Apollinaris "THE QU…

THE HOTEL METROPOLE, LONDON, W.C. See p. 1080.

SPECIAL EDITION (In CLOTH), 3s. 6d. POST FREE, 3s. 11d. | No. 794. | JUL…

OFFICIALLY

Under the Patronage of HIS M…
The Royal Family, both Houses of Parliam…
Banks, and other Public …

BRADSHAW'S
CONTINENTAL GUIDE,

FOR TRAVELLERS THROUGH EUROPE,

WITH AN EPITOMIZED DESCRIPTION OF EACH COUNTRY,
and Maps of Europe, showing the lines of Railways Opened.

CONTENTS TABLE, see page XVIII.

A B C DIRECT ROUTES, see page LXXIII.

HENRY BLACKLOCK & CO., LTD. (PROPRIETORS, PRINTERS, and PUBLISHERS),
BRADSHAW HOUSE, SURREY STREET, STRAND, LONDON, W.C.

HARWICH ROUTE TO THE CONTINENT

VIA THE

Hook OF Holland

(BRITISH ROYAL MAIL ROUTE) DAILY;

ALSO VIA ANTWERP DAILY (SUNDAYS EXCEPTED)

Through Corridor Carriages from Manchester and Liverpool via Lincoln; Bradford (Exchange) and Leeds via Doncaster; and from Birmingham (L. & N. W.) via March.

	Week-days.	Sundays.
LONDON (Liverpool Street Station) ......dep	8 30 p.m.	8 30 p.m.
EDINBORO' (Waverley Sta.) dep	10 0 a.m.	...
Do. (Princes Street) ,,	10 5 ,,	...
GLASGOW (Queen Street) ,,	8 45 ,,	...
Do. (Central) .... ,,	10 0 ,,	...
LIVERPOOL (Lime Street)... ,,	2 0 p.m.	9 20 a.m.
Do. (Central) .... ,,	2 30 ,,	10 40 ,,
Do. (Mid.) .... ,,	12 55 ,,	...
Do. (Exchange) ... ,,	2 10 ,,	8 45 ,,
MANCHESTER (L. & N. W.) ,,	2 10 ,,	9 0 ,,
Do. (Gt. Central) ,,	3 20 ,,	12 5 p.m.
Do. (Victoria)... ,,	2 55 ,,	10 40 a.m.
Do. (Mid.) ...... ,,	1 15 ,,	...
YORK (N.E.R.) .... ,,	4 0 ,,	12 20 p.m.
LEEDS (G.N.R.) .... ,,	3 50 ,,	1 10 ,,
BRADFORD (G.N.R.) .... ,,	3 12 ,,	12 15 ,,
DONCASTER........................ ,,	4 47 ,,	2 35 ,,
BIRMINGHAM (L. & N. W.) ,,	4 0 ,,	12 55 ,,
Do. (Mid.) ..... ,,	3B15 ,,	7 0 a.m.
HARWICH (Parkeston Quay) arr	9 35 ,,	8 25 p.m.
HARWICH (Parkeston Quay)..............dep	10 0 ,,	10 0 ,,
HOOK OF HOLLAND...........................arr	5E10 a.m.	5E10 a.m.
ROTTERDAM (via the Hook of Holland) ,,	6E11 ,,	6E11 ,,
AMSTERDAM ditto ,,	7E30 ,,	7E30 ,,
HAMBURG ditto ,,	2 47 p.m.	2 47 p.m.
BERLIN (Fried St.) ditto ,,	4 54 ,,	4 54 ,,
COLOGNE ditto ,,	11 15 a.m.	11 15 a.m.
LONDON (Liverpool Street Station) ...dep	8 40 p.m.	...
HARWICH (Parkeston Quay)............ ,,	10 10 ,,	...
ANTWERP Sud (by Steamer) ....arr	8 0 a.m.	...
BRUSSELS (via Antwerp) .... ,,	9 11 ,,	...

BRUSSELS (via Antwerp) .... ,,	5 29 p.m.
ANTWERP Sud (by St'mr) Weekdays ,,	7 0 ,,
HARWICH (Parkeston Quay)............ ,,	6 0 a.m.
LONDON (Liverpool Street Station) ...arr	7 35 ,,
COLOGNE (via the Hook of Holland) ...dep	7 21 p.m.
BERLIN (Fried St.) ditto ,,	1 5 ,,
HAMBURG ditto ,,	2 58 ,,
AMSTERDAM ditto ,,	9E45 ,,
ROTTERDAM ditto ,,	11E10 ,,
HOOK OF HOLLAND............................ ,,	11F30 ,,

Through Corridor Carriages to Birmingham (L. & N. W.) via March and Peterboro'; to Manchester and Liverpool via Lincoln, & to Bradford (Exchange) and Leeds via Doncaster.

	Week-days.	Sundays.
HARWICH (Parkeston Quay)..............dep	6 35 a.m.	6 35 a.m.
LONDON Liverpool Street Station) ...... ,,	8 0 ,,	8 0 ,,
HARWICH (Parkeston Quay) dep	7 2 ,,	7A0 ,,
BIRMINGHAM (L. & N. W.) arr	12 11 p.m.	1 53 p.m.
Do. (Mid.)......... ,,	2 35 ,,	9 25 ,,
DONCASTER........................ ,,	11 48 a.m.	2 50 ,,
BRADFORD (G.N.R.) .... ,,	1 17 p.m.	5 1 ,,
LEEDS (G.N.R.)................ ,,	12 41 ,,	4 30 ,,
YORK (N.E.R.) .... ,,	12 35 ,,	3 56 ,,
MANCHESTER (L. & N. W.) ,,	2 30 ,,	4 20 ,,
Do. (Gt. Central) ,,	2 0 ,,	5K25 ,,
Do. (Victoria) ... ,,	2 7 ,,	...
Do. (Mid.)......... ,,	2 38 ,,	10 47 ,,
LIVERPOOL (Lime Street)... ,,	2 35 ,,	4 5 ,,
Do. (Central)......... ,,	2 45 ,,	6 50 ,,
Do. (Mid.) .... ,,	3 50 ,,	11 35 ,,
Do. (Exchange) ... ,,	2 50 ,,	10 10 ,,
GLASGOW (Queen Street) ,,	7 35 ,,	7 23 a.m.
Do. (Central)......... ,,	6 15 ,,	6 45 ,,
EDINBORO' (Waverley Sta.) ,,	6 15 ,,	5 55 ,,
Do. (Princes Street) ,,	6 15 ,,	6 50 ,,

A—The Train via Lincoln leaves at 8.50 a.m. on Sundays. B—Leaves Birmingham at 2.40 on Saturdays.
E—Amsterdam Time. F—Greenwich Time. K—Central Station.

Corridor Vestibuled Trains. Through Carriages and Restaurant Cars.

TURBINE STEAMERS only on the Hook of Holland Service.
Wireless Telegraphy and Submarine Signalling on the G. E. R. Steamers.

GHENT INTERNATIONAL EXHIBITION.—May-November.

Return Tickets at Reduced Fares via Antwerp-Brussels.
1st Class, **47/2**; 2nd class, **28/8.**

OPENING OF THE PEACE PALACE AT THE HAGUE.

Exhibition of Art, Industry, Shipping, Agriculture, and display of Customs and Costumes in many Dutch Towns. QUICKEST ROUTE is via HARWICH and the HOOK of HOLLAND.

SEASON TICKETS in Holland at reduced rates during July, August and September, 1st Class, £1 13s. 4d.; 2nd Class, £1 5s. 0d.; available 8 days.

SERVICE to ESBJERG, via Harwich, for Denmark and Norway, four times per week by the Danish Royal Mail Steamers of the Forenede Line of Copenhagen.

SERVICE to HAMBURG, via Harwich.—TWICE WEEKLY, by the General Steam Navigation Company's steamers, fitted with Submarine Signalling.

SERVICE to GOTHENBURG, via Harwich, every Saturday (May-Sept.), by the Swedish Royal Mail Steamers (fitted with wireless telegraphy) of the Thule Line.

For Time Books (free) and any further information, apply to the Continental Traffic Manager, Great Eastern Railway, Liverpool Street Station, London, E.C.

[See pages 237C, 237D, 238, 238A, 239, 239A.]

INDEX TO HOTELS, PENSIONS, Etc.

In the following places, arranged Alphabetically, without regard to Geographical Position.

The towns to which the word "Bad" is more or less usually attached will be found under their separate headings (see page 756).

Continued on page vi.

[SEE OVER.

SOUTH EASTERN and CHATHAM RAILWAY.

TABLE OF THROUGH SERVICES from LONDON to the

CHIEF TOWNS OF EUROPE.

(LIABLE TO ALTERATION).

The italics to the left of the times indicate the number of hours from London.
Night figures 6 0 p.m. to 5 59 a.m. are shown in dark type, thus 6 0 p.m.

Over the S. E. & C. System all services are 1 & 2 class, but the 10.0 a.m. and 2.5 p.m. Boulogne, the 2.5 p.m. Ostend, and the 9.0 p.m. Calais and Ostend Mail Services also carry 3rd Class passengers. They run daily (Sundays included) except where otherwise stated.

London—											
Charing Cross dep	9 0 a.	9 0 a.	...	10 0 a.	...	2 5 p.	2 5 p.	4 30 p.	...	9 0 p.	9 0 p.
Victoria .... "	...	...	10 0 a.	...	11 0 a.	...	...	Until	8 30 p.	...	...
Holborn......... "	...	...	9 55 —	...	...	...	...	Oct. 31.	8 25 —	...	...
St. Paul's ...... "	...	...	9 56 —	...	...	...	...	(Not on	8 27 —	...	...
Herne Hill ... "	...	...	10 10 —	...	...	...	...	Sundays).	8 40 —	...	...
ROUTE. *via*	CALAIS.	OSTEND.	FLUSHING.	BOULOGNE	CALAIS.	BOULOGNE	OSTEND	CALAIS.	FLUSHING.	CALAIS.	OSTEND.
Amsterdam ......arr	*(12)* 9 27 p.	*(15)* 12 15 a.	*(14)* 11 0 p.	...	...	..	...	...	*(11)* 8 0 a.	*(14)* 11 1 a.	*(14)* 11 22 a.
Antwerp .... "	*(9)* 6 9 —	*(10)* 6 9 p.	*(13)* 10 47 —	...	*(10)* 9 8 p.	...	*(10)* 11 54 p.	...	*(12)* 7 50 —	*(11)* 6 47 —	*(11)* 6 47 a.
Bâle.................. "	*(15)* 12f18 a.	*(20)* 5 50 —	*(24)* 12 16 p.	...	...	*(15)* 6 34 a.	*(20)* 11 15 a.	*(14½)* 7 58 a.	*(20)* 5 45 —	*(15)* 12b48—	*(19)* 5 31 —
Berlin................ "	*(21½)* 7c29 a.	*(21½)* 7c29 —	*(21½)* 7 57 a.	...	...	*(27½)* 3 46 p.	*(24½* 3 48 p.	...	*(19)* 4 54 —	*(23)* 9 26 —	*(21)* 7 0 p.
Berne .... "	...	*(23)* 9 32 —	...	*(22)* 9 32 a.	*(20)* 9 5 a.	*(18)* 9 32 a.	*(25)* 4 12 —	*(20)* 12 55 p.	...	*(17)* 4b17—	*(23)* 9 7 p.
Bremen .... "	*(20)* 5 2 a.	*(20)* 5 2 —	*(19)* 5 2 a.	...	...	*(21)* 12 40 p.	*(24)* 5 20 —	...	*(15)* 1 8 p.	*(22)* 7 48 —	*(17)* 3 22 p.
Brindisi .... "	...	...	...	...	*(57)* 9 55 —	*(54½)* 9 55 p.	*(55)* 9 55 p.	*(45)* 2 30—	...	*(43)* 5*57 —	*(43)* 11 30 p.
Brussels............ "	*(7)* 4 41 p.	*(8)* 5 20 p.	*(14)* 11 11 p.	...	*(8)* 6 55 —	*(9)* 11 14 —	*(8)* 10 31 p.	...	*(13)* 8 32 a.	*(8½)* 5 21 a.	*(8½)* 5 24 a.
Budapest .... "	*(37)* 11c5 p.	*(37)* 11c5 p.	...	*(36)* 11c5 p.	...	...	...	...	*(40)* 1 40 p.	*(40)* 1 40 p.	*(40* 1 40 p.
Cannes .... "	*(28½* 1 26 p.	...	...	*(25)* 9t39 a.	*(25)* 12 7 p.	..	...	...	...	*(32)* 5 20 a.	...
Cologne .... "	*(14)* 11 1 p.	*(14)* 10†46—	*(15½)* 1 40 a.	...	...	*(14)* 5 40 a.	*(14)* 5 40 a.	...	*(12)* 9 56 a.	*(14)* 11 14 a.	*(13)* 9 51 a.
Constantinople "	*(66)* 10§17 a.	*(66)* 10§17 a.	...	*(65)* 10§17 a.	...	...	...	...	...	...	...
Copenhagen...... "	*(32)* 4 48 p.	*(32)* 4 48 p.	*(32)* 4 48 p.	...	...	...	...	...	*(37)* 10 5 a.	*(37)* 10 5 a.	*(36)* 10 5 a.
Dresden .... "	*(25)* 11 13 a.	*(25)* 11 13 a	*(25)* 11 13 a.	...	...	*(31)* 8 41 p.	*(31)* 8 41 p.	...	*(23)* 8 27 —	*(27½)* 1 36 a.	*(27½)* 1 36 a.
Florence............ "	*(39)* 1 20 a.	*(50)* 11 22 p.	...	*(38)* 1 20 a.	*(37)* 1 20 a.	*(34)* 1 20 a.	*(39)* 6 38 a.	*(33)* 3 35 a.	...	...	*(42)* 1 10 p.
Frankfort .... "	*(21)* 6 3 a.	*(17½)* 3 28 a.	*(21)* 6 5 a.	...	...	*(21)* 11 15 —	*(19)* 11 15 a.	...	*(16)* 2 10 p.	*(19)* 3 6 p.	*(18)* 2 11 p.
Geneva .... "	...	*	...	*(22)* 7 53 a.	*(21)* 7 53 —	*(21)* 11 20 a.	...	...	...	*(22½)* 6 49 —	...
Genoa .... "	...	...	...	*(32)* 6 16 p.	*(31)* 6 16 p.	*(28)* 6 45 p.	...	*(31)* 12 10—	...	*(36)* 10 30 a.	...
Hague, The ...... "	*(13½)* 10 28—	*(14)* 11 35 p.	*(13)* 10 3 p.	...	...	...	...	...	*(10)* 7 34 a.	*(13)* 10 4 a.	*(13)* 10 24 a.
Hamburg .... "	*(21)* 6 55 a.	*(21)* 6 55 a.	*(21)* 6 55 a.	...	...	*(23)* 2 27 p.	*(23)* 5 4 p.	...	*(17)* 2 47 p.	*(24)* 9 40 p.	*(19)* 5 3 p.
Karlsbad........... "	*(26)* 12k21 p.	*(26)* 12k21 p.	...	...	...	...	*(40)* 7 6 a.	...	...	...	...
Leipsic .... "	*(23)* 9 6 a.	*(23)* 9 6 a.	*(22½)* 9 6 —	...	...	*(26)* 6 11 —	*(26)* 6 11 —	...	*(21)* 6 23 p.	*(26)* 11 30 —	*(26)* 11 38 —
Lille.................. "	*(5½)* 2 37 p.	...	...	...	*(6)* 4 34 —	*(6½)* 8 49 p.	...	...	...	*(6)* 3 12 a.	...
Lisbon.............. "	...	...	...	...	*(61)* 12 33 a.	...	...	...	...	*(50)* 10c50 p.	...
Lucerne .... "	...	*(23)* 8 59 a.	..	...	*(21)* 8 59 a.	*(18)* 8 59 a.	*(24)* 3 49 p.	*(17)* 10 48—	*(22)* 8 15 p.	*(17½)* 3b49—	*(22)* 8 15 p.
Madrid .... "	...	...	...	*(37)* 10 58 p.	*(44)* 7 0 —	*(41)* 7 0—	...	...	...	*(40½)* 2c12 p.	...
Marseilles......... "	*(23½)* 8 30 a.	...	...	*(22)* 6t26 a.	*(21½)* 8 40 —	*(24)* 2 32 p.	...	...	...	*(25)* 10 14 p.	...
Mentone............ "	*(30½)* 3 34 p.	...	...	*(25)* 11t18 a.	*(27)* 2 0 p.	...	...	...	...	*(35)* 7 38 a.	...
Milan .... "	...	*(29)* 3 5 p.	...	...	*(28)* 3 5 p.	*(24)* 3 5 —	*(31)* 10 25 —	*(26½)* 7 47 p.	...	*(24)* 10b25 —	*(32)* 6 32 a.
Monte Carlo ...... "	*(30½)* 3 16—	...	...	*(25)* 10t59 a.	*(27)* 1 41 —	...	...	...	...	*(34½)* 7 19 a.	...
Munich .... "	*(25)* 11c18 a.	*(25)* 11c18 a.	*(26)* 12 58 p.	*(24)* 10c21 a.	...	*(22)* 12 58 p.	*(29)* 9 8 p.	...	*(23)* 8 52 p.	*(24)* 10 20 p.	*(23)* 8 50 p.
Naples.............. "	...	*(51)* 12 10 p.	...	...	*(49)* 3 5 p.	*(46)* 1 36—	*(51)* 5 50 p.	*(47)* 4 30—	...	*(56)* 6 50 a.	*(56)* 11 55 a.
Nice.................. "	*(29)* 2 20—	...	...	*(24)* 10t17 a.	*(36)* 12 50 —	...	...	...	...	*(33½)* 6 10 a.	...
Paris .... "	*(8)* 4 40 p.	...	...	*(8)* 5 20 p.	*(7½)* 6 20 p.	*(7)* 9 16 p.	...	*(7)* 11 25—	...	*(10)* 5 40 a.	...
Rome .... "	...	*(45)* 8 25 a.	...	...	*(43)* 8 25 a.	*(40)* 8 25 a.	*(46)* 1 10 p.	*(39)* 8 50 a.	...	*(49)* 10 35 p.	*(48)* 6 50 p.
Rotterdam.......... "	*(12)* 8 7 p.	*(13½)* 10 31 p.	*(12)* 9 32 p.	...	...	...	...	...	*(9)* 6 32 a.	*(12½)* 9 36 a.	*(12½)* 9 36 a.
San Remo .... "	*(32)* 5 50—	...	...	...	*(29)* 4 39 p.	...	..	...	...	*(40)* 2 5 p.	...
St. Petersburg... "	*(49)* 11†54 a.	*(49)* 11†54 a.	*(55½)* 6 15—	...	...	...	...	...	*(60)* 8 15 a.	*(60)* 8 15 a.	*(58)* 8 15 a.
Stockholm......... "	*(47½)* 8 59 a.	*(47½)* 8 59 a.	*(47)* 8 59 a.	...	...	...	...	...	*(59)* 7 0 —	*(59)* 7 0 —	*(59)* 7 0 a.
Stuttgart .... "	*(19)* 4 52 a.	*(21)* 6c40 a.	*(22)* 9 10 a.	...	*(19)* 6c40 a.	*(18)* 9 2 a.	*(22)* 12 42 p.	...	*(21)* 6 28 p.	*(21)* 6 28 p.	*(21)* 6 28 p.
Turin .... "	...	...	...	...	*(26½)* 2 33 p.	*(23)* 2 33 p.	...	...	...	*(35)* 6 33 a.	...
Venice.............. "	...	*(37½)* 11 55 p.	...	...	*(35½)* 11 55 p.	*(32)* 11 55 p.	*(37)* 4 23 a.	*(32)* 4 16—	...	*(38)* 12 10 p.	*(38)* 12 10 p.
Vienna .... "	*(30)* 6 c 0 p.	*(30)* 6 c 0 p.	*(35)* 9 28 p.	*(29)* 6 c 0 p.	*(28)* 6 c 0 p.	*(31)* 9 35 p.	...	...	*(33)* 7 30 a.	*(33)* 7 30 a.	*(33)* 7 30 a.

*—P. & O. Express, Fridays only from London. †—Nord Express, 1st cl. with extra fare, Wednesdays and Saturdays from London.
§—Mondays, Wednesdays, Thursdays, & Saturdays only from London, 1st Class with extra fare.
b—From London every Friday until September 26.
c—Daily Train de Luxe (Orient, Vienna, Nord, or Sud), 1st cl. only with extra fare.
f—Winter only.
k—Train de Luxe 1st cl. with extra fare—until September 15. t—Winter only.

Details of most of these Services will be found in the S. E. and C. Co.'s. Continental Time-book, to be obtained post free for 3 stamps from the Enquiry Offices, S. E. and C. R., Victoria or Charing Cross Stations. For full details of the "Via Ostend" Services apply to Mr. Defrance, Representative of the Belgian State Railways, 47, Cannon Street, London, E.C.

BRADSHAW'S GUIDE, ENQUIRY DEPT.

TARIFF CARDS and BOOKLETS

OF THE VARIOUS

Hotels, Boarding Houses,

and Hydropathic Establishments

AT THE

CHIEF PLACES OF RESORT

At HOME and on THE CONTINENT

May be inspected or obtained at any of the following Addresses:—

LONDON - - Henry Blacklock & Co. Ltd., Bradshaw House, Surrey St., Strand, W.C.

MANCHESTER - Henry Blacklock & Co. Ltd., 12 and 13, Albert Square.

LIVERPOOL - - Liverpool Printing & Stationery Company, 6, Castle Street Arcade.

GLASGOW - - James Reid and Son, 45, Mitchell Street.

DUBLIN - - - Wilson Hartnell & Co., Commercial Buildings.

For **ENQUIRIES** by **POST** address the **LONDON OFFICE**, enclosing Stamps (2d.), and write "tariffs" on outside of envelope. The localities for which tariffs or prospectuses are wanted must be specified.

SCHOOLS at home or abroad. Advice and full information free. State age, locality, and approximate fees.

TRAIN SERVICE ENQUIRIES

Should be addressed to the

LONDON OFFICE,

BRADSHAW HOUSE

SURREY STREET,

STRAND

and must be accompanied either by the annexed Coupon from the current issue or stamps (6d.), otherwise they cannot be answered.

This enquiry is to be used only for the purpose of elucidating difficulties and not merely to save the trouble of referring to the train services given in the Guide.

TRAIN SERVICE ENQUIRY.

JULY ISSUE.

This Coupon* must be detached and forwarded, or Stamps (6d.) must accompany the enquiry or it cannot be answered.

*-N.B.—Letters enclosing Coupons from out of date issues will not be answered.

BRADSHAW'S SCHOOL DIRECTORY—Continued.

GIRLS. **SEASCALE, Cumberland.**

The Calder Girls' School.

Principals: Miss A. L. HILTON WILSON, Newnham College and the Training College, Cambridge. Miss F. A. WILSON, Newnham College, Cambridge, and St. Mary's Training College, London.

Two large houses which border the seashore. Caldersyde is for senior girls over 15. Calder House suitable for girls beginning school life. Boarders only. Combination of mountain and sea air, bracing, sunny, dry, and most healthy. Efficient resident staff, including mistress for gymnastics and games. Good music. Safe bathing. Good sands. Escort from Euston, Crewe, Leeds, Glasgow, Belfast, etc. Illustrated prospectus.

BOYS.

SOUTHPORT Modern School.

Scarisbrick New Road.

AN IDEAL SCHOOL FOR BOYS.

Principal: Major J. C. UNDERWOOD, A.C.P., F.R.G.S. Vice-Principal: E. W. SHANAHAN, M.A., L.C.P.

Splendid buildings. Healthy locality. Excellent Staff, including B.A., B.Sc., F.C.V., L.R.A.M., Mus. Bac., etc. The curriculum includes Classics, Languages, Science, Commercial Subjects, Physical Culture, and Drill. Numerous "Honours" and "Distinctions" gained at Exams. The School has Cricket, Football, Swimming, and Gymnastic Clubs, also a Cadet Company, Miniature Rifle Range, etc. Foreign boys received.

GIRLS.

LAUSANNE, Switzerland.

Château des Apennins.

Principals: Mlles. BOLLINGER.

Thorough General Education. Special attention paid to French and other modern Languages. Music. Drawing Lessons by University and Conservatoire Professors. Needlework. Special attention to Health. Family Life. Sports. Superb situation.

HIGHEST REFERENCES.

TECHNICAL COLLEGES.

Penningtons, University Tutors.

254, Oxford Road, Manchester Established 1878.

Correspondence and Oral Courses for Civil, Mechanical, Electrical, and Sanitary Engineers, Surveyors, Architects, Accountants, and Solicitors by Experts in each profession. Courses in Ferro-Concrete, Electric Equipment, & Plumbers' work. Classes for Matriculation and all Entrance Exams. Residence for Students from abroad.

Full particulars respecting other schools are published monthly in "Bradshaw's Railway Guide" for Great Britain and Ireland.

BOYS' SCHOOLS.

BLACKHEATH, S.E. .... Christ's College.
BOGNOR .... Holyrood House.
DOLLAR (N.B.) .... The Dollar Institution.
FOLKESTONE .... Feltonfleet School.
HARROGATE .... Pannal Ash College.
PANGBOURNE (Berks.) .... Clayesmore School.
RAMSGATE .... St. Lawrence College.
ROCESTER (Derbyshire) .... Abbotsholme.

GIRLS' SCHOOLS.

DOLLAR (N.B.) .... The Dollar Institution.
EDINBURGH .... Grange, Strathearn College.
KINGSGATE (Thanet) .... Brondesbury.
LEE, near Blackheath .... Burnt Ash Hill.

SCHOOLS ON THE CONTINENT (BOYS).

BRUGES .... Pembroke School.

SCHOOLS ON THE CONTINENT (GIRLS).

BRUGES .... Mme. Burnier de Lutry.
DORNHOLZHAUSEN .... Victoria College.
LAUSANNE .... La Bergeronnette.
LUGANO .... Pension at Cunier.
VEVEY .... Les Charmettes.

PRIVATE TUITION.

EYPE, near Bridport .... Mr. R. O. Jourdain.
LONDON, 20, West Cromwell Rd., S.W. .... Mr. A. Klemin Schmidt.
NORTH QUEENSFERRY (Fife) .... Mr. W. H. Elder.

TECHNICAL COLLEGES.

254, OXFORD ROAD, Manchester .... Penningtons.

PURCHASE OR SALE OF SCHOOLS.

Particulars of Schools for Sale forwarded on application to the MANAGER, Bradshaw House, Surrey Street, Strand, W.C.

Apollinaris "THE QUEEN OF TABLE WATERS."

SPECIAL EDITION (In CLOTH), 3s. 6d. POST FREE, 3s. 11d.	No. 794. JULY, 1913.	PRICE (In PAPER COVER), 2s. Parcels Post, 2s. 4d.

OFFICIALLY  EVERY MONTH.

Under the Patronage of HIS MAJESTY THE KING, The Royal Family, both Houses of Parliament, all the Government Offices, Banks, and other Public Offices, &c., &c.

BRADSHAW'S CONTINENTAL GUIDE,

FOR TRAVELLERS THROUGH EUROPE,

WITH AN EPITOMIZED DESCRIPTION OF EACH COUNTRY, and Maps of Europe, showing the lines of Railways Opened.

CONTENTS TABLE, see page XVIII.
A B C DIRECT ROUTES, see page LXXIII.

HENRY BLACKLOCK & CO., LTD. (PROPRIETORS, PRINTERS, and PUBLISHERS), BRADSHAW HOUSE, SURREY STREET, STRAND, LONDON, W.C.

NOTICE.—*While every effort has been made to ensure the correctness of the information given in this book,* **NO RESPONSIBILITY** *can be accepted by the Publishers for any inaccuracies.*

CONTENTS.

Sunday Trains.—Continental Trains run the same on Sunday as on week-days.

Bold Figures—Thus **(24)** are placed against stations where other lines run in, and refer to pages of the Guide where these lines will be found.

Classes—"1 cl.," "1 & 2," 1, 2, 3," etc.—at the head of each table refer *only* to the trains running over the line described in the title of the table, and *not* to the trains from or to connecting stations.

"Ex. 1," "Ex. 2," "Ex. 3," at the head of a train, signify 1st class Express, 1st and 2nd class Express, 1st, 2nd, and 3rd class Express. These distinctions are necessary where shewn, the fares by Express trains being higher than those by ordinary train

The **"a"** and **"p"** occasionally inserted in the tables denote **"a.m."** and **"p.m."**

Trains de Luxe.—Tickets for the Trains de Luxe, etc., organised by the International Sleeping Car Co. can be obtained from their Office, at 20, Cockspur Street, London, S.W.

LONDON:—HENRY BLACKLOCK & CO., LTD., PROPRIETORS, BRADSHAW HOUSE, SURREY STREET, STRAND, (W.C.), and ALBERT SQUARE, MANCHESTER.
GLASGOW:—JAMES REID & SON, 45, MITCHELL STREET (Sole Agents for Advts. in Scotland)
JOHN MENZIES & CO., 90, WEST NILE STREET, GLASGOW, and ROSE STREET, EDINBURGH.
DUBLIN:—WILSON HARTNELL & CO., COMMERCIAL BUILDINGS (Sole Agents for Advts. in Ireland).

DEPÔTS FOR THE SALE OF BRADSHAW'S CONTINENTAL GUIDE:

The CONTINENTAL BRADSHAW may be obtained at many of the chief Railway Stations on the Continent and also from the following persons:—

BASLE:—P. SCHMIDT, Station Bookstalls.
BERLIN:—THOMAS COOK & SON, Unter den Linden.
BOULOGNE-SUR-MER:-MERRIDEW, 60, Rue Victor Hugo
BREMEN:—THOMAS COOK & SON, 36, Bahnhofstrasse.
BRUSSELS:—LIBRAIRIE KIESSLING & CIE., 48, Rue Coudenberg, Passage 1—3.
CANNES:—VIAL, 34, Rue d'Antibes.
COLOGNE:—J. G. SCHMITZ, Station Bookstalls and
" THOMAS COOK & SON, 1, Domhof.
DRESDEN:—THOMAS COOK & SON, 43, Pragerstrasse.
FLORENCE:—SEEBER, 20, Via Tornabuoni.
HAMBURG:—THOMAS COOK & SON, 39, Alsterdamm.
HEIDELBERG:—Bangel & Schmitt, Leopoldstr., 5.
HOMBURG:—F. SCHICK.
HYERES:—J. HOOK, 26, Place des Palmiers.
LAUSANNE:—PERRIN & Co., 15, Place St. Francois.
LUCERNE:—E. HAAG (late EISENRING), Librairie Doleschal
" GEBHARDT, Schweizerhof Quai.
MARSEILLES:—PINET, 4 Rue Noailles.
MENTONE:—LIBRAIRIE CENTRALE, 3, Rue St. Michel
MILAN:—SACCHI & FIGLI, Corso Venezia, 13.
MONTREUX:—C. B. FAIST, English Library.
MUNICH:—OFFICIAL B. T. OFFICE, Promenadeplatz, 16.
NAPLES:—B. JOHANNOWSKY, Piazza Plebiscito.
NEW YORK:—BRENTANO, 225, Fifth Avenue.
PARIS:—THE GALIGNANI LIBRARY, Rue de Rivoli, 224.
" BRENTANO, 37, Avenue de l'Opera.
" W. H. SMITH & SON, 248, Rue de Rivoli.
PORT SAID:—COLONIAL BOOK STORES.
ROME:—PIALE, Piazza di Spagna.
ST. MORITZ:—LIBRAIRIE BRANZKE and GANDOLFO GALLERIE.
ST. MORITZ BAD:—C. B. FAIST, English Library.
ST. RAPHAEL AND VALESCURE:—W. F. KING, 6, Rue Charles Gounod.
SAN REMO:—LIBRAIRIE BRANZKE and GANDOLFO GALLERIE.
STUTTGART:—HERMANN WILDT, 38, Königs-Strasse.
VIENNA:—THOMAS COOK & SON, 2, Stefansplatz.
WIMEREUX: ENGLISH CIRCULATING LIBRARY and Reading Room, Place Carnot

THE RAILWAYS OF THE CONTINENT, ARRANGED UNDER THE HEADINGS OF THE RESPECTIVE COUNTRIES.

For list of Stations on all the Lines consult the INDEX pp. xxiv to lxi.

FRANCE.

FRANCE—State Railways—*continued.*

Southern Company ....pages 43 to 47

Paris, Lyons, and Mediterranean Company.......................................pages 48 to 63B

BELGIUM—State Railways—*(continued).*

Minor Belgian Lines:—

HOLLAND.

State Railways ....pages 113 to 118

Holland Co.:—

Minor Dutch Lines:

GERMAN EMPIRE.

Prussian State Railways—

District Administrations:

Altona	Dantsic	Hanover	Posen
Berlin	Elberfeld	Kattowitz	St. Johann-Saarbrucken
Breslau	Erfurt	Königsberg	Schwerin
Bromberg	Essen	Magdeburg	Stettin
Cassel	Frankfort	Mayence	
Cologne	Halle	Münster	

GERMAN EMPIRE—*continued.*

GERMAN EMPIRE—*(continued).*

Alsace & Lorraine Railway ...pp. 207A to 212A

Baden State Railways ....pages 139A to 145

AUSTRIA.

Austrian State Railway—

Buschtehrad Railway

ITALY.

SPAIN.

PORTUGAL.

DENMARK.

NORWAY.

SWEDEN.

RUSSIA.

RUSSIA—*continued.*

GREECE.

RUMANIA.

BULGARIA.

SERVIA & TURKEY.

EGYPT.

SOUDAN GOV. RYS.

ALGERIA.

TUNIS.

INDEX OF TOWNS, &c.,

SHOWING THE PRINCIPAL RAILWAY STATIONS UPON THE CONTINENT OF EUROPE

Together with the Steamboat and Diligence Stopping Places.

PAGES BELOW 378 REFER TO RAIL, STEAMER, AND DILIGENCE TABLES ABOVE 378, TO DESCRIPTIVE MATTER.

Italic figures [*673*] refer to pages in the Special Edition, with Extra Maps and Plans of 29 Cities, price 3/6.

Where the page numbers are separated by three dots (...) the numbers after the dots are of pages where the station is given as a connection only.

To avoid multiplying figures in this Index, the route in connection with each town is only given once, the **Return Journey** will, in many cases, be found on the following page.

Note.—Italic figures [*675*] refer to pages in the Special Edition, with Extra Maps and Plans of 29 Cities, price 3/6.

C ROUTES from LONDON pages lxxiii. to cxvii.; SAILINGS from BRITISH and FOREIGN PORTS, pp. 336 to 360.

Note.—Italic figures [673] refer to pages in the Special Edition, with Extra Maps and Plans of 29 Cities, price 3/6.

Pages below 373 refer to RAIL, STEAMER, and DILIGENCE TABLES; above 373, to DESCRIPTIVE MATTER.

Note.—Italic figures [673] refer to pages in the **Special Edition**, with Extra Maps and Plans of 28 Cities, price 3/6.

B

A B C ROUTES from LONDON pages lxxiii. to cxvii.; SAILINGS from BRITISH and FOREIGN PORTS, pp. 336 to 360.

Note.—Italic figures [*678*] refer to pages in the Special Edition, with Extra Maps and Plans of 29 Cities, price 3/6.

Note.—Italic figures [*673*] refer to pages in the Special Edition, with Extra Maps and Plans of 23 Cities, price 3/6.

Note.—Italic figures [*578*] refer to pages in the Special Edition, with Extra Maps and Plans of 29 Cities, price 3/6.

Pages below 378 refer to RAIL, STEAMER, and DILIGENCE TABLES; above 378, to DESCRIPTIVE MATTER.

Note.—Italic figures [675] refer to pages in the Special Edition, with Extra Maps and Plans of 25 Cities, price 3/6.

A B C ROUTES from LONDON pages lxxiii. to cxvii.; SAILINGS from BRITISH and FOREIGN PORTS, pp. 336 to 360.

Pages below 378 refer to RAIL, STEAMER, and DILIGENCE TABLES; above 378, to DESCRIPTIVE MATTER.

Note.—Italic figures [673] refer to pages in the Special Edition, with Extra Maps and Plans of 29 Cities, price 3/6.

A B C ROUTES from LONDON pages lxxiii. to cxvii.; SAILINGS from BRITISH and FOREIGN PORTS, pp. 336 to 360.

Note.—Italic figures [673] refer to pages in the "Special Edition, with Extra Maps and Plans of 23 Cities, price 3/6.

Note.—Italic figures [*673*] refer to pages in the **Special Edition**, with Extra Maps and Plans of 29 Cities, price 3/6.

Note.—Italic figures [*673*] refer to pages in the Special Edition, with Extra Maps and Plans of 20 Cities, price 3/6.

A B C ROUTES from LONDON pages lxxiii. to cxvii.; SAILINGS from BRITISH and FOREIGN PORTS, pp. 336 to 360.

Note.—Italic figures [*678*] refer to pages in the Special Edition, with Extra Maps and Plans of 29 Cities, price 3/6.

Note.—Italic figures [673] refer to pages in the Special Edition, with Extra Maps and Plans of 29 Cities, price 3/6.

A B C ROUTES from LONDON pages lxxiii. to cxvii.; SAILINGS from BRITISH and FOREIGN PORTS, pp. 336 to 360.

Note.—Italic figures [*578*] refer to pages in the Special Edition, with Extra Maps and Plans of 29 Cities, price 3/6.

Note.—Italic figures [*678*] refer to pages in the Special Edition, with Extra Maps and Plans of 28 Cities, price 3/6.

A B C ROUTES from LONDON pages lxxiii. to cxvii.; SAILINGS from BRITISH and FOREIGN PORTS, pp. 336 to 360.

Note.—Italic figures [*672*] refer to pages in the Special Edition, with Extra Maps and Plans of 29 Cities, price 2/6.

Note.—Italic figures [*673*] refer to pages in the Special Edition, with Extra Maps and Plans of 29 Cities, price 3/6.

A B C ROUTES from LONDON pages lxxiii. to cxvii.; SAILINGS from BRITISH and FOREIGN PORTS, pp. 336 to 360.

Note.—Italic figures [*675*] refer to pages in the Special Edition, with Extra Maps and Plans of 23 cities, price 3/6.

Note.—Italic figures [*678*] refer to pages in the Special Edition, with Extra Maps and Plans of 29 Cities, price 3/6.

Note.—Italic figures [*678*] refer to pages in the **Special Edition**, with Extra Maps and Plans of 29 Cities, price 3/6.

Note.—Italic figures [*673*] refer to pages in the Special Edition, with Extra Maps and Plans of 29 Cities, price 3/6.

Pages below 378 refer to RAIL, STEAMER, and DILIGENCE TABLES; above 378, to DESCRIPTIVE MATTER.

Note.—Italic figures [673] refer to pages in the Special Edition, with Extra Maps and Plans of 59 Cities, price 3/6.

Note.—Italic figures [*673*] refer to pages in the **Special Edition**, with Extra Maps and Plans of 29 Cities, price 3/6.

A B C ROUTES from LONDON pages lxxiii. to cxvii.; SAILINGS from BRITISH and FOREIGN PORTS, pp. 336 to 360.

Note.—Italic figures [*673*] refer to pages in the Special Edition, with Extra Maps and Plans of 29 Cities, price 3/6.

Note.—Italic figures [*673*] refer to pages in the **Special Edition**, with Extra Maps and Plans of 29 Cities, price 3/6.

Note.—Italic figures [673] refer to pages in the Special Edition, with Extra Maps and Plans of 23 Cities, price 3/6.

Note.—Italic figures [*673*] refer to pages in the Special Edition, with Extra Maps and Plans of 25 Cities, price 3/6.

A B C ROUTES from LONDON pages lxxiii. to cxvii.; SAILINGS from BRITISH and FOREIGN PORTS, pp. 336 to 360.

Note.—Italic figures [673] refer to pages in the Special Edition, with Extra Maps and Plans of 28 Cities, price 3/6.

ROUTES from LONDON pages xxiii. to cxvii.; SAILINGS from BRITISH and FOREIGN PORTS, pp. 330 to 360.

Note.—Italic figures [673] refer to pages in the Special Edition, with Extra Maps and Plans of 29 Cities, price 3/6.

Note.—Italic figures [*687*] refer to pages in the Special Edition, with Extra Maps and Plans of 28 Cities, price 3/6.

Note.—*Italic figures* [*678*] refer to pages in the Special Edition, with Extra Maps and Plans of 29 Cities, price 2/6.

Pages below 373 refer to RAIL, STEAMER, and DILIGENCE TABLES; above 373, to DESCRIPTIVE MATTER.

Note.—Italic figures [673] refer to pages in the Special Edition, with Extra Maps and Plans of 29 Cities, price 3/6.

Note.—Italic figures [*673*] refer to pages in the Special Edition, with Extra Maps and Plans of 28 Cities, price 2/6.

A B C ROUTES from LONDON pages lxxiii. to cxvii.; SAILINGS from BRITISH and FOREIGN PORTS, pp. 336 to 368.

Note.—Italic figures [673] refer to pages in the Special Edition, with Extra Maps and Plans of 28 Cities, price 2/6.

A B C ROUTES from LONDON pages lxxiii. to cxvii.; SAILINGS from BRITISH and FOREIGN PORTS, pp. 336 to 360.

Note.—Italic figures [*673*] refer to pages in the Special Edition, with Extra Maps and Plans of 29 Cities, price 3/6.

Note.—Italic figures [*675*] refer to pages in the Special Edition, with Extra Maps and Plans of 23 Cities, price 3/6.

Note.—Italic figures [*673*] refer to pages in the Special Edition, with Extra Maps and Plans of 29 Cities, price 3/6.

Note.—Italic figures [*673*] refer to pages in the Special Edition, with Extra Maps and Plans of 29 Cities, pric. 3/6.

A B C ROUTES from LONDON pages lxxiii. to cxvii.; SAILINGS from BRITISH and FOREIGN PORTS, pp. 336 to 360.

Note.—Italic figures [673] refer to pages in the Special Edition, with Extra Maps and Plans of 23 Cities, price 3/6.

Note.—Italic figures [67…) pages in the **Special Edition**, with Extra Maps and Plans of 29 Cities, price 3/6.

Note.—Italic figures [*673*] refer to pages in the Special Edition, with Extra Maps and Plans of 23 Cities, price 3/6.

Note.—Italic figures [*678*] refer to pages in the Special Edition, with Extra Maps and Plans of 29 Cities, price 3/6.

A B C ROUTES from LONDON pages lxxiii. to cxvii.; SAILINGS from BRITISH and FOREIGN PORTS, pp. 336 to 360.

Pages below 373 refer to RAIL, STEAMER, and DILIGENCE TABLES; above 373, to DESCRIPTIVE MATTER.

Note.—Italic figures [675] refer to pages in the Special Edition, with Extra Maps and Plans of 28 Cities, price 3/6.

Note.—Italic figures [*675*] refer to pages in the Special Edition, with Extra Maps and Plans of 23 Cities, price 3/6.

TO TRAVELLERS.

THE best thanks of the Editor will be given to any Traveller who may do him the favour to point out inaccuracies in this Work, or furnish any information which will be useful to Travellers in general—addressed "BRADSHAW HOUSE, 5, SURREY STREET, STRAND, LONDON, W.C." With this view, a few leaves of writing-paper, for stray remarks, are introduced at the end of the Special Edition. Please write only on *one* side of the sheet, if possible; and note the *article*, *page*, and *date* of the CONTINENTAL GUIDE referred to. All *names of Places and Persons* should be written very distinctly.

The Editor will also be happy to reply to inquiries having reference to the tables, etc., should difficulties be encountered in using the GUIDE.

The SPECIAL EDITION of the CONTINENTAL GUIDE contains additional information, together with Thirty-two Maps, price 3s. 6d. (per post, 3s. 11d.).

I.—TRAVELLING ON THE CONTINENT.

How to reach your destination.—There should be little or no difficulty encountered whilst tracing the best route to any part of the Continent. Should the proposed destination be a town of historical or commercial importance, a notable pleasure resort, or a prominent watering place, it is almost certain to be included in the list of places to which routes from London are traced on pages lxxiii to cxvii. If these routes are carefully followed through the tables on the pages referred to, and section by section on the map, the journey will be easily traced. When the destination is a place of minor importance, the traveller, by the aid of the Index, should first find the table in which it appears, then, guided by the names of leading stations on the same line, the position on the map of the destination may be discovered; this ascertained, it is only needful to look on the map for the nearest large place to which a route is traced.

Tourist Agencies.—Messrs. COOK and SON, Ludgate Circus; The Polytechnic Touring Association, 309, Regent Street, W.; Cruising Company Limited, 5, Endsleigh Gardens, Euston Road; Messrs. DEAN and DAWSON, 82, Strand, W.C. At their head or branch offices, at home and abroad, particulars may be obtained of Excursions, by single, return, and circular tickets, or by International Travelling Tickets; including Coupon for board and lodging for one or more persons, or for parties personally conducted. The Routes comprise the chief towns on the Continent, in the East, the United States and Canada; also trips round the World, or by Steamers of the various Companies to all parts of the globe. Each firm issues a periodical List, giving full information.

CUSTOM-HOUSE REGULATIONS.

In practically all European Countries no merchandise is allowed to enter free of duty. In the case of travellers the custom-house officials have a certain latitude allowed them, and in France, for instance, the question, "Have you anything to declare?" if answered in the negative is very frequently followed, in the absence of any suspicious circumstances, by the traveller being allowed to pass almost without examination.

As regards articles usually taken by travellers, we have, after careful enquiry from officials, drawn up the following information, in order to meet frequently expressed wishes, but it must be clearly understood that the only way to avoid trouble is to be perfectly open in stating what there is in the baggage, and to exercise reasonable courtesy towards the officials.

Cut Tobacco.—As a rule enough for the railway journey, say an *opened* packet (of not more than 1½ ounces).

Cigars.—In France or Germany, enough for the railway journey (about ten). Cigarettes, about twenty. Spain, only a few, not more than 20. In Italy, half-a-dozen. In Portugal, one *opened* box.

Spirits or Wine.—A small bottle, which must have been uncorked and used from. In Italy, under two gills.

Patent Medicines.—What is needed for the journey; in France, subject to duty, in Germany free, excepting pills. In Portugal, only one bottle free, rest pays duty.

Sporting Guns and Rifles.—Must pay duty according to weight in Germany, Portugal, and Belgium. For Spain, a permit must be obtained previously from the Civil Governor of District (cost about 60 pesetas each gun). Military rifles, as a rule, are forbidden.

ENGLAND.

Passengers are allowed duty free, 1 pint of drinkable Spirit, ½ pint of Liqueur or perfumed Spirit (eau de Cologne, etc.), and ½ lb. of Cigars or Tobacco; Passengers from the Channel Islands are only allowed half these quantities. The goods must be produced, and if the above quantities are exceeded, duty is charged *on the whole*.

STEAMER SERVICE.—PRIVATE CABINS.

In all cases requests for reserved accommodation should be made in advance.

Via Dover and Calais.—Extra Charges for Private Cabins irrespective of the number of Passengers occupying them:—

	£	s.	d.
MAIN DECK STATE CABIN	3	0	0
PROMENADE DECK HALF-STATE CABIN	2	0	0
MAIN DECK HALF-STATE CABIN	1	10	0
MAIN DECK SMALL CABIN	1	0	0

For extra charges on Turbine Steamers see below, Folkestone and Boulogne Route.

EXCESS FARES.—Passengers holding Second Class Tickets can pay the excess for Saloon on board. From Dover to Calais, or vice versa, 2s. Excess for Third Class Passengers, 3s.

Apply to Continental Inquiry Office, Victoria Station, or Charing Cross Station, London; or to Capt. Dixon, Dover; in Calais, to Capt. Blomefield, Gare Maritime; in Paris, to Capt. Churchward, 14, Rue du 4 Septembre.

Via Folkestone and Boulogne (Turbine Steamers)—

	£	s.	d.
PROMENADE DECK STATE CABIN	4	0	0
„ „ HALF-STATE CABIN	2	0	0
„ „ LARGE CABIN...	1	10	0
„ „ SMALL CABIN	1	0	0

Passengers holding Second Class Tickets can pay excess for Saloon on board. From Folkestone to Boulogne, or vice versa, 2s. Excess for Third Class Passengers, 3s.

Apply to Continental Inquiry Office, Victoria Station, or Charing Cross Station, London; or to Capt. Dixon, Folkestone Harbour; in Boulogne, to Major Stevens, Quai Chanzy; in Paris, to Capt. Churchward, 14, Rue du 4 Septembre.

Via Dover and Ostend.—PRIVATE CABIN, in addition to First Class Fare, 5s. 8d. ("Princesse Clementine" only); Double Cabin 11s. 3d. On the "Jan Breydel," "Pieter de Coninck," "Princesse Elisabeth," "Princesse Henriette," "Princesse Josephine," "Leopold II," "Princesse Clementine," "Rapide" and "Marie Henriette," the extra charge for Cabins is as follows:—Double Cabin, 11s. 3d.; Special Cabin*, £1 2s. 5d.; State Room, £3.

***—The "Rapide," "Princesse Henriette," and "Princesse Josephine" have no Special Cabin.**

EXCESS FARES.—Second Class Passengers may travel Saloon on the Dover and Ostend Boats on payment of 2s. on board.

Apply to Belgian Mail Office, 53, Gracechurch Street, London; or to Messrs. Friend & Co., Strond Street, Dover; at Ostend, to the Chef de Gare, Quai Station.

Via Folkestone and Queenborough and Flushing.—

	£	s.	d.	
The Night Steamers, besides the ordinary Berth Cabins, have one				
Imperial State Deck Cabin, charge	3	0	0	
Two Royal State Cabins, charge	2	0	0	
23 Deck and 4 Inside Deck Cabins, charge (two berths each)	1	0	0	each cabin.
The Day Steamers have two State Deck Cabins, charge	1	0	0	each cabin.

EXCESS FARES.—Second Class Passengers may travel in Saloon on board the Day or Night Flushing Steamers on payment of 8s. (Children between 4 and 10 years 4s.); or 13s. return Adults (children between 4 and 10 years, 6s. 6d).

Passengers by the Night Service from London, wishing to break the journey at Flushing, may remain in their berths till about 7.0 a.m., so as to leave the Boat at a more convenient hour.

Via Newhaven and Dieppe.—

	Per Cabin. £	s.	d.	
QUARTER DECK CABINS, with two or more berths, one Passenger	0	16	0	These rates are in addition to the First Class Fares.
Do. Do. Do. two or more Passengers...	1	0	0	
GRANDE CABINE DE LUXE (Turbine Steamers only)	2	0	0	

Second Class Passengers may use the First Saloon of the Steamboats by payment on board of 5s., and Third Class Passengers may use Second Saloon of the Night Boats on payment of 3s. 6d., but are not allowed to use the First Saloon.

First Class Passengers can reserve Sofa Berths in the Ladies' and Gentlemen's Saloons of the Steamers on payment of a fee of 1s. (1fr. 25c. in France) per berth. Second Class Berths cannot be reserved.

Apply to the Marine Superintendent, Newhaven; at Dieppe, to the Chef de Gare Maritime.

Via Southampton and Havre.—The cabins are two berth and four berth. Berths in cabins on the promenade deck, 2s. 6d. extra. No extra charge for berths in cabins on main and lower decks. Exclusive use of cabin on promenade deck, £1, and cabins on main and lower decks, 10s. per unoccupied berth.

Apply to the Docks and Marine Manager, L. and S. W. Rly., Southampton.

Via Harwich and Hoek van Holland and Harwich and Antwerp.—STATE ROOMS, extra charge if occupied by two persons 10s., if reserved for one person 20s. DECK CABINS.—An extra charge of 5s. per Berth in these Cabins, but if an entire Cabin is specially reserved, the extra charge will be as follows:—

	£	s.	d.
If reserved for one person	1	10	0
Do. two persons	1	0	0
Do. three or four persons in one party	0	15	0

Passengers desiring a Cabin in the First Class General Sleeping Saloon to be reserved for themselves will be charged 13s. for each unoccupied Berth.

Passengers holding Tickets available Second Class on the Steamer can travel First Class (Saloon) on board the Hook of Holland and Antwerp Steamers by an extra payment of 7s. on a single and 11s. on a return ticket.

Apply to the Marine Superintendent, Parkeston Quay, Harwich; at Hoek van Holland or at Antwerp, to the Great Eastern Railway Co.'s Agent.

Children.—Children travel free up to the age of three years throughout the greater part of the Continent. In Belgium children between three and eight pay half price; in France and Italy, between three and seven, half price; in Germany and Holland, between four and ten; in Switzerland between four and twelve.

The Registration of Luggage saves the Passenger from all trouble and expense of landing and shipping the Luggage and conveying it between the Train and Boat, Harbour Dues, and other imposts hitherto made; secures in some cases an allowance (25 kilos. or 56 lbs.) of Luggage free of charge, also the privilege of paying before departure the charge for the conveyance of Excess Luggage, according to a Fixed Through Rate. Occasionally at inland places of lesser importance Customs Examinations are not made late at night nor on Sunday. As a rule, **all luggage**, registered or not, is examined at the frontier station of each country by the customs authorities, and travellers are advised to personally attend the examination. Almost the only exceptions are in the case of luggage registered to Paris, when the examination is made at Paris, and in the case of some Trains de Luxe, when the examination is made in the train.

REGISTRATION FEES

Via Dover and Calais..........6d. per passenger.	Via Southampton and Havre........1s. per passenger.
,, Dover and Ostend...........6d. ,, ,,	,, Queenborough and Flushing...6d. per package.
,, Folkestone and Boulogne 6d. ,, ,,	,, Folkestone and Flushing ......6d. ,, ,,
,, Newhaven and Dieppe ...1s ,, ,,	,, Harwich and Hoek v. Holland 6d. ,, ,,
	,, Harwich and Antwerp............6d. ,, ,,

Continental Luggage Rates.—No free allowance of luggage is made by the German Railway Administrations, and the Dutch Railways make no free allowance of luggage in transit through Holland; on the other hand passengers holding ordinary through tickets to Belgium, France, Holland, and Spain, are allowed 56 lbs. free luggage per ticket; passengers to Switzerland, Austria, Hungary, Italy, Denmark, Norway, Sweden, and Russia, are granted a free allowance of 56 lbs. as far as the German or Swiss frontier.

The English Companies register luggage to destinations in Germany, and the luggage charges take into account the free allowance as far as Herbesthal, or Flushing, or Hoek van Holland, as the case may be. There are fifteen luggage zones in Germany, and, as the charges are reduced according to the number of tickets, it is impossible to reproduce the extensive series of tables prepared for use by the English Companies.

At the top right and left hand corners of the Railway Table pages the luggage rates will generally be found. See also for Austria page, 237b; Belgium, page 424; France, page 383; Germany, page 462; Holland, page 440; Hungary, page 233b; Italy, page 269; Portugal, page 577. Switzerland, page 511; Spain, page 565;

Cycles.—The French Customs tax Cycles entering France at the rate of 2 fr. 20 c. per kilogramme (about 10d. per lb.), but this charge will be refunded on leaving France, provided that the passenger declares at the time of payment his intention of reclaiming it. Similarly entering Italy, charges of 1 lr. 70 c. per chilogrammo (about 8½d. per lb.), and entering Switzerland, 1fr. 45c. per kilogramme (about 7d. per lb.) are made, which are refunded on leaving. The Refund Permit is valid 12 months. Cyclists belonging to a club will not be charged duty, on production of their cards of membership. Entering Holland, 5 per cent. on their value, but Cyclists accompanying their own machines will not be charged duty. Entering Belgium, a minimum charge of 18 frs. is made, which is refunded when leaving. Entering Germany, no duty is charged, unless the machines are for commercial purposes. Entering Austria, a charge of about 41s. 8d. (50 kronen) is made (refunded on leaving the Country), and there are no special facilities to members of clubs.

Passengers wishing to cycle in France must apply to the Customs Authorities on landing for the necessary permit. This permit, which is supplied on payment of 60 centimes, is available for three months.

Motor Cars.—Detailed information regarding Motor Car regulations upon the Continent will be found in the Handbook of the Automobile Club.

Sunday Services Abroad.—CHURCH OF ENGLAND SERVICES are mostly supplied by the *Society for the Propagation of the Gospel in Foreign Parts* (15, Tufton Street, Westminster, S.W.); and the *Colonial and Continental Church Society* (9, Serjeants' Inn, Fleet Street, E.C.) A few Embassy and Consular Chaplains are still appointed or partly supported by the Foreign Office.

II.—POSTAL REGULATIONS.

Postage.—The rates of postage to be prepaid on letters posted in Great Britain addressed to places abroad are; For all British Colonies and Possessions, for Egypt, and for the United States of America, 1d. per ounce; for all other places abroad, 2½d. for the first ounce, and 1½d. for each additional ounce. Post Cards are 1d.; Newspapers, ½d. per 2oz.; 1d. per 4oz.; Books, ½d. per 2oz. In most countries of the Postal Union the letter postage to Great Britain will be at the rate of 25 centimes or their equivalent for the first 20 grammes or 1 ounce, according to the system of weights in use, and 15 centimes or their equivalent for every additional 20 grammes or 1 ounce. The European countries not accepting the general rule are France, Greece, Italy, Montenegro, Russia, Servia, and Turkey. Within the Union, Prepayment by postage stamps of the country from which the Letter is sent, is compulsory. If a Letter be insufficiently prepaid, the extra charge is double the deficiency. For Registered Letters 2d. extra is charged. Newspapers are not allowed to be sent through the post in Russia.

Poste Restante.—Letters for the Continent should be addressed very legibly, particularly the *Christian* and *Surname*, which latter should be UNDERLINED, omitting "Esquire," "Bart.," or other title, which Officers of Foreign Post Offices are apt to take for a name. Persons applying for letters should present a *Card* with the name written plainly. It is always better to direct letters to the care of a Banker or an Hotel, as Letters and parcels addressed "Poste Restante" are apt to get lost.

International Express Service.—Letters from Great Britain marked "Express," upon which a special fee of 3d. in addition to the postage has been paid, will be delivered by Express Messenger in the following countries:

Austria	France	Italy	Portugal
Belgium	Germany	Luxemburg	Servia
Bosnia-Herzegovina	Holland	Montenegro	Switzerland
Denmark	Hungary	Norway	

When the address is beyond the usual postal delivery an additional charge will be levied at the destination.

Reply Coupons.—Coupons exchangeable for stamps of the value of 25 centimes (2½d.) can be purchased at any Money Order Office in Great Britain at a cost of 3d. for the purpose of prepaying replies to letters. The coupons are exchangeable at the Post Office of the place of destination for local postage stamps. This system is available for:—

Algeria	Crete	Germany	Hungary	Roumania	Tunis
Austria	Denmark	Gibraltar	Italy	Sweden	Turkey
Belgium	Egypt	Greece	Luxemburg	Switzerland	
Bulgaria	France	Holland	Norway		

Telegrams.—Charges from any part of the United Kingdom to the following countries:—

In no case is a lower sum than tenpence accepted for a telegram or reply.

	Per Word.		Per Word.		Per Word.
Algeria	2½d.	France	2d.	Portugal	3d.
Austria	2½d.	Germany	2d.	Rumania	3d.
Azores	9d.	Gibraltar	3d.	Russia-in-Europe	4½d.
Belgium	2d.	Greece and Greek Islands	5½d. to 6d.	,, ,, Caucasus	4½d.
Bosnia-Herzegovina	3½d.	Holland	2d.	,, ,, Asia	4½d.
Bulgaria, Eastern Roumelia	3½d.	Hungary	2½d.	Servia	3½d.
Canary Islands	9d.	Iceland	5½d.	Spain	3d.
Cyprus	1s. 0d.	Italy	2½d.	,, Via Marseilles Cable	5d.
Denmark	2½d.	Luxemburg	2½d.	Sweden	2½d.
Egypt: Alexandria	1s. 0d.	Malta	4d.	Switzerland	2½d.
Egypt: Suakim	1s. 4d.	Montenegro	3½d.	Tripoli (Africa)	7d.
Egypt: Other places, 1st Region	1s. 0d.	Morocco: Tangier	4d.	Tunis	2½d.
Egypt: Other places, 2nd Region	1s. 1d.	Morocco: Other places	3d. to 9d.	Turkey-in-Europe, or in Asia	6d.
Egypt: Other places, 3rd Region	1s. 4d.	Norway	2½d.		

III.—INFORMATION RESPECTING PASSPORTS.

Travellers to any part of the Continent wishing to save trouble or unnecessary expense can obtain Passports through the London Office of BRADSHAW'S GUIDE, BRADSHAW HOUSE, 5, SURREY STREET, STRAND, LONDON, W.C. Special printed forms of application will be sent on receipt of stamped envelope, and the Passport, duly visé if necessary, can be forwarded by post if desired.

Fee for obtaining Passport 5s., including Foreign Office charge; ditto for each *visa*, 2s. in addition to the Consulate charges. Passport cases 2s. and 3s. 6d. Name lettered in gold, 1s. 6d. Passports mounted on linen, 1s. 6d.

Passports Abroad.—As every police officer abroad is authorised to inspect a Passport, it should be carried about the person. To protect it from friction, it should be bound in a pocket book.

Regulations respecting Passports.

1.—Passports are granted to such persons as are known to the Secretary of State, or recommended to him by some person who is known to him; or upon the production of a *Certificate of Identity and Recommendation* signed by any *Banking Firm* established in the United Kingdom, or by any *Mayor, Magistrate, Justice of the Peace, Minister of Religion, Barrister-at-Law Physician, Surgeon, Solicitor, or Notary,* resident in the United Kingdom. The applicant's Certificate of Birth may also be required, in addition to the Certificate of Identity and Recommendation.

Special printed forms must be used, they may be obtained from *Bradshaw's Guide Office, Bradshaw House, 5, Surrey Street, Strand, London, W.C.*

Passports are granted only (1) to natural-born British subjects, *viz.*, persons born within His Majesty's Dominions, and to persons born abroad who derive British nationality from a father or paternal grandfather born within His Majesty's Dominions, and who, under the provisions of the Acts 4 George II, cap. 21, and 13 George III, cap. 21, are to be adjudged and taken to be natural-born British subjects; (2) to the wives and widows of such persons; and (3) to persons naturalised in the United Kingdom, in the British Colonies, or in India.

A married woman is deemed to be a subject of the State of which her husband is for the time being a subject.

2.—If the applicant for a Passport be a Naturalized British subject, the Certificate of Naturalization must be forwarded to the Foreign Office with the Declaration or Letter of Recommendation. Naturalized British subjects, if resident in London or in the Suburbs, must apply *personally* for their Passports at the Foreign Office; if resident in the Country, the Passport will be sent, and the Certificate of Naturalization returned, to the person who may have verified the Declaration for delivery to the applicant.

Naturalized British subjects will be described as such in their Passports, which will be issued subject to the necessary qualifications.

3.—Passports are only available for five years from the date of issue.

4.—A Passport cannot be issued by the Foreign Office, or by an Agent at an outport, on behalf of a person already abroad; such person should apply for one to the nearest British Mission or Consulate.

5.—Travellers who intend to visit the Russian Empire, the Turkish Dominions, or the Kingdom of Rumania, Persia, Colombia, Venezuela, Hayti, or Eritrea, in the course of their travels, must not leave the United Kingdom without having had their Passports *vises* by the Consuls of these Countries. Travellers about to proceed to any other country need not obtain the *visa* of the Diplomatic or Consular Agents of such country.

Austria and Hungary.—Although Passports are not legally necessary, travellers are advised to carry them. For purposes of residence a Passport or other document to prove identity is necessary.

Belgium.—It is desirable for travellers to possess Passports. For purposes of residence registration at the Police Office of the district is required, and a Passport is accepted as evidence of identity.

Bulgaria.—Travellers should carry Passports of recent date.

Denmark.—No Regulations in force. But Passports or similar documents may be required by the Police from persons accepting employment in Denmark before furnishing them with an "opholdsbog' (situation book), or from music hall artistes. ICELAND.—No Regulations in force.

Egypt.—Passports not required by law, but travellers are advised to carry them. For travelling in other parts of the Ottoman dominions, see TURKEY.

France.—The possession of a Passport may save inconvenience, since evidence of identity may at any time be required. For permanent residence, or to exercise profession or trade, a declaration must be made at the Mairie of the Commune within a few days of arrival. ALGERIA and TUNIS.—Regulations similar to France.

German Empire.—The possession of a Passport is not obligatory, but as evidence of identity may at any time be required, it is very desirable for travellers, especially if they intend to reside for any length of time, to be provided with Passports. Children sent to schools in Germany should carry Passports.

Greece.—No Regulations in force, except as regards persons entering the country by the land frontier, who are sometimes required to be in possession of Passports.

Italy.—The possession of a Passport is not obligatory, but travellers may at any time be required to give a satisfactory account of themselves, and to establish their identity.

Montenegro.—No special Regulations exist, but a Passport properly *visé* is required for travelling through the surrounding Turkish and Austrian territories.

Morocco.—It is advisable for travellers to be provided with Passports. Any one wishing to travel into the interior should consult His Majesty's Minister at Tangier or the British Consul for the district through which his route lies.

Netherlands.—The possession of a Passport is not strictly necessary, but is recommended for purposes of identification.

Norway.—No Regulations in force.

Portugal.—Travellers are advised to provide themselves with Passports. For residence, proof of nationality is required, and in travelling a Passport may save the bearer much inconvenience. AZORES.—A passport is advisable. MADEIRA.—No Regulations in force.

Rumania.—Passport necessary. It must be *visé* by a Rumanian Consul in the United Kingdom.

Russia.—Visitors to Russia must be provided with Passports bearing the *visa* of a Russian Diplomatic or Consular officer. Without such *visa* they will not be allowed to enter the country. To persons of the Jewish faith the *visa* is only granted in special circumstances. The *visa* must be of recent date, no traveller can enter Russia with a *visa* more than six months old.

The Passport will enable the holder to reside in Russia for six months, when it must be exchanged at the Prefecture of St. Petersburg, or at the Chancery of a Provincial Governor, for a Russian "Billet de Séjour" to be renewed annually.

The cost of such a "Billet de Séjour" varies from 7r. 15c. to 1r. 29c. Each "Billet de Séjour," on first issue or renewal, must be delivered to the local police officer for inscription or *visa*. For non-renewal of a "Billet de Séjour" at the time of its expiration a fine is exacted.

On leaving Russia a Police Certificate must be obtained, or, if resident more than six months, the "Billet de Séjour" must be returned, when the Passport will be handed back to the owner with the necessary authorization to leave.

Servia.—Travellers are required to produce Passports on entering the country.

Spain.—It is most advisable for travellers to be provided with Passports. The *visa* of a Spanish Consul is not necessary, but will be found useful in travelling in provincial towns and country districts. CANARY ISLANDS.—No Regulations in force.

Sweden.—No Regulations in force.

Switzerland.—A Passport or similar document is necessary in order to obtain a "Permis de Séjour." Children sent to schools in Switzerland should carry Passports.

Turkish Empire.—A Passport bearing the *visa* of a Turkish Consular officer is required on entering the country. On leaving Turkey the *visa* of a British Consul should be obtained,

3 [July]

FOREIGN AMBASSADORS, MINISTERS, CONSULS, &c., IN LONDON.

FOR REGULATIONS AS TO PASSPORTS SEE PRECEDING PAGES.

United States of America—
Ambassador........................ The Hon. Walter H. Page.
1st Secretary of Legation ... Mr. William Phillips.
Office of Legation, 123, **Victoria Street, S.W.; hours, 11 to 3. Passports and Visas granted on personal application and identification at the Legation.**
Consul-General ......Mr. J. L. Griffiths, 42 to 45, New Broad Street, E.C.

Argentine Republic—
Minister .... Senor Vicente L. Dominguez, 2, Palace Gate, W.
Consul-General ...... Senor S. G. Uriburu, 601, Salisbury House, Finsbury Circus, E.C.

Austria Hungary—
Ambassador .... **Count Mensdorff Pouilly-Dietrichstein**, G.C.V.O., 18, Belgrave Sqr., S.W.
Consul-General ...... **Baron Alfred de Rothschild, 22 and 23, Laurence Pountney Lane, E.C.**

Belgium—
Minister.............. ... **Count de Lalaing, 15, West Halkin Street, Belgrave Square, W.**
Consul-General......... **Monsieur E. Pollet**, 40, Finsbury Square. E.C.

Brazil—
Minister.................. **Senhor Regis de Oliveira**, 1, Halkin Street, S.W.
Consul.................... **Senhor F. Alves Vieira, Coventry House, South Place**, Finsbury, E.C.

Bulgaria—
Minister.................. **Monsieur** Michel Madjaroff, 51, Queen's Gate, S.W.

Chili—
Minister .... **Senor Agustin Edwards**, 48, Grosvenor Square, W.
Consul..................... **Senor Vicente Echeverria Lariain**, 4, Lloyd's Avenue, Fenchurch Street, E.C.

China—
Minister.................. **Liu Yuk-lin, 49, Portland Place, W.**

Colombia—
Minister.................. **Señor S. Perez Triana**, 45, Avenue Road, Regent's Park, N.W.
Consul-General........ Don José M. Nuñez, Sicilian Avenue, Southampton Row, W.C.

Denmark—
Minister .... **Monsieur** de Grevenkop-Castenskiold, 29, Pont Street, S.W.
Consul-General ...... **J. W. Faber, Esq., 8, Byward Street, Gt. Tower Street, E.C.**

France—
Ambassador .... **Monsieur Paul Cambon**, G.C.V.O., **Albert Gate House, Hyde Park, W.**
Consul-General ...... **Monsieur de Coppet**, 51, Bedford Square, W.C.; **(11 to 4, 11 to 1 Sats.).**

German Empire—
Ambassador .... Prince Karl Max Lichnowsky, **9, Carlton House Terrace. S.W.**
Consul-General ...... Herr Johannes, 21A, Bedford Place, **Russell Square, W.C.**

Greece—
Minister.................. **Monsieur J. Gennadius**, 14, De Vere Gardens, S.W.
Consul-General .... **Monsieur J. Stavridis, 40, Old Broad Street, E.C.; 12 to 4 (12 to 1 Saturdays).**

Italy—
Ambassador .... Marquis G. Imperiali di Francavilla, 20, **Grosvenor Square, W.**
Consul-General........ Marquis Alessandro **Faà di Bruno, 44, Finsbury Square. 11 to 3, Saturday, 11 to 1.**

Japan—
Ambassador .... Monsieur Inouye.
Consul-General .... ————————.

Mexico—
Minister.................. Señor Don Miguel Cavarrubias, **98, Cromwell Road, S.W.**
Consul .... **Adolfo Bülle, Esq. 7, Broad Street House, New Broad Street, E.C.**

Montenegro—
Consul-General ...... Sir J. Roper Parkington, 24, **Crutched Friars, E.C.**

Netherlands—
Minister.................. **Baron Dr. K. W. Gericke van Herwijnen, 8, Grosvenor Gardens, S.W.**
Consul-General........ **Jonkheer H. S. J. Maas**, Finsbury Circus House, Blomfield Street E.C.

Norway—
Minister.................. Monsieur P. B. Vogt, 25, The Boltons, S.W.
Consul-General ...... **Monsieur** W. Eckell, 22, Great St. Helen's, E.C.

Persia—
Minister .... Mirza Mehdi Khan Mushir el Mulk, 36, Queen's Gate Terrace, S.W.
Consul-General......... **H. Seymour Foster, Esq., 82, Victoria Street, S.W.**

Peru—
Minister .... Senor Don Carlos G. Candamo (resident in Paris).
Consul-General......... Eduardo Lembcke, Esq., 104 Victoria Street, S.W.

Portugal—
Minister .... Senhor Teixeira Gomez, 12, Gloucester Place, Portman Sq., W.
Consul-General........ Senhor Demetrio Cinatti, 6, South Street, Finsbury, E.C.

Rumania—
Minister .... Monsieur M. C. G. Mano, 4, Cromwell Place, S.W.
Consul General........ ——————

Russia—
Ambassador .... Count A. de Benckendorff, Chesham House, Chesham Place, S.W.
Consul-General .... Baron de Heyking, 20, Great St. Helens, E.C. 11 to 3 (11 to 1 Saturdays).

Servia—
Charge d'Affaires ... ——————.

Spain—
Ambassador .... Don Wenceslao de Villa-Urrutia, G.C.V.O., 1, Grosvenor Gardens, S.W.
Consul-General......... Senor J. M. Torroja y Quinzá, 40, Trinity Square, E.C. 10 to 4.

Sweden—
Minister .... Count H. Wrangel, 73, Portland Place, W.
Consul-General......... Monsieur D. Danielsson, 63, Finsbury Pavement, E.C. 10 to 4 (10 to 2 Saturdays).

Switzerland—
Minister .... Monsieur Gaston Carlin, 3, Portland Place, W. Hours, 11 to 4 (11 to 2 Saturdays).

Turkey—
Ambassador .... Ahmed Riza Bey, 69, Portland Place, W.
Consul-General......... Mundji Bey, 7, Union Court, Old Broad Street, E.C. Hours, 10 to 3 (10 to 2 Saturdays.)

Uruguay—
Minister.................. Senor Don Frederico R. Vidiella, 194, Queen's Gate, S.W.

CONTINENTAL TIME.

SIMULTANEOUS TIME.

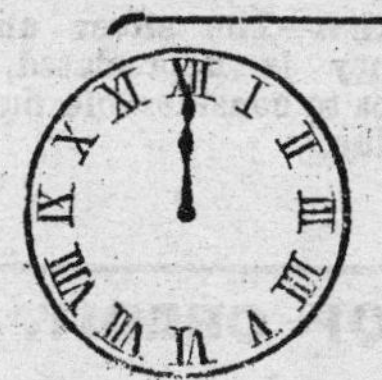

WEST EUROPE TIME.
[GREENWICH TIME.]

MID EUROPE TIME.
One hour in advance of Greenwich Time.

EAST EUROPE TIME
Two hours in advance of Greenwich Time.

In BELGIUM, FRANCE, SPAIN, and PORTUGAL the railway services are arranged according to *West Europe (Greenwich) Time*; in HOLLAND, according to *Amsterdam Time*, which is 20 minutes in advance of Greenwich Time; in GERMANY, AUSTRIA, HUNGARY, SWITZERLAND, ITALY, SERVIA, DENMARK, NORWAY, SWEDEN, and part of TURKEY, according to *Mid Europe Time*, which is one hour in advance of West Europe Time; in BULGARIA, RUMANIA, and part of TURKEY, according to *East Europe Time*, which is one hour in advance of Mid Europe Time, and two hours in advance of West Europe Time; in GREECE, according to Athens Time; in RUSSIA, the train services in this Guide are according to St. Petersburg Time, but the railway authorities usually issue time tables also shewing the services by local time, such as Warsaw and Moscow Time, etc.

West Europe (Greenwich) Time is 20 minutes later than Amsterdam Time.
" " " 1 hour " " Mid Europe Time.
" " " 1 hr.35min. " " Athens Time.
" " " 2 hours " " East Europe Time.
" " " 2 hr. 1 min. " " St. Petersburg Time.

IN BELGIUM, FRANCE, ITALY, SPAIN, AND PORTUGAL TIME is reckoned to 24 o'clock.

A CONCISE TABLE OF FOREIGN MONEYS,

REDUCED FROM ENGLISH into the CURRENCY of OTHER COUNTRIES AT PAR.

England.	France, Italy, Belgium, Switzerland.	Germany	Holland.	United States.	Austria and Hungary in Notes.	Russia in Notes
£ s. d.	Frs. Cts.	Mks. Pfg.	Fl. Cts.	Dols. Cts.	Kronen.	Roubles
0 0 0½	0 052	0 04	0·02^{5}	0 01	·04	·01
0 0 1	0 104	0 08	0 05	0 02	·08	·0
0 0 2	0 208	0 17	0 10	0 04	·18	·0
0 0 3	0 312	0 25	0 15	0 06	·26	·1
0 0 4	0 416	0 33	0 20	0 08	·38	·14
0 0 5	0 520	0 42	0 25	0 10	·48	·18
0 0 6	0 625	0 50	0 30	0 12	·56	·21
0 0 7	0 729	0 58	0 35	0 14	·66	·25
0 0 8	0 833	0 67	0 40	0 16	·76	·28
0 0 9	0 937	0 75	0 45	0 18	·86	·32
0 0 10	1 040	0 84	0 50	0 20	·96	·36
0 0 11	1 144	0 92	0 55	0 23	1·04	·39
0 1 0	1 25	1 0	0 60	0 25	1·20	·47
0 2 0	2 50	2 0	1 20	0 50	2·40	·95
0 3 0	3 75	3 0	1 80	0 75	3·60	1·42
0 4 0	5 0	4 0	2 40	1 0	4·80	1·90
0 5 0	6 25	5 0	3 0	1 25	6·	2·37
0 6 0	7 50	6 0	3 60	1 50	7·20	2·85
0 7 0	8 75	7 0	4 20	1 75	8·40	3·32
0 8 0	10 0	8 0	4 80	2 0	9·60	3·80
0 9 0	11 25	9 0	5 40	2 25	10·80	4·27
0 10 0	12 50	10 0	6 0	2 50	12·	4·75
0 11 0	13 75	11 0	6 60	2 75	13·20	5·22
0 12 0	15 0	12 0	7 20	3 0	14·40	5·70
0 13 0	16 25	13 0	7 80	3 25	15·60	6·17
0 14 0	17 50	14 0	8 40	3 50	16·80	6·65
0 15 0	18 75	15 0	9 0	3 75	18·	7·12
0 16 0	20 0	16 0	9 60	4 0	19·20	7·60
0 17 0	21 25	17 0	10 20	4 25	20·40	8·07
0 18 0	22 50	18 0	10 80	4 50	21·60	8·55
0 19 0	23 75	19 0	11 40	4 75	22·80	9·02
1 0 0	25 0	20 0	12 0	5 0	24·	9·40
2 0 0	50 0	40 0	24 0	10 0	48·	18·80
3 0 0	75 0	60 0	36 0	15 0	72·	28·20
4 0 0	100 0	80 0	48 0	20 0	96·	37·60
5 0 0	125 0	100 0	60 0	25 0	120·	47·
6 0 0	150 0	120 0	72 0	30 0	144·	56·40
7 0 0	175 0	140 0	84 0	35 0	168·	65·80
8 0 0	200 0	160 0	96 0	40 0	192·	75·20
9 0 0	225 0	180 0	108 0	45 0	216·	84·60
10 0 0	250 0	200 0	120 0	50 0	240·	94·

EXPLANATION OF THE CURRENCIES OF THE VARIOUS COUNTRIES.

In **France, Belgium, Switzerland,** and **Italy,** 1 franc=100 centimes. **Germany,** 1 mark=100 pfennig. **Holland,** 1 florin or gulden = 100 cents. **Norway, Sweden, and Denmark,** 1 krone=100 öre. **United States,** 1 dollar=100cents. **Spain,** 1 peseta =100 centimos. **Austria,** 1 krone =100 heller. **Hungary,** 1 korona =100 fillér. **Portugal,** 1 milreis =1000 reis. **Greece,** 1 drachma =100 leptas. **Turkey,** 1 piastre = 40 paras. **Russia,** 1 rouble =100 kopecks.

In France, Belgium, Switzerland, Italy, and Greece, 5 franc pieces are legal tender in each country, irrespective of the country of origin. Smaller Italian coins only pass in their own country; French, Belgian, and Swiss small silver coins pass indiscriminately, but not the copper or nickel centimes

Spain.—The silver and paper currency is depreciated, and is subject to considerable fluctuations in value.

IV.—FOREIGN MONEY—LETTERS OF CREDIT.

Drafts and Letters of Credit Payable in Foreign Money may be had on the principal towns abroad from Foreign bankers in London, which are subject to no deduction for exchange or commission; the sums payable being fixed on this side; they only require a foreign bill stamp according to the law of the country where they are made payable.

Circular Notes of small denomination are issued (£10, £20) for the convenience of the traveller by most of the principal London bankers, and form a very safe and convenient kind of Letter of Credit. A Letter indicating the name of the correspondent abroad accompanies the note, which must be produced on presenting it for payment; and tourists should be careful to keep the letter always separate from the notes.

The traveller should be always provided with small change in the legal current coin of the country through which he passes, as every exchange entails a consequent loss. English Money and Bank Notes can be exchanged in the principal Continental Cities, but it is better to be provided with Foreign Currency before leaving for the Continent, especially as half-sovereigns, etc., are sometimes refused abroad or changed under value.

GOLD AND SILVER COIN TABLE.—Showing the approximate values of the following Gold and Silver Coins abroad, subject to variations according to the fluctuations in the rates of exchange. Corrected monthly by **Messrs. A. KEYSER & CO.**, 21, Cornhill, London, E.C., from whom drafts and letters of credit on the principal towns abroad may be obtained.

DESCRIPTION OF COIN	Value in English.			United States.		France, Belgium, Switzerland.		German Empire.		Holland.		Austrian and Hungarian Paper.		Italian.	
GOLD.	£	s.	d.	Doll.	Cts.	Frs.	Cts.	M.	Pf.	Gl.	Ct.	Kr.	H.	Lire	Cts.
English Sovereign	1	0	0	4	87½	25	23	20	44	12	15	24	12½	25	90
Twenty Franc Piece	0	15	10	3	84	20	0	16	13	9	51	19	25	20	0
German 20 Mark Piece	0	19	6	4	74	24	70	20	0	11	77	23	50	24	70
Dutch 10 Florins	0	16	4	3	96	20	80	16	60	10	0	19	80	20	80
Imperial (Russian)	0	15	10	3	85	20	0	16	13	9	54	18	70	20	0
Twenty Kroner (Swedish, Norwegian, and Danish)	1	1	9	5	25	27	40	22	20	13	10	24	92	27	40
Half-Eagle (5 dolls. U.S.)	1	0	6	5	0	25	85	20	90	12	38	24	50	25	85
SILVER.															
English Shilling	0	1	0	0	24	1	25	1	0	0	60	1	14	1	25
Five Franc Piece	0	3	11½	0	95	5	0	4	0	2	37½	4	54	5	0
One Franc Piece	0	0	9½	0	19	1	0	0	80	0	47½	0	92	1	0
One Mark	0	0	11¾	0	24	1	22	1	0	0	59	1	12	1	22
One Florin (Dutch)	0	1	7¾	0	40	2	05	1	70	1	0	1	88	2	05
One Krone (Danish, Swedish, and Norwegian)	0	1	1	0	27	1	30	1	18	0	66	1	24	1	30
One Peseta (Spanish)	0	0	8	0	16	0	80	0	7	0	35	0	75	0	80
One Dollar (U.S.)	0	4	1	1	0	5	10	4	10	2	46	4	70	5	10

THE METRIC SYSTEM OF WEIGHTS AND MEASURES, WITH ENGLISH EQUIVALENTS.

Linear Measure
- 1 Centimètre = 0·3937 inch.
- 1 METRE = 39·3701 inch = 3·28 feet = 1·093 yard.
- 1 Kilomètre = 1093·6 yards = 0·62137 mile.

Weight ...
- 1 Milligramme = 0·015 grains troy.
- 1 GRAMME = 15·43 ,, ,,
- 1 Kilogramme = 2·205 lb. avoirdupois
- 1 Quintal métrique = 100 kilogramme = 220·5 ,, ,,
- 1 Tonneau = 1000 ,, = 2205 ,,

Measure of Capacity ... 1 LITRE = 1·76 pint.

The Metric System of Weights and Measures, with trifling variations of denomination, has been adopted in the following countries:—

AUSTRIA	GERMANY	ITALY	SERVIA	SWITZERLAND
BELGIUM	*GREECE	NORWAY	SPAIN	§TURKEY
DENMARK	HOLLAND	PORTUGAL	SWEDEN	
FRANCE	HUNGARY	§RUMANIA		

*—In Greece the following weights may be used—

1 Oke = 2.80 lbs. avoirdupois.

1 Stater = 44 Oke = 123.2 lbs. avoirdupois.

§—In Turkey and Rumania the following weights are also used—

1 Oke = 2.83 lbs. avoirdupois.

1 Kintal = 44 Oke = 125 lbs. avoirdupois.

RUSSIAN WEIGHTS AND MEASURES.

Verst = 0.663 mile. 1 Pood = 40 Pund = 36.12 lbs. avoirdupois. Vedro = 2.7 imperial gallons.

DISTANCE AND MEASURE TABLES.

Kilomètre and Mètre Tables.

Distances on Continental Railways are generally measured by the *Kilometre* (kilometer, chilometro, etc.) of 1,000 mètres. One mètre=1·094 English yard=3·281 feet=39·37 inches=1 1/10th yard nearly. Hence, to convert mètres into yards, add 1/10th; to convert yards into mètres, subtract 1/11th. Hence, again, 10 mètres=32·81 feet; 100 mètres=328·1 feet; 1,000 mètres (or kilomètre)=3,281 feet, or 5 furlongs nearly. Hence, a kilomètre=⅝th of an English mile; or 5 miles=8 kiloms., nearly; or 10 miles=16 kiloms.

To convert English statute miles into geographical (or sea) miles, subtract ⅛th. One sea mile=1·15 English mile=1·85 kilomètre. Hence 100 sea miles=115 English miles=185 kilomètres.

TABLE OF KILOMETRES AND ENGLISH MILES.

Kils.	Mls.	Mls.	Kils.
1=	0·621	1=	1·609
2=	1·243	2=	3·219
3=	1·864	3=	4·828
4=	2·485	4=	6·437
5=	3·107	5=	8·047
6=	3·728	6=	9·656
7=	4·349	7=	11·27
8=	4·971	8=	12·87
9=	5·592	9=	14·48
10=	6·214	10=	16·09
11=	6·835	11=	17·7
12=	7·456	12=	19·31
13=	8·078	13=	20·92
14=	8·699	14=	22·53
15=	9·321	15=	24·14
16=	9·942	16=	25·76
17=	10·563	17=	27·36
18=	11·185	18=	28·97
19=	11·806	19=	30·58
20=	12·427	20=	32·18
30=	18·64	30=	48·28
40=	24·85	40=	64·37
50=	31·07	50=	80·47
60=	37·28	60=	96·56
70=	43·49	70=	112·65
80=	49·71	80=	128·74
90=	55·92	90=	144·84
100=	62·14	100=	160·93
200=	124·28	200=	321·86
300=	186·41	300=	482·79
400=	248·55	400=	643·72
500=	310·69	500=	804·65
600=	372·83	600=	965·59
700=	434·97	700=	1126·52
800=	497·10	800=	1287·45
900=	559·24	900=	1448·38
1000=	621·38	1000=	1609·31

Centimètres	Inches
0	0
2½	1
5	2

TABLE OF METRES, YARDS, AND FEET.

mètres	yards	feet
1=	1·09 =	3·281
2=	2·18 =	6·562
3=	3·27 =	9·843
4=	4·36 =	13·123
5=	5·45 =	16·404
6=	6·54 =	19·685
7=	7·63 =	22·966
8=	8·72 =	26·247
9=	9·81 =	29·527
10=	10·936=	32·809
11=	12·03 =	36·09
12=	13·12 =	39·37
13=	14·22 =	42·65
14=	15·31 =	45·93
15=	16·4 =	49·21
16=	17·5 =	52·49
17=	18·59 =	55·76
18=	19·68 =	59·06
19=	20·78 =	62·34
20=	21·87 =	65·618
30=	32·81 =	98·427
40=	43·74 =	131·236
50=	54·68 =	164·045
60=	65·616=	196·84
70=	76·58 =	229·66
80=	87·49 =	262·47
90=	98·42 =	295·28
100=	109·36 =	328·09
200=	218·72 =	656·18
300=	328·08 =	984·27
400=	437·44 =	1312·36
500=	546·8 =	1640·45
600=	656·16 =	1968·54
700=	765·52 =	2296·63
800=	874·88 =	2624·72
900=	984·24 =	2952·81
1000=	1093·63 =	3280·9
8000= 5 miles, nearly.		

THERMOMETRIC SCALES.

Deg. Centi-grade	Deg. Fahr-enh'it	Deg. Réau-mur.	
100	212	80	WATER BOILS (bar. at 30 inch = 760 mm.)
95	203	76	
90	194	72	
85	185	68	
80	176	64	
78·3	173	62·7	ALCOHOL BOILS
75	167	60	
70	158	56	
65	149	52	
60	140	48	
55	131	44	
50	122	40	
45	113	36	
40	104	32	
37·8	100	30·2	Fever heat commences.
36·7	98	29·3	Blood Heat.
35	95	28	
30	86	24	
25	77	20	Summer heat.
20	68	16	
15	59	12	Normal temp.
10	50	8	Temperature of Spring Water
5	41	4	
0	32	0	WATER FREEZES
—5	23	—4	
—10	14	—8	
—15	5	—12	
—18	0	—14·4	Zero Fahrenheit.

BAROMETER.

Millim.	Inches.
715 =	28·15
720 =	28·35
725 =	28·54
730 =	28·74
735 =	28·94
740 =	29·13
745 =	29·33
750 =	29·53
755 =	29·73
760 =	29·92
765 =	30·12
770 =	30·32
775 =	30·51
780 =	30·71
785 =	30·91
790 =	31·10

Inches.	Millim.
31 =	787·4
30 =	762·0
29 =	736·6
28 =	711·2
27½ =	698·5

Intermediate heights—to be added to above

Millim.	Inches.
1 =	·039
2 =	·079
3 =	·118
4 =	·158
5 =	·197

Inches.	Millim.
0·1 =	2·5
0·2 =	5·1
0·3 =	7·6
0·4 =	10·1
0·5 =	12·7
0·6 =	15·2
0·7 =	17·8
0·8 =	20·3
0·9 =	22·9

Barometer.—The weather glass and rainfall in France are measured by the Millimètre = 1/1000th of a Mètre=·0394 inches=4/100th of an Inch. Thus, 724 Millimètres (mm.) correspond to 28½ inches; 736½ mm. to 29 inches; 749½ mm. to 29½ inches; 762 mm. to 30 inches; 775 mm. to 30½ inches. (See Table above). For comparison, remember that the Mean Temp. of London is 39° in winter, 50½° annual; and the Rainfall, 25 to 26 inches.

Thermometer Table.—On the Continent thermometers are frequently graded for both Centigrade and Reaumur.

Weights and Measures.—A Penny weighs ⅓ oz., or 10 grammes; a halfpenny, ⅙ oz. A French centime or cent. weighs a gramme; its diameter equals a centimètre; and 100 cents. in a row equal a mètre. 1 Centimètre=10 Millimètres=4/10th of an Inch; or 2½ Centimètres=1 Inch. An inch is the diameter of a halfpenny. A penny is 1/10th foot in diameter.

A B C DIRECT ROUTES
TO THE
PRINCIPAL CITIES, WATERING PLACES, and RESORTS in EUROPE,
WITH QUICKEST TRAINS
From LONDON, pages lxxiii to cxvii.

Note.—At the pages referred to in the Routes will be found *full particulars* of departure and arrival of Trains, Steamers, and Diligences.

English Railways connecting with the Continent—

Via Dover and Calais, via Dover and Ostend, via Folkestone and Boulogne, and via Queenborough and Flushing—
The South Eastern and Chatham Railway Co..........(Advert., pp. vii to x).
The Belgian State Railway and Mail Packet Service ....(Advert., pp. 714-715).

Via Newhaven and Dieppe—
The London, Brighton, and South Coast Railway Co. ...(Advert., p. 713).

Via Southampton, Havre, Cherbourg, and St. Malo—
The London and South Western Railway Co. ....(Advert., p. 716).

Via Harwich and Hoek van Holland and Harwich and Antwerp—
The Great Eastern Railway Co...............................(Advert., first page opposite Cover).

From LONDON to	ROUTES.		FARES. 1st Cl. £	s.	d.	2nd Cl. £	s.	d.	Validity of Ticket. Days	Departure from London.	Arrive Destination.	Time of Journey HRS	Excess luggage per 20 lb
Aix-la-Chapelle ...	London to Ostend, Bruges, and Ghent	102								**OhX** 9 a0	10 p9	₵12	
Via Ostend-Malines.										,, 9 p0	8 a41	₵11¾	
314 miles.	On to Malines and Louvain ...	101											
Thro' Table p. 9.	,, Liege, Verviers, and Herbesthal	104											See page lxiv.
	,, **Aix-la-Chapelle**	122	2	10	0	1	15	0	15				
	Return fare		4	8	5	3	2	2	60				
Via Calais.	London to Calais and Lille ...	26								**OhX** 9 a0	9 p48	₵11¾	
339 miles.	On to Tournai, Enghien, and Brussels	103								,, 2p§5	4 a15	13¼	
Thro' Table p. 9.										,, 9 p0	10 a4	₵12	
	,, Liege, Verviers, and Herbesthal	104								§—Via			See page lxiv.
	,, **Aix-la-Chapelle**	122	3	1	11	2	3	3	15	Boulogne			
	Return fare		5	7	10	3	17	4	60				
Via Ostend and Brussels.	London to Ostend, Bruges, Ghent, and Brussels	102								**OhX** 2 p5	4 a15	₵13¼	
318 miles.	On to Liege, Verviers, and Herbesthal	104											See page lxiv.
Thro' Table p. 9.	,, **Aix-la-Chapelle**	122	2	10	0	1	15	0	15				
	Return fare		4	8	5	3	2	2	60				
Via Antwerp.	London to Harwich, Antwerp	110								**Liverpool**			See page lxiv.
302 miles.	On to **Aix-la-Chapelle**	99	1	19	2	1	4	6	15	**Str** 8 p40 Not Sun.	2 p41	17	

₵—Through Carriage from Boulogne, Calais, Dieppe, Flushing, H. v. Holland, Ostend—as the case may be.—

From LONDON to	ROUTES	PAGE	FARES. 1st Cl. £ s. d.	FARES. 2nd Cl. £ s. d.	Validity of Ticket. Days	Departure from London.	Arrive Destination.	Time of Journey HRS	Excess luggage per 20 lb
Aix-les-Bains	London to Boulogne, Abbeville, Amiens, and Paris......	18				**ChX** 2p 5	6 a47	16¾	
Via Boulogne.	On to Dijon 48; Bourg	63B							
607 miles.	„ Aix-les-Bains	60	5 3 4	3 10 11	15				4/-
Thro' Table p. 1.	**Return fare**		8 16 0	6 8 0	60				
Via Calais.	London to Calais, Boulogne, Abbeville, Amiens, and Paris	18				**Vic** 11a0	6 a 7	19	4/2
635 miles.	On to Dijon 48; Bourg	63B				**ChX** 9 p0	5 p42	20¾	
Thro' Table p. 1.	„ Aix-les-Bains	60	5 3 4	3 15 11	15				
	Return fare		8 16 0	6 8 0	60				
Via Dieppe.	London to Dieppe, Rouen, and Paris	76				**Vic** 10a0	6 a 7	20	
594 mile						„ 8p45	5 p42	21	
Thro' Table 1.	On to Dijon 48; Bourg	63B							
	„ Aix-les-Bains	60	4 12 0	3 4 5	15				3/6
	Return fare		7 6 9	5 5 5	60				
Via Havre.	London to Havre, Rouen, and Paris	76				**Waterloo** 9p45	10p55	25	
689½ miles.	On to Dijon 48; Bourg	63B				Not Sun. night.			
Thro' Table p. 1.	„ Aix-les-Bains	60	4 13 4	3 4 0	15				
	Return fare		7 8 3	5 5 2	60				
Alassio.........	London to Calais, Boulogne, Amiens, and Paris...............	18				**Vic** 11 a0	6p11	31¼	
1027 miles via Calais.						**ChX** 9 p0	11a14	38¼	
	On to Dijon, Macon, Lyons, Marseilles......................	48							¶
	„ Cannes, Nice, Menton, Ventimiglia 54; Alassio	272	8 4 11	5 13 2	20				
Via Marseilles.	Fare via Boulogne, Paris, Marseilles......................					**ChX** 10 a0	6p11	32¼	¶
999 miles via Boulogne.	¶—5/10 to Ventimiglia; thence -/2.		8 4 11	5 13 2	20				
986½ miles via Dieppe.	London to Dieppe, Rouen, Paris	76							
	Paris to Alassio as above (Single and Return tickets issued to Ventimiglia)		7 7 0	5 1 9	20	**Vic** 10 a0	6p11	32¼	
						„ 8 p45	11a14	38½	
Via Turin.	See Routes to Turin.								
	On to Savona 272; Alassio......	272A				**ChX** 2 p 5	10p39	31¾	
855 miles......	Fare via Boulogne and Turin...		7 9 1	5 2 9	20				
843 miles......	Fare via Dieppe and Turin......		6 11 1	4 11 3	20				3/11
Alexandria.. *Via Naples.* 2557 miles.	See Routes to Naples, or Through Tables London to Naples pages 1 & 5. Societa Nazionale Steamer from Naples every Thursday at 4.0 p.m.; leave London Tues. aft., arr. Alexandria Monday		19 4 6	13 1 0	......				
	Norddeutscher Lloyd Steamer July 11th at 12.0 noon.		... ...	... ...	......				
Via Brindisi. 2437 miles.	See Routes to Brindisi, or Through Tables London to Brindisi, via Mont Cenis p. 1, via St. Gothard p. 5. The Austrian Lloyd Co. steamer from Brindisi every Tues. and Sat.		21 9 0	14 8 6	......				

From LONDON to	ROUTES.	Page	FARES. 1st Cl. £	s.	d.	2nd Cl. £	s.	d.	Validity of Ticket. Days	Departure from London.	Arrive Destination.	Time of Journey HRS	Excess luggage per 20 lb.
ALEXANDRIA—*continued.*	See Simplon Express via Paris to Trieste........................	1											
Via Trieste. 2491 miles.	Austrian Lloyd steamer from Trieste every Sun. and Fri. 1.0 p.m..........................		23	13	3	...	...	...	......				
Via Marseilles. 2565 miles.	See Train Service from London to Marseilles, page civ.												
	Messageries Maritimes steamer from Marseilles every Friday. Leave London Thurs., arrive Alexandria Tuesday		20	17	3	14	1	5	......				
	Norddeutscher Lloyd Steamer July 2nd and 16th.		21	15	2	14	12	11	......				
Via Constantin'ple 3170 miles.	See Orient or Ostend-Vienna Express to Constantinople...	8											
	Khedivial Mail Steamer from Constantinople every Tuesday aft. Leave London Sat., arrive Alexandria Sat.		25	11	0	...	...	...	......				
Via Constanza (Kustendje).	By Orient or Ostend-Vienna Express to Constanza (Kustendje)	8											
	Rumanian State Rly. Steamer from Constanza every Tues. night arr. Alexandria Mon.		25	16	10	...	...	...	......				
Algiers .... Thro' Table p. 1. *Via Calais.* 1239 miles.	See routes to Marseilles. Thence Cie. Generale Transatlantique steamers on Sun., Tues., Wed., and Fri.; Cie. de Navigation Mixte steamer on Monday and Thursday.........		10	14	11	7	10	7	22				
	Return fare		16	4	7	11	18	8	90				
Amsterdam *Via Hoek van Holland.* 258 miles.	London to Hoek van Holland and Schiedam	112											
	On to The Hague & Amsterdam	119	1	14	9	1	3	11	15	**Liverpool Str** 8 p30	7 a30	₵10¾	1/3
	Return fare		2	15	11	1	18	7	60				
Via Flushing. 310 miles.	London to Flushing, Rosendaal, and Breda..................	113								**Vic** 10 a0	10p50	₵12½	
	On to Tilburg 116; Utrecht ...	115								" 8 p30	8 a10	₵11½	
	" Amsterdam	118	1	14	9	1	3	11	15				1/6
	Return fare		2	15	11	1	18	7	60				
Via Calais. 384 miles.	London to Calais and Lille......	26								**ChX** 9 a0	12a29	15	
	On to Brussels 103; Rosendaal	110	[No Throu			gh Ticket]				" 9 p0	11a22	14½	
	,, Rotterdam 117; Amsterdam	119	3	4	6	2	5	5	...				
Via Ostend. 364 miles.	London to Ostend and Brussels	102								**ChX** 9 a0	12a29	15	
	On to Rosendaal 110; Rotterdam	117	[No Throu			gh Ticket]				" 9 p0	11a22	14½	
	,, Amsterdam	119	2	14	6	1	18	9	...				

₵—Through Carriage from Boulogne, Calais, Dieppe, Flushing, H. v. Holland, Ostend—as the case may be.—₵

From LONDON to	ROUTES.		FARES. 1st Cl.			2nd Cl.			Validity of Ticket.	Departure from London.	Arrive Destination.	Time of Journey	Excess luggage per 20 lb
		PAGE	£	s.	d.	£	s.	d.	Days			HRS	
Antwerp	London to Ostend, Bruges,												
Via Ostend.	and Ghent	102								ChX 9 a0	6 p28	9½	
	On to Antwerp	101	1	18	4	1	7	0	7	„ 9 p0	8 a0	11	
235 miles.	**Return fare**		3	8	9	2	8	7	30				2/3
	London to Calais and Lille ...	26								ChX 9 a0	6 p 9	9	
Via Calais.	On to Blandain, Tournai, and									Vic 11 a0	8 p16	9¼	
269 miles.	„ Brussels 103 ; Antwerp	110	2	10	5	1	15	1	7	ChX 2p§5	1 a2	11	
	Return fare		4	9	3	3	3	10	30	„ 9 p0	6 a47	9¾	2/4
										§—Via B	oulo	gne.	
	London to Flushing and									Vic 10 a0	9 p46	11¾	
Via Flushing.	Rosendaal	113								„ 8 p30	7 a6	10½	
242 miles.	On to Esschen and Antwerp ...	110	1	13	8	1	3	10	7				2/-
	Return fare		2	19	1	2	3	9	30				
Via Harwich.	London to Harwich and									Liverpool			
209 miles.	Antwerp	110	1	7	0	0	16	6	7	Str 8†p40	8 a0	11¼	1/-
	Return fare		2	2	0	1	6	0	60	†-Not on	Sun.		
Arcachon ...	London to Boulogne and Paris	18								ChX 2 p5	8 a51	18¾	
Via Boulogne.	On to Orleans, Blois, Tours,												
662 miles.	Poitiers, and Bordeaux	34											
Thro' Table p. 7.	„ Arcachon	45A											4/3
	Return fare		9	4	9	6	14	5	60				
	London to Calais and Paris ...	18								Vic 11 a0	8 a2	21	
Via Calais.	On to Orleans, Blois, Tours,									ChX 9 p0	6 p11	21¼	
690 miles.	Poitiers, and Bordeaux	34											
Thro' Table p. 7.	„ Arcachon	45A											4/4
	Return fare		9	4	9	6	14	5	60				
	London to Dieppe, Rouen, and									Vic 10 a0	8 a2	22	
	Paris	76								„ 8 p45	6 p11	21½	
Via Dieppe.	On to Orleans, Blois, Tours,												
64 miles.	Poitiers, and Bordeaux	34											
Thro' Table p. 7.	„ Arcachon	45A	4	17	9	3	8	3	15				3/8
	Return fare		7	15	1	5	11	7	60				
Athens	See Routes to Brindisi.												
Via Brindisi.	From Brindisi, Austrian Lloyd,												
Thro' Table p. 1.	Societa Nazionale, or Greek												
1860 miles.	steamer, Sun., Mon., Wed.,												
	Fri., and Sat. for Corfu												
	and Patras	350											
	On to Athens	325	13	9	0	9	4	9	...	... ...	...	...	...
	See Routes to Trieste.												
	From Trieste by Austrian												
Via Trieste.	Lloyd Steamer on Sun. and												
	Tues. for Corfu and Patras...	350											
	On to Athens	325	16	12	6	11	10	3	...	... ...	...	...	...
	See Routes to Marseilles.												
	From Marseilles by Messageries												
Via Marseilles.	Maritimes Cie. steamer for												
	Piræus. See Steamer List.												
2270 miles.	On from Piræus to Athens...	325	...	...	...	...	...	...	...	... ...	...	...	...
	[Fares from Marseilles £6 8s.]												
	By Orient or Ostend-Vienna												
	Express to Bucharest and												
Via	Constanza (Kustendje)........	8											
Constanza	Rumanian State Ry. Steamer												
(Kustendje).	to Piræus Tuesday 11.30 p.m.												
	arrive Piræus Sat. morning												
	On from Piræus to Athens ...	325	21	0	10	...	...	...	...	... ...	...	...	...

The "a" and "p" inserted in the departure and arrival times denote "a.m." and "p.m."

From LONDON to	ROUTES	PAGE	FARES. 1st Cl. £ s. d.	FARES. 2nd Cl. £ s. d.	Validity of Ticket. Days	Departure from London.	Arrive Destination.	Time of Journey HRS	Excess luggage per 20 lb
Avranches... 285 miles.	London to Southampton, Cherbourg, and Lison	79				Waterloo 8p15	1 p 2	16¾	
	On to Avranches	75A	2 2 8	1 9 2	7	Tues. and Thurs. only			
	Return fare		3 11 5	2 8 5	60				
Baden-Baden... *Via Ostend.* 535½ miles.	London to Ostend Bruges, Ghent, and Brussels	102				ChX 9 a0	5a45	19¾	
	On to Namur, Jemelle, Arlon, Bettingen, and Luxemburg	103A				„ 2 p5	10a13	19¼	
	„ Metz, Strassburg, and Appenweier	210				„ 9 p0	5p14	19¼	
	„ Oos and Baden	141	3 19 0	2 14 3	15				See page lxiv.
	Return fare		7 4 2	4 18 11	60				
Via Flushing. 590 miles.	See Flushing route to Cologne					Vic 10 a0	9 a18	22¼	
	On from Cologne to Mayence...	122				„ 8p30	4 p2	18½	
	On to Mannheim	139							
	„ Oos and Baden	140A	4 1 5	2 13 3	15				See page lxiv.
	Return fare		7 9 5	4 19 0	60				
Via Hoek van Holland. 605 miles.	See Hoek v. Holland route to Cologne, and on to Baden as in previous route		4 1 5	2 13 3	15	Liverpool Str 8p30	5 p31	20	See page lxiv.
	Return fare		7 9 5	4 19 0	60				
Via Boulogne or Calais and Paris. 635 miles via Calais.	By Orient Express, see Through Table	8				ChX §10a0	4 a52	18	
	London to Calais, Boulogne, Abbeville, Amiens, & Paris	18				Vic 11 a0	6 a53	19	
	On to Nancy and Deutsch Avricourt	64				ChX 9 p0	5 p55	20	
	„ Strassburg & Appenweier	210							
	„ Oos and Baden	141	5 9 0	3 14 8	15				
	§—By Orient Express from Paris.								
Via Boulogne-Laon 553½ miles.	London to Boulogne & Amiens	18				ChX 2 p5	6 a53	15¾	
	On to Tergnier and Laon	21				„ 4§p30	10a13	16¾	
	„ Avricourt	64A							
	„ Strassburg	210				§—Not on Sunday from London.			
	„ Baden-Baden	141	4 12 9	3 3 3	15				
Via Dieppe. 595 miles.	London to Dieppe, Paris, and as in previous route		4 10 11	3 3 0	15	Vic 10 a0	6 a53	20	
	Return fare		7 12 0	5 6 9	60	„ 8 p45	5 p55	20¼	
Barcelona ... *Via Montauban.* 1000 miles.	London to Paris	18 or 76				ChX 10 a0	3 ‡40	29¾	
	On to Montauban	32				Vic 8 p45	7 a53	35½	
	„ Toulouse and Narbonne	45B				ChX 9 p0	7 a53	35	
	„ Portbou	46							
	„ Barcelona	295	...	...	...				
	[Fares from Paris, £5 4s. 9d. and £3 12s. 3d.]								
	‡—Barcelona Express, extra fare from Paris.								
Via Lyons. 1046 miles.	London to Paris	18 or 76				ChX 10a0	7 ‡32	32½	
	On to Tarascon	48				„ 9 p0	7 a53	35	
	„ Cette	57							
	„ Narbonne	45B							
	„ Portbou	46							
	„ Barcelona	295	...	...	...				
	[Fares from Paris, £5 11s. 6d. and £3 16s. 10d.]								

The "a" and "p" inserted in the departure and arrival times denote "a.m." and "p.m."

From LONDON to	ROUTES.	PAGE	FARES. 1st Cl. £ s. d.	FARES. 2nd Cl. £ s. d.	Validity of Ticket. Days	Departure from London.	Arrive Destination.	Time of Journey. HRS	Excess luggage per 20lb
						Vic 11 a0	5 a58	₵18	
Basle...........	London to Calais and Lille...	26				ChX 4‡p30	7 a58	₵14½	
	On to Douai.........................	23				ChX 9§p0	12p42	₵14¾	
Via Calais-Laon.	„ St. Quentin and Laon ...	21							
	„ Reims...........................	67							
584 miles.	„ Chalons	67							
Thro' Table p. 5.	„ St. Dizier and Chaumont	66							
	„ Belfort and Alt-Munsterol	68							
	„ Basle	207A	4 15 8	3 6 1	15				3/5
	Return fare		7 19 11	5 15 7	60				
	‡—From London on Week-days only								
	§—This service is from London on Friday night only.								
Via Boulogne-Laon	London to Boulogne Abbeville Amiens	18				ChX 2 p5	6 a34	₵15½	
560 miles.	On to Tergnier	21							
Thro' Table p. 5.	„ Laon	21							
	Thence as in previous route....		4 15 8	3 6 1	15				3/5
	Return fare		7 19 11	5 15 7	60				
	London to Ostend, Ghent, and					ChX 9 a0	5 a43	₵19¾	
	Brussels..........................	102				„ 2 p5	11a15	₵20¼	
Via Ostend.	On to Namur, Jemelle Arlon,					„ 9 p0	5 p36	₵19½	
588 miles.	Bettingen, Luxemburg...	103A							
Thro' Table p. 5.	„ Metz and Saarburg	210							See page lxiv.
	„ Strassburg	211							
	„ Mulhausen and Basle ...	208	4 4 11	2 17 6	15				
	Return fare		7 15 11	5 3 6	60				
Via Calais-Paris.	London to Calais, Abbeville,					Vic 11 a0	4 ‡45 a	16¾	
613 miles.	Amiens, and Paris..............	18				„ 11 a0	5 a58	18	
	On to Belfort and Alt-Munsterol	68				ChX 9 p0	5§p15	19¼	
	„ Basle	207A	5 1 8	3 11 6	15				
	‡—Engadine Express. Train de Luxe, extra fare £1 3s. 5d.								
	§—Via Belfort-Delle p. 68, forward p. 266								
Via Boulogne-Paris	London to Boulogne and Paris	18				ChX 2 p5	5 a58	15¾	
585 miles.	On as in previous route		4 17 0	3 6 6	15				
Via Dieppe-Paris.	London to Dieppe, Rouen, and					Vic 10 a0	5 a58	19	
577 miles.	Paris	76				„ 8 p45	5§p15	19½	
	On to Belfort and Alt-Munsterol	68							
	„ Basle	207A	4 5 7	2 19 10	15				3/1
	Return fare		6 19 5	4 19 3	60				
	See route to Cologne via Flushing.					Vic 8 p30	5 p47	₵20	
	Cologne to Coblence & Bingerbruck	122							
Via Flushing.	On to Kreuznach (125) and Neustadt	206							
Thro' Table p. 5. 672½ miles via Strassburg;	„ Strassburg and Basle ...	208	4 12 6	2 19 3	15				See page
690 miles via Carlsruhe.	**Return fare**		8 11 8	5 11 0	60				
	Or—from Cologne to Mayence	122				Vic 10 a0	11 a0	24¼	lxiv.
	On to Mannheim	136							
	„ Carlsruhe and Basle......	140	4 12 6	2 19 3	15				
	Return fare		8 11 8	5 11 0	60				
Via Hoek van Holland.	See route to Cologne via Hoek van Holland and on as in					Liverpool Str 8 p30	7 p56	₵22½	See page lxiv.
Thro' Table p. 5. 687 miles.	previous route....................		4 12 6	2 19 3	15				
	Return fare		8 11 8	5 11 0	60				

₵—Through Carriage from Boulogne, Calais, Dieppe, Flushing, H. v. Holland, Ostend—as the case may be.—₵

From LONDON to	ROUTES.	PAGE	FARES. 1st Cl. £ s. d.	FARES. 2nd Cl. £ s. d.	Validity of Ticket. Days	Departure from London.	Arrive Destination.	Time of Journey HRS	Excess luggage per 20lb.
Baveno	See routes to Lausanne.					**Vic** 11 a0	10§30	Ȼ22¾	
Via Lausanne.	On to Domodossola	263B	[No Throu	ghTicket]		„ 11 a0	11a48	Ȼ23¾	
	„ Baveno	274	... ...	... ...		**ChX** 2 p5	5p42	27¾	
Via Calais.	758 miles		6 6 1	4 7 6		„ 9 p0	10p45	24¾	
Via Boulogne.	730 miles		6 6 1	4 7 6		**Vic** 10 a0	11a48	Ȼ24¾	
Via Dieppe.	715 miles		5 8 7	3 16 3		„ 8 p45	10p45	25	
	§—Simplon Express, train de luxe.								
Bayreuth ...	See routes to Cologne.					**ChX** 9 a0	3 p21	29¼	
	On to Mayence & Aschaffenburg	122				„ 9 p0	10p42	24¾	
Via Ostend.	„ Wurzburg......................	196							See
701 miles.	„ Nürnberg......................	195A							page
	„ Bayreuth	202	4 19 10	3 5 4	15				lxiv.
Via Calais.	See routes to Cologne, and on					**ChX** 9 a0	3 p21	29¼	See
726 miles.	as above		5 11 9	3 13 8	15	„ 2§p5	3 p21	24¼	page
	§—Via Boulogne, Laon, Muhlacker, Nurnberg.								lxiv.
Via Flushing.	See routes to Cologne, and on								See
704 miles.	as above		4 15 6	3 1 9	15	**Vic** 10a0	3 p21	28¼	page
	Return fare		8 17 8	5 16 0	60	„ 8 p30	10p42	25	lxiv.
Via Hoek van Holland.	See routes to Cologne, and on								See
718 miles.	as above		4 15 6	3 1 9	15	... ...	... ..	.....	page
	Return fare		8 17 8	5 16 0	60				lxiv.
St. Beatenberg	See routes to Berne.								
	On from Berne to Thun	267							
	On to Beatenbucht	268F							
	Thence climbing rail in 14 min. to St. Beatenberg		... ...	... ...	......				
Beaulieu......	London to Calais, Amiens and					**ChX** 9 a0	1 p54	29	
	Paris	18				**Vic** 11 a0	1 p54	28	
Via Calais,	On to Dijon, Macon, Lyons, and					**ChX** 9 p0	6 a53	34	
971 miles.	Marseilles	48							
	„ Toulon, Cannes, Nice, and Beaulieu	54	7 15 10	5 6 11	15				
	Return fare		12 4 10	8 17 6	60				5/9
Via Boulogne.	London to Boulogne, Amiens,					**ChX** 10 a0	1 p54	28	
943 miles.	Paris	18							
	On to Dijon, Macon, Lyons, and								
	Marseilles	48							
	„ Toulon, Cannes, Nice, and Beaulieu	54	7 15 10	5 6 11	15				5/7
	Return fare		12 4 10	8 17 6	60				
Via Dieppe.	London to Dieppe, Rouen,					**Vic** 10 a0	1 p54	28	
930 miles.	and Paris	76				„ 8p45	6 a53	34¼	5/1
	On as in previous route		6 17 11	4 15 5	15				
Via Havre.	London to Havre, Rouen, and					**Water-**			
1025 miles.	Paris	76				**loo** 9p45	1 p5	41¼	
	On as above		... ...	... ...	......	Not Sun.			5/1

The "a" and "p" inserted in the departure and arrival times denote "a.m." and "p.m."

From LONDON to	ROUTES	PAGE	FARES. 1st Cl. £ s. d.	FARES. 2nd Cl. £ s. d.	Validity of Ticket. Days	Departure from London.	Arrive Destination.	Time of Journey HRS	Excess luggage per 20 lb
Belgrade...... *Orient Express* 1544 miles.	London to Paris via Calais or Boulogne .... On from Paris by Orient Express, see Through Table	18 8	14 10 0	... ...	......	ChX 10 a0 Mon., Wed., Thurs., Sat.	5 a58 Wed Fri. Sat., Mon	43	
Ostend-Vienna Express. 1363 miles.	London to Vienna by Ostend-Vienna Express, and on from Vienna by Orient Express, see Through Table	8	13 1 6	... ...	......	ChX 9 a0 Mon., Wed., Thurs., Sat.	5 a58 Wed Fri. Sat., Mon	44	
	[Also see routes to Vienna, and thence.]								
Bergen............ *Via Copenhagen.* 1570 miles.	See routes to Copenhagen. On to Helsingborg..................... " Gothenburg .... " Mellerud .... " Christiania .... " Bergen .... Fares from Christiania to Bergen, 1st class £1 10s., 2nd class 19s. 3d. For fares to Christiania see routes to that place.	 311 309A 306 304A 305A							
Via Hull.	Wilson steamer every Thursday —fare from Hull		2 16 0	2 5 0	......				
Via Newcastle.	Steamer on Tues., Thurs., and Sat.								
Berlin .... *Nord Express.* 726½ miles.	By Nord Express, see Through Table from London .... Ticket of Sleeping Car Co. Fare via Ostend	9	 6 10 5			ChX 9 a0	7 a29	§21½	
Via Flushing. 664½ miles. Thro' Table p. 9.	London to Flushing & Breda On to Boxtel.............................. " Goch and Wesel..................... " Oberhausen .... " Dortmund, Hamm, Minden, Hanover, Stendal, and Berlin .... Return fare	113 116 120 132 161	4 3 0 7 12 8	2 14 10 5 2 3	15 60	Vlo 10a0 " 8p30	7 a57 4 p54	§21 §19½	See page lxiv.
Via Ostend. 720 miles. Thro' Table p. 9.	London to Ostend, Bruges, Ghent, and Brussels .... On to Liege Verviers, and Herbesthal .... " Aix-la-Chapelle, Cologne " Elberfeld 134A; Soest...134A " Paderborn and Hameln " Hildesheim .... " Brunswick .... " Magdeburg .... " Berlin............................... Return fare	102 104 122 134A 164 155 159 162 161	5 1 11 9 12 3	3 6 8 6 5 5	15 60	ChX 9 a0 " 2 p5 " 9 p0	8 a54 3 p48 6 p12	22¾ 24¾ 20¼	See page lxiv.

§—Through Carriage from Boulogne, Calais, Dieppe, Flushing, H. v. Holland, Ostend—as the case may be.—§

From LONDON to	ROUTES	PAGE	FARES 1st Cl. £	s.	d.	FARES 2nd Cl. £	s.	d.	Validity of Ticket.	Departure from London.	Arrive Destination.	Time of Journey HRS	Excess luggage per 20lb
BERLIN —*contd.*													
Via Calais.	London to Calais and Lille ...	26								ChX 9 a0	8 a54	22¾	
747 miles.	On to Enghien and Brussels ...	103								" 2§15	3 p48	28¼	
Thro' Table p. 9.	" Liege, Verviers, and Herbesthal	104								" 9 p0	9 p:8	23¼	
	" Aix la Chapelle, Cologne	122								§—Via Boulogne			See page lxiv.
	" Dusseldorf, Dortmund, Hamm, Hanover Stendal and Berlin	161	5	13	10	3	14	11	15				
	Return fare		10	11	8	7	0	8	60				
Via Hoek van Holland.	London to Hoek van Holland and Rotterdam	112								Liverpool Str 8 p30	4 p54	C19½	
628 miles.	On to Utrecht	118											See page lxiv.
Thro' Table p. 9.	" Amersfoort	115A											
	" Rheine 118B; Lohne ...	156A											
	" Hanover and Berlin	161	4	3	0	2	14	10	15				
	Return fare		7	12	8	5	2	3	60				
Berne .... *Via Boulogne-Laon.* 626 miles.	London to Boulogne & Amiens	18								ChX 2 p5	8a35	17½	
	On to Tergnier 21; to Laon ...	21											
	" Reims 67; to Chalons ...	67											
	" Chaumont....................	66											
	" Belfort & Alt-Munsterol	68A											3/5
	" Basle 207A; Olten.........	258											
	" Berne	257	4	18	3	3	7	8	15				
	Return fare		8	6	1	6	0	4	60				
Via Calais-Laon. 656½ miles.	London to Calais and Lille......	26								Vio 11 a0	7 a40	19¾	
	On to Douai	23											
	" St. Quentin and Laon ...	21											
	" Reims 67; Chalons ...	67											
	" St. Dizier and Chaumont	66											
	" Belfort & Alt-Munsterol	68A											
	" Basle 207A; Olten	258											3/10
	" Berne	257	5	1	1	3	10	0	15				
	Return fare		8	6	1	6	0	4	60				
Via Ostend. 654 miles.	See Ostend route to Basle.									ChX 9 a0	9 a20	23¼	
	Basle to Olten	258								" 2 p5	3 p44	24½	
	On to Berne	257	4	13	0	3	3	2	15	" 9 p0	8 p53	23	3/3
Via Calais or Boulogne-Paris. 635 miles via Calais. 607 miles via Boulogne. Thro' Table p. 1.	London to Calais, Boulogne, and Paris	18								Vio 11§a0	6 a8	18	
	On to Dijon	48								ChX 2 p5	8 a35	C17½	
	" Pontarlier....................	52								" 9 p0	6 p55	21	
	" Neuchatel	265											
	" Berne	259B	5	1	1	3	10	0	15				4/3
	Return fare		8	6	1	6	0	4	60				
	§—By Simplon and Oberland Express, Train de Luxe, first departure from London July 8th.												
Via Dieppe-Paris. 594 miles. Thro' Table p. 1.	London to Dieppe and Paris...	76								Vio 10 a0	8 a35	21½	
	On to Berne via Pontarlier...		4	9	8	3	3	0	15	" 8 p45	6 p55	21¼	3/1
	Return fare		7	3	11	5	3	3	60				
	Or, from Paris to Belfort and Delle	68								Vio 10 a0	7 a40	20¾	
	On to Delemont 266; to Biel...	264A								" 8 p45	6 p5	20¼	3/1
	" Berne	265	4	9	8	3	3	0	15				
	Return fare		7	3	11	5	3	3	60				

The "a" and "p" inserted in the departure and arrival times denote "a.m." and "p.m."

From LONDON to	ROUTES	PAGE	Fares 1st Cl. £	s.	d.	Fares 2nd Cl. £	s.	d.	Validity of Ticket	Departure from London	Arrive Destination	Time of Journey	Excess luggage per 20lb
									Days			HRS	
Biarritz	London to Calais and Paris	18								**Vic** 11 a0	7 a29	20½	4/10
Via Calais.	On to Orleans, Tours, Bordeaux	34								**ChX** 9 p0	9 p 5	24	
784 miles.	„ **Biarritz**	45	6	9	6	4	9	3	15				
Thro' Table p. 7.	**Return fare**		10	5	2	7	9	2	60				
Via Boulogne.	London to Boulogne and Paris	18								**ChX** 10 a0	7 a29	21½	
756½ miles.	On to **Biarritz as in previous**									„ 2 p 5	11a58	21¾	
Thro' Table p. 7.	**route**		6	9	6	4	9	3	15				4/8
	Return fare		10	5	2	7	9	2	60				
Via Dieppe.	London to Dieppe, Rouen, and									**Vic** 10 a0	7 a29	21½	
744 miles.	Paris	76								„ 8 p45	9 p 5	24¼	4/2
Thro' Table p. 7.	On to **Biarritz as in first route**		5	11	4	3	17	6	15				
	Return fare		8	15	7	6	6	3	60				
Bologna	See routes to Basle.												
	On to Olten and Lucerne.........	258											
Via Basle.	„ Bellinzona, Lugano, and Chiasso	259											
	„ Como and Milan	269A											
	„ Bologna................................	279											§
926½ miles......	Boulogne and Basle.................									**ChX** 2 p 5	7 p0	28	
951 miles......	Calais and Basle									**Vic** 11 a0	7 p0	31	
										Vic 10 a0	7 p0	32¼	
944 miles......	Dieppe and Basle...................									„ 8 p45	10a10	36½	
954½ miles......	Ostend and Basle									**ChX** 2p 5	12a12	33¼	
1039 miles......	Flushing and Basle									**Vic** 8p30	10a12	36½	
1053½ miles......	Hoek v. Holland and Basle ...									**Liv St** 8p30	10a12	36½	
	Ostend or Calais and Basle......									**ChX** 9 p0	10a12	36¼	
	See routes to Turin.									**ChX** 2p 5	11p41	32¾	
Via Turin.	On to Alessandria	270								„ 9 p0	1 p34	39½	
	„ Piacenza	273											
944 miles......	„ Bologna.............................	279											
Bordeaux ...	London to Calais, Boulogne,									**Vic** 11a0	3 a43	16¾	
Via Calais.	Abbeville, Amiens, and Paris	18								**ChX** 9 p0	4 p49	19¾	
655 miles.	On to Orleans Tours, Poitiers,												
Thro' Table p. 7.	Bordeaux	34	5	10	6	3	16	5	15				4/2
	Return fare		8	16	10	6	8	9	60				
Via Boulogne.	London to Boulogne, Amiens,												
627 miles.	Paris	18								**ChX** 10 a0	3 a43	17¾	
Thro' Table p. 7.	On to Orleans, Tours, Poitiers,									„ 2 p 5	6 a58	17	
	Bordeaux	34	5	10	6	3	16	5	15				4/-
	Return fare		8	16	10	6	8	9	60				
Via Dieppe.	London to Dieppe, Rouen,									**Vic** 10a0	3 a43	17¾	
614 miles.	and Paris	76								„ 8p45	4 p49	20	
Thro' Table p. 7	On to Orleans, Tours, Bordeaux	34	4	12	5	3	4	9	15				3/6
	Return fare		7	7	2	5	5	10	60				

§—5/6 to Chiasso, thence 1/-

The "a" and "p" inserted in the departure and arrival times denote "a.m." and "p.m."

From LONDON to	ROUTES	PAGE	FARES. 1st Cl. £ s. d.	FARES. 2nd Cl. £ s. d.	Validity of Ticket. Days	Departure from London.	Arrive Destination.	Time of Journey HRS	Excess luggage per 20lb
Bordighera.. 992 miles.	London to Calais, Boulogne Paris	18							
	On to Lyons, Marseilles	48							
	„ Nice and Ventimiglia	54				Vic 11 a0	4 p21	28¼	
	„ Bordighera	272	7 19 2	5 9 2	20	ChX 9 p0	9a40	35½	‡
	‡—5/10 to Ventimiglia, and 1d. thence each 20lbs., with minimum charge of 8d.								
Via Marseilles									
964 miles. ...	Fare via Boulogne, Paris, Marseilles		7 19 2	5 9 2	20	ChX 10 a0	4 p21	29¼	
	London to Dieppe, Rouen, and Paris	76				Vic 10 a0	4 p21	29¼	
						„ 8 p45	9 a40	36	‡‡
951 miles. ...	Paris to Bordighera as above		7 1 3	4 17 8	20				
‡‡—5/2 to Ventimiglia, and 1d. thence each 20lbs., with minimum charge of 8d.									
Via Turin.	See routes to Turin.								
	On to Savona 272; Bordighera 272A								
895½ miles ...	Fare via Boulogne and Turin...		7 13 7	5 5 11	20	Vic 10 a0	12 a8	37	
883 miles ...	Fare via Dieppe and Turin......		6 15 8	4 14 4	20	ChX 2 p 5	12 a8	33	3/11
Boulogne........ 100½ miles.	London to Folkestone and Boulogne	18	1 7 2	0 19 3	7	ChX 10 a0	1 p30	3½	¾d.†
						„ 2 p 5	5 p50	3¾	
	Return fare		2 13 7	1 18 4	60			†per	lb.
Bourboule, La *Via Calais.* 572 miles.	London to Calais and Paris	18				Vic 11 a0	7 a20	20¼	
	On to Orleans and Vierzon......	32				ChX 9 p0	5 p15	20¼	
	„ Montlucon & Laqueuille	37							
	„ La Bourboule	37	4 18 11	3 8 7	15				3/8
	Return fare		7 19 5	5 16 3	60				
Via Boulogne. 544 miles.	London to Boulogne and Paris	18				ChX 10 a0	7 a20	21¼	
	On to La Bourboule as in previous route		4 18 11	3 8 7	15				3/7
	Return fare		7 19 5	5 16 3	60				
Via Dieppe. 532 miles.	London to Dieppe and Paris	76				Vic 10 a0	7 a20	21¼	
	On to La Bourboule as in first route					„ 8 p45	5 p15	20½	
	Return fare		6 9 2	4 12 11	60				3/-
Bremen .... *Via Flushing.* Thro' Table p. 9. 498 miles.	London to Flushing, Rosendaal, Breda	113				Vic 10 a0	4 a19	₵17½	
						„ 8 p30	1 p12	₵15½	
	On to Boxtel	116							
	„ Goch and Wesel	120							
	„ Oberhausen	132							See
	„ Munster and Bremen ...	132	3 2 4	2 2 0	15				page
	Return fare		5 11 3	3 16 8	60				lxiv.
Via Hoek van Holland. 461 miles.	London to H. v. Holland and Rotterdam	112				Liverpool Str 8 p30	1p12	₵15¾	
	On to Utrecht 118; Amersfoort	115A							
	„ Bentheim and Rheine...	118B							
	„ Osnabruck	156C							See
	„ Diepholz and Bremen...	132	3 2 4	2 2 0	15				page
	Return fare		5 11 3	3 16 8	60				lxiv.
Via Ostend. Thro' Table p. 9. 565½ miles.	See route to Cologne via Ostend.					ChX 9 a0	5 a2	18¾	See
	On from Cologne to Bremen ...	132	4 2 0	2 15 10	5	„ 2 p 5	12p44	21¾	page
	Return fare		7 12 5	5 3 0	60	„ 9 p0	3p22	17¼	lxiv.
Via Calais. Thro' Table p. 9. 590½ miles.	See route to Cologne via Calais.					ChX 9 a0	5 a2	18¾	See
	On from Cologne to Bremen ...	132	4 13 11	3 3 9	15	„ 2 § 5	12p44	21¾	page
	§—Via Boulogne. **Return fare**		8 11 10	5 18 3	60	„ 9 p0	7 p48	21¾	lxiv.

₵—Through Carriage from Boulogne, Calais, Dieppe, Flushing, H. v. Holland, Ostend—as the case may be.—₵

From LONDON to	ROUTES.	PAGE	FARES. 1st Cl. £ s. d.	FARES. 2nd Cl. £ s. d.	Validity of Ticket. Days	Departure from London.	Arrive Destination.	Time of Journey HRS	Excess luggage per 20lb
Breslau	See routes to Berlin.								
	On to Breslau	179							
	Via Ostend and Berlin		... ...	... .	....	**ChX** 9 p0	12 0	26	
	Fare via Flushing and Berlin		5 10 6	3 10 4	15	**Vic** 10 a0	2 p0	27	
	Return fare		10 7 8	6 13 3	60	„ 8p30	12 0	26½	
	Fare via H.v. Holland & Berlin		5 10 6	3 10 4	15	**Liverpool**	nght		
	Return fare		10 7 8	6 13 3	60	**Str.** 8p30	12 0	26½	
Brindisi	London to Calais and Paris ...	18				**Vic** 11 a0	2p30	50½	
Via Calais and Paris.	On to Dijon 48; to Bourg	63B				**ChX** 9§p0	5§p54	₵44	
1450 miles.	„ Modane........................	60							
Thro' Table p. 1.	„ Alessandria 270; Piacenza	273							
	„ Bologna 279; Brindisi...	285							
	§—From London Fri. only, arrive		Brindisi Sun.						
Via Boulogne and Paris.	London to Boulogne and Paris	18				**ChX** 2 p5	2p30	47½	
1422 miles.	On to Dijon 48; Bourg...........	63B							
Thro' Table p. 1.	„ Modane 60; Alessandria	270							
	„ Piacenza........................	273							
	„ Bologna 279; Brindisi ...	285							
Via Dieppe and Paris.	London to Dieppe and Paris...	76				**Vic** 10 a0	2p30	51½	
1410 miles.	On to Dijon 48; Bourg	63B							
Thro' Table p. 1	„ Modane........................	60							
	„ Alessandria 270; Piacenza	273							
	„ Bologna 279; Brindisi ...	285	8 11 9	5 16 10	30				
Via Ostend and Basle.	See routes from London via Ostend to Basle.					**ChX** 2 p5	2p30	47½	
Thro' Table p. 5.	Basle to Lucerne	258							
1428 miles.	On to Chiasso 259; Milan	269A	[No Through	Ticket]					
	„ Bologna 279; Brindisi...	285	9 2 9	6 3 4	20				
Brunswick	See route to Cologne via Ostend.					**ChX** 9 a0	5a29	19½	
Via Ostend.	On from Cologne to Elberfeld	134A				„ 2 p5	2p34	23½	
Thro' Table p. 9.	On to Soest	134A				„ 9 p0	4p35	18½	
578½ miles.	„ Paderborn (p. 164) and Hameln	155							
	„ Hildesheim	155	[No Through	Ticket]					
	„ Brunswick	159	4 5 7	2 17 3	......				
Via Calais.	See route to Cologne via Calais.					**ChX** 9 a0	5a29	19½	
Thro' Table p. 9.	On from Cologne to Hanover		[No Through	Ticket]		„ 2§p5	2p34	26¾	
624 miles.	and Brunswick	161	4 16 9	3 5 6	......	„ 9 p0	7p43	21¾	
					§—	Via Boulogne.			
Via Flushing.	London to Flushing, Rosendaal, Breda	113				**Vic** 10 a0	5a29	₵18½	
Thro' Table p. 9.	On to Boxtel	116				„ 8p30	3p15	17¾	
531½ miles.	„ Goch and Wesel............	120							See page lxiv.
	„ Oberhausen	131A							
	„ Hanover and Brunswick	161	3 7 3	2 5 6	15				
	Return fare		6 1 0	4 3 8	60				
Via Hoek van Holland.	London to H. v. Holland and Rotterdam	112				**Liverpool Str** 8p30	3p15	17¾	
Thro' Table p. 9.	On to Utrecht........................	118							
505 miles.	„ Amersfoort	115A							See page lxiv.
	„ Rheine 118B to Lohne	156C							
	„ Hanover and Brunswick	161	3 7 3	2 5 6	15				
	Return fare		6 1 0	4 3 8	60				

The "a" and "p" inserted in the departure and arrival times denote "a.m." and "p.m."

From LONDON to	ROUTES.	PAGE	FARES. 1st Cl. £ s. d.	FARES. 2nd Cl. £ s. d.	Validity of Ticket. Days	Departure from London.	Arrive Destination.	Time of Journey HRS	Excess luggage per 20lb
Brussels	London to Calais and Lille ...	26				**ChX** 9 a0	4p41	₵ 7¾	
Via Calais.	On to Blandain, Tournai,					**Vic** 11a0	6p55	₵ 8	
242 miles.	Enghien, **Brussels**	103	2 7 10	1 13 4	7	**ChX** 9p0	5a21	₵ 8¼	2/2
	Return fare		4 5 4	3 1 2	30				
Via Ostend.	London to Ostend, Bruges,					**ChX** 9 a0	5 p6	₵ 8	
231 miles.	Ghent, **Brussels**	102	1 17 10	1 6 8	7	,, 2 p5	10p25	₵ 8¼	2/3
	Return fare		3 8 0	2 8 0	30	,, 9 p0	5a24	₵ 8½	
Via Boulogne.	London to Boulogne	18A				**ChX** 2 p5	11p14	₵ 9	
268½ miles.	On to Calais..........................	19A							
	Thence as in first route.		2 7 10	1 13 4	7				2/2
	Return fare		4 5 4	3 1 2	30				
						Not on Sun.			
Via Antwerp.	London to Antwerp and					**Liverpool**			
236 miles.	Brussels..............................	110	1 11 8	0 19 0	7	**Str** 8p40	9a11	₵ 12½	1/3
	Return fare		2 8 7	1 10 7	30				
Via Flushing.	London to Vlissingen and								
269 miles.	Rosendaal	113							
	On to Brussels	110	1 17 3	1 6 3	7	**Vic** 10a0	10p29	12½	2/3
	Return fare		3 4 10	2 7 8	30	,, 8p30	8 a24	12	
Bucharest ...	London to Paris via Boulogne	18				**ChX** 10 a0	6 p34	55½	
Orient Express.	On from Paris by Orient Express, see Through Table, page 8. Leave London on Sunday, Tuesday, & Friday.								
1839 miles.			16 0 0	... ...	......				
Ostend-Vienna Express.	London to Vienna and Bucharest by Ostend-Vienna Express, see Through Table, page 8. Leave London on Sunday, Tuesday, & Friday.					**ChX** 9 a0	6p34	56½	
1686 miles.			14 11 4	... ...	......				
	[Also see routes to Vienna, and		thence].						
Via Berlin.	See Flushing Route to Berlin.					**Vic** 10 a0	7 p45	56	
1801 miles.	On to Breslau	179				**ChX** 2 p5	6 a55	62¾	
	,, Kandrzin 218; Oderberg	219							
	,, Cracow	222							
	,, Lemberg 246A; Burdujeni	246A							
	,, Pascani 324B; Bucharest	324	... ...	... ...	......				
	[Fares from Berlin, 1st class,		£6 10s. 4	d., 2nd c	lass,	£4 4s. 11d	.]		
Budapest ...	London to Paris via Calais or					**ChX** 10 a0	11 p5	36	
Orient Express	Boulogne	18							
1293 miles.	On by Orient Exp., see Through								
	Table, page 8		12 9 7	... ...	......				
Ostend-Vienna Express.	London to Vienna and Budapest by Ostend-Vienna Express, Through Table, p. 8............					**ChX** 9 a0	11 p5	37	
1139 miles.			10 14 1	... ...	......				
	[Also see routes to Vienna, and		thence.]						
Via Berlin.	See Routes to Berlin.								
	On to Breslau	179							
	,, Oderberg	218							
	,, Ruttka.............................	253A							
	,, Budapest	232A							
	Via Boulogne and Berlin..		... ...	... ...	......	**ChX** 2 p5	9 a40	42½	
	Via Ostend and Berlin................		... ...	... ...	......	" 9 p0	12p50	38¾	
1273 miles.	Via Vlissingen and Berlin		... ...	... ...	......	**Vic** 8p30	12p50	39¼	
1237 miles.	Via Hoek van Holland and Berlin		... ...	... ...	......	**Liverpool**			
						Str 8p30	12p50	39¼	

₵—Through Carriage from Boulogne, Calais, Dieppe, Flushing, H. v. Holland, Ostend—as the case may be—₵

From LONDON to	ROUTES.		FARES. 1st Cl.	FARES. 2nd Cl.	Validity of Ticket.	Departure from London.	Arrive Destination.	Time of Journey	Excess luggage per 20 lb
			£ s. d.	£ s. d.	Days			HRS	
Cairo............	London to Brindisi by P. & O. Express, see Through Table, page 1. From Brindisi on Sunday night by P. & O. steamer to Port Said or Ismailia, rail from Port Said to Ismailia and Cairo page 328.								
Via Brindisi. 2668 miles.	Leave London Friday night arrive Cairo Wednesday		23 10 0						
	By ordinary train service to Brindisi, and steamer thence		19 10 0						
Via Marseilles. 2710 miles.	London to Paris and Marseilles by P. & O. Marseilles Express, see Through Table page 1. Steamer thence on Friday to Port Said or Ismailia, rail from Port Said to Ismailia and Cairo page 328.		¶	¶—In addition a "Surtax" of ten per cent.					
	Leave London Thursday arrive Cairo Wednesday		23 10 0						
	By ordinary train service to Marseilles, and steamer thence		20 15 0	14 3 0					
Via Trieste.	London to Trieste by Simplon Express, see Through Table, page 1. From Trieste Austrian Lloyd Steamer to Port Said in four to six days								
Via Alexandria.	See routes to Alexandria. On from Alexandria to Cairo p. 327 (18s. from Alexandria)								
Cannes.........	London to Calais, Amiens, Paris	18				**Vic** 11 a0	12p40	25¾	
Via Calais. 948 miles.						**ChX** 9 p0	4 a57	32	
	On to Dijon, Macon, Lyons, Marseilles	48							
	,, Toulon and Cannes......	54	7 12 6	5 4 9	15				5/8
	Return fare		11 19 10	8 14 0	60				
Via Boulogne. 920 miles.	London to Boulogne, Amiens, Paris	18				**ChX** 10 a0	12p40	26¾	
	On to Dijon, Macon, Lyons, Marseilles	48							
	,, Toulon and Cannes......	54	7 5 10	4 19 8	15				5/6
	Return fare		11 19 10	8 14 0	60				
Via Dieppe. 907½ miles.	London to Dieppe, Rouen, and Paris	76				**Vic** 10 a0	12p40	26¾	
						,, 8p45	4 a57	32¼	
	On to Dijon, Macon, Lyons, Marseilles	48							
	,, Toulon and Cannes......	54	6 14 7	4 13 2	15				5/-
	Return fare		10 10 7	7 11 5	60				
Via Havre. 1004 miles.	London to Havre, Rouen, and Paris	76				**Waterloo** 9p45 Not Sun. night.	12p40	39	
	On to Dijon, Macon, Lyons, Marseilles	48							
	,, Toulon and Cannes......	54	6 15 10	4 12 10	15				
	Return fare		10 12 2	7 11 2	60				

The "a" and "p" inserted in the departure and arrival times denote "a.m." and "p.m."

From LONDON to	ROUTES. PAGE	FARES. 1st Cl. £ s. d.	FARES. 2nd Cl. £ s. d.	Validity of Ticket. Days	Departure from London.	Arrive Destination.	Time of Journey HRS	Excess luggage per 20lb
Carlsbad	See route to Cologne via Ostend.				ChX 9 a0	12§21	26¼	
	On from Cologne to Aschaffenburg 122				" 9 a0	5 p31	31½	
Via Ostend.	On to Wurzburg 196							
769½ miles.	,, Nurnberg 195A							
Thro' Table p. 13.	,, Eger 202							
	,, Carlsbad 251	5 8 5	3 11 8	30				2/10
	§—By Ostend-Vienna Express, Train de Luxe.							
Via Flushing. 772½ miles.	See routes to Cologne, via Flushing, and on as above...	5 10 8	3 10 3	30	Vic 10 a0	5 p31	30½	1/-
Via Calais and Cologne. 794½ miles. Thro' Table p. 13.	See route to Cologne via Calais, and on as first route	5 18 11	3 18 8	30	ChX 9 a0	5 p31	31½	2/10
Via Hoek van Holland. 787 miles.	See route to Cologne via Hoek van Holland, and on as first route	5 10 8	3 10 3	30				
	Return fare	10 0 11	6 7 8	60				
Cassel .... *Via Ostend,* 529 miles.	See Ostend route to Cologne.				ChX 2 p5	10a59	19¾	
	From Cologne to Elberfeld and Hagen 134A				" 9 p0	6 p39	20½	See page lxiv.
	On to Warburg and Cassel......135A	3 17 11	2 12 9	15				
Via Flushing. 500 miles.	London to Flushing and Breda 113				Vic 10 a0	10a59	24	
	On to Boxtel 116; Wesel 120				" 8 p30	6 p39	21	
	,, Oberhausen..........131A							
	,, Essen and Witten......... 135							
	,, Hagen 133E; Cassel......135A	3 10 6	2 7 2	15				See page lxiv.
	Return fare	6 7 8	4 5 10	60				
Via Hoek van Holland. 519 miles.	See Hoek v. Holland route to Dusseldorf.				Liverpool Str 8 p30	6 p39	21¼	
	From Dusseldorf to Elberfeld and Hagen 134A							
	On from Hagen to Cassel 135A	3 10 6	2 6 8	15				See page lxiv.
	Return fare	6 7 8	4 5 10	60				
Via Calais. 554 miles.	See Calais route to Cologne and on as in routes above †—Via Boulogne.	4 9 10	3 1 0	15	ChX 2†p5 " 9 p0	10a59 6 p39	19¾ 20½	See page lxiv.
Cauterets	See routes to Paris.				Vic 11 a0	12p49	25¾	
	On from Paris to Bordeaux ... 34							
	On to Morcenx 45							
	,, Tarbes 45							
809½ miles.	,, Lourdes and Pierrefitte 43							
	,, Cauterets 47	... ...	... ...	...	... ...			
	(£4 0s. 4d. and £2 14s. 10d. from Paris).							

Ȼ—Through Carriage from Boulogne, Calais, Dieppe, Flushing, H. v. Holland, Ostend—as the case may be—Ȼ

From LONDON to	ROUTES.	PAGE	FARES. 1st Cl. £ s. d.	FARES. 2nd Cl. £ s. d.	Validity of Ticket. Days	Departure from London.	Arrive Destination.	Time of Journey HRS	Excess luggage per 20lb
	London to Calais, Boulogne,					Vic 11 a0	10a13	23½	
	Abbeville, Amiens, Paris......	18				ChX 9 p0	10p48	25¾	
Chamonix ...	On to Dijon 48; Bourg............	63B							
Via Calais.	,, Bellegarde 60; Annemasse	61A							
	,, Le Fayet de St. Gervais	61A							
734½ miles.	,, Chamonix..................	61B	6 3 7	4 4 4	15				4/7
	Return fare		9 16 5	7 1 6	60				
Via Boulogne.	London to Boulogne and Paris	18				ChX 10 a0	10a13	24½	
	On as in previous route		6 3 7	4 4 4	15	,, 2 p5	4p34	25½	4/6
707 miles.	**Return fare**		9 16 5	7 1 6	60				
Via Dieppe.	London to Dieppe and Paris	76				Vic 10 a0	10a13	24¼	
694 miles.	On as in route above..............		5 5 8	3 12 10	15	,, 8 p45	10p48	26	3/11
	Return fare		8 7 1	5 19 0	60				
Chemnitz	See routes to Leipsic								
	On to Chemnitz	184A							
713 miles	Fare via Flushing		4 18 4	3 1 2	15	Vic 10 a0	1 p59	27	
	Return fare		8 15 10	5 14 10	60	,, 8 p30	8 p30	22¾	
687 miles	Fare via Hoek van Holland ...		4 10 3	2 19 5	15	Liverpool			
	Return fare		8 7 0	5 11 5	60	Str 8p30	8 p13	22¾	
784 miles	Via Ostend		... .	... ...	......	ChX 9 a0	1 p59	28	
						,, 9 p0	11p46	25¾	
Christiania	See routes to Copenhagen via Kiel and via Warnemunde.								
	On to Helsingborg&Gothenburg	303							
	,, Mellerud	306							
Via Hamburg-Copenhagen	,, Fredrikshald	306							
or	,, Christiania	304A				Vic 10 a0	12 0	49	
Via Hamburg-Stralsund.	Or, see routes to Hamburg.								
	On to Lubeck 213A; to Rostock	213							
	,, Stralsund..	181A							
	,, Sassnitz and Trelleborg	181							
Thro' Table p. 9.	,, Malmo 311; Gothenburg	309A							
	,, Mellerud	306							
	,, Fredrikshald	306							
	,, Christiania	304A				Vic 8 p30	9p43	48	See page lxiv.
1239 miles......	Via Flushing and as above......		7 17 6	5 5 3	30				
	Return fare		14 13 6	9 17 4	60				
1202 miles	Via Hoek van Holland............		7 17 6	5 5 3	30	Liverpool			
	Return fare		14 13 6	9 17 4	60	Str 8 p30	9p43	48¼	5/-
1306 miles......	Via Ostend		8 18 2	5 17 10	30	ChX 9 a0	12 0	50	7/9
						,, 9 p0	9 p13	47¾	
1331 miles......	Via Calais..........................		9 9 11	6 5 10	30	ChX 9 a0	12 0	50	6/9
	See routes to Berlin.								
Via Berlin.	On to Sassnitz and Trelleborg	181							
Thro' Table p. 9.	,, Malmo 311; Gothenburg	309A							
	,, Mellerud & Fredrikshald	306							
	,, Christiania	304A							
1331 miles......	Via Flushing and Berlin.........		8 13 2	5 13 5	30	Vic 10 a0	12 0	49	
	Return fare		16 4 9	10 13 9	60	,, 8 p30	9p43	48	
1295 miles......	Via Hoek v. Holland & Berlin		8 13 2	5 13 5	30	Liverpool			
	Return fare		16 4 9	10 13 9	60	Str 8p30	9p43	47¾	4/9
1387 miles......	Via Ostend and Berlin............					ChX 9 a0	12 0	50	
			... ...	... ...	......	,, 9 p0	9p43	47¾	
1414 miles......	Via Calais and Berlin		... ...	... ...	......	ChX 9 a0	12 0	50	
						,, 2 p5	9p43	54½	

The "a" and "p" inserted in the departure and arrival times denote "a.m." and "p.m."

From LONDON to	ROUTES	PAGE	FARES. 1st Cl. £ s. d.	FARES. 2nd Cl. £ s. d.	Validity of Ticket. Days	Departure from London.	Arrive Destination.	Time of Journey HRS	Excess luggage per 20lb
Chur (Coire) ...	See routes to Basle.						a		
	On to Zurich	261				Vic 11 a0	9 §25	21½	
	,, Chur	268B				,, 11 a0	11a25	23½	
Via Calais-Laon. Through Table p. 5.	Fare via Calais-Laon-Basle......		5 12 10	3 18 1	15				
712½ miles.	Return fare		9 7 4	6 14 11	60				3/5
	§—Engadine Express. Train de Luxe, extra fare £1 8s. 2d.								
Via Boulogne-Laon. Through Table p. 5. 688 miles.	Fare via Boulogne-Laon-Basle		5 12 10	3 18 1	15	ChX 2 p5	11a25	20¼	3/5
	Return fare		9 7 4	6 14 11	60				
Via Ostend. 715 miles.						ChX 9 a0	11a25	₵25½	
						,, 2 p5	4 p53	25¾	
	Fare via Ostend-Brussels-Basle		5 1 3	3 8 11	15	,, 9 p0	11p38	25½	3/3
Via Dieppe-Basle 706 miles.	Fare via Dieppe-Paris-Basle ...		5 2 9	3 11 11	15	Vic 10 a0	11a25	24½	3/1
	Return fare		8 6 11	5 18 7	60	,, 8 p45	11p38	26	
Coblence...... *Ostend-Vienna Express.* 419½ miles.	London to Ostend, Brussels, Cologne, and Coblence, see Through Table	8	3 16 11	... ...	...	ChX 9 a0	1 a24	₵15¼	
Via Ostend. 415 miles. Thro' Table p. 13.	See Ostend route to Cologne.					ChX 9 a0	2 a50	16¾	See
	On from Cologne to Coblence...	122	3 4 4	2 4 2	15	,, 2 p5	8 a27	17¼	page
	Return fare		5 17 0	4 0 5	60	,, 9 p0	11a27	13½	lxiv.
Via Calais. 440 miles. Thro' Table p. 13.	See Calais route to Cologne.					ChX 9 a0	2 a50	16¾	See
	On to Bonn, Rolandseck, and					,, 2†p5	8 a27	17¼	page
	Coblence	122	3 16 3	2 12 5	15	,, 9 p0	12p48	14¾	lxiv.
	Return fare		6 16 5	4 15 8	60	†—Via	Boulogne.		
Via Flushing. 418 miles. Thro' Table p. 13.	See Flushing route to Cologne.					Vic 10 a 0	3 a30	₵16½	See
	On to Bonn, Rolandseck, and					,, 8 p30	11a34	₵14	page
	Coblence	122	3 0 0	2 0 4	15				lxiv.
	Return fare		5 6 8	3 13 3	60				
Via Hoek van Holland. 422 miles. Thro' Table p. 13.	See Hoek van Holland route to Cologne.					Liverpool Str 8p30	12p48	₵15¼	See page lxiv.
	On to Bonn and Coblence ...	122	3 0 0	2 0 4	15				
	Return fare		5 6 8	3 13 3	60				
Cologne ...... *Nord Express.* 362 miles.	London to Ostend, Brussels, and Cologne, see Through Table	9	3 6 6	... ...	......	ChX 9 a0	10p46	₵12¾	
Ostend-Vienna Express. 362 miles.	London to Ostend, Brussels, and Cologne, see Through Table	8	3 6 6	... ...	......	ChX 9 a0	11p52	₵14	
Via Ostend-Ghent. 357½ miles. Thro' Table p. 9.	London to Ostend, Bruges, and Ghent	102				ChX 9 a0	11p24	₵13¼	
	On to Malines and Louvain ...	101							
	,, Herbesthal	104							See
	,, Aix-la-Chapelle and Cologne	122	2 16 0	1 18 9	15				page lxiv.
	Return fare		5 0 5	3 9 8	60				
Via Ostend-Brussels. 362 miles. Thro' Table p. 9.	London to Ostend and Brussels	102				ChX 2 p5	5 a40	₵14½	
	On to Louvain and Herbesthal	104				,, 9 p0	9 a51	₵12	See
	,, Aix-la-Chapelle, Cologne	122	2 16 0	1 18 9	15				page
	Return fare		5 0 5	3 9 8	60				lxiv.

₵—Through Carriage from Boulogne, Calais, Dieppe, Flushing, H. v. Holland, Ostend—as the case may be—₵

From LONDON to	ROUTES.	PAGE	FARES. 1st Cl. £ s. d.	FARES. 2nd Cl. £ s. d.	Validity of Ticket. Days	Departure from London.	Arrive Destination.	Time of Journey HRS	Excess luggage per 20 lb
COLOGNE—*contd.*									
Via Calais. 382½ miles. Thro' Table p. 9.	London to Calais, Hazebrouck, Lille	26				**ChX** 9 a0 " 2p†5 " 9 p0	11 pl 5 a40 11a14	₵13 ₵14½ ₵13¾	See page lxiv.
	On to Blandain, Tournai, Enghien, and Brussels	103							
	" Louvain, Liege, and Herbesthal	104				†—Via Boulogne.			
	" Aix-la-Chapelle, Cologne	122	3 7 11	2 7 0	15				
	Return fare		5 19 10	4 4 10	60				
Via Calais and Namur. 393 miles.	London to Calais and La Madeleine	26				**ChX** 9 a0	11 pl	₵13	See page lxiv.
	On to Valenciennes	29A							
	" Aulnoye & Erquelinnes	25							
	" Namur and Liége	92							
	" Herbesthal	104							
	" Cologne	122	3 7 11	2 7 0	15				
	Return fare		5 19 10	4 4 10	60				
Via Flushing. 360½ miles. Thro' Table p. 13.	London to Flushing, Rosendaal, Breda	113				**Vic** 10 a0 " 8 p30	1 a50 9 a56	₵14¾ ₵12½	See page lxiv.
	On to Boxtel	116							
	" Goch and Wesel	120							
	" Oberhausen 131A; Cologne	160A	2 11 9	1 14 9	15				
	Return fare		4 10 0	3 2 0	60				
Via Hoek van Holland. 375 miles. Thro' Table p. 13.	London to Hoek van Holland and Rotterdam	112				**Liverpool Str** 8 p30	11a15	₵13¾	See page lxiv.
	On to Geldermalsen, Tiel, and Nymegen	119							
	" Kleve, Kempen, Neuss, and Cologne	121	2 11 9	1 14 9	15				
	Return fare		4 10 0	3 2 0	60				
Constantinople *Via Bucharest.* Thro' Table p. 8.	ORIENT EXPRESS.—London to Paris, Stuttgart, Vienna, Bucharest, Constanza, and Constantinople	8	19 0 0	... ...		**ChX** 10 a0 Sun., Tu, Fri.	noon 12 0	Wd.	Fri, Mon.
	OSTEND-VIENNA EXPRESS.—London to Brussels, Cologne, Vienna, Bucharest, Constanza, and Constantinople	8	17 13 3	.. .. ..		**ChX** 9 a0 Sun., Tu, Fri.	noon 12 0	Wd.	Fri, Mon.
Via Berlin.	See Routes to Berlin.								
	On to Breslau	179							
	" Kandrzin 218; Oderberg	219							
	" Cracow	222							
	" Lemberg 246A; Burdujeni	246A							
	" Pascani 324B; Bucharest	324							
	" Constanza	324A							
	" Constantinople	360B	... ...	... ...					
	Fares from Berlin to Constantinople, 1st class £9 8s., 2nd class £6 1s. 3d.								

₵—Through Carriage from Boulogne, Calais, Dieppe, Flushing, H. v. Holland, Ostend—as the case may be—₵

From LONDON to	ROUTES.	PAGE	FARES. 1st Cl. £ s. d.	FARES. 2nd Cl. £ s. d	Validity of Ticket. Days	Departure from London.	Arrive Destination.	Time of Journey. HRS	Excess luggage per 20lb
Contrexeville	London to Calais and Amiens	18				ChX 4§p30	5 a45	13	
	On to Tergnier	21				,, 9‡p 0	12p31	15½	
Via Calais. 486 miles.	,, Laon 21; Reims	67							
Thro' Table p. 5.	,, Chalons	67							
	,, St. Dizier, Chaumont	66							
	,, Langres	68A							
	,, Contrexeville	68A	4 2 3	2 17 0	15				3/1
	Return fare		6 16 11	4 19 7	30				
	‡—From London Friday night only.								
	§—From London on Tuesday and Friday only.								
Via Boulogne. 462 miles.	London to Boulogne and Amiens	18				ChX 2 p 5	4 a48	14¾	
	On as in previous route		4 2 3	2 17 0	15				3/1
	Return fare		6 16 11	4 19 7	30				
Copenhagen *Via Ostend and Kiel.* 859 miles. Thro' Table p. 9.	See Ostend route to Cologne.					ChX 9 a0	4 p48	30¾	
	From Cologne to Oberhausen	161				,, 9 p0	10 a4	36	
	On to Bremen and Hamburg	132							
	,, Kiel and Korsoer	168							
	,, Copenhagen	302A	6 2 10	4 3 9	30				See page lxiv.
Via Ostend & Warnemunde. 901 miles. Thro' Table p. 9.	Or, on from Hamburg to Lubeck	213A				ChX 9 a0	6 p41	32¾	
	On to Warnemunde	213				,, 9 p0	9 a42	35¾	
	,, Gjedser and Copenhagen	302A	6 2 10	4 3 9	30				
Via Calais. Thro' Table p. 9.	See Calais route to Cologne, and thence as in preceding routes		6 14 6	4 11 10	30	Same times as above.			See page lxiv.
	Return fare		14 6 11	9 12 0	60				
	London to Flushing, Breda, and Boxtel	113				Vic 10 a0	4 p48	29¾	
						,, 8 p30	10 a4	36½	
	On to Goch and Wesel	120							
	,, Oberhausen	131A							
	,, Bremen and Hamburg	132							
Via Flushing. 792 miles. Thro' Table p. 9.	,, Kiel and Korsoer	168							
	,, Copenhagen	302A	5 1 10	3 10 11	30				
	Return fare		9 10 3	6 14 5	60				
	Or, on from Hamburg to Lubeck	213A							
	On to Warnemunde	213							See page lxiv.
834 miles.	,, Gjedser and Copenhagen	302A	5 1 10	3 10 11	30	Vic 10 a0	6 p41	32	
	Return fare		9 10 3	6 14 5	60	,, 8 p30	9 a42	36	
	London to Hoek van Holland and Rotterdam	112				Liverpool Str 8 p30	8 a12	34¾	
	On to Utrecht	118							
Via Hoek van Holland. 797 miles.	,, Amersfoort	115A							
	,, Bentheim and Rheine	118B							
	,, Osnabruck	156C							
	,, Bremen and Hamburg	132							
	,, Vamdrup 168; Fredericia	303							See page lxiv.
	,, Copenhagen	302	5 1 10	3 10 11	30				
	Return fare		9 10 3	6 14 5	60				
	Or, on from Hamburg to Korsoer	168				Liverpool			
755 miles.	On to Copenhagen	302A				Str 8 p30	10 a4	36½	

The "a" and "p" inserted in the departure and arrival times denote "a.m." and "p.m."

From LONDON to	ROUTES	PAGE	FARES. 1st Cl. £	s.	d.	2nd Cl. £	s.	d.	Validity of Ticket. Days	Departure from London.	Arrive Destination.	Time of Journey HRS	Excess luggage per 20lb.
Cracow	**See routes to Berlin.**									**Vic** 10 a0	8 p10	33	
	On from Berlin to Breslau	179								,, 8 p30	5 a30	32	
	On to Kandrzin	218								**ChX** 2 p5	3 a7	36	
	,, **Oderberg**	219								,, 9 p0	5 a30	31½	
	,, **Cracow**	222	...	...	...	...	...	...	......	**Liverpool Str** 8 p30	5 a30	32	
1088 miles via Flushing; 1052 miles via H. v. Holland.	**Fares via either Queenborough — Flushing, or Harwich — Hoek van Holland**............		6	13	6	4	5	9	30				
	Return fare		12	13	8	8	4	0	60				
Crefeld......... *Via Flushing.* 326 miles.	London to Flushing and Breda	113								**Vic** 8 p30	8 a58	11½	
	On to Boxtel 116 ; to Goch	120											
	,, Crefeld	121	2	7	10	1	12	2	15				
	Return fare		4	2	3	2	16	10	60				
Via Hoek van Holland. 340 miles.	London to Hoek van Holland and Rotterdam	112								**Liverpool Str** 8 p30	10 a5	12½	
	On to Nymegen	119											
	,, Crefeld	121	2	7	10	1	12	2	15				
	Return fare		4	2	3	2	16	10	60				
Davos Platz	**See routes to Basle.**									**Vic** 11 a0	12‡15	24¼	
	On to Zurich	261								,, 11 a0	2 p10	26¼	
	,, **Landquart**	268B								**ChX** 4§p30	2 p42	21¼	
	,, **Davos Platz**..................	268D											
Via Calais. **735½ miles.**	**To Basle viá Calais and on as above**..............................		6	2	10	4	4	9	15				3/5
	Return fare		10	3	4	7	5	6	60				
	‡—Engadine Express. Train de Luxe, extra fare £1 8s. 2d.												
	§—From London on weekdays only—service until 14th Sept.												
Via Boulogne. **711 miles.**	**To Basle via Boulogne and on as above**..............................		6	2	10	4	4	9	15	**ChX** 2 p5	2 p10	23	3/5
	Return fare		10	3	4	7	5	6	60				
Via Dieppe. **724 miles.**	**To Basle via Dieppe, and on as above**		5	12	10	3	18	6	15	**Vic** 10 a0	2 p10	27¼	3/1
	Return fare		9	2	11	6	9	2	60				
Dieppe............ **120½ miles.**	**London to Newhaven and Dieppe**	76	1	8	7	1	0	0	3	**Vic** 10 a0	3 p0	5	
										,, 8p45	2a30	5¾	1/-
	Return fare		2	5	3	1	11	1	30				
Dinan .... ***Via St. Malo.***	**London to Southampton, St. Malo, and Dol**	82											
	On to Dinan............................	79	1	19	0	1	8	0	15				
	Return fare		2	18	5	2	4	7	45				
Dinard......... ***Via St. Malo.***	**London to Southampton and St. Malo. Thence local Steamer (15 min.) to Dinard.**		Fares to St. Malo.										
			1	15	10	1	5	10	7				
	Return fare		2	13	8	2	1	2	180				

The "a" and "p" inserted in the departure and arrival times denote "a.m." and "p.m."

From LONDON to	ROUTES.	PAGE	FARES. 1st Cl. £	s.	d.	2nd Cl. £	s.	d.	Validity of Ticket. Days	Departure from London.	Arrive Destination.	Time of Journey HRS	Excess luggage per 20 lb.
Dortmund ...	London to Flushing, Rosendaal,									**Vic** 10 a0	1a42	14¾	
	Breda	113								,, 8p30	12p16	14¾	
Via Flushing.	On to Boxtel	116											
365 miles.	,, Goch and Wesel.............	120											See
	,, Oberhausen	131A											page
	,, **Essen and Dortmund** ...	160	2	13	6	1	15	6	15				lxiv.
	Return fare		4	13	8	3	3	8	60				
Via Hoek van Holland.	London to Hoek van Holland									**Liverpool**			
366 miles.	and Rotterdam	112								**Str** 8p30	12p16	14¾	
	On to Geldermalsen, Nymegen	119											See
	,, Crefeld	121											page
	,, **Dortmund**	161	2	13	6	1	15	6	15				lxiv.
	Return fare		4	13	8	3	3	8	60				
Dresden	See Ostend route to Cologne.									**ChX** 9 a0	11a20	25¼	
	On to Elberfeld	134A								,, 2 p5	8p27	29¼	
	,, Soest	134A								,, 9 p0	10p14	24¼	
Via Ostend.	,, Paderborn.........................	164											
Thro' Table p. 9.	,, Hameln	155											
770 miles.	,, Hildesheim	155											
	,, Halle	166											See
	,, Leipsic	158											page
	,, **Dresden**........................	188	5	10	8	3	11	3	15				lxiv.
	Return fare		10	9	8	6	14	8	60				
Via Flushing.	London to Flushing and Breda	113								**Vic** 10 a0	11a20	₵24¼	
Thro' Table p. 9.	On to Boxtel	116								,, 8p30	8 p27	₵23	
736 miles.	,, Goch and Wesel	120											
	,, Oberhausen	132											
	,, Hanover and Brunswick	161											
	,, Magdeburg, Halle, and												See
	Leipsic	158											page
	,, **Dresden**..	188	4	13	9	3	0	8	15				lxiv.
	Return fare		8	14	0	5	13	10	60				
Via Calais.	See Calais route to Cologne.									**ChX** 9 a0	11a20	25½	
Thro' Table p. 9.	On to Hanover and Oebisfelde	161								,, 2p†5	8 p27	29¼	
832 miles.	,, Magdeburg	160C								,, 9 p0	1a43	27¾	See
	,, Halle and Leipsic	158											page
	,, **Dresden**........................	188	6	2	6	3	19	6	15				lxiv.
	Return fare		11	9	0	7	9	10	60				
	†—Via Boulogne.												
Via Hoek van Holland.	See Hoek van Holland route to									**Liverpool**			
Thro' Table p. 9.	Hanover.									**Str** 8p30	8 p27	23	See
710 miles.	On to Stendal, 161A; Magdeburg	163											page
	,, Leipsic	158											lxiv.
	,, **Dresden**........................	188	4	13	9	3	0	8	15				
	Return fare		8	14	0	5	13	10	60				
Dusseldorf...										**ChX** 9 a0	11§33	₵13½	
Via Ostend.										,, 9 a0	12 a9	14	See
382½ miles.	See Ostend route to Cologne.									,, 2 p5	6 a22	15¼	page
	On to Dusseldorf	161	2	18	0	2	0	3	15	,, 9 p0	10a40	12¾	lxiv.
	§—Nord Express.												
Via Calais.	See Calais route to Cologne.									**ChX** 9 a0	12 a9	14	See
Thro' Table p. 9.	On to Dusseldorf	161	3	9	11	2	8	6	15	,, 2p†5	6 a22	15¼	page
407½ miles.	†—Via Boulogne.									,, 9 p0	12p32	14½	lxiv.

₵—Through Carriage from Boulogne, Calais, Dieppe, Flushing, H. v. Holland, Ostend—as the case may be.—₵

From LONDON to	ROUTES.	PAGE	FARES. 1st Cl. £ s. d.	FARES. 2nd Cl. £ s. d.	Validity of Ticket. Days	Departure from London.	Arrive Destination.	Time of Journey HRS	Excess luggage per 20lb
DUSSELDORF-*Con*	*tinued.*								
Via Flushing.	London to Flushing and Breda	113				**Vic** 10 a0	1 a11	14¼	
354 miles.	On to Boxtel	116				" 8p30	9a30	12	
	" Goch and Wesel	120							See
	" Oberhausen	131A							page
	" Dusseldorf	160A	2 9 11	1 13 5	15				lxiv.
	Return fare		4 6 5	2 19 5	60				
Via Hoek van Holland.	London to Hoek van Holland								
359 miles.	and Rotterdam	112				**Liverpool**			
	On to Geldermalsen, Nymegen	119				**Str** 8p30	10a33	13	
	" Kleve, Kempen, Neuss...	121							See
	" Dusseldorf	134A	2 9 11	1 13 5	15				page
	Return fare		4 6 5	2 19 5	60				lxiv.
Ems	See Ostend route to Cologne.					**ChX** 9 a0	5 a9	19	See
Via Ostend.	On to Coblence	122				" 2p5	9 a13	18	page
Thro' Table p. 13. 426 miles.	" Ems	146	3 5 5	2 4 10	15	" 9 p0	12p36	14½	lxiv.
Via Calais.	See Calais route to Cologne.					**ChX** 9 a0	5 a9	19	See
Thro' Table p. 13.	On to Coblence	122				" 2p†5	9 a13	18	page
450 miles.	" Niederlahnstein and Ems	146	3 17 4	2 13 2	15	" 9 p0	1p48	15¾	lxiv.
	†—Via Boulogne.								
Via Flushing.	See Flushing route to Cologne.					**Vic** 10 a0	5 a9	18	See
Thro' Table p. 13.	On to Coblence	122				" 8p30	12p36	15	page
429 miles.	" Niederlahnstein and Ems	146	3 1 3	2 1 2	15				lxiv.
	Return fare		5 9 0	3 14 10	60				
Via Hoek van Holland.	See H. v. Holl. route to Cologne.								
	On to Coblence	122				**Liverpool**			See
Thro' Table p. 13. 433 miles.	" Niederlahnstein and Ems	146	3 1 3	2 1 2	15	**Str** 8p30	1 p48	16¼	page
	Return fare		5 9 0	3 14 10	60				lxiv.
Essen	London to Flushing and Breda	113				**Vic** 10 a0	12a44	13¾	
	On to Boxtel	116				" 8 p30	10a30	13	
Via Flushing.	" Goch and Wesel	120							
	" Oberhausen	131A							
345 miles.	" Essen	161	2 10 4	1 13 11	15				
	Return fare		4 7 3	3 0 5	60				
Via Hoek van Holland.	London to Hoek van Holland					**Liverpool**			
	and Rotterdam	112				**Str** 8 p30	11a37	14	
365 miles.	On to Nymegen	119							
	" Crefeld	121							
	" Essen	135	2 10 4	1 13 11	15				
	Return fare		4 7 3	3 0 5	60				
Evian	London to Calais and Paris	18				**Vic** 11 a0	7 a51	21	
Via Calais.	On to Dijon	48				**ChX** 9 p0	7 p54	23	
690 miles.	" St. Amour and Bourg ...	63B							
	" Bellegarde 60; Evian ...	61A	... ...	... ...	...				4/5
Via Boulogne.	London to Boulogne and Paris	18				**ChX** 10 a0	7 a51	22	
662½ miles.	On as in previous route		... ...	... ...	...	" 2 p5	1 p27	23¼	4/3
Via Dieppe.	London to Dieppe and Paris ...	76				**Vic** 10 a0	7a51	22	
650 miles.	On as in previous route		5 0 0	3 9 9	15	" 8 p45	7p14	23¼	3/9
	Return fare		7 18 7	5 13 11	60				

The "a" and "p" inserted in the departure and arrival times denote "a.m." and "p.m."

From LONDON to	ROUTES.	PAGE	FARES. 1st Cl. £	s.	d.	2nd Cl. £	s.	d.	Validity of Ticket. Days	Departure from London.	Arrive Destination.	Time of Journey HRS	Excess luggage per 20 lb
Florence	See routes to Paris.									Vic 11 a0	1 a50	37¾	
Via Paris-Turin	On from Paris to Dijon	48								ChX 9 p0	3 p12	41¼	
	On to Bourg 63B; Modane	60											
Through Table p. 1.	,, Turin, Genoa, and Pisa	270											
	,, Florence..........................	270A											
1020 miles......	Fare via Calais, Paris, Turin ...		8	3	11	5	12	1	20				
995 miles	Fare via Boulogne, Paris, Turin		8	3	11	5	12	1	20	ChX 2 p5	1 a50	34¾	‡
	‡—4/7 to Modane; thence 1/6.												
	Fare via Dieppe, Paris, Turin		7	6	0	5	0	7	20	Vic 10 a0	1 a50	38¾	
	Return fare		12	9	0	8	14	10	60	" 8 p45	3 p12	41½	3/11
	See routes to Paris.												
	On from Paris to Dijon	48											
Via Paris-Milan.	On to Pontarlier.......................	52											
	,, Lausanne, Domodossola	263B											
	,, Milan 274; Florence	279											
1000 miles	Fare via Boulogne and Paris...		7	15	3	5	6	3	10	ChX 10 a0	11p16	36½	
989 miles......	Fare via Dieppe and Paris		7	4	11	5	0	6	20	Vic 10 a0	11p16	36½	3/1
	See routes to Basle.									Vic 11 a0	11p16	35½	
	On from Basle to Lucerne	258											
	On to Lugano and Chiasso	259											
Via Basle-Milan.	,, Como and Milan	269A											
	,, Bologna and Florence ...	279											
Thro' Table p. 5.	Fare via Calais, Laon, Basle, Milan—1033 miles		8	3	2	5	12	8	20				‡
	‡—3/1 to Chiasso; thence 1/3.												
	Fare via Boulogne, Laon, Basle, Milan—1009 miles ...		8	3	2	5	12	8	20	ChX 2 p5	11p16	32¼	‡
										ChX 2 p5	3 a26	36¼	
1022 miles	Fare via Ostend, Basle, Milan		7	11	7	5	3	6	20	" 9 p0	1 p25	39½	
										Vic 10 a0	11p16	36¼	
1037 miles	Fare via Dieppe, Paris, Basle		7	13	0	5	6	5	20	" 8 p45	1 p25	39½	3/1
Flushing......... 170 miles.	London to Queenborough (morn) or Folkestone (night) and									Vic 10 a0	6 p40	8¼	
										" 8 p30	4 a0	7	1/-
	Flushing	113	1	10	5	0	18	10	7				
	Return fare		2	8	2	1	11	8	21				
Frankfort-on-the-Main *Ostend-Vienna Express*	London to Ostend, Brussels, Cologne, and Frankfort, see Through Table	8	4	9	9	...	...	...	......	ChX 9 a0	3 a26	₵17½	
Via Ostend. 500 miles.	See Ostend route to Cologne.									ChX 9 a0	6 a53	21	See
	On to Coblence and Frank-									" 2 p5	11a11	20	page
Thro' Table p. 13.	fort	122	3	14	2	2	10	4	15	" 9 p0	1 p57	₵16	lxiv.
	Return fare		6	16	8	4	12	10	60				
Via Calais. 520½ miles.	See Calais route to Cologne.									ChX 9 a0	6 a53	21	See
	On to Coblence, Mayence,									" 2p†5	11a11	20	page
Thro' Table p. 13.	Frankfort	122	4	6	0	2	18	8	15	" 9 p0	3 p5	₵17	lxiv.
	†—Via Boulogne. **Return fare**		7	16	0	5	8	0	60				
Via Flushing. 498½ miles.	See Flushing route to Cologne.									Vic 10 a0	6 a16	₵19¼	See
	On to Coblence, Mayence,									" 8 p30	1 p57	₵16¼	page
Tho' Table p. 13.	Frankfort	122	3	9	10	2	6	2	15				lxiv.
	Return fare		6	6	3	4	4	10	60				

₵—Through Carriage from Boulogne, Calais, Dieppe, Flushing, H. v. Holland, Ostend—as the case may be—₵

From LONDON to	ROUTES.	PAGE	FARES. 1st Cl. £	s.	d.	2nd Cl. £	s.	d.	Validity of Ticket. Days	Departure from London.	Arrive Destination.	Time of Journey HRS	Excess luggage per 20 lb
FRANKFORT—continued.													
Via Hoek van Holland.	See Hoek van Holland route to Cologne.									**Liverpool Str** 8 p30	3 p5	‡17¾	See page lxiv.
513 miles.	On to Coblence, Mayence,												
Thro' Table p. 13.	Frankfort	122	3	9	10	2	6	2	15				
	Return fare		6	6	3	4	4	10	60				
Via Calais or Boulogne-Laon.	London to Boulogne & Amiens	18											
	On to Tergnier and Laon	21								**ChX** 2 p5	10a14	19¼	
	„ Nancy and Metz	64A								„ 4§p30	2 p17	20¾	
	„ Bingerbruck	125A							§—Not on	Sunday from	London.		
640 miles.	„ Frankfort	123	...	...	...	...	...	...	......				
Franzensbad... *Via Cologne.*	See routes to Cologne.									**ChX** 9 a0	11§37	25½	
	On to Mayence and Ashchaffenburg 122; Wurzburg	196								„ 9 a0	4 p21	30¼	
	„ Nurnberg 195A; Eger	202								**Vic** 10 a0	4 p13	29¼	
	„ Franzensbad (from Cologne £2 10s. & £1 11s.)	197											
§—Travelling by	Ostend-Vienna Express as far as		Eger.										
Via Leipsic.	See routes to Leipsic.												
	On to Reichenbach	187											
	„ Franzensbad (from Leipsic 16s. 6d. and 10s. 9d., in 4 to 5 hours)	188	...	...	...	...	...	...	......	....	... ...	......	... ...
Freiburg...... *Via Calais or Boul'gne-Laon.*	See routes to Basle.												
	On from Basle to Freiburg	141	...	...	...	...	...	...	......	**ChX** 2 p5	8 a42	17½	
601 miles.	§—Not on Sunday from London.									„ 4§p30	10a27	17	See
Via Calais.	See routes to Strassburg.									**ChX** 9 a0	8a41	22¾	page
577 miles.	On to Appenweier	145								„ 2 p5	11a19	20¼	lxiv.
	„ Offenburg and Freiburg	140								„ 9 p0	6 p43	20¾	
	Fare via Calais and Brussels		4	11	6	3	2	0	15				
	Return fare		8	6	11	5	14	8	60				
Via Ostend.										**ChX** 9 a0	8a41	22¾	See
557 miles.	Fare via Ostend and Brussels		4	2	3	2	15	10	15	„ 2 p5	11a19	20¼	page
	Return fare		7	10	6	5	2	2	60	„ 9 p0	6 p1	20	lxiv.
Via Flushing.	See Flushing route to Cologne.									**Vic** 10 a0	10 a5	23	
651½ miles.	On from Cologne to Mayence	122								„ 8 p30	6 p1	‡20½	See page lxiv.
	On to Mannheim	139											
	„ Carlsruhe and Freiburg	140A	4	10	3	2	17	9	15				
	Return fare		8	7	0	5	8	0	60				
Via Hoek van Holland.	See Hoek van Holland route to Cologne, and on as in previous									**Liverpool Str** 8 p30	7 p0	‡21½	See page lxiv.
666 miles.	route		4	10	3	2	17	9	15				
	Return fare		8	7	0	5	8	0	60				
Gastein ...... *Via Basle.*	See routes to Basle.												
	On to Zurich	261											
	„ Sargans 268B; Buchs	268A											
	„ Feldkirch, Innsbruck, Schwarzach St. Veit	238A											
	„ Gastein	237D	...	...	...	...	...	...	......	....	... ...	......	... ...
	[Basle to Gastein £2 13s. 1d.		and £1			15s. 1d.]							
Via Munich.	See routes to Munich.												
	On to Rosenheim and Salzburg	200											
	„ Bischofshofen	239											
	„ Schwarzach St. Veit	238											
	„ Gastein	237B	...	...	...	...	...	...	......	....	... ...	......	... ...
	[Munich to Gastein £1 5s. 8d. an		d 16s.			3d.]							

The "a" and "p" inserted in the departure and arrival times denote "a.m." and "p.m."

From LONDON to	ROUTES.	FARES. 1st Cl.	FARES. 2nd Cl.	Validity of Ticket.	Departure from London.	Arrive Destination.	Time of Journey	Excess luggage per 20lb.
		£ s. d.	£ s. d.	Days			HRS	
Geneva	London to Calais and Paris 18				**Vic** 11 a0	8 a38	20½	
Via Calais.	On to Dijon 48; Bourg............ 63B				**ChX** 9 p0	7 p38	21½	
668 miles.	,, Culoz, Bellegarde, and							
Thro' Table p. 1.	Geneva 60	5 13 11	3 18 7	15				4/3
	Return fare	9 1 11	6 12 3	60				
	London to Boulogne, Amiens,				**ChX** 10 a0	8 a38	21½	
	Paris 18				,, 2 p5	12 p3	21	
Via Boulogne.	On to Dijon 48; Bourg............ 63B							
640 miles.	,, Culoz, Bellegarde, and							
Thro' Table p. 1.	Geneva 60	5 7 3	3 13 7	15				4/2
	Return fare	9 1 11	6 12 3	60				
	London to Dieppe and Paris 77A				**Vic** 10 a0	8 a38	21½	
	On to Dijon 48; Bourg............ 63B				,, 8 p45	7 p38	22	
Via Dieppe.	,, Culoz, Bellegarde, and							
627 miles. ...	Geneva 60	4 16 0	3 7 1	15				3/7
Thro' Table p. 1.	**Return fare**	7 12 8	5 9 8	60				
	Or, Paris to Dijon 48				**Vic** 10 a0	9a57	23	
	On to Pontarlier..................... 52				,, 8 p45	7 p22	21½	
	,, Lausanne 263B							
617 miles. ...	,, Geneva 263A	4 10 10	3 3 10	15				3/1
	Return fare	7 5 8	5 4 5	60				
Genoa	See routes to Turin.				**ChX** 2 p5	6p30	27½	
Via Turin.	On to Alessandria and Genoa... 270				,, 9 p0	9a35	35¼	
871 miles via Calais	Fare via Calais or Boulogne,							
Thro' Table p. 1	Paris, Turin........................	7 6 1	5 0 10	20				
	Return fare	11 16 11	8 11 1	60				
	Fare via Dieppe, Paris, Turin	6 8 2	4 9 3	20	**Vic** 10 a0	6p30	31¼	3/11
	Return fare	10 7 7	7 8 6	60	,, 8p45	9a35	35¾	
	See routes to Lausanne.				**Vic** 11 a0	5 p25	29½	
	On to Domodossola 263B				**ChX** 2 p5	11p25	33¼	
Via Lausanne.	,, Arona 274; Novara......274A							
882 miles via	,, Alessandria.................. 269							
Calais.	,, Genoa 270							
854 miles via Boulogne.	Fare via Calais or Boulogne ...	7 7 1	5 2 1	20				
841 miles	Fare via Dieppe....................	6 9 1	4 10 0	20	**Vic** 10 a0	5 p25	30½	3/1
	Return fare	10 11 4	7 10 6	60				
	See routes to Madrid.							
Gibraltar ...	On to Alcazar 296				**Vic** 11 a0	6§p30		
	,, Cordoba 296A					4th		
Via Madrid.	,, Bobadilla 294					day.		
1636 miles.	,, Algeciras and Gibraltar 299	§-Arrive	2.35 p.	m.	on Sun.	and	Wed.	
	(Fare from Paris £10 13s. and £7	16s.)						
Steamer direct.	Steamer from London, see List	9 0 0	6 0 0					
1320 miles......	**Return fare**	13 10 0	9 0 0		four	days		
					Liverpool			
Gothenburg ...	London to Harwich, thence ♣	4 0 0	2 15 0	—	**Str** 4p10	9 a0		
	steamer direct **Return fare**	7 0 0	4 5 0		Sat.	Mon		
The Hague...	London to Hoek van Holland				**Liverpool**			
Via Hoek van	and via Schiedam to The				**Str** 8p30	6 a27	₵ 9¾	
Holland.	Hague ....112 and 119	1 12 1	1 1 7	15				1/2
219 miles.	**Return fare**	2 10 10	1 13 11	60				
	London to Flushing & Rosendaal 113				**Vic** 10a0	10 p5	₵11¾	
Via Flushing.	On to Dordrecht and Rotterdam 117				,, 8p30	7 a19	₵10¾	
266½ miles.	,, Delft and The Hague...... 119	1 12 1	1 1 7	7				1/5
	Return fare	2 10 10	1 13 11	60				

₵—Through Carriage from Boulogne, Calais, Dieppe, Flushing, H. v. Holland, Ostend—as the case may be—₵

From LONDON to	ROUTES	PAGE	FARES. 1st Cl. £ s. d.	FARES. 2nd Cl. £ s. d.	Validity of Ticket. Days	Departure from London.	Arrive Destination.	Time of Journey HRS	Excess luggage per 20lb
Hamburg ...	London to Flushing Rosendaal					Vic 10 a0	6 a31	₵19½	
	Breda	113				" 8p30	2 p47	₵17¼	
Via Flushing.	On to Boxtel	116							
570 miles.	,, Goch and Wesel	120							
Thro' Table p. 9.	,, Oberhausen	132							See page lxiv.
	,, Osnabruck, Bremen, Hamburg	132	3 11 4	2 7 9	15				
	Return fare		6 9 3	4 8 0	60				
Via Hoek van Holland.	London to Hoek v. Holland and Rotterdam	112				Liverpool Str 8p30	2 p47	₵17¼	
533 miles.	On to Utrecht	118							
	,, Amersfoort	115A							
	,, Bentheim and Rheine	118B							See page lxiv.
	,, Osnabruck	156C							
	,, Bremen and Hamburg	132	3 11 4	2 7 9	15				
	Return fare		6 9 3	4 8 0	60				
Via Calais and Ostend.	See Calais and Ostend routes					ChX 9 a0	6 a55	20¾	
637 miles via Ostend.	to Cologne.					" 2 p5	2 p28	23¼	See page lxiv.
	From Cologne to Hamburg ...	132				" 9 p0	5 p3	19	
	Fare via Ostend and Cologne...		4 11 6	3 1 2	15				
	Return fare		8 11 5	5 14 5	60				
Thro' Table p. 9.	†—Via Boulogne.					ChX 9 a0	6 a55	20¾	See page lxiv.
662 miles.	Fare via Calais and Cologne ...		5 3 5	3 9 5	15	" 2p†5	2 p28	23¼	
	Return fare		9 10 10	6 9 8	60	" 9 p0	9 p42	23¾	
Hanover	London to Flushing and Breda	113				Vic 10 a0	4 a17	₵17¼	
Via Flushing.	On to Boxtel	116				" 8 p30	1 p20	₵15¾	
493½ miles.	,, Goch and Wesel	120							See page lxiv.
Thro' Table p. 9.	,, Oberhausen	132							
	,, Hamm and Hanover	161	3 3 0	2 2 5	15				
	Return fare		5 12 8	3 17 5	60				
Nord Express. 565½ miles.	By Nord Express, see Through Table from London (Fare via Ostend)	9	5 1 10	... ...	...	ChX 9 a0	3 a49	₵17¾	
Via Ostend.	See Ostend route to Cologne.					ChX 9 a0	4 a32	18½	
557 miles.	On to Elberfeld	134A				" 2 p5	12p13	21¼	
Thro' Table p. 9.	,, Hagen and Soest	134A				" 9 p0	2 p56	17	See page lxiv.
	,, Paderborn & Altenbeken	164							
	,, Hameln and Hanover ...	155	4 1 4	2 14 11	15				
	Return fare		7 11 0	5 2 0	60				
Via Calais.	See Calais route to Cologne.					ChX 9 a0	4 a32	18½	See page lxiv.
586 miles.	On to Minden and Hanover ...	161	4 13 3	3 3 3	15	" 2†p5	12p13	21¼	
Thro' Table p. 9.	**Return fare**		8 10 5	5 17 3	60	" 9 p0	5 p56	20	
	†—Via Boulogne.								
Via Hoek van Holland.	London to Hoek van Holland ♣ and Rotterdam	112				Liverpool Str 8 p30	1 p20	₵16	
467 miles.	On to Utrecht	118							
Thro' Table p. 9.	,, Amersfoort	115A							See page lxiv.
	,, Rheine 118B; to Lohne	156C							
	,, Hanover	161	3 3 0	2 2 5	15				
	Return fare		5 12 8	3 17 5	60				
Havre .... 200 miles.	Rail to Southampton, steamer thence	76	1 10 6	1 1 6	3	Waterloo 9p45 ‡	6 a30	8¾	
	Return fare		2 7 0	1 15 0	30				
	‡—From London not on Sunday night.								

The "a" and "p" inserted in the departure and arrival times denote "a.m." and "p.m."

From LONDON to	ROUTES.	PAGE	FARES. 1st Cl. £ s. d.	FARES. 2nd Cl. £ s. d.	Validity of Ticket. Days	Departure from London.	Arrive Destination.	Time of Journey. HRS	Excess luggage per 20 lb.
Heidelberg ..	See route to Cologne.					ChX 9 a0	7 a29	21½	
Thro' Table p. 13.	On to Mayence and Darmstadt	122				" 2 p5	12p27	21¼	
	,, Heidelberg	136				" 9 p0	3 p0	17	
	[Or, from Mayence to Mannheim p. 139, on to Heidelberg p. 140.]								See page lxiv.
Via Ostend.	Fare via Ostend and Cologne...		3 18 3	2 12 11	15				
531 miles.	**Return fare**		7 4 10	4 18 0	60				
Via Boulogne-Laon	London to Boulogne & Amiens	18				ChX 2 p5	9 a56	19	
604 miles.	On to Laon 21; Avricourt	64A				" 4§p30	11a18	17¾	
	,, Appenweier & Carlsruhe	210							
	,, Heidelberg....................	141	4 14 4	3 4 6	15				
	Return fare		8 4 8	5 16 6	60				
	§—Weekdays only from London.								
Via Calais.	Fare via Calais and Cologne ...		4 10 2	3 1 3	15	ChX 9 a0	7 a29	21½	See
556 miles	**Return fare**		8 4 3	5 13 3	60	" 2†p5	12p27	21¼	page
	†—Via Boulogne.					" 9 p0	4 p20	18½	lxiv.
Via Flushing.	Fare via Flushing and Cologne		3 13 11	2 8 9	15	Vic 10 a0	7 a29	20½	See p
534 miles.	**Return fare**		6 14 5	4 10 0	60	" 8 p30	3 p0	17½	lxiv.
Via Hoek van Holland.	Fare via Hoek van Holland and Cologne..........................		3 13 11	2 8 9	15	Liverpool Str 8 p30	4 p20	₵19	See page
548 miles.	**Return fare**		6 14 5	4 10 0	60				lxiv.
Homburg Bad...	See routes to Cologne.					ChX 9 a0	7 a1	21	
Thro' Table p. 13.	On to Mayence and Frankfort	122				" 2 p5	12p45	21¾	See
	,, Homburg Bad	150				" 9 p0	3 p31	17½	page
	[Or, Cologne to Frankfort p. 128.]								lxiv.
Via Ostend.	Fare via Ostend and Cologne...		3 15 5	2 11 3	15				
504 miles.	**Return fare**		6 19 3	4 14 8	60				
Via Calais.	Fare via Calais and Cologne ...		4 7 4	2 19 6	15	ChX 9 a0	7 a1	21	See
529 miles.	**Return fare**		7 18 8	5 9 10	60	" 2†p5	12p45	21¾	page
						" 9 p0	3 §55	18	lxiv.
	†—Via Boulogne.			§—Via Wiesbaden page 128.					
Via Boulogne-Laon	London to Boulogne & Amiens	18				ChX 2 p5	11a21	20¼	
651½ miles.	On to Laon 21; Metz	64A				" 4§p30	3 p31	22	
	,, Bingerbruck 125A; Frankfort	123							
	,, Homburg Bad	150	... ...	... ...	......				
	§—Weekdays only from London.								
Via Flushing.	Fare via Flushing and Cologne		3 11 2	2 7 0	15	Vic 10 a0	7 a1	20¼	See p
511 miles.	**Return fare**		6 8 10	4 6 8	60	" 8 p30	3 p31	18	lxiv.
Via Hoek van Holland.	Fare via Hoek van Holland and Cologne.......................		3 11 2	2 7 0	15	Liverpool Str 8 p30	3 §55	₵18½	See page
507 miles.	**Return fare**		6 8 10	4 6 8	60				lxiv.
Hyères........	London to Calais and Paris ...	18				Vic 11a0	11a49	25¾	
Via Calais.	On to Dijon, Macon, Lyons, Marseilles	48							5/4
887 miles.	,, Toulon and Hyères......	54	7 3 1	4 18 3	15				
	Return fare		11 5 7	8 3 8	60				
Via Boulogne.	London to Boulogne and Paris	18							
859½ miles.	On to Lyons and Marseilles ...	48				ChX 10 a0	11a49	26¾	
	,, Toulon and Hyères......	54	6 16 5	4 13 3	15				
	Return fare		11 5 7	8 3 8	60				5/2
Via Dieppe.	London to Dieppe and Paris...	76				Vic 10 a0	11a49	26¾	
847 miles.	On to Lyons and Marseilles ...	48							
	,, Toulon and Hyères......	54	6 5 1	4 6 9	15				
	Return fare		9 16 4	7 1 1	60				4/8

₵—Through Carriage from Boulogne, Calais, Dieppe, Flushing, H. v. Holland, Ostend—as the case may be.—₵

From LONDON to	ROUTES.	FARES. 1st Cl.	FARES. 2nd Cl.	Validity of Ticket.	Departure from London.	Arrive Destination.	Time of Journey	Excess luggage per 20 lb
HYERES—*cont'd.*	PAGE	£ s. d.	£ s. d.	Days			HRS	
	London to Havre, Rouen, and Paris 76							
Via Havre. 941 miles.	On to Dijon, Macon, Lyons, Marseilles 48							
	„ Toulon and Hyères...... 54	6 6 4	4 6 4	15	... ...	...	...	
	Return fare	9 17 11	7 0 11	60				
Innsbruck ...	See routes to Basle.				Vic 11 a0	3 p25	27½	
	On to Brugg and Zurich 261				ChX 2 p5	3 p25	24¼	
Via Basle.	„ Sargans 268B				„ 4 §p30	6 p55	25¼	
	„ Buchs 268A							
	„ Feldkirch, Landeck, Innsbruck 238							
	Fare via Boulogne, Laon, Basle	6 13 10	4 9 3	30				3/5
	808 miles. Return fare	11 9 7	8 0 8	60				
	§—Weekdays only from London.							
836 miles.					ChX 9 a0	3 p25	29½	
	Fare via Ostend, Brussels, Basle	... ...	... ...	......	„ 9 p0	5 a50	32	
825½ miles.	Via Dieppe, Paris, Basle.........	6 3 6	4 4 6	30	Vic 10 a0	3 p25	28½	3/1
	Return fare	10 8 9	7 4 0	60	„ 8 p45	5 a50	32	
Interlaken...	See routes to Paris.				Vic 11 a0	7 ‡35	19½	
Via Paris.	On to Dijon 48; Pontarlier ... 52				„ 11 a0	10a20	22½	
	„ Neuchatel 265; Berne...259B				ChX 9 p0	9 p5	23	
	„ Interlaken 267							
‡—Simplon	Express, Train de Luxe, first arrival July 9th, extra fare £1 14s. 10d.							
	Via Boulogne and Paris	5 4 2	3 11 8	15	Chx 2 p5	10a20	20¼	
	Return fare	8 15 6	6 6 10	60				
	See routes to Paris.				Vic 10 a0	9 a28	22½	
Via Dieppe.	On to Belfort and Delle 68				„ 8 p45	7 p45	22	
	„ Delemont 266; Biel 264A							
	„ Berne 265; Interlaken... 267	4 15 7	3 7 1					
	Return fare	7 13 6	5 9 9					
Via Laon-Basle.	See routes to Berne.				Vic 11 a0	9 a28	21½	
	On to Interlaken 267				ChX 2 p5	10a20	19¼	
	§—Weekdays only from London.				„ 4§p30	3 p25	22	
					ChX 9 a0	10a55	25	
691 miles.	Via Ostend, Basle				„ 2 p5	5 p58	26¾	
Ischl	See routes to Munich.							
	On to Salzburg 200							
894 miles.	„ Ischl (from Munich £1 5s. 9d. and 16s. 3d.) 248A							
Kissingen ...	See routes to Cologne.				ChX 9 a0	11a53	26	
Thro' Table p. 13.	On to Niederlahnstein and Frankfort 128; Gemunden 196				„ 9 p0	8 p15	22½	
Via Ostend.	„ Schweinfurt 196A; Kissingen 195							See page
605 miles.	Fare via Ostend and Cologne...	4 9 0	2 19 6	15				lxiv.
Via Calais.								See
630 miles.	Fare via Calais and Cologne ...	5 0 11	3 7 10	15	ChX 9 a0	11a53	26	page
	†—Via Boulogne.				„ 9 p0	8 p15	22¼	lxiv.
Via Flushing.					Vic 10a0	11a53	25	See p
608 miles.	Fare via Flushing and Cologne	4 4 8	2 15 4	15	„ 8 p30	8 p15	22¾	lxiv.
Via Hoek van Holland.	Fare via Hoek van Holland and				Liverpool			See
622 miles.	Cologne........................	4 4 8	2 15 4	15	Str 8 p30	8p15	22¾	page
	Return fare	7 15 10	5 3 3	60				lxiv.

The "a" and "p" inserted in the departure and arrival times denote "a.m." and "p.m."

From LONDON to	ROUTES.	PAGE	FARES. 1st Cl. £ s. d.	FARES. 2nd Cl. £ s. d.	Validity of Ticket. Days	Departure from London.	Arrive Destination.	Time of Journey. HRS	Excess luggage per 20lb.
Kreuznach...	See Calais route to Cologne.					**ChX** 9 a0	5 a6	19	
Via Calais.	On to Bingerbruck	122				" 2†p5	10a13	19¼	See
488 miles.	" Kreuznach	125	... ...	... ...	...	" 9 p0	2 p14	16¼	page
									lxiv.
	†—Via Boulogne.								
Via Ostend.	See Ostend route to Cologne.					**ChX** 9 a0	5 a6	19	
463 miles.	On to Bingerbruck............	122				" 2 p5	10a13	19¼	See
	" Kreuznach	125	... ...	... ...	...	" 9 p0	12p56	15	page
									lxiv.
Via Flushing.	See Flushing route to Cologne.					**Vio** 10a0	7 a40	21	
466 miles.	On to Bingerbruck	122				" 8p30	12p56	15½	See
	" Kreuznach	125	3 6 3	2 3 10	15				page
	Return fare		5 19 0	4 0 3	60				lxiv.
Via Hoek van Holland.	See Hoek van Holland route to Cologne.					**Liverpool**			
480 miles.	On to Bingerbruck	122				**Str** 8p30	2 p14	16¾	See
	" Kreuznach	125	3 6 3	2 3 10	15				page
	Return fare		5 19 0	4 0 3	60				lxiv.
Lausanne ...	London to Calais, Boulogne,					**Vio** 11a0	5 ‡50	₵18	
	Abbeville, Amiens, and Paris	18				" 11a0	7 a10	₵19¼	
	On to Fontainebleau and Dijon	48				**ChX** 9 p0	6 p15	20¼	
Via Calais.	" Pontarlier	52							
619 miles. Thro' Table p. 1.	" Lausanne	263B	5 4 8	3 12 6	15				3/10
	Return fare		8 8 7	6 2 5	60				
	‡—Simplon Express, train de luxe,		extra fare £1 12s. 5d.						
Via Boulogne.	London to Boulogne, Abbeville,								
591 miles.	Amiens, and Paris	18				**ChX** 10a0	7 a10	20¼	
Thro' Table p. 1.	On as in first route		4 18 0	3 7 6	15	" 2 p5	9 a48	18¾	3/8
	Return fare		8 8 7	6 2 5	60				
Via Dieppe.	London to Dieppe, Rouen, and					**Vio** 10 a0	7 a10	₵20½	
579 miles.	Paris	76				" 8 p45	6 p15	20½	
Thro' Table p. 1.	On as in first route		4 6 10	3 1 0	15				3/1
	Return fare		6 19 3	5 0 0	60				
Via Havre.	London to Havre and Paris ...	76				**Waterloo**			
674 miles.	On as in first route		4 8 1	3 0 8	15	9 p45	11p54	25	
	Return fare		7 0 11	4 19 10	60	Not Sun.			
Leipsic	See Flushing route to Brunswick.					**Vio** 10a0	9 a6	₵22	See
Via Flushing.	On from Brunswick to Leipsic	158	4 3 8	2 15 3	15	" 8 p30	6p23	20¾	page
662 miles.	**Return fare**		7 13 10	5 3 0	60				lxiv.
Thro' Table p. 9.	See Ostend route to Cologne.					**ChX** 9 a0	9 a6	23	
	On to Hamm, Hanover, and					" 2 p5	6 p11	27	
Via Ostend.	Oebisfelde	161				" 9 p0	8 p6	22	See
733 miles.	" Magdeburg	160C							page
Thro' Table p. 9.	" Halle and Leipsic	158	5 0 4	3 5 8	15				lxiv.
	Return fare		9 9 0	6 3 5	60				
	See Calais route to Cologne.					**ChX** 9 a0	9 a6	23	
	On to Hamm, Hanover, and					" 2†p5	6 p11	27	
Via Calais.	Oebisfelde..................	161				" 9 p0	11 p9	25	
Thro' Table p. 9.	" Magdeburg	160C							See
758 miles.	" Halle and Leipsic	158	5 12 3	3 13 11	15				page
	Return fare		10 8 9	6 18 8	60				lxiv.
	†—Via Boulogne.								

₵—Through Carriage from Boulogne, Calais, Dieppe, Flushing, H. v. Holland, Ostend—as the case may be.—₵

From LONDON to	ROUTES.	PAGE	FARES. 1st Cl. £	s.	d.	2nd Cl. £	s.	d.	Validity of Ticket. Days	Departure from London.	Arrive Destination.	Time of Journey HRS	Excess luggage per 20lbs
LEIPSIC—*Cont'd*													
Via Hoek van Holland.	See Hoek van Holland route to Hanover.									Liverpool Str 8 p30	6 p23	21	See page lxiv.
Thro' Table p. 9.	On to Stendal 161A; Magdeburg	163											
635½ miles.	„ Leipsic	158	4	3	8	2	15	3	15				
	Return fare		7	13	10	5	3	0	60				
Liege	London to Ostend, Bruges, and Ghent........................... ..	102								ChX 9 a0	7 p28	₵10½	
Via Ostend.										„ 2 p5	1§a23	₵11¼	
279 miles.	On to Malines and Louvain ...	101								„ 9 p0	7 §24	₵10½	
	„ Liege	104	2	4	10	1	11	4	7				2/9
	Return fare		3	19	0	2	15	7	30	§-Via Brussels.			
Via Calais.	See Calais route to Brussels.									ChX 9 a0	6 p47	₵ 9¾	
304 miles.	On to Liege	104	2	15	1	1	18	4	7	„ 2†p5	1 a23	₵11¼	
	Return fare		4	17	0	3	9	1	30	„ 9 p0	7 a24	₵10½	2/8
	†—Via Boulogne.												
Via Calais and Namur.	London to Calais and La Madeleine	26								ChX 9 a0	6 p47	₵ 9¾	
314 miles.	On to Valenciennes	29A											
	„ Aulnoye and Erquelinnes	25											
	„ Namur and Liege	92	2	18	0	2	1	1	7				2/7
	Return fare		5	1	2	3	14	0	30				
Lisbon	See routes to Paris.									Vic 11 a0	2 p31	51½	
Thro' Table p. 7.	On to Bordeaux	34								ChX 2p5	11p53	58	
	„ Irun	45											
	„ Valladolid and Medina	291A											
	„ Salamanca	290A											
1440 miles	„ Villar Formoso	299											
	„ Pampilhosa	301											
	„ Entroncamento	300											
	„ Lisbon	300	11	9	10	...	...	...	......	....	... ...	......	... ...
	(£8 16s. and £6 7s. from Paris).												
Sud Express.	London to Paris via Calais or Boulogne	18											
	On from Paris to Lisbon by Sud Express, see Through Table	7	14	19	3	...	...	...	......	....	... ...	......	... ...
Lucerne	See routes to Basle.												
Thro' Table p. 5.	On to Olten and Lucerne.........	258											
Via Calais.	Fare via Calais, Laon, Basle ...		5	3	8	3	11	8	15	Vic 11 a0	8 a59	21	3/1
644 miles.	Return fare		8	12	8	6	4	7	60	ChX 4§p30	10a48	17¼	
	§—Weekdays only from London.												
Via Boulogne.	Fare via Boulogne, Laon, Basle		5	0	11	3	9	4	15	ChX 2 p5	8 a59	₵17¾	3/9
619 miles.	Return fare		8	12	8	6	4	7	60				
										ChX 9 a0	8 a59	23	
Via Ostend.	Fare via Ostend, Brussels,									„ 2 p5	1 p56	22¾	
647½ miles.	Basle		4	12	1	3	2	6	15	„ 9 p0	8 p15	22¼	3/3
Via Dieppe.	Fare via Dieppe, Paris, Basle		4	13	7	3	5	5	15	Vic 10a0	8 a59	22	3/1
637 miles.	Return fare		7	12	3	5	8	3	60	„ 8 p45	8 p15	22½	
Via Hoek van Holland.	Fare via Hoek van Holland									Liverpool			
746½ miles.	and Basle		5	0	8	3	4	11	15	Str 8 p30	11p42	26¼	1/-
	Return fare		9	3	2	5	18	10	60				
Via Flushing.	Fare via Flushing, Cologne,									Vic 10 a0	1 p56	27	
732 miles.	and Basle		5	3	4	3	6	11	15	„ 8 p30	8 p15	22¾	

₵—Through Carriage from Boulogne, Calais, Dieppe, Flushing, H. v. Holland, Ostend—as the case may be.—₵

From LONDON to	ROUTES.	PAGE	FARES. 1st Cl. £	s.	d.	2nd Cl. £	s.	d.	Validity of Ticket. Days	Departure from London.	Arrive Destination.	Time of Journey HRS	Excess luggage per 20 lb
Lugano	See routes to Basle.												
	On to Olten and Lucerne	258											
	,, Bellinzona and Lugano...	259								**Vic** 11 a0	1 p17	25¼	
768 miles.	Via Calais or Boulogne		6	5	10	4	7	2		**ChX** 2 p5	1 p17	22¼	
	§—Weekdays only from London.									,, 4§p30	4 p56	25¼	
772 miles.	Via Ostend									**ChX** 9 a0	1 p17	27¼	
										,, 2 p5	6 p44	27¾	
761 miles.	Via Dieppe		5	15	9	4	1	0		**Vic** 10 a0	1 p17	26¼	
Lyons	London to Calais, Boulogne,									**ChX** 9 a0	3 a2	18	
Via Calais.	Abbeville, Amiens, and Paris	18								**Vic** 11 a0	3 a59	𝕮17	
610 miles.	On to Dijon, Macon, and									**ChX** 9 p0	4 p43	19¾	
Thro' Table p. 1.	Lyons	48	5	8	10	3	11	9	15				3/11
	Return fare		8	6	9	6	1	4	45				
Via Boulogne.	London to Boulogne, Amiens,									**ChX** 10 a0	3 a2	17	
582 miles.	Paris	18								,, 2 p5	7 a10	17¼	
Thro' Table p. 1.	On to Dijon, Macon, and Lyons	48	4	17	2	3	6	9	15				3/9
	Return fare		8	6	9	6	1	4	45				
Via Dieppe.	London to Dieppe, Rouen, and									**Vic** 10 a0	3 a59	18	
569 miles.	Paris	77A								,, 8 p45	5 p1	20¼	
Thro' Table p. 1.	On to Dijon, Macon, and Lyons	48	4	5	11	3	0	3	15				3/3
	Return fare		6	17	5	4	18	9	45				
Via Havre.	London to Havre, Rouen, and									**Waterloo**			
665 miles.	Paris	76								9 p45	11 p8	25¼	
Thro' Table p. 1.	On to Dijon, Macon, and Lyons	48	4	7	2	2	19	10	15	Not Sun.			
	Return fare		6	19	0	4	18	6	45	night.			
Madrid	London to Paris via Calais or												
Sud Express.	Boulogne	18											
	On from Paris to Madrid by												
	Sud Express, see Through												
	Table	7	12	0	6	...	...	...	......				
Thro' Table p. 7.	Or from Paris by ordinary express to Bordeaux	34											
	On to Bayonne and Irun	45											
	,, Alsasua, Burgos, Medina,												
	El Escorial, and Madrid	291A	...	...	...	...	...	...	......				
1196 miles.	Via Calais.........................		9	13	2	6	16	11	......	**Vic** 11 a0	10p58	36	
1168 miles.	Via Boulogne		9	7	0	6	11	11	......	**ChX** 10 a0	10p58	40	
										,, 2p5	7 a0	41	
1156 miles.	Via Dieppe		8	15	7	6	5	3	......	**Vic** 10 a0	10p58	37	
	Return fare		14	19	1	9	4	5	30				
Mannheim...	See routes to Cologne.												
	On to Coblence and Mayence...	122								**ChX** 9 a0	6a45	20¾	
Via Ostend.	,, Mannheim ....139 or	136								,, 2 p5	12 p1	20¾	See
519½ miles.	Fare via Ostend and Cologne...		3	16	10	2	12	2	15	,, 9 p0	2 p22	16¼	page
	Return fare		7	2	0	4	16	5	60				lxiv.
Via Calais.	Fare via Calais and Cologne		4	8	9	3	0	5	15	**ChX** 9 a0	6a45	20¾	See
544 miles.	**Return fare**		8	1	5	5	11	8	60	,, 2†p5	12 p1	20¾	page
	†—Via Boulogne.									,, 9 p0	3 p46	17¾	lxiv.
Via Flushing.	Fare via Flushing and Cologne		3	12	6	2	7	11	15	**Vic** 10a0	6 a45	19¾	See p.
522 miles.	**Return fare**		6	11	8	4	8	5	60	,, 8 p30	2 p22	𝕮17	lxiv.
Via Hoek v.	Fare via H. v. Holland and									**Liverpool**			See
Holland.	Cologne		3	12	6	2	7	11	15	**Str** 8 p30	3 p46	𝕮18¼	page
537 miles.	**Return fare**		6	11	8	4	8	5	60				lxiv.

The "a" and "p" inserted in the departure and arrival times denote "a.m." and "p.m."

From LONDON to	ROUTES	PAGE	FARES. 1st Cl. £	s.	d.	2nd Cl. £	s.	d.	Validity of Ticket. Days	Departure from London.	Arrive Destination.	Time of Journey HRS	Excess luggage per 20lb
	See route to Cologne via Ostend.									ChX 9 a0	12 §3	26	
Marienbad	On fr. Cologne to Aschaffenburg	122								" 9a 0	5 p7	31	
	On to Wurzburg......................	196											
Via Ostend.	,, Nürnberg 195A; Eger ...	202											2/10
756½ miles.	,, Marienbad	243A	5	6	0	3	9	11	30				
	§—Travelling by Ostend-Vienna		Express			as far as			Eger.				
Via Calais.	See route to Cologne via Calais									ChX 9 a0	5 p7	31	
781½ miles.	and on as above		5	16	6	3	16	11	30				2/10
Via Flushing.	See route to Cologne via Flushing-									Vic 10 a0	5 p7	30	1/-
759½ miles.	ing and on as above		...	...	...	...	...	...	......				
Via Hoek v. Holland.	See route to Cologne via Hoek												
	van Holland, and on as above		5	8	3	3	8	5	30				1/-
774 miles.	**Return fare**		9	16	2	6	4	0	60				
	London to Calais, Boulogne,									ChX 9 a0	8 a30	23½	
	Abbeville, Amiens, and Paris	18								Vic 11 a0	8 a58	22	
Marseilles ...	On to Dijon, Macon, Lyons									ChX 9 p0	10p35	25½	
Via Calais.	Marseilles	48	6	15	2	4	12	11	30				
827 miles.	**Return fare**		10	13	9	7	15	2	60				5/-
Thro Table p. 1.													
Via Boulogne.	London to Boulogne and Paris	18								ChX 10 a0	8 a30	22½	
800 miles.	On to Dijon, Macon, Lyons,									" 2p5	2 p38	24½	
Thro' Table p. 1.	Marseilles	48	6	8	6	4	7	11	30				4/11
	Return fare		10	13	9	7	15	2	60				
Via Dieppe.	London to Dieppe and Paris ...	77A								Vic 10 a0	8 a58	23	
787 miles.	On to Dijon and Marseilles ...	48	5	17	3	4	1	5	30	" 8p45	10p35	26	
Thro' Table p. 1.	**Return fare**		9	4	6	6	12	7	60				4/4
Via Havre.	London to Havre and Paris ...	76								Waterloo			
882 miles.	On to Dijon and Marseilles ...	48	5	18	7	4	1	1	30	9p45	5 a0	31	
Thro' Table p. 1.	**Return fare**		9	6	3	6	12	6	60	Not Sun.	night.		
Martigny (Vosges)	London to Calais and Amiens	18								ChX 4§p30	5a24	13	
	On to Tergnier	21								9‡p0	12p16	15	
Via Calais.	" Laon 21; Reims	67											
	" Chalons	67											3/1
480 miles.	" St. Dizier, Chaumont ...	66											
Thro' Table p. 5.	" Langres 68A; Martigny	68A	4	2	3	2	17	0	15				
‡—Friday	only from London. §—Tuesday and Fridays from London.												
Via Boulogne.	London to Boulogne, Amiens	18								ChX 2p5	4a33	14½	
455 miles.	On as in previous route		4	2	3	2	17	0	15				3/1
Mayence......	London to Ostend, Frankfort,												
Ostend-Vienna Express.	and Mayence, see Through									ChX 9 a0	12a48	₵16¾	
477 miles.	Table		4	5	6	...	...	...	......				
Thro' Table p. 13.	See routes to Cologne.									ChX 9 a0	5a25	19½	See
	On to Coblence and Mayence...	122								" 2p5	10a22	19¼	page
Via Ostend.	Fare via Ostend and Cologne...		3	10	9	2	8	8	15	" 9 p0	1 p7	15	lxiv.
472 miles.	**Return fare**		6	9	10	4	9	5	60				
Via Calais.	Fare via Calais and Cologne ...		4	2	8	2	16	11	15	ChX 9 a0	5a25	19½	See
497 miles.	**Return fare**		7	9	3	5	4	8	60	" 2†p5	10a22	19¼	page
	†—Via Boulogne.									" 9 p0	2p22	16½	lxiv.
Via Flushing.	Fare via Flushing and Cologne		3	7	3	2	4	6	15	Vic 10a0	5a25	18½	See p.
475 miles.	**Return fare**		6	1	0	4	1	8	60	" 8p30	1 p7	₵15½	lxiv.
Via Hoek v. Holland	Fare via Hoek v. Holland and									Liverpool			See
	Cologne		3	7	3	2	4	6	15	Str 8p30	2p22	₵17	page
490 miles.	**Return fare**		6	1	0	4	1	8	60				lxiv.

The "a" and "p" inserted in the departure and arrival times denote "a.m." and "p.m."

From LONDON to	ROUTES.	PAGE	FARES. 1st Cl. £	s.	d.	2nd Cl. £	s.	d.	Validity of Ticket. Days	Departure from London.	Arrive Destination.	Time of Journey HRS	Excess luggage per 20 lb
Menton	London to Calais and Paris...	18								**Vic** 11 a0	2 p37	27½	
Via Calais.	On to Lyons and Marseilles ...	48								**ChX** 9 p0	7 a38	34½	
982 miles.	,, Cannes, Nice, Menton ...	54	7	17	9	5	8	2	15				5/10
	Return fare		12	7	8	8	19	7	60				
Via Boulogne.	London to Boulogne, Amiens, and Paris	18								**ChX** 10 a0	2 p37	28½	
954 miles.	On as in previous route		7	11	1	5	3	2	15				5/8
	Return fare		12	7	8	8	19	7	60				
Via Dieppe.	London to Dieppe and Paris ..	77A								**Vic** 10 a0	2 p37	28½	
942 miles.	On as above		6	19	10	4	16	8	15	,, 8p45	7 a38	35	5/2
	Return fare		10	18	4	7	17	0	60				
Via Havre	London to Havre and Paris...	76											
1036 miles.	On as above		7	0	11	4	16	2	15				
	Return fare		10	19	8	7	16	7	60				
Meran	See routes to Basle.												
Via Basle.	On to Brugg and Zurich	261											
	,, Sargans 268B; Buchs 268A												
	,, Feldkirch, Landeck, and Innsbruck	238											
	,, Botzen-Gries 235; Meran	237A	...	...	...	...	...	...	......				
	[Basle to Meran, £2 13s. 6d., 1st cl., £1 17s. 1d., 2nd cl.]												
911 miles.	Via Boulogne, Laon, Basle......									**ChX** 2 p5	8 p28	29¼	
929 miles	Fare via Dieppe, Paris, Basle		6	19	3	4	17	0	30	**Vic** 10 a0	8 p28	33½	3/2
	Return fare		11	19	3	8	8	1	60	,, 8 p45	11a35	37¾	
	Via Ostend and Basle		...	...	...	...	...	...	......	**ChX** 9 a0	8 p28	34½	
										,, 9 p0	11a35	37½	
Milan	See routes to Paris.									**Vic** 11 a0	12§12	₵24¼	
Via Paris and Lausanne.	On to Dijon 48; Pontarlier ...	52								,, 11 a0	1 p30	25½	
Thro' Table p. 1.	,, Lausanne and Domodossola	263B								**ChX** 9 p0	12a15	26¼	
812½ miles via Calais, 785 miles via Boulogne.	,, Milan	274	6	12	0	4	11	6	20	§—Simplon Express, train de luxe.			
	Return fare		10	18	2	7	17	4	60				
	Fare by Simplon Express		7	19	0	...	...	...	......				
Via Dieppe.	Fare via Dieppe, Paris, Simplon		5	17	1	4	2	3	20	**Vic** 10 a0	1 p30	₵26½	3/1
772 miles.	**Return fare**		9	8	10	6	14	9	60	,, 8 p45	12a15	26½	
Via Berne.	See routes via Laon to Berne.									**Vic** 11 a0	2 p10	26¼	
	On to Thun and Spiez	267								**ChX** 2 p5	3 p45	24½	
	,, via the Lotschberg to Brig	268F											
	,, Domodossola	263B											
	,, Milan	274	...	...	...	...	...	...	......				
Via Basle.	See routes to Basle.												
Thro' Table p. 5.	On to Olten and Lucerne	258											
	,, Bellinzona, Lugano, Chiasso	259											
	,, Como and Milan	269A	...	...	...	...	...	...	......				
Via Calais and Basle.	Fare via Calais, Laon, & Basle									**Vic** 11 a0	3 p5	27	‡
816½ miles.	**Return fare**												
	‡—3/5 to Chiasso; thence -/3.												
Via Boulogne and Basle.	Fare via Boulogne, Laon, Basle									**ChX** 2 p5	3 p5	24¼	‡
792 miles.	**Return fare**									‡-3/5 to Chiasso; thence -/3.			
										ChX 9 a0	3 p5	₵30	
Via Ostend and Basle.	Fare via Ostend, Brussels, and									,, 2 p5	8 p40	₵29½	
	Basle (820 miles).................		6	0	5	4	2	4	20	,, 9 p0	6 a22	32¾	
Via Dieppe and Basle.	Fare via Dieppe, Paris, Basle		5	17	1	4	2	3	20	**Vic** 10 a0	3 p5	28	3/11
	(805 miles). **Return fare**		9	8	10	6	14	9	60	,, 8 p45	6 a22	32¾	

₵—Through Carriage from Boulogne, Calais, Dieppe, Flushing, H. v. Holland, Ostend—as the case may be.—₵

From LONDON to	ROUTES.	PAGE	FARES. 1st Cl. £	s.	d.	2nd Cl. £	s.	d.	Validity of Ticket. Days	Departure from London.	Arrive Destination.	Time of Journey HRS	Excess luggage per 20lb
										Vic 11 a0	2 p18	27¼	
Monte Carlo	London to Calais and Paris......	18								**ChX** 9 p0	7 a19	34¼	
Via Calais.	On to Lyons and Marseilles ...	48											
978 miles.	,, Cannes, Nice, MonteCarlo	54	7	16	10	5	7	7	15				
	Return fare		12	6	3	8	18	7	60				5/10
	London to Boulogne, Paris ...	18								**ChX** 10 a0	2 p18	28¼	
Via Boulogne.	On to Lyons and Marseilles ...	48											
950 miles.	,, Cannes, Nice, Monte Carlo	54	7	16	10	5	7	7	15				5/8
	Return fare		12	6	3	8	18	7	60				
Via Dieppe.	London to Dieppe and Paris...	76											
937 miles.	On as in previous route		6	18	11	4	16	0	15	**Vic** 10 a0	2 p18	28¼	5/2
	Return fare		10	17	0	7	16	0	60	,, 8p45	7 a19	34½	
Via Havre.	London to Havre and Paris ...	76											
1032 miles.	On as above		7	0	2	4	15	8	15				
	Return fare		10	18	7	7	15	10	60				
	London to Calais and Paris ...	18								**Vic** 11a0	6 ‡26	₵18½	
Montreux ...	On to Fontainebleau and Dijon	48								,, 11a0	7 a47	₵19¾	
Via Calais.	,, Pontarlier......................	52								**ChX** 9 p0	6 p57	21	
635 miles.	,, Lausanne and Montreux	263B	5	6	9	3	13	11	15				
Thro' Table p. 1.	**Return fare**		8	11	11	6	4	10	60				3/10
	‡—Simplon Express, train de Luxe.												
Via Boulogne.	London to Boulogne & Paris...	18								**ChX** 10 a0	7 a47	20¾	
607 miles.	On as in first route		5	6	9	3	13	11	15	,, 2 p5	11a42	18½	3/8
Thro' Table p. 1.	**Return fare**		8	11	11	6	4	10	60				
Via Dieppe.	London to Dieppe and Paris...	77A											
594 miles.	On as in first route.................		4	8	11	3	2	5	15	**Vic** 10 a0	7 a47	₵20¾	3/1
Thro' Table p. 1.	**Return fare**		7	2	8	5	2	3	60	,, 8 p45	6 p57	21¼	
Via Havre.	London to Havre and Paris ...	76								**Water-**			
689 miles.	On as in first route		4	10	2	3	2	1	15	**loo** 9p45	12a37	26	
	Return fare		7	4	3	5	2	1	60	Not Sun.			
Moscow	See routes to Warsaw.									**ChX** 9 a§0	8 p18	57¼	
	On to Brest-Litewski	315								,, 9 p0	1 p25	62½	
	,, Minsk, Wjasma, Moscow	315								§—Nord	Expr	ess,	
1937 miles......	Fare via Ostend and Warsaw...		10	7	3	6	17	7	30	from L	ondo	n on	
	Return fare		20	2	10	13	7	3	60	Monda	y on	ly.	
1957 miles......	Fare via Boulogne and Warsaw		10	18	11	7	5	8	30	**ChX** 2 p5	1 p25	68¾	
	Return fare		21	1	11	14	2	3	60				
1867 miles......	Fare via Flushing and Warsaw		9	12	3	6	6	2	30	**Vic** 8 p30	1 p25	62½	
	Return fare		18	10	11	12	4	10	60				
1831 miles......	Fare via H. v. Holland, Warsaw		9	12	3	6	6	2	30	**Liverpool**			
	Return fare		18	10	11	12	4	10	60	**Str** 8 p30	1 p25	62½	
Munich	London to Paris and thence by									**ChX** 10 a0	10a16	23¼	
Orient Express	Orient Express (830½ miles) ...	8	7	16	6	...	...	...	......				
Ostend-Vienna	London to Ostend and thence									**ChX** 9 a0	11a15	25¼	
Express.	by Ostend-Vienna Express...	8	6	4	2	...	...	...	......				

From LONDON to	ROUTES.	PAGE	FARES. 1st Cl. £ s. d.	FARES. 2nd Cl. £ s. d.	Validity of Ticket. Days	Departure from London.	Arrive Destination.	Time of Journey HRS	Excess luggage per 20 lb
MUNICH—*Cont'd.*									
Via Calais or	London to Boulogne & Amiens	18				**ChX** 2 p5	1 p8	22	
Boulogne-Laon	On to Laon 21; Avricourt......	64A				" 4§p30	5 p9	23½	
776 miles.	" Appenweier & Carlsruhe	210				§—Week	days	only	
	" Stuttgart and Munich ...	192	6 0 0	4 0 4	15	from	London		
Via Ostend-	See Ostend route to Cologne.					**ChX** 9 a0	1 p8	27	See
Cologne. 757 miles.	On to Frankfort	128				" 9 p0	8 p55	₢22½	page
Thro' Table p. 13.	" Aschaffenburg & Munich	196	5 5 6	3 9 8	15				lxiv.
	Return fare		9 19 5	6 11 5					
Via Calais-	See Calais route to Cologne,					**ChX** 9 a0	1 p8	27	See
Cologne. 777mls.	and on as above		5 17 5	3 17 11	15	" 2†p5	8 p55	29¾	page
Thro' Table p. 13.	†-Via Boulogne. **Return** fare		10 18 10	7 6 8		" 9 p0	10p25	24½	lxiv.
Via Flushing.	See Flushing route to Cologne.					**Vic** 10 a0	1 p8	₢26	
755 miles.	On to Frankfort	128				" 8 p30	8 p55	₢23½	See
Thro' Table p. 13.	" Aschaffenburg & Munich	196	5 3 10	3 5 5	15				page
	Return fare		9 14 3	6 3 5	60				lxiv
Via Hoek van	See Hoek v. Holland route to					**Liverpool**			
Holland.	Cologne.					**Str** 8 p30	10p25	₢25	
769 miles.	On to Niederlahnstein and								See
Thro' Table p. 13.	Frankfort	128							page
	" Aschaffenburg & Munich	196	5 3 10	3 5 5	15				lxiv.
	Return fare		9 14 3	6 3 5	60				
Via Paris.	London to Calais and Paris ...	18				**Vic** 11 a0	1 p8	25	
858 miles	On to Chalons and Deutsch-					**ChX** 9 p0	11p23	25½	
[Break allowed at	Avricourt 64; Strassburg	210							
any station be-	" Appenweier	145							
yond Paris.	" Carlsruhe 141; Muhlacker	141							
	" Stuttgart, Ulm, Munich	192							
823 miles.	Via Dieppe, Paris, and as above		5 18 2	4 0 1	15	**Vic** 10 a0	1 p8	26	
	Return fare		10 6 7	7 0 11	60	" 8 p45	11p23	25¾	
Naples	See routes to Rome via Paris and Turin.					**ChX** 2 p5	noon 12 5	45	
	On to Naples	276				" 9 p0	nght 12 0	50	
Via Calais or Boulogne.	Fare via Calais, or Boulogne, Turin, and Rome		9 4 4	6 5 0	20				*
Through Table p. 1.	*—4/7 to Modane; thence 2/-.								
Via Dieppe.	Fare via Dieppe, Turin, Rome		8 6 6	5 13 6	20	**Vic** 10 a0	12 p5	49	3/11
1296 miles.	**Return** fare		16 3 6	11 4 5	60	" 8 p45	12 0	50½	
Nauheim, Bad	See routes to Frankfort.					**ChX** 9 a0	8 a58	23	
Via Calais or	On to Nauheim (3s. 8d. and					" 2 p5	12p52	21¾	
Ostend.	2s. 5d. from Frankfort).........	157				" 9 p0	2 *56	17	
544 miles via	Fare via Calais........................		4 8 9	3 0 4	15.	" 9 p0	4 ‡28	18½	
Calais; 521½	Fare via Ostend		3 16 10	2 12 0	15				
miles via Ostend.	*—Via Ostend-Frankfort. ‡—		Via Ost	end or C	alai	s and Wi	esba	den.	
Via Flushing.	**Fare via Flushing**		3 12 6	2 7 10	15	**Vic** 10 a0	7 a38	20½	See p
522 miles.	**Return** fare		6 11 8	4 8 3	60	" 8 p30	2 p56	17¼	lxiv.
Via Hoek van						**Liverpool**			See
Holland	**Fare via Hoek v. Holland......**		3 12 6	2 7 10	15	**Str** 8 p30	4 §28	19	page
536 miles.	**Return** fare		6 11 8	4 8 3	60				lxiv.
					§—	Via Wie	sbad	en.	
Neuenahr, Bad....	See routes to Cologne.								
397 miles.	On to Bonn and Remagen	122							
	" Neuenahr (5s. 6d. and 3s. 9d. from Cologne)...	124							

₢—Through Carriage from Boulogne, Calais, Dieppe, Flushing, H. v. Holland, Ostend—as the case may be.—₢

From LONDON to	ROUTES	PAGE	1st Cl. £	s.	d.	2nd Cl. £	s.	d.	Validity of Ticket. Days	Departure from London.	Arrive Destination.	Time of Journey HRS	Excess luggage per 20 lb
Nice	London to Calais, Amiens,									**Vic** 11 a0	1 p25	$26\frac{1}{4}$	5/9
Via Calais.	and Paris	18								**ChX** 9 p0	6 a17	$33\frac{1}{4}$	
967 miles.	On to Dijon, Macon, Lyons,												
	Marseilles	48											
	„ Toulon, Cannes, and Nice	54	7	15	4	5	6	7	15				
	Return fare		12	4	0	8	17	0	60				
Via Boulogne.	London to Boulogne, Amiens,									**ChX** 10 a0	1 p25	$27\frac{1}{4}$	
939 miles.	Paris	18											
	On to Dijon, Macon, Lyons,												
	Marseilles	48											
	„ Toulon, Cannes, and Nice	54	7	8	8	5	1	7	15				5/7
	Return fare		12	4	0	8	17	0	60				
Via Dieppe.	London to Dieppe, Rouen, and												
927 miles.	Paris	76								**Vic** 10 a0	1 p25	$27\frac{1}{4}$	
	On as in previous route		6	17	5	4	15	0	15	„ 8p45	6 a17	$33\frac{1}{2}$	5/1
	Return fare		10	14	9	7	14	5	60				
Via Havre.	London to Havre, Rouen, and												
1022 miles.	Paris	76											
	On as above		6	18	8	4	14	8	15	... ...	...	...	
	Return fare		10	16	3	7	14	2	60				
Nurnberg ...	London to Ostend, Brussels,												
Ostend-Vienna Express.	Cologne and Nurnberg, see									**ChX** 9 a0	7 a56	₵22	
648 miles.	Through Table	8	5	12	6	...	...	...	...				
	See routes to Cologne.									**ChX** 9 a0	11a39	$25\frac{1}{2}$	
Through Table p. 13	On to Mayence & Aschaffenburg	122								„ 9 p0	6 p54	22	
	„ Wurzburg	196											See
	„ Nurnberg	195A											page
Via Ostend.	Fare via Ostend and Cologne...		4	11	6	3	1	2	15				lxiv.
643 miles.	**Return fare**		8	11	5	5	14	5	60				
	Fare via Calais and Cologne ...		5	3	5	3	0	5	15	**ChX** 9 a0	11a39	$25\frac{1}{2}$	See
Via Calais.	**Return fare**		9	10	10	6	9	8	60	„ 2†p5	6 p54	$27\frac{3}{4}$	page
68 miles.	†—Via Boulogne.									„ 9 p0	9 p22	$23\frac{1}{2}$	lxiv.
	London to Boulogne & Amiens	18								**ChX** 2 p5	11a48	$20\frac{3}{4}$	
Via Boulogne-Laon	On to Laon 21; Avricourt	64A											
727½ miles.	„ Strassburg 210; Carlsruhe...	141											
	„ Bietigheim 192; Backnang...	194											
	„ Crailsheim 191; Nurnberg...	204	5	14	9	3	16	10	15				
										Vic 10 a0	11a39	₵$24\frac{1}{2}$	See page
Via Flushing.	Fare via Flushing and Cologne		4	9	0	2	16	11	15	8 p30	6 p54	$21\frac{1}{4}$	lxiv.
646 miles.	**Return fare**		8	4	8	5	6	5	60				
Via Hoek van Holland.	Fare via Hoek v. Holland and									**Liverpool**			See page
660 miles.	Cologne		4	9	0	2	16	11	15	**Str** 8 p30	9 p22	24	lxiv.
	Return fare		8	4	8	5	6	5	60				

The "a" and "p" inserted in the departure and arrival times denote "a.m." and "p.m."

From LONDON to	ROUTES	PAGE	FARES 1st Cl. £	s.	d.	FARES 2nd Cl. £	s.	d.	Validity of Ticket. Days	Departure from London.	Arrive Destination.	Time of Journey HRS	Excess luggage per 20 lb
Odessa	See routes to Berlin.												
	On to Breslau	179											
	,, Kandrzin 218; Oderberg	219											
	,, Cracow	222											
	,, Lemberg&Podwoloczyska	246A											
1832 miles.	,, Schmerinka 320; Odessa	320											
1770 miles.	Via Ostend		...	...	...	...	...	...	...	ChX 9 p0	9 a25	58½	
	Via Flushing		...	...	...	...	...	...	...	Vic 8 p35	9 a25	59	
	Fare via Hoek van Holland									Liverpool			
1734 miles.	and Berlin		...	...	...	...	...	...	...	Str 8 p30	9 a25	59	
										ChX 9 a0	2 p0	5	
Ostend	London to Dover and Ostend...	102	1	8	4	1	0	2	7	" 2 p5	7 p30	5¼	1/4
145½ miles.	**Return fare**		2	12	9	1	17	9	60	" 9 p0	2 a0	5	
Paris...........	London to Calais, Boulogne,									ChX 9 a0	4 p40	₵ 7¾	
Via Calais.	Abbeville, Amiens, and Paris	18								Vic 11 a0	6 p20	₵ 7¼	
286¾ miles.			2	16	8	1	19	8	7	ChX 4‡p30	11p25	₵ 7	1/1†
	‡-Not run on Sunday **Return fare**		4	15	9	3	9	10	30	" 9 p0	5 a40	₵ 7¾	† per
	London to Boulogne, Abbeville,									ChX 10 a0	5 p20	₵ 7½	10lb.
Via Boulogne.	Amiens, and Paris..............	18	2	10	0	1	14	8	7	" 2 p5	9 p0	₵ 7	1/0†
259 miles.	**Return fare**		4	7	10	3	3	0	30				
Via Dieppe.	London to Dieppe, Rouen, and									Vic 10 a0	6 p3	₵ 8	10d.
225 miles.	Paris	77A	1	18	7	1	8	0	7	" 8 p45	6 a3	₵ 9¼	per
	Return fare		3	6	3	2	7	1	30				10lb.
Via Havre.	London to Havre, Rouen, and									Water-			
341½ miles.	Paris	76	1	16	10	1	6	10	7	loo 9‡p45	11a24	₵13½	
	Return fare		3	2	4	2	4	4	30	‡-Week d	ays o	nly.	
Pau	See routes to Paris.									ChX 10 a0	7 a59	22	
	On to Orleans, Blois, Tours,									" 2p5	12p25	22¼	
	Poitiers, Bordeaux ...	34											
	,, Dax and Puyoo 45; Pau	43											
Via Boulogne. 772 miles.	Fare via Boulogne and Paris ...		6	11	5	4	10	6	15				4/9
Through Table p. 7.	**Return fare**		10	8	1	7	11	3	60				
Via Calais, 800 miles.	Fare via Calais and Paris		6	11	5	4	10	6	15	Vic 11 a0	7 a59	21	4/11
Through Table p. 7.	**Return fare**		10	8	1	7	11	3	60	ChX 9 p0	9 p25	24½	
Via Dieppe.	Fare via Dieppe and Paris		5	13	4	3	18	10	15	Vic 10 a0	7 a59	22	4/3
759 miles.	**Return fare**		8	18	6	6	8	5	60	" 8 p45	9 p25	24¾	
Through Table p. 7.													
Pöstyén	See routes to Vienna.												
Ostend Vienna	On to Galantha	227								ChX 9 a0	10p11	36¼	
Express.	" Pöstyén	233B	9	9	2	...	...	...	...				
1204 miles.	Via Ostend and Berlin...........		...	...	...	...	...	...	...	ChX 2 p5	6 a14	39¼	
										" 9 p0	10a32	35½	
1142 miles.	Via Flushing and Berlin.........		...	...	...	...	...	...	...	Vic 10 a0	12a41	37½	
										" 8 p30	10a32	36	
1105 miles.	Via Hoek van Holland and									Liverpool			
	Berlin		...	...	...	...	...	...	...	Str 8 p30	10a32	36	
Prague	See routes to Dresden.		*—Via			Ostend.				ChX 9 a0	3 p17	29¼	
Via Calais	On to Bodenbach	188	‡—Via			Calais.				" 9 p0	5 *50	32	
or Ostend.	,, Aussig and Prague	252A	...	...	...	...	...	...	...	" 9 p0	6 ‡25	32½	
Via Flushing.	Fare via Flushing and Dresden		5	12	2	3	12	0	30	Vic 10 a0	3 p17	28½	
855 miles.	**Return fare**		10	10	10	6	16	8	60	" 8 p30	5 a50	32½	
Via Hoek v. Holl.	Fare via Hoek van Holland ...		5	12	2	3	12	0	30	Liverpool			
829 miles.	**Return fare**		10	10	10	6	16	8	60	Str 8 p30	5 a50	32½	

₵—Through Carriage from Boulogne, Calais, Dieppe, Flushing, H. v. Holland, Ostend—as the case may be.—₵

From LONDON to	ROUTES.	PAGE	FARES. 1st Cl. £ s. d.	FARES. 2nd Cl. £ s. d.	Validity of Ticket. Days	Departure from London.	Arrive Destination.	Time of Journey. HRS	Excess luggage per 20 lb
Ragaz	See routes to Basle.								
	On to Zurich ...261; Ragaz ...	268B							
Via Calais. 700 miles.	Via Calais, Laon, and Basle......		... ...	... ...	.. ...	**Vic** 11a 0	10a59	23	4/5
	§—From London on		Weekda	ys only.		**ChX** 4§p30	12p 7	18½	
Via Boulogne. 676 miles.	Via Boulogne, Laon, Basle		... ...	... ...	......	**ChX** 2 p5	10a59	20	4/5
Via Dieppe. 694 miles.	Via Dieppe, Paris, Basle..........					**Vic** 10 a0	10a59	24	
						" 8 p45	11 p7	25¼	
Rapallo .... 862 miles via Boulogne.	See routes to Turin.								
	On to Genoa and Rapallo	270				**ChX** 2 p5	8 p19	29¼	
	Fare via Calais, Boulogne, Paris, Turin		7 8 7	5 2 6	20				
850 miles.	Fare via Dieppe, Paris, Turin		6 10 9	4 11 0	20	**Vic** 10 a0	8 p19	33½	3/11
Rome .... *Via Basle.* Thro' Table p. 5.	See routes to Basle.					**Vic** 11 a0	6a45	42¾	
	On from Basle to Lucerne	258							
	On to Bellinzona, Lugano, and Chiasso	259							
	" Como and Milan	269A							
	" Florence and Rome	279							
Via Calais-Basle 1221 miles.	Fare via Calais, Laon, and Basle		8 19 1	6 2 5	20				
	Return fare		15 16 8	11 1 1	60				
	§—5/6 to Chiasso; thence 1/9.								
Via Boulogne-Basle. 1196 miles	Fare via Boulogne, Laon, Basle		8 19 1	6 2 5	20	**ChX** 2 p5	6a45	39¾	
	Return fare		15 16 8	11 1 1	60				
Via Paris and Modane. 1149 miles via Boulogne. Thro' Table p. 1.	London to Boulogne, Amiens, Paris	18				**ChX** 2 p5	7 a0	40	
	On to Dijon	48				" 9 p0	7 p15	45¼	
	" St. Amour and Bourg ...	63B							
	" Culoz and Modane.........	60							
	" Turin, Genoa, Pisa, Rome	270	8 16 9	5 19 11	20				‡
	Return fare		15 3 11	10 18 0	60				
	‡—4/5 to Modane; thence 1/10.								
Via Dieppe-Modane. 1141 miles.	London to Dieppe and Paris ...	76				**Vic** 10 a0	7 a0	44	3/11
	From Paris to Rome as above		7 18 10	5 8 5	20	" 8p45	7 p15	45¼	
	Return fare		13 14 7	9 10 5	60				
Via Paris and Simplon. 1226 miles via Calais. 1198 miles via Boulogne. 1185 miles via Dieppe.	London to Calais and Paris ...	18				**Vic** 11 a0	6 a45	42¾	
	On to Dijon 48; Pontarlier ...	52				**ChX** 9 p0	6 p55	45	
	" Lausanne & Domodossola	263B							
	" Milan 274; Rome	279	8 16 11	6 0 7	20				
	Via Dieppe, Paris, and Simplon		7 19 0	5 9 1	20	**Vic** 10 a0	6 a45	43¾	
	Return fare		13 17 5	9 11 9	60	" 8p45	6 p55	45	3/1
1280 miles.	Via Havre, Paris, and Simplon		... ...	... ...	Not	**Waterloo** Sun. 9 p45	6 p55	44	
Rotterdam *Via Hoek v. Holland.* 211 miles.	London to Hoek v. Holland and Rotterdam	112	1 11 11	1 1 1	15	**Liverpool Str** 8 p30	5a43	₵ 9	1/2
	Return fare		2 10 6	1 13 10	60				
Via Flushing. 252½ miles.	London to Flushing and Rosendaal..............................	113				**Vic** 10 a0	9 p20	₵11	
						" 8 p30	6 a46	₵ 9½	
	On to Zevenbergen, Dordrecht, and Rotterdam	117	1 11 11	1 1 1	15				1/2
	Return fare		2 10 6	1 13 10	60				
	London to Tilbury, thence steamer direct		1 1 0	0 13 0	......	**Fench'rh St.** 4‡p48	...	11	
	Return fare		1 12 0	1 0 0	......	‡—Not on Sun.			

₵—Through Carriage from Boulogne, Calais, Dieppe, Flushing, H. v. Holland Ostend—as the case may be.—₵

Travel and Hotel Enquiries—See page XII.

From LONDON to	ROUTES.	PAGE	FARES. 1st Cl. £	s.	d.	2nd Cl. £	s.	d.	Validity of Ticket. Days	Departure from London.	Arrive Destination.	Time of Journey HRS	Excess luggage per 20 lb.
Rouen	London to Dieppe and Rouen	76	1	13	7	1	4	0	7	**Vic** 10 a0	5p19	7¼	7d. per
Via Dieppe.	**Return fare**		2	13	3	1	18	1	30	" 8 p45	7 a14	10½	10 lb.
159 miles.													
Via Calais.	London to Calais and Amiens	18								**Vic** 11 a0	9 p33	10½	
	On to Rouen	21	2	14	8	1	18	3	7	**ChX** 9 p0	9 a22	12½	†1/1
278 miles.	†—Per 10 lb. **Return fare**		4	15	7	3	9	9	30				
Via Boulogne.	Fare via Boulogne, and on as above		2	8	1	1	13	4	7	**ChX** 10 a0	9 p33	11½	
250½ miles.	**Return fare**		4	4	11	3	0	11	30	" 2 p5	11 p9	9	†1/0
Via Havre.	London to Havre and Rouen...	76	1	12	4	1	3	4	7	**Waterloo**			
254½ miles.	‡—Weekdays only. **Return fare**		2	10	4	1	16	4	30	9‡p45	9 a17	11½	
	See routes to Paris.									**ChX** 9 p0	5p20	20¼	
Royat	On to Vierzon 32; Montlucon....	37											
	,, Lapeyrouse 36; Royat.....	36	...	...	...	...	...	...	...				
	Fare via Boulogne & Paris (528 miles)		...	...	...	...	...	...	...	**ChX** 2 p5	9a42	19½	3/6
	Fare via Dieppe & Paris (515 miles)		3	18	2	2	15	0	15	**Vic** 10 a0	9 a42	23¾	3/-
										" 8p45	5p 20	20½	
St. Moritz ...	See routes to Basle.									**Vic** 11 a0	12§25	24½	
	On to Zurich	261								" 11 a0	3 p17	27¼	
	,, Sargans and Chur	268B											5/3
	,, St. Moritz	268B	...	...	...	...	...	...	......				
768½ miles.	...Fare via Calais		6	13	2	4	11	9	15				
	Return fare		10	19	11	7	16	7	60				
	§—Engadine Express, Train de Luxe.												
744 miles.	...Fare via Boulogne		6	13	2	4	11	9	15	**ChX** 2 p5	3 p17	24½	5/3
	Return fare		10	19	11	7	16	7	60				
772 miles.	...Fare via Ostend		6	1	8	4	2	6	15	**ChX** 9 a0	3 p17	29½	6/2
										" 2 p5	9 p15	30½	
757 miles.	...Fare via Dieppe		6	3	1	4	5	6	15	**Vic** 10 a0	3 p17	28¼	
	Return fare		9	19	6	7	0	3	60				
St. Petersburg	By Nord Express, see Through Table from London, page 9;									**ChX** 9 a0	10a30	47½	
Nord Express,	Ticket of Sleeping Car Co. On Wed. and Sat. only.												
1745 miles.	Fare via Ostend		14	1	8	...	...	...	......				
Via Flushing.	See Flushing route to Berlin.									**Vic** 10a0	11a35	47½	
	On from Berlin to Konigsberg and Eydtkuhnen	176								" 8p30	8 a15	57¾	
1683 miles. Thro' Table p. 9.	On to Wirballen and St. Petersburg	313	9	12	4	6	6	11	30				
	Return fare		18	11	3	12	6	4	60				
Via Calais.	See Calais route to Berlin.									**ChX** 9 p0	8a15	57¼	
1766 miles.	On from Berlin to Eydtkuhnen	176											
Thro' Table p. 9.	On to Wirballen and St. Petersburg	313	10	19	2	7	5	7	30				
	Return fare		21	2	6	14	2	2	60				
Via Ostend.	See Ostend route to Berlin.									**ChX** 9 p0	8 a15	57¼	
1739 miles.	On from Berlin to Eydtkuhnen	176											
Thro' Table p. 9.	On to Wirballen and St. Petersburg	313	10	7	6	6	17	7	30				
	Return fare		20	3	5	13	17	2	60				
Via Hoek v. Holland.	See Hoek van Holland route to Berlin.									**Liverpool Str** 8p30	8a15	57¾	
1647 miles.	On from Berlin to Eydtkuhnen	176											
Thro Table p. 9.	On to Wirballen and St. Petersburg	313	9	12	4	6	6	11	30				
	Return fare		18	11	3	12	6	4	60				

The "a" and "p" inserted in the departure and arrival times denote "a.m." and "p.m."

From LONDON to	ROUTES.	PAGE	1st Cl. £	s.	d.	2nd Cl. £	s.	d.	Validity of Ticket. Days	Departure from London.	Arrive Destination.	Time of Journey HRS	Excess luggage per 20lb
	London to Calais, Boulogne,									**Vic** 11 a0	4 p39	28½	
	Amiens, and Paris............	18								**ChX** 9 p0	9 a58	36	
San Remo ...	On to Dijon, Macon, Lyons,												¶
· 999 miles.	Marseilles	48											
	,, Cannes, Nice, Menton,												
	Ventimiglia	54								¶—5/10 to	Venti	migl	ia,
	,, San Remo................	272	8	0	3	5	10	0	20	thence	-/2.		
	Return fare		12	12	9	9	3	2	60				
Via Marseilles.	Fare via Boulogne, Paris, and												
971 miles.	Marseilles..........................		8	0	3	5	10	0	20	**ChX** 10 a0	4 p39	29½	
	Return fare		12	12	9	9	3	2	60				¶
958 miles.	London to Dieppe, Rouen, and									**Vic** 10 a0	4 p39	29½	
	Paris	76	7	2	5	4	18	6	20	,, 8p45	9 a58	36¼	5/4
	Paris to San Remo as above												
	See routes to Turin.									**Vic** 10 a0	11p49	36¾	
Via Turin.	On to Savona 272; San Remo 272A									**ChX** 2 p5	11p49	32¾	
888 miles......	Fare via Boulogne and Turin...		7	12	9	5	5	4	20				
876 miles ...	Fare via Dieppe and Turin......		6	14	10	4	13	10	20				
Langen-	See routes to Cologne.									**ChX** 9 a0	8 a8	22	
Schwalbach	On to Wiesbaden	128								,, 2 p5	11a24	20¼	
	,, Langenschwalbach........	146	...	...	...	...	...	...	......	,, 9 p0	3 p37	17½	
Via Flushing.	Fare via Vlissingen and Cologne									**Vic** 10 a0	8 a8	21	See p
490 miles.										,, 8 p30	3 p37	18	lxiv.
Via Hoek v.	Fare via Hoek v. Holland and									**Liverpool**			See
Holland.	Cologne..............................		3	8	10	2	5	6	15	**Str** 8p30	3 p37	18	page
504 miles.	**Return** fare		6	4	3	4	3	8	60				lxiv.
Spa.............	See routes to Brussels.									**ChX** 9 a0	8‡p33	11½	
	On to Liege and Pepinster ...	104								,, 9 p0	8a36	11½	
	,, Spa	111											
Via Ostend.	Fare via Ostend and Brussels...		2	6	10	1	12	9	7	‡—Via G	hent-		2/10
299 miles.	**Return** fare		4	2	5	2	17	11	30	Louvain	page	101.	
Via Calais.	Fare via Calais and Brussels ...		2	17	2	1	19	9	7	**ChX** 9 a0	8 p0	11	2/9
324 miles.	**Return** fare		5	0	4	3	11	4	30	,, 9 p0	8 a36	11½	
										Liverpool			
Via Antwerp.	London to Antwerp & Malines	110								**Str** 8p40	11a28	14¾	
318 miles.	On to Louvain 101 : to Pepinster	104								Not Sun.			
	,, Spa	111	1	18	7	1	4	0	7	night.			
	Return fare		3	0	4	1	18	7	30				1/8
	See routes to Copenhagen, via												
Stockholm..	Kiel or via Warnemunde.												
Via	On to Malmo (steamer) and												
Hamburg-	Stockholm	308A											
Copenhagen,	Or, see routes to Hamburg.												
or	On to Lubeck 213A; to Rostock	213											
Via Hamburg-	,, Stralsund....................	181A											
Stralsund.	,, Sassnitz and Trelleborg	181											
Thro' Table p. 9.	,, Malmo	311											
	,, Stockholm	308A	...	...	...	...	...	...	...				
1307 miles.	Via Ostend and Hamburg		8	3	1	5	8	5	30	**ChX** 9 a0	8 a49	46¾	
										,, 9 p0	6 a58	57	

The "a" and "p" inserted in the departure and arrival times denote "a.m." and "p.m."

From LONDON to	ROUTES.	PAGE	FARES. 1st Cl. £	s.	d.	2nd Cl. £	s.	d.	Validity of Ticket.	Departure from London.	Arrive Destination.	Time of Journey	Excess luggage per 20 lb
STOCKHOLM-*cont.*									Days	ChX 9 a0	8 a49	46¾	
1332 miles.	Via Calais and Hamburg.........		8	14	9	5	16	6	30	" 9 p0	6 a58	57	
1196 miles.	Fare via Flushing and Copenhagen to Stockholm		7	2	4	4	15	10	30	Vic 10a0 " 8 p30	8 a49 6 a58	45¾ 57½	See page lxiv.
	Return fare		13	11	3	9	4	3	60				
1159 miles.	Fare via Harwich and Hoek van Holland to Stockholm		7	2	4	4	15	10	30	Liverpool Str 8 p30	6 a58	57½	See page lxiv.
	Return fare		14	18	0	9	15	0	60				
Via Berlin. Thro' Table p. 9.	See routes to Berlin.									ChX 9 a0	8 a49	46¾	
	On to Sassnitz and Trelleborg	181								" 2 p5	6 p46	51¾	
	" Malmo	311											
	" Stockholm (from Berlin £3 12s., £2 8s. 8d.)	308A	...	...	...	...	...	...	...				
1307 miles.	Via Flushing and Berlin.........		7	15	9	5	1	3	30	Vic 10a0	8a49	45¾	
	Return fare		14	18	0	9	15	0	60	" 8 p30	6p46	45¼	
1271 miles.	Via Hoek v. Holland & Berlin		7	15	9	5	1	3	30	Liverpool			
	Return fare		14	18	0	9	15	0	60	Str 8 p30	6p46	45¼	
1363 miles.	Via Ostend and Berlin		...	...	...	...	...	...	...	ChX 9 a0 " 2 p5	8 a49 6p46	46¾ 51¾	
1390 miles.	Via Calais and Berlin		...	...	...	...	...	...	...	ChX 9 a0 Vic 11a0	8 a49 6p46	46¾ 53¾	
Via Harwich-Gothenburg.	London to Harwich, thence Steamer to Gothenburg									Liverpool Str 4 p10 Sat.	9 p8 Mon		
	On to Cathrineholm...............	309											
	" Stockholm	308A	5	11	6	3	14	6	...				
	Return fare		10	2	6	6	3	6	...				
Strassburg *Via Boulogne-Laon.* 517 miles.	London to Boulogne & Amiens	18	§—Wee			kdays o		nly		ChX 2 p5	5 a50	14¾	
	On to Laon 21; Avricourt	64A	from			London.				" 4§p30	8 a14	15¼	
	" Strassburg	210	4	6	0	2	18	10	15				
Thro' Table p. 5.	See routes to Brussels.									ChX 9 a0	3 a27	₵17½	
	On to Namur & Luxemburg ...	103A								" 2 p5	8 a44	₵17¾	See
	" Metz and Strassburg......	210								" 9 p0	3 p19	₵17¼	page
Via Ostend. 499 miles.	Fare via Ostend and Brussels...		3	14	0	2	10	8	15				lxiv.
	Return fare		6	14	2	4	11	9	60				
Via Calais. 520 miles.	Fare via Calais and Brussels ...		4	3	4	2	16	10	15	ChX 9 a0	3 a27	17½	See
	Return fare		7	10	6	5	4	3	60	" 2p†5	8 a44	17¾	page
	†—Via Boulogne.									" 9 p0	3 p19	17¼	lxiv.
Via Paris. 599 miles.	See routes to Paris.									Vic 11 a0	5 a50	18	
	On to Chalons, Nancy, and									ChX 9 p0	4 p41	18¾	
	Deutsch-Avricourt.........	64											3/-
	" Strassburg	210											
	Fare via Calais and Paris		...	...	...	...	...	...	...				
559 miles.	Fare via Dieppe and Paris......		4	4	1	2	18	7	15	Vic 10 a0	5 a50	19	3/4
	Return fare		6	18	5	4	17	11	60	" 8 p45	4 p41	19	
Orient Express. 571 miles.	London to Paris thence by Orient Express	8	5	16	6	...	...	...	...	ChX 10 a0	3 a38	16½	
Via Hoek van Holland. 598 miles.	See Hoek van Holland route to Cologne.									Liverpool Str 8 p30	6 p17	20¾	
	On from Cologne to Bingerbruck	122											
	On to Kreuznach and Munster	125											See
	" Hochspeyer & Neustadt	206											page
	" Strassburg....................	208	4	0	9	2	12	10	15				lxiv.
	Return fare		7	8	0	4	18	3	60				
Via Flushing 584 miles	See Flushing route to Cologne and on as in previous route...		4	0	9	2	12	10	15	Vic 10a0 " 8 p30	10 a1 3 p48	23 ₵17	See page
	Return fare		7	8	0	4	18	3	60				lxiv.

₵—Through Carriage from Boulogne, Calais, Dieppe, Flushing, H. v. Holland, Ostend—as the case may be.—₵

From LONDON to	ROUTES.	PAGE	FARES. 1st Cl. £	s.	d.	2nd Cl. £	s.	d.	Validity of Ticket. Days	Departure from London.	Arrive Destination.	Time of Journey HRS	Excess luggage per 20 lb
Stuttgart ...	London to Boulogne and									**ChX** 2 p5	9 a2	18	
Via Boulogne-	Amiens	18								„ 4 §p30	12p42	19¼	
Laon.	On to Laon	21											
627 miles.	„ Avricourt	64A											
	„ Appenweier & Carlsruhe	210											
	„ Stuttgart	192	5	1	2	3	9	0	15				
	§—Weekdays only from London.												
	See routes to Paris.									**Vic** 11 a0	9 a2	21	
	On to Chalons, Nancy, and									**ChX** 9 p0	7 p42	21¾	
	Deutsch Avricourt.........	64											
	„ Strassburg & Appenweier	210											
Via Paris.	„ Oos and Carlsruhe..........	141											
709 miles.	„ Pforzheim & Muhlacker	141											
	„ Stuttgart	192											
	Fare via Calais and Paris												
669 miles.	**Fare via Dieppe and Paris......**		4	19	4	3	8	10	15	**Vic** 10 a0	9 a2	22	4/-
	Return fare		8	8	10	5	18	3	60	„ 8 p45	7 p42	22	
Orient Express.	London to Paris thence by									**ChX** 10 a0	6 a40	19¾	
681 miles.	Orient Express	8	6	15	9	...	...	...	...				
Via Ostend-	London to Ostend and Brussels	102											
Carlsruhe.	On to Luxemburg	103								**ChX** 9 a0	9 a2	23	See
609 miles.	„ Appenweier 210; Carlsruhe	141								„ 2 p5	12p42	21¾	page
	„ Muhlacker 141; Stuttgart	192	4	8	5	2	19	2	15	„ 9 p0	7 p42	21¾	lxiv.
Thro' Table p. 13.	See routes to Cologne.									**ChX** 9 a0	9 a19	23¼	
	On to Mayence and Darmstadt	122								„ 9 p0	4 p47	18¾	
Via Cologne.	„ Heidelberg	139											
Thro' Table p. 13.	„ Bruchsal	140											
	„ Muhlacker and Stuttgart	192											See
Via Ostend-													page
Cologne. 601 miles.	**Fare via Ostend and Cologne...**		4	8	5	2	19	2	15				lxiv.
Via Calais-										**ChX** 9 a0	9 a19	23¼	See
Cologne.	**Fare via Calais and Cologne ...**		5	1	2	3	9	0	15	„ 9 p0	6 p29	20½	page
626 miles.													lxiv.
Via Flushing-													See
Cologne. 604 miles.	**Fare via Flushing and Cologne**		4	4	2	2	14	11	15	**Vic** 10 a0	9 a19	22¼	page
	Return fare		7	14	10	5	2	5	60	„ 8 p30	4 p47	₵19¼	lxiv.
Via Hoek van Holland and	**Fare via Hoek van Holland and**									**Liverpool**			See
Cologne. 618 miles.	**Cologne ....**		4	4	2	2	14	11	15	**Str** 8 p30	6 p29	₵21	page
	Return fare		7	14	10	5	2	5	60				lxiv.
Trieste	From Calais by Simplon Ex-												
Via Paris.	press, see Through Table, p. 1		11	12	8		...		...	**Vic** 11 a0	9 p0	₵33	
	Via Cologne, Frankfort, and												
	Munich (see routes to)												
Via Cologne.	From Munich to Salzburg	200											
	On to Bischofshofen...............	239											
	„ Villach, Rosenbach, and												
	Trieste	237D											
1130 miles.	Fare via Ostend		8	0	0	5	1	6	30	**ChX** 9 p0	9 a1	35.	
1108 miles.	Fare via Flushing....................		7	19	8	5	1	2	30	**Vic** 8 p30	9 a1	₵35½	
	Return fare		14	18	11	9	9	5	60				
1122 miles.	Fare via Hoek van Holland ...		7	19	8	5	1	2	30	**Liverpool**			
	Return fare		14	18	11	9	9	5	60	**Str** 8p30	11a25	38	
1109 miles.	Fare via Calais		8	12	9	5	10	7	30	**ChX** 9 p0	11a25	37½	

₵—Through Carriage from Boulogne, Calais, Dieppe, Flushing, H. v. Holland, Ostend—as the case may be. ₵

From LONDON to	ROUTES	PAGE	1st Cl. £	s.	d.	2nd Cl. £	s.	d.	Validity of Ticket. Days	Departure from London.	Arrive Destina-tion.	Time of Journey HRS	Excess luggage per 20lb
Turin	London to Calais, Boulogne,									**Vic** 11 a0	2 p 5	26	
	Amiens, Paris	18								**ChX** 2 p5	2 p 5	23	
Via Calais or	On to Dijon	48								" 9 p0	12 a5	26	
Boulogne.	" St. Amour and Bourg ...	63B											
741 miles.	" Culoz, Modane	60											
Thro' Table p. 1.	" Turin	270	6	10	9	4	10	2	20				
	Return fare		10	8	10	7	11	5	60				§
	§—4/7 to Modane; -/5 thence.												
Via Dieppe.	London to Dieppe, Rouen, and									**Vic** 10 a0	2 p 5	27	
728 miles.	Paris	76								" 8 p45	12a 5	26¼	
Thro' Table p. 1.	On to Turin as above		5	12	11	3	18	8	20				3/11
	Return fare		8	19	6	6	8	10	60				
Venice	See routes to Milan via Basle.									**ChX** 2 p5	11p30	32½	
	On to Verona, Padua, and Venice	280											
Via Basle.	Fare via Boulogne Laon, Basle, Milan (956¾ miles)............		7	17	0	5	8	10	20				§
Thro' Table p. 5.	§—5/5 to Chiasso; 1/1 thence.												
										ChX 9 a0	11p30	37½	
985 miles.	Fare via Ostend, Brussels,									" 2 p5	4 a19	37¼	
	Basle, Milan		...	...	...	...	...	...	20	" 9 p0	11a25	37½	
975 miles.	Fare via Dieppe, Paris, Basle...		7	6	11	5	2	7	20	**Vic** 10 a0	11p30	36½	6/1
	Return fare		12	0	5	8	10	7	60	" 8 p45	11a25	37¾	
Via Paris.	From Calais by Simplon Express, see Through Table, p. 1		10	10	10	...	...	...	...	**Vic** 11 a0	4p40	₵28¾	
949 miles.	See routes to Milan, via Paris.									**Vic** 11 a0	11p30	35½	
Thro' Table p. 1.	On to Venice (Fare via Boulogne)	280	7	17	3	5	8	8	20	**ChX** 2 p5	11p30	32¼	
986 miles.	Fare via Dieppe, Paris, Turin		7	6	4	5	0	10	20	**Vic** 10 a0	11p30	36½	3/11
Vernet-les-Bains...	See routes to Paris.												
895 miles.	On to Toulouse and Narbonne	32								**ChX** 10 a0	10a38	24½	
	" Perpignan	46								**Vic** 8p45	7 a12	22½	
	" Villefranche Vernet-les-									**ChX** 9 p0	7 a12	22¼	5/5
	Bains	46	7	5	1	4	19	9	15				
	Return fare		11	8	8	8	6	1	60				
Vichy	London to Calais and Paris ...	18								**Vic** 11 a0	3 a15	16¼	
Via Calais.	On to St. Germains-des-Fosses									**ChX** 9 p0	3 p35	18½	
518 miles.	and Vichy	58											3/5
	Return fare		7	7	0	5	7	1	60				
Via Boulogne.	London to Boulogne and Paris	18								**ChX** 2 p5	5 a11	15¼	
491 miles.	On to St. Germains-des-Fosses												
	and Vichy	58											3/3
	Return fare		7	7	0	5	7	1	60				
Via Dieppe.	London to Dieppe and Paris ...	76								**Vic** 10 a0	3 a15	17¼	
478 miles.	On to St. Germains-des-Fosses									" 8 p45	3 p35	18¾	
	and Vichy	58	3	12	9	2	11	4	15				2/9
	Return fare		5	17	8	4	4	6	60				
Via Havre.	London to Havre and Paris ...	76								**Waterloo**			
573 miles.	On to Vichy	58	3	14	0	2	11	0	15	9 p45	6 p30	20¾	
	Return fare		5	1[illegible]	3	4	4	3	60	Not Sun.			

The "a" and "p" inserted in the departure and arrival times denote "a.m." and "p.m."

From LONDON to	ROUTES.	PAGE	FARES. 1st Cl. £	s.	d.	FARES. 2nd Cl. £	s.	d.	Validity of Ticket. Days	Departure from London.	Arrive Destination.	Time of Journey. HRS	Excess luggage per 20lb
Vienna......... *Ostend-Vienna*	By Ostend-Vienna Express, see									ChX 9 a0	6 p0	₵32	
Express.	Through Table from London	8	8	12	1	...	...	...	......				
967 miles.	By Orient Express. See									ChX 10 a0	6 p0	31	
Orient Express 1121 miles.	Through Table from London	8	10	13	3	...	...	...	......				
	London to Boulogne & Amiens	18								ChX 2 p5	9 p50	30¾	
Via	On to Laon 21; Avricourt	64A											
Boulogne-Laon	,, Appenweier & Carlsruhe	210											
1047 miles.	,, Bietigheim 192; Backnang	194											
	,, Crailsheim 191; Nürnberg	204											
	,, Passau 195A; Vienna ...	239A	8	6	0	5	8	9	30				
	Return fare		15	5	10	10	3	11	60				
	See routes to Cologne.												
Ostend or	On to Frankfort	128								ChX 9 a0	9 p50	35¾	
Calais and	,, Aschaffenb. & Wurzburg	196								" 9 p0	7 a20	33½	
Cologne.	,, Nurnberg and Passau ...	195A											
Thro' Table p. 13.	,, Wels 239B; Vienna	239A											
963 miles.	Fare via Ostend		7	0	0	4	9	2	30				
	Return fare		13	8	7	8	10	6	60				
88 miles.	Fare via Calais		7	12	11	4	18	2	30				
	Return fare		14	7	9	9	5	6	60				
Via Flushing-Dresden.	See Flushing route to Dresden.									Vic 10 a0	9 p36	₵34½	
Thro' Table p. 9.	On to Tetschen 188; Vienna...	224	7	0	0	4	7	11	30	" 8 p30	7 a22	₵33¾	
1058 miles.	**Return fare**		12	19	9	8	3	0	60				
Via Hoek van	See H. v. Holland to Dresden									Liverpool			
Holland.	and on as in previous route...		7	0	0	4	7	11	30	Str 8 p30	7 a22	33¾	
1032 miles.	**Return fare**		12	19	9	8	3	0	60				
Vittel	London to Calais and Amiens	18								ChX 4‡p30	6 a0	13½	
Via Calais.	On to Tergnier	21								" 9*p0	12p43	15¾	
489 miles.	" Laon 21; Reims	71											
Thro' Table p. 5.	" Chalons	67											
	" St. Dizier, Chaumont ...	66											
	" Langres 68A; Vittel	68A	4	2	3	2	17	0	15				3/1
	Return fare		6	16	11	4	19	7	30				
	‡—From London on Tues. and Fri. only. *—From London on Fri. only.												
Via Boulogne.	London to Boulogne, Amiens	18								ChX 2 p5	4 a59	14¾	
465 miles.	On as in previous route		4	2	3	2	17	0	15				3/1
Warsaw	From London once a week, on									ChX 9 a0	7 p14	33½	
Nord Express.	Monday. See Through												
Via Ostend.	Table	9	9	18	9	...	...	...	......				
1126 miles.	See Ostend route to Berlin.									ChX 9 a0	1 a29	38½	
Via Ostend.	On to Frankfort-on-Oder	179								" 9 p0	8 a7	34	
Thro' Table p. 9.	,, Posen 182; Thorn.........	178											
1126 miles.	,, Alexandrowo	176											
	,, Warsaw	316	7	11	6	4	19	1	......				
Via Calais.	Fares via Calais and Berlin									ChX 9 a0	1 a29	38½	
1146 miles.	and as in previous route		8	3	2	5	7	2	......	" 9 p0	1 p22	38¼	
	See Flushing route to Berlin.									Vic 10 a0	1a29	37½	
Via Flushing.	On to Custrin, Schneidemuhl,									" 8 p30	8 a7	34¼	
1056 miles.	Bromberg, and Thorn ...	176											
	,, Alexandrowo 176; Warsaw	316	6	15	9	4	7	3	30				
	Return fare		12	18	0	8	6	11	60				
Via Hoek van	Fare via Hoek van Holland and									Liverpool			
Holland.	as above............................		6	15	9	4	7	3	30	Str 8 p30	8 a7	34½	
1020 miles.	**Return fare**		12	18	0	8	6	11	60				

The "a" and "p" inserted in the departure and arrival times denote "a.m." and "p.m."

From LONDON to	ROUTES.	FARES. 1st Cl. £ s. d.	FARES. 2nd Cl. £ s. d.	Validity of Ticket. Days	Departure from London.	Arrive Destination.	Time of Journey HRS	Excess luggage per 20lb
Wiesbaden......	See route to Cologne.				**ChX** 9 a0	5 a0	19	
Thro' Table p. 13.	On to Niederlahnstein and				" 2 p5	11a26	20¼	See
	Wiesbaden 128				" 9 p0	2 p26	₵16½	page
Via Ostend. 472 miles.	Fare via Ostend and Cologne...	3 10 9	2 8 8	15				lxiv.
	Return fare	6 9 10	4 9 5	60				
Via Calais. 497 miles.	Fare via Calais and Cologne ...	4 2 8	2 16 11	15	**ChX** 9 a0	5 a0	19	See
	Return fare	7 9 3	5 4 8	60	" 2†p5	11a26	20¼	page
	†—Via Boulogne.				" 9 p0	2 p26	₵16½	lxiv.
Via Flushing. 475 miles.	Fare via Flushing and Cologne	3 7 3	2 4 6	15	**Vic** 10 a0	5 a8	₵18	see p
	Return fare	6 1 0	4 1 8	60	" 8 p30	2 p26	₵17	lxiv.
Via H.v.Holl'nd 489 miles.	Faro via H. v. Holland & Cologne.	3 7 3	2 4 6	15	**Liverpool**			see p
	Return fare	6 1 0	4 1 8	60	**Str** 8 p30	2 p26	17	lxiv.
Wildungen	See routes to Cassel.				**ChX** 2 p5	3 p52	24¾	
Via Cassel.	On to Wabern 156A; Wildungen 156A				**Vic** 8p30	8 p27	22¾	
532 miles.	Fare via Flushing	3 14 3	2 9 0	15	**ChX** 9 p0	8 p27	22¼	
	Return fare	6 15 0	4 10 8	60				
551 miles.	Fare via Hoek v. Holland	3 14 3	2 9 0	15	**Liverpool**			
	Return fare	6 15 0	4 10 8	60	**Str** 8p30	8 p27	23	
560½ miles.	Via Ostend or Calais	[No Through Ticket]						
Zermatt	See routes to Lausanne.							
	On to St. Maurice and Visp ...263B							
	„ Zermatt...................... 266							
727 miles.	Fare via Calais	6 8 11	4 13 3	15	**Vic** 11a0	12p36	24½	3/10
	Return fare	10 7 3	7 15 10	60				
699 miles.	Fare via Boulogne	6 2 3	4 8 4	15	**ChX** 10a0	12p36	25½	3/8
	Return fare	10 7 3	7 15 10	60	" 2 p5	5p58	26¾	
686 miles.	Fare via Dieppe	5 11 0	4 1 10	15	**Vic** 10a0	12p36	25½	3/1
	Return fare	8 18 0	6 13 3	60				
Zurich	See routes to Basle.				**Vic** 11a0	6 §45	18¾	
	On to Brugg and Zurich 261				" 11a0	8 a35	20½	
Via Calais, 639 miles.	Fare via Calais, Laon, Basle...	5 3 0	3 11 3	15	**ChX** 4‡p30	9 a58	16½	3/5
	Return fare	8 11 8	6 3 11	60				
	§—Engadine Express, Train de Luxe.							
	‡—Weekdays only from London.							
Via Boulogne. 615 miles.	Fare via Boulogne, Laon, Basle	5 3 0	3 11 3	15	**ChX** 2 p5	8 a35	17½	3/5
	Return fare	8 11 8	6 3 11	60				
					ChX 9 a0	8 a35	22½	
Via Ostend,					" 2 p5	1 p13	22¼	
643 miles.	Fare via Ostend, Brussels, Basle	4 11 6	3 2 1	15	" 9 p0	7 p55	21¾	3/3
Via Dieppe, 633 miles.	Fare via Dieppe, Paris, Basle...	4 13 0	3 5 0	15	**Vic** 10 a0	8 a35	21½	
	Return fare	7 11 3	5 7 7	60	" 8 p45	7 p55	22	
Via Flushing, 728 miles.	Fare via Flushing, Cologne, Basle	5 2 9	3 6 6	15	**Vic** 10 a0	1 p13	26¼	
					" 8 p30	7 p55	22	1/-
Via Hoek van Holland, 742 miles.	Fare via Hoek van Holland,				**Liverpool**			
	Cologne, Basle.....................	5 0 0	3 4 6	15	**Str** 8 p30	11p25	26	1/-
	Return fare	9 2 2	5 18 2	60				

₵—Through Carriage from Boulogne, Calais, Dieppe, Flushing, H. v. Holland, Ostend—as the case may be.—₵

"Swiss" = Swiss Railway Station. "Badish" = Baden Railway Station.

From BASLE to	ROUTE.	PAGE	FARES. 1st class. fr.	c.	2nd class. fr.	c.	Validity of Ticket. Days.	Departure from Basle.	Arrve destin ation.	Time of J'rney
Berne	To Olten	258						**Swiss** 7a15	9a20	2
66½ miles.	On to Berne..........................	257	11	15	7	85	...	" 7a40	10a27	2¾
	Return fare		16	70	10	70	10	" 10a40	1p32	2¾
								" 1p42	3p55	2¼
								" 1p50	4p12	2½
								" 3p40	6 p0	2½
								" 6p20	8p53	2½
								" 9p45	12 a8	2½
								" 12ngt	2a35	2½
Brussels	To Mulhausen and Strassburg	209						**Swiss** 10a22	8p11	10¾
364 miles.	On to Metz and Luxemburg ...	210A						" 12p15	9p26	10¼
	„ Arlon, Namur, & Brussels	103B	59	25	38	90	4	" 7p32	5a26	11
								" 11p40	8a28	9¾
Chur (Coire)...	To Brugg and Zurich	261						**Swiss** 5§a10	9a25	4¼
128½ miles.	On to Ziegelbrucke, Sargans,							" 7 a5	11a25	4¼
	and Chur	268B	21	45	15	5	...	" 8‡a20	12p32	4¼
	Return fare		32	15	20	60	10	" 8a50	2p25	5½
								" 11a30	4p53	5½
§—Engadine E	xpress, Train de Luxe, from 2nd		July un		til 15th		Sept.	" 1p37	6p47	5
	‡—Runs until 15th Sept.							" 6p15	11p38	5½
Cologne	To Strassburg, Weissenburg,							**Swiss** 10a14	6 p5	7¾
	Neustadt	209						" 1p45	10p15	8½
Via Munster-am-Stein.	On via Munster-am-Stein (p.							" 4p37	12a55	8¼
312 miles.	206) to Bingerbruck	125A						" 9p33	5a21	7¾
	„ Coblence, Bonn, & Cologne	123B	51	50	32	75	4			
Via Worms.	To Strassburg, Weissenburg							**Swiss** 9a29	6 p5	8½
334 miles.	Worms, and Mayence ...	209						" 11p48	9a50	10
	On to Coblence, Bonn, Cologne	123B	51	50	32	75	4			
Via Carlsruhe.	To Freiburg, Carlsruhe, and							**Badish** 9a50	6 p5	8¼
329½ miles.	Mannheim	141						" 10a42	7 p7	8½
	On to Mayence	136						" 1 p0	10p30	9½
	„ Coblence, Bonn, & Cologne	123B	51	50	32	75	4	" 3p33	12a55	9¼
	[Or, from Basle to Heidelberg							" 9p41	5a42	8
	141, on to Darmstadt 139, on							" 11p52	9a50	10
	to Mayence 123A.]									
Davos-Platz ...	To Brugg and Zurich..............	261						**Swiss** 5§a10	12p15	7
151½ miles.	On to Ziegelbrucke, Sargans,							" 7 a5	2p10	7
	and Landquart	268B						" 8‡a20	2p12	6¼
	„ Davos-Platz.....	268D	34	0	23	35	...	" 8a50	5 p2	8¼
§—Engadine E	xpress, Train de Luxe, from 2nd		July un		til 15th		Sept.	" 11a30	7 p35	8
	‡—Runs until 15th Sept.							" 1p37	9p25	7¾
Dresden	To Carlsruhe and Heidelberg	141						**Badish** 7a53	10p14	14¼
524½ miles.	On to Frankfort 136-139; Bebra	149						" 9 a50	11p52	14
	„ Corbetha and Leipsic ...	171						" 5 p18	8 a13	15
	„ Dresden........................	188	87	50	53	15	4	" 11p52	2p55	15
Frankfort ...	To Freiburg, Carlsruhe, and							**Badish** 7 a53	12p39	4¾
Via	Heidelberg	141						" 9a50	2p33	4¾
Carlsruhe.	On to Darmstadt and Frankfort	139	36	25	23	50	4	" 10a42	4p25	5¾
210½ miles.								" 1 p0	6p25	5½
								" 2p33	8p20	5¾
								" 3p33	8p32	5
								" 5p18	10p11	5
								" 5p33	10p53	5½
								" 11p52	5a32	5¾
Via	To Strassburg, Neustadt, and							**Swiss** 7a40	12p40	5
Strassburg.	Ludwigshafen	209						" 9a29	2p33	5
230½ miles.	On to Mannheim	205						" 12p15	5 ‡36	5¼
	„ Frankfort	136						" 3p19	8‡p13	5¼
			36	25	23	50	4	" 4p59	10p25	5½
	‡—Via Worms.							" 11p48	5 a48	6

The "a" and "p" inserted in the departure and arrival times denote "a.m." and "p.m."

From BASLE to	ROUTE	PAGE	FARES 1st class fr. c.	FARES 2nd class fr. c.	Validity of Ticket.	Departure from Basle.	Arrve destination.	Time of J'rney
		PAGE	fr. c.	fr. c.	Days.	**Swiss** 7a15	1p13	6
Geneva........	To Olten	258				" 10a40	6 p0	7¼
Via Berne.	On to Berne	257				" 1 p12	6p55	5¼
165¾ miles.	" Lausanne and Geneva ...	263A	27 45	19 80	...	" 1 p50	7 p22	5½
	Return fare		41 20	26 40	10	" 3p40	9p15	5½
						" 6 p20	1 a8	6¾
						" 12ngt	6 a10	6¼
Via Biel.	To Biel, Neuchatel, &Lausanne	264A				**Swiss** 7a30	12p52	5½
159¾ miles.	On to Geneva	263A	27 45	19 20	...	" 3p40	9 p0	5¼
	Return fare		41 20	26 40	10	" 6p44	12 a8	5½
						Swiss 7a15	10a55	3¾
Interlaken......	To Olten	258				" 7a40	12p40	5
103¾ miles.	On to Berne 257; Interlaken...	267	18 45	11 95	...	" 10a40	3 p25	4¾
	Return fare		28 10	17 60	10	" 1 p50	5p58	4¼
						" 3p40	7p45	4
Lausanne ..	To Biel, Neuchatel, and					**Swiss** 7a25	11a40	4¼
Via Biel.	Lausanne	264A	20 10	14 10	...	" 3p40	8 p7	4½
121¼ miles.	**Return fare**		30 10	19 30	10	" 6p44	11 p7	4½
Via Berne.	To Olten	258				**Swiss** 7a15	11a55	4¾
127¼ miles.	On to Berne	257				" 10a40	4p23	5¾
	" Lausanne	263A	21 15	14 85	...	" 1p42	5p55	4¼
	Return fare		31 70	20 30	10	" 1p50	6p14	4½
						" 3p40	8 p7	4½
						" 6p20	11p27	5¼
						" 12ngt	4a44	4¾
London	Basle to Alt-Munsterol	207A						
Via Laon-Boulogne.	On to Belfort and Chaumont...	69				**Swiss** 9a40	10p45	14
559¾ miles.	" St. Dizier and Chalons ...	66				" 11p33	3p25	16¾
	" Reims 67; Laon..........	67						
	" Tergnier 21; Amiens ...	21						
	" Boulogne and London ...	19A	119 50	82 55	15			
Via Laon-Calais.	See route above as far as Laon.							
584 miles.	Thence to St. Quentin	21				**Swiss** 9p25	10§15	13¾
	On to Douai 24; Lille	23				" 11p33	5p10	18½
	" Calais and London.........	27	119 50	82 55	15	§—Not on Sunday.		
Via Ostend.	Basle to Strassburg	209				**Swiss** 10a22	5a43	20½
588 miles.	On to Metz and Luxemburg ...	210A				" 11p40	5p10	18½
	" Brussels	103B						
	" Ostend and London	102A	106 45	72 10	15			
Via Paris-Calais.	Basle to Alt-Munsterol	207A				**Swiss** 10a41	5a43	20
613 miles.	On to Belfort and Paris	69	‡—Via	Delle.		" 11‡p33	5p10	18
	" Calais and London.........	19	127 10	87 70	15	" 12§a30	5p10	17¾
§-Engadine Express, Train de Luxe, via Delle and Chaumont. Runs from July 2 until Sept. 15.								
Via Paris-Boulogne.	Basle to Delle	264A						
585 miles.	On to Belfort and Paris	69				**Swiss** 7a35	10p45	16¼
	" Boulogne and London ...	19	127 10	87 70	15	11p33	3p25	16½
Via Paris-Dieppe.	Basle to Alt-Munsterol	207A						
577 miles.	On to Belfort and Paris	69	‡-Via	Delle.		**Swiss** 10a41	7a30	21[illegible]
	" Dieppe and London	77	106 95	74 75	15	" 11‡p33	6p10	19[illegible]
Via Flushing.	Basle to Neustadt	209				**Badish** †10a42	7 a48	22½
672¾ miles.	On to Munster-am-Stein	206				" 9†p41	7 p34	23
	" Bingerbruck..........................	125						
	" Cologne 123B; Oberhausen	161						
	" Wesel 132; Boxtel	120			†-Via	Mannheim page 141A.		
	" Vlissingen and London...	113	115 65	74 0	15			
Via Hoek van Holland.	Basle to Cologne as in previous route					**Swiss** 10a14	8 a0	22¾
687 miles.	On to Nymegen 121; Rotterdam	119A						
	" Hoekv. Holland & London	112	115 65	74 0	15			

From BASLE to	ROUTE.		FARES, 1st class.		2nd class.		Validity of Ticket.	Departure from Basle.		Arrve destination.	Time of J'rney
		PAGE	fr.	c.	fr.	c.	Days.	**Swiss**	7 a0	8 a59	2
Lucerne	To Olten and Lucerne	258	10	0	7	0	3	"	7 a30	9 a28	2
59½ miles.	**Return** fare		15	0	9	60	10	"	8 a25	10a48	2½
								"	12p2	1 p56	2
								"	1 p50	3 p49	2
								"	6 p10	8 p15	2
								"	7 p55	9 p55	2
								"	9 p45	11p42	2
								"	11p20	1a12	2
Milan	To Olten and Lucerne	258						**Swiss**	7 a0	3 p5	8
232½ miles.	On to Göschenen, Lugano, and							"	12p2	8 p40	8½
	Chiasso	259						"	1 p50	10p25	8½
	„ Como and Milan	269A	45	40	31	80	4	"	9 p45	6 a22	8¾
	Return fare		73	95	48	70	10	"	11p20	8 a53	9¾
Munich	To Brugg and Zurich	261						**Swiss**	7‡a10	5 p15	10
258 miles.	On to Romanshorn	262	‡—Via Bulach.					"	8 a50	7 p5	10¼
	„ Romanshorn to Lindau	368						"	1‡p18	9 p55	8½
	„ Kempten and Munich ...	199	45	15	30	35	3	"	9 p39	7 a5	9½
Paris	To Mulhausen and Alt-Munsterol	207A						**Swiss**	7‡a35	2 p49	8¼
326½ miles.								"	10a41	5 p45	8
	On to Belfort, Chaumont, Paris	69	58	70	39	80	5	"	5 p6	11p48	7¾
								"	10 p0	6 a25	9½
‡—Via Delle.								"	11‡p33	7 a28	9
§—Engadine	Express, Train de Luxe. Runs from 2nd July until 15th Sept.								12§a30	8 a42	9¼
Rome	To Olten and Lucerne	258						**Swiss**	7 a0	6 a45	23¾
646 miles.	On to Göschenen, Bellinzona,							"	12p2	8 a50	20¾
	and Chiasso	259						"	1 p50	1 p5	23¼
	„ Milan	269A						"	9 p45	6 p55	21¼
	„ Rome..............................	279	104	70	70	75	10	"	11p20	10p55	23½
St. Moritz	To Brugg and Zurich	261						**Swiss**	5§a10	12p25	7¼
184½ miles.	On to Ziegelbrucke and Chur...	268B						"	7 a5	3 p17	8¼
	„ St. Moritz	268B	44	70	30	55	...	"	8‡a20	4 p20	8
	Return fare		69	30	45	40	10	"	8 a50	6 p15	9½
§— Engadine	Express, Train de Luxe; from 2nd July to 15th Sept.							"	11a30	9 p15	9¾
‡—Runs until	15th September.							"	1 p37	10p20	8¾
Stuttgart								**Badish**	7a53	12p42	4¾
178½ miles.	To Offenburg and Carlsruhe ...	141						"	8 a0	2 p24	6½
	On to Pforzheim and Mühlacker	141						"	10a42	4 p47	6
	„ Bietigheim and Stuttgart	192	31	95	20	55	2	"	1 p0	6 p29	5½
								"	2 p33	7 p42	5¼
								"	3 p33	9 p21	5¾
								"	5 p33	10p42	5
								"	9 p41	3 a4	5½
								"	11p52	4a52	5
Thun	To Olten	258						**Swiss**	7 a15	10 a5	2¾
85½ miles.	On to Berne	257						"	10a40	2 p25	3¾
	„ Thun ....257 or	267	14	25	9	5	...	"	1 p50	5 p0	3¼
	Return fare		21	40	13	0	10	"	3 p40	6 p50	3¼
								"	6 p20	10p37	4¼
Turin	To Olten and Lucerne	258						**Swiss**	7 a30	7 p15	11¾
295 miles.	On to Göschenen and Bellinzona	259						"	8 a25	9 p45	13¼
	„ Luino... 259B; Novara...	269						"	12p2	11p50	11¾
	„ Vercelli and Turin.........	269	58	75	41	20	5	"	9 p45	9 a50	12
								"	11p20	12p35	13¼
								Swiss	6 a45	8 a35	2
Zurich	To Brugg and Zurich	261	9	25	6	50	...	"	8‡a20	9 a58	1¾
55½ miles.	**Return** fare		13	90	8	90	10	"	8 a50	10a37	1¾
								"	11a30	1 p13	1¾
	‡—Runs until 15th September.							"	1 p37	3 p29	1¾
								"	6 p15	7 p55	1¾
								"	6 p38	8 p58	2¼
								"	9 p39	11p25	1¾

From BERLIN to	ROUTE.	FARES. 1st class.	2nd class.	Validity of Ticket.	Departure from Berlin.	Arrve destin ation.	Time of J'rney
Bucharest	To Breslau 179	M. Pf.	M. Pf.	Days.	**Fried** 8 a36	7 p45	34¼
1136 miles.	On to Kandrzin 218; Oderberg 219				" 4 p39	6 a55	37½
	„ Cracow 222						
	„ Lemberg 246A; Burdujeni 246A						
	„ Pascani 324B; Bucharest 324	130 30	84 90				
Budapest ... *Via Vienna.*	See routes to Vienna.				**Anhalt** 8 p10	1 p40	17½
614 miles.	On from Vienna to Budapest 225B	79 60	51 10	...			
Via Breslau.	To Frankfort-o-O. and Breslau 179	‡—Via	Ruttka		**Fried** 4 p39	9 a40	17
609 miles.	On to Kandrzin 218; Oderberg 219	and Z	ólyom.		" 7 p33	12‡50	17¼
	„ Zsolna 253A; Galánta...233B				" 12n'ght0	6 p20	18¼
	„ Budapest.........................227	79 60	51 10	...			
Cologne	**To Hanover, Hamm, Cologne** 160	47 80	29 20	...	**Fried** 8‡a0	3 p56	8
364½ miles.					" 8‡a59	5 p41	8¾
					" 11a40	9 p9	9½
					" 12‡p16	8 p36	8¼
					" 1 p21	10p58	9½
					" 3 p32	11p39	8
	‡—Via Elberfeld page 134C.				" 9 p34	7 a15	9¾
	§—Nord Express.				" 10§p58	8 a2	9
	To Magdeburg and Soest 165				**Ptsdm** 1 p0	10p26	9½
358½ miles.	**On to Cologne**..........................134C	47 80	29 20	...	" 10p13	8 a52	10½
Constantinople...	See routes to Budapest.						
	On to Belgrade 225A						
	" Constantinople 325A	177 50	117 50	...	[Service sus	pend	ed].
	See route to Bucharest as far as	Pascani.				noon	
1521 miles.	On to Buzeu............................ 324				**Fried** 8 a36	12 0	50½
	" Faurei 324; Fetesci 324B				Mon., Wed.,	Wed	
	" Constanza and Constantinople 324A	187 10	121 20	...	Sat.	Fri., Mon	
Copenhagen ...	To Neu-Strelitz 181				**Stettn Bhf** 8 a49	6 p41	10
278½ miles.	On to Rostock & Warnemünde 178B						
	On by Steamer to Gjedser				" 11p15	9 a42	10½
	On from Gjedser to Copenhagen 302	40 0	27 90	...			
Dresden	**Via Elsterwerda or via Röderau** 188	16 20	10 50	...	**Anhalt** 6a55	9 a48	2¾
111¾ miles.					" 8 a5	11 a6	3
					" 9 a20	12 p4	2¾
					" 1 p20	4 p15	3
					" 4 p30	6 p56	2½
					" 6 p45	9 p48	3
					" 8 p10	10p46	2½
					" 11p15	2 a16	3
					Anhalt 8 a0	3 p46	7¾
Frankfort ... *Via Bebra.*	**To Halle, Erfurt, and Bebra** ... 170				" 9 a5	4 p54	7¾
335 miles.	**On to Frankfort** 149	43 40	27 50	...	" 2 p15	9 p23	7¼
					" 3 p35	11p40	8
					" 10p15	6 a53	8¾
					Fried 8 a17	5 p52	9½
Via Cassel.	To Kreiensen 165				" 7p‡52	5 a42	9¾
363 miles.	On to Frankfort 156	43 40	27 50	...	" 8 p50	6 a7	9¼
	‡—Via Hanover and Göttingen.				" 9 p50	7 a18	9½
Hamburg	**To Wittenberge and** Hamburg 167	24 70	15 90	...	**Lehter** 6 a18	9a49	3½
178 miles.					" 9 a5	12p58	3¾
					" 9 a10	1 p8	4
					" 1 p15	4p50	3½
					" 3 p8	6p57	3¾
					" 5 p25	8p52	3½
					" 7 p12	11 p2	3¾
					" 8 p55	12 a9	3¼

From BERLIN to	ROUTE	PAGE	FARES, 1st class. M.	Pf.	2nd class. M.	Pf.	Validity of Ticket. Days.	Departure from Berlin.	Arrve destination.	Time of J'rney HRS.
Leipsic .... 107½ miles.	To Bitterfeld and Leipsic	187	15	20	9	90	...	**Anhalt** 7 a10	9 a18	2¼
								" 7 a30	9 a26	2
								" 8 a55	11 a0	2
								" 10a50	1 p13	2½
								" 12p45	3 p44	3
								" 3 p50	6 p5	2¼
								" 4 p50	7 p37	2¾
								" 6 p30	8 p43	2¼
								" 7 p45	9 p41	2
								" 10p50	12a58	2¼
London ...... *Nord Express.*	By Nord Express, see Through Table from Berlin	11	127	90				**Fried** 10p58	§7 p5	21
									‡10p0	24
	§—Via Namur-Calais, slight extra charge.							‡—Via Ostend.		
726½ miles.	Berlin to Hanover, Hamm, and Oberhausen	160B						**Fried** 1 p5	7 a48	19¾
Via Flushing.	On to Wesel 132; Boxtel	120						" 10p28	7 p34	22
664½ miles.	" Breda	116								
	" Vlissingen and London...	113	83	0	54	80	...			
	Return fare		152	60	102	20	60			
Via Ostend.	Berlin to Hanover, Hamm, and Cologne	160B						**Fried** 8 a59	5 a43	21¾
720 miles.	On to Herbesthal	123B						" 8 p32	5 p10	26¾
	" Brussels........................	104						" 9 p34	10 p0	25½
	" Ostend and London	102A	101	90	66	60	...			
	Return fare		192	20	125	40	60			
Via Calais 747 miles.	Berlin to Hanover, Hamm, and Cologne	160B						**Fried** 8 a59	5 a43	21¾
	On to Herbesthal	123B						" 8 p32	5 p10	26¾
	" Brussels 104; Lille	103						" 9 p34	7 p5	22¼
	" Calais and London.........	27	113	80	74	90	...			
	Return fare		211	60	140	60	60			
Via Hoek van Holland. 628 miles.	Berlin to Hanover and Lohne...	160B						**Fried** 1 p5	8 a0	20
	On to Rheine	156C								
	" Amersfoort	118C								
	" Utrecht........................	115A								
	" Rotterdam	118A								
	" Hoek van Holland and London	112	83	0	54	80	...			
	Return fare		152	60	102	20	60			
Munich ...... *Via Hof.* 407½ miles	To Leipsic and Hof	187	53	20	32	70		**Anhalt** 7 a30	6 p14	10¾
	On to Regensburg and Munich	203						" 10a50	10p10	11¼
	§—Berlin-Tyrol Express, Luxuszug.							" 3 §p5	12a33	9½
								" 10p50	9 a23	10½
Via Weissenfels. 436½ miles.	To Halle and Weissenfels	170						**Anhalt** 10a30	8 p34	10
	On to Gera and Probstzella......	173						" 1p10	10 p5	9
	" Lichtenfels 195; Munich	197	53	20	32	70	...	" 1p45	12p40	11
								" 8p50	7 a14	10½
Paris.......... *Via Hanover-Cologne.* 671 miles.	To Hanover, Hamm, and Cologne	160						**Fried** 8 a0	11p30	16½
	On to Aix-la-Chapelle and Herbesthal	123B						" 9 p34	4 p0	19½
	" Verviers and Liege	104								
	" Namur and Erquelinnes	93								
	" Tergnier and Paris.........	24	89	30	57	60	...			
	Return fare		161	10	104	80	20			
Nord Express.	By Nord Express, over preceding route		120	80	...	...	...	**Fried** 10p58	4 p0	18

The "a" and "p" inserted in the departure and arrival times denote "a.m." and "p.m."

From BERLIN to	ROUTE.	PAGE	FARES. 1st class. M. Pf.	FARES. 2nd class. M. Pf.	Validity of Ticket. Days.	Departure from Berlin.	Arrve destination.	Time of Jrney HRS.
PARIS—*Continued.*								
Via Soest-Cologne. 665 miles.	To Magdeburg and Soest	165				**Ptsdm** 1 p0	7 a35	19½
	On to Elberfeld 134B; Cologne	134B				" 9 p26	4 p0	19½
	" Aix-la-Chapelle and Herbesthal	123B				" 10p13	6 p5	20¾
	" Verviers and Liege	104						
	" Namur and Erquelinnes	93						
	" Tergnier and Paris	24	89 30	57 60	...			
	Return fare		161 10	104 80	20			
Pöstyén 477 miles.	To Breslau	179				**Fried** 8 a36	12a38	16
	On to Kandrzin and Oderberg	218				" 4 p39	6 a11	13½
	" Zsolna	253A				" 7 p33	10a27	15
	" Pöstyén	233B	60 10	38 60	...	" 12n'gt0	2 p49	14¾
Prague 239 miles.	To Bodenbach	188				**Anhalt** 8 a5	3 p17	7¼
	On to Aussig and Prague	252A	34 50	22 20	...	" 4 p30	10p57	6½
	‡—Via Tetschen, page 224.					" 8 p10	2‡a41	6½
						" 11p15	6 a25	7½
St. Petersburg 1019 miles.	To Eydtkuhnen	176				**Fried** 8a17	11a35	26¼
	On to Wilna, Dwinsk, and					" 11p47	8 a15	31½
	St. Petersburg	313	115 0	73 15	...			
Nord Express.	By Nord Express, over preceding route		160 70	... ...	...	**Fried** 7 a32 Sun. & Thurs.	10a30	26
Stockholm 643 miles.	To Sassnitz	181				**Stettn Bhf** 11 a9	8 a49	21¾
	Steamer to Trelleborg.					" 8 p15	6 p46	22½
	On to Malmo	311						
	" Stockholm	308A	71 90	48 60	...			
Vienna *Via Breslau.* 510 miles.	To Breslau	179				**Schles** 8 a54	9 p50	13
	On to Kandrzin	218				" 4 p57	6 a0	13
	" Oderberg	219				" 7 p45	8 a7	12¼
	" Vienna	222	69 80	43 60	...	" 12a16	3 p10	15
Via Tetschen. 441½ miles.	To Dresden and Tetschen	188				**Anhalt** 8 a5	9 p36	13½
	On to Nimburg, Deutschbrod,					" 6 p45	7 a22	12¾
	and Vienna	224	69 80	43 60	...	" 8 p10	8 a0	11¾
Via Bodenbach 493½ miles.	On to Dresden and Bodenbach	188				**Anhalt** 8 a5	9 ‡45	13¾
	" Prague and Vienna	252A	69 80	43 60	...	" 4 p30	6 a55	14½
	‡—Via Gmund p. 243.					" 11p15	12‡48	13½
Warsaw *Via Posen.* 400 miles.	To Frankfort-on-Oder	179				**Fried** 7a§32	7 p14	10¾
	On to Posen	182				" 9 a42	1 a29	14¾
	" Thorn	178				" 3 ‡p5	7 a20	15¼
	" Alexandrowo	176				" 7‡p20	8 a7	11¾
	" Warsaw	316	52 80	34 70	...	" 11‡p24	1 p22	13
	§—Nord Express, Tuesday only.		‡—Via Landsberg, page 176.					
Via Kalisz. 419 miles.	To Frankfort and Sagan	179				**Fried** 11p50	2 p15	13½
	On to Lissa and Kalisz	218A						
	" Lodz and Warsaw	316	49 50	31 5	...			

The "a" and "p" inserted in the departure and arrival times denote "a.m." and "p.m."

A B C ROUTES from BRUSSELS with best Direct Trains.

From BRUSSELS to	ROUTE.		FARES. 1st class. fr.	c.	2nd class. fr.	c.	Validity of Ticket.	Departure from Brussels.	Arrve destination.	Time of J'rney
		PAGE	fr.	c.	fr.	c.	Days.			HRS.
Amsterdam ...	To Antwerp and Rosendaal ...	110						**Midi** 6 a0	11a22	5
142½ miles.	On to Rotterdam	117						**Nord** 7a56	12p43	4½
	" The Hague and Amsterdam	119						" 9a33	2p40	4¾
								Midi 12p33	5p17	4½
	or from Rotterdam to							" 4p54	9p 53	4½
	Amsterdam	115A	17	40	12	50	...	**Nord** 6p54	12a29	5¼
	Return fare		31	50	22	90	4			
Basle..............	To Namur, Arlon, and Luxem-							**Nord** 6 a8	5p36	10½
366½ miles.	burg	103A						" 7 a49	7 p22	10½
	On to Metz and Strassburg......	210						" 10a20	9 p13	10
	" Mulhausen and Basle ...	208	59	0	38	70	...	" 6 p35	5a43	10¼
	Return fare		110	50	72	50	7	" 11p28	11a15	10¾
Berlin	To Liége and Herbesthal.........	104						**Nord** 5a45	9p28	14¾
505 miles.	On to Aix-la-Chapelle and							" 10a54	12a21	12½
	Cologne	122						" 1p32	7a20	16¾
	" Hamm, Hanover, and							" 5 p0	8a54	15
	Berlin............................	161	81	10	50	90	...	" 5§p22	7a29	13
	Return fare		156	30	97	50	10	" 11p24	3p48	15½
	§—Nord Express.									
Cologne	To Liége and Herbesthal........	104						**Nord** 5a45	11a14	4½
141 miles.	On to Aix-la-Chapelle and							" 10a54	4p19	4½
	Cologne	122	23	70	15	80	...	" 1p32	7p40	5¼
	Return fare		41	80	27	70	4	" 5 p0	11 p1	5
								" 5§p22	10p46	4½
	§—Nord Express.							" 6‡p38	11p52	4¼
	‡—Ostend-Vienna Express.							" 11p24	5a40	5½
Copenhagen ...	To Liége and Herbesthal.........	104						**Nord** 5a45	9a42	27
684 miles.	On to Aix-la-Chapelle and							" 5a45	10a§4	27¼
	Cologne	122						" 5 p0	4 §48	22¾
	" Bremen and Hamburg ...	132						" 5 p0	6p41	24¾
	" Lubeck	213A								
	" Warnemunde	213						§–Via Kiel.		
	" Copenhagen	302	108	50	73	10	...			
	Return fare									
Dresden	To Liége and Herbesthal........	104						**Nord** 11p24	6 p36	18¼
	On to Cologne	122								
	" Elberfeld and Hagen	134A								
Via Cassel.	" Cassel	135A								
558½ miles.	" Bebra...............................	173A								
	" Leipsic	171								
	" Dresden..	188								
			92	0	56	60	...			
	To Liége and Herbesthal	104						**Nord** 5 a45	1 a43	19
	On to Cologne........................	122						" 1 p32	10a26	20
Via Magdeburg	" Hanover and Brunswick	161						" 5 p0	11a20	17¼
590½ miles.	" Magdeburg, Halle, and							" 11p24	8 p27	20
	Leipsic	158								
	" Dresden........................	188	92	0	56	60	...			

The "a" and "p" inserted in the departure and arrival times denote "a.m." and "p.m."

From BRUSSELS to	ROUTE.	PAGE	FARES. 1st class. fr. c.	FARES. 2nd class. fr. c.	Validity of Ticket. Days.	Departure from Brussels.		Arrve destination.	Time of J'rney HRS.
Dusseldorf......	To Liége and Herbesthal........	104				**Nord**	5 a45	1 p14	6½
152½ miles.	On to Aix-la-Chapelle	122				"	7 a31	2 p54	6¼
	" **Dusseldorf**	134A	26 60	18 10	...	"	10a54	4 p51	5
	Return fare		47 20	31 90	4	"	1 p32	8 p46	6¼
						"	3 p3	11p19	7¼
						"	5 p0	12 a3	6
Frankfort ... *Via Wiesbaden.* 279 miles.	To Liege and Herbesthal	104				**Nord**	5 a45	3 p19	8¾
	On to Cologne	122				"	8 a17	7 p57	10¾
	" Frankfort	128	46 20	30 20	...	"	5 p0	6 a53	13
Via Coblence. 281 miles.	To Liege and Herbesthal	104				**Nord**	5 a45	3 p5	8¼
	On to Cologne and Frankfort...	122	46 20	30 20	...	"	10a54	10 p7	10¼
	§—Ostend-Vienna Express—extra fare.					"	1 p32	12 a8	9½
						"	6p§38	3 a26	7¾
						"	11p24	11a11	10¾
Hamburg ... *Via Wesel.* 385 miles.	To Antwerp and Rosendaal ...	110				**Nord**	11a53	12 a9	11¼
	On to Breda 113; on to Boxtel	116							
	" Wesel 120; on to Haltern	130							
	" Hamburg	132	60 90	41 70	...				
	Return fare		118 20	79 40	8				
Via Cologne. 420½ miles.	To Liége and Herbesthal.........	104				**Nord**	5a45	9p42	15
	On to Aix-la-Chapelle and Cologne	122				"	5 p0	6a55	13
	" Osnabruck, Bremen, Hamburg	132	68 20	44 0	...	"	11p24	2p28	14
	Return fare		130 40	83 80	8				
London .... *Via Ostend.* 221 miles.	To Ghent, Ostend and London	102A	47 25	33 25	...	**Nord**	8a‡6	5p10	9
	Return fare		84 90	60 0	30	"	8a46	5p10	8½
	‡—Vienna-Ostend Express.					"	11§a37	10p 0	10½
	§—Nord Express					"	1p13	10p 0	8¾
						"	8p40	5a43	9
Via Calais. 242 miles.	To Lille	103				**Midi**	8a52	5p10	8¼
	On to Calais and London	27	59 75	41 65	...	"	11a20	7 p5	7¾
	Return fare		106 65	76 45	30	"	2p14	10*45	8½
	*—Via Boulogne.					"	10 p3	5a43	7¾
Via Antwerp. 236 miles.	To Antwerp and London.........	110	39 5	23 70	...	**Nord**	5p29	7a35	14
	Return fare		60 70	38 20	30	Not on Sun.			
Via Flushing. 269 miles.	To Antwerp and Rosendaal ...	110				**Nord**	5a59	7 p34	13½
	On to Vlissingen and London	113	46 55	32 75	...	"	7p42	7 a48	12
Paris.............. 192½ miles.	To Mons and Maubeuge	108				**Midi**	8a21	12p51	4½
	On to Tergnier and Paris	25	34 35	23 25	...	"	1 p1	5 p15	4¼
	Return fare		52 95	37 55	5	"	6p15	10p46	4½
						"	12 a7	5a32	5½
Strassburg ... 278 miles.	To Namur, Arlon, and Luxemburg	103A				**Nord**	6 a8	3 p19	8¼
	On to Metz and Strassburg......	210	45 50	30 10	...	"	7 a49	4 p41	8
	Return fare		83 50	55 20	6	"	10a20	7 p12	8
						"	6 p35	3 a27	8
						"	11 p28	8 a44	8¼

The "a" and "p" inserted in the departure and arrival times denote "a.m." and "p.m."

From COLOGNE to	ROUTE.	FARES. 1st class. M. Pf.	FARES. 2nd class. M. Pf.	Validity of Ticket. Days.	Departure from Cologne.	Arrve destination.	Time of Jrney
Amsterdam *Via Emmerich.* 162 miles.	To Dusseldorf and Oberhausen 161				**Haupt** 5 a30	9 a45	5
	On to Emmerich 131A			...	" 10 a6	2 p35	5¼
	" Utrecht and Amsterdam 118A	19 0	13 70		" 2 p27	6 p42	5
					" 4 p47	8 p35	4½
					" 6 p15	10p20	4¾
Via Kleve. 153½ miles.	To Kempen, Kleve, and Nymegen 121				**Haupt** 7 a5	11a25	5
					" 2p23	6 p50	5
	On to Amersfoort, Amsterdam 118C	19 0	13 70	...	" 4p54	8p51	4¾
					" 7p21	10p57	4¼
Antwerp...... *Via Liege.* 152½ miles.	To Aix-la-Chapelle and Herbesthal 123B				**Haupt** 6 a0	11a20	6¼
					" 10 a5	2 p51	5¾
	On to Verviers, Liege, and Louvain...................... 104				" 1 p44	6 p9	5½
					" 3 p12	8‡p16	6
	" Malines 101; Antwerp ... 110	20 10	13 40	...	" 6 p13	10 p0	4¾
	Return fare	35 10	23 30	4	‡—Via Brussels.		
Via Roermond. 133 miles.	To Neuss 121				**Haupt** 7 a5	10a48	4¾
	On to Munchen Gladbach 134C				" 8 a51	12p23	4½
	" Roermond 127; Antwerp 99	17 0	11 40	...	" 1 p4	5 p57	6
	Return fare	31 20	20 90	4	" 4 p54	8 p46	5
Via Maestricht. 136½ miles.	To Aix-la-Chapelle 123B				**Haupt** 9 a10	2 p28	6½
	On to Maestricht and Antwerp 99	17 40	11 60	...	" 1p38	6 p27	5¾
	Return fare	31 20	20 80	4	" 4 p19	9 p52	6½
Baden-Baden... 115 miles	See routes to Heidelberg.				**Haupt** 1a58	8a46	6¾
	On from Heidelberg to Oos and Baden............................140	30 40	19 50	...	" 9‡a32	3 p36	6
					" 10‡a3	4 p2	6
					" 11‡a20	5 p31	6¼
	‡—Via Schwetzingen.				" 12‡p10	6p52	6¾
					" 1 p5	8 p4	7
					" 8 p2	3 a6	7
					" 10‡p33	4 a52	6¼
Basle .... *Via Mayence.* 329½ miles.	To Bonn, Coblence, & Mayence 122				**Haupt** 1 a58	11a 0	9
	On to Mannheim 136				" 9 a32	5 p38	8
	" Heidelberg, Carlsruhe, and Basle 140				" 11a20	7 p56	8½
					" 12p10	8 p55	8¾
	[Or, from Mayence to Darmstadt 123, to Heidelberg 139, thence to Basle 140.]	41 20	26 20	...	" 1 p5	10p21	9¼
					" 8 p2	5 a38	9½
Via Strassburg. 312 miles. 334½ miles	To Bonn, Coblence, and Bingerbruck.................... 122				**Haupt** 10 a3	5 p47	7¾
					" 12p10	8 p20	8¼
	On to Kreuznach and Munster-am-Stein 125				" 10§p22	6a14	7¾
					" 10p33	6 a24	7¾
	" Enkenbach & Neustadt 206	41 20	26 20				
	" Weissenburg, Strassburg, and Basle 208			§—In July and Aug. only.			
	[Or, from Bingerbruck to Mayence p. 123, thence to Basle p. 208.]						
Berlin .... 364½ miles.	To Hamm, Hanover, & Berlin 161	47 80	29 20	...	**Haupt** 7 a20	3 p48	8½
					" 10a14	6p12	8
					" 12p58	9 p28	8½
	§—Nord Express				" 4 p24	12a21	8
					" 9 p42	7 a20	9¾
					" 10§p58	7 a29	8½
					" 11p33	8 a54	9¼
Brunswick.. 241½ miles.	To Hamm, Hanover, and Brunswick 161	31 0	19 90	...	**Haupt** 7 a20	2 p34	7¼
					" 10a14	4 p35	6½
					" 12p58	7 p43	6¾
					" 4 p24	10p39	6¼
					" 9 p42	4 a19	6½
					" 11p33	5 a29	6
Via Soest. 216½ miles.	To Elberfeld 134A; Hagen & Soest 134A				**Haupt** 8 a26	2 p34	6¼
	On via Altenbeken (p. 164) to Hameln 155; Hildesheim 155						
	" Brunswick 159	31 0	19 90	...			

The "a" and "p" inserted in the departure and arrival times denote "a.m." and "p.m."

From COLOGNE to	ROUTE.	PAGE	FARES. 1st class. M. Pf.	FARES. 2nd class. M. Pf.	Validity of Ticket. Days.	Departure from Cologne.	Arrve destination.	Time of Jrney HRS.
Brussels	To Aix-la-Chapelle and Herbesthal	123B				Haupt 4‖a41	7 a52	4¼
141 miles.	On to Liege and Brussels	104	19 20	12 80	...	" 6 a0	10a25	5½
	Return fare		33 80	22 40	4	" 7 a56	11a26	4½
						" 8§ a7	11a31	4½
						" 9 a10	1 p3	5
	§—Nord Express. ‖—Ostend-Vienna Express.					" 10a 5	2 p51	4¾
						" 3 p12	6 p57	4¾
						" 4 p19	8 p0	4¾
						" 6 p13	9 p45	4½
						" 12 a5	3 a56	4¾
Carlsbad .... 407½ miles.	To Mayence, Darmstadt, and Aschaffenburg	122				Haupt 1 a58	5 p31	15½
	On to Würzburg	196						
	,, Nürnberg 195A; Eger ...	202						
	,, Carlsbad	250	55 40	34 20				
Ostend-Vienna Express. 412 miles.	To Mayence and Frankfort	122						
	On to Würzburg	196				Haupt 11p57	12p21	12½
	Thence as in preceding route.		......	......	...			
Cassel	To Elberfeld and Hagen	134A				Haupt 6 a 0	10a59	5
171 miles.	On to Warburg and Cassel	135A	23 0	15 30	...	" 8 a36	1 p27	5
						" 9 a 6	3p 30	6½
						" 1 p30	6 p39	5
						" 5 p56	11p31	5½
						" 8 p18	2 a35	6¼
Christiania *Via Berlin.* 1031 miles	To Hanover and Berlin	161				Haupt 10a14	9 p43	35½
	On to Sassnitz and Trelleborg	181					noon	
	,, Malmo 311; Gothenburg	309A				" 11p33	12 0	36½
	,, Mellerud & Fredrikshald	306						
	,, Christiania	304A	... ...	... ...	...			
Via Hamburg-Sassnitz. 974 miles	To Bremen and Hamburg	132				Haupt 10 a6	9 p43	35½
	On to Lubeck 213A; Rostock...	213					noon	
	,, Stralsund	181A				" 11p40	12 0	36¼
	,, Sassnitz and Malmo	181						
	,, Gothenburg, Christiania	309A	124 0	81 60	...			
Via Copenhagen. 949 miles.	To Bremen and Hamburg ...	132					noon	
	On to Lubeck 213A; Warnem'de	213				Haupt 11p40	12 0	36¼
	,, Copenhagen	302						
	,, Malmo and Gothenburg	309A						
	,, Mellerud	306						
	,, Fredrikshald	306						
	,, Christiania	304A	124 0	81 60				
Copenhagen ... 544 miles.	To Osnabruck, Bremen, and Hamburg	132				Haupt 10 a6	8‡a12	22
	On to Lubeck	213A				" 1 p45	9 a42	20
	,, Warnemunde	213				" 1 p45	10§a4	20¼
	,, Copenhagen	302	68 30	47 30	...	" 11p40	4 §48	17
						" 11p40	6 p41	19
	§—Via Kiel. (502 miles)			‡—Via Vamdrup and Fredericia.				
Dresden ...... *Via Goslar.* 396 miles.	To Elberfeld and Hagen	134A				Haupt 6 ‡a0	6 p36	12½
	On to Holzminden 135A; Seesen	164	‡—Via Cassel and Bebra.			" 8 a36	8 p27	11¾
	,, Goslar 163; Halle	166				" 1‡p30	1 a43	12¼
	,, Leipsic 158; Dresden...	188	54 0	33 20	...			
Via Magdeburg. 450 miles.						Haupt 7 a20	8 p27	13
	To Hanover and Brunswick ...	161				" 10a14	10p14	12
	On to Magdeburg, Halle, and Leipsic	158				" 12p58	1 a43	12¾
						" 9 p42	10a26	12¾
	,, Dresden	188	54 0	33 20	...	" 11p33	11a20	11¾

The "a" and "p" inserted in the departure and arrival times denote "a.m." and "p.m."

From COLOGNE to	ROUTE.	PAGE	FARES. 1st class. M. Pf.	FARES. 2nd class. M. Pf.	Validity of Ticket. Days.	Departure from Cologne.	Arrve destination.	Time of Jrney
Ems .... *Via Ehrenbreitstein.* 67½ miles.	To Niederlahnstein	128				Haupt 8 a8	11 a3	3
	On to Ems	146	9 50	6 20	...	" 9 a10	11a46	2½
						" 11a27	1 p48	2¼
						" 3 p38	6 p10	2½
						" 6 p18	8 p59	2¾
Via Coblence. 68½ miles.	To Bonn and Coblence............	122				Haupt 6 a17	9 a13	3
	On to Ems	146	9 50	6 20	...	" 9 a32	11a46	2¼
						" 10 a3	12p36	2½
						" 11a20	1 p48	2½
						" 12p10	2 p54	2¾
						" 12p32	3 p34	3
						" 5 p56	8 p59	3
						" 8 p2	11 p9	3
						" 10p33	12a56	2¼
Frankfort ... *Via Niederlahnstein.* 140½ miles.	To Niederlahnstein and Frankfort	128	19 20	12 40	...	Haupt 1 a58	6 a16	4¼
						" 8 a8	12p34	4½
						" 9 a10	1 p32	4¼
						" 11a27	3 p19	3¾
						" 3 p38	7 p57	4¼
						" 6 p18	11 p0	4¾
Via Mayence 138 miles.	To Coblence, Mayence, and Frankfort	122	19 20	12 40	...	Haupt 9 a32	1 p36	4
						" 10 a3	1 p57	3¾
						" 11a20	3 p5	3¾
						" 12p10	4 p8	4
						" 1 p5	5 p29	4½
						" 2 p31	6 p33	4
						" 5 p56	10 p7	4¼
	†—Ostend-Vienna Express.					" 6 p33	10p44	4¼
						" 8 p2	12 a8	4¼
						" 10p33	2 a34	4
						" 11†57	3 a26	3½
Hamburg ...... 279¾ miles.	To Osnabruck, Bremen, and Hamburg	132	37 40	23 70	...	Haupt 7 a4	2 p28	7½
						" 10 a6	5 p3	7
						" 1 p45	9 p42	8
						" 4 p55	12 a9	7¼
						" 11p40	6 a55	7¼
Hanover .... 203½ miles.	To Hamm and Hanover	161	27 20	17 50	...	Haupt 7 a20	12p13	4¾
						" 10a14	2 p56	4¾
						" 12p58	5 p56	5
						" 4 p24	8 p53	4½
	†—Nord Express.					" 9 p42	3 a12	5½
						" 10†p58	3 a49	4¾
						" 11p33	4 a32	5
Heidelberg ..... 173¼ miles.	To Mayence and Darmstadt ...	122				Haupt 1 a58	7 a29	5½
	On to Heidelberg.................	136	23 20	15 40	...	" 9 a32	2 p46	5¼
						" 10 a3	3 p0	5
						" 11a20	4 p20	5
						" 12p10	4 p57	4¾
						" 1 p5	6 p30	5½
						" 8 p2	1 a0	5
Homburg Bad *Via Niederlahnstein.* 152¼ miles.	To Niederlahnstein & Frankfort	128				Haupt 1 a58	7 a1	5
	On to Homburg Bad	150	20 50	13 70	...	" 8 a8	1 p25	5¼
						" 9 a10	2 p20	5¼
						" 11a27	3 †55	4½
						" 3 p38	8 p53	5¼
						" 6 p18	11p43	5½
Via Mayence. 149¾ miles.	To Mayence and Frankfort......	122				Haupt 9 a32	2 p20	4¾
	On to Homburg Bad	150	20 50	13 70	...	" 10 a3	3 p31	5½
						" 11a20	3 p47	4½
	†—Via Wiesbaden.					" 12p10	5 p24	5¼
						" 1 p5	6 p16	5¼
						" 6 p33	11p43	5¼
						" 8 p2	1a 2	5

From COLOGNE to	ROUTE.	PAGE	FARES. 1st class. M. Pf.	FARES. 2nd class. M. Pf.	Validity of Ticket. Days.	Departure from Cologne.	Arrve destination.	Time of Jrney HRS.
Kissingen ...	To Niederlahnstein & Frankfort	128				**Haupt** 11a27	8 p15	8¾
Via Frankfort.	On to Aschaffenburg and					" 12p10	9 p23	9¼
	Gemunden	196				" 8 p2	6 a32	10½
247½ miles.	,, Schweinfurt	201				" 11§p57	8 a18	8¼
	,, Kissingen	195	33 60	21 60	...	" 1 a58	11a53	10
	§—Ostend-Vienna Express as far as Wurzburg.							
Leipsic	To Soest	134A				**Haupt** 6‡a0	4 p28	10½
	via Paderborn (p. 164) and					" 8 a36	6 p11	9¾
Via Soest. 321½ miles.	Altenbeken to Hameln	155	‡—Via Cassel & Bebra			" 1‡p30	11p34	10
	On to Hildesheim and Goslar	155						
	,, Halle 166; Leipsic	158	43 90	27 90	...			
						Haupt 10a14	8 p6	10
Via Hanover. 372 miles.	To Hanover and Brunswick	161				" 12‡p58	11 p9	10¼
	On to Halle and Leipsic	158	43 90	27 90	...	" 11p33	9 a6	9½
	‡—Via Stendal.							
London ...... *Vienna-Ostend Express.* 362 miles.	Cologne to Brussels, Ostend, and London, see Through Table	8	64 0	... ...	...	**Haupt** 4 a41	5 p10	13½
Via Ostend. 362 miles.	Cologne to Herbesthal	123B				**Haupt** 10 a5	10 p0	13
	On to Brussels	104				" 6 p13	5 a43	12½
	,, Ostend and London	102A	56 0	38 70	...	" 12 a5	5 p10	18
Via Calais. 382½ miles.	Cologne to Herbesthal	123B				**Haupt** 7a§56	7 p5	12¼
	On to Brussels	104				" 9 a10	10†45	14½
	,, Lille	103				" 6 p13	5 a43	12½
	,, Calais and London	27	67 90	47 0	...	" 12 a5	5 p10	18
	†—Via Boulogne.							
§—The 7.56 a.m.	from Cologne for Calais travels via Namur, tickets via Brussels not available.							
Via Flushing. 360¾ miles.	Cologne to Oberhausen	161				**Haupt** 5 a47	7 p34	14¾
	On to Wesel 132; Boxtel	120				" 7 p14	7 a48	13¾
	,, Vlissingen and London	113	51 70	34 70	...			
Via Hoek van Holland. 375 miles.	Cologne to Nymegen	121				**Haupt** 7 p21	8 a0	13¾
	On to Rotterdam	119A						
	,, Hoek van Holland and London	112	51 70	34 70	...			
Lucerne	See routes to Basle.					**Haupt** 10 a3	8 p15	10¼
	On from Basle to Olten and					" 12p10	11p42	11½
389 miles.	Lucerne	258	49 30	31 90	...	" 1 p5	1 a12	12
	Return fare		95 10	61 30	45	" 10p33	8 a59	10½
Milan	See routes to Basle.					**Haupt** 12p10	6 a22	18¼
	On from Basle to Lucerne	258				" 1 p5	8 a53	20¼
562 miles.	On to Bellinzona and Chiasso	259				" 10p33	3 p5	16½
	,, Como and Milan	269A	78 0	52 0	...	" 1 a58	8 p40	18¾
						Haupt 1‡a58	2 p0	12
Munich	To Niederlahnstein & Frankfort	128				" 10a‡3	8 p55	10¾
397 miles.	On to Würzburg and Munich	196	51 40	31 50	...	" 11a27	10p25	11
	‡—Via Coblence.					" 12‡p10	12a40	12½
	§—Ostend-Vienna Express, Luxus Zug.					" 6 ‡p33	7 a20	12¾
						" 8 ‡p2	9 a29	13½
						" 11§p57	11a15	11¼
Paris .... 306 miles.	To Aix-la-Chapelle and					**Haupt** 7 a56	4 p0	9
	Herbesthal	123B				" 8§a7	4 p0	9
	On to Verviers and Liege	104				" 9 a10	6 p 5	10
	,, Namur and Erquelinnes	93				" 3 p12	10p46	8½
	,, Maubeuge, Tergnier, and					" 4 p19	11p30	8¼
	Paris	24	43 10	29 40	...	" 10p52	7 a35	9¾
	Return fare		69 30	49 0	20	§—Nord Express.		

The "a" and "p" inserted in the departure and arrival times denote "a.m." and "p.m."

From COLOGNE to	ROUTE.	PAGE	FARES. 1st class. M. Pf.	FARES. 2nd class. M. Pf.	Validity of Ticket. Days.	Departure from Cologne.	Arrve destin ation.	Time of Jrney HRS.
Prague	To Mayence and Aschaffenburg	122				**Haupt** 1a‡58	9p43	19¾
503 miles.	On to Gemunden & Würzburg	196				" 10a3	6 a55	20¾
	,, Nürnberg	195A				" 8 p2	5p14	21¼
	,, Schwandorf and Furth...	204						
	,, Pilsen and Prague	243B	70 60	43 10	...	‡—Via Eger.		
St. Petersburg (*Nord Express*)	To Hanover, Stendal, & Berlin	161				**Haupt** 10p58	10a30	34½
	On to Eydtkuhnen	176						
1,383 miles.	,, Wilna and St. Petersburg	313	219 40	... ...	...			
	Ordinary express over preceding route		155 70	101 65		**Haupt** 12p58 " 9 p42	8 a15 11a35	42¼ 36¾
Stockholm... *Via Berlin.*	To Hanover and Berlin	161				**Haupt** 10a14	6 p46	32½
	On to Sassnitz and Trelleborg	181				" 11p33	8 a49	33¼
1007 miles.	,, Malmo 311; to Stockholm	308A	118 70	75 60	10			
Via Hamburg Sassnitz.	To Bremen and Hamburg	132				**Haupt** 10 a6	6 p46	32¾
	On to Lubeck 213A; to Rostock	213				" 11p40	8 a49	33¼
	,, Stralsund	181A						
	,, Sassnitz and Trelleborg	181						
950 miles.	,, Malmo 311; to Stockholm	308A	108 80	72 20	10			
Via Copenhagen.	To Bremen and Hamburg	132				**Haupt** 11p40	8 a49	33¼
	On to Kiel and Korsoer	168						
	,, Copenhagen	302A						
906 miles.	,, Stockholm	308A	108 80	72 20	10			
Stuttgart	To Mayence and Darmstadt ...	122				**Haupt** 1 a58	9 a19	7¼
243½ miles.	On to Heidelberg	139				" 10 a3	4 p47	6¾
	,, Bruchsal	140				" 11a20	6 p29	7¼
	,, Bietigheim and Stuttgart	192	33 10	21 30	...	" 12‡p10	7 p42	7½
	‡—Via Mannheim.					" 1 p5	9 p21	8¼
						" 8 p2	3 a4	7
Vienna .... *Ostend-Vienna Express.*	By Ostend-Vienna Express, see Through Table, Cologne to Vienna	13	110 70	... ...	...	nght **Haupt** 11 57	6 p0	18
605½ miles.								
Via Mayence.	To Mayence, Darmstadt, Aschaffenburg	122				**Haupt** 1 a58	9 p50	20
	On to Würzburg	196						
	,, Nürnberg and Passau ...	195A						
600 miles.	,, Wels 239B; Vienna	239A	84 80	52 50	...			
Via Frankfort.	To Niederlahnstein & Frankfort	128				**Haupt** 1 a58	9 p50	20
	On to Aschaffenburg and					" 12p10	7 a20	19¼
	Würzburg	196				" 8 p2	6 p32	22½
608 miles.	,, Nürnberg and Passau ...	195A						
	,, Wels 239B; Vienna......	239A	84 80	52 50	...			
Wiesbaden......	To Niederlahnstein & Wiesbaden	128	16 60	10 80	...	**Haupt** 8 a8	11a42	3½
Via Niederlahnstein.						" 9 a10	12p40	3½
						" 11a27	2 p26	3
115 miles.						" 3 p38	7 p5	3½
						" 6 p18	10 p2	3¾
Via Coblence.	To Bonn and Coblence............	122				**Haupt** 9a32	1 p19	3¾
115½ miles.	On to Rudesheim & Wiesbaden	128	16 60	10 80	...	" 5p56	10 p2	4
						" 8 p2	1 a13	5¼
						" 1a58	5 a8	3¼
						Haupt 10 a3	5 p24	7¼
Wildbad	To Mayence	122				" 12p10	8 p40	8½
248 miles.	On to Mannheim 139; Carlsruhe	140A				" 1 p5	10p35	9½
	,, Pforzheim 141; Wildbad	194A	31 20	20 0	...	" 10p33	6 a26	8

The "a" and "p" inserted in the departure and arrival times denote "a.m." and "p.m."

From COPENHAGEN to	ROUTE.	PAGE	FARES, 1st class. K	ö	2nd class. K	ö	Validity of Ticket. Days.	Departure from Copenhagen.	Arrve destination.	Time of J'rney HRS.
Berlin	To Masnedsund, Gjedser,							11 a0	8 p55	10
278¼ miles.	Warnemunde	302						8p10	6a38	10½
	On to Rostock and Neu-Strelitz	178B								
	,, Berlin........................	181	33	0	23	0	...			
Christiania ...	To Elsinore and Helsingborg...	303						7 a0	9 p43	14¾
405 miles.	On to Halmstad, Gothenburg	309A							noon	
	,, Mellerud	306						9 p5	12 0	15
	,, Fredrikshald	306								
	,, Christiania	304A	50	70	32	10				
Hamburg ... *Via Warnemde* 264 miles.	To Gjedser and Warnemunde	302						11a 0	8 p23	9¼
	On to Lubeck 213; Hamburg	213A	24	0	19	0	...	8 p10	6a15	10
Via Kiel. 222 miles.	To Korsœr and Kiel	302						12p55	11 p4	10
	On to Neumunster, Hamburg	168	24	0	19	0	...	7p50	7a27	11½
Via Fredericia 324 miles.	To Fredericia and Vamdrup ...	302						night		
	On to Hamburg	168	24	0	19	0	...	12 0	11a31	11½
London ...... *Via Ostend.* 901 miles via Warnemunde.	To Korsœr and Kiel (Steamer)	302						12p55	10 p0	34¼
	On to Hamburg	168						8§p10	5a43	34½
	,, Bremen and Cologne	133								
	,, Herbesthal	123B								
	,, Louvain 104; Ghent......	101					§—Via Warnemunde.			
	,, Ostend and London	102A	120	0	86	50	...			
Via Calais. 926 miles via Warnemunde.	As in route above to Cologne.							12p55	7 p5	31¼
	From Cologne to Brussels	104						8§p10	5a43	34½
	On to Lille	103								
	,, Calais and London.........	27	128	50	92	70	...			
Via Flushing. 834 miles via Warnemunde.	To Korsœr and Kiel (Steamer)	302						12p55	7p34	31¾
	On to Hamburg	168						12 ‡0 night	7a48	32¾
	,, Bremen and Oberhausen	133								
	,, Wesel 132; Boxtel.........	120					‡—Via Fredericia (302) and			
	,, Vlissingen and London...	113	91	50	64	50	...	Vamdrup (168).		
Via Hoek van Holland. 857 miles.	To Fredericia	302						night		
	On to Vamdrup 303; Hamburg	168						12 0	8 a0	33
	,, Bremen and Osnabruck	133								
	,, Rheine 156C; Amersfoort	118C								
	,, Utrecht 115A; Rotterdam	118A								
	,, H. v Holland and London	112	91	50	64	50	...			
Paris............. 808½ miles.	To Korsœr and Kiel (Steamer)	302						12p55	4 p0	28
	On to Neumunster, Hamburg	168						8§p10	10p46	27½
	,, Bremen, Osnabruck, and							night		
	Cologne	133						12 ‡0	7a35	32½
	,, Aix-la-Chapelle and Her-									
	besthal	123B					§—Via Warnemunde.			
	,, Verviers and Liége	104	‡—Via Fredericia (302) and Vamdrup (168)							
	,, Namur and Erquelinnes	93								
	,, Maubeuge and Paris......	24	99	0	73	0	10			
	Return fare		145	50	111	50	30			
Stockholm...... 404 miles.	To Malmo (steamer) and Stock-							5 a40	6 p46	13
	holm	308A	35	30	21	90	...	7 p50	8 a49	13
Vienna......... 720 miles.	To Masnedsund, Gjedser,							11 a0	12p48	25¾
	and Warnemunde	302						8p10	9‡36	25½
	On to Neu-Strelitz 178B; Berlin	181			‡—Via Tetschen page 224.					
	,, Dresden and Bodenbach	188								
	,, Prague 252A; Vienna	243	87	20	61	50	...			

The "a" and "p" inserted in the departure and arrival times denote "a.m." and "p.m."

A B C ROUTES from DRESDEN with best Direct Trains.

From DRESDEN to	ROUTE.	PAGE	FARES. 1st class. M. Pf.	FARES. 2nd class. M. Pf.	Validity of Ticket. Days.	Departure from Dresden.	Arrve destination.	Time of J'rney HRS.
Berlin	Via Röderau or Elsterwerda...	189	16 20	10 50	...	Haupt 5 a36	8 a8	2½
111½ miles.						,, 7 a20	10a20	3
						,, 10 a0	12p48	2¾
						,, 2 p12	5 p1	2¾
						,, 4 p20	6 p51	2½
						,, 5 p14	7 p57	2¾
						,, 7 p15	10p26	3¼
						,, 10p 3	12a49	2¾
Cologne	To Leipsic	189				Haupt 3 a41	3 p56	12¼
Via Magdeburg	On to Magdeburg and Hanover	158				,, 5§a36	5 p48	12¼
450 miles.	,, Cologne	160	54 0	33 20	...	,, 8 a0	9 p9	13
	‡—Via Falkenberg-Magdeburg.		§—Via	Berlin.		,, 7‡p15	7 a40	12¼
Via Goslar.	To Leipsic	189				Haupt 10a35	10p26	11¾
396 miles.	On to Halle	158				,, 8 p6	8a52	12¾
	,, Goslar and Hildesheim...	166						
	,, Altenbeken	155						
	,, Soest	165						
	,, Elberfeld and Cologne...	134c	53 40	32 80	...			
Frankfort	To Leipsic	189				Haupt 3 a41	1 p27	9¾
314 miles.	On to Corbetha, Erfurt, and					,, 7 a15	3 p46	8½
	Bebra	170				,, 8 ‡a0	4 p54	9
	,, Frankfort	149	40 90	25 90	...	,, 10a35	7 p36	9
	‡—Via Halle.					,, 1‡p18	9 p23	8
						,, 8 p6	5 a6	9
London	See route above to Cologne.					Haupt 3 a41	5 a43	27
Via Ostend.	Thence to Aix-la-Chapelle	123B				,, 7 p15	10 p0	27¾
770 miles.	On to Brussels	104						
	,, Ostend and London	102A	110 60	71 20	...			
Via Flushing.	To Leipsic	189				Haupt 8 a0	7 a48	24¾
736 miles.	On to Magdeburg and Hanover	158				,, 7 p15	7 p34	25¼
	,, Oberhausen	160A						
	,, Wesel 132; to Boxtel ...	120						
	,, Breda	117						
	,, Vlissingen and London	113	93 70	60 60	...			
Via Hoek van Holland.	To Leipsic	189				Haupt 8 a0	8 a0	25
710 miles.	On to Magdeburg and Hanover	158						
	,, Lohne 160; Rheine	156c						
	,, Amersfoort	118c						
	,, Utrecht	115A						
	,, Rotterdam	118						
	,, Hoek v.Holland & London	112	93 70	60 60	...			
Via Calais.	See routes above to Cologne.					Haupt 3 a41	5 a43	27
832 miles.	Thence to Aix-la-Chapelle	123B				,, 7 p15	7 p5	25
	On to Brussels	104						
	,, Calais and London...........	103	122 50	79 50	...			
Munich	To Chemnitz and Reichenbach	186				Haupt 8a30	6 p14	9¾
337½ miles.	On to Hof................................	187	43 70	27 70	...	,, 12p54	10p10	9¼
	,, Regensburg and Munich	203				,, 10p45	7 a50	9
Vienna...........	To Tetschen	188				Haupt 11a30	9 p36	10
Via Tetschen.	On to Deutschbrod and Vienna	224	54 50	33 40	...	,, 9p55	7 a22	9½
322 miles.						,, 10p53	8 a0	9
Via Bodenbach.	To Bodenbach	188				Haupt 2 a30	12‡48	10¼
374 miles.	On Prague and Vienna	252A	54 50	33 40	...	,, 7 a10	6 p28	11¼
						,, 11a30	9 ‡45	10¼
	‡—Via Gmund p. 243.					,, 7 p 5	6 a55	12

The "a" and "p" inserted in the departure and arrival times denote "a.m." and "p.m."

From FRANKFORT to	ROUTE.	PAGE	FARES. 1st class. M. Pf.	FARES. 2ndclass. M. Pf.	Validity of Ticket. Days.	Departure from Frankfort.	Arrve destination.	Time of J'rney HRS.
Berlin	To Bebra	149				6 a4	2 p39	$8\frac{1}{2}$
335 miles.	On to Halle and Berlin	171	48 40	27 50	...	8 a23	3 p34	$7\frac{1}{4}$
						9 a40	6 p42	9
						12p53	8 p55	8
	§—Via Cassel, page 157.					1 p 5	10p38	$9\frac{1}{2}$
						2 p46	11 p2	$8\frac{1}{4}$
						10p25	7 a36	$9\frac{1}{4}$
						§10p36	7 a49	$9\frac{1}{4}$
Dresden	To Bebra	149				6 a4	2 p55	$8\frac{3}{4}$
314 miles.	On to Corbetha and Leipsic ...	171				9 a40	6 p36	9
	„ Dresden........................	188	40 90	25 90	...	1 p 5	10p14	$9\frac{1}{4}$
						2 p46	11p52	$9\frac{1}{4}$
						10p25	8 a13	$9\frac{3}{4}$
Hamburg	To Hanover and Hamburg	157	43 0	27 20	...	5 a58	3 p23	$9\frac{1}{2}$
340 miles.						12‡p53	10p14	$9\frac{1}{4}$
	‡—Via Bebra.					2‡p55	11p43	$8\frac{3}{4}$
						8§p27	6 a8	$9\frac{3}{4}$
	§—Until 31st August.					8 p55	6 a44	$9\frac{3}{4}$
						11‡p25	8 a22	9
London	To Mayence and Cologne	123A	§—Vienna-Ostend Express			1 a§1	5 p10	$17\frac{1}{4}$
Via Ostend.	On from Cologne to Herbesthal	123B				5 a20	10 p0	$17\frac{3}{4}$
500 miles.	On to Brussels	104				2 p18	5 a43	$16\frac{1}{2}$
	„ Ostend and London	102A	74 10	50 30	...	6 p9	5 p10	24
	To Mayence and Cologne	123A				2 p18	5 a43	$16\frac{1}{2}$
	Or to Niederlahnsteir & Cologne	129				1 a44	7 p5	$18\frac{1}{4}$
Via Calais.	On from Cologne to Herbesthal	123B						
520½ miles.	On to Brussels 104 ; to Lille...	103						
	„ Calais and London.........	27	86 0	58 60	...			
	To Mayence and Cologne	123A				2 p50	7 a48	18
Via Flushing.	Or to Niederlahnstein &Cologne	129				1 a44	7 p34	19
498½ miles.	On from Cologne to Oberhausen	161						
	On to Wesel 132 ; Boxtel.........	120						
	„ Vlissingen and London...	113	69 80	46 10	...			
Via Hoek van	To Niederlahnstein & Cologne	129				2 p50	8 a0	$18\frac{1}{4}$
Holland.	On to Kleve and Nymegen	121						
513 miles.	„ Rotterdam	119A						
	„ H. v. Holland & London	112	69 80	46 10	...			
Munich	To Aschaffenburg and Treucht-					3a§36	11a15	$7\frac{3}{4}$
257 miles.	lingen..................................	196				6 a26	2 p 0	$7\frac{1}{2}$
	On to Munich	197				2 p23	8 p55	$6\frac{1}{2}$
			33 40	21 50	...	3 p36	10p25	$6\frac{3}{4}$
						4 p36	12a40	8
	§—Ostend-Vienna Express		—Luxus zug.			11p13	7 a20	$8\frac{1}{4}$
						12a21	9 a29	$9\frac{1}{4}$
Paris	To Mayence and Bingerbruck	123A				7 a32	6 p40	12
Via Metz.	On to Saarbrucken & Forbach	125				1p33	11p47	$11\frac{1}{4}$
424½ miles.	„ Metz & Pagny 212; Frouard	72				5 p7	5 a0	13
	„ Chalons and Paris	65	60 20	39 90	...	8 p35	8 a25	$12\frac{3}{4}$
	To Worms	139				9a44	9p20	$12\frac{1}{2}$
	On to Strassburg	208				8p25	8a25	13
Via Strassburg	„ Deutsch Avricourt	210A				12 10n'gt	12p16	13
454 miles.	„ Chalons and Paris.........	65	60 20	39 90	...			
Vienna	To Aschaffenburg & Wurzburg	196				3a§36	6 p0	$14\frac{1}{2}$
467 miles.	On to Nurnberg and Passau ...	195A				8 a29	9 p50	$13\frac{1}{4}$
§—Ostend-	„ Wels	239B				4 p36	7 a20	$14\frac{3}{4}$
Vienna Express.	„ Vienna	239A	68 0	42 30	...	12a21	6 p32	$18\frac{1}{4}$

The "a" and "p" inserted in the departure and arrival times denote "a.m." and "p.m."

From GENEVA to	ROUTE.	PAGE	FARES. 1st class. fr.	c.	2nd class. fr.	c.	Validity of Ticket. Days.	Departure from Geneva.	Arrve destination.	Time of Jrney HRS.
Basle	To Lausanne	263						7 a12	1 p3	5¾
Via Biel.	On to Neuchatel, Biel, and							10a47	3 p57	5¼
159½ miles.	Basle	264	27	45	19	30	...	1 p30	7 p35	6
	Return fare		41	20	26	40	5	5 p23	10p53	5½
								6 a50	1 p12	6¼
	To Lausanne and Berne	263						10a10	3 p57	5¾
Via Berne.	On to Olten	257						12p49	7 p35	6¾
165½ miles.	,, Basle	258	27	45	19	30	...	5 p5	11p 3	6
	Return fare		41	20	26	40	5	1 a0	7 a25	6½
London	To Bourg 61; on to Dijon........	63B						6 a53	5 a43	24
668 miles.	On to Paris	51						§10a45	5a43	20
	,, London, via Calais........	19	141	75	97	50	...	9 p10	5 p10	21
§—Savoie Express. Train de Luxe, from 6th July until 14th September.										
627 miles.	To Paris as in first route, thence						15	6 a53	7 a30	25¾
	via Dieppe	76	118	40	82	30	45	9 p10	6p10	22
	To Lausanne	263								
	On to Pontarlier	263C								
617 miles.	,, Dijon 52; Paris............	51								
	,, Dieppe and London	77	113	45	79	70	15	9 p0	6p10	22¼
	Return fare		182	5	130	50	60			
Lucerne	To Lausanne and Berne	263						6 a50	1 p48	7
158¾ miles.	On to Langnau and Lucerne ...	265	26	35	18	50	...	10a10	3†49	5½
	Return fare		39	50	25	30	....	12p49	7 p45	6¾
								5 p5	10p52	5¾
	†—Via Olten.							1 a0	8 a32	7½
								6 a53	10a15	4½
Lyons	To Culoz and Ambérieu	61						12§p55	4 p21	4½
105 miles.	On to Lyons........................	53	18	80	12	70	1	1 p33	4 p32	4
	Return fare		28	20	20	30	4	8 p5	11p12	4
§—From	11th August until 20th September.							9 p10	1 a17	5
Marseilles	To Culoz and Ambérieu	61						6 a53	5 p51	12
322½ miles.	On to Lyons	53						1 p33	10p35	10
	,, Valence, Avignon, Mar-							8 p5	5 a0	10
	seilles	49	57	70	38	95	1	9 p10	8 a30	12¼
								5 a30	1 p30	
Milan	To Lausanne	263						7 a12	3 p15	8½
231¼ miles.	On to Domodossola	263B						10a47	7 p45	8¾
	,, Milan	274	44	65	31	45	4	5 p5	12a15	7¼
	Return fare		69	90	46	80	10	10p0	6a25	8½
Paris............	To Culoz and Bourg	61						6 a53	6 p8	12½
376 miles.	On to Dijon	63B						10§a45	6 p32	7¾
	,, Paris	51	70	15	47	30	3	2 p30	10p50	9¼
§—Savoie Express. Train de Luxe, from 6th July until 14th Sept.								9 p10	7 a0	11
	To Lausanne	263						5 a30	2 p[illegible]	10
	On to Pontarlier....................	263C						1 p30	11 [illegible]	10½
	,, Dijon 52; Paris............	51	63	50	43	15	3	5 p23	4 a55	12½
	Return fare		95	30	67	40	10	9 p0	6 a45	10¾
Turin	To Bellegarde and Culoz.........	61						7 a38	7 p7	11½
184 miles.	On to Chambéry and Modane..	60						3 p0	12 a5	9
	,, Turin	270	36	35	25	0	...	9 p10	5 a50	8½
Zurich	To Lausanne	263						7 a12	1 p3	5¾
179¾ miles.	On to Neuchatel and Biel.........	264						10a47	4 p8	5½
	,, Neu-Solthurn and Olten	257B						1 p30	7 p46	6¼
	,, Aarau	257						5 p23	10p50	5½
	,, Brugg and Zurich	262	28	50	20	0	...			
	Return fare		42	75	27	40	5			

The "a" and "p" inserted in the departure and arrival times denote "a.m." and "p.m."

From LUCERNE to	ROUTE.	PAGE	FARES. 1st class. fr. c.	FARES. 2nd class. fr. c.	Validity of Ticket. Days.	Departure from Lucerne.	Arive destination.	Time of J'rney HRS.
Berlin	To Olten and Basle	258				5 a5	8 p55	15¾
605 miles.	On to Offenburg and Heidelberg	141				7 a0	11 p2	16
	,, Darmstadt and Frankfort	139				2 p2	7 a36	17½
	,, Hanau and Bebra	149				9p10	2 p39	17½
	,, Eisenach, Erfurt, and Berlin..........................	171	100 85	62 30	7			
	Return fare		196 90	121 20	45			
Brussels	To Olten and Basle	258				7 a0	8p11	14¼
426 miles.	On to Mulhausen & Strassburg	209				9 a55	9p23	12½
	,, Metz and Luxemburg ...	210A				4 p57	5a26	13½
	,, Arlon, Namur, and Brussels	103A	69 15	45 85	5	9 p10	8a28	12¼
	Return fare		133 85	88 50	45			
Chur (Coire)...	To Rothkreuz, Zug, & Thalweil	260				7a35	11a25	3¾
109 miles.	On to Ziegelbrucke, Sargans and Chur	268B	15 50	10 90	...	9a15	12§32	4¾
						11 a5	4p53	5¾
						2†p16	6p47	4½
	Return fare		23 25	14 90	10	4p 5	9 p0	5
†—Via Zurich.	§—After 15th Sept. arrive 2.5 p.m					6p20	11p38	5¼
Cologne ...... *Via Carlsruhe.* 389 miles.	To Olten and Basle	258				7 a0	6 p5	11
	On to Carlsruhe and Mannheim	141				10a10	12a55	14¾
	,, Mayence	136				2 p2	5 a9	15¼
	,, Coblence and Cologne ...	123B	61 55	39 80	4	7 p0	5a42	10¾
	Return fare		118 65	76 40	45	9p10	9a50	12¾
Via Strassburg. 372 miles.	To Olten and Basle	258				7 a0	6 p5	11
	On to Strassburg and Neustadt	209				10a10	10p15	12
	,, Munster-am-Stein	206				2 p2	12a55	11
	,, Kreuznach and Bingerbruck	125				7 p0	5a21	10¼
	,, Coblence and Cologne ...	123B	61 55	39 80	4			
	Return fare		118 65	76 40	45			
Davos-Platz ...	To Rothkreuz, Zug, & Thalweil	260				7a35	2 p10	6½
132½ miles.	On to Ziegelbrucke, Sargans, and Landquart	268B				9a15	2 §42	7¾
						11 a5	7 p35	8½
	,, Davos-Platz....................	268D	28 5	19 20	...	2†p16	9 p25	7
	Return fare		43 45	28 40	...			
	§—After 15th Sept. arrive 5.2 p.m.					†—Via Zurich.		
Geneva...........	To Langnau and Berne	265				7a38	1p13	5½
158¾ miles.	On to Fribourg, Lausanne, and Geneva	263A				10a54	6 p0	7
						1p [illegible]6	6p55	5
	Return fare		26 35	18 50	...	2†p2	7p22	5¼
			39 50	25 30	10	7p10	1 a8	6
	†—Via Olten.					9†p10	6a10	9
						9 a8	6p45	9½
Genoa	To Bellinzona and Chiasso	259				9 a47	8p20	10½
267 miles.	On to Milan and Genoa	269A	55 50	38 95	5	2 p22	12a10	9¾
	Return fare		89 15	60 40	10	11p52	9a20	9½
						1a52	12p30	11¼
Lausanne	To Berne	265				7a38	11a55	4¼
120½ miles.	On to Fribourg and Lausanne	263A	20 10	14 10	...	10a54	4p23	5½
						1p56	5 p55	4
	Return fare		30 10	19 30	10	2†p2	6p14	4¼
	†—Via Olten.					7p10	11p27	4¼
						9†p10	4 a44	7½

The "a" and "p" inserted in the departure and arrival times denote "a m." and "p.m."

From LUCERNE to	ROUTE.	PAGE	FARES. 1st class. fr.	c.	2nd class. fr.	c.	Validity of Ticket. Days.	Departure from Lucerne.	Arive destination.	Time of J'rney HRS.
London	To Olten and Basle	258						9p10	3p25	19¼
	On to Alt-Munsterol...........	207A								
	,, Chaumont...........	69A								
Via Boulogne.	,, St. Dizier and Chalons...	66								
619 miles.	,, Reims...........	67								
	,, Laon 67; Tergnier........	21								
	,, Amiens	21								
	,, Boulogne and London ...	19	129	50	89	55	15			
Via Calais.	Route as above		129	50	89	55	15	9p10	5p10	21
644 miles	**Return fare**		215	80	155	70	60	10§p13	5p10	20
	§—Engadine Express, Train de Luxe.									
	To Olten and Basle	258						7 a0	5a43	23¾
	On to Strassburg...........	209						9p10	5p10	21
Via Ostend.	,, Luxemburg	210A								
647½ miles.	,, Brussels	103B								
	,, Ostend and London	102A	115	10	78	10	15			
	To Olten and Basle	258						7 a0	7a48	25¾
	On to Neustadt	209						7 p0	7p34	25½
Via Flushing.	,, Bingerbruck...........	125								
732 miles.	,, Cologne 123A; Oberhausen	161								
	,, Wesel and Boxtel	132								
	,, Vlissingen and London...	113	119	85	76	20	...			
	To Olten and Basle	258						7 a0	8 a0	26
	On to Neustadt 209; Bingerbruck	125								
Via Hoek van	,, Cologne...........	123A								
Holland.	,, Nymegen 121; Rotterdam	119A								
746½ miles.	,, H. van Holland & London	112	119	85	76	20	...			
	To Olten and Basle	258						7 a0	7 a30	25½
Via Dieppe.	On to Belfort 207A; Paris	69						9p10	6 p10	22
637 miles.	,, Dieppe and London	77	116	95	81	75	15			
	Return fare		190	25	135	30	60			
Milan	To Göschenen, Lugano, and							9 a8	3 p5	6
172½ miles.	Chiasso	259						9a47	4p40	7
	On to Como and Milan	269A	35	95	25	20	3	2p22	8p40	6¼
	Return fare		58	95	39	10	10	4 p0	10p25	6½
								11p52	6a22	7
								1a22	8a53	7½
Paris...........	To Olten and Basle	258						5 a5	2p49	10¾
Via Delle.	On to Delemont 264A; Delle ...	266						7 p0	6a25	12¼
398 miles.	,, Belfort, Troyes, and Paris	69	68	70	46	80	5	10§p13	8a42	11½
	§—Engadine Express, Train de Luxe.									
	To Olten and Basle	258								
Via	On to Mulhausen and Alt-							7 a0	5p45	11¾
Mulhausen.	Munsterol	207A						2 p2	11p48	10¾
386 miles.	,, Belfort, Troyes, & Paris	69	68	70	46	80	5	9p10	7a28	11¼
St. Moritz	To Rothkreuz, Zug & Thalweil	260						7a35	3p17	7¾
165½ miles	On to Ziegelbrucke, Sargans,							9a15	4 §20	9
†—Via Zurich.	and Chur	268B						11 a5	9p15	10¼
§—After 15th	,, St. Moritz...........	268B	38	75	26	40	...	2†p16	10p20	8
Sept. arr, 6p15.	**Return fare**		60	40	39	70	10			
Venice	To Bellinzona and Chiasso	259						9a47	11p30	13½
337½ miles,	On to Como and Milan	269A						4 p0	4a19	12¼
	,, Verona, Padua, & Venice	280	67	60	47	20	6	11p52	11a25	11½
								1a22	2 p15	13[illegible]

The "a" and "p" inserted in the departure and arrival times denote "a.m." and "p.m."

From PARIS to	ROUTE.	PAGE	FARES. 1st class. fr. c.	FARES. 2nd class. fr. c.	Validity of Ticket. Days.	Departure from Paris.		Arive destination.	Time of Jrney HRS.
Barcelona ...	To Bordeaux	34				**Orsay**	12§p16	7 a53	19¾
Via	On to Narbonne	45B				"	10p10	7 p32	21¼
Bordeaux.	,, Port Bou	46							
790 miles.	,, Barcelona	295	145 25	99 95	6				
	§—Sud Express; fare 155 fr. 35 c.								
	To Macon, Lyons, and Tarascon	48				**P.L.M.**	9 a15	7 a53	22¾
	On to Nimes, Lunel, and Cette	57				"	9 p0	7 p32	22½
Via Lyons.	,, Narbonne	45B							
754½ miles.	,, Perpignan and Portbou	46							
	,, Gerona and Barcelona ...	295	139 30	95 95	6				
	To Limoges and Montauban ...	32				**Orsay**	7 §p0	3 p40	20¾
Via	On to Toulouse and Narbonne	45B				"	8 p30	7 p32	23
Montauban.	,, Perpignan and Portbou	46							
710½ miles.	,, Gerona and Barcelona ...	295	130 90	90 25	6				
	§—Paris-Barcelona Express, Train-de-Luxe, Extra fare.								
Basle	To Troyes, Belfort, and Alt-Munsterol	68				**Est**	8 a55	5 p28	7½
Via Mulhausen.	On to Mülhausen and Basle...	207A	58 70	39 80	5	"	1p 0	9 p20	7¼
326¼ miles.	**Return** fare		90 85	64 55	10	"	9 p45	5 a58	7¼
	To Troyes, Belfort, and Delle	68				**Est**	8 a0	5 p15	8¼
Via Delle.	On to Delemont	266				"	7§p47	4 a45	8
338 miles.	,, Basle	264	58 70	39 80	5	"	9 p0	6 a7	8
	Return fare		90 85	64 55	10				
	§—Engadine Express, Train de Luxe. Runs until 14th Sept.								
Berlin	By Nord Express, Paris to Cologne	24							
	On to Hanover and Berlin	161	149 85	... ...	...	**Nord**	1 p45	7 a29	16¾
	To Maubeuge and Erquelinnes	24				**Nord**	7 a50	12a21	15½
	On to Namur and Liége	92				"	1 p45	8 a54	18¼
Via Cologne-Hanover.	,, Herbesthal	104				"	6 p20	3 p48	20½
671 miles.	,, Aix-la-Chapelle and Cologne	122				"	11p15	6 p12	18
	,, Hamm, Hanover, and Berlin	161	110 50	71 30	5				
	Return fare		199 50	129 80	20				
Berne	To Laroche and Dijon	48				**P.L.M.**	8 a30	6 p55	9½
Via	On to Dole and Pontarlier	52				"	2 p20	12 a1	8¾
Pontarlier.	,, Neuchâtel	265				"	7§p45	6 a8	9½
343 miles.	,, Berne	259B	62 50	42 60	5	"	10p15	8 a35	10
	Return fare		93 50	66 25	10				
	§—Simplon Express.								
	To Belfort and Delle	68				**Est**	8 a0	6 p5	9
Via Delle.	On to Delemont 266; to Biel...	261A				"	1 p0	12 a2	10
	On to Berne	265	62 50	42 60	5	"	9 p0	7 a40	9¾
						Nord	8 a10	12p12	4
Brussels	To Tergnier and Maubeuge	24				"	12p35	4 p38	4
192¾ miles.	On to Mons and Brussels	108	34 35	23 25	...	"	7 p10	11p 5	4
	Return fare		52 95	37 55	5	"	11p15	5 a15	6
Cologne	To Tergnier and Erquelinnes...	24				**Nord**	7 a50	4 p19	7½
306 miles.	On to Namur and Liége	92				"	8 a10	5 p55	8¾
	,, Herbesthal	104				"	1p§45	10p46	8
	,, Aix-la-Chapelle and Cologne	122	53 10	36 20	4	"	6 p20	5 a40	10¼
						"	10 p0	8 a0	9
	Return fare		85 40	60 40	20	"	11p15	9 a51	9½
	§—Nord Express.								

The "a" and "p" inserted in the departure and arrival times denote "a.m." and "p.m."

From PARIS to	ROUTE.	PAGE	FARES. 1st class. fr.	c.	2nd class. fr.	c.	Validity of Ticket. Days.	Departure from Paris.		Arrve destination.	Time of Jrney HRS.
Constantinople...	By Orient Express via Bucharest, see Through Table	8	398	70	...	...	...	Est	7 p13 Sunday, Tuesday, Friday	noon 12 0 Wed Fri., Mon	61
1998 miles.	See route to Vienna.							Est	10p15 Mon, Thur, Sat.	noon 12 0 Fri., Mon Wed	83¾
	On to Budapest & Verciorova	227									
	,, Bucharest	324A									
	,, Constanza	324A									
	By steamer to Constantinople		326	15	209	90	10				
Dresden .... 756 miles.	To Maubeuge and Erquelinnes	24						Nord	1 p45	11a20	20¼
	On to Namur and Liége	92						"	10 p0	8 p27	21½
	,, Herbesthal	104						"	11p15	10p14	22
	,, Cologne........................	122									
	,, Hanover and Brunswick	161									
	,, Magdeburg and Leipsic	158									
	,, Dresden.......	188	122	10	77	50	5				
	Return fare		222	70	142	20	20				
Florence...... *Via Turin.* 731 miles.	To Dijon 48; on to Bourg	63B						P.L.M.	2p20	3 p12	24
	On to Culoz and Modane.........	60						"	10p15	1a50	26½
	,, Turin and Pisa	270									
	,, Florence	270A	132	90	89	55	10				
	Return fare		225	80	157	40	30				
Via Milan. 737 miles.	To Dijon 48; on to Pontarlier	52						P.L.M.	2p20	1 p25	22
	" Lausanne&Domodossola	263B						"	9 p30	11p16	24¾
	" Milan 274; Florence......	279	131	55	89	40	10				
Frankfort ... *Via Metz.* 424½ miles.	To Chalons and Frouard	64						Est	9 a0	9 p20	11¼
	On to Pagny-sur-Moselle	72						"	5 p15	5 a38	11¼
	,, Metz and Saarbrucken...	212						"	9 p5	10a14	12¼
	,, Kreuznach and Bingerbruck	125									
	,, Mayence and Frankfort	123	74	65	49	50	5				
	Return fare		127	80	87	15	20				
Via Strassburg. 454 miles.	To Deutsch Avricourt	64						Est	9 a0	10 p0	12
	On to Strassburg & Appenweier	210						"	12 0	1 a16	12¼
	,, Carlsruhe	141						"	5 p15	5 a32	11½
	,, Frankfort ....141 and	136	74	65	49	50	5	"	9 p5	11a40	13½
	Return fare		127	80	87	15	20	"	10p15	12p39	13½
Via Cologne. 444½ miles.	To Erquelinnes	24						Nord	7 a50	10 p7	13¼
	On to Namur and Liége	92						"	8 a10	10p44	13½
	,, Herbesthal	104						"	6 p20	11a11	16
	,, Cologne and Frankfort...	122	74	65	49	50	5	"	10 p0	1 p36	14½
	Return fare		127	80	87	15	20	"	11p15	1 p57	13¾
Geneva .... *Via Culoz.* 376 miles.								P.L.M.	8 a40	7 p38	10
	To Dijon 48; on to Bourg	63B						"	9 a15	11p25	13½
	On to Culoz and Geneva	60	70	15	47	30	5	"	9 p35	8 a38	10
								"	10p25	12p 3	12¾
Via Lausanne. 365½ miles.	To Dijon 48; on to Pontarlier	52						P.L.M.	8 a30	7 p22	10
	On to Lausanne 263B; Geneva	263A	63	50	43	15	8	"	2 p20	1 a8	9¾
	Return fare		95	30	67	40	10	"	9 p30	8 a20	9¾
Genoa .... 580 miles.	To Dijon 48; on to Bourg	63B						P.L.M.	2p20	9 a35	18¼
	On to Culoz and Modane..........	60						"	10p15	6 p30	19¼
	,, Turin and Genoa	270	110	60	75	35	10				
	Return fare		174	10	124	50	30				

The "a" and "p" inserted in the departure and arrival times denote "a.m." and "p.m."

From PARIS to	ROUTE.	PAGE	FARES. 1st class. fr. c.	FARES. 2nd class. fr. c.	Validity of Ticket. Days.	Departure from Paris.	Arrve destination.	Time of Jrney HRS.
Lausanne	To Dijon	48				**P.L.M.** 8 a30	6 p15	$8\frac{3}{4}$
$337\frac{1}{2}$ miles.	On to Dole and Pontarlier	52				" 2 p20	11p54	$8\frac{1}{2}$
	" Lausanne	263B	58 90	40 5	3	" 7§p45	5 a50	9
	Return fare		88 20	63 0	10	" 9 p30	7 a10	$8\frac{3}{4}$
	§—Simplon Express, Train de Luxe.							
Lisbon	By Sud Express, see Through Table	7	323 45	... ...	...	**Orsay** 12p16	10p52	$35\frac{1}{4}$
$1175\frac{3}{4}$ miles.	To Orleans, Tours, and Bordeaux	34				**Orsay** 7p38	2 p31	43
	On to Bayonne and Irun........	45				" 10p10	11p53	$49\frac{3}{4}$
	" Burgos, Valladolid, and Medina	291A						
	" Salamanca	290A						
	" Villar Formoso	299						
	" Pampilhosa.....................	301						
	" Entroncamento	300						
	" Lisbon	300	220 60	159 85	...			
London .... *Via Boulogne.* 259 miles.	Paris to Amiens, Boulogne, and London........................	19	62 50	43 35	7	**Nord** 8 a25	3 p25	7
	Return fare		109 85	78 80	30	" 4 p0	10p45	$6\frac{3}{4}$
Via Calais. $286\frac{3}{4}$ miles.	Paris to Amiens, Calais, and London	19	70 80	49 55	7	**Nord** 9 a50	5 p10	$7\frac{1}{4}$
						" 12 0	7 p5	7
	Return fare		119 75	87 35	30	" 9 p20	5 a43	$8\frac{1}{2}$
	‡—Not run on Saturday midnight.					" 12‡a30	10a15	$9\frac{3}{4}$
Via Dieppe. $246\frac{1}{2}$ miles.	Paris to Dieppe and London ...	77	48 25	35 0	7	**Lazar** 10 a0	6 p10	$8\frac{1}{4}$
	Return fare		82 75	58 75	30	" 9 p20	7 a30	10
Via Havre. $341\frac{1}{2}$ miles.	Paris to Rouen, Havre, and London	77	45 75	33 25	7	**Lazar** 7‡p48	9 a0	$13\frac{1}{4}$
	Return fare		77 65	55 15	30			
	‡—On weekdays only, also on Sundays from July 27th							
Madrid	By Sud Exp. see Through Table	7	226 50	... ...	...	**Orsay** 12p16	2 p12	26
904 miles.	To Orleans, Tours, and Bordeaux	34				**Orsay** 7 p38	10p58	$26\frac{1}{2}$
	On to Bayonne and Irun.........	45				" 10p10	7 a0	$32\frac{3}{4}$
	" Burgos, Valladolid, and Madrid	291A	171 25	121 55	...			
Milan	To Dijon	48				**P.L.M.** 8 a30	12a15	$14\frac{3}{4}$
Via Lausanne. 521 miles.	On to Pontarlier..........................	52				" 2 p20	6 a25	$15\frac{1}{4}$
	" Lausanne and Domodossola..........................	263B				" 7§p45	12p12	$15\frac{1}{4}$
	" Milan............................	274	96 80	66 65	10	" 9 p30	1 p30	$14\frac{3}{4}$
	Return fare		150 65	107 30	30			
	§—Simplon Express, Train de Luxe.							
Via Basle. 559 miles.	To Belfort and Alt-Munsterol	68				**Est** 8 ‡a0	12a15	$15\frac{1}{4}$
	On to Basle	207A				" 1 p0	6a22	$16\frac{1}{4}$
	" Lucerne 258; Chiasso ...	259				" 9 ‡p0	2 p10	$16\frac{1}{4}$
	" Milan............................	269A	96 80	66 65	10	" 9 p45	3 p5	$16\frac{1}{4}$
	Return fare		150 65	107 30	30	‡—Via Delle.		

The "a" and "p" inserted in the departure and arrival times denote "a.m." and "p.m."

From PARIS to	ROUTE	PAGE	FARES, 1st class. fr. c.	FARES, 2nd class. fr. c.	Validity of Ticket. Days.	Departure from Paris.		Arrve destination.	Time of Jrney HRS.
Munich	By Orient Exp. see Thro' Table	8	125 25	... ...	...	**Est**	7p13	10a16	14
571 miles.	To Nancy and D.-Avricourt ...	64				**Est**	9 a0	11p23	13½
	On to Strassburg & Appenweier	210				"	12 0	7 a20	18¼
	" Carlsruhe 141; Muhlacker	141				"	5 p15	8 a35	14¼
	" Stuttgart, Ulm, Munich	192	99 45	65 10	5	"	9 p5	1 p8	15
	Return fare		175 45	117 35	20	"	10p15	5 p9	18
Pöstyén	See routes to Vienna.					**Est**	7§p13	10p10	26
953 miles.	On to Galanta 227; Pöstyén..	233B	176 0	112 20	...	"	10p15	10a55	35¾
	Return fare		327 35	211 60	25				
	§—By Orient Express, Train de Luxe, fare about 40 fr. extra.								
Rome .... *Via Genoa.* 890 miles.	To Dijon 48; on to Bourg	63B				**P.L.M.**	2 p20	7 p15	28
	On to Culoz and Modane.........	60				"	10p15	7 a0	31¾
	" Turin, Genoa, and Rome	270	148 90	99 30	10				
	Return fare		257 80	176 90	45				
Via Bologna. 964 miles.	To Dijon 48; on to Bourg	63B				**P.L.M.**	2 p20	10p55	31½
	On to Culoz and Modane.........	60				"	10p15	8 a50	33½
	" Turin and Alessandria...	270							
	" Piacenza 273; Rome......	279	... ...	... ...	...				
Via Milan. 934 miles.	To Dijon 48; on to Pontarlier	52				**P.L.M.**	2p20	6 p55	27½
	On to Lausanne & Domodossola	263B				"	9p30	6 a45	32¼
	" Milan 274; Florence & Rome	279	149 15	100 20	10				
Stuttgart	Orient Express, Through Table	8	95 55	... ...	...	**Est**	7 p13	6 a40	10½
422 miles.	To Nancy and D.-Avricourt ...	64				**Est**	9 a0	7 p42	9¾
	On to Strassburg & Appenweier	210				"	12 0	12a15	11¼
	" Carlsruhe 141; Muhlacker	141				"	5 p15	4 a52	10½
	" Stuttgart	192	75 85	50 95	5	"	9 p5	9 a2	11
	Return fare		128 20	89 10	20	"	10p15	12p42	13½
St. Petersburg	Nord Express; Paris to Cologne	24				**Nord**	1 p45	10a30	42¾
1690 miles.	Through Table, Cologne to St. Petersburg	9	340 25	... ...	...	Wed. & Sat.			
	See routes to Berlin.					**Nord**	7a50	11a35	49¾
	On from Berlin to Eydtkühnen	176				"	11p15	8 a15	55
	On to St. Petersburg..............	313	243 80	160 70	10				
	Return fare		465 90	308 60	60				
Turin	To Dijon 48; on to Bourg	63B				**P.L.M.**	8 a40	12 a5	14½
477 miles.	On to Culoz and Modane.........	60				"	2 p20	5 a50	14½
	" Turin	270	91 50	62 15	10	"	10p15	2 p 5	14¾
	Return fare		148 60	107 35	30				
Vernet-les-Bains ...	To Toulouse and Narbonne ...	32				**Orsay**	8a20	7 a12	23
608 miles.	On to Perpignan.....................	46				"	7 p0	10a38	15½
	" Villefranche Vernet ...	46	109 50	73 90	...	"	8 p30	4 p52	20½
Vienna..........	Orient Express, Through Table	8	192 50	... ...	...	**Est**	7 p13	6 p0	21¾
861½ miles. *Via Strassburg.* 861½ miles.	To Nancy and D.-Avricourt ...	64				**Est**	9 a0	8 a10	22¼
	On to Strassburg & Appenweier	210				"	5 p15	6 p32	24¼
	" Carlsruhe 141; Muhlacker	141				"	9 p 5	9 p50	23¾
	" Stuttgart and Munich ...	192				"	10p15	6 a0	30¾
	" Rosenheim and Salzburg	200							
	" Wels, Linz, and Vienna	239A	155 10	98 85	10				
	Return fare		285 55	184 90	25				
Via Basle. 913 miles.	To Altmunsterol and Basle ...	68				**Est**	1 p0	5 p25	27½
	On to Zurich 261; Buchs	268B				"	9 p45	6 a0	31¼
	" Innsbruck and Vienna	238A	155 10	98 85	10				
	Return fare		285 55	184 90	25				

The "a" and "p" inserted in the departure and arrival times denote "a.m." and "p.m."

From ST. PETERSBURG to	ROUTE	PAGE	FARES. 1st class. R. k.	FARES. 2nd class. R. k.	Validity of Ticket. Days.	Departure from St. Petersburg.	Arive destination.	Time of J'rney HRS.
Archangel	To Vologda	319				12a35	2p27	38
766 miles.	On to Archangel........................	315	24 0	14 40	...			
Berlin .... *Nord Express.*	To Vilna and Eydtkuhnen	313				7§p45	10p38	28
1019 miles.	On to Konigsberg, Schneidemuhl, Berlin	177	70 0	... ...				
	§—Wed. and Sat. only.							
	By ordinary Express over preceding route.		53 15	33 85	...	7 p5 11 p0	7 p25 5 a42	25¼ 31¾
Copenhagen ...	To Vilna and Eydtkuhnen	313				7 p5 11 p0	9 a42 6p41	39½ 44¾
1297 miles.	On to Konigsberg, Schneidemuhl, Berlin	177						
	,, Neu-Strelitz	181						
	,, Warnemunde and Gjedser	178B						
	,, Masnedsund and Copenhagen	302	77 0	48 50	...			
Dresden	To Vilna and Eydtkuhnen ...	313				7 p5 11 p0	10p46 9 a48	28¾ 35¾
1138 miles.	On to Konigsberg and Berlin...	177						
	,, Dresden........................	188	59 15	38 15	...			
Hamburg	To Vilna and Eydtkuhnen	313				7 p5 11 p0	12 a9 12p58	30 39
1197 miles.	On to Konigsberg, Schneidemuhl, Berlin................	177						
	,, Wittenberge and Hamburg...........................	167	62 75	40 45	...			
London .... *Nord Express.*	By Nord Express, see Through Table	11				7p45 Wed. and Sat.	10 p0	52¼
1745 miles.	Fare via Ostend		140 0	... ...	...			
Via Flushing. 1683 miles.	To Vilna and Eydtkuhnen	313				11 p0	7a48	58¾
	On to Berlin........................	177						
	,, Hanover & Oberhausen	160B						
	,, Wesel........................	132						
	,, Boxtel........................	120						
	,, Vlissingen and London	113	89 95	58 70	...			
Via Ostend. 1739 miles.	To Vilna and Eydtkuhnen	313				11 p0	5a43	56¾
	On to Berlin........................	177						
	,, Hanover and Cologne ...	160B						
	,, Herbesthal	123B						
	,, Louvain........................	104						
	,, Ghent........................	101						
	,, Ostend and London	102A	96 85	64 15	...			
Via Calais. 1766 miles.	To Vilna and Eydtkuhnen	313				11 p0	5 a43	56¾
	On to Berlin........................	177						
	,, Hanover and Cologne ...	160B						
	,, Herbesthal	123B						
	,, Brussels........................	104						
	,, Lille	103						
	,, Calais and London.........	7	102 30	68 9	...			

The "a" and "p" inserted in the departure and arrival times denote "a.m." and "p.m."

From ST. PETERSBURG to	ROUTE.		FARES. 1st class	FARES. 2nd class.	Validity of Ticket.	Departure from St. Petersburg.	Arive destination.	Time of Jrney
			R. k.	R. k.	Days.			HRS.
LONDON—*cont.*	To Vilna and Eydtkuhnen	313				11p0	8 a0	59
Via Hoek van Holland.	On to Berlin...........................	177						
1647 miles.	,, Hanover and Lohne	160B						
	,, Rheine	156C						
	,, Amersfoort	118C						
	,, Utrecht.........................	115A						
	,, Rotterdam	118A						
	,, Hoek van Holland and London	112	88 95	58 70				
Moscow .... 404 miles.	To Moscow	314	26 55	17 25		10 a0 9 p30 11 p0	8 p0 8 a10 10a0	10 10¾ 11
Odessa .... 1205 miles.	To Vilna	313				7 p25	9 a10	37¾
	On to Rowno	314						
	,, Kasjatin........................	320						
	,, Odessa	320	31 50	18 90	...	... ...	...	...
						Wed. and Sat. only		
Paris .... 1690 miles.	To Vilna and Eydtkuhnen	313				7p45	4 p0	46½
Nord Express.	On to Konigsberg, Schneidemuhl, Berlin	177						
	,, Hanover and Cologne ...	160						
	,, Aix-la-Chapelle and Herbesthal	123B						
	,, Liége	104						
	,, Namur and Erquelinnes	93						
	,, Maubeuge and Paris	24	137 50	... ...	...			
	By ordinary express over preceding route.		91 0	60 0	...	7 p5 11p 0	4 p0 11p30	47 50½
Stockholm... about 500 miles. *Via Abo.*	To Riihimaki, Toijala, & Abo	312				9 a45	9 a0	24½
	Steamer to Stockholm	360A	26 4	20 42	...			
Vienna........... 1127 miles.	To Vilna and Warsaw	313				6 p45	6 a0	36¼
	On to Granica	316						
	,, Trzebinia	222						
	,, Oderberg and Vienna ...	222	53 5	35 20				
Warsaw .... 693 miles.	To Vilna and Warsaw	313	22 50	13 50	...	6 p45	12p47	18

The "a" and "p" inserted in the departure and arrival times denote "a.m." and "p m."

From STOCKHOLM to	ROUTE.	FARES. 1st class.	2nd class.	Validity of Ticket.	Departure from Stockholm.	Arive destination.	Time of J'rney
Berlin	To Malmo and Sassnitz 308	K. ö.	K. ö.	Days.			HRS.
Via Sassnitz.	On to Neu-Strelitz and Berlin 181	64 0	43 20.	10	10a27	8 a35	22¼
642¾ miles.					8 p30	6 p34	22
Christiania ...	To Gnesta and Cathrineholm 308				8a38	10p27	13¾
357 miles.	On to Hallsberg and Laxa 309				9p35	10a30	13
	„ Kil and Charlottenberg... 308						
	„ Christiania 304A	37 60	23 80	90			
	Return fare	64 90	43 50	90			
London	To Malmo and Copenhagen ... 308						
	On to Korsœr and Kiel............ 302						
	„ Hamburg 168						
Via	From Hamburg to London,						
Copenhagen.	see Through Table......... 11						
1263 miles.	Via Copenhagen and Ostend ...	158 40	105 60		8 p30	10 p0	50½
1288 miles.	Via Copenhagen and Calais ...	158 40	105 60		8 p30	7 p5	47½
1196 miles.	Via Copenhagen and Flushing	126 50	85 20	30	8 p30	7p34	48
		241 10	163 80	60			
	To Malmo and Sassnitz 308						
	On to Stralsund and Berlin ... 181						
	From Berlin to London, see						
	Through Table 11						
	Or, to Malmo and Sassnitz....... 308						
	On to Stralsund 181; to Rostock 181A						
	On to Lubeck 213; to Hamburg 213A						
Via	From Hamburg to London,						
Sassnitz.	see Through Table......... 11						
1363 miles.	Via Sassnitz and Ostend..........	158 40	105 60	...	10a27	5 a43	42¼
					8p30	10 p0	50½
1390 miles.	Via Sassnitz and Calais	158 40	105 60	...	10a27	5 a43	42¼
					8p30	7 p5	47½
1307 miles.	Via Sassnitz and Flushing.......	138 40	90 0	30	10a27	7 a48	46½
					8p30	7 p34	49
1271 miles.	Via Sassnitz & Hoek v. Holland ...	138 40	90 0	30	10a27	8 a0	46½
Paris............	To Malmo and Copenhagen .. 308						
	On to Korsœr and Kiel............ 302						
	„ Neumunster & Hamburg 168				8 p30	4 p0	44½
Via	„ Bremen, Osnabruck, and						
Copenhagen.	Cologne 133						
1212 miles.	„ Herbesthal 123B; Liege 104						
	„ Namur and Erquelinnes 93						
	„ Maubeuge and Paris 24	136 50	90 20	15			
	Return fare	257 30	171 10	45			
	To Malmo and Sassnitz 308				10‡a27	5 a32	44
	Or to Stralsund and Berlin...... 181				8p30	4 p0	44½
Via	„ Hanover and Cologne ... 160						
Sassnitz.	„ Herbesthal 123B; Liege... 104						
1314 miles.	„ Namur and Erquelinnes 93				‡–Via Stralsund-Hamburg.		
	„ Maubeuge and Paris 24	144 10	94 40	15			
	Return fare	272 40	179 40	45			
St. Petersburg	Steamer to Abo....................... 358				7p30	10 p0	25¼
	Rail on to Toijala.................... 312						
	„ Riihimaki............ 312						
	„ St. Petersburg....... 312	...	...	...			

The "a" and "p" inserted in the departure and arrival times denote "a.m." and "p.m."

 A B C ROUTES from VIENNA with best Direct Trains.

From VIENNA to	ROUTE.		FARES. 1st class.	FARES. 2nd class.	Validity of Ticket.	Departure from Vienna.	Arive destination.	Time of Jrney
		PAGE	kronen.	kronen.	Days.			HRS.
Belgrade......	To Galantha and Budapest......	227				Staats 6p51	5a58	11
Orient Express	On to Szabadka and Belgrade	225A	103 35	......	...	Tu, Thr, Fri,		
395¾ miles.						Sun. only.		
Ordinary	To Bruck and Budapest	225B				Staats 9a10	10p38	13¾
Express.	On to Belgrade	225A	70 35	45 70	10	" 10p20	2p14	16
Berlin	To Oderberg	222				Nord 7a34	8p16	12¾
510 miles.	On to Kandrzin	219				" 3p55	5 a8	13¼
Via Oderberg.	" Breslau	218				" 7p45	7 a35	11¾
	" Berlin	179	82 20	51 40	4	" 10p15	10a50	12½
Via Tetschen.	To Deutschbrod and Tetschen	224				Nd Wst 8a50	10p26	13½
441½ miles.	On to Dresden and Berlin	189	82 20	51 40	4	" " 8p20	8 a8	11¾
						" " 9p40	10a20	12½
Via Bodenbach	To Brunn and Bodenbach	252				F.J. Bhf 6‡30	6 p51	12½
493½ miles.	On to Dresden and Berlin	189	82 20	51 40	4	" 8 a25	10p26	14
	‡—Via Gmünd.					Staats 10p 0	12p48	14¾
Breslau	To Prerau and Oderberg	222				Nord 7a34	3p10	7½
284 miles.	On to Kandrzin	219				" 3p55	11p48	8
	, Breslau	218	52 65	32 95	4	" 7p45	3a24	7½
						" 10p15	5a56	7¾
Brussels	See route to Cologne.					West 7a25	10a25	28
	On from Cologne to Aix-la-					" 1 p0	12‡55	25
Via Passau.	Chapelle and Herbesthal......	123B				" 8p40	9 ‡26	25¾
746 miles.	On to Liege and Brussels.........	104	124 90	76 60	10			
	‡—Via Ulm and Strassburg.							
Vienna-O.	By Vienna-Ostend Express over					noon		
Express.	preceding route		156 60	......	...	West 12 0	7 a52	21
Bucharest ...	To Budapest and Verciorova...	227				Staats 6p51	6p34	22¾
Orient or	On to Bucharest...	324A	138 0	......	...	Mon. Wed.		
Ostend-Express						& Sat. only.		
719 miles.	By other express over preceding					Staats 9a25	11a25	25
	route		92 60	61 0	10			
	To Bruck and Budapest	225B				Staats 9 a10	11a40	25½
Via Predeal.	On to Predeal	233				" 4 p50	9 p20	27½
730½ miles.	" Ploesci 324A ; Bucharest	324	91 60	61 0	10			
Budapest	To Pozsony and Budapest	227	36 60	23 30	...	Staats 9a25	2 p0	4½
Via Marchegg.						" 2p10	6 p40	4½
173¾ miles.						" 2p55	7 p10	4¼
						" 4p50	9 p5	4¼
	By Orient and Ostend-Constantinople Expresses over preceding route		49 50	......	...	Staats 6p51	11 p5	4¼
Via Bruck.						Staats 9a10	1 p40	4½
167¾ miles.	To Bruck and Budapest	225B	36 60	23 30	...	" 1p55	6 p35	4¾
Cologne	To Amstetten and Wels	239				West 7a25	12a55	17½
605 miles.	On to Neumarkt and Passau...	239B				" 1†p0	9 a50	20¾
	" Nurnberg and Würzburg	195A				" 8p30	4 p32	20
	" Aschaffenburg & Frankfort	196B	†—Via	Munich.				
	" Niederlahnstein and Cologne	129	99 80	61 90	5			
Vienna-O.	By Vienna-Ostend Express					noon		
Express.	over preceding route...........		125 70	......	...	West 12 0	4a35	16¾

The "a" and "p" inserted in the departure and arrival times denote "a.m." and "p.m."

From LONDON to	ROUTES.	PAGE	FARES. 1st Cl. £ s. d.	FARES. 2nd Cl. £ s. d.	Validity of Ticket. Days	Departure from London.	Arrive Destination.	Time of Journey HRS	Excess luggage per 20lb
Turin	London to Calais, Boulogne, Amiens, Paris	18				Vic 11 a0	2 p 5	26	
Via Calais or Boulogne.	On to Dijon	48				ChX 2 p5	2 p 5	23	
741 miles.	" St. Amour and Bourg ...	63B				" 9 p0	12 a5	26	
Thro' Table p. 1.	" Culoz, Modane	60							
	" Turin	270	6 10 9	4 10 2	20				
	Return fare		10 8 10	7 11 5	60				§
	§—4/7 to Modane; -/5 thence.								
Via Dieppe.	London to Dieppe, Rouen, and Paris	76				Vic 10 a0	2 p 5	27	
728 miles.						" 8 p45	12a 5	26½	
Thro' Table p. 1.	On to Turin as above		5 12 11	3 18 8	20				3/11
	Return fare		8 19 6	6 8 10	60				
Venice	See routes to Milan via Basle.					ChX 2 p5	11p30	32½	
	On to Verona, Padua, and Venice	280							
Via Basle.	Fare via Boulogne Laon, Basle, Milan (956¾ miles)..............		7 17 0	5 8 10	20				§
Thro' Table p. 5.	§—5/5 to Chiasso; 1/1 thence.								
965 miles.	Fare via Ostend, Brussels, Basle, Milan		... ...	... ...	20	ChX 9 a0	11p30	37½	
						" 2 p5	4 a19	37¼	
						" 9 p0	11a25	37½	
975 miles.	Fare via Dieppe, Paris, Basle...		7 6 11	5 2 7	20	Vic 10 a0	11p30	36½	6/1
	Return fare		12 0 5	8 10 7	60	" 8 p45	11a25	37¾	
Via Paris.	From Calais by Simplon Express, see Through Table, p. 1		10 10 10	... ...	...	Vic 11 a0	4p40	28¾	
949 miles.	See routes to Milan, via Paris.					Vic 11 a0	11p30	35½	
Thro' Table p. 1.	On to Venice (Fare via Boulogne)	280	7 17 3	5 8 8	20	ChX 2 p5	11p30	32¼	
986 miles.	Fare via Dieppe, Paris, Turin		7 6 4	5 0 10	20	Vic 10 a0	11p30	36½	3/11
Vernet-les-Bains...	See routes to Paris.								
895 miles.	On to Toulouse and Narbonne	32				ChX 10 a0	10a38	24½	
	" Perpignan	46				Vic 8p45	7 a12	22½	
	" Villefranche Vernet-les-Bains.....................	46	7 5 1	4 19 9	15	ChX 9 p0	7 a12	22¼	5/5
	Return fare		11 8 8	8 6 1	60				
Vichy	London to Calais and Paris ...	18				Vic 11 a0	3 a15	16¼	
Via Calais.	On to St. Germains-des-Fosses and Vichy..................	58				ChX 9 p0	3 p35	18½	3/5
518 miles.	**Return fare**		7 7 0	5 7 1	60				
Via Boulogne.	London to Boulogne and Paris	18				ChX 2 p5	5 a11	15¼	
491 miles.	On to St. Germains-des-Fosses and Vichy..................	58							3/3
	Return fare		7 7 0	5 7 1	60				
Via Dieppe.	London to Dieppe and Paris ...	76				Vic 10 a0	3 a15	17¼	
478 miles.	On to St. Germains-des-Fosses and Vichy..................	58	3 12 9	2 11 4	15	" 8 p45	3 p35	18¾	2/9
	Return fare		5 17 8	4 4 6	60				
Via Havre.	London to Havre and Paris ...	76				Waterloo			
573 miles.	On to Vichy..........................	58	3 14 0	2 11 0	15	9 p45	6 p30	20¾	
	Return fare		5 19 3	4 4 3	60	Not Sun.			

The "a" and "p" inserted in the departure and arrival times denote "a.m." and "p.m."

From VIENNA to	ROUTE.	PAGE	FARES. 1st class.	FARES. 2nd class.	Validity of Ticket.	Departure from Vienna.		Arrve destin ation.	Time of Jrney
London			kronen.	kronen.	Days.		noon		HRS.
Vienna-Ostend Express.	By Vienna-Ostend Express, see Through Table	8	[About] 203 30	... ...		**West**	12 0	5 p10	30½
Orient Express. 1121 miles.	By Orient Express, see Through Table	8	[About] 253 50	... ...		**West**	noon 12 0	5 p10	30½
Via Laon and Calais. 1094 miles.	Vienna to Salzburg 239; Munich	200				**West**	8 p40	5 a43	34
	On to Stuttgart and Carlsruhe	192A							
	,, Avricourt..........................	210A							
	,, Chalons and Laon..	65A							
	,, Calais and London	19A							
Via Cologne-Ostend. 963 miles.	Vienna to Wels	239				**West**	7 a25	10 p0	40½
	On to Passau	239B				"	8 p30	5 a43	34¼
	,, Nurnberg & Wurzburg	195A							
	,, Aschaffenburg & Frankfort 196A; Cologne	129							
	,, Herbesthal 123B; Brussels	104							
	,, Ostend and London	102A	168 0	107 0	30				
Via Cologne-Calais. 988 miles.	From Vienna to Brussels as above					**West**	7 a25	7 p5	36½
	On from Brussels to Lille	103				"	8 p30	5 a43	34¼
	On to Calais and London.........	27	180 90	115 40	30				
Via Dresden-Flushing. 1058 miles.	Vienna to Tetschen	224				**Nd West**	8a50	7 p34	35¾
	On to Dresden and Falkenberg	189				"	9 p40	7 a48	35
	,, Zerbst and Magdeburg...	172							
	,, Hanover 158; Oberhausen	160B							
	,, Wesel 132; Boxtel.........	120							
	,, Breda.............................	117							
	,, Vlissingen and London..	113	168 0	105 50	30				
Via Dresden-Hoek van Holland. 1032 miles.	Vienna to Tetschen	224				**Nd West**	9p40	8 a0	35¼
	On to Dresden and Leipsic......	189							
	,, Magdeburg and Hanover	158							
	,, Lohne 160B; Rheine......	156C							
	,, Amersfoort 118C; Utrecht	115A							
	,, Rotterdam	118A							
	,, Hoek van Holland and London	112	168 0	105 50	30				
Lucerne .... 581 miles.	To Amstetten & Bischofshofen	239				**West**	12p35	8 a25	20
	On to Innsbruck, Feldkirch, and Buchs 238; Sargans	268				"	7 p50	3 p14	19½
	,, Ziegelbrucke & Thalweil	268C				"	10p10	9 p35	23½
	,, Zug and Lucerne	260	92 30	59 10	6				
Milan .... 620 miles.	To Amstetten	239				**Sud**	7 a35	6 a10	22¾
	On to St. Michael (Or to Bruck and St. Michael page 234)					**West**	9 p15	6 p40	21½
	Villach, and Pontebba...	241				**Sud**	9†p30	6 p40	21¼
	,, Udine and Mestre.........	285A		†—Via	Graz	and Nabresi	na.		
	,, Padua, Verona, & Milan	280	99 60	67 0	15				
Moscow .... 1245 miles.	To Oderberg and Trzebinia......	222				**Nord**	10p15	3 p44	40½
	On to Granica 222; Warsaw...	316							
	,, Brest-Litewski	315							
	.. Minsk and Moscow......	315	141 10	93 70	8				
Munich ...... *Via Salzburg.* 290½ miles.	To Wels and Salzburg	239				**West**	8 a15	5 p0	8¾
	On to Rosenheim and Munich	200	55 10	34 30	4	"	1 p0	10 p0	9
						"	8 p40	6 a30	9¾
	By Orient Express over route via Salzburg........................		66 30	... ...	...	**West**	noon 12 0	7 p45	7¾

The "a" and "p" inserted in the departure and arrival times denote "a.m." and "p.m."

From VIENNA to	ROUTE.	FARES. 1st class.	FARES. 2nd class.	Validity of Ticket.	Departure from Vienna.	Arrve destination.	Time of Jrney
		kronen.	kronen.	Days.			HRS.
Nice	See route to Genoa.						
830 miles.	On from Genoa to Ventimiglia 272						
	On to Monte-Carlo and Nice ... 55	121 80	80 70	30	**Sud** 7a35	3 p25	32¾
	By Vienna-Nice Express over preceding route	171 90	... ...	...			
Odessa	To Oderberg and Cracow......... 222				**Nord** 7 a34	6 p58	34½
939 miles.	On to Lemberg & Woloczyska 246A				" 10p15	9 a25	34¼
	" Schmerinka.................. 320						
	" Odessa 320	141 40	88 90	7			
Paris...............	By Orient Express, see Through Table 8	184 60	... ...	...	**West** noon 12 0	8 a56	22
Via Munich. 861¾ miles.	To Wels and Salzburg 239				**West** 1 p0	12p16	27¼
	On to Rosenheim and Munich 200				" 8 p40	9 p20	25¾
	" Ulm, Stuttgart, and Muhlacker 192A						
	" Carlsruhe......................141A						
	" Appenweier.................... 140						
	" Strassb'rg & D.Avricourt210A						
	" Nancy, Chalons, & Paris 65	148 90	94 90	10			
	Return fare	274 15	177 50	25			
Via The Arlberg. 926½ miles.	To Amstetten & Bischofshofen 239				**West** 12p35	5 p45	30¼
	On to Innsbruck, Feldkirch, and Buchs..................... 238				" 7 p50	11p48	29
	" Sargans 268						
	" Ziegelbrucke and Zurich 268C						
	" Brugg and Basle............. 261						
	" Mülhausen and Alt-Münsterol......................207A						
	" Belfort, Troyes, & Paris 69	148 90	94 90	10			
	Return fare	274 15	177 50	25			
Pöstyén	To Pozsony 227; Lipotvar...... 226				**Staats** 7 a45	10a55	3¼
91½ miles	On to Pöstyén........................233B				" 9 a25	3 p44	6¼
	Or, to Galantha 227				" 6§p51	10p10	3¼
100 miles......	On to Pöstyén 233B	18 70	11 90	...	" 7p30	12a13	4¾
	§—Luxuszug—extra fare.						
Rome	To Neustadt and Bruck 234				**Sud** 7 a35	1 p5	29½
761½ miles.	On to Leoben 235				**West** 9 p15	6 a45	33½
	" St. Michael 241				**Sud** 9†p30	6 a45	33½
	" Villach and Pontebba ... 241						
	" Udine and Mestre.........285A		†—Via	Graz	and Nabresi	na.	
	" Padua and Bologna 279A						
	" Florence and Rome 279	119 40	79 30	15			
Serajevo	To Budapest via Bruck 225B				**Staats** 9 a10	8 a10	23
617¾ miles.	On to Szabadka 225A						
	" Bosna Brod 230						
	" Doboj and Serajevo 247B	91 22	61 4	...			
St. Petersburg ...	To Oderberg and Trzebinia...... 222				**Nord** 10p15	12p15	37
1127 miles.	On to Granica 222						
	" Warsaw 316						
	" Wilna & St. Petersburg 313	134 80	89 40	7			
Warsaw	To Oderberg and Trzebinia...... 222				**Nord** 3 p55	7 a47	15
434½ miles.	On to Granica 222				" 10p15	2 p17	15
	" Warsaw 316	76 60	48 80	4			

The "a" and "p" inserted in the departure and arrival times denote "a.m." and "p.m."

LONDON TO THE MEDITERRANEAN, SWITZERLAND, ITALY, ALGIERS, EGYPT, AND GREECE.—Mont-Cenis and Simplon Routes.

LONDON—	a.m.		a.m.		a.m.	a.m.	a.m.	a.m.	a.m.	a.m.				p.m.	p.m.	p.m.	p.m.				p.m.
VICTORIA .... dep	...	...	11 0	...	11 0	11 0	11 0	11 0	11 0	11 0	...	...	...	...	...	...	...	...	...	...	...
CHARING CROSS .... dep	9 0	...	...	...	...	...	...	...	...	...	...	...	...	9 0	9 0	9 0	9 0	...	...	...	9 0
DOVER .... arr	10a40	...	12p45	...	12p45	12p45	12p45	12p45	12p45	12p45	...	...	...	10p40	10p40	10p40	10p40	...	...	...	10p40
DOVER .... dep	11 a5	...	12p55	...	12p55	12p55	12p55	12p55	12p55	12p55	...	...	...	11 p5	11 p5	11 p5	11 p5	...	...	...	11 p5
CALAIS (Pier) .... 18 dep	1 p15	...	2 p40	...	2 p50	2 p57	2 p50	2 p50	2 p50	2 p50	...	...	...	1 a30	1 a30	1 a30	1 a30	...	...	...	1 a3
BOULOGNE .... 18 arr		...	...	...	...	...	...	...	...	...	...	...	...	2 a12	2 a12	2 a12	2 a12	...	...	...	
CHARING CROSS .... dep		10 a0	D	10 a0	...	B	...	...	...	...	2 p5	2 p5	2 p5	...	...	...	...	...	...	...	
FOLKESTONE .... dep		11a55	...	11a55	...	...	...	...	...	...	3 p55	3 p55	3 p55	...	...	...	...	...	...	...	
BOULOGNE .... 18 dep		2 p12	...	2 p12	...	...	...	...	...	...	6 p2	6 p2	6 p2	2 a12	2 a12	2 a12	2 a12	...	...	...	
AMIENS .... 18 arr	3 p8	...	4 p35	...	4 p47	4p51	4 p47	4 p47	4 p47	4 p47	...	...	...	3 a54	3 a54	3 a54	3 a54	...	...	...	3 a3
" .... 18 dep	3 p13	...	4 p41	...	4 p50	4p55	4 p50	4 p50	4 p50	4 p50	...	...	...	3 a59	3 a59	3 a59	3 a59	...	...	...	3 a8
PARIS (Nord) .... 18 arr	4 p40	5 p20	6 p15	5 p20	6 p20		6 p20	6 p20	6 p20	6 p20	9 p0	9 p0	9 p0	5 a40	5 a40	5 a40	5 a40	...	...	...	
PARIS (Nord) .... dep	...	5 p39	6 p25	5 p39	7 p31		7 p31	7 p31	7 p31	7 p31	9 p25	9 p25	9 p25	...	6 a38	6 a38	6 a38	...	...	...	
PARIS (P.L.M.) .... arr	...	6 p26	6 p59	6 p26	8 p3		8 p3	8 p3	8 p3	8 p3	9 p55	9 p55	9 p55	...	7 a18	7 a18	7 a18	...	...	...	
LONDON—																					
L.B. Ry. VICTORIA .... dep	...	...	...	...	...		10 a0	...	...	...	...	...	...	...	8 p45	...	...	...	...	...	ORIENTAL EXPRESS.
L.B. Ry. LONDON BRIDGE dep	...	...	...	...	...		...	...	...	...	...	...	...	...	8 p45	...	...	...	...	...	
L.B. Ry. NEWHAVEN .... dep	...	...	...	...	...		11a30	...	...	...	...	...	...	...	10p25	...	...	...	...		
DIEPPE .... 77A dep	...	...	...	...	...		3 p11	...	...	...	...	...	...	...	3 a5	...	...	...	...		
PONTOISE .... 77A arr	...	...	...	...	...		...	...	...	...	...	...	...	...	...	...	...	...	...		
PARIS (St. Lazare) 77A arr	...	...	...	...	...		6 p3	...	...	...	...	...	...	...	6 a3	...	...	...	...		
PARIS (P.L.M.) .... arr	...	...	...	...	...		8 p14	...	...	...	...	...	...	...	7 a52	...	...	...	...		
LONDON—WATERLOO dep	...	...	...	...	...		...	...	...	...	...	...	...	...	...	...	...	...	9 p45	Week nights only from London.	
SOUTHAMPTON .... dep	...	...	...	...	...		...	...	...	...	...	...	...	...	...	...	...	...	12a15		
HAVRE .... 76 dep	...	...	...	...	...		...	...	...	...	...	...	...	...	...	...	...	...	8 a0		
ROUEN .... 76 arr	...	...	...	...	...		...	...	...	...	...	...	...	...	...	...	...	...	9 a12		
PARIS (Ouest) .... 76 arr	...	...	D	...	C		...	...	...	...	...	...	...	...	...	...	...	E	11a22		
		p.m.	p.m.	p.m.	p.m.		p.m.	p.m.	p.m.	p.m.	p.m.	p.m.	p.m.	a.m.	a.m.	a.m.	a.m.	a.m.	p.m.	p.m.	
PARIS (P.L.M.) .... 48 dep	...	7 0	7 45	7 50	8 50		9 0	9 10	9 30	9 35	10 15	10 25	10 50	7 10	8 30	8 40	9 15	11 35	2 20	3 45	See note at side PENINSULAR AND
DIJON .... 48 arr	...	11p52	12a13	12a32	1 a8		1 a20	1 a30	1 a42	2 a4	2 a57	3 a20	3 a37	12p23	12p36	1 p4	2 p9	3 p30	6 p29	8 p11	9 a59
DIJON .... 52 dep	...	...	12a28	1 a7	...		...	...	1 a48	...	3 a4	...	3 a47	...	12p46	...	...	...	6 p42	...	
PONTARLIER .... 52 arr	...	...	2 a53	3 a46	...		...	...	4 a10	...	5 a11	...	6 a26	...	3 p15	...	...	...	8 p50	...	
LAUSANNE .... 263B arr	...	...	5 a50	7 a10	...		...	...	7 a10	...	...	...	9 a48	...	6 p15	...	...	...	11p54	...	
DOMODOSSOLA 263B arr	...	...	9 a32	10a55	...		...	...	10a55	...	...	...	...	...	10 p3	...	...	...	3 a40	...	
MILAN .... 274 arr	...	...	12p12	1 p30	...		...	...	1 p30	...	...	...	...	...	12a15	...	...	...	6 a25	...	
FLORENCE .... 279 arr	...	...		11p16	...		...	...	11p16	...	...	...	...	...	...	...	...	...	1 p25	...	
ROME .... 279 arr	...	...		6 a45	...		...	...	6 a45	...	...	...	...	...	...	...	...	...	6 p55	...	
NEUCHATEL .... 265 arr	...	...	●5a10	7 a17	...		...	...	...	...	7 a35	...	9 a20	...	5 p46	...	...	...	11 p9	...	
BERNE .... 259B arr	...	...	●6 a8	8 a35	...		...	...	...	...	8 a35	...	10a32	...	6 p55	...	...	...	12 a1	...	
INTERLAKEN .... 267 arr	...	...	●7a35	10a20	...		...	...	...	...	10a20	...	12p40	...	9 p5	...	...	...	...	...	
DIJON .... 48 dep	...	12a12		12a40	1 a15		1 a26	1 a40	...	2 a10	3 a12	3 a30	...	1 p3	...	1 p32	2 p19	3 p36	6 p47	8 p35	10 a6
MACON .... 48 arr	...	1 a58		2 a19			3 a0	...	...	...	...	5 a39	...	3 p16	...	...	3 p59	...	...	10 p4	
MACON .... 60 dep	...	...		...			...	...	...	...	...	6 a20	...	...	...	...	4 p23	...	...	...	
CULOZ .... 60 arr	...	...		...			...	5 a35	...	5 a49	6 a26	9 a12	...	...	...	5 p0	8 p6	6 p49	10p22	...	1 p25
GENEVA .... 60 arr	...	...		...	Evian arr. 7.51; Chamonix arr. 10.13.		...		...	8 a38		12 p3	...	...	...	7 p38	11p25	9 p22		...	
MACON .... 48 dep	...	2 a1		2 a22			3 a3		...	...		5 a48	...	3 p23	...		4 p2			10 p9	
LYONS .... 48 arr	...	3 a2		3 a21			3 a59		...	...		7 a10	...	4 p43	...		5 p1			11p 8	
LYONS .... 48 dep	...	3 a18		...			4 a8		...	...		8 a0	...	5 p52	...		5 p21			11p37	
MARSEILLES .... 49 arr	...	8 a30		...		6 a36	8 a58		...	...		2 p38	...	12 a9	...		10p35			5 a0	
(P. & O.						a.m.															
MARSEILLES (steamer) dep	Friday.			...		10 0	...		...	...		...	...	...	...		...			...	
PORT SAID (steamer)... arr	Tues. 6th		day	...		...	...		...	...		...	...	...	...		...			...	
CAIRO .... 327 arr	Wed. 7th		day	...		5 p5	...		...	...		...	...	...	...		...			...	
MARSEILLES .... dep	...	...		...		...	☾§		...	...		...	...	...	...		...			...	
ALEXANDRIA (st'mr) arr	...	...		...		...	...		...	...		...	...	...	...		...			...	
CAIRO .... 327 arr	...	...		...		...	9 p15		...	...		...	...	...	...		...			...	
1	2	3	4	5	6	7	8	9	10	11	12	13	14	15	16	17	18	19	20	21	22

NOTES.

Steamer and Train Connection.—The Trains run from alongside the steamers at Calais, Boulogne, and Dieppe; at Havre a tramcar conveys Paris Passengers from Steamer to Station. At **Marseilles and Brindisi** travellers will have to find their way from train to steamer, except in the case of the P. & O. Marseilles Express, which runs down to the Mole, at Marseilles, and the P. & O. Brindisi Express, which runs down to the Port at Brindisi.

FARES—See A B C Through Routes from London, pages lxxiii to cxvii.

B—P. and O. Marseilles Express, running from Calais on Thursday only.

C—Runs until 19th Sept.

D — Simplon Express, Train de Luxe, leaving Calais daily. Take tickets in advance of Sleeping Car Co. ●—These arrivals are only from July 9th until 15th September.

E—Savoie Express, Train de Luxe, will run daily from Paris from 5th July until 12th September.

1	2	3	4	5	6	7	8	9	10	11	12	13 ‡	14	15	16	17	18	19	20	21	22
MARSEILLES (steamer) dep	...	...		...		...	p.m. 1 0	Mon.(6p0),Tu,Wed,Thur.(11a45),Fri.Sun.									...			...	
ALGIERS (steamer) ...arr	...	...		...		...	1 p0	Tues., Wed., Thurs., Fri., Sat., Mon.									...			...	
MARSEILLES ...54 dep	...	...		...		...	9 a20		...	...		...	...	12a46	...		12a46			...	
TOULON ...54 arr	...	...		...	B	...	10a25		...	...		...	...	2 a7	...		2 a7			...	
HYERES ...54 arr	...	...		...		...	11a49		...	...		...	...	...	...		...			...	
ST. RAPHAEL ...54 arr	...	...		...		...	12p10		...	...		...	...	4 a24	...		4 a24			...	
CANNES ...54 arr	...	...		...		...	12p40		...	...		...	...	4 a57	...		4 a57			...	
NICE ...54 arr	...	...		...		...	1 p25		...	...		...	...	6 a17	...		6 a17			...	
MONTE CARLO ...54 arr	...	...		...		...	2 p18		...	...		...	...	7 a19	...		7 a19			...	
MENTON ...54 arr	...	...		...		...	2 p37		...	...		...	...	7 a38	...		7 a38			...	
BORDIGHERA ...272 arr	...	...		...		...	4 p21		...	...		...	...	9 a40	...		9 a40			...	
SAN REMO ...272 arr	...	...		...		...	4 p39		...	...		...	...	9 a58	...		9 a58			...	
MACON ...60 dep	...	...		...		...	...		...	...		6 a20	...	...	...		4 p23			...	
CULOZ ...60 dep	...	...		...		...	...	5 a47	...	...	6 a27	9 a45	...	...	...	5 p22	9 p19	7 p1	10p35	...	1 p32
AIX-LES-BAINS ...60 arr	...	...		...	5 a26	...	...	6 a7	...	...	6 a47	10a15	...	...	...	5 p42	9 p47	7 p21	10p55	...	1 p54
MODANE ...60 arr	...	...		...	...	...	...	...	...	...	9 a54	2 p20	...	...	...	8 p20	...		1 a41	...	4 p38
TURIN ...270 arr	...	...		...	...	...	...	...	...	...	2 p5	7 p7	...	...	...	12 a5	...		5 a50	...	8 p49
TURIN ...269 dep	...	...		...	...	...	...	...	...	...	3 p5	8 p0	...	...	...	...	...	Chambery arr. 7.46 p.m.	6 a35	...	
MILAN ...269 arr	...	...		...	...	...	...	...	...	...	5 p55	10p57	...	...	...	...	...		9 a10	...	
" ...280 dep	...	...	12p25	...	...	...	...	...	...	...	6 p20	11p25	...	...	...	...	...		9 a45	...	
VENICE ...280 arr	...	...	4 p40	...	...	...	...	...	...	...	11p30	4 a19	...	...	...	...	...		2 p15	...	
MILAN ...280 dep	...	...	12p25	...	...	...	...	...	...	...	...	...	...	...	...	...	...		...	...	
MESTRE ...280 arr	...	...	4 p20	...	...	...	...	...	...	...	...	...	...	...	...	...	...		...	...	
CORMONS ...285A arr	...	...	7 p20	...	...	...	...	...	...	...	...	...	...	...	...	...	...		...	...	
TRIESTE ...234 arr	...	...	9 p0	...	...	...	...	...	...	...	...	...	...	...	...	...	...		...	...	
TURIN ...270 dep	...	...	...	...	...	...	...	...	...	...	3 p0	8 p10	...	...	...	...	...		6 a25	...	
ALESSANDRIA ...270 arr	...	...	...	...	...	...	...	...	...	...	4 p29	9 p39	...	...	...	...	...		7 a45	...	
GENOA ...270 arr	...	...	...	...	...	...	...	...	...	...	6 p30	11p25	...	...	...	...	...		9 a35	...	
SPEZIA ...270 arr	...	...	...	...	...	...	...	...	...	...	10 p0	1 a50	...	...	...	...	...	...	11a53	...	
PISA ...270 arr	...	...	...	...	...	...	...	...	...	...	11p44	3 a17	...	...	...	...	...	...	1 p19	...	
PISA ...270A dep	...	...	...	...	...	...	...	...	...	...	12a23	3 a42	...	...	...	...	...	...	1 p36	...	
FLORENCE 270A arr	...	...	...	...	...	...	...	...	...	...	1 a50	5 a44	...	...	...	...	...	...	3 p12	...	
PISA ...270 dep	...	...	...	...	...	...	...	...	...	...	12 a5	3 a26	...	...	...	...	...	...	1 p33	...	
ROME ...270 arr	...	...	...	...	...	...	...	...	...	...	7 a0	9 a30	...	...	...	...	...	...	7 p15	...	
ROME ...276 dep	...	...	...	7 a30	...	...	...	...	7 a30	...	7 a30	10 a0	...	...	...	...	...	...	8 p0	...	
NAPLES ...276 arr	...	...	...	12 p5	...	...	...	...	12 p5	...	12 p5	2 p10	...	...	...	...	...	...	12 0	...	
TURIN ...270 dep	...	...	...	...	...	...	...	...	...	...	3 p0	...	...	...	...	...	...	...	7 a15	...	9 p15
ALESSANDRIA ...270 arr	...	...	...	...	...	...	...	...	...	...	4 p29	...	...	...	...	...	...	...	8 a42	...	10p44
PIACENZA ...273 arr	...	...	...	...	...	...	...	...	...	...	8 p25	...	...	...	...	...	...	...	10a50	...	12a28
BOLOGNA ...279 arr	...	...	...	...	...	...	...	...	...	...	11p41	...	...	...	...	...	...	...	1 p34	...	3 a2
BOLOGNA ...279 dep	...	...	...	...	...	...	...	...	...	...	12a31	...	...	...	...	...	...	...	2 p3	...	
FLORENCE ...279 arr	...	...	...	...	...	...	...	...	...	...	3 a26	...	...	...	...	...	...	...	5 p18	...	
ROME ...279 arr	...	...	...	...	...	...	...	...	...	...	8 a50	...	...	...	...	...	...	...	10p55	...	
BOLOGNA ...285 dep	...	...	...	...	...	...	...	...	...	...	12a30	...	...	...	...	...	...	...	2 p25	...	3 a18
ANCONA ...285 arr	...	...	...	...	...	...	...	...	...	...	3 a42	...	...	...	...	...	...	...	7 p43	...	6 a35
FOGGIA ...285 arr	...	...	...	...	...	...	...	...	...	...	10a10	...	...	...	...	...	...	...	...	...	1 p25
BRINDISI ...285 arr	...	...	...	...	...	...	...	...	...	...	2 p30	...	...	...	...	...	...	...	...	...	5 p54
☾—Arrival is at Piræus. BRINDISI (steamer) ...dep						nght 12 *0 Sun.		a.m. 1 †30 Tues.		p.m. 11†30 Wed.		p.m. 7 *0 Fri.		p.m. 11 ¶0 Sat.		...	...	...	...	...	
CORFU (steamer) ...arr						...		1 p30 ,,		10a30 Thur.		7 a15 Sat.		10 a0 Sun.		...	...	...	...	...	
PATRAS (steamer) ...arr						8 p0 Mon.		5 a0 Wed.		4 a0 Fri.		9 p45 ,,		5 a0 Mon		...	...	...	...	...	
ATHENS ...325 arr						☾7 a0 Tues.		4 p40 ,,		4 p40 ,,		☾9 a15 Sun.		4 p40 ,,		...	...	...	...	...	
BRINDISI ...dep (P. & O. Steamer, Sunday)							...	...	...	...	...	...	...	...	...	...	...	...	...	...	
PORT SAID arr (Tuesday night, 4th day from London)							...	...	...	...	...	...	...	...	...	...	...	...	...	...	12 0 nght
CAIRO 327 arr (Wednesday, 5th day from London)							...	...	...	...	...	...	...	...	...	...	...	...	...	...	5 p5

Peninsular & Oriental Express. on Friday in each week, leaving London by 9.0 p.m., in connection at Calais with a Special Train (Peninsular and Oriental Express), consisting of Sleeping Cars and a Restaurant Car running through direct to Brindisi. Special fare by this service.

☾—Norddeutscher Lloyd Steamer from Marseilles 10.30 a.m. or 3.0 p.m. on July 2nd, 9th, and 16th.

§—Messageries Maritimes Steamer from Marseilles on Friday (usual departure 12.0

*—Società Nazionale steamer.

†—Austrian Lloyd Steamer.

‡—Compagnie Générale Transatlantique or Cie. de Navigation Mixte.

¶—Greek Steamer.

The heavier figures refer to pages where the various sections of the routes may be traced in detail.

HOMEWARD SERVICES, see next page.

EGYPT, GREECE, ITALY, SWITZERLAND, AND THE MEDITERRANEAN TO LONDON.

	p.m.	p.m.	p.m.		a.m.						
ATHENS ....325 dep	1 0Mon.	1 0Tues.	1 0Thur.	†—Austrian Lloyd Steamer.	7 5 Fri.	...	...	...	...	...	...
PATRAS steamer ...dep	11p†0 „	11†p0 „	9‡p0Thur.	*—Società Nazionale Steamer.	7p30 „	...	...	...	...	...	...
CORFU steamer ......dep	4 p0Tues.	2 p30Wed.	4 p0 Fri.	‡—Greek Steamer.	...	...	...	...	...	...	...
BRINDISI steamer ...arr	3 a0Wed.	2 a30Thurs	4 a0Sat.		3p30 Sat.	...	...	...	...	...	...

1	2	3	4	5	6	7	8	9	10	11	12	13	14	15	16	17	18	19	20	21	22	23
		a.m.			p.m.									p.m.								
BRINDISI ......285A dep	...	6 35	...	...	12 5	...	...	...	...	...	...	...	...	5 25	...	...	...	...	...	...	...	...
FOGGIA ....285A dep	...	12 p5	...	...	4 p30	...	...	...	...	...	...	...	...	10p40	...	...	...	...	...	...	...	...
ANCONA ....285A dep	...	8 p45	...	...	11 p5	...	...	...	...	...	...	...	...	5 a15	...	...	...	...	...	...	...	...
BOLOGNA ......285A arr	...	12a45	...	...	2 a35	...	...	...	...	...	...	...	...	9 a57	...	...	...	...	...	...	...	...
ROME ....279B dep	...	6 p5	...	...	9 p5	...	...	...	...	...	...	...	...	11p50	...	...	...	...	...	...	...	...
FLORENCE ......279B dep	...	11p39	...	...	2 a15	...	...	...	...	...	...	...	...	6 a20	10a50	...	...	...	...	...	...	...
BOLOGNA ....279B arr	...	2 a42	...	...	5 a15	...	...	...	...	...	...	...	...	9 a34	2 p15	...	...	...	...	...	...	...
BOLOGNA ....279B dep	...	2 a55	...	...	5 a33	...	...	...	...	...	...	...	...	10a17	2 p38	...	...	...	...	...	...	...
PIACENZA ....279B arr	...	5 a20	...	...	8 a0	...	...	...	...	...	...	...	...	1 p0	5 p20	...	...	...	...	...	...	...
„ ....273 dep	...	5 a30	...	...	8 a15	...	...	...	...	...	...	...	...	1 p20	5 p35	...	...	...	...	...	...	...
ALESSANDRIA ....271 dep	...	7 a10	...	...	11a10	...	...	...	...	...	...	...	...	5 p24	9 p55	...	...	...	...	...	...	...
TURIN ....271 arr	...	8 a41	...	...	12p40	...	...	...	...	...	...	...	...	7 p0	11p25	...	...	...	...	...	...	...
NAPLES ....276 dep	3 p10	...	...	...	7 p30	...	...	...	...	...	...	...	...	...	4 a20	...	...	...	...	1 p45	1 p45	...
ROME................276 arr	8 p25	...	...	...	11p35	...	...	...	...	...	...	...	...	...	8 a20	...	...	...	...	5 p45	5 p45	...
ROME....................271 dep	...	...	...	...	11p55	...	...	...	...	...	...	...	...	...	9 a0	...	...	...	...	...	6 p15	...
PISA.......................271 arr	...	...	...	...	5 a45	...	...	...	...	...	...	...	...	...	2 p41	...	...	...	...	...	12a14	...
FLORENCE ...270A dep	...	...	...	...	3 a50	...	...	...	...	...	...	...	...	7 a30	11a50	...	...	...	...	...	9 p25	...
PISA ....270A arr	...	...	...	...	5 a46	...	...	...	...	...	...	...	...	8 a55	1 p46	...	...	...	...	...	11p40	...
PISA.......................271 dep	...	...	...	...	6 a5	...	...	...	...	...	...	...	...	9 a5	2 p55	...	...	...	...	...	12a27	...
SPEZIA ....271 dep	...	...	...	...	7 a53	...	...	...	...	...	...	...	...	11a24	4 p35	...	...	...	...	...	2 a7	...
GENOA ....271 dep	...	...	...	...	11a15	...	...	...	...	...	...	...	...	3 p5	8 p0	...	...	...	...	...	5 a0	...
ALESSANDRIA ......271 dep	...	...	...	...	1 p35	...	...	...	...	...	...	...	☞Runs from 2nd July.	5 p24	9 p55	...	...	Savoie Express, Train de Luxe, runs from 6th July until 14th Sept. ☞	...	...	7 a10	...
TURIN ....271 arr	...	...	...	...	3 p12	...	...	...	O	...	...	...		7 p0	11p25	...	...		...	...	8 a41	...
TRIESTE...................234 dep	...	...	...	...	...	...	...	...	7 a50	...	...	...		...	...	...	...		...	...	...	...
CORMONS ....285A dep	...	...	...	...	...	...	...	...	9 a25	...	...	...		...	...	...	...		...	...	...	...
MESTRE ....280 dep	...	...	...	...	...	...	...	...	12p21	...	...	...		...	...	...	...		...	...	...	...
MILAN.....................280 arr	...	...	...	...	...	...	...	...	4 p25	...	...	...		...	...	...	...		...	...	...	...
VENICE.................280 dep	...	...	...	...	8 a0	...	...	...	12 0	...	...	...		9 a30	2 p0	...	...		...	...	...	...
MILAN ....280 arr	...	...	...	...	12p25	...	...	...	4 p25	...	...	...		3 p7	6 p40	...	...		...	...	...	...
„ ....269 dep	...	...	...	...	12p50	...	...	...		...	...	...		4 p20	8 p50	...	...		...	...	4 a0	...
TURIN ....269 arr	...	...	...	...	3 p25	...	...	...	O	...	...	...		7 p15	11p50	...	...		...	...	7 a55	...
TURIN ....271 dep	...	...	...	...	4 p5	...	...	...		...	...	...		...	12a30	...	...		...	...	9 a10	...
MODANE ....61 dep	12p12	...	...	...	6 p40	...	...	...		...	...	...		...	3 a0	...	...		...	...	11a25	...
AIX-LES-BAINS...61 dep	3 p50	...	...	...	9 p25	...	...	...		...	...	10p47	11p46	...	5 a19	...	7 a7	10a48	...	...	2 p31	...
CULOZ ....61 arr	4 p18	...	...	...	9 p45	...	...	...		...	...	11 p9	12a10	...	5 a4[illegible]	...	7 a38	11a10	...	...	2 p56	...
MACON ....61 arr	8 p42	...	...	...		...	...	...		...	...			...		...	10a40		...	...		...
SAN REMO...............272 dep	5 a11	...	...	...		...	...	...		...	1 p28			...		...	...		11p49	...		...
BORDIGHERA ....272 dep	5 a35	...	...	...		...	...	...		...	1 p48			...		...	...		12a 8	...		...
MENTONE...................55 dep	5 a46	...	...	...		...	...	...		...	2 p30			...		3 p29	...		12a17	...		...
MONTE CARLO ....55 dep	6 a3	...	...	...		...	...	...		...	2 p48			...		3 p47	...		12a31	...		...
NICE ....55 dep	7 a2	...	...	...		...	...	...		...	3 p40			...		4 p44	...		1 a18	...		...
CANNES ....55 dep	7 a49	...	...	...		...	...	...		...	4 p25			...		5 p39	...		2 a3	...		...
ST. RAPHAEL............55 dep	8 a23	...	...	...		...	...	...		...	5 p1			...		6 p25	...		2 a36	...		...
HYERES....................55 dep	8 a41	...	...	...		...	...	...		...	4 p48			...		8 p17	...		...	...		...
TOULON ....55 dep	10a13	...	...	...		...	...	...		...	6 p46			...		9 p19	...		4 a23	...		...
MARSEILLES...........55 arr	11a25	...	...	...		...	...	...		...	7 p55			...		10p54	...		5 a38	...		...

NOTES.

F—The train from Marseilles at 3.41 p.m runs in connection with the incoming Bombay steamer. It leaves Marseilles (Quay de la Joliette only) on Sunday (possibly on Saturday), according to steamer arrival. The departure time from Marseilles is announced on board the steamer.

O—Simplon Express, Train de Luxe.

*—These departures from Interlaken, Berne, and Neuchatel are from July 9th until September 15th.

1	2	3	4	5	6	7	8	9	10	11	12	13	14	15	16	17	18	19	20	21	22	23
CAIRO ....327 dep	(Friday)			...		...	...	...		...	...			...		...	...		12 0	...		...
ALEXANDRIA stmr dep	(Wed.‡, & Sat.§)			...		...	...	...		...	...			...		...	...		2 p0	...		...
MARSEILLES............arr	...	...	...	...		...	...	...		...	—	‡		...		...	...		4 a0	...		...
ALGIERS steamer ...dep	...	...	...	...		...	...	...		...	12p30 Tues, Thurs, Fri, Sun					...	...		...	...		...
MARSEILLES stmr ...arr	...	...	...	...		...	...	...		...	1 p0 Wed., Fri., Sat., Mon.					...	...		...	...		...
MARSEILLES ....50 dep	11a50	...	...	...		...	3 p41	...		...	8 p10			...		11p28	...		9 a0	...		...
LYONS ....50 arr	6 p46	...	...	...		...		...		...	1 a9			...		6 a28	...		2 p19	...		...
LYONS ....50 dep	7 p40	...	8 p40	...		...		...		11p54	1 a19			...		7 a20	9 a39		2 p34	...		...
MACON ....51 arr	8 p51	...	9 p54	...		...		...		12a53	2 a13			...		8 a44	10a51		3 p33	...		...
GENEVA..................61 dep	3 p0	...	...	...		...		9 p10		...	...			...		...	6 a53	10a45	...	...	2 p30	...
CULOZ ....61 dep	4 p44	...	...	...	9 p55	...		10p34	O	...	...	11p15	12a28	...	5 a45	...	7 a59	11a26	...	...	3 p15	...
MACON ....61 arr	8 p42	...	...	...		...		12a31		...	...		...	...	...	...	10a40		...	...		...
MACON ....51 dep	9 p4	...	10 p2	...		...	F	12a41		12a58	2 a16		...	...	...	8 a52	10a59		3 p36	...		...
DIJON ....51 arr	11 p9	...	12a23	...		...		2 a22		2 a46	3 a52		4 a16	...	9 a36	11a13	1 p8	2 p41	5 p23	...	6 p31	...
INTERLAKEN ...267 dep	3 p38	...	...	6 p15		7 p45		...	9 p40	* ...	...		...	...	...	...	...		7 a40	11a35		...
BERNE ....259B dep	5 p40	...	...	8 p20		9 p25		...	11 p5	* ...	...		...	...	6 a40	...	6 a40		9 a19	2 p10		...
NEUCHATEL......266 dep	6 p43	...	...	9 p53		11 p7		...	12 a5	* ...	...		...	...	7 a30	...	8 a0		10a40	3 p13		...
ROME ....279B dep	9 p5	...	...	...		11p50		...		...	...		...	...	9 a5	...	...		...	6 p5		...
FLORENCE ...279B dep	2 a15	...	...	...		6 a20		...	O	...	...		...	...	2 p30	...	...		...	11p39		...
MILAN ....274 dep	10a50	...	...	...		3 p25		...	4 p30	...	...		...	...	11p45	...	...		...	8 a0		...
DOMODOSSOLA 263C dep	1 p42	...	...	...		6 p22		...	7 p15	...	...		...	...	2 a35	...	...		...	10a55		...
LAUSANNE ....263C dep	6 p53	...	...	9 p42		10p47		...	11p39	...	...		...	...	6 a42	...	6 a55		10 a0	3 p0		...
PONTARLIER ....52 dep	8 p15	...	...	11p20		12 a5		...	12a43	...	...		...	...	7 a56	...	9 a18		12p25	4 p25		...
DIJON ....52 arr	11p17	...	...	1 a39		2 a10		...	2 a30	...	...		...	...	9 a49	...	12p47		4 p44	6 p47		...
DIJON ....51 dep	11p37	...	12a42	1 a52	2 a4	2 a16		2 a28	2 a40	2 a52	3 a58	4 a10	4 a22	...	10 a1	11a40	1 p25	2 p47	5 p35	6 p56	6 p46	...
PARIS (P.L.M.) ......51 arr	4 a55	...	6 a0	6 a20	6 a35	6 a45		7 a0	7 a15	7 a23	8 a0	8 a12	8 a37	...	2 p25	5 p10	6 p8	6 p32	10 p0	11 p0	10 p50	...
PARIS (P.L.M.) ......dep	...	...	7 a5	7 a5	7 a5	7 a5		8 a47	8 a47	8 a47	8 a47	8 a47	...	...	3 p2	...	7 p23	7 p23	...	...	...	...
PARIS (Nord) .... arr	...	...	7 a43	7 a43	7 a43	7 a43		9 a21	9 a21	9 a21	9 a21	9 a21	...	...	3 p35	...	7 p59	7 p59	...	...	...	...
PARIS (Nord) ....19 dep	...	...	8 a25	8 a25	8 a25	8 a25		9 a50	9 a55	9 a50	9 a50	9 a50	...	...	4 p0	...	9 p20	9 p20	● 12a30	● 12a30	● 12a30	...
AMIENS.....................19 arr	...	...	...	...	...	...	9 a15	...	11a22	...	...	...	...	...	...	...	10p55	10p55	...	...	...	...
" ....19 dep	...	...	...	...	...	...		...	11a25	...	...	...	...	...	...	...	11 p0	11 p0	...	...	...	...
BOULOGNE ....19 dep	...	...	11a45	11a45	11a45	11a45		...	...	...	...	...	...	...	7 p10	...	...	...	...	...	...	...
FOLKESTONE ....dep	...	...	1 p40	1 p40	1 p40	1 p40	F	...	...	...	...	...	...	...	9 p5	...	...	...	...	...	...	...
CHARING CROSS ....arr	...	...	3 p25	3 p25	3 p25	3 p25		...	...	...	...	...	...	...	10p45	...	...	...	...	...	...	...
BOULOGNE ....19 dep	...	...	...	...	...	...		...	...	...	...	...	...	...	...	...	12a42	12a42	...	...	...	...
CALAIS (Pier)............19 arr	...	...	...	...	...	...	11a28	1 p5	1 p10	1 p5	1 p5	1 p5	...	...	...	...	1 a23	1 a23	6 a20	6 a20	6 a20	...
DOVER ....arr	...	...	...	...	...	...	2 p35	2 p35	2 p35	2 p35	2 p35	2 p35	...	...	...	...	2 a55	2 a55	...	...	...	...
DOVER ....dep	...	...	...	...	...	...	3 p20	3 p20	3 p20	3 p20	3 p20	3 p20	...	...	...	...	3 a45	3 a45	...	...	...	...
CHARING CROSS............arr	...	...	...	...	...	...	5 p10	5 p10	5 p10	5 p10	5 p10	5 p10	...	...	...	...	5 a43	5 a43	10a15	10a15	10a15	...
VICTORIA ....arr	...	...	...	...	...	...	...	...	...	...	...	...	...	...	...	...	...	...	...	...	...	...
PARIS (P.L.M.) ....dep	...	...	...	...	...	...	...	...	...	Via Pontoise 77 A	8 a51	...	...	...	...	...	7 p42	...	...	...	...	...
PARIS (St. Lazare)...77 dep	...	...	...	...	...	...	...	...	...		10 a0	...	...	...	...	...	9 p20	...	...	...	...	...
ROUEN ....77 dep	...	...	...	...	...	...	...	...	...		...	...	...	...	...	...	11p37	...	...	...	...	...
DIEPPE ....dep	...	...	...	...	...	...	...	...	...		1 p0	...	...	...	...	...	1 a25	...	...	...	...	...
NEWHAVEN ....arr	...	...	...	...	...	...	...	...	...		4 p40	...	...	...	...	...	5 a30	...	...	...	...	...
LONDON BRIDGE ....arr	...	...	...	...	...	...	...	...	...		...	...	...	...	...	...	7 a30	...	...	...	...	...
VICTORIA ....arr	...	...	...	...	...	...	...	...	...		6 p10	...	...	...	...	...	7 a30	...	...	...	...	...
PARIS (Ouest) ....77 dep	...	...	...	...	...	...	...	...	...		...	...	...	...	...	...	7 p48	On Weekdays only; also Sundays from July 27th.	...	...	...	...
ROUEN ....77 dep	...	...	...	...	...	...	...	...	...		...	...	...	...	...	...	9 p51		...	...	...	...
HAVRE ....dep	...	...	...	...	...	...	...	...	...	...	...	...	...	...	...	...	12 0		...	...	...	...
SOUTHAMPTON..............arr	...	...	...	...	...	...	...	...	...	...	...	...	...	...	...	...	...		...	...	...	...
WATERLOO ....arr	...	...	...	...	...	...	...	...	...	...	...	...	...	...	...	...	9 a0		...	...	...	...

PENINSULAR AND ORIENTAL EXPRESS, HOMEWARD SERVICE.—A Special Express Train composed of Restaurant & Sleeping Cars is despatched from Brindisi on the arrival of the P. & O. Steamer.

‡ — Norddeutscher Lloyd Steamer.

§-Messageries Maritimes Steamer.

●—Not from Paris on Saturday midnight

The heavier figures refer to pages where the various sections of the routes may be traced in detail.

LONDON TO THE VOSGES, BASLE, SWITZERLAND, ITALY—St. Gothard Route.

LONDON—					A		E
VICTORIA ....dep	11 a0	...	...	...	...	...	11 a0
CHARING CROSS ......dep	...	...	...	...	4 p30	...	...
DOVER ....dep	12p55	...	...	...	6 p15	...	12p55
CALAIS ....26 dep	2 p46	...	...	...	8 p10	...	2 p40
LILLE ....26 arr	4 p30	...	...	...	A	...	18 & 68A
DOUAI ....23 arr	5 p12	...		...	...	...	
ST. QUENTIN ....25 arr	6 p5	...		...	...	...	
LAON ....21 arr	7 p22	...		...	11p20	...	
CHARING CROSS ...dep	...	2 p5		...	...	...	Via Paris, see p.
FOLKESTONE ....dep	...	3 p55		...	...	...	
BOULOGNE ....18 dep	...	6 p8		...	...	...	
AMIENS ....18 arr	...	...		...	...	...	
TERGNIER ....21 arr	...	...		...	...	...	
LAON ....21 arr	...	9 p13		...	...	...	
LAON ....67 dep	7 p32	9 p23		...	11p25	...	
REIMS ¶ ....67 arr	8 p15	10p29		...	...	...	
CHALONS ....67 arr	9 p17	11p10		...	12a49	...	
CHALONS ....64A dep	9 p22	11p28		...	12a52	...	
CHAUMONT .... 66 arr	...	1 a15		...	2 a32	...	11 p9
MARTIGNY ......68A arr	...	4 a33		...	5 a24*	...	...
CONTREXEVILLE 68A arr	...	4 a48		...	5 a45*	...	...
VITTEL ....68A arr	...	4 a59		...	6 a0*	...	...
BELFORT ....68A arr	2 a45	3 a45	...	...	4 a45	...	1 a25
BELFORT ....68A dep	3 a20	3 a53	...	...	4 a50	...	...
BASLE ....207A arr	5 a58	6 a34	...	...	7 a58	...	...
BELFORT ....68A dep	2 a53	3 a55	Until 15th September.	...	...	...	1 a28
DELLE ....68A arr	3 a27	4 a21		...	...	...	1 a57
DELEMONT ....266 arr	5 a40	6 a35		...	...	...	
DELEMONT ......264A dep	5 a45	6 a36		...	...	...	
BIEL ....264A arr	6 a57	7 a50		...	...	...	
BERNE ....265 arr	7 a40	8 a35		...	...	...	
BERNE ...257 or 267 dep	8 a0	8 a50	...	...	...	...	
THUN ......257 or 267 arr	8 a33	9 a28	...	...	...	...	
INTERLAKEN 267 arr	9 a28	10a20	...	...	...	...	
DELEMONT ....264 dep	...	...	...	...	...	...	
BASLE ....264 arr	...	...	...	...	...	...	4 a45
BASLE ....261 dep	6 a45	6 a45	...	...	8 a26	...	5 a10
ZURICH ....261 arr	8 a35	8 a35	...	...	9 a58	...	6 a45
RAGAZ ....268B arr	10a59	10a59	...	...	12 p7	...	8 a59
COIRE ....268B arr	11a25	11a25	...	...	12p32	...	9 a25
" ....268B dep	11a55	11a55	...	...	1 p20	...	9 a35
ST. MORITZ ......268B arr	3 p17	3 p17	...	...	4 p20	...	12p25
BASLE ....258 dep	7 a0	7 a0	...	...	8 a25	...	5 a52
LUCERNE ....258 arr	8 a59	8 a59	...	...	10a48	...	7 a50

¶—For Reims change at the "halte" of Betheny.

LONDON—		a.m.	a.m.		p.m.	p.m.								
CHARING CROSS ......dep	...	9 0	9 0	...	2 5	9 0	...	...	...	...	...	...	...	...
DOVER ....dep	...	11 a5	...	...	...	11 p5		...	...	...	...	...	...	...
CALAIS ....26 dep	...	12p53	...	...	...	1 a19		...	...	...	...	...	...	...
BRUSSELS Nord 103 arr	...	4 p41	...	...	11‡14	5 a21		...	...	...	...	...	...	...
DOVER ....dep	...	...	11 a0	...	4 p30	11 p0		...	...	...	...	...	...	...
OSTEND ....102 dep	...	...	4 p20	...	8 p47	3 a42		...	...	...	...	...	...	...
BRUSSELS Nord 102 arr	...	...	6 p3	...	10p31	5 a24		...	...	...	...	...	...	...
BRUSSELS Nord 103A dep	...	6 p35		...	11p28	6 a8	...	...	...	...	...	...	...	...
LUXEMBURG ......103A arr	...	12 a3		...	4 a55	11a36	...	...	...	...	...	...	...	...
" ....210 dep	...	12a11		...	5 a3	11a41	...	...	...	...	...	...	...	...
METZ ....210 arr	...	1 a5		...	6 a3	12p44	...	...	...	...	...	...	...	...
STRASSBURG ....210 arr	...	3 a27		...	8 a44	3 p19	...	...	...	...	...	...	...	...
" ....208 dep	...	3 a35		...	9 a14	3 p26	...	...	...	...	...	...	...	...
BASLE ....208 arr	...	5 a43		...	11a15	5 p36	...	...	...	...	...	...	...	...

‡—Via Boulogne.

A—Not on Sunday from London.

B—From London on Friday night only.

E—Engadine Express, Train de Luxe, running until 14th September.

*—These arrivals are on Wednesday and Saturday only.

	B
CHARING CROSS ......dep	9 p0
DOVER ....arr	10p40
DOVER ....dep	11 p5
CALAIS ....18 dep	12a58
AMIENS ....18 arr	2 a51
" ....21 dep	2 a55
LAON ....21 arr	4 a16
REIMS ¶ ....67 arr	5 a12
" ....67 dep	10p40
CHALONS ....67 arr	5 a46
" ....64 dep	5 a50
CHAUMONT ....66 arr	7 a37
MARTIGNY ......68A arr	12p16
CONTREXEVILLE 68A arr	12p31
VITTEL ....68A arr	12p43
CHAUMONT ....68 dep	7 a43
BELFORT ....68 arr	10 a0
" ....68 dep	10 a5
BASLE ....207A arr	12p42

BRINDISI ...285A dep	...	...	12 p5	...	...	5 p25	...	...	5 p25	...
FOGGIA ......285A dep	...	...	4 p30	...	...	10p40	...	...	10p40	...
ANCONA ......285A dep	...	...	11 p5	...	...	5 a15	...	...	5 a15	...
BOLOGNA ...285A arr	...	...	2 a35	...	...	9 a57	...	...	9 a57	...
NAPLES ......276 dep	4 a20	4 a20	1 p45	3p10	3 p10	6 p0	...	3 p10	6 p0	...
ROME ....276 arr	8 a20	8 a20	5 p45	8p25	8 p25	10p50	...	8 p25	10p50	...
ROME ....279B dep	9 a5	9 a5	6 p5	9 p5	9 p5	11p50	...	9 p5	11p50	...
FLORENCE ...279B dep	2 p30	2 p30	11p39	2a15	2 a15	6 a20	...	2 a15	6 a20	...
BOLOGNA ......279B dep	6 p8	6 p8	2 a55	5a33	5 a33	10a17	...	5 a33	10a17	...
MILAN ....279B arr	9 p45	9 p45	6 a45	9a10	9 a10	2 p25	...	9 a10	2 p25	...
NAPLES ......276 dep	4 a20	4 a20	7a45	1p45	3 p10	6 p0	...	3 p10	6 p0	...
ROME ....276 arr	8 a20	8 a20	11a55	5p45	8 p25	10p50	...	8 p25	10p50	...
ROME ....271 dep	9 a0	9 a0	2 p0	6 p15	9 p0	11p55	...	9 p0	11p55	...
PISA ....271 arr	2 p41	2 p41	9p41	12a14	2 a40	5 a45	...	2 a40	5 a45	...
FLORENCE ......270A dep	11a50	11a50	8p15	9p25	9 p40	3 a50	...	9 p40	3a50	...
PISA ....270A arr	1 p46	1 p46	9p50	11p40	11p38	5 a46	...	11p38	5 a46	...
PISA ....271 dep	2 p55	2 p55	10p 5	12a27	2 a56	6 a5	...	2 a56	6 a5	...
SPEZIA ....271 dep	4 p25	4 p25	11p45	2 a7	4 a25	7 a53	...	4 a25	7 a53	...
GENOA ....271 arr	7 p10	7 p10	2 a9	4a15	6 a45	10a35	...	6 a45	10a35	...
" ....269A dep	7 p45	7 p45	2a40	5a50	8 a20	11a10	...	8 a20	11a10	...
MILAN ....269A arr	10p55	10p55	6 a50	9 a5	11a55	1 p55	...	11a55	1 p55	...
VENICE ....280 dep	6 p10	6 p10	12a10	...	8 a0	...	...	8 a0	...	...
MILAN ....280 arr	11p20	11p20	6 a10	...	12p25	...	...	12p25	...	...
MILAN ....269A dep	11p35	11p35	7 a25	9 a35	12p40	2 p40	...	12p40	2 p40	...
COMO ....269A dep	12a37	12a37	8 a26	10a42	1 p36	3 p42	...	1 p36	3 p42	...
CHIASSO ....269A arr	12a45	12a45	8 a35	10a50	1 p44	3 p50	...	1 p44	3 p50	...
" ....259A dep	1 a5	1 a5	8 a50	11a10	1 p54	4 p4	...	1 p54	4 p4	...
LUCERNE ....259A arr	6 a40	6 a40	1 p51	4 p44	6 p50	9 p0	...	6 p50	9 p0	...
" ....258 dep	7 a0	7 a0	2 p2	4 p57	7 p0	9 p10	...			...
BASLE ....258 arr	8 a57	8 a57	4 p6	6 p58	9 p0	11 p3	...			...
BASLE Swiss Sta. dep	10 a0	9 a25	5 p7	...	9 p20	...	...			...
" Baden Sta. dep	10a42	9 a50	5 p18	...	9 p41	...	...			...
CARLSRUHE ...141 dep	1p57	12p33	8 p9	...	12a28	...	...			...
MANNHEIM ...141 arr	2p44	1 p19	9 p13	...	1 a15	...	...			...
MAYENCE ......139 arr	3p59	2 p51	11 p5	...	2 a28	...	...			...
MAYENCE ...123A dep	4 p2	2 p54	12 a2	...	2 a28	...	...			...
COLOGNE ...123B arr	7 p7	6 p5	5 a9	...	5 a42	...	...			...
BASLE ....209 dep	10a14	...	...	...	9 p33	...	...			...
STRASSBURG ..209 dep	12p17	...	...	...	11p41	...	...			...
NEUSTADT ......209 arr	1 p52	...	...	...	1 a10	...	...			...
BINGERBR'K 125A arr	3 p31	...	...	...	2 a46	...	...			...
BINGERBR'K 123A dep	3 p40	...	...	...	2 a51	...	...			...
COLOGNE ...123A arr	6 p5	...	...	...	5 a21	...	...			...
COLOGNE ...161 dep	7 p14	...	...	...	5 a47	...	...			...
OBERHAUSEN 131A dep	...	...	...	...	7 a2	...	...			...
WESEL ....120 dep	...	...	...	...	7 a28	...	...			...
BOXTEL ....117 dep	9 p57	...	...	...	8 a42	...	...			...
FLUSHING ......113 arr	11p52	...	...	...	10a45	...	...			...
FOLKESTONE ......arr	5 a30	...	...	...	...	...	...			...
QUEENBOROUGH ..arr	...	...	...	...	5 p55	...	...			...
HOLBORN VDT. arr	7 a48	...	...	...	7 p34	...				...
VICTORIA ...... arr	7 a48	...	...	...	7 p34	...	...			...
COLOGNE ...120A dep	...	7 p21	...	...	...	...	...			...
NYMEGEN ...120A arr	...	9 p1	...	...	...	...	...			...
NYMEGEN ...119A dep	...	9 p26	...	...	...	...	...			...
ROTTERDAM 119A arr	...	11p10	...	...	...	...	...			...
HOEK V. HOL. 112 arr	...	11p35	...	...	...	...	...			...
HARWICH ....arr	...	6 a20	...	...	...	...	...			...
LIVERPOOL STR. ...	[illegible]	[illegible]								

LONDON													
VICTORIA ....dep	...	...	...	10 a0	...	8 p30	...	...	§—Via Goch, page 121.	...	...	...	...
HOLBORN VIAD'T dep	...	...	...	9 a55	...	8 p25	...	...		...	...	...	...
QUEENBOROUGH dep	...	...	...	11a30	...	...	...	...		...	...	...	...
FOLKESTONE ......dep	...	...	...	...	...	10p35	...	...		...	...	...	...
FLUSHING ......113 dep	...	...	...	7 p0	...	4 a20	...	...		...	...	...	...
BOXTEL ....116 arr	...	...	...	8 p57	...	6 a10	...	...		...	...	...	...
WESEL ....120 arr	...	...	...	11p44	...	...	...	...		...	...	...	...
OBERHAUSEN ...131A	...		...	12a11	...	§	...	...		...	...	...	...
COLOGNE ...160C arr	...	...	...	1 a50	...	9 a56	...	...	...	...	...	...	...
LONDON L'pool St. dp	...	...	...	...	...	...	...	8 p30	...	...	...	...	...
HARWICH...........dep	...	...	...	...	...	...	...	10 p0	...	...	...	...	...
HOEK V. HOL. 112 dep	...	...	...	...	...	...	...	5 a18	...	...	...	...	...
ROTTERDAM 119 dep	...	...	...	...	...	...	...	⋮	...	...	...	...	...
NYMEGEN ......119 arr	...	...	...	...	...	...	...	7 a33	...	...	...	...	...
NYMEGEN ......121 dep	...	...	...	...	...	...	...	7 a35	...	...	...	...	...
COLOGNE......121 arr	...	...	...	...	...	...	...	11a15	...	...	...	...	...
COLOGNE......122 dep	...	...	...	...	...	10 a3	...	11a20	...	...	...	...	...
BINGERBR'K...122 arr	...	...	...	...	...	12p33	...	1 p47	...	...	...	...	...
BINGERBR'K...125 dep	...	...	...	...	...	12p39	...	1 p56	...	...	...	...	...
NEUSTADT......208 dep	...	...	...	...	...	2 p15	...	4 p30	...	...	...	...	...
STRASSBURG ..208 arr	...	...	...	...	...	3 p48	...	6 p17	...	...	...	...	...
BASLE ....208 arr	...	...	...	...	...	5 p47	...	8 p20	...	...	...	...	...
COLOGNE......122 dep	...	...	...	1 a58	...	...	...	11a20	...	...	...	...	...
MAYENCE ......122 arr	...	...	...	5 a25	...	...	...	2 p22	...	...	...	...	...
MAYENCE ......139 dep	...	...	...	5 a30	...	...	...	2 p32	...	...	...	...	...
MANNHEIM ...140 dep	...	...	...	7 a10	...	...	...	3 p51	...	...	...	...	...
CARLSRUHE 140A arr	...	...	...	8 a1	...	...	...	4 p39	...	...	...	...	...
BASLE Baden Sta. ar	...	...	...	11 a0	...	...	...	7 p56	...	...	...	...	...
„ Swiss Sta. arr	...	...	...	11a21	...	...	...	8 p20	...	...	...	...	...
BASLE ....258 dep	7 a0	7 a0	7 a30	12 p2	12 p2	6 p10	...	9 p45	...	...	...	...	...
LUCERNE ....258 arr	8 a59	8 a59	9 a28	1 p56	1 p56	8 p15	...	11p42	...	...	...	...	...
„ ....259 dep	9 a8	9 a8	9 a47	2 p22	2 p22	...	...	11p52	...	...	...	...	...
CHIASSO..............259 arr	1 p54	1 p54	3 p20	7 p19	7 p19	...	...	5 a5	...	...	...	...	...
„ ....269A dep	2 p5	2 p5	3 p38	7 p40	7 p40	...	...	5 a20	...	...	...	...	...
COMO ....269A arr	2 p11	2 p11	3 p44	7 p46	7 p46	...	...	5 a26	...	...	...	...	...
MILAN ....269A arr	3 p5	3 p5	4 p40	8 p40	8 p40	...	...	6 a22	...	...	...	...	...
MILAN ....280 dep	6 p20	6 p20	6 p20	11p25	11p25	...	...	7 a5	...	...	...	...	...
VENICE.........280 arr	11p30	11p30	11p30	4 a19	4 a19	...	...	11a25	...	...	...	...	...
MILAN .... 269A dep	3 p35	3 p35	5 p0	8p55	8p55	...	...	6 a40	...	...	...	...	...
GENOA.................269A arr	6 p45	6 p45	8 p20	12a10	12a10	...	...	9 a20	...	...	...	...	...
„ ....270 dep	7 p10	7 p10	10p25	12a25	12a25	...	...	9 a45	...	...	...	...	...
SPEZIA ....270 arr	10 p0	10 p0	12a50	3a31	3a31	...	...	11a53	...	...	...	...	...
PISA...................270 arr	11p44	11p44	2 a28	5a43	5a43	...	...	1 p19	...	...	...	...	...
PISA ....270A dep	12a23	12a23	3 a42	6 a2	6 a2	...	...	1 p36	...	...	...	...	...
FLORENCE ...270A arr	1 a50	1 a50	5 a44	8 a7	8 a7	...	...	3 p12	...	...	...	...	...
PISA...................270 dep	12 a5	12 a5	2 a35	...	...	...	...	1 p33	...	...	...	...	...
ROME.................270 arr	7 a0	7 a0	8 a40	...	...	...	...	7 p15	...	...	...	...	...
ROME............276 dep	7 a30	7 a30	10 a0	...	...	...	...	8 p0	...	...	...	...	...
NAPLES ......276 arr	12 p5	12 p5	2 p10	...	...	...	...	12 0	...	...	...	...	...
MILAN ....279 dep	3 p30	3 p30	9 p0	9 p0	9 p0	...	...	7 a0	...	...	...	...	...
BOLOGNA ....279 arr	7 p0	7 p0	12a12	12a12	12a12	...	...	10a12	...	...	...	...	...
FLORENCE ......279 arr	11p16	11p16	3 a26	3 a26	3 a26	...	...	1 p25	...	...	...	...	...
ROME...............279 arr	6 a45	6 a45	8 a50	8 a50	8 a50	...	...	6 p55	...	...	...	...	...
ROME............276 dep	7 a30	7 a30	10 a0	10 a0	10 a0	...	...	8 p0	...	...	...	...	...
NAPLES ......276 arr	12 p5	12 p5	2 p10	2 p10	2 p10	...	...	12 0	...	...	...	...	...
BOLOGNA ......285 dep	7 p25	7 p25	12a30	12a30	12a30	...	...	10a25	...	...	...	...	...
ANCONA.........285 arr	11p13	11p13	3 a42	3 a42	3 a42	...	...	2 p55	...	...	...	...	...
FOGGIA ....285 arr	6 a0	6 a0	10a10	10a10	10a10	...	...	10p23	...	...	...	...	...
BRINDISI.......285 arr	11a50	11a50	2 p30	2 p30	2 p30	...	...	...	...	...	...	...	...

BASLE ....209 dep	10a22	...	...	7 p32	...	11p40	...	...	...	...
STRASSBURG ....209 arr	12p25	...	...	9 p50	...	1 a34	...	...	...	...
„ ....210A dep	12p33	...	...	10 p5	...	1 a40	...	...	...	...
METZ ....210A dep	3 p4	...	...	12a37	...	4 a0	...	...	...	...
LUXEMBURG ....210A arr	4 p8	...	...	1 a44	...	5 a1	...	...	...	...
„ ....103B dep	4 p24	...	...	1 a50	...	5 a7	...	...	...	...
BRUSSELS Nord 103B arr	8 p11	...	...	5 a26	...	8 a28	...	...	...	...
BRUSSELS Nd. 102A dep	8 p40	...	...	...	...	8 a46	...	...	...	...
OSTEND ....102A arr	10p26	...	...	...	...	10a29	...	...	...	...
DOVER ....arr	2 a15	...	...	...	...	2 p0	...	...	...	...
BRUSSELS Nord 103 dep	...	...	...	8 a30	...	...	10a58	...	...	...
CALAIS....................27 arr	...	...	...	1 p0	...	...	3 p21	...	...	...
DOVER ....arr	...	...	...	2 p45	...	...	5 p0	...	...	...
VICTORIA ....arr	...	...	...	...	...	...	7 p5	...	...	...
CHARING CROSS.........arr	5 a43	...	...	5 p10	...	5 p10	...	...	...	E

BASLE ....207A dep	9 a40
BELFORT................69 arr	10a17
BELFORT................69 dep	10a21
CHAUMONT ....69 arr	12p38
VITTEL ....69A dep	8‡27
CONTREXEVILLE 69A dep	8‡39
MARTIGNY ......69A dep	8‡54
CHAUMONT ....66 dep	12p43
CHALONS ....65 arr	2 p24
CHALONS ....67 dep	2 p35
REIMS ....67 dep	2 p58
LAON ....67 arr	4 p0
LAON ....21 dep	4 p5
TERGNIER ....21 dep	4 p29
AMIENS ....19 dep	5 p33
BOULOGNE..........19 arr	7 p2
FOLKESTONE ....dep	9 p5
CHARING CROSS......arr	10p45

LUCERNE ......258 dep	...	7 p0	9 p10	10p13
BASLE ....258 arr	...	9 p0	11 p3	12a10
ST. MORITZ ......268C dep	...	11a20	3 p5	4 p30
COIRE ....268C arr	...	2 p10	6 p5	7 p18
COIRE ....268C dep	...	3 p5	6 p20	7 p30
RAGAZ..................268C dep	...	3 p29	6 p46	7 p55
ZURICH ....261 dep	...	6 p40	9 p12	10 p5
BASLE ....261 arr	...	8 p28	10p58	11p45
BASLE ....264A dep	...	...	11p33	12a30
DELEMONT..........264A arr	...	...	12a18	...
INTERLAKEN 267 dep	...	5 p58	7 p45	...
THUN ....267 dep	...	6 p50	9 p46	...
BERNE ....267 arr	...	7 p23	10p18	...
BERNE ....266 dep	...	7 p43	10p38	...
BIEL ....266 arr	...	8 p20	11p18	...
BIEL......................264 dep	...	8 p22	11p21	...
DELEMONT ....264 arr	...	9 p32	⋮	...
DELEMONT ....266 dep	...	9 p35	12a20	...
DELLE ....69 dep	...	9 p25	12a48	1 a50
BELFORT..................69 arr	...	10 p0	1 a13	2 a29
BASLE ....207A dep	...	9 p25	...	...
BELFORT ....69 arr	...	10 p2	...	...
BELFORT.................69 dep	...	10 p9	1 a23	2 a42
CHAUMONT..............69 arr	...	12a15	...	5 a0
VITTEL ....69A dep	...	9 p0	...	...
CONTREXEVILLE 69A dep	...	9 p10	...	...
MARTIGNY........69A dep	...	9 p24	...	...
CHAUMONT ....66 dep	...	12a20	...	5 a5
CHALONS..................65 arr	...	1 a55	6 a25	...
CHALONS ....67 dep	...	1 a58	6 a27	...
REIMS ....67 dep	...	...	6 a47	...
LAON.........................67 arr	...	3 a15	7 a30	...
LAON.....................21 dep	...	...	7 a53	...
TERGNIER ....21 arr	...	...	8 a11	E
AMIENS.................19 dep	...	...	9 a12	...
BOULOGNE..........19 arr	...	...	10a57	...
FOLKESTONE ....dep	...	...	1 p40	...
CHARING CROSS......arr	...	...	3 p25	...
LAON.........................21 dep	...	3 a20	8 a0	...
ST. QUENTIN ....24 arr	...	...	8 a46	...
DOUAI ....23 dep	...	...	10a13	...
LILLE ....27 dep	...	...	11a31	...
CALAIS ....27 arr	... §	6 a45	1 p0	1 p10
DOVER ....arr	...	...	2 p35	2 p35
CHARING CROSS.........arr	... §	10a15	5 p10	5 p10

‡—On Wednesday and Saturday Vittel depart 10.12, Contrexeville dep. 10.22, Martigny dep. 10.37.

E—Engadine Express, runs from 2nd July until 15th September.

§—Not arrive at Calais nor London on Sunday.

LONDON TO BORDEAUX, ARCACHON, PAU, SPAIN, AND PORTUGAL.

LONDON—		a.m.		Cote d'Argent Express, Train de Luxe.			
VICTORIA .... dep	...	11 0	...	...	...	...	...
CHARING CROSS .... dep	...	...	...	...	...	9 p0	...
DOVER .... arr	...	12p45	...	...	...	10p40	...
DOVER .... dep	...	12p55	...	...	...	11 p5	...
CALAIS (Pier) ...... 18 dep	...	2 p50	...	...	...	1 a30	...
BOULOGNE .... 18 arr	...	⋮	...	...	...,	2 a12	...
CHARING CROSS ...... dep	...	⋮	...		2 p5	...	...
FOLKESTONE .... dep	...	⋮	...		3 p55	...	...
BOULOGNE .... 18 dep	...	⋮	...		6 p2	2 a12	...
AMIENS .... 18 arr	...	4 p47	...		...	3 a54	...
„ .... 18 dep	...	4 p50	...		...	3 a59	...
PARIS Nord .... 18 arr	...	6 p20	...		9 p0	5 a40	...
LONDON—							
L. B. & S. C. Ry. VICTORIA .... dep	...	10 a6	...		...	8 p45	...
LONDON BRIDGE dep	...	...	...		...	8 p45	...
NEWHAVEN ...... dep	...	11a30	...		...	10p25	...
DIEPPE .... 76 dep	...	3 p11	...		...	3 a5	...
PARIS St. Lazare ... 76 arr	...	6 p3	...		...	6 a3	...
	A						
	p.m.	p.m.	p.m.	p.m.	p.m.	a.m.	a.m.
PARIS Quai Orsay 34 dep	12 16	7 38	8 15	9 0	10 10	7 50	9 46
„ Quai Austerlitz 34 dep	12p26	7 p48	8 p27	9 p10	10p21	8 a0	9 a56
POITIERS .... 34 arr	4 p16	12a20	12a59	1 a23	2a53	1 p0	2 p3
BORDEAUX .... 35 arr	7 p9	3 a43	5 a5	4 a27	6a58	4 p49	5 p7
BORDEAUX ...... 45A dep	7 p35	...	6 a32	...	7 a33	5 p15	5 p15
ARCACHON ...... 45A arr	9 p14	...	8 a2	...	8 a51	6 p11	6 p11
BORDEAUX .... 45 dep	7 p19	4 a0	...	4 a37	8 a23	...	5 p26
DAX .... 45 arr	9 p7	6 a9	...	6 a30	10a39	...	7 p47
DAX .... 45 dep	...	6 a42	...	6 a42	10a51	...	7 p55
PAU .... 44 arr	...	7 a59	...	7 a59	12p25	...	9 p25
DAX .... 45 dep	9 p12	6 a22	...	6 a37	10a45	...	7 p56
BAYONNE .... 45 arr	9 p49	7 a3	...	7 a18	11a26	...	8 p37
BIARRITZ .... 45 arr	10p10	7 a29	...	7 a48	11a58	...	9 p5
IRUN .... 45 arr	11 p5	8 a10	...	8 a25	12p41	...	9 p48
IRUN .... 291A dep	11p40	8 a42	...	...	2 p35	...	...
SAN SEBASTIAN ... 291A arr	12a 2	9 a 3	...	...	3 p 4	...	...
BURGOS .... 291A arr	6 a2	3 p16	...	...	10p24	...	...
MEDINA .... 291A arr	9 a7	6 p21	...	...	1 a42	...	...
EL ESCORIAL ...... 291A arr	1 p16	...	...	...	5 a57	...	...
MADRID .... 291A arr	2 p12	10p58	...	...	7 a0	...	...
MEDINA .... 290A dep	9 a17	6p38	...	...	2 a20	...	...
SALAMANCA ... 290A arr	11 a1	9 p0	...	...	4 a33	...	...
VILLAR FORMOS. 299 arr	2 p11	1a39	...	...	...	...	...
PAMPILHOSA ... 301 arr	6 p58	9a25	...	...	5 p0	...	...
ENTRONCAM'TO 300 arr	9 p21	12p46	...	...	10 p4	...	...
LISBON .... 300 arr	10p52	2p31	...	...	11p53	...	...

		Cote d'Argent Express.				A
LISBON .... 300 dep	9 p55	...	...	6 p55	...	11a39
ENTRONCA'TO 300 dep	12a36	...	...	8 p21	...	12p55
PAMPILHOSA 301 dep	10a40		...	11p15	...	2 p52
VILLAR FORM. 299 dep	4 p46		...	6 a23	...	7 p51
SALAMANCA 290A dep	10p10		...	11 a2	...	11p11
MEDINA ...... 290A arr	12a23		...	1 p31	...	12a55
						A
MADRID .... 291 dep	9 p0		...	9 a15	...	8 p0
EL ESCORIAL ... 291 dep	10p15		...	...	...	9 p13
MEDINA .... 291 dep	2 a10		...	1 p48	...	1 a14
BURGOS .... 291 dep	5 a37		...	5 p3	...	4 a20
SAN SEBASTIAN 291 dep	11a32		...	10p37	...	9 a28
IRUN .... 291 arr	12 0		...	11 p0	...	9 a51
IRUN .... 291 dep	12p10		8 p12	11 p3	...	9 a53
BIARRITZ .... 45 dep	3 p8	9 p15	9 p41	12a48	6 a33	11 a9
BAYONNE .... 45 dep	3 p46	9 p55	10p15	1 a31	7 a17	11a31
DAX .... 45 arr	4 p30	10p36	10p58	2 a20	8 a7	12 p9
PAU .... 44 dep	3 p7	9 p27	9 p27	...	6 a55	9 a36
DAX .... 45 arr	4 p24	10p36	10p36	...	8 a10	12 0
DAX .... 45 dep	4 p40	10p46	11 p8	2 a30	8 a19	12p14
BORDEAUX .... 45 arr	6 p53	12a35	1 a10	5 a17	10a45	1 p58
ARCACHON ... 45A dep	5 p43	9 p27	9 p27	...	9 a20	12p40
BORDEAUX ... 45A arr	6 p42	11p13	11p13	...	10a27	1 p42
BORDEAUX ...... 35A dep	7 p45	12a41	1 a22	6 a0	11 a4	2 p. 3
POITIERS .... 35A dep	11p39	...	4 a51	9 a35	2 p6	4 p58
PARIS Austerlitz 35B arr	4 a46	8 a5	9 a27	2 p6	6 p7	8 p45
„ Quay Orsay 35B arr	4 a56	8 a15	9 a36	2 p15	6 p16	8 p54
PARIS Nord ...... 19 dep	8 a25	...	9 a50	4 p0	9 p20	12a30
AMIENS .... 19 arr	...	...	⋮	...	10p55	...
„ .... 19 dep	...	...	⋮	...	11 p0	...
BOULOGNE .... 19 arr	11a25	...	⋮	6 p58	⋮	B
FOLKESTONE ...... dep	1 p40	...	⋮	9 p5	⋮	...
CHARING CROSS ... arr	3 p25	...	⋮	10p45	⋮	...
BOULOGNE .... 19 dep	...	...	⋮	...	⋮	...
CALAIS (Pier) ...... 19 arr	...	...	1 p5	...	1 a23	6 a20
DOVER .... arr	...	...	2 p35	...	2 a55	...
DOVER .... dep	...	...	3 p20	...	8 a45	...
CHARING CROSS ...... arr	...	...	5 p10	...	5 a43	10a15
PARIS St. Lazare 77 dep	...	...	10 a0	...	9 p20	...
DIEPPE .... dep	...	...	1 p0	...	1 a25	...
NEWHAVEN .... arr	...	...	4 p40	...	5 a30	...
LONDON BRIDGE ... arr	...	...	...	...	7 a30	...
VICTORIA .... arr	...	...	6 p10	...	7 a30	...

Transit across Paris.—Tickets from London for Stations on the Orleans Railway, and beyond, contain a Coupon for the Omnibus drive from the Gare du Nord or from St. Lazare to the Quai d'Orsay Station.

A—Sud Express.—Tickets to be taken in advance of Sleeping Car Co., 20, Cockspur Street, London, S.W.

B—The 12.30 night service from Paris does not run from Paris on Saturday night.

LONDON TO NANCY AND METZ, VIA SEDAN.

LONDON—	a.m.		
CHARING CROSS .... dep	9 0	...	...
DOVER .... dep	11 a5	...	...
CALAIS .... 26 dep	12p50	...	...
LILLE .... 26 arr	...	...	...
VALENCIENNES .... 29A arr	3 p1	...	...
AULNOYE .... 29A arr	3 p40	...	...
HIRSON .... 29A arr	4 p30	...	...
MEZIERES-CHARLEVILLE .... 71 arr	5 p44	...	...
SEDAN .... 70 arr	6 p14	...	...
LONGUYON .... 70 arr	7 p22	...	...
NANCY .... 72 arr	9 p30	...	...
METZ .... 210 arr	10p55	...	...

METZ .... 210A dep	8 a42	...	...
NANCY .... 72 dep	7 a42	...	...
LONGUYON .... 71 dep	9 a47	...	...
SEDAN .... 71 dep	10a53	...	...
MEZIERES-CHARLEVILLE .... 71 dep	11a18	...	...
HIRSON .... 71 dep	12p29	...	...
AULNOYE .... 29A dep	1 p10	...	...
VALENCIENNES .... 29A dep	1 p39	...	...
LILLE .... dep	...	...	...
CALAIS .... 27 arr	3 p31	...	...
DOVER .... arr	5 p0	...	...
LONDON-VICTORIA .... arr	7 p5	...	...

The heavier figures refer to pages where the various sections of the routes may be traced in detail.
FOR FARES, see Through Routes from London, pages lxxiii to cxvii.

LONDON, VIENNA, BUDAPEST, AND CONSTANTINOPLE.

ORIENT EXPRESS and OSTEND-VIENNA EXPRESS. Sleeping and Restaurant Cars only.

Services organised by the International Sleeping Car Co., 20, Cockspur Street, London, S.W. Tickets to be taken in advance; on journey take up passengers only when places are vacant. Customs examination en route.

The Services between London and Vienna run daily each way, between Vienna and Constantinople only on certain days, as shown.

ORIENT EXPRESS.

Station	Table		Time
LONDON—			a.m.
CHARING CROSS		dep	10 0
FOLKESTONE		dep	11a55
BOULOGNE	18	dep	2 p12
PARIS Nord	18	arr	5 p20
			p.m.
PARIS Est	64A	dep	7 13
CHALONS	64A	arr	9 p27
CHALONS	64A	dep	9 p32
D.-AVRICOURT	64A	arr	1 a18
STRASSBURG	210	arr	3 a38
APPENWEIER	210	arr	⋮
OOS (Baden)	141	arr	4 a30
CARLSRUHE	141	arr	4 a59
MUHLACKER	141	arr	⋮
STUTTGART	192	arr	6 a40
ULM	192	arr	8 a13
MUNICH	192	arr	10a16
MUNICH	200	dep	10a28
SALZBURG	200	arr	12p45
VIENNA West	239A	arr	6 p0

OSTEND-VIENNA EXPRESS.

Station	Table		Time
LONDON—			a.m.
CHARING CROSS		dep	9 0
DOVER		arr	10a40
DOVER (Steamer)		dep	11 a0
OSTEND	102	dep	4 p36
BRUSSELS	102	arr	6 p14
BRUSSELS	106	dep	6 p38
HERBESTHAL	106	arr	10 p5
AIX-LA-CHAPELLE	122	arr	10p43
AIX-LA-CHAPELLE	122	dep	10p45
COLOGNE	122	arr	11p52
COLOGNE	122	dep	11p57
BONN	122	arr	12a30
COBLENCE	122	arr	1 a24
MAYENCE	123	arr	2 a48
FRANKFORT	123	arr	3 a26
FRANKFORT	196	dep	3 a36
HANAU	196	dep	4 a1
ASCHAFFENBURG	196	arr	4 a22
ASCHAFFENBURG	196	dep	4 a27
WURZBURG	196	arr	5 a50
MUNICH	197	arr	11a15
WURZBURG	195A	dep	6 a8
NURNBERG	195A	arr	7 a56
NURNBERG	195A	dep	8 a15
PASSAU	195A	arr	12 p7
PASSAU	239B	dep	12p55
VIENNA	239A	arr	6 p0

Station	Table		Time	Days
VIENNA West		dep	6 p19	Daily.
VIENNA Staats	227	dep	6 p51	"
GALANTA	227	arr	8 p47	"
BUDAPEST	227	dep	11p45	Mon., Wed , Sat.
VERCIOROVA	227	arr	9 a40	Tues., Thurs., Sun.
VERCIOROVA	324A	dep	10a50	" " "
BUCHAREST	324A	arr	6 p34	" " "
BUCHAREST	324A	dep	6 p47	" " "
CONSTANZA	324A	arr	11 p5	" " "
" (steamer)		dep	11p30	" " "
CONSTANTINOPLE		arr	12 ‡0	Wed., Fri. Mon. ‡—noon.
CONSTANTINOPLE Stm		dep	3 p0	Thurs. } Roumanian
ALEXANDRIA		arr	mrn.	Mon. } Steamer.
VIENNA West		dep	6 p19	Daily.
VIENNA Staats	227	dep	6 p51	"
GALANTA	227	arr	8 p47	"
BUDAPEST	227	arr	11 p5	"
BELGRADE	225A	arr	5 a58	Wed., Fri., Sat., Mon.
BELGRADE	325A	dep	6 a13	" " "
NISH	325A	arr	11a22	" " "
TZARIBROD	325A	dep	2 p40	" " "
SOFIA	325A	arr	4 p18	" " "
ADRIANOPLE	325A	arr	...	
CONSTANTIN'PLE	325A	arr	...	

Station	Table		Time	Days
CONSTANTIN'PL	325A	dep	...	
ADRIANOPLE	325A	dep	...	
SOFIA	325A	dep	1 p42	
TZARIBROD	325A	arr	3 p52	
NISH	325A	dep	5 p11	
BELGRADE	325A	arr	10p25	
BELGRADE	225A	dep	10p39	Mon., Tues., Thurs., Sat.
BUDAPEST	227A	dep	6 a50	Daily.
GALANTA	227A	dep	9 a3	"
VIENNA Staats	227A	arr	11 a4	"
VIENNA West		arr	11a35	"
ALEXANDRIA Steamer		dep	4 p0	... Fri. } Roumanian
CONSTANTINOPLE		arr	mrn.	... Tues. } Line.
CONSTANTINOPLE (steamer)		dep	2 p30	Sat., Tues., Thurs.
CONSTANZA		arr	5 a0	Sun., Wed., Fri.
CONSTANZA	324A	dep	8 a0	" " "
BUCHAREST	324A	arr	12p35	" " "
BUCHAREST	324A	dep	12p50	" " "
VERCIOROVA	324A	arr	8 p40	" " "
VERCIOROVA	227A	dep	7 p50	" " "
BUDAPEST	227A	dep	6 a50	Daily
GALANTA	227A	dep	9 a3	"
VIENNA Staats	227A	arr	11 a4	"
VIENNA West		arr	11a35	"

ORIENT EXPRESS.

Station	Table		Time
			noon
VIENNA West	239	dep	12 0
SALZBURG	200	dep	5 p32
MUNICH	200	arr	7 p45
MUNICH	192A	dep	7 p55
ULM	192A	dep	9 p59
STUTTGART	192A	dep	11p32
MUHLACKER	141A	dep	...
CARLSRUHE	140B	dep	1 a6
OOS (Baden)	140B	dep	1 a36
APPENWEIER	210A	dep	...
STRASSBURG	210A	dep	2 a31
D.-AVRICOURT	65	dep	3 a45
CHALONS	65	arr	6 a14
CHALONS	65	dep	6 a19
PARIS Est	65	arr	8 a56
PARIS Nord	19	dep	9 a55
CALAIS		arr	1 p10
DOVER		dep	3 p20
CHARING CROSS		arr	5 p10

VIENNA-OSTEND EXPRESS.

Station	Table		Time
			noon
VIENNA	239	dep	12 0
PASSAU	239B	arr	5 p1
PASSAU	195A	dep	5 p17
NURNBERG	195A	arr	8 p30
MUNICH	197C	dep	4 p45
TREUCHTLINGEN		dep	7 p11
NURNBERG	195A	dep	8 p49
WURZBURG	195A	arr	10p30
WURZBURG	196C	dep	10p38
ASCHAFFENBURG	196C	arr	11p55
ASCHAFFENBURG	196C	dep	12 0
HANAU	196C	arr	...
FRANKFORT	196C	arr	12a46
FRANKFORT	123A	dep	1 a1
MAYENCE	123A	dep	1 a39
COBLENCE	123B	dep	3 a5
BONN	123B	dep	4 a1
COLOGNE	123B	arr	4 a35
COLOGNE	123B	dep	4 a41
AIX-LA-CHAPELLE	123B	arr	5 a54
AIX-LA-CHAPELLE	123B	dep	5 a56
HERBESTHAL	104	dep	6 a19
BRUSSELS	104	arr	7 a52
BRUSSELS	102A	dep	8 a6
OSTEND	102A	arr	9 a52
DOVER (Steamer)		arr	2 p0
DOVER		dep	3 p20
LONDON— CHARING CROSS		arr	5 p10

LONDON TO NORTH GERMANY, BERLIN, DENMARK, SWEDEN, AND RUSSIA.

LONDON:—				a.m.	a.m.	a.m.	a.m.		p.m.					p.m.		p.m.		
Charing Cross dep	...	...	...	9 0	9 0	9 0	9 0	...	2 5	...	...	...	...	9 0	...	9 0	...	...
Victoria dep	...	...	...	...	...	...	C	11 a0	...	...	...	...	...	...	...	...	...	...
Dover (Steamer) dep	...	...	...	11 a5	11 a5	...	...	12p55	...	...	...	...	...	...	...	11 p5	...	...
Calais 26 dep	...	...	...	12p53	12p50	...	...	2 p46	7 p2	...	...	...	...	...	...	1 a19	...	...
Brussels Nord 103 arr	...	...	...	4 p41		...	...	6 p55	11p14	...	...	...	...	...	...	5 a21	...	...
Dover (Steamer) dep	...	...	...	...		11 a0	11 a0		4 p30	...	...	...	...	11 p0	...	...	...	...
Ostend 102 dep	...	...	...	...		4 p5	3 p30	...	8 p41	...	...	...	...	3 a25	...	...	...	...
Brussels Nord 102 arr	...	...	...	...		¶	5 p12	...	10p25	...	...	...	...	...	...	...	...	...
Brussels Nord 104 dep	...	...	...	5 p0			5 p22	...	11p24	...	...	...	...	...	...	5 a45	...	...
Valenciennes 29A dep	...	...	...	...	3 p4		...	...	...	...	...	...	...	...	...	...	...	...
Erquelinnes 92 dep	...	...	...	...	4 p41		...	...	...	...	...	...	...	...	...	...	...	...
Liege 92 arr	...	...	...	...	6 p47		...	...	...	...	...	...	...	...	...	...	...	...
Herbesthal 104 arr	...	...	...	8 p58	8 p58	9 p28	9 p7	...	3 a35	...	...	...	...	8 a4	...	9 a22	...	...
Aix-la-Chapelle 122 arr	...	...	...	9 p48	9 p48	10 p9	9 p37	...	4 a15	...	...	...	...	8 a41	...	10 a4	...	...
Cologne 122 arr	...	...	...	11 p1	11 p1	11p24	10p46	...	5 a40	...	...	...	...	9 a51		11a14	...	...
Cologne 161 dep	...	...	...	11p33	—		10p58	...	7 a20	8 a26	...	...	...	10a14		12p58	...	...
Dusseldorf 161 arr	...	...	...	12 a9	...		11p33	...	7 a55		...	...	...			1 p33	...	...
Oberhausen 161 arr	...	...	...		...			...			...	...	...				...	...
LONDON:—	a.m.	a.m.										p.m.	p.m.					
Victoria dep	10 0	10 0	...		...			...			...	8 30	8 30				...	...
Holborn Viaduct dep	9 a55	9 a55	...		...			...			...	8 p25	8 p25				...	...
Queenborough dep	11a30	11a30	...		...			...			...	...	...				...	...
Folkestone dep	...	...	...		...			...			...	10p30	10p30				...	...
Flushing 113 dep	7 p10	7 p10	...		...			...			...	4 a36	4 a36				...	...
Boxtel 116 arr	9 p7	9 p7	...		...			...			...	6 a26	6 a26				...	...
Wesel 120 arr	12 0	12 0	...		...			...			...	9 a7					...	...
Oberhausen 131A arr			...		...			...			...						...	...
Cologne 132 dep		B	...		11p40			...		Cologne to Berlin and Dresden via Soest, Hameln, and Hildesheim (see Table at Side).	7 a4				10 a6		1 p45	...
Oberhausen 132 dep			...		12a52	...		...			...				11a17		3 p1	...
Haltern 132 dep			...		...	...		...			...				12p15		4 p11	...
Bremen 132 arr	4 a19		...		5 a2	...		...			12p44	1 p12			3 p22		7 p48	...
Hamburg 132 arr	6 a31		...		6 a55	...		...			2 p28	2 p47			5 p3		9 p42	...
Hamburg 213A dep	9 a13		...		9 a13	...		...			...	...			12 0		12 0	...
Lubeck 213A arr	10 a8		...		10 a8	...		...			...	...			1 a0		1 a0	...
Rostock 213 arr	12p20		...		12p20	...		...			...	...			3 a2		3 a2	...
Warnemunde 178B arr	12p39		...		12p39	...		...			...	...			3 a29		3 a29	...
Gjedser (steamer) arr	3 p2		...		3 p2	...		...			...	...			5 a45		5 a45	...
Copenhagen 302 arr	6 p41		...		6 p41	...		...			...	...			9 a42		9 a42	...
Hamburg 168 dep	7 a5		...		7 a5	...		...			3 p37	3 p37			11p10		11p10	...
Altona 168 dep	7 a25		...		7 a25	...		...			3 p55	3 p55			11p33		11p33	...
Kiel 168 arr	9 a5		...		9 a5	...		...			5 p29	5 p29			1 a16		1 a16	...
Kiel (steamer) dep	9 a15		...		9 a15	...		...			...	...			1 a32		1 a32	...
Korsoer 302 dep	3 p0		...		3 p0	...		...			...	...			8 a3		8 a3	...
Copenhagen 302 arr	4 p48		...		4 p48	...		...			...	...			10 a4		10 a4	...
Copenhagen (steamer) dep	8 p0		...		8 p0	...		...			...	...			11 a5		11 a5	...
Malmo 308A dep	10p12		...		10p12	...		...			...	...			3 p0		3 p0	...
Stockholm 308A arr	8 a49		...		8 a49	...		...			...	...			6 a58		6 a58	...
Hamburg 213A dep	9 a13		...		9 a13	...		...			...	5 p20			5 p20		...	...
Rostock 213 arr	12p20		...		12p20	...		...			...	8 p59			8 p59		...	...
Stralsund 181A arr	2 p26		...		2 p26	...		...			...	11p30			11p30		...	...
Sassnitz 181 arr	4 p36		...		4 p36	...		...			...	1 a57			1 a57		...	...
Trelleborg (steamer) arr	8 p56		...		8 p56	...	C	...			...	6 a17			6 a17		...	...
Malmo 311 arr	9 p50		...		9 p50	...		...			...	7 a12			7 a12		...	...
Stockholm 308A arr	8 a49		...		8 a49	...		...			...	6 p46			6 p46		...	...
Gothenburg 309A arr	4 a20		...		4 a20	...		...			...	1 p42			1 p42		...	...
Christiania 304A arr	12 0		...		12 0	...		...			...	9 p43			9 p43		...	...
1	2	3	4	5	6	7	8	9	10	11	13	14	15	16	17	18	19	

NOTES.

Unbroken Connection.—The Services shewn in this table have close connection, that is the trains run into and out of the same Stations, and the Steamers start from alongside the trains, with the following exceptions: At **Berlin**, the Stettin Bahnhof is about ¾ mile from the Friedrichstrasse Bahnhof; at **Copenhagen**, the pier of the Malmo Steamers is about 2 miles from the railway station; at **St. Petersburg**, the Station for Moscow is about 2¼ miles from Warsaw Station, where trains arrive from Berlin; at **Warsaw**, the Station for Moscow is about three miles from the Station where trains arrive from Berlin.

The Through Services from London are 1st and 2nd class, except the Nord Express.

FARES. — See Through Routes from London, pages lxxiii to cxvii.

A—Travels from Berlin to Thorn via Schneidemuhl and Bromberg (p. 176).

B—The 7.10 p.m. from Flushing travels onward from Wesel to Osnabruck, p. 132, thence via Lohne to Hanover, p. 156A.

C—Nord Express, Daily via Ostend between England and Berlin; from Berlin to St. Petersburg on Sunday and Thursday only. From Berlin to Warsaw on Tuesday only. Take Tickets in advance from Sleeping Car Co.

D—The 1.10 p.m. from Hanover has a connection (see page 158) via Hildesheim arriving at Leipsic 6.11 p.m.

1	2	3	4	5	6	7	8	9	10	11	13	14	15	16	17	18	19	
OBERHAUSEN ....161 dep	...		...		...	...		...			...	...			...		...	...
HAMM ....161 dep	...		...	2 a15	...	...		...	9 a54		...	...			...	3 p35	...	...
HANOVER ....161 arr	...	4 a17	...	4 a32	...	...	3 a49	...	12p13		...	...	1 p20	2 p56	...	5 p56	...	...
LONDON LIVERPOOL ST. dep	...		...		...	...		...			...	...	8 p30		...	...	...	...
HARWICH ....dep	...		...		...	...		...			...	...	10 p0		...	...	...	...
HOEK V. HOLLAND ...112 dep	...		...		...	...		...			...	...	5 a18		...	...	...	...
ROTTERDAM ....112 arr	...		...		...	...		...			...	...	5 a43		...	...	...	...
ROTTERDAM ....118 dep	...		...		...	...		...			...	...	5 a46		...	...	...	...
UTRECHT ....118 arr	...		...		...	...		...			...	...	6 a42		...	...	...	...
AMERSFOORT ....115A arr	...		...		...	...		...			...	...	7 a2		...	...	...	...
OSNABRUCK ....118B arr	...		...		...	...		...			...	...	11a19		...	...	...	...
BREMEN ....132 arr	...		...		...	...		...			...	...	1 p12		...	...	...	...
HAMBURG ....132 arr	...		...		...	...		...			...	...	2 p47		...	...	...	...
OSNABRUCK ....156C dep	...		...		...	...		...			...	...	11a37		...	...	...	...
HANOVER ....161 arr	...		...		...	...		...			...	...	1 p20		...	...	...	...
HANOVER ....161A dep	...	4 a37		4 a37	...	...		...	1 p10		...	...	1 p36	3 p34	...	6 p41	...	...
BRUNSWICK ....161A arr	...	5 a29	5 a37	5 a29	...	...			2 p34	2 p34	...	...	3 p15	4 p35	...	7 p43	...	...
MAGDEBURG ....158 arr	...		6 a46		...	...			3 p57	3 p57	...	...	4 §23	6 p2	...	8 §59	...	...
MAGDEBURG ....158 dep	...		7 a10		...	...		D			...	...	4 p28	6 p10	...	9 p6	...	...
LEIPSIC ....158 arr	...		9 a6		...	...	C	6 p11			...	...	6 p23	8 p8	...	11 p9	...	...
LEIPSIC ....188 dep	...		9 a32		...	...		6 p47			...	...	6 p47	8 p40	...	12 0	...	...
DRESDEN ....188 arr	...		11a20		...	...		8 p27			...	...	8 p27	10p14	...	1 a43	...	...
DRESDEN ....188 dep	...		11a30		...	...		9 p55			...	...	9 p55	10p53	...	...	...	...
TETSCHEN ....188 arr	...		12p39		...	...		10p52			...	...	10p52	11p51	...	...	...	...
VIENNA ....224 arr	...		9 p36		...	...		7 a22			...	...	7 a22	8 a0	...	...	...	...
HANOVER ....161A dep	...	4 a22	...	4 a37	...	...	3 a57	...	12p18		...	...	1 p25	3 p1	...	6 p1	...	...
STENDAL ....161A arr	...	...	...		...	...	5 a46	...	...		...	...	3 p14	...	...	7 p48	...	...
BERLIN Friedrichstrasse arr	...	7 a57	...		...	...	7 a29	...	3 p48		...	...	4 p54	6 p12	...	9 p28	...	...
„ 161A Alexanderplatz arr	...	8 a6	...		...	...	C	...	3 p58		...	...	5 p3	6 p21	...	9 p38	...	...
„ Schlessis. Bahnf. arr	...	8 a12	...		...	...	7 a41	...	4 p4		...	...	5 p9	6 p27	...	9 p44	...	...
„ 164 Potsdamer Bahnf. arr	...	...	...	8 a54	...	...	...	...	...	6 p1	...	...	...	...	...	...	...	...
BERLIN—Stettin Bhf. 181 dep	...	8 a49	...	...	...	...	...	...	...	...	...	...	...	...	...	11p15	...	...
NEU-STRELITZ ....181 arr	...	10a30	...	...	...	...	...	...	...	...	...	...	...	...	...	12a57	...	...
WARNEMUNDE ....178B arr	...	12p50	...	...	...	...	...	...	...	...	...	...	...	...	...	3 a29	...	...
GJEDSER (Steamer) ....arr	...	3 p2	...	...	...	...	...	...	...	...	...	...	...	...	...	5 a45	...	...
COPENHAGEN ....302 arr	...	6 p41	...	...	...	...	...	...	...	...	...	...	...	...	...	9 a42	...	...
BERLIN—Stettin Bf. 181 dep	...	...	...	11 a9	...	...	...	...	8 p15	...	...	...	8 p15	8 p15	...	...	...	...
SASSNITZ Hafen ....181 arr	...	...	...	4 p36	...	...	...	...	1 a57	...	...	...	1 a57	1 a57	...	...	...	...
TRELLEBORG (Steamer) arr	...	...	...	8 p56	...	...	...	...	6 a17	...	...	...	6 a17	6 a17	...	...	...	...
MALMO ....arr	...	...	...	9 p50	...	...	...	...	7 a12	...	...	...	7 a12	7 a12	...	...	...	...
STOCKHOLM ....308A arr	...	...	...	8 a49	...	...	...	...	6 p46	...	...	...	6 p46	6 p46	...	...	...	...
MALMO ....309A dep	...	...	...	10p16	...	...	...	...	7 a40	...	...	...	7 a40	7 a40	...	...	...	...
GOTHENBURG ....309A arr	...	...	...	4 a20	...	...	...	...	1 p42	...	...	...	1 p42	1 p42	...	...	...	...
FREDRIKSHALD ...304A arr	...	...	...	8a 57	...	...	...	...	6 p32	...	...	...	6 p32	6 p32	...	...	...	...
CHRISTIANIA ...304A arr	...	...	...	12 0	...	...	C	...	9 p43	...	...	...	9 p43	9 p43	...	...	...	...
BERLIN—Schles. Bhf. 176 dep	...	8 a30	...	...	...	...	7 a58	...	...	...	...	...	...	...	...	11p30	...	...
EYDTKUHNEN ....176 arr	...	6 p27	...	...	...	...	5 p50	...	...	...	...	...	...	...	...	10a15	...	...
EYDTKUHNEN ....313 dep	...	7 p48	...	...	...	...	6 p56	...	...	...	...	...	...	...	...	11a31	...	...
ST. PETERSBURG ......313 arr	...	11a35	...	...	...	...	10a30	...	...	...	...	...	...	...	...	8 a15	...	...
BERLIN—Schls. Bhf. 179 dep	...	9 a57	...	9 a57	...	...	7 a52	...	...	...	...	...	...	7 p35	...	11p21	...	...
FRANKFORT-A-O. ......182 dep	...	11 a7	...	11 a7	...	...	9 a3	...	...	...	...	...	...	A	...	12a29	...	...
POSEN ....182 arr	...	1 p51	...	1 p51	...	...	11a27	...	...	...	...	...	...		...	3 a1	...	...
THORN ....178 arr	...	4 p4	...	4 p4	...	...	1 p29	...	...	...	...	...	...	1 a2	...	5 a28	...	...
ALEXANDROVO ......176 arr	...	4 p53	...	4 p53	...	...	C	...	...	...	...	...	...	1 a30	...	6 a15	...	...
WARSAW ....316 arr	...	1 a29	...	1 a29	...	...	7 p14	...	...	...	...	...	...	8 a7	...	1 p22	...	...
WARSAW ....315 dep	...	...	...	...	...	...	8 p30	...	...	...	...	...	...	9 a52	...	3 p25	...	...
MOSCOW ....315 arr	...	...	...	...	...	...	8 p18	...	...	...	...	...	...	1 p25	...	3 p44	...	...

¶—The Carriages for Aix-la-Chapelle and Cologne by this Service travel via Ghent, Malines, and Louvain (p. 101), avoiding Brussels.

§—To Magdeburg via Stendal.

The heavier figures refer to pages where the various sections of the routes may be traced in detail.

HOMEWARD SERVICES, see next page.

COLOGNE to BERLIN and DRESDEN, via Soest.

COLOGNE ....134A dep	8 a26	...
ELBERFELD ....134A dep	9 a15	...
SOEST ....134A arr	10a48	...
SOEST ....164 dep	10a49	...
HAMELN ....155 arr	1 p4	...
HILDESHEIM ....155 arr	1 p52	...
BRUNSWICK ....159 arr	2 p34	...
MAGDEBURG ....158 arr	3 p57	...
BERLIN ....164 arr	6 p1	...
HILDESHEIM ......166 dep	1 p56	...
GOSLAR ....166 arr	2 p52	...
HALLE ....166 arr	5 p30	...
LEIPSIC ....158 arr	6 p11	...
DRESDEN ....188 arr	8 p27	...
DRESDEN ....189 dep	10a35	...
LEIPSIC ....158 dep	1 p0	...
HALLE ....166 dep	1 p41	...
GOSLAR ....166 dep	4 p15	...
HILDESHEIM ......166 arr	4 p59	...
BERLIN ....165A dep	1 p0	...
MAGDEBURG ....158 dep	2 p59	...
BRUNSWICK ....159 dep	4 p28	...
HILDESHEIM ....155 dep	5 p11	...
HAMELN ....155 dep	5 p59	...
SOEST ....165A arr	8 p6	...
SOEST ....134D dep	8 p7	...
ELBERFELD ....134D arr	9 p38	...
COLOGNE ....134D arr	10p26	...

RUSSIA, SWEDEN, DENMARK, BERLIN, NORTH GERMANY, AND LONDON.

1	2	3	4	5	6	7	8	9	10	11	12	13	14	15	16	17	18	19
																	D	
MOSCOW ....315 dep	...	...	2 p0	...	...	6 p0	...	...	...	...	...	...	...	...	...	...	10a45	...
WARSAW ....315 arr	...	...	2 p25	...	...	9 p40	...	...	...	...	...	...	...	...	...	...	10a50	...
WARSAW ....316 dep	...	...	5 p12	...	...	11p52	...	...	...	5a57	...	...	...	...	...	...	12p22	...
ALEXANDROVO ....177 dep	...	...	10p15	...	...	4 a10	...	...	...	11a31	...	...	...	...	...	...	3 p49	...
THORN ....178 dep	...	...	11p36	...	...	5 a21	...	...	...	12p40	...	...	...	...	...	...	4 p46	...
POSEN ....178 arr	...	...	1 a51	...	...	⋮	...	...	...	3 p12	...	...	...	...	...	...	6 p48	...
POSEN ....182 dep	...	...	2 a6	...	...	⋮	...	...	...	3 p20	...	...	...	...	...	...	6 p52	...
FRANKFORT-A-O. ...182 arr	...	...	4 a36	...	...	⋮	...	...	...	6 p4	...	...	...	...	...	...	9 p27	...
BERLIN—Schl. ......179 A arr	...	...	5 a51	...	...	11a10	...	...	...	7 p12	...	...	...	...	...	...	10p38	...
ST. PETERSBURG ....313 dep	...	...	11 p0	...	...	...	...	...	...	7 p5	...	...	...	...	...	7 p5	7 p45	...
EYDTKUHNEN ....313 arr	...	...	5 p30	...	...	...	...	...	...	10a15	...	...	...	...	...	10a15	11a25	...
EYDTKUHNEN ....177 dep	...	...	5 p42	...	...	...	...	...	...	10 a7	...	...	...	...	...	10 a7	11 a0	...
BERLIN—Schles. Bhf. 177 arr	...	...	5 a51	...	...	...	...	...	...	7p25	...	...	...	...	...	7p25	10p38	...
CHRISTIANIA ...304 A dep	...	...	...	...	...	7 a44	...	...	...	5 p45	...	...	...	...	...	...	D	...
FREDRIKSHALD...304 A dep	...	...	...	...	...	10a40	...	...	...	8 p50	...	...	...	...	...	...	...	...
GOTHENBURG......309 A dep	...	...	...	...	...	3 p33	...	...	...	1 a33	...	...	...	...	...	...	...	...
MALMO ....309 A arr	...	...	...	...	...	9 p31	...	...	...	7 a36	...	...	...	...	...	...	...	...
STOCKHOLM ....308 dep	...	...	...	...	...	10a27	...	...	...	8 p30	...	...	...	...	...	...	...	...
MALMO ....dep	...	...	...	...	...	9 p57	...	...	...	7 a54	...	...	...	...	...	...	...	...
TRELLEBORG (Steamer) dep	...	...	...	...	...	10p45	...	...	...	8 a46	...	...	...	...	...	...	...	...
SASSNITZ ....181 dep	...	...	...	...	...	3a10	...	...	...	1 p11	...	...	...	...	...	...	...	...
BERLIN Stettin Bhf. 181 arr	...	...	...	...	...	8 a35	...	...	...	6 p34	...	...	...	...	...	...	...	...
COPENHAGEN ....302 dep	...	...	8 p10	...	...	...	...	...	...	...	11 a0	...	...	...	...	...	...	...
GJEDSER (Steamer)..........dep	...	...	12a14	...	...	...	...	...	...	...	2 p38	...	...	...	...	...	...	...
WARNEMUNDE ....178 B dep	...	...	2 a32	...	...	...	...	...	...	...	4 p51	...	...	...	...	...	...	...
NEU-STRELITZ ....181 dep	...	...	5 a0	...	...	...	...	...	...	...	7 p13	...	...	...	...	...	...	...
BERLIN —Stettin Bhf. 181 arr	...	...	6 a38	...	...	...	...	...	...	...	8 p55	...	...	...	...	...	...	...
			a.m.			p.m.	p.m.			p.m.				p.m.		p.m.	p.m.	
BERLIN—Potsd. Bhf. 165 dep	...	...	...	...	...	...	...	...	...	...	...	...	...	9 26	...	...	...	...
" Schl. Bhf....160 dep	...	...	8 43	...	...	12 48	3 15	...	...	9 18	...	...	...	...	...	10 12	10 45	...
" Alexanderplatz dep	...	...	8 a49	...	...	12p54	3 p21	...	...	9 p24	...	...	...	...	...	10p18	D	...
" Friedrichstrasse dep	...	...	8 a59	...	...	1 p5	3 p32	...	...	9 p34	...	...	...	...	...	10p28	10p58	...
STENDAL ....160 dep	...	...	10a46	...	...	...	...	...	...	11p32	...	...	...	...	...	...	12a53	...
HANOVER ....160 arr	...	...	12p36	...	...	4 p27	6 p53	...	...	1 a47	...	...	...	1 a55	...	2 a16	3 a1	...
DRESDEN.....................189 dep	...	...	3 a41	...	...	8 a0	...	...	...	...	...	...	...	7‡p15	...	7‡p15	⋮	...
LEIPSIC ....189 arr	...	...	5 a29	...	...	9 a53	...	...	...	...	...	...	...	...	...	...	⋮	...
LEIPSIC ....158 dep	...	...	6 a57	...	...	10a25	...	...	...	...	...	...	...	9 p32	...	9 p32	⋮	...
MAGDEBURG ....158 arr	...	...	8 a54	...	...	12p20	...	...	...	...	...	...	...	11§42	...	11§42	⋮	...
MAGDEBURG...........158 dep	...	...	9 a39	...	...	12p43	2 p59	...	...	...	...	...	...	11p50	...	11p50	⋮	...
BRUNSWICK............160 dep	...	...	11a12	...	...	2 p19	4 p36	...	...	...	...	...	...	1 a18	...	1 a18	⋮	...
HANOVER ....160 arr	...	...	12p10	...	...	3 p18	6 p20	...	...	...	...	...	...	2 a10	...	2 a10	⋮	...
HANOVER ....160 dep	...	...	...	...	...	4 p32	...	...	...	...	...	...	...	...	...	...	⋮	...
OSNABRUCK ....156 C dep	...	...	...	...	...	6 p36	...	...	...	...	...	...	...	...	...	...	⋮	...
HAMBURG...............133 dep	...	...	...	...	...	2 p58	...	...	...	...	...	...	...	...	...	...	⋮	...
BREMEN ....133 dep	...	...	...	...	...	4 p40	...	...	...	...	...	...	...	...	...	...	⋮	...
RHEINE ....118 C dep	...	...	...	...	...	7 p29	...	...	...	...	...	...	...	...	...	...	⋮	...
AMERSFOORT.........115 A dep	...	...	...	...	...	9 p20	...	...	...	...	...	...	...	...	...	...	⋮	...
UTRECHT.................118 A dep	...	...	...	...	...	9 p39	...	...	...	...	...	...	...	...	...	...	⋮	...
ROTTERDAM ....118 A arr	...	...	...	...	...	10p45	...	...	...	...	...	...	...	...	...	...	⋮	...
ROTTERDAM..............112 dep	...	...	...	...	...	10p50	...	...	...	...	...	...	...	...	...	...	⋮	...
HOEK V. HOLLAND 112 arr	...	...	...	...	...	11p15	...	...	...	...	...	...	...	...	...	...	⋮	...
HARWICH ....arr	...	...	...	...	...	6 a29	...	...	...	...	...	...	...	...	...	...	⋮	...
LONDON LIVERPOOL ST. arr	...	...	...	...	...	8 a0	...	...	...	...	...	...	...	...	...	...	⋮	...
HANOVER ....160 dep	...	...	12p45	...	...	4 p32	6 p58	...	...	1 a53	...	...	...	2 a28	...	2 a22	3 a7	...
HAMM ....160 A dep	...	...	3 p17	...	...	⋮	9 p13	...	...	4 a33	...	...	...	5 a4	...	⋮	D	...
OBERHAUSEN.............160 A arr	...	...	⋮	...	...	⋮	...	...	...	⋮	...	...	...	⋮	...	⋮	⋮	...

NOTES.

A—From Copenhagen to Fredericia page 302, on to Vamdrup page 303, on to Hamburg page 168.

D—Nord Express. Daily between Berlin and Ostend. From St. Petersburg to Berlin on Wednesday and Saturday. From Moscow on Friday only, from Warsaw on Saturday only. Tickets of Sleeping Car Co.

*—Carriages in the 9.10 a.m. and 6.13 p.m. from Cologne for Ostend travel via Louvain, Malines, and Ghent (page 101), avoiding Brussels.

‡—Via Falkenberg pages 189 and 172) and Zerbst.

§—Via Zerbst, page 164.

1	2	3	4	5	6	7	8	9	10	11	12	13	14	15	16	17	18	19
CHRISTIANIA 304A dep	...	7 a44		...	7 a44	Via Osnabruck, pages 156A, 133.		7 a44	...		...	5 p45	5 p45		...			...
GOTHENBURG ...309A dep	...	3 p33		...	3 p33			3 p33	...		...	1 a33	1 a33		...			...
STOCKHOLM ......308 dep	...	10a27		...	10a27			10a27	...		...	8p30	8 p30		...			...
MALMO ....311 dep	...	9 p57		...	9 p57			9 p57	...		...	7 a54	7 a54		...			...
TRELLEBORG (Steamer) dp	...	10p45		...	10p45			10p45	...		...	8 a46	8 a46		...			...
SASSNITZ ....181 dep	...	3a10		...	3a10			3 a10	...		...	1 p11	1p11		...			...
STRALSUND.........181A dep	...	5a 8		...	6 a51			6 a51	...		...	3 p22	3 p22		...			...
ROSTOCK ....213 dep	...	6 a56		...	10a34			10a34	...		...	5 p19	5 p19		...			...
HAMBURG.........213A arr	...	9 a51		...	2 p25			2 p25	...		...	8 p23	8 p23		...			...
STOCKHOLM ....308 dep	...	...		...	...			...	...		...	8 p30	8 p30		...			...
MALMO ....308 arr		...		...	...			...	...		...	7 a30	7 a30		...			...
COPENHAGEN (stmr.) arr	...	...		n'gt	...			...	...		...	9 a45	9 a45		...			...
COPENHAGEN ......302 dep	7 p50	...		12 0	...			...	...		...	12p55	12p55		...			...
KORSOER.................302 arr	9 p46	...			...			...	...		...	2 p44	2 p41		...			...
KIEL (Steamer) ....arr	4 a55	...			...			...	...		...	8 p25	8 p25		...			...
KIEL ....168 dep	5 a27	...		A	...			...	...		...	9 p 0	9 p0		...			...
ALTONA ....168 arr	6 a51	...			...			...	...		...	10p38	10p38		...			...
HAMBURG ....168 arr	7 a27	...		11a31	...			...	...		...	11 p4	11 p4		...			...
COPENHAGEN ...302 dep	8 p10	...			...			...	...		...	11 a0	11 a0		...			...
GJEDSER (Steamer) ...dep	12a14	...			...			...	...		...	2 p38	2 p38		...			...
WARNEMUNDE ...178B dep	2 a40	...			...			...	...		...	4 p59	4 p59		...			...
ROSTOCK ....213 dep	3 a0	...			...			...	...		...	5 p19	5 p19		...			...
LUBECK ....213A dep	5 a13	...			...			...	...		...	7 p28	7 p28		...			...
HAMBURG.........213A arr	6 a15	...			...			...	...		...	8 p23	8 p23		...			...
HAMBURG ....133 dep	7 a39	9 a59			2 p58			4 p31	...		...	11p30	11p14		...			...
BREMEN ....123 dep	9 a29	11a44		...	4 p40			6 p27	...		...	2 a4	1 a9		...			...
HALTERN ....133 arr	12p42	3 p14		...				...	...		...		4 a45		...			...
OBERHAUSEN ....133 arr	1 p47	4 p25		...				...	...		...		5 a50		...			...
COLOGNE ....133 arr	3 p2	5 p48		...				11p49	...		...		7 a10		...			...
OBERHAUSEN ....131A dep	...			...					...		...		...		...			...
WESEL ....131A arr	...			...	8 p20				...		...	6 a45	...		...	6 a45		...
HALTERN ....130 dep	...			...	...				...		...	...	...		...	...		...
WESEL ....120 dep	...			...	8 p26				...		...	6 a55	...		...	6 a55		...
BOXTEL ....117 dep	...			...	9 p43	9 p43			...		...	8 a22	...		...	8 a22		...
FLUSHING ....113 arr	...			...	11p38	11p38			...		...	10a20	...		...	10a20		...
FOLKESTONE ....arr	...			...	5 a30	5 a30			...		...	...	...		...	...		...
QUEENBOROUGH ....arr	...			...	...	...			...		...	5 p40	...		...	5 p40		...
LONDON—VICTORIA.....arr	...			...	7 a48	7 a48			...		...	7 p34	...		...	7 p34		...
HOLBORN VIADUCT ......arr	...			...	7 a48	7 a48			...		...	7 p34	...		...	7 p34		...
OBERHAUSEN...........160A dep	...			...	...	...			...		...	...	...		...	...		...
DUSSELDORF ....160A dep	...		5 p12	...	...	...	11 p4		...	6 a39	...	...	...	7 a4	...	...	7 a27	...
COLOGNE ....160A arr	...		5 p48	...	...	...	11p39		...	7 a15	...	...	...	7 a40	...	...	8 a2	...
COLOGNE...............123B dep	...		6 p13	...	...	...	12 a5		7 a56	7 a56	...	...	7 a56	9 a10	10 a5	...	8 a7	...
AIX-LA-CHAPELLE ...123B dep	...	...	7 p27	...	...	...	1 a29	...	9 a12	9 a12	...	...	9 a12	10a32	11a23	...	9 a23	
HERBESTHAL ....123B arr	...	...	7 p47		...	...	1 a52	...	9 a32	9 a32	...	...	9 a32	10a52	11a43	...	9 a43	
HERBESTHAL ....104 dep	...	...	7 p54		...	...	2 a0	...	9 a36	9 a36	...	...	9 a36	10a59	11a50	...	9 a53	
LIEGE ....93 dep	...	...	...		...	...	...	...	10a15	...	...	...	10a15	...	...	...	...	
ERQUELINNES ....93 arr	...	...	...		...	...	...	...	12p34	...	...	...	12p34	...	...	...	...	
VALENCIENNES.......29A dep	...	...	...		...	...	...	...	1 p42	...	...	...	1 p42	...	...	...	...	
BRUSSELS Nord ....104 arr	...	...	...		...	...	3 a56	...	...	11a26	...	...	...	1 p3	...	...	11a31	
BRUSSELS Midi ....104 arr	...	...	*	9 p58	...	...	...	...	...	...	...	...	...	2 p8	...	...	...	
BRUSSELS Nord ...102A dep	...	...	...	...	...	...	8 a46	...	...	1 p13	...	...	...	...	...	...	11a37	
OSTEND.................102A arr	...	...	11 p1	...	...	...	10a29	...	...	3 p1	...	...	...	...	3 p23	...	1 p15	
DOVER (Steamer) ....arr	...	...	2 a15	...	...	...	2 p0	...	...	6 p30	...	...	...	...	6p30	...	6 p30	
BRUSSELS Nord........103 dep	...	...	...	...	...	...	8 a30	...	...	...	...	...	...	...	...	B—Via Boulogne.	...	
BRUSSELS Midi........103 dep	...	...	...	10 p3	...	...	8 a52	...	...	...	...	...	...	2 p14	...	...	...	
CALAIS.......................27 arr	...	...	...	1 a36	...	...	1 p0	...	3 p31	...	...	...	3 p31	...	...	...	...	3 p31
DOVER (Steamer)............arr	...	...	...	3 a0	...	...	2 p45	...	5 p 0	...	...	...	5 p9	B	...	...	...	5 p0
LONDON—VICTORIA........arr	...	...	...	...	...	...	...	...	7 p5	...	...	...	7 p5	...	...	...	...	7 p5
CHARING CROSS..............arr	...	...	5 a43	5 a43	...	...	5 p10	...	...	10 p0	...	...	...	10p45	10 p0	...	10 p0	...

The heavier figures refer to pages where the various sections of the routes may be traced in detail.

LONDON, COLOGNE, CENTRAL GERMANY, AND VIENNA.

1	2	3	4	5	6	7	8	9	10	11	12	13	14	15	16	17	18	19	20	21	22	23	24	25	26	27
LONDON—	a.m.		a.m.	a.m.				a.m.	a.m.			a.m.	p.m.			p.m.		p.m.								
VICTORIA .... dep	...	...	...	...	...	...	...	...	...	...	...	11 0	...	...	...	...	...	...	...	...	...	...	...	...	...	...
CHARING CROSS .... dep	9 0	...	9 0	9 0	...	...	...	9 0	9 0	...	...	...	2 5	...	...	9 0	...	9 0	...	...	...	...	...	...	...	...
DOVER .... arr	10a40	...	10a40	10a40	...	...	...	10a40	10a40	...	...	12p45	...	...	...	10p40	...	10p40	...	...	...	...	...	...	...	...
DOVER (Steamer) .... dep	11 a5	...	11 a5	...	...	...	...	...	A	...	...	12p55	...	...	...	...	...	11 p5	...	...	...	...	...	...	...	...
CALAIS .... 26 dep	12p53	...	12p50	...	...	...	...	...	...	...	...	2 p46	7 p2	...	...	...	...	1 a19	...	...	...	...	...	...	...	...
BRUSSELS Nord .... 103 arr	4 p41	...		...	...	...	...	...	...	...	...	6 p55	11p14	...	...	...	...	5 a21	...	...	...	...	...	...	...	...
DOVER (Steamer) .... dep	...	...		11 a0	...	...	...	11 a0	11 a0	...	...	...	4 p30	...	...	11 p0	...	11 p0	...	...	...	...	...	...	...	...
OSTEND .... 102 dep	...	...		4 p5	...	...	...	3 p24	4 p36	...	...	...	8 p41	...	...	3 a25	...	3 a42	...	...	...	...	...	...	...	...
BRUSSELS Nord .... 102 arr	...	...		§	...	...	...	5 p6	6 p14	...	...	...	10p25	...	...	§	...	5 a24	...	...	...	...	...	...	...	...
BRUSSELS Nord .... 104 dep	5 p0	...		...	...	...	...		6 p38	...	...	...	11p24	...	...	...	...	5 a45	...	...	...	...	...	...	...	...
VALENCIENNES .... 29A dep	...	...	3 p4	...	...	...	...	...	...	...	...	...	...	...	...	...	...	...	...	...	...	...	...	...	...	...
ERQUELINNES .... 92 dep	...	...	4 p41	...	...	...	...	...	...	...	...	...	...	...	...	...	...	...	...	...	...	...	...	...	...	...
LIEGE .... 92 arr	...	...	6 p47	...	...	...	...	...	...	...	...	...	...	...	...	...	...	...	...	...	...	...	...	...	...	...
HERBESTHAL .... 104 arr	8 p58	...	8 p58	9 p28	...	...	...	...	10 p5	...	...	...	3 a35	...	...	8 a4	...	9 a22	...	...	...	...	...	...	...	...
HERBESTHAL .... 122 dep	9 p27	...	9 p27	9 p50	...	...	...	...	10p24	...	...	...	3 a56	...	...	8 a22	...	9 a45	...	...	...	...	...	...	...	...
AIX-LA-CHAPELLE .... 122 arr	9 p48	...	9 p48	10 p9	...	...	...	...	10p43	...	...	...	4 a15	...	...	8 a41	...	10 a4	...	...	...	...	...	...	...	...
AIX-LA-CHAPELLE .... 122 dep	9 p52	...	9 p52	10p12	...	...	...	...	10p45	...	...	...	4 a20	...	...	8 a43	...	10 a7	...	...	...	...	...	...	...	...
COLOGNE .... 122 arr	11 p1	...	11 p1	11p24	...	...	...	...	11p52	...	...	...	5 a40	...	...	9 a51	...	11a14	...	...	...	...	...	...	...	...
										a.m.						p.m.						p.m.				
VICTORIA .... dep	...	...			...	...	...	...	...	10 0	...	...	...	...	...	8 30	...	...	...	...	...	8 30	...	...	...	...
HOLBORN VIADUCT .... dep	...	...			...	...	...	...	...	9 a55	...	...	...	...	...	8 p25	...	...	...	...	...	8 p25	...	...	...	...
ST. PAUL'S .... dep	...	...			...	...	...	...	...	9 a56	...	...	...	...	...	8 p27	...	...	...	...	...	8 p27	...	...	...	...
QUEENBOROUGH .... dep	...	...			...	...	...	...	...	11a30	...	...	...	...	...	...	...	...	...	...	...	...	...	...	...	...
FOLKESTONE .... dep	...	...			...	...	...	...	...	...	...	...	...	...	...	10p30	...	...	...	...	...	10p30	...	...	...	...
FLUSHING .... 113 dep	...	...			...	...	...	...	...	7 p0	...	...	...	...	...	4 a15	...	...	...	...	...	4 a15	...	...	...	...
BOXTEL .... 116 arr	...	...			...	...	...	...	...	8 p57	...	...	...	...	...	6 a5	...	...	...	...	...	6 a5	...	...	...	...
WESEL .... 120 arr	...	...			...	...	...	...	...	11p44	...	...	...	...	...		...	...	...	...	...	D	...	...	...	...
OBERHAUSEN .... 131A arr	...	...			...	...	...	...	...	12a11	...	...	...	...	...		...	...	...	...	...		...	...	...	...
OBERHAUSEN .... 160C dep	...	...			...	...	...	...	...	12a33	...	...	...	...	...	D	...	...	...	...	...		...	...	...	...
COLOGNE .... 160C arr	...	...			...	...	...	...	...	1 a50	...	...	...	...	...	9 a56	...	...	...	...	...	9 a56	...	...	...	...
LIVERPOOL STREET .... dep	...	...			...	...	...	...	...	...	...	...	...	...	...	...	...	8 p30	...	...	...	8 p30	...	...	...	...
HARWICH .... dep	...	...			...	...	...	...	...	...	...	...	...	...	...	...	...	10 p0	...	...	...	10 p0	...	...	...	...
HOEK VAN HOLLAND 112 dep	...	...			...	...	...	...	...	...	...	...	...	...	...	...	...	5 a25	...	...	...	5 a25	...	...	...	...
ROTTERDAM .... 112 arr	...	...			...	...	...	...	...	...	...	...	...	...	...	...	...		...	...	...		...	...	...	...
ROTTERDAM .... 119 dep	...	...			...	...	...	...	...	...	...	...	...	...	...	...	...		...	...	...		...	...	...	...
NYMEGEN .... 119 arr	...	...			...	...	...	...	...	...	...	...	...	...	...	...	...	7 a33	...	...	...	7 a33	...	...	...	...
NYMEGEN .... 121 dep	...	...			...	...	...	...	...	...	...	...	...	...	...	...	...	7 a35	...	...	...	7 a35	...	...	...	...
CREFELD .... 121 arr	...	...			...	...	...	...	...	...	...	...	...	...	...	...	...	10 a5	...	...	...	10 a5	...	...	...	...
COLOGNE .... 121 arr	...	...			...	...	...	...	...	...	...	...	...	...	...	...	...	11a15	...	...	...	11a15	...	...	...	...
COLOGNE .... 128 dep	11p45				...	...	...	...	...	1 a58	...	...	...	8 a8	9 a10	...	...	11a27	...	...	...	11a27	...	...	...	3 p38
NIEDERLAHNSTEIN .... 128 arr	2 a36				...	...	...	...	...	...	...	...	...	10 a1	11 a0	...	...	1 p0	...	...	...	1 p0	...	...	...	5 p25
EMS .... 146 arr	5 a9	...	...	...	...	...	...	...	...	...	...	...	...	11 a3	11a46	...	...	1 p48	...	...	...	1 p48	...	...	...	6 p10
NIEDERLAHNSTEIN .... 128 dep	2 a41	...	...	...	...	...	...	...	...	...	...	...	...	10 a5	11 a2	...	...	1 p4	...	...	...	1 p4	...	...	...	5 p29
WIESBADEN .... 128 arr	5 a0	...	...	...	...	...	...	...	...	5 a8	...	...	...	11a42	12p40	...	...	2 p26	...	...	...	2 p26	...	...	...	7 p5
FRANKFORT .... 128 arr	6 a53		...	...	...	...	...	...	...	6 a16		...	...	12p34	1 p32	...	...	3 p19			...	3 p19	...	...	...	7 p57
FRANKFORT .... 150 dep	7 a0	8 a29	...	...	...	...	...	...	...	6 a22	8 a29	...	...	12p44	1 p50	...	...	...	...	3 p36	...	...	...	...	...	8 p24
HOMBURG BAD .... 150 arr	7 a45		...	...	...	...	...	...	...	7 a1		...	...	1 p25	2 p20	...	...	3 †55	...	B	...	3 †55	...	...	...	8 p53
COLOGNE .... 122 dep	1 a58		...	...	...	...	...	...	11p57	1 a58		...	6 a17	...	9 a32	10 a3	...	11a20	...		...	12p10	...	...	1 p5	...
COBLENCE .... 122 arr	3 a30		...	...	...	...	...	...	1 a24	3 a30		...	8 a27	...	11 a4	11a34	...	12p48	...		...	1 p41	...	...	2 p47	...
WIESBADEN .... 128 arr	5 a8	B	...	...	...	...	...	...		5 a8	B	...	11a26	...	1 p19	2 p26	...	2*46	...		...	4 p42	...	...	6 p40	...
EMS .... 146 arr	5 a9		...	...	...	...	...	...		5 a9		...	9 a13	...	11a46	12p36	...	1 p48	...		...	2 p54	...	...	3 p34	...
BINGERBRUCK .... 122 arr	...		...	...	...	...	...	...		...		...	9 a44	...	12 p9	12p33	...	1 p47	...		...	2 p41	...	...	4 p2	...
BINGERBRUCK .... 123 dep	...		...	...	...	...	...	...	A	...		...	9 a47	...	12p11	12p36	...	1 p50	...		...	2 p49	...	...	4 p7	...
MAYENCE .... 123 arr	5 a25						...	...	2 a48	5 a25		...	10a22	...	12p43	1 p7	...	2 p22	...			3 p21	...	...	4 p39	...
MAYENCE .... 123 dep	...			...	...		...	...	2 a49	...		...	10a28	...	12p58	1 p13	...	2 p25	...			3 p28	...	...	4 p43	...
FRANKFORT .... 123 arr	...			...	...		...	...	3 a26	...		...	11a11	...	1 p36	1 p57	B	3 p5	...			4 p8		...	5 p29	...
FRANKFORT .... 150 dep	...			...	...		...	...	3 a36	...		...	12p18	...	1 p50	2 p45	2 p23	3 p21	...			4 p43	4 p36	...	5 p35	...
HOMBURG BAD .... 150 arr	...			...	...		...	...		...		...	12p45	...	2 p20	3 p31		3 p47	...			5 p24	B	...	6 p16	...

1	2	3	4	5	6	7	8	9	10	11	12	13	14	15	16	17	18	19	20	21	22	23	24	25	26	27
MAYENCE 123 dep	5 a54			...	...		...	...		5 a54		...	...	...	1 p32	1 p32		...	...			...		...	4 p48	...
DARMSTADT 123 arr	6 a33			...	...		...	...		6 a33		...	...	...	2 p12	2 p12		...	...			...		...	5 p29	...
ASCHAFFENBURG 123 arr	7 a24	9 a17		...	...		...	...	4 a22	7 a24	9 a17	...	...	...	3 p3	3 p3	3 p7	...	...	4 p26		...	5 p27	...	...	...
ASCHAFFENBURG 196 dep	7 a33	9 a19		...	...		...	...	4 a27	7 a33	9 a19	...	...	...	3 p12	3 p12	3 p12	...	...	4 p28		...	5 p33	...	...	...
GEMUNDEN 196 arr	8 a35			...	...		...	...		8 a35		...	...	...	...	...	...	...	...			...	6 p31	...	...	...
SCHWEINFURT 201 arr	10a44			...	...		...	...		10a44		...	...	...	...	...	...	...	...			...	...	...	...	...
KISSINGEN 195 arr	11a53			...	...		...	...		11a53		...	...	...	...	...	...	...	...			...	...	...	...	...
GEMUNDEN 196 dep	8 a37			...	...		...	...		8 a37		...	...	...	...	...	...	...	...			...	6 p32	...	...	...
WURZBURG 196 arr	9 a12	10a47		...	...		...	...	5 a50	9 a12	10a47	...	...	...	4 p36	4 p36	4 p36	...	...	5 p51		...	7 p3	...	...	...
WURZBURG 198 dep	10 a0	11 a7		...	...		...	...	6 a0	10 a0	11 a7	...	...	...	...	...	...	...	...	6 p10		...	7 p15	...	...	...
SCHWEINFURT 198 arr	10a47	12p23		...	...		...	...	7 a6	10a47	12p23	...	...	...	...	...	...	...	...	7 p21		...	8 p10	...	...	...
KISSINGEN 195 arr	11a53	1 p44		...	...		...	...	8 a18	11a53	1 p44	...	...	...	...	...	...	...	...	8 p15		...	9 p23	...	...	...
WURZBURG 196 dep	9 a26	...		...	...		...	...	6 a10	9 a26	...	...	...	...	4 p45	4 p45	4 p45	...	...	5 p56		...	7 p22	...	...	...
TREUCHTLINGEN 196 arr	11a57	...		...	...		...	...	8 a55	11a57	...	...	...	...	...	...	...	...	...	8 p27		...	...	...	...	...
MUNICH 196 arr	2 p0	...		...	...		...	...	11a15	2 p0	...	...	...	...	8 p55	8 p55	8 p55	...	...	10p25		...	12a40	...	...	...
MUNICH 200 dep	4 p10	...		...	...		...	...	1 p30	4 p10	...	...	...	...	9 p30	9 p30	9 p30	...	...	11p49		...	...	...	...	...
SALZBURG 200 arr	6 p50	...		...	...		...	...	4 p5	6 p50	...	...	...	...	12 a8	12 a8	12 a8	...	...	2 a10		...	...	...	...	...
VIENNA 239A arr	6 a0	...		...	...		...	...	9 p50	6 a0	...	...	...	...	8 a10	8a 10	8 a10	...	...	8 a10		...	...	...	...	...
WURZBURG 195A dep	9 a32	10a53		...	...		...	...	6 a8	9 a32	10a53	...	...	...	5 p0	5 p0	5 p0	...	...	...		...	7 p22	...	...	...
NURNBERG 195A arr	11a39	12p41		...	...		...	...	7 a56	11a39	12p41	...	...	...	6 p54	6 p54	6 p54	...	...	...		...	9 p22	...	...	...
NURNBERG 202 dep	...	1 p5		...	...		...	...	8 a25	...	1 p5	...	...	...	7 p22	7 p22	7 p22	...	...	...		...	...	...	...	...
EGER 202 arr	...	3 p48		...	...		...	...	11 a9	...	3 p48	...	...	...	12a57	12a57	12a57	...	...	...		...	...	...	...	...
EGER 251 dep	...	4 p28		...	...		...	...	11a24	...	4 p28	...	...	...	...	...	...	...	...	...		...	...	...	...	...
CARLSBAD 251 arr	...	5 p31		...	...		...	...	12p21	...	5 p31	...	...	...	...	...	...	...	...	...		...	...	...	...	...
NURNBERG 195A dep	...	12p51		...	...		...	...	8 a15	...	12p51	...	...	...	...	...	...	...	...	...		...	9 p40	...	...	...
PASSAU 195A arr	...	4 p15		...	...		...	...	12 p7	...	4 p15	...	...	...	...	...	...	...	...	...		...	1 a25	...	...	...
PASSAU 239B dep	...	4 p40		...	...		...	...	12p55	...	4 p40	...	...	...	...	...	...	...	...	...		...	1 a57	...	...	...
WELS 239B arr	...	6 p8		...	...		...	...	2 p17	...	6 p8	...	...	...	...	...	...	...	...	...		...	3 a22	...	...	...
WELS 239A dep	...	6 p16		...	...		...	...	2 p35	...	6 p16	...	...	...	...	...	...	...	...	...		...	3 a24	...	...	...
VIENNA 239A arr	...	9 p50		...	...		...	...	6 p0	...	9 p50	...	...	...	...	...	...	...	...	...		...	7 a20	...	...	...
MAYENCE 123 dep	5 a30	...	5 a30	5 a54	...	7 a51	9 a0	...	...	5 a30	...	...	10a33	...	12p52	1 p13	...	2 p32	2p32	...	3 p23	3 p23	...	...	4 p48	
DARMSTADT 123 arr	...	...	...	6 a33	...	8 a50	9 a57	...	...	...	...	...	...	...			...		...	...	...		...	...	5 p29	
HEIDELBERG 136 arr	...	...	7 a29	7 a53	...	10a45	11 a3	...	...	...	...	...	12p27	...			...		4p20	...	4 p57		...	...	6 p30	
HEIDELBERG 140 dep	...	...	7 a34	8 a11	8 a52	...	11 a8	12p12	...	...	...	...	...	...			...		4p28	...	5 p13		...	...	6 p34	
BRUCHSAL 140 arr	...	...	8 a0	8 a38	9 a18	...	11a34	12p38	...	...	...	...	...	...		3 p16	...		4p56	...	5 p38		...	...	...	7 p42
CARLSRUHE 140 arr	8 a1	...	8 a18	8 a58	9 a37	...	11a53	1 p1	...	8 a1	...	...	...	...	2 p52	3 p18	...	4 p39	...	...	5 p59	6 p9			7 p11	...
CARLSRUHE 140 dep	8 a6	...	8 a38	9 a3	9 a42	...	12 p3	1 p6	...	8 a6	...	...	...	...	2 p56	3 p24	...	4 p48	...	...	6 p18	6 p13	...	6 p13	7 p21	...
OOS 140 arr	8 a33	...	9 a6	9 a34	10a10	...	12p30	1 p35	...	8 a33	...	...	...	...	3 p23	3 p51	...	5 p19	...	...	7 p10	6 p39	...		7 p48	...
BADEN-BADEN 140 arr	8 a46	...	9 a18	9 a46	10a24	...	12p44	1 p52	...	8 a46	...	...	...	...	3 p36	4 p2	...	5 p31	...	...	7 p19	6 p52	...		8 p4	...
BASLE 140 arr	11 a0	...	...	12p16	12p43	...	2 p55	4 p41	...	11 a0	...	...	...	...	5 p38	...	...	7 p56	...	...	...	8 p55	...	C	10p21	...
BRUCHSAL 192 dep	...	...	8 a5	...	10 a3	...	...	12p50	...	8 a5	...	...	...	...	...	3 p20	...	...	4p58	...	...	...	...		...	8 p6
STUTTGART 192 arr	...	...	9 a19	...	11a28	...	...	2 p24	...	9 a19	...	...	...	...	...	4 p47	...	...	6p29	...	...	...	...	7 p42	...	9 p21
STUTTGART 192 dep	...	...	9 a29	...	11a37	...	...	2 p31	...	9 a29	...	...	...	...	...	4 p55	...	...	6p42	...	...	...	...	7 p53	...	...
ULM 192 arr	...	...	10a51	...	1 p12	...	...	4 p2	...	10a51	...	...	...	...	...	6 p58	...	...	8p29	...	...	...	...	9 p22	...	...
ULM 192 dep	...	...	11 a8	...	1 p17	...	...	4 p12	...	11 a8	...	...	...	...	...	7 p17	...	...	...	...	...	...	...	9 p28	...	...
MUNICH 192 arr	...	...	1 p8	...	3 p25	...	...	9 p35	...	1 p8	...	...	...	...	...	9 p40	...	...	...	...	...	...	...	11p23	...	...
MUNICH 200 dep	...	...	1 p30	...	4 p10	...	...	11p40	...	1 p30	...	...	...	...	...	11p40	...	...	...	...	...	...	...	11p40	...	...
SALZBURG 200 arr	...	...	4 p5	...	6 p50	...	...	2 a10	...	4 p5	...	...	...	...	...	2 a10	...	...	...	...	...	...	...	2 a10	...	...
VIENNA 239A arr	...	...	9 p50	...	6 a 0	...	...	8 a10	...	9 p50	...	...	...	...	...	8 a10	...	...	...	...	...	...	...	8 a10	...	...

§—The Carriages for Aix-la-Chapelle and Cologne by this Service travel via Ghent, Malines, and Louvain (page 101), avoiding Brussels.

A—Ostend-Vienna Express. Secure tickets in advance of International Sleeping Car Co., 20, Cockspur Street, London, S.W.

B—From Frankfort, via Hanau to Aschaffenburg (page 196).
C—From Carlsruhe via Pforzheim, table at foot of page 141.

D—From Boxtel, via Goch, p. 121.
†—Via Wiesbaden.

The heavier figures refer to pages where the various sections of the routes may be traced in detail.

VIENNA, CENTRAL GERMANY, COLOGNE, AND LONDON.

Station	2	3	4	5	6	7	8	9	10	11	12	13	14	15	16	17	18	19	20
VIENNA ....239 dep	...	10p55	...	8a15	...	...	1 p0	...	...	...	8 p49	...	...	...	...	...	...	...	...
SALZBURG ....239 arr	...	8 a14	...	2 p0	...	...	6p58	...	...	...	2 a50	...	...	...	...	...	...	...	...
SALZBURG ....200 dep	...	9 a7	...	2p25	...	...	7 p20	...	...	...	3 a25	...	...	...	5 a40	...	...	...	...
MUNICH ....200 arr	...	12p10	...	5 p0	...	...	10 p0	...	...	...	6 a30	...	...	...	8 a2	...	...	...	...
MUNICH ....192A dep	...	2 p50	...	5 p20	...	...	10p25	...	...	...	...	...	...	...	8 a22	...	...	...	...
ULM ....192A arr	...	5 p4	...	7 p24	...	...	12a28	...	...	...	...	...	...	...	10a37	...	...	...	...
ULM ....192A dep	...	5 p12	...	8 p55	...	...	12a38	...	...	8 a5	...	...	...	...	10a48	...	...	...	...
STUTTGART ....192A arr	...	6 p41	...	10p28	...	...	2 a 9	...	...	9 a45	...	...	...	...	12p16	...	...	...	...
STUTTGART ....192A dep	...	6 p59	...	10p38	...	...	2 a19	...	6 a58	10a 3	...	...	...	...	12p22	...	...	...	...
BRUCHSAL ....192A arr	...	:	...	:	...	...	:	...	9 a1	11a25	...	...	...	...	1 p45	...	...	...	...
BASLE ....141 dep	...	5 p33	...	9 p41	...	...	11p52	...	4 a30	8 a0	...	...	...	...	10a42	...	...	...	...
BADEN-BADEN ...141 dep	...	7 p50	...	11p42	...	...	2 a13	...	8 a13	10a33	...	...	...	...	1 p13	...	...	1 p25	...
OOS ....141 dep	...	8 p2	...	11p54	...	...	2 a24	...	8 a30	10a45	...	...	...	...	1 p26	...	...	1 p41	...
CARLSRUHE ....141 arr	...	8 p30	...	12a20	...	...	2 a55	...	9 a1	11a13	...	...	...	...	1 p52	...	...	2 p11	...
CARLSRUHE ....141 dep	...	8 p38	...	12a28	...	...	3 a 5	5 a8	9 a5	11a17	...	...	...	...	1 p57	12p43	...	2 p20	..
BRUCHSAL ....141 dep	...	8 p58	...	:	...	...	3 a24	5 a33	9 a29	11a48	...	...	...	...	:	1 p10	...	2 p41	...
HEIDELBERG ....141 arr	...	9 p25	...	:	...	...	3 a51	6a 0	9 a56	12p15	...	...	...	...	:	1 p39	...	3 p8	...
HEIDELBERG ....136 dep	...	9 p29	...	:	11p47	...	4 a10	6 a10	10 a2	12p24	...	...	...	...	2 p19	1 p43	...	3 p13	...
DARMSTADT ....123A dep	...	10p28	...	:	...	...	5 a19	8 a11	11a12	1 p42	...	...	...	...	:	2 p53	...	4 p31	...
MAYENCE ....123A arr	A	11p23	...	2 a28	2 a28	...	5 a56	8 a55	:	2 p23	...	...	...	...	3 p59	3 p28	...	5 p13	...
VIENNA ....239 dep	12 0	...	...	7 a25		...	...	...	:	8 p30	...	...	8 p30	...	...	...	...	...	...
WELS ....239 arr	3 p31	...	...	11a42		...	...	...	:	12a25	...	...	12a25	...	...	...	...	...	...
WELS ....239B dep	3 p43	...	...	11a52		...	...	...	:	12a28	...	...	12a28	...	...	...	...	...	...
PASSAU ....239B arr	5 p1	...	...	1 p18		...	...	...	:	1 a54	...	...	1 a54	...	...	...	...	...	...
PASSAU ....195A dep	5 p17	...	...	1 p35		...	...	...	:	2 a28	...	...	2 a28	...	...	...	...	...	...
NURNBERG ....195A arr	8 p30	...	...	4 p55		...	...	...	:	6 a40	...	...	6 a40	...	...	...	...	...	...
CARLSBAD ....250 dep	4 p52	...	...	12p19		...	...	...	:	...	1 a39	...	...	...	1 a39	...	1 a39	...	...
EGER ....250 arr	5 p52	...	...	1 p35		...	...	...	:	...	3 a0	...	...	...	3 a0	...	3 a0	...	...
EGER ....203 dep	6 p7	...	...	1 p55		...	...	...	:	...	3 a54	...	...	...	3 a54	...	3 a54	...	...
NURNBERG ....203 arr	8 p23	...	...	4 p34		...	...	...	:	...	7 a35	...	...	...	7 a35	...	7 a35	...	...
NURNBERG ....195A dep	8 p49	...	...	5 p8		8 p35	...	...	:	7 a0	9 a20	...	7 a0	...	9 a20	...	9 a20	...	...
WURZBURG ....195A arr	10p30	...	...	6 p45		10p48	...	...	:	8 a58	11a20	...	8 a58	...	11a20	...	11a20	...	...
MUNICH ....196B dep	:	...	...	4 p25		4 p45	10p18	...	:	...	7 a 5	...	...	...	9a 0	...	9 a0	...	...
TREUCHTLINGEN ......196B dep	:	...	...	...		7 p11	12a21	...	:	...	9 a 6	...	...	...	...	...	...	...	...
WURZBURG ....196B arr	:	...	...	8 p29		10p48	2 a41	...	:	...	11a25	...	...	...	12p25	...	12p25	...	...
KISSINGEN ....195 dep	:	...	...	6 p30		7 p36	11 p0	...	:	7 a17	9 a45	...	7 a17	...	9 a45	...	9 a45	...	...
SCHWEINFURT ....198 dep	:	...	...	7 p30		8 p30	11p42	...	:	7 a58	10a30	...	7 a58	...	...	...	...	...	...
WURZBURG ....198 arr	:	...	...	8 p13		9 p52	12a55	...	:	8 a52	11a25	...	8 a52	...	...	...	...	...	...
WURZBURG ....196B dep	10p38	...	...	8 p45		11 p5	2 a50	...	:	9 a15	11a37	...	9 a15	...	12p33	...	12p33	...	...
GEMUNDEN ....196B arr	:	...	...	9 p20		...	...	...	:	9 a51	12p 6	...	9 a51	...	...	...	...	...	...
KISSINGEN ....195 dep	:	...	...	...		...	...	...	:	5 a35	...	...	5 a35	...	...	...	...	...	...
SCHWEINFURT ....196A dep	:	...	...	...		...	...	...	:	7 a15	...	...	7 a15	...	...	...	...	...	...
GEMUNDEN ....196B dep	:	...	...	9 p21		...	...	...	:	9 a53	12p 7	...	9 a53	...	...	...	...	...	...
ASCHAFFENBURG ....196B arr	11p55	...	...	10p24		12a23	4 a21	...	:	10a57	1 p0	...	10a57	...	1 p48	...	1 p48	...	...
ASCHAFFENBURG ....123A dep	12 0	...	...	10p37		12a29	4 a35	...	B	11 a8	1 p3	...	11 a8	...	2 p2	...	2 p2	...	...
DARMSTADT ....123A dep	:	—	...	11p30		:	5 a19	...	:	12 p3	:	...	12 p3	...	2 p53	...	2 p53	...	...
MAYENCE ....123A arr	:	...		12a12		:	5 a56	...	:	12p47	:	...	12p47	...	3 p28	...	3 p28	...	...
HOMBURG BAD ....150 dep	:	9 p37		11 p5		:	...	7 a40	:	12p57	1 §49	...	12p57	1§p49	1§p49	...	2 p59	5 p9	...
FRANKFORT ....150 arr	12a46	10 p6		11p38		1 a19	...	8 a18	:	1 p35	...	...	1 p35	...	...	...	3 p26	5 p36	...
FRANKFORT ....123A dep	1 a1	10p49		1 a44		1 a44	5 a20	8 a30	:	1 p51	2 p18	...	1 p51	...	...	...	3 p30	6 p9	...
MAYENCE ....123A arr	1 a37	11p53		2 a21		2 a21	6 a3	9 a7	:	2 p35	:	...	2 p35	...	...	...	4 p13	6 p52	...
MAYENCE ....123A dep	1 39	12 a2	12a35	2 a28		2 a28	6 a10	9 a20	:	2 p54	page 129.	...	2 p54	...	4 p2	...	4 p27	6 p58	...
BINGERBRUCK ....123A arr	:	12a52	1 a11	3 a 9	—	3 a 9	6 a45	9 a52	:	3 p25	:	...	3 p25	...	4 p33	...	5 p2	7 p33	...
BINGERBRUCK ....123B dep	A	12a57	2 a51	3 a10	...	3 a10	6 a48	9 a55	:	3 p40	:	...	3 p40	...	4 p34	...	5 p4	7 p35	...
EMS ....147 dep	:	12a33	...	...	...	...	6 a20	10a12	:	3 p9	:	...	3 p9	5 p0	5 p14	...	5 p20	7 p59	...
WIESBADEN ....129 dep	:	...	11†46	1†17	...	1a†17	5†35	8 a56	:	2†p8	3 p15	...	2†p8	3 p51	3 p51	...	3 p51	6†30	...
COBLENCE ....123B dep	3 a5	2 a37	3 a50	4 a11	...	4 a11	8 a3	11 a1	:	4 p38	...	...	4 p38	5 p37	5 p44	...	6 p19	8 p40	...
COLOGNE ....123B arr	4 a3[illegible]	5 a9	5 a[illegible]	5 a42	...	5 a42	9 a50	12p48	[illegible]	6 p5	6 p8	...	6 p5	7 p7	7 p14	...	8 p[illegible]5	10p30	...

NOTES

A—Vienna - Ostend Express, consisting of Sleeping and Restaurant Cars. Secure Tickets in advance of International Sleeping Car Co.

B—Travels from Heidelberg to Frankfort page 136.

†—Via Mayence.

1	2	3	4	5	6	7	8	9	10	11	12	13	14	15	16	17	18	19	20
Homburg Bad .... 150 dep	...	...	...	...	...	...	...	9 a2	...	...	1§p49	...	...	1§p49	...	...	4 p1	...	...
Frankfort .... 150 arr	...	...	...	...	...	...	...	9 a29	11a40	...	...	...	...	...	...	...	4 p40	...	...
Frankfort .... 129 dep	...	...	...	...	...	...	...	10 a1	12p28	...	2 p18	...	...	2 p50	...	...	5 p1	...	...
Wiesbaden .... 129 dep	...	...	...	...	...	...	...	10a56	1 p17	...	3 p15	...	...	3 p51	...	...	5 p55	...	...
Niederlahnstein .... 129 arr	...	...	...	...	...	...	...	12p27	2 p44	...	4 p37	...	...	...	...	...	7 p35	...	...
Ems .... 147 dep	...	...	...	...	...	...	...	11a58	2 p16	...	4 p11	...	...	...	...	...	6 p29	...	...
Niederlahnstein .... 129 dep	...	...	...	...	...	...	...	12p31	2 p48	...	4 p41	...	...	...	...	...	7 p39	...	...
Cologne .... 129 arr	...	...	...	...	...	...	...	2 p17	4 p32	...	6 p8	...	...	7 p7	...	...	9 p30	...	...
Cologne .... 161 dep	...	...	...	5 a47	...	...	...	...	...	...	6 p32	...	...	7 p14	...	...	...	...	...
Oberhausen .... 161 arr	...	...	...	6 a54	...	...	...	...	...	...	7 p46	...	...	...	...	...	...	...	...
Oberhausen .... 131A dep	...	...	...	7 a2	...	...	...	...	...	...	7 p51	...	...	C	...	...	...	...	...
Wesel .... 120 dep	...	...	...	7 a28	...	...	...	...	...	...	8 p26	...	...	...	...	...	...	...	...
Boxtel .... 117 dep	...	...	...	8 a42	...	...	...	...	...	...	9 p43	...	...	9 p57	...	...	...	...	...
Flushing .... 113 arr	...	...	...	10a45	...	...	...	...	...	...	11p38	...	...	11p52	...	...	...	...	...
Folkestone .... arr	...	...	...	...	...	...	...	...	...	...	5 a30	...	...	5 a30	...	...	...	...	...
Queenborough .... arr	...	...	...	5 p55	...	...	...	...	...	...	...	...	...	...	...	...	...	...	...
London—St. Paul's .... arr	...	...	...	7 p32	...	...	...	...	...	...	7 a45	...	...	7 a45	...	...	...	...	...
Holborn Viaduct .... arr	...	...	...	7 p34	...	...	...	...	...	...	7 a48	...	...	7 a48	...	...	...	...	...
Victoria .... arr	...	...	...	7 p34	...	...	...	...	...	...	7 a48	...	...	7 a48	...	...	...	...	...
Cologne .... 120A dep	...	...	...	...	...	...	...	...	...	...	...	...	...	...	7 p21	...	...	...	...
Crefeld .... 120A dep	...	...	...	...	...	...	...	...	...	...	...	...	...	...	8 p17	...	...	...	...
Nymegen .... 120A arr	...	...	...	...	...	...	...	...	...	...	...	...	...	...	9 p 1	...	...	...	...
Nymegen .... 119A dep	...	...	...	...	...	...	...	...	...	...	...	...	...	...	9 p26	...	...	...	...
Rotterdam .... 119A arr	...	...	...	...	...	...	...	...	...	...	...	...	...	...	11p 8	...	...	...	...
Rotterdam .... 112 dep	...	...	...	...	...	...	...	...	...	...	...	...	...	...	11p10	...	...	...	...
Hoek Van Holland 112 arr	...	...	...	...	...	...	...	...	...	...	...	...	...	...	11p35	...	...	...	...
Harwich .... arr	...	...	...	...	...	...	...	...	...	...	...	...	...	...	6 a20	...	...	...	...
Liverpool Street .... arr	...	...	...	...	...	...	...	...	...	...	...	...	...	...	8 a0	...	...	nght	...
Cologne .... 123B dep	4 a41	...	6 a0	7 a56	...	...	10a 5	3 p12	...	6 p13	6 p13	...	6 p13	...	...	...	...	12 5	...
Aix-la-Chapelle .... 123B arr	5 a54	...	7 a32	9 a9	...	...	11a19	4 p25	...	7 p24	7 p24	...	7 p24	...	...	...	...	1 a29	...
Aix-la-Chapelle .... 123B dep	5 a56	...	7 a37	9 a12	...	...	11a23	4 p29	...	7 p27	7 p27	...	7 p27	...	...	...	...	1 a32	...
Herbesthal .... 123B arr	6 a16	...	8 a7	9 a32	...	...	11a43	4 p49	...	7 p47	7 p47	...	7 p47	...	...	...	...	1 a52	...
Herbesthal .... 104 dep	6 a19	...	8 a15	9 a36	9 a36	...	11a50	4 p56	...	7 p54	7 p54		7 p54	...	...	...	...	2 a 0	...
Liege .... 93 dep	...	...	...	10a15	...	...	...	...	...	...	...		...	...	...	...	...	...	...
Erquelinnes .... 93 arr	...	...	...	12p34	...	...	...	...	...	...	...		...	...	...	...	...	...	...
Valenciennes .... 29A dep	...	...	...	1 p42	...	...	...	...	...	...	...		...	...	...	...	...	...	...
BRUSSELS Nord .... 104 arr	7 a52	...	10a25	...	11a26	...	...	6 p57	...	9 p45	9 p45		9 p45	...	...	...	...	3 a56	...
BRUSSELS Nord .... 102A dep	8 a6	...	...	...	1 p13	...	...	8 p40	...	*	*		*	...	...	...	...	8 a46	...
Ostend .... 102A arr	9 a52	...	...	...	3 p1	...	3 p23	10p26	...	11 p1	11 p1		11 p1	...	...	...	...	10a29	...
Dover (Steamer) .... arr	2 p0	...	...	...	6 p30	...	6 p30	2 a15	...	2 a15	2 a15		2 a15	...	...	...	...	2 p0	...
BRUSSELS Nord .... 103 dep	...	...	10a58	...	...	...	...	...	...	...	...		...	...	...	...	...	8 a30	...
BRUSSELS Midi .... 103 dep	A	...	11a20	...	...	...	...	10 p3	...	...	...	10 p3	...	...	...	...	...	8 a52	...
Calais .... 27 arr	...	...	3 p21	3 p31	...	...	...	1 a36	...	...	...	1 a36	...	...	...	...	...	1 p0	...
Dover (Steamer) .... arr	...	...	5 p0	5 p0	...	...	...	3 a20	...	...	...	3 a20	...	...	...	...	...	2 p30	...
Dover .... dep	3 p20	...	5 p20	5 p20	7 p55	...	7 p55	3 a45	...	3 a45	3 a45	3 a45	3 a45	...	...	...	...	3 p20	...
London { Victoria .... arr	...	...	7 p 5	7 p 5	...	...	...	...	...	...	...	...	...	...	...	...	...	...	...
London { Charing Cross arr	5 p10	...	...	...	10 p0	...	10 p0	5 a43	...	5 a43	5 a43	5 a43	5 a43	...	...	...	...	5 p10	...

§—Via Wiesbaden.

*—Carriages in the 6.13 p.m. from Cologne for Ostend travel via Louvain, Malines, and Ghent (page 101), avoiding Brussels.

C—From Cologne via Goch page 121.

The heavier figures refer to pages where the various sections of the routes may be traced in detail.

LONDON TO CHINA AND JAPAN via Siberia.

Via Moscow depart from London by ordinary express on Friday and Sunday. The NORD EXPRESS leaves London for for Moscow on Monday only.

	Nord Express.	Via Ostend.	Via Boulogne	Via H. v. Holland.	Via Flushing.
	a.m.	p.m	p.m.	p.m.	p.m.
London ...dep	9 0	9 0	2 20	8 30	8 35
Moscow ...arr	8 p18	1 p25	1 p25	1 p25	1 p25

Via St. Petersburg depart London Wednesday night.

	Via Harwich.	Via Flushing.	Via Ostend.	Via Calais.
	p.m.	p.m.	p.m.	p.m.
London ....dep	8 30	8 35	9 0	9 0
St. Petersburg arr	8 a15	8 a15	8 a15	8 a15

English Miles from Moscow.	Days from London.						
			p.m.				
—	...	Moscow ....dep	9 10	Mon.	Wed.		
732	...	Samara ....dep	10p14	Tues.	Thurs		
1356	5th	Chelyabinsk ....arr	8 p50	Wed.	Fri.		
...	...	Chelyabinsk ....dep	9 p20	Wed.	Fri.	Mon.	Siberian Railway.
1850	...	Omsk ....arr	3 p27	Thurs	Sat.	Sun.	
2380	...	Taiga (for Tomsk) arr	11a41	Fri.	Sun.	Wed.	
2708	...	Krasnoyarsk.........arr	1 a28	Sat.	Mon.	Thurs	
3377	9th	Irkutsk ....arr	5 a10	Sun.	Tues.	Fri.	
...	...	Irkutsk ....dep	6 a9	Sun.	Tues.	Fri.	
4086	...	Karimskaya.........arr	9 a45	Mon.	Wed.	Sat.	
4321	...	Manchuria ....arr	7 p24	"	"	"	
4901	11th	Harbin ....arr	3 p50	Tues.	Thurs	Sun.	Chinese Railway.
...	...	Harbin ....dep	4 p15	"	"	"	
5385	12th	Vladivostock ...arr	1 p35	Wed.	Fri.	Mon.	
5948	15th	Tsuruga (stmer) arr	6 a0	Sat.	Mon.	Thurs	
			p.m.				
...	...	Harbin ....dep	5 45	Tues.	Thurs	Sun.	Chinese Railway.
5049	...	Chang-chun ....arr	12 a5	Wed.	Fri.	Mon.	
...	...	" ....dep	7 a0	"	"	"	
5238	12th	Mukden ....arr	1 p50	"	"	"	SOUTH MANCHURIA RAILWAY (See opposite page).
...	...	Mukden ....dep	9 a0	Thurs	Fri (3p55)		
5762	13th	Pekin ....arr	7 a50	Fri.	Sat. (1p35)		
			p.m.				
...	...	Mukden...........dep	2 10	Wed.	Fri.	Mon.	
5485	12th	Dairen.............arr	10p20	"	"	"	
...	13th	Port Arthur ......arr	9 a20	Thurs	Sat.	Tues.	
...	...	Dairen (stmr) dep	noon	"	"	...	
6015	15th	Shanghai " arr	m'rn	Sat.	Mon.	...	
...	...	Mukden..............dep	2 p40	Wed.	Fri.	Mon.	SOUTH MANCHURIA RAILWAY.
5408	...	Antung ....arr	9 p40	"	"	"	
5990	13th	Fusan ....arr	7 p50	Thurs	Sat.	Tues.	
...	15th	Tokyo .... arr	1 p50	Sat.	Mon.	Thurs.	

	p.m.	
St. Petersburg dep	2 55	Sat.
Viatka ....dep	3 p17	Sun.
Chelyabinsk...arr	8 p16	Mon.

Tokyo ....dep	8 a30	Sat.	Mon.	Thurs.
Fusan..................dep	9 p50	Sun.	Tues.	Fri.
Antung...............dep	4 p40	Mon.	Wed.	Sat.
Mukden ....arr	11p10	"	"	"
Shanghai ......dep	m'rn	...	Mon.	Wed.
Dairen ....arr	m'rn	...	Wed.	Fri.
	a.m			
Port Arthur ......dep	11 0	Mon.	Wed.	Sat.
Dairen ....dep	3 p20	"	"	"
Mukden ....arr	11p25	"	"	"
	p.m.			
Pekin...................dep	9 45	...	Tues.	Fri. (7p30)
Mukden.................arr	8 p30	...	Wed.	Sat. (6 p0)
Mukden.................dep	11p50	Mon.	Wed.	Sat.
Chang-chun ....arr	6 a50	Tues.	Thurs	Sun.
" ....dep	1 a35	"	"	"
Harbin ....arr	7 a35	"	"	"
	p.m.			
Tsuruga (stmer) dep	5 0	Fri.	Mon. (6p0)	Wed. (6p0)
Vladivostock ...dep	12p15	Mon.	Wed.	Sat.
Harbin ....arr	9 a5	Tues.	Thurs	Sun.
Harbin ....dep	9 a35	"	"	"
Manchuria ....dep	7 a4	Wed.	Fri.	Mon.
Karimskaya.........dep	4 p40	"	"	"
Irkutsk ....arr	8 p54	Thurs	Sat.	Tues.
Irkutsk ....dep	10p20	"	"	"
Krasnoyarsk.........dep	3 a12	Sat.	Mon.	Thurs
Taiga ....dep	4 p56	"	"	"
Omsk ....dep	1 p22	Sun.	Tues.	Fri.
Chelyabinsk ....arr	7 a45	Mon.	Wed.	Sat.
	a.m.			
Chelyabinsk.........dep	8 20	"	Wed.	
Samara ....arr	7 a11	Tues.	Thurs	
Moscow ....arr	9 a10	Wed.	Fri.	

Chelyabinsk dep	8 a50	Sat.
Viatka ....arr	1 p51	Sun.
St. Petersburg arr	2 p15	Mon.

	Via Ostend or Calais.	Via Flushing.	Via H. v. Holland.	Nord Express
	p.m.	p.m.	p.m.	
Moscow dep	2 0	2 0	2 0	10a45
London arr	5a43	7a48	8 a0	10p0

Leave Moscow Wednesday and Friday; arrive London Saturday and Monday.
NORD EXPRESS from Moscow on Fri. only, arrives London Sunday.

	Via Ostend or Calais.	Via Flushing.	Via H. v. Holland.
	p.m.	p.m.	p.m.
St. Petersburg dep	7 5	7 5	11 0
London ....arr	10 p0	7 p34	8 a0

Leave St. Petersburg Monday, arrive London Wednesday

FARES FROM LONDON. See pages cvi and cxi.

FARES FROM MOSCOW.

	1st class. £	s.	d.	2nd class. £	s.	d.
Chelyabinsk......	8	4	5	5	8	6
Irkutsk	18	2	3	11	18	8
Harbin	30	3	2	19	14	0
Shanghai	44	8	0	32	0	4
Pekin..............	35	19	2	23	3	11
Dairen	33	19	4	21	11	7
Port Arthur	34	2	8	21	13	0
Tsuruga...........	39	14	0	27	6	3

SOUTH MANCHURIA RAILWAY.

Shortest, Quickest, and Cheapest Route between Europe and the Far East.

LONDON to SHANGHAI, via Dairen, in 14 days.
„ HONGKONG, „ in 18 days.

The South Manchuria Railway, in connection with the Trans-Siberian Express Trains and the Company's own Dairen-Shanghai Mail Steamer Service, forms the Shortest, Quickest, and Cheapest Route between Europe and any place in the Far East.

Dairen-Shanghai Direct Service is maintained Twice Weekly with the fast Passenger and Mail Boats, "Kobe Maru" and "Saikio Maru." Both steamers are thoroughly equipped with the latest facilities for the comfort and safety of passengers, including wireless telegraphy, and a highly qualified surgeon is carried on each.

LONDON to TOKYO, via Mukden and Fusan, in 14 days.
„ PEKING, via Mukden, in 12½ days.
TOKYO to PEKING, via Fusan and Mukden, in 3½ days.

The South Manchuria Railway Co.'s new Mukden-Antung Line, opened on standard gauge on November 1st, 1911, passes through magnificent scenery, and furnishes the last link in the Newest Highway Round the World. The Manchuria-Chosen Express Service through Manchuria and Korea is the best and quickest to Japan, with only a short sea voyage between the mainland and Japan proper.

SOUTH MANCHURIA RAILWAY HOTELS.

Yamato Hotels at Dairen, Port Arthur, Mukden, Changchun, and Hoshigaura. All on European lines, and under the Company's management. Comfortable Accommodation. Excellent Cuisine. Moderate Terms. Cook & Son's Coupons accepted. Rooms reserved by Letter or Wire. Telegraphic Address: "Yamato."

GUIDE BOOKS.

Illustrated Guide Books, Time Tables, the Company's Railway and Steamer Tickets, and information obtainable at Thos. Cook & Son's Offices; the Agencies of the International Sleeping Car and Express Trains Co.; the Reisebureau der Hamburg-Amerika Linie; the Nordisk Reisebureau; or direct from the

SOUTH MANCHURIA RAILWAY COMPANY, DAIREN.

Telegraphic Address: "Mantetsu." Codes:—A B C 5th Ed., A1, and Lieber's.

NORTHERN RAILWAY COMPANY.—(CHEMIN DE FER DU NORD).

[Paris Terminus, Rue de Dunkerque.]

☞ On the Railways of France Time is reckoned from Midnight to Midnight. The morning hours are reckoned in the same manner as hitherto, but after 12.0 noon the hours are numbered 13 o'clock, 14 o'clock, and so on to 24 o'clock, which is Midnight. The first hour of the day is written, 0.5, 0.10, 0.30, equivalent to 5 minutes past midnight, etc.

LONDON to PARIS via CALAIS and via BOULOGNE.

CALAIS, BOULOGNE, ABBEVILLE, AMIENS, and PARIS.

English Miles from Dover.	Station																
	London Charing Cross ....dep	...	...	...	...	...	...	...	...	...	...	9 a0	...	9 a0	...	...	...
	London Victoria ....dep	...	...	...	...	...	...	...	...	...	...	...	...	...	...	...	11 a0
	Dover ....dep	...	...	...	...	...	...	...	...	...	...	11 a5	...	11 a5	...	...	12p55
25	CALAIS Gare Maritime ....arr	...	...	...	...	...	...	...	...	...	...	12p25	...	12p25	...	...	2 p20
		1,2,3	1,2,3	1,2,3	1,2,3	1 &2	1 &2	1,2,3	1,2,3	1,2,3	1,2,3	1 & 2	1,2,3	1,2,3	1,2,3	1,2,3	Lux
	CALAIS Gare Maritime ....dep	...	...	...	...	...	...	...	...	...	...	13 15	...	13 30	...	...	14 40
26¾	Calais Ville ....dep	...	...	5 58	...	...	...	7 20	9 8	10 13	...		...	13 37	...	...	
31¼	Fréthun	...	...	...	...	...	...	7 34	...	10 29	...		...	...	...	...	
42½	Marquise Rinxent	...	...	6 30	...	...	...	8 3	9 34	10 56	...		...	...	...	...	
48½	Wimille Wimereux	...	...	6 42	...	...	...	8 21	9 46	11 10	11 43		...	...	...	...	
51¾	Boulogne Tintelleries	...	...	6 52	...	...	...	8 31	...	...	...		...	...	...	...	
52¼	BOULOGNE Ville ....arr	...	...		...	...	...	8 35	9 54	11 19	11 58		...	14 19	...	...	
...	London Charing Cross ...dep	...	...		...	...	...	...	...	...			10a0	10 a0	...	10 a0	
...	Folkestone ....dep	...	...		...	...	...	...	...	...			1155	11a55	...	11a55	
...	Boulogne ....arr	...	...		...	...	...	...	...	...			1330	13 30	...	13 30	
...	Boulogne Maritime ....dep	...	...		...	...	...	...	...	...			1412	...	...	14 28	
...	BOULOGNE Ville ....dep	...	5 3		6 16	...	8 45	9 0	10 9	11 31	2 30		1420	14 29	12 37	14 33	
55¼	Pont de Briques	...	5 12		6 25	...	...	...	10 17	11 40	12 38			...	12 46	14 42	
57¾	Hesdigneul 19A	...	5 18		6 33	...	...	9 12	10 23	11 47				...	12 53	...	
60¾	Neufchâtel	...	5 27		6 41	...	...	9 23	10 31	11 56			L	...	13 1	...	
64½	Dannes-Camiers ●	...	5 36		6 49	...	9 4	9 32	10 39	12 5				...	13 9	14 59	
69	Etaples ¶ 28	...	5 49	7 18	6 57	...	9 12	9 45	10 47	12 19	13 5			14 56	13 17	15 7	
76	Rang-du-Fliers-Verton 30A	...	6 6	7 31		...	9 26	10 6		12 38	13 2	RC		15 15			
82¾	Quend Fort Mahon ☽	...	6 21	...	...	...	9 40	10 26	...	12 54	13 36			...	...		
86½	Rue	...	6 29	7 46	...	...	...	10 36	...	13 3	...			...	...		
92¾	Noyelles 22A	...	6 47	7 57	...	...	9 56	10 58	...	13 20	13 54			...	...		
100¾	Abbeville 20	5 10	7 22	8 11	...	...	1013	11 32	...	13 43	14 11			15 43	14 44		
106¼	Pont-Rémy	5 21	7 33	...	...	...		11 43	...	...				...	14 54		
112	Longpré 21 ....arr	5 36	7 48	...	...	...		11 58	...	14 0				...	15 9		
120	Picquigny	5 57	8 9	...	...	...		12 22	...	...				...	15 45		
127½	St. Roch 30A	6 17	8 30	...	...	...		12 48	...	...				...	16 5		
128¾	Amiens ....arr	6 22	8 35	8 44	...	...		12 53	...	14 28	14 45	15 8		16 15	16 10		16 35
177¾	Tergnier 21 ....arr	8 44	11 27	11 27	...	...		17 23	...	...	...	...		18 4	18 4		...
195¾	Laon 21 ....arr	10 11	12 20	12 20	...	...		16 21	...	...	...	...		19 8	19 8		...
228	Reims 67 ....arr	11 17	13 46	13 46	...	C ...		17 20	...	...	...	...		20 15	20 15	...	...
263½	Chalons 67 ....arr	12 2	16 43	16 43	...	C ...		17 48	...	...	...	...		21 17	21 17	...	...
201½	Rouen 21 ....arr	..	10 53	10 53	...	...		17 30	1,2,3	...	...	...		21 33	21 33	...	...

English Miles from Dover.	Station																		
...	Amiens ....dep			6 33	9 12	8 49	8 56	1028		13 24	15 28	15 34	14 53	15 13		16 20	17 57	...	16 41
131¾	Longueau			6 41	9 22	...	...	1044		...	...	15 53	...	...		...	...	...	...
134¼	Boves 29			6 48	9 30	...	...	...		13 36	...	16 0	...	...		...	18 10	...	...
140½	Ailly-sur-Noye			7 5	9 51	...	...	...		13 51	...	16 13	...	...		...	18 25	...	...
151¼	Breteuil			7 28	10 20	...	...	...		14 12	...	16 34	...	...		...	18 5	...	...
160½	Saint Just 29A		6 40	7 52	10 52	...	9 42	RC		14 38	...	17 37	...	...		17 2	19 20	...	...
169¼	Clermont 29A	5 52	7 10	8 8	11 30	...	9 56	...		15 0	16 16	18 1	...	...		...	19 42	...	...
174¼	Liancourt	6 2	7 22	8 19	11 40	...	10 5	...		15 1[illegible]	...	18 11	...	...		...	19 50	...	...
178½	Creil 22 ....arr	6 14	7 34	8 33	11 49	...	10 13	...		15 25	16 29	18 23	15 53	...		17 25	20 2	...	...
	Creil 22 ....dep	6 30	7 39	8 39	11 51	...	10 15	...		15 31	16 31	18 27	15 55	...		17 27	20 5	...	...
184¾	Chantilly	6 41	7 49	8 50	12 1	...	...	...		15 41	...	18 37	...	...		17 37	20 15	...	...
210¼	PARIS Nord ....arr	7 25	8 37	9 38	12 42	10 30	10 55	12 7	1212	16 2[illegible]	17 10	19 25	16 35	16 40	1720	18 10	20 56	...	18 15

Runs 5th July to 30th Sept. Not on Sunday. — Runs until Oct. 3rd. — Until 31st August only. ☞ — Simplon and Engadine Express, see Note X.

JUNCTION TRAINS—For passengers from Stations on Nord Co.'s line to places served by the P.L.M. Line.

‡—Thursday only.

	1 & 2	1 & 2	1 & 2	1 & 2	1 & 2	Lux	1 & 2	1 &2	...
Paris Nord Station ....dep	6 38	11 2	13 9	17 ‡1	17 39	18 25	19 31	2125	...
Paris P.L.M. Station ...arr	7 18	11 35	13 48	17 35	18 26	18 59	20 34	2155	...

Children—Under 3 years free; three to seven, half-fare; over seven, full fare.

Luggage, 30 kilogrammes (66 lbs.) allowed free; excess Luggage, 1 centime per 44 lbs. per kilometre. *Only 25 kilogrammes (56 lbs.) of registered luggage from London to Paris allowed free.*

Customs Examination.—Unregistered Luggage and Hand Luggage examined at Calais and Boulogne. Luggage registered to Paris examined at Nord Station, Paris.

Private Cabins on Steamers.—See page lxiii.

Bicycles.—Dover to Calais or Folkestone to Boulogne, 3s.

¶—Station for Le Touquet—2 miles.

☽-Station for Quend Plage and Fort Mahon—tramway.

●—Station for Ste. Cecile.

A—Also takes at Boulogne 3rd class for Paris only; will take for all Stations 3rd class from England and Calais.

B—Special Service from London every Friday.

C—Will not admit 2nd class at Amiens.

RC Restaurant Car attached.

For Continuation of Trains, see next page.

NORTHERN RAILWAY.

LONDON to PARIS via CALAIS and via BOULOGNE.

CALAIS, BOULOGNE, ABBEVILLE, AMIENS, and PARIS.

THROUGH CARRIAGES.
- Boulogne to Basle—in 18.8 (1st and 2nd Class, Lits-Salon, Wagon-Lit).
- Boulogne to Berne, Interlaken, and Lucerne—in 18.8 (1st and 2nd class and Lits-Salon).
- Calais to Basle—in 20.10 and 0.58 (1st and 2nd class, Lits-Salon).
- Calais to Geneva—in 14.50 (1st and 2nd class and Lits-Salon).
- Calais to Milan, via the Simplon—in 14.50 (1st and 2nd Class).

Station		1	2	3	4	5	6	7	8	9	10	11	12	13	14	15	16	17	18
London Charing Cross dep		...	...	...	...	...	...	...	...	...	...	4p30	4 p30	...	...	...	9 p0	9 p0	9 p0
London Victoria dep		11 a0	...	...	...	...	...	...	...	...	...	...	...	...	...	...	8 p45	...	...
Dover dep		12p55	...	...	...	...	...	...	...	...	...	6p15	6 p15	...	...	...	11 p5	11 p5	11 p5
CALAIS Gare Maritime arr		2 p20	...	...	...	...	...	...	...	...	...	...	...	1,2,3	...	...	12a20	12a20	12a20
		1 & 2	1,2,3	1,2,3	1 & 2	1 & 2	1 & 2	1,2,3	1,2,3	1,2,3	1,2,3	1& 2	1 & 2	Enquire as to this Service.	1,2,3	1,2,3	1 & 2	Lux	1 & 2
CALAIS Gare Maritime dep		14 50	...	...	15 57	...	...	...	...	...	...	20 0	20 10		...	...	0 58	1 3	1 30
Calais Ville dep		14 56	...	13 55	16 3	...	...	15 0	16 58	18 12	1924				20 30	2255		SC	1 37
Fréthun			...	14 8	...	...	...	...	17 11	K	1937				20 46	23 9			...
Marquise Rinxent			...	14 37	...	...	...	15 30	17 42	...	20 8				21 15	2341	B		A
Wimille Wimereux			...	14 54	...	...	...	15 42	18 1	18 46	2027				21 29	2359			...
Boulogne Tintelleries			...	15 4	...	...	...	...	18 12	...	2037				21 39	0 8			2 12
BOULOGNE Ville arr			...	15 8	16 48	...	...	15 50	18 16	18 54	2041				21 44	0 12			
London Charing Cross dep			...	...	...	2 p5	2 p5	...	...	...	...			5 p5	...	Until 30th Sept.			
Folkestone dep			...	...	...	3 p55	3 p55	...	...	...	...			6 p42	...				
Boulogne arr			...	...	...	17 50	17 50	...	...	...	...			20 20	...				
Boulogne Maritime dep			...	...	1,2,3	18 8	18 8	...	...	†	*			20 50	...				
BOULOGNE Ville dep			16 0	16 4	16 58	18 25	18 32	17 37	19 4	19 50	1938			20 57	22 3				
Pont de Briques			...	16 12	...		...	...	...	19 59	1948				22 11	...	SC		
Hesdigneul 19A			...	16 18	...		...	17 49	...	20 5	1955				22 17	...			
Neufchâtel		C	...	16 28	...	M	G	17 57	H	20 13	20 3				22 26	...			
Dannes-Camiers ●			...	16 36	...		...	18 5	...	20 2[illegible]	2010				22 34	...			
Etaples ¶ 28			16 24	16 48	17 25		...	18 13	19 29	20 28	2022			21 22	22 50	...			
Rang-du-Fliers-Verton 30A			16 39	17 7	17 41		...		19 45		2039				23 12	...			
Quend Fort Mahon ☽			...	17 22	...		...	...	19 56	...	2053				0 27	...	RC		
Rue			...	17 30	...	RC	RC	...	20 2	...	21 1				23 35	...			
Noyelles 22A			17 2	17 46	18 9		...	...	20 16	...	2118		Does not run on Sunday.	From London on Fri. only, from July 11th to Sept. 12th.	23 53	...		from London Friday only, not entering Paris. Tickets of Sleeping Car Co.	
Abbeville 20	1624		...	18 4	18 22		SC	...	20 32	19 43	2138				0 17	...			3 18
Pont Rémy	1641		...		...		...	...	...	19 54	2148				...	...			...
Longpré 21 arr	1650		...	...	18 49		...	...	...	20 10	22 2				0 35	...			...
Picquigny	1711		...	...	...		...	...	...	20 28	2227				...	...			...
St. Roch 30A	1733		...	...	...		...	...	...	20 48	2251				...	...		...	...
Amiens arr	1738	16 47	From 10th July until 15th September only.	...	19 14		19 58	...	21 5	20 52	2256				1 5	...	2 51	3 3	3 54
Tergnier 21 arr		19 55		...	...		...	...	23 23	...	...	Does not run on Sunday.			5 26	...	...		...
Laon 21 arr		...		...	...		21 13	...	2 8	...	...		23 20		6 48	...	4 16		...
Reims 67 arr		...		...	...		22 29	...	4 13	...	...		...		8 25	...	5 12		...
Chalons 67 arr		...		...	...		23 10	...	6 33	...	...		0 49		10 0	...	5 46		...
Rouen 21 arr		21 33		...	...		23 9	...	23 9	23 9	6 10		...		6 10	...	6 10	Brindisi,	9 a22
Amiens dep		16 50		20 20	19 22		...	...	21 12	21 18	...		...		1 25	1 39		3 8	3 59
Longueau		...		20 28	...		...	...	...	...	...		...	...	...	1 48		P. & O. Express for	...
Boves 29		...		20 35	...		...	...	J	...	...		...	...	...	1 55	From London on Friday only.		...
Ailly-sur-Noye		...	...	20 48	...		...	...	...	...	...		...	...	...	2 11			...
Breteuil		...	...	21 26	...		...	...	...	...	...		...	...	2 12	2 34			...
Saint Just 29A		...	...	21 47	...		...	...	21 57	22 3	...		...	...	2 33	2 55			...
Clermont 29A	19‡26	...	...	...	...		...	...	22 11	22 17	...		...	...	2 52	3 13			...
Liancourt	19 35	...	...	...	...		...	...	22 20	22 26	...		...	...	...	...			...
Creil 22 arr	19 47	...	...	...	...		...	...	22 2[illegible]	22 34	...		...	...	3 10	3 30			...
Creil 22 dep		...	...	...	...		...	...	22 3[illegible]	22 37	...		...	...	3 18	3 39			...
Chantilly		...	...	...	...		...	...	22 4[illegible]	22 47	...		...	...	3 29	3 51			...
PARIS Nord arr		18 20	19 15	...	21 5	21 0	...	...	23 19	23 25	...	2325	...	...	4 15	4 37		...	5 40

G—Train for Switzerland. Only takes those 2nd class passengers who come from England or who are travelling from a station on NORD CO.'s line to a station on EST CO.'s line, or beyond.

H—Only takes those 3rd class passengers who come from England; down to Noyelles, will also admit 3rd class for Paris.

J—Between Amiens and Paris runs until 3rd October only.

K—Third class passengers taken when going to England.

L—Train reserved for passengers from England for Paris; exceptionally admits at Boulogne 1st and 2nd class for Paris without registered luggage.

M—Second class passengers from Boulogne must be without registered luggage.

X—**Simplon and Engadine Express.**—Train de Luxe; take tickets in advance from Sleeping Car Co.

*—Until 30th Sept. Boulogne dep. 19.22 on Sunday.
†—Until 15th October only.
‡—Sunday excepted.
SC—Sleeping Car attached.

661bs. of Luggage free.] **NORTHERN RAILWAY.** [Excess Luggage, 1 cent. per 44 lbs. per kilometre.

PARIS to LONDON via BOULOGNE and via CALAIS.

PARIS to AMIENS, BOULOGNE, ABBEVILLE, and CALAIS.

Only 25 kilogrammes (55 lbs.) of registered luggage from Paris to London allowed free.

1 Cl. fr. c. Fro	2 Cl. fr. c. m P	3 Cl. fr. c. aris.		1,2,3 (Until 30th Sept.)	1,2,3	1,2,3	1 Cl.	1,2,3	1 & 2	1,2,3	1 & 2	1,2,3 (From 10th July until 15th Sept. only.)	1,2,3	1,2,3	1,2,3	1 & 2 (For Travellers to England only.)	Lux·
			PARIS Nord ...dep	...	...	...	...	5 17	...	7 15	8 25	8 30	8 33	8 40	9 0	9 50	9 55
4 60	3 10	2 0	Chantilly ...	...	...	...	...	6 14	...	7 †46			9 5	9 12	9 36		...
5 70	3 85	2 50	Creil ...arr	...	...	...	...	6 24	...	7 55			9 14	9 21	9 45		...
			Creil ...dep	...	5 12	...	...	6 34	...	7 58			9 16	9 22	9 54		M
6 50	4 40	2 85	Liancourt ...	...	5 23	...	...	6 51	...	8 7			...	...	10 5		...
7 40	5 0	3 25	Clermont ...	...	5 34	...	...	7 11	...	8 16	C		...	...	10 14		...
8 95	6 5	3 95	Saint Just ...	...	5 54	...	...	7 37	...	8 31			O	...	10 29	RC	...
10 65	7 20	4 70	Breteuil ...	...		...	...	8 0	...	8 46			...	...			...
12 55	8 45	5 50	Ailly-sur-Noye ...	...	...	...	...	8 26	...	...			...	...	...		...
13 65	9 20	6 0	Boves ...	...	...	...	...	8 33	...	...			...	...	...		...
14 10	9 55	6 20	Longueau ...	...	...	...	...	8 40	...	9 9			...	...	...		...
14 65	9 90	6 45	**Amiens** ...arr	...	...	...	...	8 47	...	9 15			10 12	10 18	...		11 22
...	...	...	ROUEN 21 ...dep	...	...	...	...	...	...	...			8 6	...	8 6		
...	...	...	CHALONS 67 ...dep	...	...	...	6 27	...	...	...			...	...	...		
...	...	...	REIMS 67 ...dep	...	...	...	6 47	...	...	...			...	...	...		
...	...	...	LAON 21 ...dep	...	...	...	7 53	...	...	...			8 0	...	...		
...	...	...	TERGNIER 21 ...dep	...	...	...	8 11	...	...	...			8 30	...	...		
...	...	...	**Amiens** ...dep	...	4 44	7 7	9 12	...	...	9 20			10 17	...	10 32		11 25
14 90	10 5	6 55	St. Roch ...		4 52	7 17	...	...	...	...			...	...	...		
16 25	10 95	7 15	Picquigny ...		5 13	7 36	RC	...	...	...			O	...	...		
17 70	11 95	7 80	Longpré ...dep		5 35	7 59	...	...	...	...			...	...	10 59		
18 70	12 65	8 25	Pont-Rémy ...		5 52	8 15	...	...	...	...			...	...	...		
19 70	13 30	8 65	**Abbeville** ...		6 11	8 30	...	...	...	9 52			10 53	...	11 16		M
21 15	14 30	9 30	Noyelles ...arr (Until October 15.)		6 29	8 47	G	...	...	...		10 39	11 6	...	12 15		
22 30	15 5	9 80	Rue ...		6 49	9 6	...	...	...	...		...	...	...	12 32		
22 95	15 50	10 10	Quend Fort Mahon ...		6 57	9 15	...	...	...	...		...	11 24	...	12 40		
24 20	16 35	10 65	Rang-du-Fliers-Verton		7 17	9 33	...	...	...	10 27		11 4	11 38	...	12 58		
25 40	17 15	11 20	**Etaples** (Le Touquet) ...7 26	6 37	7 38	9 52	...	...	...	10 40		11 16	11 53	11 34	13 17		
26 20	17 70	11 55	Dannes-Camiers ...7 36	6 46	7 49	10 1	...	...	...	...		...	...	11 44	13 26		
26 90	18 15	11 85	Neufchâtel ...7 44	...	7 58	10 10	...	...	...	...		...	...	11 52	13 34		
27 45	18 50	12 5	Hesdigneul ...7 51	...	8 5	10 17	...	...	...	...		...	...	11 58	13 41		
27 90	18 80	12 25	Pont de Briques ...7 57	7 0	8 11	10 23	...	...	...	...		...	...	12 4	13 47		
28 45	19 20	12 50	**BOULOGNE** Ville ...arr 8 4		8 18	10 30	10 47	...	...	11 3	11 15	11 39	12 16	12 11	13 54		
...	...	...	Boulogne Maritime ...arr		...	...	10 54	...	...	...	11 25	...					
...	...	...	BOULOGNE ...dep		8*45	..	11 45	...	...	...	11 45	...	...	...	...		
40 30	28 55	21 5	FOLKESTONE ...dep		10*25	...	1 p40	...	...	...	1 p40	...	...	...	...		
62 50	43 35	28 35	CHARING CROSS ...arr		12*12	...	3 p25	...	..	...	3 p25	...	...	...	...		
...	...	...	**BOULOGNE** Ville ...dep		8 33	10 55	...	...	11 38	11 48	...	...	...	13 12	...		
28 55	19 30	12 55	Boulogne Tintelleries ...	7 13	8 39	11 0	...	...	...	11 53	...	...	...	13 17	...		
29 10	19 65	12 80	Wimille-Wimereux ...	7 21	8 51	11 13	...	...	...	...	...	...	...	13 28	...		
30 25	20 40	13 30	Marquise Rinxent ...	7 33	9 10	11 34	...	...	...	...	...	...	...	13 48	...		
32 25	21 75	14 20	Fréthun ...	...	9 36	12 2	...	...	...	...	...	...	...	14 16	...		
33 5	22 30	14 55	Calais Ville ...arr	7 57	9 48	12 13	...	...	12 21	12 39	...	...	...	14 27	...		
33 40	22 55	14 70	**CALAIS** Gare Maritime ...arr		...	...	...	...	12 27	12 46	...	...	...	...	...	13 5	13 10
			CALAIS Gare Maritime ...dep	...	...	...	...	...	...	...	...	...	...	...	...	1 p25	1 p25
47 5	33 70	24 15	DOVER ...arr	...	...	...	...	...	...	...	...	...	...	...	...	2 p35	2 p35
			London VICTORIA ...arr	...	...	...	...	...	...	...	...	...	...	...	...	...	...
70 80	49 55	32 30	London CHARING CROSS ...arr	...	...	...	...	...	...	...	...	...	...	...	...	5 p10	5 p10

*—From Boulogne on Monday, July 14th, 21st, 28th; Tuesday, August 5th, and each Monday from August 11th to September 15th.

†—Takes up only.

§—Leaves Boulogne, Maritime Station, at 13.55.

RC—Restaurant Car attached.

A—Takes 3rd class from Paris for Boulogne, Calais, and from all Stations for England.

B—2nd class for Calais and England only. Restaurant Car (2nd class passengers admitted at meal times only).

C—Takes 1st, 2nd, and 3rd class for England or for Transatlantique steamer; also takes 1st and 2nd class for Boulogne, in case of second class passengers must be without registered luggage.

D—Takes 2nd class for England or Transatlantique steamer; 2nd class for Boulogne must be without luggage.

G—Coming from Switzerland; carries 2nd class from Eastern Co.'s line. Restaurant Car generally attached (travellers are warned to enquire).

H—Takes 3rd class for England only.

L—Also carries 2nd class from Est. Co.'s line.

M—**Simplon and Engadine Express.** Train de Luxe.

O—Runs until 3rd October.

P—Runs until 30th September.

For Continuation of Trains, see next page.

66 lbs. of Luggage free.] **NORTHERN RAILWAY.** [Excess Luggage, 1 cent. per 44 lbs. per kilometre.

PARIS to LONDON via BOULOGNE and via CALAIS.

PARIS to AMIENS, BOULOGNE, ABBEVILLE, and CALAIS.

		1,2,3	1 & 2	1,2,3	1,2,3	1,2,3	1,2,3	1,2,3	1,2,3	1 & 2	1 Cl.	1 & 2	1 & 2	1,2,3	1,2,3	1,2,3	1,2,3	1 & 2	&2
PARIS Nord ....dep		9 55	12 0	12 3	13 0	13 15	1430	15 20	15 50	16 0	...	1710	1720	18 0	21 20	2015	22 20	0 30	...
Chantilly		1051	...	12 36	13†33	13 56	15 4	...	16 53		...		...	18 37	...	21 7	23 17		...
Creil ....arr		11 1	...	12 45	...	14 6	1513	...	17 3		...		...	18 47	21 55	2117	23 27		...
Creil ....dep		11 6	...	12 48	...	14 10	1518	...	17 10		...		...	18 49	21†56	2159	23 45		...
Liancourt		1120	RC	12 57	...	14 25	1528	...	17 23		...		...	19 2	...	2213	23 56		...
Clermont		1136	...	13 7	...	14 41	1538	...	17 35		...		RC	19 12	...	2227	0 9		...
Saint Just		1159	B	13 22	...	15 8	1553	O	18 18	D	...		...	19 29	...	2243	0 31		...
Breteuil		1222	...	...	...	15 31	16 8	...	18 42		...		...	19 48	A	23 1	0 51		...
Ailly-sur-Noye		1240	...	...	...	15 50	...	...	19 4		...		...	20 2	...	2323	1 7		...
Boves		1254	...	...	...	16 4	...	...	19 20		...		...	...	...	2336	...		...
Longueau ....arr		13 0	...	...	...	...	...	...	...		...		1839	20 14	...	2342	1 22		...
Amiens ....arr		13 8	1326	13 57	14 36	16 17	1633	16 50	19 32		...		1853	20 22	22 55	0 5	1 31		...
ROUEN 21 ....dep		8 37	8 37	8 37	...	13 26	...	...	...		13 26		...	18 6	18 12	...	...		...
CHALONS 67 ....dep		...	...	...	...	7 52	...	...	7 52		14 35		...	14 22	18 43	...	...		1 58
REIMS 67 ....dep		9 2	9 2	9 2	...	11 8	...	...	11 8		14 58	Runs from 5th July until 30th September, and not on Sundays.	...	16 1	19 40	...	...		...
LAON 21 ....dep		1032	1032	10 32	...	12 38	...	...	12 38		16 5		...	17 21	20 32	...	...		3 20
TERGNIER 21 ....dep	1,2,3	1131	1131	11 31	...	14 26	...	...	14 26		16 29		...	18 26	21 3	...	...		...
Amiens ....dep	1128	1422	1331	14 9	...	17 41	...		16 55		17 33		...	20 51	23 0	0 17	2 2	Not from Paris on Saturday night (Sunday morn.)	
St. Roch	1134	1430		...	...	17 50	...		...		...		...	20 59	...	0 22	...		
Picquigny	1152	1451		...	...	18 10	...		...		...		...	21 19	...	0 42	...		
Longpré ....dep	1212	1514		...	...	18 33	...		H		L		...	21 42	...	1 1	2 34		
Pont-Rémy	1229	1531		...	...	18 50	...		...		...		...	21 59	...	1 17	...		
Abbeville	1238	1540	RC	14 47		19 17	...	Until 31st August.	17 29	RC	...	1914	...	22 15	23 35	1 27	2 59		
Noyelles ....arr				15 5	Depart from Maritime Station.	19 35	...		...		...	1927	...	22 29			3 16		
Rue		...		15 25		19 56	...		...		RC	1938	...	22 49		...	3 †28		Not on Sunday morn.
Quend Fort Mahon		...		15 33		19 57	...		...		...	1945	...	22 57		...	...		
Rang-du-Fliers-Verton		...		15 51		20 24	...	...	18 5		...	1957	...	23 18		...	3 52		
Etaples		14 3		16 10		20 44	1711	17 42	18 18		...	2010	2227	23 38		...	4 10		
Dannes-Camiers		1412	B	...		20 53	1720	17 50	...		...	2018	...	23 48		...	...		
Neufchâtel		1420		...		21 2	1728	...	...		...		...	23 56		...	...		
Hesdigneul		1427		16 31		21 12	1735	...	...		...		2247	...		...	4 37		
Pont de Briques		1433				21 19	1741	18 7	...		...		...	0 7		...	4 44		
BOULOGNE Ville ....arr		1440				21 27	1749	18 14	18 41	18 51	18 56		2258	0 15		...	4 51		
Boulogne Maritime ....arr					18 6	...			...	18 58	19 2			...		...	...		
BOULOGNE ....dep		...			...	...	...	...	...	19 10	19 10		...	...		...	...		
FOLKESTONE ....dep		...			...	...	...	...	...	9 p5	9 p5		...	...		...	...		
CHARING CROSS ....arr		...			...	...	...	...	...	10p45	10p45		...	...		...	...		
BOULOGNE Ville ....dep		14§1			18 15	21 37	1910		18 50	...	...		...	0 47		...	4 59		
Boulogne Tintelleries		P		16 48	...	21 43	1916		18 56	...	...	2038	...	0 53	0 42	...	5 6		
Wimille-Wimereux		1410		17 0	...	21 54	1925	Until Sept. 30.	19 5	...	...	2044	...	1 2	...	...	5 15		
Marquise Rinxent		1422		17 20	...	22 14	1944		19 19	...	...		...	1 16	...	...	5 32		
Fréthun		...		17 48	...	22 42	2012		...	...	...	...	...	...	...	...	5 57		
Calais Ville ....arr		1445	1525	18 0	19 2	22 53	2023	...	...	...	...	...	...	1 41	1 15	...	6 9		
CALAIS Gare Maritime ....arr		1452	1526	...		...	...	...	...	...	...	...	...	...	1 23	...	...	6 20	6 34
CALAIS Gare Maritime ....dep		...	3p45	...		...	...	...	...	...	...	...	...	...	1 a40	...	...	6 45	6 45
DOVER ....arr		...	5 p0	...	To Lille.	...	...	...	...	...	...	...	...	...	2 a55	...	...	...	...
London VICTORIA ....arr		...	7 p5	...		...	...	...	...	...	...	...	...	...	...	...	...	...	...
London CHARING CROSS ....arr		...	...	...		...	...	...	...	...	...	...	...	...	5 a43	...	...	1015	10 15

CALAIS and DUNKIRK.

E.M.																		
—	**Calais** ....dep	...	6 36	8 33	12 49	1540	19 16	21 21	**Dunkirk** ..dep	4 49	...	8 55	11 27	13 18	...	17 23	21 36
3	St. Pierre	...	6 50	8 45	13 1	...	19 28	21 33	Bourbourg	5 15	6 19	9 28	11 52	13 57	1643	17 58	22 8
14¼	Gravelines	6 36	7 20	9 14	13 36	1613	20 2	22 0	Gravelines	5 23	6 26	9 40	12 0	14 8	1650	18 10	22 18
18	Bourbourg	6 43	7 29	9 26	13 53	1623	20 13	22 11	St. Pierre	5 51	—	10 9	...	14 38	—	18 41	22 47
29¼	**Dunkirk** (94) ....arr	...	8 1	9 59	14 24	1647	20 45	22 37	**Calais** (18) arr	6 3	...	10 19	12 31	14 48	...	18 52	22 58

BOULOGNE and ST. OMER.

*—Until 30th September. ‡—17.9 p.m. on Sunday.

Dist. E.M.	1 Cl. fr. c.	2 Cl. fr. c.	All 1,2,3 Class.													
			Boulogne ....dep	5 13	8 48	12 0	14*43	17‡19	20 59	**St. Omer** ....dep	4 46	9 46	12 20	18 10	21 43	...
5½	1 10	0 70	Hesdigneul	5 30	9 8	12 21	15 3	17 40	21 20	Wizernes	5 6	10 12	12 40	18 30	22 4	...
10	1 80	1 20	Samer	5 43	9 22	12 42	15 16	17 53	21 34	Lumbres	5 23	10 30	12 55	18 47	22 29	...
15½	2 80	1 90	Desvres	6 10	9 44	13 6	15 32	18 14	21 55	Desvres	6 3	11 8	13 35	19 25	23 6	...
28½	5 15	3 50	Lumbres (22A)	6 48	10 26	13 48	—	18 50	22 31	Samer	6 16	11 22	13 49	19 38	23 19	...
33½	6 5	4 10	Wizernes	7 2	10 40	14 2	...	19 5	22 45	Hesdigneul	6 29	11 35	14 1	19 50	23 31	...
40½	6 85	4 90	**St. Omer** (26) ..arr	7 22	10 59	14 21	...	19 26	23 2	**Boulogne** (18) ...arr	6 43	11 50	14 15	20 4	23 45	...

ARRAS and DOULLENS.

Dist E.M							
	Arras ......dep	5 18	9 30	11 31	16 35	19 24	...
16⅝	Mondicourt-Pas......	6 4	10 15	12 17	17 25	20 8	...
23	**Doullens (20)** ......arr	6 20	10 31	12 34	17 41	20 22	...

Doullens ......dep	6 38	9 28	13 40	16 33	20 25	...	...
Mondicourt-Pas	6 57	9 48	14 1	16 53	20 45	...	...
Arras (23) ......arr	7 42	10 36	14 47	17 39	21 28	...	...

BETHUNE, ABBEVILLE, & LE TRÉPORT.

	1,2,3	1,2,3	1,2,3	1,2,3	1& 2	1,2,3	1,2,3	1,2,3
Béthune ...dep	7 13	...	8 36	11 2		14 8	...	19 3
Lapugnoy	7 33	...	8 52	11 19	...	1425	...	19 21
Brias	8 9	...	9 22	11 52	§—Until Oct. 1st.	1458	...	19 53
St. Pol ......arr	8 19	...	9 31	12 2		15 7	...	20 2
" ......dep	—	5 28	9 47	12 31		1532	16 42	20 48
Frevent	...	5 54	10 12	12 57		1556	17 9	21 16
St. Riquier......	...	6 51	11 3	13 51		—	18 3	22 11
Abbe-ville arr	...	7 9	11 22	14 10	...	...	18 22	22 30
dep	4 6	7 19	11 35	15 52	1746	...	19 14	—
Chépy	4 37	7 59	12 13	16 33	...	...	19 49	...
Feuquières......	4 44	8 8	12 20	16 41	§	...	19 56	...
Eu	5 13	8 37	12 45	17 6	1845	...	20 29	...
Dieppe (85) arr	7 34	1211	14 4	18 39	...	...	21 56	...
Treport ...arr	5 20	8 42	12 50	17 11	1849	...	20 34	...

Le Treport dp	...	...	6 50	9 29	...	13 26	...	1716	2110
Dieppe.....dep	...	...	...	6 41	...	10 37	...	1319	20 7
Eu	...	...	6 59	9 41	...	13 35	...	1725	2125
Feuquières	...	...	7 22	10 5	...	13 57	...	1747	2153
Chépy	...	...	7 28	1012	...	14 5	...	1754	22 0
Abbeville 18 ar	...	...	8 0	1045	...	14 36	...	1825	2233
" ...dep	353	6 32	—	—	1124	15 48	...	1926	—
St. Riquier......	4 9	6 53	...	...	1142	16 9	...	1947	...
Frevent...(20)...	459	7 59	...	...	1234	17 10	1912	2048	...
St. Pol ......arr	520	8 22	...	...	1256	17 32	1934	2111	...
" (28) dep	551	8 30	...	...	13 5	17 38	20 3	—	...
Brias	6 3	8 41	...	...	1316	17 49	2015	...	...
Lapugnoy	631	9 13	...	...	1341	18 19	2042	...	...
Béthune (26) a	645	9 28	...	...	1356	18 34	2058	...	...

Feuquières ......dep	...	...	...	...	...
Ault-Onival ......arr	...	...	...	...	...
Ault-Onival ......dep	...	...	...	...	...
Feuquières ......arr	...	...	...	...	...

VERBERIE and ESTREES-St.-DENIS.

Verberie (29)......dep	7 12	8 34	1020	1448	1858	21 20	...	...
Estrées-St.-Denis arr	7 37	9 4	11 8	1517	1926	22 4	...	...
Estrées-St.-Denis dep	6 29	7 53	9 21	12 26	1557	1947	...	...
Verberie ......arr	6 59	8 19	10 7	12 56	1628	2017	...	...

VALENCIENNES and HIRSON.

Valenciennes...dep	...	5 10	...	7 18	10 11	13 25	...	17 57	20 8
Bavai (30A)	5 12	6 2	7 16	8 13	11 2	14 14	17 3	18 49	21 7
Maubeuge ...arr	5 44	6 32	7 42	8 40	11 30	14 41	1734	19 23	2139
Solre-le-Chateau	—	7 31	—	—	12 27	16 21	—	20 59	—
Fourmies (29A)	...	8 5	...	9 29	13 3	16 55	...	21 32	...
Anor	...	8 12	...	9 38	13 11	17 3	...	21 40	...
Hirson ......arr	...	8 39	...	9 47	13 20	17 14	...	21 49	...
Hirson ......dep	...	...	4 45	...	9 17	1241	...	17 33	...
Anor	...	...	4 57	...	9 28	1254	...	17 46	...
Fourmies	...	...	5 5	...	9 41	13 7	...	17 54	...
Solre-le-Chateau	...	...	5 37	...	10 12	1340	...	18 29	...
Maubeuge ...dep	4 4	6 17	6 43	9 44	11 30	1623	1813	19 25	2034
Bavai	4 42	6 49	7 16	1012	12 4	1659	1848	19 57	21 8
Valenciennes ar	5 26	...	8 3	...	12 52	1748	1914	20 42	2154

DOUAI and ORCHIES.

Douai ......arr	6 4	8 26	1135	16 5	18 7	19 7	2020	2317	...	...
Orchies 29 dep	6 56	9 10	1216	1651	1856	1952	21 2	2357	...	...
Orchies.....dep	4 42	6 6	9 24	1250	1710	18 6	1859	2115	...	...
Douai ......arr	5 34	6 48	10 4	1336	1759	1852	1942	2152	...	...

AMIENS and FREVENT.

E.M.									
—	**Amiens** ......dep	5 47	...	1037	...	...	1659	...	2119
6¾	Bertangles-Poulain	6 10	...	11 0	...	...	1725	...	2140
16½	**Canaples** ......arr	6 35	8 51	1125	1257	1559	1751	1940	22 5
27¼	**Doullens** ......arr	7 7	9 20	1155	1326	1627	1823	20 9	2234
38½	**Frevent (20)** ...arr	7 47	...	1228	...	...	1859	...	23 5

Frevent......dep	6 3	...	...	1022	13 2	...	1717	...
Doullens ......dep	6 35	7 48	1035	1053	1332	1354	1752	2027
Canaples ......dep	7 8	8 18	11 4	1128	14 1	1427	1821	2055
Bertangles-Pouln	7 36	8 46	—	1156	1429	...	1851	...
Amiens (19)...arr	7 53	9 7	...	1221	1449	...	19 8	...

VALENCIENNES and HIRSON.

Valenciennes......dep	...	5 24	8 20	8 46	11 0	1356	1754	1916	...
Solesmes ......arr	...	6 10	8 43	9 33	11 45	1442	1838	20 2	...
Le Cateau	...	6 39	9 2	10 7	12 9	1513	1914	2037	...
Busigny......dep	3 14	7 11	9 17	1050	12 23	1514	20 4	2148	...
Le Nouvion......	4 22	8 8	...	1139	—	1631	2053	—	...
Hirson (71) ......arr	5 36	8 55	10 7	1226	...	1721	2149	...	...

Hirson .....dep	5 3	...	8 50	...	1333	1734	19 21	21 7
Le Nouvion ...	5 47	...	9 34	...	1414	1817	20 1	...
Busigny ...arr	6 33	...	10 18	13 3	1457	19 1	20 43	2154
Le Cateau ...	7 9	...	10 53	1319	1541	1937	—	2215
Solesmes	7 34	8 21	11 19	1342	16 7	20 6	...	2229
Valencien arr	8 19	8 55	12 7	1428	1653	2051	...	2253

WATTEN-EPERLECQUES and GRAVELINES.

Watten-Eper. ......dep	5 52	8 49	1323	1554	2140
Bourbourg ......arr	6 13	9 10	1345	1615	22 1
Gravelines (19A) ...arr	6 26	9 35	14 4	1642	2215

Gravelines ......dep	6 36	9 14	1336	18 10	22 0	...
Bourbourg ......dep	6 49	9 36	14 7	18 25	22 18	...
Watten-Eper....arr	7 11	9 57	1428	18 45	22 39	...

LENS and DON SAINGHIN.

Lens (26) ......dep	4 39	6 7	9 14	1145	1311	1520	1832	...
Henin-Lietard......	5 6	6 33	9 45	1248	14 5	1642	1918	...
Carvin (29B)	5 32	7 6	10 11	1314	1431	17 9	1944	...
Bauvin-Provin (30)	5 38	7 14	10 17	1322	1437	1717	1951	...
Don Sainghin arr	5 45	7 23	10 24	1331	1445	1726	20 0	...

Don Sainghin dep	6 24	7 49	11 3	12 8	1458	18 7	21 21	...	...
Bauvin-Provin	6 34	7 57	1113	12 16	15 5	1815	21 29	...	...
Carvin	6 43	8 4	1123	12 23	1512	1821	21 36	...	...
Henin-Lietard...	7 9	8 26	1148	12 47	1535	1844	22 0	...	...
Lens ......arr	7 37	9 0	1253	13 15	1752	1925	22 25	...	...

ENGHIEN and MONTMORENCY.

Enghien......dep	5 50	6 45	7 14	And half-hourly until 22.45; also at 0.7 & 0.44.
Montmorency arr	5 57	6 53	7 22	

Montmorency dep	5 32	6 1	6 56	7 24	And half-hourly until 22.56; also at 0.18.
Enghien (20)...arr	5 40	6 12	7 4	7 32	

PARIS (Ouest) and PARIS (Nord).

Paris—Rue St. Lazare ...dep	7 4	8 2	8 30	And hourly, at about 30 min. past the hour, until 22 35 from St. Lazare to Nord Station. Extra at 6.29, 12.10, 16.3, 16.55, 18.8, and 23.44.
Asnières......	7 14	8 12	8 40	
Bois de Colombes	7 18	8 16	8 45	
Colombes	7 22	8 20	8 50	
Argenteuil	7 29	8 27	8 58	
Sannois	7 34	8 33	9 6	
Ermont	7 39	8 44	9 13	
Enghien 20	7 47	8 52	9 22	
Epinay	7 54	8 59	9 30	
Saint Denis	7 59	9 5	9 36	
Paris (Nord) ...arr	8 7	9 13	9 44	

Paris-Nord...dep	7 2	8 8	9 5	And hourly, at about 5 min. past the hour, until 23.5 from Nord Station to St. Lazare. Extra at 4.20, 6.20, 11.50, 16.33, 17.38, and 18.40.
Saint Denis	7 14	8 19	9 15	
Epinay	7 19	8 24	9 21	
Enghien......	7 27	8 32	9 29	
Ermont	7 34	8 40	9 38	
Sannois	7 38	8 44	9 51	
Argenteuil	7 48	8 55	9 58	
Colombes	7 54	9 1	10 4	
Bois de Colombe	7 58	9 6	10 8	
Asnières......	8 3	9 11	10 12	
Paris Ouest...arr	8 11	9 19	10 20	

Excess Luggage, 1 cent. per 44 lbs. per kilometre.] **NORTHERN RAILWAY.**

TERGNIER to AMIENS and ROUEN.

Reims 67 ....dep	...	...	...	...	...	...	6 47	6 47	9 2	11 8	14 58	13 47	16 1	19 40
Laon 21..............dep	...	...	...	3 20	5 20	...	7 53	8 0	10 32	12 38	16 5	15 30	17 21	20 32
	1,2,3	1,2,3	1,2,3		1,2,3	1,2,3	1 Cl.	1,2,3	1,2,3	1,2,3	1 Cl.	1,2,3	1,2,3	1,2,3
Tergnier ....dep	...	...	...	Calais arr. 6.34.	6 19	...	8 11	8 30	11 31	14 26	16 29	16 48	18 26	21 3
Ham 29B	...	...	...		6 59	...	:	8 47	11 56	14 56	...	17 21	18 58	21 26
Nesle	...	...	...		7 20	...	A	8 58	12 10	15 15	...	17 39	19 15	21 42
Chaulnes 29	...	...	...		7 39	...	:	9 8	12 25	15 35	RC	17 59	19 31	21 56
Rosieres	...	...	...		7 53	...	RC	...	12 35	15 45	...	18 13	19 40	22 7
Villers-Bretonneux......	...	...	...		8 19	...	:	...	12 57	16 9	...	18 41	20 5	22 31
Amiens ....arr	...	...	...		8 40	...	9 10	9 45	13 16	16 30	17 28	19 4	20 43	22 50
Boulogne 19 ......arr	...	...	...		11 3	...	10 54	12 16	16 48	18 41	18 56	20 15	0 15	0 42
Amiens..................dep	3 25	...	5 24		8 58	9 1	...	Runs until 30th Sept.	14 5	17 45	Until 30th September.	21 36	21 16	RC—Restaurant Car.
Saleux	...	...	5 42	...	...	9 20	...		14 23	18 1		21 52	...	...
Namps Quevauvillers...	...	...	6 2	...	...	9 40	...		14 43	18 30		22 12	...	...
Poix	...	...	6 22	...	...	10 0	...		15 1	18 40		22 31	...	...
Abancourt 30	4 51	5 1	7 14	...	9 44	10 53	...		15 44	19 20		23 4	22 2	...
Serqueux 77A.........arr	5 13	5 30	7 46	...	10 3	11 21	...		16 13	19 50		—	22 19	
" ....dep	5 16	5 32	8 1	...	10 4	11 25	...		16 16	20 13		...	22 21	
Sommery	...	5 45	8 16	...	...	11 38	...		16 31	20 26		...	...	
Montérollier-Buchyarr	5 36	5 59	8 30	...	10 20	11 52	...		16 45	20 41		...	22 38	
Montérollier ......dep	5 51	...	...	...	10 25	12 0	...	...	16 53	...		...	22 46	
Clères 76	6 29	...	...	...	10 55	12 39	...	...	17 55	...		...	23 23	
Motteville ....arr	7 2	...	...	...	11 26	13 17	...	...	18 39	...	...	...	23 56	
Havre 77 ....arr	9 25	...	...	...	12 35	14 57	...	...	19 42	...	...	...	1 9	
Montérollier ....dep	5 43	6 1	8 39	...	10 22	12 2	...	...	16 48	20 47	...	...	22 41	
Darnetal	...	6 41	9 16	...	10 47	12 39	...	...	17 24	21 27	...	...	...	
Rouen....................arr	6 10	6 47	9 22	...	10 53	12 45	...	...	17 30	21 33	...	...	23 9	

A—Only takes 2nd class from or to England, or from or to the Eastern Co.'s Line.

Extra.—Tergnier to Amiens 9.37. Abancourt to Amiens 7.10.

	2 & 3	1,2,3	1,2,3	1,2,3	1,2,3	1 Cl.	1,2,3	1,2,3	1,2,3	1 Cl.		1,2,3	1,2,3	1,2,3
Rouen (Martainville)......dep	...	...	6 0	8 13	8 37	...	...	13 26	...	...	...	18 6	18 12	19 53
Darnetal	...	...	6 10	...	8 46	...	...	13 35	...	...	...	18 13	18 21	20 2
Montérollier-Buchyarr	...	...	6 58	8 34	9 31	...	...	14 21	...	...	...	18 39	19 10	20 47
Havre 76.........dep	...	...	...	6 7	6 13	...	...	9 40	...	...	...	16 0	...	...
Motteville ....dep	...	...	...	7 20	8 4	...	...	12 13	...	...	...	17 14	...	19 12
Clères..................dep	...	...	...	8 5	8 51	Runs until 30th September.	...	13 51	Runs until 30th Sept.	...	...	18 1	...	20 0
Montérollier ......arr	...	...	...	8 29	9 21		...	14 21		...	...	18 32	...	20 33
Montérollier ....dep	Runs until 30th Sept. on Saturdays only.	...	7 4	8 38	9 39		...	14 32		...	...	18 42	19 18	20 48
Sommery		...	7 21	...	9 51		...	14 46		...	...	...	19 32	21 3
Serqueux ....arr		...	7 33	...	10 2		...	14 57		...	...	18 58	19 42	21 14
" ....dep		...	7 44	...	10 7		...	15 7		...	...	19 2	19 59	21 18
Abancourt		...	8 16	9 12	10 55		...	15 50		...	...	19 26	20 39	21 48
Poix		...	8 44	...	11 26		...	16 21		...	...	19 46	21 11	—
Namps Quevauvillers...		...	9 0	...	11 42		...	16 38		...	Calais dep. 20.10.	...	21 28	...
Saleux		...	9 17	...	11 59		...	16 55		...		...	21 44	...
Amiens 19..................arr		...	9 30	9 51	12 14		...	17 15		...		20 11	22 0	...
Boulogne ....dep		2 12	6 52	...	9 0	12 30	14 29	...	16 58	18 8		19 4	...	22 3
Amiens..................dep	2 55	6 36	9 57	11 29	14 5	15 5	16 26	17 47	19 27	20 2		21 21	...	2 59
Villers-Bretonneux	...	7 3	10 16	11 51	14 23	:	16 45	18 12	...	RC	:	21 44	...	3 24
Rosieres	...	7 29	10 32	12 13	14 51	:	17 6	18 38	...	A	:	22 9	...	3 47
Chaulnes	RC	7 44	10 43	12 26	15 5	RC	17 17	18 54	20 0	:	:	22 25	...	4 6
Nesle	...	8 0	10 53	12 39	15 19	:	17 28	19 8	20 10	:	:	22 39	...	4 23
Ham	...	8 18	11 6	12 58	15 34	:	17 41	19 27	20 21	:	:	22 56	...	4 47
Tergnier ....arr	...	8 44	11 27	13 23	16 13	:	18 4	19 55	20 38	:	:	23 23	...	5 26
Laon 21..................arr	4 16	10 11	12 20	15 18	17 23	16 21	19 8	...	...	21 13	23 20	2 8	...	6 48
Reims 67 ....arr	5 12	11 17	13 46	17 0	19 0	17 20	20 15	...	...	22 29	...	4 13	...	8 25

TRÉPORT and CANAPLES.

‡—Runs until 30th Sept.

E.M.									
—	Tréport ....dep	...	5 53	8 48	9‡58	13 20	16 25	...	...
9¼	Longroy-Gm........	...	6 23	10 32	10 30	14 1	17 10	...	...
18¾	Martaineville	...	6 48	10 59		14 26	17 37	...	...
29¾	Airaines	...	7 20	11 32	—	14 58	18 13	...	21 13
34½	Longpré.........arr	5 50	7 30	11 42	...	15 6	18 23	19 5	21 26
38	Flixecourt......dep	6 2	8 28	12 33	...	15 36	—	19 16	—
41	St. Leger-l-D.......	6 15	8 38	12 43	...	15 45	...	19 27	...
45½	Canaples 20 ...arr	6 28	8 49	12 54	...	15 57	...	19 38	...

Canaples ...dep	7 10	...	11 6	14 29	...	20 57	...	...
St. Leger-l-D.	7 22	...	11 18	14 43	...	21 8	...	...
Flixecourt	7 32	...	11 28	14 55	...	21 20	...	...
Longpré 19......	8 8	...	12 24	15 35	19 6	22 14	...	...
Airaines	8 21	‡	12 36	15 46	19 17	22 25	...	...
Martaineville...	8 54		13 8	16 19	19‡46	22 57	...	...
L.-Gamaches...	9 16	9 18	13 30	16 41	—	23 19	...	...
Tréport......arr	10 55	9 42	14 11	17 25	...	23 49	...	...

LAON and TERGNIER.

Reims 67 ...dep	...	...	5 27	6 47	6 47	6 47	9 2	11 8	13 47	14 58	16 1	17 50	19 40	20 52	...	...
Laon..............dep	3 20	5 20	6 54	7 53	8 0	8 40	10 32	12 38	15 30	16 5	17 21	19 15	20 32	22 28	...	...
La Fere	:	5 58	7 26	...	8 18	9 11	11 4	13 11	16 6	...	17 56	19 48	...	22 59	...	...
Tergnier 24......arr	:	6 4	7 34	8 10	8 26	9 19	11 12	13 19	16 14	16 28	18 4	19 56	20 55	23 7	...	...
St. Quentin arr	:	...	8 12	...	8 46	...	12 7	14 4	17 12	...	18 34	20 25	21 21	0 7	...	...
St. Quentin dep	§	5 6	7 37	8 48	9 43	11 5	13 47	:	15 59	17 47	18 38	:	:	21 23	0 14	...
Tergnier.........dep	:	6 6	8 24	9 27	:	11 41	14 34	:	16 40	18 28	18 58	:	:	21 48	1 29	...
La Fere	:	6 16	8 34	9 38	:	11 51	14 45	:	16 51	18 38	...	:	:	21 59	1 40	...
Laon ....arr	4 16	6 48	9 4	10 11	10 22	12 20	15 18	16 21	17 23	19 8	19 22	21 13	23 20	22 31	2 8	...
Reims 67 ......arr	5 12	8 25	...	11 17	11 17	13 46	17 0	17 20	19 0	...	20 15	22 29	...	23 59	4 13	...

§—Runs on Saturday only until 30th Sept.

LILLE and COIMNES

Lille..............dep	4 58	7 34	10 20	12 20	17 4	19 53
La Madeleine	5 13	7 46	10 35	12 35	17 15	20 7
Quesnoy-s-Deule..	5 33	8 1	10 52	12 49	17 27	20 23
Comines Fr. 90 arr	5 53	8 16	11 8	13 3	17 40	20 36

Comines ...dep	6 13	8‡57	11 28	14 50	18 0	21 0
Quesnoy-s-D...	6 45	9 27	12 4	15 23	18 28	21 38
La Madeleine	7 6	9 46	12 20	15 40	18 43	22 4
Lille 26 ......arr	7 20	9 59	12 33	15 52	18 55	22 17

‡—Until 30th Sept. will run 10 mins. earlier on Monday.

MAUBEUGE and COUSOLRE.

Maubeuge ......dep	5 2	8 3	9 35	11 39	15 10	17 55	20 17	
Cousolre ....arr	5 33	8 34	10 7	12 19	16 15	18 27	20 57	
Cousolre ....dep	5 43	8 46	10 18	13 15	16 25	18 37	21 9	...
Maubeuge 25......arr	6 13	9 18	10 56	13 46	16 55	19 14	21 39	...

NORTHERN RAILWAY. [66 lbs. of Luggage free.

CREIL, BEAUVAIS, and GOURNAY.

Creil ......dep	...	6 50	8 18	11 9	12 55	1542	19 0	21 50	...
Cires-les-M'lo	...	7 13	8 35	1127	13 13	16 1	19 20	22 9	...
Mouy-Bury ...	...	7 28	8 46	1137	13 23	1612	19 32	22 20	...
Hermes (22A)	...	7 42	8 58	1149	13 25	1625	19 46	22 34	...
Beauvais arr	...	8 5	9 19	1212	13 57	1648	20 10	22 55	...
,, dep	5 12	—	9 39	—	15 0	1731	20 22	—	...
Saint Paul ...	5 27	...	9 54	...	15 15	1747	20 36	...	...
St. Germer ...	5 54	...	10 25	...	15 45	1818	21 5	...	...
Gournay 77A	6 4	...	10 35	...	15 55	1829	21 14	...	...

Gournay ...dep	5 18	...	9 14	12 57	...	1741	...	20 53	...
St. Germer ...	5 29	...	9 25	13 9	...	1752	...	21 6	...
Saint Paul......	5 55	...	9 53	13 42	...	1829	...	21 40	...
Beauvais arr	6 8	...	10 6	13 56	...	1843	...	21 52	...
,, dep	6 28	8 42	11 9	15 15	16 9	1917	2123	—	...
Hermes	6 50	9 5	11 33	15 39	1633	1946	2146	...	...
Mouy-Bury ...	7 3	9 18	11 46	15 52	1649	20 2	22 1	...	...
Cires-les-M'llo	7 13	9 28	11 56	16 3	17 0	2015	2213	...	...
Creil 24......arr	7 30	9 44	12 12	16 21	1717	2036	2228	...	...

GISORS and BEAUVAIS.

Gisors.........dep	7 20	9 58	14 7	1756	21 55
Trie-Chateau......	7 25	10 3	1412	18 1	22 0
Auneuil	8 0	10 37	1447	1836	22 34
Beauvais 22 arr	8 20	10 57	15 7	1857	22 53

Beauvais ...dep	5 56	8 39	12 32	1628	20 29
Auneuil	6 18	9 1	12 54	1653	20 52
Trie-Chateau ...	6 48	9 33	13 24	1725	21 22
Gisors 77A arr	6 52	9 37	13 28	1729	21 26

PARIS to CREIL, via LOUVRES and CHANTILLY.

	123	123	1,2,3	123	123	12 3	1,2,3	12 3	1,2,3	1 &2	1,2,3	1,2,3	1,2,3	1,2,3	1,2,3	1,2,3	1,2,3
Paris ...dep	517	610	7 0	7 3	718	8 40	8 51	9 0	9 55	1025	1036	12 3	1223	1315	1332	1430	1550
Saint Denis	...	...	...	...	...	...	...	...	...	...	1047	...	...	...	1313	...	...
Louvres ...	547	646	...	736	...	...	...	...	...	...	1116	...	...	...	1417	...	...
Survilliers	556	655	...	745	...	...	9 28	...	1034	...	1125	...	1259	...	1427	...	1635
Chantilly ...	614	716	...	8 3	755	9 2	9 43	9 36	1051	11 0	1140	1236	1317	1356	1443	15 4	1653
Creil ...arr	624	726	7 37	813	8 4	9 11	...	9 45	11 1	11 9	...	1245	1327	14 6	...	1513	17 3

	1,2,3	1,2,3	1,2,3	1,2,3	1,2,3	1,2,3	1,2,3	1& 2	1,2,3	1,2,3	1,2,3	1,2,3	1,2,3	1,2,3	1,2,3	1,2,3	
Paris ...dep	16 5	1640	1645	1739	18 0	18 3	1826	1835	1910	2010	2015	2040	21 2	2220	2317	0 35	...
Saint Denis	...	...	...	...	...	...	...	...	...	...	...	...	2112	2233	2326	0 46	...
Louvres ...	...	...	...	...	...	...	19 0	...	1916	...	...	...	2139	...	2353	1 16	...
Survilliers	...	...	...	1811	...	...	19 8	...	1956	...	2049	...	2148	...	0 2	1 25	...
Chantilly ...	1641	1718	1722	1825	1837	1845	1923	1911	2017	2046	21 7	2114	22 9	2317	0 17	1 42	...
Creil ...arr	1650	1728	...	1835	1847	...	...	1920	2027	2055	2117	2123	2219	2327	...	1 52	...

	1,2,3	1,2,3	1,2,3	1,2,3	1,2,3	1,2,3	1,2,3	1,2,3	1,2,3	1,2,3	1,2,3	1,2,3	1,2,3	1,2,3	1,2,3	1,2,3
Creil ....dep	3 1	3 18	3 39	5 40	6 30	...	...	7 39	7 50	8 15	...	8 39	10 25	...	1151	...
Chantilly	...	3 22	3 53	5 57	6 44	6 52	7 38	7 52	8 4	...	8 46	8 52	10 37	1046	12 3	12 9
Survilliers	...	...	...	6 17	...	7 10	7 52	...	8 21	...	...	9 11	...	11 3	...	1228
Louvres	...	...	...	6 26	...	7 18	...	...	8 31	...	...	...	...	...	...	...
Saint Denis......	...	...	...	...	...	...	...	...	9 2	...	...	...	...	...	...	...
Paris ....arr	4 5	4 15	4 37	6 56	7 25	7 48	8 18	8 37	9 10	8 55	9 24	9 38	11 10	11 29	1242	1256

	1,2,3	1,2,3	1,2,3	1,2,3	1,2,3	1,2,3	1,2,3	1,2,3	1 &2	1,2,3	1,2,3	1,2,3	1,2,3	1,2,3	1,2,3	1,2,3
Creil ....dep	1220	...	14 5	15 3	1531	1645	17 6	1727	1755	1827	19 2	20 5	...	21 1	2237	2333
Chantilly	1235	1312	1419	1515	1543	1658	1720	1738	18 6	1840	1916	20 18	2035	2115	2248	2346
Survilliers	...	1329	1436	...	...	1716	...	...	...	...	1934	...	2053	...	...	0 3
Louvres	...	1337	...	...	...	...	...	...	...	...	1942	...	21 1	...	...	0 12
Saint Denis......	...	14 8	...	...	...	...	...	...	...	...	...	...	2131	...	...	0 38
Paris ....arr	1315	1417	15 3	1550	1620	1743	1759	1810	1840	1925	2012	20 56	2140	2156	2325	0 47

Extra.—Creil to Paris, 4.53, 8.7, 10.15.

Paris Nord and St. Denis.—A local service of about three trains per hour is maintained from 5.28 until 22.35.

PARIS and CREIL, via ST. OUEN-L'AUMONE.—ERMONT, VALMONDOIS, and PERSAN-BEAUMONT.

Paris ....dep	5 35	8 0	9 0	9 30	10 0	1030	11 30	1330	17 0	1735	1755	1819	1858	1930	2130	23 0
Enghien	5 48	8 13	9 12	9 42	1012	1042	11 42	1342	1712	⋮	⋮	⋮	...	...	2142	2312
Ermont ....arr	5 52	8 17	9 16	9 45	1016	1046	11 46	1346	1716	⋮	⋮	⋮	1914	1944	2145	2316
Ermont.........dep	5 54	8 18	9 17	...	1018	...	...	...	1717	⋮	⋮	⋮	1917	...	...	2317
St-Leu (S.-et-O.)	6 9	8 30	9 30	...	1030	...	...	...	1729	⋮	1818	⋮	1929	...	...	2329
Valmondois...arr	6 36	8 54	9 54	...	1055	...	...	...	1753	⋮	1839	1851	1953	...	...	2353
Ermont.........dep	⋮	⋮	⋮	9 48	⋮	1048	11 47	1347	⋮	⋮	⋮	⋮	⋮	1946	2148	...
Pontoise	⋮	⋮	⋮	1024	⋮	1123	12 22	1422	⋮	18 6	⋮	⋮	⋮	2022	2223	...
St.-Ouen-l'Aum...	⋮	⋮	⋮	1027	⋮	1125	12 25	1424	⋮	18 9	⋮	⋮	⋮	2025	2226	...
Valmondois	6 38	8 55	9 55	1047	1056	1142	12 44	1442	1754	1829	1840	1853	1954	2043	2243	2354
Isle-Adam-Parm	6 45	9 1	10 1	1052	11 2	1148	12 49	1448	1759	1834	1845	1859	1959	2048	2249	2359
Persan Beaum't	7 0	9 16	1011	11 2	1112	12 6	12 58	1458	1813	1842	1856	1910	2016	21 3	23 3	0 9
St.-Leu d'E.	7 23	9 39	—	—	1145	1228	—	1520	1836	—	—	1932	2040	2129	2327	—
Creil (19) ......arr	7 30	9 46	...	...	1153	1236	...	1528	1843	...	...	1940	2048	2137	2335	...

Creil... ....dep		5 22	7 9	7 55	8 56	...	1041	1259	...	1539	1746	2046	2241
St.-Leu d Esserent		5 31	7 18	8 3	9 5	...	1050	13 8	...	1547	1754	2056	2250
Persan Beaum't		7 11	7 42	8 26	9 36	1039	1137	1336	1536	1631	1832	2136	2316
Isle-Adam-Parm.		7 22	7 51	8†35	9 47	1050	1148	1348	1548	1643	1845	2148	2325
Valmondois		7 27	7 55	8†39	9 51	1054	1152	1352	1552	1647	1849	2152	2330
St.-Ouen-l'Aumon		7 48	⋮	⋮	⋮	⋮	⋮	⋮	⋮	⋮	⋮	⋮	2350
Pontoise.........	7 25	8 †0	⋮	⋮	⋮	⋮	⋮	⋮	⋮	⋮	⋮	⋮	2359
Ermont ...arr	7 58	⋮	⋮	⋮	⋮	⋮	⋮	⋮	⋮	⋮	⋮	⋮	0 19
Valmondois dp ...		⋮	7 57	8†40	9 54	1056	1154	1354	1553	1648	1851	2154	...
St-Leu(S.-et-O.)...		⋮	⋮	9† 5	1021	1124	1222	1422	1620	1719	1923	2222	...
Ermont ....arr ...		⋮	⋮	⋮	1032	1134	1232	1432	1630	1730	1933	2232	...
Ermont ...dep	8 0	⋮	⋮	⋮	1033	1135	1233	1433	1632	1732	1936	2233	0 10
Enghien.........	...	⋮	⋮	⋮	1038	1140	1238	1438	1638	1738	1943	2238	0 26
Paris.........arr	8 16	8†25	8 30	9†24	1050	1152	1250	1450	1650	1750	1955	2250	0 41

Extra.

Paris..................dep	5 10	7 0	7 30	11 0	12 0	14 0	1430	15 0	16 0	1630	1725	1835	1933	20†0	2030	21 0	0 30	...	...	...	...	...	...	...	...
Persan-Beaumont arr	6 41	8 13	9 1	12 9	1310	1510	16 4	16 9	1716	18 1	1832	1846	2043	21 8	2155	2210	1 36	...	...	...	...	...	...	...	...

Persan-Beaumont dep	5 15	5 46	5 58	6 29	8 0	8 33	8 51	9 46	1148	1238	1351	14†38	1644	1731	1746	18 48	1938	1945	20 30	2047	2146	...	...	...
Paris ....arr	6 28	7 19	7 13	7 44	9 18	9 50	1020	1125	1320	1351	1522	15 50	1823	1850	1920	20 23	2050	2120	21 52	2222	2320	...	...	...

†—Weekdays only.

SOMAIN and PERUWELZ.

Somain ......dep	3 38	5 2	7 3	9 2	1155	1322	1540	1852	21 6
Denain-Mines......	3 54	5 18	7 19	9 19	1211	1338	1557	19 8	2122
Anzin	4 11	5 36	7 36	9 37	1229	1356	1617	1923	2140
⋮ Valenciennesdep	...	...	...	...	1223	...	1611	...	...
Bruay-s-l'E. dep	4 18	5 43	7 43	9 44	1236	14 3	1625	1933	2147
Vieux-Condé	4 36	6 3	8 1	10 2	1254	1422	1644	1951	22 5
Péruwelz 100 ar	4 45	...	8 10	1011	13 3	1431	1653	20 0	...

Péruwelz dep	...	5 26	...	8 56	1115	1322	1446	18 6	2052
Vieux-Condé	5 5	5 49	7 7	9 23	1139	1341	15 8	1833	2115
Bruay.........arr	5 22	6 6	7 24	9 40	1157	1358	1525	1851	2132
Valenciennes ar	...	...	...	9 58	...	1414	...	...	...
Anzin..............	5 34	6 14	7 36	9 49	1211	1413	1536	19 6	2141
Denain-Mines ...	5 51	6 31	7 53	10 6	1229	1428	1556	1924	2158
Somain 23...arr	6 5	6 46	8 8	10 21	1244	1443	1611	1939	2213

ANVIN and CALAIS.

Anvin (28) ......dep		...	...	...	1012	1248	15 51	21 15
Fruges		...	...	8 32	1144	1325	16 50	21 58
Fauquembergue		...	...	9 20	1233	—	17 40	—
Lumbres (**19A**) ...arr		...	...	10 5	1324	...	18 23	...
BOULOGNE ......arr		...	...	11 50	...	...	20 4	...
Lumbres ......dep		...	6 48	10 26	1318	...	18 50	22 31
St. Omer ......arr		...	7 22	10 59	1421	...	19 26	23 2
Lumbres ....dep		...	—	10 35	1355	...	18 56	—
Tournehem		7 12	...	11 36	15 5	...	19 58	...
Ardres		7 39	...	12 2	1532	18 3	20 25	...
Guines..............	5 58	8 7	...	12 26	16 0	1828	20 50	...
Calais Ville arr	6 27	8 35	...	12 52	1628	1855	21 16	...

Calais Ville ......dep		7 30	...	1055	...	1530	17 5	1920	2130
Guines		8 9	...	1130	...	16 8	1735	1958	22 0
Ardres		8 33	...	12 3	...	1637	1755	2026	—
Tournehem		9 0	...	1228	...	17 5	—	2048	...
Lumbres..............arr		10 4	...	1329	...	1818	...	—	...
St. Omer ......dep		9 46	...	1220	...	1810	...	...	2143
Lumbres.........arr		10 25	...	1253	...	1843	...	...	2217
BOULOGNE ......dep		8 48	...	12 0	...	1719	...	...	—
Lumbres ....dep		10 34	...	1410	...	1858	...	...	...
Fauquembergue		11 11	...	1510	...	1948	...	...	...
Fruges	8 10	11 49	1415	1553	1340	2028	...	...	...
Anvin.........arr	8 55	12 25	1450	...	1925	...	...	...	...

DERCY-MORTIERS and LA FERE.

E.M.					
	Dercy-Mortiers 28 dep	7 26	1155	12 59	1810
5	Pouilly-sur-Serre (Nord) 28	8 0	1215	15 2	1836
13½	**Versigny** ....arr	8 36	—	15 45	1930
16¾	**La Fére** .... ,,	9 10	...	16 4	1946
20½	TERGNIER 21..............arr	9 19	...	16 14	1956

TERGNIER..........dep	9 27	...	1640	1828	...
La Fére..........dep	9 42	...	1651	1838	...
Versigny........... ,,	10 0	...	17 3	20 3	...
Pouilly-sur-Serre	1058	1225	1733	2128	...
Derey-Mortiers arr	1140	1240	1749	...	...

PERSAN-BEAUMONT and HERMES.

Persan-Beau. arr	7 13	8 53	12 3	15 2	1823	...
Ercuis	7 43	9 42	1230	1528	1849	...
Hermes 22 ......arr	8 48	11 7	1325	1618	1939	...

Hermes.......dep	5 29	9 18	1155	1637	1950	...
Ercuis	6 19	1020	13 3	1733	2050	...
Persan-B. 30 arr	6 43	1046	1338	18 2	2117	...

BOISLEUX & CAMBRAI.

Arras ....dep	...	8 6	11 35	...	18 55
Boisleux........dep	...	8 28	11 58	...	19 22
Marquion	4 48	9 25	12 57	17 4	20 30
Cambrai 30A...arr	5 52	10 17	13 52	1815	...

Cambrai ......dep	...	8 15	10 40	16 11	19 1
Marquion	6 0	9 27	12 1	17 6	20 9
Boisleux........arr	7 24	10 52	...	18 20	...
Arras 26.........arr	7 38	11 6	...	18 34	...

NOYELLES, CAYEUX, and LE CROTOY.

Noyelles ....dep	3 30	7 8	8‡5	9 2	11*18	12§27	12‡38	13§25	14 *0	1520	18‡12	18§20	19 50	20 20	22 46	24 0	...
St. Valery-sur-Somme ...	3 42	7 25	8 17	9 14	11 32	12 40	13 30	13 37	14 12	1535	18 27	18 32	20 3	20 32	22 58	0 12	...
Cayeux...................arr	...	7 59	...	...	12 3	13 12	13 34	...	...	16 7	18 57	...	20 36	21‡14	23‡35	...	...

Cayeux ....dep	...	6 46	9 54	...	...	12‡28	14§2	...	16‡13	17§5	19‡0	...	...	20‡8	22‡30	...	...	...
St. Valery-sur-Somme ...	6 12	7 21	1028	1155	12 52	13 6	1434	1444	17 18	1740	1930	19§5	1934	20 50	23 28	...	...	...
Noyelles 18 ....arr	6 24	7 33	1040	12 7	13 4	13 18	...	1456	17 30	1751	...	1917	1946	21 2	23 40	...	...	...

Noyelles...	6*54	9 *0	11‡15	1225	1518	18‡15	19‖32	20‡19	22‡40
Le Crotoy	7 12	9 20	11 33	1243	1538	18 33	19 48	20 35	23 0

Le Crotoy	6 6	7*25	10 25	11‡51	12 53	17‡15	19‖0	19‡43	20‡48
Noyelles...	6 23	7 41	10 42	12 8	13 10	17 32	1918	20 0	21 4

*—From 10th July until 22nd September.
§—From 4th October.
‡—Runs until 3rd October.
‖—Weekdays only from 5th July until 30th September.

PARIS to ORSAY and LIMOURS.

Paris- Luxembourg dep	5 20	6 7	7 6	8 16	9 3	9 48	1055	1150	1317	1414	1544	1648	1719	1745	1829	1923	1948	2118	2249	0 35	...
Bourg-la-Reine ...	5 41	6 23	7 25	8 35	9 22	...	1116	12 9	1336	1434	16 3	17 5	...	...	...	1942	20 8	2141	2311	0 54	...
Orsay...............	6 13	6 57	7 57	9 9	9 56	1026	1153	1243	14 2	15 8	1635	1739	18 3	1819	1918	2017	2040	2216	2342	1 23	...
St. Rémy-les-Chev	6 32	7 16	8 16	9 25	10 12	1039	1210	13 0	1421	1522	1652	1758	1817	1830	1937	2034	2055	2237	2358	—	...
Limours ...arr	6 50	7 32	8 32	9 41	10 27	1054	1226	1315	1437	...	17 8	1813	...	1845	1957	2049	2111	2252	0 13	...	...

Limours .....dep	...	...	5 51	...	6 53	7 38	8 3	8 52	9 51	1056	1139	1235	14 7	1534	...	1743	1818	1921	2012	2115	2223
St. Rémy-les-Chev.	...	...	6 6	...	7 10	7 53	8 17	9 7	10 7	1111	1154	1250	1422	1549	1653	1758	19 3	1939	2027	2130	2238
Orsay	4 37	5 34	6 22	6 40	7 25	8 8	8 27	9 22	1022	1125	12 9	13 5	1437	16 4	17 8	1813	1918	1957	2043	2145	2253
Bourg-la-Reine ...	5 8	6 11	...	7 12	7 59	...	...	9 54	1054	12 0	1240	...	15 9	1637	1741	1844	1950	2034	2111	2219	2324
Luxembourg ar	5 26	6 28	7 16	7 30	8 18	8 53	9 0	1010	1111	1220	1257	1352	1526	1654	1759	19 0	20 7	2051	2127	2235	2340

NOYON and LASSIGNY.

Noyon ....dep	9 18	12 50	19 22
Lassigny .... arr	9 57	13 28	20 0

Lassigny......dep	6 35	11 20	18 12	...
Noyon **24** ...arr	7 13	12 10	18 50	...

NOYON and HAM.

Noyon......dep	8 40	13 7	19 27	...
Ham.........arr	9 55	14 31	20 25	...

Ham......... dep	6 10	11 10	17 56	...	...
Noyon **24** ...arr	7 8	12 19	18 55	...	...

FERRIERES & EPANNES.

E.M.					
	Ferrières d'Aunis ...dep	5 15	10 36	15 5	16 51
15½	Epannes 42A............arr	6 22	11 43	16 23	18 10

Epannes.......................dep	7 55	12 30	17 7	18 50
Ferrières d'Aunis 46A arr	9 0	13 48	18 26	20 8

SAINT-QUENTIN and GUISE.

Saint-Quentin dp	2 45	6 41	8 53	1052	13 40	15 0	1652	1752	1910
Itancourt	2 57	6 51	9 5	11 4	13 49	1511	17 2	18 1	1922
Ribemont..........	3 22	7 12	9 23	1127	14 7	1529	1721	1819	1940
Longchamps-B.	3 59	7 41	9 50	1152	14 38	1554	—	1849	20 9
Guise (28)......arr	4 15	7 53	10 3	12 4	14 50	16 6	...	19 2	2022

Guise ......dep	6 8	8 23	10 43	12 13	1426	1619	1837	2045	...
Longchamps	6 20	8 35	10 55	12 25	1440	1631	1851	2057	...
Ribemont......	6 49	9 2	11 28	12 53	15 7	17 1	1918	2125	...
Itancourt......	7 8	9 21	11 47	13 12	1527	1721	1938	2144	...
St. Quentin 24	7 18	9 32	11 55	13 22	1535	1730	1945	2154	...

66 lbs. of Luggage free. **NORTHERN RAILWAY.** [Excess Luggage, 1 cent. per 44 lbs. per kilomètre.

ARRAS to DOUAI, LILLE, MOUSCRON, and VALENCIENNES.

Frequent Extra Service between Lille and Tourcoing.

E.M		1,2,3	1,2,3	1,2,3	1,2,3	1 2 3	1,2,3	1,2,3		1,2,3	1,2,3	1,2,3	1& 2	1,2,3	1&2	1,2,3	1,2,3	1,2,3	1,2,3	1,2,3
—	PARIS 27.........dep	2120	...	...	2220	...	...	...	...	...	...	...	...	...	8 0	...	...	...	8 40	...
120	**Arras** ....dep	1 16	...	...	4 15	...	...	...	...	6 23	...	8 41	⋮	...	1013	...	1029	...	11 22	...
125	Rœux	...	...	...	4 29	...	...	...	...	6 41	...	8 54	⋮	...	...	...	1047	...	...	...
129¼	Vitry	...	...	...	4 42	...	...	...	...	6 52	...	9 4	⋮	...	...	...	1058	...	...	...
135½	**Douai** ....arr	1 46	...	...	5 0	...	...	...	...	7 12	...	9 22	10 8	...	1032	...	1120	...	11 41	...
...	**Douai** ....dep	1 53	...	4 7	5 28	...	...	7 21	...	7 35	8 57	9 35	1013	...	1035	10 44	—	11 32	11 45	1211
141¾	Libercourt 29B......	...	...	4 36	5 55	...	...	D	...	8 0	9 25	10 3	A	...	...	11 9	...	...	...	1236
146¾	Seclin	...	...	4 48	6 9	...	...	...	...	8 14	9 45	1016	...	...	...	11 23	...	...	...	1251
153½	**Lille** ....arr	2 30	...	5 12	6 29	...	...	7 51	...	8 31	10 3	1036	1042	...	11 0	11 43	...	11 59	12 10	13 4
...	OSTEND 90....arr	...	...	8 44	9 49	...	...	1014	...	...	...	...		...	1425		...	...		...
...	CALAIS ¶ 26...dep	1 19	...	...	...	...	...	...	...	...	6 21	...	...	...	...	...	...	...		9 49
...	**Lille**................dep	3 20	4 53	5 37	6 42	7 30	8§11	8 22	...	9 25	10 6	1050	...	11 9	1128	...	...	12 17		1331
158¼	Croix	3 33	5 6	5 50	6 55	7 43	...	8 33	...	...	...	11 3	...	...	...	...	...	12 29		1344
159½	Roubaix..................	3 45	5 14	5 56	7 1	7 49	8 25	8 39	...	9 38	1020	11 9	...	11 22	1142	...	...	12 34	...	1348
161¼	Tourcoing...............	3 50	5 23	6 3	7 8	7 55	8 31	8 45	...	9 42	1027	1118	...	11 26	1154	...	...	12 47	...	1354
164¾	**Mouscron** ....arr	—	5 31	6 11	7 16	8 2	8 37	8 53	...	—	1035	1126	...	11 45	12 2	...	...	12 55	...	—
200	GHENT 89 ...arr	...	7 32	7 45	8 35	—	1046	1046	...	...	1151	1358	...	13 3	1323	...	...	14 7	...	...
		1,2,3	1,2,3		1,2,3	1,2,3			1,2,3		1,2,3	1,2,3			1,2,3				1,2,3	
...	**Douai** ....dep	2 7	...	...	5 17	...	...	...	7 31	...	8 31	10 0	...	...	1040	...	...	...	11 55	...
138½	Somain 29A	2 26	...	...	5 45	...	...	...	8 1	...	9 5	1025	...	...	11 3	...	...	...	12 16	...
155½	**Valenciennes** ...arr	2 48	...	...	6 15	...	...	...	8 28	...	9 45	1051	...	...	1128	...	...	...	12 43	...
...	" ...dep	2 53	5 43	...	6 23	6 57	...	...	8 34	...	—	11 0	...	...	1133	...	...	...		...
162¾	Blanc-Misseron	3 9	6 4	...	6 45	7 12	...	...	8 59	...	...	1119	...	...	1150	...	...	...	...	...
163½	**Quiévrain** ....arr	3 13	6 7	...	6 48	7 15	...	...	9 2	...	...	1122	...	...	1153	...	...	...	...	...
175¾	MONS 108.........arr	3 51	—	...	7 44	7 48	...	...	9 54	...	...	1220	...	...	1224	...	...	...	...	...
213¾	BRUSSELS ......arr	5 6	...	...	8 50	8 50	...	...	1134	...	...	1338	...	...	1338	...	...	...	...	...

VALENCIENNES to MOUSCRON, LILLE, DOUAI, and ARRAS.

Frequent Extra Service between Tourcoing and Lille.

BRUSSELS 108...dep	...	...	...	...	...	5 8	6 57	...	...	...	8 21	...	...	...	8 57	...	9 40	...	13 6
MONS 108.........dep	...	...	...	...	...	7 22	8 10	...	...	...	9 41	...	...	...	10 40	...	12 22	...	14 11
		1,2,3		1,2,3	1,2,3	1,2,3	1,2,3				1,2,3		1,2,3		1,2,3		1,2,3		1,2,3
Quiévrain ....dep	...	4 22	...	...	...	8 4	8 37	...	...	...	1010	...	...	...	11 38	...	13 5	...	14 34
Blanc-Misseron.........	...	4 38	...	6 1	...	8 18	8 54	...	...	...	1026	...	...	...	11 56	...	13 30	...	14 53
Valenciennes......arr	...	4 58	...	6 21	...	8 36	9 7	...	...	...	1042	...	...	...	12 16	...	13 46	...	15 6
" ....dep	...	5 40	...	6 33	7 5	8 45	9 15	...	...	...	1055	...	1058	...	13 0	...	14 21	...	16 3
Somain.....................	...	6 10	...	7 1	7 53	9 12	9 45	...	...	...	1116	...	1149	...	13 31	...	15 4	...	16 29
Douai..................arr	...	6 29	...	7 18	8 14	9 27	10 4	...	...	...	1129	...	12 7	...	13 51	...	15 23	...	16 44
	1,2,3	1,2,3	1,2,3	1 &2	1,2,3		1,2,3	1 & 2	1 &2	1,2,3		1,2,3	1,2,3	1,2,3	1,2,3	1,2,3	1,2,3	1,2,3	1,2,3
GHENT 89 ......dep	...	...	...	...	4 39	...	6 35	...	...	...	...	8 17	...	9 20	11 0	...	...	...	11 43
Mouscron ......dep	...	...	5 47	...	6 48	...	7 44	8 27	...	8 39	...	9 43	...	1112	12 13	...	12§35	...	13 50
Tourcoing	5 20	5 55	6 7	6 33	7 14	...	8 10	8 35	8 45	9 8	...	10 10	...	1134	12 36	...	12 56	13 3	14 16
Roubaix	5 28	6 3	6 12	6 39	7 20	...	8 16		8 51	9 17	...	10 19	...	1140	12 42	...	13 2	13 9	14 20
Croix.....................	5 33	...	6 18	...	7 25	...	...	...	RC	9 22	...	10 24	...	1145	12 47	...	13 7	13 14	...
Lille..................arr	5 45	6 15	6 28	6 50	7 34	...	8 27	...	9 2	9 31	...	10 35	...	1156	12 56	...	13 15	13 23	14 33
CALAIS 27 ......arr	...	...	—	9 1	...	...	...	...	...	...	...	13 0	...	...	15 21	...	—	15 21	...
OSTEND 91 ...dep	...	...	...	...	...	...	5 17	...	7 0	...	...	7 7	...	7 46	11 11	...	...	—	...
Lille ....dep	5 58	6 30	...	7 0	7 44	...	8 39	...	9 10	9 50	...	11 0	...	1216	13 33	1349	...	...	15 35
Seclin	6 13	6 43	...	...	...	...	8 57	...	...	10 4	...	11 14	...	1237	...	14 6	...	...	15 54
Libercourt 1,2,3	6 28	6 54	...	...	...	...	9 11	...	RC	1019	...	11 28	...	1252	...	1423	...	...	16 10
Douai..........arr a.m.	6 53	7 7	...	7 25	8 11	...	9 40	...	9 35	1035	...	11 50	...	1315	13 59	1445	...	...	16 35
Douai............dep 6 38	...	7 11	...	7 27	8 26	...	10 19	...	9 37	—	...	—	1215	1321	14 4	1535	...	...	17 25
Vitry..................6 57	...	...	...	...	8 49	...	10 39	...	...	...	...	...	1237	1337	...	1556	...	...	17 44
Rœux..................7 7	...	...	...	...	9 1	...	10 49	...	...	...	...	...	1248	1347	...	16 8	...	...	17 55
Arras..........arr 7 20	...	7 35	...	7 46	9 18	...	11 0	...	9 56	...	...	...	13 5	1358	14 25	1625	...	...	18 6
PARIS 26 ...arr ...	...	9 57	...	9 57	12 7	...	16 20	...	12 7	...	...	...	...	1710	17 10	...	...	...	...

French Customs Examination at Tourcoing and Blanc Misseron; Belgian Customs Examination at Mouscron and Quiévrain.

§—Runs until 30th September.

¶—See page 26 whether from Ville or Maritime Station at Calais.

*—10 mins. earlier after 30th September.

A—Calais-Belfort Express.

D—Between Douai and Lille weekdays only, for passengers without luggage, *(May not be running.)*

RC—Restaurant Car in this train.

For Continuation of Trains, see next page.

NORTHERN RAILWAY. [Excess Luggage, 1 cent. per 44 lbs. per kilometre.

ARRAS to DOUAI, LILLE, MOUSCRON, and VALENCIENNES.

Frequent Extra Service between Lille and Tourcoing.

	1,2,3	1,2,3	1,2,3	1,2,3	1,2,3	1 & 2	1,2,3	1,2,3	1,2,3	1,2,3	1,2,3	1 & 2		1,2,3	1,2,3	1 & 2	1,2,3	1,2,3	1 & 2	1,2,3
PARIS 27 .... dep	8 40	...	...	...	...	...	13 0	...	...	...	14 30	1720	...	...	...	1925	19 25	...	21 0	...
Arras .... dep	12 4	1257	...	...	...	...	16 2	1515	...	1644	17 49	1929	...	...	1936	2136	21 42	2148	2315	...
Rœux	1215	1315	...	...	...	...	...	1526	...	17 5	...	...	...	...	1954	RC	...	22 7	...	...
Vitry	1224	1326	...	...	...	...	...	1535	...	1718	...	RC	...	...	20 5	...	...	2217	...	...
Douai .... arr	1241	1347	...	...	...	...	1622	1551	...	1742	18 8	1947	...	...	2026	2154	22 4	2238	2333	...
Douai .... dep	1254	—	13 55	...	1530	...	1627	—	1723	1816	18 14	1949	...	19 55	2111	2156	22 17	2256	2335	2341
Libercourt 29B	1320	...	...	...	1553	...	...	...	1751	1844	18 29	...	...	20 9	2140	...	22 31	2310	...	0 4
Seclin	1332	...	...	...	16 4	...	...	...	18 8	1856	18 38	...	...	20 20	2155	...	22 44	...	...	0 18
Lille .... arr	1349	...	14 24	...	1617	...	1652	...	1824	1919	18 50	2014	...	20 32	2211	2221	22 57	2327	24 0	0 35
OSTEND 90 ... arr	18 9	...	...	...		...	1854	...	...		...	2225	...	...		...	...	...	...	
CALAIS ¶26 ... dep	9 49	...	12 53	...	...	§	1446	1446	...	1630	...	...	...	19 7	...	19 7	...	...	...	...
Lille .... dep	14 4	...	15 31	1616	...	17 1	17 6	1758	19 5	1959	20 30	2020	...	21 5	...	2226	23 3	2335	0 7	...
Croix	1417	...	...	1627	...	...	1717	18 9	...	2011	20 43	...	...	21 16	...	2236	23 17	...	...	...
Roubaix	1424	...	15 45	1631	...	1713	1723	1813	1922	2017	20 49	2032	...	21 22	...	2243	23 23	2348	0 20	...
Tourcoing	1431	...	15 53	—	...	1720	1729	1821	1931	2021	21 8	2036	...	21 26	...	2247	23 28	2352	0 24	...
Mouscron ...... arr	1439	...	16 1	...	...	1726	1737	1829	1939	...	21 17	2052	§ ...	21 41	...					...
GHENT 89 ..... arr	1645	...	—	...	...	...	1856	...	—	...	22 40		...	...	...	...	...	...	...	...

	1,2,3	1,2,3	1,2,3		1,2,3			1,2,3	1,2,3		1,2,3	1,2,3	1,2,3		1,2,3		1,2,3			1,2,3
Douai .... dep	1251	14 9	14 52	...	...	...	...	1643	1719	...	18 24	20 1	...	...	2034	...	22 12	...	...	2346
Somain 29A	1319	1429	15 16	...	...	...	...	17 8	1743	...	18 42	2017	...	...	21 2	...	22 32	...	...	0 11
Valenciennes ..... arr	1348	1454	15 41	...	...	...	...	1741	1830	...	19 2	2042	...	...	2130	...	22 56	...	...	0 39
" ..... dep	1415	—	15 46	...	1618	...	...	18 0	—	...	19 41		21 12	...		...		...	...	
Blanc-Misseron	1440	...	16 3	...	1633	...	...	1826	...	...	20 16	...	21 32	...	...	...	...	...	...	...
Quiévrain .... arr	1443	...	16 6	...	1636	...	...	1830	...	...	20 19	...		...	...	...	...	...	...	...
MONS 108 .... arr	1540	...	17 15	...	1715	...	...	1945	...	...	21 6	...	...	...	...	...	...	...	...	...
BRUSSELS .... arr	1756	...	18 30	...	1830	...	...	2130	...	...	22 16	...	...	...	...	...	...	...	...	...

VALENCIENNES to MOUSCRON, LILLE, DOUAI, and ARRAS.

Frequent Extra Service between Tourcoing and Lille.

BRUSSELS 108 ... dep	...	13 6	...	...	...	...	...	...	...	...	...	...	15 8	...	...	18 3	...	19 27	...	...
MONS 108 .... dep	...	1429	...	...	...	...	...	...	...	...	...	...	1715	...	...	19 4	...	20 59	...	...
		1,2,3						1,2,3					1,2,3		1,2,3	1,2,3		1,2,3		
Quiévrain .... dep	...	1514	...	...	...	...	...	...	...	...	...	...	18 3	...	1927	20 7	...	21 31	...	...
Blanc-Misseron	...	1538	...	...	...	...	...	...	...	...	...	...	1824	...	1946	2028	...	21 53	...	...
Valenciennes ...... arr	...	1554	...	...	...	...	...	...	...	...	...	...	1845	...	1959	2046	...	22 10	...	...
" ...... dep	...	1612	...	...	...	...	...	1840	...	...	...	...	20 8	...		2114	...	22 20	...	...
Somain	...	1652	...	...	...	...	...	19 9	...	...	...	...	2046	...	...	2148	...	22 52	...	...
Douai .... arr	...	1713	...	...	...	...	...	1928	...	...	...	...	21 6	...	...	22 9	...	23 10	...	...

	1,2,3		1 & 2 §	1 & 2	1 & 2	1,2,3	1,2,3	1,2,3	1,2,3	1,2,3	1 & 2	1 & 2	1,2,3			1,2,3	1,2,3	1,2,3	1,2,3	1,2,3
GHENT 89 ...... dep	13 8		...	...	...	...	1642	...	...	17 2	...	...	...	...	...	1843	18 43	19 16	2053	...
Mouscron ...... dep	15 13		1539	...	...	1638	1755	...	...	1820	18 40	...	...	...	...	1957	20 33	21 19	2215	...
Tourcoing	15 43		1546	16 0	...	1712	1823	...	...	1841	18 46	19 5	1915	...	...	2018	20 59	21 45	2242	...
Roubaix	15 51		—	16 6	...	1718	1829	...	...	1848	—	1911	1923	...	...	2024	21 5	21 53	2249	...
Croix	15 56		—	...	...	1723	...	...	...	1853	—	...	1928	...	...	2029	...	21 58	2255	...
Lille .... arr	16 5		...	1617	...	1732	1840	...	...	19 2	...	1922	1939	...	...	2040	21 16	22 7	23 7	...
CALAIS 27 ...... arr	18 5		...	18 5	...	2228	2228	...	...	—	...	...	...	...	...	...	...	1 36	1 36	...
OSTEND 91 ... dep	—		...	1414	1414	...	—	15 2	...	...	...	1718	...	...	...	...	...	18 0	—	...
Lille .... dep	...		...	1627	1645	1742	...	19 0	19 3	...	...	1930	1940	1948	...	2058	21 33	22 25	...	0 55
Seclin	...		...	...	A	...	...	...	19 23	...	...	...	1955	2015	...	2122	...	22 44	...	1 17
Libercourt	...		...	...	...	18 1	...	1920	...	...	...	...	20 8	2028	...	2136	21 54	22 57	...	1 31
Douai .... arr	...		...	1652	1712	1815	...	1934	19 59	...	...	1955	2029	2057	...	22 0	22 8	23 18	...	1 54
Douai .... dep	...	1723	...	1554	1715	18 1	...	1939	—	...	...	1957	—	2115	...	2221	—	23 28	...	—
Vitry	...	To Lille.	...	...	To Cambrai.	1849	...	...	...	...	...	RC	...	2140	...	2212	...	...	...	...
Rœux	...		...	...		19 1	...	...	...	...	...	...	...	2152	...	2255	...	...	...	...
Arras .... arr	...		...	1713		1918	...	20 0	...	...	...	2016	...	2210	...	23 8	...	23 56	...	...
PARIS 26 .... arr	...		...	1920		...	...	2226	...	...	...	2226	...	...	...	4 15	...	4 37	...	...

PARIS to BRUSSELS (via Maubeuge) and to COLOGNE (via Erquelinnes)

Dist	1 Cl.	2 Cl.		1,2,3	1,2,3	1,2,3	1,2,3	1,2,3	1 & 2	1,2,3	1,2,3	1 & 2	1& 2	1 & 2	1,2,3	1,2,3	1,2,3	1 &2		1& 2	1 & 2
E.M From	fr. c. from	fr. c. Paris.	PARIS—Gare du Nord ......dep	...	...	...	5 17	...	...	7 0	...	7 50	8 10	...	9 0	...	1025	1235		...	13 45
4¼	0 80	0 55	St. Denis	...	...	...	...	...	A	...	...	...	F	...	...	...	...	G			C
25½	4 60	3 10	Chantilly	...	...	...	6 14	...	...	...	...	...	...	...	9 36	...	11 0	...			
31¾	5 70	3 85	Creil .... arr	...	...	...	6 24	...	From Laon.	7 37	...	...	...	...	9 45	...	11 9	...		From Calais (12.50, page 26).	Nord Express.
...	...	...	Creil .... dep	...	...	...	6 45	5 15		7 40	...	...	...	...	9 52	10 0	1112	...			
38½	6 95	4 70	Pont Ste Maxence	...	...	...	7 8	5 33		...	...	...	...	...	10 4	1020	1124	...			
44¾	8 5	5 45	Longueil-S-Marie	...	...	...	7 26	5 47		...	...	RC	...	...	...	1036	...	...			
52¼	9 40	6 35	Compiegne 29......	...	...	...	8 12	6 8		8 9	...	...	...	...	1028	1157	1145	RC			
67	12 10	8 15	Noyon	5 14	...	...	9 55	6 50		8 30	...	...	...	...	1051	1240	12 5	...			
77	13 90	9 35	Chauny 29B.........	5 44	...	...	1031	7 20		8 47	...	...	...	...	11 9	1310	1221	...			
81½	14 65	9 90	Tergnier 21 ...arr	5 56	...	...	1043	7 31	8 26	8 55	...	...	...	...	1118	1322	1228	...			C
...	...	...	,, ...dep	—	5 25	...	—	7 42	8 28	8 58	...	...	...	...	1136	1332	1233	...			...
95¾	17 25	11 65	St. Quentin arr	...	5 53	...	...	8 12	8 46	9 16	...	9 23	9 46	...	12 7	14 4	1252	1411			15 19
			St. Quentin dep	...	5 57	...	...	8 19	8 49	9 29	...	9 26	9 49	...	1212	1419	1258	1414			15 22
112½	20 25	13 70	Busigny 28 arr	...	6 38	...	...	8 59	9 12	9 55	...	⋮	...	...	1255	15 3	1321	...			⋮
			Busigny 28 dep	...	—	7 8	...	—	9 15	9 59	10 15	⋮	...	...	—	15 7	1328	...			⋮
118	21 30	14 35	Le Cateau..........	...	...	7 27	...	...	...	...	10 57	⋮	...	...	...	1519	1344	...		⋮	⋮
134¼	24 20	16 35	Aulnoye ... arr	...	...	8 8	...	...	To Lille (arr. 10.44)	10 25	11 35	⋮	1032		a.m.	1552	1422	1457		1540	⋮
			Aulnoye ... dep	4 56	7 8	8 21	...	...		10 27	11 45	⋮	1035	10 41	1046	1626	1430	1458	15 11	1545	⋮
139½	25 10	16 95	Hautmont..........	5 13	7 22	8 37	...	...		10 36	11 57	⋮	⋮	RC	11 0	1640	1440	⋮	15 20	⋮	⋮
142¼	25 65	17 30	Maubeuge......arr	5 25	7 33	8 48	...	...		10 42	12 7	⋮	⋮	10 52	1110	1651	1446	⋮	15 29	⋮	Nord Express.
143½	...	...	FEIGNIES ...arr	6 45	7 58	...	...	...		11 7	...	⋮	1049	...	...	1714	15 3	1511	...	⋮	⋮
146	26 70	18 5	QUEVY 108 ...arr	6 52	8 5	...	...	...		11 13	...	⋮	1054	...	...	1720	15 8	1516	...	⋮	⋮
192¾	34 35	23 25	BRUSSELS ...arr	8 50	10 18	...	...	...		13 6	...	⋮	1212	...	...	2025	...	1638	...	RC	⋮
225	38 5	25 75	ANTWERP 110 ar	...	...	...	...	...	...	...	...	⋮	1324	...	...	...	...	1745	...	⋮	⋮
340¼	54 40	38 10	AMST'DAM 119ar	...	...	...	...	...	...	...	...	⋮	5p17	...	...	...	...	9p53	...	⋮	⋮
...	...	...	Maubeuge......dep	5 30	7 53	8 52	...	...	13 20	10 45	12 13	⋮	...	10 53	1125	17 4	15 0	...	15 33	⋮	⋮
148	26 65	18 0	Jeumont	5 50	8 8	9 13	...	...	13 43	10 55	12 32	⋮	...	11 3	1144	17 25	1515	...	15 46	16 4	16 21
149¼	26 90	18 15	Erquelinnes ¶ arr	...	8 12	9 17	...	...	13 47	10 58	12 35	10 21	...	11 6	1147	1729	1519	...		16 7	16 24
167¾	29 80	20 15	CHARLEROI ...arr	...	9 7	1021	...	...	...	11 51	13 37	10 57	...	11 51	...	1834	1635	...	...	17 8	17 8
190¼	33 40	22 55	NAMUR 92......arr	...	10 46	1135	...	...	...	12 30	15 41	11 35	...	12 30	...	...	1935	...	...	1747	17 47
228	39 10	26 45	LIEGE (Guillem)	...	13 1	1226	...	...	...	13 35	17 43	12 26	...	13 35	...	...	...	...	...	1847	18 47
306½	53 10	36 20	COLOGNE 122 arr	...	...	...	...	...	...	5 p55	...	4 p19	...	5 p55	...	...	...	...	...	11p1	10p46
671	11050	71 30	BERLIN 161 ...arr	...	...	...	...	...	...	7 a20	...	12a21	...	7 a20	...	...	...	...	...	8a54	7 a29
586¼	97 50	64 40	HAMBURG 132arr	...	...	...	...	...	...	...	...	12 a9	...	...	...	...	...	...	...	6a55	6 a55

COLOGNE and BRUSSELS to PARIS.

		1,2,3	1 Cl.	1,2,3	1,2,3	1,2,3	1,2,3	1,2,3	1,2,3	1 Cl.	1Cl.	1,2,3	1,2,3	1,2,3	1 &2	1& 2	1,2,3	1,2,3	1 & 2	1,2,3	1,2,3
HAMBURG 133 dep		...	2 p45	...	...	...	...	...	...	...	...	...	...	...	11p14	11p14	...	...	...	11p14	...
BERLIN 160B dep		...	12p16	...	...	...	...	...	...	...	...	...	...	...	9p34	10p58	...	...	...	9 p34	...
COLOGNE 123B dep		...	10p52	...	...	...	...	...	...	...	...	...	...	...	7a56	8 a7	...	...	...	9 a10	...
LIEGE 93 ......dep		...	1 1	...	...	...	...	...	...	7 20	...	6 27	6 27	7 38	1015	1015	...	9 7	...	11 32	...
NAMUR 93 ...dep		...	2 12	...	...	...	...	3 44	...	8 16	...	7 34	7 38	9 38	1121	1121	...	1051	...	12 45	...
CHARLEROI 93 dep		...	3 0	...	...	...	...	5 38	...	9 0	...	8 43	9 36	11 1	12 6	12 6	...	1224	..	13 36	1352
Erquelinnes ......dep		...	3 34	...	...	...	...	6 50	...	9 30	...	9 57	1034	1158	1235	1235	...	1322	...	14 9	1457
Jeumont ¶		...	4 15	4 32	5 10	5 56	...	7 16	9 5	9 46	...	10 11	1057	1224	1249	13 2	13 8	1355	...	1436	1516
Maubeuge ....arr		...	A	4 42	5 27	6 18	...	7 32	9 24	9 54	...	10 30	1111	1238	⋮	D	1326	14 8	...	1445	1530
AMSTERDAM 119 dep		...	⋮	...	...	...	...	...	...	...	...	...	...	...	⋮	⋮	...	...	8a40	...	...
ANTWERP 110 dep		...	⋮	...	...	...	...	...	...	...	7 12	...	...	...	⋮	⋮	...	...	11 53	...	...
BRUSSELS...108 dep		...	⋮	...	...	...	...	...	6 57	...	8 21	8 57	...	...	⋮	⋮	9 40	...	13 1	...	13 6
FEIGNIES 108...dep		...	⋮	...	5 18	6 3	...	7 36	9 6	...	9 59	11 3	...	...	⋮	⋮	1253	...	14 34	...	1514
MAUBEUGE ......arr		...	⋮	...	5 34	6 18	From Lille. (dep. 7.44.)	7 48	9 21	...	⋮	11 14	...	...	⋮	⋮	13 8	...	⋮	...	1526
Maubeuge ....dep		...	⋮	4 45	5 39	6 32		7 50	9 27	9 55	⋮	11 27	1135	...	⋮	Nord Express.	1328	1412	⋮	1449	1539
Hautmont		...	SC	4 54	5 54	6 45		8 4	9 42	E	⋮	11 37	1147	...	⋮		1341	1421	⋮	...	1551
Aulnoye .... arr		...	⋮	5 2	6 7	6 57		8 13	9 56	10 7	1012	11 45	1156	...	13 5		1354	1430	⋮	15 1	16 0
Aulnoye .... dep		...	⋮	5 7	—	7 6		8 31	—	1019		11 50	12 2	...	1310		1359	—	⋮	1510	16 5
Le Cateau		...	⋮	5 42	...	7 43	...	9 12	...	RC		12 19	1239	...	To Calais (arr. 15.36, page 27.)		1434	...	⋮	...	1641
Busigny .... arr		...	⋮	5 55	a.m.	7 57	9 11	9 27	...	1043		12 30	1254	...			1447		⋮	1535	1655
Busigny .... dep		4 21	⋮	5 58	6 59	8 3	9 20	9 59	...	1044		12 40	13 0	...			—	15 9	⋮	1537	17 3
St. Quentin...... arr		5 3	5 25	6 32	7 34	8 44	9 40	10 36	...	11 2		13 8	1343	...		14 4	...	1545	15 24	1555	1742
St. Quentin...... dep		5 6	5 30	6 35	7 37	8 48	9 43	10 41	...	11 5		13 13	1347	...		14 8	...	16 2	15 28	1559	1747
Tergnier .... arr		5 36	5 49	6 53	8 5	9 18	⋮	11 12	...	1121		13 36	1417	...		...	...	1631	...	1616	1817
Tergnier .... dep		6 0	5 50	6 57	8 40	9 29	To Laon.	11 45	...	1122		13 42	1431	...		...	...	1636	...	1620	1833
Chauny		6 13	...	7 6	8 49	9 43		12 0	...	...		13 53	1445	...		...	...	1647	...	...	1848
Noyon		6 43	...	7 22	9 6	1015		12 28	...	...		14 9	1513	...		D	...	17 4	RC	...	1918
Compiègne..........	6 48	7 37	6 27	7 45	9 39	11 6		13 11	...	1154		14 33	1618	...		...	...	1725	...	1655	20 2
Longueil.............	7 5	7 48	...	...	9 54	1128		13 28	...	...		...	1623	...		...	...	...	...	...	2019
Pont Ste Maxence	7 25	...	...	8 3	10 8	1145		13 42	...	...		...	1646	...		...	...	...	...	...	2038
Creil .... arr	7 42	8 5	...	8 13	1022	12 3	...	14 0	...	...		15 1	17 3	...	...	...	...	1753	...	1720	2055
Creil .... dep	—	8 7	...	8 15	1025	1220	...	14 5	...	...		15 3	17 6	...	...	...	...	1755	...	1722	21 1
Chantilly		...	...	...	1036	1235	...	14 16	...	...		15 15	1720	...	...	...	...	...	...	...	2118
St. Denis..................		...	...	...	...	...	...	...	...	...		...	...	...	...	...	...	...	...	...	...
PARIS Nord...... arr		8 50	7 35	8 55	1110	1315	...	15 3	...	1251		15 50	1759	...	...	16 0	...	1840	17 15	18 5	2156

PARIS to BRUSSELS and COLOGNE.

	1,2,3	1,2,3	1,2,3	1,2,3	1,2,3	1&2	1&2	1,2,3	1,2,3	1,2,3	1,2,3	1&2	1,2,3	1,2,3
PARIS—														
Gare du Nord dep	...	12 23	16 5	...	16 40	1820	1910	...	1739	20 10	2040	22 0	2315	0 35
St. Denis	...	...	...	...	...	...	...	...	...	...	...	H	J	0 46
Chantilly	...	13 17	1641	...	17 18	‡	...	From Laon.	1825	20 46	2116	...	...	1 43
Creil arr	...	13 27	1650	...	17 28	1858	...		1835	20 55	2123	...	...	1 52
Creil dep	...	13 30	1654	...	17 36	19 1	...		19 4	20 58	2127	...	SC	1 59
Pont Ste Maxence	...	13 51	...	...	17 56	RC	RC		1922	21 18	...	SC	...	2 15
Longueil	...	14 7	...	...	18 10	...	...		1937	21 32	...	...	...	2 27
Compiègne 29	...	15 7	1725	...	18 31	1929	...		1953	22 1	2158	...	0 30	2 45
Noyon	...	15 50	1746	...	19 13	...	...	...	—	22 41	2215	...	...	3 17
Chauny 29B	...	16 21	18 2	...	19 41	...	...	...	...	23 8	2234	...	...	3 35
Tergnier 21 arr	...	16 33	1810	...	19 53	20 4	...	2055	...	23 19	2242	...	1 12	3 45
,, dep	...	16 43	1815	18 29	—	20 6	...	21 0	2034	23 40	2245	...	1 17	3 51
St. Quentin arr	...	17 12	1834	19 1	...	2025	...	2121	21 5	0 7	23 4	2350	1 36	4 18
St. Quentin dep	...	17 17	1839	19 4	...	2029	...	2126	21 8	0 12	23 9	2355	1 39	4 21
Busigny arr	...	17 53	19 7	19 46	...	2052	21 4	2156	2146	0 49	2332	:	...	4 59
Busigny dep	...	18 7	19 9	21 22	...	2054	21 9	22 2	—	1 5	2335	:	...	5 6
Le Cateau	...	18 24	1919	21 40	...	...	:		...	1 18	2345	:	...	5 20
Aulnoye arr	...	19 4	1944	22 17	...	2121	:	To Lille (arr. 23.27).	...	1 49	0 7	:	...	5 55
Aulnoye dep	17 55	19 11	1953	22 40	...	2123	:		2348	1 55	0 11	:	...	6 6
Hautmont	18 9	19 22	20 2	22 55	...	...	:		2357	2 5	0 20	:	...	6 18
Maubeuge arr	18 20	19 34	20 8	23 7	...	2135	:		0 6	2 11	0 29	:	2 43	6 28
FEIGNIES arr	18 44	20 31	2031	...	...	...	2143		...	...	...	:	3 22	6 45
QUEVY 108 arr	18 51	20 36	2036	...	...	...	2148	...	...	...	...	:	3 27	6 52
BRUSSELS arr	21 30	22 16	2216	...	...	...	23 5	...	...	...	...	:	5 15	8 50
ANTWERP 110 arr	...	...	...	...	...	...	0 13	...	...	...	...	:	6 56	...
AMSTERDAM 119 ar	...	...	...	...	...	...	...	...	...	...	...	:	1122	...
Maubeuge dep	18 24	20 21	...	23 10	...	2136	...	...	0 8	...	0 31	:	2 52	6 38
Jeumont	18 45	20 40	...	23 27	...	2146	...	...	0 21	...	0 40	1 0	3 4	7 0
Erquelinnes arr	18 49	20 44	...	...	...	2149	...	...	—	...	0 43	1 4	3 7	7 3
CHARLEROI arr	20 9	21 46	...	...	...	2236	...	...	...	...	...	2 1	4 2	...
NAMUR 92 arr	...	23 10	...	...	...	2315	...	...	...	...	...	2 45	4 52	...
LIEGE (Guillem) arr	...	...	...	...	...	0 19	...	...	...	...	...	3 51	6 0	...
COLOGNE 122 arr	...	...	...	...	...	5a40	...	...	...	...	...	8 a0	9a51	...
BERLIN 161 arr	...	...	...	...	...	3p48	...	...	...	...	...	6p12	6p12	...
HAMBURG 132 arr	...	...	...	...	...	2p28	...	...	...	...	...	5 p3	5 p3	...

‡—Will not set down at Creil.

A—Belfort and Calais Express.

C—**Nord Express**, for Berlin and St. Petersburg. Taking for beyond Erquelinnes only. Will take 2nd class for Erquelinnes and beyond. At Liege this train becomes exclusively a Train de Luxe.

F—Takes 2nd class for Feignies and beyond and 2nd class for Erquelinnes and beyond.

G—Takes at Paris 2nd class for St. Quentin and beyond; will also take 2nd class for Erquelinnes, Feignies, and beyond.

H—Does not take 2nd class for French Stations.

J—Does not admit 3rd class for Compiègne, Tergnier, St. Quentin, or Maubeuge.

¶—Customs Examination.

COLOGNE and BRUSSELS to PARIS.

		1 Cl	1,2,3	1,2,3	1,2,3	1,2,3	1&2	1&2	1,2,3	1&2	1,2,3	1,2,3	1,2,3		
HAMBURG 133 dep		...	...	...	...	...	7a39	...	...	7a39	...	...	9a59	...	...
BERLIN 160B dep		...	...	...	...	...	...	...	...	8 a0	...	...	8a59	...	...
COLOGNE 123B dp		...	...	...	...	1126	3p12	...	...	4p19	...	...	6p13	...	...
LIEGE 93 dep		...	...	11 40	...	1353	1710	...	...	1835	...	18 0	:	...	...
NAMUR 93 dep		...	...	14 49	...	16 3	1811	...	...	1926	...	1952	C :	...	...
CHARLEROI 93 dp		...	...	16 10	...	1750	1854	...	...	20 8	19 25	2120	:	...	...
Erquelinnes dep		...	...	17 5	18 9	1853	1922	...	...	2036	20 55	2217	:	...	...
Jeumont		...	17 5	17 25	18 35	19 9	1940	...	1956	2055	21 30	2242	:	...	...
Maubeuge arr		...	1722	17 46	18 52	1926	19‡49	...	20 9	:	21 46	2259	:	...	...
AMSTERDAM 119 dp		...	...	...	...	...	...	1 p45	...	:	...	...	8 p0	...	...
ANTWERP 110 dep		...	...	...	...	...	...	17 6	...	:	...	...	2257	...	...
BRUSSELS 108 dep		B	...	...	15 3	...	...	18 15	...	:	...	...	0 7	...	...
FEIGNIES 108 dep		From Lille (dep. 16.45)	...	17 8	18 21	...	...	19 55	20 0	:	20 47	...	2 16	...	...
MAUBEUGE arr			...	17 24	18 36	...	...	:	2011	:	20 58	...	:	...	...
Maubeuge dep			1725	17 53	19 7	1929	19‡50	:	2016	:	21 59	23 4	F :	...	...
Hautmont			1738	18 8	19 30	1940	RC	:	2023	:	22 11	2316	:	...	...
Aulnoye arr			1747	18 23	19 40	1958	20 1	20 8	2031	:	22 20	2329	2 29	...	...
Aulnoye dep			—	18 29	20 37	—		20 15	2033	RC	22 33	—	2 34	...	...
Le Cateau		...	...	19 7	21 47	...	...	...	...	:	23 8	...	...	...	...
Busigny arr		1812	...	19 18	22 2	...	...	RC	2059	:	23 20	...	SC	...	...
Busigny dep		1816	...	19 35	22 17	...	...	...	21 1	:	23 31	...	...	...	...
St. Quentin arr		1835	...	20 17	23 6	...	...	21 0	2120	2150	0 9	...	3 20	...	...
St. Quentin dep		1838	...	20 21	23 25	...	...	21 4	2123	2153	0 14	...	3 23	...	...
Tergnier arr		1856	...	20 51	0 2	...	...	...	2140	...	0 43	...	3 43	...	...
Tergnier dep		1858	2010	—	—	...	...	...	2142	...	1 0	...	3 44	...	...
Chauny	1,2,3		2022	...	...	...	...	...	2152	...	1 12	...	...	...	...
Noyon	...		2051	...	...	...	...	...	22 8	...	1 33	...	...	...	...
Compiègne	1748	To Laon.	2130	...	22 44	...	...	...	2240	...	2 7	5 32	4 23	...	...
Longueil	18 5		—	...	23 0	...	...	...	...	...	2 22	5 50	...	...	...
Pont Ste Maxen	1820		...	...	23 14	...	...	...	...	...	2 36	6 8	...	...	...
Creil arr	1841	...	...	...	23 30	...	...	...	23 7	...	2 51	6 27	4 51	...	...
Creil dep	19 2	...	...	...	23 33	...	...	...	2310	...	3 1	6 30	4 53	...	...
Chantilly	1916	...	...	...	23 46	...	...	...	...	...	...	6 44	...	...	...
St. Denis	...	...	...	...	0 38	...	...	...	...	...	...	...	...	...	...
PARIS Nord arr	2012	...	...	...	0 47	...	...	22 46	2355	2330	4 5	7 25	5 32	...	...

‡—At Maubeuge takes up and sets down passengers only—without luggage.

¶—Customs Examination.

A—Bringing 2nd class passengers from Germany and Belgium; and at stations in France taking up 2nd class for Paris only.

B—Calais and Belfort Express.

C—This train from Cologne (6.13 p.m.) has a connection with the Midi Station at Brussels.

D—**Nord Express**, from St. Petersburg and Berlin; brings forward 1st and 2nd class. At St. Quentin takes 1st class for Paris.

E—Bringing forward 2nd class from Belgian Stations; takes up 2nd cl. at Jeumont and Feignies only.

F—Bringing forward 3rd class from Belgian Stations.

RC—Restaurant Car in this train.

SC—Sleeping Car attached.

LONDON, CALAIS, LILLE, ARRAS, and PARIS.

THROUGH CARRIAGES. } Calais to Basle—in 14.46 from Calais. Calais to Cologne—in 12.50 (via Liège) and 12.53 from Calais. Calais to Brussels in 12.53, 14.46, and 1.19 from Calais. Calais to Frankfort—in 1.19 from Calais.
A Coupé-Lits-Toilette carriage will be run from Calais to Brussels, if ordered in advance, for three 1st Class fares, and three extra fares of 13 fr. 65 c. each.

	1,2,3	1,2,3	1,2,3	1,2,3	1,2,3	1,2,3	1 & 2	1,2,3	1,2,3	1,2,3	1,2,3	1,2,3	1,2,3	1,2,3	1 & 2	1,2,3	1 & 2	1 &2	1,2,3	1,2,3	1,2,3	1 &2	1,2,3	1,2,3	1,2,3	1,2,3	1,2,3	1,2,3	1,2,3
London: Charing Cross ...dep	...	...	...	...	...	...	...	...	...	...	...	...	...	...	9 a0	...	9 a0	...	...	...	...	...	...	...	...	2 p5	...	...	9 p0
Victoria ...dep	...	...	...	...	...	...	...	...	...	...	...	...	...	...	...	...	...	...	...	...	...	11a0	...	...	...	H	...	...	...
Dover ...dep	...	...	...	...	...	...	...	...	...	...	...	...	...	...	11a5	...	11 a5	...	...	...	...	1255	...	...	...	...	...	...	11 p5
Calais (Maritime) ...dep	...	...	...	...	...	...	...	...	...	A	...	...	...	...	1250	...	12 53	...	...	...	...	1446	...	...	...	...	...	...	1 19
„ (Ville) ...dep	...	...	...	...	...	...	...	...	6 21	8 2	...	...	...	9 49	...	...	12 59	...	1342	...	...	1452	16 10	...	1758	19 7	...	21 59	1 25
Watten-Eperl (20)	...	...	...	...	...	...	...	7 13	7 20	...	...	...	9 58	10 47	RC	...	G	...	1440	...	1429	...	1724	...	1858	H	...	22 53	...
Saint-Omer (19A)	...	...	6 0	...	...	...	...	7 24	7 42	8 39	...	...	10 17	11 8	...	...	13 29	...	1458	14 33	1439	1525	17 38	...	1920	1942	20 8	23 12	1 57
Hazebrouck ...arr	...	...	6 28	...	...	...	...	—	8 9	8 58	...	...	10 46	11 38	1338	...	13 46	...	1521	15 0	—	1544	18 5	...	1948	1959	20 37	23 37	2 15
Dunkirk ...dep	...	...	5 29	6 0	...	...	...	7 26	...	A 8 0	...	...	...	9 59	...	13 19	...	...	1430	...	...	...	1740	...	1817	...	19 18	22 38	...
Bergues	...	...	5 43	...	...	...	...	7 39	...	8 14	...	...	...	10 14	...	12 26	...	...	1446	...	...	...	1750	...	19 2	...	19 41	22 51	...
Cassel	...	...	6 15	...	...	...	...	8 8	...	8 44	...	...	...	10 50	...	13 13	...	...	1518	...	...	...	1811	...	1915	...	20 29	23 21	...
Hazebrouck ...arr	...	...	6 26	6 35	...	...	...	8 18	...	8 54	...	...	...	11 1	...	13 24	...	...	1528	...	...	...	1821	...	1946	...	20 41	23 32	...
Hazebrouck ...dep	4 46	6 4	6 41		...	...	...	...	8 28	9 1	...	9 30	11 5	11 52	1339	14 25	13 47	...	16 1	...	...	1547	1835	1912	2013	20 2	21 49	23 45	2 18
Bailleul	5 9	6 24	6 56	...	...	...	...	...	8 48	9 16	...	9 57	11 25	12 18	...	14 49	...	...	1624	...	...	...	1852	1932	2035	...	22 16	0 2	...
Armentières 30, 95	5 27	6 45	7 9	...	7 40	...	...	...	9 8	9 28	...	1028	11 41	12 44	...	15 22	14 6	...	1648	...	...	1611	19 6	1953	21 0	2026	23 2	0 17	...
Perenchies	5 38	6 58	...	...	7 53	...	...	...	9 18	A	...	...	...	12 54	...	15 33	G	...	1658	...	...	...	...	20 6	2110	...	23 12	...	...
La Madeleine	5 43	7 13	7 23	...	8 8	...	...	...	9 29	...	...	...	...	13 8	1410	15 48	14 32	...	1715	...	...	...	1923	2020	2126	...	23 30	0 34	...
Lille ...arr	6 5	7 25	7 31	...	8 19	...	...	...	9 40	9 49	...	1049	12 3	13 20		15 59	14 38	...	1728	...	...	1630	1933	2014	2138	2045	23 41	0 44	2 55
BRUSSELS 103 arr	8 56	—	11 2	...	11 2	...	...	...	13 46	13 46	...	—	—	16 41		...	16 41	...	2121	...	...	1855	...	...	...	2314	—	—	5 21
Hazebrouck ...dep	4 59	...	...	6 39	...	6 54	...	8 25	8 40	...	...	...	...	11 54	To Valenciennes (page 29A), and Liège (arr. 18.47 page 92).	13 34	...	...	1537	...	...	...	1826	...	2025	...	...	...	...
Steenbecque	5 9	...	...	...	...	7 4	...	...	8 50	...	...	...	...	12 4		13 44	...	...	1547	...	...	...	...	...	2035	...	...	...	RC Restaurant Car in this train.
Berguette	5 37	...	...	...	...	7 25	...	8 42	9 6	A—Runs until 30th September.	...	...	...	12 21		14 3	...	...	16 2	...	...	...	1842	...	2056	...	...	...	
Lillers	5 49	...	...	...	...	7 37	...	8 50	9 18		...	...	...	12 34		14 13	...	...	1614	...	...	...	1851	...	21 9	...	...	...	
Chocques	6 0	...	...	...	...	7 46	...	...	9 27		...	...	...	12 43		14 22	...	...	1624	...	...	...	...	...	2119	...	...	...	
Bethune (20, 29B)	6 20	...	...	7 *7	...	8 26	...	9 5	9 43		11 5	...	...	12 59		14 35	...	...	1639	...	1746	...	19 9	...	2143	...	22 22	4 59	
Bully Grenay (30)	6 41	...	...	...	...	8 50	...	...	10 3		1126	...	...	13 20		14 58	...	...	1659	...	18 9	...	1926	...	22 7	...	22 49	5 26	
Lens (29B, 30)	6 54	...	...	...	7 50	9 4	...	9 27	10 16		1140	1158	...	13 38		15 31	...	...	1719	...	1832	...	1937	...	2233	0 25	23 22	5 46	
Farbus	7 13	...	...	...	8 9	—	...	...	10 35			1215	...	13 57		15 49	...	...	1738	...	1850	...	...	...	2252	0 45	...	6 5	
Arras ...arr	7 28	1&2	...	7 41	8 27	...	...	9 48	10 53		...	1233	...	14 11		16 8	...	...	1752	...	19 9	1&2	1955	...	23 6	1 8	23 51	6 27	
LILLE ...dep	7 0	7 0	7 0	—	—	...	9 10		...		...	—	13 33	—		—	...	1627	1627	19 0	—	1930	—	2058	—	—	22 25	...	
Arras ...dep	7 55	7 50	8 0	...	...	...	10 0		11 8		...	...	14 29	...		...	14 56	1717	1817	20 4	...	2021	...	2319	...	...	0 7	6 32	
Boisleux (22A)	...	...	8 12	...	...	...	...	—	11 21		...	...	...	...		...	15 9	...	1830	...	...	...	...	2332	...	...	...	6 44	
Achiet (30A)	...	F	8 28	...	...	...	...	...	11 38	...	...	‡	...	...		...	15 26	...	1846	...	...	...	...	2346	...	...	0 33	6 59	
Albert (29B)	8 27	...	8 54	...	...	...	RC	...	12 4	...	...	1416	14 59	...	...	...	15 52	...	1917	20 33	...	RC	...	0 17	...	...	0 57	7 25	...
Corbie	...	...	9 19	...	...	...	...	...	12 31	...	...	1441	...	...	...	1 Cl.	16 19	...	1944	...	...	...	...	0 38	...	...	...	7 52	...
Longueau (Buffet) ...arr	...	8 32	...	...	...	...	10 42	...	12 52	...	...	...	...	...	...	p.m.	...	...	...	...	...	...	...	...	...	...	...	8 14	...
Amiens (Buffet) ...arr	8 51	...	9 42	...	...	...	10 56	...	...	...	...	15 6	15 23	...	...		16 40	...	20 8	20 57	...	...	...	0 55	...	...	1 23	8 33	...
„ (18, 21) ...dep	8 56	8 19	—	...	...	...	10 28	...	13 24	...	...	—	15 28	...	...	16 50	17 57	...	—	21 18	...	...	...	1 25	...	...	1 39	8 49	...
Longueau ...dep	...	8 34	...	...	...	...	10 44	...	...	...	...	...	...	...	...	...	...	...	...	...	...	...	...	...	...	...	...	...	...
Clermont	9 56	...	...	...	...	...	...	...	...	...	...	...	16 16	...	...	...	19 42	...	...	22 17	...	...	...	2 52	...	...	3 13	...	...
Creil	1015	...	...	...	...	...	...	...	15 31	...	...	...	16 31	...	...	...	20 5	...	...	22 37	...	...	...	3 16	...	...	3 39	...	...
Paris ...arr	1055	9 57	...	...	...	...	12 7	...	16 20	...	...	...	17 10	...	...	18 20	20 56	1920	...	23 25	...	2226	...	4 15	...	...	4 37	10 50	...

*—Stops only for passengers without luggage.
‡ On Sun., Wed. & Sat.
F—Will not take up 2nd Class after leaving Arras.
H—Via Boulogne. Brings forward 3rd cl. from England.
G—Carriages for Brussels do not run into Lille Station.
Extra.—Armentieres to Lille 10.33, 13.17, 18.15.

Excess Luggage, 1 cent. per 44 lbs. per kilometre.] **NORTHERN RAILWAY.**

PARIS, ARRAS, and CALAIS—LILLE, CALAIS, and LONDON.

Station		1,2,3				1,2,3	1,2,3	1,2,3	1 & 2	1,2,3	1,2,3	1,2,3	1,2,3	1,2,3		1,2,3
Paris (Nord) ......dep		...	...	...	...	...	7 15	...	8 0	8 40	...	5 17	...	...	...	...
Creil		...	...	...	...	...	7 58	...	...	9 22	...	6 34	...	...	...	...
Clermont		...	...	...	...	...	8 17	...	B	...	...	7 12	...	...	...	...
Longueau ....arr		...	...	...	...	...	9 8	...	9 22	...	...	8 39	...	...	...	...
Amiens ....arr		...	...	...	...	...	9 15	...	...	1018	...	8 47	...	...	From Liége (10,15, page 93), and Valenciennes (page 29A)	†
,, ...dep		...	...	...	...	...		6 40	9 12	1023	...	9 46	...	...		1233
Longueau ....dep		...	...	...	...	...	...	...	9 24	...	...	...	...	...		...
Corbie		...	...	...	...	...	...	7 3	...	...	...	10 10	...	...		13 5
Albert		...	...	...	...	...	...	7 31	...	1050	...	10 59	...	...		1337
Achiet		...	...	...	...	...	...	7 59	...	...	...	11 31	...	...		
Boisleux		...	...	...	...	...	...	8 14	...	...	...	11 46	...	...		...
Arras ....arr		...	...	...	...	...	...	8 24	10 8	1118	...	11 56	...	...		...
LILLE **23** ....arr		...	...	...	...	...	...	10 36	11 0	1210	...	13 49	...	...		...
Arras ....dep		3 51	...	...	...	7 15	9 25	8 36	10 19		11 28	12 35	...	1310		...
Farbus		4 13	...	...	...	7 34	9 44	8 50	...		11 43	12 53	...	1332		...
Lens		4 32	...	...	...	7 53	10 3	9 10	10 37		12 3	13 8	13 20	1353		...
Bully Grenay			...	...	...	8 8	10 19	9 24	...	...	12 19		13 33			...
Bethune		...	...	...	...	8 41	10 37	9 47	10 56	...	12 39	...	13 55	...		...
Chocques		...	...	...	...	8 53		9 59	...	...	12 50	...	14 7	...		...
Lillers		...	...	...	...	9 2	...	10 9	11 9	...	12 59	...	14 16	...		...
Berguette		...	...	...	...	9 16	...	10 22	11 17	...	13 8	...	14 29	...		...
Steenbecque		...	...	...	...	9 31	...	10 37	...	...	...	...	14 43	...		...
Hazebrouck 90 arr		...	...	...	...	9 41	...	10 47	11 30	...	13 24	...	14 52	...		...
BRUSSELS..dep		...	...	...	...	7 2	7 2	8 52	...	...	8 52	11 20	...	1120		1414
(103)		1,2,3	1,2,3	1,2,3	1,2,3	1,2,3	1,2,3	1 & 2	1,2,3	1,2,3	1,2,3	1 & 2	1,2,3	1& 2	1&2	I& 2
Lille ....dep		5 17	7 0	7 §9	8 19	1017	9 44	11 31	...	...	11 35	13 38	13 14	1355	...	1637
La Madeleine		5 31	7 12	7 21	8 31	...	9 59	...	...	...	...	...	13 27	14 4	1419	...
Perenchies		5 43	...	...	8 44	...	10 12	...	...	...	11 50	...	13 39		...	C
Armentières dp		5 58	7 29	7 35	8 57	1042	10 27	...	...	...	12 0	13 57	14 0		...	1656
Bailleul		6 16	...	...	9 19	11 2		...	...	...	12 12	...	14 21	...	...	...
Hazebrouck arr		6 34	7 53	8 3	9 38	1120	...	12 6	...	...	12 38	14 18	14 40	...	1446	1716
Hazebrouck ...dep		6§45	7 59	...	...	1136	...	11 36	...	1212	13 29	...	15 8	...	...	...
Cassel		6 57	8 12	...	...	1148	...	11 48	...	...	13 41	...	15 22	...	...	...
Bergues		7 26	8 42	...	...	1217	...	12 17	...	...	14 9	...	15 58	...	...	...
Dunkirk .. arr	1,2,3	7 38	8 54	...	...	1229	...	12 29	...	1245	14 21	...	16 13	...	...	...
Hazebrouck dep	6§43	...	8 6	...	...	1136	...	12 8	12 14	...	12 42	14 20	14 59	...	1447	1718
Saint-Omer	7 15	...	8 27	...	8 35	12 4	...	12 25	12 48	...	13 5	14 41	15 34	...	...	1736
Watten Eperlecq's	7 28	...	...	...	8 45	...	...	...	12 59	...	13 18	...	15 48	...	...	...
Calais (Town) arr	8 21	...	9 1	...		...	...	12 54	...	...	14 14	15 15	16 44	...	...	18 5
,, (Quai) arr	...	...	...	...	...	...	...	13 0	...	...	...	15 21	...	...	1531	⋮
London DOVER ....arr		...	...	...	...	...	...	2p35	...	...	...	5 p0	...	...	5 p0	F
London VICTORIA ....arr		...	...	...	...	...	...	...	...	...	...	7 p5	...	...	7 p5	⋮
London CHARING CROSS arr		...	...	...	...	...	...	5p10	...	...	...	...	...	...	...	1045

Station	1,2,3	1,2,3	1,2,3		1,2,3	1,2,3	1,2,3	1,2,3	1,2,3	1 Cl.	1& 2	1,2,3	1,2,3	1,2,3	1,2,3
Paris (Nord) ......dep	9 55	...	13 0	...	1430	1720	...	...	18 35	19 25	21 0	...	20 40	2120	2220
Creil	11 6	...	...	...	1518	RC	...	...	19 22	A	2136	...	21 25	2156	2345
Clermont	1136	...	...	...	1541		...	...	...	RC	...	...	22 27	...	0 9
Longueau ....arr	13 0	...	...	...	...	1839	...	...	20 25	20 47	2226	...	23 42	...	1 22
Amiens ....arr	13 8	...	14 36	...	1633	1856	...	...	20 43	21 3	...	...	0 5	2255	1 31
,, ...dep	1327	...	14 43	...	1644	1826	17 28	...	20 15	20 32	2211	2115	23 36		2 20
Longueau ....dep	...	...	...	...	...	1843	...	...	20 31	20 50	2229	...	23 54	...	...
Corbie	1350	...	15 0	...	...	...	17 50	...	...	...	...	2139	0 10	...	2 46
Albert	1418	...	15 17	...	1712	...	18 18	...	20 56	...	...	22 6	0 29	...	3 8
Achiet	1445	...	15 39	...	...	...	18 46	...	...	...	...	2234	0 52	...	3 37
Boisleux	15 0	...	...	...	...	..	19 0	...	...	...	...	2249	...	...	3 50
Arras ....arr	1510	...	15 56	...	1741	1927	19 10	...	21 26	21 34	2313	23 1	1 9	...	4 4
LILLE **23** ....arr	...	...	16 52	...	1850	2014	20 14	...	22 21	22 21	24 0		2 30	...	6 29
Arras ....dep	1518	1638	17 28	..		1935	19 39	2141	21 46		2322	...		...	5 22
Farbus	1531	1656	17 44	...	...		19 58	...	22 0	...	2340	...	...	...	5 41
Lens	1547	1717	18 9	...	...	1952	20 21	...	22 14	...	0 9	...	...	...	6 11
Bully Grenay	1558	1733	18 23	...	...	..	20 35	...	22 25	...	0 22	...	...	...	6 26
Bethune	1615	1752	18 41	...	...	2010	21 9	...	22 41	...	0 37	...	...	...	6 45
Chocques	1627		18 55	...	...	...	21 14	...	22 52	...		...	...	...	6 57
Lillers	1636	...	19 6	...	...	...	21 26	...	23 2	...	...	...	...	...	7 9
Berguette	1648	...	19 21	...	...	...	21 42	...	23 10	...	...	...	...	...	7 22
Steenbecque	17 2	...	19 38	...	...	...	21 56	...	...	...	...	...	...	...	7 38
Hazebrouck 90 arr	1711	...	19 48	...	...	2040	22 5	2240	23 26	...	...	...	...	...	7 48
BRUSSELS..dep	...	1414	...	...	1644	...	18 29	1829	...	...	...	22 3	22 3	...	...
(103)	1,2,3	1,2,3	1,2,3	1,2,3	1,2,3	1,2,3	1,2,3	1,2,3				1,2,3	1,2,3		1,2,3
Lille ....dep	1541	1722	19 0	1934	21 8	...	22 30	2151	...	...	...	0 11	0 29	...	6 19
La Madeleine	1553	...	...	1949	2124	...	22 42	...	...	...	...	...	0 40	...	6 34
Perenchies	16 5	...	...	20 4	2138	...	22 52	...	...	...	...	...	0 50	...	6 47
Armentières dp	1618	1745	19 24	2058	2152	...	23 2	2211	...	...	...	...	1 4	...	6 59
Bailleul	1638	1759	19 45	2117	2210	...	23 22	...	...	...	...	...	1 22	...	7 19
Hazebrouck arr	1657	1813	20 5	2135	2229	...	23 40	2236	...	...	...	0 43	1 42	...	7 38
Hazebrouck ...dep	...	1818	20 48	...	...	2042	...	2243	...	...	...	...	3 50	...	7 59
Cassel	...	1830	21 2	...	...	...	...	2254	...	...	...	...	4 3	...	8 12
Bergues	...	1858	21 37	...	...	...	...	2314	...	...	...	...	4 37	...	8 42
Dunkirk .. arr	...	1912	21 49	...	...	2115	...	2323	...	...	...	...	4 53	...	8 54
Hazebrouck dep	1727	...	20 11	...	...	2050	...	2245	...	...	...	0 44	3 45	...	8 27
Saint-Omer	18 2	...	21 21	...	...	2114	...	2314	...	...	...	1 1	4 27	...	9 3
Watten Eperlecq's	1814	...	21 34	...	...		...		...	...	...	...	4 45	...	9 17
Calais (Town) arr	1910	...	22 28	...	...	...	...	...	...	...	...	1 32	5 56	...	1014
,, (Quai) arr	...	...	...	...	...	...	...	...	...	...	...	1 36	...	...	
London DOVER ....arr	...	...	...	...	...	...	...	...	...	...	...	2a55	...	...	...
London VICTORIA ....arr	...	...	...	...	...	...	...	...	...	...	...	...	...	...	...
London CHARING CROSS arr	...	...	...	...	...	...	...	...	...	...	...	5a43	...	...	...

A—Also takes, at Paris, 2nd class for beyond Longueau.

B—At Paris will only take those 2nd class Passengers who are for Arras and beyond. Takes up 1st class without registered luggage only at Longueau.

C—Will take 3rd class for England.

F—Via Boulogne.

§—Runs until 30th September only.

†—Sunday, Wednesday, and Saturday only.

RC—Restaurant Car attached.

Extra—Lille to Armentieres 12.7, 16.41, 18.31, 20.23.

NORTHERN RAILWAY.

[66 lbs. of Luggage free.

PARIS, SOISSONS, LAON, and HIRSON.

	1,2,3	1,2,3	1,2,3	1&2	1,2,3	1,2,3	1,2,3	1,2,3	1,2,3	1&2	1,2,3	1,2,3	1,2,3
Paris Nord....dep	...	5 53	7 55	9 0	9 20	1215	...	1448	17 0	1810	19 0	20 40	0 40
Le Bourget-Dran	...	6 8	...	...	9 38	...	...	...	...	...	...	...	0 58
Aulnay-s-Bois ...	...	6 18	...	...	9 47	...	...	1454	...	...	1917	...	1 9
Dammartin.........	...	6 49	8 31	...	1020	1257	...	1531	1736	...	1957	...	1 52
Nanteuil	...	7 10	8 50	...	1039	1320	...	1552	1756	...	2016	...	2 15
Crépy-en-Valois.	...	7 31	9 9	...	11 0	1352	...	1615	1818	...	2032	21 43	2 41
Villers Cotterets..	5 52	7 56	9 34	...	1127	1418	...	1647	1845	...	—	22 8	3 11
Longpont	6 8	8 12	9 50	...	1145	1434	...	17 5	19 2	...	...	22 21	...
Soissons.........arr	6 28	8 33	1010	1020	12 7	1454	...	1729	1922	1932	...	22 41	3 44
Reims 74a...arr	7 58	10 24	1130	1130	1340	1626	...	19 4	2147	2147	...	0 6	5 1
Soissons ....dep	6 43	...	1028	1023	1232	1459	...	1758	1946	1935	...	22 51	5 33
Anizy-Pinon ...	7 16	...	11 1	1039	13 5	1528	...	1833	2020	1951	...	23 21	6 12
Laon (21).....arr	7 40	...	1128	1054	1332	1551	1733	19 3	2045	20 6	...	23 44	6 44
Dercy-Mortiers	9 39	...	1251	1113	—	1619	1755	1939	—	...	...	—	7 22
Marle...............	9 55	...	13 6	1122	...	1633	1811	1955	...	2031	...	...	7 39
Vervins.............	1019	...	1329	1138	...	1656	1834	2016	...	2047	...	...	8 8
Hirson (71)..arr	1048	...	1356	1157	...	1724	19 4	2045	...	21 7	...	...	8 40
Mezieres-Ch.	1345	...	1726	1345	...	1946	2159	2159	...	2351	...	...	11 0

	1,2,3	1,2,3	1,2,3	1,2,3	1&2	1,2,3	1,2,3	1,2,3	1,2,3	1,2,3	1 & 2	1,2,3	1,2,3
Mezieres-Ch. dp	...	...	3 5	...	...	6 39	8 40	12 6	...	14 56	14 56	17 35	...
Hirson ....dep	...	...	5 13	...	7 35	9 3	10 40	1347	...	16 57	18 8	19 17	...
Vervins..............	...	...	5 42	...	7 54	9 31	11 10	1416	...	17 26	18 27	19 59	...
Marle	...	...	6 4	...	8 8	9 51	11 32	1437	...	17 47	18 42	20 23	...
Dercy-Mortiers ...	...	...	6 19	...	...	10 4	11 48	1452	...	18 3	...	20 38	...
Laon ....dep	...	...	7 5	7 29	8 34	1034	12 36	1532	1626	19 17	19 7	21 10	...
Anizy-Pinon	...	...	7 27	7 55	8 51	1058	13 5	1558	1657	19 46	19 23	21 36	...
Soissons.........arr	...	...	7 53	8 25	9 7	1125	13 35	1628	1728	20 17	19 38	22 4	...
Reims...........dep	...	4 54	4 54	7 41	7 41	8 54	12 19	1430	1828	18 28	18 28	20 49	1 19
Soissons ....dep	5 14	7 10	7 56	9 21	9 15	1132	13 49	1633	1948	20 24	19 44	22 14	2 36
Longpont	5 37	7 33	...	9 44	...	1156	14 15	1657	2011	20 47	...	...	...
Villers-Cotterets ...	5 59	7 52	8 25	10 6	...	1216	14 36	1718	2027	21 7	...	22 44	3 12
Crépy-en-Valois ...	6 42	8 20	8 43	1033	...	1242	15 4	1747	—	21 43	...	23 2	3 38
Nanteuil	7 0	8 39	...	1051	...	13 0	15 22	18 4	...	22 2	...	...	...
Dammartin...........	7 20	9 15	9 9	1111	...	1320	15 43	1824	...	22 23	...	23 27	4 8
Aulnay-s-Bois	7 53	9 53	...	...	...	...	...	1843	...	...	...	...	4 34
Le Bourget-Drancy	8 4	10 4	...	...	...	...	...	...	...	...	...	...	4 42
Paris Nord ......arr	8 19	10 24	9 39	1141	1038	1350	16 13	1858	...	22 54	21 0	0 1	4 58

Extra								
Paris.........dep	20 0	22 45	...	...	...	...	...	...
Crépy ......arr	21 27	0 21	...	...	...	...	...	...
Crépy ......dep	5 44	18 53	...	...	...	...		
Paris.........arr	7 13	20 41	...	...	...	...		

A—From 6th July until 30th Sept.

ARRAS and ETAPLES.

Dist. E.M.		1,2,3	1,2,3	1,2,3	1,2,3	1,2,3	1,2,3	1,2,3
—	Arras ....dep	4 19	8 35	8 10	1126	14‡17	1937	...
12½	Aubigny............	4 52	9 12	8 33	1156	14 52	2014	...
24¼	Saint-Pol ....arr	5 19	9 39	8 53	1223	15 19	2041	...
...	,, (30) ...dep	5 30	9 45	8 58	1227	15 25	2050	...
30½	Anvin (22A	5 48	10 4	9 11	1243	15 42	21 8	...
34¾	Blangy-s-Ter ...	5 57	10 15	A	1252	15 53	2120	...
42¼	Hesdin..............	6 17	10 34	9 32	1310	16 13	2145	2158
56	Montreuil-s-Mer	6 54	11 13	9 54	1346	16 52	22 8	2245
62¾	Etaples 19 ...arr	7 8	11 29	10 8	14 1	17 7	2221	23 5
79½	Boulogne arr	8 4	12 11	1037	1440	17 49	2258	0 15

‡—Depart 14.35 on Mon., Fri., and Sat. until 30th September.

	1,2,3	1,2,3	1,2,3	1,2,3	1,2,3	1,2,3	1,2,3
Boulogne	...	6 16	10 9	1237	1737	1845	19 50
Etaples..dep	4 27	7 43	1054	1328	1823	1920	20 52
Montreuil ...	4 45	8 4	1115	1349	1841	1935	21 9
Hesdin.........	5 20	8 41	12 1	1428	1914	20 1	21 42
Blangy-s-T..	5 37	8 58	1224	1445	1931	A	—
Anvin	5 50	9 12	1242	1459	1942	2024	...
Saint-Polarr	6 4	9 28	1258	1515	1955	2036	...
,, dep	6 18	9 43	13 8	1520	20 8	2042	...
Aubigny......	6 50	1015	1341	1551	2040	21 3	...
Arras.....arr	7 25	1049	1413	1625	2114	2124	...

CHANTILLY & CREPY-EN-VALOIS.

Chantilly dep	7 59	9 45	12 41	17 2	1724	1846	23 58
Senlis..............	8 24	10 13	13 8	1726	1746	1915	0 22
Crépy ......arr	8 58	10 47	13 44	18 2	...	1951	0 57
Crepy(28)dep	6 35	9 35	11 5	15 21	...	1953	22 4
Senlis..............	7 14	1019	11 44	16 3	18 4	2032	22 44
Chantilly arr	7 36	1042	12 7	16 27	1827	2057	23 9

‡—10.47 on Wed. and Sun.]

LILLE, ARMENTIERES, and ST. OMER.

Dist.										
—	Lille .....dep	5 17	7 0	...	10 17	12 7	...	16 40	18 49	...
13	Armentièr's	6 12	7 36	...	10 48	12 56	...	17 30	19 23	...
34¾	Berguette ...	7 27	9 18	10 28	12 34	14 32	18 45	19 25	21 46	...
38	Aire-s.-Lys.	7 41	9 29	10 40	12 46	14 43	18 54	19 38	21 59	...
48½	Arques	8 10	9 59	—	—	15 11	—	20 7	22 26	...
51½	St. Omer ...	8 17	10 6	...	...	15 18	...	20 14	22 33	...

St. Omer (26) dp	4 40	7 38	...	1120	...	15 2	...	19 56
Arques	4 48	7 46	...	1128	...	15 13	...	20 5
Aire-sur-la-Lys	5 17	8 20	11 ‡1	12 0	1343	15 45	19 2	20 38
Berguette	5 32	9 18	11 29	12 9	14 2	17 7	1912	21 47
Armentières......	6 35	1021	12 36	...	15 7	18 11	—	22 53
Lille (23)......arr	7 25	11 7	13 20	...	1551	18 46	...	23 41

COMPIEGNE and VILLERS-COTTERETS.

Compiègne dp	5 25	8 26	1249	1525	1733	2040
Rethondes...	5 38	8 35	1258	1534	1742	2049
Pierrefonds	5 59	8 51	1315	1552	1756	21 6
Villers-C.	...	9 26	1351	1627	—	2141
Villers-C.	...	6 30	1039	1321	...	1856
Pierrefonds	6 17	7 4	1118	1358	1823	1929
Rethondes ...	6 30	7 17	1131	1411	1843	1942
Compièg.	6 38	7 25	1139	1419	1855	1950

LILLE, ASCQ, and TOURCOING.

Lille........dep	4 37	7 9	8 36	...	12 45	1618	1819	1913
Ascq	5 3	7 30	8 46	10 25	13 16	1640	1844	1943
Roubaix-W...	5 25	7 51	—	10 48	13 37	1658	19 6	2011
Tourcoing arr	5 38	8 1	...	11 0	13 50	17 9	1921	2024

Tourcoing	4 16	6 45	9 35	10 46	1322	1710	1938
Roubaix ...	4 30	7 1	9 52	11 3	1336	1726	1952
Ascq	5 2	7 28	1022	11 48	1356	1748	2021
Lille ...arr	5 21	7 45	1039	12 5	1410	18 2	2039

VILLERS-COTTERETS and LA FERTE-MILON.

Dist. E.M.									
	Villers-Cotterets ......dep	6 27	10 18	1443	1724	1850	2032	...	...
8¾	La Ferté-Milon (74B) arr	6 49	10 40	15 5	1746	1912	2054	...	...
...	La Ferté-Milon ....dep	5 23	8 51	12 49	16 5	1817	1930	2122	...
...	Villers-Cotterets (28) arr	5 45	9 19	13 14	1629	1839	1953	2155	...

LAON and BUSIGNY.

E.M.										
	Laon ....dep	...	7 31	...	10 29	12 34	1559	...	17 37	21 4
9¼	Pouilly-sur-Serre 22A	...	7 55	...	10 48	12 57	1619	...	17 59	21 26
23½	Sains Richaumont ...	...	8 33	...	—	13 35	—	...	18 38	22 4
31	Guise.........................	5 34	8 56	...	...	14 2	...	...	19 8	22 24
41¾	Wassigny	6 12	9 29	9 58	...	14 36	...	1840	20 24	—
49¾	Busigny 24......arr	6 33	9 50	1018	...	14 57	...	19 1	20 43	...

Busigny......dep	3a14	...	...	7 11	...	9 17	10 50	13 8	15 44	20 4
Wassigny	3 39	...	...	7 45	...	9 29	11 13	13 30	16 24	20 39
Guise..................	—	5 11	...	8 59	...	—	—	14 3	17 23	21 10
Sains Richaumont ...		5 33	...	9 22	...	...	...	14 25	17 48	—
Pouilly-sur-Serre......		6 9	7 56	9 57	12 3	...	...	15 0	18 29	...
Laon 21 ....arr		6 30	8 17	1018	12 24	...	...	15 21	18 50	...

Excess Luggage, 1 cent per 44 lbs. per kilometre.]

NORTHERN RAILWAY.

COMPIEGNE and AMIENS.

Station						Station					
Compiegne ......dep	4 26	8 46	15 6	17 55	20 13	**Amiens** ......dep	4 40	9 3	13 1	17 25	20 32
Estrees-St-Denis ...arr	4 48	9 9	15 25	18 18	20 32	Boves	4 55	9 18	1316	17 40	20 49
Montdidier	5 32	9 56	16 9	19 10	21 14	Montdidier	5 42	10 12	1357	18 42	21 36
Boves	6 15	10 45	16 57	19 59	21 57	Estrées-St-Denis..	6 18	10 54	1433	19 34	22 14
Amiens 19A.........arr	6 29	10 59	17 10	20 13	22 11	**Compiegne** arr	6 37	11 14	1450	19 51	22 31

COMPIEGNE and CREPY-EN-VALOIS.

Station						Station					
Compiegne...dep	5 17	7 59	12 42	1628	2016	Crepy-en-V. ...dep	6 31	9 14	14 7	18 22	21 49
Verberie	5 40	8 28	13 5	1652	2043	Verberie	7 7	9 47	1443	18 54	22 25
Crepy-en-Val. 29	6 15	9 2	13 45	1732	2127	Compiegne ...arr	7 30	10 7	1510	19 15	23 49

*—Weekdays only.

ST. JUST-EN-CHAUSEE to EPEHY and DOUAI.

B—Basle Express.

Station			From Busigny.								
St. Just ....dep		...	...	...	8 39	10 41	...	1522	18 5	19 58	20 5
Montdidier		...	...	5 54	9 35	11 13	...	1611	1914	20 20	2038
Roye		...	...	6 26	10 11	11 50	...	1646	1947	20 47	2114
Chaulnes ....arr		...	...	7 26	10 30	12 10	...	17 5	20 6	20 59	2133
,, ...dep	4 16	...	...	8 25	10 50	12 29	1542	1725	2010	21 1	2231
Pont-les-Brie	4 34	...		8 45	11 8	12 47	16 2	1743	2028	...	2249
Peronne(La C.) dp	4 42	...		8 55	11 18	12 54	1611	1752	2035	...	2257
Peronne (Flm.) dp	4 45	6 4		9 3	11 23	13 0	1614	18 0	2041	21 20	23 0
Roisel	—	6 28		9 30	11 47	13 22	—	1824	21 4	21 33	—
Epéhy		6 43		9 46	12 2	13 37	...	1839	2118	...	...
Marcoing ....arr		7 2	...	10 6	12 22	13 55	1750	19 1	2137	21 54	...
Cambrai.........arr	5 26	7 16	9 43	1023	12 35	14 8	18 5	1917	2152	22 4	2229
Aubigny-au-B.arr	5 52	8 56	B	1051	—	15 49	19 7	—	—	—	...
Arleux ....dep	6 4	9 5	...	11 0	...	16 0	1916	...	...	...	...
Douai (23) ...arr	6 22	9 24	10 8	1117	...	16 18	1933	...	...	...	2254

Station								To Busigny.			
Douai ....dep	5 20	...	...	8 13	8 34	12 5	...	17 15	1722	20 4	2224
Arleux	5 40	...	...	...	8 54	1225	...	B	1744	2024	2243
Aubigny-au-Bac..	5 48	...	...	...	9 0	1233	...	...	1753	2031	2250
Cambrai	6 20	5 39	7 35	8 39	10 6	1310	15 2	17 42	1916	2057	2313
Marcoing	6 36	5 56	7 45	9 17	1021	1325	1519		1933	2220	—
Epéhy	—	6 20	...	—	1044	1350	1545		1958	2243	...
Roisel	...	6 35	8 7	...	1058	14 4	16 0		2013	2257	...
Peronne Flamc'rt	4 6	7 0	8 20	8 27	1129	1428	1629		2039	2318	...
Peronne La Chap.	4 10	7 4	...	8 31	1133	1432	1633		2043	—	...
Pont-les-Brie	4 17	7 11	...	8 38	1142	1439	1640	...	2050	...	...
Chaulnes.........arr	4 33	7 29	8 37	8 56	12 0	1457	1658	...	21 8	...	...
,, ...dep	4 36	7 50	8 39	9 12	1233	—	1725	...	2230	...	...
Roye	4 58	8 13	8 50	9 33	13 0	...	1754	...	2253	...	...
Montdidier	6 0	8 47	9 11	1010	1359	...	1839	...	2320	...	...
St. Just (19A) arr	6 30	9 17	9 31	1040	1430	...	1910	...	—	...	...

Extra.—Aubigny to Cambrai. 19 8; Douai to Cambrai 14*33; Cambrai to Douai, 21.5.

Station									
Marcoing ......dep	8 10	10 56	13 30	15 23	19 30	20 39	21 18	...	...
Cambrai ....arr	8 27	11 12	13 47	15 40	19 45	20 56	21 35	...	...
Cambrai ......dep	6 9	9 0	12 13	14 22	16 21	18 50	20 22	...	...
Marcoing ... ..arr	6 25	9 17	12 29	14 39	16 38	19 6	20 38	...	...

Station										
Marcoing ....dep	6 37	7 49	9 22	1025	12 30	1441	1649	19 9	2041	...
Masnieres ....arr	6 42	7 54	9 27	1030	12 35	1446	1654	1914	2045	...
Masnieres......dep	6 49	8 0	9 55	10 50	1341	15 4	1738	1921	2110	...
Marcoing ......arr	6 54	8 5	10 0	10 55	1346	15 9	1743	1926	2115	...

Station										
Aubigny-au-Bac..dep	6 8	9 7	1237	1757	2141	...	...	...	...	...
Somain 29A ....arr	6 44	9 37	13 6	1825	2217	...	...	...	...	...
Somain ....dep	5 10	8 17	11 54	1518	1834	21 1	...	...	...	...
Aubigny-au-Bac ..arr	5 38	8 46	12 22	1545	19 2	2128	...	...	...	...

‡—Runs until 15th September.]

ANICHE and VALENCIENNES.

[*—Runs until 30th September.

Station																							
Aniche ....dep	...	5 30	...	...	...	8 40	...	11 28	...	...	13 43	...	...	...	17 15	...	...	19 29	...	...	23 20	...	...
Somain	4 53	5 45	...	...	...	9 5	...	12 16	...	...	13 54	...	17 8	...	17 43	...	...	19 40	...	...	0 11	...	...
⁝ Denain ....dep	...	...	...	7 0	8 5	...	10 52	...	...	12 57	...	16 7	...	...	...	...	18 23	...	...	21 7	...	...	...
Wallers	5 14	5 57	...	7 19	8 22	9 22	11 35	12 26	...	13 35	14 11	16 38	1724	17‡30	18 1	...	19 3	19 57	...	21 39	0 22	...	...
St. Amand ....arr	...	...	5 55	7 34	8 39	...	11 52	...	12 54	13 52	...	16 55	...	17 47	...	18‡40	19 19	...	21 36	21 55	...	...	...
Valenciennes ......arr	5 37	6 15	6 18	8 2	9 21	9 45	...	12 43	13 16	14 23	14 34	17 46	1741	...	18 30	18 54	19 53	20 20	22 4	22 40	0 39	...	...

Station																									
Valenciennes...	4 21	6 27	6 33	7 5	9 15	...	9 3	10 58	11 45	1227	...	1421	14 53	1522	16 12	...	17 53	1758	...	...	21 17	21 20	22 20	...	...
St. Amand	4 50	6 56	...	...	...	...	10 3	...	12 11	...	12‡57	...	15 20	1533	...	17 3	...	1819	18‡25	19 35	22 0	...	...	...	...
Wallers	5 17	7 17	...	7 30	9 32	...	10 21	11 24	12 30	1254	13 12	1440	15 38	—	16 32	17 29	18 45	—	18 40	20 36	22 51	21 46	22 38	...	...
⁝ Denain ....arr	5 36	7 33	...	...	...	...	10 37	...	12 46	...	—	...	15 54	...	...	17 45	...	...	—	20 52	23 8	...	...	...	...
Somain	—	—	7 4	8 6	9 42	11 4	—	11 54	—	1322	...	1518	—	...	16 55	—	19 2	...	...	—	—	22 2	22 57	...	...
Aniche ....arr	...	...	7 11	8 13	...	1115	...	12 5	...	1333	...	1528	...	...	17 6	...	19 13	—	...	...	...	...	23 8	...	...

DOUAI and ANICHE.

Station								Station									
Douai ...dep	4 41	12 51	14 28	17 28	20 34	...	...	Aniche......dep	7 20	1256	14 43	15 37	18 23	22 5	...	...	...
Aniche ...arr	5 11	13 33	15 15	18 5	21 10	...	...	Douai ....arr	7 55	1351	15 23	16 13	18 58	23 10	...	...	...

CREPY and MAREUIL.

E.M.	Station					Station				
	Crepy-en-Valois ...dep	6 29	9 19	13 56	19 30	**Mareuil**...dep	7 45	12 5	17 §8	20 30
16¾	**Mareuil-sur-Ourcq** arr	7 7	10 3	14 35	20 10	**Crépy** (28) arr	8 30	12 44	17 52	21 11

§—16 56 on Sunday.

LAON and LIART.

E.M.	Station								Station									
	Laon ....dep	5 49	7 51	12 35	15 59	21 2	...	...	**Liart**...............dep	5 2	8 45	13 27	17 23	2010	...	...	...	...
16¼	Clermont-les-F.	6 35	8 39	13 19	16 37	21 44	...	...	Rozoy	5 30	9 11	13 55	17 52	2036	...	...	...	...
26¾	Rozoy	7 4	9 9	13 45	17 4	22 10	...	...	Clermont-les-Fermes	5 57	9 36	14 21	18 17	21 4	...	...	...	...
37¼	**Liart** 74 ......arr	7 33	9 42	14 15	17 29	22 38	...	...	**Laon** 28 ....arr	6 40	1016	15 7	18 59	2146	...	...	...	...

LILLE and SOMAIN.

Station									Station								
Lille ....dep	4 37	8 7	11 24	12 45	...	1725	1955	...	**Somain** ....dep	...	...	5 21	8 30	11 57	1521	18 9	21 7
Ascq	4 59	8 29	11 47	13 13	...	1752	2022	...	Orchies	4 21	5 40	6 31	9 40	12 34	1556	19 3	2137
Cysoing	5 20	8 49	12 7	14 11	...	1814	2041	...	Cysoing	4 40	5 59	6 49	9 58	12 53	1614	1921	—
Orchies	6 17	9 42	12 34	14 48	17 1	1833	2111	...	Ascq	5 2	6 22	7 14	1022	13 12	1644	1942	...
Somain ....arr	6 47	1011	13 7	...	1729	1931	2138	...	**Lille** ....arr	5 21	6 42	7 26	1039	13 26	1657	20 0	...

ROUBAIX, TOURCOING, and MENIN.

Station												Station											
Roubaix ...dep	...	6 16	8 18	9 42	11 42	1350	1633	1723	1844	1922	2122	**Menin**.........dep	...	7 12	9 21	11 41	13 1	15 5	1716	1813	...	20 35	...
Tourcoing	4 32	...	...	9 47	11 52	1359	...	1738	...	1934	2135	Halluin	5 10	7 30	9 39	11 58	1321	1519	1731	1831	1945	20 53	22 11
Halluin	4 55	6 43	8 44	1014	12 16	1424	1658	1756	1912	20 1	2158	Tourcoing	5 45	...	10 3	12 23	...	1538	...	1856	20 7	21 22	22 32
Menin.........arr	...	6 47	8 48	1018	12 20	1428	17 2	18 0	...	20 5	...	**Roubaix** ...arr	...	7 54	1015	12 40	1347	1547	1752	1919	2022	21 50	22 47

LAON and CHAUNY.

Laon.........dep	7 5	10 34	1626	1957	**Chauny** ......dep	6 20	9 47	...	12 7	18 8
Anizy-Pinon	7 38	11 5	17 1	2027	Coucy-le-Chateau	6 48	1014	...	12 35	1841
Coucy-le-Chateau	8 0	11 26	1723	2049	Anizy-Pinon	7 16	1039	11 1	12 55	19 4
Chauny (24) arr	8 27	11 53	1752	2120	**Laon** (28)......arr	7 40	1054	1128	13 32	1928

CLERMONT and BEAUVAIS.

Clermont dep	7 34	...	...	1138	1814	2231	Beauvais dep	6 15	8 35	1031	...	1633	1949
La Rue St. P.	7 49	...	...	1153	1829	2246	Rochy-Condé	6 28	8 46	1044	...	1648	20 4
St. Just dep	6 13	8 10	9 52	1115	1635	1938	**La Rue St. P.**	6 46	9 0	11 3	1238	17 9	2026
Bulles	6 30	8 27	10 9	1132	1653	1955	Bulles	7 10	9 16	...	1250	1850	2015
La Rue St. P	7 51	8 38	1022	1155	1833	2248	**St. Just** arr	7 27	9 31	...	13 7	19 7	21 2
Rochy-Condé	8 12	—	1042	1216	1855	2310	**La Rue St. P.**	6 48	9 1	11 8	—	1712	2028
Beauvais arr	8 22	...	1052	1226	19 5	2320	**Clermont** arr	7 3	9 16	1123	...	1727	2043

COMPIEGNE and ROYE.

Compiegne 29 dep	5 12	10 35	1521	1937	**Roye** ....dep	6 30	1316	1752	2052	...
Ressons..............	5 45	11 11	1556	20 8	Ressons	7 1	1347	1824	2122	...
Roye (29) ......arr	6 15	11 41	1627	2038	**Compiegne** ...	7 30	1416	1854	2151	...

CLERMONT and COMPIEGNE

Clermont...........dep	7 9	11 37	17 45	20 46	**Compiegne**...........dep	5 53	10 32	16 15	20 52	...
Catenoy	7 23	11 51	17 59	21 1	**Estrees-St.-Denis** dep	6 25	10 56	16 47	21 29	...
Estrees St. Denis..	7 46	12 18	18 33	21 29	Catenoy	6 49	11 18	17 11	21 53	...
Compiegne (24)...arr	8 3	12 37	18 52	21 46	**Clermont** (19).........arr	7 2	11 30	17 24	22 10	...

HIRSON and GUISE.

E.M.						
	Hirson ......dep	6 32	10 38	12 34	1921	...
24¾	Guise (28)...arr	7 52	11 55	13 52	2038	...
...	Guise.........dep	5 28	8 41	12 12	1732	...
...	Hirson ......arr	6 51	10 3	13 39	19 2	...

COMPIEGNE and SOISSONS.

Compiegne......dep	4 0	8 34	12 11	17 41	20 32	**Soissons** 28......dep	6 20	9 12	13 47	18 0	20 58
Rethondes	4 9	8 43	12 20	17 50	21 41	Attichy	7 3	9 54	14 29	18 46	21 22
Attichy.....................	4 26	9 6	12 38	18 10	20 58	Rethondes.................	7 21	10 12	14 47	19 5	21 40
Soissons (23) ...arr	5 6	9 50	13 21	18 53	21 39	**Compiegne** 29A arr	7 29	10 20	14 55	19 13	21 48

†—Change trains at La Madeleine.

LILLE, ORCHIES, and VALENCIENNES.

Lille ....dep	4 59	8 43	1154	13 55	1615	1742	18 1	1812	19 44	2024	2133	22 31
Orchies 29............dep	5 32	9 19	1231	Calais dep 12.50	1658	...	1826	19 4	20 15	21 9	...	23 9
St. Amand 102B ...arr	5 52	9 37	1250		1717	...	1839	1923	20 28	2128	...	—
Blanc-Misseron...arr	7 50	1031	15 4		...	...	...	2011	...		...	...
St. Amand ....dep	5 55	9 40	1254		1722	...	1810	1930	20 30	2136	...	22 13
Valenciennes...arr	6 18	10 2	1316	15 1	1746	19 2	1854	1953	20 50	22 4	2256	22 40

Valenciennes dep	5 14	5 37	8 27	9 3	10 55	11 45	13 58	13 39	1522	17 58	1840	1943	21 17
St. Amand ....arr	5 34	5 52	8 49	9 18	...	12 1	14 13	Calais arr 15.31	1533	18 19	⋮	20 7	21 39
Blanc-Misseron dep	...	...	8 0	8 0	...	10 41	...		...	16 18	⋮	...	20 43
St. Amand ....dep	5 38	5 55	8 53	9 19	...	12 5	14 16		1534	18 23	⋮	20 9	21 45
Orchies...............dep	5 58	6 13	9 18	9 35	...	12 31	14 39		...	18 47	⋮	2029	22 8
Lille 26 ....arr	...	6 48	9 55	10 0	11 59	13 0	15 16	14 38	16 7	19 25	2032	—	22 45

VALENCIENNES and AULNOYE.

Valenciennes dep	4 49	5 48	6 57	10 14	13 22	14 41	15 4	18 2	18 12	19 6	20 12	22 59
Le Quesnoy	5 33	6 32	7 40	10 55	14 0	15 31	...	18 35	18 54	19 28	20 52	23 25
Aulnoye 29A ...arr	5 58	6 58	8 7	11 19	14 25	15 52	15 40	18 59	19 20	19 45	21 16	23 43

Aulnoye ....dep	4 15	7 8	8 24	10 18	12 13	1310	14 43	1632	17 55	20 6	22 36	...
Le Quesnoy 30A	4 45	7 43	8 40	10 33	12 49	...	15 1	1711	18 13	20 34	23 3	...
Valenciennes ...arr	5 17	8 14	8 58	10 50	13 19	1336	15 19	1745	18 30	21 4	23 33	...

HIRSON and AULNOYE.

Hirson...dep	5 40	7 0	...	9 17	10 17	1229	1349	14 4	...	1642	1814	...	21 21
Anor ......dep	5 54	7 13	...	9 28	10 30	...	...	1415	...	1654	1827	...	21 33
Fourmies	6 4	7 23	...	9 35	10 40	...	14 6	1422	...	17 2	1835	...	21 43
Solre-C. dep	5 51	...	8 51	...	...	...	...	...	16 2	...	...	2118	...
Avesnes.........	6 36	7 52	9 31	9 56	11 10	...	1425	1446	1656	1729	19 7	2156	22 7
Aulnoye arr	6 56	8 14	9 52	10 9	11 31	13 2	1438	15 2	1716	1745	1930	2211	22 28

Aulnoye ....dep	4 36	6 18	7 18	8 34	10 46	1155	14 35	1550	1613	1722	1931	1952	2020	22 30
Avesnes.........................	4 56	6 39	7 42	8 57	11 8	1220	14 58	...	1636	1747	1951	20 7	2047	22 54
Solre-le-Chateau arr	5 33	...	8 37	...	—	1358	...	...	...	...	—	21 5	...	...
Fourmies 20	—	7 3	8 15	9 29	...	1253	15 26	...	17 6	1819	...	2030	2119	23 22
Anor 20, 93.........dep	...	7 11	8 30	9 38	...	13 2	15 35	...	1714	1829	...	2038	2130	23 30
Hirson 28 ....arr	...	7 20	8 39	9 47	...	1311	15 44	1630	1723	1838	...	2046	2139	23 39

BUSIGNY and SOMAIN.

Somain ....dep	...	...	...	...	7 54	...	10 58	13 17	15 18	...	17 38	...	18 49	21 5	...	...
Lourches	...	...	6 56	...	8 5	...	11 9	13 29	15 30	...	17 49	1833	19 3	21 19	...	...
Cambrai Annexe	...	...	...	...	8 29	...	11 34	13 54	15 55	A	18 16	19 0	19 36	21 50	...	...
Cambrai ....arr	...	...	7 17	...	8 33	...	11 38	13 59	16 0	...	18 21	19 5	19 41	21 55	...	...
,, ...dep	5 12	6 1	...	8 42	9 0	10 4	11 46	14 15	16 7	1745	18 27	...	20 4	22 3	0 2	...
Busigny 20......arr	5 49	6 45	...	9 9	9 42	10 33	12 28	15 0	16 51	1812	19 12	...	20 47	22 53	0 43	...

Busigny ....dep	2 35	5 23	...	7 20	9 15	9 20	10 26	...	1328	1515	...	18 4	1928	...	21 6	22 2	23 44
Cambrai 30A ...arr	3 5	6 0	...	8 2	9 41	10 0	11 0	...	14 8	1557	...	1841	20 9	...	21 40	2227	0 27
,, ...dep	—	6 7	7 25	8 45	9 43	—	11 6	12 22	1417	16 2	17 6	—	2014	...	21 45	2238	—
Cambrai Annexe	...	6 14	7 32	8 50	B	...	11 12	12 29	1423	16 6	1712	...	2020	...	21 52	...	...
Lourches	...	6 41	7 57	9 18	...	...	11 37	12 54	1449	1633	1739	...	2046	2122	22 16	2257	...
Somain 22A ...arr	...	6 50	8 8	9 29	...	...	11 46	13 5	1458	1642	...	...	2055	2134	22 25	2335	...

Valenciennes	5 5	6 30	7 9	10 7	12†25	1445	1651	...	18 6	2027	...
Denain.........	6 13	6 49	7 43	1044	12 55	1514	1731	1824	1841	21 1	2313
Lourches arr	6 24	6 55	7 51	1052	13 2	1522	1739	1832	1848	21 9	2321

Lourches...dep	6 46	9 24	11 42	14†55	1641	18 8	2053	22 58	...	...
Denain...........	6 57	9 37	11 53	15 4	1653	1818	21 3	23 5	...	...
Valenciennes...	7 34	10 4	12 20	15 34	1722	1850	2133	23 23	...	...

†—Runs until 30th Sept.

A—Calais-Basle Express.
B—Basle-Calais Express.

CARVIN and LIBERCOURT.

Carvin ....dep	6 20	7 35	8 50	10 45	12 10	13 55	15 30	1725	18 40	1948	20 58	...	...	...	...	...	...	...
Libercourt (23) ......arr	6 35	7 50	9 5	11 0	12 25	14 10	15 45	1740	18 55	20 3	21 13	...	...	...	...	...	...	...
Libercourt ....dep	7 0	8 31	9 38	11 20	13 0	14 28	16 15	18 7	19 25	20 17	22 0	...	...	...	...	...	...	...
Carvin (20) ....arr	7 15	8 46	9 53	11 35	1315	14 43	16 30	18 22	19 40	20 32	22 15	...	...	...	...	...	...	...

CHAUNY and SAINT-GOBAIN.

E.M.																
	Chauny (24) ......dep	8 55	12 25	1318	2055	...	...	...	St-Gobain......dep	6 5	7 50	10 20	15 30	17 0	...	...
9½	St-Gobain ....arr	9 22	12 53	1346	2130	...	...	...	Chauny ....arr	6 40	8 17	10 47	16 7	1737	...	...

CAMBRAI, CATILLON, and ST. QUENTIN.

†—At or from St. Quentin (Cambrésis).

E.M.																	
	Cambrai ......dep	6 30	8 0	8 50	12 5	14 0	1521	1915	**Catillon**.........dep	5 50	...	...	11 30	...	...	18 33	...
8¾	Caudry-Cambrésis	7 13	8 33	9 38	12 52	1433	1611	20 3	Le Cateau..............	6 38	9 5	11 0	12 17	1533	1735	19 24	...
16¼	Le Cateau	7 42	9 0	1022	13 22	15 0	1655	2045	Caudry-Cambrésis	7 12	9 42	1127	12 55	16 9	18 2	20 2	...
21¾	**Catillon** ....arr	...	...	11 0	...	...	1733	2124	**Cambrai** 29 ...arr	7 52	1022	12 0	13 40	1649	1835	2045	...

Denain......................dep		...	6 20	11 20	...	18 5	...	...	**St. Quentin** (Nord) dep	6†a30	8 40	12†55	17†0	19†39	...
Caudry-Cambrésis		...	9 42	13 0	16 14	20 8	...	...	Le Catelet-Gouy	7 48	10 58	14 15	1838	20 43	...
Caudry (Nord)		...	9 57	13 10	16 35	2032	...	...	Caudry (Nord)	9 5	12 15	15 39	1938	—	...
Le Catelet-Gouy	6 40	8 34	1110	15 1	18 25	2129	...	...	Caudry-Cambrésis	9 40	12 23	15 47	1946	...	...
St. Quentin Nord 24	8 12	10 8	1249	16 47	19†37	...	..	...	**Denain** 29..................arr	11 4	...	17 37	...	...	...

VALMONDOIS and MARINES.

Valmondois dep	8 58	11 3	15 0	18 57	21 57	...	...	**Marines**... ...dep	6 48	9 57	12 45	1632	20 40	...	...	...
Epiais-Rhus	9 33	11 39	1552	19 32	22 33	...	...	Epiais-Rhus	7 10	10 17	13 16	1654	21 0	...	...	...
Marines.........arr	9 52	11 58	1617	19 51	22 52	...	...	**Valmondois** 22	7 47	10 51	13 46	1735	21 35	...	...	...

DOULLENS and ALBERT.

Doullens ....dep	7 56	15 50	20 33	...	**Albert** ....dep	...	9 5	16 0	...
Beauquesne	8 35	16 30	21 9	...	Beauquesne	6 6	10 30	17 25	...
Albert 26..............arr	10 11	18 2	...	...	Doullens 20..........arr	6 53	11 12	18 8	...

ALBERT and HAM.

Albert......dep	...	9 0	12 10	...	19 25	Ham ......dep	...	8 50	...	14 0	19 35	...
Peronne.........	5 20	11 22	14 16	17 2	21 40	Offoy	...	9 10	...	14 20	19 57	...
Offoy 37	6 33	12 36	—	18 31	—	Peronne (29)	5 20	10 31	11 55	16 25	21 15	...
Ham 21 ...arr	6 48	12 51	...	18 46	...	Albert (26) arr	7 13	...	14 8	18 7	...	...

ALBERT and MONTDIDIER.

Albert ....dep	5 45	...	9 0	16 20	Montdidier ....dep	6 3	10 22	16 30	...	...
Rosières	7 19	7 58	12 38	18 45	Rosières	8 21	12 45	18 2	...	...
Montdidier (29) ...arr	...	8 59	13 50	20 8	Albert (26)............arr	10 19	14 8	20 11	...	...

ABBEVILLE and DOMPIERRE.

†—Thurs. at 2.50 p.m.

Abbeville 18......................dep	7 44	12†44	19 22	...	Dompierre ....dep	5 20	9 35	16 40
Forest l'Abbaye ....arr	8 29	13 27	20 4	...	Crecy-Estrees	5 37	9 54	17 1
Noyelles ....dep	8 2	12 40	19 37	...	Forest l'Abbaye ......arr	5 54	10 11	17 18
Forest l'Abbaye..............dep	8 32	13 32	20 8	...	Noyelles 18 ....arr	6 26	10 43	17 55
Crecy-Estrees	8 53	13 53	20 28	...	Forest l'Abbaye......dep	6 0	10 15	17 24
Dompierre-sur-Authie .....arr	9 10	14 10	20 48	...	Abbeville ....arr	6 44	10 57	18 10

HAZEBROUCK and HONDSCHOOTE.

‡-Monday, dep. 10.16 a.m.

Hazebrouck...dep	...	...	8 30	...	12 40	...	1548	19 2	...	Hondschoote dep	6 0	7 23	1010	11 10	1346	1430	16 30	18 0
Bergues	...	8‡28	...	1240	...	1530	...	19 52	...	Rexpoede	6 14	7 36	1023	11 24	14 5	1445	16 43	1814
Rexpoede	6 40	9 0	9 45	1310	14 2	1558	1726	20 25	...	Bergues 26 ...	...	8 8	...	11 58	...	1512	...	1847
Hondschoote arr	6 54	9 13	9 58	1323	14 15	1611	1740	20 39	...	Hazebrouck arr	7 47	...	1138	...	1520	...	18 5	...

Hondschoote to Bray-Dunes, 7.20, 10.37, 17.50. From Bray-Dunes, 6.12, 9.18, 15.15.

LE TREMBLOIS and PETITE-CHAPELLE.

E.M.																
	Le Tremblois ......dep	7 32	9 36	...	13 20	17 5	1858	21 3	Petite-Chapelle ...dep	...	8 27	11 48	1545	1810	...	...
7½	Rocroi	8 2	10 5	11 24	14 35	1736	1926	2131	Rocroi........................	6 25	8 44	12 8	1612	1825	20 4	...
10½	Petite-Chapelle ...arr	8 13	...	11 36	14 47	1748	...	...	Le Tremblois (71) arr	6 54	9 12	12 36	1641	1848	20 32	...

NOUZON and GESPUNSART.

E.M.														
	Nouzon......dep	6 26	9 30	13 7	1514	1759	2044	Gespunsart dep	5 28	7 10	11 18	1355	1638	1850
5	Gespunsart arr	6 51	9 56	13 33	1541	1825	21 8	Nouzon (20) arr	5 52	7 31	11 45	1420	17 4	1915

BETHUNE and LILLE.

Bethune......dep	...	5 27	8 33	9 50	13 5	14 7	1647	1850	2149	...
Violaines ...arr	...	5 47	8 50	1010	13 18	1427	17 7	1910	2210	...
Bully-Gre'y dp	...	...	...	9 30	...	1341	...	1847	...	...
Violaines ...arr	...	...	...	9 50	...	14 3	...	19 7	...	...
Violaines ...dep	...	5 48	8 51	1012	13 19	1429	17 8	1912	2212	...
Don Sainghin ...	4 59	6 25	9 12	1045	13 39	1458	1738	1943	2235	23 22
Wavrin.............	5 6	6 31	9 17	1050	...	...	1745	1956	2241	23 29
Lille Pte d'Arras	5 31	6 59	9 41	...	...	...	18 9	2023	23 4	...
Lille (Nord) arr	5 41	7 9	9 48	1112	14 3	1525	1819	2035	2314	23 57

Lille (Nord) dp	4 32	7 6	9 15	1115	14 24	17 5	18 2	2027
Lille Pte d'Ar	4 44	...	9 26	1128	...	...	19 4	2039
Wavrin	5 16	7 35	9 50	1156	14 47	1731	1927	21 9
Don Sainghin	5 26	7 47	10 4	12 6	15 5	1746	1937	2122
Violaines ..arr	5 49	8 10	1026	1228	15 23	18 9	...	2144
Violaines dep	...	8 15	...	1240	...	1820	...	...
Bully-Grenay	...	8 35	...	13 0	...	1838	...	...
Violaines dep	5 54	8 12	1027	1231	15 24	1811	...	2147
Bethune(Nord)	6 13	8 31	1046	1250	15 40	1830	...	22 8

Extra: Don Sainghin to Lille 12.1 Lille to Don Sainghin 4.1, 12.19.

BETHUNE and DOUAI.

Bethune ....dep	4 59	6 20	...	...	8 26	9 43	11 5	...	1259	...	1435	1639	1746	19 9	...	...	...	2142	22 22	...
Lens.........................dep	6 7	6 50	7 0	8 13	9 14	1044	1145	12 35	1341	1429	1520	1723	1832	1934	2044	...	...	2219	23 1	0 5
Libercourt...... arr	6 39	—	...	...	9 47	...	1217	...	1414	...	1559	...	19 7	—	2116	...	...	—	—	...
Libercourt...... dep	6 54	...	...	...	1019	...	1252	.	1423	...	1610	...	1920	...	—	2136	2257	...	...	...
Douai 23...............arr	7 7	...	7 54	9 9	1035	1139	1315	13 24	1445	1522	1635	18 8	1934	...	...	22 0	2318	...	...	0 54

Douai ....dep	4 19	...	5 28	6 43	7 35	9 2	1044	1155	1211	12 54	...	1425	...	1653	1755	1816	2111	...	22 56	...
Libercourt ... arr	...	...	5 54	...	7 58	...	11 7	...	1233	13 18	...	...	...	...	1825	1843	2138	...	23 9	...
Libercourt ... dep	...	...	6 0	...	8 26	...	1117	...	1242	—	1430	...	1737	...	—	1848	—	...	23 31	...
Lens.........................dep	5 17	6 11	6 35	7 53	9 11	10 4	12 2	1253	1320	...	15 2	1547	18 0	18 9	...	1952	...	2214	0 9	...
Bethune 27 ....arr	...	6 41	...	8 27	9 38	10 37	1235	...	1330	...	...	1612	—	1836	...	20 9	...	2239	0 37	...

NORTHERN RAILWAY. [66 lbs. of Luggage free.

PARIS, BEAUVAIS, ST. OMER-EN-CHAUSSEE, LE TREPORT, and AMIENS.

D—On Saturday only from Beauvais. E—On Sunday only.

	123	1,2,3	1,2,3	1,2,3	1,2,3	1,2,3	1,2,3	1 &2	1,2,3	1,2,3	1,2,3	1,2,3	1,2,3	1,2,3	1,2,3	1,2,3
Paris Nord...dep	...	...	...	...	...	5 17	6 0	8 5	8 35	8 45	1140	1440	1721	18 0	1850	...
Persan-Beau...dep	...	...	...	...	...	B	7 10	8 41	9 19	1018	1228	1614	18 7	B	1931	...
Meru	...	...	...	...	...	...	7 45	8 58	...	1047	13 4	1644	1830	...	1950	...
Beauvais(22)...arr	...	...	...	...	...	8 5	8 29	9 23	10 5	1126	1350	1720	1858	2010	2015	
,, ...dep	5 9	5 45	...	7 40	...	8 52	9 32	9 26	10 8	—	14 7	1728	1915	2036	—	2018
St.Omer-en-C. arr	536	6 3	...	8 7	...	9 19	9 50	⋮	⋮	...	1433	1757	1944	2052	...	⋮
St.Omer-C....dep	...	6 4	A	8 10	...	...	9 54	⋮	A	...	1437	18 2	...	2055	...	D
Grandvilliers ...	...	6 36	...	8 40	...	...	1023	⋮	⋮	...	1511	1841	...	2126	...	⋮
Abancourt...dep	...	6 59	7 15	9 0	9‡22	...	11 0	1012	1058	...	1548	1935	...	2155	...	2111
Aumale	...	—	7 33	—	9 39	...	1118	...	...	...	16 6	1956	...	22 6	...	
Blangy	...	...	8 8	...	1012	...	1152	§	...	...	1640	2031	...	2236	...	RC
Longroy G....arr	...	...	8 20	9‡18	1023	...	12 5	...	...	1341	1651	2012	2321	2245	C	
Eu	...	...	8 51	9 37	1050	...	1232	11 1	1159	14 6	1720	2110	2344	23 0	0 50	22 0
Le Treport..arr	...	...	8 56	9 42	1055	...	1237	11 5	12 3	1411	1725	2115	2349	23 5	0 55	22 4
St. Omer-en-C.dep	557	...	...	...	...	9 21	...	...	...	...	1445	1812	21 1	...	...	...
Crevecœur	6 4	...	...	...	...	9 49	...	...	...	...	1512	1839	2128	...	...	...
Conty	634	...	...	...	...	1021	...	...	...	...	1544	1911	2156	...	...	...
Saleux	7 2	...	...	...	...	1049	...	...	...	...	1612	1946	2222	...	...	...
Amiens (18) ...arr	717	...	...	...	...	1110	...	...	...	...	1630	20 5	2237	...	...	...

		1,2,3	1,2,3	1 &2	1,2,3	1,2,3	1,2,3	1,2,3	1,2,3	1,2,3	1,2,3	1,2,3	1,2,3	1,2,3
Amiens ....dep		6 3	...	...	9 53	1156	...	...	16 9	...	...	...	1841	...
Saleux		6 24	...	...	1012	1213	...	...	1628	...	...	...	19 0	...
Conty		6 53	...	...	1042	1241	...	...	1658	...	...	...	1933	...
Crevecœur		7 29	...	...	1119	1316	...	...	1733	..	...	...	2021	...
St. Omer-en-C....arr		7 50	...	...	1140	1335	...	...	1753	‡	...	A	2040	...
Treport.........dep		...	5 8	8§20	8 48	...	13 5	1320	...	1745	1625	1830	...	20 0
Eu		...	5 20	8 30	8 57	...	1314	1329	...	1753	1634	1838	...	20 8
Longroy G.		...	5 44	...	9 28	...	A	14 0	...	...	1712	19 0	...	2022
Blangy		...	5 58	...	9 43	...	...	1414	...	E	1729	1918	...	2032
Aumale		...	6 40	9 9	1024	...	...	1457	...	...	1819	1959	...	2057
Abancourt.....dep		...	7 10	9 22	11 1	1241	14 4	1549	...	1848	1932	2019	...	2110
Grandvilliers......		...	7 33	9 36	1125	13 5	⋮	1611	...	RC	1958	—	...	2125
St. Omer-C. ...arr		...	8 2	...	1152	1338	⋮	1637	...	⋮	2031	...	...	2141
St Omer-en-C. dep		7 51	8 3	...	1157	1342	⋮	1638	1757	⋮	2033	...	2041	2142
Beauvais ....arr		8 13	8 30	1010	1223	14 8	1449	17 3	1834	1933	2053	...	21 7	22 0
,, (22)...dep	7 0	8 42	8 46	1013	1233	1415	1454	17 8	1917	1937	2117	...	2123	22 5
Meru	7 29	B	9 35	1039	1316	1459	...	1751	B	20 3	22 8	2042	B	2231
Persan-B. ...arr	7 45	...	10 4	1054	1343	1526	B	1821	...	2018	2235	2115	...	2246
Paris Nord ar	8 35	1055	1120	1130	1457	1616	1610	19 3	2156	21 0	0 31	2245	2325	2325

Extra									
Longroy...dep	15‡30	17*48	Treport...dep	5 53	9‡58	1147	14‡34	17*0
Eu	16 5	18 21	Eu..........	5 59	10 5	1155	14 41	17 8
Le Treport arr	16 12	18 28	Longroy arr	6 22	1030	1219	15 6	1733

B—Via Chantilly. ‡—Runs until 30th September.
§—Between Beauvais and Treport until 3rd October only. *—Runs until 2nd October.
A—Runs until 3rd October. C—From 14th July until 30th September.

LENS, BULLY-GRENAY and ST. POL.

†—Weekdays only.

Lens ....dep	6 11	10 3	13 20	...	18 9
Bully-Grenay...ar	6 22	10 17	13 31	...	18 20
,, (26) dep	6 47	10 25	13 42	†	18 44
Bruay	7 19	10 56	14 13	1444	19 14
Houdain	7 29	11 5	14 22	1457	19 25
Brias..........	7 54	11 29	14 46	1524	19 45
Saint-Pol(20, 28)ar	8 3	11 39	14 56	1534	19 54

Saint-Pol dep	3†36	...	7 29	11 50	15 34	20 47
Brias	3 52	...	7 42	12 2	15 46	20 59
Houdain	4 14	...	8 3	12 23	16 6	21 20
Bruay	4 24	4 52	8 14	12 34	16 17	21 31
Bully- arr	—	5 18	8 40	13 1	16 44	21 57
Grenay dep	...	5 26	8 50	13 20	16 59	22 7
Lens ....arr	...	5 42	9 4	13 29	17 8	22 19

LENS and ARMENTIERES.

‡—Not on Sunday.

Lens (30)..........dep	4 13	5 31	9 49	1410	15 27	1840	2236	
Pont-à-Vendin ....arr	4 26	5 48	10 7	1428	15 44	19 0	2253	
Violaines ....arr	...	7 2	1050	...	16 50	1936	...	
Bauvin-Provin.........dep	4 39	6 4	1021	1441	15 57	1912	23 7	
Don Sainghin (20) ...arr	4 48	6 12	1029	1450	16 7	1922	2317	
Wavrin..........	...	6 26	1046	1529	16‡19	1954	2328	
Armentieres (26) arr	...	6 49	11 9	1552	...	2019	—	
Armentieres......dep	...	7 6	11 24	...	17 1	...	2039	...
Wavrin	...	7 29	11 48	...	1725	1928	21 3	...
Don Sainghin	4 49	7 54	12 13	1622	1744	1950	2128	...
Bauvin-Provin (20)......	5 1	8 3	12 22	1632	1754	20 0	2135	...
Violaines ....dep	...	7 15	11 0	...	1715	...	1939	...
Pont-à-Vendin	5 15	8 14	12 33	1644	18 7	2012	2146	...
Lens..........arr	5 35	8 32	12 50	17 2	1825	2030	22 5	...

PARIS, MONTSOULT-MAFFLIERS, to LUZARCHES and PERSAN-BEAUMONT.

E.M																											
	Paris ....dep	5 15	6 0	7 15	8 5	8 45	10 40	11 40	11 53	12 40	14 40	16 40	17 21	17 29	18 3	18 50	18 53	1917	19 40	2022	21 45	0 40	...	...	...	...	...	...
4¼	Saint-Denis	5 25	...	7 24	...	8 54	10 49	...	...	12 50	14 49	16 49	...	...	18 12	...	...	1928	19 49	2031	21 55	0 49	...	...	...	...	...	...
6¾	Epinay..........	5 30	...	7 29	...	8 59	10 54	...	12 4	12 56	14 54	16 54	...	17 40	18 17	...	19 6	1933	19 54	2036	22 0	0 55	...	...	...	...	...	...
11¾	Ecouen-Ezanville	5 53	...	7 48	...	9 19	11 15	...	12 22	13 18	15 16	17 14	...	18 5	18 38	...	19 27	1950	20 12	2053	22 18	1 14	...	...	...	...	...	...
15½	**Montsoult M.** ar	6 8	6 27	8 2	...	9 34	11 29	12 5	12 36	13 33	15 31	17 27	17 49	18 21	18 52	19 15	19 41	—	20 26	—	22 32	1 28	...	...	...	...	...	...
22¼	**Luzarches** arr	...	7 10	...	...	10 0	...	12 36	—	14 4	...	...	18 16	...	19 25	...	20 10	...	...	...	23 0	...	...	...	...	...	...	...
23	**Persan-Beau** 30	...	6 52	8 25	8 40	9 57	11 53	12 21	...	13 57	15 55	17 51	18 5	...	19 16	19 30	20 5	...	20 49	...	22 55	1 51	...	...	...	...	...	...
...	**Persan-B.** ....dep	4 53	...	6 14	6 47	7 48	7 56	...	10 15	10 55	11 22	...	13 48	15 33	16 25	17 13	18 25	18 37	...	21 26	22 48	23 24	...	...	...	...	...	
...	**Luzarches**...... ,,	...	...	5 58	...	7 36	...	...	10 10	...	...	12 51	...	15 29	...	...	...	18 26	...	21*18	...	...	...	...	...	...	...	
...	**Montsoult**	5 19	...	6 40	7 17	8 11	8 20	8 45	10 40	...	11 45	13 21	14 12	16 3	16 49	17 39	18 41	19 2	20 40	21 55	...	23 48	...	...	...	...	...	
...	Ecouen-Ezanville	5 32	6 15	6 55	7 30	...	8 34	8 58	10 58	...	11 58	13 34	14 25	16 16	17 1	17 52	...	19 16	20 55	22 10	...	0 1	...	...	...	...	...	
...	Epinay..........arr	5 49	6 33	7 15	...	...	8 52	9 16	11 10	...	12 15	...	14 44	16 33	17 18	18 14	...	19 38	21 16	22 31	...	0 18	...	...	...	...	...	
...	Saint-Denis .... ,,	5 53	...	...	...	...	8 56	9 21	...	...	12 19	...	14 48	16 37	17 22	18 19	...	19 42	21 20	22 35	...	0 22	...	...	...	...	...	
...	**Paris**.......... ,,	6 2	6 43	7 25	7 48	8 35	9 7	9 30	11 20	11 30	12 28	14 0	14 57	16 46	17 32	18 30	19 3	19 51	21 30	22 45	23 25	0 31	...	...	...	...	...	

*—12 minutes earlier on Sunday.

CAMBRAI and ROISIN.

Dist E.M										
	Cambrai ...dep	3 38	6 21	...	...	11 34	1359	1619	...	20 21
13¾	Solesmes 20......	4 14	7 3	...	...	12 16	1447	17 6	...	21 12
24¾	Le Quesnoy ...	5 36	7 47	10 59	...	12 54	1520	1744	1932	23 32
33	Bavai.....arr...	5 55	8 7	11 24	1233	13 14	1537	18 4	1951	23 51
38	Roisin 94 ...arr	6 17	8 31	—	1249	—	1550	1821	...	—

Roisin ......dep	...	6 41	8 58	...	13 0	16 27	...	18 37
Bavai 20	4 16	7 8	9 26	10 19	13 32	16 40	19 1	20 4
Le Quesnoy ...	4 50	7 45	11 2	10 46	14 9	18 40	1919	20 37
Solesmes	5 16	8 14	11 34	—	14 52	19 16	—	21 8
Cambrai 29A ar	5 53	8 53	12 18	...	15 30	19 57	...	21 47

VELU and ST. QUENTIN.

Velu 30A ....dep	...	9 25	12 36	16 45	19 50	...	...
Ytres-Etricourt......	5 22	9 47	12 54	17 12	20 15	...	...
Epehy 29...............	6 7	10 31	13 24	18 0	20 57	...	...
Roisel 29...............	6 36	11 0	14 26	18 42	—	...	...
St. Quentin 24 arr	7 29	12 0	15 19	19 55	...	..	...

St. Quentin 22A dep	5 25	...	8 25	9 56	12 30	14 25	18 50	...
Roisel....................	6 20	...	9 28	11 0	13 42	15 48	19 51	...
Epehy....................	—	6 5	9 48	13 55	14 26	16 25	20 14	...
Ytres-Etricourt	...	6 43	10 17	14 20	—	17 14	20 49	...
Velu ....arr	...	7 1	10 34	14 35	...	17 33	...	...

ACHIET and MARCOING.

Dist.							
	Achiet............dep	8 35	11 48	15 50	19 0	...	...
4¼	Bapaume	8 57	12 10	16 13	19 25	...	...
10½	Velu 30A	9 22	12 37	16 42	19 50	...	...
15½	Havrincourt	9 42	12 59	17 17	20 13	...	...
20½	Marcoing 29...arr	10 0	13 17	17 40	20 31	...	...

Marcoing ...dep	6 31	9 23	14 2	1650	...	...
Havrincourt ...	6 49	10 1	1418	1719	...	...
Velu	7 8	10 38	1438	1743	...	...
Bapaume..........	7 32	11 5	15 0	1815	...	...
Achiet 26 ...arr	7 48	11 21	1515	1831	...	...

ESVRES and LE GRAND PRESSIGNY.

Esvres ....dep	...	...	9 5	...	1420	...	1750
Ligueil ....arr	...	...	1026	...	1536	...	1910
Loches.........dep	5 25	8 15	—	15 2	—	17 5	—
Ligueil ......arr	6 13	9 5	...	1549	...	1752	...
Ligueil ....dep	6 21	9 14	...	—	...	1756	...
Le Grand Pres. arr	7 10	10 5	...	...	...	1845	...

Grand Pressigny	...	7 35	...	1454	1912
Ligueil ....arr	...	8 21	...	1544	1956
Ligueil ......dep	...	8 26	11 0	1558	20 0
Loches.........arr	...	9 15	1150	1612	2044
Ligueil ....dep	7 5	11 46	—	1553	—
Esvres 38 ......arr	8 29	13 8	...	17 4	...

Loches ...	7 20	9 50	1812
Montresor	8 25	11 4	1920
Ecueille	9 18	12 0	2018
Ecueille	5 50	9 55	18 5
Montresor	6 50	11 0	1915
Loches ...	7 48	12 0	2018

PERIGUEUX and ST. YRIEIX.

E.M.						
	Perigueux dep	5 55	11 10	17 12	...	...
13	Savignac	6 58	12 24	18 20	...	...
22½	Excideuil 35B......	7 53	13 40	19 22	...	...
32¼	Lanouaille............	8 49	14 43	20 21	...	...
41¾	La Juvenie	9 41	15 40	21 17	...	...
46½	St. Yrieix 32 arr	10 3	16 6	21 44	...	...

St. Yrieix ...dep	5 32	11 15	16 55	...	...
La Juvenie.........	5 54	11 38	17 17	...	...
Lanouaille	6 45	12 40	18 11	...	...
Excideuil............	7 49	13 55	19 17	...	...
Savignac............	8 33	14 48	20 3	...	...
Périgueux 39A	9 37	16 7	21 15	...	...

PERIGUEUX and ST. PARDOUX LA RIVIERE.

Périgueux..............dep	6 45	11 0	17 2	...
Chateau l'Evêque	7 25	11 40	1750	...
Brantome	8 42	13 5	1910	...
St. Pardoux 35B......arr	9 37	14 5	20 9	...

St. Pardoux ......dep	6 58	10 55	15 30	...
Brantome	7 58	12 10	16 38	...
Chateau l'Evêque..............	9 4	13 22	17 50	...
Périgueux 39A ......arr	9 44	14 6	18 35	...

PERIGUEUX and VERGT.

Perigueux Place Francheville...dep	6 10	10 10	16 45
Vergt ....arr	7 35	11 35	18 5

Vergt ....dep	7 55	11‡55	18 30
Perigueux.........arr	9 20	13 15	19 50

‡—15.10 p.m. on Friday.

ST. ROCH (Amiens) and AUMALE.

St. Roch............dep	6 §5.6	40	11 25	18 7	19*20
Molliens	7 16	7 54	12 41	1923	20 29
Aumale (30) ...arr	8 45	9 25	14 15	2047	...

Aumale ....dep	...	5 45	9 44	16†15
Molliens..................	4*21	7 15	11 15	17 51
St. Roch (18) ...arr	5 30	8 20	12 22	18 55

*—Weekdays only. †—18.2 on Saturday. §—Runs until 4th October.

AIRE-SUR-LA-LYS and BERCK.

[*—Runs until 30th September.

Aire...........dep	...	8 30	...	1452	...	1950	...
Fruges...............	5 51	11 7	...	1635	...	2138	...
Wicquinghem ...	6 44	12 7	*	1725	...	—	...
Montreuil	8 29	14 8	17 5	1849	1943	...	...
Verton..............	9 10	14 53	1743	1930	2030	...	...
Rang-Verton......	9 18	15 0	1751	1933	2050	...	...
Berck-Ville	9 28	15 10	18 2	1947	21 0	...	...
„ Plage ...arr	9 33	15 15	18 7	1952	21 5	...	...

Berck-Plage. dep	...	6 35	12 30	17 32	18 32	...	...
Berck-Ville	...	6 45	12 37	17 38	18 39	...	...
Rang-Verton	...	7 5	13 0	17 50	18 50	...	...
Verton	...	7 9	13 3	17 53	18 53	...	...
Montreuil	...	8 30	14 4	18 55	19 28	...	...
Wicquinghem	...	9 49	15 20	20 9	—	...	...
Fruges	5 47	1154	16 15	21 1	...	...	...
Aire ....arr	7 30	1332	18 50	...	...	...	...

‡—Runs until 3rd October.

Extra. { Rang-Verton to Berck 7.41, 10.18, 10.40, 11‡50, 13.10, 13‡30, 15.22, 16.5, 17.51, 18.12, 18*29, 20.0, 20.50, 23.25, 0*12.
Berck to Rang-Verton, 5.25, 7.5, 8.55, 10.2, 11‡15, 12.6, 12‡42, 14.35, 15.25, 16.40, 17.15, 17.32, 19.15, 22.40.

Berck Plage and Paris Plage—Service four times a day each way.

BAVAI and HON-HERGIES.

Bavai..............dep	7 28	13 23	19 11	...	...
Houdain....................	7 59	13 53	19 35	...	...
Bavai Annexe	9 14	15 0	20 16	...	...
Hon-Hergies arr	8 16	14 8	19 47	...	...

Hon-Hergies...dep	8 34	14 26	19 53	...	...
Bavai Annexe	9 27	15 13	20 21	...	...
Houdain	9 55	16 1	20 31	...	...
Bavai (20).........arr	10 49	16 52	20 56	...	...

ARGENT and LE BLANC.

Argent ....dep	...	...	...	6 22	...	...	1315	...	17 55
Salbris	...	...	...	7 58	10 25	...	1459	16 30	19 50
Romorantin	...	...	8 5	—	11 43	...	—	19 37	20 54
Gievres	...	...	8 40	...	12 11	...	...	20 12	—
Valencay	...	6 15	9 17	...	12 58	...	1640	20 49	...
Ecueille (30A)...........	...	7 7	—	...	14 9	...	1732	—	...
Buzancais	7 0	8 6	...	1141	15 12	1625	1831	...	...
Mezières-en-Brenne...	7 56	—	...	1247	—	1737	—	...	...
Le Blanc (38) ...arr	8 46	...	...	1345	...	1835	...	...	...

Le Blanc dep	...	...	6 0	9 10	...	16 35	...
Mezières	...	...	6 57	1012	...	17 40	...
Buzancais	...	...	8 36	1110	13 7	18 40	1930
Ecueille	...	...	9 37	—	14 6	—	2029
Valencay.........	5 45	...	10 26	...	16 30	...	2121
Gievres	6 22	...	11 3	...	17 21	...	—
Romorantin ...	6 58	...	11 29	...	18 7	...	...
Salbris	8 2	10 26	12 40	1335	19 8	...	...
Argent 38 arr	...	12 3	...	1521	21 10	...	...

UZERCHE and ARGENTAT.

Uzerche (33)...dep	6 24	...	11 27	17 45	...	...	...
Seilhac	7 14	...	12 23	18 37	...	...	...
Tulle (33)	8 1	8 18	13 13	19 38	...	...	...
Argentat ....arr	...	9 42	15 0	21 2	...	...	...

Argentat dep	...	6 30	...	9 55	...	15 47	...	...	...
Tulle	6 20	8 0	8 30	1125	11 58	17 16	...	...	...
Seilhac	7 13	—	9 29	—	13 2	18 47	...	...	...
Uzerche arr	...	...	10 9	...	13 40	19 24	...	...	...

Seilhac.............dep	7 30	13 0	18 43	...	...	...
Treignac ....arr	8 48	14 18	19 58	...	...	...

Treignac.........dep	6 0	11 0	17 0	...	...	...
Seilhac..............arr	7 10	12 18	18 19	...	...	...

ORLEANS RAILWAY COMPANY—(CHEMINS DE FER D'ORLEANS).

D—From Quimper forward admits 3rd class when travelling at least 62 miles.

SAVENAY and LANDERNEAU.

‡—Until 9th October.

		1,2,3	1,2,3	1,2,3	1,2,3	1,2,3	1,2,3	1,2,3	1,2,3	1,2,3	1,2,3
NANTES 39 dep		3 46	...	...	6 40	5 58	9 50	12 45	1533	1618	1920
Savenay ...dep		⋮	...	...	⋮	6 55	11 0	14 1	1625	1732	2042
Pont Chateau...		⋮	...	...	⋮	7 12	1120	14 20	1639	1748	2059
Redon (32)...arr		5 8	...	...	8 4	7 49	12 1	15 0	17 4	1825	2136
" ...dep		5 12	...	6 0	8 9	8 18	1222	15 7	17 9	1836	2142
Malansac		...	...	6 26	...	8 42	1248	15 33	...	19 2	22 3
Questembert ...		C	...	6 41	8 36	8 58	13 4	15 53	...	1918	2216
Elven	1,2,3	...	...	7 1	...	9 14	1324	16 14	...	1937	...
Vannes	5 25	6 7	...	7 19	9 1	9 31	1342	16 34	18 2	1955	2243
Auray 31A	5 53	6 34	6‡46	7 50	9 26	10 4	1424	17 0	1827	2029	23 8
Landevant	—	...	7 9	8 7	...	1021	1444	17‡34	...	2045	...
Hennebont		...	7 29	8 23	9 51	1037	15 0	17‡51	1852	21 1	2333
Lorient	4 49	7 13	7 41	8 40	10 6	1122	1518	18‡2	19 7	2121	2342
Quimperlé	5 12	7 34	—	9 12	1026	1153	1550	—	1932	2149	—
Rosporden	5 41	7 59	...	9 55	1050	1228	1632	...	20 2	2221	...
Quimper ...	6 12	8 18	9 0	1020	1126	1340	1657	...	2036	2240	...
Châteaulin	6 59	—	9 49	—	12 6	1425	1755	...	2115	—	...
Quimerc'h	7 21	...	1010	...	1229	1448	1818	...	...	...	...
Landerneau	8 25	...	11 6	...	1327	1557	1922	...	2224	...	...
BREST 80...	9 7	...	1151	...	14 8	1638	20 6	...	23 5	...	...

A—Between Landerneau and Redon admits 2nd & 3rd class for Nantes and beyond; or for Rennes and beyond.
B—Between Lorient and Redon will not take 2nd & 3rd cl. local passengers.
C—At Redon admits passengers from branch lines only; from Vannes forward takes 1st class without restriction, 2nd and 3rd class travelling at least 62 miles.
E—Admits 3rd class when travelling at least 93 miles.

BREST (81) dep		...	5 22	...	7 11	...	...	10 50	...	13 45	...	7 27	...
		1,2,3	1,2,3	1,2,3	1,2,3	1,2,3	1,2,3	1,2,3	1,2,3	1,2,3	1,2,3	1,2,3	1,2,3
Landerneau ...dep		...	5 50	...	7 48	...	...	11 27	...	14 20	...	18 0	18 17
Quimerc'h		...	...	...	8 45	...	...	12 30	...	15 21	...	A	19 22
Châteaulin ...dep		...	6 58	...	9 9	...	...	12 54	...	15 46	...	19 10	19 47
Quimper		...	7 38	6 49	1022	...	1230	13 51	1613	16 38	1729	20 2	21 0
Rosporden		...	8 1	7 25	1052	...	1255	14 24	1641	17 0	1758	20 25	21 31
Quimperlé		...	8 27	8 4	1135	...	—	14 58	—	17 23	1833	20 50	22 11
Lorient		5 0	8 52	9 7	12 0	12‡30	1251	15 31	1659	17 47	1915	21 15	22 23
Hennebont		5 12	9 2	9 20	—	12 40	13 7	15 42	1713	D	1926	...	22‡51
Landevant		5 29	...	9 37	...	...	1324	15 58	1731	...	1942	...	...
Auray		6 7	9 35	10 7	...	13 13	14 7	16 26	18 4	18 27	2019	21 55	23‡31
Vannes		6 40	9 56	1039	...	13 34	1440	16 53	1830	18 48	2049	22 16	23‡51
Elven		7 0	...	1059	...	...	15 0	17 10	—	...	...	A	—
Questembert		7 25	1023	1124	...	E	1525	17 29	...	19 13	2124	...	...
Malansac		7 40	B	1139	...	...	1540	17 43	...	...	...	...	...
Redon ....arr		8 2	1046	12 1	...	14 21	16 2	18 3	...	19 38	2155	23 3	...
" ......dep	5 35	8 16	1053	1225	...	14 23	1613	18 13	...	19 45	22 4	23 11	...
Pont Chateau	6 20	8 59	1117	13 8	...	14 54	1656	18 49	...	...	2233	⋮	...
Savenay...arr	6 38	9 17	⋮	1326	...	15 8	1714	19 4	...	20 22	2252	⋮	...
NANTES (39)	7 59	11 0	1214	1448	...	16 10	1829	20 20	...	21 14	2353	0 32	...

Lorient ....dep	5 20	9 0	13 4	17 47
Plouay	6 21	10 1	14 3	18 52
Meslan	7 3	10 42	—	19 30
Gourin...........arr	8 26	12 9	...	20 55

Gourin..........dep	5 4	9 20	...	15 35
Meslan................	6 23	10 40	...	17 1
Plouay................	7 5	11 20	15 28	17 46
Lorient.........arr	8 5	12 19	16 30	18 45

Locminé ....dep	5 0	10 0	...	16 3
Vannes..................	7 50	11 20	1357	1720
Surzur ....arr	8 26	—	1430	1913
Port Navalo arr	9 54	...	1553	2035
La Roche Bernard	9 41	...	1541	2022

La Roche Bernard	4 39	10 31	16 49	...
Port Navalo dep	4 29	10 19	16 40	...
Surzur	5 54	11 45	18 0	...
Vannes................	7 29	13 55	19 6	...
Locminé ....arr	8 46	15 15	20 25	...

Plouay ....dep	7 6	14 5	18 55	...
Baud	7 55	14 56	19 46	...
Locminé	8 52	15 55	20 33	...
Moulin-Gilet	9 18	16 18	20 58	...
Ploermel .... arr	10 54	17 42	22 30	...

Ploermel ......dep	...	7 47	14 2	18 45
Moulin-Gilet	...	9 14	15 29	20 55
Locminé	4 30	9 42	15 59	21 19
Baud................	5 24	10 28	16 45	—
Plouay ....arr	6 16	11 18	17 36	...

Moulin-Gilet dep	9 25	1620	20 56	
Pontivy ....arr	1010	17 6	21 37	

Pontivy...........dep	8 25	14 35	20 0	...
Moulin-Gilet ...arr	9 10	15 20	20 45	...

Pontivy...dep	8 35	1335	1723	...	...
Meslan ...arr	1035	1642	1925	...	...

Meslan...dep	10 44	17 3	...	...	...
Pontivy arr	12 37	1853	...	...	...

Questembert..........dep	9 7	15 56	19 45	...	...	...
Ploermel (77B).........arr	10 4	16 46	20 47	...	...	...

Ploermel ....dep	7 35	14 5	18 5	...	...
Questembert 31 ......arr	8 28	15 9	18 56	...	...

Rosporden ...dep	8 10	11 0	13 0	14‡44	18 10	20‡28
Concarneau ...arr	8 43	11 33	13 33	15 13	18 44	21 1

Concarneau... dep	6 41	9 9	11 45	13‡44	1530	19‡23	...
Rosporden 77B arr	7 10	9 38	12 14	14 13	1619	19 52	...

Quimper ......dep	6 16	8 25	11 15	14 5	1740	20‡53	...
Pont l'Abbé ...arr	7 14	9 0	11 54	14 42	1817	21 30	...

Pont l'Abbé dep	6 45	9 23	11 27	12‡54	1513	1916	...
Quimper 31 arr	7 25	9 57	12 17	13 31	16 0	1953	...

Quimper ....dep	6 33	8 31	11 23	14 0	1735	20‡46	...
Douarnenez......arr	7 34	9 7	12 4	14 38	1813	21 24	...

Douarnenez......dep	6 39	9 30	11 8	12‡47	1514	19 11
Quimper ....arr	7 18	10 4	12 1	13 23	16 5	19 47

‡—Until 9th October.

Quimperlé ....dep	...	9 23	12 30	16 5	18 45	...
Pont-Aven......................	7 35	10 28	13 38	17 10	19 40	...
Concarneau..................arr	8 29	11 22	14 32	18 4	...	...

Concarneau 31 ....dep	...	9 15	12 42	16 11	18 24
Pont-Aven.........................	7 0	10 19	13 45	17 17	19 17
Quimperlé 31..............arr	7 55	11 14	14 40	18 12	...

PONT l'ABBE and ST. GUENOLE.

E M						
	Pont l'Abbé ......dep	9 15	12 10	15 5	19 0	...
9¼	Penmarch	9 58	12 53	15 49	19 43	...
11¼	St. Guénolé ......arr	10 7	13 2	15 58	19 52	...
	St. Guénolé ....dep	5 37	10 19	13 30	17 30	...
	Penmarch	5 46	10 28	13 39	17 39	...
	Pont l'Abbé ....arr	6 27	11 11	14 22	18 22	...

DOUARNENEZ and AUDIERNE.

E.M.						
	Douarnenez ...dep	7 45	9 25	11 15	15 0	18 55
12½	Audierne ......arr	8 44	10 24	12 10	15 55	19 50
	Audierne ....dep	5 32	8 10	9 52	13 35	17 32
	Douarnenez 31 arr	6 22	9 5	10 47	14 30	18 27

BREST and PORSPODER.

E.M					
	Brest ......dep	7 41	10 0	13 41	1753
10½	St. Renan.........	8 33	10 50	14 30	1844
13¾	Lanrivoare	8 46	11 4	14 44	1858
20¼	Ploudalmezeau	9 12	11 30	15 10	1924
26¾	Porspoder arr	9 45	12 3	15 44	1957

Porspoder dp	6 20	10 53	15 0	17 5
Ploudalmezeau	6 55	11 28	1536	1740
Lanrivoare	7 18	11 51	1559	18 3
St Renan.........	7 31	12 4	1612	1816
Brest ......arr	8 22	12 53	17 1	19 7

LANDERNEAU and BRIGNOGAN.

Landerneau......dep	7 24	9 48	14 7	18 15	...
Lesneven................	8 30	10 45	15 0	19 10	...
Plouider 31.............	8 46	11 8	15 16	19 37	...
Brignogan ......arr	9 10	11 32	15 40	20 1	...

Brignogan ......dep	7 22	9 30	16 2	17 0
Plouider	7 47	9 55	1640	17 27
Lesneven................	8 13	10 14	17 5	17 41
Landerneau ......arr	8 58	11 0	1750	18 57

BREST and L'ABER-WRACH, and PLOUESCAT.

E.M.							
	Brest ....dep	6 56	7 21	9 10	1325	1530	1743
11¼	Plabennec	7 44	8 12	9 59	1412	1617	1832
18¾	Lannilis	⋮	8 46	1039	1452	⋮	1912
22¼	L'Aber-Wrach arr	⋮	9 4	1057	1510	⋮	1930
—	Plabennec ...dep	7 47	...	10 3	1416	1622	1836
8	Lesneven	8 28	...	1043	1456	1710	1920
11¼	Plouider 31	8 56	...	1112	1515	1728	1938
20½	Plouescat ...arr	9 36	...	1152	...	18 8	2018

Plouescat ...dep	...	7 16	10 26	...	15 48	...
Plouider	...	7 57	11 11	...	16 30	1727
Lesneven	6 29	8 16	11 31	...	16 49	1750
Plabennec ...arr	7 8	8 57	12 10	...	17 29	1829
L'Aber-Wr'ch dep	6 17	⋮	11 19	1526	16 38	⋮
Lannilis	6 38	⋮	11 40	1547	16 59	⋮
Plabennec	7 13	9 2	12 15	1620	17 34	1833
Brest ....arr	8 4	9 51	13 3	17 8	18 33	1921

E.M					
	Plouescat...........dep	6 47	9 40	11 57	18 13
8¾	St. Pol de Leon 81 arr	7 27	10 19	12 36	18 52
	St. Pol de Leon...dep	6 33	9 41	15 5	17 30
	Plouescat ....arr	7 13	10 21	15 43	18 9

ORLEANS RAILWAY.

LIMOGES and CLERMONT-FERRAND.

‡—Until 20th September.

E.M	Station																		
—	Limoges—Bénédictins......dep	...	...	...	...	...	...	4 26	...	...	8 56	...	...	...	...	1521	17‡27	1842	...
15	St. Leonard	...	...	...	...	...	...	5 11	...	...	9 41	...	...	...	...	16 3	18 12	1929	...
19¾	St. Denis-des-Murs ...	...	...	...	...	...	...	5 26	...	...	9 56	...	...	...	...	1619	18 1	1944	...
31	Eymoutiers	...	...	...	...	...	...	6 8	...	...	1044	...	...	...	...	1655	19 9	2017	...
44	Viam	...	...	...	...	...	...	6 55	...	...	1128	...	...	...	...	1741	19 54		...
52½	Barsanges	...	...	...	...	...	...	7 26	...	...	1156	...	...	...	...	1810	20 23	...	...
61½	Meymac	...	...	...	...	...	...	7 56	...	...	1229	...	...	...	...	1840	20 56	...	...
70¾	Ussel (32)	3 26	...	...	5 48	...	...	8 50	...	...	13 9	...	1557	...	...	1911	21 15	2152	...
81½	Eygurande-Merlines.	3 55	...	6 ‡3	6 26	...	...	9 31	...	...	1340	...	1626	16 ‡3	...	1941		2222	...
95	Laqueuille (37)		...	6 38	7 15	...	...	1021	13‡12	...	1451	...	1725	16 41	...	2044	...		...
111¼	Pontgibaud	...	...		8 1	...	...	11 8	13 50	...	1535	...	18 4		...	2130	...	...	...
122½	Volvic (46A)	...	...	...	8 44	9 18	...	1148	14 24	...	1610	1653	1836	...	21 46	22 7	...	...	...
131¾	Royat	...	6‡45	8‡29	9 17	9 42	12 ‡4	1216	14 50	15‡21	1632	1720	1858	21‡39	22 13	2235	...	...	...
134¾	Clermont-Ferrand arr	...	6 56	8 40	9 27	9 52	12 15	1226	15 0	15 32	1641	1730	19 7	21 50	22 23	2245	...	...	...

Station																			
Clermont-Ferrand dp	...	...	4 25	4 45	6 48	8‡56	9 18	11 2	...	...	15 41	16‡45	17 35	18‡12	...	1935	...	...	...
Royat	...	...	4 39	5 0	7 2	9 8	9 34	1118	...	...	15 55	16 56	17 49	18 23	...	1949	...	...	...
Volvic	...	...	5 11	5 36	7 28	9 34	10 6	1154	...	...	16 31		18 21		...	2023	...	...	...
Pontgibaud	...	...		6 10	7 58	10 6		1226	...	...	17 3	...		...	...	2056	...	...	...
Laqueuille	...	...	...	7 9	8 44	1054	...	1320	15‡11	...	17 59	...	...	...	21‡32	2152	...	...	...
Eygurande	...	4 35	...	7 53	9 22	1125	...	1413	15 45	1640	18 41	...	...	...	22 6	2236	...	...	...
Ussel	4 12	5 3	...	8 30	9 48	12 6	...	1552		1723	19 10	...	...	...		23 4	...	...	...
Meymac	4 34		...	8 54		1239	...	1615	...			...	...	...	...		...	...	...
Barsanges	5 6	...	...	9 26	...	...	...	1647	...	...	...	...	...	...	...	...	...	...	...
Viam	5 32	...	...	9 51	...	...	...	1713	...	...	...	...	...	...	...	...	...	...	...
Eymoutiers	6 23	...	...	1031	14 4	14 4	...	1757	...	...	...	...	...	...	...	...	...	...	...
St. Denis-des-M.	6 57	...	...	11 0	14 36		...	1832	...	...	...	...	...	...	...	...	...	...	...
St. Leonard	7 12	...	...	1117	14 52	...	...	1848	...	...	...	...	...	...	...	...	...	...	...
Limoges (35) ......arr	7 58	...	...	1157	15 35	...	...	1934	...	...	...	...	...	...	...	...	...	...	...

ST. DENIS-PRES-MARTEL, AURILLAC, and ARVANT.

E.M.	Station															
	St. Denis-pres-Martel		...	4*10	5†46	...	...	9*20	9†34	...	...	...	1352	1628	...	20 5
10½	Bretenoux-Biars		...	5 9	6 18	...	...	9 52	1048	...	...	...	1429	1652	...	2039
35½	Miecaze		...	6 27	7 36	8 1	...	11 12		...	...	...	1548	1758	...	22 1
38½	Viescamp-s-Jallès		...	6 36	7 45	8 10	8 42	11 24	...	...	From 21st Sept.	1241	1557	18 7	...	2213
47¼	Aurillac (36) ......arr		4 31	6 56	8 5	8 30	9 1	11 44	...	...		13 2	1623	1823	19 8	2233
49¾	Arpajon (Cantal)		4 39	7 13			9 27		...	...		1321	1631	...	19 16	
59¾	Vic-sur-Cère		5 6	7 40	...	...	9 56	...	...	...		1349	17 0	19 0	19 46	...
70¼	Le Lioran		6 1		...	...	1044	...	...	11§50		1437	1748	Until 5th Sept.	20 34	...
77	Murat	5 21	6 42	...	...	...	1119	...	...	12 17	1216	15 8	1818		21 2	...
82¾	Neussargues 45A	5 35	6 56	...	...	...	1135	...	...	12 29	1234	1522	1831		21 15	...
...	"	...	7 17	...	...	...	1244	...	...			1536	1841			...
98¼	Massiac		7 58	...	...	...	1325	...	...	...	...	1620	1924		...	...
113	Arvant (58) ......arr		8 33	...	...	...	14 2	...	...	...	...	1657	20 1		...	...

Station															
Arvant ......dep	...	...	...	...	...	5 45	...	9 22	...	...	...	15*11	15†11	18 22	...
Massiac	...	...	...	...	...	6 23	...	9 56	...	...	...	15 51	15 50	19 1	...
Neussargues......arr	...	...	...	...	...	7 5	...	1039	...	...	...	16 48	16 48	19 59	...
" ......dep	...	...	6 10	...	...	7 18	...	11 1	...	...	1525	17 48	17 0	20 39	...
Murat	...	...	6 31	...	...	7 32	7 44	1121	...	...	1545	18 1[illegible]	17 18	21 5	...
Le Lioran	...	...	6 59	...	...		8 35	1152	...	...	1613	18 44	17 49	21 34	...
Vic-sur-Cère	...	...	7 46	...	8§18	...	9 30	1236	...	...	1658	19 27	18 31	22 19	...
Arpajon (Cantal)	...	...	8 11	...	...	...	1016	13 2	...	...	1724	19 55	18 58	22 55	...
Aurillac (31A)	4 32	...	8 18	9 11	9 18	...	1031	1311	1451	17*5	1732	20 3	19 7	23 6	...
Viescamp-sous-Jallès...	4 53	...	8 49	9 35	9 53	...		1357	1515	1727	1824	20 32			...
Miecaze	5 2	...		9 44	10 2	...	...		1524	1736	1835	20 41	...	...	...
Bretenoux-Biars	6 19	7 52	...	11 6		...	...	...	1651	1851		22 0	...	...	...
St. Denis-pres-Mart. 38	6 46	8 22	...	1136	...	...	...	...	1719	1917	...	22 33	...	...	...

*—Until 9th October.
†—From 10th October.
§—Until 20th September.

AURILLAC and EYGURANDE.

‡—Until 20th September.

Station								
Aurillac ......dep	4 56	‡33	...	Until 9th Oct.	13‡45	...	18 0	...
Viescamp	5 17	9 53	...		14 6	...	1824	...
Miécaze	5 26	10 3	...		14 15	...	1835	...
Mauriac	6 47	1128	...		15 36	...	2012	...
Largnac	7 29	1212	‡		16 9	...	2056	...
Bort (Correze)...	8 10	1239	1245	15 2	17 5	...	2133	...
Port Dieu	8 30	...	13 6	...	17 26	2118	2152	...
Eygurande arr	9 7	...	1314	1550	18 6	22 6	2227	...

Station									
Eygurande dep	4 11	4 28	6‡[illegible]7	9 45	...	16 ‡0	20 2	...	...
Port Dieu	...	5 17	7 10	1018	...	...	2037	...	...
Bort (31A)	4 55	5 25	7 30	1045	...	16 55	2057	...	...
Largnac		5 53		1113	...	...	2218	...	...
Mauriac	...	6 46	...	12 9	16‡22	18 3	2258	...	...
Miécaze	...	8 1	...	1325	17 40	19 16		...	...
Viescamp	...	8 10	...	1336	17 49	19 26	...	...	...
Aurillac (36) arr	...	8 30	...	1356	18 9	19 44	...	...	...

BORT and NEUSSARGUES.

‡—Until 20th September.

Station						
Bort (Correze) ......dep	4 59	8 5	12 51	17‡38	...	...
Riom-ès-Montagnes	5 40	8 52	13 38	18 4	...	...
Allanche	6 42	10 3	14 44	19 32	...	...
Neussargues (45A) arr	7 9	10 32	15 13	20 1	...	...

Station						
Neussargues......dep	5 45	7 55	12 41	19 1	...	...
Allanche	6 17	8 27	13 12	19 33	...	...
Riom-ès-Montagnes	7 25	9 37	14 20	20 37	...	...
Bort (31A) ......arr	8 2	10 19	14 57	21 14	...	...

AURAY and PONTIVY.

Station				
Auray ......dep	5 58	10 18	1414	20 39
Saud	6 39	11 5	1457	21 23
Pontivy 77B ...arr	7 17	11 45	1535	22 1

Station						
Pontivy......dep	4 37	7 58	12 33	18 20	...	...
Baud	5 17	8 39	13 14	19 4	...	...
Auray 31 ......arr	5 57	9 19	13 57	19 46	...	...

PARIS, ORLEANS, VIERZON, and MONTAUBAN.

WAGON-COUCHETTE and WAGON-LIT Compartments—in 19.0, 19.50, 20.27, and 22.30 from Paris.
THROUGH CARRIAGE—Paris to Narbonne and Villefranche Vernet-les-Bains in 19.0 from Paris.
☞ **Barcelona Express**—Attached to the 19.0 from Paris are carriages de luxe running to Barcelona, arriving there 15.40; see page 295.

Dist.	1 Cl.	2 Cl.		1,2,3	1,2,3	1,2,3	1,2,3	1,2,2	1,2,3	1,2,3	1,2,3	1,2,3	1,2,3	1,2,3	1,2,3	1,2,3	1,2,3	1,2,3	1,2,3	1,2,3
E.M.	fr. c.	fr. c.	PARIS—																	
	Fro	m	Quai d'Orsay ......dep	7 10	8 20	8 30	8 36	10 0	1157	14 0	16 3	16 3	19 0	1910	1950	2027	20 43	2230	22 51	0 35
Quai	d'Or	say.	Quai d'Austerlitz dep	7 22	8 30	8 40	8 47	10 10	12 8	1410	16 13	16 13	19 10	1920	20 0	2037	20 53	2241	23 4	0 50
14½	2 60	1 75	Juvisy	...	...	...	9 5	...	1233	...	...	...	...	...	...	...	...	...	23 28	1 32
22½	4 5	2 70	Bretigny	...	A	...	9 26	C	13 4	...	...	RC	B	RC	G	G	F	SC	23 48	2 6
37½	6 70	4 55	Etampes	8 9	...	...	9 58	...	1352	...	...	...	...	...	2047	...	...	2329	0 20	2 56
76¼	13 80	9 30	Les Aubrais ....arr	9 5	9 56	10 8	1110	11 43	1523	1543	17 46	17 46	...	2053	2138	2210	22 29	0 25	1 41	4 40
77¾	14 0	9 45	Orléans .... arr	9 20	10 9	10 23	1118	11 56	1533	1555	17 53	17 53	...	21 4	2153	2220	22 48	0 39	1 59	4 47
			Orléans .... dep	8 55	9 49	10 1	12 7	11 37	16 3	—	18 10	17 59	20 32	2044	2132	22 3	22 26	0 19	1 36	5 29
...	...	...	Les Aubrais ....dep	9 11	10 2	10 13	...	11 48	...	...	...	...	20 48	2057	2143	2215	22 38	0 31	1 51	...
91½	16 45	11 10	La Ferté St. Aubin ...	9 37	...	...	1238	...	1632	...	18 39	...	...	2120	...	...	...	...	2 14	6 2
100¾	18 15	12 25	Lamotte-Beuvron 46A	9 57	RC	...	13 2	RC	1655	...	19 2	...	RC	2138	...	SC	...	...	2 33	6 27
112½	20 25	13 70	Salbris	1019	...	...	1328	...	1719	...	19 28	...	...	22 0	...	...	...	...	2 54	6 55
126¾	22 85	15 40	**Vierzon** ....arr	1043	11 0	11 11	1355	12 54	1744	...	19 53	19 5	21 49	2224	2249	2319	23 42	1 37	3 16	7 22
205	36 95	24 95	MONTLUCON 37...arr	1332	13 32	13 32	1755	17 55	2129	...	...	...	...	...	...	...	1 56	3 34	...	1250
276½	49 85	33 65	LAQUEUILLE 37 arr	1641	16 41	16 41	...	...	...	...	...	...	...	...	...	...	6 38	6 38	...	...
...	...	...	**Vierzon** ....dep	1112	11 5	☞ Runs until 5th September only.	1458	12 58	...	1918	...	19 11	21 54	...	2254	2321	...	...	3 30	7 50
138½	25 0	16 85	Reuilly	1134	...		1525	...	...	1942	...	...	...	...	...	...	...	...	3 52	8 17
149½	26 90	18 15	Issoudun (32)	1153	...		1553	13 29	...	2010	...	19 42	SC	...	2324	...	...	...	4 13	8 44
156½	28 20	19 5	Neuvy-Pailloux	12 6	...		16 9	...	...	2026	...	...	...	...	G	...	...	...	4 28	9 0
166	29 90	20 20	**Châteauroux (38)**	1220	11 50		1629	13 53	...	2045	...	20 5	22 42	...	2348	0 14	...	...	4 44	9 20
185½	33 40	22 55	**Argenton (38)**	1253	...		1747	14 26	1437	2133	...	20 42	...	...	0 21	...	...	...	5 33	1022
202½	36 50	24 65	St. Sebastien (33)	—	RC		1839	15 3	1527	—	...	...	...	...	...	SC	...	...	6 27	1125
214½	38 65	26 10	La Souterraine	...	...		1910	15 22	1556	...	...	21 33	...	...	1 12	...	...	...	6 58	1156
230½	41 55	28 5	**St. Sulpice** ...... arr	...	13 30		1949	...	1635	...	...	21 58	...	...	...	1 54	...	...	7 37	1235
...	...	...	**Lauriere** ... dep	1054	13 34		20 0	...	1710	18‡5	23 12	22 1	...	1 9	...	1 57	...	6 53	7 45	1259
251	45 25	30 55	**Limoges** arr	1141	14 2		2055	16 15	1757	1834	23 56	22 30	0 47	1 41	2 4	2 27	...	7 37	8 34	1348
...	...	...	(Benedictins) dep	—	14 12		—	16 34	1827	—	—	—	0 53	—	2 12	2 36	3 16	—	9 10	1425
263½	47 50	32 5	Pierre Buffière	...	...		...	16 56	19 4	...	...	...	...	...	...	...	3 52	...	9 43	1456
273½	49 30	33 25	St. Germain-les-Belles	...	...		...	17 14	1940	...	...	...	...	SC Sleeping Car in this train.	...	G	4 28	...	10 18	1529
287	51 75	34 95	Uzerche	...	...		...	17 37	2024	...	...	...	...		3 10	...	5 13	...	11 1	1612
302	54 45	36 75	Allassac	...	...		...	17 58	21 1	...	...	...	...		3 31	...	5 50	...	11 37	1649
312½	56 35	38 5	**Brive** ....arr	...	15 41	...	...	18 16	2130	...	...	...	2 29		3 48	4 5	6 18	...	12 5	1717
371½	67 0	45 20	CAPDENAC (32) arr	...	...	...	...	21 4	...	...	...	...	4 41		RC Restaurant Car attached.	6 19	10 35	...	15 30	21 4
...	...	...	**Brive** ....dep	...	15 48	...	1558	18 42	...	1925	‡—Until 9th October.	...	2 35			4 14	6 45	...	13 12	...
335½	60 50	40 80	Souillac	...	...	...	1654	Via Capdenac.	...	2043		...	...			4 52	7 45	...	14 10	...
338	60 95	41 15	Cazoulès	...	...	...	17 2		...	2052		...	SC			SC	7 53	...	14 18	...
349½	62 95	42 50	Gourdon	...	...	...	1740		...	2133		...	...			5 17	8 31	...	14 56	...
374½	67 55	45 60	**Cahors** .... arr	...	17 18	...	1843		...	2241		...	4 5			5 53	9 32	...	15 57	...
			Cahors .... dep	7 0	17 23	...	1858		...	—		...	4 9			5 58	9 41	...	16 7	...
399	71 90	48 55	Caussade	8 19	18 0	...	20 2		...	...		...	...			6 35	10 45	...	17 17	...
413½	74 60	50 35	**Montauban** ....arr	8 58	18 26	...	2036		...	...		...	5 9			7 1	11 19	...	17 54	...
...	...	...	,, ...dep	9 25	18 32	...	2047		...	...		...	5 16			...	11 45	...	18 46	...
445½	80 30	54 20	**Toulouse (45B)**......arr	1036	19 16	...	2157	0 23	...	...		...	6 0			7 50	12 31	...	20 7	...
539	...	...	NARBONNE (45B) arr	...	0 57	...	...	...	...	...		...	8 56	...		...	15 49	...	...	...
608	...	...	VILLEFR. VERNET 46	...	7 12	...	...	...	...	...		...	10 38	...		...	21 8	...	...	...

A—Takes 2nd and 3rd class when travelling 125 miles or 187 miles respectively, or those coming off branch lines; at Paris admits 3rd cl. for Chateauroux & beyond, at Limoges for Cahors & beyond, at Vierzon admits from or for branches.
B—At Paris will take 1st class for Vierzon and beyond, and 2nd and 3rd class for Limoges and beyond only; between Orleans and Limoges takes up for Montauban or beyond, and for Capdenac and beyond.
C—Between Paris and Orleans admits 3rd class travelling at least 94 miles; between Vierzon and Allassac those travelling 31 miles. **F**—Down to Vierzon only takes 3rd cl. travelling at least 62 m. or coming from branch lines.
G—Takes 2nd cl. travelling at least 125 miles and 3rd cl. travelling at least 187 miles, or from or to branch lines.

LIMOGES and BRIVE. Via Nexon.

E.M.										
	Limoges-B. dep	3 9	5 45	9 0	10 47	1456	1623	18 7	1822	18 42
12½	Nexon	3 39	6 31	9 39	11 25	1530	1646	1840	1854	19 9
25½	St. Yrieix	4 15	8 9	1021	—	1612	—	—	1940	—
51½	Objat	5 33	—	1139	...	1734	...	...	21 3	...
61½	**Brive (33)** ...arr	6 10	...	1219	...	1811	...	...	2144	...

Brive ...dep	5 0	6 46	12 42	1816	...
Objat	5 31	7 25	13 18	1855	...
St. Yrieix	6 39	8 46	14 36	2017	...
Nexon	7 19	9 29	15 16	2057	0 9
Limoges 35	7 48	10 2	15 42	2129	0 31

BRIVE and USSEL.

‡—Until 20th September. §—Until 9th October.

Brive ......dep	3 6	...	5 15	7‡34	10‡15	1246	1632	1850	2210	0§31
Tulle	3 36	3‡48	6 9	8 32	10 55	1331	1711	1937	2248	1 1
Eyrein	—	...	6 57	9 17	...	1416	—	2021	—	—
Egletons	...	4 50	7 30	9 46	12 5	1445	...	2050	...	...
Meymac	...	5 21	8 10	1028	12 40	1525	...	2127	...	...
Ussel 31A arr	...	5 39	8 29	1046	12 58	1544	...	2145	...	...

Ussel ......dep	...	...	5 48	8‡50	10‡4	...	15 3	2033	23‡10
Meymac	...	...	6 10	9 11	1026	...	1528	2055	23 31
Egletons	...	...	6 47	9 48	11 0	...	16 4	2136	0 1
Eyrein	...	...	7 19	1017	...	...	1634	22 4	...
Tulle	3§37	5 28	8 18	1054	12 1	1445	1725	2249	1 3
Brive (33) arr	4 4	6 7	8 55	1216	1228	1530	18 1	2325	1 36

BRIVE and TOULOUSE.

‡—Until 10th October.
§—Until 5th September.

Brive ....dep	...	2‡47	3 55	4 22	...	...	7 55	...	12 41	15§53	...	18 42	19 7	...	...
St. Denis-Martel 31A	...	3 19	4 32	4 55	...	...	8 45	...	13 34	16 23	...	19 25	19 51	...	...
Rocamadour	...	...	—	5 17	...	...	9 18	...	14 8	—	...	19 53	—	...	...
Figeac	...	4 30	...	6 8	...	...	10 24	...	15 19	...	17 10	20 53	...	...	...
Capdenac ......arr	...	4 41	...	6 19	...	...	10 35	...	15 30	...	17 23	21 4	...	...	...
,, (38) dep	...	—	...	6 26	7 2	...	10 58	...	16 5	...	—	21 13	...	...	...
Villefranche-de-Rou.	...	...	5 35	7 5	7 55	...	11 58	...	16 59	...	...	22 4	...	...	...
Lexos (37)	...	...	6 25	7 44	8 50	...	12 57	...	17 56	...	19 41	22 46	...	...	...
Tessonnières (33) ...	5 33	...	7 19	8 28	9 44	11 2	14 2	1724	19 2	...	20 51	23 26	...	...	...
Gaillac	5 42	...	7 27	8 36	9 52	1111	14 14	1735	19 14	...	21 0	23 32	...	...	...
St. Sulpice (Tarn) 46A	6 22	...	8 7	9 2	10 25	1147	14 57	1818	19 58	...	21 37	23 53	...	...	...
Toulouse ......arr	7 15	...	8 55	9 35	10 56	1235	15 53	1913	20 49	...	22 31	0 23	...	...	...

Excess Luggage, 1 cent. per 44lbs. per kilometre.] **ORLEANS RAILWAY.**

MONTAUBAN, VIERZON, ORLEANS, and PARIS.

Wagon-Couchette and Wagon-Lit Compartments—in 20.45 from Toulouse.

VILLEFRANCHE VERNET dep			...	...	...	...	...	...	5 0	8 48	8 48	...	...	1243	...	...	18 24	...
NARBONNE.........dep	...	...	...	...	...	1 47	6 13	...	9 38	1313	13 13	...	...	1647	...	...	20 33	...
	1,2,3	1,2,3	1,2,3	1,2,3	1,2,3	1,2,3	1,2,3	1,2,3	1,2,3	1,2,3	1,2,3	1,2,3	1,2,3	1,2,3	1,2,3	1,2,3	1,2,3 §	1,2,3
Toulouse ....dep	...	...	...	...	...	6 0	9 16	...	13 0	1547	16 45	...	1742	2045	...	...	23 37	...
Montauban...... arr	...	...	...	...	...	6 44	1024	...	1314	1627	17 29	...	Via Capdenac.	2125	...	...	0 20	...
Montauban...... dep	...	...	...	...	...	7 15	1047	...	1349	1637	17 37	...		2134	...	...	0 27	...
Caussade	...	...	...	...	...	7 56	1125	...	...	1716	17 59	...		2157	...	...	...	...
Cahors .... arr	...	...	...	...	...	9 7	1227	...	1415	1821	18 36	...		2235	...	...	1 23	...
Cahors .... dep	...	...	5 50	...	...	9 30	—	15 32	1449	19 4	18 43	...		2240	...	...	1 27	...
Gourdon....................	...	...	7 11	...	...	10 38	...	16 42	D	2017	19 24	...		2322	...	...	...	...
Cazoulès	...	...	7 44	...	...	11 8	...	17 12	...	2049	...	...		...	...	...	D	...
Souillac....................	...	...	8 4	...	...	11 18	...	17 33	1548	21 3	19 47	...		2346	...	...	...	...
Brive ....arr	...	...	9 7	...	...	12 11	...	18 26	1623	22 2	20 22	...	2347	0 22	...	...	2 58	...
CAPDENAC 33 ...dep	...	...	...	...	...	10 12	...	16 17	1318	...	16 17	...	2118	2118	...	...	0 29	...
Brive ....dep	...	5 11	...	9 25	...	12 56	...	18 41	1628	...	20 31	...	2358	0 28	...	...	3 5	...
Allassac....................	...	5 38	...	9 52	...	13 23	...	19 9	...	...	...	...	...	0 45	...	...	SC	...
Uzerche	...	6 20	...	1033	...	14 2	...	19 48	17 7	...	21 10	...	...	...	...	...	3 47	...
St. Germain-les-Belles	...	7 1	...	1114	...	14 41	...	20 28	...	...	...	...	...	SC	...	...	...	...
Pierre Buffière	...	7 27	...	1141	...	15 6	...	20 53	...	...	...	...	...	...	...	...	...	...
Limoges ....arr	...	7 56	...	1210	...	15 35	...	21 22	18 0	...	22 3	...	1 35	2 3	...	...	4 45	...
(Benedictins) ......dep	5 42	8 15	7 33	1245	12 56	15 55	1632	—	18 8	1913	22 19	...	1 48	2 13	...	3 3	4 52	0 41
St. Sulpice ...... arr	6 37	8 52	8 29	1322	13 54	16 32	1730	...	1844	20 9	22 58	...	2 25	2 50	...	3 44	5 28	1 18
St. Sulpice ...... dep	6 45	8 56	—	1326	14 11	16 37	1736	...	1846	—	23 3	...	2 28	2 58	...	3 50	5 29	—
La Souterraine	7 23	9 24	...	...	14 56	17 4	1817	...	...	...	23 29	...	...	K	...	4 19	...	...
St. Sebastien	7 50	9 44	...	E	15 30	17 28	1845	...	...	...	...	...	D	...	...	4 42	D	...
Argenton....................	8 29	10 14	1345	...	16 10	17 55	1951	...	RC	...	0 10	...	...	4 7	...	5 19	...	...
Chateauroux	9 18	11 19	1428	1459	17 3	18 30	2046	...	2011	...	0 46	...	4 6	4 47	...	6 3	6 54	...
Neuvy-Pailloux..........	9 38	...	—	...	17 23	...	21 7	...	...	...	...	...	...	...	...	6 19	...	...
Issoudun	9 54	11 46	...	1524	17 43	18 55	2124	...	D	...	...	...	...	5 13	...	6 36	...	...
Reuilly	1016	...	...	...	18 13	...	2148	...	...	...	...	...	...	...	...	6 56	...	...
Vierzon ....arr	1039	12 18	...	1554	18 38	19 25	2213	...	2057	...	1 37	...	5 3	5 45	...	7 18	7 40	...
LAQUEUILLE 37...dep	...	...	...	8 44	13 20	...	...	15 10	...	...	...	2152	...	...	...	...	...	...
MONTLUCON 37...dep	...	8 11	...	1333	16 40	...	1854	18 28	...	...	...	0 48	...	...	...	...	...	6 13
Vierzon ....dep	1121	12 31	1440	16 2	18 59	19 39	2326	20 16	21 6	...	1 44	3 9	5 10	5 52	6 28	7 58	7 47	9 12
Salbris......................	1146	12 54	15 9	...	19 25	20 2	2352	...	...	...	H	...	...	...	6 51	8 27	...	...
Lamotte-Beuvron	1212	13 14	1537	...	19 49	20 22	0 17	‡	RC	...	...	...	D	...	7 15	8 53	D	...
La Ferté St. Aubin......	1233	13 30	16 2	...	20 11	20 39	0 38	...	...	...	...	E	...	...	7 36	9 15	...	...
Les Aubrais ....arr	...	...	1633	17 9	20 37	21 1	1 6	21 21	22 7	...	2 51	4 16	6 31	7 1	...	9 43	8 52	1013
Orléans .... arr	13 2	13 55	1651	1722	20 50	21 17	1 20	21 33	2220	...	3 2	4 31	6 45	7 17	8 5	10 0	9 7	1024
Orléans .... dep	—	14 4	1634	17 6	20 23	20 53	0 58	21 14	22 3	...	2 45	4 10	6 25	6 59	—	9 49	8 45	1012
Les Aubrais ....dep	...	14 10	1645	1720	20 43	21 7	1 15	21 26	2213	...	2 58	4 24	6 39	7 11	...	10 1	8 58	1024
Etampes....................	...	15 7	...	1819	...	RC	2 29	...	...	...	...	...	7 43	...	...	10 59	...	...
Bretigny....................	...	15 30	...	...	...	...	2 58	...	...	...	...	...	...	...	...	...	...	...
Juvisy........................	...	15 42	...	...	...	...	3 17	...	...	...	...	...	...	...	...	...	...	...
PARIS Austerlitz arr	...	16 2	18 7	19 5	22 16	22 46	3 37	22 58	2345	...	4 36	5 57	8 34	8 47	...	11 45	10 32	1156
,, Quai d'Orsay arr	...	16 12	1816	1914	22 25	22 55	...	23 7	2354	...	4 46	6 7	8 43	8 56	...	11 55	10 41	12 5

Extra.		
Limoges......dep	10‡21	21 15
St. Sulpice...arr	10 58	21 59

D—Takes 2nd class travelling at least 125 miles and 3rd class travelling at least 187 miles; also takes forward 2nd & 3rd class from branch lines.

§—Through carriage de Luxe from Barcelona attached to this train. ‡—Until 9th October only.

E—Takes 3rd class travelling at least 93 miles, or coming from branch lines.

H—2nd class must be going at least 62 miles, and 3rd class 187 miles, or coming off branch lines.

K—After Limoges only admits 3rd class travelling at least 93 miles, or coming from branch lines.

ALBI and TESSONNIÈRES.

Albi..............dep	1 10	5 0	6 38	7 54	9 2	1025	1312	1648	18 11	20 2	22 51	...	...	...
Tessonnières...arr	1 34	5 25	7 4	8 16	9 28	1052	1338	1716	18 40	2028	23 15	...	...	...
Tessonnières...dep	1 47	7 25	8 37	9 48	1116	1241	14 10	1547	1740	19 5	21 0	23 30	...	...
Albi (43) .....arr	2 11	7 53	9 1	1014	1144	1310	14 38	1616	18 8	1933	2127	23 54	...	...

ISSOUDUN and ST. FLORENT.

Issoudun............dep	7 44	11 56	20 20	...	...	...
St. Florent 37 ...arr	8 50	12 28	20 52	...	...	...
St. Florent............dep	5 20	10 46	19 19	...	...	...
Issoudun 32 ....arr	6 4	11 20	19 55	...	...	...

ST. SEBASTIEN and GUERET.

St. Sebastien dep	6 45	15 31	18 50	...	...	...	
Dun-le-Palleteau...	7 22	16 5	19 25	...	...	...	
Guéret (36).....arr	8 12	17 1	20 20	...	...	...	
Guéret ....dep	4 50	12 10	1529	...	...	...	...
Dun-le-Palleteau	5 45	13 30	1635	...	...	...	...
St. Sebastien (33) arr	6 18	14 9	17 8	...	...	...	...

TOULOUSE and BRIVE.

‡—Until 10th October. §—From 11th October.

Toulouse dep	...	...	...	5 26	8 0	9 50	...	11 0	12 55	14 0	...	15 25	17 42	18 43	...	...	0 30	...
St. Sulpice.........	...	...	...	6 21	9 0	1024	...	11 51	13 27	14 55	...	16 24	18 16	20 2	...	...	1 7	...
Gaillac	...	...	...	7 1	9 35	1052	...	12 26	13 49	15 34	...	17 12	18 45	20 40	...	...	1 34	...
Tessonnières......	...	2§20	...	7 20	9 43	11 3	11 13	12 33	14 0	15 42	...	17 36	18 57	21 6	...	...	1 42	1‡55
Lexos	...	3 35	...	8 21	—	1144	12 54	—	14 42	—	...	18 38	19 39	22 17	...	...	—	2 39
Villefranche	5 ‡5	5 5	...	9 18	...	1231	14 24	...	15 27	...	16 5	19 51	20 24	23 17	23‡24	...	...	3 20
Capdenac arr	6 6	6 6	...	10 1	...	13 5	15 33	...	16 0	...	1726	20 38	20 58	—	0 5	‡	...	3 57
,, dep	—	—	7 16	10 12	...	1318	—	...	16 17	...	—	—	21 18	...	—	0 29	...	—
Figeac...............	...	...	7 30	10 25	...	1330	...	...	16 31	...	...	...	21 31	...	...	0 41	...	...
Rocamadour........	...	...	8 41	11 24	...	1432	...	...	17 29	...	...	...	22 37	...	...	...	...	...
St. Denis-Martel	4 56	...	9 17	11 55	...	1458	...	17 26	17 57	...	...	...	23 7	...	...	1 54	...	...
Brive 32......arr	6 18	...	9 59	12 33	...	1538	...	18 10	18 33	...	...	...	23 47	...	...	2 25	...	...

66lbs. of Luggage free. Excess Luggage, 1 cent. per 44 lbs. per kilometre.] ORLEANS RAILWAY.

PARIS, ORLEANS, TOURS, POITIERS, AND BORDEAUX.

THROUGH CARRIAGES, 1st Class. } Paris to Arcachon—in 9.46 from Paris. Paris to Pau—in 19.38. Paris to Irun—in 19.38, and 22.10 from Paris. RC—Restaurant Car attached. SC—Sleeping Car attached.

WAGON-COUCHETTE and WAGON-LIT Compartments—19.38, 20.15, and 22.10 from Paris.

Dist E.M		1,2,3	1,2,3	1,2,3	1,2,3	1,2,3	1,2,3	1,2,3	1 Cl	1,2,3	1,2,3	1,2,3	X	1,2,3	1,2,3	1,2,3	1,2,3	1,2,3	1,2,3	1 &2	1,2,3		1,2,3	1,2,3	1,2,3	1,2,3	1,2,3	1,2,3	1,2,3	1,2,3	1,2,5
	PARIS—																					Z			‡						
—	Quai d'Orsay ......dep	0 35	...	5 40	7‡50	...	8 36	9 0	9 46	...	11 5	1157	1216	1340	14‡0	1445	1615	1734	1826	1938	2015	21 0	2110	2120	2210	...	...	...	...	2344	...
...	Pont St. Michel ...dep	0 38	...	5 43	...	...	8 39	...	...	...	RC	12 0	...	1343	...	1449	...	1737	1829	SC	...	...	...	...	...	...	...	...	...	2347	...
...	Quai Austerlitz ...dep	0 50	...	5 50	8 0	...	8 47	9 10	9 56	...	1115	12 8	1226	1351	1410	15 0	1625	1745	1837	1948	2027	2110	2120	2130	2221	...	...	...	...	2358	...
6¼	Vitry	1 3	...	6 2	...	...	...	...	...	...	...	...	...	...	...	...	...	...	...	...	...	...	...	...	...	...	...	...	...	...	...
14¼	Juvisy	1 32	...	6 25	...	...	9 5	...	D	...	C	1233	...	1413	...	1523	G	...	RC	J	E	...	...	B	...	...	...	...	...	0 24	...
22¼	Bretigny 37	2 6	...	6 57	...	...	9 26	...	...	...	...	13 4	RC	1446	...	1542	RC	1813	...	...	...	...	...	...	...	...	...	...	...	0 42	...
37¼	Etampes	2 56	6 5	7 40	RC	...	9 58	...	RC	...	12 3	1352	...	1532	...	1610	...	1837	1925	RC	...	...	...	...	SC	...	...	...	...	1 12	...
57¾	Toury	3 53	7 1	9 50	...	...	1039	...	...	...	...	1442	...	1626	...	1652	...	1924	...	...	...	...	...	...	...	...	...	...	...	1 53	...
76½	Les Aubrais ......arr	4 40	7 49	1030	9 33	...	1110	...	1122	...	1256	1523	1347	1711	1543	1721	...	20 5	2019	...	22 0	2242	2253	23 7	2354	...	...	...	...	2 24	...
77¾	Orléans 32, 33 { arr	4 47	7 59	1039	9 49	§	1118	...	1134	...	13 8	1533	1358	1722	1555	1732	...	2014	2027	...	2214	...	...	2321	0 7	...	...	...	...	2 40	...
...	Orléans { dep	5 32	8 11		9 23	9 35	1140	1028	1115	...	1250	16 6	1340		1533	1820	1748		2023	2121	2154	2237	2248	2258	2347	...	...	...	...	2 19	...
...	Les Aubrais ......dep	...	...	...	9 38	9 48	...	1045	1126	...	13 2	...	1351	...	1548	...	18 4	...	2033	2133	22 6	2246	2259	2313	2359	...	...	...	...	2 33	...
88¾	Meung-sur-Loire	6 0	8 39	...	...	10 5	12 8	...	...	...	...	1636	...	...	...	1852	...	...	2052	⋮	...	⋮	...	2332	...	...	...	...	...	2 53	...
93¼	Beaugency	6 13	8 52	...	...	1015	1221	...	...	...	1326	1649	...	...	...	19 6	...	...	21 2	⋮	...	⋮	2323	...	...	...	...	...	...	3 4	...
107½	Ménars	6 44	9 23	...	...	...	1252	...	...	...	...	1720	...	...	...	1939	...	...	...	⋮	...	⋮	...	...	...	...	...	...	...	...	...
113	Blois 40	7 3	9 40	...	1028	1044	13 9	...	...	...	1355	1741	...	...	1635	1959	1852	...	2137	⋮	2253	⋮	...	0 12	...	...	...	...	...	3 42	...
122½	Onzain	7 23	10 0	...	...	11 1	1329	...	...	...	14 9	18 3	...	...	...	2020	...	...	2153	⋮	...	⋮	0 1	...	...	...	...	...	...	3 58	...
133	Amboise	7 50	1026	...	...	1118	1356	...	...	...	1426	1832	...	...	...	2051	...	...	2212	⋮	...	⋮	0 19	...	...	...	...	...	...	4 19	...
141	Vouvray	8 11	1047	...	...	...	1417	...	...	...	...	1854	...	...	...	2114	...	...	...	⋮	...	⋮	...	...	...	...	...	...	...	...	...
146	St. Pierre des Corps	8 23	1059	...	1114	1136	1429	12 4	1242	...	1445	19 6	15 3	...	1715	2127	1932	...	2232	⋮	2333	⋮	0 37	0 56	1 23	...	...	...	...	4 43	...
148	Tours ......arr	8 31	11 9	...	1129	1151	1438	⋮	1256	...	15 1	1915	1518	...	1727	2138	1943	...	2240	⋮	2348	⋮	⋮	1 15	1 40	...	...	...	...	4 52	...
213¾	¶ANGERS 39 ......arr	...	1316	...	1316	1316	1652	1339	1415	...	1652	2117	...	...	2055	0 40	2117	...	0 40	⋮	...	⋮	2 11	2 56	3 47	...	...	...	...	7 44	...
267¾	NANTES 39 ......arr	...	1450	...	1450	1450	1847	15 7	1526	...	1847	2235	...	...	...		2235	...		⋮	...	⋮	3 33	4 34	5 40	...	...	...	...	9 35	...
...	Tours ......dep	1014	...	13 3	11 9	...	...	☞ Until 9th October.	1231	...	1458	...	1458	1736	17 4	...	2010	...	...	2249	2322	2355	...	☞ Until 8th October only.	1 11	☞ Until 9th October.	...	...	...	5 9	7 10
...	St. Pierre des Corps	...	...	...	1123	...	...		1248	...	1519	...	15 9	...	1722	...	...	...	...	23 5	2340	0 8	...		1 30		...	...	...	...	...
160½	Villeperdue	1047	...	1335	...	...	...		...	...	...	...	...	18 6	...	...	2042	...	...	...	...	...	...		...		...	...	...	5 41	7 47
167¼	Ste. Maure	11 1	...	1348	RC	...	...		...	...	1551	...	...	1820	...	...	2056	...	...	...	...	...	...		...		...	...	...	5 54	8 2
174½	Port-de-Piles 35B	1117	...	14 3	...	...	...		RC	...	16 3	...	...	1835	18 2	...	2111	...	...	J	...	...	...		SC		...	...	...	6 11	8 25
188¼	Châtellerault 40	1152	...	1440	1230	...	...		...	...	1628	...	...	1913	...	...	2147	...	...	...	...	...	...		2 27		...	...	...	6 47	9 10
193¼	Les Barres	12 3	...	1451	...	...	...		...	...	...	...	...	1923	...	...	2158	...	...	...	...	...	...		...		...	...	...	6 58	9 21
208¾	Poitiers 38, 42A { arr	1243	...	1534	13 0	...	...		14 3	...	1657	...	1616	20 0	1847	...	2238	...	...	0 20	0 59	...	...		2 53		...	...	...	7 38	10 4
...	Poitiers { dep		...		1313	...	...		14 8	1425		1727	1620		1857	...		...	...	0 25	1 6	1 23	...		2 58	1 40	5 2	...	...	7 50	1028
211½	St. Benoit	...	...	...	...	...	...		...	1434	...	1735	...	...	...	...	...	...	...	...	...	...	...		...	...	5 10	...	...	7 58	1037
230	Couhé Verac	...	...	...	...	...	...	...	...	1524	...	1816	...	...	...	...	...	...	...	...	...	...	...		...	2 16	5 58	...	...	8 38	1128
241	St. Saviol 35	...	...	...	...	...	...	...	...	1551	...	1949	RC	...	1940	...	...	...	...	...	...	...	...		...	2 36	6 25	...	...	9 1	1155
249¾	Ruffec 40	...	...	...	14 6	...	...	...	...	1611	...	20 8	...	...	RC	...	...	...	...	...	...	...	...		...	2 52	6 47	...	...	9 20	1214
256	Salles-Moussac	...	...	...	...	...	...	...	...	1623	...	2019	...	...	...	...	...	...	...	...	...	...	...	...	...	...	6 59	...	...	...	1227
279	Angoulême 41B { arr	...	...	...	1446	...	...	...	1526	1713	...	21 9	1734	...	2031	...	...	...	...	1 49	2 34	...	...	...	4 32	3 40	7 47	...	...	1012	1324
...	Angoulême { dep	...	...	...	1452	...	1542	...	1532	1746	...	2124	1739	...	2037	...	...	...	...	1 54	3 0	2 52	5 17	...	4 39		7 56	...	...	1040	1334
300¼	Montmoreau	...	...	...	⋮	...	1614	...	⋮	1841	...	2216	⋮	...	...	...	...	...	...	⋮	3 32	⋮	6 10	...	...	...	8 49	...	...	1135	1424
310¾	Chalais	...	...	...	⋮	...	1629	...	⋮	19 5	...	2232	⋮	...	...	...	...	...	...	⋮	...	⋮	6 31	...	5 29	...	9 9	...	...	1157	1443
313¾	Parcoul-Médillac 39A	...	...	...	⋮	...	1638	...	⋮	1914	...	2246	⋮	...	...	...	...	...	...	⋮	...	⋮	6 39	...	⋮	...	9 17	...	...	12 5	...
329¾	Coutras 41B ......arr	...	...	...	⋮	...	17 4	...	⋮	1949	...	2317	⋮	...	2142	...	...	...	...	⋮	4 11	⋮	7 11	...	⋮	...	9 48	...	...	1236	1517
...	LYONS ......dep	...	...	...	⋮	...	...	...	⋮	...	9 50	...	⋮	...	...	...	...	...	1611	⋮	...	⋮	...	...	⋮	...	...	...	...	...	...
...	LIMOGES ......dep	...	...	...	⋮	...	...	...	⋮	1435	1842	1842	⋮	...	...	...	...	...	1 50	⋮	...	⋮	2 25	...	⋮	...	5 45	...	...	...	...
	1	2	3	4	5	6	7	8	9	10	11	12	13	14	15	16	17	18	19	20	21	22	23	24	25	26	27	28	29	30	31

	1	2	3	4	5	6	7	8	9	10	11	12	13	14	15	16	17	18	19	20	21	22	23	24	25	26	27	28	29	30	31
...	**Coutras** ....dep	2 21	3 54	...		...	1713	...		20 4	2128	2332		...	2146	...	...	...	4 59		4 13		7 18	...		...	9 57	1130	1333	1244	1523
340	**Libourne** 36	3 15	4 37	6 49	1615	...	1736	1850		2030	2144	2358		1917	22 2	...	...	1056	5 18		4 30		7 46	...	6 17	9 3	1022	1159	1413	13 6	1646
345½	Vayres 36	3 29	4 52	7 5	...	...	...	...		2045	Until Oct. 9	...		1933	...	...	...	1111	...		...		8 1	...	...	...	...	1216	1428	...	17 1
351	Saint Loubes	3 43	5 6	7 19	...	...	1755	...		21 0		...		1947	...	...	...	1125	...		...		8 15	...	...	9 22	...	1231	1442	...	1715
358½	Lormont......................	4 4	5 31	7 45	...	...	...	...		2124		...		2013	...	...	...	1150	...		...		8 41	...	...	...	...	1259	15 7	...	1743
361¾	**Bordeaux** Bastide arr	4 13	5 39	7 53	...	...	1819	1931		2132	2215	0 36		2021	...	...	...	1158	5 54		...		8 49	...	...	9 45	11 1	13 8	1515	1337	1751
365¼	" St. Jean...arr	...	...	8§11	1649	...	...	...	17 7	2158	...	...	19 9	...	2235	...	...	...	6 35	3 43	5 5	4 27	9 12	...	6 58	...	...	14 0	1622	14 0	...
400	ARCACHON 45A...arr	...	...	...	1811	...	...	...	1811	0 36	...	...	2114	...	0 36	...	...	...	8 51	...	8 2	8 2	1112	...	8 51	...	...	1555	1811	1555	...
510	PAU 44 ....arr	...	...	1225	2125	...	...	...	2125	...	...	...	...	...	5 19	...	...	...	11 4	7 59	11 4	7 59	1639	...	1225	...	...	2125	2125	2125	...
494½	BIARRITZ 45 ......arr	...	...	1158	21 5	...	...	...	21 5	4 51	...	...	2210	...	4 51	...	...	...	11 0	7 29	...	7 48	1639	...	1158	...	...	1921	21 5	1921	...
512	IRUN 45 ....arr	...	...	1241	2148	...	...	...	2148	5 47	...	...	23 5	...	5 47	...	...	...	1152	8 10	...	8 25	1732	...	1241	...	...	2017	2148	2017	...
904	MADRID 291A......arr	...	...	...	...	...	...	...	...	...	...	...	1412	...	...	...	...	...	7 0	2258	...	...	...	...	7 0	...	...	...	...	...	...

‡—Only takes 3rd class when travelling at least 94 miles.
§—Until 9th October only.
B—Takes 2nd class travelling at least 125 miles and 3rd class travelling at least 187 miles. Exceptionally between Paris and Tours will take 2nd and 3rd class for beyond Tours; also takes, irrespective of distance, 2nd and 3rd class to and from Branch Lines.
C—Takes 3rd class travelling at least 31 miles, or for Branch Lines. Will not admit 3rd class for Etampes.
D—Admits for beyond Orleans only.

E—Takes 2nd class travelling at least 125 miles, and 3rd class travelling at least 187 miles; also admits for Branch Lines. At Paris takes 2nd and 3rd class for Blois. At Orleans takes 2nd class for Blois. At Blois takes 2nd class for Tours, and 3rd class for stations beyond Tours.
G—At Paris admits for Blois and beyond only.
J—At Paris (only) will take 1st class for Poitiers and beyond, but otherwise only takes passengers for beyond Bordeaux to Stations on Midi Cie Line.
X—Sud Exp., Sleeping Car Co.'s Special Service. Take Tickets in advance of Sleeping Car Co. Extra Fares.
Z—Cote d'Argent Express—Train de Luxe. *Runs until 1st Nov.* Take tickets in advance of Sleeping Car Co.

SAINT-SAVIOL and LUSSAC-LES-CHATEAUX.

E.M.										
	St. Saviol......dep	6 40	1239	...	1847	Lussac.........dep	7 0	1120	1736	1915
4¼	Civray	6 52	1251	...	19 1	L'Isle-Jourdain	7 36	1356	1815	1949
10½	Charroux	7 11	1310	...	1925	Le Vigean.........	7 48	1413	1824	20 2
24¼	Le Vigean............	7 49	1347	18 1	20 6	Charroux	8 24	1454	19 1	—
27½	L'Isle-Jourdain 35	8 0	1431	1812	2017	Civray	8 41	1511	1920	...
39½	**Lussac-Chat** 38arr	8 42	1511	1844	2051	**St. Saviol** 34 arr	8 50	1519	1929	...

BORDEAUX and EYMET.

E.M.												
	Bordeaux dep	7 26	1040	14 6	1556	18 0	**Eymet** ......dep		6 17	8 34	1518	...
8¾	Citon-Cenac	7 58	1116	1437	1635	1837	La Sauvetat		6 26	8 43	1527	...
18	La Sauve...........	8 30	1145	15 6	17 7	1915	Sauveterre de G.		7 36	9 55	1615	...
34¾	Sauveterre de G.	9 18	—	—	1756	20 2	La Sauve......	6 30	8 33	1045	1728	2020
61½	La Sauvetat	1030	...	...	19 5	2111	Citon-Cenac	6 59	9 5	1114	1758	2052
64½	**Eymet** 35 ...arr	1038	...	...	1913	2119	**Bordeaux**	7 29	9 35	1143	1833	2124

*—Until 8th October.

ANGOULEME and LIMOGES.

[Le Quéroy-P. to Angoulême 19.39.

Angoulême ...dep	5 2	4 7	8 27	1117	1057	1455	17 0	18 0	21*42	**Limoges B.** dep	4 6	...	6 44	8 50	12 7	1235	1641	18*53
Ruelle	5 13	4 18	...	1128	11 8	15 7	1712	1811	...	Verneuil-sur-V. ...	4 47	...	7 26	9 29	...	1328	1725	...
Le Quéroy-Pran. 35B	5 29	4 36	...	1145	1124	1523	1730	1830	...	Saint Junien	5 15	5 58	8 2	10 1	1311	1412	1755	19 53
La Rochefoucauld ...	—	4 57	9 6	12 2	—	1540	—	1851	22 22	Saillat-Chassenon	5 31	6 14	8 20	1012	1325	1445	1813	...
Roumazieres-Loub't ...	...	5 39	9 42	1245	...	1617	...	1933	22 51	Chabanais	5 42	—	8 33	—	1336	15 0	1825	...
Chabanais	...	6 2	10 2	13 5	...	1637	...	1953	...	Roumazieres-L. ...	6 8	...	8 57	...	1354	1531	1850	20 32
Saillat-Chassenon 36	5 38	6 16	1015	1321	1610	1648	1839	20 7	...	La Rochefoucauld	6 50	...	9 41	...	1431	1617	1935	21 3
Saint Junien...........	5 49	6 30	1027	1335	1625	17 0	1846	2022	23 31	LeQuéroy-Pranzac	7 12	8 16	9 58	1340	...	1638	1954	...
Verneuil-sur-Vienne	—	7 1	...	14 7	17 1	1728	—	2051	...	Ruelle..................	7 31	8 32	1014	1358	15 0	1656	2012	...
Limoges Benedictins..		7 44	1129	1447	1750	1815	...	2135	0 29	**Angoulême 34**	7 41	8 42	1024	14 9	1510	17 7	2022	21 39

BERGERAC and MARMANDE.

Bergerac dep	448	9 37	1413	18 9
Eymet 35 ...	550	1050	1527	1929
Marm'nde45B	646	1149	1620	2023
Marmande...	5 0	9 30	1430	1828
Eymet	6 16	1047	1548	1982
Bergerac (36)	7 29	1150	1657	2044

BERGERAC and MUSSIDAN

Bergerac ...dep	7 45	1310	1715	2057
Mussidan 39 arr	8 36	14 3	18 0	2148
Mussidan ....dep	6 10	9 26	11 46	1840
Bergerac (36)arr	7 4	1019	12 37	1935

RUFFEC and L'ISLE JOURDAIN.

E.M.																
	Ruffec ....dep	...	7 5	...	12 22	...	1631	L'Isle Jourdain......dep		...	...	8 39	...	1445	...	1953
16¾	Vieux Cerier...............	...	7 56	...	13 9	...	1737	Le Vigean		...	...	8 50	...	1456	...	20 8
28½	Roumazières-Loubert...	6 24	9 46	...	14 35	...	1944	Confolens	5 3	...	8 2	9 40	12 5	16 1	18 0	2051
39¼	Confolens	6 59	1010	13 0	15 15	1715	20 8	Roumazières-L. 35	5 31	6 35	8 47	—	12 33	—	1940	—
55¼	Le Vigean	7 42	—	14 3	—	18 1	—	Vieux Cerier		7 11	—	...	13 44	...	2024	...
58	L'Isle Jourdain 35 arr	8 11	...	14 16	...	18 8	...	Ruffec.....................arr		8 3	...	...	14 37	...	2131	...

CHAMPILLET-URCIERS & LAVAUFRANCHE

E.M.				
	Champillet..................dep	8 1	12 0	1851
23½	Lavaufranche (36) ......arr	9 0	14 13	1953
	Lavaufranche ....dep	5 15	9 37	17 10	...
	Champillet (38) ....arr	6 15	11 17	18 10	...

ORLEANS and GIEN.

Orleans (34) dep	5 8	8 38	12 2	1547	1834	**Gien** ....dep	5 51	8 45	12 24	17 0	1924
St. Denis-Jargeau	5 44	9 13	12 37	1622	1913	Les Bordes 38	6 41	9 27	13 15	1744	2015
Châteauneuf-s-L....	5 57	9 26	12 49	1635	1926	Châteauneuf-s-L.	7 6	9 54	13 40	1812	2044
Les Bordes (Loiret)	6 35	10 1	13 19	17 8	2011	St. Denis-Jargeau	7 19	10 6	13 52	1825	21 4
Gien (58) ......arr	7 14	1040	13 58	1748	2053	**Orléans** (35B)arr	7 55	1042	14 28	19 6	2145

ORLEANS and MONTARGIS

Orleans ......dep	6 13	1028	1748	2023	Montargis 56dep	5 0	7 30	1129	18 9
Vennecy............	6 38	1054	1816	2048	Bellegarde-Quier	5 47	8 10	1216	19 5
Combreux	7 10	1127	1847	2120	Combreux	6 14	8 37	1244	1933
Bellegarde-Qs. 38	7 50	1156	1916	2158	Vennecy	6 46	9 9	1317	20 9
Montargis ...arr	8 27	1234	1952	2235	Orleans 35B...arr	7 10	9 34	1344	2035

BORDEAUX, POITIERS, TOURS, ORLEANS, AND PARIS.

WAGON-COUCHETTE COMPARTMENTS—in 19.45 and 20.34; Wagon-Lits in 22.30 from Bordeaux.
RESTAURANT CAR—in 8.26 and 11.4 from Bordeaux; in 8.46 and 18.52 from Tours.

MADRID ....291 dep	...	...	...	...	9 15	...	...	...	...	...	...	...	...	...	...	20 0	...	...	...	21 0	...	...	21 0	...	...	...	...
IRUN .... 45 dep	...	...	...	...	23 3	...	...	...	...	...	...	...	...	...	...	9 53	...	...	...	12 10	...	...	14 14	...	...	...	20 12
BIARRITZ ..... 45 dep	...	21 41	...	...	0 48	...	...	...	...	...	...	...	6 33	...	6 33	11 9	...	...	...	13 46	...	...	15 8	17 53	...	...	21 25
PAU .... 43 dep	...	21 27	...	...	...	...	...	...	...	...	...	...	6 55	...	6 55	9 36	...	...	...	12 26	...	15 7	15 7	18 2	...	...	21 27
ARCACHON ..45A dep	...	...	...	...	...	...	...	...	...	5 17	7 22	7 33	9 20	...	...	12 40	...	...	14 12	16 40	14 12	17 43	17 43	20 58	...	...	...
	1,2,3	1 & 2	1,2,3	1,2,3	1,2,3	1,2,3	1,2,3	1,2,3	1,2,3	1,2,3	1,2,3	1,2,3	1 Cl.	1,2,3	1,2,3	X	1,2,3	1,2,3	1,2,3	1,2,3	1,2,3	1,2,3	1,2,3	1,2,3	1,2,3	1,2,3	Z
Bordeaux—																											
St. Jean ....dep	...	1 22	...	...	6 ‡0	...	...	...	6 32	7 22	8 26	9 16	11 4	...	12 10	14 3	...	...	17 18	18 33	17 18	20 34	19 45	22 30	...	23 34	0 41
Bastide ....dep	...		...	...	...	6 45	5 17	7 19	...	7 43	...	9 47		11 13	...		14 17	16 1	17 51	...	18 55	...	C	SC	22 47	0 50	
Lormont	...	G	...	...	...	...	5 26	...	...	7 52	A	...		11 22	B		...	...	...	...	19 4	...	...	...	...	0 59	
Saint Loubes	...		...	...	...	...	5 50	...	...	8 16	RC	...		11 46	...		...	...	18 15	...	19 28	...	...	D	...	1 18	
Vayres	...		...	...	...	...	6 4	...	...	8 30	...	...		12 0	...		...	...	...	...	19 42	...	...	SC	...	1 31	
Libourne	...		...	...	6 32	7 22	6 18	7 53	7 7	8 44	9 8	10 25	RC	12 25	12 52		15 1	16 45	...	19 16	20 2	21 11	20 25	23 6	23 22	2 3	
Coutras ....arr	...		...	...		7 42			7 22	9 33		10 41		12 45	13 7		15 21	17 5	18 33	19 35	20 19	21 27		23 22	23 38	2 23	
LIMOGES 39A ....arr	...		...	...		12 20	...	...	10 12	...		...		...	17 47		...	21 55	...	...	...	0 31		...	...	...	
LYONS 51B ....arr	...		...	...		...	...	...	19 41	...		...		...	...		...	...	...	...	...	9 40		...	...	...	
Coutras ....dep	...		...	...		7 56	...	5 2	Until 5th October.	...		10 43		...	13 10		15 33	17 9	...	19 38	...	...		23 28	...	...	
Parcoul-Médillac 39A ...	...		...	...		8 34	...	5 35		...		11 15		...	...		16 11	17 40	...	20 11	...	...		...	...	...	
Chalais	...		...	...		8 44	...	5 45		...		11 23		...	13 41	RC	16 23		...	20 20	...	...		...	...	...	
Montmoreau..................	...		...	...		9 10	...	6 9		...		11 41		...	13 58		16 49	...	...	20 42	...	...		...	...	...	
Angoulême 41B arr	...	3 11	...	...	7 49	10 0	...	6 52		...	10 29	12 21	12 38	...	14 27	15 33	17 37	...	...	21 22	...	...	21 47	0 36	...	...	
Angoulême 41B dep	...	3 16	...	...	7 55	10 50	4 44	7 1		...	10 36		12 42	15 47	14 37	15 38	18 18	21 29	...		...	...	21 54	0 45	...	...	
Salles-Moussac..............	...	...	...	...	...	11 48	5 38	8 2		...	...	...	...	16 40	...	...	19 25	...	...	...	...	...	...	...	...	...	
Ruffec	...	...	...	...	8 35	12 7	5 54	8 45		...	...	...	...	17 0	15 28	...	19 53	22 19	...	...	...	...	22 40	1 30	...	...	
Saint-Saviol..................	...	...	...	...	...	12 29	6 17	9 6		...	11 31	...	...	17 26	15 43	...	20 29	...	...	...	...	...	...	...	...	...	
Couhé-Verac	...	...	...	...	...	12 56	6 42	9 32		...	...	...	...	17 50	16 6	...	21 1	E	...	...	...	...	...	SC	...	...	
St. Benoit	...	...	...	...	...	13 41	7 26	10 18	...	...	...	...	...	18 32	...	...	21 52	...	...	...	...	...	...	...	...	...	
Poitiers 38, 42A arr	...	4 45	...	...	9 27	13 47	7 33	10 25	...	...	12 15	...	14 1	18 38	16 36	16 53	21 59	23 15	...	...	...	...	23 32	2 26	...	...	
Poitiers 38, 42A dep	...	4 51	5 0	...	9 33	14 22	7 48		...	10 38	12 22	...	14 6		17 6	16 58		23 23	...	18 0	...	20 33	23 39	2 36	...	...	
Les Barres	...	...	5 37	...	...	15 6	8 33	...	...	11 18	...	...	...	...	...	...	...	...	...	18 41	...	21 14	...	...	...	...	
Châtellerault	...	...	5 52	...	10 0	15 27	8 49	...	...	11 34	12 50	...	...	...	17 40	...	...	23 54	...	18 55	...	21 31	0 10	3 8	...	...	
Port-de-Piles	...	...	6 27	...	...	16 13	9 26	...	...	12 12	...	...	...	...	18 4	...	...	0 14	...	19 33	...	22 14	0 30	...	...	...	
Ste.-Maure	...	...	6 45	...	...	16 37	9 43	...	...	12 32	...	...	...	...	18 19	...	...	...	...		...	22 32	...	...	...	...	
Villeperdue	...	...	7 1	...	...	17 2	10 1	...	...	12 50	...	...	...	...	...	...	...	E	...	...	...	22 50	...	...	...	...	
St. Pierre des Corps	...	6 10	...	...	10 55	...	...	...	...	...	13 47	...	15 16	...	18 48	18 4	...	...	...	...	...	...	1 10	4 8	...	...	
Tours ....arr	...	6 30	7 29	...	11 9	17 36	10 32	...	...	13 22	14 5	...	15 32	...	19 8	18 19	...	0 56	...	...	...	23 20	1 28	4 28	...	...	
NANTES ......39 dep	...	...	...	6 15	...	...	...	9 27	...	...	...	...	12 40	...	16 18	...	...	...	...	...	...	21 29	21 29	0 42	0 42	...	
ANGERS......39 dep	...	...	...	7 29	...	...	...	10 59	...	11 27	...	...	13 48	...	17 30	...	...	...	...	...	...	22 50	22 50	2 6	2 6	...	
Tours ¶ ....dep	5 13	6 2	7 45	8 46	10 46	...	11 9	12 31	9 0	14 17	13 42	...	15 10	17 4	18 52	17 54	20 12	...	...	19 20	...	0 17	1 1	4 0		...	
St. Pierre des Corps......	5 21	6 17	7 52	9 0	11 2	...	11 18	12 45	9 7	14 25	13 55	...	15 24	17 12	19 11	18 9	20 24	...	...	19 32	...	0 33	1 21	4 14	3 45	...	
Vouvray.........................	5 36	...	...	...	...	...	11 33	...	9 23	14 39	...	...	...	17 25	...	...	...	...	...	19 48	...	...	...	...	...	...	
Amboise	5 59	...	8 14	...	...	...	11 59	13 6	9 49	14 58	...	...	...	17 44	RC	...	20 46	...	...	20 12	...	0 53	...	D	...	...	
Onzain..........................	6 24	...	8 32	RC	...	...	12 26	13 24	10 17	15 20	...	...	...	18 6	...	...	21 5	...	...	20 42	...	...	...	SC	F	...	
Blois 36	7 3	G	8 51	...	...	...	12 52	13 44	10 42	16 10	14 43	...	...	18 49	20 0	...	21 25	...	...	21 3	...	1 25	2 9	5 1	...	...	
Ménars	7 15	...	...	...	...	...	13 4	...		16 23	...	...	...	19 0	...	...	21 37	...	...		...	...	...	...	SC	...	
Beaugency	7 48	...	9 25	...	...	...	13 38	14 17	...	16 58	...	...	...	19 30	...	...	22 7	...	...	...	...	...	2 36	5 28	...	...	
Meung-sur-Loire	7 59	...	9 35	...	...	...	13 49	14 26	...	17 10	...	...	...	19 41	...	...	22 16	...	...	...	...	...	...	...	...	...	
Les Aubrais..................	...	7 43	9 54	10 20	12 28	...	...	14 45	...	...	15 31	...	16 40	...	20 48	19 22	22 42	...	...	...	...	2 16	3 0	5 52	5 16	...	
Orleans ....arr 1,2,3	8 30	7 59	10 9	10 32	12 40	...	14 20	14 56	...	17 42	15 46	...	16 51	20 10	20 58	19 33	22 54	...	...	...	...	2 30	3 19	6 8	5 29	...	
Orleans ¶ ....dep 8 0	8 45	7 36	9 49	10 12	12 22	10 47		14 38	...	18 37	15 22	17 22	16 34		20 32	19 16	22 37	22 48	...	...	...	2 9	2 56	5 46	5 10	5 35	
Les Aubrais............8 6	8 58	7 49	10 1	10 24	12 33	10 53	...	14 51	...	18 43	15 37	17 29	16 45	...	20 55	19 26	22 55	23 2	...	...	...	2 23	3 9	6 0	5 22	5 41	
Toury 8 49	...	...	10 28	...	...	11 44	...	15 17	...	19 53	...	18 27	...	...	...	...	23 24	23 52	...	...	...	2 49	...	...	...	6 47	6 20
1	2	3	4	5	6	7	8	9	10	11	12	13	14	15	16	17	18	19	20	21	22	23	24	25	26	27	28

1		2	3	4	5	6	7	8	9	10	11	12	13	14	15	16	17	18	19	20	21	22	23	24	25	26	27	28
Etampes 35B	9 33	...	...	10 59	...	...	12 36	...	15 45	...	20 39	16 28	19 17	...	...	21 44	...	23 55	0 40	...	...	...	3 20	4 0	...	...	7 45	...
Bretigny	10 7	...	...	RC	RC	...	13 2	...	16 7	...	21 20	...	20 2	RC	...	...	...	0 20	1 13	...	...	...	...	...	...	F	8 29	...
Juvisy	1021	...	...	...	...	...	...	...	...	...	21 39	...	20 32	...	...	RC	...	...	1 43	...	...	...	...	...	...	...	8 58	...
Vitry	...	...	...	...	...	...	...	...	...	...	21 59	...	20 52	...	...	...	...	...	2 4	...	...	...	...	...	...	...	...	...
PARIS Q. Austerlitz	1040	10 32	9 27	11 45	11 56	14 6	13 32	...	16 34	...	22 10	17 15	21 2	18 7	...	22 35	20 45	0 51	2 16	...	...	...	4 14	4 46	7 49	7 3	9 17	8 5
PARIS Pt. St. Michel	1046	...	...	11 51	...	...	13 38	...	...	...	22 15	...	21 7	...	...	...	...	...	...	...	...	...	...	...	...	...	9 23	...
PARIS Quay d'Orsay	1050	10 41	9 36	11 55	12 5	14 15	13 43	...	16 43	...	22 19	17 25	21 11	18 16	...	22 44	20 54	1 1	...	...	...	...	4 24	4 56	7 58	7 12	9 27	8 15

Extra							
Bordeaux B......dep	13 14	17 9	21 31	...	...	...	...
Libourne.........arr	14 15	18 16	22 29	...	...	...	...

A—Takes 3rd class only when coming from or going to Branch Lines, or, between Angoulême and Paris, travelling not less than 94 miles.

B—Takes 3rd class when coming from or going to Branch Lines, or when travelling not less than 94 miles; exceptionally will admit at Angoulême 3rd class for Poitiers and beyond, and at Poitiers those for Tours.

C—Takes 2nd class travelling at least 125 miles, and 3rd class travelling at least 187 miles, or when coming from or to Branch Lines. Also admits 2nd and 3rd class for Beaugency, and at Beaugency 2nd and 3rd cl. for Paris.

D—Takes 3rd class only when coming from or going to Branch Lines, or when travelling not less than 94 miles. At Bordeaux will not take up for Libourne or Coutras or branches.

E—Runs from 1st August until 8th October only.

F—Sets down only on the running shown in this table.

G—2nd class must be travelling not less than 125 miles.

X—Sleeping Car Co.'s "Sud Express." Take tickets in advance.

Z—Cote d'Argent Express, Train de Luxe. Runs until 3rd November.

¶—Passengers for **Tours** should note whether they must change at **St. Pierre des Corps**, and those for **Orléans** whether they must change at **Les Aubrais**; the Express Trains not always running into **Tours** and **Orléans**.

‡—Until 9th Oct.]

PARIS, BRETIGNY, and DOURDAN.

Paris Quai d'Orsay dep	5 40	7 2	7 55	8 36	10 6	1228	...	1340	1457	17 1	1718	1756	1837	1956	2032	2136	23 9	...
,, Austerlitz...dep	5 50	7 14	8 5	8 47	10 17	1239	...	1351	15 5	1712	1729	18 7	1848	20 7	2043	2144	2321	...
Juvisy	6 25	7 36	8 41	9 5	10 38	1259	...	1413	1536	1731	1751	...	19 5	2026	...	2213	24 0	...
Bretigny ....arr	6 53	7 52	9 6	9 17	10 53	1314	1327	1443	16 3	1747	1817	1838	1926	2039	2112	2239	0 50	...
Dourdan ....arr	7 47	8 30	10 7	9‡41	11 42	1339	14 6	1538	1649	1825	19 4	1922	2015	2124	2137	2318	1 20	...

Dourdan...dep	4 17	5 46	6 47	7 44	8 32	9 31	1050	1132	1215	13 0	1442	1621	1654	1723	2015	2117	2157	0 56	...
Bretigny...dep	4 55	6 31	7 31	8 28	9 12	9 55	1131	1214	13 1	1346	16 1	1713	1720	1814	2120	22 2	2222	1 32	...
Juvisy	5 20	6 56	7 57	...	9 37	...	1157	1243	1328	1416	1628	1739	...	1840	2139	2221	...	2 5	...
Paris Austerlitz	5 53	7 16	8 16	8 58	9 56	1022	1220	13 2	1347	1438	1645	1758	1747	1859	2210	2240	2252	2 36	...
,, d'Orsay arr	6 2	7 26	8 26	9 8	10 6	1032	1228	1312	1357	1448	1653	18 7	1756	19 9	2219	2250	23 2	...	...

ETAMPES and AUNEAU.

E.M.							
	Etampes ....dep	7 57	12 15	16 52	19 33	...	...
20½	Auneau 37.......arr	8 52	13 50	17 47	20 25	...	...
...	Auneau ....dep	6 27	9 32	14 34	20 57	...	...
...	Etampes 34.......arr	7 20	10 25	16 5	21 52	...	...

ANGOULEME and THIVIERS.

Angoulême dep	5 2	...	1057	17 0	...
Le Quéroy-Pranzac	5 30	...	1125	1732	...
Marthon	5 50	...	1144	1754	...
Nontron	6 29	9 27	1216	1846	...
St. Pardoux-R. 30A	6 41	9 41	—	19 1	...
Thiviers 39A arr	7 14	1018	...	1939	...

Thiviers ....dep	6 26	1129	...	2030	...	...
St. Pardoux-la-Riviere	7 1	1211	...	21 3	...	...
Nontron	7 20	1239	1838	2117	...	...
Marthon	7 53	1316	1916	—	...	...
Le Quéroy-Pranzac	8 13	1338	1938	...	...	...
Angoulême 41B arr	8 42	14 9	20 6	...	...	...

HAUTEFORT and SARLAT.

Hautefort dep	5 55	...	10 25	...	1830	...
Terrasson	6 33	7 11	11 17	14 26	19 8	2033
Condat	—	7 22	—	14 39	—	2045
Sarlat 38......arr	...	8 26	...	16 28	...	2148

Sarlat...........dep	5 27	9 0	...	18 26	...
Condat	6 32	10 39	...	19 41	...
Terrasson	7 5	10 48	15 15	19 50	2051
Hautefort 35B arr	7 45	...	16 10	...	2131

SARLAT and GOURDON.

Sarlat...........dep	9 12	13 29	20 43	...	...
Gourdon 32 ...arr	9 52	14 19	21 21	...	...
Gourdon.........dep	7 36	10 58	17 42	...	...
Sarlat 35B .....arr	8 17	11 51	18 21	...	...

PORT DE PILES and LE BLANC.

E.M						
	Port de Piles...........dep	6 42	12 20	...	1411	1842
13	Le Grand Pressigny (30A)...	7 27	12 47	...	1449	1914
31¾	Tournon St. Martin	8 28	13 33	1435	1543	2021
41¾	**Le Blanc** (38) ....arr	9 0	13 58	15 5	1616	2047

Le Blanc ....dep	6 7	9 2	16 0	1950	...	...
Tournon St. Martin	6 36	9 35	1630	2024	...	...
Le Grand Pressigny	7 26	1028	1716	2129	...	...
Port de Piles (34)...arr	7 54	11 8	1741	2159	...	...

CHATELLERAULT and LE BLANC.

E.M.				
	Chatellerault ...dep	6 52	13 5	1925
14½	Pleumartin	7 38	1351	2010
28½	Tournon-St. Martin ...	8 13	1429	2048
38½	**Le Blanc** (32) ...arr	9 0	15 5	2114

Le Blanc..............dep	6 39	13 2	1925	...
Tournon-St. Martin	7 20	13 36	1955	...
Pleumartin	8 8	14 25	2045	...
Chatellerault (34) .. arr	8 40	15 5	2117	...

BOURGES and COSNE.

E.M.					
	Bourges...........dep	6 53	12 2	18 0	...
13¾	Les Aix d'Angillon ...	7 27	1236	1835	...
33½	Sancerre	8 19	1327	1926	...
42½	**Cosne 58** ....arr	8 41	1349	1948	...
...	**Cosne** ....dep	7 9	1410	1927	...
...	Sancerre	7 36	1436	1953	...
...	Les Aix d'Angillon ...	8 30	1525	2016	...
...	**Bourges 37** ......arr	9 1	1555	2117	...

THIVIERS and BRIVE.

Thiviers.........dep	6 32	11 12	16‡55	1957
Excideuil	7 18	11 48	17 31	2035
Hautefort 35B	7 54	12 12	17 53	2058
Le Burg	8 51	13 9	—	2144
Brive (32) ....arr	9 16	13 33	...	22 4

‡—Until 9th Oct.

Brive..............dep	...	7 50	13 45	...	17 28
Le Burg	...	8 11	14 8	...	17 57
Hautefort	6 12	9 12	14 55	15 ‡1	18 53
Excideuil 30A	6 34	9 42	—	15 28	19 18
Thiviers ....arr	7 11	10 25	...	16 7	19 56

PENNE and TONNEINS.

Station									
Penne......dep	7 20	8 43	13 0	1355	1541	18 25	1938	2038	2148
Villeneuve-s-Lot	7 43	9 3	1315	1417	1558	18 50	1959	2052	2211
Ste. Livrade	7 57	9 17	—	1431	1610	19 11	2013	—	2223
Tonneins 45B	8 43	...	...	...	1652	19 57	...	...	23 1

Station								
Tonneins dep	...	6 49	...	12 25	...	1750	...	2030
Ste. Livrade ...	5 40	7 31	1152	13 6	1445	1832	1940	21 7
Villeneuve-s-Lot	5 56	7 50	1211	13 21	15 2	1854	1958	2120
Penne 39A arr	6 10	8 5	1226	13 35	1516	19 9	2015	2133

BORDEAUX and LE BUISSON.

E.M.	**Bordeaux—**									
—	(Bastide) ......dep		5 17	7 19	1113	1314	1117	16 1	17 9	1752
16¾	Vayres..................		6 4	...	12 0	14 1	...	...	18 1	...
22¼	**Libourne** 36......		6 46	8 2	1219	1415	1456	1638	1843	1833
27¼	Saint Emilion......		7 0	8 17	1231	—	1512	1650	1859	—
33½	Castillon..............		7 24	8 33	1253	...	1536	17 5	1922	...
41	Velines.................		7 46	...	1315	...	1559	...	1945	...
46½	Ste-Foy-la-Grande		8 9	8 58	1332	...	1619	1732	20 3	...
52¼	Gardonne..............		8 23	...	1344	...	1632	...	2017	...
60¼	**Bergerac** ...	4 56	8 49	9 30	1418	...	1655	18 6	2039	...
73¼	Lalinde	5 32	—	10 3	1450	...	—	1837	—	...
83¼	**Le Buisson**	6 4	...	1032	1519	...	...	19 7	...	...

Station								
Le Buisson dep	...	6 32	...	1051	1545	...	1941	...
Lalinde	...	7 2	...	1123	1616	...	2014	...
Bergerac 35 ...	5 0	7 40	8 19	12 3	17 8	1717	2017	...
Gardonne..........	5 21	...	8 43	1229	...	1745	—	...
Ste-Foy-Grande..	5 34	8 6	9 1	1242	1735	1758	...	...
Velines............	5 52	...	9 17	1259	...	1814	...	...
Castillon	6 14	8 31	9 40	1331	18 7	1837	...	...
Saint Emilion.....	6 33	8 45	9 59	1352	1825	1857	...	...
Libourne dep	6 49	9 3	1022	1413	1850	1917	...	...
Vayres	7 5	...	...	1428	...	1933	...	...
Bordeaux arr	7 53	9 45	11 1	1515	1931	2021	...	...

ST. SULPICE, MONTLUÇON, and GANNAT.

*—From 10th Oct.] [‡—Until 9th Oct.

Station											
St. Sulpice dep	3 5	...	5 45	9 5	...	11‡3	1413	...	19 0	22 8	1 24
Vieilleville ...	3 30	...	6 25	9 37	...	...	1449	...	1937	2245	...
Guéret (36) ...	4 0	...	7 24	1019	...	1157	1529	1713	2027	2325	2 13
Busseau......	4 22	4 36	8 0	1058	...	1217	1558	1735	2057	2348	2 32
Parsac...........	...	5 23	8 40	1132	...	...	1631	—	2128	—	...
Lavaufranche	5 5	6 0	9 10	1159	...	...	17 3	...	2156	...	...
Huriel............	5 29	—	9 41	1226	...	...	1729	...	2223	...	...
Montluçon	5 47	...	10 1	1245	...	1324	1748	...	2242	...	3 39

Station					‡			
St. Germain dep	2 34	...	5 3	10 19	1325	1513	18 9	20 20
Gannat ...dep	4 24	...	7 36	11 16	1352	1635	1840	21 3
St. Bonnet 42B...	4 39	...	8 8	11 33	...	1642	19 2	...
Bellenaves	4 56	...	8 37	11 47	...	1658	1925	21 29
Lapeyrouse	5 24	7 12	9 35	12 20	1444	1730	20 9	21 54
Commentry 42B	5 50	7 42	1019	12 50	15 7	18 0	21 1	22 17
Chamblet-Néris	7 57	7 50	1029	12 58	1514	18 8	21 9	...
Montluçon ar	6 8	8 3	1047	13 10	1525	1818	2122	22 34

Station				‡	*	‡					
Montluçon	6 18	8 19	...	1315	1347	1352	1820	...	...	...	3 47
Chamblet-N...	6 33	8 39	...	1332	14 0	14 7	1838	...	...	...	...
Commentry....	6 44	8 52	...	1347	14 9	1416	1853	...	...	...	4 8
Lapeyrouse 36	7 10	9 29	...	1420	1435	1440	1923	...	...	...	4 32
Bellenaves ...	7 51	10 9	...	1527	15 5	...	20 3	...	...	...	...
St.Bonnet de R	8 7	1026	...	1542	1518	...	2020	...	...	...	...
Gannat 59 ar	8 25	1045	...	16 0	1533	1553	2038	...	...	...	5 19
St. Germ. arr	9 10	1134	...	1644	1644	1644	2132	...	...	...	6 7

Station						‡			
Montluçon dp		6 34	8 36	...	13 39	1533	19 0	...	22 43
Huriel..............		7 3	9 1	...	14 3	...	1927	...	...
Lavaufranche 35		7 36	9 37	...	14 30	16 9	1958	...	...
Parsac		8 4	10 6	...	14 56	...	2025	...	...
Busseau..	4 19	8 41	1050	1456	15 26	1650	21 3	...	23 53
Guéret.........	5 14	9 18	1126	1519	15 53	1711	2133	...	0 15
Vieilleville	5 56	10 4	1213	—	16 30	...	2217	...	...
S. Sulpice	6 30	1036	1245	...	17 0	1758	2251	...	1 2

LA CHATRE and GUERET.

Station					
La Chatre...dep	6 23	11 10	1833	...	...
Bonnat	7 51	12 54	20 1	...	...
Gueret 36 ...arr	8 42	13 51	2051	...	...

Station					
Gueret ....dep	5 27	14 8	1725	...	...
Bonnat	6 22	15 0	1826	...	...
La Chatre 38 ......arr	7 52	1929	20 8	...	...

BUSSEAU D'AHUN and USSEL.

Station							
Busseau-d'Ahun dep	4 39	8 45	1050	1742	2116	2356	...
Lavaveix-les-Mines......	4 52	8 58	11 2	1754	2128	0 8	...
Aubusson	5 25	9 38	1140	1826	2158	0 33	...
Felletin	5 54	10 1	12 3	1845	—	—	...
Mas-d'Artiges	6 54	1053	1254	1935	...	...	...
Ussel 32.............arr	8 12	1149	1344	2025	...	...	...

‡—Until 9th Oct.

Station							
Ussel..............dep	...	6 15	...	1158	1757	...	...
Mas-d'Artiges.........	...	8 8	...	1255	19 1	...	...
Felletin..................	...	9 19	‡	1337	1951	2240	...
Aubusson	3 33	9 50	1131	14 5	2013	23 1	...
Lavaveix-les-Mines	3 57	1017	1155	1434	2040	2326	...
Busseau-d'Ahun	4 10	1031	12 5	1447	2051	2338	...

Station							
Vieilleville ......dep	6 30	12 19	15 15	19 55	22 52	...	...
Bourganeuf......arr	7 23	12 54	16 12	20 28	23 25	...	...

Station								
Bourganeuf ......dep	5 15	11 26	13 31	18 50	21 12	...	...	...
Vieilleville 36......arr	5 49	11 59	14 39	19 24	22 0	...	...	...

LAPEYROUSE, VOLVIC, and CLERMONT-FERRAND.

†—Until 30th Sept.]

E.M.	Station							
	Lapeyrouse ....dep	7 15	9 53	1240	1450	1750	1940	22 0
5¼	St. Eloy..........................	7 36	1020	13 7	1511	1814	20 4	2225
16¼	St. Gervais-Chateauneuf ...	8 14	—	—	1548	—	2040	—
35¼	Volvic	9 18	...	...	1653	...	2146	...
44¾	Royat	9 42	...	...	1720	...	2213	...
47¾	Clermont-Ferrand 31A arr	9 52	...	...	1730	...	2223	...

Station								
Clermont-Ferr. dep	4 25	...	9 18	...	...	...	1735	...
Royat	4 39	...	9 34	...	...	...	1749	...
Volvic....................	5 14	...	10 9	...	...	...	1824	...
St.Gervais-Chatea.	6 18	...	1113	...	16†2	...	1930	...
St. Eloy	6 50	8 44	1145	1352	1634	1645	20 3	21 19
Lapeyrouse 36 arr	7 8	9 10	12 5	1419	...	17 9	2022	2143

ORLEANS and MALESHERBES.

Station								
Orléans............dep	...	5 18	...	11 59	...	1755	20 32	...
Neuville-aux-Bois......	...	6 3	...	12 47	...	1838	21 18	...
Pithiviers.................	4 59	6 30	8 0	13 24	1658	1911	21 48	...
Malesherbes (56) ar	5 33	...	8 33	13 57	1734	1949	...	...

Station							
Malesherbes...dep	7 25	9 38	...	1427	1755	0 35	...
Pithiviers...............	8 1	10 10	11 16	1511	1810	1 2	...
Neuville-aux-Bois ...	8 30	—	11 47	1545	1925	—	...
Orléans..........arr	9 14	...	12 29	1632	2020	...	...

VILLEFRANCHE-SUR-CHER and BLOIS.

Station									
Villefranche dep	5 0	7 9	8 43	10 12	1147	1335	1522	1749	20 5
Romorantin	5 14	7 24	8 54	10 23	12 1	1349	1536	18 6	2019
Fontaine-Soings	—	7 52	—	—	1231	—	—	1843	—
Vineuil-St.-Claude		8 22	...	...	13 2	...	...	1917	...
Blois 34 ....arr		8 43	...	...	1324	...	...	1939	...

Station									
Blois...........dep	5 7	...	...	...	1055	...	...	1745	...
Vineuil-St.-Cl...	5 29	...	...	...	1121	...	...	18 6	...
Fontaine-Soings	6 0	...	...	...	12 0	...	...	1841	...
Romorantin	6 38	8 3	9 30	1111	1258	1438	1714	1914	2032
Villefranche arr	6 47	8 20	9 47	1128	1312	1455	1731	1927	2045

AUBIGNE and SABLE.

E.M.	Station				
	Aubigne.......dep	5 20	8 11	13 17	18 11
21¾	**La Flèche**	6 14	9 8	18 9	19 49
41¾	**Sablé** 75 ....arr	...	10 14	17 23	20 45

Station							
Sablé..............dep	4 48	8 55	...	...	18 8	...	...
La Flèche..........	6 45	9 58	11 50	16 6	19 3	21 8	...
Aubigné ....arr	7 37	...	12 45	17 11	...	22 0	...

CAPDENAC and AURILLAC.

§—Until 5th Sept.] [‡—From 6th Sept.

Station							
Capdenac......dep	7 3	10 55	16§25	16§25	21 24	...	...
Figeac	7 16	11 9	16 39	16 39	21 37	...	...
Maurs..................	7 46	11 41	17 14	17 12	22 9	...	...
Viescamp-s-Jallés	8 42	12 41	18 17	18 14	23 5	...	...
Aurillac 31A...arr	9 1	13 2	18 38	18 35	23 26	...	...

Station									
Aurillac ....dep	4 21	8 26	13 32	18 14	...	...	...	...	...
Viescamp-s-Jallé	4 43	8 49	13 57	18 39	...	...	...	...	...
Maurs................	5 44	9 42	14 55	19 36	...	...	...	...	...
Figeac	6 19	1013	15 30	20 10	...	...	...	...	...
Capdenac 32ar	6 30	1024	15 41	20 21	...	...	...	...	...

SAILLAT & ST. YRIEIX

E.M.	Station						
	Saillat-Chassenon 35 dep	...	6 44	...	1345	1811	...
16¾	Champagnac	...	7 56	...	1437	19 0	...
28	Bussière-Galant	7 27	8 46	12 3	1511	1933	2052
42¼	St. Yrieix 32............arr	8 24	...	1337	...	...	2147

Station					
St. Yrieix ....dep	...	5 44	8 57	...	1745
Bussière-Galant	3 55	6 39	1040	1610	1925
Champagnac	4 29	...	1127	1644	...
Saillat-Chassenon arr	5 18	...	1239	1734	...

VIERZON, MONTLUCON, and LAQUEUILLE.

‖—Until 9th October. §—Until 29th Sept. ‡—Until 20th September.

Dist E.M		1,2,3	1,2,3	1,2,3	1,2,3	1,2,3	1,2,3	1,2,3	1,2,3	1,2,3	1,2,3	1,2,3	1,2,3	1,2,3
	PARIS Orsay 32 dep	2230	2230	2230	...	...	0 35	7 10	8 30	10 0	14 0	16 3	1950	2043
	Vierzon ......dep	1‡44	1 55	2 42	...	...	8 5	1050	1117	1416	1752	1931	2310	2345
9¼	Mehun-s-Yevre	:	2 20	...	...	...	8 28	1111	‡	1439	1815	1952	2333	...
19¼	**Bourges (38)**...arr	:	2 42	3 11	...	...	8 52	1132	1146	15 1	1837	2013	2357	0 14
...	**Bourges** ......dep	:	3 39	3 20	...	7 14	9 39	12 0	...	1525	1846	2143	0*23	:
41¾	Nérondes	:	4 35	...	...	8 13	1038	1257	...	1622	1953	2239	1 *1	:
56	**Saincaize** ......arr	SC	5 17	4 18	...	8 51	1120	1332	...	17 3	2035	2315	1*27	:
...	**Bourges** ....dep	:	3 24	—	4 45	—	1011	12 3	1152	15 9	1845	—	0 35	0 24
23½	Saint Florent (33)...	:	3 49	...	5 26	...	1040	1235	1213	1538	1914	...	0 59	...
47¼	St. Amand Mont 42B	:	4 35	...	6 30	...	1138	1333	1248	1540	2018		—	1 14
72¾	Les Trillers	:	5 27	...	7 32	...	1234	1429	..	1740	2114		...	...
78¼	**Montluçon**......arr	3 34	5 39	...	7 48	...	1250	1444	1332	1755	2129		...	1 56
97½	LAPEYROUSE 36 ar	4 32	7 10	...	9 29	...	1420	...	1440	1923	—		...	4 32
142¼	ROYAT 36 ......arr	...	9 42	...	—	...	1720	...	1720	2213	...		...	...
...	**Montlucon** ...dep	3 53	6 25	...	...	...	—	15‡2	1343	1837	...		2§21	2 3
95¾	Evaux	...	7 14	...	...	...	...	1558	1421	1931	...		2 58	...
107	Auzances	4 50	7 41	...	...	1128	...	1630	1444	20 1	...		3 21	3 0
118	Letrade	...	8 16	...	...	1218	...	1710	1510	2036	...		...	3 24
136	Eygurande-M.	6 3	9 31	6 26	...	1333	1641	1810	1551	2130	1953		4 19	4 1
149¾	**Laqueuille** 37 arr	6 38	1012	7 7	...	1441	1718	...	1641	...	2031	...	...	...

*—Mon., Tues., and Fri. only.

	1,2,3	1,2,3	1,2,3	1,2,3	1,2,3	1,2,3	1,2,3	1,2,3	1,2,3	1,2,3	1,2,3	1,2,3	1,2,3	1,2,3
Laqueuille ...dep	...	...	...	...	7 9	8 44	10‡54	1320	13‡20	1510	...	1759	21‡32	2152
Eygurande	...	...	...	4 49	7 46	9 55	1124	1446	14 31	1610	...	20 5	22 18	2237
Letrade	...	...	...	5 55	—	1048	—	1550	15 11	...	...	2119	...	2319
Auzances	...	...	...	6 36	...	1123	...	1632	15 35	1719	...	2157	23 17	2343
Evaux	...	...	...	7 13	...	1155	...	17 2	15 57	...	...	—	...	0 5
Montluçon ... arr	...	...	...	8 11	...	1245	...	1750	16 30	1813	...	...	0 8	0 38
ROYAT..........dep	...	...	...	4 39	...	9 34	...	—	...	...	...	...	—	1749
LAPEYROUSE dep	...	5 24	...	7 12	...	1220	...	...	14 44	1730	...	1730	...	2154
Montluçon .. dep	...	6 13	...	8 11	...	1333	...	14 2	16 40	1828	...	1854	...	0 48
Les Trillers..........	...	6 28	...	8 36	...	...	...	1419	...	:	...	1910	...	...
St. Amand-Mont ...	...	7 19	...	9 33	...	1424	...	1534	17 24	:	...	2016	...	1 33
Saint Florent	...	8 12	8 58	1029	1233	15 5	1521	1643	...	A	...	2112	...	...
Bourges ....arr	...	8 31	9 26	1056	13 0	:	1551	1711	18 15	:	...	2136	...	2 24
Saincaize ...dep	4 44	...	8 17	...	1226	:	—	1547	...	:	1835	1956	21 32	...
Nérondes	5 20	...	8 57	...	1258	:	...	1627	...	:	1913	2037	...	...
Bourges arr......	6 10	...	9 47	...	1334	:	...	1717	...	:	1954	2129	22 27	...
Bourges.........dep	6 50	8 38	10 4	1124	1344	:	...	1726	18 23	:	20 9	2158	22 35	2 33
Mehun-s-Yevre	7 11	...	1028	1145	14 5	:	...	1749	...	:	2029	2222	...	...
Vierzon ....arr	7 32	9 7	1049	12 6	1424	1514	...	1810	18 52	2010	2050	2243	23 6	3 2
PARIS 33 ......arr	1041	12 5	...	1612	1816	1914	...	2225	22 25	23 7	2354	3†37	3†37	6 7

Extra.						
Vierzon...dep	13 6	17‖25	2110	Bourges...dep	9‖55
Bourges...arr	1350	17 54	2157	Vierzon ...arr	1024

A—Admits 2nd class travelling 124 miles, and 3rd class travelling at least 186 miles, or for or from beyond Montlucon. †—At Austerlitz Station.

LAQUEUILLE to LA BOURBOULE and MONT-DORE.

‡—Runs until 20th September.

E.M														
	Laqueuille dep	6‡50	7 35	9‡12	11‡15	...	1332	15‡2	16‡48	...	18‡5	20‡42	22 2	...
2½	St. Sauves	6 59	7 44	9 21	11 24	...	1341	1511	16 59	‡	1814	20 51	2211	...
5¼	La Bourboule......	7 20	8 1	9 40	11 41	13‡10	14 0	1528	17 15	1755	1832	21 9	2227	...
8¾	**Mont-Dore** arr	7 34	8 15	9 53	11 55	13 24	1414	1542	17 29	18 8	1846	21 22	2241	...

Mont-Dore ...dep	6 10	7‡47	9‡24	1215	12‡35	13‡41	14 22	16‡23	17‡30	1935	20‡46	...
La Bourboule	6 28	8 8	9 42	1236	12 48	13 59	14 40	16 42	17 43	1954	21 4	...
St. Sauves	6 41	8 21	9 56	1249	—	14 13	14 53	16 58	—	20 7	21 17	...
Laqueuille 37 arr	6 49	8 29	10 4	1257	...	14 21	15 1	17 6	...	2015	21 25	...

MONTLUCON and MOULINS.

Montluçon ...dep	6 4	8 34	1338	1843
Commentry	6 28	9 7	1359	1913
Doyet La Presle	6 42	9 22	1410	1928
Villefranche d'A.......	6 57	9 33	1420	1940
Chavenon	7 12	9 52	1433	1958
Souvigny..............	7 55	1042	1514	2050
Moulins 58 ......arr	8 11	11 2	1530	2111

Moulins ....dep	5 32	8 36	1122	16 0	1922	...
Souvigny................	5 52	8 55	1139	1617	1912	...
Chavenon	6 41	9 54	1221	17 0	2040	...
Villefranche 42B......	6 58	1014	1233	1714	2054	...
Doyet La Presle	7 12	1032	1245	1726	2110	...
Commentry	7 33	1056	13 1	1742	2132	...
Montluçon 38 arr	7 53	1116	1320	18 0	2152	...

MONTAUBAN and LEXOS.

Montauban (V. B.)	6 31	11 0	1634
,, (V. N.)	6 42	1112	1618
Bruniquel	7 22	1153	1729
Lexos (32) ......arr	8 12	1245	1824

Lexos ....dep	8 56	1315	18 55
Bruniquel............	9 45	14 5	19 45
Montaub (V.N.)	10 28	1447	20 31
,, (33) (V.B.)	10 37	1456	20 40

PARIS to TOURS viâ VENDOME.

Dist E.M	Paris—												
	Quai d'Orsay...dep	...	...	7 2	8‡36	10 6	12 28	...	17 1	1956	20 32	23 9	23 44
	Austerlitz ......dep	...	...	7 14	8 47	10 17	12 39	...	17 12	20 7	20 43	23 21	23 58
22¼	Bretigny	...	...	7 55	9 19	10 56	13 16	1327	17 50	2041	21 14	0 45	0 40
37¼	Dourdan	...	6 29	8 32	9 43	11 47	13 42	1415	18 28	2148	21 39	1 24	
50¼	Auneau 35B...........	...	7 1	9 3	...	12 28	14 5	1445	18 58	2217	22 1	1 54	—
64	Voves	...	7 45	9 34	...	13 15	14 28	—	19 54	—	22 22	2 23	
85½	Châteaudun	6 0	8 32	10 23	1055	14 7	15 22	18 5	20 56	...	23 0	3 13	
101¼	Freteval................	6 43	—	10 58	...	—	16 0	1847	21 36	...	...	...	
111¾	Vendome	7 15	...	11 41	1131	...	16 30	1936	21 59	...	23 45	4 6	
121¼	St. Amand-de-Vend.	7 39	...	12 2	—	...	16 50	1958	—	...	0 3	4 27	
130½	Châteaurenault 87...	8 7	...	12 26	...	...	17 13	2026	...	...	0 19	4 48	
144¼	Nôtre-Dame-d'Oé ...	8 45	...	12 59	...	...	17 46	21 4	...	...	0 45	5 18	
148	**Tours** 38 ....arr	9 16	...	13 27	...	...	18 16	2135	...	...	1 5	5 43	

‡—Runs until 9th October.

Tours.............dep	...	...	5 30	...	8 48	...	13 10	...	15 23	17 27	20 45
Nôtre-Dame-d'Oé ...	...	...	6 3	...	9 22	...	13 35	...	15 54	18 0	21 14
Châteaurenault	...	...	6 35	...	9 58	...	14 1	...	16 31	18 34	21 42
St. Amand-de-Vend.	...	...	6 57	...	1024	...	14 17	...	16 55	18 56	22 0
Vendome	...	...	7 20	8 10	1050	...	14 38	...	17 26	19 29	22 21
Freteval	...	...	7 37	8 35	1116	...	14 54	...	17 51	19 51	22 42
Châteaudun............	5 42	...	8 10	9 25	1213	...	15 28	...	18 45	20 41	23 21
Voves....................	6 33	...	8 46	10 20	1322	...	16 6	...	19 53	...	0 3
Auneau..................	7 10	8 45	9 9	10 59	14 5	15 49	16 29	...	20 36	...	0 27
Dourdan.................	7 44	9 13	9 31	11 32	1442	16 18	16 54	1723	21 17	21 57	0 56
Bretigny..................	8 28	—	9 55	12 14	1530	—	17 20	1814	22 2	22 22	1 32
Paris Austerlitz arr	8 58	...	10 22	13 2	16 2	...	17 50	1858	22 40	22 52	2 36
,, Q. d'Orsay arr	9 8	...	10 32	13 12	1612	...	18 1	19 8	22 50	23 2	...

AURAY and QUIBERON.

‡—Until 9th Oct.

Auray......dep	6‡51	8‡8	1023	13‡24	14‡30	17‡17	18‡47	20 49	...	...	...
Plouharnel Car	7 16	8 33	1046	13 47	14 52	17 40	19 11	21 15	...	...	...
Quiberon arr	7 38	8 55	11 8	14 9	15 15	18 2	19 33	21 37	...	...	...
Quiberon dep	6‡48	8‡3	12‡10	13 0	15‡21	17‡13	1846	20‡50	...	...	...
Plouharnel Car	7 15	8 31	12 35	13 28	15 48	17 39	1913	21 19	...	...	...
Auray 31 ...arr	7 35	8 51	12 55	13 50	16 8	17 59	1934	21 38	...	...	...

NANTES and CHATEAUBRIANT

Châteaubriant dep	6 17	11 14	1652	2024	**Nantes**.........dep	8 26	12 21	1622	1954
Abbaretz................	6 56	11 53	1735	2113	Sucè	8 57	12 52	1653	2025
Sucè.......................	7 36	12 32	1817	2152	Abbaretz	9 38	13 33	1734	2111
Nantes 39 ....arr	8 7	13 4	1851	2222	**Châteaubriant**	1017	14 12	1813	2150

‡—Until 9th October.]

TOURS and LE MANS.

Tours ...dep	1 40	6 6	11 16	12‡33	1544	18 10	20 20
Mettray	2 1	6 33	11 44	12 54	16 9	18 38	20 46
Neuillé-Pont-Pierre (37)	2 19	6 56	12 10	13 11	1631	19 4	21 16
Château-du-Loir 42	2 42	7 29	12 43	13 33	17 6	19 34	21 54
Aubigné 36	2 58	7 49	13 7	13 50	1728	—	22 23
Mayet	3 9	8 2	13 24	...	1748	...	22 41
Le Mans 30 ...arr	3 42	8 47	14 14	14 28	1845	...	23 33

Le Mans ...dep	2 6	...	6 51	9 ‡0	12 7	16 48	21 11
Mayet	2 43	...	7 36	...	12 50	17 44	21 56
Aubigné	3 0	...	7 55	9 40	13 5	18 2	22 15
Château-du-Loir	3 21	5 34	8 20	9 54	13 31	18 29	22 36
Neuillé-Pont-Pierre	3 49	6 8	8 56	1018	14 6	19 5	23 10
Mettray	4 9	6 31	9 18	1034	14 28	19 26	23 31
Tours 35A ...arr	4 28	6 57	9 41	1051	14 50	19 51	23 50

TOURS and VIERZON.

Tours ...dep	446	5 2	7 37	11 2	1446	15‡16	1533	16 40	20 0	2256	0 27
Veretz	...	522	7 58	1124	1510	...	...	17 2	2020	2316	...
Chenonceaux	529	554	8 34	1155	—	...	1615	17 39	2052	2347	...
St. Aignan-Noyer	6 9	—	9 15	1241	...	16 23	1658	—	2138	—	1 39
Villefranche-s-C.	7 1	...	10 2	1329	...	16 54	1753	19‡36	2229	...	2 10
Vierzon (37) ...arr	735	...	1036	14 4	...	17 20	1832	20 10	23 5	...	2 36

Vierzon ...dep		325	7 52	10‡32	11 5	1433	...	1918	23 12
Villefranche-s-C.		427	8 29	11 0	1142	15 9	...	1957	23 43
St. Aignan-Noyer		555	9 13	...	1223	1548	...	2046	0 16
Chenonceaux	4 16	656	9 55	...	13 2	1626	1848	2130	...
Veretz	4 43	731	1037	...	1330	...	1939	22 7	...
Tours 34 ...arr	5 2	752	1059	12 26	1349	17 6	1959	2227	1 15

TOURS and MONTLUÇON.

Tours ...dep		5 38	8 7	11 7	1334	1635	20 28	23 1
Montbazon		6 11	8 39	...	14 5	17 9	21 0	2330
Esvres (30A)		6 23	8 48	1139	1415	1719	21 9	2340
Loches		7 13	9 31	1213	1459	18 5	21 56	0 9
Châtillon-s-Indre		7 51	9 59	1239	1530	1838	22 27	—
Buzancais		8 29	10 33	13 4	1610	1913	23 1	...
Châteauroux ...arr		9 6	11 13	1332	1645	1957	23 35	...
„ dep	5 1	9 57	—	—	17 8	—	—	0 51
Mers	5 34	10 28	...	...	1744	...	...	1 22
La Châtre	6 1	11 1	...	...	18 7	...	...	1 41
Champillet (35)	6 23	11 28	...	...	1830	...	...	—
Chateaumeillant	6 35	11 39	...	...	1843	...	...	...
Courcais	7 22	12 24	...	...	1925	...	...	...
Montluçon 37	7 55	12 59	...	...	20 6	...	...	...

Montluçon ...dep		...	6 21	...	1453	19 18	...
Courcais		...	6 58	...	1531	19 57	...
Chateaumeillant		...	7 42	18 14	1614	20 38	...
Champillet-Urciers		...	7 55	18 29	1626	20 52	...
La Châtre		3 46	8 16	—	1649	21 22	...
Mers		4 3	8 35	...	17 9	21 41	...
Châteauroux 32 arr		4 34	9 9	...	1748	22 12	...
„ dep		6 7	10 51	14 59	1841	0 53	...
Buzancais		6 50	11 32	15 41	1933	1 27	...
Châtillon-s-I		7 28	12 3	16 19	2019	1 57	...
Loches	6 5	8 7	12 41	16 57	2112	2 28	...
Esvres	6 47	8 49	13 22	17 46	2153	3 3	...
Montbazon	6 56	9 1	13 33	17 59	22 1	3 11	...
Tours 35A ...arr	7 23	9 34	14 7	18 34	2228	3 40	...

LIMOGES and LE DORAT.

E.M.					
	Limoges-Béné dep	4 0	8 7	12 50	17 41
10	Nieul	4 27	8 35	13 26	18 12
18¾	Vaulry	...	9 5	14 0	18 45
26¾	Bellac	5 11	9 27	14 26	19 10
34¾	**Le Dorat** 38 ...arr	5 33	9 50	14 49	19 35

Le Dorat dep	6 0	12 1	15 20	20 14
Bellac	6 27	12 29	15 52	20 41
Vaulry	6 49	12 51	16 14	21 3
Nieul	7 22	13 29	16 50	21 34
Limoges B. arr	7 51	13 57	17 21	22 3

LE BUISSON and ST. DENIS PRES MARTEL.

Le Buisson dep	...	6 38	...	1058	1532	1942	...
Sarlat 35B	6 50	7 33	...	1158	1640	2054	...
Souillac	7 56	—	1010	1250	18 2	2145	...
St. Denis 31A	8 31	...	1140	1326	1840	...	...

St. Denis-Martel ...dep	...	...	6 54	...	12 14	...	...	20 1
Souillac	...	5 52	7 29	8 0	12 48	1310	...	2058
Sarlat	4 55	6 40	—	9 17	—	1422	1832	2151
Le Buisson ...arr	5 51	...	...	10 9	...	1521	1925	...

MONSEMPRON-LIBOS and CAPDENAC.

Monsempron-Libos ...dep	...	7 48	...	1518	21 9
Puy-L'Evêque	...	8 22	...	1550	2139
Cahors (32) arr	...	9 19	...	1642	2231
„ dep	7 11	—	1331	1829	—
St. Gery	7 49	...	14 8	19 7	...
Cajarc	8 48	...	15 1	1950	...
Capdenac 38 ar	9 34	...	1548	2029	...

Capdenac ...dep	...	...	7 28	1044	...	1731
Cajarc	...	...	8 4	1122	...	1816
St. Gery	...	...	8 48	12 2	...	1910
Cahors ...arr	...	...	9 18	1232	...	1944
„ ...dep	6 3	7 28	—	1240	1852	—
Puy-L'Evêque	6 58	9 11	...	1334	1958	...
Monsempr'n-L. ar	7 29	1011	...	14 4	2033	...

POITIERS and ST.-SULPICE-LAURIERE.

‡—Until 9th October.

E.M.						
	Poitiers ...dep	3 27	8 ‡5	9 9	12 27	17 39
7½	Mignaloux-N.	3 46	8 21	9 31	12 49	18 2
13¾	Fleuré	...	...	9 49	13 8	18 20
25½	Lussac-les-Chât.	4 26	8 58	10 20	13 40	18 52
33¾	Montmorillon	4 47	9 15	10 45	14 7	19 18
51½	Le Dorat 38	5 39	9 55	11 39	15 4	20 20
64	Château-Ponsac	6 12	1019	12 14	15 39	20 54
78½	St. Sulpice L. arr	6 48	1047	12 51	16 17	21 30

St. Sulpice-L. dep	4 18	8 36	14 0	18 55
Château-Ponsac	4 55	9 14	1434	19 30
Le Dorat	5 40	9 56	15 7	20 12
Montmorillon	6 26	10 42	1552	21 1
Lussac-Chât. 35	6 47	11 2	1616	21 21
Fleuré	7 20	11 31	1646	21 49
Mignaloux-N.	7 40	11 50	17 4	22 9
Poitiers 34 ...arr	7 57	12 7	1722	22 26

Le Dorat ...dep	6 2	10 10	1517	2033
Magnac-Laval ...arr	6 16	10 24	1531	2050

Magnac-Laval ...dep	5 12	9 29	1435	1915
Le Dorat ...arr	5 27	9 45	1450	20 0

POITIERS, LE BLANC, and ARGENTON.

‡—Tues., Thurs., and Sat.

Poitiers ...dep	6 0	7 ‡0	10 20	...	17 20
Mignaloux-Nouailli	6 23	8 29	10 36	...	17 37
Chauvigny	7 1	9 52	11 12	...	18 10
St. Savin	7 34	—	11 47	...	18 42
Le Blanc 39A ...arr	8 13	...	12 22	...	19 16
„ ...dep	9 5	...	12 33	1627	21 44
Ciron	9 24	...	12 53	1649	22 6
Argenton 32 ...arr	9 59	...	13 31	1729	22 45

Argenton ...dep	6 2	...	13 2	18 6	20 45
Ciron	6 46	...	13 41	18 48	21 22
Le Blanc ...arr	7 10	...	14 2	19 13	21 43
„ ...dep	7 27	...	14 8	19 32	—
St. Savin	8 10	...	14 48	20 16	...
Chauviguy	8 45	10‡44	15 18	20 53	...
Mignaloux N. ...arr	9 23	11 27	15 54	21 31	...
Poitiers 34 ...arr	9 52	11 48	16 11	21 51	...

Argenton ...dep	8 56	14 50	19 48	...	...	...
La Chatre (38) ...arr	10 25	15 40	21 9	...	...	...

La Chatre ...dep	6 34	10 55	18 13	...	...
Argenton (38) ...arr	8 21	12 11	19 29	...	...

RODEZ and CAPDENAC.

‡—Until 10th Oct.

Rodez ...dep	4 44	8 10	1116	1343	1847	22§33
St. Christophe	5 33	8 57	12 3	1432	1933	23 23
Cransac	6 1	9 22	1228	1458	1958	23 45
Viviez	6 19	9 38	1245	1515	2017	24 0
Capdenac 38 ...arr	6 45	10 3	1310	1541	2044	0 20

[§—Until 9th Oct.

Capdenac dep	4‡49	6 43	1111	1627	21 25
Viviez	5 13	7 15	1140	17 0	21 54
Cransac	5 28	7 35	1158	1719	22 11
St. Christophe	5 56	8 8	1229	1746	22 40
Rodez ...arr	6 47	9 11	1322	1839	23 38

ETAMPES and BOURGES.

Etampes ...dep	...	5 32	8 17	10 3	1411	1616	1941
Pithiviers	...	6 42	9 11	1111	15 6	1731	2056
Auxy ...dep	5 8	...	...	1134	15 0	1826	...
Beaune-la-Rolande	5 28	7 22	9 46	1155	1540	1846	2139
Bellegarde-Quiers (35)	5 43	7 36	10 1	1218	16 2	1919	2154
Les Bordes	6 34	9 22	1044	1318	17 4	2018	2233
Argent (38) ...arr	7 18	—	1127	14 5	1750	21 7	2317
Aubigny	7 44	...	1147	1431	1819	2138	—
Henrichemont	8 25	...	1227	...	19 3	—	...
Bourges (37) ...arr	9 8	...	13 9	...	1947	...	...

Bourges ...dep	...	...	6 15	...	1020	...	...	1645
Henrichemont	...	...	7 1	...	11 5	...	...	1735
Aubigny	...	5 30	7 42	...	1146	1354	...	1826
Argent	...	5 45	7 57	...	1211	14 9	...	1858
Les Bordes (35)	...	6 47	8 45	10 2	1259	15 5	1819	20 7
Bellegarde-Quiers	...	7 39	9 26	1045	—	1555	1920	2050
Beaune-la-Rolande	5 50	7 58	9 45	11 2	...	1618	1943	2114
Auxy ...arr	...	8 34	...	1120	...	1637	...	2127
Pithiviers	6 36	8 30	1021	—	...	17 2	2025	2155
Etampes 35B) ...arr	7 33	9 25	1121	...	...	18 2	2131	2232

ARGENT and GIEN.

E.M.						
	Argent ...dep	8 4	14 25	18 43	...	...
14½	Gien 58 ...arr	8 40	15 24	19 19	...	...

Gien ...dep	6 5	11 21	1656	...	...
Argent 30A ...arr	7 11	11 59	17 34	...	...

Excess Luggage, 1 cent. per 44 lbs. per kilometre.] **ORLEANS RAILWAY.**

TOURS to SAUMUR, ANGERS, NANTES, and LE CROISIC.

Station																					
PARIS Orsay 34 dep		2210	...	...	23 44	...	2344	2344	0 35	7 50	9 0	9 46	9 46	11 5	...	14 0	1615	...	1826	2110	2120
		1,2,3	1,2,3	1,2,3	1,2,3	1,2,3	1,2,3	1,2,3	1,2,3	1,2,3	1,2,3	1 Cl.	1,2,3	1,2,3	1,2,3	1,2,3	1,2,3	1,2,3	1,2,3	1,2,3	1,2,3
Tours ....dep		1 48	...	...	5 4	...	6‡18	6 50	1039	11 22	11 55	1231	13 1	1434	...	1750	1920	21 1	2247	0 27	0‡42
St. Pierre des Corps		...	...	...	...	...	...	...	...	11 44	12 11	1254	...	1452	...	...	1944	...	...	0 44	1 3
Savonnières		...	...	...	5 22	...	...	7 11	11 0	...	...	...	1319	...	...	1811	...	2122	...	...	...
Langeais		2 15	...	...	5 41	...	...	7 29	1120	12 6	‡	...	1331	1517	...	1832	20 6	2141	2311	...	1 27
Port Boulet 42A		2 39	...	...	6 11	...	...	8 1	1153	...	...	...	1355	1539	...	19 9	2024	2215	2332	...	1 50
Saumur 42		3 0	...	...	6 41	...	7 20	8 29	1350	12 38	13 3	1342	1413	16 1	...	1942	2042	2240	2356	1 35	2 12
La Menitré		3 22	...	...	7 10	...	...	9 2	1431	12 56	...	...	→	1626	...	2018	...	—	0 17	...	2 33
Angers 41A ... arr		3 47	...	...	7 44	...	8 3	9 37	1517	13 16	13 39	1415	...	1652	...	2055	2117	...	0 40	2 11	2 56
Angers 41A ... dep		4 8	...	5 39	8 33	8 10		9 54	1547	13 23	13 46	1423	1431	1711	19 0	2134	2123	...	—	2 20	3 6
Possonnière 42A		4 26	...	6 5	8 59	8 26	—	1024	1614	13 39	14 2	...	1454	1738	1935	2157	...	...	...	...	3 23
Varades		4 52	...	6 44	—	...	...	11 9	1656	...	...	...	—	18 0	2017	2320	...	...	...	D	3 49
Ancenis		5 8	...	7 4	...	9 4	...	1131	1717	14 18	14 38	A	...	1814	2042	2345	22 6	...		...	4 3
Clermont-sur-Loire		...	...	7 22	...	...	...	1150	1736	...	...	...	...		21 3	—	...	...	Extra.—Nantes to St. Nazaire, 16.18.	...	...
Mauves		...	...	7 34	...	...	...	12 3	1748	...	‡	...	...	1833	2116	...	...	...		...	...
Thouaré		...	...	7 41	...	...	...	1212	1756	14 40	...	...	...	...	2125	...	...	...		...	...
Nantes 41 arr	1,2,3	5 40	...	7 55	...	9 35		1229	1812	14 50	15 7	1526		1847	2142	...	2235			3 33	4 34
Nantes 41 dep	5 17	5 58	7 0	8 32	9 21	9 50	1245	1327	—	14 59	15 15	1533	19 7	1920	—	1726	—	2240		3 46	4 46
Savenay 31...arr	6 28	6 48	8 10	9 27	10 28	10 45	1355	1439	...	15 50	16 6	1621	20 0	2030	...	...	...	...		To Landerneau	...
Montoir 39	—	7 14	8 44	9 52	—	11 16	—	1513	...	...	...	...	‡	21 9	...	...	...	‡			...
St. Nazaire ......arr		7 23	8 54	10 1	13 29	11 26	...	1523	...	16‡17	16 33	1652	2031	2117	...	1831	...	2351			5 57
Pornichet		7 59	9‡26	1032	13 54	11‡54	...	16 1	...	—	17 3	1723	2111	—	...	19 5	...	—			6 28
Escoublac-la-B.		8 6	9‡32	1039	14 1	12‡1	...	16 7	...	...	17 8	1729	2118	...	...	1912	...	5‡46			6 35
⁝ Guérande 39 ...arr		8 29	9‡55	11 0	14 30	12 19	...	1635	...	...	18 0	18 0	2155	...	...	1934	...	5 56			6 55
Le Croisic ....arr		8 36	9‡59	11 4	14 33	12‡26	...	1634	...	...	17 37	1755	2152	...	...	1941	...	...	...		7 14

Station																						
	1,2,3	1,2,3	1,2,3	1,2,3	1,2,3	1,2,3	1,2,3	1,2,3	1 Cl.	1,2,3	1,2,3	1,2,3	1,2,3	1,2,3	1,2,3	1,2,3	1,2,3	1,2,3		1,2,3	1,2,3	1,2,3
Le Croisic...dep	...	...	...	5‡13	...	7 0	7 39	...	10§20	1131	1332	...	...	1520	...	17 8	...	18‡43	...	21 7	22‡3	From Landerneau
⁝ Guérande dep	...	6‡17	...	5 11	...	7 5	...	9‡11	10 16	1131	1333	...	...	1522	...	1651	...	18 46	...	21 3	21 3	
Escoublac-la-B	...	6 31	...	5 36	...	7 27	8 12	9 25	10 45	12 2	14 2	...	...	1547	...	1740	...	19 13	...	2134	2233	
Pornichet	...	—	...	5 44		7 36	8 23	—	10 53	1212	1411	...	...	16 2	...	1750	...	19 21	...	2146	2242	
St. Nazaire dep	...	...	...	6 4	6 12	8 8	8 56	...	11 23	1243	1441	...	...	1630	...	1824	...	19 41	1948	2215	23 9	
Montoir	...	...	...	—	6 21	...	9 10	...	...	1253	1450	...	...	1638	...	1833	...		1956	2224	...	
Savenay	...	...	...	...	6 53	...	9 45	...	...	1334	1520	...	...	17 5	1719	19 1	1911	—	2029	2258	...	
Nantes ... arr	...	...	...	...	7 59	9 17	11 0	...	12 28	1448	1610	...	...	18 3	1829	20 2	2020	...	2114	2353	0 14	0 32
Nantes ... dep	...	...	6 15	6 23	8 13	9 27	1150	...	12 40	15 2	1618	...	1738	1940	—	2030	—	...	2129	—		0 42
Thouaré	...	...	...	6 37	8 28	...	12 4	...	...	1513	...	...	1753	1955	...	...	...	...	...	...	—	...
Mauves	...	...	...	6 45	8 36	...	1213	...	...	...	...	...	18 1	20 3	...	...	...	...	...	...	...	...
Clermont sur L.	...	...	...	6 56	8 48	...	1224	...	B	...	‡	...	1813	2015	...	...	...	...	C	...	...	...
Ancenis	...	...	6 40	7 15	9 9	9 57	1313	...	...	1539	...	...	1836	2033	...	21 0	...	...	...	...	...	1 11
Varades	...	...	...	7 32	9 28	1010	1331	...	...	...	...	...	1854	—	...	2113	...	...	...	...	...	...
Possonnière	...	...	...	8 17	1012	1036	1417	...	...	1621	...	...	1942	...	...	2143	...	...	...	...	...	...
Angers ... arr	...	...	7 22	8 42	1038	1051	1442	...	13 43	1637	1724	...	20 8	...	...	2159	...	...	2242	...	...	1 58
Angers ... dep	...	6 31	7 29	9 24	1127	1059	1454	...	13 48	1647	1730	1830	—	...	...	22 7	...	...	2250	...	...	2 6
La Menitré	...	7 5	...	10 1	1157	...	1531	...	...	1710	...	19 6	...	...	...	2230	...	...	...	...	...	...
Saumur	5 44	8 11	8 3	1040	1233	1139	1616	...	14 21	1736	18 4	1950	...	...	...	2256	...	...	2329	...	...	2 44
Port Boulet	6 8	8 36	...	11 5	1256	1156	1614	...	...	1755	...	2020	...	...	...	2314	...	...	...	...	...	...
Langeais	6 41	9 14	...	1140	1328	...	1724	...	...	1816	...	21 0	...	...	...	2334	...	...	...	...	...	...
Savonnières	6 57	9 33	...	1157	1343	...	1747	...	...	...	...	2119	...	...	...	...	...	...	...	...	...	...
St. Pierre Corps	...	...	8 52	...	...	1237	...	...	15 10	...	1855	...	...	...	...	...	...	...	0 23	...	...	3 38
Tours 35A ...arr	7 17	9 54	9 9	1218	14 2	1256	18 8	...	15 32	1810	19 8	2142	...	...	...	2358	...	...	0 40	...	...	3 58
PARIS ......arr	1155	1415	12 5	1643	1816	1643	2244	...	18 16	2244	2244	...	...	...	...	4 24	...	...	4 24	...	...	7 12

A—At Angers admits 2nd class coming from connecting lines.

B—Down to Saumur also admits 2nd class for Vierzon and beyond.

C—Admits 3rd class travelling 62 miles or from or for branch lines.

D—Between Paris and Nantes admits passengers for Nantes and beyond only.

§—From 10th October runs 20 minutes earlier between Le Croisic and St. Nazaire.

‡—Until 9th October only.

ANGERS and LA FLÈCHE.

E.M.												
	Angers ....dep	4 45	8 57	1355	1749	La Flèche ...dep	6 29	1143	16 1	19 14	...	...
13	Seiches	5 21	9 36	1433	1826	Seiches	7 15	1229	16 47	20 0	...	...
30½	La Flèche ...... arr	6 7	10 27	1520	1912	Angers 39......arr	7 50	13 7	17 25	20 38	...	...

LA FLECHE and LA SUZE.

E.M.												
	La Flèche.........dep	6 26	9 59	17 32	...	...	La Suze......dep	8 54	16 16	2010	...	...
19¼	La Suze (75)......arr	7 18	10 51	18 26		...	La Flèche ...arr	9 45	17 10	21 1	...	...

SAUMUR and LA FLECHE.

E.M.															
	Saumur..............dep	4 50	8 36	1439	19 45	...	...	La Flèche ......dep	6 20	10 41	16 0	17 39	...	...	...
33	La Flèche (39)......arr	6 10	9 54	1555	20 58	...	...	Saumur (39) ...arr	7 36	12 7	1719	18 56	...	...	...

‡—Not on Sunday. **ST. NAZAIRE and LA ROCHE BERNARD.**

St. Nazaire ....dep		8 14	1015	11 47	13 45	1536	17 0	1853	La R. Bernard dep	450	...	...	...	...	...	...	16 0	...
Trignac	7 25	8 27	1029	12 1	13 57	1547	1714	19 7	Herbignac..........	548	...	...	...	...	...	...	1628	...
Montoir 39.........	7 35	8 44	—	12 41	14 10	1556	1728	1923	Montoir ......dep	712	925	...	...	13 28	...	16 0	1733	...
Herbignac	—	10 0	...	—	—	—	—	2044	Trignac	726	936	1058	1230	13 38	15 0	16 9	18 4	...
La Roche Bernard arr		1021	...	...	...	...	...	21 5	St. Nazaire 39 arr	741	950	1112	1245	...	1514	1620	1818	...

Herbignac......dep	5 20	1520	...	...	Guérande ......dep	8 40	1840	...	...
Guérande 39...arr	6 45	17 0	...	...	Herbignac......arr	9 57	2025	...	...

LA POSSONNIÈRE and LA ROCHE ST. JEAN de LINIÈRES.

La Possonnière.................dep	7 35	10 15	14 21	...	La Roche St. Jean de L.......dep	9 42	14 31	16 57	...	...	...
La Roche St. Jean de L. (83) arr	8 6	10 46	14 53	...	La Possonnière (39) ....arr	10 11	15 1	17 26		...	...

Excess Luggage, 1 cent. per 44 lbs. per kilometre.] **ORLEANS RAILWAY.**

COUTRAS, PERIGUEUX, and BRIVE.

BORDEAUX (Bastide) 35A dep	...	...	6‡32	...	6 45	...	12‡10	1417	16 1	...	20‡34	20‡34	2247	...
Coutras ......dep	...	...	7 25	...	7 47	...	13 20	1527	1714	...	21 29	21 50	2313	...
Mussidan (35)	5*16	...	A	...	8 52	...	14 25	1626	1811	1853	22 4	22 46	0 23	...
Périgueux ...arr	6 11	...	8 29		9 42	...	15 23	1719	1845	2030	22 37	23 38	1 0	
LIMOGES 39A arr	—	...	1012		1220	...	17 47	—	2155	—	0 31	1 28	...	
Périgueux ...dep	...	5 27	—	8 38	1014	13 2	—	...	19 5	...	—	—	1 7	
Niversac............	...	5 44	...	B	1031	13 21	...	...	1923	...	...	...	1 20	
Thenon	...	6 22	...	...	1111	14 9	...	...	20 8	...	...	...	...	
Condat	...	6 45	...	9 36	1134	14 34	...	...	2034	...	...	...	2 6	...
Brive 32,33 arr	...	7 24	...	10 6	1214	15 26	...	...	2119	...	...	...	2 37	...

*—Sun. and Wed. only.

Brive ....dep	1 46	...	...	6 27	...	10 7	13 3	...	...	1832	...	18 55	...	...
Condat..............	2 19	...	...	7 9	...	1047	1343	...	...	19 4	...	19 40	...	...
Thenon	...	...	...	7 35	...	1113	14 8	...	...	B	...	20 6	...	...
Niversac..............	3 11	...	...	8 12	...	1152	1416	...	...	...	...	20 45	...	...
Périgueux ......arr	3 24	...	...	8 28	...	12 8	15 2	...	...	20 9	...	21 1	...	...
LIMOGES ....dep	—	1 50	2 25	5 45	...	—	...	14 35	*		18 42	18 42	...	...
Perigueux ......dep	...	3 48	5 5	8 41	10 35	...	1510	17 33	1825		20 24	21 23	2355	...
Mussidan	...	...	6 2	9 16	11 32	...	16 5	18 30	1919	...	A	22 17	1 0	...
Coutras ....arr	...	4 52	7 3	9 49	12 29	...	17 1	19 31	—	...	21 25	23 14	1 58	...
BORDEAUX 35 arr	...	5 54	8 49	11 1	13 37	...	1819	21 32	...	...	22 15	0 36	4 13	...

A—Until 9th Oct. B—Until 20th Sept. ‡—From St. Jean Station, Bordeaux.

§—Wed. and Sat. only. **LIMOGES and AGEN.** A—Until 9th Oct.

PARIS Orsay (32) ....dep	19 0	19 50	...	2027	2251	...	8 20	10 0	10 0	...	...	...
Limoges-Bénédictins ...dep	1 50	2 25	...	5 45	9 0	10 47	14 35	1623	18 7	18 42	...	...
Bussière-Galant	...	3 12	...	6 53	10 4	11 58	15 47	17 8	19 42	...	...	...
Thiviers 35B..................	...	3 41	...	7 27	1038	—	16 18	1733	20 17	A	...	...
Périgueux..................arr	3 37	4 17	...	8 20	1130	...	17 9	18 6	21 8	20 15	...	...
„ (39A) ....dep	—	4 33	4 46	8 52	12 0	...	17 25	1813	—	—	...	...
Niversac........................	...	4 46	5 0	9 10	1217	...	17 42	...	...	...	...	...
Mauzens-Miremont	...	...	5 35	9 47	1253	...	18 18	...	A	...	...	...
Le Buisson (36)..................	...	5 40	6 16	1043	1335	...	18 52	1912	19 17	...	...	...
Monsempron (38)..................	...	6 50	7 50	1211	15 7	...	21 5	—	20 13	...	...	...
Penne (36)	...	7 12	8 28	1241	1536	18§38	21 43	...	20 36	...	...	...
Agen (45A) ....arr	...	7 45	9 10	1325	1617	19 26	22 29	...	21 5	...	...	...

Agen ....dep	...	...	...	5 41	7 24	...	13 0	...	18 38	19 54	...	...
Penne	...	...	...	6 27	8 22	...	1348	...	19 30	20 34	...	...
Monsempron........................	...	...	...	6 55	8 53	...	1418	...	20 2	21 4	...	...
Le Buisson (36)	...	...	...	8 22	10 47	...	1551	...	21 34	22 15	...	...
Mauzens-Miremont	...	...	...	8 58	11 33	...	1629	...	22 13	...	...	...
Niversac........................	...	...	...	9 34	12 12	...	17 4	...	22 48	23 11	...	...
Péri- ....arr	...	...	...	9 49	12 28	...	1720	...	23 1	23 23	...	...
gueux ....dep	5 14	...	8 37	10 1	12 44	1545	1853	22 44	—	23 50	...	...
Thiviers........................	6 12	...	A	11 1	13 43	1628	20 6	23 25	...	...	...	...
Bussière-Galant	6 51	8 57	...	11 36	14 22	17 6	2050	...	...	0 52	...	...
Limoges-Bénédictins ...arr	7 48	10 2	1012	12 20	15 14	1747	2155	0 31	...	1 28	...	...
PARIS 33 ....arr	1612	...	...	19 14	22 55	2354	4 46	8 43	...	8 43	...	...

PERIGUEUX and PARCOUL.

Perigueux ....dep	5 23	10 21	...	17 50	...	...	**Parcoul-Med.** dep	7 0	...	12 23	1750	--	...
Lisle	6 6	11 2	...	18 29	...	...	Riberac	8 6	10 20	13 24	1848	19 0	...
Riberac 39A................	7 3	11 30	1452	18 57	19 9	...	Lisle	8 38	11 7	...	...	1929	...
Parcoul-Medillac 35	8 5	...	1545	...	20 4	...	**Perigueux** 30A arr	9 15	11 51	...	...	20 5	...

DOYET LA PRESLE (37) and BEZENET—in 15 min. Doyet La Presle...dep. 7.20, 10.39, 12.56, 14.25, 17.30, 19.38. Bezenet...dep. 6.24, 9.1, 12.25, 13.51, 17.3, 19.5.

VIVIEZ (38) and FONTVERGNE—in 10 min. Viviez dep. 5‡20, 6.21, 7.20, 9.51, 11.50, 12.50, 15.21, 17.5, 20.26, 22.0. Fontvergne...dep. 5.54, 6.43, 9.11, 11.9, 12.22, 14.45, 16.28, 19.49, 21.14, 23‡25.

‡—Until 9th October only.

MONTMORILLON and LE BLANC.

Montmorillon ...dep	6 33	11 6	1953	...	...	...	**Le Blanc** ....dep	9 12	1425	19 43	...	...	...	...
La Trimouille	7 2	11 34	2021	...	...	...	La Trimouille..............	9 49	15 1	20 19	...	...	...	...
Le Blanc (38) ...arr	7 41	12 5	2052	...	...	...	**Montmorillon** ...arr	1012	1529	20 47	...	...	...	...

ANGOULEME and MUSSIDAN.

Angouleme......dep	...	6 3	14 5	16 42	...	...	...	**Mussidan** ......dep	...	9 20	1434	1835	...	...	...	...	...
Ruelle	...	6 14	14 18	16 57	...	...	...	Riberac ...... arr	...	1010	1555	1921	...	...	...	...	...
Magnac Touvre......	...	6 22	14 26	17 4	...	...	...	Riberac ...... dep	6 51	12 5	—	1927	...	...	...	...	...
Laroche-Beaucourt	...	7 2	15 26	17 44	...	...	...	Laroche-Beaucourt	7 56	1315	...	2021	...	...	...	...	...
Riberac ...... arr	...	7 56	16 46	18 40	...	...	...	Magnac Touvre ...	8 39	14 2	...	21 0	...	...	...	...	...
Riberac ...... dep	4 20	1022	17 0	—	...	...	...	Ruelle	8 45	14 9	...	21 6	...	...	...	...	...
Mussidan 35... arr	5 41	1113	17 52	...	...	...	...	**Angouleme**......arr	8 57	1421	...	2116	...	...	...	...	...

ANGOULEME and BARBEZIEUX.

Angoulême-Etat..........dep	5 28	8 28	12 24	17 38	...	**Barbezieux-Etat**...........dep	6 43	11 33	14 47	17 45	...	...
Blanzac	7 8	10 8	14 28	19 36	...	Blanzac	7 42	12 35	15 45	18 39	...	...
Barbezieux-Etat ....arr	8 1	11 1	15 23	20 33	...	**Angoulême-Etat** ....arr	9 19	14 15	17 25	20 25	...	...

BARBEZIEUX and COGNAC.

Barbezieux-Etat...........dep	5 15	11 30	16 43	...	...	**Cognac**.........................dep	8 10	14 38	19 45	...	...	...
Archiac	6 12	12 26	17 47	...	...	**Archiac**	9 50	16 16	21 35	...	...	...
Cognac ....arr	7 39	14 4	19 12	...	...	**Barbezieux**..................arr	10 36	17 12	22 21	...	...	...

Pons ....dep	8 15	15 15	19 35	...	...	Barbezieux ....dep	5 40	12 0	16 43	...	...
Barbezieux 40 ....arr	10 32	17 15	21 38	...	...	Pons 41........................arr	7 27	14 8	18 44	...	...

Pons ....dep	...	9 5	14 50	18 55	...	St. Ciers-sur-Gironde ...dep	5 10	8 40	14 0	17 35	...
La Bergerie	6 35	10 30	15 55	19 50	...	La Bergerie	6 26	10 35	15 56	18 46	...
St. Ciers-sur-Gironde 42B arr	7 57	11 58	17 17	20 58	...	Pons 41........................arr	7 23	11 34	17 5	...	...

STATE RAILWAYS OF FRANCE—(CHEMINS DE FER DE L'ETAT)—[Paris Time kept at all Stations. 30 kilog. of luggage (66 lbs.) allowed free; excess Luggage, 1 centime per 44 lbs. per kilometre.]

CHARTRES and AUNEAU.	E.M									
*—13.6 on Thurs. and Sats.		**Chartres** ...dep	7 32	11*28	19 23	**Auneau** ...dep	9 31	14 31	20 51	...
	7¼	Sours-Nogent-le-Phaye	7 49	11 48	19 41	**Auneau** Ville ...	9 37	14 37	20 56	...
	16¾	**Auneau** Ville ...	8 10	12 11	20 3	Sours-Nogent-la-Phaye	10 1	15 3	21 19	...
	18	**Auneau** (37) ...arr	8 16	12 15	20 9	**Chartres** 42A ...arr	10 16	15 21	21 35	...

PONT DE BRAYE and BLOIS. †—Until 9th October.											
Pont-de-Braye dep	5 50	1027	...	1812	**Blois** ...dep	5 40	7 40	11†16	...	18 4	...
Montoire-s-Loir ...	6 24	1055	...	1847	Vendome ...	6 46	8 55	12 20	1556	1925	...
Vendome (37) ...	7 23	1138	15†51	1935	Montoire (40) ...	—	9 36	—	1636	20 5	...
Blois (34) ...arr	8 22	1240	17 7	2038	**Pont-de-Braye** 42	...	10 0	...	17 2	2031	...

LOUDUN and AIRVAULT												
Loudun ...dep	2 41	8 4	1341	1740	...	**Airvault** ...dep	6 51	1431	1550	22 13	...	...
Arçay ...	...	8 14	1351	1759	...	Moncontour ...	7 40	1453	1614	22 32	...	...
Moncontour de P. ...	3 1	8 37	14 8	1814	...	**Arçay** ...	7 58	1511	1631	22 45	...	...
Airvault (42) ...arr	3 15	9 0	1430	1836	...	**Loudun** (41A) ...arr	8 8	1520	1640	22 54	...	...

BESSE-S-BRAYE and ST. CALAIS.												
Bessé-s-Braye	6 8	1025	12 19	15†4	1823	St. Calais ...dep	8 13	11 8	14†9	1635	21 5	†—Until
St. Calais 86 ..	6 29	1047	12 41	1534	1855	Bessé-s-Braye 42 arr	8 35	1127	1431	17 6	2138	9th Oct.

LOUDUN and CHATELLERAULT.	E.M.								
		Loudun ...dep	8 43	1534	21 26	**Chatellerault** dp	6 16	11 5	1924
	20¼	Lencloitre ...	9 46	1635	22 29	Lencloitre ...	6 50	12 32	20 6
	31½	**Chatellerault** 34	1023	1712	23 6	**Loudun** (41A) arr	7 41	13 26	21 7

*—3rd Class only. **NOGENT-ROTROU and COURTALAIN.**

E.M.											
	Nogent-le-Rotrou ...dep	5 40	7*23	10 36	17 59	Courtalain-St.-Pellerin ...dep	7 45	12 15	14 33	2043	...
28	Courtalain-St.-Pellerin 42...arr	6 59	10 31	12 0	19 27	Nogent-le-Rotrou 80 ...arr	9 19	13 35	16 53	22 6	...

†—Mon., Wed., and Sat. only.] **VELLUIRE and NIORT.** [*—Until 9th October.

Velluire (41) dep	7 2	...	...	1156	13†30	17 4	...	1944	21*36	**Niort** ...dep	...	4 59	6 40	...	1127	...	1659	...
Fontenay-le-Comte	7 21	8 59	10 0	1225	13 53	1725	1811	20 0	21 54	Benet ...	...	5 12	7 37	...	1151	...	1721	...
Benet ...	—	9 33	11 29	13 0	—	—	1852	⋮	—	Fontenay-le-C.	5 15	5 59	8 57	9 51	1237	16 †3	1751	20 15
Niort (42A) arr	...	9 55	12 13	1322	...	...	1921	⋮	...	**Velluire** arr	5 27	6 18	...	1013	1259	16 25	...	20 37

Fontenay-le-Comte ...dep	5 58	13 11	...	18 1	...	20 9	21*59	BRESSUIRE...dep	4 11	...	7 2	13 17	...	...	18 11
Breuil-Barret ...arr	6 46	14 9	...	18 47	...	20 50	22 42	Breuil-Barret..dep	4 40	...	8 2	15 31	...	...	19 15
BRESSUIRE 42A ...arr	7 38	15 58	...	19 46	...	21 21	23 16	Fontenay-le-Comte	5 10	...	8 49	16 26	...	...	20 1

NIORT and RUFFEC.	E.M																
		Niort (42A) ...dep	5 55	1256	17 6	...	...	...	**Ruffec** ...dep	6 17	9 24	1620	...	...	...	...
	20¼	Melle ...	7 6	1353	1817	...	...	...	Melle ...	7 57	11 1	1813	...	...	...	...
	51¼	**Ruffec** (34) ...arr	8 25	1520	1945	...	...	...	**Niort** ...arr	8 53	1159	1917	...	...	...	...

SAUJON and LA GREVE.—ROYAN and SAINTES.

Saujon ...dep	6 *7	8 56	1258	16 46	22 4	**La Grève** ...dep	4‡59	7*34	11 10	1149	18 0	‡—In connection
La Tremblade...arr	6 55	9 47	14 9	17 37	22 56	La Tremblade ...	5 11	7 46	11 35	1456	1825	with steamer.
La Grève ...arr	7 7	10 5	1425	17 50	...	**Saujon** (41A) ...arr	5 57	8 32	12 42	1624	1917	

Royan dep	5 37	5 45	6 9	6 45	...	8 20	10*2	11 4	1233	1254	16 19	16 57	1920	1928	2023	21§24	23*28	...	...	...	...
Saujon ...	D	6 6	6 26	⋮	...	8 44	1015	⋮	1250	1318	16 44	17 14	1933	1948	21 43	22 8	23 43	...	...	...	...
Pons ...	...	7 4	...	A	7 §9	9 51	...	B	...	1431	...	18 16	C	2058	...	...	...	...	...	...	...
Saintes arr	6 7	8 17	7 37	⋮	7 59	10 28	1042	⋮	1343	16 9	17 27	18*51	2012	2126	2118	22 58	0 10	...	...	...	...

Saintes ...dep	4*40	...	6 39	7 14	9 4	11 12	...	1427	14 32	⋮	18 4	⋮	18 9	18 33	21 15	...	21 47	23 10	...	...
Pons 41 ...	...	...	7 46	...	1040	...	...	1522	...	F	C	E	19 42	...	*	21*7	G	C	...	...
Saujon ...	5 12	6 17	8 52	8 2	1142	12 10	12§53	1638	15 12	⋮	18 36	⋮	20 52	19 30	21 48	21 58	...	⋮	...	...
Royan ...arr	5 23	6 36	9 6	8 14	1154	12 24	13 12	1654	15 24	1756	18 47	18 57	21 7	19 46	21 59	22 9	22 20	23 46	...	...

A—From 2nd July until 1st October to Bordeaux (arr. 8 50), not on Sunday.
B—From 2nd July until 6th October to Paris (arr. 18.20).
D—Monday only; runs until 6th October.
E—From Bordeaux (dep. 16.55) until 30th September, not on Sunday.
F—From Paris (dep. 10.55) until 5th October.
C—Until 6th October.
*—Until 7th October.
§—Until 9th October.
G—Saturdays only; runs until 4th October.

CHATEAUNEUF and ST. MARIENS.											
Chateauneuf-s-C. dep	6 10	9 59	1240	16 55	20 29	**St. Mariens** ...dep	6 25	...	13 44	...	20 5
Barbezieux (39A) ...	6 46	11 1	14 2	17 44	21 10	Barbezieux ...	7 43	1047	15 29	18 38	21 45
St. Mariens (41) ...arr	8 0	12 39	...	19 16	...	**Chateauneuf** (41B)	8 21	12 1	16 8	19 29	22 19

SARGE and TOURS. †—Until 9th October.												
Sargé ...dep	4 49	8 50	11 53	17 10	...	**Tours** ...dep	...	7 29	12 1	17 15	19 13	...
Montoire-sur-le-Loir	5 41	9 44	12 32	17 45	...	Chateaurenault arr	...	8 32	13 15	18 19	20 20	...
Chateaurenault arr	6 27	10 26	13 13	18 22	...	Chateaurenault dep	4†52	8 43	13 24	—	20 27	...
Chateaurenault dep	6 39	10 30	13 16	18 25	...	Montoire-sur-le-Loir 40	5 30	9 47	14 17	...	21 13	...
Tours 42A ...arr	7 43	11 36	14 21	19 29	...	**Sargé** (42) ...arr	6 7	10 30	14 56	...	21 48	...

LA ROCHELLE and LA PALLICE.

La Rochelle dep	5 0	6 30	9 59	1314	1637	1822
La Pallice ...arr	5 29	6 59	10 29	1344	17 7	1852
La Pallice ...dep	5 38	7 16	10 39	14 4	1729	19 7
La Rochelle 42A	6 7	7 46	11 9	1434	1759	1937

ILE DE RE.

LA PALLICE ...		7 35	11 5	1730	**Les Portes** ...dep	4 10	7 15	1340	1559
Sablanceaux dep		8 30	11 45	18 5	St. Martin de Ré	5 35	8 43	1521	1715
St. Martin ...	5 40	9 34	12 46	1915	**Sablanceaux** arr	6 29	9 42	1619	...
Les Portes ...	6 58	1058	13 55	2030	LA PALLICE ...	7 7	1027	17 2	...

†-Only when the tide serves.] **ROCHEFORT and LE CHAPUS.**

E.M														
	Rochefort ...dep	7 39	10 13	1334	18 41	...	OLERON-CHATEAU (Stm.)	...	8 30	13 20	1730	...	...
4¼	Tonnay-Charente ...	7 48	10 22	1344	18 50	...	**Le Chapus** ...dep	6 14	9 26	14 37	1818	...	...
21½	Marennes (41A) ...	8 51	11 26	15 3	19 55	...	Marennes ...	6 31	9 43	15 8	1858	...	...
25½	**Le Chapus** ...arr	9 3	11 28	1519	20 7	...	Tonnay-Charente ...	7 27	10 35	16 13	20 0	...	...
...	OLERON-CHATEAU (Stm)	1010	12†15	1610	20 45	...	**Rochefort** (41) ...arr	7 35	10 43	16 21	20 9	...	...

ST. TROJAN and ST. DENIS (Ile d'Oleron).												
St. Trojan ...dep	7 15	9 45	16 0	...	...	**St. Denis**...dep	6 10	1045	15 0	...	...	...
Le Chateau-d'Oleron...	8 5	10 30	1650	...	...	St. Pierre ...	7 11	1145	1557	...	...	...
St. Pierre ...	8 55	11 20	1741	...	...	Le Chateau (40)	8 0	1235	1655	...	...	...
St. Denis ...arr	9 42	12 4	1830	...	...	**St. Trojan** arr	8 30	13 2	1725	...	...	...

St. Pierre ...dep	6 42	15 48	...	...	Boyardville ...dep	8 45	12 50	17 35	...	...
Boyardville ...arr	7 9	16 12	...	...	St. Pierre ...arr	9 10	13 15	18 3	...	...

STATE RAILWAYS.

30 kilog. of luggage (66 lbs.) allowed free; excess Luggage, 1 centime per 44 lbs. per kilometre.

NANTES, LA ROCHE-SUR-YON, SAINTES, and BORDEAUX.

Dist. E.M			1,2,3	1,2,3	1,2,3	1,2,3	1,2,3	1,2,3	1,2,3	1,2,3	1,2,3	1,2,3 (Until 8th October. To Angoulême arr. 21.33)	1,2,3	1,2,3	1,2,3	1,2,3	1,2,3	1,2,3
	Nantes (Etat)......dep		...	...	...	...	6 20	9 5	9 45	...	1251	...	12 57	17 38	18 43	1631	...	22 5
—	Nantes (Orleans) dep		...	...	...	...	6 9	8 56	9 40	...	1233	...	12 44	...	18 36	1628	...	22 1
4¼	Vertou		...	...	...	...	6 41	9 22	10 5	...	...	...	13 15	...	...	1650	...	...
16¾	Clisson (41B)		...	...	...	...	7 23	9 43	10 49	...	A		13 47	...	19 20	1717	...	2253
24¼	Montaigu-Vendée		...	...	...	...	7 45	9 57	11 12	...	...		14 3	...		1737	...	23 9
47¾	La Roche- ......arr		...	...	...	...	8 40	10 35	12 18	...	1357		14 51	18 46	...	1830	...	2357
...	sur-Yon 42A...dep		...	...	4 42	...	9 11	10 45		...	14 0		15 1	18 51	...	1915	...	0 15
70¾	Luçon		...	...	5 46	...	1018	11 25	...	...	...		16 4	...	...	2024	...	1 1
85¾	Velluire (40)		...	5 30	6 34	...	1059	11 51	...	...	...		16 51	...	...	21 9	...	1 30
97	Marans (46A)		...	5 48	7 2	...	1128	12 12	...	...	...		17 22	...	...	2143	...	1 52
111¾	La Rochelle......arr		.	6 12	7 41	...	12 6	12 38	...	...	1529		18 4	...	...	2218	...	2 17
...	,, 42A.........dep		4 52	6 40		9 29		12 51	18*18	14 50	1534	19 0	19 8	...	19 58	22*45	...	2 38
125	S. Laurent la Prée 41B		5 29	7 20	...	10 5	...	...	18 53	15 32	...	...	...	...	20 53	23*21	...	...
129¾	Rochefort.........arr		5 41	7 32	...	1017	...	13 18	19 13	15 44	1559	--	19 40	...	21 8	23*33	...	3 8
...	,, (42A).........dep		5 49	7 49	...	1027	...	13 27		16 8	16 2	19 28	19 50	...	21 24		...	3 17
133½	Tonnay-Charente		5 57	7 58	...	1036	...	13 36	...	16 17	...	...	19 58	...	21 50	...	...	3 27
146¾	Saint Savinien		6 27	8 30	...	1111	...	...	...	16 55	...	...	20 33	...	22 33	...	...	...
151	Taillebourg ....arr		6 35	8 40	...	1120	...	...	...	17 3	...	...	20 41	...	22 45	...	...	...
157½	Saintes (41B) arr	1,2,3	6 52	8 56	...	1143	...	14 9	...	17 31	1637	20 3	20 53	...	23 2	...	...	4 7
...	,, ...dep	4 43	7 1	9 4	9 40	1427	...	14 19	17 59	18 9	1642	...	21 3	...	23 41	...	...	4 29
162¾	Beillant 41B	5 5	7 16	9 22	...	1443	...	...	18 12	18 28	...		21 19	...	0 1	...	...	...
172½	Pons	5 39	7 34	9 49	1029	15 7	...	14 47	18 31	18 59	...		21 41	...	0 36	...	...	4 52
177¾	Mosnac-s.-Seugne	5 59	...	10 3	1050	1521	...	...	...	19 13	...		...	...	...	...	...	...
184	Jonzac	6 27	7 55	1019	1120	1538	...	15 7	18 51	19 35	A		22 4	...	1 11	...	...	5 12
197	Montendre	7 26	8 20	1050	1223	1614	...	15 29	...	20 16	...		22 31	...	1 55	...	...	5 34
207½	St. Mariens (41B)	7 54	8 42	1115	1310	1642	...	15 52	19 32	20 58	...		22 57	...	2 32	5 0	6 41	5 54
210	Cavignac		8 49	1121	1317	1649	...	...	...	21 10	...		...	...	2 43	5 7	6 49	...
218¾	St. André Cubzac		9 5	1149	1347	1710	1837	16 11	19 51	21 40	...		23 18	...	3 11	5 34	7 32	6 12
235½	Bordeaux St. J. arr		9 30	...	...	1749	...	16 36	20 17	22 20	1824	...	...	...	4 51	...	...	6 40
231¾	,, Etat...arr		...	1227	1429	...	1917	.	...	...	...	...	23 48	...	3 56	6 15	8 16	...

To Les Sables (arr. 19.22) on Wed. and Sat. from 12th July; daily (Sun. excepted) from 30th July until 6th September.

		1,2,3	1,2,3	1,2,3	1,2,3	1,2,3	1,2,3	1,2,3	1,2,3	1,2,3	1,2,3	1,2,3	1,2,3	1,2,3	1,2,3	1,2,3	1,2,3 (Until 9th Oct. From Angoulême, dep. 21.45.)	1,2,3
Bordeaux— Etat ......dep		...	...	...	...	6 56	...	...	10 0	1355	...	...	17 2	1812	...	...		...
,, St. Jean dep		...	...	...	5 11	..	8 32	11 41	...	...	1216	1432	...	...	1920	19 5		22 16
St. André-de-Cubzac		...	...	...	5 45	7 38	9 0	...	10 43	1437	13 0	1515	17 34	1857	...	1934		...
Cavignac		...	...	...	6 3	8 4	...	...	11 10		1324	1539	17 57	1924	2015			...
Saint Mariens		...	...	...	6 16	8 19	9 23	A	11 17	...	1336	1553	18 9	1931	2043	1958		23 5
Montendre		...	...	...	6 40	8 45	9 42	...		...	14 5	1619	18 33		2048	2017		...
Jonzac		...	...	...	7 8	9 18	10 1	...	...	...	1440	1644	19 4	...		2036		23 40
Mosnac-sur-Seugne		...	...	...	7 23	9 33	...	...	...	...	1455	1656	19 19	...	...	..		...
Pons		...	...	...	7 42	9 51	10 22	...	...	...	1525	1711	19 37	...	...	2058		23 58
Beillant		...	...	...	8 3	1014	10 39	...	...	...	1553	1730	20 6	...	...	2116		...
Saintes......arr		..	...	...	8 17	1028	10 49	13 15	...	--	16 9	1741	20 22	...	...	2126		0 20
,, ...dep		...	...	6 42	8 29		10 59	13 19	...	1414	1641	19 1		...	...	2148	23 8	0 35
Taillebourg		...	...	6 57	8 45	...	...	...	...	1431	1658	1920	...	...	...	22 1	...	...
Saint Savinien		...	...	7 9	8 56	...	..	...	...	1442	1714	1935	...	...	...	2213	...	...
Tonnay-Charente		...	...	7 43	9 28	...	11 33	...	...	1514	1751	2012	...	...	...	2236		--
Rochefort.........arr		...	...	7 50	9 35	...	11 40	13 53	...	1521	1759	2021	...	...	...	2243	23 45	1 13
,, ...dep		...	...	8 3	9 44	...	11 45	13 55	13 12	1530	1843	2029	..	...	...	2250	...	1 21
St. Laurent de la Prée		..	...	8 20	10 4	...	...	...	13 27	1547	1858	2045	20† 4	...	...	..	...	...
La Rochelle......arr		..	...	8 53	1036	,,	12 11	14 19	13 58	1625	1932	2119	20†31	*	...	2321	0 14	1 48
,, ...dep		..	5 35	9 8		...	12 24	14 23	15 17	1850	20 1			2043	...			2 6
Marans		...	6 16	9 54	...	...	12 51	...	16 4	1920	2036	...	...	2112	...	...	...	...
Velluire (Font. C.)		...	6 46	1032	...	...	13 13	A	16 40	1937	21 8	...	...	2129	...	...	...	...
Luçon			7 30	1123	...	...	13 38	...	17 29		2141	...	...		...	...	...	3 10
La Roche-sur- arr		7 53	8 37	1222	...	...	14 25	15 53	18 38	...	2233	...	...	...	...	...	...	3 50
Yon ....dep	6 6	7 56	8 57	1246	...	...	14 41	15 55	19 19	1720	2248	...	...	...	...	...	...	4 4
Montaigu-Vendée	6 58	...	9 54	1340	...	...	15 16	...	20 15	1811	2332	...	...	...	...	...	...	...
Clisson (41B)	7 24	...	10 20	14 2	1237	17 7	15 52	...	20 42	1832	2351	1841	...	...	...	...	...	4 55
Vertou	7 58	...	10 56	1436	1259	1742	15 54	...	21 16	1854	0 14	1914	...	...	...	...	...	...
Nantes Orleans arr	8 17	...	11 17	1454	1318	18 4	16 11	17 16	21 38	1911	0 31	1931	...	...	...	...	...	5 35
Nantes (Etat)..arr	8 14	9 0	11 14	1453	1316	18 0	16 10	17 0	21 32	19 9	0 30	1930	...	...	...	...	...	5 33

From Les Sables (dep. 7.20) on Mon. and Fri. from 18th July; daily (Sun. excepted) from 31st July until 8th September.

A—Until 2nd November.

*—Until Oct. 9. †—Until Oct. 7. §—Until Nov. 15.

Extra.			
Bordeaux (E.)	6§49	17†21	1812
St. Mariens ...	7 43	18 9	1932
Rochefort ...	13†12	16*52	
La Rochelle	14 2	17 50	
La Rochelle			
Rochefort ...			
Nantes (Etat) dep	16 0	2048	
Clisson ......arr	1651	2138	

BORDEAUX and LA POINTE-DE-GRAVE.

Dist E.M	Bordeaux—								
	(St. Louis).........dep	6 29	8 25	9 46	1234	17 2	...	18 8	...
15½	Margaux	7 19	8 59	1035	1323	1728	...	1855	...
25½	St. Laurent St. J.	7 44	...	11 6	1349	..	...	1920	...
29¼	Pauillac	7 58	9 27	1115	14 2	1754	18 4	1932	...
32¼	St. Estèphe	8 10	9 39		1414	...	1816	1944	...
41¾	Lesparre 42B	8 38	1014	...	1441	1819	1842	2020	...
57¾	Soulac-les-Bains	9 28	1059	...	1530	1849	1926	21 9	...
62¼	Le Verdon	9 38	11 9	...	1540	1858	1935	2118	...
64	Pointe-de-Grave ...arr	9 46	1117	...	1547	19 6	...	...	...

Pointe-de-Grave dep	...	...	8 40	1428	1823	19 3	...
Le Verdon	5 5	6 53	8 49	1437	1832	1936	...
Soulac-les-Bains	5 16	7 5	9 1	1448	1847	1945	...
Lesparre	6 5	7 35	9 54	1541	1940	2017	...
St. Estèphe	6 28	...	1018	16 4	20 4	...	...
Pauillac	6 42	8 1	1032	1619	21 0	2043	...
St. Laurent St. J.	6 52	...	1042	1628	2110	...	...
Margaux	7 22	8 24	1110	1653	2136	21 7	...
Bordeaux St. L. ...arr	8 10	8 51	1157	1744	2223	2140	...

Margaux ...dep	9 10	13 30	19 10	...	...
Avensan	9 24	13 47	19 28	...	...
Castelnau ...arr	9 32	13 55	19 36	...	...

Castelnau ......dep	7‡13	10 20	16 18	...	...
Avensan	7 22	10 37	16 27	...	...
Margaux.........arr	7 35	10 50	16 40	...	...

‡—Not on Sunday.

STATE RAILWAYS.

ANGERS and POITIERS.

Angers St. Laud. ..dep	4 50	6 37	...	11 22	...	...	14 35	17 58	20 44	...	...	...
Maitre-Ecole	4 55	6 42	...	11 27	...	...	14 47	18 4	20 51	...	...	...
Les Ponts-de-Cé	5 9	6 56	...	11 41	...	...	...	18 19	...	...	...	...
La Possonnière dep	...	6 27	...	10 55	...	...	...	16 43	...	...	...	...
St. Aubin de Luigné	...	6 59	...	11 30	...	...	...	17 12	...	...	...	...
Per.-Jouannet. .arr	...	7 34	...	12 21	...	...	...	18 2	...	...	...	...
Perray-Jouannet dep	5 56	7 45	...	12 31	...	...	17 3	19 24	21 34	...	...	...
Douè-la-Fontaine 41B	6 27	8 21	...	13 4	...	...	18 23	20 14	21 58	...	...	...
Montreuil Bel. ...arr	6 54	8 48	...	13 32	...	...	19 1	20 48	22 14	...	...	...
„ (42) dep	7 18	—	12 53	13 53	...	17 3	—	—	22 22	...	...	...
Lamotte Bourbon	7 26	...	13 13	14 1	...	1711	...	...	22 32	...	...	...
Loudun (40) ....arr	7 53	...	14 10	14 27	1515	1737	...	...	22 57	...	...	...
Arcay (42A) ....arr	8 13	...	—	14 47	1532	1750	...	...	23 20	...	...	...
Moncontour	8 31	...	...	15 10	1639	1813	18§23	...	23 35	...	...	...
Mirebeau-en-P.	9 2	...	...	15 40	1754	—	18 58	...	24 0	...	...	...
Neuville-de-Poitou	9 32	...	...	16 10	1853	...	19 26	19 33	0 19	...	...	...
Poitiers (34) ....arr	9 58	...	...	16 18	...	...	...	20 19	0 39	...	...	...
								†				
Poitiers ....dep	...	6 11	...	6 25	12 12	...	...	17 23	20 6	...	...	...
Neuville-de-Poitou	...	6 45	...	7 58	12 52	...	...	18 1	20 34	...	...	...
Mirebeau-en-P.	...	7 9	...	9 15	13 19	...	...	18 30	20 58	...	...	...
Moncontour	...	7 40	...	10 15	13 50	...	...	19 6	21 27	...	...	...
Arcay ....arr	...	7 56	...	10 43	14 8	...	...	19 24	21 42	...	...	...
Loudun ....arr	...	8 8	...	11 16	14 18	...	16 0	19 37	21 53	...	...	...
Lamotte Bourbon	...	8 48	...	13 15	14 53	...	16 33	—	22 33	...	...	...
Montreuil Bel. ...arr	...	8 57	...	13 28	15 2	...	16 44	...	22 42	...	...	...
„ dep	7 23	9 12	...	—	15 18	15 26	17 10	...	23 25	...	...	...
Doué-la-Fontaine	7 57	9 40	...	...	15 39	16 50	17 43	...	23 52	...	...	...
Perray-Jouannet arr	8 30	10 6		...	15 57	17 55	18 13	...	0 17	...	...	...
Perry-Jouan....dep	8 38	...	12 55	...	...	...	19 22	...	...	...	...	...
S. Aubin de Luignè	9 15	...	13 31	...	...	...	19 56	...	...	...	...	...
La Possonnière arr	9 45	...	14 1	...	...	...	20 25	...	...	...	...	...
Les Ponts-de-Cé	9 21	...	—	...	...	..	19 7	...	...	...	...	...
Maitre-Ecole ......arr	9 35	10 59	...	...	16 36	21 33	19 21	...	0 57	...	...	...
Angers St. Laud...arr	9 43	11 9	...	...	16 42	21 43	19 28	...	1 2	...	...	...

†—Tuesday and Saturday only.

§—Until 9th October.

‡—Until 2nd November.

POITIERS and NIORT.

Dist E.M.						‡						
	Poitiers.........dep	2 38	7 57	14 14	17 13	20 30	...	...	...	...	...	...
6¾	Lusignan	3 13	8 41	14 54	17 56	21 10	...	...	...	...	...	...
34¼	Saint Maixent	3 51	9 30	15 43	18 46	21 52	21 57	...	...	...	...	...
48¾	**Niort 42** ....arr	4 20	10 4	16 16	19 19	...	22 26	...	...	...	...	...
...	**Niort** ....dep	7 17	10 5	13 57	17 5	...	20 39	...	...	...	...	...
...	Saint Maixent	7 54	10 38	14 41	17 43	17‡46	21 29	...	...	...	...	...
...	Lusignan	8 39	11 23	15 44	...	18 43	22 26	...	...	...	...	...
...	**Poitiers**........arr	9 18	11 57	16 23	...	19 21	23 3	...	...	...	...	...

LA LOUPE and BROU.

La Loupe ....dep	6 12	10 27	18 27	...	...	...	...	...	...	...	...
Brou (42) ....arr	7 36	12 35	19 58	...	...	...	...	...	...	...	...
Brou.......................dep	8 7	15 44	20 23	...	...	...	...	...	...	...	...
La Loupe (80).........arr	9 32	17 38	21 48	...	...	...	...	...	...	...	...

SAINTES and MARENNES.

Saintes (Etat).........dep	7 20	11 †55	18 25	...	...	...	Marennes ....dep	4 40	10 50	14 55	...	...	...
Marennes (40) ......arr	10 18	14 36	21 14	...	...	...	Saintes (Etat) (41B) arr	6 45	13 48	17 40	...	...	...

†—From and at Saintes Ville.

SAUJON and MARENNES.

Saujon ....dep	6 40	8 30	13 10	17 5	...	...	Marennes ....dep	6 50	9 50	15 15	18 36	..	...
Marennes (40) ......arr	7 54	9 35	14 25	18 20	...	...	Saujon (40) ....arr	8 0	11 10	16 27	19 36	...	...

PORNIC and PAIMBŒUF.

E.M.													
	Pornic (Etat.) ...dep	5 50	9 0	16 53	19 38	...	...	Paimbœuf 42A dep	...	6 45	1350	16 45	...
6¼	La Plaine..........arr	6 13	9 23	17 16	20 1	...	...	St. Brevin-l'Ocean	...	7 36	1437	17 37	...
7¼	Préfailles.........arr	6 19	9 29	17 22	20 7	...	...	Préfailles ...dep	5 10	8 16	1522	18 17	...
14¼	St. Brevin-l'Ocean ...	7 3	10 9	18 6	—	...	...	La Plaine	5 16	8 22	1528	18 23	...
24¾	Paimbœuf (Etat.) arr	7 54	11 0	18 54	...	...	...	Pornic (42A) ...arr	5 39	8 45	1552	18 45	...

CORSICAN RAILWAYS.

E.M.				‡								‡		
	Bastia ....dep	8 25	6 32	11 45	12 5	1255	15 25	**Ajaccio** ....dep	...	...	6 35	11 45	12 2	15 25
10½	Borgo	9 8	7 8	...	12 41	1331	16 1	**Carbuccia**	...	...	7 26	...	12 52	16 16
13¾	Casamozza ....arr	9 19	7 19	12 19	12 51	1342	16 2	**Bocognano**	...	...	8 45	13 29	14 12	17 41
	dep	—	7 29	12 23	12 56	—	16 25	**Vizzavona**	...	...	9 18	13 56	14 45	18 14
29½	Ponte Leccia ......arr	...	8 27	13 9	13 54	...	17 31	**Vivario**	...	...	9 52	14 23	15 21	18 48
	dep	...	8 35	13 13	14 0	...	17 48	Corte ....arr	...	...	10 53	15 13	16 21	19 45
46	Corte ....arr	...	9 46	14 10	15 11	...	19 0	dep	...	7 10	11 23	15 22	16 31	—
	dep	5 20	10 11	14 20	15 23	...	—	Ponte Leccia ....arr	...	8 16	12 27	16 17	17 35	...
59¾	**Vivario**	6 34	11 27	15 22	16 37	...	...	dep	...	8 28	12 33	16 21	17 40	...
66¼	**Vizzavona**	7 20	12 13	15 57	17 17	...	...	Casamozza ....arr	...	9 30	13 41	17 6	18 33	...
72¾	**Bocognano**	7 47	12 40	16 21	17 43	...	...	dep	7 32	9 39	13 49	17 10	18 37	16 29
85¼	**Carbuccia**	8 44	13 39	..	18 35	...	...	Borgo	7 45	9 50	14 0	...	18 48	16 40
98¾	**Ajaccio** ....arr	9 30	14 25	17 45	19 20	...	...	**Bastia**...............arr	8 24	10 25	14 35	17 45	19 22	17 15

E.M.											
	Casamozza ....dep	9 36	14 0	...	...	...	...	**Ghisonaccia** ...dep	4 45	13 40	...
...	Folelli-Orezza	10 4	14 31	...	...	...	...	**Prunete-Cervione**	6 18	15 14	...
16½	Prunete-Cervione	10 39	15 9	...	...	...	...	Folelli-Orezza	6 53	15 48	...
40¼	**Ghisonaccia** ......arr	12 8	16 38	...	...	...	...	**Casamozza** ....arr	7 20	16 15	...

‡—Will not take passengers for less than 21 miles.

E.M.													
	Ponte-Leccia ...dep	8 40	17 45	...	...	...	...	**Calvi** ....dep	5 5	14 10	...	...	...	...
18	Palasca	9 56	19 1	...	...	...	...	Ile Rousse	5 55	15 0	...	...	...	...
32	Ile Rousse	10 56	20 1	...	...	...	...	Palasca	7 2	16 7	...	...	...	...
46	**Calvi** ....arr	11 40	20 45	...	...	...	...	**Ponte-Leccia** arr	8 14	17 19	...	...	...	...

66 lbs. of Luggage free.] STATE RAILWAYS.

SAINTES and ANGOULEME.

E.M.																				
—	**Saintes** ....dep	4§36	7 19	7 56	9 4	1051	1441	1824	20 12	2019	21 3	...	0 31	...	...	...	...	...	...	...
6¼	**Beillant**	4 50	7 33	8 15	9 28	11 8	15 0	1845	20 24	2049	2127	...	0 48	...	...	...	...	...	...	...
16¾	Cognac 46A	5 9	7 56	8 50	1010	1143	1540	1923	20 45	2129	2146	22 5	1 11	...	...	...	...	...	...	...
25¼	Jarnac-Ségonzac..	—	8 15	9 15	—	12 9	16 7	1948	A	—	—	2247	—	...	...	...	...	...	...	...
34¼	**Châteauneuf** ...	...	8 34	9 42	...	1236	1636	2016	...	...	...	2325	...	...	...	...	...	...	...	...
48½	**Angoulême** 39A	...	9 8	1022	...	1319	1720	2055	21†33	...	...	0 33	...	...	...	...	...	...	...	...

Angoulême..dep	4 26	...	8 12	1140	1537	...	19 7	21†45	22*4	...	...	...	...	...	...	...	...	...	...	...
Châteauneuf ...	5 4	...	8 57	1226	1620	...	1946	...	22 50	...	...	...	...	...	...	...	...	...	...	...
Jarnac-Ségonzac...	5 26	...	9 22	1251	1643	...	20 9	A	23 7	...	...	...	...	...	...	...	...	...	...	...
Cognac	5 50	6 18	9 52	1322	1711	19 2	2034	22 37	23 29	...	...	...	...	...	...	...	...	...	...	...
Beillant	6 16	7 35	1022	1352	1742	1951	2057	...	23 50	...	...	...	...	...	...	...	...	...	...	...
Saintes 41......arr	6 30	7 59	1036	14 6	1756	...	21 8	23 3	0 1	...	...	...	...	...	...	...	...	...	...	...

A—Runs until 8th October. *—Until 2nd November. §—Runs until 7th October. †—Orleans Co.'s Station.

NANTES and LA ROCHE-SUR-YON, via Challans.

E.M.										
	Nantes (Etat)..................dep	6 44	11 35	...	18 15	20 52	...	...	...	...
16¾	Ste. Pazanne 42A	7 40	12 25	...	19 1	21 17	...	...	...	...
36¾	Challans	8 38	13 16	15 8	19 56	23 7	...	...	...	...
43¾	Commequiers 41B	9 1	13 37	15 42	20 24	—	...	...	...	...
69	**La Roche-sur-Yon 41**...arr	9 59	14 33	18 35	21 27	...	...	...	...	...

La Roche-sur-Yon..dep	...	6 22	9 3	15 17	19 12	...	...	...	...	...	...
Commequiers 41B..............	...	9 13	10 16	16 23	20 26	...	...	...	...	...	...
Challans............................	5 57	9 47	10 40	16 51	20 55	...	...	...	...	...	...
Ste. Pazanne......................	6 57	—	11 44	17 59	22 11	...	...	...	...	...	...
Nantes 41 ....arr	7 46	...	12 38	18 4	23 4	...	...	...	...	...	...

ST. LAURENT and FOURAS.

ROCHEFORT ......dep	7 6	8 ‡13	9 ‡51	13‡29	1530	17‡35	18‡51	20 29	...	...	...	...
St. Laurent......dep	7 ‡30	8 35	10 12	13‡51	1550	17‡50	19 12	20 58	...	...	...	...
Fouras..............arr	7 40	8 45	10 22	14 1	16 0	17 59	19 22	21 8	...	...	...	...

Fouras..............dep	5‡14	6 53	8 ‡4	9 39	12‡38	1511	17‡13	1837	19‡47	20 24	0 *46	...	...
St. Laurent......arr	5 23	7 3	8 13	9 48	12 47	1528	17 22	1847	19 57	20 33	0 55	...	...
ROCHEFORT ......arr	5 41	7‡18	8 36	10 ‡2	12 58	1544	17 50	1913	...	20‡47	1 8	...	...

*—Until 30th September. ‡—Until 7th October.

ST. MARIENS and COUTRAS.

St. Mariens......dep	6 17	9 44	11 30	17 9	1810	2044	...	...	...	...	...	...	...
Marcenais	6 33	9 58	11 46	1725	1827	2059	...	...	...	...	...	...	...
Coutras 34........arr	7 9	...	12 23	...	19 8	2139	...	...	...	...	...	...	...

Coutras ....dep	5 6	7 50	...	14§22	...	...	19 58	...	...	...	...	...	...
Marcenais 41B	5 46	8 35	8 51	15 7	1517	17*27	20 41	...	...	...	...	...	...
St. Mariens 41 arr	6 0	8 49	9 6	15 22	1533	17 44	20 56	...	...	...	...	...	...

*—Tuesday and Friday only. §—Until 1st November.

LIBOURNE and MARCENAIS.

Libourne ...dep	5 *6	8 0	1443	16†50	1945	...
Marcenais arr	5 37	8 30	1517	17 24	2025	...

Marcenais...dep	6 41	10 1	17 28	21*11	...
Libourne 35 arr	7 14	1034	18 1	21 48	...

*—From 14th July until 7th October. †—Tuesday and Friday only.

BLAYE and SAINT-MARIENS.

Blaye ...dep	5 1	7 20	1445	17†5	1836	...	...
St. Mariens	5 44	8 4	1534	1751	1921	...	...

St.Mariens	6 30	9†34	1125	1812	21 5	...
Blaye (42B)	7 14	1017	1210	1856	21 53	...

†—Until 9th October.

COMMEQUIERS and ST. GILLES.

Commequiersdep	9 *4	1021	1340	16 33	2034
St. Gilles ......arr	9 31	1048	14 7	17 12	21 1

St .Gilles	7 57	9*40	12 56	1521	1937
Commequiers 41B	8 37	10 7	13 23	1548	20 4

*—From 14th July until 7th October.

CHOLET and CLISSON.

Cholet ......dep	6 5	9 5	1144	17 23	19 34	...
Clisson 41 arr	7 1	10 5	1232	18 20	20 36	...

Clisson dep	7 31	10 43	17 1	1922	2148	...
Cholet 42A	8 36	11 43	18 5	2012	2248	...

LIGRE RIVIERE and RICHELIEU.

Ligré-Rivière 42A.........dep	9 27	1354	17†55	2145	...	...	...	...	...	...	...	...
Richelieu ....arr	9 56	1434	18 25	22 12	...	...	...	...	...	...	...	...
Richelieu ....dep	6 3	1036	16 †5	19 30	...	...	...	...	...	...	...	...
Ligré-Rivière ....arr	6 30	1114	16 32	19 59	...	...	...	...	...	...	...	...

†—Thursday and Saturday only.

NANTES and CHOLET.

Nantes (P.O. Anjou) dep	5 55	9 28	14 38	18 6	...
Loroux	6 53	10 37	15 44	19 19	...
Puiset-Doré-le-Fuilet	7 37	11 43	16 36	20 14	...
Beaupréau	8 15	12 29	17 21	20 58	...
Cholet (42A) ....arr	9 35	13 48	18 43	...	...

Cholet ....dep	...	7 8	11 42	...	16 10
Beaupréau	5 5	8 29	12 37	13 20	17 35
Puiset................................	6 6	9 20	—	14 21	18 27
Loroux	6 56	10 7	...	15 17	19 17
Nantes (P.O. Anjou) arr	7 59	11 16	...	16 26	20 20

†—On Sunday arrives Nantes 17.26.

Beaupréau............dep	6 0	8 30	12 40	1748	...	...
La Possonnière ......arr	7 25	9 56	14 4	1915	...	...

La Possonnière...dep	6 33	10 40	15 15	1742	...	...
Beaupréau ....arr	8 10	12 11	16 46	1921	...	...

SAUMUR and CHOLET.

Saumur Etat dep	...	7 32	12 0	16 38	...
Doué-la-Fontaine ...	...	8 40	13 10	17 43	...
Vihiers	5 45	10 0	14 29	18 52	...
Cholet 42A......arr	7 3	11 18	15 47	20 10	...

Cholet ....dep	5 50	10 5	14 36	18 58	...	...
Vihiers	7 12	11 40	16 8	20 16	...	...
Doué-la-Fontaine (41A)...	8 41	13 16	17 42	—	...	...
Saumur Etat ....arr	9 35	14 10	18 34	...	...	...

STATE RAILWAYS. [66 lbs. of Luggage free.

PARIS, CHARTRES, SAUMUR, SAINTES, and BORDEAUX.

Dist E.M	PARIS—	1,2,3	1,2,3	1,2,3	1,2,3	1,2,3	1,2,3	1,2,3	1,2,3	1,2,3	1,2,3	1,2,3	1,2,3	1,2,3	1,2,3	1,2,3	1,2,3	1,2,3	1,2,3
—	Montparnasse.........dep	...	...	...	...	§—Depart from or arrive at Invalides Station.	5§23	8 15	9 55	10‡45	10‡55	1250	1440	...	1725	20 30	21 10	2135	2320
10¼	Versailles	...	...	...	...		5 59	8 37	1018	RC	...	1312	RC	...	1749	20 55	21 34	2157	2346
54¾	**Chartres (80)** ......arr	...	...	...	...		7 49	9 43	1115	...	...	1419	1549	...	19 8	21 52	22 31	22 [illegible]0	1 5
...	" ....dep	...	...	...	5 29		8 25	9 50	1232	11 52	12 3	1427	1553	...	1919	21 59	22 38	2256	1 14
70½	Illiers	...	...	...	6 7		9 19	1015	1320	...	...	15 7	...	...	20 0	...	23 2	...	1 50
77¾	Brou (41A)	...	...	...	6 27		9 41	1029	1343	...	...	1527	G	...	2020	...	23 15	...	2 6
88¼	Courtalain-St. Pellerin...	...	...	...	7 30		1059	1051	1413	...	...	16 3	...	...	2059	...	23 35	2354	2 29
107	Sargé (40)	...	...	...	8 24		1147	1121		...	...	17 8	17 2	...	2154	A	...	...	3 12
115	Bessé-Braye	5 10	...	...	8 47		12 9	1135	...	...	...	1728	...	2040	2213	...	0 16	...	3 30
120	Pont-de-Braye (40)	5 46	...	...	9 2		1226	...	...	...	RC	1746	...	21 2	2227	...	0 25	...	3 42
125½	La Chatre (87)	6 21	...	...	9 19		1241	RC	...	...	...	18 1	...	2117	2241	...	...	...	3 55
135¼	Chateau-du-Loir ......arr	7 1	...	7 46	9 43		13 5	12 2	‡—Will not set down at Chartres.	...	...	1823	1739	2140	23 3	23 44	0 46	1 11	4 11
157¾	Noyant-Méon		From Royan (dep. 6.45) Runs until 2nd October.	9 34	1125	...	15 9	1243		...	...	1934	...			...	1 31	...	5 20
177¾	**Saumur** (Orleans) ...arr	...		1053	1218	B—Coming from Nantes. Runs until 2nd November.	1552	13 9		...	...	2019	1834	...	...	0 47	1 57	2 16	6 2
...	" " ......dep	...			1219		1612	1318		...	...	2030	1838	...	...	0 51	2 2	2 22	6 36
182	**Saumur** (Etat) ......arr	...		...	1423		18 4	...		...	...	2052	...	...	A—Runs until 6th Octob. r.	...	...	...	7 38
...	" " ......dep	...		8 7	1225		16 0	...		...	...	2011	G	...		A	...	...	6 32
191¼	Montreuil Bellay	...		9 20	1312		1654	1342		...	...	2115	...	...		...	2 23	...	7 22
202½	**Thouars (42A)** ......arr	...		10 1	1343		1721	1358		...	15 1	2140	1910	...		1 26	2 44	2 59	7 49
...	" ....dep	4 40		1257			1750	1414		C	15 7		1918	2315		1 34	2 56	...	8 15
217½	Airvault (40) ...	5 21		1312	...		1842	1439		...	...	...	...	0 17		...	3 26	☞	9 8
230½	Parthenay (42A)	6 4		1436	...		1920	15 6		...	...	...	...	1 6		2 14	3 49	Runs until 7th October.	9 52
258	**Niort (41A)** ....arr	7 3		1533	...		2016	1550	...	14 42	16 19	...	2031	2 31		2 57	4 31		1048
...	" ....dep				...		2056	1638	...	14 54	16 27	1648	2043	5 18	...	3 9	5 4		1146
270¾	Beauvoir-sur-Niort	...	...	...	...		2132	...	...	...	To Royan (until 5th Oct) arrive 17.56.	1722	...	6 6	...	...	5 27		1222
288¾	St. Jean-d'Angely	...	Not on Sundays.	...	...		2222	1724	...	...		1820	...	7 23	...	3 52	6 1		1313
305¾	**Saintes** ....arr	...		...	...	...	2257	1751	...	16 5		1910	2111	8 38		4 16	6 31		1353
...	" ....dep	4 43		9 4	1427	1642	2341	1759	18 9			21 3	2147	9 40	4 29		7 1		1419
312	Beillant	5 5		9 22	1413	...	0 1	1812	1828	...		2119	...	...	...	...	7 16		...
320¾	Pons	5 39		9 49	15 7	...	0 36	1831	1859	...		2141	To Royan arr. 22.20.	1029	4 52	...	7 34	...	1447
333	Jonzac..........1,2,3	6 27		1019	1538	...	1 11	1851	1935	...		22 4		1120	5 12	...	7 55	...	15 7
356	St. Mariens-St. Yzan 6 41	7 54		1115	1642	B	2 32	1932	2058	...		225		1253	5 54	5 0	8 42	...	1552
358½	Cavignac.........6 49			1121	1649	...	2 43	...	2110	...		...		1317	...	5 7	8 49	...	...
367¾	St. Andre-de-Cubzac 7 32	...		1149	1710	...	3 11	1951	2140	...		2318		1347	6 12	5 34	9 5	...	1611
381	**Bordeaux** Etat arr 8 16	...	8 50	1227	...	...	3 56	...	...	...		2348	...	1429	...	6 15	...	...	...
384	" St. Jean arr	...	...	...	1749	1824	4 51	2017	2220	...		...	...	...	6 40	...	9 30	...	1636

G—Between Paris and Niort runs on Tues., Thur., and Sat.; between Niort and Royan on Sat. only from 5th July until 4th October. C—Wed. and Sat. only from 12th July until 13th September.

	1,2,3	1,2,3	1,2,3	1,2,3	1,2,3	1,2,3	1,2,3	1,2,3	1,2,3	1,2,3	1,2,3	1,2,3	1,2,3	1,2,3	1,2,3	1,2,3	1,2,3	1,2,3	1,2,3
Bordeaux- Etat ....dep (See also page 41.)	...	...	From Royan depart 5.37.	6 56	...	From Royan (Until 6th October) depart 11.4.	...	...	10 0	...	...	...	1655	17 2	1812	...	...	19 20	...
St. Jean ......dep	...	5 11		...	...		8 32	...	...	1141	12 16	1432	Not on Sunday.	...	...	...	19 5	...	2216
St. Andre-de-Cub.	...	5 45		7 38	...		9 0	...	1043	...	13 0	1515		1731	1857	...	1934	20 15	...
Cavignac	...	6 3		8 4	...		RC	...	1110	RC	13 24	1539		1757	1924	...	...	20 43	...
St. Mariens-St. Yzan ...	...	6 16		8 19	...		9 23	...	1117	...	13 36	1553		18 9	1931	From 2nd July until 9th October. ☞	1958	20 48	23 5
Jonzac	...	7 8		9 18	...		10 1	...		...	14 40	1644	To Royan (arr. 18.57) Runs until 30th September.	19 4	E—Mon. and Thur. from 28th July until 14th August; daily (except Sunday) from 15th August until 6th October.		2036		2310
Pons	...	7 42		9 51	...		1022	...	...	...	15 25	1711		1937			2058	...	2358
Beillant	...	8 3		1014	...		1039	...	...	...	15 53	1730		20 6			2116	...	...
Saintes ....arr	...	8 17	6 7	1028	...		1049	...	...	1315	16 9	1741		2022			2126	...	0 20
" ....dep	...		6 11		7 3		11 6	1111	1420	1319		1810					2140	...	0 30
St. Jean-d'Angely	...	...	D	...	8 8		1135	12 3	1458	☞ To Nantes. Until 2nd Nov. only.	15 5	19 1		...			22 7	...	0 55
Beauvoir-sur-Niort	...	...	...	...	9 9		...	1255			15 54	1954		...			...	...	F
Niort ....arr	...	...	7 8	...	9 42		1219	1325	...		16 23	2022		...			2252	...	1 34
" ....dep	...	...	7 20	4 55	1016	12 41	13 3	1349	1252		17 10	2046		1943			23 4	...	1 42
Parthenay	...	...	8 5	6 13	1139	...	1355	15 5	...		19 3[illegible]	2140		2058			2353	...	2 32
Airvault	...	...	RC	6 48	1214	...	1416	1536	...		20 13	22 5		2127		☞	...	...	...
Thouars ....arr	...	...	8 40	7 26	1252	13 55	1438	1610	1411		21 9	2228		22 0			0 30	...	3 8
" ....dep	...	6 23	8 49	8 13	1312	14 4	1450	1624	1420		21 43	2241				0 24	0 41	...	3 18
Montreuil-Bellay	...	7 1	9 6	9 15	1341	...	1510	17 9	...		22 25	23 1		...		0 43	0 59	...	...
Saumur (Etat) ......arr	...	7 33	...	10 3	1423	...	...	18 4	...		22 59	...		...		...	...	...	...
" " ......dep	...	6 30	...	1047	1225	...	...	16 0	...			...		...		...	...	...	...
Saumur (Orleans) arr	...	7 33	9 23	11 7	1415	...	...	1759	...		...	2321		...		1 2	1 13	...	3 49
" " ...dep	...	7 41	9 27	1114	1453	RC	1540	18 0	...		...			...		1 6	1 22	...	3 53
Noyant-Méon	...	8 26	D	1210	1536	...	16 9	1910	...	...	...	...		RC—Restaurant Car attached.		1 36	1 55	...	...
Chateau-du-Loir ......dep	4 59	9 27	10 24	1340	17 7	...	1648	2040	...	...	...	...	...			2 18	2 38	...	4 52
La Chartre	5 23	9 52	...	14 8	1737	...	RC	2115	...	...	...	...	...			...	...	...	...
Pont-de-Braye ....dep	5 39	10 9	...	1424	1756	...	1710	2140	E	...	...	...	...			2 41	3 0	...	...
Bessé-Braye ....dep	5 53	1024	...	1444	1813	...	1720	2159	...	...	...	†—Sets down only.	...			2 51	3 10	...	...
Sargé	6 13	11 7	11 1	15 7	1840	...	...	2229	...	...	...		...			...	...	2 & 3	F
Courtalain-St. Pellerin...	7 19	1224	...	1649	1945	...	18 5	2338	...	...	...		...			3 35	3 56	4 43	...
Brou	7 51	1255	...	1721	2019	...	1821	0 7	...	...	...		...			3 51	4 13	5 14	...
Illiers	8 15	1316	...	1746	2046	†	1835	0 30	...	...	...		...			...	...	5 38	...
Chartres ....arr	8 53	1352	12 8	1827	2126	17 6	1858	1 8	...	...	...		...			4 25	4 47	6 18	6 35
" ....dep	9 10	1425	12 12	1848	2144	...	19 6	1 23	...	...	...		...			4 32	4 54	6 47	6 40
Versailles	1012	1520		20 0	2255	...	2010	2 55	...	...	...	...	...			5 35	6 3	8 22	7 49
Paris Montparnasse arr	1035	15§48	13 25	2025	2320	18 20	2035	3 37	1835	...	...	...	...	...		6 0	6 30	8 46	8 15

D—Between Niort and Paris on Mon., Wed., and Fri. between Royan and Niort on Mon. only from 7th July until 6th October. F—Until 7th October.

Station														
Tours ......dep	...	1 1	...	...	5 50	10 7	12 0	...	...	...	...	1518	...	19 1
Joue-les-Tours	...	...	...	...	6 3	1022	12 12	...	...	1254	...	1531	...	1913
Azay-le-Rideau	...	1 47	...	...	6 35	1054	12 39	...	...	14 5	...	16 3	...	1953
Chinon (42A)	...	2 14	...	...	7 17	1132	13 10	...	...	1523	...	1654	...	2046
Loudun (40)	...	2 49	...	...	8 15	1312	13 32	...	...	—	15 3	1740	...	2139
Arcay	...	...	...	...	8 29	—	14 15	A	...	...	1528	18 2	...	2151
Thouars	3 10	3 13	4 54	...	8 55	...	14 40	1512	From Nantes.	1520	1615	1823	B	2214
Bressuire ...	3 45	4 16	5 54	...	1029	7 50	—	1548		1635	—	20 8	2016	—
Chantonnay ...	—	5 10	7 38	...	1146	11 2	12 43	1641		1757	...	—	...	...
Roche- arr	...	5 46	8 31	...	1236	—	14 19	1712		1841	...	...	2145	...
sur-Yn dep	...	5 58	9 4	1053	1252	...	15 15	1719	1851	19 1	...	...	2150	...
La Mothe-A. ...	...	6 22	9 35	1121	1318	...	15 46	...	C	1929	...	...	...	...
Olonne	...	..	9 50	1136	1333	...	15 59	...	...	1941	...	...	...	...
Les Sables ...	...	6 39	9 58	1143	1340	...	16 8	1750	1922	1948	...	...	2221	...

Station													
Les Sables dp	...	...	5 7	7 20	7 45	9 39	...	...	1125	1331	...	17 55	21 5
Olonne	...	...	5 16	...	7 54	9 49	...	...	...	1332	...	18 3	F
Mothe-Achard	...	...	5 33	D	8 14	10 4	...	...	...	1351	...	18 18	21 23
La Roche arr	...	...	5 57	7 53	8 43	1031	...	...	E	1422	...	18 44	21 41
,, dep	...	...	6 30	To Nantes.	9 8	1049	...	...	...	1511	...	18 59	21 51
Chantonnay ...	...	..	7 35		1042	1144	...	12 2	...	16 4	...	19 50	22 28
Bressuire ...	...	6 55	9 27		—	1310	...	1529	...	1820	...	21 41	23 38
Thouars	...	7 41	1024		...	1341	1416	—	14 5	1933	...	22 23	0 11
Arcay	...	8 7	1050		...	—	1446	...	—	20 2	...	...	—
Loudun	...	8 26	11 9	—	...	...	1529	1555	...	2013	2027	23 6	...
Chinon	6 54	9 5	1151	...	...	...	1553	1733	...	—	2116	23 29	...
Azay-le-Rideau	7 44	9 48	1242	...	...	...	1623	1817	...	...	22 8	23 56	...
Joue-les-Tours	8 21	1026	1320	...	...	...	1648	1849	...	...	2247	...	...
Tours(34) arr	8 33	1038	1332	...	...	...	1659	19 0	...	...	23 0	0 45	...

A—Until 7th October.
B—Sat. only until 27th Sept.
F—Until 9th October.

C—Wed. and Sat. only from 12th to 26th July; daily except Sunday from 30th July until 6th Sept.
D—Mon. and Fri. from 18th to 28th July; daily, Sunday excepted, from 31st July until 8th Sept.
E—Mon. and Thurs. from 28th July until 14th August; daily, except Sunday, from 15th August until 6th Oct.

NIORT to LA ROCHELLE & ROCHEFORT.

Station							
Thouars ....dep	2 56	3 10	4 40	8 15	15 7	15 7	17 56
Niort (42)	4 41	......	7 19	11 3	1634	1643	20 47
Epannes	...	......	7 42	11 27	...	17 5	21 8
Mauzé	5 7	......	7 56	11 43	...	1720	21 23
Surgeres (46A)	5 23	......	8 18	12 5	17 9	1741	21 45
Aigrefeuille	5 37	......	8 40	12 27	1724	18 2	22 4
La Rochelle 41 ...arr	6 6	6 12	9 18	13 5	1746	1840	22 36
Aigrefeuille ...dep	5 52	...	8 55	12 36	1734	18 8	22 13
Rochefort .....arr	6 17	...	9 24	13 5	1753	1833	22 39

Station								
Rochefort...dep	5 28	7 57	9 †58	1113	16 37	1821	21 26	...
Aigrefeuille arr	4 59	8 22	10 27	1132	17 6	1846	21 45	...
La Rochelle dep	5 1	7 52	10†0	1121	1638	1823	2131	
Aigrefeuille	5 40	8 29	1040	1143	1719	19 0	2158	
Surgeres	6 5	8 56	11 9	1157	1754	1925	2213	
Mauzé	6 23	9 14	1132	...	181[illegible]	1945	2227	
Epannes (22A) ...	6 38	9 29	1148	...	1849	1959	...	
Niort	7 0	9 51	1210	1227	1913	2018	2248	
Thouars ....arr	8§40	1252	1855	1355	22 0	2228	0 30	

†—Until Oct. 9.
§—Mon., Wed. & Fri. only.

CHANTONNAY and FONTENAY-LE-COMTE.					
Chantonnay ....dep	7 44	12 24	19 47	...	...
Vouvant-Cezais............	8 31	13 48	20 30	...	...
Fontenay-le-Comte arr	8 49	14 18	20 52	...	...
Fontenay-le-C. ...dep	5 58	9 33	16 27	...	...
Vouvant-Cezais	6 34	10 10	16 48	...	...
Chantonnay (42A) arr	7 16	11 22	17 30	...	...

PORT-DE-PILES and PORT BOULET.					E.M.
Port-de-Piles ......dep	5 20	10 31	...	18 9	
L'Ile-Bouchard	6 8	11 3	...	19 42	9½
Ligré-Rivière 41B............	6 40	11 26	...	20 19	12½
Chinon 42A...........dep	7 28	12 2	1740	21 19	20
Port Boulet 39......arr	7 52	12 26	18 2	21 59	33

Station						
Port Boulet ...dep	8 38	12 41	...	...	19 15	...
Chinon ....arr	8 57	13 2	1320	1335	19 40	2124
Ligré-Rivière	9 17	—	1338	134[illegible]	—	2138
L'Ile-Bouchard	9 37	...	1420	...	...	22 7
Port-de-Piles 34 arr	10 8	...	1550	...	...	2247

POITIERS and BRESSUIRE. E.M.	Station					
	Poitiers ....dep	4 23	8 24	12 49	19 0	...
10½	Neuville-de-P. 41A	4 56	8 49	13 24	19 33	...
34¾	Parthenay 42	6 35	9 47	14 46	20 42	22 11
56	**Bressuire** 42A arr	7 29	1023	15 39	...	23 1

Station					
Bressuire...dep	6 57	13 12	...	18 16	21 29
Parthenay	8 8	14 13	15 22	19 25	22 15
Neuville-de-P. ...	9 13	—	16 36	20 32	22 57
Poitiers 41A arr	9 41	...	17 6	21 4	23 17

NANTES to PORNIC, and PAIMBŒUF. §—Runs 14th July until 7th Oct.

Station										
Nantes Etat dep	6*44	7 9	10 *3	11*35	1324	17†29	1743	1815	2052	§
Ste-Pazanne ...	7 43	8 3	10 53	12 22	14 1	17 58	1840	1 52	2156	2213
St. Hilaire-de-C.	7 48	8 11	11 4	12 41	1411	..	1847	19 2	—	2223
La Bernerie	:	8 42	11 36	:	1442	18 21	1917	...	*—Until 9th Oct.	2255
Pornic(41A)...arr	:	8 55	11 49	:	1455	18 30	1930	...		23 7
St. Hilaire dep	7 57	...	...	12 44	...	...	...	19 4		...
Paimbœuf arr	8 39	...	...	13 34	...	...	...	1946		...

Station									
Paimbœuf dep	5 59	...	9 17	...	...	1659	...	...	
St.Hilaire arr	6 41	...	10 7	...	...	1742	*	...	
Pornic ......dep	5 57	7†21	9 25	...	1619	...	1831	21§1	†—Until 4th Oct.
La Bernerie ...	6 13	7 3[illegible]	9 45	...	1637	*	1847	2117	
St. Hilaire dep	6 45	7 52	1014	...	1711	1 44	1915	2150	
Ste.Pazanne ar	6 52	...	1021	1144	1719	1751	1922	2159	2211
Nantes Etat arr	7 46	8 21	1117	1238	1528	1848	2015		23 4

ANGERS and NIORT.

Station							
Angers..............dep		4 8	9 54	1431	1711	...	21 2
La Possonnière dp		4 37	1031	15 2	1739	...	2122
Chemillé		5 10	11 5	1546	1815	...	2151
Cholet (41B)		5 43	1151	1643	1844	20 20	2218
Châtillon-St-Aub. ...		6 13	1222	1723	—	20 47	—
Bressuire	4 11	7 2	1317	1811	...	21 14	...
Breuil-Barret......	4 39	7 59	1418	19 1	...	—	...
Benet	—	9 7	1538	1955	...	...	...
Niort (42) ....arr		9 29	16 3	2014	...	...	...

Station									
Niort ....dep	...	5 12	...	...	13 45	17 24	...	...	...
Benet	...	5 34	...	...	14 9	17 47	...	...	†
Breuil-Barret	...	6 53	...	...	15 17	19 4	...	2051	2245
Bressuire(42A)......	4 30	7 48	1034	...	16 14	19 47	...	2121	2318
Châtillon-St-Aub. ...	5 6	8 24	11 8	...	16 51	—	...	—	—
Cholet	5 28	8 46	1128	1253	17 15	18 14	2019	...	...
Chemille	6 10	9 28	—	13 7	—	18 48	2047	...	...
La Possonnière arr	6 44	10 0	...	1343	...	19 21	2118	...	...
Angers...............arr	7 6	1038	...	1442	...	20 8	2159	...	...

†—Until 9th October.

CHARTRES and ORLEANS.								
Chartres(80)dep	6 52	12 27	...	1441	19 5	...	2112	...
Voves (37)..........	7 44	13 20	...	1535	1951	...	2150	...
Patay	8 34	14 9	16 0	1630	2034	2110	2224	...
Orléans (34) arr	9 17	14 52	1627	1713	2114	2149	2258	...

Station							
Orléans dep	4 56	5 23	6 1	10 32	11 30	15 1	18 7
Patay (42A)	5 44	7 29	6 29	11 2	12 22	1548	1859
Voves..............	6 34	1026	6 57	—	13 12	1633	20 0
Chartres 42	7 12	1158	7 31	...	13 51	1717	2050

Station				
Voves.....................dep	7 50	13 35	20 18	...
Toury (34)...............arr	9 30	14 30	21 15	...
Toury.....................dep	5 29	11* 0	18 43	
Voves (42A) ....arr	6 19	12 32	19 32	

*—Tues. and Sat. 11.58

CONNERRE-BEILLE and PATAY

Station								
Connerre-Beillé dep	5 20	8 47	...	1310	...	1739	...	...
Thorigné	5 34	9 18	...	1327	...	1756	...	...
Montmirail-Melleray...	6 15	1038	...	14 4	...	1842	...	...
Courtalain-St.Pellerin	7 2	12 5	1222	1450	16 8	1946	21 9	...
Chateaudun (37)	7 45	—	13 7	1527	1731	2024	2148	...
Patay(42A)...........arr	8 22	...	1351	1555	1845	21 4	...	...

Station									
Patay ....dep	5 39	...	11 6	1123	1217	...	...	...	19 5
Chateaudun	6 21	9 59	1139	1228	1310	...	1513	1849	1956
Courtalain-St. P.	7 5	1042	1212	—	14 5	1451	1518	1924	2053
Montmirail-M. ...	7 49	—	1250	...	—	1621	—	—	2139
Thorigné	8 26	...	1326	...	...	1754	...	...	2214
Connerré-B.arr	8 41	...	1341	...	...	18 9	...	...	2229

†—At and from Saintes Ville.] **SAINTES, PORT MAUBERT, and JONZAC.** [§—Tues. and Fri. only.

Station							
Saintes Etat ....dep	...	6 50	10†25	15†15	18 18	...	...
Gemozac Etat	...	8 30	12 10	16 50	20 23	...	...
Touvent (42A)	5 6	9 4	12 55	17 27	21 2	...	...
St. Fort-s-Gironde	5 26	9 22	13 14	17 45	21 20	...	...
Port Maubert ......arr	...	...	13 35	...	21 38	...	...
La Bergerie	6 16	10 20	15 56	18 52	—	...	...
Jonzac (41)............arr	7 §9	11 10	16 32	19 22	...	...	...
Touvent ....dep	6 5	10 5	13 15	17 35	21 1	...	...
Mortagne Port ......arr	6 33	10 34	13 41	18 0	21 19	...	...

Station								
Jonzac ....dep	...	7 §25	...	9 30	...	15 0	1910	...
La Bergerie..........	...	7 55	8 15	10 29	...	15 50	1950	...
Port Maubert dep	5 10	—	...	...	14 0	...	...	..
St. Fort-s-Gironde...	5 31	...	9 25	12 35	1415	16 30	2037	..
Touvent..............	6 0	...	10 5	13 10	—	16 57	2056	..
Gemozac Etat.........	6 32	...	11 5	14 10	...	17 55	—	..
Saintes Etat ...arr	8 7	..	12†16	15 48	...	19 13	...	...
Mortagne Port ...dep	4 40	5 25	8 25	12 0	1610	...	...	
Touvent (42A)......arr	5 1	5 50	8 52	12 30	1640	...	...	

ETIVAL and SENONES.

†—Until 31st October.

Etival...dep	5†37	6 42	8 26	10 7	11 31	1426	1529	1715	1850	2019	...	**Senones**dep	5 †5	6 7	7 25	9 24	1052	1350	1455	1614	1812	1933	...
Senonesarr	5 54	6 59	8 49	1029	11 52	1443	1546	1732	19 7	2036	...	**Etival**...arr	5 22	6 24	7 48	9 45	11 9	14 7	1512	1631	1829	1950	...

NIZAN and LUXEY.

Nizan (44) ....dep	9 35	1630	1920	...	**Luxey** ....dep	5 10	7*30	14‡0	...	16*45	...	*—Thurs. & Sats. excepted.
St. Symphorien 42B	1051	18 0	20 1	...	St. Symphorien	6 10	8 25	1442	1450	17 36	18 2	‡-On Thurs. & Sat. only.
Luxey..............arr	1141	1850	21 8	...	**Nizan**.........arr	6 50	...	...	1545	...	1850	

LESPARRE and FACTURE.

E.M.															
	Lesparre (41) dep	...	5 30	10 0	...	1545	**Facture** ...dep	...	8 14	...	11 40	1525	...	1830	...
13¾	Hourtin..................	...	6 12	1048	...	1628	Taussat..............	...	8 47	...	12 6	1552	...	19 0	...
28¼	**Lacanau**	...	6 59	1145	1440	1819	Arès	6 10	9 30	...	12 20	1627	...	1918	...
43¼	Arès 5 15	7 5	9 55	—	16 0	19 6	**Lacanau**...42B	7 56	1028	12 5	—	1714	1816	—	...
48¼	Taussat...............5 29	7 20	1013	...	1620	—	Hourtin	8 45	—	13 1	...	—	19 8	...	...
56¾	**Facture**45A arr 5 55	7 48	1048	...	1647	...	**Lesparre** arr	9 27	...	13 55	...	...	1954	...	...

FACTURE and HOSTENS.

Facture............dep	8 15	11 50	18 35	...	...	**Hostens**.........dep	6 34	9 25	16 5	...	...	...
Hostens (42B) ...arr	9 22	13 10	19 44	...	...	**Facture** (45A) arr	7 40	10 49	17 10	...	...	...

BEAUTIRAN and ST. SYMPHORIEN.

Beautiran..................dep	9 5	...	14 35	18 15	**St. Symphorien**...dep	6 0	8 40	...	15 5	...	...	...	...	...
Hostens................................	10 17	13 45	15 41	19 37	Hostens (42B)	6 45	9 13	9 55	15 53	...	...	...	...	...
St. Symphorien 42B arr	10 45	14 18	...	20 18	**Beautiran** (45B) ...arr	8 5	...	11 0	17 9	...	...	...	...	...

BORDEAUX and LACANAU-OCEAN.

Bordeaux.................dep	6 10	9 45	16 30	...	...	...	**Lacanau-Ocean**...dep	6 40	11 10	16 55	...	...	...	...
Lacanau (42B) ....arr	7 52	11 52	18 12	...	...	...	**Lacanau**........................	7 14	12 0	17 30	...	...	...	...
Lacanau-Océan........arr	8 27	12 31	18 47	...	...	...	**Bordeaux** ....arr	8 54	14 9	19 17	...	...	...	...

St. ANDRE-DE CUBZAC and St. CIERS-SUR-GIRONDE.

E.M.													
	St. Andre-de-Cubzac ......dep	7 48	14 42	19 2	...	...	**St. Ciers-sur-Gironde**dep	5 8	9 5	16 3	...	...
17½	Blaye	9 1	16 25	20 13	...	...	Blaye (41B)................................	6 5	10 22	17 11	...	...
31½	**St. Ciers-sur-Gironde** (39A)	9 54	17 27	21 5	...	...	**St. Andre-de-Cubzac** 42	7 14	11 35	18 20	...	...

MOULINS and COSNE-SUR-L'ŒIL.

Moulins ....dep	6 25	13 20	1625	...	**Cosne-sur-l'Œil** ...dep	5 10	9 1	16 27	...
Bourbon l'Archambault...	7 29	14 23	1745	...	Bourbon l'Archambault......	6 42	10 9	17 37	...
Cosne-sur-l'Œil (42B)	8 35	15 29	1910	...	**Moulins** (58) ....arr	7 55	11 9	18 36	...

VARENNES and MARCILLAT.

Varennes dep	...	5 58	9 15	1010	13 46	16 1	19 39	21 37	**Marcillat** ......dep	...	...	5 8	...	11 30	...	1635	...	...
St. Pourcain ...	...	6 25	9 52	1111	14 10	1632	20 3	22 1	Commentry	...	...	6 34	...	12 43	14 30	1745	19 2	...
Chantelle	...	7 15	10 40	—	—	1728	—	—	Bezenet.....................	...	...	7 17	...	—	15 10	—	1938	...
Montmarault ...	6 14	8 26	11 51	...	...	1854	...	...	Montmarault	...	5 50	8 0	...	...	16 5	...	2012	...
Bezenet.............	6 45	—	12 16	...	...	1919	...	...	Chantelle	...	7 16	9 2	...	...	17 30	...	—	...
Commentry 36...	7 45	...	12 47	1410	19 0	1958	...	...	St. Pourcain	4 58	8 17	9 54	13 0	14 36	18 45	2049	...	...
Marcillat...arr	9 0	...	...	1524	20 11	...	...	...	**Varennes** (58) arr	5 22	8 43	10 16	1326	15 0	19 11	2113	...	...

CHANTELLE and EBREUIL.

Chantelle ....dep	7 20	...	14 10	...	18 0	...	...	Ebreuil ....dep	5 45	7 32	9 50	14 34	16 5	19 40	...	...
St. Bonnet de R. 36	8 15	11 40	15 24	16 46	19 8	2028	...	St. Bonnet de Rochefort	6 14	7 55	1013	14 59	1645	20 3	...	...
Ebreuil...............arr	8 37	12 2	15 49	17 8	19 30	2050	...	Chantelle 42B...........arr	6 51	8 53	...	...	1722	...	...	...

St. Victor (51B) **to Bourg-de-Thizy and Cours.**—7.45, 12.0, 15.30, 17.12, 20.24. From Cours to St. Victor 6.10, 10.5, 14.0, 15.45, 18.50.—**St. Victor to Thizy-Ville.**—5.55, 7.35, 9.30, 12.0, 15 19, 17.10, 20.35. From Thizy-Ville to St. Victor 5.0, 6.40, 8.7, 10.35, 14.20, 16.15, 19.10.

MARLIEUX and CHATILLON-SUR-CHALARONNE.

Marlieux ....dep	9 30	15 9	1855	Châtillon-s-Chaldep	7 45	14†0	1620	† 25 min earlier
Châtillon-s-Chal.arr	10 0	1539	1925	Marlieux ....arr	8 15	1430	1650	on Saturdays.

BOURGES and LAUGERE.

E.M.														
	Bourges......dep	4 45	11 55	16 7	...	...	...	**Laugère**.........dep	7 9	12 46	19 2	...	...
13	Levet......................	5 34	12 54	1657	...	...	...	Dun-sur-Auron	8 0	13 45	19 54	...	...
21	Dun-sur-Auron ...	6 5	13 36	1730	...	...	...	Levet.......................	8 32	14 24	20 28	...	...
34¾	**Laugère** 42B arr	6 50	14 21	1815	...	...	...	**Bourges** (38) arr	9 25	15 27	21 20	...	...

ANGERS and NOYANT-MEON.

Angers St. Laud dep	6 45	...	11 35	...	15 40	1740	Noyant-Meon...dep	6 0	10 40	13 5	16 10	...
Baugé	9 12	11 41	13 54	14 25	17 58	1950	Baugé	6 55	11 35	14 2	17 4	...
Noyant-Meon ......arr	10 6	12 35	...	15 24	18 52	...	Angers St. L. ...arr	9 16	13 53	1617	19 26	...

LA GUERCHE and CHATEAUMEILLANT.

[†-At St. Amand Ville.

La Guerche ....dep	...	5 7	...	11 3	1319	...	...	1712	**Chateaumeillant** dep	...	7 50	...	...	1147	...	1846
Sancoins	...	5 50	...	11 38	1354	...	...	1755	St. Amand Montrond......	6 5	9 17	...	1145	1336	1730	20 8
Laugère (42B)	...	7 1	...	12 37	—	1432	...	19 7	Laugère	6 55	—	...	1229	1425	1820	—
St. Amand Montrond	5 50	7†33	9 50	13 15	...	1514	1637	1949	Sancoins	7 54	...	1158	—	1525	1924	...
Chateaumeillant...arr	7 14	...	1120	...	...	...	18 8	...	**La Guerche** ....arr	8 24	...	1233	...	1555	1954	...

SANCOINS and LAPEYROUSE.

Sancoins ....dep	...	...	6 40	9 48	1413	18 2	...	**Lapeyrouse** ....dep	...	5 29	...	12 22	1740	...	...
Couleuvre	...	...	7 31	10 38	15 6	1850	...	Villefranche d'Allier	...	7 10	10 18	14 30	1948	...	...
Cosne-sur-L'Œil	6 20	...	8 57	11 56	1635	1954	...	Cosne-sur-L'Œil (42B)	5 45	8 54	10 40	15 38	2021	...	...
Villefranche d'Allier (37)	6 41	7 5	9 18	12 56	1726	—	...	Couleuvre	6 55	10 3	...	16 45	2129	...	...
Lapeyrouse ....arr	...	9 4	...	14 18	1910	...	...	**Sancoins** ....arr	7 43	1052	...	17 28	2214	...	...

LA VOULTE and DUNIERES.

La Voulte-sur-Rhone.. dep	...	8 0	15 43	20 57	...	**Dunières**..................dep	...	8 55	14 25	21 25	...
Le Cheylard	4 0	10 40	17 38	23 10	...	Raucoules-Brossettes...	...	9 30	14 58	22 0	...
St. Agrève	5 20	11 55	18 47	—	...	St. Agrève	4 0	10 44	16 20	23 15	...
Raucoules-Brossettes (46A)	6 54	13 14	20 0	...	...	Le Cheylard (46A)	5 10	12 5	17 55	—	...
Dunières ....arr	7 20	13 40	20 26	...	...	**La Voulte** (62) ......arr	7 15	14 17	20 10	...	...

ANGOULEME and MATHA.

E.M.													
	Angoulême (C.F.D.) dp	...	6 10	11 6	16 5	**Matha** ....dep	5 30	9 50	15 21	19 12	...	...
11¼	Hiersac..............................	...	7 0	12 3	16 56	Siecq	6 0	10 22	15 54	19 44	...	...
22¼	Rouillac	5 21	7 52	13 3	17 50	Rouillac	6 52	11 13	16 45	20 24	...	...
31	Siecq	5 59	8 29	13 42	18 27	Hiersac	7 39	12 6	17 34	—	...	...
38½	**Matha** (46A)..............arr	6 27	8 57	14 11	18 55	**Angoulême** (41B)	8 28	12 55	18 23	...	...	...

OLORON and SAUVETERRE.

E.M.								
	Oloron......dep	7 0	1420	1728	**Sauveterre**dep	7 9	10 24	17 2
12¾	**Navarrenx**......	8 24	1543	1852	Navarrenx	8 16	11 31	18 7
24¾	**Sauveterre**arr	9 21	1640	1949	Oloron 45A arr	9 30	12 45	1923

OLORON and MAULEON.

Oloron ...dep	8 28	1412	1725	**Mauleon** ...dep	7 19	13 5	1740
Lanne	9 30	1513	1826	**Lanne**	8 58	1443	1919
Mauleon 42Bar	11 8	1650	20 4	Oloron 45A arr	9 59	1543	2019

TOULOUSE, ST. GIRONS, BAGNERES-DE-LUCHON, PIERREFITTE, and BAYONNE.

	1,2,3	1,2,3	1,2,3	1,2,3	1,2,3	1,2,3	1,2,3	1,2,3	1,2,3	1,2,3	1,2,3	1,2,3	1,2,3	1,2,3	1,2,3	1,2,3	1,2,3	1,2,3	1,2,3	1,2,3	1,2,3	1,2,3	1,2,3
Toulouse Matabiau ...dep	0 48	...	...	4 50	...	5 15	6 35	8 16	9 21	...	9 46	...	1250	...	1311	...	...	1431	1557	1810	1947	...	23 6
Muret	1 15	...	...	J	...	5 49	J	E	D	...	1020	...	1314	...	1334	...	...	15 1	§	1844	*	...	2330
Carbonne (46A)...	...	...	...	...	...	6 22	...		...	...	1054	...	...	...	A	...	...	1534	J	1917	J	...	...
Boussens ......arr	1 59	...	...	5 47	...	6 57	7 33	9 18	10 18	...	1130	...	1354	...	1414	...	...	1611	1656	1953		...	0 17
Boussens ...dep	...	...	...	...	...	...	7 57	...	...	...	1145	...	...	...	1426	...	...	1627	...	2011		...	...
Salies-du-Salat	...	...	...	...	...	...	8 18	...	...	...	12 4	...	...	...	1443	...	...	1646	...	2029		...	...
Prat-Bonrepau	...	...	...	...	...	...	8 43	...	...	...	1227	...	...	...	15 6	...	...	1711	...	2059		...	...
St. Girons arr	...	...	...	...	...	...	9 5	...	...	...	1247	...	...	...	1520	...	...	1732	...	2120		...	...
Boussens ......dep	2 4	...	...	5 51	...	7 3	7 37	9 23	10 23	...	1135	...	1354	...	1419	...	...	1621	17§1	20 3		...	0 22
Saint Gaudens ...	2 34	...	...	6 18	...	7 45	8 3	9 53	10 51	...	1216	...	1427	...	1447	...	...	17 5	1723	2045	21 9	...	0 52
Montrejeau arr	2 49	...	...	6 32	...	8 3	8 19	10 7	11 5	...	1234	...	1443	...	15 3	‡—From 20th July until 21st September.	...	1723	1742	21 7	2125	...	1 6
Montre-jeau ......dep	...	...	6*45	...	...	...	8*26	1012	11 26	...	1245	14*4	...	...	1528		...	1750	1750	*2154	*2130	...	...
Loures-Barbaz	...	...	6 59	...	...	...	8 36	1027	11 36	...	1256	1415	...	...	1538		...	18 5	18 5	2215	2140	...	...
Salechan	...	...	7 10	...	...	...	...	1040	...	...	13 7	1426	...	...	1548		...	1819	1819	2228	...	...	...
Marignac-St. ...	...	...	7 23	...	...	...	...	1055	11 52	...	1318	1435	...	...	16 2		...	1835	1835	2242	...	...	...
Luchon ......arr	...	...	7 42	...	...	...	9 7	1125	12 11	...	1340	1454	...	...	1624		...	19 5	19 5	2310	2211	...	...
Montrejeau dep	3 3	4 0	...	6 42	...	8 15	8 40	1020	11 17	...	1257	...	1453	...	1513		...	18 4	1755	...	2140	2141	1 19
Lannemezan 46	3 30	4 55	...	7 4	...	8 50	9 18	1043	11 38	...	1325	...	1518	...	1537		...	1842	1816	...	22 2	23 4	1 47
Capvern	3 45	5 18	...	7 15	...	9 4	9 31	1054	11 49	...	1339	...	1530	...	1548		...	1853	1827	...	2213	2315	1 59
Tournay	4 7	5 58	...	7 36	...	9 27	9 57	1116	12 11	...	14 1	...	1 52	...	1610		...	1918	1849	...	2235	2337	2 21
Tarbes ....arr	4 38	7 0	...	7 58	...	9 57	1033	1138	12 33	...	1426	...	1614	H	1632	‡	B	1950	1911	*	2257	24 0	2 46
,, (45)...dep	4 5		6 35	8 10	8‡20	1015	11 5	1212	13 3	1325	1443	1520		1628	1650	...	1945	20 9	1922	2121	23 5	*	3 4
Ossun	5 13	...	6 55	...	8 40	1035	1124		...	1340	15 0	1538	☞	...	...	...	...	2026	§	2150	*	...	...
Lourdes.........arr	5 29	...	7 14	8 35	8 55	1053	1142	1241	13 27	1353	1515	1556		1652	1720		20 9	2043	1946	2220	2329	...	3 28
Lourdes ...dep	5*45	6*42	7*49	...	9 5	11 6	...	13 0	...	1423	1530	...	From 27th July until 31st August.	...	1740	1825	...	2058	20*4	...	...	...	...
Lugagnan	...	...	8 3	...	...	1119	...	...	...	1432	1543	...		...	1754	...	...	21 8	...	...	...	...	...
Boo-Silhen......	...	...	8 17	...	...	1129	...	...	...	1441	1552	...		...	18 8	*	...	2117	2 24	...	...	...	...
Argeles-Gaz'st	6 4	7 7	8 25	...	9 23	1143	...	1323	...	1451	16 2	...		...	1819	1848	...	2125	2033	...	...	...	...
Pierrefitte arr	6 14	7 16	8 34	...	9 38	1152	...	1332	...	15 0	1611	...		...	1828	1857	...	2138	2042	...	...	...	...
CAUTERETS 47	7 7	8 15	9 29	...	1033	1249	...	1425	...	1 53	1712	...		...	1928	1952	B	2236	2136	...	...	...	...
Lourdes ......dep	5 43	...	7 28	8 45	...	11 8	1155	1256	13 37	14 3	...	16 8		17 7	1730	...	2041	2056	1956	§—Runs from 10th July.	*—Until 21st September.	...	3 36
Coarraze-Nay ...	6 11	...	8 5	...	...	1140	1233	E	...	1435	...	1645		...	1756	...	...	2131	§			...	...
Pau..............arr	6 29	...	8 34	9 25	...	12 5	1259	1332	14 16	1455	...	1713		1745	1812	...	2117	22 0	2035			...	4 15
,, 45A dep 5 40	6 55	...	8 49	9 36	...	1226			14 30	1518	15 7	18 9		18 2	1844	...	2127					...	4 35
Lescar......... 5 49	C	...	8 58	...	...	1235	...	...	...	1527	...	1819		...	...	...	...	...	...			...	...
Orthez 6 40	...	...	9 51	1014	...	1326	...	...	15 8	1612	...	1933	...	...	1923	...	...	...	...			...	5 13
Puyoo ...arr 6 59	7 42	...	1010	1029	...	1345	...	...	15 21	1631	1553	1953	...	1848	1938	...	2210	...	...	...	...	...	5 28
,, ...dep	7 52	...	1050	1034	...	14 0	...	...	15 31	1 43			...		1948	...		...	...	...	...	...	5 38
Peyrehorade	8 21	...	1119	...	...	1445	...	...	...	1710	...	...	...	...	2014	...	...	...	...	...	...	...	5 56
Bayonne ......arr	9 22	...	1220	1122	...	1547	...	...	16 25	1810	...	...	...	...	21 4	...	...	...	...	...	...	...	6 41

A—Between Toulouse and Pau admits 3rd class only when travelling not less than 62 miles; or 31 miles for passengers [from Toulouse.
B—Only takes passengers travelling at least 93 miles.
C—Only takes at Pau 3rd class when travelling not less than 62 miles.
D—From 20th July until 21st Sept. will only admit at Toulouse passengers for beyond Pau, or those arriving by connecting trains.
E—Runs from 20th July until 21st Sept. Admits 3rd class only when travelling not less than 62 miles, or 31 miles if from Toulouse. J—Takes 3rd class only when travelling at least 62 miles.
H—Takes 2nd and 3rd cl. only when travelling at least 93 miles; exceptionally admits 2nd class at Tarbes for Lourdes.

CASTELNAUDARY and CARMAUX.

[*—One hour earlier from 25th Aug. until 9th Oct.

Castelnaudary dp	...	5 0	8 21	...	†—3rd class.	14 6	1620	1810	19 19
Revel-Sorèze.........	...	5 35	8 58	...		1441	17 8	1835	19 57
Castres (46) ...arr	...	6 17	9 41	...		1522	1750	19 4	20 43
,, ...dep	5 23	6 36		1132		1537			20 57
Laboutarie	6 8	7 22	...	1225	...	1626	...	...	21 37
Albi 33 { Orléans 4 30	6 45	7 59	10†29	1320	15 0	17 8	1945	...	22 7†
Albi 33 { Midi ...4 35		8 20	10 36	1326	1511	1725	1950	...	22 23
Carmaux...arr 5 3	...	8 48	11 20	1356	1555	1755	2016	...	22 49

Carmaux ...dep	...	5 45	...	7 17	...	1223	1559	...	18 6	2130
Albi.. { Midi	...	6 16	...	7 44	...	1254	1634	...	1855	22 9
Albi.. { Orléans	5 3	6 22	...	8 1	9 39	1345	1640	17 20	1943	2217
Laboutarie	6 7		...	8 44	1011	1426		18 6	2041	
Castres ......arr	7 23	...	...	9 28	1049	1513	...	18 53	2148	...
,, ...dep		5 36	7 3	9 42	1151		1615	20*44		...
Revel-Sorèze ...	...	6 24	7 34	1026	1536	...	1715	21*38	...	...
Castelnaudary	...	6 56	7 58	1058	13 8	...	1756	22*17	...	...

Albi—Orleans......dep	6 51	8 13	10 30	17 25	...	...
St. Juéry ....arr	7 17	8 31	10 48	17 43	...	...

St. Juéry..............dep	7 31	12 34	19 9	...	...	...	...	...
Albi—Orleans 43 ...arr	7 49	12 52	19 27	...	...	...	...	...

CARMAUX and RODEZ.

Carmaux ....dep	5 11	9 4	16 19	2020
Naucelle	6 20	10 0	17 16	2117
Rodez 45A ....arr	7 34	11 2	18 20	2220

Rodez..............dep	5 6	9 39	1347	1911	...	...	...
Naucelle	6 15	1046	1451	2017	...	...	...
Carmaux 43......arr	7 9	1147	1546	2119	...	...	...

CASTRES and BEDARIEUX.

Castres ...dep	6 27	7 29	1011	1111	1532	1546	16 0	19 9	2058	22 30
Mazamet	7 9	7 55	1047	1151	1559	1616	17 25	1938	2149	22 58
St. Amans-S.	7 24	8 14		12 8	1613	1630	17 58	1952	22 7	
St. Pons...4 13	8 13	8 53	...	25 9	1655	1720		2032	2255	...
Olargues 4 44	8 42	...	...	32 8	...	1749	...			...
Lamalou 5 15	9 11	9 38	1114	1355	1734	1817	...	...	...	...
Bédarieux 5 27	9 22	9 47	1125	14 6	1744	1828	...	...	...	...

Bédarieux dep	...	6 1	8 21	8 39	1050	1446	1812	1920	...	22 17
Lamalou	...	6 15	8 31	8 53	11 2	15'4	1829	1931	2024	22 30
Olargues	...	6 45	...	9 31		1531			...	22 57
St. Pons.........	5 35	7 21	9 27	10 5	11 5	16 5	...	...	21 2	23 25
St. Amans-S.	6 16	8 17	10 0	1050	1334	17 2	...	1820	2134	
Mazamet 4 45	6 32	8 40	1017	11 6	1439	1720	...	1848	2150	...
Castres arr 5 16	6 58	9 18	1040	1137	1517	1746	...	1939	2213	...

PUYOO, ST. PALAIS, and MAULEON.

Puyoo ....dep	7 22	7 55	...	1055	14 5	1558	1647	1946	2046
Salies de Bearn ...	7 37	8 8	...	1111	14 18	1611	1714	1959	21 1
Autevielle	7 59		9 58	1133			1749		2123
St. Palais......arr	8 27	...	10 18	1210	...	...	1835	...	2150
Sauveterre-de-B.	8 10	...		1148	...	...	1840	...	2134
Mauléon 42B...arr	8 39	...	...	1223	...	...	20 5	...	22 9

Mauléon dep	5 25	...	9 4	...	...	1242	17 7	...	...
Sauveterre B.	6 0	...	9 39	...	...	1350	1755	...	...
St. Palais dp	5 46	...	9 21	11 15	...	...	172	...	20 49
Autevielle ...	6 11	...	9 50	12 5	...	1422	18 4	...	21 8
Salies Bearn	6 37	9 33	10 15	13 15	15 0	1528	1832	20 9	
Puyoo 45...arr	6 49	9 48	10 27	13 35	15 15	1552	1845	2023	...

BAYONNE, PIERREFITTE, LUCHON, ST. GIRONS, and TOULOUSE.

	1,2,3	1,2,3	1,2,3	1 &2	1,2,3	1,2,3	1,2,3	1,2,3	1,2,3	1,2,3	1,2,3	1,2,3	1,2,3	1,2,3	1,2,3	1,2,3	1,2,3	1,2,3	1,2,3	1,2,3	1,2,3
Bayonne......dep	...	...	...	...	...	5 32	...	...	9 20	...	8 43	...	...	...	1340	15 3	...	...	...	1831	2020
Peyrehorade......	...	...	...	...	...	6 37	...	...	10 3	...	9 37	B	...	B	1455	1550	...	...	...	1936	2054
Puyoo .... arr	...	...	...	...	...	7 3	...	...	1026	...	10 3	...	...	...	1524	16 8	...	...	...	20 9	2110
Puyoo .... dep	4 1	...	...	7 10	...	7 28	...	1011	1039	...	1049	1125	...	1540	1626	1616	...	...	2030	2124	2115
Orthez	4 25	...	...	...	...	7 51	...	1026	1058	...	1112	1144	...	1559	1651	1632	...	...	2046	2146	2132
Lescar..............	...	...	A	F	...	8 44	...	A	G	...	12 1	...	...	...	1743	A	...	...	...	2236	...
Pau......... arr	5 19	...	...	7 59	...	8 53	...	11 4	1137	...	12 9	1225	...	1639	1752	1712	...	...	2125	2244	2211
Pau......... dep		5 30	6 50	8 10	8 30	9 13	...	1124	1154	...	1222	1318	1516	1657	18 7	1726	...	...			2224
Coarraze-Nay...	...	5 56	7 11	...	9 1	9 49	...	C	...	...	1255	...	1544	1721	1839	1747	...	...	...	...	B
Lourdes ......arr	...	6 28	7 40	8 58	9 40	1029	...	1211	1242	...	1338	1412	1619	1747	1918	1813	...	...	...	...	2319
CAUTERETS dep		...	5 29	7 8	...	8 55	...	...	1038	...	1139	1237	...	1519	1737	1618	1737	1918	...	2115	...
Pierre-fitte......dep	...	...	6 23	8 0	...	9 50	...	...	1133	...	1235	1333	...	1612	1832	1720	1832	2012	...	2220	...
Argelès-Gaz'st	...	...	6 34	8 10	...	10 1	...	...	1145	...	1247	1343	...	1624	1846	1732	1846	...	...	2233	...
Boo-Silhen ...	...	...	6 41	8 18	...	10 8	...	...	‡	...	1254	...	...	...	...	1739	...	‡	...	‡	...
Lugagnan......	...	...	6 55	8 27	...	1017	...	...	...	...	13 9	‡	...	...	19 3	1756	19 3	...	...	...	...
Lourdes ...arr	...	...	7 7	8 37	...	1029	...	...	12 6	§	1322	14 3	...	1644	1910	1810	1910	2036	...	2252	...
Lourdes ......dep	...	6 41	7 48	9 9	9 53	1044	11 51	1222	1252	1333	1351	1422	1630	18 2	1940	1823	1934	...	...	...	2333
Ossun..............	...	6 58	A	...	1010	11 4	...	C	...	1347	14 5	...	1647	1816	20 0	...	‡	...	...	...	B
Tarbes ... arr	...	7 14	8 12	9 34	1024	1122	12 15	1246	1316	14 5	1422	1446	17 3	1829	2018	1847	1958	...	...	...	2359
Tarbes ... dep	4‡50	7 43	8 26		1057		12‡30	1256	1326		15 6	1456	1711			19 5	20 8	...	...	...	0 9
Tournay...........	5 15	8 17	8 48	...	1126	...	12 53	1319	1347	...	1541	1521	18 7	...	...	1926	2029	...	...	...	0 33
Capvern............	5 51	8 58	9 22	...	1159	...	13 27	1352	1419	...	1623	1555	1853	...	...	1959	21 3	...	...	...	1 7
Lannemezan ...	6 3	9 12	9 34	...	1210	...	13 38	14 1	1428	...	1636	16 8	1910	...	...	20 9	‡	...	...	...	...
Montrejeau arr	6 26	9 40	9 54	...	1230	...	13 57	1420	1446	...	17 6	1628	1951	...	...	2027	2127	...	...	‡	1 33
Luchon ...dep	5 26	...	8 15	9*20	1126	...	...	...	1350	...	16 0	1543	...	...	...	1919	2042	...	...	2130	...
Marignac St...	5 56	...	8 54	9 41	1153	...	...	...	1411	...	1630	...	...	...	...	1950	...	...	...	2155	...
Salechan	6 8	...	9 7	9 50	12 2	...	...	...	1425	...	1639	...	...	...	...	20 2	‡	...	...	22 5	...
Loures Barb.	6 21	...	9 21	10 0	1212	...	...	...	1437	...	1650	1616	...	...	...	2016	2115	...	...	2216	...
Montrejeau ar	6 33	...	9 35	1011	1223	...	...	...	1447	...	17 1	1626	...	...	...	2028	2125	...	...	2226	...
Montre-jeau ...dep	6 46	5 20	10 6	...	1240	...	...	1430	1456	*1512	1719	1638	...	...	...	2039	‡2137	...	...	...	1 42
Saint Gaudens...	7 9	5 41	1025	...	13 0	...	...	1445	1513	1535	1743	1657	...	...	...	2055	2152	...	...	...	...
Boussens......arr	7 46	6 15	1050	...	1332	...	...	:	1535	16 9	1817	1723	...	...	...	2116	...	...	...	...	2 18
St. Girons dep	...	5 3	9 10	...	...	...	...	C :	1417	...	1642	...	...	...	...	2014	...	...	...	...	...
Prat-et-Bonre	...	5 25	9 31	...	...	...	...	:	1438	...	1714	...	...	...	...	2029	...	...	...	...	...
Salies-du-Sal.	...	5 51	9 56	...	...	...	...	:	15 6	...	1743	...	...	...	...	2046	...	...	...	...	...
Boussens...arr	...	6 7	1011	...	...	...	...	:	1523	...	18 5	...	...	...	...	21 1	...	...	...	...	...
Boussens ...dep	7 53	6 24	1055	...	1335	...	...	:	1542	1624	1823	1728	...	...	...	2119	...	...	...	...	2 23
Carbonne	8 34	7 2	...	...	1411	...	...	:	...	17 2	19 3	...	...	...	...	2143	...	...	...	...	...
Muret..............	9 7	7 31	1131	...	1441	...	...	1542	...	1736	1938	18 6	...	...	...	22 1	...	...	...	...	...
Toulouse......arr	9 42	8 4	1153	...	1512	...	...	16 5	1637	18 7	20 9	1827	...	...	...	2223	23 8	...	...	...	3 18

*—From 13th July until 21st Sept. ‡—Runs until 21st September. §—From 20th July until 21st Sept.
A—Takes 3rd class travelling at least 62 miles, or 31 miles if for Toulouse.
B—Only admits 3rd class travelling at least 62 miles. **C**—Between Pau and Toulouse runs from 10th July.
F—Takes 2nd class travelling at least 93 miles. Exceptionally takes for Argelès, Pierrefitte, and beyond, and for Bagnères de Bigorre.
G—Takes 2nd and 3rd class only when travelling at least 62 miles, or 31 miles for Toulouse passengers. Exceptionally takes up for all destinations passengers arriving at Bayonne at 9.0 from Hendaye line.

ELNE and ARLES-SUR-TECH.

Elne ....dep	7 20	11 10	15 0	1923	
Ceret	8 11	11 59	15 51	2014	
Amelie-les-Bains	8 29	12 13	16 6	2032	
Arles-sur-Tech arr	8 36	12 19	16 12	2039	
Arles-sur-Tech dep	5 25	8 42	13 26	1650	...
Amelie-les-Bains	5 33	8 50	13 35	1659	...
Ceret	5 49	9 4	13 48	1714	...
Elne (46) ....arr	6 35	9 49	14 30	18 0	...

NERAC and MONT DE MARSAN.

E.M.															
	Nerac ....dep	...	7 50	11 14	15 0	19 12	21 37	**Mont de Marsan** dep	...	7 40	10 51	1513	1813	...
9¼	Mezin	...	8 14	11 44	1524	19 35	21 56	Gabarret	5 52	9 13	12 42	17 2	1951	...
26	Gabarret	5 46	9 6	12 50	1614	20 22		Mezin	6 47	10 4	13 38	1759		...
58½	Mont de Marsan 45 arr	7 25	10 28	14 10	1743	...	...	Nerac 44..........arr	7 13	10 25	14 3	1824	...	...

PORT STE. MARIE and RISCLE.

Port S. Marie dep	...	6 45	10 13	†	1333	17 47	20 57	**Riscle**......dep	...	6 35	...	12 2	16 15	22 15
Nerac 44..............	...	7 35	10 47	11 48	1410	18 53	21 29	Nogaro..............	...	7 12	...	1236	16 49	22 49
Condom	...	8 16	11 25	13 21	1444	19 32	22 6	Eauze	6 1	7 52	...	13 9	17 23	23 15
Eauze	4 37	9 35	12 27	16 10		20 34	23 0	Condom	7 0	8 52	9 58	14 5	18 18	
Nogaro..............	5 6	10 10	13 2	17 46	...	21 6		Nerac	7 41		10 50	1444	18 59	...
Riscle 45 ......arr	5 39	10 47	13 35	18 58	...	21 39	...	**Pt. Marie** 45B	8 13	...	11 29	1515	19 33	...

†—3rd Class only.

MARMANDE and MONT de MARSAN.

E.M.														
	Marmande ....dep	...	7 35	9 42	...	1645	...	**Mont de M.** dep	6 14	11 25	1645	1815	...	...
38½	Bourriot	6 13	9 7	1246	...	1915	...	Roquefort	6 46	12 2	1723	1851	...	...
46½	Roquefort	6 44	9 29	1311	1524	1942	...	Bourriot	7 12	12 42	1745	1912	...	...
61	**Mont de Marsan 45** arr	7 19	10 0	1340	1628	2015	...	**Marmande** 45B	9 3	14 17	1936	...	...	...

LANGON and BOURRIOT.

Langon dep	8 45	10 54	17 18	18 35	...	...	**Bourriot** ...dep	...	7 11	13 53	19 18	...	...	...
Nizan (43B) ...	9 24	11 14	17 38	19 5	...	...	Bazas..............	6 39	8 49	15 37	20 21	...	...	...
Bazas..............	9 53	11 29	17 54	19 36	...	...	Nizan	7 18	9 15	16 0	20 34	...	...	...
Bourriot (44)	11 7	12 20	18 57	...	...	...	**Langon** (45B) ar	7 49	9 41	16 24	20 54	...	...	...

PAU and PONTACQ.

E.M.									
	Pau (Centre) .... dep	5 25	9 0	17 0	Pontacq ....dep	7 10	10 45	1845	...
11¼	Espoey	6 29	10 6	18 6	Espoey	7 36	11 11	1911	...
16¾	Pontacq ....arr	6 55	1031	18 31	Pau (Centre) (44) ....arr	8 40	12 15	2015	...

PAU and AIRE-SUR-ADOUR.

Pau (Centre) dep	5 50	1250	1815	...	**Aire** (Gare) dep	4 45	1049	1715	...
St. Laurent de B.	7 15	1415	1940	...	Garlin	6 0	12 2	1830	...
Garlin	8 40	1530	21 3	...	St. Laurent de B.	7 20	1313	1948	...
Aire (Gare) (45)	9 45	1635	22 8	...	**Pau** (Centre) arr	8 40	1435	21 8	...

St. Laurent de Bretagne ....dep	7 30	14 25	19 50	...
Lembeye ....arr	8 35	15 30	20 55	...
Lembeye ....dep	6 5	11 55	18 33	...
St. Laurent de Bretagne ....arr	7 12	13 0	19 40	...

PAU and MONEIN.

Pau—Gare Midi...dep	9 0	13 0	18 15	...	...	**Monein** ......dep	6 15	10 50	16 15	...	...
Monein..............arr	1025	1425	19 40	...	...	**Pau** (43) ......arr	7 40	12 15	17 40	...	...

BORDEAUX, MORCENX, DAX BAYONNE, and IRUN.

PARIS Orsay 34 dep	1938	21 0	...	...	...	20 15	2210	2210	...	...	23 44	9 46	9 46	12 16	14 0	14 0
	1&2	Y	1,2,3	1,2,3	1,2,3	1,2,3	1,2,3	1,2,3	1,2,3	1,2,3	1,2,3	1,2,3	1,2,3	Z	1,2,3	1,2,3
Bordeaux— St. Jean ......dep	4 0	4 37	...	...	5 27	6‡50	8‡23	7‡33	1047	13 40	14 20	1726	1736	19 19	2322	2345
Facture (42B).........	SC	...	...	...	6 33	7 34	...	...	1133	14 49	15 6	...	1818	...	...	...
Lamothe (45A)...	A	...	...	...	6 41	7 42	...	8 17	1141	14 55	15 16	B	1826	...	0 15	0 39
Labouheyre	...	...	...	...	7 38	8 25	9 44	...	1238		16 13	...	1923	...	...	1 34
Morcenx (45) arr	5 31	...	...	...	8 3	8 44	10 2	9 20	13 3	...	16 38	19 8	1945	...	1 18	1 57
,, ...dep	5 36	...	...	...	8 13	8 51	10 6		1315	...	16 43	1915	1953	...		2 10
Rion-des-Landes......	...	...	...	...	8 29	9 5	...	...	1331	...	16 58	...	20 7	Z	...	...
Dax ....arr	6 9	6 30	...	...	9 7	9 31	1039	...	14 9	...	17 37	1947	2031	21 7	...	2 47
Dax........dep6 5	6 42		...	...	...	9 40	1051	9 47	1420	...	18 28	1955	...	...	...	3 15
Puyoo ...arr6 45	7 7		...	...	...	10 6	1120	1024	15 7	...	19 17	2026	...	...	...	3 53
PAU **44** arr7 59	7 59	...	...	...	...	11 4	1225	1137	1639	...	21 25	2125	...	...	...	5 19
Dax...............dep	6 22	6 37	...	7 42	9 46	9 41	1045	...	1427	...	17 47	1956	2038	21 12	...	3 7
Saint Vincent ...1,2,3	...	Y	...	8 24	10 25	10 3	...	...	15 9	...	18 14	...	21 0	...	...	3 33
Bayonne ...arr B	7 3	7 18	...	9 8	11 5	10 25	1126	...	1551	...	18 44	203	2125	21 49	...	4 3
,, (43)dep6 55	7 7	7 21	8 25	9 41		10 35	1135	1250	1610	16 45	18 54	2043	2132	21 52	...	4 23
La Negresse ..arr7 6	7 18	7 32	8 40	9 54	...	10 48	1147	13 3	1623	16 59	19 7	2054	2143	22 3	...	4 36
Biarritz .arr7 19	7 29	7 48	8 52	10 9	...	11 0	1158	1319	1639	17 10	19 21	21 5	2157	22 10	...	4 51
Ville dep6 58	6 58	6 58	8 28	9 44	...	10 37	1134	1257	1613	16 46	18§58	2048	2125	22 16	...	4 23
La Negresse..dep7 10	7 26	7 37	8 42	9 58	...	10 55	1155	1310	1631	17 7	19 13	21 1	2149	22 26	...	4 43
Guethary 7 20	7 36	7 47	8 56	1011	...	11 9	12 5	1323	1644	17 20	19 27	2111	2159	...	...	4 56
St. Jean de Luz 7 29	7 46	7 58	9 6	1024	...	11 21	1216	1336	17 0	17 33	19 41	2124	2210	22 42	...	5 11
Hendaye ...arr7 43	8 1	8 13	9 24	1042	...	11 36	1231	1354	1715	17 51	20 0	2138	2225	22 55	...	5 30
Irun ¶.........arr7 50	8 10	8 25	9 31	1057	...	11 52	1241	1410	1732	18 5	20 17	2148	2235	23 5	...	5 47
MADRID (291A) ar	2258	...	...	...	...	...	7 0	7 0	...	10 59	4 30	...	...	14 12	...	6 8

Extra. { Bayonne ....dep 14 47; Irun ....arr 15 50 }

RC—Restaurant Car attached.
SC—Sleeping Car attached.

MADRID (291) dep	...	..	...	20 0	...	21 0	...	..	...	...	...	...	...	...	...	...	9 15
IRUN (291) ...dep	...	D	...	9 53	...	1210	...	14 14	...	...	...	1819	...	...	...	2119	23 3
	1,2,3	1,2,3	1,2,3	Z	1,2,3	1,2,3	1,2,3	1,2,3	1,2,3	1,2,3	1,2,3	1,2,3	1,2,3	Y	1,2,3	1,2,3	1,2,3
Hendaye ¶ ...dep	5 10	6 5	7 54	1021	1157	13†15	1342	14‡42	1455	17‡22	1655	1851	2033	2057	2113	2146	0 22
St. Jean de Luz	5 29	6 24	8 17	1036	1221	1335	14 2	15 1	1518	1741	1717	1910	2052	2114	2131	22 5	0 41
Guethary	5 38	6 33	8 27	...	1232	1346	1411	15 10	1528	1750	1727	1920	21 1	2123	2140	2214	...
La Negresse ......arr	5 50	6 43	8 39	1050	1244	1355	1423	15 18	1540	1759	1739	1932	2113	2131	2149	2226	0 56
Biarritz { ....arr	6 5	6 57	8 52	11 0	1256	1410	1440	15 31	1556	1814	1752	1951	2124	2157	2157	2240	1 14
Ville { ...dep	5 40	6 33	8 28	11 9	1232	1346	1415	15 8	1532	1753	...	1926	...	2125	2141	2216	0 48
La Negresse ......dep	5 57	6 52	8 47	1116	1252	14 2	1430	15 26	1548	18 9	1744	1940	2120	2139	2157	2228	1 6
Bayonne 44...arr	6 10	7 5	9 0	1128	13 5	1415	1443	15 38	16 1	1822	1757	1953	2133	2151	22 9	2241	1 19
,, ...dep	6 23	7 17	1020	1131	1323	1425		15 46	1614	1832	1842	...		2155	2215	...	1 31
Saint Vincent	7 7	7 45	11 2	...	14 7	...	...	...	1656	RC	19	...	...	...	...	...	...
Dax..................arr	7 45	8 7	1141	12 9	1443	1511	...	16 30	1732	1918	20 5	...	...	2236	2258	...	2 20
PAU (43) ...dep	5 4	6 55	9 36	9 36	Extra.—Hendaye to Bayonne 9.49.	1226	...	15 7	1518	18 2	...	1844	...	2127	2127	...	...
Puyoo.........dep	7 14	7 45	1121	1121		1416	...	15 59	1645	1855	...	2040	...	2211	2211	...	...
Dax...............arr	7 51	8 10	12 0	12 0		1455	...	16 24	1725	1922	...	2127	...	2236	2236	...	...
Dax ....dep	8 28	8 19	1220	1214		1518	...	16 40	1749	1932	...	...	...	2246	23 8	...	2 30
Rion-les-Landes......	9 8	D	13 0	...		1551	...	...	1830	‡	...	...	...	...	...	...	...
Morcenx.........arr	9 23	8 58	1315	...		16 6	...	17 17	1845	2014	...	...	...	...	...	...	3 10
,, ...dep	9 34	9 8	1325	...		1614	...	17 22	19 5	2019	...	...	3 46	Y	A	6 33	3 26
Labouheyre	10 0	...	1352	...		1640	...	...	1931	RC	...	...	4 7	...	...	7 0	...
Lamothe	11 1	10 4	15 0	...		1733	...	...	2029	2119	...	...	5 5	...	...	8 6	...
Facture	1111	...	15 9	...		1741	...	...	20*34	...	...	...	...		...	8 15	...
Bordeaux St.Jean	1158	1045	1617	1358		1821	...	18 53	2117	22 0	...	...	5 56	0 35	1 10	9 6	5 17
PARIS (35B)...arr	2244	1816	...	2054		4 56	...	4 56	...	7 58	...	...	1415	8 15	9 36	...	1415

A — For passengers travelling at least 93 miles; also admits 1st class without luggage at Dax.

B—At Bordeaux and Morcenx will take 2nd and 3rd class for Payoo and beyond.

D—Only takes 2nd and 3rd class for Bordeaux or who are travelling at least 62 miles.

Y—Pyrénées-Côte d'Argent Express, Train de Luxe; runs until 9th October.

Z—Sud Express.

*—Restaurant Car, Dax to Irun.

§—After 9th August depart 18.45.

¶—Customs Exam.

‡—Takes 2nd and 3rd class travelling at least 78 miles.

*—Sets down only.

†—From Hendaye to Bayonne takes for Dax and beyond.

BAYONNE to BIARRITZ, Local Line.—From Bayonne (station outside Fortifications) 7.0, 8.0, 9.0, 10.0 and half-hourly from 10.30 to 20.0, also at 21.0, and 22.0.

Biarritz (station in the town) to **Bayonne**, 6.30, 7.30, 8.30, 9.30, and half-hourly from 10.0 to 19.30, also at 20.30, and 1.30.

Mont-de-Marsan & Luxey.—28½ miles in 2 hrs. From Mont de Marsan 10.43 and 18.8. From Luxey 6.25 and 15.20.

MORCENX and BAGNERES DE BIGORRE.

K.M														
	Morcenx ....dep	1 37	...	5 55	...	...	9 26	...	9 37	...	1332	1651	1959	A
24¼	**Mt-d-Marsan**	2 22	...	7 8	7 36	...	10 8	...	1036	...	1425	1755	2051	21 0
44	**Aire**	2 57	5 26		8 22	...	1041	...	1119	...	1534	1840		2136
53½	**Riscle 44**	3 20	5 57	...	8 52	...	11 1	...	1151	...	16 6	1914	...	2159
69	Maubourguet..............	3 51	6 37	...	9 31	...	...	...	1231	...	1651	1958	...	...
74½	Vic-en-Bigorre (45A)	4 3	6 56	...	9 44	...	1135	...	1248	...	17 9	2014	...	2233
85¾	**Tarbes** ....arr	4 26	7 22	...	10 5	...	1155	...	1313	...	1741	2046	B	2253
...	,, (43, 45A)...dep	5 23	8 34	9 39		11 6		13 6		1525	1749	21 2	2013	23 9
90¾	Bernac-Debat	...	8 56	...	...	1128	...	...	...	1551	1810	...	2033	...
93¾	Montgaillard..............	5 46	9 14	B	...	1148	...	...	...	16 2	1821	...	2053	
98¾	**B. de Bigorre** ...arr	5 56	9 27	10 6	...	12 7	...	1334	...	1614	1838	2134	21 4	2335

A—From 1st August until 21st Sept.

Bag. de Bigorre dep	5 28	7 12	...	8 46	11 36	1213	...	14 3	15 35	1758	19 10	23 45	...
Montgaillard..............	5 4	7 23	...	9 8	11 47	...	...	1413	...	1822	...	...	...
Bernac-Debat	5 58	7 31	...	9 19	11 55	...	...	1420	...	1834	A	B	...
Tarbes ....arr	6 19	7 48	...	9 38	12 13	1240	...	1438	16 1	1858	19 37	0 11	
,, ...dep5 5			8 28		12 26	B	12 55	1452		20 3			0 2
Vic-en-Bigorre......5 27	...	...	8 51	...	12 50		13 16	1517	...	2042	...	...	0 39
Maubourguet.........5 40	...	...	9 5	...	13 1	...	...	1530	...	21 1	...	...	0 49
Riscle 6 25	...	...	9 49	...	13 30	...	13 52	1618	...	22 0	...	...	1 16
Aire (44) 6 52	...	...	10 15	...		...	14 11	1649	...	2235	...	...	1 33
Mt-d-Marsan ...7 45	...	...	11 35	...	...	...	15 0	1753	...	2322	23 45	...	2 14
Morcenx (45) arr 8 38	...	...	12 33	...	...	...	15 54	1845	...	...	1 3	...	3 1

B—Runs until 21st Sept.

BAYONNE & ST. ETIENNE-DE-BAIGORRY.

Bayonne dep	7 16	9 59	13 25	19 34	...	...
Cambo-les-B.	8 1	10 36	14 7	20 13	...	...
Ossès	8 38	11 14	14 47	20 53	...	...
St.Jean p.d.P'rt	8 57	11 31	15 7	21 14	...	...
St.Etienne ar	9 5	12 25	15 11	21 16	...	...
St.Etienne dp	6 30	10 49	16 8	18 57	...	...
St.Jean......dep	6 31	11 47	16 10	18 57	...	...
Ossès..............	6 51	12 4	16 31	19 22	...	...
Cambo-les-B.	7 32	12 45	17 14	20 10	...	...
Bayonne 44 arr	8 5	13 18	17 50	20 47	...	...

BORDEAUX, LAMOTHE, and ARCACHON.

B—From 1st August.

Paris 34 dep	2015	2210	...	...	...	...	9 46	9 46	...	...	...	...	14 0
	1,2,3	1,2,3	1,2,3	1,2,3	1,2,3	1,2,3	1Cl.	1,2,3	1,2,3	1,2,3	1,2,3	1,2,3	1,2,3
Bordeaux-St. Jean dep	6 32	7 33	10 0	1047	13 0	1420	1715	1736	1744	1935	...	2120	2322
Facture (42B)	7 19	A	...	1133	...	15 6	...	1818	1856	2031	...	...	...
Lamothe arr	7 23	8 17	1042	1138	...	1511	1755	1823	19 1	2036		...	0 5
,, (45) dep	7 27	8*26	1045	1147	...	1520	1757	1830	19 5	2043	2127	...	0 20
Gujan-Mest's.	7 41	9*38	1054	1159	1346	1535	...	1838	1920	2057	2143	22 8	...
La Teste	7 56	8*46	11 6	1212	1354	1549	...	1846	1933	21 8	2157	2217	...
Arcachon	8 2	8*51	1112	1218	1359	1555	1811	1851	1939	2114	22 4	2223	0 36

	1,2,3	1Cl.	1,2,3	1,2,3	1,2,3	1,2,3	1,2,3	1,2,3	1,2,3	1 Cl.	1,2,3	1,2,3	1,2,3
Arcachon dep	5 17	7 22	7 33	9‡20	1032	1240	1412	1640	17 0	17 43	2058	2127	2231
La Teste	5 28	...	7 41	9 27	1042	1246	1423	1652	1711	...	A	2138	2237
Guj.-Mes.	5 43		7 49	9 39	1056	1254	1438	17 6	1727	...	...	2153	...
Lamothe arr	5 55	7 36	7 58	...	11 8	...	1450	1713	1739	17 58	2112	22 5	B
Lamothe dep	6 0	7 39	8 6	...	1116	...	15 0	1716	1742	18 0	2119	2210	...
Facture	6 11	...	8 15	...	1126	...	15 9	1726	1822	...	...	2218	...
Bordeaux	7 18	8 17	9 6	1027	1233	1342	1617	18 3	1926	18 42	22 0	2313	2333
Paris arr	1725	1725	...	1816	...	...	...	4 56	4 56	4 56	7 58	...	...

*—15 minutes later on Sunday.
A—Takes 2nd & 3rd class travelling at least 78 miles.
‡—Takes for Bordeaux and beyond only.
Extra.—Bordeaux to Lamothe 5.27, 9.10, 13.40.

BEZIERS and NEUSSARGUES.

†—3rd Cl. only. §—Until 9th October. *—Until 25th September.

Béziers dep		...	4 35	6 23	9 45	13 0	...	14§3	1730	2016
Faugères		...	5 35	7 18	1024	14 6	...	1443	1830	2135
Bédarieux (45A)		...	6 0	8 11	11 1	15 8	...	15 0	1914	2153
Ceilhes Roqu'r'donde		...	7 6	9 16	A	1615	...	—	2029	—
Tournemire	4 41	...	8 17	1024	1253	1727	19†35	...	2138	...
Millau	5 29	...	8 55	11 9	1331	1816	2053	...	2217	..
Séverac-le-C. 45A	6 37	8*37	11†18	1217	1431	1925	—	...	—	2030
Le Monastier arr	8 4	9 35	—	1339	...	—	...	19 0	...	2134
Marvejols	8 23	9 52	...	1359	1545	...	...	1925	...	2147
St. Chély	9 41	—	...	15 5	1651	...	--	2042	...	—
St. Flour	11 5	...	9 40	1613	1733	...	1928	2140	5 0	...
Neussargues 31A	1140	...	1046	1648	1829	...	2029	—	5 40	...

Neussargues dep	...	...	...	...	...	7 19	...	8 32	11 45	1535	1845	2124
St. Flour	4 47	...	...	...	...	7 55	...	9 38	13 0	1623	1924	22 1
St. Chély	5 46	...	...	...	...	8 42	...	1047	—	1737	—	—
Marvejols	6 44	...	...	...	...	9 34	...	1156	...	1844	...	...
Monastier	6 57	...	...	...	...	A	...	1212	...	19 5	...	...
Séverac-le-C.	8 10	...	6 5	8§22	9†34	11 5	...	1350	...	2050	...	...
Millau	—	4 0	7 12	9 16	1230	12 5	...	15 2	18 7	2218	...	...
Tournemire	...	4 48	8 2	9 53	14 3	1250	...	1555	19 23	2258	...	...
Ceilhes Roq.	...	5 38	8 51	A	—	...	...	1655	20 9	—	...	...
Bédarieux	4 50	6 58	10 0	1133	...	1424	16 0	18 0	21 15	...	...	...
Faugères	5 10	7 34	1025	1153	...	1444	1653	1854	21 44	...	...	...
Béziers (45B) arr	6 6	8 35	1115	1227	...	1522	1837	1944	22 30	...	...	...

A—Admits 3rd class when travelling 93 miles, or from or for branch lines.

MARVEJOLS and MENDE.

Marvejols dep	7 48	9 55	16 0	...	...	...	...	...
Le Monastier dep	8 20	10 7	1616	19 25	...	...	...	...
Mende (45A) arr	9 40	10 57	17 8	20 17	...	...	...	...

Mende dep	5 35	8 16	13 55	17 52	-	...
Le Monastier (45A)	7 6	9 11	14 52	18 50	-	...
Marvejols arr	7 17	9 22	15 3	...	...	...

SEVERAC-LE-CHATEAU and RODEZ.

E.M.							
	Severac-le-Chateau dep	6 46	8 41	1149	1453	19†35	20 35
16¾	Bertholene (45A)	7 34	1010	1242	1545	20 15	21 23
28	Rodez (38) arr	8 2	1046	1311	1615	20 38	21 52

Rodez dep	4 39	7† 2	9 30	12 12	1430	1857	...
Bertholene	5 9	7 32	9 57	12 45	1543	1929	...
Severac-le-C. (45a) arr	5 55	8 12	1038	13 32	1731	2020	...

†—Until 9th October.

Bertholene dep	10 2	15 55	19 42	...	...	...	...
Espalion arr	11 2	17 4	20 46	...	...	...	...

Espalion dep	6 12	11 26	1758	...	...	...	...
Bertholene (45A) arr	7 25	12 30	1911	...	...	...	...

MENDE and LA BASTIDE.

Mende dep	6 52	11 8	1842	...
Bagnols-Chadenet	7 40	1148	1931	...
La Bastide-St. Laurent-les-Bains (58) arr	9 15	13 4	2049	...

La Bastide—St. Laurent-les-B. dep	6 13	10 28	14 13	18 12
Bagnols-Chadenet	7 32	11 53	16 27	19 35
Mende (45A) arr	8 6	12 27	17 13	20 9

BEZIERS and PAULHAN.

Beziers dep	5 15	1035	15 2	1825	...	...	...	...
Vias (45B)	5 39	11 8	1525	1858	...	...	...	...
Pezenas	6 12	1144	1558	1940	...	...	...	...
Paulhan (45A) arr	6 27	12 0	1613	1956	...	...	...	...

Paulhan dep	7 20	1224	1638	2035	...	...	...	...
Pezenas	7 41	1242	1658	2055	...	...	...	...
Vias	8 16	1314	1735	2134	...	...	...	...
Béziers (45A) arr	8 38	1336	18 3	2157	...	...	...	...

PAULHAN and LODEVE.

Paulhan dep	7 25	1235	1652	2038	...	...	...	...
Clermont-l'Hérault	7 48	1255	1714	21 0	...	...	...	...
Lodève arr	8 27	1334	1748	2133	...	...	...	...

Lodève dep	5 40	10 53	1457	1850	...	...	...	...
Clermont-l'Hérault	6 12	11 31	1542	1935	...	...	...	...
Paulhan arr	6 29	11 50	16 0	1953	...	...	...	...

MONTPELLIER and BEDARIEUX.

Montpellier dep	5 10	6 2	8 20	1048	1453	1855	...	...
Montbazin-Gigean	5 50	6 36	8 56	1132	1536	1940	...	...
Paulhan	6 35	7 7	9 27	1230	1635	2037	...	...
Faugères arr	7 24	7 44	10 3	1321	1724	2137	...	...
Bedarieux arr	7 46	8 2	1021	1341	1746	22 3	...	...

Bedarieux dep	5 37	1050	1435	1459	18§10	18‡43	1852	...
Faugères dep	5 58	1111	15 1	1520	18 31	19 3	1918	...
Paulhan (45A)	6 50	12 3	1538	16 9	19 5	19 37	2010	...
Montbazin Gigean	7 43	13 2	1610	1712	19 42	20 12	2120	...
Montpellier (57) arr	8 26	1340	1640	1748	20 13	20 43	2158	...

‡—From 10th October. §—Until 9th October.

AGEN and TARBES.

Dist.							
	Agen dep	...	5 57	8 15	10 37	15 8	19 40
22¼	Lectoure	...	6 58	9 6	11 36	16 3	20 47
43½	Auch (47) arr	5 20	7 50	9 49	12 26	16 52	21 44
56½	L'Isle-de-Noé	5 52	8 42	10 37	13 7	17 40	—
61	Mirande	6 9	9 1	10 53	13 22	17 57	...
79½	Rabastens	7 6	9 58	11 45	14 17	19 7	...
84	Vic-en-Bigorre arr	7 16	10 7	11 54	14 26	19 17	...
92	Tarbes (43) arr	7 56	1041	12 19	14 51	19 50	...

Tarbes dep	...	7 27	10 7	13 28	15 15	2025
Vic-en-Bigorre (45)	...	7 57	10 33	14 0	15 37	2059
Rabastens	...	8 7	10 45	14 16	15 47	2110
Mirande	...	9 6	11 49	15 16	16 40	2211
L'Isle-de-Noé	...	9 18	12 1	15 28	16 52	2224
Auch	5 18	10 10	12 34	16 10	17 41	2256
Lectoure	6 9	11 5	...	17 11	18 31	—
Agen (45B) arr	7 10	12 9	...	18 8	19 24	...

E.M.									
	Tournemire dep	5 15	8 10	10†25	1322	17 30	23 10	...	...
9¼	St. Affrique arr	5 42	8 37	10 52	1349	17 57	23 34	...	...

St. Affrique dep	4 7	7 18	11 51	15 0	1828	...	...
Tournemire 45A arr	4 37	7 48	12 21	15 30	1858	...	...

E.M.									
	Bédarieux dep	8 29	10 46	15 16	19 35	22 15	...	...	...
6¾	Graissessac-Est. arr	9 0	11 14	15 47	20 11	22 43	...	...	...

Graissessac dep	4 15	5 52	9 15	13 18	1718	...	...
Bédarieux (45A) arr	4 36	6 29	9 39	13 48	1748	...	...

PAU and LARUNS-EAUX-BONNES.—PAU and OLORON.

Dist E.M.												
	Pau dep	6 47	8‡11	9 35	...	1247	1435	...	1825	...	...	...
12½	Buzy arr	7 22	8 37	10 7	...	1319	15 9	...	19 2	...	...	...
21½	Oloron 42B arr	7 58	9 1	1036	...	1349	1551	...	1940	...	...	...
...	Buzy dep	7 34	8‡40	1013	11 19	1324	1515	1649	1913	...	...	...
24½	Laruns arr	8 16	9 4	1045	11 57	1356	1549	1747	1935	...	...	...

Laruns dep	6 30	9 24	10 16	1242	1410	16 5	1815	20§14
Buzy arr	7 8	10 1	10 57	1314	1453	1631	1853	20 39
Oloron dep	6 42	—	10 37	1245	—	1610	1820	20 20
Buzy	7 23	...	11 8	1321	...	1636	19 3	20 45
Pau (44) arr	7 59	...	11 44	1354	...	17 6	1939	21 13

‡—From 10th July. §—From 10th July; dep. 20.2 on Sunday.

BORDEAUX, TOULOUSE, NARBONNE, and CETTE.

☞ Carriages of the Sleeping Car Co.'s Train de Luxe, Paris-Barcelona Express, are attached to the 5.18 from Montauban to Narbonne and the 20.33 from Narbonne to Montauban.

	1,2,3	1,2,3	1Cl.	1,2,3	1,2,3	1,2,3	1,2,3	1,2,3	1,2,3	1,2,3	1,2,3	1,2,3	1,2,3	1,2,3	1,2,3	1,2,3	1,2,3	1,2,3	1,2,3	1,2,3	1,2,3	1,2,3
Bordeaux— St. Jean ...dep	...	...	...	0 30	...	5 1	7 40	7 55	8 15	9 22	1056	...	...	14 0	1535	1650	1735	18 41	1846	1950	2010	2245
Beautiran 42B	...	...	...	0†56	...	5 33	...	8§12	8 52	9 54	11 15	...	...	1432	16 8	1724	1755	B	1918	...	2043	23 4
Cérons	...	...	...	1†18	...	5 56	...	8§25	9 18	1018	11 30	...	...	1456	1632	1750	1810	...	1943	D	21 7	2317
Langon	...	...	...	1 54	...	6 25	...	8 39	9 40	1047	11 44	...	...	1522	17 2	18 9	1827	...	20 2	...	2137	2332
Saint-Macaire	...	...	...	...	...	6 31	B	B	—	1053	...	...	...	1528	17 8	—	1833	...	—	SC	2143	...
La Reole	...	...	...	2 24	...	7 0	...	8 57	...	1122	12 8	...	...	1558	1737	...	19 1	...	...	...	2213	2351
Marmande 35	...	...	...	2 48	...	7 31	...	9 18	9 45	1157	12 25	...	...	1633	1812	...	1927	19 51	20 0	...	2239	0 13
Tonneins 36	...	...	...	3 31	...	7 54	...	9 37	10 28	1217	12 44	...	...	17 1	1842	...	—	...	2023	...	—	0 31
Aiguillon	...	...	...	3 50	...	8 13	...	9 49	10 58	—	12 57	...	...	1720	19 4	...	...	...	2041	...	...	0 43
Port-Ste.-Marie 44	4‡53	...	...	4 7	8 18	8 31	...	10 3	11 35	...	13 11	1524	...	1742	1917	1940	...	...	2125	...	...	0 53
Agen 45A ...arr	5 46	...	...	4 33	8 38	9 0	9 20	1021	11 27	...	13 30	1619	...	1812	—	20 9	...	20 36	2155	2130	...	1 12
" ...dep	—	6 8	...	4 57	—	9 33	9 26	1031	—	...	13 38	—	16 5	1835	...	—	...	20 43	—	2136	...	1 18
Valence-d'Agen	...	7 15	...	5 43	...	1015	...	1054	...	...	14 18	...	1653	1917	...	...	...	...	...	...	...	1 43
Moissac	...	7 58	...	6 10	...	1040	...	1111	...	...	14 42	...	1725	1942	...	...	...	...	...	...	...	2 1
Castelsarrasin 46	...	8 19	...	6 25	...	1053	...	1122	...	...	14 56	...	1744	1958	...	...	...	...	...	...	...	2 13
Montauban ...arr	...	9 1	...	6 51	...	1116	10 18	1140	...	...	15 18	1 &2	1811	2021	...	...	...	21 42	...	2228	...	2 32
" 37 ...dep	5 18	—	7 6	7 16	9 25	1152	10 22	1145	...	...	15 31	1832	1842	2047	...	...	...	21 47	...	2232	...	2 42
Toulouse (Matab) arr	6 0	...	7 50	8 37	1036	13 4	11 1	1231	...	...	16 46	1916	20 0	2157	...	...	...	22 28	3 Cl	2311	...	3 31
" 44, 46 ...dep	6 28	6 38	—	9 35	—	—	11 11	1257	14 20	1740	17 5	—	—	—	2022	...	...	22 40	2327	2321	...	3 45
Villefranche-de-Laur	B	7 27	...	10 24	...	...	...	1331	15 11	1835	17 42	...	...	...	A		...	...	0†26	...	...	4 19
Castelnaudary 43	7 25	8 9	...	11 10	...	...	RC	1359	15 53	1925	18 14	...	...	...	2116	†—Stops to set down only.	...	23 34	1 18	...	...	4 47
Bram 46A	7 40	8 36	...	11 34	...	...	...	1410	16 20	1952	18 33	...	...	...	...		...	...	1 45	...	...	5 9
Carcassonne ...arr	7 57	9 4	1,2,3	12 0	...	...	12 27	1437	16 48	2022	18 51	...	...	...	2145		...	0 3	2 11	0 37	...	5 34
" 46 ...dep	8 4	9 14	1055	12 41	...	...	12 31	1446	17 8	—	19 16	...	1930	...	2149		...	0 7	2 26	0 41	...	5 44
Moux 46	8 26	9 57	1146	13 22	...	...	...	1514	17 54	...	19 44	...	2016	...	...		...	...	...	...	...	6 25
Lezignan (Aude)	8 38	1012	12 5	13 37	...	...	...	1527	18 11	...	19 58	...	2033	...	2219		...	0 37	3 21	...	...	6 40
Narbonne ...arr	8 56	1044	1243	14 9	...	...	13 15	1549	18 46	...	20 20	...	21 9	...	2229		...	0 57	3 58	1 25	...	7 10
" 46 ...dep	9 11	1059	—	14 19	1227	1643	13 24	1559	19 10	...	20 30	...	—	...	2244		...	1 5	—	1 35	4 20	7 24
Béziers 45A ...arr	9 31	1137	...	14 54	1250	1719	13 44	1622	19 51	...	21 3	...	...	...	23 7		...	1 28	...	1 55	5 8	8 2
Vias	RC	1213	...	15 46	1322	1753	...	...	20 30	...	21 40	...	...	...	A		...	...	...	...	6 15	8 33
Agde	9 59	1222	...	15 55	1327	18 3	...	1650	20 40	...	21 47	...	...	...	...		...	...	...	...	6 33	8 43
Cette 57 ...arr	1021	1252	...	16 25	1347	1833	14 24	1715	21 13	...	22 12	...	...	...	2349	...	...	2 12	...	2 34	7 10	9 12
MARSEILLES 49 ...arr	1438	1820	...	—	1810	0 9	18 20	2351	...	...	...	...	...	...	...	...	...	6 50	...	6 50	...	...

		1,2,3	1,2,3	1,2,3	1,2,3	1,2,3	1,2,3	1,2,3	1,2,3	1,2,3	1Cl.	1,2,3	1 Cl.	1,2,3	1,2,3	1,2,3	1,2,3	1,2,3	1,2,3	1,2,3	1,2,3	1,2,3	1,2,3	1,2,3	
MARSEILLES dep		...	...	...	1955	2035	...	2328	...	2328	...	...	...	...	6 0	8 10	...	8 10	1017	1150	...	...	...	1955	...
								B				B							B						
Cette ...dep		...	...	...	0 29	1 56	...	5 0	...	5 13	...	8 15	...	8 33	1030	12 6	...	1423	1527	1748	...	1910	21 0	0 2	...
Agde		...	...	...	B	2 31	...	5 21	...	5 46	...	8 37	...	9 5	1019	B	1231	1456	1549	1820	...	1932	2136	D	...
Vias		...	...	...	...	...	...	5 26	...	5 53	...	...	...	9 3	11 5	...	...	15 4	...	1828	Until 9th October.	RC	2145	SC	...
Béziers ...dep		...	...	...	1 9	3 18	...	5 46	...	6 35	...	9 2	...	9 44	1131	1247	1312	1532	1612	1853		1957	2210	0 43	...
Narbonne ...arr		...	...	...	1 30	3 51	...	6 7	...	7 14	...	9 23	...	1020	12 6	13 8	—	16 8	1635	1934		2018	2315	1 3	...
" ...dep		...	...	...	1 47	4 13	...	6 13	...	7 34	...	9 38	...	1034	1226	1313	...	17 1	1647	1948		2033	—	1 13	...
Lezignan		...	...	...	2 12	4 48	...	6 38	...	8 12	...	10 4	...	1112	1257	...	...	1739	1713	2022		21 0	...	...	...
Moux		...	...	...	...	5 2	...	6 51	...	8 31	...	1018	...	1129	1312	RC	3Cl.	1757	1728	2036		...	...	...	...
Carcassonne arr		...	...	...	2 46	5 40	...	7 19	...	9 15	...	1043	...	1210	1350	1411	..	1840	1756	2113	...	2139	...	2 10	...
" dep		...	...	...	2 55	5 52	...	7 24	...	9 27	...	1058	...	1223	1428	1416	1655	1860	18 5	—	2121	2147	...	2 15	...
Bram		...	...	...	...	6 26	...	7 45	...	10 0	...	1115	...	1255	15 0	...	1743	1924	1827	...	...	22 9	...	...	...
Castelnaudary		...	...	...	3 36	7 5	...	8 6	...	1027	...	1141	...	1326	1528	1452	1823	1956	1848	...	22 0	2233	...	...	...
Villefranche		...	...	...	...	7 41	...	8 28	...	11 1	...	12 3	...	1359	16 2	...	—	2030	19 9	...	...	2254	...	...	...
Toulouse ...arr		...	...	...	4 23	8 28	...	8 56	...	1146	...	1232	...	1445	1648	1537	1,2,3	2115	1937	1Cl.	2246	2322	1 Cl	3 36	...
" ...dep		...	...	...	5 15	—	...	9 8	9 16	—	13 0	1315	16 45	15 1	1710	1547	18 3	—	—	2045	—	2358	2337	3 48	...
Montauban arr		...	...	...	6 23	...	...	9 48	1024	...	1344	14 1	17 29	16 8	1753	1627	1925	...	...	2125	...	0 44	0 20	4 31	...
" dep		...	...	5 34	6 43	7 24	...	9 52	1054	...	—	14 6	—	1643	18 2	1635	1940	...	...	—	...	0 54	—	4 36	...
Castelsarrasin		...	...	6 0	7 28	8 8	...	...	1119	...	...	1426	...	1711	1821	...	2011	...	...	...	...	1 15	...	...	...
Moissac		...	...	6 15	7 14	8 37	...	...	1133	...	...	1437	...	1726	1832	...	2027	...	...	...	...	1 27	...	...	...
Valence-d'Agen		...	...	6 38	7 30	9 17	...	...	1156	...	...	14 4	...	1751	1848	...	2049	...	...	...	...	1 45	...	...	...
Agen ...arr		...	...	7 16	7 52	1021	...	1046	1234	...	...	1519	1,2,3	1833	1910	1729	2127	...	...	...	...	2 7	...	5 31	...
" ...dep		4 38	6 5	—	8 1	—	9 32	1052	1247	...	...	1525	16 26	—	1932	1735	—	...	1943	...	...	2 17	...	5 41	...
Port-Ste.-Marie		5 11	6 34	...	8 24	1010	10 1	...	1326	...	...	1548	17 3	...	1957	...	...	...	2024	...	...	2 39	...	F	...
Aiguillon		5 21	—	...	8 35	1024	—	...	1339	...	...	1558	17 15	...	20 7	...	...	...	—	...	...	2 50	...	...	...
Tonneins	1,2,3	5 40	...	...	8 56	1046	...	...	14 0	...	...	1611	17 35	...	2021	...	...	...	...	...	...	3 5	...	...	...
Marmande	4 35	6 57	...	9 26	9 18	1112	12 3	1138	1432	...	...	1631	18 30	...	2041	1821	...	...	...	...	...	3 30	...	6 30	...
La Reole	5 2	7 25	...	9 54	9 37	—	1231	...	15 2	...	...	1649	18 59	...	21 0	...	...	...	...	...	...	3 51	...	...	...
St. Macaire	5 28	7 51	...	1020	...	...	1257	...	1529	...	1,2,3	...	19 25	...	...	...	1,2,3	...	...	...	...	...	...	...	...
Langon	5 43	7 56	8 17	1030	9 57	...	1312	...	1551	...	1722	1712	19 45	...	2121	...	2130	...	...	...	...	4 16	...	...	...
Cérons	6 6	8 21	8 41	1053	...	...	1336	...	16 7	...	1747	1724	20 8	...	...	...	2150	...	...	...	...	4 29	...	...	...
Beautiran	6 34	8 36	9 6	1121	...	...	14 1	...	1626	...	1813	1737	20 36	...	...	...	2215	...	...	...	...	4 41	...	...	...
Bordeaux arr	7 12	8 58	9 45	12 0	1032	...	1437	1236	1648	...	1851	1757	21 11	...	2156	1920	2252	...	...	...	...	5 1	...	7 39	...

A—From 25th August until 5th October.

B—Admits 3rd class travelling at least 62 miles, or 31 miles at or for Toulouse.

D—2nd and 3rd class passengers must be travelling at least 93 miles.

F—At Agen admits 2nd cl. for Bordeaux and beyond.

SC—Sleeping Cars in these trains.

‡—Until 31st October. §—Takes up only.

BORDEAUX and CADILLAC.

E.M.										
	Bordeaux ...dep	5 55	8 0	10 15	13 50	16‡55	17 18	1848	...	...
5½	La Tresne	6 22	8 26	10 41	14 15	17 15	17 45	1913	...	...
20½	Cadillac ...arr	8 6	9 50	12 16	15 40	18 25	19 23	2043	...	...

Cadillac ...dep	5 10	7 35	8 40	11 50	14‡30	16 40	18‡58	...
La Tresne	6 47	8 45	10 21	13 16	17 20	18 6	20 47	...
Bordeaux 34 arr	7 12	9 5	10 45	13 40	17 50	18 30	21 12	...

‡—Not on Sunday.

NARBONNE and CERBERE

Dist E M														
	CETTE 45B ......dep	0 29	...	1 56	5 13	...	8 15	8 33	12 6	...	1527	1910	...	...	...
		1,2,3	1,2,3	1,2,3	1,2,3	1 &2	1,2,3	1,2,3	1,2,3	1,2,3	1,2,3	1,2,3			
	Narbonne ......dep	1‡45	...	5 25	7 43	9 2	9‡33	11 3	13†28	...	1650	2037	...	...	...
13¾	La Nouvelle	...	...	6 10	8 20	..	9 53	1139	13 47	...	1727	21 5	...	...	...
34¾	Rivesaltes	...	...	7 30	9 12	B	1024	1236	14 20	...	1818	2154	...	...	...
39¾	Perpignan	2 36	6 50	7 44	9 22	9 48	1033	1247	14 29	1745	1828	22 4	...	...	...
69	VILLEFRANCHE 46 arr	7 12	...	9 22	...	1038	1210	...	16 52	...	21 8	—	...	...	...
48½	Elne 44	...	7 15	8 34	9 57	—	1058	1324	14 49	18 5	19 6	...	...	...	...
58½	Port Vendres	3 12	7 50	9 20	1029	...	1117	14 0	15 8	1835	1938	...	...	...	...
61½	Banyuls-sur-Mer	...	8 2	9 39	1040	...	...	1411	...	1844	1949	...	...	...	...
65¼	Cerbere ......arr	3 25	8 13	9 59	1052	...	1131	1422	15 22	1856	20 1	...	...	...	...
66¼	PORTBOU ¶......arr	3 36	8 36	1042	...	...	1138	1440	15 30	19 5	2017	...	...	...	...
171½	BARCELONA 295...arr	7 53	...	...	...	...	1540	...	19 32	...	...	...	...	...	...

BARCELONA 295 ......dep	...	...	...	...	5 0	10 0	...	...	1416	...	1851	...	...	...
	1,2,3	1,2,3	1,2,3	1,2,3	1,2,3	1,2,3	1,2,3	1,2,3	1,2,3	1,2,3	1,2,3			
Cerbere ¶ ......dep	...	...	5 48	9 25	12 33	14†17	1521	1713	1830	...	23 5	...	...	...
Banyuls-sur-Mer	...	...	6 1	9 37	12 47	...	1535	1725	RC	...	*	...	...	...
Port Vendres	...	...	6 11	9 48	12 59	14 33	1545	1737	‡	...	2321	...	...	...
Elne	B	A	6 45	1017	13 35	14 51	1629	1821	...	...	...	...	...	...
VILLEFRANCHE ......dep	...	...	5 0	8 48	12 43	...	15 4	...	1824	1824	...	...	...	...
Perpignan 45A	4 35	5 40	7 18	1045	14 8	15 14	17 3	1841	1919	2035	2351	...	...	...
Rivesaltes	4 45	5 50	7 34	1056	14 22	15 26	1721	—	1929	2053	0 1	...	...	...
La Nouvelle	5 35	6 40	8 26	1142	15 13	15 59	1820	...	...	2217	0 31	...	...	...
Narbonne ......arr	5 59	7 4	8 57	12 7	15 41	16 20	1855	...	2015	23 3	0 50	...	...	...
CETTE 45B ......arr	9 12	9 12	1021	1347	17 15	18 33	2113	...	2212	...	2 12	...	...	...

A—From 10th October.

B—Until 9th October.

*—Takes 3rd cl. travelling at least 93 miles, and at Port Vendres 3rd class arriving by Algerian steamers.

†—Takes 3rd cl. travelling at least 62 miles.

‡—Takes 2nd and 3rd cl. travelling at least 93 miles.

¶—Customs Examination.

RC—Restaurant Car attached.

PERPIGNAN and VILLEFRANCHE VERNET-LES-BAINS.

B—Until 9th October.

E M								
	Perpignan ......dep	5 26	8 2	9 53	11A0	1115	1517	1930
10½	Millas	6 7	8 27	...	11 20	1225	1547	20 3
25½	Prades	7 0	9 10	B	12 1	—	1640	2056
29¼	Villefranche-Vernet-Bains arr	7 12	9 22	1038	12 10	...	1652	21 8

Villefranche-V. dep	5 0	8 48	12A43	15 4	1723	1824
Prades	5 19	9 9	12 55	1519	1738	B
Millas	6 6	9 52	13 32	16 7	1821	...
Perpignan (46) arr	6 39	1025	13 57	1636	1850	1910

A—Through Carriages (with lits-toilette and couchettes) between Paris and Villefranche-Vernet in these trains.

VILLEFRANCHE and BOURG MADAME.

†—Until 9th October.

Villefranche ......dep	7 31	9†34	12 30	17 7	Bourg Madame dep	5 10	9 41	14 6	17 30
Olette	7 55	10 0	12 53	1732	Saillagouse	5 49	10 8	1433	18 0
Thuès-les-Bains	8 16	10 15	13 8	1752	Mont Louis	6 44	10 48	1518	18 46
Mont Louis	9 7	11 18	13 59	1850	Thuès-les-Bains	7 37	11 39	16 5	19 33
Saillagouse	9 53	12 28	14 45	1932	Olette	7 56	11 53	1620	19 48
Bourg Madame arr	10 24	12 58	15 10	20 0	Villefranche ......arr	8 27	12 12	1642	20 8

PERPIGNAN, RIVESALTES and QUILLAN.

Perpignan ......dep	...	7 18	1148	1553	1755	...	Quillan ......dep	5 28	8 7	1435	17 7	...
Rivesaltes ......dep	...	7 41	12 8	1621	1820	...	St. Paul-de-F. ,,	6 30	9 23	1543	18 25	...
St. Paul-de-Fenouillet ,,	4 5	8 42	13 7	1735	1920	...	Rivesaltes ...arr	7 24	10 18	1645	19 21	...
Quillan (46) ......arr	5 9	9 53	1411	1848	...	...	Perpignan arr	7 44	10 33	1723	19 42	...

NARBONNE and BIZE.

Narbonne dep	7 28	1118	1656	2043	Bize ......dep	5*10	6 ‡0	8 43	1348	18 15	*—Until 9th Oct.
Bize ......arr	8 10	1236	1742	2124	Narbonne arr	5 57	6 47	9 25	15 0	18 56	‡—From 10th Oct.

MOUX & CAUNES.

Moux ......dep	6 56	10 23	15 22	18 6	Caunes ...dep	7 6	9 45	12 4	16 27	...	...	...
Caunes ...arr	8 5	11 29	16 12	19 8	Moux (45B) arr	8 14	11 0	13 0	17 21	...	...	...

CETTE and MONTBAZIN-GIGEAN.

E.M.											
	Cette ......dep	5 10	10 57	1450	1857	Montbazin-Gigean dep	9 1	1314	1713	2016
3¾	Balaruc-les-Bains	5 20	11 5	15 2	19 8	Balaruc les-Bains	918	1337	1730	2037
8	Montbazin Gigean 45A	5 40	11 21	1527	1930	Cette (45B) ......arr	925	1346	1737	2044

MONT-DE-MARSAN and DAX.

Mont-de-Marsan dep	5 35	11 27	15 17	1750	Dax ......dep	...	8 29	10 20	15 26	1810
St. Sever	6 3	11 54	15 52	1823	Montfort-en-Chalosse	...	9 6	11 30	16 8	19 3
Montfort-en-Chalosse	6 50	12 57	16 48	19 8	St. Sever	6 54	9 49	13 26	17 0	1955
Dax (45) ......arr	7 31	13 41	17 30	1945	Mont-de-Marsan 45 arr	7 20	10 16	13 55	17 27	2022

St. Sever ......dep	6 15	10 10	12 0	18 30	...	...	...	St. Sever ......dep	5 25	9 10	11 14	16 17	...	...	...	...
Hagetmau ......arr	6 49	10 44	12 30	19 0	...	...	...	Hagetmau ......arr	5 52	9 41	11 41	16 44	...	...	...	...

TOULOUSE and AX-LES-THERMES.

Toulouse-Matabiau ......dep	4 55	7 11	8 10	9 6	1340	17 26	...	...	Ax ......dep	4 30	8 12	1223	1450	1722	17 43	...	...
Portet-St.-Simon	5 15	7 31	...	9 26	1359	17 45	...	...	Tarascon	5 15	9 10	1311	1537	18 4	18 38	...	...
Auterive	5 51	8 11	...	...	1436	18 23	...	...	Foix (46)	5 57	9 55	1347	1615	1832	19 20	...	...
Pamiers 46A	6 45	9 1	9 29	1054	1527	19 26	...	...	Pamiers	6 37	1043	1423	17 1	1857	20 10	...	...
Foix	7 15	9 31	9 47	1124	1556	19 58	...	...	Auterive	7 29	1124	1523	1754	...	21 4	...	...
Tarascon	8 2	—	1016	12 6	1637	20 44	...	...	Portet-St.-S.	8 14	1159	16 3	1843	...	21 43	...	...
Ax-les-Thermes ar.	8 49	...	1055	1250	1721	21 31	...	...	Toulouse (45B)	8 37	1215	1625	19 3	1957	22 5	...	...

FOIX and ST. GIRONS.

Foix ......dep	7 40	14 50	20 10	...	St. Girons ......dep	5 45	9 17	17 42	...
Labastide-de-Sérou	8 12	15 27	20 48	...	Labastide-de-Sérou	6 39	10 11	18 35	...
St. Girons (43) ......arr	8 56	16 25	21 38	...	Foix (46) ......arr	7 10	10 42	19 5	...

CARCASSONNE and QUILLAN.

Carcassonne...dep	6 2	10 0	15 0	19 11	Quillan ......dep	5 20	10 10	14 47	19 22	...
Limoux 46A	7 1	11 8	15 55	20 15	Alet	6 1	10 47	15 27	19 59	...
Alet	7 15	11 23	16 10	20 29	Limoux	6 22	11 10	15 53	20 23	...
Quillan 46 ......arr	7 51	12 0	16 48	21 6	Carcassonne 45B arr	7 12	11 59	16 43	21 11	...

MONTAUBAN and CASTRES

‡—3rd class only.

Montauban dep	5 29	7 17	...	12 8	18 33	Castres ......dep	7 18	10 54	...	18 7	22 21	...
Villemur	5 55	7 54	...	1250	19 18	Lavaur	8 22	11 54	‡	1913	23 4	...
St. Sulpice 32 ...	6 23	8 27	10‡30	1330	19 57	St. Sulpice	9 6	12 20	1514	1955	23 25	...
Lavaur	6 40	8 52	12 10	1355	20 21	Villemur	9 36	12 49	1646	2026	...	...
Castres 43 ...arr	7 18	9 56	...	1459	21 29	Montauban arr	1012	13 24	1819	21 5	0 5	...

LANNEMEZAN and ARREAU-CADEAC.

Lannemezan ......dep	9 42	1215	16 41	20 30	Arreau-Cadéac ...dep	7 30	1046	13 32	17 47
Arreau-Cadéac ......arr	10 26	13 1	17 27	21 20	Lannemezan (43) arr	8 17	1130	14 19	18 32

Castelsarrasin (45B) to Beaumont-de-Lomagne, in 1 hour, 7.30, 11.30, 18.33. From Beaumont-de-Lomagne 5.5, 9.35, 16.46.

BRAM and LAVELANET.

Bram..........dep	8 2	15 2	1628	18 48
Belvèze (46A) ...	8 32	15 29	1650	19 15
Moulin-Neuf......	8 57	16 2	1715	20 4
Lavelanet......arr	10 13	17 13	...	21 35

Lavelanet ....dep	5 27	...	5 50	10 33	15 49	...
Moulin-Neuf (46A)...	6 29	7 37	9 10	11 51	17 16	...
Belvèze	6 54	8 2	10 8	12 19	17 45	...
Bram (45B) ....arr	7 17	8 24	10 59	12 42	18 12	...

Belvèze ....dep	8 51	12 30	19 25	...	...
Limoux (46)....arr	9 37	13 11	20 0	...	...

Limoux..............dep	7 15	11 20	16 3	...	...
Belvèze (46A) ...arr	7 51	12 7	16 39	...	...

Moulin-Neuf......dep	5 21	9 10	17 25	20 23	...
Pamiers (46) ......arr	6 15	10 3	18 46	21 26	...

Pamiers ....dep	6 42	10 46	15 32	19 30	...
Moulin-Neuf 46A arr	7 34	11 42	16 59	20 22	...

ARCACHON and CAZAUX.

Arcachon ...dep	7 30	17 0	...
La Teste (45A)	8 45	18 45	...
Cazaux ....arr	9 25	19 25	...

Cazaux......dep	6 45	16 0	...	...
La Teste...........	7 25	16 40	...	...
Arcachon arr	8 9	16 46	...	...

GERZAT and MARINGUES.

E.M.					
	Gerzat...........dep	8 4	13 8	17 45	...
12½	Maringues......arr	9 3	14 6	18 42	...

Maringues ....dep	6 0	10 55	15 50	...	...
Gerzat (58).........arr	7 3	11 57	16 55	...	...

RIOM and VOLVIC.

E.M.							
	Riom ....dep	6 13	8 0	13 35	1812	...	...
5	Volvic (Bourg)	6 34	8 32	14 7	1833	...	...
11	„ (Orleans Sta.)31	...	9 5	14 40	...	...	

Volvic (Orleans Sta) dp	...	9 19	16 55	...	...
„ (Bourg)............	6 40	10 2	17 49	18 38	...
Riom (58) ....arr	7 2	10 25	17 59	19 0	...

ST. JEAN d'ANGELY and COGNAC.

E.M.							
	St. Jean d'Angely dep	5 43	8 40	14 6	18 16	...	...
11¼	Matha (42B)	6 32	9 40	15 6	19 1	...	...
28¾	Cognac (Etat) (41B) arr	7 40	11 12	16 32	20 10	...	...

Cognac (Etat) ......dep	6 1	8 6	12 38	17 32	...	...
Matha	7 10	9 26	14 27	19 2	...	...
St. Jean d'Angely ar	7 49	10 11	15 20	19 48	...	...

ST. JEAN d'ANGELY and ST. SAVIOL.

E.M.							
	St. Jean d'Angely dep	5 37	...	13 57	...	19 36	...
29¾	Chef-Boutonne.............	7 51	14 35	16 27	19 0	21 44	...
44¾	St. Saviol (35) ....arr	8 44	15 30	...	20 0	...	...

St. Saviol ....dep	...	5 45	...	9 10	16 2	...
Chef-Boutonne	5 15	6 46	9 0	10 3	1656	17 6
St. Jean d'Angely ar	7 18	...	11 21	...	...	18 52

ST. JEAN d'ANGELY and MARANS.

E.M.					
	St. Jean d'Angely dep	6 32	10 22	15 30	...
20½	Surgères (Etat)	8 30	12 12	17 5	18 5
32¾	Ferrieres-d'Aunis (22A)	9 11	13 5	—	19 3
41½	Marans (Etat) (41)...arr	9 40	13 42	...	19 40

Marans (Etat) ......dep	5 0	10 0	16 6	...	...
Ferrieres-d'Aunis	5 34	10 40	1641	...	...
Surgères (Etat)	6 54	12 10	1722	17 53	...
St. Jean d'Angely ar	8 30	13 45	...	19 21	...

*†—Not on Tuesday.]

TOULOUSE and BOULOGNE-SUR-GESSE.

E.M.								
—	Toulouse (Gare Roguet) dp	6 0	8 30	1010	12†40	1710	1840	...
11¼	Fonsorbes..........................	6 52	9 19	11 9	13 29	18 0	1929	...
16¾	Ste. Foy-de-Peyrol...arr	...	9 45	...	13 55	...	1955	...
37½	Lombez..............................	8 44	—	1320	—	1955	—	...
61	Boulogne-s-Gesse ......arr	1020	...	1526*	...	2130	...	...

Boulogne-s-Gesse dep	...	5 0	...	...	9 20	...	16 0
Lombez	...	6 39	...	...	1124	...	1734
Ste. Foy-de-Peyrol dp	6 25	...	1035	†	...	1635	...
Fonsorbes	6 50	8 28	11 2	11 6	1328	17 8	1928
Toulouse ....arr	7 47	9 25	...	12 0	1416	18 0	2030

TOULOUSE and CADOURS.

E.M.					
	Toulouse (Gare Roguet) dep	6 50	9 45	18 10	...
30	Cadours...........................arr	9 3	12 6	20 20	...

Cadours ....dep	5 38	11 15	17 5	...
Toulouse ....arr	7 54	13 34	19 15	...

PERPIGNAN and LE BARCARES.

E.M.								
	Perpignan ....dep	7 55	10 50	17 8	18 54	...	...	...
6¼	Pia	8 29	11 22	17 49	19 26	...	...	...
14½	Le Barcares ....arr	9 5	11 58	18 31	20 2	...	...	...
...	Le Barcares ....dep	5 40	9 10	12 40	15 45	...	...	...
...	Pia	6 18	9 53	13 27	16 28	...	...	...
...	Perpignan (46)..............arr	6 44	10 20	13 58	16 54	...	...	...

PIA and BAIXAS.

E.M.								
	Pia ....dep	6 20	11 0	13 33	16 46	...	...	...
6¾	Baixas ....arr	6 54	11 34	14 41	17 40	...	...	...
...	Baixas...........................dep	7 58	11 43	14 58	17 50	...	...	...
...	Pia (46A) ....arr	8 28	12 16	16 17	18 52	...	...	...

PERPIGNAN and THUIR.

E.M.								
	Perpignan ....dep	6 51	10 55	15 15	17 5	19 12	...	...
10	Thuir.............................arr	7 33	12 5	15 57	17 48	19 55	...	...
...	Thuir ....dep	5 50	8 15	13 5	16 7	18 12	...	...
...	Perpignan (46) ....arr	6 33	9 25	13 48	16 50	18 51	...	...

TOULOUSE and SABARAT.

Toulouse (Gare Roguet) ...dep	5 45	10 0	1655
St. Sulpice-sur-Lèze	8 0	1238	19 7
Pailhes	9 42	14 0	2022
Sabarat..............................arr	1035	1439	2054
Sabarat (46A) ....dep	5 0	9 40	1555
Pailhes..................................	5 36	10 18	1633
St. Sulpice-sur-Lèze	7 6	11 47	1753
Toulouse..............................arr	9 15	14 0	1959

ST. GAUDENS and ASPET.

E.M.					
	St. Gaudens.....dep	8 45	13 50	17 50	...
13	Aspet.................arr	9 50	14 55	18 55	...
...	Aspet ....dep	6 35	11*30	15 50	...
...	St. Gaudens 43 arr	7 40	12 35	16 55	...

*—10.15 on Thursday.

CARBONNE and LE MAS D'AZIL.

E.M.					
	Carbonne (S.O.) dep	7 15	11 15	19 30	...
19¼	Sabarat..................	8 46	12 52	20 58	...
22¼	Le Mas d'Azil ...arr	9 5	13 10	21 15	...
...	Le Mas d'Azil ...dep	4 40	11 45	16 45	...
...	Sabarat (46A)	5 3	12 9	17 6	...
...	Carbonne (43) ...arr	6 26	13 44	18 33	...

ARLES-SUR-TECH and PRATS-DE-MOLLO (Service from day of opening).

E.M.								
	Arles-sur-Tech ....dep	8 51	8 57	1311	1317	2054	21 0	...
6¼	Manyaques	9 41	9 44	14 1	14 4	2142	2147	...
11¾	St. Laurent-de-Cerdans	...	1022	...	1442	...	2223	...
13	Prats-de-Mollo ....arr	1033	...	1453	...	2234	...	...

Prats-de-Mollo.........dep	...	6 54	...	1120	...	1510	...
St. Laurent-de-Cerdans	7 2	...	1127	...	1517	...	...
Manyaques	7 37	7 43	12 4	1210	1554	16 0	...
Arles-sur-Tech 44 ...arr	8 21	8 27	1248	1254	1638	1644	...

LA VOUTE-SUR-LOIRE and RAUCOULES-BROSSETTES.

La Voute-sur-Loire ...dep	...	6 25	9 50	...	1523	...	20 20
Yssingeaux	5 10	8 15	11 1	11 55	1634	1840	21 31
Raucoules-Brossettes 42B	6 15	9 20	...	13 0	...	1945	...

Raucoules-Brossettes dep	6 40	9 50	...	1515	...	2158
Yssingeaux	7 44	10 52	13 15	1617	18 45	23 0
La Voute-sur-Loire 59 arr	8 45	...	14 15	...	19 45	...

TOURNON and LE CHEYLARD.

E.M.						
	Tournon ......dep	7 43	14 50	20 0	...	...
20¼	Lamastre	9 27	16 36	21 35	...	...
33	Le Cheylard (42B)	10 31	17 31	22 30	...	...

Le Cheylard.........dep	5 12	12 0	15 45	...
Lamastre...................	6 7	13 2	16 53	...
Tournon (62) ......arr	7 20	14 20	18 17	...

BLOIS and LAMOTTE-BEUVRON.

Blois (Vienne).........dep	6 37	11 44	16 32	...	...	...
Bracieux	7 29	12 36	17 26	...	...	...
Lamotte-Beuvron 32 arr	9 37	14 41	19 32	...	...	...

Lamotte-Beuvron ...dep	7 41	11 0	16 12	...	...	...	...
Bracieux	9 46	13 7	18 21	...	...	...	...
Blois (Vienne).........arr	10 33	14 0	19 8	...	...	...	...

AIX-LES-BAINS and ANNECY.

A—From 2nd July until 20th Sept.

Aix-les-Bains......dep	5 33	6 25	9 22	9 58	11 5	1246	16 45	1757	2341
Grésy-sur-Aix	...	6 34	9 33	...	1114	1255	16 55	18 6	2350
Bloye	A	6 54	9 54	...	1134	1317	17 16	1826	...
Rumilly	...	7 2	10 2	...	1143	1325	17 25	1834	0 20
Lovagny	...	7 20	1020	...	12 0	1342	17 46	1852	0 37
Annecy 61A arr	6 28	7 31	1030	1050	1210	1352	17 56	19 2	0 47

Annecy dep	4 5	8 10	12 27	14 1	1520	1735	1940	2131	2248
Lovagny	4 14	8 19	12 37	1411	1531	1744	...	2140	..
Rumilly	4 31	8 37	12 55	1428	1550	18 2	...	2158	A
Bloye	4 38	8 44	13 2	1435	1557	18 9	...	22 5	...
Grésy-sur-A.	4 56	9 2	13 23	1454	1616	1832	...	2224	...
Aix-les-B.	5 2	9 8	13 29	15 0	1623	1838	2031	2230	2338

ANNECY and ALBERTVILLE

Annecy......dep	6 40	1115	16 27	21 0	...	...
St. Jorioz	7 2	1133	16 45	21 18	...	...
Lathuille	7 8	1139	16 51	21 24	...	...
Ugine	7 53	1225	17 ?8	22 8	...	...
Albertville arr	8 8	1240	17 53	22 23	...	...

Albertville dep	5 52	8 34	13 2	19 2	...	...
Ugine	6 10	8 53	1320	1921	...	...
Lathuille	6 47	9 32	1358	1959	...	...
St. Jorioz	7 0	9 47	1411	2012	...	...
Annecy 61A arr	7 16	10 4	1427	2028	...	...

ANNECY and THONES.

Annecy dep	4 45	8 *0	11 0	13†30	16 30	19§35		
Alex	5 46	8 51	1157	14 21	17 27	20 32		
Thones arr	6 10	9 10	1220	14 40	17 50	20 55		

Thones ...dep	6 30	9*30	12 40	15 †0	18 10	21§15	...	...
Alex	6 52	9 52	13 0	15 22	18 30	21 37	...	...
Annecy 47 arr	7 45	1045	13 50	16 15	19 20	22 30	...	...

*—Until 15th Sept. †—Until 30th Sept. §—Mon., Thurs., and Sat. only from 10th July until 10th Sept.

MEYRARGUES and DRAGUIGNAN.

*—May not run.

E.M.							
	Meyrargues ...dep	...	7 10	13 *0	16 30	1830	
12½	Rians	...	8 4	14 1	17 23	1922	
26¾	Barjols	4 54	9 14	15 12	18 20	2018	
42¼	Salernes	5 55	1025	16 26	19 24		
61	Draguignan ....arr	6 57	1135	17 44	20 28		...

Draguignan ......dep	...	4 40	9 *30	12 45	18 2	
Salernes	...	5 56	11 18	14 5	1917	
Barjols	4 40	7 1	12 37	15 21	2014	
Rians	5 40	8 3	13 55	16 28		
Meyrargues 63A arr	6 18	8 40	14 36	17 6		..

DRAGUIGNAN and GRASSE-S. F.

*—May not run.

Draguignan ......dep	4 48	9*15	13 35	18 3
Fayence	6 30	11 12	15 18	19 47
Montauroux	6 54	11 44	15 45	20 12
Grasse-S. F. 47...arr	7 45	12 35	16 36	21 1

Grasse-S. F. ....dep	5 45	8 35	14*24	16 44
Montauroux	6 36	9 29	15 22	17 37
Fayence	7 3	9 53	15 52	18 5
Draguignan 47.........arr	8 41	11 37	17 39	19 49

GRASSE and NICE.

*—May not run.

Grasse-s. F. dep	5 46	7 59	13*25	1649	...
Vence (53C)	6 49	9 17	14 55	1756	...
Colomars	7 23	10 2	15 46	1841	...
Nice ....arr	7 56	10 33	16 25	1912	...

Nice ....dep	5 50	8 *0	14 0	18 5	...
Colomars	6 32	8 55	1442	18 54	...
Vence	7 23	10 1	1527	19 45	...
Grasse-s. F. (47) arr	8 23	1114	1629	20 45	...

DIJON (Port Neuve) and CHAMPLITTE.

Dijon ....dep	6 18	11 8	1754	...	...
Mirebeau	7 56	12 38	1924	...	...
Fontaine-Française	8 43	13 30	2011	...	...
Mornay	9 9	13 59	2037	...	...
Champlitte 74A arr	9 31	14 21	2059	...	...

Champlitte ...dep	5 6	10 40	16 4	...
Mornay	5 28	11 5	16 27	...
Fontaine Française	5 55	11 34	16 53	...
Mirebeau	6 47	12 30	17 45	...
Dijon (63B) ......arr	8 15	14 7	19 14	...

Dijon (Port Neuve)...dep	7 9	10 18	18 0	...	...	...
Val-Suzon-Haut	8 16	11 26	19 9	...	...	...
St. Seine-l'Abbaye ...arr	8 57	12 7	19 50	...	...	...

St. Seine l'Abbaye ... dep	6 18	12 14	16 45	...	...	...
Val-Suzon-Haut	6 59	12 55	17 26	...	...	...
Dijon (Port Neuve) ...arr	8 3	13 59	18 37	...	...	...

PIERREFITTE, CAUTERETS, and LUZ ST. SAUVEUR.

Service liable to modification. ‡—Until 22nd Sept.

Pierrefitte dep	6‡29	7 37	8‡50	9 55	12 8	1347	1513	1632	1849	19‡12	20‡57	21 58
Nestalas	...	...	8 53	10 2	1212	1354	...	...	1855	...	...	...
Calypso	...	...	9 19	1026	1236	1418	...	...	1919	...	...	...
Cauterets arr	7 7	8 15	9 29	1033	1249	1425	1553	1712	1928	19 52	21 36	22 36

Cauterets dep	5 29	7 8	8 55	10‡38	1139	12‡37	1519	1618	17‡37	19‡18	21‡15	...
Calypso	5 37	7 13	9 4	10 38	1146	...	1519	1627	17 45	...	21 20	...
Nestalas	6 3	7 39	9 28	11 4	1212	...	1547	1653	18 10	...	21 48	...
Pierrefitte(43)	6 7	7 46	9 35	11 16	1218	13 18	1557	1658	18 15	19 56	21 53	...

Pierrefitte dep	6‡29	7 37	8‡50	9 55	12 8	13 47	1518	16 27	1845	19‡12	20‡55	21 54
Nestalas	...	...	8 56	10 0	1212	13 54	1524	...	...	...	...	...
Luz ....arr	7 13	8 21	9 37	1041	1255	14 32	16 3	17 14	1930	19 57	21 41	22 44

Luz.........dep	5 24	7 1	8 39	10‡29	1133	12‡23	15 7	16 16	17‡30	19‡0	21‡10	...
Nestalas	6 3	...	9 25	11 10	1212	...	1550	16 53	18 10	...	21 53	...
Pierrefitte arr	6 8	7 46	9 25	11 14	1218	13 9	1554	17 3	18 15	1947	21 55	...

TOURNEMIRE and LE VIGAN.

Tournemire ....dep	...	9 10	13 25	1558
Sauclieres	7 15	10 36	14 55	1714
Alzon	7 31	10 49	15 23	1727
Le Vigan 53B ......arr	8 16	11 29	16 49	18 8

Le Vigan ....dep	5 10	9 16	11 40	1813
Alzon	6 14	10 17	13 37	1916
Sauclieres	6 41	10 55	14 45	1945
Tournemire 45A...arr	7 47	12 8	17 11	2048

PONTCHARRA-SUR-BREDA, LA ROCHETTE, and ALLEVARD-LES-BAINS.

‡—Until 14th Sept.

E.M.														
—	**Pontcharra** P.L.M.Stn.dep	...	6 22	6 45	...	9 5	...	1249	14 24	15‡46	...	1815	...	...
—	,, Ville	...	6 27	6 50	...	9 10	...	1254	14 29	15 51	...	1820	...	...
5	Détrier	...	...	7 11	8 14	9 31	11 43	1315	14 50	16 12	1716	1841	1945	...
6¾	**La Rochette** ....arr	...	...	7 21	8 24	9 44	11 53	1329	15 5	16 25	1726	1854	1955	...
...	Détrier ....dep	4 50	6 48	...	...	9 34	12‡10	1319	14‡55	16 15	...	1844	...	...
9¼	**Allevard-les-Bains**...arr	5 15	7 13	...	...	9 59	12‡35	1344	15‡20	16 40	...	19 9	...	...

Allevard-les-Bains...dep	...	5 33	...	7 46	...	11 15	...	1250	14 25	16 48	...	1920	...	...	...	...	...
Détrier ....arr	...	5 58	...	8 11	...	11 40	...	1315	14 50	17 13	...	1945	...	...			...
La Rochette ....dep	4 40	...	5 25	8 1	9 21	11 30	12 ‡0	13 5	14‡40	17 3	18 31	...	...	...	...	...	...
Détrier	4 50	5 58	5 35	8 14	9 31	11 43	12 10	1319	14 55	17 16	18 41	...	...	...	...	...	...
Pontcharra Ville		6 18	5 55	8 34		12 3	...	1339	15 15	17 36		...	...	...	...	...	...
,, P.L.M. Sta. 62A...arr	...	6 22	6 0	8 38	...	12 7	...	1343	15 19	17 40	...	...	...	...	...	...	...

TOULOUSE and AUCH.

Toulouse Matabiau dep	6 17	9 28	1320	17 8	...
Colomiers	6 56	10 0	1355	17 44	...
Mérenvielle	7 42	1030	1425	18 13	...
L'Isle Jourdain (Gers)	7 56	1043	1443	18 25	...
Aubiet	8 47	1141	1534	19 23	...
Auch 45A ....arr	9 18	1211	16 4	19 53	...

Auch ....dep	5 30	10 5	12 53	17 44	...
Aubiet	6 0	10 35	13 23	18 14	...
L'Isle Jourdain	6 59	11 29	14 10	19 13	...
Mérenvielle	7 8	11 39	14 27	19 20	...
Colomiers	7 43	12 11	14 56	19 51	...
Toulouse Matab.	8 20	12 43	15 31	20 25	...

Auch to Castera-Verduzan in 45 min. From Auch 10.15, 16.20, 20.22 From Castera-Verduzan 8.56, 15.0, 18 40.

For Notes and Continuation of Trains, see page 49a.

PARIS, DIJON, MACON, LYONS, and MARSEILLES.

SALOON CARRIAGES.
- Paris to Chambery, 14.20, 21.10 and 22.15 (Lits-Salon, Wagon-Lit).
- Paris to Evian, 20.50 (Lits-Salon, Wagon-Lit).
- Paris to Geneva, 21.35 (Wagon-Lit, Lits-Salon).
- Paris to Interlaken, 22.15 (Lits-Salon, Wagon-Lit).
- Paris to Lausanne and Milan, 14.20 and 21.30 (Lits-Salon, Wagon-Lit).
- Paris to Rome, 22.15 (Wagon-Lit, Lits-Salon).
- Paris to Turin, 14.20 (Wagon-Lit).

LUGGAGE, 66 lbs. allowed free; excess Luggage, 1 centime per 44 lbs. per kilometre.

RC—Restaurant Car attached.
SC—Sleeping Car attached.

From Paris E.M. Dist.	1 Cl. fr. c.	2 Cl. fr. c.	Station	1	2	3	4	5	6	7	8	9	10	11
			Calais 18 ... dep		...	1 3	1 30	1 30	...	1 30	1 30	...	5 58	...
			Boulogne 18 ... dep		...	For Friday	2 12	2 12	...	2 12	2 12	...	6 52	...
			Paris (Gare du Nord) ... arr		...		5 40	5 40	...	5 40	5 40	...	10 30	...
			Paris (Gare du Nord) ... dep		...		...	6 38	...	6 38	6 38	...	...	...
			arr		...		...	7 18	...	7 18	7 18	...	...	...
						Lux	Exp.	Exp.		Exp.	Rpde	Lux	Exp.	
			PARIS (Gare P.L.M.) Boulevard Diderot	1,2,3	1,2,3		1,2,3	1 & 2	1,2,3	1 & 2	1 & 2		1,2,3	1,2,3
			dep	6 0	...	Brindisi from London on night only. See note **BB**.	7 10	8 30	8 33	8 40	9 15	11 35	11 40	12 5
3	0 55	0 40	Charenton ...	... (See also p. 63.)	...		**B**	RC	...	...	**A**	...	**B**	...
9¼	1 70	1 15	Villeneuve St. Georges ...	6 18	...		...	**L**	...	...	...	**E**	...	...
13¾	2 45	1 65	Brunoy ...	6 31	...		...	...	9 5	...	...	...	...	12 38
28	5 5	3 40	Melun ...	7 5	...		...	Via Héricy.	9 44	...	Via Héricy.	...	12 27	13 20
36¾	6 60	4 45	Fontainebleau ...	7 27	...		...		10 12	...		...	12 48	13 44
41¾	7 50	5 5	Moret ...	7 41	...		...		10 32	...		...	...	14 0
49	8 85	5 95	**Montereau 63** ...	7 57	...		8 21		10 57	...		...	13 11	14 33
70¼	12 65	8 55	**Sens 63B** ...	9 14	...		8 54		11 42	...		...	13 48	15 54
79	14 20	9 60	Villeneuve-sur-Yonne ...	9 33	...		...		12 2	...		...	...	16 14
90¾	16 35	11 5	Joigny ...	9 59	...		9 25	...	12 28	...	RC	...	14 23	16 41
96¼	17 35	11 60	**Laroche 56** ... arr	10 9	...	7 41	9 35	10 27	12 38	10 47	11 36	13 28	14 34	16 52
			dep		3 10	7 46	9 43	10 32	12 53	10 52	11 41	13 33	14 44	17 17
107½	19 40	13 10	St. Florentin ...		3 33	...	10 4	...	13 17	...	...	...	15 3	17 41
122½	22 5	14 90	**Tonnerre** ... arr		4 1	...	10 25	...	13.45	...	...	...	15 27	18 9
			dep		4 4	...	10 26	...	14 15	...	...	...	15 29	18 39
127½	22 95	15 50	Tanlay ...		4 15	...	...	...	14 26	...	...	...	...	18 50
139¾	25 20	17 0	**Nuits-sous-Ravieres 57** ...		4 48	...	10 53	...	15 2	...	...	...	16 1	19 24
151	27 20	18 35	Montbard ...		5 13	...	11 11	...	15 28	...	...	...	16 23	19 52
159¾	28 80	19 45	Les Laumes 63A ... dep		5 43	...	11 29	...	15 56	...	...	...	16 44	20 19
179	32 25	21 75	Blaisy-Bas ...		6 33	...	12 1	...	16 43	...	...	...	17 23	21 9
195¾	35 30	23 80	**Dijon** ... arr		7 15	9 59	12 23	12 36	17 22	13 4	14 9	15 30	17 46	21 48
282¾	51 0	34 40	Pontarlier 52 ... arr		...	...	...	15 15	...	...	...	...	...	...
316¼	56 90	38 65	Neuchatel 265 ... arr		...	...	...	5p46	...	...	...	...	...	...
343	62 50	42 60	Berne 259B ... arr		...	...	...	6p55	...	...	...	...	...	...
327½	58 90	40 5	Lausanne 263B ... arr		...	...	...	6p15	...	...	...	...	...	...
444¼	81 15	55 65	Domodossola 263B ... arr		...	...	...	10 p3	...	...	...	...	...	...
520¾	96 80	66 65	Milan 274 ... arr		...	...	...	0 15	...	...	...	...	...	...
...	...	...	**Dijon** ... dep		8 45	10 6	13 3	...	18 31	13 22	14 19	15 36	18 10	22 32
202½	36 50	24 65	Gevrey-Chambertin ...		8 58	Via St. Amour.	...	...	18 45	⋮	...	...To Chambery (arr. 19.46).	...	22 45
206¼	37 20	25 10	Vougeot ...		9 7		**B**	...	18 54		...		...	22 54
209½	37 75	25 50	Nuits-St. Georges ...		9 17		...	...	19 5		...		...	23 3
218¾	39 40	26 60	Beaune 87 ...		9 44		13 37	...	19 38		...		18 51	23 27
228	41 10	27 75	**Chagny 53A, 56** ...		10 22		13 58	...	20 15		...		19 17	23 58
238	42 90	28 95	**Chalon** Saone ... arr		10 49		14 15	...	20 41		...		19 36	0 19
			dep		11 0		14 20	...	21 28		...		19 46	
253½	45 70	30 85	Tournus ...		11 38		14 46	...	22 4		...		20 15	...
273½	49 30	33 25	**Macon** ... arr		12 22		15 16	...	22 46		15 59		20 48	...
389	70 15	47 30	Geneva 60 ... arr		20 21	⋮	23 25	...	...	19 38	23 25	21 22	...	...
431¼	77 75	52 45	Modane 60 ... arr		...	16 38	...	...	...	20 20	...	...	...	...
496¼	91 50	62 15	Turin 270 ... arr		...	20 49	...	...	...	0 5	...	...	...	...
580	110 60	75 35	Genoa 270 ... arr		...	...	...	...	...	...	...	...	...	...

Station	12	13	14	15	16	17	18	19	20	21	22
Calais 18 ... dep	...	...	...	...	...	14 57	...	14 40	...	14 50	14 50
Boulogne 18 ... dep	...	...	...	...	...	...	14 12	...	14 12	...	...
Paris (Gare du Nord) ... arr	...	...	...	...	...		17 20	18 15	17 20	18 20	18 20
Paris (Gare du Nord) ... dep	13 9	...	...	...	...		17 39	18 25	17 39	19 31	19 39
arr	13 48	...	...	...	...	19 4	18 26	18 59	18 26	20 34	20 34
	Exp.		Exp.		Exp.		Rpde	Lux	Rpde	Rpde	Rpde
PARIS (Gare P.L.M.) Boulevard Diderot	1 & 2		1 & 2	1,2,3	1,2,3		1,2,3	**C**	1,2,3	1 & 2	1 Cl.
dep	14 20	...	15 45	16 5	18 0	Calais-Marseilles-Bombay Express, from Calais on Thurs. only, enquire of P. & O. Co.	19 0	19 45	19 50	20 50	21 0
Charenton ...	...	...	**Y**	...	...		**I**	Simplon **C** Express.	...	...	**J**
Villeneuve St. Georges ...	...	...	...	...	**B**		...		...	...	...
Brunoy ...	...	...	...	...	...		...		**G**	**M**	...
Melun ...	**AA**	...	...	16 52	18 40		Via Héricy.		...	...	...
Fontainebleau ...	...	...	...	17 15	18 57				...	...	SC
Moret ...	...	...	...	17 27	...				...	...	...
Montereau 63 ...	...	...	...	17 46	19 18				...	...	...
Sens 63B ...	...	...	...	18 32	19 50				...	...	...
Villeneuve-sur-Yonne ...	...	...	...	18 52	...				...	...	...
Joigny ...	...	...	...	19 19	20 20		...		...	...	...
Laroche 56 ... arr	16 16	...	17 44	19 30	20 30		21 18	21 48	22 3	22 51	23 3
dep	16 21	...	17 54	19 47	20 35		21 23	21 53	22 8	22 56	23 8
St. Florentin ...	...	...	...	20 9	...		...	...	...	...	...
Tonnerre ... arr	...	...	...	20 35	21 12		...	...	...	...	...
dep	...	...	...	20 38	21 14		...	...	...	...	...
Tanlay ...	...	...	...	20 48	...		...	...	...	...	...
Nuits-sous-Ravieres 57 ...	...	...	...	21 19	21 43		...	...	...	...	...
Montbard ...	...	...	...	21 42	22 2		...	...	...	...	...
Les Laumes 63A ... dep	...	...	...	22 0	22 18		...	...	...	...	...
Blaisy-Bas ...	...	...	...	22 35	22 53		...	...	...	...	...
Dijon ... arr	18 29		20 11	23 0	23 15		23 52	0 13	0 32	1 8	1 20
Pontarlier 52 ... arr	20 50		...	...	...		...	2 53	...	...	...
Neuchatel 265 ... arr	11 p9		...	...	...		...	5 ‡10	...	...	...
Berne 259B ... arr	12 a1		...	...	...		...	6 ‡8	...	...	...
Lausanne 263B ... arr	11p54		...	...	...		...	5 a50	...	...	...
Domodossola 263B ... arr	3 a40		...	...	...		...	9 a32	...	...	...
Milan 274 ... arr	6 25		...	...	...		...	12 12	...	...	...
Dijon ... dep	...	18 47	20 23	...	...		0 12	‡—First arrival 9th July.	0 40	1 15	1 26
Gevrey-Chambertin ...	...	Via St. Amour.	...	...	...		...		...	...	...
Vougeot ...	...		...	...	...		**I**		...	...	SC
Nuits-St. Georges ...	...		...	...	...		...		...	To Evian (arr. 7.51.)	...
Beaune 87 ...	...		...	...	...		...		...		**J**
Chagny 53A, 56 ...	...		21 2	22 22	...		...		...		...
Chalon Saone ... arr	...		21 17	22 47	...		1 6		...		...
dep	...		21 20		...		1 9		...		...
Tournus ...	...		...	...	...		...		...		...
Macon ... arr	...		22 4	...	...		1 58		2 19	...	3 0
Geneva 60 ... arr	...		...	...	...		...		...	...	...
Modane 60 ... arr	...	1 41	...	...	...		...		...	...	...
Turin 270 ... arr	...	5 50	...	...	...		...		...	...	...
Genoa 270 ... arr	...	9 35	...	...	...		...		...	...	...

For Notes and Continuation of Trains, see page 49a.

			1	2	3	4	5	6	7	8	9	10	11	12	13	14	15	16	17	18	19	20	21	22
...	...	...	**Macon** dep	13 30	...	15 22	...	...	...	16 2	...	20 58	...	...		22 9	...	...		2 1		2 22	...	3 3
283¼	51 5	34 45	Romanèche	13 56	...	...	...	...	...	...	...	...	...	...	...	...	...	...		...	...	...	...	...
287¾	51 85	35 0	**Belleville 63**	14 9	2 & 3	15 44	2 & 3	...	...	...	...	21 24	...	...	...	...	...	...		...	...	...	2 & 3	...
297	53 55	36 15	Villefranche-sur-Saône	14 39	12 31	16 1	16 45	...	...	...	...	21 43	...	...	...	22 41	...	...		...	...	...	5 0	SC
302	54 45	36 75	**Quincieux-Trévoux**	14 56	12 43	...	16 57	...	...	A	...	...	...	...	...	...	...	...		...	...	...	5 12	...
305¾	55 10	37 20	Saint-Germain-Mt-d'Or	15 6	12 53	16 18	17 6	...	...	...	...	...	...	...	...	...	...	...		...	...	...	5 21	...
307	55 35	37 35	Villevert-Neuville	...	12 58	...	17 11	...	...	...	...	...	...	...	...	...	...	...		...	...	...	5 26	...
310¾	56 0	37 80	Collonges Fontaines	...	13 12	B	17 23	...	...	...	...	...	...	...	...	...	...	...		...	...	...	5 38	...
315	56 80	38 35	**Lyons** (Vaise) arr	15 24	13 26	16 33	17 36	...	...	...	...	22 13	...	...	...	...	...	...		...	...	...	5 51	...
			Lyons (Vaise) dep	15 31		16.37		...	...	...	...	22 16	...	...	...	...	...	...		...	...	...		...
318¼	57 35	38 70	**Lyons** (Perrache) arr	15 38	...	16 43	...	...	...	17 1	...	22 23	...	...	...	23 8	...	...		3 2	...	3 21	...	3 59
393¼	70 90	47 85	GRENOBLE 63A arr	20 2	...	20 2	...	...	...	20 2	...	4 19	...	...	...	4 19	...	...		6 37	...	6 37	...	...
...	...	...	GENEVA 61 dep	13 33	...	13 33	...	...	...	13 33	...	20 5	...	...	...	20 5	...	...		21 10	...	...	...	...
				1,2,3	1,2,3	1,2,3		1,2.3		1 & 2		1,2,3	1,2,3			1 & 2	1,2,3			1,2,3	1,2,3	1,2,3		1 Cl.
...	...	...	**Lyons** (Perrache) dep	16 38	...	17 52	...	18 17	...	17 21	...	23 47	21§37	...	...	23 37	...	...		3 18	...	4 14	...	4 8
331¼	59 70	40 30	**Chasse 56**	17 10	...	...	...	18 55	...	...	...	...	22 9	...	...	...	...	...		...	...	...	...	...
337½	60 80	41 5	**Vienne**	17 23	...	18 22	...	19 13	...	A	...	0 19	22 22	...	...	...	...	...		...	...	...	...	J
344¾	62 15	41 95	Les Roches de Condrieux		...	...	...	19 31	...	...	...	...		...	...	Y	...	...		...	...	...	...	...
355½	64 5	43 25	**St. Rambert** arr	...	...	18 47	...	20 0	...	...	...	0 44	...	...	...	...	...	...		I	...	...	...	...
			St. Rambert dep	...	...	18 52	...		...	...	...	0 46	...	...	...	...	...	...		...	...	...	...	...
363½	65 50	44 25	Saint-Vallier	...	...	19 6	...	...	...	RC	...	...	...	...	...	...	...	...		...	...	...	...	...
372¼	67 10	45 30	Tain	...	...	19 22	...	...	...	...	...	1 11	...	...	...	...	...	...		...	...	...	...	...
384	62 90	46 70	**Valence 62A** arr	...	...	19 38	...	...	...	18 44	...	1 28	...	...	...	1 5	...	...		4 45	...	5 40	...	5 29
			Valence 62A dep	...	...	19 51	...	...	...	18 51	...	1 36	...	...	...	1 8	...	...		4 53	...	5 46	...	5 32
394½	71 10	48 0	**Livron 56, 63B** arr	...	...	20 7	...	...	...	...	...	...	...	...	...	...	...	...		...	...	...	...	...
			Livron 56, 63B dep	...	...	20 13	...	...	...	...	...	...	...	...	...	...	...	...		...	...	...	...	...
396½	71 45	48 25	Loriol	...	...	...	...	...	...	...	...	...	...	...	...	...	...	...		...	...	...	...	...
411¼	74 15	50 5	Montélimar	...	...	20 38	...	...	...	...	...	2 18	...	...	...	...	...	...		...	...	...	...	...
417	75 15	50 75	Châteauneuf-du-Rhone	...	...	...	...	...	...	...	...	...	...	...	...	...	...	...		...	...	...	...	...
424½	76 50	51 65	Pierrelatte (49B)	...	...	20 59	...	...	...	...	...	...	...	...	...	...	...	...		...	...	...	...	...
431¾	77 85	52 55	Bollène La Croisière	...	...	B	...	...	...	...	...	2 48	...	...	...	...	...	...		...	...	...	...	...
443¾	79 95	54 0	Orange 62	...	...	21 29	...	...	...	...	...	3 9	...	...	...	...	...	...		...	...	...	...	...
448¾	80 85	54 60	Courthezon	...	...	...	...	...	...	...	...	...	...	...	...	...	...	...		...	...	...	...	...
454¾	82 0	55 35	**Sorgues 56**	13 47	18 47	21 46	...	...	...	...	...	...	...	...	...	...	...	...		...	...	...	...	...
461	83 10	56 10	**Avignon 63A** arr	14 6	19 6	21 56	...	...	...	20 29	...	3 35	...	...	...	2 50	...	...		6 33	...	7 23	...	7 5
...	...	...	,, (Rive Gauche) dep			22 7	...	...	...	20 38	...	3 45	...	...	...	2 56	...	...		6 45	6 58	7 37	...	7 15
464¾	83 80	56 55	Barbentane 74B	...	...	...	...	...	...	...	...	...	...	...	...	...	...	...			...	...	...	
474¾	85 55	57 75	**Tarascon** arr	...	...	22 29	...	...	...	21 0	...	4 7	...	...	...	3 18	...	...			7 16	7 57	...	
540	97 30	65 70	CETTE 57 arr	...	...	1 30	...	...	...	23 40	...	7 57	...	...	...	6 37	...	...			10 10	10 10	...	
582¾	10465	70 70	NARBONNE 45B arr	...	...	3 51	...	...	...	1 3	...	9 23	...	...	1,2,3	9 23	...	...			12 6	12 6	...	
754¼	13930	95 95	BARCELONA 295 arr	...	...	...	...	...	...	7 53	...	15 40	...	...	p.m.	15 40	...	...			19 32	19 32	...	
...	...	...	**Tarascon** dep	...	...	22 39	...	...	...	21 9	...	4 19	...	...	3 8	3 31	5 20	...			7 20	...	...	
482¾	87 0	58 5	**Arles 57** arr	...	...	22 52	...	...	...	...	...	4 32	...	...	...	...	5 33	...			7 32	...	...	
			Arles 57 dep	...	...	22 57	...	...	...	...	...	4 36	...	...	...	...	5 39	...		I	7 35	...	...	
503¼	90 70	61 25	Miramas 63A	...	...	...	...	...	...	...	...	5 8	...	...	...	...	...	...			...	...	...	RC
506½	91 30	61 60	Saint-Chamas	...	...	...	...	...	...	...	...	...	...	...	...	...	...	...			...	...	...	
519½	93 65	63 20	**Rognac 49B**	...	...	...	...	...	...	...	...	...	...	...	...	...	...	...			...	...	...	
525	94 65	63 90	Pas-des-Lanciers 74B	...	...	...	...	...	...	...	...	...	...	...	...	...	...	...			...	...	...	
529¾	95 40	64 40	L'Estaque	...	...	...	...	...	...	...	...	...	...	...	...	...	...	...			...	...	...	
535¾	96 55	65 15	**MARSEILLES** St. Charles arr	...	...	6 9	...	...	...	22 35	...	5 55	...	...	4 50	5 0	6 50	...	6§36	8 30	8 43	...	...	8 58
656¼	11830	79 80	CANNES 54 arr	...	...	4 57	...	...	...	...	...	11 40	...	...	...	...	...	...	...	13 26	13 26	...	...	12 40
675½	12175	82 15	NICE 54 arr	...	...	6 17	...	...	...	...	...	12 33	...	...	...	...	...	...	...	14 20	14 20	...	...	13 25
690½	12445	83 95	MENTON 54 arr	...	...	7 38	...	...	...	...	...	13 48	...	...	...	...	...	...	...	15 38	15 34	...	...	14 37

Extra. Paris......dep 17 55; Sens ......arr 20 23

§—Arrive Joliette Quay.

PARIS, DIJON, MACON, LYONS, and MARSEILLES—continued.

RC—Restaurant Car attached. SC—Sleeping Car attached.

1	2	3	4	5	6	7	8	9	10	11	12	13	14	15	16
CALAIS 18A ....dep	14 50	14 50	14 50	...	...	...	...	...	...	...	...	...	...	...	...
BOULOGNE 18A ....dep	...	...	...	18 2	...	18 2	...	...	...	...	...	...	...	...	...
PARIS (Gare du Nord)....arr	18 20	18 20	18 20	21 0	...	21 0	...	...	...	...	...	...	...	...	...
" ....dep	19 31	19 31	19 31	21 25	...	21 25	...	...	...	...	...	...	...	...	...
PARIS (Gare P.L.M.) Boulevard Diderot... arr	20 34	20 34	20 34	21 55	...	21 55	...	...	...	...	...	...	...	...	...
	Exp.	Exp.	Exp.	Exp.		Exp.	Exp.								
	1,2,3	1 & 2	1,2,3	1 & 2	2 & 3	1,2,3	1,2,3	1,2,3	1,2,3	1,2,3	1,2,3	1,2,3	1,2,3		1,2,3
dep	21 10	21 30	21 35	22 15	...	22 25	22 50	23 0	...	...	...	...	...	...	...
Charenton	...	...	...	...	...	...	...	...	...	...	...	...	...	...	...
Villeneuve St. Georges	...	...	O	N	...	V	P	...	...	...	...	...	...	...	...
Brunoy	F	H	...	...	...	...	...	...	...	...	...	...	...	...	...
Melun	SC	SC	...	SC	...	SC	...	23 46	...	...	...	...	...	...	...
Fontainebleau	...	...	...	...	...	...	...	0 8	...	...	...	...	...	...	...
Moret	...	...	...	...	...	...	...	0 23	...	...	...	...	...	...	...
Montereau 63	...	...	...	...	...	23 35	...	0 45	...	...	5 40	...	...	...	...
Sens 63B	...	...	...	...	...	0 6	...	1 33	...	...	6 29	...	...	...	...
Villeneuve-sur-Yonne	...	...	...	...	...	...	...	1 50	...	...	6 49	...	...	...	...
Joigny	...	...	...	...	...	0 36	...	2 16	...	...	7 16	...	...	...	...
Laroche 56 .... arr	23 13	23 28	23 43	0 28	...	0 46	1 6	2 26	...	...	7 27	...	...	...	...
dep	23 18	23 33	23 48	0 33	...	0 51	1 11	—	...	6 10	8 15	...	...	...	...
St. Florentin	...	...	...	...	...	...	...	...	...	6 33	8 39	...	...	...	...
Tonnerre .... arr	...	...	...	...	...	1 27	...	...	...	7 1	9 7	...	...	...	...
dep	...	...	...	...	...	1 28	...	...	...	7 4	9 11	...	...	...	...
Tanlay	...	...	...	...	...	...	...	...	...	7 15	9 22	...	...	...	...
Nuits-sous-Ravieres 57 ...	...	...	...	...	...	...	...	...	...	7 46	9 53	...	...	...	...
Montbard	...	...	...	...	...	2 11	...	...	...	8 11	10 18	...	...	...	...
Les Laumes 63A ....dep	...	...	...	...	...	2 26	...	...	...	8 43	10 40	...	...	...	...
Blaisy-Bas	...	...	...	...	...	...	...	...	...	9 36	11 28	...	...	...	...
Dijon ....arr	1 30	1 42	2 4	2 57	...	3 20	3 37	...	...	10 25	12 8	...	...	...	...
PONTARLIER 52 ....arr	...	4 10	...	5 11	...	...	6 26	...	...	...	...	...	...	...	...
NEUCHATEL 265 ....arr	...	7a17	...	7 a35	...	...	9 a20	...	...	...	...	...	...	...	...
BERNE 259B ....arr	...	8a35	...	8 a35	...	...	10a32	...	...	...	...	...	...	...	...
LAUSANNE 263B ....arr	...	7a10	...	...	...	...	9 a48	...	...	...	...	...	...	...	...
DOMODOSSOLA 263B ....arr	...	10a55	...	...	...	...	—	...	...	...	...	...	...	...	...
MILAN 274 ....arr	...	13 30	...	...	...	...	...	...	...	...	...	...	...	...	...
Dijon ....dep	1 40	...	2 10	3 12	...	3 30	5 55	A	5 10	11 14	14 37	...	...	...	...
Gevrey-Chambertin	Chambery arr. 6.37. Via St. Amour.	...	⋮	Via St. Amour.	...	...	...	...	5 24	11 27	14 51	...	...	...	...
Vougeot		...	⋮		...	V	...	...	5 33	11 36	15 0	...	...	...	...
Nuits-St. Georges		...	⋮		...	...	...	...	5 42	11 46	15 10	...	...	...	...
Beaune 87		...	⋮		...	4 3	6 26	...	6 35	12 16	15 39	...	...	...	...
Chagny 53A, 56		...	⋮		...	4 23	6 46	...	7 21	12 58	16 13	12 23	...	...	...
Chalon Saone .... arr		...	⋮		...	4 40	7 2	...	7 49	13 22	16 39	12 48	...	...	...
dep		...	⋮		...	4 46	7 8	...	8 31	13 39	16 49	—	...	...	4 55
Tournus		...	⋮		...	...	7 32	...	9 9	14 11	17 26	...	...	...	5 29
Macon ....arr		...	⋮		...	5 39	8 1	...	9 53	14 52	18 9	...	...	...	6 10
GENEVA 60 ....arr		...	8 38	⋮	...	12 3	16 17	...	...	23 25	0 43	...	...	...	...
MODANE 60 ....arr	...	...	...	9 54	...	14 20	...	...	...	...	...	...	...	...	...
TURIN 270 ....arr	...	...	...	14 5	...	19 7	...	...	...	...	...	...	...	...	...
GENOA 270 ....arr	...	...	...	18 30	...	23 25	...	...	...	...	...	...	...	...	...

EXTRA FARES
FROM PARIS BY TRAINS DE LUXE
(In addition to 1st Class Fare).

	fr. c.
Aix-les-Bains (Savoie Express)	18.0
Chambèry (Savoie Express)	18.0
Evian (Savoie Express)	21.0
Geneva (Savoie Express)	21.0
Lausanne (Simplon Express)	18.30
Milan (Simplon Express)	30.95

NOTES.

A—Takes 1st class travelling at least 125 miles; between Paris and Macon 2nd class travelling at least 250 miles, and from Lyons forward takes 2nd class travelling at least 149 miles. Exceptionally will take at Dijon 1st class passengers for Lyons, and at Tarascon 1st and 2nd coming from direction of Cette.

AA—Only takes for Mouchard and beyond towards Pontarlier (page 52), or for Bourg towards Italy (page 60). 2nd class must be travelling at least 155 miles. Exceptionally will take 1st class for beyond Dijon towards Dole (page 52).

B—Takes 2nd and 3rd Class Passengers going at least 62 miles.

BB—**Péninsulaire Express**, runs from Nord Co.'s line on to P.L.M. line without entering Paris; runs on Saturday morning only. Though principally intended for passengers to Brindisi from England and the Nord Co.'s line this train will take, when places are available, passengers for Culoz, Aix-les-Bains, Chambéry, Modane, Turin, and Alessandria.

C—**Simplon Express**, Train de Luxe. *Take tickets in advance of Sleeping Car Co.*

E—**Savoie Express**, Train de Luxe. Will run daily from Paris to Chambèry; first departure on 5th July. Runs until 12th Sept.

F—This train will only take passengers going beyond Bourg (page 60), and then not those for the line beyond Culoz towards Bellegarde; 2nd class must be travelling at least 155 miles and 3rd class at least 248 miles. Exceptionally will take 1st and 2nd class for beyond Laroche towards Auxerre and for Dijon and beyond towards Belfort; and will take 3rd class for Besancon (page 52) and beyond.

G—From Paris to Macon will only take passengers travelling at least 310 miles. From Lyons to Valence only those travelling at least 94 miles.

H—Takes only those passengers who are travelling beyond Andelot (page 52), beyond Pontarlier (page 52), and beyond Mouchard (page 52). 2nd class must be travelling at least 155 miles. Until the 29th September travellers for beyond Pontarlier towards Berne and Interlaken will not be taken by this train.

1	2	3	4	5	6	7	8	9	10	11	12	13	14	15	16
Macon ....dep	...	...	...	...	...	5 48	8 8	8 48	10 7	16 10	18 24	...	21 25	4 41	6 53
Romaneche	...	...	...	...	...	...	...	9 9	10 32	16 40	18 50	...	21 49	5 6	7 19
Belleville 63	...	...	...	...	...	6 12	8 31	9 18	10 44	16 54	19 2	...	22 0	5 19	7 30
Villefranche-sur-Saône	...	...	...	...	9 48	6 29	8 47	9 35	11 7	17 20	19 26	20 24	22 49	5 41	7 54
Quincieux Trévoux	...	...	...	...	10 1	...	...	...	11 21	17 37	19 42	20 37	23 5	5 55	8 9
Saint Germain-Mt-d'Or.	...	...	...	...	10 10	6 45	9 2	...	11 31	17 49	19 52	20 46	23 15	6 4	8 19
Villevert-Neuville	...	...	...	...	10 15	...	...	...	11 36	17 56	19 59	20 54	...	6 10	8 25
Collonges Fontaines	...	...	...	...	10 30	...	...	...	11 48	18 10	20 12	21 6	...	6 21	8 38
Lyons (Vaise) .... arr	...	...	...	...	10 40	7 0	9 17	10 §9	12 0	18 23	20 23	21 16	23 35	6 32	8 50
Lyons (Vaise) .... dep	...	...	...	...		7 4	9 21		12 5	18 32	20 31		23 41	6 38	8 56
Lyons (Perrache) ....arr	...	...	...	...	...	7 10	9 27	...	12 12	18 39	20 39	...	23 48	6 45	9 3
GRENOBLE 63A ....arr	...	...	...	...	...	...	12 26	...	18 54	0 9	...	...	4 19	10 2	12 26
GENEVA 61 ....dep	...	...	...	...	...	...	6 53	7 38	7 38	14 30	...	...		...	6 53
					1,2,3	1,2,3	1,2,3	1,2,3	1,2,3	1,2,3	1,2,3	1,2,3	1,2,3	1,2,3	1,2,3
Lyons (Perrache) ....dep	...	...	...	...	5 13	8 0	12 15	13 26	14 40	19 31	...	6 §58	...	8 15	10 56
Chasse 56	...	...	...	...	5 53	8 22	...	13 59	15 21	20 15	...	7 33	...	8 54	11 36
Vienne	...	...	...	...	6 15	8 35	12 42	14 12	15 43	20 36	...	7 47	...	9 14	11 57
Les Roches de Condrieux	...	...	...	...	6 33	...	...		16 4	20 55	...		...	9 33	12 16
St. Rambert .... arr	...	...	...	...	7 4	8 59	13 6	...	16 36	21 25	...	...	...	10 2	12 45
St. Rambert .... dep	...	...	...	...	7 17	9 2	13 9	...	17 0	21 40	5 56	...	...	10 11	13 17
Saint-Vallier	...	...	...	...	7 37	...	Z	...	17 22	22 0	6 16	...	...	10 33	13 37
Tain	...	...	...	...	7 58	9 27	...	...	17 47	22 21	6 37	...	...	10 56	14 0
Valence 62A .... arr	...	...	...	...	8 20	9 43	13 45	...	18 11	22 43	6 59	...	...	11 20	14 22
Valence 62A .... dep	...	...	...	...	10 0	9 52	13 56	...	18 58	23 6		6 9	16 12		14 46
Livron 56, 63B .... arr	...	...	...	...	10 26	10 8	14 12	...	19 25	23 31	...	6 35	16 41	...	15 12
Livron 56, 63B .... dep	...	...	...	...	10 37	10 13	14 15	...	19 37	23 35	...	6 46		...	15 24
Loriol	...	...	...	...	10 43	...	...	...	19 43	23 41	...	6 52	...	...	15 30
Montélimar	...	...	...	...	11 20	10 38	14 40	...	20 48	0 16	...	7 27	...	...	16 13
Châteauneuf-du-Rhone	...	...	...	...	11 32	...	...	...	21 0	...	...	7 39	...	...	16 26
Pierrelatte	...	...	...	...	11 54	10 58	...	...	21 20	0 40	...	7 56	...	...	16 52
Bollène La Croisière	...	...	...	...	12 12	11 10	...	...	21 37	0 55	...	8 19	...	...	17 12
Orange	...	...	...	...	12 51	11 30	15 24	...	22 12	1 18	5 30	8 55	...	...	17 54
Courthezon	...	...	...	...	13 3	...	...	...	22 23	...	5 41	9 6	...	...	18 6
Sorgues 56	...	...	...	...	13 20	11 47	...	...	22 40	...	6 1	9 24	...	10 10	18 25
Avignon 63A .... arr	...	...	...	...	13 37	11 57	15 47	...	22 57	1 46	6 18	9 41	...	10 27	18 42
,, (Rive Gauche) dep	...	...	...	...	16 20	12 7	15 57	...		1 57	8 35	12 28	4 20		19 20
Barbentane 74B	...	...	...	...	16 37	...	...	...	...	...	8 49	12 42	4 31	...	19 32
Tarascon ....arr	...	...	...	...	16 58	12 29	16 18	...	...	2 20	9 13	13 5	4 51	...	19 54
CETTE 57 ....arr	...	...	...	...	...	15 12	18 49	...	...	4 45	11 45	15 12	...	...	23 40
NARBONNE 45B ....arr	...	...	...	...	...	16 35	20 18	...	...	6 7	13 7	16 35	...	...	1 2
BARCELONA 295 ....arr	...	...	...	...	...	...	...	...	...	...	19 32	...	...	...	7 53
Tarascon ....dep	...	...	...	...	17 19	12 57	16 28	...	16 44	...	9 30	13 22	5 33	...	20 40
Arles 57 .... arr	...	...	...	...	17 39	13 10	...	...	16 57	...	9 50	13 42	5 51	...	21 1
Arles 57 .... dep	...	...	...	...	17 49	13 14	...	...	17 1	...	10 10	13 52	6 7	...	21 27
Miramas 63A	...	...	...	...	18 48	13 46	...	...	17 34	...	11 20	14 42	6 54	...	22 28
Saint-Chamas	...	...	...	...	18 57	...	...	...	...	...	11 28	14 50	7 2	...	22 37
Rognac 49B	...	...	...	...	19 34	14 12	...	...	...	...	12 6	15 24	7 33	...	23 9
Pas-des-Lanciers 74B	...	...	...	...	20 3	...	...	...	...	...	12 22	15 37	7 46	...	23 22
L'Estaque	...	...	...	...	...	...	...	...	...	...	12 35	15 50	7 57	...	23 36
MARSEILLES St. Charles arr	...	...	...	...	20 21	14 38	17 51	...	18 20	...	12 49	16 4	8 10	...	23 51
CANNES 54 ....arr	...	...	...	...	...	...	22 35	...	...	...	...	...	...	...	...
NICE 54 ....arr	...	...	...	...	...	...	23 23	...	...	...	...	...	...	...	...
MENTON 54 ....arr	...	...	...	...	...	...	0 33	...	...	...	...	...	...	...	...

I—At Paris and stopping stations takes for beyond Avignon, conditionally that at least 150 miles are travelled. Exceptionally will take up at Dijon from branch lines; and at Chalons will take up passengers travelling at least 310 miles.

J—Only for travellers going at least 310 miles. Exceptionally, at Lyons will take for Marseilles and for beyond Cette; and at Valence and Avignon for beyond Les Arcs.

L—At Paris will not take for Laroche, nor at Laroche for Dijon; after Dijon takes only those passengers who are travelling at least 46 miles.

M—Takes for beyond Bellegarde (page 60) towards Evian as well as for Annecy and beyond towards Chamonix; 2nd class must be travelling at least 155 miles. *This train will only run until the 19th September.*

N—Takes 1st class for Aix-les-Bains and beyond, and 2nd class for same destinations when travelling at least 155 miles. Until 29th September 1st and 2nd class for Pontarlier and beyond towards Berne and Interlaken will be taken by this train.

O—Takes passengers for beyond Culoz towards Bellegarde (page 60) only, with the condition that 2nd class must be travelling at least 155 miles and 3rd class at least 249 miles.

P—Taking passengers for Dijon and beyond only.

V—Takes 2nd and 3rd class travelling at least 93 miles.

Y—Takes 2nd class travelling at least 125 miles.

Z—Takes 3rd class travelling at least 62 miles.

§—At or from Brotteaux Station, Lyons.

Extra			
Extra	St. Germain-Mt-d'Or...dep	6 51	7 53
	Lyons (Vaise) ....arr	7 22	8 23

PIERRELATTE and NYONS.

Pierrelatte ....dep	5 58	12 10	18 15	...	...
St. Paul-Tr.-Chat.	6 10	12 27	18 33	...	...
Valreas	7 11	13 29	19 31	...	...
Nyons ....arr	7 44	14 2	20 4	...	...
Nyons ....dep	5 46	14 38	18 46	...	...
Valreas	6 23	15 15	19 24	...	...
St. Paul-Tr.-Chateaux ...	7 20	16 19	20 16	...	...
Pierrelatte 49 ....arr	7 32	16 31	20 28	...	...

AIX and ROGNAC.

Aix ....dep	5 18	9 52	13 58	15 56	19 0
Roquefavour	5 47	10 19	14 27	16 41	19 47
Rognac 49 ....arr	6 10	10 38	14 50	17 4	20 23
Rognac ....dep	6 52	8 10	12 30	15 42	19 55
Roquefavour	7 34	8 34	12 56	16 6	20 19
Aix ....arr	8 21	9 9	13 32	16 41	20 54

66 lbs. of Luggage free. [Excess Luggage, 1 cent. per 44 lbs. per kilometre.

MARSEILLES, TARASCON, LYONS, MACON, DIJON, and PARIS.

RC—Restaurant Car attached.

1	2	3	4	5	6	7	8	9	10	11	12	13	14	15	16	17	18	19	20	21	22	23	24	25	26	27
MENTON 55 ....dep	...	...	...	...	...	...	...	...	...	...	...	0 17	...	...	...	...	...	5 46	...	...	...	...	...	...	...	...
NICE 55........dep	...	...	...	...	...	...	...	...	...	...	...	1 18	...	...	...	...	...	7 2	...	...	...	...	...	...	...	...
CANNES 55 ....dep	...	...	...	...	...	...	...	...	...	...	...	2 3	...	...	...	...	...	7 49	...	...	...	...	...	...	...	...
	1,2,3	1,2,3		1 & 2	1,2,3			1,2,3	1,2,3	1,2,3	1,2,3	1,2,3	1,2,3	1 & 2	1,2,3	1,2,3		1,2,3		1,2,3	1,2,3			1,2,3		1,2,3
MARSEILLES— St. Charles ......dep	...	...	...	...	...	...	...	...	...	...	4 45	6 0	7 5	9 0	8 10	10 17	...	11 50	...	...	...	...	...	...	...	14 12
L'Estaque	...	...	...	...	...	...	...	...	...	...	5 3	T	7 19	M	...	...	...	...	...	...	...	...	...	...	...	14 28
Pas-des-Lanciers	...	...	...	...	...	...	...	...	...	...	5 15	...	7 30	...	...	...	...	T	...	...	...	...	...	...	...	14 41
Rognac ....arr	...	...	...	...	...	...	...	...	...	...	5 29	6 24	7 40	...	...	10 45	...	12 19	...	...	...	...	...	...	...	14 56
Saint Chamas	...	...	...	...	...	...	...	...	...	...	6 4	...	8 14	...	...	11 16	...	...	...	...	...	...	...	...	...	15 35
Miramas	...	...	...	...	...	...	...	...	...	...	6 19	6 53	8 26	...	...	11 30	...	12 47	...	...	...	...	...	...	...	15 50
Arles 57 ....arr	...	...	...	...	...	...	...	...	...	...	7 3	7 20	9 7	...	9 24	12 12	...	13 15	...	...	...	...	...	...	...	16 37
dep	...	...	...	...	...	...	...	...	...	...	7 31	7 24	9 35	...	9 26	12 22	...	13 22	...	...	...	...	...	...	...	16 47
Tarascon ....arr	...	...	...	...	...	...	...	...	...	...	7 52	7 38	9 54	10 23	9 40	12 41	...	13 36	...	...	...	...	...	...	...	17 6
BARCELONA 295......dep	...	...	...	18 51	...	...	...	...	...	...	...	...	...	...	...	...	...	...	...	...	...	...	...	...	...	...
NARBONNE 45B ......dep	...	...	...	1 35	...	...	...	...	...	...	...	...	4 20	4 20	...	9 11	...	9 11	...	...	...	...	...	...	...	13 24
CETTE 57 ....dep	...	...	...	3 0	...	...	...	...	...	...	4 5	4 5	7 20	7 20	...	10 50	...	10 50	...	...	...	...	...	...	...	14 40
Tarascon ....dep	...	...	...	5 18	5 40	...	...	...	...	...	8 20	7 48	10 37	10 29	...	13 3	...	13 44	...	...	...	...	...	...	...	17 31
Barbentane........	...	...	...	...	6 5	...	...	...	...	...	8 46	...	11 0	...	...	13 25	...	...	...	...	...	...	...	...	...	18 1
Avignon 63A ......arr	...	...	...	5 40	6 14	...	...	...	...	...	8 55	8 7	11 9	10 51	...	13 34	...	14 6	...	...	...	...	...	...	...	18 10
dep	...	...	...	5 48		...	...	...	5 57	8 24	9 20	8 15	11 50	10 57	...		...	14 20	...	...	16 0	...	...	...	...	18 57
Sorgues	...	...	...	...	...	...	...	...	6 17	8 40	9 40	...	12 10	...	...	...	...	14 33	...	...	16 20	...	...	...	...	19 22
Courthezon........	...	...	...	...	...	...	...	...	6 34		9 56	...	12 26	RC	...	...	...	...	...	...	16 37	...	...	...	...	19 38
Orange	...	4 47	...	Y	...	...	...	...	6 52	...	10 15	8 42	12 47	...	...	...	...	14 56	...	...	16 57	...	...	...	...	19 57
Bollène La Croisière	...	5 9	...	...	...	...	...	...	7 24	...	10 47	9 1	13 19	...	...	...	...	15 16	...	...	17 36	...	...	...	...	20 35
Pierrelatte	...	5 28	...	...	...	...	...	...	7 48	...	11 9	9 14	13 39	...	...	...	...	T	...	...	17 54	...	...	...	...	21 43
Châteauneuf-du-Rhone ...	...	5 46	...	...	...	...	...	...	8 7	...	11 29	...	13 58	...	...	...	...	...	...	...	18 14	...	...	...	...	22 2
Montelimar ....arr	...	5 57	...	7 0	...	...	...	...	8 18	...	11 41	9 33	14 9	...	...	...	...	15 47	§—Lyons Brotteaux Station.	...	18 25	...	...	...	...	22 13
dep	...	6 1	...	7 2	...	...	...	...	8 28	...	12 13	9 37	14 17	...	...	...	...	15 52		...	18 32	...	...	...	...	22 50
Loriol	...	6 33	...	...	...	...	...	...	9 2	...	12 46	...	14 51	...	...	...	...	...		...	19 6	...	...	...	...	22 52
Livron ....arr	...	6 38	...	...	...	...	...	...	9 7	...	12 51	9 59	14 56	...	...	...	...	16 17		...	19 11	...	...	...	...	22 57
dep	...	6 47	...	...	...	...	...	...	9 13	11 43	12 57	10 4	15 10	...	...	...	...	16 21		18 25	19 23	...	...	21 1	...	23 2
Valence 62A ......arr	...	7 14	...	7 41	...	...	...	...	9 40	12 7	13 23	10 20	15 36	12 43	...	...	...	16 38		18 52	19 50	...	...	21 27	...	23 26
dep	5 30		...	7 49	...	...	...	8 38	10 42		13 59	10 30	15 53	12 49	...	...	...	16 52			20 26	...	...		...	
Tain	5 55	...	...	...	...	...	...	9 3	11 7	...	14 25	...	16 18	...	...	...	...	17 11		...	20 52	...	...	...	...	...
Saint-Vallier	6 17	...	...	...	...	...	...	9 25	11 29	...	14 48	...	16 40	...	...	...	...	...		...	21 15	...	...	...	...	...
St. Rambert......arr	6 34	...	...	...	...	...	...	9 42	11 46	...	15 5	11 7	16 57	...	...	...	...	17 38		...	21 33	...	...	...	...	...
dep	6 56	...	...	...	...	...	...	9 55	11 57	...	15 24	11 10	18 23	...	...	...	...	17 41		...	22 2	...	...	...	...	...
Les Roches de Condrieux	7 27	...	...	...	...	...	...	10 26	12 28	...	16 4	...	19 4	...	...	...	...	...		...	22 16	...	...	...	...	...
Vienne	7 49	...	...	...	...	...	...	10 51	12 51	...	16 16	11 36	19 16	...	...	...	...	18 10		...	23 10	...	...	...	...	...
Chasse 56........	8 11	...	...	...	...	...	...	11 13	13 11	...	16 39	...	19 37	...	...	...	...	18 25		...	23 32	...	...	...	...	...
Lyons Perrache ......arr	8 44	...	...	9 19	...	...	...	11 50	13 47	...	17 13	12 2	20 10	14 19	...	...	...	18 46	...	...	0 3	...	...	...	...	...
GENEVA 60 ....arr	...	...	...	16 17	...	...	...	16 51	19 38	...	0 43	16 51	...	19 38	...	...	...	0 43	...	...	...	...	...	...	...	...
GRENOBLE 63A ......dep	...	...	...	6 35	...	...	6 35		...	11 48		8 18	15 22	...	...	...	...		15 22	15 22	...	...	...	19 10	...	...
		1,2,3	1,2,3	1 & 2	2 & 3	Lux.	1,2,3	1,2,3	1,2,3	1,2,3		1,2,3	1,2,3	1 & 2	1 & 2	1,2,3	1,2,3	1,2,3	1 Cl.	1,2,3	1 & 2	1,2,3		1,2,3	1,2,3	
Lyons Perrache......dep	...	3 58	7 34	9 39	...	...	10 38	...	15 2	17 30	...	13 5	20 53	14 34	...	...	...	...	19 40	20 40	...	...	...	23 17	...	...
Lyons Vaise ......arr	...	4 4	7 41	...	...	...	10 45	...	15 9	17 37	...	13 11	21 0	...	...	...	...	...	19 46	20 46	...	...	...	23 24	...	...
dep	...	4 9	7 50	RC	8 21	...	10 52	¶	15 15	17 44	...	13 15	21 7	...	...	...	...	...	19 50	20 49	...	...	...	23 26	22 8	...
Collonges Fontaines........	...	4 21	8 5	...	8 31	...	11 7	13 27	15 30	...	...	T	21 20	M	...	...	...	...	...	...	...	...	...	...	22 21	...
Villevert-Neuville	...	4 33	8 19	...	8 46	...	11 21	13 37	15 44	...	...	...	21 33	...	...	...	...	...	...	T	...	...	...	...	22 33	...
Saint Germain	...	4 41	8 29	Y	8 51	...	11 30	13 42	15 54	18 6	...	13 31	21 42	...	...	...	...	...	...	21 5	...	...	...	23 42	22 38	...
Quincieux-Trevoux	...	4 49	8 38	...	8 59	...	11 40	13 50	16 4	18 15	...	...	21 51	...	...	...	...	...	...	...	...	...	...	...	22 46	...
Villefranche-sur-Saône ...	...	5 8	8 55	10 14	9 10	...	11 58	14 2	16 26	18 34	...	13 47	22 10	...	...	...	...	...	20 16	21 19	...	...	...	23 58	22 57	...
Belleville 63	...	5 30	9 17	...		...	12 22	14 19	16 48	18 55	...	14 4	22 31	...	...	...	...	...	20 31	21 34	...	...	...	0 14		...
Romanèche........	...	5 41	9 29	...	...	...	12 34	14 28	16 59	19 5	...	...	22 42	...	...	...	...	...	...	...	...	...	...	...	...	...
Macon........arr	...	6 5	9 54	10 51	...	...	13 1	14 49	17 25	19 30	...	14 25	23 5	15 33	...	...	...	...	20 51	21 54	...	...	...	0 38	...	...

For Notes and Continuation

of Trains, see page 51a.

1	2	3	4	5	6	7	8	9	10	11	12	13	14
Genoa 271 ......dep	...	...	...	20 0	...	...	...	¶—From Lyons Brotteaux dep. 13.13.	...	...	...	...	...
Turin 271 ......dep	...	...	...	9 30	...	...	...		...	...	...	...	...
Modane 61 ......dep	...	...	...	3 0	...	...	...		...	...	...	...	...
Geneva 61 ......dep	...	...	...	6 53	...	...	7 38		11 15	...	...	7 38	...
Macon ......dep	4 22	7 2	10 10	10 59	...	From Chambéry (dep. 10.25)	13 39		17 54	19 57	...	14 31	...
Tournus	5 10	7 55	10 58	...	...		14 28		18 42	20 49	...	15 1	...
Chalon Saone ...... arr	5 50	8 34	11 33	11 55	...		15 3		19 15	21 24	...	15 26	...
Chalon Saone ...... dep	6 24	9 5	12 7	11 57	...		15 47		19 35		13 29	15 32	18 50
Chagny 53A	7 11	10 32	12 47	12 19	...		16 46		20 22	...	13 58	16 0	19 17
Beaune	7 38	10 59	13 13	...	...	...	17 13		20 54	...		16 18	
Nuits-St. Georges	8 5	11 26	13 40	RC	...		17 40		21 21	...	...	16 34	...
Vougeot	8 13	11 34	13 48	...	...	X	17 48		21 30	...	...	T	...
Gevrey-Chambertin	8 22	11 43	13 58	...	...		17 58		21 40	...	...	...	...
Dijon 52 ......arr	8 35	11 56	14 11	13 8	...	14 41	18 12		21 53	...	...	16 58	...
Milan 274 ......dep	...	...	...	23 45	...	...	...		...	...	...	8 0	...
Domodossola 263c dp	...	...	...	2 a35	...	...	...		...	...	...	10a55	...
Lausanne 263c ......dep	...	...	...	6 a55	...	...	...		...	...	...	3 p0	...
Berne 259b ......dep	...	...	...	6 a40	...	...	...		...	...	...	2 p10	...
Neuchatel 266 ......dep	...	...	...	8 a0	...	...	...		...	...	...	3 p13	...
Pontarlier 52A ...dep	...	...	...	9 18	...	...	...		...	...	...	16 25	...
Dijon ......dep	9 6	12 25	15 4	13 25	...	14 47	19 28	...	...	...	...	19 5	...
Blaisy-Bas	9 54	13 15	15 51	...	...	...	20 14	...	...	...	...	...	...
Les Laumes	11 3	14 0	16 35	...	...	...	20 58	...	...	...	...	20 0	...
Montbard	11 22	14 43	16 51	...	...	...	21 15	...	...	...	...	20 13	...
Nuits-sous-Ravières	12 0	15 9	17 18	...	...	X	22 11	...	...	...	...	20 30	...
Tanlay	12 32	15 47	17 44	Y	...	...	22 40	...	...	...	...	...	...
Tonnerre ...... arr	12 36	16 15	17 53	...	...	...	22 50	...	...	...	...	20 53	...
Tonnerre ...... dep	12 52	16 30	17 56	...	...	...	22 55	...	...	...	...	20 55	...
St. Florentin	13 10	16 44	18 25	...	...	...	23 50	...	...	...	...	21 16	...
Laroche 56 ...... arr	13 34	17 6	18 45	15 45	...	16 35	23 50	...	...	...	...	21 31	...
Laroche 56 ...... dep	14 33	17 26	19 5	15 50	...	16 40	0 10	...	...	...	...	21 36	...
Joigny	14 46	17 39	19 17	...	...	...	0 24	...	...	...	...	21 46	...
Villeneuve-sur-Yonne	15 13	18 6	19 43	...	...	...	0 52	...	...	...	...	...	...
Sens 73	15 40	18 29	21 1	...	...	...	1 13	...	...	...	...	22 15	...
Montereau	17 16	19 33	22 4	...	...	...	2 7	...	...	...	...	22 42	...
Moret	17 50	19 54	22 20	...	...	...	2 25	...	...	...	...	...	...
Fontainebleau	18 8	20 11	22 35	...	...	...	2 39	...	...	...	...	23 1	...
Melun	18 34	20 34	22 56	...	...	...	3 1	...	...	...	...	23 16	...
Brunoy	18 54	21 13	23 22	...	...	...	3 40	...	...	...	...	...	...
Villeneuve St. Georges ...	...	...	...	...	...	...	3 51	...	...	...	...	...	...
Charenton	...	...	...	...	...	...	4 13	...	...	...	...	...	...
PARIS Gare (P.L.M.) arr	19 20	21 38	23 45	18 8	...	18 32	4 20	...	...	...	...	23 55	...
PARIS Gare (P.L.M.) dep	...	...	...	19 23	...	19 23	...	...	...	...	...	...	...
Paris (Nord) ...... arr	...	...	...	19 59	...	19 59	...	...	...	...	...	...	...
Paris (Nord) ...... dep	...	...	...	21 20	...	21 20	...	...	...	...	...	...	...
Boulogne 19 ......arr	...	...	...	...	...	...	...	...	...	...	...	...	...
Calais 19 ......arr	...	...	...	1 23	...	1 23	...	...	...	...	...	...	...

1	15	16	17	18	19	20	21	22	23	24	25	26	27
Genoa 271 ......dep	...	...	...	11 15	...	5 0	...	...	...	...	‡—These departures are only from 9th July until 15th September.	...	...
Turin 271 ......dep	...	...	...	16 5	...	9 10	...	...	...	...		...	...
Modane 61 ......dep	...	...	...	18 40	...	12 12	...	...	...	...		...	...
Geneva 61 ......dep	...	...	...	⋮	14 30	15 0	...	...	21 10	...		...	...
Macon ......dep	15 36	...	...	⋮	⋮	21 4	22 2	...	0 41	Simplon Express.		...	...
Tournus	...	...	...	⋮	⋮	21 33	22 35	...	...			...	...
Chalon Saone ...... arr	...	...	...	⋮	⋮	21 55	22 57	...	SC			...	...
Chalon Saone ...... dep	M	...	...	⋮	⋮	21 59	23 5	...	...			...	...
Chagny 53A	...	...	...	⋮	⋮	22 22	23 31	...	...			...	...
Beaune	...	...	...	⋮	⋮	22 37	23 47	...	O			...	...
Nuits-St. Georges	...	...	...	⋮	⋮	...	0 3	...	...			...	...
Vougeot	...	...	...	⋮	⋮	...	...	...	...			...	...
Gevrey-Chambertin	...	...	...	⋮	⋮	Q	T	...	...			...	...
Dijon 52 ......arr	17 23	...	...	1 55	18 31	23 9	0 23	...	2 22	Lux.		...	...
Milan 274 ......dep	...	8 0	...	...	...	10 50	10 50	15 2[illegible]	...	16 30		...	...
Domodossola 263c dp	...	10a55	...	...	...	1 p42	1 p42	6 p22	...	7 p15		...	...
Lausanne 263c ......dep	10 a0	3 p0	9p42	...	...	6 p53	6 p53	10p47	...	11p39		...	...
Berne 259b ......dep	9 a19	2 p10	8p20	...	...	5 p40	5 p40	9p25	...	11‡ 5		...	...
Neuchatel 266 ......dep	10a40	3 p13	9p53	...	...	6 p43	6 p43	11p 7	...	12‡ 5		...	...
Pontarlier 52A ...dep	12 25	16 25	23 20	...	...	20 15	20 15	0 5	...	0 43	...	...	...
Dijon ......dep	17 35	18 56	1 52	2 4	18 46	23 37	0 42	2 16	2 28	2 40	...	...	...
Blaisy-Bas	...	...	...	...	...	0 11	SC	...	...	...	...	...	...
Les Laumes	RC	RC	...	...	...	0 39	1 42	Z	...	...	...	...	...
Montbard	...	...	C	...	...	0 53	1 56	...	...	...	...	...	...
Nuits-sous-Ravières	...	Z	...	...	...	1 10	...	SC	O	...	...	...	6 12
Tanlay	...	...	...	...	...	...	...	...	...	...	...	...	6 38
Tonnerre ...... arr	...	...	...	...	...	1 34	2 36	...	...	...	...	...	6 46
Tonnerre ...... dep	...	...	...	...	...	1 35	2 38	...	...	...	...	4 55	6 47
St. Florentin	...	...	...	...	...	Q	T	...	...	...	...	5 21	7 14
Laroche 56 ...... arr	19 45	20 57	4 3	4 15	20 47	2 9	3 13	4 27	4 39	4 51	...	5 39	7 33
Laroche 56 ...... dep	19 50	21 2	4 8	4 26	20 52	2 19	3 18	4 32	4 44	4 56	...	6 33	...
Joigny	...	...	...	...	...	2 30	3 28	...	...	...	...	6 45	...
Villeneuve-sur-Yonne	...	...	...	...	...	...	...	...	...	...	...	7 10	...
Sens 73	To Héricy.	...	...	...	...	3 0	3 58	...	...	...	5 55	7 33	...
Montereau		...	...	...	...	3 32	4 30	Z	...	...	6 36	8 16	...
Moret		Z	C	...	...	...	...	...	...	...	6 50	8 48	...
Fontainebleau		...	...	...	...	3 53	Via Héricoy.	...	...	...	...	9 1	...
Melun		...	...	...	...	4 11	5 17	...	...	...	...	9 23	...
Brunoy		...	...	...	...	...	...	...	...	...	...	9 51	...
Villeneuve St. Georges ...	...	...	...	...	...	...	...	...	...	...	...	...	...
Charenton	...	...	...	...	...	...	...	...	...	...	...	...	...
PARIS Gare (P.L.M.) arr	22 0	23 0	6 20	6 35	22 50	4 55	6 0	6 45	7 0	7 15	...	10 17	...
PARIS Gare (P.L.M.) dep	...	...	...	...	...	...	7 5	7 5	8 47	8 47	...	...	...
Paris (Nord) ...... arr	...	...	...	...	...	...	7 43	7 43	9 21	9 21	...	...	...
Paris (Nord) ...... dep	...	...	...	...	...	...	8 25	8 25	9 50	9 55	...	...	...
Boulogne 19 ......arr	...	...	...	...	...	...	11 25	11 25	...	...	...	...	...
Calais 19 ......arr	...	...	...	...	...	...	...	...	13 5	13 10	...	...	...

Extra.

Vienne ......dep	6 11	8 58	14 58	18 23	...
Lyons. ......arr	6 57	9 41	15 49	19 9	...
Lyons Vaise......dep	11 25	13 49	18 44	...	
Villefranche......arr	12 13	14 38	19 33	...	

NIMES to ARLES-TRINQUETAILLE.

Nimes-Camargue......dep	6 30	12 25	17 15	...	...	...	...
Arles-Trinquetaille......arr	7 55	13 45	18 35	...	...	...	...
Arles-Trinquetaille......dep	8 5	12 15	18 45	...	...	...	...
Nimes-Camargue......arr	9 25	13 30	20 0	...	...	...	...

ARLES-TRINQUETAILLE to GIRAUD and SAINTES MARIES.

Arles-Trinquetaille......dep	8 10	14 5	19 0	...	...	...	...
Le Salin de Giraud ......arr	9 45	15 40	20 30	...	...	...	...
Arles-Trinquetaille......dep	8 15	14 0	18 55	...	...	...	...
Saintes Maries-de-la-Mer arr	9 50	15 25	20 20	...	...	...	...
Le Salin de Giraud ......dep	6 0	10 15	16 45	...	...	...	...
Arles-Trinquetaille......arr	7 35	11 55	18 25	...	...	...	...
Saintes Maries-de-la-Mer dep	6 15	10 10	17 5	...	...	...	...
Arles-Trinquetaille......arr	7 40	11 45	18 30	...	...	...	...

MARSEILLES, TARASCON, LYONS, MACON, DIJON, and PARIS.

MENTON 55 ....dep	...	...	...	...	...	14 30	...	...	13 5	...	...	15 29
NICE 55 ....dep	...	...	...	...	...	15 40	...	...	14 18	...	...	16 44
CANNES 55 ....dep	...	...	...	...	...	16 25	...	...	15 9	...	...	17 39
	1,2,3	1,2,3	1,2,3	1,2,3	1,2,3	1 Cl.	...		1,2,3	1,2,3		1,2,3
MARSEILLES—												
St. Charles ......dep	...	16 39	18 0	...	19 55	20 10	...	...	20 25	20 35	...	23 28
L'Estaque	...	16 55	T	...	...	⋮	...	...	⋮	...	...	...
Pas-des-Lanciers	...	17 11	...	...	...	RC	...	...	⋮	20 56	...	R
Rognac ....arr	...	17 25	...	...	...	⋮	...	...	⋮	21 5	...	SC
Saint Chamas	...	18 0	...	...	...	P	...	...	W	21 34	...	...
Miramas	...	18 15	18 50	...	...	⋮	...	...	⋮	21 43	...	0 20
Arles 57 .... arr	...	18 59	19 18	...	...	SC	...	...	⋮	22 16	...	0 50
dep	...	19 50	19 23	...	...	⋮	...	...	⋮	22 26	...	0 58
Tarascon ....arr	...	20 12	19 37	...	21 19	⋮	...	...	⋮	22 44	...	1 8
BARCELONA 295......dep	5 0	...	...	10 0	...	⋮	...	...	⋮	...	...	14 16
NARBONNE 45B ......dep	15 59	13 24	13 24	16 43	...	⋮	...	...	⋮	...	...	20 30
CETTE 57 ....dep	17 35	15 0	15 0	18 55	...	⋮	...	...	⋮	...	...	22 30
Tarascon...............dep	⋮	20 25	20 4	21 0	...	⋮	...	...	⋮	23 10	...	1 25
Barbentane......................	⋮	20 51	...	...	...	⋮	...	...	⋮	...	...	...
Avignon 63A ...... arr	19 46	21 0	20 30	21 23	...	21 53	...	...	22 13	23 32	...	1 49
dep	20 15	22 35	20 39		21 40	22 3	...	...	22 25		...	1 57
Sorgues	...	22 51	...	...	21 52	...	...	...	...	...	...	...
Courthezon......................	...	23 6	...	...		...	...	...	...	...	...	...
Orange............................	...	23 16	21 7	...	...	...	...	...	...	...	...	2 29
Bollène La Croisière	...		...	...	...	...	...	...	W	...	...	2 51
Pierrelatte	...	...	21 35	...	...	...	...	...	...	...	...	...
Châteauneuf-du-Rhone ...	S	...	...	...	...	...	...	...	...	...	...	...
Montelimar........... arr	...	...	21 54	...	...	...	...	...	...	...	...	3 24
dep	...	...	21 57	...	...	...	...	...	...	...	...	3 27
Loriol	...	...	...	...	...	...	...	...	...	...	...	...
Livron .... arr	...	...	T	...	...	...	...	...	...	...	...	3 55
dep	...	...	...	...	...	...	...	...	...	...	...	3 58
Valence 62A ...... arr	21 57	...	22 35	...	...	23 43	...	...	0 19	...	...	4 17
dep	22 2	...	22 43	...	...	23 46	...	...	0 23	...	...	4 37
Tain	...	...	...	...	...	...	...	...	...	...	...	...
Saint-Vallier	...	...	...	...	...	SC	...	...	...	...	...	...
St. Rambert...... arr	...	...	...	...	...	...	...	...	...	...	...	R
dep	...	...	...	...	...	P	...	...	...	...	...	...
Les Roches de Condrieux	...	...	...	...	...	...	...	...	...	...	...	...
Vienne	...	...	23 46	...	...	...	...	...	...	...	...	5 52
Chasse 56.....................	...	...	23 58	...	...	...	...	...	...	...	...	6 6
Lyons Perrache ......arr	23 30	...	0 18	...	...	1 9	...	...	2 1	...	...	6 28
GENEVA 60 ....arr	...	...	...	...	...	...	...	...	...	...	...	12 3
GRENOBLE 63A ......dep	20 50	...	20 50	...	...	...	...	...	...	...	...	...
			1,2,3	1,2,3		1 Cl.	1,2,3	1 & 2	1,2,3	1,2,3	1 & 2	1,2,3
Lyons Perrache ......dep	23 54	...	0 40	...	...	1 19	...	...	2 16	...	...	7 20
Lyons Vaise........ arr	...	...	0 46	...	...	...	...	...	...	...	...	7 26
dep	...	...	0 49	...	...	...	...	...	...	...	...	7 30
Collonges Fontaines	...	...	...	...	...	...	...	...	...	...	...	...
Villevert-Neuville/	...	...	...	...	...	...	...	...	...	...	...	...
Saint Germain	S	...	T	...	...	...	...	...	...	...	...	7 49
Quincieux-Trevoux	...	...	...	...	...	...	...	...	...	...	...	...
Villefranche-sur-Saône ...	...	...	1 19	...	...	...	...	...	...	...	...	8 6
Belleville 63	...	...	1 36	...	...	...	...	...	...	...	...	8 23
Romanèche......................	...	...	...	...	...	...	...	...	...	...	...	...
Macon.....................arr	0 53	...	1 58	...	...	2 13	...	...	3 17	...	...	8 44
1	2	3	4	5	6	7	8	9	10	11	12	13

NOTES.

BB—Coming from Pontarlier line. **At Dijon will take up for Paris, and also take** forward passengers from Modane line.

C—Will not take up 3rd class at Dijon nor Laroche.

D—Coming from the Chambèry and Aix-les-Bains line; carrying 2nd class passengers travelling at least 155 miles and 3rd class at least 248 miles.

M—Taking 1st class travelling at least 125 miles; and 2nd class at Marseilles travelling at least 150 miles, and at Lyons travelling at least 248 miles. Exceptionally will take up at Lyons 1st class for Dijon.

O—Bringing forward 1st, 2nd, and 3rd class from the Geneva line; not taking up at stations shown in this table.

P—Only for passengers travelling at least 310 miles; exceptionally, at Marseilles will take up passengers for Lyons.

Q—At Dijon (only) will take up 2nd class coming from branch lines, and 2nd class who are going direct to Paris.

R—Takes 2nd class passengers going at least 62 miles, and 3rd class going at least 125 miles.

S—From Avignon to Valence will only take up passengers travelling at least 149 miles; at Lyons and forward will only take up passengers travelling at least 310 miles.

T—Takes 2nd and 3rd class travelling at least 62 miles.

W—Taking from Marseilles and Avignon travellers proceeding at least 149 miles.

X—**Savoie Express,** Train de Luxe, leaving Chambèry daily from 6th July until 13th September.

Y—Takes 2nd class travelling at least 62 miles.

Z—Bringing forward passengers from the Pontarlier line; **not taking** up at either Dijon or Laroche.

RC—Restaurant Car attached.

SC—Sleeping Car attached.

SAINT GERMAIN-DES-FOSSES and LYONS.

	1,2,3	1,2,3	1,2,3	1,2,3	1,2,3	1,2,3	1,2,3	1,2,3	1,2,3	1 & 2	1,2,3	1,2,3	1,2,3	1,2,3	1,2,3	1,2,3	1,2,3	1,2,3
St. Germain-des Fosses......dep	2 20	...	...	...	5 19	6 21	...	...	10 27	12 9	15 10	...	16 17	17 6	17 22	18 19	...	20 20
Lapalisse (53B)......	2 42	...	From Moulins (depart 4.4.)	...	5 50	...	...	...	10 54	...	15 29	...	...	17 27	17 49	...	...	21 9
St.Martin-Sail-les-Bains......	3 4	...		...	6 18	...	...	...	11 19	B	15 46	...	D	...	18 14	...	...	21 48
St. Germain l'Espinasse	3 26	...		...	6 45	...	...	...	11 45	...	...	...	...	...	18 40	...	...	22 31
Roanne......arr	3 37	...		...	7 0	7 23	...	...	11 59	13 3	16 12	...	17 19	18 9	18 54	19 15	...	23 2
,, ...dep		5 5		6 42		7 28	7 57	11 22	12 24	13 8		16 22	17 26				19 28	
St. Victor-Thizy (42B)	...	5 46		7 15	...	A	8 42	11 51	13 2	...	...	17 2	...	...	...	...	20 5	...
Tarare ......dep	...	6 28		7 52	...	8 37	9 24	12 25	14 14	14 6	...	17 44	18 31	...	...	...	20 46	...
L'Arbresle (62)	2 & 3	7 3		8 11	9 35	8 54	9 58	12 42	14 53	...	...	18 14	...	...	...	...	21 11	...
Lozanne (53A)	6 32	7 12	8 9		9 45	9 3	10 7		15 8	...	...	18 24	...	...	...	...	21 20	21 45
S. Germain-au-Mt.-d'Or	6 50	7 34	8 23	...		9 17	10 30	...	15 34	...	...	18 47	...	...	...	...	21 35	22 8
Lyons Vaise ......arr		8 2	8 37	...	...	9 31	10 58	...	16 6	...	...	19 16	...	...	...	...	21 51	22 33
,, Brotteaux ......arr	...	...	...	...	...	...	...	...	...	14 51	...	...	19 19	...	...	...	...	...
,, Perrache ......arr	...	8 18	8 48	...	...	9 40	11 12	...	16 22	15 11	...	19 28	19 41	...	...	...	22 5	22 45

	1,2,3	1,2,3	1,2,3	1,2,3	1,2,3	1,2,3	1,2,3	1,2,3	1,2,3	1,2,3	1,2,3	1,2,3	1,2,3	1,2,3	1,2,3	2 & 3	1,2,3	1,2,3
Lyons Perrache......dep	...	...	4 56	7 0	...	8 36	9 50	...	12 20	...	14 55	16 9	...	...	17 4	...	21 11	...
,, Brotteaux......dep	...	...	...	...	...	...	10 11	...	...	...	...	16 30	...	...	...	...	...	...
,, Vaise ......dep	...	...	5 11	7 8	...	8 49	D	...	12 35	...	C	C	...	...	17 17	...	21 25	...
St. Germain	...	...	5 29	7 24	...	9 9	10 32	...	12 57	...	15 16	16 50	...	...	17 52	19 50	21 46	...
Lozanne......	...	...	5 53	7 36	7 46	9 33	...	...	13 24	...	...	17 6	...	...	18 19	20 8	22 12	...
L'Arbresle	...	...	6 10	To Moulins (arr. 11.10.)	8 14	9 51	...	...	13 48	...	...	17 19	...	17 45	18 48		22 30	...
Tarare......dep	...	...	6 53		8 45	10 34	11 19	...	14 29	...	16 3	17 47	...	18 22	19 32	...	23 17	...
St. Victor-Thizy	...	...	7 35		9 21	11 15	...	...	15 9	...	...	18 21	...	19 1	20 14	...	0 3	...
Roanne......arr	...	...	8 9		9 51	11 49	12 11	...	15 44	...	16 54	18 43	...	19 32	20 47	1,2,3	0 35	...
,, ...dep	5 40	7 29	8 35			12 34	12 16	15 12		15 59	16 59	18 49	19 6			21 34		1 1
St. Germain l'Espinasse	5 55	...	8 50		...	12 52	...	15 26	...	...	...	...	19 23	...	...	...	...	...
St. Martin-Sail-les-Bains......	6 20	...	9 17	...	...	13 22	...	15 50	...	...	...	...	19 53	...	...	...	...	2 20
Lapalisse	6 41	...	9 40	...	...	13 46	...	16 11	...	...	...	...	20 18	...	...	...	...	2 56
St. Germain-d-F.......arr	7 1	8 22	10 0	...	...	14 9	13 15	16 29	...	16 52	17 57	19 48	20 39	...	...	22 35	...	3 29

A—Admits 2nd and 3rd cl. passengers travelling at least 62 miles.
B—Admits 2nd class passengers travelling at least 56 miles.
C—Only takes 2nd and 3rd class travelling at least 62 miles, **or for beyond Roanne.**
D—Takes 2nd class travelling 50 miles and 3rd class travelling 186 miles.

1	2	3	4	5	6	7	8	9	10	11	12	13
GENOA 271 ......dep	...	...	...	...	...	...	...		...	...	20 0	...
TURIN 271 ......dep	...	...	...	...	...	...	...		...	...	0 30	...
MODANE 61 ......dep	...	...	...	...	...	...	...		...	...	3 0	...
GENEVA ......dep	...	...	...	...	...	...			...	...	:	...
Macon ......dep	0 58	...	2 38	...	...	2 16	From Chambéry (dep. 22.15).	From Evian (dep. 21.30). Runs July 2 to Sept. 20.	3 20	...		8 52
Tournus	...	...	3 10	...	...	...			...	...		9 22
Chalon Saone...... arr	...	...	3 37	...	...	...			4 11	...		9 47
Chalon Saone...... dep	...	...	3 45	4 26	...	...			4 13	...		9 53
Chagny 53A......	...	...	4 46	4 45	...	SC			4 33	...		10 19
Beaune......	...	...	5 6		...	...			W	...		10 37
Nuits-St. Georges	...	...	5 25	...	...	...			...	...		...
Vougeot	...	...	...	...	...	...			...	...		R
Gevrey-Chambertin......	...	...	...	...	...	...			...	...		...
Dijon 52......arr	2 46	...	5 50	...	...	3 52	4 4	4 16	5 21	...	9 36	11 13
MILAN 274 ......dep	...	...	...	...	...	...	...	...	...	...	23 45	...
DOMODOSSOLA 263C dp	...	...	...	...	...	...	...	...	...	...	2 a35	...
LAUSANNE 263C......dep	...	...	...	...	...	...	...	...	...	...	6 a42	...
BERNE 259B......dep	...	...	...	...	...	...	...	...	...	...	6 a40	...
NEUCHATEL 266......dep	...	...	...	...	...	...	...	...	...	...	7 a30	...
PONTARLIER 52A ...dep	...	...	...	...	...	...	...	...	...	...	7 56	...
Dijon ......dep	2 52	...	6 25	...	...	3 58	4 10	4 22	5 36	6 33	10 1	11 40
Blaisy-Bas	...	...	...	...	...	...	...	...	...	7 14	...	12 14
Les Laumes......	...	...	7 17	...	...	...	...	...	...	8 25	RC	12 42
Montbard......	...	...	7 30	...	...	...	...	...	...	8 41	...	12 56
Nuits-sous-Raviers	S	...	7 50	...	...	...	...	...	...	9 7	BB	...
Tanlay	...	...	...	...	...	...	D	...	...	9 34	...	...
Tonnerre ...... arr	...	...	8 12	...	...	...	...	...	...	9 43	...	13 35
Tonnerre ...... dep	...	...	8 14	...	...	...	...	...	...	9 46	...	13 36
St. Florentin	...	...	...	...	...	...	...	...	...	10 15	...	R
Laroche 56...... arr	5 3	...	8 46	...	...	5 56	6 8	6 20	7 50	10 35	12 11	14 11
Laroche 56...... dep	5 8	...	8 54	...	...	6 1	6 13	6 25	8 2	10 50	12 16	14 22
Joigny	...	...	9 4	...	...	...	...	...	...	11 2	...	14 33
Villeneuve-sur-Yonne......	...	...	...	...	...	...	...	...	...	11 28	...	...
Sens 73	...	...	9 32	11 10	...	Via Héricy.	...	...	...	11 51	...	15 4
Montereau	...	...	9 59	11 55	...		...	...	...	12 52	...	15 40
Moret......	...	...	...	12 13	...		...	...	...	13 19	...	...
Fontainebleau	...	...	...	12 25	...		...	...	...	13 36	...	...
Melun	...	...	...	12 46	...		...	...	...	14 1	...	...
Brunoy......	...	...	...	13 16	...		...	...	...	14 38	...	...
Villeneuve St. Georges ...	...	...	...	13 29	...	...	...	...	...	14 52	...	...
Charenton	...	...	...	...	...	...	...	...	...	...	...	...
PARIS—(Gare P.L.M.) arr	7 23	...	11 8	13 45	...	8 0	8 12	8 37	10 15	15 8	14 25	17 10
PARIS—(Gare P.L.M.) dep	...	...	...	...	...	8 47	8 47	...	11 0	...	15 0	19 23
PARIS (NORD) ... arr	...	...	...	...	...	9 21	9 21	...	11 28	...	15 35	19 59
PARIS (NORD) ... dep	8 35	...	...	...	...	9 50	9 50	...	12 0	...	16 0	21 20
BOULOGNE 19......arr	11 25	...	...	...	...	...	...	...	...	...	18 58	...
CALAIS ......arr	...	...	...	...	...	13 5	13 5	...	15 26	...	...	1 23

VILLEFRANCHE-SUR-SAONE and TARARE.

Villefranche-s-S. dep	5 56	9 40	14 6	1632	**Tarare (P.L.M.)** ...dep	6 26	9 56	1322	17 †4	...
Legny	7 33	11 17	15 43	18 9	Legny......	7 12	1048	1415	17 45	...
Tarare (P.L.M.) arr	8 32	12 16	16†33	19 8	**Villefranche-s-S.** ...arr	8 32	12 8	1535	19 5	...

VILLEFRANCHE and MONSOLS.

Villefranche-s-S. dep	5 52	9 38	13 12	1634	**Monsols** ......dep	6 0	9 42	13 17	...	1636
Beaujeu	7 50	11 29	15 10	1831	Beaujeu......	6 48	1030	14 1	14 5	1724
Monsols ......arr	8 46	12‡30	16 7	1928	**Villefranche-s-S.** ...arr	8 30	1212	‡	1547	19 6

†—At or from Tarare-Ville. ‡—Sunday and Wednesday only.

PARIS, LYONS, and MEDITERRANEAN RAILWAY. [66 lbs. of Luggage free.

DIJON to DOLE and PONTARLIER—DOLE, BESANCON, and BELFORT.

Dist. From E.M	1 Cl. m Di fr. c.	2 Cl. jon. fr. c.	3 Cl. fr. c.																	
				PARIS (48)...dep	19 50	2130	21 30	2215	2250	2250	...	...	...	...	8 30	...	1420	...	15 45	1945
				DIJON ....arr	0 32	1 42	1 42	2 57	3 37	3 37	...	...	...	...	1236	...	1829	...	20 11	0 13
					1,2,3	1 &2	1,2,3	1 &2	1,2,3	1,2,3	1,2,3	1,2,3	1,2,3	1,2,3	1 &2	1,2,3	1 &2	1,2,3	1,2,3	Lux
—	—	—	—	**Dijon** ....dep	1 7	1 48	1 58	3 4	3 47	4 20	5 44	9 0	...	1140	1246	15 1	1842	1855	20 30	0 28
8¾	1 55	1 5	0 70	Magny-Fauverney	...	...	...	...	...	...	6 5	9 19	...	12 0	...	1521	...	1914	...	...
14½	2 60	1 75	1 15	Collonges	...	...	...	B	E	...	6 23	9 34	...	1216	RC	1539	...	1923	...	...
20	3 60	2 40	1 60	**Auxonne** ......arr	1 30	A	2 25	...	4 12	4 51	6 39	9 48	...	1232	C	1555	F	1942	20 58	Q
...	...	...	...	,, ...dep	1 33	...	2 28	...	4 15	4 54	6 59	9 57	...	1238	...	1610	...	1949	21 0	...
26¾	4 80	3 25	2 10	Champvans	...	...	...	...	...	...	7 16	10 14	...	1255	...	1627	RC	20 5	...	...
29½	5 25	3 55	2 30	**Dôle (56)** ......arr	1 44	SC	2 42	...	4 23	5 10	7 22	10 21	...	13 2	1322	1633	...	2011	21 14	...
...	...	...	...	**Dôle**..........dep	1 54	...	:	...	4 33	5 28	7 56	:	1139	:	1332	17 1	...	2032	:	...
38	6 85	4 60	3 0	Montbarrey	2 9	...	:	...	...	5 47	8 17	:	12 4	:	...	1723	...	2054	:	...
44½	8 5	5 45	3 55	Arc-Senans..........	2 21	...	:	...	...	6 3	8 35	:	1227	:	...	1741	...	2114	:	...
49	8 85	5 95	3 90	**Mouchard** arr	2 28	2 52	:	4 3	5 6	6 12	8 44	:	1238	:	14 1	1750	1941	2124	:	1 36
...	...	...	...	,, (53) dep	2 37	2 57	:	4 8	5 11	6 32	9 23	:	1327	:	14 6	1849	1946	—	:	1 41
55½	9 95	6 75	4 40	Mesnay Arbois...	...	...	:	...	...	6 50	9 44	:	1346	:	...	19 5	...	...	:	...
64	11 55	7 80	5 10	**Andelot (51)** ...	3 8	3 28	:	...	...	7 20	10 23	:	1451	:	1435	1936	2012	...	:	Q
71½	12 90	8 70	5 65	Boujeailles	3 26	3 48	:	...	6 3	7 45	10 54	:	1521	:	1454	20 1	2030	...	:	2 28
79½	14 35	9 70	6 30	La Rivière	...	...	:	...	...	8 3	11 17	:	1548	:	...	2019	...	...	:	...
87	15 70	10 60	6 90	**Pontarlier** arr	3 46	4 10	:	5 11	6 26	8 20	11 36	:	1610	:	1515	2035	2050	...	:	2 53
119½	21 45	14 60	9 70	NEUCHATEL arr	7a17	...	:	7a35	9a20	1p47	8 p28	:	7p49	:	5p46	...	11p9	...	:	5‡10
146½	25 75	17 65	11 85	BERNE 259B arr	8a35	...	:	8a35	1032	3p31	5 p0	:	1015	:	6p55	...	12a1	...	:	6‡a8
131½	23 40	15 95	10 60	LAUSAN263B arr	7a10	7a10	:	...	9a48	1135	4 p13	:	7p57	:	6p15	...	1154	...	:	5a50
...	...	...	...	**Dôle**..............dep	...	...	2 53	...	...	5 23	7 38	10 40	...	1337	...	1647	...	2022	21 21	...
38½	6 95	4 70	3 5	Orchamps	...	...	...	...	...	5 48	8 2	11 6	...	14 1	...	1711	...	2047	...	...
40½	7 30	4 90	3 20	**Labarre**	...	...	...	...	...	5 55	8 8	11 13	...	14 6	...	1717	...	2054	...	...
46	8 30	5 60	3 65	Saint-Vit	...	...	3 20	...	...	6 10	8 24	11 30	...	1421	...	1734	...	21 9	...	...
57½	10 30	6 95	4 55	**Besançon 52** arr	...	...	3 38	...	...	6 36	8 49	11 55	...	1445	...	18 0	...	2135	22 0	...
...	...	...	...	,, Viotte dep	...	...	3 59	...	...	6 57	9 15	12 4	1348	17 0	...	1928	...	2148	—	...
77	13 90	9 35	6 10	Baume-les-Dames	...	...	4 36	...	...	7 47	10 7	12 32	1441	1750	...	2027	...	2310	...	...
93½	16 80	11 35	7 40	L'Isle-s-le-Doubs...	...	...	5 5	...	...	8 26	10 47	...	1523	1828	...	2113	...	—	...	...
103½	18 60	12 55	8 20	Voujaucourt	...	...	5 31	...	...	8 54	11 19	...	1552	1856	1,2,3	2147	...	...	...	...
105½	19 5	12 85	8 40	**Montbéliard**(57)	...	...	5 38	...	...	9 2	11 27	13 11	16 0	19 4	1445	2155	...	...	...	...
110½	19 95	13 45	8 75	Héricourt..........	...	...	6 2	...	...	9 33	12 6	...	1627	1934	15 0	2232	...	...	...	...
116½	21 5	14 20	9 25	**Belfort** ....arr	...	...	6 13	...	...	9 46	12 18	13 31	1640	1946	1515	2247	...	...	...	...
147½	...	...	...	MULHAUSEN 207A	...	...	8 a49	...	...	1p23	3 p28	3 p44	8p45	1045	...	...	...	...	...	...

A—2nd class must be travelling at least 155 miles; until 30th Sept. will not take for Pontarlier and beyond towards Berne and Interlaken.
B—Runs until 30th September. Only takes for Salins, Pontarlier, and beyond towards Berne and Interlaken.
C—Takes only passengers travelling at least 46 miles.
E—Takes passengers for Switzerland only.
F—2nd class must be travelling at least 155 miles
Q—"Simplon Express," Train de Luxe.
RC—Restaurant Car attached.
SC—Sleeping Car attached.
‡—From 9th July until 15th September only.

GRAY and BESANCON.

E.M.							
	Gray ....dep	...	5 1	9 40	...	15 27	18 35
13½	Montagney ....arr	4 55	5 41	10 22	13 0	16 11	19 17
24½	Labarre .... ,,	5 31	...	...	1350	17 4	...
...	Montagney ....dep	—	5 43	10 24	—	—	19 18
35½	**Besancon** Viotte 52arr	...	6 44	11 25	...	...	20 23

Besançon Viotte dep	...	7 36	...	1215	...	18 45
Montagney ....arr	...	8 39	...	1317	...	20 1
Labarre ....dep	6 16	...	11 40	...	1838	...
Montagney ....dep	7 19	8 42	12 11	1321	1930	20 4
Gray (56) ....arr	8 10	9 20	...	14 2	...	20 40

PONTARLIER and GILLEY.

EM								
	Pontarlier......dep	5 57	9 36	16 35	...	...	...	...
15	**Gilley** ....arr	6 48	10 51	17 19	...	...	...	...

Gilley..........dep	8 24	11 37	20 53	...	...	...
Pontarlier ......arr	9 8	12 50	21 39	...	...	...

BESANÇON and MORTEAU.

Besançon Viotte ...dep	4 37	9 8	...	15 4	1828	...	...
L'Hopital-G-B...	5 37	1012	...	16 7	1927	...	...
‡Lods ....arr	7 2	12 7	...	1717	2037	...	...
Avoudrey	6 26	11 0	...	1656	2014	...	...
Gilley	6 59	1133	...	1729	2045	...	...
Morteau ...arr	7 20	1153	16 7	1750	21 6	...	...
LOCLE 255 ...arr	8 a0	1233	4p33	6p29	9p36	...	...

LOCLE ....dep	...	7a14	...	1150	1 p21	5p27	8†p1	...	...
Morteau ......dep	4 10	7 52	1024	12 8	14 2	18 9	2022	...	...
Gilley	4 33	8 20	1057	—	14 29	1838	—	...	...
Avoudrey	4 58	8 46	—	...	14 57	19 4	...	...	...
‡Lods ....dep	4 41	8 25	...	...	13 15	1813	...	...	...
L'Hopital-Gros-B.	5 39	9 27	...	...	15 40	1949	...	...	...
Besançon 52 arr	6 32	1024	...	...	16 43	2055	...	...	...

†—Until 28th September depart 7p49 on Sunday.

MONTBELIARD and ST. HIPPOLYTE.

Montbéliard ...dep	5 27	11 54	16 0	1929	...	...	...
Voujaucourt	5 40	12 6	16 13	1944	...	...	...
Pont-de-Roide	6 17	12 43	16 46	2023	...	...	...
St. Hippolyte...arr	6 35	13 1	17 7	2044	...	...	...

St. Hippolyte...dep	7 17	9 45	1326	1735	...	...	...
Pont-de-Roide	7 41	10 3	1344	1757	...	...	...
Voujaucourt	8 32	1044	1423	1833	...	...	...
Montbéliard (52)arr	8 40	1052	1431	1841	...	...	...

ANDELOT and LEVIER.

Andelot..........dep	7 25	1615	...	...	...
Levier..........arr	8 25	1745	...	...	...

Levier ....dep	9 0	1820	...	...	...
Andelot (52)........arr	10 0	1920	...	...	...

66 lbs. of Luggage free.] **PARIS, LYONS, and MEDITERRANEAN RAILWAY.**

BELFORT, BESANCON, DOLE–PONTARLIER, DOLE, and DIJON.

MULHAUSEN (207A) ......dep	...	...	...	...	7 a36	9 a36	...	1 p4	2p45	5 p38	...	...	5p44	8p48	...	...	...	...	...
	1,2,3	1,2,3	1 &2	1,2,3	1,2,3	1,2,3	1& 2	1,2,3	1,2,3	1,2,3	1,2,3	1,2,3	1,2,3	1,2,3	1& 2	Lux			
Belfort ....dep	...	4 15	...	...	7 55	10 44	...	14 10	15 28	18 10	...	...	1845	2150	...	...	...	...	...
Hèricourt	...	4 31	...	...	8 8	10 59	...	14 26	...	18 24	...	...	19 1	22 8	...	...	...	...	...
Montbéliard	...	4 52	...	...	8 30	11 23	...	14 48	15 50	18 43	...	...	1948	2222	...	...	...	...	...
Voujaucourt	...	5 2	...	...	8 40	11 33	...	14 59		18 53	...	...	20 0	—	...	...	...	...	...
L'Isle-sur-le-Doubs......	...	5 29	...	...	9 6	11 59	...	15 26	...	19 19	...	...	2033		...	...	...	...	...
Baume-les-Dames	...	6 11	...	...	9 44	12 36	...	16 4	...	19 57	...	...	2118	...	...	...	...	...	...
Besançon............arr	...	7 7	...	...	10 32	13 25	...	16 53	17 10	20 45	...	...	2215	...	...	...	...	...	...
,, (Viotte)...dep	5 0	8 0	...	...	10 48	13 51	17 3	17 45	—	21 9	...	...	—	...	...	...	...	...	...
Saint-Vit.....................	5 28	8 30	...	...	11 13	14 19	...	18 13		21 32	...	...		...	...	...	...	...	...
Labarre ....dep	5 45	8 50	...	...	11 27	14 35	...	18 31	...	...	...	...	...	...	...	...	...	...	...
Orchamps	5 52	8 56	...	...	11 32	14 42	...	18 38	...	21 48	...	...	...	...	...	...	...	...	...
Dôle ....arr	6 16	9.22	...	...	11 54	15 6	1743	19 2	...	22 3	...	...	...	...	...	...	...	...	...
LAUSANNE 263C dep	...	...	6a42	6a55		10 a0	3 p0	3 p0	...		6 p53	9p42	...	...	1047	1139	...	...	...
BERNE 259B ......dep	...	...	6a40	6a40		9a19	2p10	2 p10	...		5 p40	8p20	...	...	9p25	11§5	...	...	...
NEUCHATEL 266 dep	...	...	7a30	8 a0		10a40	3p13	3p13	...		6 p43	9p53	...	...	11p7	12§5	...	...	...
Pontarlier ¶ ...dep	...	5 46	7 56	9 18		12 25	1625	16 50	...		20 15	2320	...	...	0 5	0 43		...	...
La Riviére	...	6 4	...	9 36		12 43	...	17 8	...		20 32	...	...	...	...	...		...	...
Boujeailles.................	...	6 23	...	9 55		13 2	...	17 27	...		20 49	H	...	...	...	...		...	...
Andelot	...	6 47	D	1014		13 23	17 1	17 49	...		21 8	...	...	...	...	S		...	...
Mesnay Arbois...........	...	7 5	...	1032		13 44	...	18 9	...		21 26	...	...	...	...	...		...	...
Mouchard ......arr	...	7 17	8 46	1044		13 57	1723	18 22	...		21 38	0 15	...	...	...	...		...	...
,, ...dep	5 40	7 58	8 49	11 2		14 7	1727	18 32	...		21 49	0 19	...	...	J	...		...	...
Arc-Senans	5 50	8 8	...	1111		14 17	C	18 42	...		21 57	...	...	...	...	...		...	...
Montbarrey	6 7	8 26	...	1127		14 35	...	18 59	...		22 11	...	...	...	...	...		...	...
Dôle..................arr	6 27	8 46	...	1146		14 55	1753	19 19	...		22 25	0 48	...	...	...	...		...	...
Dôle ....dep	6 38	9 37	RC	1222	12 2	15 21	18 5	19 36	...	22 11	22 29	0 53	...	...	...	...		...	...
Champvans	6 45	9 43	...	1229	...	15 27	...	19 42	...	...	...	...	...	...	SC	...		...	...
Auxonne ....arr	7 0	9 58	...	1244	12 15	15 42	...	19 57	...	22 24	22 41	1 6	...	...	...	...		...	...
,, ...dep	7 20	10 9	...	1248	12 18	15 54	RC	20 17	...	22 27	22 44	1 9	...	...	...	...		...	...
Collonges	7 36	10 25	...	13 3	...	16 9	...	20 34	...	...	...	...	...	...	...	...		...	...
Magny-Fauverney......	7 52	10 41	...	1319	...	16 25	...	20 52	...	...	...	...	...	...	...	...		...	...
Dijon ....arr	8 12	11 1	9 49	1338	12 47	16 44	1846	21 12	...	23 1	23 17	1 39	...	...	2 10	2 30		...	...
DIJON ....dep	...	11 40	10 1	...	13‡25	17 35	1856	23‡37	...	23‡37	23‡37	1 52	...	...	2 16	2 40	...	...	...
PARIS (51) ....arr	...	17 10	1425	...	18 8	22 0	23 0	4 55	...	4 55	4 55	6 20	...	...	6 45	7 15	...	...	...

§—These departures are from 9th July until 15th September.

C—Takes only passengers travelling at least 46 miles. **J**—Carries passengers from Switzerland only.
D—Only admits at Pontarlier and Mouchard 2nd class travelling at least 155 miles.
S—"Simplon Express," Train de Luxe. †—1st Class. ‡—1 & 2 class. ¶—Customs Examination.
H—From Mouchard forward admits 3rd class only when travelling at least 249 miles.

ST. ETIENNE and LANGEAC.

St. Etienne dep	4 56	...	6 22	8 49	...	1155	1631	...	1821	2054
Firminy	5 48	...	7 10	9 33	...	1244	1714	...	1915	2129
Fraisse-Unieux	—	...	7 17	9 40	...	1251	1720	...	1927	—
Pont-de-Lignon.		...	8 1	1029	...	1336	1758	...	2013	...
Retournac		...	8 21	1049	...	1355	—	...	2033	...
La Voute-s-Loire ...		...	8 56	1124	...	1430	...	...	21 7	...
Le Puy	4 40	7 56	9 11	1139	14 0	1445	...	1645	2122	...
Darsac 62A	5 26	8 45	—	1250	1447	—	...	1743	—	...
St. Georges d'A.	6 22	9 37	...	—	1542	1615	...	1836	...	...
Langeac ...arr	6 48	10 5	...	...	—	1624	...	1859	...	...

Langeac ..dep	...	...	6 24	9 40	...	1537	...	...	19 15
St.Georg. d'A.	...	...	6 58	1015	...	1625	...	...	19 36
Darsac	...	...	8 8	1126	...	1755	...	...	20 54
Le Puy ...dep	5 0	...	9 18	12 0	1450	1832	...	1952	21 29
LaVoutesurL.	515	...	9 34	—	15 7	—	...	2016	—
Retournac ...	549	...	10 9	...	1544	...	...	2050	...
Pont-de-Lig.	610	...	1031	...	16 5	...	1827	2110	...
Fraisse-Un ...	652	...	1114	...	1650	...	1910	2153	...
Firminy	7 5	9 3	1123	1217	17 9	...	1933	22 7	22 27
St.Etienne ar	743	9 38	1158	1255	1755	...	2018	2246	23 5

Le Puy...........dep	6 20	10 0	19 0	...
Langogne 58 ...arr	8 18	1159	2057	...

Langogne ......dep	5 40	1131	1655
Le Puy 52A ...arr	7 38	1328	1850

LYONS and ST. MARCELLIN.

E.M														
—	**Lyons**-Monplaisir ....dep	...	...	...	5 55	8 26	...	14 0	...	18 34	...	...	...	...
28½	St. Jean-de-Bournay....................	...	...	...	8 33	11 2	...	16 38	...	20 55	...	...	...	...
39¾	La Cote-St. André (Ville)...............	...	5 10	7 46	9 33	13 25	16 41	17 41	1953	21 45	...	...	...	...
40½	La Cote-St. André (P.L.M.)............	...	6 42	8 6	9 53	14 31	17 1	18 28	2013	—	...	...	...	...
56	Roybon..	4 0	8 16	—	—	16 15	—	19 44	—	...	...	...	...	...
72¾	**St. Marcellin** (62A) ....arr	5 45	10 6	...	...	18 0	...	...	...	...	...	...	...	...

St. Marcellin.....................dep	...	...	...	6 30	...	...	...	...	...	...	14 10	...	...	18 30
Roybon	...	4 13	...	8 15	...	...	...	12 23	...	...	16 0	16 40	...	20 20
La Cote-St. André (P.L.M.) (62A)..	...	6 41	8 26	—	...	1010	...	14 30	...	17 18	—	18 20	20 33	—
La Cote-St. André (Ville)............	4 55	7 1	8 46	...	9 50	1030	12 40	14 50	16 50	17 38	...	18 40	20 53	...
St. Jean-de-Bournay....................	5 52	—	—	...	10 58	—	13 47	—	17 53	—	...	—	—	...
Lyons-Monplaisir.....................arr	8 5	...	...	...	13 2	...	16 18	...	20 17	...	...	...	...	...

La Cote-St. André (Ville) dep	6 33	12 5	18 5	...	...
Grand-Lemps ....arr	7 28	13 0	19 0	...	...

Grand-Lemps ....dep	7 50	15 0	2033	...	...
La Cote-St. André (Ville) arr	8 45	1555	2128	...	...

LYONS, BESANCON, and VESOUL.

Marseilles (50)...dep	2025	...	20 25	...	23 28	2328	23 28	...	...	...	...	6 0	6 0	9 0	9 0	...	...	1150	11 50	...	...
	1,2,3	1,2,3	1,2,3	1,2,3	1,2,3	1,2,3	1,2,3	1,2,3	1,2,3	1,2,3	1,2,3	1,2,3	1,2,3	1 &2	1,2,3	1,2,3	1,2,3	1,2,3	1,2,3	1,2,3	1,2,3
Lyons Perrache ......dep	2 30	...	3 46	...	7 0	7 20	7 30	...	...	1014	...	1230	13 3	1445	16 32	...	1812	1916	19 55	1939	...
„ Brotteaux ... „	2 45	5 56	4 3	5 10	7 15	7 32	7 49	9 23	...	1032	11 3	1244	13 22	15 6	16 51	1659	1827	1936	20 6	1953	21 7
„ St. Clair ...... „	...	...	4 17	5 16	7 22		7 56	9 29	...	1039	11 9	...	13 29	...	16 59	17 5	1834	1943		20 0	2113
Montluel	A	...	4 47	Via Sathonay.	...	Via Sathonay.	8 35	Via Sathonay.	...	...	1143	...	13 55	...	17 29	Via Sathonay.	1914	...	Via Sathonay.	2027	2141
Meximieux	...	...	5 8		...		8 55		...	...	12 3	...	14 14	...	17 51		1935	...		2048	22 1
Ambérieu ....arr	3 44	6 40	5 28		8 3		9 17		...	1131	1223	1325	14 34	1543	18 11		1957	2020		21 7	2221
Geneva (60).........arr	8 38	1130	11 30		12 3		16 17		...	1617	...	1651	19 38	1938	23 25		0 43	0 43		...	...
Lausanne (263)...arr	...	1p50	1 p50		2 p10		6 p10		...	6p10	...	6p10	10p15	1015	2 a10		2a10	2a10		...	...
Basle 258 or 264...arr	...		...		7 p35		10p53		..	1053	...	1053	...	...	...			7a25		...	...
Strassburg 209...arr	...	...	...		11p35		1 a34		...	1a34	...	1a34	...	...	...		...	9a29		...	...
Ambérieu..............dep	...	...	6 11		...		...		10 54	...	...	..	14 56	...	18 42		...	...		22 9	...
Pont d'Ain		...	6 29		...		...		11 13	...	...	...	15 15	...	19 0		...	...		2231	...
Bourg ....arr	A—Runs from 2nd July until 20th September.	...	6 56	7 8	...	8 35	...	11 34	11 41	...	...	...	15 42	...	19 27	1910	...	...	21 8	2255	...
„ (60, 62) ....dep		4 1	7 33		...	8 40	...		12 3	...	...	...	16 52	...			2010	...	21 13		...
Coligny.........................		4 34	8 3	...	...	...	...	...	12 36	...	...	...	17 28	...	...	...	2044	...	...	...	...
St. Amour (63B)		4 46	8 13	...	...	...	...	...	12 49	...	...	...	17 44	...	...	...	2055	...	...	...	...
Cuiseaux		4 59	8 25	...	...	...	...	...	13 3	...	...	...	17 57	...	...	...	21 8	...	...	...	...
Beaufort		5 15	8 40	...	...	...	...	...	13 20	...	...	...	18 17	...	...	...	2123	...	...	...	...
Lons-le-Saunier......arr		5 40	9 5	...	...	9 45	...	...	13 45	...	...	...	18 45	...	...	...	2148	...	22 11	...	...
„ (62)...dep		5 51	9 13	...	...	9 53	...	...	14 2	1627	...	...	19 35	...	...	...		...	22 16	2235	...
Domblans......................		6 13	9 34	...	...	...	...	...	14 25	1651	...	...	19 59	...	...	...	...	...	...	2258	...
Poligny (56)		6 41	10 0	...	...	...	...	...	14 55	1721	...	...	20 31	...	...	...	...	...	22 49	2326	...
Arbois		7 1	10 19	...	...	...	...	...	15 15	1742	...	...	20 54	...	...	...	...	...	...	2346	...
Mouchard (52).........arr		7 14	10 31	...	...	1051	...	...	15 28	1756	...	...	21 8	...	...	...	...	...	23 13	24 0	...
„ ......dep 6 10	...	7 27		...	...	1054	...	12 25	15 43	1844	...	...	21 59	...	...	...	...	...	23 16		...
Montferrand 7 1	...	8 13	...	...	...	...	...	13 11	16 28	1936	...	...	22 46	...	...	...	...	...	...	...	...
Besancon Viotte arr 7 22	...	8 32	...	...	...	1139	...	13 30	16 48	1957	...	...	23 6	...	...	...	...	...	23 59	...	...
Belfort (52) ......arr	...	1218	...	...	...	1331	...	16 40	19 46	...	...	...	...	...	...	...	...	...	...	...	...
Mulhausen 207A arr	...	3p28	...	...	...	3p44	...	...	10p45	...	...	...	...	...	...	...	...	...	...	...	...
Strassburg (209) arr	...	...	...	...	...	5p18	...	...	1 a34	...	...	1,2,3	...	...	...	...	...	...	...	...	...
Besancon Viotte......dep	...	9 23	...	...	...	...	...	14 0	17 23	...	...	19 2	...	...	...	...	...	...	...	...	4 41
Auxon-Dessus	...	9 42	...	...	...	...	...	14 19	17 40	...	...	1921	...	...	...	...	...	...	...	...	5 2
Loulans-les-Forges	...	1027	...	...	...	...	...	15 7	18 22	...	...	20 9	...	...	...	...	...	...	...	...	5 46
Montbozon	...	1038	...	...	...	...	...	15 20	18 35	...	...	2022	...	...	...	...	...	...	...	...	6 0
Vesoul (66) ....arr	...	1114	...	...	...	...	...	16 0	19 10	...	..	2059	...	...	...	...	...	...	...	...	6 35

	1,2,3	1,2,3	1,2,3	1,2,3	1,2,3	1,2,3	1,2,3	1,2,3	1,2,3	1,2,3	1,2,3	1,2,3	1,2,3	1,2,3	1,2,3	1,2,3	1,2,3	1,2,3	1,2,3	1,2,3
Vesoul ....dep	...	...	...	...	...	...	5 23	...	...	...	...	...	...	...	9 52	...	14 47	...	17 7	19 0
Montbozon..................	...	...	...	...	...	...	6 8	...	...	...	...	...	...	...	10 34	...	15 31	...	17 51	20 0
Loulans-les-Forges	...	...	...	...	...	...	6 17	...	...	...	...	...	...	...	10 42	...	15 39	...	18 0	20 15
Auxon-Dessus..............	...	...	...	...	...	...	7 0	...	...	...	...	...	...	...	11 25	...	16 20	...	18 43	21 14
Besancon Viotte ......arr	...	...	...	...	...	...	7 19	...	...	...	...	...	...	...	11 43	...	16 37	...	19 2	21 38
Strassburg (208)dep	...	...	...	...	...	...	...	...	...	...	...	...	...	...	6 a0	7a40	12p54	12p54	3 p53	...
Mulhausen 207A dep	...	...	...	...	...	...	...	...	...	...	...	...	...	...	7 a36	9a36	2 p45	2 p45	5 p38	...
Belfort 52A ......dep	...	...	...	...	...	4 15	4 15	...	...	...	...	...	...	...	7 55	1044	15 28	15 28	18 10	...
Besancon Viotte......dep	...	...	...	...	4 42	7 35	7 46	...	...	...	...	...	...	...	11 59	1445	17 30	17 20	21 33	...
Montferrand	...	...	...	...	5 4	...	8 8	...	...	...	...	...	...	...	12 20	15 6	17 51	...	21 54	...
Mouchard ....arr	...	...	...	...	5 51	8 20	8 58	...	...	...	...	...	...	...	13 6	1550	18 39	18 9	22 39	...
„ ....dep	...	...	...	3 50	6 31	8 25	9 12	...	...	...	...	...	...	...	14 14	1610	18 52	18 14	22 47	...
Arbois	...	...	...	4 3	6 44	...	925	...	...	...	...	...	...	...	14 27	1623	19 6	...	23 0	...
Poligny	...	...	...	4 23	7 6	8 48	947	...	...	...	...	...	...	...	14 47	1645	19 27	...	23 21	...
Domblans		...	...	4 48	7 31	...	1014	...	...	...	...	...	...	...	15 11	1710	19 53	..	23 48	...
Lons-le- ....arr		...	...	5 8	7 51	9 18	10 34	...	...	...	...	...	...	...	15 30	1730	20 13	19 15	0 9	...
Saunier 62 ....dep		...	...	5 21	8 5	9 24	11 20	...	...	C—From 11th August until 20th September.	...	...	...	...	16 51		20 27	19 35		...
Beaufort		...	...	5 45	8 29	...	11 45	...	...		...	...	...	...	17 17	...	20 53	...	...	...
Cuiseaux		...	...	6 1	8 46	...	12 2	...	...		...	...	...	...	17 35	...	21 13	...	...	...
St. Amour		...	...	6 16	9 1	9 57	12 47	...	...		...	...	...	...	17 57	...	21 35	20 10	...	...
Coligny		...	...	6 24	9 10	...	12 57	...	...		...	...	...	...	18 7	...	21 44	...	...	...
Bourg ....arr	B—Runs from July 3rd until 21st September.	...	...	6 57	9 40	1022	13 34				...	...	...	...	18 47	...	22 17	20 39	...	...
„ ....dep		4 57	...	7 23	10 33	1030		11 17	...	...	14 4	16 30	...	...	19 26	...	22 40	20 47	...	...
Pont d'Ain		Via Sathonay.	...	7 45	11 5	Via Sathonay.	...	Via Sathonay.	...	...	1434	Via Sathonay.	...	...	19 51	...	23 12	Via Sathonay.	...	...
Ambérieu ....arr			...	7 57	11 22		...		...	...	1451		...	...	20 6	a.m.	23 32		...	...
Strassburg 208 dep			8 p36	...	...		...		...	4 a28	4a28		...	...	...	1113	...		12p54	...
Basle 258, 264A...dep			12 0	...	...		...		...	7a30	7a30		...	...	...	2p2	...		3 p40	...
Lausanne 263A...dep	...		5 a5	...	5 a20		...		9 a17	11a50	1210		12 15	12p15	...	6p29	...		7 p53	...
Geneva 61 ....dep	...		6 53	...	7 38		...		11 15	12 55	1333		14 30	15 0	...	20 5	...		21 10	...
Amberieu ......dep 1 46	5 47		9 15	9 26	11 35		12 22		14 27	15 0	1538		17 16	19 0	20 56	2219	...		23 58	6 58
Meximieux	6 12		...	9 47	11 55		12 42		14 47	...	...		17 43	19 22	21 17	...	...		...	7 20
Montluel .... B	6 35		...	10 4	12 15		12 59		15 8	C	...		18 6	19 45	21 35	...	...		...	7 41
Lyons St. Clair arr ...	7 17	7 6	...	1036	12 42		13 30	13 48	15 35	...	...	18 39	18 49	20 13	22 4	...	...		...	8 10
„ Brott'ux arr 2 28	7 22	7 11	9 54	1041	12 47	1127	13 35	13 53	15 40	15 55	1615	18 44	18 54	20 13	22 9	2257	...	21 42	0 43	8 15
„ Perrache arr 2 42	7 44	...	10 15	...	13 9	1142	...		16 1	16 21	1632	...	19 15	20 39	...	2312	...	21 56	1 17	8 35
Marseilles (49) 8 30	1438	...	17 51	...		1751	...	..	22 35	22 35	2235	...	...	...	...	5 0	...	5 0	8 30	...

ST. JEAN-DE-LOSNE and LONS-LE-SAUNIER.										
	St. Jean-de-Losne...dep	5 11	10 0	17 7	...	Lons-le-Saunier...dep	6 45	13 10	1855	...
	Chaussin	5 54	11 12	17 51	...	Chaussin	8 31	14 36	20 11	...
	Lons-le-Saunier ......arr	7 5	12 42	19 2	...	St. Jean-de-Losne arr	9 26	15 21	20 53	...

PARIS, LYONS, and MEDITERRANEAN RAILWAY.

ROANNE, MONTCHANIN, NEVERS, CHAGNY, ETANG, EPINAC.

Roanne ......dep	...	...	...	6 34	...	8 22	...	...	...	...	...	...	16 30	...	1935	...
Iguerande........	...	...	...	7 23	...	9 3	...	...	...	...	...	...	17 10	...	2015	...
Paray-le- ...... arr	...	...	...	8 15	...	9 50	...	...	...	...	...	...	17 57	...	21 4	...
Monial.........dep	...	...	7 3		...	10 14	...	1032	1330	14 0	...	...	18 30	...		...
Genelard	...	...	7 33	...	...	...	...	11 2	14 0	15 18	...	...	19 11	...	...	...
Montceau-les-Mines	4 47	...	7 59	...	9 35	10 57	...	1126	1425	16 45	...	...	19 48	...	...	...
Montchanin...arr	5 10	...	8 25	...	10 32	11 16	...	1151	1447	17 17	...	...	20 20	...	...	...
Nevers..........dep	1 55	...	...	...	6 50	:	...	...	...	13 25	...	16 45	...	1848	...	†—Not on Sunday.
Cercy-la-Tour 63B...	2 55	...	...	...	8 13	:	...	...	...	14 50	...	17 55	...	2010	...	
Remilly	...	...	...	...	8 35	:	...	...	...	15 12	...	18 15	...	2031	...	
Etang .... arr	4)	...	...	...	9 30	:	...	...	...	16 6	...	18 56	...	2128	...	
,, ...dep	4 15	4†53	6 50	...	9 46	:	...	1255	...	16 25	...	19 2	19 52	2135	...	
Marmagne	4 47	5 25	7 24	...	10 12	:	...	1329	...	16 57	...	...	20 21	...	...	
Le Creusot........	5 8	5 57	7 56	...	10 30	:	11 30	1342	1420	17 20	18†20	19 34	20 40	2214	...	
Mont- ....arr	5 20	6 7	8 10	...	10 40	:	11 44		1434	17 32	18 31	19 44	20 51	2225	...	
chanin ....dep	5 36		8 50	...	10 51	11 27		...	1458	17 58	18 36		21 8	2235	...	...
Chagny (48)......arr	6 25	...	9 50	...	11 42	11 57	...	...	1546	18 51	19 33	...	21 58	23 5	...	...
Etang ....dep	4 8	...	6 46	...	10 0	...	...	13 0	...	16 30	...	19 57	...	2145	...	...
Autun (63A)	4 36	...	7 40	...	10 34	...	...	1356	...	17 5	...	20 42	...	22 8	...	...
Dracy-St. Loup	4 47	...	7 56	...	10 46	...	...	14 8	...	17 16	...	20 54	...		...	...
Epinac	5 24	...	8 40	...	11 20	...	...	1445	...	17 52	...	21 25	...	...	...	...
Chagny..........arr	6 12	...	9 35	...	12 9	...	...	1533	...	18 40	...	22 10	...	...	...	...

Chagny ...dep	...	4 27	...	...	...	7 30	10 30	...	...	...	...	...	1435	16 45	...	...	2121
Epinac	...	5 17	...	...	...	8 24	11 22	...	...	...	...	...	1545	17 45	...	...	2212
Dracy-St. Loup	...	5 43	...	...	...	8 50	11 48	...	...	...	...	...	1613	18 16	...	...	2237
Autun	...	6 3	...	...	...	9 10	12 12	...	...	...	1527	...	1624	19 2	20 55	...	2247
Etang ......arr	...	6 23	...	...	...	9 32	12 34	...	...	...	1550	...		19 25	21 18	...	
Chagny ...dep	...	4 2	5 8	...	5 18	7 20	10 42	10 55	...	1330	1425	...	...	17 3	19 37	2112	...
Mont- arr	...	5 14	5 46	...	6 16	8 16	11 20	11 52	...	1426	15 0	...	...	17 59	20 29	22 4	...
chanin...dep	...	5 20	6 0	7 0	:	8 40	11 34	:	1212		1512	17†35	...	18 20	20 43	2212	...
Le Creusot........	...	5 55	6 11	7 10	:	9 2	11 51	:	1246	...	1529	18 18	...	18 43	21 2	2223	...
Marmagne	...	6 4		...	:	9 13	12 0	:		...	1537	18 27	...	18 52	...		...
Etang ......arr	...	6 30	...	7 36	:	9 42	12 26	:	...	...	16 1	18 53	...	19 18	21 25	...	...
,, ...dep	...	6 56	...	7 40	:		12 42	:	...	...	16 6		...	19 48		...	...
Remilly	...	7 54	...	8 21	:	...	13 34	:	...	...	1648	...	...	20 42	...	...	...
Cercy-la-Tour...	6 20	8 15	...	8 49	:	...	14 2	:	...	...	17 8	...	...	21 10	...	...	...
Nevers......arr	7 44	...	...	9 55	:	...	15 9	:	...	...	18 0	...	...	22 19	...	...	...
Mont-chanin dep	...	...	...	...	6 30	8 31	...	12 0	...	...	1522	...	...	18 45	21 5	...	2233
Montceau-les-M.	...	...	...	...	7 0	9 2	...	12 28	...	...	1552	...	...	19 18	21 36	...	2253
Genelard	...	...	...	...	7 21	9 22	...	12 50	...	...	1612	...	...	19 42		...	
Paray-le-Marr	...	...	...	...	7 50	9 50	...	13 19	...	...	1640	...	...	20 16	...	...	...
,, dep	6 6	...	...	...		10 40	...		1357	...		18 35	...		...	...	...
Iguerande........	6 54	...	...	...	...	11 32	...	...	1452	...	...	19 29	...	...	...	...	...
Roanne (56) ar	7 43	...	...	...	...	12 25	...	...	1532	...	...	20 12	...	...	...	...	...

DIJON and EPINAC.

Dijon ....dep	5 15	10 58	18 5	...	...	Epinac-les-Mines	5 54	8 45	16 33	...	...	...
Pont d'Ouche	6 34	12 56	19 29	...	...	Pont d'Ouche	7 6	10 31	17 46	...	...	...
Epinac-les-Mines arr	7 40	14 35	20 36	...	...	Dijon............arr	8 25	12 42	19 7	...	...	...

BELLEGARDE and DIVONNE.

Bellegarde............dep	7 28	10 28	19 24	**Divonne** ....dep	4 57	12 3	18 10	...
Collonges-Fort l'Ecluse ...	7 42	10 42	19 43	Gex........................	5 15	12 21	18 28	...
Thoiry........................	8 14	11 14	20 15	Thoiry	5 41	12 47	18 54	...
Gex	8 46	11 45	20 47	Collonges-Fort l'Ecluse......	6 11	13 18	19 25	...
Divonne ....arr	9 1	12 0	21 2	**Bellegarde (60)** ......arr	6 22	13 29	19 36	...

MOUCHARD and SALINS.

Mouchard ......dep	4 25	6 22	7 29	9 13	11 10	14 22	16 7	18 50	21 52	23 23	...	...	...	...
Salins ....arr	4 40	6 37	7 44	9 28	11 25	14 37	16 22	19 5	22 7	23 38	...	...	...	...
Salins ....dep	5 19	6 58	8 4	10 31	13 6	15 22	17 4	21 12	22 27	23 58	...	...	...	...
Mouchard .....arr	5 30	7 9	8 15	10 42	13 17	15 33	1715	21 23	22 38	0 9	...	...	...	...

FIRMINY and ST. JUST-SUR-LOIRE.

E.M.									
	Firminy....................dep	5 58	9 7	1330	1721	**St. Just.** ......dep	7 32	11 32	18 44
1¾	Fraisse-Unieux	6 5	9 15	1336	1728	Fraisse-Unieux ...	8 30	12 21	19 17
11¾	**St. Just-sur-Loire 63B** arr	6 34	10 9	14 4	1757	**Firminy (63)** arr	8 36	12 27	19 23

PARAY-LE-MONIAL and LOZANNE.

Paray-le-Monial.....dep	...	5 49	...	11 11	...	1816	**Lozanne**...............dep	6 18	7 38	10 8	1328	1746	1919	...
La Clayette-Baudemont......	...	6 34	...	12 5	...	1914	Ternand	6 48	...	10 41	14 6	1821	1951	...
Chauffailles..................	...	6 56	...	12 31	...	1942	Lamure-sur-Azergues.........	7 13	8 13	11 15	1435	1856	2017	...
Lamure-sur-Azergues	6 10	7 38	7 55	13 30	1828	2033	Chauffailles..................		8 56	12 4		1946		...
Ternand..	6 34	...	8 18	14 2	1854	21 0	La Clayette-Baudemont.......	...	9 15	12 25	...	20 9	...	...
Lozanne 51B ....arr	7 0	8 7	8 46	14 40	1922	2133	**Paray-le-Monial 62** arr	...	9 54	13 10	...	2054	...	...

Lozanne ....dep	7 7	1241	13 26	15 45	19 33	Givors ....dep	...	7 53	1111	...	1753	...
Tassin	7 47	1312	14 3	16 54	20 9	Tassin	6 30	9 8	1152	17 0	1843	...
Givors (56) ....arr	8 32	1352	...	17 35	...	Lozanne...................arr	7 2	9 40	1224	17 36	1915	...

NEVERS and CORBIGNY.

Nevers......dep	6 18	13 3	16 0	17 30	Corbigny...dep	6 35	10 50	16 25	...	...	...	
St. Saulge	8 22	15 21	18 2	19 57	St. Saulge	8 13	12 34	18 6	...	...	...	
Corbigny...arr	9 53	16 21	19 27	21 18	Nevers ......arr	10 2	14 45	20 14	...	...	...	

St. Saulge ....dep	...	8 23	14 25	1757	...	...	Moulins-Engilbert...dep	6 17	8 39	...	15 3	...
Tamnay-Chatillon (57)..	7 16	9 17	15 26	1849	...	...	Tamnay-Chatillon.........	7 15	9 16	1120	16 0	...
Moulins-Engilbert...arr	7 51	1018	...	1947	...	...	St. Saulge ....arr	8 7	...	1218	1658	...

LE MARTINET and TARASCON.

E.M							
—	**Le Martinet** ....dep	...	6 25	11 50	1430	16 52	1955
6½	**St. Julien-les-** ... arr	...	6 50	12 14	15 4	17 24	2028
...	**Fumades** .... dep	...	8 17	12 50	—	18 55	—
19½	Euzet-les-Bains	...	8 52	13 25	...	19 32	...
30½	**Uzès**.........(63B).......arr	5 15	9 27	14 0	...	20 10	...
39½	Pont-du-Gard	5 40	9 58	14 41	...	20 46	...
42½	**Remoulins**.............arr	5 49	10 7	14 50	...	20 55	...
...	,, (62) dep	6 5	1036	15 22	...	21 23	...
43½	Lafoux	6 8	1040	15 26	...	...	...
56	**Tarascon** (57) ......arr	6 47	1121	16 11	...	22 12	...

Tarascon ....dep		5 3	...	9 20	...	14 20	20 22
Lafoux		5 49	...	10 1	...	15 0	21 0
Remoulins ....arr		5 52	...	10 4	...	15 3	21 3
,, ...dep		6 8	...	10 24	...	15 17	21 25
Pont du Gard		6 18	...	10 34	...	15 27	21 35
Uzès ....arr		6 43	...	10 59	...	15 52	21 59
Euzet-les-Bains		7 23	...	11 39	...	16 43	—
St. Julien-les- ......arr		7 57	..	12 13	...	17 18	...
Fumades...dep	7 19	—	11 5	12 35	1534	18 52	...
Le Martinet...arr	7 49	...	1129	13 6	1627	19 20	...

LUNEL, ALAIS, and LE VIGAN.

Lunel (57)......dep		6 5	...	9 22	...	...	14 25	...	18 37
Gallargues		6 15	...	9 32	...	...	14 35	...	18 49
Sommières 57arr		6 34	...	9 51	...	...	14 54	...	19 13
Nimes ....dep		5 39	...	9 7	...	...	14 5	...	18 30
St. Césaire		5 45	...	9 13	...	...	14 11	...	18 36
Congenies...............		6 25	...	9 49	...	...	14 47	...	19 16
Sommières..........		6 50	...	10 10	...	...	15 11	...	19 43
Quissac		7 37	...	10 51	...	...	15 59	...	20 34
Le Vigan (47)...arr		8 52	...	11 58	...	...	17 12	...	21 54
Quissac ......dep		7 55	...	11 6	...	...	16 2	...	20 39
Lezan............	5 40	8 20	9 35	11 31	12 35	16 6	16 25	2043	21 3
Mas-des-Gard.	5 53	8 34	9 48	11 45	12 50	16 21	16 39	2056	21 19
Alais (58) ...arr		8 49	...	12 0	13 5	16 36	16 54	...	21 34

Alais ....dep	5 1	...	8 58	...	13 53	1725	18 40	...
Mas-des-Gardies	5 19	6 28	9 16	10 20	14 12	1743	18 58	22 0
Lezan..................	5 32	6 41	9 29	10 33	14 25	1756	19 11	22 13
Quissac ......arr	5 57	—	9 54	—	14 53	—	19 39	—
Le Vigan ......dep	4 55	...	9 4	...	13 50	...	18 25	...
Quissac	6 9	...	10 16	...	15 4	...	20 5	...
Sommières ...arr	6 44	...	10 51	...	15 39	...	20 41	...
Congenies................	7 2	...	11 11	...	16 2	...	21 13	...
St. Césaire	7 36	...	11 45	...	16 41	...	21 54	...
Nimes ....arr	7 42	...	11 51	...	16 47	...	22 0	...
Sommières ...dep	7 7	...	11 10	...	16 10	...	20 55	...
Gallargues	7 27	...	11 29	...	16 30	...	21 38	...
Lunel ....arr	7 35	...	11 37	...	16 38	...	21 50	...

LEZAN and ST. JEAN DU GARD.

Lezan.......................dep	6 43	10 49	1436	17 57	19 27	22 19	...
Anduze	7 1	11 5	15 7	18 11	19 46	22 32	...
St. Jean du Gard...arr	7 40	11 54	16 4	...	20 32	...	...
St. Jean du Gard...dep	...	6 45	11 18	1514	...	19 51	...
Anduze	5 10	7 52	12 6	1552	18 36	20 30	...
Lezan ....arr	5 23	8 8	12 22	16 4	18 49	20 42	...

MONTBOZON and LURE.

Montbozondep	6 15	11 8	1852	**Lure** ....dep	9 6	1250	1817
Villersexel	6 56	1152	2023	Villersexel............	9 42	1353	1858
Lure (68) ...arr	7 30	1228	2132	**Montbozon** (53)arr	1022	15 7	1945

GRAND-SERRE and SAINT-VALLIER.

Grand Serre......dep	5 20	1055	1640	St. Vallier...dep	6 24	1145	1738
St. Vallier(P.L.M) a	7 22	1310	1850	Grand Serre arr	8 37	14 2	1955

VEYNES and GAP.

‡—Until 30th September.

Veynes ......dep	4 55	8 47	10 20	11‡38	11 50	17 15	22 35
Montmaur	5 8	9 0	10 30	...	12 0	17 25	22 45
Gap (62A)...arr	5 45	9 37	11 2	12 6	12 31	17 57	23 16
Gap ....dep	4 0	9 45	12 14	15 26	16‡56	21 20	...
Montmaur	4 32	10 33	12 46	16 7	...	22 13	...
Veynes ......arr	4 41	10 45	12 55	16 17	17 27	22 25	...

GAP and BRIANÇON.

‡—Until 30th September.

Gap ....dep	6 0	12 ‡9	12 40	18 2	...	...
Chorges	6 24	12 29	13 4	18 26	...	...
Embrun	7 8	13 5	13 47	19 11	...	...
Mt. Dauphin-Guillestre	7 38	13 28	14 17	19 41	...	...
L'Argentière..................	8 6	13 45	14 43	20 9	...	...
Briançon ....arr	8 35	14 7	15 9	20 38	...	...
Briançon ....dep	6 1	12 45	14‡55	18 45	...	...
L'Argentière	6 23	13 7	15 16	19 7	...	...
Mt. Dauphin-Guillestre	6 47	13 32	15 34	19 32	...	...
Embrun...	7 21	14 4	15 59	20 5	...	...
Chorges	8 3	14 47	16 34	20 47	...	...
Gap 53B ....arr	8 27	15 11	16 53	21 11	...	...

ROMANS, TAIN, and ST. DONAT.

Romans ......dep	5 30	6 40	9 46	12 38	14 20	15 51	18 7
Tain	...	7 42	...	13 40	...	16 53	...
St. Donat. arr	6 15	...	10 46	...	15 19	...	19 6
St. Donat dep	6 30	...	12 30	...	15 45	...	19 19
Tain	...	9 35	...	14 10	...	1758	...
Romans ......arr	7 28	10 36	13 29	15 12	16 44	19 0	20 6

DOMPIERRE-SEPT-FONDS and LAPALISSE.

Dompierre ......dep	5 45	12 28	16 51	...	...	...
Sorbier-Peublanc...	6 41	13 50	17 51	...	...	...
Lapalisse 51B ...arr	8 21	15 10	19 13	...	...	...
Lapalisse ......dep	6 30	11 1	17 17	...	...	...
Sorbier-Peublanc...	8 3	12 35	18 43	...	...	...
Dompierre ......arr	8 51	13 55	19 55	...	...	...

MONTELIMAR and DIEULEFIT.

Montelimar dep	5 20	8 33	12 5	1630
Dieulefit ... arr	6 46	1025	14 0	1828
Dieulefit ...dep	6 15	11 50	1615	1945
Montelimar arr	8 8	13 44	1812	2115

PONT-EN-ROYANS and ROMANS.

Pont-en-Royansdep	...	6 18	10 7	...	16 55	1855
Bourg-de-Péage	5 23	8 40	12 23	16 33	19 19	2115
Romans (62A) ......arr	5 33	8 50	12 38	16 43	19 29	2125

Romans ....dep	5 53	10 11	13 35	16 59	19 45	21 40	...
Bourg-de-Péage	6 10	10 28	13 52	17 16	19 55	21 50	...
Pont-en-Royans arr	8 32	12 50	16 7	19 39	...	...	...

VALENCE and BOURG-DE-PEAGE.

Valence ....dep	6 27	11 0	1410	1722	...	...
Chabeuil	7 21	11 55	1458	1817	...	...
Bourg-de-Peage......arr	8 32	13 10	...	1928	...	...

Bourg-de-Peage ...dep	6 34	11 34	...	17 11	...	...
Chabeuil	7 53	12 57	1520	18 31	...	...
Valence (49)...........arr	8 37	13 40	16 2	19 13	...	...

VOIRON and ST. BERON.

*—Sun., and Thurs. only, until 15th Sept. ‡—Until 9th October.

Voiron ....dep	4*45	...	7 12	9 45	12 42	1625	1944	22*0
St. Laurent-du-Pont	5 42	5 46	8 19	10 56	13 52	1750	2[illegible]50	23 0
Entre-Deux-Guiers	—	6 2	8 34	11 13	14 7	1810	21 4	—
St. Beron (57) arr	...	6 40	9 7	11‡50	14 40	1850	...	...

St. Beron dep	..	7 21	9 40	13‡5	...	1640	19 44	...
Entre-Deux-G.	5 18	7 54	10 24	1334	13 37	1726	20 16	...
St. Laurent-d-P	5 42	8 15	10 48	—	14 0	18 0	20 30	...
Voiron ...arr	6 38	9 12	11 45	...	15 0	19 0	21*46	...

Tramway

St. Beron (P.L.M.)dep	...	7 15	9 25	...	1455	1630	1940	...
Pont de Beauvoisin	4 55	7 43	9 53	1415	1520	17 0	20 8	...
Aoste St. Genix arr	5 27	8 20	1030	1452	...	1737	2045	...

Aoste-St. Genix dep	5 40	..	9 0	1324	15 5	18 5	2130	...
Pont de Beauv.	6 18	8 30	9 40	14 7	1544	1847	22 4	...
St. Beron (P.L.M.)ar	6 43	8 55	...	1432	16 9	1913	...	...

E.M				
	Pont-de-Beauvoisin...dep	8 43	16 20	...
16½	Bonpertuis ....arr	10 54	18 16	...

Bonpertuis ....dep	8 35	14 0	...
Pont-de-Beauvoisin53Barr	11 18	18 47	...

CANNES and GRASSE (12 miles).

Cannes...dep	6 38	8 47	10 5	1348	1516	1745	2248	...	...	...
La Bocca ...	6 45	8 54	1012	1355	1523	1752	2255	...	...	...
Mouans-Sar.	7 7	9 19	1034	1417	1545	1814	2311	...	...	...
Grasse ...arr	7 26	9 38	1053	1436	16 4	1833	2324	...	...	...

Grasse......dep	5 30	6 49	9 2	12 35	13 59	1621	19 14	...	...
Mouans-Sarto.	5 46	7 9	9 21	12 51	14 19	1637	19 30	...	...
La Bocca	6 5	7 27	9 39	13 9	14 37	1655	19 48	...	...
Cannes 55 arr	6 10	7 32	9 44	13 14	14 42	17 0	19 53	...	...

CARNOULES and GARDANNE.

E.M.						
	Carnoules dep	4 32	...	6 55	14 48	20 37
15	Brignoles	5 20	...	8 4	15 36	21 20
26	St. Maximin	5 47	...	8 47	16 7	21 48
37½	Trets	6 15	...	9 20	16 35	22 15
44	La Barque	6 36	8 30	9 49	16 56	22 35
49	Gardanne 63A	6 49	8 48	10 5	17 9	22 48

Gardanne ....dep	3 59	7 17	11 13	17 55
La Barque	4 10	7 30	11 29	18 9
Trets	4 27	7 52	11 53	18 30
St. Maximin	4 52	8 20	12 28	18 58
Brignoles	5 25	8 54	13 9	19 32
Carnoules (55) ...arr	6 7	9 34	13 56	20 11

TOULON, HYERES, and ST. RAPHAEL.

Toulon.....................dep	...	5 20	6 23	7 33	9 15	1054	1140	1255	1355	1453	1724	1810	1943	...	...	...
Le Pradet	...	5 49	6 51	7 50	9 42	1113	12 7	1324	1424	1510	1752	1837	2010	...	...	...
Carqueiranne	...	6 6	7 4	8 1	9 54	1131	1222	1341	1438	1519	18 5	1846	2024	...	...	...
San Salvadour	...	6 17	7 13	8 7	10 3	1143	1232	1353	1448	1525	1815	1853	2033	...	...	...
Hyères Ville ....arr	...	6 30	7 26	8 17	1016	1156	1245	14 6	15 1	1535	1828	19 2	2046	...	...	...
" ....dep	...	6 43		8 29		1210				1547		1913		...	...	...
Bormes	...	7 23	...	9 6	...	1246	...	...	...	1628	...	1950	...	...	...	...
Le Lavandou....................	...	7 33	...	9 14	...	1252	...	...	...	1635	...	1958	...	...	...	...
La Croix.........................	...	8 45	...	1025	...	1358	...	...	...	1743	...	21 5	...	...	...	...
La Foux	5 47	9 15	...	1055	...	1427	...	...	...	1810	...	2120	...	...	...	...
Ste Maxime	6 12	9 44	...	1123	...	1447	...	...	...	1833	...		...	...	...	...
Frejus	6 54	1026	...	12 5	...	1525	...	...	...	1913	...	...	...	...	...	...
St. Raphael ....arr	7 2	1034	...	1213	...	1533	...	...	...	1921	...	...	...	...	...	...

St. Raphael ....dep	...	...	...	4 40	...	8 52	...	...	...	1329	...	1620	2020	...	...	...
Frejus	...	...	...	4 48	...	9 2	...	...	...	1337	...	1630	2030	...	...	...
Ste. Maxime	...	...	...	5 28	...	9 47	...	...	...	1418	...	1711	2112	...	...	...
La Foux	...	...	...	5 59	...	1020	...	...	13 4	1450	...	1739	2129	...	...	...
La Croix.........................	...	...	...	6 21	...	1045	...	...	1328	1510	...	1759		...	...	...
Le Lavandou....................	...	...	...	7 29	...	1158	...	...	1441	1620	...	19 4	...	...	...	...
Bormes	...	...	...	7 38	...	12 9	...	...	1452	1631	...	1911	...	...	...	...
Hyères Ville ....arr	...	...	...	8 15	...	1246	...	...	1531	1710	...	1950	...	...	...	...
" ....dep	5 10	6 2	7 37	8 30	1035	1256	1338	1431	1543	1722	1758	20 5	...	...	...	...
San Salvadour	5 25	6 21	7 52	8 42	1050	13 8	1355	1447	1558	1735	1814	2017	...	...	...	...
Carqueiranne	5 33	6 33	8 2	8 48	1058	1314	14 6	1456	16 6	1741	1823	2023	...	...	...	...
Le Pradet	5 47	6 50	8 15	8 57	1111	1323	1422	1511	1618	1751	1838	2033	...	...	...	...
Toulon ....arr	6 13	7 16	8 41	9 12	1137	1349	1448	1537	1644	18 6	19 4	2059	...	...	...	...

COGOLIN and ST. TROPEZ.

Cogolin ......dep	5 24	8 41	9 57	1241	14 3	1713	21 7	...	...
La Foux............	5 54	9 9	1047	13 6	1447	18 7	2135	...	...
St. Tropez ...arr	6 16	9 31	11 9	1328	15 9	1829	2157	...	...
St. Tropez ...dep	5 18	8 35	9 51	1235	1357	17 7	21 1	...	...
La Foux............	5 55	9 10	1048	13 7	1443	18 8	2136	...	...
Cogolin.........arr	6 11	9 26	11 4	1325	15 4	1824	2152	...	...

NICE and DIGNE.

E.M.							
	Nice ....dep		4 50	7 13	9 26	14 18	17 44
8	Colomars......................		5 30	7 47	10 8	14 52	18 31
15½	La Vésubie 53c............		5 58	8 14	1037	15 21	19 0
36¾	Puget Theniers..............		7 18	9 27	1157	16 40	20 21
44	Pont-de-Gueydan..........		7 47	9 52	1226	17 9	20 50
49	Annot..........................	4 5	8 25	1021	13 4	17 46	21 17
66½	St. André....................	5 45	1012	1140	1450	19 24	
79	Chaudon-Norante ..	6 34	11 4	1221	1543	20 12	...
93¾	Digne.............arr	7 33	12 5	1310	1645	21 8	...

Digne ....dep	...	5 0	8 12	11 2	14 50	17 27
Chaudon-Norante...	...	5 59	9 16	12 19	15 42	18 30
St. André.............	...	7 1	1030	13 31	16 33	19 32
Annot	3 45	8 35	13 5	15 33	17 41	20 42
Pont-de-Gueydan...	4 2	8 56	1325	15 55	17 55	
Puget Theniers.......	4 29	9 31	1352	16 32	18 20	...
La Vésubie............	5 33	1039	1457	17 45	19 20	...
Colomars	6 5	1112	1530	18 20	19 49	...
Nice (47).........arr	6 37	1145	1556	18 53	20 15	...

LA VESUBIE and ST. MARTIN-VESUBIE.

E.M.								
	La Vésubie ....dep	6 15	8 28	1055	1547	1930	...	...
21¾	St. Martin-Vésubie ...arr	8 45	11 0	1326	1820	22 1	...	...

St. Martin-Vésubie...dep	2 45	7 23	12 5	1441	16 2	...	...
La Vésubie 53c ......arr	5 16	9 56	1436	1714	1835	...	...

GRASSE and CAGNES.

Grasse (P.L.M.) dep	...	...	731	9 43	1058	1236	16 9	...	1838	...
" (Ville).........	5 38	7 21	751	10 3	1120	14 0	1636	1725	1919	2020
Chateau.-Pré-du-Lac	6 2	7 41	9 1	...	1141	1420	1658	1747	1941	2040
Cagnes (S.F.) ...arr	7 9	...	100	...	...	...	1756	...	20 9	...

Cagnes...dep	...	...	5 57	...	9 43	...	...	1525	...	1840
Chateauneuf	5 10	5 59	6 57	8 12	1043	1253	1518	1625	...	1940
Grasse Ville	5 30	6 19	7 17	8 33	11 3	1329	1543	1645	1812	20 0
" P.L.M.	...	6 39	...	8 53	1225	1349	1613	...	1832	...

CAGNES and VENCE.

E.M.						
	Cagnes ....dep	6 15	8 50	1255	1510	1830
6¼	Vence (S.F.) 47...arr	7 5	9 40	1345	16 0	1920

Vence (S.F.)......dep	5 58	7 25	1011	1356	1711	2 18
Cagnes ....arr	6 48	8 16	11 0	1446	18 0	21 7

MONTE CARLO & LA TURBIE. FARES.—Upward, 3 fr. 10 c., 2 fr. 30 c. Downward, 1 fr. 55 c., 1 fr. 15 c.

Monte Carlo Bd. Nord dep	7 50	9 50	11 20	14 0	15 0	16 0	17 0	18‡35	...	...
Monte Carlo supérieur	7 54	9 54	11 24	14 4	15 4	16 4	17 4	18 39	...	...
Bordina	7 57	9 57	11 27	14 7	15 7	16 7	17 7	18 42	...	...
Route de la Corniche...........	8 8	10 8	11 38	14 18	15 18	16 18	17 18	18 53	...	...
La Turbie ....arr	8 11	10 11	11 41	14 21	15 21	16 21	17 21	18 56	...	...

‡—Until 30th Sept.

La Turbie ....dep	8 13	10 30	13 20	14 23	15 23	16 23	17 23	19 ‡0	...	...
Route de la Corniche...........	8 16	10 33	13 23	14 26	15 26	16 26	17 25	19 3	...	...
Bordina	8 27	10 44	13 34	14 37	15 37	16 37	17 37	19 14	...	...
Monte Carlo-supérieur	8 30	10 47	13 37	14 40	15 40	16 40	17 40	19 17	...	...
Monte Carlo Bd. Nord arr	8 34	10 51	13 41	14 44	15 44	16 44	17 44	19 21	...	...

AUXERRE and GIEN.

Auxerre...................dep	6 35	11 40	16 35	...	...
Toucy-Moulins	8 10	13 30	18 30	...	...
Fontenoy	8 22	13 42	18 41	...	...
Gien (58)...............arr	10 35	15 23	20 16	...	...

Gien ....dep	4 8	11 50	16 0	...	...
Fontenoy	6 28	13 44	17 46	...	...
Toucy-Moulins (63B)..	6 58	14 7	18 35	...	...
Auxerre ....arr	8 0	15 8	20 10	...	...

MARSEILLES, TOULON (HYERES), CANNES, NICE, MENTON, and VENTIMIGLIA. [66 lbs. Luggage free.

Dist.	1 Cl.	2 Cl.																													
...	...	...	PARIS 48 ... dep	...	9 15	...	1545	...	...	1545	...	1545	21 0	21 0	...	...	...	...	...	...	...	...	...	...	...	...	...	...	...	...	...
...	...	...	LYONS 49 ... dep	...	1752	...	2337	...	...	2347	...	2347	4 8	4 8	...	...	...	...	...	...	...	...	...	1215	1215	...	...	...	...	...	...
				1,2,3	1,2,3	1,2,3	1,2,3	1,2,3	1,2,3	1,2,3	1,2,3	1,2,3	1 Cl	1,2,3	1,2,3	1,2,3	1,2,3	1,2,3	1,2,3	1,2,3	1,2,3	1,2,3	1,2,3	1,2,3	1,2,3	1,2,3	1,2,3				
E.M	fr. c.	fr. c.																													
Fr.	Mars	eille	**MARSEILLES** ... dep	...	0 46	...	5 12	5 38	...	7 20	...	7 32	9 20	9 40	...	...	11 1	...	1155	1348	1635	1725	1753	1850	19 2	...	21 6	...	...	...	...
5½	1 0	0 70	St. Marcel ...	...	...	...	...	5 55	...	...	...	7 48	...	A	...	...	1119	...	1212	14 8	1654	1743	...	...	1919	...	2125	...	...	...	...
10½	1 90	1 30	**Aubagne** 57 ...	...	1 13	...	5 41	6 13	...	...	...	8 3	...	R C	...	...	1136	...	1230	1427	1711	18 2	1823	...	1937	...	2142	...	...	...	...
23	4 15	2 80	La Ciotat ...	...	...	...	6 8		...	...	...	8 29	...	...	...	...	12 4	...		1458	1739		1852	...		...	2212	...	...	...	...
41¾	7 50	5 5	**Toulon** ... arr	...	2 7	...	6 56	...	...	8 39	...	9 15	1025	1054	...	...	1255	...	...	1552	1831	...	1941	20 3	...	...	23 4	...	...	...	...
...	...	...	**Toulon** ... dep	...	...	...	7 10	...	...	9 44	...	...	...	...	1117	...	1324	...	...	1612	...	18 3	...	...	...	2047	...	...	...	...	...
48½	8 75	5 90	La Pauline ...	...	...	...	7 26	...	...	10 0	...	...	...	...	1134	...	1341	...	...	1628	...	1819	...	...	...	21 4	...	...	...	...	...
54¾	9 85	6 65	**Hyères** ... arr	...	...	...	7 41	...	...	1015	...	...	...	...	1149	...	1356	...	...	1643	...	1834	...	...	...	2119	...	...	...	...	...
57¼	10 30	6 95	„ La Plage ... arr	...	...	...	7 56	...	...	1031	...	...	...	...	12 6	...	1411	...	...	1657	...	1849	...	...	...	2134	...	...	...	...	...
59¾	10 75	7 25	„ Salins ... arr	...	...	...	8 4	...	...	1039	...	...	...	...	1214	...	1419	...	...	17 5	...	1857	...	...	...	2142	...	...	...	...	...
...	...	...	**Toulon** ... dep	...	2 20	...	...	5 33	...	8 51	...	9 25	1035	11 6	...	...	13 9	...	...	1631	1845	...	...	2016	...	...	...	...	...	...	...
48½	8 75	5 90	La Pauline ...	...	...	...	...	5 53	...	9 9	...	9 44	...	...	...	...	1329	...	...	1652	19 5	...	...	...	...	...	...	...	...	...	...
56	10 10	6 80	Cuers ...	...	...	...	...	6 22	...	...	...	1011	...	...	...	...	1357	...	...	1721	1933	...	...	...	...	...	...	...	...	...	...
63½	11 40	7 70	Carnoules 62A ...	...	3 16	...	...	6 49	...	9 52	...	1033	...	R C	...	...	1422	...	...	1748	1954	...	...	21 3	...	...	...	...	...	...	...
75¼	13 55	9 15	Le Luc et Cannet ...	...	...	...	...	7 18	...	1012	...	11 4	...	...	...	...	1450	...	...	1817	2052	...	...	...	...	...	...	...	...	...	...
80¾	14 55	9 85	Vidauban ...	...	...	...	...	7 31	...	...	...	1118	...	...	...	...	15 2	...	...	1830	21 4	...	...	...	...	...	...	...	...	...	...
84½	15 25	10 30	**Les Arcs** ... arr	...	3 47	...	...	7 38	...	1027	...	1125	1143	1223	...	...	15 9	...	...	1837	2111	...	...	2131	...	...	...	...	...	...	...
			Les Arcs ... dep	...	3 52	4 50	...	7 53	...	1032	...	1235	1145	1227	...	...	1527	...	...	1852		...	...	2134	...	...	...	...	...	...	...
98¼	17 70	11 95	Frejus ...	...	4 16	5 27	...	8 29	...	1057	...	1311	...	...	...	...	16 5	...	...	1930	...	...	...	2158	...	...	...	...	...	...	...
100¾	18 15	12 25	St. Raphael 53C ...	...	4 24	5 34	...	8 39	...	11 4	...	1319	1210	1254	...	...	1614	...	...	1940	...	...	...	22 5	...	...	...	...	...	...	...
102½	18 50	12 45	Boulouris ...	...	...	5 41	...	8 46	...	...	...	1326	...	...	...	...	1621	...	...	1947	...	...	...	...	...	...	...	...	...	...	...
105¾	19 5	12 85	Agay ...	...	...	5 50	...	8 55	...	...	...	1335	...	A	...	...	1631	...	...	1956	...	...	...	...	...	...	...	...	...	...	...
111¾	20 15	13 60	Le Trayas ...	...	...	6 3	...	9 8	...	...	...	1348	...	...	...	...	1645	...	...	2010	...	...	...	...	...	...	...	...	...	...	...
115½	20 85	14 5	La Napoule ...	...	...	6 15	...	9 20	...	...	...	14 0	...	...	...	...	1657	...	...	2022	...	...	...	...	...	...	...	...	...	...	...
118¾	21 40	14 45	La Bocca ...	...	...	6 23	...	9 28	...	...	...	14 8	...	...	...	...	17 6	...	...	2031	...	...	...	...	...	...	...	...	...	...	...
120½	21 75	14 65	**Cannes** ... arr	...	4 57	6 28	...	9 33	...	1140	...	1413	1240	1326	...	...	1711	...	...	2036	...	...	...	2235	...	...	...	...	...	...	...
133	23 0	16 15	GRASSE 53C ... arr	...	7 26	7 26	...	1053	...	...	...	16 4	1436	1436	...	...	1833	...	...	...	...	...	...	2324	...	...	...	...	...	...	...
...	...	...	**Cannes** ... dep	...	5 12	6 41	7 57	9 51	...	1150	12 5	1423	1247	1336	...	...	1728	1839	...	2056	...	...	...	2245	...	...	...	...	...	...	...
124¼	22 40	15 10	Golfe-Juan ...	...	5 23	6 52	8 7	10 1	...	12 0	1215	1433	1256	1346	...	...	1739	1849	...	21 6	...	...	...	2254	...	...	...	...	...	...	...
126¼	22 75	15 35	Juan-les-Pins ...	...	5 30	6 58	8 14	10 7	...	...	1221	1439	...	...	...	...	1746	1855	...	2112	...	...	...	...	...	...	...	...	...	...	...
127½	22 95	15 50	Antibes ...	...	5 36	7 4	8 19	1013	...	12 9	1227	1445	13 4	1355	...	...	1752	19 0	...	2118	...	...	...	...	...	...	...	...	...	...	...
132½	23 85	16 10	Cagnes ...	...	5 52	7 19	8 35	1026	...	...	1242	1457	...	R C	...	...	18 9	1912	...	2131	...	...	...	...	...	...	...	...	...	...	...
136	24 55	16 55	Var ...	...	6 8	7 35	8 51	1038	...	...	1258	15 9	...	...	...	...	1825	1925	...	2143	...	...	...	...	...	...	...	...	...	...	...
139¾	25 20	17 0	**Nice** ... arr	...	6 17	7 43	9 0	1046	...	1233	13 6	1517	1325	1420	...	...	1833	1933	...	2151	...	...	...	2323	...	...	...	...	...	...	...
			Nice ... dep	5 30	6 33	7 59	9 10	11 1	1140	1256	1318	1529	1340	1440	...	1715	1853	1943	...		...	...	...	2339	...	...	0 25	...	...	...	...
141	25 40	17 15	Nice-Riquier ...	5 39	6 41	8 7	9 18	11 8	...	...	1325	1536	...	...	...	1722	19 0	1949	...	...	...	...	...	...	...	...	0 31	...	...	...	...
142½	25 65	17 30	Villefranche-sur-Mer ...	5 44	6 47	8 12	9 23	1113	...	13 4	1330	1541	1348	1448	...	1727	19 6	1954	...	...	...	...	...	2348	...	...	0 36	...	...	...	...
143½	25 85	17 45	Beaulieu ...	5 51	6 53	8 18	9 28	1119	1151	13 9	1335	1546	1354	1454	...	1733	1912	20 0	...	...	...	...	...	2354	...	...	0 41	...	...	...	...
145¾	26 20	17 70	Eze ...	5 57	6 59	8 24	9 34	1125	...	...	1341	1552	...	...	...	1739	1918	20 6	...	...	...	...	...	...	...	...	0 47	...	...	...	...
147¼	26 55	17 90	Cap d'Ail—La Turbie ...	6 4	7 6	8 31	9 41	1132	...	...	1348	1559	14 7	15 7	...	1746	1925	2013	...	...	...	...	...	...	...	...	0 54	...	...	...	...
149	26 90	18 15	Monaco ... arr	6 9	7 11	8 36	9 46	1137	12 3	1325	1353	16 4	1412	1512	...	1751	1930	2018	...	...	...	...	...	0 10	...	...	0 59	...	...	...	...
			Monaco ... dep	6 15	7 15	8 40	9 51	1142	12 5	1329	1358	16 8	1415	1517	...	1757	1935	2022	...	...	...	...	...	0 14	...	...	1 2	...	...	...	...
150¼	27 10	18 30	**Monte Carlo** ... arr	6 19	7 19	8 44	9 55	1146	12 9	1333	14 2	1612	1418	1520	...	18 1	1939	2026	...	...	...	...	...	0 18	...	...	1 6	...	...	...	...
			Monte Carlo ... dep	6 25	7 24	8 48	10 0	1150	1212	1337	14 5	1616	1424	1525	...	18 7	1943	2031	...	...	...	...	...	0 22	...	...	1 8	...	...	...	...
152½	27 45	18 50	Cabbe-Roquebrune ...	6 32	7 31	8 55	10 7	1157	...	...	1412	1623	1431	1532	...	1814	1950	2038	...	...	...	...	...	...	...	...	1 15	...	...	...	...
154¾	27 90	18 80	**Menton** ... arr	6 39	7 38	9 2	1014	12 4	1223	1348	1419	1630	1437	1538	...	1821	1957	2045	...	...	...	...	...	0 33	...	...	1 22	...	...	...	...
			Menton ... dep	6 45	7 44	9 8	1019	12 8		1352	1426	1636	1444	1543	...	1828	20 3		...	...	...	...	...	0 38	...	...		...	...	...	...
155¾	28 10	19 0	Menton-Garavan ...	6 51	7 50	9 14	1025	1214	...	1358	1432	1642	1449	1548	...	1834	20 9	...	...	...	...	...	...	0 44	...	...	...	...	...	...	...
161½	29 30	19 85	**VENTIMIGLIA** ¶ ... arr	7 2	8 1	9 25	1036	1225	...	14 9	1443	1653	1459	1558	...	1845	2020	...	...	...	...	...	...	0 55	...	...	...	...	...	...	...
171½	31 35	21 30	SAN REMO 272 ... arr	9 58	9 58	1131	1324	...	...	1639	1639	1914	1639	1750	...	21 9	...	...	...	...	...	...	...	2 56	...	...	...	...	...	...	...
255½	48 50	33 30	GENOA 272 ... arr	1350	1350	17 5	1720	...	...	2150	2150	2310	2150	2310	...	2 10	...	...	...	...	...	...	...	7 40	...	...	...	...	...	...	...

MARSEILLES, TOULON (HYERES), CANNES, NICE, MENTON, and VENTIMIGLIA.

Station																					
PARIS 48 ... dep	...	...	...	...	...	...	...	...	...	...	...	...	...	...	...	...	...	...	...	...	...
LYONS 49 ... dep	...	...	...	...	...	...	...	...	...	...	...	...	...	...	...	...	...	...	...	...	...
MARSEILLES ... dep	...	...	...	...	...	...	...	...	...	...	...	...	...	...	...	...	...	...	...	...	...
St. Marcel	...	...	...	...	...	...	...	...	...	...	...	...	...	...	...	...	...	...	...	...	...
Aubagne 57	...	...	...	...	...	...	...	...	...	...	...	...	...	...	...	...	...	...	...	...	...
La Ciotat	...	...	...	...	...	...	...	...	...	...	...	...	...	...	...	...	...	...	...	...	...
Toulon ... arr	...	...	...	...	...	...	...	...	...	...	...	...	...	...	...	...	...	...	...	...	...
Toulon ... dep	...	...	...	...	...	...	...	...	...	...	...	...	...	...	...	...	...	...	...	...	...
La Pauline	...	...	...	...	...	...	...	...	...	...	...	...	...	...	...	...	...	...	...	...	...
Hyères ... arr	...	...	...	...	...	...	...	...	...	...	...	...	...	...	...	...	...	...	...	...	...
,, La Plage ... arr	...	...	...	...	...	...	...	...	...	...	...	...	...	...	...	...	...	...	...	...	...
,, Salins ... arr	...	...	...	...	...	...	...	...	...	...	...	...	...	...	...	...	...	...	...	...	...
Toulon ... dep	...	...	...	...	...	...	...	...	...	...	...	...	...	...	...	...	...	...	...	...	...
La Pauline	...	...	...	...	...	...	...	...	...	...	...	...	...	...	...	...	...	...	...	...	...
Cuers	...	...	...	...	...	...	...	...	...	...	...	...	...	...	...	...	...	...	...	...	...
Carnoules 62A	...	...	...	...	...	...	...	...	...	...	...	...	...	...	...	...	...	...	...	...	...
Le Luc et Cannet	...	...	...	...	...	...	...	...	...	...	...	...	...	...	...	...	...	...	...	...	...
Vidauban	...	...	...	...	...	...	...	...	...	...	...	...	...	...	...	...	...	...	...	...	...
Les Arcs ... arr	...	...	...	...	...	...	...	...	...	...	...	...	...	...	...	...	...	...	...	...	...
Les Arcs ... dep	...	...	...	...	...	...	...	...	...	...	...	...	...	...	...	...	...	...	...	...	...
Frejus	...	...	...	...	...	...	...	...	...	...	...	...	...	...	...	...	...	...	...	...	...
St. Raphael 53C	...	...	...	...	...	...	...	...	...	...	...	...	...	...	...	...	...	...	...	...	...
Boulouris	...	...	...	...	...	...	...	...	...	...	...	...	...	...	...	...	...	...	...	...	...
Agay	...	...	...	...	...	...	...	...	...	...	...	...	...	...	...	...	...	...	...	...	...
Le Trayas	...	...	...	...	...	...	...	...	...	...	...	...	...	...	...	...	...	...	...	...	...
La Napoule	...	...	...	...	...	...	...	...	...	...	...	...	...	...	...	...	...	...	...	...	...
La Bocca	...	...	...	...	...	...	...	...	...	...	...	...	...	...	...	...	...	...	...	...	...
Cannes ... arr	...	...	...	...	...	...	...	...	...	...	...	...	...	...	...	...	...	...	...	...	...
GRASSE 53C ... arr	...	...	...	...	...	...	...	...	...	...	...	...	...	...	...	...	...	...	...	...	...
Cannes ... dep	...	...	...	...	...	...	...	...	...	...	...	...	...	...	...	...	...	...	...	...	...
Golfe-Juan	...	...	...	...	...	...	...	...	...	...	...	...	...	...	...	...	...	...	...	...	...
Juan-les-Pins	...	...	...	...	...	...	...	...	...	...	...	...	...	...	...	...	...	...	...	...	...
Antibes	...	...	...	...	...	...	...	...	...	...	...	...	...	...	...	...	...	...	...	...	...
Cagnes	...	...	...	...	...	...	...	...	...	...	...	...	...	...	...	...	...	...	...	...	...
Var	...	...	...	...	...	...	...	...	...	...	...	...	...	...	...	...	...	...	...	...	...
Nice ... arr	...	...	...	...	...	...	...	...	...	...	...	...	...	...	...	...	...	...	...	...	...
Nice ... dep	...	...	...	...	...	...	...	...	...	...	...	...	...	...	...	...	...	...	...	...	...
Nice-Riquier	...	...	...	...	...	...	...	...	...	...	...	...	...	...	...	...	...	...	...	...	...
Villefranche-sur-Mer	...	...	...	...	...	...	...	...	...	...	...	...	...	...	...	...	...	...	...	...	...
Beaulieu	...	...	...	...	...	...	...	...	...	...	...	...	...	...	...	...	...	...	...	...	...
Eze	...	...	...	...	...	...	...	...	...	...	...	...	...	...	...	...	...	...	...	...	...
Cap d'Ail—La Turbie	...	...	...	...	...	...	...	...	...	...	...	...	...	...	...	...	...	...	...	...	...
Monaco ... arr	...	...	...	...	...	...	...	...	...	...	...	...	...	...	...	...	...	...	...	...	...
Monaco ... dep	...	...	...	...	...	...	...	...	...	...	...	...	...	...	...	...	...	...	...	...	...
Monte-Carlo ... arr	...	...	...	...	...	...	...	...	...	...	...	...	...	...	...	...	...	...	...	...	...
Monte-Carlo ... dep	...	...	...	...	...	...	...	...	...	...	...	...	...	...	...	...	...	...	...	...	...
Cabbe-Roquebrune	...	...	...	...	...	...	...	...	...	...	...	...	...	...	...	...	...	...	...	...	...
Menton ... arr	...	...	...	...	...	...	...	...	...	...	...	...	...	...	...	...	...	...	...	...	...
Menton ... dep	...	...	...	...	...	...	...	...	...	...	...	...	...	...	...	...	...	...	...	...	...
Menton Garavan	...	...	...	...	...	...	...	...	...	...	...	...	...	...	...	...	...	...	...	...	...
VENTIMIGLIA ¶ ... arr	...	...	...	...	...	...	...	...	...	...	...	...	...	...	...	...	...	...	...	...	...
SAN REMO 272 ... arr	...	...	...	...	...	...	...	...	...	...	...	...	...	...	...	...	...	...	...	...	...
GENOA 272 ... arr	...	...	...	...	...	...	...	...	...	...	...	...	...	...	...	...	...	...	...	...	...

NOTES.

Excess Luggage, 1 centime per 44 lbs. per kilometre.

¶—Customs Examinations.

RC—Restaurant Car.

A—Between Marseilles and Antibes will only admit 2nd and 3rd class travelling at least 87 miles.

VENTIMIGLIA, MENTON, NICE, CANNES, (HYERES), TOULON, and MARSEILLES.

Station																							
GENOA (272A) ......dep	...	...	...	...	...	0 20	...	...	...	4 30	7 10	...	...	9.45	...	9 45	1050	...	1240	...	1710	...	2010
SAN REMO (272A)......dep	...	...	...	...	...	5 11	...	...	7 51	9 20	1138	1243	...	1328	...	1328	1541	...	1754	...	2011	...	2349
	1,2,3	1,2,3	1,2,3	1,2,3	1,2,3	1,2,3	1,2,3	1,2,3	1,2,3	1,2,3	1,2,3	1,2,3	1,2,3	1Cl.	1,2,3	1,2,3	1,2,3	1,2,3	1,2,3	1,2,3	1,2,3	1,2,3	1,2,3
VENTIMIGLIA ......dep	...	...	...	...	...	5 25	...	7 17	8 31	1030	1220	1244	...	14 9	...	15 7	1617	...	18 8	1925	2120	...	2355
Menton-Garavan	...	...	...	...	...	5 36	...	7 29	8 43	1042	1232	1256	...	1420	...	1519	1629	...	1820	1937	2132	...	0 7
Menton ......arr	...	...	...	...	...	5 41	...	7 35	8 49	1048	1238	13 1	...	1425	...	1525	1635	...	1826	1943	2138	...	0 13
Menton ......dep	...	...	...	...	...	5 46	...	7 40	8 56	1053	1245	13 5	1410	1430	...	1529	1641	1731	1833	1948	2143	2320	0 17
Cabbe-Roquebrune	...	...	...	...	...	5 53	...	7 48	9 4	11 1	1253	1312	1418	1437	...	1537	1649	...	1841	1956	2151	2328	...
Monte-Carlo ......arr	...	...	...	...	...	5 59	...	7 54	9 10	11 7	1259	1318	1424	1443	...	1543	1655	1742	1847	20 2	2157	2334	0 28
Monte-Carlo ......dep	...	...	...	...	...	6 3	...	7 57	9 13	1111	13 2	1322	1427	1448	...	1547	1659	1745	1851	20 5	22 0	2337	0 31
Monaco ......arr	...	...	...	...	...	6 6	...	8 1	9 17	1115	13 6	1326	1431	1451	...	1551	17 3	1749	1855	20 9	22 4	2341	0 35
Monaco ......dep	...	...	...	...	...	6 10	...	8 4	9 21	1119	1310	1329	1434	1454	...	1554	17 7	1751	1859	2011	22 6	2344	0 38
Cap d'Ail—La Turbie	...	...	...	...	...	6 16	...	8 10	9 27	1125	1316	1335	1440	15 0	...	...	1713	...	19 5	2017	2212	2350	...
Eze	...	...	...	...	...	6 22	...	8 17	9 34	1132	1323	...	1447	...	...	...	1720	...	1912	2024	2219	2357	...
Beaulieu	...	...	...	...	...	6 29	...	8 23	9 40	1139	1330	1346	1453	1510	...	16 8	1727	18 5	1919	2030	2226	0 3	0 51
Villefranche-sur-Mer	...	...	...	...	...	6 34	...	8 28	9 45	1144	1335	1351	1458	1515	...	1614	1732	...	1924	2035	2231	0 8	...
Nice-Riquier	...	...	...	...	...	6 40	...	8 34	9 51	1150	1341	B	15 4	...	...	...	1738	...	1930	2040	2236	0 13	...
Nice ......arr	...	...	...	...	...	6 45	...	8 39	9 56	1155	1346	14 1	15 9	1525	...	1624	1743	1814	1935	2045	2241	0 18	1 3
Nice ......dep	...	...	...	...	5 0	7 2	7 35	8 49	1013	1210		1418	1550	1540	...	1644	1759			2057			1 18
Var	...	...	...	...	5 9	A	7 44	8 58	1021	1219	...	...	1558	...	...	...	18 7	...	...	21 6	...	...	...
Cagnes	...	...	...	...	5 24	...	7 59	9 11	1037	1234	...	RC	1613	C	...	...	1823	...	...	2120	...	...	...
Antibes	...	...	...	...	5 40	7 23	8 15	9 24	1053	1250	...	1444	1629	16 2	...	1710	1839	...	...	2134	...	...	1 38
Juan-les-Pins	...	...	...	...	5 45	...	8 20	9 29	1058	1255	...	...	1634	...	...	...	1844	...	...	2139	...	...	...
Golfe-Juan	...	...	...	...	5 52	7 32	8 27	9 36	11 5	13 2	...	1453	1641	1610	...	1719	1851	...	...	2146	...	...	1 46
Cannes ......arr	...	...	...	...	6 0	7 39	8 35	9 45	1113	1310	...	15 1	1649	1617	...	1728	1859	...	...	2155	...	...	1 53
GRASSE (53C) ......dep	...	...	...	...	5 30	6 49	...	...	9 2	...	...	1359	1621	...	...	1621	...	...	...	...	...	...	...
Cannes ......dep	...	...	...	...	6 18	7 49	8 54	...	1129	...	...	15 9	1659	1625	...	1739	19 8	...	...	...	...	...	2 3
La Bocca	...	...	...	...	6 24	...	9 0	...	1136	...	...	...	17 5	...	...	...	1914	...	...	...	...	...	...
La Napoule	...	...	...	...	6 32	...	9 8	...	1144	...	...	...	1713	...	...	...	1922	...	...	...	...	...	...
Le Trayas	...	...	...	...	6 44	...	9 20	...	1158	...	...	B	1725	...	...	...	1934	...	...	...	...	...	...
Agay	...	...	...	...	6 59	...	9 35	...	1213	...	...	...	1739	...	...	...	1948	...	...	...	...	...	...
Boulouris	...	...	...	...	7 8	...	9 44	...	1222	...	...	...	1748	...	...	...	1957	...	...	...	...	...	...
St. Raphael	...	...	...	...	7 19	8 23	9 53	...	1233	...	...	1549	1756	17 1	...	1825	20 5	...	...	...	...	...	2 36
Frejus	...	...	...	...	7 26	8 29	10 0	...	1243	...	...	...	18 3	...	...	1833	2011	...	...	...	...	...	2 42
Les Arcs ......arr	...	...	...	...	8 5	8 54	1039	...	1324	...	...	1623	1843	...	...	19 7	2047	...	...	...	...	...	3 5
Les Arcs ......dep	...	...	5 30	...	8 17	8 57	1051	...	1336	...	...	1626		...	1646	1932		...	...	...	...	...	3 9
Vidauban	...	...	5 41	...	8 28	...	11 2	...	1348	...	...	...	...	C	1657	...	...	...	...	...	...	...	...
Le Luc et Cannet	...	...	5 58	...	8 45	...	1119	...	14 5	...	...	...	...	...	1715	...	...	...	...	...	...	...	...
Carnoules	...	...	6 34	...	9 17	...	1156	...	1447	...	...	RC	...	...	1814	2031	...	...	...	...	...	...	3 48
Cuers	...	...	6 52	...	10 2	...	1215	...	15 7	...	...	...	...	...	1831	...	...	...	...	...	...	...	...
La Pauline	...	...	7 15	...	1024	...	1237	...	1533	...	...	...	...	...	1854	2056	...	...	...	...	...	...	...
Toulon ......arr	...	...	7 29	...	1038	10 3	1253	...	1550	...	...	1743	...	1834	19 8	21 7	...	...	...	...	...	...	4 15
Hyères Salins ......dep	...	4 35	6 20	8 21	...	...	1143	...	1422	...	1623	...	...	...	...	1951	...	...	...	...	...	...	...
„ La Plage ...dep	...	4 43	6 28	8 29	...	...	1151	...	1430	...	1631	...	...	...	...	1959	...	...	...	...	...	...	...
„ Town ......dep	...	4 59	6 42	8 41	...	...	12 5	...	1447	...	1648	...	...	...	...	2017	...	...	...	...	...	...	...
La Pauline	...	5 17	6 59	8 53	...	...	1223	...	15 7	...	17 8	...	...	...	...	2035	...	...	...	...	...	...	...
Toulon ......arr	...	5 33	7 14	9 13	...	...	1238	...	1524	...	1725	...	...	...	...	2050	...	...	...	...	...	...	...
Toulon ......dep	...	5 48	7 41	...	1051	1013	13 6	...	1612	...	...	1757	...	1846	1920	2119	...	...	...	...	...	...	4 23
La Ciotat	...	6 44	8 38	...	1145	...	14 1	1,2,3	1711	...	...	...	...	...	2015	...	1,2,3	...	...	...	...	...	4 57
Aubagne ......arr	6 45	7 15	9 8	...	1218	...	1433	1350	1742	...	...	...	1828	...	2043	...	2025	...	...	...	...	...	5 20
St. Marcel	7 2	7 39	9 23	...	...	...	1447	14 8	1756	...	...	...	1849	...	2057	...	2043	...	...	...	...	...	...
MARSEILLES ......arr	7 19	8 0	9 39	...	1242	1125	15 5	1425	1813	...	...	1920	19 6	1955	2114	2254	2059	...	...	...	...	...	5 38
LYONS (50) ......arr	...	1419	...	...	...	1846	...	...	1 9	...	...	1 9	...	1 9	...	6 28	...	...	...	...	...	...	12 2
PARIS (51) ......arr	...	22 0	...	...	...	4 55	...	...	8 0	...	...	8 0	...	8 0	...	1710	...	...	...	...	...	...	2355

NOTES.

A—Takes 2nd and 3rd class only when travelling not less than 62 miles; exceptionally at Ventimiglia and forward will take for Nice, and at Toulon for Marseilles.

B—Between Ventimiglia and Toulon only admits 2nd and 3rd class travelling not less than 87 miles.

C—Between Ventimiglia and Marseilles only takes passengers travelling not less than 93 miles.

RC—Restaurant Car.

DIJON and ST. AMOUR.

E.M.								P. & O. Express.		Savoie Express.					
—	Dijon ....dep	1 15	1 40	2 10	3 12	4 0	8 54	10 6	1322	1536	1548	1847	1949	...	...
13	Aiserey	...	...	...	...	4 34	9 28		...	...	1622	...	2026	...	...
19½	St. Jean-de-Losne	...	...	...	...	4 54	9 50		...		1642	...	2049	...	...
28½	Seurre	...	...	...	...	5 22	1024		...		17 7	...	2112	...	...
37¼	St. Bonnet-B.......	...	...	...	...	5 57	1049		...		1756	...	—	...	...
54¾	Louhans	...	...	...	...	7 13	1152		...		1858	1959	...	...	...
70¼	St. Amour 53......	...	...	...	...	7 54	1234		...		1940	...	...	...	...
88¼	Bourg ......arr	3 24	3 49	4 19	5 8	9 40	1334	12 1	1516	1730	2039	2050	...	...	...

							Savoie Express.					
Bourg ....dep	1 18	2 8	...	4 0	7 24	12 3	1248	1637	1652	23 36	...	...
St. Amour ......dep	...	...	...	5 40	...	1324	...	...	18 0	...	...	...
Louhans	...	...	...	7 6	...	1420		...	1920	0 36	...	...
St. Bonnet-en-B. ...	...	...	...	8 21	...	1512		...	2015	...	...	...
Seurre	...	...	6 29	9 14	...	1540		...	2045	...	...	...
St. Jean-de-Losne	...	...	6 59	9 47	...	1615		...	2117	...	...	...
Aiserey	...	...	7 14	10 4	...	1633		...	2133	...	...	...
Dijon (48) ....arr	4 4	4 16	7 50	1040	9 36	1711	1441	1831	22 6	1 55	...	...

CLAMECY and CERCY-LA-TOUR.

Clamecy ....dep	5 23	...	1346	1717
Corbigny	6 25	...	1450	1816
Tamnay-Chatillon	7 13	1258	16 3	19 5
Vandenesse	7 42	1331	1636	1934
Cercy-la-Tour arr	7 55	1345	1650	1947

Cercy-la-Tour ...dep	3 25	8 46	1445	18 5
Vandenesse	3 40	9 0	15 0	1819
Tamnay-Chatillon	4 18	9 34	1532	1859
Corbigny	5 6	1024	—	1945
Clamecy ....arr	6 1	1115	...	2036

CORBIGNY to SAULIEU.

Corbigny.........dep	...	7 5	14 53	1950	...
Lormes	...	7 57	15 38	2035	...
Ouroux	4 43	9 0	16 36	2124	...
Alligny-en-M.	6 1	10 34	17 55	—	...
Saulieu ....arr	6 45	11 22	18 39	...	...

Saulieu............dep	...	5 12	9 41	14 21	...
Alligny-en-M.	...	6 4	10 33	15 6	...
Ouroux	4 36	7 52	12 6	16 31	...
Lormes	5 27	8 55	—	17 23	...
Corbigny ....arr	6 6	9 37	...	18 1	...

LES LAUMES and EPINAC.

E.M							
	Les Laumes ...dep	5 42	12 50	17 15	...	...	...
34½	Arnay-le-Duc......	7 31	14 50	20 5	...	...	...
46½	Epinac ....arr	8 7	15 32	20 54	...	...	...
...	Epinac ....dep	5 25	8 38	18 0	...	...	...
...	Arnay-le-Duc......	6 18	9 30	18 55	...	...	...
...	Les Laumes ...arr	8 7	11 17	20 43	...	...	...

CLAMECY and TRIGUERES.

Clamecy ....dep	5 20	...	11 50	16 55	...	...
Surgy	5 30	...	12 1	17 5	...	...
Fontenoy	6 23	7 34	13 13	17 57	...	...
Toucy-Moulins 53c.........	—	8 19	14 10	18 22	...	...
Charny	...	9 45	15 40	19 25	...	...
Triguères 63B...........arr	...	10 14	16 10	19 50	...	...

Triguères ....dep	4 54	11 32	16 58	...	...	...	...
Charny	5 24	11 55	17 21	...	...	...	...
Toucy-Moulins............	7 1	14 0	18 43	...	...	...	...
Fontenoy	7 13	14 15	18 55	...	...	...	...
Surgy	8 2	15 25	19 49	...	...	...	...
Clamecy 63B ....arr	8 11	15 35	19 58	...	...	...	...

†—From or at Port Neuve.]

DIJON, IS-SUR-TILLE, and CULMONT-CHALINDREY.

Dijon (ville) (48) .. dep	6 0	6 10	9 9	11†11	1327	14†54	1737	18†12	1942	0 45
St.-Julien-Clenay	...	6 46	9 48	11 42	...	15 29	...	18 47	2023	...
Is-sur-Tille (74) ......arr	6 35	7 5	10 7	12 23	1410	16 10	1815	19 28	2042	1 30
Vaux-s-Aubigny	—	7 46	1043	—	...	17 2	...	—	2135	...
Culmont-Chalindrey 68	...	8 20	1119	...	15 6	17 37	19 2	...	2211	2 28
Langres (68)...........arr	...	8 44	1133	...	1530	18 5	1927	...	2251	2 51

Langres ....dep	5 48	...	11 10	1143	1448	...	1534	1921	2211
Culmont-Chal. dep	6 5	...	...	12 2	15 5	...	16 4	1946	2233
Vaux-s-Aubigny	6 38	...	...	1234	1540	...	...	2023	..
Is-sur-Tille	7 28	9 30	12 5	1315	1610	1632	17 7	2115	2317
St.-Julien-Clenay	7 48	10 5	...	1337	...	1652	...	2137	...
Dijon (ville) ...arr	8 26	10†36	12 36	1420	...	1733	1746	2221	2348

UZES and NOZIERES.

E.M.				
	Uzès ....dep	5 54	1215	16 0
11¾	Nozières 59 arr	6 29	1250	1653
...	Nozières......dep	8 45	1355	1730
...	Uzès 53B ......arr	9 20	1430	1823

SENS and MONTARGIS

E.M							
	Sens ....dep	5 32	...	9 21	...	1542	1855
16¾	Courtenay	6 18	...	1047	...	1629	1947
24¾	Triguères 63B	6 38	10 24	1115	1213	1653	2015
38½	Montargis 58......arr	7 13	11 5	...	1245	1729	2055

Montargis ......dep	4 1	8 38	10 45	15 50	20 0
Triguères	4 46	9 12	11 17	16 45	2042
Courtenay	—	9 29	12 26	17 11	21 3
Sens ....arr	...	10 5	13 37	17 58	2142

CLAMECY and COSNE.

Clamecy ......dep	6 25	11 38	17 23
Cosne 58......arr	9 0	13 37	19 18
Cosne ....dep	4 28	10 20	17 35
Clamecy 63Barr	6 19	12 50	19 35

COSNE and ST. AMAND.

E.M									
	Cosne ....dep	6 23	10 52	1736	...	...	...	...	...
13¾	St. Amand-en-Puisaye ....arr	7 22	11 59	1843	...	...	...	...	...

St. Amand ....dep	7 53	12 31	19 5	...	...	...	...	...
Cosne (58) ....arr	9 2	13 41	2014	...	...	...	...	...

LIVRON and PRIVAS.

E.M.									
	Livron (49)dep	6 2	7 13	10 40	1426	1523	1655	2021	...
3¾	La Voulte.........	6 35	7 35	10 58	1442	1534	1713	2036	...
6¾	Le Pouzin (62)...	6 50	7 45	11 10	1457	—	1734	2049	...
19¾	Privas ......arr	7 36	8 19	11 47	1530	...	18 8	2123	...

Privas dep	5 25	8 50	10 14	1354	...	16 27	19 38	...
Le Pouzin...	6 2	9 27	11 13	1432	...	17 42	20 20	...
La Voulte...	6 20	9 41	11 27	1443	15 54	17 59	20 41	...
Livron arr	6 31	9 52	11 38	1454	16 5	18 10	20 52	...

ARLES and ST. LOUIS.

Arles ....dep	7 40	13 53	19 35	...	...
St. Louis...............arr	9 0	15 29	20 50	...	...
St. Louis...............dep	5 33	10 37	17 35	...	...
Arles ....arr	6 58	12 4	19 0	...	...

§—Tuesday only, until 26th August.]

CLERMONT and SAINT-ETIENNE.

[‡—Monday and Thursday only.

E.M.												
—	Clermont-Ferrand......dep	...	5 0	10 2	...	...	13 0	...	...	1651	1758	20 25
10	Vertaizon..............	...	5 25	1027	...	...	1324	...	...	1714	1827	20 51
21¾	Pont-de-Dore	...	6 10	11 5	...	...	1357	...	..	1738	1921	21 21
23	Courty (62A)	...	6 32	1112	12 3	13§14	14 5	...	16 50	1745	1928	21 28
24¼	Thiers	...	7 0	1129	1220	13 31	143[illegible]	...	17 7	18 2	1955	21 45
38	Noiretable	...	7 59	—	—	—	15[illegible]	...	—	1836	2045	—
54	Boen	5 30	9 6	...	...	...	1[illegible]8	...	...	1920	2138	...
64½	Montbrison	6 0	9 50	1217	1435	...	[illegible]6	17 29	...	1941	2218	...
74	Bonson (63)	6 30	1023	1247	1457	...	1732	18 2	...	1959	2243	...
77¾	Saint Just..............	6 46	1037	13 2	15 8	...	1745	18 22	...	20 8	2255	...
85¼	St-Etienne ...arr	7 16	1057	1332	...	...	18 6	18 53	...	2024	2315	...

Saint-Etienne ......dep	...	...	6 31	6 59	...	11 0	1152	...	...	15 50	17 48	21 0	...
Saint Just..............	...	...	6 45	7 26	...	11 26	1217	...	...	16 15	18 16	2129	...
Bonson	...	...	6 55	7 44	...	11 44	1233	...	...	16 30	18 33	2144	...
Montbrison	...	...	7 15	8 16	...	12 13	13 0	...	...	16 52	18 58	2215	...
Boen	...	...	7 38	8 45	...	12 42	—	...	...	17 32	—	2241	...
Noiretable	5‡18	...	8 26	9 50	...	13 45	...	...	...	18 38	...	—	...
Thiers	5 54	6 4	9 0	1035	1131	14 30	...	16§37	17 58	19 47	...	...	...
Courty	—	6 18	9 14	1048	1143	14 44	...	16 49	18 11	20 0	...	...	...
Pont-de-Dore	...	6 40	9 22	11 7	—	14 53	...	—	18 27	20 20	...	...	...
Vertaizon..............	...	7 13	9 52	1143	...	15 28	...	...	19 1	20 54	...	...	...
Clermont ......arr	...	7 37	1020	1210	...	15 56	...	...	19 25	21 18	...	...	...

PARIS, LYONS, and MEDITERRANEAN RAILWAY. [66 lbs. of Luggage free

†—Runs until Sept. 30th.

SAINT-AUBAN and DIGNE.

St-Auban dep	6 46	9 10	10†0	1330	1450	2041
Mallemoisson	7 7	9 35	1021	14 0	1523	21 6
Digne......arr	7 25	9 55	1039	1420	1543	2126

Digne ....dep	5 51	7 55	12 22	13 40	18 2
Mallemoisson ...	6 9	8 15	12 40	13 58	18 25
St-Auban 63A arr	6 29	8 43	13 0	14 18	18 45

SORGUES and CARPENTRAS.

Sorgues...........dep	8 46	1029	17 0	22 2	...
Althen-les-Paluds ...	9 2	1047	1715	22 17	...
Carpentras 62 arr	9 21	1110	1733	22 35	...

Carpentras ...dep	5 23	9 39	1257	1755	...
Althen-les-Paluds ...	5 39	9 55	1318	1818	...
Sorgues ....arr	5 52	10 8	1337	1838	...

BEAUNE and ALLEREY.

Beaune ....dep	6 40	11 12	16 51	...	...	...	...
Allerey (56) .....arr	7 15	11 41	17 21	...	...	...	...

Allerey ....dep	8 54	12 21	18 39	...	...	...	...	...
Beaune (48) ....arr	9 32	12 53	19 12	...	...	...	...	...

LES ARCS and DRAGUIGNAN.

Les Arcs .... dep	4 5	8 19	10 49	12 39	15 16	1654	1920	21 41
Draguignan (47)...arr	4 28	8 43	11 25	13 3	15 40	1725	1944	22 4

Draguignan ...dep	2 38	7 15	9 32	11 59	1433	1558	18 0	20 55
Les Arcs (55)...arr	2 55	7 35	10 10	12 19	1453	1618	18 28	21 15

DOLE and CHAGNY.

Dist							
	Dole (56) ......dep	4 30	6 50	10 35	16 5	20 48	...
28	St.Bonnet-en-Bresse	5 53	8 7	11 37	17 47	21 55	...
39¾	Allerey (56)...........	6 23	8 33	12 3	18 14	22 18	...
52¼	**Chagny**...........arr	6 59	10 0	13 12	19 4	...	...

Chagny ....dep	4 23	7 5	12 18	16 30	...	...	...	...	...	...
Allerey	5 19	7 47	13 13	17 16	19 32	...	...	...	...	...
St. Bonnet-en-Bresse	6 0	8 13	13 43	18 0	20 20	...	...	...	...	...
Dole ....arr	7 10	9 25	15 2	19 23	21 31	...	...	...	...	...

GRAY and CHALON-SUR-SAÔNE.

Dist								
	Gray (66, 74) dep	...	5 33	8 37	14 32	...	18 29	2110
23	**Auxonne**........arr	...	6 26	9 37	15 35	...	19 30	22 8
...	,, ...dep	...	7 10	10 32	16 18	...	—	—
30½	St.Jean-de-Los, 63B	...	7 47	11 11	16 58	...	...	...
39¾	Seurre	...	8 14	11 40	17 25	...	...	...
51½	Allerey (56)	6 29	8 56	12 27	18 28	22 24	...	...
62¾	**Chalon**-Ville ...arr	6 56	9 25	13 0	19 5	22 48	...	...

Chalon-Ville 48 dp	...	4 30	6 58	...	12 30	...	16 35	18 55	...
Allerey	...	5 13	7 27	...	13 39	...	17 4	19 24	...
Seurre	...	5 46	—	...	14 23	...	18 16	—	...
St. Jean-de-Losne......	...	6 15	...	...	14 52	...	18 47	...	...
Auxonne ....arr	...	6 49	...	...	15 25	...	19 20	...	...
,, ...dep	3 0	7 31	...	1022	—	16 30	—	...	20 8
Gray ....arr	4 11	8 31	...	1122	...	17 32	...	...	21 7

DOLE and POLIGNY.

E.M.					
	Dole (53) ....dep	8 5	10 50	17 53	...
13¾	Mont-sous-Vaudrey	8 43	11 27	18 35	...
25¼	**Poligny (53)** ....arr	9 19	12 3	19 11	...

Poligny ....dep	6 12	13 0	20 37	...	...	...	...	...
Mont-sous-Vaudrey	6 49	13 32	21 9	...	...	...	...	...
Dole ....arr	7 27	14 10	21 46	...	...	...	...	...

Extra.—St. Etienne to Lyons 4.43, 13.6, Lyons to St. Etienne 0.3.

ROANNE to SAINT-ETIENNE and LYONS (Perrache).

Roanne ......dep		3 47	5 15	7 51	9 1	...	...	1330	1618	...	1820	1921	2011	...
Balbigny		...	6 10	...	9 55	...	...	1422	...	...	19 4	...	21 2	...
Feurs.................		...	6 27	8 40	1014	...	...	1442	...	...	1915	...	2119	...
Montrond (62)		4 37	6 46	8 56	1035	...	...	15 5	17 6	...	1929	...	2135	...
St. Galmier		...	6 58	9 7	1049	...	...	1520	...	...	1941	...	2147	...
St. Just (63B)...		4 54	7 12	...	11 6	13 2	...	1538	1723	1745	...	...	22 0	2255
St.-Etienne...ar		5 10	7 38	9 37	1137	1332	...	16 7	1736	18 6	2010	2037	2230	2315
,, 52A, 63B dep		6 42	8 0	10 5	1220	1431	1534	17 0	—	1829	2048	—	—	2340
St.-Chamond ...		7 3	8 17	1022	1241	1453	1550	1723	...	1851	2113	...	...	0 0
Rive-de-Gier ...		7 22	8 33	1038	13 2	1513	16 3	1745	...	1912	2134	...	...	0 14
Givors	6 26	7 48	8 49	11 0	1331	1540	1618	1813	1750	1941	22 1	...	1955	0 31
Lyons ...arr	7 14	8 21	9 21	1150	1359	1634	1649	1857	1838	20 7	2252	...	2050	0 59
Givors......dep		7 55	1024	...	1429	...	1645	...	...	1945	...	...	...	...
Chasse 50 arr		8 8	1039	...	1443	..	17 0	...	...	1958	...	...	...	...

Lyons ...dep	...	...	4 4	7 6	7 27	9 46	1112	14 2	1310	16 3	1734	1823	2115
Givors.........	...	...	4 39	7 37	8 19	1021	12 7	1450	14 6	1636	18 6	1916	2149
Rive-de-Gier	...	...	5 11	7 52	8 48	1044	1236	—	1435	1654	1827	1946	2220
St. Chamond	...	...	5 41	8 7	9 14	1111	13 1	...	15 4	1716	1849	2013	2248
St. Etienne a	...	...	6 28	8 22	9 36	1130	1323	...	1526	1736	19 8	2036	2310
,, dep	4 47	6 18	6 38	—	10 0	1152	1445	14 8	1612	1816	20 5	21 0	—
St. Just	5 12	...	6 58	...	1025	1215	...	1429	1632	1838	...	2124	...
St. Galmier	5 26	...	7 8	...	1038	—	...	1440	1646	1853	...	—	...
Montrond ...	5 39	...	7 21	...	1053	...	1510	1521	17 4	1913	2033	...	...
Feurs	5 57	...	7 35	...	11 7	...	...	1533	1720	1931	...	...	...
Balbigny......	6 13	...	7 49	...	1118	...	...	1544	1736	1945	...	...	...
Roanne 58 ar	7 6	7 25	8 26	...	12 3	...	1554	1621	1828	2034	2124	...	...
Chasse dep	...	...	...	7 3	...	9 26	1127	...	...	1530	...	1844	2051
Givors ...ar	...	...	...	7 17	...	9 39	1141	...	...	1545	...	1857	21 4

†—1st class only.]

PARIS and MONTARGIS.

Paris ....dep	6 35	8 15	10 0	12 0	1520	18 5	20†15	2025	21 0	2235	0 35
Juvisy	7 9	...	1033	1232	1552	...	...	21 7	2145	...	1 14
Corbeil	7 33	†	1054	1256	1617	1851	...	2137	22 5	2322	1 43
La Ferté Alais	8 4	...	1124	1326	1651	1923	...	22 9	—	2352	2 40
Malesherbes......	8 46	9 33	12 7	1410	1740	2010	21 23	2246	...	0 27	4 5
Auxy-B.la Rolande	9 23	9 57	1245	1449	1822	2049	...	—	...	—	5 10
Montargis ...arr	9 51	1020	1313	1517	1858	2118	22 2	...	...	...	6 10

Montargis........dep	4 32	...	8 16	...	1055	13 0	15†28	...	1754	21†18	2252	...
Auxy-B. la Rolande	5 2	...	8 46	...	1127	1331	...	...	1823	21 39	2336	...
Malesherbes	6 0	6 59	9 26	9 38	1215	1422	16 22	1745	19 7	22 5	0 15	...
La Ferté-Alais	6 42	7 31	...	1015	1250	15 1	16 47	1821	1945	...	...	...
Corbeil	7 26	8 10	1014	1053	1329	1541	17 11	19 4	2023	22 45	1 6	...
Juvisy	7 41	8 24	...	1115	...	...	...	1929	2045	...	1 23	...
Paris.................arr	8 11	8 46	1049	1158	14 8	1618	17 45	2016	2115	23 15	2 5	...

MORET and MALESHERBES.

Dist. E.M.					
	Moret (58).........dep	6 29	12 19	16 22	19 59
7½	Bourron..................	6 46	12 42	16 44	20 20
24¼	Malesherbes......arr	7 20	13 41	17 27	21 4

Malesherbes ...dep	5 50	9 44	14 21	20 13
Bourron	6 26	10 52	15 5	21 4
Moret.............arr	6 41	11 16	15 25	21 25

NEVERS and LAROCHE.

Nevers...dep	...	4 18	9 0	...	1340	...	19 7
Guerigny	...	4 44	9 27	...	1415	...	1932
Clamecy ...	...	6 30	1140	13 2	1620	...	2113
Cravant	558	7 35	1252	1525	1740	2012	2223
Auxerre arr	626	8 3	1320	1557	18 8	2036	2251
,, dep	7 5	8 12	1330	1610	1816	2047	23 3
Chemilly	723	8 30	1348	1635	1834	21 3	2321
Laroche arr	735	8 42	14 0	1650	1846	2113	2333

Laroche	2 42	5 52	8 0	1053	1455	18 0	2045
Chemilly ...	2 56	6 5	8 11	11 6	15 8	1813	2056
Aux-erre arr	3 14	6 22	8 26	1123	1525	1830	2111
dep	3 24	6 44	9 5	1135	1533	1838	2120
Cravant......	4 2	7 24	9 29	1217	16 1	1922	2144
Clamecy	5 41	8 46	—	1335	17 5	21 0	—
Guerigny ...	7 12	1017	...	1525	—	2240	...
Nevers arr	7 35	1040	...	1555	...	23 5	...

Extra.—Auxerre to Laroche, 5.20. Laroche to Auxerre, 23.25.

LIVRON and VEYNES.

Livron dep	6 53	10 42	16 53	20 25	...
Crest	7 24	11 16	17 45	21 4	...
Saillans	7 50	11 43	18 24	21 43	...
Die..........dep	8 29	12 55	19 57	22 30	...
La Beaume...	9 40	15 11	21 24	—	...
Aspres..........	10 0	15 38	21 47	...	...
Veynes arr	10 10	15 51	22 2	...	...

Veynes dep	...	5 45	...	13 7	16 35
Aspres..........	...	6 0	...	13 29	16 47
La Beaume...	...	6 30	...	14 12	17 9
Die	4 30	8 0	12 25	16 10	18 22
Saillans	5 25	8 43	13 17	—	18 57
Crest	6 1	9 18	14 4	...	19 29
Livron arr	6 29	9 46	14 49	...	19 54

NIMES and LE GRAU-DU-ROI.

Nimes.........dep	5 15	7 10	11 13	1610	19 5
St.-Cesaire	5 22	7 17	11 20	1617	19 12
Le Cailar 57......	6 2	8 23	12 2	1728	20 0
Aimargues	6 9	8 31	12 11	1737	20 10
Aigues Mortes...	6 32	8 56	12 35	18 6	20 40
Grau du Roi arr	6 46	9 10	12 49	1820	20 54

Grau du Roi dp	4 5	7 27	11 5	1635	19 53
Aigues-Mortes	4 20	7 50	11 21	1652	20 10
Aimargues	5 3	8 14	12 15	1715	20 38
Le Cailar.........	5 11	8 22	12 23	1725	20 48
St.-Cesaire	5 57	9 4	13 5	18 9	21 35
Nimes.........arr	6 4	9 11	13 12	1816	21 42

Excess Luggage, 1 cent. per 44lbs. per kilometre.] **PARIS, LYONS, MEDITERRANEAN RY.**

ARLES and TARASCON to MONTPELLIER and CETTE.

§—Takes 2nd and 3rd class travelling at least 31 or 47 miles respectively.

	1,2,3	1,2,3	1,2,3	1,2,3	1,2,3	1,2,3	1,2,3	1,2,3	1,2,3	1,2,3	1,2,3	1,2,3	1,2,3	1,2,3	1,2,3
MARSEILLES 50 dep	...	...	...	4 45	...	...	8 10	...	...	...	11 50	18 0	...	...	...
Arles ...dep	...	...	4 0	7 13	...	...	1040	...	...	...	16 12	1935	...	...	...
Saint-Gilles	...	...	4 27	7 40	...	...	11 9	...	...	...	16 41	20 2	...	...	...
Le Cailar 56	...	...	4 58	8 13	...	...	1141	...	...	...	17 15	2034	...	...	...
Aimargues	...	...	5 5	8 21	...	...	1150	...	...	...	17 21	2041	...	...	...
Lunel ...arr	...	...	5 18	8 38	...	...	12 5	...	...	...	17 34	2055	...	...	...
MARSEILLES 50 dp	2328	...	...	...	6 0	8 10	8 10	1017	1150	...	...	1412	18 0	19 55	2035
Tarascon ...dep	2 58	3 38	4 27	6 15	8 6	9 49	1014	1317	14 7	...	16 40	1750	2032	21 44	23 7
Beaucaire	...	3 44	4 31	6 20	...	...	1018	...	1411	...	16 44	1755	2037	...	...
Manduel	...	...	4 51	6 44	...	§	1041	...	1435	...	17 7	1822	21 1	...	...
Nimes ...arr	3 4	4 12	5 0	7 0	8 35	1016	1056	1343	1450	...	17 20	1838	2117	22 10	2333
„ (56)...dep	3 16	4 35	5 25	8 0	8 45	1026	1127	1353	15 3	16 54	17 30	2020	—	22 20	2354
Vergèze	...	...	5 56	8 31	...	...	1158	...	1533	17 25	...	2053	...	...	...
Lunel ...dep	3 43	5 4	6 21	9 18	9 11	1050	1223	1417	1556	18 2	17 55	2123	...	22 45	0 22
Montpellier...arr	4 4	5 27	7 4	10 1	9 34	1111	13 8	1438	1633	18 45	18 16	22 6	...	23 6	0 47
„ (57) dep	4 16	5 56	7 17	1011	9 44	1121	1320	1447	1655	19 5	18 25	2232	...	23 16	0 57
Frontignan	4 36	6 27	7 47	1040	...	...	1351	...	1729	19 37	...	23 0	...	...	...
Cette (45B) ...arr	4 45	6 37	7 57	1050	1010	1145	14 1	1512	1738	19 47	18 49	2310	...	23 40	1 30
BORDEAUX ...arr	1648	...	1757	1920	1920	1920	...	...	5 17	...	5 17	...	...	7 39	...
PORT BOU ...arr	1138	...	1138	1530	1530	1530	...	2017	...	...	...	...	...	3 36	...
BARCELONA 295 arr	1540	...	1540	1932	1932	1932	...	...	...	...	...	...	...	7 53	...

		1,2,3	1,2,3	1,2,3	1,2,3	1,2,3	1,2,3	1,2,3	1,2,3	1,2,3	1,2,3	1,2,3	1,2,3	1,2,3	1,2,3	1,2,3
BARCELONA 295 dep		1851	...	...	...	...	...	...	...	...	...	...	5 0	10 0	...	14 16
CERBERE 46 ...dep		23 5	...	...	...	...	...	5 50	...	9 75	...	...	12 33	14 17	...	18 30
BORDEAUX 45B dep		1950	...	...	...	...	2215	...	...	7 40	...	...	8 0	8 0	8 0	10 56
Cette ...dep		3 0	...	4 5	6 0	7 20	9 45	1050	1310	1440	15 0	1735	17 45	18 55	1955	22 30
Frontignan		...	...	4 14	6 11	7 29	9 54	...	1319	§	15 9	...	17 56	...	20 7	22 39
Montpellier ...arr		3 25	...	4 33	6 39	7 57	1023	1112	1348	15 3	1539	1758	18 26	19 18	2038	22 57
„ ...dep		3 31	...	4 40	6 49	8 7	1038	1121	1358	1513	1551	18 6	18 36	19 28	2055	23 7
Lunel ...arr		3 52	...	5 22	7 31	8 29	1120	1140	1440	1532	1634	1825	19 20	19 47	2138	23 27
Vergèze		...	...	5 44	7 59	...	—	...	15 6	...	17 6	...		...	22 7	...
Nimes ...arr		4 20	...	6 15	8 30	9 0	...	12 6	1537	1558	1739	1850		20 13	2240	23 55
„ ...dep	2 30	4 31	4 45	6 25	—	9 20	...	1216	1627	16 8	1826	1858		20 23	—	0 28
Manduel		...	4 59	6 41	...	9 36	...	...	1643	...	1843			...		...
Beaucaire		...	5 20	7 2	...	9 57	...	...	17 4	...	19 5			...		0 50
Tarascon (49)	2 57	4 53	5 23	7 5	...	10 0	...	1238	17 7	1633	19 8			20 45		0 53
MARSEILLES	4 50	6 50	8 10	8 43	...	...	...	1438	2021	1820	2351			0 9		
Lunel ...dep		4 40	...	...	7 45	...	...	1149	...	...	1648		19 40	...		
Aimargues		4 55	...	...	8 23	...	...	12 4	...	...	1727		19 58	...		
Le Cailar		5 1	...	...	8 31	...	...	1211	...	...	1737		20 7	...		
Saint-Gilles		5 31	...	...	9 3	...	...	1241	...	...	1812		20 43	...		
Arles (49) ...arr		5 55	...	...	9 27	...	...	13 5	...	...	1836	...	21 9	...		
MARSEILLES ...arr		8 10	...	...	1244	...	...	1438	...	...	...	...	23 51	...		

To Avignon arr. 19.46.

Extra.—Lunel to Nimes, 12.14. Nimes to Tarascon, 12.44.

NUITS-RAVIERES and CHATILLON-SUR-SEINE.									
Nuits-Raviers	8 9	16 12	22 0	...	**Chatillon**	5 44	13 20	1947	...
Laignes	8 42	17 4	22 45	...	Ste. Colombe	5 57	13 26	1953	...
Ste. Colombe	9 12	17 50	23 16	...	Laignes	6 43	14 3	2026	...
Châtillon arr	9 16	17 55	23 21	...	**Nuits-Raviers**	7 25	14 42	2059	...

ANDELOT and MOREZ.												
Andelot 53 dep	5 5	10 35	14 57	1757	21 15	**Morez** dep	4 37	7 19	1435	...	1715	...
Champagnole	5 37	11 11	15 35	1835	21 36	St. Laurent	5 10	7 50	15 6	...	1746	...
St. Laurent	6 30	12 0	16 23	1923	—	Champagnole	6 14	8 34	1610	17 7	1850	...
Morez ...arr	7 0	12 30	16 53	1953	...	**Andelot** arr	6 37	10 3	1633	1730	1 13	...

Champagnole ...dep	6 24	8 44	1841	...	...	Lons-le-Saunier ...dep	8 12	1657	2027	...	...	...	...
Lons-le-Saunier ...arr	7 42	10 3	20 1[illegible]	...	...	Champagnole ...arr	9 30	1813	2147	...	...	...	...

TAMNAY-CHATILLON and CHATEAU-CHINON							
Tamnay-Chatillon dep	4 45	9 40	1556	Chateau-Chinon ...dep	6 10	12 0	17 45
Chateau-Chinon ...arr	5 34	1029	1645	Tamnay-Chatillon 63B arr	6 59	1249	18 34

AUBAGNE and LA BARQUE.

Aubagne ...dep	6 21	11 40	14 44	...	18 30	19 44	**La Barque** ...dep	5 18	...	11 38	...	18 23	...
Valdonne	7 22	12 55	15 55	16 56	19 16	20 30	Valdonne	6 29	7 51	12 59	16 50	19 35	...
La Barque ...arr	8 22	...	16 51	17 51	...	...	**Aubagne** ...arr	7 8	8 58	13 38	17 29	20 18	...

ST. ANDRE-LE-GAZ and CHAMBERY.										
St. André-le-Gaz	632	8 37	11 25	1418	1855	**Chambéry**	610	8 32	121[illegible]	1541	2042
Pressins	653	8 55	11 44	1435	1914	Lepin	643	9 7	1249	1615	2116
Pont de Beauvoisin	7 3	9 5	11 54	1145	1926	St. Béron 53B	654	9 2[illegible]	13 0	1626	212[illegible]
St. Béron	714	9 17	12 6	1456	1939	Pont de Beauvoisin	7 5	9 32	1310	1636	2140
Lepin	724	9 27	12 16	15 8	1950	Pressins	716	9 42	1319	1644	2148
Chambéry	753	9 56	12 46	1538	2020	**S. André-le-Gaz** arr	733	10 0	1335	17 0	22 4

ST. ANDRE-LE-GAZ and VIRIEU-LE-GRAND.

St. André-le-Gaz dep	...	6 58	...	...	1432	1744	...	...	Virieu-le-Grand dep	5 32	8 23	9 50	1322	1718	21 45	...
Pressins	...	7 18	...	...	15 2	18 5	...	...	Belley	5 54	8 50	11 0	1349	18 6	22 8	...
Aoste	...	7 36	...	...	1535	1823	...	...	Aoste	6 32	—	1230	—	1850	—	...
Belley	7 22	8 26	1153	1535	1655	1914	2055	...	Pressins	6 55	...	1253	...	1917	...	...
Virieu-le-Grand ..arr	7 44	8 51	1227	16 0	...	1937	2115	...	St. André-le-Gaz arr	7 15	...	1320	...	1934	...	...

CERCY-LA-TOUR and GILLY-SUR-LOIRE. (53A)												
Cercy-la-T.	6 25	8 25	...	1452	20 5	**Gilly** ...dep	5 55	9 30	10 54	1430	1755
Bourbon-Lancy	8 24	9 59	1159	1624	2116	Bourbon-Lan.	6 21	9 56	11 15	1558	1838
Gilly (63) arr	8 50	1025	1220	1650	2140	**Cercy-T.** arr	7 44	...	13 49	1655	1940

Montpellier and Sommières.

Montpellier dep	5 50	9 10	14 8	18 48
Castries	6 12	9 32	14 30	19 5
Sommières 53B ar	6 40	10 0	14 58	19 33
Sommières ...dep	7 20	11 3	15 55	20 52
Castries	7 49	11 32	16 24	21 25
Montpellier ...arr	8 10	11 53	16 45	21 47

MONTBELIARD and DELLE.

Montbéliard ...dep	6 5	9 12	11 44	16 20	19 24	Delle ...dep	7 19	10 5	13 25	17 3	20 42
Beaucourt	6 32	9 39	12 14	16 49	19 53	Morvillars	7 34	10 20	13 40	17 18	20 57
Morvillars	6 50	9 55	12 30	17 5	20 11	Beaucourt	7 54	10 39	13 58	17 39	21 16
Delle (266) ...arr	7 6	10 9	12 44	17 19	20 26	Montbéliard ...arr	8 17	11 2	14 20	18 4	21 38

STE. CECILE d'ANDORGE and FLORAC.							
Ste. Cecile d'Andorge...dep	8 30	1145	19 45	Florac.........dep	5 0	7 51	16 30
Florac ....arr	11 2	1415	22 15	Ste. Cecile ...arr	7 17	10 10	18 47

A—Takes from Paris down to Riom 2nd & 3rd Cl. travelling at least 93 miles or to or from branch lines.
C—At St. Germain takes up 1st class only or to or from branch lines.
D—Between Paris and Moulins takes up for Gannat and beyond only; between Gannat and Le Breuil admits 2nd and 3rd class for beyond Arvant only; from La Levade forward admits 2nd and 3rd class for beyond Nimes only. Exceptionally admits all passengers to and from branch lines.
F—Admits 2nd class travelling 55 miles and 3rd class travelling 186 miles; also admits for beyond Gannat towards Montlucon (3rd class must be travelling at least 62 miles).
V—**Vichy Express.** Train de Luxe; runs until 7th September. Take tickets in advance of Sleeping Car Co. Extra fare, Paris to Vichy 12 fr.

PARIS, ST. GERMAIN-DES-FOSSES, and VICHY, CLERMONT FERRAND, ALAIS, NIMES.

Dist. E.M From Paris	1 Cl. fr. c.	2 Cl. fr. c.		2 & 3	1,2,3	1,2,3	1,2,3	1,2,3	1,2,3	1,2,3	1,2,3	1,2,3	1,2,3	1,2,3	1,2,3	1 Cl	1,2,3	1,2,3	Lux	1,2,3	1,2,3	1,2,3	1,2,3 ‡	1,2,3	1,2,3
			Paris Boulevard Diderot dp	...	...	...	...	...	...	...	...	...	7 25	8 15	...	1110	1115	1230	16 0	...	...	17 5	2015	2030	22‡10
36¾	6 60	5 45	**Fontainebleau**	...	...	...	...	...	...	...	...	...	8 35	A	...	12 0	1229	...	...	...	...	1814	...	...	
41¾	7 50	5 5	**Moret**	...	...	...	...	...	...	...	...	5 47	8 48		...	...	1242	...	...	...	...	1830	...	...	
49	8 85	5 95	Bourron	...	...	...	...	...	...	...	...	6 4	9 4	Via Males'bes	...	E	1259	...	V	...	...	1848	...	D	Via Males'bes
54	9 75	6 60	Nemours	...	...	...	...	...	...	...	...	6 17	9 17		...	...	1311	...	...	...	...	19 2	...	...	
60¼	10 85	7 35	Souppes (63)	...	...	...	...	...	...	...	...	6 31	9 31		...	...	1324	RC	...	...	...	1916	...	...	
73¼	13 20	8 90	**Montargis** arr	...	...	...	...	...	...	...	...	7 5	10 3	10 20	...	1250	1355	1412	1728	...	...	1947	22 2	2228	0 19
...	...	...	,, (56, 63B) dep	...	...	...	...	...	...	...	...	7 27	1040	10 23	...	1256	1430	1417	1732	...	...	2017	22 5	2231	0 22
96¼	17 35	11 70	**Gien** (35)	...	...	...	...	...	...	...	...	8 23	1234	10 59	...	...	1549	1451	...	...	...	2110	2239	...	1 1
102¼	18 50	12 45	Briare	...	...	...	...	...	...	...	...	8 35	1249	11 11	...	...	16 2	...	...	...	...	2123	...	...	1 13
121¾	21 95	14 80	Cosne 63B	...	...	4 55	6 2	...	...	...	...	9 28	1414	11 44	...	14 2	1654	1531	...	...	...	2210	2316	2343	1 46
127¼	22 95	15 50	Tracy-Sancerre	...	...	5 6	6 14	...	...	...	...	9 41	1426	11 56	...	...	17 6	...	...	...	...	2222	2327	...	...
141	25 40	17 15	La Charité	...	...	5 37	6 49	...	...	...	...	1016	15 4	12 19	...	...	1740	...	...	...	...	2256	2349	...	2 20
149½	27 0	18 20	Pougues-les-Eaux	...	...	5 52	7 9	...	...	...	...	1030	1525	12 34	...	1443	18 0	...	19 5	...	...	2313	0 2	...	...
157¾	28 45	19 20	**Nevers** (53A, 56)	...	4 10	6 8	7 27	11 55	13 30	...	...	1054	1545	12 48	1525	1455	1818	1624	1917	1933	21 0	2331	0 14	0 37	2 47
164	29 55	19 95	**Saincaize** (37)	...	4 39	6 47	8 4	12 6	13 40	...	...	1132	1710	RC	1535	...	2025	...	...	1944	2118		0 36	...	...
174½	31 45	21 25	St. Pierre-le-Moutier	...	4 55	7 14				...	...	12 9	1749	13 41		...	2126	...	...			...	0 54	D	...
194¼	35 5	23 65	**Moulins-s-Allier** arr	...	5 21	7 53	...	...	...	...	...	1246	1828	14 10	...	1552	2232	1724	20 6	...	...	...	1 19	1 39	3 49
...	...	...	,, (37)...dep	...	5 24	8 21	...	...	...	...	...	1258	1852	14 14	1521	1554		1726	20 7	...	...	...	1 30	1 42	4 3
212½	38 30	25 80	Varennes-s.-Allier	...	5 50	9 3	...	...	...	...	...	1340	1933	14 44	1554	...	...	...	...	...	...	...	...	...	...
220½	39 75	26 85	**St. Germ.-d-Fos.** arr	...	6 2	9 21	...	...	...	...	...	1359	1952	14 57	16 8	1626	...	18 1	2039	...	...	...	2 4	2 19	4 41
...	...	...	**St. Germain** dep	...	6 30	9 48	...	...	...	...	...	1520	20 4	15 20	1622	1634	...	1816	2040	...	...	...	3 0	3 0	4 56
226¾	40 90	27 60	**Vichy** arr	...	6 45	10 6	...	...	...	...	...	1535	2019	15 35	1637	1654	...	1830	2054	...	...	...	3 15	3 15	5 11
Frm	S. G'	ma'n	**St. Germain** dep	...	...	...	...	7 39	10 19	...	1325	1434	...	15 13	1639	...	...	18 9	...	...	2020	2053	...	2 34	5 3
3½	0 35	0 25	Saint Remy	...	...	...	...	7 49	10 30	...	F	1445	...	...	...	...	...	...	...	...	C	21 3	...	...	...
14¾	2 70	1 80	**Gannat** (36) arr	...	...	...	...	8 17	10 59	...	1347	1516	...	15 39	17 6	...	...	1832	...	...	2047	2132	...	3 4	5 27
...	...	...	,, dep	6 26	...	...	...	8 37	11 15	12 1		1610	...	15 44	17 8	...	...	1833	...	...		2138	...	3 7	5 31
21¾	3 90	2 65	Aigueperse	6 46	...	...	...	8 53	11 32	...	...	1628	...	...	...	...	...	...	...	...	...	2153	...	...	5 44
32¼	5 80	3 95	Riom 46A, 59	7 18	...	...	...	9 17	11 56	1227	...	1659	...	16 10	1744	...	...	1856	...	...	...	2214	...	3 35	6 12
36	6 50	4 40	Gerzat	7 32	...	...	...	9 30	12 12	...	...	1713	...	...	...	...	...	...	...	...	...	2226	...	...	6 20
40½	7 30	4 90	**Clermont-** arr	7 46	...	...	...	9 40	12 22	1242	...	1723	...	16 30	1759		...	1912	2&3	...	...	2236	...	3 54	6 29
...	...	...	**Ferrand** (63B) ...dep		...	...	7 0	10 12	13 10	...	...	1830	...	16 55			...		20 0	...	...		...	4 8	
49¾	8 95	6 5	Les Martres-de-Veyres	...	...	...	7 27	10 38	13 33		...	1858	...	...	...		...	...	2036	...	...	...	...	4 28	...
62	11 20	7 55	Issoire	...	...	...	8 2	11 11	14 7		...	1937	...	17 40	...		...	...	2129	...	...	...	...	4 58	...
67¾	12 20	8 25	Le Breuil	...	...	...	8 19	11 26	14 22		...	1955	...	...	...		...	...	...	...	...	...	...	5 10	...
77¾	14 0	9 45	**Arvant** arr	...	...	...	8 48	11 32	14 47		...	2024	...	18 12	2&3		...	...	22 3	...	...	...		5 33	...
...	...	...	,, (45A) dep	...	...	...	8 59	12 1	14 58		...		...	18 40	2055		...	...		...	...	...		5 36	...
84	15 10	10 20	Brioude	...	...	...	9 26	12 22	15 26		...	...	...	19 5	2135		...	...	...	...	...	...		6 0	...
98¾	17 80	12 0	St. Georges d'Aurac 52A	...	...	...	10 8		16 5		...	...	...	19 50	2231		...	...		...	...	...		6 40	...
103	18 60	12 55	**Langeac** (52A)	...	...	...	10 27	...	16 24		...	...	...	19 58	2247		...	...		...	...	...		6 57	...
144¾	26 10	17 60	Langogne 52A	...	5 25	...	13 2	17 35			...	...	...	22 3	...		...			...	...	...		8 55	...
156½	28 20	19 5	La Bastide St. L.	...	6 0	...	13 41	18 9	...		...	...	...	22 54	...		...			...	...	...		9 31	...
169½	30 60	20 65	Villefort	...	6 41	...	14 18	18 46	...		...	...	...	23 30	...		...			...	...	...		10 6	...
177¾	32 5	21 60	Genolhac	...	7 4	...	14 44	19 9	...		...	...	...	23 55	...		...			...	...	...		1029	...
185¼	33 40	22 55	Ste. Cecile d'Andorge	...	7 32	...	15 11	19 38	...		...	...	...	...	...		...			...	...	...		1052	...
188¼	33 95	22 90	La Levade 4 55	...	7 45	11 14	15 23	19 49	...	...	...	...	...	0 28	...		...			...	...	...		11 2	...
190	34 25	23 15	Grand Combe La P.5 5	...	7 54	11 24	15 32	19 58	...	...	...	...	...	0 36	...		...			...	...	...		11 9	...
198¾	35 85	24 20	**Alais** arr5 39	...	8 22	12 12	15 57	20 25	...	...	...	...	...	0 59	...		...			...	...	...		1132	...
...	...	...	,, (62A) dep	6 2	8 40	13 3	16 27		19 0	...	...	2123	...	1 8	...		...			...	...	...		1140	...
205	36 95	24 95	Mas-de-Gardies	6 19	8 57	13 20	16 48	...	...	...	...	2145	...	...	...	...	...			...	...	...		...	...
211¾	38 20	25 80	**Nozières** (63B)	6 43	9 21	13 44	17 13	...	19 23	...	...	2211	...	1 27	...	...	...			...	...	...		12 0	...
216¾	39 10	26 40	Fons	6 57	9 35	13 59	17 28	...	...	...	...	2226	...	...	...	...	...			...	...	...	...	...	...
229¼	41 35	27 90	**Nimes** (57) arr	7 28	10 6	14 31	18 0	...	19 59	...	...	2258	...	2 4	...	...	...			...	...	...	...	1234	...
277¼	...	...	CETTE arr	10 10	1145	17 38	23 10	...	23 10	...	...	1 30	...	4 45	...	...	...	...		...	...	...	...	1512	...
489¾	...	...	BARCELONA (295) arr	...	1926	...	7 53	...	7 53	...	...	...	...	15 40	...	...	...	...	...	...	...	...	...	...	...

Thursday only until 28th August. To Royat.

E—Only admits for beyond Montargis. *Runs until 29th September.*

‡—Admits at Paris 2 & 3 Cl. for Gien and beyond only.

RC—Restaurant Car attached.

Extra. { Nevers ......dep 18 10 / Saincaize...arr 18 21

*—Until 29th Sept. **RIOM and CHATEL-GUYON.** ‡—Until 30th Sept.

Riom ....dep	6 20	7 53	9 30	1040	13‡25	1623	1755	19*10	2230	Chatel G. dep	5 41	6 56	8 36	10 1	1130	12‡26	1525	1659	18*34	2148
Chatel Guyon arr	6 39	8 12	9 49	1059	13 51	1645	1817	19 29	2249	Riom.......arr	5 55	7 10	8 50	1015	1144	12 40	1539	1713	18 48	22 2

BRIOUDE and ST. FLOUR.										
	Brioude..............dep	6 3	7 5	12 54	19 10	St. Flour ....dep	5 12	12 5	16 53	18 20	...
	St. Flour 45A ......arr	7 38	9 3	14 44	20 57	Brioude 58 ....arr	6 58	13 49	18 44	19 45	...

H—Will not take 2nd or 3rd class for St. Germain.
J—From Brioude forward only admits 2nd and 3rd class travelling at least 93 miles, or those from or for branch lines.
K—From Issoire takes only 2nd and 3rd cl. travelling not less than 93 miles, or those from or for branch lines.
L—Admits 2nd and 3rd class travelling 93 miles or from or for branch lines.
V—Vichy Express, Train de Luxe, until 8th September.
RC—Restaurant Car attached.

NIMES, SAINT GERMAIN-DES-FOSSES, and PARIS.

BARCELONA 295 dep	...	...	...	...	...	...	...	...	1416	...	...	...	...	...	1851	...	...	...	...	...	...	...	...	...	10 0	...
CETTE 57 ....dep	...	...	...	...	...	...	...	...	2280	...	...	...	...	...	3 0	...	...	...	4 5	7 20	1050	...	10 50	1440	1855	...
	1,2,3	1,2,3	2&3	1,2,3	1,2,3	1,2,3	Lux	1,2,3	1,2,3	1,2,3	1,2,3	1 Cl	1,2,3	1,2,3	1,2,3	1,2,3	1,2,3	1,2,3	1,2,3	1,2,3	1,2,3	1,2,3	1,2,3	1,2,3	1,2,3	1,2,3
Nimes..............dep	...	...	...	...	...	...	...	...	0 15	...	...	Runs until 30th September. Will not take up beyond Cosne except at Montargis, where 1st class from branch lines are admitted.		...	4 55	...	From Royat; runs on Thursday only until 28th August. Takes passengers only, no luggage.		7 50	9 26	§ 1228	...	12 50	1615	2040	...
Fons	...	...	...	...	...	...	...	...	...	...	...			...	5 29	...			8 24	...	...	...	13 24	1650	2114	...
Nozières 63B	...	...	...	...	...	...	...	...	0 51	...	...			...	5 44	...			8 39	10 1	13 1	...	13 39	17 6	2128	...
Mas-des-Gardies	...	...	...	...	...	...	...	...	...	...	...			...	6 9	...			9 4	1014	...	...	14 4	1731	2152	...
Alais .... arr	...	...	...	...	...	...	...	...	1 11	...	...			...	6 23	...			9 18	1025	1321	...	14 18	1745	22 6	...
dep	...	...	...	...	...	...	...	...	1 19	...	...			...		7 6			9 33		1330	...	14 50	18 5		2227
Grand Combe la Pise	...	...	...	...	...	...	...	...	1 46	...	...			...	...	7 37			10 3	...	1357	...	15 34	1837	...	23 5
La Levade	...	...	...	...	...	...	...	...	1 55	...	...			...	...	7 49			1014	...	14 6	...	15 42	1853	...	2313
Ste. Cecile d'Andorge	...	...	...	...	...	...	...	...	J	...	...			...	...	8 5			1029	...	1417	...	16*30	19 9	...	...
Genolhac	...	...	...	...	...	...	...	...	2 31	...	...			...	...	8 36			11 2	...	1443	...		1943	...	...
Villefort	...	...	...	...	...	...	...	...	3 3	...	...			...	...	9 15			1135	...	1517	...	...	2016	...	...
La Bastide St. L.	...	...	...	...	...	...	...	...	3 57	...	...			...	...	1015			1224	...	1615	...	...	2114	...	...
Langogne 52A..........	...	...	...	...	...	...	...	...	4 32	...	...			...	...	1044			1349	2&3	1640	17 5	...	2140	...	...
Langeac 52A	...	...	...	...	...	...	...	...	6 15	6 24	...			1135	...				1537	1915		1847	...		...	...
St. Georges d'Aurac...	...	...	...	...	...	...	...	...	6 33	6 37	7 5			1148	...	...			16 8	1953	...	1922	...	...	...	...
Brioude	...	...	...	...	...	...	...	4 36	7 9		7 56			1232	...	14 2			1645	2048	...	20 0	...	...	...	...
Arvant 31A...... arr	...	...	...	...	...	...	...	4 50	7 23	...	8 16			1252	...	1416			17 8	2119	...	2014	...	...	...	...
dep	...	...	...	...	...	...	...	5 1	7 29	...	8 52			13 3	...	1421			1724		...	2040	...	...	...	...
Le Breuil	...	...	...	...	...	...	...	5 27	...	...	9 17			1329	...	...			1751	...	...	...	...	...	...	...
Issoire	...	...	...	...	...	...	...	5 44	7 54	...	9 34			1349	...	1447			1811	1940	...	21 6	...	...	...	...
Les Martres-de-Veyres	...	...	...	...	Runs until 30th September.	L	...	6 13	J	...	10 7		...	1423	...	...		...	1845	2025	...	M	...	...	...	...
Clermont Ferr arr	...	...	...	...		...	...	6 39	8 33	...	1032		...	1451	...	1523		...	1915	21 5	...	2142	...	...	...	...
31A dep	...	...	4 20	...		7 10	...	7 20	8 52	10 7		1235	1250		...	1539	17 5	1715	1945		...	22 0	...	...	...	...
Gerzat	...	...	4 34	...		...	...	7 30	...	1016	...	...	13 2	...	...	K	...	1725	1955	...	...	...	...	...	...	...
Riom 59.................	...	...	4 49	...		7 25	...	7 43	9 9	1026	...	1256	1316	...	...	1554	1719	1737	20 8	...	...	2213	...	...	...	...
Aigueperse	...	...	5 20	...		...	...	8 10	...	1050	...	...	1342	...	...	...	...	18 4	2032	...	...	...	...	...	...	...
Gannat 36 ...... arr	...	...	5 36	...		7 49	...	8 22	9 33	11 1	...	1317	1354	...	...	1615	1743	1815	2044	...	...	2248	...	...	...	...
dep	...	...		5 45		7 50	...	8 35	9 35	11 3	...	1319	1357	...	1541	1618	1744	1823	2055	...	...	2250	...	...	...	...
Saint-Remy	...	...	...	H		...	...	9 1	...	1125	...	...	1422	...	O	...	...	1852	2122	...	...	...	...	...	...	...
St. Germain.........arr	...	...	1,2,3	6 7		8 13	V	9 10	9 58	1134	...	1340	1431	...	16 7	1644	18 7	19 2	2132	...	...	2313	...	...	...	...
Vichy ....dep	...	...	4 32	...	7 10	8 6	9 15	...	9 31	...	...	1333	14 0	...	...	1638	...	1925	...	...	2215	23 6	...	...	...	...
St. Germain...arr	...	...	4 47	...	7 25	8 21	9 30	...	9 46	...	...	1350	1415	...	...	1656	...	1940	...	...	2230	2321	...	...	...	...
St. Germ.-d.-F. ...dep	...	...	5 12	...	7 31	8 33	9 31	9 38	1017	...	...	14 0	1445	...	...	17 9	...	20 8	2150	...	2250	2331	...	...	...	...
Varennes-sur-Allier...	...	...	5 33	...	...	...	...	9 57	1031	...	...	...	15 4	...	...	K	...	...	2213	...	...	...	...	...	...	...
Moulins-sur-Allier arr	...	...	6 11	...	8 8	9 9	10 3	1033	11 0	...	...	1431	1539	...	...	1743	...	2041	2254	2&3	2326	0 11	...	...	...	...
dep	...	...	6 25	...		9 13	10 4	1048	1127	...	...	1433	1620	...	...	1748	...	2043		2120	2335	0 20	...	...	...	...
St. Pierre-le-Moutier	...	...	7 7	...	...	...	...	1126	1157	...	...	...	17 2	...	...	...	...	...	...	2225	0 3	...	...	...	...	...
Saincaize ....arr	4 30	...	7 30	9 5	...	L	...	1146	1214	1350	...	...	1723	...	...	1825	2048	2119	...	23 2	...	...	1‡35	...	...	...
Nevers ....arr	4 42	...	7 51	9 17	...	10 1	1047	1210	1231	14 9	...	1516	1746	16 6	...	1837	2110	2140	...	2350	0 26	1 15	1 45	...	...	...
Pougues-les-Eaux......	5 14	...	8 55		...	...	11 5	1329	13 0		...	1534	1932	1625	...	1913			...		0 52	...		...	...	...
La Charité	5 31	...	9 16	...	...	RC	...	1351	1317	...	...	...	1952	1644	...	1927	...	...	...	...	1 6	...	...	...	...	...
Tracy-Sancerre	6 0	...	9 47	...	...	...	...	1424	1342	...	...	...	2022	1713	...	RC	...	...	...	...	1 27	...	...	...	...	...
Cosne....................	6 19	...	10 5	...	...	11 9	V	1443	1357	...	...	16 7	2040	1723	...	1958	...	...	...	...	1 39	2 22	...	...	...	...
Briare	7 4	...	1051	...	...	...	...	1531	1429	...	...	...	2127		...	2025	...	...	...	...	...	...	...	...	...	...
Gien 53C	7 24	...	1116	...	...	1145	...	1553	1443	...	...	...	2147	...	...	2035	...	...	...	...	2 15	...	...	...	...	...
Montargis .... arr	8 7	...	12 0	...	...	1217	1232	1641	1521	...	...	17 1	2233	...	...	2113	...	...	...	...	2 47	3 34	...	...	...	...
dep	8 16	9 3	1320	...	...	1222	1235	1750	1528	1542	...	17 5	2252	...	...	2118	...	...	...	...	2 50	3 37	...	...	...	...
Souppes..................	Via Males'bes.	9 39	1357	...	...	Via Males'bes.	...	1826	Via Males'bes.	1614	...	...	Via Males'bes.	...	...	Via Males'bes.	...	...	...	...	Via Males'bes.	Via Males'bes	...	...	...	...
Nemours		9 56	1415	...	...		...	1842		1628	...	...		...	...		...	...	...	...			...	...	...	...
Bourron		10 7	1426	...	...		...	1853		1639	...	...		...	...		...	...	...	...			...	...	...	...
Moret		1024	1450	...	...		...	1913		1655	...	...		...	...		...	...	...	...			...	...	...	...
Fontainebleau		1042	15 8	...	...		...	1929		1710	...	1753		...	...		...	...	...	...			...	...	...	...
Paris ....arr	1049	1155	1635	...	...	1415	14 3	2038	1745	1820	...	1840	2 5	...	...	2315	...	...	...	...	4 40	5 40	...	...	...	...

§—Between Nimes and Grand Combe admits 2nd and 3rd class for beyond La Levade only.

M—From Issoire down to Riom takes 2nd and 3rd class only when travelling not less than 93 miles, or those from or for branch lines.

O—Admits passengers from Orleans Co.'s line (3rd class must be travelling at least 62 miles.)

*—Not on Sunday.

‡—On Monday, Tuesday, and Friday only.

MACON and GENEVA.—CULOZ, AIX-LES-BAINS, and MODANE.

[66 lbs. of Luggage free.

Dist.	1 Cl.	2 Cl.	3 Cl.	PARIS 48......dep	2050	1950	2110	2135	2215	...	2225	...	...	...	...
				MACON........arr	:	2 19	:	:	:	...	5 39	...	...	...	...
E.M.	fr. c.	fr. c.	fr. c.		1 &2	1& 2	1,2,3	1,2,3	1& 2	1,2,3	1,2,3	1,2,3	1,2,3		1,2,3
From Macon			...	**Macon** ....dep	Via St. Amour	2 30	Via St. Amour	Via St. Amour	Via St. Amour	3 55	6 20	...	9 9	Via St. Amour	...
5	0 90	0 60	0 40	Pont-de-Veyle		...				4 8	6 32	...	9 22		...
10½	1 90	1 30	0 85	Vonnas..............		G				4 20	6 42	...	9 34		...
13¾	2 45	1 65	1 10	Mézériat		...				4 28	6 49	...	9 42		...
17½	3 15	2 10	1 40	Polliat		...				4 38	6 58	...	9 52		...
23½	4 25	2 85	1 85	**Bourg 53, 62** arr	3 24	3 4	3 49	4 19	5 8	4 51	7 10	...	10 5	12 1	...
...	...	...	...	dep	3 27	—	4 3	4 22	5 10	5 17	7 23	...	1033	12 2	...
29¼	5 25	3 55	2 30	La Vavrette	...	...	...	...	...	5 32	...	...	1046	A	...
35¼	6 40	4 30	2 80	Pont d'Ain	...	...	F	B	D	5 50	7 45	...	11 5	...	...
42¾	7 75	5 20	3 40	**Amberieu**......arr	3 58	...	4 34	4 53	5 37	6 7	7 57	...	1122	1229	...
...	...	...	...	LYONS.........dep	2 30	...	2 30	...	3 46	5*56		7 0	1014	...	1230
...	...	...	...	**Amberieu**......dep	4 9	...	4 40	4 59	5 42	6 54		8 13	1146	1239	1330
49¾	8 95	6 05	3 95	St. Rambert en-B.	...	...	...	...	...	7 13	—	...	12 4	...	...
54	9 75	6 60	4 30	Tenay	...	...	...	...	...	7 25	...	8 37	1215	...	...
62½	11 30	7 65	5 0	Rossillon	E	...	...	...	D	7 45	...	...	1235	...	...
66¼	12 0	8 10	5 25	Virieu-le-Grand...	...	...	5 24	...	...	7 56	...	9 1	1247	...	...
74	13 35	9 0	5 85	**Culoz**......... arr	5 1	1,2,3	5 35	5 49	6 26	8 14	...	9 12	13 4	1325	1416
...	...	...	...	dep	5 12	6 14	:	6 0	:	8 30	...	9 24	1323	:	1430
83¼	15 0	10 15	6 60	Seyssel	...	6 36	:	...	:	8 51	...	...	1344	:	...
94½	17 0	11 50	7 50	**Bellegarde** ar	5 47	7 5	:	6 40	:	9 19	...	10 6	1412	:	15 5
...	...	...	...	*** 61A dp	To Evian (arr. 7.51.)	7 37	:	6 54	:	9 33	...	1016	1422	:	1511
101¼	18 25	12 30	8 5	Collongs-Ecluse		7 52	:	...	:	9 47	...	...	1436	:	...
103¼	18 60	12 55	8 20	Chancy (Switz)		8 0	:	...	:	9 55	...	...	1445	:	...
109¼	19 70	13 30	8 65	Satigny¶		9 17	:	...	:	1115	...	...	16 2	:	...
115½	20 85	14 5	9 15	**Geneva** ¶ ...arr		9 31	:	8 38	:	1130	...	12 3	1617	:	1551
					1 &2		1,2,3		1 &2	1,2,3	1 &2	1,2,3	1,2,3	:	1,2,3
...	...	...	...	**Culoz** ....dep	5 6	...	5 47	...	6 27	8 33	9 27	9 45	1347	1332	1445
87½	15 75	10 65	6 95	**Aix-les-Bains 47**... arr	5 26	...	6 7	...	6 47	9 1	9 47	1015	1418	1354	15 7
...	...	...	...	dep	To Chamonix (10.13). From July 2 to Sept. 20 only.	...	6 19	...	6 58	9 18	To Chamonix (arr. 14.53.)	1025	1429	1356	1514
90¾	16 35	11 5	7 20	Viviers		...	...	...	...	9 26		1033	1437	...	...
96¼	17 35	11 75	7 60	**Chambéry 62** arr		...	6 37	...	7 13	9 38		1045	1449	1412	1530
...	...	...	...	d'p		...	6 52	...	7 30	—		1112	—	1421	1612
102½	18 45	12 50	8 10	Chignin-les-Marc.		...	...	...	...	...		1125	...	...	1625
105	18 90	12 80	8 30	Montmelian		...	7 10	...	...	...		1135	...	...	1635
112	20 15	13 60	8 85	St. Pierre Alb. 62A		...	7 26	...	...	...		12 0	...	A	1657
114¼	20 70	14 0	9 10	Chamousset.........		...	—	...	...	...		12 7	...	...	17 6
126¼	22 70	15 35	10 0	Epierre		...	...	...	8 19	...	...	1234	...	1513	1733
140¼	25 30	17 10	11 10	St. Jean de Maur.		...	...	...	9 5	...	...	1321	...	1549	1823
148	26 65	18 0	11 70	St. Michel		...	...	...	...	...	...	1344	...	...	1846
154¼	27 75	18 75	12 20	La Praz		...	...	...	...	...	...	14 7	...	...	19 9
157¾	28 45	19 20	12 50	**Modane** *** ...arr		...	...	...	9 54	...	...	1420	...	1638	1922
...	...	...	...	MODANE It.Tm. dep		...	...	...	1130	...	...	16 5	...	1815	2137
222	42 20	28 90	19 0	TURIN 270 ...arr	...	...	...	...	14 5	...	...	19 7	...	2049	0 5

PARIS 48......dep	...	8 40	...	...	1135	...	...	9 15	...	1420	...
MACON........arr	...	:	...	...	:	...	...	1559	...	...	...
	1,2,3	1 &2	1,2,3		:			1,2,3	1,2,3	1,2,3	1,2,3
Macon ....dep	1236	Via St. Amour	...	...	Via St. Amour	...	...	1623	18 30	Via St. Amour	1945
Pont-de-Veyle	1249		...	...		...	...	1636	18 42		1958
Vonnas..............	13 3		...	...		...	...	1649	18 52		2010
Mézériat	1312		...	...		...	...	1657	18 59		2017
Polliat	1322		...	...		...	...	17 6	19 7		2026
Bourg 53, 62 arr	1336	1516	...	...	1730	...	...	1719	19 18	2050	2040
dep	14 4	1520	...	...	1731	...	...	1739	19 26	2054	2240
La Vavrette	1417	...	...	...	...	...	...	1752	19 38	...	2254
Pont d'Ain	1434	...	...	...	...	...	...	18 9	19 51	...	2312
Amberieu......arr	1451	1546	...	...	1757	...	...	1825	20 6	2120	2332
LYONS.........dep	13 3	1445	...	...	...	...	...	1632	19 16	1939	—
Amberieu......dep	1513	16 1	...	...	18 2	...	...	1845	20‡40	2136	...
St. Rambert en-B.	1531	...	...	...	...	...	...	19 4	20 57	...	...
Tenay	1542	...	...	...	...	...	...	1916	21 9	SC	...
Rossillon	16 2	...	...	...	C	...	...	1936	...	...	...
Virieu-le-Grand...	1613	1648	...	...	...	...	...	1948	21 35	...	...
Culoz......... arr	1632	17 0	...	...	1849	...	...	20 6	21 46	2222	...
dep	1647	1717	...	...	:	18 59	...	2023	22 4	:	...
Seyssel	17 7	...	...	...	:	...	...	2044	22 21	:	...
Bellegarde ar	1735	1750	...	...	:	19 31	...	21 9	22 49	:	...
*** 61A dp	1821	18 1	19 9	...	:	19 43	...	2125	22 54	:	...
Collongs-Ecluse	1836	...	1927	...	:	...	...	2139	23 9	:	...
Chancy (Switz)	1845	...	1935	...	:	C	...	2148	...	:	...
Satigny¶	20 6	...	2052	...	:	...	...	23 9	...	:	...
Geneva ¶ ...arr	2021	1938	21 6	...	:	21 22	...	2325	0 43	:	...
	1,2,3	1 &2	1,2,3	1,2,3	:	...	1,2,3	1,2,3	1,2,3	1,2,3	1,2,3
Culoz ....dep	...	1722	...	...	19 1	...	2025	2119	21 59	2235	4 25
Aix-les-Bains 47... arr	...	1742	...	...	1921	...	2045	2147	22 21	2255	4 53
dep	1635	1751	...	1855	1930	...	21 0	2157	22 45	23 2	5 11
Viviers	1643	§	...	19 3	...	...	...	22 5	...	§	5 19
Chambéry 62 arr	1655	18 7	...	1915	1946	...	2115	2217	23 2	2319	5 30
d'p	1715	1816	1840	20 6	—	...	2128	—	—	2327	6 20
Chignin-les-Marc.	1728	...	1853	2019	...	...	...	...	...	...	6 33
Montmelian	1733	1830	19 2	2028	...	...	2143	...	...	...	6 45
St. Pierre Alb. 62A	—	RC	1918	2047	...	...	To Grenoble. (arr. 22.6)	...	...	...	7 6
Chamousset.........	...	...	To Moutiers-Salins.	2055	...	...		...	...	...	7 13
Epierre	...	...		2123	...	...		...	...	...	7 39
St. Jean de Maur.	...	1933		22 9	...	...		...	...	0 49	8 26
St. Michel	...	...		2232	...	...		...	...	1 8	8 49
La Praz	...	...		2255	...	...		...	...	...	9 12
Modane *** ...arr	...	2020		23 8	...	...		...	...	1 41	9 25
MODANE It.Tm. dep	...	2137		...	...	...	...	...	...	3 15	...
TURIN 270 ...arr	...	0 5		...	...	...	...	...	...	5 50	...

SC — Sleeping Car attached.

*—From Brotteaux Station at Lyons.

‡—From Amberieu forward will only take 3rd class travelling at least 31 miles.

§—At Aix-les-Bains will not take up for Chambéry or Montmelian.

¶—Mid Europe time observed at these stations.

A—P.&O. Expressover this line on Sat. only, leaving London on Friday night for Brindisi.

B—Takes 2nd and 3rd class travelling at least 155 miles, and 249 miles respectively. Exceptionally takes at Culoz for all stations, and at Bellegarde for Geneva and beyond.

C—SAVOIE Express. Runs from 5th July until 13th Sept.

D—Taking Passengers for Aix-les-Bains and beyond only (2nd class must be travelling at least 155 miles). Exceptionally at Amberieu, will take up passengers from Lyons for Aix-les-Bains.

E—Runs from 2nd July until 20th Sept.; takes only for beyond Bellegarde towards Evian and Chamonix — 2nd class must be travelling at least 155 miles.

F—Admits 2nd class travelling at least 155 miles, and 3rd class travelling 249 miles; takes only for Bourg and beyond. Exceptionally takes for beyond Culoz towards Bellegarde.

G—After 20th Sept. will leave Macon at 2.55, arr. Bourg 3.29.

*** Customs Examinations at Bellegarde for Switzerland, at Modane for Italy

Extra.			
Aix-les-Bains......dep	0 2	7 20	Culoz..............dep 16 51
Chambéry...........arr	0 21	7 40	Aix-les-Bains ...arr 17 19
			Chambéry.........arr 17 53

MODANE, GENEVA, and MACON.

[SLEEPING CAR, Geneva to Paris—in 21.10 from Geneva.

Customs Examination at Bellegarde and Modane.

Station																															
TURIN 271 ......dep	...	...	0 30	...	...	2340	...	...	...	...	...	...	5 40	...	9 10	...	...	...	...	...	...	...	...	...	1415	16 5	...	...	...	...	...
MODANE ....arr	...	...	3 15	...	...	3 46	...	...	...	...	...	...	9 0	...	11 48	...	...	...	...	...	...	...	...	...	1740	19 0	...	...	...	...	...
		1,2,3	1 &2	1,2,3	1,2,3	1,2,3	1,2,3	1,2,3	1,2,3	Lux	1,2,3		1,2,3		1 & 2			1,2,3	1,2,3	1,2,3	1,2,3	1,2,3	1,2,3	1& 2	1,2,3	1,2,3		1,2,3	1,2,3	1,2,3	1& 2
Modane French Time...dep	...	...	3 0	...	...	4 38	...	From Grenoble. (dep. 8.15)	...	...	...	...	9 0	...	11 25	...	...	...	1212	...	...	...	...	From Chamonix. (dep. 15.12)	1654	1840	...	...	...	...	From Chamonix. (dep. 18.38)
La Praz	...	...	...	...	...	4 51	...		...	...	...	...	9 13	...	...	...	...	...	1225	...	...	...	...		17 7	...	...	...	...	...	
St. Michel	...	...	SC	...	...	5 15	...		...	...	...	...	9 37	...	RC	...	...	...	1249	...	...	...	...		1731	RC	...	...	...	...	
S. Jean de Maurienne	...	...	3 48	...	...	5 38	...		...	...	...	...	10 1	...	12 14	...	...	...	1314	...	...	...	...		1755	1928	...	...	...	...	
Epierre	...	...	...	...	...	6 11	...		...	...	...	...	1032	...	...	...	...	...	1348	...	...	...	...		1830	...	...	...	...	...	
Chamousset	...	...	...	...	...	6 34	...		...	...	...	...	1057	...	...	...	...	...	1411	...	...	...	...		1854	...	...	B	...	...	
St. Pierre d'Albigny	...	...	E	...	...	6 48	...		9 10	...	...	...	11 7	...	...	...	...	...	1426	...	...	...	...		1912	...	...	1933	...	...	
Montmelian	...	...	...	...	...	7 9	...	9 1	9 29	...	10 0	...	1127	...	...	...	...	...	1445	1548	...	18 22	...		1931	...	...	1950	...	...	
Chignin-les-Marches	...	...	...	...	...	7 16	...	...	9 36	...	10 7	...	1134	...	...	...	...	...	1452	...	...	18 29	...		1938	...	...	...	...	...	
Chambéry ....arr	...	...	4 54	...	...	7 27	...	9 14	9 47	...	1018	...	1145	...	13 7	...	...	...	15 3	16 1	...	18 49	...		1949	2031	...	20 5	...	...	
,, ...dep	...	5 43	5 0	6 35	...		8 5	9 24		1025	1035	...	1215	...	13*25	...	...	14 0	1520	16 9	1725	18 55	1935			2057	...		2215	23 7	
Viviers	...	5 56	...	6 48	...	...	8 18	...	...	C	1048	...	1227	...	...	...	...	1413	1533	...	1738	19 8	1948		...	...	...	...	...	...	
Aix-les-Bains......arr	...	6 3	5 14	6 55	...	...	8 25	9 40	...	1040	1055	...	1234	...	13 41	...	...	1420	1540	1626	1745	19 15	1955	2031	...	2116	...	...	2232	2324	B
,, (47)...dep	...		5 19	7 7	...	...	8 33		...	1048	1112	...	1241	...	13 52	...	...	1431	1550	1637		19 25		2039	...	2125	...	...	2247		2346
Culoz..................arr	...	...	5 41	7 38	...	...	8 58	...	...	1110	1143	...	13 6	...	14 12	...	...	1456	1618	1658	...	19 54	...	21 0	...	2145	...	...	23 9	...	0 10
	1,2,3	1,2,3	1 &2	1,2,3	1,2,3				Lux	:	1,2,3	1,2,3		1,2,3		1,2,3	1 &2		1,2,3				1,2,3	1,2,3		1,2,3	1,2,3	1,2,3	:		1& 2
Geneva¶ ....dep	...	...		6 53	7 38	...	...	...	1045		1115	1255	...	...		1333	1430	...	15 0	...	...	...	1845	20 5	...		2110	2225		...	From Evian.
Satigny ¶	...	...		...	7 54	...	...	...	...		1124	...	...	...		...	...	...	1518	...	...	...	19 1	...	...		...	2241		...	
Chancy	...	...		A	7 9	...	...	...	C		1046	D	...	...		...	...	...	1435	...	...	...	1816	...	...		...	2156		...	
Collonges	...	...		...	7 17	...	...	...	...	C	1054	...	...	...		...	...	...	1444	...	...	...	1824	1939	...		...	22 4		...	
Bellegarde ......arr	...	...		6 35	7 28	...	...	...	1019		11 5	1231	...	...		1314	14 3	...	1456	...	...	...	1836	1951	...		2053	2215		...	2318
,, ...dep	...	...		7 13	8 8	...	...	...	1046		1149	13 1	...	...		1352	1431	...	1542	...	...	...	1911	2032	...		2132	2249		...	2342
Seyssel..................	...	...		7 33	8 35	...	...	...	...		1216	...	...	...		...	...	...	16 9	...	...	...	1938	...	...		...	2313		...	...
Culoz.................arr	...	...		7 47	8 53	...	...	...	1115		1234	1332	...	...		1421	15 0	...	1627	...	...	...	1956	21 1	...		22 3	2328		...	0 15
Culoz.................dep	...	4 35	5 45	7 59	9 18	...	...	...		1126	1252	1345	...	...		1438	1515	...	1644	...	...	...	2014	2114	...	2155	2216		2315	...	0 28
Virieu le Grand	...	4 54	...	8 17	9 41	...	...	...	...	...	1314	...	...	...	...	...	...	...	17 8	...	...	...	2037	2132	...	...	2234	...	...	...	...
Rossillon	...	5 5	...	...	9 52	...	...	...	...	...	1325	...	...	...	...	...	...	...	1724	...	...	...	2049	...	...	...	...	...	...	...	B
Tenay	...	5 27	...	8 48	1014	...	...	...	...	...	1347	D	...	...	...	...	...	...	1751	...	...	...	2114	...	...	SC	F	...	...	...	...
St. Rambert-en-B. ...	...	5 38	...	8 57	1025	...	...	...	...	...	1357	...	...	...	...	...	...	...	18 2	...	...	...	2123	...	...	...	...	...	...	...	...
Ambérieu ....arr	...	5 54	6 33	9 7	1040	...	...	...	...	1216	1412	1450	...	...	...	1533	16 3	...	1817	...	...	...	2140	2214	...	2253	2319	...	0 30	...	1 26
LYONS (53) ......arr	...	8 35	8 35	10 15	13 9	...	...	...	...	...	16 1	1621	...	...	...	1632	1915	...	2039	...	...	...	2312	2312	...	1 17	1 17	...	...	...	2 42
Ambérieu ....dep	...	6 11	6 51	9 27	1054	...	...	...	...	1221			...	1456	...		16 8	...	1842	...	...	...	2225		...	2258	2324	...	0 36	...	1 38
Pont-d'Ain	...	6 29	...	9 40	1113	...	...	...	...	...	...	...	...	1515	...	...	...	...	19 0	...	...	...	2247	...	...	...	SC	...	...	...	...
La Vavrette	...	6 44	...	...	1128	...	...	...	...	...	...	...	...	1530	...	...	...	...	1915	...	...	...	2259	...	...	...	...	...	...	...	...
Bourg ....arr	...	6 56	7 19	9 58	1140	...	...	...	...	1247	...	...	...	1542	...	...	1634	...	1927	...	...	...	2311	...	...	2329	2355	...	1 13	...	2 7
,, (53, 62) ...dep	5 35	7 40	7 24	10 6	1159	...	...	...	...	1248	...	...	...	1645	...	...	1637	...	1945	...	...	...	2332	...	...	2336	2358	...	1 18	...	2 8
Polliat....................	5 49	7 54	Via St. Amour	...	1213	...	...	...	...	Via St. Amour	...	...	...	1658	...	...	Via St. Amour	...	1959	...	...	...	...	...	...	Via St. Amour	...	...	Via St. Amour	...	Via St. Amour
Mézériat..................	5 59	8 4		...	1223	...	...	...	...		...	...	...	17 7	...	...		...	20 9	...	...	...	...	...	...		...	...		...	
Vonnas	6 7	8 12		...	1231	...	...	...	...		...	...	...	1715	...	...		...	2018	...	...	...	...	...	...		...	...		...	
Pont-de-Veyle	6 21	8 26		...	1244	...	...	...	...		...	...	...	1727	...	...		...	2032	...	...	...	...	...	...		...	...		...	
Macon ....arr	6 32	8 36		10 40	1254	...	...	...	...		...	...	...	1737	...	...		...	2042	...	...	...	0 9	...	...		0 31	...		...	
MACON............dep	...	8 52		10†59	1431	...	...	...	...		...	...	...	...	...	...		...	21§4	...	...	...	0 41	...	...		0 41	...		...	
PARIS (51) ......arr	...	1710	1425	18 8	2355	...	...	...	...	1832	...	...	...	...	...	...	2250	...	4 55	...	...	...	7 0	...	...	6 35	7 0	...	8 12	...	8 37

A—3rd class must be travelling not less than 31 miles.
B—Runs from 2nd July until 20th September.
C—**Savoie Express**, Train de Luxe. Runs from 6th July until 14th Sept.
D—Runs from 11th August until 20th September only.
E—From Modane to Bourg only takes 2nd class travelling at least 155 miles. Exceptionally will take passengers for beyond Culoz towards Geneva, Evian, & Divonne; for Chambéry & beyond towards St. Andre-le-Gaz; for Aix-les-Bains and beyond towards Annecy; and for beyond Ambérieu towards Lyons.

F—Between Geneva and Culoz takes 2nd and 3rd class travelling at least 155 miles and 249 miles respectively. Exceptionally takes for beyond Culoz towards Aix-les-Bains, and for beyond Ambérieu towards Lyons.
†—1st and 2nd class only.
§—1st class only.
*—1,2,3 class.
¶—Mid Europe time observed at these stations.

PARIS, LYONS, and MEDITERRANEAN RAILWAY.

BELLEGARDE, EVIAN, and BOUVERET.

Dis.	1 cl.	2 cl.	3 cl.		1,2,3	1,2,3	1 & 2	1 & 2	1,2,3	1,2,3	1,2,3	1,2,3	1,2,3	1,2,3	1 & 2	1,2,3	Lxu	1,2,3	
E M	fr. c.	fr. c	fr. c																
Fro	mBe	lleg	arde	**Bellegarde** ....dep	4 5	...	5‡52	7 7	7 18	...	...	1136	1523	...	1812	1852	1954	...	...
15	2 70	1 80	1 20	St. Julien-en-Genevois	4 43	...	6 29	7 39	7 56	...	...	1118	16 2		1843	1934	2023	...	...
24½	4 35	2 95	1 90	Annemasse .... arr	5 11	...	6 55	7 56	8 23	...	...	1143	1627	*	19 2	20 2	2044	...	...
				dep		6 6	7 1	8 9	8 45	...	1015	1217	1650	1746	19 7		2047	2139	...
28	5 5	3 40	2 20	St. Cergues	...	6 16	C	D	8 55	...	1024	1227	17 0	1756	B	...	A	2149	...
42¾	7 75	5 20	3 40	Thonon..............................	...	7 1	7 39	8 46	9 43	...	11 7	1314	1744	1841	1944	...	2118	2236	...
47¼	8 50	5 75	3 75	Amphion	...	7 10	...	...	9 52	...	1116	1323	1753	1850	...	...	...	2245	...
48½	8 75	5 90	3 85	**Evian** ....arr	...	7 14	7 51	8 56	9 56	1027	1120	1327	1757	1854	1954	...	2128	2249	...
49	8 85	5 95	3 90	Bains d'Evian....................	...	7 35				1032		1337	1810			...			...
59	10 65	7 20	4 70	St. Gingolph	...	8 7	...	...	...	11 8	...	1413	1840	...	...	...	...	...	...
62¾	11 30	7 65	5 0	**Bouveret** ....arr	...	8 14	...	...	...	1117	...	1420	1847	...	...	...	...	...	...

	1,2,3	1,2,3	1,2,3	Lux	1,2,3	1,2,3	1 &2	1,2,3	1,2,3	1,2,3	1 &2	1,2,3	1 & 2	1,2,3					
Bouveret ....dep	...	...	6 32	...	...	...	...	1154	...	1637	...	...	...	2033	Sunday only.	...	...	...	...
St. Gingolph	...	...	6 40	...	...	...	...	12 2	...	1645	...	...	C	2043		...	...	...	...
Bains d'Evian........................	...	...	7 9	¶	...	...	*	1233	...	1714	...	...	...	2116		...	...	...	...
Evian ....dep	4 22	5 50	7 23	9 0	...	1050	1230	1253	1530	1728	19 2	1928	21‡30	2120		...	...	...	...
Amphion	...	5 55	7 28	...	...	...	...	1258	1535	1733	...	1933	...		2143	...	...	...	...
Thonon	4 35	6 7	7 41	9 11	...	11 4	1242	1312	1549	1747	1915	1945	21 45	...	2148	...	...	...	...
St. Cergues	5 13	6 45	8 19	...	...	1136	...	1350	1627	1825	D	2026	...	...	22 0	...	...	...	...
Annemasse .... arr	5 21	6 53	8 27	9 42	...	1144	1315	1358	1635	1833	1954	2034	22 21	...	2243	...	...	...	...
dep	5 42			9 45	1011	1212	1326	14 8	17 0	19 4	2025		22 26	...	2251	...	...	...	...
St. Julien-en-Genevois	6 10	...	...	10 3	1042	1234	1345	1439	1731	1932	2047	...	22 48	...		...	...	...	...
Bellegarde (60) ......arr	6 49	...	...	1031	1117	13 3	1413	1515	18 8	20 7	2115	...	23 18	...	...	...	...	...	...

*—Runs until 20th September.
‡—From 2nd July until 20th September.
¶—From 6th July until 14th September.

A—From 5th July until 13th September.
B—Runs until 19th September.
C—Takes 2nd class travelling at least 155 miles.
D—Runs from 21st to 30th September.

ANNEMASSE, LE FAYET ST. GERVAIS, and ANNECY.

...	GENEVA Eaux Vives 61B dep	5 5	6 30	7 38	8 12	1110	1225	1450	17 5	...	1720	1815	1910	1945	...	...	...	...	...
Dis.		1,2,3	1 & 2	1 & 2	1,2,3	1 &2	1,2,3	1,2,3	1 &2	1 &2	1,2,3	1,2,3	1 &2	1,2,3	1 &2				
E M																			
—	**Annemasse** ....dep	5 35	7 10	8 7	8 42	1137	1254	1520	1730	...	1749	1847	1938	2016	...	...	...	...	...
1¾	Monnetier-Mornex	5 47	...	...	8 54	...	13 7	1529	...	...	18 1	1859	...	2025	B	...	...	...	...
5½	Reignier	5 57	B	C	9 4	§	1317	1539	§	§	1815	19 9	§	2035	...	...	...	...	...
10	La Roche-sur-Foron ......arr	6 12	7 35	8 32	9 19	12 4	1332	1554	1753	18 5	1830	1924	20 9	2050	2130	...	...	...	...
...	La Roche-sur-Foron ...dep	6 22	7 47	8 33	9 38	1218	1340	16 6	...	:	1832	:	2011	2058	:	...	...	...	...
16¾	Bonneville	6 40	8 3	8 50	9 57	1239	1358	1624	...	:	1852	:	2027	2120	:	...	...	...	...
21¼	Marignier	6 52	...	...	10 12	...	14 9	1635	...	:	19 3	:	...	2131	:	...	...	...	...
25½	Cluses	7 6	...	...	10 23	13 0	1423	1649	...	:	1917	:	2051	2149	:	...	...	...	...
29¾	Magland	7 19	...	...	10 33	...	1440	17 6	...	:	1930	:	...	2156	:	...	...	...	...
35½	Sallanches.........................	7 37	8 47	9 31	10 47	1325	15 0	1724	...	:	1946	:	2116	2218	:	...	...	...	...
39¼	Fayet St. Gervais 61B arr	7 48	8 57	9 39	10 55	1335	15 7	1736	...	:	1957	:	2124	2227	:	...	...	...	...
...	CHAMONIX ....arr	9 10	10 13	11 13	12 15	1453	1634	1859	...	:	2134	:	2248	2355	:	...	...	...	...
19½	Evires..................................	6 57			9 57		1417		...	:		20 2			:	...	...	...	...
23¾	Groisy-la-Caille	7 11	...	...	10 7	...	1427	...	...	:	...	2012	...	...	:	...	...	...	...
33½	**Annecy 47**.................arr	7 35	...	...	10 31	...	1455	...	...	19 0	...	2036	...	...	2227	...	...	...	...

1 cl.	2 cl.	3 cl.		1,2,3	1 & 2	1,2,3	1,2,3	1 & 2	1 & 2	1 & 2	1,2,3	1 & 2	1,2,3	1 &2	1,2,3	1 &2	1,2,3	
fr. c.	fr. c	fr. c																
—	—	—	**Annecy** ....dep	4 55	6 42	8 0	...	...	11 10	...	14 36	...	...	...	19 37	...	...	...
1 75	1 25	0 80	Groisy-la-Caille	5 28	:	8 33	...	...	:	...	15 10	...	...	...	20 14	...	...	...
2 55	1 75	1 15	Evires	5 42	:	8 47	...	...	§	...	15 24	§	...	...	20 28	B	...	...
...	...	...	CHAMONIX ....dep	...	:	6 0	7 49	...	:	9 52	12 40	15 12	16 13	1646	:	1838	...	...
...	...	...	Fayet St. Gervais ......dep	4 27	:	7 20	9 14	...	:	11 29	14 8	16 42	17 43	1818	:	20 1	21 3	...
...	...	...	Sallanches	4 40	B	7 35	9 29	...	:	11 39	14 22	16 52	17 57	1828	:	2011	2119	...
...	...	...	Magland	4 54	:	7 49	9 43	...	:	B	14 37	...	18 11	C	:	...	2133	...
...	...	...	Cluses.................................	5 8	:	8 3	9 57	...	:	12 0	14 51	17 14	18 27	1852	:	...	2147	...
...	...	...	Marignier	5 21	:	8 18	10 10	...	:	...	15 3	...	18 40	...	:	...	22 0	...
...	...	...	Bonneville	5 33	:	8 32	10 22	...	:	12 20	15 15	17 35	18 54	1920	:	2055	2212	...
...	...	...	La Roche-sur-Foron ...arr	5 55	:	8 58	10 44	...	:	12 43	15 37	17 58	19 16	1946	:	2124	2234	...
4 35	2 90	1 90	La Roche-sur-Foron ....dep	6 15	7 39	9 21	10 48	12 25	12 9	12 47	15 57	18 3	19 26	1947	20 57	2134	2237	...
5 0	3 45	2 25	Reignier..............................	6 28		9 34	11 1	§	...	...	16 10	...	19 39	...	21 10	...	2247	...
5 70	3 0	2 55	Monnetier-Mornex	6 37	...	9 43	11 10	...	...	B	16 19	...	19 48	...	21 19	...	2256	...
6 5	4 10	2 70	**Annemasse 61B**.........arr	6 47	...	9 53	11 17	12 49	...	13 12	16 26	18 28	19 58	2014	21 26	2158	23 3	...
6 75	4 65	3 5	GENEVA Eaux Vives ...arr	7 20	...	1020	11 42	13 12	...	13 40	17 13	19 2	20 22	2058	21 52	2224	2325	...

§—Runs until 20th September.

B—From 2nd July until 20th September.
C—Runs from 21st to 30th September.

GENEVA and ANNEMASSE.

†—Until 19th September.]

E M	fr. c																					
		Geneva E. V.	5 5	5 36	6*30	7‡38	8 12	9 43	11§10	11 45	1225	14 50	16 15	17§ 5	1720	18 15	19† 0	19 45	21 9	21 37	...	...
1¾	0 30	Chene	5 12	5 47	6 37	7 45	8 19	9 50	11 17	11 52	1232	14 57	16 22	17 12	1727	18 22	19 17	19 52	21 16	21 49	...	...
3¾	0 60	**Annemasse**	5 20	5 55	6 45	7 53	8 27	9 58	11 25	12 0	1240	15 5	16 30	17 20	1 35	18 30	19 25	20 0	21 24	21 59	...	...

Annemasse ....dep	5 38	7 8	8 40	10 8	11 30	12 2	13§0	13§28	1412	1648	1850	20 10	2046	2140	22*12	2313	...	...	...	...
Chene	5 45	7 15	8 47	1015	11 37	12 9	13 7	13 35	1419	1657	1857	20 17	2053	2147	22 19	2320	...	...	...	...
Geneva ....arr	5 50	7 20	8 52	1020	11 42	1214	1312	13 40	1424	1713	19 2	20 22	2058	2152	22 24	2325	...	...	...	...

*—From 2nd July until 20th September. ‡—Runs from 21st to 30th September. §—Runs until 20th September.

LE FAYET—ST. GERVAIS and CHAMONIX.

E M	1 cl. fr. c	2 cl. fr. c	All 1 & 2 class.	‡				*	§			‡		‡		‡		‡		†	
—	—	—	**Le Fayet St. Gervais** dep	4 53	6 10	...	8 3	9 12	10 5	...	1110	1255	1350	1425	1527	...	1752	18 49	2027	2142	2250
3¾	0 65	0 30	Chedde..........................	5 1	6 18	‡	8 11	...	1013	‡	1118	13 3	...	1433	1535	...	18 0	18 57	2037	2151	2258
8¾	1 55	0 70	Servoz	5 18	6 40	7 52	8 30	...	1033	1112	1135	1320	1413	1451	1552	1739	1817	19 16	2054	22 8	2315
15	2 70	1 20	Les Houches	5 36	6 58	8 11	8 48	...	1051	1130	1153	1338	1431	15 9	1610	1758	1835	19 34	2112	2226	2333
20	3 60	1 60	Les Bossons	5 48	7 12	8 23	9 0	10 3	11 3	1142	12 5	1350	1443	1523	1624	1810	1849	19 49	2124	2238	2345
24¼	4 35	1 90	**Chamonix** ....arr	5 58	7 22	8 33	9 10	1013	1113	1152	1215	14 0	1453	1533	1634	1820	1859	19 59	2134	2248	2355

	‡		‡		‡		‡	‡		‡	‡			§		*		‡	‡	
Chamonix ....dep	5 15	6 0	6 59	7 49	8 49	9 52	1030	1154	1240	1317	1410	1512	1613	1646	1735	1838	1938	2051	2311	...
Les Bossons	5 25	6 10	7 10	7 59	9 2	10 4	1040	12 6	1250	1327	1420	1522	1623	1656	1745	1848	1948	21 1	2321	...
Les Houches	5 37	6 20	7 20	8 10	9 12	1014	1052	1216	13 0	1339	1432	1532	1634	17 6	1757	...	1958	2113	2335	...
Servoz	5 57	6 39	7 38	8 29	9 30	1034	1136	1242	1321	1357	1453	1553	1654	1727	1818	...	2017	2132	2354	...
Chedde................................	6 19	6 58	—	8 48	—	1053	1155	13 4	1340	—	1512	1612	1713	...	1837	...	2036	2152	0 13	...
Le Fayet St. Gervais arr	6 26	7 5	...	8 55	...	11 0	12 2	1311	1347	...	1519	1619	1720	1751	1844	1939	2043	2159	0 20	...

*—From 2nd July until 20th September. †—Runs until 19th September.
‡—Runs until 20th September. §—Runs from 21st to 30th September.

CHAMONIX and ARGENTIERE.

All 1 & 2 class. †—From 2nd July until 20th Sept.

		*			*		*	†			*		*	*		*			*		*		‡
Chamonix dep	4 26	6 15	655	8 1	8 45	915	9 55	1034	11 0	12 0	1251	1323	1357	1424	15 0	1526	1611	1648	1754	1913	2012	2147	23 1
LesPraz-de-Cham.	4 34	6 23	7 3	8 9	8 53	923	10 3	1042	11 8	12 8	1259	1331	14 5	1432	15 8	1534	1621	1656	18 2	1921	2020	2157	23 9
Les Tines	4 39	6 28	7 8	814	9 0	928	10 9	1047	1113	1214	13 4	1338	1412	1437	1514	1539	1626	17 3	18 9	1926	2025	22 2	2314
Argentiere 257A	4 55	6 44	724	830	9 16	944	1025	11 3	1129	1230	1320	1354	1428	1453	1530	1555	1642	1719	1825	1942	2041	2218	2330

			*		*		*		*		*			*		*	*		*	*		‡
Argentiere.........dep	525	651	7 32	843	9 51	1030	1132	1156	1321	1355	1456	1559	1646	1724	1752	1831	1859	1943	21 0	2135	2233	2345
Les Tines	541	7 9	7 48	859	10 8	1048	1148	1213	1337	1411	1513	1615	17 2	1740	18 8	1847	1915	1959	2116	2151	2249	0 1
Les Praz-de-Chamonix	546	714	7 53	9 4	1013	1053	1153	1218	1342	1416	1518	1620	17 7	1745	1813	1852	1922	20 4	2121	2156	2254	0 6
Chamonix ....arr	552	720	7 59	910	1019	1059	1159	1224	1348	1422	1524	1626	1713	1751	1819	1858	1928	2010	2127	22 2	23 0	0 12

*—Runs until 20th September. ‡—Runs until 19th September.

CHAMONIX and MONTENVERS.—Service until 15th Sept.

From Chamonix (in 55 minutes), 8.15, 9.45, 11.20, 14.5, 15.30.
From Montenvers, 9.30, 11.0, 12.40, 15.10, 16.40. 18.0.
Fares—Single: 1st Class 12 fr. 50c.; 2nd Class 8 fr. 25c. Return: 1st Class 17fr. 10c.; 2nd Class 12. fr.

LE FAYET and GLACIER DE BIONNASSET.

*—Until 1st Sept.] [‡—Until 20th Sept.

	‡	‡	‡		‡		*	‡
Le Fayet ....dep	8 0	9 15	11 10	1314	13 55	18 0	2010	21 35
Les Bains	8 5	9 20	11 15	1319	14 0	18 5	2015	21 40
St. Gervais	8 20	9 30	11 30	1329	14 17	18 15	2025	21 50
Motivon	8 43	—	11 53	—	14 40	—	—	—
Col de Voza	9 16	...	12 16	1345	15 20	...	...	...
Glacier de Bionnasset arr	10 0	...		1425	16 0	...	...	...

		‡	‡		‡	‡		
G.de Bion.dep	...	11 15		...	15 30	17 15	...	...
Col de Voza...	...	12 0	13 30	...	16 30	18 3	...	...
Motivon	‡	—	13 54	...	16 54	18 27	*	‡
St. Gervais...	9 35	10 30	14 30	15 45	17 21	18 55	20 30	22 0
Les Bains....	9 47	10 42	14 42	15 57	17 33	19 7	20 42	22 12
Le Fayet arr	9 50	10 45	14 45	16 0	17 36	19 10	20 45	22 15

Extra.					
Le Fayet.........dep	6 35	8 5	10 0	15 25	...
St. Gervais ......arr	6 50	8 20	10 15	15 40	...

Extra.					
St. Gervais.........dep	6 55	8 25	13 33	18 20	...
Le Fayet...........arr	7 10	8 40	13 48	18 35	...

ANNEMASSE to SAMOENS and BONNEVILLE.—Steam Tramway.

Dist. E.M.						
	Annemasse-Gare.........dep	5 40	9 15	14 30	18 55	...
5½	Bonne-sur-Menoge...............	6 15	9 50	15 5	19 32	...
12½	St. Jeoire	7 19	10 44	15 57	20 34	...
20½	Taninges..............................	8 3	11 32	16 45	21 18	...
27¼	**Samoens** ....arr	8 30	12 5	17 17	21 45	...

Samoens ....dep	5 0	9 5	15 30	18 25	...	...
Taninges	5 33	9 37	16 2	18 57	...	...
St. Jeoire	6 23	10 24	16 49	19 44	...	...
Bonne-sur-Menoge	7 25	11 20	17 45	20 40	...	...
Annemasse-Gare.........arr	7 55	11 50	18 15	21 10	...	...

Dist. E M.					
	Annemasse-Gare ......dep	7 0	10 50	20 10	...
5½	Bonne..............................	7 25	11 20	20 40	...
13¾	**Bonneville**................arr	8 15	12 10	21 30	...

Bonneville..................dep	5 25	9 0	18 40	...	...	...	...
Bonne	6 15	9 50	19 30	...	...	...	...
Annemasse-Gare ....arr	6 45	10 20	20 0	...	...	...	...

Dist E M.					
	St. Jeoire dep	6 5	9 15	17 0	2027
5½	Marignier...ar	6 40	9 50	1735	21 2

Marignier dep	7 2	1027	1916	22 9
St. Jeoire arr	7 37	11 2	1951	2244

E.M.		
	Samoens dep	Omnibus service, 40 minutes, connecting with the Tramway service at Samoens.
3½	Sixt ......arr	

MORTEAU and TREVILLERS.

E M	fr. c.	fr. c.						
			Morteau ....dep	7 50	12 19	18 7	...	...
11¼	2 35	1 80	Le Russey..........................	8 44	13 13	19 1	...	...
21¾	4 55	3 50	Maiche........................arr	9 40	14 9	19 57	...	...
28	5 85	4 50	**Trevillers**............arr	10 32	14 57	20 49	...	...

Trevillers ....dep	4 39	10 47	15 7	...	...	...
Maiche ....dep	5 26	11 34	15 54	...	...	...
Le Russey	6 28	12 34	16 55	...	...	...
Morteau ....arr	7 17	13 23	17 44	...	...	...

LYONS and TREVOUX.

Lyons (Croix R.)dep	6 28	9 25	10 43	1342	1659	1814	1846	2052
Sathonay	6 52	9 51	11 2	1411	1725	1825	19 5	2112
Neuville-sur-Saone	7 17	1017	11 33	1451	1753	1843	1931	2136
Trévoux...........arr	7 38	1041	11 57	1530	1817	1858	1952	2155

Trévoux...........dep	6 4	6 59	7 55	11 6	12 33	...	1557	19 2	2040
Neuville-sur-Saone	6 26	7 18	8 18	1131	12 59	...	1636	1930	21 3
Sathonay	6 54	7 40	8 47	12 2	13 34	1530	1730	20 2	2135
Lyons (Croix R.) arr	7 12	7 50	9 5	1221	13 53	1548	1754	2023	2152

Extra.—Lyons to Sathonay, 12.5, 14.46. Sathonay to Lyons, 12.41.

PARIS, LYONS, and MEDITERRANEAN RAILWAY.

66 lbs. of Luggage free.

LYONS to MONTBRISON.

Station									
Lyons-Saint-Paul........dep	6 6	7 9	8 38	11 45	14 21	1629	1744	1848	2029
Lyons-Gorge-de L. ...	...	7 14	8 44	11 51	14 27	1635	..	1854	2036
Charbonnières..........	6 23	7 33	9 7	12 11	14 50	1659	18 2	1916	2059
L'Arbresle (51B)	7 7	8 5	10 7	13 4	15 27	1737	1838	1954	2133
Sain Bel	7 16	—	10 14	13 13	—	1744	—	20 2	—
Viricelles-Chazelles...	8 23	...	11 8	14 23	...	1842	...	21 2	...
Montrond (56)...........	9 3	...	11 34	14 42	...	19 0	...	—	...
Montbrison 63B ...arr	9 30	...	12 0	15 42	...	20 6	...	..	...

Station								
Montbrison...dep	...	...	6 43	...	10 15	1424	...	1828
Montrond	...	...	7 33	...	11 7	1518	...	1937
Viricelles-Chazel.	...	5 52	8 1	...	11 44	1544	...	2012
Sain-Bel	...	6 48	8 58	...	12 41	1638	..	2115
L'Arbresle	6 18	7 15	9 11	1038	12 58	1655	1821	2136
Charbonnières ...	6 58	7 47	9 42	1110	13 32	1734	1859	2215
Lyons-Gorge-de L	7 22	8 10	10 4	1126	13 52	1753	1917	2236
Lyons-St.-Paul ar	7 26	8 14	10 8	1129	13 56	1757	1921	2241

Extra.—L'Arbresle to Lyons S.P., 8.20, 14.51 Lyons to L'Arbresle, 5.0

Station					
Lyons-St.-Paul ....dep	11 30	12 3	12 30	18 17	19 27
Charbonnières ....arr	11 52	12 27	12 52	18 44	19 49

Station							
Charbonnières..................dep	6 10	12 47	13 9	16 27	19 17	20 17	...
Lyons-St.-Paul ....arr	6 31	13 9	13 29	16 52	19 44	20 39	

‡—Perrache Station, Lyons.]

LYONS, BELLEGARDE, and CHALON-SUR-SAONE.

Station		1,2,3	1,2,3	1,2,3	1,2,3	1,2,3	1,2,3	1,2,3	1,2,3
Lyons—Croix-Rousse...dep		5 3	7‡20	8 12	9 46	13 18	1722	19‡55	2010
Sathonay		5 43	7 §52	8 28	10 5	13 37	1742	2026	2034
Villars-Chalamont		6 23	...	9 12	10 50	14 29	1827	§	2121
Marlieux (42B).........		6 34	...	9 24	11 2	14 43	1840	...	2133
Bourg (53, 60)......arr		7 3	8 35	9 52	11 34	15 17	1910	21 8	22 7
Bourg ......dep	4 13	7 34	...	...	12 11	16 0	1952	...	...
Simandre-s-S.	5 7	8 28	...	...	13 10	16 59	2053	...	...
La Cluse 62 ...	5 35	8 55	...	...	13 42	17 29	2122	...	...
Nantua	5 58	9 19	...	...	14 5	17 55	2151	...	...
St. Germ.-d-J.	6 23	9 44	...	...	14 31	18 21	2216	...	...
Bellegarde arr	6 44	10 5	...	...	14 52	18 42	2237	...	...
Bourg ....dep		7 50	...	...	...	15 27	1957	...	...
Montrevel		8 19	...	...	...	15 58	2029	...	...
Ratenelle		9 11	...	...	...	16 51	2123	...	...
S. Germain-du-Plain		9 52	...	...	...	17 47	22 4	...	...
Chalon-s-Saône arr		1025	...	...	...	18 24	2237	...	...

Station		1,2,3	1,2,3	1,2,3	1,2,3	1,2,3	1,2,3	1,2,3	1,2,3
Chalon-s-Saone dep		...	...	7 13	...	1210	16 24	...	...
S. Germain du Plain		...	...	7 50	...	1246	16 56	...	...
Ratenelle		...	...	8 30	...	1325	17 37	...	...
Montrevel		...	...	9 23	...	1429	18 35	...	...
Bourg ....arr		...	...	9 51	...	15 2	19 4	...	...
Bellegarde......dep		4 36	...	7 48	11 43	...	16 16	...	2030
St. Germ.-d-J.......		5 1	...	8 13	12 9	...	16 43	...	2057
Nantua		5 26	...	8 38	12 34	...	17 11	...	2128
La Cluse ......dep		5 46	...	8 57	12 54	...	17 32	...	2148
Simandre-s-Suran		6 17	...	9 27	13 25	...	18 4	...	2222
Bourg ....arr		7 9	...	10 17	14 17	...	18 57	...	2318
Bourg ....dep	4 57	7 59	10 30	11 17	14 32	1630	19*40	2047	...
Marlieux	5 25	8 35	...	11 56	15 10	17 5	20 11	...	...
Villars-Chala ...	5 36	8 50	...	12 14	15 25	1718	20 23	...	...
Sathonay	6 28	9 44	11†14	13 13	16 20	1810	21 10	21†30	...
Lyons (C.R.) arr	6 40	9 57	11‡45	13 27	16 35	1826	21 25	21‡56	...

†—Sets down only. §—Takes up only.

*—20.57 on Sunday.

La CLUSE and ST. CLAUDE.

Station					
La Cluse ....dep	6 8	9 23	14 0	18 0	22 0
Oyonnax	6 40	9 55	14 30	18 32	22 30
St. Claude.........arr	7 50	10 59	15 33	19 39	23 27

Station					
St. Claude.........dep	4 0	7 3	11 6	15 36	19 41
Oyonnax	5 5	8 15	12 17	16 50	20 55
La Cluse (62) ......arr	5 30	8 40	12 42	17 15	21 20

Station						
St. Claude.........dep	5 55	12 50	15 53	20 21	...	...
Morez (57) ....arr	7 0	14 2	16 58	21 31	...	...

Station							
Morez ....dep	7 25	9 52	14 5	20 15	...	...	...
St. Claude (62) ...arr	8 23	10 50	15 10	21 14	...	...	...

MACON and PARAY-LE-MONIAL.

Station						
Macon ....dep	3 58	6 59	11 1	1345	1752	...
La Roche-V.-Milly............	4 23	7 25	11 27	1411	1821	...
Cluny (63) ....arr	4 46	7 48	11 52	1435	1846	...
Clermain..........................	5 28	8 24	—	1511	1924	...
Beaubery	6 3	8 58	..	1546	20 1	...
Charolles	6 27	9 22	12 41	16 9	2024	...
Paray-le-Monial 53A...arr	6 50	9 45	13 8	1632	2051	...

Station						
Paray-le-Monial dep	...	5 55	8 33	1018	1343	18 13
Charolles	...	6 24	8 59	1047	1412	18 41
Beaubery	...	6 48	—	1110	1436	19 7
Clermain	..	7 22	...	1143	1513	19 46
Cluny......................	4 48	8 7	...	1221	1552	20 20
La Roche-V.-Milly ...	5 21	8 34	...	1250	1622	20 47
Macon.................arr	5 38	8 59	...	1315	1653	21 15

CHALON and LONS-LE-SAUNIER.

E.M.	Station				
	Chalon-s-Saone ...dep	5 32	10 28	17 15	...
10½	St.-Germain-du-Plain	6 4	11 0	17 55	...
17½	Montret	6 20	11 17	18 15	...
23¾	Louhans (63B)	7 4	12 9	19 14	...
34½	Savigny-Beaurepaire	7 29	12 34	19 42	...
42½	Lons-l-Saunier 53 arr	7 54	13 1	20 10	...

Station						
Lons-le-Saunier ...dep	6 0	10 46	1750	...	...	...
Savigny-Beaurepaire	6 22	11 10	1816	...	...	...
Louhans....................	7 8	12 0	1924	...	...	...
Montret	7 25	12 18	1943	...	...	...
St.-Germain-du-Plain	7 44	12 37	20 3	...	...	...
Chalon-s-Saone ...arr	8 21	13 16	2038	...	..	...

MONTALIEU-VERCIEU and AMBERIEU.

E.M.	Station					
	Montalieu dep	5 11	9 48	13 16	17 42	...
2¼	Sault-Brenaz..	5 24	10 3	13 31	17 56	...
11¼	Ambérieu arr	6 0	10 41	14 10	18 30	...

Station							
Ambérieu ......dep	7 0	11 44	15 55	2043	...	...	...
Sault-Brenaz	7 35	12 23	16 30	2113	...	...	...
Montalieu ......arr	7 47	12 37	16 42	2137		...	...

ORANGE and L'ISLE-SUR-SORGUE.

E M	Station				
	Orange ....dep	6 29	11 38	17 58	...
13⅝	Carpentras .... arr	7 42	12 30	18 43	...
	Carpentras .... dep	8 13	13 15	19 12	...
23½	L'Isle-sur-Sorgue ......arr	8 58	14 5	19 52	...

Station					
L'Isle-sur-Sorgue .....dep	6 12	9 50	17 50	...	...
Carpentras 56........ arr	6 50	10 36	18 30	...	...
Carpentras 56........ dep	7 13	11 27	18 53	...	...
Orange 49 ....arr	8 17	12 36	19 45	..	...

LYONS, LE TEIL, and NIMES.

Station								
Lyons-Perrache dp	...	...	6 7	...	10 30	11 24	15 57	2031
Givors-Canal...dep	...	...	6 55	...	10 55	12 19	16 47	2115
Chavanay	...	...	7 51	...	11 33	13 9	17 40	2158
Peyraud ....dep	5 57	...	8 41	...	11 59	13 47	18 32	2218
Tournon	6 38	...	9 40	...	12 41	14 39	19 25	—
Soyons	7 7	...	10 16	...	13 7	15 12	19 59	...
La Voulte ......arr	7 26	...	10 40	...	13 26	15 34	20 21	...
,, ...dep	7 46	6 24	—	11 11	13 30	15 46	20 51	...
Le Pouzin	7 56	6 33	...	11 21	13 40	15 58	21 5	...
Cruas	8 13	6 49	...	11 38	13 59	16 16	21 22	...
Le Teil ....arr	8 34	7 9	...	11 58	14 20	16 38	21 43	...
,, ...dep	—	7 26	...	12 32	—	17 33	22 5	...
Bourg-St-Andeol...	...	7 57	...	13 3	...	18 8	22 35	...
Pont-St-Esprit	4 16	8 21	...	13 26	...	18 36	22 54	...
L'Ardoise...............	4 50	9 2	...	14 1	...	19 28	—	...
Pont d'Avignon ...	5 24	9 39	...	14 40	...	20 10	...	...
Remoulins ......arr	5 54	10 11	...	15 10		20 48	...	...
,, ...dep	6 12	10 22	12 40	15 15	18 55	21 16	...	...
Grezan..................	6 41	10 56	13 9	15 45	19 24	21 51	...	...
Nimes 57 ....arr	6 48	11 4	13 16	15 52	19 31	21 59	...	...

Station									
Nimes ....dep	...	...	...	5 9	11 0	9 41	1415	1756	2035
Grezan..............	...	...	...	...	...	9 48	1423	18 3	2042
Remoulins ...arr	...	...	...	5 46	11 23	1014	1455	1829	21 8
,, ...dep	...	...	...	6 2	11 26	—	1520	1832	—
Pont d'Avignon	...	...	...	6 41	12 0	...	16 9	19 8	...
L'Ardoise	...	...	...	7 15	12 34	...	1652	1939	...
Pont-St-Esprit ...	4 10	...	...	7 55	13 9	...	1737	2014	...
Bourg-Andeol ...	4 29	...	...	8 17	13 30	...	18 2	2034	...
Le Teil.........arr	4 55	...	...	8 46	13 58	...	1835	21 0	...
.........dep	—	5 14	7 4	10 20	14 11	1640	1920	—	...
Cruas	...	5 34	7 24	10 43	14 31	17 3	1944	...	...
Le Pouzin ...dep	...	5 53	7 41	11 3	14 48	1728	20 4	...	...
La Voulte ...arr	...	6 1	7 48	11 11	14 55	1736	2012	...	...
,, ...dep	...	6 26	—	11 29	14 59	1745	2042	...	...
Soyons..............	...	6 50	...	11 53	15 20	1811	21 2	...	...
Tournon	...	7 32	...	12 33	15 48	1854	2133	...	...
Peyraud............	6 7	8 38	...	13 37	16 34	20 2	2310	...	...
Chavanay	6 32	9 7	...	14 6	16 59	2033	—	...	...
Givors-Canal ...	7 20	1037	...	15 1	17 47	2135	...	...	...
Lyons-Perrache	8 5	1057	...	15 51	18 16	2226	...	...	...

Station							
Le Teil ...dep	...	5 4	8 59	1221	1435	17 7	2229
Vogué ...arr	...	5 53	9 52	13 8	1530	1758	2317
Vogué ...dep	...	6 15	10 10	1328	1545	1819	2330
Vals-les-Bains	...	6 56	10 49	14 6	1623	19 0	0 2
Lalevade-d'Ardèche-P.	...	7 5	10 58	1415	1632	19 9	0 10
Vogué ...dep	...	6 10	10 15	1335	—	1833	—
Ruoms	...	6 33	10 37	1357	...	1857	...
Robiac ...arr	...	7 28	11 31	1449	...	20 1	...
„ ...dep	5 6	7 38	11 45	1458	1625	2011	...
Alais 58 ...arr	5 54	8 30	12 46	1553	18 8	21 8	...

Station							
Alais ...dep	...	6 35	10 34	...	14 55	1817	2214
Robiac ...arr	...	7 27	11 24	...	16 0	1910	23 3
„ ...dep	...	7 39	11 34	...	16 15	1920	—
Ruoms	...	8 36	12 29	...	17 21	2020	...
Vogué ...arr	...	8 57	12 50	...	17 42	2041	...
Lalevade d'Ardèche-P.	4 43	8 5	12 3	1438	17 2	1951	2215
Vals-les-Bains	4 52	8 19	12 16	1450	17 15	20 3	2224
Vogué ...arr	5 22	8 55	12 53	1522	17 51	2035	2253
Vogué ...dep	5 35	9 12	13 14	1537	18 10	2058	—
Le Teil 62 ...arr	6 21	9 56	13 57	1622	18 56	2143	...

Station								
Robiac ...dep	7 50	11 48	15 4	16 22	1923	2015	23 5	...
Bessèges ...arr	8 0	11 54	1510	16 32	1933	2025	23 10	...

Station								
Bessèges ...dep	4 58	7 15	11 18	14 39	1558	17 0	19 0	19 50
Robiac ...arr	5 6	7 24	11 27	14 48	16 5	17 9	19 9	19 59

Station	
Robiac ...dep	17 35
La Valette arr	17 42

Station	
La Valette ...dep	6 34
Robiac ...arr	6 40

Station			
Vogué ...dep	6 25	10 20	18 29
Largentière ...arr	7 7	11 4	19 6

Station				
Largentière ...dep	4 34	8 7	1656	...
Vogué ...arr	5 12	8 45	1741	...

ST. GERMAIN-DES-FOSSES and DARSAC.

Station					To Thiers				A—Tues. only, until 26th Aug.	B—Thurs. only, until 28th Aug.
St. Germain-des Fosses ...dep	6 30	4 56	9 48	1030	...	1520	1622	1816	21 1	2325
Vichy ...arr	6 45	5 11	10 6	1045	1224	1535	1637	1830	2119	2340
Ris-Chateldon	—	5 43	—	1120		16 7	1727	—	—	—
Courty (63B) ...arr	...	6 14	...	1150	1310	1637	1759	...		
Pont-de-Dore (63B)	...	6 35	...	12 4	A	—	18 6	...		
Giroux	...	7 47	...	1319	...	...	2015	...		
Ambert	5 10	8 35	...	1410		...	2114	...		
Arlanc	5 40	9 14	...	1438		...	2143	...		
La Chaise-Dieu	6 44	1020	...	16 5		...	—	...		
Sembadel	7 2	1035	...	1624		...	...	...		
Darsac ...arr	7 48	1116	...	17 7	...	...	...	...		

Station				To Royat			From Thiers		
Darsac ...dep		...	5 53		...	...	...	13 1	18 0
Sembadel		...	7 3		...	...		1354	19 0
La Chaise-Dieu		...	7 16		...	...		14 4	1912
Arlanc		4 12	8 33		...	...		16 5	2012
Ambert		4 38	9 15		...	...		1640	2036
Giroux		5 23	10 1		...	...	...	1730	—
Pont-de-Dore		6 0	1040		1139	--	A	1811	2030
Courty ...dep		6 55	—		1153	1537	1718	—	2039
Ris-Chateldon		7 26	...	B	1223	16 6	...	...	2110
Vichy 58	4 32	8 6	9 31	1120	1249	1638	18 7	1925	2215
St. Germain	4 47	8 21	9 46	...	...	1656	...	1940	2230

Station							
St. Germain ...dep	3 0	1330	1634	17 2	18 2	20 4	20‡40
Vichy ...arr	3 15	1349	1654	1717	1816	2019	20 54

Station										
Vichy ...dep	5 42	7 10	9*15	11 45	1255	13 33	14 0	1540	1737	23 6
St. Germain arr	5 57	7 25	9 30	11 59	1310	13 50	1415	1555	1752	2321

*—Runs until 8th September. ‡—Runs until 7th September.

GRENOBLE and BOURG d'OISANS.

*—From 16th Sept. ‡—Until 15th Sept.

Station																	
Grenoble (P.L.M.) ...dep	...	5 50	6‡55	6 58	7 55	...	...	1058	1129	12 54	...	...	15 55	...	17 30	...	2039
„ (Sq. des Postes)	4 45	6 2	7 2	7 12	8 5	9 10	1010	1110	1210	13 10	14 10	15 10	16 10	17 10	18 0	19 5	2049
Gieres	5 5	6 22	...	7 33	8 25	9 30	1030	1130	1230	13 30	14 30	15 30	16 30	17 30	18 19	19 25	21 9
Uriage	5 27	6 44	7 39	7 57	8 47	9 52	1052	1152	1252	13 52	14 52	15 52	16 52	17 52	18 42	19 50	2131
Vizille-Ville ...arr	5 53	7 10	8 0	8 24	9 13	1018	1118	1218	1318	14 18	15 18	16 18	17 18	18 18	19 7	20 16	2158
Sechilienne	6 35	—	...	9 *1	9‡56	—	—	—	—	—	—	—	—	—	19 50	—	—
Bourg d'Oisans ...arr	7 50	...	9 20	10*20	11‡14	...	...	...	...	...	...	...	...	...	21 5	...	...

Station																		
Bourg d'Oisans ...dep	...	...	4 20	...	...	...	8 48	...	...	...	...	1345	...	...	...	17*40	18‡10	1840
Sechilienne	...	...	5 30	...	...	...	10 0	...	...	...	...	15 0	...	...	...	18 50	...	1950
Vizille-Ville ...dep	4 15	5 5	6 5	7 27	8 42	9 42	1034	1149	1242	1335	1442	1535	1649	1742	1850	19 26	19 20	2033
Uriage	4 46	5 36	6 36	8 0	9 12	1012	11 2	1212	1312	14 5	1512	16 5	1712	1812	1921	20 1	19 49	21 5
Gieres	5 4	5 54	6 53	8 18	9 31	1031	1123	1231	1331	1423	1531	1623	1731	1831	1940	20 19	20 5	2122
Grenoble (Sq. des Postes)...	5 25	6 15	7 14	8 37	9 54	1054	1143	1249	1349	1441	1549	1642	1749	1849	20 2	20 38	20 25	2140
„ (P.L.M.) ...arr	5 31	6 21	7 20	...	10 0	11 0	1149	...	...	1446	...	1648	...	...	20 8	...	20 50	...

Station																		
Vizille (Pl. Chât.) ...dep	5 20	6 45	8 0	10 50	14 0	1430	1710	1845	2115	...	...	...	...	...	...	...	...	...
Jarrie-Vizille (P.L.M.) arr	5 33	6 58	8 13	11 3	1413	1453	1723	1858	2128	...	...	...	...	...	...	...	...	...
Jarrie-Vizille (P.L.M.) dep	4 37	6 12	7 22	10 7	13 10	1347	1555	18 0	1930	...	...	...	...	...	...	...	...	...
Vizille (Pl. Chât.) ...arr	4 50	6 25	7 35	1020	13 23	14 0	16 8	1813	1943	...	...	...	...	...	...	...	...	...

GRENOBLE, LANCEY, and FROGES.

Station					
Grenoble ...dep	5 15	6 33	7 38	8 40	And hourly at 40 mins. past the hour until 17.40; also at 18.43 and 19.44.
Gieres	5 36	6 52	8 0	9 0	
Domene	5 53	7 9	8 16	9 16	
Lancey	6 5	7 22	8 31	9 31	
Froges ...arr	6 19	7 38	8 45	9 45	

Station						
Froges ...dep	4 45	6 39	7 48	9 15	...	And hourly at 15 mins past the hour until 18.15; also at 19.20 and 20.20.
Lancey	5 1	6 55	8 3	9 30	...	
Domene	5 15	7 8	8 16	9 43	...	
Gieres	5 36	7 2	8 34	10 1	...	
Grenoble ...arr	5 57	7 46	8 53	1020	...	

ST. RAMBERT, RIVES, and GRENOBLE.

Dist	Station					
	Saint Rambert ...dep	5 35	7 19	13 23	17 12	21 2
13	Beaurepaire	6 8	7 52	13 55	17 46	21 35
23	La Côte-St.-Andre	6 36	8 20	14 22	18 15	22 3
34¾	**Rives (63A)** ...arr	7 8	8 52	14 54	18 49	22 35
57½	GRENOBLE ...arr	8 0	1012	16 2	20 2	0 9

Station						
GRENOBLE ...dep	...	8 18	11 48	15 22	18 42	...
Rives ...dep	5 10	9 32	13 25	16 41	19 53	...
La Côte-St.-Andre 52A	5 42	10 4	13 59	17 13	20 26	...
Beaurepaire	6 11	10 31	14 36	17 42	20 54	...
Saint Rambert ...arr	6 40	10 58	15 5	18 10	21 26	...

VALENCE and CHAMBERY.

Station									
Valence ...dep	...	6 3	4 32	8 32	1050	13 0	1659	2015	2333
Romans	...	7 10	5 7	9 5	1130	1324	1733	2054	0 13
St. Marcel	...	8 30	5 55	9 50	—	1357	1819	2143	—
Moirans	...	—	6 44	1037	...	1431	19 9	2234	...
Grenoble ...	...	...	7 10	11 3	...	1449	1935	23 0	...
„ ...dep	5 15	8 15	8 31	1117	17 0	15 1	2027	—	...
Gières-Uriage	...	...	8 41	1126	17 9	...	2036	...	...
Goncelin	5 56	.	9 22	12 3	1747	...	2114	...	...
Pontcharra-s-B	6 13	8 50	9 41	1220	18 5	153[illegible]	2131	...	...
Montmélian ...	6 30	9 1	10 0	1237	1822	1548	2147	...	...
Chambéry ...	6 47	9 14	1018	1255	1840	16 1	22 2	...	...

Station									
Chambery dep	5 10	...	6 5	8 15	...	1330	1715	1950	2128
Montmélian...	5 32	...	6 22	8 38	...	1351	1737	2013	2148
Pontcharra 47	5 48	...	6 35	8 55	...	14 6	1752	2029	2152
Goncelin	6 4	...	...	9 11	...	1422	18 8	2045	...
Gières Uriage	6 42	...	...	9 51	...	15 1	1847	2123	...
Grenoble...	6 50	...	7 13	9 59	...	15 9	1855	2131	2226
„ ...	—	4 51	7 30	1048	...	1547	1933	—	—
Moirans	...	5 18	7 50	1117	...	16 9	20 3	...	...
St. Marcellin	...	6 14	8 34	12 9	...	17 5	2056	...	...
Romans	3 50	7 6	9 10	1257	1447	1754	2144	...	...
Valence arr	4 22	7 34	9 31	1325	1525	1822	2212	...	...

ST. PIERRE d'ALBIGNY & MOUTIERS SALINS.

‡—Runs until September 20th.

Station					
CHAMBERY ...dep	6 5[illegible]	...	11 12	1612	1840
St. Pierre d'Albigny dep	7 29	10‡36	12 10	17 7	1927
Albertville ...arr	8 5	11 7	12 46	1745	20 3
„ ...dep	8 20	11 34	13 9	1810	2018
Cevins	8 43	...	13 32	1837	2041
Moutiers Salins ...arr	9 6	12 14	13 55	19 0	21 4

Station					
Moutiers Sal. dep	5 0	7 23	12 3	1712	18‡1
Cevins	5 23	7 48	12 30	1735	...
Albertville ...arr	5 44	8 10	12 51	1756	18 39
„ ...dep	5 55	8 30	13 25	1816	18 54
St. Pierre d'A. arr	6 31	9 7	14 7	1852	19 25
CHAMBERY 61 arr	7 27	9 47	15 3	...	19 49

MOUTIERS and BRIDES-LES-BAINS. Tramway.—From Moutiers (in half-an-hour), service about hourly from 5.30 to 19.30. From Brides, service about hourly from 6.10 to 18.35.

PARIS, LYONS, and MEDITERRANEAN RAILWAY. [66 lbs. of Luggage free.

AVALLON and NUITS-sous-RAVIERES.	E.M.									
		Avallon dep	5 35	12 15	1752	**Nuits-sous-Ravieres** dep	8 5	12 2	17 25	...
	8½	L'Isle-sur-Serein	6 22	13 20	1819	L'Isle-sur-Serein	9 1	13 10	18 21	...
	27½	Nuits-sous-Ravieres (48) arr	7 26	14 40	1911	**Avallon (63A)** arr	9 30	13 50	19 0	...

PARIS, FONTAINEBLEAU, and MONTEREAU.

	1,2,3	1Cl.	1,2,3	1,2,3	1,2,3	1,2,3	1,2,3	1,2,3	1,2,3	1,2,3	1,2,3	1 Cl.	1,2,3	1,2,3	1,2,3	1,2,3	1,2,3	1,2,3	1,2,3	1,2,3	1 Cl	1,2,3	1,2,3	1,2,3	1 Cl	1,2,3	1,2,3	1,2,3
Paris—Boulevard Diderot dp	6 0	7 10	7 25	7 40	8 33	9 15	9 25	9*57	1015	1040	1115	11 40	12 5	1355	1450	16 5	16 0	17 5	1725	1755	18 0	1845	1940	2140	2225	2240	23 0	0 35
V.-St.-Georges ...	6 18	...	...	...	...	9 44	...	...	1043	...	...	...	...	...	1519	...	16 8	...	1742	...	...	...	...	...	...	2311	...	...
Brunoy	6 31	...	...	8 8	9 5	9 57	...	10 26	1058	...	...	...	1233	1428	1533	...	16 3	...	1756	1824	...	1917	2013	...	...	2326	...	1 4
Melun	7 5	...	8 12	8 42	9 44	—	1011	11 2	1132	1123	12 4	12 27	1320	15 7	16 6	1652	17 5	17 51	1827	1853	1940	1950	2050	2228	...	24 0	2346	1 39
Fontainebleau ...	7 27	...	8 35	9 5	10 12	...	1034	11 23	—	1142	1229	12 48	1344	1531	—	1715	—	18 14	—	1914	1957	—	2114	2251	...	—	0 8	2 3
Moret	7 41	...	8 44	9 20	10 32	...	1046	11 41	...	1152	1238	...	14 0	1547	...	1727	...	18 25	...	1928	...	...	2123	23 0	...	...	0 23	2 15
Montereau arr	7 57	8 19	...	9 37	10 48	...	...	11 58	...	...	...	13 8	1417	16 3	...	1740	...	...	...	1944	1916	...	...	...	2334	...	0 39	2 29

Other Stations: Charenton, Maisons-Alfort, Montgeron, Combs-la-Ville, Lieusaint, Cesson, Bois-le-Roi, Thomery, St. Mammes.

	1,2,3	1 Cl	1,2,3	1,2,3	1 Cl	1,2,3	1,2,3	1,2,3	1,2,3	1,2,3	1Cl.	1,2,3	1,2,3	1,2,3	1,2,3	1,2,3	1 Cl	1,2,3	1,2,3	1,2,3	1,2,3	1,2,3	1,2,3	1,2,3	1,2,3	1Cl.
Montereau dep	2 7	3 32	...	4 27	4 30	5 46	6 36	...	8 16	9 10	9 59	...	1018	1155	1252	...	1540	1550	...	1716	1746	...	1933	...	22 4	2242
Moret	2 25	...	4 10	4 46	...	...	7 6	...	8 48	9 29	...	1019	1037	1213	1319	1450	...	1610	17 0	1750	...	1913	1954	21 8	2220	...
Fontainebleau ...	2 39	3 53	4 22	5 2	...	...	7 24	...	9 1	9 46	...	1033	1053	1225	1333	15 8	...	1627	1713	18 8	...	1929	2011	2122	2235	23 1
Melun	3 1	4 11	4 43	5 24	5 8	6 49	7 48	8 24	9 23	1010	...	1056	1116	1246	14 1	1531	...	1651	1735	1834	1853	1951	2034	2139	2256	2316
Brunoy	3 33	...	5 19	6 1	...	7 23	...	9 3	9 51	1048	...	...	1153	1316	1438	16 8	...	1730	...	...	1929	...	2113	...	2322	...
Villeneuve-S-G ...	3 51	...	5 35	...	...	...	...	9 18	...	11 3	...	...	12 7	1329	1452	...	...	...	...	...	1948	...	...	...	...	...
Paris arr	4 20	4 55	5 50	6 33	6 0	7 48	8 30	9 36	1017	1121	11 8	1142	1223	1345	15 8	1635	1710	1755	1820	1920	20 0	2038	2138	2220	2345	2355

Via CORBEIL.

Paris-Boulevard Diderot ...dep	5 10	7 34	9 25	10 0	14 0	1450	1640	1723	18 5	1940	2025
Corbeil	6 24	8 42	...	11 0	15 9	...	1726	1815	1858	...	2131
Melun	7 11	9 26	1020	11 43	1548	1610	18 9	—	1942	2123	2210
Montereau arr	8 11	1048	1121	13 19	...	1710	1911	...	...	2223	...

Montereau dep	...	5 46	...	8 16	...	9 47	...	...	1410	1550	1746	1952
Melun	6 32	6 49	7 12	9 26	...	1056	12 35	...	1514	1656	1853	2110
Corbeil	7 26	:	7 53	1014	1053	:	13 29	1438	:	1740	:	22 0
Paris ...arr	8 11	7 49	8 46	1049	1158	1142	14 8	1545	1635	1835	20 0	2258

ST. RAMBERT D'ALBON and FIRMINY.

St. Rambert ...	...	...	7 15	8 10	10 33	12 0	1319	1820	1933	22 8
Peyraud (63) ...	...	...	7 23	8 36	10 44	12 8	1345	1836	1957	2230
Annonay	...	6 16	7 51	9 27	11 12	1345	1416	1924	2042	23 1
Bourg-Argental	4 43	6 47	—	10 4	—	1422	—	20 4	21 8	—
Dunières	5 51	7 55	...	1111	...	1537	...	2120	—	...
Firminy 52A arr	6 45	8 53	...	12 4	...	1632	...	2216	...	...

Firminy ...dep	...	...	7 21	...	10 0	13 6	...	...	1728	1934
Dunières	...	...	8 37	...	11 9	1417	...	...	1834	2047
Bourg-Argental	4 26	...	9 33	...	12 0	1511	...	...	1931	2143
Annonay	5 3	7 25	1013	1215	—	1554	1720	1919	20 8	22 7
Peyraud	5 40	8 43	1045	1250	...	1638	1752	20 5	2043	—
St. Rambert a.	5 45	8 49	1050	1255	...	1643	1757	2010	2048	...

MOULINS and PARAY-LE-MONIAL.

E.M.							
	Moulins dep	4 4	8 23	11 35	16 2	20 0	...
17¼	Dompierre-Sept-Fons	4 41	9 2	12 15	1644	21 9	...
23	Gilly (57)	4 59	9 20	12 34	17 3	21 50	...
34¾	Digoin	5 24	9 48	13 2	1732	22 32	...
41¾	**Paray-Monial** ...arr	5 37	10 1	13 15	1746	22 55	...

Paray-le-M. ...dep	8 28	9 59	13 32	1654	2114				
Digoin	8 45	10 14	13 49	1712	2132	...	...	...	...
Gilly	9 12	10 34	14 18	1740	22 0	...	...	...	...
Dompierre-Sept-Fons	9 29	...	14 35	1757	2217	...	...	...	...
Moulins 58 ... arr	10 5	1110	15 11	1833	2253	...	...	...	...

BONSON and SEMBADEL.

Bonson ...dep	...	7 57	12 55	...	1651	18 47	...	...
St. Bonnet	5 25	9 6	14 3	...	18 3	19 57	...	...
Craponne	6 17	9 57	14 50	1542	—	20 46	...	...
Sembadel ...arr	6 45	10 25	...	1610	...	...	...	...

Sembadel ...dep	...	7 19	14 5	18 58	...	...	...	...	...
Craponne	4 32	8 4	15 13	19 33	...	...	...	...	...
St. Bonnet	5 18	9 4	16 9	20 23	...	...	...	...	...
Bonson (63B) ...arr	6 19	10 8	17 15	21 21	...	...	...	...	...

BEAUJEU and BELLEVILLE.

Beaujeu ...dep	4 49	7 30	10 10	13 11	18 16	2047	...	...
Belleville (49) arr	5 9	8 12	10 30	13 50	18 41	2110	...	...
Belleville dep	6 20	9 26	12 26	17 0	1913	22 39	...	...
Beaujeu ...arr	7 0	9 49	12 46	17 40	1936	22 59	...	...

ROANNE and CHALON.

Dist. E.M.										
	Roanne dep	...	4 55	6 34	8 22	11 15	13 13	...	1630	1935
11¾	Pouilly-s.-Charlieu	...	5 23	7 1	9 2	11 40	13 38	...	17 7	1959
27½	La Clayette-Baud	...	6 42	—	10 12	—	14 22	...	18 5	—
47½	Clermain	...	7 40	...	11 24	...	—	*	1922	...
53¾	Cluny (63)	6 34	8 14	...	12 25	...	...	1622	2015	...
66¾	St. Gengoux (63)	7 18	8 50	...	13 7	...	...	17 0	2054	...
84¾	**Chalon (48)** arr	8 17	9 41	...	14 9	...	...	18 6	2147	...

*—Sat. and Sun. only.

Chalon dep	...	6 13	10 19	...	1214	...	17 1	19*54
St. Gengoux	...	7 12	11 22	...	1311	...	18 1	20 52
Cluny	...	8 28	11 59	...	15 9	...	1924	21 29
Clermain	...	8 51	—	...	1536	...	1950	—
La Clayette-Baud	6 18	10 14	...	...	1642	...	2055	...
Pouilly-s.-Charlieu	7 0	11 43	13 22	15 7	1735	1944	2146	...
Roanne (51B) arr	7 43	12 25	13 49	1532	18 5	2012	2215	...

MONTEREAU and SOUPPES.

E.M							
	Montereau ...dep	...	8 55	...	1435	...	1955
19¼	Egreville	7 5	1028	1236	1615	1737	2135
28	**Souppes (58)** arr	7 43	...	1314	...	1815	...

Souppes dep	...	9 40	14 8	...	1924
Egreville	6 20	10 30	14 47	16 45	20 3
Montereau (63) arr	7 49	11 59	...	18 19	...

Souppes dep	6 38	9 39	14 6	19 25	...	...
Chateau Landon arr	6 55	9 56	1423	19 42	...	...
Chateau Landon dep	5 50	9 3	13 0	18 0	...	...
Souppes arr	6 6	9 19	13 16	18 16	...	...

ST. GENGOUX and MONTCHANIN.

E.M							
	St. Gengoux depart	7 22	13 23	20 58	...	...	...
16¼	**Montchanin (53A)** arrive	8 20	14 43	21 59	...	...	...

Montchanin depart	5 55	11 28	1620	...	...
St. Gengoux (63) arrive	6 47	12 37	1750	...	...

66 lbs. of Luggage free. [Excess Luggage, 1 cent. per 44 lbs. per kilometre.

MARSEILLES, TARASCON, LYONS, MACON, DIJON, and PARIS.

RC—Restaurant Car attached.

1	2	3	4	5	6	7	8	9	10	11	12	13	14	15	16	17	18	19	20	21	22	23	24	25	26	27	
MENTON 55 ....dep	...	...	...	...	...	...	...	...	...	...	...	0 17	...	...	...	...	...	5 46	...	...	...	...	...	...	...	...	...
NICE 55..............dep	...	...	...	...	...	...	...	...	...	...	...	1 18	...	...	...	...	...	7 2	...	...	...	...	...	...	...	...	...
CANNES 55 ....dep	...	...	...	...	...	...	...	...	...	...	...	2 3	...	...	...	...	...	7 49	...	...	...	...	...	...	...	...	...
	1,2,3	1,2,3		1 & 2	1,2,3			1,2,3	1,2,3	1,2,3	1,2,3	1,2,3	1,2,3	1 & 2	1,2,3	1,2,3		1,2,3		1,2,3	1,2,3			1,2,3		1,2,3	
MARSEILLES—																											
St. Charles ......dep	...	...	...	...	...	...	...	...	...	...	4 45	6 0	7 5	9 0	8 10	10 17	...	11 50	...	...	...	...	...	...	...	14 12	...
L'Estaque	...	...	...	...	...	...	...	...	...	...	5 3	T	7 19	M	...	...	...	...	...	...	...	...	...	...	...	14 28	...
Pas-des-Lanciers	...	...	...	...	...	...	...	...	...	...	5 15	...	7 30	...	...	...	...	T	...	...	...	...	...	...	...	14 41	...
Rognac ....arr	...	...	...	...	...	...	...	...	...	...	5 29	6 24	7 40	...	...	10 45	...	12 19	...	...	...	...	...	...	...	14 56	...
Saint Chamas	...	...	...	...	...	...	...	...	...	...	6 4	...	8 14	...	...	11 16	...	...	...	...	...	...	...	...	...	15 35	...
Miramas	...	...	...	...	...	...	...	...	...	...	6 19	6 53	8 26	...	...	11 30	...	12 47	...	...	...	...	...	...	...	15 50	...
Arles 57 .... arr	...	...	...	...	...	...	...	...	...	...	7 3	7 20	9 7	...	9 24	12 12	...	13 15	...	...	...	...	...	...	...	16 37	...
Arles 57 .... dep	...	...	...	...	...	...	...	...	...	...	7 31	7 24	9 35	...	9 26	12 22	...	13 22	...	...	...	...	...	...	...	16 47	...
Tarascon ....arr	...	...	...	...	...	...	...	...	...	...	7 52	7 38	9 54	10 23	9 40	12 41	...	13 36	...	...	...	...	...	...	...	17 6	...
BARCELONA 295......dep	...	...	...	18 51	...	...	...	...	...	...	...	...	...	...	...	...	...	...	...	...	...	...	...	...	...	...	...
NARBONNE 45B ......dep	...	...	...	1 35	...	...	...	...	...	...	...	...	4 20	4 20	...	9 11	...	9 11	...	...	...	...	...	...	...	13 24	...
CETTE 57 ....dep	...	...	...	3 0	...	...	...	...	...	...	4 5	4 5	7 20	7 20	...	10 50	...	10 50	...	...	...	...	...	...	...	14 40	...
Tarascon..............dep	...	...	...	5 18	5 40	...	...	...	...	...	8 20	7 48	10 37	10 29	...	13 3	...	13 44	...	...	...	...	...	...	...	17 31	...
Barbentane.....................	...	...	...	...	6 5	...	...	...	...	...	8 46	...	11 0	...	...	13 25	...	...	...	...	...	...	...	...	...	18 1	...
Avignon 63A ...... arr	...	...	...	5 40	6 14	...	...	...	...	...	8 55	8 7	11 9	10 51	...	13 34	...	14 6	...	...	...	...	...	...	...	18 10	...
Avignon 63A ...... dep	...	...	...	5 48		...	...	...	5 57	8 24	9 20	8 15	11 50	10 57	...		...	14 20	...	...	16 0	...	...	...	...	18 57	...
Sorgues	...	...	...	...	...	...	...	...	6 17	8 40	9 40	...	12 10	...	...	...	...	14 33	...	...	16 20	...	...	...	...	19 22	...
Courthezon.....................	...	...	...	...	...	...	...	...	6 34		9 56	...	12 26	RC	...	...	...	...	...	...	16 37	...	...	...	...	19 38	...
Orange..........................	...	4 47	...	Y	...	...	...	...	6 52	...	10 15	8 42	12 47	...	...	...	...	14 56	...	...	16 57	...	...	...	...	19 57	...
Bollène La Croisière	...	5 9	...	...	...	...	...	...	7 24	...	10 47	9 1	13 19	...	...	...	...	15 16	...	...	17 36	...	...	...	...	20 35	...
Pierrelatte	...	5 28	...	...	...	...	...	...	7 48	...	11 9	9 14	13 39	...	...	...	...	T	...	...	17 54	...	...	...	...	21 43	...
Châteauneuf-du-Rhone ...	...	5 46	...	...	...	...	...	...	8 7	...	11 29	...	13 58	...	...	...	...	...	...	...	18 14	...	...	...	...	22 2	...
Montelimar............ arr	...	5 57	...	7 0	...	...	...	...	8 18	...	11 41	9 33	14 9	...	...	...	...	15 47	...	...	18 25	...	...	...	...	22 13	...
Montelimar............ dep	...	6 1	...	7 2	...	...	...	...	8 28	...	12 13	9 37	14 17	...	...	...	...	15 52	...	...	18 32	...	...	...	...	22 50	
Loriol	...	6 33	...	...	...	...	...	...	9 2	...	12 46	...	14 51	...	...	...	...	...	...	...	19 6	...	...	...	...	22 52	
Livron .... arr	...	6 38	...	...	...	...	...	...	9 7	...	12 51	9 59	14 56	...	...	...	...	16 17	...	...	19 11	...	...	...	...	22 57	
Livron .... dep	...	6 47	...	...	...	...	...	...	9 13	11 43	12 57	10 4	15 10	...	...	...	...	16 21	...	18 25	19 23	...	...	21 1	...	23 2	
Valence 62A ...... arr	...	7 14	...	7 41	...	...	...	...	9 40	12 7	13 23	10 20	15 36	12 43	...	...	...	16 38	...	18 52	19 50	...	...	21 27	...	23 26	
Valence 62A ...... dep	5 30		...	7 49	...	...	...	8 38	10 42		13 59	10 30	15 53	12 49	...	...	...	16 52	...		20 26	...	...		...		
Tain	5 55	...	...	...	...	...	...	9 3	11 7	...	14 25	...	16 18	...	...	...	...	17 11	...	...	20 52	...	...	...	...	...	
Saint-Vallier	6 17	...	...	...	...	...	...	9 25	11 29	...	14 48	...	16 40	...	...	...	...	...	...	...	21 15	...	...	...	...	...	
St. Rambert...... arr	6 34	...	...	...	...	...	...	9 42	11 46	...	15 5	11 7	16 57	...	...	...	...	17 38	...	...	21 33	...	...	...	...	...	
St. Rambert...... dep	6 56	...	...	...	...	...	...	9 55	11 57	...	15 24	11 10	18 23	...	...	...	...	17 41	...	...	22 2	...	...	...	...	...	
Les Roches de Condrieux	7 27	...	...	...	...	...	...	10 26	12 28	...	16 4	...	19 4	...	...	...	...	...	...	...	22 16	...	...	...	...	...	
Vienne	7 49	...	...	...	...	...	...	10 51	12 51	...	16 16	11 36	19 16	...	...	...	...	18 10	...	...	23 10	...	...	...	...	...	
Chasse 56...................	8 11	...	...	...	...	...	...	11 13	13 11	...	16 39	...	19 37	...	...	...	...	18 25	§	...	23 32	...	...	...	...	...	
Lyons Perrache ......arr	8 44	...	...	9 19	...	...	...	11 50	13 47	...	17 13	12 2	20 10	14 19	...	...	...	18 46	...	...	0 3	...	...	...	...	...	
GENEVA 60 ....arr	...	...	...	16 17	...	...	...	16 51	19 38	...	0 43	16 51	...	19 38	...	...	...	0 43	...	...	...	...	...	...	...	...	
GRENOBLE 63A ......dep	...	...	...	6 35	...	...	6 35		...	11 48		8 18	15 22	...	...	...	...		15 22	15 22	...	...	...	19 10	...	...	
		1,2,3	1,2,3	1 & 2	2 & 3	Lux.	1,2,3	1,2,3	1,2,3	1,2,3		1,2,3	1,2,3	1 & 2	1 & 2	1,2,3	1,2,3	1,2,3	1 Cl.	1,2,3	1 & 2	1,2,3		1,2,3	1,2,3		
Lyons Perrache......dep	...	3 58	7 34	9 39	...	...	10 38	...	15 2	17 30	...	13 5	20 53	14 34	...	...	...	...	19 40	20 40	...	...	...	23 17	...	...	
Lyons Vaise ...... arr	...	4 4	7 41	...	...	...	10 45	...	15 9	17 37	...	13 11	21 0	...	...	...	...	...	19 46	20 46	...	...	...	23 24	...	...	
Lyons Vaise ...... dep	...	4 9	7 50	RC	8 21	...	10 52	¶	15 15	17 44	...	13 15	21 7	...	...	...	...	...	19 50	20 49	...	...	...	23 26	22 8	...	
Collonges Fontaines.........	...	4 21	8 5	...	8 31	...	11 7	13 27	15 30	...	...	T	21 20	M	...	...	...	...	...	...	...	...	...	...	22 21	...	
Villevert-Neuville	...	4 33	8 19	...	8 46	...	11 21	13 37	15 44	...	...	...	21 33	...	...	...	...	...	...	T	...	...	...	...	22 33	...	
Saint Germain	...	4 41	8 29	Y	8 51	...	11 30	13 42	15 54	18 6	...	13 31	21 42	...	...	...	...	...	...	21 5	...	...	...	23 42	22 38	...	
Quincieux-Trevoux	...	4 49	8 38	...	8 59	...	11 40	13 50	16 4	18 15	...	...	21 51	...	...	...	...	...	...	...	...	...	...	...	22 46	...	
Villefranche-sur-Saône ...	...	5 8	8 55	10 14	9 10	...	11 58	14 2	16 26	18 34	...	13 47	22 10	...	...	...	...	...	20 16	21 19	...	...	...	23 58	22 57	...	
Belleville 63	...	5 30	9 17	...		...	12 22	14 19	16 48	18 55	...	14 4	22 31	...	...	...	...	...	20 31	21 34	...	...	...	0 14		...	
Romanèche.....................	...	5 41	9 29	...	...	...	12 34	14 28	16 59	19 5	...	...	22 42	...	...	...	...	...	...	...	...	...	...	...	...	...	
Macon....................arr	...	6 5	9 54	10 51	...	...	13 1	14 49	17 25	19 30	...	14 25	23 5	15 33	...	...	...	...	20 51	21 54	...	...	...	0 38	...	...	

§—Lyons Brotteaux Station.

For Notes and Continuation

A—Runs until 30th September.

LYONS, GRENOBLE, AIX, and MARSEILLES.

Lyons—															
Perrache ......dep		...	...	...	...	3 50	6 53	8 24	9 56	12 8	15 0	1824	1730	2022	0 33
St-Quentin-Fallav.		...	...	...	...	4 15	...	9 2	...	1248	1543	19 3	...	21 3	...
Bourgoin		...	...	...	...	4 33	7 37	9 24	1035	1318	1616	1925	18 9	2134	1 27
La Tour-du-P. 63A		...	...	...	...	4 59	8 6	—	1057	1350	1646	—	1831	2211	2 2
St. André G.		...	...	...	...	5 15	8 29	...	1112	1416	1713	...	1847	2232	2 25
Chabons		...	...	...	...	5 39	8 55	...	...	1442	1739	...	...	2258	...
Rives (62A)		...	...	...	7 12	5 59	9 18	...	1148	15 7	18 1	...	1924	2321	3 20
Voiron (53B)		...	...	...	7 25	6 11	9 34	...	12 0	1523	1816	...	1936	2335	3 42
Moirans (62A)		...	...	...	7 35	...	9 47	...	12 9	1537	1829	...	1945	2344	3 54
Grenoble.........arr		...	...	...	8 0	6 37	1012	...	1226	16 2	1854	...	20 2	0 9	4 19
„ (62A)..dep		4 40	...	5 19	—	7 24	—	...	1315	—	—	18 5	2041	—	—
Jarrie-Vizille		5 1	...	...	...	7 47	...	...	1336	...	...	1826	21 8	...	...
St.Georges-de-Com		5 13	...	...	...	7 59	...	...	1349	...	...	1838	2121	...	...
Vif		5 17	...	5 49	...	8 8	...	...	1359	...	...	1846	2125	...	...
Clelles		—	...	7 1	...	9 23	...	...	1515	...	...	2013	—	...	...
Veynes...........arr		...	...	8 37	...	1058	...	...	1650	...	...	2147	...	...	...
„ ....dep		5 0	...	—	...	1130	...	...	1711	...	18 8	—	...	...	...
Chabestan		5 12	...	...	...	1142	...	...	1723	...	A	...	...	...	...
Sisteron		6 13	...	...	...	1247	...	...	1828	...	1914	...	...	...	...
Saint Auban ...arr		6 36	...	...	...	1310	...	...	1851	...	1933	...	...	...	...
„ (56)...dep		6 43	...	...	...	1315	...	...	1858	...	1936	...	...	...	...
Volx (63A)		7 24	...	...	...	14 0	...	...	1944	...	2014	...	...	...	...
Mirabeau		8 8	...	...	...	1440	...	...	2025	...	2047	...	...	...	...
Pertuis...........arr		8 25	...	...	...	1457	...	...	2042	...	21 4	...	...	...	...
„ ....dep		8 43	...	1236	...	1517	...	17 9	2127	...	2114	...	...	...	4 57
Meyrargues		8 55	...	1249	...	1529	...	1723	2143	...	2124	...	...	...	5 13
Aix.........arr	...	9 42	...	1343	...	1618	...	1819	2234	...	22 0	...	...	...	6 18
„ (49B) dep	8 40	9 54	1249	1356	...	1632	1716	1831	2250	...	22 2	...	...	5 36	6 38
Gardanne	9 2	1017	13 8	1418	...	1654	1741	1852	2314	...	2217	...	...	5 56	7 1
Septemes	9 24	1035	1330	1440	...	1710	18 4	1914	2334	...	...	...	...	6 18	7 26
Marseilles arr	9 53	11 0	14 1	15 9	...	1744	1835	1942	24 0	...	2257	...	...	6 54	7 55

Marseilles ......dep		0 42	...	...	...	4 10	6 4	6 34	8 14	10 0	1339	16 0	1643	18 40	2220
Septemes		1 11	...	...	...	4 39	6 36	A	...	10 37	1411	...	1718	19 15	...
Gardanne........arr		1 28	...	...	...	5 0	6 57	7 16	8 58	10 58	1434	1644	1739	19 36	23 6
Aix..............arr		1 44	...	...	...	5 25	7 18	7 31	9 17	11 19	1455	17 5	18 1	19 56	2324
„ ....dep		—	...	...	8 42	5 40	—	7 35	—	11 33	1513	1719	—	20 11	—
Meyrargues		...	...	...	9 34	6 32	...	8 10	...	12 22	1618	1813	...	21 1	...
Pertuis...........arr		...	...	...	9 43	6 42	...	8 19	...	12 31	1631	1822	...	21 12	...
„ ....dep		...	...	...	—	7 3	...	8 27	...	12 52	—	1844	...	—	...
Mirabeau		...	...	...	...	7 21	...	8 44	...	13 10	...	19 2	...	...	...
Volx		...	...	...	...	8 9	...	9 18	...	13 55	...	1947	...	...	...
Saint Auban...arr		...	...	...	...	8 48	...	9 48	...	14 34	...	2029	...	...	...
„ ...dep		...	...	...	...	8 56	...	9 49	...	14 39	...	2034	...	...	...
Sisteron		6 15	...	...	...	9 26	...	1010	...	15 8	...	21 2	...	...	...
Chabestan		8 4	...	...	...	1035	...	...	...	16 11	...	2211	...	...	...
Veynes...........arr		8 22	...	...	...	1047	...	1110	...	16 23	...	2223	...	...	...
„ ....dep		—	...	4 51	...	1120	...	—	...	16 48	1750	—	...	...	...
Clelles		...	...	6 28	...	1259	...	...	...	18 29	1918	...	...	...	...
Vif		...	6 0	7 32	1015	14 6	1553	...	...	19 40	2012	...	...	...	...
St.Georges-de-Com		...	6 21	7 36	1021	1411	16 5	...	...	19 46	A	...	...	...	...
Jarrie-Vizille		...	6 35	7 45	1034	1421	1618	...	...	19 57	2023	...	...	...	...
Grenoble...arr	...	...	7 2	8 3	11 1	1439	1644	...	...	20 15	2030	...	...	...	...
„ (62A) dep	4 0	6 35	7 30	8 18	1148	1522	—	1842	19 10	—	—	2050	...	22 6	...
Moirans	4 26	6 54	7 47	8 44	1215	1549	...	1910	19 31	...	...	21 7	...	22 54	...
Voiron	4 43	7 7	—	9 1	1233	16 3	...	1926	19 45	...	...	2120	...	23 24	...
Rives	5 23	7 25	...	9 22	1254	1625	...	1941	20 5	...	...	2138	...	24 0	...
Chabons	5 51	...	...	9 48	1321	1652	...	—	20 32	...	...	...	...	...	...
St. André G.	6 17	8 8	...	1018	1348	1724	...	...	21 1	...	...	2219	...	1 25	...
La Tour-du-P.	6 27	8 17	...	1031	1359	1733	...	...	21 16	...	...	2227	...	1 45	...
Bourgoin	6 50	8 33	...	1055	1422	1754	...	1821	21 41	...	...	2243	...	2 13	5 44
St.-Quentin F.	7 20	...	...	...	1450	1810	...	1848	22 11	...	...	...	...	—	6 8
Lyons Perr'he	8 2	9 10	...	1133	1531	1836	...	1930	22 55	...	...	2320	...	...	6 45

VOLX and FORCALQUIER.

Volx..............dep	6 45	...	...	...	...	...
St. Maime	7 15	8 55	1435	2025	...	...
Forcalquier arr	7 35	9 15	1455	2045	...	...

Forcalquier dep	6 35	8 0	12 25	1830	...	...	...
St. Maime	6 53	8 20	12 45	1848	...	...	...
Volx (63A)......arr	...	...	...	...	...	...	...

E.M						
	La Tour-du-Pin dep	8 30	14 10	1835	2126	...
—	Les Avenières ...arr	9 59	15 37	1958	2246	...
	Les Avenières.........dep	6 26	11 55	15 39	1957	...
	La Tour-du-Pin 63A arr	7 50	13 28	17 14	2110	...

CAVAILLON and VOLX.

Cavaillon...dep	...	5 40	9 45	1538	2051
Bonnieux	...	6 53	1021	1626	2137
Apt	5 45	7 15	11 9	1710	2159
Céreste	6 28	—	12 2	18 5	—
St. Maime	7 4	...	13 4	19 2	...
Volx (63A)...arr	7 16	...	1320	1915	...
Volx...........dep	...	8 17	14 5	...	20 0
St. Maime	...	8 45	1421	...	2020
Céreste	...	9 48	15 6	...	21 1
Apt	7 54	1110	16 7	1830	2140
Bonnieux	8 16	1129	1625	1858	—
Cavaillon ...arr	9 6	12 9	17 4	20 3	...

AVIGNON, MIRAMAS, and PERTUIS.

Avignon ....dep	3 58	8 22	...	13 52	1655	...	1922	22 37
Morières	4 15	8 39	...	14 9	1712	...	1939	22 54
L'Isle-sur-Sorgue...	4 45	9 13	...	14 44	1742	...	2017	23 21
Cavaillon ....arr	4 57	9 28	...	14 59	1757	...	2032	23 33
Cavaillon ......dep	5 32	9 50	...	15 31	—	...	20 3	—
Orgon	5 48	10 9	...	15 49	...	...	2111	...
Salon	6 22	10 47	13 0	16 47	...	18 6	2152	...
Miramas ......arr	6 41	11 7	1322	17 6	...	1828	2214	...
Cavaillon.........dep	5 17	10 4	—	15 20	...	—	21 3	...
Cadenet	6 28	11 24	...	16 27	...	...	2213	...
Pertuis (63A) ...arr	6 46	11 51	...	16 45	...	...	2244	...

Salon.........dep	6 30	11 0	1624	...
Aix ....arr	8 5	13 2	1751	...

Pertuis ....dep	4 8	7 19	...	...	12 46	...	...	18 42	...
Cadenet	4 26	7 48	...	...	13 8	...	...	19 5	...
Cavaillon ......arr	5 27	9 1	...	...	14 13	...	...	20 12	...
Miramas.....dep	...	7 30	8 45	11 45	13 7	1611	...	19 6	2220
Salon	...	8 0	9 57	12 6	13 36	1632	...	19 34	2241
Orgon	...	8 35	10 46	—	14 10	—	...	20 9	—
Cavaillon ...arr	...	8 50	11 5	...	14 23	...	...	20 22	...
Cavaillon ......dep	5 43	9 20	12 36	...	14 39	...	1720	20 40	...
L'Isle-sur-Sorgue	6 0	9 44	12 53	...	15 2	...	1745	21 3	...
Morières	6 26	10 12	13 19	...	15 28	...	1815	21 30	...
Avignon.........arr	6 42	10 28	13 35	...	15 44	...	1832	21 46	...

Aix.........dep	8 10	13 7	1830	...	...
Salon ......arr	9 38	15 37	1958	...	...

‡—Runs until 30th September.

CRAVANT and AUTUN.

Cravant (56) ...dep	4 9	7 40	9 40	12 50	1623	1916	21‡55
Arcy-sur-Cure	4 30	8 7	10 6	13 17	1653	1946	22 15
Avallon	5 24	9 39	1125	14 14	18 5	2030	22 50
Maison-Dieu	5 36	9 50	1137	14 25	1817	—	—
Saulieu	6 52	—	1258	—	1929	...	...
Dracy-St.-Loup	7 54	...	1410	...	2030	...	...
Autun 53) ......arr	8 4	...	1421	...	2040	...	...

Autun ....dep	...	...	7 19	...	1240	...	18 2	...
Dracy-St.-Loup	...	...	7 30	...	1254	...	1814	...
Saulieu	...	...	8 52	...	1422	...	1926	...
Maison-Dieu	4 36	...	9 54	...	1532	‡	2022	...
Avallon	4 52	6 18	11 2	14 2	16 7	19 13	2046	...
Arcy-sur-Cure	5 31	6 53	1140	1446	1656	19 48	2124	...
Cravant ......arr	5 53	7 15	12 8	1516	1728	20 6	2150	...

AVALLON and LES LAUMES.

Avallon .....dep	5 38	9 39	1414	...	2042	...	...
Maison-Dieu	5 51	9 51	1426	...	2054	...	...
Semur	6 35	10 36	1514	19 15	2239	...	...
Laumes .....arr	7 9	11 7	1545	19 48	2210	...	...
Laumes .....dep	3 15	8 40	13 0	1655	2025	...	...
Semur	3 57	9 28	14 3	1735	21 2	...	...
Maison-Dieu	4 36	1013	14 28	1821	—	...	...
Avallon.....arr	4 47	1025	14 40	1833	...	...	...

DIRECT COMMUNICATION BY EXPRESS TRAINS

From LONDON AND FROM PARIS to SWITZERLAND and ITALY.

Sleeping Car, Coupés-Lits, Through Carriages 1 & 2 class, between Boulogne or Calais-Basle-Berne-Milan and Paris-Milan.

St. Gothard Route.

Read Down. (1)	(3)	(2)				Read Up. (3)		(4)
2 p5	4p30	9 p0	dep	**London**	arr	10a15	5a43	10p45
§	7p40	12a58	dep	Calais	arr	6a34	1a36	§
9p23	11p25	4a22	dep	Laon	arr	3a15	8p24	4 p0
10†18	...	4†48	dep	Reims	arr	...	7p35	3†33
11p28	12a48	5a50	dep	Chalons	arr	1a54	6p26	2p24
1a24	2a32	7a43	dep	Chaumont	arr	12a13	2p10	12p38
3a45	4a45	10 a0	arr	Belfort	dep	10 p9	11a41	10a21
7a50	12p15	5p15	arr	Bienne	dep	8p22	7a19	
8a35	1p32	4‡p12	arr	Berne	dep	7p43	6‡a50	
9a28	2p25	5‡p6	arr	Thun	dep	6p50	5¦a55	
10a20	3p25	5‡p58	arr	Interlaken	dep	5p58	—	
6a34	7a58	12p42	arr	**Basle**	dep	9p25	10a41	9a40
8a35	9a58	3p29	arr	Zurich	dep	6p40	7 a16	
10a57	1̶2 p5	6p17	arr	Ragatz	dep	3p29	4 a24	
11 a7	12p15	6p27	arr	Landquart	dep	3p20	4 a14	
11a25	12p32	6p47	arr	**Coire**	dep	3 p5	4 a0	
3p25	4p20	10p20	arr	St. Moritz	dep	11a20	...	
8a59	10a48	3p49	arr	**Lucerne**	dep	7 p0	7 a0	
12p25	3p55	7p33	arr	Bellinzona	dep	3p13	2a30	
1p25	4p52	8p15	arr	Locarno	dep	1 p7	11 p2	
1p17	4p56	8p26	arr	Lugano	dep	2p29	1a42	
1p54	5p52	9 p0	arr	Chiasso	dep	1p54	1 a5	
2p11	6p22	9p24	arr	Como	dep	1p35	12a37	
3 p5	7p47	10p25	arr	**Milan**	dep	12p40	11p35	

Lötschberg-Simplon Route.

Read Down.						Read Up. (3)		
...	11 a0	2 p5	dep	**London**	arr	10a15	3p25	...
...	2p46	...	dep	Calais	arr	6a34	...	...
...	...	6 p8	dep	Boulogne	arr	...	11 a5	...
...	7p32	9p23	dep	Laon	arr	3a15	7a45	...
...	8p31	10†18	dep	Reims	arr	...	7†18	...
...	9p22	11p28	dep	Chalons	arr	1a55	6a21	...
...	11p53	...	dep	Nancy	arr	...	4 a4	...
...	1 a4	☽	dep	Epinal	arr	☽	3 a0	...
...	2a53	3a55	dep	Belfort	arr	10 p2	1a13	...
...	3a27	4a21	arr	Delle	dep	9p35	12a48	...
...	6a57	7a50	arr	Bienne	dep	8p22	11p21	...
...	7a40	8a35	arr	Berne	dep	7p43	10p38	...
...	8a33	9a28	arr	Thun	dep	5p50	9p46	...
...	9a28	10a20	arr	Interlaken	dep	5p58	7p45	...
...	9a14	10a46	arr	Frütigen	dep	4p23	9 p6	...
...	9a43	11a12	arr	Kandersteg	dep	4 p1	8p42	...
...	10a32	11a57	arr	Brig	dep	3p 9	7p48	...
...	3p10	3p10	arr	Zermatt	dep	9a15	5p20	...
...	11a36	1 p0	arr	Domodossola	dep	1p42	6p22	...
...	12p56	2p25	arr	Arona	dep	12p16	4p55	...
...	6p30	...	arr	Genoa	dep	6a55	11a1	...
...	2p10	3p45	arr	**Milan**	dep	10a50	3p2⁵	...

(1) Permanent service, via Chaumont—Petit-Croix. Dining car between Boulogne and Laon. From July 1st to Sept. 15th through service between Boulogne and Berne via Delle.

(2) Temporary service, departure from London Friday from June 1st to September 30th. Dining car between Calais and Petit-Croix.

(3) Only on weekdays.

(4) Departure from Basle, Mondays in January and February; Mondays and Fridays from April 1st to June 14th; Mondays and Fridays in October; every day from June 15th to September 30th. Dining car between Petit-Croix and Boulogne.

†—Travellers from or for Reims change at Betheny.

‡—Via Basle. ☽—Via Chaumont.

§—Via Boulogne—Folkestone.

													(3)
9 p0		...	11 a0	2 p20	dep	**London**	arr	...	3 p25	10p45	5 a43	10a15
1 a30		...	2 p50	§	dep	Calais	arr	...	§	§	1 a23	6a20
5 a40		...	6 p20	9 p16	arr	**Paris** (Nord)	dep	...	8 a25	4 p0	9 p20	12a30
8 a0	8 a55	1 p0	9 p45		dep	**Paris** (Est)	arr	6 a25	7 a28	2 p49	5 p45	11p44
5 p15	5 p2?	9 p20	5 a58		arr	**Basle**	dep	10 p0	11p33	7 a37	10a41	5 p6
6 p15		9 p39	6 a45		dep	**Basle**	arr	8 p28	10p58	...	9 a3	4 p12
7 p55		11p25	8 a35		arr	Zurich	dep	6 p40	9 p12	...	7 a16	2 p30
11p38		...	11a25		arr	**Coire**	dep	1 p20	5 p42	...	4 a0	11a37
...		...	3 p35		arr	St. Moritz	dep	9 a5	2 p20	...	...	6 a45
St. Gothard Route. 6 p10		9 p45	7 a0		dep	**Basle**	arr	9 p0	11 p3	7 a10	8 a57	4 p6
8 p25		11p40	8 a59		arr	**Lucerne**	dep	7 p0	9 p10	5 a5	7 a0	2 p0
...		6 a22	3 p5		arr	**Milan**	dep	12p40	2 p40	9 p5	11p30	7 a25

8 a0	1 p0	9 p0	dep	**Paris** (Est)	arr	7 a28	2 p49	11p48
1 p37	7p29	2 a42	dep	Belfort	arr	12a54	9 a7	6 p0
2 p3	7p54	3 a8	arr	Delle	dep	12a28	8 a42	5 p35
5 p21	11p21	6 a57	arr	Bienne	dep	8 p52	7 a19	3 p57
6 p5	12 a2	7 a40	arr	Berne	dep	8 p7	6 a38	3 p18
6 p50	12a48	8 a33	arr	Thun	dep	7 p10	5 a55	2 p35
7 p45	...	9 a28	arr	**Interlaken**	dep	6 p15	...	1 p30
Lötschberg-Simplon Route. 7 p32	...	9 a16	arr	Frutigen	dep	9 p6	...	1 p56
10 [illegible]3	3a40	11a36	arr	Domodossola	dep	6 p22	2 a35	11a22
11 p6	4a52	12p56	arr	Arona	dep	4 p55	1 a13	9 a39
12p15	6a25	2 p10	arr	**Milan**	dep	3 p25	11p45	8 a15

Train de Luxe—Calais-Paris-Lucerne-Engadine-Express,

Composed exclusively of Sleeping and Dining Cars (with supplementary fare) belonging to the International Wagons-Lits Company, will run as follows:—

	Station		Time
Express Train.	London	dep	11 0 a.m.
	Paris (Nord)	dep	6 45 p.m.
	Paris (Est.)	dep	7 47 p.m.
	Lucerne	arr	7 50 a.m.
	Coire	arr	9 25 a.m.
Trains in connection for	Thusis	arr	10 23 a.m.
	Samaden	arr	12 14 p.m.
	Pontresina	arr	12 28 p.m.
	Saint Moritz	arr	12 25 p.m.
	Innsbruck	arr	3 25 p.m.
	Bozen	arr	7 11 p.m.
	Meran	arr	8 28 p.m.

	Station		Time
Trains in connection from	Meran	dep	7 30 a.m.
	Bozen	dep	8 47 a.m.
	Innsbruck	dep	12 54 p.m.
	Saint Moritz	dep	4 30 p.m.
	Pontresina	dep	4 27 p.m.
	Samaden	dep	4 44 p.m.
	Thusis	dep	6 32 p.m.
Express Train.	Coire	dep	7 30 p.m.
	Lucerne	dep	10 13 p.m.
	Paris (Est.)	arr	8 42 a.m.
	Paris (Nord)	arr	9 55 a.m.
	London	arr	5 10 p.m.

OUTWARD JOURNEY.

From July 1st to Sept. 14th.

Daily Service: Calais and Paris to Basle, Lucerne, and Coire.

HOMEWARD JOURNEY.

From July 3rd to Sept. 16th.

Daily Service: Coire, Lucerne and Basle to Paris and Calais.

DIRECT COMMUNICATION BY EXPRESS TRAINS

From LONDON and from PARIS to

SOUTH GERMANY—AUSTRIA—TURKEY.

		●			1.—Via Belgrade.			●				
9 p0	9 a0	10 a0	11 a0	dep	**London**	arr	...	5 p10	...	...	...	...
5 a40	4 p40	5 p20	6 p20	arr	**Paris** (Nord)	dep	...	9 a55	...	...	...	...
9 a0	5 p15	7 p13	9 p5	dep	**Paris** (Est)	arr	8 a25	8 a56	12p15	4 p38	9 p20	...
...	...	11 a0	2 p5	dep	**London** (via Laon-Reims)	arr	3 p25	3 p25	...	10*45	5 a43	...
...	...	9 p17	11p15	arr	Chalons-sur-Marne	dep	6 a27	6 a27	...	2 p35	6 p43	...
10a54	7 p18	9 p32	11p21	dep	Chalons-sur-Marne	arr	4 a55	6 a14	10 a5	2 p30	6 p38	...
1 p13	9 p36	12 a0	1 a48	arr	Nancy	dep	2 a23	4 a3	7 a35	12p17	4 p15	...
...	9 a0	...	...	dep	**London** (via Méz-Hirson)	arr	...	...	7 p5	...	...	...
...	9 a30	...	...	arr	Nancy	dep	...	...	7 a42	...	...	...
1 p19	9 p51	12 a7	1 a56	dep	Nancy	arr	2 a13	3 a51	7 a22	11a59	4 p5	...
4 p52	1 a39	3 a38	5 a50	arr	Strasburg	dep	12a34	2 a31	5 a40	10 a8	2 p18	...
6 p8	3 a1	4 a59	7 a11	arr	Carlsruhe	dep	11 p8	1 a6	4 a10	8 a38	12p44	...
7 p42	4 a52	6 a40	9 a2	arr	Stuttgart	dep	9 p17	11p32	2 a19	6 a58	10a52	...
11p23	8 a35	10a16	1 p8	arr	Munich	dep	5 p20	7 p55	10p25	...	7 a0	...
2 a10	12p28	12p45	4 p5	arr	Salzburg	dep	2 p25	5 p32	7 p20	...	3 a25	...
11a29	...	...	...	arr	Trieste	dep	...	...	7 a40	...	6 p0	...
8 a10	6 p32	6 p0	9 p50	arr	**Vienna**	dep	8 a15	12 p0	1 ‡p0	...	8 p40	...
1 p40	6 a25	11 p5	8 a10	arr	Budapest	dep	9 p30	6 a50	10p55	...	2 p5	...
...	7 p50	5 a58	...	arr	Belgrade	dep	...	10p39	1 p57	...	5 a41	...
...	6 a59	11a22	...	arr	Nisch	dep	...	5 p11	5 a50	...	10p40	...
...	7 a39	4 p18	...	arr	Sofia	dep	...	2 p10	12 a0	...	5 p40	...
...	...	10a17	...	arr	**Constantinople**	dep	...	7 p15	...	...	8 p23	...
					2.—Via Constanza.							
...	...	6 p51	...	dep	**Vienna**	arr	...	11 a4	...	...	6 p12	...
...	...	11 p5	...	arr	Constanza	dep	...	8 a0	...	...	6 a30	...
...	nght	11 30	...	dep	(Steamer)	arr	...	5 a0	...	...	5 a0	...
...	noon	12 0	...	arr	**Constantinople**	dep	...	3 p0	...	...	3§p0	...

●—Trains de Luxe, "Orient-Express," Dining and Sleeping Cars only.

*—Mondays and Fridays until June 14th; from June 15th daily.

‡—From June 1st.

§—Tues., Thurs., and Sat.

A—Between PARIS—BUDAPEST, daily.

B—Between PARIS—CONSTANTINOPLE, via Belgrade, Four times a Week.

OUTWARD, via Belgrade.—Paris depart, Mon., Wed., Thur., and Sat.; Constantinople arrive Thurs., Sat., Sun., and Tues.

RETURN, via Belgrade.—Constantinople depart Mon., Wed., Fri., and Sun.; Paris arrive Thurs., Sat., Mon., and Wed.

Between PARIS—CONSTANTINOPLE, via Constanza, Thrice a Week.

OUTWARD, via Constanza.—Paris depart, Sun., Tues., and Fri.; Constantinople arrive, Wed., Fri., and Mon.

RETURN, via Constanza.—Constantinople depart, Sat., Tues., and Thurs.; Paris arrive, Tues., Fri., and Sun.

EXPRESS SERVICES between LONDON AND THE FOLLOWING WATERING PLACES:

MARTIGNY—CONTREXEVILLE—VITTEL.

Twice a week until September 30th, without change of carriage on the Continent.

LONDON departure TUESDAYS AND FRIDAYS.					WEDNESDAYS AND SATURDAYS.
4 30 p.m.	dep	**London** (Charing Cross)	arr	10 45 p.m.	
7 40 „	dep	Calais	arr	...	
...	dep	Boulogne	arr	7 2 „	
11 20 „	arr	Laon	dep	4 5 „	
...	arr	Rheims	dep	2*58 „	
12 45 a.m.	arr	Châlons-sur-Marne	dep	2 35 „	
2 27 „	arr	Chaumont	dep	12 43 p.m.	
5 21 „	arr	**Martigny**	dep	10 37 a.m.	
5 40 „	arr	**Contrexéville**	dep	10 22 „	
5 55 „	arr	**Vittel**	dep	10 12 a.m.	

*—Change at Betheny.

EASTERN RAILWAY COMPANY (CHEMINS DE FER DE L'EST).

66 lbs. of Luggage free; Excess Luggage, 1 centime per 44 lbs. per kilometre.

PARIS, CHALONS, BLESME, PAGNY, FROUARD, NANCY, and AVRICOURT.

THROUGH CARRIAGES 1st and 2nd class.
- Paris to Frankfort—in 9.0, 17.15, and 21.5 from Paris.
- Paris to Munich—in 9.0, 17.15, and 21.5 from Paris.
- Paris to Stuttgart—in 12.0 from Paris.
- Paris to Vienna—in 9.0 and 17.15 from Paris.

RESTAURANT CAR—in 9.0 and 12.0 from Paris; and in 19.18 from Chalons.

Dist. E.M	1 Cl. fr. c.	2 Cl. fr. c.	3 Cl. fr. c.	PARIS (Gare de l'Est)	1,2,3	1,2,3	1,2,3	1 &2	1,2,3	1,2,3	1,2,3	1,2,3	1,2,3	1,2,3	1,2,3	1,2,3	1 & 2	1,2,3	1,2,3
F	rom	Pari	s.	Rue de Strasbourg ...dep	...	...	0 35	...	...	6 58	...	...	5 30	8 0	8 15	...	9 0	9 6	10 35
17½	3 15	2 10	1 40	Lagny-Thorigny	...	...	1 7	...	...	...	...	...	6 1	...	...	...	B	9 39	10 54
28	5 25	3 20	2 10	Meaux	...	...	1 44	...	...	7 47	...	...	6 29	A	8 55	...	:	10 5	11 30
41	7 40	5 0	3 25	La Ferte-s-Jouarre 64	...	...	2 15	...	...	8 14	...	...	7 2	...	9 14	...	RC	1034	12 0
59	10 65	7 20	4 70	Château-Thierry ...dep	...	...	2 55	...	...	8 48	...	5 17	7 49	...	9 40	1010	:	11 8	13 45
72¾	13 10	8 85	5 75	Dormans	...	...	3 17	...	7 32		...	5 48	8 21	...	9 59	1039	:		14 13
78¼	14 10	9 55	6 20	Châtillon Port-à-B.	...	...	...	...	7 47	...	...	6 4	8 36	..	...	1053	:	...	14 26
88¼	15 90	10 75	7 0	Epernay ...arr	...	...	3 40	...	8 8	...	...	6 25	8 55	9 38	10 19	1113	:	...	14 45
107	17 45	11 80	7 70	REIMS 74A ...arr	...	...	4 49	...	9 22	...	...	7 27	...	...	12 11	1211	:	...	...
...	...	...	...	Epernay ...dep	...	...	3 50	Calais dep. 0.58.	...	...	...	6 32	8 59	9 41	10 41	1121	:	1435	...
98¾	17 80	12 0	7 85	Jalons-les-Vignes	...	...	4 8		...	...	...	6 56	9 23	...	...	1145	:	15 2	...
107½	19 40	13 10	8 55	Chalons ...arr	...	...	4 21		...	...	...	7 15	9 42	10 4	11 12	12 4	10 56	1522	...
206½	37 20	25 15	16 40	AMANVILLERS 67 ...arr	...	...	11 33		...	...	...	...	1515	15 15	...	...	...	2122	...
216¼	38 35	26 15	16 95	METZ 212 ...arr	...	...	1 p9		...	...	...	...	4p52	4p52	...	...	...	1057	...
...	...	...	...	BOULOGNE ...dep	...	...	...		...	...	...	...	...	...	...	...	...	...	...
...	...	...	...	LAON ...dep	...	...	...	4 22	...	...	...	...	...	...	...	...	...	...	...
...	...	...	...	Chalons ...dep	2 51	3 10	4 40	5 50	...	...	7 33	7 44	1019	10 10	11 52	...	11 1	...	12 26
127½	22 95	15 50	10 10	Vitry-le-François	3 23	3 40	5 30	...	...	...	8 1	8 38	11 8	10 37	13 3	...	...	...	12 53
135½	24 40	16 50	10 75	Blesme 66 ... arr	...		5 44	To Basle; see note "G"	...	...	...	8 52	1122	...	13 17	...	...	...	
				dep	...	...	5 45		...	...	...	8 55	1123	...	13 18	...	...	...	...
143½	25 85	17 45	11 40	Sermaize	3 50	...	6 3		...	...	...	9 14	1143	...	13 37	...	...	...	...
148½	26 75	18 5	11 80	Révigny	...	5 20	6 19		...	...	...	9 26	1154	...	13 49	1324	...	...	16 26
157¾	28 45	19 20	12 50	Bar-le-Duc	5 0	5 45	7 8		...	...	8 45	9 59	1219	11 18	14 12	1350	12 0	...	16 52
164½	29 70	20 5	13 5	Nancois-Tronville	5 18		7 29		...	...	...	10 23		...	14 30		:	...	
179½	32 35	21 85	14 25	Lerouville 72	6 14	7 5	8 9		9 0	...	...	11 6	1117	...	15 7	...	:	...	17 39
183¼	33 5	22 30	14 55	Commercy	6 25	7 14	8 20		9 10	...	9 24	11 15	1127	11 55	15 17	...	:	1441	17 49
191½	34 50	23 30	15 20	Pagny-sur-Meuse 72 arr	6 44		8 40			...	...	11 34	1146	...	15 37	...	:	15 6	
				dep	6 49	...	8 44		...	...	...	11 39		...	16 0	...	:	15 9	...
198¾	35 85	24 20	15 75	Toul 74	7 10	8 0	9 5		...	1043	9 46	11 54	...	12 18	16 22	...	:	1529	...
210	37 85	25 55	16 65	Liverdun	7 33	8 22	9 28		...	11 6	:	13 23	...	:	16 47	...	:	...	...
214½	38 65	26 10	17 0	Frouard ...arr	7 42	8 31	9 36		...	1115	:	13 32	...	:	16 56	...	:	1557	...
232½	...	...	...	PAGNY-MOSELLE 72 arr	8 18	10 5	...	...	...	1221	:	14 9	...	14 9 (Via Nancy)	18 0	...	14 9 (Via Nancy)	1636	...
244¾	...	...	...	METZ ...212 arr	10 a5	1156	...	...	...	2p19	:	4 p3	...	4 p3	7 p54	...	4 p3	6p41	...
293¾	53 25	35 85	23 35	SAARBRUCKEN ...212 arr	...	...	...	...	...	...	:	5 p29	...	5 p29	9 p25	...	5 p29	8p50	...
381¾	68 0	45 85	29 45	BINGERBRUCK ...125A arr	...	...	...	...	...	...	:	8 p34	...	8 p34	...	...	8 p34	...	...
401	70 40	47 35	30 45	MAYENCE ...123 arr	...	...	...	...	...	...	:	8 p39	...	8 p39	...	...	8 p39	...	...
424½	74 65	49 50	31 95	FRANKFORT ...123 arr	...	...	...	...	...	...	:	9 p20	...	9 p20	...	...	9 p20	...	...
...	...	...	...	Frouard ...dep	7 47	8 32	9 42	...	...	1120	:	13 35	...	:	16 58	...	:	1559	...
219¼	39 55	26 70	17 40	Nancy 66, 72 ... arr	8 2	8 47	9 57	...	...	1135	1015	13 50	...	12 47	17 13	...	13 15	1612	...
				dep	8 20			...	11 32	1219		14 0	1550	12 55		17 5	13 21		18 48
227½	41 0	27 65	18 5	Varangeville St. Nicolas	8 40	...	...	...	11 53	1239	...	14 18	1610	...	...	1723	...	...	19 8
230½	41 55	28 5	18 30	Rosières-aux-Salines	8 52	...	...	1,2,3	12 4	1249	...	14 28	1620	...	...	1733	...	...	19 18
233¾	42 10	28 45	18 55	Blainville-la-Grande .. 1,2,3	9 1	...	...	1150	12 14	1256	...	14 39	1632	...	...	1742	...	...	19 27
239¾	43 25	29 20	19 0	Lunéville 74 ... 5 30	9 16	...	...	12 5	12 34	1313	...	15 0	1647	13 25	...	18 6	13 49	...	19 47
249¾	45 0	30 40	19 80	Embermenil ... 5 55	9 46	...	...		13 1		...	15 25		...	...	1831	...	...	20 12
254¾	45 90	31 0	20 20	Igney Avricourt arr 6 7	9 58	...	...	...	13 12	...	...	15 37	...	13 51	...	1843	14 12	...	20 24
				dep	10 12	...	...	...	13 30	...	...	15 44	...	13 56	...	1849	14 20	...	
256	46 30	31 25	20 40	Deutsch Avricourt ...arr	10 15	...	...	...	13 33	...	...	15 47	...	13 59	...	1853	14 23	...	...
312½	56 45	37 80	24 50	STRASSBURG ...210 arr	...	...	...	...	4 p41	...	...	7 p12	...	4 p41	...	...	4 p52	...	...
326	59 85	40 35	26 15	APPENWEIER ...210 arr	...	...	...	...	...	...	...	...	...	...	...	...	...	...	...
366	67 60	45 20	29 30	CARLSRUHE ...141 arr	...	...	...	...	6 p8	...	...	...	...	6 p8	...	...	6 p8	...	...
422	75 85	50 95	32 90	STUTTGART ...192 arr	...	...	...	...	7 p42	...	...	...	...	7 p42	...	...	7 p42	...	...
571½	99 45	65 10	42 15	MUNICH ...192 arr	...	...	...	...	11p23	...	...	...	...	11p23	...	...	11p23	...	...
861¾	155 10	98 85	63 65	VIENNA ...239A arr	...	...	...	...	...	...	...	...	...	8 a10	...	...	8 a10	...	...

A—At Paris takes 2nd and 3rd class travelling at least 93 miles.

B—Between Paris and Nancy only takes such 2nd class passengers as are travelling at least 217 miles, or for Avricourt or Pagny and beyond.

C—Takes 2nd class for Avricourt and beyond and for Pagny-sur-Moselle and beyond, or when travelling at least 217 miles; 3rd class carried only when travelling to Avricourt or Pagny and beyond.

E—Takes 3rd class who are travelling at least 62 miles.

F—At Paris admits only 2nd class travelling at least 155 miles. Between Paris and Nancy only takes 3rd class travelling at least 217 miles, or for Avricourt or Pagny and beyond.

G—Calais to Basle Express; will run every Saturday until 30th Sept.

H—At Paris admits 3rd class travelling at least 217 miles; at Chalons and Bar-le-Duc admits 3rd class travelling 124 miles.

Œ—ORIENT EXPRESS—Train de Luxe. Tickets should be taken in advance from Sleeping Car Co.

LA FERTE-SOUS-JOUARRE and MONTMIRAIL.	E.M										
		La Ferté-s-Jouarre dep	8 55	14 17	19 45	...	Montmirail ...dep	5 25	11 10	15 45	...
	13	Sablonnieres	10 4	15 22	20 54	...	Sablonnieres	6 28	12 15	16 50	...
	28	Montmiral ...arr	11 4	16 24	21 54	...	La Ferté-s-Jouarre arr	7 32	13 21	17 53	...

EASTERN RAILWAYS.

PARIS, CHALONS, BLESME, PAGNY, FROUARD, NANCY, and AVRICOURT.

RC—Restaurant Car attached. SC—Sleeping Car attached.

	1,2,3	1,2,3	1,2,3	1,2,3	1,2,3	1,2,3	1,2,3	1,2,3	1,2,3	1,2,3	1,2,3	1 Cl.	1 Cl	1,2,3	1,2,3	1,2,3	1,2,3	1,2,3	
PARIS (Gare de l'Est)																			
Rue de Strasbourg ...dep	12 0	12 20	...	...	13 0	1423	1548	1715	1717	1720	1822	19 13	1915	20 7	21 5	22 0	22 15	22 18	...
Lagny-Thorigny	:	...	...	...	...	1455	1621	:	...	...	1836	...	...	20 37	...	...	...	22 48	...
Meaux	H	...	...	...	13 46	1525	1658	:	...	18 3	19 7	...	...	20 59	C	...	...	23 10	...
La Ferte-s-Jouarre	:	...	...	...	14 8	1555	1727	F	...	1825	1936	...	...	21 26	...	...	...	23 39	...
Château-Thierry ...dep	RC	13 39	...	...	14 47	1644	18 1	:	1832	1859	2010	Œ	K	22 32	SC	...	23 33	0 17	...
Dormans	:	E	...	...	15 18	1713	☞	:	...	1931		...	...	23 2	...	...	23 36		...
Châtillon Port-à-B.	:	...	...	...	15 33	1728		:	...	1947	...	...	...	23 17	...	...	23 56	...	...
Epernay ...arr	:	14 14	...	...	15 53	1748		:	19 7	20 7	...	21 2	2126	23 37	22 49	23 54	0 19	...	...
REIMS 74A ...arr	:	15 11	...	...	17 37	19 5	Runs until 30th September.	:	2042	2222	...	...	...	...	...	0 40	1 52	...	
Epernay ...dep	:	14 17	...	...	16 0	18 0		:	1910	2143	1 & 2	21 3	2127	...	22 51	23 57	0 22	...	From Calais.
Jalons-les-Vignes	:	...	...	...	16 24	1825		:	1917	22 8	Calais dep. 14.46.	...	...	...	...	...	...	...	
Chalons ...arr	14 1	14 41	...	...	16 43	1845		1911	1938	2227		21 27	2151	...	23 15	0 22	0 49	...	
AMANVILLERS 67 ...arr	21 22	21 22	...	...	...	...		...	...	...		...	...	...	...	...	6 45	...	
METZ 212 ...arr	10 57	10p57	...	...	...	...		...	...	...		...	...	1 & 2	...	...	9 a12	...	
BOULOGNE ...dep	...	...	...	...	...	...		...	...	...		...	...	18 8	18 8	...	20 10	●	
LAON ...dep	...	...	...	...	...	...		...	...	...	1932	...	...	21 23	21 41	...	23 25	...	●
Chalons ...dep	14 9	14 48	...	1510	17 12	...	...	1919	1944	2235	2122	21 32	2156	23 28	23 21	...	0 57	...	...
Vitry-le-François	...	15 17	...	1556	18 19	...	...	...	2035	2317	:	...	...	Basle Express, runs direct to St. Dizier and Chaumont p. 66.	...	...	1 28	...	...
Blesme 66 arr	...	...	...	1610	18 33	...	...	F	2048		:	...	...		...	...	...	...	...
Blesme 66 dep	H	...	...	1611	18 35	...	...	...	2049	...	:	...	...		C	...	...	...	...
Sermaize	...	...	...	1630	18 55	...	...	RC	2110	...	:	...	...		...	...	1 55	...	...
Révigny	...	...	1819	1640	19 14	1946	...	...	2121	2225	:	...	...		...	...	...	...	...
Bar-le-Duc	15 9	16 1	1844	1717	20 27	20 9	...	2019	2150	2250	:	22 34	2257		0 27	...	2 23	3 0	...
Nancois	:	16 14		1735	20 44		...	:	...		:	:	:		‡—Connection via Nancy.	...	...	3 15	...
Lerouville 72	:	16 38	...	1813	21 18	...	...	:	2230	...	:	:	:			...	...	3 48	...
Commercy	:	16 50	...	1823	21 24	...	...	:	2240	...	:	Œ	K			...	3 10	3 56	...
Pagny-sur-Meuse 72 arr	:	...	...	1842		...	...	:	2259	...	:	:	:			...	...	4 14	...
Pagny-sur-Meuse 72 dep	:	...	...	1844	...	20 5	...	:	2322	...	:	:	:			...	...	4 18	...
Toul 74	:	17 13	18 4	19 4	19 43	2021	2129	21 9	2340	...	:	:	:			...	3 36	4 45	...
Liverdun	:	...	...	...	20 7		2154	:	:	...	:	:	:			...	:	5 8	...
Frouard ...arr	:	17 35	1826	1931	20 15	...	22 4	:	:	...	:	:	:			...	:	5 17	...
PAGNY-MOSELLE 72 arr	18 0	18 47	1950	2030	...	...	...	2235	1‡22	...	:	:	:		2 ‡53	...	5 ‡30	6 a37	...
METZ ...212 arr	7 p54	8 p41	9p36	...	...	...	...	1221	:	...	:	:	:		4 ‡16	...	7 a29	8 a28	...
SAARBRUCKEN ...212 arr	9 p25	11p30	...	...	...	...	...	1a47	:	...	:	:	:		6 a12	...	9 a21	10a26	...
BINGERBRUCK...125A arr	:	...	...	...	...	...	...	4a18	:	...	:	:	:		9 a30	...	...	1 p30	...
MAYENCE ...123 arr	:	...	...	...	...	...	...	4a58	:	...	:	:	:		9 a32	...	1 p27	1 p27	...
FRANKFORT ...123 arr	:	...	...	...	...	...	...	5a38	:	...	:	:	:		10a14	...	2 p17	2 p17	...
Frouard ...dep	:	17 37	1829	1934	20 16	...	22 6	:	:	...	:	:	:		...	...	:	5 21	...
Nancy 66, 72 arr	16 23	17 48	1839	1947	20 31	...	2223	2137	0 13	...	2345	24 0	0 22		1 48	...	4 9	5 35	...
Nancy 66, 72 dep	16 43		1932	2050		...		2151	0 35	2233	2353	0 7	0 27		1 56	6 36	4 19	6 22	...
Varangeville St. Nicolas	...	...	1953	2110	...	...	...	...	0 53	2253	From Nancy page 66, Belfort (p. 68A) arr 2.45	...	...		...	6 57	...	...	...
Rosières-aux-Salines	17 4	...	20 4	2120	...	...	...	...	1 3	23 3		...	...	...	...	7 9	...	...	...
Blainville-la-Grande	...	...	2011	2127	...	...	...	...	1 14	2315		...	...	...	...	7 19	...	6 46	...
Lunéville 74	17 17	...	2028	2147	...	...	...	2222	1 26	2330		0 42	1 9	...	2 28	7 34	4 56	7 0	...
Embermenil	...	...			...	...	...	...				...	...	...	...		...	7 24	...
Igney Avricourt arr	17 42	...	...	...	...	...	...	2251	...	...		1 12	1 45	...	2 58	...	5 22	7 35	...
Igney Avricourt dep	17 52	...	...	...	...	...	...	2256	...	...		1 15	1 55	...	3 2	...	5 25	7 39	...
Deutsch Avricourt ...arr	17 55	...	...	...	...	...	...	2259	...	...		1 18	1 58	...	3 6	...	5 28	7 42	...
STRASSBURG ...210 arr	8 p38	...	...	...	...	...	...	1a39	...	...		3 a38	4a28	...	5 a50	...	8 a44	10a30	...
APPENWEIER ...210 arr	9 p9	...	...	...	...	...	...	...	...	...		...	...	...	...	...	9 a23	12p15	...
CARLSRUHE ...141 arr	10 p6	...	...	...	...	...	...	3 a1	...	...		4 a59	5a47	...	7 a11	...	10a30	1 p52	...
STUTTGART ...192 arr	12a15	...	...	...	...	...	...	4a52	...	...		6 a40	...	...	9 a2	...	12p42	4 p34	...
MUNICH ...192 arr	7 a20	...	...	...	...	...	...	8a35	...	...		10a16	...	...	1 p8	...	5 p9	9 p40	...
VIENNA ...239A arr	...	...	...	...	...	...	...	6p32	...	...	...	6 p0	...	...	9 p50	...	6 a0	8 a10	...

K—Carlsbad Express, Train de Luxe, runs until 27th September.

ST. DIZIER and BAR-LE-DUC.

E.M.																	
	St. Dizier ...dep	4 37	7 32	1235	1538	19 0	...	...	**Bar-le-Duc** ...dep	6 12	9 17	14 9	1747	2058	...	...	...
17½	Révigny (64)	5 20	8 15	1324	1626	1946	...	...	Révigny	6 33	9 40	1435	18 6	2124	...	...	...
26¾	**Bar-le-Duc** ...arr	5 45	8 39	1350	1652	20 9	...	...	**St. Dizier** (66) ...arr	7 17	1030	1523	1851	22 7	...	...	...

BRAY-sur-SEINE to SABLONNIERES.

E.M.																	
	Bray-s-Seine...dep	...	...	6 50	...	12 5	18 0	...	**Sablonnières** dep	...	7 50	...	...	1520	...	1843	...
20¼	Nangis	...	...	9 39	...	14 55	1957	2024	St. Siméon	...	8 34	10 19	...	1626	...	1955	...
31½	Jouy-le-Châtel	7 0	...	1044	...	16 10		2114	Jouy-le-Châtel	7 55		12 1	...	1747	...	2112	...
47¼	St. Siméon	8 33	10 18	1158	1627	17 28	1956		Nangis	9 40	...	12 56	1450	1846	20 26		...
55½	**Sablonnières**...arr	...	11 4	...	17 9	...	2037	...	**Bray-s-Seine** arr	1144	...		17 2	...	22 26	...	...
—	Jouy-le-Châtel ...dep	6 15	11 55	1550	...	...	...	...	Marles (Est) ...dep	9 17	1350	19 18	...	...	...	...	...
15	Marles (Est) ...arr	7 28	13 20	1715	...	...	...	...	Jouy-le-Châtel arr	1039	15 4	20 20	...	...	...	...	...

EASTERN RAILWAY. [66 lbs. of Luggage free.

AVRICOURT, NANCY, CHALONS, and PARIS.

Station		1,2,3	1,2,3	1Cl.	1,2,3	1Cl.		1,2,3	1,2,3	1,2,3	1,2,3	1,2,3	1,2,3	1,2,3	1,2,3	1,2,3	1 & 2	1,2,3	1 &2
VIENNA (239) ....dep		...	...	...	8a15	12 0	...	...	...	...	...	...	...	1 p[illegible]	...	...	...	1 0	...
MUNICH (192A) ....dep		...	...	...	5p20	7p55	...	...	...	...	...	...	...	1025	...	...	...	10p25	...
STUTTGART [192A)......dep		...	...	...	9p17	1132	...	...	...	...	...	...	...	2a29	...	...	...	2 a29	6a58
CARLSRUHE (140) ......dep		...	...	1045	11p8	1 a6	...	...	...	...	...	...	...	4a10	...	...	...	4 a10	8a38
APPENWEIER [210A)...dep		...	...	...	12a5	...	...	...	...	...	...	...	...	5a10	...	...	...	5 a18	...
STRASSBURG (210A) ...dep		...	...	1219	1234	2a31	...	...	...	...	...	...	...	5a40	...	...	...	6 a16	10a8
Deutsch Avricourt***...dep		...	...	1 40	1 57	3 45	...	...	...	...	...	...	...	7 4	...	...	...	8 42	1135
Igney-Avricourt ***......arr		...	...	1 43	2 0	3 48	...	...	...	...	...	...	...	7 7	...	...	...	8 45	1138
" [Customs ex.]dep		...	...	0 55	1 21	3 0	...	...	3 38	...	...	...	5 25	6 25	...	...	...	8 14	11 3
Embermenil		...	...	...	...	...	...	...	3 47	...	...	...	5 35	...	...	...	...	8 24	RC
Luneville.................. arr		...	...	1 16	1 42	3 22	...	...	4 7	...	...	...	5 59	6 47	...	...	...	8 48	1125
Luneville.................. dep		...	...	1 17	1 43	3 22		...	4 9	...	...	...	6 2	6 49	...	7 49	...	9 20	1126
Blainville-la-Grande		...	...	...	1 44	...	Belfort dep. 1.23.	...	4 27	...	...	...	6 21	7 0	...	8 24	...	9 36	1137
Rosières-aux-Salines		...	...	K	SC	...		...	4 34	...	...	...	6 30	...	...	8 32	...	9 44	H
Varangeville St. Nicolas ...		...	...	...	...	...		...	4 45	...	...	...	6 43	...	...	8 42	...	9 54	...
Nancy .... arr		...	...	1 46	2 13	3 51		...	5 7	...	...	...	7 3	7 22	...	9 5	...	10 15	1159
Nancy .... dep		...	...	1 55	2 23	4 3	4 10	...		...	...	6 3		7 35	7 52	9 19	...	10 25	1317
Frouard ....arr		...	...	⋮	⋮	⋮	⋮	...	...	...	...	6 16	...	G	8 2	9 32	...	10 38	⋮
FRANKFORT (123A) ...dep		...	...		8p35			...	...	...	...	...	...		...	1148	...	...	
MAYENCE (123A).........dep		...	...		9p15			...	...	...	...	...	...		...	1235	...	...	
BINGERBRUCK (125) ...dep		...	...		9p50			...	...	...	...	...	...		...	1a27	...	...	
SAARBRUCKEN (212)...dep		...	...		1236	ŒE		...	...	...	...	...	...		...	5a50	...	7 a47	
METZ (212)..................dep		...	...		1a51			...	...	...	...	...	...	6a15	...	7a54	...	9 a40	
PAGNY-S-MOSELLE 72 dep		...	...		1 33			...	...	...	...	4 45	...	6‡17	...	7 48	...	9 29	
Frouard.........................dep		...	...					...	...	...	...	6 19	...		8 3	9 34	...	10 40	
Liverdun		...	...					...	...	...	...	6 29	...		...	9 44		10 50	
Toul...............................dep		...	...		2 53			...	7 16	...	...	6 58	...	8 8	8 31	10 9		11 18	H
Pagny-sur-Meuse...... arr		...	...		...			...	7 37	...	...	7 19	...	...				11 37	
Pagny-sur-Meuse...... dep		...	...		...			...		...	...	7 26	...	...	...	...		11 41	
Commercy		...	...		3 16			...	...	...	6 35	7 48	...	8 33	...	8 49		12 1	
Lerouville		...	...		SC			...	...	...	6 45	7 59	...	...	...	8 56		12 12	
Nancois..............................		...	...		...			...	...	...	...	8 38	...	...	...			12 48	
Bar-le-Duc		...	...	3 24	3 53	5 21		5 10	6 12	...	7 30	9 15	9 17	9 11	...	...	From Basle to Boulogne;	13 13	1337
Révigny		...	...	...	...	...		5 34	6 32	...	7 50	9 32	9 39	...	...	...		13 44	...
Sermaize		...	...	...	...	...		5 44		...	...	9 41		...	...	...		13 56	RC
Blesme .... arr		...	...	...	...	...		6 3	...	...	...	9 58	...	G	...	...		14 14	...
Blesme .... dep		...	...	...	...	...		6 4	...	...	...	9 59	...	...	...	...		14 17	...
Vitry-le-Francois		...	...	...	4 29	...		6 21	...	6 48	8 25	10 16	...	...	...	1310		14 36	...
Chalons ....arr		...	...	4 20	4 55	6 14	6 25	6 49	...	7 35	8 51	10 57	...	10 5	...	1359	14 24	15 23	1430
LAON... (67) ....arr		...	...	...	7 30	...	7 30	...	...	...	...	...	...	...	...	...	16 0	...	16 0
BOULOGNE (19) ......arr		...	...	...	1057	...	10 57	...	...	...	...	...	...	...	...	...	19 2	...	19 2
METZ (212)....................dep		...	...	...	...	...	...	...	...	...	...	6 a7	...	...	...	...	...	10a34	...
AMANVILLERS (67)......dep		...	...	...	...	...	...	...	...	...	...	6 0	...	...	...	...	...	10 19	...
Chalons ....dep		...	5 25	4 25	5 20	6 19	...	6 56	...	7 46	8 57	11 8	10 27	1013	1319	1455	...	16 25	1436
Jalons-les-Vignes.............		...	5 44	...	...	...	...	...	...	8 5	...	...	10 45	⋮	1337	1515	...	16 43	...
Epernay...... ....arr		...	6 9	4 49	5 45	6 42	. .	7 22	...	8 29	9 23	11 34	11 10	⋮	14 2	1540	...	17 8	...
REIMS (74A) ....dep		...	5 17	...	...	...	...	...	...	7 13	8 31	10 42	...	⋮	13 0	1445	...	...	...
Epernay ....dep		...	6 50	4 50	5 48	6 43	...	7 24	...	8 39	9 27	11 37	11 53	⋮	14 8	1547	...	...	...
Châtillon		...	7 10	...	...	...	...	...	...	9 0	...	RC	12 15		1428	16 8	...	...	...
Dormans	1,2,3	...	7 25	...	...	...	...	...	...	9 16	...	...	12 32		1445	1624	...	...	...
Chateau-Thierry	6 16	7 30	7 54	K	6 41	...	...	8 6	9 16	1116	10 9	12 18	13 10		1543	1729	...	...	...
La Ferte-s-Jouarre	6 57	8 11		...	...	...	...	8 32	9 54	12 1	10 35	...	13 49		1629	18 8	...	...	...
Meaux	7 27	8 39	...	...	...	...	...	8 54	10 24	1246	10 56	...	14 17		17 5	1838	...	...	...
Lagny Thorigny	7 50	...	...	...	...	...	...	...	10 43	...	...	...	14 38		1731	1857	...	...	...
PARIS Est. ....arr	8 20	9 28	...	7 21	8 25	8 56	...	9 35	11 14	1337	11 37	13 42	15 12	1216	1810	1928	...	...	1639

***—German Time

B—From Nancy forward takes 2nd class travelling at least 93 miles, 3rd class travelling at least 155 miles or from branch lines.

E—From Nancy forward takes 3rd class only when travelling at least 93 miles, or those coming from Longuyon to Bar-le-Duc.

F—At Nancy will not take up 3rd class for Frouard or Toul, except passengers from branch lines.

G—From Nancy forward only takes 3rd class travelling at least 217 miles, or for beyond Epernay towards Reims; at Chalons will only take up 1st class.

H—At Igney-Avricourt 2nd class are taken for all destinations, but elsewhere only when travelling at least 217 miles.

K—Carlsbad Express, Train de Luxe, runs until 30th September.

ŒE—ORIENT EXPRESS, Train de Luxe, coming from Vienna.

EASTERN RAILWAY.

AVRICOURT, NANCY, CHALONS, and PARIS.

VIENNA (239) ....dep	...	...	...	...	8p 40	...	...	...	...	...	...	...	...	...	...	...	...	...
MUNICH (192A) ....dep	...	...	...	...	7 a0	...	...	...	...	...	...	...	...	8a22	...	8 a22	...	...
STUTTGART (192A)......dep	...	...	...	...	10a52	...	...	...	...	...	...	...	...	1248	...	12p48	...	...
CARLSRUHE (140) ......dep	...	...	...	...	12p44	...	...	...	...	...	...	...	...	4p48	...	4 p48	...	...
APPENWEIER (210A)...dep	...	...	...	...	1 p47	...	...	...	...	...	...	...	...	6p10	...	6 p10	...	...
STRASSBURG (210A) ...dep	...	...	...	...	2 p18	...	...	...	...	2p18	4p40	...	...	7p14	...	7 p26	...	...
	1,2,3	1,2,3	1,2,3	1,2,3	1,2,3	1,2,3	1,2,3	1,2,3	1,2,3	1,2,3	1,2,3	1,2,3	1,2,3	1,2,3	1,2,3	1,2,3	1,2,3	1,2,3
Deutsch Avricourt***...dep	...	...	...	...	15 41	...	...	...	...	1626	1812	...	...	2053	...	22 2	...	...
Igney-Avricourt***......arr	...	...	...	...	15 47	...	...	...	...	1639	1815	...	...	2057	...	22 5	...	...
,, [Customs ex.]dep	...	11 18	...	13 22	15 9	...	...	...	...	1610	1733	...	...	2017	...	21 31	...	...
Embermenil	...	11 28	...	13 32	...	...	...	...	...	1620	...	...	...	2027	...	F	...	...
Luneville .... arr	...	11 52	...	13 56	15 31	...	...	...	...	1644	18 0	...	...	2049	...	21 54	...	...
Luneville .... dep	1024	11 55	1253		15 34	...	...	...	...	1650	18 9	...	19 49	21 2	...	21 59	22 26	...
Blainville-la-Grande	1059	12 11	13 8	...	...	...	...	...	1614	1711	1824	...	20 7	2115	...	22 10	22 41	...
Rosières-aux-Salines	11 7	12 19	1316	...	L	...	...	...	1622	1721	...	...	20 15	2122	...	...	22 49	...
Varangeville St. Nicolas ...	1117	12 29	1326	...	...	...	...	...	1632	1735	E	...	20 2	2134	F	...	23 0	...
Nancy .... arr	1139	12 50	1347	...	16 5	J	...	...	1653	1758	1846	...	20 48	2151	...	22 35	23 21	...
Nancy .... dep	1222	13 10	1415	15 26	16 15	1635	...	1753		1822	19 0	2010			22 28	23 5	0 20	...
Frouard ....arr	1235	13 19	1428	15 41	:	1644	...	18 2	...	1835	19 9	2019	...	...	22 38	23 14	0 30	...
FRANKFORT (123A) ...dep	...	7 a32	7a32	...	:	...	...	...	...	8a30	1p33	...	...	...	...	5 p7	...	...
MAYENCE (123A) ......dep	...	8 a10	8a10	...	:	...	...	...	...	9a20	2p13	...	...	...	...	5 p47	...	...
BINGERBRUCK (125)...dep	...	8 a45	8a45	...	:	...	...	...	...	10a4	1p56	...	...	...	...	5 p45	...	...
SAARBRUCKEN (212)...dep	...	11a28	1128	...	:	...	...	...	...	2p48	5 p7	...	...	...	...	8 p59	...	...
METZ (212)...............dep	...	12 48	1248	3 p10	3 p10	3p53	...	...	...	5p18	6p31	7 p1	...	...	...	10p27	...	...
PAGNY-S-MOSELLE (72)dep	...	12 37	1258	15 5	15 ‡5	1547	...	...	...	1737	1822	1845	...	...	21 49	22 19	...	...
Frouard..................dep	1236	13 27	1431	15 47	:	1645	...	18 3	...	1841	1914	2020	...	...	22 45	23 16	0 32	...
Liverdun	1245	...	1442	15 57	:	...	...	...	...	1853	RC	2029	...	...	...	...	0 42	...
Toul.......................dep	1316	13 52	1513	16 24	16 46	1710	...	1831	...	1947	1936	2052	...	...	23 9	23 40	1 7	...
Pagny-sur-Meuse ... arr	...	B	1534	16 45	...	...	...	1842	...	20 9	...		...	...	23 26	...		...
Pagny-sur-Meuse ... dep	...	...	1539	17 3	...	...	...	1849	...	2017	...	...	...	...	23 28	...	...	...
Commercy	1348	14 18	16 8	17 23	L	1735	...	19 9	1854	2046	E	...	...	...	23 42	0 5	...	...
Lerouville		...	1618		...	1743	...	1918	19 2	21 5	...	...	...	...	23 49	...	...	...
Nancois........................	...	...	1659	...	...	1810	...	...		2143	...	...	...	...	...	...	...	...
Bar-le-Duc	14 9	15 0	1757	16 7	17 42	1826	17 47	1957	2058	22 9	2033	...	...	...	0 31	0 48	...	...
Révigny	1431	...	1822	16 32	...	1841	18 4		2120	2240	...	...	...	...	...	...	...	...
Sermaize		...	1832	16 42	...	...		...		2251	...	...	...	...	...	...	...	...
Blesme .... arr	...	...	1850	17 0	...	...	...	...	...	23 9	...	...	...	...	1 0	...	...	...
Blesme .... dep	...	...	1851	17 1	...	...	...	...	...	2310	...	...	...	...	1 1	...	...	...
Vitry-le-Francois	...	15 40	19 5	17 18	...	1912	18 0	2020	...	2335	...	...	...	...	1 13	...	...	...
Chalons ....arr	...	16 6		18 5	18 38	1935	18 26	21 8	...	0 10	2129	...	...	...	1 39	1 51	...	...
LAON (67) ....arr	...	18 59	...	...	20 24	...	...	...	...	...	...	...	...	...	...	3 15	...	...
BOULOGNE (19) ......arr	...	...	§—Arrive Calais.	...	1§23	...	...	...	...	...	...	...	...	...	...	6 §45	...	...
METZ (212) ....dep	...	10a34		1 p55	1 p55	...	...	...	...	...	4p28	...	...	...	...	...	...	...
AMANVILLERS (67) ...dep	...	10 19		13 41	13 41	...	...	...	...	...	1618	...	...	...	...	...	...	...
Chalons.....................dep	...	16 12		19 0	18 50	1945	...	2030	...	0 20	2136	...	...	...	...	2 4	...	...
Jalons-les-Vignes	...	B		19 18	...	...	...	2048	...	0 35	RC	...	...	...	...	...	...	...
Epernay......................arr	...	16 37	...	19 43	19 15	2010	...	2114	...	0 52	22 0	...	...	...	...	2 30	...	...
REIMS (74A)..............dep	1,2,3	14 45	...	...	18 11	...	...	2010	...	2258	2010	...	...	...	...	1 15	...	...
Epernay......................dep	1840	16 40	...	20 21	19 18	2013	...	2215	...	1 0	22 2	...	...	...	...	2 34	5 0	...
Châtillon	19 1	...	...	20 44	...	...	...	2236	...	...	...	...	...	...	...	...	5 23	...
Dormans	20 0	...	...	21 0	RC	J	...	2251	...	1 26	...	...	...	...	...	2 58	5 38	...
Chateau-Thierry	2032	17 20	1920	21 34	...	2053	...	2320	...	1 52	...	...	...	...	...	3 22	6 7	...
La Ferte-s-Jouarre		...	1958	22 15	...	...	...		...	2 23	...	...	...	...	...	3 53		5 29
Meaux	...	...	2027	22 43	...	2140	...	...	...	2 50	...	...	...	...	...	4 14	...	5 59
Lagny Thorigny	...	...	...	...	...	...	...	...	...	3 10	...	...	...	...	...	4 31	...	6 22
PARIS Est. ....arr	...	18 40	2115	23 30	21 20	2230	...	...	...	3 45	2347	...	...	...	...	5 0	...	7 9

J—Will not admit 3rd class at Chateau-Thierry. At Meaux sets down only.

L—Admits 3rd class only for beyond Chalons and Epernay towards Reims. Exceptionally admits 3rd class at Igney Avricourt for all destinations.

NANCY to EPINAL and GRAY.

		1,2,3	1,2,3	1,2,3	1,2,3	1,2,3	1,2,3	1,2,3	1,2,3	1 &2	1 & 2	1,2,3	1,2,3	1,2,3	1,2,3	1,2,3	1,2,3	1,2,3	1,2,3	1 &2
Nancy ....dep		1 32	5 50	7 0	9 20	10 22	...	...	11 3	...	13 40	...	13 46	1631	1643	18 18	...	...	22 5	2353
Varangeville-St.-Nic.		...	...	...	9 38	...	...	...	11 25	...	B	...	...	...	...	...	...	...	...	
Rosières-aux-Salines		...	...	...	9 48	...	...	...	11§35	...	...	...	...	...	...	...	...	...	...	
Blainville-la-Grande		5 1	...	7 30	9 !7	10 42	...	...	11 46	...	14 2	...	14 12	...	1713	18 39	...	...	2232	
Charmes 71		5 47	...	8 16	10 36	...	...	...	12 30	...	...	...	14 53	...	1757	19 9	...	1920	23 8	
Epinal 70 ....arr		6 32	6 59	8 57	11 16	11 32	...	...	13 11	...	14 52	...	15 34	1731	1840	19 36	...	2011	2348	
,, ...dep		—	7 5	9 23	12 6	11 35	...	...	—	...		...	15 51	1742	—	19 45	19 58	—	—	
Xertigny		...	7 30	9 51	12 34	...	...	...	...	...		...	16 19	...	...	...	20 27	...	...	
Bains-les-Bains		...	7 45	10 7	12 51	...	...	...	...	...		...	16 35	...	...	20‡19	20 45	...	...	
Aillevillers ....arr		...	7 58	1023	13 7	12 13		A	...	...			16 51	1820	...	20 33	21 1	...	...	
Aillevillers ......dep		5 50	8 50	...	...	12§2	14‖25	1439	16§40	...		16‖59	17 §7	1837	...	...	21‡19	...	...	
Plombières........arr		6 14	9 31	...	...	12§47	14 47	15 1	17 2	...		17 21	17§24	19 7	...	...	21‡41	...	...	
AILLEVILLERS dep		—	8 3	1032	...	12 49	—	—	—	...		—	16 58	1833	...	...	21 30	...	...	
LURE 71 ....arr		...	8 49	1122	...	13 35	...	...	...	...		...	17 49	1927	...	...	22 11	...	...	
Aillevillers ....dep		5 45	8 8	1030	13 15	—	...	...	14 21	1442		...	18 27	—	...	20 46	21 13	...	...	
Saint-Loup-Luxeuil...		5 58	8 16	1038	13 24	...	...	...	14 52	...		...	18 34		...	...	21 25	...	...	
Conflans-Varigney ...		6 15	8 26	1048	13 34	...	...	...	15 20	A		...	18 43	...	...	...	21 37	...	...	
Faverney		6 39	8 43	11 5	13 51	...	...	...	15 4	...		...	18 58	...	...	...	21 55	...	...	Belfort ...... (p. 68A) arr. 2.45.
Port-d'Atelier 68		7 24	9 3	1120	14 6	...	...	...	16 26	15 7	To Gerardmer.	...	19 10	...	...	21 14	22 15	...	...	
Port-sur-Saone		7 36	9 15	1132	14 18	...	...	...	16 37	—		...	19 22	...	...	—	22 28	...	...	
Vesoul 53, 68 arr	...	7 55	9 34	1149	14 37	...	..	...	16 55	...		...	19 42	...	...	..	22 45	...	...	
Vesoul 53, 68 dep	6 0	—	9*25	1250	—	...	...	...	16*45	...		...	19*29	...	...	...	—	...	...	
Vellexon	6 52	...	1018	1339	...	...	...	...	17 36	...		...	20 20	...	...	...	...	...	...	
Gray 52.........arr	7 34	...	11 4	1421	...	...	...	...	18 19	...		...	21 2	...	...	...	...	...	...	

		1,2,3	1,2,3	1,2,3	1 & 2	1,2,3	1,2,3	1,2,3	1,2,3	1,2,3	1,2,3	1 & 2	1,2,3	1,2,3	1,2,3	1,2,3	1 &2			
Gray ....dep		...	...	5 21		...	...	9 30	...	...	...	...	1430	...	17 50	20 2		...	...	...
Vellexon		...	...	6 2		...	...	1012	...	...	...	...	1513	...	18 32	2045		...	...	...
Vesoul..................arr		...	D	6 49		...	...	11 1	...	...	...	...	1559	...	19*21	2134		...	...	...
,, ...dep		3 50	...	7 3		...	...	1122	...	...	...	...	1613	...	19 17	—	Belfort dep. 1.23.	...	...	...
Port-sur-Saone		4 7	...	7 26		...	...	1144	...	...	...	...	1635		19 41	...		...	...	...
Port-d'Atelier..............		4 35	4 55	7 46		...	...	12 2	...	...	...	16§36	1656	20 2	20 11	...		...	...	...
Faverney		4 42	5 2	7 56		...	...	1210	...	...	-	...	17 5	...	20 20	...		...	...	...
Conflans-Varigney ...		4 58	5 18	8 11		...	...	1226	...	...	...	...	1726	...	20 36	...		...	...	...
Saint-Loup-Luxeuil...		5 10	5 30	8 25		...	...	1237	...	...	...	..	1734	...	20 48	...		...	...	...
Aillevillers ....arr		5 17	5 37	8 32	To Gerardmer.	...	...	1244	...	...	...	17 2	1741	2032	20 54	...		...	...	...
LURE 71 ....dep		4 36	—	7 46		...	...	1152	12 56	...	...	—	1524	1949	19 49	...		...	...	...
AILLEVILLERS arr		5 22	...	8 34		...	...	1250	13 38	A	...	...	1618	2025	20 25	...		...	...	...
Plombières ......dep		5 ‡2	...	7 24		...	...	1142	13§10	1420	16 0	...	1727	1950	19 50	...		...	...	...
Aillevillers ......arr		5‡24	...	7 45		...	...	12 5	13§30	1437	16 31	...	1748	2018	20 18	...		...	...	...
Aillevillers ....dep		5 30	...	8 45		1017	...	13 0	13 42	—	—	...	1753	2040	21 3	...		...	...	...
Bains-les-Bains		5 55	...	9 9		...	...	1324	14 ‡1	...	...	...	1821	21§3	21 27	...		...	...	...
Xertigny		6 12	...	9 25		...	...	1340	...	...	...	...	1839	...	21 43	...		...	...	...
Epinal ....arr	1,2,3	6 35	...	9 48		1058	...	14 3	14 26	...	...	...	19 3	2130	22 6	...		...	...	...
,, ...dep	5 11	7 0	...	9 58	10 45	11 1	1144	1444	14 36	1658	17 17	...	1953	2140	22 21	...		...	...	...
Charmes..............	5 53	7 40	...	10 41	...	...	1223	1525	...	1739	18 5	...	2042	...	23 0	...		...	...	...
Blainville-la-Gr.	6 29	8 15	...	11 22	...	...	13 8	16 0	...	1816	—	...	2125	2226	23 26	...		...	...	...
Rosières-aux-Sa.	6 37	...	...	...	B	...	1316	...	...	...	...	...	...	...	23 44	...		...	...	...
Varangeville-St-N	6 49	...	...	...	...	...	1326	...	...	...	...	...	...	...	23 55	...		...	...	...
Nancy 65........arr	7 10	8 47	...	11 48	11 54	12 4	1347	1623	15 45	1841	...	...	2156	2248	0 11	...	4 4	...	...	...

*—Connection via Valvre. ‡—Until 20th September. §—Until 20th September.
‖—From 21st September. **A**—Until 21st September.
B—Runs daily until 15th Sept.; from 16th to 30th Sept. on Tues., Thurs., and Sat. only.
D—Runs until 15th September.

BLESME and CHAUMONT.

	1 &2	1,2,3	1,2,3	1 & 2	1,2,3	1,2,3	1,2,3	1,2,3	1,2,3	1,2,3	1 & 2	1,2,3	1 & 2							
CHALONS 64 dep	0 52	3 10	4 40	5 50	7 44	10 9	10 19	12 26	1435	1712	17 51	1944	23 28	...	...	...	...	...	...	...
Blesme ......dep		4 8	6 48		9 4	11 0	11 35		1535	1826		21 8		...	...	...	...	...	...	...
Saint Dizier ...		4 45	7 33		9 28	1130	12 20	13 30	16 4	19 1		2212		...	...	...	...	...	...	...
Ancerville-Guë...		4 54	7 42		—	1138	—	...	1613	19 9		2219		...	...	...	...	...	...	...
Eurville..............		5 2	7 50	C	...	1146	...	13 42	1621	1917	A	2226		...	...	...	...	...	...	...
Joinville		5 40	8 26		...	1227	...	14 1	1658	1953		2254		...	...	...	...	...	...	...
Gudmont		6 4	8 47		...	1249	...	...	1719	2013		—		...	...	...	...	...	...	...
Bologne (72)...		6 37	9 18		...	1318	...	...	1748	2041		...		...	...	...	...	...	...	...
Chaumont arr	2 32	7 2	9 40	7 37	...	1340	...	14 44	1810	21 3	19 31	...	1 15	...	...	...	...	...	...	...

	1& 2	1,2,3	1,2,3	1,2,3	1,2,3	1 & 2	1,2,3	1,2,3	1,2,3	1,2,3	1,2,3	1 &2								
Chaumont dep	3 46	...	5 29	...	1023	12 43	...	1455	1615	1638	2039	0 20	...	...	...	...	...	...	...	...
Bologne	...	...	5 49	...	1042		...	1515	...	1659	2056	...	...	...	...	...	...	...	...	...
Gudmont............	...	...	6 17	...	11 9		...	1543	...	1727	2125	...	...	...	...	...	...	...	...	...
Joinville	...	...	6 42	...	1130		1324	16 7	1655	1753	2148	...	...	...	...	...	...	...	...	...
Eurville	...	...	7 11	...	1159	A	1353	1635	1714	1827	2217	...	...	...	...	...	...	...	...	...
Ancerville-Guë...	...	...	7 19	...	12 7		14 1	1642	...	1839	2226	...	...	...	...	...	...	...	...	...
Saint Dizier...	4 52	5 15	7 36	9 20	1216		1413	1659	1729	1930	2240	...	...	...	...	...	...	...	...	...
Blesme ......arr		5 40	8 2	9 46	1239		1439	1725		1956	23 6	...	...	...	...	...	...	...	...	...
CHALONS 65 ar	5 43	6 49	8 51	10 57	1359	14 24	16 6	1826	1826	21 8	0 10	1 55	...	...	...	...	...	...	...	...

A—Runs daily until 30th September. **C**—Runs every Saturday until 30th September.

CONFLANS-JARNY and VILLERUPT-MICHEVILLE.

Conflans-Jarny dep	...	5 1	6 15	7 15	9 20	11 27	14 56	17 35	21 0	...	...	...
Briey	4 36	5 37	6 56	7 44	10 5	11 55	15 33	18 9	21 28	...	...	...
Audun-le-Roman	5 16	...	...	8 33	10 55	...	17 5	18 54	...	...	...	...
Villerupt-M. ......arr	5 50	...	...	...	11 29	...	17 38	19 22	...	...	...	...
Villerupt-M. ......dep	...	...	6 42	...	9 58	...	14 43	...	18 15	...	...	...
Audun-le-Roman	...	...	7 23	...	10 50	13 6	15 23	...	19 0	...	...	...
Briey	5 0	6 0	8 13	10 14	11 20	13 44	16 5	18 22	19 42	...	...	...
Conflans-Jarny arr	5 32	6 33	8 44	10 46	...	14 16	16 37	18 59	20 11	...	...	...

Audun-le-R. ...dep	7 42	11 6	15 34	19 11
Baroncourt... ..arr	8 20	11 46	16 12	19 49

Baroncourt ......dep	6 18	9 35	14 15	18 6	...
Audun-le-R. ...arr	6 59	10 16	14 56	18 45	...

LAON and REIMS.

Laon ......dep	2 22	4 22	...	7 10	1032	11 1	12 33	1535	16 26	1735	1932	1940	2123	2141	2241	2325
Guignicourt..	...	C	5 52	7 54	...	1143	13 15	1625	A	1826	...	...	...	...	2328	:
Betheny	...	5 3	...	...	...	...	...	...	17 7	...	...	...	2220	2226	...	X
Reims .....arr	4 13	5 12	6 23	8 25	1117	1214	13 46	17 0	17 20	19 0	2015	2020	2229	2237	2359	:

Reims.....dep	:	4 56	5 27	6 47	9 2	11 8	1347	1458	16 1	1750	1940	2052
Betheny	:	...	...	...	...	...	...	1520	...	...	...	...
Guignicourt..	:	5 36	5 58	...	9 34	1139	1418	A	1632	1820	...	2125
Laon 21...arr	3 15	...	6 44	7 30	1018	1222	15 4	16 0	1714	1859	2024	2210

A—Runs daily until 30th September. C—Runs every Saturday until 30th September. X—Chalons arrive 0.49.

RC—Restaurant Car.]

CHALONS, ST. HILAIRE, and REIMS.

Paris dep	...	0 35	0 35	...	...	8 15	1216	...	12 20	1242	14 20	1717	22 15
	1 &2	1,2,3	1 & 2	1 &2	1,2,3	1,2,3	1,2,3	1 &2	1,2,3	1,2,3	1,2,3	1,2,3	1,2,3
Chalons dep	1 58	5 3	5 48	6 27	7 52	1117	1422	1435	16 17	1843	19 6	22 5	1 50
St. Hil- arr	Laon arr. 3.15	5 26	...	...	8 15	1139	1443	...	16 40	RC	19 29	2228	2 10
aire ...dep	:	5 27	...	...	8 20	1140	1450	...	16 42	...	19 32	2238	2 19
Mourmelon	:	5 43	...	...	8 36	1156	15 7	A	16 58	19 9	19 49	2255	2 45
Wez-Thuisy	:	5 57	...	...	8 50	12 9	1521	...	17 12	...	20 3	23 9	...
Sillery.........	:	6 8	...	...	9 1	1220	1532	...	17 23	...	20 14	2320	...
Betheny	:	...	...	...	...	...	...	1519	...	...	...	...	...
Reims ...arr	:	6 26	6 36	6 47	9 19	1237	1550	1533	17 41	1935	20 32	2338	4 9

	1,2,3	1 & 2	1,2,3	1,2,3	1,2,3	1,2,3	1,2,3	1,2,3	1,2,3	1& 2	1,2,3	1 &2	1,2,3	1 &2	1 &2	
Reims...dep	1 11	4 48	5 8	6 35	8 35	9 42	1127	1235	1516	1651	1752	2031	2139	2211	22 3	Laon dep. 23.25
Betheny ...	...	5 4	...	...	...	...	...	...	...	17 8	...	...	...	2227	2223	:
Sillery	...	...	5 24	...	8 51	9 59	RC	1252	1532	...	18 8	...	2158	...	...	:
Wez-Thuisy	...	C	5 36	...	9 3	1011	...	13 4	1544	A	1820	...	2210	...	...	:
Mourmelon	1 48	...	5 53	7 4	9 22	1029	1155	1321	16 0	...	1836	...	2228	...	...	:
St. Hil- arr	2 0	...	6 7	...	9 37	1044	...	1336	1614	...	1850	...	2243	...	...	:
aire...dep	2 10	...	6 12	...	9 39	1050	...	1338	1622	...	1851	...	2245	...	...	:
Chalons arr	2 28	5 46	6 33	7 28	10 0	1111	1220	1359	1643	1748	19 9	2117	23 6	2315	2310	0 49
Paris 65	...	...	9 33	1135	12 15	...	1630	1630	...	...	2230	...	3 45	3 45	...	...

A—Runs daily until 30th September. C—Runs every Saturday until 30th September.

CHALONS ST.-HILAIRE-AU-TEMPLE, VERDUN, and BATILLY.

E.M Dist											
	Paris (64) dep	22 15	...	0 35	8 0	...	12 20	17 17	...	...	...
		1,2,3	1,2,3	1,2,3	1,2,3	1,2,3	1,2,3	1,2,3			
—	**Chalons** ......dep	1 50	...	5 32	10 28	...	15 48	19 50	...	...	...
10¼	**St.-Hilaire** ...arr	2 10	...	5 55	10 53	...	16 13	20 13	...	...	...
...	Reims ......dep	1 11	...	5 8	9 42	...	15 16	17 52	...	...	...
...	**St.-Hilaire**...dep	2 17	...	6 12	10 59	...	16 19	20 16	...	...	...
20¼	Suippes	2 36	...	6 33	11 20	...	16 40	20 38	...	...	...
32¼	Valmy	...	...	6 59	11 46	...	17 6	21 4	...	...	...
38½	Sainte-Menehould	3 13	...	7 30	12 5	...	17 27	21 30	...	...	...
46½	**Clermont (72)**	3 34	...	7 53	12 26	...	17 48	21 51	...	...	...
62¾	Baleicourt	4 8	...	8 27	13 0	...	18 22	22 27	...	...	...
66½	**Verdun (72)**	4 29	7 50	9 44	13 19	1544	19 0	22 35	...	...	...
92	**Conflans Jar. 67**	5 28	8 47	10 46	14 20	1644	20 3	—	...	...	...
97	**Batilly**	6 34	—	11 23	15 5	1740	21 12	...	...	...	...
98¾	**Amanvillers** arr	6 45	...	11 33	15 15	1750	21 22	...	...	...	...
08¾	Metz(212) ...arr	9 a12	...	1 p9	4p52	7p29	10p57	...	...	...	...

Metz (212) ...dep	...	6 a7	10a34	1 p55	4 p28	...	...	8p29	...
	1,2,3	1,2,3	1,2,3	1,2,3	1,2,3	1,2,3	1,2,3	1,2,3	
Amanvillers dp	...	6 0	10 19	13 41	16 18	...	...	20 9	...
Batilly	...	6 22	10 41	14 4	16 46	...	...	2029	...
Conflans J. dep	...	6 51	11 7	14 35	17 30	...	19 8	2115	...
Verdun	6 1	8 10	12 19	15 46	19 3	...	20 8	2218	...
Baleicourt	6 9	8 18	12 27	15 54	19 11	...	—	—	...
Clermont	6 47	8 58	13 7	16 34	19 53	...	...	...	...
Sainte-Menehould	7 12	9 22	13 35	16 58	20 18	21 29	...	...	...
Valmy	7 23	9 33	13 46	17 9	...	21 40	...	...	...
Suippes	7 51	10 2	14 16	17 38	20 52	22 10	...	...	...
St.-Hilaire ...arr	8 11	1022	14 36	17 58	:	22 30	...	...	...
Reims ......arr	9 19	...	15 50	...	:	23 38	...	...	...
St.-Hilaire...dep	8 18	1024	14 41	18 1	:	22 34	...	...	...
Chalons (65) arr	8 39	1042	15 2	18 22	21 25	22 55	...	...	...
Paris ......arr	11 35	1349	18 38	21 20	23 45	3 45	...	...	...

Conflans Jarny......dep	5 1	6 15	7 15	9 20	11 27	1456	17 35	21 8
Homecourt Joeuf arr	5 35	6 45	7 47	9 52	11 58	1530	18 7	21 33

Homecourt Joeuf dep	4 57	6 3	8 9	10 13	1337	1555	1829	1935
Conflans Jarny ......arr	5 32	6 33	8 44	1046	1416	1637	1859	20 3

LANGRES and POINSON-BENEUVRE.

E.M.							
	Langres-Marne 68 ....dep	9 31	16 3	20 6	...	...	...
3¼	**Langres-Ville**	9 46	16 18	20 25	...	...	...
18	Vaillant	10 27	16 55	21 18	...	...	...
29½	Poinson-Beneuvre 74 ......arr	10 52	17 18	21 56	...	...	...

Poinson-Beneuvre......dep	6 46	11 57	17 48	...	...	...	...	...	...	...
Vaillant	7 31	12 25	18 17	...	...	...	...	...	...	...
Langres-Ville	8 31	13 0	18 53	...	...	...	...	...	...	...
Langres-Marne ....arr	8 41	13 8	19 1	...	...	...	...	...	...	...

MONTMEDY and ECOUVIEZ.

Montmedy ....dep	4 43	5 42	8 52	1210	13 45	1535	1834	2048
Ecouviez 95 ....arr	4 53	5 54	9 4	1223	13 57	1548	1844	21 1

Ecouviez ....dep	4 0	5 11	6 24	9 38	13 1	1430	16 23	19 39
Montmedy 71 ....arr	4 12	5 23	6 34	9 50	13 12	1442	16 38	19 54

LANGRES and ANDILLY.

Dist. E.M.												
	Langres 68 dp	3 5	3*33	6 50	7 38	1018	13 0	15 †0	15‡30	16‡9	1713	1921
11¼	Andilly 66 ar	3 26	4 2	7 15	:	1058	1320	15 25	:	:	1745	1946

Andilly dp	7 57	:	13 6	1424	§ :	1616	1758	1850	22‖35	23*29	...
Langres ar	8 40	10 41	14 1	1443	1615	1648	1822	1911	23 4	23 0	...

*—Runs until 15th Sept. †—30 minutes later from 21st Sept. ‡—Runs until 20th Sept. §—Until 21st Sept. ‖—Runs from 16th Sept.

JUSSEY and EPINAL

E.M.							
	Jussey (68) ....dep	4 10	9 27	13 36	17 19	...	...
24½	Darney	5 14	10 28	14 37	18 25	...	...
49	**Epinal (66)** ....arr	6 24	11 39	15 46	19 46	...	...

Epinal ....dep	6 58	11 22	1459	20 0	...	...
Darney	8 14	12 34	16 9	21 17	...	...
Jussey ....arr	9 14	13 33	17 7	22 17	...	...

CARIGNAN and MESSEMPRE.

Dis.					
	Carignan ....dep	13 12	...	...	...
4¼	Messempré ....arr	13 39	...	...	...

Messempré ....dep	14 37	...	...	...
Carignan 71 ....arr	1457	...	...	...

PARIS, TROYES, CHAUMONT, VESOUL, and BELFORT.

THROUGH CARRIAGES { Paris to Basle—in 8.55, 13.0, 21.45, and 22.0 from Paris.
Paris to Milan—in 21.45 from Paris.
Paris to Vienna via The Arlberg—in 13.0 and 21.45 from Paris.

Dist E.M From Paris	1 Cl. fr. c.	2 Cl. fr. c.	3 Cl. fr. c.	**PARIS** (Gare de l'Est)	1 & 2	1,2,3	1,2,3	1,2,3	1,2,3	1,2,3	1,2,3	1,2,3	1,2,3	1 &2	1,2,3	1,2,3	1,2,3	1 &2	1,2,3
			...	Rue de Strasbourg...dep	...	0 20	...	...	5 22	7 0	8 0	8 3	...	8 55	...	8 58	9 2	1110	...
5½	1 0	0 70	0 45	Noisy-le-Sec	...	...	...	...	...	..	...	...	...	B	...	...	9 37	...	...
20¾	3 15	2 20	1 60	Ozoir-la-Ferrière	...	...	...	...	...	...	H	...	...	...	...	...	1014	...	...
24¾	3 70	2 75	1 90	**Gretz**	...	0 58	...	...	6 13	7 53	...	8 38	8 43	...	...	...	1023	RC	...
33	5 95	4 0	2 60	Verneuil-l'Etang	...	1 15	...	...	6 35	8 12	...	...	9 4	RC	...	9 44	1045	...	...
43½	7 85	5 30	3 45	Naugis	...	1 37	...	...	6 59	—	RC	...	9 29	...	...	10 1	1110	...	...
55¼	9 95	6 75	4 40	**Longueville**	...	1 58	...	5 17	7 27	...	...	9 18	9 52	...	...	1020	1136	G	...
59¾	10 75	7 25	4 75	**Flamboin**	...	...	...	5 29	7 38	...	...	...	—	...	...	1030	1146	...	...
69	12 45	8 40	5 45	Nogent-sur-Seine	...	2 19	...	5 58	8 0	...	...	9 37	...	...	...	1051	—	...	...
80¼	14 45	9 75	6 35	**Romilly 70**	...	2 37	...	6 35	8 34	...	...	9 53	...	...	...	1121	...	...	1448
103¾	18 70	12 65	8 25	**Troyes 73, 74** arr	...	3 11	...	7 38	9 38	...	9 53	1022	...	1054	...	1222	...	13 9	1550
				dep	...	4 0	...	7 50	—	...	9 56	1027	...	1057	..	1325	...	1312	1555
123¾	22 30	15 5	9 80	Vendeuvre	...	4 51	...	8 43	...	...	...	1054	...	...	...	1415	...	...	1641
130½	23 50	15 90	10 35	Jessains	...	5 10	...	9 4	...	...	...	...	...	...	...	1436	...	...	1658
137¼	24 75	16 70	10 90	**Bar-sur-Aube 74**	...	5 29	7 11	9 23	...	...	...	1115	...	...	...	1452	...	...	1714
155¼	28 0	18 90	12 30	**Bricon**	...	6 16	7 57	1012	...	...	...	1221	...	...	...	1536	...	...	1755
162¾	29 35	19 80	12 90	**Chaumont**...arr	...	6 38	8 16	1034	...	...	11 5	1240	...	12 9	...	1556	...	1428	1815
...	...	...	...	CHALONS (64)...dep	5 50	3 10	4 40	...	...	...	...	...	...	...	10 9	...	1226	...	...
...	...	...	...	BLESME (66)...dep	...	4 8	6 48	...	...	...	...	...	...	...	11 0	...	1125	...	...
...	...	...	...	**Chaumont**...dep	7 43	7 53	9 53	...	...	...	1110	1248	...	1215	1354	1617	1455	1439	...
...	...	...	...	Foulain	⋮	8 9	10 9	...	...	...	...	13 3	...	...	14 8	1632	...	...	...
184½	33 25	22 45	14 65	**Langres**	⋮	9 27	1049	1156	...	...	1138	1338	...	1245	1456	17 7	1534	1520	...
...	...	...	...	DIJON...dep	⋮	6 10	...	9 9	...	...	⋮	—	...	⋮	1327	1454	...	...	1737
191½	34 50	23 30	15 20	**Culmont-Chalindrey**	D	9 58	11 2	1211	...	...	⋮	...	...	⋮	15 8	1748	1545	1535	1911
...	...	...	...	MARTIGNY...68A arr	⋮	12 16	...	...	...	...	⋮	...	1422	⋮	⋮	...	...	1643	⋮
...	...	...	...	CONTREXEVILLE 68A arr	⋮	12 31	...	...	...	...	⋮	...	1438	⋮	⋮	...	...	17 1	⋮
...	...	...	...	VITTEL...68A arr	⋮	12 43	...	...	1,2,3	...	⋮	...	1450	⋮	⋮	...	...	1714	⋮
201¼	36 30	24 50	15 95	Charmoy	⋮	10 18	...	1231	G	...	⋮	...	...	⋮	1533	18 7	...	⋮	⋮
208¾	37 65	25 40	16 55	**Vitrey**	⋮	10 37	...	1251	14 10	...	⋮	...	...	⋮	1548	1825	...	1611	⋮
220	39 65	26 75	17 45	: **Bourbonne-les-Bains** ar	⋮	11 25	...	...	14 39	...	⋮	...	...	RC	1649	1920	...	1649	⋮
215½	38 85	26 25	17 10	Jussey 67	⋮	10 56	...	1338	—	...	⋮	...	...	⋮	16 3	1847	...	...	⋮
224½	40 45	27 30	17 80	**Port d'Atelier 66**	⋮	11 14	...	1355	...	...	⋮	...	...	⋮	1623	1910	...	1633	1955
...	...	...	...	PLOMBIERES 71...arr	RC	12 47	...	...	...	...	⋮	...	...	⋮	1724	...	...	1724	—
234¼	42 20	28 50	18 60	**Vaivre**	⋮	11 43	...	1422	...	...	⋮	...	...	⋮	1650	1936	...	—	...
236¾	42 65	28 80	18 80	**Vesoul 53, 66** arr...	⋮	11 49	...	1428	...	...	1237	...	...	1345	1655	1942	...	...	...
				dep6 9	⋮	12 48	11 4	—	...	...	1240	...	...	1348	17 5	1955	...	...	...
256¼	46 5	31 5	20 25	**Lure 71**...6 59	⋮	13 29	1153	...	...	...	...	...	...	...	1815	2047	...	...	...
275¼	49 60	33 50	21 85	**Belfort**...arr7 45	10 0	14 28	1240	...	...	...	1327	...	...	1438	19 4	2137	...	...	...
...	...	...	...	LYONS (53)...dep ...	...	7 20	...	...	7 20	...	...	...	...	7 20	...	...	...	...	...
...	...	...	...	BESANCON (52) dep3 59	6 57	12 4	...	9 15	12 4	...	...	...	...	12 4	17 0	...	1348	...	...
...	...	...	...	**Belfort**...dep7 55	10 5	16 30	...	1252	13 33	1411	...	...	...	1445	20 3	...	1813	...	...
282¾	50 95	34 40	22 40	Petit-Croix...8 10	10 19	16 45	...	13 7	13 45	1431	...	...	...	15 2	2018	...	1831	...	...
284½	51 30	34 65	22 60	Alt-Munsterol ¶...arr8 20	10 23	17 0	...	1320	13 53	1435	...	...	...	15 6	2028	...	1845	...	...
326¼	58 70	39 80	26 0	BASLE 207A...arr1115	12 42	8 p11	...	4p25	5 p28	5p28	...	...	...	5p28	12 8	...	9p20	...	...
...	...	...	...	**Belfort**...dep	...	...	1150	...	...	...	1337	...	⋮	1525	1936	2145	...	...	...
284	51 20	34 55	22 50	Morvillars	...	...	1212	...	...	...	1352	...	⋮	1547	1958	22 8	...	...	...
289	52 10	35 15	22 90	**Delle 266 ¶**...arr	...	...	1226	...	...	...	14 3	...	⋮	16 1	2012	2222	...	...	...
338	58 70	39 80	26 0	BASLE 264...arr	...	...	5 p7	...	...	...	5p15	...	⋮	8p23	...	...	...	...	...
...	...	...	...	BERNE 265...arr	...	...	...	...	...	...	6 p5	...	⋮	1023	...	...	...	...	...
...	...	...	...	MILAN 274...arr	...	...	...	...	...	...	1215	...	⋮	6a25	...	...	...	...	...
...	...	...	...	BASLE...dep	...	...	6p15	...	6 p15	...	6p15	...	6p15	9p39	...	...	9p39	...	...
381½	67 95	46 30	30 65	ZURICH 261...arr	...	...	7p55	...	7 p55	...	7p55	...	7p55	1125	...	...	1125	...	...
...	...	...	...	BASLE...dep	...	...	6p10	...	6 p10	...	6p10	...	6p10	9p45	...	...	9p45	...	...
386	68 70	46 80	31 0	LUCERNE 258...arr	...	...	8p15	...	8 p15	...	8p15	...	8p15	1142	...	...	1142	...	...
558¾	104 85	72 40	47 70	MILAN 259A...arr	...	...	...	...	...	...	...	...	...	6a22	...	...	6a22	...	...

A—Will only admit 3rd class for Petit-Croix and beyond, or for Delle and beyond. At Lure admits passengers without luggage only.

B—Takes 2nd class travelling at least 125 miles. Exceptionally admits 2nd class for Petit-Croix, or Delle, or beyond.

C—Taking 2nd class passengers coming from England, and taking up 2nd class for beyond Delle or Petit Croix. Will also receive on Eastern Co.'s Lines 2nd class from Laon and Stations on Nord Co.'s Lines.

D—Runs every Saturday until 30th Sept.

E—ENGADINE EXPRESS, Train de Luxe, running until 14th Sept. Take tickets in advance of Sleeping Car Co.

G—Runs until 20th September.

H—Takes 3rd class for beyond Troyes only.

J—Takes 3rd class who are travelling at least 125 miles.

K—Will only take 2nd class for Petit-Croix and beyond, and for Delle and beyond.

L—At Paris will only take 2nd class for Chaumont and beyond, and 3rd class for Vesoul and beyond.

M—Taking 3rd class who are travelling at least 125 miles. This train runs until 14th September.

¶—Customs Examination. Alt-Munsterol is also named "Montreux Vieux."

*—The times (of service to Berne) will only apply from 2nd July until 15th September.

FOULAIN and NOGENT-EN-BASSIGNY.

Foulain...dep	8 29	13 18	16 47	18 56	...	...	...	**Nogent-en-B.** ...dep	7 12	11 14	14 14	17 46	...	...	...
Nogent-en-B. ...arr	9 19	13 58	17 31	19 42	...	...	...	**Foulain (68)** ...arr	7 54	11 56	14 54	18 26	...	...	...

PARIS, TROYES, CHAUMONT, VESOUL, and BELFORT.

RC—Restaurant Car attached. SC—Sleeping Car attached.

Paris Nord ....dep	...	...	...	...	..	...	...	18 57	..	...	...	...	...	...	...	...	...	...
Paris Est. ....arr	...	...	...	...	...	...	...	19 18	..	...	...	...	...	...	...	...	...	...
	1,2,3	1,2,3	1,2,3	1,2,3	1,2,3	1,2,3	1,2,3	1 Cl.	1,2,3	1,2,3		1 &2	1 &2	1 & 2	1,2,3	1,2,3	1 & 2	1,2,3
PARIS (Gare de l'Est)																		
Rue de Strasbourg...dep	1430	13 2	13 0	1530	1633	1729	18 54	19 47	20 5	21 0	...	...	2145	...	22 0	22 20	...	22 24
Noisy-le-Sec	1447	...	...	...	1651	...	...	...	...	...	...	...	K	...	...	...	...	22 37
Ozoir-la-Ferrière	1528	13 40	A	...	1732	...	...	...	...	...	...	...	...	...	J	...	...	...
Gretz	1539	13 49	...	...	1744	1812	19 35	...	...	...	...	...	SC	...	...	M	...	23 19
Verneuil-l'Etang	1625	14 12	...	1617	18 3	1834	19 51	...	20 50	L	...	...	...	...	...	...	...	23 41
Nangis 1,2,3	1653	14 39	...	1634		1859	20 15	E	21 10	...	...	...	...	...	...	...	...	0 5
Longueville arr17 5	1719	15 5	...	1651	1850	1922	20 41	...	21 27	...	...	...	...	...	...	...	...	0 23
Flamboin arr1718		15 20	RC	...	19 9		20 52	...	21 37	SC	...	...	...	...	...	...	...	
Nogent-sur-Seine	...	15 48	...	1714	1935	...	21 19	...	21 52	...	...	...	...	...	...	...	...	...
Romilly 70	...	16 27	...	1735	2020	...	21 50	...	22 13	...	...	...	...	...	...	...	...	...
Troyes 73, 74 .... arr	...	17 30	1453	1812	2122	...	23 21	21 48	22 47	22 57	...	...	2338	...	0 7	0 52	...	...
Troyes 73, 74 .... dep	...	18 26	1457			...		21 57		22 59	...	...	2341	...	0 13	0 57	...	...
Vendeuvre	...	19 16	...	...	...	...	...	...	...	...	...	...	...	...	0 45	...	...	...
Jessains	...	19 35	...	...	...	...	...	...	...	...	...	...	...	...	0 59	...	...	...
Bar-sur-Aube 74	...	19 55	...	...	...	...	...	...	...	...	...	...	...	...	1 12	...	...	...
Bricon	...	20 39	...	...	...	...	...	...	...	...	...	...	...	...	1 47	...	...	...
Chaumont..................arr	1,2,3	20 59	16 6	...	...	...	...	23 9	...	0 11	...	...	0 50	...	2 3	2 30	...	...
Chalons (64) ....dep	1435	17 12	...	...	...	...	...	...	...	...	...	2122	...	23 28	...	0 52	0 52	...
Blesme (66)............dep	1535	18 26	...	...	...	...	...	...	...	...	...		...	...	...	...	...	...
Chaumont................dep	1825	21 12	1611	...	...	...	...	23 15	...	0 16	...		0 55	1 24	2 10	2 36	2 37	4 39
Foulain	1841	21 29	...	...	...	...	...		...		...				...	...		4 53
Langres	1921	22 11	1639	1827	...	...	...		...		...				2 40	3 10		5 25
Dijon..................dep	...	19 42		...	...	...	...		...		...			C	0 45	...		...
Cul.-Chalindrey	1934	22 56		1840	...	...	...		...		...				3 7	3 38		5 49
Martigny 68A ......arr	2127	...		...	...	...	...		...		...				4 33	5 §24		...
Contrexeville 68A arr	2141	...		...	...	...	...		...		...				4 48	5 §45		...
Vittel 68A ....arr	2151	...		...	...	...	...		...		...				4 59	6 §0		...
Charmoy	...	23 16		...	...	...	...		...		...					...		6 21
Vitrey	...	23 34		...	...	...	...		...		...				3 35	4 10		6 39
Bourbonne-les-Bains ar	...	...		...	...	...	...		...	SC	...	Via Nancy, page 66.		SC	4 15	5 32		7 38
Jussey 67	...	23 49		...	...	...	...		...		...				3 53	...		7 1
Port d'Atelier 66	...	0 5		...	...	...	...	E	...		...				4 12	4 43		7 19
Plombieres 71 ......arr	...	...		...	...	...	...		...		...				6 14	...		9 31
Vaivre	...	...		...	...	...	...		...		...				...	5 13		7 49
Vesoul 53, 66 .... arr	...	0 26	1738	...	...	...	...		...	1 41	...				4 37			7 55
Vesoul 53, 66 .... dep	...		1740	...	...	...	...		...	1 43	...				4 47	...		8 12
Lure 71	...	...	18 6	...	...	2215	...		...	...	...				5 25	...		9 2
Belfort ....arr	...	...	1834	...	...	23 2	...	1 25	...	2 33		2 45	3 11	3 45	6 6	...	4 45	9 49
Lyons....................dep	...	...	...	...	...	...	...		...	...			...	...	...	...	...	...
Besancon (52) ......dep	...	...	...	...	...	...	...		...	...			...	...	3 59	...	...	6 57
Belfort ....dep	...	...	1839	...	...	...	...		...	...			3 20	3 53	6 28	4 52	4 50	10 30
Petit-Croix	...	...	1851	...	...	...	...		...	...		...	3 33	4 6	6 43	5 5	...	10 45
Alt-Munsterol ¶ ....arr	...	...	1859	...	...	...	...		...	...		...	3 42	4 10	6 55	5 19	...	10 58
Basle 207A ....arr	...	...	9p20	...	...	...	...		...	...		...	5a58	6 a34	10a10	...	7 a58	2 p27
Belfort ....dep	...	...	...	...	...	...	...	1 28	...	2 42	2 53	...	...	3 *55	6 52	4 26	...	10 3
Morvillars	...	...	...	...	...	...	...	1 46	...	2 57	3 14	...	...	4 *10	7 22	4 46	...	10 30
Delle 266 ¶ ....arr	...	...	...	...	...	...	...	1 57	...	3 8	3 27	...	...	4 *21	7 41	5 0	...	10 44
Basle 264 ....arr	...	...	...	...	...	...	...	4 a45	...	6 a7	...	...	...	...	...	9 a40	...	...
Berne 265..........arr	...	...	...	...	...	...	...	...	...	7a40	7 a40	...	...	8a35	...	10a20	...	...
Milan 274 ....arr	...	...	...	...	...	...	...	...	...	2 p10	2 p10	...	...	3 p45	...	...	...	...
Basle.................dep	...	...	9p39	...	...	...	...	5 a10	...	6 a45	...	...	6a45	6 a45	10a34	...	...	4 p12
Zurich 261 ....arr	...	...	1125	...	...	...	...	6 a45	...	8 a35	...	...	8a35	8 a35	12p48	...	...	6 p57
Basle...............dep	...	...	9p45	...	...	...	...	5 a52	...	7 a0	...	...	7 a0	7 a0	10a40	...	...	2 p50
Lucerne 258 ...arr	...	...	1142	...	...	...	...	7 a50	...	8 a59	...	...	8a59	8 a59	1 p40	...	...	6 p15
Milan 269A ......arr	...	...	6a22	...	...	...	...	...	...	3 p5	...	...	3 p5	3 p5	...	...	...	...

§—These arrivals are on Wednesday and Saturday only.

CULMONT—CHALINDREY, CONTREXEVILLE, and NANCY.

Paris.................dep	...	...	22 0	22 20	...	...	...	0 20	8 55	...	11 10	11 10	...	...	...	...
Chaumont ....dep	...	...	2 10	2 36	...	4 39	...	7 53	12 15	...	14 39	...	...	...	18 25	...
Langres ....dep	...	...	3 5	3 33	...	6 50	...	10 18	13 30	...	15 20	15 30	...	...	19 21	...
Culmont Chalindrey......dep	...	...		C	...	6 38	...	10 32		...	15 44	E	...	...	19 25	...
Andilly	...	...	3 29	4 5	...	7 17	...	11 3	13 22	...	16 7		...	...	19 59	...
Merrey	...	...	3 59	4 39	5 52	8 10	...	11 40	13 49	...	16 31	16 12	...	16 55	20 50	...
Martigny-lès-Bains	...	...	4 33	5 24	6 30	8 48	...	12 16	14 22	...	Via Neufchateau.	16 43	...	17 33	21 27	...
Contrexeville	...	...	4 48	5 45	6 44	9 4	...	12 31	14 38	...		17 1	...	17 48	21 41	...
Vittel	...	...	4 59	6 0	6 53	9 17	...	12 43	14 50	...		17 14	...	17 59	21 51	...
Hymont-Mattaincourt...	...	...	5 31	6 36	7 27	9 52	...	13 19	15 15	...		17 39	...	18 38	22 24	...
Mirecourt	...	5 2	5 44	6 42	7 55	10 3	...	13 33	15 20	15 30		17 44	...	19 1	22 29	...
Frenelle	...	5 16	5 55		8 8	10 14	...	13 47		15 41			...	19 18		...
Vezelise	4 34	5 53	6 19	...	8 46	10 41	11 3	14 24	...	16 19		...	...	20 4	...	...
Pont-St. Vincent	5 18	7 0	6 48	...	9 29	11 4	11 47	15 6	...	17 3		...	1825	20 50	...	...
Nancy (64) ....arr	5 53	7 37	7 18	...	10 6	11 27	12 27	15 41	...	17 44	18 39	...	19 1	21 30	...	...

C—On Wednesday & Saturday.
E—Until 20th Sept.

EASTERN RAILWAY.

BELFORT, VESOUL, CHAUMONT, TROYES, AND PARIS.

Station																				
MILAN 269A dep		...	...	...	...	...	...	9 p5	...	...	...	1135	...	11p35	11p35	...	...	...	...	...
LUCERNE ...dep		...	...	...	...	...	...	5 a5	...	...	...	7 a0	...	7 a0	7 a0	...	...	...	...	1010
BASLE 258 ...arr		...	...	...	...	...	...	7a10	...	...	...	8a57	...	8 a57	8 a57	...	...	...	...	1p12
ZURICH ....dep		...	...	...	...	...	...	...	...	4a52	...	7a16	...	8 a25	8 a25	...	...	...	9 a45	1138
BASLE 261 ......arr		...	...	...	...	...	...	...	...	7a35	...	9 a3	...	10 25	10a25	...	...	...	11a56	1p18
MILAN ....dep		...	...	...	...	...	...	1145	...	...	...	...	...	|	...	...	...	...	...	...
BERNE 266 ......dep		...	...	...	...	...	...	6a38	...	...	...	...	...	|	...	...	...	...	...	...
BASLE *** 264A dep		...	...	...	...	...	...	7a35	...	7a45	...	...	7 a45	|	10a44	...	...	...	10a44	...
Delle ¶ 266 ....dep		...	...	...	...	5 35	...	8 42	7 3	9 45	...	...	10 42	|	12 55	...	...	...	13 38	...
Morvillars		...	...	...	...	5 48	...	8 51	7 20	9 59	...	...	10 56	|	13 4	...	...	...	13 53	...
Belfort ....arr		...	...	...	...	6 10	...	9 7	7 43	1024	...	...	11 22	|	13 21	...	...	...	14 16	...
BASLE *** 207A ...dep		...	...	...	...	4 a58	...	...	6a33	7a58	...	9a40	10a41		...	...	...	...	12p15	1p45
Alt-Munsterol.........dep		...	...	...	...	5 59	...	...	7 19	9 41	...	9 52	10 57		11 45	...	...	...	13 19	1424
Petit Croix ¶ ....dep		...	...	...	...	6 21	...	...	7 37	1016	...	10 5	11 23	...	12 16	...	...	...	13 38	1451
Belfort ....dep		...	...	...	...	6 37	...	...	7 53	1033	...	1017	11 36	...	12 29	...	...	...	13 54	15 6
BESANCON 52 ......arr		...	...	...	...	10 32	...	...	1032	1325	...	1325	...	...	...	...	...	...	16 53	1710
LYONS 53 ....arr		...	...	...	...	...	...	...	...	...	...	...	...	...	...	...	...	...	21 56	2156
		1,2,3	1,2,3	1,2,3	1,2,3	1,2,3	1,2,3	1,2,3	1,2,3	1,2,3		1 &2	1 & 2	1,2,3	1,2,3	1,2,3	1,2,3	1,2,3	1,2,3	1,2,3
Belfort ....dep		Until 15th September.	3 48	...	...	6 47	...	9 12	...	1043	Wednesday and Saturday only.	1021	11 41	12 25	13 26	...	...	...	14 27	1710
Lure			4 31	...	...	7 37	...	...	...	1135		C	E	12 53	13 56	...	...	...	15 14	18 0
Vesoul .... arr				...	...	8 15	...	9 57	...	1216		⋮	12 29		14 20	...	...	...	15 51	1840
Vesoul .... dep			...	3 50	...	8 25	...	9 59	...	1235		⋮	12 31	...	14 23	...	...	...	16 28	
Vaivre			...	3 56	...	8 33	...	⋮	...	1242		⋮	⋮	...	...	...	B	...	16 36	...
PLOMBIERES 71 ......dep			...	...	...	7 24	...	⋮	...	...		⋮	⋮	...	11 42	...	1420	...	...	...
Port d'Atelier			...	4 22	...	9 0	...	⋮	...	1311		RC	RC	...	14 43	...	15 8	1654	17 1	...
Jussey			...	4 44	...	9 24	...	⋮	...	1343		⋮	⋮	...	14 58	...	...	1712	17 29	...
: Bourbonne-l-Bains dep		5 50	...	4 23	...	8 48	...	⋮	...	13 1		⋮	⋮	...	13 1	...	1453		17 5	...
Vitrey		6 21	...	5 0	...	9 41	...	⋮	...	14 2	☞	⋮	⋮	...	15 11	...	1532	...	17 47	...
Charmoy			...	5 17	...	9 58	...	⋮	...	1420		⋮	⋮	...	⋮	...	⋮	...	18 6	...
VITTEL 69A ....dep		...	...	...	6 13	...	...	8 27	...	...	10 12	⋮	⋮	...	12 50	1250	1442	...	15 41	...
CONTREXEVILLE 69A dp		...	...	...	6 22	...	...	8 39	...	...	10 22	⋮	⋮	...	13 2	13 2	1454	...	15 50	...
MARTIGNY 69A ......dep		...	...	...	6 36	...	...	8 54	...	...	10 37	⋮	⋮	...	13 18	1318	15 9	...	16 4	...
Culmont-Chalindrey		...	...	6 0	8 30	10 27	...	⋮	1119	1451		⋮	⋮	...	15 44	1515	16 3	...	18 37	1912
DIJON 55A ....arr		...	...	8 26	...	12 36	...	⋮	1420			RC	⋮	...	17 46	...	...	...	22 21	...
Langres		...	4 14	6 21	8 49	10 55	10 16	11 9	1140	...		⋮	13 42	14 37	16 1	1533	1627	1658	19 9	1927
Foulain		...	4 39	6 51	9 21		10 49	...	1211	...		⋮	...	15 9	...	...	...	1731	19 41	
Chaumont...................arr		...	4 53	7 9	9 39	...	11 10	1136	1229	...		1238	14 10	15 27	16 29	16 2	1655	1751	19 58	...
BLESME 66 ....arr		...	8 2	...	1239	...	...	...	...	...	...	...	17 25	...	19 56	...	...	...	23 6	...
CHALONS 65 ....arr		...	8 51	...	1359	...	...	...	...	...	...	1424	18 26	...	21 8	1826	...	...	0 10	...
Chaumont ....dep		...	5 9	7 22	...	...	11 5	1139	...	...	...	...	14 16	15 34	16 45	...	17 2	1840	20 44	...
Bricon		...	5 22	7 40	...	...	12 12	...	...	...	...	...	...	15 51	...	...	...	1857	21 1	...
Bar-sur-Aube		...	5 58	8 20	1110	...	12 54	...	...	...	...	...	...	16 29	17 19	...	...	1952	21 41	...
Jessains..........................		...	6 13	8 41	1127	...	13 10	RC	...	...	...	...	...	16 45	...	...	RC	20 8	21 5	...
Vendeuvre		...	6 31	9 1	1146	...	13 30	...	...	...	...	...	...	17 3	17 40	...	...	2027	22 11	...
Troyes .... arr		...	7 14	9 48	1233	...	14 17	1246	...	...	...	1,2,3	15 26	17 53	18 7	...	1814	2114	22 53	...
Troyes .... dep		7 25	7 33	11 15		...	14 36	1251	...	1328	...	1538	15 31	18 58	18 32	...	1819		23 4	2040
Romilly		8 3	8 37	12 24	...	...	15 16	...	...	1450	...	1644	...	20 19	19 6	...	...	...	0 2	2142
Nogent-sur-Seine		8 22	9 6	12 51	...	...	15 38	...	...	1519	...	1714	RC	20 49	19 23	...	...	...	0 28	
Flamboin....................	4 27	...	9 35	13 13	...	...	15 55	...	1646	1542	...	1741	...	21 15	...	...	...	...	0 47	...
Longueville................	4 57	8 48	9 54	14 45	1236	...	16 9	...	17 6		...	2012	...	21 37	19 45	...	...	...	1 5	...
Nangis	5 27	9 9	1030	15 22	13 6	...	...	...	1745	...	...	2042	...	22 1	...	...	...	...	1 33	...
Verneuil-l'Etang	5 4[illegible]	9 25	1056	15 52	1328	14 18	16 47	...	1812	1857	...	21 5	...	22 18	...	...	...	...	...	...
Gretz-Armainvilliers	6 15	9 41	1122	16 20	1349	14 41	...	...	1836	1926	...	2142	...	...	...	...	...	...	2 13	...
Ozoir-la-Ferrière		...	1132	...	...	...	...	...	...	1933	...	...	...	...	...	...	...	...	...	...
Noisy-le-Sec....................		...	1213	...	...	...	...	...	...	20 9	...	...	...	...	...	...	...	...	2 55	...
PARIS Est. ....arr	7 0	1010	1228	16 59	1430	15 35	17 37	1449	1914	2026	...	22 5	17 45	23 8	21 0	...	2031	...	3 11	...

GERARDMER, LA SCHLUCHT, and LE HONECK.

*—Runs until 21st September. ‡—Until 21st September. §—Until 19th October.

E.M.	fr. c.																		
						*	§	*	§	*		§	*	§	*	§			
—	—	**Gérardmer** ...dep	5§50	...	...	7 0	7 55	8 50	9 50	10 40	...	13 20	14 10	15 0	16 0	16 50	17*40	...	...
6¾	1.90	Retournemer..........	6 30	6*35	7§ 0	7 55	8 48	9 40	10 34	11 22	13*15	14 5	15 0	15 54	16 46	17 36	18 20	...	...
11¼	2.40	La Schlucht 211		7 0	7 22	8 20	9 10	10 2	10 56	11 44	13 41	14 29	15 24	16 18	17 10	17 58	...	...	...
13	3.30	**Le Honeck**....arr	...	...	7 42	8 40	9 34	10 20	11 14	13‡ 0	13 55	14 48	15 44	16 36	17 28	...	-	...	...

E.M.	fr. c.																		
				*	§	*	§	*		*	§	*	§	*	§				
—	—	**Le Honeck**...dep	...	...	8 6	8 56	9 48	10 42	11‡30	...	13 20	14 15	15 10	16 4	16 56	17*44	...	...	...
1¾	0.60	La Schlucht..........	...	7 26	8 23	9 18	10 4	10 58	11 42	11 46	13 39	14 32	15 28	16 20	17 12	18 2	18§ 6	...	...
7¼	1.35	Retournemer	7§ 0	7 55	8 50	9 50	10 40	11 30		12 10	14 10	15 0	16 0	16 50	17 40	18 30	18 28	...	...
13	2.25	**Gérardmer**....arr	7 40	8 40	9 30	10 30	11 20	12 10	...	...	14 50	15 40	16 40	17 30	18 20	19 10	...	...	...

SEDAN and BOUILLON.	**Sedan**.......................dep	7 13	9 46	13 43	16 24	**Bouillon**...........dep	7 46	10 25	14 20	16 50	...
	Balan Bazeilles	7 29	10 2	13 59	16 39	Corbion (frontier)	8 23	11 12	14 58	17 31	...
	Corbion (frontier)	8 13	10 53	14 48	17 21	Balan Bazeilles	9 12	12 8	15 52	18 19	...
	Bouillon (Belg.) 96 arr	8 55	11 37	15 32	18 4	**Sedan**...................arr	9 26	12 24	16 7	18 33	...

EASTERN RAILWAY.

BELFORT, VESOUL, CHAUMONT, TROYES, AND PARIS.

Station											
MILAN 269A dep	7 a25	...	7 a25	9 a35	...	12p40	...	...	2p40	...	...
LUCERNE ...dep	2 p2	...	2 p2	4 p57	...	7 p0	...	...	9p10	10p13	...
BASLE 258 ...arr	4 p6	...	4 p6	6 p58	...	9 p0	...	...	11p3	12a10	...
ZURICH ....dep	2 p48	...	2 p48	2 p48	...	6 p40	...	9 12	9p12	10 p5	...
BASLE 261......arr	4 p29	...	4 p29	4 p29	...	8 p28	...	1058	1058	11p45	...
MILAN ....dep	8 a15	...	...	...	10a50	...	...	3p25	...	...	...
BERNE 266.........dep	3 p18	...	...	4 p12	7 p43	...	...	1038	...	...	...
BASLE *** 264A dep	4 p17	...	...	6 p44	...	...	..	1145	1133	12a30	...
Delle ¶ 266 ....dep	17 35	...	17 45	20 26	21 35	...	...	0 48	0 28	1 50	...
Morvillars	17 44	...	17 59	20 39	...	...	...	...	0 37	2 4	...
Belfort ....arr	18 0	...	18 22	21 4	22 2	...	...	1 13	0 54	2 29	...
BASLE *** 207A ...dep	5 p6	5 p6	5 p58	7 p32	9 p25	10 p0	10p11	...	:	:	...
Alt-Munsterol ....dep	17 13	1751	19 20	20 55	...	22 20	23 43	...	:	:	...
Petit Croix ¶ ....dep	17 41	1810	19 44	21 15	...	22 50	0 2	...	:	:	...
Belfort ....arr	17 54	1827	20 0	21 29	22 2	23 3	0 16	...	:	:	...
BESANCON 52 ......arr	20 45	2215	...	...	...	...	...	...	:	:	...
LYONS 53 ....arr	...	...	...	...	...	...	...	...	:	:	...
	1,2,3	1,2,3	1,2,3		1 & 2	1,2,3	1,2,3	1 &2	1,2,3	1 Cl.	
Belfort ....dep	18 6	1920	20 35	...	22 9	23 15	...	1 23	1 30	2 42	..
Lure	18 32	1948	21 11	...	:	23 44	...	:	1 56	:	...
Vesoul .... arr	18 55	2037	21 37	...	:	0 9	...	:	2 19	:	...
Vesoul .... dep	18 58	—	21 44	...	:	0 15	...	:	2 22	:	...
Vaivre	:	...	...	...	:	:	...	To Boulogne and Calais.	:	:	...
PLOMBIERES...........dep	:	1950	19 50	...	:	:	...	:	:	:	...
Port d'Atelier	:	2118	22 17	...	:	E	...	:	J	G	...
Jussey	RC	...	22 34	...	:	:	...	:	:	:	...
: Bourbonne-l-Bains dep	:	2058	...	...	:	SC	...	:	:	:	...
Vitrey	:	2143	...	...	:	:	...	:	:	:	...
Charmoy	:	:	22 57	...	:	:	...	:	:	:	...
VITTEL 69A ....dep	17 25	...	21 0	...	:	:	...	:	:	:	...
CONTREXEVILLE 69A dp	17 36	...	21 10	...	:	:	...	:	:	:	...
MARTIGNY 69A ......dep	17 51	...	21 24	...	:	:	...	:	:	:	...
Culmont-Chalindrey	:	2218	23 23	...	:	:	...	:	:	:	...
DIJON 55A..............arr	L	2348	...	...	:	:	...	:	:	:	...
Langres	20 5	—	23 41	...	:	1 31	...	:	3 29	:	...
Foulain........................	...	...	...	...	:	...	...	:	...	:	...
Chaumont.................arr	20 32	...	0 10	...	0 15	2 0	...	:	3 56	5 0	...
BLESME 66...............arr	23 6	...	...	...	...	...	...	:	...	...	...
CHALONS 65 ....arr	0 10	...	...	...	1 55	...	...	6 25	...	...	...
Chaumont ....dep	20 38	...	0 18	...	...	2 10	...	...	4 1	5 5	...
Bricon	...	...	0 30	...	...	...	...	...	...	...	...
Bar-sur-Aube	...	...	0 57	...	...	...	...	...	...	...	...
Jessains.......................	...	...	1 9	...	...	...	...	...	...	...	...
Vendeuvre	...	...	...	...	...	...	...	...	...	...	...
Troyes .... arr	21 45	...	1 45	...	...	3 24	...	...	5 8	6 9	...
Troyes .... dep	21 50	...	1 59	...	...	3 29	4 27	...	5 13	6 19	...
Romilly	...	...	2 35	...	...	...	5 42	...	...	...	...
Nogent-sur-Seine	...	...	2 53	...	...	...	6 10	...	...	...	...
Flamboin......................	...	...	3 8	...	...	...	6 38	...	...	...	...
Longueville..............dep	RC	...	3 20	...	...	SC	7 12	...	...	...	...
Nangis	...	...	3 42	...	...	...	7 48	...	...	G	...
Verneuil-l'Etang	...	...	4 2	...	...	...	8 13	...	...	...	...
Gretz-Armainvilliers......	...	...	4 19	...	...	...	8 39	...	...	...	...
Ozoir-la-Ferrière	...	...	...	...	...	...	8 48	...	...	...	...
Noisy-le-Sec.................	...	...	...	...	...	...	...	...	...	...	...
PARIS Est. ....arr	23 48	...	4 55	...	...	6 25	9 25	...	7 28	8 42	...
PARIS Est. ....dep	...	...	...	...	...	...	...	...	...	8 51	...
PARIS Nord ....arr	...	...	...	...	...	...	...	...	...	9 14	...

NOTES.

☞ Passengers to and from Basle via Delle may have to change carriages at Belfort.

Luggage, 30 kilo. (66 lbs.) allowed free; excess Luggage, 1 centime per 44 lbs. per kilometre.

B—This train will run until 21st September.

C—Train running to Boulogne daily until 30th September.

E—Carries 2nd class travelling at least 125 miles, and 3rd class travelling at least 190 miles; exceptionally will take for all stopping places 2nd cl. and 3rd cl. coming from beyond Petit-Croix or Delle.

G—ENGADINE EXPRESS, Train de Luxe; will run from 3rd July until 16th September.

J—Taking 2nd class travelling at least 125 miles and 3rd class travelling at least 190 miles; exceptionally, 2nd and 3rd class from beyond Petit-Croix or Delle taken for all stopping places.

L—Will only carry those 3rd cl. passengers who are travelling from beyond Petit-Croix or Delle.

RC—Restaurant Car attached.

SC—Sleeping Car attached.

*****—Differences of Time.** The Basle departures are by Mid-Europe Time.

¶—Customs Examination.

Extra		
Extra	Belfort ......dep	18 10
	Lure ....arr	18 58
	Flamboin ...dep	8 18
	Longueville arr	8 31

NANCY, CONTREXEVILLE, and CULMONT-CHALINDREY.

Station																		
Nancy ....dep	...	5 1	7 40	7 52	...	9 25	...	1222	14 5	...	1620	1652	1730	...	1838	1919	2045	...
Pont-S.-Vincent............	...	5 44	8 21	Via Neufchateau	...	10 6	...	1257	1446	...	1653	1713	1813	...	19 3	1952	2120	...
Vezelise	...	6 35	9 5		...	1055	B	1340	1536	...	—	1742	1857	C	1932	—	22 2	...
Frenelle-la-G.................	...	7 16	—		...	1135	...	1419	1621	...	...	1816	—	...	1957	...	2235	...
Mirecourt ....dep	5 30	7 38	...		A	12 0	14 9	1458	1634	16 50	...	1846	...	19 44	2024	...	2247	...
Hymont-Mattaincourt dp	5 38	7 47	...		...	1210	14 15	15 5	—	16 57	...	1852	...	19 50	2034	...	—	...
Vittel	6 13	8 27	...		10 12	1250	14 42	1541	...	17 25	...	1930	...	20 27	21 0	...	...	...
Contrexéville	6 22	8 39	...		10 22	13 2	14 54	1550	...	17 36	...	1941	...	20 37	2110	...	...	...
Martigny-les-Bains	6 36	8 54	...	:	10 37	1318	15 9	16 4	...	17 51	...	1954	...	20 51	2124	...	...	...
Merrey	7 11	9 31	...	10 3	:	1354	15 32	1640	...	18 20	...	2029	...	21 24	2157	*	...	...
Andilly	7 51	10 7	...	:	:	1422	:	1715	...	18 48	...	—	...	21 53	2255	2233	...	...
Culmont-C. ....arr	8 16	1032	...	11§2	:	15 8	:	1741	...	19§34	...	...	...	22 13	:	2251	...	...
LANGRES ....arr	8 40	1039	...	1041	12 2	1443	16 15	1822	...	19 11	...	...	...	...	23 4	...	...	...
CHAUMONT (69).......arr	9 39	1136	...	1136	12 38	16 2	16 55	1958	...	...	...	...	...	...	0 10	0 10	...	...
PARIS (69) ....arr	...	1449	...	1449	...	21 0	20 31	2344	...	...	...	...	...	...	4 55	4 55	...	...

C—Runs until 15th September.

*—Runs from 16th September.

§—Via Langres. **A**—On Wednesdays and Saturdays until 30th September. **B**—Until 21st September.

PARIS, MEAUX, REIMS, MEZIERES-CHARLEVILLE, GIVET, and AUDUN-le-ROMAN.

	1,2,3	1,2,3	1,2,3	1,2,3	1,2,3	1,2,3	1,2,3	1,2,3	1,2,3	1,2,3	1,2,3	1,2,3	1,2,3	1,2,3	1,2,3	1,2,3	1,2,3	1,2,3	1,2,3
Paris-Est ....dep	...	...	0 35	...	5 30	8 10	9 4	1035	8 15	...	13 0	13 55	15 48	16 55	1720	18 20	18 22	21 15	...
Meaux ....dep	...	...	1 44	...	6 35	...	...	1140	8 58	...	13 55	...	16 46	...	1813	...	19 15	21 52	22 2
Trilport	...	...	Via Epernay	...	6 44	...	...	1149	9 7	...	14 4	...	16 55	...	1822	...	19 24	...	22 11
Lizy-sur-Ourcq	...	...		...	7 0	...	...	12 6	9 23	...	14 21	...	17 12	17 48	1838	...	19 39	...	22 27
La Ferté-Milon............	...	4 43		...	7 36	A	10 6	1233	10 20	...	15 10	14 59	17 41	18 8	19 5	...	20 46	22 26	22 54
Oulchy-Breny	...	5 6		...	7 59	...	...	—	10 48	...	15 34	...	—	18 30	—	RC	21 7	...	—
Fere-en-Tardenois......	...	5 22		...	8 15	...	...	...	11 5	...	15 50	...	...	18 45	...	...	21 23	22 53	...
Fismes	...	5 52		...	8 46	...	...	...	11 38	...	16 21	...	...	19 13	...	...	21 53	23 11	...
Reims............... arr	...	6 28	4 19	...	9 25	9 56	11 3	...	12 17	...	17 0	15 58	...	19 35	...	20 20	22 17	23 33	...
Reims............... dep	...	—	5 40	8 21	10 34	10 0	11 10	...	12 54	...	17 15	16 5	...	—	2233	20 28	—	23 44	0 50
Bazancourt (**74A**)	...	...	6 6	8 48	11 0	...	...	...	13 20	...	17 45	...	...	...	23 0	...	...	...	1 11
Rethel	...	...	6 43	9 23	11 50	...	11 44	12 1	13 56	...	18 23	16 39	...	...	2334	21 1	21 13	0 27	1 40
Amagne-L. (74)......	...	...	7 6	9 43	12 4	...	...	1211	14 14	...	18 46	...	...	...	2344		21 28	0 39	1 53
Mohon	...	...	8 19	10 52	13 12	...	...	—	15 22	...	19 58	...	...	...	—	...	—	...	...
Mezieres-Char. arr	...	...	8 23	10 56	13 16	11 9	12 29	...	15 26	...	20 2	17 24	...	...	...	21 46	...	1 29	2 46
Mezieres-Ch....dep	6 5	...	9 2	...	...	...	12 44	1451	...	...	...	17 34	20 21	...	...	22 17	...	...	3 2
Nouzon (**29B**)	6 17	...	9 16	...	...	...	12 57	15 3	...	...	...	17 48	20 34	...	...	22 30	...	...	3 15
Montherme	6 37	...	9 37	...	...	...	13 18	1521	...	...	...	18 9	20 55	...	...	22 51	...	...	3 36
Vireux-Molhain (**97**)	7 34	...	10 37	...	...	...	14 14	1614	...	...	...	19 6	21 50	...	...	23 46	...	...	4 57
Givet (92).........arr	7 49	...	10 52	...	...	...	14 29	1629	...	...	...	19 21	22 5	...	...	0 1	...	...	5 18
BRUSSELS ....arr	10 37	...	15 6	...	...	...	17 35	21 8	...	...	...	23 12	...	...	...	...	...	...	8 29
Mezieres Charleville...dep	6 5	6 38	8 39	11 50		11 38	12 42	...	15 36	18 11	20 20	17 52	...	22 53	...	22 9	...	1 45	2 59
Mohon	6 10	...	8 46	11 55		...	12 47	...	15 41	18 16	20 25	...	...	22 58	...	...		...	...
Vrigne-Meuse	6 32	...	9 10	12 14		...	13 6	...	16 0	18 38	20 45	...	...	23 17	...	...		...	...
Sedan (72)..........dep	7 19	7 2	9 39	12 26		...	13 35	...	16 45	18 57	20 58	18 14	...	23 29	...	22 33		2 11	3 30
Pont-Maugis	7 25	...	9 47	—		12 1	13 43	...	16 51	19 5	—	...	...	—	...	...		...	...
Bazeilles	7 29	...	9 51	...		...	13 47	...	16 55	19 11	...	18 35	...	...	...	...		...	...
Carignan (**67**) 1,2,3	7 58	7 22	10 21	...		12 26	14 18	...	17 23	19 40	...	19 1	...	...	...	22 58		...	4 3
Montmédy (**67**)......4 20	8 47	7 47	11 10	...		12 53	15 7	...	18 10	20 28	...	...	...	...	...	23 26		3 7	4 38
Velosnes-Torgny ...4 30	8 56	...	11 19	...		...	15 16	...	18 19	20 37	...	...	...	...	...	...		...	...
Longuyon ...arr4 50	9 19	8 6	11 39	...		13 14	15 36	...	18 41	20 57	...	19 22	...	...	...	23 47		3 31	5 4
" ....dep	10 3	—	—	...	...	13 31	16 10	...	—	—	...	19 44	...	...	...	—	RC	—	5 16
Audun-Roman arr	10 41	...	...	...	...	14 9	16 52	...	...	...	...	20 28	...	...	...	...		...	5 53
FONTOY (Fentsch) dp	12p57	...	...	...	...	3p45	—	...	...	...	...	10p3	...	...	...	...	...	...	7a20
METZ (**210**) .....arr	2 p22	...	...	...	...	4p54	...	...	...	...	...	10p55	...	...	...	...	...	...	8 a47

A—Admits 3rd class for beyond Reims only.

RC—Restaurant Car attached.

EPERNAY and ROMILLY-SUR-SEINE.

Epernay dep	6 20	...	8 22	9 52	11 53	16 55	19 32	21 9	...
Oiry............dep	6 30	...	8 31	10 3	12 2	17 7	19 42	2120	...
Vertus	7 0	...	9 3	10 41	12 29	17 40	20 12	2150	...
Fère-Champeno	—	...	9 43	11 13	13 7	18 14	20 53	2224	...
Sezanne	4 47	7 5	10 25	11 41	13 53	19 10	21 23	2252	...
St.Quentin-le-V	5 5	7 26	10 45	—	14 11	19 32	—	—	...
Romilly...arr	5 30	7 53	11 11	...	14 34	20 0	...	...	...

Romilly ....dep		...	8 31	...	1226	...	1647	1741	...	22 25
St. Quentin-le-V.		...	8 55	...	1250	...	1713	18 6	...	22 49
Sezanne 4 41	4 41	...	9 18	1145	1315	...	1738	1825	1933	23 9
Fère-Champenoise	5 14	...	9 49	1219	1343	1411	1811	—	20 7	—
Vertus	5 49	7 23	1019	13 0	—	1448	1843	...	2048	...
Oiry.........................	6 15	7 54	1042	1326	...	1515	1910	...	2116	...
Epernay 65 arr	6 25	8 7	1052	1335	...	1524	1924	...	2128	...

NANCY, ST. DIE, LAVELINE, and EPINAL.

Nancy.........dep	5 53	3 45	...	6 22	9 15	1319	1643	17 5	1826	22 5
Blainville	6 33	4 27	...	6 46	9 41	...	17 4	1742	1851	22 35
Luneville	6 46	5 14	...	7 10	10 3	14 6	1730	1815	19 9	22 53
Baccarat	—	6 1	...	7 50	10 49	1446	1812	1856	1936	23 29
Etival	...	6 32	...	8 19	11 22	1520	1842	—	20 7	23 49
St. Dié........arr	...	6 49	...	8 36	11 39	1537	1859	...	2023	0 5
" ....dep	4 30	7 2	...	8 50	11 54	1555	19 5	...	—	—
St. Leonard ...arr	4 46	7 18	...	9 7	12 11	1612	1921	...	...	...
Fraize ......dep	4*28	6 13	...	8 42	11 45	1547	19 3	20 2	...	21 57
St. Leonard arr	4*38	6 28	...	8 57	12 0	16 2	1920	2015	...	22 10
St. Leonard ...dep	4 47	7 22	...	9 10	12 14	1615	1926	—	...	—
Laveline ...arr	5 23	7 59	...	9 50	12 55	1654	20 5	...	...	...
" ......dep	5 26	8 7	9 49	9 56	13 4	17 5	2010	...	2039	...
Bruyeres (**74**)......	5 34	8 18	9 56	10 3	13 14	1716	2021	...	2048	...
Jarmenil	6 3	8 47	...	1031	13 45	1748	2050	...	...	...
Arches (73) arr	6 10	8 54	A	1038	13 52	1756	2057	...	B	...
" ......dep	6 11	8 55	...	1039	13 54	1758	2058	...	...	...
Epinal (66) arr	6 29	9 13	1037	1054	14 15	1817	2116	...	2125	...

Epinal ......dep		4 40	7 10	7 18	10 7	12§15	1324	1459	1555	2020
Arches ......arr		4 57	...	7 35	1027	...	1342	...	1612	2037
" ......dep		4 58	B	7 36	1029	...	1344	A	1614	2040
Jarmenil		5 5	...	7 43	1036	...	1351	...	1621	2047
Bruyeres............		5 49	7 53	8 21	1114	13 1	1430	1544	17 4	2129
Laveline ...arr		5 55	7 59	8 27	1121	13 7	1436	1550	1710	2136
" ......dep		5 57	—	8 31	1130	—	1441	—	1715	2143
St. Leonard ...arr		6 34	...	9 8	12 8	...	1518	...	1759	2221
St. Leonard dep		7 34	...	9 23	1225	...	1524	1617	1816	2230
Fraize......arr		7 52	...	9 39	1243	...	1539	1635	1832	2246
St. Leonard...dep		6 35	...	9 11	1212	...	1520	—	18 4	2223
St. Dié arr		6 50	...	9 26	1227	...	1534	...	1819	2237
" dep	5 11	7 40	...	9 38	1240	14 6	1625	...	1945	—
Etival	5 30	7 58	...	9 56	1259	14 21	1644	...	20 9	...
Baccarat......	6 3	8 30	...	1025	1330	14 45	1722	1812	2047	...
Luneville	6 49	9 11	...	11 4	1412	15 15	18 9	1852	2126	...
Blainville ...	7 0	...	...	1122	1428	...	1824	1910	...	...
Nancy 65 ar	7 22	9 48	...	1148	15 7	15 50	1846	1951	22 3	...

Extras											
Laveline...dep	15§56	Epinal ...dep	1849	Fraize ....dep.	13 30	17 33	St. Leonard...dep.	4*55	19 35	21 1
Epinal ......arr	16 48	Laveline...arr	20 0	St. Lecnard. arr.	13 43	17 46	Fraize ....arr.	5 11	19 53	21 19

A—Runs until 15th September, and on Tuesday, Thursday, and Saturday from 16th to 30th September.

B—From 10th July until 20th September. *—Runs until 15th September. §—Runs until 20th September.

Gerardmer dep	4 50	7 24	9 16	10§42	1222	15‖30	1627	1918	20‡9	21 4
Aumontzey......	5 14	7 48	9 39	11 8	1246	...	1651	1948	...	2128
Laveline ...arr	5 21	7 5[illegible]	9 44	11 14	1253	15 52	1658	1955	2036	2135

Laveline ...dep	6 5	8 4	8 37	1132	13‖9	1448	15†53	1720	2015	2149
Aumontzey......	6 10	‡	8 42	1137	...	1453	...	1725	2020	2154
Gerardmer arr	6 43	8 31	9 9	12 6	1336	1527	16 20	1754	2049	2228

†—Runs until 15th September; Tues., Thurs., and Sat. only from 16th to 30th September.

‡—From July 10th until September 20th. §—Runs until September 30th. ‖—Runs until September 2[illegible]th.

E.M.							
	Baccarat ......dep	6 10	10 57	14 58	19 5	...	...
8½	**Badonviller** ...arr	6 41	11 28	15 41	19 37	...	...

Badonviller ....dep	5 22	9 45	12 40	16 37	...	...	...	...
Baccarat (70) ......arr	5 53	10 16	13 20	17 8	...	...	...	...

[Excess Luggage, 1 cent. per 44 lbs. per kilometre.] EASTERN RAILWAY.

AUDUN-le-ROMAN, GIVET, REIMS, MEAUX, and PARIS. RC—Restaurant Car attached.

Station																					
Metz (210A)..........dep			...	...	...	...	...	...	6 a26	...	8 a42	...	10a10	...	...	...	...	4p44	...	...	...
Fontoy (Fentsch)...arr			...	...	...	...	...	...	7 a44	...	9 a28	...	12p14	...	...	...	...	5p41	...	...	...
			1,2,3	1,2,3	1,2,3	1,2,3	1,2,3	1,2,3	1,2.3	1,2,3	1,2,3	1,2,3	1,2,3	1,2,3	1,2,3	1,2,3	1,2,3	1,2,3	1,2,3	1,2,3	1,2,3
Audun-le-Roman ¶..........dep			...	...	4 15	...	...	...	7 24	...	8 55	...	11 52	...	...	...	...	1716	...	...	...
Longuyon ....arr			...	...	4 52	...	...	...	7 59	...	9 33	...	12 30	...	...	...	...	1752	...	...	...
„ ....dep			...	...	5 5	...	...	6 24	8 19	...	9 47	...	13 9	...	11 30	14 15	16 19	18 7	1916	20 7	...
Velosnes-Torgny..........			...	...	5 23	...	...	...	8 36	...	...	...	...	...	11 49	14 37	16 37	...	1935	20 24	...
Montmedy			...	...	5 36	...	...	6 46	8 47	...	10 7	...	13 31	...	12 3	14 51	16 50	1828	1944	20 34	...
Carignan			...	...	6 23	...	...	7 12	9 33	...	10 31	...	13 57	...	12 53	15 39	17 37	1854	—	21 20	...
Bazeilles..........			...	...	6 51	...	...	...	9 59	...	...	...	...	...	13 20	16 6	18 3	...	...	21 45	...
Pont-Maugis..........			...	...	6 57	...	...	...	10 5	...	...	...	...	...	13 26	16 13	18 10	...	...	21 51	...
Sedan ....dep			...	4 54	7 10	...	...	7 37	10 16	...	10 53	1123	14 25	...	13 50	16 29	18 43	1918	2133	22 0	22 21
Vrigne-Meuse			...	5 9	7 23	...	...	...	10 28	...	...	1136	...	...	14 1	16 44	18 56	...	2145	...	22 33
Mohon			...	5 30	7 44	...	...	...	10 49	...	...	1157	...	...	14 23	17 6	19 18	...	22 6	...	22 44
Mezières-Charlv. arr			...	5 35	7 48	...	...	7 59	10 53	...	11 13	12 1	14 46	...	14 27	17 10	19 22	1939	2210	22 22	22 58
Brussels Q. L. ...dep (103A)			...	...	...	...	...	...	...	...	7 5	...	...		9 8	12 30	...	...	...	17 22	
Givet ....dep			...	2 58	...	...	6 6	...	...	8 54	10 26	...	...	...	12 59	15 43	17 53	...	...	20 40	
Vireux-Molhain			...	3 24	...	...	6 23	...	...	9 12	10 44	...	...	...	13 16	15 59	18 10	...	...	20 57	
Montherme..........			...	4 50	...	...	7 21	...	...	10 10	11 39	...	...	...	14 13	16 56	19 6	...	...	21 57	
Nouzon			...	5 16	...	...	7 41	...	...	10 30	11 57	...	...	...	14 32	17 16	19 25	...	...	22 18	
Mezières-Charl. arr			...	5 30	...	...	7 53	...	...	10 42	12 8	...	...	...	14 43	17 28	19 36	...	...	22 29	
								1& 2													
Mezières Charleville ...dep			...	5 40	...	...	...	8 9	8 18	...	12 55	1215	15 1	...	15 8	17 40	...	2012	...	22 50	
Mohon			...	5 45	...	...	...	B	8 25	...	...	1220	...	...	15 13	17 45	...	...	...	...	
Amagne-Lucquy..........			...	6 46	...	6 56	8 25	...	9 39	10 53	13 35	1426	...	...	16 17	18 54	20 5	...	...	23 50	
Rethel			...	6 57	...	7 10	8 38	8 51	9 52	11 7	13 45	1441	...	...	10 32	19 7	20 20	2052	...	0 3	
Bazancourt			...	...	...	7 50	—	...	10 27	—	...	1517	...	...	17 6	19 47	—	...	...	0 35	
Reims ....arr			...	7 31	...	8 19	...	9 22	10 54	...	14 19	1544	16 16		17 27	20 17	...	2124	...	0 54	
„ ....dep		5 23	6 44	7 37	9 45		...	9 29	—	13 17	14 25	—	16 23	1811	19 19	—	...	2131	1 36	—	
Fismes..........		5 49	7 23	7 59	1026	...	...	...	...	13 57	...	...	...	⋮ Via Epernay	20 1	...	¶—Customs Examination.	2152	2 1	...	
Fere-en-Tardenois ...		6 24	7 57	...	11 2	...	...	...	...	14 33	...	...	...	⋮	20 37	...		2212	...	...	
Oulchy-Breny..........		6 38	8 10	...	1116	...	...	RC	...	14 48	...	...	...	⋮	20 51	...		...	...	...	
La Ferte-Milon	5 50	7 5	9 14	8 43	1147	...	13 8	...	...	15 49	15 24	...	...	⋮	21 22	18 48		2235	2 55	...	
Lizy-sur-Ourcq	6 18	7 32	9 45	...	1218	...	13 37	...	...	16 22	...	...	...	⋮	21 53	19 16		...	...	...	
Trilport	6 34	7 47	10 1	...	...	...	13 53	...	...	16 38	...	...	...	⋮	22 11	19 32		...	...	...	
Meaux ......arr	6 42	7 54	10 9	...	1239	...	14 1	...	...	16 46	...	...	...	...	22 19	19 40		...	3 28	...	
Paris Est ...arr	7 45	8 50	1113	9 50	1337	...	15 11	1123	...	18 10	16 29	...	18 22	2120	23 30	20 16		2340	4 34	...	

¶—Customs Examination.

B—Admits also 3rd class travelling at least 149 miles or from Charleville and beyond.

MEZIERES-CHARLEVILLE and HIRSON.

Dist. E.M.	Station												
	Mezieres-Charleville...dep	3 5	6 39	8 4	...	8 40	1118	12 6	1456	1735	1845	1952	2015
5½	Tournes..........	3 16	6 52	8 14	8 25	8 53	...	1219	15 9	1748	19 4	20 2	2028
13¾	Le Tremblois 29B	...	7 24	...	...	9 22	...	1246	1534	1814	...	...	2055
20	Auvillers	3 58	7 43	...	9 6	9 44	...	13 2	1550	1829	1945	2033	2110
34⅝	Hirson..........arr	4 34	8 23	9 11	...	1030	1224	1340	1628	19 7	...	21 0	2150

Dist.	Station											
...	Hirson..........dep	6 1	...	9 25	10 12	12 5	...	15 53	1640	18 2	2053	22 5
...	Auvillers	6 43	6 48	10 7	10 40	12 46	1636	16 34	...	18 51	2121	22 50
...	Le Tremblois	7 4	⋮	1025	...	13 9	⋮	16 53	...	19 12	...	...
...	Tournes..........	7 36	7 23	1048	11 7	13 33	17 9	17 14	...	19 34	2148	23 37
...	Mezieres-Ch. arr	7 48	...	11 0	11 18	13 45	...	17 26	1744	19 46	2159	23 51

Station						
Liart.....dep	6 5	9 56	1424	1750	...	...
Tournes......	6 48	10 36	15 5	1832	...	...
Mezières arr	7 3	10 48	1518	1845	...	...
Mezières dep	6 49	8 4	12 16	1620	1845	...
Tournes......	7 3	8 14	12 32	1634	1859	...
Liart......arr	7 43	8 40	13 10	1714	1947	...

PORT D'ATELIER-AMANCE, PLOMBIERES, and LURE.

Station	1,2,3	1,2,3	1,2,3	1,2,3	1,2,3	1,2.3	1,2,3	1,2,3	1 & 2	1,2,3	1,2,3	1,2,3	1,2,3	
Port d'Atelier-A. dep	4 35	4§55	...	7 46	⋮	...	12 2	...	15‡36	...	1656	20 2	2011	...
Conflans-Varigney..........	4 58	5 18	...	8 11	⋮	...	12 26	...	...	...	1720	...	2036	...
Aillevillers ....arr	5 17	5 37	...	8 32	1213	...	12 44	...	17 2	...	1741	2032	2054	...
Aillevillers......dep	5 50		...	8 50	⋮	...	12*25	...	17 7	...	1837	...		...
Plombières... arr	6 14	—	...	9 31	⋮	...	12*47	..	17 24	...	19 7	...		...
Aillevillers ....dep	5 47	...	8 3	1033	1214	1249	—	1658	17 19	1823	1833	2120		...
Fontaine-le-Luxeuil ...	6 1	...	8 15	1046	A	...	...	1711	...	B	1847	2133	...	...
Luxeuil-les-Bains	6 12	...	8 27	1058	⋮	1310	...	1725	17 39	⋮	19 1	2147	...	...
Lure (66, 52B) ......arr	6 38	...	8 49	1122	⋮	1335	...	1749	...	⋮	1927	2211	...	...

Station	1,2,3	1,2,3	1,2,3	1,2,3	1,2,3	1,2,3	1,2,3	1 & 2	1,2.3	1,2,3	1.2.3	1,2,3		
Lure ....dep	4 36	...	7 46	⋮	11 52	12 56	1335	*	1524	19 1	1949	...	‖—Runs until 20th Sept.	...
Luxeuil-les-Bains	5 2	...	8 12	C	12 23	13 18	1358	14 14	1553	1931	2010	...		...
Fontaine-le-Luxeuil ...	5 11	...	8 21	⋮	12 36	...	...	...	16 5	1943	...	...		...
Aillevillers ....arr	5 22	...	8 34	1016	12 50	13 38	1415	14 32	1618	1955	2025	...		...
Plombières...dep	5 ‖2	7 24	—	—	11 42	—	...	14 20	1727	1950		...		...
Aillevillers ...arr	5‖24	7 45	...	...	12 5	...	...	14 37	1748	2018		...		...
Aillevillers ....dep	5 45	8 8	10 30	...	13 15	...	1421	14 42	1827	2046		2113		...
Conflans-Varigney	6 15	8 26	10 48	...	13 34	...	1520	...	1843	...	...	2137		...
Port d'Atelier-A. arr	6 49	8 50	11 12	...	13 58	...	16 7	15 7	19 5	2114	...	22 2	...	...

*—Runs until 21st Sept.
‡—Runs until 20th Sept.
B—To Belfort arrive 19.20.
§—Runs until 15th September.
A—To Belfort arrive 13.19.
C—From Belfort depart 9.20.

LONGWY and VILLERUPT.

Station							
Longwy dep	6 5	9 17	14 4	1840	2012	22 55	...
Villerupt arr	6 35	9 47	14 34	1911	2044	23 25	...
Villerupt arr	5 12	6 53	11 45	1634	1749	19 40	...
Longwy dep	5 44	7 25	12 17	17 7	1820	20 12	...

CHARMES & RAMBERVILLERS.

Station						
Charmes (66) ...dep	6 8	1055	1818	...	...	...
Rehaincourt..........	6 53	1139	1851	...	...	...
Rambervillers arr	7 30	1222	1919	...	...	...
Rambervillers dep	4 37	9 13	1613	...	...	...
Rehaincourt..........	5 6	9 48	1648	...	...	...
Charmes ....arr	5 35	1037	1728	...	...	...

CHAUMONT, NEUFCHATEAU, PAGNY-SUR-MEUSE, EPINAL. [66 lbs. of Luggage free.

Chaumont ...dep	...	3 55	7 30	...	11 25	15 16	18 25	21 33
Bologne	...	4 12	7 49	...	11 45	15 35	18 47	21 54
Andelot	...	4 33	8 11	...	12 6	15 57	19 9	22 15
Rimaucourt	...	4 39	8 16	...	12 12	16 4	19 16	22 21
Neufchâteau arr	...	5 16	9 3	...	13 1	16 55	20 8	23 9
Neufchâteau dep	...	6 5	9 27	...	13 28	17 3	22 17	...
Châtenois	...	6 43	9 59	...	14 1	17 36	22 50	...
Mirecourt ...arr	...	7 17	10 31	*	14 34	18 11	23 20	...
„ (66) dep	5 42	8 2	10 35	13 18	14 41	18 35	—	...
Hymont-Mat	5 51	8 12	10 42	13 29	14 50	18 45	...	...
Dompaire	6 7	8 29	10 57	13 45	15 7	19 2	...	...
Epinal (66) ...arr	6 39	9 2	11 28	14 16	15 40	19 34	...	...

*—Runs until 15th September.

Epinal ....dep		...	6 52	11 11	14 20	15 44	18*11	19 26
Dompaire		...	7 23	11 44	14 47	16 16	...	19 57
Hymont-M. 66 ...		...	7 39	11 59	15 1	16 31	18 47	20 13
Mirecourt ...arr		...	7 44	12 4	15 6	16 36	18 52	20 18
„ ...dep	4 25	...	7 56	12 10	—	16 42	—	20 25
Châtenois ...	5 1	...	8 32	12 46	...	17 18	...	21 0
Neufchâte'u	5 32	...	9 3	13 17	...	17 49	...	21 31
Neufchâteau dep		4 33	9 27	13 35	15 5	18 5	...	22 15
Rimaucourt		5 18	10 11	14 25	16 49	18 51	...	23 6
Andelot		5 24	10 17	14 30	17 0	18 57	...	23 11
Bologne		5 47	10 44	14 58	17 48	19 20	...	23 32
Chaumont ...arr		6 9	11 14	15 23	18 10	19 42	...	23 52

Neufchateau dep	...	6 1	10 3	13 40	18 20	21 52	...
Domrémy-M. ...	...	6 18	10 20	13 57	18 37	22 19	...
Vaucouleurs	...	6 57	11 2	14 37	19 21	22 40	...
Pagny-Meuse ar	...	7 16	11 23	14 56	19 40	22 59	...

Pagny-Meuse ...dep	4 26	7 46	11 58	15 47	20 24	...	...	...
Vaucouleurs	4 48	8 8	12 22	16 6	20 46	...	...	...
Domrémy-M.	5 22	8 43	12 57	16 41	21 21	...	...	...
Neufchâteau ......arr	5 38	8 59	13 13	16 57	21 37	...	...	...

Rimaucourt ......dep	5 27	13 30	19 20	...	...	...
Gudmont ....arr	6 12	14 51	20 6	...	...	...

Gudmont ....dep	8 53	15 47	20 20	...	...	...	...	...
Rimaucourt ......arr	9 57	16 45	21 9	...	...	...	...	...

LEROUVILLE and SEDAN.

Dist.									
—	**Lerouville** ...dep	...	6 3	9 2	9 52	14 3	16!5	1929	2236
10½	St. Mihiel	...	6 30	9 31	1015	1431	1716	1959	2259
34¾	**Verdun** (67) arr	...	7 29	1034	—	1530	1821	21 4	—
...	„ ......dep	4 31	8 46	1115	...	1558	1845	—	...
42¼	Cumières	4 51	9 6	1135	...	1619	19 7	...	...
58¾	Dun-Doulcon ...	5 35	9 51	1221	...	17 6	1953	...	...
67	Stenay	5 57	1015	1245	...	1731	2018	...	...
87½	Remilly	6 45	11 4	1333	...	1823	21 8	...	...
88¾	**Pont-Maugis** ...	6 50	11 9	1338	...	1830	2113	...	...
91¼	**Sedan** ....arr	6 56	1115	1344	...	1836	2119	...	...

Sedan ....dep		...	6 53	...	9 32	1246	1625	1925	...
Pont-Maugis ...dep		...	7 1	...	9 39	1252	1631	1931	...
Remilly..................		...	7 6	...	9 45	1258	1636	1937	...
Stenay		...	7 56	...	1038	1350	1725	2029	...
Dun-Doulcon		...	8 17	...	11 1	1412	1746	2051	...
Cumieres		...	9 0	...	1146	1456	1831	2135	...
Verdun ....arr		...	9 21	...	12 7	1517	1852	2154	...
„ ....dep	4 35	...	9 35	...	1325	1550	19.2	—	...
St. Mihiel..........	5 40	7 19	1044	1316	1428	1657	2027	...	...
Lerouville...arr	6 4	7 45	11 9	1348	1452	1721	2054	...	...

NANCY, PAGNY-SUR-MOSELLE, CONFLANS-JARNY, LONGUYON, & LONGWY.

Dist. E.M.	¶—Customs Exam.	1,2,3	1,2,3	1,2,3	1,2,3	1,2,3	1,2,3	1,2,3	1,2,3	1,2,3	1,2,3	1,2,3	1,2,3	1,2,3	1,2,3	1,2,3	1,2,3	1,2,3	1,2,3
—	**Nancy** ....dep	2 4	4 23	5 29	7 0	7 42	9 1	11 15	12 13	1330	1357	16 0	17 0	17 39	19 10	19 27	2150	22 18	0 25
5½	**Frouard**	2 15	4 39	5 47	7 15	7 52	9 17	11 32	...	1340	1413	16 10	1712	17 54	19 20	19 42	...	22 33	0 40
6¾	Pompey (74A).........	...	4 45	5 53	7 20	...	9 22	11 37	...	RC	1418	...	1717	18 0	...	19 48	...	22 38	...
18	Pont-à-Mousson	2 40	5 16	6 23	7 49	8 9	9 51	12 7	12 39	1359	1448	16 27	1746	18 33	19 40	20 19	2224	23 8	1 11
23½	**Pagny-s-Mos.** arr	2 53	5 30	6 37	8 3	8 18	10 5	12 21	12 48	14 9	15 2	16 36	18 0	18 47	19 50	20 30	2235	23 21	1 22
36	METZ (212)......arr	4a46	7 a29	8 a28	10a5	10 a5	11a56	2 p19	4 p3	4 p3	5p11	6 p41	7p54	8 p41	9 p36	—	1221	1 a14	—
...	**Pagny-s-Moselle** dep		5 38	—	8 33	8 20	10 8	13 0	12 49	—	15 9	16 37	—	18§52	19 54	...	—	—	...
28½	Onville........................		5 52	...	8 50	...	10 21	13 15	...	...	1525	...	...	19 §4	20 9	...	RC —Restaurant Car.	...	...
38	Mars-la-Tour		6 17	...	—	...	10 45	13 45	...	...	1554	...	§—Not on Sunday.	—	20 34	...		...	...
43½	**Conflans-Jarny**		6 30	...	...	8 51	10 58	13 59	13 20	...	16 9	17 8		...	20 47	...		...	...
51½	Gondrecourt-Aix		7 14	...	...	...	11 52	—	...	...	1748	...		...	21 27	...		...	...
69½	**Longuyon** (71) ......arr		7 55	...	...	9 40	12 35	...	14 3	...	1828	17 54		...	22 8	...		...	...
...	„ ......dep	5 18	8 17	11 49	...	9 49	12 45	13 25	14 8	1657	1855	18 0		19 30	22 20	23 52	RC	3 45	5 0
79½	**Longwy** 103A ¶ arr	5 44	8 44	12 17	...	10 17	13 13	13 44	14 26	1725	1923	18 18		19 48	22 48	0 11		4 8	5 31

		1,2,3	1,2,3	1,2,3	1,2,3	1,2,3	1,2,3	1,2,3	1,2,3	1,2,3	1,2,3	1,2,3	1,2,3	1,2,3	1,2,3	1,2,3	1,2,3	1,2,3	1,2,3
Longwy ....dep		6 0	4 23	7 32	8 53	9 15	1055	12 5	12 58	...	15 22	...	...	17 25	18 33	19 0	...	...	19 42
Longuyon ....arr		6 19	4 51	8 0	9 21	9 34	1123	12 33	13 19	...	15 50	...	...	17 44	19 6	19 19	...	...	20 1
„ ....dep		—	5 27	8 12	—	9 52	—	—	13 24	...	15 55	...	...	—	—	19 36	19 46	...	—
Gondrecourt-Aix........		...	6 10	...	...	10 35	...	...	14 6	...	16 35	...	...	...	...	...	20 28	...	...
Conflans-Jarny dp		...	6 51	8 56	...	11 22	...	...	14 28	14 44	16 55	...	17 20	...	...	20 21	20 52	...	...
Mars-la-Tour		...	7 9	...	...	11 42	...	...	...	15 2	...	...	17 36	...	...	...	21 10	...	...
Onville		...	7 31	...	...	12 7	...	...	...	15 25	...	...	18 1	...	...	...	21 33	...	...
Pagny-s-Mos. ...arr		...	7 43	9 27	...	12 19	...	...	15 3	15 37	17 26	...	18 13	...	...	20 52	21 45	...	...
METZ................dep		6a 15	7 a54	9a40	9a40	12p48	...	...	3 p10	3 p53	5 p18	5 p18	6 p31	7 p1	8 p24	8 p24	...	10p27	1a51
Pagny-s-M. dep	4 45	6 17	7 48	9 29	10 2	12 37	...	12 58	15 5	15 47	17 27	17 37	18 22	18 45	20 16	20 54	21 49	22 19	1 33
Pont-à-Mousson...	5 1	6 33	8 5	9 40	1021	12 52	...	13 15	15 17	16 3	17 39	17 55	18 36	19 1	20 32	21 4	22 4	22 36	1 43
Pompey	5 33	7 1	8 33	...	1052	...	...	13 45	15 35	16 31	...	18 28	RC	19 34	21 0	...	22 30	...	...
Frouard	5 39	7 6	8 38	...	1057	13 16	...	13 50	15 40	16 36	...	18 33	19 0	19 39	21 5	...	22 35	23 0	2 3
Nancy ....arr	5 57	7 23	8 56	10 6	1114	13 39	...	14 8	15 53	16 56	18 5	18 52	19 19	19 56	21 22	21 30	22 57	23 18	2 13

Extra.—Onville to Pont-a-Mousson 5§14. Longwy to Longuyon, 6.30, 12.39. Nancy to Pagny, 18.34.

ONVILLE and THIAUCOURT.

‡—Not on Sunday.

Onville ......dep	5 15	8 52	1035	12 19	1541	18 9	19 ‡5	2020	...
Thiaucourt arr	6 42	9 19	11 2	12 54	16 7	1833	19 29	2046	...

Thiaucourt arr	4‡50	7 1	9 50	11 30	1436	17 17	1938	21 0	...
Onville .....dep	5 14	7 24	10 14	11 53	15 8	17 41	20 2	2123	...

CHATEAU-THIERRY and ROMILLY-SUR-SEINE.

E.M.							
—	**Château-Thierry** ......dep	3 59	...	9 45	1250	1728	2017
21¾	Montmirail	5 5	...	1046	14 5	1841	2120
34¼	**Esternay** (73)	5 39	7 30	1123	15 5	1918	2152
54¾	**Romilly** (68) ....arr	6 29	8 22	1213	1558	2011	...

Romilly ....dep	...	6 34	9 0	...	1225	1626	2221
Esternay	4 0	7 47	9 57	1121	1326	1727	2317
Montmirail (64)	4 33	8 24	—	1155	14 0	18 0	—
Chateau-Thierry ...arr	5 35	9 28	...	1252	15 2	19 6	...

BAR-LE-DUC and VERDUN.

*—On Thursdays only.

Bar-le-Duc............dep	6 18	10 24	16 21	1745
Beauzee.................arr	7 18	11 27	17 10	1842
Clermont-en-A....arr	8 27	12 20	*	1941
Beauzee ....dep	7 21	11 32	17 13	1846
Verdun ....arr	8 34	12 57	18 21	20 4

Verdun...............dep	5 17	9 31	16 26	19 *5	...
Beauzee ....arr	6 33	10 44	17 47	20 15	...
Clermont.........dep	5 31	9 35	16 46	...	...
Beauzee ....dep	6 36	10 47	17 52	20 18	...
Bar-le-Duc ....arr	7 39	11 49	18 58	21 12	...

Excess Luggage, 1 cent. per 44 lbs. per kilometre.] **EASTERN RAILWAY.**

PARIS, VINCENNES, BRIE-COMTE-ROBERT, and VERNEUIL-L'ETANG.

* Sundays excepted.

Station																											
Paris (Bastille) dep	6 0	7 33	8 25	9 5	9 30	10 6	10 8	1133	1219	1325	14 1	15 5	1610	17 0	17 5	1758	18 1	18 39	19 2	1927	20 0	2030	21 1	22 5	2235	2310	0 30
St. Mandé	6 10	...	...	9 15	9 40	...	1018	...	...	...	...	1515	1620	...	1715	...	...	...	...	...	...	...	2115	...	2245	2320	0 40
Vincennes	6 14	...	...	9 20	9 44	...	1022	...	1227	...	...	1519	1624	...	1719	...	18 9	...	...	...	20 8	...	2119	...	2249	2325	0 44
Joinville-le-Pont	6 26	7 49	8 40	9 33	9 56	...	1034	1145	1239	1342	1417	1532	1636	1716	1731	...	1821	18 55	...	...	2020	2042	2132	2221	23 1	2338	0 56
Champigny	6 38	8 2	8 52	9 46	10 8	1024	1046	1157	1251	1354	1429	1544	1648	1728	—	1816	1833	19 *7	1920	1947	2033	2054	2144	2233	—	2350	1 8
La Varenne Chenne	6 42	8 6	8 56	9 50	1012	1028	1050	12 1	1255	1359	1433	1548	1652	1732	...	1820	1837	19*11	1924	1951	2037	2058	2149	2237	...	2354	1 12
Boissy-St. Leger	6 52	8 17	9 7	—	—	1039	11 2	12 6	13 6	1410	1445	1559	17 3	1745	...	1831	—	—	1934	20 1	2047	21 9	—	2248	...	0 5	1 23
Brie-Cte-Robert	7 22	8 47	—	...	...	11 9	—	1241	1336	—	1515	—	—	1816	...	19 1	...	...	—	2031	—	2139	...	2318	...	—	1 54
Verneuil-l'Etang	7 52	9 17	...	...	...	1139	...	...	14 5	...	1545	...	...	1847	...	1931	...	...	...	21 0	...	...	...	2348	...	...	2 24
Verneuil-l'Etang dep	...	...	...	6 2	...	7 5	...	...	...	9 36	...	...	11 6	...	...	...	1445	...	1614	...	...	1817	...	1912	...	2120	...
Brie-Cte-Robert	...	5 24	...	6 31	...	7 34	8 20	...	...	10 6	...	...	1136	13*3	...	...	1515	...	1649	...	...	1847	...	1944	2041	2157	2248
Boissy-St. Leger	5*23	5 53	6 20	7 4	7 35	8 4	8 48	9*36	...	1034	1116	...	12 4	1331	1421	...	1543	1616	1717	...	1815	1915	...	2014	2110	2232	2316
La Varenne Chenne	5 33	6 4	6 31	7 15	7 46	8 16	8 58	9 46	9 57	1045	1127	1157	1215	1340	1432	1527	1553	1627	1728	1743	1825	1927	1957	2027	2121	2243	2327
Champigny	5 37	6 8	6 36	7 19	7 51	8 21	9 2	9 50	10 1	1049	1131	12 1	1219	...	1436	1531	1557	1631	1732	1747	1829	1932	20 2	2031	2125	2247	2331
Joinville-le-Pont	5 49	...	6 50	...	8 4	...	9 14	10 2	1014	...	1143	1213	1231	...	1448	1543	16 9	1643	...	1759	1841	1945	2015	2043	2133	2259	2343
Vincennes	...	...	...	...	...	...	...	...	1026	...	1155	1225	1243	...	15 0	1555	...	1655	...	1811	1853	...	2027	2055	2150	...	2355
St. Mandé	...	...	...	...	...	...	...	...	1028	...	1157	1227	...	...	15 2	1557	...	1657	...	...	...	...	2029	2057	2152	...	2357
Paris (Bastille)...arr	6 4	6 34	7 3	7 41	8 19	8 41	9 29	1017	1039	1111	12 8	1238	1250	14 0	1513	16 8	1634	1711	1750	1818	19 0	20 2	2042	21 8	22 5	2312	0 8

Paris to La Varenne Chenne, 6.40, 7.2, 7.55, 8.50, 10.35, 11.3, 12*0, 12.3, 12.35, 14.35, 15.35, 16.35, 17*36, 18.22, 18.25, 19.5, 19.30, 19.42, 20.35, 23.50, 0.55; vice-versa, 4.49, 5.12, 5*58, 6.43, 7*7, 7.23, 7.39, 8.25, 10.24, 10.57, 12.58, 13.27, 13.57, 14.57, 16.57, 17.11, 18.47, 19.23.

Extra.—PARIS TO VINCENNES AND JOINVILLE-LE-PONT every half hour from 6.0 until 23.50, and vice versa every half hour from 5.8 until 23.43.

SAINT-DIZIER and DOULEVANT-LE-CHATEAU.

St. Dizier......dep	5 25	9 34	1417	1919	**Doulevant** dep	5 30	9 58	14 5	17 5
Eclaron	5 45	10 6	1444	1940	Vaux Montreuil...	5 57	10 25	1443	1733
Wassy...arr	6 8	10 39	1511	20 3	Wassy...arr	6 7	10 35	15 2	1741
Vaux Montreuil ...	6 22	11 33	1533	2017	Eclaron	6 33	11 5	16 3	1821
Doulevant ...arr	6 51	12 15	16 2	2045	**St. Dizier** 66 arr	6 53	11 25	1634	1842

NANCY and MONCEL (CHAMBREY).

Nancy d	543	840	1120	14 1	1620	1731	1846	2020	Moncel	451	655	9 46	1235	15 9	1725	1843	2122
Laitre	6 9	9 8	1130	1427	1648	18 5	1922	2047	Laitre..	514	719	10 9	1259	1533	1749	19 7	2145
Moncel	632	931	1215	1452	1711	1828	1945	2110	Nancy	547	751	103[illegible]	1330	16 2	1819	1939	2214

TROYES and ST. FLORENTIN.

Troyes ...dep	4 55	8 19	13 24	18 33	...	**St. Florentin**	5 34	8 52	12 20	18 35	...
Ervy	5 53	9 19	14 26	19 32	...	Ervy	6 5	9 26	12 53	19 18	...
St. Florentin	6 21	9 47	14 53	20 1	...	**Troyes**... ..arr	7 4	10 28	13 56	20 21	...

CHALONS-SUR-MARNE, TROYES, and SENS.

E.M Dis.		1,2,3	1,2,3	1,2,3	1,2,3	1,2,3	
—	**Chalons** ......dep	...	4 45	10 47	15 28	18 54	...
18	Sommesous	...	5 32	11 34	16 17	19 43	...
28½	Herbisse	...	5 55	11 56	16 42	20 6	...
35½	Arcis-sur-Aube	...	6 14	12 15	17 4	20 27	...
46	Charmont	...	6 41	12 44	17 33	20 56	...
57¼	Troyes Preize......arr	...	7 10	13 12	18 2	21 25	...
58½	**Troyes** ....arr	...	7 13	13 15	18 5	21 28	...
...	,, ...dep	5 20	8 55	13 25	18 40	—	...
...	Troyes Preize ...dep	5 24	8 59	13 29	18 44	...	...
75¼	Aix-en-Othe-Villem	6 12	9 51	14 17	19 35	...	...
83¾	Villeneuve-l'Arche	6 34	10 20	14 40	19 58	...	...
98	**Sens** (Est.) ......arr	7 18	11 13	15 24	20 42	...	...
100	**Sens** (Lyon Sta.) arr	7 22	11 17	15 28	20 46	...	...

		1,2,3	1,2,3	1,2,3	1,2,3	1,2,3	1,2,3	
...	**Sens** (Lyon Station) dep	...	5 6	...	10 17	15 50	1855	...
...	**Sens** (Est. Station)	...	5 11	...	10 22	15 56	19 3	...
...	Villeneuve-l'Arche	...	5 57	...	11 5	16 43	1952	...
...	Aix-en-Othe-Villem	...	6 21	...	11 28	17 14	2018	...
...	Troyes Preize......arr	...	7 7	...	12 13	18 7	2111	...
...	**Troyes** ....arr	...	7 10	...	12 16	18 10	2114	...
...	,, ...dep	4 54	—	7 45	13 4	18 43	—	...
...	Troyes Preize ...dep	4 57	...	7 49	13 8	18 47	...	...
...	Charmont	5 28	...	8 20	13 39	19 19	...	...
...	Arcis-sur-Aube	6 0	...	8 51	14 9	19 52	...	...
...	Herbisse	6 16	...	9 7	14 25	20 8	...	...
...	Sommesous	6 43	...	9 35	14 54	20 39	...	...
...	**Chalons** (64-67) arr	7 26	...	10 20	15 35	21 21	...	...

‡—Sunday and Thursday only.

EPINAL and BUSSANG.

Epinal...	...	7 25	9 58	12 25	16 6	18 10	20 10	21*40
Arches.....	‡	7 43	1015	12 44	1625	1829	20 33	22 0
Remirem't	5 46	8 18	1048	13 16	17 0	1856	21 10	22 26
Rupt........	6 9	8 39	11 8	13 39	1729	—	21 33	—
St. Maurice	6 42	9 13	1140	14 13	18 7	...	22 7	...
Bussang	6 51	9 21	1148	14 22	1815	...	22 16	...
Bussang	4 30	7 8	9‡43	12 4	16 49	1917	...	...
St. Maurice	4 37	7 15	9 50	1212	16 57	1924	...	...
Rupt........	5 6	7 44	1019	1242	17 32	1955	...	...
Remirem't	5 32	8 16	1042	13 8	18 1	2021	...	...
Arches.....	6 0	8 45	11 9	1336	18 33	2049	...	...
Epinal...	6 18	9 4	1127	1355	18 52	21 4	...	...

*—Until 15th Oct. ‡—Until 2nd November between Bussang & Remiremont.

GRETZ and SEZANNE.

Gretz........ dep	...	6 30	8 52	10 1‡	14 45	18 26	19 41	23 22	**Sézanne** ...... dep		...	6 50	10 30	...	1555	18 10	19 0
Marles	...	6 46	9 7	10 36	15 4	18 43	19 59	23 39	**Esternay**		...	7 39	11 24	...	1639	18 41	1930
Mortcerf	...	6 58	9 17	10 48	15 17	18 54	20 8	23 50	La Ferté-Gaucher		6 9	8 28	12 7	1553	1728	—	2018
Coulommiers ...	5 55	7 25	9 49	11 25	15 55	19 29	20 38	0 15	Coulommiers...	5 17	6 56	9 17	12 48	1645	1818	...	21 5
La Ferté-Ga. ...	6 38	8 ‡18	10 28	12 5	16 37	20 6	21 16	—	Mortcerf	5 44	7 25	9 49	13 16	1716	1849	...	2133
Esternay 72 ...	7 56	—	11 34	—	17 32	—	22 7	...	**Marles**	5 55	7 42	10 3	13 30	1733	19 2	...	2145
Sézanne 70 arr	8 23	...	12 1	...	17 59	...	22 33	...	**Gretz** ....arr	6 8	7 58	1018	13 44	1749	1917	...	2158

SEZANNE and VITRY-LE-FRANCOIS.

Sezanne ....dep	4 25	9 18	13 15	18 33
Fère-Champenoise	4 57	9 51	13 48	19 5
Sommesous	5 42	10 18	14 15	19 45
Vitry-le-François ...arr	6 26	11 3	14 5*	20 28
Vitry-le-François ...dep	7 25	11 40	16 10	21 0
Sommesous	8 24	12 28	17 0	21 48
Fère-Champenoise	8 51	12 54	17 29	22 12
Sezanne ....arr	10 11	13 35	17 59	22 40

TROYES to CHATILLON-SUR-SEINE, GRAY, and CHAUMONT.

Troyes ....dep	3 20	7 55	11 4	12 30	1610	1850	2310
Bar-sur-Seine ...dep	4 1	8 49	1155	13 29	17 6	1953	2359
Chatillon-sur- arr	4 53	9 47	—	14 21	18 6	2055	—
Seine...dep	5 1	9 58	...	14 26	1828	—	...
Poinson-Beneuvre...	6 19	11 17	...	15 50	1958	...	...
Is-sur-Tille 63B...arr	6 57	11 53	...	16 27	2038	...	...
,, ...dep	7 17	13 7	...	17 5	21 1	...	...
Mirebeau-sur-Bèze	7 51	13 41	...	17 40	2134	...	...
Gray 74...........arr	8 28	14 19	...	18 16	2211	...	...

Gray ....dep	...	...	5 45	...	...	11 29	15 0	19 25
Mirebeau-sur-Bèze..	...	...	6 24	...	...	12 9	15 42	20 4
Is-sur-Tille ....arr	...	...	6 59	...	...	12 43	16 19	20 40
,, ...dep	...	...	7 18	...	10 29	14 26	—	21 8
Poinson-Ben'vre dep	...	...	8 2	...	11 19	15 13	...	22 3
Chatillon-sur-S. arr	...	...	9 9	...	12 25	16 26	...	23 8
,, dep	...	5 22	9 14	...	12 31	16 30	19 41	—
Bar-sur-Seine ...dep	4 25	6 22	10 14	12 23	13 30	17 30	20 40	...
Troyes 68 ....arr	5 15	7 15	11 6	13 16	14 23	18 21	21 30	...

Chatillon-sur-Seine .....dep	5 42	9 55	12 55	18 25	...	...
Bricon 69	6 51	11 0	15 36	19 37	...	...
Chaumont ....arr	7 11	11 17	15 56	19 57	...	...

Chaumont......................dep	7 36	11 48	15 0	18 15	...	...
Bricon 68	7 56	12 6	15 18	18 33	...	...
Chatillon-sur-Seine ......arr	8 56	13 10	16 19	19 36	...	...

LAGNY and MORTCERF.—Chemins de Fer de Seine et Marne. Depart from Lagny 8†5, 15.36, 19.0. Mortcerf depart 6.5, 12.0, 17.26. In 1 hour. †—9.55 on Sundays and Fridays.

HAIRONVILLE and TRIAUCOURT.

Haironville ......dep	...	6 2	11 20	1448	...
Lisle-en-Rigault ...	...	6 33	11 43	15 8	...
Revigny ....arr	...	8 3	13 0	1615	...
,, ...dep	5 23	8 35	—	1643	...
Lisle-en-Barrois arr	6 40	10 20	...	18 3	...
Rembercourt...dep	7 11	11 20	...	1836	...
Triaucourt ....arr	7 55	12 8	..	1922	...

Triaucourt ....dep	...	6 4	9 56	...	17 23	...
Rembercourt ...arr	...	6 52	10 53	...	18 16	...
Lisle-en-Barrois ...	...	7 25	11 37	...	18 51	...
Revigny............arr	...	8 58	12 56	...	20 16	...
,, ...dep	6 47	9 40	—	1825	—	...
Lisle-en-Rigault ..	8 22	10 53	...	1949	...	...
Haironville.......arr	8 48	11 12	...	2015	...	...

GRAY and VESOUL.

Gray (Est)...dep	4 25	9 25	17 8	...
Gray (Ville)......	4 37	9 45	1723	...
Velesmes.........	4 54	10 5	1744	...
Gy	5 20	10 40	1817	...
Bucey	5 28	10 49	1825	...
Frétigney	6 5	11 27	19 3	...
Grandvelle ...arr	6 21	11 45	1919	...
Vesoul ......arr	7 35	13 8	2030	...

Vesoul ...dep	5 10	10 43	18 5	...
Grandvelle dep	6 35	12 0	19 35	...
Frétigney	6 49	12 16	19 53	...
Bucey	7 21	12 50	20 31	...
Gy..................	7 30	13 3	20 42	...
Velesmes..........	7 55	13 32	21 9	...
Gray (Ville) 74	8 15	13 55	21 30	...
Gray (Est) arr	8 28	14 10	...	...

Marnay ....dep	...	6 30	16 5	19 45	...
Gy	4 46	7 22	17 5	20 43	...
Bucey.............arr	4 48	9 53	17 13	20 51	...
Bucey ....dep	4 55	7 21	10 15	17 40	20 55
Gy........................	5 19	7 29	11 15	18 18	21 3
Marnay ....arr	6 0	...	12 7	19 10	...

BARISEY and MIRECOURT.

Barisey.....................dep	4 58	8 27	14 23	1753
Vandeléville	5 57	9 26	15 0	1836
Frenelle-la-Grande	6 43	10 7	15 33	1916
Mirecourt 72 ....arr	7 0	10 24	15 44	1928

Mirecourt ....dep	4 23	12 18	15 15	19 51
Frenelle-la-Grande.........	4 40	12 34	15 32	20 7
Vandeléville	5 20	13 11	16 17	20 47
Barisey 74................arr	6 15	13 54	17 6	21 25

TOUL and NEUFCHATEAU.

†—Not on Sunday.

Toul ....dep	4 15	7 45	8 33	1029	1328	1630	19†10	20 55
Blenod-les-Toul	...	8 5	...	1050	1349	1650	19 31	21 15
Barisey 74....................	4 42	8 24	...	11 8	14 7	17 7	19 49	21 32
Neufchateau ....arr	...	8 57	9 21	1146	1446	1747	...	22 9

Neufchateau ....dep	5 48	9 24	13 35	17 16	18 12	21 48
Barisey	6 27	10 0	14 20	17 42	18 56	22 23
Blenod-les-Toul	6 41	10 14	14 38	...	19 14	22 38
Toul ....arr	7 2	10 35	14 57	18 1	19 37	22 55

REMIREMONT & CORNIMONT.

‡—Until 20th Sept.

Remiremont.........dep	5 ‡50	8 30	13 30	18 7	21 17
Vagney	6 12	8 52	13 52	18 29	21 39
Thiefosse	6 24	9 4	14 4	18 41	21 51
Cornimont ....arr	6 43	9 23	14 24	19 0	22 10

Cornimont ....dep	4‡30	7 1	12 0	15 56	19 20
Thiefosse.....................	4 48	7 19	12 18	16 14	19 38
Vagney	5 0	7 31	12 30	16 26	19 49
Remiremont ....arr	5 20	7 51	12 50	16 46	20 9

VITRY-LE-FRANÇOIS and BAR-SUR-AUBE.

E.M.					
	Vitry-le-Francois ...dep	5 0	8 44	13 1	19 14
10	Gigny-Brandonvillers ...	5 24	9 8	13 25	19 40
21	Valentigny ....arr	5 52	9 37	13 53	20 8
24¾	Brienne	6 2	10 8	14 9	20 38
33	Jessains	6 54	10 40	14 50	21 5
39¾	Bar-sur-Aube (68) ...arr	7 9	10 57	15 5	21 20

Bar-sur-Aube ......dep	4 53	8 6	12 40	19 40
Jessains	5 9	8 40	13 17	19 56
Brienne	5 39	9 5	13 49	20 47
Valentigny..........dep	5 51	9 14	13 58	20 57
Gigny-Brandonvillers	6 19	9 44	14 26	21 25
Vitry-le-Fran. 64...arr	6 43	10 9	14 50	21 49

LUNEVILLE and BRUYERES.

Lunéville dep	5 14	7 28	9 3	12 15	1420	1745	1939
Gerbéviller	5 52	8 6	9 32	12 50	1450	1815	20 7
Rambervillers...	6 58	—	1020	—	16 8	19 3	—
Bruyères...arr	7 44	...	11 6	...	1655	1948	...

Bruyères ..dep	...	6 15	8 29	...	11 23	...	14 32	17 20	...	21 23
Rambervillers	5 0	7 39	9 8	..	12 44	...	15 59	18 3	...	22 12
Gerbéviller	5 47	8 31	—	10 3	13 35	14 45	—	19 0	20 24	—
Lunéville (65) arr	6 14	9 0	...	10 37	14 0	15 7	...	19 28	20 51	...

AMAGNE-LUCQUY, APREMONT, and REVIGNY.

Amagne (Est) dep	2 7	...	7 11	9 45	12 16	14 25	19 3	21 33
Attigny.....................	2 28	...	7 29	10 3	12 33	14 42	19 21	21 51
Vouziers	3 10	4 43	7 58	10 34	13 0	15 12	19 50	22 19
Challerange......arr	3 50	5 9	8 22	11 0	13 24	15 36	20 14	—
Challerange...dep	—	...	8 35	12 14	—	16 10	20 34	...
Grandpré	...	...	8 55	12 31	...	16 53	20 51	...
Apremont......arr	...	...	9 20	12 57	...	17 52	21 17	...
Challerange......dep	...	5 45	8 25	11 5	...	15 57	20 22	...
Ste. Menehould..arr	4 23	7 17	9 14	12 13	...	17 24	21 27	...
Revigny (64) ...arr	5 13	8 7	...	13 5	...	18 16	22 18	...

Revigny ....dep	...	...	6 17	9 46	13 55	20 25	...
Ste. Menehould dep	4 22	...	7 25	10 45	14 50	21 27	...
Challerange.......arr	5 10	...	8 13	11 33	15 38	22 15	...
Apremont ...dep	4 26	...	...	10 15	13 47	19 25	...
Grandpré...........	4 50	...	...	10 39	14 44	19 49	...
Challerange...arr	5 8	...	...	10 57	15 20	20 7	...
Challerange ...dep	5 20	...	8 17	12 9	16 15	22 17	...
Vouziers	5 44	7 2	8 45	12 36	17 6	22 44	...
Attigny	6 11	7 44	9 12	13 4	17 41	23 11	...
Amagne (Est.) arr	6 27	8 9	9 28	13 20	18 1	23 27	...

AMAGNE-LUCQUY and HIRSON.

E.M						
—	**Amagne-Lucquy** ......dep	7 3	9 49	1424	1857	...
6¼	Novion-Porcien	7 16	10 3	1438	1911	...
21¾	Liart	8 1	10 49	1524	20 0	...
38½	**Hirson** (71) ......arr	8 43	11 31	16 6	2042	...

Hirson ....dep	4 58	9 1	12 33	1635	22 2
Liart	5 44	9 51	13 18	1736	22 48
Novion-Porcien ...	6 19	1025	13 52	1810	23 23
Amagne-L. ...arr	6 34	1040	14 7	1825	23 35

GRAY and JUSSEY.

Gray (Est) ....dep	4 25	9 25	17 8	...	...
Gray (Ville)	4 45	9 50	17 18	...	...
Jussey (Est) ......arr	8 15	13 19	21 5	...	...

Jussey (Est) ......dep	4 55	9 42	17 31	...	...	...
Gray (Ville)........ arr	8 10	13 25	20 42	...	...	...
Gray(Est)...........arr	8 28	14 10	21 0	...	...	...

GRAY and DOLE.

Gray (Est).........dep	4 25	9 25	17 8	...	...
Apremont	5 14	11 25	17 55	...	...
Dole (P.L.M. ...arr	7 45	14 24	20 22	...	...

Dole (P.L.M.) ...dep	4 25	10 35	17 2	...	...	...
Apremont	7 8	13 15	19 45	...	...	...
Gray (Est) ....arr	8 28	14 10	21 0	...	...	...

CULMONT-CHALINDREY GRAY.

Station					
Culmont-Chalindrey dep	3 20	6 35	1156	1555	1846
Champlitte	3 50	7 14	1230	1633	1923
Gray (52,56) arr	4 17	7 44	1259	17 3	1954

Station					
Gray dep	4 35	8 41	13 2	1723	2115
Champlitte	5 8	9 11	1333	1754	2146
Culmont-Chalindrey 63B ar	5 50	9 50	14 9	1833	2225

FLAMBOIN and MONTEREAU.

Dist. E M.	Station				
	Flamboin dep	6 54	10 50	16 20	21 45
5¼	Vimpelles	7 15	11 4	16 37	22 4
18¾	**Montereau** arr	7 41	11 31	17 6	22 35

Station					
Montereau dep	8 39	12 18	14 30	18 37	...
Vimpelles	9 9	12 46	14 58	19 17	...
Flamboin arr	9 23	13 0	15 10	19 34	...

BELFORT and GIROMAGNY.

Station						
Belfort dep	6 28	6 47	11 1	1527	1842	2155
Bas Evette	6 48	7 44	11 21	1547	19 1	2215
Giromagny	7 2	7 58	11 35	16 1	1917	2229

Station							
Giromagny dep	5 20	7 16	9 5	1312	17 4	2028	...
Bas Evette	5 38	7 35	9 23	1230	1722	2046	...
Belfort 69 arr	5 49	7 45	9 34	1340	1733	2057	...

AILLEVILLERS and FAYMONT.

Dist. E M	Station					
	Aillevillers dp	5 55	8 50	14 20	18 28	21‡30
5¼	Fougerolles	6 14	9 8	14 39	18 46	21 49
12¾	**Faymont** arr	6 39	9 33	15 4	19 10	22 14

Station					
Faymont dep	4‡35	7 10	1123	15 52	19 38
Fougerolles	4 59	7 36	1146	16 16	20 1
Aillevillers (71)	5 14	7 50	12 0	16 30	20 15

‡—Until 20th September.

POMPEY and NOMENY.

Station				
Pompey (72) dep	6 9	9 54	1429	1836
Faulx	6 28	10 12	1448	1856
Moivron	6 46	10 30	15 9	1914
Nomeny arr	7 1	10 45	1523	1929

Station							
Nomeny dep	4 37	7 22	12 41	17 6	...	...	...
Moivron	4 52	7 37	12 56	17 21	...	...	...
Faulx	5 12	7 58	13 16	17 41	...	...	...
Pompey arr	5 26	8 12	13 30	17 55	...	...	...

EPERNAY and REIMS.

Station														
PARIS (64) dep	0 35	...	...	...	8 15	...	1220	13 0	1423	17 17	...	22 0	22 15	...
Epernay dep	4 4	5 40	6 37	8 36	11 24	12 49	14 29	16 48	1818	19 52	21 35	23 59	1 10	...
Ay	4 10	5 46	6 45	8 43	11 32	12 57	14 35	16 57	1826	19 59	21 41	0 5	1 16	...
Reims arr	4 49	6 25	7 27	9 22	12 11	13 36	15 11	17 37	19 5	20 42	22 22	0 40	1 52	...

Station														
Reims dep	5 17	7 15	8 31	10 42	11 38	13 0	14 45	16 45	18 11	20 10	21 39	22 58	1 15	...
Ay	5 58	7 56	9 12	11 21	12 18	13 39	15 25	17 25	18 51	20 50	22 19	23 40	1 49	...
Epernay arr	6 4	8 4	9 18	11 29	12 24	13 47	15 33	17 33	18 57	20 56	22 25	23 46	1 55	...
PARIS (65) arr	9 35	...	1137	13 42	...	18 10	18 40	...	21 20	23 45	...	3 45	5 0	...

LONGUEVILLE, PROVINS, and ESTERNAY.

Station																					
Longueville dep	5 33	7 30	8 54	9 22	10 2	1030	1142	1335	1516	17 5	1730	18 5	1930	2011	2051	2140	0 29	2 3	...	...	...
Provins	5 45	7 42	9 7	9 34	1013	1042	1154	1347	1528	1716	1742	1817	1942	2021	21 3	2152	0 41	2 11	...	...	...
Esternay arr	7 10	...		...	11 8	...	...	...	...	...	1847	...	...	...	...	...	...	...	...	...	...

Station																					
Esternay dep	...	...	...	7 34	...	...	...	1129	...	...	...	...	...	1851	...	...	...	...	...	...	...
Provins	4 35	6 8	6 50	8 28	9 35	9 49	1116	1220	1423	1543	1630	1829	1910	1950	2026	2113	0 48	...	...	...	...
Longueville arr	4 45	6 20	7 2	8 38	9 47	10 1	1128	1230	1435	1555	1642	1841	1922	20 2	2035	2124	1 0	...	...	...	...

SOISSONS and REIMS.

Station													
Soissons dep	3 55	6 38	8 45	10 32	10 42	12 19	15 15	17 45	...	20 24	22 57	...	...
Fismes	4 31	7 19	9 45	11 4	11 38	13 1	15 58	18 27	19 22	21 8	23 34	...	...
Reims arr	5 1	7 58	10 24	11 30	12 17	13 40	16 26	19 4	20 1	21 47	0 6	...	...

Station														
Reims dep	4 54	7 41	8 54	11 28	12 19	14 30	1630	17 53	18 28	20 49	1 19	...	...	...
Fismes	5 30	8 20	9 34	12 14	12 59	15 10	1710	18 33	18 55	21 27	1 50	...	...	...
Soissons 28 arr	6 14	9 1	10 15	...	13 40	15 51	17 51	19 15	19 30	22 6	2 24	...	...	...

TROYES and ST. DIZIER.

Station					
Troyes dep	4 29	7 56	12 41	1910	...
Brienne	5 51	9 35	14 4	2029	...
Valentigny (74)	6 3	9 45	14 14	2042	...
Montier-en-Der	6 30	10 14	14 40	21 6	...
Eclaron (**72**)	6 57	10 42	15 6	2132	...
St. Dizier (73) arr	7 15	11 2	15 24	2150	...

Station					
St. Dizier dep	4 36	7 56	12 32	19 8	...
Eclaron	4 54	8 15	12 51	1926	...
Montier-en-Der	5 23	8 48	13 25	1954	...
Valentigny	5 44	9 9	13 47	2018	...
Brienne	6 10	9 54	14 16	2031	...
Troyes arr	7 7	10 51	15 13	2129	...

MONTIÉR-EN-DER and PAGNY-SUR-MEUSE.

Station					
Montiér-en-Der dep	...	7 14	1018	1456	1843
Wassy	...	7 39	1047	1521	19 7
Joinville	5 45	9 1	1255	1754	1944
Gondrecourt	6 44	1024	1413	19 4	—
Sorcy	7 28	11 7	15 7	1947	...
Pagny-sur-Meuse arr	7 36	1115	1515	1957	...

Station					
Pagny-sur-Meuse dep	...	4 29	9 3	12 5	1746
Sorcy	...	4 40	9 15	1216	1756
Gondrecourt	...	5 46	1021	1450	1856
Joinville	4 20	7 31	1116	1716	1947
Wassy	4 58	8 14	1258	1754	—
Montiér-en-D. arr	5 16	8 33	1316	1812	...

TOUL and PONT ST. VINCENT.

Station				
Toul dep	4 54	10 40	17 23	...
Pont St. Vincent (**66**) arr	5 34	11 24	18 3	...

Station				
Pont St. Vincent dep	6 55	13 2	18 29	...
Toul (**64**) arr	7 34	13 42	19 11	...

REIMS and CHALLERANGE.

Station							
Reims dep	6 10	8 8	10 8	1355	18 5	21 30	...
Bazancourt	6 37	8 36	10 35	1422	1832	22 3	...
Betheniville	7 12	9 7	11 8	1455	19 8	22 42	...
Somme-Py	7 45	—	11 39	1527	1940	—	...
Challerange ar.	8 10	...	12 4	1552	20 5	...	...

Station							
Challerange dep	...	5 18	...	11 43	1545	2025	...
Somme-Py	...	5 47	...	12 11	1613	2054	...
Betheniville	5 20	6 18	9 20	12 41	1645	2126	...
Bazancourt	5 53	6 54	9 58	13 13	1719	22 1	...
Reims arr	6 21	7 21	1031	13 39	1745	2227	...

MARLES and VERNEUIL L'ETANG.

Station								
Marles dep	6 26	7 47	8 57	10 44	1338	1512	1737	20 4
Verneuil l'Etang arr	6 49	8 8	9 18	11 9	1359	1540	1758	2036

Station								
Verneuil l'Etang dep	5 26	7 10	8 20	9 50	12 47	1420	1655	1815
Marles arr	5 49	7 33	8 43	1011	13 17	1443	1716	1836

PARIS and GARGAN.

†—Weekdays only.

Station		
Paris Est dep	5 5	Dep. from Paris Est. at 5.5, 6.27, 7.23, 8.26, 10.37, 11.25, 12.6, 12.25, 13.35, 15.11, 16.32, 17.38, 18†17, 18†41, 18.59, 19†25, 19†30, 19.46, 20.42, 21.35, and 23.13.
Bondy	5 28	
Gargan arr	5 38	

Station		
Gargan dep	5 7	Dep. from Gargan 5.7, 5†34, 6.5, 6†30, 7.11, 7†25, 8.12, 9.34, 11.23, 12.18, 13.24, 13.49, 14.21, 16.17, 17.18, 18.24, 18†53, 19.38, 20.36, 21.23, 22.20, and 22.59.
Bondy	5 19	
Paris Est. arr	5 40	

EASTERN RAILWAY.

[66 lbs. of Luggage free.

BAR-LE-DUC and NEUFCHATEAU.

E.M.									
—	Bar le-Duc dep	5 5	7 35	9 31	1234	1519	17 14	18 5	2054
7½	Nancois-Tron ...	5 27	7 55	9 53	1258	1540	17 36	1825	2115
10	Ligny	5 40	8 4	10 2	13 7	1549	17 46	1834	2123
13¾	Menaucourt	5 49	8 11	10 10	1315	1556	17 54	1841	—
23¼	Demange.	6 18	—	10 39	1344	—	18 23	—	...
28½	Gondrecourt	6 45	...	10 59	14 6	...	19 0	...	...
43¼	Sionne-Midrev.	7 25	...	11 36	1443	...	19 37	...	...
49½	Neufchâteau ...	7 39	...	11 52	1459	...	19 53	...	...

Neufchâteau ......dep	4 48	...	9 16	1328	...	...	1758
Sionne-Midrevaux ..	5 2	...	9 30	1342	...	...	1812
Gondrecourt	5 52	...	10 18	1433	...	...	19 5
Demange-aux-Eaux	6 8	...	10 34	1450	..	...	1921
Menaucourt	6 36	7 55	11 3	1521	1627	18 53	1951
Ligny	6 45	8 4	11 12	1532	1638	19 5	20 0
Nancois-Tronville ...	6 54	8 15	11 22	1541	1649	19 16	20 7
Bar-le-Duc 64 ......arr	7 11	8 35	11 40	1559	1710	19 36	2021

Extra.—Bar-le-Duc to Ligny, 9.59. Ligny to Bar-le-Duc, 12.17, 20.15, 21.41.

NEUFCHATEAU and MERREY.

Neufchateau 72 dep	6 8	9 24	9 40	1514	2014	...
Bourmont............	6 41	...	10 16	1547	2047	...
Merrey 66 ......arr	7 16	10 0	10 51	1620	2120	...

Merrey......dep	8 6	11 45	1635	1645	2037	...
Bourmont	8 37	12 21	...	1717	21 8	...
Neufchateau	9 6	12 53	1712	1747	2138	...

IGNEY-AVRICOURT and CIREY.

Dist							
	Igney-Avricourt	6*28	8 18	1324	1755	2032	...
11½	Cirey ....arr	7 5	8 55	14 1	1832	21 9	...

Cirey ....dep	5*39	7 28	1015	1525	1926	...
Igney-Avricourt	6 15	8 4	1051	16 1	20 2	...

*—Until 10th October only.

CHATEAU THIERRY and LA FERTE MILON.

Chateau Thierry	3 58	7 0	9 53	1342	1930
Bezu-St.-Germain......	4 20	7 23	10 15	14 3	1957
La Ferté Milon arr.	5 18	8 23	11 15	15 0	2059

Ferte Milon 28	7 45	10 49	1515	17 51	21 3
Bezu-St.-Germain...	8 49	11 53	1619	18 54	22 7
Château T. 64 ar	9 6	12 10	1636	19 11	2224

SEDAN and RAUCOURT.

E.M.							
	Sedan ....dep	5 33	7 50	10 5	12 15	1637	1937
3¾	**Pont-Maugis**	5 40	7 58	1013	12 23	1645	1945
7½	Remilly	5 47	8 5	1020	12 30	1652	1952
10	**Raucourt** arr	6 4	8 21	1036	12 46	17 8	20 8

Raucourt dep	6 17	8 53	11 23	1337	1756	2038
Remilly	6 33	9 9	11 39	1353	1812	2054
Pont-Maugis	6 40	9 16	11 46	14 0	1820	21 1
Sedan ....arr	6 47	9 23	11 53	14 7	1827	21 8

§—Sun. and Thurs. until 8th Sept.

CAEN and BAYEUX.

Service liable to modification.

									‡
Caen St. Pierre dep	...	6 32	9 32	1230	14‡0	15 8	...	1750	2036
Benouville ......arr	...	7 2	10 2	13 0	1430	1538	...	1820	21 6
Benouville ...dep	...	7 10	1010	13 7	...	1546	...	1828	2118
Cabourg	...	8 5	11 5	14 2	...	1641	...	1923	22 4
Dives ....arr	...	8 10	1110	14 7	...	1646	...	1928	22 8
Benouville ......dep	...	7 9	10 9	13 6	1432	1544	...	1827	2113
Ouistreham	...	7 25	1025	1322	1448	16 0	‡	1843	2129
Riva Bella	...	7 33	1033	1327	1453	16 6	1731	1850	2134
Lion-sur-Mer.........	...	7 50	1050	1342	15 8	1623	1743	19 8	2149
Luc-sur-Mer 74C ...	6 0	7 59	11 9	1351	1517	1638	1758	1915	2158
St. Aubin-sur-Mer..	6 12	—	1121	—	—	1650	—	—	—
Courseulles 74C......	6 34	...	1159	...	...	1716	...	...	
Ryes ....arr	7 20	...	1245	...	...	18 7	...	...	‡—Until 8th Sept.
Arromanches dep	7 3	8§45	1228	14 4	...	1750	1847	...	
Ryes ....dep	7 21	9 §3	1250	1419	...	1814	19 2	...	
Bayeux............arr	8 4	9 43	1330	—	...	1852	—	...	
Bayeux.........dep	8 20	—	1410	...	...	1913	...	...	
Port-en-Bessin ar	9 0	...	1450	...	...	1953	...	...	...

Port-en-Bessin...dep		...	9 12	...	...	...	...	1710	20 3
Bayeux ......arr		...	9 54	...	...	...	...	1752	20 45
Bayeux ....dep		6 40		10§27	13 41	...	...	1822	—
Ryes ....arr		7 20	...	11 7	14 21	...	18 15	19 4	...
Arromanches arr		7 41	1252	11 25	14 42	...	18 30	1924	...
Ryes...............dep		7 24	13 7	—	14 26	...	—	19 7	...
Courseulles		8 33	—	...	15 28	...	...	1956	...
St. Aubin		8 49	...	...	15 44	...	...	2012	...
Luc-sur-Mer...	6 15	9 10	1213	14 47	16 4	1728	18‡26	2033	20‡28
Lion-sur-Mer	6 24	9 20	1222	14 57	16‡13	1738	18 34	—	20 38
Riva Bella ...	6 39	9 39	1237	15 16	16‡28	1757	18 50	...	20 52
Ouistreham ..	6 44	9 45	1242	15 22	—	18 3	18 56	...	20 57
Benouville arr	7 0	10 0	1258	15 46	...	1818	19 12	...	21 13
Dives ...dep	6 0	9 0	12 3	14 37	...	1718	...	...	20 11
Cabourg......	6 6	9 6	12 8	14 43	...	1724	...	...	20 16
Benouville...	7 0	10 0	1258	15 37	...	1818	...	...	21 6
Benouville dep	7 7	10 7	13 3	15 44	...	1825	19 15	...	21 17
Caen St. P. arr	7 37	1037	1333	16 14	...	1855	19 45	...	21 47

PAS-DES-LANCIERS and MARTIGUES.

*—Not on Sunday.

Pas-des-Lanciers dep	7 33	1249	17 9	1933	...
Marignane	7 48	13 4	1724	1948	...
Martigues ....arr	8 18	1334	1754	2018	...

Martigues dep	5 55	11 25	1440	17*10	1830
Marignane ...	6 21	11 51	15 6	17 50	1856
P. d'Lanciers	6 40	12 10	1525	18 10	1915

BARBENTANE and ORGON.

Barbentane ...	4 0	9 0	13 40	1810
Orgon	5 30	10 0	15 30	1950

Orgon	5 55	1055	1655	2015
Barbentane (49)	8 15	1215	1915	2135

MIRAMAS and PORT-DE-BOUC.

Miramas ....dep	4 20	7 20	12 58	19 3
Rassuen	...	8 11	13 46	1934
Port-de-Bouc...arr	5 14	8 58	14 31	20 5

Port-de-Bouc...dep	5 36	9 26	1526	20 27
Rassuen	6 4	10 20	1620	20 55
Miramas.........arr	6 35	11 0	17 0	21 25

TARASCON and ORGON.

Tarascon...dep	8 10	13 50	1720	2010	...	...	...
Saint-Rémy ...	9 0	14 40	1820	2050	...	...	...
Orgon 63A arr	10 0	15 30	1950	...	...	...	...

Orgon ...dep	10 55	...	1655	...	...	...	...
Saint-Rémy	12 0	15 40	19 0	...	...	...	...
Tarascon ar	12 30	16 20	1930	...	...	...	...

ARLES and SALON.

Arles...dep	3 50	8 0	...	1320	14 0	17 10	...
Fontvieille	4 10	8 20	...	1330	1419	17 30	...
Eyguieres	5 40	10 5	1225	1535	—	19 5	...
Salon...arr	6 0	1025	1245	1555	...	19 25	...

Salon 63A...dep	...	8 10	10 30	13 40	...	17 0	19 35	...
Eyguieres	5 35	8 30	10 55	14 0	...	1735	20 35	...
Fontvieille	7 1	—	12 11	—	15 51	19 1	21 51	...
Arles ....arr	7 20	...	12 30	...	16 10	1920	22 0	...

EYGUIERES and MEYRARGUES.

Eyguières (74B) dep	5 45	10 15	15 5	20 0
Lamanon	6 0	10 30	15 20	2010
Meyrargues (47) arr	7 50	12 10	17 10	...

Meyrargues......dep	...	8 25	1325	1825	...
Lamanon	5 20	10 40	1620	2020	...
Eyguières (74B) arr	5 30	10 50	1630	2030	...

LAROCHE and L'ISLE-ANGELY.

Laroche ....dep	5 45	10 45	14 45	19 45
Chablis..........................	7 6	12 20	16 7	21 7
Noyers..........................	8 11	13 32	17 12	—
L'Isle-Angely ...arr	8 56	14 24	17 59	...

L'Isle-Angely ......dep	...	6 9	10 16	15 0
Noyers	...	6 57	11 14	1553
Chablis	6 15	8 10	12 30	1715
Laroche (48) ......arr	7 32	9 25	13 54	1840

LANDES LOCAL RAILWAYS.

Labouheyre ....dep	10 18	17 3	...	Mimizan ....dep	5 36	14‡10	...	...
Mimizan ....arr	12 1	18 43	...	Labouheyre ....arr	7 25	15 56	...	...

Sabres ....dep	6 26	14*51	...	Labouheyre ....dep	10 20	16 58	...	...
Labouheyre ....arr	7 13	15 38	...	Sabres ....arr	11 8	17 44	...	...

Morcenx ....dep	9 46	17 5	...	St. Julien-en-Born ....dep	6 9	14 10	...	...
Sindères	10 10	17 29	...	Sindères	7 30	15 31	...	...
St. Julien-en-Born ....arr	11 18	18 33	...	Morcenx ....arr	7 45	15 46	...	...

Sindères ....dep	10 10	17 29	...	Lit-et-Mixe ....dep	5 57	13 58	...	...
Lit-et-Mixe ....arr	11 38	18 49	...	Sindères ....arr	7 21	15 22	...	...

Ychoux ....dep	10 35	17 10	...	Moustey ....dep	5 49	14‖28	...	...
Moustey ....arr	11 39	18 14	...	Ychoux ....arr	6 57	15 35	...	...

Ychoux ....dep	10 30	17 5	20 0	Biscarrosse ....dep	5 56	14§21	18 35	...
Parentis	11 8	17 43	20 23	Parentis	6 37	15 2	19 3	...
Biscarrosse ....arr	11 31	18 6	20 40	Ychoux ....arr	7 7	15 30	19 33	...

Laluque ....dep	10 10	13 55	18 35	Tartas ....dep	7 37	13 1	16 20	...
Tartas ....arr	10 48	14 23	19 13	Laluque ....arr	8 17	13 29	17 0	...

Laluque ....dep	10 5	18 35	...	St. Girons-en-Marensin dep	6 10	14 55	...	...
St. Girons-en-Marensin arr	11 55	20 20	...	Laluque ....arr	8 10	16 55	...	...

St. Vincent ....dep	8 32	11 25	18 40	Léon ....dep	5 6	...	14 40	...
Soustons	9 13	12 4	19 20	Soustons	6 15	10 7	16 4	...
Léon ....arr	...	13 10	20 17	St. Vincent ....arr	6 47	10 43	16 38	...

*—On Labouheyre Fair days depart at 12.23.
‡—On Labouheyre Fair days depart at 12.20.
§—On Labouheyre Fair days depart at 11.20.
‖—On Labouheyre Fair days depart at 11.25.

†—From 12th July until 14th Sept.]

CAEN and COURSEULLES.

Caen (Etat) ....dep	...	5 25	9 10	...	†	...	12 40	†	15 25	...	...	17 5	1952	...	...	...	...	...	...
Caen St. Martin	...	8 0	10 0	...	11 10	12 30	...	1430		...	17 †5	17 55	2030	...	...	...	...	...	...
Douvres	...	8 32	10 35	...	11 30	13 2	13 26	15 1	16 10	...	17 25	18 28	21 3	...	...	...	...	...	...
Luc-sur-Mer	5 52	8 46	10 48	11 17	11 36	13 15	13 37	15 9	16 21	16 44	17 31	18 40	2111	...	...	...	...	...	...
Langrune	5 58	8 52	10 53	11 23	11 40	13 21	13 43	1513	16 27	16 50	17 35	18 46	2116	...	...	...	...	...	...
St. Aubin-sur-Mer...	6 4	9 1	11 0	11 29	11 44	13 28	13 52	1517	16 35	16 56	17 39	18 55	2122	...	...	...	...	...	...
Courseulles ....arr	6 10	9 12	11 11	11 43	11 53	13 39	14 3	1526	16 46	17 10	17 48	19 6	2133	...	...	...	...	...	...

Courseulles ....dep	6 20	8 †5	8 20	9 55	12 25	13†10	1430	15 23	15†55	17 50	18†45	19 57	20 25	...	...	...	...	...	...
St. Aubin	6 33	8 16	8 35	1012	12 40	13 26	1442	15 44	16 7	18 3	18 56	20 12	20 39	...	...	...	...	...	...
Langrune	6 38	8 20	8 41	1018	12 45	13 32	1446	15 50	16 11	18 8	19 0	20 18	20 44	...	...	...	...	...	...
Luc-sur-Mer	6 44	8 24	8 46	1027	12 53	13 41	1452	15 55	16 17	18 15	19 4	20 23	20 53	...	...	...	...	...	...
Douvres	6 53	8 31	—	1036	13 4	13 47	15 2	—	16 23	18 26	19 10	—	21 2	...	...	...	...	...	...
Caen St. Martin ...	7 23	8 51	...	11 9	13 36	14 12	1533	...	16 43	18 55	19 30	...	21 32	...	...	...	...	...	...
Caen (Etat) ....arr	7 52	...	...	1140	15 2	...	1615	...	...	19 22	...	...	...	...	...	...	...	...	...

ALENÇON and CONDE-SUR-HUISNE.

E.M													
	Alençon ....dep	5 40	10 10	14 18	...	18 0	**Conde-s-Huisne** ....dep	5 42	10 27	14 19	20 45	...	...
13¾	Le Mesle-s-Sarthe	6 16	10 47	14 52	...	18 39	Regmalard	6 6	10 43	14 35	20 59	...	...
23	**Mortagne**	6 57	11 37	15 17	15 45	19 22	**Mortagne**	7 22	11 33	15 27	21 41	...	...
36	Regmalard	7 27	12 10	—	16 30	19 57	Le Mesle-s-Sarthe	8 4	12 3	15 54	22 5	...	...
41¾	**Conde-s-Huisne** 80	7 40	12 25	...	16 49	20 10	**Alençon** 75 ....arr	8 49	12 42	16 28	22 39	...	...

* From or at Orleans Co.'s Station.

ROUEN, ELBEUF (ST. AUBIN), and SERQUIGNY.

Dist E.M																					
—	**Rouen** rt. bank dep	5*8	...	...	8 11	8*31	8 51	...	11*37	1223	...	1447	1527	17*13	1811	19*33	...	2046	22*23	2243	0 48
...	,, left bank dep	540	6 15	...	7 43	⋮	8 48	10 5	11 5	1214	1338	...	1550	16 32	18 5	18 56	1945	2149	22 1	2345	0 49
8¾	**Oissel** ....dep	552	6 40	7 51	8 31	⋮	9 30	1045	11 32	1252	14 5	1549	1619	16 55	1851	19 19	2021	22 8	22 19	0 3	1 26
14¼	**Elbeuf St. A.** (86)...	613	—	8 6	8 46	⋮	9 45	11 0	11 49	—	1424	16 4	1634	17 18	19 6	19 39	2036	2225	22 36	0 17	1 40
20	La Londe-la-Bou...	648	...	—	8 59	9 7	—	—	12 18	...	1441	—	—	18 0	—	20 6	—	2239	23 0	—	...
33½	Glos Montfort (85)	722	...	...	—	9 33	...	...	12 50	...	1515	...	...	18 46	...	20 32	...	—	23 39	...	2 21
45½	**Serquigny** (78) arr	749	...		...	9 58	...	...	13 20	...	1546	...	...	19 24	...	20 54	...	...	0 6	...	2 47

Serquigny dp	...	...	...	6 23	...	8 29	...	10 36	...	...	...	13 47	...	...	...	1821	...	21 34	...	0 43	...
Glos Montfort	...	...	...	6 55	...	9 2	...	10 59	...	...	...	14 20	...	...	...	18[illegible]2	...	22 3	...	1 12	...
La Londe-la-B	...	...	...	7 23	...	9 37	...	11 24	1131	...	...	14 49	1457	...	...	1922	2021	22 35	23 6	...	...
Elbeuf St. A.	5 21	6 27	7 11	7 55	8 22	10 8	1044	⋮	1145	...	1430	⋮	1513	1638	1810	1945	2041	...	2317	1 59	...
Oissel ....arr	5 41	6 41	7 27	8 10	8 38	1024	1111	⋮	12 0	1337	1446	⋮	1530	1653	1825	1959	2057	...	2332	2 12	...
Rouen lft bnk	6 1	7 22	...	8 34	1018	...	1130	⋮	1220	14 9	...	⋮	1620	1713	1847	2021	...	...	0 12	2 51	...
,, right bnk	6 44	7 8	8 9	7*57	9 8	10*15	12 8	11*55	1233	14 9	1559	15*24	...	...	...	20*2	2219	23*11	...	2 40	...

66 lbs. of Luggage free.] **STATE RAILWAYS.** [Excess Luggage, 1 cent. per 44 lbs. per kilometre.

CAEN and LE MANS.

A—Monday, Wednesday and Friday only. B—Tuesday, Thursday, and Saturday only.

Dist. E.M.		1,2,3	1,2,3	1,2,3	1,2,3	1,2,3	1,2,3	1,2,3	1,2,3	1,2,3	1,2,3
—	Caen.......dep	8 40	5 23	...	9 7	13 19	...	15 30	18 40	22 19	...
15	Mezidon	9 9	6 3	9 47	10 5	13 58	...	16 18	19 24	22 58	...
26¾	Coulibœuf	9 43	6 38	...	10 31	14 35	...	16 49	19 55	23 29	...
29¾	Fresné-la-Mère ...	—	6 47	A	10 45	14 45	...	16 59	20 4	...	...
42½	Argentan	...	8 0	1033	11 50	15 14	15 51	17 39	20 41	0 7	...
51	Surdon	...	8 30	...	12 16	—	16 10	18 6	21 3	...	2 7
69	Alençon (42B)	6 18	9 23	11 7	13 1	...	16 50	18 53	21 47	0 57	2 43
78¼	La Hutte-Coulomb	6 38	9 55	...	13 29	...	17 14	19 17	22 13	1 13	—
85¾	Vivoin-Beaumont	6 52	10 14	...	13 45	...	17 30	19 37	22 30	...	...
91¼	Montbizot	7 7	10 34	...	14 3	...	17 48	19 56	22 48	...	...
103¾	Le Mans (81) ...arr	7 29	10 59	1158	14 28	...	18 12	20 22	23 13	1 51	...

	1,2,3	1,2,3	1,2,3	1,2,3	1,2,3	1,2,3	1,2,3	1,2,3	1,2,3	1,2,3	1,2,3	1,2,3	1,2,3
Le Mans ......dep	1 15	...	5 23	...	...	9 5	9 18	...	12 43	15 40	19 3	...	22 21
Montbizot	1 35	...	5 49	...	...	...	9 44	...	13 9	16 7	19 26	...	22 46
Vivoin-Beaumont	1 47	...	6 8	...	...	B	10 3	...	13 28	16 27	19 40	...	23 2
La Hutte Coulomb	2 5	...	6 28	...	...	...	10 20	...	13 46	16 47	19 55	...	23 21
Alençon (42B)	2 37	...	7 2	...	...	9 59	10 55	...	14 15	17 26	20 21	21 53	23 45
Surdon	3 17	...	7 44	...	...	...	11 36	12 5	14 54	18 10	20 56	22 35	—
Argentan	3 49	7 13	8 1	8 59	...	1038	11 54	1254	15 25	18 55	21 24	23 36	...
Fresné-la-Mère ...	4 14	7 37	—	9 23	...	...	—	1338	15 51	19 20	...	—	...
Coulibœuf	4 25	7 45	...	9 34	10 38	...	...	14 1	15 57	19 30	21 51	...	...
Mezidon	5 6	8 15	...	10 15	11 0	1115	12 7	15 0	16 29	20 5	22 16	...	...
Caen.......arr	5 36	8 4	...	10 46	...	...	13 36	1611	16 58	20 35	22 42	...	...

Coulibœuf ....dep	4 35	6 53	8 15	9 52	10 56	14 44	16 55	20 4	21 36	23 34
Falaise 83 ....arr	4 50	7 8	8 31	10 0	11 8	15 0	17 11	20 19	22 8	23 50

Falaise.......dep	4 0	6 14	7 23	9 5	10 14	13 40	15 33	19 0	21 19	23 0
Coulibœuf ....arr	4 13	6 27	7 36	9 19	10 27	13 53	15 47	19 13	21 32	23 13

CAEN and FALAISE.

Caen (Etat) ....dep	6 10	12 0	17 30	...	...
Bretteville-sur-Laize	7 34	13 24	18 54	...	...
Falaise (Etat) ....arr	9 29	15 19	20 49	...	...

Falaise (Etat) ....dep	5 54	11 44	17 14	...	...
Bretteville-sur-Laize	7 55	13 45	19 15	...	...
Caen (Etat) ....arr	9 13	15 6	20 36	...	...

LE MANS and ANGERS.

A—Until 5th October.

PARIS *** ...dep	0 5	...	7 30	9 32	11 33	...	...	1625	...	1725	20 0	2144	2213
	1,2,3	1,2,3	1,2,3	1,2,3	1,2,3	1,2,3	1,2,3	1,2,3	1,2,3	1,2,3	1,2,3	1,2,3	1,2,3
Le Mans.......dep	5 16	8 17	11 51	12 34	15 21	15 43	18 19	1931	19 45	22 7	23 23	0 50	2 0
La Suze	5 47	8 45	12 17	...	...	16 10	18 43	...	20 9	2229	...	1 7	...
Noyen	6 0	8 57	12 28	..	15 41	—	18 54	...	—	2240	A	...	2 25
Sablé (36) ....arr	6 25	9 22	12 54	13 14	16 1	...	19 19	20 5	...	23 6	24 0	1 33	2 43
,, ...dep	6 35	9 33	13 29	13 19	16 6	...	19 22	20 8	...	2310	0 4	—	3 0
Morannes	6 53	9 51	13 47	...	16 20	...	19 40	...	...	2328	...	...	...
Etriche-Chateaun..	7 9	10 7	14 2	...	16 30	...	19 53	...	...	2339	...	...	3 21
Angers St.Serge...	8 0	1056	14 50	...	...	...	20 39	...	...	...	...	...	...
Maitre-Ecole	7 51	1046	14 39	...	...	...	20 28	2046	...	0 12	...	...	3 46
Angers.......arr	7 56	1051	14 44	14 4	16 57	...	20 33	2050	...	0 18	0 45	...	3 52
NANTES (39) arr	9 35	1450	18 12	15 26	18 47	...	22 35	2235	...	...	3 33	...	5 40

	1,2,3	1,2,3	1,2,3	1,2,3	1,2,3	1,2,3	1,2,3	1,2,3	1,2,3	1,2,3	1,2,3	1,2,3
NANTES 39 dep	0 42	6 15	6 23	...	9 27	9 27	...	1150	15 2	...	2030	0 42
Angers.....dep	5 19	7 33	8 49	...	11 3	1215	...	1552	17 3	1918	2232	2 10
Maitre-Ecole ...	5 25	...	8 55	...	11 9	1221	...	1559	...	1927	...	...
Angers St. S...	5 13	...	8 41	...	...	1211	...	1542	...	1917	...	A
Etriche-Chat. ...	5 59	...	9 28	...	1129	1258	...	1642	1726	2012	23 0	...
Morannes	6 13	...	9 39	...	...	1312	...	17 0	...	2030	...	...
Sablé.......arr	6 35	8 15	9 59	...	1151	1335	...	1724	1746	2058	2327	2 51
,, ...dep	6 44	8 18	10 4	...	1154	1352	...	1812	1751	2110	2342	3 1
Noyen	7 11	...	10 29	...	...	1422	...	1844	18 8	2143	0 3	...
La Suze	7 26	...	10 40	10 52	...	1434	1833	19 1	1818	2158	...	...
Le Mans...arr	7 51	8 54	11 5	11 17	1231	1459	1854	1928	1840	2227	0 31	3 43
PARIS (81)...	12 15	1215	15 48	...	1548	1810	...	2 44	2211	4 48	4 51	7 16

***—See page 80 for Paris departure station.

DOMFRONT and AVRANCHES.

‡—Until 5th October. §—Daily until 5th October, after 6th October not on Tuesday.

Domfront.......dep	4‡57	...	...	...	9 10	1459	21§35	...
Romagny	5 41	5 49	6‡35	9 32	10 9	1549	22 25	2248
St. Hilaire-du-Har.	—	6 20	7 1	9 50	10 29	16 2	—	2312
Pontaubault	...	6 58	—	—	11 26	1655	...	—
Avranches 79 arr	...	7 11	...	...	11 36	17 4	...	...

Avranches dep	...	7 5	...	9 33	1748	...
Pontaubault	...	7 14	...	9 53	18 6	...
St. Hilaire-du-H.	5 38	7 54	8‡36	11 8	1858	1914
Romagny	6 24	8 11	8 55	11 33	1916	1939
Domfront arr.	7 16	...	9 45	12 31	...	2033

PRE-EN-PAIL and MAYENNE.

E.M.					
	Pré-en-Pail ....dep	5 57	10 38	15 45	...
19¼	La Chapelle-au-Riboul	6 49	11 48	17 6	...
28½	**Mayenne** (83).......arr	7 13	12 15	17 35	...

Mayenne ....dep	8 15	13 3	18 5	...	...
La Chapelle-au-Riboul	8 37	13 43	18 30	...	...
Pré-en-Pail (75).......arr	9 38	15 10	19 40	...	...

ALENÇON and DOMFRONT.

Alençon ....dep	4 50	9 18	14 21	18 50	...	...	...
Pré-en-Pail	5 54	10 35	15 26	19 47	...	...	...
Couterne ....arr	6 24	11 21	16 26	20 23	...	...	...
Domfront ....arr	7 13	12 38	18 10	21 8	...	...	...

Domfront ....dep	5 25	8 25	13 4	18 57	...	...	...	...
Couterne ....dep	6 38	9 10	14 17	19 41	...	...	...	...
Pré-en-Pail	7 46	9 51	15 27	20 28	...	...	...	...
Alençon (74C) ....arr	8 38	10 47	16 19	21 19	...	...	...	...

LAIGLE and CONCHES.

Conches ....dep	3 40	7 35	11 33	15 34	18 53	21 5	...	...
Le Fidelaire	4 0	7 53	11 49	15 50	19 8	21 27	...	...
Lyre	4 13	8 2	11 57	15 58	19 15	21 41	...	...
Rugles-Bois-Arnault	4 32	8 20	12 14	16 15	19 31	22 7	...	...
Laigle 82 ....arr	4 51	8 37	12 28	16 29	19 45	22 28	...	...

Laigle ....dep	4 52	7 15	9 24	13 46	17 20	22 8	...	...	...
Rugles-Bois-Arnault ...	5 10	7 31	9 45	14 2	17 36	22 32	...	...	...
Lyre	5 26	7 48	10 7	14 20	17 53	22 58	...	...	...
Le Fidelaire	5 36	7 56	10 17	14 28	18 1	23 8	...	...	...
Conches 78 ....arr	5 54	8 10	10 35	14 42	18 15	23 24	...	...	...

LISON and LAMBALLE.

E.M.										Until 4th October.								A	*	A	
—	Lison ....dep	...	...	3 44	...	7 35	9 48	...	...	...	...	1345	...	...	...	16 0	1912	2110	2140	2153	...
11¾	Saint-Lo 83........ ..	...	...	4 18	6 43	8 59	10 26	...	...	...	...	1420	...	...	...	1640	1946	2138	2217	2229	...
20	Carantilly-Marigny	...	...	4 41	7 6	9 25	10 52	...	...	...	...	1443	...	...	...	17 4	—	—	2240	2252	...
29¾	Coutances........arr	...	...	5 7	7 32	9 55	11 17	...	...	...	...	15 9	...	...	...	1731	...	...	23 5	2317	...
...	,, 85 ......dep	...	...	5 15	7 45	—	11 29	...	...	...	...	1517	...	...	...	1747	...	...	2313	2325	...
34	Orval-Hyenville ...	...	...	5 25	7 55	...	11 46	...	...	...	...	1531	...	...	...	1757	...	...	2323	2335	...
47½	Folligny 82 ......arr	...	...	6 4	8 34	...	12 25	...	...	...	...	1610	...	...	...	1845	...	...	0 3	0 16	...
...	,, ...dep	...	...	6 20	8 54	...	12 3	1355	...	...	...	—	1644	...	...	1910	...	...	0 9	0 35	...
58½	Avranches 75...arr	...	...	6 50	9 24	...	13 2	1421	...	...	...	...	1711	...	...	1949	...	...	0 36	1 0	...
...	,, ...dep	4 12	...	6 51	9 33	...	13 6	1424	...		‡	...	1716	‡	...	2021	...	...	—	—	...
72	Pontorson 77B	4 43	...	7 32	1016	...	13 40	1454	...	...	1729	...	1748	1810	...	2110	...	...	...	...	...
85¾	Dol 82..............arr	5 10	A	8 7	1049	...	14 9	1516	*	...	1758	...	1817	1940	...	2143	...	...	...	...	...
...	,, ...dep	5 21	5 44	8 41	—	1236	14 14	—	1659	1724	—	...	1852	—	1954	...	...	...	...	...	...
93¾	Miniac Chat. 83.....	5 46	...	9 7	...	1 57	14 38	...	1723	...	...	...	1922	...	2013	...	...	...	...	...	...
103¾	Dinan..............arr	6 9	6 30	9 40	...	1322	15 2	...	1750	18 6	...	...	1954	...	2036	...	...	...	...	...	...
...	DINARD 82......arr	7 2	7 2	1044	...	14 4	15 43	...	—	1834	...	...	2137	...	2137	...	...	...	...	...	...
...	Dinan ....dep	6 16	—	9 51	§	—	15 10	...	...	—	...	§	20 5	...	—	...	...	...	...	...	...
114¼	Plancoet	6 50	...	1020	1349	...	15 37	...	...	...	...	1923	2037	...	...	...	...	...	...	...	...
128¾	Lamballe ....arr	7 21	...	1050	1417	...	16 8		...	...	...	1951	211	...	...	...	...	...	...	...	...

													§						
Lamballe...........dep	4†20	...	...	6 3	...	...	...	...	10 10	...	...	1330	1710	18 48	...	...	...	20 †1	...
Plancoet.................	4 53	...	...	6 43	...	...	...	...	10 49	...	...	1419	1739	19 25	...	...	...	20 30	...
Dinan ....arr	—	...	...	7 10	...	...	...	...	11 15	...	...	1454	—	19 57	...	A	...	—	A
DINARD ....dep	...	...	...	5 30	...	8 38	...	...	10 24	...	...	1413	16 7	—	...	18 50	...	...	21 44
Dinan ....dep	...	4 15	...	7 17	...	9 7	...	...	11 21	...	...	1514	1653	...	20*20	20 54	...	...	22 22
Miniac Chateau	...	4 39	...	7 48	...	A	...	...	11 52	...	...	1544	1728	...	20 59	21 20	...	..	..
Dol....................arr	...	4 59	...	8 12	...	9 41	...	...	12 16	...	...	16 9	1759	...	21 34	21 47	...	...	23 3
,, ...dep	...	5 22	...	8 42	...	—	10‡24	...	12 42	14 54	1540	1645	1828	...	—	—	2225	...	—
Pontorson................	...	5 47	...	9 21	...	...	10 56	...	13 19	15 21	1618	1730	1917	...	...	...	2258	...	...
Avranches ....arr	...	6 11	...	9 56	A	...	—	...	13 52	15 48	1653	1810	1953	...	...	...	2330	...	...
,, ...dep	...	6 14	7 58	1011	1156	...	...	...	13 58	15 51	1720	1815	—	20 5	...	...	2333	...	...
Folligny ....arr	...	6 38	8 33	1047	1228	...	...	...	14 34	16 19	1755	185	...	21 12	...	...	0 5	...	...
,, ...dep	3 42	6 52	8 57	1110	—	...	...	...	14 56	—	1823	1917	...	—	...	...	...	...	...
Orval-Hyenville	4 17	7 32	9 34	11 5	...	...	...	...	15 36	...	1858	1948	...	...	...	...	...	...	...
Coutances ....arr	4 28	7 44	9 45	1157	...	...	...	...	15 47	...	19 9	1958	...	...	...	...	...	...	...
,, ...dep	4 37	7 54	9 56	1215	...	...	...	...	16 3	...	1919	2013	...	...	...	...	...	...	...
Carantilly-Marigny	5 11	8 26	1027	1245	...	...	...	...	16 33	...	195	2040	...	...	...	...	...	...	...
Saint-Lo..................	5 49	9 1	1054	1315	...	...	...	14 25	17 5	17 48	2016	2057	...	...	...	...	...	...	...
Lison 79 ....arr	6 22	9 30	1123	1344	...		...	14 53	...	18 17	20 5	...	...	...	...	...	...	...	...

*—From 6th October. †—From 10th July until 14th Sept. ‡—From 14th July until 15th Sept.
§—From 10th July until 3rd October. A—Until 5th October.

†—Monday at 5.14. **CARENTAN and CARTERET.** Service until 5th October.

Carentan ....dep	4 30	...	8 5	...	14 10	16 30	...	2125
La Haye-du-Puits (85)	5 6	6 55	9 15	10 30	14 40	17 19	1821	2212
Carteret...............arr	5 44	7 36	9 49	11 17	15 14	...	19 0	2253
GOREY (Jersey) arr	Sea passage in one hour.						...	...

GOREY (stm.) dep	...	...	...	...	...	...	...
Carteret ....dep	5†46	7 46	9 17	12 36	1533	16 52	1830
La Haye-du-Puits	6 17	8 25	9 54	13 14	1630	17 30	1925
Carentan ...arr	...	8 54	...	13 45	...	17 59	2011

The Steamers between Carteret and Gorey ply once daily each way—for times see bills posted locally.

‡—Until 5th October. **NEUILLY and ISIGNY.** *—From 6th October.

Neuilly dep	3 52	7 43	12 1	1353	1610	1930	2.*56	22‡10	...
Isigny ...arr	4 5	8 0	12 16	1410	1625	1945	22 13	22 27	...

Isigny...... dep	3 13	5 56	8 57	1236	14 45	1710	2015	...	...
Neuilly 78 arr	3 26	6 14	9 12	1251	15 0	1725	2030	...	...

Isigny ....dep	...	10 45	1430	...	...	...	...	...	...	...
Vierville	5 38	12 12	1653	...	...	...	...	...	...	...
Le Molay-Littry (78)	6 51	13 45	1813	19 12	...	...	...	...	...	...
Balleroy ....arr	8 23	14 28	...	19 55	...	...	...	...	...	...

Balleroy ......dep	6 8	1435	...	1747	...	...	...
Le Molay-Littry	7 25	1517	16 21	1829	19 0	...	...
Vierville.............	8 41	...	17 50	...	2018	...	...
Isigny .... arr	10 5	...	19 14	...	...	...	...

St. Martin des Besaces dep	7 0	12 57	16 3	...	...
Balleroy	8 43	14 40	17 45	...	...
Bayeux ....arr	9 52	15 49	18 54	...	...

Bayeux...........................dep	7 59	12 55	18 57	...	...
Balleroy	9 17	14 8	20 10	...	...
St. Martin des Besaces ......arr	10 52	15 43	...	...	...

LAVAL and CHATEAU GONTIER.

Laval.........dep	8 13	10 3	1536	20 0	...	...
Arquenay-Baz.	8 36	10 29	1558	2023	...	...
Gennes-Long'fuy	9 5	10 55	1620	2047	...	...
Chât.-Gont arr	9 15	11 6	1630	2057	...	...

Chat.-Gont 83 dep	8 21	1123	1715	2247	...	...
Gennes-Long'fuye ..	8 33	1138	1726	2256	...	...
Arquenay-Baz.	8 56	12 0	1748	2319	...	...
Laval ....arr	9 17	1221	1810	2341	...	...

BARENTIN and CAUDEBEC.

Barentin (76) dep	3 35	7 48	12 59	18 16	...	...
Duclair..................	4 11	8 24	13 35	18 52	...	...
Yainville-Jumièges	4 17	8 30	13 41	18 58	...	...
Caudebec ......arr	4 34	8 50	14 1	19 1	...	...

Caudebec......dep	6 10	10 2	15 1	20 24	...
Yainville-Jumièges.	6 33	10 25	15 24	20 .3	...
Duclair..................	6 41	10 33	15 32	21 4	...
Barentin ......arr	7 19	11 11	16 10	21 43	...

PONTORSON and MONT ST. MICHEL.

Pontorson ....dep	7 50	9 30	1115	15 5	17 45	...	...
Mont St. Michel arr	8 20	9 55	1145	1530	18 15	...	...

M. St. Michel dep	8 35	10 5	14 15	1530	18 30	...	...
Pontorson ......arr	9 5	10 30	14 45	16 8	19 0	...	...

STATE RAILWAYS.

Luggage, 30 kilo. (66 lbs.) allowed free; excess Luggage, 1 centime per 44 lbs. per kilometre.

LONDON to PARIS via HAVRE and via DIEPPE.

THROUGH CARRIAGES—Dieppe to Lausanne and Milan—in 15.11 from Dieppe (1st and 2nd class).

"Compartiments à Couchettes" in 3.5 from Dieppe (extra fare on 1st class, 5 fr.—if reserved 6 fr).

FARES	1 Cl. Fr.c.	2 Cl. Fr.c.	3 Cl. Fr.c.
Havre and Paris...	25 55	17 25	11 25
Dieppe and Paris	20 80	12 70	8 30

RC—Restaurant Car attached.

SC—Sleeping Car in this train.

Distance. Eng. Mils.	Station																													
	London (Waterloo) dep	...	...	...	...	...	...	...	9p45	Service on week nights only.								...	...	...	...	...	...	8a57	Service from London on Sats. only from 26th July.					...
	Southampton ......dep	...	...	...	...	...	...	...	1215									...	...	...	...	...	...	11a15						...
	Havre ....arr	...	...	...	...	...	...	...	6a30									...	...	...	...	...	...	5p30						...
		1,2,3	1,2,3	1,2,3	1,2,3	1,2,3	1,2,3	1,2,3	1 &2	1,2,3	1,2,3	1,2,3	1,2,3	1,2,3	1 Cl	1,2,3	1,2,3	1 &2	1,2,3	1,2,3	1 &2	1,2,3	1,2,3	1 &2	1,2,3	1 Cl	1,2,3	1,2,3		
	HAVRE..................dep	...	...	...	...	...	6 7	6 13	8 6	8 21	9 40	1127	12 0	1245	13 2	13 9	...	...	1436	1320	16 0	...	1737	1854	1859	2047	2052	22 9	...	...
3¾	Harfleur	...	...	...	...	...	...	6 26	A	8 33	9 52	1138	1212	D	E	...	...	...	1448	1331	C	...	1748	B	1911	...	21 7	2218	...	...
15½	**Bréauté** arr	...	...	...	...	...	6 34	6 59	8 29	9 4	1024	1211	1243	13 7	1327	1340	...	...	1522	14 4	1625	...	1821	1920	1941	...	2142	2251	...	...
	Beuzeville 77A... dep	...	...	...	...	...	6 40	7 8	8 32	9 9	1030			1314	1332	1345	...	...	1528		1629	...		1928	1945	...		23 0	...	...
31	Yvetot	...	...	...	...	...	7 4	7 47	...	9 44	11 7	...	...	...	1357	1423	...	...	16 4	...	1652	...	1825	1953	2020	...	...	2335	...	...
36	**Motteville 21, 77A**	...	...	...	...	...	7 19	8 1	...	9 56	1132	...	...	...	1414	1434	...	...	1618	...	17 3	...	1833	2011	2030	...	2132	2347	...	...
44	Barentin **78**..................	...	...	...	...	...	7 33	8 18	...	1015	1149	...	...	...	...	1452	...	...	1638	...	1716	...		2024	2047	...	2159	0 4	...	...
49	Malaunay	...	...	...	...	...	...	8 27	...	1025	12 0	...	...	...	...	15 2	...	...	1649	...	...	...	...	RC	2056	...	2216	0 19	...	...
54¾	**Rouen** (right bank) ...arr	...	...	...	...	...	7 49	8 40	9 17	1037	1212	...	...	1358	1436	1515	...	...	17 2	...	1731	...	...	2039	21 9	2146	2231	0 32	...	...
...	**LONDON**-Victoria...dep	...	8p45	...	...	...	...	...	...	...	...	...	...	Not on Sunday. Runs until 30th Sept.	...	...	...	10a0	...	...	...	...	...	...	...	...	...	...	...	...
...	London Bridge ...dep	...	8p45	...	...	...	...	...	...	...	...	...	...		...	...	...	...	...	...	...	...	...	...	...	...	...	...	...	...
...	Newhaven ....dep	...	1025	...	...	...	...	...	...	...	...	...	...		...	...	...	1130	...	...	...	...	...	...	...	...	...	...	...	...
...	Dieppe ....arr	...	2 30	...	...	...	...	...	...	...	...	...	...		...	...	...	15 0	...	...	...	...	...	...	...	...	...	...	...	...
E.M	**DIEPPE** Quai dep	...	3 5	...	...	...	...	...	...	...	...	...	...		...	...	...	1511	...	RC	...	...	...	F	...	...	...	...	...	...
—	**DIEPPE** Gare dep	...	3 18	...	...	...	5 47	...	8 7	...	9 38	...	...		...	1239	...	1521	...	1629	1623	...	...	1924	1826	2048	...	22 5	...	...
18¾	Saint-Victor	...	Via Pontoise, page 77A.	...	...	...	6 32	...	...	...	1028	...	...		...	1325	...	⋮	...	1718	...	...	...	...	1911	...	...	2249	...	...
24¾	**Clères 21** ....arr	...		...	...	...	6 43	...	8 43	...	1040	...	...		...	1336	...	RC	...	1732	1659	...	...	1957	1922	G	...	23 0	...	...
32¼	Malaunay	...		...	...	...	7 1	...	...	...	1116	...	...		...	14 3	...		...	1752	...	...	...	...	1943	...	...	2323	...	...
38	**Rouen** (rt. bank) arr	...		...	...	..	7 14	...	9 3	...	1129	...	...		...	1416	...		...	18 5	1719	...	...	2017	1956	2134	...	2336	...	...
...	**Rouen** (right bank) ...dep	...		...	...	...	8 0	8 51	9 27	...	1223	...	...	14 3	1447	1527	...	Via Pontoise, page 77A.	17 9	1811	1741	...	...	2053	2116	2153	2243	0 48	...	...
57¼	**Rouen** (left bank)...dep	...		5 40	7 0	6 15	...	...	...	10 5	...	...	1550	...	E	...	1731		18 5	...	...	1837	1945	...	23 6	...	...	...	...	...
63¼	**Oissel**	...		6 1	7 16	6 49	...	9 46	...	1030	13 2	...	1611	...	15 5	16 0	1749		1847	1836	...	19 0	2010	2114	2339	...	2314	1 21	...	...
67¾	Pont de l'Arche **86**	6 54		6 10	7 24	7 0	...	10 0	...	1040	1314	...	1619	...	...	1610	...		1857		...	1910	2019	...	2352	...		1 34	...	...
75¼	**St. Pierre-du-Vauvray** arr	7 10		6 26	7 35		...	1014	...		1329	...		...	1520	1626	...		1913		...		2035	2131	0 5	...	...	1 49	...	...
	St. Pierre-du-Vauvray dep			6 34	7 38	...	...	1021	...	...	1338	...	...	...	1523	1632	...		1918	...	...	...	2042	2136	0 19	...	...	1 52	...	...
83¼	Gaillon	...		6 50	...	...	...	1037	...	...	1354	...	...	...	...	1647	...		1933	...	...	...	2058	RC	0 37	...	...	2 11	...	...
92	**Vernon 86**	5 53		7 16	8 2	9 5	...	11 0	...	...	1417	16 0	...	...	1546	17 9	...		20 0	...	...	...	2121	2159	0 56	...	...	2 32	...	...
105¾	**Mantes** (Junction).. arr	6 20		7 46	...	9 30	...	1129	...	...	1447	1625	...	...	...	1737	...		2028	...	...	...	2150	2222	1 21	...	...	3 0	...	...
	Mantes (Junction).. dep	6 32	SC	7 54	...	9 38	...	1139	...	...	1456	1644	...	...	...	1749	...		2036	...	...	...	22 4	2225		...	...	3 6	...	...
106¼	**Mantes** (Station) ......dep	6 37		...	...	...	...	...	...	...	...	1648	...	...	...	⋮	...		...	...	...	...	⋮	...	...	...	...	...	...	...
116¼	Les Mureaux	7 1		8 16	...	...	...	...	...	...	...	1710	...	...	...	⋮	...		...	...	...	...	⋮	...	...	...	...	3 23	...	...
125	Poissy	7 23		...	...	...	...	1214	...	...	...	1733	...	...	...	⋮	...		...	...	...	...	⋮	...	...	...	...	3 39	...	...
131	Maisons Laffitte	7 36		...	...	...	...	...	...	...	...	1749	...	...	...	⋮	...		...	...	...	...	⋮	...	...	...	...	3 51	...	...
141¾	**PARIS**—St. Lazare... arr	7 57	6 3	8 57	9 6	1027	9 58	1242	1124	...	16 9	1817	...	1559	1650	19 4	...	18 3	2135	...	1935	...	2353	2318	...	2333	...	4 17	...	...
...	Paris St. Lazare ...dep	...	6 54	...	...	...	...	...	...	...	...	...	...	...	...	...	...	1916	Junction Trains for passengers with through tickets to places served by the Lyons Co.'s Line.											
...	Paris Lyons Station arr	...	7 52	...	...	...	...	...	...	...	...	...	...	...	...	...	...	2014												

A—At Havre will not take 2nd class for Bréauté Beuzeville.

B—From Havre to Rouen (included) will take up 3rd class for Paris.

C—Between Havre and Rouen will take 3rd cl. for Paris; also takes 3rd cl. for branch lines beyond Bréauté Beuzeville and branch lines beyond Motteville.

E—Between Havre and Rouen takes 2nd and 3rd class for Paris. Exceptionally takes 2nd class between Havre and Motteville for Rouen.

F—Between Dieppe and Rouen only runs until 5th October.

G—Between Dieppe and Rouen only runs from 13th July until 14th September.

66 lbs. of Luggage free.] STATE RAILWAYS.

PARIS to LONDON via DIEPPE and via HAVRE.

PARIS, MANTES, ROUEN, and HAVRE—ROUEN and DIEPPE.

RC—Restaurant Car. SC—Sleeping Car attached.

PARIS—	1,2,3	1,2,3	1,2,3	1,2,3	1,2,3	1,2,3	1,2,3	1,2,3	1 Cl	1,2,3	1 &2	1,2,3	1 &2	1,2,3	1,2,3	1,2,3	1,2,3	1,2,3	1,2,3	1 &2	1,2,3	1,2,3	1,2,3	1,2,3	1 &2	1,2,3	1 &2	1 &2	1,2,3	1,2,3
Gare St. Lazare ...dep	...	...	...	4 52	...	6 26	6 55	8 0	8 17	...	8 32	...	10 0	1030	13 9	1440	1448	...	...	1622	1711	1717	18 4	1948	20 0	2055	2120	2120	2327	0 45
Maisons Laffitte	...	...	...	5 11	...	6 51	...	:	...	...	...	...	:	:	:	...	...	...	...	...	...	:	1831	...	...	:	...	...	:	1 12
Poissy	...	...	...	5 21	...	7 20	E	:	...	...	RC	...	RC	:	:	...	...	...	...	...	...	:	1849	...	...	:	...	...	:	1 29
Les Mureaux	...	...	...	5 38	...	7 41	...	:	...	...	...	From Orleans.	:	:	:	...	M	...	...	...	C	:	1911	H	F	:	B	...	D	1 50
Mantes	...	...	...	...	...	8 3	...	:	...	...	...		:	:	:	...	...	...	...	...	...	:	1931	...	...	:	...	...	:	...
Mantes Junction { arr	...	...	...	5 53	...	8 13	7 42	9 14	...	...	9 21		Via Pontoise, page 77A.	1138	14 3	...	...	...	...	...	...	1828	1935	...	2048	2157	...	...	0 20	2 14
Mantes Junction { dep	...	...	...	6 5	...	8 19	7 44	9 30	...	...	9 24		:	1153	14 6	...	...	...	...	A	...	1833	1949	...	2051	2220	SC	SC	0 29	2 48
Vernon	...	...	...	6 35	...	8 44	8 4	10 3	...	...	9 46	...	:	1223	1431	...	...	...	...	...	1819	19 6	2014	...	2112	2251	...	...	0 59	3 27
Gaillon	...	...	...	6 52	...		...	1021	...	...	...	...	:	1240	1449	...	...	...	...	...	...	1924		...	...	2310	...	...	1 16	3 42
St. Pierre-du-Vauvray { arr	...	...	...	7 4	...	...	8 24	1034	...	...	10 8	9 55	:	1253	15 2	J	...	...	...	...	1839	1937	...	...	2133	2323	...	...	1 29	3 55
St. Pierre-du-Vauvray { dep	...	...	...	7 12	...	...	8 27	1041	...	...	1011	10 0	:	1258	15 8	...	...	...	...	...	1845	1942	...	...	2138	2327	...	...	1 37	4 5
Pont-de-l'Arche	...	...	6 51	7 30	8 16	...	8 42	1059	...	9 53	1023	...	:	1318	1528	...	...	...	...	...	1859	20 1	2230	...	...	2341	...	...	1 52	4 23
Oissel	5 41	6 48	7 1	7 41	8 26	...	8 51	1111	...	10 1	1034	...	:	1329	1542	...	...	1634	...	...	19 8	2015	2242	...	2159	2352	...	...	2 23	4 40
Rouen (left bank) arr	6 1	...	7 22	...	8 45	...	...	...	...	1018	...	...	:	...	...	...	...	...	...	...	1921	2034	23 1	...	...	0 12	...	...	...	...
Rouen (right bank) arr	6 44	7 8	...	8 9		...	9 8	12 8	9 55		1050	1029	:	14 9	1559	1635	1651	17 3	...	1813				2136	2219		2326	2326	2 40	5 7
Rouen (right bank) dep	7 59	7 17	...	...	...	...	9 26	1239	10 8	...	1112	...	Via	...	1621	...	1656	1710	...	1833	1926	...	...	...	2241	...	2331	...	3 19	...
Malaunay	8 14	7 31	...	...	...	...	...	1255	...	...	...	...	:	...	...	...	...	1729	...	...	1947	...	...	...	2257	...	...	...	3 33	...
Clères ...arr	8 32	7 48	...	...	...	...	9 45	1312	K	...	1130	...	:	...	L	Weekdays only.	...	1747	...	1851	2010	...	...	...	2317	...	...	...	3 52	...
Saint Victor	8 55		...	...	...	...	...	1329	...	...	...	...	RC	...	...		...	18 8	...	...	2031	...	...	...	2333	...	...	...	4 9	...
DIEPPE { Gare...arr	9 38	...	...	...	...	...	1022	1415	1055	...	12 6	...	1236	...	1717		1750	1853	...	1929	2115	...	...	...	0 16	...	0 28	...	4 56	...
DIEPPE { Quai...arr	...	...	...	...	...	...	...	...	...	...	...	...	1246	...	...		...		...	...		...	...	...	...	...	0 43	...	...	...
DIEPPE ...dep	...	...	...	...	...	...	...	...	...	...	...	...	13 0	...	...		Runs July 5th, 12th, 19th, and 26th.	...	...	...	...	...	...	...	...	...	1 25	...	...	...
NEWHAVEN ...arr	...	...	...	...	...	...	...	...	...	...	...	...	4p45	...	...			...	...	...	...	...	...	...	...	...	5a30	...	...	...
LONDON B'IDGE arr	...	...	...	...	...	...	...	...	...	...	...	...	...	...	...	...		...	...	...	...	...	...	...	...	...	7a30	...	...	...
VICTORIA ...arr	...	...	...	...	...	...	...	...	...	...	...	...	6p10	...	...	...		...	...	...	...	...	...	...	...	...	7a30	...	...	...
Rouen (right bank) dep	6 55	...	...	8 17	...	...	9 15	1218	10 0	...	11 1	...	...	1429	16 9	1644		...	1738	1821	...	2017	...	2142	2228	...	...	2343	2 52	5 19
Malaunay	7 14	...	...	8 33	...	...	...	1236	...	...	...	...	...	1448	...	...		...	1757	...	...	2034	...	...	2244	...	...	G	3 6	5 37
Barentin	7 29	...	...	8 43	...	...	9 32	1251	...	...	1121	...	...	15 1	1629	J		...	18 9	...	...	2049	...	22 1	2259	...	...	...	3 20	5 52
Motteville	7 56	...	...	9 4	...	...	9 50	1322	...	...	1141	...	...	1525	1646	1721		...	1833	1852	...	2111	...	2220	2322	...	...	0 19	3 40	6 21
Yvetot	8 7	...	...	9 13	...	...	10 0	1334	...	...	1151	...	...	1536	1656	...		...	19 6	19 1	...	2121	...	2229	2336	...	...	0 27	3 53	6 33
Bréauté-Beuzeville { arr	8 40	...	...	9 42	...	...	1018	14 9	...	...	1210	...	...	16 7	1720	1747		‡	1937	1919	...	2152	...	2247	0 6	...	...	0 46	4 22	7 7
Bréauté-Beuzeville { dep	8 45	...	...	9 45	...	...	1022	1417	...	...	1214	1313	...	1611	1725	1753		18 4	1944	1922	...	2156	...	2252	0 12	...	...	0 47	4 34	7 15
Harfleur	9 14	...	...	1012	...	...	...	1445	...	...	...	1338	...	1639	...	...		1829	2012	...	...	2222	...	...	0 33	...	...	...	4 58	7 44
HAVRE ...arr	9 25	...	...	1022	...	...	1042	1457	11 1	...	1235	1348	...	1650	1747	1815	...	1839	2023	1942	...	2233	...	2312	0 44	...	...	1 9	5 9	7 53
HAVRE ...dep	...	...	...	...	...	...	...	...	...	...	...	...	...	...	...	...	...	...	...	...	...	...	...	24 0	Week nights only; also on Sunday from July 27th.					
SOUTHAMPTON ...arr	...	...	...	...	...	...	...	...	...	...	...	...	...	...	...	...	...	...	...	...	...	...	...	...						
LONDON (Waterloo) ar	...	...	...	...	...	...	...	...	...	...	...	...	...	...	...	...	...	...	...	...	...	...	...	9a 0						

A—Takes 2nd class at Paris for Motteville and beyond, and for Clères and Dieppe; at Rouen 2nd class for Yvetot and beyond.

B—Also takes 3rd class for England.

C—At Paris will take 3rd class for beyond Pont de l'Arche; at St. Pierre will also take up 3rd class coming from branch lines.

D—At Paris takes 3rd class for Rouen and beyond; at Junctions will also take up 3rd class coming from branch lines.

E—At Paris takes 3rd class for Rouen and beyond, and at Rouen will take 3rd class for Havre.

F—At Paris will take 3rd cl. for beyond Mantes; also takes up 3rd class coming off branch lines.

G—From Rouen forward will take up 3rd class for Havre.

H—At Paris will take 3rd class for Rouen and beyond towards Havre; at Rouen will take 3rd class for Havre.

J—Runs on weekdays only—takes 3rd class for Havre, Dieppe, and branch lines. Until 30th Sept.

K—Between Rouen and Dieppe only from 13th July to 4th September.

L—Between Rouen and Dieppe until 5th October only.

M—At Paris will take 3rd class for Dieppe and beyond.

Customs Examination.—Luggage registered to Paris examined at St. Lazare Station, Paris; at Dieppe or Havre for other destinations.

‡—Weekdays only.

PARIS and DIEPPE, via PONTOISE.

E.M.	Station																		
...	LONDON-VICTORIA dep	8 p45	...	...	...	...	...	...	...	...	...	10 a0	...	...	...	...	...	...	...
...	LONDON BRIDGE ...dep	8 p45	...	...	...	...	...	...	...	...	...	...	...	...	...	...	...	...	...
...	NEWHAVEN ....dep	10p25	...	...	...	...	...	...	...	...	...	11a30	...	...	...	...	...	...	...
...	DIEPPE ....arr	2 30	...	...	...	...	...	...	...	...	...	14 15	...	...	...	...	...	...	...
E.M.		1,2,3	1,2,3	1,2,3	1,2,3	1,2,3	1,2,3	1,2,3	1,2,3	1,2,3	1,2,3	1 & 2	1,2,3	1,2,3	1,2,3	1,2,3	1,2,3	1,2,3	
	DIEPPE Quai........dep	3 8	...	...	...	...	...	...	...	...	...	15 11	...	...	...	...	...	A	...
—	DIEPPE Gare ....dep	3 18	...	...	...	6 0	6 16	7 49	9 46	12 30	14 35	15 22	...	15 35	...	18 3	...	0 10	...
3¾	Arques-la-Bataille	...	...	...	...	6 12	6 27	...	9 59	12 41	14 44	...	...	15 45	...	18 16	...	0 22	...
15½	Bures	...	...	...	...	6 46		...	10 30	13 11	...	...	...	16 15	...	18 51	...	0 52	...
...	Neufchâtel-en-B.	...	...	...	...	7 7	...	8 23	10 49	13 28	15 13	...	...	16 46	...	19 11	...	1 12	...
...	Nesle Saint-Saire............	...	...	...	...	7 19	...	...	11 2	13 39	...	...	...	17 9	...	19 25	...	1 25	...
30½	Serqueux ....dep	...	...	...	5 39	7 53	...	8 42	11 50	13 57	15 32	...	...	17 54	...	20 6	...	1 42	...
...	Forges-les-Eaux	...	...	...	5 44	7 58	...	...	11 56	14 2	15 38	...	...	18 11	...	20 13	...	1 48	...
46	Gournay ....arr	...	...	...	6 12	8 26	...	9 3	12 27	14 31	15 57	...	...	18 57	...	20 43	...	2 17	...
...	" ....dep	...	...	...	6 15	8 33	...	9 7	12 37	14 40	16 1	...	17 40		...	20 58	...	2 20	...
61½	Gisors	...	5 47	6 55	7 5	9 48	...	9 33	13 23	15 25	16 25	...	18 34	...	19 13	21 51	22 7	2 51	...
...	Chars	...	6 24	7 21	7 49	10 33	...	9 56	14 3	16 9	16 51	...	19 25	...	20 25	22 24	22 51		...
86¼	Pontoise	...	7 1	7 44	8 29	11 12	...	10 13	14 38	16 50	17 8	...	20 3	...	21 24	22 45	23 28	...	...
...	Achères	...	...	...	8 48	...	...	...	...	...	...	...	20 33	...	...	...	...	...	...
104½	Paris St. Lazare.........arr	6 3	8 10	8 35	9 15	12 0	...	10 50	15 22	17 40	17 48	18 3	21 9	...	22 59	23 37	0 22	...	...

	Station																		
	Paris—Rue	1,2,3	1,2,3	1,2,3	1,2,3	1,2,3	1,2,3	1 & 2	1,2,3	1,2,3	1,2,3	1,2,3	1,2,3	1,2,3	1,2,3	1,2,3	1,2,3	1,2,3	
...	St. Lazare ....dep	...	...	...	5 40	7 49	8 53	10 0	10 4	11 24	...	15 16	...	16 52	17 21	18 0	19 0	20 30	...
...	Achères	...	...	...	6 9	...	...	...	...	...	...	15 44	...	...	...	18 25	...	21 10	...
...	Pontoise......................arr	...	...	...	6 34	8 42	9 29	...	10 58	12 19	...	16 12	...	17 34	18 7	18 53	20 17	21 43	...
...	Chars (77A).....................	...	...	...	7 15	9 22	9 50	...	11 36	12 59	...	16 58	...	17 56	18 35	19 32	20 56	22 25	...
...	Gisors (86)	...	...	...	8 3	10 26	10 16	...	12 14	13 39	...	17 40	...	18 19	19 4	20 10	21 31	23 12	...
...	Gournay.......................arr	...	B	...	8 41	11 2	10 37	...		14 15	...	18 16	...	18 40		20 46		23 53	...
...	" ....dep	...	5 52	6 43	8 53		10 40	...	...	14 19	...	18 55	...	18 43	...	21 18	...	23 58	...
...	Forges-les-Eaux	...	6 29	7 24	9 40	...	11 6	...	...	14 53	...	19 30	...	...	...	22 6	...	0 39	...
...	Serqueux	...	6 40	7 54	10 16	...	11 13	...	...	15 11	...	20 7	...	19 13	...	22 28	...	0 46	...
...	Nesle Saint-Saire	...	6 50	8 4	10 27	...	...	...	...	15 21	...	20 19	...	...	...	22 43	...		...
...	Neufchâtel	...	7 2	8 14	10 46	...	11 28	...	...	15 34	17 24	20 35	...	19 28	...	22 55	...	...	...
...	Bures	...	7 16	8 28	10 54	...	...	...	...	15 49	17 37	20 49	...	...	...		...	...	...
...	Arques-la-Bataille.........	7 6	7 43	8 59	11 25	...	11 50	...	...	16 21	18 4	21 18	19 2	...	...	...	...	...	...
...	DIEPPE Gare........arr	7 20	7 55	9 11	11 37	...	11 59	12 36	...	16 34	18 14	21 30	19 16	19 56	...	...	...	...	...
...	DIEPPE Quai.........arr	...	...	...	...	...	...	12 46	...	...	...	...	...	...	...	...	...	...	...
...	DIEPPE ....dep	...	...	...	...	...	...	13 0	...	...	...	...	...	...	...	...	...	...	...
...	NEWHAVEN ....arr	...	...	...	...	...	...	4 p45	...	...	...	...	...	...	...	...	...	...	...
...	LONDON BRIDGE ...arr	...	...	...	...	...	...	...	...	...	...	...	...	...	...	...	...	...	...
...	LONDON-VICTORIA arr	...	...	...	...	...	...	6 p10	...	...	...	...	...	...	...	...	...	...	...

A—On Sunday and Monday only until end August. B—On Saturday and Sunday only until 30th September.

MAGNY-EN-VEXIN and CHARS.

E.M.							
	Magny dep	6 39	8 42	12 16	16 7	21 35	...
8	Chars ...arr	7 7	9 12	12 46	16 41	22 9	...

Chars 77A...dep	7 55	10 1	14 10	18 2	22 39	...
Magny.........arr	8 22	10 32	14 40	18 28	23 6	...

Service until 5th October.]

BREAUTE-BEUZEVILLE and ETRETAT.

Breaute-B. dep	4 37	7 27	9 24	1037	1227	1430	1732	17‡58	1829	1954	2311
Les Ifs arr	4 53	7 43	9 43	1052	1247	1445	1747	18 12	1845	2010	2326
Les Ifs dep	5 27	8 16	9 58	11 4	1257	1454	1820	—	1857	2020	2336
LogesVaucottes	5 47	8 32	1019	1120	1313	1513	1840	—	1913	2036	2352
Etretat ......arr	5 57	8 42	1029	1130	1323	1523	1850	...	1923	2046	24 0

Etretat ...dep	5 34	7 15	9 7	10 4	1150	1459	1617	1813	1938	2140
Les Loges V.	5 46	7 29	9 21	1018	12 4	1515	1631	1825	1950	2152
Les Ifs arr	6 2	7 46	9 38	1035	1221	1532	1648	1841	20 9	22 9
Les Ifs dep	6 11	8 3	9 53	1147	1233	1545	17 0	1855	—	2222
Breaute-B.76	6 26	8 17	10 8	12 4	1252	1559	1715	19 9	...	2236

‡—Until 30th September, and not on Sunday.

BRÉAUTÉ-BEUZEVILLE and FECAMP.—BRÉAUTÉ-BEUZEVILLE and LILLEBONNE.

‡—Until 30th September and not on Sunday.

Breaute Beuzeville	4 37	7 27	9 24	1037	1227	1430	1732	17‡58	1829	1954	2311
Les Ifs	4 57	7 58	9 49	1057	1252	1450	1751	18 16	1850	2015	2329
Fecamp arr	5 10	8 11	10 4	1110	13 5	15 3	18 4	18 29	19 3	2028	2342

Fecamp dp	5 48	7 41	9 32	1126	12 9	1329	1525	1642	1832	22 3
Les Ifs	6 11	8 3	9 53	1147	1233	1347	1545	17 7	1855	2222
Breaute-B.	6 26	8 17	10 8	12 4	1252	14 1	1559	1715	19 9	2236

Breaute-Beuzeville dep	4 42	7 30	9 20	10 40	12 30	1427	1755	1837	1957	23 8
Bolbec	4 55	7 59	9 33	10 52	12 42	1439	18 7	1854	20 9	2318
Lillebonne ....arr	5 12	8 16	9 50	11 9	12 59	1456	1824	1911	2026	2333

Lillebonne dp	6 0	7 42	11 32	1222	1527	1835	2047	22 3
Bolbec	6 17	8 0	11 49	1244	1544	1852	21 8	2220
Breaute-Beu.	6 29	8 12	12 1	1256	1556	19 4	2121	2233

‡—Until 5th October.]

MOTTEVILLE and ST. VALERY-EN-CAUX

Motteville ......dep	5 38	8 15	10‡5	11 45	1320	17‡31	18 57	...	22‡29
St. Vaast-Bosville	6 24	8 53	1042	12 20	1414	18 6	19 33	21‡3	23 2
St. Valery-en-C.arr	6 45	9 14	11 3	12 41	1435	18 25	19 54	2124	23 23

St. Valery-en-C. dp	6 0	10 9	13‡2	15 6	1857	20‡21	22 ‡5	...
St. Vaast-Bosville	6 27	1039	1329	1533	1929	20 47	22 32	...
Motteville ....arr	6 57	1111	1359	16 5	1959	...	23 7	...

MANTES and VERSAILLES via Plaisir-Grignon.

Mantes ....dep	5 14	8 25	11 48	15 2	16 53	19 52	...
Epone-Mezieres.....................	5 57	8 44	12 4	15 22	17 48	20 15	...
Plaisir-Grignon....................	6 35	9 23	12 52	16 3	18 29	21 19	...
Versailles Chantiers...arr	7 6	9 51	13 17	16 30	18 57	21 52	...

Versailles Chantiers..dep	6 39	10 7	13 1	1617	18 35	21 45
Plaisir-Grignon.....................	7 8	10 32	13 42	1642	18 56	22 20
Epone-Mezieres.....................	7 53	11 33	14 51	1724	19 30	23 1
Mantes.............................arr	8 6	11 47	15 7	1737	19 44	23 17

ST. PIERRE-DU-VAUVRAY and LOUVIERS.

St. Pierre-du-Vauvray......dep	6 32	7 15	8 30	10 26	10 46	13 45	15 28	1639	18 46	19 47	21 44	2 0	...	...	...	...	...	...
Louviers...........................arr	6 45	7 28	8 43	10 39	10 59	14 0	15 41	1654	18 59	20 0	21 57	2 13	...	...	...	...	...	...
Louviers...........................dep	6 2	6 52	8 8	9 27	9 44	9 54	12 37	14 42	16 7	18 7	21 13	1 6	...	...	...	...	...	...
St. Pierre-du-Vauvray.. ...arr	6 15	7 5	8 21	9 40	9 55	10 6	12 50	14 55	1620	18 20	21 26	1 19	...	...	...	...	...	...

ST. PIERRE-DU-VAUVRAY and LES ANDELYS.

St. Pierre-du-V. ...dep	7 44	8 57	10 48	1343	1641	1948	2146
Muids	7 53	9 7	10 58	1353	1654	1958	2156
Les Andelys ....arr	8 9	9 25	11 16	1411	1715	2016	2214

Les Andelys.....................dep	5 54	8 20	9 36	12 8	1429	1754	2044
Muids..	6 10	8 36	9 54	12 30	1447	1816	21 2
St. Pierre-du-Vauvray ...arr	6 20	8 46	10 5	12 45	1458	1831	2113

SAINT-BRIEUC and PONTIVY.

Station					
Saint Brieuc 80 dep	5 54	10 49	1323	17 59	20 9
Quintin	6 24	11 9	1358	18 27	20 41
Plœuc-l'Hermitage	6 42	11 26	1415	18 44	20 58
Uzel	6 54	11 38	1425	18 55	21 10
Loudéac	7 18	11 58	1449	19 15	21 31
Pontivy (31A)......arr	7 51	12 24	1518	19 40	21 56

Station					
Pontivy ....dep	7 23	11 57	15 45	20 44	...
Loudéac	8 1	12 46	16 23	21 28	...
Uzel	8 22	13 6	16 41	21 48	...
Plœuc-l'Hermitage	8 33	13 16	16 52	21 58	...
Quintin	8 51	13 33	17 11	22 14	...
St. Brieuc ....arr	9 18	14 0	17 40	22 40	...

St. Brieuc to Collinée 6.50, 10.35 and 17.45.
Tréguier to Plouec 6.30, 9.20, 14.55, 19.5
Tréguier to Perros and Lannion 6.10, 9.50, 17.20, 19.38.

LA BROHINIERE and PLOERMEL.

Station					
La Brohiniere ......dep	6 18	9 24	12 1	1652	...
Mauron	6 52	11 1	13 0	1725	...
Ploermel 31...........arr	7 25	12 5	13 42	1758	...
Ploermel ....dep	4 45	10 12	14 5	18 2	...
Mauron	5 18	10 45	1514	1835	...
La Brohiniere 80...arr	5 50	11 18	1625	19 7	...

CHATEAUBRIANT and RENNES.

Station						
Châteaubriant ...dep	5 23	10 52	14 18	18 49	...	...
Martigné Fer .....arr	5 49	11 14	14 37	19 10	...	...
Martigné Fer dep	6 7	12 5	...	19 22	...	...
La Guerche-de-B.	6 49	13 4	...	19 50	...	...
Vitré 80............arr	7 36	14 7	...	20 28	...	...
Martigné Fer.....dep	5 53	11 17	14 49	19 15	...	...
Corps-Nuds	6 38	12 0	15 21	19 58	...	...
Rennes 80...........arr	7 5	12 28	15 46	20 24	...	...
Rennes ....dep	4 13	8 57	13 0	17 41	...	...
Corps-Nuds	4 43	9 29	13 30	18 17	...	...
Martigné-Fer .....arr	5 20	1015	14 10	19 14	...	...
Vitré..................dep	3 50	8 25	...	17 57	...	...
La Guerche-de-B.	4 40	9 35	...	18 35	...	...
Martigné-Fer arr	5 8	1010	...	19 1	...	...
Martigné-Fer ....dep	5 23	1018	14 12	19 20	...	...
Châteaubriant ...arr	5 46	1039	14 37	19 47	...	...

NANTES and LEGE.

E.M.	Station				
	Nantes ....dep	6 37	12 12	17 50	
14¼	St. Philibert	7 50	13 20	18 59	
28	Legé ....arr	8 46	14 15	19 57	
...	Legé ....dep	5 49	9 24	16 21	
...	St. Philibert	6 48	10 26	17 25	
...	Nantes ....arr	7 54	11 31	18 35	

CAEN and DOZULE-PUTOT.

Service until 5th October.

Station										
Caen...dep	6 13	8 32	9‡38	12 7	14 14	15 37	16 42	18 4	21 47	
Troarn ...	6 39	9 2	9 58	12 33	14 43	16 15	17 2	18 34	22 13	
Dozulé arr	6 56	9 19	10 11	12 50	15 0	16 39	17 15	18 51	22 30	
Dozulé dep	7 10	8 45	1022	11‡5	1326	1427	1542	18 17	19 44	0§14
Troarn	7 30	9 1	1042	1121	1347	1445	1611	18 33	20 4	0 31
Caen 79 arr	7 53	9 19	11 5	1139	1410	15 3	1641	18 51	20 27	0 50

‡—Until 28th September. §—Until 15th September.

SAINTE GAUBURGE and BERNAY.

Station							
Ste. Gauburge dep	5 22	...	1131	1714	...	...	...
Echauffour	5 40	...	1142	1733	...	...	...
La Ferté-Fresnel	6 27	...	1215	1815	...	...	...
La Trinité-de-R. (77B)	7 6	9 24	1243	1850	...	...	...
Broglie	7 18	9 33	1250	1914	...	...	...
Bernay (78) ......arr	7 41	9 56	1311	1937	...	...	...
Bernay ....dep	5 10	8 37	14 0	18 1	...	...	
Broglie	5 43	9 1	14 30	18 29	...	...	
La Trinité-de-Reville	5 54	9 9	14 45	18 53	...	...	
La Ferté-Fresnel	6 30	—	15 29	19 38	...	...	
Echauffour	7 6	8 13	16 9	20 25	...	...	
Ste. Gauburge...arr	7 24	8 23	16 21	20 55	...	...	

SAINTE GAUBURGE and MESNIL MAUGER.

Station								
Ste. Gauburge dep	3 44	8 37	13 11	1740	2028	...	...	...
Echauffour (77B)...	4 0	8 49	13 23	1755	2038	...	...	...
Gace	4 34	9 25	13 55	1837	21 1	...	...	...
Vimoutiers	5 37	1039	15 10	1947	2138	...	...	...
Livarot	6 3	1112	15 43	2029	2154	...	...	...
Mesnil-Mauger arr	6 36	1145	16 21	2110	2216	...	...	...
Mesnil-Mauger dep	4 42	7 55	1343	...	1844	2325	...	...
Livarot	5 11	8 42	1415	...	1926	2354	...	...
Vimoutiers	5 48	9 24	1447	1852	20 0	0 14	...	...
Gace	6 35	1025	1554	1936	2119	—	...	...
Echauffour	7 14	1054	1631	1959	2150	...	...	...
Ste. Gauburge arr	7 24	11 6	1643	20 9	22 1	...	...	...

LA HUTTE-COULOMBIERS and MAMERS.

Station						
La Hutte-Coulombiers dp	4 35	7 10	10 35	1719	23 22	...
St. Rémy du Plain	5 3	7 54	11 33	1747	23 50	...
Mamers 84 ....arr	5 18	8 24	12 5	18 2	0 4	...
Mamers..................dep	5 22	8 49	15 5	21 0	...	...
St. Rémy du Plain	5 46	9 10	15 35	21 19	...	...
La Hutte-Coulombiers 85	6 20	9 44	16 17	21 48	...	...

VITRE and PONTORSON.

†—Mon., Tues., and Sat.] [‡—Mon., Tues., Wed. and Sat.

E.M.	Station							
	Vitré ....dep	3 56	...	9 10	12 7	...	1754	2140
11¾	Châtillon-en-Vend.	4 29	...	9 48	1241	...	1832	2218
19¼	La Selle-en-L. (85)...	4 49	...	1013	13 3	†	1855	2242
23	Fougères (85)	5 5	7 23	1025	1321	1421	1930	2253
34¼	St. Brice-en-Coglès	5 45	8 15	—	14 1	1545	2017	—
42½	Antrain	6 9	8 45	...	1424	1653	2043	...
48½	Pontorson (79)...arr	6 26	9 5	...	1441	1722	21 0	...

Station									
Pontorson ....dep	...	4 54	9 24	10‡13	...	...	1622	...	1922
Antrain	...	5 12	9 40	10 45	...	...	1642	...	1943
St. Brice	...	5 44	10 5	11 35	...	...	1710	...	2022
Fougères	5 52	6 17	1042	12 29	1259	1349	1742	1912	2111
La Selle-en-L.	6 0	—	1050	—	13 7	14 0	—	1923	—
Châtillon-en-Vend.	6 20	...	11 9	...	1327	1428	...	1944	...
Vitré (80) ....arr	6 55	...	1143	...	14 3	1512	...	2023	...

MORLAIX and CARHAIX.

Station					
Morlaix..............dep	8 4	12 55	16 0	22 3	...
Huelgoat	9 14	14 10	17 32	23 17	...
Carhaix 77B......arr	9 51	14 49	18 18	23 56	...

Station						
Carhaix..............dep	4 58	10 25	12 38	19 0	...	...
Huelgoat	5 35	11 3	13 31	1934	...	...
Morlaix 80 ......arr	6 50	12 20	14 59	2043	...	...

CARHAIX and LOUDEAC.

Station						
Carhaix...dep	4 30	5 39	9 59	17 19	...	...
Rostrenen	5 15	6 54	10 45	18 18	...	...
Caurel	6 6	8 35	11 31	19 10	...	...
Loudeac arr	7 2	10 8	12 36	20 20	...	...

Station						
Loudeac dep	8 36	12 2	16 15	21 35	...	...
Caurel	9 41	13 38	17 14	22 34	...	...
Rostrenen	10 52	15 28	18 16	23 33	...	...
Carhaix ...arr	11 34	16 24	18 55	0 12	...	...

LA BROHINIERE and LOUDEAC.

Station				
La Brohiniere...........dep	4 37	12 5	16 58	...
St. Lubin-le-Vaublanc	6 18	14 35	18 48	...
Loudeac..................arr	6 59	15 39	19 34	...

Station				
Loudeac.....................dep	8 8	13 43	16 21	...
St. Lubin-le-Vaublanc	8 57	14 28	17 15	...
La Brohiniere...........arr	10 51	16 16	19 20	...

CARHAIX and CHATEAULIN.

Station				
Carhaix.....................dep	4 50	10 20	19 15	...
Chateauneuf du Faou	6 29	11 26	20 22	...
Pleyben	7 18	12 1	20 57	...
Chateaulin (Orléans) 31 arr	8 23	12 41	21 40	...

Station					
Chateaulin (Orleans) dep	7 9	10 5	15 55	...	...
Pleyben	7 53	11 28	16 42	...	...
Chateauneuf du Faou...	8 26	12 28	17 22	...	...
Carhaix ....arr	9 25	14 8	18 26	...	...

LISIEUX and LA-TRINITE DE-REVILLE.

E.M.	Station					
	Lisieux.........dep	7 45	13 6	17 21	22 32	...
5	St. Martin-de-Mail	8 1	1322	17 37	22 47	...
11¾	Orbec	8 34	1351	18 6	23 10	...
20	La Trinité ...arr	9 2	1422	18 33	—	...

Station							
Trinite Reville	...	10 52	1515	1910	...	...	...
Orbec	6 19	11 26	1549	1941	...	...	...
St. Martin-de-Mail	6 42	11 52	1614	20 6	...	...	...
Lisieux (78) arr	6 58	12 8	1630	2022	...	...	...

PAIMPOL and ROSPORDEN.

Station								
Paimpol..............dep		4 40	7 40	...	1139	15 3	2047	...
Pontrieux		5 18	8 20	...	1218	1542	2126	...
Guingamp 80 ...... arr		6 13	9 25	...	1320	1643	2230	...
Guingamp 80 ...... dep		7 1	—	12 0	1425	1945	—	...
Mousterus Bourbriac ...		7 36	...	1230	1455	2015	...	...
Callac		8 45	...	1325	1549	2111	...	...
Carhaix 77B... arr		9 26	...	14 4	1627	2150	...	...
Carhaix 77B... dep	6 36	1012	...	1423	1910	—	...	...
Gourin	7 45	11 0	...	1515	20 2	...	...	...
Scaer	8 43	1138	...	1555	2014	...	...	...
Rosporden 31....arr	9 13	12 6	...	1622	2112	...	...	...

Station								
Rosporden ....dep	...	...	7 33	...	1058	1259	1650	...
Scaer	...	...	8 6	...	1143	1329	1720	...
Gourin	...	...	8 47	...	1240	14 8	18 0	...
Carhaix arr	...	...	9 30	...	1328	1450	1842	...
Carhaix dep	...	5 58	9 41	...	15 0	—	1919	...
Callac	...	6 43	1025	...	1546	...	2018	...
Mousterus Bourbriac ...	...	7 38	1117	...	1639	...	2121	...
Guingamp arr	...	8 0	1138	...	17 1	...	2145	...
Guingamp dep	6 33	1015	1221	1443	1936	...	—	...
Pontrieux	7 33	1126	1332	1543	2037	...	...	...
Paimpol ....arr	8 8	12 6	14 7	1618	2114	...	...	...

PARIS to TROUVILLE, HONFLEUR, CAEN, and CHERBOURG.

	1,2,3	1,2,3	1,2,3	1,2,3	1,2,3	1,2,3	1 & 2	1,2,3	1,2,3	1,2,3	1 & 2	1,2,3	1,2,3	1,2,3	1,2,3	1,2,3	1,2,3	1Cl.	Lux	1 & 2	1,2,3	1,2,3	1,2,3	1,2,3	1,2,3	1,2,3	1,2,3	1,2,3		
PARIS—Rue St. Lazare......dep	...	0 45	...	4 52	...	6 48	7 45	U till 5th October only.	7*55	...	8 45	...	9 4	...	1120	...	1227	1326	1555	16‡5	...	16 0	17 0	RC 18*25	18 4	2055	A 22 5	2348	...	...
Mantes-Gassicourt........	...	3 34	5 16	6 0	...	8 53	D		8 45	...	...	...	10 0	1056	12 8	...	1327		...	...	...	17 0	...	19 32	1950	22 3	...	0 52	...	...
Bueil (86)	...	4 11	5 59	...	...	9 26	...		9 9	...	...	...	1026	1125	...	...	14 7	C	L	...	...	1735	RC	19 59	2027	2234	...	1 25	...	...
Evreux (85, 86)	...	4 41	6 30	6 45	...	9 55	9†17		9 32	...	1031	...	1056	1218	1254	...	1434		...	17 35	...	1811	1840	20 27	21 1	2259	2350	1 52	...	...
Conches (75)..................	...	5 23	7 23	...	...		...		9 54	...	...	...	1116	1244	RC	...	1527			...	...	19 4	Until Aug. 31.	20 46		2337	SC	2 25	...	...
Serquigny...............arr	...	5 53	7 51	...	...	...	...		1013	...	...	...	1140	1310	1326	...	1555			18 8	...	1935		21 6	...	0 3	0 23	2 53	...	...
ROUEN ....dep	...	...	6 8	...	...	...	...	8 31	8 31	...	RC	...	RC	1137	1137	...	1338		July 5 to Sept. 7.	...	...	1713		19 33	...	2223	2223	0 49	...	...
Serquigny...............dep	...	6 1	8 8	...	§	...	...	10 2	1018	...	...	...	1144	1337	1328	...	1612			18 10	...	1953		21 10	...	0 39	0 32	3 5	...	...
Bernay (77B)	...	6 18	8 23	...	8 51	...	...	1013	1029	...	...	...	1157	1350	...	...	1625			18 21	...	2015	1924	21 23	...	0 51	...	3 20	...	...
Lisieux (77B) ....arr	...	6 56	9 0	8 7	9 18	...	10†26	1042	1058	...	1132	...	1231	1427	14 9	...	17 3			18 50	...	2056	1955	21 58	...	1 25	1 7	3 56	...	...
Lisieux ....dep	...	7 28		8 12		...	1030	...	1112	...		...	1310		1414	...	1725				19 8		1959	22 12	...	...		4 20	...	...
Pt. l'Eveque...........arr	...	7 55				B		...	1130	...		...	1337			...	1751				1930		2013	22 30	...	...		4 41	...	...
Pt. Eveque ....dep	...	8 8				9 20		...	1132	...		...	1341			...	1756				1940		2015	22 31	...	...		4 55	...	...
Trouville ....arr	...	8 25		8 40		9 38	1652	...	1146	...		...	1358		1436	...	1812	1622	1837		1958		2026	22 45	...	...		5 10	...	...
Pt. l'Eveque ....dep	...	8 1				...		...	1140	...		...	1348		...	...	1817	...	...		1954		...	22 50	...	...		4 48	...	...
Quetteville	...	8 33		Runs until 15th September only.		...		...	12 0	...		...	1410		...	...	1841	...	...		2014		...	23 10	...	...		5 10	...	...
Honfleur ....arr	...	8 50				...		...	1215	...		...	1427		...	...	1858	...	...		2031		...	23 27	...	...		5 27	...	...
Lisieux ....dep	4 54	7 18	9 28		9 22	...		...	11 3	...	1137	...	1257	1448	1413	...	1738	...	...	18 54	...	2120	...	22 3	...	...	1 11	4 1	...	...
Mesnil-Mauger (77B)	5 31	7 49	9 49		...	...		...	...	...	...	...	1319	1513	...	...	18 9	...	...	...	...	2157	...	22 25	...	...	...	4 23	...	...
Mezidon (78)	6 4	8 15	1015		9 42	...		12 7	1129	...	...	...	1331	1520	...	1629	1817	...	...	19 19	B	22 7	...	22 35	...	...	...	4 35	...	...
Caen (74B, 83) ....arr	6 34	8 46	1046		...	...		1236	1147	...	1219	...	1356	1611	1453	1658	1852	...	...	19 36		2321	...	22 57	...	...	1 52	5 1	...	...
Caen ....dep	8 20	10 0	1157			...	Runs until 15th September only.			...	1231	...	1425		...	1730	2014	...	...		20 1		...		23 8	...	2 6	5 50	...	...
Bretteville Norrey..........	8 38	1024	1215			...		...	...	...	...	...	1445	...		1750	2034	...	...	...	...	...	...	...	2329	...	2 22	6 9	...	...
Bayeux.........................	9 3	1053	1235		To Le Mans.	...		...	...	...	13 4	...	1516	...		1816	21 2	...	...	...	2031	...	...	...	2350	...	2 47	6 36	...	...
Le Molay-Littry	9 21	1114		...		...		...	...	...	...	...	1529	...	Runs until 15th August only.	1838	2123	...	...	...	...	...	...	...		...	3 4	6 57	...	...
Lison (75A) ....arr	9 34	1129	...	...		...		...	...	...	1328	...	1542	...		1851	2136	...	...	...	2052	...	...	...	...	...	3 16	7 10	...	...
Lison (75A) ....dep		1140	...	...		...	...	...	...	...	1334	1514	1551	...		19 6	2146	...	...	...	2056	...	...	...	...	...	3 31	7 21	...	...
Neuilly (75A)	...	1150	...	...		...	...	...	...	...	1343	1528	1613	...		1918	2159	...	...	...	B	...	...	...	...	...	3 41	7 30	...	...
Carentan (75A)	...	12 5	...	...	...	...	...	...	...	...	14 0	1550	1620	...		1940	2217	...	...	...	2113	...	...	...	...	...	4 0	7 48	...	...
Montebourg (85)	...	1234	...	...	...	...	...	...	...	...	...	1617	1648	...		20 9	2245	...	...	...	...	...	...	...	...	...	4 29	8 19	...	...
Valognes (85)...............	...	1249	...	...	...	...	...	...	...	...	1430	1642	17 4	...		2029	23 0	...	...	...	2139	...	...	...	...	...	4 43	8 36	...	...
Sottevast (85)	8 13	13 5	1146	...	...	...	...	...	...	1550	...	1658	1721	1919		2045	2313	...	...	...	...	22 9	...	...	...	...	4 57	8 52	...	...
Cherbourg...............arr	8 45	1338	1217	...	...	...	...	...	...	1630	1457	1729	1751	1951	...	2115	2342	...	...	...	22 3	2237	...	...	...	...	5 24	9 25	...	...
CHERBOURG ....dep	...	...	...	...	...	...	...	...	...	...	...	...	From Cherbourg to Southampton on Monday, Wednesday, and Friday.								23 0	...	...	...	...	...	...	...	...	...
SOUTHAMPTON ......arr	...	...	...	...	...	...	...	...	...	...	...	...									8 0	...	...	...	...	...	...	...	...	...
LONDON (Waterloo) arr	...	...	...	...	...	...	...	...	...	...	...	...									11 5	...	...	...	...	...	...	...	...	...

RC—Restaurant Car attached.
SC—Sleeping Car attached.
*—At Paris takes 3rd class for Lisieux and beyond.
†—Stops to take up only.

‡—At Paris will take 3rd class for Caen and beyond, also for Honfleur, Trouville, and beyond.

§—On Monday, Wednesday, and Friday only.
A—From Paris to Lisieux takes 2nd and 3rd class for beyond Caen.

B—Runs until 5th October only.
C—Runs until 17th Sept. (not run on July 6th, 14th, 27th, and August 15th).

D—Runs until 15th Sept. Takes up only for Trouville and beyond.
L—Train de Luxe, tickets of Sleeping Car Co.

TROUVILLE-DEAUVILLE and MEZIDON.

E.M																		
	Trouville ....dep	5 25	...	7 28	8 51	9 †55	11 *7	12 3	13 13	14 12	14 57	16*30	17 0	18 24	18‡49	19 22	20 38	22 59
6¾	Villers-s-Mer..............	5 52	...	7 55	9 18	10 21	11 31	12 29	13 42	14 37	15 33	16 53	17 30	18 50	19 8	19 48	21 1	23 27
12½	Houlgate	6 13	7 34	8 18	9 42	10 42	11 52	12 55	14 3		16 13	17 14	17 52	19 13	19 29	20 20	21 27	23 49
14¼	Dives-Cabourg	6 29	7 42	8 28	9 56	10 49	11 57	13 8	14 12	...	16 32	17 20	18 1	19 24	19 34	20 41	21 33	23 58
19¼	Dozulé-Putot..............	7 2	7 53	8 40	10 45	10 59	...	13 20	14 22	17 22	16 48	...	18 12	19 38		20 53	...	0 9
31¾	**Mezidon** (78)........arr	7 52	8 24	...	11 43	...	...	...	...	18 12	...	...	...	...	...	21 57	...	...
...	**Mezidon** ....dep	B	...	6 21	8 45	†	...	...	...	14 24	...	...	...	...	20 21	...	23 3	...
...	Dozulé-Putot	...	‡	7 18	9 30	10 16	12‖25	12 55	...	15 8	...	17 26	18 58	...	21 4	22 36	23 41	...
...	Dives-Cabourg	6 31	7 25	7 40	9 50	10 29	12 38	13 11	14§30	15 24	...	17 41	19 12	19 35	21 19	22 58	23 59	...
...	Houlgate....................	6 39	7 36	7 48	9 58	10 39	12 49	13 19	14 39	15 33	...	17 54		19 45	21 29	23 6	0 4	...
...	Villers-s-Mer	7 1	7 54	8 14	10 24	11 4	13 15	13 47	15 0	15 58	16 57	18 19	...	20 12	21 52	23 29		...
...	**Trouville** ....arr	7 22	8 11	8 32	10 43	11 25	13 36	14 7	15 18	16 16	17 24	18 42	...	20 32	22 11	23 50	...	...

*—Until 15th September.
†—From 14th July until 28th September.
‡—From 5th July until 7th September.
§—From 2nd July until 18th September.
‖—Leaves Dozulé-Putot 13 mins. earlier from Aug 16
B—From 7th July daily, until 1st Sept.; and on Mon. only to 29th Sept.

CHERBOURG and PARIS.

LONDON (Waterloo) dep	...	...	...	...	...	...	...	...	...	8p15	From Southampton to Cherbourg on Tuesday, Thursday, and Saturday nights.									...	...	...	...	...
SOUTHAMPTON ......dep	...	...	...	...	...	...	...	...	...	11p15										...	...	...	...	...
CHERBOURG ....arr	...	...	...	...	...	...	...	...	...	6a15										...	...	...	...	...
	1,2,3	1,2,3	1,2,3	1 &2	Lux	1,2,3	1,2,3	1,2,3	1,2,3	1,2,3	1,2,3	1,2,3	3Cl.	1,2,3	1Cl.	1,2,3	1,2,3	1,2,3	1,2,3	1,2,3	1,2,3	1,2,3	1,2,3	1,2,3
Cherbourg ....dep	4 54	...	4 39	...	...	6 0	...	...	...	8 0	8 38	...	9 44	...	...	1121	13 §0	...	1526	1636	17‡15	...	1912	2024
Sottevast	5 23	...	5 8	...	...	A	...	...	...	8 27	9 7	...	1034	...	...	1154	...	...	16 4	17 5	...	...	1940	2054
Valognes	5 36	...		...	...	6 24	...	...	...	8 38		...		...	...	12 6	13 28	...	1626		17 42	...	1953	
Montebourg	5 47	...	...	...	...	...	...	...	...	8 47	...	...	...	...	...	1219	...	...	1641	...	RC	...	20 4	...
Carentan	6 17	...	...	...	...	6 48	...	...	...	9 14	...	...	...	...	...	1251	13 55	...	1724	...	18 8	...	2031	...
Neuilly	6 32	...	...	...	...	...	...	...	...	9 28	...	...	...	...	...	13 5	...	...	1746	...	...	...	2045	...
Lison (75A) ......arr	6 40	...	...	...	...	7 1	...	...	...	9 35	...	From Le Mans.	...	...	...	1313	14 10	...	1753	...	18 23	...	2051	...
Lison (75A) ......dep		...	...	...	...	7 5	...	...	...	9 43	...		...	...	...	1325	14 15	1531	1840	...	18 29	...	21 2	...
Le Molay Littry	...	...	...	...	...	7 19	...	...	...	9 58	...		...	...	...	1340	...	1552	19 0	...	18 44	...	2117	From 6th July until 5th October. ℘
Bayeux	...	5 21	...	...	...	7 35	...	...	...	10 20	...		...	...	...	14 4	14 43	1620	1926	...	19 3	...	2136	
Bretteville-Norrey	...	5 46	...	...	...	...	...	...	...	10 40	...		...	...	...	1426	...	1647	1949	...	...	...	SC	
Caen ....arr	...	6 5	...	...	...	8 0	RC	...	...	10 56	...		1,2,3	...	...	1443	15 10	17 7	20 8	3Cl.	19 30	...	22 4	
Caen ....dep	5 23	6 20	...	...	...	8 10	8 40	9 7	...	12 0	...	¶	1126	...	...	1530	15 21	1752	⌊	2035	19 42	...	2219	
Mezidon	5 51	6 42	...	...	...	8 35	9 1	1010	...	...	...	1136	1153	...	...	1631	...	1823		2135	20 7	...	2254	
Mesnil-Mauger		6 51	...	...	...	...	9 8	1019	...	...	...	...	12 4	...	...	1639	...	1833	...	2158	...	...	23 4	
Lisieux ....arr	...	7 10	...	...	...	8 58	9 26	1045	...	12 44	...	1158	1228	...	...	1659	16 3	1857	...	2218	20 31	...	2326	
Honfleur ....dep	...	5 43	...	...	...	...	8 12	...	...	10 42	...	⋮	⋮	...	...	1517	...	17 6	...	...	18 45	...	2138	
Quetteville	...	6 2	...	...	...	...	8 32	...	...	11 1	...	⋮	⋮	...	...	1536	...	1727	...	...	19 6	...	22 6	
Pt. l'Eveque ....arr	...	6 21	...	E	...	...	8 49	...	...	11 20	...	⋮	⋮	...	...	1556	...	1746	...	...	19 25	†	2224	
Trouville ....dep	...	6 12	...	7 37	8 25	...	8 44	...	...	11 13	...	⋮	⋮	14 2	1530	1545	...	1749	...	...	19 28	2050	2228	0 22
Pt. l'Eveque ....arr	...	6 26	...	7 48	⋮	...	8 56	...	...	11 30	...	⋮	⋮	⋮	F	16 1	...	18 8	...	...	19 43	⋮	2244	0 35
Pt. l'Eveque ....dep	...	6 34	...	7 49	⋮	...	8 58	...	...	11 39	...	⋮	⋮	⋮	⋮	16 9	...	1816	...	...	19 51	⋮	2252	0 36
Lisieux ....arr	...	7 1	...	8 3	⋮	...	9 14	...	...	12 8	...	⋮	⋮	1426	⋮	1638	...	1842	...	...	20 20	2114	2316	0 56
Lisieux ....dep	4 32	7 15	...	8 8	C	9 4	9 38	...	12†23	12 55	...	12 2	13 0	1429	⋮	17 9	16 8	1910	...	...	20 41	2118	2340	...
Bernay	5 14	7 50	...	E	⋮	...	1014	...	1310	13 28	...	1230	1357	...	⋮	1751	...	1956	...	...	21 14	...	0 19	...
Serquigny ....arr	5 25	7 59	...	...	⋮	...	1024	...	1322	13 37	...		14 8	D	⋮	18 1	16 40	20 7	...	...	21 24	...	0 30	...
ROUEN (77A) ....arr	7 57	1015	...	...	⋮	...	1155	...		15 24	...	...	...	...	⋮	20 2	...	RC	...	...	23 11	...	2 51	...
Serquigny ....dep	5 33	8 3	8 12	...	⋮	...	1028	...	...	13 45	...	...	1420	...	⋮	18 6	16 42	2012	...	...	21 29	...	0 40	...
Conches	6 8	8 26	8 42	...	⋮	...	1054	...	...	14 16	...	...	15 4	...	⋮	1837	...	2059	...	...	RC	...	1 16	...
Evreux	6 45	8 47	9 56	9 25	⋮	1022	1114	1148	...	14 43	...	...	16 1	1551	⋮	1920	17 28	2139	...	...	22 10	2234	1 45	...
Bueil	7 18	9 12	1053	...	⋮	...	1139	1224	...	15 9	...	...	1649	...	⋮	20 8	...	2211	...	...	...	...	2 22	...
Mantes-Gassicourt	8 6	9 38	1139	1010	⋮	...	12 3	1315	...	15 35	...	...	1749	...	⋮	2049	...	23 5	...	...	22 57	2319	2 52	...
PARIS St. Lazare ......arr	9 24	1027	1242	11 1	1110	1155	1257	15 3	...	16 31	...	...	19 4	1735	1825	2148	18 58	0 36	...	...	23 45	0 6	4 10	...

†—Until 5th October.

‡—At Cherbourg only takes 3rd class for Caen & beyond; between Cherbourg and Lisieux admits 3rd class for Paris; between Cherbourg and Caen 3rd class for beyond Serquigny towards Rouen.

§—From Cherbourg to Caen admits 3rd class for Paris only.

¶—On Tues., Thurs., and Sat. only.

A—From Cherbourg down to Caen will take up 3rd class for Paris, also takes up 3rd class for stations between Lison and Caen.

C—Train de Luxe, from 6th July until 8th Sept. Tickets of Sleeping Car Co.

D—From 16th August until 5th October.

E—Until 1st Sept. daily; Sunday only until 29th Sept.

F—Runs from 2nd July until 18th Sept. (Not on July 14th).

RC—Restaurant Car attached.

SC—Sleeping Car attached.

BRIOUZE and COUTERNE.

Briouze ....dep	3 15	...	6 55	...	1123	...	1340	15 †8	...	16†37	...	1938	22 7
La Ferte-Mace	3 42	5 30	8 0	1038	1149	1315	1421	15 35	15‡40	17 3	1858	20 3	2233
Bagnoles	4 ‡7	6 0	8 30	1058	12 6	1339	1439	...	16 0	17 21	1916	2020	2250
Couterne ....arr	...	6 16	8 46	1110	...	1350	...	...	16 12	...	1928	...	...

Couterne ....dep	...	...	6 51	9 38	1135	...	14‡35	...	17 3	...	2039	...	...
Bagnoles	4‡22	...	7 14	9 57	12 8	14†5	14 50	...	1729	1812	2055	2335	...
La Ferte-Mace	4 37	4 42	7 36	1017	1251	1424	15 7	15†41	1744	1831	2115	2352	...
Briouze ....arr	...	5 12	...	1036	1310	1444	...	16 2	...	1850	2134	...	...

†—Until 5th October. ‡—Until 15th September.

ORVAL and REGNEVILLE.

Orval-Hyenville ......dep	5 55	8 4	1155	1548	19 4	...	...	...	...
Regneville ....arr	6 11	8 27	1222	16 4	1919	...	...	...	...

Regneville ....dep	6 53	1056	1449	1725	1926	...	...	...	...
Orval-Hyenville ......arr	7 22	1125	1518	1743	1942	...	...	...	...

STATE RAILWAYS.

[66 lbs. of Luggage free.

LA BROHINIERE and DINAN. *—Until 1st November. ‡—Until 5th Oct.

La Brohinière......dep	5 55	11*58	17 2	Dinan..........dep	4 *40	9 48	12‡40	17 56
Le Quiou-Evran	6 32	12 34	17 41	Le Quiou-Evran.........	5 12	10 21	13 16	18 32
Dinan ....arr	7 7	13 10	18 26	La Brohinière 80 arr	5 45	10 56	13 50	19 10

*—Until 1st Nov. ‡—Until 5th Oct.] **PLOUARET and LANNION.** [§—From 6th Oct.

Plouaret......dep	5‡47	7 26	9 42	1152	1455	1851	20 9	22 5	Lannion ......dep	6 31	8 41	10§18	10‡28	1234	1550	17‡8	19*20	21‡21
Lannion ......arr	6 13	7 52	10 8	1217	1534	1916	2040	2230	Plouaret ......arr	6 57	9 7	11 0	10 59	13 1	1617	1750	19 47	21 47

PARIS to LE MANS, RENNES, and BREST.

SC—Sleeping Car. RC—Restaurant Car.

Dist		1,2,3	1,2,3	1,2,3	1,2,3	1,2,3	1,2,3	1,2,3	1,2,3	1&2	1,2,3	1&2	1,2,3	1,2,3	1,2,3	1,2,3	1,2,3	1,2,3	1,2,3	1,2,3	1,2,3	1,2,3	1,2,3	1,2,3	1,2,3	1,2,3	1,2,3
E M	Paris St. Lazare...dep	...	...	...	7 2	...	A	F	...	...	D	...	...	...	M	...	1629	...	...	1915	1915	B	...	...	D	2221	C
...	„ Invalides.........	...	...	5 23	G	...	...	...	1043	...	1133	...	...	...	...	1623	...	...	1857	...	...	...	2144	21 58	2213	...	...
...	„ Montparnasse...	...	...	...	7 30	8 20	9 32	9 55	...	1018	...	11 5	1250	13 5	1625	1634	1725	1820	...	20 0	2011	2048	E	...	2215	...	0 5
10½	**Versailles**	...	...	5 59	7 54	8 46	9 55	1018	1116	1041	12 2	1141	1312	1334	1649	17 0	1749	1846	1925	2026	2037	2114	...	22 27	2245	23 9	0 32
13¾	St. Cyr	...	...	6 8	...	8 55	...	...	1125	J	RC		...	1343	...	17 9	...	1855	1934	L	...	...	...	...	...	2318	...
29¾	Rambouillet	...	...	6 53	8 22	9 37	...	...	12 3	...	1233		1342	1426	...	1750	1824	1936	2015	...	H	2144	...	23 12	2315	2359	...
42¾	Maintenon 85	...	...	7 21	8 40	10 5	...	...	1229	...	1252	...	14 0	1457	...	1820	1848	20 4	2040	...	...	22 2	...	K	...	0 23	...
54¾	**Chartres 42A** ... arr	...	...	7 49	8 58	1034	1051	1115	1256	1138	1312	...	1419	1525	1746	1849	19 8	2033	21 3	2128	2140	2220	23 4	23 30	2348	0 52	1 38
	dep	4 6	...	7 58	9 3	1148	1056	1120		1143	1317	...		1543	1750		1913	2040		2134	2147	2226	23 9	23 35	2353	1 53	1 44
77	La Loupe 84	4 57	...	8 52	9 39	1234	...	...	...	...	1352	...	...	1641	...	...	20 1	2132	...	...	...	23 1	...	...	0 31	2 39	...
87½	Conde-s-H. 42B	5 23	7 51	9 15	9 57	1256	...	...	...	...	14 7	...	...	17 8	RC	...	2020	2152	...	...	...	SC	...	...	SC	3 2	...
92½	Nogent-Rotrou 40......	5 43	8 0	9 27	10 9	13 8	RC	RC	...	...	1417	...	...	1722	...	...	2032	22 0	...	SC	SC	2324	...	...	0 50	3 14	...
105¾	La Ferté-Bernard	6 11	8 21	9 52	1027	1332	...	...	...	...	1436	...	...	1749	...		21 1		...	...	...	2341	...	..	1 11	3 35	...
116¼	**Connerré 86**	6 36	8 56	1010	1042	1351	...	...	...	...	1450	...	...	1812	...		2120	...	2235	...	...	2355	...	...	...	3 52	...
131	**Le Mans** ....arr	7 15	9 32	1049	11 5	1432	1224	1254	...	1316	1511	...	...	1852	1922		2157	...	2257	23 7	2333	0 18	0 38	1 15	1 43	4 15	3 34
191½	ANGERS 75.........arr	1051	...	...	...	...	14 4	...	...	...	1657	...	...	...	2050		0 18	...	...	...	...	...		...	3 52	7 56	7 56
246	NANTES 39.........arr	...	...	...	...	...	1526	...	...	...	1847	1,2,3	...	...	2235		3 33	...	...	...	...	...		...	5 40	9 35	9 35
...	**Le Mans** ....dep	8 14	...	1128	1117	...	1238	13 2	...	1324	1527	Runs until 9th October only.	1621	20 2	1939	E—Runs until 9th October only; takes for Sable and beyond. Exceptionally takes 1 & 2 class for Le Mans.	2214	...	...	2317	2344	0 41	To Redon and St. Nazaire.	1 24	L—Until 5th Oct. Takes only for Angers and beyond, and for Morlaix and beyond.	4 39	3 55
153½	Sillé-le-Guillaume ...	9 18	...	1227	...	...	...	...	...	...	16 7		1721	21 3	...		23 1	†—Stops to pick up only.	F—Until 9th October. Takes 3rd class for Plouaret and beyond only.	...	...	1 16		...		5 35	4 34
167¾	Evron	9 51	...	1256	...	...	...	F	...	...	1630		1753	2136	...		2326			...	...	1 36		...		6 5	4 55
179½	La Chapelle-Anth. ...	1019	...	1320	...	...	...	...	...	...	1649		1820	2210	...		2349			...	...	...		...		6 31	...
187	**Laval 78, 83**...... arr	1037	...	1336	1234	...	1351	1419	...	1448	17 2		1836	2229	2051		0 4			0†40	1 10	2 3		2 51		6 48	5 23
	dep	1053	...		1241	1510	14 0	1429	...	1456	1712		1920		21 1					0†48	1 18	2 11		3 1		6 58	5 35
208¾	**Vitre 77B**............	1156	...	...	1313	16 4	1432	15 1	...	...	1742		2020	...	2130		...			...	...	2 41		...		7 41	6 7
232½	**Rennes** .... arr	1248	...	...	1344	1653	15 2	1531	RC	16 0	1812		2133	...	22 0		...			1 50	2 24	3 16	...	4 7		8 34	6 55
	dep		4 40	...	14 5		1517	1541	1556	To St. Malo and Dinard, runs until 4th Oct. only.		1822		2053			...			2 †0	2 37	3 30	...	To St. Malo and Dinard, runs until 4th Oct. only.		1033	7 25
246	Montfort-sur-Meu	...	5 9	...	1430	...	...	...	1622			...	...	2120	...		...			...	...	3 54	...			11 3	7 54
255¼	**La Brohinière**	...	5 32	...	1457	...	...	...	1649		...	...	...	2141	...		...			...	SC	4 13	...			1130	8 19
282¾	**Lamballe 79**	7 25		1056	1555	1612	...	1655	1743		2121	1936	...	2237	...		...			...	3 56	5 7	...			1227	9 15
295¾	**St. Brieuc 77B**.. arr	7 52	...	1125		1638	1653	1722	1813		2151	1957	...	23 6	...		...			3†36	4 27	5 36	...			13 0	9 50
	dep		8 8		...		17 6	1735	1828			20 5	...	2311	...		...			3 53	4 39	5 46	...			1317	10 8
314½	**Guingamp 77B**		8 45	...	...	...	1733	18 2	19 5		...	2032	...	2351	...		...			...	5 6	6 23	...			1356	1054
330½	**Plouaret 80**..............	...	9 23	...	...	...	18 2	1835	1950		...	21 2	...		...		...			...	5 42	7 2	...			1441	1138
335½	Plounérin..................	...	9 42	...	...	...	...	To Lannion. Until Oct. 9.	2013		...	...	...	...	...		...			...	To Lannion. Until Oct. 4th.	7 22	...			15 0	1159
350½	**Morlaix 81** ...... arr	...	1012	...	...	...	1835		2043		...	2136	...	...	...		...			5 22		7 52	...			1533	1229
	dep	6 0	1019	...	...	...	1840		2057		...	2141	...	...	...		...			5 27		7 59	...			1541	1241
359¾	St. Thégonnec............	6 22	1041	...	...	...	...		2119		...	...	...	...	...		...			...		8 21	...			16 5	13 8
366¾	Landivisiau	6 39	1057	...	...	...	...		2137		...	...	...	...	...		...			...		8 38	...			1623	1325
376	**Landerneau**...arr 8 35	7 1	1114	1337	1615	1935	1916		2155		2234	2218	...	...	...		6 35			6 5		8 56	...			1642	1346
387¾	**Brest** ....arr 9 7	7 31	1154	14 8	1645	20 6	1942		2225		23 5	2243	...	...	...		7 5	...		6 34		9 38	...			1725	1427

Extra				
Paris (Montp.).........dep	8 15	21 10	23 20	0 31
Chartres ....arr	9 43	22 31	1 5	2 23

A—At Paris will take 3rd class for Plouaret and beyond, and at Le Mans forward to Rennes 3rd class from branch lines going to Rennes and beyond.
B—Admits at Paris 3rd class for beyond Vitré. At Chartres and Le Mans takes 3rd class from branch lines. At Rennes takes up 3rd class for beyond La Brohinière.
C—At Paris and Versailles will not take up 3rd class for Chartres.
D—At Paris will take 3rd class for Le Mans and beyond.

G—At Paris and at Versailles takes 3rd class only for beyond Chartres; from Rambouillet forward admits 3rd cl. only for beyond Le Mans.
H—Takes 3rd class for Rennes and beyond.
J—Takes 2nd class for beyond Rennes only.
K—Runs until 4th October. Takes only for beyond Rennes towards St. Malo and Redon. At Paris admits 3rd cl. for St. Malo & Dinard.
M—Admits 1st and 2nd class for beyond Chartres, and 3rd class for beyond Le Mans only.

Morlaix..............dep	8 40	1340	1930	Primel-Tregastel dep	6 20	1035	1730
Plouézoc'h..............	9 19	1419	20 9	Lanmeur ....dep	6 40	1055	1750
Lanmeur ....arr	9 46	1446	2041	Plouézoc'h	7 6	1121	1816
Primel-Tregastel arr	10 3	15 3	2053	Morlaix..............arr	7 45	12 0	1855

Plouescat ....dep	6 0	10 0	1550	La Feuillée ....dep	6 0	1010	1440	
Landivisiau	7 49	1220	1739	Landivisiau	7 46	12 0	1627	
La Feuillée..............arr	9 46	1417	1936	Plouescat 31..............arr	9 31	15 0	19 5	
La Feuillée ....dep	5 50	9 55	1455	Rosporden ....dep	...	8 35	1430	18 8
Chateauneuf du Faou.....	7 56	12 1	1740	Chateauneuf du F...	7 8	1044	1730	2016
Rosporden ....arr	1027	1614	1949	La Feuillée ....arr	9 16	1432	1935	...

66 lbs. of Luggage free.]

STATE RAILWAYS.

MORLAIX and ROSCOFF.

‡—Until 5th October. *—Until 1st November.

Morlaix.........dep	5 49	9 15	10‡44	1318	1555	1854	22*0	...	**Roscoff** ....dep	5*31	7 59	1114	1354	1654	1837	20‡36	...	...
Taule-Henvic......	6 8	9 37	11 2	1345	1628	1915	2220	...	St. Pol-de-Léon ...	5 42	8 10	1125	1421	17 5	1913	20 47	...	...
Plouenan	6 21	9 51	11 14	14 1	1646	1930	2234	...	Plouenan	5 51	8 19	1134	1432	1714	1934	20 56	...	...
St. Pol-de-Léon ...	6 29	9 59	11 27	1411	17 7	1939	2241	...	Taule-Henvic........	6 8	8 31	1147	1449	1727	20 2	21 9	...	...
Roscoff ....arr	6 38	10 8	11 36	1424	1723	1948	2252	...	**Morlaix 80**......arr	6 27	8 48	12 5	1516	1744	2029	21 28	...	...

BREST, RENNES, LE MANS, and PARIS.

VOITURE DE LUXE (Couchette)—In 17.0 and 20.51 from Brest; 0.54 from Le Mans.

	1,2,3	1,2,3	1,2,3	1,2,3	1,2,3	1,2,3	1,2,3	1,2,3	1,2,3	1,2,3	1,2,3	1 &2	1,2,3	1,2,3	1,2,3	1,2,3	1,2,3	1,2,3	1,2,3	1,2,3	1,2,3	1,2,3	1,2,3	1,2,3	1,2,3	1,2,3	1,2,3	1,2,3
Brest ....dep	...	...	...	...	...	...	...	...	...	...	5 22	Until Oct. 5.-After Rennes will not take up 2nd cl.	5 0	8 5	8 50	7 11	1055	1036	1138	1342	1410	1548	17 0	1723	19 5	2130	...	2051
Landerneau	...	...	...	...	...	...	...	...	...	...	5 40		5 33	...	9 20	7 38	1120	11 1	1154	1410	1431	1619	...	1750	1945	22 3	Until 5th Oct.	2110
Landivisiau	...	...	...	...	...	...	...	...	...	Until 9th Oct.			6 3	...	9 43			1135	...		1454	1643	...		20 7			...
Saint-Thégonnec	...	...	...	...	...	...	...	...	...		...		6 24	A	10 2	...	...	1155	F	...	1514	17 3	B	...	2026	...		A
Morlaix 81 ...... arr	...	...	...	...	...	...	...	...	...		...		6 47	8 58	1021	...	...	1218	1233	...	1533	1727	1759	...	2044	...		2150
Morlaix 81 ...... dep	...	...	...	...	...	...	...	...	...		...		7 0	9 2	1028	...	...	1248	1238	...	1542		18 6	...	2056	...		2158
Plounerin..............	...	...	...	...	...	...	...	...	...		...		7 37	...	11 0	...	...	1328	...	...	1617	...	...	...	2130	...		...
Plouaret	...	...	...	...	...	...	...	...	...	9 14	...		7 56	9 36	1114	...	...	1348	1312	...	1634	...	1848	...	22 6	...	2155	...
Guingamp	...	...	...	...	...	...	...	...	...	9 37	6 47		8 38	10 2	1150	...	...	1426	1338	...	1712	...	1915	...	23 8		2221	2256
Saint Brieuc ... arr	...	...	...	...	...	...	...	...	...	10 4	7 23		9 19	1030	1227	...	...	15 4	14 7	...	1751	...	1945	...	2348	Until 6th Oct.	2250	2325
Saint Brieuc ... dep	...	...	...	...	...	...	5 28	...	...	10 19	7 37		9 30	1045	1241	...	...	1516	1415	...	18 3	...	1954	...			23 4	2337
Lamballe 79	...	...	...	...	...	...	5 53	...	...	10 44	8 3		10 3	11 9	13 9	...	...	1543	1437	...	1831	...	2018	...	...		2328	...
La Brohiniére	...	...	...	...	...	...		...	6 9	RC	8 59		12 3	1153	1410	...	...	1642	RC	...	1935	...	...	...	...		...	SC
Montfort-sur-Meu......	...	...	...	...	...	...	...	...	6 38	...	9 17		1223	...	1427	...	...	17 0	...	...	1954	...	...	...	...		...	...
Rennes .... arr	...	...	...	...	...	...	...	...	7 7	12 3	9 44		1251	1231	1458	...	...	1730	1553	...	2023	...	2136	...	...	...	0 47	1 13
Rennes .... dep	4 45	...	...	...	...	6 35	...	...	7 27	12 15	1023	11 3	1325	1243	1515	...	...		16 7	1630	2037		2148	...	...	0 30	0 59	1 23
Vitre....................	5 34	...	...	...	...	7 5	...	...	8 23	12 50	1152	...	1435	...	16 1	...	...	...	1642	1732	2138		2223	...	...	D	...	1 59
Laval.............. arr	6 14	...	...	...	...	7 32	...	...	9 8	13 20	1236	1210	1526	1344	1641	...	...	...	1713	1819	2221		2254	...	...	1 39	2 5	2 30
Laval.............. dep		...	...	...	5 37	7 40	...	...	9 24	13 28	1246	1219		1350		...	...	...	1720	1835	2231		23 7	...	...	1 47	2 13	2 38
La Chapelle Anth ...	...	...	...	...	5 57	...	...	...	9 45	...	13 4	...	...	RC	...	...	...	...	1736	1855	2247		2324	...	...	...	...	...
Evron	...	...	...	...	6 25	...	...	...	1012	C	1331	RC	...	...	...	1 &2	...	...	1755	1923	2310		...	...	...	...	G	...
Sillé-Guillaume 85 ...	...	...	...	...	7 1	...	...	...	1046	...	1448	...	...	1437	...	H	...	...	1820	20 1	2336		...	...	...	...	...	...
Le Mans..............arr	...	...	...	...	7 45	8 49	...	...	1131	14 43	1531	1335	...	15 4	...	RC	...	...	1849	2047	0 9		0 27	...	...	3 6	3 29	3 52
NANTES 39 ......dep	...	...	...	...	0 42	6 15	9 27	...	6 23	...	9 27	...	...	9 27	...	15 2	...	15 2	...	...	...		2030	2030	...	...	...	0 42
ANGERS 75 ......dep	...	...	...	...	5 19	7 33	11 3	...	8 49	...	1215	...	...	1215	...	17 3	...	17 3	17 3	...	...		2232	2232	...	...	...	2 10
Le Mans ....dep	...	4 50	...	6 5	8 1	9 5	1241	...	1145	14 58	1543	1343	...	1519	1656	1912	...	1919	19 4	21 6	...		0 41	0 54		3 16	3 38	4 0
Connerré	...	5 13	...	6 43	8 49	...	13 1	...	1226	...	1621	...	...	...	1741	1935	...	1959	...	2149	...		...	1 21		...	...	...
La Ferté Bernard......	...		...	7 9	9 11	...	L	...	1250	...	1644	...	...	...	18 5	1954	...	2027	...	2216	...		1 15	SC		...	...	...
Nogent-le-Rotrou	5 17	...	...	7 40	1010	9 56	1332	...	1345	C	1713	...	...	...	1831	2021	...	2059	F	2251	...		1 36	...		D	...	4 50
Conde-s.-Huisne	5 27	...	...	7 53	1026	...	RC	...	1356	...	1725	...	...	...	1841	2033	...	2120	...	23 5	...		SC	E		...	...	...
La Loupe..................	5 58	...	...	8 21	1114	1022	...	...	1426	...	1755	...	...	...		21 0	...	2158	...	2336	...		2 5	...		...	...	...
Chartres .... arr	6 41	...	...	9 0	1156	1047	1420	...	15 6	16 27	1838	1522	...	1649	...	2134	...	2252	2042	0 19	...		2 32	2 53		5 3	5 25	5 44
Chartres .... dep	6 47	...	8 12	9 10	1218	1052	1425	14 5	1535	16 32	1922	1527	...	1654	...	2144	2153	23 4	2047	0 38	1 23		2 38	3 0		5 10	5 30	5 49
Maintenon	7 18	...	8 40	...	1248	11 8	...	1444	16 7	...	20 5	...	...	...	...	...	2224	...	...	1 3	...		2 55	...		...	...	...
Rambouillet	7 52	8 3	9 12	...	1321	1127	...	1514	1641	...	2040	...	...	...	...	2224	2255	2353	...	1 34	2 17		3 21	...		...	...	...
St. Cyr	...	8 42	9 51	...	14 2	...	...	1555	...	...	2122	...	...	...	...	...	2338	...	...	...	...		...	...		...	...	...
Versailles Chantiers	8 22	8 50	10 1	1012	1410	1153	1520	16 3	1713	17 27	2130	1624	...	1747	...	2255	2345	0 32	2147	2 7	2 55		3 53	4 13		6 15	6 37	6 49
Paris Montparnasse...	8 46	...	...	1035	1436	1215	...	1627	...	17 50	22 2	1646	...	1810	...	2320	...	1 10	2211	2 44	3 37		4 18	...		...	7 6	7 16
,, Invalides ...arr	...	9 20	...	...	...	...	1548	...	1741	...	...	...	...	...	...	...	...	...	...	...	...		...	4 51		6 44	...	...
,, St. Lazare ...arr	...	...	1035	...	...	...	...	...	...	...	...	...	...	...	...	...	0 25	...	...	...	...		...	...		...	...	...

D—At Rennes and Le Mans will take 3rd class from branch lines for Versailles and Paris.

‡—Until 9th October only.

Extra								
Chartres ....dep	4 32	4 54	5 57	6‡40	9 29	1848	19 6
Paris (Montp.).........arr	6 0	6 30	7 56	8 15	1149	2025	2035

A—At Brest and stations to St. Brieuc will admit 3rd class for Paris and at Rennes will admit 3rd class from branch lines for Paris.

B—Down to Lamballe admits 3rd class for Rennes and beyond; at Rennes takes 3rd class for Le Mans and beyond; at Le Mans admits 3rd class from branch lines.

C—Down to St. Brieuc takes 3rd class for Versailles and Paris only.

E—At Le Mans will take up 3rd class from branch lines.

F—Until 9th October only.

G—Takes 3rd class from beyond Plouaret for Versailles and Paris, also those coming from Redon and beyond towards Quimper.

H—Takes 3rd class arriving by connecting trains, and those at Le Mans for Versailles and Paris.

L—Takes at Le Mans 2nd class passengers for Paris, and 3rd class coming from beyond Le Mans.

ST. BRIEUC and GUINGAMP, via St. Quay.

E.M	fr. c.	fr. c.									
			St. Brieuc (Etat)...dep	4 50	6 15	8 35	10 20	1320	1550	18 5
8¾	1 10	0 70	Binic	5 38	7 14	9 33	11 19	1420	1645	19 5
13¾	1 70	1 15	Portrieux	6 4	7 43	10 2	11 48	1449	1714	19 35
14¼	1 80	1 20	St. Quay	6 10	7 51	10 8	11 54	1455	1719	19 43
18¾	2 30	1 55	Plouha	6 31	8 11	1030	12 10	1515	1744	20 0
34	4 25	2 85	**Guingamp**...........arr	7 40	9 15	1135	...	1620	1855	...

Guingamp ....dep	6 5	9 25	1155	...	1810	...	...
Plouha	7 6	1029	1256	15 50	1911	20 53	...
St. Quay	7 27	1048	1315	16 10	1930	21 12	...
Portrieux	7 38	1059	1326	16 20	1943	21 23	...
Binic.......................	8 6	1124	1352	16 45	2010	21 43	...
St. Brieuc (Etat)...arr	9 0	1215	1450	17 37	21 5	22 35	...

PARIS, LAIGLE, ARGENTAN, FLERS, and GRANVILLE.

G—Admits 3rd class at Granville and Folligny for Paris.

Paris—	1,2,3	1,2,3	1,2,3	1,2,3	1,2,3	1,2,3	1,2,3	1&2	1,2,3	1,2,3	1& 2	1 & 2	1,2,3	1,2,3
St. Lazare dep	...	...	5 58	7 2	...	...	...	A	...	...	1629	...	...	...
Invalides...dep	...	...	...	7 31	8 13	...	8 31	1225	...	1623	1725	...	...	...
Montparnasse	...	...	6 27	7 30	...	...	...	...	1236	...	1634	...	1750	22 15
Versailles	...	...	6 59	7 59	8 41	...	9 3	1256	13 2	1654	1754	...	1816	22 36
Houdan	...	...	8 10	C	...	...	1018		1420	18 7	E	...	1931	...
Dreux (84) ...	...	5 19	9 10	9 0	D	10 30	1047	14 2	1510	1836	19 1	19 27	2029	23 50
Nonancourt	...	5 41	9 30	...		10 51		...	1534		RC	19 56	2054	0 10
Verneuil (84) ...	...	6 24	9 54	9 33	1016	11 50	...	...	16 7	...	1937	20 30	2130	0 37
Laigle ......arr	...	6 54	1056	9 52	...	12 20	...	1455	1637	...	20 0	E—Admits 3rd class at Paris and Versailles for beyond Vire only.	22 0	1 4
„ (84) dep	...	6 59	11 1	9 56	...	12 33	...	15 0	1643	...	20 5		22 7	1 9
Ste Gauburge ...	...	7 31	1128	1012	RC	13 2	...	...	1712	...	2021		2242	1 27
Le Merlerault ...	...	7 48	1144	...	...	13 22	...	...	1728	...	...		2258	1 39
Surdon (75)	3 17	8 15	12 5	1034	...	13 51	1454	A	1751	...	2046		2319	1 58
Almenèches	3 23	8 21	1211	...	...	14 1	15 0		1757	...	...		2325	...
Argentan (75)	4 40	8 52	1243	1052	1132	14 12	1510	1554	1839	...	2118		0 12	2 22
Ecouché	4 54	9 6	1258	...	...		1626	...	1853	...	...		0 35	2 33
Briouze (79)......	5 24	9 37	1330	1121	...	...	17 4	1626	1923	...	2148		1 28	3 1
Flers (83) arr	5 47	10 0	1353	To Bagnoles, arr. 12 6.	1214	...	1748	1642	1946	...	22 3		2 6	3 16
dep	6 19	10 20	1418		1219	...		1647	20 2	...	22 8		‡—Until 15th Sept. only.	3 27
Montsecret Vass	6 33	10 35	1432		1232	...	...	...	2019	...	...			3 46
Tinchebrai......	7 40	11 7	15 8		...	...	...	...	2141	...	...			...
Les Maures arr	8 16		1559		...	...	...	...	...	...				...
Vire (82).........	7 5	11 10	15 0		1252	...	...	1720	21 2	...	2240			4 20
Folligny arr	8 42	12 12	1612		1343	...	...	1813	22 6	...	2325			5 17
dep	9 12	12 38	1625		1347	14 45	19 2	1818	2211	0 30	2328			5 24
Granville...arr	9 32	13 1	1644	...	14 1	15 5	1919	1831	2230	0 47	2341		‡	5 42

GRANVILLE dep } Steamer from Granville to Jersey, every Tuesday
JERSEY ......arr } and Saturday.

JERSEY......dep } Steamer from Jersey to Granville, every Tuesday
GRANVILLE arr } and Friday.

	1,2,3	1,2,3	1,2,3	1,2,3	1,2,3	1,2,3	1,2,3	1 & 2	1,2,3	1,2,3	1&2 G	1,2,3	1,2,3	1,2,3	1,2,3 ‡
Granville...dep	5 50	...	6 30	8 10	...	1035	11 40	12 48	13 20	14 9	1613	1733	1826	19 22	20 51
Folligny arr	6 10	...	6 45	8 30	...	1059	12 4	13 3	13 44	1435	1629	1753	1850	19 38	21 15
dep	6 15	...	6 48	8 45	...	1122		13 6		1514	1639		19 4	19 43	21 22
Vire	7 10	4 57	7 38	9 43	...	1253	...	13 58	...	1640	1731	1739	2010	20 47	22 29
Les Maures dep		...	...	9 5	...	...	...	...	...		...	...	From Bagnoles.	16 46	RC—Restaurant Car attached.
Tinchebrai	...	4 50	...	9 36	...	1238	...	B	...	...	...	...		19 39	
Montsecret	...	5 26	...	10 4	...	1321	...	...	...	...	...	1818		21 10	
Flers ...... arr	...	5 43	8 8	10 20	...	1338	...	14 28	...	...	18 4	1841		21 25	
dep	1150	6 5	8 12	10 25	...	14 4	...	14 38	...	...	18 8	1949		21 33	
Briouze..............	12 7	6 31	...	10 51	...	1428	...	15 0	...	...	...	2021	1852	21 57	
Ecouché		6 53	...	11 13	...	1449	...	...	...	...	...	2049	F	22 17	
Argentan...dep	...	7 27	9 0	11 36	12 4	1541	...	15 35	...	1752	1859	21 2	1940	22 44	
Almenèches.......	...	7 39	...	RC	1216	1553	...	...	...	18 8	...	F—Takes 3rd class coming from Bagnoles & La Ferté.	...	22 56	
Surdon	...	7 52	...	11 51	1226	16 1	...	...	...	1819	...		...	23 10	
Le Merlerault ...	...	8 13	...	12 11	1246	1621	...	...	...	1843	RC		...	23 33	
Ste Gauburge ...	...	8 34	...	12 25	13 7	1650	...	...	...	19 8	...		2018	23 56	
Laigle arr	...	8 54	...	12 40	1328	1712	...	16 21	...	1932	...		2031	0 19	
dep	6 3	9 1	...	12 44	1338	1730	...	16 26	...	2046	...		2038	0 28	
Verneuil..........	6 37	9 33	...	13 7	14 6	18 4	...	...	...	2131	...		21 1	0 58	...
Nonancourt.........	7 1	9 57	...	13 27	1431	1829	...	B	...	22 7	...		...	1 26	...
Dreux..............	7 25	1015	10 35	13 51	1510	1930	17 31	17 19	...	2230	...		2138	1 55	6 15
Houdan	7 52			14 12		1958	17 57	...	...		...		...	2 28	6 41
Versailles......	9 5	...	11 36	15 14	17 4	2129	19 17	18 28	...	...	2140		2249	3 48	8 4
Paris M'par arr	9 25	...	11 57	...	1727	2152	...	...	...	...	...		...	4 8	...
Invalides arr	...	...	...	15 37	...	...	19 43	18 53	...	...	22 7		2313	4 51	8 28
St. Lazare arr	...	...	...		...	...	...	...	...	...	...		...	...	...

Extra.—Paris (Montparnasse) to **Dreux**, 10.3, 19.7, 21.15, 0.46. Dreux to Paris (Montparnasse), 5.29, 9.2, 11.30, 15.10. Folligny to Granville 6.47, 10.57.

A—Until 5th October. From Paris to Laigle takes 1st and 2nd class for beyond **Argentan**, at Argentan admits from branch lines. At Paris also takes 3rd class for Briouze and beyond. **B**—Until 5th October. At Granville, Foligny, and Briouze takes 3rd class for Paris. **C—At Paris and Versailles takes 3rd class for Aigle** and beyond; at Dreux admits 3rd class from branches for beyond Argentan towards Granville; at Argentan 3rd class for beyond Briouze. **D**—Down to Verneuil only takes for Flers and beyond; exceptionally takes at Argentan 3rd cl. for Vire and beyond arriving by connecting trains. After Argentan admits 1 & 2 cl. only.

ST. MALO and RENNES.

*—Until 5th October.] [§—Until 4th October.

London ......dep }
SOUTHAMPTON dep } From London (Waterloo) and Southampton
ST. MALO........arr } to St. Malo see Advt. p. 716.

JERSEY ....dep } Steamer from Jersey to St. Malo, every Monday
ST. MALO........arr } and Wednesday.

‡—14th July until 15th Sept.	1,2,3	1,2,3	1,2,3 *	1 &2 *	1,2,3 ‡	1,2,3	1,2,3	1&2 ‡	1,2,3	1,2,3	1,2,3	1,2,3 *
Saint Malo dp	4 42	7 33	8 28	9 25	9 47	1150	1420	1459	1553	17 34	21 15	2245
La Gouesnière...	4 56	7 45	...	...	9 57	12 5	1431	1511	1613	17 45	21 30	...
Dol ...... arr	5 13	8 2	8 51	9 48	1014	1226	1448	1528	1632	18 2	21 51	23 9
dep	5 34	8 20	8 56	9 56		1250			1651	18 25	22 6	2316
Bonnemain	5 46	8 31	...	...	...	13 4	...	...	17 4	18 36	22 20	...
Combourg.........	5 57	8 43	...	RC	...	1321	...	...	1719	18 46	22 34	...
St. Germain-s-I.	6 33	9 14	...	...	...	14 4	...	...	18 0	19 16	23 7	...
Rennes (81) arr	7 0	9 37	9 50	1053	...	1437	...	...	1828	19 39	23 38	0 19

	123	123 §	1,2,3	1,2,3	1,2,3	1,2,3	1,2,3	1,2,3 §	1,2,3	1,2,3	1,2,3	1,2,3 §	1,2,3
Rennes ....dep	345	422	7 15	...	1050	...	1354	16 8	...	1639	...	20 4	2039
St. Germain-s-I.	412	...	7 40	...	1117	...	1423	...	...	17 8	...	...	21 6
Combourg	442	...	8 10	...	1148	...	1459	...	...	1744	...	...	2136
Bonnemain	455	...	8 23	...	12 1	...	1513	...	...	1758	...	...	2149
Dol (79) arr	5 7	533	8 35	‡	1213	§	1527	1713	*	1810	‡	2112	22 1
dep	518	540	8 46	1055	1228	1522	1532	1718	18 5	1824	20 1	2116	2210
La Gouesnière...	538	...	9 4	1113	1246	...	1552	...	1826	1842	2019		2228
Saint Malo arr	547	6 5	9 13	1122	1253	1544	16 1	1740	1837	1851	2028	2138	2237

ST. MALO.....dep } Steamer from St. Malo to Jersey, every Monday
JERSEY ....arr } and Thursday.

ST. MALO........dep }
SOUTHAMPTON arr } From St. Malo to Southampton and
London ....arr } London see Advt. page 716.

RENNES and REDON. ‡—Until 5th Oct.

Rennes...dep	3 10	4 0	5 49	6 3	10‡2	10 14	15 29	16 20	1745	19 50
Guichen	...	5 13	...	6 37	...	10 43	...	16 49	...	20 24
Messac (83).....	3 56	5 50	6 32	7 1	1041	11 2	16 12	17 10	1829	20 46
Massérac	4 25			7 33		11 34	16 37	17 46		21 12
Redon ....arr	4 43	...	...	7 54	...	11 52	16 52	18 4	...	21 30

Redon (31)...dep	5 20	...	8 22	11 2	13 8	17 11	...	18 43	23 19
Massérac	5 39	...	8 41	11 18	13 28	17 31	...	19 2	23 30
Messac..................	6 9	8 5	9 13	11 42	14 15	18 5	19 9	19 31	0 6
Guichen.................	6 36	...	9 32	...	14 35	18 29	...	19 50	...
Rennes (81) arr	7 4	8 47	10 0	12 21	15 4	18 56	19 48	20 20	0 39

DINAN and DINARD. ‡—Until 4th October.

	1,2,3	1,2,3	1,2,3	1,2,3	1,2,3	1,2,3	1,2,3	1,2,3	1,2,3	...
DOL ....dep	5‡44	...	8 41	1236	1414	17‡24	1724	1852	1954	...
Dinan...dep	6 36	7 27	10 9	1332	15 9	18 11	1835	2010	21‡8	...
Dinard arr	7 2	8 3	10 44	14 4	1543	18 34	1911	2044	2137	...

	1,2,3	1,2,3	1,2,3	1,2,3	1,2,3	1,2,3	1,2,3	1,2,3	1,2,3	1,2,3	...
Dinard...dep	5 30	8‡38	8 55	10‡24	11‡58	14 13	16 7	17 9	1850	21‡44	...
Dinan.....arr	6 6	9 2	9 34	11 0	12 34	14 56	1643	1745	1924	22 17	...
DOL(75A)arr	8 12	9 41	...	12 16	[illegible]	16 9	1759	[illegible]	[illegible]	[illegible]	...

VIRE and FOUGERES.

Vire ....dep	4 28	7 56	...	14 0	...	20 5
Sourdeval...........	5 16	8 55	...	14 49	...	22
Mortain-le-Neu....	5 40	9 20	...	15 14	...	22 3
Romagny	5 49	9 32	10 9	15 25	1549	22 4
St. Hilaire-du-H,...	6 12	9 50	1029	15 43	16 4	23 1
Fougères.........arr	7 15	12 0	...	...	1841	...

Fougères ....dep	...	6 25	...	1344	1751	...
St. Hilaire-du-H.	5 38	7 54	11 8	1528	1858	19 1
Romagny	6 0	8 12	1133	1551	1917	19 3
Mortain-le-Neuf.	6 11	8 23	...	16 2	1928	...
Sourdeval..........	6 36	8 48	...	1628	1954	...
Vire (82).........arr	7 14	9 27	...	17 7	2033	...

SABLE, CHATEAUBRIANT, and ST. NAZAIRE.

	1,2,3	1 2 3	1,2,3	1,2,3	1,2,3	1 2 3	1 2 3	1,2,3
Le Mans 75 dep	0 50	2 0	5 16	...	12 34	15 1	...	19 31
Sablé ....dep	1 41	2 51	7 37	...	13 45	1616	1627	20 25
Agets-St-Brice ...	...	...	7 48	...	13 55	...	1644	20 36
Gennes-L. **78**......	...	...	8 16	9 5	14 20	...	1725	21 2
Château-Gon.	...	3 22	8 31	9 19	14 32	1650	18 8	21 20
Chemazé **83**	...	...	8 46	9 34	14 46	17 3	1838	21 34
Segré (83) ...arr	...	3 45	9 6	9 53	15 5	1717	19 7	21 52
,, ...dep	2 38	4 4	9 36	—	—	1731	—	22 9
Pouancé	2 43	4 44	10 13	...	...	18 8	...	22 47
Château- arr	3 29	5 9	10 35	...	...	1829	...	23 10
briant (37) dep	3 39	6 13	11 22	...	...	1844	...	—
St. Vincent	3 51	6 33	11 40	...	...	19 0	...	...
Blain	4 37	7 24	12 59	...	...	1959	...	*
Pont Chateau dp	5 *6	8 11	13 29	11 43	18 16	2013	...	22 25
Besné-P.-Château	5 21	8 39	13 52	11 50	18 23	2038	...	23 10
St. Nazaire...arr	5 48	9 13	14 25	...	...	21 6	...	23 33

*—Until 1st November.

	1,2,3	1 2 3	1,2,3	1,2,3	1 2 3	1,2,3	1,2,3	1,2,3	1,2,3
St. Nazaire dep		4*22	6 21	...	11 38	...	18 25	*	22 45
Besné-Pont-Chât.		4 47	6 48	...	12 1	14 0	18 49	20 42	23 9
Pont Chateau ar		4 54	7 3	...	12 27	14 7	18 49	20 49	...
Blain		—	7 44	9 4	13 1	—	19 36	—	23 51
St. Vincent		...	8 29	9 51	13 50	...	20 23	...	0 28
Château- arr		...	8 47	10 9	14 8	...	20 41	...	0 44
briant ......dep		6 0	8 58	—	14 55	1540	20 52	...	0 51
Pouancé.............		6 21	9 20	...	15 18	1627	21 12	...	A
Segré ...arr		6 57	9 59	...	15 54	1722	21 46	...	1 35
,, ...dep	5 5	7 5	10 14	...	16 13	—	22 2	...	1 45
Chemazé	5 26	...	10 36	...	16 34	...	22 22	...	...
Château-Gon.	5 37	7 31	10 50	...	16 48	...	22 35	...	...
Gennes-Long	5 48	...	11 4	...	17 0	...	22 45	...	...
LesAgets-St-B	6 12	...	11 28	...	17 25	...	23 8	...	...
Sablé ...arr	6 22	8 2	11 37	...	17 35	...	23 17	...	2 40
Le Mans 75	7 51	8 54	12 31	...	18 40	...	0 31	...	3 43

A—From 15th July until 5th October.

†—From 2nd July until 5th Oct.

RENNES and NANTES.

E.M								
	Rennes ....dep	...	5 49	10†2	10 14	16 20	17 45	...
33	Beslé	6 15	6 52	11 1	11 37	17 47	18 52	...
47¾	Blain	7 0	7 41	1136	13 5	18 41	19 35	20 17
74½	Nantes (Etat) ...arr	...	8 50	1232	14 16	...	20 28	21 25

Nantes (Etat) ...dep	5 50	...	11 24	17 11	18 3	...	...
Blain	6 55	7 47	12 56	18 8	19 16	20 25	...
Beslé	7 45	8 52	13 53	18 50	—	21 27	...
Rennes ....arr	8 47	10 0	15 4	19 48	...	...	...

CHATEAUBRIANT and REDON.

Chateaubriant dep	3 50	10 45	19 0	...
St. Vincent des Landes	4 6	11 0	19 17	...
Derval	4 24	11 17	19 48	...
Massérac	4 58	11 49	20 41	...
Redon (83) ...arr	5 16	12 6	21 5	...

Redon ....dep	6 15	12 14	18 59
Massérac	6 36	12 37	19 14
Derval	7 15	13 14	19 46
St. Vin. des Landes..	7 48	13 37	20 6
Châteaubriant arr	8 10	13 54	20 22

Chemazé dep	9 41	1453	17 16	...
Craon ...arr	1012	1522	17 48	...
Craon ...dep	7 42	1032	15 50	...
Chemazé arr	8 7	11 5	16 15	...

CHATEAUBRIANT and PLOERMEL.

Chateaubriant ...dep	4 55	10 59	16 49
Erce-Teillay	5 28	11 32	17 33
Messac 83...........arr	6 0	12 4	18 16
,, ...dep	7 15	12 18	19 14
Ploermel ....arr	9 33	13 47	21 29

Ploermel..............dep	4 30	10 10	16 52	...
Messac ....arr	5 58	12 17	18 20	...
,, ...dep	7 20	12 38	18 44	...
Erce-Teillay	7 46	13 21	19 33	...
Chateaubriant 83 arr	8 30	14 2	20 16	...

SEGRÉ and NANTES.

Segré dep	3 53	5 22	10 10	17 34	...	...
Cande	4 22	5 58	10 40	18 5	...	...
S.Mars Jail	4 38	6 18	11 0	18 22	...	...
Ligne	5 14	6 58	11 35	18 58	...	...
Nantes...	6 0	7 55	12 21	19 53	...	...

Nantes...dep	7 11	1329	1928	...	...
Ligne............	8 0	1416	2017	...	...
St.Mars-Jaille	8 34	1450	2051	...	...
Cande...........	8 52	1512	21 9	...	...
Segré 83 ...	9 24	1545	2139	...	...

SEGRE and ANGERS (St. Serge.)

Segré (83) ....dep	7 7	10 7	15 15	17 36	22 6	...	...
Angers..............arr	8 12	11 9	16 22	18 51	23 10	...	...
Angers ....dep	5 31	8 18	14 59	17 50	20 47	...	...
Segré ....arr	6 34	9 21	16 6	19 0	21 51	...	...

CANDE and ANGERS (St. Laud).

Candé-Anjou dep	6 50	9 26	...	1727
La Roche St. J (39)	8 13	1051	1454	1850
Angers ....arr	8 40	1118	1521	1917
Angers ....dep	6 42	14 0	1718	...
La Roche St. J. ...	7 11	1430	1748	...
Candé-Anjou arr	8 33	1551	1910	...

FALAISE and FLERS.

E.M						
—	**Falaise**..........dep	5 25	1133	1737	...	...
6¼	Martigny..................	5 46	1159	1758	...	...
13	Mesnil-Vil.-P.-des-V	6 6	1232	1818	...	...
18	**Berjou** (83)	6 34	1316	1851	...	...
23	Condé-s-Noireau ...	7 7	1333	19 9	...	...
30½	**Flers** (82, 83)....arr	7 58	1355	1934	...	...

Flers ....dep	5 57	14 35	15 56	20 12	...
Condé-sur-Noireau......	6 17	14 57	16 18	20 35	...
Berjou	7 21	15 22	—	21 45	...
Mesnil-Vil.-P.-des-V.	7 41	15 56	...	22 3	...
Martigny	8 14	16 37	...	22 27	...
Falaise (75) ....arr	8 34	17 0	...	22 46	...

CAEN and LAVAL.

Caen ....dep	...	3 42	...	8 8	12 1	...	17 24	...	20 8
Saint-Rémy	...	4 37	5 20	9 1	1254	...	18 23	...	2112
Berjou-Cahan	...	5 4	6 34	9 23	1316	...	18 51	...	2136
Condé-sur-Noireau	...	5 21	7 7	9 41	1333	1642	19 9	2037	2151
Flers ....arr	...	5 56	7 58	10 8	1355	1714	19 34	21 7	2216
,, (82, 83)...dep	3 40	6 48	—	10 43	1411	1729	20 15	—	—
Domfront Orne	4 19	7 35	...	11 27	1457	1827	21 14	...	...
Ambrières	4 47	8 21	...	11 59	1532	—	21 46	...	...
Mayenne (85)......	5 14	9 5	...	12 27	16 1	1745	22 16	2127	...
Chapelle-Anthen...	5 40	9 33	...	12 56	1629	18 9	22 47	2159	...
Laval (78, 80) arr	5 57	9 52	...	13 15	1647	1824	23 5	2217	...

Laval ....dep	3 5	6 33	1027	...	14 1	1655	1857	23 48
La Chapelle-Anth.	3 23	6 52	1049	...	1421	1714	1919	0 13
Mayenne	3 53	7 23	1123	...	1447	1749	1955	0 40
Ambrières............	4 18	7 48	12 4	...	—	1813	2020	—
Domfront Orne	4 58	8 22	1257	1456	...	1855	2119	...
Flers ....arr	5 37	9 0	1340	1631	...	1936	2154	...
,, ...dep	5 57	9 14	1435	—	17 4	2012	2233	...
Condé-sur-Noireau	6 17	9 40	1457	...	1723	2035	2252	...
Berjou-Cahan	6 32	9 56	1514	...	1738	2052	—	19 20
Saint-Rémy	6 53	1016	1536	...	1756	2113	...	20 43
Caen (78).......arr	7 47	11 9	1633	...	1852	22 9	...	...

MINIAC and LA GOUESNIERE-CANCALE.

Miniac (75A ....dep	...	5 55	9 13	1519	17 32	19 26	...	...
Châteauneuf	4 35	6 6	9 31	1530	17 43	19 36	...	...
La Gouesnière-C. arr	4 49	6 19	9 48	1544	17 56	...	...	...

La Gouesnière-C.	5 9	6 59	13 48	16 46	1850	...
Châteauneuf	5 24	7 20	14 3	17 1	19 5	...
Miniac ....arr	5 35	7 33	14 14	17 12	1916	...

CAEN and VIRE.

Caen ....dep	5 13	...	11 18	1419	1719	...
La Besace	6 31	...	12 33	1559	1846	...
Guilberville	6 41	8 21	12 52	1611	19 3	...
Vire...............arr	7 13	9 35	13 25	1649	1940	...
Guilberville ...dep	8 5	12 50	19 1	...	...	...
St. Lo (79)......arr	8 48	14 7	20 3	...	...	...

Vire........ dep	5 11	7 24	11 29	...	15 8	17 45	...	...
Guilberville ...	5 57	8 20	12 18	12 43	15 51	18 35	...	...
La Besace	6 5	8 34	—	13 0	16 2	18 47	...	...
Caen.........arr	7 35	1026	...	16 5	17 15	20 3	...	...
St. Lo...........dep	4 35	11 0	17 13	...	...	...	...	
Guilberville ...arr	5 46	12 24	18 23	...	...	...	...	

PARIS to VERSAILLES.

Via St. Cloud.

Stations	
Paris—Rue St. Lazare	Service about hourly, from 4.47 until 0.46.
Courbevoie	
Suresnes	
St. Cloud-Montret	
Sèvres, Ville d'Avray	
Versailles Rive Droite	

Via Clamart.

Stations	
Paris-Boulevard Montparnasse	Service about hourly, from 5.40 until 0.48.
Clamart	
Meudon	
Sèvres	
Versailles (Rive Gauche)	

Via Issy.

Stations	
Paris—Invalides	Electric trains maintain a frequent service (half-hourly or oftener), from 5.3 until 0.40.
Champ-de-Mars	
Issy	
Meudon-Val-Fleury	
Viroflay	
Versailles (Rive Gauche)	

PARIS to ST. GERMAIN.

Via Marly.

Stations	
Paris—St. Lazare	Service from 5.20 until 19.32.
Puteaux	
St. Cloud	
Marly-le-Roi	
St. Germain Gde. Ceinture	
,, Ouest	

Via Rueil.

Stations	
Paris—St. Lazare	A frequent service from 4.55 until 0.44.
Nanterre	
Rueil	
St. Germain (Ouest)	

PARIS to SCEAUX.

Stations									
Paris-Luxembourg dp	5 27	5 52	...	And from Paris every half hour until 21.4. Also at 22.2, 23.7, 0.2, and 0.43, preserving the same relative time as shown in columns.	...	...	...	...	...
Sceaux-Ceinture	5 39	6 4	...		...	...	...	...	...
Arcueil-Cachan	5 46	6 10	...		...	...	...	...	...
Bourg-la-Reine	5 52	6 16	...		...	...	...	...	...
Fontenay	5 57	6 21	...		...	...	...	...	...
Sceaux arr	6 0	6 26	...		...	...	...	...	...

HAVRE, FECAMP, and DIEPPE.

‡—Until 5th October. *—From 6th October.

Stations								
Havre dep	...	6 42	11 0	...	16 20	...	18 5	2033
Harfleur	...	6 52	1113	...	16 30	...	1815	2043
Rolleville	...	7 12	1141	...	16 50	...	1844	2120
Les Ifs arr	4 57	7 50	1227	...	17 30	...	1921	2211
Fecamp arr	5 10	8 24	1249	...	17 43	*	1937	2233
,, dep	5 20	9 0	1310	14‡27	18 19	1920	—	—
Cany	6 3	10 3	1355	15 12	19 4	20 7	...	...
St. Vaast B.	6 31	10 44	1424	16 25	19 15	2029	...	...
Luneray	6 58	11 13	1456	16 54	20‡22	21 3	...	...
Dieppe arr	7 38	11 54	1543	17 35	21‡ 3	2144	...	...

Stations						‡	
Dieppe dep	...	5 8	8 14	10 42	1415	1746	1939
Luneray	...	5 48	8 54	11 29	1457	1826	2023
St. Vaast Bosvl	...	6 28	9 27	12 23	1538	1857	2055
Cany	...	6 42	9 41	12 37	1552	—	21 9
Fecamp arr	...	7 26	10 24	13 21	1635	..	2152
,, dep	6 46	7 41	10 36	13 44	1710	20 2	22 3
Les Ifs dep	7 2	8 3	11 0	13 59	1753	2022	2222
Rolleville	7 48	...	11 43	14 37	1830	21 2	...
Harfleur	8 12	...	12 10	14 57	1851	2125	...
Havre arr	8 22	9 25	12 20	15 12	19 1	2134	2312

For other trains between Havre and Les Ifs and Fecamp via Bréauté-Beuzeville, see pages 76, 77 & 77A.

Extra.—Cany to St. Vaast, 8.30, 11.51, 13‡6, 17‡43. St. Vaast to Cany 9.3, 10.48, 13‡35, 14.17, 18‡12, 19*38. St. Vaast to Dieppe 12‡30, 16*25. Fecamp to Cany 21‡14. St. Vaast to Fecamp 19‡38.

MORTAGNE and SAINTE GAUBURGE.

Stations				
Mortagne dep	7 10	15 25	19 25	...
Lignerolles	7 35	15 50	19 52	...
Moulins-la-Marche	8 4	16 22	20 28	...
Sainte Gauburge (82) arr	8 25	16 44	20 51	...

Stations				
Sainte Gauburge dep	5 23	9 17	17 34	...
Moulins-la-Marche	5 46	9 49	17 57	...
Lignerolles	6 17	10 28	18 28	...
Mortagne arr	6 46	11 1	18 55	...

ROUEN and CHARTRES.

Stations												
Rouen (Orleans) dep		...	5 51	6 31	10 3	13 2	1422	1545	16 6	...	...	2022
Elbeuf arr		...	6 36	7 17	1049	1348	1458	1620	1652	...	...	2112
Louviers		...	7 34	8 1	1157	1429	1546	1654	18 1	1843	...	2155
Pacy	5 14	...	8 33	—	1327	—	1625	—	1858	1918	1928	—
Dreux	7 9	5 31	9 59	...	1458	...	1738	...	—	2018	2140	...
St. Sauveur-Chateauneuf		6 4	1110	...	—	...	1813	...	...	...	2210	...
Chartres arr		6 41	1147	...	...	...	1849	...	...	21 2	2247	...
ORLEANS 42A arr		9 17	1452	...	...	...	2114	...	...	2258	...	...
ORLEANS dep		...	4 56	4 56	...	...	...	...	...	15 1	18 7	...
Chartres dep		...	7 36	7 46	...	...	1219	...	...	1729	2143	...
St. Sauveur Chateauneuf		...	...	8 26	...	...	13 0	...	...	1812	2235	...
Dreux		5 6	8 22	9 10	10 7	...	1328	1538	...	19 2	2312	...
Pacy		6 58	9 12	1118	1333	...	—	17 7	...	2020	—	...
Louviers	5 58	8 11	9 47	1222	1426	17 4	...	1815	19 7	2115	...	...
Elbeuf	6 45	9 2	1026	1318	—	1759	...	1933	2030	2157	...	...
Rouen (Orleans) arr	7 30	9 47	1058	1351	...	1843	...	2025	2115	2229	...	...

MAMERS, MORTAGNE and LAIGLE.

Stations				
Mamers dep	5 21	9 4	13 0	18 5
Vaunoise	5 41	9 32	13 33	18 25
Bellême-St.-Martin	6 1	10 4	14 8	18 41
Mortagne (42B) arr	6 30	10 48	15 0	19 11
,, dep	7 0	11 27	—	19 32
Tourouvre	7 38	11 50	...	20 15
Crulai	8 16	12 16	...	21 2
Laigle (82) arr	8 50	12 36	...	21 31
Laigle dep	4 56	11 17	17 55	...
Crulai	5 33	11 46	18 19	...
Tourouvre	6 14	12 19	18 45	...
Mortagne arr	6 49	12 50	19 9	...
,, dep	7 13	13 0	19 40	21 46
Bellême-St.-Martin	7 55	14 0	20 16	22 26
Vaunoise	8 13	14 21	20 33	22 46
Mamers arr	8 41	14 53	20 56	23 17

LAVAL and CHATEAUBRIANT

E.M.	Stations				
	Laval dep	6 25	14 35	18 59	...
23	Craon (83)	7 37	15 38	20 9	...
38	Pouancé	8 32	16 20	20 56	...
47¾	Chateaubriant (83) arr	8 52	16 40	21 17	...

Stations				
Chateaubriant dep	4 9	10 24	18 23	...
Pouancé	4 30	10 45	18 45	...
Craon	5 16	11 23	19 30	...
Laval (80) arr	6 20	12 30	20 35	...

LA LOUPE and EVREUX.

Stations						
La Loupe dep	5 6	1032	1443	...	20 8	...
Verneuil	6 43	1158	1610	1948	2119	...
Damville	7 34	1252	1710	2045	—	...
Evreux (78) arr	8 15	1334	1751	2126	...	...

Stations							
Evreux dep	4 34	7 42	10‡ 3	...	1615	...	1928
Damville	5 20	8 27	11 55	...	17 1	...	2012
Verneuil	6 51	9 22	13 43	1618	1754	19 32	21 5
La Loupe arr	8 8	11 8	...	1719	...	20 49	...

‡—After 8th September, depart 9.44.

CHERBOURG and COUTANCES.

‡—3rd class only.

E.M.	Station							Station							
	Cherbourg ......dep	4 39	8 38	9‡44	...	1636	2024	**Coutances** dep	5 22	...	10 12	...	16 0	...	2010
11½	**Sottevast (78)**......arr	5 8	9 7	10 34	...	17 5	2054	Periers	5 52	...	11 43	...	16 37	...	2040
16¾	Bricquebec	5 23	9 25	11 51	...	1720	21 9	Lessay	6 7	...	12 17	...	16 56	...	2056
33	La Haye-du-Puits (78)	6 25	10 12	13 13	14‡46	18 3	2150	La Haye-du-Puits	6 37	10 23	12 44	13 48	17 15	18 0	2114
38½	Lessay	6 39	10 27	—	15 26	1818	—	Bricquebec	7 47	11 26	—	15 20	—	18 59	2153
44¾	Periers	6 56	10 44	...	16 8	1835	...	**Sottevast**	8 13	11 46	...	15 50	...	19 19	22 9
57¾	**Coutances (79)** ...arr	7 24	11 12	...	17 5	19 3	...	**Cherbourg 78**	8 45	12 17	...	16 30	...	19 51	2237

CHERBOURG and BARFLEUR.

Station								Station									
Cherbourg.........dep	7 0	9 52	1315	1530	18 33	...	...	Barfleur...........dep	6 0	7 53	10 37	1522	17 1	...	...	...	...
Barfleur ....arr	8 32	1120	1442	17 0	20 1	...	...	Cherbourg ....arr	7 29	9 22	12 7	1652	1830	...	...	...	...

LA HUTTE-COULOMBIERS and SILLE-LE-GUILLAUME.

E.M.	Station						Station						
	La Hutte-Coulom. dp	6 45	10 30	13 56	17 34	20 1	**Sillé-le-Guillaume** dep	5 10	8 40	12 34	15 40	21 15	...
10½	Segrie-Vernie	7 34	10 56	14 30	18 9	2027	Segrie-Vernie	5 29	8 59	12 53	15 59	21 34	...
18	**Sillé-le-Guill. (80)** arr	8 10	11 16	15 2	18 44	2048	**La Hutte-Coul. 75** arr	5 55	9 26	13 20	16 26	22 1	...

SILLE-LE-GUILLAUME and SABLE.

Station						Station						
Sillé-le-Guillaume dep	5 49	12 30	18 23	...	...	**Sable**............dep	5 12	12 42	18 1	...	...	...
Loue	6 34	13 11	19 6	...	...	Juigné-sur-Sarthe........	5 21	12 55	18 10	...	...	...
Juigné-sur-Sarthe........	7 14	13 54	19 44	...	...	Loue	6 1	13 41	19 5	...	...	...
Sablé (83) ....arr	7 22	14 2	19 52	...	...	**Sille-le-Guillaume (80)** arr	6 47	14 24	19 52	...	...	...

MAYENNE and FOUGERES.

Dist.	Station							Station						
	Mayenne (83)......dep	5 33	14 58	17 57	...	...	...	**Fougères** ....dep	6 41	13 30	19 42	...	...	...
18¾	Ernée	6 28	16 37	18 47	...	...	...	**La Selle-en-L.** dep	6 56	13 40	19 51	...	...	...
29½	**La Selle-en-L. 77B** ar	6 55	17 20	19 14	...	...	...	Ernée	7 49	14 25	20 23	...	...	...
36	**Fougères (77B)** ...arr	7 3	17 32	19 22	...	...	...	**Mayenne (83)** ...arr	9 0	15 44	21 21	...	...	...

DIEPPE and LE TREPORT.

E.M.	Station								Station							
	Dieppe..........dep	6 41	10 37	1319	1726	20 7	...	...	**Le Treport** dep	6 22	10 41	12 45	1723	20 12	...	...
10	Envermeu........	7 12	11 8	1353	1755	2036	...	...	ABBEVILLE...dep	4 6	7 19	11 35	1552	19 14	...	...
26	**Eu**	7 50	11 47	1431	1832	2114	...	...	**Eu**	6 30	10 51	12 55	1733	20 27	...	...
47¾	ABBEVILLE (20) arr	1045	14 36	1825	...	2233	...	...	Envermeu........	7 10	11 37	13 38	1815	21 25	...	...
28	**Le Tréport (20)** arr	8 4	11 57	1441	1840	2125	...	...	**Dieppe** ....arr	7 34	12 11	14 4	1839	21 56	...	...

AUNEAU and DREUX.

E.M.	Station								Station							
	Auneau ......dep	6 23	9 13	14 10	16 59	19 6	...	...	**Dreux** ....dep	6 19	9 6	...	15 14	19 6	...	...
14¼	Maintenon	7 52	11 20	16 33	19 0	20 14	...	...	Nogent-le-Roi ...	6 52	9 36	...	15 45	19 39	...	...
20½	Nogent-le-Roi ...	8 8	11 37	16 48	19 40	20 30	...	...	Maintenon (80)	7 54	9 50	1124	16 31	20 25	...	...
31	**Dreux (84)** arr	8 43	12 10	17 23	20 42	21 3	...	...	**Auneau** ......arr	8 33	...	12 2	17 9	21 9	...	...

EVREUX and GLOS MONTFORT

E.M.	Station							Station						
	Evreux ....dep	5 17	12 29	17 6	1925	...	...	**Glos Montfort** dep	...	7 43	12 58	19 17	...	...
15¼	Le Neubourg	6 2	13 11	17 49	20 5	...	...	Le Neubourg	5 27	8 30	13 45	20 12	...	...
29¾	**Glos Montfort (77A**	6 43	13 50	18 30	...	...	...	**Evreux (78)**......arr	6 10	9 9	14 24	20 56	...	...

PONT-AUDEMER and HONFLEUR.

E.M.	Station								Station						
	Pont-Audemer dep	7 54	13 28	16 14	1948	0 10	...	...	**Honfleur** ....dep	5 28	7 33	...	12 20	16 41	1957
10½	Quetteville	8 33	13 56	17 3	2046	0 41	...	...	Quetteville	5 44	7 49	8 40	12 39	17 0	2022
18	**Honfleur (78)** ...arr	8 50	14 11	17 25	21 5	0 58	...	...	**Pont-Audemer (86)**	6 10	8 19	9 7	13 7	17 27	21 3

DREUX and EVREUX.

E.M.	Station								Station							
	Dreux.........dep	7 29	9 35	15 5	20 31	...	...	...	**Evreux**......dep	4 49	7 13	12 7	18 0	...	...	...
5½	St. Georges-Motel	7 45	9 51	15 21	20 50	...	...	...	Prey........	5 8	7 33	12 27	18 20	...	...	...
20½	Prey	8 21	10 29	15 57	21 27	...	...	...	St. Georges M....	5 47	8 16	13 5	18 59	...	...	...
26¾	**Evreux (78)** arr	8 34	10 44	16 10	21 42	...	...	...	**Dreux (82)** arr	6 5	8 32	13 24	19 18	...	...	...

VALOGNES and MONTEBOURG to BARFLEUR.

Dist E.M	Station							Station						
Dist	**Valognes** ....dep	5 50	9 33	1240	1746	1957	...	**Barfleur** ....dep	...	...	6 0	9 7	1410	1715
E.M	**Montebourg** ......dep	6 0	9 27	1255	1742	...	2015	St. Vaast-la-Hougue........	...	...	6 35	9 56	1450	18 1
6¼	St. Martin-d'Audouville V.	6 23	10 8	1325	1819	2018	2031	Quettehou........	...	...	6 53	1011	1456	18 9
13¾	Quettehou........	6 52	1048	1359	1852	—	—	St. Martin d'Audouville V.	5 0	5 12	7 21	1042	1524	1840
15½	St. Vaast-la-Hougue........	7 7	11 8	1421	1911	...	...	**Montebourg** ......arr	...	5 29	8 0	1125	1550	1917
22¼	**Barfleur**........arr	7 34	1137	1452	1941	...	...	**Valognes (78)** ....arr	5 22	...	7 57	1116	1559	1915

GRANVILLE and SOURDEVAL-LA-BARRE.

Station								Station						
Granville (Etat) ......dep	...	7 28	...	13 32	1515	...	...	Sourdeval-la-Barre dep	5 35	10 0	...	14 50	...	...
St. Pair	...	7 46	...	13 50	1533	...	...	Avranches	7 45	1152	12 56	17 15	...	...
Jullouville-Bouillon......	...	7 59	...	14 4	1545	...	...	St. Jean-le-Thomas	8 24	—	13 36	17 55	...	...
Champeaux	...	8 17	...	14 22	16 3	...	...	Champeaux	8 32	...	13 44	18 3	...	...
St. Jean-le-Thomas	...	8 25	...	14 27	16 9	...	...	Jullouville-B.	8 50	...	14 5	18 21	...	...
Avranches 79	6 30	9 7	11 0	15 7	1650	...	...	St. Pair	9 3	...	14 18	18 34	...	...
Sourdeval-la-B. 82........	8 25	...	1255	...	1913	...	...	Granville 82 ....arr	9 21	...	14 36	18 52	...	...

GRANVILLE and CONDE.

E.M.	Station								Station							
	Granville (Etat) dep	...	7 14	10 43	...	17 10	...	...	Condé ....dep	...	8 38	11 48	...	17 58	...	...
11¾	Cerences	...	8 31	12 1	...	18 50	...	...	Percy	6 44	10 13	13 8	16 38	19 18	...	...
26¾	Percy	6 48	10 7	13 25	16 10	20 14	...	...	Cerences	8 32	12 0	...	18 49	—	...	...
41¾	Condé ....arr	8 8	11 26	...	17 31	...	...	...	Granville......arr	9 26	12 50	...	19 39	...	...	...

LAVAL and MAYENNE.

E.M.	Station								Station							
	Laval..........dep	...	5 30	11 32	17 40	...	...	...	**Mayenne** ......dep	...	6 28	12 7	18 0	...	...	...
25½	Ernée-Echange ...	...	7 42	13 42	19 53	...	...	...	Landivy	5 5	9 10	15 0	20 29	...	...	...
42½	Landivy	5 25	9 27	15 12	21 12	...	...	...	Ernée-Echange ...	6 16	10 22	16 14	—	...	...	...
72	**Mayenne** ......arr	7 57	1157	17 40	...	...	...	...	**Laval**........arr	8 26	12 35	18 23	...	...	...	...

ELBEUF and DREUX.

Extra.—Elbeuf to Louviers 7.22, 13.51

Elbeuf ...dep	6 44	1058	15 1	1621	1658	...	...	2112	**Dreux** ......dep		5 6	...	8 22	9 10	10 7	1538	...	19 2
Louviers dep	7 34	1157	1546	17 1	18 1	1843	19 4	22 7	Croth-Sorel		5 31	...	...	9 44	10 41	16 8	...	19 27
Acquigny arr	7 41	12 6	1552	17 8	18 8	...	1911	2214	Ivry-la-Bataille		5 44	...	...	9 57	10 58	1623	...	19 43
Acquigny dp	7 49	1230	...	17 9	...	...	1912	2216	**Bueil** ....arr		5 52	7 24	8 55	10 4	11 6	1632	...	19 51
Brosville	8 8	1248	...	1724	...	...	1931	2235	**Pacy-s-Eure**		6 58	7 43	9 12	11 18	13 33	17 7	...	20 20
Evreux...arr	8 37	1315	...	1745	...	...	1959	23 2	Chambray		7 14	—	...	11 36	13 50	1725	...	20 36
Chambray [86	8 9	1250	...	—	1840	...	—	—	**Evreux** dep		6 40	8 50	...	11 18	...	1654	...	20 0
Pacy-s-Eure	8 33	1317	1625	...	1858	1918	1928	5 14	Brosville		7 7	9 8	...	11 41	...	1725	...	20 27
Bueil ...(78)...	9 15	14 9	1648	...	—	...	20 6	6 5	**Acquigny** ar		7 25	9 23	...	11 57	...	1743	...	20 45
Ivry-la-Bataille	9 21	1418	1656	...	...	...	2014	6 14	**Acquigny** dep		7 44	9 24	...	12 7	14 19	1752	...	21 1
Croth-Sorel	9 32	1433	17 9	...	...	...	2028	6 37	**Louviers**	5 58	7 51	9 31	9 42	12 14	14 26	1759	19 7	21 15
Dreux(85) arr	9 59	1458	1731	...	...	2014	2057	7 9	**Elbeuf** arr	6 40	8 57	1021	1021	13 12	17 46	19 2	19 42	21 54

PACY-S-EURE and GISORS.

Extra.—Vernon to Pacy 15.3.

Pacy-s-Eure ...dep		6 19	9 17	13 21	17 25	...	...	...	**Gisors—** (Etat).........dep		5 15	8 13	...	13 56	...	17 50
Vernon (76)	3 41	7 12	10 13	14 52	18 7	19 55	...	...	Gisors (Ville)......		5 27	8 17	...	14 2	...	18 4
Vernonnet...........	3 48	7 21	10 30	14 59	—	20 6	...	...	Dangu		6 6	8 36	...	14 24	...	18 24
Gasny	4 2	7 42	11 18	15 17	...	20 27	...	...	Bordeaux-St.-Cl.		6 30	8 47	...	14 38	...	18 41
Bordeaux-St.-Clair	4 28	8 19	12 25	15 46	...	21 8	...	...	Gasny		7 58	9 16	...	15 19	...	19 16
Dangu	4 35	8 35	12 40	15 55	...	21 20	...	...	Vernonnet		8 34	9 34	...	15 39	...	19 36
Gisors (Ville)	4 53	8 55	13 6	16 13	...	21 40	...	...	**Vernon**......	7 22	8 46	9 39	1024	15 48	18 25	19 44
Gisors (Etat) arr	4 56	8 59	13 13	16 17	...	21 45	...	...	**Pacy**......arr	8 8	...	...	1110	...	19 10	...

PONT-DE-L'ARCHE and GISORS.

Dis.																		
	P. de-l'Arche	4 43	7 6	10 45	13 22	16 23	19 17		**Gisors** (Etat) dep	4 58	...	8 1	13 45	16 58	1830	20 28
9	Charleval	5 23	7 49	11 29	13 59	15 58	19 57		,, (Ville)... ,,	5 3	...	8 6	13 49	17 4	1834	20 36
13½	Menesqueville ...	5 33	7 59	11 39	14 8	17 6	20 6		Etrepagny	5 32	...	8 34	14 10	17 34	1857	21 12
23½	Etrepagny	6 9	8 37	12 9	14 42	17 36	20 37		Menesqueville	6 3	...	9 2	14 38	18 5	1922	21 42
29½	**Gisors** (Ville)...	6 36	9 5	12 33	15 6	17 58	21 4		Charleval	6 12	7 44	9 21	11 45	18 13	1927	21 54
33½	,, ...(Etat) 77A	6 41	9 11	12 38	15 11	18 6	21 8		**P. de-l'Arch(76)**	6 47	8 13	9 50	15 13	18 48		22 28

CHARLEVAL and SERQUEUX.

Charleval.........dep	6 17	11 32	17 3	20 3	Serqueux.........dep	7 56	11 45	1635	...	2025	...
Vascœuil	6 35	12 8	1725	2020	Forges-E.-Thermal	8 3	12 3	1642		2032	...
Forges-Etabl.-Th.	7 28	13 39	1842	2115	Vascœuil..............	8 55	13 58	1740	1931	2127	...
Serqueux ....arr	7 36	13 49	1851	2123	Charleval (86)...arr	9 13	14 36	1758	1949	2145	...

MAMERS and SAINT-CALAIS.

E.M.								
	Mamers 84 ....dep	6 38	10 45	15 56	Saint-Calais ....dep	6 48	11 2	16 12
17½	Bonnetable..................	7 51	11 42	16 46	Thorigné....................	7 54	11 59	17 13
28	Connerré (O.) 80.......arr	8 30	12 18	17 34	Connerré (Ville)	8 6	12 8	17 22
...	,, ...dep	9 6	14 3	18 28	Connerré (O.).........arr	8 11	12 15	17 27
29½	Connerré (Ville)	9 18	14 12	18 37	,, ...dep	8 48	13 58	18 25
31½	Thorignè 42A..............	9 27	14 24	18 50	Bonnetable	9 27	14 37	19 12
47½	Saint-Calais 40 ....arr	10 27	15 28	19 53	Mamers..................arr	10 22	15 32	20 12

GLOS MONTFORT and PONT-L'EVEQUE.

Glos Montfort dep	...	7 40	15 25	19 5	Pont l'Eveque dep	...	8 15	12 †0	...	1820	...
Cormeilles	6 50	10†20	16 55	20 35	Cormeilles	5 10	9†15	12 50	16 50	1910	...
Pont l'Eveque arr	7 40	11 10	17 45	...	Glos Montfort arr	6 40	1045	...	18 20	...	...

†—Later on Fridays.

GLOS-MONTFORT and PONT-AUDEMER.

(85)																
Glos-Montfort	7 23	1110	13 1	1525	1859	2343	...	Pont-Audemer	6 16	8 23	1827	1737	1936	2117	...
Condé-s-R. ...	7 38	1128	1314	1538	1917	2356	...	Condé-s-R.	6 28	8 35	1345	1758	20 3	2133	...
Pont-Audemer	7 52	1147	1326	1550	1933	0 7	...	Gros-Mont.	6 42	8 48	14 5	1815	2019	2152	...

MONTPELLIER, BEZIERS, and St. CHINIAN.

E.M.														
—	Montpellier ....dep	7 5	5 42	8 46	...	13 45	18 0	St. Chinian ...dep	...	7 5	...	1157	1628	1856
12½	Montbazin(Hérault)	8 17	6 29	9 40	...	14 45	18 54	Cessenon	...	7 30	...	1221	1656	1920
15	Poussan..................	8 23	6 39	9 54	...	15 0	19 4	Cazouls-lès-Bézi.	...	7 58	...	1248	1744	1947
22½	Meze.....................	—	7 12	10 37	...	16 5	19 43	Lignan	...	8 21	...	1312	1817	2012
30½	Montagnac..............	...	7 58	11 24	...	16 49	20 21	Béziers ....arr	...	8 35	...	1330	1833	2030
34½	Pezenas	...	8 15	11 49	...	17 14	20 38	,, ...dep	5 35	8 44	1144	1730	—	—
42½	Servian....................	...	8 53	12 34	...	18 6	21 9	Servian	6 4	9 23	1232	18 9	...	...
49½	Béziers ....arr	...	9 27	13 9	...	18 38	21 37	Pezenas..............	6 39	10 0	1325	1844	...	...
	,, 45A ......dep	5 15	10 0	14 0	17 0	...	...	Montagnac	6 52	1020	1349	19 2	...	...
52½	Lignan..................	5 28	10 11	14 17	1711	...	...	Meze...................	7 39	1113	1545	1950	...	...
57½	Cazouls-lès-Bézier.	5 51	10 37	15 1	1741	...	...	Poussan..............	8 8	1148	1641	2019	1812	...
64	Cessenon	6 18	11 7	15 46	18 9	...	...	Montbazin	8 16	1156	1649	2027	1822	...
69½	St. Chinian ......arr	6 42	11 30	16 9	1832	...	...	Montpellier ...arr	9 5	1250	1752	2117	1937	...

Mèze... ....dep	7 12	10 37	15 55	19 43	...	...	Agde ....dep	6 4	9 30	1350	18 30	...
Florensac	7 51	11 18	16 42	20 25	...	...	Florensac	6 43	10 9	1435	19 4	...
Agde 45B ....arr	8 22	11 51	17 31	21 3	...	...	Mèze ....arr	7 24	11 2	1526	...	...

BILLOM and VERTAIZON.

Billom......dep	4 53	6 36	11 6	1751	...	...
Vertaizon arr	5 17	7 0	1130	1815	...	...
(63B)						
Vertaizon dep	5 36	7 55	1342	1839	...	...
Billom ......arr	6 0	8 19	14 6	19 3	...	...

MONTPELLIER and PALAVAS.

Extra trains on Sundays.

(Espl.) **Montpellier** dp	6 0	10 0	1340	17 0	...	...	...	...	...	...	...	...
Palavas (rive)...	6 22	1023	14 3	1723	...	...	...	...	...	...	...	...
,, (Pl.) arr	6 24	1025	14 5	1725	...	...	...	...	...	...	...	...
Palavas (Pl.) dep	6 31	1056	1536	1756	...	...	...	...	...	...	...	...
,, (rive) dep	6 34	1058	1538	1758	...	...	...	...	...	...	...	...
Montpellier ar	7 0	1124	16 6	1824	...	...	...	...	...	...	...	...

Montpellier	5 58	10 43	...	14 30	17 0	Rabieux ...	6 26	11 30	1326	1510	1748	1930
Aniane 515	7 18	12 14	14 4	16 15	1827	Aniane......	7 12	12 15	1355	1610	1836	20 7
Rabieux 553	7 58	12 49	1433	16 59	19 3	Montpellier	8 28	13 32	...	1742	20 0	...

GUE-ANCERVILLE and NAIX-MENAUCOURT.

Gué-Ancerville	...	8 15	1220	1625	1920
Savonnières-P.	6 30	9 7	13 25	1728	2010
Naix-Menauc't	7 40	...	14 31	1834	...
Naix-Menaucourt...	...	8 20	...	16 1	19 6
Savonnières-P.	6 20	10 25	1430	1729	20 5
Gué-Ancerville	7 4	11 20	1532	1824	...

St. GEORGES-DE-COMMIERS and LA MURE.

St. Georges-de-Com.	...	5 35	...	9 16	...	...	14 14	...	1847	La Mure ....dep	5 41	...	8 30	...	12 12	...	1758	...
La Motte-d'Aveillans	6 48	6 51	8 30	10 34	10 31	1212	15 29	1758	20 2	: Notre D. de V....	5 54	7 1	8 43	10 44	12 25	1541	1811	2016
: Notre Dame de V. ar	6 56	...	8 38	..	10 39	1220	15 36	18 6	2011	La Motte-d'Aveil	6 8	7 9	8 57	10 52	12 39	1549	1825	2024
La Mure ....arr	...	7 13	...	10 56	...	...	15 52	...	2026	St. Georges-de-C.	7 11	...	10 0	...	13 44	...	1930	...

LYONS and AOSTE ST. GENIX.

Lyons (Est)......dep	7 59	6 15	9 43	13 20	1454	16 50	18 50	2017
Meyzieu	8 24	6 41	10 8	13 43	1518	17 13	19 16	2042
Cremieu	8 56	7 24	10 46	14 15	1555	17 47	19 59	2114
St. Hilaire de B.	—	7 40	11 2	—	1611	—	20 15	—
Soleymieu		7 57	11 18	...	1627	...	20 33	...
Quirieu		8 29	11 55	...	1715	...	21 5	...
Montalieu-Ville......arr		8 42	12 8	...	1728	...	21 16	...
Montalieu (62)...arr		8 46	12 12	...	1732	...	...	...
Aoste-St.-Genix ...arr		8 53	12 20	...	1717	...	21 28	...

Aoste-St.-G. ...dep		5 54	...	1014	...	15 40	...	18 22
Montalieu ...dep		...	...	10 4	...	15 39	...	18 20
Montalieu-Ville ...		6 0	...	10 9	...	15 44	...	18 25
Quirieu		6 12	...	1021	...	15 56	...	18 37
Soleymieu		6 47	...	11 1	...	16 31	...	19 21
St. Hilaire de B.		7 5	...	1120	...	16 46	...	19 40
Cremieu	6 6	7 25	9 51	1140	15 1	17 6	1841	20 0
Meyzieu	6 42	8 6	10 27	1216	1537	17 43	1917	20 41
Lyons (Est)	7 6	8 34	10 51	1242	16 1	18 9	1941	21 9

St. Hilaire de B. ......dep	7 44	11 25	1650	20 20	
Jallieu......arr	8 8	11 49	1718	20 44	
Jallieu......dep	6 26	10 20	15 32	18 57	...
St. Hilaire de B. ...arr	6 54	10 50	16 0	19 25	...

LYONS and VAUGNERAY.

Lyons— St. Just......dep; Craponne; Messimy; **Mornant** arr; **Vaugneray** arr — Dep. from Lyons at 5.0 and 5 30, and about twice hourly until 20.30.

Only certain trains run to Mornant.

Vaugneray dep; **Mornant** dep; Messimy; Craponne; **Lyons** ......arr — Dep. from Vaugneray (Gare) at 6.40, and hourly at 40 mins. past the hour until 21.40.

Dep. from Mornant at 5.33, 6.33, 8.33, 9.33, 11.33, 12 33, 14.33, 15.33, 17.33, 18.33, and 20.33.

ALAIS and L'ARDOISE.

E.M.					
	Alais (58)......dep	6 45	9 28	17 0	...
6¼	Célas	7 6	9 52	17 23	...
26	Cavillargues	8 15	11 8	18 32	...
36¾	**L'Ardoise (62)**......arr	8 49	12 22	19 17	...

L'Ardoise ...dep	5 0	14 10	19 45	...	...
Cavillargues	5 50	14 53	20 32	...	...
Célas	8 0	15 54	21 44	...	...
Alais ......arr	8 24	16 12	22 7	...	...

PORT BOULET and CHATEAU-RENAULT.

Port Boulet (42A)...dep	...	5 0	8 35	...	1546	1915
Gizeux-Continvoir ...	...	5 51	9 26	...	1640	20 9
Rillé-Hommes	...	6 28	9 55	...	17 8	2038
Neuillé-Pont-Pierre ar	7 15	8 43	1338	1646	1845	2218
Marray	8 15	1021	...	1733	...	...
Châteaurenault....arr	9 24	1130	...	1843	...	...

Châteaurenault (37) dp		...	6 40	...	1353	1642	...
Marray		...	7 51	...	1512	1756	...
Neuillé-Pont-P ...	4 50	7 16	8 49	1218	1644	1843	...
Rillé-Hommes......	6 27	9 37	—	1358	1835	—	...
Gizeux-Continvoir	6 54	1011	...	1426	19 4	...	...
Port Boulet....arr	7 47	1125	...	1523	20 3	...	...

Rillé-Hommes......dep	6 26	9 ‡56	17 13	...	...
Fondettes......arr	7 32	11 2	18 29	...	...
Fondettes......dep	7 47	15 28	18 45		
Rillé-Hommes......arr	9 12	16 45	20 4		

‡—12.5 on Tuesday.

LE MANS, ST. JEAN-SUR-ERVE, LAVAL.

Le Mans ......dep	5 27	12 2	1712
Loué (85)	7 27	1351	1920
St. Jean-s-Erve arr	8 35	1455	2027
St. Jean. dep	5 10	9 0	1515
Loué	6 19	10 6	1623
Le Mans arr	8 6	1150	1815

St. Jean-s-Erve dep	5 35	9 25	16 7
Laval ......arr	6 58	1048	1730
Laval ......dep	7 20	13‡45	18 30
St. Jean-sur-Erve arr	8 47	15 12	19 57

‡—13.0 on Sunday.

LE MANS and LA CHARTRE.

Le Mans dp	5 40	8 15	12 5	1818
Parigne ...	6 40	9 11	1259	1912
Grand Luce	7 40	1010	1356	2010
La Chartre	8 35	11 3	1453	21 3
LaChartre	5 10	9 7	15 6	18 8
GrandLuce	6 12	10 7	1610	19 9
Parigne ...	7 10	11 3	17 6	20 8
Le Mans	8 5	1156	18 1	21 3

AIGNAY-LE-DUC and CHATILLON-SUR-SEINE.

Aignay-le-Duc ...dep	6 30	11 40	1655
Aisey-sur-Seine	7 41	12 51	18 6
Chatillon (P.L.M) arr	8 43	13 53	19 8
Chatillon (P.L.M.) dep	6 26	11 36	16 56
Aisey-sur-Seine	7 37	12 47	18 2
Aignay-le-Duc ...arr	8 43	13 53	19 26

Aisey-sur-Seine ...dep	11*16	1810	...
Baigneux-les-Juifs arr	12 31	1928	...
Baigneux-les-Juifs dep	6 0	1630	...
Aisey-sur-Seine ......arr	7 21	1746	...

*—Tues., Thurs., and Sat. 13.0

BEAUNE and SEMUR.

Beaune ......dep	...	6 17	...	...	12 43	17 50
Bligny	...	7 58	...	...	14 24	19 50
Arnay-le-Duc	...	8 45	9 50	...	15 11	20 35
Sussey-le-Maupas ...	...	—	10 46	...	16 24	21 36
Saulieu	4 52	...	11 27	13 10	17 20	22 16
Precy-sous-Thil	5 43	...	—	14 1	18 11	—
Semur P.L.M. arr	6 23	...	...	14 41	18 52	...

Semur P.L.M. dep	...	4 45	...	9 50	...	1738
Precy-sous-Thil	...	5 51	...	10 51	...	1836
Saulieu	...	7 5	...	11 38	13 30	1923
Sussey-le-Maupas ...	...	7 50	...	—	14 15	2025
Arnay-le-Duc	5 45	8 42	9 0	...	15 7	2120
Bligny	6 52	—	10 7	...	17 29	—
Beaune (48) arr	8 39	...	11 41	...	19 5	...

OFFOY and ERCHEU.

E.M.						
	Ercheu ......dep	6 35	11 25	1645	...	...
6¼	Nesle ......arr	7 10	11 55	1720	...	...
...	" ......dep	8 20	13 24	...	19 21	...
12½	**Offoy** ......arr	8 55	14 10	...	19 58	...

Offoy ......dep	6 35	11 0	1625	...	...	...
Nesle ......arr	7 8	11 45	17 5	...	...	...
" ......dep	8 21	12 50	...	19 30	...	...
Ercheu ......arr	8 52	13 20	...	20 0	...	...

ESTREES ST. DENIS and CRÈVECŒUR-LE-G.

Estrees-St. Denis......dep	5 31	...	13 10	1825
St. Just-en-Chaussee arr	6 27	...	14 18	1913
" dep	—	8 48	15 32	1953
Froissy	...	10 3	16 18	2039
Crèvecœur-le-G. ......arr	...	10 29	16 42	21 3

Crevecœur ......dep	6 18	...	1248	...	1755
Froissy	6 43	...	1319	...	1820
St. Just-en-Chaussee arr	7 28	...	1423	...	19 5
" dep	—	8 53	—	1527	1946
Estrees-St. Denis......arr	..	1012	...	1636	2042

DIGOIN and ETANG.

Digoin......dep	...	6 5	10 28	14 0	1742	21 40	...
Toulon-sur-Arroux	5 36	8 32	11 30	1518	1843	22 44	...
Etang 53A ......arr	6 30	9 25	...	1611	1931	...	...

Etang......dep	7 20	...	13 0	1640	1950	...
Toulon-sur-Arroux	8 28	11 45	15 9	1950	21 7	...
Digoin 63 ...arr	9 34	12 47	16 31	21 2	2213	...

Toulon-sur-Arroux ......dep	5 29	8 42	18 50	...	...	...
Cressy-sur-Somme	7 9	10 33	20 12	...	...	...
Bourbon-Lancy (P.L.M.)...arr	8 4	11 50	20 58	...	...	...
Bourbon-L. (P.L.M.)...dep	6 29	10 6	1835	...	...	...
Cressy-sur-Somme	7 8	12 40	1942	...	...	...
Toulon-sur-Arroux ...arr	8 26	14 26	21 2	...	...	...

MAUBEUGE and VILLERS-SIRE-NICOLE.

[†—Not on Sunday

Maubeuge ......dep	7 †0	9 22	11 48	14 58	18†9	18 40	...
Mairieux	7 37	9 58	12 23	15 34	1845	19 16	...
Villers-Sire-Nicole arr	7 55	10 14	12 37	15 50	19 1	19 32	...

Villers-Sire-Nicole dep	5 †30	6 †5	10 23	12 44	16 †0	1643
Mairieux	5 47	6 22	10 40	12 58	16 17	17 2
Maubeuge ......arr	6 22	6 57	11 18	13 33	16 55	1740

LAPUGNOY and RIMBERT.

Lapugnoy dep	7 37	9 20	11 24	1428	1928
Rimbert...arr	7 56	9 39	11 43	1447	1945
Rimbert......dep	6 8	8 28	13‡14	1744	
Lapugnoy (20)...arr	6 24	8 46	13 32	18 2	

‡—13.8 on Tuesday.

COUTANCES and LESSAY.

Coutances......dep	8 0	13 20	1750	...	...	...
Tourville	8 35	13 53	1825	...	...	...
Agon	8 40	13 58	1830	...	...	...
Coutainville	8 45	14 3	1835	...	...	...
Pirou	9 34	14 52	1924	...	...	...
Lessay 85......arr	9 50	15 8	1940	...	...	...

Lessay......dep	6 55	10 30	17 7	...	...	...
Pirou	7 11	10 45	1723	...	...	...
Coutainville	8 0	11 32	1812	...	...	...
Agon	8 5	11 37	1817	...	...	...
Tourville	8 10	11 42	1824	...	...	...
Coutances ......arr	8 46	12 13	1856	...	...	...

NOISY-LE-SEC, VERSAILLES, and NOISY-LE-SEC.—Grande Ceinture de Paris.

									‡
Paris Est ......dep		5 33	7 22	8 8	9 50	1047	1320	15 0	1813
Noisy-le-Sec. ...dep		5 56	7 38	8 24	1010	11 6	1339	1511	1825
Nogent-le-P. Bry...		6 40	7 50	8 48	1025	1120	1352	1531	1839
Champigny............		6 50	8 8	9 23	1047	1151	1430	1545	1912
La Varenne C.		6 58	8 12	9 28	1052	1155	1436	1554	1918
Villeneuve-St.-Geor		7 38	—	—	1125	—	15 8	—	1951
Juvisy 32 ....arr		7 52	...	...	1137	...	1519	...	20 2
,, ...dep		8 6	6 12	9 7	1157	1423	1545	18 2	2030
Massy-Palaiseau ...		8 51	6 43	9 50	1226	1455	1623	1831	21 4
Versailles ....arr		9 18	7 10	1022	1253	1522	1652	1858	2131
,, (Chant) dep	5 36	9 37	7 31	1037	13 5	1545	1718	19 2	2141
St. Cyr	5 49	9 50	7 44	1050	1318	1558	1731	1913	2154
Mareil-Marly ...	6 11	1012	8 5	11 8	1336	1619	1749	1930	2212
St. Germain.....	6 25	1019	8 18	1114	1342	1625	1755	1936	2218
Achères	6 40	1034	8 38	1145	14 0	1644	18 8	1950	2235
Argenteuil	7 25	11 6	9 34	12 8	1428	17 8	1845	2025	—
Epinay	7 37	—	—	1219	1437	1720	—	2031	...
Le Bourget......	7 57	...	...	1237	1459	1742	...	2050	...
Noisy-le-Sec....	8 7	...	...	1246	1510	1753	...	21 0	...

Noisy-le-Sec. ...dep	...	6 33	8 43	...	1313	1537	...	...	20 5
Le Bourget	...	6 43	8 53	...	1323	1547	...	...	2015
Epinay	...	6 58	9 8	..	1340	16 5	...	...	2034
Argenteuil	...	7 7	9 16	1138	1350	1615	1724	1933	2044
Achères...................	5 56	7 43	10 4	1220	1430	1652	1828	2010	2121
St. Germain............	6 11	8 1	1020	1235	1446	17 8	1843	2025	2137
Mareil-Marly	6 18	8 7	1026	1241	1453	1715	1850	2031	2143
St. Cyr	6 39	8 35	1047	13 1	1516	1737	1912	2054	22 5
Versailles ....arr	6 49	8 44	1057	1311	1526	1747	1922	21 4	2215
(Chantiers) ...dep	7 7	9 8	11 3	1325	1539	1759	1939	2130	—
Massy-Palaiseau ...	7 42	9 41	1141	14 4	1622	1832	2029	22 2	...
Juvisy..............arr	8 8	1013	12 9	1432	1650	19 4	21 1	2229	...
,, ...dep	8 29	—	1220	1550	—	—	2113	—	...
Villeneuve-St.-Geo.	8 40	...	1234	16 3	...	...	2125	...	...
La Varenne Chen....	9 3	1045	1345	1635	1722	2027	2148	2243	...
Champigny............	9 7	1048	1349	1641	1736	21 0	2159	2251	...
Nogent-le-P. Bry ...	9 28	11 4	14 1	1652	1756	2123	2216	23 5	...
Noisy-le-Sec. ...arr	9 39	1115	1412	1717	18 9	2135	2227	2318	...
Paris-Est ......arr	9 57	1133	1425	1730	1826	2152	2245	2333	...

Extra.—Paris(Est) to La Varenne Chen., 6.35, 9.2, 12.8, 16 0, 16 33, 17.32, 18.41, 18.57, 19.25, 19.59, 22.24; *vice versa*, 5.21; 6.4, 6.31, 7.39, 8.16, 10.57, 12.15, 14.32, 15.53, 19.23, 19 57 ‡—Not on Sunday.

PARIS CEINTURE (GIRDLE) RAILWAY.—

Paris (St. Lazare) dep	A frequent Service is maintained throughout the day from St. Lazare to Auteuil and *vice versa*. From 6.3 until 23.42 the trains run about every ten minutes, afterwards at 24.0, 0.18, 0.36, and 0.54
Batignolles	
Courcelles Levallois ...	
Neuilly (Porte Maillot)	
Bois de Boulogne	
Avenue-Henri-Martin	
Passy	
Auteuil ....arr	

Courcelles Ceinture ...	5 33	A frequent Service is maintained throughout the day from Courcelles Ceinture round to Courcelles Ceinture and *vice versa* until 18.18.
Courcelles Levallois ...	5 34	
Neuilly (Porte Maillot)	5 37	
Bois de Boulogne	5 39	
Avenue-Henri-Martin	5 41	
Passy	5 43	
Auteuil	5 48	
Point-du-Jour	5 52	
Grenelle	5 56	
Vaugirard-Issy	5 59	
Ouest-Ceinture..........	6 3	
Montrouge	6 6	
Parc-de-Montsouris ...	6 10	
La Maison-Blanche ...	6 14	
Orlèans-Ceinture	6 17	
La Rapée-Bercy	6 21	
Bel-Air	6 26	
Avenue de Vincennes	6 29	
Charonne	6 31	
Ménilmontant	6 37	
Belleville-Villette	6 41	
Pont-de-Flandre.........	6 44	
Est-Ceinture..............	6 46	
La Chapelle-St. Denis	6 51	
Boulevard Ornano......	6 53	
Avenue de St.-Ouen ...	6 56	
Avenue de Clichy	6 59	
Courcelles Ceinture ...	7 2	

Paris (St. Lazare)...dep	6 17	7 46
Clichy-Levallois	6 23	...
Asnières	6 27	...
Courbevoie	6 37	8 0
Puteaux	6 46	8 6
Suresnes-Longchamp...	6 50	8 11
Pont-de-St.-Cloud	6 58	8 19
Pont-de-Sevres...........	7 2	8 23
Le Bas Meudon...........	7 8	8 30
Les Moulineaux-Bil. ...	7 11	8 32
Pont de Grenelle	7 31	8 59
Champ-de-Mars	7 35	9 3
Les Invalides ....arr	7 42	9 10

The service is continued as follows:—
St. Lazare to Les Invalides, 8.57, 9.46, 10.45, 11.54, 12.45, 13.50, 14.44, 16.38, 17.47, 19.4, 19.57, 20.40, 22.50.

Return Service. Les Invalides to St. Lazare, 6.0, 6.28, 7.4, 8.16, 8.55, 10.6, 10.58, 12.8, 12.57, 13.39, 14.49, 15.57, 17.33, 18.10, 19.9, 20.45, 22.1, 23.20.

METROPOLITAIN RAILWAY.

Fares for any distance, 25c. 1st class, 15c. 2nd class.
Trains from each end every few minutes from 5.30 a.m. until 12.30 a.m.

Vincennes and Porte Maillot Line.—Stations: Vincennes, Nation, Reuilly, Lyon, Bastille, Saint-Paul, Hôtel-de-Ville, Châtelet, Louvre, Palais-Royal, Tuileries, Concorde, Champs-Elysées, Rue Marbeuf, Alma, Etoile, Obligado, Porte Maillot.

Place de la Nation and Porte Dauphine Line.—Stations: Place de la Nation, Avron, Bagnolet, Philippe-Auguste, Pere-Lachaise, Menilmontant, Couronnes, Belleville, Combat, Allemagne, Aubervilliers, Chapelle, Barbés, Anvers, Pigalle, Blanche, Clichy, Rome, Villiers, Monceau, Courcelles, Ternes, Etoile, Victor Hugo, Porte Dauphine.

Place Gambetta and Porte Champerret Line.—Stations: Place Gambetta, Martin-Nadaud, Père Lachaise, Saint Maur, Parmentier, Republique, Temple, Arts-et-Métiers, Sebastopol-Réaumur, Sentier, Bourse, Quatre Septembre, Opera, Caumartin, Saint Lazare, Europe, Avenue de Villiers, Malesherbes, Wagram, Pereire, Porte Champerret.

Porte de Clignancourt and Porte d'Orleans Line.—Stations: Porte de Clignancourt, Simplon, Marcadet, Chateau Rouge, Barbes Rochechouart, Gare du Nord, Gare de l'Est, Chateau d'Eau, Saint Denis, Reaumur Sebastopol, Etienne, Marcel, Halles, Chatelet, Cité, Saint Michel, Odeon, Saint Germain des Prés, Saint Sulpice, Vaugirard, Montparnasse, Vavin, Raspail, Denfert Rochereau, Mouton Duvernet, Alesia, Porte d'Orleans.

Gare du Nord and Place de l'Etoile Line.—Stations: Gare du Nord, Gare de l'Est, Lancry, Republique, Oberkampf, Richard Lenoir, Breguet-Sabin, Bastille, Arsenal, Austerlitz, Orleans, Saint Marcel, Campo Formio, Italie, Corvisart, La Glacière, Saint Jacques, Denfert Rochereau, Raspail, Edgar Quinet, Place du Maine, Pasteur, Sevres, Cambronne, La Motte Picquet, Dupleix, Grenelle, Passy, Trocadero, Boissière, Kleber, Place de l'Etoile.

Place de la Nation and Italie Line.—Stations: Place de la Nation, Saint Mandé, Bel Air, Daumesnil, Charenton, Bercy, Gare, Chevaleret, Nationale, Italie.

Porte de la Villette and Opera.—Stations: Porte de la Villette, Flandre, Crimée, Riquet, La Villette, Louis Blanc, Château Landon, Gare de l'Est, Poissonnière, Cadet, Le Peletier, Chaussée d Antin, Opera.

Place Pigalle and Porte de Versailles Line.—Stations: Place Pigalle, Saint-Georges, Notre Dame de Lorette, Trinité, St. Lazare, Madeleine, Concorde, Chambre des Députés, Solferino, Bac, Sevres, Rennes, Notre Dame des Champs, Montparnasse, Falguière, Pasteur, Volontaires, Vaugirard, Convention, Porte de Versailles.

Saint-Lazare and Porte de Saint-Ouen Line.—Stations: Saint-Lazare, Berlin, Clichy, La Fourche, Marcadet, Porte de Saint-Ouen.

No free Luggage is allowed, except Hand-Luggage to the amount of 55 lbs.
Luggage rate, centimes 1.50 per 25 kilog. (55 lbs.) per kilometre, minimum charge 50 centimes.

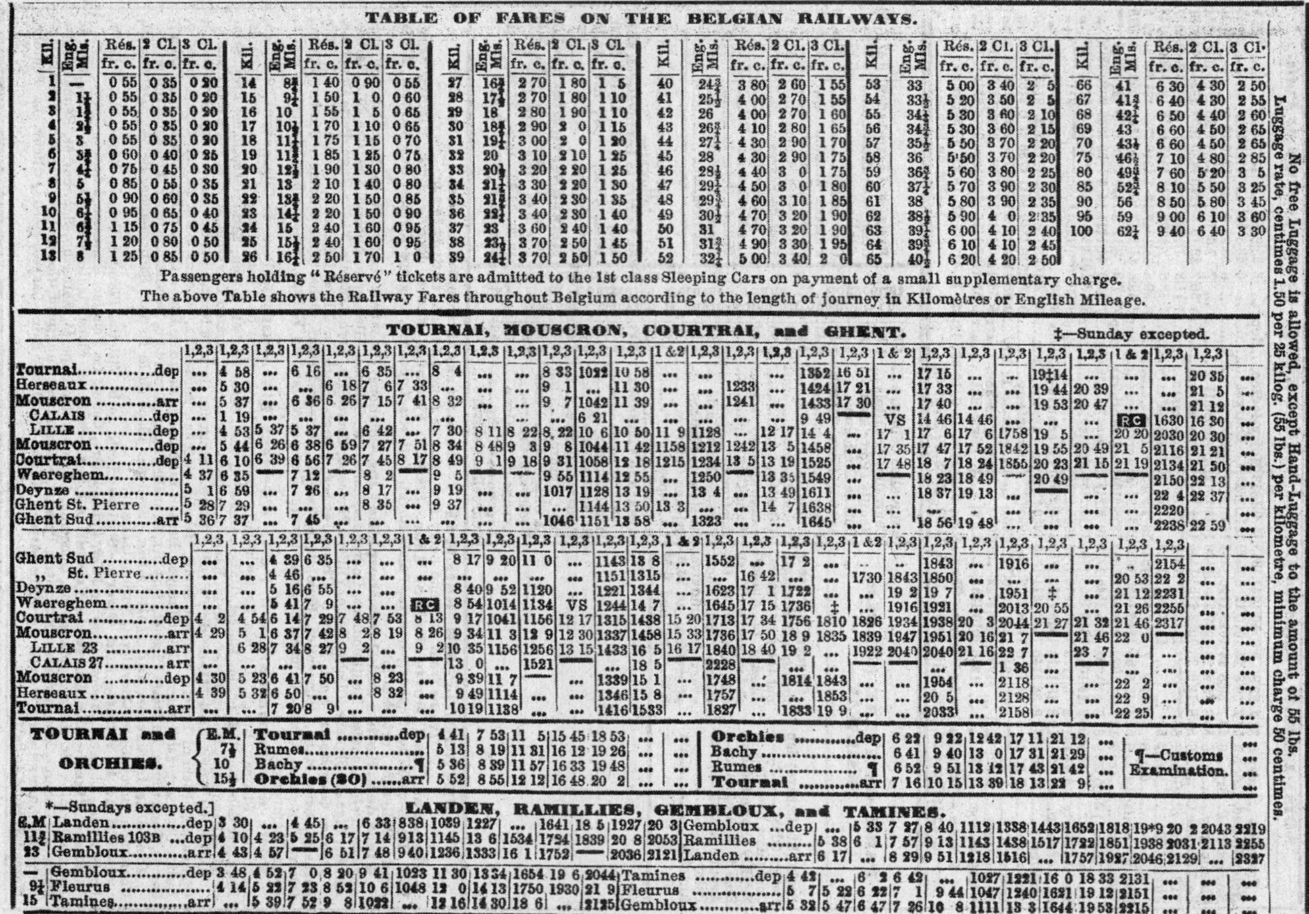

TABLE OF FARES ON THE BELGIAN RAILWAYS.

Kil.	Eng. Mls.	Rés. fr. c.	2 Cl. fr. c.	3 Cl. fr. c.	Kil.	Eng. Mls.	Rés. fr. c.	2 Cl. fr. c.	3 Cl. fr. c.	Kil.	Eng. Mls.	Rés. fr. c.	2 Cl. fr. c.	3 Cl. fr. c.	Kil.	Eng. Mls.	Rés. fr. c.	2 Cl. fr. c.	3 Cl. fr. c.	Kil.	Eng. Mls.	Rés. fr. c.	2 Cl. fr. c.	3 Cl. fr. c.	Kil.	Eng. Mls.	Rés. fr. c.	2 Cl. fr. c.	3 Cl. fr. c.
1	—	0 55	0 35	0 20	14	8¾	1 40	0 90	0 55	27	16¾	2 70	1 80	1 5	40	24¾	3 80	2 60	1 55	53	33	5 00	3 40	2 5	66	41	6 30	4 30	2 50
2	1¼	0 55	0 35	0 20	15	9¼	1 50	1 0	0 60	28	17½	2 70	1 80	1 10	41	25½	4 00	2 70	1 55	54	33½	5 20	3 50	2 5	67	41¾	6 40	4 30	2 55
3	1¾	0 55	0 35	0 20	16	10	1 55	1 5	0 65	29	18	2 80	1 90	1 10	42	26	4 00	2 70	1 60	55	34¼	5 30	3 60	2 10	68	42¼	6 50	4 40	2 60
4	2½	0 55	0 35	0 20	17	10½	1 70	1 10	0 65	30	18¾	2 90	2 0	1 15	43	26¾	4 10	2 80	1 65	56	34¾	5 30	3 60	2 15	69	43	6 60	4 50	2 65
5	3	0 55	0 35	0 20	18	11¼	1 75	1 15	0 70	31	19¼	3 00	2 0	1 20	44	27¼	4 30	2 90	1 70	57	35½	5 50	3 70	2 20	70	43½	6 60	4 50	2 65
6	3¾	0 60	0 40	0 25	19	11¾	1 85	1 25	0 75	32	20	3 10	2 10	1 25	45	28	4 30	2 90	1 75	58	36	5 50	3 70	2 20	75	46½	7 10	4 80	2 85
7	4¼	0 75	0 45	0 30	20	12½	1 90	1 30	0 80	33	20½	3 20	2 20	1 25	46	28½	4 40	3 0	1 75	59	36¾	5 60	3 80	2 25	80	49¾	7 60	5 20	3 5
8	5	0 85	0 55	0 35	21	13	2 10	1 40	0 80	34	21¼	3 30	2 20	1 30	47	29¼	4 50	3 0	1 80	60	37¼	5 70	3 90	2 30	85	52¾	8 10	5 50	3 25
9	5½	0 90	0 60	0 35	22	13¾	2 20	1 50	0 85	35	21¾	3 40	2 30	1 35	48	29¾	4 60	3 10	1 85	61	38	5 80	3 90	2 35	90	56	8 50	5 80	3 45
10	6¼	0 95	0 65	0 40	23	14¼	2 20	1 50	0 90	36	22½	3 40	2 30	1 40	49	30½	4 70	3 20	1 90	62	38½	5 90	4 0	2 35	95	59	9 00	6 10	3 60
11	6¾	1 15	0 75	0 45	24	15	2 40	1 60	0 95	37	23	3 60	2 40	1 40	50	31	4 70	3 20	1 90	63	39¼	6 00	4 10	2 40	100	62¼	9 40	6 40	3 30
12	7½	1 20	0 80	0 50	25	15½	2 40	1 60	0 95	38	23½	3 70	2 50	1 45	51	31¾	4 90	3 30	1 95	64	39¾	6 10	4 10	2 45					
13	8	1 25	0 85	0 50	26	16¼	2 50	1 70	1 0	39	24¼	3 70	2 50	1 50	52	32¼	5 00	3 40	2 0	65	40½	6 20	4 20	2 50					

Passengers holding "Réservé" tickets are admitted to the 1st class Sleeping Cars on payment of a small supplementary charge.

The above Table shows the Railway Fares throughout Belgium according to the length of journey in Kilomètres or English Mileage.

TOURNAI, MOUSCRON, COURTRAI, and GHENT.

‡—Sunday excepted.

	1,2,3	1,2,3	1,2,3	1,2,3	1,2,3	1,2,3	1,2,3	1,2,3	1,2,3	1,2,3	1,2,3	1,2,3	1,2,3	1 & 2	1,2,3	1,2,3	1,2,3	1,2,3	1,2,3	1 & 2	1,2,3	1,2,3	1,2,3	1,2,3	1,2,3	1 & 2	1,2,3	1,2,3	
Tournai ....dep	...	4 58	...	6 16	...	6 35	...	8 4	...	...	8 33	1022	10 58	...	...	...	...	1352	16 51	...	17 15	...	...	19‡14	...	...	...	20 35	...
Herseaux	...	5 30	...	...	6 18	7 6	7 33	...	...	...	9 1	...	11 30	...	...	1233	...	1424	17 21	...	17 33	...	...	19 44	20 39	...	...	21 5	...
Mouscron ....arr	...	5 37	...	6 36	6 26	7 15	7 41	8 32	...	...	9 7	1042	11 39	...	...	1241	...	1433	17 30	...	17 40	...	...	19 53	20 47	...	...	21 12	...
CALAIS ....dep	...	1 19	...	...	...	...	...	...	...	...	...	6 21	...	...	...	...	...	9 49	—	VS	14 46	14 46	...	...	...	RC	1630	16 30	...
LILLE ....dep	...	4 53	5 37	5 37	...	6 42	...	7 30	8 11	8 22	8 22	10 6	10 50	11 9	1128	...	12 17	14 4	...	17 1	17 6	17 6	1758	19 5	...	20 20	2030	20 30	...
Mouscron ....dep	...	5 44	6 26	6 38	6 59	7 27	7 51	8 34	8 48	9 3	9 8	1044	11 42	1158	1212	1242	13 5	1458	...	17 35	17 47	17 52	1842	19 55	20 49	21 5	2116	21 21	...
Courtrai ....dep	4 11	6 10	6 39	6 56	7 26	7 45	8 17	8 49	9 1	9 18	9 31	1058	12 18	1215	1234	13 5	13 19	1525	...	17 48	18 7	18 24	1855	20 23	21 15	21 19	2134	21 50	...
Waereghem	4 37	6 35	—	7 12	—	8 2	—	9 5	—	—	9 55	1114	12 55	...	1250	—	13 35	1549	...	—	18 23	18 49	—	20 49	—	—	2150	22 13	...
Deynze	5 1	6 59	...	7 26	...	8 17	...	9 19	...	...	1017	1128	13 19	...	13 4	...	13 49	1611	...	...	18 37	19 13	...	—	...	...	22 4	22 37	...
Ghent St. Pierre	5 28	7 29	...	...	...	8 35	...	9 37	...	...	...	1144	13 50	13 3	...	...	14 7	1638	...	...	...	...	...	...	...	...	2220	...	...
Ghent Sud ....arr	5 36	7 37	...	7 45	...	...	...	...	...	...	1046	1151	13 58	...	1323	...	...	1645	...	...	18 56	19 48	...	...	...	...	2238	22 59	...

	1,2,3	1,2,3	1,2,3	1,2,3	1,2,3	1,2,3	1 & 2	1,2,3	1,2,3	1,2,3	1,2,3	1,2,3	1,2,3	1 & 2	1,2,3	1,2,3	1,2,3	1,2,3	1 & 2	1,2,3	1,2,3	1,2,3	1,2,3	1,2,3	1,2,3	1,2,3	1,2,3		
Ghent Sud ....dep	...	...	4 39	6 35	...	...	...	8 17	9 20	11 0	...	1143	13 8	...	1552	...	17 2	...	...	...	1843	...	1916	...	...	...	2154	...	...
„ St. Pierre	...	...	4 46	...	...	...	...	...	...	...	...	1151	1315	...	...	16 42	...	...	1730	1843	1850	...	...	...	...	20 53	22 2	...	...
Deynze	...	...	5 16	6 55	...	...		8 40	9 52	1120	...	1221	1344	...	1623	17 1	1722	...	...	19 2	19 7	...	1951	‡	...	21 12	2231	...	...
Waereghem	...	...	5 41	7 9	...	...	RC	8 54	1014	1134	VS	1244	14 7	...	1645	17 15	1736	‡	...	1916	1921	...	2013	20 55	...	21 26	2255	...	...
Courtrai ....dep	4 2	4 54	6 14	7 29	7 48	7 53	8 13	9 17	1041	1156	12 17	1315	1438	15 20	1713	17 34	1756	1810	1826	1934	1938	20 3	2044	21 27	21 32	21 46	2317	...	...
Mouscron ....arr	4 29	5 1	6 37	7 42	8 2	8 19	8 26	9 34	11 3	12 9	12 30	1337	1458	15 33	1736	17 50	18 9	1835	1839	1947	1951	20 16	21 7	—	21 46	22 0	—	...	...
LILLE 23 ....arr	...	6 28	7 34	8 27	9 2	...	9 2	10 35	1156	1256	13 15	1433	16 5	16 17	1840	18 40	19 2	...	1922	2040	2040	21 16	22 7	...	23 7	...	...	...	...
CALAIS 27 ....arr	...	...	...	...	—	...	—	13 0	...	1521	—	...	18 5	—	2228	—	...	...	—	—	...	—	1 36	...	—	...	...	...	...
Mouscron ....dep	4 30	5 23	6 41	7 50	...	8 23	...	9 39	11 7	—	...	1339	15 1	...	1748	...	1814	1843	...	...	1954	...	2118	...	...	22 2	...	...	...
Herseaux	4 39	5 32	6 50	...	...	8 32	...	9 49	1114	...	...	1346	15 8	...	1757	...	...	1853	...	...	20 5	...	2128	...	...	22 9	...	...	...
Tournai ....arr	...	...	7 20	8 9	...	...	...	10 19	1138	...	...	1416	1533	...	1827	...	1833	19 9	...	...	2033	...	2158	...	...	22 25	...	...	...

TOURNAI and ORCHIES.

E.M.																
—	**Tournai** ....dep	4 41	7 53	11 5	15 45	18 53	...	...	**Orchies** ....dep	6 22	9 22	12 42	17 11	21 12	...	...
7½	Rumes	5 13	8 19	11 31	16 12	19 26	...	...	Bachy	6 41	9 40	13 0	17 31	21 29	...	...
10	Bachy ....¶	5 36	8 39	11 57	16 33	19 48	...	...	Rumes ....¶	6 52	9 51	13 12	17 43	21 42	...	...
15½	**Orchies (80)** ......arr	5 52	8 55	12 12	16 48	20 2	...	...	**Tournai** ....arr	7 16	10 15	13 39	18 13	22 9	...	...

¶—Customs Examination.

LANDEN, RAMILLIES, GEMBLOUX, and TAMINES.

*—Sundays excepted.]

E.M.																												
—	Landen ....dep	3 30	...	4 45	...	6 33	838	1039	1227	...	1641	18 5	1927	20 3	Gembloux ...dep	...	5 33	7 27	8 40	1112	1338	1443	1652	1818	19*9	20 2	2043	2219
11½	Ramillies 103B ...dep	4 10	4 23	5 25	6 17	7 14	913	1145	13 6	1534	1724	1839	20 8	2053	Ramillies	5 38	6 1	7 57	9 13	1143	1438	1517	1722	1851	1938	2031	2113	2255
23	Gembloux ....arr	4 43	4 57	—	6 51	7 48	940	1236	1333	16 1	1752	—	2036	2121	Landen ....arr	6 17	...	8 29	9 51	1218	1516	...	1757	1927	2046	2129	...	2327

—	Gembloux ....dep	3 48	4 52	7 0	8 20	9 41	1023	11 30	1334	1654	19 6	2044	Tamines ....dep	4 42	...	6 2	6 42	...	1027	1221	16 0	18 33	2131	...	...	...
9¼	Fleurus	4 14	5 22	7 23	8 52	10 6	1048	12 0	14 13	1750	1930	21 9	Fleurus	5 7	5 22	6 22	7 1	9 44	1047	1240	1621	19 12	2151	...	...	...
15	Tamines ....arr	...	5 39	7 52	9 8	1022	...	12 16	14 30	18 6	...	2125	Gembloux ....arr	5 32	5 47	6 47	7 26	10 8	1111	13 3	1644	1953	2215	...	...	...

FOR FARES SEE PAGE 89. [Luggage, cent. 1·50 per 55 lbs. per kilometre.

LILLE, BRUGES, and OSTEND.

PARIS Nord 23...... dep	2120	...	...	...	2220	2220	2220	...	--	...	8 0	8 0	8 40	...	...	13 0 VS	13 0	...	1430	1720
Lille ....dep	4 53	...	...	5 55	6 42	7 59	8 11	...	9 25	1050	11 9	1128	1331	14 4	1616	17 1	17 6	1825	19 5	2020
Roubaix........	5 14	...	...	6 16	7 1	8 18	8 25	...	9 38	11 9	1122	1142	1350	1424	1633	1713	1723	1844	1922	2032
Tourcoing ...... arr	5 19	...	...	...	7 5	...	8 29	...	9 42	1113	1126	1146	1354	1428	...	1717	1727	...	1926	2036
Tourcoing ...... dep	—	...	6 22	...	7 8	...	8 31	...	9 47	1152	1137	1154	1359	1431	...	1720	1738	...	1934	2046
Halluin	...	...	:	6 43	:	8 44	:	...	1014	1216	:	:	1424	:	1658	:	1756	1912	20 1	:
Menin ...... arr	...	...	C	6 47	C	8 48	C	...	1018	1220	C	C	1428	C	17 2	C	18 0	—	20 5	C
Menin ...... dep	...	...		7 4		9 12		9 22	1034	1231							1812	1836	2040	
Roulers ...... arr	...	...	7 27	7 30	8 21	9 33	9 31	9 43	11 1	1257	1240	13 3	...	1633	...	1814	1833	19 3	21 7	2145
Roulers ...... dep	5 11	6 7	—	7 34	8 24	9 38	9 32	9 46	1121	—	1241	13 6	1515	1637	...	1815	1843	1910	2122	2146
Lichtervelde........	5 37	6 22	...	7 46	8 44	9 50	9 43	9 58	1137	...	RC	1323	1526	17 1	...	...	1855	1928	2138	RC
Thourout ....arr	5 43	6 31	...	7 54	8 50	9 57	9 49	10 5	1143	...	1255	1329	1532	17 7	...	1829	19 1	1934	2144	22 0
Thourout ....dep	5 47	6 33	...	8 1	8 51	10 0	...	...	1144	...	...	1333	1533	1710	...	...	19 3	1936	...	22 5
Zedelghem	6 0	6 44	...	8 13	9 2	...	...	...	1156	...	...	1344	...	1722	...	...	...	1948	...	D
Bruges ....arr	6 17	6 58	...	8 28	9 15	1021	...	...	1210	...	...	1355	1558	1737	...	...	1926	20 3	...	2227
Thourout ....dep 4 41	5†53	...	...	7 59	9 2	...	9 50	10 6	...	11 4	1256	1336	1635	1719	...	1830	19 7	1945	...	22 1
Snaeskerke 5 20	6 31	...	...	8 34	9 39	..	...		...	1143	...	1414	1713	1758	...	...	...	2024	...	...
Ostend ....arr 5 31	6 42	...	...	8 44	9 49	...	1014	1034	...	1153	1320	1425	1723	18 9	...	1854	1945	2034	...	2225

RC—Restaurant Car. **Extra**—Menin to Roulers 15 49, Lille to Halluin 21.5.
C—Via Courtrai. †—Not on Sunday. Customs Examination at Menin.
D—Between Thourout and Bruges runs until 15th September.

ROULERS, COURTRAI, POPERINGHE, HAZEBROUCK.

Roulers ......dep	5 12	5 4	6 0	6 43	7 43	8 23	8 35	10 7	1113	1151	13 5	1349	1353	1428	1454	1627	1717	1758	1938	...	20 5	2152
Ingelmunster	:	5 25	6 17	7 8	...	8 49	:	1021	1132	...	1324	14 8	:	1147		1648	1733	...	20 0	...	2022	22 9
Courtrai ......arr	:	5 44	6 35	7 22	8 4	9 7	:	1033	1144	1212	—	1426	:	15 6	1515	17 6	1745	1819	2019	...	2034	2227
,, ...dep	:	6 19	—	7 51	—	—	:	1047	1231	—	...	1442	:	—	—	1715	1817	—	—	2011	2046	—
Menin	5 42	6 41	...	8 11	...	...	9 7	11 5	1252	...	...	1459	1424	...	...	1732	1835	...	...	2033	21 5	...
Comines ......arr	5 54	6 54	...	8 23	...	...	9 19	1117	13 4	...	...	1511	1436	...	...	1744	1847	...	...	2045	2117	...
,, ...dep	6 11	7 0	...	8 26	...	...	9 23	1119	13 9	...	...	1513	—	...	...	1748	1849	...	...	2049	2119	...
Ypres	6 36	7 18	7 39	9 4	...	1050	9 40	1140	1327	...	1431	1536	..	...	...	18 9	1914	...	2014	21 5	2141	...
Poperinghe ...	6 51	—	7 52	9 19	...	11 3	—	1155	—	...	1444	1556	...	...	...	1825	1928	...	2027	2118	2154	...
Godewaersvelde ...	7 21	...	—	9 43	...	—	...	1219	...	...	—	1617	...	...	...	1846	—	...	—	—	—	...
Hazebrouck ¶	7 40	...	...	10 2	...	...	...	1238	...	...	...	1636	...	...	...	19 5	...	...	...	...	...	...

¶—Customs Examination.

B—To Brussels (Midi arr. 8.54. **MANAGE and OTTIGNIES.** [*—Sunday excepted.

Manage ...dep	4 24	...	5 9	6 4	6 55	8 3	8 23	10 2	12 19	13 33	15 10	...	...	1654	18*12	18 21	...	1930	20 31	22 1
Nivelles (Nord)..	4 45	...	5 32	6 24	7 18	:	8 46	1024	12 41	13 55	15 32	16 21	...	1717	18 27	18 44	...	1953	20 54	22 21
Baulers	4 48	5*22	5 37	6 34	7 32	:	8 57	1029	12 48	14 1	15 36	16 25	1659	1740	18 39	18 48	19 14	20 0	20 57	22 24
Genappe........	—	5 32	5 50	6 44	7 45	:	9 10	1042	13 1	14 14	15 47	—	1712	1753	18 52	—	19 27	2013	—	—
Ottignies...arr	...	—	6 17	7 5	8 11	B	9 35	11 9	13 25	14 39	16 10	...	1737	1818	19 20	...	19 52	2038	...	...

MONS and MANAGE.

[*—Sunday excepted.

Mons ...dep	3 26	4*21	4 40	6 25	6 51	7 4	7 58	8 2	9 24	10 17	...	12 23	14 15	...	15 44	16 24	17 *1	1715	1833	...	20 42
Havré-Ville	3 39	4 39	5 3	6 43	...	7 22	...	8 21	...	10 35	...	12 41	14 33	...	16 1	...	17 20	1733	1851	...	21 0
La Louvière	4 5	5 2	5 41	7 7	7 16	7 47	8 25	8 45	9 47	11 0	12 1	13 5	14 54	16 15	16 23	16 46	17 45	1754	1912	20 14	21 24
Manage 107	4 19	...	5 55	7 20	7 26	8 0	8 35	8 58	9 57	11 14	12 14	13 18	15 8	16 29	16 35	16 56	18 0	18 7	1926	20 24	21 38

Extra.—La Louviere to Manage 6*23, 8.38, 18.49.

†—Sunday excepted. **MONS, BONNE-ESPERANCE, and CHARLEROI.**

Mons ....dep	...	4†15	4 54	6 51	...	7 20	7 58	7 58	...	10 9	...	1226	1324	...	16 24	...	17 13	...	...	1849	21 30
Estinnes	...	4 47	5 29		...	7 49		8 33	...	1041	...	1256	1355	...		...	17 43	...	...	1921	22 0
Faurœulx ...dep	...	...	5 53		6 53	7 32		...	9 44	1037	12 19	...	...	1533		1635	...	...	†	1929	...
Bonne-Espérance	...	4 56	5 59	Via Manage and Luttre.	6 58	7 57	Via Manage and Luttre.	8 41	9 49	1049	12 24	13 5	14 2	1538	Via Manage and Luttre.	1640	17 50	...	1912	1934	22 8
Binche	4 7	5 3	6 7		7 6	8 4		8 45	9 54	1054	12 29	1310	14 9	1545		1646	17 56	...	1919	1940	22 14
Haine St. P. ...arr	4 21	5 23	6 28		7 24	8 22		—	1011	1112	12 49	—	1427	16 4		17 4	18 15	1914	1941	20 0	22 32
Piéton........arr	4 48	5 58	7 1		7 48	8 45		...	—	1135	13 13	...	1448	1629		...	18 37	1934	—	2029	22 57
Marchiennes	5 22	6 21	7 30		8 11	9 11		...	...	12 0	13 38	...	1512	1721		...	19 3	—	...	2059	23 20
Charleroi...arr	5 30	6 29	7 38	8 5	8 17	9 18	9 27	...	...	12 8	13 45	...	1520	1728	17 32	...	1911	...	...	21 7	23 27

Extra.—B. Espéranceto Haine St. P. 5.40, 7.38, 11.29. Haine St. P. to Piéton, 7.35, 9.23, 18.4.

Haine St. Pierre...dep	5 28	6†12	6 54	7 33	8 27	10 21	11 53	12 54	14 37	16 7	17 32	18†15	18 38	20 6	†—Sunday	...
La Louviere........arr	5 38	6 21	7 4	7 43	8 34	10 30	12 0	13 1	14 47	16 14	17 39	18 23	18 48	20 13	excepted.	...

La Louviere........dep	5†20	5†56	6 30	7 19	8 16	11 3	11 35	13 51	15 30	17 2	17 52	18†32	1936	1955	22 15	22 55	...	...
Haine St. Pierre...arr	5 27	6 5	6 39	7 26	8 23	11 12	11 42	14 0	15 37	17 9	18 2	18 39	1946	20 2	22 22	23 2	...	...

ANTWERP and GHENT

Steamer across the Scheldt at Antwerp. †—Sunday excepted.

E.M																			
	Antwerp Waas ...dep	...	5 12	6 46	7 32	9 5	1039	12 12	14 6	15 4	17 8	17†45	1818	18†47	19 †5	1948	2024	21 41	...
3	Zwyndrecht-Burg	...	5 32	7 8	7 52	...	1059	12 30	...	15 24	...	18 5	1841	19 5	19 26	...	2044	...	...
6¼	Beveren (Waas.)	...	5 46	7 20	8 2	9 29	1111	12 42	1432	15 36	1738	18 18	1853	19 15	19 38	2014	2056	22 6	...
11¾	**St. Nicholas (96)** ...	4 34	6 7	7 44	8 17	9 46	1132	13 2	1449	15 56	1753	18 36	1918	19 31	19 57	2033	2114	22 20	...
15½	Sinay........	4 46	6 19	7 55	...	9 56	1143	13 14	...	16 8	18 3	—	1930	—	—	2043	—	...	...
20	**Lokeren (97)**........	5 3	6 34	8 10	8 36	10 7	12 2	13 32	15 7	16 24	1815	...	1946	...	...	21 1	...	22 39	...
26¼	Loochristi........	5 24	6 54	8 32	...	1025	1223	13 53	...	16 44	1834	...	20 6	...	...	...	...	...	...
31	**Ghent** (Sud) ....arr	5 55	7 25	9 10	9 20	11 0	1252	14 28	1548	17 29	19 4	...	2037	...	...	2147	...	23 17	...

Luggage, cent. 1·50 per 55 lbs. per kilometre.] **FOR FARES SEE PAGE 89.**

OSTEND, BRUGES, and LILLE.

[Customs Examination at Halluin.

Ostend ......dep	...	5 17	7 0	7 7	...	7 46	9 52	1111	12 18	1414	15 2	...	...	16 2	1718	...	...	18 0	19 3	...	20 8
Snaeskerke......	...	5 28	RC	7 18	...	7 58	10 4	VS	12 28	...	15 13	...	...	...	RC	...	...	18 11	...	...	20 19
Thourout ...arr	...	6 5	7 24	7 53	...	8 36	10 39	1135	13 5	1438	15 50	...	...	16 41	1742	...	...	18 48	1931	...	20 56
Bruges ...dep	...	5 42	6 58	7 25	8 9	9 16	10 21	...	12 40	...	15 26	...	...	16 28	...	...	19 8	18 24	...	1945	20 53
Zedelghem ...	...	5 59	D	7 39	8 24	9 29	10 36	...	12 55	...	15 43	...	...	...	...	...	...	18 41	...	20 2	21 10
Thourout arr	...	6 10	7 18	7 51	8 34	9 39	10 46	...	13 7	...	15 55	...	...	16 48	...	...	1931	18 53	...	2014	21 22
Thourout ...dep	4 39	6 12	7 25	7 55	8 43	9 41	10 48	1135	13 16	1439	15 58	...	...	16 51	1743	...	1940	19 0	1932	2016	21 24
Lichtervelde ...	4 46	6 21	7 32	8 3	8 51	9 49	10 58		13 29		16 6	...	...	17 3	...	...	1947	19 18	...	2024	21 35
Roulers... arr	5 1	6 36	7 42	8 18	9 6	10 4	11 8	1150	13 44	1453	16 21			17 13	1757	...	1957	19 32	1949	2039	21 50
Roulers... dep	5 4	6 39	7 43	8 35	—	10 7	11 11	1151	13 53	1454	16 27	16 43	1717	17 20	1758	...	20 0	19 36	1951	2041	...
Menin	:	7 12	:	9 21	...	:	11 41	:	15 5	:	:	17 16	:	17 42	:	18 13	2023	20 §2	2012	:	...
Halluin... arr	C	7 17	C	9 25	...	C	11 45	C	15 9	C	C	17 20	C	—	C	18 17		20 40		C	...
Halluin... dep	:	7 30	:	9 39	...	:	11 58	:	15 19	:	:	17 31	:	19 45	:	18 31	—	20 53	—	:	22 11
Tourcoing arr	6 56	...	8 33	10 3	...	11 22	12 23	1241	15 38	1546	18 6	...	1828	20 7	1846	18 56	...	21 22	...	2225	22 32
Tourcoing dep	7 14	...	8 45	10 10	...	11 34	12 36	1256	15 43	16 0	18 23	...	1841	20 18	19 5	19 15	...	21 45	...		22 42
Roubaix	7 20	7 57	8 51	10 19	...	11 40	12 42	13 2	15 51	16 6	18 29	17 54	1853	20 24	1911	19 28	...	21 53	...	—	22 49
Lille (23) ...arr	7 34	8 13	9 2	10 35	..	11 56	12 56	1315	16 5	1617	18 40	18 8	19 2	20 40	1922	19 39	...	22 7	...	...	23 7
PARIS Nord ar	12 7	12 7	12 7	...	...	17 10	17 10	1710	19 20	1920	22 26	...	2226	4 15	2226	...	...	4 37	...	...	...

Extra—Roulers to Menin, 5.12, 10.9; Thourout to Lichtervelde 10.41; Halluin to Tourcoing 5.10; Menin to Lille 13.1.
C—Via Courtrai. **D**—Between Bruges and Thourout until 15th September only. §—Depart 20.35.

HAZEBROUCK, POPERINGHE, COURTRAI, and ROULERS.

Hazebrouck ...dep		...	...	...	...	...	...	...	8 33	...	...	...	...	...	13 31	...	15 56	...	18 27	...	20 46
Godewaersvelde.........		...	...	...	...	...	...	6 36	8 55	...	...	...	...	...	13 50	...	16 18	...	18 48	...	21 8
Poperinghe ¶ dep		4 51	5 35	6 10	7 26	...	...	7 52	9 22	...	...	1036	1156	...	14 15	...	16 43	1745	19 14	...	21 28
Ypres		5 8	5 51	6 25	7 39	8 1	...	8 20	9 43	...	...	1056	1212	...	14 32	...	17 0	1758	19 36	20 33	21 41
Comines ....arr		5 26	6 5	6 39	—	8 19	...	8 38	9 56		...	1114	1230	...	14 45	...	17 17	—	19 54	20 48	—
„ ....dep		5 28	6 7	6 44	...	—	...	8 40	9 58	10 13	...	1122	1232	...	14 47	1533	17 19	...	19 56	—	...
Menin		5 43	6 20	6 56	7 19	...	...	8 54	10 12	10 25	1115	1139	1249	...	15 1	1545	17 44	...	20 13	...	...
Courtrai.............arr		6 1	6 37	:	7 36	...	..	9 11	10 30	:	1134	1154	13 7	...	15 17	—	18 2	...	20 31	...	...
„ ......dep	4 28	—	6 56	:	7 45	8 54	9 10	—	10 43	:	1219	1234	1312	1440	15 55	1753	18 28	1813	20 41	21 24	21 48
Ingelmunster	4 49	...	7 10	:	8 5	9 8	...	...	11 2	:	...	1251	1333	15 0	16 16	...	18 49	1827	21 1	...	22 10
Roulers ......arr	5 7	...	7 27	7 30	8 21	9 24	9 31	...	11 18	11 1	1240	13 3	1350	1513	16 33	1814	19 7	1840	21 17	21 45	22 31

¶—Customs Examination.

OTTIGNIES and MANAGE.

[*-Sun. excepted.

Ottignies ....dep		...	...	4*34	...	6 38	8 6	8 43	9 39	11 54	13 32	14 57	...	1616	...	1751	18 30	20*14	21 12	...
Genappe		4 *0	4*49	5 3	6 *1	7 8	8 24	9 11	10 7	12 28	14 0	15 24	...	1640	...	1817	18 59	20 44	21 40	...
Baulers	3 35	4 13	5 12	5 32	6 13	7 30	8 35	9 27	10 20	12 51	14 29	15 53	1610	17 0	17*28	1838	19 12	20 56	22 14	...
Nivelles (Nord)...	3 39	—	5 16	5 36	—	7 34	8 39	9 31	10 24	12 55	14 33	15 58	1613	17 4	17 34	1842	19 16	—	22 18	...
Manage ......arr	4 0	...	5 38	5 58	...	7 56	8 55	9 54	10 45	13 17	14 55	16 20	—	1726	17 56	19 4	19 38	...	22 39	...

MANAGE and MONS.

*—Sun. excepted.] [†—From Charleroi (Sud).

Manage ...dep	4 19	5 46	6 11	6 55	8 2	8 23	9 6	1020	1047	1120	1333	1514	1648	1733	18†7	18*21	19†8	1921	1943	20 3	22 1
La Louvière......	4 35	6 3	6 28	7 9	8 18	8 39	9 16	1034	11 1	1134	1349	1527	17 0	1749	1818	18 36	1918	1935	1953	2019	2213
Havré-Ville......	4 54	6 22	6 47	7 24	...	8 57	...	...	1120	...	14 8	1545	—	18 8	...	18 55	...	—	—	2038	—
Mons ....arr	5 11	6 39	7 4	7 35	8 41	9 13	9 36	1055	1137	...	1424	16 1	...	1825	1840	19 14	1939	...	...	2055	...

Extra.—Manage to La Louviere 5*42, 22.42.

CHARLEROI, BONNE-ESPERANCE and MONS.

[†—Not on Sunday.

Charleroi...dep	4 34	5 41	6 38	7 11	...	8 32	9 18	...	1057	1158	...	1359	14 49	1622	...	1734	1744	1837	...	19 11	21 26
Marchiennes	4 42	5 50	6 46	7 21	...	Via Luttre and Manage.	9 27	...	11 5	12 6	...	14 7	14 58	1631	...	Via Manage & La Louvière.	1753	Via Manage & La Louvière.	...	19 18	21 35
Piéton	5 10	6 19	7 10	8 0	...		9 55	...	1128	1229	...	1431	15 24	1659	...		1815		18 39	19 44	21 57
Haine St. Pierre	5 33	6 36	7 32	8 25	...		10 22	11 15	1146	1257	14 3	1449	15 46	1720	1732		1841		19 5	20 9	22 26
Binche	5 52	7 30	7 51	8 44	8 51		10 40	11 33	—	1317	14 23	1543	16 4	1738	1753		19 0		19 49	20 27	22 45
Bonne-Esperance	5 59	7 37	7 57	8 50	8 57		10 46	11 39	...	1323	14 29	1549	16 10	1744	1759		19 6		19 56	20 33	22 51
Faurœulx ...arr	...	...	8 2	8 55	...		11 9	...	...	...	14 34	1554	...	1756	18 4		1911		...	...	22 56
Estinnes	6 9	7 50	—	—	9 5		10 56	11 47	...	1332	—	—	16 18	1756	—		—		20 5	20 41	—
Mons (91) ...arr	6 38	8 17	...	...	9 33	9 35	11 28	1213	...	14 4	...	...	16 46	1826	...	1840	...	1939	20 34	21 8	...

Extra.—Piéton to H. St. Pierre 5.0, 8.47, 21.22. H. St. Pierre to B. Espérance 5.14, 5.22, 17†47, 19.12.

MALDEGEM and BRESKENS. (Steam Tramway.)

Maldegem......dep	8 15	10 25	13 42	16 30	19 5	...	...	
Breskens ......arr	10 7	12 18	15 43	18 26	21 9	...	...	

Breskens.........dep	6 0	8 11	10 22	12 58	16 15	...	...	...
Maldegem (93) arr	7 52	10 12	12 16	14 59	18 14	...	...	...

GHENT and ANTWERP.

†—Sunday excepted.]

Ghent Sud.......dep	...	...	...	4 11	...	...	6 1	7 22	8 39	10 20	12 14	1346	16 0	1658	1747	1920	2035	2112	...	...
Loochristi..............	...	...	...	4 42	...	...	6 53	...	9 14	10 54	12 50	...	1631	...	1822	1953	21 8	...	...	...
Lokeren	...	...	4†31	5 6	...	...	7 16	8 4	9 33	11 16	13 12	1433	1652	1745	1845	2017	2131	2155	...	...
Sinay	...	...	4 45	5 18	...	...	7 30	...	9 44	11 30	13 26	...	17 6	...	1859	2029	2143	...	...	...
St. Nicholas	4 14	4†54	5 1	5 34	5†49	6†26	7 44	8 23	9 56	11 44	13 41	1452	1720	18 3	1919	2040	2154	2211	...	...
Beveren..................	4 34	5 8	5 21	5 48	6 9	6 39	8 3	8 36	10 9	12 3	14 0	15 5	1739	1816	1940	2057	22 7	—	...	...
Zwyndrecht............	4 46	...	5 33	...	6 21	...	8 15	...	...	12 15	14 12	...	1751	...	1952	21 7	2217	...	...	...
Antwerp Waas arr	5 3	5 33	5 52	6 13	6 38	7 2	8 33	8 57	1030	12 32	14 30	1528	18 7	1839	2010	2124	2233	...	...	...

FOR FARES SEE PAGE 89. Luggage, cent. 1·50 per 55 lbs. per kilometre.

RC—Restaurant Car.

ERQUELINNES, CHARLEROI, NAMUR, and LIEGE.

PARIS(Nord) 24 dep		22 0	23 15	...	...	...	...	...	...	...	...	...	7 50	...	...	...	8 10	...	...	...	10 25	...	13 45	...	...	16 5	1820
		1 & 2	1,2,3	1,2,3	1,2,3	1,2,3	2 & 3	1,2,3	1,2,3	1,2,3	2 & 3	1,2,3	1 & 2	1,2,3	2 & 3	2 & 3	1 & 2	2 & 3	2 & 3	2 & 3	1,2,3	1,2,3	1 & 2	1,2,3	1,2,3	1,2,3	1 & 2
Maubeuge ......dep		⋮	2 52	...	...	...	...	...	...	6 38	...	7 53	⋮	...	8 52	...	1053	...	1213	...	15 0	17 4	⋮	...	1824	2021	2136
Jeumont		1 0	3 4	...	...	...	...	5 18	...	7 0	...	8 8	⋮	...	9 13	...	11 3	...	1232	...	15 15	1725	16 21	...	1845	2038	2146
Erquelinnes ...arr		1 4	3 7	...	...	...	...	5 21	...	7 3	...	8 12	1021	...	9 17	...	11 6	...	1235	...	15 19	1729	16 24	...	1849	2044	2149
CALAIS 26.........dep		...	...	...	...	...	...	...	...	...	...	...	...	...	...	...	...	...	...	...	...	...	12 50	...	...	...	...
Erqul'ns¶Belg. dep		1 32	3 33	...	...	...	...	5 35	...	7 15	...	8 17	1030	...	9 24	1041	1123	...	1241	...	15 36	1738	16 41	...	1912	2053	22‡7
Lobbes		...	...	...	...	...	...	5 59	...	7 40	...	8 38	...	...	9 48	11 7	...	...	13 4	...	16 4	18 1	...	...	1938	2116	...
Charleroi.........arr		2 1	4 2	...	...	...	...	6 33	...	8 11	...	9 7	1057	...	1021	1139	1151	...	1337	...	16 35	1834	17 8	...	20 9	2146	2236
,, (107)...dep		2 4	4 8	4 52	3 34	...	...	6 41	7 0	8 22	8 34	9 28	1058	...‡	1046	1213	1153	...‡	1357	15 24	18 8	1933	17 10	1738	—	2154	2238
Châtelineau		2 14	4 18	5 11	3 55	...	...	6 54	7 14	8 36	8 52	9 43	...	...	1059	1230	...	...	1432	15 39	18 28	1954	RC	1748	...	2216	...
Tamines		...	4 29	5 31	4 16	...	...	7 6	7 31	8 47	9 11	10 4	B	1121	1118	1250	A	...	1453	16 8	18 49	2020	...	18 1	...	2236	...
Namur..............arr		2 45	4 52	6 20	5 10	...	...	7 30	8 12	9 10	9 52	1046	1135	12 6	1141	1336	1230	...	1541	16 54	19 35	21 3	17 47	1829	2 & 3	2310	2315
,, (92, 103A)	3*56	2 47	4 54	—	5 47	...	6*40	7 35	8 18	9 22	9 55	11 0	1136	1241	14 2	13‡51	1233	...	1545	17‡16	20 26	—	17 49	1833	1840	—	2317
Marche-Dames ...	...	...	...	...	6 3	...	6 56	...	8 31	...	10 9	1113	⋮	1257	1417	...	...	...	1558	17 29	20 40	‡—1, 2, 3 class.	⋮	...	1856	...	...
Namêche	...	A	...	...	6 7	...	7 0	...	8 36	9 36	1013	1118	RC	13 1	1422	...	RC	...	16 3	17 34	20 45		D	...	19 0	...	...
Andenne-Seilles	4 18	...	5 14	2 & 3	6 22	...	7 16	7 55	8 49	9 48	1026	1132	⋮	1315	1437	1410	...	...	1617	17 48	21 0		⋮	1853	1913	...	2337
Statte (98).........	4 43	...	5 25	5*31	6 40	...	7 40	8 6	9 5	10 0	1043	1149	⋮	1332	1458	1421	...	16 7	1639	18 5	21 20		⋮	19 4	1930	...	...
Huy.........	4 49	3 17	5 28	5 40	6 43	6 57	7 43	8 9	9 •8	10 3	1051	12 4	⋮	1336	15 2	1424	13 2	16 9	1642	18 24	21 23		18 18	19 7	1935	...	2349
Amay	5 3	⋮	⋮	5 50	6 53	7 11	7 56	...	9 20	...	11 3	1216	⋮	1346	1514	...	..	1620	1655	18 37	21 36		⋮	...	1948	...	⋮
Engis........	5 17	⋮	⋮	6 4	7 3	7 26	8 11	...	9 31	...	1117	1227	⋮	14 0	1527	...	...	1633	17 8	18 50	21 48		⋮	...	20 2	...	⋮
Flemalle-H. ar	5 23	⋮	⋮	6 10	7 9	7 36	8 20	8 26	9 37	1020	1126	1233	⋮	14 9	1533	1441	1320	1639	1714	18 56	21 55		⋮	1926	2011	...	⋮
Flemalle.dep	5 25	⋮	⋮	6 12	7 12	7 37	8 36	8 27	9 40	1021	1127	1236	⋮	1411	1537	1442	1325	1658	1717	18 59	21 58	Nord Express.	⋮	1930	2012	...	⋮
Seraing.........	5 35	⋮	⋮	6 25	7 23	7 49	8 50	8 35	9 50	1028	1140	1246	⋮	1420	1548	1450	1334	17 7	1727	19 10	22 9		⋮	1939	2025	...	⋮
Liege Long....	5 52	⋮	⋮	6 42	7 40	8 8	9 9	8 45	10 5	1038	1159	13 1	⋮	1434	16 3	15 0	1350	1720	1744	19 26	22 25		⋮	1953	2045	...	⋮
Flemalle-H.dp	...	⋮	⋮	6 11	7 10	7 37	...	8 30	9 43	1022	1129	1236	⋮	1410	1538	1443	1321	1640	1716	18 59	22 1		⋮	1927	2014	...	⋮
Jemeppe-sur-M.	...	⋮	⋮	6 20	7 18	7 47	...	8 39	9 51	1031	1139	1246	⋮	1420	1548	1451	...	1649	1725	19 9	22 11		⋮	...	2023	...	⋮
Liege (Guillem)	...	3 51	6 0	6 37	7 33	8 4	...	8 55	10 5	1047	1156	13 1	1226	1437	16 2	15 6	1335	17 6	1743	19 23	22 24		18 47	1940	2038	...	0 19
VERVIERS (104) arr		4 34	6 50	8 a7	8 18	9 36	...	9 45	11 4	12 7	...	1427	1314	16 2	1755	16 2	1427	1755	1850	...	23 50	1949	19 40	2122	2147	...	1 22
AIX-CHAPELLE arr		6a47	8 a41	10a4	11a5	...	...	1211	1254	2p44	...	4p39	3 p8	6p19	8p21	...	4p39	8p21	9p48	...	...	9p37	9 p48	...	...	...	4a15
COLOGNE (122) arr		8 a0	9 a51	1114	...	...	...	...	2p24	4p34	...	5p55	4p19	7p40	10p28	...	5p55	1028	11p1	...	...	1046	11 p1	...	...	...	5a40

A—Brings forward 3rd class from French Stations, and takes up 3rd class for Herbesthal and beyond. *—Sunday excepted.

D—Attached to this train is a Car of the Nord Express; at Charleroi, Namur, & Huy admits 2cl. for beyond Liége, or coming from branch lines.

Extra.						
Charleroi dep	6 1	1258	1749	2051	22 51	...
Namur ....arr	7 25	1347	1910	2214	23 40	...

B—Admits only passengers coming from France or for Herbesthal and beyond.

¶—Customs Examination. Frequent trains between Flémalle-Haute and Liége.

GIVET and NAMUR.

¶—Customs Examination.

E.M.																				
	Givet ....dep	5 53	6‡37	...	8 1	8 55	...	12 1	...	14 40	...	17 49	19 51	...	...	...	...	...	...	...
2½	Heer-Agimont ¶	6 5	6 49	...	8 14	9 17	...	12 18	...	14 57	...	18 5	20 2	...	...	...	...	...	...	...
5½	**Hastiere 93**	6 15	6 59	7 45	8 22	9 28	11 8	12 28	14 16	15 8	...	18 16	20 13	...	...	...	...	...	...	...
8¾	Waulsort.........	6 24	7 8	7 55	8 30	9 37	11 18	12 37	14 27	15 17	...	18 26	20 24	...	...	...	...	...	...	...
14¼	**Dinant 96**	6 37	7 22	8 10	8 41	9 50	11 35	12 49	14 43	15 30	16 55	18 55	20 40	...	...	...	...	...	...	...
18¾	Yvoir.........	6 49	7 34	8 25	8 52	10 2	11 48	13 1	14 57	15 42	17 8	19 6	20 54	...	...	...	...	...	...	...
21¼	Godinne	6 56	7 41	8 34	...	10 9	11 56	13 8	15 5	15 49	17 16	19 13	21 2	...	...	...	...	...	...	...
23	Lustin	7 2	7 47	8 40	...	10 15	12 2	13 14	15 10	15 55	17 21	19 19	21 7	...	...	...	...	...	...	...
26¾	Dave	7 13	7 57	8 51	...	10 25	12 14	13 25	15 22	16 5	17 33	19 29	21 19	...	...	...	...	...	...	...
29¾	Jambes.........	7 22	...	8 59	...	10 33	12 22	13 33	15 30	16 13	17 40	19 38	21 27	...	...	...	...	...	...	...
31	**Namur (103B)** ...arr.	7 27	8 8	9 4	9 17	10 38	12 27	13 38	15 35	16 18	17 45	19 44	21 32	...	...	...	...	...	...	...

Namur ....dep	6 1	8 16	9 34	10 58	12 46	13 56	1549	17 19	17‡51	18 38	19 18	20 4	...	...	...	...	...	...	...	...	...	...
Jambes.........	6 6	8 22	9 39	11 4	12 51	14 2	1554	17 25	...	18 43	...	20 10	...	...	...	...	...	...	...	...	...	...
Dave	6 15	8 30	9 48	11 12	13 1	14 10	16 4	17 33	18 3	18 53	...	20 18	...	...	...	...	...	...	...	...	...	...
Lustin	6 27	8 40	10 1	11 22	13 13	14 20	1616	17 44	18 13	19 5	...	20 30	...	...	...	...	...	...	...	...	...	...
Godinne	6 33	8 46	10 8	11 28	13 18	14 26	1622	17 51	18 19	19 12	...	20 37	...	...	...	...	...	...	...	...	...	...
Yvoir.........	6 40	8 53	10 15	11 35	13 26	14 33	1631	17 58	18 26	19 20	19 44	20 45	...	...	...	...	...	...	...	...	...	...
Dinant	6 56	9 7	10 31	11 48	13 41	14 47	1644	18 14	18 39	19 37	19 55	20 59	...	...	...	...	...	...	...	...	...	...
Waulsort.........	7 9	9 19	10 42	11 59	13 54	14 58	—	18 25	18 50	19 49	20 6	21 11	...	...	...	...	...	...	...	...	...	...
Hastiere (93) ...arr.	7 19	9 28	10 52	12 8	14 5	15 7	...	18 34	18 59	20 0	20 13	21 19	...	...	...	...	...	...	...	...	...	...
Heer-Agimont	7 28	9 41	—	12 20	—	15 19	...	18 49	19 10	—	20 21	21 30	...	...	...	...	...	...	...	...	...	...
Givet ¶ (71, 98)...arr.	7 35	9 48	...	12 27	...	15 26	...	18 56	19 17	...	20 27	21 37	...	...	...	...	...	...	...	...	...	...

‡—Sunday excepted.

LUTTRE and CHATELINEAU.

Luttre ....dep	5 0	5 56	6 35	7 2	7 56	8 49	1025	11 56	1259	14 8	14 32	15 42	16 9	17 25	1834	18 39	19 0	20 30	22 37
Gosselies-Ville..........	5 19	6 14	6 53	7 20	8 14	9 5	1043	12 14	1317	14 26	14 50	15 56	16 27	17 42	⋮	18 56	19 17	20 48	22 52
Jumet-Brulotte.........arr	5 30	6 24	7 4	7 31	8 25	9 14	1054	12 23	1328	14 36	15 1	16 2	16 38	17 51	⋮	19 7	19 25	20 54	23 0
Jumet-Brulotte dep	5 34	⋮	7 6	7 40	—	9 18	—	12 28	—	14 38	—	16 4	—	...	⋮	19 10	⋮	20 56	⋮
Charleroi ....arr	5 54	⋮	7 27	7 58	...	9 33	...	12 46	...	14 56	...	16 22	...	...	1857	19 31	⋮	21 14	⋮
Chatelineau ....arr	6 13	6 50	...	8 8	...	9 41	...	12 54	...	15 5	...	16 26	...	18 18	...	...	19 50	21 24	23 22
Chatelineau ....dep	5 2	6 35	7 18	...	8 53	...	...	11 52	...	13 32	...	15 27	...	1714	...	18 38	...	21 52	2216
Charleroi ....dep	5 7	6 42	⋮	7 42	8 52	10 8	...	12 1	...	13 47	...	15 27	...	⋮	17 47	18 40	20 19	⋮	⋮
Jumet-Brulotte arr	5 27	7 0	⋮	8 4	9 10	10 29	...	12 19	...	14 5	...	15 45	...	⋮	18 6	19 0	20 40	⋮	⋮
Jumet-Brulotte.........dep	5 32	7 2	7 43	8 5	9 19	10 30	1142	12 23	13 33	14 7	15 5	15 49	1635	1742	18 8	19 6	20 41	22 19	22 41
Gosselies-Ville..........	5 43	7 12	7 52	8 16	9 29	10 41	1153	12 33	13 50	14 17	1517	15 59	1647	1752	18 20	19 15	20 53	22 27	22 51
Luttre ....arr	5 59	7 27	8 6	8 32	9 43	10 57	12 9	12 46	14 6	14 32	1533	16 12	17 8	18 7	18 35	19 29	21 9	22 41	23 7

Luggage, cent. 1·50 per 55 lbs. per kilometre.] FOR FARES SEE PAGE 89.

LIEGE, NAMUR, CHARLEROI, and ERQUELINNES.

RC—Restaurant Car.

Station																														
COLOGNE 123B dep		10p52	...	...	...	...	...	...	6 a0	...	...	7a56	8 a7	9 a10	...	...	11a26	...	...	1237	1p42	3p12	...	...	...	4 p19	...	6 p13	...	...
AIX-CHAPELLE dep		12a10	...	...	...	...	...	...	7a37	...	...	9a12	9a23	10a32	...	...	12p56	...	...	2p46	3p16	4p29	...	...	...	5 p47	...	7 p27	...	...
VERVIERS 104...dep		0 17	3 50	5 19	...	6 7	6 56	...	7 55	...	...	9 11	9 23	10 43	10 53	...	13 9	1352	...	15 0	1525	1630	1650	...	...	17 43	18 8	20 8	...	...
		1 & 2	1,2,3	1,2,3	2&3	1 & 2	1,2,3	2&3	1,2,3	2&3	1,2,3	1 &2		1,2,3	1,2,3	1,2,3	1,2,3	1,2,3	1,2,3	2&3	2&3	1,2,3	1,2,3	1,2,3	1,2,3	1 & 2	2 & 3	1,2,3	1,2,3	2 & 3
Liege Guillem dep		1 1	5 28	6 27	6 33	7 20	7 38	8 22	9 7	...	10 26	1015	Nord Express	11 32	11 40	12 18	1353	15 0	...	1547	1621	1710	1731	...	18 9	18 35	19 43	21 19	...	...
Jemeppe-sur-Meuse..		A	5 45	...	6 48	:	7 53	8 36	9 19	...	10 43	: B		...	11 55	12 35	14 8	1516	...	16 4	1636	:	1745	...	1826	:	19 56	21 33	...	...
Flemalle-H'te arr		‡	5 54	6 41	6 57	:	8 1	8 44	9 28	...	10 53	:		11 45	12 4	12 45	1416	1525	...	1613	1646	:	1754	...	1836	:	20 4	21 42	...	...
Liege Longdoz dep		:	5 30	6 18	...	:	7 35	8 22	9 3	...	10 30	:		11 20	11 40	12 15	1350	1455	16 0	1530	1615	:	1728	18 0	1820	:	19 27	21 15	2155	23 15
Seraing..................		:	5 48	6 32	...	:	7 51	8 35	9 19	...	10 44	:		11 34	11 57	12 36	14 7	1512	1611	1549	1628	: A	1746	18 12	1838	:	19 49	21 32	22 6	23 28
Flemalle-H. arr		:	5 59	6 41	...	:	8 0	8 44	9 28	...	10 53	:		11 43	12 6	12 50	1417	1522	1617	16 2	1637	:	1756	18 18	1848	:	20 4	21 42	:	23 37
Flemalle-H'te dep		:	6 2	6 42	6 58	:	8 3	8 46	9 30	...	10 54	:		11 46	12 8	12 51	1418	1528	1618	1623	1646	:	1759	18 20	1850	:	20 7	21 44	...	23 38
Engis.....................		:	6 9	...	7 7	:	8 10	8 52	9 37	...	11 3	:		...	12 15	13 0	1425	1536	...	1631	1654	:	18 6	...	1857	C	20 17	21 54	22‡19	23 45
Amay		:	6 20	...	7 21	:	8 22	9 6	9 46	...	11 17	:		...	12 27	13 14	1437	1549	...	1645	—	:	1817	...	19 9	:	20 33	22 11	22‡27	23 56
Huy....................		1 35	6 32	7 1	7 50	7 48	8 35	—	9 58	...	11 34	1049	—	12 6	12 40	13 28	1449	16 3	1637	17 1	...	1740	1830	18 39	1921	:	20 50	22 26	2236	0 6
Statte (98)...............		...	6 36	...	7 53	...	8 39	...	10 2	...	11 36	...	...	12 9	12 47	13 30	1452	16 6	1640	17 3	...	...	19 3	18 42	—	:	20 52	—	2239	—
Andenne-Seilles		A	6 52	7 13	8 9	...	8 54	...	10 14	...	11 52	RC	...	12 20	13 4	—	15 8	1623	1651	1718	...	...	1919	18 53	...	RC	21 6		2250	...
Namêche		...	7 5	...	8 24	...	9 8	...	10 28	...	12 6	...	...	...	13 19	...	1522	1638	...	1733	...	RC	1931	...	...	:	21 21		...	...
Marche-les-Dames ...		...	7 10	...	8 28	...	9 13	...	...	...	12 10	...	...	E	13 24	...	1527	1643	...	1737	...	...	1936	...	...	:	21 25		...	...
Namur (111)......arr		2 9	7 23	7 32	8 44	8 14	9 26	1,2,3	10 42	...	12 26	1118	1,2,3	12 38	13 37	...	1540	1657	1710	1753	...	18 9	1948	19 12	...	19 25	21 39		2310	1,2,3
,, ...dep	5 24	2 12	7 38	7 34	9 33	8 16	9 38	1047	10 51	1159	—	1121	14 2	12 45	14 49	...	16 3	1720	1716	—	1857	1811	—	19 52	...	19 26	21 51	¶—Customs Examination.	2316	3 44
Tamines	6 12	...	8 27	8 0	10 4	...	10 25	1113	11 32	1245	...	...	14 47	13 11	15 15	...	1651	18 9	1742	...	1958	A	...	20 39	...	...	22 38		2342	4 36
Châtelineau ...	6 33	2 46	8 51	8 11	1015	...	10 44	1125	11 58	1311	...	...	15 8	13 22	15 28	...	1712	1831	1753	...	2018	...	...	21 0	...	...	22 58		2353	5 6
Charleroi ...arr	6 48	2 56	9 8	8 21	1028	8 57	10 59	1139	12 15	1326	...	12 5	15 23	13 32	15 41	...	1727	1847	18 7	...	2033	1852	...	21 15	...	20 7	23 13		0 5	5 24
,, ...dep	7 4	3 0	9 36	8 43	—	9 0	11 1	—	12 24	—	...	12 6	—	13 36	16 10	13 52	1750	1925	—	...	—	1854	...	21 20	...	20 8	—		—	5 38
Lobbes	7 37	...	10 8	9 25	...	...	11 32	...	12 57	...	...	...	...	E	16 41	14 26	1827	1959	...	...	...	...	...	21 53	...	...	...		...	6 18
Erquelinnes	8 1	3 31	10 31	9 49	...	9 29	11 57	...	13 21	...	...	1234	...	14 7	17 4	14 51	1851	2024	...	...	...	1921	...	22 16	...	20 35	...		...	6 43
CALAIS (27)......arr		...	...	...	...	...	...	...	...	...	...	1531	...	...	...	...	...	...	...	...	...	...	...	...	...	...	...		...	...
Erquelinnes...dep		3 34	10 34	9 57	...	9 30	11 58	...	13 22	...	...	1235	...	14 9	17 5	14 57	1853	2055	...	...	...	1922	...	22 17	...	20 36	...		...	6 50
Jeumont ¶		4 15	10 57	1011	...	9 46	12 24	...	13 55	...	...	13 2	...	14 36	17 25	15 16	19 9	2130	...	...	...	1940	...	22 40	...	20 55	...		...	7 16
Maubeuge ......arr		:	11 11	1030	...	9 54	12 38	...	14 8	...	...	:	...	14 45	17 46	15 30	1926	2146	...	...	...	1949	...	22 59	...	:	...		...	7 32
PARIS (Nord) 24 arr		7 35	15 50	1550	...	12 51	...	...	...	...	...	16 0	...	18 5	...	21 56	2246	4 5	...	...	...	22 46	...	...	...	23 30	...		...	...

‡—Sets down only.

Frequent trains between Liege & Flemalle-Haute.

A—Admits 3rd Class for Jeumont and beyond.

B—Attached to this train is a Car of the Nord Express.

C—Admits only passengers from Germany or for Jeumont and beyond.

Extra.—Namur to Charleroi, 4.33, 6.40. Liege (Longdoz) to Namur, 3.47.

E—From Namur to Charleroi inclusive will only take up in 3rd class passengers for Erquelinnes and beyond.

GHENT, EECLOO, and BRUGES.

E.M													
	Ghent (Sud)......dep	...	6 14	7 14	8 58	1031	1229	1550	1738	1923	2017	2131	...
3¾	,,(Porte d' Anvers)	...	6 33	7 26	9 14	1044	1244	16 6	1756	1941	2033	2144	...
10½	Sleydinge	...	6 55	7 48	9 36	11 6	13 6	1630	1819	20 3	2055	22 4	...
16¼	**Eecloo**..............	5 27	7 20	8 3	9 55	1121	1322	1649	1836	2018	2112	2218	...
22¼	Maldegem	5 46	7 40	8 22	1014	1140	1341	17 8	1856	2039	2129	—	...
33½	**Bruges** ....arr	6 18	8 12	8 54	1044	1212	1413	1740	1928	2111	2157	...	...

Bruges..............dep	...	5 12	6 29	8 57	10 8	1227	1537	1757	1941	2158	...	...
Maldegem..................	...	5 45	7 2	9 30	1041	13 0	1610	1830	2014	2227	...	...
Eecloo	5 23	6 6	7 22	9 55	11 6	1322	1630	1854	2038	2243	...	...
Sleydinge..................	5 38	6 21	7 37	1010	1121	1337	1645	19 9	2053	—	...	...
Ghent (P. d' A.)...arr	5 59	6 43	7 58	1029	1142	1358	17 6	1930	2115	...	...	...
,, (Sud) ...... ,,	6 16	7 1	8 9	1042	1158	14 9	1719	1949	2126	...	...	...

LUTTRE and BOULEVARD CENTRAL.

Luttre ....dep	7 56	1025	1121	1259	1432	16 9	...	...	...
Jumet-Brulotte	8 26	1055	1155	1336	15 5	1639	...	...	...
Boulevard Central........	8 44	1113	1212	1353	1523	1657	...	...	...

Boulevard Central	9 25	1123	1314	1446	16 7	1714	...	...	...	...
Jumet-Brulotte	9 44	1142	1338	15 5	1626	1732	1742	...	...	...
Luttre ....arr	1012	12 9	14 6	1533	1653	...	18 7	...	...	...

HASTIERE and ANOR.

¶-Customs Examination.

E.M Dist							
	NAMUR 92 ....dep	...	8 16	10 58	13 56	17 19	...
	Hastiére ....dep	6 16	9 30	12 10	15 20	18 41	...
6¾	Doische	6 33	9 50	12 32	15 42	19 3	...
18¾	Mariembourg	7 11	10 26	13 2	16 20	19 50	...
24¾	Aublain	7 28	10 44	13 18	16 40	20 6	...
28½	Chimay	7 46	11 2	13 34	16 58	20 22	...
31	Villers-la-Tour	7 54	11 10	13 41	17 6	20 30	...
36	Momignies	8 12	11 28	13 57	17 24	20 48	...
41	**Anor** ¶.....................arr	8 21	11 37	14 7	17 34	20 57	...

Anor ....dep	5 56	9 40	12 46	15 40	18 33	...	...
Momignies ¶	6 15	10 2	13 8	16 2	18 54	...	...
Villers-la-Tour..............	6 30	10 18	13 24	16 18	19 10	...	...
Chimay	6 38	10 30	13 33	16 28	19 18	...	...
Aublain	6 50	10 44	13 47	16 40	19 32	...	...
Mariembourg 97	7 14	11 4	14 4	17 1	19 52	...	...
Doische	7 51	11 36	14 37	17 40	20 25	...	...
Hastiére ....arr	8 8	11 50	14 52	17 58	20 40	...	...
NAMUR (92)...........arr	9 17	13 38	16 18	19 44	...	...	...

FOR FARES SEE PAGE 89. [Luggage, cent. 1·50 per 55 lbs. per Kilometre.

GHENT, DIXMUDE, NIEUPORT, and DUNKIRK.

¶—Customs Examination.

Station													
Ghent Sud......dep	...	4 59	6 12	...	...	...	...	11 33	1540	1552	17 [illegible]	...	19 27
„ St. Pierre „	...	...	6 19	7 27	8 50	...	...	11 40	...	...	...	18 14	19 34
La Pinte	...	...	6 32	7 38	...	...	...	11 55	...	16 9	1758	...	19 44
Deynze	...	5 20	6 48	7 50	9 7	1017	...	12 12	1612	1626	1814	18 31	19 55
Thielt............	...	5 46	7 14	8 13	9 29	1040	...	12 39	1633	1649	1840	18 51	20 21
Pitthem............	...	5 54	7 22	8 22	...	—	...	12 47	1641	—	1848	...	20 29
Lichtervelde	...	6 28	7 54	8 42	9 51	...	1139	13 28	17 0	...	1929	19 9	20 48
Cortemarck	...	6 39	8 9	8 56	10 2	...	1150	13 43	1714	...	1940	19 20	21 19
Dixmude ......arr	...	7 3	8 32	9 19	1016	...	1214	14 6	1737	...	20 3	19 34	21 42
Dixmude ......dep	...	7 26	8 48	9 43	1020	1153	1229	14 17	1746	1834	2023	19 37	21 51
Nieuport (Town)	...	7 59	9 8	10 16	1037	1226	13 2	14 50	1819	1859	21 2	19 54	22 19
„ (Baths) arr	...	8 5	9 14	10 22	1043	1232	13 8	14 56	1825		...	20 0	22 25
Dixmude ......dep	...	7 15	8 34	9 21	1026	...	1222	14 11	1739	—	20 5	19 42	21 44
Furnes	5 30	7 43	9 2	9 52	1047	...	1250	14 40	18 5	...	2032	20 3	22 5
Adinkerke Panne...	5 37	7 54	9 9	10 4	1054	11 8	1257	14 56	1814	1618	—	20 21	22 29
Ghyvelde ¶	6 51	8 13	—	10 38	—	1136	—	15 36	1838	1648	...	20 47	22 47
Rosendael............	7 9	8 34	...	11 2	...	1155	...	15 59	1859	17 7	...	21 8	23 7
Dunkirk (26) arr	7 17	8 43	...	11 12	-	12 3	...	16 9	19 9	1715	...	21 18	23 17

Station													
Dunkirk.........dep	...	5 4	5 49	...	9 0	10 5	1052	...	1255	1446	1656	...	19 24
Rosendael............	...	5 14	5 59	...	9 9	10 14	11 4	...	13 6	1457	17 6	...	19 33
Ghyvelde	...	5 36	6 21	...	9 28	10 34	1127	...	1328	1525	1729	...	19 50
Adinkerke Panne ¶	...	6 0	6 41	...	9 45	11 14	1147	1326	1336	1543	1750	1853	20 24
Furnes	4 31	6 8	6 49	...	9 53	11 33	1155	1344	—	1551	18 3	19 1	20 32
Dixmude ......arr	4 53	6 28	7 15	...	1019	11 49	1222	1411	...	1618	1829	1925	20 52
Nieuport (B.) dep	...	6 10	6 28	8 35	9 45	11 5	...	1325	...	1532	1736	1855	20 31
„ (Town) „	...	6 16	6 34	8 41	9 51	11 11	...	1331	...	1538	1745	19 1	20 37
Dixmude ......arr	...	6 33	7 8	9 15	1011	11 44	...	14 5	...	1611	1818	1935	20 58
Dixmude ......dep	4 54	6 39	7 17	...	1021	11 50	1236	1413	...	1621	1831	...	21 5
Cortemarck	5 21	6 59	7 45	...	1047	12 10	13 8	1437	...	1648	19 1	...	21 24
Lichtervelde	5 32	7 8	8 5	...	1056	12 19	1327	—	...	17 5	1936	...	21 33
Pitthem............	5 53	7 21	8 24	...	1114	...	1348	...	...	1726	20 0	...	...
Thielt............	6 2	7 29	8 33	9 8	1123	12 37	1357	1523	...	1735	2020	...	21 51
Deynze	6 27	7 47	8 54	9 32	1144	12 58	1422	1546	...	18 0	2046	...	22 9
La Pinte	6 43	...	9 6	—	...	...	1439	1624	...	1817	21 0	...	...
Ghent St. Pierre arr	6 57	8 3	...	...	...	...	...	1633	...	1831	2112	...	22 25
„ Sud **97** arr	7 4	...	9 24	...	12 7	13 18	1454	1645	...	1838	2119	...	...

MONS, DOUR, and QUIEVRAIN.

Station														
Mons.........dep	†	...	5 38	7 28	8 57	10 4	11 43	...	1433	16 5	1719	1844	1945	21 22
Flénu-Produits	...	...	5 55	7 43	9 12	1019	11 58	...	1449	1622	1734	19 0	20 0	21 39
Warquignies ...	4 54	...	6 19	8 1	9 30	1035	12 15	...	15 9	1647	1748	1918	2018	21 57
Dour	5 4	5 49	6 29	8 12	—	1044	12 25	1340	1520	1658	1758	1927	2028	22 7
Roisin ...arr	...	6 13	7 16	8 40	...	1110	12 55	14 3	1549	—	1824	1951	...	...
Bavai 30A arr	...	6 54	...	9 11	...	...	13 13	—	1640	...	1850	—	...	...
Elouges............	5 10	—	6 37	8 19	...	1051	12 40	...	1526	...	18 5	...	2034	22 13
Quievrain arr	5 18	...	6 45	8 27	...	1059	12 48	...	1534	...	1813	...	2042	22 21

†—Sunday excepted.

Station													
Quievrain dep	...	5 28	6 26	7 32	8 59	11 21	12 31	13 8	1439	16 13	18 41	...	21 10
Elouges............	...	5 37	6 36	7 41	9 8	11 30	12 40	13 17	1448	16 22	18 51	...	21 19
Bavai 20 dep	...	...	6 4	...	8 18	...	...	12 33	...	15 39	18 8	...	...
Roisin ...dep	...	...	6 22	7 22	8 48	11 16	...	13 2	1426	15 59	18 31	19 58	...
Dour	†	5 44	6 46	7 49	9 15	11 38	12 45	13 26	1454	16 28	19 0	20 21	21 25
Warquignies ...	4 59	5 56	6 57	8 0	9 26	11 47	12 57	13 39	15 6	16 37	19 11	20 29	21 36
Fl-Produits......	5 17	6 18	7 13	8 18	9 42	12 3	13 14	...	1523	16 54	19 29	—	21 53
Mons 100 ...arr	5 33	6 33	7 28	8 32	9 56	12 16	13 29	14 10	1537	17 8	19 43	...	22 7

ANSEGHEM and INGELMUNSTER.

E.M.	Station						
—	**Anseghem** dep	7 12	1049	14 10	16 21	19 28	
6½	Waereghem	7 33	1138	14 30	16 49	20 18	
15¼	**Ingelmunster**	7 59	12 4	14 53	17 19	20 45	

Station							
Ingelmunster	5 42	9 18	13 7	15 6	17 40	20 25
Waereghem	6 12	9 46	13 36	15 33	18 24	20 52
Anseghem arr	6 31	10 36	13 55	15 52	18 43	...

*—Sun. excepted.]

HAINE ST. PIERRE, HOUDENG, and SOIGNIES.

E.M.	Station								
	Haine St. Pierre dep	3*59	5 40	...	8 40	...	1433	1836	2013
3	Houdeng (98)	4 8	5 53	6 57	8 52	10 7	1443	1847	2023
11¼	Soignies (108) ...arr	4 36	6 22	7 22	9 20	1035	15 9	1914	2049

Station									
Soignies ...dep	4*42	6 27	7 34	9 29	1057	12 7	1646	1921	2054
Houdeng......arr	5 12	6 51	8 2	9 58	1127	1236	1717	1950	2121
Haine S.P. 98arr	5 24	...	8 11	...	1138	1246	1728	20 0	2132

Dist. *—Sunday excepted.

ST. GHISLAIN and WARQUIGNIES.

E.M.	Station						
	St. Ghislain 108 dep	4*40	6 2	7 44	11 19	14 50	17 20
3	Warquignies 94...arr	4 49	6 13	7 55	11 31	15 1	17 32

Station										
Warquignies .dep	6 13	8 15	9 31	11 48	1339	1517	1639	1752	1915	2035
St. Ghislain....arr	6 24	8 26	9 42	11 59	1350	1528	1650	18 3	1924	2044

ATH and ST. GHISLAIN.

E.M.	Station					
	Ath ....dep	5 2	8 42	12 42	16 3	19 58
6¾	Vaudignies-Neufmaison	5 26	9 6	13 6	16 27	20 25
14¼	St. Ghislain 108 ....arr	5 55	9 33	13 35	16 54	2053

Station						
St. Ghislain ....dep	6 31	7 47	10 59	13 56	18 13	19 37
Vaudignies-Neufmaison ...	7 0	8 14	11 26	14 25	18 44	20 4
Ath 102B.......................arr	7 23	8 36	11 47	14 44	19 7	20 26

THIELT and INGELMUNSTER.

Station										
Thielt..........	7 38	8 29	1041	1134	1246	1425	1652	1750	1920	2030
Ingelmunster	7 55	8 46	1057	1150	13 3	1440	1710	18 5	1937	2047

Station										
Ingel.	7 11	8 7	8 48	11 4	1211	1339	15 6	1654	1852	20 0
Thielt	7 26	8 23	9 3	1120	1228	1354	1522	1711	1910	2015

‡—Not on Sunday.

TIRLEMONT and TONGRES.

E.M.	Station								
	Tirlemont dep	4 16	6 49	8 20	12 50	‡	14 50	18 15	20 57
7½	Drieslinter **98**	4 36	7 9	8 36	13 3	1444	15 10	18 35	21 17
10	Léau	4 44	7 22	8 44	13 11	1451	15 19	18 43	21 28
13¾	St. Trond **99** ...	4 59	7 38	9 10	13 24	15 9	15 48	18 57	21 42
28	**Tongres 116**ar	5 49	8 27	10 0	14 11	16 1	16 38	19 49	22 30

Station							
Tongres ...dep	4 11	7 9	10 42	12 58	14 23	18 29	20 30
St. Trond	5 9	8 10	11 33	13 47	15 8	19 21	21 17
Léau	5 20	8 21	11 44	13 58	15 19	19 32	21 28
Drieslinter	5 27	8 28	11 51	14 5	15 26	19 39	21 36
Tirlemont arr	5 50	8 51	12 14	14 24	15 47	20 2	21 50

BLATON and BERNISSART.

Station										
Blaton arr	4 27	5 19	7 0	8 40	1050	1240	1430	1645	1752	1940
Bernissart	4 39	5 31	7 13	8 52	11 3	1252	1442	1657	18 4	1952

Station										
Bernissart dep	4 50	6 38	7 59	1024	1213	14 4	1613	1724	1911	20 2
Blaton (100)arr	5 2	6 50	8 11	1036	1225	1416	1625	1736	1923	2014

†—Sun. excepted.]

BLATON and QUEVAUCAMPS.

Station											
Blaton	5 30	7 0	8 40	1050	1245	1430	1642	1748	18†40	1939	2038
Quevaucamps	5 46	7 16	8 56	11 6	13 1	1446	1658	18 4	18 56	1955	2054

Station											
Quevau	6 35	8 2	1019	1210	1356	16 0	1715	18†14	19 6	20 5	21 4
Blaton	6 51	8 18	1035	1226	1412	1616	1731	18 30	1922	2020	2120

SAINT-GHISLAIN and JURBISE.

E.M.	Station								
	St. Ghislain ...dep	4 37	6 29	7 45	9 55	12 43	15 43	18 10	19 42
8	Jurbise 108 ......arr	4 58	6 48	8 8	10 13	13 5	16 5	18 32	20 4

Station							
Jurbise ....dep	7 6	8 22	10 24	14 16	16 47	19 3	2037
St. Ghislain ...arr	7 24	8 43	10 45	14 37	17 8	1921	2055

Luggage, cent. 1·50 per 55 lbs. per kilometre.] FOR FARES SEE PAGE 89.

ANTWERP to HOOGSTRAETEN and TURNHOUT.

†—Sunday excepted.

(Zurenborg)																	
Antwerp ....dep		6 50	9 16	1130	1411	1630	1740	1919	0 0	**Hoogstraeten**.........dep	5 20	7 36	10 0	1217	1449	1712	20 1
Wyneghem..................		7 21	9 47	12 4	1441	17 2	1811	1950	0 41	Oost-Malle	6 13	8 14	1039	1255	1529	1752	2040
Oost-Malle	6 7	8 10	1034	1251	1528	1749	1858	2037	1 34	Wyneghem..................	7 1	9 1	1126	1342	1616	1839	2127
Hoogstraeten arr	6 42	8 50	1116	1331	16 8	1828	...	2117	...	**Antwerp** (Zurenborg)	7 32	9 32	1157	1411	1647	1910	2158

E.M.																			
	Oost-Malle ...dep	1 37	6 5	8 16	1040	1255	1531	1752	19†1	2041	**Turnhout** dep	5 24	6†22	7 40	10 1	1216	1450	1713	20 0
8¾	**Turnhout** ......arr	2 10	6 40	8 51	1115	1330	16 6	1827	1940	2116	**Oost-Malle** arr	6 2	6 59	8 12	1036	1251	1525	1748	2035

ROULERS and YPRES.

Roulers ......dep	5 28	7 48	8 29	1012	11 24	1356	1722	19 40	**Ypres** ....dep	5 25	6 43	7 44	1014	12 20	1433	1537	18 7	19 41
Moorslede-Pass.	5 45	8 6	8 42	1025	11 41	14 9	1738	19 53	Moorslede-Pass.	5 44	7 9	8 4	1041	12 39	1452	16 3	18 26	20 16
Ypres (90)...arr	6 10	8 31	9 0	1043	12 6	1427	18 3	20 11	**Roulers** ......arr	5 56	7 25	8 16	1057	12 51	15 4	1619	18 38	20 32

MARBEHAN and ECOUVIEZ.

‡—Sunday excepted.

Dist. E.M.																		
	Marbehan...dep	...	4 37	7 37	1046	1130	13 19	...	16 54	20‡13	22 23	**Ecouviez** ...dep	4 58	9 5	...	12 29	14 1	18 45
7½	Croix-Rouge ...	...	4 58	7 58	...	1152	13 39	...	17 15	20 34	22 44	**Lamorteau** ¶...	5 14	9 20	...	13 15	1436	18 55
15	Virton	...	5 24	8 22	1124	1216	14 2	...	17 42	20 58	23 10	Virton-St-Mard	6 12	9 37	1222	13 33	1452	19 7
16¼	Virton-St-Mard	4 6	5 55	8 44	1128	1224	14 8	1554	17 46	21 2	23 14	Virton	6 17	9 42	1227	—	1457	19 12
20	Lamorteau	4 17	6 6	8 55	—	1235	14 18	16 5	18 18	—	—	Croix-Rouge ...	6 44	10 8	1249	...	1523	19 38
24¾	Ecouviez ¶ (67)	4 32	6 16	9 25	...	1252	14 25	1615	19 12	...	...	**Marbehan** ...arr	7 4	1028	13 8	...	1543	19 57

Extra						
Ecouviez.............dep	5 55	1550	Virton-St-M....dep	3 29	15 56	¶—Customs
Virton St. Mard arr	7 37	1637	Marbehan ......arr	4 27	16 35	Examination.

THOUROUT and YPRES.

*—Sundays excepted.

Thourout ....dep	6 20	7 57	8 37	13 20	15 51	17 0	19 17	20 59	...	...
Cortemarck......................	6 30	8 6	8 47	13 30	16 1	17 10	19 27	21 9	...	...
Staden	6 54	—	9 9	13 54	—	17 26	19 57	—	...	...
Langemarck	7 12	...	9 26	14 11	...	17 44	20 14	...	...	...
Ypres (95) ....arr	7 26	...	9 40	14 25	...	17 59	20 28	...	...	...

Ypres ....dep	...	...	6 54	...	9 56	1219	...	15 37	...	...	18 10	...
Langemarck	...	...	7 10	...	10 11	1234	...	15 52	...	...	18 25	...
Staden................	...	*	7 28	...	10 29	1251	...	16 9	...	...	18 43	...
Cortemarck	4 25	5 41	7 47	8 27	10 51	13 6	14 42	16 24	16 50	18 32	19 6	...
Thourout (90)...arr	4 34	5 51	7 56	8 37	11 1	1316	14 52	16 34	17 0	18 43	19 16	...

COMINES and ARMENTIERES.

Comines........................dep	6 16	8 28	1132	15 21	17 51	21 20	...	...	...	...
Le Touquet	6 37	8 48	1154	15 42	18 14	21 46	...	...	...	...
Houplines ¶	6 44	8 57	12 6	15 53	18 26	21 58	...	...	...	...
Armentières ....arr	6 49	9 2	1212	15 58	18 32	22 4	...	...	...	...

Armentières...dep	4 36	7 33	10 35	14 4	16 36	19 14	...	...	...	
Houplines	4 44	7 39	10 42	14 11	16 43	19 22	...	...	...	¶—Customs
Le Touquet ¶	4 56	7 52	10 54	14 24	16 56	19 33	...	...	...	Examination.
Comines (21,90) arr	5 19	8 9	11 11	14 41	17 13	19 50	...	...	...	

‡—At Stelplaats.]

OSTEND and PANNE.

Ostend Station ....dep	4‡35	5 56	7 40	9 40	1044	1226	1414	1730	2010	...	...	...	...	...	...	...	...	...	...
Nieuport	5 24	6 56	8 40	1040	1142	1324	1512	1831	21 4	...	...	...	...	...	...	...	...	...	...
Furnes	5 57	8 5	9 50	1124	1232	1418	16 6	1924	2154	...	...	...	...	...	...	...	...	...	...
Panne.........................arr	6 13	8 27	1012	1140	...	1440	1628	1946	...	...	...	...	...	...	...	...	...	...	...

Panne ....dep.	...	6 18	8 34	...	1028	1210	...	1450	1732	19 54	...	...	...	...	...	...	...	...	...	...
Furnes..............................	5 0	6 50	8 50	10 4	1050	1226	1310	1516	18 4	20 20	...	...	...	...	...	...	...	...	...	...
Nieuport.............................	5 51	7 41	9 36	105	—	13 1	14 1	16 7	1857	21 3	...	...	...	...	...	...	...	...	...	...
Ostend Station...........arr	6 50	8 40	1035	1154	...	14 0	15 0	17 5	1956	21‡50	...	...	...	...	...	...	...	...	...	...

LIBRAMONT and GOUVY.

Libramont...dep	...	6 47	8 19	11 16	1424	16 54	21 3	...	**Gouvy** ......dep	...	6 5	8 47	12 9	14 24	1732	...	21 30	...
Bernimont.........	...	6 58	8 30	11 27	1435	17 5	21 18	...	**Bastogne**.........	5 50	6 59	9 30	1257	15 15	1821	19 30	22 19	...
Morhet	...	7 16	8 52	11 48	1457	17 27	21 43	...	**Morhet**............	6 8	7 18	9 46	1317	15 33	—	19 48	—	...
Bastogne (95) ...	4 6	7 33	9 36	12 20	1516	17 46	22 4	...	Bernimont	6 30	7 40	10 4	1340	15 55	...	20 10	...	...
Gouvy 100 ...arr	4 52	8 13	1023	13 11	16 5	18 36	...	...	**Libramont**......	6 40	7 50	10 13	1350	16 5	...	2026	...	...

BASTOGNE and BENONCHAMPS.	Bastogne ....dep	9 10	12 5	16 13	1838	...	**Benonchamps** ....dep	8 39	11 32	14 43	1912	...
	Benonchamps......arr	9 26	1222	16 31	18 56	...	**Bastogne** ....arr	8 56	11 54	15 12	1929	...

PIETON and FLEURUS.

Piéton ....dep	4 53	...	7 5	8 47	13 3	16 0	...	...	17 3	1833	**Fleurus** ...dep	...	6 28	8 51	1159	...	...	...	20 3
Trazegnies	5 3	5 21	7 16	8 58	1314	1511	...	...	17 13	1843	Vieux-Camp.	...	6 36	...	...	1411	1735	...	2011
Courcelles-Centre	5 9	5 27	7 22	9 4	1320	1519	1538	...	17 19	1849	Ransart	...	6 42	9 3	1210	1421	1741	...	2017
Jumet- arr	5 25	5 43	7 35	9 17	1333	1535	1554	...	17 35	19 2	**Jumet-** arr	...	6 56	9 13	1221	1434	1754	...	2029
Brulotte ...dep	5 34	—	7 45	9 20	1334	1551	—	1759	—	19 9	**Brulotte** dep	5 44	7 9	9 21	1225	1441	1757	1915	2045
Ransart	5 47	...	7 58	9 30	1348	16 2	...	1813	—	1927	Courcelles-C.	5 58	7 22	9 35	1239	1459	1810	1929	2059
Vieux-Campinaire	5 53	...	—	9 36	1353	16 7	...	1819	...	1932	Trazegnies......	6 5	7 28	9 41	1246	15 6	1826	1937	21 6
Fleurus...........arr	6 0	...	...	9 43	...	...	...	1836	...	...	**Piéton** ......arr	6 15	7 37	9 52	1256	1516	1836	1948	2116

ANTWERP, BOOM, and ALOST.

Antw'p Sud.	4 55	6 42	8 14	9 49	10 5	1340	1522	17 4	19 4	2020
Hoboken	5 3	6 50	8 23	9 57	...	1348	1530	1712	1912	2028
Boom	5 38	7 24	8 49	1027	1142	1416	1559	1742	1943	2056
Willebroeck...	5 47	7 32	8 57	1036	1319	—	16 9	1750	1957	21 4
Londerzeel W	6 14	—	—	11 2	1346	...	1645	—	2017	—
Opwyck	6 36	...	...	1124	14 6	...	17 7	...	2039	...
Alost ...arr	7 0	...	...	1147	1429	...	1731	...	21 3	...

Alost dep	345	...	...	9 2	...	1155	1448	...	18 0	1950
Opwyck ...	421	...	...	9 29	...	1219	1515	...	1827	2016
Londerzeel	5 4	...	...	9 54	...	1241	1548	...	1849	—
Willebroeck	525	7 40	9 4	1015	...	13 6	16 9	18 0	1910	...
Boom	540	7 49	9 13	1025	1211	1314	1619	1816	1926	...
Hoboken ...	610	8 18	9 40	1054	1240	15 1	1646	1845	1955	...
Antwerp	617	8 25	9 47	11 1	1247	15 8	1653	1852	20 2	...

TERMONDE and ST. NICHOLAS.

Dist.							
	Termonde............dep	6 49	8 53	11 33	15 21	18 18	20 44
1¾	Grembergen (Etat)	6 57	9 1	11 41	15 29	18 26	20 52
3¾	„ (Moerzeke)	7 3	9 7	11 47	15 35	18 32	20 58
6¼	Hamme	7 10	9 14	11 54	15 42	18 39	21 5
13¾	**St. Nicholas** (90) ...arr	7 37	9 40	12 21	16 9	19 5	21 32

St. Nicholas dep	5 43	7 51	10 23	12 35	...	16 1	19 37
Hamme.................	6 11	8 15	10 51	13 3	1447	16 29	20 5
Grembergen (Moer.)	6 18	8 26	10 58	13 10	1454	16 36	20 12
„ (Etat) ...	6 24	8 32	11 4	13 16	15 0	16 42	20 18
Termonde (97) ar	6 31	8 39	11 11	13 23	15 7	16 49	20 25

TERNEUZEN, SAINT NICHOLAS, and MALINES.

		a.m.	a.m.		p.m.		p.m.
Terneuzen *_*...dep	...	6 58	10 0	...	1 48	...	6 12
Sluyskil 97	...	7 5	10 8	...	1 56	...	6 20
Hulst.....................	...	7 7	10 18	...	14 2	...	1826
Saint Gilles 97	...	7 29	10 45	...	1426	...	1851
St. Nicholas......arr	...	7 38	10 54	...	1435	...	19 2
„ 90 dep	6 23	8 22	10 57	1220	15 0	17 52	1914
Tamise	6 36	8 35	11 13	1232	1512	18 4	1928
Puers 101	6 51	8 51	11 26	1245	1527	18 16	1942
Willebroeck 96	7 1	9 0	11 35	1254	1536	18 25	1953
Malines 110 ......arr	7 22	9 17	11 55	1314	1557	18 46	2014

_ Amsterdam Time at Terneuzen and Sluyskil.

Malines...............dep	6 37	8 40	10 32	1329	1618	18 1	2046
Willebroeck	7 3	9 1	10 52	1355	1638	18 26	21 9
Puers......................	7 13	9 9	11 0	14 5	1646	18 34	2119
Tamise	7 26	9 21	11 15	1420	1659	18 51	2132
St. Nicholas... ....arr	7 40	9 33	11 27	1432	1712	19 3	2143
„ 96 dep	7 45	—	11 43	15 5	—	19 15	—
Saint Gilles	7 54	...	11 55	1516	...	19 25	...
Hulst [Dutch Customs	8 9	...	12 14	1532	...	19 41	...
Sluyskil *_*	8 56	...	1 19	4 22	...	8 27	...
Terneuzen ....arr	9 4	...	1 26	4 28	...	8 34	...

GEMBLOUX and TAMINES.

Gembloux.....dep	3 38	5 5	5 59	7 35	8 40	1138	1432	1654	1910	2047
Jemeppe-s.-S. ...	4 8	5 36	6 29	8 4	9 10	12 7	1459	1726	1950	2116
Tamines 96...arr	4 19	5 47	6 40	8 15	...	1218	1510	1737	20 1	2127

Tamines ....dep	4 55	6 12	...	1026	1328	16 1	1654	1811	1916
Jemeppe-s.-S.	5 6	6 22	9 23	1036	1339	1612	17 4	1822	1925
Gembloux 103A...arr	5 47	6 57	9 50	11 9	1412	1644	1740	1855	20 0

BERTRIX and HOUYET.

Bertrix..dep	4 11	...	7 23	11 24	1221	1434	1554	17 34	21 29
Paliseul 96...	4 35	...	7 47	11 47	1245	1459	1618	17 58	22 9
Gedinne	5 6	...	8 17	12 17	1315	1529	1648	18 31	22 40
Beauraing...	5 42	7 6	8 51	12 51	1350	16 3	1722	19 6	...
Houyet...arr	5 57	7 20	9 6	13 5	14 4	1617	1736	19 20	...

Houyet ...	...	5 2	6 19	7 44	1018	13 34	15 23	18 27	2115	...
Beauraing	...	5 18	6 35	8 0	1034	13 50	15 39	18 43	2131	...
Gedinne...	5 7	5 56	—	8 40	1112	14 28	16 17	19 19	22 8	...
Paliseul...	5 39	6 28	...	9 11	1145	14 59	16 49	19 52	2241	...
Bertrix ...	6 2	6 51	...	9 34	12 8	15 22	17 12	20 15	23 4	...

LIBRAMONT, BERTRIX, and ATHUS.

Libramont dep	...	6 45	...	...	1029	1117	14 6	1653	1852	2149
Bertrix	4 2	7 10	...	...	1055	1141	1431	1719	1912	22 7
Florenville	4 36	7 45	...	...	1130	—	15 6	1756	—	2243
Virton St. Mard	5 31	8 37	1023	1155	14 8	1716	1551	1846	...	2329
Athus 103A arr	6 24	9 25	1112	1243	1454	1820	...	1934	...	...

Athus ...dep	4 36	7 36	1018	1231	1546	1752
Virton St. M.	5 36	8 29	1151	1417	1640	1846
Florenville...	6 24	9 15	1240	15 6	1728	1934
Bertrix	7 13	9 52	1322	1547	1814	2019
Libramont ar	7 36	1013	1345	1610	1840	2040

PALISEUL and BOUILLON.

Paliseul...... dep	6 45	8 10	9 20	11 54	15 10	17 0	18 40	...
Bouillon 69...arr	7 40	9 8	10 8	12 40	16 0	1745	19 24	...

Bouillon dep	5 22	6 25	8 7	1032	13 50	16 50	18 36	...	...
Paliseul arr	6 12	7 34	8 56	1120	14 40	17 40	19 25	...	...

TAMINES and DINANT.

Tamines ...	4 39	6 44	8 51	1132	1326	1521	16 3	1814	1850	2049
Fosse.........	5 1	7 6	9 13	1154	1348	1543	1627	1836	1914	2112
Mettet	5 30	7 44	9 36	1220	14 7	16 1	1657	1855	1939	2148
Ermeton s B	5 47	7 54	9 50	1231	1422	—	1715	19 4	1949	22 2
Anhée	6 18	8 25	1023	13 4	1453	...	1751	—	2021	2233
Dinant ...	6 30	8 39	1035	1316	15 5	...	18 3	...	2033	2245

Dinant	3 42	...	6 51	...	9 23	11 0	13 4	...	1625	1916	2050
Anhée ...	3 55	...	7 3	...	9 37	1115	1316	...	1644	1936	21 2
Ermeton	4 45	6 26	7 34	...	1014	1147	1353	...	1714	2011	2137
Mettet ...	5 9	6 40	7 46	9 17	1029	1159	14 7	16 8	1724	2024	2149
Fosse ...	5 36	7 5	8 3	9 40	1047	1219	1424	1627	1740	2042	22 8
Tamines	5 55	7 23	8 21	9 59	11 5	1238	1442	1645	1758	21 1	2226

ACOZ and METTET.

Acoz ......dep	7 3	8 38	9 28	1124	13 9	1617	1859	21 5
Mettet......arr	7 34	9 7	9 59	1153	1338	1649	1929	2134

Mettet...dep	5 25	7 0	7 54	1030	1216	1414	1727	2026
Acoz ......arr	5 53	7 29	8 23	1059	1244	1442	1755	2055

BAULERS and CHATELINEAU.

Baulers ....dep	3*27	...	4 15	6 38	9 31	11 12	1537	...	17 3	18*41	...	19 15	20 44
Nivelles (Est)	3 31	...	4 19	6 42	9 35	11 16	1541	...	17 8	18 45	...	19 19	20 48
Chassart	4 2	...	4 51	7 13	10 8	11 47	1612	...	17 40	19 17	...	19 51	21 19
Fleurus.....................	4 11	4 18	5 0	7 30	1025	11 57	1619	1719	17 49	19 26	19 31	20 0	21 35
Vieux-Campinaire ...	—	4 37	—	7 38	1033	12 5	—	1727	—	—	19 39	—	21 42
Chatelineau ....arr		4 56	...	7 56	1052	12 24	...	1745	...	...	19 57	...	22 2

Chatelineau......dep	...	5 10	7 2	8 59	1127	13 36	...	18 33	2022	...	...	...
Vieux-Campinaire...	...	5 30	7 22	9 19	1147	13 56	...	18 54	2042	...	...	...
Fleurus	4*20	5 40	7 36	9 27	1158	14 12	1625	19 6	2049	2111	...	...
Chassart	4 31	5 50	7 47	9 37	12 9	14 22	1635	19 20	—	2125	...	...
Nivelles (Est)	5 3	6 21	8 17	10 7	1239	14 52	17 6	19 50	...	2155	...	...
Baulers ....arr	5 6	6 24	8 20	10 10	1242	14 55	17 9	19 53	...	2158	...	...

*-Sunday excepted.

‡-Sunday arr. 15.20.

BRAINE-LE-COMTE and BRAINE-L'ALLEUD.

Braine-le-Comte ....dep	4 26	...	7 25	...	10 23	13 33	...	16 24	...	18 39	20 10
Tubize................................	5 17	7 6	8 14	10 11	10 58	14 8	15 52	17 7	...	19 14	20 59
Clabecq	5 42	7 10	8 20	10 16	11 2	14 20	15 57	17 11	18 13	19 41	—
Braine-l'Alleud (107) ...arr	6 11	...	8 50	10 44	...	14 50	16 27	...	18 43	20 11	...

Braine-l'Alleud ....dep	4 59	6 49	...	10 51	...	13 41	16 47	18 53	20 22	...	...
Clabecq	5 34	7 22	8 8	11 23	13 2	14 16	17 31	19 40	20 49	21 18	...
Tubize	5 45	7 26	8 14	11 30	13 7	14 20	17 43	19 44	21 0	21 33	...
Braine-le-C. (107)........arr	6 21	...	8 48	12 4	13 41	15‡52	18 16	...	21 34	22 7	...

TURNHOUT and TILBURG.

Turnhout dp	5 8	7 42	12 25	16 44	18 58	...
Weelde-Merx...	5 20	7 54	12 37	16 56	19 9	...
Baarle ¶	5 58	8 29	1 12	5 36	7 44	...
Alphen	6 5	8 36	1 20	5 44	7 51	...
Tilburg 115ar	6 22	8 52	1 38	6 2	8 7	...

		a.m.	a.m.	p.m.	p.m.	
Tilburg ...dep	...	6 55	1015	3 20	6 21	...
Alphen	...	7 14	1033	3 39	6 38	...
Baarle	a.m.	7 22	1042	3 47	6 45	...
Weelde-Merx ¶	4 45	7 20	1039	15 47	18 40	...
Turnhout arr	4 56	7 31	1050	15 58	18 51	...

Amsterdam Time between Baarle and Tilburg.
¶—Customs Examination.

Luggage, cent. 1·50 per 55 lbs. per kilometre.] **FOR FARES SEE PAGE 89.**

SENZEILLE and ERMETON SUR BIERT.

Senzeille.........dep	4 16	5 51	7 30	1026	1228	1542	1755	2010
Philippeville	4 29	6 19	8 47	1041	1243	1616	1825	2025
Florennes (C.)......	5 10	7 5	9 18	11 9	1311	1649	1853	21 0
Ermeton s/B....arr	5 30	7 25	9 38	1129	1331	17 9	1913	2120

Ermeton s/B....dep	4 31	5 44	7 55	1012	1238	1420	17 20	20 21	...
Florennes (C.)......	4 52	6 5	8 16	1044	13 0	1444	17 58	20 49	...
Philippeville	5 22	6 34	8 43	1123	1326	1512	18 26	21 16	...
Senzeille.........arr	5 36	6 48	9 34	1137	1442	1527	18 40	21 30	...

Florennes (C.) dep	3†34	3†50	5 19	6 25	7 2	8 57	10 53	11 15	13 5	15 7	15 22	16 44	18 15	19 33	20 57
Walcourt.........arr	4 16	4 23	5 59	6 59	7 43	9 29	11 34	11 44	13 38	15 47	15 54	17 13	18 59	20 7	21 30

†—Sunday excepted.

Walcourt ......dep	4 34	4 53	6 29	6 36	9 21	9 29	12 14	12 24	14 33	14 40	17 41	17 49	19 33	...	...	...	...	...	...
Florennes (C.) arr	5 7	5 32	7 1	7 15	9 54	10 9	12 54	12 57	15 6	15 19	18 14	18 46	20 9	...	...	...	...	...	...

BERZEE and LANEFFE.

Berzee ......dep	5 20	6†20	7 20	9 11	1143	13 0	1435	17†12	18†30	19 16	...	...	...	...	...
Laneffe ....arr	5 36	6 36	7 34	9 27	1157	1316	1451	17 26	18 46	19 32	...	...	...	...	...

Laneffe...dep	4 †5	5 50	6†53	7 41	1032	12 4	1358	16†16	17†33	18†53	19 39	...	...
Berzee 97 arr	4 21	6 6	7 8	7 55	1048	1218	1414	16 32	17 47	19 9	19 55	...	...

†—Sun. excepted

MARIEMBOURG and COUVIN.

Mariembourg dep	4 43	5 30	5 48	7 15	10 27	13 5	15 20	17 0	19 50	21 17	...	...	...	...	...
Couvin............arr	4 53	5 42	6 0	7 27	10 39	1317	15 32	17 12	20 2	21 29	...	...	...	...	...
Couvin ....dep	5 5	6 8	6 46	9 38	10 47	1453	16 38	19 15	20 48	21 35	...	...	...	...	...
Mariembourg arr	5 17	6 20	6 58	9 50	10 59	15 5	16 50	19 27	21 0	21 47	...	...	...	...	...

GHENT, SELZAETE, and TERNEUZEN.

Ghent (Sud)......dep	5 17	8 19	11 50	14 15	17 4	20 3
Wondelghem	5 37	8 39	12 11	14 35	17 24	20 23
Selzaete (97) ...arr	6 1	9 3	12 34	14 59	17 48	20 47
" ......dep	6 12	9 10	12 43	15 2	17 55	20 59
Sas-de-Gand ***	6 42	9 40	1 15	3 32	6 25	9 10
Sluyskil	6 57	9 55	1 30	3 47	6 40	9 45
Terneuzen (96) arr	7 5	10 3	1 38	3 55	6 48	9 53

	a.m.	a.m.	p.m.	p.m.	p.m.	p.m.	
Terneuzen *** ...dep	5 56	8 52	12 19	3 5	5 31	8 35	...
Sluyskil	6 4	9 0	12 27	3 13	5 39	8 43	...
Sas-de-Gand	6 19	9 15	12 43	3 30	5 55	8 59	...
Selzaete.............arr	6 4	9 0	12 28	15 15	17 40	20 44	...
" (Belg. time) ...dep	6 16	9 7	12 41	15 20	17 50	20 59	...
Wondelghem	6 40	9 30	13 5	15 43	18 14	21 23	...
Ghent (Sud.) ......arr	7 4	9 50	13 24	16 2	18 26	21 41	...

‡—Not on Sunday. ***—Amsterdam time between Sas-de-Gand and Terneuzen.

BRUSSELS and TERMONDE.

Brussels Nord...	7 30	8 9	1015	1215	14 3	1535	1655	1759	1820	1924	2137
Jette	7 42	8 18	1027	1227	1415	1544	17 7	18 8	1833	1936	2149
Assche	8 2	...	1048	1248	1435	1558	1727	1823	1854	1957	22 7
Opwyck............	8 19	...	11 5	13 3	1454	...	1748	...	1911	2012	2222
Termonde ...arr	8 36	8 49	1122	1316	1511	1620	18 5	1841	1929	2032	2239

Termond	6 45	8 56	9 34	1131	1238	1333	1420	1727	2034	2042
Opwyck	7 3	9 14	...	1147	1252	...	1438	1745	2044	2058
Assche ...	7 25	9 36	...	12 8	1313	1359	15 1	18 7	2057	2117
Jette	7 45	9 54	10 6	1230	1329	1411	1520	1826	21 8	2134
Brussels	7 56	10 4	1014	1241	1340	1419	1531	1837	2116	2145

ALOST and EECLOO.

Alost ....dep	4 1	6 13	...	7 37	8 27	...	1050	...	...	1442	1520	...	1744	...	1913	2110
Termonde ....arr	4 25	6 37	...	8 1	8 49	...	1116	...	...	15 6	1537	...	18 6	...	1937	2134
" ....dep	4 30	6 45	...	—	9 2	...	1128	...	...	1516	—	1630	1811	1850	1947	—
Grembergen	4 38	6 53	...	...	9 10	...	1136	...	...	1524	...	1638	1819	1858	1955	...
Lokeren..................arr	4 59	7 12	...	...	9 30	...	1156	...	...	1543	...	1658	1839	1917	2015	...
St. Gilles (Waes)...dep	4*49	6 54	7 59	...	...	1120	...	12 0	...	...	1526	...	...	...	1930	...
Moerbeke ....dep	5 31	7 34	8 39	...	9 52	1152	1217	1230	1521	16 0	1555	1721	19 6	1934	2037	...
Selzaete	6 13	7 54	9 10	...	—	—	1238	—	1543	—	—	1750	1928	—	21 0	...
Eecloo...................arr	7 7	...	9 51	...	...	...	1319	...	1624	...	...	1833	2012	...	2158	...
Eecloo ....dep	...	...	5 11	...	...	8 12	...	10 2	...	1138	1327	...	1652	...	19 5	2038
Selzaete	...	...	6 9	...	8 9	9 12	...	1046	...	1247	1410	...	1749	...	20 3	2121
Moerbeke ....arr	5 40	5 36	6 31	7 40	8 32	9 32	1031	11 6	1241	1310	1430	16 4	18 9	1919	2023	2141
St. Gilles (Waes) ...arr	6 9	...	7 18	...	...	1034	...	1145	...	1350	—	...	1847	2015	...	—
Lokeren.................dep	—	5 57	6 50	8 17	8 49	—	1051	—	13 1	1332	...	1625	—	1946	2057	...
Grembergen	...	6 19	7 11	8 37	9 9	...	1112	...	1321	1352	...	1647	...	20 8	2119	...
Termonde..............arr	...	6 26	7 18	8 44	9 16	...	1119	...	1328	1359	...	1654	...	2015	2126	...
" ....dep	6 21	6 46	7 20	—	9 30	...	1126	...	—	14 8	1546	1711	...	2035	2128	2150
Alost ....arr	6 36	7 10	7 37	...	9 54	...	1148	...	...	1430	1610	1733	...	2059	2152	22 7

*—Mon., Wed., and Fri. only.

PIETON and CHARLEROI.

†—Sunday excepted.

E.M.								
	Piéton ....dep	6 40	8 39	10 21	13 54	16 13	18 41	1951
3	Trazegnies	6 50	8 49	10 31	14 4	16 23	18 51	20 1
5½	Courcelles-Centre	6 56	8 55	10 37	14 10	16 29	18 57	20 7
9½	Marchienne-au-Pt.	7 11	9 14	10 56	14 34	16 44	19 14	2021
11¾	**Charleroi 98** ar	7 17	9 22	11 4	14 42	16 51	19 20	2028

Charleroi ...dep	7 38	9 14	13 9	...	...	17 53	18 44
Marchienne..........	7 45	9 23	13 17	...	...	18 1	18 54
Courcelles-Centre	7 59	9 42	13 32	14 59	...	18 17	19 22
Trazegnies............	8 6	9 48	13 39	15 6	1649	18 26	19 28
Piéton ....arr	8 15	9 57	13 48	15 16	1658	18 36	19 38

Fauroeulx......dep	...	5 57	8 3	9 44	14 9	1534	1757	1912	20†4
Merbes-Ste-Marie	5 43	6 6	8 12	9 53	1418	1543	18 5	1921	2028
Piéton............arr	6 8	6 34	8 34	1016	1443	16 8	1830	1942	2130

Piéton ....dep	5 7	6 20	8 21	10 2	1355	1522	1845	...
Merbes-Ste-Marie ...	5 32	6 44	8 44	1028	1421	1546	1911	...
Fauroeulx............arr	...	6 52	8 52	1036	1429	1554	1919	...

COUILLET and JAMIOULX.

†—Sunday excepted.

E.M.								
—	Couillet...........dep	4 25	6 16	10 54	13 43	16†42	18 3	...
5½	Jamioulx (97) ...arr	4 49	6 46	11 18	14 18	17 11	18 27	...

Jamioulx.........dep	5 15	8 20	12 42	14 40	17†26	1843	...
Couillet............arr	5 39	8 40	13 2	15 8	17 50	1912	...

BERZEE and THUILLIES.

E.M.										
—	Berzée...dep	4 30	4 47	6 23	8 10	9 17	1224	1430	1755	1940
5	Thuillies ar	4 43	5 2	6 36	8 25	9 32	1237	1445	18 8	1955

Thuillies ...dep	5 45	6 50	7 41	8 40	9 55	1336	1523	1850	2042
Berzée ......arr	6 0	7 5	7 55	8 55	1010	1350	1538	19 5	2057

CHARLEROI and VIREUX.

*—23.18 on Sunday.] ‡—19.5 on Sunday.

									*	
Charleroi (Sud)...dep	3 40	5 34	6 26	8 25	11 3	1340	1629	1811	1822	1936
La Sambre...	3 46	5 40	6 33	8 31	11 9	1346	1635	1817	1830	1942
Jamioulx ...	4 2	5 57	6 53	8 48	1124	14 3	1652	1833	1850	1959
Berzee.........	4 22	6 15	7 15	9 7	1141	1422	1710	1852	1914	2018
Walcourt ...	4 40	6 27	7 25	9 18	1153	1435	1722	19 3	1922	2029
Cerfontaine	5 1	6 48	—	9 39	1214	1456	1744	1924	—	2050
Mariemborg	5 20	7 7	...	10 0	1233	1515	18 6	1944	...	2113
Treignes	5 52	7 40	...	1025	1258	1542	—	2012	...	2145
Vireux ...arr	5 57	7 45	...	1030	13 3	1547	...	2017	...	2150

Vireux ....dep		4 49	...	6 26	9 14	1048	1434	...	1616	19 9
Treignes		4 58	...	6 39	9 30	1059	1448	...	1630	1925
Mariembourg ...		5 22	6 22	7 8	10 0	1125	1516	...	1659	1951
Cerfontaine		5 44	6 47	7 30	1024	1149	1538	‡	1721	2012
Walcourt dep	4 29	6 6	7 10	7 51	1046	1213	16 0	1629	1743	2034
Berzee ...dep	4 39	6 14	7 19	7 59	1054	1221	16 8	1639	1751	2042
Jamioulx ...	4 58	6 33	7 38	8 18	1113	1240	1627	1659	1810	2059
La Sambre ...	5 15	6 49	7 56	8 32	1130	1257	1643	1719	1826	2112
Charleroi arr	5 20	6 54	8 1	8 37	1135	13 2	1648	1724	1831	2117

Extra—Charleroi to Walcourt, 12.13. Walcourt to Charleroi, 9.35.

BRUSSELS to ERQUELINNES and CHIMAY.

[†—Not on Sunday.

	1,2,3	1,2,3	1,2,3	1,2,3	1,2,3	1,2,3	1,2,3	1,2,3	1,2,3	1,2,3	1,2,3	1,2,3	1,2,3	1,2,3	1,2,3	1,2,3	1,2,3	1,2,3	1,2,3	1,2,3
Brussels (Midi) dep	...	...	...	4†51	6 49	...	8 24	10 36	12 27	1337	...	15 52	...	...	...	1723	17 46	18 17	18 51	20 6
Hal	...	...	...	5 21	7 6	...	8 44	11 6	12 44	14 7	...	...	...	...	...	1740	...	18 44	19 23	20 37
Lembecq-lez-Hal	...	...	...	5 27	7 11	...	8 49	11 11	12 49	1412	...	...	...	...	...	1745	...	18 49	19 30	20 42
Clabecq (96)	...	4†13	...	5 35	7 18	...	8 56	11 21	12 55	1423	...	...	...	...	...	1752	...	18 54	19 38	20 52
Ecaussines	4 46	4 54	...	6 25	7 58	8 37	9 50	11 59	13 33	15 1	...	16 37	16 58	...	...	1830	18 36		20 21	21 37
Houdeng (94)	5 0	5 9	...	6 39	8 12	8 48	10 4		13 47		...	16 48	17 13	...	...	1844	18 50	...	20 35	21 52
Haine St. Pierre	5 14	5 22	5 38	7 32	8 25	8 58	1014	...	14 3	...	15 24	17 20	17 32	17†47	18 41	1853	19 5	19 12	20 45	22 26
Binche	5 33	5 40	6 0	7 51	8 44		1058	13 54	14 23	...	15 43	17 45	17 53	18 7	19 0		19 17	19 35		22 44
Bonne-Espérance 90	5 40	5 48	...	7 58	8 51	...	11 5	14 0	14 30	...	15 50	17 52	18 0	18 14	19 7	...	...	19 43	...	22 52
Fauroeulx arr	5 44	5 52	6 8	8 2	8 55	...	11 9	14 8	14 34	...	15 54	17 56	18 4	18 18	19 11	...	...	19 47	...	22 56
Fauroeulx ...dep	...	5 55	6 9	...	8 57	...	1110	...	14 37	...	15 55	...	18 19	18 19	...	...	...	19 58	...	22 57
Erquelinnes (93)	...	6 12	6 26	...	9 13	...	1126	...	14 53	...	16 11	...	18 32	18 32	...	...	...	20 14	...	23 13
Fauroeulx dep	5 49			8 3	8 59	...		14 9	14 39	...		17 57	18 7		19 12	...	...	19 56	...	
Merbes-Ste-Marie	5 58	...	...	8 11	9 8	...	...	14 17	14 48	...	...	18 4	18 16	...	19 20	...	19 34	20 5	...	...
Lobbes (92)	6 21	...	...		9 21	...	1319		15 2	...	...		18 29	...		...	19 45	20 18	...	...
Thuillies (97) ...4 50	6 39	...	...	...	9 37	2&3	1335	...	15 18	...	...	...	18 48	...	...	...	20 1	20 36	...	...
Beaumont ...5 9	6 56	...	...	...	9 54	10†59		...	15 34	...	...	...	19 5	...	...	...	20 15	20 53	...	...
Froidchapelle ...5 39	7 25	...	...	...	10 23	12 8	...	...	16 3	...	...	...	19 36	...	...	...	...	21 22	...	...
Chimay (93) arr 6 1	7 44	...	...	...	10 45	1243	...	...	16 25	...	...	...	19 58	...	...	...	20 58	21 44	...	...

E.M.																			
—	**Chimay** dep	...	3 58	...	6 15	...	6 41	7 57	...	9 50	...	13 46	...	...	...	...	...	...	17 36
8¾	Froidchapelle	...	4 21	...	6 38	...	...	8 20	...	10 9	...	14 9	...	...	...	...	...	...	17 59
18¾	Beaumont	...	4 50	...	7 11	...	7 24	8 49	...	10 37	...	14 38	...	...	...	...	...	...	18 28
24½	Thuillies	...	5 8	...	7 27	...	7 38	9 7	...	10 52	12 38	14 53	...	...	...	...	...	...	18 46
28½	Lobbes	...	5 26	...		...	7 52	9 22	...	11 7	12 54	15 10	...	...	...	...	...	...	19 4
34½	Merbes-Ste-Marie	...	5 40	6 44	...	...	8 3	9 35	10 28	11 19		15 23	...	15 46	...	...	...	...	19 19
37½	**Fauroeulx** arr	...	5 48	6 52	...	...	...	9 43	10 36	⋮	...	15 31	...	15 54	...	...	...	†	19 27
...	**Erquelinnes** dep	3 45	5 29	...	7 14	...	...	9 23	...	⋮	12 1	15 12	...	...	16 18	...	17†35	1847	19 3
...	**Fauroeulx** arr	⋮	5 46	...	7 31	...	...	9 39	...	⋮	12 18	15 29	...	...	16 34	...	17 52	19 5	19 21
37½	**Fauroeulx** dep	⋮	5 53	6 53	7 32	...	...	9 44	10 37	⋮	12 19	15 33	...	15 56	16 35	...		19 7	19 29
39½	Bonne-Espérance	⋮	5 59	6 58	7 38	...	...	9 49	10 42	11 29	12 24	15 38	...	16 1	16 40	...	17 50	1912	19 34
41	Binche	4 7	6 7	7 6	7 45	...	8 18	9 54	10 47	11 35	12 29	15 45	...	16 7	16 46	...	17 56	1919	19 40
46½	Haine St. Pierre	4 26	6 44	7 24	8 4	9 8	8 30	10 17	11 12	11 55	13 7	16 10	16 13		17 20	...	18 27	1941	20 8
49¾	Houdeng	4 37	6 55		8 15	9 16	8 40	10 27		12 6	13 17	16 18	16 23	...	17 28	...	18 38		20 18
54¾	**Ecaussines** ...6 21	4 53	7 22	...	8 29	9 27	8 52	10 41	...	12 18	13 39	16 30	16 45	...	17 39	...	19 0	...	20 38
66½	Clabecq ...6 58	5 43	8 2	...			...	11 20	...	...	14 15	...	17 23	...		19 23	19 36	...	21 14
69	Lembecq-lez-Hal ..7 †4	5 49	8 8	...	...	...	...	11 26	...	...		16 57	17 29	...	...	19 28		...	
70¼	Hal ...7 †9	5 54	8 13	8 44	...	...	...	...	...	...	...	...	...	...	...	19 33	...	...	...
79	**Brussels (Midi)** ..arr 7†36	6 13	8 29	9 12	...	...	9 37	11 44	...	13 1	...	17 13	17 45	...	...	20 1	...	...	...

TIRLEMONT, DIEST and MOLL.

E.M										
	Tirlemont dep	516	...	8 6	1024	1237	1539	...	...	1948
7¼	Drieslinter	541	...	8 29	1047	1258	16 2	...	...	2011
20¼	**Diest** arr	617	8 41	9 5	1124	1334	1636	1859	...	2047
24¾	Deurne-lez-Diest	7 1	8 53	1122		15 9	1723	1911	...	2134
35½	Bourg-Leopold	734	9 27	1154	...	1546	1755	1945	2125	22 7
43½	**Moll (97)** arr	754	9 45	1212	...	16 6	1815	20 3	2143	2227

Moll dep	511	714	9 8	...	1318	1524	1645	...	1833	2029
Bourg-Leopold	533	734	9 28	...	1338	1546	17 5	...	1855	2050
Deurne-lez-Diest	6 2	8 3	9 57	...	14 7	1615	1735	...	1924	
Diest arr	613	814	10 8	1337	1418	1626	1746	1853	1935	...
Drieslinter	7 9	913	1132	1414			1829	1930		...
Tirlemont (104) arr	734	932	1156	1438	...	...	1853	1947	...	...

†—Sunday excepted. *—Florennes Est.

LODELINSART and GIVET.

Lodelinsart dep	5 51	...	9 21	1040	1515	17 46	20 0	2154
Charleroi (Ville-Haute)	5 56	...	9 26	1045	1520	17 51	20 5	2159
Châtelineau ...3 55	6 39	9 2	9 37	11 5	1543	18 22	2026	2214
Châtelet (Ville) ...3 59	6 43	9 6		11 9	1547	18 26	2030	
Acoz (96) ...4 14	6 58	9 21	...	1122	16 0	18 42	2045	...
Oret ...4 44	7 29	9 49	...	1145	1625	19 8	2112	...
Florennes (Central) ...5 12	7 56	1018	...	12*2	1652	19 37	2127	...
Merlemont ...5 35	8 19	1042	...	1220	1717	19 57	22 4	...
Doische (Bel. Front) ...5 52	8 36	1059	...	1237	1734	20 18	2221	...
Givet (Fr. Frontier) ...6 1	8 45	1118	...	1246	1743	20 28	2230	...

Givet (92) (Fr. Front.) dep	3 55	5 28	6 39	10 58	1249	1557	1934
Doische (Bel. Frontier)	4 16	5 52	7 0	11 19	1310	1618	1955
Merlemont	4 36	6 12	7 20	11 39	1330	1638	2019
Florennes (Central)	5 16	6 54	7 53	12 *1	1410	1724	2054
Oret	5 33	7 11	8 7	12 21	1426	1740	2112
Acoz	6 0	7 33	8 30	12 46	1448	18 3	2135
Châtelet (Ville)	612	7 45	8 42	12 57	15 0	1815	2147
Châtelineau ...4 23	637	7 48	8 54	13 6	15 3	1838	2157
Charleroi (Ville-H.) ...4 41	655		9 12	13 21	1744	1856	2216
Lodelinsart (100) arr 4 45	659	...	9 16	1325	1748	19 0	2220

Extra.—Châtelineau to Florennes 5.32, 14.26, 18†37, 19.34. Florennes to Châtelineau, 3†50, 4†59, 10.36, 16.7.

†—Sundays excepted.

LANDEN, HUY and CINEY.

Dist E M											
	Landen dep	...	4 6	4†50	6 31	8 38	1039	1228	1440	16 40	20 3
6¼	Hannut	...	4 28	5 37	6 49	8 59	1059	1246	15 2	17 2	2025
10½	Braives	...	4 44	6 4	7 3	9 14	1111	1258	1518	17 20	2041
14¼	Fumal	...	4 58	6 26	7 15	9 28	1124	13 9	1531	17 34	2055
21¼	**Statte** arr	...	5 20	7 18	7 38	9 51	1144	1328	1552	17 57	2118
...	,, (92)...dep	4 32	6 43	7 40		10 3	1244	1415	1641	18 49	2119
22¼	Huy (Sud)	4 39	6 50	7 46	...	1010	1251	1422	1646	18 57	2125
29¼	Modave	5 6	7 13		...	1039	1318	1446	1711	19 24	
36¾	Havelange	5 33	7 40	...	...	11 5	1348	1511	1737	19 51	...
42¼	Hamois	5 51	7 57	...	...	1123	14 6	1527	1755	20 7	...
47¼	Ciney (103A)...arr	6 9	8 15	...	...	1141	1424	1543	1813	20 21	...

Ciney dep	4 42	6 40	8 36	...	1253	1444	1627	1918
Hamois	4 57	6 56	8 51	...	13 9	1458	1646	1937
Havelange 6 †0	5 14	7 10	9 8	...	1324	1512	17 4	1951
Modave ...6 52	5 38	7 32	9 29	...	1347	1535	1730	2013
Huy (Sud) 7 33	6 5	7 53	951	1216	14 8	16 0	1756	2037
Statte ...arr	6 12	8 0	958	1223	1414	16 4	18 0	2041
,, 93 dep 5 3	6 41	9 7	10 6	1244	1416	1642	1845	
Fumal ...5 27	7 4	9 28	1030	13 8	1437	17 5	19 5	...
Braives ...5 41	7 15	9 42	1044	1322	1449	1719	1917	...
Hannut ...5 56	7 27	9 57	11 0	1338	15 3	1734	1932	...
Landen arr 6 13	7 43	1018	11 20	1359	1520	1752	1952	...

Extra.—Statte to Huy (Sud), 5.30, 11.53, 15.53, 18.7. Huy (Sud) to Statte, 6.22, 8.55, 16.25, 18.25, 21.33.

CINEY and ANHEE.	Ciney ...dep	4 11	4 52	6 43	9 2	1156	1337	1545	1830	1928
	Spontin	...	5 11	7 1	9 23	1215	1358	16 3	1850	1947
	Yvoir	4 46	6 51	7 40	9 56	1242	1425	1635	1924	2050
	Anhée ...arr	4 52	6 59	7 46	10 2	1250	1431	1641	1932	2058

Anhée dep	5 11	7 20	8 37	1041	1320	1445	1723	1945	2117
Yvoir	5 20	7 36	8 56	1048	1330	1452	1730	1955	2124
Spontin	5 48	8 4	9 24	1116	1359	1520	1758	2023	2151
Ciney ...arr	6 7	8 23	9 41	1133	1416	1537	1815	2040	22 8

SICHEM and MONTAIGU.	Sichem	6 0	6 45	8 12	8 32	1050	1247	1440	17 3	1847	20 5
	Montaigu	6 10	6 55	8 22	8 42	11 0	1257	1450	17 13	1857	2015

Mont'gu	6 15	755	1011	12 0	1410	15 2	1611	1750	1920	2025	...
Sichem	6 25	8 5	1021	1210	1420	1512	1621	18 0	1930	2035	...

Luggage, cent. 1·50 per 55 lbs. per kilometre.

FOR FARES SEE PAGE 89.

ANTWERP and ROERMOND.

¶—Customs Examination. Extra.—Herenthals to Moll 14.20.

THROUGH CARRIAGE—Antwerp to Cassel and Leipsic in 8.6 from Antwerp. Amsterdam Time between Budel and Roermond.

Dist. E.M.			1,2,3	1,2,3	1,2,3	1,2,3	1,2,3	1,2,3	1,2,3	1,2,3	1,2,3	1,2,3	1,2,3
	Antwerp Centrale ...dep		5 36	8 6	8 35	1029	1342	1543	...	...	1833	1836	1943
—	Bouchout		5 55	...	8 54	1044	14 1	...	...	...	...	1855	...
9¼	**Lierre** ...dep		6 4	8 23	9 22	1052	1410	...	...	...	1851	19 4	2021
...	Nylen	1,2,3	6 19	...	9 37	11 7	1422	...	...	...	...	1919	2036
21¼	**Herenthals**...dep	4 17	6 37	8 42	10 7	1126	1441	...	1548	1747	1910	1938	21 6
34¾	**Moll**	4 55	7 12	9 6	1048	12 1	1522	...	1639	1822	1934	2012	2136
49	Neerpelt	5 36	7 54	9 28	1133	1236	16 3	...	1724	19 5	1956	2050	—
54¾	Hamont	5 50	8 11	9 39	1147	1250	1619	17 1	1738	1918	20 7	21 8	...
56	Budel ¶	—	8 50	1012	—	1 22	4 52	5 39	—	—	8 41	9 42	...
...	Baexem		9 19	...	...	1 49	5 19	...	...	...	9 9	...	...
77¾	**Roermond 127**...arr		9 36	1049	...	2 5	5 37	6 14	...	...	9 27	1020	...
101½	M. GLADBACH...arr		1135	1230	...	3p57	7p37	7p57		...	1112	...	...
118	DUSSELDORF 134A...arr		1237	1p14	...	4p58	8p36	8p36	...	...	12a3	...	...
130¾	COLOGNE ...arr		1p19	2 p0	...	5p14	...	9p22	...	...	1a50	...	...

COLOGNE ...dep		...	...	7 a5	7a52	8a51	...	1010	1 p4	...	4p54	...	5p25
DUSSELDORF ...dep		...	...	7a25	8a35	9a17	...	1020	1259	...	5p16	...	6p29
M. GLADBACH ...dep		...	...	8 a9	9a20	10a0	...	1139	2 p0	...	6p 1	...	7p32
		1,2,3	1,2,3	1,2,3	1,2,3	1,2,3	1,2,3	1,2,3	1,2,3	1,2,3	1,2,3	1,2,3	1,2,3
		a.m.	a.m.	a.m.	a.m.	a.m.		p.m.	p.m.		p.m.		p.m.
Roermond...dep		...	6 20	8 34	9 54	1025	...	1218	2 45	...	6 26	...	8 12
Baexem		...	6 39	...	1013	...	...	1238	3 3	...	6 44	...	8 32
Budel		...	7 9	9 13	1042	11 2	...	1 8	3 34	...	7 14	...	9 3
Hamont ¶		6 13	7 15	9 16	1043	11 3	1216	—	1536	18 1	19 14	1928	21 5
Neerpelt	1,2,3	6 28	7 30	9 27	1117	...	1231	..	1552	1816	19 25	1943	2122
Moll	4 30	7 13	8 13	9 49	1154	...	1317	1049	1629	1859	19 47	2028	22 1
Herenthals	5 3	7 46	8 56	1013	1231	...	1352	1127	17 7	1934	20 11	2056	2237
Nylen	—	8 23	9 13	...	1248	...	—	1145	...	—	...	2123	2254
Lierre...dep		8 39	9 30	1032	13 6	...	...	12 3	1733	...	20 30	2140	23 7
Bouchout		8 48	9 39	...	1315	...	...	...	1742	...	...	...	2316
Antwerp Centrale arr		8 59	9 54	1048	1333	1223	...	1244	1757	...	20 46	2220	2332

ANTWERP, MAESTRICHT, and AIX-LA-CHAPELLE.

¶—Customs Examination.

Amsterdam Time between Simpelveld and Maestricht. Mid Europe Time at Aix-la-Chapelle.

Dist E.M			1,2,3	1,2,3	1,2,3	1,2,3	1,2,3	1,2,3	1,2,3	1,2,3	1,2,3	1,2,3
	Antwerp Centrale...dep		...	...	6 21	9 7	10 40	12 53	...	16 34	...	19 10
8¾	Lierre		...	...	6 49	9 37	11 5	13 24	...	17 4	...	19 38
26¾	**Aerschot**...arr		...	...	7 45	10 19	11 53	14 8	...	17 52	...	20 33
...	" ...dep		...	6 15	8 5	10 24	12 5	14 16	14 57	18 20	19 24	20 47
34¾	Sichem...arr		...	6 36	8 24	10 42	12 26	14 31	15 18	18 41	19 38	21 8
37¾	Diest		...	6 47	8 34	10 51	12 36	14 40	15 30	18 51	19 48	21 17
50¾	**Hasselt**		...	7 34	9 16	11 31	13 19	15 12	16 15	19 35	20 16	22 5
57¾	Beverst		...	7 50	9 33	11 48	13 39	15 27	16 35	19 52	20 31	22 22
62¼	Munsterbilsen		...	7 57	9 40	11 55	13 46	...	16 42	19 59	...	22 29
67¾	**Lanaeken**		...	8 12	9 57	12 10	14 5	15 41	17 2	20 15	20 45	22 45
69½	**Maestricht 111**...arr	1,2,3	...	8 21	10 6	12 19	14 14	15 50	17 11	20 24	20 54	22 54
...	" ¶...dep	5 10	8 3	9 38	10 31	12 48	3 12	4 17	6 43	8 54	9 22	—
76¼	Fauquemont	5 34	8 21	1014	10 52	1 6	3 42	4 36	7 14	9 14	...	...
84½	**Simpelveld**	5 56	8 42	1052	11 11	1 28	4 10	4 56	7 42	9 34	...	...
90¾	**Aix-la-Chap. West**	6 52	9 38	—	12 5	2 25	—	5 50	—	10 31	10 41	...
92½	" Hauptbahnhof	7 9	9 54	...	12 22	2 42	...	6 7	...	10 43	10 56	...
136	COLOGNE 122...arr		1114	...	2 p24	4 p19	...	7 p40	...	..	...	...

COLOGNE ...dep		...	...	...	...	7a56	9 a10	...	1028	1 p38	4 p19	8p15
		1,2,3	1,2,3	1,2,3	1,2,3	1,2,3	1,2,3	1,2,3	1,2,3	1,2,3	1,2,3	1,2,3
		a.m.		a.m.	a.m.	a.m.	a.m.	a.m.	p.m.	p.m.	p.m.	p.m.
Aix-la-Chapelle Haupt.		...	...	...	6 46	9 45	10 38	...	1246	3 4	5 41	9 46
" West		...	...	...	6 55	9 53	10 47	...	1255	3 13	5 50	9 55
Simpelveld (Holl.) ¶		...	...	5 31	6 39	9 36	10 30	11 10	1246	3 3	5 40	9 47
Fauquemont		...	...	6 1	6 57	...	10 50	11 39	1 5	3 20	5 59	10 4
Maestricht ...arr		...	...	6 28	7 15	10 0	11 6	12 4	1 21	3 35	6 15	1022
" (111, 113) dep		4 32	...	6 33	8 35	9 43	10 51	—	1436	15 22	18 3	22 7
Lanaeken (Belg.) ¶		4 48	...	6 50	8 51	10 5	11 9	...	1455	15 41	18 27	2226
Munsterbilsen		5 5	...	7 7	9 6	...	11 23	...	1512	...	18 42	2242
Beverst	1,2,3	5 12	...	7 14	9 13	1021	11 30	...	1519	15 57	18 49	2249
Hasselt	3 32	5 38	6 51	7 40	9 38	1040	11 52	13 44	1538	16 17	19 11	23 5
Diest	4 9	6 23	7 18	8 20	1020	11 5	12 33	14 25	—	16 43	19 52	—
Sichem	4 17	6 31	7 26	8 29	1028	...	12 41	14 33	...	...	20 0	...
Aerschot 100 ...arr	4 38	6 52	7 41	8 48	1046	1125	13 1	14 51	...	17 3	20 20	...
" ...dep	5 58	6 58	—	8 57	11 8	—	13 7	15 1	...	17 37	20 27	...
Lierre	6 50	7 50	...	9 42	12 3	...	14 1	15 50	...	18 11	21 25	...
Antwerp Cen. ...arr	7 18	8 18	...	10 9	1244	...	14 28	16 17	...	18 27	21 52	...

HERENTHALS and AERSCHOT.

E.M.										
	Herenthals dep.	5 6	7 5	8 55	9 37	12 12	17 8	19 40	...	...
8¾	Westmeerbeek	5 33	7 32	9 13	9 52	12 39	17 35	20 2	...	...
14¼	Aerschot ...arr.	5 48	7 47	9 25	10 7	12 54	17 49	20 17	...	...

Aerschot ...dep.	5 54	8 10	10 30	14 59	18 0	18 22	20 25	...	...	...
Westmeerbeek	6 8	8 25	10 45	15 14	...	18 37	20 40	...	...	...
Herenthals arr.	6 34	8 51	11 11	15 35	18 28	19 3	21 1	...	...	...

MAESEYCK and HASSELT.

Maeseyck ...dep	6 10	10 5	13 40	17 45	19 *5	...	...	...	...
Asch	6 41	10 37	14 11	18 16	20 18	...	...	...	...
Hasselt (99) ...arr	7 20	11 16	14 50	18 55	21 32	...	...	..	...

Hasselt ...dep	4 36	9 13	12 0	15 15	19 38	...	*—Sunday at 19.46.	...
Asch	5 16	9 53	12 43	15 55	20 18	...		...
Maeseyck ...arr	5 46	10 23	13 13	16 25	20 48	...		...

LANDEN, SAINT-TROND, and HASSELT.

†—Not on Sunday.

E.M													
—	**Landen** ...dep	6 23	7 48	8 40	10 37	1240	1523	16†17	18 11	20 6	...	...	...
6¾	**Saint-Trond**... arr	6 42	8 6	8 59	10 53	13 0	1542	16 36	18 31	2025	...	...	...
18	**Hasselt (116)**...arr	7 19	8 40	9 35	11 23	1334	16 9	17 9	19 6	21 5	...	...	...

Hasselt ...dep	...	6 35	7 36	9 35	11 29	14 10	15 †9	16 50	15 57	19 58	...	...
Saint-Trond	5 53	7 10	8 7	10 6	11 58	14 42	15 43	17 23	18 38	20 32	...	...
Landen (98) arr	6 13	7 30	8 26	1026	12 18	15 2	16 3	17 43	18 58	2051	...	...

FOR FARES SEE PAGE 89.

ANTWERP, LOUVAIN, and CHARLEROI.

Station				From Antwerp (Sud) dep. 6.32.							From Antwerp (Sud) dep. 17.39.		†		
Antwerp Centrale dep		...	5 20		6 21	7 51	9 7	1140	12 53	...		1634	1836	1910	2045
Bouchout		...	5 39		6 40	...	9 26	1159	13 12	...		1655	1855	1929	21 4
Lierre 102B		...	5 50		6 49	8 8	9 37	1212	13 24	...		17 4	1914	1938	2114
Berlaer		...	6 4		7 4	...	9 50	1227	13 37	...		1717	1929	1953	2128
Boisschot		...	6 27		7 31	...	10 9	1244	13 58	...		1740	1955	2019	2151
Aerschot arr		...	6 41		7 45	8 41	1019	1256	14 8	...		1752	20 7	2033	22 3
„ dep		...	6 57		7 51	8 42	1022	13 6	14 12	17 7		1755	2023	2037	—
Rotselaer		...	7 8		8 9	...	1038	1317	14 28	...		1811	2034	2052	...
Louvain (104) arr	...	...	7 17	7 15	8 21	9 0	1048	1326	14 40	17 25	18 23	1823	2043	21 1	...
„ dep	5 20	6 39	—	7 21	8 39	—	1158	—	15 18	17 34	18 29	1932	—	—	20†7
Weert-St.-Georges	5 40	6 59	...	...	8 59	...	1218	...	15 38	17 54	...	1952	...	...	2027
Wavre	6 5	7 26	8 3	7 48	9 18	1018	1241	1423	16 1	18 14	18 56	2015	...	2129	2048
Ottignies (90) arr	6 17	7 40	8 15	7 55	9 28	1029	1252	1434	16 11	18 25	19 3	2027	...	2140	2058
„ dep	6 27	8 1	8 34	7 58	9 35	1040	1310	—	16 20	18 34	19 8	2040	...	—	—
Villers-la-Ville	6 55	8 24	8 50	...	9 53	11 4	1337	...	16 43	18 57	...	21 3	...	...	...
Tilly	7 7	8 33	...	...	10 3	1113	1347	...	16 52	19 6	...	2113	...	...	...
Ligny	7 21	8 45	...	...	1015	—	14 1	...	17 5	19 19	...	2126	...	...	...
Fleurus	7 29	8 51	9 6	8 26	1022	...	14 9	...	17 11	19 40	19 36	2132	...	2221	...
Lodelinsart 98	7 48	9 9	9 20	8 39	1038	...	1431	...	17 29	19 58	19 49	2148	...	2238	...
Charleroi (Ouest)	7 57	9 17	—	8 46	1049	...	1441	...	17 41	20 6	19 56	—	...	—	...
Charleroi (Sud) 82	8 9	...	...	...	11 1	...	1453	...	17 53	...	...	...	...	...	...

Extra—Antwerp to Aerschot, 10.40.

Station																‡	
Charleroi (Sud) ...dep				...	...	...	...	8 56	...	13 6	...	...	16 53	...	...	...	18 49
Charleroi (Ouest)				...	6 15	...	6 52	9 9	...	13 19	...	1538	17 7	...	18 4	1828	19 2
Lodelinsart (98) arr				4 57	6 23	...	7 1	9 18	...	13 28	...	1547	17 16	17 49	1811	1837	19 11
Fleurus				5 18	6 41	...	7 29	9 48	...	13 51	...	1614	17 39	18 5	1830	19 4	19 36
Ligny				5 24	...	...	7 35	9 54	...	13 57	...	1620	17 45	...	...	1911	19 42
Tilly				5 37	...	...	7 47	10 6	1118	14 9	...	1632	17 57	...	...	1924	19 54
Villers-la-Ville				5 47	...	...	7 56	1015	1127	14 18	...	1641	18 6	18 21	...	1933	20 3
Ottignies arr				6 8	7 8	...	8 17	1036	1149	14 35	...	17 3	18 27	18 36	1857	1956	20 24
„ (103A) dep			4 25	6 22	7 11	7 35	8 23	1041	1235	15 5	...	1717	18 42	To Brussels (Q.L.) arr. 19.5	19 4	2011	20 42
Wavre			4 38	6 36	7 19	7 46	8 36	1052	1246	15 18	...	1729	18 55		1914	2023	20 55
Weert-St.-Georges			5 2	7 0	...	—	9 0	1113	—	15 42	...	1835	19 19		...	—	21 24
Louvain arr			5 20	7 18	7 47	...	9 18	1131	...	16 0	...	1853	19 37		1944	...	21 42
„ 101, 104 dp		5 28	5 46	7 26	7 51	8 38	10 1	1235	1424	16 36	1719	19 4	19 49		1947	2015	22 5
Rotselaer		5 40	5 56	7 36	To Antwerp Sud arr. 8.35.	...	1011	1245	1436	16 48	...	...	19 59		To Antwerp Sud arr. 20.32.	2027	22 15
Aerschot arr		5 50	6 13	7 50		8 55	1021	13 0	1453	17 5	1736	1921	20 15			2044	22 25
„ dep	4†30	5 58	6 58	—		8 57	11 8	13 7	15 1	17 11	1737	—	20 27			—	—
Boisschot	4 45	6 12	7 12	...		9 8	1120	1321	1514	17 26	...	...	20 42			...	...
Berlaer	5 11	6 35	7 35	...		9 27	1139	1346	1536	17 51	...	...	21 8			...	...
Lierre	5 27	6 50	7 50	...		9 42	12 3	14 1	1550	18 17	1811	...	21 25			23 7	...
Bouchout	5 36	7 0	8 0	...		9 51	...	1410	1559	18 26	...	...	21 34			2324	...
Antwerp	5 54	7 18	8 18	...		10 9	1244	1428	1617	18 44	1827	...	21 52			2332	...

Extra.

Aerschot	4 8	4 46	7 43	8 50	9 27	10 53	1126	1453	1645
Louvain	4 38	5 16	8 1	9 8	9 45	11 11	1144	1511	17 5
Louvain dep	7 34	1138	1355	1737	17 53	...	...	...	
Aerschot arr	8 1	12 0	1412	1755	18 17	...	...	...	

Antwerp dep	1218	15 †3	19 26	...
Lierre ....arr	1245	15 28	19 52	...
Lierre ...dep	4†48	13 25	14 15	20 2
Antwerp arr	5 15	13 52	1442	20 26

†—Sunday excepted. ‡—Does not run on Saturday and Sunday.

MONS, BLATON, and TOURNAI. BLATON, and GHENT.

Station											
Mons ...dep	4 17	7 38	9 41	9 46	1145	1332	1652	1835	1846	1947	2047
Jemappes	4 25	...	...	9 54	1152	1340	17 0	1844	...	1955	...
St. Ghislain	4 38	7 51	9 54	10 9	12 5	1353	1712	19 5	19 0	20 7	2115
Blaton arr	5 7	8 18	1011	1038	1234	1422	1741	1933	1919	2036	2138
Blaton	5 10	8 32	1012	1046	1240	1428	1747	1940	1920	2037	2139
Péruwelz	5 28	8 45	1021	1058	13 8	1441	18 0	1953	1930	2051	2152
Antoing	5 53	9 7	1037	1152	1331	15 5	1822	2015	1946	2114	2213
Tournai	6 6	9 20	1046	12 5	1344	1518	1835	2028	1955	2127	2226
Blaton .dep	5 15	8 24	...	...	1236	1424	1744	1937	...	...	...
Leuze	5 47	8 50	...	...	1259	15 8	18 8	20 4	...	...	...
Renaix	6 20	9 23	...	1050	1329	1538	1841	2036	...	...	...
Audenarde	6 54	9 53	...	1124	1355	1612	19 7	21 6	...	...	...
La Pinte	7 25	1024	...	1159	1427	1643	1938	2137	...	...	...
Ghent Sud	7 41	1039	...	1214	1448	1659	1954	2156	...	...	...

Station										
Ghent (Sud) ....dep		5 54	...	8 48	1019	12 12	1413	1711	20 8	1811
La Pinte		6 13	...	9 7	1038	12 28	1434	1733	2026	1831
Audenarde		6 58	...	9 54	1117	12 57	15 9	18 9	21 6	19 5
Renaix		7 25	...	1019	1144	—	1538	1842	2131	1934
Leuze		8 2	...	—	1214	...	16 9	1913	—	20 5
Blaton arr		8 24	...	...	1234	...	1630	1929	...	2025
Tournai...dep	6 47	7 39	8 35	1030	1141	15 13	1540	...	1840	1932
Antoing	6 57	7 53	8 46	1045	1155	15 23	1554	...	1855	1947
Péruwelz	7 13	8 18	9 2	1114	1218	15 39	1615	1720	1921	2010
Blaton arr	7 22	8 31	9 11	1126	1230	15 48	1627	1735	1934	2022
Blaton dep	7 23	8 34	9 12	1127	1236	15 49	1633	—	1936	2030
St. Ghislain	7 42	9 2	9 37	12 1	13 4	16 7	1659	...	20 4	21 0
Jemappes	...	9 13	9 47	1213	1315	...	...	...	2015	2111
Mons arr	7 53	9 20	9 54	1220	1322	16 18	1710	...	2022	2118

LIEGE, JEMELLE, and TROIS VIERGES (ULFLINGEN).

Station						¶—Customs Exam.								*—Earlier on Sunday from these stations.				Via Pepinster.		*** German Time at Trois-Vierges.		‡—Sunday excepted.
Liége-Guillem	...	4 27	5 45	5 54	6 37	6 43	9 13	10 9	1137	12 6	13 7	14 3	1533	1615	17 8	1816	18‡43	19 3	1910	19 19	19 45	2139
Angleur	...	4 40	5 53	6 2	6 45	6 52	9 21	10 17	1145	1216	1315	1411	15 41	1623	1716	1824	18 52		...	19 28	19 53	2147
Tilff	...	4 58	6 3	6 12	...	7 3	9 31	10 27	1156	1235	1325	1422	15 51	1640	1726	1834	19 2		...	19 46	20 3	2157
Esneux	...	5 11	6 16	6 25	...	7 15	9 44	10 40	12 8	1246	1338	1434	16 3	1652	1739	1846	19 15		...	19 58	20 15	2211
Rivage arr	3 56	5 30	6 29	6 38	7 9	7 28	9 57	10 53	1221	13 4	1351	1447	16 16	1711	1752	1859	19 29		1939	—	20 28	2224
Hamoir	4 17	...	6 53	...	...	7 49	...	11 13	...	...	1410	...	16 33	—	1811	...	20 4		...	...	20 48	2244
Barvaux	4 41	...	7 12	...	...	8 11	...	11 35	...	...	1432	...	16 57		1829	...	20 24		...	...	21 8	
Melreux	4 56	...	7 26	...	7 42	8 26	...	11 50	...	...	1447	...	17 11		1844	...	20 39		2012	...	21 23	
Marche	5 14	...	7 41	...	7 55	8 43	...	12 6	...	...	15 3	...	17 27		19 0	...	20 56		2025		21 40	
Marloie	5 24	...	7 47	...	...	9 12	...	12 19	...	...	1515	...	17 35		1912	...	21 6		...		21 51	
Jemelle...arr	5 32	...	7 55	...	8 6	9 19	...	12 26	...	...	1522	...	17 42		1920	...	21 14		2036		21 58	
Rivage dep	—	5 35	—	6 39	—	—	9 59	—	1222	13 6	—	1450	16 43		—	19 1	—		—		20 34	
Aywaille	...	5 51	...	6 58	...		1019	...	1242	1322	...	15 8	17*12		...	1920	...		...		21*12	
Remouchamps	...	—	...	7 4	...		1025	...	1248	—	...	1514	17*23		...	1926	...		...		21*21	
Stoumont	...	...	...	7 25	...		1045	...	13 8	...	...	1535	17*58		...	1946	...		...		21*52	
Trois Ponts	5 ‡7	...	...	8 1	...		1123	...	1338	...	...	1613	18*39		...	2017	...	2051	...		22*21	
Vielsalm	5 31	...	...	8 22	...		1144	...	1359	...	...	1635	—		...	2038	...	21 8	...		—	
Gouvy	5 52	...	...	9 0	...		1210	...	1425	...	...	17 6	...	...	...	21 3	...	2127	...		...	
T. Vierges ***¶	...	...	...	1016	...	...	1 26	...	3 41	...	...	6 22	...	...	...	1019	...	1040	...		...	...

Melreux......dep	6 26	9 0	10 14	13 10	15 55	18 50	20 16
Laroche ......arr	7 41	10 9	11 27	14 33	17 4	19 59	21 22

Laroche......dep	50	6 55	8 18	10 25	13 10	15 37	17 20	...	...	...
Melreux......arr	5 58	8 8	9 34	11 35	14 23	16 50	18 28	...	...	...

ANTWERP and TERMONDE, LOUVAIN, MALINES, and GHENT.

	1,2,3	1,2,3	1,2,3	1,2,3	1,2,3	1,2,3	1,2,3	1,2,3	1,2,3	1,2,3	1,2,3	1,2,3	1,2,3	1,2,3	1,2,3	1,2,3	1,2,3	1,2,3	1&2	1,2,3	1,2,3
Antwerp Centrale dep	4 52	6 27	7 0	8 0	...	9 3	10 §5	1044	1231	1235	13 47	1410	16 4	...	1643	17 58	19 2	19 52	From Herbesthal (dep. 7.54 p.m.)	...	23 0
Vieux-Dieu	5 6	6 41	...	8 15	...	9 13	:	1110	:	1245	14 1	1420	...	...	1657	18 12	1916	20 4		...	2314
Boom	5 36	6 59	7 22	8 38	...	9 34	10 36	1131	:	1318	14 25	1439	1626	...	1722	18 36	1947	20 26		...	2338
Puers	5 49	7 13	...	8 54	...	9 43	10 50	—	:	1330	—	1448	...	...	1734	—	20 0	20 38		...	—
St. Amand-lez-Puers	6 2	...	...	9 6	...	...	11 3	...	:	1342	...	C	...	...	1746	...	2012	20 47		...	...
Termonde arr	6 17	7 10	7 47	9 20	...	10 0	11 17	...	:	1356	1 & 2	15 5	1651	...	18 0	...	2027	21 1		...	...
Louvain dep	4 23	...	...	...	8 32	8 37	9 36	10 3	:	1155	13 12	...	...	1520	...	17 17	...	18 2		2118	2122
Wespelaer	4 42	...	...	...	...	8 56	9 55	...	:	1214	B	...	...	1589	...	...	...	18 21		To Antwerp (arr. 22.0.)	2140
Malines arr	5 10	...	...	...	8 52	9 19	10 20	1025	:	1240	13 32	...	...	16 2	...	17 37	‡	18 47	2118		22 4
Malines dep	5 41	...	...	...	8 56	9 25	10 36	⌐	:	1317	13 39	...	...	1612	...	17 41	1835	19 27	2123		2227
Londerzeel (Ouest)	6 10	...	...	...	:	9 41	11 1	—	:	1355	:	...	...	1639	...	...	19 4	19 54	:		2252
Malderen	6 18	...	...	...	:	9 48	11 8	...	:	14 2	:	...	...	1646	...	...	1911	20 1	:		2259
Termonde arr 1,2,3	6 35	...	...	...	:	10 1	11 24	...	:	1416	:	...	...	17 2	...	18 4	1927	20 17	:		2312
Termonde dep 4 31	6 40	7 33	7 49	9 22	:	10 4	11 30	...	:	1421	:	1510	1657	17 5	18 4	18*10	...	21 6	:	...	...
Wetteren 5 2	7 11	...	...	...	:	10 21	12 1	1359	:	1452	RC	...	...	1736	...	...	...	21 37	:	...	...
Melle 5 14	7 23	...	...	...	:	10 30	12 12	1411	:	...	:	C	...	1748	...	...	...	21 49	:	...	...
Ghent (St. Pierre) ...	...	...	8 18	...	9 45	...	...	...	1335	...	14 26	...	...	...	...	...	...	...	22 8	...	...
Ghent (Sud) arr 5 28	7 37	8 6	...	10 6	...	10 38	12 20	1423	:	15 8	...	1539	1726	18 2	1833	18 39	...	21 57	...	...	...
OSTEND (102A) arr	9 24	9 31	9 24	1118	11 0	12 12	...	...	1434	1646	15 23	1646	1844	...	2115	21 15	...	...	23 1	...	...

A—Connecting carriages from Ostend run in at Ghent St. Pierre. ‡—Sunday excepted.

B—Takes 1st and 2nd class only for Ghent and beyond; also admits 3rd class for England.

C—Wagon-Salon between Antwerp and Ostend. *—Only takes up for beyond Ghent. §—From Antwerp Sud Station.

	1,2,3	1,2,3	1,2,3	1,2,3	1,2,3	1,2,3	1,2,3	1,2,3	1,2,3	1,2,3	1,2,3	1,2,3	1,2,3	1,2,3	1,2,3	1,2,3	1,2,3	1&2	1,2,3	1,2,3	1,2,3	1,2,3
OSTEND dep	...	3 42	6 27	6 27	6 34	...	7 5	8 48	8 51	...	...	11 34	1330	11 34	From Antwerp Central (dep. 17.26)	1430	1510	16 5	...	17 27	1740	20 10
Ghent (Sud) dep	...	5 20	...	7 50	..	...	8 30	10 7	1050	12 2	1221	13 37	:	13 50		1556	1651	16 45	...	19 15	20 0	...
Ghent (St. Pierre)	...	...	7 33	...	7 43	...	...	...	...	...	...	...	1430	...		...	...	17 1	18 3	...	...	21 17
Melle	...	5 34	...	...	...	...	8 42	10 23	...	...	1235	...	:	14 6		16 9	...	A	:	19 31	...	...
Wetteren	...	5 46	...	8 7	...	...	8 54	10 36	11 6	1218	1247	13 53	:	14 18		1621	...	:	:	19 54	...	...
Termonde arr	...	6 16	8 7	8 25	8 12	...	9 24	11 9	1122	1234	1320	14 9	:	14 48		1651	1719	RC	:	20 24	2030	21 46
Termonde dep	5‡28	6 40	8 8	...	...	1036	9 26	11 27	⌐	...	...	...	:	15 15		17 1	...	:	:	20 48	...	...
Malderen	5 45	6 57	...	...	...	1050	9 43	11 44	...	...	...	...	:	15 32		1718	...	:	:	21 6	...	...
Londerzeel (O.)	5 53	7 4	...	...	...	1059	9 53	11 51	...	...	...	...	:	15 40		1736	...	:	:	21 14	...	...
Malines arr	6 20	7 31	8 34	...	...	1120	1020	12 18	...	...	...	...	:	16 7		18 3	...	17 48	1853	21 40	...	...
Malines dep	6 47	7 44	8 52	...	...	—	1030	12 36	...	...	1335	...	:	16 19		1830	...	17 52	1858	22 29	...	...
Wespelaer	...	8 16	...	...	...	...	1056	13 1	...	...	...	...	:	16 45		1855	...	D	...	22 56	..	...
Louvain arr	7 10	8 28	9 12	...	...	...	1114	13 19	...	...	1359	...	:	17 3	18 7	1913	...	18 11	1918	23 14	...	...
Termonde 4 7	...	6 43	...	8 27	8 15	8 55	...	...	1126	1235	...	14 12	:	...	...	1733	1721	...	...	...	2037	21 50
St. Amand-l-P. 4 22	...	6 58	...	8 40	...	9 10	...	...	1141	...	...	14 27	:	...	...	1748	...	...	...	...	2052	...
Puers 4 36	...	7 10	...	8 53	...	9 23	...	...	1153	...	...	14 40	:	...	...	18 0	1741	1,2,3	...	...	21 5	...
Boom 4 51	...	7 24	...	9 8	8 41	9 37	...	13 16	12 6	13 0	...	14 52	:	15 44	...	1813	1751	19 20	...	21 34	2119	22 17
Vieux-Dieu 5 18	...	7 48	...	9 26	...	10 3	...	13 45	1227	...	...	15 19	:	16 2	...	1839	18 7	19 45	...	22 0	...	...
Antwerp C. 5 30	...	8 0	...	9 39	9 3	1015	...	13 57	1235	1319	...	15 31	1534	16 10	...	1848	1815	19 58	...	22 12	2142	22 38

Extra.										
Louvain...dep	5 35	7 11	1346	Malines...dep	5 40	9 31	1659	1922	Termonde...dep	4 9
Malines ...arr	6 17	7 50	14 7	Louvain...arr	6 0	9 50	1719	20 6	Louvain......arr	6 41

D—Will only take up passengers for Liege and beyond, exceptionally admits at Malines passengers arriving at 17.27 from Holland.

POIX and ST. HUBERT.

E.M.																					
	Poix dep	625	8 40	1015	1150	1445	16 0	1720	20 5	2130	St. Hubert dep	5 40	7 40	9 25	11 0	1355	1520	1635	1915	2030	...
1½	Arville	635	8 50	1025	12 0	1455	1610	1730	2015	2140	Arville	5 50	7 50	9 35	1110	14 5	1530	1645	1925	2040	...
4½	St. Hubert arr	645	9 0	1035	1210	15 5	1620	1740	2025	2150	Poix 103A arr	6 0	8 0	9 45	1120	1415	1540	1655	1935	2050	...

JEMELLE and DINANT.

Jemelle dep	4 4	5 25	6 10	8 25	9 38	1254	1531	1748	2117	22 0	Dinant	4 3	7 3	9 28	1044	1152	1347	1512	...	1853	2010	2042	...
Rochefort	...	5 31	6 16	8 31	9 44	13 0	1537	1754	2123	22 6	Houyet	4 33	7 34	9 57	1113	1219	1419	1546	1652	1926	2042	21 9	...
Eprave	...	5 37	6 22	8 37	9 50	13 6	1543	18 0	2129	—	Wanlin	4 43	7 44	10 8	1123	—	1429	1557	17 2	1936	2052	—	...
Villers-s-L.	...	5 43	6 28	8 43	9 56	1312	1549	18 6	2135	...	Villers	4 52	7 54	1018	1132	...	1438	16 6	1711	1945	21 1	...	...
Wanlin	...	5 52	6 37	8 52	10 6	1321	1558	1815	2144	...	Eprave	4 58	8 0	1024	1138	...	1444	1612	1717	1951	21 7	...	...
Houyet	4 31	6 7	6 49	9 11	1028	1334	1620	1826	2154	...	Rochef'rt	5 5	8 8	1031	1145	...	1451	1619	1724	1958	2120	...	...
Dinant arr	...	6 33	7 15	9 39	1055	14 1	1646	1852	2220	...	Jemelle	5 12	8 15	1038	1152	...	1458	1626	1731	20 5	2129	...	...

Extra—Houyet to Dinant, 12.29, 15.52, 17.42, 19.26. Dinant to Houyet, 14.51, 17.30.

TROIS VIERGES (ULFLINGEN), JEMELLE, and LIEGE.

						a.m.	a.m.	a.m.			a.m.			p.m.				p.m.			p.m.			
Trois Vierges *,*	...	...	...	...	...	5 43	...	9 10	...	...	11 3	...	...	2 58	...	...	...	5 16	...	...	8 9	...	...	
Gouvy ¶	...	...	...	...	...	5 7	7‡17	8 31	...	...	1027	...	...	1422	...	...	...	1641	...	...	1934	...	...	
Vielsalm	...	...	...	...	...	5 30	7 40	8 52	...	...	1043	...	...	1445	...	...	...	17 4	...	...	1956	...	...	
Trois Ponts	...	...	...	...	...	5 57	8 0	9 19	...	...	11 1	1225	...	15 9	...	...	...	1729	...	...	2020	...	...	
Stoumont	...	...	...	...	...	6 22	—	9 43	...	...	:	1249	...	1534	...	...	...	1756	...	..	2044	...	...	
Remouchamps	...	...	...	...	...	6 42	...	10 3	...	...	:	1310	...	1554	...	...	...	1816	...	...	21 4	...	...	
Aywaille	4 17	...	6 5	...	...	6 47	...	10 8	...	...	:	1324	1359	1559	...	...	...	1821	...	...	2110	...	...	...
Rivage arr	4 31	...	6 24	...	...	7 3	...	1024	...	...	:	1340	1416	1615	V S	...	...	1837	...	...	2128	...	...	...
Jem'lle dep	...	3 55	...	5 38	6 46	...	8 23	—	9 10	...	:	12 4	...	...	15 2	...	1749	...	18 1	1929	...	2151	...	
Marloie	...	4 8	...	5 51	...	...	8 36	...	9 22	...	:	1239	...	...	1527	...	...	..	1819	1948	...	22 5	...	
Marche	...	4 15	...	5 57	6 59	...	8 42	...	9 28	...	:	1245	...	...	1533	...	18 2	...	1825	1954	...	2211	...	
Melreux	...	4 31	...	6 13	7 10	...	8 57	...	9 42	...	:	13 0	...	...	1548	...	1813	...	1839	20 9	. .	2226	...	
Barvaux	...	4 45	...	6 27	...	...	9 10	...	9 55	...	:	1313	...	...	16 1	...	...	...	1852	2022	...	2237	...	
Hamoir	...	5 6	...	6 47	...	...	9 29	...	1014	...	:	1331	...	...	1619	...	...	...	1913	2040	...	2256	...	
Rivage dep	4 32	5 25	6 28	7 10	...	7 18	9 47	...	1033	1158	:	1349	1419	1617	1641	1730	1844	1849	1933	2058	2129	2314	...	
Esneux	4 46	5 39	6 46	...	...	7 32	10 1	...	1046	1212	:	14 2	1438	1631	1655	1751	...	19 2	1947	2111	2142	2328	...	
Tilff	4 58	5 51	6 59	...	...	7 44	1014	...	1058	1224	:	1414	1450	1643	17 7	18 7	...	1914	1959	2121	2154	2338	...	
Angleur	5 8	6 1	7 19	...	...	7 54	1025	...	11 8	1234	:	1424	15 8	1657	1717	1825	...	1924	20 9	2131	22 5	2349	...	
Liege-G'mn.	5 17	6 8	7 8	7 38	8 7	8 1	1032	...	1115	1241	1259	1431	1517	17 4	1724	1836	1911	1931	2016	2138	2212	2356	...	

Via Pepinster.

‡—Not on Sunday

, German Time at Trois-Vierges.

LONDON to OSTEND and BRUSSELS.

OSTEND, BRUGES, GHENT, and BRUSSELS.

THROUGH CARRIAGES
- Ostend to Basle—in 3.42, 16.20, and 20.47 from Ostend Quai.
- Ostend to Cologne—in 3.25, 16.5, and 20.41 from Ostend Quai.
- Ostend to Frankfort and Munich—in 3.42 from Ostend Quai
- Ostend to Milan—in 16.20 from Ostend Quai.

SLEEPING CARRIAGES.—Ostend to Basle—in 16.20 from Ostend Quai.

RC—Restaurant Car

Distance from Ostend Station (E.M.)	Station	1 & 2 Direct Service Ostend–Cologne.	1,2,3 Every Saturday until 20th September.	1,2,3	1,2,3	1,2,3	2 & 3 VS	1,2,3	2 & 3 VS	From Blankenberghe. C VS Not on Sunday.
	London—									
	VICTORIA dep	...	...	...	...	...	...	...	...	...
	CHARING CROSS dep	9 p0	9 p0	9 p0	...	...	...	...	...	
	DOVER dep	11 p0	11 p0	11 p0	...	...	...	...	...	
	OSTEND Quai arr	2 a0	2 a0	2 a0	...	...	...	...	...	
	OSTEND Quai dep	3 25	3 32	3 42	...	...	...	6 27	...	
	Ostend Station dep		...	...	...	5 1	5 57	...	6 34	
8¾	Jabbeke		...	...	...	5 23	...	...	...	C
14¼	Bruges (111) arr		3 52	4 2	...	5 37	6 21	6 50	6 58	VS
	Bruges (111) dep		3 54	4 3	...	5 40	6 24	6 53	7 3	7 29
18¾	Oostcamp			...	...	5 49	...	...	...	
21¾	Beernem			...	...	5 57	...	...	...	
28	Aeltre			...	...	6 11	...	...	...	
31¾	Hansbeke			...	...	6 24	...	...	...	
33½	Landegem			...	...	6 30	...	...	...	
37¼	Tronchiennes			...	...	6 40	...	...	...	
39¾	Ghent St. Pierre			4 34	...	6 47	7 1	7 28	7 41	8 0
42¼	Ghent Sud arr			4 45	...	6 54	:	7 33	...	:
74½	MALINES (101) arr			7 31	...	...		8 34	...	
85¼	ANTWERP (101) arr			8 0	...	...		9 3	9 3	
90	LOUVAIN (101) arr			8 28	...	...		9 12	...	
168¼	AIX-LA-CHAP. 122 arr	8 a41		...	...	...		1254	...	
212	COLOGNE (122) arr	9 a51		...	...	...		2p24	...	
...	Ghent Sud dep	...		4 20	5 42	7 11	:	8 43	...	:
...	Ghent St. Pierre	...		4 35	...	...	7 2	...	...	8 1
43	Meirelbeke	...		...	...	...	...	...	...	...
44¾	Melle	...		...	...	...	...	...	...	C
48½	Wetteren	...		...	...	7 27	...	...	...	...
50¼	Schellebelle	...		...	...	...	...	9 4	...	...
56½	Alost (97) arr	...		...	6 10	7 42	7 29	9 21	...	...
	Alost (97) dep	...		...	6 12	7 44	7 31	9 26	...	...
58½	Erembodegem	...		...	...	...	...	9 32	...	...
61	Denderleeuw arr	...		...	6 19	7 52	...	9 38	...	...
...	,, 102B dep	...		...	6 21	7 54	...	9 39	...	...
65¼	Ternath	...		...	...	...	...	9 54	...	...
72¾	Jette (97)	...		...	...	...	...	1021	...	...
74	Laeken	...		...	...	...	...	1026	...	...
75¾	BRUSSELS Nord arr	...	5 *18	5 24	6 44	8 19	8 3	1032	...	8 50
138	LIEGE (104) arr	...	...	7 24	8 56	11 22	9 53	1224	...	11 22
172¾	AIX-LA-CHAP. 122 arr	...	...	10 a4	12p11	2 p20	...	3 p8	...	2 p44
216¼	COLOGNE (122) arr	...	...	11a14	...	4 p19	...	4p19	...	4 p19
216¾	LUXEMBURG (103A) arr	...	10a39	11a36	1p23	...	...	...	...	...
353¾	STRASSBURG (210) arr	...	1 p57	3 p19	4p41	...	...	...	...	...
442¼	BASLE (208) arr	...	4 p0	5 p36	7p22	...	...	...	...	...

Station	1,2,3 From Nieuport.	From Zee Brugge dep. 8.0. Wed., & Fri. only. Runs on Sun.	1,2,3	2 & 3 VS	C VS Weekdays only.	1,2,3 From Blankenberghe.	1,2,3	1.2.3	1,2,3	2 & 3 From Blankenberghe. Runs from 28th July until 2nd September, and not on Sunday.
VICTORIA dep	...	...	...	...	...	...	...	...	...	...
CHARING CROSS dep	...	...	...	...	...	...	...	...	...	...
DOVER dep	...	...	...	...	...		...	...	...	
OSTEND Quai arr	...	...	...	...	...		...	...	...	
OSTEND Quai dep	...		...	...	...		8 43	...	...	
Ostend Station dep	...		6 39	7 5	7 20		...	8 48	8 51	
Jabbeke	...		7 1	...	...		...	...	9 13	
Bruges (111) arr	...		7 15	7 29	7 41		9 6	9 11	9 27	...
Bruges (111) dep	...	8 29	7 50	7 33	7 43	9 3	9 10	9 18	9 29	10 55
Oostcamp	...		7 59	...	...	...	...	...	9 38	
Beernem			8 7	...	...	E	...	...	9 46	V S
Aeltre			8 21	...	...	...	...	...	10 0	
Hansbeke			8 34	...	...	...	...	...	10 13	
Landegem			8 40	...	...	...	...	...	10 19	
Tronchiennes			8 50	...	...	...	...	...	10 29	
Ghent St. Pierre		9 1	8 57	8 11	8 14	9 41	9 47	...	10 36	
Ghent Sud arr		...	9 4	8 17	:	:	...	9 57	10 43	
MALINES (101) arr			...	10 20			...	12 18	12 18	
ANTWERP (101) arr			...	11 20			...	...	12 35	
LOUVAIN (101) arr			...	11 14			...	13 19	13 19	
AIX-LA-CHAP. 122 arr			...	...			...	6 p19	...	
COLOGNE (122) arr	...		...	...			...	7 p40	...	
Ghent Sud dep	...	...	9 28	8 22	:	:	...	10 2	10 55	
Ghent St. Pierre	8 6	9 2	...	...	8 15	9 45	...	...	...	
Meirelbeke	...		...	...		...	...	...	11 4	
Melle	...		...	...		...	...	...	11 10	
Wetteren	...		9 44	...		E	...	...	11 22	
Schellebelle	...		...	...		...	...	...	11 28	
Alost (97) arr	...	9 25	9 59	8 51		10 13	...	...	11 45	
Alost (97) dep	...	9 26	10 1	8 54		10 17	...	...	11 50	
Erembodegem	...		...	...		...	...	...	11 56	
Denderleeuw arr	...		10 9	...		...	...	...	12 2	
,, 102B dep	...		1011	...		...	...	...	12 3	
Ternath	...		1020	...		...	...	...	...	
Jette (97)	...		1034	...		...	...	...	...	
Laeken	...		1039	...		...	...	...	...	
BRUSSELS Nord arr	8 56	9 54	1045	9 26	9 4	10 50	...	10 54	12 28	12 32
LIEGE (104) arr	1122	11 46	1224	11 46	11 22	13 50	...	13 50	15 15	15 15
AIX-LA-CHAP. 122 arr	2p44	2 p44	3 p8	2 p44	2 p44	5 p20	...	5 p20	6 p19	6 p9
COLOGNE (122) arr	4p19	4 p19	4p19	4 p19	4 p19	7 p24	...	7 p24	7 p40	7 p40
LUXEMBURG (103A) arr	...	3 p48	...	3 p48	3 p48	...	...	6 p35	...	...
STRASSBURG (210) arr	...	7 p12	...	7 p12	7 p12	...	...	10p31	...	...
BASLE (208) arr	...	9 p13	...	9p13	9 p13	...	...	...	...	...

Station	2 & 3 VS	2 & 3 From Blankenberghe.	1,2,3	1,2,3	1,2,3 To Duisburg.	1,2,3 From 28th July until 2nd September, and not on Sunday.	2 & 3 VS	1,2,3 From Blankenberghe.	1,2,3
VICTORIA dep	...		...	...	...	...	...	...	...
CHARING CROSS dep	...		...	...	...	...	...	...	...
DOVER dep	...		...	...	...	...	...		...
OSTEND Quai arr	...		...	...	...	...	...		...
OSTEND Quai dep	...		...	...	1330	...	...		...
Ostend Station dep	10 42		11 19	11 34	...	...	14 30		15 10
Jabbeke	...		...	11 56	...	...	...		...
Bruges (111) arr	11 6	VS	11 43	12 10	1351	...	14 54	...	15 32
Bruges (111) dep	11 9	11 29	—	12 15	1356	14 50	14 57	15 14	15 34
Oostcamp	...	...	...	12 24	...		...	...	...
Beernem	...	...	...	12 32	...		...	...	...
Aeltre	RC	RC	...	12 46	...		...	...	...
Hansbeke	...	...	...	12 59	...		...	...	...
Landegem	...	...	...	13 5	...		...	...	...
Tronchiennes	...	...	...	13 15	...		...	...	...
Ghent St. Pierre	11 45	...	...	13 23	1428		...	15 50	...
Ghent Sud arr	:	12 10	...	13 29	:		15 38	:	16 10
MALINES (101) arr		...	...	16 7			17 48		17 48
ANTWERP (101) arr	13 19	...	...	15 31	1534		18 15		18 15
LOUVAIN (101) arr		...	...	17 3			18 11		18 11
AIX-LA-CHAP. 122 arr		...	...	...			10p 9		10 p9
COLOGNE (122) arr		...	...	...			11p24		11p24
Ghent Sud dep	:	12 18	13 32	13 40			15 47	:	16 24
Ghent St. Pierre	11 47	...	...	...			...	15 53	...
Meirelbeke	...	...	...	13 49			...	...	...
Melle	...	...	...	13 55			...	...	...
Wetteren	...	...	...	14 7	...		...	...	...
Schellebelle	...	...	...	14 13	...		...	...	...
Alost (97) arr	...	12 46	14 1	14 30	...	15 55	...	16 21	16 48
Alost (97) dep	...	12 48	14 5	14 33	...	15 57	...	16 24	16 50
Erembodegem	...	...	...	14 39	...	...	...	...	...
Denderleeuw arr	...	...	14 14	14 44	...	...	...	...	...
,, 102B dep	...	...	14 16	14 46	...	...	...	...	...
Ternath	...	...	...	15 1	...	...	...	...	...
Jette (97)	...	...	...	15 28	...	...	...	...	...
Laeken	...	...	...	15 33	...	...	...	16 53	...
BRUSSELS Nord arr	12 44	13 20	14 40	15 39	...	16 29	16 44	16 59	17 20
LIEGE (104) arr	15 15	15 28	17 2	18 4	..	18 4	18 47	...	21 27
AIX-LA-CHAP. 122 arr	6 p19	6 p19	8 p21	...	...	...	9p48	...	...
COLOGNE (122) arr	7 p40	7 p40	10p28	...	..	...	11p 1	...	...
LUXEMBURG (103A) arr	...	8 p25	...	...	..	...	...	...	12 a3
STRASSBURG (210) arr	...	...	...	...	...	...	...	...	3 a27
BASLE (208) arr	...	...	...	...	...	...	...	...	5 a43

Belgian Railway Time.—See Note on page 89.

LONDON to OSTEND and BRUSSELS.

OSTEND, BRUGES, GHENT, and BRUSSELS.

Stations																						
London—						From Blankenberghe.				September only. Runs until 2nd										Weekdays only. From Nieuport.	From Blankenberghe.	
Charing Cross	dep	9 a0	9 a0	9 a0	9 a0	9 a0		...	...	...	...	...	...	...	...	...	...	...	2 p5	2 p5	...	...	...
Dover	dep	11 a0	11 a0	11 a0	11a0	11 a0		...	...	...	...	...	...	...	...	...	...	...	4 p30	4 p30	...		...
Ostend Quai	arr	2 p0	2 p0	2 p0	2 p0	2 p0		...	...	...	...	...	...	...	...	...	...	...	7 p30	7 p30	...		...
			A	B	G	H													D				
		2 & 3		1 & 2	1,2,3			2 & 3	1,2,3	2 & 3	2&3	1,2,3	1,2,3	1,2,3	1,2,3	2 & 3	1,2,3	2 & 3	1 & 2	1,2,3	1,2,3	2 & 3	1,2,3
		VS	Lux		VS	Lux		VS		VS	VS					VS		VS	VS				
Ostend Quai	dep	15 24	15 30	16 5	1620	16 36		...	...	...	...	...	...	...	...	...	...	...	20 41	20 47	...		...
Ostend Station	dep	:	...	...	...	...		17 8	...	17 27	1737	...	...	17 40	18 35	19 1	20 10	20 23	...	...	20 27		23 15
Jabbeke		F	...	...	...	...		...	...	...	:	...	...	18 2	...	...	...	...	RC	J	20 46		...
Bruges (111)	arr	:	...	16 25	RC	...	1,2,3	...	...	17 51	:	...	...	18 16	...	19 25	20 34	20 47	21 1	21 7	20 57	...	23 29
Bruges (111)	dep	:	...	16 29	...	...	17 45	K	...	17 54	:	...	...	18 20	...	19 31	20 38	20 50	21 3	21 9		21 37	23 42
Oostcamp		RC	...	...	...	...	:	...	...	...	:	...	...	18 29	...	:	...	...	...	...		...	...
Beernem		:	...	...	...	...	:	...	...	...	:	...	...	18 37	...	:	...	...	...	...		VS	...
Aeltre		:	...	RC	...	...	:	...	...	...	:	...	...	18 51	...	:	...	...	...	...		...	...
Hansbeke		:	...	...	...	...	:	...	...	RC	:	...	...	19 4	...	:	...	...	...	...		RC	...
Landegem		:	...	...	...	...	:	...	...	...	:	...	...	19 10	...	:	...	...	...	...		...	...
Tronchiennes		:	...	...	...	...	:	...	...	...	:	...	...	19 20	...	:	...	...	...	J		...	...
Ghent St. Pierre		16 15	16 20	17 0	1711	17 25	:	18 6	...	...	1835	...	...	19 27	19 32	:	21 15	...	21 34	21 40		...	...
Ghent Sud	arr	:	:	:	:	:	:	:	...	18 35	:	...	...	19 35	:	:	:	21 31	:	:		22 13	0 23
Malines (101)	arr	:	:	17 48	:	:	:	:	...	21 40	:	...	...	...	:	:	:	...	:	:		...	...
Antwerp (101)	arr	:	:	18 28	:	:	:	:	...	21 42	:	...	...	21 42	:	:	22 38	...	:	:		...	...
Louvain (101)	arr	:	:	18 11	:	:	:	:	...	23 14	:	...	...	...	:	:	...	...	:	:		...	...
Aix-la-Chap. 122	arr	:	:	10 p9	:	:	:	:	...	4 a15	:	...	...	...	:	:	...	...	:	:		...	...
Cologne (122)	arr	:	:	11p24	:	:	:	:	...	5 a40	:	...	...	...	:	:	...	...	:	:		...	...
Ghent Sud	dep	:	:	...	:	:	:	:	...	18 59	:	19 3	...	20 10	:	:	...	21 50	:	:	:	22 16	0 29
Ghent St. Pierre		16 16	16 21	...	1712	17 26	:	18 8	18 25	...	1837	...	19 13	...	19 34	:	...	...	21 35	21 41	22 28	...	...
Meirelbeke		...	:	...	...	:	:	...	...	...	:	...	...	20 19	...	:	...	...	...	...	...	...	...
Melle		...	:	...	...	:	:	...	...	...	:	...	...	20 25	...	:	...	...	...	...	...	...	...
Wetteren		RC	:	...	...	:	:	...	...	19 15	:	19 21	19 29	20 37	...	:	...	...	...	...	...	...	...
Schellebelle		...	:	...	RC	:	:	...	...	...	:	...	...	20 43	...	:	...	...	...	...	...	...	...
Alost (97)	arr	...	:	...	...	:	:	18 35	...	19 30	:	19 36	19 44	20 59	...	:	...	22 18	...	...	22 53	22 44	...
Alost (97)	dep	...	:	17 37	...	:	:	18 36	...	19 32	:	19 37	19 45	21 8	...	:	...	22 20	...	...	22 54	22 45	...
Erembodegem		...	:	17 43	...	:	:	...	...	...	:	...	...	21 14	...	:	...	...	...	...	...	...	...
Denderleeuw	arr	...	:	17 49	...	:	:	...	...	...	:	...	19 53	21 20	...	:	...	...	...	...	...	...	...
" (102B	dep	...	:		...	:	:	...	...	...	:	-	19 54	21 25	...	:	...	...	...	...	...	...	...
Ternath		...	:	...	...	:	:	...	...	19 51	:	19 56	...	21 40	...	:	...	...	...	...	...	...	...
Jette (97)		...	:	...	...	:	:	...	...	...	:	...	...	22 7	...	:	...	...	...	...	...	...	...
Laeken		...	:	...	...	:	:	...	...	...	:	...	...	22 12	...	:	...	...	...	...	...	...	...
BRUSSELS Nord	arr	17 6	17 12	...	18 3	18 14	19 16	19 8	19 23	20 12	1934	20 17	20 23	22 18	20 28	21 2	...	22 51	22 25	22 31	23 24	23 17	1 26
Liege (104)	arr	20 29	18 58	...	2029	20 6	22 32	22 32	22 32	23 25	2325	23 25	23 25	...	23 25	23 25	...	1 23	1 23	1 23	...	...	...
Aix-la-Chap. 122	arr	...	9 p37	...	1228	10p43	...	...	...	...	...	...	...	...	...	...	...	4 a15	4 a15	4 a15	...	...	...
Cologne (122)	arr	...	10p46	...	...	11p52	...	...	...	...	...	...	...	...	...	...	...	5 a40	5 a40	5 a40	...	...	...
Luxemburg (103A)	arr	12 a3	...	...	12a3	...	...	...	...	...	...	...	...	...	...	...	...	4 a55	4 a55	4 a55	...	...	...
Strassburg (210)	arr	3 a27	...	...	3a27	...	...	...	...	...	...	...	...	...	...	...	...	8 a44	8 a44	8 a44	...	...	...
Basle (208)	arr	5 a43	...	...	5a43	...	...	...	...	...	...	...	...	...	...	...	...	11a15	11a15	11a15	...	...	...

(Column 2: Nord Express. Column 5: Ostend-Vienna Express.)

☞ Belgian Railway Time.—See Note on page 89. ☜

Extra. Ostend ....dep 1438 21†54; Ghent Sud...arr 17 4 23 3 ‖ Bruges........dep 22§13; Ghent ....arr 22 54 ‖ Ghent Sud...dep 4 42 15 0 1733; Brussels N...arr 6 13 16*30 20 7 ‖ Ostend Stat dep 19‡35; Bruges........arr 20 11 ‖ Ghent Sud...dep 21 53; Alost..........arr 22 37 ‖ †—In August only, and not on Sunday.

‡—Runs until 7th Sept. only. §—Runs on Sats. only until 6th Sept. E—Runs from 28th July until 2nd September, and on weekdays only.

V.S.—Attached to these trains are carriages known as "Voitures-Salon." Holders of 2nd class tickets may use them on payment of an excess fare of three centimes per kilometre. The excess fare may be paid in the carriage

TABLE OF FARES ON BELGIAN RAILWAYS.—See page 89.

NOTES.

*—Arrives at Quartier Leopold Station.

A—Nord Express, for Berlin and St. Petersburg, consisting of Restaurant and Sleeping Cars, at extra fares. Tickets of Sleeping Car Co.

B—The 16.5 from Ostend takes along passengers arriving by the Mail Steamer, and at Ostend (for passengers not arriving by the steamer), and Bruges only those for Malines and beyond towards Louvain; at Ghent (St. Pierre) only takes up for beyond Liege.

C—This train is composed entirely of Wagons-Salons.

D—Takes for Louvain and beyond only. Also takes for all destinations passengers from England using the "Voitures Salon," and those travelling to Malines or Antwerp

F—Will not take local passengers at Ostend.

G—Takes forward for all destinations Passengers coming direct from England, or holding through tickets from England; also takes all passengers using the "VS" carriage; at Ostend and Ghent will also take passengers for Arlon (p. 103A) and beyond.

H—Ostend-Vienna Express, consisting of Sleeping and Restaurant Cars; at extra fare. Tickets of Sleeping Car Co.

J—Except in the case of travellers with through tickets from England will only take up for Namur and beyond.

K—At Ostend takes for beyond Ghent only.

RC—Restaurant Car in this train.

10

BRUSSELS to OSTEND and LONDON.

BRUSSELS, GHENT, BRUGES, and OSTEND.

Station																											
BASLE 209A ....dep	7p32	7p32	...	...	...	...	...	...	...	...	...	...	...	11p40	11p40	...	...	...	...	...	...	...	...	...	...	...	...
STRASSBURG 210A ...dep	10p5	10p5	...	...	...	...	...	...	...	...	...	...	...	1 a40	1 a40	...	...	...	...	...	...	...	...	...	...	...	...
LUXEMBURG 103B ...dep	1a50	1a50	...	...	...	...	...	...	...	...	...	...	...	5 a7	5 a7	...	...	...	...	...	...	...	...	...	...	6 a49	...
COLOGNE 123B.........dep	12a5	12a5	...	...	...	...	...	...	...	...	...	4 a41	...	...	...	...	...	...	...	...	...	6 a0	6 a0	8 a7	...	7 a56	7a56
AIX-LA-CHAPL. 123Bdep	1a32	1a32	...	...	...	...	...	...	...	...	...	5 a56	...	...	...	...	...	...	...	...	...	7a37	7 a37	9a23	...	9 a12	9a12
LIEGE 104..............dep	2 16	2 16	...	...	...	...	...	...	...	...	...	6 28	4 53	4 53	4 53	4 53	6 52	7 43	7 43	...	...	8 35	8 35	10 7	...	9 53	9 53
	1,2,3	1,2,3	2&3	2 & 3	2 & 3	1,2,3	1,2,3	1,2,3	1,2,3	1,2,3	1,2,3	Lux	1,2,3	1,2,3	2, Cl.	1,2,3	2 & 3	1,2,3	2 & 3	1,2,3	1,2,3	1,2,3	1,2,3		1,2,3	1,2,3	1,2,3
			VS	VS								H		VS	VS		VS		VS			A		Lux			VS
BRUSSELS Nord......dep	5 40	5 58	6 44	6 55	...	...	...	7 7	7 40	7 47	7 53	8 6	8 25	8 46	8 50	8 59	9 15	9 27	9 32	...	10 10	10 41	10 44	11 37	...	11 40	12 25
Laeken	...	6 5	6 51	...	...	...	...	7 14	...	...	...		...				...	...	...	...	...	...	10 51		...	...	...
Jette	...	...	...	...	...	...	...	7 19	...	...	...		...	K			...	...	9 42	...	...	...	10 56		...	...	...
Ternath..................	...	...	...	...	...	...	...	7 46	...	...	D		...				...	...	10 1	...	...	...	11 23		...	...	...
Denderleeuw ....arr	...	6 28	...	...	...	...	...	8 0	...	...	...		...				...	...	10 11	...	...	A	11 37		...	12 4	...
,, (102B) ...dep	...	6 29	RC	RC	...	...	...	8 17	...	...	...		...				...	...	10 12	10 26	...	...	11 39		...	12 5	RC
Erembodegem..............	...	...	...	...	...	...	...	8 24	...	...	...		...				...	...	...	...	...	...	11 46		...	...	...
Alost (96)................	6 8	6 40	7 22	7 28	...	...	...	8 38	8 12	8 16	8 22		9 0				...	9 59	10 24	1036	10 43	11 18	12 6		...	13 17	12 55
Schellebelle.............		6 57	...		...	...	...	8 57		...			...				...	...	...				12 25		...	...	
Wetteren		7 3	...		...	...	...	9 3		...			...	RC			...	10 15	10 40	...			12 31		...	12 35	
Melle (107)		...	...		...	...	...	9 15		...			...				...		...	...			...		...	12 47	
Meirelbeke		...	...		...	...	...	9 21		...			...				...		...	...			...		...	12 53	
Ghent Sud...............arr		7 19	7 50		...	...	...	9 27		8 42			9 30				10 11		10 56	...			12 47		...	13 1	
COLOGNE 123B.........dep		...	12a5		...	...	...	...		...		Ostend Express	...						...	...			...		From Duisburg.	6 a0	
AIX-LA-CHAPL. 123Bdep		...	1a32		...	...	...	...		...			...						...	...			...			7 a37	
LOUVAIN 101...........dep		...	4 23		...	...	4 23	...		...			...			8 32			8 37	8 37			...			10 3	
ANTWERP 101 ....dep		...	4 52		7 0	...	6 27	...		...			...	7 J26		...	8 0		9 3	9 3			...		12 31	12 31	
MALINES 101 ....dep		...	5 41		...	...	5 41	...		...			...	7 J56		8 56			9 25	9 25			...			10 36	
Ghent Sud ....dep		...	7 58		...	8 21	8 24	...		...			...				10 16		11 3	11 7			...			13 34	
Ghent St. Pierre	6 32	...	...		8 20		8 31	...	8 39	...	8 46	8 58	...	9 36		9 57	...	10 32	...	11 14	11 10	11 48	...	12 25	13 37	13 41	13 19
Tronchiennes	...	...	...		...		8 39	...		...	To Nieuport.	Vienna-	...	...		...	...	...	...	11 22		...	...	Nord Express.	...	13 49	...
Landegem	...	...	...		...		8 49	...	...	...			...	...		...	...	...	...	11 32	...	...	...		...	13 59	...
Hansbeke....................	...	...	...		...		8 55	...	...	...			...	...		...	...	...	...	11 38	...	A	...		...	14 19	...
Aeltre	...	...	...		...		9 17	...	...	...			...	...		...	...	...	...	11 50	...	...	...		...	14 45	...
Beernem	...	...	...		...		9 31	...	...	...			...	...		...	...	...	...	12 4	...	...	...		...	14 59	...
Oostcamp....................	...	...	...		...		9 39	...	...	...			...	...		...	...	...	...	12 12	...	...	...		...	15 7	...
Bruges (111) ... arr 1,2,3	7 3	...	8 39		8 57	9 4	9 47	...	...	...		9 31	...	10 7	10 12	10 33	...	11 9	11 44	12 20	...	12 24	...		14 9	15 15	13 51
Bruges (111) ... dep 5 †9	7 8	...	8 43		9 0	9 7	9 50	...	...	...	...	9 32	...	10 9	10 15	10 36	...	11 13	11 48	12 26	...	12 29	...		14 13	15 18	13 55
Jabbeke......................5 24	...	...			...	...	10 5	...	...	...	...	...	...	...	...	...	...		...	12 41	...		...		...	15 33	...
OSTEND Station arr 5 45	...	...		8 53	9 24	9 31	10 26	...	...	...	...	...	...	...	10 37	11 0	11 18		12 12	13 2	...		...		...	15 54	...
OSTEND Quai.. arr ...	7 28	...		...	...	...	...	...	...	...	...	9 52	...	10 29	...	...	...		...	...	...		...	13 15	14 34	...	14 16
OSTEND ....dep	...	...	To Blankenberghe.	...	...	...	...	...	...	...	...	10 47	...	10 47	...	...	...	To Blankenberghe.	...	...	...	To Blankenberghe.	...	15 30	15 30	...	...
DOVER.....................arr	...	...		...	...	...	...	...	...	...	...	2 p0	...	2 p0	...	...	...		...	...	...		...	6 p30	6 p30	...	...
CHARING CROSS ......arr	...	...		...	...	...	...	...	...	...	...	5 p10	...	5 p10	...	...	...		...	...	...		...	10 p0	10 p0	...	...

†—Not on Sunday.
A—Runs from 28th July until 2nd September, Sunday excepted.
B—At Brussels will only take for England.
C—Will also take 3rd class for England. D—Takes for beyond Ghent only.

H—Vienna-Ostend Express, Sleeping and Restaurant Cars only.
J—These connections are via Brussels.
K—This train takes 1st and 2nd class for Ostend and England; takes 3rd class for England via Ostend; at Brussels only will take 1st class for Ghent.

V.S.—Attached to these trains are carriages known as "Voitures-Salon." Holders of 2nd class tickets may use them on payment of an excess fare of three centimes per kilometre. The excess fare may be paid in the carriage.

Belgian Railway Time—See Note on page 89.

For Continuation of Trains and Notes, see next page.

BRUSSELS to OSTEND and LONDON.

BRUSSELS, GHENT, BRUGES, and OSTEND.

Station	1	2	3	4	5	6	7	8	9	10	11	12	13	14	15	16	17	18	19	20	21	22	23	24	25	26	27	28
Basle 209 ...dep	...	...	...	...	...	...	...	...	...	...	...	...	...	...	...	...	...	...	...	...	...	...	...	10a22	...	12p15	...	...
Strassburg 210A ...dep	...	5 a52	...	...	...	...	...	...	7 a30	7 a30	7a30	7 a30	7a30	...	7 a30	...	...	...	...	...	...	...	...	12p33	...	2 p18	...	...
Luxemburg 103B ...dep	...	9 a38	...	...	...	...	...	...	11a27	11a27	1127	11a27	11a27	...	11a27	...	...	...	...	...	12p48	12p48	...	4 p24	...	5 p58	...	...
Cologne 123B ...dep	...	9 a10	...	...	...	9 a10	9 a10	10 a5	11a26	11a26	1126	11a26	11a26	...	11a26	...	...	...	...	12p37	12p37	12p37	3p12	4 p19	...	8 p13	6 p13	...
Aix-la-Chap. 123B dep	...	10a32	...	...	...	10a32	10a32	11a23	12p56	12p56	1256	12p56	12 56	...	12p56	...	...	...	...	2 p46	2 p46	2 p46	4p29	5 p47	...	7 p27	7 p27	...
Liege 104 ...dep	...	11 30	...	...	...	11 36	11 36	13 5	13 49	13 49	1349	13 49	13 49	...	13 49	...	...	...	...	15 47	15 47	15 47	17 35	18 32	...	20 7	20 54	...
	1,2,3	1,2,?	1 & 2	2 & 3	1,2,3	2 & 3	2 & 3	2 & 3	1,2,3	D	D	1,2,3	1,2,3	1,2,?	2 & 3	1,2,3	1,2,3	1,2,3	1,2,3	1,2,3	2 & 3	1,2,3	2 & 3	1,2,3	1 & 2	1,2,3	1,2,3	1,2,3
	A	VS				VS	VS	VS		...		E			VS						VS		VS					
BRUSSELS Nord ...dep	12 31	13 13	...	...	13 24	14 22	14 35	14 42	15 57	16 14	1621	16 25	16 25	...	16 28	17 6	17 13	...	...	17 56	18 8	18 14	19 52	20 40	...	22 21	23 55	0 6
Laeken ...	...		...	...	13 31	...	...	...	...			...		...	...	...	...	...	...	...	...	...	...	...	...	...	...	H
Jette ...	...	B	...	...	13 36	...	...	...	...			...			...	...	...	...	...	...	...	...	...	...	...	...	...	0 15
Ternath ...	...		...	...	14 3	...	A	RC	...			...			...	...	...	...	...	...	...	...	...	...	...	...	...	0 33
Denderleeuw ...arr	A		...	...	14 17	...	...	...	...			...			16 52	17 29	...	...	...	...	...	...	20 18	...	...	22 46	0 27	0 42
" (102B) ...dep	...	RC	...	...	14 20	...	...	...	...			...			16 54	17 30	...	...	...	...	...	...	20 19	...	...	22 47	0 28	0 43
Erembodegem ...	...		...	...	14 27	...	...	...	...			...			...	...	...	...	...	...	...	...	...	...	...	...	...	...
Alost (96) ...	13 2		...	...	14 34	14 58	15 6	15 15	16 26			16 55			17 5	17 39	17 44	...	...	18 31	18 38	18 44	20 30	21 8	...	22 57	0 39	0 55
Schellebelle ...			...	...	14 53	RC		...	...						...	...		...	...			...	...		...	...		...
Wetteren ...			...	...	14 59			...	16 39						...	...		...	...			18 58	...		...	...		1 12
Melle (107) ...			...	...	15 11		A	...	...	Sunday excepted.	Sunday excepted.		until 6th September.		...	...		...	...			...	...		...	...	Not Sunday.	...
Meirelbeke ...			...	...	15 17			...	...						...	...		...	...			...	...		...	...		...
Ghent Sud ...arr			...	...	15 23			15 43	16 53						17 32	18 5		...	...			19 12	20 58		...	23 22	1 9	1 30
Cologne 123B ...dep			10 a5	...	...			...	...					On Saturday only: in August daily, Sunday excepted.	...	...		1p42	...			1 p42	...		6p13	...	...	...
Aix-la-Chap. 123B ...dep			11a23	...	...			...	...						...	...		3p16	...			3 p16	...		7p27	...	...	...
Louvain 101 ...dep			13 12	...	...			...	...						...	...		1717	...			17 17	...		...	...	...	...
Antwerp 101 ...dep			...	14 10	14 10			14 10	...						16 4	...		1643	...			16 43	...		2015	...	...	...
Malines 101 ...dep			13 39	VS	13 12			...	...						...	...		1741	...	until 6th Sept.		17 41	...		2123	...	...	...
Ghent Sud ...dep				15 44	16 0			15 56	...					17 30	17 37	...			...			19 22	21 4			...	1 20	1 39
Ghent St. Pierre ...	13 30	14 3	14 27	...	16 7			...	...	17 6	1713	17 22		...	...	...	18 10	1842	18 53			19 29	21 11	21 33	22 9	...	...	...
Tronchiennes ...	...	...	C	...	16 15			...	...	...	...	...		...	...	...		...	...			19 37	...	...	...	...	...	...
Landegem ...	...	...	...	...	16 25			...	...	...	...	...		...	...	...		...	...			19 47	...	...	...	...	...	...
Hansbeke ...	A	...	RC	...	16 31			...	...	D	...	E	Saturday only,	...	...	...	To Nieuport.	...	...	Saturday only,		19 53	...	...	...	...	...	H
Aeltre ...	...	...	...	...	16 43			...	...	...	...	...		...	...	...		...	...			20 5	...	...	...	...	...	...
Beernem ...	...	...	...	...	16 57			...	...	...	...	...		...	...	...		...	...			20 19	...	...	...	...	...	...
Oostcamp ...	...	...	...	...	17 5			...	...	...	...	...		...	...	...		...	...			20 27	...	...	...	...	...	...
Bruges (111) ... arr	14 1	14 35	14 58	16 20	17 13		16 7	16 37	...	...	1744	17 53	17 54	18 11	18 17	...		1914	19 25	19 30	19 35	20 35	21 48	22 4	2239	...	2 5	2 20
Bruges (111) ... dep	14 4	14 40	15 3	16 24	17 16		16 10	16 41	18 35	...	1747		17 57	18 14	18 21	...	...	1918	19 28	19 32	19 39	20 39	21 53	22 6	2241	...		
Jabbeke ...		...	...	...	17 31				18 50	...		...		...	...	...	...	...	...		...	20 54	...	...	...	...	...	...
OSTEND ... Stat. arr		...	...	16 46	17 52	16 21			19 11	17 58		...		18 38	18 44	...	...	1940	...		20 1	21 15	22 17	...	...	...	...	...
OSTEND ... Quai arr		15 1	15 23	...	...	...			...	...		...		...	...	...	...	...	19 51		...	...	...	22 26	23 1	...	...	...
Ostend ...dep	To Blankenberghe.	15 30	15 30	...	...	...	To Blankenberghe.	To Blankenberghe.	...	...	To Blankenberghe.	...	To Blankenberghe	...	...	...	...	...	...	To Blankenberghe.	...	...	...	23 8	23 8	...	...	...
Dover ...arr		6 p30	6 p30	...	...	...			...	...		...		...	...	...	...	...	...		...	...	...	2 a15	2a15	...	...	...
Charing Cross ...arr		10 p0	10 p0	...	...	...			...	...		...		...	...	...	...	...	...		...	...	...	5 a43	5a43	...	...	...

Extra.				
Denderleeuw ...dep	7 50	20 35	22 34	...
Alost ...arr	8 2	20 47	22 44	...

†—Not on Sunday.
§—From Quartier Leopold Station.
D—Train composed of Wagons-Salons only.
E—On Sunday, Wednesday, and Friday only.
H—On Monday early morn. only.
RC—Restaurant Car attached.

Belgian Railway Time.—See Note on page 89.

NOVILLE-TAVIERS and EMBRESIN.

E.M.	Noville-Taviers							
—	Noville-Taviers...dep	6 0	8 20	10 6	13 12	1451	1710	19 5
6¼	Embresin ....arr	6 35	8 55	1041	13 47	1526	1745	1940

Embresin ....dep	5 0	7 15	9 10	1215	1355	16 5	18 0
Noville-Taviers 103B arr	5 35	7 50	9 45	1250	1430	1640	1835

ANTWERP, LIERRE, and TURNHOUT.

Dist E.M	Antwerp—								
	Centrale dep	5 44	8 35	1033	1414	...	1752	1943	22 20
3¾	Vieux-Dieu	5 59	...	1047	1424	...	18 6	1957	22 31
6¾	Contich............	6 12	...	11 1	1435	1641	1814	20 6	22 42
10½	Lierre	6 26	9 22	1116	1454	17 8	1828	2021	22 56
15½	Nylen	6 41	9 37	1131	15 9	1723	1843	2036	—
23	Herenthals......	7 2	9 58	1153	1541	1744	1913	21 5	...
33½	Turnhout ...arr	7 28	1024	1219	16 7	18 7	1939	2131	...

Turnhout.dep	3 46	6 4	7 37	8 29	10 58	13 42	16 21	1827	20 33
Herenthals ...	4 16	6 38	8 6	8 56	11 27	14 12	16 51	1853	21 6
Nylen	4 36	6 56	8 23	9 13	11 45	14 30	17 9	1911	21 23
Lierre 100......	4 59	7 12	8 39	9 30	12 3	14 48	17 26	1927	21 41
Contich	5 17	7 28	...	...	12 22	15 4	17 45	1941	21 58
Vieux-Dieu ...	5 29	7 38	...	...	12 32	15 14	17 52	1952	22 8
Antwerp C. ar	5 41	7 46	8 59	9 54	12 44	15 26	18 4	20 4	22 20

ANTWERP to LIERRE, via Wilryck.

Antwerp Sud.	4 42	7 11	8 9	12 7	...	1316	1441	1546	1857
Hoboken	4 50	...	8 19	...	...	...	1450	...	19 6
Vieux-Dieu. .	5 12	...	8 40	12 20	...	1413	1512	...	1929
Contich.........	5 27	8 6	9 3	...	13 3	...	1521	16 5	1938
Lierre ......arr	5 40	8 19	9 16	...	1315	...	...	1654	2019

Lierre......dep	5 50	8 44	1019	12 3	1244	...	15 53	...	19 27
Contich.......	6 20	8 59	1120	12 22	1254	...	17 25	18 6	19 57
Vieux-Dieu...	6 29	9 10	1130	13 6	—	1448	17 35	1814	20 5
Hoboken	...	9 31	1151	...	...	15 9	...	1835	20 30
Antwerp..arr	6 42	9 33	1158	13 19	...	1516	17 48	1842	20 37

DENDERLEEUW, ATH, and MONS.

†—Except Sunday.]

												†	
Denderleeuw ...dep		4†16	5 54	8 6	1017	12 8	1447	...	1659	18 5	1850	2033	2154
Ideghem		4†47	6 27	8 34	1050	1240	1514	...	1731	1839	1922	2127	2226
Grammont......		5 15	6 57	8 56	11 2	1254	1528	...	1743	1855	1932	2142	2238
Lessines..............		5 39	7 13	9 13	1115	1310	1541	...	1759	19 8	2016	—	2252
Ath ....arr		6 0	7 34	9 33	1135	1330	16 1	...	1819	1930	2038	†	2314
„ ....dep	5 †7	6 15	7 39	9 45	1235	1332	16 8	1746	—	1938	—	2117	—
Maffle............	5 13	6 19	7 44	9 50	1240	1337	1613	1751	...	1943	...	2122	...
Jurbise......	5 43	6 46	810	1016	13 6	14 3	1639	1819	...	20 9	...	2149	...
Mons......arr	6 6	7 13	831	1036	1321	1421	1658	1835	...	2035	...	22 4	...

Mons ......dep		5 16	6 43	8 45	1141	1347	1723	1830	1950
Jurbise dep		5 40	7 6	9 14	12 6	14 8	1749	1858	2022
Maffle		6 6	7 33	9 41	1233	1435	1816	1924	2049
Ath ....arr		6 10	7 37	9 45	1237	1439	1820	1928	2053
„ ...dep	4 25	6 16	7 47	1012	1250	1547	1849	1945	2118
Lessines ...	4 46	6 37	8 8	1036	1311	1613	1912	2015	2138
Gramm't	4 59	6 59	8 34	1054	1328	1633	1930	2039	2152
Ideghem ...	5 43	7 11	8 46	11 6	1340	1645	1942	2051	22 4
Dend'l'w	6 16	7 44	9 19	1135	1413	1718	2015	2122	2233

BLATON and ATH.	E.M.									
		Blaton.. dep	5 25	6 59	8 42	1058	1433	1745	18†48	2038
	11¾	Ath 103 arr	6 3	7 36	9 22	1137	15 4	1823	19 28	2115

Ath ....dep	4 22	6 14	742	958	1246	1545	1825	1940	†Not
Blaton 100 arr	5 4	6 53	821	1041	1328	1626	19 4	2019	Sun.

LIEGE, BATTICE, and VERVIERS.

Dist. E.M.	Liege								
	(Guillemins) ....dep	4 21	6 40	9 19	1134	1416	1649	19 5	2112
8	Beyne......................	4 57	7 14	9 53	12 8	1450	1722	1936	2143
16¾	Battice.....................	5 31	7 49	1031	1247	1525	1755	20 9	2215
24¾	Verviers..............arr	6 1	8 20	11 4	1319	1559	1827	2042	2245

Verviers ....dep	4 55	6 40	9 44	1212	1355	17 6	19 0	2128
Battice	5 30	7 16	1019	1247	1432	1742	1936	22 1
Beyne......................	6 3	7 50	1053	1323	15 5	1816	2011	2233
Liege (Guil.).......arr	6 39	8 23	1123	1355	1535	1850	2045	23 3

E.M										
	Battice ....dep	5 47	7 55	10 36	12 57	15 28	18 1	20 20	22 16	
13¾	Bleyberg ....arr	6 40	8 42	11 26	13 53	16 15	18 54	21 12	23 6	
	Bleyberg ...dep	4 23	6 10	9 13	11 42	1326	1636	1827	2045	...
	Battice ......arr	5 24	7 12	10 13	12 43	1426	1737	1927	2144	...

TOURNAI and ST. AMAND.

E.M.							
—	Tournai ....dep	4 25	7 26	10 53	15 49	18 51	...
4¼	Antoing	4 39	7 41	11 8	16 4	19 6	...
8¾	Bleharies..........................	4 57	8 0	11 26	16 24	19 27	...
13¾	Maulde-Mortagne	5 14	8 18	11 43	16 45	19 44	...
16¼	Saint Amand 29A........arr	5 27	8 32	11 56	16 58	19 57	...

Saint Amand ....dep	6 5	9 43	14 2	18 47	20 36	...
Maulde-Mortagne	6 21	9 58	14 16	19 1	20 54	...
Bleharies	6 36	10 10	14 28	19 12	21 6	...
Antoing	6 53	10 29	14 46	19 31	21 25	...
Tournai ....arr	7 5	10 41	14 58	19 43	21 37	...

AUDENARDE and MOUSCRON.

[‡—Except Sunday.

Dist. E.M.										
	Audenarde.dep	...	6 9	7 16	...	11 21	15 47	19 29	...	21‡10
11¼	Avelghem 102B	5 42	6 56	7 49	1039	11 54	16 26	20 3	2116	21 45
21¼	Herseaux 89.....	6 18	7 33	8 20	1117	12 33	1656	20 39	2151	22 20
23½	Mouscron 89arr	6 26	7 41	8 26	1123	12 41	...	20 47	22‡0	22 26

Mouscron..dep	4 30	5 23	8 23	8 54	11 36	...	...	‡	...
Herseaux........	4 41	5 34	8 38	9 6	11 46	1428	1758	1919	2013
Avelghem	5 14	6 15	9 9	9 37	12 18	15 14	1829	20 2	2050
Audenarde arr	...	6 47	9 40	...	12 50	1546	19 0	2034	...

HERSEAUX and ROUBAIX-WATTRELOS.

Herseaux ....dep	5 41	7 38	9 7	1135	16 57	18 25	...	...
Roubaix-Wattrelos...arr	6 4	7 57	9 32	1153	17 18	18 50	...	...
Roubaix-Wattrelos...dep	6 16	8 9	10 49	13 49	17 35	19 14	...	...
Herseaux ....arr	6 30	8 25	11 4	14 5	17 48	19 29	...	...

BRUSSELS, DENDERLEEUW, and COURTRAI.

Brussels (Nord)	441	614	8 15	9 6	12 9	1324	16 7	1716	18 17	19 8	20 0
Denderleeuw.	534	636	8 38	9 29	1241	1451	16 31	1756	18 47	1941	2024
Burst...............	554	...	8 58	VS	13 1	1515	...	1816	...	20 2	...
Sottegem...dep	616	657	9 12	9 50	1317	1531	16 57	1830	19 9	2017	2046
Audenarde arr	645	713	9 41	10 6	1347	16 2	17 16	1859	19 25	2047	21 2
Anseghem	7 6	...	9 58	...	14 6	1626	...	1921	VS	—	...
Courtrai ...arr	735	743	1027	1035	1435	1657	17 41	1949	19 58	...	2129

Courtrai......dep	6 8	642	748	9 25	1038	12 9	1232	1529	1818	19 0
Anseghem	637	...	...	...	11 5	1238	VS	1558	1847	...
Audenarde...arr	651	7 8	814	9 51	1116	1252	1258	16 9	19 1	1926
Sottegem ...dep	739	730	837	1016	1151	1338	1321	1648	1939	1951
Burst	753	...	...	...	12 5	1352	...	17 3	20 4	...
Denderleeuwarr	812	VS	...	1036	1224	1411	1339	1722	2024	2011
BrusselsNordarr	846	810	918	11 0	1312	1440	14 8	1757	2053	2035

Extra. {Audenarde......dep 8 19 | 19 40 | ... ; Courtrai ....arr 9 6 | 20 28 | ...

Courtrai ......dep 17 12 | 20 55 | ... ; Audenarde......arr 17 55 | 21 40 | ...

Sottegem......dep 9 25; Brussels ......arr 10 45

COURTRAI, TOURNAI, RENAIX, and ENGHIEN.

Courtrai ....dep		4 48	...	8 23	...	10 41	14 36	17 34	18 22	2043
Avelghem		5 19	...	8 49	...	11 8	15 5	18 9	1852	2111
Tournai ......dep		4 56	6 11	7 59	8 35	10 50	14 46	...	18 40	...
Renaix		5 55	7 5	9 13	9 27	11 40	15 39	18 35	19 35	2136
Lessines........	8 26	6 38	7 44	—	10 6	12 13	16 9	—	20 13	—
Bassily	8 46	6 57	8 0	...	—	1228	16 28	...	2028	...
Enghien...arr	—	7 10	8 12	...	...	1240	16 40	...	20 42	...

Enghien..dep	5 7	8 1	...	...	10 5	...	14 20	17 38	...	1912
Bassily.........	5 20	8 11	...	...	10 18	...	14 35	17 51	...	1925
Lessines	5 38	8 29	...	...	10 42	...	14 53	18 7	...	1941
Renaix ...arr	6 14	9 3	9 23	9 34	11 20	1331	15 30	18 40	1933	2018
Tournai arr	7 17	10 5	1017	...	12 38	...	16 38	20 31	...	2114
Avelghem ...	6 54	—	—	10 2	—	14 0	16 31	19 19	20 6	...
Courtrai arr	7 25	...	...	10 29	...	1438	16 59	19 52	2038	...

FOR FARES SEE PAGE 89. [Luggage, cent. 1·50 per 55 lbs. per kilometre.

LONDON, LILLE, TOURNAI, and BRUSSELS.

THROUGH CARRIAGES.—Calais to Brussels and Cologne—in 1.19 and 12.53 from Calais.

Station																				
CHARING CROSS......dep	9 p0	...	...	...	...	...	...	...	...	...	...	...	9 a0	...	...	...	...	...	2 p5	...
VICTORIA STATION ,,	...	...	...	...	...	...	...	...	...	...	...	...	...	...	11 a0	11a0	...	...	...	...
DOVER ,,	11 p5	...	...	...	...	...	...	...	...	...	...	...	11 a5	...	12p55	1255	...	...	D	...
CALAIS 26 ,,	1 19	...	...	...	...	...	...	...	...	...	...	...	12 53	...	14 46	1446	...	...	19 7	...
LILLE ......arr	2 55	...	...	...	...	...	...	...	...	...	...	...	⋮	...	16 30	1630	...	...	2045	...
	1,2,3	1,2,3	1,2,3	1,2,3	1,2,3	1,2,3	1,2,3	1,2,3	1,2,3	1,2,3	1,2,3	1,2,3	1 & 2	1,2,3	1 & 2	1,2,3	1,2,3	1,2,3	1,2,3	1,2,3
Lille ......dep	3 0	...	...	...	...	6 20	...	8 36	...	10 41	12 13	13 55	⋮	...	16 35	17 1	17 46	19 32	2055	22 28
La Madeleine ......dep	...	...	...	...	...	...	...	...	...	...	...	...	⋮	...	...	...	...	...	...	...
Ascq......	...	...	...	...	...	6 32	...	8 47	...	10 52	12 24	14 6	A	...	...	...	17 57	19 46	...	22 39
Baisieux (France) ...dep	3 14	...	...	...	...	6 43	...	8 56	...	11 2	12 35	14 15	14 35	...	16 53	1716	18 7	19 54	21 9	22 49
Blandain (Bel.) ¶ arr	3 19	...	...	...	...	6 50	...	9 4	...	11 9	12 43	14 22	14 40	...	16 59	1722	18 14	20 1	2114	22 56
Blandain (Bel.) ¶ dep	3 35	...	...	...	...	7 3	...	9 14	...	11 19	12 54	14 32	14 51	...	17 11	1732	18 25	20 11	2124	23 1
Tournai (Doornik) arr	3 43	...	...	...	...	7 15	...	9 27	...	11 32	13 7	14 43	14 59	...	17 19	1740	18 38	20 24	2134	23 12
,, (89) ......dep	3 50	...	5 7	5 38	...	7 24	7 30	9 35	10 48	11 43	14 18	⌣	15 §6	15 38	17 26	1747	18 42	20 48	2141	—
Havinnes	...	...	5 21	...	...	...	7 40	...	11 1	11 53	14 29	—	...	15 48	...	...	18 52	21 2	...	...
Barry-Maulde	...	...	5 31	...	...	...	7 48	...	11 10	12 2	14 37	...	...	15 56	...	...	19 1	21 12	...	...
Leuze	B	4† 35	5 45	5 59	...	7 45	7 58	9 55	11 21	12 14	14 48	...	15 27	16 8	...	18 9	19 14	21 23	22 1	...
Ligne	...	4 47	5 57	...	...	...	8 9	...	11 32	12 26	15 0	...	...	16 20	...	...	19 25	21 36	...	...
Ath (102B) arr	4 19	4 57	6 7	6 11	...	7 57	8 18	10 7	11 40	12 33	15 7	...	15 39	16 27	...	1821	19 33	21 46	2213	...
Ath (102B) dep	4 21	—	6 18	6 13	...	8 1	8 23	10 9	11 44	12 39	15 9	...	15 41	16 31	...	1825	19 48	—	2214	3†42
Ghislenghien	...	...	6 35	...	...	...	8 40	...	12 1	...	15 26	...	...	16 48	...	...	20 6	...	...	4 3
Bas-Silly (102B)	...	...	6 48	...	...	...	8 50	...	12 14	...	15 36	...	...	17 1	...	...	20 19	20 28	...	4 15
Enghien (107) arr	...	...	7 2	6 36	...	8 24	9 4	1031	12 28	13 6	15 50	...	...	17 15	...	1847	20 33	20 42	...	4 32
Enghien (107) dep	...	4†47	7 17	6 39	8†13	8 26	9 12	1032	12 29	13 9	16 5	...	...	17 18	...	1848	20 47	20 52	...	—
Saintes......	...	5 4	7 34	...	...	...	9 28	...	12 46	...	16 21	...	...	17 35	...	...	...	21 9	...	...
Hal	...	5 18	7 47	6 58	...	...	9 41	...	12·59	13 29	16 35	...	...	17 48	...	...	21 5	21 22	...	...
Buysingen	...	5 23	7 52	...	...	...	9 46	...	...	...	16 40	...	...	17 53	...	...	...	21 27	...	...
Loth......	...	5 28	7 57	...	...	...	9 51	...	...	...	16 45	...	...	17 58	...	...	...	21 32	...	...
Ruysbroeck	...	5 34	8 3	...	...	...	9 57	...	...	...	16 51	...	...	18 4	...	...	...	21 38	...	...
Forest (Midi)	...	5 39	8 8	...	...	...	10 2	...	...	...	16 56	...	...	18 9	...	...	...	21 43	...	...
BRUSSELS Midi...arr	...	5 46	8 15	7 14	8 42	8 56	10 9	11 2	13 15	13 46	17 3	...	...	18 16	...	1917	21 21	21 50	...	...
BRUSSELS Nord. arr	5 21	...	...	...	...	...	...	...	...	...	...	...	16 41	...	18 55	...	...	...	2314	...

A—Carriages from Calais for Brussels do not enter Lille, but run on to line for Brussels at La Madeleine, outside Lille.
B—This train brings forward 3rd class from French stations and takes up 3rd class for Brussels Nord and beyond.
D—Via Boulogne.

†—Sunday excepted. ¶—Customs Examination. §—1,2,3 Class.

BRUSSELS, TOURNAI, LILLE, and LONDON.

Dist. E.M.	Station																			
			1,2,3	1,2,3	1,2,3	1,2,3	1,2,3	1,2,3	1,2,3	1 & 2	1,2,3	1,2,3	1,2,3	1,2,3	1,2,3	1,2,3	1,2,3	1,2,3	1,2,3	1,2,3
	BRUSSELS Nord ...dep		...	...	...	...	...	8 30	...	10 58	...	13 50	...	...	...	...	...	...	...	...
...	Schaerbeek......dep		...	...	...	...	...	...	...	...	...	...	...	...	...	...	†	...	...	21 45
—	**BRUSSELS** Midi ...dep		4 18	5 53	7 *2	7 20	7 55	8 52	11 0	11 20	13 9	14 14	16 4	16 44	17 27	1829	1834	19 5	20 3	22 3
2¼	Forest (Midi)......		...	6 1	...	7 28	8 3	...	...	...	1317	...	16 12	...	17 35	...	...	1913	...	...
4¼	Ruysbroeck		...	6 6	...	7 33	8 8	...	...	...	1322	...	16 17	...	17 40	...	...	1918	...	...
6¼	Loth		...	6 12	...	7 39	8 14	...	...	...	1328	...	16 23	...	17 46	...	...	1924	...	...
7¾	Buysingen	1,2,3	...	6 17	...	7 44	8 19	...	...	...	1333	...	16 28	...	17 51	...	...	1929	...	...
8¾	Hal	3‡42	4 35	6 23	7 19	7 49	8 25	...	11 17	...	1339	...	16 34	...	17 57	...	...	1935	2021	...
13½	Saintes	...	4 49	6 36	...	—	8 38	...	11 29	...	1352	...	16 47	...	18 12	...	...	1948	...	...
16¾	**Enghien**...... arr	4 0	5 3	6 51	7 36	...	8 54	9 24	11 43	11 48	14 7	14 44	17 2	17 17	18 29	19 3	19 9	20 3	2038	22 31
	Enghien...... dep	4 17	5 7	6 52	7 37	8 1	9 4	9 25	11 54	11 49	14 10	14 45	—	17 20	18 39	19 7	—	20 15	2043	22 32
24¼	Bas-Silly......	4 31	5 19	7 6	...	...	9 17	...	12 7	...	14 21	...	...	...	18 53	...	...	20 31	...	...
26¼	Ghislenghien......	4 41	—	7 18	...	...	9 26	...	12 16	...	14 31	...	...	...	19 5	...	...	20 43	...	...
33	**Ath** ...... arr	4 58	...	7 34	7 58	...	9 42	9 50	12 32	12 10	14 46	15 7	...	17 42	19 22	1930	...	21 0	21 5	22 53
	Ath ...... dep	5 16	...	7 40	7 59	...	9 55	9 52	12 39	12 12	14 48	15 9	...	17 46	19 37	1932	...	21 19	21 7	22 54
36¾	Ligne	5 26	...	7 48	...	...	10 5	...	12 47	...	1456	...	...	...	1947	...	...	21 29	...	...
41	Leuze	5 41	...	7 59	8 12	9 47	10 17	10 6	13 4	12 25	15 8	15 22	...	18 1	20 4	1948	...	21 41	2122	23 8
44	Barry-Maulde	5 53	...	8 9	...	...	10 29	...	13 16	...	15 19	C	...	...	20 15	...	...	21 53	...	...
47¾	Havinnes......	6 1	...	8 17	...	...	10 37	...	13 24	...	15 27	...	...	...	20 23	...	...	22 1	...	C
52½	**Tournai** (Doornik) arr	6 12	...	8 25	8 30	10 5	10 48	10 25	13 35	12 43	15 35	15 40	...	18 19	20 31	20 7	...	22 12	2140	23 26
...	**Tournai** (Doornik) dep	6 28	7 57	8 39	⌣	—	10 52	10 30	—	12 47	—	15 45	15 59	18 39	20 41	⌣	...	23 41	2146	23 28
56¼	Blandain (Frontier)	6 44	8 13	8 54	—	...	11 8	10 43	...	12 59	...	15 57	16 14	18 55	20 54	...	...	23 53	2158	23 38
59¾	Baisieux ¶ arr	6 51	8 19	9 0	...	...	11 14	10 49	...	13 5	...	16 2	16 20	19 1	21 0	...	...	23 59	22 4	23 45
	Baisieux ¶ dep	7 4	8 33	9 13	...	...	11 26	11 6	...	13 19	...	16 15	16 38	19 19	21 14	...	...	0 9	2217	23 54
62¾	Ascq	7 14	8 43	9 22	...	...	11 36	...	...	...	...	...	16 44	19 28	21 23	...	...	...	...	...
67¾	**Lille**......arr	7 26	8 55	9 34	...	...	11 49	11 20	...	13 32	...	16 27	16 57	19 38	21 34	...	...	0 24	2229	0 6
...	LILLE......dep		...	...	...	...	...	11 31	...	13 38	...	16 37	...	B—Via Boulogne.	...	...	...	...	0 11	0 11
136	CALAIS (27) ......arr		...	...	...	...	...	13 0	...	15 21	...	18 5	...		...	...	...	...	1 36	1 36
161	DOVER ...... ,,		...	...	...	...	...	2p45	...	5 p0	...	B	...		...	...	...	...	3 a0	3 a0
237½	CHARING CROSS ...... ,,		...	...	...	...	...	5 p10	...	...	...	10p45	...		...	...	...	...	5a43	5 a43
...	VICTORIA STATION ,,		...	...	...	...	...	...	...	7 p5	...	...	...		...	...	...	...	...	...

C—This train carries forward from beyond Tournai 3rd cl. for England. 3rd Cl. passengers for French stations change at Tournai. *—Will not take passengers for Hal. ‡—Between Hal and Ath does not run on Sunday.

☞ Belgian Railway Time.—See Note on page 89. ☜

Luggage, cent. 1·50 per 55 lbs. per kilometre.] **FOR FARES SEE PAGE 89.**

BRUSSELS, NAMUR, ARLON, and LUXEMBURG.

*** —At Kleinbettingen and Luxemburg the trains run according to Mid Europe time, 60 minutes in advance of Belgian train time.
THROUGH CARRIAGES.—Brussels to Basle, in 6.8, 18.35, and 23.28 from Brussels Nord. RC—Restaurant Car. SC—Sleeping Car.

Dist. E.M.	BRUSSELS—		1,2,3	1,2,3	1,2,3	1,2,3	1,2,3	1,2,3	2&3	1,2,3	1,2,3	1,2,3	1,2,3	1,2,3	1,2,3	1,2,3	2 & 3
	Nord ...dep		...	...	...	5 29	6 8	6 30	6 51	...	7 49	8 40	9 43	...	1020	1114	12 10
...	Schaerbeek ...dep		...	...	...	...	...	...	...	7 14	...	...	...	...	...	...	...
4¼	Quartier Leopold dep		...	...	5 24	5 50	6 20	6 57	7 5	7 33	8 3	9 3	9 56	10 6	1033	1137	12 30
7½	Boitsfort		...	...	...	...	...	...	...	...	...	...	...	...	...	1153	...
10¼	Groenendael		...	...	D	...	...	...	VS	...	...	...	...	...	VS	12 0	VS
13¾	La Hulpe		...	...	...	...	RC	...	...	...	VS	...	...	...	...	1211	...
15½	Rixensart		...	...	...	...	...	...	...	...	...	...	...	...	RC	1220	...
18¾	**Ottignies**		3 57	5†21	...	6 23	...	7 23	7 31	8 4	RC	9 40	...	1034	...	1230	12 59
22¼	Mont-St.-Guibert		4 8	5 32	RC	6 33	C	...	...	8 14	...	9 50	...	...	...	1240	...
28	Gembloux		4 31	6 0	...	7 2	...	7 43	7 51	8 44	...	10 12	...	1055	...	13 6	13 22
33	St. Denis-Bovesse		4 49	6 17	...	7 19	...	...	...	9 1	...	10 28	...	...	...	1321	...
34¾	Rhisnes		4 54	6 22	...	7 24	...	...	...	9 6	...	10 34	...	...	...	1327	...
38½	**Namur** ...arr	1,2,3	5 2	6 30	6 18	7 32	7 14	8 2	8 10	9 15	8 54	10 42	10 47	1114	1125	1335	13 41
...	" ...dep	3 43	5 43		6 22	7 38	7 17		8 15	9†34	9 3	1055		1150	1128	1354	13 49
43¼	Nannine	3 58	6 3	...	...	7 58	...	...	...	9†54	...	11 15	...	1210	...	14 9	...
49¾	Assesse	4 18	6 21	...	...	8 17	...	...	8 38	1013	...	11 35	...	1229	...	1427	14 13
56¼	**Ciney** (98)	4 38	6 57	...	D	8 35	...	...	8 51	1030	...	12 0	...	1247	...	1442	14 26
62¾	Haversin	4 56	7 15	...	...	8 51	...	...	9 4		...	12 17	...		...	1457	...
70¼	**Marloie**	5 15	7 35	5 24	...	9 12	...	...	9 18	...	...	12 40	...	...	1219	1515	14 53
74	**Jemelle** (101) ...arr	5 22		5 32	7 20	9 19	8 15	...	9 25	...	9 59	12 47	...	...	1226	1522	15 1
...	" ...dep		...	5 40	7 26	9 34	8 21	...	9 30	...	10 9	12 58	...	...	1231	1528	15 8
79½	Grupont		...	5 58	...	9 47	...	...	...	...	...	13 14	...	...	...	1540	...
85¾	Poix (101)		...	6 16	...	10 3	...	...	9 52	...	...	13 32	...	...	...	1554	...
94½	**Libramont** (95)		5 28	6 43	...	1024	9 0	7 53	1016	...	1046	13 56	...	...	13 9	1614	15 51
100	Longlier		5 40	6 58	...	1033	...	8 8	1027	...	...	14 8	...	...	...	1623	16 3
110	**Marbehan** (95)	4 47	6 15	7 30	...	1112	...	8 38	1044	...	...	14 39	...	...	1333	1650	16 21
114½	**Habay**	4 59	6 27	7 42	D	1124	...		...	...	...	14 51	...	...	...	17 2	16 31
118	**Fouches**	5 6	6 34	7 50	...	1131	...	...	...	...	...	14 58	...	...	...	17 9	...
123	**Arlon** (103A) ...arr	5 18	6 46	8 2	8 41	1143	9 42	...	11 5	...	1127	15 10	...	...	1353	1721	16 45
...	" ...dep		7 9	8 13	8 47	1156	9 48	...		...	1133	15 29	...	...	1358	1731	16 50
129¼	**Sterpenich**		7 26	8 32	9 0	1213	...	...	...	...	1146	15 47	...	...	1411	1748	17 3
129¾	Kleinbettingen*** ar		8 28	9 34	10 2	1 15	11 1	...	...	...	1248	4 49	...	...	3 13	6 50	6 5
...	(German-Cust.) dp		8 38	9 48	1019	1 25	1116	...	...	...	1 3	4 59	...	...	3 28	7 2	6 15
141	**Luxemburg** ...arr		9 3	1018	1039	1 50	1136	...	...	...	1 23	5 27	...	...	3 48	7 30	6 35
164	WASSERBILLIG 212 arr		1031	...	1239	2p49	1239	...	...	...	2p49	6 p57	...	...	5p16	...	7 p56
173	TREVES (125) ...arr		1057	...	1 p9	3p15	1 p9	...	...	...	3p15	7 p14	...	...	5p40	...	8 p25
179½	METZ (210) ...arr		1046	1244	1138	3p47	1244	...	...	...	2p22	7 p52	...	...	4p54	9a27	7 p52
278	STRASSBURG (210) arr		1p17	3p19	1p57	...	3p19	...	...	...	4p41	10p31	...	...	7p12	...	10p31
366½	BASLE (208) ...arr		...	5p36	4 p0	...	5p36	...	...	...	7p12	...	...	...	9p13	...	...

Dist. E.M.	BRUSSELS—	1,2,3	1,2,3	1,2,3	1,2,3	1,2,3	1,2,3	2&3	1,2,3	1,2,3	2&3	1,2,3	1,2,3	1,2,3	1,2,3	1,2,3
	Nord ...dep	...	1419	...	...	...	...	17 4	...	1835	1843	...	1934	20 6	2238	2328
...	Schaerbeek ...dep	...	...	1517	†	...	1655	...	1736	...	...	...	...	...	...	...
4¼	Quartier Leopold dep	1345	1435	1540	1641	16 45	1711	1722	1756	1847	1858	1914	1950	2026	2256	2340
7½	Boitsfort	14 0	...	...	...	...	...	...	...	SC	...	1930	20 5	2038	2311	...
10¼	Groenendael	14 7	...	...	...	...	...	VS	...	RC	...	1938	2012	...	2318	...
13¾	La Hulpe	1418	...	...	...	...	...	...	...	...	...	...	2019	...	2325	B
15½	Rixensart	1427	...	...	...	...	...	...	1819	VS	...	1952	2028	...	2333	...
18¾	**Ottignies**	1443	15 1	1616	...	17 16	1745	...	1831	...	...	2010	2042	21 4	2341	...
22¼	Mont-St.-Guibert	1453	...	1626	...	17 26	...	...	1842	...	...	2020	2053	...	2351	...
28	Gembloux	1513	1521	1649	1727	17 48	18 5	1810	19 3	A	...	2041	2114	2125	0 7	...
33	St. Denis-Bovesse		...	1659	...	18 3	...	...	1918	...	...		...	...	...	...
34¾	Rhisnes	...	...	17 4	...	18 9	...	...	1924	...	...	...	...	...	0 20	...
38½	**Namur** ...arr	...	1539	1713	1745	18 19	1824	1830	1932	1938	1949	...	2133	2144	0 28	0 34
...	" ...dep	1554	1547	1724		19 14		1835	20 3	1943	1958	...				0 40
43¼	Nannine	1614	...	1746	...	19 31	...	...	2023	...	...	...	...	...	...	...
49¾	Assesse	1633	...	18 5	...	19 50	...	19 1	2043	...	...	...	...	...	...	...
56¼	**Ciney** (98)	1658	1620	1825	...	20 7	...	1914	21 0	...	2029	...	...	...	...	...
62¾	Haversin	1715	...	1843	...		...	1929	2118	...	...	...	...	...	...	...
70¼	**Marloie**	1735	...	1912	...	...	...	1947	2142	...	...	...	...	...	...	...
74	**Jemelle** (101) ...arr	1742	1648	1920	...	...	...	1954	2149	2039	2057	...	...	...	...	1 38
...	" ...dep	1750	1653	1925	...	...	...	20 8		2044	21 2	...	...	...	...	1 43
79½	Grupont	18 7	17 4	1941	...	...	...	2022	...	...	2113	...	...	...	...	...
85¾	Poix (101)	1826	1719	1959	...	...	...	2037	...	...	2128	...	...	...	...	...
94½	**Libramont** (95)	1850	1738	2023	...	...	...	2056	...	...	2146	...	...	...	...	...
100	Longlier	19 3	1750	2036	...	...	...	21 8	...	...	2158	...	...	...	...	...
110	**Marbehan** (95)	1934	18 8	21 7	...	...	...	2129	...	...	2216	...	...	3 31	...	...
114½	**Habay**	1947	1818	2120	...	...	...	2139	...	...	2225	...	...	3 44	...	...
118	**Fouches**	1954	...	2127	...	...	...	...	...	...	...	...	...	3 51	...	...
123	**Arlon** (103A) ...arr	20 6	1832	2139	...	...	...	2153	...	2159	2239	...	...	4 3	...	3 1
...	" ...dep		1838		...	...	...		...	2210		...	3 47		5 7	3 6
129¼	**Sterpenich**	...	1851	...	...	...	...	...	...	...	...	...	4 1	...	5 21	...
129¾	Kleinbettingen*** ar	...	7 53	...	...	...	...	...	...	1123	...	...	5 3	...	6 23	4 19
...	(German-Cust.) dp	...	8 5	...	...	...	...	...	...	1143	...	...	5 10	...	6 28	4 34
141	**Luxemburg** ...arr	...	8 25	...	...	...	...	...	...	12 3	...	...	5 40	...	6 53	4 55
164	WASSERBILLIG 212 arr	...	11p9	...	...	...	...	...	...	...	...	...	7 a6	...	7a41	7 a6
173	TREVES (125) ...arr	...	1135	...	...	...	...	...	...	...	...	...	7a32	...	8 a2	7a32
179½	METZ (210) ...arr	...	...	...	...	...	...	...	...	1 a5	...	...	7a29	...	8a47	6 a3
278	STRASSBURG (210) arr	...	...	...	...	...	...	...	...	3a27	...	...	...	...	...	8a44
366½	BASLE (208) ...arr	...	...	...	...	...	...	...	...	5a43	...	...	...	...	...	1115

A—Will take Voiture-Salon and Sleeping Car passengers for all destinations; other passengers taken at Brussels, Namur, and Jemelle for Kleinbettingen and beyond, or for Mont.-St.-Martin and beyond. At Arlon admits all classes.

B—Admits 3rd class at Brussels for Jemelle and beyond only.
C—Takes 3rd class for Arlon and beyond only.
D—Will run every Saturday until 20th Sept.

†—Sunday excepted.

Extra.					
Gembloux ...dep	14 14	16 55	20 8	21 30
Namur ...arr	14 44	17 26	20 40	22 0
Ottignies ...dep	10 40	...	...	...
Namur ...arr	11 55	...	...	...

ARLON and LONGWY. ¶ Customs Examination.										
Arlon ...dep	4 8	5 21	6 20	7 6	9 53	12 0	14 25	15 17	17 25	22 42
Athus 96	4 35	5 48	6 49	7 35	10 17	12 32	14 52	15 44	17 57	23 9
Mont-St.-Martin ¶			6 57	7 43		12 40	15 1		18 5	23 17
Longwy 72 ...arr	...	...	7 3	7 49	...	12 44	15 7	...	18 11	23 23

Longwy ...dep	6 0	9 6	10 27	...	...	14 33	...	18 27	...	20 6	...
Mont-St.-Martin	6 7	9 12	10 33	...	...	14 40	...	18 35	...	20 14	...
Athus ¶	6 27	9 29	10 46	11 19	12 53	14 57	18 22	18 50	19 35	20 26	...
Arlon 103A ...arr	6 54	9 57	11 14	11 46	13 20	15 22	18 55	19 18	20 3	20 55	...

Belgian Railway Time.—See Note on page 89.

Luggage, cent. 1 50 per 55 lbs. per kilometre.]

FOR FARES SEE PAGE 89.

LUXEMBURG, ARLON, NAMUR, and BRUSSELS.

***—The departures from Luxemburg are according to Mid Europe Time. Belgian Time begins at Sterpenich.

Station																														
Basle 209 ...dep		11p40	...	...	...	...	...	...	...	...	...	...	...	...	...	...	...	...	...	...	...	...	...	10a22	1215	...	...	...	...	7p32
Strassburg 210A dep		1 a40	...	...	...	...	...	...	...	...	...	5 a52	...	...	...	7a30	...	...	...	...	...	...	...	1233	2p18	...	...	...	...	10 p5
Metz 210A ...dep		4 a0	...	...	...	...	...	...	...	...	6a30	8 a21	...	...	...	1010	...	...	...	...	...	...	1248	3 p4	4p44	...	...	4 p58	7p35	12a37
Treves 125 ...dep		...	...	...	...	...	...	...	...	...	6 a0	8 a8	...	...	...	8a15	...	...	11a38	...	...	...	1p27	2p50	...	5 p4	...	...	6p29	11 p8
Wasserbillig 212 dep		...	...	...	...	...	...	...	...	4a30	6a31	8 a26	...	...	...	8a45	...	...	11 54	...	...	...	1p54	3p16	...	5 p21	...	...	6p58	11p36
		1,2,3	1,2,3	2&3	1,2,3	1,2,3	1,2,3	1,2,3	2&3	1,2,3	1,2,3	1,2,3	1,2,3	1,2,3	1,2,3	2&3	1,2,3	1,2,3	1,2,3	2 & 3	1,2,3	1,2,3	1,2,3	1,2,3	1,2,3	1,2,3	1,2,3	1,2,3	1,2,3	1,2,3
		a.m.							VS	a.m.	a.m.	a.m.				a.m.			p.m.	VS			p.m.	p.m.	p.m.	p.m.		p.m.	p.m.	a.m.
Luxemburg *** ...dep		5 7	...	...	...	...	...	...	...	6 49	8 59	9 38	...	...	...	1127	...	...	12 48	...	...	...	3 17	4 24	5 58	6 20	...	7 7	9 21	1 50
Kleinbettingen		5 30	...	...	...	...	...	...	...	7 18	9 27	10 0	...	...	...	1154	...	...	1 16	...	...	...	3 45	4 48	6 20	6 48	...	7 56	9 48	2 12
Sterpenich (Belgian Cust.) arr		4 32	...	...	...	...	...	...	...	6 21	8 29	9 2	...	...	...	1056	...	...	12 18	...	...	...	1447	1550	1722	17 50	...	18 39	2051	1 15
Sterpenich (Belgian Cust.) dep		4 57	...	...	...	...	...	...	...	6 33	8 34	9 18	...	...	...	11 6	...	...	12 24	...	...	...	1455	1610	1740	17 58	...	18 46	2059	1 43
Arlon ...arr		5 9	...	...	...	...	...	...		6 50	8 52	9 30	...	...	...	1118	...	...	12 42				1512	1622	1752	18 16	...	19 3	2116	1 55
Arlon ...dep		5 11	...	...	...	...	...	5 22	6 57	7 1	8 55	9 34	...	...	10 2	1124	...	...	12 46	13 27	15 30	...	1534	1628	1758	18 21	...	19 24	2120	2 1
Fouches		...	...	...	...	...	...	5 36	...	7 15	9 8	...	...	...	1015	...	...	...	12 59	...	...	...	1547	...	...	18 35	...	19 38	2134	SC
Habay		...	...	...	...	...	...	5 44	7 14	7 22	9 15	...	...	...	1022	VS	...	...	13 6	13 42	...	...	1554	G	...	18 43	...	19 46	2142	...
Marbehan		...	...	...	...	...	...	5 57	7 24	7 34	9 26	VS	...	...	1035	1146	...	...	13 19	13 52	15 51	16 36	16 6	RC	VS	18 55	...	20 0	2153	...
Longlier		G	...	...	...	...	...	6 26	7 44	8 3	9 53	RC	...	...	11 1	12 8	...	...	13 46	14 9	...	16 53	1633	...	...	19 24	...	20 30		...
Libramont		...	4†30	...	...	...	...	6 43	7 58	8 19	10 7	10 18	...	...	1115	1216	...	...	14 4	14 22	16 19	17 5	1650	1715	1843	19 42	...	20 48	...	...
Poix		...	4 46	...	...	...	...	7 1	8 12	8 35		...	...	...	1132	...	...	...	14 20	14 35	...		17 7	...	RC	19 58	...	21 5	...	...
Grupont		...	5 3	...	5†52	...	...	7 16	8 25	8 50	...	...	...	...	1144	...	...	...	14 36	...	...	...	1722	...	...	20 14	...	21 20	...	...
Jemelle ...arr		6 24	5 19	...	6 7	...	...	7 32	8 35	9 5	...	10 48	...	...	1157	1246	...	...	14 51	14 56	16 49	...	1738	1745	1914	20 29	...	21 36	...	3 15
Jemelle ...dep		6 30		5 30		...	...	7 37	8 42	9 10	...	10 52	1059	...	12 4	1252	...	...	14 56	15 2	16 53	...	18 1	1755	1923	21 51	...	21 46	...	3 20
Marloie 100		RC	...	5 42	...	...	8 38	7 49	8 53	9 20	...	...	11 8	...	1216	...	...	...	15 28	15 13	...	...	1814	...	...	22 3	...	21 56	...	...
Haversin	1,2,3	...	...	6 6	...	...	9 0	8 11	9 9	9 42	...	...	1129	...	1234	...	...	...	15 50	15 30	...	...	1836	...	...		...	22 14	...	...
Ciney	4 7	...	5†25	6 23	...	...	9 14	8 27	9 21	10 0	...	...	1145	...	1249	1320	...	...	16 10	15 47	17 23	17 8	1851	...	F	...	20 45	22 29	...	...
Assesse	4 28	...	5†46	6 43	...	...		8 47	9 34	1017	...	...	12 5	...	13 9	...	...	...	16 31	16 1	...	17 39	1911	...	...	...	21 5	22 44	...	...
Nannine	4 45	...	6 †2	6 59	...	...	...	9 3	...	1033	...	...	1221	...	1325	...	...	...	16 48	...	...	17 56	1927	...	...	...	21 21	...	...	...
Namur 92 ...arr	5 1	7 21	6 †17	7 15	...	...	...	9 19	9 53	1045	...	11 43	1236	†	1340	1347	...	...	17 4	16 19	17 49	18 14	1942	1851	2014	...	21 36	23 2	...	4 13
Namur 92 ...dep	5 19	7 23	6 42	7 36	7 42	8 18	8 50	9 31	9 58	1054	...	11 48	1246	1342	1358	1352	15 5	1719	17 26	16 28	17 55	18†25	1954	1859	2020	20 0	21 45	23 19	3†56	4 17
Rhisnes	5 30	...	6 53	...	7 53	...	9 1	...	...	11 5	...	...	...	...	14 8	...	15 17	...	17 36	...	...	18 36	...	...	...	20 11	21 58	...	4 7	...
St.-Denis-Bovesse	5 37	...	7 0	...	8 0	...	9 8	...	...	1112	...	...	...	...	1414	...	15 24	...	17 42	...	...	18 42	...	...	...	20 18	22 5	...	4 30	...
Gembloux	5 53	...	7 16	8 1	8 16	8 39	9 24	9 54	1021	1127	...	...	13 8	14 9	1430	1416	15 46	...	18 0	16 51	18 16	18 58	2020	...	...	20 42	22 19	23 43	4 47	E
Mont-St.-Guibert	6 12	...	7 35	...	8 35	...	9 47	...	...	1146	...	...	...	...	1448	...	16 5	...	18 19	...	...	19 17	...	...	...	21 0	22 35	...	5 6	...
Ottignies	6 27	VS	7 46	8 21	9 5	...	9 54	1010	1040	1153	1334	...	1329	1426	1458	1442	16 16	...	18 34	17 9	...	19 23	2041	...	F	21 9	22 44	23 59	5 19	...
Rixensart	...	...	...	...	9 15	...		...	...	...	1346	...	...	...	1510	...	16 28	...	...	...	...		...	...	...	21 21	...	...	5 32	...
La Hulpe	...	...	...	VS	9 25	...	...	...	...	...	1354	...	...	...	1518	...	16 37	...	...	...	...	...	...	...	...	21 30	...	...	5 43	...
Groenendael	...	...	...	...	9 42	...	...	...	...	...	14 6	...	...	...	1535	...	16 48	...	...	...	...	...	...	...	...	21 39	...	...	5 53	...
Boitsfort	6 53	...	...	...	9 49	...	...	...	...	...	1416	...	...	...	1542	...	16 55	...	...	...	...	...	...	...	...	21 46	...	...	6 2	...
BRUSSELS Q. Leol. arr	7 1	8 15	8 12	8 47	10 1	9 17	...	1037	11 7	1220	1429	12 40	1353	1459	1554	15 6	17 7	1811	19 1	17 35	18 54	...	21 8	1955	2114	21 58	23 12	0 25	5 15	5 13
BRUSSELS Schb'k arr	7 46	...	...	9 23	...	...	...	1057	...	1236	1456	...	...	...	1610	...	17 27	...	...	...	...	...	...	...	...	...	...	...	6 40	...
BRUSSELS Nord ...arr	7 21	8 28	...	9 8	1021	...	...	...	1123	...	...	12 55	14 8	...	...	1522	...	1826	19 19	17 53	19 7	...	2140	2011	2126	22 16	...	0 38	...	5 26

†—Sundays excepted.

G—Only brings forward such 3rd class as are from Arlon and beyond, and those travelling to England via Ostend.

E—At Namur admits 3rd class for Ghent and beyond only.

F—Brings forward passengers from Jemelle and beyond only.

Extra.						
Namur ...dep	2 51	3 14	1215	16 1	18 33	19 15
Gembloux arr	3 25	3 47	1252	16 39	19 4	19 48

TIRLEMONT and NAMUR.

E.M.																						
	Tirlemont ...dep	3 28	*	5 56	7 48	8 16	9 13	1222	14 52	...	...	...	1810	19 7	19 50	...	22 22	...	...	...	...	...	...
13	Ramillies ...dep	4 17	5 44	6 40	8 27	8 58	9 53	13 3	15 31	1537	1723	18 35	1853	2034	20 29	21 6	22 54	...	...	...	...	...	...
16½	Noville-Taviers ...	4 25	5 54	6 48	8 35		10 1	13 11		1545	1731	18 43	19 1	2042		2114		...	...	...	...	...	...
27½	**Namur** ...arr	5 6	6 34	7 27	9 13	...	1039	13 50	...	1623	1816	19 22	1940	2120	...	2148	...	...	...	...	...	...	...
...	**Namur** ...dep	...	4*29	5 14	...	7 38	...	10 51	14 6	1626	1729	1855	1956	...	21 49	*—Sunday excepted.		...	...	...	...	...	
...	Noville-Taviers ...		5 10	5 54	...	8 19	...	11 32	1446	17 7	1815	1943	2041	...	22 31			...	...	...	...	...	
...	Ramillies ...dep	4 *35	5 18	6 3	6 58	8 27	1019	11 41	1459	1723	1849	1950	2048	2118	22 [illegible]			...	...	...	...	...	
...	**Tirlemont 104** ...arr	5 13	...	6 41	7 36	9 4	1057	12 17	1537	18 2	1928			2156	23 31			...	...	...	...	...	

Belgian Railway Time.—See Note on page 89.

BRUSSELS to LIEGE, VERVIERS, HERBESTHAL, and COLOGNE.

THROUGH CARRIAGES.—Brussels to Cologne—in 5.45, 10.10, 13.32, and 23.24 from Brussels Nord

Dist. E.M.		Carries 3rd Class for beyond Herbesthal only.	2&3	1,2,3	1,2,3	1 & 2	1,2,3	2&3	1,2,3	1,2,3	1,2,3	1 &2	1,2,3	1,2,3	2 & 3	1,2,3	2&3	1,2,3	1,2,3	2&3	1 &2
	Ostend 102 ......dep		...	...	...	...	...	...	...	...	...	3 42	...	...	...	...	5 57	...	5 57	...	7 5
	Calais 26 ....dep		...	...	...	...	...	...	...	...	...	1 19	...	...	...	...	...	...	...	...	...
...															VS		VS			VS	
—	BRUSSELS Nord dep		...	...	...	...	...	...	...	4 44	5 0	5 45	6 16	6 48	7 31	7 20	8 17	...	8 27	9 18	1010
1¾	Schaerbeek		...	...	...	...	...	...	...	...	5 8	RC	6 23	6 56	⋮	...	⋮	...	8 34	9 27	RC
10	Cortenberg		...	...	...	...	...	...	...	...	5 33	...	6 42	...	⋮	...	⋮	...	8 59	...	...
18¾	Louvain ....arr		...	...	...	...	...	...	...	5 22	6 5	6 12	7 6	7 21	⋮	7 50	⋮	...	9 22	9 52	1038
...	Antwerp 110...dep		...	...	...	...	...	...	...	...	...	5 7	5 7	5 59	⋮	...	⋮	8 17	8 17	8 54	...
...	Ostend 102......dep		...	...	...	3 25	...	...	...	...	...	...	...	...	⋮	...	⋮	6 27	6 27	...	...
...	Ghent 101 ......dep		...	...	...	|	...	...	...	...	...	...	...	...	⋮	...	⋮	7 33	7 33	...	...
...	Louvain..............dep		...		...	|	...	...	...	5 30	...	6 18	7 8	7 28	⋮	...	⋮	9 14	9 24	9 55	1040
29¾	Tirlemont		...		3 19	|	...	...	...	6 7	...	...	7 53	7 50	⋮	...	⋮	...	10 0	1016	...
38	Landen.........................		...	†—Sundays excepted.	3 46	|	...	4 30	5 57	6 47	...	RC	8 30	8 5	⋮	...	⋮	...	1038	1032	RC
46¼	Waremme		...		4 12	|	...	4 59	6 24	7 18	...	...	8 55	8 21	⋮	...	⋮	...	11 4	1048	...
58¾	Ans................................		...		4 51	|	...	5 44	7 4	7 58	...	7 13	9 33	8 43	8 52	...	9 42	10 8	1154	11 9	1135
62½	Liége Guillemins arr	1,2,3	...		5 6	|	...	5 59	7 19	8 13	...	7 24	9 48	8 56	9 3	...	9 53	1019	12 9	1122	1146
...	Paris 24 ....dep	22 0	...	...	...	|	23 15	...	...	...	...	...	...	...	...	...	...	...	...	...	...
...	Maubeuge 92...dep	...	...	...	...	|	2 52	...	...	...	...	...	...	...	...	2&3	...	...	...	6 38	6 38
...	Liége Guillemins dep	4 3	...	4 40	5 14	⌣	6 16	6 30	7 40	8 33	...	7 28	10 1	9 3	9 11	1012	9 58	1023	...	1129	1150
64½	Chênée	⋮	...	4 51	5 25	...	⋮	6 43	...	8 43	...	...	1010	...	...	1031	...	...	...	...	⋮
66½	Chaudfontaine	⋮	...	5 1	5 35	...	⋮	6 53	...	8 53	...	...	1018	9 17	...	1040	...	...	...	...	⋮
74¼	Pepinster ....arr	⋮	...	5 33	6 7	...	⋮	7 25	8 9	9 22	...	7 55	1044	9 34	9 39	1111	1025	1050	...	1156	⋮
82	Spa 111 ....arr	⋮	...	6 58	6 58	...	⋮	8 36	8 36	9 59	...	8 36	1128	9 59	9 59	1233	1053	1128	...	1233	⋮
...	Pepinster............dep	⋮	...	5 34	6 10	...	⋮	7 27	8 10	9 24	...	7 56	1058	9 37	9 41	...	1027	1052	...	1159	⋮
77¾	Verviers Ouest arr	4 34	...	5 46	6 22	...	⋮	7 39	8 18	9 36	...	...	11 6	9 45	9 49	...	1035	...	...	12 7	1221
	Verviers Ouest dep	4 41	4 58	6†29	6 55	...	⋮		8 28		...	...		⌣	9 56	...		...	11 6	1213	1237
80¼	Verviers Est..............	...	5 5	6†36	7 2	...	6 50	...	...	...	...	8 7	...	...	10 3	...	...	11 4	1113	1220	RC
82¾	Dolhain.........................	...	5 16	6†47	7 13	...	...	...	8 39	...	...	...	...	...	1014	...	...	...	1121	1229	1248
86½	Welkenraedt	...	5 29	6†57	7 26	...	...	...	8 47	...	...	...	...	...	1027	...	...	...	1131	1239	...
93½	Bleyberg	...	5 51	...	8 11	...	...	...	...	...	...	...	...	...	1050	...	...	...	...	13 0	...
99½	Aix-la-Chapelle arr	...	7 12	...	9 33	...	...	...	...	...	...	...	...	...	1211	...	...	...	...	2p20	...
87½	Herbesthal ** ...arr	6 0	...	...	8 29	...	8 4	...	9 50	...	...	9 22	...	...		...	...	1219	1234		1 57
97	Aix-la-Chap ...arr	6a47	...	...	9a22	...	8a41	...	11a5	...	...	10a4	...	...	...	...	...	1254	1p15	...	2p44
140¾	Cologne 122...arr	8 a0	...	...	1143	...	9a51	...	...	...	...	1114	...	...	...	...	...	2p24	3p15	...	4p34

RC—Restaurant Car.

Extra.—Brussels to Louvain, 7.44.

COLOGNE to HERBESTHAL, VERVIERS, LIEGE, and BRUSSELS.

	1,2,3	1 & 2	1,2,3	1,2,3	1,2,3	1,2,3	1,2,3	1,2,3	Lux	1,2,3	1,2,3	1,2,3	2&3	1,2,3	1& 2	1,2,3	2&3	1,2,3	1& 2	Lux
Cologne 123B dep	10p52	12 a5	...	...	...	...	...	...	4a41	...	...	...	...	6 a0	...	...	...	7a56	...	8 a7
Aix-la-Chap....dep	12a10	1 a32	...	...	...	...	...	...	5a56	...	...	...	...	7a37	...	...	...	9a12	...	9 a23
	a.m.	a.m.							a.m.					a.m.				a.m.		a.m.
Herbesthal ** ...dep	12 43	2 0	...	...	...	...	...	...	6 19	...	...	...	...	8 15	...	...	...	9 36	...	9 53
Aix-la-Chapelle dep	...	...	...	...	...	...	...	...	...	...	...	...	...	...	...	7 a29	...	...	...	...
Bleyberg	...	...	...	...	...	...	...	...	...	...	...	...	...	...	...	6 58	...	...	...	...
Welkenraedt	...	...	...	...	...	...	...	...	5§34	4 49	...	5 †23	...	...	...	7 21	...	8 §53	...	9 §5
Dolhain..........................	H	1 10	...	...	...	...	...	...	Œ	4 58	...	5 †34	...	7 25	...	7 31	...	...	...	A
Verviers Est.	...	...	...	...	...	...	...	...	5 51	5 8	...	5 †44	...	VS	...	7 39	...	9 11	...	9 23
Verviers Ouest arr	0 1	1 20	...	...	...	...	...	...	⋮	5 13	...	5 †49	VS	7 35	...	7 44	...	...	...	⋮
Verviers Ouest dep	0 17	1 37	...	...	...	3 50	...	...	⋮	5 19	6 7	6 24	6 56	7 51	...	7 55	8 11	...	...	⋮
Pepinster ....arr	0 25	1 44	...	...	...	4 1	...	...	⋮	5 30	6 15	6 35	7 4	7 58	...	8 6	8 22	9 20	...	⋮
Spa 111 ....dep	...	...	...	...	...	...	...	...	⋮	4 58	5 33	5 33	6 37	7 12	8 47	7 12	7 31	8 47	...	⋮
Pepinster ....dep	0 26	1 45	...	...	...	4 2	...	...	⋮	5 32	6 18	6 36	7 9	8 3	9 27	8 8	8 23	9 22	...	⋮
Chaudfontaine...........	...	...	...	...	...	4 26	...	...	⋮	6 1	...	7 5	...	RC	...	8 32	8 52	...	...	⋮
Chênée........................	...	...	...	...	...	4 33	...	...	⋮	6 10	...	7 14	...	...	...	8 41	9 2	...	...	⋮
Liége Guillemins arr	0 51	2 11	...	...	...	4 43	...	...	6 24	6 18	6 47	7 24	7 35	8 29	9 53	8 51	9 14	9 48	⌣	9 59
Maubeuge 93 ...arr	...	...		...	...	...	...	...	...	...	9 54	12 38	1238	...	...	14 8	...	...	|	...
Paris 24............arr	7 35	...		...	...	...	...	...	...	...	12 51		...	...	...	...	...	16 0	|	16 0
Liége Guillemins dep	...	2 16		...	...	4 53	...	5 51	8 28	6 35	6 52	7 23	7 43	8 35	...	8 59	...	9 53	1015	10 7
Ans................................	...	...	*—To Brussels Midi (arrive 6.41).	...	...	5 16	...	6 10	Vienna & Ostend Exp.	7 13	7 9	...	7 59	8 50	...	9 21	...	...	Via Namur (p. 93).	Nord Express.
Waremme.....................	...	...		...	...	5 52	...	7 5	⋮	7 57	7 27	...	⋮	9 9	...	10 2	...	...	⋮	⋮
Landen.........................	...	...		...	...	6 19	...	7 29	⋮	8 36	7 47	...	⋮	9 23	1,2,3	1046	...	...	⋮	⋮
Tirlemont.....................	3 48	3 8		5 17	...	6 44	...	7†54	⋮	8 57	8 2	...	⋮	9 36	9 39	11 7	...	...	⋮	⋮
Louvain...............arr	4 20	3 24		5 52	...	7 16	...		⋮	9 29	8 21	8 28	⋮	9 55	1011	11 26	...	10 55	⋮	⋮
Ghent 101.........arr	7 37	...		...	...	9 45	...	...	⋮	12 20	9 45	9 45	⋮	...	...	...	...	...	⋮	⋮
Ostend 102 ....arr	9 24	...		...	...	11 0	...	...	⋮	...	11 0	11 0	⋮	...	...	...	...	...	⋮	⋮
Antwerp 110.....arr	6 34	...		...	...	9 48	...	...	⋮	11 20	9 48	9 48	⋮	11 20	...	13 24	1,2,3	13 24	⋮	⋮
Louvain...............dep	4 53	3 26	5 37	5 54	6 48	7 31	7 36	...	⋮	9 31	8 27	9 24	⋮	9 57	1017	11 31	1153	10 57	⋮	⋮
Cortenberg.................	5 31	...	*	6 32	7 8	7 47	8 8	...	⋮	9 52	...	...	⋮	...	1049	...	...	...	⋮	⋮
Schaerbeek..................	5 59	...	6 3	7 0	7 30	8 0	8 32	...	⋮	10 12	...	...	⋮	...	1114	11 56	...	...	⋮	⋮
BRUSSELS Nord arr	6 5	3 56	⋮	7 6	7 40	8 8	8 39	...	7 52	10 18	8 58	9 53	9 14	10 25	1121	12 3	1227	11 26	⋮	11 31
Calais 27 ....arr	...	...	...	...	...	13 0	...	...	...	15 21	...	...	...	15 21	...		...	...	1531	...
Ostend 102 ......arr	...	7 28	...	...	...	1029	1029	...	9 52	...	11 18	...	1212	...	...	14 16	...	...	...	13 15

Belgian Railway Time.—See Note on page 89

For Notes and continuation of Trains see pages 105 and 106.

BRUSSELS to LIEGE, VERVIERS, HERBESTHAL, and COLOGNE.

No free Luggage allowed, except Hand-Luggage to the amount of 55 lbs.
Luggage rate, centimes 1·50 per 55 lbs. per Kilometre.

Station																					
Ostend 102 ....dep		7 5	...		8 48	...	...	1042	1042	...	...	...	1134	...	...	...	14 30	...	...	15 30	...
Calais 26 ....dep		...	...		...	...	...	...	...	...	...	...	...	...	...	...	12 53	1250	...	...	...
		1,2,3	2&3		1,2,3	1,2,3	1,2,3	2&3	1,2,3	1,2,3	1,2,3	1,2,3	1,2,3	2&3	1,2,3	1,2,3	1,2,3		1,2,3	Lux	1,2,3
			VS					VS						VS		VS	M			A	
BRUSSELS Nord ...dep		1013	1054	Carries 3rd Cl. for beyond Herbesthal only. See Note F.	10 59	12 3	1250	1316	1332	14 8	15 3	...	1557	1633	...	1641	17 0	Via Namur (p. 92).	...	17 22	...
Schaerbeek		1021	:		11 6	12 12	1259	...	C	1416	...	...	16 4	:	...	...	VS		...	...	...
Cortenberg..................		1045	:		...	12 42	1320	...	...	1441	...	...	1628	RC	...	...	RC		...	...	...
Louvain..................arr		1117	:		11 31	13 16	1341	1346	14 3	1513	1532	...	1655	:	...	1710	17 27		...	17 50	...
Antwerp 110 ......dep		9 30	:		9 30	...	1311	1132	1311	...	...	...	...	:	...	1522	16 26		...	Nord Expr.	...
Ostend 102 ....dep		7 5			7 5	...	8 51	8 51	8 51	...	...	...	...		...	1134	11 34		...		...
Ghent 101...........dep		8 30			8 30	...	1050	1050	1050	...	...	...	...		...	1350	13 50		...		...
Louvain..................dep		1144			11 40	...	1412	1351	14 8	...	1535	...	...	:	...	1713	17 31		...	17 52	1756
Tirlemont.....................		1219			12 1	...	1454	1412	1429	...	1556	16 2	...		...	1734	17 49		...		1831
Landen					12 28	...	1524	1426	...	...	1611	16 27	...		...	1750	18 2		...		
Waremme......................		...			12 54	...	1549	1441	...	...	1627	16 53	1740	:	...	18 6	18 17		...		...
Ans 116		...	1213		13 33	...	1628	15 2	1514	...	1649	17 31	1820	1753	...	1827	18 36		...	18 47	...
Liége Guillemins ...arr		...	1224	1,2,3	13 50	...	1643	1515	1528	...	17 2	17 46	1835	18 4	...	1840	18 47	1847	...	18 58	...
Paris 24..............dep		...	7 50	8 10	...	...	...	...	...	...	...	...	...	...	...	...	13 45		1345	13 45	...
Maubeuge 92 dep	1,2,3	...	...	1053	...	2 & 3	...	...	...	2&3	...	12 13	...	...	...	...	...		...	...	1 &2
Liége Guillem. dep	1215	...	1239	1348	13 56	12 57	1654	1520	1536	1617	1712	17 53	...	1811	18 22	1846	18 59		19 3	19 13	1917
Chênée	1226	...	:	...	14 5	13 10	17 3	...	...	1630	...	18 5	...	...	18 33	...	...	...	...	:	...
Chaudfontaine	1236	...	E	F	14 15	13 19	1712	1534	...	1640	1729	18 15	...	...	18 43	19 0	M	...	...	A	...
Pepinster ....arr	1313	...	:	1415	14 41	13 51	1738	1551	16 4	1712	1745	18 52	...	1839	19 14	1917	19 26	...	1930	:	1944
Spa 111 ....arr	1431	...	:	1511	15 11	14 31	1814	1620	1640	...	1814	19 51	...	1911	19 51	1951	20 0	...	20 0	:	2012
Pepinster.........dep	1315	...	:	1419	14 44	13 56	1740	1554	16 9	...	1747	18 55	...	1842	19 41	1920	19 29	...	...	:	...
Verviers Ouest.... arr	1327	...	1 & 2 cl. from Liege	1427	14 56	14 7	1752	16 2	...	...	1755	19 7	...	1850	19 53	1927	...	...	...	:	1,2,3
Verviers Ouest.... dep	1336	...	:	1441	15 3			1622	...	...	18 2	19 13	...				...	...	...	:	2046
Verviers Est.	1343	...	1314	...	15 10	...	...	1629	1621	...	18 9	19 20	...	...	...	...	19 40	...	...	19 49	2053
Dolhain	1354	...	:	...	15 21	...	...	1638	...	...	1820	19 31	...	...	...	...	19 49	...	...	...	21 2
Welkenraedt	14 6	...	:	F	15 34	...	...	1651	1637	...	1832	19 41	...	...	...	...	...	...	...	...	2112
Bleyberg..............		...	:	...	...	...	...	1718	...	...	19 4	...	...	...	...	...	...	...	...	...	2135
Aix-la-Chapelle...arr		...	:	...	...	...	...	6p39	...	...	8p25	...	...	...	...	...	...	...	...	...	1056
Herbesthal *,*.......arr		...	2 29	4 0	4 37	...	...		5 40	...	7 35	8 44	...	...	...	...	8 58	...	...	9 7	
Aix-la-Chap. 122 arr		...	3 p8	4p39	5p20	...	...	...	6p19	...	8p21	9 p48	...	...	...	...	9 p48	...	...	9 p37	...
Cologne 122......arr		...	4p19	5p55	7p24	...	...	...	7p40	...	1028	11 p1	...	...	...	...	11 p1	...	...	10p46	...

COLOGNE to HERBESTHAL, VERVIERS, LIEGE, and BRUSSELS.

Station																			
Cologne 123B...dep	...	7a56	...	9 a10	...	...	10 a5	...	...	...	11a26	...	...	12p37	1p44	...	3p12	...	...
Aix-la-Chapelle dep	...	9 a12	...	10a32	...	...	11a23	...	...	...	12p56	...	...	2 p46	3p16	...	4p29	...	...
	1,2,3	1,2,3	2&3	1,2,3	1 & 2	2&3	1,2,3	2&3	1,2,3	1,2,3	2 & 3	1,2,3	2 & 3	2 & 3	1,2,3	1,2,3	1,2,3	1,2,3	2 & 3
		a.m.	VS	a.m.			a.m.		a.m.		p.m.			p.m.	p.m.		p.m.		VS
Herbesthal *,* ......dep	...	10 12	...	10 59	...	...	11 50	...	...	...	1 33	...	...	3 30	3 43	...	4 56	...	...
Aix-la-Chapelle...dep	9a16	...	1022	...	...	...	...	...	...	...	...	1p29	...	...	...	...	...	...	...
Bleyberg	8 45	...	9 49	...	...	...	...	...	...	...	...	1256	...	...	...	...	...	...	...
Welkenraedt	9 11	...	1012	...	...	...	J	...	11 15	...	...	1319	...	VS	...	...	RC	...	...
Dolhain....................	9 21	9 26	1020	...	B	...	...	...	11 24	...	12 43	1329	...	14 40	...	...	...	...	...
Verviers Est.	9 29	9 34	1028	...	VS	...	...	...	11 34	...	...	1339	...	14 48	...	...	...	...	...
Verviers Ouest.... arr	9 34	9 39	1033	10 17		...	11 8	...	11 39	...	12 53	1344	...	14 53	15 1	...	1614	...	...
Verviers Ouest.... dep		9 46	1053	10 43	10 48	...	11 25	...	11 49	...	13 9	1352	14 27	15 0	15 25	...	1630	16 33	16 50
Pepinster...............arr	...	9 57	11 2	10 50	10 55	...	11 32	...	12 0	...	13 16	14 3	14 38	15 8	15 32	...	:	16 44	16 58
Spa 111 ....dep	...	8 47	1017	10 17	10 17	1017	11 10	...	11 32	11 59	12 51	1335	13 50	14 42	14 42	...	:	16 12	16 36
Pepinster..............dep	...	9 59	11 5	10 52	11 0	1117	11 37	...	12 1	12 31	13 18	14 4	14 39	15 12	15 34	...	:	16 47	17 3
Chaudfontaine	...	10 22	1121	...	RC	12 1	RC	...	12 25	...	VS	1428	15 8	...	...	...	O	17 10	...
Chênée	...	10 31	...	...	...	1211	...	...	12 36	...	...	1437	15 18	...	...	...	:	17 19	...
Liége Guillemins ...arr	...	10 39	1132	11 17	11 26	1223	12 2	...	12 44	12 59	13 44	1445	15 30	15 41	16 0	...	1659	17 27	17 30
Maubeuge 93......arr	...	14 45	1445	14 45	...	...	...	VS	...		19 26	2146	...	...	19 49	...	1940	22 59	...
Paris 24...............arr	...	18 5	18 5	18 5	...	...	...		...		...	...	...	...	22 46	...	2246	...	...
Liége Guillemins...dep	...	10 44	1136	...	11 30	...	12 6	13 5	12 54	...	13 49	1451	...	15 47	16 6	16 28	17 7	17 46	17 35
Ans	...	11 6	1153	...	:	...	...	1322	13 24	...	14 6	1511	...	16 4	...	16 47	...	18 7	:
Waremme	...	11 43	1210	...	:	...	RC	:	13 57	...	14 24	1547	...	16 21	...	17 22	1741	18 43	:
Landen........................	1123	12 28	1223	...	:	...	J	:	14 22	15 22	...	1611	...	16 34	...		1755	19 15	:
Tirlemont....................	1144	12 58	1236	...	:	...	...	:	14 54	15 49	14 49		...	16 47	...	...	18 8	19 37	:
Louvain ....arr		13 30	1255	...	:		13 10	:	15 26	16 21	15 8	...	...	17 6	17 12	...	1826	20 9	:
Ghent 101.............arr	...	...	1426	...	:		14 26	:	...	...	18 2	...	...	18 39	18 39	...	...	...	:
Ostend 102 ....arr	...	...	1523	...	:		15 23	:	...	...	...	...	...	21 15	21 15	...	...	...	:
Antwerp 110 .....arr	...	14 51	1451	...	:		14 51	:	...	...	16 58	...	...	18 9	18 9	...	22 0	22 0	:
Louvain.................dep	12 6	13 35	1257	...	:	1339	...	:	15 28	16 26	15 15	1630	17 39	17 9	...	17 35	1828	20 17	:
Cortenberg	1254	...	...		:	14 6	...	:	15 53	16 42	...	17 2	18 11	...	...	...	O	20 43	:
Schaerbeek................	1320	...	1323	13 50	:	1444	...	:	16 12	16 59	...	1726	18 35	17 35	...	...	...	21 4	:
BRUSSELS Nord ...arr	1326	14 5	1332	...	13 3	1451	...	1436	16 20	17 9	15 44	1734	18 44	17 44	...	18 8	1857	21 12	19 3
BRUSSELS Midi ...arr	...	...	...	14 8	...	...	...	...	...	...	...	...	...	...	...	...	...	...	...
Calais 27 ....arr	...	...	...	18 5	...	...	...	...	...	...	...	...	...	...	...	...	...	...	...
Ostend 102.........arr	...	16 21	...	...	15 1	...	...	1758	18 44	...	18 44	...	...	20 1	...	21 15	2217	...	22 17

For other Trains and Notes, see previous and following pages.

Belgian Railway Time.—See Note on page 89.

BRUSSELS to LIEGE, VERVIERS, HERBESTHAL, and COLOGNE.

OSTEND 102 ....dep	...	15 24	16 36	1620	1620	...	17 8	1727	19 1	...	...	2047
CALAIS 26 ....dep	...	...	...	...	...	...	14 46	...	...	...	...	19 2
	1 & 2	1,2,3	Lux	1,2,3	2&3	1,2,3	1,2,3	1,2,3	2 & 3	1,2,3	1 &2	1 &2
					VS				VS			
BRUSSELS Nord ...dep	...	17 32	18 38	1827	1846	1857	19 28	2021	21 24	22 26	...	2324
Schaerbeek	...	17 39	Ostend-Vienna Exp	...	...	19 7	19 37	2028	21 34	22 34	...	N
Cortenberg	...	18 3	:	...	...	1931	...	2058	...	23 0	...	...
Louvain ....arr	...	18 25	:	1857	1921	1958	20 2	2132	21 58	23 23	...	2354
ANTWERP 110A ...dep	17 26	17 39	:	1821	1821	...	18 21	...	...	21 52	...	2152
OSTEND 102 ....dep	16 5	16 5	:	...	16 5	...	...	...	...	17 27	...	...
GHENT 101...........dep	17 1	17 1	:	...	18 3	...	...	...	...	19 15	...	...
Louvain..................dep	18 23	18 29	:	1920	1925	...	20 12	...	22 2	23 28	...	2357
Tirlemont	RC	19 23	:	...	1946	...	20 50	...	22 22	23 50	...	0 18
Landen	D	20 5	:	...	20 1	...	21 14	...	22 36		...	0 35
Waremme	...	20 32	:	...	2017	...	21 41	...	22 51	...	...	N
Ans	19 17	21 12	19 55	2018	2039	...	22 17	...	23 12	...	...	1 9
Liége Guillemins.....arr	19 28	21 27	20 6	2029	2052	...	22 32	...	23 25	1 & 2	...	1 23
PARIS 24 ....dep	13 45	...	...	...	...	...	...	...	...	18 20	...	...
MAUBEUGE 92 .....dep	...	...	...	2&3	...	...	...	...	...	21 36	...	...
Liége Guillemins....dep	19 34	21 35	20 11	2013	21 2	...	22 44	...	23 32	0 44	...	1 36
Chênée	RC	21 46	:	2026	...	...	22 58	...	...	...	...	...
Chaudfontaine	...	21 54	Œ	2036	2116	...	23 8	...	...	P	...	...
Pepinster ....arr	19 58	22 21	:	21 8	2133	...	23 35	...	0 8	1 12		2 4
SPA 111 ....arr	20 33	22 53	:	...	2253	...	...	...	...	...		...
Pepinster ....dep	20 1	22 25	:	2110	2135	...	23 38	...	0 10	1 14	2 11	2 6
Verviers Ouest ... arr	RC	22 38	:	2122	2147	...	23 50	...	0 22	1 22	2 20	...
Verviers Ouest ... dep	...	22 53	:		2210	...		...	0 31	2 1		...
Verviers Est................	20 13	23 0	20 47	...	2217	...	...	...	0 38	...	...	...
Dolhain........................	...	23 9	...	...	2226	...	...	...	0 47	2 13	1,2,3	...
Welkenraedt	...	23 19	...	...	2236	...	...	...	0 56	...	4†41	2 33
Bleyberg	...		...	...	...	...	...	...		...	5 3	...
Aix-Chapelle ....arr	...	...	...	...	...	...	...	...	...	...	6a24	...
Herbesthal ***.........arr	9 28	...	10 5	...	1139	...	...	...	...	3 23	...	3 35
AIX-LA-CHAP. 122 arr	10 p9	...	10p43	...	1228	...	...	...	...	4 a15	...	4a15
COLOGNE 122 ......arr	11p24	...	11p52	...	...	...	...	...	...	5 a40	...	5a40

NOTES.

Fares.—See Table on page 89.

***—The time at Herbesthal is Mid Europe time.

V. S.—Attached to these trains are carriages known as "Voitures-Salon," the property of the International Sleeping Car Co. The excess fare may be paid in the carriage.

†—Not on Sunday.

A—Nord Express. Tickets of Sleeping Car Co.

B—At Verviers, Pepinster, and Liege, takes up for Brussels and beyond only.

C—At Brussels takes for Louvain only such passengers as come from the direction of Courtrai and Ostend.

D—At Louvain only takes such passengers as come from Antwerp line or for Spa. At Liege only takes up for Herbesthal and beyond or for Spa; will also admit passengers for Pepinster and Verviers coming from beyond Liege.

E—At Liege and Verviers Est takes only passengers for Herbesthal and beyond. 1 & 2 class from Liége.

F—Until 30th September will at Liege take only for Herbesthal and beyond.

Œ — Ostend - Vienna Express. Tickets of Sleeping Car Co.

COLOGNE to HERBESTHAL, VERVIERS, LIEGE, and BRUSSELS.

COLOGNE 123B ...dep		4 p19	4p19	...	5 p33	6p13	...	...	...	...	...	6p53	...
AIX-LA-C. 123B ...dep		5 p47	5p56	...	6 p58	7p27	...	...	...	...	...	9p10	...
		1 & 2	1,2,3	1,2,3	1,2,3	1& 2	1 & 2	1,2,3	1,2,3	2&3	1,2,3	1,2,3	1,2,3
		p.m.	p.m.		p.m.	p.m.						p.m.	
Herbesthal *** ......dep		6 9	6 34	...	7 24	7 54	...	...	...	VS	...	9 58	...
Aix-Chapelle ......dep		...	...	5 p36	...	...	...	...	...	7p42	...	...	9p18
Bleyberg	1,2,3	Q	...	17 10	...	...	...	...	...	1912	...	...	2052
Welkenraedt	17 0	17§26	...	17 33	...	...	...	18 28	...	1935	...	...	2115
Dolhain..................	1711	...	1748	17 41	...	RC	...	18 39	...	1943	...	21 7	2123
Verviers Est	1718	17 43	...	17 51	...	...	...	18 49	...	1953	...	2115	2131
Verviers Ouest ... arr	1724	:	1759	17 56	18 43	1912		18 55	...	1958	...	2120	2136
Verviers Ouest ... dep	1748	:		18 8	19 3	1929	19 31	19 37	...	20 8	2032	2134	2154
Pepinster ....arr	1759	:	2&3	18 19	19 14	:	19 38	19 48	...	2016	2043	2145	22 6
SPA 111 ....dep		:	1636	17 45	...	:	18 36	18 36	...	1954	...	2047	2135
Pepinster ....dep		:	1722	18 20	...	K	19 40	19 49	...	2021	2045	2146	2210
Chaudfontaine		:	1751	18 43	...	:	...	20 18	...	2037	21 9	22 7	2236
Chênée........................		:	18 1	18 53	...	:	...	20 27	...	...	2119	2225	2244
Liége Guillemins ...arr		18 16	1813	19 1	...	1958	20 4	20 35	...	2048	2129	2237	2252
MAUBEUGE 93......arr		...	...	...	...	...	...	...	...	...	...	...	...
PARIS 24..............arr		23 30	...	...	...	...	...	...	...	...	...	...	...
Liége Guillemins ...dep		18 32	1840	19 6	...	20 1	20 7	...	2013	2054	2144	...	...
Ans................................		:	19 2	19 26	...	:	...	...	2031	2112	22 6	...	...
Waremme		VS	1950	19 45	...	:	RC	...	21 8	2131	2242	...	...
Landen		:	2054	20 1	...	:	...	...	2132	2147	23 6	...	...
Tirlemont		RC	2113	20 19	...	:	...	...		22 2		...	...
Louvain ....arr		:		20 38	...	:	21 8	...	...	2221	...	...	...
GHENT 101...........arr		:	...	...	...	22 8	...	...	...	...	...	...	...
OSTEND 102 ....arr		:	...	...	...	23 1	...	...	...	...	...	...	...
ANTWERP 110 ......arr		:	...	22 0	...	...	22 0	...	...	...	...	...	...
Louvain..................dep		:	...	20 49	...	...	21 12	1,2,3	2148	2223	...	...	...
Cortenberg		:	...	...	...	...			2216	...	...	...	...
Schaerbeek		:	...	21 14	...	...	21 35	21 45	2241	2249	...	...	...
BRUSSELS Nord...arr		20 0	...	21 23	...	...	21 45	...	2252	2256	...	...	...
BRUSSELS Midi ...arr		...	...	...	...	...	...	21 58	...	...	...	...	...
CALAIS 27 ....arr		...	...	...	...	...	...	1 36	...	...	...	...	...
OSTEND 102..........arr		22 26	...	...	...	...	...	...	...	...	...	...	...

H—Takes 1st & 2nd class for Liege & beyond towards Erquelinnes (p. 93); brings 3rd class from German stations and will take up 3rd class for beyond Erquelinnes (p. 93).

J—Takes 1,2,3 class coming from Germany, or going to England, and 1 & 2 class for Malines and beyond.

K—At Verviers and forward only takes for Malines and beyond.

M—At Brussels will only take such passengers as come from Tournai or the Ostend line; also, at Brussels will only take 1st and 2nd class passengers for beyond Louvain; exceptionally admits 3rd class for Germany. At Liège will take only passengers for Dolhain and beyond.

N—Takes also 3rd class passengers from England.

O—At Verviers (Ouest) only takes 3rd class for Jeumont (French frontier, page 93) and beyond; at Liége only takes up 3rd class coming from or going to branch lines.

P—Between Liége and Verviers will also take 3rd class coming from Namur and beyond.

Q—Takes only passengers from Germany, or for Jeumont and beyond.

Customs Examination.—At Herbesthal when entering Germany; at Verviers when entering Belgium.

§—Stop for Customs Exam. only.

☞ Belgian Railway Time.—See Note on page 89. ☜

For other Trains see previous two pages.

†—Sunday excepted.

BRUSSELS, CHARLEROI, and NAMUR.

A—At Luttre will not take up for Charleroi.
[‖—Braine-l'Alleud to Baulers, Sunday excepted.

Station												VS	Via Braine-le-Comte.							VS												
Brussels (Midi) dep		...	...	...	5 32	6 8	6 47	6 52	7 35	7 46		8 27	8 57	10 24	9 50	...	11 46	1232	14 11	14 46	...	15 1	1617	16 28	1658	1725	1753	18 0	19 7	19 30	20 35	2130
Forest (Est)		...	...	...	5 39	...	...	6 59	...	...	...	...		...	9 57	...	11 53	1239	14 18	...	...	15 8	...	16 35	...	...	...	18 7	...	19 38	20 42	...
Rhode-S.-Genèse		...	...	4†35	6 1	6 28	...	7 21	...	...	...	...		...	10 19	...	12 15	13 2	14 40	...	...	15 30	...	16 57	...	1744	...	1832	...	20 0	21 4	2147
Waterloo		...	...	4†44	6 9	6 36	...	7 29	...	...	...	...		...	10 27	...	12 23	1310	14 48	...	...	15 38	...	17 5	...	1752	...	1840	19 34	20 9	21 12	...
Braine-l'Alleud		3‖54	...	4†51	6 16	6 41	7 13	7 35	...	8 11	...	...		10 49	10 32	...	12 29	1316	14 56	...	A	15 44	1642	17 11	...	1759	...	1847	19 40	20 16	21 18	2158
Baulers		4 22	5 5	5 20	6 32	—	7 27	7 50	...	8 24	...	...		11 7	—	...	12 43	1341	15 10	...	...	15 58	1656	17 39	...	...	1834	19 1	20 1	20 31	21 34	2211
Nivelles (Est.)		4 26	...	5 24	6 36	...	7 31	7 53	...	8 28	...	9 4		11 11	...	...	12 50	1345	15 46	15 23	...	—	17 0	17 43	...	1812	1838	—	20 5	—	21 38	2215
Luttre		4 55	5 24	5 48	6 57	7 45	7 49	—	...	8 54	9 3	9 21	10 18	11 32	11 49	1320	—	1414	16 7	15 40	17 14	17 16	1727	18 4	...	1841	1856	1936	20 32	...	21 59	2244
Courcelles-Motte		5 6	5 35	5 59	7 5	...	7 57	...	...	9 3	...	9 29	10 27	11 41	12 0	1331	...	1423	16 18	...	...	17 25	1738	—	...	1849	...	1947	20 41	...	22 8	2253
Marchiennes Pont		5 18	5 49	6 11	7 16	...	8 8	...	...	9 14	...	9 40	10 37	11 52	12 11	1342	...	1434	16 30	15 54	...	17 36	1751	...	...	19 0	1914	1958	20 52	...	22 19	23 4
Charleroi (Sud) arr		5 26	5 57	6 19	7 24	8 5	8 14	...	8 40	9 22	9 27	9 46	10 43	11 58	12 19	1350	...	1442	16 38	16 0	17 32	17 44	1759	...	18 3	19 7	1920	20 6	20 58	...	22 25	2310
„ (100) dep	2 4	5 42	6 1	6 41	7 45	—	8 22	7 0	8 47	9 28	—	—	10 46	12 13	12 58	1357	...	1524	16 55	16 7	17 38	17 49	—	18 8	—	1910	1933	2051	21 54	22 51	22 38	—
Châtelineau	2 14	5 59	6 18	6 54	8 3	...	8 36	7 14	8 58	9 43	—	...	10 59	12 30	13 13	1432	...	1539	17 10	16 22	17 48	18 6	...	18 23	...	1925	1954	21 7	22 9	23 4	...	...
Tamines	...	—	6 39	7 6	—	8 10	8 47	7 31	—	10 4	...	1121	11 18	12 50	13 24	1453	...	16 8	—	—	18 1	18 28	...	18 49	...	—	2020	2128	22 36	23 15	...	...
Floreffe	...	...	7 7	...	...	8 39	...	7 58	...	1032	...	1149	...	13 18	...	1521	...	1636	18 8	...	...	18 55	...	19 17	...	...	2048	2156	...	...	...	...
Namur (103A)	2 45	...	7 25	7 30	...	8 58	9 10	8 12	...	1046	...	12 6	11 41	13 36	13 47	1541	...	1654	18 23	...	18 29	19 10	...	19 35	...	...	21 3	2214	23 10	23 40	23 15	...

Station						From Manage, dep. 8.3.					Ghent (Sud) arr. 10.52.							* 17 59 on Sun.					Via Ecaussines.								
Namur dep	...	3 44	...	4 33	5 24	...	...	6 40	...	7 34	...	...	7 38	9 33	9 38	10 47	10 51		1159	1245	...	14 2	14 49	...	...	16 3	...	1716	17 20	1857	19 52
Floreffe	...	4 3	...	4 52	5 43	...	...	6 59	...	...	...	...	7 55	...	9 55	...	11 5		1216	...	...	14 19	...	...	...	1622	...	...	17 38	1914	20 11
Tamines	...	4 36	...	5 25	6 12	...	...	7 32	...	8 0	...	...	8 27	10 4	1025	11 13	11 32		1245	1311	14 1	14 47	15 15	...	...	1651	...	1742	18 9	1958	20 39
Châtelineau	...	5 6	...	5 48	6 33	...	7 17	8 0	...	8 11	8 20	8 20	8 51	1015	1044	11 25	11 58		1311	1322	1428	15 8	15 28	1630	...	1712	...	1753	18 31	2018	21 0
Charleroi arr	...	5 24	...	6 6	6 48		7 35	8 16	...	8 21	8 38	8 38	9 8	1028	1059	11 39	12 15		1326	1332	1446	15 23	15 41	1646		1727	*	18 7	18 47	2033	21 15
„ (90) dep	4 5	5 31	5 51	6 15	7 1		7 46	8 21	...	8 32	8 41	8 49	9 14	1032	—	11 53	12 27		1411	1355	—	16 26	15 49	1656	1736	1739	18 3	1844	19 4	2038	21 23
Marchiennes Pont	4 12	5 42	6 0	6 24	7 10		7 53	...	...	...	8 48	8 58	9 23	1041	...	12 2	12 34		1418	14 2	...	16 34	15 56	17 3	...	1749	1814	1854	19 13	2045	21 30
Courcelles-Motte	4 23	5 53	6 11	6 35	7 21		...	...	...	...	...	9 9	9 34	1052	...	12 13	VS		1429	1413	...	16 45	16 7	VS	...	18 2	1828	19 5	19 24	2056	21 41
Luttre	5 6	6 7	6 19	6 49	7 35		8 10	...	8†25	8 49	9 2	9 17	9 54	11 0	...	12 24	12 49	...	1438	1421	...	16 58	16 15	1718	...	1812	1844	1916	19 34	21 7	21 55
Nivelles (Est)	5 25	6 26	—	7 10	7 54		8 26	...	8†44	—		9 33	10 13	1115	...	12 43	13 4	13 8	1457	1436	...	17 19		1733	...	1831	19 5	—	19 55	—	22 14
Baulers	5 40	6 31	...	7 25	7 59		8 31	...	8 58	...		9 39	10 30	...	...	12 49	...	13 16	15 3	...	1626	17 27		1737	...	1836	1916	...	20 3	...	22 29
Braine-l'Alleud	5 56	6 47	6 54	7 41	8 15		...	...	9 14	...		...	10 47	...	1058	13 2	...	13 32	1519	...	1643	17 55		1750	...	1851	1932	...	20 19	...	22 45
Waterloo	6 2	6 53	7 0	7 47	...		...	...	9 20	...		...	...	...	11 4	...	...	13 38	1525	...	1649	18 1		...	...	1858	1938	...	20 25	...	22 51
Rhode-S.-Genèse	6 9	...	7 7	7 54	...		...	...	9 27	...		...	...	...	1111	...	...	13 45	1532	...	1656	18 8		...	...	...	1945	...	20 32	...	22 58
Forest (Est)	6 28	...	7 26	8 13	...		...	...	9 46	...		...	...	...	1130	13 26	...	14 4	1551	...	1715	18 27		...	...	...	20 4	...	20 51	...	...
Brussels (Midi) arr	6 34	7 11	7 32	8 19	8 36	8 54	9 2	9 21	9 52	...	...	1011	11 11	1146	1136	13 33	13 40	14 10	1557	15 7	1721	18 33	17 45	1811	1839	1919	2010	...	20 57	...	23 20

BATTLEFIELD OF WATERLOO.—Light Railway from **Braine l'Alleud** to Butte du Lion (25c., 15c.), Gordon Monument (25c., 15c.), Belle Alliance (30c., 20c.), Prussian Monument (45c., 30c.) From Braine l'Alleud, 5*20, 8.16, 8.55, 11.0, 13.45, 15.52, 17.15, 18.50, 19.49. Return from Prussian Monument, 4*54, 7.34, 10.6, 13.1, 15.53, 18.55.

Light Railway from **Waterloo** Station to **Mont** Saint Jean and Gordon Monument; in half-an-hour: 45c. and 30c. From Waterloo, 7.50, 12.24, 14.52, 17.52, 19.55. Return from Gordon Monument, 7.15, 10.25, 13.12, 16.14, 19.5. *—Sunday excepted.

† Not on Sundays.

GHENT, GRAMMONT, and LUTTRE.

Station														
Ghent Sud dep		5 14	7 56	8 25	11 3	...	14 4	...	...	1634	17 8	...	1846	2014
Melle		5 30	...	8 37	1114	...	1418	...	...	...	1727	...	1859	2030
Sottegem		6 14	8 26	9 17	1150	...	1453	...	...	17 3	18 5	...	1940	21 4
Grammont	6 12	6 44	8 49	9 48	1214	...	1530	1545	...	1721	1835	19†9	2012	2131
Enghien	6 37	7 15	9 10	1018	1243	1313	1553	1620	1723	...	19 7	1941	2049	22 2
Rognon	...	7 25	...	1028	1253	1323	...	1631	1734	...	1917	1951	2058	2212
Braine-le-C.	6 58	7 43	9 36	1053	13 4	1435	1613	1649	1744	1759	1933	2010	2122	2221
Ecaussines S.	7 7	8 0	9 45	11 2	1313	1445	1622	1657	1840	18 9	1942	2023	2135	—
Manage	7 28	8 19	10 1	1121	1332	1511	1642	—	19 6	1818	20 2	2039	2157	...
Luttre arr	7 44	8 45	1017	1147	1359	1537	17 9	...	1933	1833	2029	...	2224	...

Station																
Luttre dep	4 36	5 10	6 24	7 32	8 50	9 3	...	9 51	1251	1440	1615	1618	17 0	...	1842	1931
Manage	5 9	5 44	6 53	8 7	9 5	9 22	10 5	1021	1321	1510	1633	1649	17 27	18†3	1911	2013
Ecaussines S.	5 26	6 1	7 15	8 25	9 28	9 32	1022	1043	1337	1526	1647	17 7	—	1820	1928	2042
Braine-le-C.	5 50	6 9	7 40	8 42	9 46	9 42	1030	1059	1350	1537	17 0	1719	18†2	1836	1940	2050
Rognon	5 59	—	7 49	8 51	9 55	...	—	11 8	1359	1546	...	1728	18 12	...	1949	—
Enghien	6 21	...	7 59	9 6	10 4	...	...	1119	1412	1556	1722	1737	18 23	1853	20 6	...
Grammont	6 56	...	8 29	9 36	—	1014	...	1149	1435	1630	1740	—	18 52	1922	2036	...
Sottegem	7 22	...	8 49	10 0	...	...	...	1218	1458	1656	1759	...	—	1955	21 2	...
Melle	7 52	...	9 5	1034	...	...	...	1252	1527	1727	...	...	...	2028	2132	...
Ghent Sud	8 3	...	9 14	1046	...	1052	...	13 4	1535	1742	1824	...	...	2041	2144	...

Extra—Grammont to Braine-le-C. 5.44. Braine-le-Comte to Luttre 3.47, 6.26. Manage to Luttre 6†6, 8.36, 9.1, 16.57, 18†23. Luttre to Manage 11 2, 18†59, 21.31.

PIETON and MANAGE.

Pieton dep	4 43	5†12	6 21	7 44	9 58	12 57	1550	17 3	18†1	1841	1943
Manage arr	5 1	5 30	6 38	8 0	1015	1314	1610	1721	1816	1859	20 0

Manage dep	4 27	5†43	6 44	8 22	1120	1335	1512	1641	17†31	18 9	1931	2047
Pieton arr	4 47	6 3	7 4	8 40	1137	1353	1530	1657	17 47	1828	1949	21 4

†—Sunday excepted.

FOR FARES SEE PAGE 89. [Luggage, cent. 1·50 per 55 lbs. per kilometre

BRUSSELS to PARIS, via Maubeuge and also via Quievrain.

Dist E.M		1,2,3	1,2,3	1,2,3	1,2,3	1,2,3	1,2,3	1,2,3	1,2,3	1 & 2	1,2,3	1,2,3	1,2,3	1,2,3	1,2,3	1,2,3	1 & 2	1,2,3	1,2,3	1,2,3
—	**BRUSSELS** Midi ...dep	...	...	...	5 8	6 25	...	6 57	7 40	8 21	8 57	9 18	9 40	...	1136	11 54	13 1	1216	13 6	...
4¼	**Ruysbroeck**	...	...	...	5 21	6 40	...	...	...	A	A	9 32	...	...	1149	...	A	1229	...	...
8¾	**Hal**	...	...	...	5 38	6 57	...	7 14	7 56	...	...	9 48	9 58	...	12 6	12 11	⋮	1239	...	...
10¼	Lembecq-les-Hal........	...	...	...	5 43	7 3	...	...	8 1	...	...		10 3	...	...	12 16	⋮		...	...
11¾	Tubize	...	...	...	5 50	7 10	...	...	8 7	...	...	...	10 13	...	1214	12 22	⋮	...	...	...
18¾	Braine-le-Comte ...arr	...	...	*	6 10	7 30	...	7 35	8 23	...	9 30	...	10 33	...		12 42	R.C.	...	1336	...
...	„ 107...dep	...	...	5 38	6 15	7 44	...	7 39	8 26	...	9 32	9 43	10 43	11 51	...	12 46	⋮	...	1338	13 51
22¼	Soignies	...	...	5 47	6 26	7 53	...	...	8 35	...	...	9 52	10 52	12 0	...	12 55	⋮	...	1347	13 59
26	Neufvilles	...	...	5 56	6 34	8 1	...	...	8 43	...	...		11 1		...	13 3	⋮	...	...	
30½	Jurbise 102B ......arr	...	*	6 10	6 48	8 15	...	...	8 56	...	...	...	11 14	...	...	13 16	⋮	...	...	...
...	„ ....dep	5 9	5 44	6 11	6 52	8 17	8 13	...	8 57	...	...	10 18	11 15	...	13 7	13 18	⋮	14 4	...	...
34¼	Ghlin	5 21	5 56	6 23	7 4	8 29	...	...	...	...	...	10 28	11 25	...	...	...	⋮	1413	...	...
38	**Mons** ....arr2&3	5 30	6 6	6 33	7 13	8 38	8 31	8 7	9 10	9 16	10 1	10 36	11 33	...	1321	13 37	⋮	1421	14 7	...
...	**Mons**........dep 5*18	...	...	6 48	...	...	...	8§20	9§23	9 19	10 11	...	12 §0	...	...	13§40	⋮	1426	...	16§21
41	Cuesmes 5 24	...	...	6 54	...	...	...	8 26	9 29	...	10 17	...	12 6	...	...	...	⋮	1432	...	16 27
42¼	Frameries 5 31	...	...	7 1	...	...	...	8 33	9 35	...	10 24	...	12 15	...	...	13 50	⋮	1439	...	16 37
47¼	Quévy 5 45	...	...	7 18	...	...	...	8 48		9 37	10 35	...	12 30	...	...	14 1	1411	1456	...	16 52
49¾	Feignies [Cus.arr 5 52	...	...	7 24	...	...	...	8 54	...	9 42	10 42	...	12 37	...	...	14 6	1416	15 3	...	16 58
...	„ Ex.]dep 6 3	...	...	7 36	...	...	...	9 6	...	9 59	11 3	...	12 53	...	...		1434	1514	...	17 8
54	**Maubeuge** ...arr 6 18	...	...	7 48	...	...	...	9 21	...	⋮	11 14	...	13 8	...	...	...	⋮	1526	...	17 24
59	AULNOYE 24......arr	...	...	...	...	...	...	9 56	...	10 12	11 45	...	13 54	...	...	...	⋮	16 0	...	18 23
192¾	PARIS 24........arr	...	...	...	...	...	...	...	...	12 51	15 50	...	...	...	...	...	1715	2159	...	...
...	**Mons** ....dep 4 17	5 35	6 *8	7 38	7 22	8 54	9 41	8 10	9 46	...	...	10 40	11 45	12 22	1332	...	...	1439	1411	16 10
41	Jemappes 4 25	5 43	6 16	...	7 30	9 2	...	...	9 54	...	...	10 47	11 52	12 30	1340	...	...	1437	...	16 18
42¼	Quaregnon-Wasml 4 30	5 48	6 21	...	7 35	9 7	...	...	9 59	...	...	10 52	11 58	12 35	1345	...	...	1442	...	16 23
44	**St. Ghislain 100** ...4 50	6 28	6 26	7 49	7 42	9 15	9 57	8 22	10 5	...	...	10 59	12 7	12 41	1350	...	...	1448	...	16 28
44¾	Boussu 4 55	6 33			7 46	9 20	...	...	10 10	...	...	11 3	12 11	12 45		...	...	1453	...	
47¼	Thulin 5 5	6 43	...	...	7 53	9 27	...	...	10 20	...	...	11 10	12 17	12 54	...	...	...	15 0	...	...
50½	**Quiévrain** ......arr 5 12	6 50	...	...	8 0	9 34	10 8	8 34	10 28	...	...	11 17	12 23	13 1	...	...	...	15 7	1432	...
58¼	VALENCIENNES 23 arr	...	...	...	8 36	...	1042	9 7	...	...	...	12 16	...	13 46	...	...	...	1554	15 6	...
213¾	PARIS 23 ....arr	...	...	...	12 7	...	...	1620	...	...	...	17 10	...	...	...	...	...	...	1920	...

PARIS to BRUSSELS, via Quievrain and also via Maubeuge.

PARIS 23 ....dep	20 40	...	...	...	...	...	...	22 20	...	...	...	...	...	...	...	...	...	...
VALENCIENNES 23 dep	2 53	...	...	...	...	...	...	6 23	6 57	...	...	8 34	...	...	...	...	...	...
	1,2,3	1,2,3	1,2,3	1,2,3	1,2,3		1,2,3	1,2,3	1,2,3	1,2,3	1,2,3	1,2,3	1,2,3	1,2,3	1 & 2	1,2,3	1,2,3	1,2,3
Quiévrain ¶ ....dep	3 27	5*32	...	...	...	...	5 54	7 0	7 25	...	...	9 16	...	10 20	...	...	...	...
Thulin........	...	5 40	...	...	...	...	6 2	7 8	...	...	...	9 24	...	10 28	...	...	...	...
Boussu........	...	5 49	...	...	...	...	6 10	7 17	...	...	...	9 31	...	10 38	...	...	...	...
St. Ghislain........	3 39	5 53	...	3 54	6 0	...	6 18	7 26	7 37	7 42	...	9 37	...	10 52	...	...	...	...
Quaregnon-Wasmuel ...	...		...	4 0	6 6	...	6 24	7 32	...	...	...	9 42	...	10 58	...	...	...	...
Jemappes	...	...	...	4 5	6 11	...	6 29	7 37	...	...	...	9 47	...	11 3	...	...	...	...
Mons 100........arr	3 51	...	...	4 12	6 18	...	6 36	7 44	7 48	7 53	...	9 54	...	11 10	...	...	...	...
PARIS 24........dep	...	...	23 15	...	...	...	...	...	...	...	0 35	...	...	...	8 10	...	7 0	...
AULNOYE 24 ...dep	...	...	⋮	...	...	...	...	4 56	...	...	7 8	...	...	8 21	10 35	...	10 27	...
Maubeuge ....dep	2 19	...	3 8	...	...	...	...	6§28	...	...	7 41	...	...	10 §2	⋮	...	10 52	...
Feignies	2 36	...	3 22	...	...	...	...	6 45	...	...	7 58	...	...	10 18	10 49	...	11 7	...
Quévy [Cust. Ex.] arr	2 43	...	3 27	...	...	...	...	6 52	...	...	8 5	...	...	10 25	10 54	...	11 13	...
„ ....dep	3 22	...	3 47	...	...	...	5 *49	7 0	...	...	8 14	...	...	10 33	11 9	...	11 27	...
Frameries 112	3 35	...	3 58	...	4*52	...	6 3	7 14	...	...	8 28	9 §10	...	10 48	⋮	...	11 37	...
Cuesmes	...	...	...	...	4 59	...	6 10	7 21	...	...	8 35	9 47	...	10 55	⋮	...	...	...
Mons........arr	3 47	...	4 9	...	5 4	...	6 15	7 26	...	...	8 40	9 52	...	11 0	⋮	...	11 45	...
		*																
Mons........dep	3 59	3 32	4 17	4 42	5 16	...	6 43	7 55	7 51	8 45	8 59	10 0	...	11 41	⋮	...	11 58	...
Ghlin........	...	...	...	4 52	5 28	...	6 52	8 4	...	8 57	...	10 9	...	11 50	⋮	...	...	...
Jurbise 94 ....arr	...	3 52	...	5 4	5 39	...	7 3	8 13	...	9 8	...	10 18	...	12 2	⋮	...	...	...
„ ....dep	...	3 54	...	5 5		...	7 6	8 14	...		...	10 19	...		⋮	...	...	...
Neufvilles	...	4 11	...	5 20	...	...	7 19	8 23	...	...	...	10 33	...	...	⋮	...	...	...
Soignies	...	4 46	...	5 28	6 30	...	7 28	8 31	...	...	9 25	10 41	10 5	...	⋮	...	12 24	...
Braine-le-Comte......arr	4 31	4 55	...	5 37	6 38	...	7 37	8 39	...	...	9 33	10 50	1014	...	⋮	...	12 32	...
„ ......dep	4 32		...	5 39	6 43	7*17	7 46	8 45	...	...	9 44	10 54	11 6	...	⋮	12 27	12 36	...
Tubize........	...	...	...	5 57	7 3	7 31	8 5	9 4	...	...	9 58	11 8	1125	...	⋮	12 41	...	1252
Lembecq-lez-Hal	...	...	...	...	7 9	7 37	8 12	9 10	...	...	...	...	1131	...	⋮	...	...	1258
Hal	...	...	...	6 6	7 14	7 42	8 18	9 16	...	...	...	11 18	1136	...	⋮	...	...	13 3
Ruysbroeck	...	...	...	6 15	7 29	...	...	...	...	...	...	...	1152	...	⋮	...	...	1319
BRUSSELS Midi......arr	5 6	...	5 15	6 24	7 42	7 58	8 34	9 32	8 50	...	10 18	11 34	12 4	...	12 12	13 1	13 6	1331

Luggage cent. 1·50 per 55 lbs. per kilometre.] FOR FARES SEE PAGE 69.

BRUSSELS to PARIS, via Maubeuge and also via Quievrain.

SLEEPING CAR—Brussels to Paris, in 0.7 from Brussels Midi.

	1,2,3	1,2,3	1,2,3	1,2,3	1,2,3	1,2,3	1,2,3	1 &2	1,2,3	1,2,3	1,2,3	1,2,3	1,2,3	1,2,3	1 &2
BRUSSELS Midi ...dep	15 3	1552	1619	17 8	1714	17 46	18 3	1815	...	1838	1845	1927	2029	2210	0 7
Ruysbroeck	1516	...	1632	...	...	...	...	⋮	...	...	...	...	...	2224	B
Hal	1533	...	1649	C	1730	...	...	⋮	...	1855	19 9	...	2046	2241	SC
Lembecq-lez-Hal	1538	...	1656	...	...	...	...	A	...	19 0	...	...	2051	2246	...
Tubize	1544	...	17 2	...	1739	18 8	...	⋮	...	19 8	1918	...	2057	2252	...
Braine-le-Comte arr	16 4	1626	1722	1746	1755	18 23	...	⋮	...	1926	1934	20 4	2117	2310	0 40
" 107 ...dep	1615	1631	1724	1748	1757		...	RC	18 8	1930	1941	20 6	2123	2315	0 41
Soignies	1624	1640	1734	...	18 6	...	...	⋮	1817	1938	1950	2015	2133	2323	...
Neufvilles	1632		1742	...	1813	...	...	⋮			1958	2023	2141		...
Jurbise 102B ...arr	1645	...	1755	18 8	1822	...	...	⋮	...	...	2012	2031	2154	...	...
" ...dep 1640	1651	...	1756	1810	1823	...	...	⋮	...	...	2014	2033	2155	...	...
Ghlin	17 1	...	18 8	...	...	...	...	⋮	...	...	2026	...	22 5	...	...
Mons ...arr 1658	17 9	...	1818	1823	1835	...	1856	⋮	...	...	2035	2048	2213	...	1 10
Mons ...dep	1733	§ §	...	...	1842	19 50	1858	⋮	...	...	...	2110	2239	...	1 20
Cuesmes	1739	...	...	...	1848	19 56	...	⋮	...	...	...	2119	2245	2&3	...
Frameries	1747	...	...	...	1854	20 3	19 8	⋮	...	...	...	2129	2251	4 47	1 30
Quévy ***	18 2	...	...	...	...	20 20	1919	1929	...	...	...	2141		5 2	1 41
Feignies [Customs arr	18 9	...	...	...	...	20 26	1922	1932	...	...	...		...	5 9	1 46
" Exam.] dep	1821	...	...	...	...	20 47	20 0	1955	...	...	...	...	...	5 18	2 16
Maubeuge ...arr	1836	...	...	...	...	20 58	2011	⋮	...	...	...	...	...	5 34	⋮
AULNOYE 24 ...arr	1940	...	...	...	...	22 20	2031	20 8	...	...	...	...	...	6 7	2 29
PARIS 24 ...arr	...	...	...	...	...	4 5	2355	2246	...	...	...	...	...	...	5 32
		*													
Mons ...dep 1652	1715	1742	1835	1846	1911	...	19 4	...	1947	2017	2039	2059	2221	4*28	...
Jemappes ...17 0	1723	1750	1844	...	1919	...	...	...	1955	...	2047	...	2229	4 36	...
Quaregnon-Wasm'l 17 5	1729	1755	1849	...	1924	...	...	...	20 0	...	2052	...	2234	4 41	...
St. Ghislain 100...1710	1736	18 0	1854	1858	1939	...	...	...	20 5	21 3	2059	2112	2240	4 46	...
Boussu	1740		19 1		1944	...	...	...			21 4	...	2245		...
Thulin	1749	...	1911	...	1953	...	...	...	...	...	2111	...	2252	...	...
Quiévrain ...arr	1756	...	1918	...	20 0	...	1925	...	...	...	2118	2124	2259	...	...
VALENCIENNES 23 arr	1845	...	1959	...	2046	...	1959	...	...	...	2210	2210	...	...	...
PARIS 23 ...arr	...	...	...	...	4 15	...	4 15	...	...	...	4 37	4 37	...	...	...

Fares: Brussels to Paris,
1st class, 34 fr. 35 c.
2nd class, 23 fr. 25 c.
3rd class, 14 fr. 85 c.

¶-Customs Examination

* Sundays excepted.

§—2 & 3 class only.

A—Through Carriages attached to these Trains for Paris viâ Quevy.

B-At Brussels, Braine-le-Comte and Mons, admits also Third Class for French Stations or from Holland.

C—For Mons takes passengers only, no luggage.

RC—Restaurant Car in this Train

PARIS to BRUSSELS, via Quievrain and also via Maubeuge.

PARIS 23 ...dep	...	8 0	...	...	...	...	...	...	...	...	...	...	...	13 0	...	1430	...	...	...
VALENCIENNES 23 dep	11 a0	1133	...	...	...	14 15	...	...	...	...	16 18	...	...	18 0	...	1941	...	...	...
	1,2,3	1,2,3	1,2,3	1,2,3	1,2,3	1,2,3	1,2,3	1 & 2	1,2,3	1,2,3	1,2,3	1,2,3	1,2,3	1,2,3	1,2,3	1,2,3	1,2,3	1 & 2	1,2,3
Quiévrain ¶...dep	11 35	12 3	...	...	13 8	15 0	...	...	...	...	16 51	...	17 38	18 57	...	2026	...	...	...
Thulin	11 43	...	...	...	...	15 8	...	...	...	...	...	...	17 46	19 5	...	2034	...	...	...
Boussu	11 58	...	...	...	...	15 16	...	...	...	...	...	...	17 55	19 15	...	2042	...	...	...
St. Ghislain	12 1	...	...	13 4	13 52	15 22	...	...	16 7	1635	17 4	1659	18 5	19 27	20 4	2048	...	...	21 0
Quaregnon-Wasmuel	12 7	...	...	13 10	13 58	15 28	...	...	...	1641	...	...	18 11	19 33	2010	2054	...	...	21 6
Jemappes	12 13	...	...	13 15	14 3	15 33	...	...	...	1646	...	...	18 16	19 38	2015	2059	...	...	2111
Mons 100 ...arr	12 20	1224	...	13 22	14 10	15 40	...	...	1618	1653	17 15	1710	18 23	19 45	2022	21 6	...	...	2118
PARIS 24 ...dep	...	...	...	...	...	...	10 25	12 35	...	...	...	...	...	...	...	...	16 5	19 10	...
AULNOYE 24 ...dep	...	...	...	11 45	...	...	14 30	14 58	...	...	...	...	16 26	17 55	1911	...	19 53	⋮	...
Maubeuge ...dep	...	...	...	12 45	...	14§34	14 51	⋮	...	...	...	...	16 59	18§28	§ 1932	...	20 19	⋮	...
Feignies	...	...	...	13 §1	...	14 50	15 3	15 11	...	...	...	...	17 14	18 44	1950	...	20 31	21 43	...
Quévy [Cust. Ex.] arr	...	...	...	13 7	...	14 56	15 8	15 16	...	...	...	...	17 20	18 51	1957	...	20 36	21 48	...
" ...dep	...	...	...	13 15	...	15 5	15 41	15 36	...	...	...	§	17 37	18 59	20 5	...	20 54	22 2	2&3
Frameries 112	11§54	...	...	13 29	...	15 19	15 52	⋮	...	...	...	1653	17 52	19 15	2019	...	21 4	⋮	22 7
Cuesmes	12 2	...	...	13 35	...	15 26	...	⋮	...	...	...	17 0	17 59	19 22	2026	...	...	⋮	2216
Mons ...arr	12 8	...		13 40	...	15 31	16 3	⋮	...	...	...	17 5	18 4	19 27	2031	...	21 16	⋮	2225
Mons ...dep	12 49	1227	1343	13 47	...	15 52	...	⋮	...	...	17 19	1723	18 30	19 50	...	...	21 23	⋮	...
Ghlin	13 1	...	...	13 56	...	16 2	...	⋮	...	...	...	1735	18 42	20 2	...	...	...	⋮	...
Jurbise 94 ...arr	13 13	...	...	14 7	...	16 14	...	RC	...	...	...	1748	18 54	20 14	...	...	...	RC	...
" ...dep	13 15	...	...		...	16 15	...	⋮	...	...	...		18 57	20 16	...	...	...	⋮	...
Neufvilles	13 28	...	...	...	...	16 29	...	⋮	...	...	...	...	19 11	20 30	...	...	...	⋮	...
Soignies	13 35	1253	14 9	15 15	15 45	16 37	...	⋮	...	...	17 45	...	19 20	20 39	...	...	...	⋮	...
Braine ...arr	13 4[illegible]	13 1	1418	15 23	15 55	16 46	...	⋮	...	...	17 53	*	19 29	20 48	...	...	...	⋮	1,2,3
" ...dep	13 59	13 6	1422	15 28		17 10	...	⋮	...	*	17 59	1837	19 39	20 56	...	2112	...	⋮	4 *1
Tubize	14 22	...	...	15 47	...	17 29	...	⋮	...	1818	...	1855	19 58	...	2027	2133	...	⋮	4 18
Lembecq-les-Hal	14 28	...	...	15 53	...	17 35	...	⋮	...	1833	...		20 4	...	2033	2139	...	⋮	4 24
Hal	14 34	...	...	15 58	...	17 40	...	⋮	...	1835	...	...	20 9	...	2038	2144	...	⋮	4 30
Ruysbroeck	...	...	...	16 13	...	...	...	⋮	...	1851	...	...	...	...	2054	2153	...	⋮	4 46
BRUSSELS Midi ...arr	14 50	1338	1453	16 25	...	17 56	...	16 38	...	19 3	18 30	...	20 25	21 30	21 6	22 2	22 16	23 5	4 58

Luggage, centimes 1·50 per 55 lbs. per kilometre.] (For Fares see page 89.)

ROSENDAAL, ANTWERP, MALINES, and BRUSSELS.

***—Amsterdam time at Rosendaal.

Dist E.M	Station																			
...	AMSTERDAM via Gouda 115A dep		...	...	...	...	...	...	...	...	...	...	...	...	7 a10	...	...	...	...	...
...	AMSTERDAM v. Hague 119 dep		...	...	...	...	...	...	...	...	...	...	...	...	4 a48	8 a0	8 a40	...	...	9a40
...	THE HAGUE 119.........dep		...	...	...	...	...	...	...	...	...	...	...	...	8 a 0	8 a50	9 a36	...	...	1050
...	ROTTERDAM 116.........dep		...	...	...	...	...	...	...	...	...	4a52	...	...	8 a33	9 a26	10 a2	...	...	1129
						1,2,3			1,2,3			1,2,3	1,2,3		1,2,3	1,2,3	1 & 2	1,2,3	1,2,3	1,2,3
Dist E.M									a.m.			a.m.			a.m.	a.m.	a.m.	a.m.	a.m.	p.m.
—	Rosendaal ***..............dep		...	...	...	...	...	...	6 0	...	...	7 4	...	...	9 39	10 38	:	11 6	11 49	:
5½	Esschen ¶ .... arr		...	...	...	...	...	...	5 50	...	...	6 54	...	...	9 29	10 27	10 48	1056	11 39	1216
	Esschen ¶ dep		...	...	...	4 33	...	...	6 10	...	...	7 20	7 35	...	9 48	10 47	11 10	⁄	11 49	1231
26	Antwerp Centrale.........arr		...	...	...	5 32	...	...	7 6	...	A	7 51	8 36	...	10 17	11 18	11 42	—	12 40	13 1
...	LONDON Liverpool St. dep		...	...	...	...	...	...	...	...	8p40	...	...	...	...	...	...	...	...	...
...	HARWICH..................dep		...	...	...	...	...	...	...	...	10p10	...	...	...	...	...	...	...	...	...
...	ANTWERP Quai ....arr		...	...	...	...	...	...	...	...	8 0	...	...	...	...	...	...	...	...	...
		1,2,3	1,2,3	1,2,3	2&3	1,2,3	1,2,3	1 &2	2&3	1,2,3	1,2,3	2&3	1,2,3	1,2,3	2 & 3	1,2,3	1 & 2	1,2,3	1,2,3	1,2,3
Dist E.M					VS				VS			VS			VS	VS			VS	
	Antwerp Sud ...dep	...	4 3	...	5 7	...	...	...	...	8 17	8§20	...	...	...	...	...	...	...	...	...
—	Antwerp Centrale dep	1 15	...	4 34	...	5 59	6 49	7 12	7 26	...	...	8 47	8 54	9 30	10 23	11 32	11 53	1213	12 46	1311
1¾	Berchem	...	...	4 40	...	6 5	...	...	...	...	...	...	...	9 36	...	...	:	1219	RC	...
3¾	Vieux-Dieu	...	...	4 47	5 19	6 12	6 58	...	...	...	A	...	...	9 43	...	...	:	1228	12 54	RC
6¾	Contich	...	...	4 54	5 27	6 20	...	...	7 40	...	...	9 3	9 7	9 53	10 37	...	D	1238	13 1	...
11¼	Wavre-St.-Catherine...	...	...	5 7	...	6 33	7 16	...	...	...	...	...	...	10 6	...	...	:	1251	...	...
15	Malines ....arr	1 37	4 41	5 17	5 44	6 43	7 28	7 33	7 53	8 40	8 45	9 17	9 28	1016	10 50	11 55	RC	13 1	13 14	1334
30½	LOUVAIN 101 ......arr	...	...	6 0	...	7 10	8 28	8 28	9 12	9 12	9 12	9 50	9 50	1114	...	13 19	:	1359	13 59	1359
...	Malines ....dep	1 38	4 46	5 23	5 51	6 45	7 40	7 34	7 56	8 42	8 49	9 24	9 30	1027	10 52	11 59	:	13 4	13 21	1336
21¾	Vilvorde	...	5 11	5 43	...	7 5	8 1	...	8 9	...	A	...	9 50	1047	...	12 12	:	1324	13 35	...
26	Schaerbeek......................	...	5 28	5 56	6 13	7 19	8 15	...	8 18	...	...	...	10 4	11 0	11 12	...	:	1338	...	...
27¼	BRUSSELS Nord...arr	2 1	5 34	6 2	6 19	7 25	8 21	...	8 24	9 2	9 11	9 49	1010	11 6	11 18	12 24	:	1344	13 47	1357
32¼	BRUSSELS Midi ...arr	...	...	...	...	...	...	8 5	...	...	...	...	...	...	...	...	12 44	...	...	...

EXPRESS SERVICE, without stop between Antwerp and Brussels —

Antwerp Centrale......dep	7 57	8 44	10 4	11 1	1210	1326	14 5	1519	1627	1723	1812	1919	2055	2252
Brussels Nord ....arr	8 31	9 18	1038	1135	1244	14 0	1439	1553	17 1	1757	1846	1953	2129	2326

VS.—Attached to these trains are "Voitures de Luxe."

§—From Antwerp Sud Quai Station.

¶—Customs Examination.

A—This train from Antwerp only takes passengers arriving by the Harwich Steamer. No service from London to Antwerp on Sunday night. Not run between Antwerp and Brussels on Monday.

BRUSSELS, MALINES, ANTWERP, and ROSENDAAL.

THROUGH CARRIAGE.—Antwerp to Bremen and Hamburg on 13.13 from Antwerp.

Station																			
	1,2,3	1,2,3	1,2,3	1 & 2	1,2,3	1,2,3	1,2,3	1,2,3	1,2,3	1,2,3	1,2,3	2 & 3	2 & 3	1,2,3	1,2,3	1& 2	1,2,3	1,2,3	1,2,3
BRUSSELS Midi ...dep	...	...	...	6 0	...	VS	...	VS	...	...	...	VS	VS	VS	...	1233	...	...	...
BRUSSELS Nord...dep	4 31	4 55	5 59	...	6 54	7 56	8 4	8 52	9 14	9 33	9 36	11 2	11 40	11 53	12 6	...	12 36	1327	14 5
Schaerbeek	...	5 3	6 6	F	7 2	:	8 12	...	:	9 41	9 45	11 9	...	12 3	12 23	VS	12 50	1339	...
Vilvorde	...	5 16	...	...	7 15	RC	8 24	9 6	:	...	10 7	...	...	12 11	12 36	...	12 58	1352	...
Malines ....arr	4 52	5 36	6 22	6 32	7 33	8 18	8 36	9 19	:	9 59	10 27	11 27	12 2	12 23	12 54	13 1	13 10	1410	1427
LOUVAIN 101 ......dep	...	4 23	5 35	5 35	...	7 11	7 11	8 37	:	8 37	10 3	10 3	10 3	...	...	1155	...	1346	1346
Malines..................dep	4 55	5 42	6 25	6 34	7 36	8 19	8 39	9 22	:	10 1	10 32	11 30	12 3	12 33	...	13 3	13 23	1413	1432
Wavre-St.-Catherine ...	5 7	5 54	...	...	7 47	...	...	...	:	...	10 43	...	...	...	...	...	13 34	...	...
Contich	5 24	6 10	...	F	8 1	...	8 54	...	:	...	10 58	...	...	12 48	...	...	13 48	1433	...
Vieux-Dieu	5 37	6 22	...	...	8 11	...	...	...	:	...	11 8	...	...	12 55	...	RC	13 58	1443	...
Berchem	5 44	6 29	...	...	8 18	...	...	...	:	...	11 15	...	...	...	...	...	14 5	...	...
Antwerp Centrale...arr	5 49	6 34	6 47	6 56	8 23	8 41	9 7	9 48	:	10 23	11 20	...	...	13 3	...	1324	14 10	1451	15 2
Antwerp Sud.......arr	...	...	...	...	...	...	—	...	9 56	...	...	11 53	12 30	...	...	...	...	...	—
ANTWERP Quai ...dep	...	...	...	...	...	...	...	...	...	...	...	...	...	...	...	...	...	...	...
HARWICH ....arr	...	...	...	...	...	...	...	...	...	...	...	...	...	...	...	...	...	...	...
LONDON L'pool St.arr	...	...	...	...	...	...	...	...	...	...	...	...	...	...	...	...	...	...	...
			1,2,3	1,2,3		1,2,3	1,2,3	1,2,3		1,2,3	1,2,3				1,2,3	1,2,3 VS	1,2,3		1,2,3
Antwerp Centrale dep	...	...	7 24	7 10	...	8 49	9‡58	10 1	...	10 32	12 19	...	...	...	13‡13	1332	14 34	...	1613
Esschen .... arr	...	...	8 19	7 45	...	9 18	1033	11 0	...	11 5	13 17	...	...	...	13 45	14 5	15 33	...	1646
Esschen dep	...	...	8 23	7 50	...	9 23	1039	...	...	11 9	...	...	...	...	13 49	1410	15 37	...	1652
Rosendaal ¶***......arr	...	...	8 53	8 19	...	9 53	11 9	...	...	11 38	...	...	...	...	2 18	2 39	4 7	...	1721
ROTTERDAM 117...arr	...	...	10a27	9 a50	...	1114	...	...	...	12p56	...	...	...	...	3 p50	3p50	6 p18	...	6p34
THE HAGUE 119...arr	...	...	11a16	10a24	...	1141	...	...	...	1 p31	...	...	...	...	4p27	4p27	6 p59	...	6p59
AMSTERDAM 119...arr	...	...	12p43	11a22	...	1243	...	...	...	2 p40	...	...	...	...	5p17	5p17	8 p 0	...	8 p0
AMSTERDAM 115A arr	...	...	...	...	...	...	...	...	...	...	...	...	...	...	...	...	...	...	...

***—Amsterdam time at Rosendaal. ‡—Will not take up passengers for Esschen.

F—At Brussels and Malines also admits 3rd class for beyond Esschen. RC—Restaurant Car in this train.

EXPRESS SERVICE, without stop between Brussels and Antwerp:—

Brussels Nord ....dep	7 52	8 49	9 55	10 51	1213	13 3	1422	15 17	1522	17 16	18 20	2152	23 49
Antwerp Centrale ......arr	8 26	9 23	1029	11 25	1247	13 38	1456	15 51	16 3	17 50	18 54	2226	0 23

ROSENDAAL, ANTWERP, MALINES, and BRUSSELS.

Station																				
AMSTERDAM via Gouda 115A dp			...	...	...	...	...	...	...	...	...	...	...	...	...	...	...	...	...	8p20
AMSTERDAM v. Hague 119 dp		10a8	...	1051	...	...	1p45	...	2p30	...	...	...	...	3 p0	4 p15	...	...	6 p49	8 p0	8 p0
THE HAGUE 119.........dep		11a6	...	12p4	...	...	2p39	...	3p29	...	...	...	...	4 p8	5 p13	...	...	7 p54	8p57	8p57
ROTTERDAM 116 ......dep		1147	...	1 p7	...	...	3 p3	...	3p59	...	...	...	...	4 p45	5 p47	...	...	8 p26	9p21	9p54
		1,2,3		1,2,3		1,2,3	1,2,3		1,2,3				1,2,3	1,2,3	1,2,3	1,2,3	1,2,3	1,2,3	1,2,3	1,2,3
		p.m.		p.m.			p.m.		⋮					p.m.	p.m.		p.m.	p.m.	p.m.	p.m.
Rosendaal ***............dep		1 44	...	2 52	...	...	4 14	...	⋮	...	...	...	...	6 37	7 14	...	8 12	9 27	B	1117
Esschen ¶ .... arr		1334	...	1442	...	...	16 3	...	1638	...	...	...	...	18 27	19 4	...	20 2	21 16	22 5	23 7
Esschen ¶ .... dep		1349	...		...	15 25	1620	...	1650	...	...	...	1754	18‡37	19 29	1939	20 51	21 30	2217	2328
Antwerp Centrale ......arr		1446	...	...	...	16 20	1655	...	1720	...	...	...	1855	19 5	20 2	2039	21 46	22 0	2247	2358
GRIMSBY ....dep		...	...	...	7 p0	From Grimsby on					...	...	...	...	...	...	...	...	...	...
ANTWERP ....arr		...	...	...	3 p0	Mon., Wed., and Sat.					...	...	...	...	...	...	...	...	...	...
	2&3	2&3	1,2,3	1,2,3	2&3	1,2,3	1& 2	1,2,3	1,2,3	1,2,3	1,2,3	2&3	1,2,3	1,2,3	1,2,3	1,2,3	1,2,3	1,2,3	1,2,3	
	VS	VS			VS		VS					VS			VS			VS		
Antwerp Sud. ...dep	14 7	...	...	...	1626	...	...	...	...	...	1739	...	1911	...	...	...	...	...	...	...
Antwerp Centrale dep	...	1451	1522	1558	...	16 30	17 6	1726	1731	1739	...	1821	...	19 23	20 15	2130	21 52	22 13	2257	...
Berchem	...	...	1528	...	...	...	...	⋮	...	1745	...	...	...	19 29	...	2136	...	...	...	...
Vieux-Dieu	...	...	1535	...	...	...	...	⋮	...	1752	...	1831	...	19 36	...	2143	...	...	B	...
Contich	...	15 6	1545	1612	...	16 46	E	⋮	1745	18 3	...	...	...	19 48	...	22 3	...	...	...	...
Wavre-St.-Catherine...	...	...	1558	...	...	...	...	⋮	...	1816	...	...	...	20 1	...	2216	...	...	...	...
Malines ....arr	1432	1519	16 8	1626	1652	17 4	1727	⋮	1759	1826	18*0	1852	1949	20 11	20 39	2223	22 10	22 40	2318	...
LOUVAIN 101 arr 2&3	...	17 3	17 3	1719	1719	...	1811	18 7	...	1913	1823	1918	...	...	...	2314	23 14	...	...	...
Malines ....dep 1350	1433	1521	1614	1630	1655	17 8	1728	...	18 6	1837	...	1856	...	20 18	20 42	2226	22 12	22 44	2320	...
Vilvorde 1410	...	1534	1634	1644	...	17 28	...	...	...	1857	...	1910	...	20 37	...	2246	...	22 58	B	...
Schaerbeek............1423	...	1544	1647	1653	1716	17 41	RC	...	...	1910	...	1922	...	20 51	21 2	2259	...	23 8	...	...
BRUSSELS Nord 1429	1455	1550	1653	1659	1722	17 47	...	...	1829	1916	...	1928	...	20 57	21 8	23 5	22 29	23 14	...	...
BRUSSELS Midi ...	...	...	...	...	...	...	1758	...	...	...	...	...	...	...	...	...	...	...	2349	...

B—Admits 3rd class passengers from Holland or for France via Feignies. At Antwerp takes only 1st and 2nd class for Brussels Midi and beyond.

D—At Antwerp takes for beyond Brussels only.

E—At Antwerp only takes for Brussels Midi and beyond.

RC—Restaurant Car in this train.

*—At Malines-Neckerspoel.

‡—Will not take up passengers at Esschen.

Extra. {Antwerp Sud...dep | 6 32 | 7 48 | 13 31 | Esschen.........dep | 9 0 | 22 22 | ...
{Malines............arr | 6 *53 | 8 26 | 14 9 | Antwerp C. ...arr | 9 55 | 23 14 | ...

BRUSSELS, MALINES, ANTWERP, and ROSENDAAL.

Station																			
	1,2,3	2&3	1,2,3	1,2,3	1 &2	2&3	1,2,3	2 & 3	1,2,3	1,2,3	1,2,3	1,2,3	2&3	2&3	1,2,3	1,2,3	2&3	1 &2	2 & 3
BRUSSELS Midi.........dep	...	VS	...	...	1654	VS	C	VS	...	V S	...	...	VS	...	...	...	VS	2326	V S
BRUSSELS Nord........dep	1526	1615	16 24	1628	...	1719	1729	17 55	1830	18 54	19 25	1942	2018	2047	...	2112	2256	⋮	23 57
Schaerbeek	1535	1634	...	1641	RC	...	...	18 3	1839	...	19 32	⋮	...	...	...	2126	23 5	⋮	0 4
Vilvorde	1547	1642	...	1654	...	...	...	18 13	1851	...	19 55	⋮	...	...	...	2138	2318	⋮	0 17
Malines ....arr	16 5	1653	16 41	1714	1723	1741	1751	18 27	19 9	19 16	20 13	⋮	2040	21 4	...	2157	2331	⋮	0 36
LOUVAIN 101 ....dep	1520	...	...	1717	...	1717	1717	17 17	18 2	18 2	...	⋮	...	...	2118	2122	...	⋮	...
Malines.........................dep	1610	1656	16 43	1749	1724	1743	1759	18 30	1924	19 20	...	⋮	2044	21 6	21*40	2211	2334	⋮	0 38
Wavre-St.-Catherine	1621	...	...	1757	...	...	...	...	1935	...	...	⋮	...	...	⋮	2219	...	⋮	...
Contich	1636	1718	...	1812	...	1757	...	...	1949	...	...	⋮	...	...	⋮	2234	...	⋮	...
Vieux-Dieu........................	1646	...	...	1824	...	...	C	...	1959	...	...	⋮	...	...	⋮	2244	...	⋮	...
Berchem	1653	...	...	1831	...	...	...	...	20 6	...	...	⋮	...	...	⋮	2251	...	⋮	...
Antwerp Centrale.........arr	1658	1732	17 1	1836	1745	18 9	§	...	2011	19 43	...	2016	...	2124	22 0	2256	2358	0 13	1 2
Antwerp Sud ....arr	...	...	...		...	...	1828	18 57	...	...	...	...	21 5	...	...	...	...	...	...
ANTWERP Quai ....dep	...	...	...	...	...	...	19 0	No Service				...	...	...	...	...	...	...	...
HARWICH ....arr	...	...	...	...	...	...	5a45	from Antwerp on				...	...	...	...	...	...	...	...
LONDON Liverpool St. arr	...	...	...	...	...	...	7a35	Sunday evening.				...	...	...	...	...	...	...	...
ANTWERP..............dep	...	...	...	...	...	...	19 0	From Antwerp on				...	...	...	...	...	...	...	...
GRIMSBY ....arr	...	...	...	...	...	...	3 p0	Tues., Thurs., Sat.				...	...	...	...	...	...	...	...
			1,2,3		1 &2	1,2,3		1,2,3	1,2,3	1,2,3	1,2,3								
					RC						C								
Antwerp Centrale ....dep	...	...	17 4	...	1755	1819	...	18 31	2021	19 56	19 25	2021	...	...	...	2348	...	...	4 39
Esschen .... arr	...	...	17 59	...	1830	1917	...	19 29	2115	20 31	20 25	2115	...	...	...	0 40	...	...	5 34
Esschen .... dep	...	...	18 3	...	1834	1921	...	...	2119	20 35		2119	...	...	...	...	...	...	5 40
Rosendaal ¶ ***............arr	...	...	6 33	...	7 4	7 51	...	...	9 48	9 5	...	9 48	...	...	...	...	...	...	6 9
ROTTERDAM 117.........arr	...	...	8 p33	...	8p33	9p20	...	...	12a6	10p36	...	12a6	...	...	...	...	...	...	7 a52
THE HAGUE 119.........arr	...	...	8 p57	...	8p57	10p5	...	...	...	11p22	...	...	...	...	...	...	...	...	8 a42
AMSTERDAM 119.........arr	...	...	9 p53	...	9p53	11p5	...	...	...	12a29	...	...	...	...	...	...	...	...	9 a43
AMSTERDAM 115A ......arr	...	...	...	...	...	1050	...	...	...	...	...	...	...	...	...	...	...	...	...

*—From Malines-Neckerspoel. §—Arrives Antwerp Sud Quai Station. C—Not on Sundays.

Extra. {Malines ....dep | 5 5 | 8 *15 | 8 59 | 16 50 | 20*12 | 20 50
{Antwerp Sud......arr | 5 43 | 8 35 | 9 35 | 17 26 | 20 32 | 21 26

HEYST, ZEE BRUGGE, and BRUGES (Brugge).

LIVERPOOL ...dep	...	...	...	2 p10	...	...	...	...	...	...	...	...	...	...	...	...	...	...
MANCHESTER dep	...	...	...	2 p55	...	...	...	...	...	...	...	...	...	...	...	...	...	...
BRADFORD ...dep	...	...	Not on Sunday.	3 p0	...	...	...	...	...	...	...	...	...	...	...	...	...	...
LEEDS..........dep	...	...		3 p52	...	...	...	...	...	...	...	...	...	...	...	...	...	...
HULL Steamer...dep	...	...		6 p0	Service from Hull on Tuesday, Thursday, and Saturday.										...	...	...	...
ZEE BRUGGE.....arr	...	...		7 0											...	...	...	...
Heyst..................dep	5 33	6 12	6 55	...	8 11	9 47	1020	1058	13 3	14 43	15 48	1650	17 14	1824	18*57	1947	21 6	23*2
Zee Brugge.........dep	5 46	6‡19	7 ‡2	8 §5	8 24	9‡54	1033	11‡5	1316	14‡50	15‡55	17 3	17‡24	1838	19 ‡4	20 0	21‡13	23‡9
Bruges St. Pierre	6 6	...	...	...	8 44	...	1053	...	1336	...	...	1723	...	1858	...	2020	...	...
Bruges ....arr	6 11	6 40	7 20	8 22	8 49	1012	1058	1123	1341	15 8	16 13	1728	17 39	19 3	19 22	2025	21 31	2327
GHENT 102 ....arr	7 1	7 33	8 0	9 1	9 41	...	1145	1210	1428	15 50	17 0	...	18 35	...	...	2131	22 13	0 23
BRUSSELS 102 ..arr	8 3	8 50	8 50	9 54	1050	...	1244	1320	...	16 59	18 3	...	19 16	21 2	21 2	2251	23 17	1 26
COLOGNE 122 ...arr	...	...	...	4 p19	...	...	...	...	...	...	...	...	...	...	...	...	...	...
BASLE..............arr	...	...	...	9 p13	...	...	...	...	...	...	...	...	...	...	...	...	...	...
BERLIN 161A......arr	...	...	...	12a21	...	...	...	...	...	...	...	...	...	...	...	...	...	...

‡—Zeebrugge arrival or departure is at Central Station.
§—On Sun, Wed, and Fri. only.
*—Until 15th September.
☞See page 102 whether Ghent connection is at Ghent Sud or Ghent St. Pierre.

BERLIN........... dep	...	...	...	...	...	...	...	...	...	...	...	...	9 p34	...	...	...	...	...	...	...
BASLE...............dep	...	...	...	...	...	...	...	...	...	...	...	...	11p40	...	...	...	...	...	...	...
COLOGNE......... dep	...	...	...	...	...	...	...	...	...	...	...	...	11a26	...	...	...	...	...	...	...
BRUSSELS 102A dep	...	5 40	6 44	...	8 50	9 27	9 32	12 25	13 13	14 42	14 42	16 21	16 25	16 28	18 8	18 14	20 40	20 40	...	...
GHENT 102A......dep	...	6 32	7 58	8 21	9 36	10 32	11 3	13 37	14 27	15 56	15 56	17 13	17 22	17 37	18 53	19 22	21 33	22 9	...	...
Bruges ....dep	5 15	7 18	8 49	9 9	10 24	11 20	1158	14 17	15 6	16 47	16 52	17 52	18 0	18 32	19 48	20 49	22 15	22 51	...	...
Bruges St. Pierre......	5 21	7 24	...	9 15	...	...	12 4	...	15 12	...	16 58	...	§	18 38	...	20 55	‡	...	...	...
Zee Brugge.........arr	5 42	7 44	9 3	9 35	10‡43	11‡39	1224	14‡36	15 32	17 ‡6	17 18	18‡11	18 18	18 58	20 ‡7	21 15	22 34	23‡10	...	...
Heyst ....arr	5 55	7 56	9 14	9 47	10 49	11 45	1236	14 42	15 44	17 12	17 30	18 17	...	19 10	20 13	21 27	22 40	23 16	...	...
ZEE BRUGGE ...dep	...	...	...	...	...	...	...	...	...	...	...	Not on ☞ Sunday.	19 0	Service from Zeebrugge on Sun., Wed., and Friday.						...
HULL Steamer...arr	...	...	...	...	...	...	...	...	...	...	...		8 a0							...
LEEDS ....arr	...	...	...	...	...	...	...	...	...	...	...		10a36	...	...	...	...	...	...	...
BRADFORD.......arr	...	...	...	...	...	...	...	...	...	...	...		11a18	...	...	...	...	...	...	...
MANCHESTER arr	...	...	...	...	...	...	...	...	...	...	...		11a31	...	...	...	...	...	...	...
LIVERPOOL ...arr	...	...	...	...	...	...	...	...	...	...	...		12p15	...	...	...	...	...	...	...

BRUGES and BLANKENBERGHE.

Bruges ....dep	5 0	713	843	914	1018	1029	1113	1152	12*29	1359	14*4	1422	1512	16*10	1641	1658	17†47	17‡57	1826	19‡32	1942	2043	22§10	22§45
Blankenberghe arr	5 27	740	9 1	941	1036	1047	1131	1219	12 49	1417	1422	1440	1539	16 28	1659	1725	18 5	18 15	1853	19 50	20 0	2110	22 28	23 3

Blankenberghe......dep	5 50	6 27	6 41	7 †7	8 28	10 0	10*34	10 59	1113	13 8	14*28	1445	16 1	1655	1716	1828	18§52	20 4	21 8	21‡50	23§15
Bruges ....arr	6 17	6 45	7 8	7 25	8 55	10 18	10 52	11 17	1140	1335	14 46	15 3	16 19	1722	1734	1855	19 10	2031	21 26	22 8	23 33

*—Weekdays only from 28th July until 2nd Sept. †—Not on Sunday. ‡—Sats. only until 6th Sept. §—Until 15th Sept.

BRUGES and KNOCKE.

EM											
	Bruges...dep	5 15	7 40	9 22	1150	1315	1435	16 0	1725	1850	...
10½	Westcapelle	5 50	8 15	9 57	1225	1350	1510	1635	18 0	1925	...
12½	Knocke..arr	6 0	...	...	1235	...	1520	...	1810	1935	...

Knocke..dep	6 30	8 5	1032	1115	1340	15 0	1625	...	2030	...	...
Westcapelle	6 40	8 15	1042	1125	1350	1510	1635	18 0	2045	...	...
Bruges...arr	7 15	8 50	1117	12 0	1425	1545	1710	1835	2120	...	...

KNOCKE and SLUIS.

Knocke..dep	5 40	8 5	...	1340	1625	1910	...	...	...	...	...
Westcapelle	5 50	8 15	9 57	1350	1635	1925	...	...	...	...	...
Sluis .....arr	6 10	8 35	1017	1410	1655	1945	...	...	...	...	...

Sluis ....dep	6 20	9 37	1022	1420	1740	2025	...	...	...	...	...
Westcapelle	6 40	9 52	1037	1440	18 0	2045	...	...	...	...	...
Knocke..arr	6 50	10 7	1052	1450	1810	2055	...	...	...	...	...

OSTEND and KNOCKE.

Ostend Marie José Pl. ...dep	7 0	Frequent service until 19.40.
Blankenberghe	7 55	
Zee Brugge Muur †..............	8 4	
Heyst	8 15	
Knocke ....arr	8 25	

Knocke.....................dep	6 20	Frequent service until 21.0.
Heyst	6 30	
Zee Brugge Muur †..........	6 41	
Blankenberghe	6 50	
Ostend.........................arr	7 40	

†—For Zee Brugge Quai.

VERVIERS, PEPINSTER, SPA, and TROIS-PONTS.

E.M.																						
—	**Verviers** ......dep	4 38	6 10	7 55	...	9 29	...	1043	1145	1352	1427	1525	1546	15 55	1736	1748	18 32	19 3	1931	1937	1947	2154
3	**Pepinster** ...dep	4 54	6 26	8 15	9 41	9 47	1035	11 2	12 3	14 5	1445	1540	16 2	16 8	1756	18 2	18 50	1921	1940	1954	20 7	2227
10½	**Spa** ....arr	5 26	6 58	8 36	9 59	1017	1053	1128	1233	1431	1511	1558	1620	16 40	1814	1834	19 11	1951	20 0	2012	2033	2253
...	" ....dep	—	7 3	—	—	1019	—	—	1238	—	1514	—	—	—	—	1838	—	—	20 2	—	2035	—
18	Hockai	...	7 32	...	...	1048	...	...	13 7	...	1544	...	...	...	...	19 8	...	...	...	...	21 6	...
25½	Stavelot	5 37	7 52	8 48	...	1110	...	...	1328	1442	16 4	...	...	17 12	...	1928	...	...	2042	...	2127	...
28½	**Trois-Ponts** arr	5 45	7 59	8 56	...	1118	...	...	1336	1450	1611	...	...	17 20	...	1935	...	...	2050	...	2135	...

Trois-Ponts dep		...	...	6 3	8 8	...	9 15	...	...	11 1	1125	13 49	...	...	...	15 7	1623	...	1727	...	...	2031	...
Stavelot	...	...	...	6 13	8 20	...	9 25	...	...	1110	1135	14 1	...	...	...	1517	1635	...	1737	...	...	2042	...
Hockai	...	...	...	6 37	—	...	9 49	...	...	...	12 0	—	...	...	...	1543	—	...	18 1	...	...	21 6	...
Spa ....arr	...	...	...	7 2	...	...	1012	...	...	1149	1226	...	...	...	...	16 3	...	...	1827	...	...	2129	...
" ....dep	4 58	5 33	6 37	7 12	7 31	8 47	1017	1110	1132	1159	1232	12 51	1335	1350	1442	1612	1636	1745	1836	1954	2047	2135	2330
Pepinster arr	5 29	6 4	6 59	7 43	8 10	9 15	1042	1128	1157	1222	13 3	13 9	1352	14 8	15 7	1643	1653	18 7	19 7	2011	2112	22 0	2355
Verviers...arr	5 43	6 22	7 39	7 58	8 18	9 36	1115	...	1228	1232	...	13 27	14 7	1427	1525	17 0	1713	1824	1923	...	2127	2237	0 10

***—Amsterdam time at Eysden and Maestricht.

MAESTRICHT and LIEGE.

E.M																						
—	**Maestricht** *** dep	...	...	a.m. 5 15	...	a.m. 7 35	a.m. 8 22	...	a.m. 11 12	...	p.m. 1245	...	...	p.m. 3 5	p.m. 4 7	...	...	p.m. 6 52	...	p.m. 8 55	p.m. 10 27	...
5½	Eysden....................	...	...	5 32	...	7 50	8 39	...	11 30	...	1 0	...	...	3 23	4 24	...	...	7 9	...	9 10	1042	...
8½	**Visé (Belgian Cust.)**	4 30	4 58	5 30	6 34	7 45	8 39	9 44	11 31	1159	13 1	1342	1427	15 32	1635	1722	18 20	1910	2015	2110	22 39	...
18½	**Liege(Longdoz)arr**	5 2	5 27	6 14	7 18	8 15	9 19	1024	12 5	1239	1333	1422	15 7	16 12	1715	18 6	19 0	1942	2055	2142	23 9	...

E.M																						
	Liege (Longdoz) dep	4 22	5 55	6 50	7 50	8 55	9 53	1059	1216	1315	1436	1525	1620	1649	1749	1835	1935	2049	2136	22 6	2319	...
10	**Visé**	4 48	6 29	7 30	8 37	9 33	1033	1135	1256	1355	1520	16 0	17 4	1729	1829	1925	2013	2129	2216	2241	2349	...
13½	**Eysden (Dutch Cust.)**	...	7 5	...	9 13	10 9	...	1211	...	...	3 56	4 36	5 46	...	...	8 1	8 49	...	...	1113	...	...
18½	**Maestricht (99)...arr**	...	7 21	...	9 29	1023	...	1227	...	...	4 12	4 50	6 0	...	...	8 17	9 3	...	...	1129	...	...

ALOST and RENAIX.

E.M.														
	Alost ....dep	4 17	7 40	8 59	1154	1440	17 42	**Renaix** ...dep	6 24	10 23	11 45	15 33	19 43	...
6¾	Burst	4 39	8 2	9 21	1214	15 3	18 4	Sottegem.........	7 16	11 15	12 39	16 58	20 35	2135
12½	Sottegem.........arr	4 59	8 22	9 41	1234	1523	18 24	Burst	8 6	11 37	13 6	17 20	...	2157
29¼	**Renaix** 100...arr	5 54	9 19	1046	1327	...	19 26	**Alost** 102...arr	8 25	11 54	13 26	17 39	...	2214

ST. GHISLAIN and FRAMERIES

E.M													
	St, Ghislain ......dep	6 2	11 3	17 12	1939	...	**Frameries** ....dep	7 3	11 32	17 41	20 13	...
5½	Frameries 108.....arr	6 28	1125	17 34	20 0	...	**Saint-Ghislain** ...arr	7 29	11 54	18 2	20 36	...

PIETON and LUTTRE.

Pieton ....dep	6 4	11 51	15 33	...	21 6	...
Trazegnies...........	6 15	12 3	15 44	1821	2116	...
Luttre ....arr	6 30	12 18	15 59	1837	2127	...
Luttre ....dep	4 17	4 35	11 43	1730	18 45	...
Trazegnies...........	4 32	4 52	12 0	1747	19 2	...
Piéton............arr	4 42	5 2	12 10	1757	19 12	...

BRUSSELS (QUARTIER LEOPOLD) and TERVUEREN.

Brussels (Q. Leopold) ...dep	4 45	6 2	6 47	7 56	9 20	1044	1215	13 9	1421	16 35	1743	18 25	19‡27	19 41	...		
Auderghem	4 56	6 13	6 58	8 7	9 32	1055	1226	1320	1433	16 46	1754	18 36	19 39	19 52	...		
Wesembeek-Stockel	5 6	6 24	7 9	8 18	9 43	11 6	1237	1331	1444	16 57	18 5	18 47	19 50	20 3	...		
Tervueren ....arr	5 13	6 31	7 15	8 25	9 50	1113	1244	1338	1451	17 4	1812	18 54	19 57	20 10	...		
Tervueren...................dep	4 52	5 ‡2	5 32	6 56	7 51	8 39	10 0	1139	1319	14 4	16 29	17 55	18 20	19 11	20‡11	20 35	...	...
Wesembeek-Stockel	5 2	5 10	5 40	7 4	7 59	8 47	10 8	1147	1327	14 12	16 37	18 4	18 28	19 19	...	20 43	...	...
Auderghem	5 13	5 21	5 51	7 15	8 10	8 58	1019	1158	1338	14 23	16 48	18 15	18 39	19 30	...	20 53	...	...
Brussels (Q. Leopold)......arr	5 23	5 31	6 2	7 25	8 20	9 8	1029	12 8	1348	14 33	16 58	18 30	18 47	19 40	20 38	21 3	...	...

‡—Not on Sun.

DUTCH RAILWAYS.

Amsterdam Time.

LONDON to HOEK van HOLLAND and ROTTERDAM.

THROUGH CARRIAGES.
- Hoek van Holland to Amsterdam—in 5.40 a.m. and 7.50 a.m.
- Hoek van Holland to Basle (via Strassburg or via Mayence)—in 5.25 a.m.
- Hoek van Holland to Berlin—in 5.18 a.m.
- Hoek van Holland to Cologne—in 5.25 a.m.

RC Restaurant Car.

Luggage rate, 10 cents. for 22lbs. for 50 Kilometers. 15 cents. for 22 lbs. for 100 Kilometers.

Customs Examination for all Dutch Towns at Hoek van Holland.

LONDON Liverpool St. ...dep		8 p30	8p30	8p30	...	...	...	...	...	...	...	...	...	...	...	...	...	...	...	...	...
HARWICH ....dep		10 p0	10p0	10p0	...	...	...	...	...	...	...	...	...	...	...	...	...	...	...	...	...
HOEK V. HOLLAND ....arr		5 a10	5a10	5a10	...	...	...	...	...	...	...	...	...	...	...	...	...	...	...	...	...
	1,2,3	1&2	1 &2	1 &2	1,2,3	1,2,3	1 &2	1,2,3	1,2,3	1,2,3	1,2,3	1,2,3	1,2,3	1,2,3	1,2,3	1,2,3	1,2,3	1,2,3	1,2,3	1,2,3	1,2,3
	a.m.	a.m.	a.m.	a.m.	a.m.	a.m.	a.m.	a.m.	a.m.	a.m.	p.m.	p.m.	p.m.	p m.	p.m.	p.m.	p.m.	p.m.	p.m	p.m.	p.m.
Hoek van Holland...dep	...	5 18	5 25	5 40	5†48	7 7	7 50	8 49	...	1049	...	†	1 25	2 45	...	5 1	...	6 48	...	9 32	1056
Maassluis	...	⋮	...	...	6 5	7 26	...	9 10	1027	11 8	1218	1 11	1 41	3 7	4 23	5 23	6 20	7 6	8 23	9 53	1110
Vlaardingen......................	5†17	⋮	...	...	6 16	7 38	...	9 22	1038	1119	1229	1 23	1 53	3 19	4 35	5 35	6 32	7 18	8 35	10 5	1121
Schiedam..........................	5 30	RC	RC	6 0	6 26	7 47	...	9 33	1049	1131	1240	1 34	2 4	3 30	4 46	5 46	6 43	7 29	8 46	1016	1132
Rotterdam Delft P.arr	5 37	5 43	5 50	6 11	6 36	7 56	8 15	9 42	1058	1140	1249	1 43	2 14	3 41	4 55	5 56	6 52	7 38	8 55	1025	1141
,, Beurs ...arr	...	⋮	...	...	...	...	...	...	...	...	...	...	...	...	...	...	...	...	...	...	...
,, Maas....arr	...	⋮	...	...	...	...	...	...	...	...	...	...	...	...	...	...	...	...	...	...	...
THE HAGUE 119 ....arr		⋮	...	6a27	...	...	8a50														
AMSTERDAM 119 ....arr		⋮	...	7a30	...	...	9a43														
OSNABRUCK ....arr		1119	...	...	...	...	...														
BREMEN 132 ....arr		1p12	...	...	...	...	...														
BERLIN 161A ....arr		4p54	...	...	...	...	9p28														
NYMEGEN 119.....................arr		...	7a33	...	...	...	...														
COLOGNE 121 ....arr		...	1115	...	...	...	2 p0														

Extra.		
Maassluis......dep	7a†59	7p†33
Rotterdam ...arr	8 28	8 5

†—Not on Sunday.

ROTTERDAM to HOEK van HOLLAND and LONDON.

COLOGNE 121.....................dep			...	...	...	...	...	...	...	...	...	...	...	...	...	...	...	...	...	7 p21	...
NYMEGEN 119A...................dep			...	...	...	...	...	...	...	...	...	...	...	...	...	...	...	...	...	9 p26	...
BERLIN 160B ....dep			...	...	...	...	...	...	...	...	...	...	...	...	...	...	...	1 p5	...	...	...
BREMEN 133 ....dep			...	...	...	...	...	...	...	...	...	...	...	...	...	...	...	4 p40	...	...	...
RHEINE 118C........................dep			...	...	...	...	...	...	...	...	...	...	...	...	...	...	...	7 p29	...	...	...
AMSTERDAM 119A ....dep			...	...	...	...	...	...	...	...	...	...	...	...	...	...	...	...	9 p45	...	...
THE HAGUE 119A.............dep			...	...	...	...	...	...	...	...	...	...	...	...	...	...	...	...	10p47	...	...
			1,2,3	1,2,3	1,2,3	1,2,3	1,2,3	1,2,3	1,2,3	1,2,3	1,2,3	1,2,3	1,2,3	1,2,3	1,2,3	1,2,3	1,2,3	1 & 2	1 & 2	1 & 2	1,2,3
			a.m.	a.m.	a.m.	a.m.	p.m.	p.m.	p.m.	p.m.	p.m.	p.m.	p.m.	p.m.	p.m.	p.m.	p.m.	p.m.	p.m.	p.m.	p.m.
Rotterdam Maas ......dep			...	...	...	...	...	...	...	...	...	...	...	...	...	...	...	...	⋮	...	...
,, Beurs...dep		a.m.	...	...	...	...	†	...	...	...	...	...	...	...	†	...	...	...	⋮	...	...
,, Delft P. dep	5†15	7 25	8 49	9 39	11 7	1157	1219	1 26	2 30	3 27	4 19	5 20	5 57	6 50	7 28	8 24	9 32	10 50	⋮	11 10	1118
Schiedam	5 25	7 35	8 59	9 48	1117	12 6	1229	1 35	2 39	3 26	4 28	5 30	6 6	7 0	7 37	8 33	9 42	...	11 7	...	1127
Vlaardingen	5 36	7 46	9 10	9 59	1128	1217	1240	1 46	2 50	3 37	4 39	5 41	6 17	7 11	7 50	8 44	9 53	...	...	...	1138
Maassluis	5 48	7 57	9 21	1010	1140	1228	1252	1 58	3 1	3 50	4 50	5 52	6 28	7 23	7 59	8 56	10 4	...	...	...	1150
HoekvHolland	6 8	8 16	...	1031	...	1247	...	2 19	...	4 8	...	6 13	...	7 43	...	9 13	10 23	11 15	11 27	11 35	...
HOEK VAN HOLLAND ......dep			...	...	...	...	...	...	...	...	...	...	...	...	...	...	...	11p50	11p50	11p50	...
HARWICH.......................arr			...	...	...	...	...	...	...	...	...	...	...	...	...	...	...	6 a20	6 a20	6 a20	...
LONDON Liverpool St. ...arr			...	...	...	...	...	...	...	...	...	...	...	...	...	...	...	8 a0	8 a0	8 a0	...

LONDON to VLISSINGEN (FLUSHING) and BREDA.

No free Luggage allowed to holders of local tickets. Luggage rate, 10 cents or 22 lbs. for 50 Kilometers; 15 cents for 22 lbs. for 100 Kilometers.

THROUGH CARRIAGES.
- Vlissingen to Amsterdam—in 4.45 a.m. and 7.0 p.m. from Vlissingen.
- Vlissingen to Basle—in 4.15 a.m. from Vlissingen.
- Vlissingen to Berlin—in 4.36 a.m and 7.10 p.m. from Vlissingen.
- Vlissingen to Hamburg—in 4.36 a.m. and 7.10 p.m. from Vlissingen.
- Vlissingen to Leipsic, Dresden and Vienna—in 4.36 a.m. and 7.0 p.m. from Vlissingen.
- Vlissingen to Rotterdam—in 4.45 a.m. and 7.0 p.m. from Vlissingen.

SLEEPING CAR
- Vlissingen to Berlin and Hamburg—in 7.10 p.m. from Vlissingen.
- Vlissingen to Dresden—in 7.0 p.m, from Vlissingen.

LONDON Victoria......dep	8p30	8 p30	8 p30	...	...	...	...	...	...	...	...	...	...	...	10 a0	10 a0	10 a0	...
LONDON Holborn Vt. dep	8p25	8 p25	8 p25	...	...	...	...	...	...	...	...	...	...	...	9 a55	9 a55	9 a55	...
HERNE HILL ....dep	8p40	8 p40	8 p40	...	...	...	...	...	...	...	...	...	...	...	10a10	10a10	10a10	...
QUEENBOROUGH ......dep	...	...	...	...	...	...	...	...	...	...	...	...	...	...	11a30	11a30	11a30	...
FOLKESTONE............dep	1030	10p30	10p30	...	...	...	...	...	...	...	...	...	...	...	...	...	...	...
VLISSINGEN (Flushing) arr	4 a0	4 a0	4 a0	...	...	...	...	...	...	...	...	...	...	...	6 p40	6 p40	6 p40	...
	1& 2	1 & 2	1,2,3	1,2,3	1,2,3	1,2,3	1,2,3	1,2,3	1,2,3	1,2,3	1,2,3	1,2,3	1,2,3	1,2,3	1 & 2	1 & 2	1,2,3	1,2,3
	a.m.	a.m.	a.m.		a.m.	a.m.		a.m.		p.m.	p.m.		p.m.		p.m.	p.m.	p.m.	p.m.
Vlissingen ....dep	4 15	4 36	4 45	...	6 25	7 14	...	9 10	...	12 25	1 27	...	4 50	...	7 0	7 10	7 46	7 55
Middelburg	D	C	A	...	6 35	7 23	...	9 20	...	12 35	1 36	...	5 0	...	RC	RC	7 56	8 5
Goes....................................	RC	RC	RC	...	7 3	7 48	...	9 53	...	1 4	1 55	...	5 29	...	...	:	8 17	8 36
Vlake	:	:	...	...	7 14	...	...	10 12	...	1 22	2 6	...	5 43	...	SC	SC	8 28	8 53
Woensdrecht...............a.m.	:	:	...	a.m.	7 50	...	...	10 45	...	1 54	...	...	6 16	...	D	:	...	9 29
Bergen op Zoom 5 48	:	:	...	5 48	8 0	8 23	...	10 56	...	2 3	2 33	...	6 27	...	...	C	8 57	9 40
Rosendaal arr6 12	:	:	5 45	6 12	8 16	8 36	...	11 13	...	2 19	2 46	...	6 45	...	8 2	:	9 10	9 58
ROTTERDAM ......117 arr	:	:	6 a46	...	...	9 a50	...	12p56	...	3 p50	3 p50	...	8 p33	...	9p20	:	10p36	12 a6
ANTWERP ....110 arr	:	:	7 a6	...	1017	10a17	...	12p40	...	4 p20	4 p20	...	8 p2	...	9 p46	:	10 p0	11p58
BRUSSELS............110 arr	:	:	8 a24	...	1118	11a18	...	1 p47	...	5 p1	5 p1	...	9 p8	...	10p29	:	11p14	2 a1
ANTWERP ....110 dep	:	:	...	4a39	...	7 a10	7a24	9 a58	1032	1 p13	1p32	1p32	5 p4	5p55	6p19	:	7 p56	8 p21
Rosendaal ....dep	:	:	...	7 8	...	8 44	9 51	11 23	1220	2 33	3 0	3 28	6 54	7 30	8 5	8 15	9 26	10 8
Etten-Leur	:	:	...	7 31	...	...	1014	...	1243	...	...	3 51	7 16	...	:	:	...	10 28
Breda............................arr	:	:	...	7 48	...	9 6	1031	11 45	1 2	2 54	3 21	4 10	7 28	7 51	:	:	9 48	10 46
BOXTEL ....116 arr	6 a5	6 a26	...	9 a8	...	9 a57	11a32	...	2 p5	3 p39	5p10	5 p10	8 p19	...	8 p57	9 p7	...	12a11
WESEL ....120 arr	...	9 a7	...	1256	...	12p56	5 p43	...	...	6 p21	9 p30	9 p30	...	...	11p44	12 0	...	...
VENLO ....116 arr	...	...	...	11a8	...	11 a8	1 p35	...	3p55	...	7 p8	7 p8	10 p6	...	...	...	...	...
COLOGNE...121, 160A arr	9a56	...	...	3p10	...	3 p10	5 p14	...	8 p6	...	11p12	11p12	...	...	1 a50	...	...	...
BERLIN ....161A arr	...	4 p54	...	...	...	...	...	...	...	...	...	...	...	...	...	7 a57	...	...
UTRECHT ....115 arr	...	...	...	...	...	10a55	...	1 p33	...	...	5 p2	6 p56	...	9p30	...	...	11p35	...
AMSTERDAM.....118A arr	...	...	8 §10	...	...	11a40	...	2 p15	...	...	5 p40	7 p37	...	10p8	10§50	...	12a17	...

Extra. { Bergen-op-Zoom...dep | 4 p20 | 7p24 | ... ; Rosendaal ....arr | 4 44 | 7 48 | ...

§—Via Rotterdam.

BREDA and VLISSINGEN to LONDON.

AMSTERDAM W.P. 118 dep			...	...	7 §10	...	7a35	8 a26	...	10a37	1 p18	...	...	4p16	4p16	6 p25	...	...	8§p20
UTRECHT ....115 dep		...	...	...	...	...	3a13	9 a4	...	11a15	1 p56	...	...	4p54	4p54	7 p5	...	...	:
BERLIN ....160 dep		...	...	10p28	...	...	...	...	...	...	...	...	...	...	...	...	1 p5	...	:
COLOGNE 121,161B dep		...	...	...	5 a47	...	5a48	...	...	...	9 a37	...	2p23	...	2p23	...	6 p32	7 p14	:
VENLO ....117 dep		...	5a11	...	...	...	7a55	...	8 a48	...	12p15	...	4 p2	...	4p14	...	...	...	:
WESEL.............120 dep		...	...	6 a55	7 a28	...	...	...	...	...	10a55	...	4p15	...	4p15	...	8 p26	...	:
BOXTEL ....117 dep		5 a33	7 a6	8 a22	8 a42	...	9a10	...	10a40	...	2 p20	...	5p33	...	6p17	...	9 p43	9 p57	:
	1,2,3	1,2,3	1,2,3	C runs through.	D runs through.	1,2,3	1,2,3	1 & 2	1,2, 3	1,2,3	1, 2,3	1,2,3	1,2,3	1,2,3	1,2,3	1,2,3	1 & 2	1 & 2	1,2,3
	a.m.	a.m.	a.m.				a.m.	a.m.	a.m.	p.m.	p.m.		p.m.	p.m.	p.m.	p.m.	:	:	:
Breda ....dep	6 6	6 25	8 20			...	10 2	10 43	11 33	1 9	3 39	...	6 13	6 43	7 22	8 54	:	:	:
Etten-Leur	6 24	...	8 37			...	...	...	11 50	...	...	...	...	...	7 37	...	:	:	:
Rosendaal ......arr	6 45	6 52	8 56	9 13	9 37	...	1025	11 4	12 10	1 31	4 2	...	6 35	7 5	7 59	9 16	10 36	10 50	:
ANTWERP 110 arr	7a51	7 a51	1017	10 17	10a17	...	11a18	11 42	...	2p46	4p55	...	7 p5	8 p2	9p46	10 p0	11p58	11p58	:
BRUSSELS 110 dep	...	...	...	5 a59	5 a59	7a56	7a56	...	...	9a55	1 p3	1 p3	4p24	5p16	...	6 p54	7 p42	...	:
ANTWERP 110 dep	4a39	...	...	7 a24	7 a24	8a49	8a49	...	...	10a32	2 p34	2p34	5 p4	5p55	...	7 p56	8 p21	...	:
ROTTERDAM116dp	4a52	...	...	...	8 a33	8a33	9a26	...	...	11a47	3 p3	3 p3	4p45	5p47	...	8 p26	...	...	9p54
Rosendaal ......dep	7 0	...	...	9 16	9 42	9 59	1041	...	...	1 41	4 16	4 25	6 40	7 25	...	9 34	10 38	10 52	11 2
Bergen op Zoom	7 23	...	...	1 & 2 Class.	1 & 2 Class	1018	1056	...	...	1 59	4 30	4 45	7 4	7 45	...	9 51	...	...	...
Woensdrecht	7 32	...	...			1026	...	...	...	2 7	...	4 54	—	7 54	...	...	C	D	...
Vlake...........................	8 6	...	...			1059	...	...	...	2 38	4 57	5 30	...	8 28	...	...	...	...	...
Goes	8 27	...	...			1116	1133	...	...	2 57	5 9	5 49	...	8 50	...	10 31	...	...	...
Middelburg...................	8 57	...	...			1145	1154	...	...	3 27	5 28	6 21	...	9 22	...	10 51	...	...	...
Vlissingen ....arr	9 6	...	...	10 20	10 45	1152	12 2	...	...	3 36	5 35	6 29	...	9 30	...	10 59	11 38	11 52	12 2
VLISSINGEN ......dep	...	...	...	11 a0	11 a0	...	...	...	...	...	...	...	...	...	...	12a10	12a10	12a10	...
QUEENBOROUGH arr	...	...	...	5 p40	5 p40	...	...	...	...	...	...	...	...	...	...	...	...	...	...
FOLKESTONE......arr	...	...	...	...	...	...	...	...	...	...	...	...	...	...	...	5 a30	5 a30	5 a30	...
LONDON Victoria arr	...	...	...	7 p34	7 p34	...	...	...	...	...	...	...	...	...	...	7 a48	7 a48	7 a48	...

Extra. { Rosendaal.....dep | 5a10, 3p40 ; Bergen-op-Zo arr | 5 34, 4 4 } { Breda ......dep. 4p25 ; Rosendaal arr. 5 7 }

*—On weekdays only between Breda and Rosendaal.

RC—Restaurant Car. ‡—From Brussels Midi. **A**—Takes only for Belgium and Holland, via Rosendaal.

C—North Germany Express; Seat Ticket required for this train—60c., and 1 fl. 20c., according to distance.

D—South Germany Express; Seat Ticket required for this train—60c., and 1 fl. 20c., according to distance.

Luggage, 10 cents for 22 lbs. for 50 kils.]

ZUTPHEN, HENGELO, and GRONAU (Mid Europe Time at Gronau).

¶—Customs Examination.

ARNHEM (114) dep	...	6 a9	8 a37	9a33	10 a5	11a52	12p10	2p47	5p21	...	7 p14	8 p26
	a.m.	a.m.	a.m.	a.m.	a.m.	p.m.	p.m.	p.m.	p.m.	...	p.m.	p.m.
Zutphen ....dep	...	7 14	9 27	1010	10 48	12 30	1 21	4 16	5 56	...	7 54	9 20
Lochem	*	7 36	9 51	...	11 5	...	1 45	4 39	...	...	8 17	9 42
Goor	5 48	7 54	10 11	...	11 18	...	2 5	4 58	...	...	8 35	10 0
Delden	6 4	8 6	10 26	...	...	...	2 18	5 11	...	...	8 50	10 13
Hengelo ....arr	6 11	8 13	10 33	1050	11 33	1 20	2 25	5 19	6 45	...	8 57	10 21
RHEINE (118B) arr	...	...	12p23	...	1 p36	...	...	7p49	...	...	...	...
Hengelo........dep	6 15	8 18	10 38	1055	11 41	1 25	2 42	5 24	6 50	7p38	9 0	10 35
Enschedé 117	6 25	8 28	10 48	11 5	11 51	1 35	2 52	5 34	7 0	7 48	9 10	10 45
Gronau 135B ¶ arr	7 33	1016	...	...	12 43	...	...	6 40	...	...	10 5	...

	a.m.	a.m.	a.m.	a.m.	a.m.	a.m.	a.m.	p.m.	p.m.	p.m.	p.m.	p.m.	p.m.	p.m.	p.m.
Gronau... ...dep	...	...	7 50	...	9 38	1140	...	...	...	3 8	...	...	7 15	...	1035
Enschedé ¶	5 0	6 30	7 34	8 50	9 20	1127	1151	1 38	2 32	2 52	4 48	6 0	7 20	8 49	1019
Hengelo......arr	5 12	6 40	7 42	9 0	9 30	1137	12 1	1 48	2 42	3 2	4 58	6 10	7 30	9 0	1029
RHEINE... ...dep	...	...	...	5 a37	...	...	...	...	...	2p22	...	...	6p42	...	...
Hengelo ...dep	5 17	6 45	...	9 9	...	1140	1211	...	2 50	3 7	5 3	6 15	7 35	...	...
Delden	5 26	...	...	9 18	...	...	1219	...	...	3 15	5 13	...	7 43	...	...
Goor	5 42	7 4	...	9 30	...	...	1233	...	...	3 27	5 29	...	7 55	...	...
Lochem	6 1	7 19	...	9 49	...	...	1251	...	...	3 47	5 52	...	8 16	...	...
Zutphen......arr	6 24	7 40	...	10 10	...	1220	1 12	...	3 32	4 13	6 19	7 5	8 38	...	...
ARNHEM 114 arr	7a20	8a13	...	10a47	...	1253	2 p5	...	4 p8	5 p6	7p15	7p45	9p29	...	...

ARNHEM, ZUTPHEN, and ZWOLLE.

		a.m.	a.m.	a.m.	a.m.	a.m.	a.m.	a.m.	a.m.	a.m.	p.m.	p.m.	p.m.	p.m.		p.m.	p.m.	p.m.	p.m.		p.m.	p.m.	p.m.	p.m.	p.m.	p.m.
Arnhem ...dep	...	6 9	6 45	7 30	8 37	9 33	9 40	10 5	11 15	11 52	1210	1 19	1 44	2 47	...	3 18	4 25	5 21	5 30	...	6 42	7 14	8 26	8 55	10 3	11 13
Velp	...	6 21	6 59	...	8 46	...	9 51	...	11 18	...	1224	...	1 58	3 0	...	3 28	4 38	...	5 43	...	6 53	...	8 36	...	1016	11 25
Dieren 120	...	6 36	7 24	...	9 4	...	10 8	...	11 42	...	1243	1 40	2 20	3 17	...	3 45	5 4	...	5 59	...	7 9	...	8 53	9 14	1041	11 42
Zutphen arr	a.m.	6 57	7 53	8 0	9 23	1043	1026	1035	12 11	12 24	1 3	1 56	2 51	3 35	...	4 3	5 34	5 51	6 19	p.m.	7 27	7 43	9 12	9 29	11 9	12 1
Zutphen dep	5 23	7 10	8 15	8 3	9 40	—	1037	1052	—	—	1 30	1 59	—	3 41	...	5 0	—	—	6 24	6 48	7 45	—	9 34	—	—	—
Deventer	5 40	7 37	8 45	8 23	10 7	...	1056	1122	...	...	2 0	2 18	...	4 6	4p30	5 30	...	...	6 51	7 18	8 3	8p32	9 58	...	...	...
Olst	—	7 53	...	...	1022	...	...	12 3	...	...	—	2 33	...	4 21	4 55	—	...	...	7 9	—	...	8 56	1013	...	...	...
Zwolle 115 arr	...	8 21	...	8 58	1051	...	1126	1245	...	...	...	3 2	...	4 50	5 42	...	...	...	7 38	...	8 32	9 38	1042	...	...	...

	a.m.	a m			a.m.	a.m.		a.m.	a.m.			p.m.	p.m.			p.m.	p.m	p m	p.m.			p.m.	p.m.			p.m.
Zwolle ......dep	...	6 0	...	...	7 10	8 40	...	9 21	11 8	...	...	...	1256	...	...	2 14	3 20	...	3 35	...	...	6 21	6 34	...	...	9 11
Olst	...	6 30	...	...	7 54	...	...	9 53	...	...	...	...	1 29	...	p.m.	3 0	...	...	4 6	...	...	...	7 10	p.m.	...	9 42
Deventer	6 0	6 46	...	...	8 20	9 12	...	1011	1143	p.m.	...	1235	1 47	...	2 55	3 25	3 52	...	4 26	...	5 45	6 53	7 30	7 50	...	9 59
Zutphen 118B arr	6 20	7 6	a.m.	a.m.	8 50	9 29	a.m.	1032	12 0	...	p.m.	1 5	2 5	p.m.	3 25	—	4 9	...	4 48	p.m.	6 15	7 9	—	8 20	p.m.	1021
Zutphen 118B dep	6 29	7 14	7 43	8 44	—	9 34	1014	1058	12 3	1225	1230	1 19	2 19	2 39	3 35	...	4 11	4 18	5 0	5 51	6 25	7 13	...	8 41	9 15	1027
Dieren	6 51	7 35	...	9 12	...	9 51	1029	1117	...	...	1258	1 39	2 35	3 7	3 50	...	...	4 40	5 20	6 19	6 48	7 28	...	9 1	9 43	1050
Velp	7 8	7 50	...	9 33	...	...	...	1131	...	...	1 24	1 55	...	3 33	...	...	...	4 56	5 36	6 45	7 4	...	...	9 19	10 9	11 8
Arnhem 118 ......arr	7 20	8 0	8 13	9 50	...	1010	1047	1140	1233	12 58	1 36	2 5	2 54	3 45	4 8	...	4 41	5 6	5 47	7 1	7 15	7 45	...	9 29	1025	1117

ZWOLLE and STADSKANAAL

†—Not on Sunday.

Zwolle ....dep	...	7†a0	9 a18	11a38	1p55	...	5 p0	...	9p25
Ommen	...	7 50	10 6	12 25	2 50	...	5 55	...	1012
Marienberg	...	8 13	10 36	12 50	3 13	...	6 17	10 24	1037
Coevorden	8 a5	9 26	11 25	1 45	4 1	4p30	7 11	10 54	1125
Stadskanaal arr	9 54	1111	11 58	3 21	...	6 16	8 54	...	...

Stadskanaal dep		...	7 a12	8 a30	10a45	1†p30	5p25	8 p32
Coevorden	6†a0	6 a30	8 55	10 26	12 41	3 57	7 5	10 16
Marienberg	6 45	7 19	9 37	11 16	1 33	4 47	7 47	—
Ommen	—	7 45	10 7	11 43	2 1	5 8	8 13	...
Zwolle ....arr		8 25	10 54	12 25	2 43	5 51	8 53	...

Marienberg......dep	6a†47	8 a57	11a24	1 p30	4†p50	6p22	7p57
Almelo ....arr	7 20	9 30	11 57	2 3	5 23	6 55	8 30

Almelo ....dep	7 a38	10 a0	12p42	2†p30	5 p40	7 p10	9p48	...
Marienberg ......arr	8 11	10 33	1 15	3 3	6 13	7 43	1021	...

NYMEGEN and HERTOGENBOSCH.

‡—Not on Sunday.

	a.m.	a.m.	a.m.	a.m.	a.m.	a.m.	p.m.	p.m.	p.m.	p.m.	p.m.	p.m.
Nymegen ....dep	6 45	...	7 58	9 42	...	11 20	12 28	2‡45	4 15	6 35	8 16	9 43
Ravestein	7 10	...	8 22	10 5	...	...	12 53	3 10	4 38	6 58	...	10 6
Oss	7 27	7 46	8 35	10 22	10 32	11 44	1 9	3 26	4 56	7 16	8 41	10 22
's Hertogenbosch arr	7 55	8 27	9 1	10 42	11 13	12 3	1 38	3 55	5 22	7 43	9 0	10 49

	a.m.	a.m.	a.m.	a.m.	a.m.	p.m.	p.m.	p.m.	p.m.	p.m.	p.m.	p.m.	
's Hertogenbosch dep	6 38	7 17	8 13	9 20	10 3	12 42	3‡ 0	4 18	5 50	6 9	8 48	9 48	...
Oss	7 18	7 47	8 34	10 2	10 25	1 11	3 32	4 51	6 11	6 41	9 9	10 19	...
Ravestein	—	8 1	...	—	10 39	1 26	3 46	5 6	...	6 57	...	10 34	...
Nymegen 114.........arr	...	8 25	8 58	...	11 3	1 50	4 10	5 29	6 35	7 19	9 33	10 56	...

¶—Customs Examination.]

NYMEGEN, VENLO, and MAESTRICHT.

†—Not on Sunday.

		a.m.	a.m.		a.m.	p.m.		p.m.	p.m.	p.m.		p.m.
Nymegen..dep	...	6 57	9 46	...	1145	1238	...	2 22	5 23	5 54	...	8 57
Beugen 120	...	7 29	10 8	...	1215	1259	...	2 53	...	6 30	...	9 30
Boxmeer	...	7 42	1017	...	1229	1 7	...	3 3	...	6 43	...	9 38
Venraij	...	8 6	1033	...	1253	1 23	...	3 27	...	7 6	...	9 53
Venlo 117 arr	a.m.	8 41	1055	a.m.	1 30	1 43	p.m.	4 4	6 17	7 46	p.m	1013
Venlo 117 dep	5 40	9 8	1113	1123	—	1 49	1 55	4 17	6 22	—	8 0	1018
Reuver	5 59	9 27	...	...	...	...	2 15	4 37	...	...	8 20	...
Roermond 99	6 21	9 46	1135	1145	...	2 12	2 40	5 1	6 44	...	8 41	1040
Sittard	7 4	1027	1157	12 7	...	2 35	3 22	5 47	7 6	...	9 29	11 3
Beek-Elsloo	7 18	1042	...	...	...	...	3 37	6 2	...	...	9 45	...
Maestri'ht ¶ar	7 43	11 3	1217	1228	...	2 55	3 59	6 22	7 26	...	10 6	1124
LIEGE 111 arr	9a19	12p5	1p33	1p33	...	4p12	5p15	7p42	...	...	11p9	...

LIEGE ......dep	...	...	5a55	...	7 a50	1059	...	3p25	4p20	...	...	7p35
		a.m.	a.m.		a.m.	p.m.	p.m.	p.m.	p.m.	p.m.	p.m.	p.m.
Maestricht ¶...dep	...	5 35	7 28	...	9 42	1 34	1 43	4 57	6 25	6 38	6†47	9 18
Beek-Elsloo	...	6 0	...	...	10 7	...	2 8	5 22	...	...	7 14	9 43
Sittard	...	6 14	7 50	...	10 23	1 57	2 24	5 41	6 47	7 1	7 27	10 1
Roerm'nd 127	...	7 0	8 12	...	11 4	2 20	3 10	6 27	7 9	7 24	—	1048
Reuver	...	7 18	...	...	11 25	...	3 28	6 46	...	...	...	11 5
Venlo ... arr	a.m.	7 37	8 32	a.m.	11 43	2 40	3 47	7 5	7 29	7 44	p.m.	1123
Venlo ... dep	5 43	—	8 37	8 42	11 51	2 46	4 8	—	7 43	—	8 38	—
Venraij	6 19	...	...	9 22	12 28	3 7	4 44		8 8	...	9 17	...
Boxmeer	6 40	...	...	9 49	12 47	3 22	5 3		8 25	...	9 39	...
Beugen	6 52	...	...	9 51	12 58	3 29	5 13	...	8 33	...	9 52	...
Nymegen 114 ar	7 24	...	9 31	1022	1 26	3 48	5 43	...	8 55	...	1022	...

Sittard.................dep	4†30	7a24	8a7	10a30	12p10	2p40	5p50	7p10	11 p7
Kerkrade-Rolduc (Customs)	5 35	8 16	9 2	11 24	1 3	3 32	6 47	8 4	12 0
Herzogenrath (120B)......arr	6 40	9 5	955	12 15	1 48	4 19	7 45	8 51	...

Herzogenrath dep	5†43	6a23	7†10	9a33	11a 8	1p20	5 p4	6 p5	9 p10
Kerkrade-Rolduc	5 15	5 58	6 51	9 16	10 49	1 1	4 46	5 47	8 53
Sittard ....arr	6 9	6 55	7 45	1011	11 41	1 51	5 36	6 42	9 47

†—Week-days only.

NYMEGEN and ARNHEM

‡—In July, Aug. and Sept.

Nymegen dep	6 26	6 50	7 34	8 30	9 4	9 35	9 45	1020	11 8	1233	1 40	1 55	3‡40	3 55	4 30	5 18	5 50	6 40	7 23	8 0	9 0	9 36	11 2	...	...
Arnhem ...arr	7 7	7 16	8 8	8 58	9 26	9 55	1027	1054	1143	1255	2 2	2 29	4 5	4 20	5 1	6 3	6 23	7 3	7 54	8 35	9 25	9 58	1137	...	...

Arnhem ...dep	5 20	6 0	7 30	8 12	9 9	9 33	10 7	1055	11 7	1155	12 5	1 49	2 16	3 34	4 16	4 56	5 21	5 53	6 37	7 50	8 23	9 4	9 42	1124	...
Nymegen...arr	6 5	6 35	7 55	8 51	9 37	9 56	1031	1117	1140	1220	12 29	2 17	2 38	4 2	4 55	5 18	5 43	6 26	7 5	8 12	8 47	9 38	10 5	1157	...

Luggage, 10 cents for 22 lbs. for 50 kils.]

UTRECHT, HERTOGENBOSCH, TILBURG, and BOXTEL.

	1,2,3	1,2,3	1,2,3	1,2,3	1&2	1,2,3	1,2,3	1 2 3	1,2,3	1,2,3	1,2,3	1,2,3	1,2,3	1,2,3	1 2 3	1,2,3
		a.m.	a.m.	a.m.	a.m.	a.m.	a.m.	a.m.	p.m.	p.m.	p.m.	p.m.	p.m.		p.m.	p.m.
AMSTERDAM W.P. 118 dep	...	5 15	7 35	8 4	8 26	...	1037	11 4	1 18	2 15	4 16	5 2	6 25	...	9 1	1015
Utrecht .... dep	...	7 3	8 13	8 50	9 4	9 30	1115	1222	1 56	3 22	4 54	5 41	7 5	...	9 40	1057
Culemborg	...	7 38	8 33	...	...	10 1	1135	1252	...	3 52	5 14	6 10	...	...	1013	1116
Geldermalsen 119	...	7 57	...	9 17	...	1022	...	1 6	...	4 7	5 24	6 25	7 33	...	1025	...
Zalt-Bommel	...	8 18	...	...	...	1047	1155	1 23	...	4 28	...	6 43	...	...	1042	...
Hertogenbosch ar	a.m.	8 36	9 6	9 42	9 55	11 0	12 9	1 42	2 45	4 46	5 50	7 2	7 58	p.m.	11 0	1148
Hertogenb'h dep	6†50	8 42	9 11	...	10 0	...	1214	2 0	2 50	5 27	5 55	—	8 5	8 11	1110	1152
Helvoirt	7 5	8 54	...	...	...	...	1225	2 15	...	5 41	...	...	...	8 26	1125	...
Tilburg .... arr	7 25	9 13	9 33	...	1021	...	1243	2 36	3 11	5 59	6 16	...	8 27	8 47	1144	1213
BREDA (117) arr	7 59	9 52	9 59	...	1042	...	1 6	3 17	3 36	...	6 40	...	8 52	9 43	—	1242
VLISSINGEN 113	1020	...	12 2	...	...	...	3p36	5p35	5p35	...	9p30	...	1059	...	p.m.	...
Hertogenbosch dp	...	8 39	9 15	9 46	...	1121	...	1 51	3 16	4 57	5 58	...	8 2	...	9 5	1155
Boxtel (116) ... arr	...	8 58	9 28	10 0	...	1140	...	2 8	3 32	5 13	6 13	...	8 19	...	9 18	1214

	1,2,3	1,2,3	1,2,3	1,2,3	1,2,3	1,2,3	1,2,3	1,2,3	1,2,3	1,2,3	1,2,3	1,2,3	1,2,3	1,2,3
	a.m.	a.m.	a.m.	a.m.		a.m.	p.m.		p.m.	p.m.	p.m.	p.m.	p.m.	p.m.
Boxtel .... dep	6 45	7 15	9 18	1042	...	1150	2 18	...	5 30	6 27	7 40	8 47	9 9	10 1
Hertogenb'h arr	7 4	7 35	9 35	1055	...	12 5	2 37	p.m.	5 44	6 46	7 53	9 0	9 25	1020
VLISSINGEN dp	...	...	7a14	...	a.m.	9a10	...	1 27	...	...	4p50	...	...	7p46
BREDA ...... dep	...	6a17	9 9	...	1040	1147	...	3 23	4 19	...	7p54	...	7p59	9 50
Tilburg ... dep	6 27	7 21	9 32	...	1124	12 9	...	3 45	4 58	...	8 16	...	8 35	1013
Helvoirt	6 49	7 41	...	...	1145	...	...	...	5 20	...	...	...	9 2	...
Hertogenb. ar	7 0	7 52	9 54	...	12 0	1231	...	4 6	5 34	...	8 38	...	9 15	1035
Hertogenb'h dep	7 14	8 0	9 58	11 2	—	1235	2 46	4 11	5 54	6 55	8 42	9 5	9 35	1040
Zalt-Bommel ...	7 33	8 19	...	1120	...	1251	3 5	...	6 10	7 14	...	...	9 55	...
Geldermalsen ...	7 59	8 34	1024	1136	...	1 4	3 28	...	6 25	7 43	...	...	1014	...
Culemborg	8 9	...	1036	1146	...	1 15	3 38	...	6 36	7 55	...	...	1025	...
Utrecht 118 arr	8 38	9 4	1056	1213	...	1 33	4 7	5 2	6 56	8 24	9 30	9 55	1045	1135
AMSTERDAM ar	9 18	9 45	1140	1 18	...	2 15	5 8	5 40	7 37	9 15	10 8	1037	1129	1217

Extra.			
Hertogenbosch ...... dep	6a35	8a10	8p35
Boxtel .... arr	6 54	8 28	8 52

Breda .... dep	2p56	...
Hertogenbosch ... arr	3 53	...

†—Not on Sunday.

ZWOLLE and GRONINGEN.

†—Not on Sunday.

	a.m.	a.m.	a.m.	a.m.	a.m.	a.m.	p.m.	p.m.	p.m.	p.m.	p.m.	p.m.				
Zwolle .... dep	5 16	9 10	...	9 25	1135	1143	1 49	3 10	3 33	5 20	8 45	9 0	...	...	...	...
Dedemsvaart	5 38	...	...	9 47	...	12 0	2 11	...	...	5 43	...	9 22	...	...	...	...
Meppel ...... arr	5 55	9 35	...	10 5	...	1213	2 28	3 37	4 0	6 0	9 10	9 39	...	...	...	...
Meppel ... dep	6 7	9 41	...	1015	...	1216	2 35	...	4 6	6 16	9 16	9 48	...	...	...	...
Steenwijk	6 29	9 58	†	1036	...	1232	2 57	...	4 23	6 38	9 33	1012	...	...	...	...
Heerenveen ...	7 15	1022	10 34	1119	...	1257	3 41	...	4 48	7 38	9 58	1059	...	...	...	...
Leeuwardn arr	8 1	1050	11 20	12 2	...	1 33	4 26	...	5 16	8 23	1026	1145	...	...	...	...
Meppel ...... dep	6 0	9 38	—	1020	...	—	2 41	3 40	4 3	6 10	9 13	9 44	...	...	...	...
Ruinerwold	6 7	...	...	1030	...	...	2 49	...	...	6 18	...	9 52	...	...	...	...
Hoogeveen	6 32	9 57	a.m.	1057	...	...	3 15	4 0	4 24	6 43	9 32	1016	...	...	...	...
Assen	7 15	1033	10†45	1144	1241	...	4 0	4 28	4 53	7 35	9 59	11 0	...	...	...	...
Haren	7 47	...	11 17	1218	...	...	4 32	...	...	8 7	...	1132	...	...	...	...
Groningen 115 ar	7 55	1057	11 25	1226	1 5	...	4 40	4 53	5 18	8 15	1023	1140	...	...	...	...

		a.m.	a.m.	a.m.	a.m.	a.m.	a.m.	p.m.	p.m.	p.m.	p.m.	p.m.		
...	Groningen dep	5 33	6 50	...	9 25	...	1150	1 5	1 27	3 20	7 11	8 45	...	...
...	Haren	5 42	...	...	...	...	1159	...	...	3 29	...	8 54	...	...
...	Assen	6 16	7 17	...	9 52	10 8	1239	1 33	1 55	4 5	7 38	9 34	...	...
...	Hoogeveen ...	6 58	7 43	...	...	1053	1 21	2 1	*2 23	4 51	8 4	1020	...	...
...	Ruinerwold ...	7 22	...	...	...	1117	1 44	...	...	5 15	...	1047	...	...
...	Meppel ... arr	7 29	8 0	...	...	1124	1 50	2 19	2 41	5 21	8 22	1053	...	...
...	Leeuwarden	5 30	6 47	9 5	...	9 24	1142	1 4	...	3 25	7 9	8 55	...	...
...	Heerenveen	6 19	7 18	9 36	...	1020	1237	1 36	...	4 14	7 40	9 55	...	...
...	Steenwijk ...	7 2	7 42	...	...	11 8	1 28	2 1	...	4 59	8 4	1042	...	...
...	Meppel ... arr	7 21	7 57	1013	...	1127	1 47	2 16	...	5 18	8 19	11 3	...	...
...	Meppel	7 34	8 5	1017	...	1137	1 59	2 24	2 46	5 28	8 28	1115	...	...
...	Dedemsvaart ...	7 53	...	...	...	1155	2 17	...	...	5 46	8 42	1138	...	...
...	Zwolle 114 arr	8 14	8 30	1047	11 0	1217	2 33	2 49	3 13	6 7	8 58	12 0	...	...

Assen .... dep	7a55	10 *8	10a43	12p45	2p0	4p55	7p40	10 p1	Stadsk.	6a10	7*a24	9a32	11a34	12p36	2p59	6p25	8p54
Stadskanaal arr	8 52	11 11	11 22	1 29	255	5 48	8 32	10 56	Assen..	7 5	8 20	1028	12 27	1 24	3 53	7 20	9 47

*—Weekdays only.

GRONINGEN and ROODESCHOOL.

Groningen dep	7a 5	9a54	12‡34	1p26	4‡13	6p0	8p49	11 p0
Sauwerd	7 27	10 5	12 55	1 50	4 44	624	9 15	11 22
Roodeschool ar	8 21	1058	1 49	2 44	5 36	720	10 9	12 15
Roodeschool	5a18	7a31	9a52	11a19	1‡53	4‡p3	5p22	8p33
Sauwerd	6 12	8 24	1048	12 14	2 48	4 59	6 22	9 35
Groningen ar	6 35	8 47	11 8	12 34	3 11	5 21	6 43	9 56

‡—Weekdays only.

GRONINGEN and DELFZIJL.

‡—Weekdays only.

	a.m.	a.m.	a.m.	pm	p.m.	pm	p.m.	p.m.	
Groningen dep	6 52	9 30	11‡52	2 0	4‡37	622	9 14	1045	...
Sauwerd	16	9 55	12 17	222	5 0	645	9 34	11 9	...
Stedum	7 36	1020	12 40	243	5 21	7 5	9 54	1129	...
Appingedam	8 2	1047	1 5	3 8	5 46	730	1019	1154	...
Delfzijl ...... arr	8 10	1055	1 13	316	5 54	739	1027	12 2	...

	a.m.	am	a.m.	a.m.	p.m.	p.m.	p.m.	p.m.	
Delfzijl ...... dep	5 7	716	10‡5	11 36	1 42	3‡47	5 3	8 16	...
Appingedam	5 16	725	1014	11 45	1 51	3 56	5 12	8 25	...
Stedum	5 41	751	1039	12 10	2 15	4 21	5 38	8 50	...
Sauwerd	6 1	813	11 0	12 32	2 37	4 47	6 0	9 11	...
Groningen .. arr	6 11	823	1122	12 51	2 47	5 7	6 20	9 30	...

¶—Customs Examination.]

HARLINGEN and NEUSCHANZ.

			a.m.	a.m.	a.m.		a.m.		p.m.	p.m.	p.m.	p.m.	p.m.	p.m.	p.m.
Harlingen ... dep	...	...	6 0	...	7 40	...	1030	*—Not on Sunday.	1212	...	2 40	4 27	6 5	7 54	9 54
Franeker	...	...	6 11	...	7 51	...	1047		1223	...	2 51	4 38	6 16	8 5	10 5
Leeuwarden ar	...	...	6 35	...	8 16	...	1117		1248	...	3 16	5 4	6 42	8 30	1030
,, (115) dep	...	...	7 5	8*23	8 53	...	1144		1 43	4 *5	—	5 26	—	8 40	1040
Veenwouden	...	...	7 28	...	9 14	...	12 7		2 6	...	...	5 47	...	9 3	11 3
Buitenpost	...	a.m.	7 45	...	9 31	...	1220		2 22	...	p.m.	6 3	...	9 19	1116
Grypskerk	...	7 *7	8 3	...	9 48	...	1237	...	2 40	...	5*12	6 21	...	9 36	1134
Groningen arr	a.m.	7 35	8 35	9 11	1015	a.m.	1 8	p.m.	3 8	5 0	5 49	6 50	p.m.	10 5	12 2
,, (115) dep	6 45	8 28	9 17	—	1029	11 40	1 18	2 15	4 19	5 29	5 57	7 3	9 3	1030	—
Hoogezand	7 11	8 55	9 38	...	1055	12 3	1 36	2 42	4 43	5 56	6 21	7 24	9 30	1053	...
Scheemda	7 36	9 23	10 4	...	1125	12 28	1 56	3 10	5 7	6 24	6 54	7 50	9 56	1119	...
Winschoten	7 45	9 33	1013	...	1135	12 38	2 5	3 20	5 15	6 34	7 4	7 58	10 6	1126	...
Neuschanz ¶ ar	8 0	...	1028	...	...	...	2 21	...	5 32	...	...	8 15	...	1142	...

	a.m.	a.m.	a.m.	a.m.	a.m.	a.m.	p.m.	p.m.	p.m.	p.m.	p.m.	p.m.	p.m.
Neuschanz dep	5 25	...	8 5	...	1028	...	...	1 49	...	5 32	...	9 12	...
Winschoten	5 42	6*59	8 23	9 46	1046	11 49	1250	2 7	3 54	5 50	6 44	9 29	1014
Scheemda	5 53	7 14	8 31	10 0	1057	12 4	1 1	2 19	4 8	5 58	6 59	9 36	1028
Hoogezand	6 18	7 40	8 54	10 24	1121	12 28	1 22	2 43	4 44	6 23	7 25	10 2	1052
Groningen arr	6 40	8 5	9 13	10 51	1140	12 52	1 52	3 3	5 10	6 43	7 50	1021	1117
,, ... dep	6 55	8 58	9 36	11 33	—	—	1 57	4*5	5 32	6 58	—	1031	—
Grypskerk	7 26	...	10 6	12 3	...	...	2 27	...	6 2	7 28	...	11 0	...
Buitenpost	7 42	...	1023	12 18	...	...	2 42	...	6 20	7 45	...	1117	...
Veenwouden ...	7 58	...	1039	12 30	...	...	2 57	...	6 36	8 2	...	1129	...
Leeuwarden arr	8 19	9 53	11 1	12 51	...	...	3 19	5 0	6 55	8 24	...	1150	...
Leeuwarden dep	8 30	—	1153	1 43	...	...	4 32	5 26	7 6	8 47	...	1155	...
Franeker	8 58	...	1222	2 11	...	...	4 58	5 52	7 31	9 13	...	1220	...
Harlingen arr	9 9	...	1232	2 21	...	...	5 8	6 2	7 41	9 23	...	1230	...

Zwolle ......dep	5‡a10	6‡a1	7a20	8a17	9a10	10a22	11a35	12p50	2 p6	3 p31	4p21	5p15	6p35	7p54	9 p5	10p50	12a5
Kampen ......arr	5 28	6 21	7 40	8 37	9 30	10 40	11 55	1 10	2 26	3 49	4 41	5 35	6 55	8 14	9 25	11 10	1225
Kampen ......dep	4‡a45	5‡a38	6a28	7a50	8a45	9a57	10a47	12p25	1p18	2p34	3p57	4p50	5p50	7p25	8p24	10 p0	11p20
Zwolle ......arr	5 1	5 54	6 46	8 8	9 3	1015	11 3	12 43	1 34	2 52	4 14	5 8	6 8	7 43	8 40	10 23	11 36
Utrecht dep	7‡a10	9 a25	10a25	11a25	12p30	1p28	2p35	3p24	4p20	5p35	6p25	7p22	8p45	10 10	11p10	...	...
Baarn ...arr	7 52	9 55	10 58	11 55	1 3	1 58	3 11	4 2	4 56	6 5	6 57	7 57	9 17	10 48	11 40	...	...
Baarn...dep	6‡a20	7a57	8a35	10 a5	11a12	12p18	1p20	2p33	3 p20	4p40	5p36	6p17	7p15	8p15	9 p52	‡—Sunday excepted.	
Utrecht arr	7 1	8 36	9 5	10 35	11 44	12 51	1 50	3 3	3 59	5 10	6 0	6 49	7 45	8 54	10 26		

OMMEN and DEVENTER.

Ommen ....dep	7 a0	10 a5	12p25	2 p57	5 p58	8 p22
Raalte	7 40	10 40	1 0	3 35	6 36	9 0
Deventer (114).......arr	8 27	11 20	1 40	4 15	7 15	9 40
Deventer ....dep	5 a48	8 a30	10a36	12p20	4 p27	6 p55
Raalte	6 21	9 15	11 19	1 17	5 12	7 38
Ommen (114).........arr	6 47	9 52	11 52	1 50	5 45	8 10

ROTTERDAM, THE HAGUE, and AMSTERDAM.

HULL (N.E. Co. Steamer) ....dep 6 p15 } From Hull daily except Sun.
ROTTERDAM ....arr 10a30 } (see Advt., page 731).
GRIMSBY (Great Central Co. Steamer) dep 7 p0 } From Grimsby Tues., Thurs., and Sat. (see
ROTTERDAM ....arr 8 a0 } Advt., page 735).

	a.m.	a.m.	a.m.	a.m.	a.m.	a.m.	noon	p.m.	p.m.	p.m.	p.m.	p.m.	p.m.
Rotterdam Delft Port dep	...	6 51	...	...	...	...	...	...	...	...	...	...	9 27
,, Maas ......dep	5 11	...	7 55	8 30	10 6	10 25	12 ‡0	2 57	4 ‡0	4 58	5 3	7 47	...
Gouda ....arr	5 46	7 21	8 15	:	10 23	11 0	:	3 16	:	5 18	5 38	8 7	9 58
The Hague..........dep	5 7	6 34	7 44	:	10 4	10 21	:	3 16	:	4 47	4 52	7 45	9 4
Gouda ....arr	5 50	7 16	8 10	‡	10 30	11 4	:	3 42	:	5 14	5 34	8 11	9 47
Gouda ....dep	5 55	7 22	8 17	:	10 33	11 15	:	3 43	:	5 21	5 42	8 14	10 1
Amsterdam Weesperp't arr	7 30	8 10	9 8	9 25	11 25	1 18	12 55	4 35	4 55	6 13	7 6	9 5	10 50
,, Central ...arr	7 50	8 25	9 23	...	11 40	1 37	...	4 50	...	6 28	...	9 21	11 5

	a.m.	a.m.	a.m.	a.m.	noon	p.m.	p.m.	p.m.	p.m.	p.m.	p.m.	p.m.	
Amsterdam Central...dep	...	6 55	7 56	...	12 0	...	3 26	...	5 24	6 37	8 5	9 50	...
,, Weesperport dep	5 46	7 10	8 13	8‡37	12 15	1‡48	3 40	4 ‡0	5 40	6 53	8 20	10 5	...
Gouda ....arr	7 24	7 55	9 5	:	1 37	:	4 32	...	6 33	8 10	9 8	11 0	...
Gouda ....dep	7 33	8 0	9 6	:	1 42	:	4 33	...	6 38	8 16	9 13	11 5	...
The Hague..........arr	8 17	8 43	9 32	:	2 24	:	4 59	...	7 4	8 59	9 39	11 31	...
Gouda ....dep	7 30	7 57	9 28	:	1 45	:		...	6 35	8 13	9 10	11 2	...
Rotterdam Maas.........arr	8 4	...	9 47	9 32	2 20	2 43	...	4 55	6 55	8 43	...	11 22	...
,, Delft Port arr	...	8 26	...	...	...	...	...	...	...	...	9 40	...	...

‡—Not on Sunday.

ROTTERDAM (St. Jobshaven—see Advt., page 735) ....dep 7 p0 } From Rotterdam
GRIMSBY ....arr 8 a0 } Tues, Thurs, & Sat.
ROTTERDAM (Parkhaven—see Advt., page 731) ....dep 8 p0 } From Rotterdam
HULL ....arr 11a30 } daily, except Sunday

UTRECHT and ZWOLLE.

	a.m.	a.m.	a.m.	a.m.	a.m.	a.m.	a.m.	a.m.	a.m.	a.m.	a.m.	a.m.	p.m.	p.m.	p.m.	p.m.	p.m.	p.m.	p.m.	p.m.	p.m.	p.m.	p.m.	p.m.	p.m.	p.m.	p.m.	p.m.	p.m.
Utrecht Central	...	6 25	6 42	7 40	...	...	8 28	8 50	...	1010	1030	1115	...	1 14	...	2 0	2 40	3 35	...	...	5 47	...	7 8	7 32	...	9 14	9 50	1051	...
,, Buurtstat	4 50	...	...	...	7 23	8 0	...	...	9 45	...	...	...	1225	...	1 18	...	...	...	4 15	5 20	...	6 45	...	...	8 53	...	...	1040	1145
De Bilt	...	6 37	...	...	7 35	8 17	...	9 1	10 2	...	...	1127	1237	...	1 35	...	2 53	...	4 27	5 37	...	7 2	...	...	9 8	...	10 3	11 4	12 1
Amersfoort	5 30	6 53	7 1	8 5	8 8	8 34	8 47	9 20	1040	1033	1056	1149	1 2	1 35	1 54	2 26	3 15	3 55	4 48	5 57	6 16	7 22	7 34	7 52	9 27	9 34	1023	1123	1219
Nykerk..........	5 52	7 17		...	8 30	8 54		9 32	11 2	...		12 1	1 24			...	3 28		5 10		6 28	8 0	...				1036		
Putten	6 6	7 27	...	...	8 44		...	9 42	1116	...	...	1213	1 38	...	...	...	3 38	...	5 24	...	6 38	8 13	...	...	...	...	1046	...	...
Harderwyk	6 24	7 45	...	...	9 1	...	...	9 56	1134	...	...	1229	1 56	...	...	...	3 54	...	5 40	...	6 54	8 31	...	...	...	...	11 1	...	...
Nunspeet	6 44	8 2	...	...		...	...	1013	1154	...	...	1246	2 16	...	...	...	4 13	...	6 0	...	7 12	8 50	...	...	...	...	1117	...	...
Elburg Old..........		8 14	...	...	...	...	...	1024		...	...	1259		...	...	...	4 26	...		...	7 24		...	...	...	...	1129	...	...
Hattem..........	...	8 33	...	...	...	...	...	1042	...	...	...	1 19	...	...	...	...	4 47	...	...	...	7 43	...	...	...	...	...	1148	...	...
Zwolle ...arr	...	8 44	...	9 0	...	...	...	1050	...	1123	...	1 28	...	...	...	3 26	4 55	...	...	...	7 51	...	8 34	...	...	...	1156	...	...

	a.m.	a.m.	a.m.	a.m.	a.m.	a.m.	a.m.	a.m.	a.m.	p.m.	p.m.	p.m.	p.m.	p.m.	p.m.	p.m.	p.m.	p.m.	p.m.	p.m.	p.m.	p.m.	p.m.	p.m.	p.m.	p.m.	p.m.		
Zwolle ...dep	5 10	...	...	6 50	...	8 39	...	9 25	1110	...	...	1256	...	...	2 57	...	3 45	...	...	...	6 32	...	...	...	...	9 8	...	...	...
Hattem..........	5 19	...	...	...	...	...	...	9 34	...	...	...	1 5	...	...	...	...	3 53	...	...	...	6 42	...	...	...	...	...	...	...	...
Elburg Oldebr.	5 40	...		...	...	...	...	9 55	...		...	1 26	...	...	...	...	4 12	...		...	7 5	...	...	...	...	...	...	...	...
Nunspeet..........	5 54	...	6 51	7 22	...	...		10 10	...	12 9	...	1 39	...	2 22	...	...	4 25	...	6 6	...	7 18	...	...	...	8 58	...	...	...	...
Harderwyk	6 17	...	7 12	7 36	...	...	9 18	10 31	...	12 30	...	1 57	...	2 43	...	...	4 41	...	6 27	...	7 38	...	...	...	9 18	...	...	...	...
Putten	6 33	...	7 30	7 51		...	9 35	10 49	...	12 48	...	2 11	...	3 1	...	...	4 56	...	6 43	...	7 54	...	...	...	9 32	...	...	...	...
Nykerk..........	6 48		7 44	8 0	9 2	...	9 50	11 4	...	1 2		2 23		3 15	...		5 7		6 57		8 7				9 45	...		...	...
Amersfoort	7 12	7 55	8 5	8 19	9 19	9 37	1014	11 23	12 9	1 27	2 36	2 47	2 5	3 38	3 57	4 2	5 24	6 10	7 22	7 38	8 29	8 58	9 20	9 37	9 58	1012	1132	...	...
De Bilt	7 38	...	8 45	...	9 37	...	1034	11 38	...	1 46	...	3 1	2 25	3 58	...	...	5 38	6 28	7 42	...	8 45	...	...	9 56	1041	...	1151	...	...
Utrecht Bu'rt	...	...	9 2	...	9 52	...	1051	...	...	1 56	...	...	2 39	4 13	...	...	...	6 45	7 54	...	...	...	...	1013	...	...	12 5	...	...
,, Central	7 44	8 14	...	8 40	...	9 57	...	11 50	1230	...	2 57	3 12	...	...	4 18	4 47	5 49	...	...	7 59	8 57	9 21	9 39	...	1051	1033	...	...	...

GRONINGEN and STADSKANAAL.

[‡—Not on Sunday between Groningen and Zuidbroek.

	a.m.	a.m.	a.m.	a.m.	a.m.	p.m.	p.m.	p.m.	p.m.	p.m.	p.m.	p.m.	p.m.
Groningen ...dep	6 45	8‡12	9 17	11‡13	1140	1‡33	2 15	3‡57	4 19	5 29	7 3	9 3	1030
: Delfzijl......dep	...	7 45	...	...	1114	...	1 40	...	...	5 15	...	8 45	...
Zuidbroek	7 35	8 43	9 55	11 41	1223	2 1	2 57	4 24	5 10	6 20	7 40	9 55	‡110
Stadskanaal arr	8 21	9 25	1036	12 22	1 3	2 42	3 37	5 7	5 51	7 25	8 20	1035	1150

	a.m.	a.m.	a.m.	a.m.	a.m.	a.m.	p.m.	p.m.	p.m.	p.m.	p.m.	p.m.	p.m.
Stadskanaal dep	5 18	6 38	7 39	8 58	10 7	1128	1 3	1 45	3 9	5 22	6 23	9 0	9 53
Zuidbroek	5 58	7 17	8 20	9 36	10 46	12 7	1 43	2 26	3 50	6 1	7 3	9 40	1033
: Delfzijl......arr	...	...	9 57	...	...	1 15	...	3 42	...	7 16	...	1035	...
Groningen ...arr	6 40	8 ‡5	8‡47	1051	11‡13	1252	2‡10	3 3	4‡15	6 43	7 50	1019	1117

ROTTERDAM, ZWALUWE, ROSENDAAL, and ESSCHEN.—BREDA, TILBURG, BOXTEL, and VENLO.

GRIMSBY (Great Central Ry. Steamer) dep 7 p0 / ROTTERDAM arr 8 a0 } From Grimsby Tues., Thurs., Sat. (see Advt. page 735).

HULL (N.E. Co.'s Steamer) dep 6 p15 / ROTTERDAM arr 10a30 } From Hull daily except Sunday (see Advt. page 731).

¶—Customs Examination—Greenwich Time.
†—At Brussels Midi.
A—Not on Sunday.
Extra—Rotterdam Delft to Dordrecht 12.3 night.

	1&2	1&2	1,2,3	1,2,3	1,2,3	1,2,3	1,2,3	1,2,3	1&2	1&2	1,2,3	1,2,3	1,2,3	1,2,3	1,2,3	1,2,3	1,2,3	1,2,3	1,2,3	1,2,3	1,2,3	1,2,3	1,2,3	1,2,3	1&2	1&2	1,2,3	1,2,3	1,2,3	1,2,3	1,2,3
Rotterdam			a.m.	a.m.	a.m.	a m	a.m.	a.m.	a.m.			a.m.	a.m.	p.m.	p.m.	p.m.	p.m.	p.m.	p.m.	p.m.	p.m.	p.m.					p.m.	p.m.	p.m.	p.m.	p.m.
Delft Port ...dep	...	...	4 45	6 38	8 7	8 33	8 56	9 18	10 2	...	...	1129	11 40	1 0	2 3	2 45	3 3	3 53	4 13	4 38	5 40	6 10	...	...	...	...	8 19	9 21	9 25	9 47	1041
Beurs ...dep	...	...	4 52	6 46	8 14	...	9 4	9 26		...	...	...	11 47	1 7	2 10	...	...	3 59	4 20	4 45	5 47	6 17	...	...	...	...	8 26		9 32	9 54	1048
Barendrecht	...	...	5 9	7 5	...	...	9 20	...		...	...	...	12 7	1 27	2 30	A	...		4 38	...	...	6 34	...	...	...	...	...		9 51	...	...
Dordrecht	...	...	5 27	7 24	8 39	8 56	9 39	9 50		...	...	1152	12 27	1 44	2 51	3 9	3 28		4 55	5 8	6 10	6 51	...	...	...	...	8 46		10 18	1014	1113
Zwaluwe ...arr	...	...	5 49	7 47	8 57	...	9 59	10 8		...	...		12 49	2 2	3 12	3 25	3 44		5 16	5 25	6 29	7 9	...	...	...	...	...		10 40		
Zwaluwe ...dep	...	...	5 57	8 20		...		1010		...	...		12 54	2 11	3 16	3 27	3 46			5 37	6 30		...	...	...	...	...		10 44		
Zevenbergen	...	...	6 7	8 30		...		...		...	...		1 5	2 21	3 26	...	...		...	5 47	6 40		...	...	...	...	...		10 53		
Rosendaal ...arr	...	...	6 27	8 50		9 32		1032		...	...		1 27	2 41	3 46	3 52	4 8		...	6 8	7 2		...	...	...	...	9 21		11 12	1053	
VLISSINGEN 113 arr	South Germany Express.	North Germany Express.	9 a6	1020		1045		12p2		a.m.	a.m.		3 p36	...	5p35	5p35	5p35		...	...	9 p30		p.m.	...	...	...	10p59		...	12a2	
Rosendaal ...dep			7 4	...		9 40		1038		11 6	1149		1 44	2 52	...	4 14	4 14		...	6 37	7 14		8 12	...	8 p5	8 p15	9 27		...	1117	
Esschen ¶ ...arr			6 54	...		9 29		1027	1048	10 56	1139	1216	1 34	2 42	...	4 3	4 3	4 38	...	6 26	7 4		8 2	...			9 16	10 5	...	11 7	
ANTWERP 110 arr			7a51	...		1017		1118	1142	11a42	1240	1 p1	2 p46	4 p20	...	4p55	4p55	5p20	...	7 p5	8 p2		9p46	...			10 p0	1047	...	1158	
BRUSSELS 110 arr			8a31	...		1118		1224	1244	12†44	1p47	1p57	3 p50	5 p1	...	5†58	5†58	5p57	...	7p53	9 p8		1029	...			11p14	1126	...	2 a1	
Zwaluwe ...dep			5 54	7 49	9 0	...	1013	...	...	...	...	...	12 51	2 7	...	...	3 52	...	...	5 26	6 33	7 10	...	...			1 & 2	...	10 48	...	
Breda ...arr		a.m.	6 14	8 11	9 16	a.m.	1035	...	...	...	...	...	1 13	2 23	...	...	4 14	...	...	5 40	6 48	7 31	...	...			p.m.	...	11 8	...	1145
VLISSINGEN 113 dep	4 15	4 36	...	...	7a14	7 14	...	...	...	...	9a10	...	9 a10	...	1225	...	1p27	1p27	...	...	...	4p50	p.m.	p.m.	7 p0	7 p10	7 46	...	7 p55	...	...
Breda ...dep			6 17	8 14	9 19	9 9	1040	...	...	...	1147	...	1 16	2 27	2 56	...	4 19	3 23	...	5 42	...	7 33	7 54	7 59			9 50	...	11 14	...	...
Tilburg arr			6 43	8 43	9 38	9 30	11 6	...	...	...	12 7	...	1 41	2 54	3 16	...	4 45	3 43	...	6 2	...	7 57	8 14	8 25			10 11	...	11 43	...	...
Tilburg dep			6 46	8 47	9 41		1110	...	...	...		...	1 44	2 56	3 17	...	4 48		...	6 3	...	7 59						...	11 49	...	...
Boxtel ...arr	6 5	6 26	7 8	9 8	9 57	...	1132	...	...	...	...	...	2 5	3 18	3 37	...	5 10	...	...	6 20	...	8 19	...	...	8 57	9 7	...	...	12 11	...	...
WESEL 120 ...arr	Via Goch, p. 121.	9 20	...	...	1256	a.m.	5p43	a.m.	...	...	...	...	...	...	6p21	...	9p30	...	...	...	...	...	...	...	1144	12 0	...	...	...	...	...
Boxtel ...dep		...	7 13	9 13	10 0	1010	1148	9 33	...	...	...	...	2 16	...	...	...	5 22	...	...	6 25	...	8 31	...	...	Via Oberh'sen	...	...	...	12 19	...	...
Eindhoven ...dep		...	7 44	9 39	1020	1030	1220	9 53	...	...	...	...	2 44	...	...	...	5 53	...	...	6 47	...	8 57	...	...		...	...	...	12 43	...	...
Helmond		...	8 4	9 58	1033	1044	1241		...	...	...	...	3 2	...	...	...	6 13	...	...	7 2	...	9 16	...	...		...	...	...		...	...
Deurne		...	8 16	10 8	...	...	1253	...	...	...	...	...	3 14	...	...	...	6 26	...	...	...	...	9 27	...	...		...	...	...	...	...	...
Venlo ...arr		...	8 59	1044	11 8	1118	1 35	...	...	...	...	...	3 55	...	...	...	7 8	...	...	7 39	...	10 6	...	...		...	...	...	...	...	...
COLOGNE 121 ...arr	9a56	...	1p19	...	3p10	3p10	5p14	...	...	...	...	...	8 p6	...	...	...	1112	...	...	11p32	...	...	...	...	1a50	...	...	...	...	...	...

Belgian Time between Valkenswaard and Liège.]

EINDHOVEN and LIEGE.

[Luggage, 10 cents for 22 lbs. for 50 kils.

K.M Dist		1,2,3	1,2,3	1,2,3	1,2,3	1,2,3	1,2,3	1,2,3	1,2,3	1,2,3	1,2,3	1,2,3	1,2,3	1,2,3	1,2,3
					a.m.	a.m.	a.m.			p.m.					p.m.
—	**Eindhoven** ...dep	...	...	...	5 54	...	10 12	...	...	1 40	...	...	...	...	6 18
6½	Valkenswaard	...	...	...	6 11	...	10 27	...	...	1 58	...	...	...	...	6 36
11	**Achel** ...arr	...	...	...	6 1	...	10 20	...	...	1347	...	...	...	...	1826
...	„ ...dep	...	...	...	6 16	7 47	10 32	...	1237	1358	...	16 2	...	...	1840
15½	Neerpelt 99	...	...	...	6 39	7 59	10 41	...	1246	14 7	...	1622	...	...	19 2
23	Wychmael	...	...	...	6 55	8 14	10 54	...	13 3	1425	A	1637	...	...	1917
36½	**Hasselt** 99 ...arr	...	...	...	7 31	8 51	11 21	...	1339	1459	...	1713	...	...	1953
...	„ ...dep	...	5 17	7 23	7 45		11 26	1135		15 6	15 22	1720	...	20 23	2030
...	Bilsen	...	5 45	7 45	8 13	...	11 48	12 3	...	1529	15 50	1748	...	20 46	2058
53½	**Tongeren** 94	5 30	6 10	8 1	8 38	...	12 4	1228	...	1550	16 14	1813	...	21 3	2123
61¾	**Liers** ...arr	6 0	6 41	8 24	9 7	...	12 27	1256	...	1615	16 43	1841	20 8	21 26	2152
66	**Ans** ...arr	...	6 59	8 40	9 29	...	...	1317	...	...	17 3	1858	2023	...	...
68	**Liège** (Vivegnis) ...arr	6 28	7 11	8 39	9 31	...	12 46	1321	...	1634	17 7	19 5	...	21 48	2218

		1,2,3	1,2,3	1,2,3	1,2,3	1,2,3	1,2,3	1,2,3	1,2,3	1,2,3	1,2,3
Liège (Vivegnis) dep		4 46	5 41	8 5	8 48	1157	1333	1623	1717	1930	2054
Ans ...dep		4 57	5 48	7 25	8 53	12 5	1337	...	1732	1935	2050
Liers		5 17	6 14	8 36	9 12	1227	1358	1647	1748	1959	2123
Tongeren		5 55	6 41	9 1	9 36	1254	1429	17 8	1815	2024	2152
Bilsen		6 15	7 0		9 55	1314	1445	1722	1835		2211
Hasselt ...arr		6 41	7 23	...	1018	1340	15 6	1741	19 1	...	2234
„ 99 dep	6 17		7 38	1128	1022	14 8	15 9		1934	...	
Wychmael	6 58	...	8 13	12 7	1055	1449	1537	...	2011	...	...
Neerpelt	7 14	...	8 30	1224	1112	15 6	1552	...	2054	...	...
Achel	7 40	...	8 43	1232	1126	1514	16 4	...	21 5	...	...
Valkenswaard	8 20	...	9 19		12 2		4 39	...	9 42	...	...
Eindhoven ..arr	8 40	...	9 34	...	1217	...	4 53	...	9 57	...	...

A—Between Hasselt & Tongeren runs on Weekdays only.

EDE and WAGENINGEN.

Ede ...dep	6 45	7 50	9 10	9 50	10 55	11 25	12 50	1 30	3 10	3 35	5 0	5 50	7 0	8 5	8 50	10 10	10 40	1155	...	...	...	...	...
Wageningen arr	7 15	8 20	9 40	10 20	11 25	11 55	1 20	2 0	3 40	4 5	5 30	6 20	7 30	8 35	9 20	10 40	11 10	1225	...	...	...	...	...
Wageningen dep	5 55	7 5	7 50	8 30	10 0	10 35	12 5	12 40	2 15	2 50	4 5	5 0	6 10	7 10	8 5	9 25	10 0	...	...	...	...	...	...
Ede ...arr	6 25	7 35	8 20	9 0	10 30	11 5	12 35	1 10	2 45	3 20	4 35	5 30	6 40	7 40	8 35	9 55	10 30	...	...	...	...	...	...

VENLO, BOXTEL, BREDA, ESSCHEN, ROSENDAAL, and ROTTERDAM.

[Luggage, 10 cents for 22 lbs. for 50 kils.

COLOGNE 121 .....dep	...	...	...	...	...	5 a47	5 a48	...	...	...	...	...	...	...	...	...	9 a37	...	...	2p23	...	2p23	...	5p14	5 p14	...	6 p32	7 p14	...
	1 2 3	1 2 3	1,2,3	1,2,3	1 & 2	1 & 2	1,2,3	1,2,3	1 & 2	1,2,3	1,2,3	1,2,3	1,2,3	1,2,3	1,2,3	1,2,3	1,2,3	1,2,3	1,2,3	1 2 3	1,2,3	1 2 3	1 & 2	1,2,3	1,2,3	1,2,3	1 & 2	1 & 2	1 2 3
Venlo ....dep	...	...	a.m. 5 11	...	...	Via Oberhausen	a.m. 7 55	...	...	a.m. 8 48	...	...	...	...	...	...	p.m. 12 15	...	...	p.m. 4 2	...	p.m. 4 14	...	p.m. 7 33	p.m. 7 48	...	Via Oberhausen.	Via Goch page 121.	p.m. 7 54
Deurne	...	...	5 55	...	...		8 23	...	...	9 30	...	...	...	...	...	...	12 59	...	...	4 30	...	4 58	...	...	...	...			8 36
Helmond	...	a.m.	6 7	...	...		8 33	...	...	9 41	a.m.	...	...	...	...	...	1 11	...	...	4 42	...	5 11	...	8 9	8 24	...			8 47
Eindhoven ......dep	...	5 6	6 28	...	...		8 47	...	...	10 1	11 25	...	...	...	...	...	1 33	...	...	4 58	...	5 34	...	8 23	8 38	...			9 5
Boxtel ....arr	...	5 30	6 55	...	a.m.	a.m.	9 6	...	...	10 27	11 48	...	...	...	...	...	2 2	...	...	5 17	...	6 2	...	8 42	8 56	...			9 31
WESEL 120.........dep	...	...	...	...	6 55	7 28	...	...	...	...	...	...	...	...	...	...	10a55	p.m.	...	4p15	...	4p15	...	...	5 p50	...	8 p26	:	8p26
Boxtel ....dep	...	5 33	7 6	...	8 22	8 42	9 10	a.m.	...	10 40	...	...	...	...	...	...	2 20	4 6	...	5 33	...	6 17	...	...	9 1	...	9 p43	9 p57	10 4
Tilburg .... arr	...	5 54	7 28	...	:	:	9 28	...	a.m.	11 0	...	p.m.	...	...	...	p.m.	2 42	4 28	...	5 49	p.m.	6 39	...	p.m.	9 20	n'gt	:	:	1024
Tilburg .... dep	...	5 57	7 31	...	:	:	9 30	9 37	1023	11 2	...	12 45	...	...	...	3 14	2 48	4 31	...	5 51	6 29	6 41	...	8 29	9 22	12 16	:	:	1026
Breda ....arr	...	6 22	7 59	...	:	:	9 52	9 59	1042	11 25	...	1 5	...	...	...	3 36	3 17	4 56	...	6 11	6 40	7 9	...	8 52	9 43	12 42	:	:	1049
VLISSINGEN 113...arr	...	9 a6	10a20	...	1020	10a45	12 p2	12 p2	...	3 p36	...	3 p36	...	p.m.	...	5 p35	5 p35	...	...	...	9p30	...	...	10p59	...	...	11p38	11p52	...
Breda ....dep	...	6 28	8 2	...	...	...	9 54	...	...	11 27	...	...	...	1 52	...	...	3 23	5 0	...	...	...	7 12	...	...	9 45	...	:	:	1051
Zwaluwe...........arr	...	6 50	8 21	...	...	...	10 10	...	...	11 49	...	...	...	:	...	...	3 43	5 23	...	...	...	7 33	...	...	10 2	...	:	:	11 9
BRUSSELS 110...dep	...	...	:	6 †a0	...	1,2,3	:	7 a56	8a52	:	9 a55	...	1213	:	12†33	12†33	...	1 p3	3p22	...	4p24	...	5p16	5 p19	:	6 p54	:	:	7p42
ANTWERP 110...dep	...	4a39	:	7 a10	...	7 a24	:	8 a49	9a58	:	10a32	...	1p13	:	1 p32	1 p32	...	2 p34	4p13	...	5 p4	...	5p55	6 p19	:	7 p56	:	:	8p21
Esschen ....dep	...	5 40	:	7 50	...	8 23	:	9 23	1030	:	11 9	...	1 49	:	2 10	2 10	...	3 37	4p52	...	6 3	...	6 34	7 23	:	8 35	:	:	9 19
Rosendaal ¶...arr	...	6 9	:	8 19	...	8 53	:	9 53	11 9	:	11 38	...	2 18	:	2 39	2 39	...	4 7	5 36	...	6 33	...	7 4	7 53	:	9 5	10 36	10 50	9 48
VLISSINGEN 113 dep	4a45	...	:	7 a14	...	7 a14	:	...	...	:	9 a10	9 a10	...	:	1 p27	1 p27	1p27	...	:	p.m.	...	4p50	...	7 p0	:	7 p46	...	...	7p55
Rosendaal......dep	5 49	6 18	7 46	8 50	...	9 3	:	10 16	...	:	11 56	12 15	...	:	2 52	3 4	3 9	4 49	:	6 11	...	6 54	7 28	8 16	:	9 29			1034
Zevenbergen..........	...	6 38	8 8	...	...	9 23	:	...	...	:	...	12 37	...	:	:	...	3 31	5 11	:	6 34	...	7 19	...	...	:	...			1055
Zwaluwe.........arr	...	6 47	8 17	...	...	9 32	:	...	...	:	...	12 46	...	:	:	...	3 40	5 20	:	6 45	...	7 28	...	...	:	9 53			11 4
Zwaluwe ....dep	...	6 55	8 24	...	...	9 33	10 11	...	...	11 50	...	12 49	...	:	:	...	3 46	5 27	:	6 46	...	7 36	...	...	10 3	9 55			1112
Dordrecht	6 25	7 20	8 47	9 31	...	9 52	10 31	...	...	12 11	12 36	1 13	...	2 29	3 31	3 45	4 9	5 51	6 12	7 15	...	8 16	8 10	8 58	10 23	10 15			1135
Barendrecht	...	7 36	9 3	...	...	10 8	...	...	...	12 26	...	1 29	...	...	...	...	4 25	6 6	...	7 31	...	8 33	...	...	...	...			1150
Rotter- Beurs......arr	...	7 52	9 14	9 50	...	10 27	10 54	...	...	12 41	12 56	1 48	...	...	3 50	...	4 41	6 20	...	7 37	...	8 52	...	...	10 44	10 36			12 6
dam. Delf Port arr	6 46	7 59	9 21	9 58	...	10 34	11 1	11 14	...	12 48	1 3	1 55	...	2 52	3 54	4 8	4 48	6 27	6 34	7 52	...	8 58	8 33	9 20	10 51	10 43			1213

†—From Brussels Midi. ¶—Customs Examination.

ROTTERDAM (Parkhaven—see Advt., page 731) ......dep	...	...	...	...	...	...	From Rotterdam daily except Sunday.	8 p0			
HULL ....arr	...	...	...	...	...	...		11a30			
ROTTERDAM (St. Jobshaven—see Advt., page 735)...dep	...	...	...	...	...	...	...	...	...	...	7 p0 From Rotterdam Tues., Thurs., Sat.
GRIMSBY ....arr	...	...	...	...	...	...	...	...	...	...	8 a0

HENGELO, OLDENZAAL, and RUURLO.

†—Not on Sunday. ‡—12.5 p.m. on Tues.

Hengelo ....dep	...	...	6†38	8 a35	10a54	...	2p52	5p11	6 p5	...	...	8p14	...
Boekelo ....arr	...	...	6 49	8 47	11 6	...	3 4	5 23	6 15	...	...	8 26	...
Oldenzaal ....dep	...	5†29	6 †20	8 a11	10a33	1‡20	2p31	...	5 28	...	6†18	7p53	10p7
Enschedé	5†a2	5 53	6 38	8 36	10 55	1 38	2 52	...	6 0	...	6 35	8 16	1026
Boekelo......... arr	5 15	6 6	6 50	8 49	11 8	—	3 5	...	6 12	...	—	8 29	1039
Boekelo......... dep	5 16	—	6 51	8 57	11 12	...	3 8	...	6 18	p.m.	...	8 31	—
Neede	5 49	...	7 18	9 29	12 0	...	3 43	...	6 43	7 30	...	8 59	...
Ruurlo ....arr	6 14	...	7 41	9 52	12 25	...	4 8	...	...	7 57	...	9 22	...

Ruurlo...........dep	...	...	6a17	8 p1	...	10a14	...	2p11	4p35	...	...	7p34	...	10 p1
Neede	...	5†46	6 46	8 32	...	10 43	...	2 40	5 1	...	...	8 2	...	10 33
Boekelo...... arr	†	6 14	7 14	8 57	...	11 10	...	3 8	5 26	...	†	8 27	...	10 58
Boekelo...... dep	5a39	6 15	7 20	9 0	...	11 12	...	3 12	5 30	†	7p40	8 29	...	11 0
Enschedé	5 52	6 45	7 37	9 12	9 a52	11 29	2 p2	3 50	5 46	6p49	7 57	8 46	9p42	11 12
Oldenzaal ......arr	6 11	7 3	7 55	...	10 10	11 47	2 20	4 10	6 3	7 6	—	9 4	10 0	...
Boekelo ......dep	...	6†18	7a16	9 a9	...	11 14	...	3p12	5p31	...	...	8p31	...	11p 1
Hengelo 118B arr	...	6 29	7 28	9 21	...	11 28	...	3 24	5 43	...	...	8 43	...	11 13

WINTERSWIJK and HELLENDOORN

†—Not on Sunday.

Winterswijk...dep	6† a1	...	7a55	...	10 a5	...	1p55	4 p15	7p21	...	9 p49
Neede	6 37	7 a19	8 29	...	10 39	12p11	2 31	5 10	7 58	...	10 25
Rijssen	...	8 56	9 41	11a 5	...	2 2	—	6 10	8 42	9p36	—
Hellendoorn ...arr	...	9 15	...	11 24	...	2 20	...	6 29	...	9 55	...

Hellendoorn ......dep	...	7a48	9a25	...	12p5	1 p28	4p56	...	7 p56	...
Rijssen	...	8 18	9 44	11 a5	1224	2 1	5 39	...	8 15	9p35
Neede	7†a19	9 29	—	12 1	—	2 49	6 47	9 p5	—	10 32
Winterswijk 118B arr	7 53	10 3	...	12 37	...	4 15	7 21	9 41	...	...

MOERDYCK and ZWALUWE.

Moerdyck ......dep	6 a40	7 a34	9 a53	12p35	3p33	7p57	...
Zwaluwe ....arr	6 50	7 44	10 3	12 45	3 40	8 4	...

Zwaluwe (116)......dep	7 a0	8 a50	12 0	3p20	7p40	...
Moerdyck ....arr	7 10	9 0	12 10	3 27	7 47	...

ZWALUWE and HERTOGENBOSCH.

Zwaluwe ....dep	6 a10	8 a43	1021	...	1 p6	3p57	7 p40
Geertruidenberg	6 38	9 4	1046	...	1 33	4 25	8 5
Waalwijk	7 17	9 27	1114	1 p0	2 0	5 6	8 34
Hertogenbosch ...arr	7 49	9 49	1137	1 37	2 25	5 39	857

Hertogenb'ch	6 a54	8a17	10a20	12p14	1 p54	6 p3	8 p20
Waalwijk ...	7 20	8 52	10 45	12 50	2 19	6 29	8 55
Geertruidenbg	7 49	9 29	11 12	—	2 46	6 55	9 30
Zwaluwe ...ar	8 14	9 57	11 34	...	3 10	7 19	9 58

LEIDEN and UTRECHT

Leiden dep	6a2	8a2	9a24	11a46	1p57	4p15	5 p13	8p10	9 p48
Bodegraven	639	828	9 58	12 23	2 39	4 41	5 43	8 47	10 26
Woerden ...	657	840	1013	12 40	2 57	4 53	5 58	9 4	10 43
Utrecht arr	715	858	1035	12 58	3 20	5 10	6 30	9 20	11 0
Utrecht dep	6a30	9a24	12p48	233	3p36	5p50	732	9p21	11 p8
Woerden ...	6 55	9 43	1 12	254	4 2	6 9	756	9 44	11 32
Bodegraven	7 11	9 59	1 29	310	4 18	6 21	8 8	10 0	11 44
Leiden...arr	7 47	1032	2 6	345	4 53	6 46	835	1036	12 10

ROTTERDAM, THE HAGUE, and AMSTERDAM to UTRECHT & EMMERICH.

HULL (N. E. Co.'s Steamer—see Advt., page 731) .... } From Hull daily except Sunday. } dep 6p15
ROTTERDAM .... } arr 10a30

GRIMSBY (Great Central Co.'s Steamer—see Advt., page 735) ...dep 7 p0 } From Grimsby Tues., Thurs., Sat.
ROTTERDAM ....arr 8 a0 }

¶-Customs Examination.	1,2,3	1 &2 (To Amersfoort (p. 115a) and Rheine (p. 118b).)	1,2,3	1,2,3	1,2,3	1,2,3	1,2,3 (To Amersfoort (p. 115a) and Rheine (p. 118b).)	1,2,3	1,2,3	1,2,3	1,2,3	1,2,3	1 &2	1,2,3	1,2,3	1,2,3	1,2,3	1,2,3	1,2,3	1,2,3
Rotterdam—	a.m.	a.m.	a.m.		a.m.	a.m.	a.m.	a.m.		a.m.	a.m.	a.m.	a.m.	a.m.	a.m.	a.m.	a.m.	p.m.	p.m.	
Delft Port..............dep	...	5 46	...	...	6 51	...	7 30	...	...	...	...	...	...	...	...	...	...	...	...	...
Maas ....dep	4 50		6 32	...	...	7 15		...	...	8 35	8 48	9 0	9 17	9 27	9 41	9 55	10 25	12 11	12 9	...
Nieuwerkerk....................	5 7		...	...	...	7 30		...	...	...	...	...	A		...	...	10 47	...	...	...
Gouda.....................arr	5 20		6 51	a.m.	7 21	7 40		...	...	8 55	9 8	9 20	9 37		10 1	10 15	11 0	12 31	1 8	...
The Hague.........dep	...		6 29	6 34	...	7 10		7 44	...	8 25	8 46	8 58	9 15		9 39	9 53	10 21	12 1	12 46	...
Soeterm-Zegwaard......	...	A	...	6 53	...	...	A	...	...	...	...	...	A		...	...	10 41	...	...	...
Gouda.................arr	...		6 55	7 16	...	7 36		8 10	...	8 51	9 12	9 24	9 41		10 5	10 19	11 4	12 27	1 12	...
Gouda ....dep	5 23		7 0	...	7 22	7 44		8 11	...	9 0	9 16	9 27	9 45		10 10	10 23	11 15	12 35	1 13	...
Woerden........................	5 45		...	...	7 43	...		...	...	...	...	...	...		...	...	11 42	...	...	...
Harmelen	5 52		...	...	7 49	...		...	...	...	...	...	...		...	...	11 49	...	...	...
Utrecht Central......arr	6 8	6 42	7 30	...	8 5	8 18	8 28	8 44	...	9 32	9 48	10 0	1019	1030	10 42	10 55	12 6	1 8	1 46	...
	a.m.	☞	a.m.	a.m.		a.m.	☞	a.m.	a.m.	a.m	a.m.	a.m	a.m.		a.m.	a.m.	a.m.	p.m.	p.m.	p.m.
Amster- Central dep	4 55		6 45	7 20	...	7 30		7 49	8 11	8 44	9 1	9 12	9 35	...	9 58	10 13	10 49	12 25	12 47	1 4
dam Weesperpoort dp	5 15		7 0	7 35	...	7 45		8 4	8 26	9 5	9 18	9 28	9 52	...	10 13	10 28	11 4	12 40	1 8	1 18
Nieuwersluis.................	5 42		...	...	...	...		8 24	...	...	...	9 47	...	...	...	...	11 33	...	...	...
Breukelen...	5 48		A	...	...	8 7		...	...	...	...	...	A	...	...	...	11 39	...	...	...
Utrecht Central 115 arr	6 5		7 33	8 8	...	8 22		8 41	9 0	9 35	9 51	10 3	1025	...	10 45	10 58	11 57	1 10	1 42	1 51
TILBURG 115 ....arr	9a13		...	9a33	...	...		...	10a21	...	...	...	...	...	12p43	12p43	2 p36	3 p11	3 p11	3 p11
BREDA 117 ....arr	9a52		...	9a59	...	...		...	10a42	...	...	...	...	...	1 p6	1 p6	3 p17	3 p36	3 p36	3 p36
VLISSINGEN 113...arr	...		...	12p2	...	...		a.m.	...	...	...	...	...	a.m.	3 p36	3 p36	5 p35	5 p35	5 p35	5 p35
Utrecht Central......dep	6 40		7 40	...	...	8 27		8 32	9 10	9 42	9 58	...	1031	9 32	10 52	11 5	12 20	1 18	1 51	...
Zeist Driebergen	6 57		...	...	a.m.	8 40		8 49	...	...	...	a.m.	...	9 53	...	...	12 36	...	2 12	...
Ede	7 42		A	...	8 28	9 7		9 28	...	...	1038	10 52	A		...	...	1 17	...	...	...
Arnhem.............. arr	8 5		8 32	a.m.	8 55	9 25		9 52	10 0	1032	1057	11 17	1129	...	11 45	11 55	1 40	2 8	p.m.	p.m.
Arnhem dep	8 41	...	8 34	7 33					10 10	1035	11 1		1133	...	12 2	11 57	1 48	2 11	2 15	3 33
Zevenaar........... arr	9 3	...	...	7 56	...	...	...	...	10 37	...	...	...	...	...	12 22	...	2 8	...	2 42	3 57
Zevenaar dep	9 6	...	A	7 58	...	...	...	...		...	A	...	A	...	12 25	...		...		4 42
Elten .... } MidE. ...	10 9	...	...	8 3	...	...	...	...	..	...	...	...	...	...	1 27	...	...	...	...	5 11
Emmerich¶ } Time arr	1020	...	9 44	9 14	...	...	...	...	...	1145	1211	...	1248	...	1 38	1 7	...	3 23	...	5 32
OBERHAUSEN 131A arr	1212	...	1050	1050	...	...	...	...	...	1 p0	1p32	...	2p19	...	...	2 p19	...	4 p47	...	7 p6
COLOGNE 160A.........arr	2p31	...	12p3	12p3	...	...	...	...	...	2p21	2p55	...	4p58	...	...	4p 58	...	6 p3	...	8p10
BERLIN 161A ....arr	...	...	7 p0	7 p0	...	...	...	...	...	9p28	9p28	...	...	...	...	...	...	12a21	...	...

Extra. { Rotterdam Maas ....dep 5a11 / Utrecht ....arr 7 15 | Amsterdam W.dep 7a13, 10a0, 1 p0, 2p15, 5 p8, ... / Utrecht.............arr 8 1, 1037, 1 33, 3 8, 5 41, ... | The Hague...dep 9 19 / Gouda ....arr 10 1

EMMERICH, ARNHEM, UTRECHT, AMSTERDAM, THE HAGUE, ROTTERDAM.

BERLIN 160B ....dep	...	...	...	...	9p34	9 a34	9p34	...	...	...	...	...	...	...	...	...	...	...	...	...	...
COLOGNE 161 ....dep	...	...	...	...	5a30	5 a30	5a47	...	...	...	...	...	...	...	...	...	...	7a30	10a8	...	10a6
OBERHAUSEN 131A dep	...	...	...	...	6a41	6 a41	7a35	...	...	...	8a23	...	...	...	...	...	...	9a49	11a32	...	1220
	1,2,3 (*—Arrives at Rotterdam Delft Port; To Vlissingen.)	1,2,3	1,2,3 (☞ From Rheine and Amersfoort.)	1,2,3	1,2,3	1,2,3	1,2,3	1,2,3	1,2,3	1,2,3	1,2,3	1,2,3	1,2,3	1,2,3	1,2,3	1,2,3	1,2,3	1,2,3	1,2,3	1,2,3	1,2,3
				a.m.	a.m.	a.m.	a m.				a.m.							a.m.	p.m.		p.m.
Emmerich } Mid E.dep	...	...	...	6 43	7 50	8 11	8 47	...	...	...	1014	...	...	...	...	...	...	1133	1246	...	2 11
Elten........... } Time ...	...	...	...	6 57	A	8 22	A	...	...	...	1025	...	...	...	...	...	...	1146	...	...	2 22
Zevenaar ¶........ arr	...	...	...	6 29	7 27	7 51	8 24	...	...	...	9 56	...	...	...	a.m.	...	...	1120	1223	...	1 53
Zevenaar dep	...	...	...	6 41	7 48	8 2	8 44	...	...	...	1010	...	...	...	11 8	...	...	1140	1246	...	2 3
Arnhem............... arr	...	a.m.	...	7 8	8 8	8 24	9 1	a.m.	...	a.m.	1031	...	...	a.m.	1136	...	...	12 0	1 3	p.m.	2 27
Arnhem dep		6 8	...	7 27	8 18	8 29	9 6	9 13	...	10 2	11 0	...	...	11 28		...	...	1216	1 8	2 13	2 47
Ede		6 34	...	7 50	...	8 55	...	9 41	a.m.	...	1120	...	...	11 55	...	p.m	p.m.	1243	1 27	...	3 7
Zeist Driebergen		7 16	...	8 26	...	9 35	...		10 5	...	1152	...	...		...	12 1	1 11	1 26	...	...	3 54
Utrecht Central......arr		7 31		8 40	9 8	9 50	9 58	...	1026	10 52	12 5	...	...	...	...	1222	1 32	1 40	2 1	3 10	4 6
VLISSINGEN 113...dep		...		...	...	...	...	...	7a14	7 a14	...	...	...	...	...	...	9a10	...	...	...	...
BREDA 116 ....dep		...		...	6a17	...	...	...	9 a9	9 a9	...	...	...	...	...	...	1147	...	...	...	...
TILBURG 115 ......dep		...		6a27	7a21	...	...	...	9a32	9 a32	...	p.m.	...	...	...	...	12p9	...	...	...	...
Utrecht Central...dep		7 37		8 45	9 13	10 20	10 8	...	11 5	10 58	12 8	1245	...	...	...	1250	1 38	...	2 5	3 17	4 33
Breukelen		7 55		...	...	1038	...	...	...	...	...	...	...	...	...	1 8	...	...	...	...	...
Nieuwersluis..................		8 16		9 1	...	10 44	1022	...	...	...	1225	...	...	...	...	1 14	1 56	...	...	3 33	4 56
Amster- Weesp.		8 30		9 18	9 45	11 13	1040	...	1140	11 30	1243	1 18	...	...	...	1 42	2 15	...	2 35	3 50	5 9
dam Central arr a.m.	a.m.	8 55	a.m.	9 35	10 0	11 29	1055	...	1155	11 45	1257	1 37	p.m.	p.m.	p.m.	2 1	2 30	...	2 51	4 5	5 22
Utrecht Central dep 6 30	7 15	7 53	8 14	8 52	9 18	10 27	1010	...	...	11 3	1213	...	1240	12 48	2 57	...	...	...	2 10	3 20	4 17
Harmelen 6 47	...	8 10		...	...	10 47	...	...	...	...	...	...	...	1 5		...	...	...	...	...	4 33
Woerden 7 0	7 40	8 16		...	...	10 56	...	...	...	...	1229	...	...	1 14		...	...	...	...	...	4 48
Gouda..............arr 7 24	7 55	8 39		9 26	9 48	11 19	1040	a.m.	...	11 37	1244	...	1 12	1 37		p.m.	...	...	2 40	3 53	5 10
Gouda ....dep 7 33	7 57	8 43		9 31	9 53	11 47	1045	1020	...	11 42	1249	...	1 17	1 42		2 5	...	...	2 45	3 58	5 26
Soeterm-Zegwaard 7 57		9 5	A	...	...	12 10	...	1044	...	...	...	...	...	2 5		2 29	...	...	...	...	5 43
The Hague...arr 8 17		9 24		9 57	1019	12 29	1111	11 3	...	12 8	1 15	...	1 43	2 24		2 48	...	...	3 11	4 24	6 8
Gouda ....dep 7 30		8 53		9 28	9 50	11 50	1042	...	...	11 39	1246	...	1 14	1 45		...	...	...	2 42	3 55	5 23
Nieuwerkerk..........7 44		9 7		...	...	12 4	...	...	...	...	...	...	...	1 59		...	...	...	...	...	5 38
Rotterdam Maas...8 4	8*26	9 23	9 8	9 48	10 9	12 25	11 1	...	...	11 59	1 5	...	1 34	2 20	3 48	...	...	...	3 1	4 14	5 58

ROTTERDAM, THE HAGUE. and AMSTERDAM to UTRECHT, ARNHEM and EMMERICH.

	1,2,3	1,2,3	1,2,3	1,2,3	1,2,3	1,2,3	1,2,3	1,2,3	1,2,3	1,2,3	1,2,3	1,2,3	1,2,3	1,2,3	1,2,3	1,2,3	1,2,3	1,2,3	1,2,3	1,2,3
Rotterdam—	p.m.	p.m.	p.m.	p.m.			p.m.		p.m.	p.m.	p.m.	p.m.	p.m.	p.m.		p.m	p.m.	p.m.		p.m.
Delft Port .... dep	...	...	...	...	...	...	...	...	...	...	...	6 35	...	...	...	...	...	9 27	...	...
Maas.................. dep	1 5	1 34	2 48	2 57	...	...	4 25	...	5 3	6 0	6 13	⋮	6 50	7 34	...	8 22	8 37	...	...	10 8
Nieuwerkerk	...	1 54	⋮	...	...	...	...	...	5 25	...	...	⋮	7 10	...	...	⋮	...	...	...	10 29
Gouda .... arr	1 25	2 8	⋮	3 16	...	p.m.	4 44	...	5 38	6 19	6 33	⋮	7 23	7 53	...	⋮	8 56	9 58	p.m.	10 42
The Hague .... dep	1 3	1 30	⋮	2 54	...	3 28	4 22	...	4 52	5 57	6 11	⋮	6 35	7 31	...	A	8 26	|	9 44	9 55
Soeterm-Zegwaard	...	1 50	⋮	...	...	3 40	...	...	5 12	...	...	⋮	6 56	...	...	⋮	...	|	...	10 16
Gouda .... arr	1 29	2 12	⋮	3 20	...	4 3	4 48	...	5 34	6 23	6 37	⋮	7 18	7 57	...	⋮	8 52	|	1010	10 38
Gouda .... dep	1 33	2 21	⋮	3 23	...	...	4 53	...	5 42	6 26	6 40	⋮	7 28	8 2	...	⋮	9 0		1012	10 47
Woerden	...	2 47	⋮	...	...	...	...	...	6 8	...	...	⋮	7 53	...	...	⋮	...		...	11 12
Harmelen	...	2 53	⋮	...	...	...	...	...	6 14	...	...	⋮	7 59	...	...	⋮	...	...	...	11 18
Utrecht Central......... arr	2 5	3 11	3 35	3 53	...	...	5 23	...	6 30	6 56	7 13	7 32	8 15	8 34	...	9 14	9 30	...	1045	11 34
Amsterdam—	p.m.		☞	p.m.	p.m.	p.m.	p.m.	p.m.		p.m.	p.m.	☞		p.m.	p.m.		p.m.	p.m.	p.m.	p.m.
Central .... dep	1 14	...	To Amersfoort (p. 115a) and Rheine (p. 118b)	3 0	3 9	4 1	4 46	4 56	...	6 10	6 29	To Amersfoort (p. 115a) and Rheine (p. 118b).	...	7 50	8 15	...	8 46	10 45	...	11 30
Weesperpoort ... dep	1 29	...		3 15	3 24	4 16	5 2	5 16	...	6 25	6 43		...	8 5	8 30	...	9 1	11 0	1015	11 45
Nieuwersluis	...	...		...	3 44	...	...	5 45	...	...	7 1		...	...	9 0	...	9 19	11 30	1032	12 6
Breukelen	...	...		...	...	...	...	5 51	...	...	...		...	...	9 7	...	...	11 36	...	...
Utrecht Central...... arr	2 2	...		3 50	4 1	4 49	5 33	6 9	...	7 0	7 16		...	8 37	9 25	...	9 34	11 54	1048	12 22
TILBURG 115 .... arr	...	...		...	6 p17	6p17	...	...	...	8p27	...		...	...	11p44	...	11p44	...	1213	...
BREDA 117 .... arr	...	...		...	6 p41	6p41	...	...	...	8p52	...		...	...	...	...	...	...	1242	...
VLISSINGEN 113...... arr	...	...		...	9 p30	9p30	...	...	...	1059	...		...	...	...	...	...	...	...	...
Utrecht Central ...... dep	2 10	...		3 58	4 5	5 28	5 38	6 38	...	7 25	7 21		...	8 44	...	...	9 40	...	1055	...
Zeist Driebergen..............	2 24	p.m.		...	4 20	...	...	6 56	p.m.	7 46	...		p.m.	...	...	p.m.	9 57	...	11 9	...
Ede	2 54	3 29		...	4 54	...	...	7 37	5 39	—	7 58		7 22	...	...	9 25	10 39	...	1139	...
Arnhem .... arr	3 12	3 56		4 51	5 16	6 18	6 32	8 0	6 6	...	8 16		7 49	9 34	...	9 52	11 4	...	1156	a.m.
Arnhem dep	—	4 14	...	—	—	6 20	6 35	—	6 46	...	8 21		—	9 37	...	—	—	...	—	5 10
Zevenaar .... arr	...	4 41	...	...	...	...	...	...	7 13	...	8 43		...	9 52	...	...	...	...	...	5 38
Zevenaar dep	...	—	...	...	...	A	A	...	7 26	...	8 45		...	9 53	...	...	...	...	...	5 41
Elten .... } Mid E. ...	...	...	...	...	...	...	...	...	8 25	...	9 46	...	...	A	...	...	...	...	...	6 53
Emmerich ¶ } Time arr	...	...	...	...	...	7 30	7 45	...	8 40	...	9 56	...	...	1050	...	...	...	...	...	7 5
OBERHAUSEN 131A ... arr	...	...	...	...	...	9 p5	9 p5	...	...	...	...	...	...	12a6	...	...	...	...	...	9 a30
COLOGNE 160A .. .. arr	...	...	...	...	...	1020	10p20	...	...	...	...	...	...	1a50	...	...	...	...	...	...
BERLIN 161A .... arr	...	...	...	...	...	7a20	7 a20	...	...	...	...	...	...	8a54	...	...	...	...	...	...

A—Special Seat Ticket required, 60c. or 1fl. 20c., according to length of journey.

EMMERICH, ARNHEM, UTRECHT, AMSTERDAM, THE HAGUE, ROTTERDAM.

BERLIN 160B............ dep	...	...	...	...	...	8 a0	...	8a59	...	...	...	...	...	...	...	...	...	...	...	1216	...
COLOGNE 161B......... dep	...	...	...	...	12p44	2p27	...	...	...	...	4 p47	...	...	...	4p47	...	6p15	...	...	6p32	...
OBERHAUSEN 131A... dep	...	...	...	...	2 p2	3p44	...	5 p2	...	...	5 p58	...	...	5 p2	5p58	...	7p36	...	...	8p10	...
¶—Customs Examination.	1,2,3	1,2,3	1,2,3	1,2,3	1,2,3	1,2,3	1,2,3	1,2,3	1,2,3	...	1 & 2	1,2,3	2&3	1,2,3	1,2,3	1,2,3	1,2,3	1,2,3	1,2,3	1,2,3	1,2,3
					p.m.	p.m.		p.m.			p.m.			p.m.	p.m.		p.m.			p.m.	
Emmerich } Mid E. dep	...	...	...	...	3 46	4 51	...	6 1	...	...	6 59	...	...	6 20	7 24	...	8 39	...	...	9 24	...
Elten .... } Time	...	...	...	...	3 56	...	...	A	...	...	A	...	...	6 32	7 37	...	A	...	...	9 34	...
Zevenaar ¶ .... arr	p.m	...	...	...	3 21	4 29	p.m.	5 37	...	...	6 35	...	...	6 5	7 10	...	8 15	...	...	9 3	...
Zevenaar dep	2†53	...	...	...	3 37	4 55	5 0	5 57	...	...	6 53	...	...	6 17	7 34	...	8 34	...	...	9 19	...
Arnhem .... arr	3 20	...	p.m.	p.m.	3 55	5 13	5 28	6 15	p.m.	...	7 9	p.m.	...	6 45	8 4	...	8 50	...	p.m.	9 35	...
Arnhem dep	—	...	4 32	4 13	4 25	5 18	—	6 20	6 27	...	7 12	8 0	...	7 25	8 20	...	8 52	...	1120	9 45	...
Ede..	...	...	4 59	4 33	4 45	...	p.m	...	6 52	...	A	...	p.m.	7 52	8 47	...	A	...	1145	10 5	...
Zeist Driebergen..............	...	...	—	5 2	5 14	...	6 30	...	—	...	...	...	8 5	8 33	—	...	...	...	—	1037	...
Utrecht Central .... arr	...	...	...	5 15	5 26	6 8	6 51	7 13	...	...	8 2	8 55	8 30	8 46	☞ From Rheine and Amersfoort.	...	9 42	...	...	1050	...
VLISSINGEN 113 ... dep	...	...	1p27	1p27	...	...	...	...	...	...	...	...	...	...		4p50	4p50	...	...	...	7p46
BREDA 116............ dep	...	...	3p23	3p23	...	...	4p19	4p19	...	...	...	...	...	...		7p54	7p54	...	...	7p59	9p50
TILBURG 115 .... dep	p.m.	...	3p45	3p45	...	...	4p58	4p58	p.m.	...	...	...	...	...		8p16	8p16	p.m.	p.m.	8p35	1013
Utrecht Central .... dep	4 39	...	5 7	5 19	5 29	6 12	7 0	7 16	7 25	...	8 5	9 0	8 42	9 6		9 35	9 47	10 6	1043	1056	1140
Breukelen	4 57	...	...	...	...	...	...	...	7 43	...	A	...	...	9 24		...	...	...	...	...	...
Nieuwersluis....................	5 3	...	...	...	5 45	...	7 18	...	7 49	...	...	...	8 59	9 30		...	...	1018	...	1112	1158
Amsterdam Weesppt... arr	5 30	...	5 40	5 52	6 2	6 42	7 37	7 48	8 18	...	8 35	9 33	9 15	9 53		10 8	1020	1037	1116	1129	1217
Amsterdam Cent......... arr	...	p.m.	5 55	...	6 17	6 57	7 52	8 3	8 34	p.m.	8 55	9 48	...	...	p.m.	1030	1035	1052	1131	1144	1232
Utrecht Central........ dep	4 28	4 47	...	...	5 34	6 17	...	7 21	...	7 59	8 10	9 5	...	9 11	9 39	...	9 53	10 5	1040	11 2	...
Harmelen	...	⋮	...	...	...	...	...	...	...	⋮	A	...	...	...	⋮	...	A	...	...	...	...
Woerden	...	⋮	...	...	...	...	...	...	...	⋮	...	...	...	9 29	⋮	...	...	...	...	...	...
Gouda .... arr	5 1	⋮	...	...	6 4	6 49	...	7 53	...	⋮	8 40	9 38	...	9 50	⋮	...	1023	1037	1110	1132	...
Gouda .... dep	5 6	⋮	...	...	6 9	6 54	...	7 58	...	§-Delftport	8 45	9 43	...	...	§-Delftport	...	1028	1038	1115	1137	...
Soeterm-Zegwaard........	...	⋮	...	...	...	...	...	...	...		...	...	...	...		...	A	...	...	...	...
The Hague.......... arr	5 32	⋮	...	...	6 35	7 20	...	8 24	...		9 11	10 9	...	...		...	1054	11 4	1141	12 3	...
Gouda .... dep	5 3	⋮	...	...	6 6	6 51	...	7 55	...	⋮	8 42	9 40	...	9 52	⋮	...	1025	11 2	1112	1134	...
Nieuwerkerk......................	...	⋮	...	...	...	...	...	...	...	⋮	...	...	...	10 7	⋮	...	A	...	...	...	...
Rotterdam-Maas..... arr	5 22	5 39	...	...	6 25	7 11	...	8 15	...	9 §2	9 1	10 0	...	10 27	10§45	...	1044	1122	1131	1153	...

ROTTERDAM (St. Jobshaven) .... dep	7 p0	From Rotterdam on Tues., Thurs., and Sat.—see Advt., page 735.
GRIMSBY .... arr	8 a0	
ROTTERDAM (Parkhaven) .... dep	8 p0	From Rotterdam daily except Sunday—see Advt., page 731.
HULL .... arr	11a30	

Extra—Utrecht Central to Amsterdam 6.31, 8.15, 11.37 a.m., 2.25, 3.52, 11.16 p.m. †—Not on Sunday.

AMSTERDAM, UTRECHT, AMERSFOORT, APELDOORN, WINTERSWIJK, RHEINE, and KLEVE.

THROUGH CARRIAGES from Amsterdam to Berlin, in 10.20 a.m., and 9.0 p.m. (also Sleeping Car) from Amsterdam.

	1,2,3	1,2,3	1,2,3	1,2,3	1,2,3	1,2,3	1,2,3	1,2,3	1,2,3	1,2,3	1,2,3	1,2,3	1,2,3	1,2,3	1,2,3	1,2,3	1,2,3	1,2,3	1,2,3	1,2,3	1,2,3	1,2,3	1,2,3	1,2,3	1,2,3	1,2,3	1,2,3	1,2,3	1,2,3	1,2,3
Amsterdam—		a.m.	a.m.		a.m.	a.m.	a.m.	a.m.	a.m.	a.m.	a.m.	a.m.	a.m.	a.m.	a.m.	p.m.	p.m.	p.m.	p.m.	p.m.	p.m.	p.m.	p.m.	p.m.	p.m.	p.m.	p.m.	p.m.	p.m.	p.m.
Central ....dep	...	5 35	6 10	...	7 5	8 0	8 4	8 22	8 48	8 57	9 40	9 54	1020	10 53	11 47	1 0	1 8	1 36	3‡20	3 35	3‡47	5 10	5 20	5 50	6 25	7 15	8 0	9 0	9 28	1040
Muiderpoort ...dep	...	5 43	...	...	...	...	8 12	...	...	9 5	...	10 2	...	...	11 56	...	1 16	...	...	...	...	...	5 28	5 57	6 33	...	...		...	...
Weesp	...	5 56	...	...	...	S	8 25	...	...	9 18	...	1015	S	...	12 10	...	1 29	...	...	...	...	...	...	6 9	6 46	...	...	SC	...	...
Naarden-Bussum	...	6 8	...	...	...	...	8 36	...	...	9 30	...	1028	...	...	12 22	1 27	1 41	...	...	...	4 13	5 36	5 49	6 20	6 58	...	8 25	S	...	11 6
Hilversum ....arr	...	6 16	...	...	7 33	8 28	8 43	8 51	...	9 38	10 7	1036	1047	11 21	12 30	...	1 49	2 5	3 48	...	4 20	5 44	5 57	6 28	7 6	7 43	8 32		9 57	1114
Hilversum ....dep	...	6‡30	...	...	7 38	...	8 56	...	...	...	10 12	1056	...	11 28	12 37	...	1‡57	2†11	...	...	4 25	...	6 15	6 35	7 12	...	8 37		10 2	...
Utrecht Malieb....arr	...	6‡56	...	...	7 59	...	9 22	...	...	...	10 32	1123	RC	11 48	1 3	...	2‡19	2 31	...	...	4 47	...	6 36	7 1	7 33	...	8 57		10 27	...
Utrecht Central...arr	...	...	...	...	...	...		...	...	...	10‡48	...	...	...	...	...	...	...	...	...	...	...	...	7 17	...	...	...		10 51	...
Hilversum ....dep	...	6 20	...	...	7 35	8 30	...	8 54	...	9 41	10 9	1053	1048	11 24	12 36	1 29	1 51	2 7	3 50	...	4 22	5 46	5 59	6 31	7 8	7 45	8 34		9 59	1116
Baarn	...	6 30	...	...	7 44	...	...	9 4	...	9 53	10 19	11 4	...	...	12 47	...	2 0	...	...	...	4 32	5 56	6 9	6 42	7 18	...	8 43		10 8	1126
Amersfoort ......arr	...	6 40	6 49	a.m.	7 53	8 44	...	9 13	9 27	10 3	10 28	1113	11 1	11 38	12 57	1 42	2 11	2 21	4 4	4 14	4 41	6 5	6 18	6 52	7 28	7 59	8 52	9 39	10 17	1135
Amersfoort ......dep	...			7 2	7 58	8 50	...	9 17					11 5	11 46		1 47	2 16			4 17		6 13				8 5		9 44	10 20	
Barneveld Voorthuiz..	...	...			19	...	...	9 35			...	...	...	12 5		...	2 36	...		...	...	6 31		...	...	8 22			10 41	
Apeldoorn ....arr	...	a.m.			8 52	9 26	...	10 0			...	...	1141	12 36		2 23	3 11	...		4 53	...	6 50		...	...	8 46			11 14	
Apeldoorn ......dep	...	6 26			8 56		...	10 7			...	...		12 49		2 36	3 19	...		5 5	...	7 2		...	...	8 53			11 22	
Zutphen ......arr	...	6 53			9 30		...	1030			...	...		1 13		...	3 43	...		5 29	...	7 21		...	...	9 15			11 47	
Zutphen ......dep	...	7 11			9 34		...	1037			...	...		1 24		2 56	3 49	...		...	...			...	...	9 17			...	
Ruurlo	...	7 52			10 8		...	11 2			...	...		1 59		...	4 26	...		...	...	...		...	...	9 50			...	
Lichtenvoorde-Groen.	...	8 10			10 25		...	1116			...	...		2 17		...	4 42	...		...	...	...		...	...	10 8			...	
Winterswijk...arr	...	8 23			10 37		...	1127			2 & 3	...		2 30		...	4 55	...		...	2&3	2 & 3		...	...	1021			...	
2&3	a.m.						...				a.m.										p.m.	p.m.			p.m.				p.m.	
Apeldoorn ...dep 7a 7	5‡55	...				9 29	...	10 4			10 27	...	1144	12 41		2 26	3 40	...		4 55	5 28	7 5		...	9 8	8 50			11 18	
Twello 7 26	6 11	...				...	...	1015			10 46	...	...	12 56		...	3 54	...		...	5 48	7 20		...	9 26	...			11 35	
Deventer 7 38	6 26	...				9 46	...	1026			10 58	...	12 1	1 12		2 43	4 10	...		5 12	6 0	7 30		...	9 41	9 9			11 47	
Rijssen	7 14	...				...	...	1059				...	...	1 52		...	4 52	...		5 34				...	1022	9 32				
Wierden	7 27	a.m.				...	a.m.	11 9			...	...	S	2 4		...	5 2	...		...	p.m.	p.m.		...	1035	...			p.m.	
Almelo	7 38	8 30		8 23		1018	1027	1118			...	...	1233	2 15		3 15	5 12	...		5 47	4 15	7 6		...	1042	9 45		11 6	11 13	
Borne	7 54	-				...	1041	...			...	...	...	2 27		...	5 26	...		...	...	7 20		...		9 55			11 28	
Hengelo ....arr	8 2	8 47				1032	1048	1136			...	...	1247	2 34		3 29	5 33	...		6 0	4 32	7 26		2&3	...	10 1			11 37	
ROTTERDAM 118...dep	...	...		To Osnabruck arrive 11.19.		7†30	...	...			...	...	9†27	9 a55		...	...	...		2†48	...	...		4p23	...	...		8†22	...	
THE HAGUE 118...dep	...	...				7†10	...	7a44			...	...	9†15	9 a53		...	...	...		1†30	...	...		4p21	...	...		7†31	...	
ARNHEM 114 ......dep	...	...				8a37	...	10a5			...	...	...	12 10		...	...	...		2p47	...	...		7p14	...	...			...	
Hengelo ....dep	8 6	...				1034	...	1139			...	...	1249	2 37		...	5 37	...		6 2	...	...		10 6	...	...			...	
Oldenzaal	8 21	...				1045	...	1152			...	...	...	2 51		...	5 51	...		6 13	...	...		1021	...	...		11 30	...	
Bentheim (Cust. Ex.) } Mid Eu'pe Time. arr	9 28	1 & 2		9 39		1141	a.m.	1254			...	...	1 52	3 55		...	6 56	...		7 8	p.m.	...			p.m.	...		12 26	...	
Bentheim (Cust. Ex.) dep	10 18			1013		12 4	1118	1 10			...	...	2 17	4 10		...		...		7 27	8 45	...		...	1016	...		12 46	...	
Schüttorf	10 26					...	1126	1 18			...	...	...	4 18		...	...	...		7 33	8 52	...		...	1024	...		...	...	
Salzberg'n arr	10 36					...	1137	1 26			...	...	2 29	4 29		...	...	...		...	9 3	...		...	1035	...		...	...	
Rheine ...... arr						1223		1 36			...	...	2 39	...		...	...	...		7 49	9 14	...		...		...		1 6	...	
HANOVER 161A ...arr	...			1p20		3p20	...	...			...	...	5p48	...		...	...	...		1225	...	...		...	...	...		4 a17	...	
BERLIN 161A ......arr	...			4p54		7 p0	...	...			...	...	9p28	...		...	...	...		5a55	...	...		...	...	...		7 a57	p.m.	
Amersfoort ....dep	...	From Hoek van Holland to Cologne.	6 51	...	8 20	...	...	...	9 29	10 10	...	...	...	11 44	1 4	...	...	...	4 6	4 20	...	...	6 20	...	...	...	8 55	...	10 22	
Veenendaal	...		...	...	8 53	...	...	...	...	10 39	...	...	...	12 3	1 33	...	...	...	...	4 43	...	...	6 38	...	...	...	...		10 47	
Rhenen........	...		...	...	9 4	...	...	...	...	10 48	...	...	...	...	1 44	...	...	...	...	4 53	...		...	...	...	...	...		10 57	
Kesteren ....arr	...		...	...	9 9	...	a.m.	...	9 55	10 53	...	...	...	12 16	1 49	...	...	...	4 33	4 58	...		6 52	p.m.	p.m.		9 22		11 2	
Kesteren ....dep	...		...	...	9 13	...	7‡32	...	10 1	10 55	...	...	...	12 20	1 51	...	...	...	4 35	5 1	...		6 56	7 14	1113		9 29		11 9	
Valburg	...	S	..	...	9 37	...	7 56	...	...	...	...	...	...	...	2 12	...	...	...	...	5 20	...		...	7 39	1138		...		...	
Vork	...	a.m.	...	...	9 46	...	8 3	...	...	11 18	...	...	...	12 38	2 19	...	...	...	...	5 37	...		7 14	7 47	1144		9 46		...	
Nymegen ....arr	a.m.	7 33	7 41	...	10 3	...	8 17	...	10 24	11 30	...	...	...	12 49	2 32	...	...	...	4 59	5 49	...		7 25	8 5	12 3		9 57		11 37	
Nymegen ....dep	6 11	7 35	7 44	...		1—4		...	10 26		...	...	...	1 7	2 47	...	...	...	5 2	5 53	...		7 30							
Cranenburg........arr	6 34	7 52	8 0	...	...	a.m.	...	...	10 43	...	...	...	...	1 29	3 10	...	...	...	5 19	6 15	...	...	7 52	...	...	...	...		...	
(Cust. Ex.) dep	7 31	8 53		...	...	11 0	...	...	11 39	...	...	...	...	2 29	4 2	...	...	...	6 14	7 10	...	...	8 49	...	...	...	...		...	
Kleve Mid Eu. Time arr	7 53	9 6	...	...	...	1122	...	...	11 51	...	...	...	...	2 41	4 24	...	...	...	6 26	7 32	...	...	9 1	...	...	...	...		...	
COLOGNE 121 ......arr	...	11a15	...	...	...	...	...	...	2 p0	...	...	...	...	5 p14	8 p 6	...	...	...	...	1112	...	...	11p32	...	...	...	...	...	...	...

Extra

Amsterdam Cent. dep	11a12	2p49	2p15	4p18	4‡50	5‡p0	5p35	10p15	11p13	11p55	...	...
Utrecht	...	4 7	3 19	5 27	...	6 1	6 36	11 29	12 16	...	...	...
Amersfoort ....arr	12 16	3 55	3 12	...	5 40	...	...	...	...	1 10	...	...

‡—Weekdays only.

S—Seat Ticket required.

†—Via Utrecht and Amersfoort.

KLEVE, AMERSFOORT, RHEINE, WINTERSWIJK, and AMSTERDAM. [Luggage, 10 cents. for 22lbs. for 50 kils.

Cologne 121 ....dep		...	...	...	...	...	...	...	7 a5	...	...
[Mid Europe Time at Kleve.]		1,2,3	1,2,3	1,2,3	1,2,3	1,2,3	1,2,3	2 & 3	1,2,3	1,2,3	1,2,3
Kleve ....dep		...	...	a.m. 6 5	...	...	a.m. ...	...	a.m. 9 23	a.m. 9 30	...
Groesbeek .... arr		...	...	5 55	a.m.	...	...	...	..	9 23	a.m.
(Cust. Exam.) ... dep		...	...	6 15	7 ‡45	...	...	...	...	9 35	11 10
Nymegen .... arr		a.m.	...	6 30	8 0	a.m.	...	...	9 10	9 50	11 24
(Cust. Exam.) ... dep		6 8	...	6 38		8 6	8 36	...	9 40	10 20	
Vork		6 29	...	...	...	8 17	8 51	...	9 51	10 31	...
Valburg		6 35	...	...	...	...	8 57	...	...	...	...
Kesteren .... arr		6 58	...	7 6	...	8 33	9 19	...	10 7	10 53	...
Kesteren .... dep			...	7 11	...	8 35		...	10 8	10 57	...
Rhenen............................		...	...	7 18	...	8 42	...	...	...	11 4	...
Veenendaal		...	...	7 29	...	8 51	...	...	...	11 14	...
Amersfoort ....arr		...	p.m.	7 57	...	9 8	...	...	10 35	11 37	...
Berlin 160b ....dep		...	1028	...	...	...	...	...	⋮	⋮	...
Hanover 160b ......dep		...	2a22	...	...	...	...	...	⋮	⋮	...
Rheine ...... (Mid Eu'pe Time.) dep		a.m.	a.m. 5 37	...	...	...	...	...	⋮	⋮	a.m. ...
Salzbergen ...... dep		5 33	...	...	...	...	...	...	⋮	⋮	8 29
Schüttorf		5 43	A	...	...	...	...	...	⋮	⋮	8 41
Bentheim		5 50	5 59	...	...	...	...	...	⋮	⋮	8 54
Oldenzaal ...... arr			6 13	...	...	...	a.m.	...	⋮	⋮	9 14
(Cust. Exam.) ...dep		...	6 1	...	...	...	7 24	...	⋮	⋮	8 56
Hengelo ....arr		...	⋮	...	...	...	7 39	...	⋮	⋮	9 8
Arnhem 114 ......arr		...	⋮	...	...	...	10a47	...	⋮	⋮	10a47
The Hague 118...arr		...	⋮	...	...	...	1 p15	...	⋮	⋮	1 p15
Rotterdam 118...arr		...	9 †8	...	...	...	1 p5	...	⋮	⋮	1 p5
Hengelo ....dep		a.m. 6 ‡0	⋮	...	...	...	a.m. 7 44	...	⋮	⋮	9 13
Borne		6 7	⋮	a.m.	...	...	...	...	⋮	⋮	9 22
Almelo ....dep		6 16	6 25	6‡30	...	...	8 1	...	⋮	⋮	9 38
Wierden	2&3		⋮	...	...	...	...	...	⋮	⋮	9 46
Rijssen..........................	a.m.		⋮	6 43	...	...	8 14	a.m.	⋮	⋮	9 59
Deventer........................	5‡51	...	⋮	7 8	...	...	8 37	8 11	⋮	⋮	10 43
Twello	6 5	...	⋮	...	...	...	...	8 24	⋮	⋮	10 52
Apeldoorn ...arr	6 24	...	A	7 23	...	...	8 52	8 40	⋮	⋮	11 6
Winterswijk...dep		...	⋮	6‡12	...	...	...	...	⋮	⋮	9 34
Lichtenvoorde-Groen		...	⋮	6 22	...	...	...	...	⋮	⋮	9 46
Ruurlo........................		...	⋮	6 37	...	...	...	...	⋮	⋮	10 5
Zutphen........ arr		...	⋮	6 58	...	...	...	...	⋮	⋮	10 33
Zutphen........ dep		...	⋮	7 1	...	...	8 25	...	⋮	⋮	10 39
Apeldoorn ......arr		...	⋮	7 21	...	...	8 47	...	⋮	⋮	11 5
Apeldoorn.........dep		...	⋮	7 28	...	8 8	8 57	...	⋮	⋮	11 14
Barneveld Voorthuiz...		...	⋮	7 52	...	8 46	...	1,2,3	⋮	⋮	11 44
Amersfoort arr	a.m.	a.m.	7 45	8 7	a.m.	9 7	9 32	a.m.	⋮	⋮	12 1
Amersfoort dep	7 10	7‡36	7 57	8 13	8 22	9 17	9 40	10 8	10 37	11 39	12 10
Baarn	7 22	7 48	...	8 24	8 34	9 28	...	10 20	10 48	11 50	12 21
Hilversum..................	7 31	7 57	...	8 32	8 42	9 36	9 54	10 29	10 55	11 59	12 29
Utrecht Cen. dep	...	...	...	...	...	...	...	...	10‡ 8	...	...
Utrecht Mallebdp	...	7‡17	...	7 48	...	9 11	...	10 1	10 32	11 35	11 57
Hilversum ...arr	...	7‡43	A	8 12	...	9 35	...	10 27	10 52	11 56	12 23
Hilversum ......dep	7 33	7 59	...	8 35	8 45	9 40	9 56	10 35	10 58	12 3	12 33
Naarden-Bussum......	7 43	8 8	...	...	...	9 50	...	10 45	...	12 12	...
Weesp	7 55	...	...	...	...	...	...	10 57	...	12 24	...
Amsterdam Muider ...	8 7	...	...	...	9 9	...	...	11 9	...	12 36	...
Amsterdam Central...	8 14	8 33	8 37	9 2	9 16	1014	10 22	11 16	11 25	12 46	1 0

Cologne 121 ....dep	...	...	10a10	...	...	...	...	2 p23	...
[Mid Europe Time at Kleve.]	1,2,3	1,2,3	1,2,3	1,2,3	1,2,3	1,2,3	1,2,3	1,2,3	1,2,3
Kleve ....dep	...	...	p.m. 1 8	...	§—Between Nymegen and Amersfoort on week-days only.	...	...	p.m. 4 41	...
Groesbeek .... arr	...	...	12 59	...		...	p.m.	...	p.m.
(Cust. Exam.) ... dep	...	...	1 12	...		...	3 10	...	5 4
Nymegen .... arr	...	...	1 27	p.m.		...	3 24	4 34	5 19
(Cust. Exam.) ... dep	...	...	1§35	1 48		...		4 54	
Vork	...	...	1 49	2 5		...	...	5 5	...
Valburg	...	...	...	2 10		...	...	...	...
Kesteren .... arr	...	...	2 6	2 32		...	...	5 23	...
Kesteren .... dep	...	...	2 9	2 36		...	...	5 24	...
Rhenen............................	...	...	...	2 43		...	...	...	...
Veenendaal	...	...	...	2 53		...	...	...	...
Amersfoort ....arr	...	...	2 §38	3 20		...	...	5 57	...
Berlin 160b ....dep	...	...	...	⋮		...	...	⋮	...
Hanover 160b ......dep	...	...	...	⋮		10a46	...	⋮	...
Rheine ...... (Mid Eu'pe Time.) dep	a.m. ...	p.m ...	...	⋮		p.m. 2 22	...	⋮	p.m. 1 50
Salzbergen ...... dep	11 17	1218	...	⋮		2 32	...	⋮	2 1
Schüttorf	11 27	1228	...	⋮		A	...	⋮	2 12
Bentheim	11 35	1236	...	⋮	...	...	...	⋮	2 26
Oldenzaal ...... arr	11 53	1252	...	⋮	p.m.	2 56	...	⋮	2 47
(Cust. Exam.) ...dep	11 47	1232	...	⋮	1258	2 31	...	⋮	2 45
Hengelo ....arr	12 0	1242	...	⋮	1 10	2 41	...	⋮	2 58
Arnhem 114 ......arr	2 p5	...	...	⋮	...	4 p8	...	⋮	5 p6
The Hague 118...arr	4 p24	...	...	⋮	...	--	...	⋮	7 p20
Rotterdam 118...arr	4 p15	...	...	⋮	...	5 †39	...	⋮	7p11
Hengelo ....dep	12 14	1246	...	⋮	1 14	2 42	...	⋮	3 7
Borne	12 22	...	...	⋮	1 22	...	...	⋮	3 16
Almelo ....dep	12 36	1 1	...	⋮	1 37	2 57	...	⋮	3 32
Wierden	...	...	...	⋮	1 44	...	2 & 3	⋮	3 40
Rijssen..........................	p.m.	...	...	⋮	2 0	RC	p.m.	⋮	3 56
Deventer........................	12 54	1 34	...	⋮	2 41	...	3 41	⋮	4 44
Twello	1 7	...	...	⋮	2 50	...	3 57	⋮	4 55
Apeldoorn ...arr	1 23	1 49	...	⋮	3 2	3 42	4 20	⋮	5 11
Winterswijk...dep	...	1210	...	⋮	...	...	...	⋮	4 2
Lichtenvoorde-Groen	...	1222	...	⋮	...	...	...	⋮	4 13
Ruurlo........................	...	1238	...	⋮	...	...	...	⋮	4 29
Zutphen........ arr	...	1 9	...	⋮	...	A	...	⋮	4 54
Zutphen........ dep	...	1 16	...	⋮	2 42	...	...	⋮	4 57
Apeldoorn ......arr	...	1 40	...	⋮	3 4	...	...	⋮	5 23
Apeldoorn.........dep	...	1 53	2 2	⋮	3 9	3 44	...	⋮	5 27
Barneveld Voorthuiz...	...	...	...	⋮	3 44	...	...	⋮	6 3
Amersfoort arr	...	2 28	2 39	⋮	4 0	4 19	p.m.	⋮	6 23
Amersfoort dep	...	2 33	2 41	3 30	4 5	4 21	5 25	6 0	6 34
Baarn	...	...	2 52	3 42	4 16	...	5 38	6 11	6 46
Hilversum..................	...	2 46	2 59	3 51	4 24	4 34	5 47	6 19	6 55
Utrecht Cen. dep	...	...	...	...	...	...	5 4	...	...
Utrecht Mallebdp	...	...	...	...	...	A	5 20	...	6 7
Hilversum ...arr	...	...	...	...	...	...	5 46	...	6 31
Hilversum ......dep	...	2 49	3 1	3 55	4 27	4 35	5 51	6 21	6 59
Naarden-Bussum......	...	...	...	4 5	...	...	6 1	...	7 10
Weesp	...	...	...	4 17	...	...	6 14	...	7 24
Amsterdam Muider ...	...	...	...	4 29	...	...	6 27	...	7 36
Amsterdam Central...	...	3 15	3 28	4 38	4 55	5 2	6 36	6 50	7 45

Cologne 121 ....dep	...	4 p54	3 p17	...	...	...	7p21	...	8 p11
[Mid Europe Time at Kleve.]	1,2,3	1,2,3	1,2,3	1,2,3	1&2	1,2,3	1&2	1,2,3	1,2,3
Kleve ....dep	...	p.m. 7 8	p.m. 6 45	...	...	p.m. 7 33	p.m. 9 16	...	p.m. 10 32
Groesbeek .... arr	...	...	6 52	...	...	7 26	A	...	10 22
(Cust. Exam.) ... dep	...	...	7 5	...	...	7 38	...	p.m.	10 32
Nymegen .... arr	p.m.	6 53	7 20	...	...	7 53	9 1		10 47
(Cust. Exam.) ... dep	5 56	7 18		...	...	8 26	9 26	9 16	
Vork	6 14	7 28	...	...	...	8 40	9 35	9 27	...
Valburg	6 20	...	...	...	...	8 46	To Hoek van Holland.	...	...
Kesteren .... arr	6 42	...	...	...	...	9 10		9 42	...
Kesteren .... dep	6 48	...	...	...	...	9 20		9 44	...
Rhenen............................	6 55	...	...	...	...	9 28		...	...
Veenendaal	7 5	...	...	...	...	9 38		...	...
Amersfoort ....arr	7 30	8 8	...	...	...	10 0		10 10	...
Berlin 160b ....dep	...	⋮	...	11a40	1 p5	†—Via Amersfoort and Utrecht.	...	...	...
Hanover 160b ......dep	...	⋮	...	3 p48	4p32		...	...	...
Rheine ...... (Mid Eu'pe Time.) dep	p.m. ...	⋮	...	p.m. 6 42	p.m. 7 29		...	...	p.m. ...
Salzbergen ...... dep	5 13	⋮	...	A	...		...	...	9 16
Schüttorf	5 23	⋮	...	...	A		...	...	9 27
Bentheim	5 30	⋮	...	7 3	...		1,2,3	...	9 40
Oldenzaal ...... arr	5 47	⋮	p.m.	7 17	7 59		p.m.	...	9 58
(Cust. Exam.) ...dep	5 23	⋮	6 30	6 53	7 37		7 45	...	10 18
Hengelo ....arr	5 33	⋮	6 45	7 3	⋮		7 58	...	10 29
Arnhem 114 ......arr	7 p45	⋮	...	9p29	‡		...	...	...
The Hague 118...arr	10 p9	⋮	...	10†54	⋮		...	...	...
Rotterdam 118...arr	9 †2	⋮	...	10†45	1045	...	...	...	...
Hengelo ....dep	5 39	⋮	p.m. 6 50	7 4	⋮	p.m. 7 36	8 1	...	10 36
Borne	...	⋮	...	...	⋮	...	8 9	...	10 44
Almelo ....dep	5 54	⋮	7 10	7 18	8 0	7 52	8 27	...	10 56
Wierden	...	⋮		...	⋮		8 35	...	
Rijssen..........................	6 7	⋮	...	A	⋮	p.m.	8 49	...	p.m.
Deventer........................	6 31	⋮	...	7 51	⋮	10 35	9 39	8 39	11 53
Twello	...	⋮	...	...	⋮	10 50	9 50	8 49	...
Apeldoorn ...arr	6 47	⋮	...	8 7	⋮	11 10	10 6	9 5	12 21
Winterswijk...dep	...	⋮	...	...	⋮	‡—Not on Sundays.	...	7 38	A—Seat Ticket required.
Lichtenvoorde-Groen	...	⋮	...	...	⋮		...	7 49	
Ruurlo........................	...	⋮	...	...	⋮		...	8 8	
Zutphen........ arr	...	⋮	...	...	⋮		...	8 35	
Zutphen........ dep	6 29	⋮	...	7 37	⋮		...	8 48	
Apeldoorn ......arr	6 48	⋮	...	8 4	⋮		...	9 12	
Apeldoorn.........dep	6 56	⋮	...	8 10	⋮		...	9 16	
Barneveld Voorthuiz...	...	⋮	...	RC	⋮	...	...	9 47	
Amersfoort arr	7 33	⋮	p.m.	8 46	9 18	p.m.	...	10 3	a.m.
Amersfoort dep	7 40	8 10	8 29	8 49	9 26	9 31	1047	10 16	6 35
Baarn	7 51	...	8 40	A	...	9 42	11 0	...	6 48
Hilversum..................	7 59	8 23	8 48	9 2	...	9 50	11 9	10 29	6 57
Utrecht Cen. dep	...	7 37	...	...	...	...	...	...	...
Utrecht Mallebdp	...	7 52	8 25	...	...	9 27	1024	10 0	6 ‡28
Hilversum ...arr	...	8 18	8 45	...	A	9 47	1044	10 26	6 54
Hilversum ......dep	8 1	8 25	8 52	9 4	...	9 53	1113	10 31	7 1
Naarden-Bussum......	...	...	9 1	...	...	10 2	1123	...	7 11
Weesp	...	...	...	...	...	...	1136	...	7 24
Amsterdam Muider ...	...	...	...	...	...	...	1148	...	7 37
Amsterdam Central...	8 30	8 51	9 25	9 30	10 5	10 26	1156	10 57	7 46

Extra.												
Amersfoort...............dep	...	12p33	1p34	...	...	...	...	...	...	...	...	...
Utrecht M. ....dep	8‡a27	12p30	1 11	2p42	3‡p23	4p16	5 p8	7p21	...	...	...	...
Amsterdam Central...arr	9 30	1 33	2 47	3 59	4 23	5 25	6 4	8 22	...	...	...	...

AMSTERDAM, THE HAGUE, and ROTTERDAM.

	1,2,3	1,2,3	1,2,3	1,2,3	1,2,3	1,2,3	1,2,3	1 & 2	1,2,3	1,2,3	1,2,3	1,2,3	1,2,3	1,2,3	1,2,3	1,2,3	1,2,3	1,2,3	1,2,3	1,2,3	1,2,3	1,2,3
Amsterdam	a.m.	a.m.		a.m.		a.m.	a.m.	a.m.	a.m.	a.m.	a.m.	a.m.	a.m.	a.m.		a.m.	a.m.	a.m.	p.m.	p.m.	p.m	...
Central ....dep	4‡48	6‡17	...	7 0	...	8 0	8 8	8 40	8 52	9 48	9 2	9 30	9 40	10 8	...	1043	1051	1153	1244	1 30	1 45	...
Haarlem ....arr	5 13	6 37	...	7 18	...	:	8 27	D	:	10 8	9 21	9 50	:	1026	...	:	1111	1212	1 4	:	:	...
Zandvoort........arr	6‡14	7 11	...	7 44	...	:	9 4	:	:	1025	...	1025	:	1110	...	:	1216	1 13	1 39	:	:	...
Zandvoort........dep	...	—	...	6‡32	a.m.	:	8 6	RC	:	—	8 39	9 30	:	...	...	:	1056	1138	1247	:	:	...
Haarlem ....dep	5 21	...	...	7 20	7 24	:	8 29	:	:	...	9 27	10 0	:	1028	...	:	1114	1214	1 7	:	:	...
Vogelenzang	5 34	a.m.	...	...	7 38	:	...	:	:	...	...	...	:	...	a.m.	:	...	...	...	A	:	p.m.
Leiden 117	6 24	7 4	...	7 52	8 5	:	8 59	:	:	...	9 55	1029	:	...	1055	:	1144	1241	1 37	:	:	2 30
Voorschoten..........	6 38	7 16	...	...	8 15	:	9 8	:	:	...	...	...	:	...	...	:	...	1249	...	:	:	2 39
The Hague.......arr	6 52	7 27	...	8 9	8 25	8 48	9 18	9 31	9 42	...	1011	1046	1028	11 3	1115	1131	12 1	1259	1 54	2 18	2 35	2 51
SCHEVENINGEN arr	7 25	8 5	...	8 45	9 5	9 25	9 55	1010	1010	a.m.	1040	1125	1055	1140	1155	1210	1240	1 40	2 25	2 55	3 10	3 25
SCHEVENINGEN dep	5 50	7 5	a.m.	7 35	7 55	8 15	8 55	8 55	9 15	9 15	9 35	1020	9 50	1035	11 5	11 5	1135	1235	1 20	1 50	2 5	2 20
The Hague......dep	6 57	7 31	8 0	8 14	8 30	8 50	9 21	9 36	9 44	9 51	1014	1050	1030	11 6	1139	1133	12 4	1 2	1 58	2 20	2 39	2 55
Ryswick	7 3	...	...	...	8 36	...	...	D	...	...	...	...	...	...	...	...	...	...	...	...	...	...
Delft	7 13	7 42	...	8 25	8 44	...	9 32	...	...	10 8	...	11 1	...	...	1150	...	1215	1 15	2 9	...	...	3 11
Schiedam.............	7 27	7 53	...	...	8 55	...	9 42	...	...	1022	...	1112	...	...	12 1	...	1226	1 27	2 20	A	...	3 23
HOEK v. H. ...arr	...	...	...	...	...	...	...	...	...	...	...	...	...	...	...	...	...	...	...	...	...	...
Rotterdam Delft P. arr	7 38	8 2	8 20	8 42	9 4	9 10	9 50	9 57	10 4	1032	1037	1121	1050	1127	1210	1153	1235	1 35	2 29	2 40	2 59	3 34
Rotterdam Beurs...arr	...	...	8 28	8 53	...	...	...	...	...	...	1052	...	...	...	...	...	...	...	2‡38	...	...	...
ROSENDAAL 116 arr	9a32	9a32	9a32	1032	1032	1032	...	...	...	...	...	1227	...	1p27	...	...	2p41	3p46	4 p8	4 p8	4 p8	...
VLISSINGEN 113 arr	1045	1045	1045	12p2	12p2	12p2	...	...	...	...	...	3p36	...	3p36	...	...	...	5p35	5p35	5p35	5p35	...

Extra.—The Hague to Rotterdam, 4.55, 6.50 a.m. Amsterdam to The Hague, 12.21 p.m.

A—Runs until 4th September.

D—At Amsterdam and The Hague only takes up for stations in Belgium and beyond.

ROTTERDAM Hofplein and SCHEVENINGEN Kurhaus.

	a.m.	a.m.	a.m.	a.m.	
Rotterdam Hofplein......dep	7‡11	8 0	9 0	10 0	And about hourly until 9.0 p.m.
The Hague Pijnacker ... „	7 50	8 28	9 28	1028	
Scheveningen Kurhaus arr	8 3	8 42	9 43	1043	

☞ Between Rotterdam and The Hague half-hourly from 8.0 a.m. to 10.30 p.m. ☜

ROTTERDAM, THE HAGUE, and AMSTERDAM.

GRIMSBY (Great Central Railway Steamer) ......dep 7 p0 } From Grimsby Tuesday, Thursday, and
ROTTERDAM..........arr 8 a0 } Saturday—see Advt., page 735.

HULL (N.E. Railway Steamer) .... dep 6p15 } From Hull daily except
ROTTERDAM .... arr 10a30 } Sun.—see Advt., page 731.

	1,2,3	1,2,3	1,2,3	1,2,3	1,2,3	1,2,3	1,2,3	1,2,3	1,2,3	1,2,3	1,2,3	1,2,3	1,2,3	1,2,3	1,2,3	1,2,3	1,2,3	1,2,3	1,2,3	1,2,3	1,2,3
VLISSINGEN 113 dep	...	...	...	4a45	4a45	...	...	...	...	...	...	...	7a14	...	7a14	...	...	...	...	9a10	...
ROSENDAAL 117 dep	...	...	...	5a49	5a49	...	6a18	...	...	...	7a46	7a46	8a50	...	9 a3	1016	10a16	...	...	1156	...
Rotterdam	a.m.	a.m.	a.m.	a.m.	a.m.	a.m.	a.m.	a.m.		a.m.	a.m.	a.m.	a.m.	a.m.	a.m.	a.m.	a.m.	a.m.	p.m.	p.m.	p.m.
Beurs........dep	...	...	...	...	...	...	...	...	...	8 15	...	...	9 53	...	...	...	1137	...	1229	1258	...
„ Delft Poort dep	5 54	6 26	6 36	6 56	7 48	7 52	8 4	8 30	...	8 34	9 30	9 34	10 2	1016	1043	1119	1147	1124	1239	1 8	1 32
HOEK v. H....dep	5a40	...	...	...	...	...	...	...	...	...	...	...	...	...	...	...	...	...	...	...	...
Schiedam............	6 7	6 36	6 47	...	‡	7 59	8 14	...	...	8 43	...	9 43	...	...	1052	...	...	1133	1248	...	1 41
Delft	6 18	6 49	7 2	...	...	8 11	8 30	...	...	8 56	...	9 59	...	...	11 5	...	...	1147	1 4	...	1 54
Ryswick	...	...	...	...	...	...	...	...	...	...	...	...	...	...	...	...	...	...	...	...	...
The Hague ......arr	6 27	6 58	7 13	7 19	8 8	8 20	8 42	8 50	...	9 5	9 50	1011	1024	1040	1116	1141	12 8	1157	1 16	1 31	2 3
SCHEVENINGEN arr	6 55	7 25	7 45	7 45	8 45	9 5	9 25	9 25	a.m.	9 40	1025	1040	1055	1110	1155	1210	1240	1225	1 55	2 10	2 40
SCHEVENINGEN dep	5 50	6 35	6 35	—	7 35	7 55	...	8 15	8 15	8 35	9 15	9 35	9 50	10 5	1035	11 5	1135	1150	1250	1 5	1 35
The Hague......dep	6 31	7 2	7 19	...	8‡12	8 23	...	8 53	8 59	9 8	9 52	1016	1028	1044	1119	1146	1212	1216	1 19	1 36	2 8
Voorschoten	S	...	7 31	a.m.	:	...	...	:	...	...	:	1028	:	...	1131	...	...	1229	1 31	...	...
Leiden	6 47	7 21	7 42	8 45	:	8 40	...	:	9 15	9 30	:	1036	:	11 2	1139	...	1228	1245	1 41	1 53	2 27
Vogelenzang	...	...	8 14	9 12	:	...	...	:	...	...	:	—	:	...	—	...	...	1 23	—	...	...
Haarlem ....arr	7 10	7 45	8 24	9 20	:	9 5	...	:	9 38	9 57	:	...	:	1129	...	1223	1251	1 35	...	2 18	2 52
Zandvoort ....arr	7 44	8 12	9 4	a.m.	:	...	...	:	1025	1025	:	...	:	1216	...	.	1 39	...	p.m.	2 36	3 52
Zandvoort..........dep	6‡32	7 22	8 6	8 39	:	8 39	...	:	...	9 30	:	...	:	1056	...	1138	...	1247	3 0	1 52	...
Haarlem ....dep	7 12	7 52	8 29	8 55	:	9 9	...	:	9 41	9 59	:	...	:	1132	...	1225	1253	1 39	3 17	2 21	2 56
Amsterdam Centr'l	7 30	8 11	8 49	9 16	9 2	9 28	...	9 43	10 0	1019	1040	...	1122	1152	...	1243	1 10	2 2	3 40	2 40	3 15

Extra.—Weekdays only, Rotterdam D.P. to Amsterdam, 4.42 a.m. ‡—Does not run on Sunday.

‡—Not on Sunday.]

ROTTERDAM, NYMEGEN, and ARNHEM.

[S—Seat ticket required.

		1 & 2	1,2,3	1,2,3	1,2,3	1,2,3	1,2,3	1,2,3	1,2,3	1,2,3	1,2,3	1,2,3	1,2,3	1,2,3	1,2,3	1,2,3	1,2,3	1,2,3	1,2,3	1,2,3	1,2,3
Rotterdam		a.m	a.m.	a.m	a.m.	a.m.		a.m.		a.m	a.m.	p.m.	p.m.		p.m.	p.m.			p.m.	p.m.	p.m.
Delftsche Poort...dep		5 51	From Amsterdam 6.10.	5 56	7‡24	8 23	...	8 48	From Amsterdam dep. 10.53	1047	...	...	2‡33	...	4 2	4 45	From Amsterdam dep. 5.20.	...	7 47	...	10 41
„ Beurs....dep		...		6 3	7 30	8 30	...	8 55		1054	...	...	2 41	...	4 9	4 54		...	7 54	...	10 48
Dordrecht ....dep		6 12		6 28	7 55	8 50	...	9 18		1115	1124	1‡47	3 2	...	4 35	5 16		...	8 15	8 52	11 13
Gorinchem		RC		7 8	8 42	...	...	9 48		1139	1218	2 30	3 30	...	5 21	5 42		...	8 39	9 30	11 51
Leerdam		:		7 26	—	...	...	10 3		...	1237	—	3 44	...	5 39	5 58		p.m.	...	9 46	—
Geldermalsen 115		:		7 53	...	...	...	1026		...	1 9	...	4 5	...	6 1	6 14		6 27	...	10 28	...
Tiel	6‡46	S		8 13	a.m.			1040		1215	1 27	p.m.	4 19	p.m.	—	6 27		6 52	9 12	10 46	p.m.
Kesteren 118B	7 32	:	7 18	8 33	9 13	9 51	10 1	1055	12 20	1228	1 51	5 1	4 31	4‡35	...	6 40	6 56	7 14	9 29	11 9	11 13
Vork ....arr	8 1	:	...	8 53	9 42	...	:	1114	12 37	1247	2 18	5 26	:	:	...	6 57	7 13	7 45	9 45	:	11 44
Vork ....dep	8 3	:	:	9 3	9 46	...		1118	12 38	1248	2 19	5 37	:	:	...	6 59	7 14	7 47	9 46	:	11 47
Nymegen 114 ..	8 17	7 33	7 41	9 15	10 3	...	1024	1130	12 49	1259	2 32	5 49	:	4 59	...	7 10	7 25	8 5	9 57	11 37	12 3
Vork..............dep	8 10	...	...	8 56	...	10 25	...	1115	...	1251	2 20	5 30	:	...	...	...	7 17	7 48	9 50	...	11 45
Elst	8 15	...	...	9 1	...	10 29	...	1119	...	1256	2 25	5 50	5 5	...	...	...	7 22	7 53	1055	...	11 50
Arnhem 118..arr	8 29	...	...	9 15	...	10 45	...	1135	...	1 12	2 40	...	5 22	...	...	...	7 36	8 12	1011	...	12 9

AMSTERDAM, THE HAGUE, and ROTTERDAM.

	1,2,3	1,2,3	1,2,3	1,2,3	1,2,3	1,2,3	1,2,3	1,2,3	1,2,3	1,2,3	1,2,3	1,2,3	1,2,3	1,2,3	1,2,3	1,2,3	1,2,3	1,2,3	1,2,3	1,2,3	1,2,3	1,2,3	1,2,3
Amsterdam	p.m.	p.m.	p.m.		p.m.	p.m.	p.m.	p.m.	p.m.	p.m.	...	p.m.	p.m	p.m.	p.m.	p.m.	p.m.	p.m.	p.m.	p.m.	p.m.	p.m	p.m.
Central...dep	1 51	2 30	3 15	...	3 0	3 ‡35	4 38	4 15	4 19	5 15	...	5 35	6 6	6 49	8 17	...	8 6	9 0	...	9 45	1020	10 38	1130
Haarlem ...arr	2 10	2 48	3 35	...	3 18	:	4 57	:	4 38	: ‡	...	5 54	6 25	7 7	8 36	...	8 18	9 18	...	10 3	1038	10 58	1149
Zandvoort...arr	2 36	...	3 52	...	3 52	:	5 13	:	5 13	:	...	6 27	6 53	7 41	8 52	...	...	9 45	...	1022	...	11 47	...
Zandvoort..dep	1 52	...	—	...	3 0	:	—	:	...	:	p.m.	5 33	5 58	6 37	—	...	7 14	9 4	9 4	9 42	10 7	10 38	...
Haarlem ...dep	2 12	2 50	...	...	3 21	:	...	:	4 41	:	4 45	5 57	6 28	7 9	...	7 14	8 20	9 20	9 25	10 5	1040	11 2	1151
Vogelenzang......	2 25	...	...	p.m.	...	:	p.m.	:	...	:	4 57	6 7	...	...	...	7 23	...	...	9 36	S	...	11 17	A
Leiden 117	3 0	...	...	3 16	3 50	:	4 36	:	5 10	:	5 37	6 30	6 56	7 35	...	8 15	...	9 48	1016	1030	11 6	11 40	1219
Voorschoten... ...	—	...	...	3 27	...	:	4 45	:	...	:	5 46	...	...	...	...	8 27	...	...	1025	...	...	...	-
The Hague......arr		3 25	...	3 40	4 5	4 23	4 56	5 9	5 27	6 6	5 58	6 49	7 12	7 50	...	8 40	8 54	10 4	1036	1044	1121	11 57	1234
SCHEVENINGEN arr		3 55	...	4 10	4 40	4 55	5 25	5 33	5 55	6 40	6 38	7 25	7 40	8 25	p.m.	9 10	9 25	1040	1125	1125	12 5	12 25	...
SCHEVENINGEN dep		2 50	...	3 5	3 35	3 50	4 20	4 35	4 50	5 35	5 50	6 20	6 50	7 20	7 20	8 20	8 20	9 35	1020	1020	1050	11 20	1155
The Hague......dep		3 29	...	3 45	4 8	4 25	4 58	5 13	5 30	6 9	6 20	6 52	7 17	7 54	8 0	9 2	8 57	10 7	1052	1047	1124	12 1	1237
Ryswick		...	...	...	...	...	...	...	5 36	...	...	...	...	...	8 6	9 8	...	...	...	...	...	...	...
Delft		...	...	3 59	...	...	5 9	...	5 42	‡	6 36	7 3	7 27	...	8 16	9 19	...	1018	11 6	...	...	12 12	A
Schiedam		...	...	4 13	...	...	5 20	...	5 55	...	6 50	7 14	...	...	8 28	9 33	...	1029	1120	11 3	...	12 23	...
HOEK v. H. 112 arr		...	...	...	...	...	...	...	...	...	...	...	...	...	...	...	...	...	...	1127	...	...	...
Rotterdam Delft P. arr		3 50	...	4 24	4 30	4 45	5 29	5 35	6 4	6 30	7 1	7 23	7 42	8 15	8 38	9 47	9 18	1037	1131	1115	1146	12 32	1258
Rotterdam Beurs...arr		3 58	...	...	4 50	...	...	5 45	...	...	...	...	7 52	8 24	...	...	...	1046	...	...	...	...	...
ROSENDAAL 116 ......arr			...	6 p8	6 p8	...	7 p 2	7 p 2	...	...	...	...	...	9p21	...	...	1053	...	...	...	...	...	...
VLISSINGEN 113 ......arr			...	--	---	---	9p30	9r30	...	---	...	...	...	1059	...	...	12a2	...	...	...	...	...	...

ROTTERDAM (St. Jobshaven—see Advt., page 735) dep 7 p0 } From Rotterdam Tuesday,
GRIMSBY ....arr 8 a0 } Thursday, and Saturday.
ROTTERDAM (Parkhaven—see Advt., page 731) ....dep 8 p0 } From Rotterdam daily except Sunday.
HULL ....arr 11a30 }

‡—Does not run on Sunday. S—Seat Ticket required.

SCHEVENINGEN and ROTTERDAM.		a.m.	a.m.	a.m.	a.m.	a.m.	a.m.		
	Scheveningen Kurhaus dep	7‡43	8 5	8‡15	8‡40	8 45	10 8	And at intervals of about an hour until 10.14 p.m.	‡—Not on Sunday.
	The Hague Pijnacker... ,,	8 0	8 30	...	...	9 0	10 30		
	Rotterdam Hofplein ......arr	8 26	8 56	8 47	9 11	9 29	10 56		

ROTTERDAM, THE HAGUE, and AMSTERDAM.

VLISSINGEN dp	...	...	...	...	1p27	1p27	1p27	...	...	...	...	...	...	...	...	4p50	...	...	7 p0	...	...	7 p46	7p46
ROSENDAAL dp	12p15	...	...	...	2p52	3 p4	3 p4	3 p9	3 p9	...	4p49	4p49	...	...	6p11	7p28	...	...	8p16	...	...	9 p29	9p29
	1,2,3	1,2,3	1,2,3	1,2,3	1,2,3	1,2,3	1,2,3	1,2,3	1,2,3	1,2,3	1,2,3	1,2,3	1,2,3	1,2,3	1,2,3	1 &2	1,2,3	1,2,3	1,2,3	1,2,3	1,2,3	1,2,3	1,2,3
Rotterdam	p.m.	p.m.	p.m.	p.m.	p.m.	p.m.	p.m.	p.m.	p.m.	p.m	p.m	p.m.	p.m.	p.m.	p.m.	p.m.	p.m.	p.m.	p.m.	p.m.	p.m.	p.m.	p.m.
Beurs.....dep	...	...	...	...	...	...	...	4‡49	4 49	...	...	...	...	...	7 49	...	...	9 5	...	...	9 57	...	...
,, Delft P...dep	2 3	2 50	3 1	3 29	4 7	4 15	4 43	5 5	5 15	5 51	6 38	6 42	7 10	7 20	8 0	8 36	8 43	9 15	9 43	9 54	1012	10 59	1130
HOEK v. H. dp	...	...	...	...	...	...	...	...	...	...	...	...	...	...	...	...	...	...	...	...	...	...	...
Schiedam	2 13	...	...	3 38	‡	...	4 52	...	...	6 0	...	6 51	...	...	8 9	...	8 52	9 22	...	10 3	1020	...	1139
Delft	2 29	A	3 17	3 50	...	...	5 7	...	5 34	6 13	...	7 7	...	A	8 25	...	9 5	9 34	...	1018	1032	...	1155
Ryswick	...	...	...	...	...	...	...	...	...	...	...	...	...	...	...	...	...	...	...	...	...	...	...
The Hague arr	2 49	3 10	3 25	4 1	4 27	4 37	5 16	5 25	5 43	6 24	6 59	7 19	7 32	7 44	8 37	8 57	9 14	9 43	10 5	1029	1041	11 22	12 5
SCHEVENINGEN ar	3 25	3 40	3 55	4 40	4 55	5 10	5 55	5 55	6 10	6 55	7 25	7 55	8 10	8 10	9 10	9 25	9 40	1010	1040	1055	1110	12 5	1245
SCHEVENINGEN dp	2 5	2 35	2 50	3 35	3 50	4 5	—	4 50	5 20	5 50	6 35	6 50	7 5	7 20	8 5	8 35	8 50	...	9 35	1020	10 5	10 35	1135
The Hague dp	2 43	3 12	3 28	4 5	4 29	4 42	...	5 27	5 47	6 28	7 3	7 25	7 40	7 48	8 43	9 2	9 18	...	10 8	1051	1044	11 26	12 9
Voorschoten	2 55	:	...	...	:	...	...	:	...	6 40	...	7 38	...	...	8 55	:	...	...	...	11 3	...	...	1221
Leiden...........	3 3	:	3 45	4 24	‡	...	...	‡	6 6	6 50	...	7 48	7 58	8 8	9 5	:	9 37	...	...	1116	11 1	11 43	1229
Vogelenzang	—	A	...	...	:	...	...	:	...	7 8	...	—	...	A	—	:	...	...	...	1145	...	...	—
Haarlem...arr	...	:	4 9	4 49	:	5 19	...	:	6 33	7 20	7 40	...	8 23	8 35	...	:	10 4	...	1045	12 0	1126	12 8	...
Zandvoort..arr	...	:	4 39	5 13	:	5 57	p.m.	:	6 53	7 41	...	...	8 52	8 52	...	:	1022	...	1147	...	...	...	...
Zandvoort.dep	...	:	...	...	:	4 56	5 33	:	5 58	6 37	7 14	...	...	...	...	:	9 42	...	10 7	...	1038	...	...
Haarlem..dep	...	:	4 12	4 53	:	5 21	5 50	:	6 36	7 22	7 42	...	8 26	8 38	...	:	10 7	...	1047	...	1128	12 10	...
Amsterdam C.	...	4 0	4 30	5 12	5 17	5 39	6 11	6 15	6 55	7 42	8 0	...	8 45	9 0	...	9 53	1027	...	11 5	...	1147	12 29	...

Extra.—Delft to The Hague & Haarlem 4.48 p.m. The Hague to Leiden 10.15 p.m. Leiden to Amsterdam 11a7, 8.13 p.m.

ARNHEM, NYMEGEN, and ROTTERDAM.

[S—Seat ticket required.

	1,2,3	1,2,3	1,2,3	1,2,3	1,2,3	1,2,3	1,2,3	1,2,3	1,2,3	1,2,3	1,2,3	1,2,3	1,2,3	1,2,3	1,2,3	1,2,3	1,2,3	1,2,3	1,2,3	1 &2		
	a.m.	a.m.		a.m	a.m.		a.m.	a.m.	a.m.	a.m.	p.m.	p.m.	p.m	p.m.		p.m.	p.m.	p.m.	p.m.	p.m.		
Arnhem ....dep	6 5	...	...	7 46	8 32	...	9 18	...	9 59	11 32	1 24	...	2‡10	4 35	...	5 44	6 57	8 13	8 58	...	...	...
Elst	6 22	...	...	8 1	8 45	...	9 33	...	10 16	11 47	1 40	...	2 24	4 51	...	6 1	7 11	8 30	9 14	...	...	...
Vork ....arr	6 26	...	...	8 5	8 49	...	9 37	...	10 20	11 51	1 44	...	2 28	4 55	p.m.	6 5	7 15	8 34	9 18	...	...	...
Nymegen ...dep	6 8	6 38	...	8 6	8 36	...	9 28	9 40	10 20	11 34	1‡35	1 48	2 24	4 47	4 54	5 56	7 10	8 26	9 16	9 26	...	...
Vork ....arr	6 24	:	...	8 15	8 48	...	9 37	9 49	10 30	11 47	1 45	2 0	2 34	4 57	5 3	6 12	7 19	8 38	9 25	9 35	...	...
Vork...............dep	6 29	:	a.m	8 17	8 51	...	9 39	9 51	10 31	11 53	1‡49	2 5	2 36	4 59	5 5	6 14	7 20	8 40	9 27	9 36	...	...
Kesteren	6 58	7 6	7 11	8 33	9 23	a.m.	9 55	10 7	10 53	12 26	2 6	2 32	2 58	5 17	5 23	6 55	...	9 25	9 42	...	...	...
Tiel	—	To Amsterdam arr. 9.2	7 31	To Amsterdam arr. 10.14.	9 38	9 43	10 10	To Amsterdam arr. 11.25	—	12 43	—	To Amsterdam arr. 4.38.	3 12	5 30	To Amsterdam arr. 6.50.	7 17	7 46	9 45	To Amsterdam arr. 10.57	...	...	...
Geldermalsen ...	...		7 53		—	1028	...		...	1 9	...		3 25	5 44		7 37	...	1038		S	...	...
Leerdam	a.m.		8 15		...	1049	...		p.m.	1 28	p.m.		3 43	5 59		7 57	...	1048		...	...	...
Gorinchem	7 5		8 39		...	1112	10 45		12‡17	1 46	4‡54		3 58	6 13		8 13	8 22	11 6		...	...	...
Dordrecht......arr	7 50		9 15		...	12 2	11 9		1 3	2 21	5 47		4 26	6 36		9 30	8 44	1147		1047	...	...
Rotterdam B. arr	8 13		9 37		...	1227	11 35		—	...	—		4 47	...		9 55	9 4	1213		...	...	...
,, Delft. P. arr	8 20		9 44		...	1234	11 42		...	2 52	...		4 54	7 1		10 2	9 10	1219		11 8	...	...

‡—Not on Sunday.

Luggage, 10 cents for 22 lbs. for 50 kils.]

AMSTERDAM, ZAANDAM, UITGEEST, and HELDER.

Amsterdam—	a.m	a.m.	a.m.	a.m.	a.m.	a.m.	a.m.	a.m.	p.m.	p.m.	p.m	p.m.	p.m.	p.m.	p.m.	p.m.	p.m.	p.m.	p.m.	p.m.	p.m.	p.m
Central...dep	6† 6	7 26	9 12	Via Har'l'm 9.48.	9 44	9 57	1028	1132	1257	2 20	2†53	3 38	4 8	4 46	5†11	5 25	6 23	7 34	8 40	9 5	9 39	1047
Zaandam ... arr	6 22	7 42	9 25		9 59	1010	1045	1147	1 10	2 36	3 9	3 51	4 24	4 59	...	5 39	6 36	7 50	8 52	...	9 54	11 3
Zaandam ... dep	6 26	7 43	9 26		10 0	1017	1050	1148	1 14	2 39	3 11	3 52	4 26	5 2	...	5 40	6 38	7 52	8 54	...	9 55	11 5
Wormerveer	6 39	7 55	9 34		1012	...	11 2	1159	1 27	2 51	3 24	4 3	4 38	5 13	...	5 52	6 49	8 6	9 6	...	10 7	1117
Krommenie-A ...	6 45	8 0	...		1017	...	11 7	12 4	1 32	2 56	3 29	4 8	4 43	5 18	...	5 57	6 54	8 12	9 11	...	1012	1122
Uitgeest ... arr	6 52	8 7	9 44		1024	1031	1114	1211	1 39	3 3	3 36	...	4 50	5 24	A	6 4	7 1	8 19	9 18	9 28	1019	1129
Uitgeest ... dep	6 57	8 14	9 47	...	—	1032	—	1218	1 45	3 9	—	...	5 2	—	...	6 6	7 5	8 37	—	9 32	—	1131
Alkmaar	7 21	8 29	10 6	1020	...	1051	...	1242	2 17	3 32	...	4 29	5 27	...	5 46	6 26	7 20	9 1	...	9 50	10p6	1153
Schagen	8 5	—	1029	—	...	1130	...	—	2 52	—	...	5 20	—	...	—	6 57	—	—	...	1012	1038	—
Helder ....arr	8 36	...	1050	...	...	12 1	...	...	3 23	...	...	5 52	...	...	...	7 26	...	...	...	1035	1110	...

				a.m.	a.m.		a.m.	a.m.	a.m.	p.m.		p.m.		p.m.	p.m	p.m.				p.m.		p.m.	
Helder ....dep	...	...	...	6†28	7 40	...	9 7	...	...	...	...	1245	...	1†52	...	4 10	...	...	...	7 30	...	8 35	...
Schagen.........	...	a.m.	...	7 3	8 4	...	9 40	...	...	...	p.m.	1 16	...	2 24	...	4 40	p.m.	...	p.m.	7 53	p.m.	9 9	p.m.
Alkmaar	...	6†32	...	7 49	8 30	...	1017	1032	1149	...	1 26	1 49	...	3 21	4 30	5 10	5 28	...	6 40	8 17	8 53	9 48	10 6
Uitgeest arr	a.m.	6 57	a.m.	8 14	...	a.m.	1040	1047	12 9	†	1 41	2 22	p.m.	3 41	4 53	5 27	5 52	p.m.	7 4	8 33	9 15	1010	1022
Uitgeest dep	6†12	7 0	7†40	8 19	...	9 8	1054	To Haarlem (arr. 11.7)	1216	1247	1 46	2 27	3†13	3 52	5 3	5 29	5 58	6 40	7 23	8 36	9 18	1013	1133
Krom'nie-A.	6 20	7 8	7 48	8 27	...	9 16	11 2		1224	1255	1 54	2 35	3 21	4 0	5 11	...	6 7	6 48	7 32	8 43	9 26	1021	1141
Wormerveer..	6 25	7 13	7 53	8 33	...	9 22	11 7		1229	1 0	1 59	2 41	3 26	4 5	5 17	5 40	6 13	6 53	7 39	8 49	9 32	1026	1146
Zaandam arr	6 36	7 25	8 4	8 45	8 54	9 34	1119		1240	1 11	2 10	2 52	3 37	4 16	5 29	5 47	6 25	7 4	7 52	8 59	9 43	1037	1157
Zaandam dep	6 37	7 29	8 7	8 58	8 58	9 38	1121		1241	1 13	2 12	2 56	3 38	4 19	5 35	5 50	6 28	7 6	7 55	9 1	9 46	1038	1158
Amster. C....	6 52	7 42	8 22	9 10	9 10	9 52	1137		1254	1 28	2 25	3 11	3 54	4 35	5 50	6 2	6 43	7 20	8 9	9 13	9 59	1054	1212

Extra—Amsterdam to Uitgeest, 5†19, 8†12 a.m., 12.4 night Uitgeest to Amsterdam, 5†19 a.m.

A—In July and August only. †—Not on Sunday.

Alkmaar	6†50	8a33	8a52	10a23	1p 2	1p57	3p37	5p32	7p23	9p55	Hoorn ...	6†50	8†a2	10 a6	11 a2	1 p0	2p34	4p39	7p13	8p57	9p39
Hoorn ...	7 34	8 55	9 37	10 44	1 48	2 20	4 19	6 13	7 46	1041	Alkmaar	7 33	8 46	10 28	11 43	1 22	3 16	5 22	7 58	9 35	10 2

†—Not on Sunday.

AMSTERDAM, HAARLEM, VELSEN, and UITGEEST.—VELSEN and IJMUIDEN.

Amsterdam—	a.m.	a.m.	a.m.	a.m.	a.m.	a.m.	a.m.	a.m.	a.m.	a.m.	p.m.	p.m.	p.m.	p.m.	p.m.	p.m.	p.m.	p.m.	p.m	p.m.	p.m.	p.m.
Central dep	5†50	7 0	...	7 48	8 8	8 24	9 20	...	9 48	11 9	1221	1244	2 3	3 54	4 50	5 35	6 17	...	7 26	8 17	9 9	1032
Haarlem arr	6 11	7 18	...	8 7	8 27	8 47	9 40	...	10 8	1130	1242	1 4	2 26	4 18	5 10	5 54	6 37	...	7 47	8 36	9 28	1051
Haarlem dep	6 14	7 33	7 54	8 10	8 32	9 14	9 42	9 48	1014	1135	1246	1 12	2 31	4 21	5 12	6 0	6 42	6 46	7 50	8 47	9 34	1054
Santpoort	6 25	7 43	...	8 19	8 41	9 23	...	...	1023	1145	1258	...	2 41	4 31	5 22	6 10	...	6 56	8 0	...	9 44	11 4
Velsen ......arr	6 33	7 49	...	8 27	8 49	9 29	...	9 57	1029	1154	1 7	1 22	2 50	4 40	5 32	6 17	...	7 5	8 9	8 58	9 53	1113
Ijmuiden arr	...	7 59	...	8 33	9 0	9 37	9 57	⋮	1037	12 5	...	1 31	2 59	4 53	5 41	...	...	7 11	8 32	9 7	10 3	1121
Velsen ......dep	6 37	7 51	...	—	8 50	9 30	—	⋮	1031	1157	1 12	1 23	2 52	4 42	5 34	6 19	...	—	8 14	9 0	9 55	1115
Beverwijk	6 43	7 57	...	...	8 55	9 35	...	⋮	1037	12 3	1 18	1 28	2 57	4 48	5 39	6 24	6 55	...	8 20	9 6	10 0	1120
Uitgeest ...arr	6 51	8 5	8 12	...	9 3	9 42	...	⋮	1045	1211	1 27	1 36	3 6	4 56	5 47	6 32	7 3	...	8 28	9 14	10 8	1128

	a.m.	a m	a.m.	a.m.	a.m.	a.m.		a.m.	p.m.		p.m.	p.m.	p.m		p.m.	p.m.	p.m.	p.m.	p.m	p.m.	p.m.	p.m.
Uitgeest ......dep	7†28	8 26	8 58	9 5	1030	1049	...	1125	1216	...	1 43	2 33	3 45	...	4 55	5 32	6 12	7 7	8 8	8 39	9 27	1024
Beverwijk.........	7 38	8 36	...	9 14	1039	...	...	1136	1225	...	1 51	2 43	3 55	...	5 4	⋮	6 23	7 16	8 19	8 47	9 36	1033
Velsen ....arr	7 43	8 41	...	9 19	1044	...	a.m.	1141	1230	p.m.	1 55	2 48	4 0	p.m.	5 9	⋮	6 28	7 21	8 23	8 51	9 41	1038
Ijmuiden...dep	7 33	8 33	...	9 10	1022	...	11 9	1130	1219	12 55	1 45	2 37	3 57	4 42	...	⋮	...	7 11	8 3	8 41	9 30	1028
Velsen ....dep	7 45	8 44	...	9 22	1046	...	...	1144	1232	1 1	1 57	2 51	4 5	4 49	5 10	⋮	6 34	7 25	8 27	8 53	9 43	1039
Santpoort	7 58	8 53	...	9 32	1053	...	...	1154	1240	1 11	...	3 1	4 12	4 57	5 20	⋮	6 45	7 36	8 36	...	9 51	...
Haarlem ... arr	8 8	9 2	9 19	9 41	11 2	11 7	1122	12 3	1248	1 20	2 9	3 10	4 21	5 6	5 29	5 50	6 55	7 45	8 44	9 2	10 0	1049
Haarlem ... dep	8 10	9 9	...	9 47	...	1112	1132	12 6	1253	1 23	2 12	3 17	4 26	5 9	5 50	6 15	7 1	7 49	8 50	9 12	10 7	1056
Amsterdam C...	8 30	9 28	...	10 6	...	1131	1152	1230	1 10	1 43	2 35	3 40	4 51	5 28	6 11	6 38	7 24	8 14	9 10	9 34	1027	1121

Extra											
Amsterdam (Central) dep	4a†48	6a†17	11a53	3 p0	5p52	Ijmuiden ......dep	6†a24	5p14	8p51	11p32	†—Not on Sunday.
Ijmuiden ....arr	5 41	6 55	12 39	3 52	6 35	Amsterdam ...arr	7 13	6 38	9 45	12 29	

HARLINGEN and LEEUWARDEN.

§—4.25 a.m. on Friday.] [†—Not on Sunday.

*—Not on Friday.	a.m.	a.m.	a.m.	a.m.	p.m.	p.m.	p.m.	
Harlingen ....dep	...	7† 5	8 57	10 13	1 48	4 32	6 50	...
Franeker ....dep	...	...	...	10*24	1 58	4 44	...	...
Tjummarum	6 5	7 31	9 23	10 39	2 13	5 0	7 14	...
Stiens ....arr	6 40	8 4	—	11 11	2 46	5 32	7 47	p.m.
Anjum..............dep	5§27	6 50	...	9 59	1 34	4 23	6 34	1025
Dokkum Aalsum ...	5 51	7 12	...	10 22	1 57	4 47	6 57	1044
Stiens..............arr	6 43	8 3	...	11 12	2 48	5 38	7 49	—
Stiens ....dep	6 45	8 7	...	11 20	2 51	5 42	7 53	...
Leeuwarden ....arr	7 4	8 26	...	11 36	3 10	6 1	8 11	...

	a.m.	a.m.	p.m.	p.m.		p.m.	p.m.	
Leeuwarden..dep	7 15	8 40	1213	2 30	...	5 20	8 40	...
Stiens ....arr	7 34	8 59	1232	2 49	...	5 39	8 56	...
Stiens ....dep	7 38	9 2	1236	2 54	...	5 41	9 0	...
Dokkum Aalsum...	8 33	9 57	1 33	3 50	...	6 33	9 56	...
Anjum ....arr	8 52	1017	1 52	4 9	p.m.	6 56	1015	...
Stiens ....dep	7 36	9 3	1235	—	2*55	5 43	9 1	...
Tjummarum	8 12	9 39	1 7	...	3 28	6 15	9 34	...
Franeker ....arr	...	9*54	1 23	...	3 43	6 30	...	...
Harlingen ....arr	8 37	10 4	1 34	...	3 54	6 39	...	...

ZWOLLE and ALMELO.

Dist		a.m.	a.m.	a.m.	a.m.	pm	p.m.	p.m.	p.m.	p.m.
—	Zwolle.........dep	6 28	...	9 15	...	1 4	...	4 18	6 18	9 6
11¼	Raalte..................	6 53	...	9 40	...	130	...	4 43	...	9 30
...	Hellendoorn-Nijv.	7 12	...	9 59	...	149	...	5 1	6 50	9 48
27¾	Almelo 118B arr	7 30	8 6	1015	1027	2 6	2 33	5 18	7 4	10 4
36¾	Hengelo ......arr	8 2	8 28	1032	1048	234	2 55	6 0	7 26	1030

	a.m.	a.m.	a.m.	p.m.	pm	p.m.	p.m.	p.m.	p.m.
Hengelo	7 0	9 5	1055	1214	153	3 41	5 8	7 4	9 5
Almelo ...	7 30	9 37	1110	1239	2 8	4 6	5 30	7 30	9 27
H.Nijverdal	7 48	9 58	—	1256	223	4 25	—	7 47	—
Raalte.........	8 9	1017	...	1 15	...	4 45	...	8 3	...
Zwolle arr	8 33	1043	...	1 40	252	5 8	...	8 28	...

HAARLEM and AALSMEER.

Haarlem dep	6a32	8a15	10 a9	1p10	2p25	5 p7	8 p0	9p17	...	Aalsmeer dep	6a37	...	8a56	10a13	1p18	4 p0	5p17	8 p4	...	...
Hoofddorp ...	7 1	8 40	10 38	1 41	2 50	5 36	8 31	9 42	...	Hoofddorp.....	6 55	7a45	9 12	10 39	1 36	4 17	5 40	8 30	...	...
Aalsmeer arr	7 16	8 56	10 53	1 57	3 5	5 51	8 47	9 57	...	Haarlem...arr	7 14	8 8	9 35	11 4	1 59	4 40	6 3	8 55	...	...

Hoofddorp dep	7 a4	10a40	1p42	3 p0	5p44	8p35	...	...	Leiden ......dep	5a49	8a14	12p22	4p30	7 p7	8p41	...
Leiden ......arr	8 0	11 48	2 50	3 56	6 40	9 43	...	...	Hoofddorp arr	6 45	9 10	1 30	5 26	8 15	9 37	...

AMSTERDAM and ENKHUIZEN.

Amsterdam—	a.m.	a.m.	a.m.	a.m.	a.m.	p.m.	p.m.	p.m.	p.m.	p.m.
Central ...dep	6 37	7 55	8 47	9 57	1039	1 34	3 6	5†39	7 1	9 31
Zaandam arr	6 51	8 9	9 0	1010	1055	1 47	3 19	5 55	7 13	9 44
Zaandam dep	6 53	8 12	9 2	1012	1058	1 49	3 21	5 57	7 14	9 46
Purmerend	7 17	8 30	9 26	1030	1123	2 7	3 44	6 21	7 32	10 9
Kwadijk Edam ...	7 23	...	9 33	...	1130	...	3 50	6 29	...	1015
Hoorn ....arr	7 49	8 53	1012	1053	1157	2 31	4 16	6 59	7 52	1041
Enkhuizen arr	8 31	9 17	1046	1111	1228	2 49	4 57	7 42	8 14	1124
STAVOREN (stm)	...	1032	...	1226	...	4 p7	6†19	...	9p29	...

STAVOREN (stm)	...	8a24	...	11a18	...	2p22	...	5†p2	7p56
	a.m.	a.m.	a.m.	p.m.	p.m.	p.m.	p.m.	p.m.	p.m.
Enkhuizen dep	8†11	9 46	1017	1238	1 0	3 42	3 49	6 25	9 18
Hoorn............ dep	9 3	1010	11 6	1 3	1 40	4 4	4 26	7 5	9 44
Kwadijk	9 33	...	1131	...	2 12	...	4 56	7 35	...
Purmerend	9 42	1031	1138	1 24	2 21	4 26	5 4	7 42	1010
Zaandam arr	10 6	1048	12 0	1 41	2 46	4 43	5 27	8 4	1027
Zaandam dep	10 9	1049	12 4	1 42	2 56	4 45	5 35	8 6	1028
Amsterdam arr	1025	11 2	1218	1 55	3 11	4 58	5 50	8 21	1041

†—Not on Sunday.

Extra.—Enkhuizen to Amsterdam, 5.40 a.m. Hoorn to Enkhuizen, 1.53 p.m. Enkhuizen to Hoorn, 8.20 p.m.

†—Not on Sunday.

LEEUWARDEN and STAVOREN.

	a.m.	a.m.	a.m.	p.m.	p.m.	p.m.	p.m.	p.m.	p.m.	p.m.	
Leeuwarden dep	6 26	7 29	1013	1220	1†30	1†42	3 24	5 23	7 3	9 23	...
Sneek	7 12	7 51	1035	1 4	1 51	2 23	4 2	6 17	7 25	10 8	...
Workum	7 42	...	1057	1 31	...	——	4 30	6 48	...	1036	...
Hindeloopen ...	7 49	...	11 3	1 38	...	...	4 38	6 55	...	1043	...
Stavoren arr	8 7	8 19	1113	1 55	2 17	...	4 55	7 12	7 53	11 0	...

	a.m.		a.m.	a.m.	p.m.	p.m.	p.m.	p.m.	p.m.	p.m.
Stavoren	6†30	...	1044	1115	1238	4†17	4 22	6 36	9 0	9 39
Hindeloopen	6 48	...	...	1134	...	...	4 39	6 54	9 19	...
Workum ...	7 0	a.m.	1058	1142	...	...	4 46	7 4	9 26	...
Sneek	7 29	1033	1116	1213	1 6	4 47	5 20	7 37	9 55	10 7
Leeuward	8 13	1114	1136	1256	1 25	5 7	6 4	8 18	...	1027

Extra.—Sneek to Leeuwarden, 8†35 a.m., 2†38 p.m. Leeuwarden to Sneek, 8.39 a.m.

†—Not on Sunday. §—1.44 p.m. on Saturday.

HOORN and MEDEMBLIK.

	a.m.	a.m.	a.m.	a.m.	a.m.	p.m.	p.m.	p.m.	p.m.	p.m.
Hoorn...dep	5†41	6†49	7†57	9 5	1141	2§36	4 33	7 † 4	8 0	9 54
Abbekerk	6 9	7 17	8 26	9 28	12 6	2 59	5 0	7 24	8 24	1021
Medemblik	6 33	7 41	8 50	9 48	1230	3 19	5 24	7 46	8 43	1045

	a.m.	a.m.	a.m.	a.m.	a.m.	p.m.	p.m.	p m	p.m.	p.m.
Medemblik dp	5†22	6†51	7†58	9 53	11†59	1†25	3 31	5 54	8 †0	8 55
Abbekerk......	5 47	7 16	8 24	1017	12 15	1 50	3 51	6 18	8 25	9 15
Hoorn 120 arr	6 15	7 44	8 51	1046	12 46	2 17	4 14	6 45	8 46	9 35

†—Not on Sunday.

DIEREN and HATTEM.

	a.m.	a.m.	a.m.	a.m.	p.m.	p.m.	p.m.	p.m.	p.m.	p.m.
Dieren ...dep	...	7 59	9 8	1013	1250	2 46	4 0	6 *5	7 16	9 41
Apeldoorn	6 50	9 50	9 46	1147	2 33	3 45	5 0	7 3	8 56	1023
Het Loo	7 5	10 5	——	12 2	2 48	4 0	5 15	7 20	9 11	——
Epe	7 34	1029	...	1227	3 13	4 25	5 40	7 50	9 36	...
Heerde	7 46	1039	...	1238	3 23	4 35	5 50	8 3	9 46	...
Hattem Stad ...	8 6	1057	...	1256	3 41	4 54	6 9	8 24	10 6	...
Hattem N.C.S	8 12	11 3	...	1 12	3 47	5 0	6 15	8 30	1012	...

		a.m.	a.m.	a.m.	p.m	p.m.	p.m.	p.m.	p.m.	p.m.
Hattem N.C.S. dep		...	7 19	9 41	1213	1 49	5 0	6 48	9 37	1057
Hattem Stad		5†19	7 28	9 49	1221	1 57	5 10	6 56	9 46	11 4
Heerde		5 38	7 45	10 6	1240	2 14	5 28	7 13	10 4	——
Epe......................		5 50	7 55	1016	1251	2 24	5 40	7 23	1015	...
Het Loo	a.m.	6 15	8 21	1042	1 19	2 49	6 9	7 48	1044	...
Apeldoorn	6 50	6 31	8 35	1056	1 36	3 7	6 23	8 2	1058	...
Dieren 114 arr	7 30	...	9 36	1234	2 16	3 47	7 *7	9 31	...	...

Extra.—Apeldoorn to Dieren, 8.20 a.m., 5.2 p.m. *—From and at Dieren in July and August.

ZEVENAAR and WINTERSWIJK.

†—Not on Sunday.

	a.m.	a.m.	a.m.	a.m.	a.m.	p.m.	p.m.	p.m.	p.m.	p.m.	p.m.	p.m.			
Zevenaar ....dep	...	...	...	8 1	1057	2 11	4 46	...	7 20	8 46	...	...	...	...	...
Doetinchem ....arr	...	5†43	...	8 29	1131	2 45	5 17	7 0	7 52	9 16	9 18	...	...	...	...
Ruurlo ....arr	...	6 15	...	9 54	1220	4 20	...	7 32	...	...	9 47	---	...	...	...
Doetinchem ....dep	4†41	——	6†34	8 32	1144	2 51	5 22	——	8 0	9 19	——	1032	...	...	...
Terborg	4 54	...	6 49	8 42	1157	3 4	5 33	...	8 13	9 30	...	1043	...	...	...
Winterswijk 118c arr	5 46	...	7 43	9 26	1250	3 53	6 23	...	...	1015	...	...	...	...	...

	a.m.	a.m.	a.m.	p.m.	p.m.	p.m.	p.m.	p m.	p.m.	p.m.	p.m.					
Winterswijk ...dep	5†57	8 11	1043	2 39	...	4 20	6 57	...	...	...	1028	...	...	...	...	...
Terborg	6 46	9 6	1132	3 33	...	5 5	7 41	...	8 46	...	1117	...	...	...	...	...
Doetinchem ....arr	6 57	9 18	1143	3 45	...	5 14	7 51	...	8 58	...	1128	...	...	...	...	...
Ruurlo ....dep	...	7 53	11 5	2 8	4 40	...	...	8 7	——	9 56	——	...	...	...	...	...
Doetinchem ....dep	6 59	9 25	1145	3 56	5 12	5 18	7 54	8 36	...	1028	...	...	...	...	...	...
Zevenaar 118...arr	7 31	10 1	1217	4 30	...	5 46	8 23	...	...	...	...	...	...	...	...	...

ENSCHEDE and AHAUS.

(Mid Europe time at Alstatte and Ahaus.)

	a.m.	a.m.	p.m.	p.m.	p.m.		
Enschede ....dep	5 13	9 25	1 27	4 30	8 29	...	...
Broekheurne	5 24	9 36	1 39	4 40	8 40	...	...
Alstatte.........................	6 23	10 31	2 33	5 34	9 36	...	...
Ahaus (135B) ....arr	6 42	10 50	2 52	5 51	9 55	...	...

	a.m.	a.m.	p.m.	p.m.	p.m.		
Ahaus ....dep	9 14	11 0	4 13	6 15	10 13	...	...
Alstatte	9 34	11 20	4 30	6 38	10 33	...	...
Broekheurne.................	9 7	10 55	4 4	6 13	10 7	...	...
Enschede 114.........arr	9 17	11 6	4 14	6 24	10 18	...	...

†—Not on Sunday.

BOXTEL and WESEL.

Amsterdam time between Boxtel and Gennep. Mid Europe time between Gennep and Wesel.

	2 3 4 a.m.	1—4 a.m.	Ex.2 a.m.	Ex 2 a.m.	Ex2 a.m.	1—4 a.m.	1—4 a.m.	1,2,3 a.m.	1—4 a.m.	1,2,3 p.m.	1—4 p.m.	1—4 p.m.	2&3	Ex 2 p.m.	Ex 2 p.m.			A—To Crefeld (arrive 8.58).
Boxtel ....dep	...	...	6 9	6 30	...	7 12	9 15	10 5	11 55	3 40	5 20	8 23	...	9 1	9 12	...	...	
Veghel	...	...	...	...	...	7 42	9 45	10 25	12 28	4 0	5 48	8 50	...	...	...	...	...	
Beugen **(114)**...... arr	...	...	...	...	...	8 21	10 25	...	1 15	...	6 27	9 27	...	...	...	...	...	
Gennep	...	5 30	6 54	7 15	...	8 36	11 8	11 0	1 32	4 35	6 45	9 39	...	9 48	10 1	...	...	
Goch (131) ......arr	...	6 43	7 49	8 8	...	9 49	12 24	11 55	2 54	5 28	7 59	——	p.m.	10 42	10 55	...	...	
,, (Customs Exam.)	...	7 15	:	8 44	8 55	10 7	12 40	12 12	4 25	5 35	8 11	...	9 53	11 2	11 17	...	...	
Xanten	6 †6	7 51	A	...	...	1048	1 23	12 37	5 8	5 59	8 59	...	1046	...	...	...	...	
Wesel (132) ......arr	6 40	8 28	:	9 20	9 32	1119	2 0	12 56	5 43	6 19	9 30	...	1138	11 44	12 0	...	...	

	1—4	2 & 3 a.m.	Ex2 a.m.	1—4 a.m.	Ex 2 a.m.	1—4 a.m.	1—4 p.m.	1,2,3 p.m.	1,2,3 p.m.	1—4 p.m.	Ex 2 p.m.	Ex.2	1—4 p.m.		B—From Crefeld (depart 8.29).				
Wesel ....dep	...	...	6 55	7 3	7 27	10 55	2 49	4 15	5 50	6 40	8 26	...	1015	...		...	...	...	...
Xanten	...	5 23	...	7 33	...	11 29	3 23	4 35	6 14	7 15	...	B	1046	...		...	...	...	...
Goch ....arr	...	7 5	7 39	8 5	8 12	12 5	3 56	4 59	6 40	7 55	9 6	p.m.	1138	...		...	...	...	...
,, ...dep	a.m.	——	7 44	9 8	8 15	12 40	4 3	5 1	6 50	8 15	9 8	9 22	——	...		...	...	...	...
Gennep(CustomsExam.)	5 40	...	7 29	8 59	7 56	12 43	3 52	4 43	6 32	8 8	8 52	9 6	...	...		...	...	...	...
Beugen	5 52	...	...	9 17	...	1 1	4 4	...	6 40	8 20	...	...	...	...		...	...	...	...
Veghel........................	6 32	...	...	10 1	...	1 41	4 45	...	7 14	9 1	...	...	...	...		...	...	...	...
Boxtel (117) ......arr	7 0	...	8 17	10 33	8 42	2 12	5 14	5 26	7 35	9 30	9 39	9 54	...	...		...	...	...	...

TABLE OF FARES ON THE GERMAN STATE RAILWAYS.

Kilo-meter.	English Miles.	1Cl. m pf	2Cl. m pf	3Cl. m pf	Kilo-meter.	English Miles.	1Cl. m pf	2Cl. m pf	3Cl. m pf	Kilo-meter.	English Miles.	1Cl. m pf	2Cl. m pf	3Cl. m pf	Kilo-meter.	English Miles.	1Cl. m pf	2Cl. m pf	3Cl. m pf	Kilo-meter.	English Miles.	1Cl. m pf	2Cl. m pf	3Cl. m pf
5	3	0 35	0 25	0 15	40	24¾	3 20	1 90	1 25	80	49¾	6 40	3 80	2 50	200	124¼	15 60	9 40	6 20	700	435	54 40	33 30	21 60
10	6¼	0 90	0 45	0 30	50	31	3 90	2 50	1 55	90	56	7 10	4 30	2 80	300	186½	23 40	14 30	9 20	750	466	60 50	35 60	23 10
20	12½	1 60	1 00	0 65	60	37¼	4 60	2 90	1 85	100	62¼	7 80	4 70	3 10	400	248½	30 40	18 80	12 40	800	497	64 00	37 80	24 60
25	15½	2 00	1 30	0 80	70	43½	5 30	3 40	2 20	125	77¾	9 60	6 10	3 90	500	310¾	38 60	23 70	15 40	900	559¼	71 00	43 20	27 60
30	18¾	2 50	1 50	0 95	75	46½	6 10	3 60	2 40	150	93¼	12 10	7 20	4 60	600	372¾	47 40	28 20	18 40	1000	621½	78 00	47 70	30 60

The above fares include the Government Stamp (Fahrkartensteuer).

For the EXPRESS TRAINS (SCHNELLZUGE) Extra Fares are charged as follows:—

Zone.	Kilometer.	English Miles.	1 & 2 Cl. M. Pf.	3 Cl. M. Pf.
I	1 to 75	⅝ to 46½	0 50	0 25
II	75 to 150	46⅝ to 93¼	1 00	0 50
III	Above 150	Above 93¼	2 00	1 00

COLOGNE, KEMPEN, VENLO, KLEVE, and NYMEGEN.

THROUGH CARRIAGE. {Cologne to Vlissingen—in 7.14 p.m. from Cologne. Cologne to Hoek van Holland—in 7.21 p.m. from Cologne.

*** Amsterdam Time.

	2,3,4	1—4	1,2,3	1—4	1,2,3	1,2,3	1—4	1,2,3	1—4	1—4	1,2,3	1,2,3	1,2,3	1—4	1,2,3	1—4	1,2,3	2,3,4	1—4	1—4	Ex 2	Ex 2	2,3,4	1,2,3	1—4	1,2,3	1,2,3	1—4	2,3,4
Cologne—		a.m.	a.m.	a.m.	a.m.		a.m.	a.m.	a.m.	p.m.	p.m.		p.m.	p.m.	p.m.	p.m.			p.m.	p.m.	p.m.	p.m.	p.m.	p.m.	p.m.		p.m.	p.m.	a.m.
Hauptbahnhof ......dep	...	5 48	7 5	7 52	8 51	...	9 37	1010	1138	1220	1 4	...	2 23	3 17	4 54	5 14	...	...	6 24	7 5	7 14	7 21	7 50	8 11	9 1	...	1020	11 9	12 20
Longerich	...	6 3	...	8 7	...	...	9 52	...	...	1235	...	...	...	3 31	...	5 29	...	...	6 39	7 21	:	...	8 7	...	9 16	...	...	1123	12 31
Worringen	...	6 12	...	8 16	...	...	10 2	1027	...	1244	...	...	...	3 40	...	5 38	...	...	6 48	7 38	RC	RC	8 16	...	9 26	...	...	1133	12 38
Dormagen	...	6 21	...	8 25	...	...	1011	1035	...	1252	...	...	...	3 48	...	5 47	...	...	6 56	7 46	:	...	8 35	...	9 35	...	...	1141	12 45
Neuss ....arr	...	6 45	7 38	8 48	9 23	a.m.	1035	1051	1212	1 15	1 36	p.m.	2 55	4 11	5 26	6 10	p.m.	...	7 18	8 8	:	7 52	8 59	8 43	10 1	p.m.	1052	12 3	1 1
DUSSELD'F134C ......dep	...	6a32	7a25	8a35	8 a49	9 13	1020	1039	1152	1259	...	1 52	2 p44	3p56	5p16	5 p16	5 59	...	7 p4	7p40	7 p57	7p40	9 p16	8 p35	9p46	1027	1034	1145	...
Neuss ....dep	...	6 52	7 45	8 58	9 25	:	1043	1056	1217	1 27	...	:	3 5	4 19	5 36	6 14	:	...	7 29	8 19	:	7 57	9 30	8 53	10 9	:	1056	1210	1 3
Osterath	...	7 4	...	9 9	...	:	1054	...	1228	1 39	...	:	...	4 30	...	6 25	:	...	7 40	8 31	:	...	9 41	...	1021	:	...	1221	...
Oppum	...	7 15	...	9 19	...	:	11 4	...	1238	1 51	...	:	...	4 40	...	6 35	:	...	7 50	8 41	:	...	9 51	9 9	1031	:	...	1232	...
Crefeld 135 ....arr	...	7 20	8 5	9 24	9 45	9 41	11 9	1114	1243	1 57	...	2 21	3 24	4 46	5 55	6 40	6 28	...	7 56	8 47	8 25	8 15	9 56	9 14	1036	1056	1116	1238	1 23
Crefeld 135 ....dep	...	7 26	8 9	9 50			1119	12 3	1250	2 6	...		3 28	4 56	5 57	6 52		...	8 35	9 39	8 29	8 17		9 17	11 4			1244	
Kempen ....arr	a.m.	7 42	8 22	10 5	...	...	1132	1220	1 6	2 23	...	...	3 40	5 12	6 9	7 8	...	p.m.	8 48	9 57	:	:	...	9 29	1120	...	...	1 0	...
Kempen ....dep	6 29	7 47	...	1010	...	...	1137	...	1 38	...	...	...	3 48	6 13	...	7 14	...	8 28	9 42	...	:	:	...	:	112	...	...		...
Grefrath	6 42	8 0	...	1023	...	...	1151	...	1 53	...	...	...	4 2	6 28	...	7 29	...	8 42	9 56	...	:	:	...	:	1136	...	...	...	...
Kaldenkirchen	7 0	8 19	...	1046	...	...	1211	...	2 13	...	...	...	4 20	6 54	...	7 51	...	9 1	1013	...	:	:	...	:	1154	...	...	...	...
Venlo ....arr	7 7	8 26	...	1053	...	...	1218	...	2 20	...	...	...	4 27	7 1	...	7 59	...	9 8	...	...	:	:	...	:	12 0	...	...	...	...
ROTTERDAM 117 ...arr	...	1050	...	...	...	...	4p41	...	...	...	...	...	8 p52	...	...	10p44	...	...	...	...	:	:	...	:	...	...	...	...	...
Kempen ....dep	...	7 46	8 23	10 7	...	...	1135	...	1 8	2 33	...	...	3 44	5 15	6 10	7 10	...	...	8 50	...	:	:	...	9 30	1122	...	...	...	...
Aldekerk	...	7 59	...	1019	...	...	1145	...	1 20	2 47	...	...	...	5 28	...	7 22	...	...	9 2	...	:	:	...	...	1134	...	...	...	...
Geldern 130	...	8 17	8 42	1036	...	...	12 2	...	1 39	3 5	...	...	4 2	5 44	6 28	7 38	...	...	9 18	...	:	:	...	9 48	1151	...	...	...	...
Kevelaer	...	8 33	...	1050	...	...	1217	...	1 54	3 22	...	...	...	5 59	...	7 52	...	...	9 30	...	:	:	...	9 59	12 6	...	...	...	...
Weeze	...	8 42	...	1059	...	...	1226	...	2 3	3 31	...	...	...	6 7	...	8 0	...	...	9 40	...	:	:	...	...	1215	...	p.m.	a.m.	...
Goch	...	8 52	9 5	11 8	...	...	1237	...	2 14	3 42	...	...	4 22	6 16	6 48	8 10	...	...	9 50	...	9 11	:	...	10 12	1225	...	11 5	5 37	...
BOXTEL 120 ....arr	...	1033	1033	...	...	...	2p12	...	...	5p14	...	...	5 p25	...	7p35	...	...	...	...	...	9 p54	:	...	...	...	...	...	...	...
VLISSINGEN 113 ......arr	...	...	3p36	...	...	...	5p35	...	...	...	...	...	9 p30	...	...	...	...	...	...	...	11p52	:	...	...	...	...	...	...	...
Kleve ....arr	...	9 9	9 19	1129	...	...	1258	...	2 34	4 3	...	...	4 35	6 35	7 2	8 29	...	...	1010	...	...	9 12	...	10 25	1246	...	1128	6 0	...
Kleve ....dep	...	9 30	9 23	...	...	...	1 6	...			...	...	4 41	6 45	7 8		...	...	1032	...	...	9 16	...			...		6 5	...
Groesbeek ***	...	9 35	...	...	...	...	1 10	...	...	...	...	...	...	7 5	...	...	...	...	1032	...	...	...	...	...	...	...	...	6 15	...
Nymegen *** ....arr	...	9 50	9 10	...	...	...	1 25	...	...	...	...	...	4 34	7 20	6 53	...	...	...	1047	...	...	9 1	...	...	...	...	...	6 30	...
AMSTERDAM 118C...arr	...	...	1125	...	...	...	3p28	...	...	...	...	...	6p50	...	8p51	...	...	...	...	...	...	1057	...	...	...	...	...	...	...
ROTTERDAM 119A ...arr	...	...	1135	...	...	...	4p47	...	...	...	...	...	7 p1	...	9 p4	...	...	...	...	...	...	11p8	...	...	...	...	...	...	...
HOEK V. HOLL. 112 arr	...	...	...	...	...	...	...	...	...	...	...	...	...	...	...	...	...	...	...	...	...	1135	...	...	...	...	...	...	...

†—Week-days only.

NYMEGEN, KLEVE, VENLO, KEMPEN, and COLOGNE.

HOEK V. HOLLAND 112 dp	...	...	...	...	...	...	...	...	5a25	...	...	...	...	...	...
ROTTERDAM 119 ......dep	...	...	...	...	...	...	...	...	5a51	...	...	...	...	8 a30	...
AMSTERDAM 118B ...dep	...	...	...	...	...	...	...	...	...	6a10	...	...	...	8 a48	...
	1,2,3	1—4	1—4	1,2,3	2,3,4	1,2,3	Ex 2	Ex2	Ex2	Ex2	1—4	1—4	1,2,3	1,2,3	1—4
		a.m.	a.m.						a.m.	a.m.	a.m.			a.m.	
Nymegen *,* ....dep	...	...	3 52	...	...	...	...	...	7 35	7 44	6 17	...	...	10 26	...
Cranenburg (Cust. Ex.) ...	...	...	5 8	...	...	...	...	...	8 53	8 40	7 31	...	...	11 39	...
Kleve ....arr	...	...	5 32	...	a.m.	a.m.	...	...	9 6	/	7 53	a.m.	...	11 51	...
Kleve ....dep	...	5 4	5 52	...	6 49	7 32	...	...	9 7	—	8 6	9 41	...	11 55	...
VLISSINGEN 113 ......dep	...	...	...	...	...	...	...	4a15		...	...	...	...	7 a20	...
BOXTEL 120 ....dep	...	...	...	...	...	...	...	6a25		...	6a30	...	...	10 a5	...
Goch	...	5 23	6 13	...	7 12	7 47	...	8 15		...	8 35	10 3	...	12 10	...
Weeze	...	5 32	6 23	...	7 22	...	...		RC	...	8 45	10 12	...	...	...
Kevelaer	...	5 41	6 32	...	7 31	8 1	...			...	8 54	10 21	...	...	...
Geldern	...	5 52	6 46	...	7 43	8 12	...			...	9 8	10 38	...	12 32	...
Aldekerk	...	6 8	7 2	...	8 0	...	...	RC		...	9 25	10 56	...	...	...
Kempen ....arr	...	6 23	7 14	...	8 13	8 29	...			...	9 36	11 9	...	12 49	...
ROTTERDAM 116...dep	...	...	...	...	...	...	...			...	...	4 a52	...	...	...
		a.m.	a.m.		a.m.						a.m.	a.m.			
Venlo ....dep	...	5 14	6 17	...	7 21	...	...			...	8 42	10 0	...	...	...
Kaldenkirchen	...	5 41	6 41	...	7 41	...	...			...	9 0	10 22	...	...	...
Grefrath	...	6 2	7 1	...	7 59	...	...			...	9 19	10 42	...	...	...
Kempen ....arr	a.m.	6 17	7 15	...	8 13	...	...			...	9 33	10 56	...	...	p.m.
Kempen ....dep	6 27	6 36	7 19	...	8 16	8 30	a.m.			...	9 39	11 19	...	12 51	1 7
Crefeld ....arr	6 43	6 55	7 33	a.m.	8 33	8 42		8 58	10 5	...	9 56	11 36	p.m.	1 3	1 24
Crefeld ....dep	6 52	7 2	7 41	7 56	—	8 44	9 0	9 6	10 6	...	1018	11 45	12 50	1 6	1 28
Oppum	7 4	7 10	7 49		...	8 50		...		...	1025	11 53		...	1 35
Osterath	...	7 23	7 58		...	...		...		...	1034	12 4		...	1 44
Neuss 134A ....arr	7 19	7 34	8 10		...	9 5		9 23		...	1045	12 15		1 25	1 55
DUSSELDORF 134A...arr	7 a36	7a56	8a37	8 a25	...	9a24	9 a30	...	1033	...	1121	12 37	1 p18	1 p56	...
Neuss ....dep	7 23	7 45	8 27	...	...	9 10	...	9 24		...	1054	12 22	...	1 28	2 4
Dormagen	...	8 10	...	...	...	...	...	...		...	1118	12 46	...	...	2 28
Worringen	...	8 19	...	...	...	...	...	...		...	1127	12 55	...	...	2 36
Longerich	...	8 28	...	...	...	...	...	...		...	1136	1 15	...	...	2 46
Cologne Haupt ......arr	7 56	8 42	9 0	...	...	9 41	...	9 56	1115	...	1150	1 19	...	2 0	3 1

HOEK V. HOLLAND 112 dp	...	...	...	...	...	...	...	...	...	...	...	...	...	...
ROTTERDAM 119 ......dep	8 a30	...	...	1054	...	...	...	...	...	...	...	...	2p41	4p54
AMSTERDAM 118B ...dep	8 a48	...	...	1053	...	...	...	...	...	1147	...	...	3p35	5 p29
	1—4	2 3 4	1,2,3	1,2,3	1—4	1,2,3	1,2,3	1,2,3	1,2,3	1—4	1—4	2,3,4	1—4	1,2,3
	a.m.			p.m.						p.m.	p.m.		p.m.	p.m.
Nymegen *,* ....dep	10 26	...	...	1 7	...	...	...	...	...	2 47	...	...	5 53	7 30
Cranenburg (Cust. Ex.) ...	11 39	...	...	2 29	...	...	...	...	...	4 2	...	...	7 10	8 40
Kleve ....arr	11 51	...	...	2 41	p.m.	...	...	...	...	4 24	...	...	7 32	9 1
Kleve ....dep	12 7	...	...	2 46	2 4	...	...	...	...	4 37	5 57	...	7 41	9 11
VLISSINGEN 113 ......dep	7 a20	...	...	...	...	...	...	...	...	...	1225	...	1p27	...
BOXTEL 120 ....dep	10 a5	...	...	1155	...	...	...	...	...	...	3p40	...	5p20	...
Goch	12 31	...	...	3 2	2 26	...	...	...	...	5 3	6 18	...	8 7	9 30
Weeze	12 40	...	...	...	2 35	...	...	...	...	5 12	6 27	...	8 16	...
Kevelaer	12 50	...	...	3 16	2 44	...	...	...	...	5 24	6 36	...	8 27	9 44
Geldern	1 5	...	...	3 27	3 1	...	...	...	...	5 40	6 51	...	8 39	9 56
Aldekerk	1 21	...	...	...	3 20	...	...	...	...	5 58	7 7	...	8 55	...
Kempen ....arr	1 30	...	...	3 44	3 33	...	...	...	...	6 7	7 18	...	9 7	10 14
ROTTERDAM 116...dep	8 a14	...	...	9 a4	...	...	...	...	...	1147	...	...	3 p3	4p45
	p.m.			p.m.						p.m.			p.m.	p.m.
Venlo ....dep	12 28	...	...	2 42	...	...	...	...	...	5 4	...	...	8 3	9 19
Kaldenkirchen	12 52	...	...	3 2	...	...	...	...	...	5 23	...	...	8 23	9 37
Grefrath	1 12	...	...	3 24	...	...	...	...	...	5 43	...	...	8 44	9 57
Kempen ....arr	1 26	p.m.	...	3 39	...	...	...	...	...	5 58	...	p.m.	9 0	10 11
Kempen ....dep	1 33	2 25	...	3 47	3 55	...	...	...	...	6 11	7 20	8 31	9 13	10 17
Crefeld ....arr	1 50	2 42	...	3 59	4 12	...	p.m.	p.m.	p.m.	6 28	7 36	8 48	9 29	10 30
Crefeld ....dep	2 0	2 55	...	4 7	4 18	...	5 34	6 4	6 49	6 35	7 40	8 54	9 36	10 35
Oppum	2 7	3 1	...	4 14	4 24	...		6 10		6 42	7 47	9 2	9 42	...
Osterath	2 17	3 11	...	...	4 34	...		...		6 51	7 56	9 12	9 52	...
Neuss 134A ....arr	2 29	3 22	...	4 32	4 45	...		6 25		7 2	8 7	9 23	10 3	10 54
DUSSELDORF 134A...arr	2 p54	3p45	p.m.	4p51	5p34	p.m.	6 p3	...	7p18	7p25	8p36	...	1025	11p19
Neuss ....dep	2 35	3 30	3 34	4 42	5 20	5 40	...	6 27	...	7 8	8 27	9 35	1015	11 0
Dormagen	...	...	...	...	5 43	...	...	...	...	7 33	8 50	...	1041	...
Worringen	...	...	...	...	5 51	...	...	...	...	7 42	8 59	...	1049	...
Longerich	...	...	...	...	6 0	...	...	...	...	7 51	9 8	...	1058	...
Cologne Haupt ......arr	3 10	4 2	4 28	5 14	6 14	6 45	...	7 0	...	8 6	9 22	10 10	1112	11 32

CREFELD LOCAL SERVICE.

*—From or at Moers Local Bahnhof.

	a.m.	a.m.	a.m.	a.m.	a.m.	p.m.	p.m.	p.m.	p.m.	p.m.	p.m.		
Suchteln ....dep	5†40	6 41	7 31	9 18	1138	1 15	2 6	3 15	5 20	6†30	8 4	...	...
St. Tönis	6 0	7 5	7 53	9 38	12 0	1 35	2 27	3 36	5 40	6 53	8 24	...	...
Crefeld Sud. .....arr	6 10	7 15	8 3	9 47	12 9	1 44	2 36	3 45	5 49	7 2	8 33	...	...

	a.m.	a.m.	a.m.	p.m	p.m.	p.m	p.m.	p.m.	p.m.	p.m.	p.m.		
Crefeld ....dep	7 41	8†18	1015	1220	2 15	3 2	4 20	6 40	7†20	8 15	9 45	...	...
St. Tönis	7 52	8 28	1025	1230	2 26	3 12	4 30	6 52	7 30	8 26	9 55	...	...
Suchteln ....arr	8 13	8 47	1044	1249	2 47	3 34	4 49	7 13	7 49	8 45	1014	...	...

	a.m.	a.m.	a.m.		p.m.	p.m.	p.m.	p.m.	p.m.		
Mörs ....dep	6* 7	6 44	9 24	...	1234	3 30	5 0	6 41	8 28	...	...
Huls ....arr	6 51	7 23	10 5	a.m.	1 12	4 9	5 41	7 18	9 5	...	...
Viersen ....dep	...	6 30	...	9 57	1 36	3 7	...	6 22	7 54	...	...
Suchteln ....dep	5 50	6 40	...	10 4	1 43	3 26	...	6 31	8 2	...	...
Suchtelnvorst	5 56	6 45	...	1010	1 49	3 32	...	6 36	8 8	...	...
Kempen	6 21	7 7	...	1033	2 12	3 55	...	7 1	8 32	...	...
Huls ....arr	6 36	7 23	...	1047	2 26	4 9	...	7 15	8 46	...	...
Huls ....dep	6 58	7 28	10 6	1048	2 31	4 11	5 42	7 21	9 6	...	...
Crefeld Nord ......arr	7 12	7 37	1016	1058	2 41	4 21	5 52	7 32	9 17	...	...
Crefeld Sud. ......arr	7 22	...	1026	11 8	2 51	4 31	6 2	7 42	9 27	...	...

		a.m.	a.m.	a.m.	a.m.	p.m.	p.m.	p.m.	p.m.	p.m.		
Crefeld Sud. ....dep	...	6†30	8 13	1124	1156	2 10	3 7	4 45	7†15	9 4	...	...
Crefeld Nord ....dep	...	6 42	8 24	1135	1210	2 21	3 19	4 56	7 31	9 16	...	...
Huls ....arr	...	6 51	8 33	1144	1219	2 30	3 28	5 5	7 40	9 25	...	...
Huls ....dep	...	6 52	8 35	...	1221	2 32	...	5 10	7 44	9 26	...	...
Kempen ....dep	...	7 9	8 50	...	1236	2 47	...	5 25	7 59	9 41	...	...
Suchtelnvorst	...	7 31	9 12	...	1258	3 9	...	5 47	8 23	10 3	...	...
Suchteln ....arr	...	7 36	9 17	...	1 3	3 14	...	5 52	8 28	10 8	...	...
Viersen ....arr	a.m.	8 22	9 26	...	1 16	3 41	...	6 0	8†52	...	...	...
Huls ....dep	5 58	...	8 34	1145	—	2 31	3 29	5 9	7 43	9 26	...	...
Mörs ....arr	6 36	...	9 7	1220	...	3 7	4 4	5 47	8 20	9*59	...	...

	a.m.	a.m.	a.m.	a.m.	a.m.	p.m.	p.m.	p.m	p.m.	p.m.	
Viersen ....dep	...	7 22	8†27	9 10	1130	12†15	3 55	5 13	8 †15	9 2	...
Süchteln	5†55	8 30	8 33	9 16	1136	12 23	4 5	5 19	8 21	9 8	...
Süchtelnvorst	6 0	...	...	...	...	...	4 11	...	...	...	...
Grefrath ....arr	6 11	...	...	...	...	...	4 21	...	...	...	...

	a.m.	a.m.	a.m.	a.m.	p.m.	p.m.	p.m.			
Grefrath ......dep	...	6†15	...	...	...	4 40	...	...	...	...
Süchtelnvorst ...	...	6 56	...	...	...	4 51	...	p.m.	p.m	...
Süchteln	6 15	7 2	8†49	1046	2 49	4 58	7 14	8 †2	8 46	...
Viersen ....arr	6 21	7 8	8 55	1052	2 57	5 4	7 22	8 10	8 52	...

†—Weekdays only.

KLEVE and ELTEN.

Kleve ....dep	9 a30	1 p3	4 p6	8 p34	...
Elten 118 ...arr	10 12	1 45	4 48	9 16	...
Elten ....dep	6 a45	10a35	1 p54	6 p36	...
Kleve ....arr	7 30	11 17	2 36	7 17	...

PRUSSIAN STATE RAILWAYS.

For Notes and Continuation of Trains,

Luggage Rates—see page 462.] [For Fares—see page 120A.

HERBESTHAL, COLOGNE, BINGERBRUCK, MAYENCE, FRANKFORT, and ASCHAFFENBURG.

RC—Restaurant Car.

Dist. E.M.	Station	1	2	3	4	5	6	7	8	9	10	11	12	13	14	15	16	17	18	19	20	21	22	23	24	25
...	BRUSSELS 104 ......dep	...	...	...	...	...	...	...	...	11p24	...	...	...	...	...	...	...	...	...	...	...	...	...	...	5 a45	...
										Ex.2	1—4	2,3,4	1—4		Ex 3	1,2,3	1,2,3			Ex 3				1—4	Ex.2	
										SC					SC											
										a.m.		a.m.	a.m.		a.m.	a.m.	a.m.			a.m.				a.m.	a.m.	
...	Herbesthal ....dep	...	...	...	...	...	...	...	...	3 56	...	—	5 56	...	6 28	6 58	...	...	...	8 22	Direct Train from Vlissingen.	...	...	8 50	9 45	Direct Train from Hoek van Holland.
...	Aix-la-Chapelle arr	...	...	...	...	...	...	...	...	4 15	...	—	6 26	...	6 47	7 28	...	...	...	8 41		...	...	9 22	10 4	
...	(Hauptbahnhof) dep	...	...	...	...	...	...	...	...	4 20	...	5 42	6 55	...	6 50	7 31	7 59	...	...	8 43		...	...	9 29	10 7	
...	Stolberg....................	...	...	...	...	...	...	...	...	4 32	...	6 1	7 14	...	7 2	7 43	8 19	...	...	...		...	...	9 50	RC	
...	Eschweiler	...	...	...	...	...	...	...	...	4 38	a.m.	6 8	7 21	...	—	7 49	8 26	...	...	...		...	...	9 58	...	
...	Duren ....dep	...	...	...	...	...	...	...	...	4 57	5 27	6 39	7 49	...	7 24	8 8	8 51	...	...	9 15		...	...	1044	10 38	
...	Horrem	...	...	...	...	...	...	...	...	5 17	5 58	7 8	8 17	...	—	8 35	9 16	...	...	...		...	...	1112	...	
From Cologne (Haupt.)	COLOGNE (Coln) Hauptbahnhof arr	...	...	...	...	...	...	...	...	5 40	6 35	7 40	8 50	...	8 0	8 56	9 47	...	...	9 51		...	...	1143	11 14	
			2,3,4		2,3.4		2,3,4	1—4	Ex.3	1,2,3	2,3,4	Weekdays only.	2,3,4	1—4	1,2,3	Ex 3	234	1,2,3	1—4	Ex 3	Ex 2		1—4	1—4		Ex 2
								a.m.		a.m.				a.m.	a.m.	a.m.		a.m.	a.m.	a.m.	a.m.		a.m.	a.m.		a.m.
	COLOGNE (Coln) Hauptbahnhof dep	...	...	...	...	...	...	5 48	...	6 17	...		...	7 30	8 51	9 32	...	9 38	10 12	9 56	10 3	...	1132	1150	...	11 20
1½	Cologne Westbahnhof..	...	...	...	...	...	...	5 53	...	...	...		...	7 37	...	...	...	...	10 19	...	...	...	1140	...	...	...
2¾	Cologne-Sudbahnhof ...	...	...	...	...	...	...	6 2	...	6 27	...		...	7 44	9 1	RC	...	9 49	10 26	...	...	...	1147	12 0	...	RC
10	Bruhl	...	...	...	...	...	...	6 20	...	...	...		...	8 2	9 15	...	...	10 3	10 43	RC	RC	...	12 4	1214	...	...
13	Sechtem......................	...	...	...	...	...	...	6 28	...	...	...		...	8 10	...	...	...	...	10 51	...	...	...	1212	1222	...	...
17	Roisdorf	...	...	...	...	...	...	6 37	...	...	...		...	8 19	...	...	...	...	11 0	...	...	...	1221	1231	...	...
20¾	Bonn 126 .... arr	...	a.m.	...	...	...	...	6 45	...	6 54	...	...	...	8 27	9 32	10 §7	...	10 20	11 8	10 31	10 38	...	1229	1239	...	11 53
	dep	...	4 48	...	...	...	...	6 47	...	6 57	...	...	...	8 32	9 34	10 10	...	10 24	11 12	10 33	10 40	...	1233		...	11 54
25	Godesberg....................	...	5 3	...	...	...	...	6 58	...	7 7	...	...	...	8 42	9 44	...	...	10 51	11 22	...	...	...	1244	...	...	...
26¼	Mehlem (Konigswinter)	...	5 10	...	...	...	...	7 4	...	7 13	...	...	...	8 48	...	...	...	10 57	11 28	...	...	...	1250	...	...	...
29½	Rolandseck	...	5 21	...	...	...	...	7 12	...	7 21	a.m.	...	...	8 56	...	...	...	11 5	11 36	...	...	...	1 4	...	...	...
33¾	Remagen-Bad Neuen-	...	5 41	...	...	...	...	7 25	...	7 33	6 57	...	...	9 11	10 0	...	...	11 17	11 51	...	...	...	1 21	...	...	...
36½	Sinzig............ [ahr 123D	...	5 53	...	...	...	...	7 48	...	7 40	7 4	...	...	9 18	...	...	...	...	11 58	...	...	...	1 29	...	...	...
39¾	Nieder Breisig..............	...	6 8	...	...	...	...	7 57	...	...	7 13	...	...	9 27	...	...	...	...	12 7	...	...	...	1 38	...	...	...
41½	Brohl	...	6 18	...	...	...	...	8 4	...	7 52	7 20	...	...	9 34	10 15	...	...	...	12 14	...	...	...	1 45	...	...	...
46¼	Andernach 123B...........	...	6 36	...	...	...	...	8 16	...	8 3	7 31	...	...	9 46	10 26	...	...	11 38	12 36	...	...	...	2 0	...	...	...
48¾	Weissenthurm..............	...	6 48	...	...	...	...	8 23	...	8 10	7 38	...	...	9 53	10 33	...	...	11 45	12 43	...	...	...	2 7	...	...	...
51½	Urmitz	...	7 0	...	...	...	...	8 31	...	...	7 46	...	...	10 3	...	...	...	...	12 51	...	...	...	2 15	...	...	...
57½	Coblence-Haupt. ......arr	...	7 29	...	...	...	...	8 48	...	8 27	8 ·4	...	...	10 18	10 50	11 4	...	12 3	1 8	11 27	11 34	...	2 32	...	...	12 48
68¼	EMS 146..................arr	...	8 a57	...	...	...	...	...	...	9 a13	8 a57	...	...	11 a3	11a46	11a46	...	12p36	1 p48	12p36	12p36	...	3p34	...	...	1 p48
115½	WIESBADEN 128 ...arr	...		...	...	...	...	...	...	11a26		...	...	12p40	1p19	1p19	...	2 p26	...	2p26	2p26	...	6p40	...	...	2‡p46
147	HOMBURG 128 or 150 arr	...	...	...	a.m.	...	a.m.	a.m.	...	1 p25	...	...	a.m.	2 p20	3 p31	3 p31	p.m.	3 p47	...	3 p47	3 p47	...	8p53	...	...	3‡p55
...	Coblence-Haupt. ....dep	...	...	...	4 50	...	5 55	7 55	...	8 33	...	...	9 17	10 28	...	11 9	12 18	...	1 16	11 30	11 37	...	2 59	...	‡—Via Mayence, see below.	12 51
61	Capellen	...	...	...	4 59	...	6 3	8 4	...	...	...	...	9 25	10 37	...	...	12 26	...	1 24	...	...	...	3 7	...		...
63	Rhens...........................	...	...	...	5 6	...	6 9	8 11	...	...	...	...	9 31	10 43	...	...	12 32	...	1 30	...	...	...	3 14	...		...
69¾	Boppard	...	...	...	5 23	...	6 26	8 29	...	8 53	...	...	9 51	10 59	...	11 29	12 47	...	1 46	...	...	...	3 31	...		...
72¾	Salzig...........................	...	...	...	5 31	...	6 34	8 37	...	...	...	...	9 59	11 7	...	...	12 55	...	1 53	...	...	...	3 39	...		...
79	St. Goar.......................	...	...	...	5 47	...	6 50	8 54	...	9 10	...	...	10 15	11 13	...	...	1 8	...	2 8	...	...	...	3 56	...		...
83	Oberwesel	...	...	...	5 57	...	7 0	9 4	...	9 20	...	...	10 25	11 33	...	...		...	2 28	...	...	...	4 6	...		...
87	Bacharach.....................	...	...	...	6 7	...	7 10	9 14	...	9 30	...	...	10 34	11 43	...	...	...	...	2 37	...	...	...	4 16	...		...
89	Niederheimbach	...	...	...	6 14	...	7 17	9 20	...	...	...	...	10 40	11 49	...	...	...	...	2 43	...	...	...	4 22	...		...
95½	Bingerbruck ....arr	...	...	...	6 30	...	7 33	9 35	...	9 44	...	...	10 55	12 3	...	12 9	...	...	2 57	12 26	12 33	...	4 36	...		1 47
105½	KREUZNACH ...125 arr	...	...	...	7 a40	...	8 a15	10a13	...	10a13	...	...	...	...	...	12p47	...	...	3p33	12p56	12 56	...	5p14	...	...	2 p14
223½	STRASSBURG ...208 arr	...	...	...	...	...	2 p9	2 p9	...	2 p9	...	...	...	...	...	3 p48	...	...	...	3 p48	3 p48	...	...	...	...	6 p17
312	BASLE ....208 arr	Ex 3	2,3,4	...	...	...	...		...	5 p36	1—4	...	...	...	...	5 p47	...	...	...	5 p47	5 p47	...	...	...	...	8 p20

PRUSSIAN STATE RAILWAYS

see next page.

Miles	Station																									
...	PARIS 64A ....dep	5 p15	...	...	...	...	...	...	9 p5	...	...	...	...	...	...	...	10p15	3 & 4	...		...	...	...	...	...	...
...	METZ 212 ....dep	12a35	...	2 3 4	...	1,2,3	...	...	4 a54	...	...	...	...	...	2,3,4	Ex 3	9 a25	9 a25	...	...	...	...	1121	...	...	9 a25
		a.m.	a.m.	a.m.	a.m.	a.m.	a.m.		⋮	a.m.	a.m.		a.m.	p.m.	p.m.	p.m.	⋮	p.m.	p.m.		p.m.		p.m.			p.m.
...	Bingerbruck ....dep	4 26	4 58	5 47	6 36	7 13	7 41	...	⋮	9 47	10 7	...	11 2	12 16	12 53	12 11	⋮	2 8	3 2	...	12 36	...	4 53	...	...	1 50
96¼	Bingen ....dep	4 31	5 5	5 52	6 42	7 18	7 46	...	⋮	9 52	10 14	...	11 7	12 21	12 59	12 16	⋮	2 14	3 8	...	12 41	...	5 1	...	...	1 55
101¼	Gau-Algesheim	...	5 21	6 8	6 58	...	8 2	...	⋮	...	10 31	...	11 22	12 36	1 15	...	⋮	2 30	3 24	...	...	...	5 24	...	...	...
103½	Ingelheim....................	...	5 28	6 14	7 9	7 30	8 8	...	⋮	10 4	10 38	...	11 28	12 42	1 21	...	⋮	2 36	3 30	...	...	...	5 30	...	...	...
114¾	Mayence Haupt. ......arr	4 58	6 4	6 47	7 42	7 48	8 42	...	9 32	10 22	11 12	...	12 3	1 20	1 54	12 43	1 27	3 8	4 3	...	1 7		6 2	...	...	2 22
...	WIESBADEN ....arr	5 a20	6 a23	7a31	...	8 a50	9 a22	...	10a14	10a44	11a35		12p27	1 p43	2 p23	1 p6	2 p9	3 p32	4 p30	...	1 p32		6p35	...	...	2 p46
245¾	STRASSBURG 208 arr	10a55	10a55	...	...	12p49	...	...	...	...	...	...	...	...	...	5 p10	5 p10	7 p5	...	...	5 p10		...	...	...	7 p5
334¼	BASLE Swiss 208 arr	12p58	12p58	...	...	2 p52	...	...	...	...	...	...	...	...	...	7 p22	7 p22	9 p13	...	...	7 p22		...	...	...	9p13
329½	BASLE Badische 140	11 a0	12p43	...	...	2 p55	...	...	...	...	...	...	5 p38	7 p56	...	5 p38	9 p56	8 p55	10p21	...	7 p56		...	...	...	7 p56
		Ex 2		1,2,3	2 3,4	1,2,3	2,3,4		Ex 3	1,2,3	1—4		2 3,4	1—4		Ex 3	Ex 3		1—4		Ex.2		1—4			Ex 2
		a.m.		a.m.	a.m.	a.m.	a.m.		a.m.	a.m.	a.m		p.m.	p.m.		p m.	p.m.		p.m.		p.m.	p.m.	p m.			p.m.
...	Mayence Haupt......dep	5 0	...	7 3	8 14	8 1	8 54	...	9 36	10 28	11 22	...	12 21	1 49	...	12 58	1 39	...	4 12	...	1 13	1 13	6 31	...	...	2 25
115¾	,, Sud	...	...	7 8	8 19	8 6	8 59	...	...	10 33	11 27	...	12 26	1 54	...	...	...	...	4 17	...	...	Via Mannheim.	6 37	...	...	...
122½	Rüsselsheim..................	...	...	7 21	8 39	8 17	9 18	...	...	10 45	11 46	...	12 45	2 13	...	...	...	...	4 36	...	...		6 56	...	...	...
129¼	Kelsterbach	...	...	...	8 57	...	9 37	...	...	...	12 3	...	1 2	2 31	...	...	...	...	4 55	...	...		7 15	...	...	...
134¼	Goldstein	...	...	...	9 10	...	9 50	...	...	...	12 15	...	1 14	2 45	...	...	...	...	5 9	...	...		7 28	...	...	...
135¾	Niederrad....................	...	...	...	9 16	...	9 56	...	...	...	12 21	...	1 20	2 52	...	...	...	...	5 15	...	...		7 34	...	...	...
138	FRANKFORT........arr Hauptbahnhof	5 38	...	7 47	9 22	8 44	10 2	...	10 14	11 11	12 27	...	1 26	2 58	...	1 36	2 17	...	5 21	...	1 57		7 41	...	...	3 5
		Ex 3	2,3,4	1,2,3	2,3,4		2,3,4	1,2,3		2,3,4	2,3,4		1,2,3	1—4		Ex 3	⋮	2,3,4	1,2,3	2,3 4			23 4			⋮
		a.m.	a.m.	a.m.	a.m		a.m.	a.m.		a.m.	a.m.		noon	p.m.		p.m.	⋮	p.m.	p.m.	p.m.			p.m.			⋮
...	Mayence Haupt...dep	5 54	6 15	7 9	7 51	...	9 0	9 24	...	10 38	11 41	...	12 8	2 15	...	1 32	⋮	3 54	4 48	5 11	...	Via Mannheim.	6 25	...	...	⋮
119½	Bischofsheim	...	6 35	...	8 8	...	9 17	...	...	10 55	11 58	...	12 22	2 32	...	...	⋮	4 12	...	5 31	...		6 43	...	...	⋮
125	Nauheim	...	6 46	...	8 19	...	9 28	...	...	11 6	12 10	...	...	2 44	...	...	⋮	4 24	...	5 43	...		6 55	...	...	⋮
127	Gross-Gerau	6 18	6 52	7 36	8 26	...	9 34	9 52	...	11 12	12 16	...	12 35	2 51	...	1 56	⋮	4 31	5 14	5 51	...		7 2	...	...	⋮
136	Darmstadt ....arr	6 33	7 15	7 53	8 50	...	9 57	10 8	...	11 32	12 38	...	12 50	3 14	...	2 12	⋮	4 54	5 29	6 14	...		7 25	...	...	⋮
173½	HEIDELBERG 136 arr	7 a53	8 a43	...	10a45	...	11 a3	...	...	1 p37	...	...	2 p24	5 p4	...	3 p13	⋮	...	6 p30	8 p40	...	3 p0	9p20	...	...	⋮
243¼	STUTTGART ..192 arr	...	11a28	...	2 p24	...	2 p24	...	...	4 p47	...	...	4 p47	7 p42	...	6 p29	⋮	...	9 p21	...	...	4 p47	1215	...	...	⋮
392¾	MUNICH........192 arr	...	3 p25	...	9 p35	...	9 p35	...	...	9 p40	...	...	9 p40	11p23	...	11p23	⋮	...	...	...	...	9 p40	...	...	...	⋮
329½	BASLE ....140 arr	12p16	12 43	...	2 p55	...	2 p55	...	...	5 p38	...	...	...	...	...	7 p0	⋮	...	10p21	...	...	...	...	...	...	⋮
135¾	Darmstadt ....dep	6 38	7 30	8 15	9 14	...	...	...	...	11 37	1 0	...	...	3 30	...	2 20	⋮	...	...	6 24	...	...	7 48	...	...	⋮
147	Dieburg	6 58	8 2	8 36	9 47	...	...	...	...	12 4	1 32	...	...	4 3	...	2 39	⋮	...	...	6 59	...	...	8 17	...	...	⋮
153½	Babenhausen	7 10	8 31	8 49	10 9	...	...	...	...	12 23	1 51	...	...	4 25	...	2 50	⋮	...	...	7 22	...	...	8 39	...	...	⋮
162	Aschaffenburg 196 arr	7 24	8 53	9 5	10 29	...	...	...	...	12 43	2 13	...	...	4 47	...	3 3	⋮	...	...	7 44	...	...	9 1	...	...	⋮
281	NURNBERG 195A arr	11a39	...	1241	5 p58	...	...	...	...	...	...	...	...	9 p22	...	6 p54	6 p54	...	...	...	...	...	...	...	...	9 p22
389¾	MUNICH ....196 arr	2 p0	...	...	...	...	...	...	...	...	...	...	...	12a40	...	8 p55	8 p55	...	...	...	...	...	...	...	...	10p25
680	VIENNA......239A arr	9 p50	...	9p50	...	...	...	...	...	...	...	...	...	7 a20	...	7 a20	7 a20	...	...	...	...	...	...	...	...	7 a20

FARES FROM COLOGNE.

	1 Cl. m. pf.	2 Cl. m. pf.	3 Cl. m. pf.		1 Cl. m. pf.	2 Cl. m. pf.	3 Cl. m. pf.
To Basle	41 20	26 20	16 80	To Munich	51 40	31 50	20 30
,, Darmstadt	19 0	12 30	7 80	,, Nurnberg	37 40	23 60	15 0
,, Ems..................	9 50	6 20	3 90	,, Strassburg	30 0	19 40	12 60
,, Frankfort...........	19 20	12 40	7 90	,, Stuttgart	33 10	21 30	13 70
,, Heidelberg	23 20	15 40	9 60	,, Vienna	97 10	58 70	37 70
,, Homburg	20 0	13 30	8 20	,, Wiesbaden	16 60	10 80	6 80
,, Kreuznach	15 50	10 10	6 30				
,, Mayence	16 60	10 80	6 80				

§—This stop at Bonn is only for long distance traffic and to take up.

RC—Restaurant Car.

BINGERBRUCK and RUDESHEIM.—(Steamer Service across the Rhine).

	a.m.	a.m.	a.m.	a.m.	a.m.	a.m.	a.m.	a.m.	a.m.	a.m.	a.m.	a.m.	a.m.	a.m.	a.m.	a.m.	a.m.	a.m.	p.m.	p.m.	p.m.	p.m.	p.m.	p.m.	p.m.	p.m.	p.m.	p.m.	p.m.
Bingerbruck......dep	...	...	6 58	...	...	...	8 16	8 38	...	...	...	9 45	10 0	...	...	11 0	...	11 35	...	...	...	...	...	1 13	...	...	1 53	2 32	...
Bingen	5 43	6 23	7 8	7 35	7 48	8 10	8 26	8 48	9 2	9 20	9 35	9 55	10 10	10 31	1055	11 10	11 33	11 45	1210	12 23	1238	1255	1 11	1 25	1 40	2 6	2 15	2 42	3 3
Rudesheim ......arr	5 55	6 35	7 20	7 47	8 0	8 22	8 38	9 0	9 14	9 32	9 47	10 7	10 22	10 43	11 7	11 22	11 45	11 57	1222	12 35	1250	1 6	1 23	1 37	1 52	2 18	2 27	2 54	3 15
	p.m.	p.m.	p.m.	p.m.	p.m.	p.m.	p.m.	p.m.	p.m.	p.m.	p.m.	p.m.	p.m.	p.m.	p.m.	p.m.	p.m.	p.m.	p.m.	p.m.	p.m.	p.m.							
Bingerbruck......dep	...	...	3 52	...	...	4 49	5 4	...	5 45	...	...	...	...	7 25	7 53	...	...	8 46	8 58	9 48	...	...	...	...	...	...	...	...	
Bingen	3 26	3 40	4 2	4 20	4 40	4 59	5 14	5 35	5 55	6 10	6 34	7 0	7 10	7 35	8 3	8 15	8 33	8 56	9 7	9 58	11 5	11 50	...	...	...	...	...	...	
Rudesheim.........arr	3 38	3 52	4 14	4 32	4 52	5 11	5 26	5 47	6 7	6 22	6 46	7 12	7 22	7 47	8 15	8 27	8 45	9 8	9 18	1010	1117	12 2	...	...	...	...	...	...	

PRUSSIAN STATE RAILWAYS.

Luggage Rates—see page 462.] For Fares—see page 120A.

HERBESTHAL, COLOGNE, BINGERBRUCK, MAYENCE, FRANKFORT, and ASCHAFFENBURG.

SC—Sleeping Car.

BRUSSELS 104 ......dep	...	...	...	...	...	...	...	...	8 a17	10a10	10a54	1054	...	...	...	10a59	1 p32	...	...	...	3 p3	5p22	5 p0	5 p0	6 p38	6 p46	...
		2,3,4		1—4		1,2,3	1—4		1—4	1,2,3	Ex 2	1—4	Ex 3	2,3,4	2,3,4	1—4	1,2,3	1,2,3		1—4	1—4	Ex1	Ex.3	Ex.3	Ex.1	1,2,3	1—4
Herbesthal ....dep	...	...	...	a.m. 10 36	...	p.m. 12 34	...	...	p.m. 12 46	p.m. 2 25	p.m. 2 49	p.m. 2 56	p.m. 4 20	...	...	p.m. 4 51	p.m. 6 0	p.m. ...	...	p.m. ...	p.m. 7 52	p.m. 9 18	p.m. 9 27	p.m. 9 50	p.m. 10 24	p.m. 11 59	p.m. 10 30
Aix-la-Chapelle arr	...	p.m.	...	11 5	...	12 54	...	...	1 15	2 44	3 8	3 25	4 39	...	...	5 20	6 19	...	...	...	8 21	9 37	9 48	10 9	10 43	12 28	10 59
(Hauptbahnhof) dep	...	12 1	...	11 24	...	1 7	...	...	1 20	3 17	3 12	3 29	4 42	p.m.	...	5 25	6 26	6 11	...	...	8 26	9 39	9 52	10 12	10 45		11 18
Stolberg	...	12 18	...	11 43	...	1 19	...	...	1 40	3 29	...	3 49	4 54	3 0	...	5 45	6 38	6 24	...	...	8 49	N	...	10 24	...	...	11 41
Eschweiler	...		...	11 49	...	1 25	p.m.	...	1 48	3 35	RC	3 56	5 0	3 7	...	5 52	6 44	6 31	...	...	8 57	...	...	10 30	O	...	11 57
Duren ....dep	...	...	...	12 17	...	1 44	1 53	...	2 18	3 54	3 43	4 30	5 19	3 35	p.m.	6 23	7 4	6 52	...	8 4	9 28	1010	10 25	10 48	11 16	...	12 23
Horrem..................	...	...	...	12 45	...	2 3	2 21	...	2 43	4 13	...	4 58	RC		3 34	6 53	...	...	...	8 37	9 55	...	...	RC	...	...	
COLOGNE (Coln) Hauptbahnhof arr	...	...	...	1 16	...	2 24	2 53	...	3 15	4 34	4 19	5 31	5 55	...	4 7	7 24	7 40	7 30	...	9 16	10 28	1046	11 1	11 24	11 52	...	...
	Ex 2	1,2,3	1,2,3	1,2,3	Ex.3	1—4	2 3 4	Ex 3	1—4	1—4	1—4	1,2,3	Ex 3	1,2,3	1—4	1—4	Ex 3	1—4	Ex 3	Ex3		1—4	1—4		Ex.1	1—4	Ex.3
COLOGNE (Coln) Hauptbahnhof dep	p.m. 12 10	p.m. 12 32	p.m. 1 5	p.m. 1 29	p.m. 2 31	p.m. 2 36	...	...	p.m. 3 23	p.m. 4 30	p.m. 5 20	p.m. 5 56	p.m. 6 33	p.m. 5 14	p.m. 6 39	p.m. 7 32	p.m. 8 2	p.m. 8 41	p.m. 10 22	p.m. 1033	...	...	p.m. 11 20	N—Nord Express.	p.m. 11 57	nght 12 28	a.m. 1 58
Cologne Westbahnhof...	...	...	...	1 37	...	2 44	...	...	...	...	5 27	...	...	...	6 47	7 39	...	8 48	...	...	...	...	11 28		...	...	...
Cologne-Sudbahnhof ...	RC	12 43	...	1 43	...	2 51	...	...	3 33	4 40	5 34	6 6	SC	5 24	6 54	7 45	...	8 55	...	SC	...	...	11 33		O	12 38	SC
Bruhl.....................	...	12 57	...	2 0	...	3 9	...	...	3 47	4 54	5 52	...	...	...	7 11	8 3	RC	9 12	A	...	...	...	11 52		...	12 55	...
Sechtem	...	...	...	2 8	...	3 17	...	...	...	...	6 0	...	...	...	7 19	8 11	...	9 20	...	...	...	...	12 0		...	...	...
Roisdorf	...	...	...	2 17	...	3 26	...	...	...	...	6 9	...	...	...	7 28	8 20	...	9 29	...	...	...	...	12 9		...	...	...
Bonn (126) ...... arr	12 45	1 11	1 38	2 25	3 6	3 34	...	...	4 5	5 11	6 17	6 33	7 8	5 51	7 36	8 28	8 37	9 37	10 57	11 7	...	p.m.	12 17		12 30	1 13	2 33
Bonn (126) ...... dep	12 47	1 17	1 41	2 29	3 8	3 40	...	...	4 9	5 13	6 23	6 35	7 13	5 53	7 42	8 45	8 40	9 44	10 58	11 8	...	1118	12 20		12 31	1 18	2 35
Godesberg	...	1 27	1 52	2 39	...	3 51	...	...	4 20	5 23	6 34	6 45	7 24	6 3	7 53	8 56	...	9 56	...	...	...	1129	12 31	...	...	1 28	...
Mehlem (Konigswinter)	...	1 33	...	2 45	...	3 57	...	...	4 26	5 29	6 40	...	...	6 9	7 59		...	10 2	...	...	...	1135	12 36	...	...	...	...
Rolandseck	...	1 41	...	2 53	...	4 5	...	...	4 34	5 37	6 56	...	...	6 17	8 7	...	...	10 10	...	...	...	1143		...	...	1 38	...
Remagen-Bad Neuen-	...	1 52	2 9	3 9	...	4 21	...	...	4 44	5 53	7 11	7 2	7 44	6 26	8 24	...	9 3	10 26	A	...	...	1157	...	...	...	1 49	...
Sinzig...........[ahr 123D	...	1 59	...	3 16	...	4 28	...	...	4 51	6 0	7 18	...	...		8 31	...	...	10 33	...	...	...		...	...	...	1 56	...
Nieder Breisig	...	...	...	3 25	...	4 37	...	...	5 0	6 9	7 27	...	...	...	8 40	...	...	10 42	...	...	...	...	...	...	...	2 5	...
Brohl......................	...	...	...	3 42	...	4 41	...	...	5 7	6 16	7 34	...	...	...	8 47	...	...	10 49	...	...	...	...	...	...	...	2 12	...
Andernach (123B) ...	...	2 18	...	3 54	...	4 57	...	...	5 20	6 28	7 46	...	8 6	...	9 0	...	9 24	11 1	...	...	...	...	...	...	...	2 24	...
Weissenthurm	...	...	...	4 1	...	5 4	...	...	5 27	6 35	7 53	...	...	...	9 8	...	...	11 8	...	...	...	...	...	...	...	2 31	...
Urmitz	...	...	...	4 9	...	5 12	...	...	5 35	6 43	8 1	...	...	...	9 17	...	...	11 16	...	...	...	...	...	...	...	...	...
Coblence-Haupt. arr	1 41	2 39	2 47	4 26	4 3	5 29	...	...	5 52	7 0	8 18	7 40	8 27	...	9 35	...	9 45	11 33	11 53	12 2	...	...	...	...	1 24	2 50	3 30
EMS (146)............arr	2 p54	3 p34	3 p34	...	...	6 p10	...	...	7 p9	8 p3	8 p59	8p59	9 p43	...	11 p9	...	11 p9	12a56	12a56	1256	...	...	...	...	...	5 a9	5 a9
WIESBADEN (128) arr	4 p42	6 p40	6 p40	7 p5	7 p5	8 p23	...	...	...	...		10p2	...	1—4	1 a13	...	1 a13	...	...	...	...	2 3 4	...	...	...	5 a8	5 a8
HOMBURG 128, 150 arr	6 p27	8 p53	8 p53	8p53	8p53	10p32	p.m.	...	...	...	...	1143	...	p m.		p m.	...	...	...	...	...	n'gt	...	...	...	7 a1	7 a1
Coblence-Haupt. dep	1 45	...	2 54	4 31	4 8	...	5 0	...	6 15	7 15	...	7 44	8 32	8 37	...	11 0	9 50	...	11 57	12 7	...	1230	...	...	1 28	2 55	3 36
Capellen	...	...	...	...	...	...	5 8	...	6 23	7 23	...	...	...	8 45	...	11 8	...	...	...	...	...	1239	...	...	⋮	3 2	⋮
Rhens	...	...	...	...	...	...	5 14	...	6 29	7 29	...	...	...	8 51	...	11 14	...	...	...	...	...	1246	...	...	⋮	3 8	⋮
Boppard	...	...	3 14	4 50	...	...	5 31	...	6 45	7 44	...	8 4	...	9 8	...	11 31	...	...	...	...	...	1 3	...	...	⋮	3 23	⋮
Salzig	...	...	...	...	...	...	5 39	...	6 53		...	...	...	9 16	...	11 39	...	...	...	...	...		...	...	⋮	3 30	Via Wiesbaden.
St. Goar	...	...	3 31	5 6	...	...	5 55	...	7 10	...	p.m.	...	...	9 31	...	11 55	...	...	A	...	...	...	...	...	⋮	3 45	⋮
Oberwesel	...	...	...	5 16	...	...	6 5	...	7 20	...	8 51	...	...	9 41	...	12 5	...	...	...	...	...	...	...	...	⋮	3 54	⋮
Bacharach	...	...	3 48	5 26	...	...	6 15	...	7 30	...	9 1	...	...	9 50	...	12 15	...	...	...	...	...	...	...	...	⋮	4 3	⋮
Niederheimbach...........	...	...	...	...	...	...	6 21	...	7 36	...	9 7	...	...	9 56	...	12 21	...	...	...	...	...	...	...	...	⋮	4 9	⋮
Bingerbruck ......arr	2 41	...	4 2	5 40	5 4	...	6 37	...	7 51	...	9 22	8 44	9 28	10 10	...	12 35	10 46	...	12 53	1 3	...	...	...	...	⋮	4 22	⋮
KREUZNACH (135) arr	3 p3	...	5p14	6 p14	6p14	...	7 p44	...	8 p40	...	...	9 p6	10 p8	10p59	...	1 a27	12a12	...	1a17	1a27	...	...	...	...	⋮	5 a6	⋮
STRASSBURG (208) ar	6 p17	...	...	...	...	...	...	...	12a27	...	...	1227	...	...	...	4 a22	...	...	4a10	4a22	...	...	...	...	⋮	11 a7	⋮
BASLE (208) ......arr	8 p20	...	...	...	...	...	...	...	...	...	...	...	...	...	...	6 a24	...	...	6a14	6a24	...	...	...	...	⋮	1 p19	⋮

PRUSSIAN STATE RAILWAYS.

PARIS (64)..........dep	...	...	...	...	...	...	...	9 a0	...	9 a0	...	...	9 a0	...	...	...	...	...	...	...	...	...	...	...	⋮	5 p15	⋮
METZ (212)..........dep	9a25	...	11a21	...	...	...	...	4 p11	...	4 p11	...	...	4 p11	...	Ex 3	...	...	3 Cl.	...	5p35	...	...	...	...	⋮	12a35	⋮
	p.m.		p.m.	p.m.	p.m.		p.m.	⋮	p.m.	p.m.	p.m.	p.m.	p.m.	p.m.	p.m.		p.m.	p.m.	...	a.m.	a.m.				⋮	a.m.	⋮
Bingerbruck.......dep	2 49	...	4 7	5 42	5 6	...	6 43	⋮	8 1	8 58	9 36	8 52	9 30	10 15	10 6	...	10 48	10 53	...	1 12	3 0	...	...	...	⋮	4 31	⋮
Bingen ....dep	2 54	...	4 12	5 47	5 11	...	6 48	⋮	8 9	9 3	9 41	8 57	9 35	10 20	10 11	...	...	10 58	...	1 17	3 5	...	...	...	⋮	4 38	⋮
Gau-Algesheim	...	...	...	...	...	...	7 5	⋮	8 28	9 18	9 55	...	...	10 34	...	...	...	11 12	...	...	3 22	...	...	...	⋮	4 54	⋮
Ingelheim	...	...	...	6 0	...	...	7 15	⋮	8 34	9 24	10 1	...	...	10 40	...	...	...	11 17	...	...	3 28	...	...	...	⋮	5 0	⋮
Mayence Haupt ...arr	3 21		4 39	6 18	5 38	...	7 49	8 39	9 8	9 53	10 31	9 24	10 2	11 9	10 38	...	11 16	11 46	...	1 44	3 59	...	...	...	2 48	5 30	5 25
WIESBADEN..........arr	3 p47		5 p11	6 p55	6 p19	...	8 p19	9 p4	10 p1	10p48	11p21	10p1	10p48	11p43	11p21	...	11p43	12 a8	...	3a10	4 a45	...	...	...	3 a10	5 a56	5 a56
STRASSBURG 208 arr	7 p5		...	12a27	...	...	...	...	...	...	...	...	...	3 a58	...	...	3 a58	...	...	5a34	...	...	...	...	...	10a55	10a55
BASLE Swiss 208 arr	9p13		...	...	...	...	...	...	...	...	...	...	...	6 a7	...	...	6 a7	...	...	8 a5	...	...	...	...	...	12p58	12p58
BASLE Badische 140	8 p55		10p21	...	...	...	...	...	...	...	...	...	5 a38	...	5a38	...	5 a38	...	...	...	...	...	...	...	...	...	11 a0
		1,2,3	1,2,3	1,2,3	Ex.3	Ex 3	2,3,4	Ex 3	1—4		3 Cl.	1,2,3	Ex 3	1—4	Ex 3		Ex 3			Ex3	2,3,4	2 3 4	2,3,4		Ex.1	1—4	Ex 3
		p.m.	p.m.	p.m.	p.m.	p.m.	p.m.	p.m.	p.m.		p.m.	p.m.	p.m.	p.m.	p.m.		p.m.			a.m.	a.m.	a.m.	a.m.		a.m.	a.m.	a.m.
Mayence Haupt ...dep	...	3 28	4 43	6 20	5 55	7 57	8 13	8 42	9 42	...	10 56	9 26	10 6	11 36	10 42	...	11 30	...	...	1 56	4 16	5 5	6 31	...	2 49	6 0	5 30
,, Sud	...	3 33	4 48	6 25	...	...	8 19	...	9 47	...	11 1	...	...	11 41	...	...	...	...	...	...	4 21	5 10	6 36	...	...	6 5	⋮
Rüsselsheim	...	...	5 1	6 38	...	...	8 39	...	10 9	...	11 21	9 40	...	12 0	...	...	...	...	...	...	4 42	5 31	6 55	...	...	6 26	⋮
Kelsterbach.................	...	...	...	...	...	...	9 9	...	10 39	...		...	...	12 20	...	...	...	...	...	...	5 2	5 52	7 13	...	...	6 45	⋮
Goldstein	...	...	...	...	...	...	9 23	...	10 55	...	...	...	...	12 35	...	...	...	...	...	...	5 17	6 8	7 27	...	...	6 57	⋮
Niederrad....................	...	...	...	...	...	...	9 29	...	11 1	...	...	...	...	12 41	...	...	...	...	...	...	5 23	6 15	7 33	...	...	7 3	⋮
FRANKFORT ......arr Hauptbahnhof	...	4 8	5 29	7 5	6 33	8 35	9 35	9 20	11 7	...	...	10 7	10 44	12 47	11 20	...	12 8	...	...	2 34	5 29	6 21	7 39	...	3 26	7 9	⋮
		⋮	1,2,3	1,2,3			2 3 4		2 3 4				1,2,3				⋮	2,3 4						2 3 4	⋮		⋮
		⋮	p.m.	p.m.			p.m.		p.m.				p.m.				⋮	p.m.	...					a.m.	⋮		⋮
Mayence Haupt dep	...	⋮	4 48	7 30	...	...	8 2	...	9 36	...	...	...	10 34	...	...	...	⋮	11 59	...	...	...	...	...	5 12	⋮	...	⋮
Bischofsheim	...	⋮	...	...	...	...	8 20	...	9 53	...	...	...	...	...	...	...	⋮	12 17	...	...	...	...	...	5 33	⋮	...	⋮
Nauheim	...	⋮	...	...	...	...	8 32	...	10 4	...	...	...	...	...	...	...	⋮	12 29	...	...	...	...	...	5 46	⋮	...	⋮
Gross-Gerau	...	⋮	5 14	7 57	...	...	8 40	...	10 11	...	...	...	10 59	...	...	...	⋮	12 35	...	...	...	...	...	5 55	⋮	...	⋮
Darmstadt ......arr	...	⋮	5 29	8 14	...	...	9 2	...	10 33	...	...	...	11 15	...	...	...	⋮	12 59	...	...	...	...	...	6 19	⋮	...	⋮
HEIDELBERG **136** ar	...	⋮	6 p30	9 p56	...	...	11 p4	...	12 31	...	...	...	12 41	...	...	...	⋮	...	...	...	...	...	...	7 a53	⋮	...	7 a29
STUTTGART **192** arr	...	⋮	9p21	12a15	...	...	...	...	...	...	...	...	3 a4	...	...	...	⋮	...	...	...	...	...	...	...	⋮	...	9 a19
MUNICH **192** ...arr	...	⋮	...	...	...	...	...	...	...	...	...	...	7 a20	...	...	...	⋮	...	...	...	2,3,4	...	...	...	⋮	...	1 p8
BASLE **140** ......arr	...	⋮	10p21	...	...	...	...	...	5 a38	...	...	...	5 a38	...	...	...	⋮	...	...	...	a.m.	...	...	12p16	⋮	...	12p16
Darmstadt ......dep	...	⋮	...	...	...	...	9 17	...	10 45	...	...	...	11 24	...	...	...	⋮	...	...	...	5 30	...	...	...	⋮	...	...
Dieburg.....................	...	⋮	...	...	...	...	9 43	...	11 17	...	...	...	11 43	...	...	...	⋮	...	...	...	6 2	...	...	...	⋮	...	...
Babenhausen **135**B ...	...	⋮	...	...	...	...	10 3	...	11 37	...	...	...	11 55	...	...	...	⋮	...	...	...	6 24	...	...	...	⋮	...	...
Aschaffenburg arr	...	⋮	...	...	...	...	10 21	...	11 59	...	...	...	12 10	...	...	...	⋮	...	...	...	6 46	...	...	...	4 a22	...	...
NURNBERG **195**A arr	...	9 p22	...	...	...	...	...	...	...	...	...	...	4 a52	...	...	...	4 a52	...	...	...	...	...	...	...	7 a56	...	...
MUNICH **196** ...arr	...	12a40	...	...	...	...	...	...	...	...	...	...	9 a29	...	...	...	9 a29	...	...	...	...	...	...	...	11a15	...	...
VIENNA **239**A. .arr	...	7 a20	...	...	...	...	...	...	...	...	...	...	6 p32	...	...	...	6 p22	...	...	...	...	...	...	...	6 p0	...	...

A—Runs in July and August only. O—Ostend-Vienna Express. SC—Sleeping Car.

MAYENCE and WIESBADEN (in 15 minutes). **Mayence** Hbf. dep. 2.53, 4.23 a.m., and about three times hourly until 11.50 p.m., also at 12.16 and 12.37 night. **Wiesbaden** dep. 1.17, 5.13 a.m., and about three times hourly until 11.41 p.m., also at 12.13 night.

RUDESHEIM and BINGERBRUCK.—(Steamer Service across the Rhine).

	a.m.	a.m.	a.m.	a.m.	a.m.	a.m.	a.m.	a.m.	a.m.	a.m.	a.m.	a.m.	a.m.	a.m.	a.m.	a.m.	a.m.	p.m.	p.m.	p.m.	p.m.	p.m.	p.m.	p.m.	p.m.	p.m.	p.m.	p.m.	p.m.	p.m.
Rudesheim...dep	6 8	6 40	7 30	7 55	8 10	8 30	8 45	9 5	9 20	9 39	9 50	10 10	10 30	10 55	11 15	11 33	11 50	12 10	12 25	1241	1256	1 10	1 26	1 49	2 0	2 26	2 37	3 0	3 22	3 43
Bingen	6 25	6 50	7 40	8 10	8 20	8 40	9 0	9 15	9 39	9 52	10 0	10 20	10 45	11 5	11 25	11 48	12 0	12 20	12 35	1256	1 6	1 20	1 44	1 59	2 24	2 41	2 47	3 31	3 32	3 58
Bingerbruck arr	6 30	...	...	8 15	...	...	9 5	...	9 44	9 57	...	...	10 50	...	...	11 53	...	...	...	1 1	...	...	1 49	...	2 29	2 46	...	3 36	...	4 3

	p.m.	p.m.	p.m.	p.m.	p.m.	p.m.	p.m.	p.m.	p.m.	p.m.	p.m.	p.m.	p.m.	p.m.	p.m.	p.m.	p.m.	p.m.	p.m.	p.m.	a.m.								
Rudesheim...dep	4 0	4 20	4 40	5 0	5 20	5 40	5 55	6 20	6 38	6 50	7 16	7 32	8 0	8 17	8 32	8 50	9 13	9 25	10 30	11 25	12 20	...	...	...	...	...	...	...	...
Bingen..............	4 10	4 35	4 50	5 17	5 30	5 50	6 5	6 30	6 53	7 0	7 26	7 45	8 10	8 32	8 47	9 0	9 28	9 40	10 40	11 35	12 30	...	...	...	...	...	...	...	...
Bingerbruck arr	...	4 40	...	5 22	...	...	...	...	6 58	...	...	7 50	...	8 37	8 52	...	9 33	9 45	...	...	...	...	...	...	...	...	...	...	...

For Continuation of Trains,

Luggage Rates—see page 462.] For Fares—see page 120A.

ASCHAFFENBURG, FRANKFORT, MAYENCE, BINGERBRUCK, COLOGNE, and HERBESTHAL.

Station																													
VIENNA 239 ......dep	12 0	...	7a25	...	...	...	...	...	...	...	...	...	1 p0	...	...	...	...	...	...	...	...	...	...	...	...	...	...	...	...
MUNICH 196A ...dep	...	...	4p25	...	...	...	...	...	...	...	...	...	1018	...	...	...	...	...	...	...	...	...	...	...	...	...	...	...	...
NURNBERG 195A dep	8 p49	...	6p10	8p55	...	...	...	...	...	...	...	...	9 p3	...	...	...	...	...	...	...	...	...	...	...	...	...	...	...	...
	nght		Ex3 p.m.							134			1,2,3 a.m.		1—4			2 3 4 a.m.		2 3 4	1,2,3		2 3 4 a.m.	2,3,4 a.m.		2 3 4 a.m.		1—4	
Aschaffenburg......dep	12 0	...	1037		...	...	...	...	...	...	...	...	4 35	...	...	...	...	4 47	...	...	...	...	5 36	6 45	...	8 2	...	...	...
Babenhausen		...	1053		...	...	...	...	...	...	...	...	...	...	...	...	...	5 8	...	...	...	...	6 0	7 7	...	8 31	...	...	...
Dieburg		...	11 5		...	...	...	...	...	...	...	...	...	...	...	...	...	5 29	...	...	...	...	6 21	7 27	...	8 50	...	...	...
Darmstadt ....arr		...	1124		...	...	...	...	...	...	...	...	5 14	...	...	...	...	6 0	...	...	...	...	6 52	7 57	...	9 18	...	...	...
BASLE 141 ....dep		...	5p33		9p41	...	...	...	...	...	...	...	1152	...	...	...	...	1152	...	...	...	...	...	...	...	...	...	4a30	...
MUNICH 192A ...dep	⊙	...	2p50		5p20	...	...	...	...	...	...	...	1025	...	...	...	...	1025	...	...	...	...	...	...	...	...	...	...	...
STUTTGART 192A dep		...	6p50		1038	...	...	...	...	...	...	...	2a19	...	...	...	...	2a19	...	...	...	...	...	...	...	6 a0	...	6a58	...
HEIDELBERG 136 dep		...	9p33			...	...	...	...	...	...	...	4a10	...	a.m.	...	...	4a25	...	6 a5	6a10	...	...	...	...	8 a2	...	10a2	...
Darmstadt..........dep		...	1130			...	...	...	...	a.m.	...	...	5 19	-	5 26	...	...	6 29	...	7 23	8 11	...	...	...	...	9 24	...	1114	...
Gross-Gerau		...	1147			...	...	...	...	4 50	...	...	5 35	...	5 49	...	...	6 54	...	7 48	8 31	...	...	...	...	9 49	...	1137	...
Nauheim		...	...			...	...	...	...	5 1	...	...	...	...	5 56	...	...	7 0	...	7 54	...	...	...	...	...	9.56	...	1143	...
Bischofsheim		...	...			...	...	...	...	5 16	...	...	...	...	6 7	...	...	7 12	...	8 6	...	...	...	...	...	10 8	...	1154	...
Mayence Haupt. ...arr		...	1212			...	...	...	...	5 35	...	...	5 56	...	6 25	...	...	7 28	...	8 22	8 55	...	...	...	...	1024	...	1210	...
FRANKFORT—	Ex.1 a.m.	1—4 p.m.		Ex3 a.m.									1,2,3 a.m.	Ex3 a.m.	1—4 a.m.	1—4 a.m.	1—4 a.m.	Ex3 a.m.		1—4 a.m.	Ex3 a.m.				Ex3 a.m.		1—4 a.m.	2 3 4 a.m.	
Hauptbahnhof......dep	1 1	1049		1 44	Via Mannheim.	...	...	...	...	...	...	...	5 20	5 35	4 37	5 42	6 35	7 32	...	7 17	8 30	...	...	...	9 51	...	1025	1130	...
Niederrad	...	1056		...		...	...	...	...	...	...	...	...	...	4 44	5 49	6 42	...	...	7 24	...	...	...	...	...	...	1032	1137	...
Goldstein	⊙	11 1		...		...	...	...	...	...	...	...	...	...	4 50	5 55	6 48	...	...	7 30	...	...	...	...	...	...	1038	1144	...
Kelsterbach	...	1114		...		...	...	...	...	...	...	...	...	...	5 4	6 8	7 2	...	...	7 52	...	...	...	...	...	...	1051	1158	...
Rüsselsheim	...	1130		...		...	...	...	...	...	...	...	5 45	...	5 21	6 24	7 20	...	...	8 8	...	...	...	...	1016	...	11 9	1216	...
Mayence Sud	...	1148		...		...	...	...	...	...	...	...	5 59	...	5 44	6 49	7 38	...	...	8 26	...	...	...	...	1030	...	1129	1238	...
,, Haupt. ...arr	1 37	1153		2 21	2a28	...	...	...	...	...	...	...	6 3	6 14	5 48	6 54	7 43	8 8	...	8 31	9 7	...	...	...	1034	...	1133	1242	...
STRASSBURG 209...dep		7 p7		...		...	...	...	...	...	...	...	1a53	...	...	...	...	...	...	...	6 a0	...	...	...	...	...	...	9a33	...
BASLE Swiss 209...dep		4p59		...		...	...	...	...	...	...	...	1148	...	...	...	...	...	...	...	...	...	...	...	...	...	...	7a40	...
BASLE Badische 141 dp		5p33		9p41		...	...	...	...	...	...	...	1152	...	...	...	...	...	...	...	...	...	...	...	...	...	...	4a30	...
WIESBADEN ....dep		1120	1146	1a17		...	...	...	...	...	...	...	5a35	...	6 a8	6 a45	...	7a51	...	7a51	8a59	9 a15	...	...	...	1014	1130	1236	1154
Mayence—		1—4	Ex3	Ex3			1—4	1—4	1—4		2 3 4	2,3,4	1,2,3		1—4	2,3,4	1—4	Ex3	1,2,3	1—4	Ex3	2,3,4	1,2,3			2 3 4	1—4	2 3 4	2 3 4
Hauptbahnhof ...dep	1 39	n'gt 12 2	n'gt 1235	a.m. 2 28		...	...	...	...	...	a.m. 3 55	a.m. 5 22	a.m. 6 10	...	a.m. 6 30	a.m. 7 32	...	a.m. 8 10	...	a.m. 8 37	a.m. 9 20	a.m. 9 38	...	...	...	a.m. 1048	a.m. 1151	p.m. 1 6	p.m. 1218
Ingelheim		1229	...	...	...	...	...	...	...	...	4 28	5 53	6 28	...	7 3	8 1	...	...	...	9 12	...	10 9	...	...	...	1124	1224	1 39	1250
Gau-Algesheim		1235	...	...	...	...	...	...	...	...	4 34	5 59	...	...	7 10	8 7	...	...	...	9 18	...	10 16	...	...	...	1130	1230	1 45	1256
Bingen ....arr		1248	1 6	3 3	...	...	...	...	...	...	4 48	6 13	6 40	...	7 23	8 23	...	8 36	...	9 31	9 46	10 29	...	...	...	1143	1243	1 58	1 10
Bingerbruck ....arr		1252	1 11	3 9	...	...	...	...	...	...	4 55	6 19	6 45	...	7 29	8 27	...	8 41	...	9 37	9 52	10 34	...	...	...	1149	1249	2 3	1 14
METZ 212 ....arr		7a48	7a48	1128	...	...	...	...	...	...	...	...	...	...	...	...	...	1241	...	4p56	4p56	...	...	...	...	...	6p22	...	6p22
PARIS 65 ....arr		...	...	...	...	...	...	...	...	...	...	...	...	...	...	...	...	6p40	...	1147	1147	...	...	...	...	...	1147	...	...
BASLE 209A ....dep		4p37	9p33	9p33	...	...	...	...	...	...	...	...	...	...	...	...	...		...	...	...	...	...	...	...	...	...	...	...
STRASSBURG 209 dep		6p50	1141	1141	...	...	...	...	...	...	...	...	...	...	...	...	...	...	6 a0	6 a0	6 a0	...	...	...	...	...	...	...	...
KREUZNACH 125A dep		1212	2a31	2a31	...	...	...	...	...	...	4 a2	...	5a57	...	6a40	...	...	...	9a24	9a24	9a24	...	...	...	...	1027	1213	1 p2	...
Bingerbruck............dep		a.m. 1257	a.m. 2 51	a.m. 3 10	...	...	...	...	...	...	a.m. 5 6	a.m. ...	a.m. 6 48	...	a.m. 7 34	...	...	...	a.m. 9 44	a.m. 10 3	a.m. 9 55	...	...	...	...	a.m. 1158	p.m. 1256	p.m. 2 17	...
Niederheimbach		1 12	...	...	...	...	...	...	...	...	5 21	...	...	...	7 49	...	...	...	...	1020	...	...	...	...	--	1214	1 13	2 32	...
Bacharach		1 18	...	...	...	...	...	...	...	...	5 27	...	7 3	...	7 55	...	...	...	...	1027	...	...	...	...	2 3 4	1220	1 20	2 38	...
Oberwesel		1 27	...	...	...	...	...	...	...	...	5 36	...	7 13	...	8 5	...	...	...	...	1037	...	...	...	...	p.m.	1229	1 30	2 4[illegible]	...
St. Goar		1 38	...	...	...	...	...	...	...	...	5 46	6 47	7 24	...	8 16	...	...	...	1013	1049	...	...	...	...	1 18	1239	1 40	2 58	...
Salzig		1 52	...	...	...	...	...	...	...	...	6 2	7 3	...	...	8 30	...	...	...	...	11 5	...	...	...	...	1 31	1254	1 57	3 14	...
Boppard......................		2 1	...	...	...	...	...	...	...	...	6 10	7 11	7 40	...	8 39	...	...	...	...	1115	1037	...	...	...	1 38	1 2	2 6	3 22	...
Rhens		2 16	...	...	...	...	...	...	...	...	6 28	7 27	...	...	8 55	...	...	...	...	1132	...	...	...	...	1 55	1 18	2 23	3 39	...
Capellen......................		2 22	...	...	...	...	...	...	...	...	6 35	7 33	...	...	9 1	...	...	...	.	1138	...	...	...	...	2 0	1 24	2 29	3 45	...
Coblence Haupt. ......arr	3 1	2 30	3 46	4 7	...	...	...	...	...	...	6 43	7 42	7 59	...	9 9	...	...	...	1043	1146	1056	...	...	...	2 8	1 31	2 37	3 53	...

see next page.

Station																													
HOMBURG 129 or 150 dep		...	...	1010	...	...	...	...	...	...	...	...	...	...	...	...	...	...	5 a2	7a32	7a32	...	9 a2	...	—	—	9a26	...	...
WIESBADEN 129 ...dep		...	...	1257	...	...	...	...	...	...	...	...	4a59	1—4	4a59	...	...	...	7a44	8a56	8a56	...	1056	...	...	...	1143	...	...
EMS 147 ...dep		1233	...	...	...	...	...	a.m.	5a10	...	6a20	...	6a20	8 a2	8 a7	...	...	...	9a21	1051	1012	...	1258	...	...	...	2 p1	...	...
Coblence-Haupt. ...dep	3 5	2 37	3 50	4 11	...	...	...	4 54	5 50	...	7 15	...	8 3	8 42	9 15	...	...	...	1048	12 6	11 1	...	1 45	...	...	...	2 49	...	...
Urmitz	...	...	...	...	...	...	...	5 9	6 9	...	7 29	...	...	9 0	9 32	...	...	...	...	1224	...	...	2 3	...	...	...	3 6	...	...
Weissenthurm	O	2 57	...	...	...	...	...	5 17	6 18	...	7 37	...	8 20	9 8	9 40	...	...	...	11 6	1232	...	...	2 11	...	...	...	3 14	...	...
Andernach	...	3 5	...	...	...	...	...	5 24	6 26	...	7 45	...	8 27	9 15	9 48	...	...	...	1113	1240	1122	...	2 19	...	...	...	3 36	...	...
Brohl	...	3 16	...	...	...	...	...	5 34	6 37	...	7 53	...	...	9 26	9 58	...	...	...	...	1251	...	...	2 30	...	...	...	3 46	...	...
Nieder Breisig	...	...	...	...	...	...	...	5 41	6 44	...	8 3	...	...	9 33	10 4	...	...	...	...	1258	...	...	2 37	...	...	...	3 52	...	...
Sinzig	...	3 29	...	...	...	...	...	5 50	6 53	...	8 12	...	...	9 42	1013	...	...	...	...	1 8	...	...	2 46	...	...	...	4 1	...	...
Remagen B. Neuenahr	...	3 44	...	...	...	...	...	6 1	7 0	...	8 22	...	8 48	9 52	1021	...	...	...	1135	1 17	1144	...	2 54	...	...	...	4 9	...	...
Rolandseck	...	3 55	...	...	...	...	a.m.	6 15	7 14	...	8 32	...	...	10 6	1035	...	...	...	...	1 31	...	...	3 4	...	...	...	4 23	...	...
Mehlem	...	...	...	...	...	...	5 37	6 24	7 23	...	8 40	...	...	1014	1043	...	...	...	...	1 39	...	...	3 12	...	...	...	4 31	...	...
Godesberg	...	4 5	...	...	1—4	...	5 43	6 32	7 30	...	8 47	...	9 4	1020	1049	...	...	...	1151	1 46	12 1	...	3 18	...	...	...	4 37	...	...
Bonn arr	4 0	4 14	4 45	5 6	a.m.	...	5 52	6 42	7 39	...	8 56	...	9 13	1029	1058	...	p.m.	...	12 0	1 55	1210	...	3 27	...	...	...	4 46	...	...
Bonn dep	4 1	4 17	4 47	5 8	5 31	...	5 57	6 51	7 44	...	8 58	...	9 16	1032	11 1	...	1 14	...	12 2	1 59	1213	...	3 29	...	...	...	4 51	...	...
Roisdorf	...	4 26	...	...	5 40	...	6 6	7 0	7 53	...	...	...	...	...	1110	...	1 23	...	...	2 8	...	...	...	...	...	...	5 0	...	...
Sechtem	...	4 35	...	...	5 49	...	6 15	7 9	8 2	...	...	...	...	...	1119	...	1 32	...	...	2 17	...	...	...	...	...	...	5 9	...	...
Bruhl	...	4 43	...	...	5 58	...	6 23	7 18	8 10	...	9 17	...	...	1051	1127	...	1 40	...	...	2 26	...	...	3 49	...	...	...	5 17	...	...
Cologne-Sudbahnhof	...	5 0	...	...	6 17	...	6 42	7 35	8 27	...	9 31	...	...	11 5	1144	...	1 57	...	1229	2 44	1240	...	4 3	...	...	...	5 34	...	...
Cologne-Westbahnhof	...	...	...	...	6 22	...	6 47	7 40	8 32	...	...	...	...	...	1149	...	2 2	...	...	2 49	...	...	...	...	...	...	5 39	...	...
COLOGNE (Coln) Hauptbahnhof arr	4 35	5 9	5 21	5 42	6 28	...	6 53	7 46	8 38	...	9 39	...	9 50	1114	1155	...	2 8	...	1237	2 55	1248	...	4 11	...	...	...	5 45	...	...
	Ex 1		2 3 4	1,2,3	1—4	Ex3	Ex 1	1—4		Ex3	2—4	Ex.3	1—4		1—4	1,2,3		1,2,3		1—4	1,2,3	Ex 3	Ex2	1—4	2 3 4	1,2,3	Ex2	1—4	1—4
	a.m.			a.m.	a.m.	a.m.	a.m.	a.m.		a.m.	a.m.	a.m.	a.m.		p.m.	a.m.		p.m.		p.m.	p.m.	p.m.	p.m.	p.m.		p.m.	p.m.	p.m.	p.m.
COLOGNE (Coln) Hauptbahnhof dep	4 41	...	...	6 0	6 48	7 56	8 7	8 11	...	9 10	...	10 5	1028	...	1237	11 26	...	1 33	...	3 25	1 44	3 12	4 19	5 3	...	5 33	6 13	6 53	6 33
Horrem	...	...	...	6 23	7 24	...	...	8 43	...	...	...	...	11 2	...	1 12	11 49	...	2 1	...	4 0	2 7	...	RC	5 38	...	...	RC	7 31	7 11
Duren (127) ...dep	5 22	...	...	6 46	8 1	8 37	8 48	9 13	...	9 51	...	10 47	1137	...	1 45	12 13	...	2 24	...	4 32	2 31	3 53	5 0	6 4	...	6 15	6 53	8 6	7 41
Eschweiler	O	...	...	7 9	8 28	...	N	9 41	...	1010	...	RC	12 6	...	2 13	12 32	...	2 43	...	4 58	2 50	RC	...		p.m.	6 35	...	8 35	
Stolberg (129B)	...	...	...	7 16	8 38	...	...	9 49	...	1017	1036	...	1215	...	2 21	12 39	...	2 50	...	5 6	2 57	...	...	...	7 23	6 43	...	8 42	...
Aix-Chapelle-Haupt. arr	5 54	...	a.m.	7 32	8 57	9 9	9 20	10 9	...	1029	1057	11 19	1235	...	2 40	12 52	...	3 2	...	5 25	3 10	4 25	5 32	...	7 43	6 55	7 24	9 1	...
" dep	5 56	...	8 44	7 37	9 33	9 12	9 23	11 2	...	1032		11 23	1256	...	2 46		...		...	5 56	3 16	4 29	5 47	...	7 46	6 58	7 27	9 10	...
Herbesthal ...arr	6 16	...	9 17	8 7	10 5	9 32	9 43	1134	...	1052	...	11 43	1 26	...	3 17	...	...	...	...	6 28	3 36	4 49	6 7	...	8 17	7 18	7 47	9 47	...
BRUSSELS (104) ...arr	7 a52	...	1126	1025	1 p3	1126	11a31	...	...	1 p3	...	2 p51	3p44	...	5p44	...	...	...	...	...	6 p8	6 p57	8 p0	...	...	9p45	9p45	...	...

†—Weekdays only.

N—Nord Express. O—Vienna-Ostend Express. RC—Restaurant Car.

Extra—Andernach to Mayen Ost, 12.55 p.m.

ANDERNACH and GEROLSTEIN.

Station										
Andernach	5a44	6a58	8a34	9a57	11a42	3 57	5p27	...	7p50	9p35
Plaidt	5 53	7 8	8 44	10 7	11 51	4 6	5 37	...	7 59	9 45
Niedermend	6 10	7 27	9 3	1025	12 6	4 21	5 56	...	8 15	10 3
Mayen Ost arr	6 28	7 46	9 23	1045	12 23	4 38	6 15	...	8 33	1022
Mayen Ost dep	6 34	7 58	10 4	—	12 27	4 44	6 26	7p50	8 36	1030
Monreal	6 54	8 20	1025	...	12 47	5 4	6 48	8 10	8 55	1050
Kaisersesch	7 17	8 37	1043	...	1 8	5 25	7 12	8 30	9 17	11 7
Daun	8 22	—	1142	...	2 13	6 29	8 21	—	1012	—
Gerolstein	9 8	...	1227	...	3 1	7 17	9 6	...	...	...

Station											
Gerolstein dep		...	5a19	7 a27	10a27	...	1p39	...	5p11	...	9p33
Daun		...	6 12	8 27	11 20	...	2 30	...	6 5	...	1020
Kaisersesch		5a52	7 11	9 33	12 26	...	3 33	...	7 9	8p58	1116
Monreal		6 10	7 29	9 52	12 47	...	3 51	...	7 27	9 17	1134
Mayen Ost arr		6 29	7 48	10 15	1 6	p.m.	4 13	p.m.	7 46	9 38	1153
Mayen Ost dep	5a42	6 36	8 56	10 22	1 16	2 30	4 29	5 45	7 56	9 49	—
Niedermeng	5 59	6 56	9 13	10 39	1 32	2 47	4 45	6 4	8 13	10 6	...
Plaidt	6 13	7 15	9 27	10 53	1 45	3 1	4 59	6 18	8 27	1020	...
Andernach	6 20	7 25	9 34	11 0	1 52	3 8	5 6	6 25	8 34	1027	...

	am	am	a.m.	pm	p.m.	p.m.	p.m.
Mayen Ost.	550	754	1048	110	4 44	8 3	1026
Coblence H.	720	912	12 9	226	6 9	9 26	1142

	am	am	a.m.	pm	p.m.	p.m.	p.m.
Coblence H.	614	846	11 5	3 4	6 23	8 57	1129
Mayen Ost.	738	959	1221	425	7 44	1016	1247

BINGERBRUCK and HERMESKEIL.

E.M.	Station								
	Bingerbruck ...dep	...	6 a51	10 a4	1 p21	3 p38	6 p49	8 p7	10p24
5	Langenlonsheim	...	7 13	10 22	1 38	3 57	7 10	8 34	10 47
14¼	Stromberg	a.m.	7 47	10 55	2 13	4 33	7 47	9 9	11 23
28½	Simmern	5 38	8 46	11 49	3 7	5 26	8 38	10 1	12 14
34¾	Kirchberg	6 1	9 9	12 11	3 31	5 49	—	1023	—
44¾	Hirschfeld	6 42	9 44	12 44	4 4	6 25	...	1056	...
54	Morbach	7 22	10 19	1 17	4 34	7 1	...	1128	...
73½	Hermeskeil ...arr	8 31	11 25	2 20	—	8 7	...	1232	...

Station								
Hermeskeil ...dep	...	4a53	9 a2	12 p2	...	3 p59	p.m.	8p32
Morbach	...	6 4	10 16	1 23	...	5 13	7 20	9 41
Hirschfeld	...	6 40	10 47	1 55	p.m.	5 51	7 58	1023
Kirchberg	...	7 16	11 22	2 34	4 23	6 30	8 33	11 3
Simmern	4a42	7 41	11 52	3 3	4 52	6 54	8 57	1125
Stromberg	5 37	8 31	12 43	3 54	5 47	7 47	9 52	—
Langenlonsheim	6 11	9 4	1 14	4 26	6 20	8 18	10 26	...
Bingerbruck 123 arr	6 31	9 30	1 45	4 46	6 36	8 54	10 44	...

SIMMERN and BOPPARD.

E.M.	Station							
	Simmern ...dep	5 a3	8 a51	11a55	3p15	5 p30	7 p0	10 p4
9¼	Castellaun	5 42	9 28	12 34	4 0	6 9	7 38	10 37
18¼	Pfalzfeld	6 18	10 2	1 10	4 42	6 43	8 13	...
32¾	Boppard ...arr	7 27	11 9	2 20	5 49	7 53	9 20	...

Station								
Boppard ...dep	...	6 a29	8 a56	12 p2	3p36	6 p12	9 p53	...
Pfalzfeld	...	7 36	10 5	1 12	4 46	7 30	11 0	...
Castellaun	6a57	8 6	10 42	1 47	5 33	8 9	11 33	...
Simmern ...arr	7 32	8 40	11 17	2 24	6 13	8 44	12 8	...

PRUSSIAN STATE RAILWAYS.

Luggage Rates—see page 462.] [For Fares—see page 120A.

ASCHAFFENBURG, FRANKFORT, MAYENCE, BINGERBRUCK, COLOGNE, and HERBESTHAL.

VIENNA 239 ......dep	8p30	...	...	...	...	...	...	...	8 p40	...	...	...	...	...	...	...	...	...	...	...	...	...	...	7 a25	...	...	...	...
MUNICH 196A......dep	...	...	...	...	...	...	...	...	9 a0	...	...	...	...	...	...	...	...	...	...	...	...	...	...	12p45	...	...	...	...
NURNBERG 195A dep	7 a0	...	...	...	...	...	...	...	9 a20	...	...	...	...	...	...	...	...	...	...	...	...	9a31	...	5 p8	...	...	...	...
	1,2,3 a.m.			1,2,3			234		Ex 3 p.m.	234 p.m.		234 p.m.	1,2,3						2—4	234 p.m.		234 p.m	1,2,3			234 p.m.	234 p.m.	3 Cl. ngt.
Aschaffenburg dep	11 8	...	...	...	...	...	...	...	2 2	1218	...	2 26	...	...	...	...	...	...	...	4 30	...	5 48	...		...	7 27	9 5	12 5
Babenhausen............	1123	...	...	...	...	...	...	...	2 18	1244	...	2 54	...	...	...	...	...	...	...	4 50	...	6 17	...		...	7 53	9 29	12 28
Dieburg	1135	...	...	...	...	...	...	...	2 30	1 7	...	3 14	...	...	...	...	...	...	...	5 10	...	6 37	...		...	8 13	9 48	12 47
Darmstadt ....arr	1153	...	...	...	...	...	...	...	2 48	1 38	...	3 45	...	...	...	...	...	...	...	5 41	...	7 7	...		...	8 40	10 19	1 18
BASLE 141 ....dep	4a30	...	...	8 a0	...	...	...	...	9 a50	...	...	9a50	1042	...	...	...	...	...	...	...	...	...	2 p33		...	...	5 p33	...
MUNICH 192A ...dep	...	...	...	...	...	...	...	...	7 a0	...	...	...	8a22	...	...	...	...	...	...	...	...	...	12p45		...	...	2 p50	...
STUTTGART 192A dep	6a58	...	...	10a3	...	...	...	...	10 52	...	...	...	1222	...	...	...	...	...	...	...	...	...	4 p47		...	4p47	6 p50	...
HEIDELBERG 136 dep	10a2	...	...	1224	...	...	p.m.	...	1 p43	...	...	2p12	3p13	...	...	...	...	...	...	3p35	...	5 p9	6 p51		...	6p51	9 p29	...
Darmstadt.........dep	12 3	...	...	1 42	...	...	1255	...	2 58	1 52	...	4 0	4 31	...	...	...	...	...	p.m.	5 49	...	7 13	8 12		...	8 50	10 28	...
Gross-Gerau	1223	...	...	1 59	...	...	1 20	...	3 8	2 19	...	4 25	4 49	...	...	...	...	...	5 39	6 13	...	7 36	8 28		...	9 15	10 51	...
Nauheim..................	...	...	...	...	...	...	1 26	...	...	2 26	...	4 32	...	...	...	...	...	...	5 45	6 19	...	7 42	...		...	9 21	10 57	...
Bischofsheim	...	...	...	...	...	...	1 40	...	...	2 39	...	4 47	...	...	...	...	...	...	5 56	6 30	...	7 53	...		...	9 32	11 7	...
Mayence Haupt. arr	1247	...	...	2 23	...	...	1 57	...	3 28	2 56	...	5 4	5 13	...	...	...	...	...	6 13	6 46	...	8 9	8 52		...	9 48	11 23	...
	1,2,3 p.m.	234 p.m	Ex3 p.m.		Ex.3 p.m.	1,2,3 p.m.	1—4 p.m.				1,2,3 p.m.	234 p.m.		Ex3 p.m.			Ex3 p.m.	2,3,4 p.m.		1—4 p.m.	234 p.m.		Ex 3 p.m.	Ex 3 p.m.	234 p.m.		1,2,3 p.m	2,3,4 nght
FRANKFORT— Hauptbahnhof ......dep	1215	1226	1248	...	1 33	1 51	1 59	...	...	...	3 30	3 52	...	5 7	...	...	6 9	5 14	...	6 22	7 17	...	8 35	9 1	9 12	...	11 48	12 10
Niederrad	...	1232	●	...	...	...	2 6	...	...	...	...	3 59	...	...	...	...	...	5 21	...	6 29	7 24	...	...	...	9 19	...	...	12 17
Goldstein	...	1237	...	...	...	...	2 12	...	...	...	...	4 5	...	...	...	...	...	5 27	...	6 35	7 30	...	SC	...	9 25	...	...	12 23
Kelsterbach	...	1249	...	...	...	...	2 25	...	...	...	...	4 18	...	...	...	...	...	5 41	...	6 49	7 43	...	...	...	9 39	...	...	12 37
Rüsselsheim	1239	1 15	...	...	...	2 15	2 42	...	...	...	3 55	4 34	...	...	...	...	6 34	5 57	...	7 6	7 59	...	...	...	9 57	...	12 13	12 54
Mayence Sud	1253	1 36	...	...	...	2 31	3 0	...	...	...	4 9	4 52	...	...	...	...	6 48	6 20	...	7 26	8 17	...	...	...	1015	...	12 27	1 12
" Haupt. ...arr	1257	1 40	1 29	...	2 9	2 35	3 5	...	...	...	4 13	4 57	...	5 43	...	...	6 52	6 26	...	7 32	8 22	...	9 11	9 37	1020	...	12 31	1 17
STRASSBURG 209 ...dep	9a33	...	...	1126	...	...	1126	...	...	...	...	...	...	2p14	...	...	...	...	...	...	...	...	5 p25	5 p25	...	...	7 p7	...
BASLE Swiss 209 ...dep	7a40	...	...	9a29	...	...	9a29	...	...	...	...	...	...	1215	...	...	...	...	...	...	...	...	3 p19	3 p19	...	...	4 p59	...
BASLE Badische 141dep	...	...	4a30	9a50	7 a53	...	9a50	...	10a42	...	1042	...	...	...	...	...	...	...	...	...	...	...	2 p33	2 p33	...	...	5 p33	...
WIESBADEN ... .dep	1236	1p18	1p11	2 p8	1 p40	...	2p42	...	3 p28	...	3p45	4p27	...	5p18	5p36	...	6p30	...	6 p30	7p12	7p55	...	8 p40	9 p6	10p9	...	12a13	12a13
	1,2,3	234	Ex3	Ex2	Ex 3	1—4	1—4	Ex2	Ex 2	1,2,3	1,2,3	2—4	1—4	Ex3	234	Ex3	Ex3		2,3,4	1—4	234		Ex 3	Ex.3	234	3 Cl	1,2,3	2,3,4
Mayence— Hauptbahnhof ......dep	p.m. 1 0	p.m. 1 45	p.m. 1 37	p.m. 2 54	p.m. 2 13	...	p.m. 3 10	...	p.m. 4 2	...	p.m. 4 27	p.m. 5 7	...	p.m. 5 47	p.m. 6 20	...	p.m. 6 58	...	p.m. 7 5	p.m. 7 40	p.m. 8 31	...	p.m. 9 15	p.m. 9 47	p.m. 1040	p.m. 9 53	nght 12 35	a.m. 1 21
Ingelheim	1 17	2 17	...	...	⋮	...	3 43	...	...	...	4 45	5 40	...	⋮	6 56	...	7 16	...	7 36	8 12	9 1	...	...	...	1110	1025	12 54	1 50
Gau-Algesheim	...	2 23	...	...	⋮	...	3 49	...	...	...	...	5 47	...	⋮	7 2	...	...	...	7 42	8 18	9 9	...	...	...	1116	1030	...	2 3
Bingen ....arr	1 29	2 35	2 3	3 20	⋮	...	4 2	...	4 28	...	4 57	5 59	...	⋮	7 15	...	7 29	...	7 55	8 31	9 22	...	9 41	10 13	1129	1043	1 6	2 16
Bingerbruck ......arr	1 34	2 40	2 8	3 25	⋮	...	4 9	...	4 33	...	5 2	6 6	...	⋮	7 20	...	7 33	...	8 0	8 37	9 33	...	9 46	10 18	1135	1048	1 11	2 21
METZ 212 ....arr	6p22	...	...	...	6 p22	...	10p14	...	10p14	...	10p14	...	...	1014	...	...	...	...	...	...	...	...	1 a45	...	...	...	...	...
PARIS 65 ....arr	11p47	...	...	...	11p47	...	5 a0	...	5 a0	...	5 a0	...	...	5 a0	...	...	...	...	...	...	...	...	8 a25	...	...	...	...	...
BASLE 209 ....dep	...	...	...	1014		...	10a14	...	10a14	...	...	...	...		...	1p45	1p45	...	...	...	...	...		4 p37	...	...	...	...
STRASSBURG 209 ...dep	...	...	...	1217	...	...	12p17	...	12p17	...	...	...	...	...	...	3p52	3p52	...	...	...	...	...	...	6 p50	...	...	...	...
KREUZNACH 125A dep	1 p2	...	1 p2	3p16	...	...	3p33	...	3 p33	...	...	...	...	...	5p32	7 p5	7 p5	...	...	8p13	...	...	...	10 p2	...	...	...	...
Bingerbruck ......dep	p.m. 1 36	...	p.m. 2 9	p.m. 3 40	...	...	p.m. 4 13	...	p.m. 4 34	...	p.m. 5 4	...	p.m. 5 25	...	p.m. 6 13	p.m 7 26	p.m. 7 35	p.m. 7 44	...	p.m. 8 41	...	...	...	p.m. 10 24	p.m. 1140	...	...	...
Niederheimbach	...	...	...	...	...	...	4 29	...	...	...	...	...	5 42	...	6 29	...	...	8 4	...	8 56	...	...	...	...	1155	...	...	...
Bacharach................	1 51	...	...	RC	...	...	4 36	...	...	...	5 19	...	5 49	...	6 36	RC	...	8 11	...	9 2	...	...	...	...	12 1	...	...	...
Oberwesel	2 0	...	...	...	...	...	4 57	...	...	...	5 29	...	5 59	...	6 46	...	...	8 22	...	9 12	...	...	...	...	1210	...	...	...
St. Goar	2 10	...	...	...	...	...	5 7	...	...	...	5 39	...	6 10	...	6 57	...	...		...	9 23	...	...	...	...	1221	...	...	...
Salzig	...	...	...	...	...	...	5 23	...	...	...	...	...	6 26	...	7 13	...	...	p.m.	...	9 38	...	...	...	...	1237	...	...	...
Boppard...................	2 26	...	...	...	...	...	5 31	...	...	...	5 55	...	6 34	...	7 22	...	8 17	8 27	...	9 47	...	...	...	...	1246	...	...	...
Rhens	...	...	...	...	...	...	5 48	...	...	...	...	...	6 51	...	7 39	...	...	8 43	...	10 3	...	...	...	...	1 2	...	...	...
Capellen..................	...	...	...	...	...	...	5 54	...	...	...	...	...	6 57	...	7 45	...	...	8 49	...	10 9	...	...	...	...	1 8	...	...	...
Coblence Haupt. ...arr	2 45	...	3 5	4 34	...	...	6 3	...	5 28	...	6 14	...	7 6	...	7 53	8 23	8 36	8 56	...	1017	...	...	...	11 21	1 16	...	...	...

PRUSSIAN STATE RAILWAYS.

HOMBURG 129or150dep	...	...	1153	11a53	...	...	...	1p49	1 p49	2 p6	2 p6	...	...	...	...	2p59	2p59	...	...	...	...	...	...	...	...	...	...	...
WIESBADEN 129 ...dep	...	...	1p17	1p17	...	...	...	3p51	3 p51	3p51	3p51	...	...	...	...	5p35	5p35	...	...	...	...	...	...	...	...	...	...	...
EMS 147 ....dep	...	...	2p16	3 p9	...	3 p9	5p20	5 p0	5 p14	5p14	5p20	...	6p29	...	...	7p59	7p59	8 p14	...	...	...	...	...	10p17	1233	...	...	...
Coblence-Haupt ...dep	...	..	3 10	4 38	...	4 42	6 29	5 37	5 44	5 50	6 19	...	7 15	...	...	8 32	8 40	9 1	...	1023	...	...	...	11 25	1 23	...	...	...
Urmitz	...	...	...	...	...	4 58	6 46	...	...	...	...	...	7 32	...	...	...	...	9 18	...	1041	...	...	...	...	1 46	...	...	...
Weissenthurm	...	...	...	...	...	5 7	6 54	...	...	6 6	...	...	7 40	...	...	...	8 58	9 26	...	1049	...	...	...	...	1 56	...	...	...
Andernach	...	...	...	...	...	5 15	7 2	...	...	6 13	6 39	...	7 48	...	...	...	9 6	9 33	...	1057	...	...	...	...	2 5	...	...	...
Brohl	...	...	...	...	...	5 26	7 12	...	...	6 23	...	...	7 59	...	...	...	...	9 43	...	11 8	...	...	...	RC	2 18	...	...	...
Nieder Breisig	...	...	...	...	...	5 33	7 18	...	...	...	...	...	8 6	...	...	...	RC	9 49	1,2,3	1115	...	...	...	...	2 26	...	...	...
Sinzig	...	...	...	...	...	5 42	7 27	...	...	...	...	...	8 15	...	...	...	...	9 58	p.m.	1124	...	...	...	...	2 37	...	...	...
Remagen B. Neuenahr.	...	...	...	RC	...	5 50	7 35	RC	RC	6 39	7 2	...	8 24	...	...	RC	9 28	10 5	9 47	1132	...	...	...	...	2 46	...	...	...
Rolandseck	...	...	...	...	...	6 4	7 49	...	...	6 49	...	...	8 38	...	...	...	...	10 19	9 58	1146	...	...	a.m.	...	3 0	...	...	...
Mehlem	...	...	...	...	...	6 12	7 57	...	...	6 57	...	...	8 46	...	p.m.	...	...	10 27	10 6	1154	...	...	1245	...	3 10	...	...	...
Godesberg	...	...	...	...	...	6 18	8 5	...	...	7 4	7 18	...	8 53	...	9 15	...	9 44	10 33	10 13	12 0	...	...	1252	...	3 17	...	...	...
Bonn .... arr	...	...	4 5	5 31	...	6 27	8 14	6 32	6 39	7 13	7 27	...	9 2	...	9 26	9 33	9 53	10 42	10 22	12 9	...	...	1 3	12 29	3 29	...	...	...
Bonn .... dep	...	...	4 6	5 32	...	6 44	8 19	6 33	6 40	7 15	7 30	...	9 7	...		9 38	9 55	10 44	10 24	1225	...	...		12 21		...	...	...
Roisdorf	...	...	...	...	...	6 53	8 28	...	...	...	...	...	9 16	...	...	...	...	10 53	...	1234	...	...	...	...	...	...	...	...
Sechtem	...	...	...	...	...	7 2	8 37	...	...	...	...	...	9 25	...	...	...	...	11 2	...	1243	...	...	...	...	...	...	...	...
Bruhl	...	...	...	...	...	7 11	8 46	...	...	...	...	...	9 34	...	...	...	...	11 10	...	1251	...	...	...	...	...	...	...	...
Cologne-Sudbahnhof......	...	...	...	...	...	7 28	9 4	...	...	7 42	7 57	...	9 52	...	...	...	1022	11 24	10 56	1 9	...	...	...	...	...	...	...	...
Cologne-Westbahnhof ...	...	...	...	...	...	7 33	9 9	...	...	...	...	...	9 57	...	...	...	...	...	...	1 14	...	...	...	...	...	...	...	...
COLOGNE (Coln) Hauptbahnhof arr	...	...	4 40	6 5	...	7 39	9 15	7 7	7 14	7 50	8 5	...	10 3	...	...	1015	1030	11 32	11 4	1 20	...	...	...	12 55	...	...	...	...
		1—4		Ex2			1—4	Direct Train to Vlissingen.	Direct Train to Hoek van Holland.		1,2,3	1—4					Ex3	1—4	SC Ex.3									
COLOGNE (Coln) Hauptbahnhof dep	...	p.m. 7 28	...	p.m. 6 13	...	...	p.m. 9 52			...	p.m. 8 15	p.m. 8 31	...	...	...	...	p.m. 1052	p.m. 11 32	nght 12 5	...	...	...	...	...	...	...	...	...
Horrem	...	8 6	...	RC	...	...	1027			...	...	9 6	...	...	...	...	SC	12 7	12 28	...	...	...	...	...	...	...	...	...
Duren (127) ....dep	...	8 35	...	6 53	...	...	1057			...	8 57	9 40	...	...	...	...	1134	12 36	12 50	...	...	...	...	...	...	...	...	...
Eschweiler	...		...	...	...	...	1126			...	9 16	10 7	...	...	...	...	...		1 9	...	...	...	...	...	...	...	...	...
Stolberg (129B)	...	...	...	...	...	...	1133	...		...	9 23	1015	...	...	...	...	...	...	1 16	...	...	...	...	...	...	...	...	...
Aix-Chapelle-Haupt.	...	p.m.	...	7 24	...	..	1152	...		...	9 39	1034	...	...	...	...	12 6	...	1 29	...	...	...	...	...	...	...	...	...
" dep	...	7†17	...	7 27	...	...		...	...	...		1040	...	...	...	...	1210	...	1 32	...	...	...	...	...	...	...	...	...
Herbesthal............arr	...	7 57	...	7 47	...	...	...	..	...	...	...	1114	...	...	...	...	1230	...	1 52	...	...	...	...	...	...	...	...	...
BRUSSELS (104) ...arr	...	...	...	9p45	...	...	...	...	...	...	...	...	...	...	...	...	...	...	3 a56	...	...	...	...	...	...	...	●	...

●—From Sudbahnhof at Frankfort. RC—Restaurant Car. SC—Sleeping Car.

BROHL and KEMPENICH.

Dist. E.M		a.m.	a.m.	p.m.	p.m.	p.m.	p.m.			
	Brohl ....dep	8 7	10 17	1 47	5 20	5 38	8 50	...	...	...
2¼	Bad Tönnisstein..................	8 23	10 33	2 2	5 35	5 53	9 7	...	...	...
6¼	Niederzissen	8 52	10 56	2 28		6 14	9 38	...	...	...
15	**Kempenich**...................arr	10 6	...	...	...	...	10 41	...	...	...

	a.m.	a.m.	p.m.	p.m.	p.m.				
Kempenich ....dep	5 15	...	...	...	5 33	...	...	...	...
Niederzissen	6 26	8 45	12 5	4 25	6 45	...	...	...	...
Bad Tönnisstein	6 47	9 6	12 27	4 46	7 7	...	...	...	...
Brohl...............................arr	7 0	9 19	12 40	4 59	7 20	...	...	...	...

REMAGEN and ADENAU.

†—Not on Sunday.

E.M.	**Remagen** dp	6 a0	7a47	9a15	11a18	11a54	1p30	2p13	4p18	7 p7	7p44	8p32	9†32	1025	12a2
6¼	B. Neuenahr	6 20	8 14	9 39	11 41	12 18	1 53	2 35	5 13	7 26	8 7	8 55	9 56	1047	1223
8	Ahrweiler...	6 29	8 24	9 47	11 49	12 26	2 0	2 44	5 25	7 33	8 14	9 6	10 3	1054	1230
15¾	Altenahr ...	7 2	8 57	1018	12 20	1 0		3 19	6 1		8 44	9 42			
22¼	Dümpelfeld	7 25	9 23			1 25	...	3 45	6 27	...		10 8	...	...	...
26½	**Adenau** arr	7 44	9 41	...	...	1 42	...	4 1	6 44	...	...	1028	...	...	...

Adenau dp	...	...	6a21	7a59	a.m.	11a20	...	2p12	...	4p55	...	...	7p47	...
Dümpelfeld	...	...	6 37	8 14	...	11 39	...	2 28	...	5 12	...	...	8 6	...
Altenahr ...	...	...	7 5	8 43	1026	12 7	...	2 58	4p40	5 43	...	†	8 37	10p17
Ahrweiler .	5a21	6a22	7 41	9 16	1059	12 40	2 p12	3 31	5 13	6 17	7p43	8p17	9 12	10 51
B.Neuenahr	5 29	6 29	7 51	9 23	11 8	12 49	2 21	3 39	5 22	6 26	7 51	8 26	9 20	10 59
Remagen a	5 50	6 50	8 13	9 44	1130	1 9	2 42	4 0	5 43	6 47	8 11	8 47	9 41	11 22

DIEDENHOFEN, TREVES, and COBLENCE.

[Luggage Rates—see page 462.

Dist. E.M.																				
	PARIS 64 ...dep		...	...	...	9p5	10p15	...	...	...	...	...	...	...	9 a0	...	...	9 a0	...	12p20
	METZ 210A ...dep		...	...	4 a55	6 a26	8 a21	...	10a10	12 p2	12 p8	...	...	3p10	5 p26	...	...	5 p32	...	8 p53
			1—4	2 3 4	2,3,4	Ex 3	2,3,4	2 3 4	2 3 4	1,2,3	2,3,4	1,2,3	2,3,4	1—4	Ex 3	2 3 4	2 3 4	2,3,4	3—4	2,3,4
					a.m.	a.m.	a.m.		a.m.	p.m.	p.m.			p.m.	p.m.			p.m.	p.m.	p.m.
—	**Diedenhofen** ...dep		...	...	5 55	6 57	9 5	...	1132	12 33	1 2	...	...	4 2	5 58	...	...	6 23	...	9 57
11½	Sierck ...		...	...	6 22	7 17	9 35	...	12 0	...	1 29	...	...	4 29	6 17	...	...	6 51	...	10 24
18¾	Nennig ...		...	...	6 43	7 33	9 59	...	1221	...	1 51	...	...	4 50	6 30	...	...	7 12	...	10 45
39½	**Karthaus** ...arr		...	...	7 30	8 2	10 49	...	1 7	...	2 38	...	...	5 35	6 59	...	...	7 59	...	11 30
...	" ...dep		...	...	7 32	8 3	10 53	...	1 8	...	2 40	...	...	5 39	7 0	...	...	8 3	...	11 31
43½	**Treves** ...arr		...	...	7 43	8 10	11 4	...	1 19	1 33	2 51	...	...	5 50	7 9	...	...	8 14	...	11 42
155	COLOGNE (126) ...arr		a.m.	...	...	12p15	4p50	...	5p18	5p18	8 p14	p.m.	...	...	11p14	p.m.	...	...	...	...
...	**Treves** ...dep		5 13	...	7 57	8 26	11 33	...	1 28	2 5	3 28	6 5	...	6 20	7 21	7 28	...	8 35	1047	11 53
47½	**Ehrang** ...dep		5 24	...	8 7	...	11 44	...	1 42	...	3 38	...	...	6 32	...	7 38	...	8 46	1059	12 1
65¼	**Wengerohr** (124) arr		6 8	...	8 52	9 0	12 28	...	2 30	2 39	4 27	6 39	...	7 18	...	—	...	9 32	—	12 45
65¾	Uerzig ...	2 3 4	6 18	a.m.	9 19	...	12 40	...	2 59	...	4 40	...	...	7 30	...	...	p.m.	9 44	...	12 55
...	Puenderich (126) ...	a.m.	6 31	9 7	9 33	...	12 54	...	3 14	2 57	4 54	6 55	...	7 44	...	...	9 5	9 59	...	...
76	Bullay (Bertrich) ...	5 32	6 36	9 12	9 42	9 20	1 0	...	3 20	3 4	5 1	7 3	...	7 50	...	...	9 10	10 6	...	1 8
83	Cochem ...	5 58	6 57	—	10 7	9 33	1 20	...	3 42	3 18	5 23	7 19	...	8 31	8 22	...	—	10 26	...	1 27
90	Carden ...	6 20	7 15	...	10 25	RC	1 38	...	4 0	...	5 41	...	...	8 49	...	...	...	10 44	...	1 39
93½	Moselkern ...	6 33	7 26	a.m.	10 35	...	1 49	p.m.	4 11	...	5 52	...	p.m.	9 0	...	...	...	10 55	...	...
96½	Hatzenport ...	6 45	7 36	9 15	10 45	9 53	1 59	2 59	4 21	3 38	6 2	...	7 46	9 10	...	...	...	11 5	...	1 51
106½	Cobern ...	7 11	7 58	9 39	11 5	...	2 20	3 23	4 44	...	6 26	...	8 7	9 33	...	...	...	11 25	...	2 7
108	Winningen ...	7 22	8 7	9 49	11 15	...	2 29	3 33	4 53	...	6 35	...	8 17	9 42	...	...	...	11 34	...	2 16
110	Güls ...	7 29	8 13	9 56	11 22	...	2 35	3 40	4 59	...	6 42	...	8 24	9 48	...	...	...	11 40	...	2 22
112½	**Coblence** ...arr	7 40	8 21	10 5	11 31	10 16	2 43	3 50	5 7	4 2	6 52	8 1	8 32	9 56	9 4	...	...	11 48	...	2 28

		2 3 4	2,3,4	1—4	Ex 3	2 3 4	2,3,4	1,2,3	2,3,4	2 3 4	1,2,3	2,3,4	1—4	2 3 4	1—4	Ex. 3	2 3 4	2,3,4	2,3,4
		a.m.	a.m.	a.m.	a.m.	a.m.	a.m.	a.m.	a.m.	p.m.	p.m.	p.m.	p.m.	p.m.	p.m.	p.m.		p.m.	nght
Coblence ...dep		3 6	...	6 5	8 38	7 25	8 47	11 9	11 14	1 20	2 50	2 55	4 40	6 27	7 15	8 43	...	9 0	12 8
Güls ...		3 12	...	6 15	...	7 35	8 53	...	11 23	1 30	...	3 4	4.50	6 36	7 24	...	...	9 10	12 17
Winningen ...		3 18	...	6 21	...	7 42	8 59	...	11 29	1 37	...	3 10	4 56	6 43	7 30	...	...	9 17	12 23
Cobern ...		3 27	...	6 30	...	7 52	9 8	...	11 38	1 47	...	3 19	5 5	6 53	7 39	RC	...	9 27	12 32
Hatzenport ...		3 42	...	6 52	...	8 15	9 26	...	12 0	2 10	...	3 41	5 26	7 13	8 1	...	...	9 51	12 54
Moselkern ...		...	...	7 2	...	—	9 33	...	12 10	—	...	3 51	5 35	—	8 11	...	...	10 1	1 4
Carden ...		3 54	...	7 13	...	...	9 41	...	12 21	...	...	4 2	5 46	...	8 22	...	...	10 13	1 15
Cochem ...		4 9	5 45	7 34	9 23	a.m.	9 59	11 53	12 42	...	3 34	4 22	6 5	...	8 42	9 29	p.m.	10 32	1 40
Bullay (Bad Bertrich)...		4 26	6 6	7 57	9 37	9 43	10 16	12 8	1 2	...	3 48	4 40	6 25	...	9 2	9 43	9 55	—	1 58
Puenderich ...		...	6 12	8 3	...	9 48	10 21	12 15	1 9	...	...	4 46	6 31	...	9 8	...	10 0	...	—
Uerzig ...		4 45	6 31	8 21	...	—	10 32	...	1 26	...	...	5 3	6 48	...	9 25	...	—	3—4	†-Weekdays only.
Wengerohr ...dep		4 52	6 41	8 30	9 57	...	10 39	12 34	1 35	...	4 8	5 11	6 57	p.m.	9 33	10 7	...	p.m.	
Ehrang ...dep		5 38	7 34	9 18	...	...	11 14	...	2 20	...	...	5 53	7 41	6 45	10 18	...	...	11 4	
Treves ...arr		5 45	7 45	9 28	10 29	...	11 21	1 6	2 27	...	4 40	6 0	7 50	6 55	10 25	10 39	...	11 16	
COLOGNE 126 ...dep		...	...	—	...	...	8 a2	...	9 a10	...	1p25	...	...	—	—	7 p10	...		
Treves ...dep		5 54	8 27	...	10 34	...	11 44	1 17	2 45	...	5 11	6 18	8 16	...	...	10 53	...	11 19	
Karthaus (127A)...arr		6 5	8 35	...	...	...	11 55	...	2 56	...	...	6 29	8 27	...	...	11 1	...	11 32	
" ...dep		6 6	8 36	...	...	...	11 57	...	2 57	...	...	6 33	8 30	...	...	11 2	...	11 33	
Nennig ...	a.m.	7 0	9 22	...	...	...	12 46	1 58	3 47	...	5 50	7 21	9 21	...	...	...	...	12 31	
Sierck ...	5†35	7 22	9 42	...	...	...	1 8	2 12	4 8	...	6 3	7 42	9 42	...	...	11 44	...	12 53	...
Diedenhofen arr	6 14	7 47	10 8	...	11 35	...	1 35	2 30	4 35	...	6 21	8 8	10 8	...	...	12 1	...	...	...
METZ (210) arr	7a29	8a47	10a46	...	12 p6	...	2 p22	3 p0	5 p29	...	6p51	9 p27	11p11	...	...	12a30	...	...	...
PARIS (65) ...arr		...	...	...	6 p10	...	9 p20	9 p20	11p47	...	...	5 a0	...	...	...	8 a25	...	...	...

WEMMETSWEILER and NONNWEILER.

Wemmetsweiler	...	...	7a12	9 a5	11a37	2p21	4p12	6p29	8p21	9p39	Nonnweiler	...	6a52	9a18	...	12p2	2p43	...	6 p5	8p57
Primsweiler ...	...	...	8 10	9 55	12 40	3 10	5 28	7 28	9 14	1031	Wadern ...	4a48	7 32	9 57	11a34	1241	3 14	...	6 44	9 35
Wadern ...	5a42	8 a6	8 49	1037	1 25	3 53	6 39	8 9	9 52	11 6	Primsweil'r	5 25	8 11	1033	12 17	1 20	4 1	5p27	7 23	10 8
Nonnweiler 127A	6 27	8 33	...	11 7	1 57	4 32	7 7	8 38	...	...	Wemmets'r	6 21	9 4	1122	1 22	2 20	5 0	6 18	8 18	11 0

NEUSS and VIERSEN.													
	Neuss ...dep	8 a8	10a56	1p20	3 p8	7p27	10p9	Viersen ...dep	5a56	9a35	1 p9	3p48	5p48	8p58
	Neersen Neuwerk arr	8 31	11 19	1 41	3 31	7 50	1032	Neersen Neuwerk...	6 13	9 50	1 28	4 4	6 5	9 15
	Viersen ...arr	8 48	11 35	1 54	3 44	8 5	1046	Neuss ...arr	6 40	1011	1 52	4 25	6 27	9 36

‡—Not on Sunday.]

CREFELD and M. GLADBACH.

Crefeld ...dep	6a57	8 a9	10a50	2 p0	5p10	p.m.	7p20	10 p5	M. Gladbach ..dep	5a55	8a29	9a32	1p10	4p19	5p52	7‡p20	8p57
Neersen Neuwerk...	7 22	8 37	11 21	2 26	5 34	7‡45	7 54	10 34	Neersen Neuwerk	6 17	8 41	9 49	1 24	4 32	6 8	7 32	9 13
M. Gladbach ...arr	7 36	8 51	11 35	2 40	5 47	7 59	8 9	10 48	Crefeld 121 ...arr	6 43	9 6	1011	1 49	4 58	6 32	...	9 40

SAARBRÜCKEN and ST. INGBERT. (In 20 minutes.)

From Saarbrücken, 5.10, 6.25, 7.0, 7.10, 7.55, 9.37, 11.15a.m.;12.4,1.17,2.26,3.28,5.43,6.29,6.54,7.41,9.53, 10.0,11.18 p.m.
From St. Ingbert,5.18,6.12,7.18,9.1,10.35,10.57a.m.;2.14,2.54,4.34,4.46,5.31,5.52,7.10,8.27, 8.40,10.48,11.24 p.m., 12.20 ni't.

WENGEROHR and CUES-BERNCASTEL.

Wengerohr (124) dep	6a58	9a11	1047	12p38	2p46	4p37	7p31	10p10	Cues-Berncastel	5a29	7a46	9a58	11a40	1p45	3p27	5p48	8 p41
Cues-Berncastel arr	7 36	9 48	1124	1 15	3 15	5 14	8 9	10 48	Wengerohr ...	6 6	8 21	1035	12 17	2 22	3 56	6 25	9 19

WENGEROHR and DAUN.

Wengerohr ...dep	6a43	9a15	12p40	2p49	4p32	6p58	9p38	1012	Daun ...dep	6a15	...	11a45	2p33	...	5p 0	7p29	...
Wittlich ...	6 57	9 31	1 0	3 1	4 42	7 8	9 46	1022	Schalkenmehren ...	6 28	...	1155	2 43	...	5 10	7 42	...
Manderscheid-Pantenbg.	7 39	1020	1 37	3 51	—	7 44	—	—	Gillenfeld ...	6 44	...	12 6	2 54	...	5 21	8 0	...
Gillenfeld ...	7 57	1042	1 51	4 13	...	7 59	...	...	Manderscheid-Panten.	7 4	...	1222	3 9	...	5 37	8 18	...
Schalkenmehren ...	8 8	1056	2 1	4 28	...	8 9	...	...	Wittlich ...	7 58	9a36	1 7	3 50	4p50	6 20	9 9	9p52
Daun (123B) ...arr	8 17	11 8	2 10	4 40	...	8 18	...	...	Wengerohr (124) ...arr	8 8	9 46	1 15	3 58	5 0	6 30	9 19	10 0

Extra.—Wengerohr to Wittlich, 8.32, 10.45 a.m.; 1.50, 5.18, 7.23 p.m. Wittlich to Wengerohr 5.56, 8.47 a.m.; 12.10, 2.23 p.m.

BINGERBRUCK, KREUZNACH, BAD MÜNSTER a. STEIN, SAARBRUCKEN, and FORBACH.

SC—Sleeping Car.

E.M.	Station															
...	Mayence 123A dep	3 a55	2a28	6a20	6a10	6 a30	8 a10	...	9 a20	9 a20	10 48	...	1a51	1 p0	2p13	1p45
...	Cologne 122 dep	12a28	1228	⋮	...	...	...	...	6 a17	6 a17	9 a32	10 a3	10 e3	1120	⋮	1210
		2,3,4	2 3 4	Ex3	2,3,4	2,3,4	Ex 3	2 3 4	1,2,3	2,3,4	2,3,4	Ex 3	2,3,4	Ex3	Ex 3	Ex2
E.M.		a.m.	a.m.	a.m.	a.m.	a.m.	a.m.	a.m.	a.m.	a.m.	p.m.	p.m.	p.m.	p.m.	p.m.	p.m.
—	Bingerbrück ...dep	5 3	4 36	⋮	7 9	7 45	8 45	...	9 56	10 4	12 17	12 39	1 5	1 56	⋮	2 46
5	Langenlonsheim ..	5 20	4 53	⋮	7 27	8 2	...	9 9	...	10 22	12 34	...	1 23	.	⋮	...
10	Kreuznach ... arr	5 33	5 6	⋮	7 40	8 15	9 2	9 22	10 13	10 35	12 47	12 56	1 36	2 14	⋮	3 3
...	Bad ... dep	5 35	5 10	7 0	7 43	8 17	9 4	9 23	10 15	10 37	12 50	12 57	1 38	2 15	2 52	3 4
12½	Münster a-S. ...arr	5 41	5 16	7 6	7 49	8 23	9 10	9 29	10 21	10 43	12 56	1 3	1 44	2 21	2 58	3 10
62¾	Neustadt 206 arr	8 a23	8a23	...	...	...	11a38	...	11a38	1 p19	...	2 p9	...	4p25	4 p25	4p25
133½	Strassb'g 208 arr		11a7	...	...	...	2 p9	...	2 p9	3 p48	...	3 p48	...	6p17	6 p17	'p17
...	Münster-a-S. ...dep	...	5 25	7 8	7 56	9 31	9 12	...	...	10 49	...	...	1 46	...	3 0	...
22	Staudernheim	...	5 51	...	8 20	9 53	...	...	...	11 14	...	...	2 11	...	...	...
23¾	Sobernheim..........	...	5 57	...	8 26	10 4	RC	...	...	11 20	...	...	2 17	...	...	...
29¼	Martinstein..........	a.m.	6 11	...	8 40	10 18		...	...	11 34	...	...	2 31	...	...	...
33	Kirn	5 39	6 23	7 38	8 51	10 29	9 43	...	...	11 45	...	...	2 40	...	3 31	...
37¼	Fischbach	5 54	6 36	..	9 2		...	...	...	11 57	...	...	2 50	...	...	...
42¼	Oberstein	6 11	6 55	7 56	9 19	...	10 1	...	...	12 15	...	...	3 8	...	3 50	...
46¾	Kronweiler		7 13	...	9 33	...	...	...	...	12 33	...	...	3 19	...	...	...
50	Heimbach	...	7 25	...	9 44	...	...	...	...	12 45	...	...	3 28	2 3 4	...	...
53¼	Birkenfeld Neub....	...	7 36	...	9 54	...	10 21	...	2,3,4	12 57	2,3,4	...	3 35	p.m	...	...
57	Turkismühle	a.m.	7 50	...	10 6	a.m.	...	p.m.	p.m.	1 10	p.m.	...	3 48	5 7	...	...
66	St. Wendel	6 17	8 16	...	10 49	9 30	10 43	1230	1 13	1 39	2 50	...	4 10	5 39	...	...
71½	Ottweiler	6 36	8 30	...	11 2	9 48	...	1247	1 31	1 52	3 7	2,3,4	4 23	5 57	...	...
75	Neunkirchen arr	6 44	8 37	8 44	11 9	9 55	10 57	1254	1 39	1 59	3 15	p.m.	4 30	6 5	4 38	...
	Neunkirchen dep	7 2	8 52	8 45	11 14	10 5	10 58	1 1	1 43	2 4	3 18	5 24	4 46	6 40	4 39	...
82¾	Sulzbach	7 30	9 15	...	11 39	10 29	...	1 25	2 8	2 28	3 41	5 49	5 7	7 4	...	...
88	Saar-brücken arr a.m.	7 41	9 27	9 7	11 53	10 42	11 19	1 39	2 21	2 41	3 54	6 2	5 18	7 18	5 1	...
	Saar-brücken dep 7 16	7 47	9 37		12 25		11 28			2 48	4 17	6 23	6 23	7 57	5 7	...
94¼	Forbach .....arr 7 25	8 1	9 51	...	12 39	...	11 37	...	...	3 2	4 32	6 37	6 37	8 10	5 16	...
137¼	Metz 212 ...arr	9 a29	1128	...	2 p16	...	12p41	...	...	4 p54	6 p22	8 p17	8 p17	9p50	6 p22	...
284¾	Paris 65 ...arr	...	6p40	...	...	...	6 p40	...	...	11p47	11p47	...	...	5 a0	11p47	...

E.M.	Station														
...	Mayence 123A dep	1 p45	...	4 p2	4p27	5 p47	5 p7	7 p5	7p40	9 p15	9 p47	1040	...	12a2	1235
...	Cologne 122 dep	12p10	...	1 p5	2p31	⋮	...	3 p23	5p56	6 p33	6 p33	8 p2	10p22	1033	1033
		2,3,4	2 3 4	2,3,4	2 3 4	Ex 3	2,3,4	2,3,4	1,2,3	Ex 3	2,3,4	2 3 4	Ex 3	Ex3	2 3 4
E.M.		p.m.	p.m.	p m	p.m.	p.m.	p.m.	p.m.	p.m.	p.m.	p.m.	p.m.	a.m.	a.m.	a.m.
—	Bingerbrück ...dep	3 3	...	4 44	5 45	⋮	7 12	8 7	8 49	9 50	10 26	1142	12 59	1 9	1 27
5	Langenlonsheim ..	3 20	4 28	5 1	6 1	⋮	7 30	8 27	...	...	10 46	1159	...	...	1 40
10	Kreuznach ... arr	3 33	4 41	5 14	6 14	⋮	7 44	8 40	9 6	10 8	10 59	1212	1 17	1 27	1 51
...	Bad ... dep	3 35	5 9	5 17	6 15	6 26	7 48	8 42	9 7	10 9	11 4	1215	1 18	1 28	1 53
12½	Münster a-S. ...arr	3 41	5 15	5 23	6 21	6 32	7 55	8 48	9 13	10 15	11 10	1221	1 24	1 34	1 59
62¾	Neustadt 206 arr	5 p55	...	...	...	...	10p30	10 30	1030	...	...	...	2 a32	2a42	...
133½	Strassb'g 208 arr	8 p30	...	...	...	...	12a27	12 27	1227	...	...	...	4 a10	4a22	...
...	Münster-a-S. ...dep	3 46	...	5 27	...	6 33	8 0	...	...	10 16	11 15	...	☞ Until 31st August.	...	2 0
22	Staudernheim	4 12	...	5 59	...	...	8 27	...	...	...	11 47	...		...	2 17
23¾	Sobernheim..........	4 19	...	6 6	...	RC	8 33	...	...	10 34	11 53	...		...	2 23
29¼	Martinstein..........	4 33	...	6 20	...	...	8 47	...	...	...	12 7	...		...	...
33	Kirn	4 45	...	6 38	...	7 3	9 1	...	...	10 49	12 20	...		...	2 39
37¼	Fischbach	4 58	p.m.	6 53	...	...	9 14	...	...	...	12 34	...		...	2 49
42¼	Oberstein	5 18	6 22	7 30	...	7 24	9 36	...	...	11 9	12 49	...		...	3 5
46¾	Kronweiler	5 36	6 40	7 48	...	...	9 55	...	...	...		a.m.		...	3 16
50	Heimbach	5 49	6 54	8 0	...	...	10 9	...	...	SC	...	3 35	...	...	3 25
53¼	Birkenfeld Neub....	6 3	7 6	8 11	...	7 45	10 20	...	...	11 30	...	3 47	...	...	3 33
57	Turkismühle	6 19	7 19	8 23	...	...	10 35	...	...	...	p.m.	4 8	...	...	3 44
66	St. Wendel	6 50	8 27	8 49	...	...	11 3	...	...	11 52	11 58	4 42	...	...	4 2
71½	Ottweiler	7 7	8 44	9 2	...	...	11 17	...	...	...	12 15	5 2	...	1—4	4 16
75	Neunkirchen arr	7 15	8 52	9 9	...	8 19	11 24	...	...	12 5	12 25	5 10	...	a.m.	4 23
	Neunkirchen dep	7 40	8 54	9 14	...	8 22	11 32	...	...	12 6	12 28	5 18	...	6 0	4 26
82¾	Sulzbach	8 8	9 20	9 37	...	...	11 56	1—4	...	...	12 51	5 47	...	6 23	4 47
88	Saar-brücken arr a.m.	8 22	9 34	9 50	...	8 46	12 9	p.m.	...	12 28	1 4	6 2	...	6 36	4 59
	Saar-brücken dep 7 16			9 55	...	8 59		11 43	...	12 36			...		5 50
94¼	Forbach .....arr 7 25	...	...	10 9	...	9 8	...	11 56	..	12 45	...	...	...	...	6 4
137¼	Metz 212 ...arr	...	...	1 a17	...	10p14	...	...	...	1 a45	...	...	...	...	7a48
284¾	Paris 65 ...arr	...	...	...	...	5 a0	...	...	...	8 a25	...	...	...	...	...

RC—Restaurant Car attached.

Extra.—St. Wendel to Neunkirchen, 7.13 a.m.

Birkenfeld Neubrucke...dep	8 a12	10a26	1p10	3 p50	7p10	8p21	1026	11p33	...
Birkenfeld Stadtbahnhof arr	8 25	10 39	1 23	4 3	7 20	8 34	1039	11 43	...

Birkenfeld Stadtbahnhof dep	7a15	9a32	12p23	3 p4	6p29	7p30	9p30	11 p1	...	...
Birkenfeld Neubrucke ...arr	7 28	9 45	12 36	3 17	6 42	7 40	9 43	11 14	...	...

Saarbrucken and Neunkirchen via Wemmetsweiler.

†—Not on Sunday.

Saarbrucken ... dep	†	5 a35	...	6a25	...	7a59	...	10a49	...	1 p23	...	3p26	...	5p38	...	7 p40	8p56	...	11p40	...	...	...	...
Wemmetsweiler	5a20	6 13	6a23	7 6	7 a9	8 38	9 a8	11 24	1 p27	2 8	2 p22	4 10	5 p1	6 13	6p19	8 21	9 38	11 p5	12 35	...	...	...	...
Neunkirchen ......arr	5 32	6 24	6 36	...	7 23	8 51	9 23	11 35	1 42	2 25	2 37	4 23	5 14	6 26	6 34	8 34	9 51	11 18	12 48	...	...	...	...
Neunkirchen...... dep	...	4 a53	6a50	8a46	9 a1	11a19	...	12p58	...	2 p6	2p20	3p40	4 p5	6p15	6p36	7 p57	...	9 p18	10p47	12a16	...	...	...
Wemmetsweiler	5 a0	5 11	7 6	9 1	9 17	11 32	11a36	1 12	1p30	2 19	2 37	3 53	4 23	6 28	6 52	8 10	8 p26	9 33	11 3	12 29	...	...	...
Saarbrucken ......arr	5 40	5 54	7 41	...	9 54	...	12 13		2 15	...	3 15	...	5 0	...	7 28	...	9 11	..	11 38	..	...	...	...

KARTHAUS and WASSERBILLIG.

‡—8.43 p.m. on Sunday.

E.M.		a.m.	a.m.	a.m.	a m	a.m.	a.m.	p m	pm	pm	p.m.	p.m.	p.m.	p.m.
—	Treves ....dep	6 0	6 32	8 8	8 15	1041	1138	1 27	250	5 4	6 29	7 18	...	11 8
4¼	Karthaus.........dep	6 14	6 46	8 16	8 28	1055	...	1 40	3 2	511	6 42	7 32	8‡50	1121
6¾	Igel	6 22	6 55	...	8 36	11 3	...	1 47	3 9	...	6 50	7 41	9 0	1129
9¼	Wasserbillig ...arr	6 28	7 2	8 25	8 42	11 9	1153	1 53	315	520	6 56	7 48	9 7	1135
32¼	Luxemburg ...arr	7 37	...	9 10	9 48	1220	1238	2 58	418	614	8 3	...	...	1227

Luxemburg ...dep	6 11	7 2	9 31	11 44	1249	1 55	4 20	6 20	7 1	...	1014	...	...	...
	a.m.	a m	a.m.	p.m	p.m.	p.m	p.m.	p.m.	p.m.	p.m.	p.m.			
Wasserbillig ......dep	7 7	7 42	1032	12 42	1 27	2 50	5 17	6 58	7 59	9 57	1110	...	...	...
Igel	7 12	...	1037	12 48	...	2 55	5 22	...	8 5	10 4	1115	...	...	...
Karthaus...........arr	7 19	7 52	1044	12 55	1 37	3 2	5 29	7 7	8 12	1013	1122	...	...	...
Treves ....arr	7 32	8 2	1057	1 9	1 47	3 15	5 40	7 14	8 25	1026	1135	...	...	...

EHRANG and CONZ.

†—Weekdays only.

Ehrang...........dep	5a†41	...	8a24	...	1118	...	...	2p24	3p27	5p42	8p42	10 20	...
Treves...........dep	6 1	6†30	8 42	9a42	1136	12 p6	1p33	2 42	3 47	6 2	9 1	11 10	...
Conz ....arr	6 18	6 52	...	10 0	...	12 28	1 55	...	4 4	6 21	9 20	11 27	...

Conz ....dep	5†35	7a10	10a34	11†a48	12p50	2p23	4p49	6†p5	7p34	9p30	...	...	...	...
Treves ....dep	6 6	7 43	10 53	12 9	1 12	2 56	5 10	6 24	7 55	9 51	...	...	...	...
Ehrang ....arr	6 24	8 1	11 9	...	1 23	3 13	5 28	6 58	8 13	10 9	...	...	...	...

FORBACH, SAARBRUCKEN, BAD MUNSTER a. STEIN, and BINGERBRUCK.

Station										
PARIS 64 ......dep	...	...	...	...	...	9 p5	...	...	1015	10p15
METZ 212 ......dep	...	...	...	...	...	4 a54	...	5a41	7a42	8 a34
	2 3 4	2 3 4	2,3,4	2 3 4	2,3,4	Ex 3	2,3,4	2 3 4	2 3 4	2,3,4
					a.m.	a.m.	a.m.	a.m.	a.m.	a.m.
Forbach ....dep	...	...	...	...	...	6 2	...	7 25	9 8	10 13
Saarbrücken arr	...	...	...	a.m.	...	6 12	...	7 38	9 21	10 26
Saarbrücken dep	...	...	...	6 34	6 0	6 28	7 28	8 12	10 1	11 5
Sulzbach	...	...	...	6 51	6 17	...	7 46	8 30	1020	11 20
Neunkirchen arr	...	...	...	7 13	6 40	6 53	8 9	8 51	1045	11 40
Neunkirchen dep	...	...	...	7 15	6 42	6 54		8 55	1050	11 42
Ottweiler	...	...	...	7 23	6 50	...	...	9 3	1058	11 50
St. Wendel	...	...	...	7 39	7 21	7 10	a.m.	9 22	1113	12 5
Turkismühle	...	...	a.m.		7 56	...	9 41	9 54		12 35
Birkenfeld Neub....	...	...	5 †38	...	8 9	7 37	9 51	10 6	...	12 46
Heimbach	...	...	5 48	...	8 20	...		1016	...	12 56
Kronweiler............	a.m.	...	5 59	...	8 31	...	...	1026	...	1 6
Oberstein	4 20	...	6 19	...	8 51	7 56	...	1043	...	1 23
Fischbach	4 33	...	6 31	...	9 4	...	...	1054	...	1 35
Kirn	4 46	...	6 46	...	9 20	8 12	...	11 5	...	1 48
Martinstein	4 57	...	6 57	...	9 33	...	...	1115	...	1 58
Sobernheim...........	5 11	...	7 10	...	9 47	8 28	...	1128	...	2 10
Staudernheim.........	5 17	...	7 16	...	9 53	...	...	1135	...	2 16
Münster-a-S. ...arr	5 43	...	7 41	1,2,3	10 19	8 45	...	1158	...	2 38
STRASSB'G 209 dep	...	...	...	6 a0	...	...	...	6a55	...	8a24
NEUSTADT 206 dep	...	a.m.	6 a2	7a52	...	6a 2	a.m.	9a14	...	12p10
Münster ....dep	5 47	6 32	8 49	9 16	10 20	8 46	9 46	12 3	...	2 45
Kreuznach Bad arr	5 53	6 38	8 55	9 22	10 26	...	9 53	12 9	...	2 51
Kreuznach Bad dep	5 57	6 40	8 56	9 24	10 27	8 54	9 56	1213	...	2 53
Langenlonsheim ...	6 15	6 54	9 14	...	10 41	⋮	10 16	1228	...	3 8
Bingerbrück ....arr	6 31	7 9	9 30	9 39	10 57	⋮	10 32	1244	...	3 24
COLOGNE 123B arr	9a50	1155	12p37	1237	...	⋮	...	4p40	...	6 p5
MAYENCE 123 arr	7a42	7a48	10a22	1022	12p 3	9a32	12 p3	1p54	...	4 p39

Station										
PARIS 64 ......dep	1015	...	...	...	...	...	...	...	...	9 a0
METZ 212 ......dep	9a25	...	...	11a21	1121	...	...	1p27	...	4 p11
	Ex3	2,3,4	Ex2	1,2,3	2 3 4	2,3,4	2 3 4	2 3 4	2 3 4	Ex 3
	a.m.	p.m.		p.m.	p.m.	p.m.	p.m.	p.m.	p.m.	p.m.
Forbach ....dep	1028	...	...	⋮	1259	2 3	...	3 7	4 22	5 19
Saarbrücken arr	1038	...	...	⋮	1 12	2 16	...	3 20	4 42	5 29
Saarbrücken dep	1045	12 28	...	1 20	1 38	2 40	2‡58	3 35	4 49	5 36
Sulzbach	...	12 46	...	...	1 55	2 57	3 16	3 52	5 6	...
Neunkirchen arr	11 8	1 9	...	1 44	2 17	3 18	3 41	4 16	5 29	6 1
Neunkirchen dep	11 9	1 15	...	1 45	2 20	3 21	3 47	4 26	5 33	6 2
Ottweiler	...	1 24	...	...	2 28	3 29	3 56	4 35	5 41	6 11
St. Wendel	1125	1 40	...	2 1	2 43	3 51	4 15	4 50	5 57	6 22
Turkismühle	...		...	...	3 15	4 27	4 48	5 25	6 29	...
Birkenfeld Neub....	...	...	...	...	3 27		5 1	5 37	7 3	6 49
Heimbach	RC	...	...	...	3 38	...	5 12	5 47	7 13	...
Kronweiler............	...	...	...	...	3 48	...	5 23	5 57	7 23	RC
Oberstein	12 4	...	...	2 40	4 5	...	5 38	6 17	7 39	7 8
Fischbach	...	...	...	...	4 17	...		6 32	7 51	...
Kirn	1218	...	...	2 56	4 29	...	...	6 49	8 4	7 24
Martinstein	...	...	...	...	4 40	...	...	7 1	8 14	...
Sobernheim...........	...	...	...	...	4 53	...	...	7 14	8 27	...
Staudernheim.........	...	...	...	...	4 58	...	...	7 22	8 33	...
Münster-a-S. ...arr	1244	...	...	3 24	5 21	...	Ex3	7 46	8 58	7 53
STRASSB'G 209 dep	...	...	1217	12p17	...	...	3p52	3p52	...	...
NEUSTADT 206 dep	...	p.m.	1p56	1 p56	...	p.m.	5p39	5p39	...	...
Münster ....dep	1245	12 55	3 9	3 26	5 24	6 32	6 58	7 51	9 7	7 56
Kreuznach Bad arr	...	1 1	3 15	3 32	5 30	6 38	7 4	7 57	9 13	...
Kreuznach Bad dep	1252	1 2	3 16	3 33	5 32	6 39	7 5	8 18	9 15	8 4
Langenlonsheim ...	⋮	1 17	...	...	5 47	6 54	...	8 40	9 30	⋮
Bingerbrück ....arr	⋮	1 30	3 31	3 49	6 3	7 10	7 20	8 54	9 46	⋮
COLOGNE 123B arr	⋮	4p40	6 p5	7 p7	1015	10p15	1015	...	1255	⋮
MAYENCE 123 arr	1p27	2p22	4p39	4 p39	7p49	9 p8	9 p8	9p53	1038	8 p39

Station										
PARIS 64 ......dep	...	...	...	...	...	...	...	12 20	...	5p15
METZ 212 ......dep	...	...	...	...	5p35	6 p59	...	9 p42	...	1235
	2 3 4	2,3,4	2 3 4	Ex 3	2 3 4	2,3,4	2 3 4	2,3,4	2 3 4	Ex3
	p.m.	p.m.	p.m.	p.m.	p.m.	p.m.	p.m.	p.m.	n'gt	a.m.
Forbach ....dep	...	5 59	...	...	7 14	8 37	...	11 17	...	1 37
Saarbrücken arr	...	6 12	...	...	7 27	8 50	...	11 30	...	1 47
Saarbrücken dep	5 49	6 35	7 6	7 39	7 55	9 5	11 2	11 36	1232	1 52
Sulzbach	6 6	6 52	7 23	...	8 12	9 24	1119	11 54	1249	...
Neunkirchen arr	6 27	7 16	7 46	8 2	8 34	9 51	1142	12 20	1 11	2 15
Neunkirchen dep	6 51	7 20	7 48	8 3	8 38	9 58	1149	12 23	1 15	2 16
Ottweiler	7 1	7 29	7 57	...	8 46	10 10	1158	12 32	1 27	...
St. Wendel	7 18	7 47	8 13	...	9 3	10 29	1213	12 54	1 46	2 32
Turkismühle		8 19		...	9 39			1 31		...
Birkenfeld Neub....	...		...	...	9 53	...	...	1 43	...	...
Heimbach	...	...	...	...	10 3	...	...	1 52	...	...
Kronweiler............	...	...	...	...	1013	...	...		...	...
Oberstein	...	...	...	8 51	1031	...	...	...	...	3 10
Fischbach	...	...	...	...	1043	...	...	...	...	...
Kirn	...	...	...	9 10	1056	...	...	...	...	3 26
Martinstein	...	...	...	...	11 6	...	...	...	...	...
Sobernheim...........	...	...	...	...	1120	...	...	...	...	...
Staudernheim.........	...	...	...	...	1127	...	...	...	...	...
Münster-a-S. ...arr	...	Ex 3	...	9 37	1150	Ex 3	...	...	...	3 54
STRASSB'G 209 dep	1,2,3	6 p50	...	...	6p50	11p41	...	...	2 3 4	...
NEUSTADT 206 dep	p.m.	8 p43	p.m.	...	9p40	1 a14	...	...	a.m.	...
Münster ....dep	8 5	9 55	10 0	9 38	12 3	2 24	...	...	5 0	3 55
Kreuznach Bad arr	8 11	10 1	10 6	9 44	12 9	2 30	...	...	5 6	4 1
Kreuznach Bad dep	8 13	10 2	1010	9 46	1212	2 31	...	...	5 8	4 2
Langenlonsheim ...	8 24	...	1028	...	1229	...	...	...	5 22	...
Bingerbrück ....arr	8 34	10 17	1044	10 1	1245	2 46	...	...	5 38	4 18
COLOGNE 123B arr	...	12a55	...	12a55	5 a9	5 a21	...	...	...	9a39
MAYENCE 123 arr	9p53	11p16	11p16	10p38	1a44	3 a59	...	...	...	4a58

†—Weekdays only between Birkenfeld and Oberstein. ‡—On Sunday at 2.22 p.m. §—2,3,4 class. RC—Restaurant Car.

MUNSTER-am-STEIN and GAU-ALGESHEIM.

Station																			
Munster ....dep	5a12	7 a8	8a10	8a46	9 a25	11a25	12p22	12p45	1p38	2p41	4p38	7p15	8p22	9p45	...	...	...	...	...
Kreuznach Bad	5 19	7 15	8 17	8 54	9 48	11 32	12 29	12 52	1 45	2 48	4 45	7 24	8 29	9 52	...	...	...	...	...
Gau-Algesheim 122...arr	6 54	7 56	8 59	D	10 7	...	1 2	A	2 26	3 20	5 17	8 2	9 2	1025	...	...	...	...	...
Gau-Algesheim ......dep	6 a4	...	7a12	8a13	9a27	...	12p38	1p48	B	3p52	C	6p12	7p22	8p21	9p10	...	...	...	...
Kreuznach Bad	6 39	7 a0	7 46	8 54	10 1	12 p8	1 24	2 26	2p52	4 26	6 p26	6 46	7 58	8 55	9 44	...	...	...	...
Munster ....arr	6 45	7 6	7 52	9 0	10 7	12 14	1 30	2 32	2 58	4 32	6 32	6 52	8 5	9 1	9 50	...	...	...	...

A—Arrive Mayence 1.27 p.m. B—Depart Mayence 2.13 p.m. C—Depart Mayence 5.47 p.m.
D—Arrives Mayence 9.32 a.m.

COLOGNE, EUSKIRCHEN, and TREVES.

Dist E.M	Cologne—	1—4 a.m.	1—4 a.m.	Ex 3 a.m.	1—4 a.m.	1—4 noon	Ex 3 p.m.	2 3 4	1—4 p.m.	2 3 4 p.m.	1,2,3 p.m.	1—4 p.m.	1—4 p.m.	1—4 p.m.
—	Hauptbhf dep	6 37	5 15	8 2	9 10	12 0	1 25	...	4 9	6§22	7 10	7 45	9 29	11 20
6¾	Kalscheuren ...	7 0	5 38	RC	9 34	12 25	RC	...	4 33	6 38	...	8 9	9 52	11 49
13½	Liblar	7 20	5 59	...	9 54	12 45	...	...	4 54	7 0	...	8 29	10 13	12 10
25	Euskirchen arr	7 47	6 26	8 46	10 21	1 12	2 7	...	5 21	7 29	7 55	8 56	10 40	12 38
...	" ...dep		6 43	8 49	10 28	1 18	2 11	...	5 30	7 33	8 1	9 2	10 49	
39½	Call..................	2,3,4	7 37	9 23	11 13	2 10	2 47	...	6 18	8 17	...	9 49	11 36	
49¼	Blankenheim ...	a.m.	8 10	...	11 42	2 41	...	...	6 47		...	1019	12 6	
57¾	Jünkerath-Stdt.	4 50	8 44	10 1	12 9	3 31	3 25	p.m.	7 16	...	9 9	1047	12 28	
69	Gerolstein	5 23	9 15	10 18	12 38	3 57	3 42	5 45	7 45	...	9 27	1113		
73½	Birresborn	5 33	9 25	...	12 47	4 7	...	5 55	7 55	...	...	1123	...	
76¼	Mürlenbach......	5 40	9 32	...	12 54	4 14	...	6 2	8 2	...	...	1130	2—4	
84¼	Kyllburg	6 1	9 54	10 42	1 14	4 34	...	6 23	8 21	...	...	1149	a.m.	
87¾	Erdorf.-Bitburg	6 14	10 5	10 50	1 23	4 44	4 12	6 34	8 33	...	10 0	1158	4 20	
107¾	Ehrang............	7 9	1056	...	2 11	5 34	...	7 21	9 23	...	...	1244	5 9	
111	Treves (124) arr	7 19	11 6	11 27	2 21	5 44	4 49	7 30	9 33	...	10 37	1253	6 29	
155¼	DIED'NH'F'N a	10 a8	1p35	1 p35	4 p35	8 p8	6 p21	...	12a1	...	12 a1	...	...	
176	METZ 210 arr	10a46	2p22	2 p22	5 p29	9p27	6 p51	...	1230	...	12a30	...	...	

	1—4	1—4	1—4	1—4	1—4	1,2,3	1—4	Ex3	1—4	1,2,3	1—4	Ex 3	2,34	2 3 4
METZ 210A dep	...	...	...	...	4 a55	6 a26	8 a21	12p2	12 p8	...	3p10	5 p26	5p32	8p53
DIED'NHFN dep	...	...	...	...	5 a55	6 a57	9 a5	1233	1 p2	...	4 p2	5 p58	6p23	9p57
			a.m.		a.m.	a.m.	a.m.	p.m.	p.m.		p.m.	p.m.	p.m.	nigt
Treves ....dep	...	...	4 44	...	8 8	8 36	11 26	1 55	3 8	...	6 13	7 55	9 5	12 0
Ehrang	...	...	4 54	...	8 16	...	11 35	RC	3 16	...	6 21	RC	9 13	1210
Erdorf.-Bitburg	...	...	5 51	...	9 28	9 19	12 42	2 35	4 13	...	7 19	8 37	1012	1 11
Kyllburg............	...	...	6 3	...	9 41	9 31	12 55	...	4 25	...	7 33	...	1025	
Mürlenbach	...	...	6 24	...	10 3	...	1 17	...	4 46	...	7 55	...	1047	
Birresborn	...	...	6 33	...	10 10	...	1 24	...	4 53	...	8 2	...	1054	
Gerolstein	a.m.	...	6 45	...	10 25	10 0	1.40	3 10	5 5	...	8 17	9 12	11 8	
Jünkerath-Stdtk	4 51	...	7 14	...	10 55	10 23	2 9	3 30	5 34	...	8 47	9 35	1134	
Blankenheim ...	5 19	a.m.	7 40	...	11 21	...	2 35	...	5 59	p.m.	9 13	...		
Call	5 47	7†12	8 7	...	11 46	11 2	3 0	4 9	6 24	8 37	9 40	...	...	
Euskirchen ...arr	6 25	7 50	8 42	a.m.	12 24	11 29	3 33	4 33	6 57	9 13	1017	10 33	...	
" ...dep	6 31	8 0	8 50	1029	12 31	11 31	3 40	4 38	7 3	9 17	1045	10 34	...	
Liblar	7 2	8 28	9 19	1057	12 57	...	4 10	...	7 34	9 45	1111	...	...	
Kalscheuren	7 20	8 46	9 40	1115	1 16	...	4 30	...	7 53	10 3	1129	...	...	
Cologne Hpt. arr	7 41	9 6	10 0	1134	1 36	12 15	4 50	5 18	8 14	10§16	1149	11 14	...	...

RC—Restaurant Car.

†—Weekdays only. §—Cologne West.

KLEVE and DUISBURG.

Kleve......dep	...	4a54	5a56	8a21	10a24	1p10	4p40	7p21	9 p16	...	...	...
Xanten	...	5 55	7 10	9 24	11 25	2 14	5 36	8 20	10 24	...	...	...
Menzelen	...	6 13	7 35	9 42	11 43	2 32	5 52	8 38	10 43	...	...	...
Mörs..............	4a50	7 8	8 20	1033	12 29	3 24	6 40	9 44	11 27	...	...	...
Trompet	4 59	7 17	8 30	1042	12 38	3 33	6 49	9 53	11 36	...	...	...
Duisburg arr	5 27	7 46	9 55	11 6	1 1	3 58	7 13	1016	12 3	...	...	...

Duisburg dep	... ...	6a35	8a27	11a17	1 p24	5p33	6 p1	...	8 p32	11p35	...	...
Trompet	5 a4	7 0	9 0	11 51	1 59	6 1	7 2	7p52	9 3	12 5	...	...
Mörs	5 13	7 12	9 12	12 1	2 12	6 11	7 10	8 1	9 15	12 13	...	...
Menzelen	5 59	8 0	10 3	12 50	3 3	7 0		8 49	10 4		...	...
Xanten	6 26	8 18	1022	1 9	3 23	7 20	...	9 10	10 25	...	...	...
Kleve ......arr	7 26	9 14	1125	2 14	4 24	8 17	...	1013	11 24	...	...	...

BONN and EUSKIRCHEN.

E M Dist		a.m.	a.m.	a.m.	a.m.	p.m.	pm	p.m.	p.m.	p.m.	p.m.
	Bonn ......dep	4 48	7 48	9 18	1113	2 28	414	5 54	7 48	9 40	1124
10½	Meckenheim	5 41	8 21	9 57	1152	3 7	454	6 33	8 27	1018	12 4
13¾	Rheinbach ...	5 53	8 28	10 5	1159	3 14	5 2	6 40	8 34	1025	1211
21¼	Euskirchen ar	6 22	8 45	1024	1218	3 33	521	6 59	8 53	1043	1229

(126)	am	a.m.	p.m.	p.m.	pm	p.m.	p m	p.m.	p.m.
Euskirchen	638	9 1	1227	2 23	411	5 53	8 0	9 22	1047
Rheinbach...	658	9 22	1247	2 44	431	6 13	8 21	9 42	11 7
Meckenheim	7 7	9 29	1254	2 51	438	6 20	8 28	9 49	1114
Bonn	739	10 1	1 25	3 23	5 9	6 51	8 59	1021	1145

BONN and OBERCASSEL.

	a.m.	a.m.	a.m.	p.m.	p.m.	p.m.	p m.	
Bonn (Stadt) ...dep	6 1	7 54	9 34	1249	3 38	5 30	7 49	...
Bonn (Traject)......	6 12	8 5	9 45	1 0	3 48	5 41	7 51	...
Obercassel......arr	6 27	8 20	10 0	1 15	4 3	5 56	8 5	...

	a.m.	a.m.	a.m.	p.m.	p.m.	p m	p m	
Obercassel.........dep	6 37	8 30	1018	3 0	4 50	6 45	8 32	...
Bonn (Traject)	6 54	8 48	1036	3 18	5 7	7 3	8 50	...
Bonn (Stadt).........arr	7 1	8 55	1043	3 25	5 14	7 10	8 57	...

PUENDERICH and TRABEN-TRARBACH.

	a.m.	a.m	p.m.	p.m.	p.m.	p.m.	p.m.
Puenderich.........dep	7 15	9 49	1 15	3 18	4 58	7 0	10 5
Traben-Trarbach arr	7 40	10 14	1 40	3 43	5 23	7 25	10 30

	a.m.	a.m.	a.m.	p.m.	p.m.	p.m.	p.m.
Traben-Trarbach dep	5 40	8 40	11 38	2 19	4 10	5 53	8 25
Puenderich ....arr	6 5	9 5	12 7	2 48	4 36	6 20	9 0

GEROLSTEIN and ST. VITH.

E.M.								
	Gerolstein dep	6 a48	10a32	1 p42	4 p0	5 p13	9p33	...
10	Gondelsheim......	7 22	11 6	2 15	4 34	5 46	10 7	...
15	Prüm	7 41	11 27	2 34	4 50	6 7	1029	...
20	Pronsfeld	7 56	11 43	2 50		6 22	1047	...
26½	Bleialf	8 23	12 7	3 12	...	6 52	1116	...
37	St. Vith (127)	8 52	12 37	3 41	...	7 30	1146	...

St. Vith.........dep	...	6a43	10a35	1p20	4p25	...	10p8	...
Bleialf	...	7 14	11 4	1 46	5 6	...	1036	...
Pronsfeld	a.m.	7 40	11 24	2 6	5 35	...	1057	...
Prüm	4 28	8 3	11 41	2 24	6 0	8p10	1112	...
Gondelsheim........	4 43	8 27	11 57	2 39	6 23	8 27		...
Gerolstein 126	5 14	9 0	12 27	3 5	7 3	9 0	...	...

Pronsfeld to Waxweiler and Pronsfeld to Neuerburg—local lines in each direction.

LINDERN and HEINSBERG.

‡—Weekdays only.

Lindern...dep	6‡a1	7a35	10a39	1p10	3p16	5p12	7p55	10p9	...
Heinsberg arr	6 36	8 9	11 12	1 45	3 48	5 47	8 30	1044	...

Heinsberg ...dep	5‡14	6a40	9a40	11a17	2p10	3p57	7o12	8p38	...
Lindern 134A arr	5 47	7 13	1013	11 51	2 45	4 29	7 47	9 16	...

TREVES and BULLAY (Mosel Valley Line).

		a.m.		a.m.		a.m.	p.m	p m		p.m.	p.m							
Treves Kleinbahn ...dep	...	7 50	...	8 44	...	11 51	2 16	2 48	...	6 3	9 0	...	...	...	...	...	...	...
Neumagen Dhron	a.m.	8 52	...	10 4	...	1 12	3 17	4 5	...	7 17	1017	...	...	...	...	...	...	...
Berncastel	6 55	9 32	a.m.	10 54	p.m.	2 11	4 1	4 56	p.m.	8 2	11 6	...	...	...	...	...	...	...
Trarbach	8 3	1010	1032	11 49	1 57	3 14	4 43	5 52	6 41	8 49		...	...	...	...	...	...	...
Puenderich	8 33		1059	12 16	2 24	3 42		6 19	7 8	9 11	...	...	...	...	...	...	...	...
Bullay ....arr	9 4	...	1125	12 42	2 50	4 11	...	6 45	7 34	9 37	...	...	...	...	...	...	...	...

		a.m.	a.m.	a.m.	a.m.	p.m.	p.m.	p.m.	...	p.m.		p.m.	p.m.				
Bullay.......................dep	...	6 12	8 7	...	9 53	1228	1 24	3 59	...	4 56	...	7 21	9 55		...	...	...
Puenderich.....................	...	6 39	8 34	...	1023	1256	1 51	4 26	p.m.	5 23	p.m.	7 58	1021	†—Not on Sunday.	...	...	...
Trarbach.........................	a.m.	7 6	9 1	1014	1052	1 23	2 18	4 56	5 †3	5 51	7§20	8 31		§—Sunday only.	...	...	...
Berncastel	4 59	8 1		1055	1151		3 13		5 47	6 46	8 3	9 37	...		...	...	...
Neumagen Dhron.............	5 56	8 51	...	1137	1240	...	4 5	...	6 26	7 36	8 47		...		...	...	...
Treves Kleinbahn.... arr	7 30	10 6	...	1243	1 55	...	5 25	...	7 32	8 51	9 51	...	...		...	...	...

Luggage Rates—see page 462.

PRUSSIAN STATE RYS.

STOLBERG and M. GLADBACH.

		a.m.	a.m.	a.m.	a.m.		p.m.		p.m.		p.m.		p.m.	p.m.	p.m.
Stolberg ....dep		...	...	6 18	8 51	...	12 20	...	2 10	...	7 2	...	10 28	...	11 42
Eschweiler (Thal)		...	...	6 30	9 4	...	12 33	...	2 23	...	7 14	...	10 41	...	11 56
Jülich ....arr		...	...	7 1	9 39	a.m.	1 4	...	2 55	p.m.	7 45	p.m.	11 12	...	12 28
„ ....dep		...	6 3	7 25	9 47	1120	1 9	...	—	5 30	—	9 3	—	11 24	—
Ameln	a.m.	...	6 23	7 44	10 8	1139	1 32	...	...	5 51	...	9 22	...	11 43	...
Otzenrath	5†32	...	6 45	8 2	10 28	1158	1 51	p.m.	...	6 12	...	9 41	...	12 3	...
Hochneukirch	5 44	6 30	6 58	8 10	10 37	12 6	2 5	5 52	...	6 22	...	9 49	...	12 10	...
M. Gladbach ...arr	6 12	6 57	7 23	8 33	11 2	1231	2 30	6 15	...	6 53	...	10 14	...	...	...

	a.m.	a.m.		a.m.	a.m.	a.m.	a.m.	p.m.	p.m.	p.m.	p.m.	p.m.	p.m.	p.m.
M. Gladbach ....dep	...	...	...	...	8 39	9 18	11 50	1 56	...	4 55	7 11	7 23	...	11 30
Hochneukirch	4 †44	5 53	...	7 †3	9 4	9 41	12 16	2 22	...	5 23	7 40	7 56	9 51	11 56
Otzenrath	4 52	6 2	...	7 11	9 12	—	12 25	2 30	...	5 32	—	8 5	9 59	12 4
Ameln	—	6 21	...	7 29	9 29	...	12 45	2 47	...	5 52	...	8 25	10 17	12 22
Jülich ....arr	...	6 42	a.m.	7 50	9 47	...	1 5	3 6	...	6 11	...	8 46	10 36	12 40
„ ....dep	5 20	—	7 32	—	9 51	...	1 9	—	4 7	6 25	...	8 55	—	—
Eschweiler (Thal)	5 51	...	8 3	...	10 23	...	1 45	...	4 38	6 57	...	9 26	...	...
Stolberg (127) ....arr	6 3	...	8 14	...	10 34	...	1 57	...	4 50	7 11	...	9 37	...	...

†—Weekdays only.

M. GLADBACH, VIERSEN, and VENLO. [Amsterdam Time at Venlo.

Extra—Kaldenkirchen to M. Gladbach 5‡52 a.m., 8‡42 p.m. Dülken to M. Gladbach 7.59 p.m.

	a.m.	a.m.	a.m.	p.m.	p.m.	p.m.	p.m.	p.m.	p.m.	p.m.
M. Gladbach dep	7 32	9 19	1149	1 12	3 41	4 16	6 29	7 20	8 17	1132
Viersen ...dep	7 47	9 33	12 3	1 27	3 56	4 31	6 44	7 46	8 56	1145
Dülken	7 55	9 43	1212	1 35	4 6	4 42	6 58	7 47	9 7	1154
Breyell	8 9	9 57	1226	1 49	4 20	—	7 12	—	9 21	12 8
Kaldenkirchen	8 27	10 9	1235	2 13	4 29	...	7 22	...	9 30	1218
Venlo ....arr	7 54	9 36	12 2	1 40	3 56	...	6 49	...	8 58	1144

*—Cust. Exam.

		a.m.	a.m.	a.m.	a.m.	p.m.	p.m.	p.m.	p.m.	p.m.
Venlo ....dep		5 57	8 2	9 47	1125	...	1 48	4 12	7 11	9 19
Kaldenkirchen		7 3	9 0	1047	1233	2 15	2 48	5 10	8 11	1018
Breyell		7 12	9 8	1055	1241	2 23	2 56	5 19	8 19	1026
Dülken	5‡a28	7 30	9 22	1112	1256	2 37	3 10	5 36	8 35	1043
Viersen	5 42	7 42	9 30	1121	1 5	2 45	3 24	5 45	8 44	1055
M. Gladbach	5 58	7 55	9 43	1131	1 19	2 58	3 37	5 55	8 57	1110

‡—Not on Sunday.

CREFELD and HOMBERG.

	a.m.	a.m.	a.m.	p.m.	p.m.	p.m.	p.m.	p.m.	p.m.
Crefeld ....dep	6 15	8 11	9 30	1225	5 12	7 23	8 4	9 20	1138
Uerdingen	6 33	8 22	9 45	1236	5 29	7 39	8 19	9 31	1150
Homberg ...arr	6 56	8 39	10 9	1258	5 55	...	8 39	9 48	12 2

	a.m	a.m.	a.m.	a.m.	a.m.	p.m.	p.m.	p.m.	p.m.
Homberg ...dep	6 5	6 38	8 19	9 51	1152	2 1	5 29	6 51	8 51
Uerdingen	6 28	7 1	8 45	1015	1216	2 25	...	7 16	9 15
Crefeld ....arr	6 43	7 15	9 1	1028	1229	2 41	5 52	7 31	9 25

Homberg and Ruhrort.—Steamer Service in 12 minutes. About twenty-five departures each way between 5.16 a.m. and midnight.

Rail Motors { Crefeld dep. 8.14, 11.17 a.m., 2.34, 6.18, 7.10, 8.31, 10.45 p.m.
Homberg dep. 7.7, 10.25 a.m., 12.30, 3.23, 5.56, 9.49 p.m.

HOMBERG and MÖRS.—Every fifteen minutes each way.

DUREN and JULICH.

Düren	6a49	9a12	10a49	12p20	2p33	4p49	8p10	9 p56	11p40
Jülich	7 17	9 42	11 17	12 52	3 1	5 17	8 38	10 27	12 12

Jülich	6 a0	7a26	9a56	1p12	3 p8	3p59	6p20	8p56	10p39
Düren	6 34	7 54	1024	1 40	3 36	4 27	6 48	9 24	11 11

ST. VITH and ULFLINGEN.

St. Vith dep	9a25	10a49	1p40	5 p3	9p58
Ulflingen ar	1020	11 44	2 35	5 58	10 45

Ulflingen ....dep	6a11	9 a13	12p10	3 p0	8p23
St. Vith ....arr	7 4	10 5	1 3	352	9 16

AIX-LA-CHAPELLE, and St. VITH.

		a.m	a.m.	p.m.	p.m.	p.m.	p.m.	p.m.					
Aix-la-Chapelle dep	...	7 39	1032	1 2	3 56	7 29	7‡40	8 32	...	...	...	...	...
Raeren (127A) ...	a.m.	8 22	1115	1 45	4 39	8 8	8 42	9 17	...	...	...	...	...
Montjoie	6 40	9 14	12 5	2 39	5 30	8 52	—	10 9	...	...	...	...	...
Weismes	7 59	10 4	1250	3 29	6 15	9 32	...	1054	...	...	...	...	...
St. Vith 126 ...arr	8 48	1031	1 15	3 58	6 42	9 55	...	1121	...	...	...	...	...

St. Vith ....dep	4a55	7a25	10a27	1p22	3p56	6p51	10p0	...	...	...	...	...	...
Weismes	5 24	7 54	10 56	1 54	4 24	7 22	1055	...	...	...	...	...	...
Montjoie	6 10	8 39	11 39	2 40	5 7	8 12	12 8	...	...	...	...	...	...
Raeren	6 57	9 22	12 22	3 23	...	8 55	—	...	...	...	...	...	...
Aix-Chapelle ar	7 43	10 0	1 0	4 1	6 21	9 33	...	...	...	...	...	...	...

‡—Weekdays only.

WEISMES and MALMEDY.

Weismes	6†a40	8 a0	10 a5	11a5	12p4	12p57	1p57	3p30	4p32	6p19	7p27	9p36	10p57	11p20
Malmedy	6 58	8 18	10 23	1123	1222	1 15	2 17	3 48	4 52	6 37	7 47	9 56	11 17	11 38

Malmedy dep	4a51	6†a0	7a28	9 a33	10a31	1224	1 p25	3 p1	3p57	5p47	6p47	8p52	10p25
Weismes arr	5 13	6 22	7 50	9 55	10 53	1246	1 47	3 23	4 19	6 9	7 9	9 14	10 47

†—Not on Sun.

COLOGNE and M. GLADBACH.

Cologne—	a.m.	a.m	a.m.	p.m.	p.m.	p.m.	p.m.	p.m.	p.m.
Hauptbahnhof	5 0	6 38	9 1	1 16	4 26	6 20	7 53	9 39	1043
Poulheim	5 26	7 6	9 27	1 44	4 53	...	8 21	...	11 9
Grevenbroich	6 6	7 41	10 9	2 19	5 31	6 57	8 54	1021	1152
Hochneukirch	6 30	8 1	1030	2 41	5 52	7 13	9 15	1037	1212
M. Gladbach	6 57	8 22	1049	3 2	6 15	7 32	9 35	1057	1232

	a.m.	a.m.	a.m.	a.m.	p.m.	p.m.	p.m.	p.m.
M. Gladb'h	4 12	5 22	6 34	9 18	1225	2 52	4 40	8 7
Hochn'uk'h	4 34	5 44	6 55	9 42	1247	3 14	5 2	8 30
Grevenbch.	5 8	6 10	7 9	10 6	1 10	3 37	5 30	8 55
Poulheim	5 42	6 49	...	1039	1 45	4 14	6 9	9 29
Cologne Ht.	6 9	7 18	7 46	11 6	2 12	4 41	6 36	9 54

AIX-LA-CHAPELLE and JULICH. ‡—Weekdays only.

		a.m.	a.m.	p.m.	p.m	p.m.	p.m.	p.m.	p.m.
Aix-Chapelle ...dep		5‡54	8 2	12 4	4 17	7‡20	7 48	9 5	11 10
Wurselen ....arr		6 7	8 15	1217	4 30	7 37	8 3	9 18	11 23
Wurselen ....dep		6 20	...	1229	5 11	...	8 8	...	...
Kohlscheid ...arr		6 44	...	1257	5 43	...	8 32	...	...
Wurselen ...	5a45	—	...	1230	5 11	...	...	...	...
Stolberg arr	6 8	...	...	1 2	5 41	...	...	...	...
Wurselen ....dep		6‡12	8 17	1218	4 33	7 39	8 5	9 19	11 24
Mariagrube		6 45	8 31	1232	4 48	7 52	8 19	9 34	11 38
Aldenhoven		7 3	8 50	1250	5 6	—	8 37	9 52	11 56
Julich (127) ....arr		7 18	9 5	1 5	5 21	...	8 52	10 7	12 11

		a.m.	a.m.	a.m.	p.m	p.m.	p.m.	p.m.	p.m.
Julich ....dep		5‡ 8	7 24	9 55	1 53	4 14	...	7 16	9 0
Aldenhoven		5 25	7 41	1012	2 10	4 31	...	7 33	9 17
Mariagrube		5 48	7 59	1030	2 30	4 53	...	7 52	9 37
Wurselen ....arr		6 2	8 12	1043	2 43	5 6	...	8 5	9 50
Stolberg ...dep		...	7 32	...	2 23	...	7 ‡0	...	7 23
Wurselen ...arr		...	7 56	...	2 46	...	7 19	...	7 44
Kohlscheid dep		5‡29	7 32	...	2 14	...	—	6 41	9 0
Wurselen ...arr		5‡56	7 58	...	2 44	...	...	7 28	9 29
Wurselen ...	7a15	6 7	8 17	1044	2 49	5 11	...	8 7	9 53
Aix-la-Chap.	7 35	6 27	8 32	1058	3 3	5 25	...	8 21	10 7

M. GLADBACH and ROERMOND. [*—Amsterdam time.

	a.m.	a.m.	a.m.	a.m.	a.m.	p.m	p.m.	p.m.	p.m.	p.m.
M. Gladbach dep	6 16	8 9	9 20	10 0	1139	2 2	3 50	6 1	7 32	1045
Rheindahlen	6 36	...	9 40	...	1159	2 20	4 9	...	7 52	11 4
Dalheim	6 57	8 39	10 0	1031	1224	2 40	4 31	6 31	8 18	1127
Vlodrop *		8 10	9 36	10 9	1157	2 8	—	6 4	7 51	11 0
Roermond * arr		8 25	9 52	1022	1215	2 26	...	6 22	8 9	1118

	a.m.	a.m.	a.m.		pm		p.m.	p.m.	p.m.	
Roermond * dep	5 57	9 47	1050	...	2 9	...	5 54	6 16	9 30	...
Vlodrop	6 57	1047	1147	p.m.	3 9	p.m.	6 42	7 12	1030	p.m.
Dalheim	7 12	11 0	12 2	1251	322	4 44	6 57	7 30	1043	1133
Rheindahlen	7 37	1118	...	1 17	340	5 7	18	...	...	1152
M. Gladbach	7 55	1135	1230	1 37	357	5 25	7 37	7 57	1112	12 9

PRUSSIAN STATE RAILWAYS.

Luggage Rates—see page 462.

SAARGEMUND, SAARBRUCKEN, and TREVES.

			a.m.		a.m.	a.m.	a.m.	a.m.	a m.	p.m.	p.m.	p.m.	p.m.	p.m.	p.m.	p.m.	p.m.	p.m.	p.m.	p.m.	n'gt
Saargemünd dep	...	...	5 39	...	7 4	9 13	9 22	9 57	1120	12 1	1252	1 57	2 41	4 31	5 54	5 23	6 20	8 4	9 28	1056	12 7
Saarbrücken arr	...	...	6 20	...	7 39	9 31	9 55	1036	1157	1219	1 28	2 34	3 15	5 9	6 12	6 6	6 55	8 42	9 46	1130	1225
	a.m.	a.m.	a.m.	a.m.	a.m.	a.m.	a.m	a.m.	p.m	p.m.	p.m.	p.m.	p.m	p.m.	p.m.	p.m.	p.m.	p m.	p.m	p.m.	n'gt
Saarbrücken dep	5 5	6 15	6 45	7 17	8 4	9 39	1033	1134	1230	1224	1 44	3 5	3 31	5 16	6 24	6 43	8 5	9 1	10 0	1143	1236
Völklingen	5 24	6 34	...	7 37	8 25	9 51	1053	1155	1250	...	2 4	3 25	3 51	5 33	...	7 7	8 26	9 23	1012	12 5	1255
Bous	5 33	6 42	...	7 44	8 33	...	11 1	12 3	1257	RC	2 13	3 33	3 59	5 41	RC	7 16	8 35	9 31	1019	1212	1 5
Saarlouis	5 47	6 54	7 8	7 56	8 46	10 4	1114	1216	1 11	...	2 26	3 46	4 9	5 53	6 47	7 30	8 50	9 44	1028	1224	1 17
Dillingen	5 56	7 0	...	8 2	8 54	1010	1121	1223	1 18	...	2 34	3 52	4 17	6 2	...	7 39	8 57	9 51	1034	1231	1 23
Merzig	6 20	7 31	7 24	8 21	9 18	1027	1141	1241	1 38	1258	2 58	4 12	4 36	6 21	7 3	7 59	9 18	10 9	1051	1249	1 41
Mettlach	6 34	7 42	7 34	—	9 33	1037	1154	—	1 50	...	3 10	—	4 48	6 33	...	—	9 31	—	11 0	—	—
Beurig-Saarburg	7 5	—	7 53	...	10 5	1056	1221	...	2 18	...	—	...	5 16	7 0	...	...	9 59	...	1119	...	...
Conz	7 32	...	...	...	1032	...	1246	...	2 42	...	...	...	5 41	7 25	...	...	1017	...	1134	...	...
Karthaus ... arr	7 37	...	8 10	...	1037	1112	1250	...	2 46	...	...	...	5 45	7 29	...	...	1028	...	1138	...	...
Karthaus ... dep	7 39	...	8 11	...	1039	1113	1252	...	2 48	...	...	...	5 47	7 30	...	...	1030	...	1139	...	...
Treves (126) ...arr	7 50	...	8 19	...	1051	1121	1 3	...	2 59	1 40	...	...	5 58	7 41	7 48	...	1041	...	1147	...	...

			a.m.	a.m.		a.m.	a.m.		a.m.			a.m.		p.m.		p.m.			p.m.	p.m.	p.m.	p.m.
Treves ...dep		...	4 55	6 8	...	7 59	9 49	...	1132	...	...	1151	...	2 37	...	4 56	...	...	6 9	8 6	1048	1125
Karthaus ... arr		...	5 6	6 16	...	8 10	9 57	...	...	...	...	12 3	...	2 49	...	...	...	...	6 21	8 17	...	1136
Karthaus ... dep		...	5 7	6 17	...	8 14	9 59	...	RC	...	...	12 5	...	2 51	...	RC	...	...	6 22	8 19	...	1137
Conz		...	5 12	6 22	...	8 19	10 4	...	...	...	...	1210	...	2 56	...	...	...	...	6 27	8 24	...	1142
Beurig-Saarburg		a.m.	5 38	6 39	a.m.	8 42	10 22	...	1155	...	...	1234	...	3 20	...	...	p.m	...	6 51	8 47	...	12 5
Mettlach	a.m.	5 19	6 8	6 59	8 9	9 9	10 42	a.m.	1214	p.m.	p.m.	1 2	p.m.	3 48	p.m.	...	5 22	p.m.	7 20	9 16	...	1232
Merzig	4 19	5 32	6 24	7 13	8 22	9 22	10 56	1110	1224	12 2	12 56	1 15	2 8	4 4	4 43	5 42	5 51	6 22	7 33	9 30	1133	1244
Dillingen	4 44	5 55	6 45	7 31	8 42	9 42	11 12	1131	...	1222	1 18	1 35	2 28	4 25	5 6	...	6 11	6 42	7 54	9 50	...	1 2
Saarlouis	4 52	6 2	6 52	7 38	8 43	9 48	11 18	1137	1240	1251	1 24	1 42	2 35	4 32	5 14	...	6 20	6 48	8 1	9 59	1149	1 8
Bous	5 10	6 16	7 6	...	9 0	10 0	...	1149	...	1 3	1 42	1 55	2 47	4 46	5 28	...	6 33	7 0	8 14	1015	...	1 20
Völklingen	5 19	6 25	7 18	7 52	9 8	1013	11 32	12 0	...	1 11	1 50	2 4	2 56	4 56	5 38	...	6 43	7 9	8 27	1026	12 3	1 28
Saarbrücken	5 36	6 42	7 41	8 4	9 25	1030	11 45	1219	1 2	1 28	2 10	2 21	3 13	5 14	5 59	6 16	7 2	7 26	8 46	1045	1215	1 45
	a.m.	a.m.		a.m.	a.m.	a.m.		p.m.	p.m.			p.m.	p.m.	p.m.	p.m.	p.m.		p.m.	p.m.	p.m.	a.m.	a.m.
Saarbrücken	5 47	6 45	...	8 12	9 34	1049	...	1228	1 11	...	...	2 41	3 33	5 26	6 50	6 30	...	7 43	9 56	1115	1232	4 13
Saargemünd	6 22	7 23	...	8 30	10 11	11 7	...	1 5	1 29	...	...	3 18	4 12	6 1	7 35	6 48	...	8 20	1030	1156	1 9	4 47

Extra { Saarbrücken to Saargemünd 11.24 a.m., 4.0 p.m.
Saargemünd to Saarbrücken 12.26 night.

RC—Restaurant Car.

VÖLKLINGEN and LEBACH								
Völklingen dep	6a45	8a0	11a0	3p4	6p20	7p20	11p30
Lebach ...arr	7 49	9 3	12 3	3 57	7 23	8 25	12 33

Lebach ...dep	4a50	6a22	8a30	1 p7	4p28	7p52	9p13
Völklingen arr	5 40	7 12	9 34	1 57	5 18	8 56	10 3

DILLINGEN and PRIMSWEILER.

†—Not on Sunday.] [‡—Not on Monday.

Dillingen ...dep	4a53	6†a14	7 a1	8 a10	9a27	11 36	2 p0	4p40	6 p45	8p20	1‡a3	1a37	...	...	...	...	...	...	...	...
Primsweiler ...arr	5 20	6 45	7 27	8 47	9 52	12 3	2 31	5 6	7 12	8 51	1 30	2 8	...	...	...	...	...	...	...	...
Primsweiler...dep	4 a3	5a25	6†a54	8 a13	8a52	1041	12p45	3p53	5p26	7p23	7†p51	9 p16	1a‡34	...	...	...	...	...	...	...
Dillingen ...arr	4 33	5 51	7 25	8 39	9 19	11 9	1 12	4 21	5 52	7 48	8 19	9 46	2 1	...	...	...	...	...	...	...

TREVES and HERMESKEIL.

Treves ...dep	6a35	9 a20	12p28	3p22	6p27	8p29	...	...
Sommerau	7 17	9 55	1 5	4 4	6 58	9 10	...	...
Schillingen	8 7	10 53	1 52	4 51	7 47	10 7	...	...
Hermeskeil arr	8 39	11 26	2 23	5 22	8 18	1041	...	...

Hermeskeil dep	5a31	8a58	11a30	2p30	5p23	8 p19	...	...	...
Schillingen	6 2	9 31	12 2	3 2	5 54	8 50	...	...	...
Sommerau	6 50	1022	12 48	3 49	6 40	9 37	...	...	...
Treves (125) arr	7 30	1054	1 18	4 23	7 17	10 10	...	...	...

HERMESKEIL and TURKISMUHLE.

‡—11.51 p.m. on Sats.

Hermeskeil	6a24	8a53	11a34	2p25	5p25	...	8p32	10p56	...
Nonnweiler	6 47	9 11	11 55	2 44	5 41	7p15	8 54	11 12	...
Turkismuhle	7 19	9 40	12 25	3 11	6 9	7 49	9 24	...	...

Turkismuhle	8 a2	10a40	1p34	4p33	6p50	8p26	10‡p37	...	...
Nonnweiler	8 36	11 11	2 8	5 5	7 27	8 55	11 15	...	...
Hermeskeil	8 52	11 27	2 24	5 21	7 46	9 11	11 37	...	...

HERBESTHAL and EUPEN.

†—Sunday excepted.

Herbesthal ...dep	5†a14	6a24	7a†5	8 a15	9 a8	10a15	1 p0	1p40	3p42	4p55	6p33	8†p22	10p0	...	...
Eupen ...arr	5 26	6 36	7 17	8 17	9 20	10 27	1 15	1 52	3 54	5 7	6 45	8 34	1012	...	...
Eupen ...dep	5†a39	6a†37	7a48	8a33	9a28	12p28	1p16	2 p8	4 p3	5 p43	7 p35	8 p56	9 p24	...
Herbesthal 122 arr	5 51	6 49	8 0	8 45	9 40	12 40	1 28	2 20	4 15	5 55	7 47	9 8	9 36	...

EUPEN and RAEREN.

Eupen ...dep	5†46	6a37	7a56	1p18	4p10	7p37
Raeren (127) arr	6 4	6 55	8 14	1 38	4 30	7 57

Raeren dep	6†14	7 a7	9a58	1p48	5 p0	8p58
Eupen ...arr	6 32	7 25	1017	2 6	5 20	9 16

†—Sunday excepted.

DUREN and HEIMBACH.

Duren .. dep	7a6	8a11	9a39	10a42	12p22	2p41	4p36	7p12	9p55
Kreuzau ...	724	8 29	9 57	11 0	12 43	2 59	4 55	7 31	1013
Heimbach arr	816	9 22	1049	11 52	1 36	3 55	5 51	8 24	11 5

Heimbach...	6a12	8a29	10a59	12p15	3 p4	4p53	6p31	7p32	9 p0	...
Kreuzau	7 6	9 21	11 53	1 15	3 59	5 50	7 30	8 30	9 56	...
Duren	7 24	9 38	12 10	1 36	4 16	6 7	7 47	8 47	1014	...

NEUSS, DUREN, and EUSKIRCHEN.

Dis				a m	a.m.	a.m.	a.m.	a.m.	a.m.	p.m.	p.m.	p m	p.m.	p.m.	p.m.	p m.	p.m.	p.m.	
—	Neuss ...dep	...	...	5 39	6‡16	...	7 3	9 13	10 55	1230	1 25	3 6	5 0	6 36	7‡30	7 51	8‡20	1015	...
8½	Grevenbroich (127) ...	...	...	6 11	6 39	6 44	7 19	9 37	11 21	1255	1 48	3 34	5 29	7 3	7 56	8 20	8 43	1040	...
16¾	Bedburg	...	...	6 34	—	7 6	7 32	9 59	11 43	1 17	—	3 56	5 51	7 25	—	8 42	—	11 2	...
30½	Duren (122) ...arr	a.m.	a.m.	7 2	...	—	7 55	10 25	12 9	1 43	...	4 24	6 18	7 52	...	9 10	...	1130	...
...	„ ... dep	5 24	6 ‡54	—	...	...	7 59	11 36	1 12	2 32	...	4 37	7 10	—	...	9 38	...	—	...
49	Euskirchen ...arr	6 14	7 42	...	...	...	8 43	12 21	2 0	3 21	...	5 24	7 54	...	...	1025	...	...	...

			a.m.			a.m.	a.m.	a.m.	a.m.		p.m.	p.m.	p.m.	p.m.			p m		p.m.	
Euskirchen dep	...	...	...	...	...	6 30	...	8 51	10 32	...	12 45	...	3 39	5 26	...	...	7 4	...	10 47	‡—Weekdays only.
Duren ...arr	...	...	...	...	...	7 20	...	9 35	11 23	...	1 32	...	4 23	6 9	...	p.m.	7 51	p.m.	11 28	
„ ...dep	...	...	5 17	...	a.m.	7 27	9 15	1048	12 22	...	—	2 44	4 39	—	...	7 15	8 5	10 28	—	
Bedburg	a.m.	a.m.	5 42	a.m.	7 16	7 52	9 40	1113	12 47	p.m.	...	3 9	5 4	...	p.m.	7 40	8 31	10 53	...	
Grevenbroich ..	4 ‡59	6 ‡0	6 11	7 ‡3	7 37	8 6	10 7	1136	1 12	2 22	...	3 34	5 29	...	7‡20	8 3	8 56	11 15	...	
Neuss ...arr	5 22	6 30	6 40	7 26	...	8 21	1031	1159	1 36	2 45	...	3 58	5 53	...	7 43	8 26	9 21	11 38	...	

Luggage Rates—see page 462.] [For Fares—see page 120A.

COLOGNE, EHRENBREITSTEIN, NIEDERLAHNSTEIN, RUDESHEIM, WIESBADEN, and FRANKFORT.

Dist E.M	Station																	
	BRUSSELS 104 ....dep	...	...	...	...	...	...	...	...	...	...	11p24	...	...	...	...	...	...
	AIX-LA-CHAPELLE 122 dep	...	...	...	...	...	...	...	...	...	...	4 a20	...	6 a50	7 a31	...	...	...
		Ex.3	2 3 4			2,3,4	1—4		1—4	1—4	1,2,3	1—4	1—4	1,2,3	1,2,3	2 3 4	1—4	Ex3
—	**COLOGNE** Haupt-bahnhof ....dep	a.m. 1 58	...	...	...	...	...	...	...	...	a.m. 5 30	a.m. 5 44	a.m. 7 28	a.m. 8 8	a.m. 9 10	...	...	a.m. ...
—	**Deutz**..........dep	⋮	...	...	...	...	...	...	...	...	...	...	...	...	...	...	...	1019
13	**Troisdorf**..........dep	⋮	...	...	...	...	...	...	...	...	5 53	6 25	8 3	8 31	9 33	...	...	...
18¾	Beuel (opposite Bonn)	⋮	...	...	...	...	...	...	...	...	6 5	6 42	8 19	8 43	9 45	...	...	RC
20¾	**Obercassel**..........	Via Bonn, page 122.	...	...	...	...	...	...	...	...	...	6 49	8 26	...	...	...	...	...
22½	Niederdollendorf 134	⋮	...	...	...	...	...	...	...	...	...	6 55	8 32	...	...	...	...	...
23¾	Königswinter	⋮	...	...	...	...	...	...	...	...	...	7 0	8 37	8†54	...	...	...	10†55
26¾	Honnef..........	⋮	...	...	...	...	...	...	...	...	6 20	7 11	8 48	...	...	...	...	⋮
31	Erpel	⋮	...	...	...	a.m.	...	...	...	...	...	7 24	9 1	...	...	...	...	⋮
33	Linz	⋮	a.m.	...	...	5 0	...	...	...	a.m.	...	7 30	9 15	9 11	...	a.m.	...	⋮
46¾	Neuwied..........	⋮	4 36	...	...	5 38	...	...	...	6 20	6 54	8 9	9 54	9 35	10 29	1120	...	⋮
50	**Engers 133B**..........	⋮	5 1	...	...		...	...	...	6 39	...	8 17	10 3	...	10 38	1129	...	⋮
53¾	Vallendar	⋮	5 13	...	...	...	...	...	...	6 51	...	8 29	1015	...	...		...	⋮
56½	**Ehrenbreitstein** ... arr	⋮	5 20	...	...	...	...	...	...	6 58	7 10	8 36	1022	9 51	10 50	...	...	⋮
	dep	⋮	5 23	...	...	...	...	...	...	7 0	7 11	8 38	1025	9 53	10 52	...	...	⋮
59	Horchheim..........	⋮	5 31	...	...	...	...	...	...	7 8	...	8 45	1033	...	...	...	...	⋮
60	**Niederlahnstein** ....arr	⋮	5 34	...	...	...	...	...	...	7 11	7 19	8 48	1036	10 1	11 0	...	...	1149
67¾	EMS 146..........arr	⋮	6a26	...	...		...	...	...	8 a5	8 a5	9 a13	11a3	11 a3	11a46	...	...	12p36
...	**Coblence** Hauptbahnhof ...dep	a.m. 3 36	...	...	...	...	a.m. 5 32	...	a.m. 7 26	...	...	a.m. 8 45	...	a.m. 9 51	a.m. 10 22	...	a.m. 11 9	...
...	**Niederlahnstein** ......arr	⋮	...	...	...	...	5 40	...	7 34	...	...	8 53	...	9 59	10 29	...	1117	...
		⋮	2 3 4	2.3,4		2,3,4	1—4	2 3 4	1—4		1,2,3	1—4		1,2,3	1,2,3	2 3 4	1—4	Ex2
...	**Niederlahnstein** ....dep	⋮	...	...	...	...	a.m. 5 54	...	a.m. 7 39	...	a.m. 7 23	a.m. 8 57	...	a.m. 10 5	a.m. 11 2	...	a.m. 1122	a.m. 1153
61	Oberlahnstein	⋮	...	...	...	...	5 59	...	7 44	...	7 28	9 2	...	...	11 7	...	1127	...
63½	Braubach	⋮	...	a.m.	...	...	6 6	...	7 51	...	...	9 9	...	...	...	...	1134	...
78	St. Goarshausen	⋮	...	4 50	...	...	6 41	...	8 26	...	7 55	9 43	...	...	11 34	...	1210	...
84¾	Caub..........	⋮	...	5 4	...	...	6 55	...	8 39	...	...	9 57	...	...	...	...	1234	...
88½	Lorc	⋮	...	5 17	...	...	7 7	...	8 51	...	...	10 9	...	...	...	...	1246	...
93½	Assmannshausen..........	⋮	...	5 28	...	...	7 17	...	9 2	...	...	10 20	...	10 55	...	...	1256	...
96	**Rudesheim** .... arr	⋮	a.m.	5 54	...	a.m.	7 23	a.m.	9 8	...	8 24	10 26	...	11 1	12 3	p.m.	1 2	1246
	dep	⋮	5 0	5 39	...	6 33	7 26	7 59	9 13	...	8 25	10 28	...	11 2	12 4	1211	1 3	1247
98½	Geisenheim	⋮	5 8	5 46	...	6 40	7 33	8 6	9 20	...	...	10 35	...	...	...	1217	1 10	⋮
106½	**Eltville**..........arr	4 51	5 33	6 9	...	7 3	7 57	8 29	9 44	...	8 44	10 59	...	11 21	12 23	1240	1 34	⋮
111¼	Schlangenbad ....arr	...	...	7 10	...	...	...	9 50	...	...	9 50	11 55	...	11 55	1 50	1 50	...	⋮
...	" ....dep	...	...	...	...	...	7 20	7 20	...	...	...	10 10	...	10 10	...	12 5	...	⋮
...	**Eltville**..........dep	4 51	5 33	6 9	...	7 3	7 57	8 29	9 44	...	8 44	10 59	...	11 21	12 23	1240	1 34	⋮
112	Biebrich West	...	5 52	6 27	...	7 21	8 15	8 47	10 2	...	8 56	11 18	...	11 34	...	1258	1 52	⋮
115	**Wiesbaden**..........arr	5 8	6 0	6 35	...	7 29	8 23	8 55	10 10	...	9 4	11 26	...	11 42	12 40	1 6	2 0	1 19
...	Wiesbaden..........dep	5 13	...	...	...	...	...	8 59	...	...	...	...	...	...	...	1 18	...	...
...	Biebrich Ost	...	...	...	...	...	...	9 5	...	...	...	...	...	...	...	1 25	...	...
...	Mayence Haupt..........arr	5 25	...	...	...	...	...	9 15	...	...	...	...	...	...	...	1 35	...	...

Dist	Station																		
		2—4	Ex 3	2—4	1,2,3	Ex 2	1,2,3	1—4	Ex3	1—4	1,2,3	1,2,3	1—4	1,2,3	1,2,3	1,2,3	1—4	1,2,3	Ex3
...	**Wiesbaden**..........dep	a.m. 4 23	a.m. 5 30	a.m. 6 10	a.m. 6 56	a.m. 7 30	a.m. 8 28	a.m. 8 35	a.m. 9 9	a.m. 10 23	a.m. 10 59	a.m. 9 16	p.m. 12 8	a.m. 11 7	a.m. 11 47	p.m. 12 45	p.m. 1 32	p.m. 2 4	p.m. 1 26
119¾	Castel (Mayence)	4 38	5 40	6 25	7 11	7 40	8 42	8 50	9 19	10 38	11 9	9 26	12 22	1118	11 57	1255	1 46	2 17	1 36
127	Flörsheim	4 56	...	6 42		...	...	9 7	...	10 55	...	...	12 40	...	...	...	2 3	...	...
135	Höchst	5 24	6 3	7 9	7 37	...	9 6	9 33	9 42	11 20	11 32	9 50	1 8	1142	12 21	1 19	2 29	2 41	...
146½	Homburg ....arr	...	...	...	...	...	...	...	10 5	...	12 3	...	...	...	...	...	...	...	...
160	Friedberg	...	...	...	...	...	...	...	...	...	12 29	...	...	...	...	...	...	...	...
162¼	Bad Nauheim ...arr	...	...	...	...	...	...	...	1035	...	12 35	...	...	...	...	...	...	...	...
140½	Frankfort Haupt...arr	5 42	6 16	7 21	7 50	8 13	9 19	9 46	...	11 33	...	10 3	1 21	1155	12 34	1 32	2 42	2 54	2 11
169½	ASCHAFFENBURG 196 arr		7 a24	...	9 a17	9 a17	...	12p37	...	...	...	...	...	...	...	2 p55	...	4p26	3 p7
224¾	WURZBURG 196 ....arr		9 a12	...	10a47	10a47	...	4 p0	...	...	...	...	...	...	...	4p36	...	5p51	4p36
288½	NURNBERG 195A ......arr		11a39	...	12p41	12p41	...	...	...	...	...	...	...	...	...	8p54	...	9p22	6p54
687	VIENNA 239A ....arr		9 p50	...	...	...	...	...	...	...	...	...	...	...	...	...	...	...	7a20
396¾	MUNICH 196..........arr		2 p0	...	...	9 p50	...	...	...	...	...	...	...	...	...	8 p55	...	1025	8p55

Extra. { Wiesbaden......dep | 3a51 | 4†a48 | 6a45 | — Frankfort ......arr | 5 10 | 5 58 | 8 5 |

Rudesheim...dep | 7 a0 | 12p55 — Mayence ......arr | 7 58 | 1 59

†—Not on Sunday.

NEUWIED and OBERBIEBER.—In 25 minutes. Service half-hourly.

PETERSBERG RAILWAY.—Fare: Upwards, 1 mark; downwards, 50 pf.
From **Konigswinter** to Petersberg, frequent service every few minutes, in connection with all trains on the main line and with the Rhine steamers.

DRACHENFELS RAILWAY.—Fare: Upwards, 1 mark; downwards, 50pf, (In 10 min.).
From **Konigswinter** to Drachenfels, frequent service, every few minutes, in connection with all trains on the main line and with the Rhine steamers.

[Luggage Rates—see page 462.

COLOGNE, EHRENBREITSTEIN, NIEDERLAHNSTEIN, RUDESHEIM, WIESBADEN, and FRANKFORT.

RC—Restaurant Car.

BRUSSELS 104 ....dep	...	...	5 a45	...	...	...	5 a45	...	...	8 a17	...	10a54	...	...	...	1 p32	...	3 p3	5 p0
AIX-LA-CHAPELLE122dep	7a31	8 a43	10 a7	...	...	...	10 a7	...	11a24	1 p20	...	3 p12	...	4p42	...	6 p26	...	8 p26	10p12
	1—4	1—4	Ex.2	2 3 4		2 3 4	1—4		1—4	Ex.2	1,2,3	1—4	1—4	1,2,3	1—4	1—4	1—4	1,2,3	1—4
COLOGNE Haupt-bahnhof ....dep	a.m. 9 13	a.m. 10 38	a.m. 11 27	...	...	...	p.m. 12 35	...	p.m. 2 15	p.m. 3 38	p.m. 3 42	p.m. 5 0	...	p.m. 6 18	p.m. 6 59	p.m. 8 23	p.m. 9 45	p.m. 10 35	p.m 11 45
Deutz ....dep	...	...	...	...	...	...	...	...	...	...	...	...	p.m.	...	...	...	...	...	...
Troisdorf..................dep	9 52	11 15	RC	...	...	...	1 11	...	2 52	4 1	4 16	5 40	7 3	6 41	7 41	9 2	10 25	10 59	12 21
Beuel (opposite Bonn)	1010	11 31	...	...	...	...	1 28	...	3 12	4 13	4 32	5 55	7 20	6 52	8 1	9 20	10 46	11 12	12 35
Obercassel..................	1017	11 38	...	...	...	...	1 35	...	3 19	...	4 39	6 2	7 27	...	—	9 27	10 56	11 19	12 41
Niederdollendorf 134	1023	11 44	...	...	...	...	1 41	...	3 25	RC	4 45	6 8	7 33	...	...	9 33	11 2	...	12 46
Königswinter	1028	11 49	...	...	...	...	1 46	...	3 31	...	4 50	6 14	7 38	7 3	...	9 38	11 10	11 28	12 51
Honnef	1039	12 12	...	...	...	...	1 57	...	3 42	4 28	5 2	6 25	7 49	7 11	...	9 49	11 24	11 36	1 1
Erpel	1052	12 25	...	...	...	...	2 10	...	3 56	...	5 15	6 38	8 3	...	...	10 2	11 37	...	1 14
Linz	1058	12 31	...	...	...	p.m.	2 17	...	4 2	...	5 22	6 45	8 10	7 23	p.m.	10 11	11 42	11 48	1 20
Neuwied..........................	1147	1 13	12 37	p.m.	...	5 36	2 57	...	5 4	4 59	6 0	7 26	8 49	7 45	9 29	10 54	—	12 16	2 0
Engers 133B.....................	1156	1 22	...	1 50	...	5 45	3 7	...	5 13	...	6 20	7 35	—	7 54	9 41	11 5	...	12 24	2 8
Vallendar	12 8	1 34	...	2 2	...	—	3 19	...	5 25	...	6 34	7 48	...	...	9 53	11 18	...	12 36	2 20
Ehrenbreitstein ... dep	1215	1 41	...	2 9	...	...	3 26	...	5 32	5 15	6 41	7 55	...	8 5	10 1	11 25	...	12 43	2 26
Ehrenbreitstein ... arr	1217	1 42	...	—	...	...	3 29	...	5 34	5 17	6 42	7 57	...	8 7	10 3	11 28	...	12 45	2 28
Horchheim	1225	1 49	...	...	...	...	3 37	...	5 41	...	6 50	8 4	...	...	10 11	11 36	...	...	...
Niederlahnstein ....arr	1228	1 52	1 0	...	...	...	3 40	...	5 44	5 25	6 54	8 7	...	8 15	10 15	11 40	...	12 53	2 36
EMS 146 ....arr	1253	2 p54	1 p48	...			4 p16	...	6 p10	6 p10	8 p3	8 p59	...	8 p59	11 p9	12a56	...	...	5 a9
Coblence Hauptbahnhof ...dep	p.m. 1219	p.m 1 55	...	p.m. 1 15	...	p.m. 3 31	...	...	p.m. 5 37	p.m. 4 52	p.m. 6 47	...	...	p.m. 8 7	p.m. 10 32	nght 12 8	...	...	a.m. 2 30
Niederlahnstein ......arr	1227	2 3	...	1 23	...	3 39	...	...	5 45	5 0	6 55	...	...	8 15	10 40	12 16	...	...	2 38
	1—4	1—4	Ex.2	2 3 4		2 3 4	1—4	2 3 4	1—4	Ex.2	1—4	1—4	...	1,2,3	1—4	2,3,4			1—4
Niederlahnstein ....dep	p.m. 1233	p.m. 2 7	p.m. 1 4	p.m. 1 25	...	p.m. 3 43	p.m. 3 55	...	p.m. 5 52	p.m. 5 29	p.m. 6 58	p.m. 8 40	...	p.m. 8 20	p.m. 10 45	nght 12 20	...	...	a.m. 2 41
Oberlahnstein	1238	2 13	:	1 30	...	3 47	4 1	...	5 57	...	7 3	8 45	...	8 25	10 50	12 24	...	...	2 45
Braubach	1245	2 20	:	1 36	...	—	4 9	...	6 4	...	7 10	8 52	...	...	10 57	—	...	...	2 51
St. Goarshausen	1 20	2 57	:	—	...	...	4 46	...	6 40	...	7 45	9 28	...	8 53	11 32	...	...	...	3 26
Caub...............................	1 45	3 11	:	...	...	...	5 0	...	7 0	...	—	9 42	...	...	11 46	...	...	...	3 39
Lorch	1 57	3 23	:	...	...	...	5 13	...	7 6	...	p.m.	9 55	...	...	11 58	...	...	...	3 50
Assmannshausen	2 8	3 33	:	...	...	...	5 24	...	7 17	...	7 49	10 6	...	...	12 8	...	...	...	4 0
Rudesheim .... arr	2 14	3 39	:	...	...	p.m.	5 30	p.m.	7 23	6 22	7 55	10 12	p.m.	9 22	12 14	...	...	...	4 6
Rudesheim .... dep	2 16	3 41	:	...	...	5 2	5 35	6 0	7 25	6 24	7 57	10 15	8 39	9 23	12 16	...	...	...	4 7
Geisenheim	2 24	3 49	:	...	...	5 9	5 42	6 6	7 32	...	8 5	10 23	8 48	...	12 23	...	...	...	4 14
Eltville........................arr	2 49	4 15	:	...	...	5 33	6 9	6 28	7 57	6 44	8 31	10 48	9 14	9 42	12 47	...	...	...	4 36
Schlangenbad..............arr	3 40	5 0	:	...	...	...	7 5	7 5	8 58	7 43	...	...	...	...	...	...	...	...	...
,, ...dep	2 8	3 43	:	...	...	...	5 18	5 18	7 16	6 0	7 52	...	...	9 3	...	...	...	...	...
Eltville.........................dep	2 49	4 15	:	...	...	5 33	6 9	6 28	7 57	6 44	8 31	10 48	9 14	9 42	12 47	...	...	...	4 36
Biebrich West..................	3 6	4 34	2 19	...	...	5 52	6 32	6 45	8 15	6 57	8 49	11 6	9 33	9 54	1 5	...	...	...	4 52
Wiesbaden.....................arr	3 14	4 42	2 26	...	...	6 0	6 40	...	8 23	7 5	8 57	11 14	9 41	10 2	1 13	...	...	...	5 0
Wiesbaden...............dep	...	...	...	...	...	...	...	...	...	...	9 6	...	...	...	1 17	...	...	...	...
Biebrich Ost	...	...	...	...	...	...	...	...	...	...	9 13	...	...	...	1 23	...	...	...	...
Mayence Haupt ......arr	...	...	...	...	...	...	...	6 58	...	...	9 23	...	...	...	1 33	...	...	...	[illegible]
	1—4	1—4	Ex.2	1,2,3	1,2,3	1—4	1—4		1—4	Ex.2	1,2,3	1—4	1—4	1,2,3		1—4		1,2,3	1—4
Wiesbaden..................dep	p.m. 3 20	p.m. 5 10	p.m. 2 35	p.m. 2 57	p.m. 5 46	p.m. 6 18	p.m. 7 17	...	p.m. 8 29	p.m. 7 12	p.m. 9 27	p.m. 11 37	p.m. 9 47	p.m. 10 11	...	p m. 10 50	...	p.m. 11 20	a.m. 5 41
Castel (**Mayence**)	3 35	5 27	2 45	3 7	5 59	6 31	7 31	...	8 46	7 21	9 37	11 52	10 0	10 22	...	11 4	...	11 30	5 57
Flörsheim	3 52	5 45	...	...	...	6 50	7 48	...	9 6	...	...	12 9	—	...	...	11 21	...	...	6 15
Höchst.............................	4 17	6 15	...	3 30	6 22	7 21	8 16	...	9 37	7 44	10 1	12 34	...	10 47	...	11 46	...	11 55	6 41
Homburg ....arr	...	...	...	3 55	6 52	...	...	...	...	...	10 32	...	...	...	...	...	...	12 26	...
Friedberg	...	...	...	4 22	—	...	...	...	...	...	10 58	...	...	...	...	...	...	...	...
Bad Nauheim...........arr	...	...	...	4 28	...	...	...	...	...	...	11 4	...	...	...	...	...	...	...	...
Frankfort Haupt. ......arr	4 30	6 28	3 19	...	...	7 34	8 29	...	9 50	7 57	...	12 47	...	11 0	...	11 59	...	...	6 53
ASCHAFFENBURG 196 arr	5p27	...	4 p26	...	...	...	10 17	...	...	10p17	...	...	...	12a10	...	1 a13	...	...	...
WURZBURG 196.........arr	7 p3	...	5 p51	...	...	...	1 a10	...	...	1 a10	...	...	...	2 a1	...	2 a44	...	...	...
NURNBERG 195A ......arr	9p22	...	9 p22	...	...	...	...	...	...	...	...	...	...	4 a52	...	4 a52	...	...	...
VIENNA 239A ....arr	7a20	...	7 a20	...	...	...	...	...	...	...	...	...	...	6 p32	...	6 p32	...	...	...
MUNICH 196 ....arr	12a40	...	10p25	...	...	...	...	...	...	...	...	...	...	7 a20	...	9 a29	...	...	...

Extra				
Wiesbaden...dep	4p23	4p55	9 p10	9 p33
Frankfort ...arr	5 35	5 46	10 0	10 42

Rudesheim...dep	6p32
Wiesbaden ...arr	7 28

NIEDERWALD RAILWAY. (Fare:—Upwards, 1 mk.; downward, 50 pf.)
From **Rüdesheim** to the National Monument on the Niederwald, Service in connection with trains on the main line.
From **Assmannshausen** to the Jagdschloss Niederwald, Service in connection with trains on the main line.

ST. GOARSHAUSEN and ZOLLHAUS.

†–Sunday at 10.4 p.m.

St. Goarshausen dep	6a52	...	9a47	1 p0	5p12	8†p15	...
Nastätten..................	7 45	6a10	11 2	2 5	6 11	9 25	...
Katzenelnbogen	—	7 21	12 9	—	7 7	—	...
Zollhaus 146 ......arr	...	7 54	1241	...	7 38	...	...

Zollhaus ....dep	...	...	9 a5	...	2p50	...	6p25	8 p10
Katzenelnbogen	...	...	9 35	...	3 36	...	6 57	8 46
Nastätten	5a30	8a10	1038	3p18	4 45	6p20	...	9 47
St. Goarshausen 128 arr	6 26	9 6	1126	4 11	...	7 14	...	...

Oberlahnstein......dep	7a50	12p30	...	...
Braubach	8 25	1 0	2p30	9 p0
Nastätten ....arr	10 9	3 10	4 29	1056

Nastätten ....dep	5a20	8 a10	10a55	6 p13	...	...
Braubach	7 17	10 40	12 37	7 55	...	...
Oberlahnstein 128 arr	7 30	10 53	...	...	...	...

Luggage Rates—see page 462.]

FRANKFORT, WIESBADEN, RUDESHEIM, NIEDERLAHNSTEIN, EHRENBREITSTEIN, and COLOGNE.

RC—Restaurant Car.

Station																			
VIENNA 239 ....dep	...	...	...	...	...	...	...	...	...	...	...	...	...	8 p30	...	8p30	...	...	8p40
MUNICH 196B........dep	...	...	...	...	1018	...	...	...	...	...	...	...	...	...	...	...	...	...	7 a5
NUERNBERG 195A ...dep	...	...	...	...	...	...	...	...	...	...	...	...	...	7 a0	...	7 a0	...	...	9a20
WURZBURG 196B ...dep	...	...	...	...	2a50	...	...	...	...	...	7 a20	7 a20	...	9 a15	...	9a15	...	...	1137
ASCHAFFENB'G 196Bdp	...	...	...	...	4a55	...	...	5 a38	...	...	8 a57	8 a57	...	11 a7	...	11a7	...	...	1 p3
		2 3 4			2 3 4	1,2,3	2 3 4	1,2,3	1,2,3	1—4	1,2,3	2,3,4	1—4	Ex.2	1,2,3	1,2,3	1—4	1,2,3	Ex2
FRANKFORT—		a.m.			a.m.	a.m.	a.m.	a.m.		a.m.	a.m.	a.m.	a.m.	p.m.	a.m.	p.m.	p.m.	p.m.	p.m.
Hauptbahnhof ....dep	...	5 22	...	...	6 22	7 12	7 12	7 58	...	8 32	10 1	10 25	11 48	12 28	...	1250	1 26	...	2 18
Bad Nauheim ......dep	...	...	...	...	...	...	...	...	...	...	...	...	...	...	11 47	...	...	1 10	...
Friedberg	...	...	...	...	...	...	...	...	a.m.	...	...	...	...	RC	11 54	...	...	1 20	RC
Homburg ....dep	...	...	...	...	...	...	...	...	7 32	...	...	...	...	...	12 19	...	...	1 49	...
Höchst ....dep	...	5 42	...	...	6 36	7 25	7 32	8 11	8 0	8 46	10 13	10 39	12 5	...	12 46	1 3	1 40	2 12	...
Flörsheim	...	6 6	...	...	7 2	...	7 58	...	...	9 11	...	11 4	12 32	...	...	...	2 5	...	...
Castel (Mayence)	...	6 24	...	...	7 21	7 49	8 16	8 35	8 25	9 29	10 36	11 21	12 49	1 0	1 10	1 27	2 22	2 37	2 57
Wiesbaden..............arr	...	6 40	...	...	7 39	8 4	8 32	8 51	8 40	9 44	10 51	11 36	1 4	1 13	1 26	1 40	2 37	2 50	3 10
	1—4	2 3 4	1—4	2 3 4	1—4	2 3 4	2 3 4	1,2,3	|	1—4	1,2,3	2,3,4	1—4	Ex.2	2,3,4	2 3 4	1—4	2 3 4	Ex2
		a.m.	a.m.		a.m.	a.m.	a.m.	a.m.		a.m.	a.m.	a.m.	p.m.	p.m.		p.m.	p.m.	p.m.	p.m.
Mayence Haupt....dep	...	...	4 28	...	...	7 43	8 18	...	|	...	...	...	...	...	...	1 52	...	2 11	...
Biebrich Ost............	...	...	4 38	...	...	7 53	⋮	...	|	...	...	...	...	...	...	2 2	...	⋮	...
Wiesbaden ....arr	...	...	4 4	a.m.	...	8 0	⋮		|	...	...	...	...	...	p.m.	2 9	...	⋮	...
Wiesbaden..............dep	...	6 54	4 59	5 26	7 44	8 10	⋮	8 56		9 49	10 56	11 43	1 27	1 17	1 50	2 20	2 42	⋮	3 15
Biebrich West	...	7 2	5 7	5 34	7 53	8 18	8 31	9 3	—	9 57	...	11 51	1 35	1 25	1 58	2 31	2 49	2 24	⋮
Eltville....................arr	...	7 20	5 25	5 52	8 11	8 36	8 48	9 15	...	10 15	11 11	12 9	1 53	⋮	2 15	2 49	3 7	2 42	⋮
Schlangenbad ......arr	...	...	...	7 10	...	...	...	9 50	...	...	11 55	1 50	...	⋮	...	3 40	3 40	3 40	⋮
" ...dep	...	...	...	...	7 20	...	...	...	...	...	10 10	...	12 5	⋮	...	2 8	2 8	...	⋮
Eltville ....dep	...	7 20	5 25	5 52	8 11	8 36	8 48	9 15	...	10 15	11 11	12 9	1 53	⋮	2 15	2 49	3 7	2 42	⋮
Geisenheim	...	7 44	5 50	6 16	8 35	9 0	9 10	...	...	10 39	...	12 33	2 17	⋮	2 43	3 13	3 31	3 5	⋮
Rudesheim .... arr	a.m.	7 50	5 56	6 22	8 41	9 6	9 16	9 33	...	10 45	11 29	12 39	2 23	1 50	2 49	3 19	3 37	3 11	3 44
Rudesheim .... dep	4 3	—	5 59	7 5	8 43	—	—	9 34	...	10 48	11 30	12 42	2 24	1 51	—	—	3 53	—	3 45
Assmanshausen	4 10	...	6 6	7 12	8 50	...	...	9 41	...	10 55	...	12 49	2 31	...	...	...	4 4	...	...
Lorch	4 20	...	6 16	7 22	9 0	...	...	...	...	11 6	...	12 59	2 40	...	...	...	4 10	...	...
Caub........................	4 32	...	6 29	7 33	9 12	...	...	...	...	11 18	...	1 11	2 51	...	...	...	4 44	...	...
St. Goarshausen	4 46	...	6 43	7 46	9 26	...	a.m.	...	...	11 33	11 59	1 25	3 4	...	p.m.	...	5 0	...	...
Braubach	5 22	...	7 19	8 19	10 0	a.m.	1058	...	...	12 8	...	2 0	3 37	...	2 20	p.m.	5 35	...	...
Oberlahnstein	5 29	...	7 27	8 26	10 7	8 8	11 5	10 30	...	12 15	...	2 8	3 44	...	2 28	4 53	5 43	...	...
Niederlahnstein ......arr	5 33	...	7 31	8 30	1011	8 12	11 9	10 34	...	12 19	12 27	2 12	3 48	2 44	2 32	4 57	5 47	...	4 37
Niederlahnstein ...dep	5 37	...	7 36	...	1015	8 21	1114	10 42	...	12 33	12 33	...	3 52	2 50	2 33	...	...	...	...
Coblence Haupt. ...arr	5 45	...	7 44	...	1023	8 29	1122	10 50	...	12 41	12 41	...	4 0	2 58	2 41	...	...	...	...
EMS 147 ....dep	5 a10	5a10	6 a20	8 a2	...	...	...	10a12	10a12	11a58	11a58	2 p1	3 p9	2 p16	...	...	5 p20	5 p0	4p11
	1—4	1,2,3	1—4	2 3 4	2 3 4	2 3 4		1,2,3	1—4	1—4	1,2,3	1—4	1—4	Ex.2	2,3,4	2 3 4	1—4	2 3 4	Ex2
	a.m.	a.m.	a.m.	a.m.				a.m.	a.m.	p.m.	p.m.	p.m.	p.m.	p.m.	p.m.		p.m.	p.m.	p.m.
Niederlahnstein......dep	5 43	6 0	7 50	8 22	...	...	..	10 38	10 52	12 37	12 31	2 24	4 6	2 48	...	...	6 5	5 19	4 41
Horchheim........................	5 47	...	7 54	8 26	...	...	...	...	10 57	12 41	...	2 28	4 10	RC	...	...	6 9	5 23	...
Ehrenbreitstein... arr	5 54	6 8	8 1	8 33	...	...	...	10 46	11 4	12 48	12 39	2 35	4 17	2 56	...	...	6 16	5 30	...
Ehrenbreitstein... dep	5 56	6 10	8 3	8 35	...	...	...	10 47	11 6	12 51	12 40	2 37	4 19	2 57	2 20	...	6 19	5 32	...
Vallendar	6 4	...	8 11	8 44	a.m.	...	...	...	11 14	12 59	...	2 45	4 27	...	2 28	p.m.	6 27	5 40	RC
Engers..................... ...	6 30	6 23	8 24	8 55	1039	...	...	...	11 27	1 18	...	2 58	4 46	3 14	2 41	5 2	6 40	5 53	...
Neuwied.................... ...	6 43	6 31	8 35	—	1048	...	...	11 4	11 38	1 27	12 56	3 22	5 8	...	—	5 11	6 50	6 3	...
Linz......................... ...	7 22	6 58	9 14	...	—	...	...	...	12 17	2 6	1 19	4 3	5 59	...	...	—	7 28	—	...
Erpel	7 28	...	9 20	...	...	...	...	...	12 23	2 12	...	4 9	6 5	...	...		7 34		...
Honnef	7 41	7 10	9 33	...	...	...	...	11 36	12 36	2 25	...	4 22	6 18	...	...	...	7 47	...	...
Königswinter	7 53	7 20	9 45	...	...	...	...	11 45	12 47	2 37	...	4 33	6 31	3 51	...	...	7 59	...	...
Niederdollendorf.............	7 58	7 26	9 50	...	...	...	...	...	12 52	2 42	...	4 38	6 36	...	...	...	8 4	...	...
Obercassel..............dep	8 4	7 32	9 56	...	...	p.m.	...	...	12 58	2 48	...	4 44	6 42	...	...	...	8 10	...	...
Beuel (opposite Bonn) ...	8 11	7 49	10 3	...	...	1217	...	11 56	1 5	2 55	1 42	4 51	6 48	4 2	...	...	8 17	...	...
Troisdorf................arr	8 26	7 51	10 20	...	...	1236	...	12 8	1 20	3 11	1 54	5 6	7 3	...	...	...	8 32	...	...
COLOGNE Deutz ...arr	...	...	...	...	...	—	...	...	...	...	...	6 4	...	...	...	...	...	...	...
COLOGNE Haupt....arr	8 59	8 19	11 2	...	...	...	...	12 31	2 2	3 51	2 17	...	7 45	4 32	...	...	9 13	...	6 8
AIX-LA-CHPELLE123arr	10 29	1029	12p52	...	...	...	..	2 p40	4 p25	5p 32	4 p25	...	9 p39	6 p55	...	...	11p52	...	7p24
BRUSSELS 104 ....arr	1 p3	1 p3	3 p44	...	...	...	...	5p 44	6 p57	8 p0	6 p57	...	...	9 p45	...	...	...	...	9p45

Extra. { Frankfort......dep 12p57 ... ; Wiesbaden ...arr 2 12 ... } | Wiesbaden......dep 12p47 ; Rudesheim ......arr 1 43 | Wiesbaden......dep 12p20 ; Eltville ....arr 12 45

[Luggage Rates—see page 462.

FRANKFORT, WIESBADEN, RUDESHEIM, NIEDERLAHNSTEIN, EHRENBREITSTEIN, and COLOGNE.

RC—Restaurant Car.

VIENNA 239 ....dep		8p40	...	..	...	...	...	...	...	...	...	...	...	...	...	7 a25	...	...	...	...
MUNICH 196B.........dep		7 a5	9 a0	9 a0	...	...	...	...	...	...	...	...	...	...	...	12p45	...	...	...	...
NURNBERG 195A ....dep		9a20	9a20	9 a20	...	...	...	...	...	...	...	...	...	...	...	5 p8	...	...	...	...
WURZBURG 196B ...dep		1137	1233	12 33	...	...	...	...	...	...	...	...	...	1 p40	1p40	6 p50	...	...	...	...
ASCHAFFENBURG 196B		1 p3	1p50	1 p50	...	...	...	2 p29	...	...	...	...	...	5 p3	5 p3	8 p6	...	...	...	...
		1,2,3	Ex3	Ex 2	2 3 4	1,2,3	1—4	1,2,3		2,3,4	Ex3	1—4	1,2.3	1,2,3	1—4	1,2,3	Ex 2	1,2,3	2,3,4	1—4
FRANKFORT—		p.m.	p.m	p.m.	p.m.	p.m.	p m.	p.m.		p.m.	p.m.	p.m.	p.m.	p.m.	p.m.	p.m.	p.m.	p.m.	p.m.	p.m.
Hauptbahnhof ....dep		2 28	2 50	2 ‡52	3 14	4 14	4 20	5 1	...	5 28	...	6 31	...	7 30	7 41	9 2	9 32	...	9 43	1126
Bad Nauheim ......dep		...	...	...	...	...	...	...	...	...	5 22	...	6 33	...	...	...	...	...	...	...
Friedberg		...	RC	...	...	...	...	...	...	...	...	...	6 40	...	...	...	...	...	...	...
Homburg.................dep		...	...	...	...	...	...	...	...	...	5 52	...	7 5	...	...	...	...	10 1	...	...
Höchst ....dep		2 43	...	...	3 28	4 27	4 34	5 13	...	5 44	6 15	6 48	7 32	7 43	7 56	9 15	...	1029	9 58	1143
Flörsheim		...	...	...	3 53	...	4 59	...	...	6 10	...	7 17	..	..	8 21	...	...	...	10 23	1211
Castel (Mayence)		3 7	3 21	3 28	4 11	4 52	5 16	5 37	...	6 27	6 39	7 35	7 55	8 7	8 38	9 39	10 4	1053	10 41	1230
Wiesbaden ....arr		3 22	3 34	3 41	4 27	5 8	5 31	5 50	...	6 42	6 52	7 50	8 8	8 20	8 54	9 54	10 17	11 6	10 57	1245
	3Cl.		Ex3	Ex 2	2 3 4	2 3 4	1—4	1,2,3	2—4	2.3,4	2 3 4	1—4		1,2,3	1—4	2,3,4			2,3,4	1—4
	p m.		p.m.	p m.	p.m.		p.m.	p.m.	p.m.	p.m.	p.m.	p.m.		p.m.	p.m.	p.m.			p.m.	a.m.
Mayence Haupt....	2 39	...	3 6	...	4 13	...	...	...	6 3	...	7 11	...	...	...	...	9 44	...	...	...	...
Biebrich Ost	2 49	...	...	...	4 23	...	...	...	6 13	...	⋮	...	...	...	...	9 54	...	...	...	...
Wiesbaden ......arr	2 56	...	3 20	...	4 30	p.m.	...	...	6 19	...	⋮	...	...	...	...	10 1	...	...	...	...
Wiesbaden ......dep	3 0	...	3 43	3 51	4 35	4 0	5 35	5 55	6 31	7 20	⋮	8 0	...	8 26	9 9	10 9	...	...	11 10	1257
Biebrich West.........	3 8	...	⋮	⋮	4 43	4 8	5 42	6 3	6 42	7 30	7 24	8 12	...	8 34	9 17	10 17	...	...	11 18	1 7
Eltville...............arr	3 25	...	⋮	⋮	5 2	4 25	5 59	6 15	7 0	7 49	7 41	8 26	...	8 46	9 36	10 35	...	...	11 36	1 27
Schlangenbad ......arr		...	⋮	⋮	5	5 0	6 30	--	7 46	8 28	8 28	...	...	9 33	...	...	...	...	...	...
,, ...dep		...	⋮	⋮	3 43	...	5 18	5 18	6 0	7 16	7 16	...		7 52	9 3	...	...	...	...	...
Eltville ....dep		...	⋮	⋮	5 2	...	5 59	6 15	7 0	7 49	7 41	8 26	...	8 46	9 36	10 35	...	...	11 36	1 27
Geisenheim		...	⋮	⋮	5 30	...	6 21	...	7 22	8 14	8 4	8 50	...	...	10 3	10 59	...	...	12 3	1 55
Rudesheim .... arr		...	4 12	4 20	5 37	...	6 27	6 33	7 28	8 21	8 10	8 56	...	9 4	10 9	11 5	...	...	12 9	2 1
Rudesheim .... dep		...	4 13	4 21		...	6 41	6 34	7 33			9 16	...	9 5			...	...	12 13	2 6
Assmannshausen............		...	...	⋮	...	...	6 48	...	7 39	...	...	9 23	...	...	...	...	...	...	12 20	2 13
Lorch		...	...	⋮	...	...	6 58	...		...	...	9 33	...	...	...	...	...	...	12 30	2 23
Caub..........................		...	...	⋮	...	...	7 11	...	...	...	...	9 44	...	...	...	...	...	...	12 42	2 35
St. Goarshausen		...	...	⋮	p.m.	...	7 26	7 4	p.m.	...	...	9 58	...	9 35	...	...	...	...	12 55	2 52
Braubach		...	...	⋮	6 29	...	8 2	...	9 9	...	...	10 32	...	...	...	...	...	...		3 32
Oberlahnstein		...	...	⋮	6 36	...	8 9	7 31	9 16	...	...	10 39	...	10 2	...	...	...	...	...	3 40
Niederlahnstein ......arr		...	5 7	⋮	6 40	...	8 13	7 35	9 20	...	...	10 43	-	10 6	...	...	...	...	...	3 44
Niederlahnstein ...dep		...	...	⋮	6 44	...	8 19	...	9 21	...	...	...	...	...	...	...	...	...	...	3 56
Coblence Haupt. ...arr		...	...	5 21	6 52	...	8 27	...	9 29	...	...	...	...	--	...	...	...	...	...	4 4
EMS 147 ....dep		...	4p11	⋮	6p29	...	...	6 p29	...	8 p14	...	...	...	...	1017	...	...	...	...	1233
			Ex3	⋮	2 3 4			1,2,3	1,2,3	1--4		2,3,4		1,2,3	2 3 4		1—4		1—4	1—4
			p.m.	⋮	p.m.			p.m.		p.m.				p.m.	p.m.					a.m.
Niederlahnstein......dep		...	5 11	Via Bonn, page 123D.	7 5	...	...	7 39	...	8 45	...	...	...	10 10	1050	...	...	...	...	3 58
Horchheim..................		...	...	⋮	7 9	...	...	...	...	8 50	...	...	...	...	1055	...	...	...	...	...
Ehrenbreitstein arr		...	...	⋮	7 17	...	...	7 47	...	8 57	...	...	...	10 18	11 2	...	...	...	...	4 6
Ehrenbreitstein dep		...	...	⋮	7 19	...	...	7 48	...	9 1	...	...	...	10 19	11 5	...	...	...	...	4 10
Vallendar		...	RC	⋮	7 28	...	...	...	...	9 10	...	p.m.	...	..	1113	...	...	...	...	4 19
Engers		...	...	⋮	7 43	...	...	8 1	p.m.	9 27	...	9 42	...	10 32	1125	...	...	...	a.m.	4 35
Neuwied		...	...	⋮	7 52	...	...	8 9	8 15	9 57	...	9 51	...	10 40	1140	...	a.m	...	5 28	4 46
Linz		...	...	⋮		...	...	...	8 54	10 38	...		...	11 4	1218	...	4 50	...	6 7	5 25
Erpel		...	...	⋮	...	...	...	...	9 0	10 45	...	...	...	...		...	4 56	...	6 13	5 31
Honnef		...	...	⋮	...	...	...	...	9 13	10 58	...	...	...	11 17	...	...	5 9	...	6 26	5 44
Königswinter		...	6 § 6	⋮	...	...	...	8 §45	9 26	11 12	...	...	...	11§25	...	...	5 20	...	6 37	5 55
Niederdollendorf...........		...	...	⋮	...	...	...	...	9 31	11 17	...	...	...	...	...	...	5 25	...	6 42	6 0
Obercassel..............dep		...	...	⋮	...	...	...	...	9 37	11 23	...	...	...	...	...	...	5 31	...	6 48	6 6
Beuel (opposite Bonn) ...		...	...	⋮	...	...	...	8 55	9 44	11 40	...	...	...	11 36	...	...	5 38	...	6 55	6 13
Troisdorf ....arr		...	6 24	⋮	...	...	...	9 6	9 59	11 57	...	...	...	11 50	...	...	5 56	...	7 10	6 28
COLOGNE Deutz...arr		...	6 46	⋮	...	...	...	...	...	...	...	...	...	...	...	...	...	...	...	...
COLOGNE Haupt. dep		...	...	7 7	...	...	...	9 30	1030	12 34	...	...	...	12 13	...	...	6 39	...	7 49	7 19
AIX-LA-CHAPEL123arr		...	...	...	...	...	...	11p52	12a6	...	...	...	...	...	...	...	8 a57	...	9a 9	9 a9
BRUSSELS 104 ....arr		...	...	...	...	...	...	3 a56	3a56	...	...	...	...	...	...	...	11a26	...	11 26	1126

Extra.					
Frankfort.........dep	6p†19	8p15	8p23	10p58	12 0 night.
Wiesbaden ......arr	7 34	9 4	9 37	11 49	1 11

†—Weekdays only.

‡—From Sudbahnhof at Frankfort. §—Not call on Sunday.

JÜLICH and DALHEIM.

	a.m.	a.m.	a.m.	a.m.	p.m.	p.m.	p.m.	p.m.	p.m.
Jülich......dep	5 18	6 21	7 55	9 55	1 12	3 32	6 16	...	1035
Baal	6 15	7 0	8 33	1055	1 50	4 34	6 54	7 30	1115
Dalheim ..arr	6 58	...	...	1140	2 31	5 17	...	8 14	1158

	a.m.	a.m.	a.m.	a.m.	a.m.	p.m.	p.m.	p.m.	p.m.	p.m.	p.m.
Dalheim dep	5 10	...	6 27	...	9 12	1227	2 58	...	6 39	...	8 47
Baal	5 52	6 32	7 11	9 0	1021	1 55	3 42	4 35	7 26	8 12	9 55
Jülich (127)...arr	7 10	...	9 38	1059	2 33	...	5 13	...	8 50	1033	

STOLBERG and HERZOGENRATH.

Stolberg..................dep	7 a27	11a20	5 p51	...	...	...
Herzogenrath ....arr	8 36	12 22	6 57	...	...	...
Herzogenrath ....dep	8 a46	1 p0	7 p26	...	...	...
Stolberg (127) ....arr	9 42	2 0	8 23	...	...	...

STOLBERG and WALHEIM.

Stolberg ....dep	7a20	10a22	12p42	3 p0	5 p10	7p16	...
Walheim ....arr	7 53	10 55	1 15	3 30	5 41	7 49	...
Walheim ....dep	8 a3	11a 8	2p15	4p15	5p57	9p14	...
Stolberg 127) ...arr	8 33	11 38	2 45	4 45	6 27	9 44	...

EUSKIRCHEN and MUNSTEREIFEL.

Euskirchen dep	6a52	8a55	10a33	1p20	5p 32	7 p18	8 p5	10p50
Arloff	7 14	9 15	10 53	1 40	5 52	7 40	8 29	11 10
Münstereifel arr	7 26	9 27	11 5	1 52	6 4	7 52	8 41	11 22
Münstereifel dep	5a50	8 a7	9 a43	11a46	2p52	6p16	8 p13	9p52
Arloff	6 3	8 20	9 56	11 59	3 5	6 29	8 27	10 5
Euskirchen... arr	6 24	8 39	10 15	12 18	3 24	6 50	8 46	1024

DÜLKEN and BRUGGEN.

Dülken.........dep	8a15	12p15	4p52	8p14	9p25	...	...	...	...
Amern	8 43	12 43	5 20	8 42	9 53	...	...	...	...
Bruggen ......arr	8 54	12 54	5 31	8 53	10 4	...	...	...	...
Bruggen ......dep	5a36	6a45	10a24	1p54	7 p4	...	...	...	...
Amern	5 48	6 57	10 36	2 6	7 16	...	...	...	...
Dülken (127) arr	6 15	7 25	11 3	2 34	7 45	...	...	...	...

‡—Not on Sunday.

CALL and HELLENTHAL.

	a.m.	a.m.	a.m.	a.m.	p.m.	p.m.	p.m.	p.m.	p.m.
Call..............dep	5 50	8 9	9 33	11 54	2 15	3 5	4 20	6 31	9 55
Hellenthal arr	6 35	8 54	1025	12 39	3 2	3 50	5 5	7 16	10 40

	a.m.	a.m.	a.m.	a.m.	p.m.	p.m.	p.m.	p.m.
Hellenthal ......dep	4 53	6 47	9 55	10 47	1 17	3 17	5 20	8 44
Call (126) ....arr	5 38	7 32	1040	11 34	2 2	4 3	6 5	9 31

PEINE and ILSEDE.—(4 miles, in 15 minutes).—

Peine (158) depart 5.45, 6.55, 7.50, 9.25, 11.55 a.m. 1.45, 2†55, 4†30, 5†35, 6†25, and 7†40 p.m.
Ilsede depart 5.5, 7,25, 8.40, and 10.5 a.m., 12.20, 1†20, 2†10, 3†45, 4.†55, and 6†50 p.m. †—Weekdays only.

BEUEL, HENNEF, and ASBACH.

Beuel ......dep	6a43	9a50	2p10	...	7p10	8p26	...	...	...
Niederpleis ...	7 16	1022	2 46	...	7 46	8 55	...	...	...
⁝Siegburg arr	7 30	1033	2 57	p.m.	8 8	...	...	...	...
Hennef	8 18	1110	3 9	4 32	8 50	9 18	...	...	...
Buchholz	9 47	1237	—	5 54	10 9	—	...	...	...
Asbach ......arr	1010	1257	...	6 14	1028	...	...	...	...

Asbach......dep	...	5a45	8a30	12p39	...	5p33	...	...	...	...
Buchholz	...	6 5	8 53	12 58	...	5 52	...	...	...	...
Hennef	6a45	8 0	11 0	2 15	4p30	7 19	...	...	...	...
⁝Siegburg dep	6 53	8 0	1110	2 20	...	7 26	...	...	...	...
Niederpleis ...	7 16	8 26	1129	2 45	4 58	7 45	...	...	...	...
Beuel (128) arr	7 45	8 58	1159	3 15	5 28	8 16	...	...	...	...

WALDBROL and HENNEF.

E.M.		a.m.	a.m.	a.m.	p.m
—	**Waldbrol** ....dep	5 38	8 12	1150	5 8
4½	Benroth	6 2	8 38	1217	5 34
10½	Felderhoferbrücke	6 35	9 13	1252	6 8
13	Ingersaulermühle	6 53	9 34	1 13	6 29
19	**Hennef** 133B ......arr	7 26	10 12	1 50	7 5

	a.m.	a.m.	p.m.	p.m.
Hennef..............dep	8 13	11 5	4 28	9 28
Ingersaulermühle........	8 55	11 46	5 7	10 9
Felderhoferbrücke	9 15	12 6	5 27	10 28
Benroth	9 49	12 42	6 1	11 2
Waldbrol..........arr	10 16	1 9	6 26	11 27

Niederpleis ....dep	7a28	11a30	3 p0	7p55	...	...
Rostingen................arr	8 51	12 44	4 25	9 16	...	...

Rostingen..........dep	9 a0	1p25	6p15	...	...	...	...
Niederpleis ....arr	1018	2 35	7 30	...	...	...	...

GEORGSMARIENHUTTE and HASBERGEN.

Georgsmarienhütte dep	8 a50	12p45	3 p15	6 p25	8p25	...	...
Hasbergen 132 ....arr	9 9	1 4	3 34	6 44	8 41	...	...

Hasbergen..............dep	10a25	2 p15	4 p50	7p 10	9p0	...
Georgsmarienhütte arr	10 44	2 34	5 9	7 26	9 16	...

ADENAU aud GEROLSTEIN.

E M.		a.m.	a.m.	p.m.	p.m.	p.m.	
—	Adenau ....dep	7 9	9 10	1 11	6 13	9 54	...
4	Dümpelfeld................	7 30	9 28	1 29	6 32	10 11	...
15½	Ahrdorf	8 10	10 7	2 9	7 12	10 51	...
27½	Hillesheim ....arr	8 48	10 46	2 48	7 51	11 30	...
33¾	Pelm	9 6	11 5	3 12	8 16	11 49	...
35	Gerolstein 126......arr	9 11	11 10	3 17	8 21	11 54	...

	a.m.	a.m.	p.m.	p.m.	p.m.		
Gerolstein ....dep	6 25	10 2	3 20	6 16	9 29	...	...
Pelm	6 31	10 7	3 26	6 22	9 34	...	...
Hillesheim ....dep	6 52	10 24	3 50	6 43	9 58	...	...
Ahrdorf	7 33	11 1	4 31	7 24	10 39	...	...
Dümpelfeld................	8 13	11 38	5 11	8 3	11 17	...	...
Adenau 123D ......arr	8 27	11 53	5 26	8 18	11 32	...	...

E M.								
	Hillesheim ......dep	6a26	8a54	10a52	2p50	4p50	7p52	11p33
6¼	Jünkerath 128 ...arr	6 44	9 12	11 10	3 8	5 8	8 10	11 51

Jünkerath.........dep	5a54	7a15	10 a2	12p15	3p27	6p15	9p35	...
Hillesheim ....arr	6 16	7 37	10 22	12 36	3 48	6 38	9 57	...

Ahrdorf..................dep	6a37	10a13	4p49	7p48	...
Blankenheim ....arr	7 36	11 14	5 50	9 10	...

Blankenheim......dep	5a30	8a15	2p50	6p50	...
Ahrdorf...............arr	6 23	9 41	3 43	7 38	...

WEISMES and JUNKERATH,

E M.		a.m.	a.m.	a.m.	p.m.	p.m.	
—	Weismes ....dep	5 14	8 4	10 6	3 35	9 16	...
3¼	Weywertz	5 35	8 14	10 16	3 45	9 27	...
27	Jünkerath ....arr	6 50	9 36	11 37	5 6	10 43	...

	a.m.	a.m.	p.m.	p.m.	p.m.		
Jünkerath ....dep	5 58	10 25	12 12	4 21	9 40	...	...
Weywertz	7 34	11 55	1 44	5 52	11 11	...	...
Weismes 127.........arr	7 42	12 3	1 52	6 0	11 19	...	...

LINZ and ALTENKIRCHEN.

	a.m.	a.m.	p.m.	p.m.			
Linz.....................dep	5 49	9 42	2 32	6 57	...	...	...
Neustadt (Wied)	7 13	11 6	3 56	8 21	...	...	...
Hammersfeld	8 22	12 26	4 43	9 8	...	...	...
Altenkirchen ......arr	8 40	12 45	5 3	9 25	...	...	...

	a.m.	a.m.	p.m.	p.m.			
Altenkirchen ......dep	6 32	10 56	3 18	7 44	...	...	...
Hammersfeld............	6 53	11 18	3 37	8 2	...	...	...
Neustadt (Wied)	7 25	11 47	4 10	8 33	...	...	...
Linz 128..................arr	8 56	1 15	5 41	10 4	...	...	...

PRUSSIAN STATE RAILWAYS.

[Luggage Rates—see page 462.

MUNSTER and RHEDA.

E.M.																
	Münster ....dep	a20	8a31	11a11	2p37	5p12	8 p0	11p38	**Rheda** ....dep	4a53	...	8a29	1210	2p20	5p22	8p23
16¼	Warendorf..............	6 55	10 0	12 26	3 44	6 27	9 8	12 41	Warendorf	5 51	6a45	9 43	1 21	3 46	6 35	9 34
30¾	**Rheda**..................arr	8 1	11 8	1 37	4 50	7 37	1037	...	**Münster** ....arr	6 50	7 48	1048	2 30	4 50	7 45	1035

WALDBRÖL and WISSEN.

Waldbröl ....dep	5 a0	7a48	10a52	2p10	4p35	7 p52	**Wissen**.........................dep	7a39	9 a37	12p10	3p36	6 p42	10p32
Hermesdorf	5 7	7 55	10 59	2 18	4 42	7 59	Hermesdorf	8 43	10 31	1 7	4 42	7 37	11 33
Wissen (133B).........arr	6 6	8 51	11 51	3 12	5 43	8 51	**Waldbröl (130)**.........arr	8 49	10 37	1 14	4 49	7 43	11 40

ESSEN and ALTEN-ESSEN.

	a.m.	a.m.	a.m.	a.m.	a.m.	a.m.	a.m.	a.m.	a.m.	p.m.	p.m.	p.m.	p.m.	p.m.	p.m.	p.m.	p.m.	p.m.	p.m.	p.m.	p.m.					
Essen Nord...dep	1 45	4 49	6 0	6 41	7 35	9 0	9 55	1046	1139	1227	1 10	1 51	3 3	3 39	4 32	6 2	6 38	7 49	8 46	9 18	1031	...	...	...	...	...
Alten-E. 160A arr	1 53	4 57	6 8	6 48	7 43	9 8	10 3	1054	1147	1235	1 18	1 58	3 10	3 46	4 40	6 9	6 46	7 57	8 54	9 25	1039	...	...	...	...	...
Alten-Essen dep	2 a2	5 25	6 29	6 58	8 11	9 30	1024	11 2	1158	1248	1 39	2p16	3 26	4 16	5 15	6 18	7 12	8 33	9 6	9 58	11 3	...	...	...	...	...
Essen 133D ...arr	2 10	5 32	6 36	7 6	8 19	9 38	1032	1110	12 6	1256	1 46	2 24	3 33	4 24	5 23	6 25	7 19	8 41	913	10 6	1110	...	...	...	...	...

UNNA KONIGSBORN and CAMEN.															
Unna Konigsborndep	7a18	10a2	12p31	3p20	4p50	8p41	10p43	Camen ....dep	5a46	7a45	10a36	1p30	4p 5	7p25	9p20
Camen 160A.........arr	7 32	1018	12 47	3 36	5 4	8 57	10 58	Unna Konigsb. 133Darr	6 2	7 59	10 48	1 45	4 20	7 40	9 35

VENLO and HALTERN.

(Customs Examination at Venlo). [*—Amsterdam Time.

Venlo * ....dep	...	4a50	6 a31	a.m.	a.m.	...	8a20	...	12p15	...	4p 1	p.m.	...	6p32	8 p37	p.m.	nig't	...	...
Straelen	...	5 51	7 38	A	A	...	9 23	...	1 18	...	5 0	B	...	7 33	9 43	A	A	...	...
Geldern (121)........	...	6 8	7 58			...	9 36	...	1 50	...	5 15		...	7 47	10 2			...	...
Wesel (132)......arr	a.m.	6 52	8 42	9 21	9 32	a.m.	10 21	a.m.	2 35	p.m.	6 1	6 21	p.m.	8 30	10 44	11 44	12 0	ng't	...
,, ...dep	4 56	7 52	—	—	—	9 26	—	1035	—	3 0	6 7	—	6 29	8 44	11 42	—	—	12 9	...
Hervest-Dorsten ...	5 39	8 33	...	...	...	A	...	1114	...	3 45	7 1	...	6 52	9 27	12 17	...	...	A	...
Haltern (132)...arr	5 57	8 52	...	...	...		...	1133	...	4 6	7 19	...	7 8	9 45	12 35	...	...		...

Haltern...........dep	...	...	5 a0	...	A	8a10	10a48	12p49	3 p22	...	4p48	6 p13		...	...	8 p59	...
Hervest-Dorsten ...	...	...	5 47	...		8 33	11 15	1 11	3 47	...	5 11	6 53	A	...	...	9 29	...
Wesel (120)......arr	...	...	6 24	...	6 45	9 4	11 49	1 45	4 9	p.m.	5 44	7 24	8 20	p.m.	p.m.	10 7	...
,, ...dep	4 a40	6 a55	7 14	7 a28	—	9 12	12 7	3 0	—	4 15	6 28	—	—	8 26	8 44	—	...
Geldern	5 32		7 58		...	9 57	12 50	3 47	...		7 14	...	...		9 28	...	...
Straelen	5 52	A	8 17	A	...	1013	1 9	4 5	...	B	7 31	...	...	A	9 44	...	...
Venlo *...........arr	5 27		7 48		...	9 44	12 41	3 38	...		7 3	...	...		9 16	...	...

A—To and from Vlissingen. B—To and from Antwerp.

WERDEN and ESSEN.

Werden dep	5a56	6a53	7a15	7a30	8a1	9a33	10a46	12p33	1p33	2p11	229	3p14	359	4p49	5p44	6p13	6p28	7p19	7p35	8p1	821	8p40	911	9p29	10p13	11p7	1 p18	12a5	12a26
Essen 130	6 16	7 14	7 36	7 50	822	9 53	11 6	12 53	1 53	2 31	250	3 35	419	5 9	6 5	6 33	6 50	7 39	7 49	815	840	9 1	931	9 43	10 33	1127	11 39	1227	12 48

Essen ....dep	5a10	6a12	6a37	7a44	8 a36	8a48	10a2	10a32	11a26	12p45	1 p5	1 p18	1p47	2 p42	2p56	4 p18	5p18	6 p41	7p13	8 p31	8 p47	9 p40	10p29	11p42
Werden ......arr	5 29	6 30	6 56	8 3	8 47	9 7	1020	10 43	11 45	1 4	1 24	1 37	1 58	3 1	3 15	4 29	5 36	6 59	7 32	8 50	9 6	9 59	10 48	12 1

SIEGBURG and OLPE.

Siegburg......dep	...	5a35	...	7a52	10 a0	...	12p51	4 p0	...	7p16	8p32	10p50
Bachermühle ...	...	6 13	...	8 26	10 33	...	1 27	4 39	...	7 55	9 7	11 27
Deutz ......dep	...	5a45	...	7a34	9 a35	...	1p25	4p28	...	7 5	8 21	11 32
Kalk Süd	...	5 54	...	7 43	9 45	...	1 35	4 38	...	7 13	8 30	11 43
Overath ......dep	5 a3	6 40	...	8 38	10 45	...	2 26	5 31	...	8 5	9 20	12 30
Osberghausen ...	5 49	7 18	7a45	9 29	11 30	12p18	3 16	6 30	p.m.	8 44	10 2	1 12
Dieringhausen..	6 9	7 30	8 4	9 54	11 52	12 36	3 49	6 48	7 56	8 59	1017	1 25
Derschlag	6 31	—	8 25	1020	12 17	1 1	4 15	7 16	8 21	9 19	1042	1 45
Bergneustadt ...	6 43	...	8 36	1034	12 29	1 11	4 29	7 33	8 31	9 29	1054	1 55
Olpe..............arr	7 32	...	9 20	1118	1 12	...	5 19	8 24	...	10 7	1143	...

Olpe ....dep	...	5a43	6a40	8a32	...	11a27	...	2p47	4p44	7 p49	10p7
Bergneustadt ...	5 a5	6 20	7 30	9 15	11a8	12 6	1 p18	3 39	5 56	8 44	1052
Derschlag	5 14	6 30	7 41	9 24	1118	12 16	1 27	3 49	6 7	8 57	11 2
Dieringhausen..	5 36	6 50	8 12	9 46	1143	12 39	1 56	4 33	6 42	9 48	1120
Osberghausen ..	5 52	7 5	8 25	9 59	1155	12 52	2 12	4 46	6 56	10 5	—
Overath ....arr	6 37	7 44	9 10	1037	—	1 33	2 55	5 30	7 34	10 48	...
Kalk Süd	7 28	8 31	10 5	1120	...	2 32	3 45	6 23	8 22	11 42	...
Deutz ....arr	7 35	8 38	1012	1128	...	2 39	3 52	6 30	8 29	11 49	...
Bachermühle ..	6 57	—	9 23	1110	...	1 45	3 12	5 43	7 44	10 59	...
Siegburg ......arr	7 33	...	9 59	1146	...	2 21	3 50	6 21	8 22	11 34	...

Dieringhausen	5a38	6 a8	8a14	9a51	11a46	2p17	3p40	4p44	6p35	7p20	10p18
Gummersbach...	5 53	6 21	8 29	10 6	12 3	2 32	3 55	4 59	6 48	7 36	10 31
Marienheide......	6 10	6 42	8 53	1024	12 21	2 55	4 16	5 21	7 2	7 55	10 50
Brugge.........arr	...	7 34	9 49	11 9	1 13	3 54	5 13	6 12	...	8 52	11 44

Brugge dep	5a48	7a50	8a50	...	12p13	2 p3	...	...	5 p0	6p18	...	9p33	11p32
Marienh'de	6 42	8 50	9 49	1144	1 19	2 55	4 p0	5p19	5 57	7 19	9p 8	1047	12 24
Gummersb	7 51	9 8	1010	12 5	1 36	3 13	4 20	5 39	6 19	7 41	9 29	11 8	12 42
Dieringh'n	8 2	9 20	1022	1221	1 48	3 26	4 30	5 50	6 32	7 52	9 40	1121	12 53

Osberghausen ......dep	5a54	7 a4	1012	11a57	3 p25	5 p2	6 p55	10p10	1a15	Waldbrol..............dep	4a44	...	6a43	10a25	11a32	2 p3	5 p14	8 p35	nght
Wiehl	6 11	7 25	1031	12 23	3 52	5 29	7 22	10 31	1 39	Wiehl	5 24	6a34	7 24	11 5	12 20	2 50	5 52	9 17	12 29
Waldbrol ....arr	...	8 0	11 4	1 2	4 33	...	8 4	11 12	2 12	Osberghausen ....arr	5 46	6 55	7 43	11 26	12 41	3 12	6 12	9 38	12 54

FRIEDBERG and HUNGEN.

†—Weekdays only.

	a.m.	a.m.	a.m.	p.m.	p.m.	p.m.	p.m.			a.m.	a.m.	a.m.	a.m.	p.m.	p.m.	p.m.	
Friedberg...........dep	4 †45	7 51	11 43	1 23	5 30	7 0	9 30	...	**Hungen** ....dep	4 †25	6 28	9 16	11 24	2 56	6 49	9 44	...
Beienheim	4 59	8 5	12 0	1 37	5 44	7 22	9 43	...	Beienheim........................	5 17	7 13	10 3	12 19	3 41	7 39	10 29	...
Hungen (130A) ...arr	5 48	8 51	12 48	2 20	6 28	8 10	10 25	...	**Friedberg (156A)** ...arr	5 32	7 26	10 19	12 35	3 55	7 54	10 42	...

FRIEDBERG and NIDDA. †—Weekdays only.		a.m.	a.m.	p.m.	p.m.	p.m	p.m.		a.m.	a.m.	a.m.	p.m.	p.m.	p.m.
	Friedberg.........dep	...	8 3	12 48	4 25	7 0	8 18	**Nidda**......................dep	4 †16	6 10	9 25	2 3	6 21	9 50
	Beienheim	5†17	8 18	1 0	4 39	7 15	8 32	Beienheim........................	5 11	7 5	10 14	2 52	7 16	10 42
	Nidda (130A) ...arr	6 4	9 17	1 47	5 33	8 9	9 26	**Friedberg (156A)** ...arr	5 32	7 18	10 27	3 5	7 29	10 56

Luggage Rates—see page 462.]

PRUSSIAN STATE RAILWAYS.

WESEL and WINTERSWIJK.

	a.m.	a.m.	a.m.	a.m.	p.m.	p.m.	p.m.	p.m.	p.m.	p.m.	p.m.	
Wesel ....dep	...	5 40	7 38	9 10	1229	1 56	2 55	4 16	6 27	8 44	1154	...
Bocholt ....arr	...	6 11	8 9	9 41	1 0	2 28	3 26	4 45	6 57	9 15	1225	...
,, ...dep	5 10	6 20	8 17	1046	...	...	3 34	—	7 5	...	...	...
Winterswijk ....arr	5 22	6 42	8 39	11 8	...	...	3 56	...	7 27	...	...	...

	a.m.	a.m	a.m.	a.m.	a.m.	p.m.		p.m.	p.m.	p.m.	p.m.
Winterswijk ....dep	...	5 47	7 38	9 13	1123	...	...	4 38	...	...	11 8
Bocholt ....arr	...	6 9	8 0	9 35	1145	...	p.m.	4 56	...	...	1130
,, ...dep	4 57	6 20	8 10	9 45	1156	2 8	3 30	5 5	7 48	10 4	...
Wesel (132) ....arr	5 30	6 54	8 40	1017	1228	2 38	4 1	5 36	8 20	10 35	...

EMPEL and MÜNSTER.

Empel ....dep	a.m.	5 a43	7a58	a.m.	10a54	p.m.	2 p34	7 p7	9 p18
Bocholt	4 50	6 17	8 38	10 0	11 31	1 59	3 32	7 50	9 59
Borken	5 27	6 52	9 27	10 31	12 9	2 35	4 19	8 37	10 36
Coesfeld	6 30	7 50	10 20	—	1 17	3 38	6 8	9 39	—
Münster (132) ar	7 50	8 58	11 40	...	2 31	4 50	7 24	10 49	...

Münster .dep	...	...	a.m.	7 a15	...	9 a9	11 a0	...	1 p28	4 p11	6 p44	9p11
Coesfeld	...	a.m.	6 34	8 34	a.m.	10 51	12 16	...	3 0	6 5	8 14	1027
Borken	a.m.	6 10	7 34	9 28	10 48	12 5	—	1 p27	4 18	7 9	9 25	1123
Bocholt....	4 40	6 52	8 5	10 3	11 24	1 5	...	1 58	4 54	7 53	9 57	1153
Empel ....arr	5 23	7 31	...	10 40	...	1 44	...	—	5 26	8 40	...	—

RUHRORT and STERKRADE.

Ruhrort ...dep	4a43	5a38	6a50	8a55	11a38	2p22	4p15	5p26	7p46	9p11	10p38
Sterkrade arr	5 1	5 56	7 9	9 13	11 56	2 40	4 33	5 44	8 4	9 31	10 56
Sterkrade dep	6a24	8 a7	8a33	9a59	1 p14	3p41	5p47	7 p14	8 p20	10p15	11p30
Ruhrort ...arr	6 43	8 23	8 48	10 1	1 32	4 0	6 5	7 32	8 39	10 29	11 48

STERKRADE and DORTMUND.

	a.m.		a.m.		a.m.		p.m.	p.m.		p.m.		p.m.	p.m.		p.m.
Sterkrade dep	5 9	...	7 45	...	9 18	...	12 6	...	...	2 45	...	4 52	...	...	9 39
Bottrop	5 24	...	8 4	...	10 2	...	1239	1 58	...	3 22	...	6 17	8 20	...	1041
Schalke	5 43	a.m.	8 21	a.m.	1019	a.m.	1256	2 15	p.m.	3 40	p.m.	6 35	8 39	p.m.	11 1
Wanne	6 27	6 57	9 6	10 8	1027	1150	1 19	2 23	3 36	3 48	5 48	7 6	9 0	1029	11 9
Herne	6 34	7 4	9 13	1015	—	1158	1 27	—	3 43	—	5 55	7 13	9 8	1036	—
Castrop	6 49	7 18	9 25	1028	...	1212	1 41	...	3 56	...	6 9	7 26	9 22	1047	...
Dortmund arr	7 27	7 59	10 2	11 7	...	1251	2 21	...	4 34	...	6 48	8 2	9 59	1123	...

	a.m.	a.m.	a.m.	a.m.		a.m.	p.m.		p.m.	p.m.	p.m	p.m.	p.m.	n'gt
Dortmund	5 9	...	7 28	8 53	...	1155	1 33	...	3 48	5 36	7 39	8 50	10 30	1216
Castrop	5 48	...	8 8	9 33	...	1235	2 8	...	4 26	6 11	8 15	9 24	11 9	1253
Herne	6 1	...	8 21	9 46	a.m.	1249	2 20	p.m.	4 38	6 23	8 27	9 36	11 23	1 7
Wanne ...	6 8	5 25	8 27	9 53	1127	1256	2 37	4 29	4 45	6 58	8 41	1040	11 30	1 13
Schalke	—	5 34	9 5	—	1136	—	2 45	4 37	—	7 7	8 51	1049	—	—
Bottrop		5 54	9 24	...	1153	...	3 3	4 55	...	7 25	9 10	11 8	...	...
Sterkrade arr		6 8	9 44	...	1224	...	3 36	5 13	...	...	10 1	1122	...	...

WANNE and BISMARCK I. W.

Wanne...	4a45	6a38	7a40	9a6	10a22	10a55	11a48	12p50	1p20	2p46	3p55	4p22	5p13	5p51	7p16	8p37	9p52	11p39
Bismarck	4 55	6 48	7 50	916	10 32	11 5	11 58	1 0	1 31	2 57	4 6	4 34	5 24	6 2	7 26	8 47	10 2	11 49

Bism	8a3	9a25	10a31	11a5	12p1	12p55	1p30	2p16	2p58	4p33	5p27	6p4	7p33	8p42	10p2	11p46
Wan	814	9 35	10 42	1116	1212	1 6	1 41	2 26	3 9	4 44	5p38	615	7 44	8 52	1012	11 56

BOCHUM and WANNE.

	m	a.m.	a.m.	a.m.	a.m.	a.m.	p.m	p.m.	p.m.	p.m.	p.m.	p.m	p.m.	p.m.	a.m.
Bochum dp	4 7	5 44	8 5	9 31	10 8	1054	12 9	2 59	3 15	4 39	5 59	7 41	9 21	1111	1226
Riemke....	421	5 58	8 19	9 45	1022	11 8	1223	3 13	3 29	4 53	6 13	7 55	9 35	1123	1240
Wanne arr	436	6 14	8 33	10 0	1037	1122	1238	3 28	3 44	5 8	6 28	8 10	9 48	1135	1252

	a.m.	a.m.	a.m.	a.m	a.m.	a.m.	p.m.	p.m.	p.m.	p.m.	p.m.	p.m	p.m.	p.m.	a.m.
Wanne dep	5 32	6 59	8 42	9 10	10 7	1131	1 20	2 39	3 56	5 19	6 56	8 26	9 17	1020	1224
Riemke....	5 48	7 15	8 57	9 26	1023	1147	1 34	2 53	4 11	5 35	7 12	8 39	9 30	1036	1238
Bochum arr	6 2	7 29	9 11	9 40	1037	12 1	1 48	3 6	4 25	5 49	7 28	8 53	9 44	1050	1252

RUHRORT and OBERHAUSEN.

Ruhrort ....dep	4a20	5a25	6a18	7a22	9 a17	10a32	11a53	12p15	1 p7	2p39	3 p8	4p 7	4 p56	5 p52	6p31	7p27	8p45	10p5	10p52	11p38	12a30	1 a17	...	...	...	...
Oberhausen ....arr	4 36	5 39	6 32	7 36	9 31	10 46	12 9	12 31	1 25	2 54	3 22	4 21	5 10	6 7	6 45	7 44	9 0	10 19	11 6	11 52	12 44	1 31	...	...	...	...

Oberhausen ....dep	5 a5	5a56	7 a0	7a52	8a56	10a11	11a20	12p23	1p20	2 p23	3 p4	3p34	4p32	5 p25	5 p58	7 p3	8p8	9p46	10 p28	11p17	12a10	12a55	1a39	...	...	...
Ruhrort....arr	5 19	6 10	7 15	8 6	9 10	10 25	11 36	12 39	1 36	2 37	3 19	3 48	4 48	5 40	6 12	7 19	8 22	10 0	10 43	11 31	12 24	1 9	1 55	...	...	...

OBERHAUSEN and HAMM.

Oberhausen...dep	...	6 a13	7 a53	11a19	1p17	2 p28	6 p7	8 p41	11p10
Recklinghausen	5a20	7 24	8 54	12 31	2 15	3 54	7 6	9 39	12 9
Hamm ....arr	6 36	8 42	10 46	1 47	3 17	5 10	8 39	11 16	...

Hamm ....dep	5 a8	6 a17	7a25	9 a49	12p52	...	3 p32	6 p45	9p48
Recklinghausen	6 28	7 46	9 25	11 54	2 30	3 p42	4 48	8 0	11 7
Oberhausen ...arr	7 28	8 42	10 30	12 58	3 35	4 33	...	8 58	12 42

BIEDENKOPF and STRASSEBERSBACH.

†—Week-days only.

E.M													
	Biedenkopf ....dep	...	...	...	8 a3	...	...	11a35	...	...	4p32	...	8 p28
3	Wallau	...	...	...	8 17	...	...	11 47	...	...	4 43	...	8 42
11½	Gönnern	...	4a52	...	8 58	...	...	12 24	p.m.	...	5 19	...	9 25
18	Nikolausstollen	...	5 43	7a54	9 52	...	...	1 6	2†30	...	6 3	...	10 15
23	Dillenburg....	5 a12	6 13	8 28	1019	11a25	1†p51	1 3	2 59	4p33	6 29	7p24	10 42
33	Strassebersbach....arr	5 53	6 54	9 15	...	12 19	2 32	...	3 38	5 18	7†17	8 8	11 24

Strassebersbach....dep	4a16	5a58	7 a9	...	9a51	...	12p51	2†p42	3p44	5p35	8p47
Dillenburg	5 0	6 46	7 50	9 a7	1033	11a41	1 52	3 25	5 21	6 15	9 35
Nikolausstollen....	5 27	7 16	—	9 33	—	12 10	2 16	—	5 51	—	10 1
Gönnern	6 20	—	...	10 24	...	—	3 6	...	6 43	...	1054
Wallau....	6 58	...	...	10 59	...	...	3 37	...	7 19	...	—
Biedenkopf (217) ...arr	7 11	...	...	11 11	...	...	3 48	...	7 32	...	...

LÖTTRINGHAUSEN and LANGENDREER.

	a.m.	a.m.	p.m.	p.m.	p.m.	p.m.	p.m.	
Löttringhausen dep	7 29	11 0	1 58	4 44	7 4	9 27	...	...
Witten	7 49	1121	2 19	5 4	7 23	9 45	10 50	...
Langendreer....arr	8 3	1137	2 34	5 19	7 36	9 59	11 3	...

	a.m.	a.m.	p.m.	p.m.	p.m.	p.m.	p.m.		
Langendreer 133D dp	6 14	8 18	1 2	3 15	6 13	7 47	10 20	...	...
Witten....	6 29	8 34	1 17	3 32	6 28	8 3	10 35	...	...
Löttinghausen ...arr	6 46	8 51	1 34	3 52	6 46	8 21		...	...

HOCHFELD and SPELDORF.

Hochfeld ....dep	5a43	6a45	8a16	11a28	1p25	3p55	5 p1	6p50	7p42	8p42	9 p44
Speldorf ....arr	5 54	6 56	8 27	11 40	1 37	4 6	5 10	7 1	7 54	8 51	9 56
Speldorf... dep	5a12	6 a19	7a34	9a28	12p58	3p29	4p17	5p23	6p58	7p17	8p47
Hochfeld ...arr	5 23	6 30	7 43	9 39	1 9	3 40	4 27	5 33	7 8	7 28	8 57

Luggage Rates—see page 462.]

PRUSSIAN STATE RAILWAYS.

EMMERICH and OBERHAUSEN.

	1—4	1—4	1—4	1,2,3	2 3 4	1—4	Ex2	1—4	Ex2	1—4	1—4	1—4	1,2,3	Ex3	Ex2	1—4	1—4	1—4	1,2,3	1—4	1—4	1—4	1—4	1—4	Ex3	1—4	1—4	Ex3	Ex2	
	a.m.		a.m.	a.m.	a.m.	a.m.		a.m.	a.m.	a.m.		a.m.	noon	p.m.	p.m.		p.m.		p.m.		p.m.		p.m.	p.m.	p.m	p.m.	p.m.	p.m.		
Emmerich ....dep	3 57	...	5 23	6 25	...	7 36	...	...	9 54	1030	...	11 48	12 0	1226	1 22	...	1 46	...	3 36	...	4 58	...	5 30	6 22	8 4	8 45	9 51	11 5	...	...
Wesel ....arr	4 49	...	6 20	7 2	...	8 36	...	...	1024	1121	...	12 49	12 30	1256	1 52	...	2 36	...	4 10	...	5 48	...	6 22	7 21	8 35	9 35	1042	1135	p.m.	...
Boxtel 120 ....dep	...	a.m.	...	...	...	...	6a25	...	...	7a12	p.m.		...	10a5	...	...	...	p.m.	...	p.m.	1155	1155	3p40	3p40	...	5p20	5p20	...	9 1	...
Wesel ....dep	4 53	5 39	6 35	7 9	7 24	8 46	9 33	10 0	1026	1125	12 6	...	12 32	1 7	1 54	p.m.	2 42	3 36	4 15	4 43	5 50	6 5	6 26	7 28	8 38	9 37	1050	1139	1146	...
Sterkrade	5 34	6 21	7 14	7 35	8 4	9 25	...	1038	...	12 4	1244	...	...	...	...	2 51	3 19	4 14	4 41	5 24	6 27	6 48	7 0	8 11	...	1014	1127	...	...	...
Oberhausen ....arr	5 40	6 28	7 20	7 41	8 11	9 30	9 56	1044	1050	1212	1250	...	1 0	1 3[illegible]	2 19	2 57	3 25	4 20	4 47	5 30	6 33	6 55	7 6	8 17	9 5	1020	1133	12 6	1211	...

	1—4	Ex3	Ex2	Ex3	1—4	1—4	1—4	2,3,4	1,2,3	1—4	1—4	1—4	1—4	1—4	1—4	1,2,3	1—4	Ex3	1—4	Ex2	1—4	1—4	Ex2	Ex2	1,2,3	1—4	1—4	1,2,3	1—4
	a.m.	a.m.	a.m.	a.m.	a.m.	a.m.	a.m.	a.m.	a.m.	a.m.	p.m.		p.m.	p.m.	p.m.	p.m.	p.m.	p.m.	p.m.	p.m	p.m.	p.m.	p.m.	p.m.	p.m.	p.m	p.m.	p.m.	a.m.
Oberhausen ....dep	6 5	6 41	7 2	7 35	7 56	8 23	9 49	10 55	11 32	11 48	1220	...	1 21	2 2	3 8	3 44	4 31	5 2	5 37	5 58	6 17	7 3	7 36	7 51	8 10	9 14	10 28	10 59	12 55
Sterkrade	6 13	...	...	7 42	8 5	8 30	9 56	11 2	11 39	11 55	1227	...	1 28	2 9	3 16	...	4 39	...	5 44	...	6 25	7 12	...	...	8 17	9 21	10 36	11 6	1 2
Wesel.........................arr	6 50	7 4	7 26	8 5	8 45	9 7	1031	11 38	12 2	12 34	1 5	...		2 45	3 53	4 7	5 16	5 25	6 12	6 22	7 4	7 50	8 0	8 14	8 40	9 55	11 12	11 29	1 39
Boxtel 120 ....arr	8a17	...	8a42	...		...	2p12		...		...	p.m.	...	5p14		5p25	7p35	7p35	9p30	9p30	...	9p39	9p39	9p39	...		...	...	
Wesel ....dep	7 21	7 14		8 7	...	9 14	1036	...	12 6	...	1 10	1 55	...	2 50	...	4 14	...	5 28	6 30	6 24	7 16	8 9	8 2		8 42	...	11 17	11 31	...
Emmerich..............arr	8 7	7 44	...	8 42	...	10 9	1128	...	12 40	...	2 6	2 46	...	3 41	...	4 46	...	5 57	7 16	6 54	8 6	9 3	8 31	...	9 19	...	12 22	12 11	...

ROTENBURG and BREMERVORDE.

Rotenburg.............dep	6a20	8a40	12p12	2p40	7p13	9p21	...	...	...	...
Zeven	7 12	9 55	1 17	4 0	8 12	10 13	...	...	...	...
Bremervörde..........arr	7 57	1050	2 12	5 13	9 7		...	...	...	...

Bremervörde ....dep	...	9 a0	11a32	3p59	6 p0	...	9p16	...	...	...	...	...	...
Zeven..............................	6a2[illegible]	10 5	1 10	5 27	6 55	8p13	1020	...	...	...	...	...	...
Rotenburg...............arr	7 28	1057	2 2	6 35	...	9 5	1112	...	...	...	...	...	...

MÜNSTER and GRONAU.

	a.m.	a.m.	a.m.		a.m		p.m.	p.m.	p.m.	p.m.		p.m.	
Münster ....dep	6 14	6 55	7 20	...	1017	...	1 27	4 32	6 28	9 10	...	11 7	...
Borghorst..................	6 54	...	8 4	...	1055	...	2 6	5 11	7 10	9 49	...	1147	...
Burgsteinfurt ...arr	7 1	7 25	8 12	...	11 2	...	2 13	5 18	7 18	9 56	...	1154	...
,, (131A)...dep	7 5	7 26	8 13	a.m.	11 5	a.m.	2 22	5 25	7 2[illegible]		p.m.	1155	...
Ochtrup	7 23	...	8 31	9 8	1129	11 50	2 52	5 48	7 48	...	1027	1212	...
Gronau (135B) ...arr	7 36	7 46	...	9 22	1135	12 4	3 5	6 1	8 2		1041	1225	...

	a.m.	a.m	a.m.	a.m.	a.m.	p.m.	p.m.	p.m.	p.m	p.m.		p.m.
Gronau ....dep	6 28	6 42	...	9 54	10 30	1234	12 50	3 30	6 48	7 21	...	1011
Ochtrup	6 43	6 55	8 36	10 8	10 45	1248	1 4	3 48	7 3	...	...	1029
Burgsteinfurt arr	7 2		8 57		11 3		1 20	4 5	7 20	7 43	p.m.	1046
,, dep	7 7	...	9 0	...	11 5	...	1 24	4 12	7 28	7 44	9 58	1048
Borghorst..............	7 18	...	9 11	...	11 13	...	1 33	4 21	7 39	...	10 7	1058
Münster (132) arr	7 54	...	9 50	...	11 50	...	2 15	5 0	8 30	8 17	10 46	1133

Rheine.....................dep	8 a23	11 a7	2 p7	4 p55	9 p38	...
Ochtrup ....arr	9 7	11 49	2 48	5 39	10 22	...

Ochtrup..................dep	6 a58	10 a9	12p49	3 p57	8 p4	...
Rheine ....arr	7 44	10 53	1 33	4 41	8 52	...

OBERHAUSEN and QUAKENBRUCK.

		a.m.	a.m	a.m.	a m	p.m.	p.m	p.m.	p.m.				
Oberhausen ......dep		4 49	7 47	10 23	1030	2 2	6 6	8 36	10‡35	...	...	A—Until September 20.	...
Osterfeld.....................		4 58	7 56	A	1039	2 11	6 16	8 45	10 44	...	...		...
Hervest-Dorsten		5 40	8 36	10 53	1121	2 50	6 53	9 27		...	...		...
Coesfeld		6 28	9 22	11 32	1230	3 35	7 44	1011		...	...		...
Burgsteinfurt ...	a.m.	7 15	1110	12 2	1 10	4 12	8 21	1051		...	...		...
Rheine..............	5 55	8 18	1134	12 20	2 6	4 38	9 30	1115		...	...		...
Furstenau	6 59	9 10			3 7	5 49	1032			...	...		...
Quakenbruck ...	7 50	9 52	...		3 58	6 33	1123	...		...	...		...

		a.m.	a.m.	a.m.	p.m.	p.m.	p.m.	p.m.	p.m.					
Quakenbruck ......dep	...	...	6 4	1020	B	...	2 58	4 50	7 18	...	...	B—Until September 21.	‡—Not on Sunday.	...
Furstenau	...	...	6 56	11 4	...	...	3 40	5 47	8 1	p.m.	...			...
Rheine ....dep	...	5 53	8 28	1158	1 14	1 48	4 56	7 0	8 53	1126	...			...
Burgsteinfurt	a.m.	6 19	9 32		1 35	2 15	5 23	7 25		1158	...			...
Coesfeld	4 44	7 1	1027	...	2 9	2 52	6 0	8 22	...	1236	...			...
Hervest-Dorsten	5 43	8 38	1114	...	2 46	3 44	6 54	9 26	p.m.		...			...
Osterfeld	6 26	9 11	1150	...	...	4 13	7 31	9 57	11‡31	...	...			...
Oberhausen.........arr	6 33	9 20	1159	...	3 14	4 21	7 40	10 6	11 40	...	...			...

OSTERFELD and HATTINGEN.

*—Not on Sunday.

			a.m.	a.m.	a.m.	a.m.	p.m.	p.m.	p.m.	p.m.	p.m.	p.m.
Osterfeld ......dep	...	...	6 42	...	9 12	11 51	2 15	4 16	6 18	7 43	8 48	...
Heissen	...	...	7 23	7 59	10 3	12 14	3 1	4 41	7 3	8 9	9 18	...
Ruttenscheid	a.m.	a.m.	7 37	8 9	1016	12 24	3 14	4 50	7 16	8 19	9 32	11 33
Steele	5 *45	7 26	7 52	8 22	1031	12 37	3 29	5 0	7 31	8 32	9 48	11 48
Altendorf-a-d-R.	5 55	7 36	8 2	8 31	1041	12 46	3 40	5 8	7 41	8 41	9 58	11 58
Hattingen ......arr	6 10	7 50	8 18	8 44	1057	1 5	3 56	5 24	7 56	9 4	10 24	12 13

	a.m.	a.m.	a.m.	a.m.	a.m.	p.m.	p.m.		p.m	p.m.	p.m.	p.m.	p.m.
Hattingen ......dep	4*40	6 8	6 57	9 0	1135	1 11	2 1	...	5 34	7 4	8 3	...	10 31
Altendorf-a-d-R.	4 55	6 26	7 11	9 28	1151	1 28	2 21	...	5 52	7 18	8 18	10 17	10 52
Steele	5 4	6 36	7 20	9 36	12 2	1 38	2 30	...	6 2	7 30	8 31	10 26	11 2
Ruttenscheid		6 55		9 53	1223	1 55	2 47	p.m.	6 20	7 47	8 49	10 43	11 18
Heissen	...	7 8	...	10 1	1235	2 8	2 55	5 50	6 38	7 55	9 2	10 51	...
Osterfeld 131A arr	...	7 41	...	1027	1 18	3 19	3 19	6 11	7 24	8 39	9 42	...	...

Luggage Rates—see page 462.] PRUSSIAN STATE RAILWAYS.

COLOGNE, OSNABRUCK, BREMEN, and HAMBURG.

RC—Restaurant Car. SC—Sleeping Car.

Dist. E M.	Station	Ex2	Ex2	1—4	1—4	1,2,3	2 3 4	1—4	1,2,3	Ex 3
...	BRUSSELS 104 ...dep	...	...	...	...	...	...	...	...	11p24
...	PARIS 24 ...dep	...	...	...	...	...	...	...	...	6 p20
...	AIX-LA-CHAPL. 122 dp	...	...	...	...	...	...	...	...	4 a20
...	COLOGNE— Hauptbahnhof arr	...	...	...	...	...	...	...	...	5 a40
										a.m.
—	COLOGNE— Hauptbahnhof dep	...	...	...	...	...	...	...	...	7 4
25	Dusseldorf ...... arr	...	...	...	...	...	...	...	a.m.	7 39
	Dusseldorf dep	...	...	...	a.m.	...	...	a.m.	7 32	7 41
39½	Duisburg	...	...	...	4 26	...	...	5 48	7 56	8 4
44¼	Oberhausen ...... arr	...	...	...	4 36	...	...	5 57	8 5	...
	Oberhausen dep	...	...	...	4 42	...	...	6 5	8 8	RC
59	Wanne ...... arr	...	...	a.m.	5 26	...	a.m.	6 48	8 38	8 59
	Wanne dep	...	...	4 15	5 35	...	6 7	7 3	8 41	9 3
65½	Recklinghausen	...	...	4 32	5 52	...	6 29	7 21	8 58	9 20
75¼	Haltern ...130 arr	...	...	4 55	6 16	...	6 53	7 45	9 12	⋮
...	VLISSINGEN 113 dep	7p10	...	...	...	...	...	...	...	⋮
...	ROTTERDAM 118 dep	7p34	...	...	...	...	...	...	...	⋮
...	AMSTERDAM 118 dep	8 p5	...	...	...	...	...	...	...	⋮
...	EMMERICH 131A dep	11p5	...	...	...	...	3a57	...	6a25	⋮
...	WESEL 130 ...dep	12a9	...	...	...	...	4 a56	...	7a52	⋮
...	Haltern ...dep	⋮	...	4 56	6 17	...	6 56	...	9 13	⋮
83	Dülmen 135B	⋮	...	5 11	6 32	...	7 14	...	9 27	9 46
101	Munster 133A ... arr	1 16	...			...	7 58	...	9 52	10 12
	Munster dep	1 18	...	2 3 4	5 a14	...	8 19	...	9 54	10 17
108	Westbevern	...	...	a.m.	5 30	...	8 34	...	...	...
120¼	Lengerich	...	...	7 14	5 59	...	9 2	...	1022	...
126¾	Hasbergen 129B	...	...	7 30	6 16	...	9 18	...	...	...
132	Osnabruck 156A ...arr	2 1	⁄	7 42	6 28	...	9 30	...	1041	10 58
...	HOEK v. HOLLAND dep	To Berlin (arr. 7.57)	...	...	...	...	...	...	...	...
...	AMSTERDAM 118B dep		9 p0	...	...	1,2,3	...	...	...	...
...	RHEINE 156C ...dep		1a16	...	...	a.m.	8a28	...	...	...
...	Osnabruck ...dep		2 25	...	6 41	8 5	9 38	...	...	11 3
138½	Vehrte		...	...	6 59	...	9 55	...	...	...
154½	Lemförde		...	a.m.	7 34	...	10 27	...	...	...
164½	Diepholz		SC	5 47	7 59	8 53	10 48	...	...	11 46
187½	Bassum	...	...	6 37	8 50	...	11 36	...	...	RC
198½	Kirchweyhe ...2—4	...	...	7 7	9 19	...	12 0	...	...	...
208	Bremen ...... arr a.m.	...	4 19	7 31	9 44	9 56	12 24	...	...	12 44
	Bremen dep 5 17	2 3 4	4 26	7 58	10 14	10 2	1 32	...	2 3 4	12 49
215½	Oberneuland ...5 32	a.m.	...	...	10 28	...	1 46	...	p.m.	...
234½	Rotenburg ...6 16	5 15	...	8 35	11 13	...	2 29	...	1216	1 23
260	Buchholz ...arr ——	6 9	...	9 10	12 10	...	3 23	...	1 15	...
272¼	Harburg ...arr	7 10	6 14	9 32	12 46	1120	3 58	...	1 53	2 10
279¾	HAMBURG Haupt arr	7 43	6 31	9 51	1 20	1138	4 18	...	2 43	2 28
319	LUBECK 213A ...arr	9a43	8a31	12 0	3 p29	...	6 p14	...	...	4 p11
410	WARNEMUNDE arr	...	12 39	...	...	...	...	...	...	...
544	COPENHAGEN 302	...	6p41	...	...	...	...	...	...	...
349	KIEL ...168 arr	...	9 a5	1p58	3 p36	...	7 p25	...	...	5 p29
433	KORSÖR steamer arr	...	2p38	...	...	...	...	...	...	...
502	COPENHAGEN 302 arr	...	4p18	...	...	...	...	...	...	...
906	STOCKHOLM 308A arr	...	8a49	...	...	...	...	...	...	...
478	SASSNITZ 181 ...arr	...	...	...	...	...	...	...	...	...
545	TRELLEBORG ...arr	...	...	...	...	...	...	...	...	...
949	STOCKH'M 308A arr	...	...	...	...	...	...	...	...	...

Dist. E M.	Station	Ex2	Ex2	1—4	1—4	1—4	Ex 2	1—4	1—4	1,2,3
...	BRUSSELS 104 ...dep	...	...	...	...	...	...	...	...	5 a45
...	PARIS 24 ...dep	...	...	...	...	...	11p15	...	...	11p15
...	AIX-LA-CHAPL. 122 dp	...	...	...	...	...	8 a43	...	...	11 24
...	COLOGNE— Hauptbahnhof arr	...	...	...	...	...	9 a51	...	...	1 p16
							a.m.			p.m.
—	COLOGNE— Hauptbahnhof dep	...	...	...	...	...	10 6	...	...	1 45
25	Dusseldorf ...... arr	...	...	...	...	...	10 40	...	a.m.	2 24
	Dusseldorf dep	...	...	...	...	...	10 43	...	1116	2 28
39½	Duisburg	...	...	...	...	...	11 5	...	1156	2 50
44¼	Oberhausen ...... arr	...	...	...	...	a.m.	11 14	...	12 6	2 59
	Oberhausen dep	...	...	...	...	9 49	11 17	...	1225	3 1
59	Wanne ...... arr	...	...	a.m.	a.m.	10 31	11 44	a.m.	1 6	3 32
	Wanne dep	...	...	9 42	8 26	10 49	11 45	11 50	1 12	3 34
65½	Recklinghausen	...	...	9 59	8 45	11 7	12 1	12 8	1 29	3 50
75¼	Haltern ...130 arr	...	...	10 22	9 7	11 27	12 13	12 34	1 49	4 6
...	VLISSINGEN 113 dep	4a36	...	...	...	...	...	...	...	...
...	ROTTERDAM 118 dep	...	...	...	...	6 a32	...	...	...	9 a55
...	AMSTERDAM 118 dep	...	...	...	...	7 a0	...	...	...	10a28
...	EMMERICH 131A dep	7a36	...	...	...	9 a54	...	...	...	1 p46
...	WESEL 130 ...dep	9a26	...	...	7a52	10a35	...	...	...	3 p0
...	Haltern ...dep	⋮	...	...	9 20	11 38	12 15	...	1 51	4 11
83	Dülmen 135B	⋮	...	...	9 38	11 53	RC	1,2,3	2 6	4 26
101	Munster 133A ... arr	1033	...	...	1039	12 38	12 51	p.m.	2 46	4 55
	Munster dep	1036	...	...	1155	1 3	12 58	4 33	2 48	5 8
108	Westbevern	...	...	...	1212	1 19	...	...	3 4	...
120¼	Lengerich	RC	...	...	1239	1 46	...	5 2	3 30	5 36
126¾	Hasbergen 129B	...	...	...	1255	2 3	...	5 21	3 45	...
132	Osnabruck 156A ...arr	1116	...	...	1 5	2 14	1 41		3 57	5 56
...	HOEK v. HOLLAND dep		5a18	...	...	...	...	...	...	...
...	AMSTERDAM 118B dep		6a10	2,3,4	...	8 a0	8 a0	...	...	10a20
...	RHEINE 156C ...dep		...	a.m.	...	12p28	12p28	...	...	4 p55
...	Osnabruck ...dep	To Berlin (arr. 4p54.)	1135	11 55	...	2 30	1 45	§—Via Vamdrup (page 168) and Fredericia (page 302A).	...	6 5
138½	Vehrte		...	12 12	...	2 48	...		...	...
154½	Lemförde		...	12 46	...	3 22	...		...	...
164½	Diepholz		...	1 11	...	3 44	...		...	6 48
187½	Bassum		RC	1 59	...	4 34	...		...	...
198½	Kirchweyhe ...2—4		...	2 27	2 3 4	5 5	...		2 3 4	...
208	Bremen ...... arr a.m.		1 12	2 53	p.m.	5 30	3 22		p.m.	7 48
	Bremen dep 5 17	...	1 15		4 4	5 44	3 27		6 40	7 55
215½	Oberneuland ...5 32	...	...	...	4 18	5 58	...		6 54	...
234½	Rotenburg ...6 16	...	...	...	5 4	6 47	...		7 37	8 32
260	Buchholz ...arr ——	...	...	...	6 1	7 40	...			...
272¼	Harburg ...arr	...	2 31	...	6 30	8 12	4 46		...	9 24
279¾	HAMBURG Haupt arr	...	2 47	...	7 2	8 35	5 3		...	9 42
319	LUBECK 213A ...arr	...	4p11	...	8 p4	10 p5	6 p14		...	11p23
410	WARNEMUNDE arr	...	...	...	...	...	...		...	3 a20
544	COPENHAGEN 302	...	...	...	...	...	8 §12		...	9 a42
349	KIEL ...168 arr	...	5p29	...	...	10p53	7 p25		...	1 a8
433	KORSÖR steamer arr	...	...	...	...	...	...		...	7 a30
502	COPENHAGEN 302 arr	...	...	...	...	...	...		...	10 a4
906	STOCKHOLM 308A arr	...	...	...	...	...	...		...	6 a58
478	SASSNITZ 181 ...arr	...	...	...	...	...	1 a57		...	...
545	TRELLEBORG ...arr	...	...	...	...	...	6 a17	...	...	...
949	STOCKH'M 308A arr	...	...	...	...	...	6 p46	...	...	...

Dist. E M.	Station	1—4	1—4	1—4	Ex3	1,2,3	1,2,3	1—4	1—4	Ex 3
...	BRUSSELS 104 ...dep	...	...	‡—Via Wesel.	11‡53	...	...	1 p32	...	5 p0
...	PARIS 24 ...dep	...	...		7a50	8a10	...	8 a10	...	1 p45
...	AIX-LA-CHAPL. 122 dp	...	...		3p12	4p42	...	6 p26	...	10p12
...	COLOGNE— Hauptbahnhof arr	...	...		4p19	5p55	...	7 p40	...	11p24
				p.m.	p.m.	p.m.		p.m.		p.m.
—	COLOGNE— Hauptbahnhof dep	...	...	4 18	4 55	6 32	From Essen depart 9.15.	9 34	...	11 40
25	Dusseldorf ...... arr	...	...	4 58	5 29	7 10		10 11	...	12 16
	Dusseldorf dep	...	...	5 6	5 32	7 14		10 13	p.m.	12 19
39½	Duisburg	...	...	5 31	5 53	7 37		10 35	10 45	12 41
44¼	Oberhausen ...... arr	...	...	5 40	RC	7 46		10 44	10 55	12 50
	Oberhausen dep	...	...	5 55	...	7 50		10 46	11 11	12 52
59	Wanne ...... arr	p.m.	p.m.	6 37	6 46	8 20	p.m	11 16	11 54	1 23
	Wanne dep	2 36	3 53	6 53	6 47	8 28	9 42	11 22	12 0	1 27
65½	Recklinghausen	2 56	4 12	7 12	7 3	8 45	9 58	11 41	12 18	1 42
75¼	Haltern ...130 arr	3 17	4 35	7 31	7 17	9 7	10 12	12 1	12 40	⋮
...	VLISSINGEN 113 dep	...	...	...	1225	...	...	...	...	⋮
...	ROTTERDAM 118 dep	...	9a55	...	1211	4p25	...	...	7 p34	⋮
...	AMSTERDAM 118 dep	...	1028	...	1240	5 p2	...	...	8 p5	⋮
...	EMMERICH 131A dep	...	1p46	5 p30	5p30	8 p4	...	...	11 p5	⋮
...	WESEL 130 ...dep	...	3 p0	6 p29	6p29	8p44	...	...	11p42	⋮
...	Haltern ...dep	3 19	4 37	7 33	7 21	9 48	10 13	12 2	12 48	⋮
83	Dülmen 135B	3 34	4 53	7 48	...	10 3	...	12 17	1 3	SC
101	Munster 133A ... arr		5 40	8 31	7 54	1044	10 49		1 38	2 30
	Munster dep	...	5 55	8 36	8 0	1056	10 51	...	1 50	2 36
108	Westbevern	...	6 11	8 52	...	1112	...	...	...	...
120¼	Lengerich	...	6 39	9 19	...	1139	...	...	2 25	...
126¾	Hasbergen 129B	...	6 55	9 34	...	1153	...	...	2 38	...
132	Osnabruck 156A ...arr	...	7 7	9 46	8 40	12 5	11 32	...	2 50	3 17
...	HOEK v. HOLLAND dep	...	...	...	...	...	...	...	...	...
...	AMSTERDAM 118B dep	...	...	...	3p35	...	...	2,3 4	9 p0	9 p0
...	RHEINE 156C ...dep	...	...	...	7p54	...	...	nght	1 a16	1 a16
...	Osnabruck ...dep	...	7 15	...	8 47	...	...	12 12	3 0	3 23
138½	Vehrte	...	7 33	...	...	...	...	12 29	3 16	...
154½	Lemförde	...	8 5	...	RC	...	...	1 1	4 4	...
164½	Diepholz	...	8 27	...	...	...	...	1 21	4 29	...
187½	Bassum	...	9 16	...	...	...	...		5 22	...
198½	Kirchweyhe ...2—4	...	9 45	...	...	...	...	...	5 50	...
208	Bremen ...... arr a.m.	p.m	1012	...	1025	...	...	nght	6 17	5 2
	Bremen dep 5 17	8 16		...	1031	...	...	12 14	6 38	5 8
215½	Oberneuland ...5 32	8 30	...	2,3,4	...	...	...	12 31	6 52	...
234½	Rotenburg ...6 16	9 16	...	p m.	...	...	...	1 13	7 36	5 45
260	Buchholz ...arr ——	1011	...	11 1	...	...	...		8 33	...
272¼	Harburg ...arr	1050	...	11 29	1151	...	...	...	9 15	6 37
279¾	HAMBURG Haupt arr	1119	...	11 56	12 9	...	...	...	9 43	6 55
319	LUBECK 213A ...arr	1230	...	...	1a45	...	...	...	12 0	8 a31
410	WARNEMUNDE arr	...	...	...	...	...	...	...	...	12p39
544	COPENHAGEN 302	...	...	...	...	...	...	...	...	6 p41
349	KIEL ...168 arr	...	...	...	...	...	...	...	...	9 a5
433	KORSÖR steamer arr	...	...	...	...	...	...	...	...	2 p38
502	COPENHAGEN 302 arr	...	...	...	...	...	...	...	...	4 p48
906	STOCKHOLM 308A arr	...	...	...	...	...	...	...	...	8a49
478	SASSNITZ 181 ...arr	...	...	...	...	...	...	...	...	4 p36
545	TRELLEBORG ...arr	...	...	...	...	...	...	...	...	8 p56
949	STOCKH'M 308A arr	...	...	...	...	...	...	...	...	8 a49

HAMBURG, BREMEN, OSNABRUCK, and COLOGNE.

RC—Restaurant Car. SC—Sleeping Car.

§—From Copenhagen 12.0 night, via Fredericia (page 302) and Vamdrup (page 168).

Stockholm 308 dep	...	...	...	...	...	...	...	...	...	...	...	10a27	...	...	...	...	...	...	...	...	...	...	...	...	...	...	8 p30	...	...
Trelleborg ...dep	...	...	...	...	...	...	...	...	...	...	...	10p45	...	...	...	...	...	...	...	...	...	...	...	...	...	...	8 a46	...	...
Sassnitz ...dep	...	...	...	...	...	...	...	...	...	...	...	3 a10	...	...	...	...	...	...	...	...	...	...	...	...	...	...	1 p11	...	...
Stockholm 308 dep	...	...	...	...	...	...	...	...	...	...	...	...	...	...	...	...	...	...	...	...	...	...	...	...	...	...	8 p30	...	...
Copenhagen 302 dep	...	...	...	...	...	...	...	...	...	...	7p50	...	...	...	...	...	...	...	...	...	...	...	...	...	...	...	12p55	...	...
Korsœr stmer...dep	...	...	...	...	...	...	...	...	...	...	10p0	...	...	...	...	...	...	...	...	...	...	...	...	...	...	...	2 p54	...	...
Kiel 168 ...dep	...	...	...	...	...	...	...	...	...	...	5a27	6 a31	...	6 a31	9 a18	11a22	...	...	...	...	2p24	...	...	...	5p52	...	9 p0	...	...
Copenhagen 302 dep		...	...	...	...	...	...	...	...	8 p10	8p10	...	...	...	...	12 §0	...	...	...	...	...	...	...	...	11a0	11 a0	...	...	...
Warnemund 178B dep		...	...	...	...	...	...	...	...	2 a40	2a40	5a42	...	5 a42	...	10 a5	10 a5	...	...	...	...	...	...	...	4p59	4 p59	...	...	...
Lubeck 213A...dep	...	...	...	...	...	...	...	...	...	5 a13	5a50	8a59	...	8 a59	10 a0	1 p28	1 p28	...	...	...	2 p17	...	...	...	8 p2	8 p2	9 p52	9p52	...
	2,3,4	1—4	1—4	2 3 4	2,3,4	1,2,3	1—4	1—4	1—4	1—4	Ex3	1,2,3	1—4	2 3 4	2 3 4	Ex.2	Ex 2	Ex 2	...	2,3,4	Ex.3	1—4	1,2,3	2 3 4	1,2,3	1—4	Ex.3	Ex2	Ex2
	p.m.			a.m.				a.m.		a.m.	a.m.	a.m.		a.m.	p.m.	p.m.	p.m.	...	1—4	p.m.	p.m.	p.m.	p.m.	p.m.	p.m.	p.m.	p.m.	p.m.	
HAMBURG Haupt. Bahnhof	11 48	...	...	5 19	...	...	...	6 0	...	6 25	7 39	9 59	...	10 13	12 4	2 45	2 58	...	...	3 28	4 31	5 8	6 36	7 22	9 17	9 31	11 14	1130	...
Harburg	12 23	...	...	5 47	...	...	...	6 21	...	6 48	7 57	10 16	...	10 39	12 35	3 2	3 15	...	...	3 49	4 49	5 33	6 54	7 42	9 38	10 4	11 34	1151	...
Buchholz	1 0	a.m.	...	6 22	a.m.	...	...	6 56	...	7 23	8 21	...	...	11 12	1 17	...	...	...	...	4 20	...	6 13	...	8 15	1010	10 36	SC	SC	...
Rotenburg	1 54	4 53	...		6 39	...	...		...	8 22	RC	11 7	...	12 6	2 16	RC	...	...	...	5 11	RC	7 8	7 41	9 10	1042	11 41	12 28	...	...
Oberneuland		5 39	...	...	7 22	...	...	...	...	9 3	...	...	...	12 43	2 57	...	...	...	...	5 49	...	7 50	...	9 50	...	12 26	...	...	...
Bremen arr	...	5 54	...	...	7 36	...	...	a.m.	...	9 16	9 25	11 39	...	12 56	3 10	4 21	4 37	...	...	6 2	6 9	8 3	8 13	10 4	1118	12 41	1 4	1 54	...
Bremen dep	...		...	...		...	...	6 8	...	10 3	9 29	11 44	...	1 28	4 47	4 26	4 40	From Berlin, dep. 1p5.	...	6 43	6 27	8 32	8 18		1214		1 9	2 4	From Berlin, dep. 10.28 p.m.
Kirchweyhe	...	...	...	...	...	...	...	6 33	...	10 28	...	...	...	1 53	5 11	...	...		...	7 11	...	8 56	...	...	1239	...	...	...	
Bassum	...	...	...	...	a.m.	...	...	7 2	...	10 56	...	...	...	2 21	5 40	...	RC		...	7 39	...	9 25	...	...	1 6	...	...	...	
Diepholz	...	...	...	...	5 58	...	...	7 56	...	11 49	...	12 46	...	3 14	6 32	...	...		...	8 37	...	10 17	9 20	...	1 53	...	2 20	...	
Lemförde	...	...	...	...	6 18	...	...	8 18	...	12 10	...	...	...	3 35	6 53	...	...		...	8 59	...	10 39	...	...		...	...	...	
Vehrte	...	...	...	...	6 52	...	...	8 52	...	12 43	...	...	...	4 9	7 29	...	...		...	9 33	...	11 15	...	...	...	...	...	...	
Osnabruck arr	...	...	...	...	7 6	...	...	9 5	...	12 57	1111	1 29	...	4 22	7 43	6 8	6 22	6 18	...	9 47	8 5	11 29	10 5	...	...	...	3 9	4 14	
Rheine 156C ...arr	...	...	...	...	...	...	...	10a53	...	2 p18	12 0	2 p18	...	...	8 p55	...	7 p25	7 p25	...	...	...	1 a22	...	...	...	...	5 a29	5a29	
Amsterdam 118C arr	...	...	...	1,2,3	...	...	...	...	...	5 p2	...	5 p2	...	...	...	...	10 p5	10 p5	...	...	...	...	...	...	...	...	8 a37	8a37	
Hoek v. Holl. 112 ar	...	...	a.m.	a.m.	...	a.m.	...	...	a.m.	...	...	...	...	...	...	...	11p15	11p15	p.m.	...	...	...	...	...	...	...	...		a.m.
Osnabruck ...dep	...	...	5 41	7 13	7 57	9 10	...	9 41	1142	1 5	1118	1 43	...	4 29	8 42	6 14	...	6 36	6 44	...	8 10	12 0	...	...	...	...	3 15	...	4 46
Hasbergen	...	...	5 52	...	8 8	...	...	9 52	1154	1 16	...	...	...	4 42	8 53	...	...	...	6 54	...	...	12 11	...	...	...	...	...	...	...
Lengerich	...	...	6 10	7 31	8 22	...	...	10 7	12 8	1 30	...	2 2	...	4 58	9 8	...	...	...	7 8	...	...	12 26	...	...	...	...	...	...	SC
Westbevern	...	...	6 37	...	8 47	...	...	10 32	1234	1 56	...	...	...	5 26	9 34	...	...	...	7 33	...	...	12 47	...	...	...	...	...	...	...
Munster arr	1—4	...	6 53	7 56	9 2	9 50	...	10 46	1250	2 12	1158	2 28	...	5 41	9 50	6 57	...	7 17	7 50	...	8 50	1 3	...	...	...	2,3,4	3 59	...	5 29
Munster dep	a.m.	a.m.	7 11	7 58	9 10	9 52	...	11 2	1258	2 50	12 8	2 36	p.m.	6 3	9 57	7 1	...	7 18	7 56	...	8 54		...	...	...	a.m.	4 7	...	5 34
Dülmen	5 48	7 2	7 53	⋮	9 55	⋮	...	11 52	1 41	3 34	RC	3 2	4 15	6 57	10 41	...	...	⋮	8 41	...	⋮	...	...	...	...	3‡37	4 33	...	⋮
Haltern ...arr	6 0	7 14	8 5	⋮	10 8	⋮	...	12 4	1 53	3 47	1242	3 14	4 28	7 11	10 54	7 37	...	⋮	8 53	...	⋮	...	...	...	...	3 51	4 45	...	⋮
Wesel 130 ...arr	...	...	9 a4	⋮	11 49	⋮	...	1 p45	4 p9	5 p44	1p45	4 p9	5p44	...	...	...	...	8p20	10p7	...	⋮	...	...	...	...	...	6 a24	...	6a45
Emmerich 131A arr	...	...	10 a9	⋮	12 40	⋮	...	2 p46	4p46	6 p54	2p46	4 p46	...	...	...	...	...	9 p19	12a11	...	⋮	...	...	...	...	...	7 a44	...	7a44
Amsterdam 118 arr	...	...	12p43	⋮	...	⋮	...	6 p2	6p42	8 p35	6 p2	6 p42	...	...	...	...	...	11p29	...	...	⋮	...	...	...	...	...	9 a45	...	9a45
Rotterdam 118 arr	...	...	1 p5	⋮	...	⋮	...	6 p25	7p11	9 p1	6p25	7 p11	...	...	...	...	...	11 53	...	...	⋮	...	...	...	...	...	10 a9	...	10a9
Vlissingen 113 arr	...	...	...	⋮	...	⋮	a.m.	...	...	...	...	...	...	...	...	...	...	11p38	...	...	⋮	...	...	...	...	...	10a20	...	1020
Haltern ...dep	6 2	7 15	8 10	⋮	10 11	⋮	11 4	12 6	1 58	3 48	1243	3 18	4 32	7 23	10 56	7 38	...	...	8 55	...	⋮	p.m.	...	...	...	3 52	4 46	...	...
Recklinghausen	6 25	7 39	8 32	8 47	10 32	10 42	1130	12 28	2 20	4 10	1 1	3 37	4 54	7 44	11 18	7 56	...	...	9 17	...	9 44	9 59	...	...	...	4 16	5 5	...	...
Wanne arr	6 41	7 55	8 47	9 1	10 48	10 54	1146	12 44	2 35	4 26	1 16	3 52	5 9	8 0	11 34	8 11	...	...	9 32	...	9 59	10 15	...	...	...	4 33	5 19	...	...
Wanne dep	6 55		8 50	9 3		10 55	1216	1 5	3 1	4 51	1 19	3 54			11 39	8 12	...	...		...	10 0		...	...	...		5 20	...	...
Oberhausen arr	7 24	...	9 32	...	...	...	1259	1 35	3 39	5 32	1 47	4 25	...	...	12 18	8 41	...	...	...	...	...	...	...	...	...	...	5 50	...	...
Oberhausen dep	7 33	...	9 39	...	...	...	1 3	1 37	3 44	5 40	1 50	4 28	...	...	12 25	8 43	...	...	...	...	...	...	...	...	...	...	5 55	...	...
Duisburg	7 42	...	9 48	9 57	...	11 50	1 13	1 46	3 53	5 50	2 1	4 39	...	...	12 34	8 54	...	...	...	...	10 51	...	...	...	...	...	6 7	...	...
Dusseldorf arr	8 3	...	10 17	1017	...	12 10	1 59	2 9	4 35	6 48	2 21	4 58	...	...		9 13	...	...	...	...	11 11	...	...	...	...	...	6 28	...	...
Dusseldorf dep	8 6	...	10 22	1022	...	12 14		2 13	4 40	6 54	2 24	5 1	...	...	...	9 16	...	...	...	...	11 13	...	...	...	...	...	6 32	...	...
COLOGNE Haupt. arr	8 42	...	11 1	11 1	...	12 53	...	2 55	5 36	8 1	3 2	5 48	...	...	...	10 2	...	...	...	...	11 49	...	...	...	...	...	7 10	...	...
Aix-la-Chapl. 123B	10a29	...	12p52	1252	...	...	...	4 p25	7p24	9 p39	4p25	7 p24	...	...	...	12 a6	...	...	...	...	1 a29	...	...	...	...	...	9 a9	...	...
Paris 24 ...arr	...	...	...	...	...	...	...	10p46	...	...	10p46	...	...	...	...	7 a35	...	...	...	...	...	...	...	...	...	...	4 p0	...	...
Brussels 104 ...arr	1 p3	...	...	5p44	...	...	...	6 p57	9p45	...	6 p57	9 p45	...	...	...	3 a56	...	...	...	...	3 a56	...	...	...	...	...	11a26	...	...

‡—Not on Sunday.

Luggage Rates—see page 462.]

PRUSSIAN STATE RAILWAYS.

SOEST, HAMM, MUNSTER, RHEINE, and EMDEN.

Station	1,2,3	1,2,3	Ex3	2 3 4	1—4	1—4	2 3 4	2 3 4	1,2,3	1—4	2 3 4	1,2,3	1—4	1,2,3	1,2,3	Ex3
	a.m.	a.m			a.m.	a.m.	a.m.	a.m.	a.m.		a.m.		a.m.	a.m.	a.m.	
Soest ......dep	...	...	...	...	...	5 57	6 25	8 40	...	...	...	...	10 7	...	...	...
Welver 133D	...	...	...	...	...	6 9	6 43	8 56	...	...	...	...	1026	...	...	...
Hamm ...... arr	...	...	...	...	...	6 23	7 3	9 14	...	...	...	...	1046	...	...	...
Hamm ...... dep	1 39	1 56	...	...	4 0	6 27	7 21	—	9 29	...	10 8	...	1058	1135	1150	...
Drensteinfurt	...	...	...	...	4 22	6 46	7 46	...	...	...	1031	...	1121	...	...	...
Münster 132 .... arr	2 10	2 26	...	...	4 44	7 6	8 13	...	9 58	a.m.	1054	...	1145	12 5	1219	...
Münster 132 .... dep	2 35	—	...	...	4 49	7 19	9 10	...		1017	—	...	1257	1227	—	...
Greven	...	...	...	...	5 6	7 38	9 32	...	—	1034	1,2,3	...	1 17	...	...	...
Rheine ...... arr	3 10	...	...	...	5 31	8 5	10 7	...	...	11 0	noon	p.m.	1 44	1258	...	Runs until 15th October.
Rheine ...... dep	3 12	...	...	...	5 43	8 10	—	...	...	11 2	12 4	1247	1 55	1 4	...	
Salzbergen ...... arr	...	...	...	...	5 52	8 19	...	...	...	1111	1213	...	2 4	...	...	
AMSTERDAM 118C. arr	F	...	...	...	8a37	1 p0	...	...	...	3p15	3p15	...	5 p2	...	...	
Salzbergen ...... dep	...	...	...	...	5 53	8 21	...	...	...	1112	—	...	2 6	B	...	
Lingen	...	...	...	...	6 21	8 50	...	...	...	1134	...	B	2 36	...	...	
Meppen	...	...	...	...	6 44	9 13	...	...	...	1153	...	...	3 34	...	2 3 4	
Lathen	...	...	...	a.m.	7 12	9 37	...	...	...	1217	1—4	...	3 58	...	p.m.	
Papenburg	...	Ex3	...	5 25	7 47	1011	...	...	...	1246	p.m.	...	4 32	...	3 8	...
Ihrhove	...	C	D	5 41	8 0	1022	...	...	...	1256	3 54	...	4 46	...	3 23	...
Leer ...... arr	4 58	a.m.	a.m.	5 51	8 10	1032	...	...	...	1 6	4 4	2 25	4 56	2 48	3 33	p.m.
BREMEN 151 ...... dep	...	5 22	6 0	...	...	6a23	...	...	...	10a8	—	...	1p53	...	...	2 11
Leer ...... dep	5 0	7 20	8 2	5 53	8 14	1036	...	...	...	1 10	...	2 27	4 59	2 50	3 35	4 11
Emden 133C ...... arr	5 24	7 44	8 30	6 29	8 51	11 9	...	...	...	1 44	...	2 51	5 34	3 14	4 12	4 34

Station	Ex3	Ex3	1—4	1,2,3	1,2,3	1—4	1—4	1,2,3	1—4	Ex3	1,2,3	1—4	1,2,3	2 3 4	1—4
	p.m	p.m.	p.m.	p.m.	p.m.	p.m	p.m.	p.m.	p.m.	p.m.	p.m.	p.m.	p.m.	p.m.	a.m.
Soest ......dep	1228	...	1 13	...	...	3 34	4 18	...	6 5	...	8 10	8 30	1046	1112	1248
Welver 133D	RC	...	1 31	...	...	3 50	4 35	...	6 23	...	...	8 46	11 6	1130	1 7
Hamm ...... arr	1249	...	1 51	...	...	4 6	—	...	6 40	...	8 35	9 4	1124	1150	1 29
Hamm ...... dep	1254	1 17	1 55	3 23	3 59	4 14	...	...	6 56	7 21	8 37	9 39	1132	1226	—
Drensteinfurt	...	...	2 19	...	...	4 38	...	...	7 20	...	...	10 2	...	1250	...
Münster 132 .... arr	1 23	1 47	2 42	3 52	4 28	5 1	...	...	7 43	7 50	9 6	1030	12 1	1 12	...
Münster 132 .... dep	1 28	1 57	4 0	—	—	5 50	...	8 10	8 36	—	—	1055	—	—	...
Greven	...	G	4 20	...	...	6 10	...	8 26	8 56	...	...	1115	...	...	...
Rheine ...... arr	1 59	2 30	4 48	...	...	6 38	...	8 53	9 24	...	...	1143	...	...	...
Rheine ...... dep	2 26	2 39	4 58	...	...	6 57	...	8 58	9 33	...	...	—	...	...	...
Salzbergen ...... arr	2 35	...	5 8	...	...	7 7	...	9 7	9 43	...	...	...	...	...	...
AMSTERDAM 118C. arr	5 p2	...	8p30	...	...	9p30	...	...	...	...	...	...	...	...	...
Salzbergen ...... dep	2 36	...	5 11	...	...	7 8	...	9 8	9 46	...	...	...	...	...	...
Lingen	2 58	3 9	5 42	...	...	7 37	...	9 29	1019	...	...	...	...	...	...
Meppen	3 17	3 27	6 6	...	...	—	2 3 4	9 48	1043	...	...	...	...	...	...
Lathen		G	6 32	...	...	...	p.m.	...	11 7	...	...	...	...	...	...
Papenburg	3 54	4 5	7 7	...	...	...	8 18	1025	1144	...	...	...	...	...	...
Ihrhove	...	...	7 13	...	p.m.	...	8 31	...	1156	...	...	...	...	...	...
Leer ...... arr	4 12	4 23	7 23	...	D	...	8 42	1013	12 6	...	...	...	...	...	...
BREMEN 151 ...... dep	...	...	...	...	6 15	...	6p15	...	8p32	...	...	...	...	...	...
Leer ...... dep	4 15	4 24	7 39	...	8 13	...	8 51	1014	1214	...	...	...	...	...	...
Emden 133C ...... arr	4 39	4 47	8 16	...	8 37	...	9 26	11 6	1249	...	...	...	...	...	...

Station		2,3,4	2 3 4	2,3,4	1—4	2 3 4	1,2,3	1,2,3	1—4	1,2,3	2 3 4	1—4	1,2,3	Ex3	Ex3
					a.m	a.m.	a.m.		a.m	a.m.	a.m		noon	p.m	p.m.
Emden ......dep		...	...	...	4 42	6 0	7 7	...	8 46	11 2	1131	...	12 0	1212	1223
Leer ......arr		...	...	...	5 19	6 34	7 30	...	9 22	11 25	12 4	...	12 25	1237	1249
BREMEN 151 ......arr		...	...	...	7a52	—	...	...	1226		3p55	...	...	3p55	2p43
Leer ......dep		...	...	...	5 23	...	7 32	...	9 26	11 26	12 6	...	12 28	1239	RC
Ihrhove		...	...	...	5 36	...	...	...	9 38	...	1217	...	...	...	Runs from 25th July until 18th August.
Papenburg		...	...	...	5 52	...	7 47	...	9 53	...	1230	...	...	1258	
Lathen		...	...	...	6 31	...	...	...	1029	...	—	...	...	...	
Meppen		...	a.m.	...	7 2	...	8 24	...	1054	A	...	...	G	1 37	
Lingen		...	5 0	...	7 29	...	8 43	...	1119	...	...	...	...	1 58	
Salzbergen ......arr		...	5 30	...	7 59	...	...	...	1147	...	...	...	...	2 23	
AMSTERDAM 118B ......dep		...	...	a.m.	...	...	...	...	...	...	...	8a22	...	1020	
Salzbergen ......dep		...	5 31	6 41	8 0	...	...	...	1148	...	...	1 27		2 24	
Rheine ......arr		...	5 41	6 51	8 10	...	9 12	...	1157	12 54	...	1 36	2 13	2 34	
Rheine ......dep		...	6 3	6 55	8 12	...	9 14	...	12 4	—	...	1 43	2 33	2 44	
Greven	2 3 4	...	6 34	7 28	8 43	1—4	...	...	1233	...	1,2,3	2 13	...	RC	
Münster ......arr	a.m.	a.m.	6 53	7 50	9 4	a.m.	9 47	p.m.	1251	...	p.m.	2 31	3 8	3 19	
Münster ......dep	4 12	5 53	7 0	8 6	9 9	1053	—	12 4	1259	...	2 27	2 37	3 13	3 24	—
Drensteinfurt	4 33	6 22	...	8 33	9 28	1118	...	...	1 23	...	...	...	...	...	...
Hamm ......arr	4 56	6 49	7 28	8 55	9 45	1140	...	1233	1 45	...	2 16	3 11	3 46	3 54	...
Hamm ......dep	5 7	7 18	7 31	9 24	9 58	1147	...	—	1 58	...	—	—	—	4 1	...
Welver	5 28	7 37	7 55	9 44	1020	12 4	...	...	2 27	...	...	...	...	...	...
Soest ......arr	5 45	7 53	8 7	10 0	1038	1217	...	...	2 43	...	...	...	...	4 25	...

Station	Ex 3	Ex3	1—4	1—4	1,2,3	1—4	1,2,3	2 3 4	Ex3	1—4	2 3 4	1,2,3	1—4	Ex 3	2 3 4
	p.m.			p.m.			p.m	p.m		p.m	p.m.	p.m.	p.m.	p.m.	p.m.
Emden ......dep	12 41	...	...	1 36	...	...	3 22	3 29	...	5 24	7 2	7 45	8 17	9 22	11 0
Leer ......arr	1 7	...	...	2 10	...	...	3 46	4 3	...	6 3	7 40	8 9	8 50	9 46	1134
BREMEN 151 ......arr	3 p1	...	p.m.	...	...	...	6p21	6p21	...	...	1054	...	...	11p14	...
Leer ......dep	RC	...	1 10	2 14	...	...	3 52	4 8	...	6 8	7 43	8 10	8 51	D	1140
Ihrhove	Until October 16th.	...	1 20	2 25	...	...		4 19	...	6 20	7 54	...	9 2	—	1151
Papenburg		...	—	2 39	...	...	B	4 34	...	6 36	8 7	8 27	9 13	...	12 4
Lathen		...	...	3 17	...	...		5 11	...	7 13	—	...	9 42	...	—
Meppen		...	...	3 44	...	...	4 48	5 38	...	7 43	...	9 4	10 2	...	...
Lingen		...	...	4 10	...	...	5 8	6 4	...	8 10	...	9 23	10 22	H—Until 14th September.	...
Salzbergen ......arr		p.m	...	4 39	...	...	...	6 33	...	8 39	1,2,3	...	10 44		...
AMSTERDAM 118B ......dep		1020	...	1053	...	...	...	...	...	3p35	p.m.	H	...		...
Salzbergen ......dep	—	2p30	...	4 40	...	...	...	6 37	...	8 41	8 45	...	10 45		...
Rheine ......arr	...	2 39	...	4 50	...	...	5 38	6 47	...	8 51	8 54	9 49	10 54		...
Rheine ......dep	...	—	...	4 55	...	...	5 58	6 57	...	9 1	—	9 51	10 55		...
Greven	...	2 3 4	1,2,3	5 23	...	...		7 26	...	9 31	...	...	...		...
Münster ......arr	...	p.m.	p.m.	5 42	p.m.	...	6 31	7 47	p.m.	9 49	...	10 24	11 33		...
Münster ......dep	...	3 48	5 1	5 47	7 6	...	6 41	8 0	8 57	9 57	...	10 29	11 37		...
Drensteinfurt	...	4 17	...	6 12	...	...	...	8 25	...	1021	...	...	...	...	...
Hamm ......arr	...	4 42	5 31	6 34	7 37	p.m.	7 11	8 47	9 28	1043	...	10 58	12 10	...	...
Hamm ......dep	...	5 4	5 32	6 56	—	7 26	—	—	9 40	1050	...	—	—	...	...
Welver	...	5 21	...	7 15	...	7 47	...	9 p6	10 0	1110	...	...	...	...	...
Soest ......arr	...	5 40	5 56	7 30	...	8 4	...	9 23	1017	1126	...	...	...	...	...

Extras. {Soest......dep 1p22 | 6p10 | 8p16 9p50 / Welver...arr 1 40 | 6 26 | 8 33 10 8} Welver dep 11a52 | 3p28 5p17 / Soest......arr 12 9 | 3 46 5 30 Hamm......dep 6 a2 5p31 | 6p35 / Münster ...arr 6 50 6 22 | 7 27 Münster......dep 4a49 2p46 5p33 / Hamm ......arr 5 39 3 38 6 24

A—Until 21st September. B—Until 20th September. C—Until 18th August. D—Until 15th September.
F—Until 16th September. G—From 4th to 12th August and from 30th August to 20th September.

PRUSSIAN STATE RAILWAYS

Luggage Rates—see page 462.

COLOGNE, SIEGBURG, BETZDORF, WETZLAR, and GIESSEN.

	2 3 4	2,3,4	1—4	2—4	Ex3	2 3 4	1—4	2 3 4	1—4	2 3 4	2 3 4	1—4	2 3 4	2 3 4	Ex 3	2 3 4	1—4	1,2,3	2 3 4	2 3 4	2 3 4
	a.m.		a.m.	a.m.	a.m.	a.m.	a.m.	a.m.	non	p.m.	p.m	p.m.	p.m.	p.m.	p.m	p.m.	p.m.	p.m.	p.m.	p.m.	p.m.
Cologne Haupt-bahnhof ...dep	5 44	...	6 49	8 8	8†18	9 13	9 55	1038	12 0	1235	2 15	3 9	4 33	5 0	6 3	...	7 40	8 46	9 45	1035	1133
Kalk	5 53	...	6 59	...	...	9 21	10 2	1046	12 8	1243	2 23	3 16	4 41	5 10	..	6 31	7 51	...	9 54	...	1142
Troisdorf... arr	6 23	a.m.	7 28	8 30	8 40	9 48	1030	1111	1236	1 8	2 48	3 44	5 7	5 38	6 25	7 0	8 20	9 8	1023	1057	1210
Troisdorf... dep	6 31	4 57	7 30	8 58	8 41	9 51	1034	1214	1241	1 26	3 15	3 46	5 13	5 43	6 27	7 7	8 23	9 9	1038	11 8	1211
Siegburg	6 38	5 6	7 38	9 5	8 48	9 57	1042	1222	1252	1 32	3 21	3 56	5 20	6 8	6 34	7 15	8 35	9 17	1046	1116	1221
Hennef 129B	6 47	5 15	7 48	9 14	...	—	1053	1230	1 5	—	—	4 6	5 29	6 19	6 42	7 24	8 47	9 26	—	1125	1232
Eitorf	—	5 35	8 9	9 36	...	...	1115	—	1 29	...	...	4 26	5 48	6 38	6 55	7 44	9 8	9 39	...	1144	1251
Schladern	...	5 58	8 33	10 3	...	a.m.	1138	...	1 57	...	...	4 49	6 10	—	...	8 6	9 31	...	...	—	1 13
Au 133B	...	6 13	8 47	1016	...	7 26	1153	...	2 11	...	...	5 2	6 23	...	7 15	8 18	9 44	10 1	†—Departs from Deutz.	...	1 25
Wissen 130	1—4	6 22	8 57	1025	...	7 35	12 3	...	2 20	...	...	5 11	6 32	2 3 4	7 23	8 27	9 54	1010		...	1 34
Betzdorf 216 arr	a.m.	6 41	9 16	1046	9 43	7 54	1222	...	2 40	...	...	5 29	6 51	p.m.	7 36	8 45	1014	1023		...	1 52
Betzdorf 216 dep	5 31	6 55	9 25	—	9 54	—	1229	...	2 47	...	...	5 36	—	7 49	7 44	8 53	1027	†		...	—
Herdorf	5 42	7 10	9 37	...	...	...	1241	...	2 59	...	...	5 47	...	8 1	...	9 4	1037	—		...	...
Burbach	6 3	7 36	9 58	...	...	...	1 3	...	3 19	...	2 3 4	6 8	...	8 23	...	9 24	1057	2 3 4		2 3 4	2 3 4
Haiger	6 30	8 8	1023	a.m.	...	p.m.	1 29	...	3 45	...	p.m.	6 33	...	8 51	...	9 50	1121	p.m.		a.m.	a.m.
Dillenburg 131	6 43	8 23	1046	9 5	1042	1214	1 39	...	3 54	...	4 55	6 44	...	8 59	8 33	9 59	1129	1051		4 42	5 25
Herborn	6 54	8 36	1056	9 16	...	1225	1 49	...	4 4	...	5 7	6 57	...	—	8 41	1011	1137	11 4		4 54	5 36
Ehringshausen	7 16	9 0	1117	—	...	—	2 12	...	4 25	...	5 31	7 22	...	...	...	1034	1155	—		5 19	6 0
Wetzlar	7 32	9 16	1133	...	11 8	...	2 28	...	4 39	...	5 43	7 39	...	...	9 2	1050	12 8	...	...	5 36	6 18
Giessen...arr	7 49	9 35	1150	...	1122	...	2 45	...	4 56	...	...	7 57	...	...	9 15	11 8	1225	...	...	...	6 45
FRANKFORT 156A	9a14	11a10	1p13	...	1239	...	4p56	...	6p55	...	...	1018	...	...	10p33	...	4a46	...	...	...	9 a0
CASSEL 157 ...arr	1146	12p51	3p28	...	1p37	...	5p51	...	8 p3	...	...	1145	...	...	12a21	1a49	2a35	...	...	...	9a37

Extra.

Cologne...dep	3p40	6p18	6p59	
Siegburg...arr	4 38	6 51	7 50	
Siegburg...dep	5a49	8a19	1p44	5p15
Cologne...arr	6 39	8 59	2 17	6 ‡4
Giessen...dep	1p30	...		
Wetzlar...arr	2 45	...		

GIESSEN, BETZDORF, and COLOGNE.

[‡—Arrives at Deutz.

		2 3 4	1—4	2 3 4	2 3 4	2 3 4	1—4	Ex 3	1,2,3	2,3.4	2 3 4	1—4	2 3 4	1—4	1—4	2 3 4	2,3,4	Ex3	1—4	2,3,4	2,3,4	2 3 4
CASSEL 156A...dep		...	...	...	2a50	...	4 a4	5 a40	...	...	...	7a25	...	9 a43	10a45	1p21	...	3p36	3p36	3 p36	4 p40	7 p0
FRANKFORT 157 dp		...	...	...	...	...	4a16	6 a51	...	...	...	7a45	...	10 a5	1 p2	2p52		4p57	4p57	4 p57	5 p45	8p55
					a.m.	a.m.	a.m.	a.m.				a.m.		p.m.	p.m.	p.m.		p.m.	p.m.	p.m.	p.m.	p.m.
Giessen...dep		...	...	...	4 58	4 20	6 47	8 17	...	...	...	10 0	...	12 39	3 12	5 4	...	6 9	6 13	6 35	8 16	1010
Wetzlar		...	...	...	5 46	4 38	7 4	8 30	...	...	...	1027	...	12 57	3 39	5 26	...	6 22	6 30	7 6	8 32	1028
Ehringshausen		...	...	...	6 5	4 55	7 22		...	a.m.	...	1045	a.m.	1 15	3 57	5 44	...	...	6 47	7 25	8 49	1045
Herborn		...	...	a.m.	6 31	5 18	7 47	8 55	...	8 37	...	11 9	1137	1 39	4 20	6 8	...	6 47	7 10	7 50	9 11	1110
Dillenburg		...	...	4 15	6 42	5 30	8 0	9 5	...	8 50	...	1122	1150	1 51	4 32	6 20	...	6 58	7 22	8 28	9 22	1124
Haiger		...	...	4 27	—	5 41	8 11	...	...	—	...	1133	—	2 2	4 43	6 31	...	...	7 34	8 49	—	1137
Burbach		...	...	5 5	...	6 11	8 42	...	...	...	...	12 4	...	2 31	5 15	7 0	...	...	8 5	9 26	...	1210
Herdorf	2 3 4	...	...	5 30	1,2,3	6 28	8 58	...	...	...	...	1221	...	2 47	5 31	7 16	...	...	8 21	9 43	...	1227
Betzdorf arr	a.m.	a.m.	...	5 43	a.m.	6 37	9 6	9 30	...	...	a.m.	1230	...	2 55	5 39	7 24	p.m	7 46	8 29	9 55	...	1236
Betzdorf dep	4 0	4 42	...	5 52	6 41	6 46	9 14	10 0	...	...	1135	1239	...	3 2	5 46	—	6 34	7 59	8 37	10 8	...	—
Wissen	4 18	5 0	...	6 16	6 54	7 6	9 33	10 13	...	...	1156	1 1	...	3 21	6 7	...	6 53	...	8 56	10 28	...	...
Au	4 28	5 10	...	6 26	7 3	7 14	9 43	10 22	...	...	12 5	1 11	...	3 31	6 17	...	7 2	...	9 6	10 37	...	...
Schladern	4 40	5 22	...	6 38	...	—	9 54	...	...	...	1217	1 24	...	3 42	6 28	...	7 13	...	9 17	10 48	...	...
Eitorf	5 3	5 43	a.m.	7 3	7 25	...	1016	10 43	...	p.m.	1241	1 51	1—4	4 8	6 52	...	7 41	...	9 39	11 11	...	...
Hennef	5 23	6 3	6 54	7 29	7 39	a.m.	1035	10 56	a.m.	12 40	1 2	2 13	p.m.	4 27	7 16	p.m.	7 59	...	9 59	11 31	...	p.m.
Siegburg	5 33	6 13	7 4	7 40	7 49	10 5	1045	11 5	11 57	12 59	1 12	2 24	3 4	4 38	7 26	6 28	8 9	8 50	1010	11 41	...	1126
Troisdorf arr	5 39	6 19	7 10	7 46	7 55	1011	1051	11 11	12 3	1 5	1 19	2 30	3 10	4 44	7 33	6 36	8 15	8 56	1016	11 47	...	1134
Troisdorf dep	5 41	6 21	7 13	8 4	7 57	1024	1053	11 12	12 9	—	1 23	2 32	3 14	4 46	7 39	7 7	8 36	8 58	1017	11 58	...	—
Kalk	6 7	6 49	7 41	8 33	...	1053	1118	...	...	...	1 53	2 57	3 43	5 11	8 12	7 36	9 2	...	1046	12 26	...	...
Cologne...arr	6 16	6 58	7 49	8‡45	8 19	11 2	1127	11 34	12 31	...	2 2	3 8	3 51	5 19	8 24	7 45	9 13	9‡20	1054	12 34	...	...

†—Weekdays only.]

LIMBURG, HADAMAR, and ALTENKIRCHEN.

*—Rail Motor.

	a.m.	a.m.	a.m.	p.m.	p.m.	p.m.	p.m.	p.m.	p.m.
Limburg ..dep	5 13	7 52	9*40	12 7	2 15	4*40	6 4	7 39	1047
Staffel	5 26	8 4	9 51	12 20	2 28	4 52	6 17	7 55	1058
Hadamar	5 39	8 17	10 3	12 33	2 41	5 5	6 35	8 8	1110
Westerburg	6 30	9 0	1042	1 16	3 26	5 46	7 17	8 46	1150
Korb	7 6	9 37	—	1 51	4 1	—	7 52	—	1223
Hachenburg	7 18	9 49	...	2 2	4 12	...	8 3	...	1234
Altenkirchen	7 49	1020	...	2 32	4 41	...	8 31	...	1 1

		a.m.	a.m.		a.m.	p.m.	p.m.	p.m.	p.m.
Altenkirchen dep		...	7 22	...	1125	1 47	5 40	8 6	1114
Hachenburg		4 47	7 55	*	1157	2 20	6 11	8 35	1145
Korb	a.m.	4 58	8 6	a.m.	12 8	2 31	6 22	8 46	—
Westerburg	6 38	5 32	8 40	1046	1243	3 6	6 58	9 19	...
Hadamar	7 13	6 17	9 19	1127	1 23	3 47	7 39	9 54	...
Staffel	7 25	6 29	9 32	1138	1 36	4 0	7 54	10 5	...
Limburg ...arr	7 36	6 41	9 43	1149	1 48	4 12	8 6	1017	...

*—Rail Motor.

LIMBURG, SIERSHAHN, and ALTENKIRCHEN.

Limburg ...dep	4a19	5a47	8a21	10a55	12*25	2p31	5p18	7p12	10*40
Staffel	4 32	6 0	8 34	11 10	12 38	2 44	5 30	7 25	10 53
Montabaur	5 18	6 50	9 21	11 57	1 33	3 31	6 15	8 10	11 39
Siershahn... arr	5 38	7 10	9 41	12 17	1 51	3 51	6 34	8 45	—
Siershahn... dep	5 44	7 22	9 52	12 27	—	4 5	6 40	8 55	...
Dierdorf	6 14	7 50	1023	12 53	...	4 38	7 10	9 24	...
Altenkirch'n ar	7 10	8 40	1115	1 40	...	5 33	8 3	1017	...

Altenkirchen	4a17	5a55	8a20	10a56	...	2p35	5p11	7 p14
Dierdorf	5 8	6 48	9 18	11 51	...	3 26	6 5	8 12
Siershahn arr	5 36	7 16	9 49	12 22	*	3 56	6 34	8 43
Siershahn dep	5 48	7 23	10 2	12 28	2p43	4 1	6 41	8 51
Montabaur	6 10	7 45	10 24	12 47	3 6	4 20	7 1	9 13
Staffel	6 55	8 28	11 11	1 28	3 53	5 2	7 47	9 55
Limburg ...arr	7 7	8 40	11 23	1 40	4 4	5 13	7 59	10 7

SIERSHAHN and ENGERS.

Siershahn dep	5a41	7 a30	9 a53	12p32	2p11	4 p3	6 p43	8 p55
Grenzau...arr	5 58	7 47	10 12	12 49	2 29	4 20	7 2	9 13
Hillscheid ...arr	6 28	...	10 41	1 20	...	4 58	7 31	9 45
Engers 128...arr	6 20	8 10	10 35	1 12	2 53	4 43	7 26	9 37

Engers ...dep	4 a53	6a37	9 a1	11a40	12p25	3p12	5 p53	8 p5
Hillscheid .dep	...	6 39	8 59	11 3	...	3 8	5 35	7 58
Grenzau ...dep	5 15	7 1	9 25	12 2	12 51	3 35	6 16	8 28
Siershahn.. arr	5 33	7 19	9 45	12 21	1 10	3 54	6 35	8 46

Altenkirchen dep	5a31	8a15	9a33	11a22	1p43	2p40	4p16	5p38	8p36	9p28
Au ...arr	6 8	8 42	10 4	11 49	2 8	3 16	4 54	6 5	9 1	9 57
Au ...	6a33	7a31	8a51	10a25	1p13	3p42	5p5	6p36	7p17	1042
Alten.	7 1	8 9	9 27	10 52	1 41	4 10	5 32	7 6	7 41	11 9

PRUSSIAN STATE RAILWAYS.

HERBORN and WESTERBURG.

	...	a.m.	a.m.	p.m.	p.m.	p.m.	p.m.
Herborn ....dep	a.m.	6 40	9 36	1250	4 25	7 15	1112
Rennerod	4 31	8 2	1119	2 20	6 5	8 37	1139
Fehl-Ritzhausen	4 45	8 14	1135	2 35	6 22	8 51	—
Westerburg (133B) arr	5 10	8 36	12 2	2 59	6 50	9 15	...

	a.m.	a.m.	a.m.	p.m.	p.m.	p.m.	p.m.
Westerburg ....dep	...	6 32	9 2	1 29	3 28	7 37	1154
Fehl-Ritzhausen	...	6 56	9 27	2 0	3 53	8 11	1225
Rennerod	5 4	7 9	9 40	2 19	4 5	8 36	1242
Herborn (133B) ....arr	6 19	8 29	1051	3 52	5 45	9 59	...

Fehl-Ritzenhausen........dep	6 a15	8 a23	11a37	1 p6	3 p23	6 p28	8 p10	...	...	...	...	...	...	...	...	...
Erbach (Westerw.)........arr	6 55	9 28	12 10	1 36	3 53	7 1	8 45	...	...	...	...	...	...	...	...	...
Erbach (Westerw.)........dep	7 a13	9 a45	12p18	2 p40	4 p15	7 p14	9 p0	...	...	...	...	...	...	...	...	...
Fehl-Ritzenhausen........arr	8 8	11 13	12 58	3 15	6 16	7 49	9 35	...	...	...	...	...	...	...	...	...

WESTERBURG and MONTABAUR.

Westerburg........dep	4 a0	6 a28	9 a3	1 p33	4 p18	7 p18
Montabaur (133B) arr	5 12	7 42	10 22	2 52	5 37	8 24

Montabaur........dep	6 a56	10a30	1p50	4 p35	7 p28	9 p23	...
Westerburg (133c) ...arr	8 11	11 42	3 2	5 47	8 41	10 34	...

EMDEN, NORDEN, and WITTMUND.

2, 3, and 4 class only between Norden and Wittmund.

	2 3 4	1,2,3	2 3 4	2 3 4	2 3 4	2,3,4	Ex3	Ex3	1—4	1—4	1—4	1,2,3	1,2,3	2 3 4	Ex3	Ex3	2 3 4	1,2,3	1—4	2 3 4	2 3 4	2,3,4	2 3 4
		a.m.	a.m.	a.m.	a.m.	a.m.	a.m.	a.m.	a.m.	a.m.	p.m.	p.m.	p.m.	p.m.	p.m.	p.m.		p.m.	p.m.	p.m.	p.m.	p.m.	p.m.
Emden 133A ....dep		5 39	5†50	6 35	7 7	7 30	7‡59	8 50	9 0	11 14	1 50	3 §15	3 22	3 59	4 42	4 58	...	5 10	5 42	7 †0	8 21	9 32	1111
Abelitz		6 0	6 20	7 9	7 42	8 4	8 24	A	9 32	11 51	2 26	...	C	4 32	5 3	5 18	...	5 33	6 14	7 37	8 47	10 5	1136
Norden........arr	a.m.	6 19	—	7 36	—	8 31	8 45	9 29	10 7	12 20	2 57	3 54	4 1	—	5 20	5 36	...	5 48	6 45	—	—	10 34	12 0
Norden........dep	6 15	6 26	...	7 42	...	8 39	8 50	9 32	10 11	12 24	3 1	4 0	4 7	...	5 21	5 38	...	5 52	7 12	...	...	—	—
Norddeich ...arr	6 30	6 39	a.m.	7 57	...	8 53	9 3	9 46	10 27	12 41	3 18	4 14	4 22	p.m.	5 33	5 52	p.m.	6 5	7 27	...	...	...	...
Norden ......dep	D	D	6 57	—	...	8 35	—	—	10 19	1 15	—	—	—	4 59	B	—	5 57	E	7 20	...	...	...	...
Hage			7 8	...	...	8 45	...	...	10 29	1 27	...	...	...	5 9	...	...	6 8	...	7 30	...	...	...	...
Dornum		...	7 30	...	...	9 7	...	...	10 50	1 53	...	...	...	5 30	...	...	6 32	...	7 51	...	...	...	...
Esens		...	8 5	...	...	9 46	...	...	11 23	2 29	...	...	...	6 10	...	...	7 2	...	8 23	...	...	...	...
Wittmund 151 arr		...	8 34	...	...	10 15	...	...	11 50	2 59	...	...	...	6 44	...	...	...	...	8 51	...	...	...	...

	1—4	2 3 4	2 3 4	1—4	2,3,4	2 3 4	1,2,3	1,2,3	Ex3	Ex3	Ex3	1—4	1—4	1,2,3	1—4	2 3 4	1,2,3	1—4	1—4	Ex3	2 3 4	2,3,4	
				a.m.	a.m.	a.m.	a.m.	a.m.	a.m.	a.m.	a.m.	a.m.	p.m.	p.m.	p.m.			p.m.		p.m.	p.m.	p.m.	
Wittmund 151 ...dep		...	...	5 51	8 11	8‡59	...	...	...	...	...	10 22	...	...	2 1	...	...	5 31	...	...	...	9 41	...
Esens		...	...	6 19	8 37	9 27	...	...	...	...	...	10 55	...	...	2 36	...	...	6 2	...	...	...	10 10	...
Dornum		...	...	6 50	9 7	—	...	F	...	...	...	11 35	...	C	3 9	...	...	6 33	...	...	...	10 41	...
Hage		...	...	7 9	9 25	...	...	...	...	G	...	11 59	...	...	3 30	...	...	6 53	...	...	...	11 1	...
Norden ....arr		...	...	7 19	9 35	...	...	...	...	...	...	12 9	...	...	3 40	...	* p.m.	7 2	p.m.	A	...	11 10	...
Norddeich .....dep	1—4	...	...	7 18	9 12	...	9§52	1042	11 5	1118	1143	12 3	1 33	2 15	3 40	...	6 30	6 55	8 6	8 19	9 15	—	...
Norden ....arr	a.m.	...	...	7 33	9 27	...	10 5	1056	1119	1131	1153	12 18	1 48	2 28	3 55	...	6 43	7 9	8 22	8 32	9 30		...
Norden........dep	3 39	a.m.	a.m.	7 37	9 39	...	10 7	1058	1121	1132	1154	12 25	1 51	2 30	4 1	p.m.	6 46	7 13	—	8 34	9 36	...	...
Abelitz	4 6	5 †1	7 8	8 7	10 12	...	...	...	1145	...	...	12 58	2 25	...	4 34	6 16	...	7 41	...	...	10 6		...
Emden 133A ..arr	4 34	5 35	7 43	8 28	10 55	...	1047	1142	12 6	1212	1235	1 31	2 59	3 12	5 10	6 52	7 30	8 12	...	9 14	1038	...	...

Aurich ....dep	3a26	4†a25	5a*25	6 a8	6a35	7 a26	9a 3	9 a36	11a7	12p25	1p46	3p55	4 p40	5 p42	7 p3	8p24	11 p7	...	...	...	...
Abelitz ....arr	3 56	5 0	5 55	6 39	7 7	7 57	9 33	10 8	1137	12 55	2 17	4 26	5 14	6 13	7 34	9 59	11 34	...	...	...	...
Abelitz ....dep	1a30	4a20	6*a3	6†a27	7a45	8 a15	9a42	10a14	11a49	1 p5	2p32	4p36	5p27	6 p20	7p45	8 p48	10p11	11p39	...	...	...
Aurich ....arr	1 57	4 50	6 33	6 59	8 17	8 45	1011	10 45	12 19	1 36	3 3	5 6	6 4	6 51	8 17	9 17	10 42	12 8	...	...	...

*—Until 15th September. †—Weekdays only. ‡—Until 18th August. §—Until 21st September.
A—Until 15th September. B—Until 15th October. C—Until 21st September. D—Until 16th September.
E—From 5th to 13th August, and from 30th August until 20th September.
F—From 6th to 15th August, and from 31st August to 21st September. G—From 25th July until 18th August.

HAGEN, LÖTTRINGHAUSEN, and DORTMUND (Sud).

Hagen ....dep	6a51	9 a59	11a12	12p34	1p14	3 p27	6 p38	7p55	9 p1	10p41	...	...	...	...
Löttringhausen........	7 16	10 26	11 36	12 59	1 40	3 57	7 1	8 24	9 25	11 6	...	...	...	...
Dortmund ....arr	7 32	10 41	11 54	1 14	1 55	4 12	7 15	8 39	9 40	11 24	...	...	...	...
Dortmund ....dep	6a32	8 a37	10 a3	11a33	1p22	2p42	4 p20	6p32	8 p7	11p39	...	...	...	...
Löttringhausen........	6 50	8 54	10 20	11 57	1 38	2 58	4 37	6 49	8 25	11 57	...	...	...	...
Hagen ....arr	7 12	9 15	10 43	12 22	2 2	3 20	4 58	7 12	8 49	12 21	...	...	...	...

HAGEN, WITTEN, and DORTMUND.

Hagen ......dep	6 a7	7 a5	7a33	7a50	8a49	9a10	9a54	11a0	1133	1224	12p29	12p53	2p17	2p25	2p52	3p10	3p42	5p52	7p17	7p37	8p52	9p30	10p26	10p31	11p54
Vorhalle........	6 14	7 12	...	7 58	...	9 17	10 1	11 8	...	...	12 36	1 0	...	2 32	...	...	...	...	...	7 45	8 59	9 37	...	10 38	12 1
Witten	6 36	7 28	7 51	8 15	9 6	9 32	1017	1126	...	1239	12 53	1 19	2 32	2 48	3 8	3 32	3 57	6 13	7 34	8 3	9 22	9 53	10 42	10 58	12 18
Dortmund arr	7 7	7 58	8 9	8 45	9 24	10 1	1044	1155	12 2	...	1 12	1 47	...	3 17	3 24	3 57	...	6 43	7 52	8 33	9 52	1025	...	11 28	12 48
Dortmund dep	5a47	6a30	7 a53	8a19	a.m.	9a26	9 a54	1130	11a58	...	1p21	...	2p49	3p33	3p55	4p25	5p56	6 p4	6p35	6p40	7p18	7p40	9p19	1151	12a58
Witten	6 19	7 6	8 12	8 56	9 33	9 49	10 24	1157	12 31	1p18	1 53	2p43	3 21	3 51	4 27	4 50	6 15	6 37	...	7 14	7 51	8 11	9 54	1223	1 17
Vorhalle	6 37	...	...	9 14	...	...	10 42	1212	12 46	...	2 8	...	3 39	...	4 44	...	...	6 56	...	7 29	8 10	8 27	1011	1239	...
Hagen ......arr	6 43	7 26	8 27	9 20	9 56	10 8	10 48	1218	12 52	1 34	2 14	2 58	3 45	4 6	4 50	5 5	6 31	7 2	7 8	7 35	8 16	8 33	1017	1245	1 33

Extra.—Hagen to Dortmund 2.4, 3.49, 5.9, 5.42, 6.33 p.m. Dortmund to Hagen 11.6 p.m.

PRUSSIAN STATE RAILWAYS.

Luggage Rates—see page 462.

OPLADEN, DUSSELDORF, DORTMUND, and WELVER.

	1—4	1—4	1—4	1—4	1—4	1—4	1—4	1—4	1—4	1—4	1—4	1—4	1—4	1—4	1—4	2 3 4	2,3,4	1—4	
		a.m		a.m.	a.m.		a.m.	p.m.		p.m.	p.m.	p.m.		p.m.	p.m.		p.m.	p.m.	
Opladen ....dep	...	5 †40	...	6 44	9 27	...	1138	12 34	...	2 52	5 0	5 41	...	7 10	8 42	...	10 27	11 41	...
Hilden....................	...	6 0	...	7 4	9 51	...	1158	12 55	...	3 19	5 22	6 3	...	7 42	9 11	...	10 46	12 3	...
Dusseldorf { arr	...	6 17	a.m.	7 20	10 8	a.m.	1215	1 12	p.m.	3 37	5 41	6 20	...	8 0	9 28	...	11 9	12 20	...
Hauptbhf. { dep	...	—	6 11	8 35	11 0	1155	—	1 47	3 34	—	5 44	6†30	...	8 11	—	...	—	12 48	...
Dusseldorf Derendorf	...	...	6 16	8 40	11 5	12 0	...	1 52	3 39	...	5 49	6†35	...	8 16	...	...	...	12 53	...
Ratingen	a.m.	...	6 34	8 56	11 22	1216	...	2 8	3 57	p.m.	6 4	6†49	p.m.	8 32	...	...	...	1 9	...
Speldorf	4 10	...	7 2	9 22	11 49	1240	...	2 33	4 23	5 14	6 30	—	7 2	8 58	...	...	1—4	1 34	...
Mülheim Eppinghof	4 16	...	7 9	9 28	11 54	1246	p.m	2 39	4 29	5 20	6 36	...	7 9	9 4	...	...	p.m.	1 40	...
Essen-Nord	4 38	...	7 31	9 51	12 16	1 8	1*43	3 3	4 55	5 41	6 58	...	7 30	9 25	...	...	11 18	2 1	...
Kray ....arr	4 45	...	7 39	9 58	12 23	1 15	1 52	3 10	5 3	5 48	7 6	...	—	9 32	...	...	11 26	2 8	...
Kray ....dep	5 0	...	8 7	10 10	12 30	1 29	...	3 20	5 9	5 50	7 10	†—Not on Sunday.	...	10 2	...	...	11 33	...	...
Gelsenkirch arr	5 10	...	8 17	10 20	12 40	1 38	...	3 30	5 20	6 0	7 20		...	10 12	...	...	11 42	...	...
Gelsenkirch-Watt'cd	4 55	1,2,3	7 48	10 7	12 31	1 23	2 0	3 18	5 11	6 29	7 14		...	9 40	Ex.3	...	11 43	2 16	...
Bochum	5 11	a.m.	8 3	10 23	12 48	1 36	2 15	3 33	5 39	6 44	7 29		...	9 53	p.m.	p.m.	11 57	2 26	...
Langendreer............	5 21	7 4	8 14	10 34	12 59	—	2 25	3 44	5 50	7 3	7 40		...	10 4	10 19	1126	—	—	...
Dortmund... { arr	—	7 17	8 33	10 53	1 18	p.m.	—	4 4	6 9	—	7 59		...	10 21	10 32	1144	...	...	...
Süd { dep	...	7 19	8 40	10 58	1 21	2 30	...	4 17	—	...	8 9		...	—	10 34	1147	...	...	...
Unna-Königsborn...	...	...	9 9	11 25	1 51	2 59	...	4 46	...	...	8 38		...	...	⋮	1215	...	...	...
Welver (133A) arr	...	7 50	9 37	11 51	2 19	3 27	...	5 15	...	...	9 5		...	...	⋮	—	...	...	...
SOEST ....arr	...	8 a7	10 a0	12 p9	2p43	3p46	...	5 p30	...	...	9 p23		...	...	11p15	...	...	...	...

	1—4	1—4	1—4	Ex3	1—4	1—4	1—4	1—4	1—4	1—4	1—4	1—4	1—4	1—4	1—4	1—4	1—4	2 3 4	
SOEST (133A) ......dep	...	...	...	5a43	...	6 a25	...	10 a7	...	...	1 p22	...	4 p18	6 p10	8 p16	...	10p46	...	...
				⋮		a.m.	a.m.	a.m.			p m.		p.m.	p.m.	p.m.		p.m.	ng't	
Welver..............dep	...	...	...	⋮	...	6 46	...	10 27	...	...	1 41	...	4 36	6 27	8 34	...	11 3	...	...
Unna-Königsborn	...	...	...	⋮	...	7 16	7 0	10 53	...	...	2 9	...	5 4	6 52	9 2	...	...	1249	...
Dortmund...... { arr	...	...	a.m.	6 25	...	7 43	7 28	11 19	p.m.	...	2 36	...	5 32	7 18	9 29	...	11 33	1 16	...
Süd { dep	...	...	5 48	6 26	a.m.	7 51	—	11 22	1 22	...	2 40	...	5 42	7 22	9 46	p.m.	11 34	—	...
Langendreer...............	a.m.	a.m.	6 12	To Oberhausen	6 44	8 12	8a42	11 43	1 40	p.m.	3 0	...	6 0	7 42	10 7	10 58	11 49	...	...
Bochum	3 54	5 3	6 27		6 57	8 24	8 53	11 55	1 55	2 23	3 13	...	6 12	7 53	10 19	11 9	⋮	...	...
Gelsenkirch-Wattenc'd	4 7	5 17	6 42		7 12	8 36	9 3	12 7	2 8	2 36	3 26	p.m.	6 26	8 4	10 30	11 19	⋮	...	...
Gelsenkirch ...dep	4 0	5 18	6 7		6 48	8 6	...	11 43	1 17	2 15	3 10	6 11	6 11	7 25	9 45	10 40	⋮	...	...
Kray ....arr	4 10	5 27	6 17		6 58	8 16	...	11 53	1 27	2 25	3 20	6 21	6 21	7 35	9 55	10 50	⋮	...	...
Kray ....dep	4 14	5 34	6 50		21	8 45	9 10	12 14	2 16	2 45	3 33	6 22	6 35	8 10	10 37	11 27	⋮	...	...
Essen-Nord **(130)** ...	4 26	5 44	7 0	—	7*31	8 55	9*19	12 25	2 28	2 57	3 43	6 30	6 46	8 19	10 46	11*36	12*14	...	...
Mülheim Eppinghofen	4 48	6 9	7 22	2—4	—	9 17	—	12 46	2 49	3 19	4 4	6 51	7 8	8 38	11 6	—	—	...	...
Speldorf..................	5 0	6 21	7 32	a.m.	...	9 26	...	12 53	2 59	3 24	4 11	6 56	7 13	8 44	11 14			...	...
Ratingen....................	5 26	6 47	7 57	8 43	...	9 50	...	1 17	3 22	—	4 33	—	—	9 7	11 37	...	...	...	...
Dusseldorf Derendorf...	5 42	7 3	8 14	9 0	...	10 6	1—4	1 31	3 38	...	4 49	...	...	9 25	11 53	...	...	...	...
Dusseldorf...... { arr	5 45	7 7	8 18	9 5	a.m.	10 10	p.m.	1 35	3 42	p.m.	4 53	...	p.m.	9 29	11 57	...	...	p.m.	...
Hauptbhf. { dep	5 50	—	8 20	—	9 45	—	1235	1 39	3 44	4 28	5 46	...	7 25	9 50	—	...	...	1129	...
Hilden	6 13	...	8 38	...	1010	...	1253	2 2	4 2	4 52	6 5	...	7 42	10 12	...	...	...	1153	...
Opladen ....arr	6 32	...	8 58	...	1033	...	1 14	2 23	4 22	5 13	6 26	...	8 3	10 34	...	...	...	1214	...

SPRENDLINGEN and FURFELD.

‡—Not on Sunday.

Sprendlingen...dep	6a15	8a55	11a38	1p50	3p30	6†20	9p35	† 14 min.
Wöllstein............	6 35	9 10	11 55	2 5	3 47	6 40	9 52	earlier
Furfeld ....arr	7 0	9 35	12 21	...	4 13	7 12	1016	on Sun.

Furfeld ....dep	5 a0	7a40	10a20	12p55	...	4‡55	8‡00
Wöllstein	5 26	8 6	10 45	1 23	3 p5	5 35	8 30
Sprendlingen ar	5 40	8 20	11 0	1 38	3 29	5 50	8 45

ALTENA and LUDENSCHEID.

Altena ....dep	Almost hourly, from 6.8 a.m.
Ludenscheid 133E ......arr	until 9.41 p.m.

Ludenscheid ....dep	Almost hourly, from 6.32 a.m.
Altena 216.............arr	until 8.35 p.m.

Werdohl.........dep	6 a20	7a30	10 a2	2p28	6p15	7 p54	...	...
Augustenthal	7 3	8 14	10 43	3 10	6 54	8 30	...	...
Lüdenscheid ...arr	7 23	8 36	11 4	3 31	7 15	8 50	...	...

Lüdenscheid...dep	6 a0	8a24	11 a8	2p20	3 p48	7 p20
Augustenthal	6 22	8 52	11 31	2 42	4 12	7 42
Werdohl.........arr	6 58	9 33	12 11	3 24	4 50	8 21

DUSSELDORF and WERDEN.

Dusseldorf Hpt....dep	5 a6	5a56	6a20	7a14	8a46	9a 57	11a46	12p45	1p40	3 p11	p.m.	p.m.	5 p28	p.m.	7 p1	7p30	7 p35	8p 55	9 p27	10p32	11p40
Kettwig	5 48	6 46	7 5	7 53	9 26	10 38	12 26	1 25	2 21	3 52	4 42	5 36	6 5	6 20	7 28	...	8 14	9 22	10 6	11 10	12 19
Werden......arr	5 54	6 52	7 12	7 59	9 32	10 44	12 32	1 31	2 27	3 58	4 48	5 43	6 11	6 26	7 34	8 0	8 20	9 28	10 12	11 17	12 25

Werden ...dep	5a31	6 a0	6a58	8 a5	8a48	9a 9	10a22	10a44	11a46	1p26	1p59	3p16	4p30	5 p6	5p37	6p43	7p34	9 p8	10 p1	10p49	12 a3
Kettwig	5 39	6 8	7 7	8 13	...	9 17	10 30	10 51	11 53	1 34	2 6	3 25	4 37	5 13	5 44	6 50	7 42	9 16	10 11	10 55	12 10
Dusseldorf arr	6 23	6 49	7 48	8 52	9 17	10 0	11 9	11 15	12 34	2 15	2 32	4 6	5 3	...	6 25	7 30	8 21	10 0	10 57	...	12 50

DUSSELDORF and VOHWINKEL.

Dusseldorf ...	5a50	7a9	7a55	8a43	9a45	...	1054	11a50	1p39	3 p0	3p30	pm	4p28	...	5p20	6p18	pm	6p58	...	8p54	9p50	p.m.	11p29
Ohligs	6 27	740	7 28	9 11	1018	1036	1125	12 19	2 17	3 31	4 9	441	5 12	5p26	5 50	6 54	7 4	7 30	7p59	9 24	1027	1138	12 2
Solingen ..arr	6 39	752	8 40	9 23	1032	1050	1137	12 31	2 29	3 43	4 22	453	5 24	5 38	6 3	7 6	716	7 42	8 11	9 36	1039	1150	12 14
Remscheid ar	7 3	817	9 4	9 46	1054	11 9	12 0	12 55	2 54	4 4	4 47	...	5 47	5 57	6 27	7 27	...	8 7	8 32	10 2	11 5	1215	12 40
Solingen.. dep	6 50	8 5	—	1025	—	—	—	12 40	2 45	—	—	5 2	—	—	6 10	—	720	—	—	—	1045	—	—
Vohwinkel ...	7 22	835	...	1056	...	...	...	1 14	3 19	...	...	537	...	...	6 41	...	753	...	...	...	1121	...	...

Vohwinkel ...	...	...	6 a3	...	7a28	8a58	...	10a13	...	...	1p25	...	3p49	...	...	...	7 p6	...	8p51	...	10p6	...
Solingen ..arr	...	...	6 35	...	7 58	9 29	...	10 46	...	p.m.	1 58	...	4 19	...	...	...	7 42	...	9 26	...	1036	ng't
Remscheid dp	4a49	5a50	...	7a14	7 42	9 2	9 a56	10 27	12 p4	1255	1 40	2p32	3 57	4 p14	5p44	6p51	7 57	8p18	9 8	10p4	1047	12 2
Solingen ..dep	5 11	6 13	6 47	7 37	8 5	9 24	10 13	10 50	12 20	1 17	2 3	2 54	4 23	5 1	6 5	7 13	8 15	8 42	9 30	1027	11 7	1224
Ohligs	5 22	6 24	6 56	7 50	8 28	9 39	10 21	11 15	12 31	1 37	2 17	3 7	4 34	5 9	6 17	7 30	8 23	8 58	9 41	1040	1119	1233
Dusseldorf ...	5 50	6 53	...	8 19	8 54	10 8	...	11 42	12 54	2 6	2 47	3 37	5 2	...	6 45	7 57	...	9 28	10 6	11 9	1148	1 1

VORHALLE, STEELE, and VOHWINKEL.

		a.m	a.m.	a.m.	a.m.	a.m.	a.m.	a.m.	...	p.m.	p.m.	p.m.	p.m.	p.m.		p.m.	p.m.	p.m.	p.m	p.m.		p.m.
Vorhalle dep		...	...	6 2	...	...	8 17	1017	...	..	...	1 12	...	3 42	...	5 25	...	7 53	...	...	...	1112
Hattingen		5 36	...	7 4	8 7	8 32	9 12	11 8	...	1251	1 54	2 3	2 58	4 33	...	6 18	6 59	8 43	1013	1031	...	12 7
Dahlhausen		5 44	...	7 13	...	8 40	9 20	1116	...	...	2 2	2 11	3 5	4 42	...	6 26	⋮	8 51	⋮	1039	...	1216
Steele arr	a.m.	5 52	...	7 20	8 17	8 47	9 27	1123	p.m.	1 1	2 9	2 18	3 11	4 49	p.m.	6 33	7 9	8 58	1024	1046	p.m.	1224
Steele dep	5 0	6 20	6 58	8 27	—	—	9 51	1145	1252	—	2 14	2 34	—	5 0	6 12	6 58	8 48	9 18	—	1052	1153	—
Kupferdreh	5 12	6 33	7 10	8 39	...	11a13	10 4	1158	1 4	...	2 27	2 45	...	5 12	6 20	7 10	9 0	9 31	...	11 4	12 6	...
⋮ Werden	5 27	6 50	7 26	9 1	...	11 27	1035	...	1 19	...	—	3 10	...	5 30	...	7 27	9 15	9 49	...	...	1221	...
Aprath	—	7 35	—	9 15	...	—	1043	1243	—	...	...	3 22	...	5 58	...	7 55	—	1015	...	1147	—	...
Vohwinkel arr		7 46	...	9 25	...	...	1053	1253	...	...	...	3 32	...	6 8	6 55	8 5	...	1025	...	1157	...	...

	a.m.	a.m.		am	a.m.	a.m.	a.m.	a.m.		a.m.		p.m.	p.m.	pm	p.m.	pm	p.m.	p.m.	p.m.	p.m.	p.m.	p.m.	nigt
Vohwinkel dep	...	...	...	654	...	8 59	...	1019	...	...	...	...	1 44	3 50	5 46	559	...	6 7	8 12	...	9 40	...	1229
Aprath	...	...	...	7 6	...	9 10	...	1031	...	...	...	...	1 55	4 2	...	6 9	...	6 18	8 23	...	9 51	...	1240
⋮ Werden	6 0	...	...	723	8 10	...	9 41	1049	...	1137	...	1 41	...	413	...	612	7 37	—	...	9 34	...	1020	1230
Kupferdreh dep	6 15	...	...	742	8 25	9 40	9 55	11 7	...	1220	...	1 56	2 26	433	6 16	639	7 52	...	8 59	9 49	1030	1112	1 14
Steele arr	6 27	...	a.m.	755	8 36	9 52	—	1119	p.m.	1233	p.m.	2 8	2 39	445	6 25	651	8 5	p.m.	9 12	10 2	1043	1125	1 26
Steele dep	—	6 0	7 15	821	8 43	—	1054	1131	1215	1249	2 0	2 26	—	5 8	—	7 1	8 10	8 48	—	10 9	—	1150	1 40
Dahlhausen	...	6 8	...	830	8 50	...	11 2	1139	...	1258	...	2 34	...	517	...	710	...	8 57	...	1017	...	1159	1 49
Hattingen	...	6 17	7 26	839	8 56	...	11 9	1149	1226	1 5	2 12	2 42	...	526	...	722	8 20	9 7	...	1024	...	12 8	1 57
Vorhalle arr	...	7 12	...	933	...	...	...	1239	...	...	...	3 30	...	618	...	815	...	9 58	...	...	...	1 1	...

BARMEN-RITTERSHAUSEN and BRUGGE. [‡—Not on Sunday.

			a.m.	a.m.	a.m.	a.m.	a.m.		p.m.	p.m.		p.m.	p.m.	p.m.		p.m.	p.m.	p.m.
Barmen-R. dep	...	...	5 58	6 58	8 26	8 50	10 46	...	12 21	1 43	...	3 14	4 22	6 4	...	7 15	8 18	10 20
Krebsoege arr	...	...	6 43	7 45	9 16	9 30	11 34	...	1 9	2 41	...	4 2	5 9	6 50	...	8 14	9 8	11 12
⋮ Lennep arr	a.m.	...	6 59	8 10	...	9 50	11 52	p.m.	1 24	2 57	...	4 26	5 26	7 7	...	8 35	9 37	...
Radevormwald	6 3	a.m.	—	8 16	10 17	9 57	12 12	1 33	2 19	—	p.m.	4 38	5 50	7 29	p.m.	8 45	10 0	11 48
Anschlag	6 25	6 46	...	9 14	—	...	12 36	1 56	—	...	4 22	6 1	—	7 57	8 8	—	10 48	—
Halver (133E)	6 32	6 54	...	9 21	...	10 21	12 45	2 7	...	...	4 33	6 9	...	8 3	8 20	...	10 55	...
Brügge (130) arr	...	7 13	...	9 41	...	10 37	1 4	2 27	...	...	4 54	...	...	...	8'40	...	11 14	...

			a.m.	a.m.			p.m.			p.m.			p.m.	p.m.				p.m.
Brügge dep	...	...	6 6	7 42	...	...	12 19	...	...	2 14	p.m.	...	6 24	6 36	p.m.	...	...	10 16
Halver	...	...	6 32	8 6	...	...	12 46	...	...	2 42	4 12	...	6 47	6 55	7 1	...	...	10 42
Anschlag arr	a.m.	a.m.	6.38	8 12	...	p.m.	12 52	...	p.m.	2 48	4 20	...	6 53	...	7 6	p.m.	...	10 48
Radevormwald	5 18	6 22	7 13	8 44	a.m.	12 15	1 15	p.m.	2 36	—	4 46	p.m.	—	7 19	7 45	8 55	p.m.	11 25
⋮ Lennep dep	...	6‡32	7 30	9 0	10 24	12 21	—	2 10	...	...	4 53	6 10	...	...	7 59	9 8	11 0	—
Krebsoege	5 43	6 49	7 45	9 17	10 40	12 40	...	2 22	3 8	...	5 11	6 21	...	7 43	8 15	9 21	11 13	...
Barmen-R. arr	6 37	7 40	8 28	9 59	11 29	1 26	...	3 20	3 57	...	5 59	7 19	...	8 27	9 0	10 10	12 0	...

Wipperfürth dep	6 a10	8 a39	12 p4	3 p55	7 p40	10p23
Anschlag arr	6 37	9 8	12 28	4 19	8 6	10 47

Anschlag dep	6 a40	8 a13	1 p0	2 p53	6 p54	10p49	...
Wipperfürth arr	7 0	8 33	1 21	3 20	7 14	11 7	...

BARMEN and REMSCHEID.

	a.m.	a.m.	a.m.	a.m.	a.m.	p.m.		p.m.	p.m.		p.m.		p.m.	p.m.	p.m.	p.m.	p.m.	p.m.	p.m.	a.m.
Barmen Rittershausen dep	6 30	7 44	7 57	9 40	1059	12 4	...	1 36	3 22	...	4 59	...	6 23	7 24	7 35	8 24	9 7	1026	1122	1 4
Lüttringhausen	6 53	8 8	...	10 4	1123	1229	p.m.	1 59	3 45	p.m.	5 23	p.m.	6 47	...	7 59	8 49	9 31	1050	1145	1 28
Lennep	7 4	8 16	8 53	1015	1132	1239	1 30	2 9	3 56	4 10	5 33	6 42	6 54	7 49	8 7	8 58	9 38	10!8	1152	1 37
Remscheid arr	7 11	8 23	9 0	1022	1139	1246	1 37	2 16	4 3	4 17	5 40	6 49	7 1	7 56	8 14	9 6	9 45	11 5	1159	1 44

Remscheid dep	4a41	6a21	6a53	7a25	8a19	9a50	12 p3	12p58	1 p37	3p30	4p22	5p13	5p 8	6p33	7p40	8p11	9p37	10p20	11p31
Lennep	4 52	6 31	7 2	7 40	8 29	10 0	12 14	1 8	1 48	3 40	4 33	5 20	6 7	6 48	7 57	8 24	9 44	10 32	11 43
Lüttringhausen	4 58	6 37	7 8	7 46	8 35	10 6	12 20	1 14	1 54	3 46	4 39	—	...	6 55	...	8 30	—	10 39	11 49
Barmen Ritters. arr	5 15	6 55	7 24	8 3	8 51	10 22	12 36	1 31	2 12	4 2	4 55	...	6 25	7 12	8 16	8 46	...	10 55	12 5

WERMELSKIRCHEN and HALBACH, via Remscheid.—From Wermelskirchen about hourly, from 8.5 a.m. until 8.5 p.m. From Halbach, hourly, from 9.19 a.m. until 9.19 p.m.

LUDENSCHEID, BRÜGGE, and HAGEN.

	a.m.	a.m.	a.m.	a.m.	a.m.	a.m.	p.m.	p.m.	p.m.	p.m.	p.m	p.m.	p.m.	p.m.	p.m.	p.m.	p.m.	ngt.
Lüdenscheid dep	5 30	7 19	8 23	9 32	1044	11 51	12 58	1 30	2 5	3 2	4 44	5 57	7 30	8 37	9 2	9 53	1111	1244
Brügge	5 55	7 42	8 50	9 57	1115	12 5	1 18	1 47	2 33	3 58	5 17	6 28	7 52	9 3	9 18	10 5	1149	1256
Schalksmühle	6 3	7 50	8 59	10 6	1124	—	1 27	—	2 41	4 7	5 26	6 37	8 1	9 12	—	—	1158	—
Hagen arr	6 46	8 34	9 33	1049	12 7	...	2 10	...	3 21	4 50	6 10	7 19	8 44	9 58	...	...	1227	...

		a.m.	a.m.			a.m.	a.m.		p.m.	p.m.		p.m.	p.m.	p.m.		p.m	p.m.	p.m.	a.m.
Hagen dep	...	6 31	7 47	...	...	1020	11 12	...	1 11	2 20	...	3 54	5 17	7 25	...	8 28	9 8	1031	1 0
Schalksmühle	a.m.	7 22	8 36	a.m.	a.m.	11 3	12 0	p.m.	1 50	3 9	p.m.	4 42	6 5	8 14	p.m.	9 18	9 55	1119	1 43
Brügge	6 20	7 43	8 50	9 53	1041	1118	12 12	1 30	2 3	3 22	3 58	5 17	6 19	8 37	9 0	9 30	1023	1151	1 56
Lüdenscheid arr	6 40	8 3	9 10	1013	11 1	1138	12 32	1 50	2 23	3 42	4 18	5 37	6 37	8 55	9 18	9 48	1043	1211	2 14

SCHALKSMUHLE and HALVER.

Schalksmuhle dep	8 a39	1 p55	4 p46	9 p20
Halver (133E) arr	9 20	2 36	5 27	10 1

Halver dep	7 a8	12p41	3p25	7 p15	...	...
Schalksmuhle 133E	7 43	1 16	4 0	7 50	...	...

ELBERFELD and CRONENBERG.

Elberfeld Steinb dep	6a28	8 a8	10 a0	2 p0	4p 3	5p17	7p0	10p22
Cronenberg arr	7 2	8 45	10 40	2 37	4 38	5 48	736	10 56

Cronenberg dep	5a30	7a12	9a10	12p35	2p51	4p44	5p58	7p45
Elberfeld arr	5 53	7 34	9 35	1 0	3 18	5 9	6 24	8 12

FRANKENBERG and BESTWIG.

Frankenberg dep		5a56	8a40	1p28	3p52	7 p1	9p24	...
Allendorf-a-E.		6 17	9 19	1 49	4 13	7 22	9 46	...
Winterberg	5a22	7 33	1027	3 9	5 30	8 32	1056	...
Steinhelle	6 0	8 17	11 3	3 45	6 8	9 8	—	...
Bestwig arr	6 22	8 40	1123	4 7	6 30	9 29	...	...

Bestwig dep		6a59	9a50	1226	5p40	8 p4	9p38
Steinhelle		7 35	1018	1253	6 8	8 29	10 5
Winterberg	5a54	8 26	1125	2 0	7 2	9 27	1055
Allendorf	6 56	9 22	1221	2 54	8 1	1027	—
Frank'berg arr	7 15	9 42	1241	3 14	8 21	1047	...

GRENGELSBITZE and NIEDERDOLLENDORF.

Grengelsbitze ...dep	7 a8	7a40	9 a5	12 0	1p48	2p33	5p20	5p55	7p9
Heisterbach	7 29	7 59	9 26	1220	2 8	2 53	5 41	6 16	7 40
Niederdollendorf 128	7 44	8 14	9 41	1236	2 24	3 9	5 56	6 31	7 55

Niederdoll.	6a30	6a57	8 a6	8a37	10a30	1 p0	1p52	3p32	4p50	6p38
Heisterbach	6 46	7 13	8 22	8 53	10 46	1 16	2 8	3 48	5 6	6 54
Grengelsb.	7 6	7 33	8 42	9 13	11 6	1 36	2 28	4 8	5 26	7 14

MEPPEN and HERZLAKE.

E.M.						
	Meppen...dep	...	7 a25	12p30	4p 0	8 p0
9	Haselünne	5a58	8 6	1 16	4 40	8 44
15	Herzlake arr	6 17	8 25	1 35	4 59	9 3

Herzlake ......dep	5a36	9 a37	1 p50	5 p51	1020
Haselünne	6 0	10 0	2 20	6 24	1041
Meppen 133A arr	6 35	10 35	2 59	7 6	...

‡—Weekdays only.]

BINGEN, ALZEY, and WORMS.

	a.m.	a.m.	a.m.	a.m.	a.m.	p.m.	p.m.	p.m.	p.m	p.m.	p.m
Bingen ...dep	5 15	6 45	8 15	9 23	10 33	1 12	2 55	5 25	7 19	8 59	11 3
Gensingen-H.	5 37	7 5	8 38	9 49	10 55	1 33	3 15	5 46	7 45	9 20	1127
Sprendlingen	5 49	7 17	8 51	10 1	11 9	1 45	3 28	6 3	7 58	9 32	1141
Armsheim ...	6 9	7 48	9 12	1030	11 31	2 6	3 48	6 31	8 20	9 51	12 3
Alzey...........	6 27	8 8	9 29	1052	11 52	2 25	4 6	6 54	9 1	10 9	1220
Gundersheim	6 46	8 29	9 48	1112	12 11	2 41	4 24	7 15	9 20	1028	—
Monsheim ...	7 5	8 50	10 5	1127	12 26	2 58	4 38	7 44	9 35	1044	...
Worms ...arr	7 24	9 12	1023	1147	12 45	3 15	4 56	8 3	9 54	11 1	...

		a m	a.m.	p.m.	p.m.	p.m.	p.m.	pm	p.m.
Worms ...dep	a.m.	6 33	9 40	12 5	1 21	4 22	5 40	7 20	9 7
Monsheim ...	4 39	7 5	10 7	1229	1 49	4 49	6 9	7 45	9 34
Gundersheim	5 3	7 21	1028	1245	2 5	5 5	6 27	8 1	9 49
Alzey...........	5 31	7 50	11 0	1 7	2 37	5 28	6 51	8 20	1017
Armsheim ...	5 45	8 7	1115	1 23	3 11	5 41	7 3	8 34	1038
Sprendlingen	6 6	8 26	1135	1 46	3 29	6 4	7 27	8 52	1056
G.-Horrweilr	6 18	8 39	1147	2 1	3 40	6 16	7 41	9 4	11 8
Bingen (122)	6 37	8 58	12 7	2 22	3 59	6 35	8 2	9 26	1128

Extra.

Alzey	4a37	5a54	1p10	5p37
Worms	5 43	7 1	2 3	6 41

Worms	8a21	3 p6	10p15	8p26	11p38
Alzey	9 22	4 5	11 17	9 28	12 43

Worms ...dep	5a‡40	8 a8
Monsheim arr	6 5	8 26

Alzey ..dep	4a52	...
Bingen arr	6 3	...

†—Week-days only. [*—11.7 a.m. on Sun.

WORMS and OFFSTEIN.

E.M.									
	Worms...dep	5a54	8a12	9a30	12p57	3 p3	5†p16	6p50	9 p0
7	Offstein...arr	6 23	8 42	10 1	1 32	3 33	5 50	7 22	9 34

Offstein ......dep	4†a45	6a31	8a45	11*a50	1p52	4‡40	6†‡0	7p28
Worms ......arr	5 20	6 59	9 18	12 30	2 27	5 10	6 33	8 3

WORMS and GUNDHEIM, in half-an-hour. From Worms Haupt 4‡15, 5.26, 6.32, 8.5, 10.37 a.m., 1.10, 2.15, 3.35, 5.12, 6.35, 8.26 p.m. From Gundheim 4‡50, 6.0, 7.6, 8.55, 11.16 a.m., 1.42, 2.48, 4.20, 5.47, 7.20, 9.12 p.m. ‡—Not on Sun.

‡—Sun., Wed., and Sat. only.

BODENHEIM and ALZEY.

Bodenheim...dep	6a13	7a41	11a34	...	2p29	5p19	7p35	11‡41
Gau-Odernheim	7 17	8 46	12 36	1p56	3 33	6 25	8 35	12 35
Alzey...........arr	7 40	9 10	1 0	2 20	3 57	6 48	8 58	12 59

Alzey...........dep	4a12	5a 7	8a10	11 a4	1p15	2p30	5p41	9 p5	...
Gau-Odernheim	4 40	5 34	8 42	11 35	1 38	2 53	6 10	9 29	...
Bodenheim ...arr	5 52	6 56	9 44	12 37	...	3 45	7 6	10 23	...

Gau-Odernheim ..dep	4 a39	5 a47	9 a9	11a41	3 p37	6 p26	9p35
Osthofen ....arr	5 24	6 35	10 0	12 26	4 25	7 18	1025

Osthofen ....dep	6 a14	8a 0	10a48	1 p6	5p23	8 p36	11p20
Gau-Odernheim arr	7 6	8 39	11 32	1 52	6 6	9 23	12 6

OFFENBACH and REINHEIM.

Offenbach Ostbhf.dep	...	...	7a12	a.m.	11a44	2p40	5 p5	6p30
Dieburg	6 a5	6a47	8 51	1048	1 17	4 12	7 5	8 4
Reinheim...........arr	6 35	7 14	9 14	1113	1 40	4 37	7 29	8 29

Reinheim............dep	4a22	7a34	8a21	9a20	12p32	3p25	6 p5	7p58
Dieburg	4 47	7 59	8 44	9 43	12 55	3 50	6 30	8 24
Offenbach Ostbhf.arr	6 31	9 32	...	1114	2 37	5 45	8 38	...

‡—Not on Sunday.]

BETZDORF and DAADEN.

Betzdorf.........dep	7a 3	10 a1	12p50	3 p10	6p33	8 p57	...
Daaden ....arr	7 28	10 31	1 17	3 41	6 58	9 22	...

Daaden..................dep	5a55	8 a35	11a53	2 p0	4p49	7 p21	...	...
Betzdorf (133B) ...arr	6 20	9 0	12 20	2 35	5 25	8 12	...	...

BUNDE and BASSUM.

Bünde..dep	...	6 a53	9 a2	10a53	1 p40	5p59	7 p58	11p30
Lübbecke.....	...	7 37	9 45	11 32	2 19	6 38	8 44	12 10
Rahden	4a47	8 19	10 12	11 59	2 47	7 5	9 13	12 33
Sulingen......	5 49	9 33	—	1 18	3 49	8 16	—	—
Bassum arr	6 29	10 20	...	1 53	4 28	8 56	...	...

Bassum ...dep	...	...	7 a29	11a 0	...	2p31	5 p47	9 p27
Sulingen............	...	...	8 11	11 46	...	3 8	6 35	10 11
Rahden	6 a7	7 a30	9 16	12 51	2 p51	4 12	7 46	11 14
Lübbecke............	6 37	8 13	9 48	1 22	3 24	4 39	8 20	11 42
Bünde.........arr	7 20	9 0	10 30	2 5	4 9	5 13	9 6	...

Herford	6a19	7‡a0	8a26	9a40	11a50	1p15	2p44	5p10	6p33	1014	1058
Bünde	6 43	7 23	8 51	10 6	12 14	1 38	3 9	5 35	6 58	1037	1114

Bünde...	5a39	6‡a25	7a28	7a51	9a4	10a45	12p25	2 p7	4p26	5p50	9p42
Herford	6 2	6 49	7 54	8 7	9 28	11 11	12 49	2 30	4 50	6 14	10 4

‡—Not on Sunday.

RAHDEN and NIENBURG.

Rahden............dep	5 a44	8a10	12 p3	2 p48	7 p46	...	...
Uchte	6 31	8 58	12 53	3 34	8 35	...	...
Nienburg (159)...arr	7 33	9 58	1 58	4 35	9 45	...	...

Nienburg.........dep	6 a6	7 a44	11a48	3 p8	10 p2	...	...	...
Uchte	7 15	9 3	1 3	4 35	11 8	...	...	...
Rahden ....arr	8 1	9 50	2 6	5 21	11 53	...	...	...

NIERSTEIN and UNDENHEIM.

Nierstein ....dep	7 a28	11a17	2p 0	4 p20	7 p23	9p15
Undenheim...................arr	8 5	11 55	2 31	5 0	8 0	9 45

Undenheim ....dep	5a55	9 a6	12p17	3 p12	6 p34	8 p26
Nierstein ....arr	6 25	9 44	12 47	3 39	7 5	8 54

‡—Weekdays only.

OSTHOFEN and GUNTERSBLUM.

Osthofen ......dep	5 a37	7 a58	10a50	2 p54	4p52	6 p46	8 p44
Guntersblum arr	6 18	8 37	11 40	3 44	5 34	7 32	9 30

Guntersblum .dep	4‡a33	6 a30	9 a20	12p42	3 p56	5p56	7 p46	9p57
Osthofen.........arr	5 15	7 13	10 10	1 27	4 41	6 36	8 31	10 39

‡—Saturday at 9.39 p.m. *—Sunday at 4.53 a.m.

MORLENBACH and WAHLEN.

Morlenbach ....dep	7a13	9a15	1 p4	4 p5	7 p16	10‡p58
Wahlen......................arr	8 6	1013	2 13	5 11	8 16	12 2

Wahlen ....dep	5*a 4	8a12	11a28	2 p36	5 p27	8 p21
Morlenbach ....arr	6 1	9 5	12 27	3 40	6 31	9 21

‡—Sunday depart 8.42 a.m.

LETMATHE and UNNA.

Letmathe dep	1a56	...	5a59	...	6a52	8 a5	9a29	10a59	11a59	...	1p52	...	4p35	...	6 p5	7p10	...	9 p7	10p15	11p22	12a5
Iserlohn ......arr	2 11	...	6 16	...	7 10	8 22	9 42	11 15	12 14	...	2 10	...	4 50	...	6 23	7 30	...	9 22	10 30	11 37	1220
,, ...dep	—	...	—	...	7 13	8 25	9 44	11 19	1 5	...	2 28	3p27	4 58	5p53	7 4	—	...	9 26	10 54	—	—
Menden	...	5a55	...	6a37	7 53	9 1	1020	11 59	1 47	2p30	3 9	4 5	5 38	6 37	7 45	...	9p25	10 6	11 36	...	...
Fröndenberg ...	...	6 7	...	7 11	8 15	9 12	1036	12 10	2 13	2 41	3 23	4 15	6 3	6 48	7 56	8p36	9 36	1028	12 34	...	...
Unna ....arr	...	6 58	...	7 38	8 39	...	11 0	12 48	2 40	...	3 48	...	6 31	7 44	...	9 0	...	1055	1 0	...	...

Unna ....dep	...	...	...	...	6a31	7a12	8a12	...	9a46	11a43	1p19	p.m.	2p55	...	4p37	...	...	7p13	...	9p53	11p7
Fröndenberg.......	...	...	...	6a28	7 9	7 38	8 50	9a27	1038	12 20	2 12	2 57	3 22	4p18	5 30	6 p5	6p53	7 45	8p46	1031	1131
Menden	...	...	...	6 40	7 19	—	9 3	9 38	1049	12 33	2 23	3 11	—	4 30	5 45	6 16	7 6	7 58	8 57	1044	1231
Iserlohn ......arr	...	...	...	7 22	7 57	...	9 44	—	1127	1 14	—	3 57	...	5 6	6 24	—	7 47	8 35	9 37	1123	—
,, ...dep	1a16	5 a31	6a21	7 35	...	8‡a55	9 55	...	1131	1 18	2p13	4 10	3p 8	5 23	6 50	...	7 52	8 42	...	1138	11p0
Letmathe..arr	1 28	5 43	6 33	7 47	...	9 7	10 8	...	1143	1 30	2 25	4 22	3 20	5 35	7 3	...	8 4	8 54	...	1150	1112

Luggage Rates—see page 462.

AIX-LA-CHAPELLE, DUSSELDORF, COLOGNE, ELBERFELD, and SOEST.

Station	0	1	2	3	4	5	6	7	8	9	10	11	12	13	14	15	16	17	18	19	20	21	22	23	24	25	26	27	28	29	30
BRUSSELS ....dep		...	...	...	...	...	...	...	1124	...	...	...	...	...	...	...	...	...	...	...	...	...	...	...	...	...	5a45	...	...	...	...
				1—4		1—4	1,2,3	1,2,3	1—4		1,2,3		1—4	1—4		1,2,3			Ex3	1,2,3	1—4	2,3,4	1,2,3	1—4		1—4	Ex3				1,2,3
Aix-la-Chapelle—									a.m.				a.m.	a.m.		a.m.			a.m.		a.m.					a.m.	a.m				
Hauptbahnhof ...dep		...	...	...	...	...	...	...	4 56	...	...	...	6 32	5 43	...	7 37	...	...	8 46	...	7 48	...	...	...	...	9 33	1114	...	...	...	...
West .... ,,		...	...	...	...	...	...	...	5 4	...	...	...	6 40	5 56	...	7 45	...	...	8 54	...	7 56	...	...	...	...	9 43	1123	...	...	...	...
Herzogenrath		...	...	...	...	...	...	...	5 26	...	...	...	7 2	6 21	...	...	...	...	...	...	8 17	...	...	...	...	10 6	1138	...	...	...	...
Lindern (125)................		...	...	...	...	...	...	...	5 52	...	...	...	7 28	6 48	...	...	...	...	...	...	8 41	...	...	...	...	10 34	1156	...	...	...	...
Erkelenz........................		...	...	a.m.	...	a.m.	...	a.m.	6 14	...	...	...	7 49	7 17	...	...	...	...	9 32	a.m.	9 2	a.m.	a.m.	...	...	10 59	1211	...	...	...	p.m.
Rheydt (124)..................		...	...	4 40	...	5 30	...	6 51	6 41	...	...	...	8 10	7 40	...	8 33	...	...	9 46	1016	9 21	10 24	11 0	...	...	11 22	1228	...	...	...	1 33
München Gladbach arr		...	...	4 46	...	5 36	...	6 57	6 47	...	...	...	8 16	7 46	...	8 39	...	...	9 52	1022	9 27	10 30	11 6	...	...	11 28	1233	...	...	...	1 59
CREFELD 135 ....arr		...	...	...	...	6 a43	...	...	7a34	...	...	...	9 a6	9 a6	...	9a14	...	...	1028	...	10a11	...	⋮	...	...	...	1 p8	...	...	...	...
ANTWERP ....dep		...	...	...	...	...	...	...	...	...	...	...	...	...	...	...	...	...	...	...	...	...	⋮	...	...	5 a36	8 a6	...	...	...	...
München Gladbach dep		...	...	4 48	...	5 41	...	7 0	7 8	...	...	...	8 21	8 1	...	8 47	...	...	10 0	1024	9 32	10 35	11 8	...	...	11 40	1240	...	...	...	1 44
Kleinenbroich.................		...	...	5 5	...	6 1	...	...	7 22	...	...	...	8 34	...	...	...	...	...	...	...	9 45	10 49	⋮	...	...	11 55	...	...	...	...	...
Neuss .... arr......		...	...	5 23	...	6 20	...	7 16	7 36	...	...	...	8 48	8 17	...	9 3	...	...	1016	1040	9 59	11 3	1124	...	...	12 9	1256	...	...	...	2 0
Neuss .... dep	1—4	...	...	5 28	...	6 24	...	7 23	7 40	...	...	...	8 51	8 20	...	9 11	...	...	1017	1043	10 2	11 5	1126	...	...	12 21	1258	...	...	...	2 3
Düsseldorf arr	a.m.	...	...	5 45	...	6 41	a.m.	7 36	7 56	...	a.m.	...	9 7	8 37	...	9 24	...	...	1029	1057	10 18	11 21	1139	...	...	12 37	1 14	...	...	...	2 16
Hauptbhf... dep	4 45	...	...	6 5	...		7 17	7 39	8 4	...	8 27	...		8 45	...	9 38	...	...	1038	11 0	10 23		1143	...	...	12 44	1 24	...	...	...	2 20
Hochdahl..........................	5 12	...	...	6 26	...	...	⋮	⋮	8 27	...	...	...	...	9 10	...	...	...	...	...	⋮	10 47	...	...	...	...	1 8	...	...	...	...	...
Vohwinkel ....arr	5 29	...	...	6 40	...	...	⋮	⋮	8 39	...	8 55	...	...	9 31	...	10 8	...	...	11 7	⋮	11 2	...	1215	...	...	1 23	1 51	...	...	...	2 48
		1,2,3	Ex3		1—4	1,2,3	⋮	⋮		1—4		Ex3	Ex3		1,2,3		1,2,3	Ex2		⋮		1—4		1—4	1,2,3			1,2,3	Ex3	1—4	
COLOGNE—		a.m.	a.m.		a.m.	a.m.	⋮	⋮		a.m.		a.m.	a.m.		a.m.		a.m.	a.m.		⋮		a.m.		p.m.	p.m.			p.m.	p.m.	p.m.	
Hauptbahnhof dep	...	5 26	6 0	...	6 5	6 58	⋮	⋮	...	7 34	...	8 26	8 36	...	9 6	...	10 0	1014	...	⋮	...	10 24	...	12 4	1241	...	...	1 22	1 30	1 57	...
Mülheim Rhine ...	...	5 35	RC	...	6 15	7 7	⋮	⋮	...	7 44	...	⋮	...	...	9 15	...	10 9	⋮	...	⋮	...	10 33	...	1214	1250	...	...	1 31	...	2 13	...
Opladen	...	5 48		...	6 36	7 21	⋮	⋮	...	8 4	...	RC	RC	...	9 29	...	...	RC	...	⋮	...	10 52	...	1231	1 3	...	...	...	RC	2 30	...
Ohligs	...	6 2	6 32	...	7 1	7 35	⋮	⋮	...	8 27	...	⋮	9 6	...	9 44	...	1030	⋮	...	⋮	...	11 13	...	1253	1 17	...	...	1 55	2 1	2 49	...
Vohwinkel ......arr	...	⋮	6 45	...	7 24	7 51	⋮	⋮	...	8 49	...	⋮	⋮	...	9 59	...	1044	⋮	...	⋮	...	11 34	...	1 10	1 31	...	...	⋮	⋮	3 9	...
Vohwinkel ....dep	5 33	⋮	6 46	6 50	7 32	7 52	⋮	⋮	8 41	8 51	8 58	⋮	⋮	9 33	10 0	10 9	1045	⋮	11 7	⋮	11 12	11 35	1216	1 12	1 32	1 38	1 52	⋮	⋮	3 11	2 49
Elberfeld Steinbeck	5 50	⋮	...	...	7 44	...	⋮	⋮	8 51	9 1	...	⋮	⋮	9 45	...	...	...	⋮	...	⋮	11 22	11 45	...	1 23	...	1 54	...	⋮	⋮	3 23	...
Elberfeld arr	5 53	6 24	6 55	7 1	7 47	8 1	7 56	8 14	8 54	9 4	9 8	9 13	9 27	9 48	10 9	10 18	1054	1059	1116	1139	11 25	11 48	1225	1 26	1 41	1 57	2 1	2 16	2 22	3 26	2 58
Hauptbhf... dep	5 57	6 26	6 57	7 6	8 7	8 3	7 57	8 16	8 57		9 10	9 15	9 30	9 53	10 12	10 22	1056	11 1	1118	1141	11 45	11 51	1227	1 30	1 43	2 30	2 5	2 18	2 26	3 29	3 0
Barmen .... arr	6 6	6 32	7 3	7 13	8 16	8 9	8 3	8 22	9 3	...	9 15	9 20	9 36	10 2	10 18	10 28	11 2	11 7	1124	1147	11 54	12 0	1233	1 39	1 48	2 39	2 11	2 24	2 32	3 35	3 7
Barmen .... dep	6 9	6 33	7 5	7 17	8 18	8 10	8 4	8 23	9 5	...	9 16	9 21	9 37	10 5	10 20	10 30	11 3	11 8	1125	1148	11 56	12 2	1234	1 42	1 49	2 43	2 12	2 26	2 34	3 37	3 9
Barmen Rittersh'sen	6 15	...	...	7 26	8 30	8 16	8 8	...	9 9	...	9 20	...	...	1012	10 26	10 36	11 7	...	...	1152	12 0	12 11	1240	1 46	...	2 49	2 17	...	...	3 41	...
Schwelm	6 24	...	...	7 36	8 39	...		...		...		...	...	1021	10 35	10 45		...	...			12 22	1249		...	3 0	2 26	...	...		...
Haspe	6 45	...	...	7 57	9 0	...	...	...	...	...	...	...	...	1042	...	...	...	...	...	...	...	12 43	...	Ex3	...	3 22	...	...	...	...	...
Hagen ....arr	6 50	6 56	7 28	8 3	9 5	8 36	...	8 46	1—4	...	...	9 48	10 0	1047	10 52	11 4	...	1131	1148	...	...	12 48	1 5	Dortmd dep. 3.28	2 12	3 28	2 42	2 49	2 57	...	3 38
DORTMUND133C arr	7a32	7a58	8 a9	9a24	10a1	9 a24	...	9 a24	a.m.	...	...	1041	1154	1154	11a54	11a54	...	⋮	1p12	Ex3	...	1 p47	1p55		3p17	...	3p24	3p24	3p57	...	
Hagen ....dep		7 0	7 38	8 12		8 40	...		1028	...	...	9 52	10 4		10 55	11 10	...	⋮	1151	p.m.	...	1 10			2 21	3 57	2 46		3 6	...	...
Schwerte ....dep		7 16	7 53	8 34	...	8 55	...	a.m.	1051	...	...	...	1019	a.m.	11 11	11 29	...	⋮	12 6	1216	...	1 33	...		2 38	4 26	3 2	...	3 21	...	...
Holzwickede		...		8 49	...	...	...	9 9	1111	...	...	...	⋮	10 4	...	11 40	...	⋮		...	...	1 45	...	p.m	2 50	4 39		...		...	...
Unna ....arr		7 32	...	8 58	...	9 10	...	9 18	1120	...	...	1020	⋮	1013	11 26	11 47	...	⋮		...	...	1 54	...	3 55	2 58	4 49	...	...	...	...	...
Unna ....dep		...	...	...	...	9 11	...	9 25	1156	...	...	...	⋮	1030	11 28	...	...	⋮	...	...	...	2 0	...	...	3 0	4 53	...	...	...	...	...
Hamm ....arr		...	...	...	...	9 27	...	9 52	1222	...	...	...	⋮	1048	11 44	...	...	⋮	...	1247	...	2 26	...	...	3 18	5 19	...	...	...	...	...
Unna ....dep		7 33	...	9 14	...		...			...	...	1021	⋮	1028		11 49	...	⋮	...	⋮	...	1 59	...	3 57		5 54	...	...	...	...	...
Werl		7 49	...	9 41	...	...	...	...	...	...	...	...	⋮	1056	...	12 5	...	⋮	...	⋮	...	2 23	...	4 12	...	5 19	...	...	...	...	...
Soest ....arr		8 3	...	10 3	...	...	...	...	...	...	...	1048	⋮	1121	...	12 19	...	⋮	...	⋮	...	2 44	...	4 25	...	5 41	...	...	...	...	...
BERLIN (164) ....arr		...	...	...	...	...	...	...	...	...	...	6 p1	6p54	...	...	8 p56	...	6p12	...	7 p0	...	...	...	...	...	...	...	...	...	...	...

RC—Restaurant Car.

Luggage Rates—see page 462.

AIX-LA-CHAPELLE, DUSSELDORF, COLOGNE, ELBERFELD, and SOEST.

§—Connects at Aix-la-Chapelle West. **SLEEPING CAR—in 7.0 p.m. from Aix-la-Chapelle.**

BRUSSELS ...dep		...	7a§31	...	...	...	...	9a§18	1054	...	...	...	...	...	...	...	...	...	...	...	...	1p32	...	...	...	...	...	...	3 p3	...	5 p0	...	...
			1—4	1,2,3				1—4	Ex2	Ex 3	1,2,3	1—4	1,2,3			1—4	1,2,3		2 3 4	1,2,3	2,3,4	Ex 3		1—4	1,2,3	2 3 4			1—4	1,2,3	1,2,3		1—4
Aix-la-Chapelle—			p.m.					p.m.	p.m.			p.m.	p.m.								p.m.	p.m.				p.m.			p.m.		p.m.		p.m.
Hauptbahnhof ...dep		...	12 5	...	...	...	...	2 15	3 17	...	...	4 6	4 44	...	...	...	...	...	...	...	6 1	7 0	...	...	...	7†26	...	...	8 27	...	1013	...	1050
West ... ,,		...	1216	...	...	...	...	2 26	...	...	...	4 17	...	...	...	...	...	...	...	...	6 9	7 8	...	...	...	7 39	...	...	8 36	...	1022	...	11 1
Herzogenrath ...		...	1238	...	...	...	...	2 48	...	...	...	4 40	...	...	...	...	...	...	...	...	6 32	SC	...	...	...	8 9	...	...	8 58	...	1036	...	1123
Lindern (126) ...		...	1 3	...	...	...	...	3 13	...	...	...	5 7	...	...	...	...	...	...	...	...	6 59	...	...	...	...		...	...	9 25	...	...	...	1151
Erkelenz ...		...	1 24	p.m.	...	...	...	3 34	...	...	...	5 41	5 34	...	...	...	...	...	...	p.m.	7 20	7 46	...	p.m.	...	1—4	...	...	9 47	p.m.	...	...	1215
Rheydt ...		...	1 46	3 1	...	...	...	3 55	...	...	...	6 6	5 50	...	...	...	...	...	...	7 52	7 41	8 1	...	8 43	...	9p11	...	...	1015	11 7	1114	...	1236
München Gladbach ...arr		...	1 52	3 7	...	...	...	4 1	4 9	...	...	6 12	5 56	...	...	...	...	...	...	7 57	7 47	8 6	...	8 49	...	9 17	...	...	1021	1112	1119	...	1242
CREFELD (135) ...arr		...	2p39	...	...	...	...	...	4p33	...	...	...	6p27	...	...	...	...	...	...	8p26	8 p26	8 p56	...	10p3	...	10p3	...	...	1118	...	1152	...	1a28
ANTWERP ...dep		...	8 a8	...	...	...	...	1029		p.m.	...	...	...	...	...	...	...	...	p.m.	3p43		3 p43	...	...	...	...	...	...	...	6p33		...	...
Munchen Gladbach ...dep		...	1 59	3 9	...	...	...	4 6	...	4 21	...	6 29	6 0	...	...	...	...	...	7 28	8 4	...	8 12	...	9 3	...	9 28	...	...	1026	1130	...	...	1248
Kleinenbroich ...		...	2 13	...	...	...	...	4 19	...	...	...	6 44	...	...	...	...	...	...	7 43	...	...	...	...	...	...	9 42	...	...	1040	...	...	...	1 2
Neuss ... arr		...	2 27	3 25	...	...	...	4 33	...	4 37	...	6 58	6 16	...	...	...	...	...	7 57	8 20	...	8 28	...	9 21	p.m.	9 57	...	...	1053	1148	...	...	1 16
Neuss ... dep		...	2 37	3 30	...	...	...	4 42	...	4 38	...	7 9	6 18	...	§—From Deutz	...	...	...	8 0	8 21	...	8 30	...	9 27	9 48	10 9	...	...	11 3	1150	...	...	1 20
Düsseldorf Haupt... arr		...	2 54	3 45	...	...	...	4 58	...	4 51	p.m.	7 25	6 31	...	...	p.m.	p.m.	...	8 16	8 36	...	8 46	..	9 43	10 2	1025	...	...	1119	12 3	...	...	1 36
Düsseldorf Haupt... dep		...	3 2	3 48	...	...	...	5 17	...		6 10	7 46	6 34	...	...	6 40	7 21	...			...	8 50	...		10 5	1032	...	...	1130	1211	...	...	1 47
Hochdahl ...		...	3 26	⋮	...	...	...	5 40	...	...	⋮	8 10	⋮	...	...	7 3	...	...	...	...	...	...	...	...	...	1055	...	...	1154	...	...	...	2 10
Vohwinkel ...arr		...	3 40	⋮	...	...	...	5 55	...	...	⋮	8 25	⋮	...	...	7 18	7 51	...	...	...	...	9 22	...	..	1034	11 9	...	...	1210	1241	. .	...	2 26
	1—4	1,2,3		⋮	Ex 2	1—4	Ex3		1,2,3		⋮		⋮	1—4	Ex3			1—4		Ex3	1,2,3		1—4	1,2,3			1—4	1,2,3			1,2,3	1—4	
COLOGNE—	p.m.	p.m.			p.m.	p.m.	p.m.		p.m.					p.m.	p.m.			p.m.		p.m.	p.m.		p.m.	p.m.			p.m.	p.m.			nigt	n'gt	
Hauptbahn ...dep	2 22	3 33	...	⋮	4 24	4 28	4 51	...	5 56	...	⋮	...	⋮	6 11	6§46	...	...	6 43	...	7 21	8 18	...	8 34	9 46	...	...	1045	1120	...	...	1 6	1 11	...
Mülheim Rhine dep	2 31	3 42	...	⋮	⋮	4 38	5 0	...	6 5	...	⋮	...	⋮	6 21	7 4	...	...	6 53	...	7 30	...	...	8 43	9 55	...	...	1055	...	...	...	...	1 20	...
Opladen ...	2 49	...	...	⋮	RC	4 58	5 13	...	6 18	...	⋮	...	⋮	6 36	7 17	...	...	7 21	...	...	8 40	...	9 1	1010	...	...	1113	1138	...	...	...	1 40	...
Ohligs ...	3 11	4 7	...	⋮	⋮	5 31	5 26	...	6 32	...	⋮	...	⋮	6 52	RC	...	...	7 45	...	7 54	8 54	...	9 24	1025	...	...	1134	1152	...	...	1 37	2 4	...
Vohwinkel ...arr	3 30	4 21	...	⋮	⋮	5 50	5 40	...	6 46	...	⋮	...	⋮	7 8	⋮	...	...	8 4	...	8 8	9 8	...	9 44	1039	...	...	1153	12 5	...	...	1*51	2*23	...
Vohwinkel ...dep	3 34	4 22	3 42	⋮	⋮	5 52	5 41	6 0	6 47	...	⋮	8 30	⋮	7 10	⋮	7 19	7 52	8 16	...	8 9	9 11	9 28	9 46	1040	1034	1112	1156	12 7	1212	1242	1 52	2 24	2 33
Elberfeld Steinbeck	3 45	...	3 52	⋮	⋮	6 5	...	6 9	...	...	⋮	8 44	⋮	7 20	⋮	7 30	...	8 32	...	...	...	...	9 56	...	...	1124	12 5	...	1226	1252	...	2 34	2 46
Elberfeld Hauptbhf. ... arr	3 48	4 31	3 55	4 23	5 10	6 8	5 49	6 12	6 56	...	6 43	8 47	7 11	7 23	7 49	7 34	8 1	8 35	...	8 18	9 20	9 38	9 59	1049	1043	1127	12 8	1216	1229	1255	2 1	2 37	2 49
Elberfeld Hauptbhf. ... dep	3 54	4 33	4 0	4 25	5 12		5 52	6 17	7 0	...	6 45	8 57	7 14	7 26	7 51	7 39	8 3	8 41	...	8 20	9 23	9 44	10 2	1054	1045	1130	1212	1224	1235	1258	2 2	2 44	2 53
Barmen ... arr	4 3	4 39	4 9	4 31	5 18	...	5 58	6 26	7 6	...	6 51	9 6	7 20	7 35	7 57	7 48	8 9	8 50	...	8 26	9 29	9 49	1011	11 0	1051	1139	1221	1229	1244	1 4	2 8	2 53	3 2
Barmen ... dep	4 6	4 41	4 12	4 32	5 19	...	6 0	6 29	7 8	...	6 52	9 9	7 22	7 36	7 58	7 51	8 10	8 52	...	8 28	9 31	9 51	1013	11 2	1052	1142	1225	1231	1249	1 5	2 9	2 57	3 4
Barmen Rittersh'usen	4 10	...	4 20	4 35	...	...	...	6 35	7 12	...	...	9 16	...	7 40	...	8 6	8 14	8 59	...	8 34	9 35	9 57	1017	1110	1056	1146	1229	...	1 15	1 9	2 13	3 1	3 8
Schwelm ...		...	4 28		...	...	...	6 45		...	...	9 27	...		...	8 18		9 11	...	...		...		1119				...	1 23				
Haspe ...		...	4 48	...	...	...	...	7 14	...	...	...	9 52	...	...	...	8 40	...	9 36	...	...	...	...	...	1141	...	...	...	...	1 43	...	...	...	...
Hagen ...arr		5 5	4 53	...	5 42	...	6 27	7 19	...	...	7 15	9 57	7 47	...	8 21	8 46	...	9 42	...	8 56	...	10 20	...	1147	...	...	...	1253	1 49	...	...	...	...
DORTMUND 133C ...arr		...	...	...	6 p43	...	7p15	8p39	...	...	7p52	11p24	8p39	...		9p40	...		...	9p40	...	11p24	...	1248	...	...	...	...		...	...	...	...
Hagen ...dep		5 11	5 23	...	5 46	...	6 31	7 25	...	...			7 51	...	...		...		...	A—Dortmund dep. 10.9.		10 25	...		...	...	...	1257	...	...	...	...	...
Schwerte ...		5 30	5 45	...	...	...	6 47	7 48		Dortmund dep. 8.9.	...	...	8 7	...	...	...	...	...	...		A	10 42	...	ng't	...	...	...	1 12	...	...	...	...	...
Holzwickede ...		...	5 57	...	...	...	...			8 p44	...	...		...	...	...	...	...	...		10p44	...	...	1237	...	...	...	1 23	...	...	...	...	...
Unna ...arr		5 46	6 6	...	...	...	7 2	...	...	8 50	...	...	...	...	...	...	...	...	...		10 52	10 58	...	1247	...	...	...	1 31	...	†—Weekdays only.	...	*—Sets down only.	...
Unna ...dep		...	6 18	...	...	...	7 3	...	...	...	...	...	...	...	...	...	...	...	...		11 4	...	...	1249	...	...	...	1 32	...		...		...
Hamm ...arr		...	6 43	...	6 30	...	7 20	...	...	...	...	...	...	...	...	...	...	...	...		11 29	SC	...	1 17	...	...	...	1 48	...		...		...
Unna ...dep		5 48	6 35	...	⋮	...		...		9 7	...	...	...	...	...	...	...	...	...		⋮	11 2	...		...	...	...	⋮	...	...	...	...	...
Werl ...		6 3	7 1	...	C	...	...	...	C—Via Hanover, page 161A.	9 33	...	...	...	...	...	...	...	...	...		⋮	11 17	...	...	...	...	...	⋮	...	...	...	...	...
Soest ...arr		6 16	7 25	...	⋮	...	...	...		9 57	...	...	...	...	...	...	...	...	...		⋮	11 31	...	...	...	...	...	⋮	...	...	...	...	...
BERLIN (164) ...arr		...	...	...	12a21	...	...	...		...	...	...	...	...	...	...	...	...	...	...	7 a20	8 a3	...	...	...	...	...	8a54	...	...	...	...	...

VOHWINKEL and VELBERT.

Vohwinkel	7a 6	9a 4	11a9	1p55	3p59	6 p7	8p20	10p50	1 a6
Aprath ...	7 20	9 16	1123	2 7	4 12	6 19	8 33	11 4	1 17
Wülfrath ...	7 34	9 27	1134	2 17	4 27	6 30	8 44	11 15	1 27
Velbert ...arr	7 57	9 50	1156	2 37	4 51	6 53	9 7	11 40	1 49

Velbert ...dep	5a30	8a10	9a58	12 6	2p45	5p9	7p3	9p17	11p54
Wülfrath ...	5 51	8 31	1016	1227	3 3	530	727	9 37	12 14
Aprath ...	6 1	8 40	1025	1236	3 12	540	735	9 46	12 25
Vohwinkel	6 15	8 53	1037	1247	3 23	552	748	9 58	12 38

Wülfrath ...dep	5a54	8 a9	12p38	2p48	5p23	8 p26	10p11
Ratingen 123D ...arr	6 30	8 42	1 13	3 19	5 58	9 1	10 45
Ratingen ...dep	7a16	11a37	2p10	4p10	6p10	9p15	...
Wülfrath ...arr	7 56	12 17	2 42	4 57	6 50	9 55	...

SOEST, ELBERFELD, COLOGNE, DUSSELDORF, and AIX-LA-CHAPELLE (Aachen).

[Luggage Rates—see page 462.

Station	1	2	3	4	5	6	7	8	9	10	11	12	13	14	15	16	17	18	19	20	21	22	23	24	25	26	27	28	29	30	31	32
BERLIN 165......dep	...	...	...	...	9p34	...	...	1013	...	...	...	...	...	...	...	...	...	...	...	...	...	...	...	...	...	...	...	...	...	...	...	8 a0
	1—4	1—4	1,2,3	1—4	1,2,3	1,2,3	1—4	Ex3	1,2,3	Ex 3	1,2,3	1—4	1,2,3	Ex3	1—4	1,2,3	1,2,3	1—4	1,2,3	1—4	1,2,3	1—4	1,2,3	1,2,3	1—4	1,2,3	Ex 3	1,2,3	1—4	1—4	1,2,3	Ex2
Soest......dep	...	...	...	...		...	...	a.m. 5 54	...	...	...	...	...	...	...	...	...	a.m. 6 49	...	a.m. 8 52	...	...	a.m. 11 9	...	a.m. 10 9	...	p.m. 12 34	...	...	...	...	A
Werl......	...	...	...	...		...	...	...	...	...	...	...	...	...	...	...	...	7 12	...	9 15	...	...	1124	...	1031	...	12 48	...	...	...	...	
Unna......arr	...	...	...	...		...	...	6 21	...	...	...		...	...	...	...	...	7 36		9 39	...	...	1139	...	1054	...	1 3		...	...	...	
Hamm......dep	...	...	...	...	a.m. 5 10	...	...	...	...	...	...	a.m. 5 50	...	...	...	...	...	7 13	a.m. 9 24	...	...	...	...	...	...	...	...	p.m. 1238	...	...	...	1 50
Unna......arr	...	...	...	...	5 26	...	...	...	...	...	...	6 18	...	...	...	...	...	7 38	9 40	...	...	...	...	...	...	...	†	1258	...	...	...	...
Unna......dep	...	...	...	...	5 27	...	...	6 22	...	...	...	6 31	...	...	...	...	...	7 42	9 41	9 48	...	...	1140	...	11 2	...	1 6	1 10	...	...	...	...
Holzwickede......	...	...	...	...	...	...	...	...	...	...	...	6 40	...	...	...	...	...	7 53	...	9 57	...	...	...	...	1113	...		1 20	...	...	...	RG
Schwerte......dep	...	...	...	...	5 42	...	...	6 40	...	...	...		...	...	...	...	...	8 9	9 59		...	...	1157	...	1129	...	...	1 32	...	...	...	...
Hagen......arr	...	...	...	...	5 56	...	...	6 55	...	a.m.	a.m.	...	a.m.	...	...	...	...	8 29	10 14	1,2,3	...	...	1213	...	1148	a.m.	...	1 47	...	...	...	2 35
DORTMUND 133C ...dep	...	...	...	a.m.	...	...	...	5a47	a.m.	6 30	6 32	a.m.	7 53	a.m.	...	...	8a37	8a37	9 a26	10a3	...	...	1138	...	1138	1158	...	...	...	...	...	1p22
Hagen......dep	...	...	...	5 14	5 58	...	...	6 59	7 7	7 32	7 40	8 3	8 29	8 42	...	...	9 25	9 29	10 18	1113	...	...	1228	...	1234	1 3	...	1 51	...	...	...	2 39
Haspe......	...	...	...	5 24	...	...	...	...	...	...	...	8 13	...	...	...	...	...	9 37	...	...	...	...	...	...	1243	...	1,2,3	...	...	...	...	...
Schwelm......	a.m.	a.m.	a.m.	5 47	6 18	a.m.	a.m.	...	...	...	8 4	8 37	...	...	a.m.	a.m.	...	10 2	...	1136	a.m.	p.m.	...	p.m.	1 4	1 24	p.m.	...	p.m.	p.m.	p.m.	...
Barmen Rittershausn......	4 21	5 21	5 58	6 3	6 26	6 36	6 49	...	7 33	7 58	8 14	8 46	8 56	...	9 26	9 36	...	1010	10 44	1145	1156	1217	...	1 4	1 12	1 35	1 50	...	2 9	2 22	2 55	...
Barmen......arr	4 25	5 25	6 2	6 7	6 30	6 40	6 53	7 26	7 37	8 2	8 18	8 50	9 0	9 8	9 30	9 40	9 53	1014	10 48	1149	12 0	1221	1256	1 8	1 16	1 39	1 54	2 19	2 13	2 26	2 59	3 7
Barmen......dep	4 26	5 28	6 3	6 9	6 32	6 41	6 55	7 28	7 38	8 4	8 19	8 54	9 1	9 9	9 32	9 42	9 55	1016	10 49	1151	12 1	1223	1258	1 9	1 19	1 41	1 56	2 21	2 14	2 31	3 0	3 8
Elberfeld Haupt......arr	4 32	5 37	6 9	6 18	6 37	6 47	7 5	7 34	7 44	8 10	8 25	9 3	9 7	9 15	9 38	9 48	10 1	1025	10 54	1137	12 7	1232	1 4	1 15	1 28	1 47	2 2	2 27	2 23	2 40	3 6	3 13
Elberfeld Haupt......dep	4 34	5 40	6 11	6 21	6 44	6 52	7 10	7 41	7 52	8 13	8 27	9 23	9 9	9 17	9 43	9 51	10 3	1030	10 56	12 1	12 9	1236	1 7	1 17	1 33	1 50	2 5	2 29	2 32	3 34	3 19	3 15
Elberfeld Steinbeck......	4 38	5 44	...	6 25	...	...	7 15	...	...	...	...	9 27			9 47	...		1034	...	...		1240	...	...	1 38	...	...	...	2 36	3 39		
Vohwinkel......arr	4 47	5 59	6 21	6 36	6 53	7 2	7 24	7 52	8 2	8 22	8 37	9 39			9 55	10 1		1043	11 5	1211		1254	1 17	1 26	1 49	2 0	2 17	2 38	2 47	3 51		
Vohwinkel......dep	4 48	6 1	...	...	6 54	...	7 26	...	8 3	8 23	...	...			9 56	...		1045	11 6	...		1256	1 18	...	...	2 1	...	...	2 48	...		
Ohligs......	5 2	6 24	...	...	7 6	...	7 49	...	8 18	8 36	...	...		9 36	1016	...	1025	11 4	11 18	...	1232	1 16	1 34	...	...	2 16	...	...	3 12	...		
Opladen......	5 15	6 55	...	...	7 17	...	8 10	...	8 32	8 48	...	...		9 46	1040	...	...	1124	11 29	...	...	1 33	1 47	...	...	2 28	...	...	3 42	...		
Mülheim......arr	5 30	7 15	...	...	...	...	8 29	...	...	9 4	...	...		§	1057	...	1048	1149	11 41	...	...	1 49	2 0	...	...	2 41	...	...	4 2	...		
COLOGNE Haupt....arr	5 38	7 23	...	...	7 35	...	8 37	...	8 52	9 12	...	...		1017	11 7	...	1057	1159	11 50	...	1259	1 57	2 10	...	...	2 50	...	...	4 10	...		3 56
Vohwinkel......dep	...	...	6 22	6 38	...	7 3	...	7 54	...	...	8 38	9 41		§—At Deutz.	...	10 3	...	...	11 11	1212	...	...	...	1 27	1 50	...	2 18	2 39	...	3 55		...
Hochdahl......	...	...	...	6 56	...	...	...	...	1—4	1,2,3	...	9 56			...	...	...	...	11 28	...	...	...	1—4	...	2 4	...	...	...	...	4 11		Ex3
Düsseldorf Haupt...arr	a.m.	...	6 42	7 16	...	7 23	...	8 17	a.m.	a.m	8 59	1014	9 36		...	1025	...	...	11 47	1233	...	...	p.m.	1 49	2 23	...	2 40	3 1	...	4 30	3 48	p.m.
Düsseldorf Haupt...dep	5 8	...	6 44	7 33	...	7 25	...	8 29	8 35	9 17		1020			...	1031	...	...	11 52	1247	...	...	1259	1 52	2 36	...	2 44		...	4 36		3 52
Neuss......arr	5 25	...	6 57	7 51	...	7 38	...	8 43	8 51	9 32	...	1036	...		...	1045	...	...	12 9	1 3	p.m.	...	1 15	To Crefeld arr 2.21 p.m.	2 52	...	2 57	...	...	4 53	...	4 5
Neuss......dep	5 35	...	7 0		...	7 45	...	8 46	8 57	9 34	...	1057	...		...		...	...	12 20	1 6	1 41	...	1 23		3 9	...	3 1	...	...	5 0	...	4 6
Kleinenbroich......	5 53	...	...	...	...	...	...	...	...	...	...	1113	...	...	...	...	...	...	12 35	...	...	...	1 37		3 23	...	...	...	...	5 17	...	...
München Gladbach...arr	6 7	...	7 16	...	...	8 1	...	9 2	9 13	9 50	...	1126	...	...	...	...	...	...	12 48	1 22	1 58	...	1 50		3 36	...	3 17	...	...	5 32	...	4 22
ANTWERP 99 ...arr 1—4	...	...	...	a.m.	...	10 48	...	...	...	12p23	...	...	...	...	...	...	...	...	...	5p57	...	...	5p57		...	...	...	...	...	8p46	...	
CREFELD ......dep a.m.	5a17	...	6a53	7 18	...	...	...	8a38	...	9 a30	...	1033	...	...	...	...	...	...	...	1233	...	...	...		2p48	...	2 p48	...	...	5p22	4 p2	
München Gladbach 5‡17	6 23	...	7 25	8 11	...	8 9	...	9 8	9 27	10 0	...	1143	...	...	...	...	...	...	12 50	1 26	2 0	...	2 4		3 46	...	3 20	...	...	6 6	4 30	
Rheydt...... 5 25	6 35	...	7 32	8 19	...	8 15	...	9 15	9 35	10 6	...	1151	...	...	...	...	...	...	12 56	1 33	2 6	...	2 11	...	3 56	...	3 27	...	...	6 13	...	...
Erkelenz...... 5 52	6 58	...	...	8 41	...		...	9 29	9 58		...	1213	...	...	...	...	...	...		1 51	From Cologne 1p4	...	2 33	...	4 19	...	...	...	...	6 35	...	...
Lindern...... 6 17	7 20	...	...	9 2	...	...	...	...	1019	...	...	1233	...	...	...	...	...	...	...	...		...	2 53	...	4 40	...	...	...	...	6 56	...	...
Herzogenrath...... 6 53	7 52	...	8 14	9 31	...	...	...	9 59	1047	...	...	1 0	...	...	...	...	...	...	...	2 24		...	3 21	...	5 4	...	...	...	...	7 26	...	...
Aix-la-Chap. West...arr 7 20	8 17	...	8 30	9 54	...	...	...	1015	1110	...	...	1 23	...	...	...	...	...	...	...	2 44		...	3 44	...	5 24	...	...	...	...	7 49	...	...
Aix-la-Chap. Haupt...arr 7 27	8 29	...	8 38	10 2	...	...	...	1023	1119	...	...	1 32	...	...	...	...	...	...	...	2 53		...	3 52	...	5 29	...	4 25	...	...	8 1	5 36	...
BRUSSELS 104......arr	...	...	1126	...	...	...	...	1 p3	2p51	...	...	5p44	...	...	...	...	...	...	...	6 p8	...	...	...	...	...	...	6 p57	...	...	...	8 p0	...

†—To Dortmund (arrive 1.28). ‡—Weekdays only. A—From Friedrichstrasse Station at Berlin, travels via Hanover; page 160B.

DUSSELDORF, HATTINGEN, and HAGEN.

Station	1	2	3	4	5	6	7	8	9	10	11	12	13	14	15	16	17	18	19	20	21
	a.m.		a.m.	a.m.	a.m.	a.m.	noon	p.m	a.m.	p.m.	p.m.	p.m	p.m.	p.m.	p.m.	p.m.	p.m.	p.m.	p.m.	p.m.	p.m.
Düsseldorf-Haupt dep	...	...	...	...	6 50	9 43	...	...	1154	...	...	3 13	...	...	5 22	...	7 33	...	9 46	...	1124
Mettmann......	...	...	...	...	7 23	10 8	...	...	1224	...	...	3 46	...	...	5 53	...	8 2	...	10 18	...	1153
Elberfeld-Mirke......	5 29	...	7 §16	7 26	7 51	1035	12§1	...	1253	1 57	2 §10	4 19	4 53	6 §4	6 23	7 32	8 30	9§14	10 48	11 7	1217
Barmen-Wichlinghs. arr	5 43	...	7 36	7 40	8 6	1049	1220	...	1 7	2 11	2 28	4 33	5 7	6 24	6 37	7 45	8 44	9 36	11 2	1121	1251
Barmen-Wichlinghs dp	5 46	...	7 37	7 44		1051	1221	1 10	...		2 29	...	5 13	6 25	...	7 47		9 37		1122	
Schee......	6 4	...	...	8 1	...	11 8	...	1 26	...	...	...	...	5 34	6 38	...	8 5	...		...	1138	...
Hattingen......arr	6 35	a.m.	8 6	8 27	...	1132	1250	1 50	...	...	2 57	...	6 7	6 58	...	8 36	...	1012	...	12 3	...
Barmen-Wichlinghs dep	...	7 49	Essen 8.26.	...	...	...	Essen 1.10.	...	1 13	...	Essen 3.20	4 35	...	Essen 7.19	5 42	...	...	Essen 10.31.	...	...	...
Hagen......arr	...	3 24		...	...	...		...	1 47	...		5 10	...		7 18	...	...		...	...	...

†—Weekdays only.
§—From or at Elberfeld Hauptbhf.

Rail Motor. Frequent Services are run between Dusseldorf & Barmen-Wichlingshausen and vice versa.

Luggage Rates—see page 462.] **SOEST, ELBERFELD, COLOGNE, DUSSELDORF, and AIX-LA-CHAPELLE (Aachen).**

Station	Ex3	1—4	Ex3	Ex3	1—4	1,2,3	1,2,3		1—4	Ex3	1—4	1,2,3	1,2,3	1,2,3	Ex2	1,2,3
BERLIN 165 dep	...	...	...	...	...	...	8a59	...	...	...	...	...	...	...	1216	...
Soest dep	...	...	...	...	p.m. 1 30	...	A	...	p.m. 3 36	...	...	...	...	...		p.m. 6 2
Werl	...	...	...	...	1 53	...		...	3 58	...	...	...	...	...		6 17
Unna arr	...	...	...	...	2 16	...	p.m.	...	4 22	p.m.	...	...	...	...		6 32
Hamm dep	...	...	...	...	2 9	...	3 25	...	...	4 7	...	...	...	...		6 7
Unna arr	...	...	...	...	2 35	...		...	...	4 25	...	...	...	...		6 32
Unna dep	...	...	...	...	2 43	...		...	4 32	4 27	...	...	...	...		6 35
Holzwickede	...	...	p.m.	p.m	2 55	...		...	4 45	...	...	p.m.	...	...		6 45
Schwerte dep	...	...	3 13	3 30	3 20	...		...	5 2	4 47	...	5 30	...	...		6 57
Hagen arr	p.m.	...	3 28	3 45	3 40	p.m.	4 12	...	5 22	5 3	...	5 45	...	...		7 13
DORTM'D 133C dp	1 22	...	2p42	2p49	...	3 33	3p33	...	4p25	4p25	...	4p25	...	5p56	6p35	6p35
Hagen dep	2 20	...	3 33	3 50	3 53	4 8	4 14	...	5 28	5 12	...	5 53	...	6 34	7 10	7 17
Haspe	2 28	...	...	...	4 0	...	...	1,2,3	5 36	...	...	RC	...	...	...	...
Schwelm	3 3	p.m.	RC	...	4 22	...	...	p.m.	5 58	...	p.m	...	p.m.	...	RC	7 39
Barmen-Rittershn	3 11	3 48	...	4 16	4 44	...	4 38	5 4	6 7	...	5 40	6 19	6 29	...	...	...
Barmen arr	3 15	3 52	4 0	4 20	4 48	4 36	4 42	5 8	6 11	5 39	5 44	6 23	6 33	7 2	7 38	7 48
Barmen dep	3 17	3 54	4 2	4 22	4 52	4 38	4 44	5 10	6 13	5 41	5 46	6 25	6 34	7 3	7 40	7 50
Elberfeld Hauptbhf arr	3 26	4 3	4 8	4 28	5 1	4 44	4 50	5 16	6 22	5 47	5 55	6 31	6 40	7 8	7 46	7 56
Elberfeld Hauptbhf dep	3 30	4 16	4 12	4 31	5 7	4 46	4 52	5 19	6 27	5 50	5 58	6 34	6 42	7 10	7 48	8 0
Elberfeld Steinbck	3 35	4 20	...	...	5 12				6 32	...	6 2	...	...			...
Vohwinkel arr	3 44	4 34	4 22	4 41	5 24				6 42	5 59	6 14	6 45	6 51			8 10
Vohwinkel dep	3 47	4 36	4 23	...	...				...	...	6 18	6 46	7 6			...
Ohligs	4 8	5 21	4 38	...	...		5 12		...	...	6 40	7 0	7 28			...
Opladen	4 27	5 43	...	...	...		...		...	...	6 59	7 12	7 46			...
Mülheim arr	4 44	6 2	...	...	...		5 32		...	...	7 18	7 25	8 2			...
COLOGNE Haupt	4 53	6 12	5 8	...	...	5 31	5 41		...	...	7 28	7 34	8 12		8 36	...
Vohwinkel dep	...	...	...	4 43	5 39	...	...		6 57	6 0	...	...	6 52		...	8 11
Hochdahl	...	...	...	...	5 56	...	1—4		7 11	...	...	...	...		...	...
Düsseldorf Haupt. arr	...	...	...	5 5	6 16	...	p.m.	5 51	7 42	6 21	...	...	7 14	7 38	...	8 32
Düsseldorf Haupt. dep	...	...	...	5 16	6 29	...	7 4	To Crefeld.	7 48	6 25	...	...	7 26	7 40	...	8 35
Neuss arr	...	...	...	5 30	6 45	...	7 21		8 5	6 39	...	...	7 40	7 55	...	8 48
Neuss dep	...	...	...	5 32	6 49	...	7 26		8 17	6 41	...	...		7 57	...	8 50
Kleinenbroich	...	...	...	...	7 3	...	7 41		8 33	...	...	...	...	...	...	...
München Glad. arr	...	...	...	5 48	7 16	...	7 54		8 46	6 57	...	...	...	8 13	...	9 6
ANTWERP 99 arr	...	...	...	8p46	1132	...	...	...	...	1132	...	...	...	...	...	...
CREFELD dep	...	...	...	5p22	6p18	...	7p17	...	8p14	...	...	...	...	...	...	8p38
München Glad. dep	...	...	...	5 51	7 23	...	8 2	...	8 55	7 0	...	...	...	8 15	...	9 12
Rheydt	...	...	...	5 58	7 32	...	8 8	...	9 3	7 6	...	...	...	8 21	...	9 19
Erkelenz	...	...	...	...	7 57	...		...	9 39		...	...	...		...	9 34
Linden	...	...	...	...	8 19	...	...	...	10 1	...	...	...	...	...	...	...
Herzogenrath	...	...	...	6 40	8 48	...	...	...	1031	...	...	...	...	...	...	10 4
Aix-la-Chapelle West	...	...	...	6 56	9 11	...	...	...	1055	...	...	...	...	...	...	1020
Aix-la-Chapelle Hauptbf	...	...	...	7 5	9 21	...	...	...	11 4	...	...	...	...	...	...	1029
BRUSSELS 104 arr	...	...	...	9r45	...	...	...	...	...	...	...	...	...	...	...	...

Station	1—4	1,2,3	1—4	1,2,3	Ex 3	Ex3	1,2,3	1—4	1—4	Ex3	1,2,3	1—4	1,2,3	1,2,3	1—4	1,2,3
BERLIN 165 dep	...	...	...	...	..	1 p0	1 p0	...	...	...	...	...	...	...	...	...
Soest dep	...	...	...	...	...	p.m. 8 7	p.m. 8 14	...	p.m. 8 29	...	...	...	p.m. 1054	p.m. ...	p.m. 11 7	...
Werl	...	...	...	...	...	...	8 29	...	8 52	...	...	...	1110	§	1128	...
Unna arr	...	p.m.	...	p.m.	...	...	8 44	...	9 15	p.m.	...	...	1126	...	1151	...
Hamm dep	...	6 44	...	7 41	...	...	...	...	9 1	9 30	...	...	...	11 0	1124	...
Unna arr	...	7 1	...	7 59	...	...	...	...	9 26	9 48	...	...	...	1118	1150	...
Unna dep	...	7 2	...	8 0	...	...	8 46	...	9 32	9 49	...	...	1127	1119	12 0	...
Holzwickede	...	...	...	...	...	...	Dortmund arr. 9.10.	...	9 42	...	...	p.m.	...	Dortmund arr. 11.47	1213	...
Schwerte dep	...	7 20	...	8 18	...	...		...	9 57	10 7	...	10 17	1144		1229	...
Hagen arr	...	7 35	...	8 34	...	9 0		...	10 15	1022	...	10 36	12 0		1249	a.m.
DORTM'D 133C dp	p.m.	6 p40	...	7 p40	8 p7	8 p7		...		9p19	...	...	11p6		1151	1258
Hagen dep	6 47	7 39	...	8 38	8 51	9 4		...	9p12	1026	...	10 40	12 2		1 15	1 35
Haspe	6 55	...	...	...	...	...		...	9 21	...	...	10 49	...	1—4	1 23	...
Schwelm	7 18	...	p.m.	...	RC	RC	p.m.	p.m.	9 42	...	p.m.	11 9	...	n'gt	1 44	...
Barmen-Rittershn	7 26	8 5	8 24	9 4	...	...	9 37	9 52	9 59	...	11 0	11 19	...	1210	2 6	2 1
Barmen arr	7 30	8 9	8 28	9 8	9 19	9 32	9 41	9 56	10 3	1054	11 4	11 23	1230	1214	2 10	2 5
Barmen dep	7 32	8 11	8 29	9 9	9 21	9 33	9 43	9 59	10 6	1055	11 5	11 26	1232	1215	2 17	2 6
Elberfeld Hauptbhf arr	7 41	8 17	8 35	9 15	9 26	9 38	9 49	10 8	10 15	11 0	1111	11 35	1238	1224	2 23	2 12
Elberfeld Hauptbhf dep	8 5	8 22	8 38		9 28	9 42	9 52	1012	10 20	11 2	1113	11 42	1240	1244	2 30	2 17
Elberfeld Steinbck	8 9	...	8 42	...			...	1016	10 25			11 47		1248	2 35	...
Vohwinkel arr	8 25	8 31	8 54	...			10 2	1025	10 36			12 0		1 1	2 49	2 28
Vohwinkel dep	8 48	8 32	...	...			...	1028	...			...		1 5	...	...
Ohligs	9 11	8 45	...	...	9 47		...	1049	...	1120		...	1 3	1 31	...	Extra. Hagen ......dep 8p1 / Vohwinkel arr 9 19
Opladen	9 32	8 57	...	...	...		...	11 6	...	1131		...	1 14	1,51	...	
Mülheim arr	9 50	9 11	...	...	...		...	1121	...	1144		...	1 27	2 8	...	
COLOGNE Haupt	9 59	9 20	...	...	10 14	1026	...	1130	...	1153		...	1 36	2 17	...	
Vohwinkel dep	...	...	8 55	...	...	...	10 3	...	10 38	...	...	12 4	...	...	...	
Hochdahl	...	Ex.2	9 9	1—4	...	...	...	...	10 53	...	...	12 18	...	...	...	
Düsseldorf Haupt. arr	...	p.m.	9 28	p.m.	...	...	10 24	...	11 14	...	1141	12 37	...	...	...	
Düsseldorf Haupt. dep	...	9 16	9 46	10 34	...	...	11 28	...	11 46	...		12 42	...	...	...	
Neuss arr	...	9 28	10 2	10 50	...	...	11 44	...	12 3	...	...	12 58	§—From 30th June until 14th Sept.	...	...	
Neuss dep	...		10 8	10 57	...	...	11 46	...	12 10	...	...	1 7		...	...	
Kleinenbroich	...	...	...	11 12	...	...	...	...	12 26	...	...	...		...	...	
München Glad. arr	...	...	1024	11 25	...	...	12 3	...	12 39	...	...	1 24		...	...	
ANTWERP 99 arr	...	...	...	...	...	...	...	...	...	...	...	...		...	...	...
CREFELD dep	...	...	9p38	...	...	...	11p27	...	11p45	...	...	...		...	...	...
München Glad. dep	...	...	1031	11 30	...	...	12 6	...	12 49	...	...	1 26		...	...	...
Rheydt	...	...	1038	11 36	...	...	12 12	...	12 55	...	...	1 32		...	...	...
Erkelenz	...	...	1059		...	...		...	1 16	...	...			...	...	...
Linden	...	...	1115	...	...	...	...	...		...	...	...		...	...	...
Herzogenrath	...	...	1141	...	...	...	...	...	...	...	...	...	...	...	...	...
Aix-la-Chapelle West	...	...	1157	...	...	...	...	...	...	...	...	...	...	...	...	...
Aix-la-Chapelle Hauptbf	...	...	12 5	...	...	...	...	...	...	...	...	...	...	...	...	...
BRUSSELS 104 arr	...	...	3a56	...	...	...	...	...	...	...	...	...	...	...	...	...

HAGEN, HATTINGEN, and DUSSELDORF

§–From or at Elberfeld Hauptbahnhof.

Station		a.m.	a.m.	Essen 7.6.	Essen 8.37	a.m.	a.m.		a.m.	a.m.	Essen 12.7	Essen 1.51		p.m.	p.m.		p.m.	p.m.	p.m.	Essen 8.0.	p.m.	p.m.	
Hagen dep		...	7 8			...	...	...	...	11 20	...	...	...	2 38	...	...	...	...	...		7 20	...	...
Barmen-Wichlinghs arr		...	7 50			...	...	...	...	12 2	...	...	...	3 21	...	...	...	...	...		8 4	...	...
Hattingen dep		6 19	...	7 27	8 57	...	9 14	...	11 12	...	1227	2 13	...	...	3 0	...	5 28	...	7 23	8 21	...	9 9	...
Schee		7 1	...	7 49	...	...	9 52	...	11 53	...	...	...	...	...	3 39	...	6 11	...	7 57	...	...	9 48	...
Barmen-Wichlinghs ar		7 14	...	7 59	9 28	...	10 5	a.m.	12 7	...	1257	2 42	p.m.	...	3 52	p.m.	6 24	...	8 9	8 50	...	10 1	p.m.
Barmen-Wichlin. dep	5 27	7 16	7 52	8 0	9 29	9 35	10 6	1145		12 10	1258	2 43	2 56	3 23	3 54	5 6	6 31	7 22	8 12	8 51	8 54	10 3	1124
Elberfeld-Mirke	5 44	7 30	8 9	8§20	9 §48	9 51	10 19	12 1	...	12 27	1§15	3 §1	3 10	3 41	4 8	5 19	6 53	7 36	8 26	9§10	9 11	1017	1139
Mettmann	6 10	...	8 34			1014	...	1227	...	12 53	...		...	4 5	...	5 43	7 24	8 3	...		9 40	...	12 5
Düsseldorf-Haupt	6 35	...	8 56	...	...	1036	...	1255	...	1 16	...	...	...	4 26	...	6 9	7 49	...	...	...	10 3	...	...

Schee & Silschede. In 20 min. Schee dep. 7.8, 8.6, 9.56 a.m., 1.30, 3.42, 6.15, 8.10 p.m. Silschede dep. 6.22, 7.35, 9.20, 11.10 a.m., 3.0, 4.53, 7.21, 9.7 p.m.

§—Dortmund Süd.

MUNCHEN GLADBACH, ESSEN, DORTMUND, and UNNA.

	2 3 4	Ex3	1,2,3	1—4	1—4	1,2,3	1,2,3	1—4	Ex3	1,2,3	1—4
				a.m.	a.m.	a.m.		a.m.			a.m.
M. Gladbach ......dep		...	...	5 29	...	7 5	...	6 26	...	...	7 32
Viersen		...	...	5 45	...	7 17	...	6 39	...	...	7 58
Crefeld ......arr		a.m.	...	6 9	...	7 34	...	7 3	...	...	8 23
Crefeld ......dep		5 34	...	—	5 56	7 36	a.m.	7 7	...	...	—
Uerdingen		...	a.m.	a.m.	6 17	...		7 28	a.m.	From 15th July until 20th September.	a.m.
Duisburg ......dep		6 4	6 9	6 15	7 0	8 3	8 13	8 25	8 18		9 28
Mülheim-Ruhr ......arr		6 14	6 19	6 29	7 14	8 13	8 22	8 40	8 28		9 41
Ruhrort ......dep		5 45	5 45	5 45	...	7 33	7 33	7 33	...		9 12
Mülheim ......arr		6 4	6 4	6 4	...	7 54	7 54	7 54	RC		9 32
Oberhausen ......dep		5 58	...	5 58	6 55	7 53	7 53	7 53	...		9 41
Mülheim ......arr		6 10	...	6 10	7 6	8 4	8 4	8 4	...		9 49
Mülheim-Ruhr ......dep		6 15	6 21	6 33	7 16	8 14	8 24	8 42	8 30		9 51
Mülheim-Eppinghofen		...	...	6 37	7 20	...	...	8 46	...		9 55
Essen West		...	...	6 50	7 33	...	...	9 0	...		10 7
Essen Haupt. ......arr		6 29	6 36	6 54	7 37	8 29	8 38	9 4	8 44	a.m	1011
Essen Haupt. ......dep		6 31	6 38	...	...	...	...	...	8 46	10 8	...
Kray	2 3 4	...	.	...	...	...	...	...	...	..	...
Bochum S. arr.	a.m.	6 45	6 52	...	...	...	...	...	9 0	1028	...
Essen Haupt. ......dep	5 11	...	⋮	7 0	7 46	8 34	8 43	9 18	...	...	1014
Steele Nord	5 24	...	⋮	7 14	8 2	8 42	8 52	9 32	...	...	1027
Bochum S.	5 44	6 46	6 53	7 33	8 20	—	9 5	9 51	9 1	1032	1055
Langendreer ......arr	5 54	6 56	7 3	7 43	8 30	...	9 15	10 1	...	1042	11 5
Witten ......arr	6 13	7 5	...	8 8	8 46	...	9 31	1014	...	...	1124
Dortmund ......arr	6 15	—	7§17	8 2	8 48	...	9 29	1020	9 21	1058	1124
,, ...dep		...		8 14		...	9 34	1033			1135
Hörde		...	...	8 27	...	...	9 46	1045	...	...	1147
Holzwickede		...	...	8 45	...	...	10 3	11 2	...	...	12 5
Unna (134A) ......arr		...	...	8 58	...	...	1013	1120	...	...	1215

	1,2,3	Ex2	1—4	Ex3	1,2,3	1—4	1,2,3	Ex3	1—4	1—4
	a.m.		a.m.	a.m.	p.m.	a.m.			a.m.	
M. Gladbach ......dep	8 44	...	...	10 0	...	...	...	...	1143	...
Viersen	8 55	...	...	1012	...	...	...	...	1158	...
Crefeld ......arr	9 14	...	...	1028	...	...	...	...	1220	...
Crefeld ......dep	9 17	...	...	1031	...	1014	...	...	1230	...
Uerdingen	9 33	...	...	1042	...	1029	p.m	...	1248	p.m.
Duisburg ......dep	10 4	...	1025	1111	1210	1053	1 5	...	1 14	1 38
Mülheim-Ruhr ......arr	1014	...	1049	1120	1224	—	1 15	p.m	1 24	1 52
Ruhrort ......dep	9 12	...	1024	...	1158	1158	...	1 12	...	...
Mülheim ......arr	9 32	...	1043	.	1219	1219	...	1 34	...	...
Oberhausen ......dep	9 41	...	...	RC	1129	121[illegible]	...	1 40	...	...
Mülheim ......arr	9 49	...	...	...	1140	1230	...	1 48	...	...
Mülheim-Ruhr ......dep	1016	...	1051	1122	1226	1233	1 17	1 49	1 25	1 54
Mülheim-Eppinghofen	...	...	1055	...	...	1238	...	...	1 29	1 58
Essen West	...	...	11 8	...	...	1251	...	RC	1 41	2 10
Essen Haupt. ......arr	1030	a.m.	1112	1137	1241	1255	1 32	2 3	1 45	2 14
Essen Haupt. ......dep	1032	1120	...	1140	1243	1 3	...	2 7	...	...
Kray	...	...	...	..	...	1 11	...	...	...	...
Bochum S. arr.	1046	1135	...	1155	1257	1 27	...	2 21	...	...
Essen Haupt. ......dep	...	⋮	1116	...	...	1 0	1 35	...	1 57	2 16
Steele Nord	...	⋮	1130	...	...	1 12	1 44	...	2 14	2 30
Bochum S.	1048	1136	12 5	1157	1258	1 30	1 57	2 22	2 46	2 57
Langendreer ......arr	1058	...	1215	...	1 8	1 40	2 7	2 32	2 56	3 7
Witten ......arr	...	...	1228	...	1 17	1 50	...	2 42	...	3 17
Dortmund ......arr	1111	1155	1235	1216		2 4	2 20	—	3 16	—
,, ...dep			1 5		...	2 11		...	3 50	
Hörde	...	...	1 19	...	...	2 23	...	...	4 4	...
Holzwickede	...	...	1 39	...	...	2 41	...	...	4 13	...
Unna (134A) ......arr	...	...	1 49	...	...	2 51	...	...	4 34	...

	Ex2	1—4	1—4	Ex3	2 3 4	Ex2	1—4	1—4	Ex3	1—4	Ex3
	p.m.		p.m.		p.m.	p.m.				p.m.	
M. Gladbach ......dep	1242	...	1 1	...	2 3	4 11	...	...	...	4 16	Cologne dep. 5.25 p
Viersen	1253	...	1 18	...	2 16	...	...	...	...	4 28	
Crefeld ......arr	1 8	p.m.	1 44	...	2 39	4 32	...	...	...	4 50	
Crefeld ......dep	1 10	2 47	1 55	...	—	4 34	...	...	...	4 54	
Uerdingen	1 21	2 58	2 13	p.m.	1—4	..	p.m	p.m	p.m	5 10	p.m.
Duisburg ......dep	1 58	3 23	2 58	3 46	4 p2	4 57	5 3	5 36	5 53	5 58	6 23
Mülheim-Ruhr ......arr	2 8	—	3 11	3 56	4 15	5 6	5 17	5 46	6 3	6 12	6 33
Ruhrort ......dep	...	...	2 48	3 27	3 27	...	4 27	...	5 33	5 33	...
Mülheim ......arr	...	...	3 7	3 47	3 47	...	4 46	...	5 52	5 52	...
Oberhausen ......dep	RC	...	3 3	3 44	3 44	...	5 1	...	...	5 53	...
Mülheim ......arr	.	...	3 14	3 52	3 52	...	5 12	...	...	6 4	...
Mülheim-Ruhr ......dep	2 10	...	3 18	3 57	4 17	5 7	5 19	5 47	6 4	6 15	6 34
Mülheim-Eppinghofen	...	...	3 22	...	4 21	...	5 23	5 51	...	6 19	...
Essen West	...	...	3 35	...	4 33	...	5 36	6 3	...	6 32	...
Essen Haupt. ......arr	2 24	...	3 39	4 12	4 37	5 20	5 40	6 7	6 19	6 36	6 48
Essen Haupt. ......dep	2 26	...	3 44	4 14	4 46	5 21	5 45	...	...	6 55	6 50
Kray	...	Ex3	3 52	...	4 54	..	5 58	...	...	7 3	...
Bochum S. arr.	2 40	p.m.	4 8	4 28	5 10	5 35	6 8	...	...	7 20	7 4
Essen Haupt. ......dep	...	2 44	...	...	4 40	...	...	6 24	6 25	6 40	...
Steele Nord	...	...	...	...	4 54	...	...	6 [illegible]	..	7 12	...
Bochum S.	2 42	3 0	4 9	4 30	5 14	5 36	6 10	6 4[illegible]	6 4[illegible]	7 34	7 6
Langendreer ......arr	...	3 10	4 19	4 40	5 24	...	6 20	6 59	6 50	7 44	7 16
Witten ......arr	...	4 4	...	4 49	5 38	...	6 33	7 12	7 12	8 1	...
Dortmund ......arr	3 1	3 23	4 38	—	5 44	5 54	6 38	7 1[illegible]	7 5	8 3	7 30
,, ...dep		3 28	5 15	...				7 23		8 9	
Hörde	...	...	5 32	...	...	...	...	7 36	...	8 23	...
Holzwickede	...	...	5 53	...	...	...	...	7 54	...	8 40	...
Unna (134A) ......arr	...	3 55	6 6	...	...	...	...	8 4	...	8 50	...

	1,2,3	1,2,3	1,2,3	1—4	1,2,3	1—4	1,2,3	Ex3	1,2,3	1,2,3
	p.m	p.m	p.m.			p.m.	p.m			p.m.
M. Gladbach ......dep	...	6 2	6 29	...	...	7 20	8 0	...	...	8 17
Viersen	...	6 13	6 52	...	...	7 35	8 11	...	...	8 33
Crefeld ......arr	...	6 27	7 19	p.m.	...	8 0	8 26	...	...	8 56
Crefeld ......dep	...	6 29	—	6 40	...	8 9	8 28	...	...	9 1
Uerdingen	From Cologne dep. 6 23 p.m.	6 40	1—4	6 59	p.m.	8 26	...	...	p.m.	9 22
Duisburg ......dep		7 0	7 p17	7 41	8 17	8‡42	9 12	...	9 45	9 53
Mülheim-Ruhr ......arr		—	7 31	7 56	8 27	—	9 22	p.m.	9 55	10 8
Ruhrort ......dep		...	6 49	7 34	...	...	8 40	8 40	...	9 40
Mülheim ......arr		...	7 8	7 52	...	...	9 0	9 0	...	9 59
Oberhausen ......dep		...	7 15	7 15	...	‡—Arrive Duisburg-Hochfeld S.	8 22	9 24	9 41	9 41
Mülheim ......arr		...	7 26	7 26	...		8 33	9 33	9 5[illegible]	9 52
Mülheim-Ruhr ......dep		...	7 34	8 0	8 28		9 24	9 34	9 57	1010
Mülheim-Eppinghofen		...	7 38	8 4	...		...	...	...	1014
Essen West		1—3	7 51	8 17	...		...	...	...	1027
Essen Haupt. ......arr	7 49	p.m.	7 55	8 21	8 4[illegible]		9 39	9 49	10 2	1031
Essen Haupt. ......dep	7 53	8 0	8 5	...	8 44		...	9 53	...	...
Kray	...	⋮	8 13	...	..		...	...	...	...
Bochum S. ......arr	8 8	⋮	8 30	...	8 59		...	10 7	...	...
Essen Haupt. ......dep	...	⋮	...	8 48	...		9 42	...	1014	1037
Steele Nord	...	8 8	...	9 3	...		...	...	1023	1051
Bochum S.	8 10	To Hattingen.	8 33	9 20	9 1		9 59	10 8	1036	1110
Langendreer ......arr	8 20		8 43	9 30	9 11	...	10 9	1018	1046	1120
Witten ......arr	8 57		8 57	9 44	...	...	1046	...	...	1132
Dortmund ......arr	8 33		9 4	9 50	9 24	...	1023	1032	11 0	1138
,, ...dep				10 9		...				12 6
Hörde	...		...	1021	...	...	...	...	...	1218
Holzwickede	...		...	1040	...	...	...	...	...	1236
Unna (134A) ......arr	...	...	...	1052	...	...	...	...	...	1247

	1—4	Ex3	1—4	1—4	1—4	1,2,3	1—4	1,2,3	1—4
	p.m	p.m.		p.m	p.m.		a.m.	p.m.	a.m.
M. Gladbach ......dep	...	9 38	...	9 44	1039	...	12 48	112[illegible]	...
Viersen	...	9 49	...	9 58	1055	...	1 3	1137	...
Crefeld ......arr	...	10 3	...	10 31	1118	...	1 28	115[illegible]	...
Crefeld ......dep	...	10 5	...	10 39	1128	...	—	1153	12 25
Uerdingen	...	1016	p.m.	10 57	1146	Until 15th September.	...	..	12 44
Duisburg ......dep	1013	1043	11 5	11*42	1210		...	123[illegible]	2 *1
Mülheim-Ruhr ......arr	1027	1053	11 20	11 52	—		...	1243	2 10
Ruhrort ......dep	9 40	1025	...	11 16	...		Ex 3	...	1 12
Mülheim ......arr	9 59	1044	...	11 35	...		nght	...	1 31
Oberhausen ......dep	1025	1025	11 4	11 38	...		12 22	SC	1 14
Mülheim ......arr	1037	1037	11 15	11 49	...		12 30	...	1 25
Mülheim-Ruhr ......dep	1039	1055	11 24	11 53	...		12 31	1245	2 12
Mülheim-Eppinghofen	1043	...	11 28	...	...		...	...	...
Essen West	1056	...	11 46	RC	...		...	...	RC
Essen Haupt. ......arr	11 0	11 9	11 50	12 7	...	nght	12 44	1257	2 26
Essen Haupt. ......dep	1121	1111	—	12 8	...	12 24	—	1 7	...
Kray	1129	...	...	...	...	...	1—4	...	...
Bochum S. ......arr	1144	1126	...	12 22	...	12 38	a.m.	1 21	...
Essen Haupt. ......dep	...	...	...	...	...	⋮	1 20	...	2 27
Steele Nord	...	...	...	...	...	⋮	1 36	...	...
Bochum S.	1145	1128	...	12 23	...	12 39	1 57	1 23	2 42
Langendreer ......arr	1155	...	...	12 33	...	12 49	2 7	...	...
Witten ......arr	12 5	...	...	...	...	...	2 20	...	...
Dortmund ......arr		1147	...	12 46	...	1 20	2 27	1 42	3 0
,, ...dep	—		...		...				
Hörde	...	...	...	...	...	...	...	...	...
Holzwickede	...	...	...	...	...	...	...	...	...
Unna (134A) ......arr	...	...	...	...	...	...	...	...	...

*—Ex 3 from Duisburg.

RC—Restaurant Car. SC—Sleeping Car.

WINTERSWIJK and ESSEN.

Winterswijk	4a28	7 a1	10a3	1124	...	2p28	...	...	5p43	8 p7
Borken 5	0	7 50	1036	1215	...	3 2	...	5p13	6 16	8 45
Hervest-Dor.	5 41	8 42	1116	1249	p.m.	3 47	...	5 47	6 53	9 25
Bismarck ...	6 31	9 27	12 0	1 3[illegible]	2 19	4 38	5p26	6 32	7 33	10 7
Essen(135)arr	7 0	9 56	1229	2 3	2 48	5 5	5 55	7 1	8 2	1036

Essen ......dep	4a24	7a19	9a57	1138	1p39	2p26	5p32	8p11	1114
Bismarck-i-W.	4 58	7 52	1034	1212	2 8	3 2	6 6	8 50	1152
Hervest Dorste	5 36	8 34	1127	1251	—	3 43	6 55	9 26	1226
Borken	6 9	9 14	12 8	1 26	...	4 15	7 28	10 0	1256
Winterswijk arr	6 31	9 37	1232	...	...	4 34	7 45	1022	1 17

Extra. { Bismarck to Essen, 11.7 a.m. / Essen to Bismarck, 12.23 p.m.

KETTWIG and MULHEIM-a.-d.-RUHR.

Kettwig .dep	5a42	7a15	9a30	10a55	1p50	3p55	6 p8	8p18	10p15
Saarn	6 0	7 33	9 49	11 14	2 10	4 14	6 27	8 36	10 35
Mülheim.arr	6 12	7 45	10 2	11 27	2 22	4 27	6 40	8 48	10 48
Mülheim dep	5 a1	6a31	8a40	9a43	12p46	2p49	5p10	7 p7	9p18
Saarn ...	5 15	6 44	8 54	9 57	1 0	3 2	5 23	7 20	9 31
Kettwig 134B	5 34	7 1	9 12	1016	1 18	3 20	5 41	7 38	9 50

UNNA, DORTMUND, ESSEN, and MUNCHEN GLADBACH.

	Ex3	1—4	Ex3	Ex2	1—4	2,3,4	Ex3	1,2,3	1,2,3	Ex 3	1,2,3
								a.m.			
Unna ...dep	...	...	...	...	...	...	...	5 38	...	...	...
Holzwickede	...	...	...	...	...	...	...	5 48	...	...	...
Hörde	...	...	...	...	...	...	...	6 7	...	...	From Elberfeld.
Dortmund ...arr	a.m.	a.m.	a.m	...	a.m.	a.m.	a.m	6 17	...	a.m.	
Dortmund ...dep	5 6	5 11	5 35	...	5 41	..	6 26	6 59	...	7 40	
Witten ...dep	...	5 2	...	...	5 43	6 21	...	6 45	...	7 29	
Langendreer	...	5 29	...	...	6 1	6 31	...	7 13	...	7 54	
Bochum	5 26	5 41	5 54	...	6 13	6 41	6 47	7 24	...	8 4	a.m.
Steele Nord	...	5 57	...	...	6 30	...	...	...	...	...	8 18
Essen Haupt. ...arr	...	6 8	...	...	6 42	...	...	7 39	...	RC	8 26
Bochum S. ...dep	5 27	—	5 55	...	...	6 52	6 48	...	...	8 5	—
Kray	...	...	...	...	...	7 9	...	...	...	..	...
Essen Haupt. ...arr	5 41	...	6 10	a.m.	...	7 16	7 2	...	...	8 20	...
Essen Haupt ...dep	5 44	...	6 15	6 22	6 45	7 23	7 3	7 41	...	8 24	...
Essen West	...	...	...	...	6 50	7 28	...	...	...	...	...
Mülheim-Eppinghofen	...	...	...	...	7 3	7 40	...	7 53	...	...	...
Mülheim-Ruhr. ...arr	5 58	...	6 28	6 36	7 6	7 43	7 16	...	...	8 36	...
Mülheim ...dep	6 18	...	6 37	6 37	7 17	⋮	7 17	...	...	...	...
Oberhausen ...arr	6 29	...	6 45	6 45	7 25	⋮	7 25	...	...	...	...
Mülheim-Ruhr ...dep	...	...	6 41	6 41	...	8 8	⋮	...	...	...	...
Ruhrort ...arr	...	...	7 1	7 1	...	8 28	⋮	...	...	...	...
Mülheim ...dep	5 59	a.m.	6 29	—	7 8	7 44	⋮	...	a.m.	8 37	a.m.
Duisburg ...arr	6 10	6 28	6 39	...	7 23	7 58	7 42	8 4	8 2	8 47	9 5
Uerdingen	6 41	6 53	7 37	...	—	—	—	8 37	8 22	To Colo'ne arr. 9.48.	...
Crefeld ...arr	6 51	7 11	7 52	...	...	...	...	8 52	8 33		9 28
Crefeld ...dep	6 53	7 18	7 55	...	...	...	...	—	8 38		9 30
Viersen	7 8	7 42	8 22	...	...	...	...	...	8 53		9 45
M. Gladbach ...arr	7 18	7 55	8 35	...	...	...	...	...	9 3		9 55

	1—4	1,2,3	1,2,3	1—4	1,2,3	1—4	Ex3	1—4	1,2,3	1—4
	a.m.			a.m.		a.m.				a.m.
Unna ...dep	6 31	...	...	7 51	...	8 40	...	...	...	11 8
Holzwickede	6 43	...	...	8 2	...	8 50	...	...	...	1118
Hörde	7 4	...	...	8 21	...	9 8	...	...	...	1136
Dortmund ...arr	7 14	a.m.	...	8 33	a.m.	9 19	a.m.	...	a.m.	1147
Dortmund ...dep	7 24	8 38	...	8 54	9 50	1018	1112	a.m.	11 46	1152
Witten ...dep	7 29	...	...	9 0	...	1026	1111	1144	...	..
Langendreer	7 42	8 54	...	9 14	10 3	1039	1125	1155	12 0	1210
Bochum	7 55	9 4	...	9 26	1012	1051	1135	12 5	12 12	1223
Steele Nord	8 11	9 18	...	9 42	...	11 9	...	...	12 25	1239
Essen Haupt. ...arr	8 21	9 26	...	9 53	...	1121	RC	...	12 35	1251
Bochum S. ...dep	8 10		...	9 54	1013	...	1136	12 7	...	...
Kray	8 26		...	1011	...	...	...	1224	...	...
Essen Haupt. ...arr	8 33		a.m.	1018	1027	...	1151	1231	...	...
Essen Haupt ...dep	8 40		9 31	1019	1032	1141	1153	1241	12 37	1 19
Essen West	8 45	...	...	1024	To Dusseldorf arr. 11.15.	1146	...	1246	...	1 24
Mülheim-Eppinghofen	8 58	...	...	1035		1157	...	1258	...	1 35
Mülheim-Ruhr. ...arr	9 1	...	9 44	1038		12 0	12 6	1 1	12 49	1 38
Mülheim ...dep	9 15	...	9 51	1039		12 1	...	1 9	1 9	1 43
Oberhausen ...arr	9 26	...	10 0	1050		1214	...	1 20	1 20	1 54
Mülheim-Ruhr ...dep	9 9	...	10 1	1052		...	...	1 33	...	—
Ruhrort ...arr	9 29	...	1020	1113		...	...	1 53	...	1,2,3
Mülheim ...dep	9 4	...	9 46	1046	p.m.	1213	12 7	1 2	12 50	p.m.
Duisburg ...arr	9 20	...	9 55	1057	1240	1227	1217	1 16	1 0	2 21
Uerdingen	10 6	...	—	1142	1 8	1 33	To Colo'ne arr. 1.17.	—	1 33	2 36
Crefeld ...arr	1025	...	...	1158	1 26	1 50		...	1 50	2 46
Crefeld ...dep	1033	...	...	1233	—	2 56		...	—	2 48
Viersen	1058	...	...	1258	...	3 24		...	...	3 3
M. Gladbach ...arr	1111	...	...	1 8	...	3 37		...	...	3 13

	Ex3	2 3 4	1,2,3	1—4	Ex3	1—4	1,2,3	Ex2	1—4	1,2,3
					p.m.	p.m.			p.m.	
Unna ...dep	...	...	...	...	1 6	1238	...	...	2 47	...
Holzwickede	...	...	...	...	..	1248	...	Hamm dep. 1.58	3 0	...
Hörde	...	...	...	...	..	1 6	...		3 20	...
Dortmund ...arr	...	p.m.	p.m.	...	1 28	1 17	...	2p24	3 30	p.m.
Dortmund ...dep	p.m	1239	1257	p.m.	1 33	1 36	p.m.	2 38		3 35
Witten ...dep	1240	...	..	1 18	...	..	2 33	...	—	...
Langendreer	1249	1259	1 10	1 28	1 46	1 54	2 43	...	...	3 48
Bochum	1258	...	1 22	1 38	1 56	2 6	2 52	2 57	p.m.	3 58
Steele Nord	...	...	1 34	...	...	2 26	...	...	3 12	...
Essen Haupt. ...arr	...	..	...	...	...	2 37	...	...	3 20	...
Bochum S. ...dep	1259	1 11	...	1 43	1 57	...	2 53	2 58	...	3 59
Kray	...	1 28	...	2 11	...	...	...	...	...	...
Essen Haupt. ...arr	1 14	1 35	1 43	2 18	2 12	...	3 7	3 12	...	4 14
Essen Haupt ...dep	1 16	1 48	1 47	2 20	—	2 45	3 8	3 14	3 25	4 16
Essen West	...	...	To Dusseldorf arr. 2.32 p.m.	2 25	...	2 51	...	...	3 30	...
Mülheim-Eppinghofen	...	2 2		2 37	...	3 5	...	..	3 42	...
Mülheim-Ruhr. ...arr	1 28	⋮		2 40	...	3 8	3 20	3 26	3 45	4 28
Mülheim ...dep	1 43	⋮		2 46	...	3 30	3 30	3 30	...	...
Oberhausen ...arr	1 54	⋮		2 56	...	3 39	3 39	3 39	...	...
Mülheim-Ruhr ...dep	1 33	⋮		2 51	...	3 46	3 46	3 46	3 46	...
Ruhrort ...arr	1 53	⋮		3 11	...	4 5	4 5	4 5	4 5	...
Mülheim ...dep	1 29	⋮		2 41	...	3 9	3 21	3 27	—	4 29
Duisburg ...arr	1 39	2 14		2 55	...	3 24	3 31	3 37	...	4 40
Uerdingen	—	—	...	—	...	4 10	4 10	...	...	5 10
Crefeld ...arr	...	...	...	...	...	4 26	4 26	4 0	...	5 20
Crefeld ...dep	...	...	...	...	...	4 51	4 51	4 2	...	5 22
Viersen	...	...	...	...	...	5 15	5 15	...	...	5 37
M. Gladbach ...arr	...	...	...	...	...	5 28	5 28	4 24	...	5 47

	Ex3	Ex3	1—4	1,2,3	1—4	Ex3	1,2,3	1—4	1,2,3	1,2,3	1,2,3
			p.m.					p.m.			
Unna ...dep	...	...	2 47	...	...	...	...	4 32	...	...	...
Holzwickede	...	...	3 0	...	...	...	...	4 46	...	...	...
Hörde	...	...	3 20	...	...	...	...	5 4	...	...	...
Dortmund ...arr	...	p.m	3 30	p.m.	p.m.	p.m.	...	5 15	...	From Elberfeld.	From Elberfeld.
Dortmund ...dep	p.m.	3 48	4 0	4 33	5 20	5 40	...	5 50	p.m.		
Witten ...dep	3 58	...	...	4 14	5 24	...	...	5 48	6 8		
Langendreer	4 8	...	4 20	4 46	5 40	...	...	6 11	6 19		
Bochum	4 18	4 7	4 37	4 56	5 53	6 0	...	6 33	6 29	p.m.	p.m.
Steele Nord	...	RC	4 58	...	6 11	...	...	6 55	...	6 29	7 10
Essen Haupt. ...arr	...	...	5 9	...	6 23	...	...	7 7	...	6 38	7 19
Bochum S ...dep	4 19	4 8	...	4 57	...	6 1	...	6 38	6 30	—	—
Kray	...	...	...	...	...	...	...	6 56	...	...	...
Essen Haupt. ...arr	4 34	4 23	...	5 12	...	6 16	...	7 4	6 44	...	...
Essen Haupt ...dep	4 36	4 26	5 19	5 15	6 27	6 18	...	7 9	6 47	...	...
Essen West	...	...	5 24	...	6 34	...	...	7 14	...	...	...
Mülheim-Eppinghofen	...	...	5 36	...	6 47	6 31	...	7 26	...	...	...
Mülheim-Ruhr. ...arr	4 49	...	5 39	5 27	6 50	...	...	7 29	7 0	...	...
Mülheim ...dep	4 51	...	6 45	5 34	...	...	...	...	7 1	...	...
Oberhausen ...arr	5 0	...	6 56	5 45	...	...	...	...	7 9	...	...
Mülheim-Ruhr ...dep	—	...	6 5	6 5	7 5	...	...	8 8	7 5	...	...
Ruhrort ...arr	1—4	...	6 25	6 25	7 24	...	p.m.	8 27	7 24	...	...
Mülheim ...dep	p.m.	...	5 42	5 28	6 51	...	7 17	7 31	—	...	...
Duisburg ...arr	5 21	4 47	5 56	5 38	7 6	6 45	7 30	7 46	...	...	...
Uerdingen	5 48	5 10	6 28	—	—	—	7 54	8 46	...	...	...
Crefeld ...arr	6 4	5 20	6 44	...	...	...	8 4	9 2	...	...	...
Crefeld ...dep	6 18	5 22	7 17	...	...	...	8 14	—	...	...	...
Viersen	6 42	5 37	7 42	...	...	...	8 39	...	...	...	...
M. Gladbach ...arr	6 56	5 47	7 55	...	...	...	8 49	...	...	...	...

	Ex2	Ex3	1—4	1—4	1,2,3	1,2,3	1—4	1,2,3	Ex2	Ex3	1—4
							p.m.	p.m			p.m.
Unna ...dep	...	...	...	...	...	...	6 41	8 46	...	...	9 5
Holzwickede	...	...	...	...	...	...	6 51	...	...	...	9 15
Hörde	...	...	...	...	...	...	7 10	...	...	...	9 33
Dortmund ...arr	p.m	p.m.	p.m.	...	p.m.	p.m.	7 22	9 10	p.m.	...	9 43
Dortmund ...dep	6 43	7 2	7 6	...	7 46	7 58	8 21	9 17	9 44	...	9 53
Witten ...dep	...	...	7 12	...	...	..	8 26	9 15	...	...	9 54
Langendreer	...	RC	7 26	...	7 59	8 11	8 43	9 31	RC	...	1012
Bochum	7 2	7 21	7 38	...	8 9	8 22	8 57	9 42	10 3	...	1024
Steele Nord	...	...	7 55	...	⋮	8 35	9 16	9 55	...	...	1042
Essen Haupt. ...arr	...	...	8 6	p.m.	⋮	8 45	9 27	10 4	...	...	1054
Bochum S ...dep	7 3	7 23	...	8 16	8 11	...	9 4	—	10 4	...	—
Kray	...	...	...	8 33	..	...	9 21	...	...	...	1,2,3
Essen Haupt. ...arr	7 17	7 38	...	8 40	8 26	...	9 28	...	1019	p.m.	p.m.
Essen Haupt ...dep	7 26	7 40	8 10	8 51	☞	8 47	9 33	...	1021	1026	1030
Essen West	...	...	8 15	8 56	From 16th July until 21st September.	...	9 38	...	⋮	...	...
Mülheim-Eppinghofen	..	...	8 26	9 7		...	9 50	...	⋮	...	...
Mülheim-Ruhr. ...arr	7 39	7 52	8 29	9 10		9 0	9 53	...	⋮	1039	1043
Mülheim ...dep	7 40	7 58	8 47	...		...	10 4	...	⋮	1044	1044
Oberhausen ...arr	7 49	8 6	8 58	⋮		...	1015	...	⋮	1052	1052
Mülheim-Ruhr ...dep	—	8 8	9 14	9 14		...	1048	...	⋮	1048	1048
Ruhrort ...arr	...	8 27	9 33	9 33		...	11 7	...	⋮	11 7	11 7
Mülheim ...dep	...	7 54	8 31	9 11		9 1	9 55	...	⋮	1040	11 2
Duisburg ...arr	...	8 5	8 45	9 25		9 11	1010	...	104[illegible]	1050	1118
Uerdingen	...	...	9 20	—		—	1044	...	To Colo'ne arr 11.39.	1115	—
Crefeld ...arr	...	8 36	9 33	...		...	11 0	...		1125	...
Crefeld ...dep	...	8 38	9 38	...		...	—	...		1127	...
Viersen	...	8 53	10 3	...		...	...	...		1142	...
M. Gladbach ...arr	...	9 3	1016	...	...	...	...	...		1152	...

	1—4	Ex3	1—4	1,2,3	1—4	1,2,3	1,2,3	1—4
	p.m.					p.m.	p.m.	
Unna ...dep	9 36	...	...	...	...	1119	1154	...
Holzwickede	9 46	...	...	...	...	...	12 7	...
Hörde	10 4	...	...	...	...	A	1227	...
Dortmund ...arr	1015	...	...	p.m.	p.m.	1145	1238	a.m.
Dortmund ...dep	1026	p.m.	p.m.	1134	1139	1159	1246	1 16
Witten ...dep	...	1043	1058	...	...	...	1220	1 17
Langendreer	1045	1053	11 8	1149	1159	1213	1259	1 35
Bochum		11 3	1119	1159	12 9	1223	1 9	1 48
Steele Nord	—	...	1135	...	...	...	...	2 7
Essen Haupt. ...arr	...	...	1147	...	...	...	...	2 19
Bochum S ...dep	...	11 4	...	12 0	1210	1225	1 10	—
Kray	...	...	...	...	1227	A	...	...
Essen Haupt. ...arr	...	1119	...	1214	1234	1240	1 25	...
Essen Haupt ...dep	...	1121	1150	1217	—	1244	1 27	...
Essen West	...	...	1156	...	...	...	...	...
Mülheim-Eppinghofen	...	...	1210	...	...	...	...	...
Mülheim-Ruhr. ...arr	...	1134	1213	1229	...	1254	1 39	...
Mülheim ...dep	...	1144	1224	1234	...	...	1 44	...
Oberhausen ...arr	...	12 5	1245	1245	...	...	1 55	...
Mülheim-Ruhr ...dep	...	...	1218	...	...	...	2 13	...
Ruhrort ...arr	...	...	1237	...	...	...	2 33	...
Mülheim ...dep	...	1135	1214	1230	a.m.	1256	1 40	...
Duisburg ...arr	...	1147	1228	1242	1255	1 7	1 50	...
Uerdingen	...	12 4	—	To Col'gne arr 1.50.	1 21	To Col'gne arr. 2.9.	—	...
Crefeld ...arr	p.m.	1214	...		1 35		a.m.	a.m.
Crefeld ...dep	1145	—	...		—		5 17	6 8
Viersen	12 9	...	...		...		5 42	6 34
M. Gladbach ...arr	1222	...	...		...		5 58	6 51

A—Until 14th September.

LIMBURG and FRANKFORT.

	a.m.	a.m.	a.m.	a.m.	a.m.	a.m.	p.m.	p.m.	p.m.	p.m.	p.m.	p.m.	p.m.	p.m.	p.m.	p.m.	p.m.	p.m.	p.m.
Limburg............dep	...	5 5	...	7 49	8 1	1015	...	12 7	...	...	2 30	...	...	...	5 27	7 13	...	8 15	...
Camberg..................	...	5 44	...	...	8 39	1051	...	1244	...	...	3 7	...	...	...	6 8	7 38	...	8 54	...
Niedernhausen......	5 16	6 27	7 13	8 36	9 23	1129	12 48	1 22	...	2 8	3 44	4 57	...	6 32	6 54	8 5	...	9 33	...
Eppstein	5 28	6 40	7 24	...	9 33	1137	12 59	1 31	1 55	2 19	3 55	5 8	5 41	6 44	7 8	8 †14	8 59	9 44	1123
Hochst-a-M........dep	5 59	7 12	7 52	9 0	10 0	12 6	1 27	1 59	2 23	2 48	4 23	5 35	6 9	7 12	7 43	8 33	9 38	10 14	1149
Griesheim...............arr	6 9	7 22	8 2	...	10 10	1216	1 37	2 7	2 32	2 58	4 33	5 45	6 19	7 22	7 53	...	9 48	10 24	1158
Frankfort Habf. arr	6 18	7 32	8 11	9 11	10 18	1225	1 46	2 16	2 41	3 7	4 42	5 54	6 28	7 31	8 3	8 44	9 57	10 32	12 7

	a.m.	a.m.	a.m.	a.m.	a.m.	a.m.	p.m.	p.m.	p.m.	p.m.	p.m.	p.m.	p.m.	p.m.	p.m.	p.m.	p.m.	p.m.	p.m.
Frankfort Haupt. ....dep	5 1	5 59	7 51	8 13	9 52	11 36	1218	12 59	2 9	2 38	4 2	4 35	5 28	6 30	7 20	8 11	8 46	10 29	11 11
Griesheim ....dep	5 9	6 6	...	8 20	9 59	11 43	1226	12 58	2 18	2 46	4 9	4 42	5 35	6 37	7 28	8 19	...	10 36	11 18
Hochst-a-M........dep	5 23	6 18	8 1	8 30	10 12	11 57	1238	1 10	2 31	2 57	4 19	4 52	5 49	6 47	7 46	8 30	8 56	10 49	11 28
Eppstein........................	5 55	6 48	8 21	8 59	10 42	12 26	1 7	1 30	3 5	3 27	4 48	5 22	6 19	7 17	8 2	9 2	...	11 16	11 57
Niedernhausen......	6 20	7 3	8 35	9 18	10 57	12 46	1 22	—	3 20	3 46	—	5 39	6 34	7 36	—	9 37	9 30	—	12 11
Camberg......................	6 55	—	8 56	9 46	...	1 20	—	...	—	4 17	...	6 10	—	8 10	...	10 5	...	...	...
Limburg ....arr	7 29	...	9 17	1019	...	1 53	...	...	...	4 50	...	6 41	...	8 44	...	1036	10 6	...	...

†—Weekdays only.

DARMSTADT and WIEBELSBACH.

Dis.		a.m.	a.m.	a.m.	a.m.	p.m.	p.m.	p.m.	p.m.	p.m.	p.m.	p.m.	
—	**Darmstadt** Haupt....dep	4 56	6 46	8 9	10 17	12 56	2 20	3 59	5 50	6 ‡25	7 50	11 0	...
7½	Ober Ramstadt..................	5 29	7 14	8 34	10 52	1 32	2 53	4 31	6 21	7 7	8 26	11 28	...
12	Reinheim	5 44	7 30	8 49	11 14	1 55	3 9	4 49	6 37	7 31	8 44	11 44	...
17½	**Wiebelsbach** ....arr	6 0	7 46	9 4	11 31	2 10	3 24	5 5	6 53	7 50	9 1	11 59	...
		a.m.	a.m.	a.m.	a.m.	a.m.	a.m.	p.m.	p.m.	p.m.	p.m.	p.m.	
...	**Wiebelsbach** ....dep	4‡10	4 28	6 ‡1	7 56	10 2	11 44	2 22	3 55	5 30	7 34	10 14	...
...	Reinheim	4 27	4 52	6 18	8 16	10 19	12 1	2 38	4 12	5 49	7 55	10 32	...
...	Ober Ramstadt	4 44	5 14	6 33	8 35	10 34	12 17	2 53	4 31	6 6	8 11	10 48	...
...	**Darmstadt** Haupt. ...arr	5 15	5 50	7 3	9 9	11 5	12 47	3 24	5 2	6 39	8 40	11 17	...

‡—Weekdays only.

REINHEIM and REICHELSHEIM.

E.M.															
	Reinheim.........dep	8a52	12p30	4p48	8p45	...	...	**Reichelsheim**...dep	6 a45	10a45	2p50	6 p25	...	...	...
5¼	Brensbach	9 21	1 5	5 17	9 15	...	...	Brensbach....................	7 23	11 22	3 28	7 7	...	...	...
11¼	**Reichelsheim** arr	9 57	1 53	5 53	9 53	...	...	**Reinheim** 135A...arr	7 58	11 53	4 0	7 42	...	...	...

*—On Sunday depart 12.30 p.m.

CARLSHAFEN and HÜMME.

	a.m.	a.m.	p.m.	p.m.	p.m.	p.m	p.m.			a.m.	a.m.	p.m.	p.m	p.m.	p.m.	p.m.	
Carlshafen dep	5 36	8 52	12 20	2 16	3 54	7 0	9 22	...	**Humme** ....dep	6 57	9 54	1 16	3 14	5 17	8 6	10 13	...
Trendelburg	5 59	9 19	12 47	2 39	4 16	7 31	9 47	...	Trendelburg................	7 11	1010	1 27	3 23	5 28	8 17	10 28	...
Humme......arr	6 9	9 32	12 59	2 49	4 26	7 45	9 59	...	**Carlshafen** 164A arr	7 41	1043	1 49	3 47	5 50	8 40	10 57	...

CASSEL and VOLKMARSEN.

Cassel ....dep	5a46	9a10	11a57	1p15	2p47	6p30	7‡p20	10p45	**Volkmarsen**	4‡a0	5a52	8a35	11a12	1p39	5p21	8p10
Obervellmar	6 2	9 26	12 12	1 30	3 2	6 46	7 34	10 59	Zierenberg......	4 57	6 53	9 32	12 2	2 26	6 11	9 2
Zierenberg	6 33	10 1	12 39	2 0	3 31	7 14	8 1	11 26	Obervellmar ..	5 26	7 22	10 5	12 35	2 57	6 40	9 34
Volkmarsen (156A) arr	7 19	10 52	1 15	2 53	4 20	7 59	...	12 10	**Cassel**......arr	5 41	7 37	1022	12 51	3 12	6 55	9 50

‡—Week days only.

HAGEN, HOLZMINDEN, and CASSEL.

	2 3 4	2,3,4	2 3 4	Ex3	2 3 4	1—4	Ex3	Ex3	2 3 4	1,2,3	2 3 4	2,3,4	2 3 4	Ex3	Ex3	2 3 4	2 3 4	2,3,4	1,2,3	2 3 4	1—4
COLOGNE 134A dp	...	...	...	6 a0	...	...	8a36	...	...	...	9 a6	...	1024	1p30	...	...	3p33	...	5p56	7p21	8p18
	a.m.	a.m.	a.m.	a.m.		a.m.	a.m.				a.m.		p.m.	p.m.			p.m.	p.m.	p.m.	p.m.	p.m.
Hagen.........dep	1 4	...	6 20	7 38	...	8 17	10 4	...	...	...	1116	...	1240	3 6	...	...	5 2	7 25	7 51	9 20	1125
Schwerte ....dep	1 28	...	6 45	7 54	...	8 40	1020	...	...	...	1139	...	1 35	3 30	...	...	5 30	7 52	8 12	9 47	1150
Fröndenberg dep	1 50	...	7 10	8 9	...	9 15	1036	...	...	...	1217	...	2 5	3 45	...	...	5 56	8 40	8 29	1027	1217
Arnsberg	2 32	6 15	7 52	8 37	...	9 56	1059	...	a.m.	...	1258	...	2 54	4 13	...	...	6 41	9 29	8 59	11 7	1 0
Bestwig................	3 38	7 7	9 12	9 7	...	1045	1130	...	1135	...	1 54	...	3 52	4 45	...	...	7 36	10 29	9 33	1156	—
Brilon	4 23	7 40	9 43	⋮	...	1118	RC	...	12 6	...	2 26	...	4 30	5 8	...	...	8 10	11 0	9 55	1227	...
Marsberg	5 11	8 25	—	⋮	...	1154	...	...	—	...	3 5	...	5 8	RC	...	...	8 45	11 38	...	1 2	...
Scherfede ....arr	5 39	8 52	...	⋮	...	1215	1221		...	...	3 28	...	5 28	⋮	...	...	9 8	11 59	1029	1 21	...
Scherfede ...dep	7 12	8 55	...	⋮	...	1231	1224	|	...	...	...	...	5 32	⋮	...	...	...	...	1034	...	...
Wehrden.......arr	8 16	9 53	...	⋮	...	1 20	...	|	...	...	...	...	6 30	⋮	...	...	...	...	1123	...	...
Holzminden arr	8 41	10 15	...	⋮	...	1 40	1 8	|	...	...	...	...	6 55	⋮	...	...	...	...	1146	...	...
MAGDEBURG 164 arr		...	...	⋮	...	...	4p47	|	...	...	...	...	...	⋮	...	...	...	...	...	...	...
BERLIN 164...arr	...	...	...	⋮	a.m.	...	6p54	p.m.	p m.	...	...	p.m.	...	⋮	...	p.m.	...	...	...	...	...
Scherfede.......dep	5 56	8 55	...	⋮	11 6	1217	...	1226	1 15	...	3 32	4 47	5 29	⋮	...	6 29	9 13	12 0	1030	1 22	...
Warburg ....arr	6 7	9 7	...	10 8	1120	1227	...	1236	1 27	...	3 42	4 58	5 40	5 48	p.m.	6 39	9 24	12 11	1040	1 32	Ex3
COLOGNE 134A dp	...	...	1,2,3	...	...	...	...	...	...	9 a6	...	...	...	...	1241	...	...	...	...	|	8p18
SOEST 164 ...dep	...	5 a49	8 a8	8 a8	...	8a33	...	8a33	...	1223	1240	...	2p50	2p50	4p35	...	6 p1	...	...	|	1134
Warburg dep 4a52	6 18	9 15	10 2	10 9	...	1243	...	1237	...	2p36	3 58	...	5 55	5 49	6 31	...	9 34	...	1041	⌊	1a42
Liebenau........5 5	6 31	9 28	...	...	...	1256	...	...	...	...	4 12	...	6 8	...	...	p.m.	9 46	...	...	...	...
Hümme.........5 28	6 51	9 48	...	...	...	1 12	...	...	...	2 56	4 33	...	6 24	...	...	7 57	10 7	...	...	...	...
Hofgeismar ...5 36	6 59	9 56	...	...	...	1 20	...	...	...	3 3	4 42	...	6 32	...	6 56	8 6	1016	...	...	...	2 7
Mönchehof ...6 2	7 27	10 22	...	...	...	1 45	...	...	...	...	5 11	...	6 57	...	...	8 36	1043	...	...	...	...
Obervellmar...6 8	7 33	10 28	...	...	...	1 51	...	...	...	...	5 18	...	7 4	...	...	8 43	1049	...	...	...	...
Cassel ......arr 6 20	7 46	10 39	1052	1059	...	2 4	...	1 27	...	3 30	5 31	...	7 15	6 39	7 26	8 57	11 0	...	1131	...	2 35

Extra—Warburg to Cassel 3.54 a.m., on Week days only.

DORTMUND and GRONAU.

Dist. E.M.			a.m.	a.m.	a.m.	a.m.	p.m.	p.m.	p.m.	p.m.	p.m.
	Dortmund dep		4 45	5 45	8 25	1027	1244	1 37	2 48	6 19	7 53
8½	Lünen........		5 14	6 15	8 53	1058	1 14	2 8	3 16	6 48	8 22
27¾	**Dülmen** arr	a.m.	5 57	7 2	9 34	1140	1 55	2 50	4 5	7 33	9 5
...	„ dep	7 10	6 3	8 5	10 2	12 5	—	3 11	5 4	—	9 11
37¼	**Cœsfeld**......	7 33	6 36	8 35	1027	1231	...	3 39	5 31	...	9 40
49¾	Ahaus........	—	7 7	9 12	1059	1 10	...	4 11	6 9	...	10 9
59¾	**Gronau** 131A arr		7 26	9 34	1120	1 31	...	4 33	6 30	...	1030

		a.m.	a.m.	a.m.	a.m.	p.m.		p.m.	p.m.	p.m.
Gronau........dep		...	6 20	7 39	1026	1221	...	2 33	5 40	7 19
Ahaus		...	6 47	8 3	1055	1242	...	3 2	6 10	7 40
Cœsfeld		6 30	7 18	8 42	1122	1 11	...	3 40	6 52	8 8
Dülmen...arr a.m.		6 51	7 41	9 6	1142	1 31	p.m.	4 2	7 14	8 29
„ ...dep	6 6	—	8 3	10 2	12 6	2 17	3 45	4 35	7 16	8 50
Lünen	6 51	...	8 51	1044	1246	2 59	4 25	5 19	8 1	9 36
Dortmund ar	7 18	...	9 18	1111	1 13	3 27	4 52	5 46	8 28	10 3

Extra—Dortmund to Dülmen, 11.34 p.m.; Dülmen to Dortmund, 4.0 a.m.

HANAU and EBERBACH.

	2—4	2—4	2—4	1,2,3	2—4	2—4	2—4	2—4	2—4
	a.m.	a.m.	a.m.	a.m.	a.m.	p.m.	p.m.	p.m.	p.m.
Hanau (Ost)...dep	...	5 14	6 33	8 2	1035	2 20	5 41	7 46	1049
Seligenstadt	...	5 36	6 52	8 18	1053	2 38	6 0	8 7	11 9
Babenhausen........	...	5 52	7 12	8 32	11 8	2 55	6 21	8 36	1128
Wiebelsbach-Heub	6 8	—	7 55	9 6	1142	3 30	7 0	9 11	12 4
Michelstadt........	6 45	...	8 33	9 36	1219	4 8	7 40	9 48	1241
Hetzbach........	7 8	...	8 57	9 56	1241	4 30	7 59	1014	—
Eberbach ......arr	7 48	...	9 38	1029	1 18	5 15	8 42	1056	...
NECKARELZ 143	8a28	...	...	11a5	1p56	6p24	1034	...	...

	2—4	2—4	2—4	2—4	2—4	2—4	2—4	1,2,3	2—4
NECKARELZ dep	...	...	4a44	7a23	...	1043	1p40	5p30	7p15
	a.m.	a.m.	a.m.	a.m.	a.m.	p.m.	p.m.	p.m.	p.m.
Eberbach...dep	...	...	5 44	8 5	9 43	2 0	3 32	6 4	8 18
Hetzbach........	...	...	6 38	8 57	10 39	2 49	4 28	6 44	9 8
Michelstadt........	3 28	...	7 5	9 18	11 0	3 11	4 48	7 1	9 30
Wiebelsbach-H...	4 8	...	7 56	10 4	11 49	3 52	5 35	7 32	1012
Babenhausen......	4 47	6 22	8 31	1036	12 23	4 27	6 15	7 53	1055
Seligenstadt	5 4	6 38	8 43	1054	12 39	4 42	6 32	8 4	11 9
Hanau (Ost.) ar	5 24	6 57	9 0	1113	12 58	5 1	6 53	8 16	1128

Extra—Hanau to Babenhausen, 1.10, 3.40, 7.11 and 9.6 p.m.; Babenhausen to Hanau, 6.22 a.m., 1.3, 3.0 p.m.

NIEDERNHAUSEN and WIESBADEN.

	a.m.	a.m.	a.m.	a.m.	a.m.	p.m.	p.m.	p.m.	p.m.	p.m.	p.m.	p.m.	p.m.	p.m.			
Niedernhausen	5 29	6 22	7 12	8 38	9 24	12 5	1 25	2 14	4 5	5 43	6 50	8 7	8 54	9 31	...	...	...
Igstadt	5 48	6 42	7 29	...	9 41	1224	1 43	2 31	4 22	6 0	7 10	...	9 14	9 48	...	...	...
Wiesbaden.arr	6 4	6 58	7 45	9 4	9 57	1240	1 59	2 47	4 38	6 17	7 23	8 33	9 30	10 4	...	...	...

	a.m.	a.m.	a.m.	a.m.	a.m.	a.m.	p.m.	p.m.	p.m.	p.m.	p.m.	p.m.	p.m.	p.m.			
Wiesbaden.dp	5 25	6 19	8 4	8 27	1022	1146	1 19	2 54	4 50	5 54	6 49	7 56	8 36	11 28	...	...	...
Igstadt........	5 47	6 41	...	8 51	1043	12 7	1 42	3 15	4 12	6 18	7 11	8 19	8 58	11 50	...	...	...
Niedernhausn	6 10	7 3	8 30	9 14	11 6	1232	2 5	3 36	5 35	6 40	7 32	8 40	9 20	12 13	...	...	...

ARMSHEIM and WENDELSHEIM.

	a.m.	a.m.	a.m.	a.m.	p.m.	p.m.	p.m.	p.m.	
Armsheim (137) dep	4 32	6 20	8 15	10 30	2 6	3 10	6 35	8 34	...
Flonheim........	4 48	6 36	8 31	10 56	2 20	3 26	6 51	8 48	...
Wendelsheim...arr	4 59	6 47	8 43	11 8	2 30	3 37	7 3	8 59	...

	a.m.	a.m.	a.m.	a.m.	p.m.	p.m.	p.m.	p.m.	
Wendelsheim dp	5 11	7 5	9 46	11 28	2 35	5 5	7 19	9 4	...
Flonheim	5 27	7 18	10 0	11 44	2 47	5 18	7 32	9 15	...
Armsheim...arr	5 43	7 33	1016	12 0	3 1	5 33	7 47	9 29	...

ACHERN and OTTENHOFEN.

	a.m.	a.m.	a.m.	p.m.	p.m.	p.m.	p.m.	
Achern........dep	6 45	8 10	10 50	1 27	4 23	7 19	9 50	...
Kappelrodeck	7 2	8 30	11 14	1 47	4 43	7 39	10 10	...
Ottenhofen arr	7 16	8 48	11 28	2 5	5 1	7 54	10 28	...

	a.m.	a.m.	a.m.	a.m.	p.m.	p.m.	p.m.	
Ottenhofen dep	5 50	7 27	9 36	11 55	3 8	5 55	8 14	...
Kappelrodeck......	6 8	7 41	9 54	12 13	3 26	6 13	8 32	...
Achern 140 arr	6 28	7 58	10 14	12 33	3 46	6 33	8 52	...

CASSEL, HOLZMINDEN, and HAGEN.

	Ex3	2,3,4	2 3 4	1,2,3	2 3 4	1—4	Ex3	2,3,4	2 3 4	Ex3	Ex3	2,3,4	1,2,3	2 3 4	Ex 3	Ex3	2,3,4	2 3 4	1,2,3	2,3,4	2 3 4
	a.m.	a.m.	a.m.	a.m.		a.m.	a.m.		a.m.	a.m.	p.m.	p.m.	p m.	p.m.		p.m.	p.m.	p.m.	p.m.	p.m.	p.m.
Cassel ....dep	3 0	3 6	5 21	7 30	...	8 45	9 43	...	1044	1150	2 0	2 15	3 0	4 22	...	5 18	6 12	7 5	8 10	8 16	1120
Obervellmar........	...	3 18	5 35	...	...	8 59	...	...	1056	...	...	2 29	...	4 36	...	...	6 26	7 19	...	8 30	1134
Mönchehof	...	3 26	5 43	...	...	9 6	...	...	11 4	...	...	2 37	...	4 44	...	...	6 34	7 27	...	8 38	1142
Hofgeismar	3 26	47	6 5	7 57	...	9 28	...	...	1124	1217	2 28	3 0	3 26	5 5	...	...	6 58	7 51	...	9 3	12 5
Hümme	...	3 54	6 13	...	...	9 36	...	...	1132	...	2 37	3 8	3 35	5 13	From Berlin (dep. 12.0 noon)	...	7 6	8 2	...	9 11	1214
Liebenau	...	4 14	6 33	...	...	9 52	...	...	1151	...	...	3 28	...	5 33		...	—	8 24	...	9 31	1235
Warburg ......arr	3 53	4 27	6 46	8 24	...	10 6	1033	...	12 4	1244	3 0	3 42	3 57	5 46		6 8	...	8 38	9 0	9 48	1250
SOEST (165) ...arr	5a42	...	10a0	...	...	...	1226	...	3p30	3p30	...	...	5p59	8 p6		8 p6	...	...	10p45	12a40	...
COLOGNE 134C arr	8a52	a.m.	...	...	a.m.	...	3p56	p.m.	...	...	...	...	9p20	1026		1026	...	...	1 a36	...	...
Warburg........dep	...	4 32	6 56	8 25	8 32	1038	...	12 8	1253	1245	3 2	3 49	5p15	6 34		6 9	...	9 5	...	10 8	...
Scherfede ......arr	...	4 42	7 7	⋮	8 42	1048	...	12 18	1 3	⋮	⋮	3 59	5 25	6 44		6 20	...	9 17	...	10 20	...
BERLIN 165...dep	...	⋮	1013	⋮	...	1150	...	...	...	⋮	⋮	⋮	...	8a35			...	...	...	...	...
MAGDEB'G 165 dep	...	⋮	1214	⋮	...	2a55	...	...	...	⋮	⋮	⋮	...	11a7			...	...	...	...	...
		⋮	a.m.	⋮		a.m.			a.m.	⋮	⋮	⋮		p m.	p.m.			p.m.	...	p.m.	
Holzminden dep	...	⋮	4 32	⋮	...	9 18	...	...	1140	⋮	⋮	⋮	...	3 22	⋮		...	6 45	...	...	...
Wehrden......dep	...	⋮	4 55	⋮	...	9 52	...	...	12 3	⋮	⋮	⋮	...	3 45	⋮		...	7 20	...	...	...
Scherfede ...arr	...	⋮	5 50	⋮	...	1045	...	...	1 0	⋮	⋮	⋮	...	4 42	6 23		...	8 23	...	...	...
Scherfede ......dep	...	4 49	7 11	⋮	...	1053	...	...	1 4	⋮	⋮	4 0	...	6 45	6 29		...	9 19	...	10 32	...
Marsberg........1—4	...	5 14	7 36	⋮	a.m.	1118	...	...	1 29	⋮	⋮	4 23	...	7 7	RC	...	...	9 45	...	10 56	...
Brilon ....a.m.	...	6 5	8 25	9 16	9 59	12 9	...	...	2 18	RC	⋮	5 11	...	7 52	...	...	...	1034	...	—	...
Bestwig........4 47	...	6 33	8 51	9 35	1029	1239	...	...	2 48	1 54	4 17	5 39	...	8 17	7 30	...	...	11 0	...	...	...
Arnsberg 5 32	...	7 20	9 36	10 4	1114	1 25	...	...	3 38	2 23	4 44	6 22	...	9 1	7 57	...	...	1145	...	...	...
Fröndenberg 6 10	...	8 6	1019	1033	1153	2 10	...	...	4 19	2 53	5 14	7 9	...	9 44	8 21	...	...	1127	...	...	...
Schwerte ..arr 6 34	...	8 28	1039	1048	1213	2 31	...	...	4 42	3 6	5 29	7 31	...	10 4	...	...	...	1249	...	...	...
Hagen ....arr 7 17	...	8 51	1058	11 6	1258	2 51	...	...	...	3 28	5 45	7 54	...	1036	8 47	...	...	1 9	...	...	...
COLOGNE 134C ...	...	...	1259	1259	2p50	5 p8	...	...	...	5 p8	7p34	...	...	1153	10p26	...	...	...	...	...	...

RC—Restaurant Car.] [Luggage Rates—see page 462.

FRANKFORT, DARMSTADT, MANNHEIM, and HEIDELBERG

		1—4	1—4	Ex3	1,2,3	Ex3	1—4	Ex2	1—4	1—4	Ex.3	1—4	1,2,3	1—4	1—4	1—4	Ex3	1—4	Ex3	Ex3
Frankfort—		a.m.	a.m.	a.m.	a.m.	a.m.	a.m.	a.m.	a.m.	a.m.	a.m.	a.m.	a.m.	a.m.	a.m.	p.m.	p.m.	p.m	p.m.	p.m.
Hauptbahnhof...dep		4 24	5 8	5 38	6 14	6 38	6 45	7 12	8 8	9 10	9 35	9 40	10 29	11 17	1143	1228	1250	1 0	1 43	1 58
Louisa		...	5 16	...	...	...	6 52	...	...	...	...	9 47	...	...	1151	...	...	1 7	...	...
Isenburg		4 34	5 22	...	...	RC	6 58	RC	8 18	9 20	RC	9 53	...	...	1159	1238	...	1 14	...	...
Wixhausen		5 3	5 50	...	...	...	7 24	...	8 44	...	...	10 20	...	...	1227	...	...	1 43	...	...
Darmstadt Haupt. arr	1—4	5 15	6 1	6 7	6 43	7 6	7 35	7 41	8 55	9 48	10 3	10 31	10 56	11 54	1239	1 4	1 18	1 55	2 12	2 26
MAYENCE (123)...dep	a.m.	...	...	...	5 a54	...	6a15	6a15	7a51		9a0	9 a24	9 a24	10a38	...	12p8	12p8	1p32	1p32	1p32
Darmstadt Haupt. dep	4 15	5 20	6 13	6 9	6 45	7 8	7 50	7 45	8 58	Extra.—Weinheim Haupt. to Mannheim 5.54 a.m. (Weekdays only).	10 6	10 36	10 59	11 58	...	1 7	1 20	2 46	2 21	2 36
Eberstadt	4 28	5 33	6 25	:	...	:	8 2	...	9 10		...	10 49	...	12 10	...	1 19	...	2 59	:	...
Bickenbach (136)	4 37	5 43	6 35	:	...	:	8 11	...	9 19		...	10 58	...	12 18	...	1 36	...	3 8	:	...
Zwingenberg	4 46	5 51	6 43	:	...	:	8 20	...	9 27		...	11 5	...	12 25	...	1 46	...	3 15	:	...
Bensheim (136)	4 56	6 3	6 54	:	7 6	:	8 31	...	9 38		...	11 15	11 22	12 36	...	1 59	1 41	3 27	:	...
Heppenheim	5 3	6 12	7 1	:	7 13	:	8 38	...	9 45		...	11 36	...	12 43	...	2 8	...	3 35	:	...
Weinheim Haupt. (136)	5 23	6 31	7 19	:	7 26	:	8 57	...	10 5		...	11 56	11 37	1 2	...	2 27	1 56	3 54	:	...
Ladenburg	5 41	6 58	8 3	:	...	:	9 16	...	1021		...	12 14	..	1 17	...	2 42	...		:	...
Friedrichsfeld ......arr	5 46	7 4	8 9	:	7 39	:	9 22	8 28	1026		10 49	12 19	11 51	1 22	...	2 48	2 9	...	:	3 19
Friedrichsfeld ...dep	5 55	7 17	8 17	:	7 48	:	9 29	8 34	1034		10 55	12 32	11 59	1 28	...	2 59	2 15	...	:	3 25
Mannheim (205) arr	6 10	7 32	8 30	6 58	8 0	:	9 40	8 47	1046		11 8	12 48	12 9	1 43		3 13	2 27	...	:	3 36
LUDWIGSHFN arr	6 39	8 23	9 6	7 14	8 23	:	...	9 6	1125		11 25	1 17	12 23	2 18		3 56	2 55		:	3 56
Friedrichsfeld.....dep	6 7	7 9	8 21	...	8 21	:	...	...	1028		...	12 23	...	1 25		2 54	...	...	:	...
Schwetzingen.....arr	6 16	7 18	8 30	...	8 30	:	...	...	1037		...	12 32	...	1 34		3 3	...	...	:	...
CARLSRUHE 142 arr	7a55	8 a1	9a34	...	9 a34	:	...	...	1149		...	...	...	...	2p52	4p14	...	...	:	...
Friedrichsfeld ......dep	5 49	7 7	8 12	...	7 41	:	9 25	8 31	1029		10 51	12 21	11 54	1 24	:	2 53	2 12	...	:	3 22
Heidelberg..........arr	6 4	7 19	8 27	...	7 53	8 0	9 38	8 43	1045		11 3	12 33	12 7	1 37	:	3 8	2 24	...	3 13	3 34
CARLSRUHE (140) arr	7a36	8a18	9a37	...	8 a44	8a58	...	9a37	1153		11a53	2 p10	1 p1	3 p18	:	3p59	3p18	...	3p59	4p36
BASLE (140)........arr	...	1210	1243	...	12p16	12p16	...	1243	2p55	...	2 p55	...	4 p41	...	5p38	7 p0	...	...	7 p0	7p56

HEIDELBERG, MANNHEIM, DARMSTADT, and FRANKFORT.

		Ex3	Ex 3	1—4	2,3,4	1—4	1—4	1,2,3	1—4	1—4	1—4	1,2,3	1—4	1—4	1,2,3	1—4	1—4	Ex2	1—4	1,2,3
BASLE (141) ....dep		1152	11p52	...	...	1152	...	...	...	...	...	...	...	...	4a30	...	...	7a53	7 a53	8 a0
CARLSRUHE (141)......dep		3 a5	3 a5	...	...	3 a5	...	5 a8	...	5 a8	5a14	6a55	...	7a11	9 a5	...	...	1036	10a36	11a17
		a.m.	a.m.			a.m.	a.m.	a.m.		a.m.	a.m.	a.m.		a.m	a.m.	a.m.		a.m.	a.m.	p.m.
Heidelberg ....dep		3 57	4 10	...	...	4 25	5 17	6 5	...	6 10	7 2	8 2	...	9 15	10 2	10 8	...	1123	11 29	12 24
Friedrichsfeld ....arr		4 9	:	...	...	4 38	5 31	6 17	...	6 26	7 15	8 14	..	9 30	1014	10 21	...	:	11 44	12 36
CARLSRUHE (142) dep		...	:	...	Weekdays only.	...	...	...	...	5 a7	...	6a48	...	7a56	...	...	...	:	9 a5	...
Schwetzingen..........dep		...	:	...		4 25	...	5 52	...	6 22	...	7 58	...	9 14	...	...	...	:	11 36	...
Friedrichsfeld ....arr		...	:	...		4 35	...	6 1	...	6 31	...	8 7	...	9 23	...	...	...	:	11 46	...
LUDWIGSHAFEN 205 dp		...	:	...		...	..	5 46	...	5 46	6 42	7 46	...	8 10	9 34	9 34	...	:	11 5	11 15
Mannheim..............dep		3 54	:	...		4 24	5 15	6 3	...	6 10	6 53	8 0	...	9 10	10 0	10 6	...	:	11 19	12 22
Friedrichsfeld ....arr		4 6	:	...		4 37	5 28	6 15	...	6 27	7 9	8 11	...	9 24	1012	10 18	...	:	11 33	12 34
Friedrichsfeld ....dep		4 13	:	...		4 44	5 36	6 21	...	6 32	7 20	8 18	...	9 34	1018	10 25	...	:	11 49	12 40
Ladenburg		...	:	...		4 51	5 43	...	...	6 40	7 27	...	...	9 41	...	10 32	...	:	11 55	...
Weinheim		4 27	4 35	a.m.	a.m.	5 10	6 0	6 37	...	6 59	7 45	...	...	9 57	1033	10 52	...	:	12 10	12 54
Heppenheim		...	...	4 7	5 15	5 29	6 20	6 49	...	7 17	8 5	...	...	1015	...	11 13	...	:	12 29	...
Bensheim		4 43	4 50	4 15	5 24	5 38	6 27	6 56	...	7 25	8 14	...	...	1023	1048	11 21	...	:	12 37	1 8
Zwingenberg		...	...	4 27	5 36	5 49	6 38	...	...	7 36	8 26	...	...	1034	...	11 33	...	:	12 48	...
Bickenbach		...	...	4 38	5 48	6 0	6 46	...	...	7 45	8 34	...	...	1041	...	11 40	...	:	12 58	
Eberstadt		...	...	4 48	6 0	6 11	6 58	...	...	7 54	8 41	...	...	1050	...	11 51	...	:	1 9	...
Darmstadt ....arr		5 4	5 12	5 0	6 12	6 24	7 9	7 17	...	8 5	8 56	9 1	...	11 2	11 9	12 4	...	1212	1 21	1 27
MAYENCE (123A) arr	a.m.	5a56	5 a56	...	...	7a28	...	8a22	a.m.	8 a55	1024	1024	a.m.	1210	1210	1 p57	p.m.	1p57	2 p23	2p23
Darmstadt...........dep	4 24	5 6	5 15	5 22	6 16	6 30	7 29	7 19	8 1	8 22	9 23	9 4	10 2	1118	1112	12 20	1258	1214	1 42	1 34
Wixhausen	4 38	...	...	5 35	6 30	6 44	7 41	...	...	8 35	...	...	1015	1132	...	12 33	1 12	...	1 55	...
Isenburg	5 11	...	...	6 8	7 3	7 16	8 10	...	8 32	9 4	...	...	1043	12 4	...	1 3	1 39	...	2 23	..
Louisa	5 18	...	...	6 15	7 10	7 23	...	...	...	9 11	...	...	...	1211	...	...	1 45	...	2 29	
Frankfort-Hauptbahn.	5 26	5 32	5 44	6 22	7 17	7 30	8 20	7 46	8 42	9 18	9 57	9 31	1053	1218	1140	1 14	1 52	1239	2 36	2 2

Eberstadt and Pfungstadt.—Frequent local trains connect Pfungstadt with all trains in above table stopping at Eberstadt.

WEINHEIM and FÜRTH.

[‡—11.55 p.m. on Sunday.

Weinheim dep	6a45	8a37	10a 5	12p26	2p35	4p55	6p40	8p12	10‡25
Morlenbach ...	7 11	9 6	10 39	1 2	3 0	5 30	7 12	8 39	10 56
Fürth ......arr	7 33	9 28	11 1	1 24	3 22	5 52	7 34	9 2	11 18

Fürth ....dep	5a30	6a29	8a41	11 a8	12 7	3p25	6p18	9p11
Morlenbach	5 55	6 44	9 9	11 36	12 32	3 49	6 45	9 37
Weinheim 136 arr	6 23	7 14	9 36	12 5	12 57	4 15	7 12	10 4

E.M.		
	Bickenbach dep	In 16 minutes. From Bickenbach 5*50, 6.55, 8.14, 9.25, 11.2 a.m., 12.21, 1.32, 3.12, 4.2, 5.21, 6.24, 7.14, 8.34, 9.42, 11.7 p.m., 12.46 night. From Seeheim 5*23, 6.12, 7.25, 8.58, 10.18, 11.55a.m., 12.38, 2.2, 3.33, 4.52, 5.42, 6.48, 7.45, 8.52, 10.26p.m., 12.17night. * Weekdays only.
2	Jugenheim	
2½	Seeheim......arr	

BENSHEIM and WORMS.

*—Sunday excepted.

Bensheim ....dep	4a17	6a2[illegible]	7a34	9 a44	1124	1253	2 p4	4p20	6p24	7*34	8 p15	9p12	9 p59	12 a1	...
Bürstadt...................	5 9	6 45	7 56	10 6	1144	1 17	2 24	4 41	6 44	7 56	8 39	9 34	10 19	12 25	...
Worms Bhf. ....arr	5 32	7 3	8 16	10 25	12 1	1 36	2 42	4 59	7 4	8 14	8 56	9 53	10 36	12 41	...
Worms..................dep	5a28	6a43	8a30	10 a0	11a49	1258	3p19	5p15	6p40	8p16	11p6	...	...	...	...
Bürstadt..................	5 50	7 3	8 49	10 22	12 13	1 18	3 39	5 33	7 7	8 38	1126	...	...	...	...
Benshim ....arr	6 11	7 22	9 9	10 42	12 32	1 38	3 57	5 53	7 27	8 57	1146	...	...	...	...

DARMSTADT and GRIESHEIM (4¼ miles in 24 minutes).—From Darmstadt Schloss 5‡35, 6.36, 7.43, 8.57, 9.57, 11.0 a.m., 12.24, 2.0, 3.12, 4.32, 5.26, 6‡10, 6.30, 7.35, 8.47, 10.15p.m. From Griesheim 5‡0, 6.6. 7.14, 8.25, 9.22, 10.23, 11.40 a.m.; 12‡4, 1.34, 2.30, 3.50, 4.58, 5‡37, 5.56, 7.5, 8.10, 9.30 p.m. ‡—Weekdays only.

Luggage Rates—see page 462.] [SC—Sleeping Car.

FRANKFORT, DARMSTADT, MANNHEIM, and HEIDELBERG.

	1—4	1,2,3	1—4	1—4	Ex 2	1,2,3	1,2,3	2 3 4	1—4	1—4	2 3 4	1—4	1,2,3	1—4	1—4	1,2,3	1—4	Ex 3	1—4	Ex. 3	1—4
Frankfort—	p.m.	p.m.	p.m.	p.m.	p.m.	p.m.		p.m.	p.m.	p.m.	p.m.	p.m.	p.m.	p.m.	p.m.	p.m.	p.m.	p.m.	p.m.	p.m.	n'gt
Hauptbahnhof dep	2 30	3 25	3 55	4 30	5 10	5 15	...	5 31	6 0	6 35	7*15	7 36	8 13	8 20	9 2	9 32	9 39	10 49	1110	11 45	1218
Louisa	2 37	...	...	4 37	...	...	...	5 38	6 8	6 42	7 22	7 43	...	8 27	...	...	9 47	...	1117	...	1225
Isenburg	2 44	...	4 6	4 45	RC	...	...	5 45	6 15	6 49	7 29	7 50	...	8 33	9 13	...	9 54	...	1124	SC	1232
Wixhausen	3 13	...	...	5 15	...	...	...	6 14	...	7 17	7 58	8 19	...	9 2	...	...	1023	...	1153	...	1 2
Darmstadt arr	3 25	3 53	4 34	5 27	5 38	5 46	...	6 26	6 44	7 29	8 10	8 31	8 43	9 14	9 41	10 0	1035	11 20	12 5	12 12	1 14
MAYENCE (123)...dep	2p15	2p15	...	4p48	4 p48	4p48	4p48	5p11	5p11	6p25	...	...	7p30	8 p2	...	...	9p36	10p34	...	10p34	...
Darmstadt dep	3 30	3 56	...	5 59	5 40	5 49	5 55	6 30	6 49	7 52	*—Weekdays only.	...	8 46	9 17	...	10 3	1041	11 30	1221	12 15	...
Eberstadt	3 43	...	...	6 12	:	...	...	6 43	7 1	7 45		...	...	9 29	...	...	1055	...	1234	...	...
Bickenbach (136)	3 53	...	...	6 21	:	...	...	6 53	7 10	7 54		...	...	9 38	...	...	11 4	...	1243	...	...
Zwingenberg	4 1	...	...	6 32	:	...	...	7 4	7 20	8 2		...	...	9 44	...	...	1111	...	1250	...	...
Bensheim (136)	4 24	4 17	...	6 45	:	6 9	6 16	7 16	7 32	8 13		...	9 7	9 56	...	10 5	1124	11 53	1 1	...	a.m.
Heppenheim	4 31	4 24	...	6 54	:	6 16	6 24	7 23	7 40	8 21		...	9 14	10 4	...	1032	1133	12 0	1 8	...	4 10
Weinheim (136)	4 52	4 36	...	7 16	:	6 30	6 38	—	8 3	8 42		...	9 27	1023	...	1044	1155	12 13	—	...	4 31
Ladenburg	5 9	...	...	7 34	:	...	...	...	8 19	8 58		...	...	1041	...	...	1210	...	...	...	4 49
Friedrichsfeld arr	5 15	4 49	...	7 40	:	6 43	6 53	...	8 24	9 4		...	9 41	1046	...	1058	1216	12 27	...	12 57	4 55
Friedrichsfeld ...dep	5 21	4 55	...	7 47	:	6 54	...	...	8 32	9 10		...	9 47	1053	...	11 5	1224	12 34	...	1 3	5 2
Mannheim (205) arr	5 37	5 5	...	7 59	:	7 4	...	...	8 50	9 23		...	9 57	11 4	...	1116	1235	12 45	...	1 14	5 19
LUDWIGSHAFN arr	5 55	5 19	...	8 19	:	7 16	...	...	9 53	9p53	...	...	11p0	1222	p.m.	1222	...	...	...	...	6 39
Friedrichsfeld ...dep	5 30	...	...	7 45	:	7 45	...	...	8 35	...	...	...	9 50	1047	1145	...	...	...	...	...	5 20
Schwetzingen ...arr	5 39	...	...	7 54	:	7 54	...	...	8 45	...	...	...	9 59	1056	1155	...	...	...	...	...	5 30
CARLSRUE 142 arr	...	...	...	...	:	...	...	...	10p8	...	...	...	...	1233	...	...	...	...	...	...	6a32
Friedrichsfeld ...dep	5 17	4 51	...	7 42	:	6 45	6 56	...	8 27	9 7	...	...	9 44	1049	...	11 1	1218	12 29	...	1 0	4 57
Heidelberg arr	5 35	5 4	...	7 58	6 30	6 57	7 9	...	8 40	9 20	...	...	9 56	11 4	...	1114	1231	12 41	...	1 12	5 12
CARLSRUHE (140) arr	7p11	5p59	...	...	7 p11	8 p2	8 p2	...	1056	1058	...	...	1056	1248	...	1248	2a11	2 a11	...	2 a11	7a36
BASLE (140) arr	1021	8p55	...	...	10 21	1124	1124	...	...	...	...	...	...	...	...	...	5a38	5 a38	...	5 a38	...

HEIDELBERG, MANNHEIM, DARMSTADT, and FRANKFORT.

	1,2,3	1—4	Ex3	1,2,3	1—4	1,2,3	1—4	Ex3	1—4	1—4	Ex3	Ex3	1—4	1—4	1,2,3	Ex2	Ex3	1—4	1—4	1,2,3
BASLE 141 dep	8 a0	8 a0	...	9a50	9a50	1042	1042	1 p0	...	...	2p33	2p33	2 p33	...	...	5p18	5p33	5 p33	...	...
CARLSRUHE 141 dep	1117	1117	...	1243	1243	2p20	2p20	4 p8	3p20	...	5p39	5p39	5 p39	...	7 p14	:	8p38	8 p38	...	10p31
	p.m.	p.m.		p.m.	p.m.	p.m.	p.m.	p.m.	p.m.		p.m.	p.m	p.m.	p.m.	p.m.		p.m	p.m.	p.m.	p.m.
Heidelberg dep	1239	1244	...	1 43	2 12	3 13	3 35	5 4	5 9	...	6 36	6 51	7 1	7 26	8 13	:	9 28	9 33	10 58	11 31
Friedrichsfeld arr	1251	1257	...	1 55	2 25	3 25	2 50	:	5 23	...	6 48	7 4	7 16	7 40	8 26	:	:	9 46	11 13	11 43
CARLSRUE 142 dep	...	1055	...	...	...	...	...	:	2p16	...	:	5p38	...	...	6 p20	8 p9	:	...	...	...
Schwetzingen ...dep	...	1250	...	...	2 14	...	...	:	5 0	...	:	6 56	...	...	8 10	8 49	:	9 12	11 2	11 2
Friedrichsfeld ...arr	...	1259	...	...	2 23	...	...	:	5 10	...	:	7 5	...	...	8 20	8 57	:	9 22	11 12	11 12
LUDWIGSHAFN dep	...	...	1p14	1 14	1 40	2 45	2 45	:	4 34	...	:	6 41	6 41	...	7 58	7 58	:	8 59	...	...
Mannheim dep	...	1240	1 25	1 43	2 9	3 8	3 29	:	5 8	...	:	6 52	7 0	7 26	8 10	8 40	:	9 27	10 57	11 27
Friedrichsfeld ...arr	...	1256	:	1 54	2 25	3 21	3 43	:	5 21	...	:	7 3	7 17	7 39	8 24	8 52	:	9 44	11 39	11 40
Friedrichsfeld ...dep	1252	1 1	:	1 59	2 30	3 29	3 56	:	5 2	...	6 49	7 9	7 22	7 45	8 31	8 58	:	9 51	11 19	11 47
Ladenburg	...	1 8	:	...	2 36	...	4 3	:	5 35	p.m.	...	...	7 29	7 52	...	...	:	9 58	11 26	...
Weinheim	1 6	1 24	:	2 13	2 53	3 43	4 23	:	5 53	6 20	7 4	7 25	7 47	8 9	8 46	...	:	10 14	11 43	12 2
Heppenheim	1 17	1 43	:	...	3 11	...	4 44	:	6 13	6 41	...	...	8 5	8 27	...	...	:	10 33	12 1	12 14
Bensheim	...	1 59	:	2 27	3 18	3 59	4 53	:	6 22	6 50	7 21	7 41	8 12	8 34	9 2	...	:	10 41	—	12 21
Zwingenberg	...	2 11	:	...	3 28	...	5 5	:	6 35	7 3	...	...	8 23	8 44	...	...	:	10 51	...	...
Bickenbach	...	2 22	:	...	3 34	...	5 16	:	6 45	7 12	...	...	8 33	8 50	9 13	...	:	10 58	...	...
Eberstadt	...	2 31	:	...	3 43	...	5 26	:	6 55	7 23	...	...	8 43	8 59	...	...	:	11 7	...	...
Darmstadt arr	1 40	2 42	2 14	2 47	3 54	4 21	5 39	6 1	7 7	7 36	7 43	8 3	8 54	9 11	9 29	9 41	1022	11 18	...	12 46
MAYENCE 123A ...arr	2 23	3p28	3p28	3p28	5 p4	5p13	6p46	...	8 p9	8p52	8p52	8p52	...	...	11p23	1123	1123	12a12	...	...
Darmstadt dep	...	2 56	2 16	2 49	3 56	4 23	5 45	6 4	7 18	8 12	7 51	8 5	8 58	9 51	9 32	9 44	1025	11 22	...	12 48
Wixhausen	...	3 9	...	...	...	...	...	...	7 31	8 24	...	...	9 11	10 3	...	...	...	11 35	...	...
Isenburg	...	3 38	...	...	...	...	6 16	...	8 1	8 53	...	...	9 39	1033	...	...	...	12 3	...	...
Louisa	...	3 44	...	...	...	...	...	...	...	...	...	...	9 45	1039	...	...	...	12 [illegible]	...	...
Frankfort-Hauptbahn	...	3 51	2 43	3 16	4 27	4 50	6 26	6 32	8 12	9 6	8 20	8 33	9 52	1046	10 0	1011	1053	12 16	...	1 16

Extra—Schwetzingen to Friedrichsfeld 10.10 p.m. Darmstadt to Frankfort 4.38, 6.27 p.m.

MAYENCE and ALZEY.

Mayence	am	a.m.	a.m.	pm	pm	pm	p.m	p.m.	a.m.	p.m.	p m.
Haupt dep	629	9 15	1150	2 7	319	438	6 20	7 8	8 27	9 41	11 7
Nieder-Olm	7 7	9 50	1222	241	354	510	7 3	7 51	9 1	1011	1141
Wörrstadt	726	10 8	1239	3 1	411	529	7 22	8 14	9 18	1027	1158
Armsheim	738	1020	1248	311	420	550	7 35	8 32	9 31	1036	1214
Alzey (207) arr	753	1035	1 2	325	435	6 6	7 51	8 47	9 46	1050	1229

	am	a m	a.m	a.m.	a.m.	p.m	p.m.	pm	p.m.	p.m
Alzey	443	5 56	7 42	10 8	1154	2 53	4 46	611	7 48	1045
Armsheim	5 1	6 14	7 56	1021	1210	3 10	4 59	626	8 1	1058
Wörrstadt	518	6 27	8 7	1032	1221	3 21	5 10	639	8 13	11 9
Nieder-Olm	543	6 48	8 22	1048	1239	3 38	5 27	7 1	8 30	1125
Mayence H.	624	7 22	8 51	1119	1 8	4 8	6 0	733	9 4	1155

FREI WEINHEIM and JUGENHEIM.

	a.m.	a.m.	p.m.	p.m.
Frei Weinheim ...dep	6 50	10 50	3 2	7 40
Nieder Ingelheim	7 38	11 40	4 15	8 15
Jugenheim arr	8 28	12 40	5 7	9 2

	a.m.	a.m.	p.m.	p.m.	
Jugenheim dep	5 35	9 5	1 15	5 55	...
Nieder Ingelheim	6 35	10 15	2 45	6 43	...
Frei Weinheim arr	6 45	10 26	2 56	7 35	...

†—Hauptbahnhof.]

MANNHEIM and WORMS.

Mannheim-	a.m.	a.m.	a.m.	a.m.	p m	p.m.	p m.	p.m.	pm	pm	p.m
Neckar'hof.	5†28	7†36	7†53	9 28	12 9	1†34	2† 8	3†57	4 7	7†0	1017
Lampertheim	6 2	8 17	...	10 0	1229	...	2 37	4 16	434	733	1044
Worms	6 23	8 33	8 25	1018	1255	2 7	2 55	4 30	453	750	11 2

	a.m.	a.m.	a.m.	a.m.	pm	p.m.	p.m.	p.m.	pm	pm	p.m.
Worms	6 29	8 24	10 12	11 29	128	3 15	3 32	6 28	7 6	835	1119
Lamperth	6 53	8 47	10 30	...	149	...	3 50	...	726	9 0	1139
Mannh.	7†25	9 10	10†58	12 †1	217	3†46	4†17	6†59	750	825	12 4

FRANKFORT, MAYENCE, and DARMSTADT to MANNHEIM.

Station	Ex3	Ex3	Ex2	1,2,3	2 3 4	Ex3	Ex3	Ex3	1,2,3	2,3,4	1,2,3	Ex3	2 3 4	Ex3	Ex2	Ex3	2,3,4	Ex2	Ex2	Ex3	Ex3	1,2,3	2 3 4	Ex3	1,2,3	2,3,4	1,2,3	1,2,3	2,3,4	Ex3	Ex3
			a.m.	a.m.	a.m.	a.m.	a.m.	a.m.	a.m.	a.m.		a.m.	p.m.			p.m.	p.m.			p.m.	p.m.	p.m.	p.m.		p.m	p.m.	p.m.	p.m.	p.m.	p.m.	
Frankfort-Hauptbhf. dep	...	...	5 52	6 45	7 0	7 40	8 10	9 37	9 44	10 18	...	1158	1220	...	...	1 43	2 17	...	...	4 3	4 10	4 30	5 21	...	7 46	7 52	8 25	1041	11 40	1155	...
Goldstein arr	...	...		...	7 13		...			10 30	...		1232	...	...		2 29	...	...				5 33	...	...	8 4			...		...
Frankfort Sud dep	...	...		...	6 25		...			10 3	...		...	...	...		1 53	...	...				5 8	...	...	6 43			...		...
Goldstein arr	...	...		...	6 40		...			10 18	...		...	...	...		2 8	...	...				5 23	...	...	6 55			...		...
Goldstein dep	...	...		...	7 14		...			10 31	...		1233	...	...		2 30	...	...				5 34	...	...	8 5			...		...
Dornberg-Gross-Gerau arr	...	...		7 12	7 47		8 39		1010	11 3	...		1 5	...	...		3 0	...	...			4 55	6 4	...	8 12	8 36	8 51	11 7	12 13		...
	a.m.	a.m.		a.m.	a.m.		a.m.		a.m.	a.m.	a.m.		p.m.	p m.	p.m.		p.m.	p.m.	p.m.			p.m.	p.m.	p.m.	p.m.	p.m.	p.m.	p.m.	p.m.		p.m.
Mayence Haupt. dep	1 49	5 30		5 54	6 15		8 9		9 24	10 8	1033		12 8	1252	1 13		2 15	2 32	3 23			3 54	4 48	5 45	7 30	7 41	7 30	1034	10 34		1125
Gross-Gerau				7 1	7 1		...		10 0	10 46			1 0				2 52					4 45	5 16		8 3	8 20	8 3	11 3	11 3		
Dornberg-Gross-Gerau arr				7 6	7 6		8 38		10 4	10 50			1 5				2 57					4 50	5 20		8 7	8 24	8 7	11 7	11 7		
Dornberg-Gross-Gerau dep				7 13	7 50		8 45		1016	11 5			1 18				3 2					4 56	6 5		8 17	8 41	8 52	1112	12 21		
Goddelau-Erfelden arr 2 34				7 22	8 8	8 13				11 23			1 35			2 20	3 19					5 5	6 23			8 58	9 2	1122	12 38		
a.m.				a.m.	a.m.	a.m.				a.m.						p.m.	p.m.					p.m.	p.m.			p.m.		p.m.			
Darmstadt dep 6 4	Via Worms.			7 3	7 46	7 46				11 0	Via Worms.		...			1 50	2 55	Via Worms.				4 37	5 52	Via Worms.		8 33		1055	p.m.		
Goddelau-Erfelden arr 6 28				7 20	8 10	8 10				11 24			...			2 15	3 19					5 1	6 9			8 59		1119			
Goddelau-Erfelden dep 6 30				7 23	8 19	8 14				11 26			1 46			2 21	3 22					5 6	6 24			9 10	9 3	1123	11 28		
Gernsheim 6 48				7 34	8 40					11 45			2 4				3 40					5 16	6 42		8 35	9 31		1134	11 46		
Biblis arr 7 1				7 48	8 54					11 59			2 18				3 54						6 56			9 44			11 58		
Biblis dep 7 2				7 49	9 2					12 10			2 19				3 57									9 47			12 1		
Worms Rhein arr 7 14				...	9 16					12 26			2 32				...									...			12 9		
" Haupt. arr 7 18				8 3	9 20			1034		12 31			2 36			2 48	4 13					5 36				10 4	9 29		12 19	1252	
Biblis dep				...	8 56					12 1							4 13					5 44	6 57			9 47					
Lampertheim				7 54	9 20			...		12 20			...			...	4 33					6 2	7 14		8 54	10 10	...	1153	...	...	
Mannheim Haupt. arr	3 4	6 45	7 2	8 13	9 49	8 56	9 33	...	11 4	12 48	12 1	1 8	...	2 1	2 22	...	4 57	3 46	4 33	5 9	5 20	6 30	7 42	6 59	9 10	10 41	...	1210	...	...	1232
LUDWIGSHAFEN 205 arr	...	7a14	7a14	8a23	...	9 a6	...	...	1125	...	1223	1p17	...	2p18	2p55	...	5 p19	3p56	5p19	5p19	5p55	7p16	8p19	7p16	9p53	11 p0	...	1222	...	...	...
HEIDELBERG 140 arr	3a45	7a29	7a29	8a48	10a4	9a50	10a4	...	1159	1 p24	1227	2 p0	...	2p46	3 p0	...	5 p19	4p20	4p57	5p46	5p46	7 p3	8p47	7p35	9p33	11p21	...	1 a0	...	...	1 a0

Extra.									
Darmstadt dep	7a46	5p52	6p50	Worms dep	4a57	12p51	6p20	8p51	
Worms arr	9 20	6 46	8 5	Darmstadt arr	6 20	2 7	7 38	1012	

Slow trains.					
Frankfort dep	5a26	9p26	Mannheim dep	1p50	9p44
Mannheim arr	8 0	1152	Frankfort arr	4 16	1219

‡—Weekdays only.

Station	Ex3	Ex3	2 3 4	1,2,3	2,3,4	Ex3	1,2,3	1,2,3	2 3 4	2 3 4	Ex 3	2 3 4	Ex3	1,2,3	Ex3	Ex3	Ex2	1,2,3	2 3 4	1,2,3	Ex3	Ex3	2 3 4	2 3 4	Ex3	Ex3	Ex3	1,2,3	Ex2	1—4
HEIDELBERG 141 dep	1147	...	4a21	6a16	...	7a24	...	7a55	8a30	...	10a15	1057	...	...	1233	1233	2p19	2 p26	2p26	3p20	...	...	5p35	6p46	...	7p37	8p18	...	9p13	...
LUDWIGSHAFEN 205 dep	1220	...	...	6a42	...	...	...	8a10	9 a7	...	11 a5	1115	...	...	1p14	1p14	...	2 p45	...	3p43	...	4p[illegible]4	6 p6	6p41	...	7p58	8p59	9 p20	9p20	...
	a.m.	a.m.	a.m.	a.m.	a.m.	a.m.	a.m.	a.m.	a.m.	a.m.	a.m.	a.m.	p.m.	p.m.	p.m.	p.m.	p.m.	p.m.	p.m.	p.m.		p.m.	p.m.	p.m.		p.m.	p.m.	p.m.	p.m.	
Mannheim Haupt. dep	1 19	...	5 28	7 4	...	7 53	...	8 20	9 23	...	11 24	1133	1218	...	1 24	1 34	2 51	3 0	3 32	3 57	...	5 6	6 23	7 15	...	8 18	9 10	9 38	9 58	...
Lampertheim		...	6 10	7 22	...		...		9 51	...	...	12 2		...					4 0	4 16	...		6 55	7 45	...		...	...		...
Biblis arr		...	6 25	7 35	...		...		10 8	...	...	1219		...					4 20		p.m.		7 13	8 0	p.m.		9 36	...		p.m.
Worms Haupt. dep		4 48	4 57	7 15	7 42		8 5		9 46	1040	...	...		1 16				3 8	4 1		4 36		6 20	7 37	7 47		8 51	9 35		11 13
" Rhein dep			...	7 21	7 48		...		...	...	...	...		...					...				...	...			...	...		...
Biblis arr			5 14	7 34	8 2	Via Worms.	...		10 5	1052	...	...		...					4 19	Via Worms.			6 38	7 53			9 8	9 49		11 25
Biblis dep			6 26	7 37	8 3		..		1010	1053	...	1221		...					4 21				7 14	8 1			9 37	9 50		11 26
Gernsheim			6 39	7 47	8 18		8 29		1025	11 3	...	1235		1 37					4 40				7 29	8 16				10 1		11 37
Goddelau-Erfelden arr			6 54	7 57	8 35		...		1042	1114	12 3	1253		...					5 0				7 46	8 34				10 12		11 49
Goddelau-Erfelden dep			...	8 16	8 45		...		1048		12 8	...		...					5 4				...	8 38				10 21		11 53
Darmstadt arr			...	8 42	9 10		8 56		1113		12 33	...		...					5 29				...	9 5				10 43		12 19
Goddelau-Erfelden dep			6 56	7 58	8 38		...		1043	1115	12 4	1 0		...					5 7				7 49	8 36				10 18		11 51
Dornberg-Gross-Ger. arr			7 13	8 8	8 56		...	9 7	11 1	1125	12 13	1 18		1 56				3 49	5 25			5 54	8 8	8 54				10 28		12 2
Dornberg-Gross-Ger. dep			7 26	8 17	...		...	9 23	11 6		12 17	1 36						3 51	5 34			6 2	8 14	8 57				10 36		
Gross-Gerau			7 48	8 31	...		...	9 49	1113		12 23	1 59						3 56	5 39			...	8 28	9 15				10 41		
Mayence Haupt. arr	2 28		8 22	8 55	...	9 13	...	1024	1157		12 47	2 23	1 27			2 51	3 59	4 20	6 13	5 28		6 34	8 52	9 48		9 23		11 5		
Dornberg-Gross-Gerau dep	...		7 15	8 10	8 58	...	...	9 8	11 3	1126	12 15	1 20	...	1 57		...	...	3 56	5 29	...		5 57	8 10	8 56		...		10 30		12 3
Goldstein arr	...		7 45	...	9 39	...	...	...	1133		...	1 51	...	...		...	...		6 0	...			8 50	9 30		...		...		
Goldstein dep	...		7 50	...	...	...	...	...	1141		...	...	...	...		...	...		6 6	...			...	9 39		...		...		
Frankfort-Sud arr	...		8 2	...	...	...	...	...	1153		...	...	...	...		...	...		6 18	...			...	9 51		...		...		
Goldstein dep	...		7 46	...	9 40	...	...	...	1134		...	1 52	...	...		...	...		6 1	...			8 51	9 31		...		...		
Frankfort Hauptbhf. arr	...	5 48	7 58	8 38	9 52	...	...	9 33	1146	1158	12 40	2 4	...	2 23	2 33	...	...	4 25	6 13	...	5 36	6 25	9 4	9 43	8 43	...	1025	10 58	1113	12 39

Luggage Rates—see page 462.]

BADEN STATE RAILWAYS (BADISCHE STAATS EISENBAHNEN)

BASLE, WALDSHUT, SCHAFFHAUSEN, SINGEN, and CONSTANCE.

		2&3	3 Cl	2&3	2 & 3	1,2,3	1,2,3	2&3	1,2,3	2&3	2&3	2&3	1,2,3	2&3	2&3	2&3	2&3	2&3	2&3	1,2,3	2&3	2&3
			a.m.	a.m.		a.m.		a.m.		a.m.		p.m.	p.m.		p.m.	p.m.	p.m.		p.m.	p.m.	p.m.	p.m.
Basle—Badische Bahnhof ....dep		...	5†10	5 50	...	7 37	...	7 52	...	1027	...	12 7	1 18	...	3 5	4 33	5 54	...	7 7	8 14	9 15	1145
Badisch-Rheinfelden ...		...	5 36	6 17	...	7 53	...	8 21	...	1055	...	1232	1 34	...	3 30	5 7	6 20	...	7 38	8 38	9 45	12 7
Brennet		...	—	6 37	...	...	...	8 41	...	1115	...	1250	...	...	3 47	—	6 39	...	7 59	...	10 5	1226
Säckingen		...	...	6 48	...	8 10	...	8 53	...	1124	...	1258	1 51	...	3 55	...	6 48	...	8 9	8 55	1018	—
Laufenburg (Klein)......		...	...	7 2	...	...	...	9 12	...	1139	...	1 12	...	...	4 9	...	7 2	...	8 24	9 5	1033	...
Albbruck....................		...	2&3	7 19	...	8 29	...	9 27	...	1151	...	1 24	...	...	4 20	...	7 18	...	8 37	9 14	1045	...
Waldshut 139A arr		a.m.	a.m.	7 31	a.m.	8 37	...	9 39	...	12 3	p.m.	1 36	2 13	p.m.	4 31	...	7 30	p.m.	8 50	9 22	1057	...
Waldshut 139A dep		3 20	5 28	7 38	8 14	8 45	...	9 45	...	12 8	1235	1 40	2 18	4 19	4 36	...	—	7 45	8 58	9 26	11 2	...
Thiengen		3 28	5 37	7 46	8 23	...	...	9 54	...	1217	1243	1 48	...	4 27	4 44	...	...	7 55	9 7	9 34	1111	...
Oberlauchringen 139A		3 33	5 44	7 53	8 29	...	...	10 1	...	1224	1249	1 55	...	4 33	4 50	...	p.m.	8 10	9 13	9 41	1118	...
Erzingen		—	6 7	8 15	—	...	...	1023	...	1246	—	2 18	...	—	5 10	...	6 55	8 32	—	...	1140	...
Neunkirch		...	6 20	8 30	...	...	...	1035	...	1258	...	2 30	...	1,2,3	5 21	...	7 6	8 44	...	...	1152	...
Neuhausen (Rheinfall)		...	6 36	8 48	1,2,3	9 17	...	1051	...	1 14	...	2 46	2 52	5p15	5 36	...	7 21	9 2	...	10 7	12 7	1,2,3
Schaffhausen ...arr		...	6 40	8 52	a.m.	9 21	...	1055	p.m.	1 18	...	2 50	2 56	5 20	5 40	...	7 25	9 6	...	1011	1211	ng't
„ (262)...dep		a.m.	7 1	8 58	9 37	9 24	...	11 5	1225	1 30	...	3 12	3 5	5 27	5 44	...	7 34	9 32	...	1014	1216	1237
Thayingen		5 3	7 16	9 13	...	...	...	1122	...	1 45	...	3 28	...	...	6 0	...	7 48	9 49	...	...	1232	...
Singen ....arr		5 26	7 35	9 33	9 56	9 42	...	1141	1246	2 4	Ex3	3 47	3 24	5 46	6 19	Ex3	8 2	1013	1,2,3	1034	1248	1257
IMMENDINGEN 144 arr		7 a6	8a29	1040	10a40	10a40	a.m.	...	1p40	3 p8	p.m.	5p25	5p25	6p40	7p22	p.m.	8p43	1138	p.m.	1138	...	1a58
Singen ....dep	5a31	6 17	7 55	10 8	10 1	9 47	1131	1147	1 2	2 12	2 43	4 11	3 29	5 58	6 30	7 40	8 42	1024	1043	—	1 10	—
Radolfzell arr	5 45	6 31	8 9	1022	10 11	9 57	1142	12 0	1 14	2 26	2 53	4 25	3 39	6 9	6 43	7 50	8 56	1039	1054	...	1 22	...
Radolfzell dep	5 47	6 35	8 13	1027	—	9 58	1143	1210	1 16	2 31	2 54	4 29	3 43	6 11	6 49	7 51	9 0	11 6	1055	...	1 23	..
Constance ...arr	6 20	7 7	8 45	11 0	...	10 16	12 2	1244	1 36	3 5	3 12	5 3	4 3	6 31	7 23	8 10	9 34	1138	1114	...	1 49	...

Extra.—Singen to Constance, 9.10 a.m., 5.30 p.m.

CONSTANCE, SINGEN, SCHAFFHAUSEN, WALDSHUT, and BASLE.

		2 & 3	1,2,3	2&3	Ex 3	2 & 3	Ex3	1,2,3	2&3	1,2,3	2&3	1,2,3	2 & 3	2&3	2 & 3	1,2,3	1,2,3	Ex3	1,2,3	2 & 3
		a.m.	a.m.	a.m.	a.m.	a.m.	a.m.		a.m.	p.m.	p.m.	p.m.	p.m.		p.m.	p.m.	p.m.	p.m.	p.m.	p.m.
Constance ....dep		5 0	7 12	7 30	9 16	9 22	11 5	...	1127	12 22	1 15	2 10	3 25	...	4 42	6 9	...	7 32	7 45	9 37
Radolfzell .... arr		5 35	7 31	8 8	9 36	9 57	1125	...	12 1	12 42	1 50	2 28	4 0	...	5 26	6 44	...	7 51	8 7	10 12
Radolfzell .... dep		5 42	7 32	8 14	9 39	10 2	1126	...	12 9	12 43	1 55	2 32	4 5	...	5 49	6 48	7 16	7 53	8 10	10 16
Singen ....arr		5 58	7 43	8 32	9 51	10 18	1138	...	1224	12 55	2 10	2 43	4 20	...	6 7	7 3	7 31	8 5	8 22	10 31
IMMENDINGEN ...dep	4a20	4 a20	5a56	...	...	8a31	...	11 a5	...	12p25	1 p0	...	3 p8	4p55	...	...	7 p2	...	7 p2	...
Singen..............dep	4a59	6 13	7 46	8 44	...	10 25	...	11 41	1233	1 3	2 19	2 46	4 38	5 30	6 22	7 10	7 40	...	8 25	...
Thayingen	...	6 36	...	9 10	...	10 49	...	...	1259	...	2 42	...	5 3	5 49	6 50	7 34	...	...	8 46	...
Schaffhausen arr	5 19	6 47	8 4	9 23	...	11 0	...	12 1	1 10	1 22	2 53	3 4	5 15	5 58	7 3	7 46	7 59	...	8 56	...
Schaffhausen dep	—	7 2	8 6	9 40	...	11 10	...	—	1 34	—	3 14	3 7	5 30	6 18	7 15	8 8	—	...	8 59	...
Neuhausen (Rheinfall) ...		7 8	8 13	9 49	...	11 19	...	...	1 41	—	3 21	3 14	5 39	6 25	7 22	8 16	...	...	9 6	...
Neunkirch	2&3	7 24	...	10 9	2 & 3	11 36	...	3 Cl.	1 57	2 & 3	3 37	...	5 57	6 41	7 40	8 32	...	2&3	...	...
Erzingen	a.m.	7 37	...	1030	a.m.	11 54	...	p.m.	2 11	p.m.	3 51	...	6 15	6 50	7 55	8 47	...	p.m.	9 30	a.m.
Oberlauchringen	7 20	7 52	...	1046	11 52	12 9	...	1 †26	2 28	3 10	4 5	...	6 33	—	8 11	9 2	...	9 13	9 42	4 18
Thiengen	7 28	7 58	...	1053	11 59	12 16	...	1 48	2 34	3 17	4 11	...	6 41	...	8 18	9 8		9 19	9 48	4 24
Waldshut... arr	7 35	8 5	8 45	11 0	12 6	12 23	...	1 59	2 41	3 25	4 18	3 46	6 48	...	8 25	9 15	†—Weekdays only.	9 26	9 55	4 30
Waldshut... dep	—	8 14	8 50	1115	—	12 30	...	—	2 52	—	4 32	3 52	7 6	...	8 34	—		—	9 59	4 35
Albbruck	...	8 27	...	1129	...	12 44	...	...	3 4	...	4 43	4 1	7 19	...	8 50	...		...	10 9	4 46
Laufenburg (Klein)...	...	8 39	...	1146	...	12 58	...	...	3 16	...	4 54	...	7 31	...	9 12	...		...	10 18	4 57
Säckingen	3Cl.	8 55	9 12	12 3	3 Cl.	1 17	...	...	3 38	...	5 13	4 20	7 48	...	9 23	...		...	10 34	5 14
Brennet....................	a.m.	9 3	...	1212	a.m.	1 25	...	...	3 47	...	5 21	...	7 57	p.m.	—	...		...	...	5 22
Badisch-Rheinfelden	6†20	9 33	9 28	1233	11 40	1 46	...	...	4 6	...	5 43	4 38	8 17	6 22	...	...		...	10 53	5 41
Basle-Baden Station	6 44	9 56	9 42	1 2	12 4	2 9	...	...	4 30	...	6 10	4 53	8 42	6 47	...	...	...	...	11 13	6 10

Extra.—Constance to Singen, 7.21 a.m., 2.0, 5.12, 11.18 p.m. Oberlauchringen to Waldshut, 5.49 p.m.

HEIDELBERG and SPEYER.

Heidelberg Hauptbhf ...dep	a.m. 6 25	a.m. 6 59	a.m. 1011	p.m. 1215	p.m. 2 15	p.m. 4 35	p.m. 6 25	p.m. 7 40	p.m. 9 10
Schwetzingen... arr	6 43	7 17	1031	1233	2 37	4 57	6 45	8 2	9 28
Schwetzingen... dep	—	7 30	1043	1248	2 44	5 2	7 21	—	9 42
Lusshof	...	7 54	11 3	1 15	3 4	5 29	7 51	...	10 8
Speyer Rhein Station ...	...	8 2	1111	1 23	3 12	5 37	7 59	...	1016
„ Bahnhof 207 arr ...	...	8 11	1120	1 32	3 21	5 46	8 8	...	1025

	a.m.		a.m.	p.m.	p.m.	p.m.	p.m.		p.m.
Speyer Bahnhof...	4 53	...	8 31	1255	1 54	3 34	5 59	...	8 32
„ Rhein Stat'n	5 2	...	8 40	1 5	2 4	3 43	6 9	...	8 42
Lusshof	5 10	...	8 48	1 13	2 12	3 51	6 19	...	8 50
Schwetzingen ... arr	5 36	a.m.	9 11	1 32	2 37	4 10	6 49	p.m.	9 18
Schwetzingen ... dep	5 39	7 20	9 20	1 35	2 44	4 11	6 54	8 12	9 45
Heidelberg......arr	5 59	7 40	9 44	1 55	3 4	4 31	7 14	8 32	10 9

WALDSHUT and IMMENDINGEN.

	a.m.	a.m.	p.m.	p.m.	p.m.	p.m.	p.m.
Waldshut ....dep	3 20	8 14	12 35	4 19	4 36	8 58	9 26
Oberlauchringen	3 34	8 32	12 51	4 53	4 49	9 45	9 40
Ofteringen	3 45	8 45	1 6	5 5	—	9 58	—
Stühlingen	4 1	9 3	1 28	5 21	—	10 15	—
Weizen	4 6	9 10	1 37	5 26	...	10 21	...
Fützen	4 27	9 35	2 3	5 51	...	10 45	...
Riedöschingen	4 52	10 5	2 34	6 18	...	11 13	...
Immendingen 144 ...arr	5 15	10 29	2 59	6 42	...	11 35	...

	a.m.	a.m.	p.m.	p.m.	p.m.		
Immendingen ....dep	5 29	9 57	1 4	3 53	7 27	...	...
Riedöschingen	5 55	10 28	1 36	4 25	7 54	...	...
Fützen	6 20	10 54	2 5	4 52	8 19	...	...
Weizen	6 40	11 15	2 28	5 14	8 39	...	...
Stühlingen	6 45	11 21	2 38	5 21	8 43	...	...
Ofteringen	7 2	11 39	2 56	5 37	9 0	...	...
Oberlauchringen	7 20	11 52	3 10	5 49	9 13	...	...
Waldshut 139A.........arr	7 35	12 6	3 25	6 2	9 26	...	...

RADOLFZELL and FRIEDRICHSHAFEN.

Radolfzell	4a40	7 a4	10a4	1018	12p7	2 p0	3p16	4p49	5p46	6p52	9 p1
Stahringen	4 59	7 14	1014	...	1217	2 17	3 56	5 3	5 56	7 7	9 11
Ueberling'n	5 28	7 43	11 1	1049	1246	2 52	4 19	5 39	6 24	7 45	9 37
Oberuhldin	5 45	8 0	—	11 3	1 4	—	4 33	—	6 41	—	9 53
Mimmenh'n	5 56	8 8	...	1111	1 13	...	4 41	...	6 51	...	10 2
Fricking'n	6 26	9 17	...	1138	2 12	...	5 6	...	7 45	...	1029
Friedrichsh	6 33	8 40	...	1136	1 46	...	5 11	...	7 24	...	1033

Friedrichshaf'n		5a20	8a6	...	12p9	1p17	...	3p10	...	6p30	8p52
Frickingen dep		5 30	730	...	1215	...	...	3 15	...	6 8	9 0
Mimmenhausen		5 59	837	...	1241	1 40	...	3 46	...	6 53	9 27
Oberuhldingen...		6 13	846	a.m.	1251	...	...	3 59	...	7 2	9 39
Ueberlingen	4a38	6 34	9 0	1112	1 8	1 58	3 16	4 18	6p23	7 14	9 56
Stahringen ..	5 18	7 7	923	1153	1 38	...	3 49	4 47	7 2	...	1026
Radolfzellarr	5 28	7 16	931	12 2	1 46	2 24	3 58	4 55	7 11	7 42	1035

For Fares—see page 120A.] BADEN STATE RAILWAYS. [Luggage Rates—see page 462.

MANNHEIM, HEIDELBERG, CARLSRUHE, FREIBURG and BASLE.

THROUGH CARRIAGES 1st and 2nd class). } Frankfort to Basle—in 6.38, 7.12, 9.35 a.m., 1.58, 5.15 and 11.45 p.m. from Frankfort.

RC—Restaurant Car.

Dist. E.M.		2&3	Ex3	2 & 3	2 & 3	2 & 3	1,2,3	2 & 3	2&3	Ex3	Ex3	1,2,3	Ex3	2&3	2&3	Ex 2	Ex3	2 & 3	2&3
...	COLOGNE ......122 dep	...	10p33	...	...	...	...	...	...	1a58	1a58	...	...	...	1a58	...	...	...	...
...	MAYENCE ......208 dep	...	1a49	...	...	...	...	...	...	...	...	...	...	...	...	...	...	...	...
...	MAYENCE ......139 dep	...	1a49	...	...	...	...	...	...	5a30	5a30	...	...	...	5a54	...	8 a9	...	...
			a.m.	a.m.		a.m.	a.m.		a.m.	a.m.	a.m.			a.m.	a.m.		a.m.	a.m.	a.m.
—	**Mannheim** ....dep	...	3 8	3 19	...	4 0	5 33	...	5 23	7 10	7 10	...	...	7 39	8 20	...	9 39	10 26	9 45
11½	**Heidelberg**.........arr	...		3 45	...	4 20	:	...	5 56	:	7 29	...	...	8 11	:	...	:	10 55	10 4
...	COLOGNE ......122 dep	...		...	...	...		...	...		...	1a58	1a58	...		1 a58		...	...
...	MAYENCE ......123 dep	...		...	...	...		...	...		...	5a54	5a54	...		6 a15		...	...
...	FRANKFORT...136 dep	...		...	...	...		a.m.	...		4a24	6a14	6a38	6a38		7 a12		...	...
...	**Heidelberg** ......dep	...	Via Schwetzingen.	...	...	4 28	Via Schwetzingen.	4 51	6 10	Via Schwetzingen.	7 34	7 59	8 11	8 15	Via Schwetzingen.	8 52	Via Schwetzingen.	...	10 8
20	Wiesloch	...		...	...	4 42		5 11	6 30		...	...	...	8 33		...		...	1028
26	Langenbrücken	...		...	...	4 52		5 29	6 48		...	...	RC	8 48		RC		...	1045
32	**Bruchsal** ....arr	...		...	...	5 2		5 42	6 59		8 0	8 25	8 38	9 1		9 18		...	1058
81¼	STUTTGART 192 arr	...		3 Cl.	...	...		8 a35	...		9a19	...	...	1128		11a28		...	...
	STUTTGART 192 dep	a.m.		a.m.	...	...		...	...		6 a0	6 a0	6 a0	6a58		6 a58	8 a1	...	8 a1
...	**Bruchsal**..........dep	5 7		5 45	...	5 3		5 55	7 6		8 1	8 26	8 39	9 4		9 19		...	11 4
37½	Weingarten	5 22		6 0	...	5 13		6 10	7 19		...	...	...	9 14		...		...	1118
42¼	**Durlach**	5 32		6 12	...	5 22		6 27	7 30		...	...	...	9 24		...		...	1130
45	**Carlsruhe** Hauptbahnhof arr	5 38	3 55	6 19	...	5 28	6 32	6 34	7 36	8 1	8 18	8 44	8 58	9 30	9 34	9 37	1026	...	1137
			a.m.		a.m.	a.m.	a.m.	a.m.	a.m.	a.m.	a.m.	a.m.	a.m.		a.m.	a.m.	a.m.		a.m.
	Carlsruhe Hauptbahnhof dep	...	4 10		5 0	5 36	6 39	7 0	8 4	8 6	8 38	8 50	9 3	...	9 42	9 42	1029	1,2,3	1152
49¼	Ettlingen................	...	...	Weekdays only.	5 10	5 46	...	7 11	8 14	...	...	...	...	...	...	...	...	a.m.	12 2
60	**Rastatt** ....146......	...	4 30		5 38	6 5	7 1	7 38	8 48	...	...	...	9 25	...	10 8	...	...	10 55	1230
65	**Oos** ....arr	...	4 39		5 51	6 15	7 10	7 51	8 58	8 33	9 6	9 18	9 34	...	1018	10 10	1057	11 8	1243
67¾	**Baden-Baden** arr	...	4 52		6 4	6 28	7 22	8 14	9 18	8 46	9 18	9 31	9 46	...	1036	10 24	1111	11 19	12 6
	Baden-Baden dep	...	4 17	...	5 43	6 5	7 1	7 40	9 8	8 24	8 56	9 8	9 23	...	10 2	10 2	1048		1233
...	**Oos** ....dep	...	4 40	...	5 54	6 17	7 12	7 53	9 25	8 35	9 10	9 19	9 35	...	1022	10 17	1059	...	1246
72	Bühl ....145......	...	...	...	6 12	6 29	7 24	8 12	9 52	:	:	...	...	...	1035	...	...	...	1 5
77½	Achern ....135B......	...	4 57	...	6 26	6 40	7 34	8 26	10 5	:	:	...	...	...	1045	...	...	...	1 19
81½	Renchen	...	...	...	6 36	6 48		8 37	1015	:	:	...	...	...	1052	...	...	...	1 29
85	**Appenweier** ......arr	...	5 8	...	6 43	6 55	7 46	8 44	1022	:	:	9 44	10 1	...	1059	10 42	1126	...	1 36
98½	STRASSBURG 145 arr	...	5a30	...	7 a24	7 a24	8a20	9 a25	1144	:	10a1	1043	1043	...	1144	11a44	1 p1	...	2 p8
410¾	PARIS ....65 arr	1,2,3	1216	2 & 3	...	...	...	4 p39	...	:	4 39	...	...	...	...	...	9p20	2 & 3	9p20
...	STRASSBURG 145 dep	a.m.		a.m.	6 a23	6 a23	7a18	8 a8	9a35	:		9a17	9a35	...	10a8	10 a8	11a0	11a39	1p22
...	**Appenweier** ......dep	5 13	...	5 19	7 9	7 2	7 52	8 48	1027	:	...	9 45	10 5	...	11 0	10 43	1131	12 38	1 57
89¾	**Offenburg** ....arr	5 23	...	5 32	7 22	7 14	8 2	9 1	1039	9 8	...	9 54	1015	...	1110	10 52	1140	12 53	2 10
182¼	SINGEN ....144 arr	9 a7	...	...	...	...	1129	12p59	3p56	1259	...	1259	3p56	...	3p56	3 p56	2p41	...	7p35
201½	CONSTANCE 139A arr	9a40	...	...	...	...	12p2	1 p36	5 p3	1p36	...	1p36	5 p3	...	5 p3	5 p3	3p12	...	8p10
...	**Offenburg** ....dep	...	...	5 37	8 12	7 20	...	9 17	...	9 11	...	...	1020	...	1113	10 55	...	...	2 48
101	Dinglingen (Lahr)	...	...	6 4	8 42	7 39	...	9 48	...	9 26	...	...	1036	...	1140	...	...	...	3 17
106½	Orschweier ......145......	...	...	6 16	8 54	7 49	...	10 4	...	...	...	...	...	...	1152	...	...	...	3 29
112	Kenzingen	...	...	6 34	9 13	8 3	...	10 22	...	...	...	...	...	...	12 3	...	...	...	3 42
115	Riegel	...	...	6 43	9 21	8 10	...	10 30	...	...	...	...	RC	...	1216	RC	...	...	3 57
119½	Emmendingen	...	...	6 49	9 35	8 20	...	10 44	...	...	...	...	11 1	...	1228	...	...	...	4 11
123¾	Denzlingen......142	2&3	...	7 7	9 47	8 31	...	10 56	...	...	...	...	...	...	1238	...	...	1,2,3	4 21
129	**Freiburg** 143 ... arr	a.m.	...	7 17	9 57	8 41	...	11 8	...	10 5	...	...	1119	...	1247	11 46	...	p.m.	4 33
...	**Freiburg** 143 ... dep	4 18	...	7 23	10 13	8 47	...		...	10 7	...	...	1121	...	1253	11 49	...	4 22	
138	Krotzingen................	4 36	...	7 43	10 31	9 2	...	...	...	...	...	...	...	...	1 12	...	...	4 37	...
147	**Müllheim** ....arr	4 57	2&3	8 5	10 57	9 19	...	...	...	1029	...	...	1144	...	1 35	12 11	...	4 51	...
151½	BADENW'LER 140A arr	6a13	a.m.	8 a47	11a31	11a31	...	...	...	1131	...	...	1251	...	2p15	12p51	...		...
...	BADENWEILER ...dep		4 25	7 a3	9 a52	...	...	...	...	9a52	...	...	9a52	...	1255	11a36	...	...	...
...	**Müllheim** ....dep	...	5 20	8 8	11 1	9 20	...	...	...	1029	...	...	1145	...	1 37	12 12	...	...	...
150	Efringen	...	6 3	8 47	11 39	9 42	...	...	...	...	...	...	...	...	2 14	...	...	...	...
163⅝	Haltingen	1,2,3	6 16	8 57	11 49	9 50	...	...	...	...	...	...	...	...	2 25	...	...	...	...
165½	Leopoldshohe.............	7a13	6 26	9 2	11 56	9 56	...	...	...	...	...	...	...	...	2 29	...	...	...	...
167½	**Basle**—Baden Sta. arr	7 19	6 32	9 9	12 2	10 2	...	...	...	11 0	...	...	1216	...	2 39	12 43	...	...	...
170½	BASLE-Swiss Sta. arr	...	...	10 22	12 40	10 22	...	...	...	1121	...	...	1240	...	...	1 8	...	...	...
225½	ZURICH ....261 arr	...	...	12p48	3 p29	12p48	...	...	...	1p13	...	...	3p29	...	...	3 p29	...	...	...
229¾	LUCERNE ......258 arr	...	...	1 p40	3 p49	1 p40	...	...	...	1p56	...	...	3p49	...	...	3 p49	...	...	...
402¾	MILAN.........269A arr	...	...	...	10p25	8 p40	...	...	...	8p40	...	...	1025	...	...	10p25	...	...	...

Customs Examination at Basle. ‡—Via Mannheim.

Dinglingen and Lahr, in 6 minutes. Frequent service connecting with all trains on main line stopping at Dinglingen.

BASLE Baden Station to BASLE Swiss Station.

Basle Swiss Station dep	7a35	9a15	9a25	10a0	12p18	1 p4	3p[illegible]	4p30	4p40	5 7	7p27	8§58	9p2	11p30
Basle Baden Station arr	7 42	9 23	9 35	10 8	12 26	1 12	3 8	4 38	4 48	5 15	7 35	9 6	9 18	11 38
Basle Baden Station dep	6a10	10a14	11a13	12p32	1p0	3p9	4p55	5p48	7p17	8p12	9p7	10p37	11p39	
Basle Swiss Station arr	6 18	10 22	11 21	12 40	1 8	3 17	5 3	5 56	7 25	8 20	9 15	10 45	11 47	

§—From 15th July until 15th September.

For Continuation of Trains, see next page.

BADEN STATE RAILWAYS.

MANNHEIM, HEIDELBERG, CARLSRUHE, FREIBURG, and BASLE.

Station																			
COLOGNE ......122 dep	...	...	...	...	6 a17	...	9a32	...	10a3	...	...	...	...	1120	1120	...	...	1210	1210
MAYENCE ......208 dep	...	...	...	9 a31	...	...	...	...	...	...	...	...	...	2p32	2p32	...	...	...	3p48
MAYENCE ......139 dep	8 a9	9a24	...	9 a24	10a33	...	1252	...	1p13	...	...	...	...	2p32	2p32	...	...	3p23	3p23
	Ex 3	1,2,3	Ex 3	1,2,3	2 & 3	2&3	Ex3	Ex.3	Ex3	2&3	Ex3	Ex3	2 & 3	Ex3	Ex3	1,2,3	2&3	Ex3	Ex3
	a.m.	a.m.		a.m.	p.m.	p.m.	p.m.	p.m.	p.m.	p.m.	p.m.		p.m.	p.m.	p.m.		p.m.	p.m.	p.m.
Mannheim ....dep	10 26	11 8	...	11 26	12 5	1256	2 5	1 54	2 28	2 17	2 41	...	3 13	3 51	4 1	...	4 20	4 38	5 24
Heidelberg ....arr	10 55		...	11 59	12 27	1 24		2 15		2 46	3 0	...	3 42		4 20	...	4 49	4 57	
COLOGNE 122, 128 dep	...	Via Schwetzingen.	...	5 a30	...	...	Via Schwetzi'g	8 a8		...	...	10a3	...	Via Schwetzingen.	...	1127	...		1127
MAYENCE ......123 dep	9 a0		...	9 a24	...	...		12 p8		...	...	1p32	...		...	2p15	...		...
FRANKFORT...136 dep	9 a35		...	10a29	...	...		12p50		...	...	1p58	...		...	3p25	...		4‡10
Heidelberg ....dep	11 8		...	12 12	12 45	...		2 33		...	3 7	3 45	3 50		4 28	5 13			
Wiesloch	...		...	...	1 5	...		...		...		RC	4 11		...	...	...		
Langenbrücken.........	...		...	...	1 22	...		...		...		...	4 28		...	...	...		
Bruchsal ....arr	11 34		...	12 38	1 35	1,2,3		2 59	3§16	...		4 12	4 41		4 56	5 38	...		Via Schwetzingen.
STUTTGART 192 arr	...		...	2 p24	...	p.m.		4 p47	4p47	...		6p29	6 p29		6p29	7p42	...	‡—Via Mannheim.	
STUTTGART 192 dep	10 a3		10a52	10 a3	10a26	1248		12p22		...		...	...			2p26	p.m.		
Bruchsal ....dep	11 35			12 40	1 39			3 0		...		4 14	4 46	RC	...	5 40	6 30		
Weingarten	...			...	1 52		RC	RC		...		...	4 59		...	...	6 43		
Durlach	...			12 55	2 4			...		...		4 30	5 9		...	5 54	6 53	...	
Carlsruhe Hauptbahnhof arr	11 53	1157	12 36	1 1	2 10	2 25	2 52	3 18	3 18	...	3 59	4 36	5 15	4 39	...	5 59	6 59	...	6 9
	p.m.		p.m.	p.m.	p.m.	p.m.	p.m.	p.m.		p.m.	p.m.	p.m.	p.m.		p.m.	p.m.			p.m.
Carlsruhe Hauptbahnhof dep	12 3	...	12 44	1 6	2 35	2 36	2 56	3 24		3 37	4 3	4 48	5 31		4 48	6 18	1,2,3	...	6 13
Ettlingen	...	...	...	...	2 45	...	...	...	...	...	...	...	5 41		...	6 29	p.m.	...	RC
Rastatt 146	...	...	...	1 26	3 18	3 3	...	...	...	4 13	...	5 10	6 10	...	5 10	6 57	5 44	...	...
Oos ....arr	12 30	...	1 12	1 35	3 31	3 13	3 23	3 51	...	4 23	4 31	5 19	6 20	...	5 19	7 10	5 56	...	6 39
Baden-Baden arr	12 44	...	1 25	1 52	3 47	3 36	3 36	4 2	...	4 40	4 40	5 31	6 36	...	5 31	7 19	6 5	...	6 52
Baden-Baden dep	12 18	...	1 3	1 25	3 21	...	3 10	3 39	...	4 23	4 23	5 8	6 11	...	5 8			...	6 28
Oos ....dep	12 32	...	1 17	1 37	3 33	...	3 25	3 52	...	4 42	4 35	5 22	6 21	...	5 22	...	...	...	6 41
Bühl.........145	...	...	...	1 49	4 5	...		...	...	5 2		...	6 58	...	...	...	...	...	...
Achern	...	...	...	1 58	4 19	...		...	...	5 17		...	7 15	...	...	...	...	...	...
Renchen	...	...	...	...	4 30	...		...	...	5 28		...	7 28	...	...	...	...	...	...
Appenweier ......arr	12 57	...	1 44	2 9	4 37	...		4 17	...	5 35		5 47	7 36	...	5 47	...	...	...	7 5
STRASSBURG...145 arr	...	...	2 p8	2 p51	5 p30	...		4 p48	...	6p46		6p46	8 p14	...	6p46	...	...	...	7p40
PARIS ....65 arr	...	...	9 p20	...		...		...	...	...		5 a0	...	1,2,3	5 a0	...	...	...	...
STRASSBURG...145 dep	12p17	...		1 p22	3 p58	...		3 p50	...	5p32		5p22	6 p56	6p21	5p22	...	...	...	6p21
Appenweier ......dep	12 58	...	...	2 11	4 47	...		4 18	...	6 4		5 49	7 44	7 11	5 49	...	...	...	7 6
Offenburg ....arr	1 7	...	...	2 20	5 0	...	3 57	4 27	...	6 17	5 8	5 58	7 57	7 21	5 58	...	..	...	
SINGEN ....144 arr	...	...	...	...	...	...	7p35	7 p35	...	...	...	1037	1 a0	1037	1037	2&3	...	...	
CONSTANCE 139A arr	...	...	3 Cl.	...	...	...	8p10	8 p10	...	...	...	1114	1 a49	1114	1114	p.m.	...	p.m.	
Offenburg ....dep	1 9	...	p.m.	2 28	5 40	...	3 58	...	...	...	5 10	6 5	...	...	6 5	6 25	...	8 36	
Dinglingen (Lahr)...140	1 24	...	5 30	2 44	6 30	...	...	...	...	...	...	6 20	...	...	6 20	6 54	...	9 4	
Orschweier 145	...	...	5 44	...	6 44	...	...	...	...	...	...	...	...	...	...		...	9 18	
Kenzingen	...	...	6 8	...	7 2	...	...	...	...	...	...	RC	...	...	RC	...	...	9 34	
Riegel	...	...	6 14	...	7 9	...	...	...	...	...	...	...	...	...	...	...	...	9 42	
Emmendingen	...	...	6 24	3 9	7 24	2&3	...	...	...	...	...	...	...	...	...	...	...	9 55	
Denzlingen 142	...	...	6 38	3 19	7 38	p.m.	...	...	...	...	...	...	...	...	...	...	...	10 7	RC
Freiburg ...143 arr	2 0	...	6 49	3 29	7 49		4 46	...	...	...	6 1	7 0	...	...	7 0	p.m.	p.m.	1017	8 2
Freiburg ...143 dep	2 2	...		3 33		4 55	4 48	...	...	...	6 6	7 2	...	...	7 2	7 25	8 23	1036	8 5
Krotzingen 145	...	...	...	3 46	...	5 15	...	...	...	...	...	...	...	...	...	7 51	8 45	1056	...
Müllheim ....arr	2 21	...	...	3 59	...	5 37	...	...	...	...	6 28	7 24	...	...	7 24	8 14	9 7	1118	...
BADENW'LER 140A arr	3 p55	...	...	...	...	6p38	RC	...	...	...	...	8 p4	...	...	...	9p53	9p53	1158	...
BADENWEILER......dep	12p55	...	...	2 p25	...	4p55	...	...	...	...	...	6p43	...	...	6p43		8p30	10p5	...
Müllheim ....dep	2 25	...	...	4 0	...	5 44	...	...	...	...	6 29	7 25	...	...	7 25	...	9 13	1119	...
Efringen	...	...	...	4 25	...	6 23	...	...	...	...	...	...	...	...	...	...	9 53	1157	...
Haltingen	...	...	...	4 33	...	6 34	...	...	...	...	...	..	p.m.	...	...	...	10 4	12 8	...
Leopoldshohe	...	...	...	...	...	6 46	...	...	...	...	...	...	8 18	...	...	...	10 9	1214	...
Basle—Baden Sta. arr	2 55	...	...	4 41	...	6 52	5 38	...	...	...	7 0	7 56	8 24	...	7 56	...	1015	1220	8 55
BASLE—Swiss Sta. ar	3 17	...	...	5 3	...	...	5 56	...	...	...	7p25	8p20	...	...	8p20	...	1045	...	9p15
ZURICH ....261 arr	6 p57	...	...	7 p55	...	...	7p55	...	...	...	...	1125	...	...	1125	...	...	...	1125
LUCERNE ......258 arr	6 p15	...	...	8 p15	...	...	8p15	...	...	...	...	1142	...	...	1142	...	...	...	1142
MILAN ....269A arr	...	...	...	...	...	...	...	...	...	...	...	6a22	...	...	6a22	...	...	...	6a22

RC—Restaurant Car. §—Via Graben Neudorf.

Extra.																		
Mannheim	4a35	5a57	6a18	7a20	8a25	9a21	12p27	1p28	3p37	5 p0	5p25	5p30	6p21	7p12	8p15	9 p14	...	...
Heidelberg	5 4	6 16	6 50	7 46	8 48	9 50	12 59	2 0	3 57	5 19	5 46	6 6	6 46	7 35	8 47	9 33	...	...

Extra.—Mullheim to Badenweiler, 5.40 a.m.]

MULLHEIM and BADENWEILER.

Mullheim—	a m	a.m.	p.m.	p.m.	p m	p m	p m	p m	p.m.
Bahnhof...	8 12	11 1	1218	1 45	3 20	6 7	7 30	9 20	1125
Rath.	8 25	1112	1231	1 56	3 33	6 19	7 44	9 33	1138
Niederweil.	8 32	1119	1238	2 [illegible]	3 40	6 26	7 50	9 40	1145
Oberweiler	8 38	1125	1244	2 9	3 48	6 32	7 56	9 46	1151
Badenweil.	8 47	1131	1251	2 15	3 55	6 38	8 4	9 53	1158

	a.m.	a m	a.m.	a.m.	p.m.	p.m	p m	p.m.	p.m.	p.m.
Badenweiler dep	4 25	7 3	52	1136	1255	2 25	4 55	6 43	8 30	10 5
Oberweiler	4 31	7 11	10 0	1143	1 1	2 31	5 3	6 50	8 38	1013
Niederweiler	4 37	7 17	10 6	1149	1 7	2 37	5 9	6 56	8 44	1019
Mullheim Rathh.	4 45	7 23	1014	1155	1 13	2 43	5 16	7 2	8 50	1025
Mullheim Bhf ar	4 55	7 36	1025	12 7	1 25	2 55	5 30	7 15	9 4	1038

BADEN STATE RAILWAYS.

MANNHEIM, HEIDELBERG, CARLSRUHE, FREIBURG, and BASLE.

RC—Restaurant Car. SC—Sleeping Car.

COLOGNE (122)...dep	1210	...	...	12p10	2p31	...	...	...	...	...	...	...	...	...	...	8 p2	...	...
MAYENCE (208) dep	..	...	...	3 p48	...	...	...	...	7p36	...	7 p36	...	...	...	...	...	...	...
MAYENCE (139) dep	3p23	...	...	3 p54	5p45	...	...	...	7 p30	...	7 p30	...	...	...	...	11p25	...	...
	2&3	2&3	Ex 2	1,2,3	Ex3	Ex3	1,2,3	2&3	Ex 3	Ex 1	1,2,3	Ex 3	2 & 3	1,2,3	2 & 3	Ex3	Ex.3	3Cl.
	p.m.	p.m.		p.m.	p.m.			p.m.	p.m.		p.m.		p.m.	p.m.	p m.	ng t		a.m.
Mannheim ....dep	6 2	...	...	6 33	7 4	...	...	7 39	9 17	...	9 35	...	10 51	1121	11 40	1241	...	1 9
Heidelberg ....arr	6 22	...	...	7 3	⋮	...	...	8 12	⋮	...	10 1	...	11 21	⋮	12 3	1 0	...	⋮
COLOGNE (122)...dep	...	...	1 p5	1 p5	⋮	...	...	...	⋮	...	3 p38	...	...	⋮	...	6p33	...	⋮
MAYENCE (123)...dep	4p48	...	4 p48	4 p48	⋮	...	4 p48	...	⋮	...	7 p30	...	...	⋮	...	1034	...	⋮
FRANKFORT (137) dep	5p10	...	5 p10	5 p15	⋮	...	5 p15	...	⋮	...	8 p13	...	9 p32	⋮	...	1049	11p45	⋮
Heidelberg ....dep	6 40	7 25	6 34	7 16	⋮	...	7 21	8 30	⋮	...	10 7	...	11 26	⋮	...	1 10	1 22	Via Schwetzingen
Wiesloch	6 53	7 46	⋮	...	⋮	...	...	8 50	⋮	...	...	...	11 46	⋮	...	...	SC	⋮
Langenbrücken	7 21	8 4	⋮	...	⋮	...	...	9 7	⋮	...	...	...	12 3	⋮	...	...	...	⋮
Bruchsal ....arr	7 35	8 17	⋮	7 42	⋮	...	7 49	9 20	⋮	...	10 33	...	12 16	⋮	Ex 1	1 35	1 48	⋮
STUTTGART 192 arr	9p21	...	⋮	9 p21	⋮	...	9 p21	...	⋮	...	12a15	...	3 a4	⋮	...	3 a4	4 a52	⋮
STUTTGART 192 dep	...	...	4p47	5 p44	⋮	6p50		6p13	⋮	...	...	...	...	⋮	11p32	...	10p38	⋮
Bruchsal ....dep	7 48	...	⋮	7 43	⋮	⋮	...	9 25	⋮	...	10 35	...	12 19	⋮	⋮	...	1 49	⋮
Weingarten	8 2	...	⋮	...	⋮	⋮	...	9 39	⋮	...	...	...	12 32	⋮	⋮	...	...	⋮
Durlach	8 14	...	RC	...	⋮	⋮	...	9 49	⋮	K	10 50	...	12 42	⋮	O	...	2 5	⋮
Carlsruhe Hauptbahn. arr	8 20	1,2,3	7 11	8 2	8 0	8 28	2 & 3	9 55	10 8	...	10 56		12 48	1233	1 1	...	2 11	2 17
		p.m.	p.m.	p.m.		p.m.	p.m.	p.m.		p.m.		p.m.			a.m.		a.m.	a.m.
Carlsruhe Hauptbahn. dep	...	6 31	7 21	8 10	...	8 33	8 42	1044	...	10 45	...	11 8	11p30	...	1 6	...	2 19	2 40
Ettlingen	...	6 41	...	...	...	...	8 52	1055	...	...	...	...	11 40	...	...	...	2 29	...
Rastatt (146)	...	7 7	...	8 30	...	...	9 19	1120	...	...	...	...	12 6	...	...	...	2 44	3 18
Oos...........arr	...	7 17	7 48	8 40	...	9 1	9 31	1130	...	11 15	2 & 3	11 36	12 16	...	1 35	...	2 53	3 29
Baden-Baden arr	...	7 30	8 4	8 52	...	9 14	9 51	1153	...	11 28	p.m.	11 53	12 25	...	1 47	...	3 6	4 52
Baden-Baden dep	...	7 5	7 39	8 23	...	8 53	9 22	...	...	11 6	11 25	11 25		...	1 24	...	2 42	2 42
Oos...........dep	...	7 19	7 50	8 42	...	9 5	9 35	...	...	11 18	11 45	11 38	...	...	1 36	...	2 54	3 37
Bühl (145)	...	7 37	...	8 55	...	...	9 56	...	...	⋮	12 5	...	...	...	⋮	...	3 6	3 55
Achern	...	7 50	...	9 5	...	...	10 9	...	...	K	12 20	...	...	...	⋮	...	...	3 48
Renchen	...	8 1	...	...	...	...	10 23	...	...	⋮	12 31	...	...	...	⋮	...	...	4 17
Appenweier.........arr	...	8 8	8 15	9 17	...	9 30	10 30	...	...	⋮	12 38	12 4	⌒	...	⋮	...	3 24	4 27
STRASSBURG (145) arr	...	...	8 p44	9 p54	...	9p54	11 p8	...	...	12a12	...	12a28	│	...	2 a25	...	3 a57	5a34
PARIS (65) ....arr	...	...	...	8 a25	...	8a25	8 a25	...	...	7 a21	...	8 a25	│	...	8 a56	...	...	1216
STRASSBURG (145) dep	...	7p32	7 p32	8 p45	...	...	10 p5	...	...	...	...	...	Ex 3	...	...	...	...	3a58
Appenweier ......dep	...	8 10	8 17	9 19	...	...	10 45	...	...	...	12 44	...	12a12	...	...	...	3 25	4 38
Offenburg...........arr	...	8 20	8 26	9 28	...	...	10 59	...	...	...	12 57	...	12 22	...	...	...	3 35	4 50
SINGEN (144) ....arr	...	...	1 a0	...	...	...	...	...	...	...		...	...	...	...	...	...	9 a7
CONSTANCE 139A arr	...	...	1 a49	...	...	...	...	...	...	...	...	...	...	...	...	...	...	9a40
Offenburg...........dep	...	...	8 30	9 32	...	...	11 29	...	...	...	...	...	12 26	...	...	...	3 38	...
Dinglingen (Lahr)	...	...	8 46	9 48	...	...	12 3	...	...	...	...	...	12 46	...	...	...	3 54	...
Orschweier (145)	...	3 Cl	...	...	...	...	12 20	...	...	...	...	...	12 55	...	...	...	...	...
Kenzingen	...	p.m.	RC	...	...	...	12 41	...	...	...	...	...	1 9	...	...	...	SC	...
Riegel	...	1027	...	...	...	...	12 51	...	...	...	...	...	1 16	...	...	...	...	...
Emmendingen	...	1041	...	10 11	...	...	1 30	...	...	...	...	...	1 25	...	...	...	4 19	...
Denzlingen (142)	...	1057	...	...	...	...	1 45	...	...	...	...	...	...	...	...	...	...	...
Freiburg (143) arr	...	1115	9 25	10 27	...	...	1 57	...	...	...	...	...	1 43	...	...	...	4 37	...
Freiburg (143) dep	...	1119	9 27	10 31	...	...		...	...	...	...	...		...	...	...	4 40	...
Krotzingen	...	1157	...	...	...	...	...	...	...	...	...	...	...	...	...	...	4 53	...
Müllheim ....arr	...	1224	9 49	10 53	...	...	...	...	...	...	...	...	...	...	‡—Via Mannheim.	...	5 6	...
BADENW'LER 140A arr	...		...	11p58	...	...	...	...	...	...	...	...	...	...	...	...	6 a13	...
BADENWEILER ...dep	...	...	8 p30	10 p5	...	...	...	...	...	...	...	...	...	...	...	...	4 a25	...
Müllheim ....dep	...	...	9 50	10 54	...	...	...	...	...	...	...	...	...	...	...	...	5 7	...
Efringen	...	...	...	...	...	...	...	...	...	...	...	...	...	...	...	...	...	...
Haltingen	...	...	...	...	...	...	...	...	...	...	...	...	...	...	...	...	...	...
Leopoldshohe	...	...	...	...	...	...	...	...	...	...	...	...	...	...	...	...	...	...
Basle—Baden Sta. arr	...	...	10 21	11 24	...	...	...	...	...	...	...	...	...	...	...	...	5 38	...
BASLE-Swiss Sta. arr	...	...	10 45	11 47	...	...	...	...	...	...	...	...	...	...	...	...	6 18	...
ZURICH (261) ......arr	...	...	...	...	...	...	...	...	...	...	...	...	...	...	...	...	8 a35	...
LUCERNE (258) ...arr	...	...	1 a12	...	...	...	...	...	...	...	...	...	...	...	...	...	8 a59	...
MILAN (269A) ...arr	...	...	8 a53	...	...	...	...	...	...	...	...	...	...	...	...	...	3 p5	...

K—Carlsbad Express, Luxus Zug, runs until 29th September. **O**—Orient Express.

Buhl and Obertal, 3¾ miles.—Buhl dep. 6.35, 8.18, 9.32, 10.40 a.m., 1.10, 2‡26, 4.15, 7.8, 8.19, 10.5 p.m. Obertal dep. 5.40, 7.40, 8.50, 10.0 a.m., 12.24, 1‡49, 3.33, 5.51, 7.42, 9.10 p.m. ‡—From 15th June until 15th Sept.

CARLSRUHE and HERRENALB.

Carlsruhe	6a40	8a44	10a44	11a44	1p44	2p44	4p44	6p14	8p14	11p14
Ettlingen	7 13	9 12	11 33	12 13	2 13	3 13	5 20	6 43	8 43	1143
Herrenalb	8 6	10 2	12 4	1 2	3 4	4 2	6 12	7 32	9 30	1233

Herrenalb	5a16	6a47	9a24	10a26	12p24	1p26	3p24	4p47	6p54	8p52
Ettlingen	6 5	7 39	1013	11 13	1 3	2 13	4 14	5 42	7 43	9 43
Carlsruhe	6 37	8 12	1042	11 42	1 42	2 42	4 42	6 12	8 12	1012

BASLE, FREIBURG, CARLSRUHE, HEIDELBERG, and MANNHEIM.

THROUGH CARRIAGES. 1st and 2nd class. {Basle to Frankfort—in 7.53, 9.50 a.m., 2.33 p.m. 5.33 p.m., and 11.52 p.m. from Basle. Basle to Cologne—in 10.42 a.m. and 9.41 p.m. from Basle. Basle to Vlissingen and Hoek van Holland—in 10.42 a.m. from Basle.

MILAN 269A ...dep	...	...	...	...	...	...	...	...	...	...	...	...	...	...	...	...	...	9 p5	9 p5
LUCERNE 258 ...dep	...	...	...	...	...	...	...	...	...	...	...	...	...	...	...	...	...	5 a 5	5 a 5
ZURICH 261 ...dep	...	...	...	...	...	...	...	...	...	...	...	...	...	...	...	...	...	...	...
BASLE Swiss Sta. ...dep	...	...	...	...	...	...	...	...	...	...	...	...	...	...	...	...	...	7a35	7a35
	2&3	Ex 1	1,2,3	2&3	...	1,2,3	1,2,3	3 Cl	2 & 5	Ex 3	2 & 3	1,2,3	2&3	1,2,3	2 & 3	Ex 3	2 & 3	Ex2	1,2,3
															a.m.		a.m.	a.m.	a.m.
Basle—Badische Bahnhof ...dep	...	...	...	...		...	...	...	...	...	...	...	...	...	4 30	...	6 36	7 53	8 0
Leopoldshöhe	...	...	...	...		...	...	...	...	...	...	...	...	...	4 38	...	6 43	...	...
Haltingen	...	...	...	...		...	...	...	...	...	...	...	...	...	4 44	...	6 49	RC	...
Efringen	...	...	...	...		...	...	...	...	...	...	...	...	...	4 56	...	7 1	...	...
Müllheim ...arr	...	...	...	...		...	...	...	...	...	...	...	...	...	5 34	...	7 41	...	8 29
BADENWEILER 140A arr	...	...	...	...		...	...	...	...	...	...	...	...	...	6 a13	...	8 a47	...	...
BADENWEILER ...dep	...	...	...	...		...	...	a.m.	...	...	...	...	...	...	4 a25	...	7 a3	...	...
Müllheim ...dep	...	...	...	...		...	...	4 30	...	...	...	...	...	...	5 38	...	7 47	...	8 30
Krotzingen	...	...	...	...		...	...	4 55	...	...	...	...	...	...	6 1	...	8 11	...	...
Freiburg ...arr	...	...	...	...		...	...	5 36	...	...	...	...	a.m.	a.m.	6 25	...	8 33	8 42	8 54
Freiburg ...dep	...	...	...	...		...	...	5 55	...	...	...	...	4 51	6 38	6 43	...	9 10	8 45	8 56
Denzlingen	...	...	...	...		...	...	6 18	...	...	...	...	5 2	...	6 54	...	9 21	⋮	9 5
Emmendingen	...	...	O—Orient Express, takes up if places vacant.	...	K—Carlsbad Express, Luxus Zug, runs until 28th September.	...	...	6 33	...	...	...	...	5 13	6 52	7 3	...	9 31	⋮	9 13
Riegel	...	...		...		...	...	6 46	...	...	...	...	5 26	...	7 16	...	9 43	⋮	RC
Kenzingen	...	...		...		...	...		...	...	...	...	5 33	...	7 22	...	9 50	⋮	...
Orschweier	...	...		...		...	...	...	...	...	...	...	5 52	...	7 39	...	10 7	⋮	...
Dinglingen	...	...		...		...	...	...	...	...	...	...	6 7	7 14	7 54	...	10 21	⋮	9 36
Offenburg ...arr	...	...		...		...	...	...	...	...	...	...	6 34	7 30	8 18	...	10 48	⋮	9 52
CONSTANCE 139A ...dep	...	...		...		...	...	...	...	...	...	...	...	...	...	...	7 a12	⋮	...
SINGEN 144 ...dep	...	...		...		...	...	...	a.m.	...	...	...	...	...	4 a0	...	7 a54	⋮	...
Offenburg ...dep	...	...		...		...	...	...	4 14	...	...	...	6 43	7 36	8 32	...	12 7	⋮	9 56
Appenweier ...arr	...	...		...	...	...	...	...	4 24	...	...	...	6 54	7 45	8 45	...	12 19	⋮	10 5
STRASSBURG 145...arr	...	...		...	Ex1	...	...	...	5 a34	...	...	...	7a24	8 a20	9 a25	...	1 pl	⋮	1043
PARIS 64A ...dep	...	7 pl3		...	7p15	...	...	...	...	9 p5	...	...	9 p5	9 p5	...	10p15	...	⋮	1015
STRASSBURG 145...dep	...	3 a44	O	...	4a33	...	...	...	3 a58	5 a56	...	...	6a23	7 a18	8 a8	9 a0	11a39	⋮	9a35
Appenweier ...dep	...	⋮	...	...	⋮	...	...	...	4 33	⋮	...	...	7 8	7 50	8 50	9 25	12 24	⋮	1010
Renchen	...	⋮	...	...	⋮	...	...	...	4 41	⋮	...	...	7 17	...	9 0	...	12 32	⋮	...
Achern	...	O	...	...	K	...	...	...	4 53	⋮	...	...	7 30	8 3	9 12	...	12 42	⋮	1022
Bühl	...	⋮	...	...	⋮	...	...	...	5 13	⋮	...	...	7 44	8 13	9 27	...	12 56	⋮	1032
Oos ...arr	...	4 30	...	...	5 18	...	...	...	5 32	6 41	...	...	8 2	8 24	9 45	9 53	1 13	10 0	1043
Baden-Baden arr	...	4 52	...	...	5 45	...	a.m.	...	5 45	6 53	...	...	8 14	8 36	9 57	10 13	1 25	1013	1056
Baden-Baden dep	...	4 17	...	...	5 8	...	4 32	...	5 23	6 33	...	...	7 40	8 13	10 2	9 38	1 3	9 52	1033
Oos ...dep	...	4 31	...	...	5 19	...	4 40	a.m.	5 35	6 44	...	...	8 5	8 30	10 14	9 58	1 14	10 5	1045
Rastatt	...	...	...	...	...	...	4 56	6 45	6 1	...	...	...	8 20	8 40	10 29	10 8	1 48	...	1054
Ettlingen	...	...	...	...	K	...	5 23	...	6 31	...	...	...	8 46	...	10 56	...	2 14	...	...
Carlsruhe Hauptbahnhof ...arr	...	4 59	...	...	5 47	...	5 32	7 25	6 41	7 11		...	8 55	9 1	11 5	10 30	2 23	1031	1113
	a.m.	a.m.	a.m.	a.m.		a.m.	a.m.		a.m.	a.m.	a.m.		a.m.	a.m.	p.m.	a.m.		a.m.	a.m.
Carlsruhe Hauptbahnhof ...dep	4 5	5 3	5 8	5 14	...	6 48	6 55	...	7 11	7 19	9 5	...	9 25	9 5	12 10	10 48	...	1036	1117
Durlach	4 13	⋮	...	5 26	...	Via Schwetzingen.	7 3	...	7 20	⋮	Via Schwetzingen.	...	9 35	9 12	12 21	⋮	...	⋮	1125
Weingarten	4 23	⋮	5 16	5 37	...	⋮	...	...	7 31	⋮	⋮	...	9 46	...	12 32	⋮	...	RC	...
Bruchsal ...arr	4 35	⋮	5 31	5 50	...	⋮	7 18	...	7 45	⋮	⋮	...	9 59	9 27	12 45	⋮	...	⋮	1140
STUTTGART 192 ...arr	...	6 a40	8 a35	8a35	...	⋮	9 a19	...	9 a19	9 a2	⋮	...	1128	11a28	2 p24	12p42	...	1242	2p24
STUTTGART 192 ...dep	2a19		2 a19	...	...	⋮	6 a0	1,2,3	6 a0		⋮	...	8 a1	6 a58	10a26		10 a3	⋮	10a3
Bruchsal ...dep	4 43	...	5 33	5 54	...	⋮	7 26	‡—Via Mannheim.	8 2	...	⋮	...	1015	9 29	1 15	...	12 0	⋮	1148
Langenbrücken	4 58	...	...	6 8	...	⋮	...		8 17	...	⋮	...	1029	...	1 28	...	...	⋮	...
Wiesloch	5 17	...	...	6 26	...	⋮	...		8 38	...	⋮	...	1055	...	1 45	...	...	⋮	...
Heidelberg ...arr	5 45	...	6 0	6 45	...	⋮	7 53		9 1	...	⋮	...	11 8	9 56	2 5	...	12 33	1118	1215
FRANKFORT 136 ...arr	7a46	...	7 a46	...	...	9‡33	9 a31		11a40	...	⋮	...	1239	11a40	4p27	...	...	1239	2 p2
MAYENCE 123A ...arr	8a22	...	8 a22	...	...	⋮	10a24		12p10	2 & 3	⋮	...	1p57	12p10	5 p4	...	2 p23	1p57	2p23
COLOGNE ...arr	1231	...	12p31	...	...	⋮	2 p17	a.m.	4 p32	a.m.	⋮	a.m.	6 p5	4 p32	9 p30	p.m.	6 p5	6p5	6 p5
Heidelberg ...dep	5 51	...	6 16	6 55	...	⋮	7 55	8 30	9 6	9 23	⋮	10 57	1135	10 15	2 26	12 1	...	...	1219
Mannheim ...arr	6 21	...	6 44	7 26	...	7 44	8 18	8 55	9 27	9 52	10 31	11 31	12 0	10 36	2 50	12 25	...	...	1236
MAYENCE 139 ...arr	8a55	...	8 a55	9a13	...	9a13	10a24	...	12p47	...	12 47	...	4p27	12p47	4 p20	...	...	...	2p51
MAYENCE 209 ...arr	9 a3	...	...	...	...	...	10a43	...	11a47	...	12p37	...	2p51	12p37	...	...	...	...	2p51
COLOGNE 123B ...arr	1248	...	12p48	12p48	...	12p48	...	...	...	...	4 p40	...	6 p5	4 p40	8 p5	...	...	...	6 p 5

O—Orient Express. RC—Restaurant Car.

For Continuation of Trains, see next page.

CARLSRUHE, PFORZHEIM, and MUHLACKER.

	Ex3	2&3	Ex1	2&3	Ex3	2&3	2&3	Ex 3	Ex 3	2&3	2&3	1,2,3	2&3	2&3	Ex2	2&3	Ex3	1,2,3	Ex 3	2&3	2&3	1,2,3
	a.m.	a.m.	a.m.	a.m.	a.m.	a.m.	a.m.	a.m.	a.m.	a.m.	p.m.	p.m.	p.m.	p.m.	p.m.	p.m.	p.m.	p.m.	p.m.	p.m.	p.m.	a.m
Carlsruhe ...dep	3 10	4 10	5 3	6 30	7 19	7 33	9 43	10 41	10 48	1130	1 57	2 38	3 25	5 47	6 13	6 24	6 45	8 43	10 12	1019	1130	1 4
Durlach ...dep	3 17	4 21	O	6 38	...	7 42	9 51	...	10 56	1139	2 9	...	3 33	5 55	...	6 32	RC	8 51	...	1029	1139	...
Wilferdingen	...	4 50	...	7 3	...	8 6	1012	...	...	12 4	2 34	...	3 56	6 35	...	6 57	...	...	...	1053	12 3	...
Pforzheim ...arr	3 46	5 26	5 42	7 35	7 56	8 37	1036	11 18	11 28	1236	3 5	3 12	4 24	7 11	6 47	7 46	7 20	9 23	10 51	1124	1238	1 46
WILDBAD 194A arr	...	6a26	...	9a 8	9a 8	1017	...	12p13	1 p15	3p29	...	...	5p24	8p40	8p40	...	8p40	1035	11p49	...	...	...
Pforzheim ...dep	3 49	6 13	5 44	7 43	7 59	8 45	1043		11 32	1246	3 23	3 18	4 34	7 30	6 48	8 8	7 23	9 28	10 57	1131	1244	1 49
Muhlacker ...arr	4 2	6 34	⋮	8 5	8 12	9 6	1059	...	11 45	1 7	3 44	3 31	4 56	7 52	⋮	3 30	7 36	9 41	11 12	1152	1 5	2 2
STUTTGART 192 ar	4 52	...	6a40	9a2	9 a2	...	1232	...	12p42	2p24	4p47	4p34	6p29	1035	7p42	1035	8p35	1042	12 15	...	3 a4	3 a4

Extra.				
Pforzheim ...dep	10 a5	...	...	...
Muhlacker ...arr	10 18	...	...	...

Luggage Rates—see page 462.]

BASLE, FREIBURG, CARLSRUHE, HEIDELBERG, and MANNHEIM.

RC—Restaurant Car.

MILAN 269A ......dep	...	...	1135	11p35	...	...	11p35	...	...	...	...	...	11p35	...	...	...	...	...	...
LUCERNE 258 ......dep	...	...	7 a0	7 a0	...	...	7 a0	...	...	...	...	...	7 a0	9 a55	...	1010	...	...	...
ZURICH 261 ......dep	...	...	7a16	7a16	...	...	7 a16	...	...	...	...	...	7a16	9 a45	...	1138	...	...	...
BASLE Swiss Sta. 140A	...	...	9a25	9a25	...	...	10 a0	...	...	...	...	...	10 a0	12p18	...	2 p4	...	...	...
			Ex3	Ex3	1,2,3	1,2,3	Ex.3	1,2,3	Ex 3	2&3	Ex 3	1,2,3	2 & 3	Ex 3		Ex3	Ex 2	1,2,3	Ex3
Basle—Badische			a.m.	a.m.			a.m.						a.m.	p.m.		p.m.			
Bahnhof.........dep	...	...	9 38	9 50	...	...	10 42	...	...	...	...	...	10 53	1 0	...	2 33	...	...	...
Leopoldshöhe	...	...	...	...	...	...	...	...	...	...	...	...	11 2	...	...	...	...	...	...
Haltingen	...	...	...	RC	...	...	RC	...	...	...	...	...	11 7	...	...	RC	...	...	...
Efringen	...	...	...	...	...	...	...	...	...	...	...	...	11 18	...	...	...	...	...	...
Müllheim ....arr	...	...	...	...	...	...	11 13	...	...	...	...	...	11 56	1 30	...	3 2	...	...	...
BADENW'LER 140A arr	...	...	...	...	...	...	...	...	...	...	...	...	12p51	2 p15	...	3p55	...	...	...
BADENWEILER ...dep	...	...	...	...	...	...	9 a52	...	...	...	...	...	9 a52	12p55	...	2p25	...	...	...
Müllheim ....dep	...	...	...	...	...	...	11 14	...	...	...	...	...	11 59	1 31	...	3 4	...	...	...
Krotzingen	...	...	...	...	...	...	...	...	...	...	...	...	12 23	...	...	...	...	...	...
Freiburg .... arr	...	...	1027	1039	...	...	11 41	...	...	...	...	...	12 46	1 56	...	3 28	...	...	...
Freiburg .... dep	...	...	1029	1041	...	...	11 46	...	...	...	...	...	1 [illegible]	1 59	...	3 31	...	...	...
Denzlingen	...	...	...	...	...	...	11 55	...	...	...	...	...	1 11	...	...	...	...	...	...
Emmendingen	...	...	...	...	...	...	12 4	...	...	...	...	...	1 20	...	...	...	...	...	...
Riegel	...	...	...	...	...	...	...	...	...	...	...	...	1 33	...	...	...	...	...	...
Kenzingen	...	...	...	...	...	...	...	...	...	...	...	...	1 40	...	...	...	...	...	...
Orschweier	...	...	...	...	...	...	...	...	...	...	...	...	1 58	...	...	...	...	...	...
Dinglingen	...	...	...	...	...	...	12 30	...	...	...	...	...	2 14	2 31	...	4 4	...	...	...
Offenburg ....arr	...	...	1114	1126	...	...	12 47	...	...	...	...	...	2 42	2 50	...	4 20	...	...	...
CONSTANCE 139A dep	...	...	7a12	7a12	...	...	9 a16	...	9 a16	...	11 a5	...	9 a22	...	...	...	...	...	...
SINGEN 144 ....dep	...	...	7a54	7a54	a.m.	...	10 a5	...	10 a5	p.m.	11a47	...	10a28	...	...	...	...	...	...
Offenburg ....dep	...	...	1117	1129	1056	...	12 54	...	12 59	1 36	2 p45	...	3 17	2 56	...	4 25	...	...	...
Appenweier ......arr	...	...	⋮	⋮	11 5	...	⋮	...	1 8	1 48	2 54	...	3 29	3 5	...	4 34	...	...	...
STRASSBURG 145 ...arr	...	...	⋮	⋮	1144	...	⋮	...	1 p43	2p51	3 p33	...	4 p12	...	...	5p30	...	...	...
PARIS 64..........dep	...	...	⋮	⋮	...	...	⋮	...	...	...	...	...	...	...	...	...	9a 0	...	9 a0
STRASSBURG 145...dep	...	...	⋮	⋮	...	...	⋮	...	12p17	1p22	2 p0	...	2 p51	...	...	3p58	4p57	...	5p22
Appenweier ......dep	...	...	⋮	⋮	...	...	⋮	...	1 10	1 55	2 56	...	3 38	3 7	...	4 36	⋮	...	5 45
Renchen	...	...	⋮	⋮	...	...	⋮	...	...	2 3	...	...	3 46	...	...	...	⋮	...	...
Achern	...	...	⋮	⋮	...	...	⋮	...	1 22	2 11	...	...	3 56	...	...	...	⋮	...	...
Bühl 145	...	...	⋮	⋮	...	...	⋮	...	RC	2 21	...	...	4 10	...	...	...	⋮	...	...
Oos..............arr	...	1,2,3	1148	12 0	...	...	1 25	...	1 39	2 33	3 23	...	4 28	3 33	...	5 1	5 41	...	6 10
Baden-Baden arr	...	a.m.	1212	1212	...	...	1 36	p.m.	1 52	2 44	3 36	p.m.	4 40	3 47	...	5 14	5 55	p.m.	6 23
Baden-Baden dep	...	1131	1139	1151	...	...	1 13	1 45	1 25	2 22	3 10	3 52	4 16	3 21	...	4 51	5 29	5 1	6 0
Oos ....dep	...	1139	1150	12 2	...	...	1 26	1 53	1 41	2 35	3 27	4 2	4 30	3 36	...	5 4	5 42	5 10	6 12
Rastatt	...	1155	...	RC	...	...	...	2 12	1 51	2 46	...	4 14	4 44	...	...	...	...	5 21	...
Ettlingen	...	...	...	...	...	...	RC	...	...	3 6	...	...	5 10	...	Ex 3	...	...	...	RC
Carlsruhe Hauptbahnhof arr	Ex3	1210	1216	1228	...	...	1 52	2 33	2 11	3 15	3 55	4 52	5 19	4 2		5 30	6 8	...	6 38
	a.m.		p.m.	p.m.	p.m.		p.m.		p.m.	p.m.	p.m.		p.m.	p.m.	p.m.	p.m.	p.m	p.m.	p.m.
Carlsruhe Hauptbahnhof dep	1121	...	1226	1233	1243	...	1 57	...	2 20	3 20	4 10	...	5 33	4 8	4 10	5 39	6 13	5 40	6 45
Durlach	⋮	...	⋮	⋮	1251	...	⋮	...	...	3 28	⋮	...	5 54	...	⋮	5 47	⋮	⋮	⋮
Weingarten	⋮	...	⋮	⋮	...	...	⋮	...	...	3 37	⋮	...	6 4	...	⋮	...	⋮	⋮	⋮
Bruchsal ....arr	⋮	...	⋮	⋮	1 7	...	⋮	...	2 38	3 50	⋮	...	6 16	4 26	⋮	6 2	⋮	⋮	⋮
STUTTGART 192 arr	⋮	...	⋮	⋮	4p34	...	⋮	Ex 3	4 p47	6p29	⋮	...	...	6 p29	⋮	...	7 p42	⋮	8p35
STUTTGART 192 dep	⋮	...	⋮	⋮	...	...	⋮	12p22	12p22	...	⋮	...	4 p47	...	⋮	...	...	⋮	
Bruchsal ....dep	⋮	...	⋮	⋮	1 10	...	⋮	1 47	2 41	3 53	⋮	...	6 22	4 28	⋮	6 3	...	⋮	...
Langenbrücken	⋮	...	⋮	⋮	...	...	⋮	...	...	4 6	⋮	...	6 35	...	⋮	RC	...	⋮	...
Wiesloch	⋮	...	⋮	⋮	...	...	⋮	...	...	4 24	⋮	...	6 53	...	⋮	...	...	⋮	...
Heidelberg ....arr	Via Schwetzingen,	...	⋮	Via Schwetzingen	1 39	...	Via Schwetzingen	2 14	3 8	4 44	Via Schwetzingen.	...	7 13	4 55	⋮	6 30	...	Via Schwetzingen.	...
FRANKFORT 136 ...arr	⋮	...	⋮	2‡33	3p16	...	4 ‡25	4‡25	4 p50	6p32	6 ‡25	...	10 p0	6 p32	6 ‡25	8p20	...	⋮	...
MAYENCE 123A......arr	⋮	...	⋮	⋮	3p28	...	⋮	...	5 p13	8 p9	⋮	2&3	11p23	...	⋮	8p52	...	⋮	...
COL'GNE 123B or 129 ar	⋮	...	⋮	⋮	7 p7	p.m.	⋮	...	9 p30	1213	⋮	p.m.	5 a9	...	⋮	1255	...	⋮	...
Heidelberg ....dep	⋮	...	⋮	⋮	1 50	1233	⋮	2 19	...	4 58	⋮	6 22	7 37	4 58	⋮	6 46	...	⋮	...
Mannheim ....arr	1213	...	1 12	1 19	2 17	1 1	2 44	2 37	...	5 22	5 0	6 45	8 4	5 22	5 0	7 11	...	6 38	...
MAYENCE 139 ......arr	1,2,	...	2p51	2p51	3p59	...	3 p59	3 p59	...	8p52	6 p34	...	9 p23	...	8 p34	9p23	...	9 p23	...
MAYENCE 209 ......arr	...	...	2p51	2p51	...	...	...	...	...	8p47	...	8p47	10p28	...	...	...	...	8 p47	...
COLOGNE 123B ......arr	4p40	...	6 p5	6 p5	7 p7	...	7 p7	7 p7	...	1255	10p30	1255	12a55	...	10p30	1255	...	12a55	...

For Continuation of Trains, see next page.

‡—Via Mannheim.

Extra.								
Heidelberg	dep.	7a24	3p10	3p59	5p35	6p10	7p14	7p59
Mannheim	arr.	7 46	3 41	4 27	5 58	6 38	7 41	8 23

MUHLACKER, PFORZHEIM, and CARLSRUHE.

	Ex3	2&3	2&3	2&3	Ex3	2 & 3	1,2,3	1,2,3	Ex 3	2 &3	1,2,3	2&3	Ex3	2&3	2&3	1,2,3	1,2,3	2&3	Ex3	2&3	Ex.3	Ex1
STUTTGART 192A dp	2a29	...	...	4 a8	6a58	...	8 a1	10 a3	10a52	...	1248	1248	...	2p26	4p47	5p44	6p50	7p12	9 17	9p17	10p38	1132
	a.m.		a.m.	a.m.	a.m.	a.m.	a.m.	a.m.	⋮	p.m.	p.m.	p.m	...	p.m.	p.m	p.m.	p.m.	p.m.	p.m.	p.m.	p.m.	⋮
Muhlacker ...dep	3 16	...	4 25	6 19	7 47	8 40	9 17	11 2	⋮	1212	1 39	1 50	...	4 2	5 43	6 48	...	9 6	1015	1023	11 28	O
Pforzheim ...arr	3 28	...	4 50	6 40	8 0	9 2	9 30	11 13	12 4	1237	1 52	2 14	p.m.	4 24	6 6	6 59	7 56	9 27	1028	1046	11 41	1230
WILDBAD dep	...	p.m.	...	4a43	7 a6		...	9 a55	11 a4	11a4	...	1p28	2 43	3p39	...	5p56	7 p6	8p12	...	1010	...	...
Pforzheim ...dep	3 30	4 30	5 3	6 53	8 2	...	9 34	11 13	12 7	1245	1 55	2 31	3 21	4 32	6 13	7 3	7 59	9 35	1032	1057	11 45	1231
Wilferdingen ...	...	4 56	5†31	7 18	...	...	9 58	...	RC	1 12	...	2 57	...	4 57	6 39	...	...	10 0	SC	1123	...	...
Durlach.........arr	3 55	5 23	5 57	7 42	...	...	1019	11 40	...	1 36	...	3 21	...	5 19	7 3	7 27	...	1022	...	1146	SC	...
Carlsruhe 140 arr	4 2	5 32	6 6	7 49	8 32	...	1026	11 47	12 36	1 47	2 25	3 40	3 50	5 26	7 11	7 34	8 28	1029	11 2	1155	12 15	1 1

†—Weekdays only. O—Orient Express. SC—Restaurant Car attached.

Luggage Rates—see page 462.] [For Fares—see page 120A.

BASLE, FREIBURG, CARLSRUHE, HEIDELBERG, and MANNHEIM.

SLEEPING CARRIAGES Basle to Heidelberg and Frankfort in 11.52 p.m. from Basle, 6 mk., 1st cl., 5 mk. 2nd cl.

Station																				
MILAN 269A ....dep	...	...	...	...	...	...	...	7a25	7 a25	...	...	...	...	...	9 a35	12p40	...	1240	2 p40	...
LUCERNE 258 ......dep	1235	...	...	...	...	...	10a10	2 p2	2 p2	...	...	...	...	...	4 p57	7 p0	...	7 p0	9 p10	...
ZURICH 261 ....dep	...	...	...	...	...	...	11a38	2p48	2 p48	...	...	...	...	...	...	6 p40	...	6p40	9 p12	...
BASLE Swiss Sta. dep	3 p0	...	...	...	...	...	3 p0	5 p7	5 p7	...	...	...	...	...	7 p27	9 p20	...	9p20	11p30	...
	Ex3	1,2,3	1,2,3	2&3	2 & 3	2&3	2 & 3	Ex2	Ex 3	Ex3	2&3	2 & 3	1 2 3	Ex.3	2 & 3	Ex 3	2 & 3	2&3	Ex.3	2 & 3
Basle—Badische	p.m.				p.m.	p.m.	p.m.	p.m.	p.m.		p.m.				p.m.	p.m.		p.m.	p.m.	p.m.
Bahnhof ....dep	3 33	...	...	...	1 25	3 15	3 50	5 18	5 33	...	6 30	...	...	...	7 47	9 41	...	9 50	11 52	11 20
Leopoldshöhe	...	...	...	...	1 37	3 20	3 57	...	...	...	6 43	...	...	...	7 53	...	...	9 58	...	11 26
Haltingen	...	...	...	...	1 42		4 2	RC	RC	...	6 49	...	...	...	7 58	...	...	10 3	SC	
Efringen	...	...	...	...	1 52	...	4 13	...	...	...	7 8	...	...	...	8 6	...	...	1013	...	...
Müllheim ....arr	4 3	..	...	...	2 27	...	4 49	...	6 2	...	7 44	...	...	...	8 30	...	...	1047	12 21	...
BADENW'LER 140A arr	...	...	...	...	3 p55	...	...	...	6 p38	...	...	...	...	...	9 p53	...	...	1158	...	...
BADENWEILER ...dep	2p25	...	...	...	12 55	p.m	...	...	4 p55	...	6 p43	8 p30	...	...	6 p43	...	...	10p5	...	...
Müllheim ....dep	4 4	...	...	...	2 29	4 28	4 56	...	6 3	...	7 47	9 11	...	...	8 32	...	...	1048	12 22	...
Krotzingen	...	...	...	...	2 54	4 41	5 26	...	...	...	8 12	9 34	...	...	8 50	...	...	1111	...	...
Freiburg .... arr	4 29	...	...	...	3 15	4 55	5 53	6 10	6 27	...	8 36	9 55	...	...	9 5	10 30	p.m.	1132	12 46	...
Freiburg .... dep	4 33	...	...	...	3 40	4 59	6 49	6 13	6 31	...		10 0	...	...	9 16	10 32	11 3		12 49	...
Denzlingen	...	...	...	...	3 52	5 16	7 2	...	...	...	...	10 16	...	...	9 27	...	11 14	...	...	...
Emmendingen	...	...	...	...	4 3	5 31	7 11	...	...	...	...		...	...	9 37	...	11 27	...	1 3	...
Riegel	...	...	...	...	4 17	5 44	7 23	...	...	...	...	...	...	...	9 49	...	11 40	...	...	...
Kenzingen	...	...	...	...	4 25	5 52	7 30	...	...	...	...	...	...	...	9 56	...	11 47	...	...	...
Orschweier	...	...	...	...	4 43	6 10	7 47	...	...	...	...	...	...	...	10 14	...	12 4	...	...	...
Dinglingen	5 7	...	...	...	5 15	6 22	8 2	...	7 4	...	...	...	...	...	10 30	...	12 19	...	1 26	...
Offenburg..........arr	5 23	...	...	...	5 40		8 27	7 0	7 20	...	...	...	...	...	10 56	11 17	12 44	...	1 42	...
CONSTANCE 139A dep	...	2 p10	...	...	2 p10	...	...	2p10	...	...	...	...	5p12	7 p32	7 p32	...	...	...	...	...
SINGEN 144 ....dep	...	2 p46	...	...	2 p46	...	...	2p46	...	...	p.m.	...	5p55	8 p7	8 p7	...	...	...	...	...
Offenburg..........dep	5 26	5 50	...	...	6 15	...	8 47	7 3	7 24	...	7 12	...	8 58	11 9	11‖30	11 19	...	...	1 46	...
Appenweier........arr	5 35	5 59	...	...	6 26	...	9 0	⋮	7 33	...	7 24	...	9 7	11 20	11 39	11 27	...	...	⋮	...
STRASSBURG 145 arr	...	6 p46	...	...	7 p40	...	9 p54	⋮	8 p14	...	8 p14	Ex 3	9p54	11p55	...	...	...	...	⋮	...
PARIS 64..............dep	9 a0	9 a0	...	...	...	...	12 0	⋮	9 a0	...	9 a0	12 0	...		...	...	...	...	⋮	5p15
STRASSBURG 145...dep	5p22	5 p32	...	...	...	...	8 p45	⋮	6 p56	...	6 p56	8 p45	...	...	10p58	10p58	...	...	⋮	1a45
Appenweier ....dep	5 51	6 1	...	...	6 28	...	9 26	⋮	7 35	...	7 40	9 11	9 19	...	11 43	11 28	...	...	⋮	⋮
Renchen	...	...	...	...	6 36	...	9 34	⋮	...	...	7 48	...	...	...	11 51	...	...	...	⋮	⋮
Achern	6 3	6 13	...	...	6 46	...	9 46	⋮	...	...	8 0	...	9 32	...	11 59	...	...	...	⋮	⋮
Bühl	6 12	6 23	...	...	6 58	...	10 0	⋮	...	...	8 14	...	9 42	...	12 8	...	...	...	⋮	⋮
Oos ....arr	6 23	6 34	...	...	7 15	1,2,3	10 18	7 35	8 0	...	8 32	9 37	9 53	...	12 21	11 52	...	...	2 21	2 31
Baden-Baden arr	6 33	6 52	...	...	7 30	p.m.	10 34	7 47	8 14	...	8 52	9 51	1034	...	12 33	12 5	...	...	2 43	2 43
Baden-Baden dep	6 11	6 28	...	...	7 5	6 19	10 14	7 25	7 50	...	8 23	9 22	9 43	...	12 12	11 42	...	...	2 13	2 13
Oos ....dep	6 25	6 36	...	...	7 17	6 30	10 25	7 37	8 2	...	8 36	9 39	9 55	...	12 23	11 54	...	...	2 24	2 32
Rastatt	6 34	6 4[illegible]	...	...	7 29	6 41	10 39	...	8 11	...	8 49	...	10 5	...	12 33	...	...	...	2 34	...
Ettlingen	...	...	...	...	7 51	7 8	11 5	...	...	...	9 17	...	...	...	12 49	...	...	...	...	...
Carlsruhe Hauptbahnhof arr	6 55	7 6	...	...	8 1	7 17	11 14	8 4	8 30	...	9 26	10 6	1026	1,2,3	12 57	12 20	...	...	2 55	3 1
		p.m.	p.m.	p.m.	p.m.		p.m.	p.m.	p.m.	p.m.				p.m.	a.m.	n'g't			a.m.	a.m.
Carlsruhe Hauptbahnhof dep	...	7 14	7 17	7 24	8 9	...	11 25	8 9	8 38	8 41	...	...	...	10 31	1 8	12 28	...	...	3 5	3 10
Durlach	...	7 21	Via Schwetzingen.	7 30	8 19	...	11 35	RC	RC	Via Schwetzingen	...	...	...	...	1 14	Via Schwetzingen.	...	...	...	⋮
Weingarten	...	...		7 40	8 29	...	11 45	Via Schwetzingen.	...		...	...	...	...	1 23		...	...	SC	⋮
Bruchsal ....arr	...	7 36		7 52	8 42	...	11 58		8 56		...	...	...	10 51	1 32		...	...	3 23	⋮
STUTTGART 192 arr	...	9 p21		9p21	...	...	...		10‖42		...	...	...	...	3 a4		...	Ex3	4 ‖52	4a52
STUTTGART 192 dep	4p47	5 p44		...	6 p50	...	9 p17		6 p50	6p50	...	...	...	9 p17	...		...	2a19	...	
Bruchsal ....dep	6 13	7 38		7 54	9 17	...	12 2		8 58	8 42	...	...	...	11 0	1 35		...	3 39	3 24	...
Langenbrücken............	...	...		8 7	9 32	...	12 17		...		...	...	...	...	1 45		...	...	...	...
Wiesloch	...	...		8 24	9 50	...	12 36		...		...	...	...	...	1 56		...	...	...	...
Heidelberg ....arr	6 42	8 6		8 43	10 11	...	12 58		9 25		...	...	...	11 26	2 10		...	4 5	3 51	...
FRANKFORT 136 ... arr	8p32	10 p0	10†11	...	...	...	...	10‖11	10 53		...	...	...	1 a16	...		...	5a44	5 a32	...
MAYENCE 123A ... arr	8p52	11p23	⋮	...	...	...	...	⋮	11p23		1,2,3	...	...	...	...		...	5a56	5 a56	2 & 3
COLOGNE 123B or 129 ar	1255	5 a9	⋮	...	...	...	...	⋮	5 a9		p.m.	...	...	...	...		...	9a50	9 a50	a.m.
Heidelberg ....dep	6 46	8 18	⋮	9 13	10 19	...	1 25	⋮	...		11 47	...	...	11 47	2 17		...	4 21	4 21	5 5
Mannheim..........arr	7 11	8 36	8 14	9 42	10 46	...	1 46	9 13	...	9 30	12 5	...	...	12 5	2 38	1 15	...	4 40	4 40	5 35
MAYENCE 139 ......arr	9p23	11 p5	9p23	...	...	...	...	11p5	...	11p5	...	...	...	...	...	2 a28	...	...	...	...
MAYENCE 209 ......arr	...	10p28	...	...	...	...	...	...	...	...	...	...	...	...	...	...	...	...	...	...
COLOGNE 123B......arr	1255	5 a9	1255	...	...	...	...	5 a9	...	5 a9	...	...	...	...	...	5 a42	...	...	...	...

‖—Via Carlsruhe. †—Weekdays only.

BADEN STATE RAILWAYS.

NECKARELZ and JAGSTFELD.

†—To Heilbronn (arrive 11.39.)

	a.m.	a.m.	a.m.	a.m.	p.m.	p.m.	p.m.	p.m.	p.m.
Neckarelz......dep	5 42	7 25	9 41	11 9	2 5	4 55	6 31	8 53	1048
Neckarzimmern...	5 51	7 32	9 50	⋮	2 16	...	6 40	9 3	...
Gundelsheim	6 0	7 41	10 0	1121	2 27	5 19	6 50	9 14	11 3
Jagstfeld (142) arr	6 16	7 55	1017	⋮†	2 43	5 29	7 5	9 29	1116

	a.m.	a.m.	a.m.	a.m.	p.m.	p.m.	p.m.	p.m.	p.m.
Jagstfeld ...dep	4 8	6 5	8 46	10 5	1255	4 49	6 34	7 53	11 3
Gundelsheim ...	4 23	6 20	9 2	1020	1 10	5 7	6 49	8 8	1120
Neckarzimme'n	4 32	6 29	9 11	1029	1 20	5 16	6 58	8 18	1129
Neckarelz 145	4 41	6 38	9 20	1038	1 30	5 23	7 7	8 27	1139

CARLSRUHE and MAXAU.

†—Weekdays only.

Carlsruhe ...dep	4a†34	4a55	5 a44	6a†32	7 a7	8a37	10a22	11a22	1 p26	2 p38	5 p34	6p34	7p25	8 p31
Maxau ....arr	4 56	5 18	6 6	6 53	7 29	8 59	10 43	11 44	1 48	3 0	5 55	6 55	7 47	8 53

Maxau ....dep	5 †a5	5 a53	7a†5	8 a5	9 a0	10a23	11a23	1p35	4 p2	5 p18	6 p17	8p12	9 p33	10p40
Carlsruhe ...arr	5 30	6 15	7 27	8 28	9 21	10 44	11 44	1 59	4 24	5 40	6 38	8 34	9 54	11 1

CARLSRUHE and EPPINGEN.

	a.m.	a.m.		a.m.	p.m.	p.m.	p.m.	p.m.	p.m.	
Carlsruhe	5 19	5‖54	...	9 48	2 5	5 4	6‡31	7 29	1050	...
Durlach	5 27	⋮	...	9 58	2 14	5 13	6 40	7 37	1057	...
Grötzingen	5 33	Helbr'n arr. 7.10	a.m.	10 3	2 19	5 18	6 46	7 43	11 2	...
Bretten ...	6 6		6 31	1037	2 53	5 50	7 21	8 26	1131	...
Flehingen...	—		6 52	11 2	3 15	6 12	—	8 47	1149	...
Eppingen ...			7 13	1124	3 36	6 33	...	9 8	12 9	...

	a.m.	a.m.	a.m.	a.m.	p.m.	p.m.	p.m.	
Eppingen dep	...	4 38	6 55	1028	1 7	3 59	8 1	Helbr'n dep 9.20
Flehingen	...	4 58	7 15	1050	1 27	4 19	8 21	⋮
Bretten ...arr	4 40	5 19	7 35	1110	1 46	4 38	8 41	⋮
Grötzingen ...	5 10	5 58	8 12	1144	2 19	5 8	9 18	⋮
Durlach	5 16	6 6	8 20	1153	2 25	5 14	9 25	⋮
Carlsruhe arr	5 22	6 12	8 26	1159	2 31	5 20	9 31	10‖36

‡—Week-days only. ‖—Carlsbad Express.

HEIDELBERG, MECKESHEIM, and JAGSTFELD.

	a.m.	a.m.	a.m.	p.m.	p.m.	p.m.		
Heidelberg...dep	5 17	8 16	1123	2 50	5 23	8 54	...	...
Schlierbach	5 29	8 28	1136	3 3	...	9 6	...	...
Neckargemünd..	5 37	8 37	1145	3 12	5 36	9 13	...	...
Meckesheim......	5 57	8 57	12 8	3 34	5 49	9 33	...	...
Sinsheim............	6 16	9 16	1227	3 52	6 5	9 50	...	...
Babstadt............	6 47	9 43	1256	4 19	6 33	10 20	...	...
Wimpfen	7 1	9 57	1 10	4 34	6 46	10 33	...	...
Jagstfeld 193 arr	7 5	10 1	1 14	4 38	6 50	10 37	...	...

	a.m.	a.m.	a.m.	p.m.	p.m.	p.m.		
Jagstfeld.........dep	4 35	8 4	10 30	1 49	4 42	7 14	...	...
Wimpfen	4 41	8 9	10 35	1 55	4 48	7 20	...	...
Babstadt...............	5 0	8 26	10 54	2 12	5 5	7 37	...	...
Sinsheim	5 32	8 50	11 19	2 36	5 28	8 6	...	...
Meckesheim.........	6 0	9 11	11 41	2 56	5 49	8 30	...	...
Neckargemünd ...	6 22	9 31	12 4	3 14	6 7	8 47	...	...
Schlierbach	6 30	9 38	12 11	3 20	...	8 53	...	...
Heidelberg......arr	6 45	9 49	12 22	3 31	6 19	9 5	...	...

BASLE and ZELL-i.-W.

	a.m.	a.m.	a.m.	a.m.	p.m.	p m	p.m.	p.m.	p m	p.m.	p.m.
Basle.........dep	7 11	8 5	9 19	1023	1223	1 25	2 25	3 49	4 59	6 27	8 35
Lörrach	7 31	8 32	9 44	1052	1250	1 48	2 52	4 11	5 22	6 51	9 3
Steinen	7 46	8 50	10 0	1111	1 5	2 2	3 7	4 27	5 38	7 7	9 18
Schopfheim ar	7 58	9 4	1013	1127	1 16	2 13	3 19	4 39	5 50	7 20	9 30
" dep	8 0	9 6	1020	1134	1 20	2 15	3 24	—	5 54	7 24	9 32
Zell............arr	8 16	9 22	1039	1150	1 36	2 31	3 40	...	6 10	7 40	9 49

	a m	a.m.	a.m.	a.m.	p m	p.m.	pm	p.m.	p.m	p.m.
Zell-i-W. dep	6 40	8 36	9 55	1118	1237	3 9	537	7 2	8 20	10 5
Schopfheim ar	6 55	8 50	1011	1133	1251	3 23	552	7 17	8 34	1017
" dep	7 4	8 54	1015	1137	1253	3 30	553	7 21	8 38	1019
Steinen.........	7 15	9 5	1026	1148	1 4	3 41	6 4	7 32	8 49	1029
Lörrach	7 32	9 21	1048	12 5	1 22	4 7	626	7 50	9 9	1047
Basle ......arr	7 47	9 37	11 4	1221	1 40	4 22	643	8 5	9 28	11 2

Extra.

Basle ......dep	4a50	11p30
Zell ....arr	6 2	12 38

Zell ......dep	5a20	2 p0
Basle ......arr	6 21	3 8

Basle ....dep	5a48
Schopfheim...arr	6 35

Schopfheim ...dep	6a44	4p51	10p38
Basle ....arr	7 28	5 37	12 20

SCHOPFHEIM and SACKINGEN.

Schopfheim dep	5a41	7a25	10a25	2p26	6 p2	9p34
Wehr	5 58	7 42	10 46	2 47	6 20	9 53
Säckingen ...arr	6 14	7 59	11 5	3 4	6 38	1010

Sackingen ...dep	6a22	9a15	1p19	5p13	7p54	9p52	10p35
Wehr....................	6 43	9 37	1 41	5 35	8 16	1017	10 57
Schopfheim...arr	6 59	9 54	1 59	5 51	8 32	1033	11 15

DENZLINGEN and ELZACH.

Denzlingen ......dep	5a10	6a22	7a12	8a34	9 a55	12 a0	2p24	4 25	5p16	6p57	8 p57	10p17	11p18	...	...
Waldkirch................	5 29	6 37	7 32	8 51	10 13	12 17	2 42	4 41	5 33	7 16	9 15	10 33	11 34	...	...
Elzach ....arr	6 0	7 4	8 9	...	10 45	...	3 13	...	6 3	7 47	9 45	...	...	...	...

Elzach ....dep	...	5 a19	6 a6	7 a23	8 a48	...	12p12	...	4 p8	...	6 p9	8 p4	...	...
Waldkirch	4 a39	5 58	6 36	8 9	9 23	11a29	12 46	2 p56	4 43	5 p31	6 40	8 38	10p39	...
Denzlingen ......arr	4 56	6 15	6 51	8 26	9 40	11 46	1 3	3 13	5 0	5 45	6 55	8 54	10 55	...

MANNHEIM, CARLSRUHE, and ROSCHWOOG.

	1,2,3 a.m.	2&3 a.m.	1,2,3 a.m.	2&3 a.m.	Ex3 a.m.	2&3 a.m.	1,2,3 a.m.	2&3 a.m.	1,2,3 a.m.	1,2,3	Ex3 p.m.	Ex 3 p.m.	2 & 3	2&3 p.m.	Ex3 p.m.	Ex3 p.m.	2&3 p.m.	2 & 3 p.m.	Ex3 p.m.	1,2,3 p.m.	1,2,3 p.m.	3 Cl. nght
Mannheim dep	3 8	3 42	5 33	6 30	7 10	8 20	9 39	1011	11 8	...	2 5	2 28	...	2 33	3 51	5 24	6 22	6 40	7 4	9 17	1121	1 9
Schwetzingen arr	...	4 10	5 48	6 44	7 23	8 34	...	1035	11 21	...	...	...	...	2 58	...	...	6 50	7 5	7 17	9 30	1135	1 26
Schwetzingen dep	...	4 14	5 51	6 46	7 24	8 36	...	1040	11 21	...	...	...	...	3 5	...	...	6 52	7 8	7 18	9 31	1137	1 27
Hockenheim ...	...	4 25	...	6 56	...	8 47	...	1051	...	...	...	...	...	3 15	...	...	7 5	7 31	...	...	1147	...
Waghausel......	...	4 41	...	7 9	...	8 58	...	11 5	...	...	...	...	...	3 29	...	...	7 21	7 45	...	...	1157	...
Graben-N....arr	...	4 55	...	7 21	...	9 8	...	1117	...	...	...	3 0	...	3 42	...	...	7 34	7 57	7 40	...	12 6	...
Carlsruhe arr	3 55	5 30	6 32	7 55	8 1	9 34	1026	1149	11 57	p.m.	2 52	3 18	p.m.	4 14	4 39	6 9	8 59	8 28	8 0	10 8	1233	2 17
Carlsruhe dep	4 10	5 48	—	8 40	—	9 42	—	1220	—	2 36	2 56	—	3 27	5 40	4 48	6 13	—	8 47	8 10	—	—	2 40
Rastatt ......arr	4 29	6 28	...	9 19	...	10 6	...	1 6	...	2 56	⋮	...	4 11	6 21	5 9	⋮	...	9 30	8 29	...	...	3 5
Roschwoog arr	...	6 57	...	9 48	...	...	...	1 36	...	3 13	⋮	...	...	7 14	⋮	⋮	...	9 51	...	...	...	...

	2&3	1,2,3	2&3 a.m.	2&3 a.m.	2&3 a.m.	1,2,3 a.m.	Ex3	Ex3	Ex3	Ex3 p.m.	2&3 p.m.	2 3 4 p.m.	1,2,3 p.m.	Ex3	1,2,3	2&3	1,2,3 p.m.	2&3 p.m.	Ex2 p.m.	Ex3 p.m.	2&3 p.m.	Ex 3 nght	
Roschwoog dep	...	...	6 46	8 13	...	1030	...	...	...	⋮	...	1 15	1 51	...	...	...	5 29	...	⋮	...	9 39	...	...
Rastatt ......dep	...	...	7 12	8 40	1013	1048	...	...	...	⋮	1 10	1 36	2 12	...	...	...	6 45	7 0	⋮	8 11	10 8	...	...
Carlsruhe arr	a.m.	a.m.	7 48	9 1	1049	1113	a.m.	p.m.	p.m.	1 52	1 48	2 11	2 33	p.m.	p.m.	p.m.	7 6	7 39	8 4	8 30	1044	12 20	...
Carlsruhe dep	5 7	6 48	7 56	9 5	1055	—	1121	1226	1233	1 57	2 16	—	—	4 10	5 38	6 20	7 17	7 49	8 9	8 41	1122	12 28	...
Graben-N. ...dep	5 38	...	8 27	9 30	1129	...	1141	...	...	...	2 47	...	...	...	...	7 14	7 40	8 32	...	...	1153	...	...
Waghausel	5 52	...	8 39	9 43	1155	...	...	...	...	...	3 1	...	...	...	6 3	7 32	...	8 46	...	...	12 8	...	...
Hockenheim ...	6 5	...	8 52	9 56	12 8	...	...	...	...	...	3 14	...	...	...	6 13	7 46	...	9 0	...	...	1222	...	...
Schwetzingen arr	6 14	7 28	9 1	10 5	1217	...	...	...	...	...	3 23	...	...	...	6 22	7 56	...	9 9	8 47	9 16	1232	...	...
Schwetzingen dep	6 17	7 29	9 2	10 7	1220	...	...	...	...	...	3 25	...	...	...	6 23	8 12	...	9 22	8 58	9 17	1233	...	...
Mannheim arr	6 42	7 44	9 16	1031	1244	...	1213	1 12	1 19	2 44	3 49	...	...	5 0	6 36	8 40	8 14	9 46	9 13	9 30	1258	1 15	...

†—Not on Sunday.

Luggage Rates—see page 462.]

BADEN STATE RAILWAYS.

HEIDELBERG and WURZBURG.

	2&3	2&3	Ex 3	2&3	2&3	2&3	Ex 3	Ex 3	2&3	2&3	1,2,3	2&3	2&3	2&3	Ex 3	2&3
Heidelberg—		a.m.	a.m.	a.m.	a.m.	a.m.	a.m.		p.m.	p.m.	p.m.	p.m.	p.m.	p.m.	p.m.	p.m.
Hauptbahnhof ...dep	...	4 0	6 19	6 57	8 0	8 16	10 10	...	12 40	2 29	4 0	5 8	7 19	8 54	9 39	11 40
Neckargemünd	...	4 20	6 32	7 19	8 23	8 34	10 23	...	12 56	2 47	...	5 26	7 40	9 13	9 52	12 0
Neckarsteinach (Ost.)	...	4 28	...	7 30	8 31	—	...	...	1 4	2 55	...	5 33	7 51		...	12 8
Hirschhorn	...	4 41	...	7 43	8 42	...	...	...	1 15	3 7	...	5 44	8 3	Via	...	12 21
Eberbach ....arr	...	4 51	6 53	7 53	8 52	...	10 44	...	1 24	3 16	4 31	5 54	8 13	Me'keshm	10 13	12 36
" ....dep	...	4 55	6 55	7 56	8 54	...	10 45	...	1 26	3 18	4 32	5 56	8 15		10 14	—
Neckargerach	...	5 15	...	8 17	9 11	...	...	...	1 45	3 35	...	6 15	8 36		...	...
Neckarelz ....arr	...	5 26	7 15	8 28	9 22	...	11 5	...	1 56	3 46	4 52	6 24	8 47	10 28	10 31	...
JAGSTFELD 142...arr	...	6 a16	7 55	...	10a17	...	...	...	2 p43	...	5p29	7 p5	9 p29	—	11p16	...
HEILBRONN 193...arr	a.m.	6 a44	8 a10	...	10a42	a.m.	11a39	...	3 p8	...	5p43	7 p40	9 p57	...	11p35	...
Neckarelz.........dep	7 26	5 33	7 18	8 33	9 25	10 45	11 7	...	1 58	3 51	4 53	6 29	8 55	...	10 36	...
Mosbach	7 32	5 39	7 23	8 37	9 31	10 49	11 12	...	2 3	3 56	4 58	6 38	9 1	...	10 41	...
Seckach 143	8 13	6 23	...	—	10 14	—	11 47	p.m.	2 39	4 35	...	7 22	9 47	...	...	...
Osterburken ...arr	8 25	6 35	8 1	...	10 26	...	11 56		2 49	4 46	5 34	7 34	9 59	...	11 17	...
" 193...dep	—	6 41	8 5	...	10 33	...	12 0	12 11	2 53	4 49	5 39	7 40	10 7	...	11 29	...
Königshofen	...	7 36	...	...	11 26	...	...	...	3 43	5 38	...	8 40	10 58	...	...	...
Lauda 146 ....arr	a.m.	7 40	8 40	...	11 30	...	12 38	12 49	3 47	5 42	6 17	8 44	11 2	...	12 8	...
" ....dep	5 7	7 48	8 42	...	11 33	...	12 40	12 49	3 53	5 46	6 19	8 56	—	...	12 10	...
Grünsfeld	5 20	8 1	...	...	11 45	...	...	...	4 5	5 56	...	9 9	...	...	—	...
Wittighausen	5 36	8 15	...	...	11 59	...	RC	RC	4 17	6 8	...	9 24	...	...	SC	...
Heidingsfeld	6 18	8 53	...	...	12 35	...	...	...	4 47	6 42	...	10 3	...	...	...	...
Wurzburg ......arr	6 28	9 5	9 22	...	12 45	...	1 21	1 31	4 56	6 51	7 6	10 13	...	...	12 52	...
SCHWEINF'RT 198 arr	...	10a47	10a47	...	2 p10	...	2 p10	2 p26	7 p21	8 p10	8p10	...	...	...	1 a48	...
KISSINGEN 195 ...arr	...	11a53	11a53	...	2 p50	...	2 p50	3 p30	8 p15	9 p23	9p23	...	...	...	...	...
RITSCHENHAU'N 195	...	1 p5	1 p5	...	4 p50	...	4 p50	4 p50	...	10p43	1043	...	...	...	...	...
BERLIN 171.........arr	...	...	...	...	...	...	10p38	...	...	...	...	...	...	...	9 a5	...

	2&3	2&3	2&3	Ex3	2&3	2&3	1,2,3	2&3	2&3	2&3	2&3	2&3	Ex3	Ex 3	Ex 3	2&3	Ex3
BERLIN 170 ......dep	...	...	...	8p25	...	...	...	...	...	...	...	...	...	8 a20	...	...	...
RITSCHENHAUSEN dep		...	...	...	...	1 a5	5 a4	...	5 a4	...	9 a32	...	1p12	...	...	...	5p25
KISSINGEN 195 dep	...	...	...	...	...	...	7a17	...	7 a17	...	11 a0	...	2p55	2 p55	...	...	6p30
SCHWEINFURT 198 dep		—	...	3a42	—	5 a53	7a58	...	7 a58	—	12p10	...	3p50	4 p12	—	5 p11	7p30
			a.m.	a.m.		a.m.	a.m.		a.m.		p.m.	p.m.	p.m.	p.m.		p.m.	p.m.
Wurzburg ......dep	...	...	3 35	4 30	...	7 27	9 10	...	9 58	...	2 0	4 10	4 40	5 4	...	7 9	8 37
Heidingsfeld	...	...	3 46	...	...	7 38	...	...	10 9	...	2 11	4 22	...	...	...	7 20	...
Wittighausen	...	...	4 23	...	...	8 15	...	...	10 55	...	2 51	5 1	...	RC	...	8 5	...
Grünsfeld	...	...	4 36	...	...	8 28	...	...	11 8	...	3 3	5 13	...	...	...	8 18	...
Lauda ....arr	...	...	4 47	5 19	...	8 38	9 56	...	11 19	...	3 13	5 23	5 32	5 53	p.m.	8 28	9 23
" ....dep	...	...	4 54	5 20	...	8 43	9 57	...	11 29	...	3 22	—	5 38	5 54	6 8	8 42	9 24
Königshofen	...	...	4 59	...	...	8 48	...	...	11 34	...	3 27	...	...	...	6 13	8 48	...
Osterburken ...arr	...	a.m.	5 54	6 1	a.m.	9 41	1038	...	12 32	...	4 22	...	6 19	6 31	7 9	9 52	10 1
" ...dep	...	3 50	6 23	6 13	8 45	9 45	1042	...	12 38	...	4 28	...		6 40	7 13	10 20	10 6
Seckach	a.m.	4 2	6 36	6 23	8 58	9 57	...	p.m.	12 52	p.m.	4 42	...	...	...	7 30	10 39	1016
Mosbach	4 23	4 35	7 13	6 47	9 33	10 31	1113	1215	1 28	3 40	5 18	...	...	7 10	8 11	11 25	1039
Neckarelz.........arr	4 27	4 39	7 17	6 51	9 37	10 35	⋮	1219	1 32	3 44	5 22	...	...	7 14	8 15	11 30	1043
HEILBRONN 193A dep	...	3a45	5 a50	5a50	—	9 a41	⋮	—	12p27	—	4 p33	...	...	6 p16	7p31	10p41	...
JAGSTFELD 142...dep	...	4 a8	6 a5	6 a5	...	10 a5	⋮	...	12p55	...	4 p49	...	...	6 p34	7 p53	11 p3	...
Neckarelz.........dep	4 32	4 44	7 23	6 53	...	10 43	⋮	...	1 40	...	5 30	...	...	7 15	8 31	11 51	1047
Neckargerach.......2&3	Via...	4 54	7 31	...	...	10 53	⋮	...	1 51	...	5 41	...	...	...	8 42	12 3	...
Eberbach...arr a.m	......	5 11	7 51	7 13	...	11 10	1137	...	2 8	...	5 56	...	...	7 35	8 59	12 20	11 6
" ...dep 4 39	Mekesh'm	5 13	7 53	7 14	...	11 12	1137	...	2 10	...	5 59	...	...	7 36	9 3	12 23	11 7
Hirschhorn 4 53		5 23	8 3	...	...	11 22	...	...	2 20	...	6 9	2 & 3	...	...	9 13	12 34	...
Neckarsteinach ...5 9		5 34	8 15	...	a.m.	11 33	...	noon	2 32	p.m.	6 21	p.m.	...	...	9 25	12 47	...
Neckargemünd ...5 18	6 22	5 43	8 24	7 37	9 31	11 41	...	12 4	2 41	3 14	6 29	6 7	...	7 57	9 33	12 54	1129
Heidelberg 140 5 37	6 45	6 2	8 41	7 50	9 49	11 56	12 8	1222	2 59	3 31	6 46	6 19	...	8 8	9 51	1 15	1140

FREIBURG and BREISACH.

E.M.		a.m.	a.m.	a.m.	p.m.	p.m.	p.m.	p.m.	p.m.	p.m.	p.m.	p.m.	
—	**Freiburg**......dep	5 54	7 24	10 9	12 12	1 39	3 34	4 57	6 35	7 23	8 22	11 4	...
7½	Gottenheim	6 13	7 44	10 28	12 31	1 59	...	5 16	6 57	7 40	8 37	11 24	...
14½	**Breisach** 212A arr	6 32	7 55	10 38	12 41	2 11	3 56	5 26	7 18	7 57	8 50	11 34	...

		a.m.	a.m.	a.m.	a.m.	a.m.	a.m.	p.m.	p.m.	p.m.	p.m.	p.m.	...
...	**Breisach** ...dep	4 59	5 50	6 42	7 55	9 25	10 42	12 58	2 30	5 27	8 18	1027	...
...	Gottenheim	5 17	6 13	7 0	8 11	9 43	...	1 16	2 48	5 44	8 39	1044	...
...	**Freiburg** ...arr	5 36	6 34	7 18	8 30	10 2	11 11	1 33	3 7	6 0	9 0	11 0	...

SECKACH and MILTENBERG.

†—Mon. and Sat. dep. 5.15 a.m.

Seckach ......dep	6a45	10a20	11a53	2p43	4p50	7p28	10p40	**Miltenberg** dep	a.m.	7a20	9a53	12p46	2p30	...	7p10
Walldürn	8 16	10 59	12 29	3 21	5 40	8 7	11 20	Walldürn	5†25	8 15	1059	1 49	3 39	6p28	8 53
Miltenberg 196A	9 16	12 5	1 53	...	6 36	9 5	...	**Seckach** 143...arr	6 8	8 54	1138	2 28	4 23	7 10	9 32

Walldürn ....dep	5a50	8a20	12p40	5p45	8p54	Hardheim ......dep	4a39	7a20	10a 8	2p45	7p23
Hardheim ....arr	6 17	8 46	1 9	6 18	9 20	Walldürn ......arr	5 11	7 50	10 40	3 20	7 58

EPPINGEN and SINSHEIM.

Eppingen ....dep	4a43	7a20	10a35	1p30	4p10	6p48	9p10	Sinsheim ....dep	6 a8	9a21	12p20	2p50	5p57	9 p56
Sinsheim 142 ......arr	5 20	7 55	11 13	2 30	4 47	8 13	9 45	Eppingen 142 ....arr	6 50	1013	1 4	3 28	6 38	10 32

HALTINGEN and KANDERN.

E.M.															
	Haltingen ...dep	6a54	9a15	11a15	1p48	4p36	6p55	10p8	**Kandern** ......dep	5a28	8a10	10 23	12p40	3p15	5p46	9 p0
8	**Kandern**......arr	7 34	9 55	11 55	2 28	5 16	7 35	1048	**Haltingen 140** arr	6 8	8 50	11 0	1 20	3 55	6 26	9 40

BRUCHSAL and GERMERSHEIM.

	a.m.	a.m.	a.m.	a.m.	a.m.	p.m.	p.m.	p.m.	p.m.	p.m.	p.m.	p.m.
Bruchsal ......dep	5 13	7 27	11 2	1127	1151	1 58	2 28	4 45	6 16	7 18	7 40	9 45
Graben- arr	5 31	7 40	11 15	1137	12 4	2 10	2 41	4 58	...	7 28	7 53	9 59
Neudorf dep	5 41	7 41	11 27	...	12 7	2 11	2 50	5 0	...	...	7 55	10 3
Germersheim arr	6 17	8 8	11 58	...	1233	2 34	3 20	5 26	6 41	...	8 21	1029

	a.m.	a.m.	a.m.	a.m.	p.m.	p.m.	p.m.	p.m.	p.m.	p.m.	p.m.
Germersheim dep	6 56	8 35	9 30	10 52	12 43	2 29	...	3 7	6 34	...	9 46
Graben- arr	7 24	9 2	...	11 18	1 9	2 50	...	3 41	7 1	...	10 14
Neudorf dep	7 25	9 12	...	11 26	1 10	2 51	3 4	3 48	7 3	7 44	10 17
Bruchsal 192 arr	7 38	9 26	9 58	11 39	1 26	3 2	3 14	4 6	7 19	7 59	10 31

For Fares—see page 120A.] [Luggage Rates—see page 452.

OFFENBURG, VILLINGEN, and SINGEN.

STRASSB'RG dp	...	3a58	7 a18	...	...	7a18	9a17	11a0	10 a8	...	12p17	1p22	1p22	3p50	5p32	6p21	7p32	8 p45
	2&3	1,2,3	1,2,3	Ex3	2&3	2&3	1,2,3	Ex3	2 & 3	2&3	2 & 3	1,2,3	2&3	Ex3	2&3	1,2,3	2&3	2 & 3
		a.m.	a.m.			a.m	a.m.	a.m.	a.m.		p m	p.m.	p.m.	p m.	p.m.	p m.	p.m.	p.m
Offenburg ....dep	...	5 27	8 8	...	...	8 25	10 2	1144	11 50	...	1 20	2 25	3 2	4 31	6 25	7 24	8 38	9 33
Gengenbach	...	5 38	...	...	...	8 38	...	...	12 3	...	1 33	...	3 15	...	6 42	...	8 51	9 48
Biberach Zell ..	...	5 47	...	...	...	8 49	...	...	12 15	...	1 44	RC	3 26	RC	6 56	...	9 3	10 1
Hausach	...	6 8	8 40	...	...	9 17	1032	1216	12 41	...	2 6	2 57	3 54	5 3	7 23	7 54	9 28	10 23
Hornberg	...	6 27	8 58	...	...	9 36	1047	...	12 58	...	—	3 12	4 15	5 18	—	8 13	9 49	11 25
Triberg	...	6 54	9 26	...	...	10 5	1111	1253	1 25	p.m.	...	3 37	4 48	5 41	p.m	8 39	1020	12 12
St. Georgen	...	7 23	9 53	...	...	1034	...	...	1 54	3 11	...	4 2	5 22	6 6	7 13	9 5	1051	—
Peterzell-Königs	...	7 29	9 59	...	...	1040	...	...	2 0	3 18	...	...	5 28	...	7 19	9 11	1057	...
Kirnach	...	7 37	...	...	...	1049	...	...	2 9	3 29	...	...	5 36	...	7 27	...	11 5	...
Villingen 194A arr	a.m.	7 42	10 10	...	...	1054	1147	1 29	2 14	3 36	...	4 16	5 41	6 20	7 32	9 22	1110	...
Villingen ......dep	5 50	7 49	10 15	...	...	11 3	1150	1 34	2 21	3 38	...	4 20	5 46	6 24	7 34	9 26	1116	...
Marbach	5 55	...	...	...	a.m.	1110	...	...	2 26	3 44	...	...	5 51	...	7 39	...	1121	...
Donaueschingen	6 17	8 9	10 30	...	11 5	1127	12 5	1 49	2 44	4 5	...	4 34	6 16	6 39	7 55	9 41	1141	...
Neudingen	6 28	...	...	...	1116	1228	...	...	2 56	4 16	...	...	6 27	...	—	...	1152	...
Immendingen ar	6 49	8 30	10 54	...	1139	1254	1224	2 8	3 16	4 37	1,2,3	4 54	6 52	7 1	...	10 0	1210	Ex 3
STUTTGART dp	...	2a58	...	8 a3	...	8 a3	8 a3	...	...	...	3 p21	1050	3p21	3p21	...	...	6p48	12 58
Immendingen dp	6 56	8 31	10 55	11 5	1157	1 0	1225	2 9	3 18	4 39	6 51	4 55	7 47	7 2	...	10 1	1213	4a20
Engen	7 20	8 53	11 14	...	1220	1 30	1244	...	3 44	5 15	...	...	8 13	7 21	...	1022	1238	...
Mühlhausen	7 29	...	...	...	1230	1 42	...	...	3 55	5 26	...	...	8 21	...	...	...	1248	...
Singen 139A...arr	7 40	9 7	11 29	1136	1241	1 55	1259	2 41	4 6	5 38	7 26	5 26	8 37	7 35	...	1037	1 0	4 52
CONSTANCE arr	8a45	9 40	12 p2	1244	1p36	3 p5	1p36	3p12	5 p3	6p31	8 p10	6 p3	9p34	8p10	...	1114	1a49	6a20

Extra

Singen ....dep	8 a1	...	Donaueschingen dep	9 p40	...	...
Donaueschingen...arr	9 32	...	Villingen ....arr	10 3	...	...
Immendingen......dep	1 p48	5 p53	Donaueschingen ..dep	11a35	7 p23	...
Donaueschingen ..arr	2 10	6 12	Immendingen ......arr	11 53	7 42	...

CONSTANCE 139A dp	...	...	5 a0	7a12	9a16	9 a16	9a22	11a5	1222	1 p15	2 p10	3p25	5p12	5p12	4p42	7p32	9p37
	Ex 3	2&3	2&3	1,2,3	Ex3	1,2,3	2&3	Ex3	2&3	3 Cl.	1,2,3	2&3	1,2,3	Ex3	2&3	Ex3	2&3
	a.m.	a.m.	a.m	a.m	a.m.	a.m.	a.m	a.m.	p.m	p.m	p.m.	p.m.	p.m	p.m.	p.m.	p m	p.m
Singen ....dep	1 12	4 0	6 7	7 54	10 5	10 16	1028	1147	1 0	2 13	2 46	4 30	5 55	6 5	6 28	8 7	1040
Mühlhausen	...	...	6 19	...	RC	...	1039	...	...	2 26	...	4 41	...	...	6 41	...	1052
Engen	...	4 16	6 32	...	...	10 32	1051	...	1 16	2 39	3 1	4 56	6 10	...	6 53	8 22	11 4
Immendingen.....arr	1 58	4 38	7 6	8 29	1040	10 56	1118	1224	1 40	3 8	3 22	5 25	6 33	6 40	7 22	8 43	1138
STUTTGART 193A ar	5 a45	9a55	...	...	2 p3	2 p3	6p38	...	6p38	...	...	...	...	9p27	1216	1a13	...
Immendingen ....dep	—	4 38	7 12	8 30	1041	—	1120	1227	2 9	3 28	3 23	5 30	6 35	—	7 25	8 44	1144
Neudingen...............	...	4 57	7 32	...	...	2 & 3	1145	...	2 30	3 49	...	5 52	...	...	7 47	...	12 5
Donaueschingen......	...	5 14	7 51	8 49	1059	p.m.	12 9	1246	2 43	4 20	3 42	6 16	6 58	...	8 2	9 3	1218
Marbach	...	5 32	8 10	...	...	1 43	1227	...	3 3	4 43	...	6 36	...	...	8 20	...	1235
Villingen 194A....arr	...	5 37	8 15	9 3	1113	1 50	1232	1 0	3 8	4 48	3 56	6 41	7 12	...	8 25	9 17	1240
Villingen...........dep	...	5 47	8 20	9 8	1116	2 21	1236	1 5	3 15	5 5	4 1	6 43	7 17	...	8 32	9 20	—
Kirnach	...	5 54	8 27	...	...	2 29	1242	...	3 22	5 13	...	6 50	...	...	8 40	...	...
Peterzell-Königsf....	...	6 3	8 37	9 20	...	2 41	1251	...	3 32	5 27	4 14	7 0	...	...	8 52	...	...
St. Georgen ....a.m.	...	6 10	8 44	9 26	...	2 49	1258	...	3 39	5 38	4 20	7 6	7 34	...	9 1	9 37	...
Triberg 4 30	2 & 3	6 36	9 11	9 47	1149	—	1 25	1 42	4 11	6 17	4 40	—	7 53	...	9 35	9 57	...
Hornberg.........5 6	a.m.	6 58	9 33	10 4	12 6	2 & 3	1 46	...	4 36	6 41	4 57	p.m	8 11	...	10 1	...	...
Hausach 145 ......5 36	5 41	7 16	9 53	1020	1218	11a50	2 9	2 10	5 19	7 7	5 11	8 33	8 25	...	1035	1027	...
Biberach Zell ...—	6 5	7 37	1015	...	...	12 10	2 32	...	5 40	7 30	...	8 54	...	...	1056	...	...
Gengenbach	6 21	7 50	1027	...	...	12 23	2 45	...	5 54	7 43	5 34	9 8	...	...	11 8	1050	...
Offenburg ....arr	6 35	8 3	1040	1049	1247	12 36	2 58	2 40	6 7	7 57	5 44	9 21	8 54	...	1121	11 1	...
STRASSBURG 145 arr	7 a24	9a25	1144	1144	1p43	1 p43	4p12	3p33	7p40	9 p54	6 p46	1155	9p54	...	1228	1155	...

FREIBURG and DONAUESCHINGEN.

E.M.	All 2 & 3 Class.	a.m.	a.m.	a.m.	a.m.	a.m.	a.m.	p.m.	p.m.	p m	p.m	p.m.	p.m			
—	**Freiburg** ....dep	4 55	6 48	7 25	9 †0	11 6	1123	1250	2 8	3 36	5 †0	6 34	9 34	...	...	*—3rd Class only and not on Sunday.
...	„ Wiehre ...	5 2	6 54	7 30	9 6	11 13	1129	1257	2 13	3 42	...	6 39	9 42	...	...	
8¾	Himmelreich	5 31	7 55	7 55	...	11 39	1154	1 22	2 3	4 8	...	7 2	1010	...	...	
14	Hirschsprung	5 45	8 12	8 12	9 39	11 53	12 7	1 35	2 51	4 23	5 35	7 15	1025	...	...	
18½	Höllsteig	6 5	8 33	8 33	...	12 13	1228	1 56	3 12	4 42	...	7 38	1046	...	...	
24½	Titisee (Lenzkirch)	6 29	8 59	8 59	1027	12 39	1252	2 19	3 40	5 5	6 17	8 4	11 9	...	...	
29½	**Neustadt** .... arr	6 39	9 9	9 9	1036	12 50	1 1	2 28	3 50	5 14	6 25	8 13	1119	...	...	
	dep	6 43	—	9 12	1041	Until 13th Sept.	1 4	2 31	Until 13th Sept.	5 16	6 28	8 18	—	...	...	
31¾	Kappel Gutachbrucke...	6 50	...	9 20	...		1 10	2 38		5 22	...	8 26	...	...	...	
39¼	Löffingen	7 7	...	9 36	...		1 27	2 55		5 38	6 48	8 43	...	...	...	
40¾	Reiselfingen...............	7 11	...	9 40	...		1 31	3 0		5 42	...	8 48	...	...	...	
54	**Donaueschingen** arr	7 44	...	10 12	1127		2 5	3 34		6 13	7 15	9 29	...	...	...	

		a.m.		a.m	p m.	p.m.		p.m		p.m	p.m.	p.m	p.m			
Donaueschingen dep	...	5 13	...	8 24	1217	2 †24	Until 13th Sept.	3 44	Until 13th Sept.	4 *5	6 20	6 44	8 4	...	...	†—1, 2, 3, Class.
Reiselfingen..............	...	5 48	...	8 58	1 3	...		4 18		5 17	...	7 23	8 43	...	...	
Löffingen	...	5 53	...	9 2	1 10	2 54		4 23		5 40	†	7 28	8 50	...	...	
Kappel Gutachbrucke ...	...	6 9	...	9 18	1 31	...		4 38		6 33	...	7 43	8 58	...	...	
Neustadt .... arr	a.m.	6 15	a.m.	9 24	1 38	3 12		4 44		6 46	7 4	7 49	9 4	...	...	
dep	4 54	6 18	8 34	9 27	1 42	3 15	4p14	4 47	6 p0	—	7 6	7 52	9 8	...	...	
Titisee (Lenzkirch)	5 7	6 35	8 44	9 40	1 59	3 26	4 24	5 4	6 17	...	7 17	8 5	9 19	...	...	
Höllsteig	5 25	6 55	9 3	10 0	2 36	...	4 46	5 20	6 37	...	...	8 22	9 36	...	...	
Hirschsprung	5 44	7 9	9 17	1022	2 53	...	5 11	5 33	6 52	...	...	8 36	9 50	...	...	
Himmelreich	5 59	7 17	9 26	1029	3 0	...	5 23	5 40	7 2	...	...	8 43	9 57	...	...	
Freiburg Wiehre	6 24	7 44	9 46	1048	3 18	...	5 43	5 58	7 27	...	8 10	9 3	1015	...	...	
Freiburg (140) ......arr	6 29	7 49	9 51	1053	3 23	4 12	5 58	6 3	7 33	...	8 14	9 8	1020	...	...	

RADOLFZELL, SIGMARINGEN, and MENGEN.

‡—Weekdays only.

Dist.		a.m.	a.m.	a.m.	p.m.		p.m.	p.m	p.m.	p.m.	p.m.
—	**Radolfzell** ....dep	6 5	7 37	10 28	12 7	...	2 35	4 49	6 52	8 52	11 0
11½	Stockach	6 41	8 8	11 1	12 37	p.m.	3 8	5 25	7 27	9 38	11 32
17¼	Schwackenreute ....arr	7 4	8 30	11 24	—	1 32	3 31	5 48	7 50	10 1	11 53
...	Pfullendorf 191............arr	7 40	9 10	12 3	...	2 4	4 15	6 53	...	10 39	—
23½	Messkirch	7 33	8 53	11 50	...	—	3 56	6 17	8 13	10 27	...
29¾	Krauchenwies ....arr	7 54	9 9	12 10	...	...	4 16	6 37	8 33	10 47	...
36	**Sigmaringen 194A**...arr	8 18	9 25	12 30	...	...	4 35	6 55	8 51	11 6	...
35½	**Mengen** ....arr	8 18	9 26	12 33	...	...	4 37	6 58	8 50	11 7	...

		a.m.	a.m.	a.m.	a.m.		p.m.	p.m.	p.m.	p.m	p.m.
Mengen ....dep	...	...	7 5	8 40	9 50	...	...	1 54	8 10	4 45	8 58
Sigmaringen dep	...	4 30	7 7		10 5	...	12 38	1 55	...	5 7	9 0
Krauchenwies ....dep	...	4 50	7 29	8 55	10 25	...	12 56	2 16	8 25	5 28	9 20
Messkirch	...	5 12	7 52	—	10 47	...	1 13	2 39	—	5 50	9 42
Pfullendorf.........dep	a.m	4 50	7 47	...	10 30	...	12 52	2 25	...	5 0	9 0
Schwackenreute ...dep	4 ‡40	5 36	8 18	...	11 9	a.m	1 30	3 3	...	6 15	10 5
Stockach	5 2	5 57	8 41	...	11 32	12 41	1 43	3 25	...	6 37	10 28
Radolfzell 139A arr	5 36	6 23	9 13	...	12 2	1 10	2 14	3 58	...	7 11	10 59

Luggage Rates—see page 462.]

BADEN STATE RAILWAYS.

STRASSBURG and APPENWEIER.

	2&3 a.m	2&3 a.m.	2&3 a.m	1,2,3 a.m.	2&3 a.m.	2&3 a.m	1,2,3 a.m	Ex3 a.m.	2&3 a m	1,2,3 p.m	2&3 p m	2&3 p.m.	2&3 p.m.	Ex3 p.m.	1,2,3 p.m.	Ex3 p.m.	2&3 p.m.	1,2,3 p.m	1,2,3 p.m.	1,2,3 p.m.	2&3 p.m	Ex3 p.m	2&3 p.m.	1,2,3 p.m.
Strassburg dep	6 23	7 18	8 8	9 0	9 17	9 35	10 8	11 0	1139	1217	1 22	2 0	2 51	3 50	3 58	5 22	5 32	6 21	6 56	7 32	8 10	8 45	10 5	1058
Kehl ....dep	6 35	7 30	8 23	9 10	9 27	9 45	1021	1110	1155	1231	1 35	2 13	3 4	4 0	4 11	5 31	5 42	6 38	7 8	7 45	8 30	8 55	1018	11 9
Appenweier 141	6 57	7 44	8 43	9 23	9 41	10 2	1037	1124	1215	1250	1 50	2 33	3 26	4 13	4 31	5 44	5 59	7 0	7 27	7 59	8 54	9 9	1038	1124

	Ex3 a.m	2&3 a.m	1,2,3 a.m	2&3 a.m	2&3 a.m	Ex 3 ...	1,2,3 a.m.	1,2,3 a.m.	2&3 p.m.	1,2,3 p.m	Ex3 p.m.	2&3 p.m.	Ex3 p.m.	2&3 p.m	2&3 p.m	1,2,3 p.m	2&3 p.m.	1,2,3 p.m.	1,2,3 p.m	1,2,3 p.m.	1,2,3 p.m	Ex 3 p.m.	2&3 p.m.	1,2,3 p.m.
Appenweier dep	5 10	5 18	6 59	7 50	8 52	:	1010	1111	1226	1 15	1 47	2 14	3 10	3 38	4 20	4 54	6 10	7 15	7 40	8 20	8 45	9 31	1034	1132
Kehl .....arr	5 25	5 40	7 13	8 8	9 12	9 50	1030	1131	1247	1 31	...	2 34	3 23	3 59	4 34	5 15	6 30	7 29	7 59	8 35	8 59	9 45	1054	1146
Strassburg	5 34	5 57	7 24	8 20	9 25	10 1	1043	1144	1 1	1 43	2 8	2 51	3 33	4 12	4 48	5 30	6 46	7 40	8 14	8 44	9 10	9 54	11 8	1155

Extra—Strassburg to Appenweier, 3.58 a.m.; Appenweier to Strassburg, 3.30 a.m., 9.38 p.m., 12.5 night.

APPENWEIER and OPPENAU.

	a.m.	a.m	p.m	p.m	p.m.	p.m.	p.m.	
Appenweier ...dep	7 10	10 47	2 39	4 48	6 6	9 19	11 45	...
Hubacker (Sulzb'ch)	7 40	11 17	3 8	5 18	6 36	9 56	12 15	...
Oppenau ....arr	7 49	11 26	3 17	5 27	6 45	10 8	12 24	...

	a.m	a.m	a.m.	p.m.	p.m.	p.m.	p.m.	
Oppenau ......dep	6 10	8 0	11 41	3 29	6 53	7 58	10 21	...
Hubacker (Sulzb.)	6 19	8 9	11 50	3 38	7 2	8 7	10 30	...
Appenweier ...arr	6 50	8 39	12 18	4 7	7 30	8 35	11 0	..

NECKARELZ and MECKESHEIM.

Dist.							
	Neckarelz ......dep	4a32	7a30	10a41	1 p59	3p55	7p18
11½	Helmstadt	5 9	8 13	11 13	2 30	4 43	7 51
16¾	Neidenstein..........	5 29	8 35	11 27	2 44	5 10	8 8
20¾	**Meckesheim 142** arr	5 41	8 50	11 37	2 54	5 25	8 18

Meckesheim dep	6a 7	9a12	12p17	3 p36	5p58	9 p32
Neidenstein.........	6 20	9 24	12 30	3 48	6 11	9 43
Helmstadt	6 39	9 41	12 53	4 4	6 27	9 59
Neckarelz 142 arr	7 10	1013	1 29	4 34	6 59	10 28

LORRACH and LEOPOLDSHOHE.

Lorrach ......dep	4a21	6 a4	7a11	8a40	9a26	10a44	1p20	4p2	6p24	8p2	11p10
Leopoldshohe a	4 36	6 15	7 22	8 55	9 39	10 58	1 31	415	6 35	815	11 22

Leopoldshohe dp	6a28	8a15	9a8	10a20	12p35	2p33	5p54	7p27	10p14
Lorrach ......arr	6 42	8 28	920	10 35	12 46	2 46	6 10	7 43	10 30

HAUSACH and SCHILTACH.

Hausach	6a22	8a43	9a15	10a40	12p41	2p15	5p22	8p25	9p30	10p35
Wolfach	6 31	8 50	9 24	10 49	12 54	2 24	5 33	8 34	9 41	10 44
Schiltach 194	6 45	9 1	9 38	11 4	1 14	2 39	5 50	8 49	9 58	10 59

Schiltach ...	5 a5	6a47	8 a8	9a8	9a57	11a15	1p25	437	6p29	9p59
Wolfach	5 24	7 2	8 25	924	10 8	11 24	1 44	452	6 46	1014
Hausach 144	5 34	7 11	8 35	934	10 14	11 48	1 54	5 1	6 55	1023

VILLINGEN and DURRHEIM.

Villingen...dep	6a40	8a6	9a21	12p15	2p57	4p36	6p52	8p12	9†49
Durrheim...arr	7 3	829	9 42	12 44	3 18	5 3	7 12	8 38	1015

Durrheim	7a23	8 38	10a38	1p26	3p26	5p32	7p20	8p46	10†30
Villingen	7 46	8 57	11 1	1 50	3 49	5 57	7 42	9 9	10 52

†—Until end of August.

NEUSTADT and BONNDORF.

Neustadt ......dep	6a55	9a36	2p40	5p23	8 p49	...
Kappel 144	7 4	9 51	2 49	5 32	9 2	...
Lenzkirch	7 23	10 21	3 8	5 53	9 17	...
Bonndorf ......arr	7 49	10 50	3 34	6 19	9 43	...

Bonndorf ......dep	5a17	8 a2	12p20	3 p46	6p45	...
Lenzkirch	5 47	8 42	12 49	4 15	7 17	...
Kappel	6 1	9 3	1 10	4 29	7 31	...
Neustadt ......arr	6 9	9 11	1 18	4 37	7 39	...

ZELL and TODTNAU.

*-Weekdays only.

Zell-i-W. ...dep	8 a30	9*42	12 0	3p58	6p38	9 p59
Schönau-i.-W. ...	9 10	1030	12 39	4 40	7 27	10 37
Geschwend.........	9 28	1047	12 54	4 55	7 42	10 52
Todtnau ...arr	9 36	1055	1 2	5 3	7 50	11 0

Todtnau ....dep	5 a28	7a10	10 a0	2 p0	4p11	7 p0
Geschwend	5 36	7 18	10 8	2 8	4 19	7 8
Schönau	5 52	7 38	10 28	2 25	4 37	7 26
Zell-i.-W. (142)...arr	6 30	8 17	11 6	3 3	5 15	8 4

DONAUESCHINGEN AND FURTWANGEN.

Donaueschingen dep	5a40	8 a37	12p22	4 p37	6 p57	9 p41
Hammereisenbach...	6 46	9 35	1 10	5 34	7 49	10 32
Vöhrenbach	7 9	9 52	1 24	5 52	8 4	10 47
Furtwangen ......arr	7 30	10 12	1 43	6 12	8 23	11 7

Furtwangen ......dep	6 a3	8 a55	2 p4	4 p0	7 p10	...	...	...	...
Vöhrenbach	6 25	9 15	2 24	4 28	7 34	...	...	...	...
Hammereisenbach ...	6 43	9 30	2 38	4 47	7 49	...	...	...	...
Donaueschingen arr	7 32	10 18	3 26	5 43	8 47	...	...	...	...

CARLSRUHE LOCAL RAILWAY.

[Weekday service.]

Spöck..............dep	4a42	5p20	...	7 a0	...	10a3	...	2 p1	...	...	...	5p15	...	...	...
Carlsruhe Localbhf...	5 40	6 23	7p15	7 59	9a23	11 0	12p5	3 0	4p33	5p40	5p50	6 17	6p28	8p15	...
Durmersheim arr	6 38	...	8 15	...	1022	...	1 5	4 1	5 35	6 45	7 0	...	7 32	9 14	...

Durmersheim dep	4 a40	5 a7	6 a48	9a15	...	11a 6	...	2p 0	5p13	5p38	7p11	...	...
Carlsruhe Localbhf....	5 48	6 11	7 59	10 14	11a10	12 5	1 p58	3 0	6 28	7 1	8 15	...	...
Spöck ....arr	6 47	...	8 57	...	12 11	...	2 58	...	7 26	...	9 13	...	...

KEHL and BUHL.

E.M.	**Kehl**............dep	5 a5	7 a33	12 0	4 p5	7 p0	8 p25
16½	Lichtenau-Ulm ...	6 42	9 1	1 27	5 27	8 28	9 42
24¼	**Buhl (140)** arr	7 18	9 45	2 10	6 8	9 2	...

Buhl............dep	...	6 a2	8 a50	1 p5	4 p40	7 p45
Lichtenau-Ulm ...	4 a10	6 40	9 33	1 53	5 25	8 28
Kehl (145)...arr	5 36	8 5	11 0	3 15	6 50	9 55

THE RHINE and ETTENHEIMMÜNSTER.

Rheinufer.....	...	7 a1	...	...	...	1p14	...	...	6p43	...	...
Orschweier...	6a23	7 56	9 a3	10a15	1158	2 2	3p33	4p50	7 14	7p52	9p25
Ettenheim....	6 36	8 9	9 12	10 24	1210	2 11	3 44	5 12	7 23	8 3	9 34
Ettenh'münst	6 54	8 27	...	...	1228	...	4 2	...	...	8 21	...

Etten'm.	...	7 a1	9a26	a.m.	1p17	...	4 p7	...	...	8p40	...
Ettenh'm	5a37	7 22	9 47	1134	1 40	3p13	4 27	5p27	7p30	9 1	...
Orschw'r.	6 25	7 31	9 56	1143	1 49	3 22	4 36	6 12	7 39	9 10	...
Rhei'fer.	6 52	...	...	1229	...	...	...	6 39	...	...	...

BREISACH and GOTTENHEIM.

‡—Until 30th September.

Breisach ....dep	a.m.	a.m.	...	5a43	8 a3	...	...	10a43	...	...	2p35	...	...	...	7p30	9p30	...	...
Endingen	4‡20	4 55	6a20	6 50	9 2	8a31	10 a5	11 55	1 p5	3 p25	3 51	...	6p35	...	9 4	1034	...	...
Riegel Ort.	4 30	5 5	6 30	7 0	9 11	8 47	10 16	12 5	1 16	3 36	4 1	6 p0	6 45	7p45	9 14	—	...	...
Riegel Haupt Bf.		5 10	6 35	7 6	9 16	...	10 20	12 11	1 20	3 40	4 11	...	6 52	...	9 22	...	...	...
Gottenheim...............arr	5 9	5 57	...	...	...	9 29	...	1 8	...	...	4 50	6 45	...	8 23	...	...	...	...

Gottenheim ....dep	...	...	5‡19	6a18	...	...	...	10a22	...	...	2 p0	...	5p13	7 p0	8 p40	...	...	...
Riegel Haupt Bf.	...	...	...	...	7a20	8a12	9a45	10 53	12p20	1 p45	...	4 p0	...	7 48	...	9 p49	...	...
Riegel Ort..........................	...		5 57	6 59	7 27	8 17	9 50	11 2	12 25	1 53	2 45	4 5	5 58	7 55	9 18	9.54	...	...
Endingen	4a30	5 a25	6 7	...	7 40	8 27	10 0	11 14	12 35	2 3	2 55	4 18	6 10	8 7	9 28	10 4	...	...
Breisach ....arr	5 29	6 31	...		8 56	...	...	12 28	...	...	...	[illegible]	...	9 19	...	...	...	...

KROTZINGEN and SULZBURG.

Krotzingen	6a23	7a46	1039	1p16	3 p0	5p30	8p54	11p14
Staufen	6 40	7 59	1055	1 31	3 17	5 48	9 10	11 29
Sulzburg ...	6 57	8 17	1114	51	3 37	6 7	9 29	11 46

Sulzburg ...dep	5a18	7 a4	8a24	11a40	2 p8	3p53	7 p7	10p13
Staufen	5 41	7 23	8 42	12 1	2 27	4 12	7 31	10 34
Krotzingen 140	5 54	7 36	8 57	12 15	2 43	4 30	7 44	10 48

Luggage Rates—see page 462.] [For Fares—see page 120A

COBLENCE and GIESSEN.

		3 &4	1—4	2 3 4	1—4	1,2,3	Ex 3	1—4	1—4	Ex3	1—4	1—4	1—4	1,2,3	2 3 4	2 3 4	1—4	Ex3	1—4	1—4
		a.m.	a.m.	a.m.	a.m.	a.m.	a.m.	a.m.	p.m.	p.m.	p.m.	p.m.	p.m.	p.m.	p.m.	p.m.	p.m.	p.m.	p.m.	n'gt
Coblence Haupt....dep		4 30	5 32	7 26	8 27	8 45	10 22	11 9	12 19	1 22	2 7	2 59	3 31	5 37	6 20	7 18	8 22	9 15	1032	12 8
Niederlahnstein arr		4 40	5 40	7 34	8 35	8 53	10 29	1117	12 27	1 30	2 15	3 7	3 39	5 45	6 28	7 26	8 30	9 23	1040	1216
COLOGNE 128......dep		1145	...	5a30	...	5a44	8 a8	9a10	9 a13	1127	11a27	...	12p35	3 p28	3p28	...	5 p18	6p18	...	8p23
WIESBADEN 120 dep		1257	...	4a59	5 a26	...	8 a56	...	10a56	...	11a43	1p17	1 p17	3 p43	3p43	...	5 p55	...	8p26	...
Niederlahnsteindep		4 42	6 0	7 39	8 37	8 57	10 47	1121	12 30	1 33	2 19	3 9	3 43	5 54	6 32	7 30	8 33	9 27	1046	1220
Ems Bad .... arr		5 9	6 26	8 5	8 57	9 13	11 3	1146	12 53	1 48	2 54	3 34	4 16	6 10	7 9	8 3	8 59	9 43	11 9	1256
dep		5 10	6 29	8 7	8 59	9 16	11 7	—	12 55	1 49	2 56	3 36	4 18	13	7 12	8 5	9 2	9 46	1111	—
Nassau		5 29	6 44	8 20	9 12	9 27	11 18	a.m.	1 8	...	3 11	3 48	4 31	6 24	7 25	8 12	9 18	...	1124	...
Balduinstein (Schaumb)		6 10	7 12	8 52	9 36	...	...	1122	1 33	...	3 37	—	4 56	6 44	7 50	8*45	9 47	...	1151	p.m.
Diez **146**	4a37	6 28	7 25	9 4	10 0	9 53	11 45	1212	1 44	...	3 49	4p59	5 8	6 52	8 3	8*58	9 58	...	12 4	1021
Limburg135Aarr	4 43	6 37	7 31	9 10	10 6	9 59	11 51	1218	1 50	2 24	3 55	5 5	5 14	6 58	8 9	9 *4	10 4	1020	1210	1028
" ......dep	4 46	—	7 42	—	10 9	10 2	11 54	1220	1 52	2 25	—	—	5 20	7 1	—	—	10 33	1023	—	—
Kerkerbach **153** ...	4 58	2 3 4	7 53	...	10 20	...	...	1231	2 3	...	...	...	5 33	7 8	...	...	10 43	...	...	...
Runkel	5 3	a.m.	7 58	...	10 25	...	...	1236	2 8	...	p.m.	...	5 38	7 13	...	p.m	10 47	...	...	...
Weilburg **147**	5 46	6 54	8 42	...	11 2	1033	12 25	—	2 56	...	5 7	...	6 22	7 44	...	8 40	11 23	1054	...	...
Braunfels..............	6 8	7 12	9 4	...	11 23	...	12 40	...	3 17	...	5 30	...	6 44	7 58	...	9 3	11 43	...	...	...
Albshausen............	6 19	7 24	9 14	...	11 33	...	...	...	3 28	...	5 42	...	6 54	...	...	9 15	11 53	...	...	...
Wetzlar.........arr	6 27	7 32	9 22	...	11 40	1058	12 53	...	3 36	...	5 50	...	7 1	8 10	...	9 23	12 1	1118	...	...
Giessen ....arr	6 45	7 58	9 40	...	11 58	1112	1 7	...	3 55	3 28	6‡29	...	7 22	8 25	...	9 43	12 16	1132	...	...
FRANKFORT **156A** a	9 a0	9a14	11a10	...	1 p13	1239	4p22	...	5p52	4p56	8 p42	...	8p51	10p25	...	12a5	4 a46	4a46	...	...
CASSEL **157**....arr	9a37	1146	12p51	...	3 p28	1p37	3p44	...	8 p3	5p51	...	...	11p45	12a21	...	1221	2 a35	1a49	...	...

Extra			
Coblence..............dep	12 p8	1 p30	...
Niederlahnstein ....dep	12 20	1 40	...
Ems Bad..............arr	12 36	2 5	...

Diez.........dep	6a39	9a30	11a52	1p36	3p12	6p32	7p10	8p30	...
Limburg...arr	6 46	9 37	11 59	1 43	3 19	6 39	7 15	8 37	...

*—Until 15th Sept. †—From Deutz. ‡—Weekdays only.

WIESBADEN and DIEZ.

§—In July and August only. †—Weekdays only.

E.M.																		
...	COLOGNE 128 ....dep	...	...	1 a58	...	5a30	...	...	9 a10	11a27	...	...	...	...	12p35	3 p38	6 p18	...
				a.m.	a.m.	a.m.	a.m.	p.m.	p.m.	p.m.	p.m.	p.m.	p.m.	p.m.	p.m.	p.m.	p.m.	p.m.
—	**Wiesbaden** ....dep	...	...	7 3	8§29	9 15	11 12	...	1 19	2 34	3 26	4 5	5 35	6 23	6 59	8 1	10 14	11 30
8¾	Eiserne Hand..................	...	...	7 45	9 11	10 0	11 57	...	2 0	3 14	4 4	4 46	6 17	7 2	7 40	8 41	10 57	12 13
14¾	**Langen Schwalbach** arr	...	...	8 8	9 35	1022	12 20	...	2 24	3 37	4 21	5 8	6 40	7 25	8 4	9 4	11 20	12 36
...	dep	...	...	8 13	—	1025	12 25	1 56	—	3 41	—	5 13	7 12	—	—	9 9	—	—
15½	Adolphseck	...	...	8 17	...	1029	12 28	2 0	...	3 44	...	5 16	7 16	...	...	9 12	...	...
18¾	Hohenstein	a.m.	a.m.	8 29	...	1041	12 39	2 13	...	3 57	...	5 30	7 29	...	...	9 25	...	...
26½	Zollhaus	6 7	7 †4	9 1	...	1112	1 8	2 45	...	4 27	...	6 1	8 2	...	...	9 53	...	...
33½	**Diez** ....arr	6 35	7 29	9 26	...	1136	1 32	3 10	...	4 54	...	6 27	8 27	...	...	10 17	...	...
66¾	NIEDERLAHNSTEIN 147	8a32	...	10a27	...	1p21	3 p33	5 p44	...	6 p54	...	8 p15	10p42	...	...	11p51	...	...
126½	COLOGNE 129.............arr	...	...	12p31	...	4p32	6 p8	...	...	9 p30	...	12a13	...	...	...	7 a19	...	...

...	COLOGNE 128...........dep	...	...	...	...	11p45	5 a44	8 a8	...	...	9 a13	...	1127	12p35	...	3 p28	...	...
...	NIEDERLAHNSTEIN 146	dep	...	...	...	6 a0	8 a57	10a47	...	...	12p50	...	2p19	3 p43	...	5 p54	...	...
				a.m.	a.m.	a.m.	a.m.	p.m.			p.m.		p.m.	p.m.	p.m.	p.m.	p.m.	
...	**Diez** ....dep	...	...	5 11	5 †54	7 58	10 11	12 29	...	...	2 19	...	4 20	5 37	6†28	7 26	11 42	...
...	Zollhaus	...	...	5 37	6 21	8 23	10 36	12 55	...	...	2 44	...	4 53	6 1	6 54	7 48	12 8	...
...	Hohenstein	...	...	6 10	—	8 56	11 8	1 28	...	...	3 15	...	5 29	6 31	—	8 19	—	...
...	Adolphseck	...	...	6 24	...	9 8	11 20	1 41	...	...	3 27	...	5 43	6 43	...	8 30	...	...
...	**Langen Schwalbach** arr	a.m.	a.m.	6 27	a.m.	9 11	11 24	1 44	p.m.	p.m.	3 30	p.m.	5 46	6 46	p.m.	8 34	p.m.	...
...	dep	4 15	5 13	6 35	7 45	9 14	11 29	—	12 35	1 56	3 38	5 9	5 51	6 52	7 31	8 42	9 46	...
...	Eiserne Hand	4 39	5 37	6 59	8 10	9 38	11 55	...	1 0	...	4 3	5 32	6 17	7 16	7 56	9 7	10 10	...
...	**Wiesbaden** ....arr	5 20	6 20	7 39	8 51	10 17	12 36	...	1 42	2 53	4 41	6 13	6 58	7 54	8 38	9 47	10 50	...
...	COLOGNE 129............arr	...	...	12p31	12p31	2 p17	4 p32	...	...	6 p8	9 p30	...	...	12a13	...	...	7 a19	...

OBERLAHNSTEIN and EMS.

Oberlahnstein ......dep	2p29	6 p42	7p40	12a30	...	...
Ems (146) ....arr	2 54	7 9	8 3	12 56	...	...

Ems ....dep	6 a20	9a21	...	...	...	...	...	...
Oberlahnstein 128 arr	6 50	9 50	...	...	...	...	...	...

‡—6p22 on Sun.

WERTHEIM, LAUDA, and MERGENTHEIM.

E.M													
	Wertheim ...dep	4 a0	...	6a43	...	...	1021	...	...	2p17	4p43	...	7p29
5	Bronnbach	4 13	...	6 57	a.m.	...	1035	p.m.	...	2 31	4 55	...	7 46
15	Tauberbischofsh'm	4 38	...	7 23	8 20	...	11 2	12 7	...	2 58	5 19	...	8 18
19¾	**Lauda 143** arr	4 49	...	7 36	8 33	...	1115	12 20	p.m	3 11	5 30	...	8 32
...	dep	—	6a27	7 40	8 52	10 a5	1138	—	1256	3 42	6 2	6‡p25	9 31
21	Königshofen	...	6 33	7 45	8 58	10†22	1143	...	1 1	3 47	6 7	6†38	9 36
26	**Mergentheim**	...	6 48	7 59	9 13	10†45	1157	...	1 13	4 0	6 20	7 †3	9 49

†—Earlier on Suns.

Mergenth'm dep	4a39	7 a15	8 a5	9a25	11a10	12p10	...	3p12	5p14	...	8p31	...	...	...
Königshofen	4 56	7 30	8 20	9 44	11 31	12 24	...	3 27	5 29	...	8 47	...	...	...
Lauda..... arr	5 1	7 34	8 24	9 51	11 35	12 28	p.m.	3 31	5 33	p.m.	8 51	...	...	...
dep	5 30	7 44	8 50	—	11 40	—	1 2	3 49	—	6 21	9 33	...	...	...
Tauberbischofsh'm	5 44	7 55	9 5	...	11 51	...	1 16	4 2	...	6 34	9 49	...	...	...
Bronnbach............	6 10	—	9 31	...	—	...	1 42	4 25	...	6 57	1016	...	...	...
Wertheim 196arr	6 23	...	9 44	...	...	...	1 55	4 37	...	7 8	1029	...	...	...

RASTATT and FORBACH-GAUSBACH.

Rastatt ......dep	5a55	8 a44	10a59	1p43	4pl6	7p14	8p50	11p22
Gernsbach	6 33	9 20	11 34	2 18	4 53	7 51	1015	11 54
Weisenbach......	6 52	9 40	11 54	2 38	5 14	8 11	1033	...
Forbach-Gaus	7 8	9 56	12 10	2 54	5 31	8 29	1049	...

Forbach-Gausbach	...	5a53	8a45	10a32	11a57	2p58	5p18	8p53
Weisenbach............	...	6 10	9 2	10 49	12 14	3 15	5 36	9 10
Gernsbach	5 a1	6 31	9 24	11 12	12 35	3 35	5 59	9 30
Rastatt ....arr	5 32	7 4	9 55	11 41	1 6	4 6	6 30	10 1

GIESSEN and COBLENCE.

Station																				
CASSEL 156 ....dep	...	...	2 a50	4 a4	...	...	5a40	...	7 a25	9a43	9 a43	...	...	...	1p13	1 p21	3p36	...	...	7 p0
FRANKFORT 157 ...dep	1036	...	...	...	...	5a58	6 a51	...	8 a52	10a5	10 a5	12p8	...	...	2p15	2 p52	4p35	4 p57	...	7p30
	2 3 4	2 3 4	2,3,4	Ex3	1—4	2 3 4	1,2,3	1—4	1—4	Ex3	1—4	2 3 4	Ex3	1—4	1—4	1—4	Ex3	2,3,4	3—4	1—4
	a.m.	a.m.	a.m.	a.m.		a.m.	a.m.	a.m.	a.m.	p.m	p.m.	p.m	p.m.		p.m.	p.m.	p.m.	p.m.		p.m.
Giessen ....dep	1210	5 38	4 58	6 13	...	7 20	8 10	10 0	10 12	12 8	12 14	1 30	3 18	...	3 24	5 4	5 56	6 13	...	9 18
Wetzlar ....dep	1228	6 3	5 15	6 27	...	7 37	8 24	1017	10 26	1221	12 33	1 48	...	...	3 38	5 21	6 10	6 37	...	9 37
Albshausen 147	1237	6 11	5 23	...	...	7 46	...	—	10 34	...	12 41	1 57	...	...	3 47	5 30	...	6 46	...	9 46
Braunfels	1248	6 22	5 34	...	...	7 57	8 37	...	10 45	...	12 52	2 8	...	...	3 59	5 41	6 23	6 58	p.m.	9 57
Weilburg	1 9	6 43	5 54	6 52	...	8 17	8 52	...	11 6	1245	1 11	2 29	...	...	4 22	6 2	6 37	7 19	8 43	1022
Runkel	—	—	6 33	...	...	8 54	...	...	11 42	...	1 48	—	...	...	4 59	6 41	...	—	9 25	11 1
Kerkerbach	...	...	6 38	...	...	8 59	...	...	11 46	...	1 53	1—4	...	...	5 4	6 46	...	...	9 30	11 6
Limburg 135A ......arr	a.m.	a.m.	6 48	7 22	a.m.	9 9	9 23	a.m.	11 57	1 15	2 4	p.m.	4 23	p.m.	5 15	6 56	7 7	p.m.	9 41	1117
" ....dep	5 0	5 15	6 52	7 25	7 47	9 51	9 27	10 0	12 4	1 17	2 9	2 0	4 25	4 17	5 28	7 2	7 10	9*16	1012	1124
Diez	5 7	5 22	6 58	...	8 7	9 59	9 33	10 7	12 10	1 23	2 17	2 7	...	4 33	5 36	7 23	7 16	9 23	1020	1133
Balduinstein............	—	5 35	7 9	...	8 19	1010	...	1053	12 21	...	2 29	—	...	4 43	5 48	7 34	...	9 34	1034	1145
Nassau	4a56	6 5	7 36	...	9 6	1036	9 59	1139	12 44	1 48	2 55	3p56	...	5 7	6 14	8 0	7 43	10 1	1110	1216
Ems .... arr	5 9	6 18	7 49	7 58	9 19	1049	10 9	1154	12 56	1 58	3 7	4 9	4 58	5 19	6 26	8 12	7 53	10 14	1127	1230
Ems .... dep	5 10	6 20	8 7	8 2	9 21	1051	10 12	1158	12 58	2 1	3 9	4 11	5 0	5 20	6 29	8 14	7 59	10 17	1128	1233
Niederlahnstein arr	5 35	6 55	8 32	8 18	9 55	1116	10 27	1223	1 21	2 16	3 33	4 36	5 16	5 44	6 54	8 36	8 15	1042	1151	1259
WIESBADEN 128 ...arr	8a23	9 a4	11a26	1126	1142	1p19	12 40	2p26	4 p42	...	6 p40	7 p5	7 p5	...	10p2	11p14	10p2	1 a13	...	5 a0
COLOGNE 129........arr	8a19	11a2	...	...	1231	...	12p31	2p17	4 p32	4p32	6 p8	6 p8	...	...	9p30	12a13	1213	...	...	7a19
Niederlahnstein dep	5 37	6 59	8 35	8 21	10 4	1123	10 42	1233	1 25	2 20	3 52	4 40	5 19	5 53	6 58	8 38	8 19	10 46	1152	1 4
Coblence ....arr	5 45	7 7	8 43	8 29	1012	1131	10 50	1241	1 33	2 28	4 0	4 48	5 27	6 1	7 6	8 46	8 27	10 54	12 2	1 12

Extra.											
Limburg...dep	4a20	8 a0	10a34	12p18	4 p9	5p20	6 p9	6‡p15	7p16	8p48	10p25	11p31
Diez ....arr	4 27	8 6	10 40	12 26	4 16	5 27	6 15	6 22	7 22	8 54	10 31	11 38

Ems...............dep	2p16	5p14
Niederlahnstein arr	2 41	5 30
Coblence..........arr	2 58	5 42

*—Between Limburg and Nassau until 15th Sept. only. ‡—Weekdays only.

WEILBURG and USINGEN.

E.M.	Station							
	Weilburg...........dep	6a10	8a56	11a15	1 p0	3p36	6p40	8p27
6½	Weilmünster	6 41	9 25	11 43	1 26	4 8	7 10	8 59
10	Laubuseschbach	...	9 51	12 2	...	4 33	7 30	9 15
...	Grävenwiesbach 147	7 15	1047	...	2 5	4 49	7 53	...
20¾	Usingen (150)......arr	7 57	1114	...	2 30	5 22	8 27	...

Station									
Usingen ....dep	...	8a10	...	11a23	2p40	...	5p37	...	8p33
Grävenwiesbach..	...	8 46	...	11 48	3 5	...	6 9	...	9 17
Laubuseschbach	...	...	10 a8	12 8	...	4p55	...	7p35	9 30
Weilmünster	6a17	9 31	10 22	12 30	3 44	5 11	6 46	7 52	9 49
Weilburg (146)arr	6 45	10 0	10 49	12 56	4 12	5 40	7 17	8 19	1018

Station						
Grävenwiesbach......dep	4 a15	6 a14	8 a56	3 p10	6 p33	...
Albshausen (146).....arr	5 19	7 29	10 11	4 23	7 48	...

Station							
Albshausen ....dep	6 a21	9 a31	1 p45	6 p40	9 p20	...	...
Grävenwiesbach (147) ...arr	7 27	10 46	2 58	7 46	10 24	...	...

HERSFELD and TREYSA.

Station							
Hersfeld ....dep	...	6 a52	11a10	2 p22	5 p15	6 p38	10p34
Oberaula	4 a0	8 3	12 11	3 32	6 23	8 15	11 42
Treysa ....arr	5 32	9 37	1 37	4 54	...	9 38	...

Station								
Treysa............dep	...	6 a50	10a17	3 p0	...	6 p52	1020	...
Oberaula	4 a34	8 33	12 7	4 16	6 p32	8 50	12 0	...
Hersfeld.........arr	5 39	9 32	1 4	5 6	7 33	10 4	...	...

TREYSA, NIEDERHONE, and LEINEFELDE.

Dist. E.M.	Station									
			a.m.	a.m.			a.m.	p.m.		p.m.
	Treysa ....dep		3 15	6 13	...	...	10 43	2 42	...	7 28
7	Frielendorf.........		3 38	6 39	...	...	10 58	3 6	...	7 47
12¼	Homberg		3 55	6 56	...	...	11 26	3 1	...	8 1
24¼	**Malsfeld** ....arr		4 26	7 30	...	a.m.	11 57	3 45	...	8 30
...	" 173A dep		—	7 53	...	9 46	12 25	3 57	...	8 52
37½	Burghofen		a.m.	8 28	a.m.	10 21	1 7	4 33	p.m.	9 30
41½	Waldkappel		6 3	8 42	10 0	10 33	1 17	4 46	7 21	9 47
49½	**Niederhone** ...arr		6 24	9 2	1019	10 52	1 40	5 6	7 43	10 8
...	" 149...dep		6 25	9 22	1021	11 3	1 41	5 10	7 45	10 10
51½	Eschwege ...	4 a5	6 53	9 29	1027	11 14	1 48	5 21	8 42	10 16
58½	Geismar	4 27	7 17	—	—	11 34	2 39	5 42	9 10	—
73½	Dingelstädt...	5 10	8 14	...	...	12 19	3 22	6 29	9 55	...
80	**Leinefelde** 148	5 27	8 33	...	...	12 36	3 40	6 45	1012	...

Station									
		a.m.		a.m.	a.m.	p.m.	p.m	p.m.	p.m.
Leinefelde ...dep		...	...	6 9	9 44	1 57	5 5	7 7	10 35
Dingelstädt.........		...	...	6 30	10 4	2 16	5 27	7 25	10 51
Geismar	a.m.	...	a.m.	7 10	10 40	2 55	6 1	8 6	11 35
Eschwege	4 55	5 42	8 10	7 32	11 0	3 14	6 24	8 28	11 57
Nieder- ...arr	5 2	5 48	8 16	7 42	11 6	3 19	6 30	9 25	12 15
hone...dep	5 18	5 58	8 17	9 22	11 54	3 22	6 52	9 26	—
Waldkappel	5 45	6 26	8 40	9 44	12 18	3 46	7 27	9 46	...
Burghofen ...	—	6 39	8 52	—	12 29	3 57	7 42	—	...
Malsfeld...arr	a.m.	7 18	9 19	...	12 57	4 27	8 16	...	...
" ...dep	6 15	8 30	—	...	1 12	4 37	8 49	...	...
Homberg	6 55	9 5	...	...	1 46	5 11	9 22	...	...
Frielendorf ...	7 11	9 23	...	...	2 4	5 28	9 39	...	...
Treysa ...arr	7 32	9 45	...	...	2 25	5 48	9 59	...	...

Extra.—Waldkappel to Eschwege 2.50 p.m. Eschwege to Waldkappel 1.37 p.m.

NIEDERHONE and TREFFURT.

Station							
Niederhone dep	6a25	10a21	1p57	4 p2	6p50	7p45	10p33
Eschwege.........	7 6	10 34	2 6	4 11	7 8	8 0	10 43
Treffurt ......arr	8 1	11 33	2 58	5 10	8 1	9 1	11 41

Station							
Treffurt ....dep	5a45	7a13	9a37	12p38	4p14	8p11	9 p2
Eschwege	6 39	8 5	1030	1 34	5 12	9 6	9 52
Niederhone arr	7 42	8 16	1050	1 44	6 30	9 25	1012

GIESSEN and GELNHAUSEN.

Station										
Giessen ......dep		5a42	8a18	10a15	12p34	2p16	5 p4	6p33	8p47	11p30
Hungen	a.m.	6 24	8 57	10 42	1 20	2 53	5 41	7 10	9 23	12 17
Nidda.........	4 23	6 55	9 23	11 0	1 54	3 16	6 6	7 33	9 50	12 47
Stockheim .	4 43	7 13	9 39	11 15	2 15	—	6 23	—	10 8	—
Gelnhausen	5 25	7 59	1022	11 47	3 1	...	7 5	...	1050	...

Station										
Gelnhausen dep		7a28	9a54	12p50	3p27	4p57	...	8p47	12a30	...
Stockheim	4a59	8 12	1040	1 35	4 1	5 42	...	9 30	1 14	a.m.
Nidda	5 26	8 34	1059	1 56	4 16	6 10	8p12	9 50	—	1251
Hungen ...	5 54	8 59	1123	2 25	4 34	4 40	8 52	1027	...	1 20
Giessen 146	6 35	9 39	1159	3 7	5 1	7 23	9 48	11 5	...	...

Station						
Nidda ....dep	5a54	9a 24	11a17	2 p5	6 p20	9 p55
Schotten......arr	7 38	10 8	12 8	2 55	7 10	10 45

Station						
Schotten ...dep	4 a30	7 a46	10a15	12p50	5 p8	8 p55
Nidda.........arr	5 20	8 30	10 57	1 40	5 58	9 45

LAUTERBACH, STOCKHEIM and HELDENBERGEN.

Station								
Lauterbach ......dep	...	...	6 a0	10a33	2p52	...	6 p8	8p25
Grebenhain	...	...	7 9	11 44	3 54	...	7 25	9 43
Gedern	...	5a40	8 5	12 44	4 50	6 p3	8 35	1042
Stockheim...............	5 a4	6 52	8 58	2 16	5 51	6 53	9 22	...
Heldenbergen-W arr	5 50	...	9 41	3 1	6 34	8 15	...	...

Station									
Heldenbergen-W.dep		...	7a20	a.m.	1235	...	...	4p40	6p40	8p22
Stockheim	...	5a13	8 23	1121	1 25	2p20	4p12	6 25	7 23	1012
Gedern...............	...	6 52	9 35	1236	—	3 34	5 24	7 23	—	1115
Grebenhain	4a38	8 3	1044	1 40	...	—	6 25	8 28	...	—
Lauterbach...arr	5 39	9 30	12 1	2 46	...	...	7 29	...	...	...

Station							
Heldenbergen...dep	5a11	5a52	9a44	1p45	3 p2	6p36	...
Vilbel..............arr	5 51	6 29	1022	2 25	3 40	7 14	...

Station							
Vilbel ....dep	6a39	11a44	12p52	3p55	5p57	7p32	9p48
Heldenbergen ...arr	7 17	12 23	1 30	4 33	635	8 13	1027

Station							
Hungen ....dep	5 a55	7a16	9 a10	3 p1	5 p8	7 p25	10p27
Laubach	6 22	8 0	9 46	3 34	5 49	8 5	10 55
Mücke ....arr	6 53	8 47	10 24	4 14	6 36	8 55	...

Station							
Mücke ....dep	...	7 a15	11a13	1 p5	4 p27	7p20	10p10
Laubach	5 a15	8 6	11 55	1 44	5 6	8 4	11 1
Hungen ....arr	5 45	8 36	12 25	2 18	5 35	8 34	11 26

[Luggage Rates—see page 462.

BERLIN, HALLE, SANGERHAUSEN, EICHENBERG, and CASSEL.

RESTAURANT CAR (RC)—in 8.1 a.m. from Schlesischer Bahnhof, Berlin.

Dist. E.M.	Station	2,3,4	2 3 4	2 3 4	Ex 3	2 3 4	2,3,4	Ex3	2,3,4	Ex.3	Ex3	2 3 4	2 3 4	Ex3	Ex 3
	BERLIN—	p.m.				a.m.					a.m.	a.m.			
—	Schlesisch Bhf. dep	11 25	...	...	...	4 11	...	...	...	...	8 1	8 28	...	...	...
1½	Alexanderplatz „	11 31	...	...	...	4 17	...	...	...	...	8 7	8 34	...	...	...
2½	Friedrichstrasse „	11 38	...	...	...	4 24	...	...	...	...	8 17	8 42	...	...	...
5½	Zoolog. Garten „	11 49	...	...	...	4 34	a.m.	...	...	...	8 29	8 53	...	...	...
7	Charlottenburg „	11 55	...	...	...	4 40	6 0	...	...	...	8 35	8 59	...	...	...
...	Potsdamer Bhf. „	...	...	...	...	...	...	Madgeburg dep. 8.15.	...	...	RC	...	...	...	...
15	**Wannsee** ....dep	12 13	...	...	...	4 58	6 19		...	...	8 50	9 17	...	...	...
18¾	Drewitz	12 22	...	...	...	5 6	6 28		...	...	...	9 25	...	...	...
30½	Beelitz	12 50	...	...	...	5 35	6 57		...	...	...	9 53	...	...	...
47½	Belzig	1 28	...	...	...	6 16	7 34		...	...	9 39	1033	...	...	...
76¼	Güterglück		...	...	...	7 30			...	...	1019	1143	...	...	...
88¼	Stadt-Calbe	...	...	a.m.	...	7 57	...	a.m.	a.m.	...	1038	12 9	...	...	...
98½	**Gusten 161c**	...	...	5 38	...	8 18	...	9 5	9 15	...	1059	1232	...	...	...
108½	Sandersleben	...	...	5 59	...		...	9 32	9 42	...	1119		...	...	...
118¼	Mansfeld	...	...	6 32	...	...	...	9 54	10 12	...	...	...	...	...	...
131¾	**Sangerhausen** ......arr	...	...	7 2	...	...	...	1015	10 41	...	12 4	...	...	...	...
...	DRESDEN Hpt. 189 dep		...	1225	...	3a41	...	...	...	8 a0	...	...	8 a0	1025	...
...	LEIPSIC 158 ...dep	...	...	3a29	...	5a55	6 a57	...	7 a45	10a25	...	...	1025	1215	...
...	BERLIN 170 ...dep	...	...	1230	...	...	...	...	...	9 a5	...	...	9 a5	1050	...
				a.m.	a.m.	a.m.	a.m.		a.m.	a.m			p.m.	p.m.	
...	**Halle** ....dep	...	...	5 5	5 52	6 42	7 45	...	9 0	11 9	...	...	1220	1 18	...
...	Teutschenthal	...	...	5 36	...	7 14	...	...	9 28	...	...	...	1248	...	...
...	Ober-Röblingen	...	...	5 50	...	7 28	8 14	...	9 40	11 34	...	...	1. 1	...	...
...	Eisleben	...	...	6 14	...	7 51	8 31	...	9 59	11 48	...	...	1 20	1 54	...
...	**Sangerhausen** ...arr	...	...	6 46	6 54	8 37	9 2	...	10 35	12 13	...	p.m.	2 0	2 19	...
...	**Sangerhausen**......dep	...	...	7 12	6 55	...	9 9	...	10 55	12 15	1220	1225	...	2 21	...
142	Rossla	...	...	7 35	...	...	9 33	...	11 19	...	1237	1247	...	...	...
144½	Berga-Kelbra 149	...	...	7 41	...	...	9 39	...	11 26	...	RC	1253	...	...	...
155	**Nordhausen**.........arr	...	a.m.	8 2	7 30	...	10 8	...	11 52	12 46	1257	1 15	...	2 53	...
...	„ 152, 159 dep	...	6 36	8 15	7 34	...	10 30	...	12 7	12 50	1 1		...	2 58	...
166½	Bleicherode	...	7 5	8 45	⋮	...	10 58	...	12 39	...	1 21	...	...	3 19	...
181½	**Leinefelde 147**......dep	...	7 45	9 26	⋮	...	11 40	...	1 38	1 32	1 52	...	...	3 46	...
191¼	Heiligenstadt	...	8 7	9 50	⋮	...	12 4	...	1 57	...	2 9	...	...	4 2	...
201	**Eichenberg** ....arr	Ex.3	8 30	1013	⋮	...	12 33	...	2 20	2 1	2 27	...	2 3 4	4 17	...
342¼	FRANKFORT 149A ar	a.m.	1 p27	3p46	⋮	...	...	...	7p36	7p36	7p36	...	p.m.	...	p.m.
...	**Eichenberg** ....dep	8 38	8 55	1019	⋮	...	12 40	...	2 40	2 3	2 31	...	4 43	4 18	6 5
215¼	Münden	9 2	9 28	1054	⋮	...	1 13	...	3 14	...	2 54	...	5 20	...	...
230¼	**Cassel** ....arr	9 28	10 35	1134	9 35	...	1 52	...	3 58	2 50	3 22	...	6 4	5 5	6 52
354½	FRANKFORT 156A ar	1 p13	...	...	1p13	...	5 p52	...	8 p51	7 p7	7 p7	...	...	...	10p25

Dist. E.M.	Station	2 3 4	2,3,4	1,2,3	Ex3	2 3 4	1,2,3	2,3,4	2,3,4	2,3,4	2 3 4	1,2,3	Ex3	Ex 2	2 3 4
	BERLIN—	a.m.	p.m.	p.m.				p.m.		p.m.	p.m.	p.m.		p.m.	p.m.
—	Schlesisch Bhf. dep	...	...	...	...	...	...	1 27	...	...	6 23	...	...	9 34	...
1½	Alexanderplatz „	...	...	...	...	...	...	1 33	...	...	6 29	...	...	9 40	...
2½	Friedrichstrasse „	...	...	...	...	...	...	1 41	...	...	6 37	...	...	9 50	...
5½	Zoolog. Garten „	...	...	...	...	...	...	1 53	p.m.	...	6 48	...	...	10 1	...
7	Charlottenburg „	10 32	...	...	...	...	...	2 2	4 3	6 0	6 55	...	...	10 7	8 54
...	Potsdamer Bhf. „	...	...	1 0	...	...	...	...	...	...	...	7 35	...	⋮	...
15	**Wannsee** ....dep	10 56	...	Via Magd'.	...	...	...	2 27	4 28	6 19	7 16	Via Madg'brg.	...	⋮	9 14
18¾	Drewitz	11 5	...		...	...	...	2 36	4 37	6 28	7 24		...	⋮	9 23
30½	Beelitz	11 35	...		...	...	...	3 7	5 5	6 59	7 53		...	⋮	9 54
47½	Belzig	12 13	...		...	...	...	3 50	5 42	7 38	8 37		...	⋮	1033
76¼	Güterglück		...		...	...	...	5 14		Week-days only.	9 47		...	⋮	
88¼	Stadt-Calbe	...	...		...	...	...	5 39	...		10 10		...	⋮	...
98½	**Gusten 161c**	...	2 22	3 53	...	...	...	6 5	...		10 30	10 35	...	⋮	...
108½	Sandersleben	...	2 45	4 11	...	...	...	6 26	...		11 59	10 53	...	⋮	...
118¼	Mansfeld	...	3 16	...	...	...	...	6 59	...		12 31	11 15	...	⋮	...
131¾	**Sangerhausen** ......arr	...	3 49	4 51	...	...	...	7 29	...		1 2	11 36	...	⋮	...
...	DRESDEN Hpt. 189 dep	...	10a35	|	1p18	...	1 p18	1 18	4 p0		...	...	8 p6	Via Magdeburg Kreiensen.	8 p6
...	LEIPSIC 158 ...dep	...	1 p0	|	3p10	...	4 p10	4 p20	7 p40	...	...	...	10p5	⋮	10p5
...	BERLIN 170 ...dep	...	...	|	1p45	...	2 p15	3 p35	4 p50	...	...	...	8p50	⋮	8p50
			p.m.		p.m.	p.m	p.m.	p.m.	p.m.				p.m.	⋮	ng't
...	**Halle** ....dep	...	2 10	|	3 55	4 2	4 54	6 15	9 40	...	...	...	1055	⋮	12 7
...	Teutschenthal	...	2 41	|	...	4 31	...	6 45	10 10	...	...	...	...	⋮	1235
...	Ober-Röblingen	...	2 56	|	...	4 48	...	6 59	10 27	...	...	...	...	⋮	1249
...	Eisleben	...	3 18	|	4 31	5 11	...	7 21	10 50	...	...	...	1131	⋮	1 10
...	**Sangerhausen** ...arr	p.m.	3 55	|	4 56	5 44	5 52	7 57	11 26	...	...	...	1156	⋮	1 46
...	**Sangerhausen**......dep	2 34	4 10		4 57	6 30	5 53	8 5	11 30	...	...		12 5	⋮	1 54
142	Rossla	2 59	4 36		...	7 7	...	8 28	11 52	...	p.m.	...	...	⋮	2 19
144½	Berga-Kelbra 149	3 10	4 43	...	..	7 19	...	8 34	11 58	...	9 52	...	...	⋮	2 28
155	**Nordhausen**.........arr	3 36	5 9	...	5 29	7 53	6 27	8 58	12 23	...	10 28	...	1237	⋮	2 54
...	„ 152, 159 dep	3 47	5 42	...	5 34			9 4		...	11 36	...	1242	⋮	4 26
166½	Bleicherode	4 17	6 14	p.m.	...	...	...	9 35	...	...	12 3	...	1 1	⋮	4 58
181½	**Leinefelde 147**......dep	5 5	6 59	6 6	6 18	...	...	10 33	...	...	12 41	...	1 29	⋮	5 44
191¼	Heiligenstadt	5 27	7 22	6 20	...	...	...	10 58	...	...		...	1 44	⋮	6 10
201	**Eichenberg** ....arr	5 53	7 43	6 38	6 46	...	...	11 23	...	...	...	...	⋮	⋮	6 36
342¼	FRANKFORT 149A ar	...	...	...	1140	...	p.m.	...	...	...	...	...	⋮	⋮	1p27
...	**Eichenberg** ....dep	6 17	7 50	...	7 0	...	8 15	11 46	...	...	...	...	⋮	⋮	6 43
215¼	Münden	6 51	8 24	...	7 29	...	8 42	12 22	...	...	...	...	⋮	⋮	7 24
230¼	**Cassel** ....arr	7 37	9 29	...	7 56	...	9 9	1 3	...	...	...	...	2 44	3 58	8 4
354½	FRANKFORT 156A ar	...	4 a46	...	...	...	...	...	...	...	...	...	6 a7	7 a18	1p13

Extra.—Sangerhausen to Nordhausen, 7.34 p.m.

WACHTERSBACH and ORB.

Wächtersbach dep. 6.45, 8.40, 11.0 a.m., 12.54, 2 20, 5.20, 7.10, 8.40 p.m. Orb dep. 5.35, 7.45, 10.3, 11.45 a.m., 1.14, 4.35, 6.23, 7.55, 9.15 p.m.

BLEICHERODE and HERZBERG.

Bleicherode.....................dep	...	5a26	7 a10	8a50	10a14	2 p14	5 p0	7 p38	9 p38	...
Weissenhorn-Lüderode.........	5 a11	6 29	8 14	9 44	11 8	3 18	6 0	8 40	10 30	...
Herzberg 164A ....arr	5 54	7 20	8 58	10 26	11 49	4 2	6 43	9 24	...	...

Herzberg ....dep	...	...	6 a38	8 a13	9 a40	12p32	4 p22	7 p31	10 p5	...
Weissenhorn-Lüderode	4 a 0	5 a12	7 28	9 3	11 8	1 17	5 12	8 37	10 49	...
Bleicherode 148..............arr	4 52	6 36	8 22	10 2	11 57	2 5	6 8	9 28	...	...

WULFTEN and LEINEFELDE.

E.M.												
	Wulften ....dep	...	...	7a25	8a55	11 a4	1p56	3p59	8p29	11p53	...	...
12¾	Duderstadt	4a30	5a43	8 13	9 39	11 47	2 42	4 56	9 15	12 37	...	...
24¾	**Leinefelde 148** .arr	5 27	6 43	9 11	1116	12 36	3 39	5 51	1012	...	...	...

Leinefelde ...dep	5a42	7 a10	9a35	11a41	1p55	5p27	7 p2	10p27	...	...	...
Duderstadt	6 27	7 54	1014	12 50	2 41	6 12	7 45	11 7	...	...	...
Wulften 164A arr	7 10	8 40	1054	1 36	3 24	6 55	8 27	...	...	...	...

CASSEL, EICHENBERG, SANGERHAUSEN, HALLE, and BERLIN.

Station	2 3 4	2,3,4	2 3 4	3 & 4	1,2,3	Ex3	2 3 4	2 3 4	2,3,4	1,2,3
FRANKFORT 157 dp	...	...	...	...	...	1113	...	...	11p13	1140
						a.m.			a.m.	a.m.
Cassel ... dep	...	...	...	...	...	2 52	...	...	3 54	6 35
Münden ...	...	...	...	...	...	3 17	...	...	4 34	7 0
Eichenberg ... arr	...	...	...		...	3 42	...	...	5 10	7 27
FRANKFORT 149 dp	...	...	...		...	...	...	...	...	...
Eichenberg ... dep	...	...	..	Weekdays only.	...	3 52	...	a.m.	5 15	7 28
Heiligenstadt ...	...	...	...		...	4 8	...	...	5 39	7 45
Leinefelde ... dep	...	...	...		...	4 28	...	4 45	6 8	8 6
Bleicherode ...	...	...	...		...	...	...	5 23	6 42	8 28
Nordhausen ... arr	...	...	a.m.	a.m.	...	5 3	a.m.	5 51	7 9	8 45
,, ... dep	...	...	3 49	4 16	...	5 7	5 43		7 18	8 49
Berga-Kelbra ...	...	...	4 12	4 53	...	...	6 19	...	7 43	...
Rossla ...	...	...	4 18	5 0	...	...		...	7 51	...
Sangerhausen ... arr	...	...	4 40	5 30	...	5 39	...	...	8 15	9 21
			a.m.			a.m.			a.m.	a.m.
Sangerhausen dep	...	...	4 44	...	...	5 43	...	...	8 21	9 22
Eisleben ...	a.m.	...	5 24	...	...	6 10	...	...	8 57	9 47
Ober-Röblingen ...	6†55	...	5 42	...	...	...	...	...	9 18	...
Teutschenthal ...	7 10	...	5 57	...	...	...	...	...	9 32	...
Halle ... arr	7 42	...	6 27	...	...	6 43	...	...	10 3	1020
BERLIN 171 ... arr		...	9 a5	...	...	9 a5	...	...	12p43	1243
LEIPSIC 158 ... arr	...	...	8 a9	...	...	8 a9	...	...	11 a8	11a8
DRESD'N Hpt 188 ar	...	...	10a26		a.m.	1026		...	2 p30	2p30
Sangerhausen ... dep	...	...	4 55		6 6	...		...	8 27	...
Mansfeld ...	...	...	5 30		6 34	...		...	9 3	...
Sandersleben ...	...	...	5 56	Weekdays only.	6 54	...	Weekdays only.	...	9 27	...
Gusten ...	...	...	6 20		7 17	...		...	9 50	...
Stadt-Calbe ...	...	...	6 43			...		...	10 11	...
Güterglück ...	a.m.	a.m.	7 28	a.m.		...	a.m.	...	10 38	...
Belzig ...	4 27	5 56	8 30	6 34		...	10 3	...	11 40	...
Beelitz ...	5 4	6 33	9 7	7 11	Via Magdeburg	...	1041	...	12 16	...
Drewitz-Potsdam ...	5 30	7 0	9 32	7 38		...	11 8	...	12 41	...
Wannsee ...	5 42	7 9	9 46	7 49		...	1117	...	12 52	...
BERLIN Charlottenburg arr	5 57	7 25	10 1	8 5		...	1133	...	1 9	...
BERLIN Zoolog. Garten ,,	6 3		10 7			...		...	1 15	...
BERLIN Friedrichstrasse ,,	6 13	...	1017	...		...	...	...	1 26	...
BERLIN Alexanderplatz ,,	6 20	...	1024	...		...	...	...	1 33	...
BERLIN Schlesisch Bhf. ,,	6 26	...	1030	...		...	...	...	1 39	...
BERLIN Potsdamer Bhf. ,,	...	...	...	...	10 49	...	...	...	...	...

Station	2,3,4	2,3,4	1,2,3	2 3 4	Fx3	1,2,3	2 3 4	2,3,4	1,2,3
FRANKFORT 157 dp	...	11p40	...	...	5a58	...	...	...	...
		a.m.		a.m.	a.m.			a.m.	
Cassel ... dep	...	7 9	...	9 0	1110	...	...	11 22	...
Münden ...	...	7 52	...	9 38	1135	...	...	12 1	...
Eichenberg ... arr	...	8 31	...	1013	12 1	...	...	12 36	...
FRANKFORT 149 dp	...	...	...	...	...	...	...	8 a20	p.m.
Eichenberg ... dep	...	8 43	...	1026	12 2	...	...	12 41	1 16
Heiligenstadt ...	...	9 7	...	1053	...	...	...	1 5	...
Leinefelde ... dep	...	9 36	...	1130	1239	...	...	1 35	1 51
Bleicherode ...	...	10 11	...	12 5	...	...	...	2 9	
Nordhausen ... arr	a.m.	10 38	p.m.	1235	1 13	...	p.m.	2 37	...
,, ... dep	9 20	10 43	12 40	1254	1 16	...	2 0	2 47	...
Berga-Kelbra ...	9 43	11 6	...	1 15	...	...	2 31	3 12	...
Rossla ...	9 49	11 12	...	1 21	..	...	2 40	3 18	...
Sangerhausen ... arr	10 13	11 37	1 13	1 41	1 46		3 9	3 41	2 3 4
	a.m.	a.m.	p.m.	p.m.	p.m.			p.m.	p.m.
Sangerhausen dep	10 25	11 50	1 4	2 0	1 47		...	3 46	5 40
Eisleben ...	11 4	12 25	1 39	3 0	...		...	4 23	6 19
Ober-Röblingen ...	11 25	12 43	...	3 26	...		...	4 42	6 37
Teutschenthal ...	11 41	12 58	...	3 46	...		...	4 56	6 51
Halle ... arr	12 12	1 28	2 15	4 23	2 50		...	5 27	7 22
BERLIN 171 ... arr	2 p39	3p34	4 p34	6p42	4p56		...	8 p19	...
LEIPSIC 158 ... arr	1 p1	2 p55	3 p5	6p11	4p27		...	6 p11	8 p6
DRESD'N Hpt 188 ar	2 p55	...	6 p19	8p27	6p36		...	8 p27	1014
Sangerhausen ... dep	...	11 44	...	...	...	1 52	...	3 52	...
Mansfeld ...	...	12 21	...	...	...	...	...	4 29	...
Sandersleben ...	...	12 51	...	...	...	2 33	...	4 58	...
Gusten ...	...	1 30	...	...	...	2 53	...	5 56	...
Stadt-Calbe ...	...	1 52	...	...	...		...	6 16	...
Güterglück ...	...	2 21	...	...	...		p.m.	6 50	...
Belzig ...	...	3 29	...	...	...		6 0	7 57	...
Beelitz ...	...	4 8	...	...	...		6 38	8 35	...
Drewitz-Potsdam ...	...	4 34	...	...	...	Via Magdeburg.	7 4	9 2	...
Wannsee ...	...	4 50	...	...	...		7 14	9 16	...
BERLIN Charlottenburg arr	...	5 10	...	...	...		7 33	9 32	...
BERLIN Zoolog. Garten ,,	...	5 17	...	...	...			9 39	...
BERLIN Friedrichstrasse ,,	...	5 28	...	...	...		...	9 50	...
BERLIN Alexanderplatz ,,	...	5 36	...	...	...		...	9 57	...
BERLIN Schlesisch Bhf. ,,	...	5 42	...	...	...		...	10 3	...
BERLIN Potsdamer Bhf. ,,	...	...	...	...	...	6 1	...	...	...

Station	2 3 4	Ex 3	2,3,4	2,3,4	Ex3	2,3,4	2 3 4	Ex 3	2,3,4	2,3,4
FRANKFORT 157 dp	8a52	12 p8	...	...	...	12p48	...	1 p2	4 p35	...
	p.m.	p.m.				p.m.		p.m.	p.m.	p.m.
Cassel ... dep	2 11	3 52	...	...	...	4 50	...	7 34	8 8	10 40
Münden ...	2 48	4 19	...	...	...	5 20	...	...	8 46	11 15
Eichenberg ... arr	3 23	4 45	...	...	...	5 56	...	8 23	9 21	11 50
FRANKFORT 149 dp	9a58	...	...	...	...	...	...	2 p46	...	3 p15
Eichenberg ... dep	3 33	4 46	...	...	...	6 7	...	8 24	9 27	11 52
Heiligenstadt ...	3 55	5 3	...	...	...	6 31	...	...	9 50	12 15
Leinefelde ... dep	4 23	5 25	...	...	...	7 0	...	...	10 23	12 40
Bleicherode ...	4 58	RC	...	...	...	7 34	...	...	10 56	1 13
Nordhausen ... arr	5 27	6 4	...	p.m.	...	8 1	p.m.	9 27	11 23	1 35
,, ... dep	5 40	6 8	...	6†30	...	8 6	8 53	9 31	11 42	
Berga-Kelbra ...	6 3	...	...	6 55	...	8 29	9 19	...	12 34	...
Rossla ...	6 9	6 29	...		...	8 35	9 26	...	12 46	...
Sangerhausen ... arr	6 33	6 45	.	...	...	8 57	9 51	10 4	1 29	...
		p.m.	p.m.			p.m.		p.m.		p.m.
Sangerhausen dep	...	7 2	7 7	...	...	9 3	...	10 5	...	10 11
Eisleben ...	...	7 28	7 47	...	...	9 36	...	...	...	10 45
Ober-Röblingen ...	...	...	8 7	...	...	9 53	...	...	...	11 3
Teutschenthal ...	...	...	8 22	...	...	10 5	...	...	...	11 18
Halle ... arr	...	8 1	8 53	...	...	10 30	...	11 0	...	11 48
BERLIN 171 ... arr	...	10p38	11 p2	...	...	5 a0	...	5 a0	...	5 a0
LEIPSIC 158 ... arr	...	9 p24	10p46	...	...	11 p9	...	1a15	...	1a15
DRESD'N Hpt 188 ar	...	11p52	...	...	p.m.	1 a43	...	...	...	...
Sangerhausen ... dep	...	6 54	...	...	8 37	9 16	...	...	..	...
Mansfeld ...	...	7 22	...	...	9 1	9 58	...	...	...	...
Sandersleben ...	...	7 42	...	...	...	10 22	...	...	...	...
Gusten ...	...	8 3	...	...	9 32	10 39	...		...	...
Stadt-Calbe ...	...	8 20	...	...		...	...		...	...
Güterglück ...	...	8 44	...	p.m.		...	...		...	...
Belzig ...	...	9 28	...	9 50		...	...		...	...
Beelitz ...	...	...	...	10 29		...	...	†—Weekdays only.	...	...
Drewitz-Potsdam ...	...	RC	...	10 55	To Magdeburg (arr. 10.20).	...	...		...	...
Wannsee ...	...	10 13	...	11 6		...	...		...	...
BERLIN Charlottenburg arr	...	10 27	...	11 24		...	...		...	...
BERLIN Zoolog. Garten ,,	...	10 33	...			...	...		...	...
BERLIN Friedrichstrasse ,,	...	10 43	...	...		...	...		...	...
BERLIN Alexanderplatz ,,	...	10 53	...	...		...	...	...	...	...
BERLIN Schlesisch Bhf. ,,	...	10 59	...	...	...	...	...	...	...	...
BERLIN Potsdamer Bhf. ,,	...	...	...	...	...	...	...	...	...	...

Luggage Rates—see page 462.] [For Fares—see page 120A.

FRANKFORT, BEBRA, and GOTTINGEN.

Restaurant Car in trains marked RC **Sleeping Cars** to Berlin in 10.25 p.m. from Frankfort. **A**—To Hamburg (arr. 8.22 a.m.)

Dist E.M		2 3 4	2 3 4	2 3 4	Ex 3	2 3 4	Ex2	Ex3	1,2,3	1,2,3	1,2,3	2 3 4	Ex2	Ex 3	Ex3	2 3 4	Ex2	Ex 3	2 3 4	2 3 4	2 3 4	1,2,3	Ex3	2,3,4	Ex2	Ex2	Ex 2	Ex 3
	Frankfort—			a.m.	a.m.	a.m.	a.m.	a.m.	a.m.	a.m.		a.m.	p.m.		p.m.	p.m.	p.m.	p.m.	p.m.	p.m.	p.m.	p.m.		p.m.	p.m.	p.m.	p.m.	p.m.
—	Hauptbahnhof ...dep	...	...	4 54	6 4	6 33	8 23	9 40	9 48	9 58	...	1046	1253	From Munich (dep. 9.0.)	1 5	1 27	2 46	2 55	3 15	4 48	6 45	8 27	...	8 44	1016	1025	11 25	11 35
2¾	Sudbahnhof	...	...	5 2	RC	6 41	...	9 48	9 56	10 6	...	1055	...		1 13	1 35	RC	...	3 24	4 59	6 55	8 35	From Munich (dep. 4.25)	8 53	...	...	...	...
6¼	Offenbach	...	...	5 16	6 17	6 55	...	9 57	10 5	10 15	..	11 8	...		1 22	1 47	3 0	3 9	3 38	5 13	7 9	8 45		9 6	...	1039	11 40	...
14	**Hanau** Ost.........arr	...	...	5 37	6 30	7 16	...	1011	10 19	10 29	...	1129	...		1 36	2 7	3 14	...	3 58	5 35	7 30	8 59		9 28	D	1053	...	12 3
...	" ....dep	...	...	5 45	6 33	7 21	...	1012	10 21	10 31	...	1137	...		1 37	2 22	3 15	...	4 8	5 44	7 35	9 0		9 35	...	1055	...	12 5
21	Langenselbold	...	...	6 3	...	7 43	...	...	...	...	...	12 0	...		...	2 44	...	...	4 27	6 6	7 54	...		9 56	...	SC	...	...
27½	**Gelnhausen 147**	...	...	6 20	...	8 14	...	1033	10 42	10 52	...	1224	...		1 58	3 2	...	3 44	4 46	6 29	8 15	9 21		10 17	...	...	...	12 27
34	Wächtersbach	...	...	6 36	...	8 31	...	...	10 55	...	...	1245	...		2 11		...	...	5 3	6 47	8 31	9 34		10 34	...	1129	...	...
38½	Salmünster	...	...	6 46	...	8 41	...	...	...	11 10	...	1256	...	p.m.	...	...	...	...	5 13	6 59	8 41	9 44	p.m.	10 44	...	..	...	...
51	**Elm 149**	...	...	7 23	7 37	9 47	9 40	1120	11 33	11 45	...	1 46	2 17	2 35	2 53	...	4 18	4 35	5 56	7 57	9 26	10 18	1025	11 28	1157	1210	1 10	1 21
68½	**Fulda 149A** ......arr	a.m.	...	8 26	8 6	1028	...	1148	12 1	12 13	...	2 27	...	3 3	3 21	...	4 46	5 3	6 38	8 50	10 9		1054	12 11	...	1238	⋮	...
	" ....dep	4 55	...	8 31	8 8	1032	...	1149	12 4	12 15	...	2 30	...	3 4	3 22	...	4 48	5 4	6 43	9 25	1013	...	1055		D	1240	⋮	...
79	Hünfeld	5 22	...	9 0	...	11 1	...	...	...	12 35	...	3 7	...	...	3 42	p.m.	...	...	7 13	9 54	1042	...	1115	...	...	...	⋮	...
95¼	Hersfeld	6 1	...	9 39	...	1140	...	...	12 45	...	...	3 54	...	3 45	4 8	5 7	...	...	7 56	1034	1122	...	1140	...	...	1 20	⋮	...
103½	**Bebra**..............arr	6 25	...	10 0	8 59	12 2	1050	1240	1 0	1 11	...	4 14	3 38	4 0	4 23	5 30	5 39	5 55	8 18	1056	1146	...	1155	...	1 21	1 34	⋮	2 47
234½	HALLE **171** ....arr	...	...	1 p42	12 27	...	1p42	4p38	5 p27	...	...	8p16	6p51	8 p16	8p16	...	8p58	...	...	...	...	...	...	...	5 a2	5a14	⋮	
334¾	BERLIN **171**.........arr	...	...	3 p34	2 p39	...	3p34	6p42	8 p19	...	...	1038	8p55	10p38	1038	...	11p2	...	...	...	...	...	...	...	7a30	7a36	⋮	...
139½	CASSEL **173A** ......arr	8 a37	...	11a36	10 36	1p25	...	1p46	2 p42	...	...	...	5p11	5 p11	6p25	...	7p54	7 p54	1113	...	...	...	1 a9	...	...	2a41	⋮	...
239½	LEIPSIC **171**.........arr	...	...	3 p7	12 50		3 p7	4p28	6 p6	...	...	8 p9	8 p9	8 p9	8 p9	...	9p28	11p34	...	...	...	...	...	...	...	5a36	⋮	2,3,4
		a.m.	a.m.	a.m.					p.m.		p.m.			p.m.		p.m.		p.m.	p.m.	p.m.			n'gt					a.m.
...	**Bebra** ....dep	6 57	10 0	10 56	...	...	...	...	1 16	...	1 53	...	...	4 5	...	5 35	...	5 56	9 30	8 0	...	...	12 1	...	...	...	⋮	4 48
120½	Hoheneiche	7 39	10 43	11 39	...	...	...	...	...	...	2 34	...	2 3 4	...	...	6 15	...	...	1015	8 37	...	...	...	...	...	...	A	5 32
125¼	**Niederhone** ......arr	7 50	10 54	11 50	...	...	...	...	1 53	...	2 45	...	p.m.	4 41	...	6 26	...	6 33	1027	8 46	...	...	1238	...	...	...	⋮	5 44
	" **147** ......dep	7 53	11 12	11 56	...	...	...	...	1 54	...	2 49	...	3 25	4 42	...	6 54	...	6 34	1037	8 47	...	...	1238	...	...	...	⋮	5 53
132	Allendorf-a-W.	8 9	11 27	12 12	...	...	...	...	2 6	...	3 5	...	3 42	⋮	...	7 11	...	⋮	1055	8 59	...	...	⋮	...	...	...	⋮	6 9
141½	**Eichenberg** 148A arr	8 33	11 49	12 35	...	...	...	...	2 26	...	3 28	...	4 6	⋮	...	7 36	...	⋮	1122	9 18	...	...	⋮	...	...	...	⋮	6 31
210¼	SANGERHAUSEN...arr	11a37	1p46	3 p41	2 3 4	...	...	...	...	...	6 p33	...	6p45	⋮	...	10p4	1,2,3	⋮	...	...	...	...	⋮	...	...	...	⋮	9 a21
342	BERLIN ....arr	3 p34	4p56	8 p19	a.m.	...	...	...	...	...	10 38	...	1038	⋮	...	5 a0	p.m.	⋮	...	...	...	...	⋮	...	...	...	⋮	12 43
...	**Eichenberg** ......dep	8 41	12 10	12 43	10 18	...	...	...	2 36	...	3 31	...	4 50	⋮	...	7 49	6 51	⋮	1155	9 26	...	...	⋮	...	...	...	⋮	6 45
153½	**Gottingen** ....arr	9 10	12 40	1 12	10 46	...	...	...	2 53	...	4 0	...	5 17	5 23	...	8 18	7 8	7 15	1224	9 55	...	...	1 19	...	...	...	3 55	7 18
178	KREIENSEN **157** ...arr	11a59	1 p43	...	11 59	...	...	...	3 p35	...	6 p3	...	6 p3	6 p3	...	9p37	...	7 p54	1a59	...	...	...	1a59	...	...	...	...	8 a42
354½	BERLIN **164** ......arr	6 p54	...	...	6 p54	...	...	...	8 p56	...	...	...	1159	11p59	...	...	...	11p59	7a49	...	...	...	7a49	...	...	...	...	...

D—Will run until 16th July; and from 2nd August to 1st September.

Extra.—Frankfort to Gelnhausen, 7.57 a.m. and 6.18, 11.40 p.m.

ELM and GEMUNDEN.

Elm..............dep	4 a29	a.m.	7a32	7a50	12 0	2p57	4p38	6p33	10p39	...	*—Weekdays only.	...	**Gemunden** dep	6 a8	9 a56	11a57	1p34	2p51	7p31	9 p22	11p59	...	...
Jossa	...	5*4	8 0	8 31	1250	3 29	5 29	7 15	11 19	...		...	Burgsinn	6 25	10 13	12 19	...	3 9	7 53	...	...	...	...
Burgsinn	...	5 20	...	8 47	1 11	...	5 49	7 31	11 35	...		...	Jossa	6 45	10 31	12 48	2 2	3 30	8 17	9 50	...	...	...
Gemünden 196	5 20	5 33	8 26	9 4	1 31	3 53	6 8	7 50	11 52	...		...	**Elm** 149.........arr	7 29	11 16	1 41	2 33	4 12	9 8	10 19	12 56	...	...

ROSSLA and STOLBERG-ROTTLEBERODE.

Rossla ....dep	...	7a35	11a19	12p47	2p59	4 p36	7 p7	8p28	...	...	...	**Stolberg-Rottleberode**	7 a6	10a30	12p24	1p50	4p11	5p32	7p52	9p20	...	...	...	...
Berga-Kelbra	6a30	7 48	11 30	1 20	3 15	4 46	7 18	8 38	...	...	...	**Berga-Kelbra**	7 30	10 56	12 48	2 14	4 37	5 56	8 20	9 44	...	...	...	...
Stolberg-Rottleberode	6 54	8 15	11 57	1 44	3 42	5 10	7 42	9 2	...	...	...	Rossla (**148**).........arr	7 51	11 12	1 21	2 40	...	6 9	8 35	...	...	...	...	...

Luggage Rates—see page 462.] [For Fares—see page 120A.

GOTTINGEN, BEBRA, and FRANKFORT.

		Ex 3	Ex2	Ex.2	Ex2	Ex 3	1,2,3	2,3,4	2 3 4	2 3 4	Ex.3	2 3 4	2,3,4	Ex2	2,3,4	Ex3	Ex 3	2 3 4	Ex2	1,2,3	Ex 3	2,3,4	1,2,3	Ex2	2 3 4	2 3 4	Ex 3	2 3 4	2,3,4
BERLIN 165 ....dep		...	...	...	...	10p13	...	10p13	...	...	11p50	...	11p50	...	...	...	7 a7	...	...	...	...	...	8a35	...	...	...	...	...	3 p55
KREIENSEN ....dep		...	...	...	...	3 a44	...	3 a44	...	...	7 a30	...	7 a40	...	9 a49	...	11a32	...	...	...	...	...	2 p18	...	...	5 p10	...	7p12	10 p7
			a.m.			a.m.		a.m.	a.m.	a.m.	a.m.		a.m.		a.m.	a.m.	p.m.			p.m.		p.m.	p.m.		p.m.	p.m.		p.m.	p.m.
Gottingen ....dep		...	1 38	...	...	4 29	...	4 35	6 40	7 48	8 16	...	9 20	...	11 20	1158	12 14	...	...	12 46	...	1 49	3 7	...	5 13	6 25	...	8 36	11 12
Eichenberg ......arr		...	⋮	...	...	⋮	...	5 9	7 11	8 24	8 37	...	9 54	...	11 54	⋮	⋮	...	...	1 5	...	2 24	3 28	...	5 47	6 56	...	9 16	11 42
BERLIN ....dep		...	⋮	...	...	⋮	...	...	...	...	│	...	12 30	...	...	⋮	⋮	...	...	...	...	9 a5	9 a5	...	10a50	1 p45	...	...	3 p35
SANGERHAUSEN dep		...	B	...	...	⋮	...	...	...	...	│	...	7 a12	...	9 a9	C	⋮	...	...	...	...	12p20	12p20	...	2 p34	4 p57	...	...	8 p5
Eichenberg ......dep		...	⋮	...	...	⋮	...	5 16	7 12	8 42		...	10 22	...	1 13	⋮	⋮	...	...	...	...	2 35	3 29	...	6 7	6 59	...	9 26	11 55
Allendorf-a-W.		...	⋮	...	...	⋮	...	5 37	7 31	9 2		...	10 43	...	1 33	⋮	⋮	...	...	...	...	2 55	3 45	...	6 26	7 18	...	9 47	12 15
Niederhone ......arr		...	⋮	...	...	5 12	...	5 52	7 46	9 17	...	...	10 58	...	1 48	⋮	RC	...	...	...	...	3 10	3 57	...	6 40	7 31	...	10 2	12 30
" 147 ......dep		...	⋮	...	...	5 13	...	5 54	7 47	9 18	...	...	11 11	...		⋮	⋮	...	...	...	...	3 28	3 58	...	6 43	7 32	...	1018	
Hoheneiche		...	⋮	...	...	...	...	6 6	8 0	9 30	...	...	11 24	...	...	⋮	⋮	...	...	...	...	3 41	...	...	6 56	7 42	...	1031	...
Bebra 170 ....arr		...	⋮	...	...	5 50	...	6 49	8 40	10 9	Ex 3	...	12 5	...	...	1 12	1 28	...	...	...	...	4 22	4 38	...	7 37	8 26	...	1113	...
LEIPSIC ....dep		10p45	⋮	11p50	...	...	...	...	...	...	6 a15	...		9a15	...	9a15	9 a15	...	9a15	...	12p40	12p40	12p40	...	...	...	5 p5	...	...
CASSEL ....dep		...	⋮	2 a57	...	4 a35	...	5 a5	...	...	8 a26	...	11a11	1118	...	1118	...	...	12p7	...	2p44	3 p45	3p45	...	6 p48	...	7 p34	...	...
BERLIN ....dep		...	⋮	10p15	1040	...	...	...	...	...	12a30	...	...	8 a0	...	8 a0	8 a0	...	9 a5	...	10a30	10a30	10a30	2p15	...	...	3 p35	...	...
HALLE ....dep		...	⋮	12a19	1246	...	...	...	...	...	5 a48	...	...	9a54	...	9a54	9 a54	...	11a9	...	12p34	12p34	12p34	4 p7	...	...	5 p29	...	...
		a.m.		a.m.	a.m.	a.m.	a.m.	a.m.			a.m.	a.m.	p.m.	p.m.		p.m	p.m.	p.m.	p.m.	p.m.	p.m.	p.m.	p.m.	p m.	p.m.		p.m.	p.m.	a.m.
Bebra ....dep	...	2 21	⋮	4 1	4 22	5 58	6 25	7 13	...	...	10 14	1027	12 22	1 8	...	1 17	1 34	1 50	2 19	4 9	4 40	5 1	4 55	7 2	7 59	...	9 0	9 53	1 27
Hersfeld	...	...	⋮	...	...	6 12	6 47	7 38	...	...	10 29	1049	12 43	...	...	...	...	2 14	...	4 23	...	5 27	5 9	...	8 25	...	RC	1015	1 50
Hünfeld	2 3 4	...	⋮	...	A	6 37		8 19	...	...	10 34	1126	1 22	...	...	...	...	3 8	...	4 48	...	6 11	5 34	...	9 3	...	...	1057	2 28
Fulda ....arr	a.m.	...	⋮	4 52	...	6 56	...	8 48	a.m.	...	11 12	1152	1 49	...	p.m.	2 6	2 23	3 36	...	5 7	5 31	6 42	5 53	...	9 29	...	9 49	1126	2 54
" ....dep	4 32	...	⋮	4 54	...	6 57	a.m.	8 51	6 35	...	11 15	12 0		...	2 31	2 7	2 24	3 41	...	5 8	5 33	6 47	5 55	...	9 37	...	9 50		2 56
Elm	5 36	3 39	4 29	5 30	5 46	7 29	7 34	9 44	7 42	...	11 49	1250	...	2 29	3 15	2 41	2 52	4 31	3 42	5 44	6 11	7 38	6 31	8 16	10 35	...	10 23	...	3 56
Salmünster	6 3	...	...	...	...	To Munich (arr. 2.0.)	8 1	10 18	8 13	...	...	1 21	...	...	3 45	...	To Munich (arr. 8.55)	5 1	...	6 4	...	8 9	6 51	...	11 5	...	...	...	4 28
Wächtersbach	6 21	...	...	5 56	...		8 11	10 28	8 23	a.m.	12 19	1 31	p.m.	RC	3 54	RC		5 10	...	6 13	...	8 20	7 0	...	11 15	...	...	a.m.	4 39
Gelnhausen	6 35	...	...	...	...		8 25	10 46	8 41	9 55	12 32	1 49	3 20	...	4 18	3 15		5 26	...	6 25	...	8 49	7 12	...	11 33	...	...	5 17	5 4
Langenselbold	6 53	...	...	...	...		...	11 6	9 1	10 14	...	2 9	3 40	...	4 36	...		5 43	...	...	...	9 8	...	...	11 53	...	...	5 38	5 23
Hanau Ost ...arr	7 12	...	...	6 24	...		8 45	11 27	9 19	10 32	12 53	2 29	4 0	3 18	4 55	...		6 1	...	6 45	7 0	9 29	7 31	...	12 12	...	11 12	6 0	5 43
" ....dep	7 18	...	...	6 26	...		8 46	11 36	9 29	10 50	12 55	2 33	4 3	3 19	5 5	...		6 5	...	6 46	7 2	9 37	7 33	...	12 23	...	11 13	6 33	5 46
Offenbach	7 42	...	5 29	6 40	...		9 1	12 0	9 54	11 15	1 9	2 55	4 25	3 33	5 28	3 46		6 28	4 41	7 0	7 17	10 5	7 47	...	12 48	...	11 27	7 2	6 9
Frankfort Sud.	7 53	...	...	...	...		9 10	12 11	10 8	11 26	1 17	3 8	4 36	...	5 39	...		6 39	...	7 8	7 26	10 16	7 55	...	12 59	...	...	7 17	6 20
" Haupt.	8 2	5 6	5 42	6 53	7 4	...	9 20	12 21	1019	11 35	1 27	3 20	4 44	3 46	5 49	3 59	...	6 49	4 54	7 18	7 36	10 26	8 5	9 23	1 10	...	11 40	7 25	6 30

A—Will run until 16th July; and from 2nd August to 1st September.
B—From Hamburg (dep. 9.27 p.m.).
C—From Hamburg (dep. 7.18).

Extra. { Gottingen...dep 4 p5 / Eichenberg arr 4 40

GIESSEN and FULDA.

		a.m.	a.m.		p.m.	p m	p.m.		p m	p.m.		
Giessen ....dep	...	5 37	8 11	...	12 8	2 16	3 33	...	5 52	9 21	...	...
Grünberg..............	...	6 19	8 51	...	12 45	2 44	4 12	...	6 36	9 56	...	...
Mücke	...	6 27	8 59	...	12 53	2 52	4 22	...	6 46	10 4	...	...
Burggemünden......	a.m.	6 41	9 12	...	1 6	3 4	4 38	...	7 2	10 18	...	...
Alsfeld	5 18	7 14	9 48	p.m.	1 37	3 36	5 9	p.m.	7 42	10 50	...	...
Lauterbach	5 49	7 44	1018	12 6	2 4	3 59	5 36	7 34	8 20	11 19	...	...
Bad Salzschlirf......	6 2	7 58	1033	12 22	2 17	4 8	5 50	7 48	8 34	11 32	...	...
Fulda 149 ....arr	6 30	8 25	11 1	1 0	2 49	4 31	6 17	...	9 4	11 59	...	...

	a m	a.m.	a.m.	p.m.	p.m.	p.m.	p.m.	p m	p.m.	p.m.			
Fulda ....dep	5 1	7 1	8 53	12 12	2 1	2 33	5 18	6 49	...	11 2	...	...	...
Bad Salzschlirf......	5 34	7 30	9 24	12 47	2 37	3 0	5 49	7 19	7 58	11 33	...	...	...
Lauterbach	5 50	7 45	9 39	1 3	2 48	3 10	6 1	7 36	8 10	11 46	...	...	...
Alsfeld	6 21	8 14	10 13	1 37		3 38	6 30	8 8		12 14	...	...	...
Burggemünden	6 57	8 44	10 46	2 5	...	4 9	7 2	8 45	...		...	...	...
Mücke	7 11	9 0	11 2	2 19	...	4 23	7 16	9 3	...	...	...	...	...
Grünberg..............	7 21	9 8	11 12	2 27	...	4 32	7 26	9 14	...	...	...	...	...
Giessen 133B ...arr	7 58	9 46	11 51	3 4	...	4 58	8 2	9 51	...	...	...	...	...

Grünberg ......dep	...	4a†40	...	7a32	12p52	4 p45	6†p10	7†35	10 p2	...	...
Londorf..............	4a40	5 12	6a†50	8 13	1 23	5 26	7 33	8 p8	10 42	...	...
Lollar ....arr	5 14	5 46	7 30	8 53	1 57	6 5	...	8 42	11 17	...	...

Lollar ....dep	5a55	9 a40	2p28	6†p10	7 p4	9p55	...	...
Londorf	6 33	10 17	3 5	6 47	7 37	1030	...	...
Grünberg ....arr	7 10	10 51	3 39	7 22	8 44	...	...	...

†—Weekdays only.

Bad Salzschlirf dep	6a15	9 a28	11 a0	2p41	4p10	5p53	8 p40	...	...	...	...
Schlitz..............arr	6 47	9 54	11 32	3 13	4 42	6 25	9 11	...	...	...	...

Schlitz ....dep	4a57	8 a44	10 a2	1 p39	3 p19	5 p5	6 p38	...	...	...	...
Bad Salzschlirf ......arr	5 29	9 16	10 28	2 10	3 51	5 37	7 10	...	...	...	...

FRANKFORT (Hauptbahnhof) and HOMBURG BAD.

*—Saturday dep. 4.30 p.m.

Station																				
WIESBADEN 128 ...dep	...	4a23	5a30	5a41	6a56	7a30	...	9 a9	9a16	10a59	11 a7	11 a7	11a47	...	1245	1p32	2p35	2 p57	...	3 p20
Frankfort Haupt. dep	4a53	5a48	6a22	7 a0	8 a7	8a20	9a15	...	10a40	...	12p18	12p24	12p44	1p20	1p50	2p45	3p21	:	3p51	4 *43
Rodelheim	5 7	6 7	6 36	7 16	...	8 34	9 29	...	10 54	11 42	...	12 39	12 58	1 34	1 59	3 1	...	:	4 4	4 57
Oberursel	5 29	6 30	6 55	7 38	8 28	8 55	9 50		11 15	11 57	12 39	1 0	1 19	1 55	2 14	3 25	3 41	3 49	4 24	5 18
Homburg Bad ...arr	5 36	6 37	7 1	7 45	8 34	9 1	9 56	10 5	11 21	12 3	12 45	1 6	1 25	2 1	2 20	3 31	3 47	3 55	4 30	5 24

Station																			
WIESBADEN 128A dep	...	4p55	5p46	...	5p10	5 p46	...	7 p12	7 p12	9 p10	9p27	10p11	11p20	11p20	...	...	...	...	...
Frankfort Haupt. dep	5p35	6 p0	:	6‡p19	6p32	7 p15	7p25	8p24	8 p29	10 p7	...	11 p8	...	12a21	...	...	...	...	...
Rodelheim	5 49	...	6 31	6 41	6 47	...	7 41	...	8 43	10 21	10 11	11 17	12 5	12 35	...	...	...	...	...
Oberursel	6 10	6 21	6 46	7 2	7 9	7 36	8 3	8 47	9 4	10 42	10 26	11 37	12 20	12 56	...	...	...	...	...
Homburg Bad ...arr	6 16	6 27	6 52	7 8	7 15	7 42	8 9	8 53	9 10	10 48	10 32	11 43	12 26	1 2	...	...	...	...	...

Station																				
Homburg Bad dep	4a44	5†a2	5†a53	6†a3	6a20	6a55	7a16	7a32	7a40	8a32	9 a2	9 a26	10a40	11a53	12p19	12 57	1p26	1 p49	2 p6	2 p59
Oberursel	4 53	5 10	6 3	6 13	6 28	7 4	7 24	7 39	7 48	8 39	9 10	9 34	10 48	12 1	12 25	1 6	1 34	:	2 15	3 7
Rodelheim	5 9	5 27	6 22	6 29	6 44	7 20	...	7 50	8 4	8 53	...	9 50	11 3	12 12	12 37	1 21	1 49	:	2 30	...
Frankfort Hpt. arr	5 23	5 41	6 33	...	6 58	7 36	7 43	:	8 18	9 [illegible]	9 29	10 4	11 17	12 22	...	1 35	2 3	:	2 44	3 26
WIESBADEN 129 arr	...	7a39	8 a4	...	8 a4	8a51	8a51	9a40	9a44	...	10a51	11a36	1 p4	1 p13	1 p26	3p10	3p10	2 p50	3p34	5 p8

Station																
Homburg Bad ...dep	4 p1	5 p9	5p52	5 p59	6 p42	7 p5	7p20	7p50	8 p38	9p13	9p37	10 p1	10p10	11 p5	...	†—Weekdays only.
Oberursel	4 9	5 17	:	6 7	6 51	7 12	7 29	7 59	8 48	9 21	9 45	10 8	10 19	11 13	...	‡—Weekdays only;
Rodelheim	4 24	...	:	6 24	7 6	7 23	7 44	8 15	9 3	9 36	9 56	10 19	10 34	11 28	...	dep. Frankfort
Frankfort Hpt. ...arr	4 40	5 36	:	6 38	7 20	:	7 58	8 31	9 17	9 50	10 6	:	10 48	11 38	...	Sudbhf.
WIESBADEN 129A arr	5p5[illegible]	7p24	6p52	8 p8	8 p20	8 8	9 p4	9p54	10 17	...	1p49	11 p6	11p49	1a11	...	

HOMBURG BAD and FRIEDBERG.

†—Weekdays only.]

Station	a.m.	a.m.	a.m.	a.m.	a.m.	a.m.	p.m.	p.m.	p.m.	p.m.	p.m.	p.m.	p.m.	p.m.	p.m.	p.m.	
Homburg Bad ......dep	4†52	5†10	5 49	6 43	8 37	1124	12 7	2 53	3 59	5 28	6 30	7†19	7†46	8 16	10 36	11 7	...
Friedrichsdorf	5 2	5 21	5 58	6 53	8 48	1134	...	3 3	4 6	5 40	6 44	7 31	7 57	8 27	...	11 17	...
Rosbach	5 19	5 38	6 16	7 11	9 6	1151	...	3 20	...	6 3	7 3	7 48	8 15	8 47	...	11 32	...
Friedberg ......arr	5 29	...	6 26	7 21	9 16	12 1	12 28	3 30	4 21	6 13	7 13	7 58	...	8 57	10 57	11 42	...

Station	a.m.	a.m.	a.m.	a.m.	a.m.	a.m.	a.m.	p.m.	p.m.	p.m.	p.m.	p.m	p.m.	p.m.	p.m.				
Friedberg ......dep	4 16	5 3	5 47	...	7 53	9 59	11 54	12 45	1 20	3 15	4 28	6 40	6 55	8 29	10 19	...	...	...	...
Rosbach	4 27	5 14	6 1	6†45	8 3	10 10	...	12 56	...	3 28	4 38	...	7 9	8 40	10 30	...	...	...	...
Friedrichsdorf	4 47	5 31	6 25	7 2	8 20	10 27	...	1 12	1 38	3 48	4 54	...	7 32	8 58	10 47	...	...	...	...
Homburg Bad ......arr	4 57	5 39	6 35	7 12	8 29	10 36	12 15	1 21	1 45	3 57	5 3	7 1	7 42	9 8	10 57	...	...	...	...

HOMBURG BAD and USINGEN.

‡—Weekdays only.

Station										
Homburg	4‡37	7 a5	10a22	12p26	1p35	4p33	6p30	7p19	10p52	...
Friedrichsdorf	4 47	7 15	10 33	12 40	1 46	4 44	6 42	7 35	11 2	...
Wehrheim ...	5 15	7 39	10 57	1 6	2 14	5 10	7 8	8 2	11 28	...
Usingen 147	5 35	7 58	11 17	1 26	2 33	5 2[illegible]	7 30	8 22	11 47	...

Station										
Usingen ...	4‡a49	5a51	8 a6	11a58	1p51	2p48	5p44	7p40	8p58	...
Wehrheim ...	5 16	6 13	8 27	12 18	2 15	3 12	6 6	8 3	9 23	...
Friedrichsdorf	5 37	6 35	8 46	12 41	2 39	3 34	5 28	8 24	9 48	...
Homburg	5 47	6 45	8 56	12 50	2 50	3 44	6 38	8 34	9 58	...

FRANKFORT (Hauptbahnhof) and SODEN.

*—Not on Sunday.]

Station																			
Frankfort ......dep	5*a1	5 a59	7a12	7 a12	8 a32	8 a48	10 a1	11a48	...	12p50	1 p26	2p40	4p14	5 p28	6p31	7p41	8 p23	9p18	11p26
Hochst	5 34	6 29	7 27	7 42	8 49	9 8	10 19	12 8	12p28	1 10	2 0	3 0	4 29	5 48	6 46	7 56	8 40	9 44	11 41
Soden ......arr	5 50	6 45	7 43	7 59	9 7	9 25	10 40	12 24	12 45	1 25	2 16	3 16	4 45	6 4	7 3	8 12	8 56	10 3	11 57
Soden ......dep	4*a52	5a57	6a53	7*a49	8 a5	9 a12	9 a39	10a55	12p34	12p48	1 p30	2p22	3 p2	4 p53	6 p11	7 p8	8 p18	9 p5	10p46
Hochst	5 13	6 19	7 17	8 13	8 29	9 33	10 0	11 20	12 51	1 8	1 53	2 41	3 49	5 15	6 34	7 33	8 34	9 37	11 5
Frankfort ......arr	5 32	6 38	7 31	8 32	8 48	9 46	10 18	11 33	...	1 21	2 5	2 54	4 7	5 34	6 53	7 52	9 17	9 50	11 30

HOCHST and KONIGSTEIN.

*—Weekdays only.

Station																
FRANKFORT Haupt. dep	5 a1	6a14	7a12	845	9a52	11a36	1p21	2p38	4 p2	5 p3	5p28	6p30	7p30	8p25	9p18	11p11
Hochst ......dep	5*24	6 41	7 40	9 8	1017	12 10	1 46	3 0	4 35	5 45	5*53	6 50	7 53	8 56	9 48	11 40
Königstein ......arr	6 15	7 21	8 20	942	1054	12 51	2 20	3 38	5 12	6 19	6 32	7 32	8 37	9 34	1022	12 1
Königstein ......dep	5 a0	6 a32	7a47	8 a28	10 a0	12p15	1p10	3 p2	4p34	5 p48	6 p46	7p50	9 p0	10p31	...	
Hochst ......arr	5 47	7 9	8 21	9 2	10 36	12 56	1 45	3 41	5 10	6 24	7 25	8 23	9 33	11 5	...	
FRANKFORT Haupt. arr	6 38	7 32	8 48	9 53	11 4	1 46	2 16	4 7	5 31	6 53	7 52	8 44	9 57	11 30	...	

RODELHEIM and CRONBERG.

†—Weekdays only.]

Station	a.m.	a.m.	a.m.	a.m.	a.m.	p.m.	p.m.	p.m.	p.m.	p.m.	p.m.	p.m.	p.m.	p.m.	p.m.	p.m.	p.m.			
FRANKFORT 150	5 48	7 8	8 27	9 40	1051	12 30	1 28	2 25	3 29	5 12	6 10	6 45	7 †25	8 15	9 43	10 44	11 57	...	...	...
Rodelheim dep	6 3	7 23	8 41	9 54	11 5	12 44	1 42	2 39	3 43	...	6 23	6 59	7 44	8 29	9 57	10 58	12 11	...	...	...
Eschborn	6 11	7 32	8 50	10 3	1113	12 53	1 51	2 48	3 52	5 28	6 32	7 8	7 53	8 38	10 6	11 6	12 19	...	...	...
Cronberg......arr	6 22	7 44	9 2	10 15	1125	1 5	2 3	3 0	4 4	5 40	6 44	7 20	8 5	8 50	10 18	11 17	12 30	...	...	...

Station	a.m.	a.m.	a.m.	a.m.	a.m.	a.m.	a.m.	p.m.	p.m.	p.m.	p.m.	p.m.	p.m.	p.m.	p.m.	p.m.
Cronberg ...dep	4 44	5 42	6 31	7†21	8 22	9 15	10 28	12 9	1 20	2 17	3 18	4 28	5 56	7 40	9 10	10 37
Eschborn	4 56	5 55	6 44	7 32	...	9 28	10 41	12 21	1 33	2 30	3 29	4 41	6 9	7 53	9 23	10 50
Rodelheim...arr	5 4	6 3	6 52	7 40	...	9 36	10 49	12 29	1 41	2 38	3 37	4 49	6 17	8 1	9 31	10 58
FRANKFORT arr	5 23	6 21	7 7	7 55	8 48	9 51	11 4	12 44	1 57	2 54	3 52	5 4	6 32	8 16	9 46	11 13

FULDA and GERSFELD.

Station						
Fulda ......dep	7 a6	12 p7	3p48	6p55	10 p2	...
Welkers	7 29	12 29	4 10	7 19	10 24	...
Gersfeld ...arr	8 12	1 7	4 52	8 1	11 6	...

Station					
Gersfeld......dep	5 a3	9 a55	1 p16	5 p33	8pl
Welkers	5 45	10 37	1 55	6 10	8 5
Fulda (149) ......arr	6 8	11 0	2 16	6 31	9 14

FULDA and TANN.

E.M.	Station						
	Fulda dep	...	7 a44	11a56	4 p0	6p52	9p35
10¼	Bieberstein	...	8 21	12 31	4 48	7 30	10 13
19¾	Hilders	7 a0	8 55	1 2	5 20	7 56	10 49
25½	**Tann** ...arr	7 22	9 17	1 22	5 59	8 47	11 11

Station							
Tann ...dep	4a31	5a43	9 a25	1 p32	4 p50	7 p24	...
Hilders	5 0	6 6	9 51	1 58	5 28	7 44	8 p8
Bieberstein	5 32	—	10 21	2 26	5 59	—	8 40
Fulda ...arr	6 15	...	11 0	3 2	6 37	...	9 18

OBER-ROBLINGEN and VITZENBURG.

Station										
Röblingen ...dep		6a11	9a48	...	1 p5	3p43	7 p5	...	11p8	12a52
Querfurt	5a30	7 43	1039	12p48	1 54	4 43	7 47	8 p28	1150	1 41
Vitzenburg	6 10	8 30	...	1 35	...	5 30	...	9 15	...	...

Station								
Vitzenburg dep	...	6a45	1010	...	2p25	...	6 p0	10 p0
Querfurt	4a50	8 25	1155	2 p5	3 15	5p40	6 50	10 43
Röblingen...arr	5 35	9 2	1231	2 50	...	6 27	9 47	12 36

BREMEN and WILHELMSHAVEN.

Bremen	Ex3 a.m.	Ex3 a.m.	1—4 a.m.	Ex3 a.m.	1—4 a.m.	1—4 a.m	2—4 a.m.	1—4 p.m.	Ex3 p.m.	Ex3 p.m.	2 3 4 p.m.	1—4 p.m.	Ex3 p.m.	2—4 p.m.	1—4 p.m.	2—4 p.m.	Ex3 p.m.	2 3 4 a.m.	
Haupt dep	5 22	5 58	6 23	7 28	7 40	10 8	1155	1 12	1 53	2 11	3*38	5 5	6 15	6 50	8 32	...	1128	12 2	...
Neustadt..	...	...	6 30	...	7 49	1015	12 5	1 22	1 59	...	3 44	5 16	...	7 2	8 40	10 5	...	12 9	...
Delmenhorst	‡	6 16	6 50	7 44	8 12	1031	1227	1 45	2 14	...	4 4	5 39	6 34	7 25	9 4	10 30	1145	1231	‡—Until August 18th.
Hude......arr	...	...	7 13	To Blexen.	8 34	1050	1249	2 9	2 30	...	4 25	6 1	6 48	7 49	9 26		...	1254	
,, ...dep	...	...	7 17		8 36	1052	1251	2 14	2 31	...	4 27	6 5	6 49	7 54	9 30	...	...		
Olden- arr	6 8	6 43	7 41		8 58	1110	1 15	2 38	2 48	2 58	4 50	6 27	7 6	8 18	9 52	...	1215	...	
burg...dep	—	7 2	8 0		—	1128	—	3 6	2 54	—	—	7 23	7 16	—	10 8	...	—	...	
Rastede	...	...	8 19		...	1150	...	3 25	...	...	*—Not on Sunday.	7 42	...	...	1029	...	...	...	
Varel		7 34	8 47		...	1218	p.m.	3 56	3 24	...		8 11	7 46	...	11 0	...	...	...	
Ellenserdam		...	9 1	...	...	1233	3 9	4 10	...	...		8 26	...	...	1114	...	...	...	
Sande		7 51	9 14	...	...	1247	3 20	4 23	...	...		8 38	8 1	...	1128	...	...	...	...
Wilhelmshaven		8 1	9 29	...	...	1 3	3 38	4 38	3 49	...		8 53	8 11	...	1144	...	...	...	...

	2—4	Ex3 a.m.	1—4 a.m.	2 3 4	1—4	1,2,3 a.m.	Ex3	Ex3	1,2,3 p.m.	1,2,3 p.m.	2 3 4	Ex3	1—4 p.m.	2 3 4	2—4 p.m.	1—4 p.m.	Ex3 p.m.
Wilhelmshaven dep	...	6 0	6 18	...	...	9 49	...	...	1234	1 21	...	...	3 45	...	5 58	7 50	9 53
Sande	...	6 11	6 38	...	...	10 6	...	...	1255	...	...	...	4 5	...	6 16	8 11	10 4
Ellenserdam...	...	...	6 47	...	...	10 15	...	...	1 5	...	...	...	4 14	...	6 27	8 21	...
Varel...	...	6 26	7 2	...	...	10 29	...	...	1 20	1 45	...	...	4 29	...	—	8 37	1019
Rastede	...	...	7 30	...	...	10 56	...	...	1 48	...	...	...	4 57	...	...	9 6	...
Olden- ...arr	a.m.	6 53	7 50	...	a.m.	11 9	p.m.	p.m.	2 4	2 13	p.m.	p.m.	5 15	p.m.	...	9 20	1048
burg...dep	6 18	7 0	8 4	...	10 20	11 27	1 54	2 15	2 30	2 21	3*42	5 28	6 8	7 39	...	9 35	1056
Hude.........arr	6 41	7 17	8 27	...	10 45	11 49	...	...	2 56	2 39	4 5	5 46	6 34	8 0	...	9 58	...
,, ...dep	6 43	7 19	8 30	a.m.	10 49	11 50	...	...	3 1	2 42	4 6	5 47	6 36	8 3	p.m.	10 3	...
Delmenhorst...	7 7	7 36	8 55	10 0	11 18	12 7	A	...	3 28	2 59	4 30	6 3	7 2	8 29	9 5	1028	1128
Bremen Neu.	7 27	...	9 14	1023	11 40	12 22	...	...	3 52	...	4 49	...	7 23	8 50	9 28	1048	...
Bremen Haupt	...	7 52	9 19	1029	11 45	12 26	2 43	3 1	3 58	3 16	...	6 21	7 28	8 55	...	1054	1144

A—From 25th July to 18th August.

OLDENBURG and BRAKE.

Oldenburg dep	8a22	11a27	2p54	6p30	9p57
Brake ......arr	9 19	12 32	3 50	7 34	11 0
Brake ......dep	6a43	9 a57	1p16	4p14	8p25
Oldenburg arr	7 47	11 1	2 13	5 20	9 28

AHLHORN and VECHTA.

E.M.					
	Ahlhorn. dep	9 a2	1p35	3p49	8p22
12	Falkenrott ...	9 40	2 17	4 29	9 2
12½	Vechta ....arr	9 43	2 20	4 32	9 5

Vechta ....dep	7a55	12p22	2 p48	7 p25
Falkenrott	7 59	12 26	2 52	7 29
Ahlhorn 151 ...arr	8 38	1 4	3 30	8 7

‡—Weekdays only.

WITTMUND and WILHELMSHAVEN.

	a.m.	a.m.	a.m.	a.m.	p.m.		p.m.		p.m.	p.m.
Wittmund dep	...	...	9 4	1155	3 4	...	...	...	6 52	8 55
Jever	5 54	8 33	9 28	1215	3 26	...	7‡21	...	7 31	9 24
Sande ......arr	6 27	9 1	9 58	1242	3 53	p.m.	7 42	p.m.	7 58	9 51
,, ...dep	6 35	9 14	1010	1247	4 7	6 20	—	8 1	8 12	10 4
Wilhelmsha'n	6 54	9 29	1028	1 3	4 25	6 38	...	8 11	8 30	1022

	a.m	a.m.	a.m.	p.m.	p m.	p m.	p.m.		p.m.		
Wilhelmshaven dep	6 55	...	8 48	1234	4 2	5‡50	6 ‡6	...	8 18	1110	...
Sande arr	7 13	...	9 6	1250	4 21	6 8	6 24	p.m.	8 36	1128	...
,, dep	7 18	7‡53	9 19	1 0	4 31	—	6 28	8 4	8 47	1140	...
Jever	7 52	8 23	10 0	1 42	5 12	...	7 0	8 25	9 26	1212	...
Wittmund	8 6	...	1017	1 56	5 26	...	...	...	9 40	...	...

†—Weekdays only.

HUDE and BLEXEN.

E.M.									
	Hude (151)...dep	7a22	...	8a46	11a52	3 p2	6p52	9 p34	10 p5
—	Brake	8 7	8a27	9 33	12 41	3 57	7 45	10 7	11 5
16	Nordenhamm	8 40	8 51	1014	1 20	4 49	8 24	10 30	11 40
27½	Blexen ....arr	...	9 8	1031	1 37	5 6	8 41	10 47	...

Blexen...dep	a.m.	6a29	8a59	10a31	11a55	1p45	4p26	p.m.	7p13
Nordenhamm	5 42	6 52	9 19	10 49	12 28	2 4	4 48	5 6	7 40
Brake	6 23	7 29	9 58	11 11	1 18	—	5 9	5 43	8 23
Hude ......arr	7 7	8 21	1042	11 41	2 6	...	5 40	6 27	9 12

Extra. {Nordenhamm to Blexen 6.5, 7†15, 8.30 a.m., 12†18, 2†5, 3†15, 5.52, 6.47 p.m.
{Blexen to Nordenhamm 7†48 a.m., 12†40, 5.25, 6.17, 8.47, 11.5 p.m.

†—Until Aug. 18th.

OLDENBURG and NEUSCHANZ.

[§—From 16th Sept.

Oldenburg dep	6a19	6a55	7a57	11a19	3 p3	3p10	7 p9	7p18	10p10
Zwischenahn..	...	...	8 22	11 40	...	3 35	7 25	7 37	10 35
Ocholt	†	‡	8 34	11 51	...	3 47	...	7 49	10 47
Stickhausen....	...	...	8 58	12 13	...	4 15	‡	8 14	11 13
Leer 133A 7a51	7 13	7 47	1010	1 10	4 16	4 49	8 3	8 44	11 46
Ihrhove ...8 2	—	—	1024	1 22	...	5 2	—	9 3	11 58
Weener 8 18	...	...	1041	1 40	4 36	5 20	...	9 19	12 14
Neuschanz¶833	...	...	1056	1 58	4 41	5 36	...	9 35	12 29

Neuschanz...dep	4a46	6a41	8a55	11a18	...	3p14	6p34	9‡p4	9 §46
Weener ¶	5 19	7 1	9 22	11 44	...	3 39	7 7	9 28	10 10
Ihrhove.......a.m.	5 35	7 16	9 39	12 0	...	3 54	7 24	...	10 25
Leer dep5 58	6 9	7 26	9 54	12 40	1p17	4 8	7 46	9 57	10 35
Stickhausen ...	6 33	—	1018	1 4	...	4 30	8 13	...	—
Ocholt ...	6 59	...	1042	1 29	...	4 52	8 39	...	...
Zwischenahn6 35	7 11	...	1053	1 41	...	5 2	8 51	...	...
Oldenburg...6 50	7 39	...	1113	2 3	2 16	5 20	9 11	1050	...

‡—Until 15th Sept.
¶—Customs Exam.

HERZLAKE and QUAKENBRUCK.

Herzlake ....dep	6 a18	8a29	...	1 p43	5 p12	9 p6
Lewinghausen	6 29	8 40	...	1 54	5 25	9 17
Löningen	6 55	9 2	11a42	2 19	6 21	9 35
Essen	7 37	9 39	12 14	3 4	6 56	—
Quakenbruck ...arr	7 49	9 56	12 22	3 18	7 10	...

Quakenbruck dep	...	8 a3	...	12p40	4 p8	8p43
Essen	...	8 20	9 a49	12 52	4 35	9 9
Löningen	5 a6	9 0	10 22	1 19	5 8	9 48
Lewinghausen	5 23	9 19	...	1 34	5 26	10 7
Herzlake.. 134 arr	5 33	9 29	...	1 42	5 36	10 17

OLDENBURG and OSNABRUCK.

		a.m.		a.m.		a.m	a.m.	p.m.		p.m.
Oldenburg ....dep	...	6 55	...	8 11	...	1120	1132	2 55	...	7 30
Ahlhorn 151	...	...	...	8 56	...	...	1223	3 44	...	8 20
Cloppenburg	a.m.	7 33	...	9 16	...	1158	—	4 5	...	8 42
Quakenbrück 131A	6 10	8 2	a.m.	10 0	a.m.	1223	...	4 39	p.m	9 20
Bramsche	7 7	8 42	8 58	10 42	1125	1259	2p26	5 26	6 35	1046
Osnabrück 156A arr	7 44	9 3	9 32	11 7	1159	1 18	2 59	5 42	7 12	1117

Osnabrück		a.m.	a.m.	a.m.	p.m.	p.m.	p.m.	p.m.	p.m.	n'gt
(Haupt. Bahnf) dep		6 35	8 23	1127	1 47	5 10	6 6	8 50	9 8	1210
Bramsche	a.m.	7 11	9 3	1158	2 12	5 44	6 34	9 21	9 30	1242
Quakenbrück	5 20	8 3	1015	1240	2 55	—	7 21	—	10 4	1 23
Cloppenburg	6 29	8 40	—	1 14	3 28	...	7 56	...	1030	—
Ahlhorn	6 51	9 0	...	1 31	3 46	...	8 16	...	...	...
Oldenburg arr	7 45	9 38	...	2 8	4 23	...	8 56	...	1110	...

Cloppenburg...dep	...	9a25	‡	*	4p10	...	8p45
Friesoythe	5a40	1014	1143	12p6	4 59	6p27	9 34
Scharrel	6 4	—	12 7	1230	—	6 51	—
Ocholt ....arr	6 51	...	1256	1 19	...	7 38	...

Ocholt............dep	...	8a36	...	3p51	...	8p41
Scharrel	...	9 24	...	4 39	...	9 29
Friesoythe	7a40	9 47	10a56	5 2	6p53	9 52
Cloppenburg ...arr	8 29	...	11 45	...	7 42	...

*—Until 24th July and from 19th Aug.
‡—From 25th July until 18th August.

JEVER and CAROLINENSIEL.

Jever............dep	8a25	9a58	1p44	5p10	9p23	...	...
Carolinensiel arr	9 6	1039	2 25	5 51	10 4	...	...

Carolinensiel dep	7 a2	8a33	11a23	2p34	6p30	8p20	...	...
Jever (151) ...arr	7 42	9 15	12 4	3 15	7 11	9 1	...	...

DELMENHORST and BRAMSCHE.

Delmenhorst dep		...	8a12	...	12p28	3 p2	7 p30	10p34
Wildeshausen		6a36	9 0	...	1 17	3 55	8 27	11 21
Falkenrott		7 18	9 44	a.m.	1 59	4 43	9 11	—
Vechta	5 a 5	7 22	9 51	1128	2 3	4 51	9 17	...
Lohne ....arr	5 17	7 36	10 5	1142	2 19	5 7	9 32	...
,, ...dep	5 25	7 40	10 7	1143	—	5 10	9 34	...
Holdorf	5 47	8 7	10 34	12 8	...	5 38	10 1	...
Bramsche...arr	6 58	8 49	11 15	1252	...	6 21	10 43	...

Bramsche ... dep	...	...	7 a24	...	12p29	2p29	5 p47	9p40
Holdorf	...	7 a4	8 12	...	1 4	3 11	6 32	1021
Lohne..........arr	...	7 33	8 41	no'n	1 29	3 35	6 57	1045
,, ...dep	5 a36	7 37	8 47	12 1	1 30	3 37	7 1	1050
Vechta	5 49	7 51	9 35	1218	1 46	3 54	7 18	11 6
Falkenrott	5 53	—	9 43	1222	—	3 58	7 22	—
Wildeshausen	6 40	...	10 28	1 22	...	4 46	8 8	...
Delmenhorst arr	7 25	...	11 14	2 [illegible]	...	5 31	8 55	...

Holdorf .....dep	7a13	8a42	10a35	1 p6	6p38	1023	...
Damme ......arr	7 31	9 0	10 56	1 24	6 56	1041	...

Damme.........dep	6a40	7a42	10 a2	11a45	5 p8	9 p30	...
Holdorf ....arr	6 57	7 59	10 19	12 2	5 25	9 47	...

Lohne ....dep	7a42	10 a8	2p22	5p13	7 p5	9p36	10p51	...
Dinklage.....arr	8 2	10 28	2 42	5 33	7 25	9 56	11 11	...

Dinklage ...dep	7 a9	8a25	11a16	3p10	6p30	9 p5	10p20	...
Lohne ....arr	7 29	8 45	11 36	3 30	6 50	9 25	10 40	...

ELLENSERDAM and OCHOLT.

‡—Not on Sunday. *—8.39 a.m. on Sunday.

Ellenserdam dep	6a55	9 a7	10a20	...	1 p 9	‡	6p28	...	8p26
Bockhorn	7 14	9 22	10 36	...	1 22	1p32	6 46	...	8 46
Grabstede	7 21	—	10 43	...	—	1 38	6 52	...	8 52
Westerstede 6a41	8 12	10a15	11 21	1240	4 p27	2 6	7 28	8p13	—
Ocholt arr 6 55	8 26	10 33	11 42	1258	4 41	...	7 42	8 27	...

Ocholt dep	7a30	8*55	11a55	1p15	3p50	‡	7p52	...	8p43	10p48
Westerstede	7 50	9 17	12 13	1 33	4 4	7p20	8 6	...	9 0	11 6
Grabstede	8 23	—	—	2 41	—	7 47	—	8p58	9 29	—
Bockhorn	8 36	9a59	12p12	2 52	7p55	7 53	...	9 4	9 35	...
Ellenserdam 151	8 51	10 5	12 27	3 7	8 10	...	...	—	—	...

NEUENBURG and VAREL.

†—Weekdays only. *-Sunday dep. 7.8 p.m. §-Sunday dep. 6.29 p.m.

Neuenburg dep	6 a0	...	8 a6	10a16	11a35	2p28	6p19	...	7p25	...
Bockhorn	6 17	...	8 42	10 32	12 5	2 53	6 36	...	7 48	9p43
Bramloge dep	...	7a58	...	—	...	2 32	—	7*32	—	...
Borgstede ...dep	6 35	8 13	9 6	...	12 45	3 10	4†p0	7 46	...	10 0
Varel arr	6 46	8 26	9 19	...	12 56	3 21	4 13	7 57	...	1011

Varel ...dep	7a10	8a52	...	1†p0	1p25	4p30	6§57	...	8p12	...
Borgstede	7 23	9 3	...	1 9	1 38	4 43	7 8	...	8 23	...
Bramloge	7 38	...	a.m.	...	1 55	...	7 22	...	...	...
Bockhorn	—	9 24	1040	1 26	1p28	5 15	—	6p46	8 47	9p40
Neuenburg	...	9 43	1057	...	1 46	5 42	...	7 3	9 5	9 58

CAMBURG and ZEITZ.

Camburg dep	3 a52	7a18	9 a29	11a41	4p 0	7 p41
Cauerwitz	4 32	7 53	10 8	12 18	4 45	8 13
Zeitz arr	5 32	8 46	10 56	1 13	5 42	8 57

Zeitz dep	5 a15	8 a32	12p20	1p47	6 p35	10 p4
Cauerwitz	6 15	9 41	1 11	2 33	7 28	11 3
Camburg arr	6 54	10 47	1 52	3 7	8 19	11 48

ERFURT and LANGENSALZA.

†—On Sunday at 11.8 p.m. ‡—Weekdays only.

Erfurt dep	...	6a0	8 a8	10 a5	...	1p48	5p21	6p28	8p†40
Kühnhausen	...	623	8 31	10 38	p.m.	2 14	5 44	6 49	9 2
Döllstadt	5a31	656	9 8	11 13	1236	2 51	6 17	7‡35	9 34
Gräfentonna	5 44	710	9 27	11 28	1247	3 4	6 38	7‡48	9 50
Langensalza 172A arr	...	725	9 45	11 44	1 1	3 19	6 58	—	10 8

Langensalza dep	4‡a0	4a45	7 a42	11 a8	1p30	3 p19	5p40	8p14
Gräfentonna	4 15	5 6	7 59	11 29	1 52	3 40	5 58	8 30
Döllstadt	4 27	5 33	8 13	11 45	2 5	3 54	6 13	8 42
Kühnhausen	5 3	6 20	8 47	12 21	—	4 21	6 49	9 18
Erfurt arr	5 26	6 45	9 10	12 47	...	4 43	7 13	9 38

ERFURT and NORDHAUSEN.

	a.m.	a.m.	a.m.	p.m.	p.m.	p.m.	p.m.	p.m.	p.m.
Erfurt dep	6 26	8 30	10 17	12 28	3 0	5 28	6 28	6 56	10 23
Kuhnhausen	6 45	...	10 37	12 46	3 20	5 47	6 49	...	10 46
Straussfurt	7 11	9 1	11 3	1 8	3 45	6 9	7 14	7 27	11 10
Greussen	7 27	9 11	11 22	1 23	4 0	6 24	—	7 37	11 25
Hohenebra 152	7 58	...	11 51	1 56	4 30	6 58	...	...	11 55
Sondershausen	8 8	9 42	12 0	2 8	4 42	7 8	...	8 7	12 5
Nordhausen arr	8 36	10 4	12 27	2 43	5 17	7 42	...	8 27	12 37

	a.m.	a.m.	a.m.	a.m.	p.m.	p.m.	p.m.	p.m.	p.m.
Nordhausen dep	6 36	5 29	7 41	10 23	1 19	2 14	5 56	9 15	9 38
Sondershausen	7 27	6 11	8 8	10 51	1 42	2 56	6 38	9 39	10 18
Hohenebra	—	6 24	8 21	11 4	...	3 8	6 53	...	10 31
Greussen	a.m.	6 50	8 43	11 23	2 9	3 31	7 23	10 6	10 57
Straussfurt	4 32	7 9	9 1	11 38	...	3 46	7 42	1016	11 12
Kuhnhausen	5 3	7 31	9 26	...	...	4 10	8 8	...	11 34
Erfurt 170 arr	6 26	7 52	9 46	12 16	2 44	4 30	8 31	1042	11 54

STRAUSSFURT and GROSSHERINGEN.

	a.m.	a.m.	a.m.	p.m.	p.m.	p.m.	p.m.	p.m.
Straussfurt dep	...	7 40	9 46	12 3	3 56	6 45	7 42	11 17
Sömmerda	...	8 30	10 27	12 58	4 32	7 35	8 5	11 42
Cölleda	5 43	8 46	10 44	1 17	4 56	7 53	—	12 10
Guthmannshausen	6 18	9 8	11 6	1 43	5 23	8 20	...	—
Grossheringen arr	7 7	9 56	12 0	2 29	6 19	9 3	...	...

	a.m.	a.m.	a.m.	p.m.	p.m.	p.m.	p.m.	p.m.
Grossheringen dep	...	6 30	8 30	12 55	3 53	...	7 33	10 1
Guthmannshausen	...	7 38	9 26	1 14	4 36	...	8 19	11 1
Cölleda	6 20	8 5	9 59	2 9	5 0	...	8 43	11 25
Sömmerda	6 43	8 31	10 30	2 40	5 36	8 12	9 16	—
Straussfurt arr	7 5	8 54	10 57	3 26	5 59	8 35	10 2	...

ILMENAU and GROSSBREITENBACH.

	a.m.	a.m.	p.m.	p.m.	p.m.	p.m.
Ilmenau dep	7 49	10 29	12 17	4 40	7 30	9 40
Gehren	8 17	11 0	12 57	5 12	8 0	1020
Grossbreitenbach arr	8 50	...	1 35	5 41	...	1050

	a.m.	a.m.	a.m.	p.m.	p.m.	p.m.
Grossbreitenbach dp	6 15	9 11	...	2 28	6 9	...
Gehren	6 58	9 47	1130	3 19	6 50	8 50
Ilmenau 170A arr	7 30	10 9	12 0	3 50	7 15	9 20

HOHENEBRA and MUHLHAUSEN.

Hohenebra dep	...	8 a23	11a59	...	2 p10	4 p35	6p58
Ebeleben	...	9 0	12 33	12p55	2 40	5 5	7 30
Schlotheim	6 a0	9 30	—	1 30	—	—	8 5
Mühlhausen 172A arr	6 45	10 15	...	2 20	...	...	9 0

Mühlhausen dep		7a10	...	11a10	...	4p25	9p31
Schlotheim		8 13	...	12 10	...	5 26	1021
Ebeleben	7a15	8 41	11a7	1 15	3 p48	6 6	—
Hohenebra arr	7 45	...	1142	1 45	4 18	6 35	...

WEIMAR and GERA.

	am	am	a.m.	a.m.	p.m.	pm	pm	pm	pm	p.m	p.m.
Weimar	612	743	1034	1126	1258	323	359	551	745	9 35	1111
Jena	641	819	1110	1158	1 36	358	430	622	818	1021	1151
Goschwit	649	838	1118	12 4	1 44	...	446	631	828	1028	12 0
Roda	7 2	851	1134	1215	1 56	415	459	644	844	...	1214
Gera arr	739	931	1227	1249	2 37	455	541	727	938	...	1256

	am	am	a.m.	a.m.	p.m.	pm	pm	pm	pm	p.m.	p.m.
Gera dep	653	746	9 16	1049	1241	120	339	...	710	9 6	9 59
Roda	728	825	10 0	1135	1 14	2 5	426	...	8 4	9 52	1037
Goschwitz	741	845	1014	1148	1 25	224	444	6 7	826	10 7	...
Jena	751	854	1023	1157	1 33	237	452	621	837	1017	1054
Weimar ar	824	936	1059	1238	2 7	317	524	7 3	913	1056	1125

Extra.—Weimar to Gera 5.23 a.m. Gera to Weimar 5.10 a.m.

RUHLA and WUTHA.

‡—Not on Sunday.

	a.m.	a.m.	a.m.	p.m.	p.m.	p.m.		
Ruhla dep	5‡30	6 50	10 5	2 20	6 25	8 53	...	...
Thal „	5 40	7 0	1015	2 33	6 37	9 5	...	...
Wutha 170 arr	5 55	7 15	1030	2 50	6 52	9 23	...	...

	a.m.	a.m.	p.m.	p.m.	p.m.	p.m.		
Wutha dep	6 14	8 35	12 2	3 38	7 50	10 10	...	...
Thal „	6 28	8 53	1220	3 57	8 8	10 25	...	...
Ruhla arr	6 37	9 5	1232	4 9	8 17	10 40	...	...

JENA and CROSSEN.

	am	am	am	a.m.	pm	pm	pm	pm	pm	p.m.	p.m.
Jena dep	...	7 6	...	1055	...	138	...	5 1	752	...	1044
Eisenberg	611	8 7	945	1228	145	238	527	650	855	1054	1212
Crossen 173 ar	632	827	108	1251	2 5	256	550	7 9	914	1113	...

	am	am	a.m.	pm	pm	pm	pm	pm	p.m.	p.m.
Crossen dp	650	9 0	1046	1 8	218	324	618	835	1026	1127
Eisenberg	8 0	928	1223	136	247	352	640	859	1045	1155
Jena arr	914	...	1 18	...	4 4	...	739	959	...	...

GRIFTE and GUDENSBERG.

Grifte dep	8a55	1 p55	7 p5	8p56	1142
Gudensberg arr	9 31	2 31	7 41	9 32	1214

Gudensberg dep	6 a28	10a35	5p27	7p52	1030
Grifte 156A arr	7 0	11 7	6 0	8 25	1058

TEUTSCHENTHAL and SALZMUNDE.

Teutschenthal dep	7 a35	9 a40	4 p0	7 p5
Salzmunde arr	7 59	10 8	4 24	7 40

Salzmunde dep	8a 45	2p10	5p51	8 p0	...
Teutschenthal 148 arr	9 11	2 35	6 16	8 25	...

WETZLAR and LOLLAR.

Wetzlar dep	4†a47	6 a40	10a36	1 p17	4 p17	7p12
Lollar arr	5 29	7 32	11 26	1 59	5 7	7 58

Lollar dep	4†a43	6†a36	8 a0	11a46	2p26	6 p12	8p29
Wetzlar arr	5 35	7 28	8 50	12 29	3 16	6 56	9 19

†—Weekdays only.

ARNSTADT and ICHTERSHAUSEN.

	a.m.	a.m.	p.m.	p.m.	p.m.	p.m	
Arnstadt dep	7 30	11 10	1 45	4 30	5 58	10 35	...
Ichtershausen arr	7 56	11 36	2 10	4 55	6 24	11 1	...
Ichtershausen dep	6a1	8a22	11a49	2p25	5 p15	6 p29	...
Arnstadt (170A) arr	6 26	8 47	12 14	2 50	5 40	6 55	...

SALZUNGEN, VACHA, and KALTENNORDHEIM.

	a.m.	a.m.	a.m.	p.m.	p.m.	p.m.	p.m	p.m.	p.m.
Salzungen......dep	7 5	8 58	10 32	1225	2 39	4 10	6 47	9 32	11 1
Dorndorf	7 35	9 23	11 0	1253	3 5	4 37	7 16	10 3	11 27
Vacha ....arr	7 44	9 32	11 9	1 2	3 14	4 46	7 25	1012	11 36

	a.m.	a.m.	a.m.	a.m.	p.m.	p.m.	p.m.	p.m.	p.m.
Vacha.........dep	6 7	7 17	9 35	1048	1 33	3 20	5 41	8 18	9 24
Dorndorf	6 18	7 32	9 45	11 1	1 44	3 31	5 51	8 29	9 35
Salzungen...arr	6 43	7 57	10 8	1125	2 10	3 56	6 15	8 54	10 2

Dorndorf...............dep	7 a39	11a23	1p54	3 p34	7p19	10 p5
Kaltennordheim ...arr	9 10	12 56	3 30	5 8	9 15	11 38

Kaltennordheim.....dep	4‡a30	7 a50	9 a30	1 p20	5 p35	7 p49
Dorndorf ....arr	5 52	9 17	10 53	2 48	7 0	9 26

‡—On Sunday dep. 5.55 a.m.

HALBERSTADT, BLANKENBURG, and TANNE.

E.M.			a.m.		a.m.	a.m.	p.m.	p.m.	p.m.	p.m.	p.m.	p.m.	p.m.		p m.	p.m.		
—	**Halberstadt** ....dep	...	7*16	...	8 20	11 0	12 18	A	2 17	3 0	3 55	6 35	7§27	...	9 25	11 35	...	...
2½	Spiegelsberge..........	...	7 24	...	8 30	1118	12 25	2 5	2 25	3 7	4 6	6 43	7 35	...	9 37	11 45	...	...
6	Langenstein	...	7 37	...	8 44	1129	...	2 16	2 38	...	4 23	6 58	7 48	...	9 46	11 59	...	...
9	Bornecke	...	7 46	...	8 58	1139	...	2 29	2 49	...	4 36	7 8	7 56	...	9 54	12 10	...	...
11¾	**Blankenburg** ...... arr	a.m.	7 53	a.m.	9 8	1146	12 45	To Thale. arr. 2.49.	2 56	3 27	4 45	7 15	8 4	...	10 0	12 20	...	...
	dep	6 35	—	8 §1	9 15	—	12 49		—	3 31	—	7 20	—	...	—	—	...	...
17¾	**Hüttenrode**..................	7 18	...	8 49	10 14	...	1 32		...	4 14	...	8 3	...	...	...	...	...	...
20	**Rubeland**.....................	7 34	...	9 10	10 35	...	1 47		...	4 28	p.m.	8 17	...	...	...	...	...	...
23½	**Elbingerode Westbhf.**	7 50	...	9 33	10 57	...	2 4		...	4 45	6§30	8 34	...	p.m.	...	...	...	...
27	Drei Annen Hohne ...	8 3	...	9 53	11 25	...	2 17		...	5 15	6 45	8 47	...	9 §5	...	...	...	...
30¼	Schierke	8 30	...	10 42	12 18	...	2 45		...	5 50	—	...	...	9 22	...	...	...	...
38¾	Brocken ....arr	9 8	...	11 20	1 0	...	3 25		...	6 31	...	...	...	10 0	...	...	...	...
26½	**Rothehütte**	8 18	...	—	11 19	...	2 30		...	5 3	...	8 57	...	—	...	...	...	...
30½	**Tanne**......................arr	8 33	...	...	11 34	...	2 45		...	5 18	...	9 12	...	...	...	...	...	...

					a.m.				a.m.		p.m.	p.m.		p.m.	p.m.	p.m.		
...	**Tanne** ....dep	...	...	...	7 35	...	...	...	11 44	...	...	5 23	From Thale dep. 8.15 p.m.	...	...	8 27	...	...
...	Rothehütte Konigshof...	...	...	a.m.	7 48	...	...	...	11 59	...	...	5 42		...	...	8 55	...	...
...	Brocken ....dep	...	...	7 §0	...	...	...	...	10 48	...	2 0	4 30		6 §0	...	...	...	...
...	Schierke	...	...	7 40	...	a.m.	a.m.	...	11 34	...	2 41	5 16		6 40	...	...	...	...
...	Drei Annen Hohne ...	...	...	7 55	...	8 15	10§25	...	12 2	...	3 9	5 41		7 2	...	9 2	...	...
...	**Elbingerode Wbf.**...dep	...	...	—	8 2	8 31	10 42	...	12 19	...	3 20	6 0		7 19	...	9 20	...	...
...	**Rubeland**.....................	...	...	...	8 20	8 53	11 4	...	12 37	...	3 38	6 24		7 45	...	9 45	...	...
...	**Hüttenrode**	...	...	...	8 33	9 18	—	...	12 51	...	3 54	6 40		8 3	...	10 7	...	...
...	**Blankenburg** ...... arr	a.m.	a.m.	...	9 10	10 2	...	p.m.	1 28	p.m	4 37	7 17		8 40	...	10 52	...	...
...	dep	6 15	7 20	...	9 15	10 30	...	1 0	2 20	4 50	—	7 30	A	—	8 55	—	...	...
...	**Bornecke**	6 23	7 28	...	...	10 41	...	1 10	2 28	...	...	7 38	8 38	...	9 7	...	...	...
...	**Langenstein**	6 33	7 38	...	9 31	10 54	...	1 22	2 38	...	...	7 48	8 51	..	9 20	...	...	...
...	**Spiegelsberge**...............	6 44	7 49	...	9 42	11 18	...	1 36	2 49	5 12	...	7 59	9 1	...	9 34	...	...	...
...	**Halberstadt**.............arr	6 51	7 56	...	9 49	11 27	...	1 45	2 56	5 18	...	8 6	...	...	9 43	...	...	...

*—Sunday only. §—Until 31st August. A—Sunday & Wednesday only.

Langenstein dep	8a12	8a53	11a32	12 p5	2 p40	6 p12	7 p0	9 p58
Derenburg..........	8 24	9 5	11 47	12 17	2 52	6 24	7 15	10 10
Minsleben......arr	8 41	...	...	12 34	...	6 41	...	...

Minsleben...dep	...	...	9 a28	...	1 p36	...	...	8p27
Derenburg	6a15	9 a15	9 45	1 p5	1 51	3 p30	7 p30	8 44
Langenstein arr	6 27	9 27	9 56	1 17		3 45	7 45	8 54

BLANKENBURG and QUEDLINBURG.

[§—Until 31st August.

Blankenburg ....dep	5 a0	9 a0	9 a15	10a16	1 p33	2 p20	4 p42	5 p55	7 p30	9 p20	...	...	...	...	...	...	...
Thale Bodetal..............	5 32	...	9 41	10 37	1 56	2 41	5 3	6 20	7 51	9 48	...	...	...	...	...	...	...
Quedlinburg............arr	6 44	9 38	...	11 8	2 27	...	...	7 0	8 22	10 22	...	...	...	...	...	...	...

Quedlinburg ....dep	...	...	7 a50	11a48	12p54	2 p40	5 p0	...	7 p15	...	9 p10	...	...	...	...	...	...
Thale Bodetal..............	6 a10	7 §25	8 21	12 19	1 37	2 54	5 30	6 p34	7 42	8 p30	...	...	...	...	...	...	...
Blankenburg ....arr	6 31	7 46	8 42	12 40	3 0	3 20	5 51	7 0	...	8 51	9 49	...	...	...	...	...	...

BRAUNLAGE and TANNE and WALKENRIED.

Braunlage ...dep	6a48	10a55	2 p6	4p28	7p43	...
Tanne ....arr	7 28	11 30	2 43	5 17	8 18	...

Tanne.........dep	8 a40	11a54	3 p5	5p58	9p20	...
Braunlage...arr	9 21	12 32	3 55	6 40	10 0	...

Braunlage ...dep	8 a0	10a22	1 p35	3p30	7p10	8p54
Walkenried ...arr	8 25	11 55	3 2	4 49	8 35	1018

Walkenried...dep	6 a0	10a0	12p36	3p38	6p17	9p 5
Braunlage......arr	7 20	1125	1 56	5 0	7 38	1023

WEIMAR and KRANICHFELD.

Weimar—	a.m.	a.m.	a.m.	p.m.	p.m.	p.m.	p.m.	
Stadt ...dep	5 46	9 2	9 52	1 18	2 8	5 45	9 50	...
„ **Berka** ... „	6 0	9 14	10 3	1 30	2 19	6 0	10 3	...
Berka..............arr	6 48	10 0	1046	2 16	3 2	6 45	1048	...
„ ....dep	7 0	—	1052	2 24	—	6 53	1055	...
Tannroda	7 15	...	11 7	2 39	...	7 8	1110	...
Kranichfeldarr	7 25	...	1116	2 49	...	7 18	1120	...

	a.m.	a.m.		a.m.		p.m.	p.m.	
Kranichfeld ....dep	5 30	7 52	...	1158	...	3 44	7 34	...
Tannroda	5 39	8 1	...	1210	...	3 53	7 43	...
Berka ....arr	5 48	8 20	a.m.	1227	p.m.	4 12	8 2	...
„ ....dep	6 55	8 28	1050	1235	3 34	4 20	8 12	...
Weimar—Berka „	7 46	9 19	1145	1 26	4 30	5 14	9 7	...
„ Stadt „ arr	7 53	9 26	1152	1 33	4 37	5 21	9 14	...

Weimar Stadt.dep	7a28	11a36	3p24	7 p1	10p18		
Berka............dep	8 36	12 43	4 28	8 4	11 24	...	...
Blankenhain arr	8 54	1 1	4 46	8 22	11 42	...	...

Blankenhain dep	5a34	9a35	1p48	5 p29	8 p46	...	...
Berka ....arr	5 52	9 51	2 6	5 56	9 4	...	...
Weimar ....arr	6 57	10 59	3 13	6 54	10 7	...	...

WEIMAR and RASTENBERG.

	a.m.	a.m.	p.m.	p.m.	p.m.	
Weimar ....dep	6 35	1115	1 25	3 40	8 21	...
Buttelstedt ....arr	7 23	12 5	2 15	4 29	9 11	...
„ ....dep	7 38	1215	—	4 39	9 21	...
Guthmannshausen	8 4	1243	...	5 7	9 47	...
Rastenberg arr	8 25	1 5	...	5 30	1010	...

	a.m.	a.m.		p.m.	p.m.	p.m.
Rastenberg ... dep	4 30	8 55	...	1 20	5 44	...
Guthmannshausen	4 52	9 27	...	1 45	6 6	8 20
Buttelstedt.........arr	5 20	9 53	p.m.	2 12	6 34	8 48
„ ....dep	5 30	10 3	12 5	2 22	6 44	—
Weimar (170) arr	6 15	1055	1255	3 12	7 34	...

Buttelstedt ....dep	7 a27	2 p30	9 p21	...
Grossrudestedt.............arr	8 27	3 40	10 21	...

Grossrudestedt ....dep	4 a20	10a35	5 p34	...
Buttelstedt ....arr	5 20	11 45	6 34	...

DEHRN and MENGERSKIRCHEN.

Dehrn ....dep	...	...	7 p6
Kerkerbach	8a10	2 p20	7 23
Hintermeilingen	9 11	3 21	8 22
Mengerskirchen ...arr	9 59	4 9	9 10

Mengerskirchen ...dep	5a11	11a46	4p41	...
Hintermeilingen	5 59	12 34	5 29	...
Kerkerbach	7 5	1 35	6 30	6p50
Dehrn ....arr	...	...	...	7 3

HILDBURGHAUSEN and FRIEDRICHSHALL.

E.M						
	Hildburghausen dep	8 a0	10a15	1p10	4 p0	7‡p2
9¼	Streufdorf	8 54	11 17	2 9	5 5	8 1
15½	Heldburg	9 30	11 53	2 53	5 41	8 37
18¾	**Friedrichshall** arr	9 47	12 10	3 10	5 58	8 54

Friedrichshall dep	4a55	10a18	12p52	3p48	6p46	...
Heldburg	5 14	10 37	1 12	4 9	7 5	...
Streufdorf	5 49	11 15	1 47	4 44	7 40	...
Hildburghausen (173B)	6 45	12 11	2 45	5 43	8 38	...

‡—11.12 p.m. on Sunday.

FINSTERWALDE and ZSCHIPKAU.

Finsterwalde dep	3a54	7a35	11a40	5p18	10p0
Zschipkau 183A arr	4 52	8 52	12 44	6 23	1117

Zschipkau dep	6 a4	9 p2	1 p49	6p 49	11p37
Finsterwalde 173A arr	7 9	1011	2 57	7 56	12 51

HAMBURG and CUXHAVEN.

		2 3 4	1,2,3	2 3 4	2 3 4	2 3 4	Ex3	2 3 4	2 3 4
Hamburg		a.m.	a.m.	a.m.	p.m.	p.m	p.m.	p.m.	p.m.
Haupt Bahnhof...dep		7 25	10 5	11 7	2 49	5 26	6 16	8 33	1136
Harburg Haupt...dep		7 54	1027	1129	3 13	5 49	6 35	9 0	12 0
„ Unter Elbe „		8 0	...	1137	3 19	5 56	...	9 6	12 6
Buxtehude	2 3 4	8 29	1049	12 9	3 50	6 27	...	9 37	1230
Stade	6a22	9 8	11 8	1249	4 30	7 1	7 12	1017	1258
Otterndorf	7 36	1021	1148	2 4	5 50	8 33	...	1131	1 59
Cuxhaven Stadt arr	7 53	1038	12 2	2 22	6 9	8 50	8 6	1149	2 13
HELIGOLAND...arr		...	3 p0	...	...	...	...	...	...

	2 3 4	2 3 4	Ex3	2 3 4	2 3 4	2 3 4	1,2,3	2 3 4	2 3 4
HELIGOLAND dep	...	...	...	...	...	...	¶	...	...
	a.m.	a.m.	a.m	a.m	a.m.	p.m	p.m	p.m	p.m.
Cuxhaven ...dep	4 32	6 10	7 0	8 37	1134	2 27	4 ‡3	5 4	7 44
Otterndorf	4 50	6 29	...	8 55	1154	2 46	4 16	5 23	8 4
Stade	6 12	7 58	7 51	1011	1 19	4 8	4 59	6 43	9 29
Buxtehude	6 46	8 35	...	1046	1 58	4 47	5 18	7 20	10 4
Harburg Unt. Elb.	7 22	9 9	...	1116	2 30	5 18	5 36	7 53	1038
„ Haupt. arr	7 28	9 14	8 27	1122	2 35	5 23	5 41	7 58	1044
Hamburg ...arr	8 2	9 38	8 46	1151	3 0	5 47	6 4	8 26	1110

‡—On Sundays this train leaves Cuxhaven at 8.10 p.m. **Extra.**—Hamburg to Stade, 6.8 a.m.

¶—A Steamer leaves Heligoland in connection with this train daily, except Sunday.

GEESTEMUNDE and BUCHHOLZ.

Geestemunde	5a25	7a35	9a54	a.m.	1p48	...	4p13	7p 2	...	11p7
Bremervö ...	6 38	8 57	1116	1130	3 4	3p18	5 35	8 18	8p26	1220
Hesedorf ...	6 45	9 5	1129	1138	3 12	3 26	5 43	8 26	8 34	—
Stade... ...	7 40	9 51	...	1226	3 58	...	6 31	9 14	...	...
Harsefeld	7 25	...	12 8	...	...	4 7	...	...	9 10	5 a0
Buchholz arr	8 26	...	1 9	...	...	5 27	...	...	10 5	6 15

Buchholz dep		6a28	...	9a16	...	...	1p18	...	...	6p16	...
Harsefeld		7 28	...	1018	a.m.	...	2 19	...	...	7 18	p.m.
Stade...dep		...	7a55	...	1020	2p 1	...	4p36	7p16	...	1021
Hesedorf		8 7	8 44	1057	11 6	2 49	2 57	5 21	8 4	7 55	11 6
Bremervö	6 a8	8 14	8 55	11 4	1118	2 56	3 11	5 29	8 16	8 2	1114
Geestem.	7 27	...	1010	...	1234	...	4 28	6 37	9 31	...	1220

UELZEN and BREMEN.

STENDAL dep (163)	1a35	2a40	...	7a37	10a5	10a26	11a2	1p43	5p20	8 p0	8p10	...	...
	Ex3	2 3 4	2 3 4	2 3 4	Ex3	Ex 3	2 3 4	2 3 4	2 3 4	Ex3	2 3 4		
	a.m.	a.m.	a.m.	a.m.	a.m.	p.m	p.m	p.m.	p.m	p.m.	p.m.		
Uelzen ...dep	3 15	5 32	8 9	10 3	1139	12 3	2 9	4 56	8 10	9 32	11 0	...	...
Munster	...	6 22	8 58	11 0	1212	...	2 58	5 47	9 7	...	1152	...	...
Soltau	...	6 50	9 23	1128	1230	...	3 25	6 15	9 39	...	1217	...	...
Visselhövede ...	A	7 21	9 51	1158	...	...	3 51	6 42	10 6	...		...	...
Langwedel 159	...	8 10	1030	1238	1 11	...	4 33	7 40	11 2	...	...	...	...
Achim	...	8 32	1051	1259	1 24	...	5 6	8 2	1123	...	...	...	...
Bremen ...arr	5 9	8 54	1113	1 22	1 39	2 1	5 22	8 24	1145	1120	...	...	...

	2 3 4	2,3,4	Ex3	2 3 4	2 3 4	2 3 4	Ex3	Ex 3	2 3 4	Ex3	2 3 4	Ex3	
	a.m.	a.m.	a.m.	a.m.	a.m.	p.m	p.m.	p.m.	p.m.	p.m.	p.m.	p.m.	
Bremen ...dep	5 5	6 35	8 0	...	1020	1230	2 53	4 3	4 16	6 32	7 19	1152	...
Achim	5 31	7 7	...	...	11 0	1256	...	...	4 41	...	8 4	...	...
Langwedel	5 49	7 33	...	...	1120	1 31	...	...	5 2	...	8 23	...	...
Visselhövede ...	6 28	8 25	...	...	12 1	2 10	B	...	5 47	...	9 7	A	...
Soltau	6 53	8 56	9 9	9 21	1228	3 0	...	5 18	6 18	...	9 38	...	...
Munster	7 16	—	9 26	9 46	1251	3 29	...	...	6 41	...	10 1	...	...
Uelzen ...arr	7 55	...	9 55	1027	1 33	4 16	4 47	6 8	7 20	8 16	1046	1 46	...
STENDAL 163	1036	...	1137	1p43	3p27	7p29	6p24	7 p53	1023	9p53	1a36	3a30	...

A—Until 15th September.

B—From 25th July until 18th August.

SALZDERHELDEN and DASSEL.

Salzderhelden...dep	5a35	7a55	8a48	10a3	12p10	1p36	2p25	3p40	4p30	5p25	7p27	9p30	1026	11p40
Einbeck ...arr	5 46	8 6	8 59	1014	12 21	1 46	2 36	3 51	4 41	5 35	7 38	9 41	1037	11 51
Dassel ...arr	...	...	9 55	...	1 15	...	...	4 45	...	...	8 34	...	...	...

Dassel ...dep	...	6a10	...	..	1010	p.m.	p.m.	1p50	p.m.	p.m.	5p20	p.m.	p.m.	p.m
Einbeck	4a35	7 13	8a16	9 a43	11 0	1 15	1 56	2 50	4 0	5 5	6 29	9 4	9 47	1114
Salzderhelden ...arr	4 46	7 24	8 27	9 54	1110	1 25	2 7	3 1	4 11	5 15	6 40	9 15	9 58	1125

HANOVER and SOLTAU.

Hanover ...dep		5a41	8 a6	12p28	1 p52	3p29	6p40	11p0	11p15
Herrenhausen		5 54	8 16	12 39	2 4	3 37	6 51	...	11 25
Mellendorf		6 32	8 48	1 13	2 38	4 10	7 24	...	11 54
Schwarmstedt	5 a3	7 8	9 26	1 51	3 8	4 46	8 3	1153	12 25
Walsrode	5 49	8 3	10 10	2 32	—	5 24	8 42	1220	1 2
Soltau (155)	6 43	8 58	10 53	3 20	...	6 7	9 25	1256	...

Soltau ...dep	...	...	7 a10	8 a21	9a26	11a40	2p38	6 p28	9 p50
Walsrode	...	6 a26	8 7	8 57	1012	12 39	3 54	7 14	10 53
Schwarmstedt	5a59	7 7	8 53	9 27	1050	1 23	4 47	8 2	11 43
Mellendorf	6 31	—	9 30	...	1121	1 57	5 22	8 33	—
Herrenhausen	7 11	...	10 4	...	1155	2 33	6 0	9 8	...
Hanover arr	7 22	...	10 11	10 17	12 6	2 43	6 11	9 18	...

SCHWARMSTEDT and CELLE.

†—Weekdays only.

Schwarmstedt dep	5†a10	7 a8	8 a56	10a52	1p52	4 p50	...	7p58	10p49
Wietze-Steinforde	6 20	7 59	9 30	11 17	2 22	5 20	6†39	8 28	11 20
Celle 156 ...arr	7 0	8 44	10 10	11 48	3 0	5 58	7 24	9 5	11 59

Celle ...dep	5 a3	7a13	9 a35	12p36	3p34	4†55	6p51	11p0
Wietze-Steinforde	5 49	7 56	10 17	1 17	4 13	5 38	7 28	1142
Schwarmstedt arr	6 21	8 44	10 46	1 47	4 42	7 3	7 57	1219

Schwarmstedt ...dep	6a25	9a22	10a52	1p53	4 p48	8p 5
Verden (159) ...arr	7 51	1038	12 20	3 17	6 15	9 34

Verden ...dep	7a12	9a28	11a39	3p14	6p27	9 p23	...
Schwarmstedt ...arr	8 47	1044	1 13	4 39	7 52	10 46	...

NIEDERWALGERN and HERBORN.

Niederwalgern dep	...	6 a29	9a26	1 p51	4 p51	7p15	10p17
Hartenrod	5a10	7 28	10 23	2 52	5 48	8 16	11 14
Herborn ...arr	6 23	8 32	11 27	3 56	6 42	9 17	12 16

Herborn ...dep	4 a9	6a57	9a21	1p54	4p45	7p12	11p11
Hartenrod	5 10	7 54	1022	2 51	5 46	8 16	12 12
Niederwal arr	5 59	8 39	1113	3 38	6 35	9 3	...

WALSRODE and ROTENBURG.

Walsrode ...dep	5a53	10a23	2p40	5p26	8p47
Visselhövede	6 23	11 13	3 32	5 53	9 35
Rotenburg ...arr	8 16	1 13	...	6 40	1121

Rotenburg ...dep	6a25	11a10	2p35	...	7 p18
Visselhövede	7 22	12 3	3 55	5p55	8 27
Walsrode ...arr	7 59	12 33	4 25	6 50	10 45

BLOMBERG and SCHIEDER.

Blomberg... dep	6a53	8a45	11a48	2 p8	3p33	7 p0	8p25
Schieder 151 arr	[illegible] 8	9 0	12 3	2 18	3 48	7 15	8 40

Schieder ...dep	7a47	9a53	12p18	2p33	4 p3	7 p31	8p58
Blomberg ...arr	8 7	1013	12 38	2 53	4 23	7 51	9 18

HANOVER and ALTENBEKEN.

	2 3 4 a.m.	2 3 4 a.m.	1,2,3 a.m.	2 3 4 a.m.	1,2,3 p.m.	2 3 4 p.m.	Ex3	2 3 4 p.m.	2 3 4 p.m.
Hanover ...dep	4 51	6 45	7 57	9 0	1245	1 22	...	4 23	7 56
Linden	5 3	7 0	...	9 15	1256	1 38	...	4 36	8 12
Weetzen ......arr	5 17	7 14	...	9 30	...	1 52	...	4 50	8 26
Bennigsen	5 34	7 32	...	9 47	...	2 12	...	5 5	8 42
Münder	6 4	8 2	...	1017	1 39	2 42	...	5 35	9 17
Hameln ......arr	6 22	8 19	8 52	1036	1 50	3 0	p.m.	5 52	9 34
HILDESH'M dp	...	7 a6	...	...	1051	1p55	5 11	5p22	7p50
Hameln ......dep	6 30	8 34	8 55	1127	1 51	3 15	5 59	6 42	9 46
Emmerthal	6 40	8 45	...	1137	...	3 24	...	6 51	9 56
Pyrmont	6 58	9 3	9 16	1154	2 12	3 41	6 18	7 8	1013
Schieder 154	7 14	9 47	⋮	12 9	2 26	3 55	...	7 24	1029
Bergheim	7 37	10 16	⋮	1236	...	4 18	...	7 44	1052
Altenbeken arr	8 5	10 51	⋮	1 5	3 2	4 42	7 0	8 10	1153
SOEST 165...arr	10a0	12p26	11 8	3p30	...	5p59	8 p6	10p45	...

	2 3 4	2 3 4	2 3 4	2 3 4	Ex3	2 3 4	2 3 4	1,2,3	2 3 4	1,2,3	2 3 4
SOEST.........dep		...	5a49	...	10a49	...	12p23	2p50	2 p50	6p17	6 p17
		a.m.	a.m.		p.m.		p.m.	p.m.	p.m.	p.m.	p.m.
Altenbeken...dep		6 57	8 23	...	12 6	...	1 48	4 41	4 57	7 44	8 10
Bergheim	a.m.	7 18	8 47	...	...	...	2 7	...	5 22	...	8 29
Schieder	5 1	7 41	9 7	a.m.	...	...	2 26	...	5 45	...	8 50
Pyrmont	5 17	7 57	9 24	1119	12 45	...	2 42	5 21	6 27	8 24	9 8
Emmerthal	5 33	8 14	9 40	1138	...	...	2 58	...	6 50	...	9 24
Hameln155arr	5 42	8 22	9 48	1147	1 4	...	3 6	5 38	6 58	8 41	9 33
HILDESHEIM arr		1013	...	1p38	1 p52	p.m.	4 p0	7p35	9 p0	...	11 p9
Hameln...dep	5 52	8 32	9 53	1214	...	1 12	3 19	5 40	7 10	8 43	9 44
Münder	6 8	8 55	1016	1239	...	1 38	3 43	...	7 34	...	10 6
Bennigsen	6 51	9 22	1046		...	2 9	4 12	...	8 5	...	10 33
Weetzen dep	7 7	9 35	11 1	...	...	2 23	4 27	...	8 20	...	10 45
Linden	7 21	9 49	1115	...	...	2 37	4 41	6 23	8 34	...	10 57
Hanover arr	7 35	10 0	1126	...	...	2 51	4 55	6 33	8 45	9 36	11 11

Extra. Hanover to Hameln, 12.0 night. Hameln to Pyrmont, 5‡23, 10.42 a.m., 1‡4, 4.13, 7.45 p.m. Pyrmont to Hameln, 6‡1 a.m., 1‡52, 4.59, 11.0 p.m.

Hanover dep	3a40	...	6a56	9a26	10a53	...	1p50	5p10	7 p4	8p35	...	11p14
Weetzen	4 42	...	7 24	9 56	11 26	12 p2	2 24	5 40	7 35	9 4	p.m.	11 44
Barsinghausen	6 13	7a20	7 54	1040	12 0	12 30	2 54	6 13	8 7	9 33	1033	12 12
Nenndorf	6 32	7 39	8 13	11 1	12 21	12 50	3 15	6 37	—	9 51	1053	—
Haste ......arr	6 39	7 46	8 20	11 8	12 28	12 58	3 22	6 44	...	9 58	11 3	...

Haste ......dep	6a54	8a40	11a30	12p41	1p25	3p36	6p54	8p 8
Bad Nenndorf	7 6	8 54	11 42	12 51	1 35	3 49	7 7	8 20
Lauenau	7 22	9 13	11 58	—	—	4 5	7 22	8 36
Münder	7 56	9 55	12 34	...	...	4 40	...	9 9
Hameln......arr	8 19	1036	12 54	...	...	4 59	...	9 25

Haste ......dep	...	4a50	6a46	8a28	10a1	11a55	...	2p2	4p28	6p54	8p17	10p26
Nenndorf ......a.m.		4 59	6 54	8 36	1010	12 5	...	2 11	4 38	7 5	8 28	10 34
Barsinghausen	4‡42	6 27	7 16	8 55	1030	12 27	1 p7	2 34	5 2	7 27	8 56	10 55
Weetzen	5 14	6 56	7 47	9 23	11 0	—	1 39	3 3	5 34	8 4	9 32	11 22
Hanover arr	5 47	7 22	8 16	9 52	1126	...	2 8	3 30	6 0	8 34	9 59	11 47

Hameln dep	...	6a35	9a53	...	...	1p40	...	5p17	...	9p54
Münder	...	6 58	1019	...	...	2 10	...	5 40	...	1019
Lauenau a.m.		7 31	1051	...	...	2 50	...	6 16	7p29	1054
Bad Nenrf.	4‡52	7 46	11 6	1258	1p41	3 10	4 p4	6 32	7 42	1110
Haste...arr	5 8	7 57	1117	1 7	1 50	3 22	4 15	6 44	7 53	1124

Extra.—Hanover to Barsinghausen, 3‡5 p.m ‡—Weekdays only.

C—To Cologne.

HILDESHEIM and LOHNE.

‡—Weekdays only.

Dist. E.M.	BRUNSWICK dep		...	5a40	...	8 a20	10 a8	11a18	...	...	...	...	...	4p28	4p28	...	4p28	...	6p30	7p56	...	...	...
			3 &4	2 3 4	2 3 4	2,3,4	2,3,4	2,3,4	1,2,3	2 3 4	Ex3	2 3 4	2—4	1,2,3	Ex3	3 &4	2 3 4	3 &4	2 3 4	1,2,3	2 3 4	3 & 4	2 3 4
				a.m.	a.m.	a.m.	a.m.	p.m.	p.m.	p.m.	p.m.	p.m.		p.m.	p.m.	...	p.m.	p.m.	p.m.	p.m.	p.m.		a.m.
—	**Hildesheim** dep		...	7 6	8 19	9 31	10 51	12 43	1 10	1 55	2 47	3 36	...	5 5	5 11	...	5 22	5§57	7 50	9 3	1054	...	12 32
7	**Nordstemmen**		...	7 24	8 43	9 53	11 8	12 59	...	2 12	...	3 54	...	...	...	...	5 39	6 34	8 14	9 24	1116	...	12 58
11¼	Elze............2 3 4		...	7 36	8 54	10 4	11 20	1 16	1 29	2 24	3 5	4 40	...	...	...	§	5 52	6 46	8 42	9 31	1127	...	1 9
29¼	**Hameln** arr a.m.		a.m.	8 23	—	—	12 5	—	—	3 10	3 35	5 34	p.m.	5 49	5 55	p.m.	6 36	7 35	9 38	—	1215	nght	—
...	,, 155 dep	4 52	6 3	8 31	...	...	12 9	...	...	3 17	3 38	—	4 29	6 2	5 59	6 10	7 39	—	9 43	...	—	12‡35	...
44¼	Rinteln	5 28	6 44	9 5	...	...	12 44	...	...	4 12	4 4	...	5 37	6 23	⋮	6 49	8 12	...	1018	...	...	1 11	...
58¾	Bad Oeynhau.	6 5	7 30	9 40	...	...	1 20	...	...	4 50	4 34	...	6 18	6 47	C	—	8 48	...	1053	...	...	—	...
62¼	**Lohne** ...arr	6 12	7 38	9 47	...	...	1 27	...	...	4 58	4 42	...	6 26	6 54	⋮	...	8 55	...	11 0	...	...	...	...

	2 3 4	2 3 4	2 3 4	2,3,4	2 3 4	1,2,3	3 & 4	3 &4	Ex3	2 3 4	Ex3	2,3,4	3 &4	2,3,4	2,3,4	3 &4	2—4	2—4	1,2,3	2—4	...
			a.m.		a.m.	a.m.		p.m.	p.m.	p.m.	p.m.		p.m.		p.m.	p.m.	p.m.	p.m.		p.m.	
Lohne ....dep	...	...	6 36	...	10 4	1142	...	...	⋮	1 38	2 13	...	...	...	5 15	...	7 ‡30	8 14	...	11 13	...
Bad Oeynhausen	...	...	6 46	...	1013	1151	...	‡	⋮	1 47	2 23	...	...	...	5 24	...	7 42	8 23	...	11 22	...
Rinteln	...	...	7 35	...	1048	1217	...	2 57	⋮	2 21	2 47	...	5 15	...	5 59	7 0	8 18	8 57	...	11 56	...
Hameln ....arr	a.m.	...	8 13	...	1122	1239	p.m.	3 [illegible]6	1 4	2 56	3 9	...	5 54	p.m.	6 32	7 39	—	9 31	...	12 30	...
,, ...dep	5 21	a.m.	8 29	a.m.	1134	1241	12 48	—	1 6	3 23	3 11	p.m.	—	6 0	7 5	—	...	9 41	p.m.	—	...
Elze	6 10	6 32	9 37	10 13	1242	1 16	1 50	...	...	4 12	3 41	5 26	...	7 6	8 30	...	...	10 29	11 5	...	...
Nordstemmen	6 27	6 47	9 54	10 29	1255	1 25	2 1	...	...	4 46	...	5 41	...	7 18	8 42	...	...	10 52	11 20	...	...
Hildesheim ......arr	6 45	7 5	1013	10 47	1 14	1 38	—	...	1 52	5 5	4 0	5 58	...	7 35	9 0	...	...	11 9	11 39	...	...
BRUNSWICK 159 arr.	9a20	9a20	1217	12 17	2p34	2p34	...	...	2p34	6p27	...	...	...	8 p37	10p20	...	...	12 27	...	...	...

Extra.—Hameln to Rinteln, 6.36, 10.44 a.m., 12.52, 4.29 p.m. Rinteln to Hameln, 5.0, 9.7 a.m., 12.45 p.m.

HERFORD and ALTENBEKEN.

Herford dep	6 a9	...	8 a9	8a23	9a37	11a39	1p17	2p43	5p23	5p28	10p9
Lage	6 42	7a26	8 31	9 0	10 6	12 13	1 47	3 14	5 53	7 2	1042
Detmold	6 58	7 47	8 43	9 16	1022	12 33	2 3	3 30	6 8	7 16	11 0
HornMeinb'g	7 16	8 11	...	—	1040	12 53	2 22	3 48	6 28	7 32	1119
Altenbeken	7 50	8 58	9 19	...	1112	1 30	2 56	4 22	6 53	8 4	1153

Altenbeken		6a2	8a2	...	11a23	1233	2p5	4p47	5p59	8 p2	9p46	11p3
HornMeinb'rg		636	831	a.m.	11 54	1 12	235	5 17	6 30	8 32	10 7	1133
Detmold	5 a0	713	847	1033	12 12	1 30	256	5 35	6 47	8 46	1018	1149
Lage	5 26	727	9 1	1048	12 28	1 44	312	5 51	7 4	9 2	1028	12 3
Herford	5 55	754	9 28	1116	12 58	...	340	6 18	7 36	9 30	1048	1229

Extra.

Lage.........dep	10a48	2p33	Detmold......dep	11a10	Herford ...dep	8p12	11p24	Detmold...dep	6 a4	9p52	‡—Weekdays
Detmold ...arr	11 2	2 49	Lage..........arr	11 23	Detmold ...arr	9 13	12 19	Herford ...arr	6‡50	1035	only.

GEMUNDEN and KIRCHHAIN.

Gemunden (Burg & Nieder) dep	6 a59	11a29	4 p42	10p21	**Kirchhain**.........dep	5a29	9 a35	1 p30	7 p20	...
Nieder Ofleiden	7 28	12 9	5 46	10 50	Nieder Ofleiden	6 2	10 10	2 5	7 57	...
Kirchhain ....arr	7 56	12 39	6 16	11 18	**Gemunden**.........arr	6 35	10 42	2 53	8 29	...

BUCHHOLZ and SOLTAU.

Buchholz..........dep	6 a30	9 a15	1p20	4p40	8 p18	**Soltau**............dep	6 a57	11a30	3p37	6 p20	9p41	...
Schneverdingen	7 26	10 19	2 5	5 33	9 3	Schneverdingen ...	7 30	12 13	4 25	6 51	1012	...
Soltau...............arr	7 55	11 2	2 33	6 8	9 31	**Buchholz** ....arr	8 14	1 11	5 31	7 34	1055	...

HILDESHEIM and KREIENSEN.

Hildesheim dep	5 a18	7 a11	11 a2	2 p13	6 p8	11p45	**Kreiensen** dep	...	7a36	12 p2	3 p8	7 p19	10p19
Grossdüngen	5 40	7 34	11 22	2 33	6 31	12 6	Gandersheim	...	7 46	12 26	3 18	7 28	10 44
Bodenburg	6 1	8 11	11 40	2 51	6 53	12 25	Bodenburg	6a10	8 35	1 13	4 8	8 17	11 30
Gandersheim	6 48	9 3	12 27	3 38	7 47	—	Grossdüngen	6 35	8 54	1 41	4 27	8 37	11 49
Kreiensen...arr	6 58	9 13	12 37	3 48	7 57	...	**Hildesheim** arr	6 53	9 13	2 0	4 45	8 56	12 8

For Fares—see page 120A.] PRUSSIAN STATE RAILWAYS. [Luggage Rates—see page 462.

HAMBURG, HANOVER, CASSEL, and FRANKFORT.

THROUGH CARRIAGES:
- Hamburg and Frankfort—in 7.18 a.m., 9.20 a.m., and 9.33 a.m.
- Hamburg and Basle—in 7.18 a.m. from Hamburg.
- Hanover and Basle—in 6.30 a.m. from Hanover.
- Hanover and Munich—in 10.33 a.m. from Hanover.

SC—Sleeping Car. RC—Restaurant Car.

§—From Copenhagen via Fredericia (page 302) and Vamdrup (page 168).
A—From Hamburg to Hanover only until 15th September.

FARES FROM HAMBURG.

	m. pf.	m. pf.	m. pf.
To Basle	71 90	43 70	28 30
,, Cassel	28 60	18 40	11 80
,, Frankfort	43 0	27 20	17 40
,, Mayence	45 60	28 90	18 60
,, Milan	109 10	69 70	46 70

Dist	Station																									
...	COPENHAGEN 302 dep	...	...	...	...	...	...	...	...	...	...	...	...	...	...	8 p10	...	...	...	...	...	...	...	...	...	...
...	WARNEMUNDE ...dep	...	...	...	...	...	...	...	...	...	...	...	...	...	...	2 a40	...	...	...	...	...	...	...	...	...	...
...	COPENHAGEN 302 ...dep	...	...	12p55	...	...	...	12p55	...	...	...	...	...	...	...	...	...	7 p50	...	...	...	...	...	...	7 p50	...
...	KIEL 168 ...dep	...	...	9 p0	...	...	...	9 p0	...	...	...	...	...	...	...	...	...	5 a27	...	...	...	...	...	...	6 a31	...
Dist			2,3,4	Ex 3				2,3,4					2,3,4	2,3,4	2,3,4	Ex 3	Ex 3	2,3,4	2,3,4		Ex 3				1,2,3	1,2,3
E M	**HAMBURG**—			nght				nght						a.m.	a.m.	a.m.	a.m.	a.m.							a.m.	a.m.
—	Hauptbahnhof ...dep	...	...	12 0	...	...	...	12 18	...	...	...	...	...	5 35	6 25	7 18	7 22	7 48	...	...	...	...	...	...	9 20	9 33
7½	**Harburg**	...	...	12 18	...	...	...	12 40	...	...	...	...	...	6 7	6 50	7 35	7 43	8 10	...	...	...	...	...	...	9 39	9 52
19¼	Winsen	...	...	...	...	...	...	1 12	...	...	...	...	...	6 39	7 21	...	A	8 42	...	...	...	...	...	...	9 57	...
30¾	**Lüneburg** ...arr	...	...	12 50	...	...	...	1 38	...	...	...	...	...	7 6	7 45	8 7	8 15	9 7	...	...	...	...	...	...	10 15	10 29
...	LUBECK 213A ...dep	...	...	...	...	...	...	...	...	...	...	...	...	...	...	6 a33	...	...	...	...	...	...	...	...	8 a20	...
...	**Lüneburg** ...dep	...	...	12 51	...	...	...	1 40	...	...	...	...	...	7 9	...	8 10	8 18	9 9	...	...	...	...	...	...	10 17	10 32
52¾	**Uelzen** ...arr	...	...	1 22	...	...	...	2 30	...	...	...	...	a.m.	7 55	...	8 41	8 49	9 56	...	...	...	...	...	...	10 48	11 3
...	,, ...dep	...	...	1 26	...	...	...	2 35	...	...	...	...	5 52	8 2	...	8 42	8 51	11 15	...	...	...	...	...	...	10 52	11 7
74¼	Eschede	...	a.m.	To Stendal.	...	...	...	3 28	...	...	...	...	6 43	8 55	a.m.	...	...	12 6	...	...	...	...	...	...	...	...
85½	Celle 154	...	4 59		...	...	...	3 50	...	...	...	...	7 8	9 44	8 50	9 27	9 36	12 30	a.m.	...	...	...	...	...	11 39	11 53
97½	Burgdorf	...	5 27		...	...	...	4 21	...	...	...	...	7 36	10 4	9 19	...	A	1 2	11 36	...	...	...	...	...	...	...
101½	**Lehrte** ...arr	...	5 42		...	...	...	4 35	...	...	...	...	7 53	10 24	9 33	9 52	10 0	1 17	11 50	...	...	...	...	...	12 4	12 18
130¼	BRUNSWICK 158 ...arr	...	7 a31		...	...	...	...	...	...	...	...	8 a45	11a10	11a10	11a10	11 10	3 p15	...	...	...	...	...	...	1 p6	1 p6
...	**Lehrte** ...dep	...	5 49		...	...	...	4 40	...	...	...	...	8 0	10 28	9 38	9 56	10 4	1 21	11 54	...	...	...	...	...	12 8	12 26
112¾	**HANOVER** ...arr	...	6 12		...	...	...	5 5	...	...	...	...	8 26	10 57	10 4	10 12	10 20	1 45	12 10	...	...	...	...	...	12 24	⋮
...	BREMEN 159 ...dep	...	...	...	...	...	...	...	...	...	...	...	5 a51	...	...	8 a7	8 a7	...	...	...	...	...	...	...	10a38	⋮
							2,3,4	1—4	Ex 3	2,3,4	2,3,4	Ex 3	2,3,4			Ex 3	Ex 3								1,2,3	⋮
								a.m.	a.m.		a.m.		a.m.			a.m.	a.m.								p.m.	⋮
...	**HANOVER** ...dep	...	...	...	...	...	...	5 29	6 30	...	8 0	...	9 5	...	...	10 24	10 33	...	...	...	...	...	...	...	12 43	⋮
124¼	Sarstedt	...	...	...	...	...	...	6 0	...	...	8 28	...	9 35	...	...	...	...	...	...	...	...	...	...	...	...	⋮
129¼	**Nordstemmen**	...	...	...	...	...	...	6 17	6 54	...	8 43	...	9 53	...	...	10 48	10 57	...	...	...	...	...	...	...	1 9	⋮
133¼	Elze 155	...	...	...	...	...	...	6 32	RC	...	8 55	...	10 8	...	...	RC	RC	...	...	...	...	...	...	...	1 18	1 30
143¾	Alfeld	...	...	...	...	...	...	7 0	...	...	9 22	...	10 35	...	...	⋮	...	...	...	...	...	...	...	...	1 35	1 49
149½	Freden	...	...	...	...	...	...	7 11	...	...	9 33	...	10 46	...	...	⋮	...	...	...	...	...	...	...	...	...	...
155½	**Kreiensen** ...arr	...	...	...	...	...	...	7 22	7 29	...	9 45	...	10 58	...	...	⋮	11 31	...	...	...	...	...	...	...	1 52	2 10
...	BERLIN 165 ...dep	...	...	...	...	...	...	11p50	11p50	...	...	7 a7	7 a7	...	...	⋮	7 a7	...	...	...	8 a17	...	...	...	8 a35	8 a35
...	MAGDEBURG 165 ...dep	...	...	...	...	...	a.m.	2 a55	2 a55	...	...	8 a54	8 a54	...	...	⋮	8 a54	...	...	...	10a10	...	...	...	11 a7	11 a7
...	**Kreiensen** ...dep	...	...	...	...	...	4 40	7 40	7 30	...	9 49	11 3	11 40	...	...	⋮	11 32	...	...	...	12 28	...	...	...	2 8	2 18
160½	Salzderhelden 154	...	...	...	...	...	4 51	7 53	7 40	...	9 59	11 14	11 50	...	...	⋮	...	...	...	...	...	...	...	...	2 18	...
168	**Northeim** ...arr	...	...	...	...	...	5 7	8 10	7 52	...	10 14	11 27	12 6	...	...	⋮	11 50	...	...	...	...	...	...	...	2 30	2 38
...	,, 164A ...dep	...	...	...	...	...	5 17	8 18	7 53	...	10 18	11 28	12 10	...	...	⋮	11 51	...	...	...	...	...	...	...	2 32	2 40
173¾	Nörten	...	...	...	...	...	5 30	8 32	...	...	10 32	...	12 24	...	...	⋮	...	1,2,3	...	...	...	...	...	...	...	...
180	**Gottingen** ...arr	...	...	...	...	...	5 46	8 48	8 12	a.m.	10 47	11 47	12 41	...	...	11 54	12 9	p.m.	...	...	1 3	...	...	...	2 52	3 2
...	,, ...dep	...	...	...	...	...	6 10	8 58	8 16	9 20	11 20	12 0	12 56	...	...	11 58	12 14	12 46	...	...	1 4	...	...	...	2 57	3 7
192	**Eichenberg** ...arr	...	...	...	...	...	⋮	⋮	8 37	9 54	11 54	⋮	⋮	...	...	⋮	⋮	1 5	...	...	⋮	...	...	...	⋮	3 28
230	BEBRA 149A ...arr	...	...	...	...	...	⋮	⋮	10 a9	...	...	⋮	⋮	...	...	1 p12	1 p28	...	...	...	⋮	...	...	...	⋮	4 p38
333¼	FRANKFORT 149A ...arr	...	...	...	...	...	⋮	⋮	1 p27	...	...	⋮	⋮	...	...	3 p59	4 p54	...	...	...	⋮	...	...	...	⋮	7 p36
...	**Eichenberg** ...dep	...	...	...	...	...	⋮	⋮	8 38	10 19	12 40	⋮	⋮	...	...	⋮	...	...	...	...	⋮	...	...	...	⋮	...
201	Münden	...	...	...	...	...	7 6	9 55	9 2	10 54	1 13	12 40	1 51	...	...	⋮	...	...	...	...	⋮	...	...	...	3 48	...
216	**Cassel** ...arr	...	...	...	...	...	7 46	10 35	9 28	11 34	1 52	1 6	2 35	...	...	⋮	...	...	...	...	2 9	...	...	...	4 17	...

For Continuation of

Trains see next page.

			2,3,4	2,3,4	1,2,3	Ex 3	2,3,4	2,3,4	2,3,4	Ex 3			Ex 3		1—4	1,2,3	:	2,3,4	2,3,4	2,3,4	Ex 3	Ex 3	Ex 3	2 3 4	2,3,4	1,2,3	2,3,4
				a.m.	a.m.			a.m.	a.m.	a.m.			p.m.		p.m.							p.m.	p.m.	...		p.m.	p.m.
...	**Cassel** ......dep		...	6 8	7 25	...	...	8 13	10 45	9 43	...	...	1 13	...	1 21	...		...	...	...	...	2 17	3 36	...	...	4 32	4 40
218¼	Wilhelmshöhe		...	6 16	7 33	...	...	8 21	10 52	...	...	...	...	...	1 29	...		...	...	...	...	...	...	...	...	4 40	4 48
224⅓	**Guntershausen**		...	6 33	...	...	...	8 41	11 9	...	...	...	...	...	1 45	...		...	...	...	...	...	...	...	...	4 57	5 4
227	Grifte		...	6 38	...	...	...	8 46	11 14	...	...	...	...	...	1 50	...		...	...	...	...	...	...	...	...	...	5 9
237	**Wabern 156A**		...	7 8	8 7	...	...	9 17	11 41	10 22	...	...	...	...	2 18	...		...	...	...	...	2 58	4 11	...	...	5 20	5 36
242¾	Borken		a.m.	7 23	...	...	...	9 31	11 55	...	...	...	...	...	2 32	...		...	...	...	...	...	...	...	...	...	5 51
254¾	**Treysa 147**		5 38	7 52	8 37	...	...	10 1	12 23	...	...	...	...	...	2 59	...		...	...	...	...	...	...	...	...	5 53	6 20
260	Neustadt		5 54	8 7	...	...	...	10 16	12 37	...	...	...	...	...	3 13	...		...	...	...	...	...	...	...	...	...	6 35
271½	Kirchhain 155		6 19	8 30	9 4	...	...	10 38	12 58	11 15	...	...	...	...	3 34	...		...	...	...	...	...	...	...	...	6 27	6 56
278½	**Cölbe**		6 36	8 49	...	...	p.m.	10 56	1 17	...	...	...	...	...	3 52	...		p.m.	...	...	...	...	...	p.m.	...	...	7 14
280¾	**Marburg 156A**		6 58	8 59	9 23	...	12 20	11 6	1 25	11 33	...	...	2 50	2,3,4	4 14	...		1 10	...	...	...	4 7	5 18	6 20	...	6 48	7 24
287¾	Niederwalgern 154		7 17	9 16	...	...	12 40	11 24	1 44	...	...	...	...	p.m.	4 31	...		1 33	...	...	...	...	...	6 40	...	7 3	7 42
294¼	**Lollar**		7 37	9 34	...	...	1 0	11 42	2 2	...	...	...	...	3 0	4 48	...			...	...	...	...	...	7 0	...	...	8 1
299¼	**Giessen** ......arr		7 46	9 43	9 50	...	1 10	11 51	2 11	11 59	...	...	3 16	3 9	4 57	...		...	...	...	...	4 33	5 44	7 10	...	7 22	8 10
360¾	EMS 147 ......arr	1,2,3	10 a9	12p56	12p56	...	...	1 p58	4 p58	1 p58	...		4 p58	...	7 p53	...	Via Bebra	...	...	...	...	7 p53	7 p53	...	...	...	12a30
371½	COBLENCE 147...arr	a.m.	10 50	1 p33	1 p33	a.m.	...	2 p28	5 p27	2 p28	...	p.m.	5 p27	...	8 p27	p.m.		...	...	...	...	8 p27	8 p27	...	p.m.	...	1 a12
...	**Giessen** ......dep	8 1	8 15	10 4	9 55	11 26	...	12 12	2 17	12 3		1 34		3 14	5 4	3 43		...	...	...	...	4 41	5 53	...	6 34	7 30	8 20
305¼	**Lang Göns**	...	8 33	10 21	...	...	...	12 27	2 34	...	1,2,3	1 52	2,3,4	3 31	5 18	...		...	...	...	p.m.	...	...	...	6 51	...	8 36
310½	Butzbach	8 22	8 48	10 37	...	11 47	p.m.	12 41	2 49	...	p.m.	2 11	p.m.	3 45	5 32	4 4		...	p.m.	p.m.	...	...	...	p.m.	7 7	7 52	8 50
316¾	**Nauheim Bad** ......dep	8 34	9 5	10 58	10 25	11 59	12 24	12 57	3 7	12 33	1 10	2 28	2 59	4 1	5 48	4 16		p.m.	3 50	6 33	5 12	5 9	6 24	6 41	7 24	8 7	9 5
319	**Friedberg**	8 41	9 14	11 6	10 34	12 6	12 30	1 5	3 15	12 40	1 16	2 [illegible]	3 5	4 8	5 55	4 23		6 53	3 56	6 39	5 19	Wiesbaden arr. 6.52.	6 31	6 47	7 32	8 15	9 12
322¼	Niederwöllstadt	...	9 28	11 20	...	...		1 19	3 28	...				4 21	6 5	...		7 7			...		...		7 46	...	9 25
327	Gross-Karben	...	9 40	11 31	...	...	...	1 30	3 39	...	...	...	...	4 39	6 13	...		7 18	...	...	...		...	...	7 57	...	9 35
331	Vilbel	...	9 52	11 44	...	...	...	1 41	3 50	...	...	...	...	4 51	6 24	...		7 32	...	...	...		...	...	8 9	...	9 46
333¾	Bonames	...	10 4	11 56	...	...	...	1 52	4 2	...	...	...	...	5 3	6 40	...		7 55	...	...	...		...	...	8 21	...	9 58
340¼	**FRANKFORT** ......arr	9 14	10 25	12 17	11 10	12 39	...	2 13	4 22	1 13	...	...	...	5 23	6 55	4 56	3 59	8 10	...	...	5 52		7 7	...	8 42	8 51	10 18
394¼	MANNHEIM 136 or 139 arr		12 p9	2 p27	1 p8	2 p27	...	4 p57	6 p30	3 p36	...	...	...	8 p50	...	7 p4	5 p9	...	...	...	8 p50		9 p10	...	...	11p16	12a10
439¼	CARLSRUHE ......140 arr		1 p1	3 p18	...	3 p18	...	5 p59	7 p11	4 p36	...	...	...	10 p8	...	7 p11	6 p9	...	...	...	10 p8	...	10 p8	...	...	12a33	2 a11
561¾	BASLE ......140 arr		4 p41	...	...	7 p0	...	8 p55	10p21	7 p56	...	...	...	...	...	10p21	8 p55	...	...	...	...	...	...	...	...	5 a38	5 a38
363½	MAYENCE ......123A arr		12p42	1 p40	12p42	2 p9	...	4 p13	5 p43	2 p9	...	...	...	...	8 p22	5 p43	5 p43	...	...	...	6 p52	...	8 p22	...	...	9 p37	12a31
494¾	STRASSBURG ...208 arr		...	...	...	5 p10	...	...	...	7 p5	...	...	...	...	...	...	7 p5	...	...	...	...	...	12a27	...	...	...	3 a58
582¾	BASLE ......208 arr		...	...	...	7 p22	...	...	...	9 p13	...	...	...	...	...	...	9 p13	...	...	...	...	...	...	...	...	...	6 a7
796½	MILAN ......269A arr		...	...	...	6 a22	...	...	...	6 a22	...	...	...	...	...	...	6 a22	...	...	...	...	...	...	...	...	...	3 p5

Extra. Bad Nauheim ......dep 11a47 ... ... ; Friedberg ......arr 11 53 ... ...

WABERN, WILDUNGEN, and CORBACH.

	a.m.		a.m.	a.m.	a.m.	a.m.	p.m.	p.m.	p.m.	p.m.	p.m.	p.m.	p.m.	a.m.
Wabern ......dep	4 22	...	7 12	8 22	9 18	1056	12 12	1 11	3 10	4 30	5 55	7 42	9 30	12 15
Fritzlar	4 35	...	7 28	8 38	9 31	11 9	12 26	1 23	3 25	4 47	6 8	7 57	9 45	12 29
Wildungen Bad arr	5 0	a.m.	7 55	9 5	9 56	1135	12 52	1 48	3 52	5 10	6 34	8 27	10 15	12 56
Wildungen Bad dep	5 9	6 1	8 3		10 17		1 1		4 14			8 35		
Waldeck	5 50	6 45	8 43	...	10 58	...	1 39	...	4 51	...	...	9 16	...	...
Corbach (156A) arr	...	7 49	9 44	...	11 55	...	2 34	...	5 47	...	...	10 18	...	...

		a.m.	a.m.	a.m.	a.m.	a.m.	p.m.	p.m.	p.m.	p.m.		p.m.
Corbach ......dep	...	...	6 11	8 37	9 40	1158	12 13	1 24	2 44	4 33	...	8 15
Waldeck	...	6 7	7 11	9 31	10 5	1227	1 6	1 57	3 40	5 50	...	9 22
Wildungen Bad arr	a.m.	6 43	7 45	10 3	1016	1240	1 40	2 11	4 13	6 16	p.m.	9 48
Wildungen Bad dep	5 25	7 0	8 10	10 8			2 17		4 21	6 35	8 28	9 58
Fritzlar	5 54	7 28	8 37	10 33	...	...	2 39	...	4 49	7 3	8 55	10 27
Wabern ......arr	6 7	7 42	8 49	10 45	...	...	2 50	...	5 4	7 17	9 8	10 40

WARBURG and SARNAU.

	a.m.	a.m.	a.m.	a.m.	p.m.	p.m.	p.m.	p.m.	a.m.		
Warburg ......dep	...	...	6 57	10 39	12 52	4 1	6 44	10 48	...	...	...
Volkmarsen 135A	...	...	7 27	11 7	1 30	4 29	7 12	11 20	12 14	...	...
Arolsen	...	5 21	7 53	11 29	1 56	5 0	7 34	11 42	12 40	...	...
Corbach	...	6 4	8 39	12 9	2 37	5 50	8 12		1 17	...	...
Frankenberg	4 30	7 26	9 45	1 9	3 44	6 55	9 10	...		...	...
Münchausen	5 0	8 1	10 14	1 37	4 12	7 23	9 39	...	...	...	...
Sarnau ......arr	5 28	8 30	10 43	2 5	4 40	7 52	10 7	...	...	...	...
Marburg 156A ...arr	5 45	8 47	11 12	2 22	4 57	8 21	10 22	...	...	...	...

	a.m.	a.m.	a.m.	a.m.	p.m.	p.m.	p.m.	p.m.	p.m.			
Marburg ......dep	...	4 27	7 6	9 23	2 4	4 20	6 †32	7 48	11 0	...	...	...
Sarnau ......dep	...	4 44	7 21	9 40	2 22	4 41	6 49	8 6	11 17	...	...	...
Münchausen	...	5 16	7 50	10 15	2 48	5 1	7 17	8 35	11 48	...	...	...
Frankenberg	...	5 55	8 27	10 51	3 19	5 40		9 11	12 22	...	...	...
Corbach	4 27	7 10	9 49	12 18	4 21	6 50	...	10 22		...	...	...
Arolsen	5 7	8 3	10 30	1 3	4 59	7 35	...	11 0	...	...	...	...
Volkmarsen	5 33	8 34	11 10	1 29	5 19	8 3	...		...	...	...	...
Warburg 135A ......arr	6 4	9 3	11 42	1 59	5 45	8 33	...	...	...	...	...	...

†—Weekdays only.

For Fares—see page 120A.] PRUSSIAN STATE RAILWAYS. [Luggage Rates—see page 462.

HAMBURG, HANOVER, CASSEL, and FRANKFORT.

THROUGH CARRIAGES { Hamburg and Frankfort—in 12.36 p.m., 9.27 p.m., and 11.4 p.m. from Hamburg. Hamburg and Basle—in 9.27 p.m. and 11.4 p.m. from Hamburg. Hanover and Basle—in 2.18 a.m. and 12.6 night from Hanover.

B—Runs only in July and August. SC—Sleeping Car. RC—Restaurant Car.

§—From Copenhagen via Fredericia (page 302) and Vamdrup (page 168).

Station	2—4	Ex 3	2,3,4	Ex 3	2,3,4	2,3,4	2,3,4	2,3,4	2,3,4	1,2,3	2,3,4	2,3,4	Ex 3		2,3,4	Ex 3	2,3,4	2 3 4	2,3,4	2,3,4	Ex 2	2,3,4		Ex 2	Ex 3		Ex3
COPENHAGEN 302 dep	...	...	...	...	...	...	...	...	...	...	...	...	...	...	...	...	...	...	...	...	11 a0	...	...	...	...	...	...
WARNEMUNDE dep	...	...	...	...	...	...	...	...	...	...	...	...	...	...	...	...	...	...	...	...	4 p59	...	...	...	...	...	p.m.
COPENHAGEN 302 dep	...	12 §0	...	12 §0	...	...	...	...	...	...	...	...	...	...	...	...	...	...	...	...	...	...	...	...	...	...	1255
KIEL 168 dep	...	9 a18	...	9 a18	...	...	...	...	...	11a22	11a10	...	1 p41	...	2 p24	5 p52	...	...	...	...	5 p52	...	...	...	...	...	9 p0
HAMBURG—	a.m.	p.m.		p.m.			a.m.		p.m.	p.m.	p.m.	p.m.	p.m.		p.m.	p.m.		p.m.	p.m.	p.m.	p.m.	p.m.			p.m.		p.m.
Hauptbahnhof dep	10 13	12 17	...	12 36	...	...	11 11	...	...	3 2	2 11	3 17	6 0	...	5 18	8 8	...	6 28	8 15	...	9 27	9 53	...	...	11 4	...	1119
Harburg	10 41	12 35	...	12 53	...	...	11 41	...	1 30	3 21	2 41	3 58	6 17	...	5 44	8 25	...	6 56	8 41	8 55	...	10 20	...	...	11 22	...	1138
Winsen	11 12	...	...	RC	...	...	12 14	...	2 3	...	3 17	4 31	...	...	6 15	...	...	7 31	9 4	9 28	SC	10 52	...	...	11 40	...	B
Lüneburg arr	11 38	1 8	...	1 24	...	...	12 40	...	2 32	3 51	3 44	5 0	6 48	...	6 40	8 58	...	7 56	9 28	9 57	...	11 21	...	...	11 57	...	1210
LUBECK 213A dep		10a42	...	10a42	...	...	10a42	p.m.		1 p31	1 p31		2 p56	...	...	5 p49	...	5p49	...		...	8 p55	...	...	8 p55	...	...
Lüneburg dep	...	1 10	...	1 27	...	...	12 45	1 45	...	3 53	4 0	...	6 50	...	6 59	8 58	...	8 9	9 32	...	...	11 29	...	...	11 59	...	1212
Uelzen arr	...	1 41	...	1 57	...	...	1 34	2 41	...	4 23	4 49	...	7 21	...	7 46	9 28	...	9 7	10 24	...	...	12 18	...	...	12 30	...	1245
" dep	...	1 45	...	1 59	...	...	2 4	3 10	...	4 26	4 53	...	7 25	...	7 56	9 33	...		10 55	...	...		...	...	12 34	...	1249
Eschede	...		p.m.	...	...	...	2 48	4 8	...	...	5 43	...	...	...	8 48	...	p.m.	...	11 47	...	...	...	...	...	SC	...	...
Celle 154	...	To Stendal.	2 2	2 46	...	...	3 8	4 48	...	5 9	6 4	...	8 9	...	9 13	10 18	10 28	...	12 6	...	...	...	...	...	1 18	...	1 36
Burgdorf	...		2 28	...	...	...	3 33	5 14	...	...	6 30	...	...	...	9 39	...	11 0	...	12 31	...	...	...	...	...	...	...	...
Lehrte arr	...		2 41	3 11	...	...	3 46	5 27	...	5 33	6 44	...	8 34	...	9 52	10 43	11 15	...	12 43	...	11 34	...	...	...	1 42	...	2 3
BRUNSWICK 158 arr	...		...	4 p35	...	...	4 p35	7 p43	...	7 p43	7 p43	...	9 p59	...	10p39	12 a4	12 a4	...	...	...	12a54	...	...	...	4 a19	...	4a19
Lehrte dep	...		2 45	3 15	...	...	3 51	5 45	...	5 36	6 49	...	8 38	...	9 59	10 46	11 32	...	12 54	...	11 38	...	...	...	1 46	...	2 7
HANOVER arr	...		3 11	3 31	...	...	4 17	6 9	...	5 52	7 14	...	8 54	...	10 24	11 2	11 48	...	1 18	...	11 54	...	...	...	2 2	...	2 24
BREMEN 159 dep	10 38	...	...	1 p1	...	...	1 p1	...	...	3 p51	3 p51	...	6 p27	...	10 p7	...	...	...	...	...	10 p7	...	...	...	12 a2	...	...
	2,3,4	2,3,4		Ex 3			2,3,4			1,2,3	2,3,4		Ex 3	2,3,4	2,3,4										Ex 3		Ex3
	p.m.	p.m.		p.m.			p.m.			p.m.	p.m.		p.m.	p.m.	nght						nght				a.m.		a.m.
HANOVER dep	12 50	2 54	...	3 45	...	...	4 43	...	...	6 0	7 38	...	9 1	10 30	12 14	...	...	...	...	...	12 6	...	...	...	2 18	...	2 35
Sarstedt	1 17	3 13	...	...	...	...	5 13	...	...	...	8 5	...	...	10 59	12 41	...	...	...	...	...	:	...	...	...	...	...	...
Nordstemmen	1 38	3 37	...	RC	...	...	5 31	...	...	6 24	8 23	...	9 24	11 16	12 58	...	...	...	...	...	:	...	...	...	2 43	...	3 2
Elze 155	1 55	3 49	...	4 16	...	...	5 57	...	...	...	8 36	...	9 32	11 26	1 11	...	...	...	...	...	:	...	...	...	...	...	...
Alfeld	2 24	4 17	...	4 33	...	...	6 30	...	...	6 46	9 6	...	9 49		1 39	...	...	...	...	...	:	...	...	...	...	...	...
Freden	2 36	4 29	...	...	...	...	6 41	...	...	...	9 20	...	...	...	1 50	...	...	...	...	...	:	...	...	...	...	...	B
Kreiensen arr	2 49	4 42	...	4 51	...	...	6 52	...	...	7 4	9 32	...	10 7	...	2 1	...	...	...	...	...	:	...	...	...	3 20	...	3 38
BERLIN 165 dep	...	...	...	12 0	...	...	...	...	...	...	3 p55	...	3 p55	...	...	...	...	...	...	...	:	8 p50	...	9 p50	10p13	...	...
MAGDEBURG 165 dep	...	...	...	1 p58	...	p.m.	...	...	...	...	6 p16	...	6 p16	...	...	...	...	...	...	...	:	:	...	12 a6	12a14	...	...
Kreiensen dep	2 56	...	...	5 2	...	5 10	7 12	...	...	7 5	9 50	...	10 9	...	2 4	...	...	...	...	...	:	:	...	2 19	3 28	...	3 44
Salzderhelden 154	3 7	...	...	...	...	5 22	7 25	...	...	7 16	10 3	...	10 19	...	2 14	...	...	...	...	...	:	:	...	:	...	...	...
Northeim arr	3 24	...	...	...	...	5 40	7 41	...	...	7 29	10 19	...	10 31	...	2 23	...	...	...	...	...	:	:	...	:	3 47	...	...
" 164A dep	3 30	...	...	...	...	5 56	7 48	...	...	7 31	10 38	...	10 32	...	2 40	...	...	...	...	...	:	:	...	:	3 48	...	B
Nörten	3 42	2,3,4	...	...	...	6 7	8 1	...	...	...	10 49	...	...	...	2 54	...	...	...	...	...	:	:	1—4	:	...	...	...
Gottingen arr	3 57	p.m.	...	5 38	...	6 22	8 17	...	...	7 50	11 4	...	10 50	...	3 9	...	...	...	...	...	1 34	:	a.m.	:	4 9	...	4 24
" dep	4 5	5 13	...	5 42	...	6 25	8 23	...	...	7 54	11 12	...	10 54	...	3 15	...	...	...	...	...	1 38	:	4 35	:	4 15	...	4 29
Eichenberg arr	4 40	5 47	...	6 2	...	6 56	:	...	...	8 14	11 42	...	:	...	:	...	...	...	...	...	:	:	5 9	:	:	...	:
BEBRA 149A arr	...	...	...	7 p37	...	8 p26	:	...	...	11p13	...	...	:	...	:	...	...	...	...	...	:	:	...	:	:	...	5a50
FRANKFORT 149A arr	...	...	...	...	p.m.	...	:	...	...	...	...	...	:	...	:	...	...	...	...	...	5 a42	:	...	:	:	...	...
Eichenberg dep	4 43	6 17	...	6 5	7 50	7 0	:	...	...	8 15	11 46	...	:	...	:	...	...	...	...	...	:	:	...	:	:	...	...
Münden	5 20	6 51	...	...	8 48	7 29	9 23	...	...	8 42	12 22	...	11 39	...	4 11	...	...	...	...	...	:	:	...	:	5 2	...	...
Cassel arr	6 4	7 37	...	6 52	9 29	7 56	10 4	...	...	9 9	1 3	...	12 7	...	4 57	...	...	...	...	...	:	2 44	...	3 58	5 30	...	...

	2,3,4		Ex 3	Ex 3	2,3,4	2,3,4	2,3,4	2,3,4	2,3,4				2,3,4	2,3,4							:	Ex 3		Ex 2	Ex 3	2,3,4	
	p.m.			p.m.		p.m.	p.m.															a.m.		a.m.	a.m.		
Cassel ....dep	6 29	...	...	7 0	...	8 18	11 6	...	...	...	...	...	...	...	...	...	...	...	...	...		2 50	‡—Weekdays only.	4 4	5 40	...	...
Wilhelmshöhe	6 37	...	...	...	...	8 26	11 14	...	...	...	...	...	...	...	...	...	...	...	...	...		...		...	...	...	...
Guntershausen	6 56	...	...	...	...	8 47	11 32	...	...	...	...	...	...	...	...	...	...	...	...	...		...		...	...	...	...
Grifte	7 1	...	...	...	...	8 52	11 37	...	...	...	...	...	...	...	...	...	...	...	...	...		...		...	...	...	...
Wabern 156A	7 45	...	...	7 38	...	9 24	12 7	...	...	...	...	...	...	...	...	...	...	...	...	...		...		...	6 18	...	...
Borken	8 1	...	...	...	...	9 40	12 21	...	...	...	...	...	...	...	...	...	...	...	...	...		...		...	...	a.m.	...
Treysa 147	8 35	...	...	...	...	10 13	12 51	...	...	...	...	...	...	...	...	...	...	...	...	...		...		...	6 47	4 27	...
Neustadt	8 46	...	...	...	...	10 27	1 6	...	...	...		...	...	...	...	...	...	...	...	...		...	...	...	...	4 41	...
Kirchhain 155	9 10	...	...	...	...	10 48	1 28	...	...	...	2,3,4	...	...	...	...	...	...	...	...	...		...	2,3,4	...	...	5 4	...
Cölbe	9 29	...	...	...	p.m.	11 6	1 46	...	...	...	p.m.	...	...	...	...	...	...	...	...	...		...	a.m.	...	...	5 22	...
Marburg	9 35	...	...	8 46	8 56	11 18	1 56	...	...	...	9 53	...	...	...	...	...	...	...	...	...		4 26	4‡43	5 37	7 34	5 53	...
Niederwalgern 154		...	...	...	9 16	11 36	2 12	...	p.m.	...	10 15	...	...	...	...	...	...	...	...	...		...	5 3	...	...	6 11	...
Lollar		...	...	...	9 35	11 55	2 28	...	11 18	...		...	...	...	...	...	...	...	...	...		...	5 23	...	...	6 31	...
Giessen ....arr	...	...	...	9 12	9 45	12 5	2 37	...	11 31	...	...	...	...	...	...	...	...	...	...	...		4 52	5 32	6 3	8 5	6 41	...
Ems 147 ....arr	...	...	...	12a30	...	...	...	...	...	...	...	...	...	...	...	...	...	...	...	...		7 a49	...	7 a58	10 a9	...	...
Coblence 147 ....arr	...	...	p.m.	1 a12	...	...	...	...	...	...	...	...	a.m.	...	...	...	...	...	...	...		8 a29	...	8 a29	10a50	...	...
Giessen ....dep	...	...	9 21	9 14	10 1	...	2 47	...	11 47	...	...	...	4 ‡20	...	...	...	...	...	...	...		4 56	5 35	6 13	8 10	6 49	...
Lang Göns	...	...	...	...	10 17	...	3 3	...	12 5	...	...	...	4 36	...	...	...	...	...	...	...		...	5 51	...	...	7 4	...
Butzbach	p.m.	...	...	...	10 32	p.m.	3 17	...	12 27	...	...	...	4 51	...	...	...	...	...	...	...		...	6 6	...	...	7 18	...
Nauheim Bad ....dep	8 0	...	9 53	9 44	10 49	10 12	3 33	a.m.	12 38	...	...	...	5 7	a.m.	...	...	...	...	...	...		5 26	6 22	6 42	8 41	7 40	...
Friedberg	8 6	...	10 0	9 51	10 59	10 18	3 39	4 36	12 44	...	...	...	5 17	5 45	...	...	...	...	...	...		5 34	6 31	...	8 48	7 52	...
Niederwöllstadt		...	...	...	11 11		3 49	4 49		...	...	...	5 31	6 3	...	...	...	...	...	...		...	6 44	...	...	8 17	...
Gross-Karben	...	...	...	...	11 23	...	4 0	5 0	...	...	...	...	5 53	6 18	...	...	...	...	...	...		...	7 2	...	...	8 28	...
Vilbel	...	...	...	...	11 33	...	4 11	5 13	...	...	...	...	6 6	6 35	...	...	...	...	...	...		...	7 13	...	...	8 38	...
Bonames	...	...	...	...	11 45	...	4 27	5 28	...	...	...	...	6 19	6 47	...	...	...	...	...	...		...	7 29	...	...	8 9	...
FRANKFORT ....arr	...	...	10 33	10 25	12 5	...	4 46	5 47	...	...	...	...	6 40	7 12	...	...	...	...	...	...	5 42	6 7	7 49	7 18	9 21	9 0	...
Mannheim 136 or 139 arr	...	...	12a10	12a10	...	...	7 a2	...	...	...	...	...	...	...	...	...	...	...	...	...	7 a2	8 a0	...	8 a56	11 a4	11 a4	...
Carlsruhe ....140 arr	...	...	2 a11	2 a11	...	...	8 a1	...	...	...	...	...	...	...	...	...	...	...	...	...	8 a44	8 a44	...	10a26	11a53	11a53	...
Basle ....140 arr	...	...	5 a38	5 a38	...	...	11 a0	...	...	...	...	...	...	...	...	...	...	...	...	...	12p16	12p16	...	...	2 p55	2 p55	...
Mayence ......123A arr	...	...	12a31	12a31	...	...	6 a3	...	...	...	...	...	...	...	...	...	...	...	...	...	7 a43	7 a43	...	8 a8	10a34	10a34	...
Strassburg ...208 arr	...	...	3 a58	3 a58	...	...	...	...	...	...	...	...	...	...	...	...	...	...	...	...	9 a4	10a55	...	10a55	12p49	...	...
Basle ....208 arr	...	...	6 a7	6 a7	...	...	...	...	...	...	...	...	...	...	...	...	...	...	...	...	11a15	12p58	...	12p58	2 p52	...	...
Milan ....269A arr	...	...	3 p5	3 p5	...	...	...	...	...	...	...	...	...	...	...	...	...	...	...	...	8 p40	10p25	...	10p25	...	...	...

*—Restaurant Car.

LOHNE, OSNABRUCK, and RHEINE.

		Ex3	Ex3	2 3 4	2—4	1,2,3	2 3 4	Ex 3	2 3 4	Ex3	2 3 4	Ex2	Ex2	2—4	1,2,3	2—4	2 3 4	1,2,3	2 3 4
Hanover 160 ....dep		From Hambrg	2a22	...	6a30	9 a0	9 a0	10a46	1250	3p48	...	4p32	From Altona.	3p48	5p12	5p17	7p20	9p23	12 0
				a.m.	a.m.	a.m.	a.m.	p.m.	p.m.	p.m.				p.m.	p.m.	p.m.	p.m.	p.m.	a.m.
Lohne ....dep				6 34	7 53	10 27	1034	12*22	2 28	5*11	...	*		5 42	6 58	7 30	1016	1110	1 38
Bünde				6 52	8 10	10 38	1052	12 33	2 44	5 23	...			5 57	7 9	7 45	1041	1121	1 53
Melle		a.m.		7 14	8 35	10 54	1116	12 49	3 7	5 40	...		p.m.	6 20	7 25	8 7	11 4	1137	2 16
Osnabruck ....arr	a.m.	4 14	4 21	7 46	9 4	11 12	1148	1 7	3 35	5 58	p.m.	6 18	6 22	6 50	7 43	8 37	1133	1155	2 45
" 132 dep	6 48	4 39	4 46		9 46	11 17	1218	1 36	3 42	6 1	6 14	6 36	6 36	7 48				1216	
Ibbenburen	7 28	...	To Vlissingen.	...	1024	11 43	1259	2 0	4 21	...	6 50	To Vlissingen.	...	8 26	...	...	...	1254	...
Rheine ....arr	8 2	5 29		...	1053	12 0	1 32	2 18	4 49	6 38	7 16		7*25	8 55	...	...	...	1 22	...
Amsterdam 118c arr		8a37		...	...	...	5 p2	5 p2	...	9p30	...		10p5	...	...	...	...	...	...

	2 3 4	1,2,3	2—4	2—4	1,2,3	Ex2	Ex2	2,3,4	Ex 3	2 3 4	Ex3	2—4	1,2,3	1,2,3	2 3 4	2 3 4	Ex3	Ex3
Amsterdam 118B........dep	...	...	...	...	...	6a10	From Vlis'gen	...	8 a0	8a22	1020	...	3p35	...	...	...	9 p0	From Vlis'gen
			a.m.	a.m.	a.m.			a.m.	p.m.	p.m.	p.m.	p.m.	p.m.	p.m.	p.m.	p.m.	a.m.	
Rheine ....dep	...	...	5 54	8 18	...			11 4	12*28	1 55	2*44	4 55	7 54	...	9 0	1058	1 16	
Ibbenburen........	...	...	6 29	8 49	...			11 33	12 49	2 24	3 5	5 24	8 15	...	9 29	1121	...	
Osnabruck ....arr	a.m.	a.m.	7 8	9 26	...	1119	1116	12 9	1 11	3 5	3 30	5 59	8 37	...	10 3	1146	2 4	2 a1
" ....dep	4 40	7 11	8 4	9 42	1044	1135	1137	12 15	1 21	3 12	3 38	6 14	8 45	9 52		1150	To Hamburg.	2 23
Melle........	5 12	7 32	8 35	1015	11 5	To Altona.	*	12 44	...	3 46	3 59	6 44	9 15	1013	...	1220		
Bünde	5 47	7 57	9 8	1056	1120			1 6	...	4 21	4 14	7 8	9 37	1028	...	1242		
Lohne 161........arr	6 3	8 8	9 23	1112	1131			1 20	2 0	4 37	4 26	7 22	9 53	1039	...	1255		
Hanover ....arr	7a35	9a58	1213	1 p2	1 p2		1p20	2 p49	3 p20	6p33	5p48	1044	1225	1236	...	...		4a17

ELZE and BODENBURG.

Elze ....dep	6a40	7a38	10a28	1p58	4p37	5p57	8p47	9p37	1a14
Gronau	7 0	7 48	10 46	2 7	4 47	6 6	8 55	9 47	1 24
Bodenburg ..arr	8 1	...	11 29	2 48	...	6 48	...	1032	...
Bodenburg ..dep	5a10	...	8a40	11a43	3 p5	...	...	7 p3	...
Gronau	5 54	9a10	9 40	12 23	3 56	5p10	...	7 43	9p10
Elze ....arr	6 4	9 20	9 50	12 31	4 6	5 20	...	7 51	9 18

CASSEL and WALDKAPPEL.

Dist									
	Cassel ....dep	7 a8	9a54	12p9	1p51	5 p3	6‡15	7p20	1040
1¾	Wilhelmshöhe	7 19	10 5	1220	2 2	5 14	6 26	7 31	1051
7½	Bettenhausen	7 45	1026	1240	2 23	5 35	6 50	7 52	1110
15½	Helsa	8 25	11 7	1 16	3 4	6 13	7 28	8 32	1146
21¾	Lichtenau	8 56	1139	1 44	3 34	6 45	8 4	9 1	1215
24½	Walburg ....arr	9 3	1146	1 51	3 41	6 52	8 11	9 8	1222
28½	Gross Almerode ar	9 36	1219	2 24	4 17	7 19	...	9 35	1248
30½	**Waldkappel 147** arr	9 31	1213	2 18	4 9	7 19	8 38	9 35	...
...	**Waldkappel** ....dep	5a57	9a55	1240	2p35	4p46	7p30	9p47	‡—Not on Sunday.
...	Gross Almerode dp	5 56	9 54	1242	2 36	4 44	7 24	9 41	
...	Walburg ....dep	6 30	1028	1 13	3 5	5 17	7 55	10 9	
...	Lichtenau	6 38	1036	1 21	3 13	5 25	8 3	...	
...	Helsa	7 5	11 4	1 48	3 39	5 49	8 31	1040	
...	Bettenhausen	7 36	1135	2 22	4 10	6 20	9 5	11 9	
...	Wilhelmshöhe	7 56	1157	2 43	4 30	7 8	9 27	1127	
...	**Cassel 156**........arr	8 6	12 7	2 53	4 40	7 18	9 37	1137	

Luggage Rates—see page 462.] PRUSSIAN STATE RAILWAYS. [For Fares—see page 120A.

FRANKFORT, CASSEL, HANOVER, and HAMBURG.

RC—Restaurant Car. THROUGH CARRIAGES.—Frankfort to Hamburg, in 5.58 a.m., 8.52 a.m., and 12.48 p.m. *—Weekdays only.

Station																										
MILAN 269A ....dep	...	...	...	...	...	...	...	2 p40	...	...	...	...	...	...	...	...	...	...	...	...	...	...	11p35	...	...	...
BASLE 209....dep	...	...	...	...	...	...	...	11p48	...	...	...	...	...	...	...	...	...	...	...	6 a0	6 a0	...	9 a29	...	...	...
STRASSBURG 209 dep	...	...	...	...	...	...	...	1 a53	...	...	...	...	...	6 a0	...	...	6 a0	...	6 a55	8 a24	8 a24	...	11a26	...	...	...
MAYENCE 123 ....dep	...	...	...	...	...	...	...	5 a0	...	...	6 a0	...	8 a1	8 a14	...	...	8 a14	...	10a28	11a22	11a22	...	1 p39	...	11a22	12p58
BASLE 141....dep	...	...	...	...	...	...	...	11p52	...	...	...	...	...	...	...	...	...	...	4 a30	7 a53	7 a53	...	9 a50	...	...	8 a0
CARLSRUHE 141....dep	...	...	...	...	...	...	...	3 a5	...	...	...	...	5 a8	6 a55	...	...	6 a55	...	9 a5	10a36	10a36	...	12p33	...	...	11a17
MANNHEIM 136, 139 dep	...	...	...	...	...	...	...	3 a54	3 a54	...	4 a24	...	7 a4	8 a20	...	...	8 a20	...	10 a0	11a24	11a24	...	1 p24	...	11a24	12p22
	2,3,4	2,3,4	2,3,4			2,3,4	2,3,4	Ex 3	2,3,4	Ex 3	2,3,4	2,3,4	1,2,3	Ex 3	Ex 3	1,2,3	2,3,4	2,3,4	Ex 3	Ex 3	Ex 3	2,3,4	Ex 3	Ex 3	2,3,4	1,2,3
FRANKFORT Hauptbahnhof ....dep	...	...	a.m. 4 *16	...	...	...	...	a.m. 5 58	a.m. 6 4	a.m. 6 51	a.m. 7 45	...	a.m. 8 52	a.m. 10 0	a.m. Homburg depart 10.3.	...	a.m. 10 5	a.m. 11 2	p.m. 12 8	p.m. 12 53	p.m. 12 48	...	p.m. 2 55	...	p.m. 1 2	p.m. 2 11
Bonames	...	...	4 36	...	...	...	...	...	6 24	...	8 7	...	...	...		...	10 24	11 22	...	⋮	...	...	⋮	...	1 22	...
Vilbel	...	...	4 51	...	...	...	...	RC	6 37	...	8 19	...	...	...		...	10 34	11 34	RC	⋮	RC	...	⋮	...	1 34	...
Gross-Karben	...	...	5 4	...	...	...	...	...	6 47	...	8 31	...	...	...		...	10 45	11 45	...	⋮	...	...	⋮	...	1 45	...
Niederwöllstadt	...	a.m.	5 17	...	...	a.m.	a.m.	...	6 58	...	8 44	a.m.	...	...		p.m.	10 55	11 56	...	⋮	...	p.m.	⋮	...	1 57	...
Friedberg	...	4 42	5 38	...	...	6 *7	6 58	6 37	7 12	7 30	8 58	9 18	9 26	10 36		12 29	11 9	12 11	12 42	⋮	1 22	12 55	⋮	...	2 13	2 44
Nauheim Bad	...	4 49	5 46	...	...	6 14	7 5	6 45	7 19	7 38	9 5	9 24	9 36	10 43	10 50	12 35	11 17	12 19	12 52	⋮	1 30	1 3	⋮	...	2 21	2 52
Butzbach	...	5 6	6 4	...	...		7 24	...	7 35	...	9 23		9 49		...		11 33	12 37	...	⋮	...	1 20	⋮	...	2 38	...
Lang-Göns	...	5 20	6 19	...	...	...	7 39	...	7 48	...	9 38	...	...	...	...	...	11 46	12 53	...	⋮	...		⋮	...	2 52	...
Giessen ....arr	...	5 34	6 35	...	...	...	7 55	7 13	8 1	8 6	9 52	...	10 8	...	11 18	...	12 0	1 9	1 20	⋮	1 58	...	⋮	...	3 6	3 19
COBLENCE 146 ....dep	...	...	...	...	...	...	...	...	...		5 a32	...	5 a32	...	8 a45	...	8 a45	...	10a22	⋮	10a22	...	⋮	1 p22	...	...
EMS 146....dep	...	...	...	...	...	...	...	...	...		6 a29	...	6 a29	...	9 a16	...	9 a16	...	11 a7	⋮	11 a7	...	⋮	1 p49	...	...
Giessen ....dep	a.m. 5 0	5 39	6 43	...	...	a.m. 4 0	...	7 16	8 18	Cologne arrive 10.50.	10 23	...	10 16	...	11 27	...	12 10	...	1 29	⋮	2 0	p.m. 2 7	⋮	p.m. 3 34	3 12	...
Lollar	5 10	5 50	6 54	...	...	4 10	...	...	8 28		10 33	...	...	...	...	...	12 20	...	...	⋮	...	2 22	⋮	...	3 23	...
Niederwalgern	5 29	6 8	7 14	...	...	4 27	...	...	8 47		10 53	...	...	...	...	...	12 35	...	...	⋮	...		⋮	...	3 42	...
Marburg	6 15	6 25	7 34	...	...	4 49	...	7 44	9 7		11 13	...	10 49	...	11 54	...	12 55	...	1 57	⋮	2 30	...	⋮	4 7	4 13	...
Colbe	6 22			...	...	4 56	...	...	9 14	...		...	10 57	...	...	...	1 2	...	...	⋮	...	...	⋮	...	4 20	...
Kirchhain	6 40	...	...	...	...	5 14	...	8 0	9 33	...	...	...	11 11	...	...	...	1 20	...	...	⋮	...	...	⋮	...	4 39	...
Neustadt	7 3	...	...	...	...	5 38	...	...	9 57	...	...	...	...	...	...	...	1 43	...	...	⋮	...	...	⋮	...	5 1	...
Treysa 147	7 16	...	...	...	...	5 53	...	8 28	10 10	...	...	...	11 40	...	...	...	1 55	...	2 39	⋮	...	...	⋮	...	5 13	...
Borken	7 45	a.m.	...	...	...	6 23	...	...	10 36	...	...	...	...	...	...	...	2 20	p.m.	...	⋮	...	...	⋮	...	5 38	...
Wabern 156A	7 59	5*20	...	...	...	6 39	...	8 56	10 50	...	...	...	12 8	...	1 2	...	2 33	3*34	3 5	⋮	...	...	⋮	5 14	5 50	...
Grifte	8 26	5 48	...	...	...	7 6	...	...	11 18	...	...	...	...	...	...	...	2 57	4 6	...	⋮	...	...	⋮	...	6 14	...
Guntershausen	8 32	5 54	...	...	...	7 12	...	...	11 24	...	...	...	12 30	...	...	...	3 5	4 13	3 27	⋮	3 52	...	⋮	...	6 20	...
Wilhelmshöhe	8 48	6 13	...	...	...	7 36	...	9 30	11 39	...	...	...	12 44	...	...	...	3 21	4 32	...	⋮	4 7	...	⋮	...	6 38	...
Cassel ....arr	8 55	6 20	...	...	...	7 43	...	9 37	11 46	...	...	...	12 51	...	1 37	...	3 28	4 39	3 44	⋮	4 14	...	⋮	5 51	6 45	...
			Ex 3	2 3 4		1—4	1,2,3	Ex 3	2,3,4	2,3,4	1,2,3		1,2,3	2,3,4	Ex 3	2,3,4				Ex 3	Ex 3	2,3,4	Ex 3	Ex 3	2,3,4	
Cassel ....dep	...	...	a.m. 6 45	a.m. 7 9	...	a.m. 9 0	...	a.m. 9 46	...	p.m. 12 34	...	...	p.m. 1 22	a.m. 11 22	p.m. 1 43	p.m. 2 11	...	...	...	⋮	p.m. 4 20	p.m. 4 29	⋮	p.m. 6 6	p.m. 7 3	...
Munden	...	...	7 11	7 52	...	9 36	...	10 11	...	1 19	...	...	1 50	12 1	⋮	2 48	...	...	...	⋮	4 47	5 7	⋮	6 32	7 41	...
Eichenberg ....arr	...	...	⋮	8 31	...	⋮	...	⋮	...	1 59	...	...	⋮	12 36	⋮	3 23	...	...	...	⋮	⋮	⋮	⋮	⋮	⋮	...
FRANKFORT 149....dep	...	...	⋮	...	...	⋮	...	⋮	...	...	9 a58	...	⋮	...	⋮	...	...	...	...	12p53	⋮	⋮	2 p55	⋮	⋮	...
BEBRA 149 ....dep	...	...	⋮	...	...	⋮	...	⋮	10 a0	...	1 p16	...	⋮	...	⋮	...	...	...	...	4 p5	⋮	⋮	5 56	⋮	⋮	...
Eichenberg ....dep	...	...	⋮	8 41	...	⋮	...	⋮	12 10	2 7	2 36	...	⋮	12 43	⋮	3 31	...	...	...	⋮	⋮	⋮	⋮	⋮	⋮	...
Göttingen ....arr	...	...	7 55	9 10	...	10 36	a.m.	10 56	12 40	2 35	2 53	...	2 40	1 12	2 45	4 0	...	...	...	5 23	5 31	5 56	7 15	7 12	8 30	...
Göttingen ....dep	...	...	7 59		...	11 14	11 8	11 1	12 49	3 30	2 58	...	3 4		2 46		...	...	...	5 28	5 35	6 1	7 19	7 29	8 38	...
Norten	...	...	...	...	...	11 29	...	⋮	1 4	3 46	...	...	...	...	...	...	...	...	...	...	...	6 17	...	...	8 54	...
Northeim ....arr	...	...	8 17	...	...	11 40	11 30	⋮	1 16	3 58	3 15	...	3 22	...	...	...	...	...	...	...	5 53	6 29	7 36	...	9 5	...
Northeim ....dep	...	...	8 18	...	...	11 43	11 37	⋮	1 17	4 2	3 17	...	3 25	...	...	...	...	...	...	...	5 54	6 33	7 37	...	9 10	...
Salzderhelden	...	...	8 32	...	...	12 0	11 50	⋮	1 34	4 20	...	...	3 38	...	...	...	...	...	...	...	...	6 52	...	...	9 27	...
Kreiensen ....arr	...	...	8 42	...	...	12 10	11 59	⋮	1 43	4 30	3 35	...	3 47	...	3 21	...	...	...	...	6 3	6 12	7 1	7 54	8 0	9 37	...
MAGDEBURG 164 ...arr	...	...	...	...	...	4 p47	4 p47	⋮	4 p47	...	6 p28	...	6 p28	...	5 p36	...	...	...	...	...	...	...	...	10 p4	...	...
BERLIN 164 ....arr	...	...	...	...	...	6 p54	6 p54	⋮	6 p54	...	8 p56	...	8 p56	...	7 p31	...	...	...	...	...	...	...	...	11 59	...	...

For Continuation of Trains, see

next page.

Kreiensen ....dep	...	...	8 46	...	...	12 14	12 0	⋮	2 4	4 34	3 36	...	3 56	...	...	...	...	...	...	6 8	6 19	7 9	7 55	...	9 45	...
Freden	...	...	...	...	...	12 26	...	⋮	2 17	4 47	...	...	...	...	...	...	...	...	...	...	...	7 21	...	...	9 57	...
Alfeld	...	...	9 7	...	...	12 38	12 19	⋮	2 29	4 59	...	...	4 15	...	...	...	...	...	...	...	6 39	7 31	...	...	10 8	...
Elze	...	...	9 26	...	...	1 7	12 36	⋮	3 4	5 26	...	...	4 33	...	...	...	...	...	...	6 42	6 59	7 59	8 25	...	10 36	...
Nordstemmen	...	...	...	...	...	1 30	...	⋮	3 16	5 41	4 13	...	4 43	...	...	...	...	...	...	...	...	8 14	...	...	10 51	...
Sarstedt	...	...	...	...	...	1 44	...	⋮	3 29	5 54	⋮	...	...	...	...	...	...	...	...	...	...	8 42	...	...	11 3	...
HANOVER ....arr	...	...	9 55	...	...	2 10	1 5	12 23	3 57	6 23	⋮	...	5 6	...	...	...	...	...	...	7 11	7 28	9 8	8 52	...	11 30	...
BREMEN 159........arr	...	...	12p38	...	...	5 p41	4 p20	4 p20	7 p33	9 p50	⋮	...	7 p50	...	...	...	...	...	...	...	...	...	10 53	...	1 a59	...
	2,3,4	2,3,4	Ex 3		2,3,4	2,3,4	1,2,3	Ex 3	Ex 3		⋮		1,2,3				2,3,4			Ex 3	Ex 3	2,3,4	Ex 3		2,3,4	
			a.m.		a.m.	p.m.	p.m.	p.m.			⋮		p.m.				p.m.			p.m.	p.m.	p.m.	p.m.		p.m.	
HANOVER ....dep	...	...	10 22	...	9 58	2 20	1 31	12 30	...	...	⋮	...	5 35	...	...	...	5 40	...	§—From Hanover until 15th September only.	7§24	7 38	9 42	9 4	...	11 34	...
Lehrte ....arr	...	...	10 37	...	10 23	2 45	1 48	12 46	...	...	5 5	...	5 51	...	...	...	6 2	...		7 40	7 54	9 58	9 20	...	11 54	...
BRUNSWICK 158 ......dep	...	...	9 a42	...	9 a42	...	12 25	11 12	...	...	4 p0	...	4 p36	...	...	...	4 p36	...		6 p21	6 p21	...	7 p51	...	10p40	...
Lehrte ....dep	...	...	10 41	...	10 53	2 49	1 52	12 50	...	...	5 9	...	5 57	...	...	...	6 6	...		7 44	7 58	10 5	9 24	...	12 1	...
Burgdorf	...	...	...	...	11 9	3 3	2 2	...	...	...	...	...	...	...	...	...	6 21	...		...	...	10 20	...	...	12 15	...
Celle	...	...	11 5	...		3 29	2 20	1 14	...	...	5 36	...	6 26	...	...	...	6 47	...		8 7	8 21	11 15	9 47	...	12 42	...
Eschede	...	...	...	...	...	3 51	...	...	...	...	...	...	...	...	...	...	7 8	...		...	...	11 40	...	...		...
Uelzen 163 ....arr	a.m.	...	11 48	...	...	4 33	3 11	1 59	p.m.	...	6 21	...	7 20	...	...	...	7 47	...		8 50	9 2	12 22	10 28	...	p.m.	...
Uelzen 163 ....dep	6 43	...	11 49	...	...	4 43	3 16	2 2	3 5	...	6 25	...	7 25	...	...	...	7 56	...		8 52	9 6		10 30	...	10 35	...
Lüneburg 169 ....arr	7 30	...	12 17	...	...	5 28	3 48	2 31	3 35	2,3,4	6 54	...	7 54	...	...	...	8 42	...		9 21	9 33	...	10 56	...	11 23	...
LUBECK 213A ....arr	...	p.m.	4 p9	...	...	8 p11	5 p42	...	5 p42	p.m.	8 p38	...	...	...	...	...	...	...		11p25	11p25	...	...	...	...	...
Lüneburg ....dep	7 45	1 38	12 18	...	...	5 33	3 51	2 33	3 37	7 7	6 55	...	7 57	...	...	...	8 51	...		9 23	9 35	...	10 57	...	11 29	...
Winsen	8 4	2 5	...	...	...	5 58	4 10	...	...	7 34	7 12	...	8 14	...	...	...	9 17	...		...	...	...	...	...	11 52	...
Harburg	8 30	2 40	12 50	...	...	6 36	4 32	3 5	4 10	8 15	7 31	...	8 33	...	...	...	10 1	...	...	9 57	10 8	...	11 27	...	12 21	...
HAMBURG Hauptbahnf	8 46	3 0	1 8	...	...	6 55	4 49	3 23	4 28	8 35	7 50	...	8 50	...	...	...	10 22	...	...	10 14	10 26	...	11 43	...	12 45	...
KIEL 168 ....arr	10a55	...	3 p36	...	...	10p20	7 p25	5 p29	7 p25	10p53	...	...	10 53	...	...	...	1 a16	...	...	1 a16	1 a16	...	...	...	...	...
COPENHAGEN 302 ...arr	...	...	...	...	...	...	...	...	...	...	...	...	...	...	...	...	10 a4	...	...	10 a4	10 a4	...	...	...	...	...
WARNEMUNDE 178B..	...	...	...	...	...	...	...	...	...	...	...	...	...	...	...	...	3 a20	...	...	3 a20	3 a20	...	3 a20	...	...	...
COPENHAGEN 302 arr	...	...	...	...	...	...	...	...	...	...	...	...	...	...	...	...	9 a42	...	...	9 a42	9 a42	...	9 a42	...	...	...

NORDSTEMMEN, HILDESHEIM, and LEHRTE.

	1,2,3	2,3,4	1,2,3	2,3,4	2,3,4	2,3,4	2,3,4	2,3,4	2,3,4	2,3,4	1,2,3	2,3,4	Ex 3	2,3,4	2,3,4	Ex 3	2,3,4	1,2,3	2,3,4	2,3,4	2,3,4	2,3,4	2,3,4	2 3 4	2 3 4	2,3,4	2,3,4
HANOVER ....dep	2 a18	5 a29	6 a20	...	6 a30	8 a0	9 a5	...	10a33	11 47	12p43	12p50	1 p10	2 p32	...	3 p19	3 p27	...	...	4 p43	...	6 p0	7 p38	9 p1	...	10p30	12a14
	a.m.	a.m.	⋮	a.m.	a.m.	a.m.	a.m.	a.m.	a.m.	p.m.	p.m.	p.m.	⋮	⋮	...	⋮	⋮	p.m.	p.m.	p.m.	...	p.m.	p.m.	p.m.	p.m.	p.m.	nght
Nordstemmen ....dep	3 16	6 27	⋮	6 47	7 0	8 50	9 54	10 29	11 0	12 33	1 25	1 44	⋮	⋮	...	⋮	⋮	4 13	4 46	5 41	...	6 29	8 43	9 28	1052	11 20	1 0
Hildesheim ....arr	3 31	6 45	6 55	7 5	7 19	9 11	10 13	10 47	11 15	12 50	1 38	2 1	1 46	3 14	p.m.	3 54	4 18	4 26	5 5	5 58	p.m.	6 49	9 0	9 45	11 9	11 39	1 17
Hildesheim ....dep	5 17			7 10		9 17			11 20	12 56		2 6			3 11			4 37	5 13	6 8	7 17		9 13		1116		
Algermissen	5 33	...	...	7 28	...	9 34	...	...	11 35	1 12	...	2 22	...	...	3 27	...	...	...	5 29	6 24	7 33	...	9 29	...	1132	...	...
Lehrte 160 ....arr	5 51	...	...	7 48	...	9 53	...	...	11 55	1 30	...	2 40	...	...	3 45	...	...	5 5	5 48	6 43	7 52	...	9 49	...	1150	...	...
HANOVER ....arr	6 a24	...	...	8 a26	...	10 12	...	...	12p17	2 p1	...	3 p11	...	...	4 p17	...	...	...	6 p20	7 p14	8 p46	...	10 24	...	1a18	...	...
	1,2,3	2,3,4	2,3,4	2,3,4	2,3,4	2,3,4	2,3,4	2,3,4	2,3,4	2,3,4	2,3,4	2,2,4	1,2,3	2,3,4	Ex 3	2,3,4	2,3,4	Ex 3	2,3,4	2,3,4	2,3,4	2,3,4	2,3,4	2,3,4	1,2,3	2,3,4	2 3 4
HANOVER ....dep	...	12a52	...	...	...	5 a38	6 a31	...	8 a22	...	9 a34	...	12p5	11a38	...	1 p36	2 p20	...	3 p43	...	5 p40	6 p48	...	...	...	9 p12	11p5
		a.m.				a.m.	a.m.		a.m.		a.m.		p.m.	p.m.		p.m.	p.m.		p.m.		p.m.	p.m.				p.m.	p.m.
Lehrte ....dep	...	2 0	...	...	...	6 15	7 5	...	8 43	...	10 6	...	1226	12 33	...	2 7	3 24	...	4 13	...	6 8	7 10	...	...	...	9 38	1139
Algermissen	...	2 21	...	...	...	6 34	7 24	...	9 5	...	10 26	...	...	12 54	...	2 26	3 43	...	4 36	...	6 30	7 29	...	...	...	10 1	1158
Hildesheim ....arr	a.m.	2 38	a.m.	a.m.	a.m.	6 49	7 39	a.m.	9 22	a.m.	10 43	p.m.	1250	1 11	p.m.	2 41	3 58	p.m.	4 53	p.m.	6 47	7 44	p.m.	p.m.	p.m.	10 19	1213
Hildesheim ....dep	2 24	5 50	5 17	6 28	6 58	7 6	7 51	8 53	9 31	10 23	10 51	12 43		1 55	2 41	2 53	4 15	5 17	5 22	5 57		7 50	9 3	9 53	10 36	10 54	1232
Nordstemmen ....arr	2 37	6 7	⋮	6 45	⋮	7 23	8 7	⋮	9 47	10 41	11 7	12 59	...	2 11	⋮	3 10	4 33	⋮	5 36	6 15	...	8 7	9 20	⋮	⋮	11 10	1249
HANOVER ....arr	3 a35	...	6 a13	7 30	7 a50	...	8 52	9 32	11a17	...	...	2 p10	...	...	3 p14	3 p57	5 p6	5 50	6 p23	7 p5	...	9 p8	...	10 44	11 10	11 40	...

FRIEDBERG and HANAU.

Dist. E.M		a.m.	a.m.	a.m.	a.m.	p.m.	p.m.	p.m.	p.m.	p.m.	p.m.	
	Friedberg ....dep	4 34	5 37	6 48	9 27	12 8	1 10	3 34	6 7	8 18	10 27	...
6¼	Erbstadt-Kaichen	4 51	5 54	7 8	9 43	12 25	1 31	3 56	6 26	8 38	10 46	...
10	Heldenbergen-Windck...	5 0	6 8	7 20	9 51	12 34	1 42	4 8	6 38	8 51	10 57	...
16¾	**Hanau** (Nord)	5 20	6 29	7 40	10 9	12 54	2 4	4 29	6 58	9 12	11 20	...
20	**Hanau** (Ost, 149........arr	5 30	6 39	7 51	10 17	1 2	2 15	4 39	7 7	9 22	11 29	...

	a.m.	a.m.	a.m.	a.m.	a.m.	p.m.	p.m.	p.m.	p.m.	p.m.
Hanau (Ost) ....dep	6 3	6 49	7 41	9 11	11 35	1 11	4 4	6 40	7 50	10 54
Hanau (Nord) ....dep	6 11	6 57	7 49	9 20	11 44	1 19	4 12	6 50	7 58	11 2
Heldenbergen-Windck...	6 34	7 21	8 11	9 46	12 8	1 41	4 33	7 17	8 20	11 22
Erbstadt-Kaichen	6 44	7 31	8 21	9 56	12 19	1 51	4 43	7 28	8 30	11 31
Friedberg 157 ....arr	7 1	7 47	8 37	10 13	12 35	2 7	4 59	7 45	8 46	11 45

Luggage Rates—see page 462.] PRUSSIAN STATE RAILWAYS. [For Fares—see page 120A.

FRANKFORT, CASSEL, HANOVER, and HAMBURG.

THROUGH CARRIAGES.—Frankfort to Hamburg, in 8.55 p.m. and 11.13 p.m. from Frankfort.

Station	1—4	1,2,3	1,2,3	2,3,4	1,2,3	Ex 3		2,3,4	2,3,4	2,3,4	2,3,4	2,3,4	1,2,3	2,3,4	Ex 3	Ex 3	2,3,4	2,3,4	1,2,3	2,3,4	Ex 2	Ex 2	Ex 3		2,3,4		
MILAN 269A ......dep	11p35	...	...	...	...	...	...	...	...	...	...	...	...	...	...	...	...	...	...	...	7 a25	7 a25	7 a25	...	...	...	...
BASLE 209 ......dep	9 a29	...	...	...	...	...	...	...	...	...	...	...	...	...	12p15	3 p19	...	...	...	...	4 p59	4 p59	4 p59	...	...	...	...
STRASSBURG 209..dep	11a26	...	...	...	...	...	...	...	...	...	...	...	...	...	2 p14	5 p25	...	...	...	...	7 p7	7 p7	7 p7	...	...	...	...
MAYENCE 123......dep	1 p39	...	...	...	3 p28	3 p28	...	...	...	4 p43	...	...	6 p20	...	...	7 p57	...	...	...	...	9 p26	10 p6	10 p6	...	...	...	...
BASLE 141......dep	9 a50	...	...	...	10a42	10a42	...	...	...	10a42	...	...	1 p0	...	2 p33	2 p33	...	...	...	...	5 p18	5 p33	5 p33	...	5 p33	...	...
CARLSRUHE 141......dep	12p33	...	...	...	1 p57	2 p20	...	...	...	2 p20	...	...	4 p8	...	5 p39	5 p39	...	...	...	...	8 p9	8 p38	8 p38	...	8 p38	...	...
MANNHEIM 136, 139 dep	1 p25	...	...	1 p43	3 p0	3 p0	...	...	...	3 p8	...	5 p6	5 p6	...	5 p8	6 p52	...	6 p52	...	...	9 p10	9 p58	9 p38	...	9 p58	...	...
FRANKFORT—	p.m.			p.m.	p.m.	p.m.				p.m.		p.m.	p.m.	p.m.	p.m.	p.m.		p.m.		p.m.	p.m.	p.m.	p.m.		p.m.		
Hauptbahnhof ......dep	2 52	...	...	3 55	4 35	4 57	...	...	...	5 45	...	6 38	7 30	7 34	8 27	8 55	...	9 0	...	10 15	10 36	11 25	11 13	...	11 40	...	...
Bonames	3 12	...	...	4 15	...	...	...	...	...	6 6	...	6 59	...	7 56	⋮	...	...	9 22	...	10 37	...	⋮	...	...	12 1	...	...
Vilbel	3 25	...	...	4 26	...	...	...	...	...	6 19	...	7 11	...	8 11	⋮	SC	...	9 37	...	10 55	SC	⋮	...	...	12 12	...	...
Gross-Karben	3 36	...	...	4 36	...	...	...	...	...	6 31	...	7 23	...	8 22	⋮	...	...	9 49	...	11 6	...	⋮	...	...	12 23	...	...
Niederwöllstadt	3 48	p.m.	p.m.	4 47	...	...	...	p.m.	...	6 44	p.m.	7 36	...	8 35	⋮	...	p.m.	10 0	p.m.	11 18	...	⋮	...	...	12 34	...	...
Friedberg	4 4	3 34	4 22	5 1	5 8	...	...	5 53	...	6 59	7 17	8 12	8 3	8 51	⋮	9 29	9 1	10 16	10 58	11 32	...	⋮	11 48	...	12 50	...	...
Nauheim Bad	4 13	3 40	4 28	5 7	5 17	5 36	...	6 0	...	7 7	7 23	8 19	8 11	9 0	⋮	9 38	9 7	10 24	11 4		11 13	⋮	11 56	...	12 59	...	...
Butzbach	4 30			5 53	...	...	...		...	7 24		8 35	8 24	9 18	⋮	...		10 40		...	...	⋮	12 9	...	1 15	...	...
Lang-Göns	4 45	...	...	6 9	...	...	...	...	...	7 38	...	8 49	...	9 32	⋮	...	...	10 54	...	...	...	⋮	...	...	1 29	...	...
Giessen ......arr	4 59	...	...	6 24	5 44	6 4	...	...	...	7 52	...	9 3	8 43	9 46	⋮	10 6	...	11 8	...	...	11 40	⋮	12 28	...	1 43	...	...
COBLENCE 146 ......dep	1 p22	...	...	...	...	Deutz arrive 9.20.	...	...	...	3 p31	...	...	...	...	⋮	5 p37	...	...	...	...	9 p15	⋮	9 p15	...	9 p15	...	...
EMS 146......dep	1 p49	...	...	...	...		...	...	...	4 p18	...	...	...	...	⋮	6 p13	...	...	...	...	9 p46	⋮	9 p46	...	9 p46	...	...
Giessen ......dep	5 5	...	...	6 36	5 47		...	...	...	8 7	...	p.m. 9 20	...	...	⋮	10 12	...	11 13	...	...	11 47	⋮	12 31	...	1 51	...	...
Lollar	5 17	...	...	6 49	...		...	...	...	8 18	...	9 31	p.m.	...	⋮	...	...	11 23	...	...	...	⋮	...	...	2 3	...	...
Niederwalgern	5 35	...	...	7 10	...		...	...	...	8 36	...	9 51	9 5	...	⋮	...	...	11 42	...	...	...	⋮	...	...	2 19	...	...
Marburg	6 24	...	...	7 29	6 17	...	...	...	...	9 0	...	10 11	9 28	...	⋮	10 45	...	12 23	...	...	12 16	⋮	12 59	...	2 40	...	...
Colbe	6 31	...	...		...	...	...	...	...	9 7	...			...	⋮	...	...	12 30	...	...	...	⋮	...	...	2 47	...	...
Kirchhain	6 51	...	...	...	6 33	...	...	...	...	9 27	...	...	...	...	⋮	...	...	12 51	...	...	...	⋮	...	...	3 2	...	...
Neustadt	7 14	...	...	...	...	...	...	...	...	9 51	...	...	...	...	⋮	...	...	1 16	...	...	...	⋮	...	...	3 28	...	...
Treysa 147	7 26	...	...	...	...	...	...	...	...	10 10	...	...	...	...	⋮	...	...	1 28	...	...	...	⋮	...	...	3 40	...	...
Borken	7 52	...	...	...	...	...	...	...	p.m.	10 35	...	...	...	...	⋮	...	...		...	...	...	⋮	...	...	4 6	...	...
Wabern 156A	8 5	...	...	...	7 25	...	...	...	9 *13	10 51	...	...	...	...	⋮	...	...	...	...	...	...	⋮	...	...	4 21	...	...
Grifte	8 34	...	...	...	...	...	...	...	9 45	11 15	...	...	...	...	⋮	...	...	...	...	...	...	⋮	...	...	4 47	...	...
Guntershausen	8 40	...	...	...	7 45	...	...	...	9 52	11 21	...	...	...	...	⋮	...	...	...	...	...	...	⋮	...	...	4 54	...	...
Wilhelmshöhe	8 57	...	...	...	...	...	...	...	10 11	11 38	...	...	...	...	⋮	...	...	...	...	...	...	⋮	...	...	5 9	...	...
Cassel ......arr	9 4	...	...	...	8 3	...	...	...	10 18	11 45	...	...	...	...	⋮	12 21	...	...	...	...	1 49	⋮	2 35	...	5 16	...	...
				2,3,4	1,2,3		2,3,4		2,3,4						⋮	Ex 3					Ex 2	Ex 2		2,3,4	2,3,4		
				p.m.	p.m.		p.m.		p.m.						⋮	a.m.					a.m.	⋮			a.m.		
Cassel ......dep	...	...	...	8 8	8 32	...	...	...	10 40	...	...	...	...	...	⋮	12 29	...	...	...	...	1 55	⋮	...	...	6 0	...	...
Munden	...	...	...	8 46	8 58	...	10 0	...	11 15	...	...	...	...	...	⋮	12 56	...	...	...	...	⋮	⋮	...	...	6 42	...	...
Eichenberg ......arr	...	...	...	9 21	⋮	...	⋮	...	11 50	...	...	...	...	...	⋮	⋮	...	...	...	...	⋮	⋮	...	...	⋮	...	...
FRANKFORT 149......dep	2,3,4	...	...	...	⋮	...	⋮	...	...	...	...	...	...	...	8 p27	⋮	...	...	...	...	⋮	11p25	...	...	⋮	...	...
BEBRA 149 ......dep	p.m.	...	...	...	⋮	...	⋮	...	...	...	...	...	...	...	12 a1	⋮	...	...	...	...	⋮	⋮	...	a.m.	4 a48	...	...
Eichenberg ......dep	7 49	...	...	9 26	⋮	...	⋮	...	11 55	...	...	...	...	...	⋮	⋮	...	...	...	...	⋮	⋮	...	4 2	⋮	...	...
Göttingen ......arr	8 18	...	...	9 55	9 38	...	10 48	...	12 24	...	...	...	...	...	1 19	1 40	...	...	...	...	⋮	3 55	...	4 30	7 35	...	...
Göttingen ......dep		...	...		9 42	...	10 51	...		...	...	...	...	...	1 22	1 45	...	...	...	...	⋮	4 0	...	4 37	7 41	...	...
Norten	...	...	...	...	...	...	11 6	...	...	...	...	...	...	...	...	...	...	...	...	...	⋮	⋮	...	4 52	7 57	...	...
Northeim ......arr	...	...	...	...	10 0	...	11 18	...	...	...	...	...	...	...	...	2 5	...	...	...	...	⋮	⋮	...	5 5	8 8	...	...
Northeim ......dep	...	...	...	...	10 1	...	11 20	...	...	...	...	...	...	...	...	2 6	...	...	...	...	⋮	⋮	...	5 8	8 27	...	...
Salzderhelden	...	...	...	...	10 14	...	11 36	...	...	...	...	...	...	...	...	...	...	...	...	...	⋮	⋮	...	5 25	8 44	...	...
Kreiensen ......arr	...	...	...	...	10 25	...	11 45	...	...	...	...	...	...	...	1 59	2 27	...	...	...	...	3 28	⋮	...	5 33	8 54	...	...
MAGDEBURG 164......arr	...	...	...	...	...	...	...	...	...	...	...	...	...	...	5 a38	5 a38	...	...	...	...	5 a38	⋮	...	12 p8	2 p34	...	...
BERLIN 164 ......arr	...	...	...	...	...	...	...	...	...	...	...	...	...	...	7 a49	7 a49	...	...	...	...	7 a49	⋮	...	2 p45	6 p1	...	...

Station																											
Kreiensen......dep	...	...	...	...	10 28	...	...	...	...	...	...	...	...	...	2 3	2 37	...	...	...	...	—		...	5 39	9 21	...	...
Freden	...	...	...	...	...	...	...	...	...	...	...	...	...	...	...	...	...	...	...	...	...		...	5 52	9 35	...	...
Alfeld	...	...	...	...	10 47	...	...	...	...	...	...	...	...	...	A	...	...	...	...	...	...		...	6 4	9 46	...	...
Elze	...	...	...	...	11 5	...	...	...	...	...	...	...	...	...	...	...	...	...	...	...	...		...	6 32	10 13	...	...
Nordstemmen	...	...	...	...	11 14	...	...	...	...	...	...	...	...	...	2 41	3 13	...	...	...	...	...		...	6 49	10 31	...	...
Sarstedt	...	...	...	...	...	...	...	...	...	...	...	...	...	...	...	...	...	...	...	...	...		...	7 4	10 46	...	...
HANOVER ......arr	...	...	...	...	11 40	...	...	...	...	...	...	...	...	...	3 3	3 35	...	...	...	...	...	5 37	...	7 30	11 17	...	...
BREMEN 159......arr	...	...	...	...	1 a59	...	...	...	...	...	...	...	...	...	...	5 a37	...	...	...	...	...	7 a34	...	9 a57	4 p20	...	...
							2,3,4			2,3,4					Ex 3	Ex 3	2—4	2,3,4	2,3,4		2,3,4	Ex 2		1,2,3	2,3,4		
							a.m.								a.m.	a.m.			a.m.		a.m.	a.m.		a.m.	a.m.		
HANOVER ......dep	...	...	...	...	...	...	12 41	...	...	...	...	...	...	...	3 15	3 50	...	...	5 38	...	7 53	5 52	...	8 22	11 38	...	...
Lehrte ......arr	...	...	...	...	...	...	1 7	...	...	...	...	...	...	...	3 31	4 6	...	...	6 2	...	8 17	6 8	...	8 38	12 1	...	...
BRUNSWICK 158......dep	...	...	...	...	...	...	...	...	...	...	...	...	...	...	1 a18	1 a18	...	...	4 a57	...	6 a24	4 a57	...	7 a55	11a12	...	...
Lehrte ......dep	...	...	...	...	...	...	1 13	...	...	...	...	...	...	...	3 35	4 10	...	...	6 18	...	8 22	6 12	...	8 42	12 6	...	...
Burgdorf	...	...	...	...	...	...	1 23	...	...	...	...	...	...	...	...	...	...	...	6 32	...	8 36	...	...	...	12 20	...	...
Celle	...	...	...	...	...	...	1 48	...	...	...	...	...	...	...	3 59	4 34	...	...	6 59	...	9 20	...	...	9 9	12 47	...	...
Eschede	...	...	...	...	Ex 3	...	2 12	...	...	...	...	...	...	...	A	...	...	...	7 20	...	9 42	...	...	...	1 8	...	...
Uelzen 163 ......arr	...	...	...	...	a.m.	...	2 55	...	...	...	...	...	...	...	4 44	5 18	a.m.	...	8 0	...	10 24	...	...	9 55	1 50	...	...
Uelzen 163 ......dep	...	...	...	...	3 5	...	3 18	...	...	...	...	...	...	...	4 48	5 19	5 33	...	8 9	...	10 34	...	...	10 1	2 10	...	...
Lüneburg 169 ......arr	...	...	...	...	3 55	...	4 8	...	...	...	...	...	...	...	5 17	5 47	6 21	...	8 56	...	11 20	...	...	10 31	3 1	...	...
LUBECK 213A ......arr	...	...	...	...	...	...	...	...	...	a.m.	...	...	...	...	...	7 a27	9 a24	a.m.	...	...	...	...	...	12p37	...	...	...
Lüneburg ......dep	...	...	...	...	3 56	...	4 11	...	...	5 25	...	...	...	...	5 18	5 51	6 46	8 6	9 1	...	11 26	...	...	10 33	3 5	...	...
Winsen	...	...	...	...	...	...	4 37	...	...	5 48	...	...	...	...	...	6 8	7 12	8 34	9 31	...	11 56	...	...	...	3 32	...	...
Harburg	...	...	...	...	5 2	...	5 16	...	...	7 0	...	...	...	...	5 51	6 27	7 49	9 19	10 16	...	12 33	...	...	11 6	4 4	...	...
HAMBURG Hauptbahnf	...	...	...	...	5 20	...	5 42	...	...	7 25	...	...	...	...	6 8	6 44	8 15	9 38	10 38	...	12 55	8 22	...	11 23	4 24	...	...
KIEL 168......arr	...	...	...	...	8 a21	...	...	...	...	...	...	...	...	...	...	9 a5	...	...	1 p58	...	3 p36	10a55	...	3 p36	7 p25	...	...
COPENHAGEN 302 ...arr	...	...	...	...	...	...	...	...	...	...	...	...	...	...	...	4 p48	...	...	...	...	...	...	...	...	...	...	...
WARNEMUNDE178Bar	...	...	...	...	...	...	...	...	...	...	...	...	...	...	...	12p41	...	...	...	...	...	12p41	...	...	...	...	...
COPENHAGEN 302 arr	...	...	...	...	...	...	...	...	...	...	...	...	...	...	...	6 p41	...	...	...	...	...	6 p41	...	...	...	...	...

A—Between Kreiensen and Hamburg only in the months of July and August.

BIELEFELD and OSNABRUCK.

	a.m.	a.m.	a.m.	a.m.	p.m.	p.m.	p.m.	p.m.	p.m.	p.m.	
Bielefeld......dep	5 29	7 34	8 50	11 10	1 26	3 56	...	6 12	7 36	11 35	...
Brackwede......	5 34	7 43	9 4	11 18	1 35	4 6	...	6 19	7 44	11 43	...
Dissen-Rothenfeld......	6 26	8 29	10 1	12 8	2 30	5 2	...	—	8 35	12 52	...
Wellendorf	6 51	8 48	10 25	12 29	2 53	5 26	6 56	...	8 58	1 13	...
Osnabrück 156A ......arr	7 24	9 21	10 59	1 1	3 29	5 56	7 32	...	9 37	1 43	...

	a.m.	a.m.	a.m.	p.m.	p.m.	p.m.	p.m.	p.m.	p.m.		
Osnabrück......dep	5 25	8 9	10 44	12 12	2 20	4 59	6 22	8 19	11 51	...	...
Wellendorf	6 2	8 47	11 18	12 45	2 53	5 41	6 56	8 58	12 24	...	...
Dissen-Rothenfeld	6 26	9 8	11 41	1 12	3 18	6 3	7 18	9 23	12 44	...	...
Brackwede	7 24	10 4	12 31	2 6	4 7	7 1	8 8	10 16	—	...	...
Bielefeld 160A ......arr	7 31	10 13	12 38	2 14	4 14	7 8	8 15	10 23	...	...	...

EILSLEBEN, BLUMENBERG, and STASSFURT.

	a.m.	a.m.	a.m.	a.m.	a.m.	a.m.	p.m.	p.m.	p.m.	p.m.	p.m.	p.m.
Eilsleben ......dep	5 10	...	7 5	...	1015	...	...	2 14	...	...	7 3	...
Magdeburg ......dep	...	5 55	...	7 40	...	11 7	1 26	...	3 3	4 35	7 15	11 25
Blumenberg (162) ......dep	6 1	6 37	8 3	8 21	1110	1130	2 13	3 4	3 55	5 20	8 5	12 7
Etgersleben......	—	6 54	—	8 38	—	1148	2 30	—	4 14	5 36	8 22	12 24
Egeln......	...	7 9	...	8 51	...	1210	2 43	...	4 29	—	8 34	12 37
Stassfurt (161C) ......arr	...	7 47	...	9 28	...	1248	3 20	...	5 7	...	9 10	1 12

	a.m.	a.m.	a.m.		p.m.		p.m.		p.m.		p.m.	
Stassfurt......dep	4 57	6 51	10 9	...	1 3	...	3 47	...	6 41	...	9 15	...
Egeln	5 33	7 33	1050	...	1 41	p.m.	4 26	...	7 22	...	9 53	...
Etgersleben	5 45	7 45	11 4	a.m.	1 53	2 48	4 37	p.m.	7 36	p.m.	10 5	...
Blumenberg ......arr	6 1	8 1	1120	1145	2 9	3 4	4 53	5 18	7 52	8 10	10 21	...
Magdeburg......arr	6 45	8 35	12 6	...	2 48	3 41	5 30	...	8 42	...	11 5	...
Eilsleben ......arr	7 40	9 16	...	1 1	...	...	...	6 11	...	9 10	...	...

Etgersleben ......dep	7 a48	12p36	5 p40	8 p31	...
Forderstedt......arr	8 22	1 19	6 15	9 7	...

Forderstedt......dep	6 a55	10a30	2 p5	6 p52	...
Etgersleben ......arr	7 37	11 1	2 43	7 29	...

For Fares—see page 120A.] PRUSSIAN STATE RAILWAYS. [Luggage Rates—see page 462.

HANOVER, BRUNSWICK, MAGDEBURG, and LEIPSIC.

Station			2 3 4	Ex3	Ex3		2 3 4	2 3 4	2 3 4	1,2,3	2 3 4	2 3 4	2 3 4	1,2,3		1—4	Ex3		2 3 4	Ex3	2 3 4		2 3 4		Ex3	Ex3	2 3 4	2 3 4	1,2,3	1,2,3	2,3,4
				a.m.	a.m.				a.m.	a.m.	a.m.	a.m.	a.m.	a.m.		p.m.	p.m.		p.m.	p.m.			p.m.			p.m.	p.m.	p.m.	p.m.	p.m.	p.m.
Hanover ...dep	...	...	...	3 21	4 37	...	...	...	5 58	7 41	7 48	8 12	9 34	1014	...	12 5	1 10	...	1 36	3 34	...	...	3 43	...	...	6 41	6 28	8 20	9 42	11 5	11 34
Lehrte ...dep	...	...	...	3 38	...	...	...	...	6 24	7 58	8 5	8 36	10 5	1030	...	1224	...	...	2 9	3 53	...	...	4 9	...	...	6 58	7 5	8 48	9 59	1122	11 57
Peine ...	...	...	...	3 55	SC	...	...	...	6 51	Via Oebisfelde.	8 22	9 6	1033	1047	...	1242	RC	...	2 35	4 11	...	...	4 35	...	...	7 17	7 34	9 16	1016	1140	12 21
Vechelde ...	...	...	...	SC	...	...	...	...	7 8		...	9 25	11 4	...	...	...	...	...	2 51	RC	...	...	4 52	...	p.m.	...	7 54	9 34	...	...	12 35
Brunswick Haupt. arr	...	...	...	4 19	5 29	...	...	a.m.	7 31		8 45	9 48	1129	1110	...	1 6	2 34	...	3 15	4 35	...	...	5 15	...		7 43	8 18	9 59	1039	12 4	12 54
Brunswick Haupt. dep	...	...	...	4 28	5 37	...	...	6 5	7 49		8 53	9 58		1115	...	1 17	2 44	...		4 42	...	...	5 28	...	7 51	7 59	8 42		1048	1216	
Konigslutter ...	...	...	a.m.	...	...	...	a.m.	Via Oschersleb'n	8 28		9 16	1028	...	...	...	1 53	...	...	...	5 6	...	...	6 2	...	Via Halberstadt.	8 22	9 17	...	1112	1252	...
Helmstedt ...	...	...	4 57	5 7	...	...	5 53		8 56		9 33	1053	1—4	1150	...	2 23	...	...	...	5 22	...	...	6 30	...		8 39	9 45	...	1128	1 18	...
Eilsleben arr	...	...	5 36	...	...	...	6 38		9 25		9 50	1122	p.m.	...	...	2 50	...	...	...	...	p.m.	...	6 56	...		8 56	1010	...	...		...
Eilsleben dep	...	...	5 38	...	...	...	6 41		9 28		9 51	1123	1 50	...	...	2 51	...	...	...	...	4 43	...	7 1	...		8 57	1012	...	...	...	...
Ochtmersleben ...	...	...	5 59	...	...	...	7 4		9 45		...	1141	2 8	...	...	3 9	...	...	...	...	5 2	...	...	...		...	1029	...	...	...	...
Magdeburg Hauptbahnhof ...arr	...	...	6 31	5 52	6 46	...	7 37	8 35	1011	1037	1016	12 8	2 34	1230	...	3 34	3 57	...	...	6 2	5 30	...	7 28	...		9 21	1054	...	12 7	...	...
	2 3 4	2 3 4	2 3 4	1,2,3	Ex3	2 3 4	2 3 4	1,2,3	2 - 4	Ex3	2 3 4	2 3 4		Ex3	1,2,3	Ex3	Ex3	2 3 4	2—4	Ex3	1—4	2 3 4		Ex3		1,2,3		2 3 4	2 3 4		
		a.m.		a.m.	a.m.		a.m.	a.m.	a.m.	a.m.	p.m.	p.m.	...	p.m.	p.m.	p.m.	Via Hildesheim.		p.m.	p.m.	...	p.m.	...	p.m.		p.m.		p.m.	a.m.		
Magdeburg Hauptbahnhof ...dep	...	4 30	...	6 10	7 10	...	7 52	9 14	1051	11 7	1218	1 20	...	1 10	3 12	4 28		...	4 48	6 10	...	7 18	...	9 6		9 45	...	1050	1239	...	
Schonebeck arr	...	4 48	...	6 25	7 25	...	8 10	9 28	1113	1121	1240	1 42	...	1 24	...	4 42		...	5 10	6 24	...	7 42	...	9 20		10 0	...	1112	1 3	RC	
Schonebeck dep	...	4 49	...	6 26	7 26	...	8 11	9 29	1130	1122		1 44	...	1 25	A	4 43		...	5 12	6 25	...	7 45	...	9 21			...		1 5		
Gnadau ...	...	4 57	...	...	...	...	8 19	...	1138	...	...	1 52	...	...	...	RC		...	5 20	...	...	7 53	...	...		...	...	...	1 13		
Grizehne ...	...	5 6	...	6 39	...	...	8 29	...	1147	...	...	2 1	...	...	...	...		...	5 29	RC	...	8 3	...	9 34		...	...	...	1 23		
Cothen Leipzig Bhf. arr	...	5 35	...	7 3	7 56	...	8 59	9 57	1216	1150	...	2 30	...	1 53	3 51	5 11		...	5 58	6 53	...	8 34	...	9 54		...	...	...	1 52		
Cothen Leipzig Bhf. dep	...	5 40	...	7 6	7 57	...	9 1	9 58	1218	1151	...	2 33	...	1 54	3 52	5 12		...	6 1	6 54	...	8 38	...	9 55		...	...	...	1 57		
Stumsdorf ...2 3 4	...	6 3	...	...	...	...	9 24	...	1241	...	...	2 57	...	...	...	...		...	6 25	...	...	9 4	...	...		...	...	...	2 22		
Halle 170 arr a.m.	a.m.	6 32	a.m.	7 38	8 28	a.m.	9 48	1029	1 8	1222	p.m.	3 21	...	2 25	4 22	5 44	5 30	p.m.	6 52	7 25	p.m.	9 33	...	1026	1044	n ht	...	...	2 46		
Halle 170 dep 4 50	6 10	...	7 30	7 43	8 30	9 10	1044	1032	1 50	1225	1240	3 24	...	2 29	4 25	5 47	5 35	6 30	6 58	7 30	8 24	9 45	...	1033	1054	1210	...	...	2 50		
Schkeuditz ...5 22	6 49	...	7 50	...	...	9 42	1115	...	2 23	...	1 12	3 55	...	...	...	...	...	7 2	7 26	...	8 52	1014	...	...	...	1242	...	...	3 19		
Leipsic Haupt Bf. arr 5 55	7 22	...	8 9	8 19	9 6	1015	1147	11 8	2 55	1 1	1 45	4 27	...	3 5	5 1	6 23	6 11	7 35	7 56	8 6	9 24	1046	...	11 9	1130	1 15	...	...	3 51		
DRESDEN Haupt 188 arr	...	...	...	1026	1120	...	2p55	2p30	...	2p55	4p31	6p36	...	6p19	...	8p27	8p27	...	...	1014	...	...	...	1a43	1a43	...	...	...	8 a9	...	...

Station																															
DRESDEN Haupt 189 dep	...	...	1225	3a41	...	...	...	...	...	...	7a15	...	8 a0	...	...	...	1025	1035	...	1p18	...	1p18	...	4 p0	...	...	...	...	8 p6	8 p6	...
	2 3 4		2—4	Ex3	Ex3	2 3 4	2 3 4	Ex3	2 3 4	1,2,3	2 3 4	1,2,3	Ex3				2 3 4	Ex3	1—4	1,2,3	1,2,3	2 3 4	2—4	Ex3	2 3 4		2 3 4	2 3 4	Ex3	Ex3	2—4
			a.m.	a.m.	a.m.	a.m.	a.m.	a.m.	a.m.	a.m.	t..m.	a.m.	a.m.				p.m.	p.m.	p.m.	p.m.	p.m.	p.m.	p.m.	p.m.	p.m.		p.m.	p.m.	p.m.	p.m.	p.m.
Leipsic Haupt Bhf. ...dep	...	...	3 29	5 55	...	5 15	6 20	6 57	7 45	8 25	9 5	10 5	1025	...	...	...	1215	1 0	2 25	3 10	4 10	3 30	4 20	6 30	6 55	...	7 40	8 40	9 45	10 5	1120
Schkeuditz ...	...	...	4 1	...	...	5 49	6 56	...	8 7	A	9 39	1027	...	...	...	...	1245	...	2 59	...	...	4 4	4 55	...	7 30	...	8 15	9 15	...	...	1150
Halle arr	...	...	4 25	6 29	...	6 16	7 25	7 32	8 33	8 59	10 6	1047	1059	...	...	...	1 9	1 34	3 26	3 44	4 44	4 31	5 19	7 4	7 57	...	8 42	9 42	1019	1039	1217
Halle dep	...	...	4 55		6 37	6 55		7 34		9 1	1010		11 5	...	...	...	1 40	1 41	3 54		4 47		5 55	7 15		...	8 46			1047	1222
Stumsdorf ...	...	...	5 19	...	...	7 19	...	...	...	...	1033	...	...	...	...	...	2 3	Via Hildesheim.	4 18	...	...	...	6 23	...	...	...	9 11	...	...	...	1249
Cothen Leipzig Bhf arr	...	...	5 43	...	7 7	7 43	...	8 4	...	9 30	1055	...	1135	...	...	...	2 25		4 40	...	5 15	...	6 53	7 45	...	...	9 33	...	...	1119	1 14
Cothen Leipzig Bhf dep	...	...	5 50	...	7 8	7 45	...	8 5	...	9 31	1058	...	1136	...	...	...	2 27		4 43	...	5 16	...	7 1	7 46	...	...	9 41	...	...	1121	1 19
Grizehne ...	...	...	6 21	...	...	8 12	...	...	...	...	1127	...	...	...	...	...	2 53		5 13	...	...	...	7 30	...	...	...	1012	...	...	1140	1 47
Gnadau ...	...	...	6 31	...	RC	8 21	...	...	...	A	1136	...	RC	...	...	...	3 2		5 22	...	...	...	7 39	...	...	...	1021	...	...	...	1 55
Schonebeck arr	a.m.	...	6 38	...	7 35	8 28	...	8 36	...	...	1143	...	12 4	...	...	...	3 9		5 29	...	5 43	p.m.	7 46	8 14	...	...	1028	...	...	1152	2 2
Schonebeck dep	5 7	...	6 41	...	7 36	8 30	...	8 37	...	...	1145	...	12 5	...	...	...	3 11		5 31	...	5 44	6 11	7 48	8 15	...	...	1030	...	...	1153	2 3
Magdeburg Hauptbahnhof ...arr	5 31	...	7 6	...	7 50	8 47	...	8 54	...	10 10	12 8	...	1220	...	...	...	3 34		5 54	...	5 59	6 34	8 11	8 30	...	...	1054	...	...	12 8	2 25
	2—4	1,2,3	2 3 4		Ex3	2 3 4		1,2,3				2 3 4	Ex3	2 3 4	Ex3	2 3 4	2 3 4				1,2,3	2 3 4		1,2,3	2 3 4	1—4		Ex3	Ex3		1—4
	a.m.	a.m.	a.m.		a.m.	a.m.		a.m.					p.m.	p.m.	p.m.		p.m.				p.m.	p.m.		p.m.	p.m.	p.m.		p.m.	p.m.		a.m.
Magdeburg Hauptbahnhof ...dep	5 42	6 21	7 11	...	8 0	9 3	...	9 39	...	...	...	...	1243	1 17	2 59	...	3 58		...	...	6 12	7 14	...	9 9	9 27	1014	...	1124	1150	SC	2 55
Ochtmersleben ...	6 15	...	Via Oebisfelde.	...	RC	9 37	...	...	...	...	...	...	RC	1 53	...	...	4 33		...	...	...	7 50	...	...	10 3	Via Oebisfelde.	...	SC	...		...
Eilsleben 164 arr	6 32	...		...	8 29	9 55	...	10 7	...	...	...	...	1 14	2 10	...	...	4 50		...	...	6 41	8 8	...	...	1021		...	1157	...		3 38
Eilsleben 164 dep	6 34	...		...	8 30	1014	...	10 8	...	...	...	...	1 15	2 12	RC	...	4 51		...	...	6 42	8 10	...	...	1025		...	1158	...		3 40
Helmstedt 162 ...	7 14	7 7		...	8 48	1043	...	1026	...	...	...	...	1 33	2 42	...	...	5 18		...	...	7 1	8 39	...	9 57	1051		...	...	1233		4 3
Konigslutter ...2 3 4	7 40	...		...	9 4	11 7	...	1041	...	...	...	...	1 49	3 8	...	...	5 43		...	...	7 18	9 4	...	1012			...	...	SC		4 21
Brunswick Hauptbahnhf arr a.m.	8 12	7 45		...	9 25	1141	...	11 3	...	...	...	p.m	2 11	3 43	4 18	p.m.	6 12		...	...	7 40	9 39	...	1034	...		...	1248	1 6		4 45
Brunswick Hauptbahnhf dep 6 24	8 33	7 55		...	9 42		...	1112	...	...	...	1225	2 19	4 0	4 27	4 36	6 21		...	...	7 51	9 54	...	1040	...		...	1 0	1 18		4 57
Vechelde ...6 47	8 56	...		...	...	...	...	...	...	...	...	1249	...	...	...	5 2	6 43		...	...	...	1018	...	...	...		...	...	...		5 17
Peine ...7 2	9 12	8 19		...	10 5	...	...	1136	...	...	...	1 6	2 43	4 24	...	5 21	6 59		...	...	8 14	1035	...	11 6	...		...	1 22	...		5 33
Lehrte ...arr 7 26	9 36	8 36	1048	...	1022	...	...	1153	...	...	...	1 31	3 0	4 41	...	5 49	7 24		...	...	8 31	1059	...	1124	...	1 13	...	...	1 54		5 58
Hanover ...arr 7 50	10 4	8 53	1117	...	1038	...	...	1210	...	...	...	2 1	3 18	4 57	5 50	6 20	7 50	5 50	...	...	8 48	1126	...	1141	...	1 32	...	1 55	2 10	...	6 24

RC—Restaurant Car.

A—In July and August only.

SC—Sleeping Car.

HANOVER, BREMEN, and GEESTEMUNDE.

Dist. E.M.			2 3 4	Ex3	2 3 4	2 3 4	1,2,3	2 3 4	Ex2	2 3 4	1,2,3	2 3 4	Ex3	2 3 4	1—4	2 3 4	Ex3	2 3 4	Ex3	2 3 4	2 3 4	2 3 4	Ex3	2 3 4	1,2,3
				a.m.				a.m.	a.m.		a.m.	a.m.	a.m.		p.m.		p.m.	p.m.	p.m.		p.m		p.m.	p.m.	ngt.
—	Hanover ......dep		...	3 53	...	...	...	4 41	5 57	...	8 0	8 37	1054	...	1 21	...	3 54	4 10	6 0	...	6 30	...	9 4	9 42	12 5
13¼	Wunstorf............		...	4 13	...	...	...	5 16	...	...	8 21	9 15	...	...	1 52	...	4 15	4 49	6 21	...	7 6	...	9 25	1015	1227
34½	Nienburg............		...	4 41	...	...	...	6 3	...	...	8 54	10 6	1141	...	2 42	...	4 43	5 44	6 50	...	8 1	...	9 53	11 8	1258
44	Eistrup 159.........		a.m.	SC	a.m.	a.m.	...	6 24	...	a.m.	9 9	1024	...	p.m	3 2	p.m.	RC	6 8	7 5	p.m.	8 24	p.m.	10 8	1131	1 13
53¾	Verden		4 36	5 8	5†20	6 23	...	6 47	...	7 53	9 24	1047	12 8	1221	3 26	4 8	5 11	6 35	7 20	7 25	8 51	1030	1023	1157	1 28
58¼	Langwedel 154...		4 46	...	5 29	6 40	...	6 57	...	8 10	...	1056	...	1238	3 35	4 33	...	6 46	RC	7 40	9 1	11 3	...	12 8	...
65½	Achim	2 3 4	5 3	...	5 52	7 1	...	7 31	...	8 32	9 42	1117	...	1259	3 57	4 57	...	7 8	...	8 2	9 25	1124	...	1228	1 46
76	Bremen 132...	a.m.	5 25	5 37	6 15	7 23	a.m.	7 54	7 34	8 54	9 57	1139	1238	1 22	4 20	5 22	5 41	7 33	7 50	8 24	9 50	1146	1053	1251	1 59
...	„ ...	3†53	6 6	5 49	—	—	8 0	8 20	—	—	1012	1151	1250	1 47	4 33	6 40	5 48	8 18	7 57	—	—	1152	1128	—	—
83	Burg-Lesum..	4 10	6 23	6 1	...	...	...	8 34	...	...	1025	12 8	...	2 5	4 50	6 59	6 0	8 36	...	...	...	1210	1140	...	...
102	Stubben	4 58	7 7	...	...	...	...	9 16	...	...	1058	1255	...	2 49	5 39	7 50	...	9 23	...	...	...	1253	...	...	...
114¼	Geestemünde	5 28	7 39	6 44	...	...	8 52	9 42	...	...	1123	1 26	1 42	3 18	6 10	8 21	6 43	9 54	8 49	...	...	1 20	1226	...	...

	2,3,4	2 3 4	2 3 4	1—4	Ex3	2 3 4	Ex3	2 3 4	Ex3	2 3 4	2 3 4	1,2,3	2,3,4	2 3 4	Ex3	2 3 4	1,2,3	2 3 4	2 3 4	Ex2	2 3 4	Ex3
(Bremerhaven)	a.m.			a.m.	a.m.	a.m.	a.m.	a.m.	a.m.		p.m.	p.m.		p.m.	p.m		p.m.	p.m.			p.m	p.m.
Geestemünde ....dep	3 †45	...	...	5 40	7 0	8 16	9 37	10 4	1143	...	1 34	2 44	...	4 32	5 30	...	6 25	6 31	...	...	9 40	1056
Stubben..........................	4 21	...	...	6 14	...	8 49	RC	1035	12 2	...	2 6	...	...	5 5	...	...	6 45	7 4	...	...	1012	SC
Burg-Lesum............dep	5 9	...	...	7 4	...	9 36	...	1120	1233	...	2 52	3 31	...	5 54	...	...	7 17	7 52	...	...	11 1	...
Bremen 133.............arr	5 25	a.m.	a.m.	7 21	7 51	9 52	1028	1136	1244	p.m.	3 8	3 42	p.m.	6 10	6 21	p.m.	7 28	8 8	...	p.m.	1117	1147
„ ....dep	—	5 32	5 51	8 19	8 7	1020	1038	1153	1 1	1230	3 26	3 51	4 16	6 39	6 27	7 19	7 38	8 19	...	10 7	1127	12 2
Achim	...	5 57	...	8 44	...	11 0	1055	1220	RC	1256	3 52	...	4 41	7 4	...	8 4	7 55	8 45	p.m.	...	1151	...
Langwedel	...	6 16	6 25	9 5	...	1124	...	1241	1 27	1 35	4 28	4 16	5 5	7 23	...	8 27	...	9 6	1052	...	1211	...
Verden	...	—	6 37	9 15	8 39	1139	1113	1251	1 37	1 47	4 39	4 25	5 17	7 34	6 56	8 39	8 13	9 17	11 4	...	1220	1235
Eistrup	...	a.m.	7 1	9 40	8 54	—	1128	1 15	1 52	—	5 1	...	—	7 58	...	—	8 28	9 38	—	...	—	...
Nienburg	...	4 48	7 22	10 3	9 10	...	1144	1 37	2 9	...	5 23	4 51	...	8 18	7 23	...	8 44	9 59	...	...	...	1 4
Wunstorf	...	5 42	8 19	1053	9 45	...	1215	2 24	2 42	...	6 17	5 21	...	9 20	7 53	...	9 15	1049	...	...	...	1 35
Hanover 160...........arr	...	6 17	8 54	1128	10 5	...	1235	3 35	3 3	...	6 51	5 41	...	9 56	8 13	...	9 35	1122	...	1149	...	1 55

Bremen to Grohn Vegesack, in half an hour, 5.33, 6.56, 8.9, 8.58, 9.28, 10.26, 11.14 a.m., 12.30, 1.26, 1.34, 2.0, 2.46, 3.28, 4.44, 5.28, 6.13, 7.3, 7.40, 8.3, 8.35, 9.0, 10.0, 11.9 p.m., 12.0 night.

Grohn Vegesack to Bremen, 4.49, 5.24, 7.2, 7.43, 8.9, 9.12, 9.44, 10.6, 11.17, 11.50 a.m., 1.24, 2.26, 3.4, 3.32, 4.29, 5.24, 6.14, 6.40, 7.54, 8.17, 9.0, 9.51, 10.25, 11.31 p.m.

Grohn Vegesack to Farge, 6.22, 7.47, 10.10 a.m., 2.14, 4.6, 6.53, 9.13 p.m. Farge to Grohn Vegesack, 7.3, 8.32, 11.10 a.m., 2.54, 4.46, 7.37, 9.50 p.m.

†—Weekdays only.

RC—Restaurant Car.

SC—Sleeping Car.

EISTRUP and HOYA.

Eistrup ....dep	7 a8	9 a45	11a35	1p55	3 p10	5 p25	7p14	8 p35	10p13
Hoya ....arr	7 28	10 5	11 55	2 13	3 30	5 45	7 32	8 55	10 33

Hoya...............dep	6a0	8 a30	10a52	1 p20	2p20	4p30	6p30	7 p57	9 p5	...
Eistrup 159......arr	6 18	8 48	11 12	1 40	2 38	4 50	6 50	8 15	9 23	...

GEESTEMUNDE and CUXHAVEN.

Geestemünde.........dep	6a16	7 a9	9a50	12p43	3 p23	7p14	10p35
Lehe	6 27	7 18	9 59	12 54	3 33	7 25	10 45
Dorum	7 5	7 49	1038	1 33	4 12	8 2	11 21
Cuxhaven ....arr	7 52	8 25	1125	2 20	4 59	8 52	12 7

Cuxhaven ....dep	5 a40	9 a9	12p40	2 p56	5 p1	7 p47	9 p20	...	...
Dorum	6 34	10 4	1 30	3 40	5 38	8 35	10 6	...	...
Lehe	7 16	10 49	2 11	4 20	6 9	9 13	10 43	...	...
Geestemünde ....arr	7 24	10 58	2 18	4 27	6 16	9 20	10 50	...	...

GEESTEMUNDE and BEDERKESA.

Geestemünde......dep	7a50	1p50	4 p8	7 p0	10p12	...	...
Lehe	8 1	1 59	4 17	7 9	11 2	...	...
Bederkesa...........arr	8 41	2 42	5 0	7 49	11 43	...	...

Bederkesa..............dep	5a55	10a19	2p56	5p17	8p40	...	...	...	...
Lehe	6 44	11 2	3 47	5 59	9 23	...	...	...	...
Geestemünde ....arr	6 52	11 10	3 55	6 6	9 30	...	...	...	...

BIELEFELD and HAMELN.

Bielefeld ......dep	5 a54	7a44	9 a8	...	11a16	...	2p22	4p47	6 p12	8 p5	...	11p17
Oerlinghausen........	6 18	8 8	9 30	...	11 43	...	2 46	5 16	6 38	8 31	...	11 40
Lage	6 43	9 8	1012	11a28	12 36	1p52	3 17	5 56	7 6	9 4	10p45	12 4
Lemgo	7 0	9 29	1028	11 43	1 3	2 8	3 41	6 12	7 35	9 20	11 12	12 20
Barntrup	7 36	1014	—	—	2 3	—	4 34	—	8 21	—	11 48	—
Hameln ....arr	8 23	1115	...	...	2 55	...	5 31	...	9 11	...	12 30	...

Hameln ......dep	...	...	6 a35	8 a57	...	...	1 p8	3 p41	...	7 p5	...	9 p43
Barntrup	a.m.	a.m.	7 34	9 52	a.m.	p.m.	2 7	4 37	p.m.	8 0	...	10 38
Lemgo	4 59	6 18	8 10	10 28	11 52	1 24	2 48	5 25	6 34	8 40	9 p44	11 35
Lage	5 18	6 41	9 7	10 43	12 31	1 58	3 18	5 56	7 6	9 5	10 0	11 50
Oerlinghausen......	5 38	7 1	9 29	—	12 53	2 22	3 41	6 16	7 28	9 30	—	—
Bielefeld......arr	6 8	7 25	9 55	...	1 18	2 51	4 8	6 43	7 54	9 57	...	...

LIPPSTADT and RHEDA.

Lippstadt ....dep	3a34	7 a4	10a53	12p50	3 p27	6p41	...
Wiedenbruck................	4 25	7 56	11 47	1 42	4 37	7 34	...
Rheda (160A) ......arr	4 33	8 4	11 57	1 50	4 46	7 42	...

Rheda.....................dep	8a26	11a36	2p18	5p19	8p25	11p19	...	...	...	...
Wiedenbruck................	8 35	11 44	2 26	5 27	8 36	11 30	...	...	...	...
Lippstadt(164)......arr	9 26	12 34	3 16	6 20	9 30	12 19	...	...	...	...

HILDESHEIM and BRUNSWICK

Hildesheim..............dep	5a24	7a58	11a0	1p56	2 p9	5p17	7 p59	9 p15	11p15
Hoheneggelsen..............	5 50	8 23	1129	...	2 36	5 44	...	9 39	11 42
Brunswick 160 .... arr	6 33	9 20	1217	2 34	3 22	6 27	8 37	10 20	12 27

Brunswick ....dep	5 a40	8a20	10 a8	11a18	2 p51	4p28	6p30	7p56	11p30
Hoheneggelsen	6 21	9 1	...	12 4	3 15	...	7 14	8 35	12 16
Hildesheim 155 ....arr	6 47	9 27	10 45	12 32	4 2	5 4	7 40	8 57	12 43

[Mid Europe Time—See page lxix.]

Luggage Rates—see page 462.] PRUSSIAN STATE RAILWAYS. [For Fares—see page 120A.

BERLIN, HANOVER, HAMM, DORTMUND, OBERHAUSEN, DUSSELDORF, and COLOGNE.

THROUGH CARRIAGE—Berlin to Paris and Brussels in 7.44 a.m. from Berlin.

Dist. E.M.																												
																	2,3,4				2,3,4		2 3 4	2,3,4	2,3,4	Ex.3	Ex 2	1,2,3
	BERLIN—																								a.m.	a.m.	a.m.	a.m.
—	Schlesischer Bhf. ...dep	...	...	...	...	...	...	...	...	...	...	...	...	...	...	...	...	...	...	...	...	...	...	...	...	...	7 44	7 53
1½	Alexanderplatz ...dep	...	...	...	...	...	...	...	...	...	...	...	...	...	...	...	...	...	...	...	...	...	...	...	...	...	7 50	7 59
2½	Friedrichstrasse ...dep	...	...	...	...	...	...	...	...	...	...	...	...	...	...	...	...	...	...	...	...	...	...	...	...	...	8 0	8 8
5¼	Zoolog. Garten ...dep	...	...	...	...	...	...	...	...	...	...	...	...	...	...	...	...	...	...	...	...	...	...	...	...	...	8 12	8 20
7	Charlottenburg ...dep	...	...	...	...	...	...	...	...	...	...	...	...	...	...	...	...	...	...	...	...	...	...	...	...	...	:	8 26
...	Potsdamer Bahnhof	...	...	...	...	...	...	...	...	...	...	...	...	...	...	...	...	...	...	...	...	...	...	...	...	...	:	...
...	Lehrter Bahnhof dep	...	...	...	...	...	...	...	...	...	...	...	...	...	...	...	...	...	...	...	...	...	...	...	4 53	8 55	RC	...
12	Spandau	...	...	...	...	...	...	...	...	...	...	...	...	...	...	...	...	...	...	...	...	...	...	...	5 12	9 9	:	8 38
23½	Wustermark	...	...	...	...	...	...	...	...	...	...	...	...	...	...	...	...	...	...	...	...	...	...	...	5 41	...	:	...
42	Nennhausen	...	...	...	...	...	...	...	...	...	...	...	...	...	...	...	...	...	...	...	...	...	...	...	6 17	...	:	...
48½	Rathenow	...	...	...	...	...	...	...	...	...	...	...	...	...	...	...	...	...	...	...	...	...	...	...	6 32	...	:	9 25
62	Schönhausen	...	...	...	...	...	...	...	...	...	...	...	...	...	...	...	...	...	...	...	...	...	...	...	7 1	...	:	...
70	Stendal ...arr	...	...	...	...	...	...	...	...	...	...	...	...	...	...	...	...	...	...	...	...	...	...	...	7 19	10 22	:	9 54
...	MAGDEBURG ...dep	...	...	...	...	...	...	...	...	...	...	...	...	...	...	...	...	...	...	...	a.m.	...	...	...	6 a7	...	:	9 a0
...	Stendal ...dep	...	...	...	...	...	...	...	...	...	...	...	...	...	...	...	...	...	...	...	4 25	...	...	...	7 34	10 26	:	9 58
77¾	Vinzelberg	...	...	...	...	...	...	...	...	...	...	...	...	...	...	...	...	...	...	...	4 44	...	...	...	7 54	To Bremen ☞	:	...
90	Gardelegen	...	...	...	...	...	...	...	...	...	...	...	...	...	...	...	...	...	...	...	5 14	...	...	...	8 25		:	10 28
108½	Oebisfelde ...arr	...	...	...	...	...	...	...	...	...	...	...	...	...	...	...	...	...	...	...	5 56	...	...	...	9 2		:	10 55
...	MAGDEBURG 160C dep	...	...	...	...	...	...	...	...	...	...	...	...	...	...	...	...	...	...	...	4 a14	...	...	...	7 a11		:	...
...	Oebisfelde ...dep	...	...	...	...	...	...	...	...	...	...	...	...	...	...	...	...	...	...	...	5 59	...	...	...	9 8		:	10 56
114½	Vorsfelde	...	...	...	...	...	...	...	...	...	...	...	...	...	...	...	...	...	...	...	6 10	...	...	...	9 19		:	...
120	Fallersleben	...	...	...	...	...	...	...	...	...	...	...	...	...	...	...	...	...	...	...	6 21	...	...	...	9 31		:	...
128	Jsenbüttel 162	...	...	...	...	...	...	...	...	...	...	...	...	...	...	...	...	...	...	...	6 39	...	...	...	9 51		:	11 23
143¾	Dollbergen	...	...	...	...	...	...	...	...	...	...	...	...	...	...	...	...	...	...	...	7 17	...	...	...	10 28	...	:	...
158¼	Lehrte ...arr	...	...	...	...	...	...	...	...	...	...	...	...	...	...	...	a.m.	...	...	...	7 38	...	a.m.	...	10 48	...	:	11 58
	Lehrte ...dep	...	...	...	...	...	...	...	...	...	...	...	...	...	...	...	7 6	...	...	...	7 40	...	8 52	...	10 53	...	:	12 1
163¾	Hanover ...arr	...	...	...	...	...	...	...	...	...	...	...	...	...	...	...	7 35	...	...	...	8 8	...	9 23	...	11 17	...	11 25	12 17
...	LEIPSIC via Halle 158	dep	...	...	...	...	...	...	...	...	11p20	...	...	...	...	...	...	...	...	...	...	...	...	5 a55	6 a57	...	...	6 a57
...	MAGDEBURG 158 dep	...	...	...	...	...	...	...	...	...	2 a55	...	...	...	...	...	...	6 a21	...	...	6 a21	...	...	8 a0	9 a39	...	...	9 a39
											2,3,4							1,2,3			2,3,4			Ex 3	1,2,3			1,2,3
											a.m.							a.m.			a.m.			a.m.	a.m.			a.m.
...	Brunswick ...dep	...	...	...	...	...	...	...	...	...	4 57	...	...	...	...	...	...	7 55	...	...	8 33	...	...	9 42	11 12	...	...	11 12
...	Vechelde	...	...	...	...	...	...	...	...	...	5 17	...	...	...	...	...	...	...	...	...	8 56	...	...	...	...	...	...	1 20
...	Peine	...	...	...	...	...	...	...	...	...	5 33	...	...	...	...	...	...	8 19	...	...	9 12	...	...	10 5	11 36	...	...	11 36
...	Lehrte ...arr	...	...	...	...	...	...	...	...	...	5 58	...	...	...	...	...	...	8 36	...	...	9 36	...	...	10 22	11 53	...	...	11 53
...	Hanover ...arr	...	...	...	...	...	...	...	...	...	6 24	...	...	...	...	...	...	8 53	...	...	10 4	...	...	10 38	12 10	...	...	12 10
		1,2,3	Ex3	Ex 3	Ex3	1,2,3	1,2,3	2,3,4	Ex 2	2,3,4	1,2,3	Ex3	Ex 3	1,2,3	Ex 2	2,3,4	2,3,4	1,2,3	2,3,4	1,2,3	2,3,4	Ex 3		Ex 3	2,3,4	Ex 2	Ex 2	1,2 3
								a.m.			a.m.					a.m.	a.m.	a.m.			a.m.			a.m.	p.m.		a.m.	p.m.
...	Hanover ...dep	...	...	...	...	...	...	5 33	...	...	6 30	...	...	...	...	7 11	7 39	9 0	...	...	10 26	...	...	10 46	1 11	...	11 32	12 50
176¾	Wunstorf	...	...	...	...	...	...	6 9	...	...	...	...	...	...	...	7 42	8 15	...	...	...	11 13	...	...	11 7	1 47	...	:	1 11
181	Haste	...	...	...	...	...	...	6 19	...	...	...	...	...	...	...	7 52	8 26	...	...	...	11 23	...	...	...	1 58	...	:	1 20
190¼	Stadthagen	...	...	...	...	...	...	6 40	...	...	...	...	...	...	...	8 13	8 46	...	...	...	11 43	...	...	...	2 18	...	RC	...
197¾	Bückeburg	...	...	...	...	...	...	6 59	...	...	7 14	...	...	...	...	8 31	9 4	9 48	...	...	12 1	...	...	11 39	2 38	...	:	1 44
203½	Minden ...arr	...	...	...	...	...	...	7 13	...	a.m.	7 23	...	...	...	...	8 44	9 15	9 57	a.m.	...	12 13	...	...	11 49	2 52	...	:	1 53
	Minden ...dep	...	...	...	...	...	...		...	5 54	7 25	...	...	...	...	8 48	9 20	9 58	10 40	...	12 25	...	...	11 50	2 59	...	:	1 55
206¾	Porta	...	...	...	...	...	...	...	...	6 3	...	...	...	...	...	8 56	9 28	...	10 48	...	12 32	...	...	...	3 6	...	:	...
213	B. Oeynhausen (Rehm.)	...	...	...	...	...	...	...	...	6 21	7 41	...	...	...	...	9 9	9 43	10 15	11 3	...	12 47	...	...	12 7	3 22	...	:	2 11
216½	Lohne ...arr	...	...	...	...	...	...	...	...	6 30	7 48	...	...	...	...	9 16	9 53	10 22	11 14	...	12 56	...	...	12 14	3 31	...	:	2 18
275	RHEINE 156C ...arr	...	...	...	...	...	...	...	...	...	10a53	...	...	...	...	...	12 0	12 0	2 p18	...	...	...		2 p18	...	...	:	4 p49
486	H'K v. HOLLAND 112 arr	...	...	...	...	...	...	...	...	...	...	...	...	...	...	...	...	...	...	...	...	...			...	...	:	...

see next page

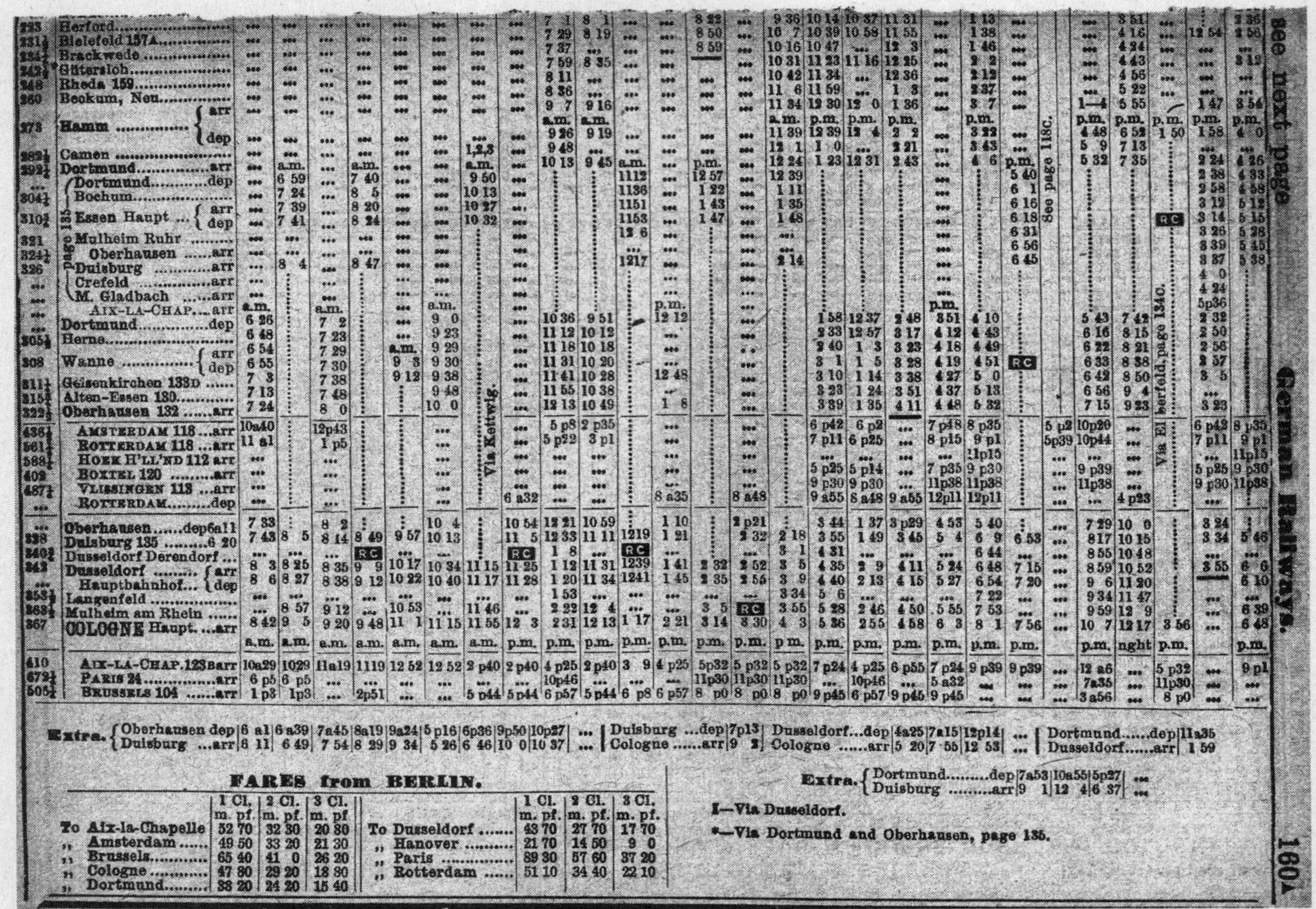

215	Herford	...	...	...	...	...	...	...	...	7 1	8 1	...	...	8 22	...	9 36	10 14	10 37	11 31	...	1 13	...		...	3 51	...	...	2 36
231½	Bielefeld 157A	...	...	...	...	...	...	...	...	7 29	8 19	...	...	8 50	...	10 7	10 39	10 58	11 55	...	1 38	...		...	4 16	...	12 54	2 58
234½	Brackwede	...	...	...	...	...	...	...	...	7 37	...	...	...	8 59	...	10 16	10 47	...	12 3	...	1 46	...		...	4 24	...	...	...
242½	*Gütersloh	...	...	...	...	...	...	...	...	7 59	8 35	...	...		...	10 31	11 23	11 16	12 25	...	2 2	...		...	4 43	...	...	3 12
248	Rheda 159	...	...	...	...	...	...	...	...	8 11	...	...	...	...	...	10 42	11 34	...	12 36	...	2 12	...		...	4 56	...	...	...
260	Beckum, Neu	...	...	...	...	...	...	...	...	8 36	...	...	...	...	...	11 6	11 59	...	1 3	...	2 37	...		...	5 22	...	...	...
273	Hamm ... arr	...	...	...	...	...	...	...	...	9 7	9 16	...	...	...	...	11 34	12 30	12 0	1 36	...	3 7	...		1—4	5 55	...	1 47	3 54
										a.m.	a.m.					a.m.	p.m.	p.m.	p.m.		p.m.			p.m.	p.m.	p.m.	p.m.	p.m.
	Hamm ... dep	...	...	...	...	...	...	...	...	9 26	9 19	...	...	...	...	11 39	12 39	12 4	2 2	...	3 22	...		4 48	6 52	1 50	1 58	4 0
282½	Camen	...	...	...	...	...	...	1,2,3	...	9 48	...	...	...	...	...	12 1	1 0	...	2 21	...	3 43	...		5 9	7 13		...	...
292½	Dortmund ... arr	...	a.m.	...	a.m.	...	...	a.m.	...	10 13	9 45	a.m.	...	p.m.	...	12 24	1 23	12 31	2 43	...	4 6	p.m.	See page 118C.	5 32	7 35		2 24	4 26
...	Dortmund ... dep	...	6 59	...	7 40	...	...	9 50	...			1112	...	12 57	...	12 39				...		5 40					2 38	4 33
304½	Bochum	...	7 24	...	8 5	...	...	10 13	...			1136	...	1 22	...	1 11				...		6 1					2 58	4 58
310½	(page 135) Essen Haupt ... arr	...	7 39	...	8 20	...	...	10 27	...			1151	...	1 43	...	1 35				...		6 16					3 12	5 12
	Essen Haupt ... dep	...	7 41	...	8 24	...	...	10 32	...			1153	...	1 47	...	1 48				...		6 18				RC	3 14	5 15
321	Mulheim Ruhr	...	...	...	...	...	...		...			12 6	...		...	...				...		6 31					3 26	5 28
324½	Oberhausen ... arr	...	...	...	...	...	...		...			...	...		...	...				...		6 56					3 39	5 45
326	Duisburg ... arr	...	8 4	...	8 47	...	...		...			1217	...		...	2 14				...		6 45					3 37	5 38
...	Crefeld ... arr	...		...		...	...		...				...		...					...							4 0	
...	M. Gladbach ... arr	...		...		...	...		...				...		...					...							4 24	
...	Aix-la-Chap. ... arr	a.m.		a.m.		...	a.m.		...				p.m.		...					p.m.							5p36	
...	Dortmund ... dep	6 26		7 2		...	9 0		...	10 36	9 51		12 12		...		1 58	12 37	2 48	3 51	4 10			5 43	7 42		2 32	
305½	Herne	6 48		7 23		...	9 23		...	11 12	10 12		...		...		2 33	12 57	3 17	4 12	4 43			6 16	8 15		2 50	
308	Wanne ... arr	6 54		7 29		a.m.	9 29		...	11 18	10 18		...		...		2 40	1 3	3 23	4 18	4 49			6 22	8 21		2 56	
	Wanne ... dep	6 55		7 30		9 3	9 30		...	11 31	10 20		...		...		3 1	1 5	3 28	4 19	4 51	RC		6 33	8 38		2 57	
311½	Geisenkirchen 133D	7 3		7 38		9 12	9 38		...	11 41	10 28		12 48		...		3 10	1 14	3 38	4 27	5 0			6 42	8 50		3 5	
315½	Alten-Essen 130	7 13		7 48			9 48		...	11 55	10 38				...		3 23	1 24	3 51	4 37	5 13			6 56	9 4	Via Elberfeld, page 134C.	...	
322½	Oberhausen 132 ... arr	7 24		8 0			10 0		...	12 13	10 49		1 8		...		3 39	1 35	4 11	4 48	5 32			7 15	9 23		3 23	
436½	Amsterdam 118 ... arr	10a40		12p43			...	Via Kettwig.	...	5 p8	2 p35		...		...		6 p42	6 p2	...	7 p48	8 p35		5 p2	10p20	...		6 p42	8 p35
561½	Rotterdam 118 ... arr	11 a1		1 p5			...		...	5 p22	3 pl		...		...		7 p11	6 p25	...	8 p15	9 pl		5p39	10p44	...		7 p11	9 pl
588½	Hoek H'll'nd 112 arr	...		...			...		...	...	...		...		...		...	...	...	...	11p15		...	...	...		...	11p15
402	Boxtel 120 ... arr	...		...			...		...	...	...		...		...		5 p25	5 p14	...	7 p35	9 p30		...	9 p39	...		5 p25	9 p30
467½	Vlissingen 118 ... arr	...		...			...		...	...	...		...		...		9 p30	9 p30	...	11p38	11p38		...	11p38	...		9 p30	11p38
...	Rotterdam ... dep	...		...			...		6 a32	...	...		8 a35		8 a48		9 a55	8 a48	9 a55	12p11	12p11		...	...	4 p23		...	
...	Oberhausen ... dep 6a11	7 33		8 2			10 4		10 54	12 21	10 59		1 10		2 p21		3 44	1 37	3 p29	4 53	5 40		...	7 29	10 0		3 24	
238	Duisburg 135 ... 6 20	7 43	8 5	8 14	8 49	9 57	10 13		11 5	12 33	11 11	1219	1 21		2 32	2 18	3 55	1 49	3 45	5 4	6 9	6 53	...	8 17	10 15		3 34	5 46
240½	Dusseldorf Derendorf	...	...	...	RC	...	...		RC	1 8	...	RC	...		...	3 1	4 31	...	...	...	6 44	...	...	8 55	10 48		...	...
243	Dusseldorf ... arr	8 3	8 25	8 35	9 9	10 17	10 34	11 15	11 25	1 12	11 31	1239	1 41	2 32	2 52	3 5	4 35	2 9	4 11	5 24	6 48	7 15	...	8 59	10 52		3 55	6 6
...	Hauptbahnhof ... dep	8 6	8 27	8 38	9 12	10 22	10 40	11 17	11 28	1 20	11 34	1241	1 45	2 35	2 55	3 9	4 40	2 13	4 15	5 27	6 54	7 20	...	9 6	11 20			6 10
253½	Langenfeld	...	...	...	...	...	...	...	...	1 53	...	...	...	...	...	3 34	5 6	...	...	...	7 22	...	...	9 34	11 47		...	...
263½	Mulheim am Rhein	...	8 57	9 12	...	10 53	...	11 46	...	2 22	12 4	...	...	3 5	RC	3 55	5 28	2 46	4 50	5 55	7 53	...	...	9 59	12 9		...	6 39
267	COLOGNE Haupt. ... arr	8 42	9 5	9 20	9 48	11 1	11 15	11 55	12 3	2 31	12 13	1 17	2 21	3 14	3 30	4 3	5 36	2 55	4 58	6 3	8 1	7 56	...	10 7	12 17	3 56	...	6 48
		a.m.	a.m.	a.m.	a.m.	a.m.	a.m.	a.m.	p.m.	p.m.	p.m.	p.m.	p.m.	p.m.	p.m.	p.m.	p.m.	p.m.	p.m.	p.m.	p.m.	p.m.		p.m.	nght	p.m.		p.m.
410	Aix-la-Chap. 123B arr	10a29	1029	11a19	1119	12 52	12 52	2 p40	2 p40	4 p25	2 p40	3 9	4 p25	5p32	5 p32	5 p32	7 p24	4 p25	6 p55	7 p24	9 p39	9 p39	...	12 a6	...	5 p32	...	9 pl
672½	Paris 24 ... arr	6 p5	6 p5	...	...	...	...	...	...	10p46	...	...	...	11p30	11p30	11p30	...	10p46	...	5 a32	...	...	...	7a35	...	11p30	...	...
505½	Brussels 104 ... arr	1 p3	1p3	...	2p51	...	...	5 p44	5 p44	6 p57	5 p44	6 p8	6 p57	8 p0	8 p0	8 p0	9 p45	6 p57	9 p45	9 p45	...	...	...	3 a56	...	8 p0	...	...

Extra.										
Oberhausen dep	6 a1	6 a39	7a45	8a19	9a24	5 p16	6p36	9p50	10p27	...
Duisburg ... arr	6 11	6 49	7 54	8 29	9 34	5 26	6 46	10 0	10 37	...

Duisburg ... dep	7p13
Cologne ... arr	9 2

Dusseldorf ... dep	4a25	7a15	12p14	...
Cologne ... arr	5 20	7 55	12 53	...

Dortmund ... dep	11a35
Dusseldorf ... arr	1 59

FARES from BERLIN.

	1 Cl. m. pf.	2 Cl. m. pf.	3 Cl. m. pf.
To Aix-la-Chapelle	52 70	32 30	20 80
,, Amsterdam	49 50	33 20	21 30
,, Brussels	65 40	41 0	26 20
,, Cologne	47 80	29 20	18 80
,, Dortmund	38 20	24 20	15 40
To Dusseldorf	43 70	27 70	17 70
,, Hanover	21 70	14 50	9 0
,, Paris	89 30	57 60	37 20
,, Rotterdam	51 10	34 40	22 10

Extra.				
Dortmund ... dep	7a53	10a55	5p27	...
Duisburg ... arr	9 1	12 4	6 37	...

I—Via Dusseldorf.

*—Via Dortmund and Oberhausen, page 135.

Luggage Rates—see page 462.] PRUSSIAN STATE RAILWAYS. [For Fares—see page 120A.

BERLIN, HANOVER, HAMM, DORTMUND, OBERHAUSEN, DUSSELDORF,—and COLOGNE.

THROUGH CARRIAGES. { Berlin to Hoek van Holland, 1st and 2nd class—in 12.48 p.m. from Berlin.
Berlin to Vlissingen (Flushing), 1st and 2nd class—in 12.48 p.m. and 10.12 p.m. from Berlin (also Sleeping Cars).
Berlin to Amsterdam, 1st and 2nd class—in 10.12 p.m. from Berlin (also Sleeping Cars).

BERLIN—	Ex.3			2,3,4	Ex3		Ex.3	Ex 2		
	a.m.			a.m.	a.m.		a.m.	noon		
Schlesischer Bhf. ...dep	8 43	...	...	...	...	...	11 23	12 0	...	...
Alexanderplatz ......dep	8 49	...	...	...	...	...	11 29	12 6	...	...
Friedrichstrasse ...dep	8 59	...	...	...	...	...	11 40	12 16	...	...
Zoolog. Garten ......dep	9 12	...	...	...	...	...	11 52	12 28	...	...
Charlottenburg ...dep	9 19	...	...	...	...	...	11 58	:	...	...
Potsdamer Bahnhof	...	...	...	...	...	...	...	:	...	...
Lehrter Bahnhof dep	RC	...	...	7 9	8 31	...	RC	RC	...	...
Spandau	...	...	...	7 29	8 47	...	...	:	...	...
Wustermark	...	...	...	7 50	...	...	...	:	...	...
Nennhausen......	...	...	...	8 26	...	...	...	:	...	...
Rathenow......	...	...	...	8 39	...	...	...	:	...	...
Schönhausen	...	...	...	9 7	...	...	...	:	...	...
Stendal ......arr	10 42	...	...	9 24	10 1	...	1 21	:	...	...
MAGDEBURG 163 dep	...	...	...	9 a33	To Bremen arr. 1.39.	...	12p32	:	...	...
Stendal ......dep	10 46	...	...	10 58		...	1 25	:	...	...
Vinzelberg	:	...	...	11 16		...	:	:	...	...
Gardelegen	:	...	...	11 43		...	:	:	...	...
Oebisfelde ......arr	:	...	...	12 17		...	:	:	...	...
MAGDEBURG 160C dep	:	...	...	10a30		...	:	:	...	...
Oebisfelde ......dep	:	...	...	12 23	...	...	:	:	...	...
Vorsfelde	:	...	...	12 34	...	...	:	:	...	...
Fallersleben	:	...	...	12 45	...	...	:	:	...	...
Isenbüttel 162......	:	...	...	1 4	...	...	:	:	...	...
Dollbergen	:	...	...	1 40	...	...	:	:	...	...
Lehrte ...... arr	:	...	...	1 58	...	...	3 7	:	...	...
Lehrte ...... dep	:	...	...	2 0	...	...	3 8	:	...	...
Hanover ......arr	12 36	...	...	2 26	...	...	3.24	3 37	...	...
LEIPSIC via Halle 158 dp	6 a57	...	...	...	...	...	10a25	10a25	...	...
MAGDEBURG 158 dep	9 a39	...	...	...	...	...	12p43	12p43	...	1 p17
	1,2,3			2,3,4			Ex.3	Ex 3		1,2,3
	a.m.			p.m.			p.m.	p.m.		p.m.
Brunswick ......dep	11 12	...	...	12 25	...	...	2 19	2 19	...	4 0
Vechelde	...	...	...	12 49	...	...	...	...	...	...
Peine......	11 36	...	...	1 6	...	...	2 43	2 43	...	4 24
Lehrte ......arr	11 53	...	...	1 31	...	...	3 0	3 0	...	4 41
Hanover ......arr	12 10	...	...	2 1	...	...	3 18	3 18	...	4 57
	Ex.3	1,2,3	2,3,4	2,3,4	.		Ex.3	Ex 2	1—4	2,3,4
	p.m.			p.m.			p.m	p.m.		p.m.
Hanover ......dep	12 45	...	...	2 42	...	...	3 48	3 43	...	5 17
Wunstorf	...	...	...	3 21	...	...	...	:	...	5 49
Haste	...	...	...	3 32	...	...	...	:	...	5 58
Stadthagen	RC	...	...	3 52	...	...	...	:	...	6 17
Bückeburg	...	...	...	4 10	...	...	...	:	...	6 34
Minden...... arr	1 33	...	...	4 22	...	...	4 36	:	...	6 45
Minden...... dep	1 35	...	...	4 48	...	...	4 38	:	...	6 50
Porta......	...	...	...	4 56	...	...	...	:	...	6 58
B. Oeynhausen (Rehm.)	1 51	...	...	5 12	...	...	4 54	:	...	7 14
Lohne ......arr	:	...	...	5 22	...	...	5 1	:	...	7 24
RHEINE 156C ......arr	:	...	...	8 p55	...		6 p38	:	...	...

BERLIN—	2,3,4	Ex 2	Ex 3	1,2,3	2,3,4	Ex 2	Ex 3	2,3,4	2,3,4
	a.m.	p.m.	p.m.	p.m.	p.m.	p.m.	p.m.	p.m.	p.m.
Schlesischer Bhf. ...dep	10 25	12 48	1 5	...	...	3 15	...	...	6 7
Alexanderplatz ......dep	10 31	12 54	1 11	...	...	3 21	...	...	6 14
Friedrichstrasse ...dep	10 38	1 5	1 21	...	...	3 32	...	...	6 23
Zoolog. Garten ......dep	10 49	1 17	1 33	...	...	3 44	...	...	6 34
Charlottenburg ...dep	10 55	:	1 39	...	...	:	...	...	6 40
Potsdamer Bahnhof	...	:	...	3 55	...	:	...	...	...
Lehrter Bahnhof dep	...	:	RC	Via Magdeburg.	2 12	RC	6 30	4 38	...
Spandau	11 10	:	1 52	:	2 36	:	...	4 58	6 55
Wustermark	11 38	:	...	:	3 7	:	...	5 25	7 26
Nennhausen......	12 14	:	...	:	3 45	:	...	6 2	8 6
Rathenow......	12 28	:	2 37	:	4 0	:	...	6 17	8 22
Schönhausen	12 56	:	...	:	4 29	:	...	6 47	8 55
Stendal ......arr	1 13	:	3 4	:	4 47	:	7 56	7 6	9 15
MAGDEBURG 163 dep	...	:	1 p15	:	3 p47	:	To Bremen	6 p6	6 p15
Stendal ......dep	2 14	:	3 8	:	5 17	:		7 11	9 46
Vinzelberg	2 34	:	...	:	5 37	:		7 31	10 6
Gardelegen	3 10	:	...	:	6 5	:		8 1	10 34
Oebisfelde ......arr	3 48	:	3 55	:	6 46	:		8 43	11 13
MAGDEBURG 160C dep	1 p46	:	1 p46	:	4 p51	:		6 p23	...
Oebisfelde ......dep	4 2	:	3 56	:	6 52	:	...	8 48	11 17
Vorsfelde	4 13	:	...	:	7 4	:	...	9 0	11 28
Fallersleben	4 24	:	...	:	7 16	:	...	9 12	11 39
Isenbüttel 162......	4 42	:	...	:	7 39	:	...	9 30	11 56
Dollbergen	5 19	:	...	:	8 14	:	...	10 6	12 31
Lehrte ...... arr	5 41	:	4 49	8 31	8 32	:	...	10 25	12 50
Lehrte ...... dep	5 45	:	4 50	8 32	8 42	:	...	10 29	12 54
Hanover ......arr	6 9	4 27	5 5	8 48	9 8	6 53	...	10 53	1 18
LEIPSIC via Halle 158 dp	...	...	...	4p10	4 p10	...	...	4 p10	...
MAGDEBURG 158 dep	2 p59	...	1 p17	6p12	6 p12	2 p59	...	7 p14	...
	2,3,4		1,2,3	1,2,3	1,2,3	2,3,4		2,3,4	
	p.m.		p.m.	p.m.	p.m.	p.m.		p.m.	
Brunswick ......dep	4 36	...	4 0	7 51	7 51	4 36	...	9 54	...
Vechelde	5 2	...	...	...	...	5 2	...	10 18	...
Peine......	5 21	...	4 24	8 14	8 14	5 21	...	10 35	...
Lehrte ......arr	5 49	...	4 41	8 32	8 32	5 49	...	10 59	...
Hanover ......arr	6 20	...	4 57	8 48	8 48	6 20	...	11 26	...
	2,3,4	Ex 2	Ex 3	1,2,3	2,3,4	Ex 2	2,3,4	2,3,4	1—4
	p.m.	p.m.	p.m	p.m.	p.m.	p.m.		p.m.	
Hanover ......dep	7 20	4 32	5 12	9 23	9 30	6 58	...	11 40	...
Wunstorf	7 56	Osn'bruck arr. 6.18	5 32	9 43	10 6	:	...	12 26	...
Haste	8 5		...	...	10 16	:	...	12 35	...
Stadthagen	8 26		RC	...	10 36	:	...	12 55	...
Bückeburg	8 44		6 1	1012	10 53	:	...	1 13	...
Minden...... arr	8 57		6 10	1021	11 6	:	...	1 25	...
Minden...... dep	9 1		6 12	1022	11 13	:	...	1 31	...
Porta......	9 9		...	...	11 21	:	...	1 39	...
B. Oeynhausen (Rehm.)	9 26		6 29	1039	11 36	:	...	1 51	...
Lohne ......arr	9 37		6 36	1046	11 46	:	...	1 59	...
RHEINE 156C ......arr	...	7 p25	...	1a22	...	:	...	...	...

BERLIN—	1,2,3	2,3,4	Ex.3	Ex 3	Ex 2	Ex.1	Ex 3	2,3,4	2,3 4
	p.m.	p.m.	p.m.	p.m.	p.m.	p.m.	p.m.	p.m.	nght
Schlesischer Bhf. ...dep	7 36	...	...	9 18	10 12	10 45	...	...	...
Alexanderplatz ......dep	7 43	...	...	9 24	10 18	...	...	...	...
Friedrichstrasse ...dep	7 52	...	...	9 34	10 28	10 58	...	...	...
Zoolog. Garten ......dep	8 3	...	...	9 46	10 40	11 10	...	...	...
Charlottenburg ...dep	8 9	...	...	9 53	:	...	...	...	...
Potsdamer Bahnhof	...	...	9 26	...	:	...	...	...	...
Lehrter Bahnhof dep	...	7 35	SC	SC	SC	...	11 41	11 46	12 18
Spandau	8 22	7 55	Via Magdeburg, page 165.	10 7	:	...	...	12 7	12 34
Wustermark	...	8 39	:	...	:	...	...	12 34	...
Nennhausen......	...	9 18	:	...	:	...	...	1 12	...
Rathenow......	9 7	9 36	:	10 58	:	B	12 52	1 25	1 43
Schönhausen	...	10 6	:	...	:	...	...	1 54	...
Stendal ......arr	9 34	10 24	:	11 28	:	12 48	1 25	2 12	2 21
MAGDEBURG 163 dep	6 p15	9 p5	:	...	:	11p25	To Bremen arr. 5.9 Until Sept. 14th.	...	12a17
Stendal ......dep	9 38	10 35	:	11 32	:	12 53		...	2 30
Vinzelberg	...	10 54	:	...	:	:		...	2 49
Gardelegen	10 7	11 22	:	12 5	:	:		...	3 18
Oebisfelde ......arr	10 32	11 57	:	:	:	:		...	3 57
MAGDEBURG 160C dep	8 p25	10p14	:	:	:	:		...	...
Oebisfelde ......dep	10 33	12 1	:	:	:	:		...	4 3
Vorsfelde	...	12 11	:	:	:	:		...	4 14
Fallersleben	...	...	:	:	:	:		...	4 25
Isenbüttel 162......	10 59	12 33	:	:	:	:		...	4 44
Dollbergen	...	...	:	:	:	:		...	5 22
Lehrte ...... arr	11 31	1 13	:	1 30	:	:	...	...	5 43
Lehrte ...... dep	11 32	1 15	:	1 31	:	:	...	...	5 49
Hanover ......arr	11 48	1 32	1 55	1 47	2 16	3 1	...	...	6 12
LEIPSIC via Halle 158 dp	6 p30	7 p40	7 p40	...	7 p40	:	...	...	...
MAGDEBURG 158 dep	9 p9	11p24	11p50	...	11p50	:	...	...	...
	1,2,3	Ex 3	Ex 3		Ex 3	:			
	p.m.	a.m.	a.m.		a.m.	:			
Brunswick ......dep	10 40	1 0	1 18	...	1 18	:	...	...	...
Vechelde	...	...	...	...	...	:	...	...	...
Peine......	11 6	1 23	...	...	...	:	...	...	...
Lehrte ......arr	11 25	...	1 55	...	1 55	:	...	...	...
Hanover ......arr	11 41	1 55	2 10	...	2 10	:	...	...	...
	1,2,3	2,3,4	Ex.3	Ex 3	Ex 2	Ex.1			1—4
	nght	a.m.	a.m.	a.m.	a.m.	a.m.			
Hanover ......dep	12 0	2 0	2 23	1 53	2 22	3 7	...	...	...
Wunstorf	12 20	2 53	...	2 13	...	:	...	...	...
Haste	...	3 3	...	...	...	:	...	...	...
Stadthagen	...	3 23	...	...	...	:	...	...	...
Bückeburg	12 49	3 40	...	2 42	A	B	...	...	...
Minden...... arr	12 58	3 51	3 21	2 51	3 10	:	...	...	...
Minden...... dep	12 59	4 5	3 23	2 53	3 16	:	...	...	...
Porta......	1 7	4 13	...	:	:	:	...	...	...
B. Oeynhausen (Rehm.)	1 18	4 25	3 38	:	:	:	...	...	...
Lohne ......arr	1 25	4 32	:	:	:	:	...	...	...
RHEINE 156C ......arr	...	...	:	:	5 a29	:	...	...	...

Lahne ......dep		...	...	5 28	...	See page 118C.	5 5		...	7 34	9 45		6 38	1047	11 51		...	2 6	...	1 28	4 37			See page 118C.		...	...	a.m. 5 35
Herford		...	p.m.	6 23	...		5 18		July 16 to Sept. 21.	7 48	10 9		6 51	1059	12 3		...	2 23	...	1 40	4 51	3 55				...	...	6 5
Bielefeld 157A	2 23	...	5 43	6 51	...		5 37	5 8		8 27	10 35		7 10	1118	1 0	8 20	...	2 45	...	1 57	5 18	4 12	3 35		4 41	...	...	Weekdays only.
Brackwede	...	...	5 52	7 0	...		...	...		8 35	10 43		...	...		...	...	2 53	...	2 5	5 26	...	...			...	...	
Gütersloh	...	...	6 17	7 35	...		...	...		8 56	11 3		7 26	1135	...	...	...	3 13	...	2 18	5 47	...	...			...	...	
Rheda 159	...	...	6 29	7 48	...		...	...			11 15		...	...	...	...	...	3 25	...	...	6 1	...	...			...	...	
Beckum Neu	...	...	6 57	8 17	...		...	...		...	11 39		...	...	...	...	...	3 49	...	—	6 29	...	...			...	...	
Hamm ......arr	3 14	...	7 30	8 48	...		6 29	6 2		...	12 9		8 8	1214	...	9 11	...	4 19	...	3 1	7 3	5 2	4 31			...	...	...
	p.m.		p.m.	p.m.			p.m.	p.m.	p.m.		a.m.		p.m.	nigt	p.m.	p.m.	p.m.	a.m.		a.m.	a.m.	a.m.	a.m.			...	...	...
Hamm ......dep	3 17	...	8 17	8 53	...		6 31	6 3	7 16	...	12 24		8 12	1215	9 36	9 13	10 48	4 38	...	3 4	7 13	5 4	4 33			...	...	...
Camen	...		8 38	9 13	...		...	...	...	...	12 46		...	...	9 57	...	11 8	4 59	...	—	7 36	...	...			...	...	...
Dortmund ......arr	3 43		9 3	9 35	...		6 57	6 29	7 43	...	1 8		8 38	1241	10 21	9 39	11 30	5 21	...	3 32	8 2	5 30	5 1		6 2	...	...	...
(page 135) Dortmund ......dep	3 48				...		7 2	6 42	7 44	...	1 16			1246		9 44			...			5 35	5 6		6 7	...	...	...
Bochum	4 8		...		...		7 23	7 2	8 11	...	1 48			1 10		10 4			...	...		5 55	5 27		...	...	...	...
Essen Haupt ...arr	4 23		...		...		7 38	7 17	8 26	...	2 19			1 25		10 19			...	...		6 10	5 41		6 40	...	...	...
Essen Haupt ...dep	4 26		...		...		7 40	7 23		...				1 27		10 21			...	...		6 15	5 44		6 41	...	...	...
Mulheim Ruhr	...		...		...		7 54	7 35	...	...	...			1 40		...			...	...		6 29	5 58		...	...	...	...
Oberhausen ......arr	...		...		...		8 6	7 43	...	...	...			1 55		...			...	...		6 45	6 29		...	...	...	...
Duisburg ......arr	4 47		...		...		8 5		...	...	...			1 50		10 41			...	...		6 39	6 10		7 3	...	...	...
Crefeld ......arr	5 20		...		...		8 36		...	...	...								...	...			6 51			...	...	...
M. Gladbach ......arr	5 47		1,2,3		Ex3		9 3		...	...	...			...					...	...			7 18			...	...	1,2,3
Aix-la-Chap. ...arr	7 p5	p.m.	p.m.		p.m.		10p29		p.m.	...	...			...					a.m.	...			8 a38			...	...	p.m.
Dortmund ......dep		3 51	6 23	9 49	7 5				7 10	...	...		8 43	...	10 30		11 36	5 41	5 11	...	8 7					...	...	11 25
Herne		4 12	6 44	10 20	7 25				7 39	...	...		9 4	...	11 3		12 8	6 16	5 42	...	8 39					...	...	11 46
Wanne ......arr		4 18	6 50	10 26	7 31				7 45	...	...		9 10	...	11 10		12 14	6 23	5 48	a.m.	8 45					...	...	11 52
Wanne ......dep		4 19	6 51	10 30	7 32				7 48	...	...		9 12	...	11 39		12 15	6 29	5 50	8 50	8 56					...	...	11 54
Gelsenkirchen 133A		4 27	6 59	10 39	7 40				7 57	...	...		9 20	...	11 47		12 22	6 39	5 59	8 58	9 13					...	...	12 3
Alten-Essen 130		4 37	7 9	10 52	7 50				8 10	...	...		9 30	...	12 0			6 52	6 12	9 12	9 26					...	...	12 14
Oberhausen 132 ......arr		4 48	7 20	11 11	8 2				8 29	...	...		9 42	...	12 18		....	7 11	6 32	9 32	9 45					...	...	12 28
Amsterdam 118 ...arr		7 p48	10p20	...	1129	9 p30		11p29	...	...	...	10p†5	...	...	...		...	10a40	9 a45	...	...		9 a45	8a37		...	...	...
Rotterdam 118 ...arr		8 p15	10p44	...	1153	10p45		11 53	...	...	...	10p45	...	...	...		...	11 a1	10 a9	...	...		10 a9	9 a8		...	...	...
Hoek H'll'nd 112 arr		...	...	...	...	11p15		...	...	...	...	11p20	...	...	...		...	...	...	...	...		...	...		...	...	...
Boxtel 120 ......arr		7 p35	...	...	...	...		9 p39	...	...	...	9 p39	...	...	...		...	...	8 a42	2pl2	2 p12		8 a42	8 a17		...	...	...
Vlissingen 113 ...arr		11p38	...	...	...	...		11p38	...	...	Ex 3	11p38	...	...	...		Ex 3	...	10a45	5 p35	5 p35		10a45	10a20		...	...	...
Rotterdam ......dep		...	...	...	...	...			...	...	4 p25	...	4 p25	...	7 p33		7 p33	...	...	...	...			...		...	...	...
Oberhausen ......dep		...	7 25	11 15	8 3	...			8 33	...	9p9	...	9 45	...	12 25		12a33	7 17	6 47	9 33	9 50			...	B	...	...	a.m.
Duisburg 135	4 49	...	7 38	11 28	8 12	...	8 10		8 58	...	9 20	...	9 56	...	12 34	10 43	12 51	7 27	7 14	9 48	10 2	6 40	6 15	...	7 4	...	...	8 34
Dusseldorf Derendorf ...	...	...	...	12 4		...	RC		9 32	...	...	...	...	...		...	...		7 49		10 42	...	...	...	...	...	...	9 19
Dusseldorf Hauptbahnhof ...arr	5 9	...	8 0	12 8	...	...	8 30		9 47	...	9 40	...	10 16	...	...	11 2	1 11	a.m.	7 53	...	10 46	7 0	6 36	...	7 24	...	...	9 23
Dusseldorf Hauptbahnhof ...dep	5 12	...	8 4		...	...	8 33	D		...	9 44	...	10 19	...	...	11 4	1 14	7 33	8 32	...	10 50	7 4	6 39	...	7 27	...	...	9 34
Langenfeld	...	...	...	...	...	...	...		...	...	...	...	...	...	...	RC	...	8 3	8 58	...	11 15	...	...	...	...	...	...	10 1
Mulheim-am-Rhein	...	...	...	...	...	...	...		...	...	...	...	10 50	...	...	...	...	8 24	9 24	...	11 36	...	...	...	...	...	...	10 23
COLOGNE Haupt ...arr	5 48	...	8 40	...	...	...	9 9	8 36	...	...	10 20	...	10 58	...	...	11 39	1 50	8 32	9 36	...	11 45	7 40	7 15	...	8 2	...	...	10 31
	p.m.		p.m.				p.m.	p.m.			p.m.		p.m.			p.m.	a.m.	a.m.	a.m.		a.m.	a.m.	a.m.	...	a.m.	...		a.m.
Aix-la-Chap. 123B arr	7 p24	...	11p52	...	...	...	11p52	...	...	...	12 a6	...	1 a29	...	...	1 a29	...	...	11a19	...	2 p40	9 a9	9 a9	...	9 a20	...	...	...
Paris 24 ......arr	5 a32	...	...	...	...	...	7 a35	...	...	...	7 a35	...	...	...	...	...	...	...	...	...	...	4 p0	4 p0	...	4 p0	...	...	...
Brussels 104 ......arr	9 p45	...	...	...	...	...	...	...	...	...	3 a56	...	3 a56	...	...	3 a56	...	...	2 †51	...	5 p44	11a26	11a26	...	11a31	...	...	...

RC—Restaurant Car. SC—Sleeping Car. †—Via Rheine, page 118C. B—Nord Express, Luxus Zug; Tickets of Sleeping Car Co.
D—Via Dortmund to Cologne, page 134D. A—From Minden will also take 3rd class.

MAGDEBURG and OEBISFELDE.

E.M. Dist		2 3 4	2,3,4	2,3,4	2,3,4	2,3,4	2,3,4	2 3 4	2,3,4	2,3,4
	Leipsic 158...dep	...	3 a29	6 a57	10a25	1 p0	4 p10	4p20	6 p30	10 p5
		a.m.	a.m.	a.m.	p.m.	p.m.	p.m.	p.m.	p.m.	a.m.
—	Magdeburg ......dep	4 14	7 11	10 30	1 46	4 51	6 23	8 25	10 14	12 31
1½	" Neustadt	4 20	7 17	10 37	1 52	4 57	6 29	8 31	10 20	12 40
11¾	Gross-Ammensleben	4 48	7 45	11 6	2 20	5 26	6 59	9 2	10 49	1 10
18¾	Neuhaldensleben	5 4	8 0	11 22	2 36	5 44	7 14	9 21	11 3	1 24
26	Flechtingen	5 20	8 16	11 38	2 53	6 0	7 30	9 42	11 28	
40	Oebisfelde ......arr	5 50	8 47	12 6	3 23	6 32	7 58	1013	11 48	...
94¾	Hanover 160 arr	8 a8	11a17	2 p26	5 p5	9 p8	10p53	1148	1 a32	...

	2 3 4	2 3 4	2 3 4	2 3 4	2 3 4	2,3,4	2,3,4	2,3,4	2,3,4	
Hanover ......dep	...	12a52	...	7a41	9a38	1 p36	4 p35	7 p2	9 p12	...
	a.m.	a.m.	a.m.	a.m.	p.m	p.m.	p.m.	p.m.	p.m.	
Oebisfelde ......dep	...	4 40	7 14	9 10	1224	4 10	6 55	9 9	11 8	...
Flechtingen	...	5 19	7 48	9 41	1259	4 46	7 30	9 42	11 36	...
Neuhaldensleben	4 31	5 45	8 1	9 55	1 14	5 5	7 46	9 56	11 49	...
Gross-Ammensleben ...	4 47	6 5	8 15	10 7	1 30	5 25	8 0	10 11	12 3	...
Magdeburg Neustadt	5 17	6 40	8 40	1032	1 59	5 57	8 29	10 37	12 28	...
Magdeburg ......arr	5 22	6 45	8 45	1037	2 4	6 3	8 34	10 42	12 33	...
Leipsic 158 ...arr	8a19	9 a6	11a8	1 p1	6p23	8 p6	11 p9	...	3 a51	...

COLOGNE (COLN), DUSSELDORF, OBERHAUSEN, DORTMUND, HAMM, MINDEN, HANOVER, and BERLIN.

Frequent Service between Cologne and Dusseldorf.

BRUSSELS 104 ...dep	...	1124	...	...	...	...	...	...	1124	1124	...	...	...	...	...
PARIS 25 ...dep	...	6p20	...	...	...	...	...	...	6p20	6p20	...	...	...	10p0	...
AIX-CHAPELLE ..dep	...	4a20	...	...	...	...	...	...	4a20	4a20	...	...	...	6a50	...
COLOGNE ... arr	...	5a40	...	...	...	...	...	...	5a40	5a40	...	...	...	8 a0	...
Hauptbahnhof	Ex3	Ex3	1,2,3	1,2,3	2 3 4	2 3 4	2,3,4	1,2,3	1,2,3	Ex3	Ex 2	2 3 4	1,2,3	1,2,3	1—4
	a.m.	a.m.	a.m.				a.m.		a.m.	a.m.		a.m.		a.m.	
dep	5 30	5 47	...	...	...	...	5 36	...	7 9	7 20	...	7 30	...	9 0	...
Mülheim-am-Rhein ...	...	...	...	...	...	...	5 45	...	7 18	...	...	7 40	...	9 9	...
Langenfeld ...	...	...	...	...	...	...	6 15	...	...	RC	...	8 4	...	...	...
Dusseldorf arr	6 5	6 22	...	...	...	...	6 40	...	7 4	7 55	...	8 29	a.m.	9 38	...
Hauptbahnhof dep	6 7	6 24	6 33	...	...	...	6 45	...	7 50	7 58	...	8 39	9 29	9 41	...
Dusseldorf-Derendorf	...	...	...	...	a.m.	a.m.	6 51	a.m.	...	...	...	8 44	...	...	a.m.
Duisburg (135) ...arr	6 26	6 44	6 53	...	4 26	5 48	7 26	8 15	8 10	8 17	...	9 17	9 50	10 2	1019
Oberhausen ...arr	6 33	6 54	7 3	...	4 36	5 57	7 38	8 24			...	9 37	10 1		1028
ROT'RDAM 118...arr	10a9	11a1	11 a1	...	...	...	1 p5	...			...	...	...		3 pl
VLISSINGEN 113 dep			...	...	...	...	...	...			4 a36	...	...		...
BOXTEL 120 ...dep	...	...	...	...	...	...	...	...			6 a30	...	...		...
HK. v. HOLLAND 112 dep		...	...	...	...	...	...	...			...	...	...		...
ROTTERDAM 118 dep	...	...	...	...	...	...	...	...			...	...	...		...
AMSTERDAM 118 dep	...	...	...	...	...	...	...	...			6 a10	...	...		...
Oberhausen ...dep	...	...	7 7	...	4 42	6 5	7 48	8 25			To Osnabruck, pages 118B and 156A.	9 49	10 5		1038
Alten-Essen (130) ...	...	...	7 19	...	5 2	6 27	8 8	8 37				1010	1019		1059
Gelsenkirchen ...	...	...	7 29	...	5 18	6 41	8 22	8 47				1024	1030		1113
Wanne ... arr	...	...	7 36	...	5 26	6 48	8 29	8 54				1031	1037		1120
Wanne ... dep	...	...	7 37	...	5 31	6 51	8 36	8 55					1040		1132
Herne ...	...	...	7 44	...	5 38	6 58	8 43	9 2				...	1047		1139
Dortmund ...arr	...	...	8 4	...	6 12	7 30	9 16	9 21				...	11 8		1216
AIX-LA-CHAP. dep (Page 135)	...	...		...								...		7a37	
M. Gladbach ...dep	...	...	...	...				...				...		8 44	...
Crefeld ...dep	...	...	...	...				...				...		9 17	...
Duisburg ...dep	...	...	...	...				...	8 13	8 18		...		10 4	...
Oberhausen ...dep	...	...	...	...				...	7 52	7 52		...		9 41	...
Mulheim Ruhr ...	...	...	...	...				...	8 24	8 30		...		1016	...
Essen ... arr	...	...	...	..				...	8 38	8 44		...		1030	...
Essen ... dep	...	...	...	...				...	8 43	8 46		...		1032	...
Bochum ...	...	1,2,3	2,3,4	...				...	9 5	9 1		...		1048	1—4
Dortmund ...arr	...	a.m.	a.m.	a.m.				...	9 29	9 21		...		1111	p.m.
Dortmund ...dep	...	4 15	5 15	6 22	6 27	8 13	10 8	...	9 34	9 26		...	1135	1117	1259
Camen ...	...	...	5 37	...	6 52	8 36	10 33	...	...	...		...	1159	...	1 26
Hamm (133A)... arr	...	4 43	5 58	6 50	7 13	8 56	10 53	...	10 3	9 52		...	1220	1143	1 47
		a.m.	a.m.	a.m.	a.m.	a.m.	a.m.		a.m.	a.m.				a.m.	
Hamm dep	...	4 45	6 2	6 54	7 20	9 2	11 6	...	10 5	9 54		...	...	1152	...
Beckum Neu (214) ...	...	...	6 36	...	7 56	9 36	11 42	...	...	...		...	...	1213	...
Rheda (159) ...	2 3 4	...	6 57	...	8 19	9 58	12 3	...	...	RC		...	...	...	...
Gütersloh ...	a.m.	5 30	7 8	7 39	8 31	10 9	12 13	...	1046	...		...	...	1237	...
Brackwede (157A) ...	7 24	...	7 33	...	8 57	1031	12 29	...	...	...		...	...	...	...
Bielefeld ...	7 36	5 52	7 43	8 5	9 10	1039	12 49	...	11 9	10 50		...	...	1259	...
Herford (155) ...	7 54	6 5	8 1	8 20	9 37	1132	1 20	...	1124			...	...	1 14	...
Lohne ...arr		6 15	8 12	8 31	9 48	1144	1 32	...	1135			...	...	1 24	...
HK. v. HOLLAND dep	...	...	...	...	...	...	...	...	...		5 a18	...	...	...	...
RHEINE 156C ...dep	a.m.	...	...	...	5a54	8a18	10a58	...	8a18		Osnab'k... arr 11.16	...	...	1058	...
Lohne ...dep	5 13	6 16	8 13	8 33	9 53	1146	1 34	...	1137			...	...	1 25	...
Bad Oeynhausen ...	5 21	6 24	8 24	8 42	10 5	1159	1 46	...	1146			...	...	1 34	...
Porta ...	5 36	...	8 40	...	1020	1214	2 12	...	...			...	...	...	...
Minden ...arr	5 43	6 38	8 47	8 56	1026	1221	2 18	...	12 0			...	...	1 48	...

BRUSSELS 104 ...dep	...	...	...	..	...	...	...	5a45	5 a45	5a45	...		10a54	...	...
PARIS 25 ...dep	1115	...	11p15	11p15	...	...	...	1115	11p15	1115	...		7a50	...	...
AIX-CHAPELLE ..dep	8a43	...	8 a43	8a43	...	...	...	10a7	10 a7	10a7	...		3p12	...	...
COLOGNE ... arr	9a51	...	9 a51	9a51	...	...	...	1114	11a14	11a14	...		4p19	...	...
Hauptbahnhof	Ex2	Ex3	Ex.3	Ex2	1—4		1,2,3	2 3 4	Ex.3	Ex2		‡—Via Rheine, page 118B.	Ex2	Ex2	2 3 4
	a.m.		a.m.	a.m.	a.m.			a.m.	p.m.	p.m.			p.m.		
dep	10 6	...	10 10	1014	9 18	...	...	1140	12 44	1253	...		4 24	..	...
Mülheim-am-Rhein ...	...	...	...		9 28	...	...	1150	...	...	...	...		...	...
Langenfeld ...	RC	...	RC		9 54	...	...	1212	RC	RC	...	...		...	...
Dusseldorf arr	1040	...	10 47		10 20	...	...	1232	1 19	1 33	...	...		p.m.	...
Hauptbahnhof dep	1043	...	10 49		11 16	...	...	1241	1 22	1 36	...	...		4 37	...
Dusseldorf-Derendorf	...	a.m.	...		11 22	...	p.m.	1246	...	...	...	...	RC	...	p.m.
Duisburg (135) ...arr	11 4	1059	11 9		11 54	...	1 40	1 17	1 42	1 56	...	...		4 47	4 2
Oberhausen ...arr	1114	11 8			12 6	...	1 49	1 31	1 55		...	...		4 57	4 11
ROT'RDAM 118...arr	3 pl	3 pl			5 p22	...	...	6p25	6 p25		...	...		8pl5	...
VLISSINGEN 113 dep	...	...			...	...	...	...	...		...	...		...	...
BOXTEL 120 ...dep	...	...			7 a12	...	...	...	...		...	...		...	...
HK. v. HOLLAND 112 dep	...	...			...	...	...	...	...		...	...		...	...
ROTTERDAM 118 dep	6a32	6a32			...	9a27	8 a48	8a48	9 a27	8a48	...	...		12pl1	9a55
AMSTERDAM 118 dep	7 a0	7 a0			...	1020	9 a18	9a18	10‡20	9a18	...	...		1240	1028
Oberhausen ...dep	1117	1110		Via Elberfeld, Barmen, Hagen.	12 25	See page 118B.	1 51	1 35	1 59	Bochum.	...	...	Via Elberfeld, page 134B.	4 58	4 15
Alten-Essen (130) ...	1129	1122			12 45		2 4	1 54	2 12		...	...		...	4 37
Gelsenkirchen ...	1138	1132			12 59		2 14	2 8	2 23		...	1—4		5 17	4 54
Wanne ... arr	1144	1139			1 6		2 21	2 15	2 30		...	p.m.		5 24	5 1
Wanne ... dep	...	1140			1 24		2 23	2 39	2 33		...	3 55		5 25	5 3
Herne ...	...	1147			1 32		2 30	2 46	2 40		...	4 2		...	5 10
Dortmund ...arr	...	12 6			2 5		2 50	3 18	3 2		...	4 30		5 53	5 43
AIX-LA-CHAP. dep (Page 135)	...		8 a46							1114	...			3p17	
M. Gladbach ...dep	...	...	10 0		...		...			1242	...			4 11	
Crefeld ...dep	...	...	10 31		...		...			1 10	...			4 34	
Duisburg ...dep	...	...	11 11		...		...			1 58	...			4 57	
Oberhausen ...dep	...	...	10 56		...		...			1 40	...			...	
Mulheim Ruhr ...	...	...	11 22		...		...			2 10	...			5 7	
Essen ... arr	...	...	11 37		...		...			2 24	...			5 20	
Essen ... dep	...	...	11 40		...		...			2 26	...			5 21	
Bochum ...	...	...	11 57		...		...			2 42	...			5 36	
Dortmund ...arr	...	...	12 16	12 2	...		...			3 1	...			5 54	
Dortmund ...dep	...	...	12 22	1212	...		...	3 35	3 11	3 6	...	4 44		6 2	6 7
Camen ...	...	...	...		...		...	3 57	...	...	...	5 8		...	6 29
Hamm (133A)... arr	2 3 4	...	12 48		...		2,3,4	4 17	3 38	3 32	...	5 27	6 30	6 29	6 50
	p.m.		p.m.				p.m.	p.m.	p.m.	p.m.				p.m.	p.m.
Hamm dep	1256	...	12 52		...		1 59	4 22	3 39	3 35	...	...		6 42	7 0
Beckum Neu (214) ...	1 31	...	...		...		2 33	4 54	...	...	...	...	...	...	7 25
Rheda (159) ...	1 56	...	RC		...		2 57	5 16	RC	RC	...	p.m.	...	...	7 48
Gütersloh ...	2 7	...	...		...		3 11	5 29	4 19	...	...	6 51	...		8 1
Brackwede (157A) ...	2 34	...	...		p.m.		3 38	5 54	...	...	...	7 19	...		8 24
Bielefeld ...	2 40	...	1 46	1 35	2 19		3 51	6 5	4 41	4 31	...	7 39	...	7 34	8 33
Herford (155) ...		...	...		2 38		4 19	6 24	4 56		...	7 56	...		8 47
Lohne ...arr	...	...	2 5		2 50		4 33	6 35	5 6		...	8 6	...		8 58
HK. v. HOLLAND dep	...	...	...		...	Ex3	...	...	...		...	...	...		...
RHEINE 156C ...dep	...	..	12p28		...	2p44	2 p44	...	2 p44		...	4p55	...		4p55
Lohne ...dep	...	...	2 7		2 51	4 27	5 14	6 37	5 9		...	8 7	...		9 1
Bad Oeynhausen ...	...	...	2 16		3 3	4 36	5 27	6 45	5 18		...	8 12	...		9 9
Porta ...	...	...	...		3 18	...	5 42	6 59	...		...	8 30	...		9 20
Minden ...arr	...	...	2 29		3 25	4 50	5 49	7 8	5 32	5 5	...	8 37	...		9 27

Station																														
Minden ......dep	5 48	6 39	9 5	8 57	1032	1238	2 37	...	12 3			...	...	1 50	...	...	..	2 31		3 31	4 53	5 55	7 14	5 34	5 6	...		...		9 0
Bückeburg	6 3	6 50	9 20	9 9	1046	1252	2 52	...	1214			...	...	2 1	...	...	...	...		3 47	5 4	6 11	7 28	5 45	...	...	...	...		9 42
Stadthagen	6 22	...	9 38	9 22	11 3	1 9	3 10	...	...			...	...	...	...	...	...	...		4 4	...	6 30	7 45	...	...	...	...	...		9 57
Haste (155)	6 43	...	9 57	...	1122	1 27	3 30	...	1237			...	...	...	...	...	...	...		4 23	...	6 50	8 3	...	...	...	...	...		1013
Wunstorf	6 55	...	10 7	...	1131	1 37	3 40	...	...			...	...	2 29	...	...	...	...		4 32	...	7 0	8 13	6 13	...	...	...	...		...
Hanover ......arr	7 28	7 35	10 40	9 58	12 0	2 10	4 13	...	1 2	1213	1 20	...	...	2 49	...	...	...	1 20	2 56	5 4	5 48	7 30	8 45	6 33	5 56	...	...	...	8 53	1044
Hanover ......dep	...	7 48	...	10 14	12 5	...	...	...	1 10	1 10	1 36	...	...	3 34	...	...	...	3 34	3 34	...	6 41	8 20	9 42	6 41	...	...	...	...	9 42	11 5
Lehrte ...... arr	...	8 4	...	10 29	1221	...	...	...	...	...	2 0	...	...	3 50	...	...	...	3 50	3 50	...	6 57	8 46	9 58	6 57	...	...	...	...	9 58	1121
Lehrte ...... dep	...	8 5	...	10 30	1224	...	...	...	...	...	2 9	...	...	3 53	...	...	...	3 53	3 53	...	6 58	8 48	9 59	6 58	...	...	...	...	9 59	1122
Peine (129B)	...	8 22	...	10 47	1242	...	...	...	...	...	2 35	...	...	4 11	...	...	...	4 11	4 11	...	7 17	9 16	1016	7 17	...	...	...	...	1016	1140
Vechelde	...	...	...	...	...	...	...	...	...	...	2 51	...	...	...	...	...	...	...	...	...	...	9 34	...	...	...	...	...	...	...	...
Brunswick ......arr	...	8 45	...	11 10	1 6	...	...	...	2 34	2 34	3 15	...	...	4 35	...	...	...	4 35	4 35	...	7 43	9 59	1039	7 43	...	...	...	...	1039	12 4
MAGDEBURG 158 arr	...	1016	...	12p30	3p34	...	...	...	3p57	3p57	...	...	...	6 p2	...	...	...	6 p2	6 p2	...	9p21	12 a7	12a7	9 p21	...	...	...	...	12a7	...
LEIPSIC via Halle 158	arr	2p55	...	3 p5	6p11	...	...	...	6p11	6p11	6 §23	...	...	8 p6	...	...	...	8 p6	8 p6	...	1130	3 a51	3a51	11p30	11§p9	...	...	...	3a51	...
	2 3 4	1,2,3	Ex 3		2 3 4				1,2,3	Ex3	Ex 2							Ex.3	Ex2	2,3,4			2 3 4	Ex.3	Ex2		2 3 4		Ex2	2 3 4
		a.m.			p.m.				p.m.	p.m.	p.m.							p.m.	p.m.	p.m.			p.m.	p.m.	p.m.		p.m		p.m.	p.m.
Hanover ......dep	...	7 41	...	...	1 36	...	...	...	1 15	1218	1 25	§—Via Stendal-Magdeburg.	...	...	...	...	From 25th July until 18th August.	3 25	3 1	4 35	...	...	9 12	6 48	6 1	...	7 2	...	8 58	1052
Lehrte ...... arr	...	7 57	...	...	2 0	...	...	...	1 32				...	...	...	...				5 1	...	...	9 34	7 4		...	7 28	...		1116
Lehrte ...... dep	...	7 58	...	...	2 2	...	...	...	1 45				...	...	...	...				5 9	...	...	9 36	7 5		...	7 30	...		1122
Dollbergen	...	...	...	...	2 21	...	...	...	...				...	...	...	...				5 30	...	...	9 55	...		...	7 49	...		...
Jsenbüttel	...	8 31	...	...	2 55	...	...	...	2 19	RC			...	...	...	...				6 5	...	...	1027	7 38		...	8 24	...		12 0
Fallersleben	...	...	...	...	3 11	...	...	...	...				...	...	...	...				6 24	...	...	1043	RC	RC	...	8 40	...		...
Vorsfelde	...	...	...	...	3 22	...	...	...	...				...	...	...	...				6 35	...	...	1054	...		...	8 50	...		...
Oebisfelde ......arr	...	8 57	...	...	3 32	...	...	...	2 46				...	...	...	...				6 45	...	...	11 4	8 3		...	9 0	...		1231
MAGDEBURG 160C ar	a.m.	1037	...	...	6 p3	...	...	...	6 p3			...	...	...	...	...				8 p34	...	...	1233	10p42		...	1042	...		...
Oebisfelde ......dep	5 55	8 58	...	...	3 31	...	...	...	2 48			...	...	...	...	...				7 14	...	...	...	8 4		...	9 3	...		1233
Gardelegen	6 35	9 23	...	...	4 10	...	...	...	3 13			...	...	...	...	...				7 55	...	...	...	8 29		...	9 42	...		1 2
Vinzelberg	7 4	9 42	...	...	4 47	...	...	...	...			...	...	...	...	...				8 28	...	...	...	...		...	1010	...		1 21
Stendal ......arr	7 23	9 53	...	...	5 1	...	...	...	3 40		3 14	...	...	...	...	...	Ex3	5 15		8 46	...	Ex 3	...	8 55	7 48	Ex3	1026	...		1 39
MAGDEBURG 163 arr	8a58	11a2	a.m.	...	6p47	...	...	...	6p47		4 p23	...	...	...	...	...	p.m.	6 p47		10p33	...	p.m.	...	10p33	8p59	p.m.	1153	...		...
Stendal ......dep	7 33	9 57	11 41	...	5 32	...	...	...	3 44		3 18	...	...	...	...	...	6 28	5 19		9 8	...	8 1	...	8 59	7 50	9 57	1114	...		1 44
Schönhausen	7 53	1012	...	...	5 51	...	...	...	...		...	...	...	...	...	...	...	...		9 29	...	...	...	...	...	...	1132	...		...
Rathenow	8 22	1032	12 11	...	6 21	...	...	...	4 14		...	...	...	...	...	...	...	...		10 1	...	8 31	...	9 30	...	...	12 4	...		2 17
Nennhausen	8 37	...	...	...	6 33	...	...	...	...		...	...	...	...	...	...	...	...		10 15	...	...	...	...	...	...	1216	...		...
Wustermark	9 14	...	...	...	7 8	...	...	...	...		...	...	...	...	...	...	...	...		11 7	...	...	...	...	...	...	1251	...		3 15
Spandau	9 44	1123	...	...	7 37	...	...	...	5 3		...	...	...	...	...	...	...	...		11 35	...	...	...	10 20	...	11 6	1 16	...		...
BERLIN Lehrter Bahnhof ar	10 3	...	1 16	...	7 55	...	...	...	...		...	...	...	...	...	...	8 0	...		11 51	...	9 38	...	...	...	1120	1 38	...		3 30
BERLIN Charlottenburg arr	...	1137	...	...	...	...	...	...	5 17		...	...	...	...	...	...	...	...		...	...	...	...	10 34	...	...	...	...		...
BERLIN Zoolog-Garten...arr	...	1144	...	...	...	...	...	...	5 24	3 36	4 42	...	...	...	...	...	...	6 48	6 0	...	...	...	...	10 41	9 16	...	...	...	12 9	3 43
BERLIN Friedrichstrasse ar	...	1154	...	...	...	...	...	...	5 34	3 48	4 54	...	...	...	...	...	...	7 0	6 12	...	...	...	...	10 52	9 28	...	...	...	1221	...
BERLIN Alexanderplatz arr	...	12 4	...	...	...	...	...	...	5 43	3 58	5 3	...	...	...	...	...	...	7 10	6 21	...	...	...	...	11 2	9 38	...	...	...	1230	3 57
BERLIN Schlesischer Bhf.ar	...	1210	...	...	...	...	...	...	5 49	4 4	5 9	...	...	...	...	...	...	7 16	6 27	...	...	...	...	11 8	9 44	...	...	...	1236	...

FARES from COLOGNE.

	1 Cl. m.pf.	2 Cl. m.pf.	3 Cl. m.pf.		1 Cl. m.pf.	2 Cl. m.pf.	3 Cl. m.pf.
To Berlin	47 80	29 20	18 80	To Hanover	27 20	17 50	11 0
,, Bremen	27 90	17 90	11 50	,, Leipsic	43 90	27 90	17 90
,, Hamburg	37 40	23 70	15 10	,, Rotterdam	20 10	14 50	9 20

For Continuation of Trains, see next page.

Extra.					
Cologne ......dep	8 a15	3 p25	7 p6	...	...
Duisburg ......arr	9 23	5 16	8 16	...	...

RC—Restaurant Car.

BRUNSWICK and OEBISFELDE.

Brunswick ...	7a35	10a45	1p23	5p17	9p41	...	...	...	...
Schandelah	7 55	11 7	1 45	5 39	10 0	...	...	...	...
Oebisfelde ...	8 52	12 4	2 40	6 37	1057	...	...	...	...

Oebisfelde ...	5a32	9a10	12p34	4 p4	6p57	...	...	...	...	...	...	...	...
Schandelah	6 33	1011	1 35	5 3	7 58	...	...	...	...	...	...	...	...
Brunswick ...	6 55	1031	1 57	5 25	8 21	...	...	...	...	...	...	...	...

OEBISFELDE and SALZWEDEL.

E.M.							
	Oebisfelde ......dep	6 a3	9a30	12p24	4p10	6 p53	10p37
22½	Beetzendorf	7 10	1054	1 30	5 18	8 1	11 41
36¾	**Salzwedel (163)**...arr	7 54	1140	2 12	6 1	8 41	12 20

Salzwedel ......dep	6 a50	9 a27	1 p10	3 p36	6p44	9p55	...	...	...
Beetzendorf	7 35	10 14	1 58	4 38	7 27	1038	...	...	...
Oebisfelde (160) arr	8 44	11 30	3 27	6 13	8 39	1149	...	...	...

SALZWEDEL and DANNENBERG

Salzwedel ......dep	4 a30	6 a45	9 a21	12p28	3 p45	7 p7	9 p30
Lüchow	5 35	7 30	10 12	1 48	4 38	7 47	10 1
Dannenberg ......arr	6 30	9 20	...	2 31	5 30	8 55	...

Dannenberg ......dep	7 a39	...	12p17	3 p40	6p20	10p10	...	...
Lüchow	8 18	11a40	1 22	4 55	7 45	11 2	...	...
Salzwedel 163 ......arr	8 46	12 13	2 5	5 41	8 17	11 33	...	...

Luggage Rates—see page 462.] For Fares—see page 120A.

COLOGNE (COLN), DUSSELDORF, OBERHAUSEN, DORTMUND, HAMM, MINDEN, HANOVER, and BERLIN.

SC—Sleeping Car RC—Restaurant Car.

BRUSSELS 104 ...dep	...	...	...	7a44	1054	...	10a54	1054	...	...	...	...	...	1p32	1p32	1 p32	1p32	...	3 p3	5 p22	...	...	5p0	...	...	5 p0	...	...	...
PARIS 24 ...dep	...	...	...	...	7a50	...	7 a50	8a10	8 a10	8a10	...	...	...	...	...	...	...	...	...	1 p45	...	...	1p45	1 p45	...	...	...	...	...
AIX-CHAPELLE 122dp	...	1124	...	1p20	3p12	...	3 p12	4p42	4 p42	4p42	...	...	...	6p26	6p26	6 p26	6p26	...	8 p26	9 p39	...	...	1012	10p13	...	10p12	...	...	...
COLOGNE Hauptbahnhof arr	...	1p16	...	3p15	4p19	...	4 p19	5p55	5 p55	5p55	...	...	...	7p40	7p40	7 p40	7p40	...	10p28	10p46	...	...	1124		...	11p24	...	...	...
		2 3 4	1,2,3	1—4	Ex2	Ex 3	Ex.3	Ex2	1,2,3	1,2,3	1—4	1,2,3	1—4	1,2,3	2 3 4	1,2,3	Ex3	Ex3	Ex 3	Ex.1	Ex2	Ex 2	Ex3	Ex 3	2 3 4	Ex 3			
		p.m.	p.m.	p.m.	p.m.	p.m.	p.m.	p.m.	p.m.	p.m.			p.m.	p.m.	p.m.	p.m.	p.m.	p.m.	p.m.	p.m.			p.m.		p.m.	a.m.			
COLOGNE Hauptbahnhof dep	...	1 57	2 27	4 18	4 47	5 0	5 25	6 15	6 23	6 32	...	...	6 38	8 11	8 14	9 34	9 42	1023	10 40	10 58	...	...	1133		1124	1 1	...	...	...
Mülheim-am-Rhein...	...	2 7	2 38	4 27		...			...	6 41	...	...	6 47	...	8 23	9 42		1032		N	...	...	...		1134	...	...	...	...
Langenfeld ...	...	2 29	...	...	RC	...	RC	RC	...	...	...	...	7 21	...	8 48	...	SC	RC	RC	...	...	...	SC		12 9	RC	...	...	...
Dusseldorf Hauptbahnhof arr	...	2 54	3 4	4 58	5 22	5 38	6 0	6 50	6 58	7 10	...	...	7 56	8 47	9 16	10 11	1018	11 2	...	11 33	...	...	12 9		1233	...	...	...	...
Dusseldorf Hauptbahnhof dep	...	3 16	3 7	5 6	5 24	5 41	6 2	6 53	7 1	7 14	...	...	8 5	8 51	9 22	10 14	1021	11 6	11 16	11 35	...	...	1211		1243	1 36	...	...	...
Dusseldorf-Derendorf	...	3 21	...	...	...	...	...	...		...	p.m.	p.m.	8 10	...	...	...	...	...	11 18	...	...	...	...	nght	1248	1 40	...	...	...
Duisburg (135) ...arr	...	3 53	3 27	5 28	5 44	6 1	6 22	7 13		7 34	7 44	8 54	8 51	9 11	9 47	10 33	1041	1127	11 38	11 55	...	...	1231	12 18	1 19	2 0	...	...	...
Oberhausen ...arr	...	4 18	3 38	5 40	5 54	6 12		7 28		7 46	7 54	9 3	9 30		10 4	10 44			1149		...	...		12 28	1 34		...	...	...
ROT'ERDAM 118A arr	...	...	7p11	9 pl	9 pl	...		1044		1154	...	...	...		...	...			...		...	...		...	...		...	...	...
VLISSINGEN 113 dep	...	...		...		...				1225	...	...	...		...	...	1p27		...		7p10	7 p0	7 p0	...	7 p0		...	...	...
BOXTEL 120 ...dep	...	...	...	...	...	...		...	Via Kettwig.	3p40	...	...	...		...	...	3p28		...		9p12	9 pl	9 pl	...	9 pl		...	...	...
HK. V. HOLLAND 112dp	...	...	...	...	...	...		...		...	...	...	...		...	...			...		...		...	...	...		...	...	...
ROTTERDAM 118 dep	...	9a55	9a55	12pl1	...	...		...		...	...	...	4p25		...	...	4p25		...		8p22		7p34	...	7p34		...	...	...
AMSTERDAM 118 dep	...	1028	1028	1240	...	...		...		...	...	...	5 p2		...	...	5 12		...		9 p0		8 p5	...	8 p5		...	...	...
Oberhausen ...dep	...	4 30	3 52	5 52	...	6 14		1—4		7 50	7 56	9 4	9 34		1024	10 46			11 51					1—4	1 41		...	...	...
Alten-Essen (130) ...	...	4 50	4 6	6 13	...	–		p.m.		8 3	8 16	9 17	9 54		1044	10 59			12 5					nght	2 0		...	...	...
Gelsenkirchen...	...	5 5	4 16	6 28	...	6 34		6 54		8 13	8 35	9 28	10 8		11 0	11 9			12 15					12 44	2 14		...	...	...
Wanne ... arr	...	5 13	4 23	6 35	...	6 40		7 1		8 20	8 43	9 35	1015		11 7	11 16			12 22					12 51	2 21		...	...	...
Wanne ... dep	...	5 32	4 30	6 56	...	6 41		7 6		8 24	8 44	9 36	1020		1123	11 17			12 23					12 56	2 23		...	...	...
Herne...	...	5 39	4 37	7 3	...	...		7 13		8 31	8 51	9 43	1028		1131	11 24			12 30					1 3	2 30		...	...	...
Dortmund ...arr	...	6 12	4 59	7 35	...	7 8		8 2		8 53	9 24	10 4	11 0		12 0	11 44			12 51	N				1 33	3 0		...	...	...
AIX-LA-CHAP. dep	...				...																		1013				...	...	...
Page 135 — M. Gladbach ...dep	...		...	...	...	...						...	...			...			...				1125	...			...	...	...
Crefeld ...dep	...		...	...	...	...						...	...			...			...				1153	...			...	...	...
Duisburg ...dep	...		...	...	...	...	6 23					...	...	9 12		...	1043	1142	...	11 56			1233	...		2 1	...	...	...
Oberhausen ...dep	...		...	...	...	...	5 53					...	...	8 22		...	1025	1138	...	...		12 22	1222	...		1 14	...	...	...
Mulheim Ruhr ...	...		...	...	...	...	6 34					...	...	9 24		...	1055	1153	...	...		12 31	1245	...		2 11	...	...	...
Essen Haupt arr	...		...	...	...	...	6 48		7 49			...	...	9 39		...	11 9	12 7	...	12 18	See page 118B.	12 44	1257	...		2 25	...	...	...
Essen Haupt dep	...		...	...	...	...	6 50		7 53			...	...	9 42		...	1111	12 8	...	12 19		(	1 7	...		2 26	...	...	...
Bochum...	...		...	...	...	...	7 6		8 10			...	...	9 59		1,2,3	1128	1223	...	---		...	1 23	...		2 41	...	...	...
Dortmund ...arr	...		...	...	...	...	7 30		8 33			...	...	1023		p.m.	1147	1246	...	12 52		...	1 42	...		3 0	...	...	...
Dortmund...dep	...	6 18	...	...	...	...		8 9		8 58	9 30	...	...		12 6	11 10	1153		...	12 57		...	1 47	...	3 12		...	...	...
Camen ...	...	6 42	...	...	...	...	...	8 36	...	...	9 55	...	...	...	1227	11 33	...	...	...			...	...	...	3 34	...	...	...	...
Hamm (133A) ... arr	...	7 3	...	...	...	...	...	8 57	...	9 28	10 16	...	...	2 3 4	1246	11 54	1221	...	...			...	2 13	...	3 54	...	...	...	...
		p.m.								p.m.				p.m.	a.m.		a.m.						a.m.		a.m.				
Hamm (133A) ... dep	...	7 12	...	...	...	...	...	...	...	9 35	...	...	...	9 40	1250	...	1225	...	§—Via Oberhausen, Essen, Dortmund.			...	2 15	...	3 58	...	...	...	...
Beckum Neu (214)...	...	7 55	...	...	...	...	...	...	...	...	...	...	...	1020	1 23	...	...	...				...	...	...	4 28	...	...	...	...
Rheda (159) ...	...	8 20	...	...	...	...	...	...	...	...	...	...	...	1047	1 58	...	...	...				...	...	...	4 49	...	...	...	...
Gütersloh ...	...	8 35	...	...	...	...	...	...	...	1016	...	...	...	11 5	2 10	...	...	...				...	...	...	5 3	...	...	...	...
Brackwede (157A) ...	...	9 2	...	...	...	...	...	...	...	...	...	...	...	1139	2 31	...	...	...				...	...	...	5 29	...	...	...	...
Bielefeld ...	...	9 15	...	...	...	...	...	...	...	1039	...	...	...	1156	2 41	...	1 36	...		2 20		...	3 7	...	5 40	...	...	...	...
Herford (155) ...	...	9 38	...	...	...	...	...	...	...	1054	...	...	...	1217	3 2	...	1 39	...				...		...	6 11	...	...	...	...
Lohne ...arr	...	9 49	...	...	...	...	...	...	...	11 4	...	...	...		3 13	...		...				...		...	6 22	...	...	...	...
H'K V. HOLLAND dep	...	...	...	...	...	...	...	...	...	...	...	...	...	...	...	...		...				...		...	...	...	...	...	...
RHEINE 156C ...dep	...	7p54	...	...	...	...	...	...	...	...	...	...	...	...	...	...		...			1a16	...		...	...	...	...	...	...
Lohne ...dep	...	10 0	...	...	...	...	...	...	...	11 6	...	...	...	...	3 33	...		...				...		...	6 28	...	...	...	...
Bad Oeynhausen ...	...	1013	...	...	...	...	...	...	...	1115	...	...	...	...	3 41	...	1 56	...				...		...	6 39	...	...	...	...
Porta ...	...	1029	...	...	...	...	...	...	...	1125	...	...	...	...	3 52	...	...	...				...		...	6 54	...	...	...	...
Minden ...arr	...	1035	...	...	...	...	...	...	...	1131	...	...	...	...	3 59	...	2 10	...			3 23	...	3 41	...	7 1	...	...	...	...

Station																													
Minden ...dep	...	1041	...	...	...	...	...	...	...	1133	...	...	...	...	...	...	2 12	...	...	...	3 25	...	3 42	...	7 8	...	...	...	...
Bückeburg	...	1057	...	...	...	...	...	...	...	1144	...	...	...	...	...	...	2 23	...	...	N	...	...	...	...	7 24	...	...	...	...
Stadthagen	...	1117	...	...	...	...	...	...	...	1157	...	...	...	...	...	...	...	...	...	...	...	...	...	...	7 41	...	...	...	...
Haste (155)	...	1141	...	...	...	...	...	...	...	...	...	...	...	...	...	...	...	...	...	...	...	...	...	...	8 2	...	...	...	...
Wunstorf	...	1152	...	...	...	...	...	...	...	1216	...	...	...	...	...	...	2 52	...	...	...	...	...	...	...	8 14	...	...	...	...
Hanover ...arr	...	1225	...	...	...	...	...	...	...	1236	...	...	...	...	...	...	3 12	...	...	3 49	4 17	...	4 32	...	8 47	...	...	...	...
																	a.m.				a.m.		a.m.		a.m.				
Hanover ...dep	...	...	...	...	...	...	...	...	...	...	...	...	...	...	...	...	3 21	...	...	...	4 37	...	4 37	...	9 34	...	...	...	...
Lehrte ...arr	...	...	...	...	...	...	...	...	...	...	...	...	...	...	...	...	3 37	...	...	...	...	...	...	...	10 0	...	...	...	...
Lehrte ...dep	...	...	...	...	...	...	...	...	...	...	...	...	...	...	...	...	3 38	...	...	...	...	...	...	...	10 5	...	...	...	...
Peine (129B)	...	...	...	...	...	...	...	...	...	...	...	...	...	...	...	...	3 55	...	...	...	...	...	...	...	1033	...	...	...	...
Vechelde	...	...	...	...	...	...	...	...	...	...	...	...	...	...	...	...	...	...	...	...	...	...	...	...	1050	...	...	...	...
Brunswick ...arr	...	...	...	...	...	...	...	...	...	...	...	...	...	...	...	...	4 19	...	...	...	5 29	...	5 29	...	1129	...	...	...	...
MAGDEBURG 158 arr	...	...	...	...	...	...	...	...	...	...	...	...	...	...	...	...	5a52	...	...	...	6a46	...	6a46	...	3p34	...	...	...	...
LEIPSIC via Halle 158	...	...	...	...	...	...	...	...	...	...	...	...	...	...	...	...	8a19	...	...	...	9 a6	...	9 a6	...	...	...	...	...	...
		2 3 4		2,34													Ex3			Ex 1	Ex2		Ex3	2,3,4	2 3 4				
		a.m.		n'gt													a.m.			a.m.	a.m.		a.m.	a.m.	a.m.				
Hanover ...dep	From 16th July until 16th September.	1252	...	1210	...	...	...	...	...	...	...	...	...	...	...	...	3 28	...	...	3 57	4 22	...	4 37	6 31	9 58	...	...	...	...
Lehrte ...arr		1 11	...	1236	...	...	...	...	...	...	...	...	...	...	...	...	...	...	...	...	...	...	Via Magdeburg, page 164	6 57	1023	...	...	...	...
Lehrte ...dep		1 12	...	1240	...	...	...	...	...	...	...	...	...	...	...	...	...	...	...	...	...	...	...	7 0	1034	...	...	...	...
Dollbergen		...	...	1 1	...	...	...	...	...	...	...	...	...	...	...	...	...	...	...	...	...	...	...	7 13	1053	...	...	...	...
Isenbüttel		...	...	1 35	...	...	...	...	...	...	...	...	...	...	...	...	...	...	...	...	...	...	...	8 5	1129	...	...	...	...
Fallersleben		...	...	1 51	...	...	...	...	...	...	...	...	...	...	...	...	...	...	...	...	...	...	...	8 23	1147	...	...	...	...
Vorsfelde		...	...	2 2	...	...	...	...	...	...	...	...	...	...	...	...	...	...	...	...	...	...	...	8 34	1159	...	...	...	...
Oebisfelde ...arr		2 22	...	2 13	...	...	...	...	...	...	...	...	...	...	...	...	...	...	...	...	...	...	...	8 44	1210	...	...	...	...
MAGDEBURG 160C ar		...	...	...	...	...	...	...	...	...	...	...	...	...	...	...	...	...	...	...	...	...	...	10a37	2 p4	...	...	...	...
Oebisfelde ...dep		2 27	...	2 35	...	...	...	...	...	...	...	...	...	...	...	...	...	...	...	...	...	...	...	9 10	1215	...	...	...	...
Gardelegen		...	...	3 22	...	...	...	...	...	...	...	...	...	...	...	...	4 58	...	...	...	...	...	...	9 52	1254	...	...	...	...
Vinzelberg		...	...	3 55	...	...	...	...	...	...	...	...	...	...	...	...	...	...	...	...	...	...	...	10 24	1 22	...	...	...	...
Stendal ...arr	Ex 3	3 31	...	4 12	...	...	...	...	...	...	...	...	...	...	...	...	5 26	...	...	5 46	...	...	...	10 43	1 38	...	...	...	...
MAGDEBURG 163 arr	a.m.	5a37	...	5a37	...	...	...	...	...	...	...	...	...	...	...	...	8a58	...	...	...	...	...	...	12p25	3p51	...	...	...	...
Stendal ...dep	3 34	3 40	...	4 20	...	...	...	...	...	...	...	...	...	...	...	...	5 30	...	...	5 50	...	...	...	11 8	2 23	...	...	...	...
Schönhausen	...	...	...	4 39	...	...	...	...	...	...	...	...	...	...	...	...	...	...	...	...	...	...	...	11 29	2 41	...	...	...	...
Rathenow	...	...	...	5 9	...	...	...	...	...	...	...	...	...	...	...	...	5 59	...	...	...	...	...	...	12 19	3 9	...	...	...	...
Nennhausen	...	...	...	5 22	...	...	...	...	...	...	...	...	...	...	...	...	...	...	...	...	...	...	...	12 33	3 21	...	...	...	...
Wustermark	...	...	...	6 11	...	...	...	...	...	...	...	...	...	...	...	...	...	...	...	...	...	...	...	1 11	3 58	...	...	...	...
Spandau	...	5 23	...	6 26	...	...	...	...	...	...	...	...	...	...	...	...	6 47	...	...	N	...	...	...	1 37	4 37	...	...	...	...
BERLIN Lehrter Bahn ...arr	5 8	...	...	6 49	...	...	...	...	...	...	...	...	...	...	...	...	...	...	...	...	...	...	...	1 56	4 53	...	...	...	...
BERLIN Charlottenburg arr	...	5 38	...	...	...	...	...	...	...	...	...	...	...	...	...	...	7 2	...	...	...	...	...	...	...	...	...	...	...	...
BERLIN Zoolog-Garten ...arr	...	5 45	...	...	...	...	...	...	...	...	...	...	...	...	...	...	7 9	...	...	7 18	7 45	...	...	...	...	...	...	...	...
BERLIN **Friedrichstrasse** ar	...	5 55	...	...	...	...	...	...	...	...	...	...	...	...	...	...	7 20	...	...	7 29	7 57	...	...	...	...	...	...	...	...
BERLIN Alexanderplatz arr	...	6 2	...	...	...	...	...	...	...	...	...	...	...	...	...	...	7 30	...	...	...	8 6	...	...	...	...	...	...	...	...
BERLIN Schlesischer Bhf. ar	...	6 8	...	...	...	...	...	...	...	...	...	...	...	...	...	...	7 36	...	...	7 41	8 12	...	...	...	...	...	...	...	...
BERLIN Potsdamer Bhf. arr	...	...	...	...	...	...	...	...	...	...	...	...	...	...	...	...	...	...	...	...	...	...	8 54	...	...	...	...	...	...

Extra.—Duisburg to Oberhausen, 10.45 and 11.48 p.m.

N—Nord Express to Berlin daily. Runs from Berlin to St. Petersburg twice a week only, leaving Berlin on Sunday and Thursday. Tickets of Sleeping Car Co.

SCHONEBECK, STASSFURT, and GUSTEN.

	a m	a.m.	a.m.	a.m.	p.m	p.m.	pm	p.m.	pm	pm	p.m.	p.m.	p.m.
Magdeburg Haupt dep	4 18	7 40	8 15	9 37	1251	3 6	320	4 40	524	634	8 39	9 45	1135
Schonebeck ...dep	4 42	8 4	8 30	10 0	1 17	3 21	346	5 3	552	658	9 1	10 1	1158
Förderstedt	5 13	8 34	...	1028	1 50	...	419	5 33	622	726	9 30	...	1226
Stassfurt 158 ...arr	5 21	8 42	8 53	1036	1 59	3 43	428	5 41	631	734	9 38	1023	1234
Gusten 148 ...arr	5 34	8 54	9 3	1050	2 16	3 52	442	5 51	646	746	9 50	1032	1246
SANGERHAUSEN ...arr	7 a2	1015	1015	12p4	3p49	4p51	...	7p29	...	...	1136	1136	...

	am	a.m.	am	am	a.m.	a.m.	a.m.	a.m.	pm	p.m.	pm	p.m.	pm	p.m.	p.m.
SANGERHAUSEN ...dep	...	...	455	6 6	...	8 27	...	1144	152	...	352	3 52	6 54	8 37	9 16
Gusten ...dep	...	5 21	625	717	...	9 52	1113	1 29	253	3 32	521	6 15	811	9 33	1043
Stassfurt ...dep	459	5 33	634	728	8 16	10 7	1122	1 41	3 3	3 45	534	6 30	823	9 42	1056
Förderstedt	510	5 44	645	...	8 27	1018	1133	1 52	...	3 56	544	6 41	833	...	11 6
Schonebeck ...arr	537	6 11	711	753	8 52	1045	1159	2 19	325	4 22	6 9	7 9	859	10 4	1130
Magdeburg Haupt arr	613	6 37	735	812	9 16	1110	1220	2 45	342	4 46	634	7 35	922	1020	1154

Extra.—Magdeburg to Schonebeck, 5.36, 6.40 a.m., 12.18, 1.46, 7.18 p.m.; Schonebeck to Magdeburg, 5.7a.m., 1.20, 5.18 p.m. Stassfurt to Güsten, 6.1, 6.55, 9.29, 10.28 a.m., 12.19, 12.58, 5.16 p.m. Güsten to Stassfurt, 5.10, 6.8, 9.8, 11.58 a.m., 12.39, 4.58, 8.58 p.m.

STENDAL and TANGERMUNDE.										
Stendal ...dep	7a37	11a2	2p20	5p27	8p10	10p47	...	...	...	...
Tangermunde arr	8 5	1130	2 48	5 55	8 38	11 15	...	...	...	...
Tangermunde ...dep	6a47	9a12	12p45	4p25	6p58	9p42	...	...	...	...
Stendal (160) ...arr	7 15	9 40	1 13	4 53	7 26	1010	...	...	...	...

For Fares—see page 120A.] **PRUSSIAN STATE RAILWAYS.** [Luggage Rates—see page 462.

ASCHERSLEBEN and COTHEN.

‡—Not on Sunday.

	a.m.	a.m.	a.m.	a.m.	p.m.	p.m.	p.m.	p.m.	p.m.	p.m.
Aschersleben...dep	5 54	7 6	8 41	10 52	1 7	3 15	4 29	7 40	9 48	1016
Güsten......arr	6 13	7 24	8 59	11 9	1 24	3 30	4 46	7 58	10 0	1034
,, ...dep	6 17	7 27	9 6	11 11	1 27	3 56	4 48	8 5	10 1	1048
Bernburg	6 33	7 45	9 23	11 29	1 47	4 21	5 6	8 24	1014	11 8
Cothen......arr	7 0	8 16	9 50	11 56	2 19	4 59	5 34	8 51	1034	1138

	a.m.	a.m.	a.m.	a.m.	a.m.	p.m.	p.m.	p.m.	p.m.	p.m.	p.m.
Cothen ...dep	4 22	6 21	8 11	9 13	11 47	1 38	3 57	5 22	7 0	9 40	1126
Bernburg ...	4 57	6 53	8 40	9 33	12 19	2 2	4 31	5 58	7 32	10 12	1155
Güsten ...arr	5 15	7 11	8 56	9 45	12 36	2 18	4 49	6 41	7 48	10 32	1213
,, dep	5 41	7 13	9 8	9 46	12 38	2 20	4 54	6 48	7 51	10 43	1248
Ascherleben	6 2	7 33	9 30	9 59	12 58	2 39	5 14	7 9	8 10	11 3	1 8

Extra. {Aschersleben to Gusten, 4.58, 6.50, 7‡35, 9.24 a.m., 2.28, 5.29, 6.32, 7‡0, 8.25 p.m., and *vice versa* 5‡10, 6.15, 8.25, 11.0 a.m., 1.12, 3.50, 6.5, 9.52 p.m.

OSCHERSLEBEN and BRUNSWICK.

E.M. Dist		a.m.	a.m.	a.m.	a.m.	a.m.	p.m.	p.m.	p.m.	
	MAGDEBURG dp	...	5 55	7 3	9 21	11 7	1 58	4 35	7 15	...
—	Oschersleben dep	...	7 1	9 3	11 8	1146	2 51	5 50	8 53	...
15½	Jerxheim	6 7	7 34	9 34	1139	12 6	3 23	6 21	9 25	...
...	BORSSUM 165 arr	...	8a22	...	1217	1229	4p10	7p11	1011	...
22½	Schöppenstedt ...	6 25	8 11	9 55	1228	...	3 44	6 44	9 57	...
33½	Wolfenbuttel......	6 57	8 37	1019	1252	...	4 8	7 10	1020	...
40½	Brunswick ....arr	7 16	8 57	1035	1 5	1 5	4 22	7 30	1037	...

	a.m.	a.m.	a.m.	a.m.	p.m.	p.m.	p.m.	p.m.	
Brunswick ....dep	6 5	8 28	1039	1148	2 16	4 24	5 31	8 28	...
Wolfenbuttel	6 26	8 44	1058	1210	2 38	4 44	5 50	8 50	...
Schöppenstedt......	6 54	9 12	1124	1237	3 9	...	6 18	9 17	...
BORSSUM.....dep	6a40	8a58	...	...	2p43	5p10	5p22	9 p4	...
Jerxheim...........	7 12	9 36	12 0	1252	3 33	...	6 38	9 35	...
Oschersleben...arr	7 40	10 5	1230	...	4 4	5 52	7 10	10 3	...
MAGDEBURG arr	8a35	1140	3p41	...	4p47	6p30	8 p4	11p5	...

SCHONINGEN and HELMSTEDT

Schoningen......dep	8a16	10 a0	1p14	4p45	6p24	10 p9	12a8
Helmstedt 158...arr	8 38	10 17	1 29	5 10	6 48	10 33	1226

Helmstedt...dep	6a50	11a0	2p26	5p40	8p48	11p30	...
Schoningen arr	7 7	1119	2 48	5 57	9 5	11 46	...

HELMSTEDT and OEBISFELDE.

Helmstedt ......dep	7a41	10a57	2p40	5p28	9 p47
Oebisfelde.......arr	8 50	12 6	3 49	6 39	10 58

Oebisfelde ......dep	5 a3	9a10	12p38	4 p4	7 p 0	...
Helmstedt ......arr	6 35	1018	1 52	5 16	8 18	...

GRIZEHNE and CÖNNERN.

Grizehne dep	...	a m	8a33	...	1150	2p10	5p58	1014
Stadt Calbe......	..	...	8 45	...	1212	2 23	6 20	1026
Nienburg-a-S.	a m	6 12	9 2	a.m.	1229	2 40	6 46	1043
Bernburg.........	5 30	7 55	9 17	1040	1244	3 9	7 23	1058
Cönnern 166	6 17	8 35	...	1128	...	3 47	8 0	...

Cönnern ...dep		6a43	8a57	a.m.	12p29	p m	4p33	8p26	...
Bernburg ...	5a43	7 23	9 45	1038	1 10	4 26	5 17	9 15	...
Nienburg ...	6 3	7 39	—	1054	1 26	4 42	—	9 32	...
Stadt Calbe	—	7 57	...	1111	1 43	4 58	...	9 49	...
Grizehne ...arr		8 8	...	1122	1 54	5 9	...	10 1	...

MAGDEBURG, OSCHERSLEBEN, and THALE.

†-Weekdays only. §—1-4 class.

		2 3 4	1,2,3	1—4	1,2,3	1,2,3	1,2,3	1—4	Ex3	1—4	1—4	2 3 4	2 3 4	1,2,3	1—4	2 3 4	2 3 4	Ex 3
Magdeburg—		a.m.	a.m.	a.m.	a.m.	a.m.	a.m.	p.m.	p.m.	...			p.m.	p.m.	p.m.	p.m.	p.m.	a.m.
Hauptbahn'f dep		5 55	7 3	9 5	9 21	11 7	1118	1232	1 58	...	...	...	4 35	6 21	7 15	9 48	1125	12 14
Langenweddingen		6 26	...	...	...	...	...	1258	...	...	...	...	5 7	...	7 48	1020	1156	...
Blumenberg 158 ...		6 34	...	9 35	...	1128	A	1 6	RC	...	...	...	5 16	...	7 57	1029	12 4	SC
Hadmersleben ...		6 45	...	9 59	...	...	...	1 16	...	...	...	...	5 27	...	8 8	1041	1215	...
Oschersleben arr		6 55	7 43	10 8	9 55	1144	1152	1 24	2 32	...	...	...	5 37	6 56	8 18	1051	1225	12 47
BR'NSW'K 162 arr		8a57	1035	...	...	1 p5	...	4p22	4p22	...	...	...	7p30	...	1037	...	...	...
Oschersleben dep		6 57	7 44	1017	9 56	—	1153	1 26	2 33	...	...	...	5 40	6 57	8 [illegible]	1053	1226	12 48
Nienhagen 162		7 14	7 55	1034	...	...	A	1 43	...	...	...	...	5 58	...	8 [illegible]	1111	1243	...
Halberstadt ...arr		7 30	8 7	1050	1017	...	1214	1 57	2 54	p.m.	p.m.	...	6 15	7 18	9 [illegible]	1128	1258	1 7
,, 166 dep	4a52	—	8 15	1058	1021	...	1226	2 8	3 3	3 18	4 2	...	6 37	7 23	9 35	—	1 16	To Goslar, p. 166.
Wegeleben arr	5 2	...	8 24	11 7	...	...	1235	2 17	To Gosl'r p. 166.	3 27	4 10	...	6 46	...	9 45	...	1 26	
,, 166 dep	5 3	...	8 25	11 8	...	...	1237	2 18		3 28	4 11	p.m.	6 47	...	9 46	...	1 27	
Quedlinburg...	5 31	...	8 45	1130	1043	...	1252	2 39		3 45	4 27	5†30	7 6	7 44	10 9	...	1 47	
Thale ......arr	5 49	...	9 4	1149	11 0	...	1 10	2 58		4 2	4 46	5 48	7 25	7 58	1028	...	2 5	

	2 3 4	Ex3	2 3 4	2 3 4	2 3 4	1,2,3	1—4	1,2,3	1—4	1—4	Ex3	1,2,3	2—4	1—4	1,2,3	2 3 4	2 3 4	
	a.m.	F'm Goslar, p. 166.		a.m.	a.m.		a.m.	a.m.	p.m.	p.m.		p.m.	p.m.	p.m.	p.m.	p.m.	p.m.	
Thale.........dep	3 55		...	6 16	7 13	...	9 27	1056	1 12	2 10	...	4 46	6†13	5 22	7 31	8 21	9 50	...
Quedlinburg ...	4 12		...	6 35	7 30	...	9 47	11 9	1 31	2 35	...	5 2	6 32	5 42	7 48	8 41	1013	...
Wegeleben arr	4 29		...	6 51	7 45	...	10 3	...	1 48	2 48	...	A	6 48	5 59	7 59	8 58	1030	...
,, dep	4 30		...	6 52	7 46	...	10 4	...	1 49	2 49	...	...	6 49	6 0	7 59	8 59	1030	...
Halberstadt arr	4 40		a.m.	7 2	7 56	a.m.	1013	1128	1 58	2 58	p m.	5 20	6 59	6 10	8 8	9 9	1039	...
,, ...dep		4a44	5 5	7 15	8 3	8 57	1018	1134	2 17	—	3 54	5 26	—	6 35	8 16	9 28	1046	...
Nienhagen	...		5 20	7 30	8 18	9 9	1034	...	2 29	...	RC	...	...	6 51	8 28	9 45	11 2	...
Oschersleben......arr		5 5	5 38	7 46	—	9 20	1051	1154	2 46	...	4 12	5 44	1,2,3	7 9	8 39	10 4	1120	...
BRUNSWICK ...dep	...		...	6 a5	...	...	8a28	...	1039	...	2p16	...	4p24	5p31	5p31	8p28	...	...
Oschersleben ...dep		5 6	5 41	7 49	...	9 21	1053	1155	2 48	2 34	4 13	5 45	5 55	7 14	8 40	10 7	1121	...
Hadmersleben.........	...		5 52	7 58	a.m.	...	11 2	...	2 58	p.m.	...	...	...	7 24	...	1018	1131	...
Blumenberg..........		SC	6 7	8 11	8 18	9 40	1115	...	3 12	4 54	...	...	...	7 38	...	1031	1145	...
Langenwedding......	...		6 15	...	8 26	...	...	...	3 20	5 2	...	...	...	...	...	1039	1153	...
Magdeburg ......arr		5 47	6 45	8 35	8 54	10 3	1140	1227	3 41	5 30	4 47	6 20	6 30	8 4	9 15	11 5	1213	...

Extra.

Nienhagen ......dep	6a17	9 a6	1p22	4p57	8 p5	10p49
Halberstadt ......arr	6 36	9 25	1 40	5 16	8 24	11 5
Halberstadt ......dep	5a43	10a28	2p 5	6p51	9p39	...
Nienhagen ......arr	5 58	10 47	2 19	7 9	9 58	...

A—July and August only.

MAGDEBURG and LOBURG.

E.M.					
	Magdeburg ...dep	7a55	12p48	5p25	11p25
5½	Biederitz	8 12	1 3	5 41	11 38
22¼	Loburg...........arr	9 5	1 59	6 34	12 32

Loburg ......dep	5a10	9 a31	2p23	6 p57
Biederitz	6 9	10 24	3 17	7 54
Magdeburg arr	6 26	10 39	3 32	8 9

JERXHEIM and NIENHAGEN.

Jerxheim ....dep	5 a8	7 a56	12p15	3p45	6 p56	9p46
Dingelstedt.................	5 43	8 31	1250	4 24	7 31	1018
Nienhagen (162) arr	6 16	9 5	1 21	4 56	8 4	1048

Nienhagen...............dep	5a59	8a19	10a48	2p20	7‡10	9 p59
Dingelstedt	6 31	8 51	11 21	2 51	7 52	10 33
Jerxheim (162)......arr	7 5	9 25	11 55	3 23	8 35	11 7

BRUNSWICK and UELZEN.

‡—Weekdays only.

Brunswick dep	...	6a58	...	1014	1p10	3p29	6 p5	10p42
Meine	...	7 40	...	1056	1 52	4 13	6 50	11 26
Jsenbuttel	4a54	8 13	9a57	1132	3 0	4 49	7 44	12 6
Gifhorn Stadt	5 5	8 21	10 6	1140	3 10	4 57	7 54	12 15
Triangel.........	5 16	8 30	—	1149	3‡20	5 6	8 4	—
Wittingen	6 48	9 24	...	1239	—	6 10	9 14	...
Uelzen ......arr	7 47	1023	...	1 38	...	7 9	1014	...

Uelzen ......dep	...	5a35	...	8 a19	12p18	...	5 p7	8 p7
Wittingen	...	6 40	...	9 40	1 33	...	6 11	9 9
Triangel	...	7 38	...	10 36	2 31	3‡45	6 59	10 4
Gifhorn Stadt	5 a7	7 48	9a34	11 10	2 42	4 23	7 8	10 6
Jsenbuttel	5 20	8 15	9 43	11 35	3 5	4 32	7 47	11 5
Meine	5 39	8 34	—	11 54	3 27	—	8 7	11 24
Brunswick arr	6 20	9 15	...	12 35	4 10	...	8 49	12 3

BITTERFELD and STUMSDORF.

Bitterfeld......dep	5a14	9 a35	11a55	5 p7	8p18
Stumsdorf......arr	5 59	10 20	12 38	6 8	9 1

Stumsdorf dep	7a40	10a37	2 p7	6p45	9p20
Bitterfeld arr	8 37	11 33	2 50	7 52	10 3

BLUMENBERG and SCHÖNEBECK.

Blumenberg......dep	6 a57	11a32	3 p50	8 p4
Schonebeck ......arr	7 47	12 36	4 55	8 55

Schonebeck ...dep	5 a11	8 a38	1p47	6p53
Blumenberg...arr	6 0	9 33	3 2	7 47

WUNSTORF and UCHTE.

Wunstorf dep	6a24	8a39	1112	...	2 p0	3p44	...	8p28	...
Rehburg-Bad	7 29	9 44	1212	p.m.	3 5	4 44	...	9 33	...
Stolzenau......	8 24	1038	—	1216	4 0	—	8 p0	1030	...
Uchte ......arr	8 53	...	...	1245	4 29	...	8 29	1059	...

Uchte.........dep	...	7a41	9a15	...	1p31	...	6p34	8p50
Stolzenau	5a57	8 40	9 44	p.m	2 2	...	7 6	9 19
Rehburg-Bad...	6 57	9 40	—	1217	3 4	6p41	8 6	—
Wunstorf...arr	7 58	1041	...	1 17	4 7	7 45	9 10	...

Luggage Rates—see page 462.] **PRUSSIAN STATE RAILWAYS.** [For Fares—see page 120A.

STENDAL and UELZEN.

[D—Until 15th September.

	Ex3	Ex3	2 3 4	3—4	2 3 4	Ex3	Ex 3	2 3 4	Ex3	2 3 4	3—4	2 3 4	Ex 3	2 3 4	2 3 4
	a.m.	a.m.	a.m.		a.m.	a.m.	p.m.	a.m.	p.m.	p.m.		p.m.	p.m.	p.m.	p.m.
Stendal ......dep	1 21	1 35	2 40	...	7 37	10 5	10 26	11 2	1 26	1 43	...	5 20	8 0	8 10	1055
Bismark	...	D	3 10	a.m.	8 4	...	...	1130	...	2 13	p.m.	5 49	...	8 35	1128
Salzwedel (161A)	2 14	2 24	4 4	7 15	8 52	1052	...	1222	2 17	3 5	4 25	6 41	8 46	9 20	1215
Bergen	...	..	4 20	7 34	9 7	..	...	1236	...	3 22	4 44	6 55	...	9 34	—
Uelzen 157A arr	3 0	3 10	5 14	8 35	9 54	1135	11 59	1 26	3 1	4 18	5 42	7 48	9 28	1025	...

	Ex3	Ex 3	2 3 4	3—4	2 3 4	Ex.3	2,3,4	3—4	Ex3	2 3 4	Ex3	2 3 4	Ex3	2 3 4	Ex3	3—4
	a.m.	a.m.	a.m.	a.m.	a.m.	a.m.	a.m.	p.m.	p.m.	p.m.	p.m.	p.m.	p.m.	p.m.	p.m.	p.m.
Uelzen ......dep	1 26	1 50	...	5 23	8 8	10 2	11 10	1 4	1 45	2 17	4 53	5 0	6 12	7 56	8 20	11 0
Bergen	...	D	...	6 24	9 0	...	12 4	2 4	...	3 11	...	5 51	...	8 42	...	1159
Salzwedel	...	2 31	5 52	6 40	9 18	10 46	12 21	2 20	2 30	3 30	E	6 10	6 58	9 14	9 5	1224
Bismark	...	...	6 51	—	1010	...	1 16	—	3 8	4 28	...	7 2	..	10 0	...	1 12
Stendal 163 arr	2 56	3 30	7 20	...	1036	11 37	1 43	...	3 24	4 57	6 24	7 29	7 53	1023	9 53	1 36

E—From 25th July until 18th August.

MAGDEBURG and WITTENBERGE.

	2,3,4	1,2,3	Ex3	2 3 4	Ex 3	Ex3	2,3,4	2 3 4	2 3 4	1,2,3	1—4	2 3 4	2 3 4	Ex3
LEIPSIC 158 ....dep	...	...	6a57	6a57	8 a25	1025	...	1025	1 p0	4 p10	4p10	6p30	7p40	10p5
	a.m.	a.m.	a.m.	a.m.	a.m.	p.m.		p.m.	p.m.	p.m.	p.m.	p.m.	p.m.	ng't
Magdeburg ....dep	5 55	6 7	9 0	9 33	10 14	1232	...	1 15	3 47	6 6	6 15	9 5	1125	1217
Wolmirstedt	6 26	...	...	9 55	A	...	...	1 40	4 10	...	6 36	9 28	1144	1234
Tangerhütte	7 2	...	...	1030		...	...	2 18	4 47	...	7 11	10 6	1222	1258
Stendal ....arr	7 24	6 58	9 50	1052	10 59	1 21	p.m.	2 40	5 10	6 52	7 33	1029	1245	1 16
,, ...dep	7 34	6 59	9 58	11 2	11 0	1 26	1 28	2 48	5 18	6 53	7 36	1037	1 22	1 21
Goldbeck	7 55	...	...	1126	...	⋮	1 51	3 10	5 42	...	7 59	11 0	1 41	⋮
Wittenberge ....arr	8 42	7 46	1042	1217	11 45	⋮	2 34	4 1	6 35	7 35	8 44	1150	2 23	⋮
HAMBURG 167 ......arr	11 44	9 a49	1258	4p12	...	4p28	...	6p57	8p52	10p26	11p2	...	5a29	5a20

	Ex3	1—4	2,3,4	2,3,4	2 3 4	1,2,3	Ex3	2 3 4	1,2,3	Ex3	2 3 4	Ex3	2,3,4	2 3 4	1,2,3
HAMBURG ....dep	12 0	1134	...	...	7a17	7 a17	8a52	9 a8	...	1217	1232	4p39	...	6p18	8p27
	a.m.	a.m.	a.m.	a.m.	a.m.	a.m.	a.m.	p.m.	p.m.	⋮	p.m	p.m.		p.m.	p.m.
Wittenberge ....dep	⋮	3 6	5 57	8 22	9 13	9 28	1124	1 0	1 28	⋮	3 15	7 1	...	9 17	1025
Goldbeck	⋮	3 50	6 49	9 16	1017	..	...	1 44	A	⋮	4 6	7 40	...	10 7	...
Stendal ....arr	2 56	4 11	7 13	9 39	1038	10 13	1211	2 3	2 13	3 24	4 29	7 57	p.m.	1027	1110
,, ...dep	3 0	4 15	7 32	—	1053	10 14	1215	2 22	2 14	3 28	5 17	8 5	9 6	1034	1111
Tangerhütte	...	4 38	7 56	...	1119	...	...	2 48	...	...	5 41	8 23	9 32	1058	...
Wolmirstedt	...	5 17	8 35	...	12 2	...	...	3 28	...	...	6 22	...	10 10	1133	...
Magdeburg ....arr	3 50	5 37	8 58	...	1225	11 2	1 5	3 51	3 2	4 23	6 47	8 59	10 33	1153	12 0
LEIPSIC (158) ....arr	...	8a19	11 a8	...	...	1 p1	3 p5	6p23	5 p1	6p23	1046	11p9	...	3a51	3a51

A—In July and August only.

GOLDBECK and WERBEN.

Goldbeck ......dep	8 a15	3 p25	8p 15
Werben ....arr	9 35	4 45	9 35
Werben ....dep	5a10	12 0	6 p0
Goldbeck ....arr	6 30	1 20	7 20

BRUNSWICK, VIENENBURG, and HARZBURG.

	1—4	2 3 4	1—4	2 3 4	2 3 4	1,2,3	2 3 4	1—4	1,2,3	1—4	2 3 4	1—4	2 3 4	1—4	1,2,3	2 3 4	Ex3	1—4	2 3 4	2 3 4	2 3 4	2 3 4
	a.m.	a.m.	a.m.	a.m.	a.m.	a.m.	a.m.	a.m.	p.m.	p.m	p.m.		p.m.	p.m.	p.m.	p.m.	p.m.		p.m.	p.m	p.m.	ng't
Brunswick ...dep	4 55	5 10	7 10	7 52	8 50	9 36	1039	1148	1 14	2 5	2 39	...	4 24	4 46	6 8	6 37	7 51	...	8 0	10 7	1058	1258
Wolfenbüttel	5 10	5 25	7 23	8 12	9 5	9 48	1058	12 4	...	2 20	2 53	p.m.	4 44	4 59	6 20	6 58	8 3	...	8 13	1023	11 5	1 14
Börssum	5 26	5 43	...	8 32	9 29	10 6	1125	1238	...	2 37	3 7	3 15	5 2	5 13	Goslar arr. 7.3	7 18	...	...	8 28	1040	1136	1 27
Vienenburg ...arr	—	6 4	7 51	8 52	...	1022	1146	1258	...	2 57	—	3 37	—	5 33		7 37	8 28	p.m.	—	11 0	—	1 46
,, ...dep	...	6 15	7 53	9 0	...	1023	1157	1 4	...	3 10	...	4 0	...	5 44		7 43	—	8 40	...	11 7	...	—
Harzburg ......arr	...	6 30	8 6	9 15	9 59	1036	1210	1 19	1 58	3 25	...	4 13	...	5 59		7 56	...	8 53	...	1122	...	...

	2 3 4	2 3 4	1,2,3	2 3 4	Ex3	1—4	2 3 4	2 3 4	2 3 4	1,2,3	1 - 4	1—4	1—4	1,2,3	1—4	2 3 4	1—4	2 3 4	1,2,3	2 3 4	2 3 4
		a.m.	a.m.	a.m.	a.m.	a.m.	a.m.	a.m.	p.m.	p.m.	p.m.	p.m	p.m	p.m.	p.m.	p.m.	p.m.	p.m.		p.m.	
Harzburg ......dep	...	5 54	7 0	7 49	...	8 29	10 7	1138	1 19	2 42	3 27	3 38	4 34	6 56	7 30	...	8 14	9 14	...	1054	...
Vienenburg ...arr	a.m.	6 5	...	8 0	...	8 40	...	1149	1 30	2 53	3 38	3 49	4 45	...	7 41	...	8 26	9 25	p.m.	11 5	...
,, ...dep	4 19	6 15	...	8 9	8 56	9 3	...	1159	1 38	~~	A	4 1	4 46	...	8 3	...	8 35	9 39	1058	1112	ng't
Börssum	4 38	6 36	...	8 32	...	9 21	1033	1219	1 57	...	—	4 27	5 13	7 17	8 22	8 47	9 1	...	..	1130	1218
Wolfenbüttel	5 2	6 57	...	8 50	9 20	9 38	1047	1237	2 15	...	...	4 42	5 31	7 32	8 38	9 4	9 17	10 5	1122	1144	1236
Brunswick ...arr	5 22	7 16	7 42	9 5	9 33	9 52	11 0	1257	2 30	...	...	4 57	5 50	7 46	8 53	9 18	9 36	1019	1135	1158	1251

A—From 16th to 30th Sept.

LANGELSHEIM and CLAUSTHAL-ZELLERFELD.

A—Goslar dep. 3.7.] [B—Goslar arr. 4.53.

*—Not on Sunday.

	a.m.	a.m.	a.m.	p.m.	p.m.	p.m.	p.m.	p.m.	p.m.
Langelsheim	*	7 4	9 58	1 27	2 17	⋮ A	5 16	7 48	10 5
Lautenthal	5 13	7 24	1018	1 47	2 41	3 33	5 36	8 8	1025
Wildemann	5 29	7 40	1034	2 3	2 57	3 49	5 52	8 24	1041
Clausthal-Zeller	5 49	7 59	1053	2 22	3 16	4 6	6 11	8 44	11 0

	a.m.	a.m.	a.m.	a.m.	p.m.	p.m.	p.m.	p.m.	p.m.
Clausthal-Zeller	4 26	5 4	8 16	1012	1 8	2 35	3 50	6 14	8 16
Wildemann	4 46	5 24	8 34	1033	1 28	2 56	..	6 34	8 40
Lautenthal	5 1	5 40	8 50	1049	1 46	3 12	4 26	6 50	8 56
Langelsheim 163	*	6 59	9 8	11 8	2 6	3 31	B:	7 9	9 15

GOSLAR, SEESEN, and HERZBERG.

	a.m.		a.m.	a.m.	a.m.	a.m.	a.m.	p.m.	p.m.	p.m.	p.m.	p.m.	p.m.	p.m.	p.m.	p.m.	p.m.	p.m.	p.m.	p.m.	p.m.	p.m.
Goslar ....dep	2 13	...	5 55	6 50	7 5	9 45	9 35	1230	1 13	2 3	2 13	3 38	4 7	4 22	5 3	6 12	7 5	7 35	8 16	9 12	9 52	11 33
Langelsheim...	A	...	6 8	7 2	7 17	9 57	9 48	1242	1 25	2 15	2 23	3 50	⋮	4 33	5 15	6 25	...	7 47	8 26	9 21	10 4	11 44
Seesen (164) arr	2 37	a.m.	6 36	—	7 53	—	1011	1 7	—	—	2 45	4 21	⋮	4 52	—	—	7 27	—	8 50	9 39	—	12 5
,, ...dep	—	5 1	6 47	...	8 2	...	1046	1 30	...	...	2 49	5 0	C	—	...	...	7 29	...	8 50	—	...	12 25
Gittelde	...	5 19	7 5	...	8 20	...	11 3	1 47	...	...	3 6	5 22	⋮	...	...	...	...	...	9 6	...	...	12 43
Osterode	...	5 29	7 14	...	8 34	...	1112	1 57	...	...	3 18	5 35	⋮	...	...	...	7 49	...	9 15	...	...	12 52
Herzberg 164A	...	5 52	7 34	...	8 57	...	1132	2 20	...	...	3 42	5 58	⋮	...	...	...	8 7	...	9 37	...	...	...

				a.m.		a.m.	a.m.		a.m.				p.m.			p.m.	p.m.		p.m.	p.m.	ngt.
Herzberg ...dep	...	...	...	6 37	...	7 45	9 25	...	1154	...	...	...	2 36	...	...	4 44	7 26	...	9 38	10 4	...
Osterode	...	...	...	6 56	...	8 6	9 48	...	1217	...	...	...	2 55	...	...	5 9	7 52	...	9 53	10 28	1 0
Gittelde	...	...	...	7 5	...	8 20	9 58	...	1227	...	...	...	3 6	...	...	5 25	8 4	...	...	10 38	1 12
Seesen ....arr	a.m.	a.m.	...	7 22	...	8 39	10 18	...	1246	...	p.m.	...	3 25	p.m.	...	5 47	8 26	...	1012	10 57	1 34
,, ...dep	3 7	4 53	a.m.	7 32	a.m.	9 12	10 25	a.m.	1259	p.m.	2 19	p.m.	3 35	4 31	p.m.	6 56	8 42	p.m.	1014	11 21	—
Langelsheim...	B	5 17	7 0	7 56	9 9	9 30	10 49	11 9	1 22	2 8	...	3 34	3 58	4 54	7 10	7 18	9 4	9 17	...	11 45	...
Goslar (166) arr	3 35	5 31	7 14	8 9	9 20	9 40	11 2	11 23	1 35	2 22	2 43	3 47	4 11	5 7	7 23	7 31	9 16	9 34	1038	11 58	...

A—From Halberstadt page 166, for Kreiensen and Holzminden page 165. B—From Holzminden and Kreiensen page 164, for Halberstadt page 166. C—Kreiensen arr. 4.51 p.m.

For Fares—see page 120A.] **PRUSSIAN STATE RAILWAYS.** [Luggage Rates—see page 462.

SOEST, WARBURG, HOLZMINDEN, MAGDEBURG, and BERLIN.

COLOGNE 134A ...dep	...	...	...	...	...	...	...	...	...	...	...	...	...	6a58	8a26	8a36	...	...	...	9 a6
AIX-LA-CHAPELLE134	A dp	...	...	...	...	...	...	...	...	...	...	...	...	4a20	6a50	Via Hagen and Scherfede (page 134A).	...	...	...	7a37
DUSSELDORF 134A dep	...	...	...	...	...	...	...	...	...	...	...	...	4a45	7a17	8a27		...	...	...	9a38
ELBERFELD 134A dep	...	...	...	...	...	...	...	...	...	...	...	...	6a26	8 a3	9a15		...	...	...	1022
	Ex2	1—4	Ex3	2 3 4	1,2,3	2 3 4	2 3 4	2 3 4	2 3 4	2 3 4	1,2,3	2 3 4	2 3 4	1—4	Ex3		Ex3	3& 4	1,2,3	1,2,3
							a.m.		a.m.	a.m.	a.m.		a.m.	a m.	a.m.			a.m.	...	p.m.
Soest ...dep	...	...	...	...	...	...	6 38	...	...	5 49	8 8	...	8 33	1010	1049		...	1056	...	1223
Lippstadt...	...	...	...	...	...	...	7 9	...	5 10	6 23	8 27	...	9 3	1042	11 8		...	1134	...	1241
Geseke ...	...	...	...	...	...	a.m.		a.m.	5 29	6 52	...	...	9 22	11 1	...		...	1158	...	1255
Paderborn (165) ...	...	...	...	...	...	5 21	...	4 30	6 15	7 26	8 58	...	1039	1151	1142		...		...	1 18
Altenbeken...arr	...	...	...	...	...	5 56	...	4 59	6 45	7 56	9 20	...	11 9	1222	12 5		...	...	...	1 40
HAMELN (155) ...arr	...	...	...	...	...	...	...	...	8a22	9a48	...	...	...	...	1 p4		...	...	...	3 p6
Altenbeken ...dep	...	...	...	...	...	...	...	5 6	6 51	8 12	9 24	...	1124	1230			...	...	...	1 54
Willebadessen ...	...	...	...	...	...	...	...	5 35	7 19	8 40	...	...	1153	1 0			...	...	...	2 17
Warburg...arr	...	...	...	...	...	...	...	6 6	7 48	9 8	10 1	...	1225	1 34			...	...	...	2 35
CASSEL (135A) arr	...	...	...	...	...	a.m.	...	7a46	...	1039	1052	a.m.	1p27	...			...	...	...	3p30
Altenbeken ...dep	...	...	...	...	...	6 9	...	5 2	7 3	8 15	9 34	1131	...	1226	12 6		...	...	...	1 58
Driburg ...	...	...	...	...	...	6 26	...	5 19	7 22	8 34	9 47	1149	...	1242	Via Hameln, Hildesheim, Brunswick.		...	...	...	2 10
Brakel ...	...	...	...	...	...	6 43	...	5 35	7 40	8 55	10 6	12 8	...	1259			...	...	...	2 22
Ottbergen164A arr	...	...	...	...	...	6 58	...	5 50	7 53	9 10	1010	1222	...	1 12			...	...	...	...
Ottbergen164A dep	...	...	...	...	...	7 2	...	6 15		9 20	1015	1224	...	1 14			...	...	...	...
Hoxter ...	...	...	...	...	...	7 19	...	6 33	...	9 37	1032	1239	...	1 30		Ex3	...	...	...	2 40
Holzminden ... arr	...	...	...	...	...	7 31	a.m.	6 46	a.m.	9 49	1044	1251	...	1 41		1 8	...	...	...	2 49
Holzminden ... dep	...	...	...	...	...		5 30	7 35	1019				...	1 46		1 9	...	...	...	2 51
Stadtoldendorf ...	...	...	...	...	...	...	5 54	7 59	1042	...	...	...	...	2 10		...	...	...	...	3 13
Naensen ...	...	...	...	...	...	...	6 22	8 27	11 9	...	...	...	...	2 38		...	...	...	...	...
Kreiensen ...arr	...	...	...	...	...	...	6 33	8 38	1120	...	1—4	...	2 3 4	2 50		1 52	...	...	...	3 44
FRANKFORT 157. dep	1036	...	...	...	...	...	11p13	1140	...	..	...	...	5a58	...		...	10a0	...	...	10a0
CASSEL 157 ...dep	1a55	...	...	...	...	...	2 a52	6a45	a.m.	...	6a45	...	9a46	...		...	1p43	...	...	1p43
Kreiensen ...dep	3 35	...	...	...	...	1—4	6 49	8 58	8 47	1—4	9 50	...	1214	2 55		1 58	3 26	...	...	3 54
Gandersheim ...		...	...	...	...	a.m.	6 59	9 7	...	a.m.	9 59	...	1229	3 4		...	...	...	...	4 3
Seesen ...		...	...	...	...	5 18	7 26	9 29	9 11	1110	1021	...	1253	3 29		2 19	...	...	...	4 25
Lutter ...		...	...	...	...	5 37	7 44	9 48		1129		...	1 12	3 48			...	...	...	...
Ringelheim 166 ...		...	...	...	...	5 47	7 59	9 59	...	1144	...	...	1 22	4 15			...	...	...	4 46
Börssum ...arr		...	...	...	...	6 20	8 29	1028	...	1214	...	...	1 54	4 48			4 22	...	...	5 4
BRUNSWICK 163 arr		...	...	...	...	...	9 a5	11a0	1,2,3	1257	...	...	2p30	5p50	2p34		4p57	Ex3	...	5p50
BRUNSWICK 163 dep		...	5a37	...	...	5a10	7a52		8a53	1148	...	...	2 p5	4p46	2p44		...	4p42	...	4p24
Börssum ...dep		...		...	...	6 40	8 58	...		1226	...	...	2 43	5 22			4 25		...	5 10
Mattierzoll ...		...		...	...	6 59	9 20	...		1244	...	...	3 5	5 44			...		...	...
Jerxheim 162 ...		...		a.m.	...	7 39	9 38	...		1255	...	...	3 36	5 57			...		...	Via Oscher-sleben
Schöningen 162 ...		...		5 4	...	8 40	10 0	...		1 15	...	...	4 10	6 21		Via Goslar.	...		...	
Völpke ...		...		5 22	...	8 58	...	...		1 36	...	1—4	4 28	6 40			...		...	
Eilsleben 158 arr		...		5 34	a.m.	9 10	11 22	...		1 48	p.m.	p.m.	4 40	6 54			...		...	
Eilsleben 158 dep		...		5 38	6 41	9 28	11 23	...	9 54	1 50	1 21	2 51	4 43	7 1			...		...	
Dreileben-Drackens...		...		5 50	6 54	9 40	11 35	...	...	2 3	1 26	3 3	4 56	...			...		...	
Niederndodeleben ...		...		6 15	7 21	9 58	11 55	...	...	2 21	1 39	3 21	5 16	...			...		...	...
Sudenburg-Magdeburg		...		6 26	7 32	10 6	12 3	...	...	2 25	1 48	3 29	5 25	...			...		...	...
Magdeburg Hpt. arr	5 38	...	6 46	6 31	7 37	1011	12 8	...	1020	2 34	1 53	3 34	5 30	7 28	3 57	4 47	5 36	6 2	...	6 28
LEIPSIC (158)...arr	8a19	...	9 a6	9 a6	1147	1 pl	3 p5	...	1 pl	6p23	...	6p23	8 p6	11p9	6p11	6§11	8 p6	8 p6	...	1046
DRESDEN Hpt. 188 arr	1026	...	1120	...	...	...	6 p19	...	2p55	8p27	...	8p27	1014	1a43	8p27	8p27	1014	1014	...	1a43
Magdeburg	a.m.	a.m.	a.m.	a.m.	a.m.	a.m	p.m.	p.m.	a.m.		p.m.	p.m.			p.m.	Ex3	p.m.		p.m	p.m.
Haupt. ...dep	5 42	6 25	6 56	8 5	8 42	1031	12 38	1220	1021	...	2 10	4 25	...	...	4 2	4 52	5 40	...	6 25	6 40
Neustadt-Magdebg...	...	6 31	...	8 11	8 48	1038	12 44	1226	1027	...	2 16	4 31	...	...	...	...	...	...	...	6 46
Biederitz...		6 41	...	8 21	...	1046	...	1235	...	...	2 26	4 40	...	...	...	...	...	...	...	...
Gerwisch...	* Arrive Fredrichstrasse.	6 47	...	8 27	...	1052	...	1240	...	...	2 32	4 46	...	...	...	...	...	...	A	...
Burg ...		7 7	...	8 47	9 8	1111	1 5	1 11	1049	...	2 52	5 23	...	...	...	5 16	..	...	...	7 8
Genthin ...		7 52	...		9 30	1141	...	1 41	1112	...		5 55	...	...	...	...	...	...	...	7 31
Brandenburg ...		8 32	7 59	...	9 55	1223	1 49	2 20	1138	...	...	6 47	...	...	5 6	6 0	...	...	7 36	7 58
Gross-Kreutz ...		8 54	...	...	...	1240	...	2 38	...	...	...	7 5	...	...	...	...	...	...	...	...
Werder...		9 6	...	...	...	1252	...	2 50	...	...	...	7 17	...	...	...	...	...	...	...	...
Wildpark ...		9 15	...	...	...	1 1	...	2 59	...	...	...	7 26	...	...	...	...	...	...	...	...
Potsdam ... arr		9 24	8 29	...	1024	1 10	2 18	3 8	12 9	...	...	7 36	...	...	5 35	6 29	...	...	8 9	8 29
Potsdam ... dep	...	9 26	8 31	...	1026	1 14	2 19	3 11	1210	...	...	7 40	...	...	5 37	6 31	...	...	8 11	8 30
BERLIN Potsdam Bf.	7*49	9 54	8 54	...	1049	1 42	2 45	3 39	1236	...	...	8 8	...	...	6 1	6 54	7 31	...	8 38	8 56

§—Via Seesen to Goslar (page 163) and to Halle (page 166). A—Runs until 31st August.

For Continuation of Trains, see next page.

MAGDEBURG and ROSSLAU.

	a.m.	a.m.	a.m.	a.m.	p.m.	p.m	p.m.	p.m.	p.m.
Magdeburg dep	3 55	6 12	7 4	10 40	1 18	4 15	6 10	7 42	1147
Biederitz ...		6 28	...	10 55	1 33	4 31	...	7 57	12 1
Gommern ...		6 50	...	11 15	1 54	4 50	6 31	8 17	1221
Gütergluck ...		7 17	...	11 37	2 25	5 11	6 45	8 49	1244
Zerbst ...		7 27	7 43	11 47	2 36	5 22	6 53	8 59	1254
Rosslau ...arr		7 49	7 56	12 8	2 58	5 45	7 13	9 22	1 11
LEIPSIC 173A	5a49	10a0	10a7	2 p12	5p46	7p37	9p20	11p53	...

LEIPSIC d	ep	4a25	6a20	9 a0	1035	1055	1p55	4 p5	7p15	9 p32
	a m.	a.m.	a.m.	a.m.	a.m.	p.m.	p.m.	p.m.	p.m.	p.m.
Rosslau dep	5 6	6 54	8 37	11 3	1139	1 0	4 26	6 8	9 11	10 47
Zerbst ...	5 23	7 14	8 51	11 25	1153	1 24	4 49	6 27	9 35	11 6
Gütergluck	5 34	7 26	...	11 36	...	1 37	5 0	6 44	9 47	...
Gommern .	5 57	7 48	...	11 53	...	1 59	5 20	7 5	1010	...
Biederitz...	6 19	8 7	...	12 12	...	2 21	5 39	7 26	1030	...
Magdeb'rg	6 35	8 22	9 27	12 27	1234	2 37	5 54	7 41	1045	11 42

SOEST, MAGDEBURG, and BERLIN.

Station	1—4	Ex3	1—4	1—4	2 3 4	2 3 4	Ex3	2,3,4	1,2,3	2 3 4	2 3 4	Ex3	Ex.3
COLOGNE 134A......dep	...	...	9 a6	...	...	...	1241	1 p30	3p33	...	...	8p11	8 p18
AIX-LA-CHAPELLE 134 dep		...	7 a37	...	...	...	10a7	...	...	...	...	6p26	7 p0
DUSSELDORF 134A dep	...	...	9 a38	...	...	...	1p24	2 p20	...	...	...	8p51	8 p50
ELBERFELD 134A dep	...	...	10a22	...	...	...	2p10	3 p0	4p33	...	...	...	9 p44
			p.m.	p.m.		p.m.	p.m.	p.m.	p.m.	p.m.	p.m.	p.m.	p.m.
Soest..................dep	...	...	12 40	2 50	...	4 42	4 35	6 1	6 17	9 10	1024	1118	11 34
Lippstadt.....................	...	...	1 28	3 22	...	5 13	4 54	6 43	6 36	9 40	1055	1139	11 54
Geseke	...	...	1 50	3 40	p.m.	—	...	7 0	6 50	9 58	1113	...	12 7
Paderborn (165) ...	...	...	2 36	4 11	4 0	5 p8	5 25	7 31	7 19	1029	1144	1216	12 26
Altenbeken ....arr	...	...	3 3	4 36	4 25	5 35	5 48	7 55	7 43	1055	1211	1240	12 53
HAMELN (155)......arr	...	...	...	5p38	—	...	...	9p33	8p41	—	...	...	...
Altenbeken......dep	...	...	3 8	4 48	...	...	5 54	8 24	...	...	...	1 3	1 3
Willebadessen	...	...	...	5 15	...	...	...	8 53	...	...	...	...	...
Warburg ....arr	...	...	3,45	5 44	...	...	6 30	9 21	...	...	...	1 41	1 41
CASSEL (135A)...arr	...	...	5 p31	6p39	...	...	7p26	11p 0	...	...	...	2a35	2 a35
Altenbeken.........dep	...	...	3 15	...	...	5 53	...	8 21	...	...	1218	...	12 57
Driburg........................	...	...	3 31	...	...	6 11	...	8 41	...	...	1235	...	...
Brakel	...	...	3 47	...	...	6 30	...	9 0	...	...	1251	...	...
Ottbergen ...... arr	...	...	4 0	...	...	6 48	...	9 13	...	...	1 4	...	...
Ottbergen ...... dep	...	...	4 3	...	...	6 56	...	9 36	...	...	1 11	...	...
Hoxter	...	...	4 18	...	...	7 17	...	9 53	...	...	1 25	...	1 33
Holzminden ... arr	...	...	4 30	...	...	7 32	...	10 7	p.m	...	1 36	...	1 42
Holzminden ... dep	...	...	4 48	...	...	8 20	...	—	1045	...	—	...	1 44
Stadtoldendorf	...	...	5 21	...	...	8 45	...	...	11 9	...	...	...	...
Naensen	...	...	5 47	...	...	9 13	...	...	1137	...	...	...	...
Kreiensen.............arr	...	...	5 59	...	Ex3	9 24	...	...	1148	...	...	...	2 30
FRANKFORT 157 ...dep	...	...	12p48	2 3 4	2,55	4p35	...	...	...	...	...	...	8 p55
CASSEL 157 ....dep	...		4p20	4p29	6 p6	8p32	p.m.	p.m.	...	...	...	...	12a29
Kreiensen ....dep	...	Harzburg dep. 6.55 p.m.	6 27	7 10	8 2	1031	9 41	8 11	1150	...	Extra { Soest ....dep 7 p35; Altenbeken...arr 9 27 }	...	2 43
Gandersheim	...		6 36	7 19	...	1041	9 50	8 20	12 0	...	...	...	...
Seesen	...		6 56	7 42	...	1115	1010	8 39	1220	...	...	...	3 7
Lutter	...		...	8 1	...	1135	—	—	—	...	...	...	...
Ringelheim 166	...		...	8 12	...	1145	...	...	...	...	...	...	...
Börssum ....arr	...	7 17	8 53	8 45	8 57	1217	1,2,3	—	...	...	...	...	...
BRUNSWICK 163 arr	...	7p46	9p36	9p18	9p36	1251	p.m.	...	...	...	...	Ex3	5a 22
BRUNSWICK 163 dep	...	6p37	8 p0	—	8 p0	—	1048	...	...	...	...	4a28	Via Goslar, Halberstadt, and Oschersleben.
Börssum ....dep	...	7 18	9 4	...	8 58	...	⋮	...	...	...		⋮	
Mattierzoll	...	...	9 23	...	...	...	⋮	p.m.	...	...		⋮	
Jerxheim 162..........	...	...	9 35	...	...	p.m.	⋮	9 39	...	...		⋮	
Schöningen 162	...	...	Via Oschersleben.	...	...	9 23	⋮	9 57	...	...		⋮	
Völpke	...	...		...	...	9 41	⋮	—	...	...		⋮	
Ellsleben 158 arr	p.m.	8 56		...	...	9 53	⋮	...	...	...		⋮	
Ellsleben 158 dep	7 7	8 57		...	...	1012	⋮	...	...	...		⋮	
Dreileben-Drackens......	7 20	...		...	...	1024	⋮	...	...	...		⋮	
Niederndodeleben.........	7 41	...		...	...	1041	⋮	...	...	...		⋮	
Sudenburg-Magdeburg	7 49	...	...	...	...	1049	⋮	...	...	...	...	⋮	
Magdeburg Hpt. arr	7 54	9 21	11 5	...	10 4	1054	12 7		...	...	...	5 52	5 47
LEIPSIC (158) ......arr	...	...	3a51	...	...	...	3a51		...	...	...	8a19	8 a19
DRESDEN Hpt. 188 arr	...	...	8 a9	2 3 4	...	...	8 a9		...	...	1—4	1026	10a26
	p.m.	p.m.		p.m.	p.m.	n'gt					a.m.		a.m.
Magdeburg Haupt. ....dep	8 41	9 31	...	1059	10 8	1225			...	...	4 15	...	5 57
Neustadt-Magdeburg ...	8 47	...	...	11 5	...	1231	...	...	...	...	4 21	...	...
Biederitz	8 56	...	...	1115	...	1239	...	...	...	...	4 30	...	...
Gerwisch	9 1	...	...	1121	...	1245	...	...	...	...	4 35	...	...
Burg	9 20	9 55	...	1139	...	1 2	...	...	...	...	4 53	...	6 20
Genthin.......................	9 52	...	...	—	...	1 33	...	...	...	...	5 25	...	6 42
Brandenburg	1050	1042	...	...	...	2 9	...	...	...	...	6 7	...	7 8
Gross-Kreutz	1123	...	...	...	...	2 25	...	...	...	...	6 26	...	...
Werder	1144	...	...	...	...	2 36	...	...	...	...	6 39	...	...
Wildpark	1149	...	...	...	...	...	...	...	...	...	6 48	...	...
Potsdam .... arr	1154	1115	...	...	...	2 50	...	...	...	...	6 58	...	7 38
Potsdam .... dep	1156	1117	...	...	...	2 52	...	...	...	...	7 0	...	7 40
BERLIN Pots. Bf. arr	1224	1142	...	...	1159	3 20	...	...	...	...	7 28	...	8 3

SCHARZFELD and ST. ANDREASBERG.

Station												
Scharzfeld ....dep	6a35	9a20	11a55	12p53	2p42	4p29	7 p0	8p25	10p13	...	...	...
Lauterberg	6 53	9 37	12 11	1 11	2 58	4 43	7 16	8 37	10 30	...	...	...
Oderthal	7 7	9 54	12 23	1 30	3 15	4 56	7 30	8 47	10 44	...	...	...
St. Andreasberg ...arr	7 37	1020	12 47	1 58	3 43	5 21	8 1	9 10	11 12	...	...	...
St. Andreasberg...dep	5a15	8a15	9a30	10a40	1 p6	2p53	6p38	7 p8	8p25	...	...	...
Oderthal	5 39	8 37	9 52	11 2	1 29	3 15	6 2	7 32	8 47	...	...	...
Lauterberg	5 54	8 53	10 6	11 16	1 43	3 31	6 20	7 46	9 1	...	...	...
Scharzfeld 164A......arr	6 8	9 7	1020	11 30	1 57	3 45	6 34	8 0	9 15	...	...	...

NORDHAUSEN, NORTHEIM, and OTTBERGEN.

Extra.—Wulften to Northeim, 3.29 and 8.32 p.m.

Station		2,3,4	2 3 4	2 3 4	1,2,3	2 3 4	2 3 4	2 3 4	2 3 4	1,2,3	1,2,3	2 3 4	2,3,4
HALLE 148 ...dep		12 a7	5a52	5a52	7a45	...	11a9	1p18	3p55	4p54	...	...	...
		a.m.	a.m.	a.m.	a.m.		p.m.	p.m.	p.m.	p.m.	p.m.	p.m.	p.m.
Nordhausen ...dep		5 19	8 11	9 21	1012	...	1 20	3 0	5 36	6 31	8 34	8 41	11 45
Ellrich..........................		5 45	8 36	9 47	1028	...	1 44	3 23	5 59	6 48	8 50	9 4	12 11
Walkenried		5 55	8 44	9 55	...	...	1 58	3 32	6 8	6 57	8 59	9 13	12 22
Scharzfeld		6 26	9 13	1026	1052	...	2 23	4 3	6 38	...	9 21	9 41	12 55
Herzberg		6 53	9 25	1036	11 0	...	2 33	4 12	6 48	7 21	9 29	9 49	1 3
Wulften	2 3 4	7 15	9 44	1057	...	...	2 48	4 29	7 5	...	...	10 7	—
Northeim...arr	a.m.	7 38	10 5	1117	1125	p.m.	3 9	4 50	7 25	7 44	9 54	1027	...
„ (157)dep	5 12	8 21	1025	—	—	1 23	3 30	4 54	7 53	7 45	—	1123	...
Carlshafen	6 23	9 28	1137	...	...	2 37	4 57	6 3	9 0	...	...	1237	...
Wehrden.........	6 46	9 50	12 8	...	...	3 1	—	6 25	9 21	...	...	1258	...
Ottbergen 164	6 57	10 0	1219	...	...	3 12	...	6 35	9 31	8 46	...	1 7	...

Station		2 3 4	2 3 4	2 3 4	1,2,3	2 3 4	1,2,3	2 3 4	2 3 4	2 3 4	1,2,3	2 3 4	2 3 4	2 3 4
			a.m.	a.m.		a.m.	a.m.	p.m	p.m.				p.m.	p.m.
Ottbergen.........dep		...	6 0	8 0	...	9 35	1011	1 26	4 4	...	...	...	7 4	9 17
Wehrden		...	6 11	8 13	...	9 46	...	1 40	4 16	...	...	...	7 20	9 28
Carlshafen		...	6 31	8 36	...	10 7	...	2 2	4 36	...	...	...	7 41	9 49
Northeim ....arr		a.m.	7 46	9 54	p.m.	1131	1113	3 12	5 49	p.m.	p.m.	p.m.	8 55	1057
„ ...dep	2 3 4	5 12	8 23	1038	12 2	1 28	1114	3 33	—	6 39	7 44	7 54	9 17	1122
Wulften ....a.m.		5 36	8 45	11 4	...	1 54	...	3 54	p.m.	7 1	...	8 19	9 41	1148
Herzberg	5 15	5 59	9 7	1136	1228	2 24	1144	4 16	6 0	7 25	8 13	—	10 6	—
Scharzfeld	5 25	6 12	9 17	1144	1236	2 37	1152	4 26	6 9	7 37	8 22	...	1020	...
Walkenried......	5 57	6 44	9 48	1223	...	3 12	1211	4 57	—	8 9	8 45	...	11 1	...
Ellrich	6 4	6 51	9 55	1230	...	3 20	1218	5 4	...	8 16	8 52	...	11 9	...
Nordhausen arr	6 26	7 12	1017	1250	1 10	3 42	1232	5 24	...	8 40	9 8	...	1131	...
HALLE (148) ...arr		10a3	1p28	2p50	2p50	...	2p50	8 p1	...	11p0	11p0	...	...	...

BUREN and LIPPSTADT.

Station						
Buren ......dep	6a16	8a15	10 a8	1 p36	4 p32	9 p20
Geseke	6 49	9 2	10 53	2 23	5 20	9 53
Lippstadt arr	...	...	11 18	...	...	...

Station						
Lippstadt dep	...	...	11a34	...	...	...
Geseke	7 a0	9 a24	12 20	2p46	7 p5	12a10
Buren ....arr	7 48	9 56	12 52	3 29	7 53	12 51

BERLIN, MAGDEBURG, HOLZMINDEN, and SOEST.

THROUGH CARRIAGES. {Berlin to Cologne, 1st, 2nd, and 3rd class—in 12.0 noon & 1.0 p.m. from Berlin. Berlin to Aix-la-Chapelle, 1st, 2nd, and 3rd class—in 8.35 a.m., 1.0 p.m., 10.13 p.m. from Berlin.

RC—Restaurant Car. A—Runs until 31st August.

Dist E.M.		2,3,4	234	2,3,4	1,2,3		234	Ex3	2,3,4	1—4	Ex 3	2,3,4	1,2,3	Ex 3	123	1,2,3	Ex3	1,2,3	1—4
	BERLIN-									a.m.	a.m.		a.m.	a.m.	a.m.	a.m.			a.m.
—	Potsdam Bahnhof ...dep	...	...	...	...	...	...	...	...	5 35	7 7	...	7 12	8 17	8 35	8 58	...	...	9 3
16½	**Potsdam** .... arr	...	...	...	...	...	...	...	...	6 2	...	...	7 35	...	9 0	9 23	...	...	9 31
	dep	...	...	...	...	...	...	...	...	6 4	...	...	7 36	...	9 2	9 26	...	...	9 33
18¾	Wildpark	...	...	...	...	...	...	...	...	6 14	...	...	...	...	...	...	...	...	9 44
22¼	Werder	...	...	...	...	...	...	...	...	6 22	...	...	...	...	...	A	...	...	9 53
29	Gross-Kreutz	...	...	...	...	...	...	...	...	6 34	...	...	...	...	...	...	...	...	10 5
38	Brandenburg	...	...	...	...	...	...	...	a.m.	6 54	...	...	8 6	...	9 37	10 0	...	...	1027
56¾	Genthin	...	...	...	...	...	a.m.	...	5 24	7 31	...	a.m.	...	...	10 6	...	...	...	11 7
73	Burg	...	...	...	...	...	4 42	...	6 0	8 1	...	9 19	...	...	1031	...	...	...	1141
81	Gerwisch	...	...	...	...	...	5 7	...	6 20	8 18	...	9 39	...	...	...	...	...	...	12 0
83	Biederitz	...	...	...	...	...	5 14	...	6 30	8 24	...	9 45	...	...	...	...	...	...	12 6
86¾	Neustadt-Magdeburg ...	...	...	...	...	...	5 25	...	6 40	8 33	...	9 54	...	...	...	...	...	...	1215
88½	**Magdeburg** Hauptarr	...	...	...	...	...	5 30	...	6 45	8 38	8 50	9 59	9 10	10 6	1057	11 13	...	...	1220
...	DRESDEN H'pt. 189 dep	...	...	...	...	...	...	3a41	3 a41	3a41	3 a41	...	3a41	...	...	...	8 a0	...	8 a0
...	LEIPSIC (158)........dep	...	...	...	...	...	...	5a55	6 a57	6a57	5 a55	...	6a57	...	...	...	1025	...	1025
						...	a.m.	a.m.	a.m.	a.m.	a.m.		a.m.	a.m.	a.m.	a.m.	p.m.		p.m.
...	**Magdeburg** Haupt.dep	...	...	...	...	...	5 42	8 0	9 3	9 39	8 54	...	9 39	10 10	11 7	11 18	1243	...	1 17
90	Sudenburg-Magdeburg	...	...	...	...	...	5 48	...	9 9	...	...	...	...	...	Via Oschersleben.	To Halberstadt arr. 12.14.	...	...	1 23
94	Niederndodeleben	...	...	...	...	...	5 59	...	9 21	...	...	...	...	...			...	...	1 35
101	Dreileben-Drackenstedt	...	...	...	...	...	6 21	...	9 43	...	...	...	...	...			...	...	1 59
106½	**Eilsleben** (158) arr	...	...	...	...	...	6 32	8 29	9 55	10 7	...	...	10 7	...			1 14	...	2 10
	dep	...	...	...	...	...	6 54	8 30		1016	...	..	10 8	...			1 15	...	2 35
111½	Völpke	...	...	...	...	...	7 5	...	...	1028	...	...	⋮	...			⋮	...	2 46
117½	**Schöningen**	...	...	...	...	...	7 25	...	...	1122	...	...	⋮	...			⋮	...	3 5
124½	**Jerxheim**	...	...	...	...	...	7 46	...	...	1146	...	...	⋮	...	12 6		⋮	...	3 38
130	Mattierzoll	...	...	...	...	...	8 0	...	...	1158	...	...	⋮	...	...		⋮	...	3 50
138¾	**Börssum**..............arr	...	...	...	...	...	8 22	10 0	...	1217	10 2	...	⋮	11 21	1229	...	⋮	...	4 10
153½	BRUNSWICK 163 arr	...	...	...	...	...	9 a5	11a0	a.m.	1257	11 a0	...	11a3	12 57	2p30	...	2p11	...	4p57
	dep	...	...	a.m.	...	...	7a52	9a36	8 50		9 a36	...		10 39	1148	...		2p39	4p24
...	**Börssum** ....dep	...	...	6 44	...	...	8 32	10 6	9 24	...	10 4	...	...	11 22	1235	...	...	3 8	5 9
150¾	**Ringelheim** (166)	...	...	7 18	...	...	...	Harzburg arr. 10.36.	9 59	...	...	...	...	...	1259	2,3,4	...	3 43	5 46
155½	Lutter	...	...	7 29	...	...	...		10 10	...	...	...	...	...	1 8	p.m.	...	3 55	5 59
164¼	**Seesen** (163)	...	...	8 7	...	...	1049		10 30	...	10 41	...	...	...	1 28	2 55	...	4 17	6 26
172¾	Gandersheim	...	...	8 27	...	...	11 8			...	...	...	...	...	1 42	3 16	...	4 37	6 47
176½	**Kreiensen**...........arr	...	...	8 35	...	...	1116		...	...	11 0	...	...	12 24	1 50	3 27	...	4 44	6 55
237	CASSEL (156) ......arr	...	...	...	...	...	2p35		...	...	1 p6	...	...	2 p9	4p17	...	...	6p52	9 p9
361¼	FRANKFORT (156) arr	...	a.m.	...	...	...	7 p7	...	...	...	4 p56	...	...	7 p7	8p51	...	...	1025	4a46
...	**Kreiensen** ....dep	...	5 13	...	...	...	1119	...	...	...	...	...	...	...	2 17	3 57	...	5 4	7 10
182¼	Naensen	...	5 29	...	...	...	1136	...	...	...	...	...	...	...	2 33	4 16	...	5 21	7 27
194¾	Stadtoldendorf	...	6 10	...	...	...	12 2	...	...	...	...	...	...	...	2 57	4 46	...	5 47	7 53
204	**Holzminden**... arr	a.m.	6 29	a.m.	...	...	1219	...	...	...	...	p.m.	...	...	3 14	5 5	...	6 4	8 10
	dep	5 20	6 30	7 23	...	...	1223	...	...	...	...	2 47	...	...	3 18	5 15	...	6 8	8 16
208¼	Hoxter	5 33	6 43	7 36	...	...	1234	...	...	...	...	2 59	...	...	3 28	5 27	...	6 21	8 28
214¼	**Ottbergen** ...... arr	5 48	6 59	7 52	...	...	1249	...	...	...	...	3 13	...	...	3 41	5 43	...	6 37	8 42
	dep	5 52	7 2	8 7	...	...	1250	...	...	...	...	3 20	...	...	3 42	5 46	...	6 43	
220¾	Brakel	6 7	7 17	8 23	...	...	1 4	...	...	...	...	3 35	...	...	3 54	6 2	...	6 58	
228¼	Driburg	6 28	7 38	8 45	...	...	1 23	...	...	...	...	3 57	...	...	4 11	6 24	...	7 21	...
234½	**Altenbeken** ....arr	6 46	7 57	9 5	...	Ex3	1 41	...	...	...	...	4 16	...	...	4 30	6 45	1—4	7 39	...
...	CASSEL (135B) ...dep	...	5a21	7 a30	...	9a43	1150	...	...	...	...	2 p0	...	...	3 p0	...	4p22	...	...
...	**Warburg**.........dep	...	6 53	8 a30	...	1034	1248	...	...	...	...	3 12	...	...	3 58	...	5 53	...	...
...	Willebadessen	...	7 25	9 3	...	...	1 19	...	...	...	...	3 49	...	...	...	...	6 24	...	...
...	**Altenbeken** ......arr	...	7 50	9 28	...	1116	1 43	...	...	...	...	4 19	...	...	4 35	...	6 49	...	...
...	HAMELN (155) ......dep	...	6a30	a.m.	8 a55	8a34	1127	...	...	1p51	...	3 p15	...	...	3p15	...	5p59	6p42	...
...	**Altenbeken**.........dep	6 55	8 13	9 32	...	1118	1 50	...	...	3 21	...	4 57	...	...	4 50	...	7 7	8 25	...
245	**Paderborn**	7 20	8 40	9 54	10 19	1138	2 14	...	a.m.	3 42	...	5 23	...	...	5 10	...	7 30	9 25	...
257½	Geseke	7 48	9 9		10 37	...	2 44	...	10 53		...	5 53	...	...	5 28	...	7 59	10 3	...
265	Lippstadt (159)	8 6	9 30	...	10 49	12 6	3 1	...	11 39	...	...	6 24	...	...	5 40	...	8 20	1032	...
277¾	**Soest**....................arr	8 36	10 0	...	11 8	1226	3 30	...	12 11	...	...	6 55	...	...	5 59	...	8 51	11 2	...
331	ELBERFELD ...134C arr	...	1 p4	...	1 p4	2p27	5p47	...	...	...	...	...	...	...	7p56	...	...	2a12	...
347¾	DUSSELDORF..134C arr	...	1p49	...	1 p49	3 p1	6p21	...	...	...	...	...	...	...	8p32	...	...	...	...
403½	AIX-LA-CHAP. 134C arr	...	4p25	...	4 p25	5p36	9p21	...	...	...	...	...	...	...	1029	...	...	...	...
359½	COLOGNE ....134C arr	...	2p10	...	2 p10	3p56	7p28	...	...	...	...	...	...	...	9p20	...	...	...	...

For Continuation of Trains, see next page.

PADERBORN and BIELEFELD.

[*—Weekdays only.

Paderborn ...dep	...	5a10	7a27	10a10	11a52	2p33	5p27	...	8p57	Bielefeld dep	5a38	8 a5	10 a0	1236	2p29	6*p25	7p15	10p43
Sennelager	*	5 39	7 52	10 35	12 18	3 1	5 54	*	9 22	Schloss Holte	6 14	8 47	10 33	1 8	2 59	6 58	7 47	11 14
Schloss Holte	5a22	6 16	8 25	11 7	12 52	3 33	6 27	7 p50	9 56	Sennelager...	6 48	9 24	11 6	1 43	3 34		8 21	11 47
Bielefeld ......arr	6 0	6 51	8 58	11 39	1 27	4 5	7 3	8 23	1030	Paderborn a	7 13	9 47	11 29	2 4	3 57	...	8 54	12 9

NEUHALDENSLEBEN and EILSLEBEN.									
Neuhaldensleben...dep	4a35	8 a5	11a42	5p 51	Eilsleben ....dep	7a20	10a25	2 p55	8p17
Schackensleben	5 13	8 42	12 26	6 25	Schackensleben	8 45	11 34	3 51	9 16
Eilsleben (164) ......arr	6 30	9 44	1 40	7 28	Neuhaldensleben 160C arr	9 22	12 10	4 23	9 46

BERLIN, MAGDEBURG, HOLZMINDEN, and SOEST.

RC—Restaurant Car. SC—Sleeping Car.

	Ex3	1–4	Ex3	1–4	2,3,4	1,2,3	1–4	1,2,3	1,2,3	2 3 4	Ex.3	Ex2	Ex3	2,3,4	Ex3	Ex 3	1–4	
BERLIN-	noon	p.m.	p.m.	p.m.		p.m.	p.m.	p.m.	p.m.	p.m.	p.m.	p.m.			p.m.	p.m.	p.m.	
Potsdam Bahnhof ......dep	12 0	12 9	1 0	2 28	...	3 55	5 32	6 54	7 35	7 52	9 26	...	...	...	1013	11 30	1150	...
Friedrichstrasse .....dep	...	...	...	...	...	...	...	...	...	...	...	9 50	...	...	...	Sunday night only.	...	...
Potsdam .... arr	1222	1236	1 23	2 55	...	4 18	6 1	7 17	7 59	8 18	9 49	...	...	...	1036		1218	...
Potsdam dep	1223	1238	1 24	2 58	...	4 19	6 4	7 18	8 1	8 20	9 50	...	...	...	1037		1221	...
Wildpark	...	1248	...	3 9	...	...	6 14	...	...	8 31	...	...	...	...	...		1232	...
Werder	RC	1257	RC	3 18	...	...	6 23	...	...	8 40	...	...	...	...	SC		1241	...
Gross-Kreutz	...	1 10	...	3 30	...	...	6 35	...	...	8 52	...	...	...	...	...		1254	...
Brandenburg	1254	1 31	1 53	3 51	...	4 50	6 56	7 49	8 32	9 12	10 19	...	...	...	11 8	12 21	1 14	...
Genthin	...	2 22	...	4 20	p.m.	5 16	7 34	8 15	...	9 49	...	...	...	...	...	12 47	1 48	...
Burg	...	2 57	...	5 3	7 5	5 39	8 7	8 37	9 17	1021	...	...	...	...	1148	1 9	2 17	...
Gerwisch	...	3 18	...	5 23	7 26	...	8 27	...	...	1039	...	...	...	...	...	...	...	...
Biederitz	...	3 24	...	5 29	7 32	...	8 33	...	...	1045	...	...	...	...	...	...	...	...
Neustadt-Magdeburg	...	3 33	...	5 38	7 42	...	8 43	...	...	1054	...	...	...	...	...	...	2 42	...
Magdeburg Haupt...arr	1 54	3 38	2 55	5 43	7 47	6 3	8 48	9 1	9 41	1059	11 20	12 2	...	...	1210	1 30	2 47	...
DRESDEN H'pt. 189 dep	...	1035	...	1p18	...	1 p18	...	4 p0	...	...	4 p0	4 p0	4 p0	8 p6	8 p6	...	8 p6	...
LEIPSIC 158 ....dep	...	1 p0	...	4p10	...	4 p10	...	6 p30	...	...	7p40	7p40	7p40	10 p5	10p5	...	1120	...
	p.m.	p.m.	p.m.	p.m.		p.m.		p.m.			p.m.	n'gt	p.m.	nght	n'gt		a.m.	
Magdeburg Haupt. dep	1 58	3 58	2 59	7 14	...	6 16	...	9 9	...	...	11 24	12 6	1150	12 18	1214	...	2 55	...
Sudenburg-Magdeburg ...		4 4		7 20	...	...	...		...	...	...			12 24		...	3 0	...
Niederndodeleben...........		4 16		7 32	...	...	...		...	...	...			12 36		...	...	...
Dreileben-Drachenstedt ...		4 39		7 56	...	...	...		...	...	...			12 58		...	...	...
Eilsleben 158...... arr		4 50		8 8	...	6 44	...		...	...	11 57			1 9		...	3 38	...
Eilsleben dep	B	4†51		8 12	...	6 45	...		1,2,3	...	11 58			1 12	B	...	3 40	...
Völpke		...		8 24	...		...		p.m.	...				1 24		...	...	...
Schöningen		6 2		9 10	...		...		From Harzburg 8.49.	...				1 39		...	...	...
Jerxheim.....................		6 39	Via	9 40	...		...			...						...	...	...
Mattierzoll		6 51		9 52	...		...			...				...		...	...	...
Börssum ....arr		7 11		1011	...		...			...				...		...	5 26	...
BRUNSWICK 163... arr		7p46	4p18	1158	...	7 p40	...	10p34		p.m.	12a48		1 a6	...	1258	...	4†45	...
BRUNSWICK 163... dep		6p36	4p28		...	8 p0	...	...		1058			1a18	...		...	4a55	...
Börssum ....dep		7 25	Hildesheim,	...	...	8 29	...	...		1139	...			...		...	5 29	...
Ringelheim 166		8 3		...	...	8 54	...	...		1217	...			...		...	6 8	...
Lutter		8 16		...	...	9 4	...	...	...	1230	...			...		...	6 21	...
Seesen 163		9 0		...	...	9 21	...	...	9 40	1 0	...			...	2 37	...	6 49	...
Gandersheim		9 21		...	...	9 35	...	...	9 54	1 23	...		Via Hanover.	...	...	...	7 11	...
Kreiensen..............arr	4 51	9 29		...	...	9 41	...	...	10 2	1 33	...	2 15		...	2 55	...	7 19	...
CASSEL 156............arr	6p52	12a7	and Hameln.	...	...	12 a7	...	...	12a7	...	...	3a58		...	5a30	...	9a28	...
FRANKFORT 156 ...arr	1025	6 a7		...	...		...	...	6 a7	...	...	7a18		...	9a21	...	1p13	...
Kreiensen ....dep	4 55	1012		...	...	...	...	...	...	...	...	...		...	3 0	...	7 40	...
Naensen	RC	1029		...	...	...	...	...	...	...	...	...		...	...	...	7 59	...
Stadtoldendorf	Via Scherfede and Hagen (page 135B).	1055		...	...	...	...	...	...	...	...	...		...	...	...	8 29	...
Holzminden...... arr		1112		...	...	...	...	...	...	...	...	...		...	3 43	...	8 48	...
Holzminden dep		1120		...	...	...	...	...	...	...	...	...		...	3 45	...	8 58	...
Hoxter		1132		1,2,3	...	...	...	...	...	...	...	...		...	3 53	...	9 13	...
Ottbergen .... arr		1148		p.m.	p.m.	...	...	...	...	...	...	...		...	...	...	9 30	...
Ottbergen dep				8 47	9 42	...	...	...	...	...	...	...		...	...	...	10 6	...
Brakel		...		8 58	10 0	...	...	...	...	...	...	...		...	...	...	1020	...
Driburg		...	RC	9 15	10 22	...	...	...	...	...	...	...		...	...	...	1041	...
Altenbeken ....arr		...	7 0	9 31	10 42	...	...	...	...	...	...	...		Ex 3	4 37	...	11 1	...
CASSEL 135B.........dep		...	5p18	8p10	8 p16	...	...	...	...	...	...	...		3 a0	3 a0	...	8a45	...
Warburg ....dep		...	6 19	9 1	9 54	...	...	...	...	...	...	...		3 54	3 54	...	1012	...
Willebadessen		...	...	...	10 25	...	...	...	...	...	...	...		...	...	...	1040	...
Altenbeken ....arr		...	6 56	9 38	10 48	2, 3, 4	...	...	...	...	...	...		4 31	4 31	...	11 7	...
HAMELN 155............dep		...	5p59	...	...	9 p46	...	...	2 3 4	...	...	...		...	...	...	8a34	...
Altenbeken...........dep		...	7 1	9 40	10 52	12 0	...	...	a.m.	...	...	...		4 41	4 48	...	1124	...
Paderborn		...	7 21	10 0	11 16	12 21	...	...	4 27	...	...	...		4 58	5 8	...	1149	...
Geseke		...	...	...	11 46		...	...	4 57	...	...	...		...	...	a.m.	1219	...
Lippstadt 159..................		...	7 47	1026	12 7	...	...	...	5 40	...	...	...		5 24	5 33	7 14	1240	...
Soest.......................arr		...	8 6	1045	12 40	...	...	...	6 12	...	...	...		5 42	5 51	7 45	1 10	...
ELBERFELD ...134C...arr		...	9p38	1111	...	...	...	...	...	...	...	...		7 a34	7a34	...	4p28	...
DUSSELDORF 134C...arr		...	1024	1141	...	...	...	...	...	...	...	...		8 a17	8a17	...	5 p5	...
AIX-LA-CHAP. 134C...arr		...	12a6	...	...	...	...	...	...	...	...	...		10a23	1023	...	7p24	...
COLOGNE.......134C...arr	1026	...	1026	1a36	...	...	...	...	...	...	...	...	7a40	8 a52	8a52	...	5p14	...

†—Runs from Eilsleben via Helmstedt. B—Via Oschersleben, Halberstadt, and Goslar.

PADERBORN and BRILON.

Paderborn dep	5a14	7 a24	9 a0	11a52	2p34	5 p28	7p33	9p15	**Brilon** ......dep	5 a2	7a41	9 a46	12p15	2p33	5p13	8 p12	...
Buren	6 16	8 12	10 2	1 2	3 40	6 38	8 35	1022	Buren	6 15	8 55	10 46	1 33	3 43	6 16	9 18	...
Brilon 135A arr	7 24	9 12	11 12	2 13	4 50	7 46	9 40	...	**Paderborn** arr	7 15	9 57	11 33	2 30	4 45	7 15	10 24	...

Paderborn and Lippspringe (in 30 minutes)—Paderborn depart 6.10, 7.34, 10.2 a.m. 12.0 noon, 1.23, 2.47, 5.44, 7.32, 9.15 p.m. Lippspringe depart 6.40, 8.11, 10.50 a.m., 12.47, 2.2, 4.33, 6.44, 8.8, 9.58 p.m.

WARSTEIN and LIPPSTADT.	**Warstein** ......dep	6 a54	10a56	2 p5	4 p25	6p35	9 p0	**Lippstadt** dep	6a21	10a14	1p28	3p39	6p45	8p22
	Belecke	7 10	11 11	2 22	4 41	6 47	9 18	Belecke	7 14	11 14	2 22	4 40	7 42	9 18
	Lippstadt (164) arr	8 0	12 0	3 13	5 35	7 39	10 8	**Warstein** ...arr	7 24	11 24	2 32	4 50	7 52	9 28

PRUSSIAN STATE RAILWAYS.

BERLIN (Potsdam Station), POTSDAM, and WERDER.

Berlin—Potsdam Bahnhof dep	6a45	7a53	9 a8	10a15	11a15	12p15	1p15	1p40	2p15	3p15	4 p5	5p15	6p15	7 p0	7p15	7p40	8p30	9p35	10p45	11p35	1 a5
Neubabelsberg	7 11	8 19	9 34	10 41	11 41	12 41	1 41	2 6	2 41	3 41	4 30	5 41	6 41	7 26	7 41	8 6	8 56	10 1	11 11	12 1	1 31
Potsdam	7 18	8 26	9 41	10 49	11 49	12 48	1 49	2 13	2 49	3 49	4 36	5 49	6 49	7 33	7 48	8 13	9 3	10 8	11 18	12 8	1 38
Charlottenhof ...	7 22	8 31	9 46	10 54	11 54	12 52	1 54	2 18	2 54	3 54	4 41	5 54	6 54	7 38	7 53	8 18	9 8	1013	11 23	12 13	1 43
Wildpark.........	7 26	8 35	9 50	10 58	11 59	12 56	1 58	2 22	2 59	3 59	4 46	5 58	6 58	7 42	7 57	8 23	9 12	1017	11 27	12 17	1 48
Werder ...arr	7 33	8 43	...	11 6	...	1 4	2 6	...	3 7	4 7	4 54	6 6	7 6	...	8 5	8 31	9 20	1025	11 35	...	1 56

Werder.........dep	5 a44	7a50	...	...	10a50	11a43	...	1p50	3 p4	3p58	4p50	5 p50	6p35	7p28	8 p35	9p29	10p14	10p46	11p44
Wildpark..............	5 53	7 58	8 a50	9 a59	10 59	11 52	12p45	1 58	3 13	4 7	4 59	5 59	6 44	7 37	8 43	9 37	10 23	10 55	11 52
Charlottenhof.........	5 57	8 2	8 54	10 3	11 3	11 56	12 49	2 2	3 17	4 11	5 3	6 3	6 48	7 41	8 47	9 41	10 27	10 59	11 55
Potsdam	6 9	8 9	9 1	10 10	11 10	12 2	12 56	2 9	3 24	4 18	5 10	6 10	6 55	7 48	8 54	9 48	10 34	11 6	12 3
Neubabelsberg	6 16	8 15	9 7	10 16	11 16	12 7	1 2	2 15	3 30	4 24	5 16	6 16	7 1	7 54	9 0	9 54	10 40	11 12	12 9
Berlin.............arr	6 41	8 40	9 32	10 41	11 41	12 31	1 27	2 40	3 55	4 49	5 41	6 41	7 26	8 19	9 25	1019	11 5	11 37	12 34

BERLIN (Potsdam Station—Wannsee Section) and POTSDAM.

Berlin Wannseebhf.	5 a0	5 a10
„ Gr. Görschenstr.	5 4	5 14
Friedenau....................	5 9	5 19
Steglitz	5 13	5 23
Lichterfelde..................	5 19	5 29
Zehlendorf....................	5 24	5 33
Schlachtensee...............	5 31	
Wannsee	5 38	...
Neubabelsberg	5 45	...
Potsdam (Wannseebhf.)	5 54	...

From Berlin Wannseebahnhof to Potsdam, every hour, at 30 minutes past the hour, from 5.30 a.m. until 10.30p.m , also at 11.10 p.m., and 12.10 & 1.10 night

Berlin to Zehlendorf, every 10 minutes, from 5.0 a.m. until 1.10 a.m.

Potsdam (Wannseebhf.)	4a40	5a50
Neubabelsberg	4 48	5 58
Wannsee.......................	4 55	6 5
Schlachtensee...............	5 2	6 12
Zehlendorf	5 9	6 19
Lichterfelde..................	5 14	6 24
Steglitz	5 20	6 30
Friedenau....................	5 24	6 34
Berlin (Görschenstr.)......	5 29	6 39
„ (Wannseebhf.)......	5 34	6 44

Potsdam to Berlin, every hour, at 50 minutes past the hour, from 5.50 a.m. until 12.50 night.

Zehlendorf to Berlin, every 10 minutes, from 5.39 a.m. until 1.19 a.m.

BEELITZ and NAUEN.

	a.m.	a.m.	p.m.	p.m.	p.m.	p.m.
Beelitz ...dep	7 10	9 20	1227	4 16	6 41	8 47
Wildpark......	7 47	10 0	1 5	4 50	7 30	9 23
Wustermark	8 30	10 33	1 37	5 28	8 5	10 8
Nauen......arr	8 48	10 45	1 49	5 39	8 17	1020

	a.m.	a.m.	a.m.	p.m.	p.m.	p.m.
Nauen ...dep	5 17	8 52	11 3	1 34	3 55	8 0
Wustermark	5 45	9 18	11 15	1 47	4 8	8 14
Wildpark......	6 28	9 52	11 46	2 27	4 50	8 48
Beelitz.....arr	6 54	...	12 26	2 57	5 19	9 44

BERLIN and POTSDAM.

Berlin Schles. Bhf. dep	5 a6	5 a36
„ Alexanderplatz...	5 11	5 41
„ Friedrichstrasse ..	5 17	5 47
„ Zoolog. Garten ...	5 30	6 0
Charlottenburg	5 37	6 7
Grunewald	5 46	6 16
Wannsee	6 1	6 31
Neubabelsberg................	6 8	6 38
Nowawes	6 13	6 43
Potsdam ....arr	6 16	6 46

Trains keeping relative time run as required about half hourly till 12.6 night

Potsdam ....dep	5a10
Nowawes	5 14
Neubabelsberg................	5 19
Wannsee	5 26
Grunewald	5 43
Charlottenburg.............arr	5 51
Berlin Zoolog. Garten.....arr	5 57
„ Friedrichstrasse ...arr	6 11
„ Alexanderplatz ...arr	6 16
„ Schles. Bahnhof ...arr	6 23

Trains keeping relative time run as required about half hourly until 12a10.

WERNIGERODE and NORDHAUSEN.

Wernigerode...dep		7a12	9a32	11a10	12p2	1p38	3p10	...	4p30	4p42	8p10
Steinerne Renne		7 38	9 59	1134	1231	2 2	3 36	...	4 55	5 7	8 35
Drei Annen-Hohne ...		8 0	10 20	1155	1252	2 23	—	4§p8	5 18	5 29	8 56
Schierke		8 25	10§29	1214	—	2 41	...	4 23	5 50	...	...
Brocken........ arr		9 8	11 20	1 0	...	3 25	...	5 4	6§31	...	...
Elend (for Schierke)...		8 22	10 40	1214	...	2 43	...	—	—	5 48	9 14
Sorge	a.m.	8 43	11 0	1233	...	3 6	...	...	...	6 11	9 35
Benneckstein	5‡20	8 57	11 13	—	...	3 30	...	...	...	6 26	9 50
Eisfelder	5 50	9 34	11 45	...	...	4 17	...	...	...	7 1	1028
Netzkater............	5 59	9 42	11 54	...	...	4 28	...	...	...	7 10	1037
Nordhausen arr	6 37	1016	12 29	...	...	5 9	...	...	...	7 46	1115

Nordhausen ......dep	6 a0	9a15	p.m.	2 p0	1p30	3p20	...	6p32	8*p10
Netzkater....................	6 37	10 0	...	2 39	2 6	3 59	...	7 9	8 53
Eisfelder	6 48	10 14	...	2 49	2 18	4 7	...	7 22	9 10
Benneckstein	7 19	10 48	...	—	2 51	4 43	...	7 54	9 42
Sorge	7 35	11 2	12 38	...	3 4	5 0	...	8 10	—
Elend (for Schierke) ...	7 55	11 24	1 3	...	3 23	5 21	p.m.	8 33	...
Brocken ....dep	7 §0	10 48	12 28	2 p0	...	4 30	6 §0	...	...
Schierke	7§40	11 34	1 10	2 41	...	5 16	6 40	...	...
Drei Annen-Hohne	8 10	11 55	1 26	2 56	3 42	5 50	6 55	8 56	...
Steinerne Renne	8 31	12 18	1 48	—	4 3	6 14	—	9 19	...
Wernigerode 166 arr	8 54	12 45	2 14	...	4 26	6 40	...	9 46	...

*—Monday, Wednesday, and Friday only.

‡—Sun., Tues., and Thurs. only. §—Runs until 31st August.

FROSE and QUEDLINBURG.

Frose ....dep		...	6 a30	8 a3	10a18	11a39	1 p26	3 p5	...	5 p49	...	8p46	...
Ballenstedt	4a45	5a41	7 3	8 45	10 49	12 8	1 56	3 40	5 p45	6 24	7p56	9 26	...
Gernrode (165B)	5 3	6 1	7 22	9 9	11 10	12 26	2 13	3 59	6 6	6 43	8 15	9 45	...
Quedlinburg (162) arr	5 20	6 20	7 42	9 27	11 27	12 43	2 30	4 16	6 23	7 0	8 32	10 2	...

Quedlinburg ......dep	...	5a40	7 a0	8 a47	11a33	12p55	2 p56	4 p32	5 p45	7 p11	8 p8	8 p41	10p16
Gernrode	...	5 59	7 20	9 11	11 51	1 13	3 15	4 50	6 3	7 30	8 26	9 0	10 34
Ballenstedt	4a44	6 17	7 47	9 32	12 10	1 31	3 34	5 7	6 23	7 47	8 50	9 19	10 52
Frose (166)...........arr	5 14	6 47	8 20	10 0	12 41	2 4	4 1	...	6 50	...	9 21	9 46	...

GERNRODE and EISFELDER.

Gernrode ...dep	7a25	9a20	1155	1p25	2p25	4p15	...	6p47	7p55
Alexisbad ....arr	8 9	10 7	1239	2 15	3 10	4 59	...	7 34	8 44
Harzgerode ...arr	8 25	1021	1254	...	3 26	5 13	...	7 49	9 2
Alexisbad.........dep	8 14	1013	—	2 25	—	5 0	...	—	8 50
Stiege..................arr	9 5	11 8	...	3 32	...	6 9	7p55	...	9 50
Hasselfelde ...arr	9 32	1132	...	3 49	...	...	8 12	...	1017
Stiege.................dep	9 8	1112	...	3 57	...	6 15	—	...	9 54
Eisfelder 165B arr	9 30	1134	...	4 6	...	6 43	...	...	1022

Eisfelder dep	...	6a51	...	10a15	...	...	3 p0	4p45	7p25
Stiege.........arr	...	7 13	...	10 37	...	...	3 26	5 11	7 47
Hasselfelde dp	...	...	...	10 15	...	...	3 7	...	7 25
Stiege ....dep	...	7 16	...	10 42	...	...	3 32	5 16	7 51
Alexisbad...arr	...	8 8	...	11 47	...	pm	4 36	6 25	8 42
Harzgerode dp	...	7 53	9a50	10 35	1 p5	258	4 42	6 46	8 25
Alexisbad dep	6a14	8 13	10 0	12 8	1 16	313	4 59	7 2	8 47
Gernrode arr	7 0	9 0	1137	1 4	2 5	4 3	5 50	7 54	9 36

HALLE, VIENENBURG, GOSLAR, and HILDESHEIM.

Dist E.M			2 3 4	2 3 4	2 3 4	Ex3	2 3 4	1—4	Ex3	2 3 4	Ex3	2 3 4	Ex3	2 3 4	2 3 4	2 3 4	1—4	1—4	2—4	1,2,3	2 3 4	1—4	Ex3
	LEIPSIC Haupt. ...dep		...	...	3a29	5a55	6a57	...	1025	1025	...	...	1 p0	...	...	2p25	...	...	4p20	6p20	7p40	10p5	...
					a.m.	a.m.	a.m.		a.m.	a.m.		p.m	p.m.			p.m.			p.m.	p.m	p.m.	p.m.	
—	**Halle** ...dep		...	...	4 46	6 37	8 2	...	1113	1128	From Magdeburg	1240	1 41	...	...	3 38	...	...	6 18	7 12	9 6	1043	From Magdeburg p. 162.
4½	Trotha ...		...	...	4 57	...	8 13	...	...	1139		1251	...	...	...	3 49	...	...	6 30	...	9 17	1053	
11¾	Nauendorf ...		...	...	5 15	RC	8 37	...	...	12 2		1 13	RC	...	...	4 12	...	...	6 54	..	9 40	1116	
18¼	Cönnern ...		...	...	5 28	...	8 55	...	1143	1218		1 30	...	...	...	4 27	...	...	7 10	7 42	9 55	1131	
29	Sandersleben ...		...	...	5 57	7 25	9 40	...	...	1247		2 0	2 31	...	...	4 57	...	...	7 44	8 2	1023	1157	
36	**Aschersleben** ...arr		...	...	6 12	7 37	9 58	p.m.	1212	1 1		—	2 42	...	p.m.	5 16	...	p.m.	8 4	8 13	1040	1211	
...	" (162) dep		...	...	6 15	7 38	10 6	1 12	1213	1 6		...	2 44	...	2 50	5 25	p.m.	5 31	8 23	8 14	1042	1213	
40¾	**Frose** ...		...	...	6 27	...	1016	1 22	...	1 16		...	...	...	3 0	5 36	6‡10	5 44	8 34	...	1053	1222	
45	Gatersleben ...		...	...	6 40	...	1028	—	...	1 27		...	...	...	—	5 49	6 23	—	8 47	...	11 4	1233	
51½	Wegeleben ...		...	...	6 58	8 2	1044	...	1236	1 43		...	...	...	...	6 7	6 40	...	9 5	...	1120	1248	...
56	**Halberstadt** ...arr		a.m.	...	7 8	8 11	1053	...	1245	1 52	p.m.	...	3 11	...	...	6 17	6 50	...	9 15	8 41	1130	1257	a.m.
...	" (162) dep		5 14	...	7 38	8 15	1058	...	1250	2 3	3 3	...	3 17	...	...	6 35	—	...	10 0	8 45	—	—	1 16
64¾	Heudeber-D. ...		5 37	...	8 1	...	1121	...	...	2 25	3 21	...	...	...	...	6 57	...	...	1023	9 2	...	...	...
70	Wasserleben ...		5 50	...	8 15	...	1133	...	...	2 37	...	...	...	...	...	7 10	...	A—Runs until 15th Sept.	1035	9 11	...	...	SC
78¾	**Vienenburg** ...arr		6 9	...	8 35	8 51	1152	2 3 4	1 26	2 55	3 43	...	3 53	...	...	7 31	2 3 4		1054	9 27	...	...	1 52
...	HARZBURG ...dep		5a54	...	8a29	—	1138	p.m	...	2p42	...	...	3p38	...	4p34	7p30	8p14		1054	9p14	...	...	...
...	**Vienenburg**..dep	5a10	6 21	...	8 58	—	1154	1 8	1 27	3 2	3 45	1,2,3	3 55	...	5 42	7 46	8 36		1110	9 29	...	...	1 54
86¾	**Goslar** ...arr	5 32	6 44	...	9 23	—	1220	1 31	1 46	3 25	4 3	p.m.	4 12	p.m.	6 7	8 8	8 58		1131	9 48	...	...	2 12
...	" ...dep	5 37	7 25	...	9 29	...	1225	—	1 51	3 42	4 7	3 36	4 15	6 18	—	8 20	—		—	9 49	...	...	—
89½	Grauhof ...	5 44	7 33	...	9 36	...	1233	...	...	3 48	Kreiensen arr. 4.51.	...	...	6 25	...	8 28	...		...	...	...	...	‡—Weekdays only.
98¼	Ringelheim ...	6 6	7 58	...	9 59	...	1 2	...	...	4 9		A	...	6 46	...	8 56	...		...	...	...	2 3 4	
109¼	Derneburg ...	6 25	8 19	a.m.	1019	...	1 23	p.m.	...	4 28		...	...	7 6	p.m.	9 18	...	...	...	...	...	p.m.	
113¾	Grossdungen ...	6 35	8 30	8 54	1030	...	1 34	4 27	...	4 38		...	...	7 16	8 37	9 28	...	...	...	...	...	1149	
120	**Hildesheim** Hpt.	6 53	8 46	9 13	1046	...	1 50	4 45	2 35	4 53		4 23	4 59	7 34	8 56	9 44	...	...	...	1032	...	12 8	
143½	HANOVER 157A...	7a50	9a32	...	1217	...	3p11	...	3p14	5p50		...	5p50	9 p8	...	1044	...	...	...	1110	...	...	

	Ex3	1—4	2 3 4	1,2,3	2 3 4	2 3 4	2 3 4	2 3 4	2 3 4	1,2,3	Ex3	Ex3	2 3 4	2 3 4	Ex3	2 3 4	1—4	2 3 4	2 3 4	Ex3	2 3 4	2 3 4	1,2,3
HANOVER ...dep	...	...	...	6a20	6a20	6a31	...	...	9 34	12p5	...	1p10	1p10	...	3p19	...	...	4p43	...	...	7p38	...	...
				a.m.	a.m.	a.m.		a.m.	a.m.	p.m.		p.m.	p.m.	p.m.	p.m.	p.m.		p.m.	p.m.		p.m.	p.m.	
Hildesheim...dep	...	...	...	6 58	7 11	8 45	...	11 2	1054	1259	...	1 56	2 6	2 13	4 7	3 20	...	6 2	6 8	...	9 16	1145	...
Grossdungen ...	...	...	...	...	7 26	9 0	...	1122	11 9	...	...	...	2 21	2 32	...	3 36	...	6 18	6 30	...	9 34	12 5	...
Derneburg ...	...	...	...	...	7 36	9 11	...	—	1119	A	...	RC	2 32	—	...	3 47	...	6 29	—	...	9 45	—	...
Ringelheim ...	...	...	...	...	7 57	9 36	...	...	1145	...	...	...	2 55	...	...	4 11	...	6 53	...	...	10 8	...	...
Goslar ...arr	a.m.	...	a.m.	7 47	8 29	1011	a.m.	...	1222	1 54	p.m.	2 52	3 30	p.m.	4 59	4 47	p.m	7 29	p.m.	...	1043	p m.	p.m.
" ...dep	3 36	...	5 42	7 48	8 32	1015	1132	...	1237	—	2 47	2 55	3 34	4 21	5 0	—	5 16	7 34	7 59	...	1045	9 18	1039
Vienenburg...arr	3 51	...	6 2	8 3	8 49	1034	1151	...	1256	...	3 1	3 9	3 53	4 41	5 14	...	5 35	7 52	8 18	...	11 2	9 35	1053
HARZBURG 163 arr	...	...	6a30	9a15	9a15	...	1210	...	1p19	...	3 25	3p25	4p13	—	...	...	5p59	8p53	8p53	p.m.	1122	—	1112
Vienenburg...dep	3 52	...	6 11	8 4	9 0	1035	—	...	1 5	...	3 3	3 11	—	...	5 15	...	5 41	8 0	—	8 33	—	...	1110
Wasserleben ...	SC	...	6 32	8 21	9 21	1054	...	...	1 27	...	...	...	...	...	...	...	6 1	8 24	...	...	...	...	1132
Heudeber-D. ...	...	...	6 46	8 32	9 36	11 6	...	...	1 42	...	...	...	...	...	...	...	6 16	8 39	...	...	...	...	114'
Halberstadt arr	4 29	a.m.	7 0	8 44	9 51	1122	...	...	1 59	...	3 38	3 46	...	p.m.	5 50	...	6 30	8 57	...	9 8	...	...	12 3
" dep	For Magdeburg p. 162.	4 45	7 40	8 48	9 58	1134	...	...	2 15	...	For Magdeburg	3 55	...	4‡10	5 55	...	6 43	9 19	...	9 12	...	...	—
Wegeleben ...		4 55	7 51	...	10 8	1145	1—4	...	2 25	...		...	1—4	4 21	6 4	1—4	6 53	9 30	...	9 21	...	...	...
Gatersleben ...		5 12	8 8	...	1023	12 1	p.m.	p.m.	2 42	...		...	p.m.	4 39	...	p.m.	7 10	9 45	p.m.	RC	...	...	...
Frose ...		5 26	8 24	...	1036	1216	1246	2 9	2 56	...		...	4 6	4 53	...	6 55	7 25	9 59	9 24	...	...	...	...
Aschersleben arr		5 35	8 33	9 17	1045	1225	1256	2 19	3 6	...		4 25	4 16	—	6 28	7 5	7 34	10 8	9 33	9 45	...	...	...
" ...dep		5 38	8 36	9 18	1049	1227	—	—	3 12	...		4 27	—	...	6 29	—	7 39	1015	—	9 47	...	...	...
Sandersleben ...		6 0	8 54	9 33	11 6	1245	...	2p30	3 31	...		4 39	...	...	...	...	7 59	1033	...	...	...	...	...
Cönnern ...		6 26	9 19	...	1131	1 9	...	2 57	3 58	...		4 58	...	...	...	...	8 24	1056	...	...	...	...	...
Nauendorf ...		6 45	9 37	...	1151	1 28	...	3 17	4 19	...	—	...	...	...	...	...	8 44	1114	...	...	...	...	...
Trotha ...	—	7 5	9 56	...	1210	1 48	...	3 37	4 39	...	...	...	...	...	...	...	9 4	1133	...	...	...	...	...
Halle ...arr	...	7 16	10 7	1021	1221	2 0	...	3 48	4 51	...	...	5 30	...	...	7 24	...	9 15	1144	...	1044	...	...	...
LEIPSIC (158) arr	...	8 a9	11a8	11a8	1 pl	3 p5	...	5 pl	6p11	...	...	6p11	...	...	8 p6	...	1046	1a15	...	11p30	...	...	...

Extra—Aschersleben to Frose, 5‡46, 7.48, 10.1, 11.33 a.m., 7‡12, 8.28, 10.17 p.m.
Frose to Aschersleben, 6‡32, 6.‡2, 10.5 a.m., 7‡56, 9.51 p.m.

HALBERSTADT, HARZBURG, and GOSLAR.

Dist. E.M		a.m.	a.m.		a.m.	a.m.	a.m.	a.m.	p.m.		p.m.	p.m.		p.m.	p m.		p.m.	p.m.	
	Halberstadt ...dep	...	6 19	...	8 23	9 35	10*24	11 6	12 20	B	2 12	3 30	...	6 26	7 26	...	9 22	11 35	...
9	Heudeber-Danstedt ...	...	6 47	...	8 44	9 59	...	11 29	12 39	p.m.	2 30	3 51	...	6 48	...	...	9 43	11 56	...
14¾	Wernigerode ...	5 5	7 9	...	9 6	10 18	11 5	11 48	1 0	2 25	2 49	4 18	p.m.	7 10	8 5	...	10 3	12 14	...
20¼	Ilsenburg ...	5 22	7 28	...	9 24	10 39	11 21	12 6	1 20	2 44	3 7	4 36	4*37	7 33	8 21	...	10 22	—	...
23¾	Eckertal ...	5 33	7 40	...	9 36	10 51	11 31	12 18	1 29	...	3 16	—	4 50	7 45	8 30	...	10 4[illegible]	...	...
29	Harzburg Bad ... arr	5 50	7 57	a.m.	9 53	11 8	11 45	12 36	1 43	3 6	3 3[illegible]	p.m.	5 6	8 1	8 44	p.m.	10 50	p.m.	...
	Harzburg Bad ... dep	6	—	8 44	10 15	11 13	—	12 40	1 55	3 15	—	6 26	—	—	—	8 49	—	10 5[illegible]	...
33¼	Oker ...	6 23	...	9 2	10 31	11 29	...	12 55	2 13	...	...	6 42	...	...	...	...	...	11 10	...
35¾	**Goslar (166)** ...arr	6 34	...	9 13	10 42	11 40	...	1 6	2 24	3 34	...	6 53	...	...	...	9 9	...	11 21	...

						a.m.	a.m.	a.m.	p.m.	p.m.	p.m.		p.m	p.m.			p.m.		p.m.
...	**Goslar** ...dep	...	...	...	...	7 55	9 42	11 54	1 20	1 55	3 16	...	4 2	5 25	...	...	7 42	...	9 38
...	Oker ...	...	...	...	...	8 2	...	12 2	1 2[illegible]	B	3 27	...	4 10	5 34	...	...	7 50	...	9 46
...	Harzburg Bad (163) arr	...	a.m.	...	...	8 16	10 1	12 18	1 [illegible]4	2 14	3 43	...	4 26	5 51	p.m.	p.m.	8 6	p.m.	10 2
...	Harzburg Bad (163) dep	...	5†37	...	...	8 20	10 7	12 26	1 54	2 20	3 48	...	4 31	6 4	6 40	6 59	8 13	9 10	—
...	Eckertal ...	...	5 56	a.m.	...	8 37	10 24	12 43	2 12	...	4 3	...	4 39	6 19	6 55	7 20	8 31	9 27	...
...	Ilsenburg ...	a.m.	6 8	6 10	a.m.	8 50	10 37	12 55	2 25	2 44	4 15	p.m.	5 3	6 31	7 7	7 36	8 42	9 39	...
...	Wernigerode ...	3 45	—	6 33	8 0	9 9	10 56	1 16	2 46	3 0	4 32	4§13	5 25	6 47	7 32	8 5	8 58	10 0	...
...	Heudeber-Danstedt ...	4 2	...	6 52	8 19	9 28	11 14	1 34	3 2	—	—	5 1	5 44	—	7 51	8 28	—	10 18	...
...	**Halberstadt (166)** ...arr	4 21	...	7 9	8 36	9 44	11 29	1 50	3 19	...	...	5 16	6 0	...	8 6	8 44	...	10 34	...

*—Until 15th September. †—Until 16th September. §—In July and August only.
B—Until 15th September.

WASSERLEBEN and BÖRSSUM.

Wasserleben ...dep	6a50	8 a28	11a44	2p45	7 p15	...	...
Börssum...........arr	8 20	9 52	1 39	4 12	8 24	...	...

Börssum ....dep	6a50	8 a35	12p32	2 p45	7 p21	...	...	...
Wasserleben (166) ......arr	8 11	10 45	1 22	5 50	8 20	...	...	...

WITTENBERGE and NEU STRELITZ.

Wittenberge ...dep	5a45	9a11	11a21	1 p5	3 p0	5p35	7 p3	9p18	2a33
Perleberg	6 26	9 35	11 45	1 30	3 28	6 0	7 28	9 50	2 56
Pritzwalk	7 35	1035	12 45	—	4 38	—	8 45	1058	—
Wittstock	8 30	1120	1 39	...	5 19	...	9 52	1147	...
Buschhof...............	9 27	12 0	—	...	5 55	...	11 0	—	...
Mirow	9 43	1217	...	4p50	6 14	...	1127	...	6a58
Neu-Strelitz ...arr	1023	1259	...	5 44	7 1	...	1216	...	7 58

Neu-Strelitz dp	5 a3	...	8a24	10a34	3p16	...	...	6p15	9p20
Mirow	6 4	...	9 4	11 13	4 12	...	...	6 58	102[illegible]
Buschhof.........	—	...	9 21	11 28	—	...	...	7 14	1029
Wittstock.........	...	6a49	9 58	12 1	...	3p42	...	7 52	1132
Pritzwalk	8a10	7 32	1039	12 45	...	4 45	...	8 45	—
Perleberg	9 55	8 22	1148	1 52	3p40	6 5	8p18	9 50	4a52
Wittenberge ...	1020	8 42	1213	2 17	4 5	6 30	8 43	1013	[illegible] 17

KIEL and FLENSBURG.

Kiel...........dep	5a20	7a23	8a30	11a18	1p13	3p42	7 p5	7p38	11p48
Gettorf	5 54	7 48	9 16	11 55	1 55	4 21	7 34	8 21	12 34
Eckernförde ...	6 18	8 8	9 45	12 18	2 22	4 46	7 54	8 49	12 55
Süderbrarup ...	6 56	8 38	1028	12 57	3 0	5 21	8 24	9 32	—
Flensburg...arr	7 45	9 22	1126	1 52	3 52	6 13	9 4	1030	...

Flensburg ...dep		6 a0	7a58	11a35	12p53	1p57	3p15	5 p4	7p10	10p32
Süderbrarup ..		6 59	9 0	12 30	1 34	3 1	4 6	5 58	8 45	11 26
Eckernförde	5a57	7 52	9 48	1 10	2 7	3 42	4 47	6 36	9 31	11 59
Gettorf	6 30	8 19	1012	1 32	2 23	—	5 8	6 55	9 53	12 15
Kiel ......arr	7 25	9 7	1057	2 16	2 50	...	5 47	7 33	10 34	12 42

ECKERNFORDE and KAPPELN.

E.M.							
	Eckernforde dep	6a30	9a47	12p34	2p21	4p47	8p46
18	Kappeln 169...arr	7 50	1112	2 2	4 0	6 8	10 9

Kappeln	6a15	8a20	11a40	3 p10	4p40	7 p50
Eckernforde	7 37	9 39	1 4	4 38	6 30	9 15

KIEL, EUTIN, and LUBECK.

		a.m.	a.m.	a.m.			a.m.	p.m.		p.m.	p.m.	p.m.	p.m.	p.m.		p.m.	p.m.
Kiel..........................dep		5 15	7 31	7 37	...	...	10 12	1 13	...	2 55	3 8	3 41	6 3	6 49	...	9 0	9 48
Preetz		5 43	7 48	8 2	...	...	10 43	1 37	...	3 32	3 26	4 12	6 35	7 18	...	9 18	10 17
Ascheberg ....arr		6 2	⋮	8 21	...	...	11 3	1 55	...	3 50	⋮	—	6 55	—	p.m.	⋮	10 37
Neumunster ....dep		—	⋮	7 42	...	...	10 19	1 16	...	3 9	⋮	...	6 20	...	6 56	⋮	9 44
Ascheberg ....arr		...	⋮	8 17	...	...	11 0	1 50	...	3 44	⋮	...	6 53	...	7 31	⋮	10 20
Ascheberg ....dep		...	⋮	8 26	...	...	11 8	1 57	...	3 55	⋮	...	6 58	...	7 32	⋮	10 41
Ploen................................		a.m.	8 7	8 36	...	a.m.	11 19	2 9	p.m.	4 4	3 45	...	7 8	...	7 42	9 37	10 51
Malente Gremsmühlen ...		7 43	...	8 52	...	11 4	11 34	2 25	3 37	4 19	3 58	...	7 26	...	7 58	9 50	11 6
Eutin ....arr	a.m.	7 51	8 22	9 0	a.m.	11 13	11 42	2 33	3 46	4 26	4 5	...	7 33	p.m.	8 6	9 58	11 14
,, ...dep	6 28	—	8 24	9 5	10 50	—	11 51	2 38	—	4 33	4 8	...	7 43	8 ‡46	—	10 2	11 20
Gleschendorf	6 47	...	...	9 19	11 8	...	12 10	2 57	...	4 47	...	...	8 4	9 1	...	10 15	11 36
Lubeck 213A ......arr	7 18	...	8 54	9 49	11 40	...	12 42	3 30	...	5 18	4 44	...	8 37	9 31	...	10 38	12 5
BERLIN 167 ......arr	...	...	12p50	4 p1	...	...	8 p22	8 p33	...	11p30	8 p33	...	5 a46	...	...	...	6 a38
BERLIN ....dep		...	...	12 0	...	...	...	9 a10	...	...	...	1 p6	...	...	...	3 p8	7 p12
			a.m.	a.m.	a.m.		p.m.	p.m.	p.m.		p.m.	p.m.		p.m.	p.m.	p.m.	p.m.
Lubeck ....dep		...	7 36	7 48	9 58	...	12 35	1 9	1 55	...	3 35	4 44	...	6 24	7 33	9 12	11 30
Gleschendorf		...	8 0	8 24	10 33	...	1 3	...	2 26	...	4 10	...	...	6 55	8 3	9 43	12 0
Eutin ....arr		a.m.	8 12	8 43	10 48	a.m.	1 19	1 43	2 38	p.m.	4 30	5 21	...	7 12	8 19	10 0	12 15
,, ...dep		5 30	8 16	8 50	10 53	11 25	1 23	1 45	—	4 4	4 37	5 25	...	7 18	—	10 7	—
Malente Gremsmühlen ...		5 39	8 25	8 59	11 1	11 34	1 33	1 54	...	4 13	4 47	5 36	...	7 28	...	10 16	...
Ploen................................		5 58	8 37	9 14	11 17	—	1 48	2 6	...	—	5 3	5 47	...	7 43	...	10 31	...
Ascheberg ....arr		6 8	⋮	9 22	11 27	...	1 57	⋮	...	...	5 11	⋮	...	7 53	...	10 41	...
Ascheberg ....dep		6 12	⋮	9 24	11 37	...	2 7	⋮	...	...	5 19	⋮	...	8 2	...	10 48	...
Neumunster.............arr		6 56	⋮	10 0	12 13	...	2 42	⋮	...	...	6 0	⋮	...	8 48	...	11 24	...
Ascheberg ....dep	a.m.	6 16	⋮	9 25	11 30	...	2 0	⋮	...	p.m.	5 16	⋮	p.m.	7 55	...	10 45	...
Preetz	5‡24	6 47	8 56	9 46	11 50	...	2 32	2 25	...	5 11	5 38	6 6	7 28	8 17	...	11 5	...
Kiel ....arr	5 55	7 19	9 13	10 10	12 16	...	2 55	2 42	...	5 40	6 3	6 23	7 59	8 43	...	11 32	...

‡—Not on Sunday.

Gleschendorf...dep	7 a10	8 a25	9 a35	10a50	1 p10	3 p5	4 p55	6 p58	8 p7	9 p45	12 a5	...
Ahrensboeck ...arr	7 29	8 45	9 55	11 10	1 30	3 25	5 15	7 18	8 27	10 5	12 25	...
Ahrensboeck...dep	6 a20	7 a38	8 a55	10a10	11a40	2 p0	3 p45	6 p15	7 p30	8 p38	11p10	...
Gleschendorf ...arr	6 40	7 37	9 15	10 30	12 0	2 20	4 5	6 35	7 50	8 58	11 30	...

EUTIN and ORTH.

Eutin ....dep	...	5a49	9a12	12p3	2p42	4p40	7p53	11p20
Neustadt	...	6 42	9 55	1 0	3 11	5 25	8 31	11 57
Oldenburg ....arr	...	8 1	1041	2 5	—	6 10	9 18	—
Heiligenhafen ......arr	6a46	9 17	1130	3 15	...	6 57	10 4	...
Fehrmarnsund	7 45	—	1210	4 0	...	7 42	—	...
Burg	8 20	...	1233	4 40	...	8 17	...	6 a0
Orth ....arr	9 7	...	1 11	5 25	...	9 1	...	6 35

Orth ....dep	...	...	6a40	...	9a33	1p47	5p31	9p11
Burg	...	...	7 20	...	1140	2 40	6 26	9 50
Fehrmarnsund	...	...	7 48	...	12 6	3 12	6 55	—
Heiligenhafen...... dep	...	5 a2	8 24	...	1243	3 49	7 33	...
Oldenburg	...	6 14	9 11	...	2 5	5 3	8 22	...
Neustadt	6a56	7 33	10 7	12p46	3 20	6 18	9 14	...
Eutin ....arr	7 23	8 11	1038	1 15	3 55	6 58	9 45	...

MALENTE GREMSMUHLEN and LUTJENBURG.

Malente Gremsmühlen ...dep	9 a0	11a38	4p20	5p45	8 p5	...
Lütjenburg ....arr	9 45	12 12	4 52	6 19	8 55	...

Lütjenburg ....dep	7a35	10a23	2p57	5 p1	6p40	...	...
Malente Gremsmühlen ..arr	8 29	10 57	3 31	5 33	7 14	...	...

NAUEN and KETZIN.

E.M.						
	Nauen......dep	8 a0	11a10	4 p30	9p45	...
10	Ketzin......arr	8 46	11 53	5 21	1027	...

Ketzin ....dep	6a40	9 a55	3p20	8 p30	...	...	...
Nauen 167 ...arr	7 30	10 35	4 10	9 17		...	...

JUBECK and GARDING.

Jübeck ....dep	5a51	9a19	...	11a40	12p45	3 p0	p.m.	4p36	p.m.	7 p53	8p50	p.m.	11p15	...	...	...	...
Husum M.	6 58	1017	1115	12 6	1 32	3 35	4 10	5 38	6 14	8 19	9 46	10 25	11 53	...	...	...	...
Büttel..................	8 4	—	1134	—	2 19	—	4 28	—	6 34	—	—	10 45	—	...	...	...	...
Tönning......... arr	8 25	...	1155	...	2 40	...	4 51	...	6 55	...	...	11 8	...	...	...	...	...
Garding ....arr	8 52	...	1225	...	3 4	...	5 16	...	7 19	...	...	11 35	...	...	...	...	...
Garding ....dep	...	5a48	9a35	...	...	12p36	...	4p33	...	...	7p20	8p53	...	...	...	...	...
Tönning.........dep	...	6 13	10 0	...	...	1 1	...	5 6	...	...	7 43	9 18	...	...	...	...	...
Büttel.................	...	6 39	1022	...	a.m.	1 24	...	5 30	p.m.	p.m.	8 4	9 42	p.m.	...	...	...	...
Husum M.	4a32	7 43	1040	11 a9	11 27	2 8	2p53	5 48	6 17	6 54	8 21	10 0	1023	...	...	...	...
Jübeck ....arr	5 17	8 37	...	11 25	12 22	2 44	3 45	...	⋮	7 36	...	...	11 2	...	...	...	...

OLDESLOE and SCHWARZENBEK.

Oldesloe ....dep	6a28	8a50	1p27	4p35	8p31	...
Schwarzenbek ...arr	7 36	9 48	2 24	6 32	9 38	...

Schwarzenbek...dep	6a50	10 a6	3p23	7p19	...	...
Oldesloe ....arr	8 7	11 3	4 22	8 20	...	...

BERLIN and HAMBURG.

RC—Restaurant Car.

E.M. Dist.	Berlin—		2 3 4	2 3 4	Ex3	1,2,3	2&3	Ex3	Ex 3	1,2,3	1—4	2,3,4	Ex3	Ex3	2 3 4	Ex3	Ex2	1,2,3	1,2,3	Ex3	Ex2	2 3 4	1—4
					a.m.	a.m.		a.m.	a.m.		a.m.	a.m.	p.m.	p.m.	p.m.	p.m.	p.m.	p.m.	p.m.	p.m.	p.m.	p.m.	n'gt
—	Lehrter Bahnhof dep		...	...	6 18	6 22	...	9 5	9 10	...	9 28	11 40	1 6	1 15	1 18	3 8	5 25	5 30	6 20	7 12	8 55	9 41	12 0
6¾	Spandau ....dep		...	...	...	6 37	...	9 20	9 24	From Leipsic.	9 44	11 56	...	...	1 36	3 23	...	5 44	6 39	...	...	10 3	12 16
21½	Nauen		...	...	...	6 58	...	...	...		10 8	12 24	...	...	2 3	...	...	6 4	6 59	...	...	1032	12 39
30½	Paulinenaue		...	...	...	7 15	...	...	...		1033	12 45	...	RC	2 23	RC	RC	6 20	7 14	RC	RC	1054	12 55
46½	Neustadt-a-Dosse 167		...	...	...	7 45	...	...	...		1110	1 22	...	...	3 2	...	...	6 46	7 42	...	...	1136	1 25
62½	Glöwen (167)		...	...	...	8 14	...	...	...		1148	2 1	...	...	3 37	...	...	7 14	8 11	...	...	1216	1 57
78¼	Wittenberge ......arr		a.m.	a.m.	7 49	8 44	...	1043	10 52	a.m.	1219	2 33	2 38	2 48	4 8	4 43	6 55	7 38	8 35	8 49	...	1247	2 24
...	" (163)...dep		4 27	6 22	7 54	8 52	...	1048	10 58	1150	1227	3 0	2 43	2 53	4 14	4 48	7 0	7 42	——	8 54	...	——	2 30
105½	Ludwigslust		5 31	7 28	...	9 42	...	1126	11 33	1226	1 27	3 58	...	...	5 14	5 24	...	8 33	...	9 30	...	...	3 22
118½	Hagenow ....arr		5 59	7 57	...	10 5	...	1145	11 52	☞	1 50	4 24	3 31	3 39	5 37	5 45	...	8 54	...	...	...	...	3 42
...	" ....dep		6 19	7 59	...	1012	...	1147	11 54		1 55	4 26	3 36	3 41	5 54	5 47	...	8 55	...	...	...	...	3 43
139¼	Boizenburg	2&3	7 7	8 45	...	1045	...	...	...		2 39	5 7	To Kiel.	...	6 35	...	...	9 27	...	...	...	2&3	4 17
147¾	Büchen ....arr	a.m.	7 29	9 5	...	11 0	a.m.	...	...		2 58	5 26		...	6 53	...	...	9 41	...	1021	...	p.m.	4 33
...	" ....dep	6 55	7 40	9 35	...	11 1	1139	...	...		3 2	5 28		...	6 59	...	...	9 42	...	1023	...	1040	4 36
154½	Schwarzenbek ...	7 13	8 2	9 55	...	...	1154	...	...	July and August only.	3 20	5 45		...	7 18	...	...	9 53	...	...	...	1058	SC
161	Friedrichsruh	7 25	8 18	10 7	...	...	12 5	...	...		3 33	5 56		...	7 30	...	...	...	...	...	...	1110	...
167½	Bergedorf	7 44	8 41	1029	...	...	1223	...	...		3 52	6 14		...	7 52	...	...	...	...	...	...	1131	5 10
178¼	Hamburg Haupt.	8 15	9 6	1054	9 49	1144	1253	1258	1 8		4 12	6 38		4 50	8 11	6 57	8 52	1026	...	11 2	12 9	12 3	5 29
181	ALTONA Hpt. arr	8 33	9 29	1114	1018	12 7	1 7	1 16	1 28		4 38	7 3		5 18	8 37	7 20	9 10	1048	...	1128	1226	1217	5 56

...	HAMBURG (Sandthor Quai)...dep	From Hamburg daily, except Sunday............	9 p0	See Advert. page 735.
...	GRIMSBY ....arr		3 a0	

GRIMSBY ....dep	...	...	...	7 p0	Great Central Railway Co. Steamer from Grimsby daily except Sunday—passage about 30 hours. See Advert., page 735.
HAMBURG..............arr	...	...	...	1 a0	

	2&3	1,2,3	2&3	Ex3	Ex3	Ex3	2,3,4	1,2,3	2 3 4	Ex2	1—4	Ex3	Ex3	Ex3	Ex2	1,2,3	Ex3	2 3 4	2&3	1—4	2&3
ALTONA Hauptbahnhof dp	4 35	5 40	6 2	6a56	...	8 25	8 43	...	9 44	1214	1 7	2 29	...	4 20	5 54	5 46	7 58	8 43	9 32	11 10	1212
Hamburg—	a.m.	a.m.	a.m.	a.m.		a.m.	a.m.		a.m.	p.m.	p.m.	p.m.	p.m.	p.m.	p.m.	p.m.	p.m.	p.m.	p.m.	p.m.	n'gt
Hauptbahnhof ......dep	4 55	6 0	6 38	7 17	From Kiel.	8 52	9 8	July and August only.	10 9	1232	1 32	3 16	From Kiel.	4 39	6 14	6 18	8 27	9 10	9 46	11 34	1226
Bergedorf	5 32	6 18	7 8	...		...	9 29		1035	...	1 55	...		...	...	6 35	...	9 38	1016	11 57	1256
Friedrichsruh............	5 53	...	7 27	...		...	9 49		11 0	...	2 15	...		...	...	...	...	10 0	1035	12 10	1 15
Schwarzenbek (166A)........	6 7	6 39	7 50	...		...	10 5		1116	RC	2 30	...		...	...	6 55	...	1015	1048	12 27	1 28
Büchen (213A)..........arr	6 21	6 50	8 4	...		9 30	10 16		1130	...	2 44	3 55		5 16	...	7 5	...	1029	11 2	12 38	1 42
" ....dep	——	6 53	——	...		9 31	10 19		1137	...	2 47	3 55		5 16	...	7 7	RC	1039	——	12 39	——
Boizenburg	...	7 9	...	...		...	10 37	☞	1154	...	3 5	...		RC	RC	7 21	...	11 0	...	SC	...
Hagenow (213) ....arr	...	7 44	...	...	a.m.	10 5	11 19		1233	...	3 46	RC	5 52	5 51	...	7 55	...	1146	...	1 34	...
" ....dep	...	7 46	...	...	1012	10 6	11 24	p.m.	1240	...	3 49	...	6 2	5 52	...	7 57	...	1155	...	1 35	...
Ludwigslust (213A)...........	2 3 4	8 11	1,2,3	...	1034	...	11 54	1244	1 12	...	4 20	4 45	6 22	6 11	...	8 21	...	1232	...	2 2	...
Wittenberge ....arr	a.m.	9 0	a.m.	9 8	11 8	1053	12 52	1 18	2 10	2 23	5 15	5 24	6 55	6 44	...	9 11	1018	1 34	...	2 57	...
" (163, 166)...dep	5 36	9 17	7 35	9 10	1113	1058	1 1	To Leipsic.	2 41	2 28	5 36	5 29	7 0	6 49	...	9 16	1023	——	...	3 6	...
Glöwen	6 16	9 44	8 2	...	...	...	1 33		3 17	...	6 8	...	...	...	...	9 41	...	...	...	3 38	...
Neustadt-a-Dosse	7 9	10 16	8 36	...	...	...	2 15		3 59	...	6 47	...	...	...	...	1012	...	...	...	4 14	...
Paulinenaue (213A)...........	7 45	10 43	9 2	...	...	...	2 50		4 33	...	7 20	...	...	...	...	1038	...	...	...	4 46	...
Nauen	8 7	10 57	9 17	...	...	...	3 9		4 55	...	7 38	...	...	...	...	1053	...	...	...	5 2	...
Spandau	8 31	11 19	9 40	...	1234	1219	3 34	...	5 22	...	8 4	6 51	...	...	...	1114	...	...	...	5 29	...
Berlin Lehrter Bhf. ......arr	8 50	11 35	9 56	1043	1250	1234	3 56	...	5 42	4 1	8 22	7 7	8 33	8 27	9 30	1130	1156	...	...	5 46	...

Extra									
Buchen..................dep	4a51	6 a7	8a17	5 p2	Hamburg......dep	7 a43	3 p34	5 p26
Hamburg ....arr	6 25	7 29	9 35	6 42	Buchen ....arr	9 2	4 42	6 38

HAGENOW and NEUMUNSTER.

Hagenow (Land) dep	...	6a15	10a13	12 0	...	2 p4	3 p36	6 p3	9 p0	Neumunster	4a38	...	7a10	10a16	12p16	...	3p14	6p57	9p40
Hollenbek..............	...	7 12	11 3	...	...	3 4	...	7 5	10 0	Oldesloe	5 50	...	8 16	11 23	1 28	p.m.	4 34	8 29	1043
Ratzeburg	...	7 33	11 19	12 44	...	3 29	4 19	7 28	1021	Ratzeburg ...	6 33	9a24	8 56	——	2 19	5 9	6 21	9 38	——
Oldesloe	5a43	8 23	12 3	——	1p52	4 38	——	8 30	1110	Hollenbek ...	6 49	...	9 12	...	2 41	...	6 41	9 59	...
Neumunster(168) arr	7 1	9 35	1 5	...	2 52	5 50	...	9 30	1222	Hagenow	7 40	10 8	10 0	...	3 35	5 52	7 41	11 5	...

Hollenbek... .....dep	7 a20	11 a5	3 p5	7 p5	...	...	...	Mölln ....dep	6 a5	8 a41	2p16	5 p45	...	...	...	...
Mölln ....arr	7 58	11 35	3 28	7 29	...	...	...	Hollenbek ....arr	6 40	9 5	2 38	6 20	...	...	...	...

WITTENBERGE, LUNEBURG, and BUCHOLZ.

E.M.	†—Weekdays only.		a.m.	a.m.	a.m.		p.m.	p.m.	p.m.		a.m.	a.m.	a.m.	p.m.	p.m.	p.m.	p.m.	p.m.	p.m.
—	Wittenberge ...dep	...	...	5 30	9 5	...	1 25	4 51	8 57	Buchholz dep	6 30	...	9 15	...	1 25	6 19	...	...	1041
8	Lanz	...	...	5 49	9 20	...	1 43	5 11	9 15	Wulfsen............	7 12	...	9 51	...	2 8	7 5	...	...	1116
23½	Dömitz (213A).........	...	4 46	6 24	9 48	...	2 23	5 54	9 49	Lüneburg arr	7 50	...	10 27	...	2 52	7 44	...	...	1154
30½	Dannenberg	...	5 1	6 38	10 2	...	2 36	6 10	10 4	" dep	——	6 26	10 39	1 40	4 20	——	8 12	10 6	——
42¾	Göhrde	...	5 33	7 8	10 29	...	3 3	6 46	1031	Göhrde		7 6	11 21	2 27	5 7	...	8 52	1056	...
63¼	Lüneburg (169) arr	a.m.	6 17	7 50	11 11	p.m.	3 44	7 36	111	Dannenberg..........		7 33	11 49	2 57	5 40	...	9 18	1125	...
...	" ....dep	6 34	——	9 13	11 45	2 †5	4 10	8 17	——	Dömitz		7 51	12 3	3 16	5 56	...	9 33	1140	...
75¾	Wulfsen	7 17	...	9 53	12 26	3 1	4 56	9 9	...	Lanz		8 22	12 32	3 50	6 31	...	9 59	——	...
87½	Buchholz (132) arr	8 13	...	1042	1 7	4 2	5 40	9 58	...	Wittenberge arr		8 40	12 50	4 8	6 51	...	1014	...	...

NEUSTADT and MEYENBURG	EM																	
	—	Neustadt-a-D dp	5a22	7a47	1116	3p13	6p50	7p44	1138	Meyenburg dep	...	6a53	...	9a46	11a49	3p56	7p54	9p45
	25½	Pritzw. 166A	5a44	7 52	9 3	1241	4 40	8 34	8 46	1255	Pritzwalk	5a32	7 30	8 58	1023	12 39	4 52	8 46	1023
	38	Meyenburg	6 22	8 45	9 41	1 15	5 18	...	9 18	...	Neustadt 167...	6 57	8 30	1010	...	2 0	6 16	10 4	...

NIEBULL and FLENSBURG.												
Niebull ....dep	6 a8	9a30	12p20	5 p27	9 p17	Flensburg.........dep	4a39	6a25	10a35	3p24	7p13	10p12
Lindholm	6 17	9 48	12 40	5 36	9 26	Nord Schl. Weiche ...	4 48	6 35	10 46	3 35	7 25	10 21
Nord Schl. Weiche	7 17	1047	1 42	7 22	11 11	Lindholm..............	5 46	7 46	11 44	4 57	8 44	11 28
Flensburg (168) ...arr	7 25	1056	1 50	7 32	11 21	Niebull (169) ...arr	5 53	7 54	11 51	5 5	8 52	11 35

GLOWEN and HAVELBERG.

Glöwen ...	7 a0	8a25	9a48	11a55	2 p7	3p50	6p10	8p15	10p15	1218	Havelberg...dep	5a45	7a37	9a10	11a19	1255	2p51	5p21	6p48	8p59	11p40
Havelberg	7 26	8 45	1013	12 15	2 27	4 15	6 30	8 35	10 40	1238	Glöwen 167 arr	6 5	7 57	9 30	11 39	1 20	3 11	5 46	7 8	9 24	12 0

ST. MARGARETHEN and BRUNSBUTTELKOOG.

‡—Not on Sunday.

St. Margarethen	6‡a22	7a58	9a40	10a22	12p40	2p7	4p40	6‡p1	7p28	8p35	12a8	Brunsbuttel	5a50	7‡a0	8a25	10a0	11a53	1p41	3p24	6‡30	7p13	1136
Brunsbuttelkoog	6 35	8 15	9 54	10 36	12 57	2 21	4 57	6 15	7 42	8 52	1225	St. Margaret	6 3	7 14	8 39	1012	12 10	1 58	3 38	6 44	7 27	1150

PRUSSIAN STATE RAILWAYS. [Luggage Rates—see page 462.

HAMBURG, ALTONA, KIEL and VAMDRUP.

SLEEPING CARRIAGES (1st & 2nd Class)—Hamburg to Copenhagen and Frederikshavn in 9.0 p.m. from Hamburg. Extra fare, 1st class 10 m., 2nd class 6 m. 75 pf.
RESTAURANT CAR (RC)—in 7.5 a.m. from Hamburg (also Sleeping Car from Cologne to Kiel in this train).

Dist E.M		1—4	Ex3	2 3 4	Ex3	Ex3	2 3 4	1,2,3	1,2,3	Ex3	Ex3	2 3 4	Ex3	1,2,3	2 3 4	Ex3	2 3 4	Ex3
	Hamburg	a.m.	a.m.	a.m.	a.m	a.m.	a.m.	p.m	p.m.	p.m.	p.m.	p.m.	p.m	p.m.	p.m.	p.m.	p.m.	p.m.
—	„ Hauptbahnh'f dep	5 38	7 5	7 10	8 38	8 56	1045	1 24	1 32	1 42	3 37	3 41	5 4	5 21	7 7	9 0	1010	1110
...	„ Dammthor......dep	5 43	7 11	7 15	8 43	9 1	1050	1 29	1 37	1 48	3 42	3 46	5 9	5 26	7 12	9 6	1015	1115
...	„ Sternschanze dep	5 48	SC	7 20	8 47	9 6	1055	1 33	1 41	A	...	3 51	...	5 31	7 17	...	1020	1120
4	**Altona** Haupt. ... arr	5 56	7 19	7 28	8 55	9 15	11 4	1 41	1 49	1 58	3 51	4 0	5 18	5 39	7 25	9 14	1028	1128
	dep	6 0	7 25	7 31	9 0	9 20	11 9	1 44	1 54	2 3	3 55	4 4	5 27	5 43	7 30	9 19	1032	1133
18	Tornesch	...	RC	8 7	...	...	1145	...	...	...	...	4 45	...	...	8 6	SC	1113	...
22½	**Elmshorn**	6 34	7 53	8 20	9 28	...	1158	2 12	2 22	...	4 21	5 0	...	6 9	8 19	9 46	1131	12 1
36	Wrist	7 1	8 14	8 58	9 50	...	1230	2 33	2 43	...	...	5 35	...	6 29	8 53	...	1159	1222
50	**Neumünster** ..arr a.m.	7 29	8 35	9 37	1011	1025	1 1	2 54	3 4	3 12	4 59	6 6	6 29	6 50	9 22	1032	1228	1243
...	**Neumünster** dep 6‡42	7 34	8 37	9 49	...	1027	1 15	...	3 6	...	5 1	6 15	...	6 52	9 35	1025	1230	1248
57½	Bordesholm 7 3	7 51	...	10 8	...	...	1 32	...	...	...	...	6 32	...	7 4	9 55	...	1246	...
69¼	**Kiel** ....arr 7 34	8 21	9 5	1034	...	1055	1 58	...	3 36	...	5 29	6 58	...	7 25	1020	1053	1 8	1 16
153½	KORSOER (steamer) arr		2p38		...		...	...		...			...		...	...		7a30
222	COPENHAGEN 302 ...arr	2 3 4	4p48	...	...		...	...	...	...	...	...	...	...	...	...	...	10a4
626	STOCKHOLM 308 ......arr	a.m.	8a49	...	...		...	...	...	...	...	p.m.	...	...	...	...	...	6a58
...	**Neumünster** ...dep 5a31	7 34	...	...	1016	A—From 10th to 13th and 25th to 29th July.	1 14	2 59	...	3 16	1,2,3	6 59	6 34	...	9 40	1033	...	1255
70¾	Rendsburg 6 14	8 20	...	...	1051		2 3	3 34	...	3 46	p.m.	7 48	7 9	‡—Not on Sunday.	1025	11 4	...	1 37
86	Schleswig-Friedrichs 6 51	8 56	...	...	1118		2 40	3 59	...	4 8	7 40	8 23	7 34		1057	1128	...	2 7
93	**Jübeck** (166A) 7 7	9 12	...	...	1131		2 58	4 11	...	4 9	7 52	8 44	7 47		1113	...	...	2 21
107½	Nord Schl. Weiche arr 7 37	9 42	2 3 4	2 3 4	...		3 30	4 33	...	To Husum arr. 4.51 p.m.	To Husum..... arr. 8.19.	9 15	...		1141	...	...	2 46
110¼	**Flensburg** ...arr 7 46	9 51	a.m.	p.m.	1157		3 40	4 41	p.m.			9 25	8 16		1150	12 5	...	2 54
...	„ ...dep	9 56	6 1	2 12	12 1			4 45	5 37			9 34				12 9	...	2 58
126½	**Tingleff**..................dep	1056	7 3	2 58	1228		...	5 12	6 30			1014	...		...	1236	...	3 23
136	**Rothenkrug** (168) arr	1057	7 28	3 22	1244		...	5 28	6 54			1036	...		...	1251	...	3 45
148¾	**Woyens** (168).........arr	1124	8 4	3 55	1 5		...	5 50	7 23			11 7	...		...	1 11	...	4 16
161½	**Vamdrup** ....arr	1159	8 43	4 42	1 29		...	6 15	8 3			1142	...		...	1 32	...	4 43
185¾	FREDERICIA 303......arr	1p38	1057	...	2p43		...	7p32	...	...	...	1 a0	...	...	...	2a30	...	5a40
324	COPENHAGEN 302 ...arr	7p51	...	...	8p32		...	...	...	...	...	...	...	...	...	8a12	...	1230
393½	FREDRIKSHVN ... 303 arr	...	...		1040		...	...	...	...		...				9a10		3p16

	Ex 3	Ex3	1,2,3	2 3 4	Ex3	2 3 4	Ex 3	2 3 4	Ex3	1—4	Ex3	2 3 4	1,2,3	Ex3	1,2,3	1,2,3	2,3,4
FREDRIKSHAVN 303 ...dep	...	...	6p47	...	...	...	...	...	...	...	...	...	6a33	...	...	...	...
COPENHAGEN 302 ......dep	...	...	7p50	8p30	12 0	...	...	...	...	...	...	...	...	...	9 a5	...	...
FREDERICIA 303.........dep	...	...	2a13	3a24	5a41	...	...	...		6 a15	...	10a0	1p41	...	3p12	...	5p12
			a.m.	a.m.	a.m.					a.m.		p.m.	p.m.		p.m.	p.m.	p.m.
Vamdrup ....dep	...	...	3 11	5 2	6 42	...	...	...	...	8 43	...	1233	2 48	From Husum dep. 4.45 p.m.	4 42	From Husum	7 0
Woyens.........................dep	...	...	3 47	5 36	7 15	...	...	...	...	9 28	...	1 19	3 24		5 32		7 41
Rothenkrug ....dep	...	...	...	6 4	7 34	...	...	...	...	10 3	...	1 51	3 44		6 3		8 12
Tingleff ....arr	...	...	...	6 26	7 49	...	...	...	--	10 28	...	2 15	3 59		6 24		8 37
Flensburg..................arr	...	...	4 45	7 3	8 15	...	...	a.m.	a.m.	11 13	...	3 4	4 27		7 1		9 19
„ ....dep	...	...	4 49	7 11	8 22	...	...	9 26	1130	11 50	...	3 16	4 33		7 6		9 24
Nord Schl. Weiche...........dep	...	...	...	7 20	...	...	...	9 37	...	12 0	...	3 26	4 41	B	7 15		9 34
Jübeck ....dep	...	...	5 23	7 49	8 49	...	...	1014	1157	12 42	...	4 7	5 4	p.m.	7 44		10 9
Schleswig-Friedrichsberg......	...	...	5 40	8 4	9 2	...	...	1034	1210	1 3	...	4 28	5 17	5 32	7 58	6 53	10 27
Rendsburg	...	...	6 12	8 38	9 28	...	...	1115	1236	1 51	...	5 8	5 44	5 57	8 26		11 5
Neumünster ....arr	...	...	6 59	9 31	10 2	...	...	12 4	1 10	2 44	...	6 1	6 16	6 30	9 3	Ex 3	11 54
STOCKHOLM 308 ....dep	...	...	...	...	...	...	...	...	...	...	...	...	...	...	...	8 p30	...
COPENHAGEN 302 ......dep	7p50	...	1—4	1,2,3	...	...	...	...	...	...	...	...	...	...	...	12p55	...
KORSOER steamer dep 2 3 4	10 p0	a.m.	a.m.	a.m.	a.m.		a.m.	a.m.	...	p.m.	p.m.	p.m.	p.m.		p.m.	2 p54	p.m.
Kiel ....dep 4a36	5a27	6 31	...	9 12	9 18	...	11 10	1122	...	1 41	2 24	5 1	5 52	...	8 17	9 0	11 6
Bordesholm..................5 3	...	6 53	...	...	9 43	...	...	1149	...	2 11	...	5 29	...	...	8 43	...	11 33
Neumunster ......arr 5 19	5 54	7 6	...	9 40	9 58	a.m.	11 39	12 6	...	2 28	2 52	5 46	6 20	...	9 0	9 28	11 51
Neumünster ....dep 5 25	5 55	7 12	7 19	9 44	10 9	1016	11 41	1221	1 14	3 2	2 56	6 32	6 25	6 34	9 8	9 30	11 59
Wrist 5 58	...	...	7 49	10 5	...	1048	...	1255	...	3 33	...	7 2	6 45	B	9 29	SC	12 27
Elmshorn 6 50	...	7 48	8 25	1025	1046	1119	12 18	1 31	...	4 7	3 33	7 34	7 6	7 13	9 49	10 9	12 54
Tornesch 7 5	...	...	8 39	...	...	1130	...	...	...	4 19	RC	7 46	...	...	...	...	...
Altona Haupt ...... arr 7 48	6 51	8 17	9 20	1053	1114	1210	12 49	2 9	2 20	4 57	4 1	8 26	7 35	7 42	1018	10 38	1 25
dep 7 51	7 9	8 25	9 25	1059	1119	1223	12 53	2 14	2 39	5 4	4 7	8 30	7 40	7 58	1022	10 46	1 34
Hamburg Sternsch arr 7 59	7 17	8 34	9 33	11 7	...	1231	...	2 22	...	5 12	4 15	8 38	7 48	8 6	1030	10 54	1 43
„ Dammthor arr 8 4	7 22	8 39	9 37	1112	1126	1236	1 2	2 27	2 37	5 16	4 20	8 43	7 53	8 11	1035	10 59	1 48
„ Hauptbnhof ar 8 9	7 27	8 44	9 42	1117	1131	1241	1 7	2 32	2 42	5 21	4 25	8 48	7 58	8 16	1040	11 4	1 53

Extra. { Vamdrup to Flensburg, 10.44 p.m. Kiel to Neumunster, 3.25 and 6.40 p.m.
Neumunster to Kiel 5‡15 a.m. and 4.24 p.m. **B**—From 16th to 19th and on 31st July.

‡—Not on Sunday.

SONDERBURG and TONDERN.

Sonderburg...dep	4a55	5a58	9a42	10a52	1 p9	2p52	4p41	5p28	8 p25
Torsbull	6 2	6 52	1036	11 48	2 0	3 36	5 43	6 26	9 19
Flensburg...arr	...	7 38	1125	...	2 47	4 16	...	7 24	10 6
Tingleff	7 7	—	—	12 19	—	4 15	6 17	—	—
Tondern ......arr	7 48	...	...	1 18	...	5 7	7 24	...	...

Tondern ...dep	...	6a3	...	9a37	...	1p33	2p59	...	5p32	...	8p35
Tingleff	...	753	...	1038	p.m.	2 25	3 51	...	6 34	...	1020
Flensburg dep	6 a8	...	9a36	...	1210	2 2	—	4p55	...	9p13	1132
Torsbull	6 53	829	1033	1116	...	2 59	...	5 43	7 13	1015	—
Sonderburg arr	7 44	928	1123	1218	1 34	3 59	...	6 39	8 19	11 6	...

Extra.—Tingleff to Tondern, 7‡52, 3.0, and 10.20 p.m., 12.40 night. Tondern to Tingleff, 7.43 and 11.31 p.m.

Rothenkrug and Apenrade (in 18 minutes)—Rothenkrug dep. 6.16, 7.37, 8.40, 10.6, 11.3 a.m., 12.48, 1.58, 3.48, 6.7, 6.59, 8.14, 10.42, 11.49 p.m., 12.54 night. Apenrade dep. 5.37, 7.15, 8.5, 9.39, 10.35 a.m., 12.25, 1.30, 3.2, 5.7, 6.36, 7.36, 9.58, 11.28 p.m., 12.34 night.

WOYENS and HADERSLEBEN.

Woyens ......dep	5a40	7a15	8a16	9a40	11a28	1p12	4p3	5p55	7p40	11p16	1a14
Hadersleben arr	6 12	7 37	8 45	1010	11 59	1 34	436	6 17	8 11	1147	1 36

Hadersleben ...dep	5a8	6a48	7a45	8a58	10a51	12p27	2p58	4p53	6p49	10p35	12a44
Woyens ....arr	531	7 10	8 7	9 22	11 15	12 55	3 20	5 26	7 22	10 57	1 6

PRUSSIAN STATE RAILWAYS.

BLANKENESE, ALTONA, HAMBURG, and OHLSDORF (Electric Rail).

Blankenese .... / Altona .... / Hamburg .... / Ohlsdorf .... } A through service, every 20 minutes, is maintained from Blankenese to Ohlsdorf, from 4.40 a.m. until 1.0 a.m. Between Altona and Hamburg a five minutes service is maintained throughout the day.

Blankenese......dep	5a23	6 a13	7 a21	7a43	8 a33	9 a33	10a53	12p43	1p51	2 p53	3 p53	4 p53	5p53	6 p43	7p43	8 p13	9 p3	10p51	12a33
Wedel ....arr	5 41	6 31	7 39	8 2	8 51	9 51	11 11	1 1	2 9	3 11	4 11	5 11	6 11	7 1	8 2	8 31	9 21	11 10	12 51
Wedel ....dep	4a57	5 a47	6 a46	7 a46	8 a55	10a17	12p17	1 p27	2p15	3 p27	4 p27	5p17	6p17	7 p6	7 p46	8 p35	9 p57	10p54	11p37
Blankenese......arr	5 15	6 5	7 5	8 5	9 15	10 35	12 35	1 45	2 33	3 45	4 45	5 35	6 35	7 26	8 5	8 55	10 15	11 15	11 55

LUNEBURG and BUCHEN.

Lüneburg.........dep	5a51	7 a11	8a28	10a45	1 p40	4 p5	5 p51	7 p1	9 p46
Lauenburg............	6 9	7 46	9 0	11 11	2 14	4 33	6 19	7 26	10 11
Büchen (167) ...arr	6 23	8 3	9 21	11 29	2 35	4 48	6 39	7 40	10 26

Büchen ......dep	5a48	7a35	9a25	11a45	3 p2	3p58	7 p9	10p40
Lauenburg	6 26	7 47	9 43	12 5	3 21	4 15	7 27	10 56
Lüneburg ...arr	6 56	8 3	10 6	12 31	3 44	4 43	7 53	11 23

NEUMUNSTER and HEIDE.

Dist. E.M.		a.m.	a.m.	a.m.	p.m.	p.m.	p.m.	
	Neumunster ....dep	5 48	7 39	1021	3 10	6 55	9 38	...
24½	Hademarschen	7 11	8 49	1153	4 28	8 16	10 57	...
38½	Heide (169) ....arr	7 51	9 31	1250	5 10	8 58	11 39	...

	a.m.	a.m.	a.m.	p.m.	p.m.	p.m.	
Heide ....dep	4 35	8 6	1144	3 24	6 52	9 40	...
Hademarschen............	5 20	8 50	1251	4 24	7 35	1022	...
Neumunster (168)...arr	6 49	10 5	2 25	5 50	8 50	1135	...

HEIDE and BUSUM.	Dist E.M		a.m.	a.m.	a.m.	p.m.	p.m.	p.m.		
		Heide ......dep	4 39	7 55	10 43	3 23	5 30	9 33	...	...
	9	Wesselburen...	5 44	8 21	11 28	4 3	6 6	10 8	...	...
	15	Büsum ......arr	6 26	8 37	11 53	4 28	6 32	10 33	...	...

	a.m.	a.m.	p.m.	p.m.	p.m.	p.m.
Büsum ...dep	6 45	8 47	1 26	5 30	7 15	10 47
Wesselburen	7 13	9 8	1 54	6 1	7 43	11 17
Heide......arr	7 49	9 35	2 35	6 34	8 20	11 51

Tondern ...	6a12	7a58	9a31	12p22	1p38	4p22	5p33	7p42	9 40	12 4
Hoyer arr	7 4	8 27	1014	12 48	2 5	4 49	6 2	8 21	1025	1233

Hoyer ...	5 a2	7a14	8a39	11a6	12p55	2p55	4p57	6p48	8p35	10p40	...
Tondern	5 30	7 45	9 7	1147	1 22	3 35	5 23	7 24	9 14	11 7	...

HEIDE and TONNING.						
	Heide ....dep	5 a29	8 a2	10a33	3 p11	9 p23
	Carolinenkoog	6 37	8 38	11 20	4 0	10 8
	Tonning (Steamer) ...arr	7 6	9 5	11 39	4 27	10 30

Tonning (Steamer) ...dep	6 a35	8 a35	1 p20	5 p22	9 p50
Carolinenkoog	6 57	8 54	1 43	5 47	10 20
Heide ....arr	7 41	9 28	2 27	6 43	11 1

‡—Not on Sunday.

HAMBURG, ALTONA, and HVIDDING (Vedsted).

	1—4	2 3 4	1—4	2 3 4	2 3 4	2 3 4	2 3 4	1,2,3	2 3 4	2 3 4	2 3 4
Hamburg	a.m.	a.m.	a.m.	a.m.	a.n.	p.m.	p.m.	p.m.	p.m.	p.m.	p.m.
Haupt. dep	5 38	5 3	7 36	9 29	1127	1 52	3 6	5 28	6 8	9 20	1135
Altona H. dp	6 0	5 25	8 0	9 49	1149	2 19	3 28	5 51	6 31	9 42	1157
Tornesch	...	6 6	...	1028	1224	2 56	4 4	...	...	1020	1239
Elmshorn ...	6 31	6 36	8 30	1043	1238	3 10	4 26	6 19	7 11	1035	1255
Gluckstadt ...		7 0	8 47	1114	1 5	3 39	4 53	6 36	7 34	1059	1 23
Itzehoe...............		7 29	9 10	1147	1 38	4 15	5 20	6 56	8 3	1132	1 51
St. Margarethen		7 54	9 34	1213	2 2	4 38	6‡ 0	7 15	8 28	12 3	—
St.Michaelisdonn		8 14	9 53	1233	2 23	4 55	—	7 28	8 47	1224	a.m.
Heide ....arr		8 47	1022	1 4	2 56	5 25	...	7 52	9 19	1259	6 37
Husum ....arr		9 36	11 4	1 53	3 48	6 10	...	8 31	1012	—	7 34
Husum Nord		9 45	1113	—	3 57	6 19	...	...	1023	5 a8	7 56
Lindholm		1038	1151	...	4 50	7 6	...	...	1121	6 3	8 50
Niebüll.........a.m.		1046	12 0	...	4 59	7 14	...	9 16	1132	6 9	9 0
Tondern arr	8 8	1110	1218	...	5 22	7 36	...	9 34	1150	7 34	9 24
Bredebro......	8 35	—	2 2	...	6 1	8 15	...	1025	—	—	—
Hvidding(V.)	9 27	...	2 49	...	6 48	9 7	...	1143	...	...	...

(303A)		2 3 4 a.m.	1,2,3 a.m.	2 3 4 a.m.	2 3 4 p.m.	2 3 4 a.m.	1—4 p.m.	2 3 4 p.m.	2 3 4 p m
Hvidding (Vedsted)		...	6 32	...	...	1133	2 58	7 3	10 0
Bredebro		...	7 20	...	...	1236	3 48	7 54	11 2
Tondern ....dep		5 35	8 1	9 14	12 4	1 4	4 23	8 40	1130
Niebüll		5 59	8 19	9 39	1229	—	4 49	9 6	—
Lindholm		6 6	...	9 48	1238	...	4 56	9 13	...
Husum Nord......	234	6 58	...	1043	1 35	p.m.	5 49	10 6	...
Husum	a.m.	7 6	9 3	1052	1 50	3 50	5 57	1016	...
Heide	5 10	7 53	9 39	1142	2 44	4 37	6 47	11 6	...
St. Michaelisdon	5 44	8 25	10 2	1216	3 22	5 2	7 23	1140	2 3 4
St. Margarethen	6 6	8 43	1016	1235	3 43	5 20	7 42	1158	a.m.
Itzehoe	6 40	9 13	1037	1 9	4 16	5 45	8 15	1228	7 5
Gluckstadt'	7 2	9 38	1054	1 36	4 42	6 11	8 43	1254	7 38
Elmshorn ...arr	7 21	10 0	11 9	1 59	5 4	6 33	9 8	1 17	8 12
Tornesch	7 36	...	...	2 11	...	6 46	9 25	1 35	8 39
Altona Hpt. arr	8 10	1036	1138	2 45	5 38	7 23	10 2	2 10	9 20
Hamburg ...arr	8 35	1059	1158	3 6	6 0	7 45	1026	2 35	9 42

Extra.—Itzehoe to Hamburg 4.45 a.m.

St. Michaelsdonn	7 a4	8a40	10a10	12p35	2‡31	3p29	5p5	7p31	9 p0	1226
Marne...........arr	7 25	9 1	10 25	12 56	2 45	3 43	526	7 45	9 15	1247

Marne dep	5a20	7a54	9a24	1150	1p46	3 p3	4p10	6p40	810	1122
St. Michael	5 41	8 8	9 45	12 4	2 7	3 17	4 31	7 0	831	1136

Bredebro ......dep	8a45	2 p4	3p50	6 p6	8p18	11 p5	...	...	...
Lügumkloster arr	9 10	2 29	4 15	6 31	8 43	11 30	...	...	...

Lügumkloster dep	6 a50	12 p3	3 p18	5 p28	7p22	9p48	...	...
Bredebro ......arr	7 15	12 28	3 43	5 53	7 47	1013	...	...

Marne ....dep	10a†29	3 p48	9 p20	...	†—Wed.	...
Friedrichskoog...........arr	11 32	4 47	10 13	...	at 11.12.	...

Friedrichskoog...........dep	6 a41	12p28	5 p12	...	...
Marne ....arr	7 44	1 30	6 17	...	...

KIEL and RENDSBURG.

Kiel ....dep	7a12	8 a40	9a31	12p40	2p23	6p10	7p14	9 p0	...
Brandsbek......	7 39	...	10 3	1 10	2 53	...	7 43	9 34	...
Rendsburg arr	8 13	9 28	1042	1 45	3 28	6 58	8 20	1018	...

Rendsburg dep	5a50	8a42	9a32	11a20	2 p7	5p48	8p30	11p38	...	...
Brandsbek	6 37	9 19	...	12 2	2 54	6 31	9 8	12 10	...	...
Kiel...........arr	7 16	9 46	1021	12 32	3 32	6 59	9 40	12 33	...	...

RENDSBURG and HUSUM.							
	Rendsburg...dep	6 a20	8 a24	9 a33	11a22	2 p6	8 p32
	Husum ....arr	7 39	9 58	10 43	1 14	3 42	10 1

Husum.........dep	4 a50	7 a55	11a45	4 p5	6 p43	10p20
Rendsburg ...arr	7 21	9 14	1 41	5 35	8 15	11 36

ALTONA (near Zollamt) and BRAMSTEDT.

Altona ....dep	7a41	1119	3p15	8p11	...	...	...	...	...
Eidelstedt............	7 56	1134	3 30	8 25	...	...	...	...	...
Kaltenkirchen ...	8 52	1241	4 29	9 46	...	...	...	...	...
Bramstedt ...arr	9 15	1 4	4 52	10 9	...	...	...	...	...

Bramstedt ...dep	5a35	10a35	3p12	7p59	...	...	...	...	...
Kaltenkirchen ...	6 1	11 3	3 37	8 25	...	...	...	...	...
Eidelstedt............	7 15	12 0	4 39	9 24	...	...	...	...	...
Altona ....arr	7 30	12 14	4 53	9 38	...	...	...	...	...

FLENSBURG and KAPPELN.

Flensburg ....dep	6a25	8a28	9 a36	1230	2p40	5p15	8 p0	11p30
Glücksburg	7 1	9 6	10 10	1 6	3 14	5 51	8 38	12 4
Kappeln (166A) ...arr	9 39	1135	...	3 47	...	8 28	1112	...

Kappeln ....dep	...	5a57	a.m.	10a37	12p45	...	5p20	7p19
Glücksburg	7 a7	8 25	1027	1 12	3 25	6 p3	7 57	9 50
Flensburg (168)...arr	7 40	9 0	11 0	1 45	3 58	6 36	8 32	1023

WRIST and ITZEHOE.

Wrist...............dep	7 a5	8a17	10a51	12p58	3 p39	7 p7	9 p35	...
Itzehoe (169)......arr	7 43	9 2	11 25	1 31	4 10	7 39	10 15	...

Itzehoe...........dep	6 a5	7 a4	9 a13	11a50	1 p50	4 p43	8 p13	...
Wrist (168)......arr	6 45	7 43	9 44	12 24	2 22	5 23	8 46	...

[Luggage Rates—see page 462.

BERLIN, HALLE—LEIPSIC, CORBETHA—WEIMAR, ERFURT, GOTHA, EISENACH, and BEBRA.

THROUGH CARRIAGE.–Berlin to Rome, via Munich, in 1.10 p.m. from Berlin (also 10.50 p.m. from Berlin, see p.187).

	Ex3	2 3 4	Ex3	1,2,3	Ex3	1,2,3	Ex3	2 3 4	2 3 4	2 3 4	Ex2	Ex3	Ex3	1 2 3	Ex 2	Ex3	Ex3	Ex3	2 3 4	2,3,4	Ex3
BERLIN—		a.m.								a.m.	a.m.	a.m.	a.m.	a.m.	a.m.			a.m.		a.m.	a m.
Anhalt Bahnhof dep	...	1230	...	...	...	...	...	...	...	5 35	8 0	8 10	8 20	8 25	9 5	...	...	1030	...	9 10	1050
Lichterfelde (Sud)	...	1248	...	...	...	...	...	...	...	...	...	...	...	...	...	...	...	...	...	9 27	...
Trebbin	...	1 22	...	...	...	...	...	...	...	6 11	...	...	...	...	...	...	...	...	...	10 11	...
Luckenwalde	...	1 43	...	...	...	...	...	...	...	6 29	...	...	...	9 10	...	...	...	...	...	10 30	...
Jüterbog arr	...	2 2	...	...	...	...	...	...	...	6 47	RC	...	RC	9 24	...	...	...	RC	...	10 49	...
Zahna	...	2 29	...	...	...	...	...	...	a.m.	7 27	...	...	...	...	...	...	...	...	...	11 19	...
Wittenberg arr	...	2 40	...	...	...	...	...	...	5 55	7 41	...	...	...	9 51	...	...	...	...	...	11 32	12 1
Pratau	...	...	...	...	...	...	...	...	6 1	7 49	...	...	...	...	...	...	...	...	...	12 20	...
Grafenhainichen	...	3 14	...	...	...	...	...	...	6 27	8 16	...	...	...	...	...	...	...	...	...	12 47	...
Bitterfeld (187) arr	...	3 33	...	...	...	...	...	...	6 47	8 36	...	...	...	1023	...	...	...	...	...	1 8	1232
Bitterfeld dep	...	3 37	...	...	...	...	...	...	6 52	8 43	...	...	...	1024	...	...	...	...	...	1 17	1234
Landsberg	...	4 3	...	...	...	...	...	...	7 15	9 7	...	...	...	...	...	...	...	...	...	1 41	...
Halle arr	...	4 23	...	a.m.	...	a m.	...	a.m.	7 34	9 25	9 50	1010	1037	1051	11 5	...	...	1230	p.m.	2 0	1259
Halle dep	...	5 48	...	7 0	...	7 55	...	8 40	—	1020	9 54	1014	1041	1116	11 9	...	...	1234	1 17	2 16	—
Merseburg (172)	...	6 7	...	⋮	...	8 13	...	8 59	...	1040	⋮	⋮	⋮	1131	⋮	...	...	⋮	1 35	2 36	...
Corbetha arr	...	6 18	...	⋮	...	8 23	...	9 11	...	1051	⋮	⋮	⋮	1141	⋮	...	...	⋮	1 46	2 47	...
DRESDEN Haup. dep	...	1225	3a41	⋮	3a41	3a41	7a15	...	7a15	...	⋮	⋮	⋮	...	⋮	1025	1035	⋮	1035	10a35	2 3 4
		a.m.	a.m.	⋮	a.m.	a.m.	a.m.		a.m.		⋮	⋮	⋮		⋮	p.m.	p.m.	⋮	p.m.	p.m.	p m.
Leipsic dep	...	5 20	6 15	⋮	7 10	7 17	9 15	...	9 35	...	⋮	⋮	⋮	...	⋮	1210	1240	⋮	1247	1 35	5 15
Markranstadt	...	5 53	⋮	⋮	⋮	7 47	⋮	...	10 8	...	⋮	⋮	⋮	...	⋮	⋮	⋮	⋮	1 17	2 14	5 52
Dürrenberg	...	6 10	⋮	⋮	⋮	8 4	⋮	...	1026	...	⋮	⋮	⋮	...	⋮	⋮	⋮	⋮	1 35	2 33	6 10
Corbetha arr	...	6 18	⋮	⋮	⋮	8 12	⋮	...	1035	...	⋮	⋮	⋮	...	⋮	⋮	⋮	⋮	1 43	2 42	6 19
Corbetha dep	...	6 23	⋮	⋮	⋮	8 24	⋮	9 12	1038	1053	⋮	⋮	⋮	1142	⋮	⋮	⋮	⋮	1 49	2 55	6 21
Weissenfels arr	...	6 33	6 56	7 29	7 51	8 33	9 57	9 23	1049	11 3	⋮	⋮	1112	1151	⋮	1251	⋮	⋮	2 0	3 5	6 32
PROBSTZELLA 173 arr	...	1259	1259	...	⋮	...	...	...	2p33	2p33	⋮	⋮	2p33	...	⋮	⋮	⋮	⋮	6p40	...	...
NURNBERG 197 ... arr	...	...	...	...	⋮	...	...	...	...	...	⋮	⋮	...	...	⋮	⋮	⋮	5p43	...	...	...
MUNICH 197 arr	...	...	...	...	⋮	...	...	...	...	...	⋮	⋮	...	...	⋮	⋮	⋮	8p34	...	...	...
Weissenfels dep	...	6 37	6 57	...	7 52	8 35	9 58	9 24	1052	1123	⋮	⋮	1114	1153	⋮	1252	⋮	⋮	2 3	3 7	6 33
Naumburg (170) 2 3 4	...	7 0	7 12	...	...	8 56	1010	9 44	11 9	1150	⋮	1053	...	1210	⋮	1 7	1 38	1 12	2 26	3 33	6 48
Koesen a.m.	...	7 10	7 21	...	...	9 4	...	9 52	1142	1159	⋮	...	...	1221	⋮	—	1 47	—	2 36	3 42	—
Grossheringen 5 38	...	7 36	7 29	...	...	9 12	...	10 0	1159	12 8	⋮	...	RC	1230	⋮	...	...	...	2 45	3 52	...
Sulza 5 43	...	7 41	...	...	...	9 17	...	10 5	12 4	1213	⋮	...	...	1236	⋮	...	...	...	2 50	4 2	...
Apolda 6 0	...	8 5	7 44	2 3 4	...	9 32	1034	1020	1217	1232	RC	...	1148	1254	⋮	...	2 8	...	3 9	4 38	...
Weimar 152 arr 6 19	...	8 30	8 1	a.m.	8 39	9 49	1048	1037	1234	1252	11 6	1127	12 4	1 13	12 21	p.m.	2 25	...	3 30	5 6	...
Weimar dep 6 21	...	8 48	8 3	7 25	8 41	9 52	1049	1115	1236	1256	11 7	1129	12 5	1 18	12 22	2 6	2 28	2 3 4	3 33	5 44	...
Erfurt 152 arr 6 49	a.m.	9 14	8 22	7 50	9 0	1011	11 7	1137	1257	1 21	1125	1146	1222	1 41	12 40	2 24	2 46	p m.	3 59	6 10	p.m.
Erfurt dep —	6 56	9 22	8 26	7 56	9 4	1015	1111	1140	1 3	1 36	1129	1150	1226	2 8	12 43	2 32	2 50	2 56	4 6	6 20	6 27
Neudietend'f 170A arr	7 8	9 38	⋮	8 13	⋮	1028	⋮	1154	1 18	1 54	⋮	⋮	⋮	2 23	⋮	2 50	⋮	3 12	4 22	6 35	6 44
RITSCHENHAUSEN arr	...	1254	⋮	...	⋮	1254	⋮	...	...	...	⋮	...	⋮	5p22	⋮	5p22	⋮	...	7p52	...	...
KISSINGEN 195 ... arr	...	3p30	⋮	...	⋮	3p30	⋮	...	...	...	⋮	3p30	4p30	7p20	⋮	7p20	⋮	...	1025	...	...
Neudietendorf dep	7 8	9 42	⋮	8 16	⋮	1029	⋮	1156	1 20	1 59	⋮	...	To Stuttg't (8p25, p.193) & Heidelb'g (8p8, p.143).	2 24	⋮	...	⋮	...	4 26	6 37	...
Gotha 172A	7 23	10 9	8 57	8 37	9 33	1048	1137	1217	1 44	2 25	1156	3 &4		2 42	1 10	...	3 21	...	4 50	7 0	3 &4
Fröttstädt (174)	...	1024	9 10	8 51	...	11 4	1150	1230	1 59	2 41	...	p.m.		2 55	...	...	3 34	...	5 4	7 23	p.m.
Wutha (152)	...	1043	...	9 12	...	1117	...	1248	2 19	3 0	...	1 19		3 7	...	...	...	2—4	5 27	7 42	5 0
Eisenach 173B arr	7 44	1049	9 25	9 18	9 55	1123	12 5	1254	2 26	3 6	1218	1 26		3 13	1 32	...	3 48	p.m.	5 36	7 48	5 8
Eisenach dep	7 47	11 1	9 29	—	9 57	1129	12 7	—	—	3 28	1220	1 40		3 16	1 34	...	3 51	6 26	5 55	8 17	5 12
Wartha	...	1118	...	...	...	...	...	...	...	...	...	1 57		...	...	...	...	6 45	...	...	5 34
Gerstungen 172 dep	8 8	1139	...	...	...	...	...	...	...	4 15	...	2 16		...	...	...	...	7 5	6 16	8 50	6 0
Bebra arr	8 30	12 5	10 9	...	1038	1214	1245	...	...	4 43	1 3	...		3 58	2 14	...	4 34	7 38	6 38	9 22	6 49
FRANKFORT 149A arr	...	3p46	1p27	...	...	3p46	3p46	...	...	8 p5	3p46	...		7p18	4 p54	...	7p36	...	9p23	...	...
CASSEL 172A arr	9a25	1p25	1136	...	1136	1p25	1p46	...	...	6p25	2p42	...		5p11	4 p47	...	6p25	...	7p54	11p13	...

Extra.									
Erfurt dep	5a58	6a15	8a33	10 a5	12 0	4p38	4p48	8p47	9 p56
Neudietendorf arr	6 14	6 30	8 47	10 20	12 16	4 51	5 2	9 2	10 11

RC—Restaurant Car.
SC—Sleeping Car.

GROSSHERINGEN and SAALFELD.

	2,3,4	1—4	1,2,3	2 3 4	2,3,4	1—4	1—4	1—4	Ex3	2 3 4	Ex 3	2,3,4	2 3 4	2 3 4	1—4	Ex2	Ex3	Ex3		...
		a.m.	a.m.	a.m.	...	a.m.	a.m.	p.m.	p.m.	p.m.	p.m.	p.m.	p.m.	p.m.	p.m.					
Naumburg dep	...	5 28	7 46	...	...	9 1	1113	1248	1 15	3 27	4 36	...	...	7 17	9 23	Berlin Dep. 8p15	Berlin Dep. 8p50	Berlin Dep. 9p50	A—From 2nd to 15th July only. B—In July & Aug. only.	...
Grossheringen dep	...	5 28	...	7 45	...	...	...	...	...	2 50	...	5 39	6 32	...	...					...
Camburg	a.m.	5 55	8 8	7 56	...	9 25	1138	1 12	RC	3 49	RC	5 48	6 45	7 40	9 46					...
Porstendorf	5 45	6 11	...	8 10	...	9 41	1153	1 29	...	4 13	...	6 3	—	7 56	10 2					...
Jena	5 58	6 34	8 25	8 18	...	9 57	1210	2 6	1 48	4 26	5 15	6 15	...	8 12	1015		12 8			...
Goschwitz	6 11	6 54	8 39	—	...	1015	1224	2 21	...	4 45	...	6 33	...	8 31	1032		...			...
Kahla	—	7 8	8 51	...	...	1029	1237	2 34	...	4 59	...	6 54	...	8 44	1045	A	SC	B		...
Orlamünde	...	7 17	...	...	...	1037	1245	2 41	...	5 7	...	7 2	...	8 52	1052		...			...
Uhlstädt	a.m.	7 28	.	...	a.m.	1049	1258	2 52	...	5 20	...	7 14	...	9 6	11 3		...			...
Rudolstadt	5 0	7 45	9 16	...	10 15	11 4	1 15	3 6	2 23	5 36	5 52	7 31	...	9 21	1117		1244			...
Schwarza	5 8	7 51	...	...	10 23	1112	1 22	3 13	...	5 44	...	7 40	...	9 29	1123		...			...
Saalfeld arr	5 18	8 0	9 27	...	10 33	1120	1 31	3 20	2 35	5 51	6 3	7 47	...	9 37	1131	1225	1256	1a46		...

Blankenburg ... dep	4 a55	6 a5	7a 5	8a20	10a35	11a40	12p27	1p58	3p27	4p48	6p25	7 p7	8 p7	9p41	12 a2	...	...	...	...	...
Schwarza arr	5 3	6 13	7 14	8 28	10 43	11 48	12 35	2 6	3 35	4 56	6 33	7 15	8 15	9 49	12 10	...	...	...	...	...

Oppurg dep	4a41	8a44	11a43	...	4p54	7 p56	...	...	...	...	...	...	...	...	...	...	...	...	...	...
Possneck	5 16	9 6	12 6	1p54	5 6	8 15	10 p0	...	...	...	...	...	...	...	...	...	...	...	...	...
Orlamünde arr	5 41	9 32	12 32	2 20	5 32	8 41	10 26	...	...	...	...	...	...	...	...	...	...	...	...	...

Luggage Rates—see page 462.]

BERLIN, HALLE—LEIPSIC, CORBETHA—WEIMAR, ERFURT, GOTHA, EISENACH and BEBRA.

THROUGH CARRIAGE.—Berlin to Zurich, in 1.45 p.m., 8.25 p.m., and 10.15 p.m. from Berlin.

	1,2,3	Ex2	2 3 4	Ex3	Ex2	Ex3	Ex3	1,2,3	1—4	Ex3	Ex3	1—4	Ex2	Ex.3	Ex3	Ex3	Ex3	Ex1	Ex2	1,2,3	2 3 4
BERLIN—	p.m.	p.m.	p.m.	p.m	p.m.		p.m.	p m.				p.m.	p.m	p.m.	p.m.	"	p.m.	p.m.	p.m.	p.m.	p.m.
Anhalt Bahnhof..dep	12 45	1 10	1 15	1 45	2 15	...	3 35	4 50	...	...	...	6 55	8 15	8 25	8 50	...	9 50	1015	1040	11 0	1125
Lichterfelde (Sud)	...	...	1 32	...	...	...	...	...	...	...	...	7 12	...	...	...	...	...	...	...	...	1142
Trebbin	...	...	2 16	...	...	...	...	...	...	...	...	7 46	Runs from 2nd to 15th July only.	...	...	...	...	...	...	...	1213
Luckenwalde	1 32	...	2 34	...	...	...	...	5 33	...	...	...	8 4		SC	SC	...	...	SC	...	1143	1232
Jüterbog ....arr	1 47	...	2 52	...	...	...	...	5 47	...	...	...	8 23		...	...	...	...	...	...	1157	1250
Zahna	...	...	3 32	RC	...	...	RC	...	...	...	...	9 0		...	...	...	...	...	...	...	1 20
Wittenberg ......arr	2 26	...	3 44	...	...	...	...	6 16	...	...	...	9 12		9 36	...	...	...	...	...	1226	1 32
Pratau	...	...	3 52	...	...	...	...	...	...	...	...	10 10		...	...	...	...	...	...	...	1 41
Grafenhainichen	...	...	4 18	...	...	...	...	...	...	...	...	10 34		...	...	...	A	...	B	...	2 8
Bitterfeld (187) arr	3 0	...	4 38	...	...	...	...	6 52	...	...	...	10 51		...	...	...	...	...	...	1 0	2 26
Bitterfeld (187) dep	3 2	...	5 17	...	...	...	...	6 54	...	...	...	10 54		...	...	...	...	...	...	1 2	2 29
Landsberg	...	...	5 40	...	...	...	...	...	...	...	...	11 15	...	...	...	...	...	...	...	...	2 50
Halle .... arr	3 30	3 0	5 58	3 47	4 5	...	5 35	7 22	p.m.	...	...	11 33	1015	10 29	1050	...	1150	1215	1240	1 29	3 8
Halle .... dep	3 35	3 4	6 6	3 51	4 7	...	5 39	7 38	8 7	...	...	12 27	1019	10 36	1054	...	1154	1219	1246		3 14
Merseburg (172)	3 50	⋮	6 25	⋮	⋮	...	⋮	7 53	8 25	...	...	12 45	...	⋮	To Jena (arr. 12.8 a.m.)	...	⋮	⋮	⋮	...	3 34
Corbetha ....arr	4 0	⋮	6 36	⋮	⋮	...	⋮	8 3	8 36	...	...	12 58	...	⋮	⋮	...	⋮	⋮	⋮	...	3 45
DRESDEN Haup. dep	1 p18	⋮	...	⋮	⋮	...	⋮	4 p0	...	7p10	8 p6	8 p6	...	⋮	⋮	8 p6	⋮	⋮	⋮	...	⋮
	p.m.		p.m.			p.m.		p.m.	p.m.	p.m.	p.m.	p.m.				p.m.				...	
Leipsic ....dep	3 10	⋮	5 15	⋮	⋮	5 5	⋮	7 20	7 25	9 30	1045	11 55	Via Saalfeld (p. 170)	⋮	⋮	1150	⋮	⋮	⋮	...	⋮
Markranstadt........	3 32	⋮	5 52	⋮	⋮	⋮	⋮	...	8 0	⋮	⋮	12 34		⋮	⋮	⋮	⋮	⋮	⋮	...	⋮
Dürrenberg........	3 42	⋮	6 10	⋮	⋮	⋮	⋮	...	8 19	⋮	⋮	12 52		⋮	⋮	⋮	⋮	⋮	⋮	...	⋮
Corbetha ......arr	3 50	⋮	6 19	⋮	⋮	⋮	⋮	7 54	8 29	⋮	⋮	1 1		⋮	⋮	⋮	⋮	⋮	⋮	...	⋮
Corbetha ....dep	4 1	⋮	6 38	⋮	⋮	⋮	⋮	8 4	8 37	⋮	⋮	1 11		⋮	⋮	⋮	⋮	⋮	⋮	...	3 52
Weissenfels ....arr	4 10	⋮	6 48	⋮	⋮	⋮	⋮	8 14	8 51	1014	⋮	1 22		⋮	⋮	1232	⋮	⋮	⋮	...	4 2
PROBSTZELLA 173 arr	9 p40	⋮	...	⋮	⋮	⋮	⋮	1250	...	...	⋮	...	...	⋮	⋮	...	⋮	⋮	⋮	...	9a42
NURNBERG 197...arr	...	7p34	...	9p26	⋮	⋮	⋮	...	...	...	⋮	...	3a36	⋮	4 a7	...	4a39	⋮	⋮	...	...
MUNICH 197 ......arr	...	10p5	...	1240	⋮	⋮	⋮	...	p.m.	...	⋮	...	7a12	⋮	7a14	...	...	⋮	⋮	...	...
Weissenfels ......dep	4 11	...	6 49	⋮	⋮	⋮	⋮	8 16	8 58	1015	⋮	1 26	...	⋮	...	1235	...	⋮	⋮	...	4 4
Naumburg 170	4 27	...	7 12	4 33	⋮	6 3	⋮	8 32	9 16	1029	1148	1 49	...	11 18	...	1247	...	1 11	⋮	...	4 23
Koesen........	4 36	...	7 20		⋮	...	⋮	8 41	9 26	1038	...	1 57	...	...	...	...	...	...	⋮	...	4 32
Grossheringen	4 58	...	7 29	...	⋮	...	⋮	...	9 33	...	...	2 6	...	...	...	...	...	...	⋮	...	4 39
Sulza........	5 4	...	7 34	...	⋮	...	⋮	...	9 38	...	...	2 11	...	...	...	...	...	...	⋮	...	4 43
Apolda........	5 17	...	7 48	...	⋮	6 23	⋮	9 4	9 54	1058	...	2 31	Ex3	11 42	...	...	...	...	⋮	...	4 58
Weimar (152) .. arr	5 35	...	8 6	...	⋮	6 37	6 56	9 21	1010	1115	...	2 52	p.m.	11 57	...	...	...	1 52	⋮	...	5 15
Weimar (152) .. dep	5 37	...	8 10	2 3 4	⋮	6 38	6 58	9 23	1012	1117	...	2 56	1126	11 59	...	2—4	...	1 54	⋮	2 3 4	5 18
Erfurt 152 ...... arr	5 56	...	8 34	p.m.	5 32	6 56	7 16	9 41	1037	1135	1238	3 22	1144	12 17	...	a.m.	...	2 12	2 40	a.m.	5 48
Erfurt 152 ...... dep	6 1	...	8 42	7 26	5 36	7 0	7 20	9 50	1048		1242	3 50	1154	12 21	...	1228	...	2 16	2 44	4 50	6 6
Neudietendorf...arr	6 15	...	8 56	7 40	⋮	⋮	⋮	⋮	11 4	...	⋮	4 7	⋮	⋮	...	1242	...	⋮	⋮	5 6	6 22
RITSCHENHAUSEN arr	...	...	1131	...	⋮	⋮	⋮	⋮	...	...	⋮	...	⋮	⋮	...	...	...	⋮	⋮	...	...
KISSINGEN 195 ...arr	...	...	5a23	...	⋮	⋮	⋮	⋮	...	...	⋮	...	⋮	⋮	...	...	...	⋮	⋮	...	...
Neudietendorf .dep	6 16	...	8 58	...	⋮	⋮	⋮	⋮	11 6	...	⋮	4 8	⋮	To Stuttg'rt (7a53, p.193 & Heidelb'g (7a50, p.143).	...	RC—Restaurant Car. SC—Sleeping Car.	...	⋮	⋮	5 7	6 24
Gotha 172A	6 36	...	9 28	...	⋮	7 1	7 49	1021	1129	...	1 8	4 33	1223		...		...	2 46	⋮	5 33	6 48
Fröttstädt (174)	6 50	...	9 42	...	⋮	...	RC	1038	1142	...	...	4 50	SC		...		...	...	⋮	5 51	7 4
Wutha (152)........	7 2	...	10 2	...	⋮	...	...	...	1159	...	...	5 11	...		...		...	...	⋮	6 12	7 23
Eisenach 173B arr	7 8	...	10 8	...	⋮	7 55	8 11	1047	12 5	...	1 29	5 18	1245		...		...	3 9	⋮	6 19	7 29
Eisenach 173B dep	7 10	...	1014	...	⋮		8 13	1052		...	1 31	5 26	1250		...		...	3 13	⋮		7 55
Wartha	...	...	1033	...	⋮	...	...	11 3	...	...	...	5 42	...		...		...	...	⋮	...	...
Gerstungen 172 dep	...	...	1053	...	⋮	...	...	1120	...	...	...	6 6	1 11		...		...	...	⋮	...	8 28
Bebra ....arr	7 53	...	1126	...	6 56	...	8 54	1150	...	...	2 6	6 42	1 35		...		...	3 55	4 16	...	8 56
FRANKFORT 149 arr	11p40	...	...	...	9p23	...	1140	..	...	...	5 a6	12p21	5 a6		...	RC SC	...	6a53	7 a4	...	1p27
CASSEL 173A ......arr	9p45	...	...	...	...	...	11p13	1 p9	...	...	...	8 a37	2a43		...		...	6a38	6a38	...	1036

Extra.					
Weissenfels dep	7a30	8a26	4 p2	5 p2	8 p6
Naumburg ...arr	7 44	8 42	4 15	5 17	8 21

A—In July and August only.
B—Runs until 15th July, and from 1st to 31st August.

A—To Schweinfurt (arr. 3.36).

NEUDIETENDORF to ILMENAU and RITSCHENHAUSEN.

ERFURT ....dep	1221	5a58	6a15	8a33	1015	11a50	12 0	1226	...	1p36	2 p8	2p32	2p56	4 p38	4p48	6 p27	7 p26	7p55	8p47	9p56	12a28
	a.m.	a.m.	a.m.	a.m.	a.m.	⋮	p.m.	p.m.	p.m.	p.m.	p.m.	p m	p.m.	p.m.	p m.	p.m.	p.m.	p.m.	p.m.	p.m.	nght
Neudietendorf...dep	⋮	6 19	6 35	8 49	1034	⋮	12 18	⋮	...	1 59	2 40	2 53	3 14	4 52	5 6	6 47	7 42	8 15	9 4	1014	12 43
Arnstadt (173C)	1243	6 43	6 52	9 6	1053	RC	12 36	1251	1 4	2 15	3 41	3 15	3 29	5 3	5 25	7 3	7 56	8 35	9 23	1036	1 0
Plaue........	...	6 59	7 5	9 24	1111	⋮		...	1 17		3 52	3 31			5 41		8 7	8 48	9 40	1048	
Gräfenroda........	...	7 11		9 35	1122	12 31	...	1 11		...		3 43	...	...	5 51	...	8 16		9 51		...
Oberhof	1 32	7 52	...	1015	1159	1 3	...	1 42	...	...	...	4 26	...	...	6 32	...	8 55	...	1030	...	...
Zella St. Blasii ...a.m.	...	8 1	...	1024	12 9	⋮	...	1 50	...	...	...	4 35	...	...	6 46	...	9 5	...	1039	...	...
Suhl 4 55	1 46	8 13	...	1034	1221	⋮	...	1 59	...	...	...	4 49	...	...	6 59	...	9 16	...	1051	...	...
Grimmenthal......5 28	⋮	8 50	...	11 1	1250	⋮	...	2 18	...	...	...	5 17	...	...	7 46	...	9 44	...	1118	...	...
Ritschenhausen	A	8 55	...	...	1254	⋮	...	⋮	...	...	...	5 22	...	...	7 52	...		...	1131	...	...
KISSINGEN 195 arr	⋮	1153	...	...	3p30	3 p30	...	4p30	...	...	...	7p20	...	...	10p25	...	...	...	5a23	...	...

		a.m.		a.m.		a.m.		a.m.	p.m.		p.m.	p.m.	p.m.			p.m.	p.m.
Plaue ....dep	...	...	...	7 8	...	9 34	...	11 24	1 20	...	2 33	3 54	5 52	...	...	8 51	10 53
Elgersburg	...	...	...	7 32	...	9 57	...	11 49	1 48	...	2 58	4 21	6 29	...	...	9 17	11 18
Ilmenau	...	5 38	...	7 59	...	10 18	...	12 7	2 13	...	3 13	4 41	6 56	...	...	9 34	11 32
Stützerbach	a.m.	6 15	a.m.	8 39	a.m.	11 0	p.m.	12 42	2 43	p.m.		5 16	7 26	p.m.	p.m.	10 12	
Schleusingen........	5 20	7 47	9 10	10 9	11 0		12 28	2 11		3 20	...	6 50		7 49	10 0	11 17	...
Themar (173B)... arr	5 54	8 11	9 34	...	11 34	...	12 52	2 35	...	3 44	...	7 14	...	8 13	10 25	11 45	...

[Luggage Rates—see page 462.

BEBRA, EISENACH, GOTHA, ERFURT, WEIMAR—CORBETHA, LEIPSIC—HALLE, and BERLIN.

A—Runs from 1st to 17th July, and from 3rd August until 2nd September.

Station																					
CASSEL 173A......dep		11p48	1148	...	...	...	...	...	Ex.3	...	2 a57	...	...	...	...	5 a5	7 a50	7a50	...	8 a26	8 a26
FRANKFORT 140 dep		10p16	1025	...	...	...	...	11p35	From Heidelberg (9p35, p.143) and Stuttgart (9p42, p.193A)	...	...	...	...	...	...	...	6 a4	...	...	6 a4	8 a23
		Ex 2	Ex2	Ex2	1,2,3	Ex 3	3& 4	Ex 3		...	Ex.3	Ex3	1,2,3	1,2,3	1—4	2,3,4	Ex 3	Ex3	1,2,3	1,2,3	Ex.2
		a.m.	a.m.				a.m.	a.m.		...	a.m.	...	a.m.		a.m.	a.m.	a.m.	a.m.	...	a.m.	a.m.
Bebra......dep		1 27	1 40	...	RC—Restaurant Car.	...	4 29	3 2		...	3 55	...	...	...	...	6 58	9 4	8 47	...	10 15	10 54
Gerstungen ......dep		A	SC	...		...	5 6	...		...	...	...	...	...	...	7 32	...	...	...	...	:
Wartha		:	...	...		...	5 25	...		...	...	...	...	...	...	7 52	RC	...	...	...	:
Eisenach ......arr		:	2 22	...		...	5 40	3 40		...	4 37	...	...	...	...	8 10	9 46	9 31	a.m.	10 57	RC
,, 173B ......dep		:	2 25	...		...	—	3 42		...	4 40	...	5 44	...	6 50	8 17	9 50	10 0	11 2	11 10	:
Wutha......		:	...	...		...	...	...		...	...	...	...	...	6 57	8 26	...	...	11 9	11 18	:
Fröttstadt		:	...	...		...	...	...		...	...	...	6 4	...	7 16	8 49	...	...	1125	11 34	:
Gotha		:	2 55	...		...	...	4 8		...	5 11	...	6 18	...	7 29	9 8	10 21	1029	1138	11 57	:
Neudietendorf arr		:	:	...		...	...	:		...	:	...	6 32	...	7 47	9 28	:	:	:	12 9	:
KISSINGEN 195...dep		:	:	...	...	...	...	:	:	...	:	...	...	...	...	...	:	:	:	7 a17	7a17
RITSCHENHAUSEN dp		:	:	...	...	...	...	:	:	...	:	...	...	...	...	6 a17	:	:	:	9 a13	9a13
Neudietendorf......dep	a.m. 5 28	:	:	...	...	...	1—4	:	:	...	:	...	6 33	...	7 48	9 31	:	:	:	1 10	:
Erfurt ... arr	5 43	3 10	3 18	...	...	...	a.m.	4 30	5 13	...	5 35	a.m.	6 45	...	8 3	9 46	10 44	1052	12 0	12 20	12 12
Erfurt ... dep	—	3 14	3 22	...	...	...	3 27	4 34	5 17	...	5 50	5 56	6 50	...	8 13	9 56	10 48	1058	12 4	12 24	12 16
Weimar... arr......		:	3 45	...	...	...	3 53	4 53	5 37	...	6 10	6 16	7 10	...	8 43	10 27	11 10	1118	1225	12 44	:
Weimar... dep ...		:	3 46	...	...	...	3 57	4 54	5 38	...	6 12	6 18	7 12	...	8 46	10 32	11 11	1119	1227	12 47	:
Apolda......	2 3 4	:	...	...	...	...	4 15	:	:	...	To Gera.	6 31	7 26	...	9 5	10 52	...	1131	1246	12 59	:
Sulza	a.m.	:	...	...	...	...	4 29	:	:	...		...	7 36	...	9 21	11 6	...	...	1258	1 9	:
Grossheringen	6 5	:	...	a.m.	...	...	4 36	:	:	...		...	7 41	...	9 29	11 12	...	...	...	...	:
Koesen......	6 12	:			...	...	4 44	:	:	...	—	...	7 49	...	9 37	11 21	...	...	1 7	1 19	:
Naumburg	6 22	:	4 31	4 38	...	...	4 57	5.25	:	...	...	6 52	8 1	...	9 46	11 56	11 45	1151	1 16	1 28	:
Weissenfels arr	6 38	:	:	4 51	...	...	5 14	:	:	...	...	:	8 15		10 3	12 15	11 57	12 6	1 31	1 41	:
MUNICH 197B ...dep		:	:	...	...	10p20	...	:	:	...	...	:	...	From Cassel via Sangerhausen (p. 148A)	...	...	...	...	...	...	:
NURNBERG 197B dep		:	:	...	...	12a55	...	:	:	2a46	2 3 4	:	...		...	...	...	...	...	...	:
PROBSTZELLA 173 dp		:	:	...	...	From Jena (dp. 5.12 a.m.)	...	:	:	:	a.m.	:	...		4a55	6 a2	6 a2	...	...	...	:
Weissenfels......dep		:	:	4 54	5 26	:	5 16	:	:	:	6 42	:	8 18		10 8	12 19	11 59	12 8	1 32	1 43	:
Corbetha......arr		:	:	:	:	:	5 27	:	6 27	:	6 53	:	8 27		1019	12 30	...	:	1 42	1 52	:
Corbetha ...dep		:	:	:	:	:	5 31	:	6 31	:	:	:	8 37		1028	12 37	:	:	1 44	2 52	:
Dürrenberg		:	:	:	:	:	5 38	:	6 38	:	:	:	...		1036	12 44	:	:	1 52	3 0	:
Markranstadt......		:	:	:	:	:	6 9	:	6 58	:	:	:	8 57		11 1	1 4	:	:	...	3 23	:
Leipsic 188 arr		:	:	5 36	:	:	6 41	6 21	7 29	:	:	7 46	9 16		1127	1 35	:	1250	2 23	3 56	:
DRESDEN Hpt.ar		:	:	8a13	:	:	...	...	...	:	:	1026	1120		2p30	4p31	:	2p55	...	--	:
		:	:		:	:	a.m.	...	a.m.	:	a.m.		a.m.		a.m.	p.m.	:		...	p.m.	:
Corbetha......dep		:	:	...	:	:	5 44	...	6 28	:	6 54	...	8 31		1022	12 35	:	...	...	1 54	:
Merseburg		:	:	...	5 46	:	6 13	...	...	:	7 6	...	8 41		1034	12 47	:	Ex3	...	2 4	:
Halle ......arr		5 2	5 14	...	6 2	6 21	6 31	...	6 48	7 50	7 25	...	8 54	a.m.	1052	1 6	12 27	p.m.	...	2 17	1 42
,, ...dep		5 10	5 18	...	—	6 25	7 0	...	6 52	7 58	—	...	8 58	10 24	1110	1 55	12 31	3 15	...	2 21	1 44
Landsberg		...	...	...	...	...	7 17	...	...	From 2nd July until 1st September.	...	...	...	...	1129	2 14	...	...	...	...	...
Bitterfeld ...... arr		A	5 43	...	...	...	7 36	...	7 16		...	...	9 23	10 48	1148	2 34	RC	3 41	...	...	...
Bitterfeld ...... dep		...	5 44	...	...	...	7 40	...	7 17		...	...	9 27	10 49	1216	2 55	...	3 46	...	...	...
Gräfenhainichen		...	...	...	...	...	8 2	...	...		...	...	...	...	1239	3 42	...	...	...	...	...
Pratau		...	...	...	...	...	8 24	...	...		...	...	...	...	1 3	4 4	...	...	...	...	...
Wittenberg ......arr		...	6 16	...	...	...	8 30	...	7 48		...	...	9 59	11 20	1 9	4 10	...	4 18	...	...	...
Zahna		...	...	...	...	...	9 12	...	...		...	...	...	...	2 3	4 43	...	...	...	...	...
Jüterbog......		...	...	...	...	...	9 52	...	...		...	...	1031	11 49	3 0	5 10	...	...	...	...	...
Luckenwalde		...	...	...	...	...	10 9	...	...		...	...	1043	12 1	3 17	5 24	...	4 58	...	...	...
Trebbin		...	...	...	...	...	1027	...	...		...	...	...	...	3 36	5 41	...	...	...	...	...
Lichterfelde (Sud)		...	...	...	...	...	11 0	...	...		...	...	...	...	4 11	6 12	...	...	...	...	...
BERLIN Anhalt ...arr		7 30	7 36	...	...	8 25	1118	...	9 5	10 4	...	...	1130	12 43	4 29	6 30	2 39	5 42	...	4 34	3 34

SAALFELD and GROSSHERINGEN.

Station	Ex3	2 3 4	Ex 3	2,3,4	1—4	2 3 4	2 3 4	Ex3	Ex3	2 3 4	1—4	2 3 4	1—4	1,2,3	2 3 4	3&4			
	a.m.	a.m.	a.m.	a.m.	a.m.	a.m.	a.m.	p.m.	p.m.	p.m.	p.m.	p.m.	p.m.	p.m.	p.m.	p.m.			
Saalfeld ......dep	4 27	5 0	5 47	7 20	8 55	9 43	1155	1241	2 32	3 35	4 58	6 40	7 15	8 21	9 57	1130	...	...	...
Schwarza	...	5 10	...	7 30	9 4	9 52	12 4	...	...	3 45	5 8	6 52	7 23	...	10 6	1211	...	...	...
Rudolstadt	4 38	5 18	...	7 39	9 12	9 58	1213	1252	2 43	3 52	5 16	7 1	7 32	8 32	1017	1219	...	...	...
Uhlstädt	...	5 34	...	7 53	9 25	—	1226	...	...	4 4	5 29	—	7 44	...	1029	—	...	...	...
Orlamünde	...	5 49	B	8 7	9 40	...	1239	RC	RC	4 16	5 42	...	7 56	8 48	1042	...	...	...	...
Kahla	...	5 56	...	8 16	9 49	...	1246	...	...	4 23	5 49	...	8 3	8 55	1054	...	...	...	...
Goschwitz	...	6 13	...	8 41	1017	...	1 0	...	...	4 42	6 2	...	8 22	9 6	11 7	...	...	...	...
Jena (152)	5 12	6 40	6 32	8 52	1032	...	1 32	1 25	3 17	4 54	6 15	...	8 41	9 15	1126	...	...	...	...
Porstendorf......	:	6 50	:	9 1	1042	...	1 41	:	...	5 3	6 25	...	8 52	...	1138	...	...	...	...
Camburg......	:	7 4	§	9 15	1056	...	1 56	:	...	5 16	6 39	...	9 7	...	1153	...	...	...	...
Grossheringen arr	*	7 20	:	9 24	...	...	3 27	†	...	...	7 9	...	...	...	...	...	...	...	...
Naumburg ...arr	:	7 38	:	...	1120	...	2 35	:	3 48	5 40	7 2	...	9 31	9 51	1218	...	...	...	...

*—Berlin arr. 8.25 a.m.
†—Berlin arr. 4.49 p.m.
§—Berlin arr. 10.14 a.m.
B—From 2nd July until 1st September.

Station																	
Schwarza ......arr	5a15	6a36	8 a0	9a30	12p36	11a20	1p42	2p48	4 p3	6p 7	6p57	7p48	8 p57	11p40	1 a0	...	...
Blankenburg ......dep	5 23	6 44	8 8	9 38	12 44	11 27	1 50	2 56	4 11	6 15	7 5	7 56	9 5	11 48	1 8	...	...

Station															
Orlamünde......dep	7 a24	10a40	12p55	2 p47	6 p0	8p55	10p58	...	...	...	...	...	...	...	...
Possneck	8 20	11 13	1 21	3 50	6 48	9 18	11 30	...	...	...	...	...	...	...	...
Oppurg (173)......arr	8 28	11 19	...	4 0	6 54	...	11 39	...	...	...	...	...	...	...	...

BEBRA, EISENACH, GOTHA, ERFURT, WEIMAR—CORBETHA, LEIPSIC—HALLE, and BERLIN.

RC—Restaurant Car.

		Ex3	Ex2	2,3,4	1,2,3	Ex3	1—4	1,2,3	Ex3	2 3 4	Ex2	Ex3	Ex3	Ex3	1,2,3	3—4	1—4	3—4	Ex2	Ex3	Ex3	2 3 4
Cassel 173A ...dep		...	...	8 e26	1111	1118	...	1118	1p36	12p7	...	...	2p44	...	3p45	...	3p45	...	3p45	6p48	7p34	7p40
Frankfort 149 dep		...	...	6 a4	8a23	9a40	...	9a58	...	9a58	1253	...	1 p5	...	1 p5	...	1 p5	...	2p46	2p55	3p15	...
				a.m.	p.m.	p.m.		p.m.		p.m.	p.m.		p.m.	From Heidelberg (10a10, p.143) and Stuttgart (10a21, p. 193A)	p.m.	p.m.	p.m.	p.m	p.m.	p.m.	p.m.	p.m.
Bebra ......dep		...	...	10 31	1210	1245	...	1 37		1 50	3 43	...	4 31		4 58	...	5 4	...	5 44	7 51	8 37	9 35
Gerstungen ......dep		...	...	11 4	...	...	...	...		2 21	RC	...	...		...	4 27	6 10	7 32	...	...	8 59	10 9
Wartha		...	...	11 28	...	...	...	...		2 41	...	...	...		...	4 46	6 31	7 51	RC	...	...	1030
Eisenach 173B arr		...	...	11 43	1248	1 25	p.m.	2 20	3 14	2 58	4 23	...	5 9		5 40	5 3	6 49	8 7	6 22	8 33	9 17	1046
Eisenach 173B dep		...	...	11 50	—	1 29	1 36	2 22	3 17	3 23	4 25	...	5 13		5 44	6 30	7 0	8 15	6 24	8 36	9 2	1052
Wutha		...	...	11 57	...	...	1 43	...	...	3 31	...	...	...		...	6 38	7 8	8 21	...	...	...	11 1
Fröttstädt		...	...	12 16	...	1 50	2 3	2 43	3 39	3 51	...	...	5 32		6 4	6 58	7 32	—	...	8 56	...	1124
Gotha		...	...	12 32	...	2 4	2 16	2 56	3 52	4 5	4 52	...	5 46		6 16	7 12	7 49	...	6 54	9 9	9 51	1139
Neudietendorf arr		...	...	12 51	...		2 35	3 4		4 26		...			6 28	7 31	8 9	...			10 3	1158
Kissingen 195...dep		...	...	7 a17	...		...	...		11a0		1p48			1p48	...	2p55	...			...	...
Ritschenhausen dp		...	...	9 a13	2 3 4		...	...		1p15					...	...	5 p7	...			...	...
Neudietendorf					p.m.									p.m.								
dorf......dep	2 3 4	...	...	12 54	1 8		2 37	3 9		4 28				6 9	6 29	7 33	8 13	...			10 4	12 0
Erfurt arr	p.m.	...	...	1 9	1 24	2 26	2 52	3 21	4 14	4 43	5 14		6 7	6 21	6 41	7 50	8 30	...	7 16	9 30	1017	1215
Erfurt dep	1235	...	...	1 33	—	2 30	2 57	3 25	4 19	4 55	5 18	5 29	6 11	6 27	6 45	—	8 45	...	7 20	9 34	1046	—
Weimar arr	1 5	...	...	2 0	...	2 51	3 18	3 46	4 40	5 20	5 38	5 47	6 32	6 50	7 11	...	9 14	...	7 40	9 54	11 6	...
Weimar dep	1 10	...	...	2 8	...	2 54	—	3 49	4 42	5 30	5 39	5 49	6 35	6 52	7 15	...	9 19	...	7 41	9 56	—	...
Apolda	1 35	...	...	2 27	...	3 7	...	4 4	...	6 5			6 49	...	7 35	...	9 43	...	...	10 9	2 3 4	...
Sulza	1 53	...	...	2 41	...	...	...	...	...	6 19			...	...	7 48	1,2,3	9 59	1,2,3	...	1018	p.m.	...
Grossheringen	2 0	...	...	2 48	Ex3	...	Ex3	...	...	6 28			...	RC	8 7	p.m.	10 4	p.m.	...	...	9 20	a.m.
Koesen	2 8	...	...	2 56	p.m	...	p.m.	4 22	5 10	6 36			...	...	8 16	9 44	1013		...	1027	9 29	12 9
Naumburg	2 16	...	...	3 10	3 52	3 30	3 59	4 32	5 19	6 51			7 12	7 27	8 29	9 53	1043	8 24	8 20	1036	9 38	1218
Weissenfels arr	3 1	...	...	3 26		3 45	4 16	4 46		7 12			7 25	7 40	8 47		11 9	8 38		1050	9 57	—
Munich 197B ......dep		5 a0	8a15	...	8a25	...	...	...		...			...	...	...		...	...	...	...	...	...
Nurnberg 197B dep		9a14	1035	...	11a0	...	...	...		...			...	12p3	...		...	...	...	...	...	...
Probstzella 173 dep				8 a53		8a53	...	...		...			...	4 p9	...		...	...	...	...	5p17	...
Weissenfels ......dep				3 28		3 46	4 17	4 48		7 17			7 27	7 44	8 50		1115	8 40		1052	9 45	2 3 4
Corbetha ...... arr		2 15		3 39			4 27	4 59		7 28					9 1		1127	8 50			9 57	a.m.
Corbetha ......dep		2 32		...			4 28	5 5		...					9 4		1147	8 51			...	4 20
Dürrenberg		...		...	RC		...	5 12		...					9 12		1155	...			...	4 28
Markranstadt		...		...			...	5 34		...					9 35		1217	9 10			...	4 53
Leipsic 188...arr		3 7		...		4 28	5 0	6 6	6 15	...			8 9		10 8		1246	9 28		1134	...	5 26
Dresden Hpt. ar		6p19		...		6p36	8p27	8p27	8p27	...			1014		1a43		...	1152		1a43	...	8a13
		p.m.		p.m.				p.m.		p.m.					p.m.		p.m.				p.m.	
Corbetha ......dep		2 17		3 44		...	...	5 0	...	7 32			...		9 6		1131	...		...	9 5	...
Merseburg		...		3 56		...	...	5 11	...	7 45			...	8 2	9 17	1025	1142	...		...	10 9	1—4
Halle arr		2 37	3 2	4 15	4 38	...	...	5 27	...	8 4	6 51	7 5	...	8 16	9 33	1039	12 1	...	8 58	...	1028	a.m.
Halle dep		2 42	3 6	5 45	4 42	...	...	5 38	...	9 20	6 55	7 11	...	8 20	—	—	1230	...	9 2	...	—	4 32
Landsberg		...	...	6 4	...	...	...	...	...	9 39	...	...	...	...	...	...	1250	...	...	...	...	4 49
Bitterfeld arr		3 6	...	6 22	...	...	...	6 4	...	9 58	...	...	...	8 45	...	...	1 11	...	RC	...	...	5 7
Bitterfeld dep		3 8	...	6 25	...	...	...	6 12	...	10 5	...	...	...	8 46	...	...	1 28	...	...	...	...	5 10
Gräfenhainichen		...	...	6 47	...	...	...	...	...	1058	...	...	...	...	...	...	1 50	...	...	...	...	5 33
Pratau		...	...	7 8	...	...	...	...	...	1121	...	...	...	...	...	...	2 14	...	...	...	...	5 54
Wittemberg ......arr		...	...	7 14	...	...	...	6 44	...	1127	...	...	...	9 18	...	...	2 20	...	...	...	...	6 0
Zahna		...	...	8 25	...	...	...	...	...	1147	...	...	...	...	...	...	2 48	...	...	...	...	6 40
Jüterbog		...	...	8 53	...	...	...	7 18	...	1215	...	...	...	...	...	...	3 20	...	...	...	...	7 43
Luckenwalde		...	...	9 11	...	...	...	7 31	...	1228	...	...	...	...	...	...	3 38	...	...	...	...	7 57
Trebbin		...	...	9 30	...	...	...	...	...	1244	...	...	...	...	...	...	4 0	...	...	...	...	8 12
Lichterfelde (Sud)		...	...	10 3	...	...	...	...	...	...	...	...	...	...	...	...	4 42	...	...	...	...	8 42
BERLIN Anhalt......arr		4 49	4 56	10 21	6 42	...	...	8 19	...	1 19	8 55	9 13	...	1038	...	...	5 0	...	11 2	...	...	9 0

Extra.															
Nieudietendorf...dep	7 a6	8 a13	9a23	11a38	4p22	5p27	7p41	8 p0	8p41	10p12	10p26	...	...	...	...
Erfurt ......arr	7 23	8 24	9 38	11 52	4 35	5 43	7 59	8 16	8 57	10 30	10 42	..	...	...	...

RITSCHENHAUSEN to ILMENAU and NEUDIETENDORF.

Kissingen 195 dp	...	...	...	...	...	...	7a17	...	...	11a0	...	1p48	...	1p48	2p55	...	...	5p 5	...
	a.m.	a.m.	a.m.		a.m.		a.m.			p.m.				p.m	p.m.			p.m.	p.m.
Ritschenhausen dep	A	...	...	...	6 17	...	9 13	...	...	1 15	...		...		5 7	...	...	7 40	...
Grimmenthal		...	5 14	...	6 50	...	9 22	...	...	1 2[illegible]	...		...	4 32	5 21	...	...	7 54	1133
Suhl	3 57	...	5 53	...	7 29	...	9 53	...	...	2 4	...	4 3	...	4 57	5 50	...	...	8 28	12 1
Zella-St-Blasii ...	...	...	6 15	...	7 50	...	1013	...	...	2 25	...	...	...	5 10	6 8	...	...	8 49	1218
Oberhof	4 19	...	6 31	...	8 8	...	1030	...	...	2 42	...	4 33	...	5 23	6 20	...	...	9 7	—
Gräfenroda	...	...	6 54	...	8 32	a.m.	1052	p.m	p.m.	3 7	...	...	p.m.	...	6 43	...	p.m.	9 32	..
Plaue ...... a.m.	...	6 28	7 4	a.m.	8 44	10 52	11 4	12 21	1 50	3 16	p.m.		4 42	5 45	6 51	p.m.	8 4	9 42	p.m.
Arnstadt 5 11	4 52	6 47	7 23	8 1	9 4	11 7	1119	12 48	2 3	3 32	4 8	5 3	5 8	5 58	7 15	7 42	8 23	9 55	1011
N'dietnd'f 5 27		7 2	7 41	8 12	9 19	11 22	1134	1 5	2 19	3 49	4 18		5 24	6 8	7 37	7 56	8 37	1010	1023
Erfurt ar 5a43	5a13	7a23	8 a3	8a24	9a38	...	1152	1p24	2p52	4 p7	4 p35	5 25	5p43	6p21	7p59	8 p16	8 57	1030	1042

A From Schwinfurt (dep. 1.49)

Themar ......dep	...	a.m.	7 a8	...	8 a26	10a25	p.m.	12 p3	1 p24	..	4 p0	6 p5	p.m.	7p 24	8 p45	11p15	...	...
Schleusingen	...	5 19	7 38	...	9 10	10 59	...	1 8	1 48	..	4 34	6 29	...	8 15	9 12	11 50	..	...
Stützerbach	a.m.	7 7	—	a.m.	10 56	—	12 39	3 6	—		6 23	—	7 54	10 7	—	—	..	...
Ilmenau	5 49	7 53	...	10 14	11 34	...	1 11	3 58	...	4p56	7 20	..	8 34	10 34	...	...	..	...
Elgersburg	6 3	8 7	...	10 28	11 54	...	1 26	4 17	...	5 11	7 38	...	8 51	—	...	...	...	...
Plaue ......arr	6 26	8 30	...	10 50	12 17	...	1 49	4 40	...	5 34	8 2	...	9 18	...	...	...	...	...

PRUSSIAN STATE RAILWAYS.

GOTHA and GRAFENRODA. †-Weekdays only.

Gotha ......dep	5a34	6a53	9 a9	1022	11a44	1p48	3 31	5 p0	6 40	7p55	10p22	11 40
Georgenthal arr	5 59	7 18	9 34	1049	12 11	2 12	3 56	5 25	7 19	8 21	10 50	12 11
Tambach arr	6 26	7 44	10 2	...	12 54	2 43	4 23	5 54	7 44	8 48	11 16	...
Georgenthal dep	6 2	7 22	9 39	1050	12 13	2 14	4 4	5 27	7 26	8 26	10 57	12 13
Ohrdruf	6 13	7 34	9 50	1059	12 24	2 23	4 14	5 42	7 40	8 38	11 5	12 23
Gräfenroda	6 50	8 14	1044	...	1 4	3 1	...	6 37	...	9 24	...	...

Gräfenroda dep	...	...	7a18	8a35	...	11a35	1 p17	3p45	...	...	7 10	9p53
Ohrdruf	4a43	5a51	8 12	9 22	11a1	12 22	2 2	5 11	6p32	...	8 16	1045
Georgenthal ...arr	4 51	6 1	8 20	9 30	11 8	12 30	2 10	5 21	6 40	...	8 25	1053
Tambach ...dep	...	5 34	6 55	9 8	...	11 45	1 43	4 57	...	6†50	7 55	1025
Georgenthal...dep	4 55	6 5	8 27	9 35	11 9	12 32	2 13	5 33	6 41	7 9	8 36	1056
Gotha 170...arr	5 22	6 30	8 51	9 59	1132	12 57	2 36	6 5	7 5	...	9 1	1120

‡—In July & August only.

ZERBST, DESSAU, FALKENBERG, and KOHLFURT.

	2,3,4	2 3 4	Ex 3	1—4	1,2,3	1—4	1—4	1—4	1—4	1,2,3
MAGDEBURG 164 dep	...	...	7 a4	...	...	10‡40	1p18	4p15	7p42	...
		a.m.	a.m.		a.m.	a.m.	p.m.	p.m.	p.m.	p.m.
Zerbst ......dep	...	...	7 44	...	8 55	11 49	2 38	5 25	9 2	...
Rosslau .....arr	...	...	7 56	a.m.	9 13	12 8	2 58	5 45	9 22	...
Dessau.........dep	...	7 46	...	6 32	9 10	12 32	3 14	6 13	9 31	10 58
Rosslau ....dep	...	7 53	8 5	6 47	9 18	12 45	3 27	6 26	9 40	11 6
Coswig	...	—	8 21	7 14	9 38	1 10	3 51	6 50	10 4	11 25
Wittenberg..arr	...	a.m.	8 34	7 36	9 53	1 30	4 11	7 9	1023	11 39
,, (170) dep	...	6 5	8 35	8 45	—	1 44	4 27	7 20	1035	—
Elster	...	6 22	...	9 2	...	2 1	4 44	7 35	1052	...
Annaburg	...	6 45	...	9 26	...	2 22	5 7	7 56	1116	...
Falkenberg...arr	...	7 10	9 16	9 51	...	2 47	5 32	8 20	1141	...
LEIPSIC ...dep	...	...	7a45	8a15	...	1 p0	3p48	6p30	—	...
		a.m.	a.m.	a.m.		p.m.	p.m.	p.m.		
Falkenberg..dep	...	7 17	9 20	1010	...	2 56	5 48	8 48	...	...
Liebenwerda	...	7 37	9 ‡33	1029	...	3 17	6 11	9 7	...	...
Elsterwerda	...	8 15	9 45	1047	...	3 38	6 35	9 24	...	...
Ruhland ......arr	a.m.	8 52	10 8	1124	...	4 15	7 18	10 0	...	...
,, (183A)dep	6 24	8 55	10 9	1129	...	4 21	7 23	10 7	...	...
Hohenboka a.m.	6 39	9 19	10 20	1144	...	4 36	7 50	1022	...	...
Hoyerswerda 4 50	7 1	9 49	10 36	1220	...	4 59	8 15	1045	...	...
Uhyst 5 16	7 24	1017	...	1246	...	5 23	—	11 9	...	...
Horka 6 15	8 20	1132	11 20	1 48	...	6 10	...	12 1	...	...
Kohlfurt arr 6 49	8 53	12 6	11 43	2 22	...	6 43	...	1233	...	...
BRESLAU ,, 9a46	1 p2	3p14	1p47	7p38	...	9 p19	...	5a50	...	...

	2 3 4	1,2,3	1—4	2 3 4	2 3 4	1—4	1—4	Ex3	2 3 4	2 3 4
BRESLAU......dep (179A)	...		11p8	...	6a11	6a23	1045	3p45	3p45	6p16
			a.m.		a.m.	a.m.	p.m.	p.m.	p.m.	p.m.
Kohlfurt..........dep	...	...	4 0	...	8 30	1030	1 5	6 7	7 5	1125
Horka (180)...........	...	...	4 40	...	9 3	1120	1 53	6 31	7 53	1155
Uhyst.....................	...	...	5 21	a.m.	9 43	1158	2 45	...	8 42	1236
Hoyerswerda ...dep	...	...	5 49	7 13	10 4	1222	3 22	7 18	9 14	1 1
Hohenboka ......dep	...	...	6 9	7 37	—	1242	3 53	7 34	9 38	1 19
Ruhland...........arr	...	...	6 23	7 52	...	1255	4 6	7 44	9 53	1 32
,, ...dep	...	...	6 29	7 56	...	1256	4 20	7 45	10 7	—
Elsterwerda (188)...	...	...	7 11	9 15	...	1 34	4 56	8 9	1058	...
Liebenwerda	...	...	7 29	9 42	...	1 51	5 11	8 20	1115	...
Falkenberg ......arr	...	...	7 48	10 4	...	2 10	5 30	8 33	1135	...
LEIPSIC 173A arr	...	...	10a1	1215	1,2,3	4p54	7p39	1034	...	...
	a.m.		a.m.	a.m.	p.m.	p.m.	p.m.	p.m.	p.m.	
Falkenberg ......dep	4 45	...	8 30	11 8	...	2 18	5 50	8 53	1150	...
Annaburg	5 10	...	8 57	1132	...	2 45	6 20	...	1216	...
Elster.....................	5 33	...	9 21	1153	...	3 9	6 43	...	1239	...
Wittenberg ......arr	5 49	a.m.	9 37	12 9	...	3 25	6 59	9 37	1255	...
,, ...dep	6 5	7 56	10 9	1213	2 31	5 15	7 47	9 41	—	...
Coswig	6 26	8 14	1032	1234	2 53	5 38	8 12	9 57	p.m.	...
Rosslau ....arr	6 46	8 32	1052	1254	3 13	5 55	8 34	1013	1020	...
Dessau ....arr	6 58	8 41	11 4	1 4	3 20	6 6	8 46	...	1028	...
Rosslau ....dep	6 54	8 37	11 3	1 1	4 26	6 9	9 11	1053	—	...
Zerbst (164)...arr	7 13	8 50	1123	1 22	4 47	6 26	9 31	11 5	...	...
MAGDEBURG ,,	8a22	9 a27	1227	2p37	5p54	7p41	1045	1142	...	...

PETERSHAIN and HOYERSWERDA.

Petershain ....dep	5a55	7a20	8a55	11a5	1p37	5 p5	6p45	8 p15	10p50
Proschim Haidemuhl	6 15	7 40	9 12	1125	1 54	5 22	7 2	8 32	11 7
Proschim H. ...dep	...	7 50	...	1135	...	5 24	...	8 34	11 15
Spremberg West arr	...	8 24	...	12 9	...	5 52	...	9 2	11 49
Proschim H. ......dep	6 17	...	9 15	—	1 55	...	7 4	—	11 9
Hoyerswerda arr	6 53	...	9 44	...	2 24	...	7 33	...	11 38

Hoyerswerda ...dep	4 a25	...	7 a8	...	11a 2	...	4 p7	...	9p20
Proschim Haidemuhl ar	4 54	...	7 44	a.m.	11 31	p.m.	4 36	p.m.	9 56
Spremberg West dep	...	5a35	...	8 40	...	1240	...	6 25	...
Proschim H.........arr	...	6 9	...	9 8	...	1 8	...	6 59	...
Proschim H. ....dep	4 56	6 16	7 46	9 13	11 33	1 10	4 38	7 4	10 0
Petershain 183A arr	5 13	6 36	8 6	9 33	11 50	1 27	4 55	7 24	1020

MERSEBURG & QUERFURT.

‡—Not on Sunday.

Merseburg dep	5 a20	8 a20	11a10	1 p40	4 p10	6 p30	8 p30	11p45
Mücheln	5 55	8 55	11 45	2 15	4 45	7 5	9 5	12 20
Querfurt ....arr	6 56	9 58	...	3 10	...	7 59	9‡54	...

Querfurt..........dep	...	5 a5	8a55	...	2p10	5 p0	...	8p25
Mücheln	4a30	6 10	9 50	12 0	3 5	6 16	7 p6	9 25
Merseburg 170 arr	5 4	6 44	1024	12 34	3 39	6 57	7 40	9 59

DESSAU and CÖTHEN.

	a.m.	a.m.	a.m.	a.m.	p.m.	p.m.	p.m.	p.m.	p.m.	
Dessau..............dep	5 43	7 4	8 49	11 9	1 7	3 23	6 16	8 58	1040	...
Cöthen ....arr	6 17	7 38	9 11	1143	1 37	3 55	6 47	9 34	1114	...

	a.m.	a.m.	a.m.	a.m.	a.m.	p.m.	p.m.	p.m.	p.m.	p.m.					
Cöthen ....dep	5 50	7 14	8 33	10 5	1158	2 38	5 38	8 55	1035	1144	...	...	...	...	...
Dessau ....arr	6 22	7 42	9 5	1034	1227	3 10	6 7	9 26	1055	1219	...	...	...	...	...

WITTENBERG, TORGAU, and EILENBURG.

Wittenberg ..dep	4a15	6a45	8a45	1p45	4 p1	7p20
Pratau	4 25	6 53	8 54	1 54	4 9	7 28
Pretzsch ....arr	5 5	7 36	9 34	2 32	4 49	8 6
‡ Torgau ....arr	6 45	...	1054	4 9	...	9 3
Bad Schmiedeberg	5 28	7 48	9 57	2 51	5 14	8 24
Düben	6 3	8 18	1041	3 27	5 51	8 53
Eilenburg ...arr	6 42	8 55	1126	4 6	6 28	9 29

Eilenburg 173A dep	4a19	5a19	9a11	1p35	4p45	7p45
Düben	4 58	5 58	10 1	2 15	5 26	8 26
Bad Schmiedeberg ...	5 29	6 29	1045	2 50	5 56	9 1
‡ Torgau ....dep	4 10	...	9 46	1 40	...	6 45
Pretzsch ....dep	5 50	6 43	11 2	3 7	6 10	9 16
Pratau	6 30	7 24	1145	3 52	6 49	9 58
Wittenberg ......arr	6 37	7 31	1152	3 59	6 56	10 5

JUTERBOG and BEELITZ.

Juterbog ...dep	5a58	9a45	11a5	3p11	7p40	10p30	...
Treuenbrietzen	6 31	1017	1140	3 45	8 16	11 8	...
Beelitz 165B arr	6 57	...	12 6	4 11	8 42	...	...

Beelitz.......dep	...	6a56	12p28	...	5p21	9 p48
Treuenbrietzen	5a55	7 27	12 58	1 p50	5 49	10 22
Juterbog ...arr	6 32	8 0	1 31	2 24	6 21	10 55

COTHEN and AKEN.

Cöthen...dp	6 a0	8a40	10a10	12p27	2p45	5p43	7p15	10p5
Aken......arr	6 22	9 3	10 41	12 57	3 7	6 19	7 44	1034

Aken...dep	5 a5	6a32	9a21	10a58	1p40	4p30	6p31	8 p15
Cöthen ar	5 27	6 54	9 44	11 29	2 11	4 59	6 54	8 44

GERSTUNGEN and GEISA.

‡—Not on Sunday.

Gerstungen...dep	6a15	7a35	8a32	...	11a45	2p22	4p35	6p20	9 p5
Heringen................	6 44	7 59	8 58	...	12 12	2 48	5 4	6 48	9 24
Vacha	7 12	8 27	9 27	...	12 40	3 16	5 33	7 17	10
Wenigentaft-Mans	8 22	—	1017	12p33	2 3	4 2	6 9	7 52	1044
Geisa...............arr	8 35	...	1031	12 46	2 18	4 17	6 24	—	1059

Gerstungen	...	5a10	8a46	9a50	12p17	1p51	...	3p46	6p35
Geisa ....dep	...	5 29	9 2	1013	12 41	2 2	...	4 10	6 51
Wenigentaft-M	4a50	6 15	9 48	1044	1 15	—	3p20	5 0	7 38
Vacha..............	5 21	6 52	1020	1112	1 43	...	3 48	5 32	8 9
Heringen	5 48	7 20	1048	1136	2 7	...	4 13	5 57	8 38

Geisa...............dep	4 ‡a1	8a42	12p47	4p20	6 p45	11 p5	...
Tann 150 ....arr	4 28	9 9	1 14	4 47	7 20	11 36	...

Tann.........dep	4‡a40	7a25	9a20	1p27	6 p2	9 p0	...	...	...
Geisa.........arr	5 8	7 56	9 48	1 49	6 31	9 31	...	...	...

Vacha ....dep	4a53	7a52	1p25	3p25	7p27
Wenigentaft-M.	5 29	9 10	2 6	4 12	7 54
Hünfeld.........arr	6 32	1023	3 5	5 23	8 53
Hünfeld ......dep	7 a5	9a12	11a30	4p10	7p39
Wenigentaft-M.	8 16	1011	12 30	5 12	8 50
Vacha...........arr	9 29	1041	1 9	5 39	9 21

NAUMBURG and ARTERN.

Naumburg ....dep	5a11	7a49	9 a5	...	11 a8	12p23	1p29	3p27	4p50	7p15	8 p56	...	...	...	...	...
Freyburg	5 28	8 4	9 22	...	11 20	12 35	1 40	3 39	5 4	7 27	9 10	...	...	...	...	...
Laucha	5 50	8 19	9 36	...	11 33	12 48	1 53	3 52	5 19	7 40	9 26	...	...	...	...	...
Vitzenburg	6 18	8 40	10 2	p.m.	—	—	2 14	—	5 43	—	9 51	...	...	...	...	...
Reinsdorf	7 15	—	10 57	1236	...	...	3 5	...	6 53	...	10 50	...	...	...	...	...
Artern ....arr	7 20	...	11 3	1241	...	...	3 10	...	7 0	...	10 55	...	...	...	...	...
Artern ....dep	...	5a26	7a38	...	11a16	...	...	12p50	...	4 p32	...	8p34	...	...	...	...
Reinsdorf..........	...	5 33	7 45	a.m.	11 22	...	...	12 56	...	4 39	...	8 39	...	...	...	...
Vitzenburg	a.m.	6 38	8 43	10 0	—	a.m.	p.m.	1 54	...	5 42	...	9 32	...	...	...	...
Laucha	5 55	7 8	9 8	1025	...	1139	1254	2 27	3p57	6 8	7p50	9 57	...	...	...	...
Freyburg-a-U.	6 8	7 23	9 24	1042	...	1152	1 7	2 43	4 10	6 25	8 3	1011	...	...	...	...
Naumburg 170 ......arr	6 19	7 36	9 37	1055	...	12 3	1 18	2 58	4 21	6 38	8 14	1024		...	...	...

SANGERHAUSEN and ERFURT.

	a.m.	a.m.	a m	a.m.	a.m.	p.m.	p.m.	p.m.	p.m.	p.m.	p.m.	ng't	a.m.	‡—Dep. 5.45 a.m. on Sun.	...	...	...
Sangerhausen dep	...	4 48	7 10	1017	10 46	1218	...	4 0	5 2	...	8 2	12 1	...		...	...	...
Artern	3‡26	5 38	7 31	1031	11 2	1238	1243	4 21	5 18	5 53	8 21	1243	12 48		...	...	...
Reinsdorf..........	3 33	—	7 36	...	11 7	1243	1249	4 26	...	5 59	8 28	—	12 54		...	...	...
Bretleben..........	3 41	...	7 44	...	11 12	1249	1255	4 33	...	6 5	8 36	...	1 0		...	...	...
Sömmerda	4 43	...	8 24	1057	11 45	1 26	—	5 19	5 48	—	9 13	...	—		...	...	...
Erfurt..........arr	5 43	...	8 57	1122	12 18	1 58	...	5 52	6 13	..	9 45	...	...		...	...	...

			a.m.	a.m.	p.m.	p.m.	p m	p.m.	p.m.	p.m.	p.m.	p m	p.m.	nig't	p.m.	...	...
Erfurt ....dep	...	...	6 10	9 52	...	1230	2 0	...	4 48	...	6 53	7 25	...	...	1115	...	...
Sömmerda ......dep	a.m.	...	6 44	1024	...	1254	2 32	...	5 21	...	7 28	7 48	...		1157	...	...
Bretleben..........	4 35	...	7 24	11 2	1216	...	3 8	4 27	6 5	7 40	8 21	...	...	12 10	1 1	...	...
Reinsdorf	4 42	a.m.	7 29	11 8	1224	...	3 13	4 35	6 12	7 47	8 26	...	1050	12 17	1 9	...	...
Artern	4 49	6 5	7 38	1115	1231	1 24	3 20	4 42	6 23	7 52	8 34	8 21	11 0	12 24	1 16	...	...
Sangerhausen...arr	5 36	6 49	8 4	1137	...	1 39	3 40	...	6 46	...	8 54	8 35	1127		...	...	...

NAUMBURG and TEUCHERN.

Naumburg ....dep	6a32	10a36	1 p3	5 p22	8 p34	...	...	...	...	...	...	...	...	...	...
Teuchern ....arr	7 19	11 24	1 48	6 5	9 21	...	...	...	...	...	...	...	...	...	...
Teuchern ....dep	5a24	7 a45	11a34	2p29	7 p20	...	...	...	...	...	...	...	...	...	...
Naumburg ....arr	6 16	8 35	12 20	3 16	8 10	...	...	...	...	...	...	...	...	...	...

WALLENDORF and PROBSTZELLA.

Wallendorf..........dep	5a 0	7†a29	9 a14	12 0	4p17	6 p0	9 p45	...	...	...	...	...	...	...	...
Probstzella ....arr	5 56	8 45	10 5	1 5	5 9	7 5	10 37	...	...	...	...	...	...	...	...
Probstzella ....dep	8 a6	10a20	1p32	3 p16	8p15	1 a1	...	...	†-Weekdays only.			...	...	...	...
Wallendorf ....arr	9 2	11 31	2 37	4 7	9 7	2 2	...	...				...	...	...	...

GOTHA and LEINEFELDE.

		a.m.	a.m.	a.m.	a.m.	a.m.	a m.	a.m.	p.m.	p.m.	p.m.	p.m.	p.m.	p.m.	p.m.	
Gotha..........dep	...	4 25	5 40	7 3	7 40	8 22	9 14	11 5	1231	2 58	4 56	6 22	7 5	8 4	10 22	...
Bufleben ....arr	...	4 37	5 52	7 14	7 55	8 31	9 26	11 19	1241	3 13	⋮	6 34	7 17	8 15	10 32	...
Bufleben ....dep	...	...	5 55	...	...	...	...	11 25	...	3 40	⋮	6 37	...	8 45	...	...
G.-Behringen ...arr	...	..	6 49	...	...	...	...	12 4	...	4 37	⋮	7 16	...	9 38	...	...
Bufleben ....dep	...	4 38	5 54	7 15	7 58	8 31	9 27	11 21	1242	3 15	⋮	6 35	7 18	8 18	10 33	...
Ballstädt	...	4 47	6 4	7 22	8 7	8 45	9 36	11 29	1249	3 22	⋮	6 43	7 26	8 27	10 40	...
Langensalza 152..........	a.m.	5 4	6 21	7 40	—	8 59	9 51	11 50	1 5	3 37	5 16	—	7 41	8 41	10 53	...
Mühlhausen	4 43	5 41	6 56	8 27	9a10	...	10 32	12 22	1 32	4 7	5 34	...	8 11	9 17	11 21	...
Leinefelde..........arr	5 37	...	7 38	9 16	1014	...	11 20	1 13	...	4 56	6 5	...	...	10 4	1 10	...

	a.m				a.m.		a.m.		a.m.	a.m.	p.m.	p.m.	p.m.	p.m.	p.m.	p.m.
Leinefelde..........dep	1 33	a.m	...	a.m.	6 19	...	8 8	...	9 37	1145	12 42	1 52	...	4 23	7 2	10 21
Mühlhausen	2 44	4 12	...	5 45	7 4	...	8 57	a.m.	1024	1238	1 22	2 23	2 35	5 5	7 41	11 1
Langensalza	—	4 42	a.m.	6 21	7 36	a.m.	9 23	9 55	1054	1 6	—	2 47	3 6	5 37	8 11	11 30
Ballstädt..........	...	5 6	6 10	6 44	7 52	8 43	9 36	10 18	1110	1 20	...	⋮	3 24	5 52	8 29	11 46
Bufleben ....arr	...	5 11	6 20	6 50	7 58	8 50	9 42	10 24	1117	1 26	...	⋮	3 30	5 57	8 35	11 52
G.-Behringen......dep	...	4 30	..	...	7 6	...	...	...	...	1230	...	⋮	...	4 50	7 26	...
Bufleben ....arr	...	5 11	...	...	7 51	...	...	...	...	1 24	...	⋮	...	5 48	8 12	...
Bufleben ....dep	...	5 15	6 21	6 51	8 1	8 51	9 43	10 26	1120	1 29	...	⋮	3 34	5 59	8 38	11 54
Gotha 170 ....arr	...	5 27	6 40	7 2	8 11	9 3	9 54	10 38	1132	1 39	...	3 12	3 46	6 11	8 50	12 5

Ballstädt..........dep	5*a7	...	8 a12	11a32	...	3 p30	...	8‡p50	...	...	...	...	...	...	...
Tennstedt	6 13	6a25	9 34	12 33	3 p10	4 36	7 p0	10 5	...	...	...	...	...	...	...
Straussfurt ....arr	...	6 52	10 53	...	3 37	5 52	7 24	...	...	...	...	...	...	...	...

Straussfurt..........dep	...	7 a16	11a41	...	4 p0	6p15	7p45	...	*—Weekdays only.
Tennstedt	4a59	7 45	12 7	1 p41	4 28	6 54	8 13	...	‡—12.2 night on Sunday.
Ballstädt ....arr	6 2	8 43	...	3 3	...	8 19	...		

MÜHLHAUSEN and TREFFURT.

Mühlhausen ...dep	6a27	10a28	2p40	6p20	9p40	...	Treffurt ....dep	4a22	8a25	12p40	4p25	8 p4	...	...
Diedorf	7 24	11 26	3 37	7 11	1038	...	Diedorf..........	4 50	8 59	1 16	4 54	8 32	...	...
Treffurt 173A...arr	7 55	11 55	4 8	7 38	1111	...	Mühlhausen 172A arr	5 39	10 0	2 12	5 41	9 13	...	...

SCHLEUSINGEN and SUHL.

Schleusingen...dep	4a47	8 a55	12p46	4p40	8p16	...	Suhl..........dep	7a30	10a45	2p10	7 p0	9p30	...
Suhl 170A..........arr	5 48	9 46	1 47	5 44	9 10	...	Schleusingen 170A arr	8 35	11 56	3 15	8 6	10 34	...

UCKRO and DAHME.

E.M.														
	Uckro..........dep	9 a25	5 p48	9 p3	...	Dahme..........dep	8 a0	3p10	7p40	...	...	...	...	...
7¾	Dahme..........arr	9 55	6 18	9 33	...	Uckro 188.....arr	8 30	3 42	8 10	...	...	...	...	...

TRIPTIS and MARXGRUN.

Triptis ....dep	...	5 a47	7 a55	10a30	2p12	4p40	...	10p38	...	...	...
Ziegenruck	...	6 54	9 10	11 52	3 19	5 46	...	11 44	...	...	...
Lobenstein (173A)	5a20	8 1	10 8	12 49	4 19	6 39	8 p35	12 39	...	...	...
Blankenstein	5 44	8 22	11 10	1 39	4 40	—	8 59	—	...	...	...
Marxgrün ....arr	6 0	8 37	11 28	1 57	4 57	...	9 20	...	...	...	...

Marxgrün ....dep	...	6 40	9 a15	12 p6	...	3p20	5 p42	10p45	...	...	...
Blankenstein	...	6 59	9 32	12 22	...	3 43	6 1	11 6	...	...	...
Lobenstein	4a42	7 26	10 53	12 40	1 p56	4 52	7 6	11 27	...	...	...
Ziegenruck..........	5 42	8 26	11 56	—	3 15	6 0	8 22	—	...	...	...
Triptis 173..........arr	6 49	9 28	1 0	...	4 21	7 17	9 50	...	...	...	...

LEIPSIC, WEISSENFELS, ZEITZ, GERA, and PROBSTZELLA.

	234	234	2,3,4	234	1,2,3	234	2,3,4	1,2,3	234	2,3,4	234	2,3,4	1,2,3	2,3,4	234	2,3,4	234	234	234	234	1,2,3	2,3,4	Ex 3	2,3,4	Ex.3	2,3,4	Ex 3	2,3,4	234
Leipsic—	a.m.		a.m.	a.m.	a.m.	a.m.	a.m.	a.m.	p.m.		p.m.	p.m.	p.m.			p.m.	p.m.	p.m.	p.m.	p.m.				p.m.	p.m.			p.m.	ng't
Hauptbhf ...dep	4 10	...	5 5	6 50	7 5	8 15	9 58	11 10		...	1 20	12 20	2 0	...	...	3 30	4 10	5 25	6 35	7 35	...	...	...	8 30	10 13	...	...	10 33	1215
Plagwitz-Linden	4 34	...	5 32	7 29	7 20	8 37	10 23	11 25	1215	...	1 45	12 43	2 14	...	...	3 56	4 33	5 49	7 0	7 58	...	...	...	8 53	10 28	...	...	10 58	1243
Eythra	4 56	...	5 54	7 50	...	8 59	10 44	...	1237	...	2 4	1 3	...	...	...	4 19	4 55	6 10	7 21	8 19	...	...	...	9 15	...	...	...	11 20	1 7
Zeitz (189A) ...arr	5 40	...	6 38	8 27	7 50	9 38	11 26	11 55		...		1 41	2 44	...	a.m.		5 37		8 2	8 57	...	...	...	9 58	11 2	...	...	12 3	1 50
BERLIN ......dep	1125	a.m.	...	1230	...	...	...	8 a20	...	...	...	8 a25	...	...	1050	...	1245	...	3p35	...	4p50	...	...	...	...	nig't	...	...	...
Weissenfels dep	4 10	5 46	...	7 1	...	8a40	...	11 20	...	...	...	12 27	...	...	2 5	...	4 59	...	6 51	...	8 24	...	...	9 4	...	12 11	...	...	...
Zeitz ....arr	4 54	6 34	...	7 46	...	9 28	...	11 51	...	p.m.	..	1 21	...	...	2 50	p.m.	5 41	...	7 31	...	9 0	...	...	9 54	...	12 56	...	...	...
Zeitz ....dep	5 48	6 53	...	8 29	7 51	9 43	...	12 0	...	12 24	...	1 51	2 45	...	2 55	5 45	5 52	...	8 6	...	9 3	...	...	10 1	11 3	1 6	..	...	2 2
Crossen (152)	6 13	7 15	...	8 49	..	1013	...	...	...	12 53	...	2 15	3 1	...	3 17	6 2	6 16	...	8 29	...	9 19	...	From 2nd until 14th July.	10 23	11 18	1 29	Until 31st August.	...	2 26
Gera (189)......arr	6 32	7 35	...	9 6	8 16	1036	...	12 24	...	1 10	..	2 37	3 15	...	3 34	6 19	6 35	...	8 46	...	9 31	...		10 40	11 29	1 47		...	2 45
,, ...dep	6 57		...	9 36	8 19	1050	...	12 33	...	1 15	...	2 59		...	3 39	6 23	6 41	...		...	9 53	...		10 46	11 31			...	4 32
Wolfsgefarth ...	7 13	...	...	9 52	...	11 9	...	...	...	1 31	...	3 18	...	...	3 55	6 36	6 56	..	...	...	...	...		11 1	...	...		...	4 49
Weida (185)	7 24	...	...	10 3	...	1128	...	12 49	...	1 44	...	3 28	...	...	4 5	6 43	7 7	...	...	...	10 8	...		11 10	11 47	...		...	5 1
Niederpöllnitz....	7 37	...	...	1014	..	1144	...	...	...	1 55	...		...	...	4 17		7 19	...	...	...	...	...		11 22	...	...		a.m.	5 14
Triptis	7 49	...	...	1024	..	12 0	...	1 10	...	2 4	...	...	...	...	4 30	...	7 32	...	...	...	1027	...		11 33	12 3	...		3 56	5 27
Neustadt-a-d-O.	8 2	...	...	1034	9 1	1215	...	1 19	...		...	...	...	...	4 40	...	7 44	...	...	...	1038	...		11 43	12 13	...		4 15	5 40
Oppurg............	8 13	...	...	1043	...	1227	...	...	...	...	Ex3	...	...	p.m.	4 52	Ex 3	7 55	...	...	...	...	...		11 53	...	Ex 3		4 34	5 49
Pössneck	8 21	...	...	1051	9 15	1239	...	1 33	p.m.	...	p.m.	...	...	3 26	5 4	p.m.	8 4	p.m.	...	...	1052	a.m.	nig't	12 4	12 25	a.m.	a.m.		5 58
Saalfeld (170) arr	8 48	...	...	1116	9 33	1 22	...	1 52	2 10	...	2 41	...	...	3 56	5 45	6 9	8 35	9 46	...	...	1111	12 1	12 31	12 34	12 42	1 2	1 52	...	6 30
Eichicht	9 14	...	...	1227	9 50		...	2 13	2 29	...	...	...	...	4 23	6 45	...	9 4	10 2	...	...		12 25	⋮			...	⋮	...	7 12
Unterloquitz	9 26	...	...	1240	...	...	...	...	2 42	...	...	...	...	4 36	6 59	...	9 18		...	...	...	12 36	⋮	...	...	...	⋮	...	7 24
Probstzella ...arr	9 42	...	...	1259	10 10	...	...	2 33	3 0	...	3 12	...	...	4 54	7 21	6 40	9 40	...	...	...	..	12 50	⋮	...	...	1 33	⋮	...	7 40
LICHTENFELS ar	1130	...	...	3p55	11a30	...	...	4 p4	...	...	⋮	...	...	...	1042	8 p0	...	...	...	...	...	...	⋮	...	...	...	⋮	...	1020
MUNICH (197) ar	...	...	...	...	5 p12	...	...	8 p34	...	...	8p34	...	...	...	...	12 40	...	...	...	...	...	...	7 a12	...	...	7 a14	8 a35	...	...

	234	1,2,3	234	Ex 3	Ex3	2,3,4	Ex 3	234	1,2,3	234	2,3,4	234	2,3,4	2,3,4	234	Ex 3	234	234	234	Ex3	234	2,3,4	1,2,3	2,3,4	234	1,2,3	2,3,4	2.3,4	1—4
MUNICH ....dep	...	...	...	10 20	...	...	11p32	...	...	...	...	...	...	...	...	...	...	a.m.	...	8a25	...	. .	8a25	...	...	12p45	...	...	...
LICHTENFELS dep	...	...	...	⋮	...	...		...	...	...	...	...	...	6 a10	...	10a37	...	1043	...	⋮	...	...	2 p2	...	...	6 p1	6 p1	...	8 p2
(195)				⋮	a.m.		⋮	a.m.				a.m.		a.m.	a.m.	⋮	p.m.	p.m.		⋮	..	p.m.	p.m.		p.m.	p.m.	p.m.		p.m.
Probstzella ......dep	...	...	...	⋮	...	...	⋮	4 55	...	...	...	6 2	...	8 53	10 16	⋮	...	1 26	...	⋮	...	...	4 9	...	5 17	7 47	8 10	...	1050
Unterloquitz...........	...	...	...	⋮	...	...	⋮	5 7	...	...	...	6 19	...	9 5	10 34	⋮	...	1 41	...	⋮	p.m.	...	...	...	5 29	...	8 23	...	11 2
Eichicht	...	...	...	⋮	.	...	⋮	5 18	...	...	...	6 31	...	9 15	10 47	⋮	12 8	1 52	...	⋮	2 21	...	4 27	...	5 41	...	8 34	...	1113
Saalfeld ....dep	...	...	...	4 18	4 35	...	5 41	5 53	...	...	...	8 31	...	10 43	11 6	12 36	1242	2 43	...	2 23	2 37	3 26	5 2	...	6 21	8 22	8 58	...	1127
Pössneck	...	...	...		4 55	...	...	6 24	...	...	...	9 0	...	11 17			1 18	3 16	...			4 0	5 23	...	6 53	8 42	9 28	p.m.	1226
Oppurg (170)............	...	...	...		...	...	From 2nd July until 1st September.	6 30	...	...	...	9 9	...	11 24	...		1 28		...	...	...	4 8	...	...	7 0	...	9 35	11 52	1232
Neustadt-a-d-Orla...	...	...	...	...	5 11	...		6 42	...	...	...	9 20	a.m.	11 37	...	...	1 40	...	...	...	...	4 20	5 37	...	7 12	8 58	9 47	12 14	1245
Triptis.....................	...	...	...	...	...	...		6 57	...	...	...	9 32	10 0	11 53	...	...	1 52	...	...	...	...	4 32	5 50	...	7 26	...	9 59	12 34	1259
Niederpöllnitz	...	...	...	...	...	a.m.		7 5	...	...	...	9 40	10 11	12 1	...	...	2 0	...	...	...	p.m.	4 40	...	...	7 34	...	10 7		1 6
Weida (185)	...	...	...	...	5 35	5 20		7 18	...	...	...	9 53	10 22	12 12	...	...	2 11	...	...	...	3 40	4 55	6 5	...	7 45	9 24	10 19	...	1 15
Wolfsgefarth	...	...	...	...	...	5 27		7 25	...	...	...	10 0	10 29	12 19	...	...	2 18	...	...	...	3 47	5 2	...	...	7 51	...	10 25	...	1 22
Gera ....arr	...	a.m.	a.m.	...	5 50	5 42		7 40	a.m.	a.m.	...	1015	10 43	12 34	...	...	2 34	...	...	...	4 3	5 18	6 19	p.m.	8 6	9 38	10 40	...	1 33
,, ...dep	...	4 25	5 0	...	5 53	6 16		7 46	8 17	8 22	...	1023	10 50	12 42	...	...	2 44	...	...	...		5 48	6 23	6 56	8 12	9 51	11 0	...	
Crossen	...	...	5 21	2,3,4	...	6 37		8 5	8 34	8 40	...	1041	11 12	1 3	...	...	3 2	...	...	...	...	6 7	6 36	7 17	8 31	10 4	11 22	...	...
Zeitz ....arr	a.m.	4 51	5 42	a.m.	6 20	6 57		8 25	8 54	8 59	...	11 1	11 35	1 23	...	...	3 22	...	...	...	...	6 29	6 51	7 37	8 52	10 19	11 41	...	..
Zeitz ....dep	4 26	4 53	...	5 47	...	7 1		...	...	9 4	...	11 8	12 40	1 30	...	...	3 28	...	...	...	...	...	6 57	7 50	9 2	...	11 50	...	...
Weissenfels ......arr	5 10	5 24	...	6 32	...	7 48	...	...	...	9 48	...	1149	1 26	2 11	...	...	4 8	...	...	...	...	...	7 31	8 35	9 43	...	12 31	...	...
BERLIN (171) ...arr		8 a25	...	...	...	11a30	...	...	...	2p39	a.m.	2p39	4p34	6 p42	..	2,3,4	8p19	...	p.m.	...	...	..	1038	...	5 a0	...	...	...	...
Zeitz..........dep 4a10	5 a0	...	6 0	...	6 21	7 51	...	...	8 53	9 38	11 7	...	p.m.	1 29	...	p.m.	3 27	...	4 52	...	p.m.	7 43	7 5	9 35	...	10 20	11 47	...	...
Eythra 4 53	5 41	...	6 50	...	...	8 24	...	...	...	10 4	11 41	...	1 18	2 3	...	2 40	4 5	...	5 32	...	6 52	8 23	...	10 12	...	..	12 24	...	...
Plagwitz-Lind. 5 22	6 8	...	7 11	...	6 50	8 43	...	...	9 22	1021	12 3	...	1 40	2 25	...	3 0	4 29	...	6 4	...	7 20	8 45	7 40	10 38	...	10 49	12 46	...	...
Leipsic Hpt. 171 5 49	6 33	..	7 38	...	7 6	9 6	...	..	9 38	1046	12 27	...	...	2 49	...	3 24	4 52	...	6 30	...	7 47	9 12	7 56	10 56	...	11 5	1 10	...	...

Niederpollnitz and Münchenbernsdorf (30 min.)—N-Pollnitz dep. 7.40, 10.18a.m., 12.10, 2.10, 5.0, 7.48 p.m. Münchenbernsdorf dep. 6.30, 9.15, 11.5a.m., 1.20, 3.40, 6.40 p.m.

PRUSSIAN STATE RAILWAYS.

Luggage Rates—see page 462.

COTTBUS and SAGAN.

	a.m.	a.m.	a.m.	p.m.	p.m	p.m.	p.m	p.m.	p.m.	p.m.	a.m.
Cottbus dep	6 55	9 45	1039	1255	3 13	4 17	5 56	7 36	1017	1128	1 46
Forst	7 25	1012	1058	1 21	3 32	4 44	6 15	8 2	1042	1157	2 6
Sorau	8 44	1113	1133	2 25	4 5	5 45	6 51	8 59	1135	1 1	2 42
Sagan ...arr	9 1	1130	1144	2 40	4 16	6 1	7 2	9 15	1148	1 16	2 53

	a.m.	a.m.	a.m.	a.m.	a.m.	a.m.	p.m.	p.m.	p.m.	p.m.	p.m.	p.m.
Sagan..	2 5	4 20	5 38	8 37	8 48	1043	1 15	1 33	4 5	6 17	7 53	1150
Sorau...	2 19	4 48	6 12	8 51	9 10	11 6	1 55	1 47	4 26	6 17	8 34	1214
Forst ...	2 47	5 39	7 6	9 23	9 56	1155	2 45	2 16	5 11	6 50	9 21	1 4
Cottbus	3 5	6 4	7 32	9 41	1020	1221	3 11	2 34	5 35	7 9	9 46	1 30

Extra—Cottbus to Sagan, 5.10 a.m Sorau to Sagan 3.19, 4.53, 9.39 a.m., 12.32 p.m Sagan to Sorau 1.15 a.m., 12.5, 8.12 p.m.

LEIPSIC, BITTERFELD, and ZERBST.

Extra.—Dessau to Bitterfeld 11.30 p m.

	2 3 4	1—4	1—4	Ex3	2 3 4	1—4	2 3 4	1—4	2 3 4	Ex.3	Ex3	2 3 4	2 3 4
Leipsic—	a.m.	a.m.	a.m.	a.m.	a.m.	p.m.	p.m.	p.m.	p.m.	p.m.		p.m.	n'gt
Haupt. Bhf. dp	4 25	6 20	9 0	1035	1055	1 55	4 5	5 10	7 15	9 32	...	1045	1233
Delitzsch	4 54	6 58	9 36	...	1135	2 36	4 43	5 48	7 53	...	...	1123	1 6
Bitterfeld ...arr	5 5	7 10	9 48	11 6	1147	2 43	4 55	6 0	8 5	10 3	...	1135	1 18
,, (170) dep	5 47	7 43	9 56	11 7	1159	3 16	5 13	6 28	8 11	10 8	...	1139	1 22
Raguhn 2 3 4	6 9	8 2	1018	...	1221	3 38	5 35	6 50	8 31	...	p.m.	12 1	1 41
Dessau 172 4a55	6 27	8 22	1038	1129	1241	3 59	5 54	7 11	8 50	10 30		1222	1 56
Rosslau......5 6	6 54	8 37	11 3	1139	1 1	4 26	6 9		9 11	10 42	1053	1240	
Zerbst 164 5 22	7 13	8 50	1123	1152	1 22	4 47	6 26	...	9 31	...	11 5	1 1	...
MAGDEBURG 6a35	8a22	9a27	1227	1234	2p37	5p54	7p41	...	1045	...	1142	...	...

	Ex3	2 3 4	2 3 4	Ex.3	1—4	2 3 4	2 3 4	1—4	1,2,3	2 3 4	2 34
	a.m.	a.m.	a.m.	a.m.	a.m.	a.m.	p.m.	p.m.	p.m.	p.m.	p.m.
MAGDEBRG dep	...	...	6 12	7 4	...	10 40	1 18	4 15	6 10	7 42	1147
Zerbst ......dep	...	5 29	7 28	7 44	8 55	11 49	2 38	5 25	6 54	9 2	1255
Rosslau ...dep	...	5 48	7 43	7 56	9 15	12 11	3 5	5 48	7 15	9 26	1 10
Dessau ...dep	4 53	6 1	7 59		9 34	12 32	3 45	6 16	7 29	9 57	1 19
Raguhn	...	6 24	8 21	...	9 58	12 54	4 11	6 33	7 51	1021	
Bitterfeld arr	5 16	6 45	8 37	...	1019	1 12	4 33	6 49	8 9	1041	...
,, ...dep	5 17	6 55	9 5	...	1049	1 20	4 52	7 0	8 24	1058	...
Delitzsch	...	7 11	9 21	...	11 5	1 36	5 8	7 14	8 41	1114	...
Leipsic Hpt. Bf.	5 49	7 49	10 0	...	1140	2 12	5 46	7 37	9 20	1153	...

HALLE, LEIPSIC, COTTBUS, and GUBEN.

Extra.—Leipsic to Eilenburg 5.10 p.m.] Falkenberg to Leipsic, 9.10 p.m.

		a.m.	a.m.	a.m.		a.m.	p.m.	p.m.	p.m.	p.m.	p.m.	p.m.	n'gt
Halle ....dep		5 32	7 45	7 55	...	1135	1245	3 10	3 25	6 15	9 5	1110	1210
Delitzsch ......dep		6 18	8 10	8 33	...	1217	...	3 35	4 5	6 56	9 46	...	1257
Eilenburg......arr		6 48	8 30	9 3	a.m.	1247	1 26	3 55	4 35	7 26	1016	1151	1 29
Leipsic ......dep		6 5	7 45	8 15	1019	12 0	1 0	3 25	3 48	6 30	9 30	1125	1225
Taucha		6 24	8 4	8 34	1042	1222	...	...	4 7	6 50	9 49	...	1245
Eilenburg ...arr		6 45	8 25	8 55	11 8	1247	1 23	3 48	4 28	7 11	1011	1148	1 6
Eilenburg dep	3a23	6 54	8 35	9 6		1254	1 30	3 59	4 39	7 31	1021	1155	1 36
Torgau	4 7	7 33	8 58	9 42	...	1 35	...	4 22	5 18	8 10	11 0	1218	2 15
Falken- arr	4 32	8 0	9 13	10 4	...	1 59	2 5	4 37	5 41	8 33	1124	1233	
berg dep	4 46		9 23	1015	...	2 17	2 6	4 39	5 48	8 50	1150	1234	...
Beutersitz	4 58	...	...	1028	...	2 30	...	...	6 0	9 3	12 2	...	...
DobrilugkKirch	5 18	...	9 43	11 0	..	2 58	...	5 1	6 19	9 39	1221	...	...
Finsterwalde ...	5 33	...	9 54	1117	...	3 12	...	5 13	6 33	9 54	1236	1 4	...
Calau..............	5 59	...	1013	1145	...	3 38	...	5 32	6 58	1019	1 1	...	...
Cottbus ...arr	6 27	...	1033	1215	...	4 7	3 7	5 51	7 26	1048	1 29	1 41	a.m.
,, ...dep	6 55	...	1044	1255	...	4 20	3 29	6 17		1127			2 42
Peitz Ost.	7 15	...	...	1 15	...	4 42	...	6 39	...	1147	...	...	3 1
Guben 179 arr	7 45	...	1113	1 42	...	5 13	4	7 11	...	1217	...	...	3 29

	a.m.	a.m.	a.m.	a.m.	a.m.	a.m.	p.m.	p.m.	p.m.	p.m.	p.m.	p.m.
Guben ......dep	1 20	...	5 19	8 46	...	1055	...	1 52	...	4 48	6 12	9 10
Peitz Ost............	1 51	...	5 50	9 18	...	1129	...	...	...	5 19	...	9 41
Cottbus ......arr	2 8	...	6 10	9 35	...	1151	...	2 26	...	5 36	6 44	10 1
,, ...dep		3 11	6 17	9 47	1026		1 20	2 40	3 36	6 0	7 17	1014
Calau	...	...	6 46	10 8	1057	...	1 55	...	4 10	6 31	7 41	1051
Finsterwalde......	...	3 49	7 15	1028	1127	...	2 27	...	4 41	7 1	8 5	1127
Dobrilugk-Kirch	...	...	7 27	1039	1140	...	2 42	...	4 59	7 14	8 17	1159
Beutersitz	...	...	7 44	...	1159	...	3 2	...	5 16	7 31	...	1220
Falkenb'rg arr	...	4 15	7 55	1057	1210	...	3 14	3 41	5 27	7 42	8 37	1232
,, ...dep	a.m.	4 16	7 59	1059	1214	...	3 50	3 42	5 38	7 50	8 53	1 7
Torgau..............	3 40	4 32	8 23	1115	1239	...	4 15	...	6 3	8 15	9 10	1 32
Eilenburg arr	4 21	4 54	9 1	1137	1 18	p.m.	4 53	4 18	6 42	8 52	9 35	2 20
Eilenbu'g dep	4 35	5 4	9 15	1143	1 30	3 15	5 5	4 28	6 52	...	9 48	
Taucha............	5 2	...	9 43	12 4	1 55	3 40	5 33	...	7 21	...	1016	...
Leipsic ...arr	5 20	5 30	10 1	1215	2 13	3 58	5 51	4 54	7 39	...	1034	p.m.
Eilenburg dep	5 8	4 58	9 5	1139	1 23		4 57	4 23	6 46	8 56	9 41	1020
Delitzsch	5 43	...	9 36	12 0	1 56	...	5 28	...	7 17	9 27	...	1052
Halle (171) arr	6 29	5 42	1013	1227	2 38	...	6 9	5 5	7 58	10 8	1025	1135

LOBENSTEIN and EICHICHT.

Lobenstein ....dep	4a48	10a22	12p50	4p11	6p24
Unterlemnitz	4 56	10 33	1 1	4 20	6 35
Hockeroda.......................	6 18	12 2	2 16	5 27	7 42
Eichicht (173) ....arr	6 24	12 7	2 20	...	7 47

Eichicht ....dep	7 a21	9a20	2 p35	...	10 p7	...	...
Hockeroda..........................	7 29	9 26	2 41	7 p0	10 13	...	...
Unterlemnitz	9 1	1034	3 56	8 17	11 34	...	...
Lobenstein (172A) ...arr	9 9	1039	4 3	8 24	11 41	...	...

EISENACH and TREFFURT.

Eisenach ....dep	5a35	8 a6	11a11	2 p40	6 p26	10p52	...
Wartha	6 4	8 31	11 35	3 7	6 51	11 8	...
Treffurt 172A ...arr	7 9	9 33	12 35	4 7	7 46	12 6	...

Treffurt ....dep	4 a5	8 a3	11a58	3 p5	5 p20	9 p8	...	...
Wartha	5 11	9 8	1 3	4 28	6 31	10 30	...	...
Eisenach ....arr	5 28	9 25	1 20	4 45	6 49	10 46	...	...

CASSEL and BEBRA.

	Ex3	1,2,3	2 3 4	2 3 4	1,2,3	2 3 4	1,2,3	1,2,3	2 3 4	Ex3	1—4	1,2,3	2 3 4	Ex3	Ex3	2 3 4	2 3 4					
	a.m.	a.m.	a.m.	a.m	a.m.	a.m.	a.m.	a.m.	p.m.	p.m.	p.m.	p.m.	p.m.	p.m.	p.m.	p.m.	p.m.					
Cassel ....dep	2 57	4 35	5 5	6 50	7 50	8 26	1111	1118	12 7	1 36	2 44	3 45	6 20	6 48	7 34	7 40	1148					
Wilhelmshöhe	...	4 43	5 13	6 58	7 55	8 34	...	1125	1215	...	2 52	...	6 28	...	...	7 48	1156	...	...	...	...	...
Guntershaus	3 14	4 59	5 31	7 18	...	8 51	...	1139	1235	...	3 12	4 1	6 45	...	7 50	8 6	1213	...	...	...	...	...
Melsungen	...	5 15	5 55	7 42	...	9 17	...	12 1	1 0	...	3 39	...	7 27	7 20	...	8 31	1237	...	...	...	...	...
Malsfeld 147	...	--	6 3	7 49	8 25	9 25	...	12 8	1 6	...	3 50	4 21	7 33	...	...	8 38	1243	...	...	...	...	...
Bebra ....arr	3 54	5 44	6 44	8 30	8 46	10 8	12 6	1238	1 42	...	4 26	4 47	8 18	7 47	8 30	9 17	1 22	...	...	...	...	...
EISENACH 171 ....arr	4a37	...	8a10	...	9a46	1057	1248	1p25	2p58	3p14	5p 9	5p40	9p17	8p33	9p17	1046	2a22	...	...	...	...	...

	Ex3	1—4	Ex3	2 3 4	Ex3	1,2,3	1—4	Ex3	1,2,3	2 3 4	1,2,3	1—4	1,2,3	2 3 4	2 3 4	1,2,3						
EISENACH ....dep	1250	5a26	7a47	7a55	9a57	1129	1129	12p7	1220	1p34	3p16	3p51	5p55	7p10	8p13	10p52						
	a.m.	a.m.	a.m.	a.m.	a.m.	p m.	p.m.	p.m.	p.m.	p.m.	p.m.	p.m.	p.m.	p.m.	p.m.	nght						
Bebra ....dep	1 40	6 54	8 32	9 2	1041	1218	1223	1247	1 42	3 11	4 12	4 50	6 44	8 4	9 39	12 7	...	...	...	...	...	...
Malsfeld	...	7 37	...	9 42	...	1245	1 2	...	...	3 53	4 33	5 31	7 8	8 46	101"	12 34	...	...	...	...	...	...
Melsungen	2 8	7 43	...	9 48	11 7	...	1 18	...	2 9	3 59	...	5 37	7 15	8 52	1023	...	...	...	...	...	...	...
Guntershaus	...	8 13	...	1013	...	...	1 42	...	...	4 24	4 53	6 1	7 34	9 18	1048	...	...	...	...	...	...	...
Wilhelmshöh..................	...	8 30	...	1029	...	1 18	1 58		...	4 40	...	6 18	7 47	9 38	11 6	1 2	...	...	...	...	...	...
Cassel 134D....................	2 44	8 37	9 25	1036	1136	1 25	2 5	1 46	2 42	4 47	5 11	6 25	7 54	9 45	1113	1 9	...	...	...	...	...	...

‡—Not on Sunday.

*—Weekdays only]

EISENACH, COBURG, and LICHTENFELS.

E.M.		Ex 3	2 3 4	2 3 4	1—4	2 3 4	2 3 4	1—4	Ex3	2 3 4	1,2,3	2 3 4	Ex 3	1—4	Ex 3	1—4	2,3,4	1—4	1—4	1 2 3
...	BEBRA 171 dep	...	...	...	3 a55	...	...	9 a4	1015	...	1210	...	p m.	1245	...	1 p50	...	4p58	...	8p37
Dist.					a.m.	a.m.	a.m.	a.m.	a.m.	p.m.	p.m.		Kissingen dep. 1.48.	p.m.	p.m.	p.m.	p.m.	p.m.	p.m.	p.m.
—	**Eisenach** dep	...	...	...	4 46	...	7 36	9 53	11 3	...	1 0	...		1 38	From Stuttgart	3 20	...	5 49	8 40	9 34
16¾	Salzungen	...	...	...	5 32	8 57	8 13	10 28	1137	1216	1 33	...		2 21		4 5	4 46	6 35	9 23	10 8
19½	Immelborn	...	...	...	5 40	9 5	8 21	10 36	...	1224	1 40	...		2 29		4 13	4 57	6 43	9 30	1014
25½	Wernshausen ...	...	...	...	5 55	—	8 38	10 51	1153	—	1 51	...		2 50		4 29	—	6 58	9 46	1025
30½	Wasungen	...	...	...	6 8	...	8 48	11 6	...	...	...	...		3 6		4 42	...	7 12	9 59	...
38	**Meiningen** arr	a.m.	a.m.	...	6 23	...	9 3	11 22	1211	p.m.	2 11	...	3 17	3 29		4 57	...	7 29	10 14	1043
...	„ dep	3 26	5 1	...	6 31	...	9 6	11 27	1214	1 8	2 15	...	3 25	3 52	4 21	5 4	...	7 37	10 19	1047
42½	Grimmenthal ...	⋮	5 13	...	6 46	...	9 23	11 40	...	1 21	2 26	...		4 2	4 28	5 30	...	8 6	10 32	1057
50½	Themar	To Erfurt (arr. 5.13)	—	...	7 4	...	9 41	12 0	...	—	2 41	p.m.	Berlin arr. 9.13.	—		5 49	...	8 28	10 51	1112
57¾	Hildburghausen		...	...	7 23	...	9 58	12 17	1245	...	2 57	3 9		...		6 9	...	8 46	11 10	1127
67½	Eisfeld		...	...	7 54	1—4	1021	12 41	...	...	3 16	3 38		2 3 4	To Berlin.	6 31	...	9 9	11 29	1144
80¾	**Coburg**......arr		a.m.	a.m.	8 19	a.m.	1045	1 7	1 21	p.m	3 37	~		p.m.		6 56	...	9 38	11 52	12 5
...	„ ...dep		4 52	6*50	8 26	9 55	1055	—	1 26	2 0	3 39	3p14		5 14		7 8	...	9 45	12 30	...
87¾	Ebersdorf		5 12	7 12	8 45	1015	1112	...	...	2 24	...	4 30	...	5 35		7 30	...	10 4	12 49	...
93¾	**Lichtenfels** ar	—	5 25	—	8 57	1031	1126	...	1 45	—	4 1	4 51	...	5 49		7 43	...	10 18	1 3	...
113¾	BAMBERG 197	...	6a27	...	10 a1	...	12p4	...	2p40	...	4p40	6 p7	...	6p21	...	8 p27	...	12 a3	1 a51	...

	Ex3	2 3 4	2 3 4	2 3 4	1—4	Ex3	1,2,3	2 3 4	2 3 4	1—4	Ex 3	2 3 4	2 3 4	1 2 3	1—4	1—4	2 3 4	1 2 3	2 3 4	1—4
BAMBERG ....dep	From Erfurt (dep. 12.21 night).	...	...	...	4a41	4a41	...	7 a0	7a 0	10a9	...	...	12p2	1p11	...	3 p37	5p28	6p50	9p49	2a20
					a.m.	a.m.		a.m.	a.m.	a.m.		p.m.	p.m.	p.m.	p.m.	p m.	p.m.	p.m.	p.m.	a.m.
Lichtenfels ......dep		...	...	...	5 57	6 32	...	8 10	9 9	1050	...	...	1240	2 15	...	4 58	6 14	8 21	11 4	2 54
Ebersdorf		...	...	...	6 16	...	...	8 25	9 48	1112	...	1238	1255	2 29	...	5 13	6 32	8 42	1137	...
Coburg 173B { arr		...	a.m.	...	6 36	6 57	...	8 41	1016	1128	Berlin dep. 8.10.	1257	1 13	2 40	...	5 32	6 53	9 0	1210	3 48
{ dep		...	4 58	...	6 44	7 1	...	9 4	—	1140		—	—	2 45	3 39	5 49	—	9 10	—	—
Eisfeld (173B)		...	5 29	...	7 35	7 27	...	9 39	⋮ ...	1220		2p26	...	3 17	4 13	6 31	...	9 48	...	...
Hildburghausen (154)		...	5 49	...	7 58	7 45	...	10 2	1—4	1244		2 52	Ex3	3 37	4 33	6 56	...	1011	...	...
Themar		a.m.	6 5	...	8 20	...	...	1020	a.m.	1 1		—	p.m.	3 54	4 50	7 19	p.m.	1033	p.m.	...
Grimmenthal (170A)	⋮	5 28	6 24	...	8 56	...	...	1037	11 2	1 21		...	2 20	4 11	5 22	7 46	9 49	1055	1129	...
Meiningen 195 { arr	2 13	5 41	6 35	a.m.	9 8	8 15	a.m.	1048	1113	1 31	1 45	...	2 27	4 20	5 34	7 58	10 0	11 6	1146	...
{ dep	—	5 50	—	6*40	9 22	8 18	1053	~	1123	1 39	1 53	...	To Stuttgart ☞	4 27	6 23	8 6	—	1111	—	...
Wasungen	...	6 7	2 3 4	6 55	9 37	...	...	...	1140	1 59	Kissingen arr. 3.32.	2 3 4		4 42	6 40	8 23	...	1125	...	...
Wernshausen (174)...	...	6 22	a.m.	7 5	9 49	8 39	1112	a.m.	1153	2 12		p.m.		4 51	6 57	8 40	...	1139	...	...
Immelborn (173B) ...	...	6 38	8 0	—	10 3	...	1122	1159	12 8	2 27		4 19		5 1	7 12	8 57	...	1152	...	...
Salzungen (153)	...	6 48	8 8	...	1013	8 54	1129	12 7	1218	2 36		4 31		5 8	7 21	9 10	...	12 0	...	...
Eisenach ....arr	...	7 29	—	...	1054	9 21	1156	—	1256	3 9		—		5 37	7 56	9 55	...	1236	...	...
BEBRA (170)......arr	...	8a30	...	...	1214	10a9	1245	...	2p14	3p58		...		6p38	8p54	11p26	...	1a35	...	...

Extra { Meiningen......dep 11p10 / Grimmenthal...arr 11 20

COBURG and LAUSCHA

Coburg ....dep	...	5a44	...	7a22	...	...	8a48	9a37	...	12p20	1p29	...	3p56	4p44	5 p41	7p39	10p32	...	12a15
Sonneberg........................	5a38	6 18	6a24	8 0	8 a5	8a20	9 43	1019	12p16	1 3	2 5	2 p9	4 42	5 33	6 34	8 23	11 10	11p16	12 51
Köppelsdorf-Ober............	5 43	6 52	6 30	—	8 11	8 26	9 52	1025	12 21	—	2 22	2 15	4 48	5 42	6 41	8 29	11 16	11 23	—
Stockheim ....arr	...	...	6 57	...	...	9 1	...	1053	...	...	...	2 41	...	6 8	7 14	9 9	11 45	...	...
Blechhammer	6 8	7 25	—	...	8 26	...	1016	—	12 44	...	2 46	—	5 11	—	—	8 44	—	11 42	...
Lauscha ....arr	6 38	8 5	...	...	8 53	...	1045	...	1 14	...	3 20	...	5 41	...	...	9 11	...	12 14	...

Lauscha ....dep	...	4 a48	...	6 a59	...	9 a7	...	12p40	1p43	3 p38	...	...	...	7 p10	9p51	...	...
Blechhammer	...	5 16	...	7 25	...	9 35	a.m.	1 12	2 11	4 4	...	...	...	7 39	1017	...	...
Stockeim ....dep	4a40	...	...	...	7a29	9 20	11 54	...	...	3 39	...	6 p48	7 p36	...	...	9p 38	...
Köppelsdorf-Oberlind	5 21	5 31	a.m.	7 44	7 58	9 54	12 25	1 33	2 37	4 22	p.m.	7 15	8 6	7 59	1034	10 22	...
Sonneberg	5 28	5 58	7 6	7 49	8 9	1010	12 37	1 49	2 51	4 34	6 20	7 26	8 11	8 23	1040	10 45	...
Coburg (173B) ....arr	...	6 35	7 45	...	8 41	1045	1 16	2 30	3 28	5 8	6 55	8 0	...	8 57	...	11 37	...

COBURG and RODACH.

Coburg ...dep	7a18	11a45	1p33	3p43	7p10	11p56	...	...
Rodach......arr	8 19	12 26	2 26	4 24	7 51	12 39	...	...

Rodach ....dep	5a38	9a34	12p35	2p37	4p30	8 p6	...	...	...
Coburg 173B arr	6 31	10 35	1 16	3 21	5 11	8 55	...	...	...

IMMELBORN and LIEBENSTEIN.

Immelborn	7 a0	9a 7	10a40	12p25	2p34	5p15	7p15	10p20
Liebenstein	7 19	9 26	11 1	12 46	3 2	5 43	7 43	10 48

Liebenstein ...	5a50	7a42	9a38	11a40	1p14	3p46	6p16	8p30	...
Immelborn 173B	6 7	7 59	9 56	11 58	1 35	4 7	6 37	8 49	...

EISFELD and UNTERNEUBRUNN.

Eisfeld........... dep	8a10	12p43	3p42	6p33	9p52	...	...
Unterneubrunn arr	9 39	1 51	4 51	7 41	11 26	...	...

Unterneubrunn dep	5a52	10a35	1p58	5 p1	7p51	...	...	...
Eisfeld 173B ...arr	7 22	12 4	3 8	6 14	9 0	...	...	...

BRETLEBEN and SONDERSHAUSEN.

Bretleben ....dep	...	7a50	11a16	12p56	3p13	4p35	6p10	8p38
Frankenhausen	5a10	8 26	11 39	1 18	3 51	5 10	6 41	9 3
Sondershausen 152 arr	6 6	9 35	...	2 2	4 37	6 30	7 51	1010

Sondershausen dep	4a58	8a13	...	12 p5	3 p0	7p10	11p 0
Frankenhausen ...	6 44	1020	11a48	2 19	3 58	7 55	11 50
Bretleben 172A arr	7 11	1051	12 13	2 48	4 23	8 15	12 9

ALLSTEDT and OBER-ROBLINGEN.

Allstedt......................dep	6a10	10a23	12p 5	3p 9	6p11	7p45
Ober-Röblingen 148 arr	6 26	10 43	12 20	3 24	6 30	8 0

Ober-Röblingen dep	8 a4	11a32	12p27	4p15	7 p5	8p55	...	...
Allstedt ....arr	8 19	11 48	12 43	4 34	7 21	9 10	...	...

DESSAU and WORLITZ

Dessau ...dep	8a55	11a15	1p26	7 p0	10p40	...
Wörlitz ...arr	9 37	11 51	2 6	7 40	11 13	...

Wörlitz ....dep	5a48	9 a52	12 0	2 p21	8 p0	...
Dessau 173A...arr	6 23	10 32	12 36	3 0	8 40	...

PLAGWITZ-LINDENAU and PORSTEN.

Plagwitz-Lindenau dep	6a55	7a25	10a25	1p55	3p 5	6p20	7p20	1115	12a50
Lausen	7 7	7 34	10 35	2 6	3 17	6 31	7 31	1125	1 0
Porsten ...arr	7 56	...	11 18	2 57	...	7 19	8 16	...	...

Porsten ......dep	...	5a30	8a55	...	12p30	4p40	...	8p42	ngt.
Lausen............	5a25	6 19	9 52	10a35	1 22	5 31	7 p3	9 31	1228
Plagwitz-L. arr	5 37	6 29	10 2	10 47	1 32	5 41	7 13	9 41	1238

LAUSEN and MARKRANSTADT.

Lausen.....................dep	7a35	3p18	6p42	1 a1	...
Markranstadt......arr	7 42	3 26	6 49	1 8	...

Markranstadt...dep	5a15	10a20	6 p0	6p55	...
Lausen..............arr	5 23	10 28	6 7	7 2	...

ARNSTADT and SAALFELD.

‡—Weekdays only.

Arnstadt ....dep		...	6a58	...	9a15	11a22	...	12p43	...	...	3 p33	5 p4	...	7 p6	...	10p33
Stadtilm		...	7 24	...	9 39	11 42	...	1 5	...	...	4 1	5 21	...	7 27	...	10 55
Paulinzella	a.m.	a.m.	7 45	a.m.	9 57	12 2	a.m.	1 22	...	...	4 19	...	p.m.	7 42	...	11 13
Rottenbach	5 ‡4	6 46	7 57	10 17	10 9	12 11	11 59	1 31	1p37	3 p11	4 29	5 41	6 40	7 51	9p22	11 25
Blankenburg	5 30	7 0	8 13	10 32	10 23	12 26	12 14	1 44	1 53	3 24	4 44	5 51	6 58	8 3	9 37	11 38
Saalfeld 173 ...arr	5 45	...	8 25	...	10 36	12 35	...	1 55	...	...	4 57	6 0	...	8 15	...	11 50
Saalfeld ....dep	4‡a25	5a14	6 a55	7a26	a.m.	9a38	a.m.	11a22	a.m.	...	2p43	...	6 p1	8 p55	p.m.	...
Blankenburg	4 42	5 28	7 6	7 41	8 13	9 50	9 40	11 37	11 43	1p54	2 59	4p13	6 18	9 10	9 17	11p50
Rottenbach	4 56	5 43	7 17	8 1	8 28	10 4	9 55	11 51	11 56	2 9	3 14	4 28	6 35	9 22	9 36	12 5
Paulinzella	—	5 53	...	8 11	—	...	—	12 1	—	—	3 25	—	6 47	9 31	—	—
Stadtilm		6 11	7 43	8 30	...	10 27	...	12 20	...	...	3 44	...	7 11	9 47	...	...
Arnstadt 170A......arr		6 32	8 0	8·49	...	10 47	...	12 42	...	...	4 5	...	7 37	10 8	...	...

ROTTENBACH, KONIGSEE and KATZHUTTE.

Rottenbach......dep	5a50	...	8a34	10a10	12p14	...	2p14	...	4p34	4p43	6p45	9p40	12 a9	...
Köditzberg.........arr	5 57	6a45	8 43	10 19	12 23	1p15	2 21	3p 3	4 42	4 50	6 52	9 49	12 17	...
: Königsee.........arr	6 13	7 0	9 2	10 38	12 45	1 30	...	3 20	...	5 8	7 10	1010	...	...
Schwarzburg	—	—	9 6	10 41	12 50	—	2 42	—	5 6	—	—	1010	12 33	...
Katzhütte ....arr	...	...	9 52	11 27	1 33	...	3 24	...	5 52	...	...	1057	1 17	...
Katzhütte ....dep	5a29	...	8a34	10a13	12 0	...	1p50	...	...	5 p6	7p50	...	...	...
Schwarzburg ......dep	6 19	a.m.	9 31	11 14	1254	...	2 40	...	p.m.	6 0	8 46	p.m.	...	...
: Königsee ....dep	6 20	8 22	9 26	11 10	1252	2 p0	...	3p57	5 55	...	8 40	10 41	...	...
Köditzberg................	6 36	8 37	9 49	11 33	1 13	2 15	3 0	4 13	6 10	6 18	9 6	10 58	...	...
Rottenbach.........arr	6 42	...	9 58	11 42	1 22	...	3 7	4 20	6 17	6 25	9 15	11 7	...	...

MERSEBURG and SCHAFSTADT.

Merseburg dep	6 a0	8a17	a.m.	11a0	1p40	4p10	7†p30	8p30
Lauchstedt.....	6 24	8 44	1028	1125	2 5	4 36	7 50	8 56
Schafstädt arr	6 38	8 58	1042	1139	2 19	4 50	...	9 10

Schafstädt......dep	4a35	†	7a10	9a30	11a 5	12p40	3 p0	6p35	...
Lauchstadt...........	4 53	6a25	7 30	9 48	11 19	1 2	3 19	6 59	7†p57
Merseburg 170 arr	5 16	6 47	7 52	1010	...	1 28	3 41	7 21	8 17

Lauchstedt..... ....dep	5a40	8a43	11a29	2 p8	3p35	7*p5	...
Schlettau ....arr	6 3	9 7	11 53	2 32	4 4	7 29	...

Schlettau .....dep	7 a0	9a58	12p35	2p43	6p30	9§14	...	...
Lauchstadt ...arr	7 25	1023	12 59	3 8	6 54	9 39	...	...

*—9.39 p.m. on Sunday. §—12.20 night on Sunday. †—Not on Sunday.

FINSTERWALDE and LUCKAU.

Finsterwalde............dep	4 a0	7a20	1p30	7 p5	...	...	...
Luckau (178A) ....arr	5 32	8 35	2 45	8 20	...	...	...

Luckau ....dep	5a50	9a55	3p30	9p25	...	...	...
Finsterwalde (173A)...arr	7 1	11 6	5 3	1058	...	...	...

CORBETHA and DEUBEN.

Corbetha ...dep	4a50	6a22	8a40	12 0	...	4p10	8 p8
Pörsten	5 10	6 42	9 1	12 22	3 p7	4 38	8 30
Deuben ......arr	...	7 16	9 36	12 58	3 41	5 16	9 11

Deuben ....dep	4a55	7a24	9a45	2p35	4 p5	6p54	...	...
Pörsten	5 20	7 59	11 21	3 15	4 36	7 28	8p29	...
Corbetha 170 ...arr	5 37	8 18	11 37	3 32	...	7 45	8 46	...

WEISSWASSER and GUBEN.

Weisswasser ....dep	5a48	...	9 a5	...	1p25	5 p0	7 p50	...	11 p0	...	...	...	...	...	...	...	...
Forst................................	6 48	7a27	10 5	12p20	2 29	6 5	8 50	10p50	12 1	...	...	...	...	...	...	...	...
Guben ....arr	...	8 30	...	1 23	3 48	7 5	...	11 53	...	...	...	...	...	...	...	...	...

Guben ....dep	...	5 a45	9 a25	1 p42	4 p55	...	9 p25	...	...	...	...	...	...	...	...	...	...
Forst	6a22	7 35	11 1	3 10	6 30	9 p22	10 27	12a15	...	...	...	...	...	...	...	...	...
Weisswasser (180) ......arr	7 26	8 40	12 1	4 10	7 30	10 21	...	1 15	...	...	...	...	...	...	...	...	...

SONNEBERG and EISFELD.

Sonneberg...dep	5 a44	10a25	12p38	4 p35	8 p18	...
Eisfeld 173B.arr	7 22	12 13	2 21	6 19	9 43	...

Eisfeld ....dep	4a31	7 a58	12p43	4 p15	6 p34	10 p2
Sonneberg ...arr	6 20	9 36	2 36	6 13	7 58	11 48

EBERSDORF and WEIDHAUSEN.

‡—Not on Sunday.

Ebersdorf ....dep	7‡27	8a48	11a22	2 p32	5p37	7p35	10p10
Weidhausen...........arr	7 50	9 12	11 47	2 57	5 56	7 54	10 35

Weidhausen..........dep	4a47	7‡58	9a25	12p17	3p42	6 p8	8p11	...
Ebersdorf 173B ......arr	5 8	8 22	9 45	12 36	4 10	8 28	8 30	...

COBURG and ROSSACH.

Coburg......dep	4 ‡7	5a44	8a46	12p36	2 p49	7p14	...
Creidlitz...........	4 17	5 53	8 59	12 52	2 59	7 24	...
Rossach ...arr	4 48	6 13	9 28	1 17	3 23	7 48	...

Rossach ......dep	4‡a59	6a19	9 a55	1 p40	4*20	8 p3	...
Creidlitz..............	5 22	6 38	10 29	2 13	5 5	8 36	...
Coburg 173B arr	5 31	6 48	10 40	2 22	5.19	8 48	...

*—4.18 p.m. on Sunday. ‡—Not on Sunday.

FROTTSTADT and GEORGENTHAL.

‡—Not on Sunday.

Fröttstadt ....dep	5a16	6‡10	7 a20	...	9a18	11a40	12p32	2 p6	3 p1	4 p0	5p12	6 p10	...	7 p35	9 p8	10 p1	10p38	11p45
Waltershausen	5 25	6 19	7 30	...	9 33	11 50	12 45	2 14	3 11	4 13	5 19	6 24	...	7 48	9 18	10 10	10 45	11 52
Reinhardsbrunn	5 36	6 34	7 43	...	9 56	12 3	1 0	2 26	3 28	4 27	5 31	6 39	...	8 4	9 32	10 23	10 56	—
Friedrichroda	5 41	6 40	7 53	9 a5	9 59	12 8	1 41	—	3 37	4 55	—	6 43	7p50	8 8	9 35	10 28	—	...
Georgenthal 173 ......arr	5 59	7 7	8 18	9 25	...	12 28	2 8	...	3 57	5 20	...	7‡11	8 20	...	...	10 47	...	...

Georgenthal.............dep	...	4‡55	6 a8	7 a28	8a30	9 a44	a.m.	12p39	...	2 p25	4 p7	...	5 p35	...	8 p34	...	...	...
Friedrichroda	...	5 18	6 31	8 3	8 50	10 21	10 45	1 5	...	2 55	4 32	...	6 10	8p16	9 3	9 p52	...	...
Reinhardsbrunn	...	5 22	6 37	8 10	—	10 27	10 54	1 11	2 p32	3 2	4 37	5p37	6 16	8 21	9 9	9 57	11p2	...
Waltershausen	4 a33	5 36	6 49	8 28	...	10 42	11 8	1 28	2 44	3 18	4 51	5 49	6 33	8 36	9 26	10 12	1113	...
Fröttstadt 170..........arr	4 44	5 44	6 57	8 38	...	10 51	11 17	1 37	2 51	3 25	4 58	5 56	6 40	8 43	9 35	10 19	1120	...

GOTTESZELL and VIECHTACH.

Gotteszell......dep	7 a22	1‡p15	5 p22	7 p30
Ruhmannsfelden ...	7 33	1 27	5 33	7 41
Teisnach	7 53	1 50	5 50	8 0
Viechtach ......arr	8 32	2 20	6 35	8 40

‡—Sun. dep. 1.10 p.m.

Viechtach ....dep	5a30	11a15	3 p10	5 p0	...	...
Teisnach	6 15	12 3	3 55	5 55	...	...
Ruhmannsfelden.........	6 41	12 29	4 21	6 19	...	...
Gotteszell (198) arr	7 0	12 46	4 40	6 33	...	...

WERNSHAUSEN and ZELLA ST. BLASII.

Wernshausen ...		6a24	8a45	9a51	10a55	12p2	2p45	4p54	7p5	9p46	1040
Schmalkalden...		6 42	9 3	10 8	11 12	1220	3 1	5 10	723	10 3	11 2
Kl. Schmalk.		7 36	9 56	—	—	1 16	4 6	...	825	—	—
Brotterode ...		8 0	1018	...	...	1 38	4 29	...	846	...	...
Schmalkald	5a15	6 51	9 16	...	...	1240	3 45	5 12	744	...	...
Zella St. Blas	6 12	7 41	10 7	...	...	1 41	4 46	6 2	842	...	...

Zella St. Blasii ...dep		6a30	8a4	10a26	...	2p30	5 p0	6p48	9p 7	...
Schmalkalden ......arr		7 39	910	11 19	a.m.	3 23	5 58	7 43	9 59	...
Brotterode ......dep		6a48	813	...	1122	2p23	...	6p40	9 0	...
Kl. Schmalkalden		7 20	842	...	1145	2 46	...	7 8	9 30	...
Schmalkalden dep	5a32	8 10	921	11 25	1 26	4 0	6 24	8 10	10 3	..
Wernshausen arr	5 49	8 30	941	11 45	1 43	4 22	6 46	8 31	1020	

BERENT and CARTHAUS.

E.M						
	Berent ....dep	6 a18	10a20	2 p31	5 p33	...
20½	Carthaus......arr	7 38	11 27	3 45	6 38	...

Carthaus.........dep	8 a35	2p10	7 p45	...	...
Berent (177A) arr	9 39	3 22	8 52	...	...

KONIGSBERG and GOLDAP.

Konigsberg Sudb.		5 a31	9 a37	...	5 p33	9p21
Lowenhagen............		6 6	10 12	...	6 6	9 53
Gerdauen...............		8 5	12 10	5p34	8 2	1148
Angerburg.........	3a52	9 41	1 39	6 46	9 40	—
Goldap ......arr	5 24	11 13	3 58	8 12	...	...

Goldap ....dep	...	...	8 a6	12p53	4 p32	8p42
Angerburg..............	...	5a43	9 44	2 33	6 41	1013
Gerdauen	5a11	6 48	11 19	3 47	8 34	—
Lowenhagen............	7 13	—	1 19	5 39	10 33	...
Konigsberg Sud...	7 42	...	1 52	6 6	11 2	...

BISCHDORF and ANGERBURG.

Bischdorf......dep	...	6a30	11a28	...	5 p20	...	8p48
Rastenburg.........	5a19	7 53	12 29	5 p26	6 54	8p25	9 35
Angerburg....arr	6 23	...	1 36	6 36	...	9 57	...

Angerburg.dep	...	6a44	...	2p31	5p49	...	7p40
Rastenburg......	4a10	7 51	10 a4	4 4	6 59	7 p16	9 24
Bischdorf....arr	5 36	...	11 8	4 57	...	8 16	...

CULMSEE and MELNO.

Culmsee..............dep	...	7 a12	12p25	4 p45	7 p15
Pfeilsdorf..................	5 a40	8 36	1 28	6 15	8 18
Melno (177A) ......arr	6 35	9 44	3 40	7 10	...

Melno....................dep	...	7 a25	12p56	4 p45	8 p40
Pfeilsdorf	5a27	8 40	1 56	5 50	9 35
Culmsee (178) ......arr	6 30	9 43	2 59	6 33	...

CULM and UNISLAW.

E.M						
	Culm ....dep	5 a15	10a40	4 p2	9 p42	...
12¼	Unislaw ......arr	6 0	11 40	5 0	10 46	...

Unislaw...........dep	6 a21	2 p54	5 p15	1 a33	...	...
Culm ....arr	7 15	3 35	5 56	2 12	...	...

LIPPUSCH and KONITZ.

E.M						
	Lippusch.........dep	5 a39	11a30	4 p56	10 p0	...
12¼	Lubnia	6 30	12 12	5 39	10 38	...
32¾	Konitz..............arr	7 34	1 14	6 38	11 31	...

Konitz ....dep	5 a35	8a48	3 p12	8 p30	...
Lubnia	6 29	9 40	4 11	9 23	...
Lippusch (177A)arr	7 2	10 14	4 53	9 59	...

SCHLOCHAU and RUMMELSBURG.

E.M					
	Schlochau ....dep	6 a16	3 p47	9 p10	...
39	Rummelsburg 178A arr	8 52	7 0	11 15	...

Rummelsburg dep	5 a40	9 a30	4 p48	...	...
Schlochau ......arr	7 57	12 33	7 39	...	...

RUMMELSBURG and BUTOW.

Rummelsburg......dep	6a14	1p42	4p33	7p40	...
Butow..................arr	7 41	3 55	5 54	9 51	...

Butow.....................dep	5a54	9 a20	1p12	6 p1	...
Rummelsburg 178A ...arr	7 37	11 14	3 25	7 23	...

BUTOW and LAUENBURG.

E.M						
	Butow ....dep	6 a32	11 a5	5 p2	7 p45	...
34¼	Lauenburg ......arr	8 29	12 48	7 12	10 5	...

Lauenburg......dep	5 a48	9 a1	2 p0	7 p55	...
Butow ....arr	7 37	10 51	3 48	10 7	...

STRASBURG and EYLAU.

E.M						
	Strasburg.........dep	5 a26	8 a45	2 p32	6 p0	...
28¼	Eylau ....arr	7 5	10 52	4 42	8 10	...

Eylau ....dep	5 a35	11a30	5p50	9 p10	...
Strasburg ......arr	8 2	1 41	7 54	10 40	...

LÖTZEN and ANGERBURG.

Lötzen...........dep	6 a36	10a36	1 p5	3 p12	9 p0
Kruglanken.........	7 15	10 59	1 32	3 33	9 41
Angerburg ......arr	7 54	11 36	2 12	...	10 37

Angerburg ....dep	6 a31	11a52	...	2 p51	6 p55
Kruglanken	7 14	12 31	1 p46	3 47	8 5
Lötzen (174A) ...arr	7 37	12 52	2 16	4 10	8 36

Kruglanken.........dep	6*a11	7 a33	3 p38	9 p46	...
Marggrabowa ......arr	7 34	9 27	4 52	11 41	...

Marggrabowa.........dep	5 a4	11a20	1*p15	6 p1
Kruglanken............arr	6 58	1 12	2 34	7 31

*-Tuesday and Saturday only.

JOHANNISBURG and LOTZEN.

Johannisburg dep	5a32	11 a5	1p23	...	6p48	...	...	...
Arys........................	6 20	11 52	2 10	5 p23	7 38	...	...	...
Lötzen............arr	7 19	12 49	3 8	6 20	8 37	...	...	...

Lötzen ....dep	5a21	10a37	a.m.	1 p9	4p15	8 p57	...	...
Arys	6 28	11 34	1158	2 12	5 12	9 53	...	...
Johannisburg arr	7 26	...	1241	2 57	...	10 35	...	...

CZERSK and LASKOWITZ.

E.M						
	Czersk ....dep	4a57	8 a3	3p 2	6 p3	...
34½	Laskowitz ....arr	7 13	10 14	5 40	9 3	...

Laskowitz ....dep	7a22	11a50	6p24	9p32	...
Czersk (176) ....arr	9 33	2 15	9 3	1136	...

FLATOW and TERESPOL.

E.M							
	Flatow...............dep	...	5a28	9a51	2p32	...	8 p8
19¼	Vandsburg	...	6 36	1056	3 48	...	9 32
40	Prust Bagnitz.........	5a10	8 40	1235	5 19	7p33	1135
63¾	Terespol (178)... arr	6 51	10 22	2 4	...	8 51	...

Terespol ....dep	...	7a45	2p38	6p38	10p35
Prust Bagnitz	5 a0	9 20	4 30	8 20	12 16
Vandsburg	7 20	1120	6 17	10 10	—
Flatow (176)......arr	8 55	1231	7 24	11 50	...

E.M					
	Prust Bagnitz......dep	5a55	9a40	12‡p45	5p26
12¾	Crone...................arr	6 50	1035	1 29	6 13

Crone.....................dep	7a40	11‡a45	3p10	6p35
Prust Bagnitz.........arr	8 42	12 30	4 8	7 24

‡—Thurs. and Sundays only.

KONIGSBERG and GRAJEWO.

Königsberg dep	...	‡	6a53	[illegible]a56	2p47	6p19	7p37	1a40
Korschen (176)	...	6a45	8 34	1150	4 51	7 59	9 38	3 33
Rastenburg	a.m.	7 54	9 56	1220	5 22	8 19	10 9	4 1
Lötzen (174)	7 42	9 1	1035	1258	6 2	8 46	1049	4 41
Lyck (177)	9 35	—	1133	2 5	7 5	9 33	1155	5 39
Prostken arr	9 55	...	1152	2 24	7 25	9 50	1215	6 0
GRAJEWO 320 arr	...	...	...	...	...	1122	...	9 a4

GRAJEWO dep	...	...	7 a9	...	...	...	7p38
Prostken dep	3 a5	5 a38	6 39	8a56	1 p15	4p31	7 37
Lyck	3 29	6 8	6 57	9 23	2 2	5 17	7 59
Lötzen	4 36	7 18	7 40	1024	3 14	6 26	8 56
Rastenburg	5 22	—	8 10	11 1	3 57	7 9	9 32
Korschen	6 17	...	8 52	1152	4 42	7 58	10 2
Königsberg 176)	7 56	...	1028	1 44	6 17	9 46	1145

‡—Not on Sunday.

KONIGSBERG and PILLAU.

Königsberg dp	8a11	9a30	1p56	2p45	3p48	5p4[illegible]	7p46	11p 8
Fischhausen...	8 58	1020	2 40	3 30	4 38	6 27	8 35	11 58
: Palmnicken	1017	...	3 20	...	5 19	...	9 18	...
Pillau arr	9 17	1038	2 59	3 50	4 57	6 46	8 55	12 17

Pillau dep	6a28	7a30	8a29	10a0	12p59	4p18	6p52	8p13	9p41	...
: Palmnicken	...	6 18	...	...	12 24	3 55	...	7 49	...	...
Fischhausen...	6 48	7 49	8 53	1020	1 19	4 38	6 52	8 35	10 1	...
Königsberg ar	7 42	8 35	...	11 5	2 7	5 29	7 35	9 31	1049	...

MARIENBURG and MLAVA.

A—Until 27th October only.

E.M.																		
	Marienburg 176 dep	...	...	[illegible]a37	9 a40	1221	...	3 p58	5 p23	7p21	p.m.	10p25	...	...	...	...	...	...
22	Riesenburg	...	...	7 21	10 36	1 14	p.m.	4 47	6 0	8 13	...	11 18	...	...	...	...	...	...
43	D. Eylau (176) arr	...	...	8 7	11 25	2 3	3 10	5 33	6 31	8 58	10 20	12 6	...	...	...	...	...	...
54½	**Zajonskowo** arr	...	...	9 7	12 2	2 51	3 47	6 11	...	9 28	10 57	—	...	...	...	...	...	...
59	**Lobau** arr	...	...	9 31	12 36	...	4 6	6 34	A	...	11 18	...	...	...	...	...	...	...
58¼	Montowo	...	a.m.	9 18	12 12	3 1	—	6 21	...	9 39	—	...	...	...	...	...	...	...
80¾	**Soldau 177A**	...	7 32	1011	1 5	3 59	...	7 10	7 31	1033	...	...	...	...	...	...	...	...
89¾	**Illowo** arr	4a59	7 52	1032	1 28	4 29	...	7 28	7 42	1052	...	...	...	...	...	...	...	...
93	**Mlava (316A)** arr	5 9	...	1053	1 50	...	...	7 59	7 59	1111	...	...	...	...	...	...	...	...
...	**Mlava** dep	...	4 a59	...	...	...	...	1145	...	3 p10	p.m.	6 p40	...	9 p40	...	...	...	...
...	**Illowo** dep	...	5 30	...	...	10a22	...	1215	...	3 37	5 51	7 0	...	10 0	...	...	...	...
...	**Soldau**	...	5 47	7a33	...	10 50	...	1232	...	4 5	6 22	7 12	...	10 30	...	...	...	...
...	Montowo	...	6 35	8 27	...	—	...	1 23	p.m.	4 58	7 21	...	...	—	...	...	...	...
...	**Lobau** dep	...	6 14	8 13	...	...	11a37	1 0	2 3	4 30	7 4	A	8 p57	...	...	...	...	...
...	**Zajonskowo** dep	a.m.	6 43	8 36	a.m.	...	11 53	1 32	2 24	5 8	7 32	...	9 17	...	...	...	...	...
...	D. Eylau	5 34	7 20	9 4	9 15	...	—	2 3	2 53	5 44	8 25	8 20	9 48	...	...	...	...	...
...	Riesenburg	6 38	8 6	—	10 8	...	...	2 52	—	6 28	9 21	8 52	—	...	...	...	...	...
...	**Marienburg** arr	7 34	8 53	...	11	...	...	3 40	...	7 10	10 10	9 25	...	...	...	...	...	...

OELS and WILHELMSBRUCK.

Oels (220) dep	7a18	11a40	3p18	7p50	9 p4	...
Gross Wartenberg	8 9	12 30	4 15	8 40	9 52	...
Kempen (219)	8 4[illegible]	1 9	4 58	9 27	1031	...
Wilhelmsbruck arr	1010	1 28	5 20	10 5	—	...

Wilhelmsbruck dep	5a30	10a25	...	1p52	6 p0	...	...
Kempen	6 20	11 0	1p49	2 56	7 12	...	...
Gross Wartenberg	6 58	11 45	2 27	3 45	7 53	...	...
Oels arr	7 50	12 44	...	4 42	8 47	...	...

MARIENBURG and ALLENSTEIN.

E.M									
	Marienburg dep		6a50	1010	1224	3 p4	5p27	7p28	8p39
24	Miswalde		7 53	11 5	1 20	4 24	6 24	8 22	9 58
34½	Maldeuten		8 22	1128	1 43	4 52	6 47	8 44	1028
42½	Mohrungen arr		8 40	1145	2 1	5 14	7 5	9 1	1046
...	" dep	5a41	8 44	1147	2 5	5 16	—	8 3	1051
66	Göttkendorf	6 54	9 39	...	3 2	6 23	...	...	1118
70¾	**Allenstein** arr	7 10	9 51	1247	3 15	6 39	...	10 1	12 0

Allenstein dep	...	5a55	8a51	9a57	1p51	3p20	...	7 p1	11p9
Göttkendorf	...	6 7		1010	2 4	3 37	...	7 16	1125
Mohrungen arr	...	7 4	9 49	11 2	2 53	4 44	p.m.	8 19	1233
" dep	4a51	7 9	9 52	11 6	2 55	4 50	7 53	8 23	—
Maldeuten	5 10	7 28	10 9	1127	3 12	5 18	8 15	8 43	...
Miswalde	6 23	8 0	1030	1156	3 34	5 47	—	9 13	...
Marienburg arr	7 33	8 53	1128	[illegible] 7	4 25	6 56	...	10 7	...

ALLENSTEIN and INSTERBURG.

			a.m.	a.m.			a.m.	p.m.		p.m.
Allenstein dep		...	5 7	8 28	...	...	1135	3 20	...	7 10
Passenheim		...	5 46	9 6	...	...	1226	4 0	...	7 48
Ortelsburg		...	6 18	9 38	...	...	1 1	4 33	...	8 17
Rudczanny		...	7 30	1039	...	...	2 50	5 42	...	9 17
Johannisburg	a.m.	a.m.	7 56	11 5	p.m.	p.m	3 21	6 13	p.m.	9 39
Lyck	3 33	6 5	9 23	1227	2 14	4 21	4 57	7 54	8 1	—
Goldap	5 42	8 2	1125	—	4 25	5 48	—	—	9 48	...
Insterburg arr	7 22	9 43	1244	...	5 4	6 55	...	...	1117	...

			a.m.	a.m.	a.m.		p.m	p.m.	p.m.
Insterburg dep		...	4 58	8 48	1041	...	2 48	6 26	9 11
Goldap		...	6 38	10 5	1212	...	4 37	8 22	1051
Lyck	a.m.	...	8 32	1128	1 57	p.m.	7 23	1037	1245
Johannisburg	5 14	...	1010	—	3 25	6 14	9 39	1218	—
Rudczanny	5 43	a.m.	1040	...	3 52	6 37	10 9	—	...
Ortelsburg	6 42	8 40	1152	...	5 0	7 43	1127	...	...
Passenheim	7 31	9 8	1224	...	5 27	8 1[illegible]	1159	...	...
Allenstein arr	8 8	9 48	1 10	...	6 5	8 47	1244	...	...

Ortelsburg	6a46	1p5	5 p2	8p12
Neidenburg	8 40	3 2	6 54	1128

Neidenburg	4a22	6a47	1231	5p18
Ortelsburg	6 14	8 34	3 36	7 22

Johannisburg	8a30	3p30	11p0
Dlottowen	9 35	4 11	1144

Dlottowen dep	6a14	1158	8p16
Johannisburg	6 55	1 6	9 0

ALLENSTEIN and KÖNIGSBERG.

Allenstein dep	5 a1	8a39	10a53	3p47	6 p56	8 p56	...	...
Wormditt	6 20	9 37	12 4	4 59	7 53	10 8	...	...
Mehlsack	6 45	9 55	12 28	5 24	8 11	10 33	...	...
Zinten	7 27	1023	1 3	6 2	8 38	11 9	...	...
Königsberg Ostbf.	8 17	1059	1 55	6 57	9 14	11 59	...	...

Königsberg dep		5a35	9a26	2 p0	5p44	8p33	11p15	...	...
Zinten		6 38	1033	3 3	6 25	9 33	11 58	...	...
Mehlsack	a.m.	7 17	1125	3 39	6 51	10 7	12 23	...	...
Wormditt	6 22	7 41	12 2	4 1	7 9	1033	12 41		...
Allenstein	7 35	9 8	1 17	5 18	8 9	1150	1 37	...	...

ALLENSTEIN and SOLDAU.

Allenstein dep	6 a6	8a23	1029	1p27	6p54
Hohenstein Ost	7 6	9 23	1127	2 25	7 58
Soldau arr	8 25	1228	1 6	4 1	9 38

Soldau dep	6 a0	1057	1p15	4 p4	6p14	...
Hohenstein Ost	7 41	1244	2 58	5 40	7 52	...
Allenstein arr	8 46	1 50	3 55	6 34	8 46	...

OSTERODE and SOLDAU.

Osterode dep	5a22	2p30	7p56	...	...
Soldau arr	7 30	5 28	10 5	...	...

Soldau dep	6a16	1134	7p17	...	...
Osterode arr	8 26	1 58	9 23	...	...

DANTSIC and STETTIN.

	1—4	1—4	1—4	2 3 4	Ex3	1—4	1,2,3	2 3 4	Ex 3	1—4	Ex3	2 3 4	2, 3,4	Ex 3	2 3 4	Ex3	2 3 4	1—4	1—4	1—4	2 3 4
Dantsic										a.m.	a.m.		a.m.			p.m.		p.m.	p.m.	p.m.	p.m.
Hauptb. dep	...	...	...	...	...	...	...	...	...	6 50	7 18	...	10 39	...	...	1231	...	1 45	5 56	9 0	1118
Zoppot	...	...	...	...	...	...	...	...	...	7 6	7 33	...	11 2	...	...	1246	...	1 59	6 12	9 17	1142
Rheda	...	...	...	...	...	...	...	...	...	7 42	RC	...	11 44	...	...	RC	...	2 36	6 50	10 3	1221
Neustadt	...	...	...	...	...	...	...	a.m.	...	8 8	8 3	...	11 59	...	...	1 16	...	2 48	7 3	1017	1233
Lauenburg	...	...	...	...	...	a.m.	...	5 13	...	8 55	8 35	...	1 3	...	...	1 53	...	3 35	7 52	1125	—
Stolp	...	...	...	...	...	4 25	...	6 49	...	1012	9 32	...	2 28	...	...	2 50	...	4 46	9 4	1242	...
Schlawe	...	...	...	...	...	5 8	...	7 51	A	1057	9 58	...	—	A	...	3 18	...	5 22	9 44	—	...
Belgard arr	...	...	...	...	...	6 41	...	9 18	a.m.	1225	11 2	...	...	p.m.	p.m.	4 20	...	6 46	11 8	...	...
Belgard dp	...	...	...	...	...	6 48	...	9 28	10 50	1232	11 8	...	...	3 15	3 43	4 25	...	6 52	1116	...	...
Schivelbein	...	...	...	...	...	7 34	...	1016	...	1 17	1140	...	...	3 47	4 32	4 58	...	7 36	12 5	...	...
Labes (179A)	...	...	...	a.m.	...	8 2	...	1046	RC	1 44	1159	...	...	4 7	—	5 18	...	8 2	1234	...	...
Ruhnow	...	...	...	6 40	...	8 26	...	11 9	11 55	2 7	1215	...	1,2,3	...	...	5 35	...	8 23	1258	...	...
Wulkow	a.m.	a.m.	a.m.	7 31	a.m.	...	a.m.	12 1	...	2 56	...	p.m.	p.m.	RC	...	...	p.m.	9 11	SC	p.m.	...
Stargard dep	4 28	5 41	6 36	7 52	9 28	9 34	9 59	1217	12 42	3 12	1258	5 8	5 48	5 2	...	6 20	7 36	9 26	1 56	1153	...
Alt Damm	5 5	6 16	7 14	8 33	9 49	1011	1020	1258	1 6	3 49	...	5 45	6 11	...	...	6 41	8 16	10 1	2 33	1227	...
Stettin arr	5 23	6 33	7 34	8 53	10 2	1028	1034	1 15	1 21	4 6	1 31	6 3	6 26	5 34	...	6 55	8 34	1016	2 51	1241	...

		1—4	1—4	2 3 4	2 3 4	2 3 4	Ex3	Ex3	1—4	1—4	2 34	1—3	1—4	Ex3	Ex 3	1—4	1—3	1—4	Ex3	1—4	2 3 4
		a.m.	a.m.	a.m.	a.m.	a.m.	a.m.	a.m.	a.m.	p.m.	p.m.	p.m.	p.m.	p.m.	p.m.	p.m.	p.m.	p.m.	p.m.	p.m.	a.m.
Stettin dep	...	2 16	5 11	6 48	9 28	9 48	1020	1031	1037	1218	2 1	2 51	4 59	5 11	5 24	7 20	7 47	8 11	9 32	1128	1 8
Alt Damm	...	2 34	5 29	7 8	9 48	10 6	A	...	1052	1236	2 22	3 5	5 16	A	...	7 39	...	8 35	9 46	1147	1 28
Stargard dep	...	3 7	6 27	7 43	1029	1038	1059	1112	1128	1 12	3 4	3 27	5 51	5 59	6 9	8 28	8 24	9 13	10 8	1222	2 8
Wulkow	...	SC	6 38	—	—	—	RC	RC	1138	—	3 15	—	—	RC	...	8 38	—	—	—	—	—
Ruhnow	...	4 6	7 38	...	...	...	1143	1157	1236	...	4 12	...	...	6 47	6 57	9 36	...	...	...	...	...
Labes	...	4 22	7 57	...	...	...	1155	12 9	1251	...	4 27	...	...	6 59	7 10	9 53	...	...	...	...	...
Schivelbein	...	4 52	8 32	...	...	...	1216	1229	1 19	...	4 59	...	...	7 21	7 33	1023	...	...	...	...	...
Belgard arr	...	5 28	9 14	...	...	...	1243	1254	1 55	...	5 36	...	...	7 49	8 0	11 0	...	...	...	...	...
Belgard dep	...	5 34	9 25	...	...	...	—	1259	2 0	2—4	5 42	...	...	—	8 7	11 9	...	...	...	A—Until 15th August.	...
Schlawe	a.m.	6 54	11 0	...	...	...	...	1 57	3 18	p.m	7 36	...	...	...	9 9	1235	...	...	...		...
Stolp dep	4 28	7 41	1142	...	...	...	...	2 27	3 56	6 10	10 0	...	...	...	9 38	1 11	...	...	...		...
Lauenburg ...1—4	5 53	8 57	1255	...	...	...	...	3 12	5 4	7 23	1119	...	...	...	1028	—	...	...	...		...
Neustadt 6a12	6 55	9 43	1 41	...	...	...	...	3 44	5 52	8 17	—	...	...	...	11 2	...	...	...	...		...
Rheda 6 24	7 13	9 53	1 51	...	...	...	...	...	6 3	8 31	...	...	...	...	RC	...	...	...	...		...
Zoppot..........7 5	8 2	1031	2 28	...	...	...	...	4 13	6 42	9 13	...	...	...	...	11 33	...	...	...	...		...
Dantsic arr 7 25	8 20	1047	2 44	...	...	...	...	4 25	6 55	9 30	...	...	...	...	11 46	...	...	...	...		...

Rheda ....dep	7a50	2 p50	6 p54	10p10	...	...
Putzig.......... arr	8 38	3 38	7 34	10 56	...	...

Putzig ....dep	6a20	12p52	4p52	7p45	...	...
Rheda..............arr	7 3	1 40	5 37	8 24	...	...

BELGARD and COLBERG.

Belgard..................dep	5a49	6a59	9 a33	11‡a12	12*p48	1 p3	2 p4	3‡p43	5 p2	5p48	7‡p58	8p13	11p15
Colberg ....arr	6 50	7 54	10 30	11 48	1 21	1 38	2 59	4 17	5 42	6 42	8 31	9 6	12 2

Colberg..................dep	4a32	5a41	8a10	9a54	10‡a11	11a19	12‡p11	1‡p39	2*p32	3 §p35	4p23	7 p0	9 p56
Belgard ....arr	5 28	6 38	9 11	10 50	10 45	12 18	12 47	2 23	3 11	4 16	5 27	7 57	10 56

§—From 16th August. *—Until 15th August. ‡—In July and August only.

ROGASEN and HOHENSALZA.

Rogasen dep 12a50	...	5a20	9 a9	12p30	6 p34	9p51	...
Wongrowitz ...1 31	...	5 56	9 44	2 52	7 42	10 25	...
Elsenau .... —	4a55	6 46	10 35	4 6	9 5	—	...
Znin	6 4	7 20	11 7	4 33	9 58	...	...
Hohensalza 176	7 14	8 22	12 22	5 35	11 10	...	...

Hohensalza.........dep	5 a0	8a54	1 p54	4p44	8 p45	...
Znin	6 8	10 1	3 12	7 2	10 0	...
Elsenau..................a.m.	6 46	10 40	4 8	8 52	10 34	...
Wongrowitz 3 50	7 50	11 22	5 0	—	11 19	...
Rogasen 179 arr 4 36	8 26	11 57	5 34	...	11 53	...

SCHOKKEN and ELSENAU.

Schokken.............dep	4 a55	8 a40	1p19	3 p46	9 p4	...	...
Janowitz	5 46	9 43	3 10	5 21	9 52	...	...
Elsenau ....arr	6 21	10 27	3 36	6 23	10 18	...	...

Elsenau ....dep	4a37	6 a44	10a42	4p54	11 p2	...	...
Janowitz	5 0	7 30	11 1	5 45	11 37	...	...
Schokken......arr	5 48	8 20	1 4	7 30	12 40	...	...

GULDENBODEN and MALDEUTEN.

Güldenboden ...dep	7a33	1028	3p20	6p28	9p32
Maldeuten 174A arr	8 18	1115	4 18	7 17	1021

Maldeuten............dep	6a 1	9 a2	11a49	5p17	8p19
Güldenboden 176 arr	6 52	9 56	12 43	6 7	9 9

ELBING and OSTERODE.

Elbing ......dep	7 a1	11a4	3p21	7p32	10p48	...
Miswalde.........	7 58	1156	4 26	9 54	11 52	...
Osterode 176 arr	9 11	1255	5 37	11 7	1 3	...

Osterode ......dep	4a20	6a32	10a34	2p32	7p47	...	...
Miswalde	5 45	7 57	12 0	3 36	9 9	...	...
Elbing 176 ...arr	6 47	8 56	1 5	4 39	1011	...	...

PRUSSIAN-STARGARD and SCHONECK.

Pr.-Stargard dp	7a55	1p45	8p56	1030	...
Schöneck ...arr	8 50	2 30	9 42	1129	...
Schöneck ....dep	6a55	758	11a10	6p45	...
Pr.-Stargard arr	7 38	858	12 6	7 44	...

LAUENBURG and LEBA.

Lauenburg...dep	9 a4	1 p57	3 p45	7 p55	...	...
Leba............arr	10 13	3 1	4 55	9 2	...	...
Leba ....dep	6 a48	11a23	6 p0	9p18	...	...
Lauenburg...arr	8 17	12 36	7 15	10 20	...	...

POSEN, WONGROWITZ, and BROMBERG.

Posen ....dep	...	...	5a35	1059	2p23	3p25	7p31
Schokken	...	a.m.	7 9	1230	3 43	4 55	9 2
Wongrowitz......	...	6 0	8 23	1 11	4 13	—	9 40
Gollantsch	...	6 40	9 14	1 50	4 44	...	1021
Exin	6a 6	7 14	10 0	2 18	5 12	...	1055
Schubin	6 50	7 52	1042	3 10	5 43	...	1132
Bromberg....arr	7 34	8 35	1127	4 7	6 24	...	1215

Bromberg.....dep	...	5 a7	9a58	...	2 p5	3p12	...	8p31	1120	...	...
Schubin	...	5 57	1046	...	3 2	4 7	...	9 17	1210	...	...
Exin	...	6 32	1123	...	3 37	5 11	...	9 52	1243	...	...
Gollantsch	a.m.	7 6	1152	...	4 7	5 41	p.m.	1025	—	...	...
Wongrowitz	5 11	7 53	1234	p.m	4 52	6 19	7 17	11 4	...	...	...
Schokken	5 54	8 32	1 12	5 7	—	—	7 53	—	...	...	...
Posen ....arr	7 23	9 55	2 33	6 30	...	...	9 20	...	...	...	...

Kolmar i Pos. ...dep	4a26	7a50	1p20	8p57	...
Gollantsch.......arr	6 19	9 10	3 28	1010	...

Gollantsch......dep	4a44	9 a34	5p43	10p30
Kolmar i Pos. arr	6 41	11 26	7 1	11 48

TERESPOL and SCHWETZ.

E.M.								
	Terespol...dep	7a41	11a30	2 p45	6p38	9 p4	10p34	...
4	Schwetz ...arr	7 56	11 48	3 3	6 56	9 20	10 50	...

Schwetz.........dep	6a36	10 a5	1p42	5 p3	8p32	9p38	...	...
Terespol 178 ...arr	6 56	10 21	2 2	5 23	8 54	9 58	...	...

MOHRUNGEN and OSTERODE.

Mohrungen......dep	5a50	11a56	8p27	...	...	...	...	Osterode.........dep	7a44	2p32	7 p7	...	...	...	...	...	...
Osterode (176)...arr	7 18	12 55	9 22	...	...	...	...	Mohrungen ...arr	8 39	4 30	8 10	...	...	...	...	...	...

GUMBINNEN and SZITTKEHMEN.

Gumbinnen ......dep	5a56	9a48	2 p10	8 p5	...	...	**Szittkehmen** ...dep	5 a16	9 a21	4 p29	8p 3	...	...	...	...
Tollmingkehmen ...	7 20	10 47	3 6	9 6	...	...	Tollmingkehmen ...	6 10	10 52	5 23	9 2	...	...	...	...
Szittkehmen......arr	8 32	11 36	3 55	9 59	...	...	**Gumbinnen** ......arr	6 59	12 2	6 7	9 51	...	...	...	...

BRAUNSBERG and MEHLSACK.

Braunsberg......dep	6a14	10a14	2p40	8p47	...	...	...	Mehlsack ....dep	7a18	12p30	5p30	10p34	...	...	...
Mehlsack ....arr	7 1	11 4	3 31	9 57	...	...	...	Braunsberg 176 ...arr	8 5	1 17	6 38	11 23	...	...	...

ROTHFLIESS and ORTELSBURG.

Rothfliess ....dep	5 a 7	11 a5	6p 5	9 p0	...	...	...	Ortelsburg ....dep	7 a5	1 p5	5 p25	8p26	...	...	...
Ortelsburg 174A...arr	6 58	12 40	7 39	11 19	...	...	...	Rothfliess ...176...arr	8 38	3 24	6 59	10 5	...	...	...

KONITZ and LASKOWITZ.

Konitz ....dep	4a55	5 a37	8 a49	1 p46	3p15	6p49	8p31	**Laskowitz**...dep	a.m.	7a22	11a48	...	6 p25	...	9 p30
Tuchel	5 49	6 19	9 39	2 38	4 12	7 40	9 23	Tuchel	6 24	8 41	12 56	5 p33	7 36	10p15	10 51
Laskowitz 177A arr	7 7	...	11 0	...	5 45	9 3	...	**Konitz** ....arr	7 8	9 30	1 37	6 23	8 21	11 10	11 34

ZOLLBRUCK and BUTOW.

Zollbruck ...dep	7 a39	10a47	2p29	6p 5	9p57	...	...	**Bütow** ....dep	5 a49	7a50	12p18	4 p2	6 p56	...	...
Barnow	8 41	11 42	3 25	7 4	10 55	...	...	Barnow........................	6 23	8 23	12 52	4 35	7 35	...	...
Bütow ....arr	9 15	12 15	3 59	7 40	11 29	...	...	**Zollbruck** (178A) arr	7 20	9 18	1 47	5 28	8 33	...	...

STETTIN and GROSS ZIEGENORT.

Stettin ....dep	5a11	7 a38	10a50	1p58	4p23	5p23	7 p15	9 p32	**Gr. Ziegenort** dep	4a11	5 a4	6a13	8a52	11a48	2 p6	5 p4	7p45
Jasenitz	6 34	9 24	12 7	3 35	5 45	6 47	8 30	10 49	Jasenitz	4 36	5 25	6 34	9 13	12 9	2 26	5 28	8 26
Gr. Ziegenort arr	6 53	9 48	12 27	3 59	6 4	7 6	8 49	11 12	**Stettin** ....arr	5 53	6 39	7 46	1026	1 23	3 50	6 49	10 7

BERLIN, SCHNEIDEMUHL, DIRSCHAU, INSTERBURG, AND EYDTKUHNEN.

Dist.		234	2—4	234	1—4	Ex1	Ex1	2,3,4	Ex2	Ex3	1—4	3 &4	Ex3	Ex 3	Ex 3	2—4	1—4	234	Ex3	1—4	234	Ex3	Ex3	234	Ex3	Ex3	Ex3	Ex3	3 &4	234
E.M	**BERLIN**—		a.m.		a.m.	a.m.	a.m.		a.m.				a.m.	a.m.	a.m.	a.m.	a.m.	p.m.	p.m.	p.m.	p.m.	p.m.	p.m.	p.m.	p.m.	p.m.	p.m.	p.m.		p.m.
From Schls. B'f.	Charlottenburg ......dep	...	4 52	...	6 23	...	...	...	7 55	...	...	...	9 3	9 19	10 14	9 30	1118	12 5	2 43	2 17	4 46	6 52	6 57	7 47	1044	1053	11 2	1118	...	1147
	Zoolog-Garten ......dep	...	4 59	...	6 30	7 20	7 20	...	8 3	...	...	...	9 11	9 27	10 21	9 37	1125	1212	2 51	2 24	4 53	6 59	7 5	7 54	1052	11 1	1110	1126	...	1155
	Friedrichstrasse ...dep	...	5 11	...	6 42	7 32	7 32	...	8 17	...	...	...	9 26	9 42	10 35	9 49	1137	1224	3 5	2 36	5 5	7 11	7 20	8 8	11 6	1115	1124	1141	...	12 7
	Alexanderplatz ......dep	...	5 17	...	6 48	...	...	...	...	...	...	...	9 33	9 48	10 41	9 56	1143	1230	3 11	2 42	5 12	7 17	7 26	8 14	1112	1121	1130	1147	...	1214
	Schlesische Bahnhof dep	...	5 25	...	7 0	7 58	7 58	...	8 30	...	...	...	9 42	9 57	10 50	10 5	1154	1242	3 20	2 54	5 21	7 26	7 35	8 26	1121	1130	1139	1155	...	1229
17¾	Strausberg	...	6 1	...	7 35	Train de Luxe, Tuesday only.	...	...	...	...	...	...	...		...	1039	1227	1 22	...	3 25	5 58	...	...	9 1		...	...	...	...	1 0
29	Dahmsdorf-Müncheberg	...	6 27	...	8 1		N	...	...	...	...	...	RC		...	11 6	1252	1 53	RC	4 7	6 26	...	RC	9 29	SC	SC	...	RC	...	1 24
42¼	Werbig........................	...	7 0	...	8 32		Nord Express.	...	...	...	...	...	...		...	1156	1 21	2 23	...	4 38	7 0	A	...	10 5		...	...	SC	...	1 51
53	**Cüstrin** Haupt. ......arr	a.m.	7 37	...	9 6			...	...	...	...	...	11 0		...	1231	1 53	2 46	4 32	5 10	7 36	...	...	1038		1241	...	1 11	...	2 24
...	„ (178B).........dep	5 45	7 43	...	9 43			...	...	...	...	...	11 2		...		1 59	2 52	4 34	5 15	7 44	...	...	1044		1242	SC	1 13	...	2 28
80	Landsberg	6 50	8 55	...	10 50			...	...	...	...	...	1142	RC	...	...	3 5	3 41	5 15	6 17	9 33	9 10	9 22	1153		1 22	1 35	1 55	...	3 34
99	Friedeberg	7 36		...	11 39			...	...	...	...	...	1211	Via Posen	...	...	3 49	4 14	...	6 59	1021	...	SC	1239	Via Posen.	...	...	...	...	4 20
117	**Kreuz (218A)** ....arr	8 15	...	...	12 20			...	...	...	...	...	1242		...	...	4 28	4 48	6 6	7 37	11 1	10 1	1012	1 19		...	2 26	2 45	...	5 2
...	„ ....dep	8 41	...	...	12 52			...	...	...	...	...	1244		...	...	4 34	5 4	6 8	7 41	11 7	10 2	1013	1 27		...	2 28	2 47	...	5 23
124	Filehne...........................	9 3	...	...	1 7		...	...	...	a.m.	...	...	...		...	...	4 50	5 17	...	7 55	1123	...	...	1 42		...	...	...	...	5 40
153¼	**Schneidemuhl** ......arr	1027	a.m.	...	2 2		1119	...	1140	...	...	...	1 33		2 10	p.m.	5 57	6 10	6 57	8 49	1225	1049	11 1	2 42		3 6	3 17	3 35	...	6 46
...	**Schneidemuhl**...dep		11 0	...				...		1155	...	...	1 46			2‡15	6 15	...	7 9	8 57	...	1051	11 6	...			3 22		...	7 1
190½	Nakel		12 54	...	...			...		1243	...	...	2 37			3 36	7 32	...	8 1	1029	...	A	...	...			4 21		...	8 27
207¼	**Bromberg** ....arr	...	1 35	...	...			p.m.		1 5	...	...	3 0			4 7	8 1	...	8 23	11 2	...	12 1	1215	...			4 43		a.m.	9 2
...	„ ....dep	...		...	...			12 28		1 8	...	...	3 9			4 43	8 40	p.m.	8 26	1129	...	12 5	1220	...			4 48		6 5	9 15
238¼	**Thorn** ....arr	...	...	...	...	1 29		1 34		1 47	...	...	4 1	4 4		5 52	9 54	7 18	9 9	1239	...	1247	1 2	...	5 28		5 34		7 22	1022
249½	Alexandrovo ......arr	...	...	...	...	1 52		...			...	...	4 53	4 53		...	1043	8 6	1043	...	...		1 30	...	6 15		6 15			1234
389½	WARSAW (316)arr	...	...	...	...	7p14		...		...	...	p.m.	1a29	1 a29		...	7a20		7a20	...	...	...	8 a7	...	1p22		1p22		a.m.	...
...	**Thorn**...................dep	...	...	...	...			2 0		...	...	3 30		4 15		7 24		...	9 21	1 10	...	...		...	5 40				6‡23	1042
254	Schönsee	...	...	...	...	...		2 58		...	...	4 48	...	4 41		8 18	...	...	9 48	1 50	...	...	...	...	RC		...		7 8	1130
274¼	**Gosslershausen** ...	...	...	...	...	...		4 3		...	...	5 35	...	5 9		9 20	...	...	1020	2 33	...	...	...	...	6 38		...		7 49	1229
296¾	Deutsch Eylau	...	...	...	...	...		4 54		...	...		...	5 41		1018	...	p.m.	1051	3 17	...	...	...	...	7 12		a.m.		8 36	1 22
314½	Osterode	...	...	...	...	...		5 41		...	...	...	...	6 10		1132	p.m.	7 5	1121	3 56	...	...	...	...	7 40		6 8		9 19	2 3
339¼	**Allenstein**	...	...	...	...	...		7 0		...	...	...	...	6 51		1218	11 7	8 0	1157	4 49	...	...	...	...	8 25		7 16		1017	3 6
358¼	Rothfliess..........................	...	...	...	...	...		8 18		...	...	...	...	7 20			12 0			5 28	...	...	...	...	8 54		7 54		1057	3 48
381¼	**Korschen** ....dep	...	...	...	...	...		10 3		...	...	...	...	7 55		...		...	...	6 22	...	...	...	...	9 29		8 34		1150	4 44
397¼	Gerdauen........................	...	...	...	...	...		10 36		...	...	...	...	8 18		234	...	...	Ex3	7 3	...	...	234	...	9 29				1226	5 21
425¼	**Insterburg** ....arr	...	...	a.m.	...	...		11 30		...	...	a.m.	p.m.	8 55		p.m.	...	p.m.	p.m.	8 11	...	...	p.m.	a.m.	1027		...		1 17	6 14
...	**Schneidemuhl**......dep	...	...	6 58	...	...	1124	...	1146	...	...	1158	1 41	RC	2 15	2 58	...	6 21	7 4	...	...	...	1110	3 49		3 11	...	3 40	Extra.—Dirschau to Marienburg, 7.18 a.m., 3.28, 5.0 p.m.	...
173¼	Flatow	...	...	7 38	...	...	...	...	...	...	...	1237	2 13		...	3 40	...	7 3	7 36	...	...	...	1159	4 29		...	...	...		...
204¾	**Konitz (175A)**.............	...	...	8 55	...	...	...	...	RC	...	...	1 44	3 2		...	4 55	...	8 6	8 27	...	...	...	1 6	5 40		4 25	...	4 53		...
222¾	Czersk (178)	...	...	9 40	...	...	...	...	...	...	...	2 20	3 27		...	5 43	...	9 21	...	...	...	...		6 29		4 49	...	...		A—Runs from 15th August until 20th September only.
249½	Pr. Stargard	...	...	1052	...	...	...	...	...	...	...	3 19	4 2		...	7 0	...	1027	9 24	...	...	...	...	7 44		5 3	...	...		
265¼	**Dirschau** ....arr	1—4	1,2,3	1125	...	...	1 41	...	2 2	...	...	3 48	4 22		4 32	7 35	...	11 0	9 45	...	...	...	...	8 22		5 43	1,2,3	6 9		
285½	DANTSIC (178) ......arr	a.m.	a.m.	1225	a.m.	...	2p42	...	2p42	p.m.	p.m.	5p15	5p15		5 p15	8p41	p.m.	1149	1030	...	p.m.	...	...	9a48		6a25	a.m.	7a11		
...	**Dirschau** ....dep	8 56	9 7	1152	11 44	...	1 46	...	2 12	2 32	2 37	4 43			4 40	7‡58	6 55	1130	9 55	...	1134	...	...			5 52	5 56	6 14		
276	**Marienburg (174A)** ...	9 19	9 26	1216	12 7	...	...	p.m.	...	2 50	3 2	5 10	...		4 56	8 23	7 17	1152	1014	...	1159	...	...	...		...	6 19	6 33		
294	Elbing (175)	1011		1 9		...	2 23	2 56	2 50	3 20	3 38	6 5	...		5 24	9 13	8 3	1234	1043	...		1—4	...	...		...	7 16	6 59		
302	**Güldenboden**	1024	...	1 24	...	...	...	3 18	...	RC		6 23	...		RC	9 29		1247	RC	...	...	a.m.	...	...		...	7 32	...		
328	**Braunsberg (175A)** ...	1120	...	2 24	...	...	...		...	4 5	...	7 25	...		6 19	1023	...	1 38	1128	...	...	4 33	...	...		...	8 27	7 44		
366¾	**Königsberg** Ost......arr	1237	...	3 49	...	...	3 51	...	4 14	4 57	...	8 54	...		7 14	1141	p.m.	2 53	1221	...	...	6 20	...	...		7 54	9 50	8 36		
...	„ 175......dep	1248	...	4 26	...	...	3 56	...	4 19		...		...		7 26	1238	7*56	3 5		...	...	6 42	...	...		8 6		8 44		
...	Wehlau	1 57	...	5 35	...	...	...	...	...	...	...	...	...		8 16	1 36	9 4	4 9	...	...	...	7 48	...	...		...	...	9 33		
422¾	**Insterburg** (177 ...arr	2 43	...	6 21	...	...	...	...	5 34	...	...	...	...		8 50	2 20	9 55	4 52	...	...	...	8 35	...	...		...	...	10 7		
...	„ ....dep	2 54	...	6 37	a.m.	...	...	...	5 36	...	...	...	...	9 7		2 31		5 5	...	...	...	8 42	...	...	1037	...	...	1037		
454¾	Stalluponen	4 7	...	7 43	8 50	...	...	...	...	...	...	...	...	9 57	...	3 37	...	6 10	...	...	...	9 48	...	...	1131	...	...	1131		
461¼	**Eydtkühnen (313)** arr	4 19	...	7 54	9 7	...	5 50	...	6 27	...	...	...	...	10 8	...	3 51	...	6 22	...	...	...	10 0	...	...	1143	1015	...	1143		
462¼	WIRBALLEN (Rus.) dep	...	...	...	...	...	7p16	...	8p40	...	...	...	...	1 a15	...	...	...	...	...	...	...	...	...	...	2p30	2p30	...	2p30	...	
1016¼	ST. PETERSBURG ...arr	...	...	...	...	...	1030	...	11a35	...	...	...	...	7 a45	...	...	...	...	...	...	...	...	...	...	8a15	8a15	...	8a15	...	

N—Nord Express, from Berlin on Sunday and Thursday. RC—Restaurant Car. SC—Sleeping Car. *—From Königsberg Süd. ‡—1-4 class.

EYDTKUHNEN, INSTERBURG, DIRSCHAU, AND BERLIN.

RC—Restaurant Car. SC—Sleeping Car. N—Nord Express, from St. Petersburg on Wednesday and Saturday.

Station	1,2,3	Ex3	1—4	1—4	Ex3	1—4	2 3 4		Ex 3	
St. Petersburg dep	...	...	...	...	...	...	...	...	...	...
Wirballen 313 arr	...	...	...	...	...	...	...	...	...	...
Eydtkühnen dep	...	...	...	...	...	a.m. 2 48	...	...	...	...
Stalluponen	...	...	...	...	...	3 5	...	...	a.m.	...
Insterburg arr	...	...	...	...	...	4 6	...	...		
" dep	...	...	...	...	...	4 21	...	...	7 42	...
Wehlau	...	...	...	...	...	5 14	...	...	8 14	...
Königsberg Ost arr	...	a.m.	...	...	a.m.	6 27	...	...	9 3	...
" dep	...	7 27	...	a.m.	6 38	8 1	...	...	9 13	...
Braunsberg	...	8 21	...	5 52	...	9 24	...	...	10 10	...
Güldenboden	...	RC	...	7 2	...	10 17	...	...	RC	...
Elbing	a.m.	9 5	...	7 20	8 6	10 37	...	...	11 0	...
Marienburg	9 2	9 31	...	8 0	...	11 14	...	...	11 27	...
Dirschau arr	9 21	9 51	...	8 31	8 43	11 36	...	...	11 47	...
Dantsic dep			...	9a10	8 a0		...	...	11 a0	...
Dirschau dep	...	...	...	9 57	8 51	...	...	...	12 0	...
Pr. Stargard	...	...	...	1031	...	...	...	...	12 28	...
Czersk	...	...	a.m.	1134	RC	...	...	...	1 8	...
Konitz	...	...	4 13	1216	...	...	...	...	1 43	...
Flatow	...	...	5 33	1 23	...	...	...	...	2 26	...
Schneidemühl arr	...	...	6 30	2 3	1115	...	...	...	2 53	...
Insterburg dep	...	...	...	...		...	...	...	a.m. 4 14	...
Gerdauen	...	...	...	...		...	...	...	5 9	...
Korschen dep	...	...	...	...		1—4	...	...	6 0	...
Rothfliess	...	...	...	...		a.m.	a.m.	...	6 54	...
Allenstein	...	...	...	...		1 0	2 54	...	7 41	...
Osterode	...	...	...	...		1 59	4 31	...	8 34	...
Deutsch Eylau	...	...	...	...		2 44	5 50	...	9 10	...
Gosslershausen	...	...	...	...		3 38	7 38	...	10 1	...
Schönsee	...	Ex3	...	...		4 24	8 20	1—4	10 45	...
Thorn arr	...	p.m.	...	...		5 7	9 5	a.m.	11 26	Ex3
Warsaw dep	...	1152	...	Ex3		...		1 20	...	5a57
Alexandrovo dep	...	4 10	...	a.m.		...	a.m.	8 50	...	1131
Thorn (178) dep	...	5 21	...	9 18		7 23	8 23	9 32	11 36	1240
Bromberg arr	...	6 9	a.m.	9 58		8 33	9 36		12 44	1 29
" dep	...	6 17	4 52	10 1		8 43		...	12 50	1 32
Nakel	...	...	5 27	...		9 18	...	...	1 23	1 58
Schneidemühl arr	...	7 30	6 50	11 8		10 44	...	...	2 39	2 50
Schneidemühl dep	...	7 35	6 58		1120	10 54	...	...	3 4	
Filehne arr	2 3 4	RC	8 0		...	11 41	...	...	...	
Kreuz arr	a.m.	8 22	8 13	...	...	11 53	...	...	3 53	...
" dep	5 3	8 24	8 33	...	...	12 5	...	...	3 57	...
Friedeberg	5 18	...	9 15	...	...	12 42	p.m.	...	4 28	...
Landsberg	7 35	9 20	10 4	...	...	1 19	4 0	...	5 0	...
Cüstrin Haupt arr	8 39	9 55	11 3	...	...	2 10	5 10	...	5 36	...
" dep	8 45	9 57	11 8	...	...	2 16	5 16	...	5 38	...
Werbig	9 19	...	11 56	...	...	2 45	6 13	...	...	...
Dahmsdorf-Münch	9 52	...	12 31	...	...	3 19	6 58	...	...	...
Strausberg	1016	...	12 58	...	...	3 43	7 28	...	...	...
BERLIN SchlessBhf arr	1045	1110	1 29	...	2 23	4 13	8 0	...	6 57	...
Alexanderplatz arr	1054	1119	1 40	...	...	4 25	8 8	...	7 7	...
Friedrichstrasse arr	11 0	1125	1 46	...	2 34	4 31	8 14	...	7 13	...
Zoolog-Garten arr	1112	1139	1 58	...	2 47	4 43	8 26	...	7 27	...
Charlottenburg arr	1119	1147	2 5		2 54	4 50	8 33	...	7 35	...

Station	Ex3	2 3 4	2 3 4	2,3,4	Ex2	Ex.1	1—4		Ex3	2 3 4
St. Petersburg dep	...	...	...	...	7 p5	7 p45	...	...	...	...
Wirballen 313 arr	...	...	...	...	9a25	10a40	...	...	...	...
Eydtkühnen dep	a.m. 6 26	...	...	a.m. 7 15	a.m. 10 7	a.m. 11 0	...	...	...	...
Stalluponen	6 39	...	...	7 31	...	...	...	...	...	...
Insterburg arr	7 27	...	...	8 26	...	11 53	...	...	p.m.	...
" dep		...	...	8 36	RC	11 55	...	...	1 8	...
Wehlau		...	...	9 28	...	...	...	...	1 39	...
Königsberg Ost arr	RC	...	...	10 40	1156	1 17	...	...	2 29	...
" dep		...	...	12 7	12 1	1 23	...	...	2 37	...
Braunsberg		...	p.m.	1 24	...	...	...	...	3 31	...
Güldenboden		...	1248	2 37	...	N	...	...	RC	p.m.
Elbing		p.m.	1 11	3 9	1 23	3 4	p.m.	...	4 17	4 57
Marienburg		2 19		3 49	...	...	4 32	...	4 45	5 46
Dirschau arr		2 40	...	4 12	1 58	3 50	4 54	...	5 3	6 11
Dantsic dep		3 42	p.m.	3 p36	1p26	2 p54		...	4p30	
Dirschau dep			1251	4 28	2 6	3 55	...	...	5 11	...
Pr. Stargard		...	1 24	5 1	...	...	...	...	5 39	p.m.
Czersk		...	2 27	5 58	...	...	...	...	...	9 25
Konitz		...	3 32	7 0	...	5 37	...	...	6 48	1025
Flatow		...	4 33	8 6	...	...	...	...	7 31	
Schneidemühl arr		...	5 9	8 46	4 23	6 48	...	1Cl.	7 58	1—4
Insterburg dep	a.m. 7 37	...	...	a.m. 10 10	...		...	Nord Express Sat. only.	...	p.m. 2 50
Gerdauen	8 17	...	...	11 9	...		...		...	3 53
Korschen dep	8 44	...	...	11 51	...		...		...	4 48
Rothfliess	9 22	...	...	12 46	...		p.m.		...	5 55
Allenstein	9 55	...	...	1 39	...		3 0		...	6 47
Osterode	1031	3 & 4	...	2 30	...		3 34		...	7 41
Deutsch Eylau	11 0	p.m.	...	3 9	...		4 2		...	8 18
Gosslershausen	11 35	12 15	...	4 1	...		4 36		...	9 12
Schönsee	RC	1 4	...	4 45	...		...		...	9 57
Thorn arr	1230	1 53	...	5 42	...		5 34	p.m.	...	1043
Warsaw dep	5a57		1—4	9 a32	...			1222	9a32	
Alexandrovo dep	1131	...	p.m.	4 p22	...		...	3p49	4p22	...
Thorn (178) dep	1240	...	1 58	5 55	...		...	4 46	5 40	...
Bromberg arr	...	...	3 7	7 6	...		...		6 27	p.m.
" dep	...	...	3 15	7 24	...		...		6 31	1120
Nakel	...	1—4	3 50	8 3	...		...		6 57	12 0
Schneidemühl arr	...	p.m.	5 8	9 27	...		...		7 51	
Schneidemühl dep		3 19	5 15	9 43	4 28	6 53	...		8 6	...
Filehne arr		4 34	6 12	1052	...	...	...		...	...
Kreuz arr		4 48	6 24	11 6	...	...	...		8 55	p.m.
" dep		5 12	6 29	11 35	...	...	...		8 57	7 54
Friedeberg		5 52	7 13	1222	...	...	...		...	9 26
Landsberg	Via Posen.	6 40	8 3	1 15	...	8 41	...		9 55	1040
Cüstrin Haupt arr		7 41	9 7	2 22	...		...		1033	1216
" dep		7 48	9 27	2 27	...	Nord Express.	...		1035	
Werbig		8 25	10 5	3 2	...		...		...	...
Dahmsdorf-Münch		9 1	1042	3 39	...		...		...	...
Strausberg		9 27	1110	4 12	...		...		...	...
BERLIN SchlessBhf arr	7 12	9 59	1143	4 54	7 25	10 38	...		1149	...
Alexanderplatz arr	7 21	10 11	1153	5 6	...	...	...		12 1	...
Friedrichstrasse arr	7 27	10 17	1159	5 12	7 38	10 53	...	1053	12 7	...
Zoolog-Garten arr	7 43	10 29	1211	5 23	7 52	11 7	...	11 7	1221	...
Charlottenburg arr	7 51	10 36	1218	5 30	7 59	...	...	...	1228	...

Station	Ex3	2 3 4	1,2,3	1—4	Ex3	1—4	Ex 3	Ex3	2 3 4
St. Petersburg dep	...	...	...	...	...	...	11 p0	11p0	...
Wirballen 313 arr	...	...	...	...	...	...	4 p20	4p20	...
Eydtkühnen dep	...	...	a.m. 1140	...	...	p.m. 4 40	p.m. 5 42	p.m. 5 52	p.m. 9 27
Stalluponen	...	...	1156	...	...	5 5	RC	RC	9 54
Insterburg arr	...	...	1256	p.m.	...	6 16	6 36	6 46	11 16
" dep	...	...	1 21	4 12	...	7 7		7 0	11 36
Wehlau	...	...	2 9	5 4	...	7 57		7 32	12 24
Königsberg Ost arr	...	...	3 14	6 15	...	9 4		8 18	1 29
" dep	...	...	3 39	6 43	...	10 2		8 26	1 51
Braunsberg	...	...	5 13	8 15	...	1126		9 26	3 14
Güldenboden	...	...	6 16	9 19	...			SC	4 8
Elbing	...	...	6 39	9 41	...	...		1017	4 25
Marienburg	...	...	7 21	10 22	...	...		1045	5 9
Dirschau arr	...	p.m.	7 46	10 46	p.m.	...		11 5	5 33
Dantsic dep	...	7 5			1014	...		1014	5 a0
Dirschau dep	...	8 12	...	...	1052	...		1110	5 51
Pr. Stargard	...	8 59	...	...	1120	...		1138	6 36
Czersk	...	1019	...	...	12 0	...		...	7 46
Konitz	...	1142	...	...	1231	...		1247	8 40
Flatow	...	1247	...	...	SC	...		...	9 50
Schneidemühl arr	...	1 24	...	2,3,4	1 36	...		1 53	10 30
Insterburg dep	...		...	p.m. 7 2		2 3 4	p.m. 6 40		
Gerdauen	...		...	8 21		p.m.	7 16		
Korschen dep	...		...	10 9		8 12	7 48		
Rothfliess	...		...	11 26		8 57	8 24		
Allenstein	...		...	12 21		9 40	8 55		
Osterode	...		...			1035	9 28		
Deutsch Eylau	...		...	...			9 56		
Gosslershausen	...		...	...		...	10 30		
Schönsee	...		...	...		...	RC		
Thorn arr	...		...	...		...	11 24		
Warsaw dep	5p12		...	...		3& 4	5 p12		
Alexandrovo dep	1015		...	...		p.m.	10p15		
Thorn (178) dep	1134		...	...		7 48	11 36		
Bromberg arr	1230		...	...		9 4	SC		
" dep	1235		...	...					
Nakel	1 1		...	...		...			
Schneidemühl arr	2 4		...	...		...			
Schneidemühl dep	2 9	2 18	...	...	1 41	...		1 58	11 27
Filehne arr	...	3 18	...	...	...	...		...	12 24
Kreuz arr	2 59	3 29	...	...	2 29	...		2 47	12 36
" dep	3 1	3 41	...	...	2 31	...		2 51	12 44
Friedeberg	...	4 25	...	...	...	...		...	1 25
Landsberg	3 59	5 14	...	...	3 28	...	Via Posen.	3 46	2 11
Cüstrin Haupt arr	4 35	6 14	...	...	4 8	...		4 23	3 14
" dep	4 37	6 23	...	...	4 10	...		4 25	3 22
Werbig	...	7 0	...	...	...	...		...	4 4
Dahmsdorf-Münch	...	7 40	...	...	...	...		...	4 41
Strausberg	...	8 9	...	...	...	...		...	5 9
BERLIN SchlessBhf arr	5 59	8 52	...	...	5 33	...	5 51	5 42	5 41
Alexanderplatz arr	6 8	9 1	...	...	5 42	...	6 0	5 51	5 53
Friedrichstrasse arr	6 15	9 7	...	...	5 48	...	6 6	5 57	5 59
Zoolog-Garten arr	6 29	9 19	...	...	6 2	...	6 20	6 11	6 11
Charlottenburg arr	6 37	9 26	...	...	6 9	...	6 27	6 18	6 18

RUHNOW and KONITZ.

Ruhnow 175 dp		4a15	5a56	8a25	...	12p16	2p20	7 p1	9p39
Falkenburg		5 15	8 20	9 22	...	1 10	3 43	7 59	1037
Tempelburg		5 41	—	9 49	...	1 34	4 16	8 24	11 3
Jastrow ......arr		7 40	...	...	...	3 8	6 32	1038	...
Neu-Stettin arr ...		6 35	...	1044	...	2 26	5 21	9 20	1156
Neu-Stettin dep	6a42	...	...	1126	1p20		6 15	9 35	...
Schlochau ...	8 7	...	...	1255	2 31	6 p10	7 48	11 6	...
Konitz 176	8 32	...	...	1 23	2 52	6 36	8 15	1131	...

Konitz dep	...	...	5a38	9a37	1p44	3p14	5 p0	...	8p30	...
Schlochau...	...	...	6 15	10 0	2 4	3 44	5 26	...	8 59	...
Neustettin {	a.m.	...	8 0	1112	3 7	5 15	—	...	1030	...
Neustettin {	5 0	...	9 37	1140	3 17	5p58	...	8p45	...	...
Jastrow dp	...	...	5 55	1010	2 30	...	...	...	...	9p13
Tempelburg	5 55	a.m.	1031	1235	4 10	6 53	...	9 56	...	1050
Falkenburg	6 22	7 20	1057	1 0	4 34	7 18	...	1029	...	
Ruhnow	7 30	8 21	1152	1 57	5 27	8 13	...	1136	...	...

Falkenburg...dep	7 a28	1 p12	3p50	8 p3	10‡p40	...
Polzin ....arr	8 42	2 20	5 10	9 5	11 48	...

Polzin ....dep	5a50	9 a38	2p27	6 p2	9‡p10
Falkenburg ......arr	7 14	10 48	3 38	7 13	10 22

‡—Until 31st Aug.

HOHENSTEIN and LIPPUSCH.

Hohenstein...dep	...	...	6 a35	...	8a34	2 p15	6 p50	...	9 p38
Schöneck	...	...	7 27	...	9 17	2 59	7 40	...	10 20
Berent	5 a5	6a28	8 28	9 a44	1015	4 14	8 45	9p25	11 22
Lippusch......arr	5 33	6 58	...	10 13	1126	4 42	...	9 55	...

Lippusch ...dep	5a40	7a10	10a25	5 p0	6p56	10p 4	...
Berent	6 15	7 41	11 6	5 38	7 35	10 35	...
Schöneck.........	7 24	—	12 14	6 42	8 39	—	...
Hohenstein arr	8 10	...	12 55	7 23	9 21	...	...

Lippusch ....dep	4 a59	7 a 6	10a18	5 p 3	10 p5	...	...
Bütow ....arr	5 41	7 48	11 0	5 45	10 48	...	...

Bütow ....dep	4 a40	9 a20	4 p6	6p 2	9 p5	...	...
Lippusch .... arr	5 28	10 4	4 50	6 46	9 50	...	...

MOGILNO and HOHENSALZA.

Mogilno...............dep	4a39	8a57	1p12	5p12	...	9p 47	...
Strelno	5 20	9 54	1 44	6 5	p.m.	10 26	...
Kruschwitz................	6 35	1134	2 43	7 25	8 59	—	...
Hohensalza ....arr	7 14	1220	3 18	8 0	9 45	...	...

Hohensalza ......dep	...	7 a38	1p35	3p45	5‡p44	10p23	...	...
Kruschwitz............	...	8 29	2 40	4 30	6 38	11 0	...	...
Strelno	7 a5	9 43	4 1	—	8 15	12 4	...	...
Mogilno.............arr	7 45	10 23	4 43	...	8 54	12 32	...	...

‡—In July and Aug. only.]

NEUSTETTIN and BELGARD.

§**Neustettin**....dep	6a47	9 a28	2 ‡p5	3 p19	6p20	8p44	...	...
Gramenz	8 0	10 14	2 46	4 1	7 12	9 47	...	...
Belgard 175 ...arr	9 13	11 3	3 38	4 50	8 1	1056	...	...

Belgard.........dep	6a51	9‡a24	11a17	12p59	2p39	8p11	...
Gramenz	8 0	10 14	12 25	1 53	4 8	9 42	...
Neustettin ....arr	8 58	10 50	1 15	2 35	5 18	1033	...

LASKOWITZ and GOSSLERSHAUSEN.

Laskowitz...	7a28	11a21	2p53	6 p24	9p30	10p46	1a22	...	...
Graudenz ...	8 16	12 8	3 40	7 8	1018	11 28	1 57	...	...

Graudenz	6a19	9a14	11a11	12p50	4p38	5 p9	8p14	...	...	...
Laskowitz	7 8	1010	11 44	1 46	5 16	5 52	9 10	...	...	...

Graudenz dep	6a18	9 a1	11a11	12p26	2p43	3p58	8p11	11p33
Melno	6 52	9 25	11 38	12 50	3 14	4 26	8 35	11 57
Gosslershausen	7 32	9 54	12 9	1 16	3 48	4 57	9 4	12 26

Gosslershausen	6a23	7a52	10a5	11a38	4 p5	5p13	7p 8	9p10	10p35
Melno	6 55	8 24	1037	12 6	4 38	5 46	7 40	9 48	11 11
Graudenz...arr	7 20	8 48	11 1	12 26	5 3	6 11	8 4	1013	11 36

‡—On Sunday and Friday only.]

GOSSLERSHAUSEN and ILLOWO.

Gosslershausen dep	...	7a55	10 a3	12p31	1 p20	5p11	9 p16	12a54
Strasburg.............	...	8 57	10 45	1 26	2 0	5 46	10 16	1 7
Soldau ....arr	7a32	1044	...	...	3 52	7 8	12 7	—
Illowo (174A) ...arr	7 52	11‡20	...	...	4 29	7 28	...	...

Illowo ....dep	...	5a30	...	12p15	...	5‡p51	...
Soldau ....dep	...	6 55	9a30	1 10	...	6 36	...
Strasburg	5a35	8 43	1056	3 2	6p20	8 8	...
Gosslershausen ar	6 19	9 52	1128	3 45	7 3	8 51	...

MEMEL and BAJOHREN.

Memel ....dep	6 a4	11a10	2 p42	6 p0	...	...	...
Bajohren ....arr	6 45	11 51	3 23	6 41	...	...	...
Bajohren.........dep	7 a5	1 p24	4 p13	7 p 6	...	...	...
Memel ....arr	7 45	2 4	4 53	7 46	...	...	...

CARTHAUS and LAUENBURG.

Carthaus ....dep	5 a57	9 a21	4p19	8 p5	...	...	...	...
Lauenburg.....arr	8 18	12 12	7 1	10 22	...	...	...	...
Lautenburg ...dep	5 a26	9 a3	3p50	7 p54	...	...	...	...
Carthaus.........arr	7 40	11 21	6 35	10 5	...	...	...	...

MEMEL and INSTERBURG.

Memel ...dep	3a54	...	8a56	1041	2p49	...	8p 2	11p2	...
Heydekrug ...	4 57	6a39	10 5	1124	3 56	...	9 5	12 4	...
Tilsit	6 10	7 54	1122	1212	5 11	7 p9	1016	—	...
Insterburg arr	7 23	9 18	1235	1258	6 21	8 51	1129	...	...

Insterburg dep	5 a2	7a39	10a33	10a45	3 p2	6p42	9 p12	...	...
Tilsit	6 16	9 0	11 22	12 12	4 35	7 52	10 21	10p34	...
Heydekrug ...	7 23	...	12 7	1 23	6 33	...	11 3	11 46	...
Memel ......arr	8 23	...	12 48	2 27	7 48	...	11 47	12 46	...

POSEN and STRALKOWO.

Posen ....dep	4a56	7a44	11a8	...	2p11	4p28	8p59	12a27	...
Wreschen............	6 27	9 50	1245	1 p20	3 42	6 11	10 38	1 56	...
Stralkowo arr	7 0	1028	...	2 8	4 21	6 58	11 37	...	...

Stralkowo...	4a40	7a10	...	11a55	2p30	5p25	9 p45	...
Wreschen	5 23	7 43	9 a50	12 55	3 37	6 18	10 47	...
Posen 182 ...	6 43	9 30	11 25	2 1	5 31	7 52	12 17	...

TILSIT and STALLUPONEN.

Tilsit ....dep	3a33	...	6a14	7a34	12p29	1p44	5 p9	10p23
Ragnit	3 55	...	6 40	7 57	12 57	2 7	5 34	10 47
Pillkallen	5 23	6a52	8 10	—	2 38	—	7 0	12 13
Stallupon. arr	5 55	7 24	8 40	...	3 8	...	7 29	12 43

Stalluponen dep	3 a33	6a17	...	12p41	...	5 p2	7p47	10p7	
Pillkallen	4 8	6 53	a.m.	1 17	...	5 43	8 19	1039	
Ragnit	5 37	8 22	1051	2 54	4p26	7 20	9 47	—	
Tilsit ....arr	6 0	8 45	1114	3 17	4 49	7 43	1010	...	

DANTSIC and CARTHAUS.

E.M.							
	Dantsic (Hauptbhf) dep	6a30	1p39	5p17	9 p8	...	...
5½	Praust (178)	6 58	2 7	5 57	9 27	...	...
12	Bölkau	7 26	2 37	6 27	9 55	...	...
31¼	**Carthaus** ....arr	8 30	3 49	7 32	11 1	...	...

Carthaus......dep	5a10	7a45	11a34	3 p52	6 p44	...	...
Bölkau	6 17	8 53	12 44	4 59	7 52	...	...
Praust................	6 49	9 33	1 19	5 33	8 27	...	...
Dantsic (Haupt)	7 11	9 48	1 33	5 46	8 41	...	...

ARNSWALDE and DRAMBURG.

Arnswalde dep	...	7a20	11a45	4 p5	7p28	11p15	...	...	...
Callies	5a54	9 18	1 23	5 51	8 50	1 8	...	...	...
Falkenburg ...	7 30	1050	3 35	7 14	1011	...	...	...	...
Dramburg arr	7 40	...	...	...	...	...	...	...	...

Dramburg dep	...	7a55	...	...	...	...	...	...	...
Falkenburg ...	...	9 24	1p16	3p50	10p45	...	...	...	...
Callies......	5a51	8a46	12 1	3 47	6 0	12 32	...	...	...
Arnswalde	7 0	9 59	1 53	5 3	7 17	...	...	...	...

WRONKE and OBORNIK.

Wronke............dep	7a17	11a43	4p23	8p15	...	...	...
Obornik ....arr	8 32	12 50	5 37	10 9	...	...	...

Obornik............dep	5a33	9 a5	1p20	6p20	...	...	...	...
Wronke 218A ...arr	7 0	1017	3 3	7 53	...	...	...	...

WEHLAU and BARTENSTEIN.

Wehlau ....dep	5 a21	9 a36	8 p20	...
Friedland	6 26	11 10	9 18	...
Bartenstein......arr	7 58	1 43	10 24	...

Bartenstein ......dep	4 a50	11a11	8 p29	...	...
Friedland	6 38	12 17	9 20	...	...
Wehlau 176 ....arr	7 40	1 25	11 59	...	...

PRUSSIAN STATE RAILWAYS.

[Luggage Rates—see page 462.

RC—Restaurant Car. §—Rail Motor. [‡—Takes up only.

BROMBERG, DIRSCHAU, and DANTSIC.

					a.m.					a.m.		p.m.		p.m.			p.m.			p.m.	p.m.	p.m.	n'ht
Bromberg...dep	...	...	...	...	6 14	...	...	...	...	10 0	...	1225	...	1 46	...	...	4 45	...	...	8 8	9 28	9 40	1223
Terespol	...	...	...	...	7 1	...	...	...	...	1051	...	...	...	2 35	...	...	5 42	...	...	9 2	10 5	1029	1 9
Laskowitz	...	...	...	a.m.	7 17	...	...	...	...	11 8	...	1 17	...	2 51	p.m.	...	6 1	...	...	9 22	1018	1041	1 21
Schmentau	...	...	...	6 10	7 55	...	...	...	...	1148	...	RC	...	3 29	5 46	...	6 44	...	...	10 0	1050	—	—
Morroschin	...	...	...	6 29	8 8	...	...	...	...	12 2	...	...	...	3 43	5 31	...	7 0	...	...	1011	...	...	...
Dirschau ... arr	a.m.	a.m.	a.m.	7 12	8 46	a.m.	a.m.	a.m.	noon	1238	p.m.	2 22	p.m.	4 19	6 15	p.m.	7 44	p.m.	p.m.	1044	1123	...	a.m.
Dirschau ... dep	5 56	6 16	6 30	—	8 59	9 24	9 58	1152	12 0	1250	2 12	2 46	4 42	5 8	6 20	7 40	7 56	9 13	10 0	1112	1142	p.m.	1213
Hohenstein	...	6 30	6 47	8a28	9 17	...	...	12‡4	12 14	1 4	...	3 1	...	5 21	6 35	7 54	8 10	9 30	...	1125	1155	1132	...
Praust	...	6 49	7 5	8 49	9 33	...	...	...	12 34	1 19	...	3 16	...	5 33	6 56	8 10	8 27	9 48	...	1137	12 7	1150	...
Dantsic ......arr	6 25	7 11	7 28	9 12	9 48	9 55	1028	1225	12 50	1 33	2 42	3 30	5 15	5 46	7 11	8 24	8 41	1012	1030	1149	1221	1212	1242

	a.m.	a.m.	a.m.	a.m.	a.m.	a.m.	p.m.		p.m.	p.m.	pm	p.m.	p.m.	p.m.	p.m.	p.m.	p.m.	p.m.	ng't				
Dantsic......dep	5 0	8 0	8 35	9 10	10§0	11 0	1 26	...	1 33	2 54	336	4 30	6 15	7 5	9 8	1014	1030	1132	1210	...	...	...	...
Praust	5 13	8 13	...	9 24	1025	1114	...	...	1 48	...	350	...	6 28	7 18	9 22	...	1053	1157	1223	...	...	...	...
Hohenstein	5 28	8 25	...	...	1043	1126	...	...	2 7	...	4 3	...	6 40	7 35	9 34	...	11 9	1215	1235	...	...	...	...
Dirschau ... arr	5 41	8 38	9 5	9 43	1059	1139	1 56	p.m.	2 24	3 27	415	4 58	6 53	7 48	9 47	1044	1124	1231	1248	...	...	...	...
Dirschau ... dep	5 50	8 49	—	10 0	—	12 0	—	1§35	—	—	430	5 12	—	7 55	—	—	1130	—	—	...	...	...	...
Morroschin	6 20	9 28	...	RC	...	1246	...	2 20	...	...	5 7	...	...	8 32	...	...	12 7	...	...	...	...	...	...
Schmentau	6 41	9 43	...	1041	...	1 3	...	2 36	...	p.m.	522	...	...	8 47	...	...	1221	...	...	...	...	...	...
Laskowitz	7 26	1024	...	1115	...	1 51	...	—	...	5 18	6 3	6 22	...	9 29	...	...	—	...	...	...	...	...	...
Terespol...	7 40	1037	...	1127	...	2 9	...	...	...	5 30	616	6 34	...	9 49	...	...	...	...	...	...	...	...	...
Bromberg...arr	8 33	1124	...	1210	...	3 3	...	...	...	6 17	7 5	7 17	...	1047	...	...	...	...	...	...	...	...	...

Pr. Stargard ...dep	5a30	7a52	1p31	3p24	9p35
Schmentau ...arr	7 39	9 22	3 19	5 12	11 5
Schmentau dep	6 a5	9 a50	3p35	6p49	8p52
Pr. Stargard arr	7 33	12 12	5 32	8 35	1130

Morroschin to Mewe, in 30 min., 6.35, 9.32 a.m., 1.0, 5.15, 8.40 p.m. Return from Mewe, 5.43, 7.30, 11.20 a.m., 3.0, 7.50 p.m.

Neufahrwasser to Dantsic (Haupt.) in 18 mins., about hourly, from 4.35 a.m. until 12.0 night,

Dantsic (Haupt.) to Neufahrwasser in 18 mins., about hourly, from 5.35 a.m. until 12.30 night.

SCHMENTAU and CZERSK.

Schmentau dep	6 a5	10a43	3p35	10p4
Skurz	6 50	11 21	4 17	1041
Konigsbruch	8 20	12 33	5 12	1137
Czersk (176) arr	9 33	12 56	5 32	1153

Czersk ...dep	4 a57	...	8 a3	3p32	9p24
Konigsbruch	5 28	...	9 15	3 48	9 48
Skurz	6 33	8a52	1025	4 39	11 6
Schmentau (178) arr	7 3	9 22	1124	5 12	...

SCHMENTAU and RIESENBURG

Schmentau dep	...	7 a8	9a44	12 0	...	5p26	9 p5	11p10	...
Marienwerder	5a47	9 54	1019	1 35	3p50	6 33	1014	1149	...
Riesenburg arr	6 31	1031	...	2 32	4 34	7 30	...	...	...
Riesenburg dep	...	6a57	...	1043	...	4p58	6p40	...	9p25
Marienwerder	5a40	8 18	9a57	1138	2 p0	5 55	7 30	9p18	1010
Schmentau arr	6 31	9 25	1037	...	3 4	...	8 37	9 55	...

THORN, GRAUDENZ, and MARIENBURG.

E.M													
			a.m.	a.m.		a.m.			p.m.	p.m.	p.m.	p.m.	p.m.	
—	**Thorn Haupt.** dep	...	6 8	6 17	...	1035	...	...	2 30	4 10	6 29	9 16	1132	...
1	Thorn Stadt	...	6 14	6 24	...	1042	...	...	2 37	4 15	6 35	9 21	1138	...
13¾	Culmsee 178A	...	6 35	7 6	a.m.	1116	...	...	3 16	4 40	7 9	9 41	1212	...
22½	**Kornatowo** .....arr	...	6 54	7 33	9 45	1139	...	...	3 46	4 56	7 30	9 58	1235	...
...	⋮ Culm ....arr	a.m.	...	8 20	1025	1235	p.m.	...	...	5 52	8 40	1037	...	...
37½	**Graudenz 177A**	5 45	7 22	8 12	—	1218	1 38	...	4 23	5 22	8 5	1022	1 11	...
56	Garnsee	6 17	7 52	9 25	...	1258	2 13	...	—	5 53	8 44	1048	1 48	...
...	Lessen ....arr	...	9 14	...	...	...	3 9	p.m.	...	7 31	10 0	...	...	...
60¾	Marienwerder	6 51	8 14	10 2	...	1 23	2 45	5 32	...	6 18	9 17	11 8	2 12	...
85	**Marienburg** ...arr	7 49	9 0	11 5	...	2 14	3 40	6 37	...	7 8	1010	1152	...	...

178A											
	a.m.		a.m.	a.m.	p.m.	p.m.	p.m.	p.m.	p.m.	ng't		
Marienburg dep	...	...	6 37	9 35	1222	...	4 2	5 21	7 22	12 6	...	...
Marienwerder ...	4 26	...	7 50	1024	1 28	3 32	5 0	6 19	8 20	1 3	...	...
Lessen ......dep	...	...	7 0	...	1253	...	—	4 57	7 59	...	...	...
Garnsee	4 54	...	8 19	1046	1 54	3 59	...	6 45	8 47	1 29	...	...
Graudenz	5 29	a.m.	8 55	11 9	2 25	4 35	...	7 17	9 18	1 58	...	...
⋮ Culm ....dep	...	6 5	8 45	1050	1 30	4 8	...	6 52	9 0	—	...	...
Kornatowo	6 10	6 39	9 32	1139	3 2	5 14	...	7 52	9 58	...	...	...
Culmsee	6 36	—	9 53	1156	3*24	5 36	...	8 14	1018	...	...	...
Thorn Stadt	7 14	...	1029	1219	4 1	6 14	...	8 53	1052	...	...	...
Thorn Haupt. arr	7 18	...	1033	1223	4 5	6 18	...	8 58	1056	...	...	...

POSEN and BROMBERG.

Dist		Ex3	2 3 4	234	2—4	Ex3	Ex3	2 3 4		2 3 4	Ex3	2 3 4	Ex3	2 3 4	2 3 4
...	BERLIN (Friedrichstrasse) dep	11p6	...	...	...	...	3a58	3a58	7a32	...	9a42	9a42	2p25	2p25	7p42
E.M		a.m.		am	a.m.	a.m.	a.m.	a.m.	a.m.	p.m.	p.m.	p.m.	p.m.	p.m.	a.m.
—	Posen ....dep	3 13	...	...	5 56	7 37	10 4	1011	1132	1238	1 59	3 10	7 3	7 46	1213
31¼	Gnesen 178A	3 57	...	454	7 19	8 21	1048	1122	⋮	1 55	2 43	4 23	7 48	8 59	1 37
49¾	Mogilno (177A)...	4 25	...	6 3	8 5	8 48	...	12 2	⋮	2 41	...	5 3	...	9 44	2 22
66½	**Hohensalza** ...arr	4 50	a.m.	733	8 39	9 10	1134	1233	B	3 15	3 31	5 36	8 36	1016	2 57
...	Hohensalza dep	4 54	7 20	—	9 18	...	1145	1 12	⋮	...	3 36	5 44	8 44	1024	—
87¾	Thorn (176) arr	5 28	8 11	...	10 5	...	1220	1 53	1 29	...	4 4	6 24	9 15	11 6	...
239	WARSAW 316	1p22	...	...	...	...	...	...	7p14	...	1a29	...	7a20	8 a7	...
...	**Hohensalza**...dep	5 2	...	...	8 46	9"14	1139	1238	...	3 40	...	5 44	8 40	1022	...
94½	**Bromberg 178** arr	6 0	...	...	9 44	9 54	1220	1 37	...	4 38	...	6 47	9 23	1115	...

		2 3 4	Ex3	2 3 4	2 3 4	Ex3	Ex3	2 3 4		Ex3	2—4	2 3 4	Ex3
		a.m.	a.m.	a.m.	a.m.	p.m.	p.m.	p.m.	p.m.	p.m.	p.m.	p.m.	
Bromberg ....dep		6 15	7 41	8 42	1131	1222	...	3 15	...	7 23	7 34	1116	...
Hohensalza ......arr		7 13	8 25	9 46	1223	1 7	...	4 13	...	8 3	8 32	12 8	...
WARSAW......dep		11p52	...	...	1a20	...	5a57	...	1222	...	9a32	—	5p12
Thorn ......dep	2 3 4	6 25	7 50	8 34	1135	...	1240	3 20	4 46	...	7 2	...	1136
Hohensalza ...arr	a.m.	7 10	8 22	9 39	1218	...	1 12	4 8	⋮	...	7 56	B—Nord Express.	1210
Hohensalza dep	3 44	7 20	8 30	9 51	1228	1 18	1 26	4 19	B	8 6	8 40		1214
Mogilno	4 20	7 53	8 54	1028	1259	...	...	4 51	⋮	...	9 16		1237
Gnesen	5 16	8 25	9 22	1113	1 37	2 8	2 26	5 32	⋮	8 52	10 2		1 10
Posen (182)...arr	6 34	9 45	10 4	1224	2 45	2 54	3 12	6 39	6 48	9 33	1119		1 51
BERLIN (179A)	1117	2 p47	2p47	...	7p27	7p27	7p27	...	1053	...	6 a6	...	6 a6

STARGARD and CALLIES.

Stargard.........dep	6 a13	8a13	12p15	3 p32	10p19
Wulkow....................	6 29	8 29	12 34	3 46	10 32
Callies ....arr	8 42	1034	3 32	5 41	1 7

Callies...........dep	6 a17	10 43	3 p6	5 p58	...	...
Wulkow	8 28	12 34	5 3	8 2	...	...
Stargard.........arr	8 41	12 46	5 16	8 15	...	...

WORMDITT and MOHRUNGEN.

Mohrungen......dep	5 a1	8a43	11 a6	2 p59	8 p32
Wormditt.........arr	5 56	9 34	11 57	3 52	9 30

Wormditt............dep	6 a14	12p11	4 p14	7p28	10p35
Mohrungen ....arr	7 6	1 6	5 11	8 20	11 33

WORMDITT and BISCHDORF.

Wormdittdep	...	6a30	...	12p15	...	5 p5	10p40
Heilsberg	4a26	7 46	10a23	1 13	2 p38	6 20	11 32
Bischdorfarr	5 38	...	11 19	...	4 8	8 25	...

Bischdorf...dep	6 a28	...	12p20	5 p18	...	9 p6
Heilsberg 5a10	7 39	10a57	2 52	6 54	8p25	10 6
Wormditt 6 8	...	11 55	3 50	...	9 50	...

NEUSTETTIN, STOLP, and STOLPMUNDE.

		a.m.		a.m.	a.m	a.m.	p.m.	p.m		p.m.
Neustettin ......dep		...	...	6 43	...	1125	3 22	5 58	p.m	10 46
Rummelsburg		5 48	a.m.	7 53	9 31	1245	4 31	7 28	8 56	12 4
Zollbrück		6 49	7 30	8 56	1044	1 52	5 32	8 39	9 55	—
Stolp ......arr......		7 24	8 10	9 27	1124	2 23	6 3	9 10	1026	...
,, ...dep	4a50	7 45	—	9 35	1p18	3 8	6 12	9 48	—	5 a55
Stolpmündearr	5 23	8 20	...	10 9	1 51	3 42	6 40	1031	...	6 29

	a.m.	a.m	a.m.	a.m.	p.m	p.m	p.m	p.m.	p.m.
Stolpmünde dp	6 40	6 3	8 43	11 10	1225	1 52	4 5	8 41	1112
Stolp ....arr	7 13	6 36	9 16	11 38	1259	2 23	4 38	9 15	1146
,, ...dep	—	6 43	10 9	11 47	1 47	3 0	5 25	9 20	—
Zollbruck.........dep		7 26	1044	12 21	2 21	3 34	6 4	9 55	...
Rummelsburg	5 a6	8 24	1140	1 22	—	4 35	7 28	1051	...
Neustettin arr	6 28	9 32	...	2 28	...	5 43	8 36	—	...

Schlawe ...dep	7 a0	11a45	3p32	9p45
Stolpmünde arr	8 18	1 23	5 30	11 7
Stolpmündedep	5a28	8 a30	1p55	6p48
Schlawe......arr	6 48	9 50	3 12	8 50

Schlawe ....dep	8 a4	11a15	3p25	6 p7	9p47
Rugenwalde ... arr	8 50	12 4	4 1	6 42	1032
Schlawe...dep	6a58	11a49	2 p1	2p58	5 p3	9p20
Zollbrück arr	7 21	12 15	2 24	3 24	5 25	9 47

Rugenwalde ...dep	6a10	9a12	2p15	4p20	8p 0
Schlawe ....arr	6 45	9 47	2 50	4 55	8 45
Zollbrück dep	7a25	9a23	12p25	1p59	5p36	8p38
Schlawe...arr	7 46	9 44	12 52	2 30	6 2	9 4

MARIENBURG and TIEGENHOF.

Marienburg dep	9 a8	11a14	4 p32	7 p21	p.m.	10p22	...
Simonsdorf	9 31	12 12	5 11	7 32	8 18	10 33	11p54
Tiegenhof ...arr	10 19	1 0	6 0	...	9 14	...	12 43

Tiegenhof ....dep	7 a5	10a32	2 p33	6p23	...	9p30	...
Simonsdorf	8 10	11 57	3 31	7 22	8 p13	10 20	11p42
Marienburg (178) arr	8 25	12 7	3 52	...	8 23	...	11 52

MARIENWERDER and GOSSLERSHAUSEN.

Marienwerderdep	7a50	12p17	1p45	6p22	9p20
Freystadt 5a50	8 56	2 0	2 45	7 30	1053
Gosslershausn7 20	9 51	3 35	...	8 43	...

Gosslershausendep	7a55	12p20	...	5p44	9p18
Freystadt 6a10	8 56	1 48	4p54	7 23	1035
Marienwerd'r7 35	9 48	2 40	5 45	8 14	...

Freystadt...dep	5 a55	9 a1	2 p0	7p17
Riesenburg arr	6 30	9 44	2 46	7 50
Riesenburg dep	8 a9	1p12	6p37	8p25
Freystadt...arr	8 48	1 44	7 10	9 14

GNESEN and NAKEL.

Gnesen......dep	5 a7	9 a23	2 p54	7 p55	...
Elsenau	6 39	10 37	4 10	9 13	...
Nakel (176) arr	7 46	12 13	5 58	10 24	...

Nakel ....dep	5 a31	9 a21	1p40	8 p15	...	...	...
Elsenau	6 44	10 42	3 59	10 32	...	...	...
Gnesen (178) arr	7 47	12 5	5 24	12 24	...	...	...

NAKEL and KONITZ.

Nakel ....dep	5 a38	9 a24	2 p2	8 p16	...
Vandsburg	7 0	11 12	4 9	9 49	...
Konitz.....................arr	8 28	12 38	6 26	11 8	...

Konitz ....dep	5 a35	9 a32	4 p52	8 p26	...
Vandsburg	6 52	11 12	6 18	10 3	...
Nakel ....arr	7 57	12 38	7 24	11 41	...

BROMBERG and SCHONSEE.

Bromberg dep	5a12	9a22	1239	1 p51	4 p13	8p33	12a38
Unislaw	6 8	10 13	1 38	2 49	5 8	9 38	1 30
Culmsee	6 38	10 37	2 10	3 32	7 18	1029	1 53
Schonsee 176	7 3	11 6	...	4 15	7 58	11 9	...

Schonsee 5a30	...	10a47	1 p8	...	4p57	10 p0
Culmsee 6 20	6a39	11 24	1 39	4 p43	5 46	10 30
Unislaw	7 1	11 48	2 5	5 8	6 19	10 56
Bromberg arr	7 50	12 38	2 56	6 4	7 16	11 47

SCHUBIN and ZNIN.

Schubin............dep	6 a4	11 a2	3 p57	9 p18	...
Znin....................arr	7 8	12 4	4 30	9 53	...

Znin....................dep	6 a10	10 a0	4p42	10p28	...
Schubin 175 ......arr	6 47	10 36	5 31	11 25	...

SCHONSEE and STRASBURG.

Schonsee...................dep	7 a12	11a39	4 p55	10 p0
Gollub	7 47	12 24	5 52	10 42
Strasburg................arr	8 52	1 37	7 32	...

Strasburg..............dep	...	8 a55	1 p58	7 p3	...
Gollub	6a10	10 1	3 41	8 56	...
Schonsee..................arr	6 53	10 35	4 27	9 41	...

OSTERODE and HOHENSTEIN.

Osterode..............dep	4 a10	10 a7	3 p38	6 p20	11p25
Hohenstein . ....arr	6 0	11 21	4 52	7 38	12 39

Hohenstein..........dep	4a38	7a12	12p44	5 p44	8 p5
Osterode ....arr	5 52	8 24	1 56	6 58	9 15

KONIGSBERG and TILSIT.

Königsbergdep	5 a47	10 a0	12p51	5 p18	9 p4
Rothenstein..........	6 18	10 21	1 15	5 42	9 28
Labiau	7 45	11 20	2 34	6 58	10 50
Mehlauken ...4a24	8 48	12 0	3 33	7 57	11 42
Tilsit......arr5 57	10 30	1 11	5 3	9 26	...

Tilsit ....dep	6 a20	9 a27	12p16	5 p32	10p25
Mehlauken 4a36	7 56	10 40	2 6	7 7	12 2
Labiau 5 35	8 57	11 19	3 6	8 10	—
Rothenstein.......................6 56	10 18	12 15	4 29	9 27	...
Königsberg (176) 7 19	10 41	12 33	4 55	9 51	...

Tilsit to Laugszargen 9.7 a.m., 1.17, 5.32, 8.43 p.m. From Laugszargen 6.20, 10.43 a.m., 3.22, 7.8 p.m.

GRAMENZ and POLLNOW.

Gramenz ...dep	8 a10	2 p0	4 p4	9p50
Bublitz	9 8	2 55	4 45	1057
Pollnow ...arr	10 21	3 42	5 29	1159

Pollnow ....dep	5 a30	8 a0	1 p0	...	5 p41	...
Bublitz	6 52	9 10	2 12	2 p41	6 30	...
Gramenz 177A ......arr	7 45	9 51	...	3 18	7 7	...

KREUZ and ROGASEN.

Kreuz.......................dep	5 a24	8 a43	1 p0	6 p32
Czarnikau	7 1	10 38	3 11	8 6
Rogasen (175) ......arr	8 28	12 5	5 12	9 33

Rogasen ....dep	5 a5	9 a6	12p38	6 p19	...
Czarnikau	6 46	1117	2 19	8 21	...
Kreuz (176 ....arr	8 9	1237	3 39	9 46	...

BEESKOW and FALKENBERG.

Beeskow ......dep	...	...	5 a30	...	9 a2	...	...	...	...	2p10	...	5 p10	...	...	...	...	...	...	...
Wittmannsdorf......	...	...	6 13	...	9 44	...	...	...	...	2 57	...	6 4	...	...	...	...	...	...	...
Lübben Nord.	...	...	7 10	7 a42	10 37	11 a0	...	...	2 p30	3 58	...	7 4	...	...	...	...	...	...	...
Luckau....................	5 a45	...	—	8 46		11 31	...	...	3 22		4p55	8 2	...	...	...	...	...	...	...
Uckro	6 2	...	...	9 17	...	11 46	...	...	4 16	...	5 15	9 10	...	...	...	...	...	...	...
Schlieben...............	—	6 a30	...	10 5	...	—	1 p0	...	5 45	...	—	10 20	...	...	...	...	...	...	...
Herzberg	5 a35	7 25	...	10 27	...	...	1 31	3 p55	6 10	...	...	10 45	...	...	...	...	...	...	...
Falkenberg 172 ar	6 3	7 49	...	10 50	...	...	2 0	4 25	7 40	...	...	...	...	...	...	...	...	...	...

Falkenberg ...dep	...	...	...	6 a13	9 a25	11 a5	...	2 p15	...	5 p46	8 p46	...	...	...	...	...	...
Herzberg	...	...	...	7 0	9 55	11 38	...	2 38	...	6 20	9 21	...	...	...	...	...	...
Schlieben................	...	...	...	7 39	—	12 5	...	3 0	...	7 2	9 48	...	...	...	...	...	...
Uckro....................	...	6 a37	...	9 30	...	—	12p30	4 15	6 p0	8 25	—	...	...	...	...	...	...
Luckau	a.m.	7 3	a.m.	9 58	p.m.	...	1 0	4 45	6 20	9 20	...	...	...	...	...	...	...
Lübben Nord..........	5 35	9 0	9 5	10 36	12 5	...	1 39	5 28	—	—	...	...	...	...	...	...	...
Wittmannsdorf	6 36	—	9 55	—	1 3	...	—	6 27	...	...	...	...	...	...	...	...	...
Beeskow ......arr	7 15	...	10 53	...	1 52	...	...	7 9	...	...	...	...	...	...	...	...	...

GOLDAP and STALLUPONEN.

Goldap.........dep	5a28	10a2	1p25	4p26	8 p20
Stallupönen arr	7 7	1136	3 57	7 5	9 49
Stallupönen dep	6 a14	9 a52	1 p35	4p23	8 p0
Goldap .... arr	7 51	11 22	4 11	6 44	9 46

ZINTEN and RUDCZANNY.

Zinten ....dep	...	6 a26	10a35	6 p9	...
Rothfliess	7 a7	9 11	12 38	8 28	...
Sensburg	8 19	10 39	1 50	9 17	...
Rudczanny......arr	9 28	...	2 45	10 2	...

Rudczanny.....dep	7 a29	10a42	...	3p51	...	...	...
Sensburg	8 21	11 41	2 p35	4 52	7 p13	...	...
Rothfliess	9 25	12 30	3 52	5 50	8 26	...	...
Zinten (174A) arr	11 26	...	5 55	...	11 1	...	...

NEUBRANDENBURG and FRIEDLAND.

Neubrandenburg dep	9 a35	2 p5	7p16	10p0
Friedland.........arr	10 38	3 8	8 14	11 3

Friedland ....dep	7a20	12p30	5p42	8p35
Neubrandenburg 181...arr	8 23	1 33	6 45	9 33

KONIGSBERG and WARNICKEN.

†—Until 31st August.

Konigsberg	5a25	8 a0	9a40	11†a10	12p50	2p0	2†p25	5 p0	§p28	7†50	9p25
Neukuhren	8 0	8 56	1016	12 10	2 33	3 0	3 13	5 51	7 35	8 50	103
Warnicken	8 40	9 23	11 2	12 36	3 4	325	3 38	6 17	8 2	9 17	11 0

Warnicken	6†20	7a25	9a26	10a8	1 p9	4†p0	5p20	6p22	7p37	9p25
Neukuhren	6 47	7 51	9 53	1038	1 35	4 30	5 50	6 51	8 6	9 51
Konigsberg	7 43	8 40	1056	12 0	2 50	5 4[illegible]	7 0	7 48	9 [illegible]	1047

MECKLENBURG-POMERANIA RAILWAY.

§—Mon., Tues., and Fri. †—Sun., Wed., and Sat.

Ferdinandshof......dep	8 a50	3 p52	6 p15	...	...	...	...
Friedland ....arr	10 47	5 20	7 59	...	...	...	...
Friedland ....dep	5 a10	12 0	3 p20	...	...	...	...
Jarmen ....arr	7 23	2 11	5 28	...	...	...	...
Anclam ....dep	4p 45	2 p40	...	...	...	...	...
Uhlenhorst ....arr	6 7	4 2	...	...	...	...	...
Anclam ....dep	...	4 a54	2 p50	...	...	...	...
Dennin	5 a10	6 10	4 31	...	...	...	...
Janow..................arr	5 37	...	4 58	...	...	...	...
Anclam ....dep	5 a38	2 p25	7†12	...	...	...	...
Leopoldshagen......arr	6 40	3 27	8 14	...	...	...	...

Friedland ....dep	5 a20	8 a50	3 p25	...	...	...	...
Ferdinandshof......arr	7 0	10 43	5 5	...	...	...	...
Jarmen ....dep	4 a53	9 a3	5 p55	...	...	...	...
Friedland ....arr	7 7	11 16	8 10	...	...	...	...
Uhlenhorst ....dep	6 a39	7p 5	...	...	...	...	...
Anclam ....arr	8 1	8 27	...	...	...	...	...
Janow..................dep	5 a43	6 p20	...	...	...	...	...
Dennin	6 25	7 7	...	...	...	...	...
Anclam ....arr	7 41	8 23	...	...	...	...	...
Leopoldshagen ... dep	6 a50	3†p35	5§p5	8†p20	...	...	...
Anclam ....arr	7 52	4 37	6 7	9 22	...	...	...

STARGARD and CUSTRIN.

Dist. E.M.			a.m	a.m.	a.m	a.m	p.m	p.m	p.m.
—	Stargard ...dep		5 15	...	8 10	11 30	3 31	6 21	10 17
15½	Pyritz		6 10	...	9 21	12 28	4 26	7 31	11 9
29½	Glasow ...a.m	a.m	7 4	8 39	1046	1 16	5 16	8 33	11 54
35	Soldin.......	4 49	7 24	8 53	1124	1 31	5 37	8 57	12 7
49½	Neudamm	5 40	8 6	9 25	1230	2 14	6 40	9 50	...
61	Custrin 176	6 16	8 35	9 51	1 12	2 43	7 15	1025	...

				a.m.	a.m.	p.m.	p.m.	p.m	p.m.	p.m.
Custrin Vorstadt dep		...	5 2	11 12	2 15	4 41	5 20	7 47	10 52
Neudamm		...	5 47	11 51	2 59	5 6	5 53	8 18	11 47
Soldin........................		...	6 35	12 52	3 55	5 41	6 37	9 2	12 58
Glasow ....a.m.	a.m.	a.m.	7 39	1 13	4 16	5 52	6 52	9 21	1 47
Pyritz....................	4 42	6 45	8 33	1 54	5 6	...	7 34	10 41	2 53
Stargard 175 arr	5 35	7 35	9 22	2 47	5 56	...	8 23	11 31	...

Pyritz ....dep	9 a40	2 p30	8 p27	...	...	...
Plönzig ....arr	10 43	3 43	9 30	...	...	...
Pyritz ....dep	5 a0	9 a50	5 p47	...	...	...
Klein-Schönfeld ...arr	6 16	11 6	7 1	...	...	...
Soldin ....dep	3 a52	7 a22	1 p43	6 p43	...	...
Landsberg 176........arr	6 17	9 8	3 31	9 12	...	...

Plönzig.................dep	6 a42	11a57	5 p27	...	...
Pyritz....................arr	7 45	1 10	6 40	...	...
Klein-Schönfeld dep	6 a29	12p37	7 p4	...	...
Pyritz.. ....arr	7 40	1 50	8 20	...	...
Landsberg ....dep	4 a32	10a54	1 p24	6 p23	...
Soldin 178B ....arr	7 0	12 46	3 16	8 51	...

NEU-STRELITZ and WARNEMUNDE.

*-From Berlin. RC—Restaurant Car attached.

SC—Sleeping Car in this train.

Dist. E.M.																			
	BERLIN 181......dep		...	...	...	8a19	...	8 a49	...	...		10a45	...	2p53	...	3p28	...	...	...	11p15
			1—4	2,3,4	1—4	1,2,3	Ex 3	Ex.3	1—4	1—4	1,2,3	1—4	1—4	1,2,3	1—4	1—4	1—4	1—4	Ex3	Ex3
*			a.m	a.m.		a.m.		a.m.	p.m			p.m.		p.m		p.m.				a.m
62¾	Neu-Strelitz ...dep		5 3	...	...	10§9	Hamburg dep. 9.13.	10 35	...	...	...	1 20	...	4§48	...	6 18	...	...	Hamburg dep. 12.0.	1 3
83½	Waren (213)............		5 55	...	a.m.	1044		11 8	...	...	..	2 30	...	5 20	...	7 15	..	p.m.		1 41
105¾	Lalendorf (213) ...	1—4	6 43	...	10 57	1120		RC	...	...	A	3 20	p.m	5 57	p.m	8 3	...	11 20		SC
115¼	Gustrow (213)......	a.m.	7 11	10 2	11 12	1136		11 57	1210	p.m.	p.m	3 51	5 46	6 13	8 22	9 16	n'gt	11 36		2 31
136½	Rostock (213)...	6 0	8 18	10 50	—	1210	12p25	12 32	1 1	2 15	2 40	4 44	6 39	6 50	8 59	1028	1254	—	3 a6	3 10
144½	Warnemünde	6 22	8 50	11 16	...	1229	12 39	12 50	1 29	2 36	2 55	5 22	7 36	7 10	9 50	1136	1 9	...	3 20	3 29
...	WARNEMUNDE dep		...	...	...	...		1 p2	...	...	...	...	...	...	...	...	...	...		3a45
170¾	GJEDSER (stm)...arr		...	...	...	...	...	3 p2	...	...	...	...	...	...	...	...	...	...	...	5a45
278½	COPENHAGEN 302 arr		...	...	...	...	...	6 p41	...	...	...	...	...	...	...	...	...	...	...	9a42
460¼	GOTHENB'RG 309A ar		...	...	...	...	...	4 a20	...	...	...	...	...	...	...	...	...	...	...	10p4
682	CHRISTIANIA 304 arr		...	...	...	...	...	12 0	...	...	...	...	...	...	...	...	...	...	...	...
682½	STOCKHOLM 308 arr		...	...	...	...	...	8 a49	...	...	...	...	...	...	...	...	...	...	...	6a58

STOCKHOLM...dep	10p0	...	...	...	...	...	...	...	...	...	...	...	...	8p30	...	...	...	...	...	...
CHRISTIANIA dep	...	...	...	...	...	...	...	...	...	...	...	...	...	5p45	...	...	...	...	...	...
GOTHENBURG dep	10a0	...	...	...	...	...	...	...	...	...	...	...	...	1a33	...	...	...	...	...	...
COPENHAGEN dep	8p10	...	...	...	...	...	...	...	...	...	...	...	...	11a0	...	...	...	...	...	...
GJEDSER(stm) dep	1214	...	...	...	...	...	...	...	...	...	...	...	...	2p38	...	...	...	...	...	...
WARNEMUNDE ar	2a14		...	...	...	...	...	...	...	...	...	...	...	4p38		...	...	...	...	...
	Ex3	Ex 3	1—4	1—4	1—4	1,2,3	1,2,3	1—4	1—4	1—4	1—4	1—4	1,2,3	Ex3	Ex3	1—4	1—4	1—4	1—4	1—4
	a.m.	a.m.	a.m	a.m.	a.m.	a.m	a.m.	a.m.	a.m.	p.m	p.m.	p.m.	p.m	p.m	p.m.	p.m	p.m.	p.m	p.m.	p.m
Warnemünde...dep	2 32	2 40	5 42	7 20	8 45	9§24	10 0	10 5	11 23	1 15	2 45	3 15	4§25	4*51	4 59	5 15	6 35	8 15	...	11 45
Rostock...............	2 51	2 55	6 9	7 42	9 5	9 46	1015	1034	11 44	2 5	3 6	4 0	4 44	5 9	5 13	6 15	7 15	8 36	11 9	12 6
Gustrow..................	3 29	Hamburg arr. 6.15.	7 16	—	—	10 27	B	12 6	—	3 11	—	5 2	5 19	5 44	Hamburg arr. 8.23.	7 1	8 30	—	1230	—
Lalendorf	SC		7 38	...	...	10 44	—	1235	...	3 31	...	5 21	5 35	SC		—	9 3	...	1248	...
Waren	4 23		8 29	...	...	11 30	...	1 55	...	—	...	—	6 14	6 35		...	9 59	...	—	...
Neu-Strelitz...arr	4 55		9 14	...	...	12 2	...	2 45	...	...	...	...	6 48	7 7		...	1048	...	...	...
BERLIN 181 ...arr	6a38		1110	...	...	1 p51	...	5p42	...	...	...	...	8p47	8p55		...	...	...	...	...

*—Until 15th September will admit at Warnemünde only passengers from the Danish Steamers.

A—From Leipzig; runs until 30th August.

B—To Leipzig; runs from 2nd July until 31st August.

§—Until 15th Sept.

LALENDORF and ROSTOCK (via Laage).

Lalendorf ...dep	6a56	...	...	3 p41	8 p5	...
Plaaz	7 16	8 a7	12p36	4 0	8 25	9p54
Laage................	7 33	8 27	12 54	4 15	8 41	10 8
Rostock ......arr	8 13	...	1 32	4 52	9 18	...

Rostock ......dep	...	6 a18	...	11 a3	2p57	7 p30
Laage................	6a25	6 57	8a42	11 44	3 38	8 10
Plaaz	6 39	7 14	8 57	12 1	3 53	8 26
Lalendorf ...arr	...	7 32	...	12 19	...	8 45

SENSBURG and LYCK.

Sensburg.........dep	8 a30	2 p10	9 p25	...	...
Nikolaiken	9 32	2 59	10 8	...	...
Arys.....................	10 54	3 52	11 1	...	...
Lyck (175) ....arr	...	...	...	...	...

Lyck ....dep	...	...	...	...	...
Arys.....................	6 a20	12 p4	4 p31	...	...
Nickolaiken	7 16	1 1	5 58	...	...
Sensburg (178A) arr	7 55	1 40	6 55	...	...

[Luggage Rates—see page 462.

BERLIN, FRANKFORT-ON-THE-ODER, KOHLFURT, and BRESLAU.

THROUGH CARRIAGE—Berlin to Bucharest in 8.36 a.m. from Friedrichstrasse.
RESTAURANT CAR—in 8.36 a.m., and 12.47 p.m. from Friedrichstrasse Bahnhof, Berlin.

Dist. E.M.		234	2,3,4	234	1,2,3	2,3,4	234	1,2,3	Ex.3	Ex 3	234	2,3,4	Ex1	2,3,4	Ex.3	Ex 3	234	2,3,4	234
	BERLIN—					a.m.		a.m.				a.m.	a.m.	a.m.	a.m.	a.m.	a.m.		a.m.
—	Charlottenburg...dep	...	...	...	...	8 39	...	6 10	...	...	...	6 39	B	7 24	8 13	9 19	10 7	...	1110
2	Zoologisch. Garten dp	...	...	...	...	3 46	...	6 17	...	...	...	6 46	7 20	7 31	8 21	9 27	1014	...	1117
4½	Friedrichstrasse dep	...	...	...	...	3 58	...	6 29	...	...	...	6 57	7 32	7 43	8 36	9 42	1026	...	1129
5½	Alexanderplatz...dep	...	...	...	...	4 4	...	6 35	...	...	...	7 3	...	7 50	8 42	9 48	1032	...	1135
7	Schlesischer Bhf. dep	...	...	...	...	4 16	...	6 47	...	...	...	7 15	7 52	8 2	8 54	9 57	1044	...	1147
36¼	Fürstenwalde	...	...	...	...	5 1	...	7 25	...	...	...	8 0	...	8 49	RC	...	1128	...	1234
57½	**Frankfort** (Oder) arr	...	...	...	...	5 49	...	7 56	...	...	...	8 49	9 0	9 25	10 4	11 5	1217	...	1 25
165	POSEN 182.........arr	...	...	...	...	9a54	...	...	...	...	...	1 p35	1127	1 p35	...	1 p51	6p23	...	6p23
405	WARSAW 316 ...arr	...	...	...	...	...	...	...	...	...	...	...	7p14		...	1 a29	...	p.m.	
...	**Frankfort** (Oder) dep	...	...	...	...	5 57	...	8 1	...	...	...	8 56	...	...	10 7	...	1225	1 31	...
71¾	Fürstenberg	...	...	...	...	6 34	...	...	...	...	...	9 32	...	...	...	...	1 0	2 8	...
87½	**Guben** ....arr	...	...	...	...	7 11	...	8 40	...	...	...	10 9	...	...	10 46	...	1 36	2 42	...
...	,, ...dep	...	...	...	...	7 15	...	8 41	From Halle, see p. 173A.	‡—Via Sorau. §—1–4 class.	...	10 15	...	...	10 47	...	1 48	3 3	...
104½	**Sommerfeld**......arr	...	a.m.	...	...	7 53	...	9 6			...	10 54	...	...	11 12	...	2 25	3 40	...
...	**Sommerfeld** ..dep	...	6 5	...	...		...	9 11			...	12 5	...	...	11 17	...	2 30		1,2,3
115	Benau	...	6 33	...	...		...	...			...	12 31	...	...	...	...	2 56		From Lissa. See p. 220A.
125	**Sagan** ....arr	...	7 1	...	From Lissa. See p. 220A.		...	9‡51			...	12 53	...	...	11 50	...	3 18		
267	KALISZ 218A...arr	...	...	...			...	...			...	...	...	...	4p55	...	...		
423	WARSAW 316...arr	...	...	...			...	...	a.m.		...	...	...	...	...	...	...		
...	**Sagan**.........dep	a.m.	7 11	...			a.m.	9 52	11 47		...	12 55	...	...	11 55	...	3 20		
156½	Reisicht 220A	6 10	8 15	...			1010	...	...	...	...	1 59	...	...	...	...	4 46		
165½	Arnsdorf	6 30	8 31	...			1030	...	...	...	...	2 18	...	...	...	...	5 3		
171¼	**Liegnitz** ...arr 2 3 4	6 44	8 44	a.m.			1044	...	12 43	...	...	2 32	...	...	12 58	...	5 12		
...	**Sommerfeld** dep a.m.			5 5		7 58		...		...	...	11 23	...	...		...	2 38	3 45	
121	**Sorau**.........arr 7 22			5 45	a.m.	8 33		9 38		...	...	11 58	...	...		...	3 12	4 21	p.m.
126¼	Hansdorf.........arr 7 36			6 1	7 43	8 50				...	...	12 12	...	...		...	3 25	4 40	5 45
137¾	Rauscha			6 29	...	9 17				...	...	12 37	...	...		...	3 48	5 11	...
146¼	**Kohlfurt**.........arr			6 52	8 12	9 38				...	...	12 53	...	...		Ex 3	4 7	5 34	6 12
...	GÖRLITZ 180......dep			6a13	...	9 a10				10a55	...	12p32	B—Nord Express, Luxus Zug, on Tuesday only.	...		12p32	3p29	6 p0	...
...	**Kohlfurt**.........dep			7 0	...	9 §53				11 48	p.m.	1 13		...		1 4	4 16	6 49	...
153¾	Siegersdorf			7 17	...	10 10				...	1225	1 30		...		...	4 35	7 6	...
162	Bunzlau			7 32	...	10 25				12 11	1242	1 47		...		1 29	4 51	7 20	...
179	Haynau			8 7	...	11 0				12 34		2 26		...		1 53	5 28	7 53	...
184½	Arnsdorf			8 18	...	11 10				...	...	2 37		...		...	5 39	8 2	...
190½	**Liegnitz** ....arr			8 32	...	11 21		10 52		12 50	p.m.	2 50		...		2 10	5 53	8 14	...
...	,, 183A......dep	6 54	9 5	8 52	...	11 29		10 55	12 46	12 53	1 14	2 58		...	1 1	2 14	6 3	8 18	...
204½	Maltsch 183A	7 22	9 32	...	...	11 59	...	...	...	...	1 39	3 25		...	...	...	6 33	8 38	...
209¾	Neumarkt	7 32	9 42	...	...	12 11	...	...	...	...		3 35		...	1 29	...	6 44	8 48	...
222½	Lissa	8 1	10 11	...	...	12 42	...	...	...	...	...	4 3		...	...	...	7 15	...	...
227¾	Klein-Mochbern	8 13	10 23	...	...	12 55	...	...	...	...	...	4 16		...	...	...	7 30	...	...
230¾	**Breslau** Haupt.....arr	8 20	10 36	9 46	...	1 2	...	11 48	1 39	1 47	...	4 23		...	2 0	3 14	7 38	9 19	...
307¼	KANDRZIN 218 arr	1149	...	...	...	...	...	3 p1	4 p2	4 p2	...	6 p35	...	...	4p 2	6 p28	...	11p36	...
343¼	ODERBERG 219...arr	1p28	...	...	...	...	...	4 p40	4 p55	4 p55	...	7p 55	...	...	4p 55	7 p55	...	12a33	...

STETTIN and SWINEMÜNDE.

	2—4	2—4	2—4	2—4	1,2,3	2—4	2—4	2 &3	2—4	2—4	2—4	1,2,3	1,2,3	2—4	2—4	2—4	2—4
		a.m.	a.m.	a.m.	a.m.	a.m.	a.m.	p.m.	p.m.			p.m.	p.m.	p.m.	p.m.	p.m.	p.m.
Stettin ....dep	...	5 1	5 18	7 52	10†5	10 54	11 10	12 1	2 25	...	...	3†41	4 ¶0	5 29	7 59	9 44	...
Alt Damm	...	5 21	5 35	8 13	1023	11 13	11 29	1216	2 48	...	p.m.	3 57	4 15	5 47	8 17	10 3	...
Gollnow	...	5 57	6 16	8 54	1058	11 55	12 12	1251	3 28	...	3 38	4 29	4 50	6 27	9 2	10 36	11 12
Wietstock	a.m.		7 19		1141		1 16			p.m.	4 31	5 16			10 1		12 0
Wollin	5 39	...	7 49	a.m.	12 3	p.m.	1 46	...	...	3†34	5 3	5 41	...	p.m.	10 33	...	12 26
Misdroy	6 15	...	8 23	10‡47	1230	12†36	2 21	...	...	4 10	5 42	6 21	...	8 †44	11 11	...	
Ostswine	6 37	...	8 47	11 13		1 2	2 45	...	...	4 36	6 6	6 48	...	9 6	11 33	...	...
Swinemünde arr	7 †9	...	9 20	11 46	...	1 29	3 12	...	...	5 3	6 33	7 15	...	9 33	...	...	...

	2—4	2—4	2—4	2—4	2—4	1,2,3	2—4	2—4	2—4	2—4	2 &3	1,2,3	2—4	2—4	2—4	2—4	
		a.m.	a.m.	a m.	a.m.			a.m.	p.m.				p.m.	p m.	p.m.		
Swinemünde dep	...	...	6 †18	...	8‡30	...	...	11 0	1†59	...	...	...	4 6	4 †48	7 54	...	...
Ostswine	...	5 15	6 50	6 51	9 1	a.m.	...	11 29	2 26	...	...	p.m.	4 38	5 19	8 19	...	...
Misdroy	a.m.	5 49		7 17	9 24	9†28	...	11 55	2 50	...	...	3†34	5 8	5 42	8 47	...	...
Wollin	4 47	6 27	...	7 45		9 55	...	12 30	3 20	...	...	4 1	5 45		9 20	...	...
Wietstock	5 15	7 14	a.m.		...	1021	p.m.	1 10		p.m.	p.m.	4 27	6 21	p.m.	9 53	p.m.	...
Gollnow	6 12	8 30	8 55	...	...	11 1	12 8	2 10	...	2 50	4 28	5 8	7 17	7 31	10 38	11 9	...
Alt Damm	6 48	9 8	9 39	...	...	1132	12 50	2 53	...	3 34	5 5	5 37	7 56	8 21		11 43	...
Stettin ....arr	7 7	9 25	9 56	...	...	1147	1 9	3 10	...	3 52	5 23	5 52	8 16	8 39	...	12 0	...

†—Until 15th September.
‡—Until 31st August.
¶—Until 27th July.

Wietstock ......dep	5a45	7a23	1 p18	4 p36	10 p4	...	...	...
Cammin	6 26	7 59	1 50	5 9	10 38	...	...	...
Nitznow		8 40	2 26	6 17	11 14	...	...	...
Treptow.........arr	...	9 22	3 4	7 2	11 51	...	...	...
Treptow.........dep	...	5 a5	10a56	...	4p20	7 p12	...	...
Nitznow	...	5 46	11 38	...	4 57	8 6	...	...
Cammin	4a37	6 27	12 21	3p46	5 36	9 6	...	...
Wietstock ......arr	5 10	7 0	12 53	4 20	6 9	9 40	...	...

Gollnow ...dep	9 a10	3 p40	9 p8
Massow ......arr	10 10	4 35	10 8
Massow ....dep	7 a38	1 p45	6 p18
Gollnow ....arr	8 35	2 35	7 18

[Luggage Rates—see page 462.

BRESLAU, KOHLFURT, FRANKFORT, and BERLIN.

RESTAURANT CAR—in 10.45 a.m. and 11.28 a.m. from Breslau.

Station																			
ODERBERG 219 dep	...	...	...	...	3 a27	3a27	3 a27	...	...	...	...	...	...	...	7 a41	...	...	...	...
KANDRZIN 218...dep	...	...	...	...	4 a18	4a18	4 a18	...	...	...	...	5a 8	...	...	8 a41	...	...	...	...
	2 3 4	1—4	2 3 4	2 3 4	Ex.3	Ex3	Ex.3	2 3 4	2,3,4	2,3 4	1,2,3	1—4	Ex3	1—4	Ex.3	Ex3	Ex 3	2,3,4	1—4
Breslau—					a.m.	a.m.	a.m.			a.m.		a.m.	a.m.		a.m.	a.m.	a.m.		p.m.
Haupt Bahnhof dep	...	...	...	...	6 6	6 11	6 45	...	...	6 23	...	8 12	8 10	...	10 45	1128	11 40	...	12 17
Klein Mochbern	...	...	...	...	...	...	...	...	...	6 31	...	8 20	...	...	...	...	...	...	12 26
Lissa	...	...	a.m.	...	...	...	...	...	...	6 45	...	8 34	...	...	RC	RC	...	...	12 41
Neumarkt	...	...	6 0	...	...	...	...	...	...	7 22	...	9 3	...	...	11 15	...	...	...	1 13
Maltsch	...	...	6 12	...	...	...	...	...	...	7 33	...	9 14	...	...	...	12 3	...	...	1 25
Liegnitz arr	...	...	6 42	a.m.	6 57	7 7	7 35	...		8 1	...	9 52	9 40	a.m.	11 41	1222	12 30	...	1 53
" dep	...	...	—	5 13	⋮	7 11	⋮	...		8 12	...	—	9 42	1112	11 44	⋮	12 33	...	2 2
Arnsdorf	...	...	...	5 25	⋮	...	⋮	...		8 26	...	...	⋮	1127	...	⋮	⋮	...	2 18
Haynau	...	...	...	5 39	⋮	7 29	⋮	a.m.		8 39	...	...	⋮	1138	12 5	⋮	⋮	p.m.	2 29
Bunzlau	...	...	...	6 20	⋮	7 54	⋮	7 4		9 14	...	...	⋮	1216	12 31	⋮	⋮	1 17	3 4
Siegersdorf	...	...	...	6 36	⋮	...	⋮	7 22		9 28	...	...	⋮	1231	12 45	⋮	⋮	1 35	3 18
Kohlfurt arr	...	...	...	6 53	⋮	8 16	⋮	—		9 43	...	...	⋮	1247	12 57	⋮	⋮	—	3 33
GÖRLITZ 179A ...arr	...	...	a.m.	7a36	⋮	8a52	⋮	...		10a40	a.m.	...	11a5	1p50	1 p50	⋮	2 p0	p.m.	4 p18
Kohlfurt dep	...	...	4 50	7 0	⋮	...	⋮	...		9 53	1114	2 3 4	...	...	1 3	⋮	...	1 20	4 12
Rauscha	...	...	5 28	7 19	⋮	...	⋮	...		10 12	...	a.m.	...	...	...	⋮	...	1 44	4 33
Hansdorf	...	a.m.	6 23	7 40	⋮	...	⋮	...		10 38	1139	1142	...	...	...	⋮	...	2 10	4 58
Sorau	...	5 10	6 45	7 53	⋮	...	⋮	...		10 51	⋮	1156	...	...	1 35	⋮	p.m.	2 27	5 14
Sommerfeld arr	a.m.	5 46	—	8 24	⋮	...	⋮	...	a.m.	11 27	⋮	—	...	...	1 55	⋮	2 3,4	3 6	5 48
Liegnitz dep	5 30	⋮	...	—	7 2	...	7 37	...	8 5	9 5	To Lissa. See p. 220A.	...	...	...	⋮	1225	1 25	⋮	
Arnsdorf	5 41	⋮	...	...	...	...	...	...	8 20	9 17		...	...	...	⋮	...	1 42	⋮	...
Reisicht	6 5	⋮	...	...	...	...	...	...	8 40	9 34		...	...	...	⋮	1246	2 3	⋮	...
Sagan arr	7 18	⋮	...	...	8 3	...	8 33	...	—	10 34		...	...	...	⋮	1 25	—	⋮	...
WARSAW 316 dep	...	⋮	...	...	...	...	... To Cottbus and Halle. See p. 173A.	...	...	...		...	...	...	⋮	...	...	⋮	...
KALISZ 218A dep	...	⋮	...	...	...	...		...	...	...		...	...	...	⋮	...	...	⋮	...
Sagan dep	7 27	⋮	...	...	8 5	...		...	...	10 33		...	...	...	⋮	1 38	...	⋮	...
Benau	7 49	⋮	...	...	RC	...		...	...	10 57	...	...	...	...	⋮	...	...	⋮	...
Sommerfeld arr	8 11	⋮	...	...	8 32	...		a.m.	...	11 19	...	...	...	...	⋮	2 5	...	⋮	...
Sommerfeld dep	—	5 51	...	...	8 37	...		8 43	...	11 33	...	...	...	...	2 0	2 9	...	3 11	...
Guben arr	...	6 25	...	...	8 59	...		9 17	...	12 6	...	...	...	...	...	2 30	...	3 48	...
" dep	...	6 29	...	...	9 1	...		9 22	...	12 13	...	...	...	...	...	2 32	...	3 54	...
Fürstenberg	...	7 7	...	...	...	...		10 2	...	12 49	...	...	...	...	...	...	...	4 32	...
Frankfort arr	Ex3	7 43	...	...	9 41	...		1037	Ex 3	1 25	...	2 3 4	...	...	2 58	3 11	...	5 8	...
WARSAW 316 ...dep	5p12	...	...	a.m.	...	1,2,3		...	11p52	..	...	a.m.	...	...	...	...	...	...	...
POSEN 182 ...dep	2 a6	...	...	4 26	...	7a10		...	10a18	...	...	1031	...	...	...	...	...	...	...
Frankfort dep	4a39	7 53	...	9 0	9 44	9 57	...	1046	1 p22	1 42	...	3 32	...	...	3 1	3 14	...	5 14	...
Fürstenwalde	...	8 33	...	9 52	...	...	...	1135	1 53	2 36	...	4 6	...	...	...	3 46	...	6 3	...
BERLIN-Schles.Bf. arr	5 51	9 19	...	1036	10 50	11 4	...	1221	2 32	3 22	...	4 50	...	...	4 5	4 25	...	6 53	...
Alexanderplatz ...arr	6 0	9 28	...	1048	11 2	1111	...	1232	2 41	3 32	...	5 2	...	...	4 17	4 34	...	7 1	...
Friedrichstrasse...arr	6 6	9 34	...	1054	11 8	1117	...	1238	2 47	3 38	...	5 8	...	...	4 23	4 40	...	7 7	...
Zoolog. Garten ...arr	6 20	9 45	...	11 5	11 21	1130	...	1250	3 1	3 50	...	5 19	...	...	4 36	4 54	...	7 18	...
Charlottenburg ...arr	6 27	9 52	...	1112	11 29	1138	...	1256	3 9	3 57	...	5 26	...	...	4 43	5 1	...	7 25	...

LABES and WIETSTOCK.

	a.m.	a.m.	a.m.	a.m.	p.m.	p.m.	p.m.	p.m.		a.m.	a.m.	a.m.	p.m.	p.m.	p.m.	p.m.
Labes dep	4 33	...	8 10	...	1218	1 14	...	8 7	**Wietstock** ..dep	...	6 17	9 12	1 19	4 32	...	10 15
Regenwalde	5 28	6 56	9 16	...	1 0	2 48	7 14	9 10	Plathe	6 4	7 39	10 31	2 22	5 32	9 59	11 35
Plathe	5 54	7 23	9 43	11 41	—	3 17	7 59	9 35	Regenwalde	6 40	8 7	10 59	2 47	6 2	10 36	12 0
Wietstock 179 arr	7 4	8 53	...	12 56	...	4 17	9 9	...	**Labes** (175)..arr	7 43	...	11 48	4 53	7 4	11 50	...

LIEGNITZ and MERZDORF.

Liegnitz ...dep	...	5a40	7a18	9a10	10 a3	2p14	4p47	5 p5	7 p9	11p15	...	...
Goldberg	...	6 42	8 9	9 47	10 54	3 2	5 26	5 50	7 56	12 5	...	...
Hermsdorf Bad ...	...	6 50	8 15	...	11 1	3 9	5 33	5 57	8 3	12 12	...	...
Schönau	4a55	7 38	—	1014	11 29	3 36	—	6 22	8 31	12 39	...	...
Ober-Kauffung ...	5 18	8 5	...	1032	11 51	3 57	...	6 44	8 51	1 0	...	...
Merzdorf ...arr	5 48	8 42	...	1056	12 20	4 27	...	7 15	9 19	...	...	...
Merzdorf ...dep	...	6a40	8a56	...	12p42	...	5p52	7p48	9 p56	...	...	...
Ober-Kauffung ...	5 a3	7 11	9 24	...	1 11	..	6 28	8 13	10 24	...	...	...
Schönau	5 25	7 33	9 45	...	1 35	...	6 54	8 33	10 46	...	...	...
Hermsdorf Bad ...	5 51	7 59	1012	1 p8	2 1	3p32	7 20	8 54	11 12	...	...	...
Goldberg	6 1	8 7	1020	1 16	2 12	3 40	7 28	9 2	11 20	...	...	...
Liegnitz 183A arr	6 47	8 48	11 5	1 54	2 54	4 21	8 11	9 40	12 2	...	...	...

KOHLFURT and GORLITZ.

Kohlfurt ......dep	1a22	3a37	5a50	6a58	8a20	9a15	9a58	1p10	3p41	5p44	6 p4	6p18	6p55	8p12	9p26	...	...	...	...	...	...
Gorlitz 180......arr	1 54	4 12	6 45	7 36	8 52	1010	1040	1 50	4 18	6 24	6 36	6 53	7 50	8 45	10 5	...	...	...	...	...	...
Gorlitz..........dep	3a20	6a13	7a25	9a10	10a42	1055	12p8	12p32	1p21	3p29	6p0	6p58	8p57	9 p10	11p21	12a37	...	...	...	...	
Kohlfurt.........arr	3 47	6 52	8 20	9 45	11 10	1133	1248	12 58	2 12	4 4	6 37	7 26	9 13	9 33	12 12	1 12	...	...	...	...	

Luggage Rates—see page 462.]

BRESLAU, KOHLFURT, FRANKFORT, and BERLIN.

RESTAURANT CAR—in 3.25 p.m. and 3.55 p.m. from Breslau.
SLEEPING CAR—in 11.3 p.m. and 11.57 p.m. from Breslau.

ODERBERG 219...dep	9a48	12p29	1229	12p29	...	...	...	...	...	...	...	...	3p45	6p15	9 p6	...	6p15	1 a4
KANDRZIN 218...dep	11a31	1 p24	1p24	1 p24	...	...	...	...	4 p9	4 p9	...	...	5p49	7p53	10 p1	...	7p53	1a54
	1—4	Ex.3	1,2,3	Ex 3	Ex1	2 3 4	1 2 3	2,3,4	Ex 3	1,2,3	2,3,4	2,3,4	2,3,4	Ex.3	Ex 3		2,3,4	Ex3
Breslau—	p.m.	p.m.	p.m.	p.m.					p.m.	p.m.	p.m.	p.m.	p.m.	p.m.	p.m.		p.m.	a.m.
Haupt. Bhf. ...dep	2 30	3 25	3 45	3 55	...	...	...	...	6 4	6 9	6 16	8 3	8 55	11 3	11 57	...	11 8	3 30
Klein-Mochbern	2 39	...	...	...	...	...	...	...	...	...	6 24	8 12	...	...	...	...	11 16	⋮
Lissa	2 54	RC	...	RC	...	...	...	...	...	...	6 38	8 30	9 12	SC	SC	...	11 32	⋮
Neumarkt	3 23	...	...	...	...	...	...	...	...	...	7 7	9 3	...	...	12 27	...	12 2	⋮
Maltsch	3 34	...	...	...	...	...	...	...	...	...	7 18	9 16	9 41	...	...	...	12 13	⋮
Liegnitz ....arr	4 0	4 19	4 40	4 48	...	...	...	...	6 56	7 5	7 44	9 48	10 3	12 4	12 54	...	12 37	⋮
" ....dep	4 6	⋮	4 44	⋮	...	...	...	...	7 1	⋮	7 49	—	⋮	12 7	⋮	...	12 42	⋮
Arnsdorf.....................	4 21	⋮	...	⋮	...	...	...	...	...	⋮	8 4	...	⋮	...	⋮	...	12 54	⋮
Haynau	4 32	⋮	5 6	⋮	...	...	...	...	7 22	⋮	8 15	...	⋮	12 26	⋮	...	1 5	⋮
Bunzlau	5 7	⋮	5 33	⋮	...	...	...	...	7 49	⋮	8 50	...	⋮	12 50	⋮	...	1 42	⋮
Siegersdorf	5 21	⋮	...	⋮	...	...	...	...	...	⋮	9 4	...	⋮	...	⋮	...	1 57	⋮
Kohlfurt ....arr	5 37	⋮	5 56	⋮	...	...	...	...	8 11	⋮	9 20	...	⋮	1 11	⋮	...	2 12	⋮
GÖRLITZ 180......arr	6 p24	⋮	6p36	⋮	...	p.m.	p.m.	...	8p45	⋮	10 p5	...	⋮	1 a54	⋮	...	4 a12	⋮
Kohlfurt...........dep	...	⋮	...	⋮	...	6 43	7 32	...	...	⋮	9 38	...	⋮	1 23	⋮	...	2 18	⋮
Rauscha	...	⋮	...	⋮	...	7 2	...	p.m.	...	⋮	9 59	...	⋮	...	⋮	...	2 37	⋮
Hansdorf	...	⋮	...	⋮	...	7 26	7 56	8 3	...	⋮	10 25	...	⋮	...	⋮	...	3 1	⋮
Sorau	2,3,4	⋮	...	⋮	...	7 40	⋮	8 17	...	8 ‡30	10 41	...	⋮	2 2	⋮	...	3 24	⋮
Sommerfeld......arr	p.m.	⋮	...	⋮	...	8 14	⋮	—	...	7 11	11 15	...	⋮	2 25	⋮	Runs until 31st October.	3 55	⋮
⋮ **Liegnitz** ....dep	2 26	4 24	...	4 52	...	4 28	To Lissa. See p. 220A.	...	...	...		...	10 9	⋮	12 56		⋮	⋮
⋮ Arnsdorf.....................	2 41	...	...	...	...	4 41		...	...	...	...	...	10 21	⋮	...		⋮	⋮
⋮ Reisicht	3 0	4 47	...	...	...	5 18		...	...	...	...	...	10 41	⋮	...		⋮	⋮
⋮ **Sagan**...................arr	4 0	5 31	...	5 55	...	6 34		...	...	8 9	...	...	11 44	⋮	1 57		⋮	⋮
⋮ WARSAW 316 dep	...	...	...	To Halle, see p. 173A	...	...		...	...	...	...	...	9 a0	⋮	3 p46		⋮	⋮
⋮ KALISZ 218A dep	8 a43	...	...		...	...		...	...	...	...	...	3 p51	⋮	9 p29		⋮	⋮
⋮ **Sagan**...................dep	4 6	5 36	...		...	7 34		...	...	8 12	...	...	11 51	⋮	2 4		⋮	⋮
⋮ Benau	4 32	...	2 3 4		...	8 0	...	...	...	...	...	...	12 14	⋮	...		⋮	⋮
⋮ **Sommerfeld** ...arr	4 56	6 1	p.m.		...	8 23	...	...	...	8 51	...	...	12 36	⋮	2 38		⋮	⋮
Sommerfeld......dep	—	6 5	6 11	—	...	8 28	...	...	...	8 56	...	...	12 41	2 43			4 0	⋮
Guben ....arr	...	6 26	6 45	...	...	9 4	...	...	...	9 19	...	...	1 14	3 6	...		4 26	⋮
" ....dep	...	6 28	6 48	...	...	9 26	...	...	...	9 20	...	...	1 17	3 7	...		4 30	⋮
Fürstenberg	...	...	7 27	...	...	10 4	...	...	...	...	...	...	1 55	...	...		5 1	⋮
Frankfort (Oder) arr	Ex.3	7 6	8 4	2,3,4	C	1040	...	...	...	10 2	...	...	2 32	3 49	...	...	5 37	6 28
WARSAW 316 ...dep	5 a57	...	...	...	1222	...	...	...	...	...	...	...	...	...	...	Ex 3	...	...
POSEN 182.........dep	3 p20	...	...	4 p20	6p52	...	...	...	...	...	...	...	8 p7	...	...	a.m.	2 a6	...
Frankfort (Oder) dep	6 7	7 9	..	8 42	9p30	1050	...	...	...	10 5	...	...	2 38	3 53	...	3 34	5 43	6 31
Fürstenwalde	...	7 39	...	9 31	...	1139	...	...	...	...	...	...	3 12	4 26	...	...	6 32	...
BERLIN-Schles.Bf. arr	7 12	8 16	...	10 14	1038	1224	...	...	...	11 14	...	...	3 57	5 8	...	4 45	7 16	7 35
Alexanderplatz ...arr	7 21	8 28	...	10 26	...	1236	...	...	...	11 23	...	...	4 9	5 20	...	4 54	7 28	...
Friedrichstrasse...arr	7 27	8 34	...	10 32	1053	1242	...	...	...	11 29	...	...	4 15	5 26	...	5 0	7 34	7 45
Zoolog. Garten ...arr	7 43	8 48	...	10 44	11 7	1254	...	...	...	11 41	...	...	4 27	5 39	...	5 14	7 46	7 59
Charlottenburg ...arr	7 51	8 57	...	10 51	...	1 1	...	...	...	11 48	...	...	4 33	5 47	...	5 22	7 53	8 7

‡—Via Sagan. C—Nord Express, Luxus Zug, on Saturday only.

HIRSCHBERG and LOWENBERG,

	a.m.	a.m.	p.m.	p.m.	p.m.	p.m.	
Hirschberg...........dep	6 35	55	2 21	4 20	7 51	1050	...
Lahn..............................	7 14	1035	2 59	5 3	8 26	1129	...
Lowenberg 181A ...arr	7 43	11 3	3 25	5 35	8 51	1157	...

	a.m.	a.m.	p.m.	p.m.	p.m.	p.m.	
Lowenberg ....dep	5 0	8 29	1215	2 46	6 35	9 3	...
Lahn	5 37	8 57	1249	3 16	7 4	9 33	...
Hirschberg 180 ...arr	6 24	9 35	1 34	3 53	7 42	1010	...

*—From or at Oppeln Ost. **BRESLAU and OPPELN.** ‡—From 1st Sept, 1 hour later.

Breslau Haupt dep	6a20	10a36	1p20	2p30	6 p7	7 p0	8p25
Tschechnitz	6 39	10 53	1 37	2 47	6 24	7 18	8 45
Meleschwitz 179A......	7 2	11 13	1 57	3 6	6 46	7 41	9 5
Laskowitz-Beckern...	7 9	11 19	2 3	3 12	6 52	7 47	9 11
Carlsmarkt 6a24	7 56	12 5	—	3 54	7 39	—	9 58
Oppeln (218) arr7*21	8 47	12 57	...	4 41	8 30	...	1052

Oppeln...........dep	3a18	...	7a53	12p28	1*p45	3p58	...	9 p0
Carlsmarkt	4 15	‡	8 47	1 21	2 58	4 48	...	9 56
Laskowitz-Beckern	5 3	6 a0	9 31	2 12	—	5 31	8p18	1041
Meleschwitz	5 9	6 5	9 37	2 18	...	5 36	8 26	1047
Tschechnitz	5 31	6 24	9 56	2 37	...	5 55	8 50	11 8
Breslau Haupt.arr	5 49	6 41	1013	2 53	...	6 13	9 8	1125

Laskowitz-Beckern.....dep	6†a51	7§a7	2p50	8 p6
Meleschwitz	7 8	7 20	3 8	8 14
Wüstendorf...................arr	7 40	7 52	3 42	8 45

Wustendorf..............dep	5†a24	6§a15	9 a0	1p40	7p10
Meleschwitz	6 6	6 53	9 38	2 20	7 48
Laskowitz-Beckern ...arr	6 14	7 0	9 45	2 27	7 55

†—Until 31st August. §—From 1st September.

Luggage Rates—see page 462.] **PRUSSIAN STATE RAILWAYS.**

BERLIN, GORLITZ, and BRESLAU. RC—Restaurant Car.

Dist.			1,2,3	1,2,3	2 3 4	1—4	2 3 4	2 3 4	1,2,3	2 3 4	2 3 4	Ex3	1,2,3	2 3 4	1,2,3	2 3 4	1,2,3	1—4	1,2,3	2 3 4
E.M.	BERLIN-		p.m.		a.m.			a.m.	a.m.		a.m.	a.m.		p.m.	p.m.	p.m.	p.m.	p.m.	p.m.	p.m
—	Görlitz Bhf. ......dep		1125	...	1240	...	...	6 55	8 40	...	9 30	1035	...	1220	3 10	3 20	5 35	7 15	8 15	9 40
4½	Johannisthal		1136	...	1252	...	...	7 9	8 53	...	9 42	1045	...	1232	3 21	3 31	5 48	7 27	8 27	9 52
17¼	K. Wusterhausen		1159	...	3 5	...	...	7 33	...	...	10 9	11 7	...	1 1	3 43	3 53	...	7 53	...	11 2
46¼	Lübben		1251	...	4 22	...	...	8 38	9 52	...	1114	1147	In July and August only.	2 6	4 23	4 56	6 47	9 0	9 28	1219
53¼	Lübbenau 183A .....dep		1 3	...	4 46	...	...	8 53	10 4	...	1130	1159		2 20	4 35	5 11	6 58	9 17	9 40	1237
71¼	Cottbus .....arr		1 35	...	5 38	a.m.	a.m.	9 31	1030	a.m.	1210	1225		3 2	5 1	5 49	7 25	9 57	10 6	1 23
...	,, 183A .....dep		1 51	...	7 6	4‡20	6 35	9 40	1040	11 5	1 5	1230		3 21	5 9	6 4	7 32	1018	1011	
86	Spremberg		2 19	...	8 1	4 57	7 11	1015	11 5	1148	1 53	1255		3 56	5 34	6 41	7 57	1054	1036	...
97½	Weisswasser 183A		2 39	...	—	5 24	7 36	1038	1124	1219	2 23	1 14		4 19	5 53	7 7	8 16	1117	1055	...
116¼	Horka (172)		...	...	...	6 12	8 18	1124		1 19		1 42		5 1	6 21	7 52	...	1159	1123	...
129¼	Görlitz .....arr		3 28	...	...	6 44	8 48	1156	1217	1 51	...	2 5		5 35	6 44	8 21	9 9	1227	1146	1—4
...	ZITTAU 180 .....arr		5a58	...	...	...	9a56	1 p4	...	3p18	...	3p18	...	...	7p52	9p54	...			a.m.
...	Görlitz .....dep			...	3&4	6 52	9 36	1227	1223	2 29	...	2 15	...	6 5	7 2	9 15	9 15	...	1—4	3*38
145¼	Lauban .....arr		...	...	a.m.	7 29	1017	1 4	1249	3 11	...	2 41	p.m.	6 43	7 32	9 59	9 50	...	a.m.	4 18
...	,, ...dep		...	...	6 20	7 34	1021	1 6	1250	3 16	...	2 44	6 46	6 52	7 36	10 7	9 55	...	4 24	
154	Greiffenberg 181A		...	...	6 50	7 58	1043	1 30	1 9	3 43	...	3 5	7 6	7 16	7 58	1036	1017	...	4 50	
167¼	Alt Kemnitz		...	...		8 35	1117	2 4	...	4 21	...	RC	...	7 52	...	1116	...	...	5 26	...
177¼	Hirschberg 182 .....arr		a.m.	a.m.	a.m.	8 55	1137	2 24	1 49	4 43	...	3 50	7 46	8 13	8 45	1137	1059	...	5 47	...
...	,, ...dep		6 41	8 4	8 15	9 0	1152	2 36	1 59	5 3	...	4 0		8 19	9 4		☞	...	5 58	...
190¼	Merzdorf		...	...	8 57	9 36	1229	3 16	...	5 44	...	4 32	...	8 57	9 36	...		...	6 36	...
194	Ruhbank 182 .....dep		7 13	2nd July to 31st August.	9 6	9 46	1243	3 27	2 30	5 57	2 3 4	4 42	...	9 7	9 47	...		...	6 48	1—4
...	LIEBAU 182 ...arr	a.m.	...		9a41	1014	1 p9	3p56	3p56	7p42	p.m.	5p16	...	...	1020	...	July and August only.	...	7a17	a.m.
203¾	Fellhammer ...dep	5 4	...			1015	1 18	3 55	2 47	6 30	4 44	5 4	...	9 34	10 8	...		...	7 19	8 2
206¾	Dittersbach	5 17	7 38		...	1026	1 31	4 18	2 55	6 43	4 52	5 15	...	9 42	1020	...		...	7 27	8 58
209	Waldenburg	5 34	7 45		...	1034	1 40	4 27	To Kattowitz.	6 52		5 22	...		1027	...		...		9 8
212¼	Altwasser	5 44	7 53		...	1043	1 50	4 36		7 2	...	5 30	...	...	1035	...		...	...	9 20
214½	N. Salzbrunn 180	5 54	8 0		2 3 4	1051	1 58	4 47		7 13	...	5 37	...	...	1042	2 3 4		2 3 4	...	9 30
225½	Königszelt .....dep	6 35	8 26	...	a.m.	1130	2 44	5 28		7 57	...	6 4	...	...	11 6	a.m.		a.m.	...	1020
243	Canth	7 16	8 52	...	9 0	12 7	3 21	6 5		8 34	...	6 31	...	...	1137	4 50	...	5†58	...	1058
255½	Breslau Freibur. B.	7 48	9 11	10 9	9 36	1240	3 53	6 37		9 5	...	6 50	...	...	1158	5 29	...	6 29	...	1129

Extra—Nieder-Salzbrunn to Königszelt, 7.5 a.m.; Görlitz to Lauban, 11.50 p.m.; Königszelt to Nieder-Salzbrunn, 12.42 p.m.; Waldenburg to Dittersbach, 2.35 p.m.

	2 3 4	2 3 4	2 3 4	2 3 4	2 3 4	1,2,3	2 3 4	2 3 4	Ex3	1,2,3	1—4	2 3 4	2 3 4	1,2,3	1,2,3	2 3 4	1—4	1,2,3	2 3 4	2 3 4
Breslau Freiburg	a.m.				a.m.	a.m.	a.m.	a.m.	a.m.		p.m.		p.m.	p.m.			p.m.	p.m.	p.m.	p.m
Bhf...dep	4‡34	...	...	...	5 16	7 0	7 17	8 58	1141	From Kattowitz.	1 13	...	3 40	5 10	...	...	6 25	7 2	8 35	1126
Canth	5 16	...	...	...	5 50	7 19	7 47	9 29	RC		1 45	...	4 14	5 29	...	...	6 58	...	9 7	1155
Königszelt		...	...	...	6 39	7 50		1022	1230		2 36	...	4 59	5 58	In July and August only.	...	7 51	Until 30th August.	10 0	1242
Nieder-Salzbrunn	...	...	...	...	7 12	8*16	...	1056	...		3 7	...	5 29	...		...	8 23		1033	1 16
Altwasser	...	...	...	...	7 26	...	From Liegnitz.	11 9	...		3 21	...	5 42	6 31		...	8 36		1042	1 28
Waldenburg	...	...	a.m.	a.m.	7 40	8 33		1120	1 8	p.m.	3 34	p.m.	5 52	6 40		...	8 48		1052	1 42
Dittersbach	...	...	5 10	5 24	7 59	8 42		1134	1 20	2 55	3 52	6 57	6 3	6 49		...	9 4		11 5	1 50
Fellhammer dep	...	...	5 19	5 33	8 11	8‖51		1146	1 30	3 5	4 5	7 6	6 12	6 57		...	9 14		1115	
LIEBAU .....dep	...	...	5a17		8 a8	...		1146	1p20	2p50	4p10		5p25	...		...	9 p11		...	...
Ruhbank .....dep	...	...	5 45	...	8 40	9 8	a.m.	1216	1 46	3 23	4 38	...	6 38	7 12	☞	...	9 43	...	1141	...
Merzdorf	...	...	5 54	...	8 55	...	11 5	1227	...	...	4 49	...	6 47	7 21		...	9 54	...	1150	...
Hirschberg.....arr	...	a.m.	6 27	...	9 26	9 38	1130	1258	2 15	3 52	5 23	...	7 13	7 45	p.m.	p.m.	10 26	9 10	1225	...
,, ...dep	...	4 57	6 32	3 &4	10 0	9 47		1 45	2 30	4 5	5 39	...			7 20	9 5	10 50			...
Alt Kemnitz	...	5 22	7 0	a.m.	1024	...	...	2 9	...	...	6 2	...	...	...	...	9 29	11 14	...	...	...
Greiffenberg	...	6 2	7 42	9 0	1059	1028	3 &4	2 45	3 14	4 47	6 37	...	...	...	7 59	10 7	11 49	...	...	...
Lauban .....arr	...	6 23	8 2	9 25	1119	1042	p.m.	3 6	3 29	5 1	6 57	...	...	...	8 13	1028	12 9	...	...	...
,, ...dep	...	6 30	8 4	9 30	1122	1044	1 0	3 10	3 32	5 2	7 0	...	...	...	8 14	1031	12*11	...	...	...
Görlitz.....arr	1,2,3	7 15	8 43	1018	12 3	11 9	1 45	3 50	4 0	5 28	7 41	2—4	...	...	8 40	1112	12*52	...	1—4	...
ZITTAU.....dep	a.m.	6a48			1054	9a37		2p58	2p58	2p58	7p33	p.m.	...	...	...	1016	...	...	a.m.	...
Görlitz .....dep	6 10	7§47	...	...	1 6	1122	...	5 58	4 9	5 36	9‡20	7 10	...	...	8 45	1125	1 15	...	4 10	...
Horka	6 29	8 12	...	...	1 40	1141	§—1-4 class.	6 36	4 28	5 59	9 47	7 39	...	...	...	1158	1 39	...	4 37	...
Weisswasser	6 56	8 48	...	...	2 16	12 8		7 16	4 55	6 27	1026		...	...	9 31	1236	2 14	...	5 18	...
Spremberg	7 14	9 9	2 3 4	...	2 37	1226		7 41	5 13	6 46	1049	...	...	...	9 49	1259	2 37	...	5 39	...
Cottbus .....arr	7 34	9 39	p.m.	...	3 6	1246		8 11	5 33	7 7	1119	p.m.	...	...	10 9	1 30	3 1	...	6 9	...
,, ...dep	7 42	9 58	1 30	...	3 22	1256		8 36	5 43	7 17		7†33	...	...	1016	3 55	3 15	...	6 35	...
Lübbenau	8 7	1038	2 10	...	4 2	1 21		9 18	6 8	7 42	...	8 29	...	...	1041	4 44	3 48	...	7 13	...
Lübben	8 19	1052	2 25	...	4 16	1 33		9 34	6 20	7 54	...	8 45	...	...	1053	5 2	4 2	...	7 28	...
K. Wusterhausen	...	1155	3 29	...	5 20	2 12	...	1040	...	...	...		...	...	...	6 31	4 55	...	8 29	...
Johannisthal	9 18	1218	3 53	...	5 43	2 33	...	11 8	7 18	8 53	...	...	...	...	1152	7 3	5 18	...	8 53	...
BERLIN—Gorlitz	9 30	1230	4 5	...	5 55	2 45	...	1120	7 30	9 5	...	...	...	...	12 4	7 15	5 30	...	9 5	...

*—Until 30th Sept. ‡—Cottbus to Gorlitz 2,3,4 class only. †—Weekdays only. ‖—Until 31st August.

Görlitz ...dep	4a52	8a56	12 p8	2 p13	4 p24	6p58	8p55	11p20
Nikrisch	5 10	9 14	12 23	2 31	4 39	7 10	9 13	11 38
Zittau .....arr	5 58	9 56	1 4	3 18	5 20	7 52	9 54	12 18

Zittau ...dep	...	6a48	9 a37	10a54	2p58	5p35	7p33	10p16
Nikrisch	5 32	7 25	10 14	11 34	3 39	6 17	8 10	10 52
Görlitz...arr	5 50	7 38	10 32	11 52	3 57	6 35	8 27	11 9

Görlitz.....dep	4a17	5a45	9a10	12p40	2p28	4p46	7 p6	9p12
Nikrisch	4 31	6 2	9 23	1 0	2 41	5 4	7 24	9 30
Seidenberg 233A	4 43	6 13	9 39	1 13	2 53	5 15	7 35	9 41

Seidenberg dp	6a43	9 a55	12p31	2p54	4p49	7p48	8p58	12 0
Nikrisch	6 54	10 6	12 42	3 5	5 0	7 59	9 9	12 12
Görlitz ...arr	7 12	10 20	12 59	3 22	5 18	8 26	9 27	12 30

KOHLFURT and LAUBAN.

Kohlfurt dep	3a52	6a58	8a23	9a50	1p30	6p16	9p25	...	...
Lauban 180	4 16	7 25	8 57	1014	2 0	6 41	9 50	...	...
Lauban ...	6a27	8a14	10a47	12 p7	3p35	7 p2	12a18	...	...
Kohlfurt	6 51	8 53	11 10	12 37	4 1	7 25	12 46	...	...

LAUBAN and MARKLISSA.

Lauban ...	4a32	8 a8	11a40	3p36	5p10	7p46	10p33	...	...
Marklissa	5 8	8 40	12 16	4 7	5 44	8 23	11 9	...	...
Marklissa ...	5a40	8a50	12p22	1p45	4p24	6p0	9 p0	1118	...
Lauban 180	6 16	9 22	12 46	2 21	4 55	635	9 36	1149	...

NIEDER-SALZBRUNN and HALBSTADT.

Nieder-Salzbrunn...dep	...	7 a17	8*a21	8†a21	...	11a5	12p33	1p14	2 p5	3 p12	6 p30	...	8 p30
Salzbrunn	...	7 26	8 30	8 29	...	1116	12 43	1 23	2 16	3 22	6 40	...	8 43
Fellhammer 180	5 a34	7 51	8 47		9 a0	1142	1 4		2 40	3 47		7 p7	9 8
Halbstadt 252A .....arr	6 0	8 40	...	...	9 41	1213	...	...	...	4 31	...	7 45	10 42

Halbstadt.dep	4a29	6 a44	...	7 a31	9 a20	12p40	...	...	...	5 p55	8 p28
Fellhammer...	5 6	7 23	...	8 1	10 18	1 22	3p17	5 *ṛ8	...	6 34	10 11
Salzbrunn	5 28	7 47	9a15		10 38	1 41	3 44	5 25	5‡p25	6 58	10 30
N. Salzbrunn.	5 36	7 54	9 22	...	10 45	1 48	3 51	5 32	5 52	7 6	10 37

*—Until 31st August. ‡—In September only.

BERLIN, NEU-STRELITZ, STRALSUND, and SASSNITZ.

THROUGH CARRIAGES { Berlin to Copenhagen, in 8.49 a.m., and 11.15 p.m. from Berlin. Berlin to Stockholm, in 11.9 a.m. and 8.15 p.m. from Berlin.

SC—Sleeping Car. RC—Restaurant Car.

Dist E.M	BERLIN—			2 3 4	1,2,3	2,3,4	1,2,3	1,2,3	Ex 3	Ex3	1—4	Ex.3	2&3	2 3 4	1,2,3	1,2,3	1—4	1—4	1,2,3	Ex.3	2 3 4	Ex3
				a.m.	a.m.	a.m.	a.m.	a.m.	a.m.	a.m.	a.m.	a.m.		p.m.	p.m.	p.m.	p.m.	p.m.	p.m.	p.m.	p.m.	p.m.
—	Stettiner Bahnhof ...dep			5 42	7 37	7 42	8 19	8 30	8 49	9 45	1045	11 9	...	1239	2 47	2 53	3 28	5 54	7 17	8 15	1017	1115
2	Gesundbrunnen			5 48	...	7 48	...		...	...	1051		...	1245	2 53	...	3 34	6 0	7 23		1024	SC
18¼	Oranienburg			6 20	8 †9	8 17	C		RC	RC	1120		...	1 16	D	...	4 7	6 41	7†51		1052	...
28½	Löwenberg			6 55	...	8 48	9 7		9 37	...	1152		...	1 49	3 38	C	4 43	7 19	8 11		1126	12 4
36	Gransee			7 16	A	9 7	9 21		9 51	...	1212	RC	...	2 10	3 51	...	5 4	7 39	8 24		1147	1218
49¾	Fürstenberg			7 51	...	9 43	9 44		...	11 3	1244		p.m.	2 44	4 14	...	5 39	8 13	8 46		1219	...
60¼	Strelitz			8 12	...	10 6	...		...	...	1 5		1 35	3 5	...	...	6 2	8 35	...		1238	...
62¼	Neu-Strelitz (178B)......arr			8 18	9 19	10 12	10 3		10 30	1123	1 10		1 42	3 11	4 33	4 43	6 8	8 41	9 9		1244	1257
144½	WARNEMUNDE ....arr			...	...	...	1229		12 50	...	5p22	Via Pasewalk.	...	...	...	7p10	1136	...	...		...	3a29
278½	COPENHAGEN (302A) arr			...	...	...			6 p41	...	...		...	...	...		...	...	...		...	9a42
682½	STOCKHOLM (308)arr a.m.			...	...	...	...		8 a49	...	...		...	...	...	...	...	...	...	Via Angermunde.	...	6a58
...	Neu Strelitz.........dep	3 32		8 24	9 24	...	...	Via Pasewalk.	...	1128	1 17		...	3 17	4 38	...	6 16	8 48	9 14		...	...
71½	Blankensee	3 49		8 44	...	...	...		...	...	1 33		...	3 34	...	...	6 34	9 6	...		...	...
79	Stargard	4 4		9 7	...	...	...		...	...	1 49		...	3 50	...	...	6 51	9 23	...		...	...
84¼	Neubrandenburg arr	4 13		9 17	10 0	...	...		...	12 1	1 58		...	3 59	5 12	...	7 0	9 32	9 45		...	
...	" dep	4 20		9 35	10 6	...	...		...	12 2	2 8		...	4 12	5 15	...	7 14	9 41	9 50			
93⅜	Treptow	4 38	2 3 4	9 54	...	...	...		...	1217	2 30		...	4 31	...	...	7 33	1015	...			
110½	Demmin	5 24	6a26	1053	...	...	...		...	1245	3 20		...	5 14	5 53	...	8 18	11 2	1032			
116	Toitz-Rustow	5 39	6 42	11 9	A	...	...		...	...	3 37		...		D	...	8 34	1118	...			
125¼	Grimmen	6 1	7 2	1129	...	1—4	...		...	1 10	3 59		2 3 4	...	6 18	...	8 53	1139	1057			
139½	Stralsund arr	6 35	7 41	12 5	1126	a.m.	...		...	1 31	4 33	2 39	p.m.		6 39	...	9 28	1222	1118	11 55		
	Stralsund dep	7 0	—	1241	1133	10 41	...	1230	...	1 37	4 54	2 45	3 29		6 48	...	9 34		⌒	12 5		
141½	Stralsund Hafen arr	7 7		1248	...	10 48	...	...	...	...	5 1	...	3 36		...	...	9 41		...	...		
	Stralsund Hafen dep	7 10		1255	...	10 52	...	C	...	...	5 8	...	3 40		...	...	9 46		...	RC		
147	Rambin	7 48		1 31	...	11 27	...	...	Ex 3	...	5 46	...	4 16		...	...	1024		...	...		
157½	Bergen-a-Rügen arr	8 15		2 1	1237	11 58	...	1 44	p.m.	2 50	6 12	...	4 43		7 50	...	1051		...	1 16		
	Bergen-a-Rügen dep	8 21		2 11	1247	12 4	...	1 50	3 ‡2	⌒	6 19	...	4 49		7 53	...	1055		...	1 18		
167¾	Sagard	8 47		2 38	1 15	12 31	...	2 14	3 25	...	6 45	...	5 16		8 16	...	1121		...	SC		...
171	Sassnitz ...arr	8 59		2 50	1 29	12 46	...	2 23	3 39	...	6 57	4 27	5 28		8 25	...	1133		...	1 48		...
172¼	Sassnitz Hafen ...arr	9*17		...	1 40	...	...	...	3 45	...	...	4 36	...		...	...	...		...	1 57		...
238¾	TRELLEBORG (ferry) arr			...	...	...	...	...	...	...	...	8 p56	...		...	...	...		...	6 a17	...	...
258¾	MALMO (311) ...arr			...	...	...	...	...	...	...	...	9 p50	...		...	...	...		...	7 a12	...	...
642½	STOCKHOLM (308).......arr			...	...	...	...	...	...	...	...	8 a49	...	...	...	...	...	...	...	6 p46	...	...

*—Until 31st August. †—Takes up only.

A—Until 31st August. §—Not on Sunday. C—Until 15th September. D—Until 31st August.

	Ex3	2 3 4	2 3 4	Ex3	1,2,3	1—4	2 3 4	1,2,3	2 3 4	1—4	1,2,3	1—4	1,2,3	Ex 3	Ex3	Ex3	1,2,3	Ex3	2 3 4	2 3 4	2 3 4
STOCKHOLM 308 dep	...	...	...	10a27	...	...	...	...	...	...	...	...	...	8 p30	...	...	...	...	...	...	...
MALMO (311)...dep	...	...	...	9p57	...	...	...	...	...	...	...	...	...	7 a54	...	...	...	...	...	...	...
TRELLE'G ferry dp	...	...	...	10p45	...	...	...	...	...	...	...	...	...	8 a46	...	...	...	...	...	...	...
				a.m.		a.m.	a.m.	a.m.		a.m.	a.m.	a.m	p.m.	p.m.	p.m.					p.m.	p.m.
Sassnitz Hafen dep	...	...	...	3*10	...	4 36	...	...	...	...	9 37	...	1228	1*11	2‡21	...	...	...	...	...	...
Sassnitz	...	...	...	3 18	...	4 49	6 56	7 44	...	9 6	9 46	1154	1237	1 20	2 30	...	...	...	...	4 16	8 46
Sagard		...	...	...	...	5 2	7 9	...	...	9 21	9 56	12 7	...	...	...	...	...	...	...	4 33	9 0
Bergen-a-Rügen arr	‡—Until 15th September.	...	...	...	...	5 25	7 34	8 13	...	9 43	1016	1230	1 5	1 48	2 57	3 7	...	...	...	5 3	9 25
Bergen-a-Rügen dep		...	...	RC	...	5 27	7 37	8 18	...	9 49	1021	1238	1 14	1 49	⌒	...	...	...	...	5 12	9 35
Rambin		...	...	...	...	5 54	8 7	...	...	1014	...	1 3	...	RC		RC	...	...	...	5 45	10 3
Stralsund Hafen arr		...	...	...	...	6 25	8 40	...	...	1048	C	1 37	A	3 0	...	...	...	...	...	6 18	1039
Stralsund Hafen dep		...	...	...	a.m.	6 38	8 46	...	...	1058	...	1 45	...	3 5	...	4 19	...	...	...	6 28	1046
Stralsund ... arr		...	a.m.	4 53	⌒	6 45	8 53	9 20	...	11 5	1123	1 52	2 24		...	4 30	...	...	...	6 35	1053
Stralsund ... dep		...	3 29	4 59	6 58	7 5	—	9 25	...	1128	1149	3 5	2 36		...		...	...	...	6 52	12 0
Grimmen		...	4 11	Via Angermunde.	7 24	7 39	...	...	...	12 6	Via Pasewalk.	3 40	...	Via Pasewalk.	...	Via Angermunde.	...	...	...	7 29	1235
Toitz-Rustow		a.m.	4 31		...	7 58	...	F	...	1226		3 58	...		...		...	...	...	7 48	1254
Demmin		6 49	4 50		7 52	8 18	...	...	...	1246		4 14	...		...		...	...	...	8 13	1 8
Treptow		7 33	5 36		RC	9 2	...	...	...	1 30		4 53	...		...		...	...	...	9 3	—
Neubranden- arr		7 50	6 0		8 33	9 19	...	1052	...	1 47		5 10	4 5		...		...	...	p.m.	9 23	...
burg...dep	...	—	6 12		8 34	9 33	...	1055	...	2 5		5 20	4 12		...		...	...	7 21	9 55	...
Stargard	...	...	6 28		...	9 49	...	...	...	2 17		5 32	...		...		...	...	7 35	10 7	...
Blankensee	...	...	6 47		9 0	10 9	...	...	...	2 37		5 48	...		...		...	...	7 57	1027	...
Neu Strelitz ...arr	...	...	7 3		9 16	1025	1,2,3	1147	...	2 53		6 4	4 57		...		...	...	8 15	1043	...
STOCKHOLM 308 dp	...	...	...		...	...	...	...	...	...		...	...		...		...	8p30	...	...	...
COPENHAG'N 302 dp	8p10	...	...		...	...	...	...	...	...		...	...		...		...	11a0	...	...	2&3
WARNEMUNDE dp	2a32	a.m.	...		5a42	...	9a24	...	p.m.	10a5		...	...		...		4p25	4p51	...	...	p.m.
Neu-Strelitz ... dep	5 a0	5 22	7 14		9 22	1031	12 9	1153	1 33	3 4		6 10	5 3		...		6 57	7 13	8 22		1115
Strelitz	...	5 30	7 20		...	1037	...	...	1 40	3 10		6 16	...		...		C	...	8 28		1122
Fürstenberg	...	5 53	7 42		9 41	11 1	...	...	2 7	3 35		6 36	A		...		7 23	7 33	8 49		—
Gransee	5 40	6 28	8 18		...	1135	...	F	2 55	4 9		7 6	...		...		7 45	7 55	9 22		...
Löwenberg	...	6 52	8 46		1017	1159	C	...	3 23	4 34		7 27	...		...		7 59	...	9 46		...
Oranienburg	SC	7 23	9 22		10*33	1227	...	...	3 53	5 5		7 57	6 *8		...		...	RC	1018		...
Gesundbrunnen	...	7 53	9 52		11 3	1257	...	1 27	4 24	5 35		8 27	6 37		...		...	...	1048		...
BERLIN ...arr	6 38	8 0	9 59	8 35	1110	1 4	1 51	1 34	4 31	5 42	3 54	8 34	6 44	6 34	...	8 16	8 47	8 55	1055	...	...

*—Sets down only.

F—Between Sassnitz and Neustrelitz runs from 25th July until 17th August; between Neustrelitz and Berlin from 1st to 24th July, and from 18th to 31st August.

Bergen-a-R....dep	1a21	5a40	8a24	9 a58	12†45	2p10	3 p2	4p53	6p30	8‡p0	9†p39
Putbus	1 41	6 0	8 49	10 18	1 6	2 36	3p30	5 13	6 53	8 20	9 59
Lauterbach ...arr	1 46	6 5	8 54	10 27	1 11	2 41	3 35	5 18	6 59	8 25	10 4
Lauterbach...dep	4a55	6a56	9a11	12 0	1†p13	2p14	4p13	5p31	7‡p13	8p39	10†p15
Putbus	5 4	7 10	9 24	1215	1 26	2 32	4 21	5 40	7 22	8 52	10 25
Bergen-a-R. ...arr	5 22	7 29	9 42	1233	1 44	2 54	4 39	5 57	7 40	9 10	10 43

†—Until 15th September.

‡—Until 31st August.

STRALSUND and ROSTOCK.

Stralsund dep	...	5a 8	6a51	9a36	12‡33	1p47	3p22	6p43	12 0
Velgast ...arr	...	A	7 22	10 8	⋮	2 28	3 49	7 14	12 31
Ribnitz	4a51	...	8 13	1055	‡	3 30	4 26	8 1	1 16
Rostock 213...	5 50	6 41	9 6	1142	⋮	4 32	5 8	8 52	...

Rostock dep	a.m	...	8a42	12p38	1249	5p46	9p23	10p18	11 p5
Ribnitz	5 3	...	9 47	1 25	1 43	6 50	1015	A	12 5
Velgast...dep	6 4	7a22	1041	2 1	2 28	7 47	1058	...	—
Stralsund arr	6 40	7 52	1117	2 26	2 58	8 25	1130	11 52	...

Velgast ...dep	6a 8	7a33	10a45	⋮	2p44	3‡56	7p48	12p38
Barth............	6 31	8 1	11 15	1 20	3 17	4 20	8 18	1 0
Prerow ...arr	...	8 41	12 12	2 1	4 16	4 58	9 11	...

Prerow ......dep	...	...	8a51	12p29	5p20	9 p34	...	...
Barth	5a33	6a52	9 39	1 27	6 35	10 24	...	...
Velgast ......arr	5 56	7 16	10 2	1 51	7 0	10 48	...	...

‡—In July and August only. A—Through train with Sleeping Car, Hamburg-Gothenburg.

LOWENBERG and PRENZLAU.

Löwenberg dep	...	7a17	12 p1	4p48	7p32	12a9	...	...
Templin ...... arr	...	8 35	1 23	5 57	8 46	1 12	...	...
Templin ...... dep	5a25	8 55	2 2	6 14	8 53	—	...	...
Prenzlau 182 arr	6 50	1023	3 40	8 18	1018	...	...	...

Prenzlau ....dep	...	7a 9	12p34	4p54	...	9p57	...
Templin .... arr	...	8 38	1 57	6 8	...	1127	...
Templin .... dep	5 a30	8 50	2 7	6 13	8 p6	—	...
Löwenberg ......arr	6 42	10 5	3 16	7 12	9 22	...	...

GREIFFENBERG and HEINERSDORF.

‡—Until 31st Aug.]

Greiffenberg dep	4 a56	6 a13	8 a6	11a10	1p40	3 p52	5 p39	7p13	8 p5	10p45
Friedeberg-a-Q...	5 21	6 38	8 32	11 37	2 10	4 22	6 1	7 43	8 33	11 3
Heinersdorf ...arr	5 44	...	8 55	12 6	2‡37	4 52	...	8 12	8 59	...

Heinersdorf ......dep		6a41	9a15	...	1p40	3‡p47	...	5p23	...	8p35	10p0
Friedeberg-a-Q	5a25	7 12	9 52	12p20	2 11	4 10	4p18	6 3	7p32	9 11	1030
Greiffenberg arr	5 50	7 31	1011	12 45	2 32	...	4 36	6 22	7 51	9 33	1137

Friedeberg dep	5a25	8a37	1139	2p10	4p25	7p40	9‡p8
Flinsberg ...arr	5 48	9 0	12 4	2 33	4 48	8 3	9 31

Flinsberg dep	6a42	9a20	1p35	3p45	5p30	8p35	10‡29
Friedeberg arr	7 2	9 40	1 55	4 5	5 50	8 55	10 50

‡—Until 14th September.

GREIFFENBERG and GOLDBERG.

Greiffenberg dp	a.m.	6a 6	8 a6	11a5	...	3p57	8p22	10p45
Löwenberg (Schl.)	4 45	7 4	9 17	1220	2p43	5 43	9 40	11 51
Hermsdorf-Bad ...	5 43	7 54	10 5	1 8	3 32	6 57	11 3	...
Goldberg......arr	5 50	8 2	1011	1 14	3 38	7 4	11 9	...

Goldberg......dep	...	6a35	8a 9	11a1	3p23	5p26	7p49	12a12
Hermsdorf-Bad ...	...	6 43	8 16	11 8	3 32	5 34	8 5	12 19
Löwenberg (Schl.)	4a30	7 40	9 12	1212	4 25	6 33	8 55	1 10
Greiffenberg arr	5 45	...	1018	1 14	5 33	7 45	9 59	...

Löwenberg...dep	9a41	12 0	4p47	8p18	12 a7
Rheinsberg. .arr	1058	1 48	6 8	9 35	1 51

Rheinsberg...dep	7a16	9 a42	2p56	4p50	7p32
Löwenberg ...arr	8 36	11 27	4 15	6 41	9 32

EBERSWALDE and FRANKFORT-on-O.

	a.m	a.m	a.m	p.m	p.m	p.m	p.m	p.m	night
Eberswalde dep	5 33	7 2	10 23	1220	2 16	4 0	6 46	8 43	12 31
Falkenberg	5 49	7 18	10 42	1239	2 32	4 18	7 3	9 0	12 55
Freienwalde arr	5 56	7 25	10 50	1247	2 39	4 25	7 10	9 7	—
,, (182) dep	6 3	7 31	10 56	—	2 46	—	7 21	9 9	...
Wriezen	6 19	7 52	11 15	...	3 14	...	7 43	9 26	...
Letschin	6 45	8 17	11 38	...	3 45	...	8 10	9 50	...
Werbig (176) ...	7 0	8 34	11 54	...	4 5	...	8 28	10 6	...
Seelow............	7 6	8 42	12 1	...	4 11	...	8 36	1012	...
Frankfort .arr	7 46	9 27	12 47	...	4 52	...	9 29	1053	...

	a.m.	a.m	a.m	a.m		p.m	p.m	p.m.
Frankfort...dep	...	6 0	9 8	11 10	...	3 49	6 11	9 11
Seelow	...	6 46	9 50	11 46	...	4 29	6 51	9 51
Werbig	...	7 1	9 57	11 54	...	4 41	7 2	10 5
Letschin	...	7 13	10 7	12 4	p.m.	4 52	7 13	10 15
Wriezen	5 41	7 46	1032	12 34	3 2	5 20	7 51	10 41
Freienwalde arr	5 57	8 1	1048	12 48	3 18	5 37	8 8	10 59
,, dep	6 8	8 7	1054	12 57	3 20	5 45	8 37	11 14
Falkenberg	6 16	8 15	11 2	1 6	3 28	5 54	8 45	11 22
Eberswalde arr	6 35	8 34	1119	1 24	3 44	6 14	9 2	11 40

WRIEZEN and KONIGSBERG N.M.

Wriezen..............dep	7 a59	11a19	3p12	6 p12	7 p49	10p40
Klemzow.....................	8 49	12 1	3 52	6 53	8 34	11 16
Jädickendorf	9 22	12 33	4 14	7 27	9 10	11 42
Konigsberg Neumark	9 35	12 46	4 48	7 38	9 18	11 50

Konigsberg ......dep	6 a2	7 a36	10a38	1 p15	6p12	8p51	...
Jädickendorf	6 19	7 54	11 2	1 34	6 28	9 43	...
Klemzow	6 48	8 17	11 30	2 4	6 55	10 2	...
Wriezen ....arr	7 32	8 56	12 16	2 50	7 34	1033	...

BERLIN and WRIEZEN.

Berlin (Schles. Bhf.) dep	5 a33	8a55	1 p5	5 p25	8p58	11p42
Lichtenberg	5 44	9 6	1 17	5 38	9 6	11 54
Werneuchen	6 35	9 58	2 3	6 33	9 47	12 41
Wriezen ....arr	7 27	10 53	2 56	7 37	10 36	1 31

Wriezen....................dep	4 a42	7 a55	9 a2	12p34	3 p9	7 p50
Werneuchen........................	5 41	9 15	9 57	1 31	4 13	8 54
Lichtenberg........................	6 28	10 12	...	2 15	5 5	9 47
Berlin (Schles. Bhf.) arr	6 36	10 21	1035	2 23	5 13	9 55

Extra. {Berlin to Werneuchen, 6.41, 10.36 a.m., 2.34, 3.33, 7.0, and 9.55 p.m.
Werneuchen to Berlin, 4†50, 6.45, 7.50 a.m., 12.7, 5.55, and 8.15 p.m. †—Not on Sunday.

REPPEN and MESERITZ.

Reppen.........dep	...	7a25	11a34	3p22	6 p43	9p37	...
Zielenzig.................	5a15	8 34	12 39	4 28	7 34	1056	...
Meseritz 182 arr	6 47	9 49	1 42	5 36	8 39	...	...

Meseritz.........dep	5 a38	10 a9	3 p22	4p30	7p12	...	...
Zielenzig	7 3	11 23	4 30	6 10	8 21	...	...
Reppen (182) arr	8 10	12 24	5 23	7 37	9 14	...	...

MESERITZ and LANDSBERG-a-W.

Meseritz ....dep	4 a18	7 a52	10 a6	3p16	5p45	7p39	...
Schwerin	5 20	8 22	10 38	3 51	6 23	8 14	...
Landsberg-a-W. ...arr	6 24	9 7	11 24	4 48	7 24	9 7	...

Landsberg-a-W....dep	3a46	6a59	12p20	2p28	6 p42	9p58	...
Schwerin	4 33	7 57	1 9	3 35	7 47	11 0	...
Meseritz...................arr	4 59	8 32	1 41	4 26	8 22	1133	...

Landsberg .... dep	4 a40	10 a6	1p40	5p20	...	...	...
Zielenzig ....arr	6 50	12 34	4 17	7 20	...	...	...

Zielenzig ....dep	5a25	9 a0	12p54	7p41	...	...	...
Landsberg...........arr	7 21	1135	3 33	9 15	...	...	...

SCHWERIN and SAMTER.

Schwerin ...dep	5 a15	9 a15	1 p11	...	4 p20	8 p17	...	...
Wierzebaum.........	6 9	10 25	1 55	...	5 34	9 17	...	...
Birnbaum	6 30	11 10	2 9	3 p0	5 52	9 50	...	...
Samter ....arr	8 25	1 10	...	5 15	...	11 43	...	...

Samter.....dep	...	7 a 3	11a19	4 p8	7 p55	...	...
Birnbaum	6 a35	9 17	2 50	6 7	10 3	...	...
Wierzebaum ...	7 12	9 34	3 7	6 28	10 18	...	...
Schwerin arr	7 51	10 18	3 47	7 35	10 57	...	...

FURSTENBERG and EBERSWALDE.

Furstenberg dep	...	7 a50	11 a5	12p55	4p43	8p55	...
Templin.............	4a44	8 49	12 11	2 3	6 18	1016	...
Joachimsthal ...	5 44	9 34	1 10	2 58	7 15	—	...
Britz	6 18	10 1	1 42	3 29	7 50	...	...
Eberswalde arr	6 27	10 7	1 49	3 40	7 57	...	...

Eberswalde ......dep	...	7 a7	...	10a18	12p28	4p 6	9 p8	...
Britz	...	7 15	...	10 26	12 42	4 18	9 17	...
Joachimsthal	...	7 51	...	10 54	1 10	4 56	9 53	...
Templin................	5a25	8 47	9a46	11 40	2 10	6 16	1048	...
Furstenberg (181) arr	7 5	...	1050	12 39	3 10	7 19	...	...

SCHIVELBEIN and GRAMENZ.

	a.m.	a.m.	p.m.	p.m.	p.m.	p.m.	p.m.	p.m.
Schivelbein	5 1	8 36	...	12 33	1 30	5 4	7 39	10 26
Polzin	6 36	9 18	...	1 7	2 26	5 51	8 36	11 45
Barwalde	7 17	9 47	12 23	...	3 0	—	9 9	—
Gramenz (178A)...	7 48	10 10	1 8	1 49	3 28	...	9 37	...

	a.m.	a.m.		a.m.	p.m.	p.m.	p.m.
Gramenz ...	...	8 6	...	10 20	3 29	4 5	7 20
Barwalde......	...	8 40	a.m.	10 49	3 50	4 36	7 54
Polzin...........	6 32	9 22	10 45	11 35	4 17	6 18	9 9
Schivelbein	7 24	10 8	11 30	12 23	4 52	7 7	9 57

Luggage Rates—see page 462.] **PRUSSIAN STATE RAILWAYS.**

FRANKFORT-on-O., GUBEN, BENTSCHEN, and POSEN.

	Ex3	Ex3	2 3 4		2 3 4	2 3 4	Ex.1	2 3 4	Ex 3	2 3 4	2 3 4	Ex3	2 3 4	2 3 4	1,2,3	2 3 4
Berlin Schles dep 179	1121 a.m	1248 a.m.	1248 a.m.	...	4a16 a.m.	...	7 a52 a.m.	8 a2 a.m	9 a57 a.m.	1147 p.m.	1 p2 p.m.	2p43 p.m.	4p57 p.m.	6 p3 p.m	7p55 p.m.	9p17 p.m.
Frankfort Oder...dep	1229	1 55	3 28	...	6 7	...	9 3	9 35	11 7	1 44	2 45	3 58	6 13	7 33	9 7	1127
Reppen (220) ......dep	...	...	4 0	...	6 36	...	...	1011	11 33	2 26	3 18	4 29	6 37	8 6	9 31	12 5
Topper	...	C	4 49	...	7 18	...	...	1056	...	3 14	—	...	—	8 51	...	—
Schwiebus	1 36	...	5 19	...	7 44	...	...	1124	12 20	3 44	...	5 16	...	9 19	1018	...
Bentschen..........arr	1 57	3 14	5 52	...	8 13	a.m.	10 22	1153	12 42	4 16	...	5 37	...	9 49	1039	...
Guben ....dep	1222	—	3 35	...	...	7 50	...	9 22	11 15	2 0	...	4 1	...	7 19	⋮	...
Crossen-a-O.	1248	...	4 13	...	...	8 26	...	9 56	11 39	2 41	...	4 27	...	7 57	⋮	...
Rothen- (220)...arr	1 8	...	4 37	...	...	8 52	A	1023	11 58	3 13	...	4 47	...	8 27	⋮	...
burg-a-O. dep	1 9	...	4 41	...	...	9 0	...	1027	11 59	3 26	...	4 48	...	8 31	⋮	...
Züllichau	1 29	3 &4	5 17	2 3 4	...	9 28	...	1051	12 18	3 48	...	5 8	2 3 4	9 0	⋮	...
Bentschen ......arr	1 55	a.m.	5 46	a.m.	...	10 8	...	1129	12 41	4 22	...	5 33	p.m.	9 40	⋮	...
Bentschen..........dep	2 1	4 10	—	5 57	8 17	—	10 26	12 0	12 48	4 32	...	5 42	5 50	10 2	1044	...
Neutomischel	...	4 41	...	6 20	8 41	...	...	1224	...	4 59	...	...	6 14	1028	11 1	...
Opalenitza..........arr	...	5 13	...	6 44	9 7	...	...	1248	...	5 27	...	6 14	6 38	1054	1119	...
Dombrowka	...	6 3	...	7 17	9 40	...	...	1 21	...	6 5	...	...	7 11	1130	...	...
Posen (178) ....arr	3 1	6 31	...	7 33	9 54	...	11 27	1 35	1 51	6 23	...	6 47	7 27	1147	1156	...

	Ex 3	Ex3 a.m	2 3 4	2 3 4 a.m.	1,2,3 a.m.	2 3 4 a.m.	Ex 3 a.m	2 3 4 a.m	3 &4 p.m.	2 3 4 p.m.	Ex3 p.m.	2 3 4 p.m.	Ex.1 p.m.	2 3 4	2 3 4 p.m	3 &4 n'gt
Posen..................dep	...	2 6	...	4 26	7 10	6 48	10 18	1031	1 35	2 24	3 20	4 20	6 52	...	8 7	1225
Dombrowka	...	...	...	4 43	...	7 6	...	1048	1 59	2 40	...	4 38	...	...	8 26	1249
Opalenitza	...	...	...	5 15	7 47	7 54	10 53	1125	—	3 15	...	5 11	B	...	9 5	1 34
Neutomischel	...	...	...	5 38	8 5	8 17	11 12	1153	2 3 4	3 40	...	5 36	...	...	9 34	2 7
Bentschen..........arr	...	3 4	...	5 59	8 20	8 38	11 28	1215	p.m	4 0	4 22	5 58	7 54	...	9 58	2 37
Bentschen ......dep	...	3 17	...	6 20	⋮	8 42	12 0	⋮	2 20	...	4 36	6 35	⋮	...	1045	—
Züllichau	...	3 56	...	7 3	⋮	9 21	12 30	⋮	3 12	...	5 2	7 19	⋮	...	1134	...
Rothenburg.......arr	...	4 15	...	7 24	⋮	9 41	12 46	⋮	3 35	...	5 18	7 40	⋮	...	1156	...
" ......dep	...	4 16	...	7 26	⋮	9 42	12 51	⋮	3 42	...	5 20	8 1	⋮	...	1159	...
Crossen-a-O.	...	4 43	...	7 57	⋮	10 9	1 13	⋮	4 10	...	5 39	8 29	⋮	...	1233	...
Guben (179) ......arr	a.m.	5 14	...	8 31	⋮	1041	1 39	⋮	4 43	...	6 3	9 1	⋮	...	1 12	...
Bentschen..........dep	2 0	3 9	...	6 12	8 24	—	11 36	1224	—	4 41	4 28	6 8	7 57	...	1010	...
Schwiebus	...	3 33	...	6 56	8 49	...	12 2	1258	...	5 20	4 53	6 42	...	...	1047	...
Topper	C	...	a.m.	7 28	...	p.m.	...	1 28	...	5 53	...	7 16	...	p.m.	1119	...
Reppen...............arr	...	...	6 16	8 11	...	1226	12 50	2 9	...	6 33	5 40	7 57	...	9 30	12 4	...
Frankfort Oder ...arr	3 30	4 36	6 42	8 48	9 54	1256	1 19	3 26	...	7 5	6 4	8 30	9 27	9 55	1237	...
Berlin 179A......arr	4 a45	5a51	9a19	1036	11a4	2p32	2p32	4p50	...	8p16	7p12	1014	10p38	1114	3a57	...

A—Nord Express, Luxus Zug, Tuesday only. C—Until 31st October.
B—Nord Express, Luxus Zug, Saturday only.

BENTSCHEN and BIRNBAUM.

	a.m.	p.m.	p.m.			
Bentschen......dep	6 5	12 49	6 8	...	...	...
Glashütte	6 40	1 24	7 26	...	...	...
Birnbaum ......arr	7 31	2 10	9 0	...	...	...

	a.m.	p.m.	p.m.			
Birnbaum......dep	9 7	2 56	6 58	...	...	...
Glashütte	10 22	3 45	8 35	...	...	...
Bentschen......arr	11 25	4 20	9 53	...	...	...

TOPPER and MESERITZ.

Topper..............dep	8 a0	1p34	5p55	7p20	9 p5
Meseritz ....arr	9 43	3 9	7 8	8 38	10 26
Meseritz ....dep	5 a48	11 a8	1p48	5p45	7p20
Topper ....arr	7 10	1 16	3 10	7 8	8 41

OPALENITZA and KOSTEN.

Opalenitza ...dep	5a27	7a52	9a20	11a27	1p5	3p30	7 p5	9 p7	1124
Grätz	6 15	8 28	1030	12 4	2 3	4 7	7 52	9 50	12 1
Kosten (218A) arr	7 3[illegible]	...	1216	...	3 9	...	9 31	11 6	...

Kosten dep	...	...	...	9 a0	11a12	...	3p36	6p25	...	10p3
Grätz	4a34	6 a4	8a29	10 9	12 11	2p25	4 31	8 7	10p5	1145
Opalenitza	5 10	6 40	9 4	1045	12 46	3 1	5 7	8 43	1041	...

BENTSCHEN and MESERITZ.

Bentschen............dep	6a45	12p48	4p37	6p13	10p45
Meseritz (182) ......arr	7 34	1 43	5 35	7 9	11 44
Meseritz ....dep	5 a3	10a20	3p22	4p31	8p44
Bentschen (182) ......arr	5 52	11 23	4 17	5 35	9 39

FRANKFORT-ON-ODER and CUSTRIN.

	am	am	am	a.m.	a.m.	p.m.	pm	pm	pm	p.m	p.m.
Frankfort	354	656	8 4	9 59	1111	1228	146	329	622	9 33	1111
Custrin Ht.	449	755	855	1050	1216	1 22	236	421	725	1028	12 9

	a.m.	a.m.	a.m.	a.m	a.m.	a.m.	p.m.	p.m	p.m	p.m	p.m.	p.m
Custrin Hauptstadt	4 42	5 25	6 35	8 52	10 2	1116	1 36	3 57	4 54	5 53	7 57	1046
Frankfort	5 38	6 26	7 37	9 41	1057	1216	2 39	4 53	5 59	7 3	8 56	1152

LIEBAU and RUHBANK.

Liebau ...	5a17	6a41	8 a8	...	11a46	1p20	2p50	4p10	5p25	8p27	9p11
Landeshut	5 32	6 58	8 26	9a26	12 2	1 34	3 6	4 25	5 43	8 51	9 29
Ruhbank	5 40	7 7	8 35	9 36	12 11	1 42	3 17	4 33	5 52	9 0	9 38

Ruhbank 180	6a50	9a14	9a49	12p43	1p55	3p30	4p48	7p16	9p51
Landeshut	7 1	9 25	9 58	12 52	2 4	3 40	4 59	7 25	10 2
Liebau 225	7 17	9 41	1014	1 9	2 25	3 56	5 16	7 42	1020

RUHLAND and LAUCHHAMMER.

Ruhland ....dep	5 a15	6a40	11a55	2 p30	4 p25
Lauchhammer......arr	5 40	7 5	12 23	2 58	4 53
Lauchhammer ......dep	5 a52	8a20	1p25	3 p30	6p15
Ruhland (183A) ......arr	6 17	8 45	1 54	3 56	6 54

HIRSCHBERG and LANDESHUT.

(180)	a.m.	a.m.	a.m.	no'n	p.m	p.m.	p.m.	p.m	p.m
Hirschberg dep	5 58	6 50	9 53	12 0	2 30	4 5	5 36	7 52	9 16
Zillerthal-Erdman.	6 28	7 20	1018	1230	2 52	4 28	6 6	8 14	9 43
Schmiedeberg 5a40	6 42	7 40	1031	1243	3 11	4 40	6 21	8 26	9 55
Landeshut 6 50	...	8 55	1155	...	4 18	...	8 32	...	...

	a.m.	a.m.	a.m.	a.m.	p.m.	p.m.	p.m.	p.m.	p.m.	p.m
Landeshut...dep	...	...	7 6	9 30	...	2 10	...	...	7 28	8 46
Schmiedeberg	5 56	7 0	8 12	11 0	1255	3 14	4 50	7 2	8 27	10 7
Zillerthal-Erd......	6 8	7 16	9 11	1118	1 14	3 30	5 4	7 19	8 38	1023
Hirschberg arr	6 23	7 36	9 32	1138	1 34	3 50	5 25	7 40	8 56	1043

BENTSCHEN and LISSA.

Bentschen dep	3a19	...	6 a17	9 a43	1 p0	5p54	6p10	10p47	...
Wollstein	3 39	4a19	6 58	10 32	1 55	6 17	6 45	11 21	...
Lissa ....arr	4 19	5 28	8 5	11 42	3 3	7 2	7 51	12 24	...

Lissa ....dep	3a52	6a10	9 a12	10a27	2 p10	5p15	8 p10	12a41
Wollstein	5 14	7 23	10 30	11 7	3 23	6 36	9 19	1 24
Bentschen (182) ...arr	5 48	7 59	11 6	11 26	4 1	...	9 52	1 46

Wollstein.........dep	4 a0	7a25	12p15	3 p22	6p55	...	...	...
Kontopp	4 50	8 20	1 16	4 51	7 53	...	...	...
Neusalz-a.-O.....arr	5 38	9 15	2 31	5 58	8 44	...	...	...

Neusalz-a.-O. ......dep	5a17	7 a20	11a18	2p48	7 p3	...	...
Kontopp..................	6 6	9 0	12 13	4 10	7 57	...	...
Wollstein............arr	6 54	10 22	1 6	5 39	8 45	..	...

POSEN and ZULLICHAU.

Posen ......dep	...	...	5 a8	...	10a30	2 p21	7p13	11p30
Grätz	...	6a 9	7 44	8 a40	12 18	4 35	9 48	12 59
Wollstein.........	5 a6	7 7	—	10 16	1 52	6 6	1112	—
Zullichau arr	6 56	...	...	12 5	3 6	8 48	1243	...

Züllichau dep	...	...	5a18	7a50	1235	3p55	9p45
Wollstein.........	...	5 26	6 48	1040	2 16	6 50	11 1
Grätz	5 a0	5 59	8 24	12 8	4 14	7 57	—
Posen ......arr	7 5	9 32	...	1 39	6 11	10 5	...

MESERITZ and ROKIETNICE.

‡—On Wed. & Sat. dep 11.46 p.m.

Meseritz ....dep	...	6a35	10 a2	1p48	5 p45	8p49	...	...
Wierzebaum............	...	7 14	10 45	2 34	6 22	9 32	...	...
Birnbaum..............	a.m.	7 34	11 1	2 54	6 40	9 48	...	...
Pinne.....................	5 28	8 23	11 56	3 52	7 26	1037	...	...
Rokietnice (218A) arr	6 19	9 12	12 57	4 58	8 16	...	...	...

Rokietnice ...dep	...	7 a22	12p10	3 p40	7 p55	10‡21	...
Pinne	6a10	8 19	1 20	4 59	8 53	11 12	...
Birnbaum	6 55	9 4	2 15	5 52	9 50	—	...
Wierzebaum.............	7 10	9 17	2 31	6 25	10 3	...	...
Meseritz (182)...arr	7 45	9 52	3 11	7 6	10 37	...	...

PRUSSIAN STATE RAILWAYS.

[Luggage Rates—see page 462.

BERLIN and STETTIN.

	3 &4	2 3 4	Ex3	1,2,3	1,2,3	Ex3	1,2,3	1—4	1—4	1—4	1,2,3	1,2,3	2,3,4	Ex3	1—4	1,2,3	1—4	1,2,3	1—4	Ex3
Berlin—Stettiner		a.m.	a.m.	a.m.	a.m.	a.m.	a.m.	a.m.	a.m.	a.m.	a.m.	a.m.	a.m.	p.m.	p.m.	p.m.	p.m.	a.m.	p.m.	p.m.
Bahnhof...dep	...	5 59	7 10	7 32	7 59	8 24	8 30	8 36	8 58	9 20	9 40	1035	10 50	1 2	1 12	1 24	1 56	2 19	2 29	3 12
Bernau............	...	6 28	...	...	B	RC	...	9 7	9 27	9 50	...	...	11 19	B	1 42	B	2 27	2 48	2 59	RC
Eberswalde ...arr	...	6 56	7 53	8 21	8 42	9 6	9 13	9 32	9 54	10 16	1026		11 44	1 45	2 10	2 16	2 50	3 11	3 23	3 55
,, ...dep	...	7 0	7 54	8 22	8 43	9 8	9 14	9 34	9 56	—	1027	K	11 54	1 47	—	2 17	2 52	3 12	3 24	3 57
Angermunde arr	‡	7 35	8 17	8 45	9 5	9 30	9 37	10 4	10 33	...	1051		12 29	2 10	...	2 41	3 30	8 10	3 52	4 21
Schwedt......arr	a.m.	8 22	...	—	...	...	—	11 1	...	...	...		1 20	—	...	...	...		4 50	...
Angermunde dep	5 45	7 39	8 18	...	9 7	9 32	...	—	10 37	...	1053		12 33	...	...	2 43	3 35	July only.	—	4 23
Passow............	6 17	8 3	...	...	...	...	...	...	11 1	...	...		12 56	...	...	...	3 58		...	...
Tantow............	6 54	8 31	...	...	...	...	...	...	11 37	...	1128		1 23	...	...	...	4 25		...	...
Stettin 175 ...arr	7 30	9 3	9 15	...	10 0	1025	...	...	12 10	...	1149	Heringsdorf arr. 2.18.	1 53	...	...	3 35	4 54	...	...	5 16

	1—4	1—4	1—4	Ex3	1—4	Ex3	2 3 4	Ex3	1—4	
Berlin—Stettiner	p.m.	p.m.	p.m.	p.m.	p.m.	p.m.	p.m.	p.m.	p.m.	
Bahnhof...dep	4 24	5 42	6 11	7 35	7 46	8 15	9 15	1120	11 30	...
Bernau............	4 54	6 13	6 41	...	8 15	...	9 45	...	11 59	...
Eberswalde ...arr	5 18	6 41	7 4	8 16	8 38	RC	1016	...	12 22	...
,, ...dep	5 19	—	7 5	8 17	8 41	...	1020	...	12 23	...
Angermunde arr	5 50	...	7 42	8 38	9 28	9 18	1054	...	12 54	...
Schwedt......arr	...	...	—	...	1015	...	...	...	1 48	...
Angermunde dep	5 55	...	...	8 39	9 34	—	1056	...	12 58	...
Passow............	6 17	...	...	...	9 59	...		...	1 19	...
Tantow............	6 42	...	...	...	1027	...	1138	...	1 43	...
Stettin 175 ...arr	7 10	...	...	9 27	11 0	...	12 0	1 0	2 8	...

RC—Restaurant Car attached.

SC—Sleeping Car attached.

	1—4	1—4	2 3 4	1—4	1—4	Ex3	Ex3	1—4	Ex3	1—4	1,2,3	1—4	1—4	Ex3	1,2,3	1,2,3	2 3 4	1,2,3	1—4	1,2,3	2, 3,4
	a.m.		a.m.		a.m.	a.m.	a.m.		a.m.	a.m.	a.m.			p.m.			p.m.	p.m.		p.m.	p.m.
Stettin ......dep	3 1	...	5 49	...	7 13	7 53	...	...	1010	10 40	1153	...	...	1 38	...	...	1 50	3 33	...	4 15	4 25
Tantow	3 34	...	6 22	...	7 46	...	...	...	...	11 13	B	...	...	RC	B	...	2 23	...	...	4 38	4 58
Passow	3 58	...	6 49	...	8 13	...	...	...	...	11 40	...	...	...	...		...	2 50	...	...	...	5 23
Angermunde arr	4 21	...	7 15	...	8 38	8 46	B	a.m.	11 2	12 5	1249	...	...	2 34		...	3 16	...	...	5 13	5 48
Schwedt ... dep	SC	...	6 16	...	...	...	...	8 45	...	11 21	...	...	p.m.	1 48		p.m.	...	...	p.m.	...	...
Angermunde dep	4 26	...	7 18	...	8 54	8 47	...	9 39	11 3	12 9	1252	...	1 43	2 36		2 45	3 20	...	4 49	5 15	5 50
Eberswalde...arr	5 2	a.m.	7 59	a.m.	9 34	9 8	1014	1012	1124	12 46	1 15	p.m.	2 11	2 59		3 7	3 53	...	5 23	5 36	6 17
,, ...dep	5 4	6 42	8 0	8 38	9 36	9 9	1015	1021	1125	12 48	1 16	1 29	2 14	3 1		3 8	3 55	...	5 24	5 41	6 24
Bernau	5 33	7 16	8 31	9 5	1010	...	...	1049	...	1 19	...	1 58	2 42	...	Heringsdorf dep. 11.51.	...	4 27	...	5 52	...	6 56
Berlin ....arr	6 1	7 45	8 58	9 34	1038	9 53	1059	1117	1211	1 46	2 5	2 25	3 9	3 18	3 20	3 54	4 55	5 34	6 19	6 29	7 23

	1,2,3	1,2,3	Ex3	2 3 4	Ex3	1—4	1—4	3 &4						
		p.m.		p.m.	p.m.		p.m.	n'gt						
Stettin.........dep	...	5 57	...	6 17	7 2	...	10 25	12‡8	...	...	...	...	...	...
Tantow	...	...	...	6 49	RC	...	10 58	1244	...	...	...	...	...	...
Passow............	...	B	...	7 15	...	...	11 24	1 18	...	...	...	...	...	...
Angermunde arr	...	6 53	p.m.	7 40	7 54	...	11 46	1 50	...	...	...	...	...	...
Schwedt... dep	p.m.	...	6 20	6 20	6 20	...	10 56	—	...	...	...	...	...	...
Angermundedep	6 15	6 55	7 12	8 3	7 56	...	11 51	...	...	...	...	...	...	...
Eberswalde...arr	6 37	7 17	...	8 37	8 18	p.m.	12 26	...	...	...	...	...	...	...
,, ...dep	6 38	7 18	RC	8 40	8 20	9 §6	12 28	...	...	...	...	...	...	...
Bernau............	...	...	..	9 9	...	9 35	12 56	...	...	...	...	...	...	...
Berlin ....arr	7 28	8 7	8 16	9 38	9 9	10 2	1 23	...	...	...	...	...	...	...

‡—Rail Motor.
§—8.58 p.m. on Sunday.
B—Until 15th Sept.
K—Until 17th August.

KONIGS-WUSTERHAUSEN and TÖPCHIN.

K. Wusterhausen dep	8*a41	1p15	6 p4	10§p45	...	...	...	...	...
Mittenwalde	9 9	1 43	6 40	11 16	...	...	...	...	...
Töpchin ....arr	9 48	2 22	7 19	12 0	...	...	...	...	...

Töpchin ....dep	...	6†a17	11a46	2p43	8 p36	...	...	...	...
Mittenwalde............	5‡a59	6 57	12 30	3 22	9 27	...	...	...	...
K. Wusterhausenarr	6 21	7 15	12 53	3 43	9 49	...	...	...	...

‡—Not on Sunday.

§—12.42 night on Sunday.

GRUNOW and KONIGSWUSTERHAUSEN.

Grunow ....dep	...	8a37	1050	11a55	...	2p10	4p35	8p10	K. Wusterh	...	5a40	8a35	...	11a15	2p15	4p38	8p 2	...
Beeskow	5a35	9 1	1115	12 16	2 p5	2 31	5 30	8 51	Beeskow ...	5a59	7 30	1017	11a15	1 1	4 0	7 20	9 42	11p0
K. Wusterhausen arr	7 19	1043	1256	...	3 48	...	7 23	1055	Grunow	6 23	7 50	...	11 35	1 55	4 20	7 40	...	1120

DITTERSBACH and GLATZ.

E.M.																				
	Dittersbach dep	4a15	5a27	8a17	8a48	10a27	1138	12p45	1p45	2p58	4 p8	5p20	6p57	9 p3	11p10	...	...	...	...	...
3¾	Charlottenbrunn ...	4 28	5 41	8 28	9 1	10 35	1152	12 57	2 0	3 7	4 19	5 33	7 9	9 15	11 22	...	...	...	...	...
18¾	Neurode	5 23	6 32	—	9 53	11 8	—	—	2 51	3 38	—	6 23	7 58	—	12 12	...	...	...	...	...
22¾	Mittelsteine 252A ...	—	6 42	...	10 3	11 18	...	...	3 1	...	...	6 33	8 10	...	12 22	...	...	...	...	...
31¾	Glatz Haupt. 219arr	...	7 6	...	1033	11 34	...	...	3 24	4 1	...	6 57	8 34	...	12 44	...	...	...	...	...

Glatz Haupt....dep	...	5a44	7a20	...	9a39	...	...	1 p9	1p45	2p50	4 p5	5p15	...	...	7p12	...	8p45	...	...	...
Mittelsteine............	...	6 11	7 39	...	10 7	...	...	1 33	...	3 12	4 31	5 48	...	...	7 38	...	9 9	...	...	...
Neurode	...	6 25	7 52	...	1020	p.m.	...	1 47	2 13	3 29	4 45	6 3	p.m.	p.m.	7 53	p.m.	9 22	...	...	...
Charlottenbrunn ...	4 a50	7 16	8 26	10a7	1115	1254	1p56	2 35	2 45	4 27	5 38	—	6 23	7 44	8 40	9 45	10 6	...	...	...
Dittersbach 180	5 5	7 29	8 34	1019	1126	1 7	2 9	2 46	2 53	4 41	5 50	...	6 35	7 57	8 1	9 57	1015	...	...	...

BERLIN, PASEWALK, WOLGAST, and STRALSUND.

Dist			1—4	2—4	1,2,3	1,2,3	1,2,3	1,2,3	1—4	1,2,3	1—4	Ex3	Ex3	Ex3	Ex 3	1—4	1—4	Ex3	Ex3	1,2,3
E.M	Berlin—Stettiner			a.m.	a.m.	a.m.	a.m.		a.m.	p.m.	a.m.	a.m.	p.m.	p.m.	p.m.	p.m.	p.m.	p.m.	p.m.	
—	Bahnhof...dep		...	5 59	7 32	7 27	8 30	From Stettin.	8 36	June 29 to 17 Aug.	1050	11 9	1249	1 2	2 19	2 29	6 11	7 5	8 15	...
44	Angermunde ....arr		...	7 35	8 45	...	9 37		10 4		1229	...	...	2 10	3 40	3 52	7 42	...	9 18	...
	„ (183)......dep		...	7 42	8 48	...	9 38		10 8		1250	RC	To Heringsdorf. Until August 31.	2 11	3 43	4 0	8 12	...	9 19	...
52¼	Wilmersdorf		a.m.	8 1	...	...	...		1027		1 13	...		...	...	4 20	8 31	A	RC	...
67½	Prenzlau (181A)		7 0	8 33	9 23	...	1011		1058		1 57	...		2 45	...	4 52	9 4	...	9 52	...
82½	Pasewalk (183)......arr		7 30	9 1	9 46	...	1031	a.m.	1126	1239	2 27	1 3		3 6	4 47	5 20	9 33	8 58	1012	p.m.
...	„ ....dep		7 53	9 14	9 51	9 36	1036	1132	1156	1244	3 22	1 8		3 16	4 52	5 35	9 55	9 2	1019	1027
89	Jatznick		8 6	9 28	...	9 41	...	1142	1210	...	3 35	...		A	...	5 49	10 8	...	...	1038
101	Ueckermünde......arr		8 54	...	...		...	...	1258	...	4 21	...		...	...	6 42	1126	...	...	1126
101½	Ducherow(183)arr	a.m.	8 33	9 54	1017	To Zinnowitz. Until July 15th.	...	12 0	1239	1 10	4 1	...		3 41	5 22	6 39	1036	9 27	...	11 4
109	Anclam	5 9	8 55	1039	—		1114	1217	1258	Heringsdorf arr. 2.18	4 17	...		—	Heringsdorf arr. 6.34.	6 39	1126	—	1055	—
119¼	Züssow ....arr	5 31	9 17	11 1	...		1131	⋮	1 22		4 39	...	...	...		7 2	1129	...	...	...
...	Züssow ....dep	6 14	1027	1137	...		1137	⋮	1 45		4 47	...	...	...		8 17	1246	...	...	...
130½	Wolgast ...arr	6 53	11 3	12 7	...		12 7	⋮	2 33		5 20	...	...	...		8 57	1 24	...	...	...
...	Züssow ....dep	5 32	9 22	11 2	...		1132	⋮	1 25		4 44	...	...	...		7 6	1134	...	...	...
130½	Greifswald...........	5 56	9 46	1125	...		1153	1251	1 48		5 10	2 11	...	...		7 32	12 1	...	1127	...
149¾	Stralsund 181 arr	6 40	1028	12 8	...		1222	1 20	2 31		5 53	2 39	...	...		8 16	1242	...	1155	...

	2 3 4	2 3 4	1—4	Ex3	1,2,3	1,2,3	1—4	1,2,3	2&3	1,2,3	Ex3	1,2,3	1—4	Ex3	1—4	Ex3	1—4	Ex3	2,3,4
			a.m.	a.m.	a.m.	a.m.	a.m	p.m.				a.m.	p.m.	p.m.	p.m.	p.m.	p.m.		p.m.
Stralsund..........dep	...	...	4 38	4 59		7 15	9 11	From July 29th until August 15th.	...	...	From Zinnowitz. Until 15th September.	1149	1216	3 5	3 19	4 30	6 56	...	11 36
Greifswald	...	...	5 37	5 28	Until Sept. 15th.	7 45	9 56		...	...		1221	1 7	...	4 1	4 59	7 43	...	12 21
Züssow ....arr	a.m.	...	6 2	...		⋮	1019		...	...		1239	1 32	...	4 23	...	8 6	Until 31st August.	12 43
Wolgast .....dep	4 45	...	...	...		⋮	8 32		...	...		12 7	1238	RC	3 38	RC	6 17		10 42
Züssow ....arr	5 20	...	...	...		⋮	9 10		...	...		1237	1 15	...	4 15	...	6 56		11 19
Züssow..............dep	5 25	...	6 6	...		⋮	1022		...	...		1240	1 36	...	4 24	...	8 10		12 44
Anclam..................	5 47	...	6 30	...		8 20	1047		...	p.m.		1 56	2 2	...	4 45	5 31	8 34		1 4
Ducherow................	6 0	a.m.	6 49	6 11	8 29	8 36	11 6		p.m.	1237		1‡11	2 23	...	5 1	5 44	8 51		—
Ueckermünde dep	—	5 22	6 36	...	...	...	1047		1234	A		...	2 3	...	4 39	...	8 30		...
Jatznick................	...	6 8	7 24	...	...	...	1136		1 19	...		...	2 50	...	5 27	...	9 21	p.m.	...
Pasewalk...........arr	a.m.	7 27	7 38	6 35	8 54	9 2	1150	1232	1 31	1 4		1 39	3 4	4 31	5 40	6 10	9 35	9 44	...
„ ....dep	5 42	—	7 52	6 40	8 59	To Stettin.	1159	1237	—	1 9		1 44	3 22	4 36	6 26	6 15	9 56	9 48	...
Prenzlau................	6 10	...	8 30	7 3	...		1232	...	...	1 32		2 8	3 57	...	6 56	6 38	1031	1041	...
Wilmersdorf.............	6 55	...	9 11	RC	...		1 7	...	...	...		...	4 29	...	7 27	...	11 3	...	...
Angermunde.......arr	7 11	...	9 23	...	...		1 26	...	...	...		2 44	4 45	...	7 44	7 11	1119	1045	...
„ ....dep	7 18	...	9 39	...	...		1 43	...	...	...		2 45	4 49	...	7 56	7 12	1151	...	...
Berlin 182A.........arr	8 58	...	1117	8 35	1059	...	3 9	2 50	...	3 14	3 20	3 54	6 19	6 34	9 9	8 16	1 23	1156	...

Angermünde 183...dep	5 a2	7 a42	10 a7	1p46	5 p19	7p48
Lüdersdorf	5 19	7 59	10 23	2 2	5 38	8 5
Freienwalde ....arr	5 50	8 32	10 51	2 30	6 11	8 34

Freienwalde 181A dep	6 a2	8 a6	9 a43	12p52	3 p43	8p12
Lüdersdorf	6 37	8 38	10 24	1 25	3 16	8 46
Angermünde.........arr	6 55	8 58	10 44	1 39	3 31	9 10

‡—Stops at Ducherow until August 17. A—Until September 15.

RC—Restaurant Car.

DUCHEROW and WOLGASTERFAHRE.

Ducherow ......dep	...	...	6a47	8a43	10a19	...	12p8	12p48	2p31	...	...	...	6p30	9 p29	...	11p8	...	...	...
Carnin	...	a.m.	7 1	8 57	10 32	p.m.	1222	1 2	2 45	‡ ⋮	A ⋮	...	6 49	A	...	1122	...	...	...
Swinemünde ...arr	...	5 35	7 39	9 35	10 56	12*15	1 0	1 41	3 23	3 40	4 17	5p25	7 39	10 10	‡	12 0	...	...	...
Heringsdorf Bad arr	a.m.	6 1	8 1	10 2	11 26	12 33	1 28	2 3	3 47	4 9	4 44	5 45	8 10	10 37	11 p6	1222	...	...	...
Zinnowitz	5 7	7 3	—	11 3	12 41	—	2 32	—	4 51	—	5 46	—	9 19	—	11 58	—	...	...	...
Wolgasterfähre arr	5 26	7 23	...	1121	1 0	...	2 52	...	5 10	...	...	...	9 36	...	...	...	...	...	...
Wolgasterfähre dep	...	5 a35	7a35	a.m.	a.m.	11a41	...	...	2 p3	3p20	5p58	9p47	...	...	...	...	...	...	...
Zinnowitz	...	6 1	7 54	...	11 0	12 3	...	...	2 29	3 48	6 19	10 5	a.m.	...	...	...	...	...	...
Heringsdorf Bad ...	a.m.	7 10	8 54	10*25	1151	12 59	1p35	3p11	3 36	4 53	7 17	—	1237	...	...	...	...	...	...
Swinemünde	5 13	7 32	9 25	10 43	1222	1 23	1 55	3 37	4 4	5 17	7 45	...	1255	...	...	...	...	...	...
Carnin	5 51	8 9	10 5	—	A ⋮	2 0	—	4 20	4 29	6 0	8 24	...	—	...	...	...	...	...	...
Ducherow ....arr	6 5	8 22	1018	...		2 13	...	4 33	4 42	6 14	8 37	...	...	...	...	...	...	...	...

*—Until 15th September. ‡—Until 31st August. A—Until 15th September.

GLASOW and ARNSWALDE.

Glasow ....dep	4a57	7a57	1p23	5p54	6p54	9p18
Berlinchen	5 35	9 2	2 9	6 28	7 39	9 59
Alt-Libbehne.........	6 10	9 38	2 55	6 59	8 19	1039
Arnswalde 177A arr	6 29	9 57	3 15	7 15	8 37	1058

Arnswalde......dep	5a10	7a16	8 a2	1135	2p15	6p38	1017
Alt-Libbehne	5 30	7 33	8 26	1154	2 49	7 0	1038
Berlinchen	6 11	8 4	9 16	1229	3 55	7 43	1139
Glasow 178B ...arr	6 56	8 37	10 6	1 8	5 2	8 23	1254

STETTIN and STRASBURG.

‡—Rail Motor.

	1—4	Ex3	1,2,3	1—4	2 3 4	2 3 4	Ex3	2 3 4	1—4	2 3 4	2 3 4	2 3 4	2 3 4			
	a.m.	a.m.	a.m.	a.m.	p.m.	p.m.	p.m.	p.m.	p.m.	p.m.	p.m.	p.m.	n'gt	...	...	...
Stettin ....dep	6 43	8 28	1040	1048	12‡4	1 57	2 24	3‡30	4 25	7 16	8 44	9 ‡6	12 9	...	...	...
Löcknitz....................	7 16	...	...	1123	1240	2 34	...	4 8	5 1	7 53	9 21	9 44	1244	...	...	...
Pasewalk 183 ...arr	7 38	9 6	1124	1145	1 2	2 54	3 7	4 30	5 24	8 16	9 41	1010	1 7	...	...	...
„ ....dep	8 5	9 11	—	12 3	—	—	3 12	—	5 45	8 21	1022	—	—	...	...	...
Strasburg ....arr	8 31	⋮	...	1230	...	...	3 33	...	6 15	8 49	1050	...	...	...	...	...
LUBECK 213 ......arr	1p24	1p24	...	...	...	...	7p56	...	12a34	...	...	...	...	...	...	...
HAMBURG 213A arr	2p25	2p25	...	...	...	...	9 p7	...	...	...	...	...	...	...	...	...

	2 3 4	2 3 4	1—4	1,2,3	1—4	2 3 4	Ex3	2 3 4	2 3 4	1—4	2 3 4	2—4	Ex3	2 3 4		
HAMBURG 213A...dep	...	...	...	...	...	...	8a50	...	...	10a30	...	...	5p20	...	...	...
LUBECK 213 ......dep	...	...	...	...	...	...	9a55	...	...	12p10	...	...	6p21	...	...	...
		a.m.	a m.	a.m.	a.m.		p.m.	p.m	p.m.	p.m.	p.m.		⋮		...	...
Strasburg ....dep	...	6 1	7 8	...	1056	p.m.	⋮	2 51	...	6 1	8 25	...	⋮	p.m.	...	...
Pasewalk ....arr	a.m.	6 31	7 31	...	1121	‡	2 4	3 11	...	6 21	8 48	p.m.	1046	‡	...	...
„ ....dep	6 13	—	7 55	9 7	12 4	1 9	2 9	3 19	4‡36	6 36	9 4	1017	1047	1058	...	...
Löcknitz....................	6 47	...	8 18	...	1230	1 32	...	3 43	4 59	6 58	9 33	1040	...	1122	...	...
Stettin 182A.........arr	7 34	...	8 54	9 42	1 4	2 7	2 45	4 14	5 31	7 36	10 9	1112	1122	12 0	...	...

JADICKENDORF and PYRITZ.

Jadickendorf ......dep	6 a20	12p40	4 p40	9 p7	11p45	...
Schonfliess	7 5	1 16	5 16	9 38	12 15	...
Pyritz (178B) ....arr	8 7	2 17	6 28	10 36	...	...

Pyritz.....................dep	...	6 a6	9 a6	2 p25	7p16	...
Schonfliess	5 a6	7 9	10 13	3 33	8 24	...
Jadickendorf (181A) arr	5 40	7 44	10 47	4 4	8 55	...

CAMENZ and RAUDTEN.

Camenz	a.m.	a.m.	a.m.	a.m.	a.m.	a.m.	p.m.	p.m.	p.m.	p.m.	p.m.
(Schl.) dep	4 12	...	6 12	8 30	10 0	1021	1242	4 38	6 6	8 19	9 33
Frankenst'n	4 24	...	6 24	8 42	1013	1032	1 4	4 49	6 19	8 32	9 45
Gnadenfrei	4 37	...	6 37	8 56	1027	...	1 19	5 0	6 33	8 47	9 58
Reichenb'ch	4 55	5 31	6 55	9 15	1126	1054	1 38	5 13	6 52	9 4	1015
Croischwitz	5 20	5 57	7 22	9 42	1153	...	2 3	5 30	7 18	9 29	1041
Schweidnitz	5 26	6 5	7 29	9 50	1211	1112	2 11	5 37	7 26	9 37	1047
Königs- arr	5 40	6 20	7 44	10 5	1224	1123	2 25	5 50	7 39	9 52	11 0
zelt ...dep	5 43	6 44	7 53	1016	1234	1126	2 45	6 8	7 54	11 9	1239
Striegau......	5 59	7 1	8 8	1031	1251	1138	3 0	6 20	8 13	1121	1255
Jauer	6 18	7 22	8 27	1051	1 13	1152	3 22	6 36	8 38	1139	1 13
Liegnitz arr	6 50	7 59	8 59	1123	1 48	1210	3 55	6 56	9 11	12 4	1 46
„ ...dep	7 1	—	9 2	1218	—	1218	4 26	7 50	1010	—	—
Raudten arr	7 55	...	9 56	1 12	...	1 12	5 20	8 48	11 6	...	...

	a.m.	a.m.	a.m.	a.m.	a.m.	p.m.	p.m.	p.m.	p.m.	p.m.	p.m.
Raudten ...dep		5 45	8 2	...	1120	3 0	...	...	7 23	...	1012
Liegnitz arr		6 44	8 55		1215	3 56	...	...	8 25	...	1112
„ dep	5 10	7 1	9 5	1126	1 7	4 10	5 4	6 24	9 1	...	1117
Jauer	5 49	7 33	9 40	1149	1 42	4 45	5 25	7 3	9 23	...	1153
Striegau......	6 10	8 3	10 0	12 7	2 4	5 6	5 40	7 24	9 39	...	1213
Königs- arr	6 26	8 18	1014	1220	2 18	5 20	5 51	7 40	9 51	p.m.	1228
zelt ...dep	6 41	8 32	1023	1237	2 39	6 16	6 10	7 52	9 55	1111	1238
Schweidnitz	6 56	8 47	1039	1 5	2 55	6 30	6 23	8 10	10 7	1126	1254
Croischwitz	7 2	8 53	1045	1 12	3 1	6 36	...	8 16	...	1132	1 0
Reichenba'h	7 27	9 22	1110	1 43	3 26	7 3	6 43	8 47	1026	1157	1 25
Gnadenfrei..	7 45	9 43	1130	2 8	3 44	7 22	...	9 6	1041	—	—
Frankenst'n	7 57	9 56	1144	2 25	3 57	7 35	7 6	9 18	1052	...	...
Camenz 219	8 7	10 6	1155	2 36	4 8	7 45	...	9 29	11 3	...	...

STRIEGAU and MERZDORF.

Striegau...dep	7a11	...	8 a18	10a38	3 p7	8p13	11p31
Rohnstock......	7 38	7a56	8 41	11 2	3 29	8 35	11 54
Bolkenhain ..	8 16	8 13	...	11 27	3 48	8 55	12 13
Merzdorf...arr	8 50	...	...	12 15	4 21	9 28	...

Merzdorf...dep	...	6a45	...	12p38	5p47	10p0	...
Bolkenhain ...	5a12	7 19	8a58	1 16	6 24	1033	...
Rohnstock......	5 32	7 38	9 23	1 36	6 44	1053	
Striegau ...arr	5 54	7 58	9 51	1 57	7 6	1113	

REICHENBACH and OBER-LANGENBIELAU.

Reichenbach ....dep	5a22	6a41	7a40	9a30	11 20	1p45	3p35	5p15	7 p8	9p10	10p30	...	...	...	...	...	...
Ober-Langenbielau ....arr	5 39	6 58	7 57	9 47	11 37	2 2	3 52	5 32	7 25	9 23	10 43	...	...	...	...	...	...

Ober-Langenbielau ....dep	4a25	6a20	7 a6	8a42	10a24	1 p5	3p 5	4p45	6p12	8p21	9 p57	10p51	...	...	...	...	...
Reichenbach ....arr	4 40	6 33	7 19	8 58	10 37	1 22	3 18	5 2	6 30	8 38	10 10	11 7	...	...	...	...	...

WEISSWASSER and MUSKAU.

Weisswasser dep	5a25	7a45	9 a5	10a50	12p20	2p30	5 p0	6p10	7p20	1125
Muskau ......arr	5 46	8 3	9 23	11 8	12 38	2 48	5 18	6 28	7 38	1142

Muskau ...	4a55	7a10	8a23	10a14	1130	1p35	3p47	5p25	6p40	10p0
Weisswa'r	5 13	7 29	8 42	10 33	1149	1 54	4 6	5 47	7 2	1019

LUBBENAU, SENFTENBERG, and KAMENZ.

†—6.15 p.m. on Sunday.

E.M									
	Lübbenau ......dep	6a15	8a58	10a10	12 p5	2p45	5p18	9p50	...
9	Calau	6 54	9 18	10 30	12 26	3 6	5 40	1022	...
25	Senftenberg	7 40	10 1	11 15	2 0	4 20	7 15	11 5	...
30½	Hohenboka	7 52	1024	11 26	2 12	4 40	7 45	1117	...
44½	**Kamenz (185)** arr	8 27	11 1	11 55	2 49	5 17	8 25	1154	...

Kamenz dep	4a30	6 a5	8a45	12p10	...	3p15	6p55	9 p0	...
Hohenboka ...	5 0	6 43	9 15	12 47	...	3 57	7 45	9 44	...
Senftenberg...	5 16	7 2	9 26	12 56	2p52	4 45	8 0	9 57	11p10
Calau............	6 5	7 42	1015	—	3 40	5 39	8 41	—	11 51
Lübbenau	6 22	7 57	1030	...	3 55	5 58	8 59	...	12 9

Senftenberg............dep	5 a45	8a30	1p30	6p25	11 p5	...	...
Zschipkau (154).......arr	6 3	8 45	1 48	6 43	11 23	...	...

Zschipkau ....dep	4a53	9 a5	12p45	6†p51	11p40	...	...
Senftenberg ....arr	5 11	9 19	1 3	7 9	11 58	...	...

HIRSCHBERG and GRUNTHAL.

Hirschberg dep	5†53	6a38	9 a5	9a52	1158	2‡22	2p37	4p10	5p45	7p55	9p18
Warmbrunn ...	6 11	6 55	9 23	10 9	1216	...	2 59	4 33	6 4	8 19	9 36
Hermsdorf.......	6 21	7 3	9 31	1017	1224	...	3 9	4 41	6 13	8 28	9 44
Petersdorf	6 34	7 19	9 43	1030	1237	2 51	3 24	4 52	6 28	8 41	10 0
Schreiberhau	7 13	8 6	1020	11 9	1 18	3 29	4 6	5 34	7 8	9 19	1040
Grünthal 225 ar	...	9 5	1112	1210	2 10	...	...	6 30	...	...	...

Grünthal dep	...	5a40	...	9a28	11a26	1p0	...	...	6p31	...
Schreiberhau	...	6 38	8 a8	1034	12 24	2 10	3p33	5p50	7 38	9p24
Petersdorf	5a50	7 21	8 45	1111	1 5	2 55	4 14	6 30	8 18	10 2
Hermsdorf......	6 1	7 32	8 56	1121	1 15	3 9	4 25	6 41	8 28	1014
Warmbrunn...	6 10	7 41	9 4	1129	1 23	3 20	4 35	6 50	8 38	1023
Hirschberg ar	6 26	7 58	9 22	1146	1 40	3 40	4 51	7 7	8 55	1040

†—Until 31st August. ‡—July and August only.

FRANKFORT-ON-THE-ODER, COTTBUS, and GROSSENHAIN.

Frankfort-a-O. dep		5a55	6a35	8 a3	1110	1p30	4 p0	7p30	11p5
Grunow		6 28	...	8 32	1146	2 2	4 33	8 2	1136
Lieberose (Jamlitz)...		6 55	...	8 56	1212	2 29	4 59	8 26	12 7
Peitz		7 11	...	9 12	1228	2 45	5 15	8 44	1224
Cottbus 180 arr	a.m.	7 30	7 45	9 31	1247	3 4	5 34	9 2	1243
„ ......dep	4 50	8 0	7 50	9 55	1 0	3 21	6 10	1014	—
Petershain 172 ...	5 20	8 3	8 11	1034	1 32	3 47	6 41	1044	...
Senftenberg	5 41	8 48	8 24	1054	1 51	4 3	7 2	11 5	...
Ruhland	5 57	9 0	...	1120	2 6	4 21	7 22	1118	...
Grossenhain ar	6 42	9 45	9 7	...	2 48	5 5	8 3	12 0	...

Grossenhain dep	4a15	7 a5	11a17	...	3p30	...	...	8p36	9p16	12 a1
Ruhland ......dep	4 58	8 0	11 28	...	4 21	...	7p23	9 17	10 6	12 39
Senftenberg	5 20	8 25	11 41	1p25	4 38	..	7 40	...	1021	12 54
Petershain	5 41	8 49	11 58	1 53	4 58	...	8 0	...	1043	1 10
Cottbus.........arr	6 7	9 15	12 22	2 25	5 24	p.m.	8 28	9 46	11 7	1 32
„ ....dep	6 50	1043	1 20	3 22	5 42	6 55	—	9 53	1130	—
Peitz	7 12	11 2	1 39	3 41	5 57	7 13	...	...	1149	...
Lieberose (Jamlitz)	7 37	1119	1 57	3 59	6 14	7 3	...	...	12 7	...
Grunow	8 3	1148	2 36	4 32	6 35	8 1	...	...	1235	...
Frankfort-a-O.	8 40	1220	3 8	5 6	7 4	8 33	...	11 0	1 8	...

LEIPSIC, DOEBELN, and DRESDEN.

Leipsic—		a.m.	a.m.	a.m.	a.m.	a.m.	p.m.	p.m.	p.m.	p.m.	p.m.	p.m.	p.m.
Hauptbahnhof dep		6 31	6 40	8 7	1010	11 25	12 27	2 53	5 37	7 19	8 20	9 20	1145
Beucha		...	7 0	8 28	1029	11 50	12 50	3 14	...	7 45	...	9 44	1211
Grimma **184**		7 0	7 22	8 51	1051	12 13	1 13	3 41	6 14	8 10	8 48	10 8	1235
Grossbothen	a.m.	...	7 32	9 1	11 1	—	1 26	3 52	6 24	8 20	...	10 20	12.6
Leisnig	5 18	7 23	7 52	9 21	1119	...	1 50	4 14	6 45	—	9 11	10 43	1 6
Döbeln ......arr	5 38	7 36	8 13	9 39	1132	...	2 12	4 35	7 3	...	9 24	11 5	—
„ **189** dep	5 47	7 42	8 18	9 51	1136	...	2 21	4 44	7 41	...	9 26	11 10	...
Rosswein **189**...	6 6	7 54	8 37	10 11	1152	...	2 41	5 4	8 3	...	9 38	11 29	...
Nossen **188A** ...	6 23	8 4	8 52	10 25	12 3	p.m.	2 56	5 19	8 18	p.m.	9 48	11 41	...
Meissen	7 4	8 27	9 27	11 1	1231	12 45	3 33	5 55	8 55	9 25	1011	—	...
Dresden Neu.	7 44	8 48	10 3	11 26	1256	1 30	3 58	6 20	9 21	10 8	1032	...	...
Dresden Hpt.	7 55	8 56	10 14	11 36	1 6	1 40	4 8	6 28	9 31	1019	1040	...	...

		a.m.	a.m.	a.m.	a.m.		p.m.	p.m.	p.m.		p.m.	p.m.
Dresden Haupt. ...dep		...	5 40	7 44	11 13	...	12 16	2 37	4 58	...	7 47	9 0
Dresden Neustadt dep		...	5 50	7 54	11 20	...	12 28	2 47	5 10	...	7 57	9 10
Meissen		...	6 21	8 26	11 42	...	12 54	3 15	5 39	...	8 22	9 48
Nossen		5 5	7 4	9 5	12 9	...	1 37	3 59	6 24	...	8 54	10 31
Rosswein		5 18	7 16	9 18	12 18	...	1 51	4 13	6 40	...	9 5	10 44
Döbeln ....arr		5 35	7 33	9 36	12 29	...	2 9	4 31	6 58	...	9 21	11 2
„ ....dep		5 44	7 45	9 52	12 37	...	2 23	4 49	7 18	...	9 32	11 14
Leisnig		6 4	8 6	10 14	12 52	...	2 45	5 10	7 42	...	9 47	11 35
Grossbothen............	a.m.	6 27	8 28	10 36	1 9	p.m.	3 8	5 34	8 4	p.m.	10 6	11 56
Grimma..................	5 28	6 39	8 38	10 46	1 18	1 30	3 19	5 46	8 15	9 12	1015	12 10
Beucha	5 52	7 4	9 1	11 9	...	1 55	3 43	6 11	...	9 38	...	12 33
Leipsic Haupt. arr	6 19	7 24	9 21	11 35	1 46	2 20	4 4	6 36	8 55	10 4	1053	12 58

Dresden—
Leipzig Bahnhof dep
Radebeul ....
Coswig ....
Meissen.................arr

A frequent Local Service in each direction is maintained throughout the day between these Stations.

BEUCHA & TREBSEN-PAUSCHWITZ.

Beucha ....dep	7a10	12p46	5p47	9p50
Brandis......................	7 20	12 59	5 56	10 2
Trebsen-Pauschwitz	7 58	1 38	6 34	1040

Trebsen-Pauschwitz	6 a0	8 a6	1p50	6p43
Brandis......................	6 44	8 47	2 31	7 24
Beucha ....arr	6 53	8 56	2 40	7 33

Extra.—Beucha to Brandis, 10.31. 11.15 a.m., 3.16, 4.22, 7.49, 8.55 p.m. Brandis to Beucha, 5‡36, 10.54 a.m., 12.26, 1‡29, 3.30, 4.59, 8‡33, 9.24 p.m. ‡—Not on Sun.

MALTSCH and STRIEGAU.

Maltsch ....dep	4a30	7 a40	1 p42	7 p22
Lohnig	5 13	8 57	2 25	8 34
Striegau 183A arr	5 43	9 46	2 56	9 27

Striegau ....dep	7a30	10a38	2 p8	8p20
Lohnig	8 11	11 7	2 37	8 49
Maltsch ....arr	9 8	11 50	3 20	9 13

A—In July only.

GOLLNOW and CÖSLIN.

E.M.											
	Gollnow ...dep		...	6 a4	9 a2	12 p2	2p52	3p33	4p51	6p32	10p42
14½	Naugard		...	6 54	9 51	12 49	1 29	4 25	...	7 19	11 26
21½	Piepenburg ...		...	7 14	1011	1 8	1 47	4 44	A	7 39	11 43
26½	Plathe	a.m.	...	7 32	1029	1 22	2 6	4 59	5 58	7 55	12 3
46½	Treptow ...	6 3	a.m.	8 36	1145	—	3 4	6 1	6 57	9 2	1 1
61½	Colberg 175	6 54	8 17	9 24	1240	...	3 51	6 50	7 41	9 52	1 41
83	Güdenhagn	8 14	9 37	1056	2 7	...	5 37	8 5	—	11 7	—
88	Cöslin...arr	8 28	9 51	1110	2 21	...	5 51	8 20	...	1122	...

Cöslin ....dep		6a20	8a50	10a40	...	1p46	4 p0	6p18	9p10
Güdenhagen		6 35	9 6	10 55	...	2 2	4 16	6 33	9 25
Colberg	5a35	8 35	1120	12 1	2p39	3 52	6 0	7 50	11 0
Treptow	6 28	9 30	1216	—	3 28	4 51	6 57	8 41	1153
Plathe	7 30	1032	1 22	...	4 28	5 56	—	9 44	—
Piepenburg	7 44	1048	1 37	...	4 45	6 14	...	9 59	...
Naugard ...	8 5	1114	2 0	...	5 3	6 36	...	1020	...
Gollnow 179	8 48	12 1	2 45	...	5 41	7 24	...	11 6	...

Extra					
	Treptow...dep	9 a31	3p26	7p15	11p54
	Colberg ...arr	10 27	4 18	8 16	12 42

Colberg ...dep	4 a 9	10 a0	3 p23	...
Treptow ...arr	4 58	10 53	4 15	...

Piepenburg ...dep	8 a0	10a15	1p50	4p51	7p50	11p54	...	...	...
Regenwalde ...arr	8 41	10 47	2 30	5 21	8 20	12 33	...	...	...

Regenwalde...dep	6a35	10 a3	1 p4	3p49	5 p33	9p20	...	...
Piepenburg ...arr	7 7	10 43	1 33	4 32	6 3	9 50	...	...

Naugard ...dep	8a18	2p10	7p30	...	...	...	...	...	...	...
Daber ......arr	9 14	3 6	8 31	..	...	...	...	...	...	...

Daber ....dep	6a53	12p18	5p15	...	...	...	...	...
Naugard ......arr	7 54	1 20	6 21	...	...	...	...	...

BERLIN and KREMMEN.

Berlin Stettin	6a46	1010	2p15	6p21	8p48	9p34	12a4	...	...
Tegel...........	7 8	1032	2 39	6 43	9 17	9 56	1226	...	...
Kremmen ...	7 47	1115	3 15	7 21	...	1034	1 9	...	...

Kremmen...	7 a49	10a21	3 p17	7p23	10p39	...	...	...
Tegel	8 24	10 56	3 53	8 2	11 15	...	...	...
Berlin Stett.	8 47	11 22	4 17	8 26	11 39	...	...	...

	a.m.	a.m.	p.m	p.m	p.m.	a.m.
Kremmen ......dep	7 52	1118	3 20	7 26	1039	1 14
Neu-Ruppin	8 42	1213	4 11	8 16	1135	2 12
Wittstock	9 46	1 23	5 12	9 30	...	...
Meyenburg......arr	11 0	3 8	6 14	1050	...	...

Meyenburg ...dep	...	7 a19	12 0	3p45	6 p34
Wittstock	...	8 29	1 24	5 18	7 58
Neu-Ruppin.........	7 a0	9 33	2 27	6 33	9 39
Kremmen ......arr	7 45	10 21	3 17	7 23	10 59

SAXONY STATE RAILWAYS—KÖNIGLICHE SACHSISCHE STAATSBAHNEN.

REICHENBERG and EIBAU.

Reichenberg..dep		5a18	7 a7	8a26	10a38	1p50	...	6p30	8p38	1115
Zittau.. arr ...		6 6	7 38	9 15	11 28	2 39	...	7 18	9 27	12 2
Zittau.. dep	4 a0	6 28	—	9 40	11 55	3 6	5p28	8 5	10 5	—
Warnsdorf ar	4 22	6 55	...	10 8	12 23	3 37	5 55	8 34	1033	...
Eibau 185 arr	4 43	7 24	...	1037	1 41	4 10	6 23	9 6	11 3	...

Eibau ....dep	...	5a40	...	9a47	12p22	3p55	6p10	8p 7	11p21	12p54
Warnsdorf .dep	...	6 12	...	10 15	12 52	4 28	7 46	8 34	11 47	1 19
Zittau .... arr	...	6 40	a.m.	10 40	1 18	4 52	8 12	9 0	12 12	1 43
Zittau .... dep	5a 7	6 49	8 47	11 0	1 37	5 30	8 25	—	1 8	—
Reichenberg arr	5 58	7 41	9 41	11 51	2 33	6 21	9 20	...	1 56	...

LOBAU and EBERSBACH.									
	Lobau dep	5a 1	5a45	8a56	11a31	3 p7	5p21	8 p8	10p25
	Ebersbach	5 19	6 31	9 21	11 54	3 31	5 45	8 42	10 49

Ebersbach dep	7a51	10a55	12p53	2 p4	4p34	6p50	9p40	11p23
Lobau 190...arr	8 15	11 16	1 38	2 25	4 57	7 26	1010	11 45

LOBAU and RADIBOR.

Löbau..............dep	...	8a32	11a58	3p10	5 p19	7p50
Weissenberg-i-S	5 a5	9 30	12 51	3 53	6 37	8 32
Grossdubrau	5 53	1018	1 42	...	7 25	...
Radibor (184)...arr	6 11	1036	2 0	...	7 43	...

Radibor...........dep	...	8a17	12p25	...	5 p8	9 p1
Grossdubrau	...	8 36	12 42	...	5 27	9 21
Weissenberg-i-S	7a32	1029	1 41	4p12	6 44	1010
Löbau ....arr	8 17	1115	2 27	4 58	7 30	...

HOYERSWERDA and BAUTZEN.

Hoyerswerda dep	...	...	7a 4	...	1011	...	2p31	...	7p41
Königswartha	5a 5	a.m.	7 48	a.m.	1058	p.m.	3 17	p.m.	8 30
Radibor	5 44	6 13	8 16	1038	1125	2 1	3 45	7 45	9 0
Bautzen (186)...arr	6 15	6 40	8 41	11 5	1150	2 27	4 10	8 12	9 25

Bautzen ....dep	5a20	7a48	9a20	11a56	2p21	4p40	7p20	8p33	11p15
Radibor (184) ...arr	5 44	8 15	9 46	12 22	2 45	5 6	7 45	8 59	11 45
Königswartha	6 12	—	1015	—	3 15	—	8 25	—	12 24
Hoyerswerda (172)	6 54	...	1057	...	3 57	...	9 7	...	...

CHEMNITZ and WECHSELBURG.

Chemnitz...............dep	5a55	10a11	3 p5	8p32	...
Schweizerthal	6 49	10 59	3 53	9 19	...
Wechselburg 184 ...arr	7 21	11 30	4 23	9 48	...

Wechselburg ......dep	8a21	12p45	4p55	9p49	...	...
Schweizerthal	8 53	1 15	5 24	1023	...	...
Chemnitz ....arr	9 45	2 7	6 11	1110	...	...

GLAUCHAU and WURZEN.

Glauchau...dep	a.m.	4a50	...	8a56	11a47	1p28	3p30	7p49	10p28
Penig..............	5 13	6 25	...	9 28	12 17	2 1	4 9	8 23	10 59
Wechselburg	5 39	7 33	a.m.	9 53	—	2 25	4 36	8 47	—
Rochlitz	5 54	7 48	7 59	10 6	12p13	2 37	5 4	9 21	...
Grossbothen	6 26	—	9 16	1032	12 42	3 41	6 30	1020	...
Grimma	6 45	...	9 39	—	1 0	3 59	6 54	1038	...
Nerchau-Trebsen	7 21	...	10 7	...	1 27	4 26	7 34	11 3	...
Wurzen 188 arr	7 44	...	1029	...	1 49	4 48	7 56	1125	...

Wurzen ....dep		6a22	...	9 a44	...	1 p4	...	4 p3	...	8p20
Nerchau-Trebsen		6 46	...	10 8	...	1 28	...	4 31	...	8 45
Grimma		7 10	a.m.	10 36	p.m.	1 53	...	5 8	...	9 13
Grossbothen ...		7 33	9 3	11 4	1 26	2 12	4 p3	6 30	p.m.	1021
Rochlitz......	5 a8	8 2	9 29	11 32	1 55	—	4 35	7 2	9 10	1047
Wechselburg...	5 21	8 16	—	11 46	2 8	...	4 52	7 16	9 54	—
Penig	6 8	8 48	...	12 17	2 37	...	5 22	7 42	11 9	...
Glauchau ...	6 39	9 22	...	12 48	3 12	...	5 54	8 14	1212	...

Extra—Wechselburg to Rochlitz, 11.33 a.m. 12.44, 9.53p.m. Rochlitz to Wechselburg, 12.25 p.m. Penig to Rochlitz 12.18p.m.

Nerchau-Trebsen ......dep	7a22	10a15	1p29	4p28	8 p46	...
Wermsdorf (190)......arr	8 7	10 59	2 12	5 11	9 30	...

Wermsdorf ....dep	6 a0	9 a3	12p35	3p36	6 p45	...	...
Nerchau-Trebsen ......arr	6 43	9 47	1 19	4 19	7 29	...	...

†—Weekdays only.

GERA and WEISCHLITZ.

Gera ...dep	...	4a48	6 a0	7a46	1018	1 p2	2 52	6p 0	...	7p33	1058
Wünsch'd'f	...	5 29	6 21	8 4	1042	1 34	3 24	6 28	...	8 3	1131
Berga	a.m.	5 42	6 35	8 14	1054	1 46	3 37	6 40	p.m.	8 17	1143
Greiz 188A	4 20	6 8	7 6	8 28	1120	2 6	4 4	7 3	7†30	8 59	12 7
Elsterberg	4 36	6 19	7 19	8 35	1131	2 18	4 15	7 15	7 43	9 12	1219
Plauen......	5 38	6 47	7 59	8 54	1222	2 46	4 43	7 43	—	9 45	1250
Weischlitz	5 58	6 59	8 3	9 3	1234	2 58	4 55	7 55	...	9 57	1 1

Wei'chlitz	513	...	8a12	1019	11a52	1p34	4 56	7 p2	...	8p18	11p4
Plauen ...	529	...	8 25	1031	12 7	1 48	5 10	7 16	p.m.	8 28	1119
Elsterberg	555	...	8 56	1057	12 34	2 16	5 36	7 44	8 28	8 49	1146
Greiz	617	...	9 11	1112	12 48	2 28	5 51	8 0	8 39	8 58	12 1
Berga	635	a.m.	9 28	1130	1 8	2 45	6 9	8 19	—	9 13	1218
Wünschd.	653	7 34	9 43	1143	1 22	2 57	6 25	8 32	...	9 25	1232
Gera ...arr	718	8 0	10 6	12 9	40	3 24	6 49	8 56	...	9 45	1257

Extra.—Gera to Wünschendorf, 9.16 a.m., 2.21, 4.32, 6.45, 9.13 p.m. Wünschendorf to Gera 1.39, 3.48, 7.12, 9.47 p.m.

SAXONY STATE RAILWAYS.

ZITTAU and OYBIN.

Zittau ......dep	...	...	6*26	7*a48	10 a5	10a56	a.m.	1p12	1p22	1p32	2§p18	4 p32	6*p34	6*p44	8 p0	10p20
Bertsdorf ...arr	...	...	6 46	8 9	1051	11 25	A	...	2 3	2 13	2 53	5 11	6 54	7 4	8 41	10 40
Bertsdorf dep	5a23	...	6 47	8 13	1054	...	11 36	...	2 5	...	2 58	5 15	§	7 6	8 43	—
Jonsdorf arr	5 38	...	7 3	8 30	1111	A	11 53	...	2 22	...	3 15	5 32	...	7 23	9 0	...
Bertsdorf ...dep	—	5a28	6 47	8 12	1054	11 27	—	...	—	2 15	2 56	5 14	6 55	7 ‡9	8 43	...
Oybin ......dep	...	5 41	7 0	8 27	11 9	11 39	...	1 57	...	2.30	3 8	5 29	7 10	7‡25	8 59	...

Oybin ......dep	5a48	7 a8	8a35	...	11a40	2 p3	2p40	...	5p43	...	...	6 p0	7p10	7§p33	9p12	...	...
Bertsdorf ...arr	5 59	7 19	8 49	a.m.	11 53	2 14	2 55	§	5 55	...	...	6 14	...	7 44	9 26	...	...
Jonsdorf dep	5 45	7 8	8 35	1118	...	...	2 37	3p33	...	5p50	...	...	...	7 28	9 5	...	...
Bertsdorf arr	5 58	7 21	8 50	1131	...	A	2 52	3 48	§	6 5	...	...	...	7 42	9 17	...	...
Bertsdorf ...dep	6 2	7 23	8 52	1134	11 55	2 16	2 57	—	5 56	—	6 p6	6 16	...	7 45	9 28	...	...
Zittau ......arr	6*19	7*40	9 32	12 6	12 32	2 48	3 33	...	6*10	...	6*22	6 55	7 47	8 20	9*44	...	...

A—Until 16th August. *—At or from Zittau Vorstadt.
‡—From 15th September. §—Until 13th September.

CHEMNITZ, BORNA, and LEIPSIC. †—Not on Sunday.

Dist. E.M.		a.m.	a.m.	a.m.	a.m.		a.m.	p.m.	p.m.	p.m.	p.m.	p.m.	p.m.	p.m.	p.m.	p.m.	p.m.	p.m.	p.m.	p.m.
	Chemnitz........dep	4†27	5 39	7 24	8 32	...	9 19	1210	1 17	1 35	2 36	3 24	4 57	5 31	6 26	7 22	7 55	8 4	9 50	1155
6½	Wittgensdorf...........	4 47	6 0	7 40	...	...	9 40	1229	...	1 58	2 59	3 47	5 19	...	6 46	7 42	...	8 20	10 13	1215
19	**Narsdorf**	—	6 29	8 13	...	...	10 14	1 1	...	—	3 30	4 23	—	6 15	—	8 14	8 26	8 52	10 49	1247
22¾	**Geithain**	...	6 43	8 26	9 11	...	10 25	1 12	...	...	—	4 34	...	6 24	...	—	...	9 4	11 0	—
29	Frohburg	a.m.	6 58	8 42	...	a.m.	10 40	1 27	...	p.m.	...	4 50	...	6 37	...	p.m.	...	9 20	11 16	...
34¼	Borna...	5 10	7 12	8 57	...	9 33	10 53	1 41	...	2 25	...	5 4	...	6 48	...	6 53	...	9 34	11 31	...
38¼	**Kieritzsch**............	5 43	7 25	9 9	...	10 0	11 5	1 53	...	3 13	...	5 16	...	...	...	7 6	...	9 46	11 44	...
45¼	Gaschwitz	6 4	7 42	9 24	...	10 30	11 21	2 11	...	3 32	...	5 32	...	...	...	7 28	...	10 3	...	...
51¼	**Leipsic** Bayr Bhf.ar	6 21	7 57	9 35	...	10 48	11 34	2 22	...	3 47	...	5 43	...	7 20	...	7 46	...	1014	12 7	...
...	„ Hauptbhf arr	...	...	...	9 58	...	...	...	2 40	...	...	...	...	...	...	...	9 12	...	...	...

			a.m.	a.m.	a.m.	a.m.	a.m.	a.m.	p.m.	p.m.	p.m.		p.m.	p.m.	p.m.	p.m.	...	p.m.	p.m.	
...	**Leipsic**—Hauptbhf	dep	...	...	...	8 47	...	...	...	1 34	...	...	...	...	6 51	...	...	...	...	...
...	„ Bayer Bhf.dep	...	5 21	6 4	7 5	...	8 51	11 34	12 45	...	2 55	...	5 27	5 59	...	6 55	...	9 27	11 35	...
...	Gaschwitz	...	5 34	6 38	7 16	...	9 5	11 46	1 0	...	3 8	...	5 48	6 15	...	7 14	p.m.	9 39	11 47	...
...	**Kieritzsch**............	...	5 51	7 0	7 27	...	9 22	12 4	1 25	...	3 29	...	6 18	6 33	...	7 31	9 †19	9 56	12 4	...
...	Borna...	...	6 4	7 12	7 35	...	9 34	12 17	1 41	...	3 42	...	6 29	6 47	...	—	9 34	10 8	12 15	...
...	Frohburg	...	6 17	—	7 45	...	9 50	12 32	—	...	3 56	...	—	7 2	...	...	—	10 21	12 29	...
...	**Geithain**	a.m.	6 36	...	7 59	9 36	10 10	12 53	...	...	4 17	p.m.	...	7 21	...	p.m.	...	10 40	12 52	...
...	**Narsdorf**........a.m.	5†38	6 50	...	8 8	...	10 25	1 4	...	...	4 30	4 42	p.m.	7 46	7 39	9 11	...	10 52	1 6	...
...	Wittgensdorf 5 50	6 14	7 27	...	8 39	...	11 5	1 39	...	...	...	5 18	7 41	8 24	...	9 52	...	11 27	1 40	...
...	**Chemnitz**...arr 6 10	6 34	7 47	...	8 51	1019	11 23	1 59	...	2 52	5 10	5 38	8 3	8 44	8 13	1013	...	11 46	1 58	...

Frohburg......dep	7 a‡2	9 a55	1 p32	4 p52	7 p10	Kohren......dep	5a42	8 a 8	11a55	3 p18	6 p4
Kohren ....arr	7 30	10 23	2 0	5 20	7 38	Frohburg ...arr	6 10	8 36	12 23	3 49	6 32

‡—Weekdays only.

KIERITZSCH and PEGAU.

Kieritzsch.....................dep	5 a35	7 a32	9 a56	2 p53	7 p9	...	Pegau ....dep	6 a33	8 a27	12 p3	5 p12	8 p22	...
Groitzsch	6 7	8 5	10 37	3 40	7 49	...	Groitzsch	6 50	8 43	12 32	5 39	8 43	...
Pegau ....arr	6 21	8 19	10 51	3 56	8 3	...	Kieritzsch ....arr	7 20	9 15	1 8	6 14	9 14	...

*—4.36 a.m. on Sunday.

LEIPSIC and GEITHAIN.

Leipsic Dresd.dep	4*48	5a20	7a1	8a47	11a29	12p23	2p49	5p58	6p39	9p10	11p29
Liebertwolkwitz	5 10	5 35	7 26	9 1	11 51	12 45	3 15	6 21	7 9	9 36	11 52
Lausig	—	6 6	7 57	9 23	12 24	—	3 47	6 55	7 39	1012	—
Geithain 184A arr	...	6 26	9 5	9 35	12 44	...	4 8	7 15	...	1032	...

Geithain	...	6a40	...	9a11	1028	...	1p15	4p37	...	9 p9
Lausig ...	...	6 56	8a47	9 24	1045	...	1 32	4 54	...	9 28
Liebertw	6a1	7 26	9 23	...	1117	1p15	2 6	5 23	7p10	10 2
Leipsic...	625	7 46	9 45	9 58	1138	1 38	2 27	5 36	7 33	1024

KLINGENBERG-COLMNITZ and FRAUENSTEIN.

Klingenberg dep	7a24	10a42	4p 5	9p20	Frauenstein......dep	5a50	9 a0	2p10	7p26
Frauenstein arr	8 30	11 58	5 21	1046	Klingenberg 186 arr	6 57	10 3	3 24	8 40

PIRNA and GROSSCOTTA.

Pirna ....dep	6a39	9 a0	1 p21	6p36	...	...	...	...	...	Grosscotta...arr	7a20	12p 2	3p33	7 p18	...	...	...	...	...
Grosscotta ...arr	7 14	9 50	2 5	7 7	...	...	...	...	...	Pirna ....dep	7 55	12 43	4 20	7 49	...	...	...	...	...

WILSDRUFF and MEISSEN TRIEBISCHTHAL.

Wilsdruff ....dep	5 a34	8 a20	11a34	4 p15	7 p42	**Meissen Triebischthal**...dep	7 a10	10a13	2 p36	6 p6	9 p56	...	...
Garsebach	6 21	9 6	12 22	5 12	8 31	Garsebach	7 26	10 30	2 53	6 20	1011	...	...
Meissen Triebischthal ...arr	637	9 19	12 35	5 27	8 44	**Wilsdruff 186**..................arr	8 19	11 19	3 41	7 8	11 0	...	...

Meissen Triebischthal...dep	6 a30	9a33	12p27	5 p55	9 p18	Lommatzsch ....dep	4a39	7a56	11 a0	1 p57	7 p43
Lothain	6 44	9 47	12 44	6 10	9 33	Lothain	5 36	8 52	11 56	2 55	8 43
Lommatzsch 183A ....arr	7 42	1044	1 43	7 11	10 31	Meissen Triebischthal...arr	5 50	9 5	12 9	3 8	8 56

DÖBELN and LOMMATZSCH.

Döbeln...........................dep	6 a0	9a50	5 p25	...	...	...	**Lommatzsch** ....dep	7 a48	2 p5	7 p35	...	...	...
Gärtitz	6 14	10 0	5 39	...	...	...	Gärtitz	9 8	3 34	9 4	...	...	...
Lommatzsch (184A)......arr	7 34	11 15	7 0	...	...	...	**Döbeln** (183A) ....arr	9 18	3 44	9 14	...	...	...

Thum ....dep	4 a42	8 a0	11a11	2p38	6 p26	9p20	Meinersdorf.......................dep	5 a45	10a18	1 p44	4 p0	7 p37	10p31
Meinersdorf (185)..............arr	5 33	8 58	12 9	3 29	7 17	1011	Thum (190) ....arr	6 49	11 10	2 37	5 6	8 43	11 23

Luggage Rates—see page 462.]

SAXONY STATE RAILWAYS.

CHEMNITZ, ADORF, and KLINGENTHAL.

	night	a.m.	a.m.	a.m.	a.m.	a.m.	p.m.	p.m.	p.m.	p.m.
Chemnitz (Haupt) dep	12 0	4 24	6 30	8 10	9 19	1045	1253	3 0	6 28	9 43
Einsiedel	1224	4 46	...	8 35	9 43	...	1 10	3 23	6 54	...
Meinersdorf	1252	5 20	7 10	9 6	10 12	...	1 39	3 53	7 23	10 25
Thalheim	1 1	5 30	7 20	9 16	10 21	1135	1 47	4 2	7 33	10 34
Zwönitz (185)	1 20	6 0	7 38	9 35	10 42	1154	2 6	4 22	7 53	10 56
Aue (189A)...arr	1 45	6 26	8 1	10 0	11 8	1217	2 29	4 48	8 17	11 21
" ...dep	—	6 33	8 18	—	11 30	1226	2 40	5 6	8 30	11 28
Wolfsgrün		6 59	8 44	...	11 59	...	3 8	5 35	8 56	11 55
Eibenstock		7 11	8 54	...	12 11	1253	3 19	5 48	9 8	12 5
Schönheiderhammer		7 19	9 1	...	12 18	1259	3 27	5 58	9 14	12 12
Wilzschhaus **185**	a.m.	7 32	9 14	p.m.	12 29	...	3 38	6 12	9 24	12 21
Muldenberg	5 3	8 0	9 43	2 55	12 55	1 28	4 6	6 43	9 51	—
Schöneck	5 16	8 13	9 58	3 12	1 9	1 42	4 19	6 59	1011	...
Zwotental.. arr	5 25	8 22	10 4	3 21	1 18	...	4 27	7 9	1022	a.m.
Zwotental dp	6 48	9 20	1010	3 23	1 28	...	4 32	7 27	1028	1 33
Klingthal arr	7 11	9 43	1029	3 46	1 51	...	4 55	7 50	1051	1 56
Zwotental..dep	5 32	8 29	10 9	3 25	1 25	...	4 29	7 20	1031	—
Markneukirchen	5 49	8 45	1026	3 41	1 40	2 3	4 43	7 35	1047	...
Adorf (188) arr	5 57	8 52	1033	3 48	1 47	2 10	4 50	7 43	1055	...

		a.m.	a.m.	a.m.	a.m.	p.m.	p.m.	p.m.
Adorf ...dep		5 0	8 0	8 33	10 45	2 20	6 46	8 46
Markneukirchen		5 8	8 7	8 44	10 53	2 29	6 57	8 54
Zwotental..arr		5 31	8 27	9 7	11 16	2 52	7 19	9 16
Klingthal dep		4 47	8 0	8 37	11 1	2 25	6 47	8 45
Zwotental ar		5 23	8 25	9 11	11 22	2 54	7 13	9 11
Zwotental..dep		5 35	8 29	9 16	11 24	2 58	7 25	9 17
Schöneck		5 49	8 42	9 32	11 39	3 13	7 40	9 31
Muldenberg	a.m.	6 3	8 53	9 46	11 51	3 24	7 52	9 43
Wilzschhaus	5 30	6 38	9 13	10 12	12 30	3 51	8 18	1010
Schönheider	5 39	6 53	9 22	10 21	12 43	4 0	8 27	1020
Eibenstock	5 49	7 7	9 30	10 30	12 55	4 10	8 37	1030
Wolfsgrün	5 57	7 16	9 38	10 38	1 3	4 18	8 45	1038
Aue...arr	6 23	7 43	10 4	11 4	1 29	4 43	9 17	11 6
" ...dep	6 32	8 3	1010	11 16	1 40	4 54	9 58	—
Zwönitz	7 5	8 36	1039	11 52	2 8	5 28	1034	...
Thalheim	7 21	8 55	...	12 12	2 22	5 47	1051	...
Meinersdorf	7 29	9 5	...	12 20	...	5 55	1059	...
Einsiedel	...	9 33	...	12 49	2 49	6 20	1127	...
Chemnitz	8 0	9 55	1127	1 6	3 5	6 38	1148	...

Extra.

Adorf ...dep	9a43	1 p1	12a49
Zwotental ...arr	10 3	1 24	1 26

Zwotental...dep	12p18
Adorf ...arr	12 46

Aue...dep	4a43	2p34
Chemnitz arr	6 15	4 22

PIRNA and ARNSDORF.

Pirna ...dep	5a40	7a43	8a44	12p4	2p48	6p38	8p33	10 p8	...	...
Dürrröhrsdf.	6 5	8 8	9 8	1229	3 13	7 4	8 57	10 33	...	...
Arnsdorf arr	6 21	...	9 25	1248	3 34	7 28	9 14	...	...	...

Arnsd'rf	6a43	...	10p35	1p22	3p51	pm	6p40	...	10p22	...	...
Dürrröh.	6 57	8 a9	10 49	1 36	4 5	533	6 57	9p0	10 36	...	...
Pirna 188	7 19	8 32	11 11	1 58	4 27	556	...	923	10 58	...	...

NEUSTADT and DURRROHRSDORF.

Neustadt ...dep	4a54	7a28	10a2	2p28	4p49	8p15	...	...
Durrohrsdorf ...arr	5 30	8 5	1039	3 7	5 26	8 52	...	...

Durrohrsdorf dep	6 a9	8 12	1236	3p30	7 p6	10p40	...	...	...
Neustadt...arr	6 49	8 52	1 16	4 10	7 46	11 19	...	...	...

Durrrohrsdorf ...dep	5a51	8 a20	12p35	5p50	...
Weissig-Buhlau...arr	6 43	9 22	1 37	6 57	...

Weissig-Buhlau dep	7a10	9a33	2p 1	7‡30	...
Durrohrsdorf ...arr	8 2	1044	3 2	8 36	...

‡—9.21 p.m. on Sunday.

KAMENZ and ARNSDORF.

Kamenz dep	5a42	8a38	12p12	3 p0	5p21	7p13	9p24	10p30	...	...
Arnsdorf arr	6 24	9 22	12 51	3 38	5 59	7 59	10 8	11 18	...	...

Arnsdorf dep	6a54	10a38	1p23	3p52	6p15	8p13	9p27	12a14	...	...
Kamenz 183A	7 35	11 19	1 59	4 31	6 50	8 53	1013	12 54	...	...

BISCHOFSWERDA and KAMENZ.

Bischofswerda dep	7a25	9a45	1p40	4p20	9 p13	...	...
Elstra	8 10	1033	2 28	5 30	10 0	...	...
Kamenz ...arr	8 34	1059	2 56	6 6	10 25	...	...

Kamenz ...dep	5a45	7a43	11a30	2p3	7p2	...	...
Elstra	6 17	8 9	11 58	230	736	...	...
Bischofswerda	7 3	8 54	12 44	321	827	...	...

PIRNA and GOTTLEUBA.

Pirna ...dep	7a32	10a22	1p36	5 p6	8p42	...	...
Berggiesshubel	8 30	11 27	2 42	6 3	9 43	...	...
Gottleuba arr	8 41	11 37	2 53	6 13	9 54	...	...

Gottleuba dep	5a52	8a55	1154	3p21	7p13	...	...	...
Berggiesshubel...	6 2	9 5	12 4	3 33	7 25	...	...	...
Pirna (185) arr	6 55	9 58	1258	4 32	8 23	...	...	...

STOLLBERG and ST. EGIDIEN.

Stollberg ...dep	6a30	9a10	12p8	2p34	6p14	9p 0	...	...	...
Neuölsnitz	6 43	9 24	1222	2 47	6 27	9 16	...	...	...
Lichtenstein-C.	7 6	9 48	1246	3 11	6 52	9 42	...	...	...
St. Egidien arr	7 13	9 55	1253	3 18	6 59	9 49	...	...	...

St. Egidien ...dep	7a49	10a45	1p28	4 p5	7p56	1012	...	...	...
Lichtenstein-Calb'g	7 58	10 56	1 38	4 16	8 6	1021	...	...	...
Neuölsnitz	8 27	11 28	2 10	4 45	8 33	1049	...	...	...
Stollberg 189 ...arr	8 39	11 40	2 22	4 57	8 45	11 1	...	...	...

‡—Not on Sunday.

HAINSBERG and KIPSDORF.

Hainsberg dep	6a35	9 a25	12p25	2p32	4p21	7 p1	9 p15	12a8	...
Dippoldiswalde	7 28	10 14	1 20	3 22	5 3	7 53	10 9	1257	...
Schmiedeberg...	7 56	10 42	1 46	3 48	5 23	8 22	10 35	1 21	...
Kipsdorf ...arr	8 10	10 56	2 0	4 2	5 35	8 36	10 49	1 35	...

Kipsdorf ...dep	4a45	7a40	9 a30	12p10	2p37	4p22	6 p3	9 p0	...
Schmiedeberg	4 59	7 54	9 44	12 25	2 52	4 39	6 19	9 16	...
Dippoldiswalde	5 26	8 16	10 13	12 52	3 20	5 2	6 47	9 44	...
Hainsberg...arr	6 14	9 1	11 1	1 41	4 8	5 45	7 37	10 38	...

WILKAU and WILZSCHHAUS.

Wilkau dep	5a17	8 a7	9a23	11a36	1p35	3p14	4p35	6p15	7p26	10p2	1138
Kirchberg...	5 46	8 34	9 58	12 5	2 5	3 49	5 6	6 49	8 5	1032	12 5
Saupersdorf	6 7	—	1020	—	—	4 11	—	7 10	—	1053	—
Rothenk'h'n	6 46	...	1114	...	...	5 2	...	8 4	...	1136	...
Schonheide	7 10	...	1148	...	...	5 36	...	8 32	...	1159	...
Wilzsch'aus	7 29	...	1210	...	...	5 57	...	9 17	...	...	...

Wilzschhaus dp	a.m.	...	7a52	...	1235	...	...	...	6p15	8p25
Schonheide...	4 25	...	8 17	...	1 0	...	...	...	6 41	9 5
Rothenkirchen	4 48	...	8 42	...	1 25	...	...	...	7 6	9 30
Saupersdorf ...	5 25	a.m.	9 22	p.m.	2 5	p.m.	p.m.	p.m.	7 51	1011
Kirchberg 4a40	5 55	8 40	9 51	1247	2 33	3 43	5 15	6 50	8 21	1038
Wilkau arr 5 6	6 18	9 3	1015	1 14	2 55	4 5	5 41	7 14	8 46	11 5

Wilzschhaus dep	7a40	9a18	12p40	6 p18	9 p28	...
Carlsfeld ...arr	8 20	9 59	1 21	6 59	10 9	...

Carlsfeld...dep	5 a58	8a32	11a44	2 p58	7 p30	...
Wilzschhaus ...arr	6 34	10 8	12 20	3 34	8 6	...

WEIDA and MEHLTHEUER.

Weida 173...dep	7a29	10a26	12p55	3p35	6p49	10p23
Triebes	8 2	10 58	1 28	4 9	7 21	10 56
Pausa	8 28	11 25	1 55	4 38	7 48	11 24
Mehltheuer 187 arr	8 43	11 40	2 10	4 53	8 3	11 39

Mehltheuer dep	6 a5	9 a6	12 p3	2p27	5p34	8p20	...
Pausa	6 19	9 20	12 23	2 41	5 49	8 34	...
Triebes	6 43	9 46	12 49	3 5	6 14	9 0	...
Weida ...arr	7 11	1016	1 21	3 34	6 44	9 30	...

†—Weekdays only.]

WERDAU and WEIDA.

	a.m.	a.m.		p.m.	p.m.	p.m.	p.m.		p.m.
Werdau ...dep	5 46	8 39	...	1221	2 22	5 21	6 47	...	1032
Teichwolframsdorf	6 6	8 58	...	1243	2 40	5 41	7 7	...	1050
Seelingstädt	6 22	9 13	a.m.	1259	2 53	5 55	—	p.m.	11 3
Wünschendorf 184	6 52	9 49	1146	1 31	3 23	6 30	7 p8	9 48	1130
Weida 173 ...arr	7 1	9 58	1155	1 39	3 31	6 39	7 17	9 57	1139

		a.m.	a.m.	a.m.	a.m.	p.m.	p.m.	p.m.	p.m.	p.m.	p.m
Weida ...dep	...	5 8	7 20	1028	1126	1 23	3 12	3 37	6 47	7 51	9 33
Wünschendf	...	5 21	7 27	1043	1135	1 30	3 23	4 57	6 55	8 3	9 41
Seelingstädt	a.m.	5 48	8 41	1112	—	—	3 51	5 25	—	8 31	—
Teichwolfra.	5 †9	6 5	8 57	1128	...	...	4 6	5 40	7p28	8 46	...
Werdau ...ar	5 29	6 22	9 13	1147	...	...	4 22	6 0	7 48	9 3	...

STOLLBERG and SCHEIBENBERG.

Stollberg ...dep	5 a15	8 a48	11a10	3p33	7 p6
Zwönitz ...arr	5 55	9 27	11 49	4 13	7 46
Scheibenberg arr	7 36	...	1 31	5 54	9 38

Scheibenberg ...dep	5 a40	...	10 a1	3 p46	8 p45
Zwönitz ...dep	7 11	9 a37	11 54	5 30	10 14
Stollberg (185)...arr	7 51	10 17	12 34	6 10	11 38

SAXONY STATE RAILWAYS.

GORLITZ, DRESDEN, CHEMNITZ, and REICHENBACH.

BRESLAU (179A)...dep	...	11 p3	...	...	...	11p8	...	...	...	...	...	6a11	8 a50	...	...	...	...	11a40	...	11a40	...	1217	...	3p45	6 p4	...	...	6 p4	...
	1—4	Ex 3	Ex 3	1—4	1—4	1—4	Ex 3	Ex 3	2 3 4	1,2,3	1—4	Ex3	Ex 3	1—4	1—4	Ex3	1—4	Ex 3	1—4	1—4	1—4	1—4	1—4	1—4	Ex 3	1,2,3	1—4	1—4	2&3
		a.m.		a.m.	a.m.	a.m.			a.m.	a.m.	a.m.	a.m.	a.m.	p.m.	a.m.			p.m.	p.m.	p.m.	p.m.	p.m.	p.m.	p.m.	p.m.			p.m.	p.m.
Görlitz ....dep	...	2 0	...	...	...	4 17	...	...	...	...	7 46	8 58	11 15	...	1121	...	...	2 11	...	2 20	...	4 24	...	6 58	8 53	...	...	9 7	1152
Löbau	...	2 25	...	...	...	4 59	...	...	...	7 31	8 30	9 23	...	...	1148	...	...	2 36	...	3 6	...	5 7	...	7 43	9 15	...	...	9 51	1248
Bautzen	...	2 46	...	3 54	...	5 36	...	...	6 46	8 9	9 8	9 44	RC	...	1224	...	...	2 57	...	3 43	...	5 42	...	8 20	9 35	...	...	1026	1 36
Bischofswerda	...	...	...	4 24	6 2	6 9	...	...	7 15	9 3	9 40	...	...	1238	1257	...	...	...	3 26	4 15	5 52	6 13	7 50	8 54	...	...	...	11 1	
Arnsdorf	...	SC	...	4 47	6 19	6 29	...	...	7 42	...	10 0	...	...	1256	1 20	...	...	RC	3 47	4 39	6 10	6 35	8 11	9 19	RC	...	...	1124	...
Klotzsche..........	...	...	...	5 8	...	...	...	...	8 4	...	...	...	...	...	...	...	...	...	...	...	...	...	...	...	...	...	...	1147	...
Dresden Neustadt arr	...	3 37	...	5 16	6 45	6 54	...	...	8 13	9 35	1025	1035	...	1 20	1 47	...	...	3 51	4 13	5 5	6 35	7 1	8 35	9 45	10 22	...	...	1156	...
" " dep	...	3 44	...	5 19	6 47	6 57	...	...	8 15	9 36	1028	1038	...	1 24	1 50	...	...	3 54	4 15	5 9	6 37	7 6	8 39	9 48	10 25	...	...	1158	...
" Haupt. ...arr	...	3 50	...	5 28	6 56	7 7	...	...	8 24	9 43	1037	1044	12 42	1 33	1 59	...	...	4 0	4 24	5 18	6 46	7 15	8 48	9 57	10 31	...	...	12 7	...
	a.m.		a.m.	a.m.			a.m.	a.m.	a.m.		p.m.	a.m.	p.m.		p.m.	p.m.	p.m.	p.m.	p.m.		p.m.	p.m.			p.m.	p.m.	p.m.	a.m.	
Dresden Haupt....dep	4 10	...	5 40	6 30	...	...	7 20	8 30	9§20	...	1220	1111	12 54	...	3 0	4 10	5 5	6 0	6 28	...	8 0	8 35	...	...	10 45	1055	1140	1 50	...
Potschappel	4 21	...	...	...	...	...	...	...	...	...	...	...	...	...	...	...	...	...	6 45	...	...	...	...	...	...	...	1154	2 4	...
Hainsberg	4 30	...	...	...	...	...	...	...	...	...	...	...	...	...	...	...	...	RC	6 55	...	...	...	...	...	SC	...	12 4	2 14	...
Tharandt..........	4 38	...	...	6 52	...	...	...	...	9 41	...	1243	RC	RC	...	3 23	...	5 26	...	7 6	...	8 17	8 56	...	...	...	...	1213	2 24	...
Klingenberg C..........	5 7	...	...	7 21	...	...	...	RC	1010	...	1 12	...	...	...	3 52	...	5 55	...	7 34	...	...	9 25	...	...	...	...	1243	2 51	...
Freiberg	5 33	...	6 30	7 48	...	...	8 13	...	1036	...	1 50	12 2	...	...	4 19	5 3	6 22	6 53	7 55	...	8 52	9 52	...	...	...	1147	1 5	3 16	...
Flöha..........	6 18	...	6 50	8 48	...	...	8 41	...	1119	...	2 33	1231	...	...	5 4	5 32	7 6	7 24		...	9 21	1040	...	...	...	1221		3 56	...
Niederwiesa	6 26	...	...	8 55	...	2 3 4	...	...	1126	...	2 40	...	...	...	5 11	...	7 13	...	...	2,3,4	...	1047	...	...	...	...	...	4 3	...
Chemnitz Hpt. { arr	6 41	...	7 12	9 9	...	a.m.	8 58	9 58	1138	...	2 52	1245	2 20	p.m.	5 25	5 47	7 25	7 41	...	p.m.	9 36	11 0	...	...	12 12	1236	...	4 15	...
{ dep	6 52	...	7 17	9 18	...	1036	9 3	10 0	1223	...	3 5	1250	2 22	4 20	6 17	5 50	7 51	7 45	...	9 12	9 40	1120	...	...	12 15	1240	...	4 25	...
Wüstenbrand..........	7 23	...	...	9 51	...	11 7	...	...	1249	...	3 41	...	...	4 53	6 48	...	8 26	...	...	9 44	...	1151	...	...	...	...	...	4 58	...
Hohenstein-Ernstthal. .	7 30	...	7 38	9 58	...	1114	...	...	1257	...	3 49	...	...	5 0	6 56	6 10	8 34	8 9	...	9 52	10 0	1159	...	...	...	...	...	5 6	...
St. Egidien ....a.m.	7 39	...	7 47	10 9	...	1123	...	...	1 7	...	4 0	...	...	5 9	7 7	...	8 44	...	...	10 1	10 8	12 9	...	...	...	...	...	5 16	...
Glauchau ....arr 6 55	7 48	...	7 55	1018	...	1132	9 35	10 30	1 16	...	4 8	1 23	...	5 18	7 15	6 25	8 53	8 23	...	10 10	10 16	1218	...	...	...	1 12	...	5 25	...
Mosel..........7 7		...	...	1052	...		...	...	1 47	...	4 24	...	...		7 30	...	9 13	...	...	10 34	...	1235	...	...	...	...	...	5 52	...
Zwickau..........arr 7 23	...	...	8 12	11 8	...	...	9 54	10 48	2 0	...	4 35	1 44	...	...	7 43	6 44	9 30	8 42	...	10 50	10 34	1246	...	...	1 0	1 31	...	6 8	...
Neumark	...	...	8 32	1142	...	...	10 13	...	2 29	...	5 6	...	...	...	8 14	...	9 58	9 5	...	...	10 53	1 3[illegible]	...	...	...	...	...	6 41	...
Reichenbach......arr	...	...	8 43	1155	...	...	10 24	11 14	2 42	...	5 19	2 15	3 29	...	8 27	7 8	1011	9 17	...	12†54	11 3	1 45	...	...	1 25	2 0	...	6 53	...
HOF (187) ....arr	...	...	10a23	...	...	...	11a50	12 34	4p48	...	9p13	3p46	4 p48	...	11p8	...	1256	11 p8	...	...	...	...	...	...	2 a43	3a55	...	9a50	...
EGER (188)..........arr	...	...	12p14	...	...	...	2 p11	2 p11	8p18	...	10p5	5 p0	8 p18	...	...	10p5	2 a3	2 a3	...	...	2 a3	...	...	...	...	5a30	...	...	...
MUNICH (203) ......arr	...	...	3 p58	...	...	...	6 p14	6 p14	...	...	...	1010	10p10	...	...	...	...	7 a20	...	...	...	...	...	...	7 a50	...	...	...	...

Extra.—Mosel to Zwickau 8.14, 11.10 a.m., 5.26, 10.11 p.m.

†—Via Werdau.:

§—1—4 class.

POTSCHAPPEL and WILSDRUFF.

	a.m.	a.m.	a.m.	a.m.	p.m.	p.m.	p.m.	p.m.	p.m	nigt.
Potschappel ....dep	6 20	7 46	9 20	10 53	1 38	3 38	4 55	6 56	8 32	12 5
Wilsdruff ....arr	6 59	8 18	9 58	11 32	2 16	4 11	5 35	7 38	9 11	12 44

	a.m.	a.m.	a.m.	a.m.	a.m.	p.m.	p.m.	p.m.	p.m.	p.m.		
Wilsdruff ....dep	5 10	6 31	8 26	9 30	11 38	2 17	3 43	5 6	7 10	11 5	...	...
Potschappel 186......arr	5 49	7 11	9 5	10 4	12 19	2 50	4 22	5 48	7 47	11 48	...	...

NOSSEN and WILSDRUFF.

	a.m.	a.m.	p.m.	p.m.	p.m.	p.m.				
Nossen ....dep	...	9 32	...	1 50	5 24	9 15	...	...	...	...
Mohorn..........	7 40	10 45	1 35	2 57	6 26	10 21	...	...	...	...
Wilsdruff ....arr	8 15	11 24	2 11	3 33	7 2	10 57	...	...	...	...

	a.m.	a.m.	a.m.	p.m.	p.m.	p.m.							
Wilsdruff..........dep	7 3	10 3	11 40	2 21	5 44	9 17	...	...	...	...	...	...	...
Mohorn..........	7 42	10 43	12 16	2 58	6 30	9 53	...	...	...	...	...	...	...
Nossen..........arr	8 43	11 44	...	3 55	7 32	...	...	...	...	...	...	...	...

LIMBACH and WUSTENBRAND.

	a.m.	a.m.	p.m.	p.m.	p.m.					
Limbach ....dep	6 15	9 5	12 2	2 45	6 55	...	...	...	...	...
Wustenbrand..........arr	7 0	9 39	12 36	3 20	7 39	...	...	...	...	...

	a.m.	a.m.	p.m.	p.m.	p.m.							
Wustenbrand..........dep	8 10	9 56	1 32	4 0	8 18	...	...	...	...	...	...	...
Limbach 189..........arr	8 45	10 30	2 6	4 34	8 52	...	...	...	...	...	...	...

REICHENBACH, CHEMNITZ, DRESDEN, and GORLITZ.

MUNICH (202) ......dep	7p20	...	...	...	...	...	1120	...	...	1120	...	...	...	...	...	...
EGER (188A)........dep	10p0	...	...	...	...	...	...	...	...	...	...	...	4a43	7a46	...	...
HOF (187)............dep	1a20	...	...	...	...	...	4a45	...	...	5 a8	...	...	...	7a50	...	...
	Ex3	1—4	2 3 4	1—4	2 3 4	1—4	Ex3	1,2,3	1—4	1,2,3	Ex 3	1—4	1,2,3	Ex3	2 3 4	1—4
	a.m.				a.m.	a.m.	a.m.		a.m.	a.m.		a.m.	a.m.	a.m.		
Reichenbach......dep	2 42	...	...	...	...	4 22	6 1	...	6 10	6 40	...	...	9 7	1017	...	...
Neumark	...	...	...	...	...	4 35	...	...	6 21	6 51	...	...	9 18	1028	...	...
Zwickau ....dep	3 7	...	...	...	5 55	4 55	6 27	...	6 44	7 8	...	8 19	9 42	1042	...	...
Mosel....................	...	...	...	...	6 10	5 5	...	...	6 59	...	...	8 34	9 53	...	a.m.	...
Glauchau (189) ......dep	3 26	...	...	...		5 20	6 43	...	7 14	7 29	...	8 50	1013	1058	1150	...
St. Egidien (185)	...	...	...	...	...	5 29	...	...	7 26	...	...	9 0	1025	...	12 1	...
Hohenstein-Ernstthal...	3 44	...	...	...	...	5 41	...	...	7 50	7 46	...	9 12	1038	RC	1214	...
Wüstenbrand	...	...	...	...	...	5 48	...	...	7 58	...	...	9 21	1047	...	1223	...
Chemnitz Hpt. arr	4 8	...	...	a.m.	...	6 14	7 12	...	8 26	8 5	...	9 48	1115	1132	1250	...
Chemnitz Hpt. dep	4 13	...	...	4 17	...	6 32	7 15	...	9 2	8 10	...		1140	1134		...
Niederwiesa	...	...	...	4 32	...	6 44	...	...	9 14	...	...	...	1156	...	...	...
Flöha......................	...	...	...	4 40	a.m.	6 51	...	...	9 24	8 26	...	...	12 6	1147	...	...
Freiberg (190)............	5 0	...	...	5 33	6 40	7 40	7 55	...	1014	9 5	...	...	1259	1220	...	...
Klingenberg Col.	...	...	a.m.	5 56	7 7	8 24	...	...	1038	...	...	...	1 22	...	...	...
Tharandt	...	...	5 48	6 16	7 28	8 44	...	...	11 0	...	...	...	1 42	...	...	...
Hainsberg (185)	...	...	5 55	...	7 34	...	...	...	11 7	...	...	...	...	...	...	...
Potschappel	...	...	6 6	...	7 43	...	...	...	...	...	...	...	...	...	...	...
Dresden Haupt....arr	5 45	...	6 18	6 33	7 54	9 0	8 35	...	1121	9 48	...	...	2 0	1 3	1—4	...
	a.m.	a.m.		a.m.	a.m.		a.m.	a.m.			a.m.	p.m.	p.m.		p.m.	p.m.
Dresden Haupt....dep	6 §2	6 16	...	7 0	8§58	...	8 45	8 50	...	...	10 19	1221	3 3	...	1 24	3 35
" Neustadt arr	6 11	6 24	...	7 8	9 6	...	8 51	8 56	...	...	10 25	1230	3 11	...	1 33	3 43
" " dep	6 14	6 27	...	7 11	9 9	...	8 53	8 58	...	...	10 30	1235	3 14	...	1 35	3 46
Klotzsche..................	...	...	...	7 25	9 23	...	RC	...	...	...	...	...	...	...	...	...
Arnsdorf ....2&3	6 47	...	..	7 54	9 50	...	...	...	...	...	RC	1 8	3 46	...	...	...
Bischofswerda ......a.m.	7 14	7 16	...	8 21	1017	...	9 30	9 35	...	...	...	1 34	4 10	...	2 22	4 32
Bautzen 4 25	7 46		...	8 46	1046	...	9 47		...	...	11 27	2 4	4 39	...		
Löbau 5 20	8 25	...	...		1124	...	10 9	...	...	...	11 50	2 41	5 15	...	...	...
Görlitz arr6 36	9 3	...	...	...	12 1	...	1031	...	...	...	12 14	3 19	5 51	...	...	...
BRESLAU 179 ......arr	1 p2	...	...	...	3p14	...	1p47	...	...	...	3 p14	7p38	9p19	...	...	...

MUNICH (202) ......dep	...	...	8a25	...	...	...	9a25	...	...	...	...	1235	12p35	...	...
EGER (188A)........dep	8a10	...	1127	...	...	...	1p30	...	...	...	2p34	4p39	4 p39	...	6p33
HOF (187)............dep	7a50	...	1p15	...	...	...	2p56	...	...	...	4p40	6p30	6 p30	7p10	...
	1—4	1,2,3	Ex3	Ex3	1,2,3	1—4	Ex3	1—4	1,2,3	1—4	1—4	Ex3	1—4	2 3 4	Ex3
	a.m.	p.m.	p m		p.m.		p.m	p.m.			p.m.	p.m.	p.m.	p.m.	p.m.
Reichenbach......dep	1138	1 55	2 28	...	2 6	...	4 30	4 55	...	...	6 37	8 0	8 38	9†47	1048
Neumark	1152	...	...	...	2 19	...	4 40	5 7	...	...	6 49	8 10	8 51	...	...
Zwickau ....dep	1228	2 20	2 51	...	2 58	...	4 56	5 34	...	...	7 13	8 25	9 19	1140	1110
Mosel....................	1239	...	...	...	3 8	...	...	5 45	p.m.	...	7 24	...	9 35	1156	...
Glauchau (189) ......dep	1255	2 37	...	...	3 25	...	5 13	6 8	6 36	...	7 38	8 41	9 54	1218	1126
St. Egidien (185)	1 7	2 46	...	...	3 36	...	...	6 19	6 45	...	7 49	...	10 8	1230	...
Hohenstein-Ernstthal...	1 19	2 57	RC	...	3 48	...	5 31	6 32	6 56	...	8 3	RC	10 23	1243	...
Wüstenbrand	1 28	...	...	...	3 56	...	...	6 41	...	...	...	...	10 33	1251	...
Chemnitz Hpt. arr	1 56	3 15	3 34	...	4 23	...	5 50	7 10	7 17	...	8 25	9 15	11 1	1 19	1155
Chemnitz Hpt. dep	2 6	3 20	3 39	...	4 36	...	5 54	7 25		...	9 45	9 19	12 5	2 5	1158
Niederwiesa	2 17	...	...	...	4 47	...	...	7 36	...	...	9 56	...	12 19	2 19	...
Flöha......................	2 25	...	...	...	4 56	...	6 10	7 43	...	p.m.	10 6	9 33	12 29	2 25	...
Freiberg (190)............	3 14	4 10	...	...	5 45	...	6 46	8 31	...	8 43	1056	10 7	1 17		1241
Klingenberg Col.	3 39	...	...	...	6 10	...	...	8 50	...	9 8	1119	...	1 41	...	...
Tharandt	3 57	...	...	...	6 30	...	RC	9 6	...	9 32	1139	...	1 59	...	...
Hainsberg (185)	...	...	...	...	...	...	...	...	...	9 40	...	...	2 5	...	...
Potschappel	...	...	...	...	...	...	...	...	...	9 49	...	...	2 13	...	...
Dresden Haupt....arr	4 13	4 50	5 0	...	6 49	...	7 28	9 22	...	10 1	1155	1047	2 25	...	1 21
	p.m.		p.n.	p.m.	p.m.	p.m.	p.m.	p.m.			a.m.				a.m.
Dresden Haupt....dep	5 20	...	5 9	7 38	8 §0	8 35	9 34	1058	...	...	1220	...	...	...	1 33
" Neustadt arr	5 29	...	5 15	7 44	8 8	8 43	9 42	11 4	...	...	1228	...	...	...	1 39
" " dep	5 31	...	5 19	7 46	8 10	8 46	9 45	11 6	...	...	1231	...	...	...	1 45
Klotzsche..................	5 45	...	...	...	...	...	...	...	...	...	1244	...	...	...	...
Arnsdorf ....2&3	6 12	...	...	...	8 45	9 24	1018	...	...	p.m.	1 10	...	...	...	SC
Bischofswerda ......a.m.	6 38	...	...	...	9 11	9 43	1045	1143	...	1147	1 37	...	...	...	...
Bautzen 4 25	7 6	...	6 10	...	9 40		1115		...	1210	2 1	...	...	...	2 36
Löbau 5 20	7 43	...	6 31	...	1018	...	1153	...	...			...	...	...	2 56
Görlitz arr6 36	8 19	...	6 52	9 5	1056	...	1230	...	...	...	...	...	...	...	3 17
BRESLAU 179 ......arr	...	...	9p30	1127	...	...	5a50	...	...	...	...	...	...	...	6 a0

Extra.—Zwickau to Mosel 9.0 a.m., 1.25, 6.7 p.m. §—1—4 class. †—Via Werdau. RC—Restaurant Car. SC—Sleeping Car.

BISCHOFSWERDA and ZITTAU.

		a.m.	a.m.			a.m.	a.m.	a.m.		p.m.	p.m.		p.m.		p.m.	p.m.		
Bischofswerda dep	...	...	7 20	...	...	9 36	...	1040	...	2 26	4 37	...	6 41	...	9 47	1144	...	...
Niederneukirch	...	...	7 39	...	...	...	...	11 1	...	2 44	4 57	...	7 0	...	10 6	...	...	...
Wilthen	...	...	7 56	...	...	...	...	1120	...	3 0	5 15	...	7 16	...	1025	...	...	...
Taubenheim	...	...	8 16	...	a.m.	...	...	1141	...	3 19	5 34	...	7 35	...	1045	...	ng't	...
Ebersbach	...	5 24	8 39	...	9 29	1018	1120	12 1	...	3 38	5 52	...	7 53	...	11 3	1235	1241	...
Eibau	a.m.	5 40	8 54	a.m.	9 47	1030	1133	1216	p.m.	3 53	6 7	p.m.	8 7	p.m.	1118	...	1254	...
Oberoderwitz	6 7	...	9 6	9 14	...	...		1228	1240	4 5	6 20	7 15	...	8 56	1129	...	...	...
Zittau ....arr	6 26	6 40	9 25	9 32	1040	1048	...	1247	1259	4 25	6 39	7 34	9 0	9 15	1147	1 0	1 43	...
	a.m.	a.m.	a.m.	a.m.	a.m.	a.m.	a.m.	a.m.	p.m.	p.m.	p.m.	p.m.	p.m.	p.m.	p.m.	p.m.	p.m.	
Zittau ....dep	4 0	6 54	7 12	...	7 45	9 40	10 9	1030	1 12	1 25	3 40	5 28	6 18	8 0	8 36	10 5	1110	...
Oberoderwitz	...	7 14	7 33	...	...	...	1028	1051	1 32	1 44	4 3	...	6 39	8 19	8 57	...	1129	...
Eibau	4 44	7 32		7 58	...	1038		11 7	1 49		4 19	6 24			9 18	11 6		...
Ebersbach	4 57	7 48	...	8 11	8 21	1051	...	1122	2 6	...	4 36	6 39	...	...	9 35	1119	...	...
Taubenheim	5 10	8 2	...		...		...	1139	2 21	...	4 50	6 53	...	...	9 51		...	...
Wilthen	5 27	8 24	...	...	...	...	...	12 0	2 44	...	5 12	7 14	...	...	1013	...	...	...
Niederneukirch	5 44	8 41	...	...	8 52	...	...	1218	3 3	...	5 31	7 31	...	...	1032	...	...	...
Bischofswerda ..arr	6 0	8 56	...	...	9 2	...	...	1234	3 20	...	5 47	7 47	...	...	1048	...	...	...

Luggage Rates—see page 462.] SAXONY STATE RAILWAYS.

BERLIN, LEIPSIC, REICHENBACH, and HOF.

SLEEPING CAR—Berlin to Munich, in 10.50 p.m. from Berlin. Extra fare, 1st class 12 m., 2nd class 9 m. 50 p.
THROUGH CARRIAGE—Berlin to Rome, via Munich, in 10.50 p.m. from Berlin (also 1.10 p.m. from Berlin, page 170).

		2,3,4			2 3 4	2 3 4	Ex3	Ex 3		Ex3			Ex3	Ex 1	1,2,3		2 3 4	Ex1	1,2,3		1,2,3	2 3 4	1,2,3	1—4	Ex3		Ex 3		1,2,3	1—4
Berlin—		a.m.			a.m.	a.m.	a.m.	a.m.		a.m.			a.m.	noon	p.m.		p.m.	p.m.	p.m.		p.m.	p.m.	p.m.	p.m.	p.m.		p.m.		p.m.	p.m.
Anhalt Bahnhof..dep	...	12 30	...	...	...	5 35	7 10	7 30	...	8 55	...	...	1050	12 5	1245	...	1 15	3 5	3 50	...	4 50	4 55	6 30	6 55	7 45	...	10 50	...	11 0	1125
Jüterbog ....arr	...	2 5	...	...	...	6 47	...	...	...	...	...	...	...	...	1 58	...	2 52	...	...	...	5 47	6 28	...	8 33	...	...	...	...	1157	1252
Wittenberg	...	2 43	...	...	5 55	7 43	...	RC	...	...	...	...	12 2	...	2 27	...	3 44	...	5 6	...	6 18	7 14	7 43	16 5	...	...	RC	...	1227	1 35
Bitterfeld .... arr	...	3 33	...	...	6 47	8 36	8 48	...	...	1030	...	...	1232	...	3 0	...	4 38	...	...	...	6 52	8 6	8 13	1051	...	...	12 28	...	1 0	2 26
Bitterfeld .... dep	...	4 25	...	...	6 55	9 5	8 49	...	...	1031	...	...	1241	...	3 7	...	4 52	...	...	...	7 0	8 24	8 14	1058	...	...	12 29	...	1 5	2 44
Delitzsch	...	4 43	...	...	7 11	9 21	...	...	...	...	...	...	...	...	3 21	...	5 8	...	...	...	7 14	8 41	RC	1114	...	...	SC	...	1 19	3 3
Leipsic Haupt Bf. arr	...	5 22	...	...	7 49	10 0	9 18	9 26	...	11 0	...	...	1 13	2 22	3 44	...	5 46	5 14	6 5	...	7 37	9 20	8 43	1153	9 41	...	12 58	...	1 42	3 42
	2 & 3	Ex 3	1—4	Ex3	1—4		Ex3	Ex 3	Ex3	Ex3	Ex3	1—4	Ex3	Ex 1	1—4	1,2,3		Ex1	2 3 4	1—4	1,2,3	1—4	1,2,3	Ex3		1,2,3	Ex 3	Ex3		1—4
	a.m.	a.m.	a.m.	a.m.	a.m.			a.m.	a.m.	p.m.		p.m.	p.m.	p.m.	p.m.	p.m.		p.m.	p.m.	p.m.	p.m.	p.m.	p.m.			p.m.	a.m.	a.m.		a.m.
Leipsic Haupt Bf. dep	6 0	7 5	...	8 36	8 29	...	...	9 40	9 57	1225	...	...	1 50	2 30	3 52	5 0	...	5 23	6 31	...	7 50	9 45	9 10	Dresden dep. 10.45p.m.	...	11 17	1 10	1 18	...	4 5
„ Bayerische Bf. arr	...	..	...	...	8 43	...	...	...	...	...	...	...	...	...	4 6	...	...	...	6 51	...	...	10 5	...		...	11 31	...	...	...	4 25
„ „ „ dep	...	...	7 34	...	9 21	...	...	...	RC	...	...	1 8	...	...	4 11	...	...	...	6 55	7 35	...	1014	RC		...	11 43	...	...	...	4 55
Gaschwitz	6 18	RC	7 52	...	9 34	...	...	...	...	...	...	...	...	...	4 22	...	...	A	7 14	...	...	1033	...		...	11 58	...	...	...	5 14
Kieritzsch	...	7 33	8 11	...	9 53	...	...	...	...	...	...	...	...	...	4 38	5 28	...	...	7 32	...	...	1052	...		...	12 17	...	1 47	...	5 31
Altenburg	6 46	7 49	8 38	9 18	1043	...	...	10 25	1038	1 7	...	1 52	...	B	5 5	5 45	...	...	7 56	8 38	8 32	1119	9 51		...	12 45	1 53	2 2	...	5 59
Gössnitz	7 0	8 3	9 3	9 32	1118	...	...	...	...	...	...	2 18	...	...	5 29	6 6	...	...		9 10	8 49	1150	10 5		...	1 11	...	2 17	...	6 26
Crimmitzschau	7 11	8 13	9 18	9 42	1134	...	...	RC	...	1 29	...	2 35	...	...	5 45	6 15	...	...	...	9 26	8 59	12 5	1015		...	1 25	SC	2 27	...	6 42
Werdau ....arr	7 22	8 24	9 37	9 53	1153	...	...	...	...	1 40	...	2 55	3 1	...	6 5	6 27	...	...	...	9 47	9 10	1224	1026		...	1 40	...	2 38	...	7 2
Neumark		8 38	9 56	10 6	1212	...	...	...	...	...	...	3 28	RC	...	6 25	6 49	...	...	...	10 8	9 23	1241	1043		...		...	...	...	7 25
Reichenbach ......arr	...	8 50	1010	1018	1225	...	...	11 23	1135	2 3	...	3 42	3 23	3 56	6 38	7 1	...	...	...	1021	9 35	1254	1055		...	...	...	3 2	...	7 38
EGER 188 ....arr	...	12p14	2p11	2p11	...	...	a.m.	2 p11	...	5 p0	p.m.	8p13	8p13	...	10p5	10p5	...	...	p.m.	2 a3	2 a3	...	2 a3	a.m.	...	...	...	5a30	a.m.	1214
Reichenbach .....dep	...	8 58	1039	1034	1250	...	1119	11 26	1150	2 25	2 30	4 6	3 36	4 1	6 56	7 18	...	...	8 40	1031	9 48	2 18	11 8	1 33	...	...	...	3 8	4 45	7 47
Herlasgrün	...	9 15	1058	...	1 15	...	...	...	...	...	...	4 26	...	...	7 17	...	...	...	9 2	1055	...	2 35	1123	...	...	...	...	3 21	5 6	8 8
Plauen	...	9 34	1130	11 2	1 57	...	1145	11 52	1216	2 55	2 58	5 0	4 2	4 26	7 53	7 47	...	7 17	9 28	1142	1016	2 57	1137	1 59	...	...	3 8	3 36	5 39	8 33
Mehltheuer	...	...	1150	...	2 22	...	RC	...	To Eger.	...	To Eger	5 24	...	To Eger	8 14		...	...	9 54	12 3	...			...	...	...	...	To Eger	6 3	8 54
Schönberg	...	...	1159	...	2 33	...	12 8	...		...		5 36	...		8 25	...	...	...		1213	...	...	...	...	...	...	...		6 16	9 4
Hof Hauptbahnhof arr	...	10 23	...	1150	3 21	...	1234	12 42		3 46		6 25	4 48		9 13	...	...	8 1	...	1256	11 8	...	...	2 43	...	...	3 55		7 5	9 50
BAMBERG ......197 arr	...	...	...	2p40	6p21	...	...	4 p40	...	6p21	...	12a3	...	...	...	...	...	...	...	...	1a51	...	...	...	...	...	6 a36	...	...	...
NURNBERG .....197 arr	...	...	...	4 p8	9p26	...	...	6 p15	...	9p26	...	2a47	...	...	...	...	...	...	...	...	3 a0	...	...	...	...	...	7 a45	...	...	...
STUTTGART.....191 arr	...	...	...	8p51	...	...	...	...	...	1252	...	...	...	...	...	...	...	...	...	...	1016	...	...	...	...	...	11a45	...	...	...
MUNICH ....203 arr	...	3 p58	...	6p14	...	...	...	6 p14	...	1010	...	...	1010	...	...	...	...	1233	...	...	7a20	...	...	7a50	...	...	9 a23	...	...	...

A—Berlin-Tyrol Express, Luxuszug.

B—Berlin-Marienbad-Carlsbad Express, Luxuszug, runs in July and August only.

REICHENBACH and LENGENFELD.

	a.m.	a.m.	p.m.	p.m.	p.m.	p.m.				
Reichenbach...dep	6 5	9 2	1 18	3 38	4 38	6 49	...	...	...	...
Goltzschtalbrücke.....	6 46	9 42	2 3	4 25	5 15	7 32	...	...	...	...
Lengenfeld ......arr	7 23	10 58	2 43	5 10	...	8 12	...	...	...	...

	a.m.	a.m.	p.m.	p.m.	p.m.	p.m.	p.m.					
Lengenfeld..........dep	8 23	...	12 5	3 0	...	6 12	10 5	...	...	...	...	...
Goltzschtalbrücke	9 10	11 25	1 30	3 45	5 28	6 56	10 50	...	...	...	...	...
Reichenbach.........arr	9 45	12 3	1 43	4 20	6 5	7 31	11 32	...	...	...	...	...

HOF, LEIPSIC, and BERLIN.

MUNICH ....dep	11p20	...	11p20	...	...	...	...	...	...	8a25	8 a25	...	...	9 a25	...	...	...	...	...	12 35	...	2p10	...	...	...	...	7 p20	7 p20
STUTTGART ....dep	...	...	8 p39	...	...	...	...	...	...	...	...	...	...	6 a0	...	...	...	8a 5	...	...	...	...	...	...	...	...	4 p0	...
NURNBERG ....dep	...	...	1 a5	...	...	...	...	1 a56	...	...	...	...	...	11 a0	...	...	...	12p 3	...	...	...	...	...	...	...	...	8 p34	...
BAMBERG ....dep	...	...	2a20	...	...	...	...	4 a41	...	...	...	...	...	12 p2	...	...	...	1 p11	...	3 p37	...	...	...	...	...	...	9 p49	...
	Ex 3	1—4	1,2,3	1—4	1—4	Ex 3	1—4	1,2,3	Ex 3	Ex 3	Ex 3	1—4	1—4	Ex 3	Ex 3		Ex 1	1,2,3	1—4	Ex 3	1—4	Ex1	1—4	1—4	Ex 3	1,2,3	Ex 3	Ex 3
	a.m.		a.m.		a.m.	a.m.	a.m.	a.m.	p.m.	p.m.	p.m.	p.m.	p.m.	p.m.				p.m.	p.m.	p.m.	p.m.	p.m.	p.m.	p.m.		p.m.	a.m.	a.m.
Hof Hauptbahnhof dep	4 35	...	5 8	...	5 30	...	7 50	10 48	...	1 15	1 23	...	1 28	2 56	...	...	...	4 40	5 0	6 30	...	7 5	7 10	...	...	10 45	1 10	1 20
Schönberg	...	...	5 40	...	6 19	...	8 39	11 40	...	...	RC	...	2 13	RC	...	...	B	5 14	5 51	RC	...	...	8 4	...	...	11 34	SC	...
Mehltheuer	...	...	5 49	a.m.	6 30	...	8 50	11 53	...	...	...	...	2 25	...	p.m.	...	p.m.	5 23	6 7	...	...	...	8 17	...	...	11 47	...	...
Plauen	5 24	...	6 2	6 7	7 12	9 39	9 9	12 18	12 51	1 57	2 8	2 15	2 47	3 45	3 33	...	4 57	5 38	6 30	7 23	7 30	8 1	8 46	9 50	...	12 44	1 59	2 7
Herlasgrün	...	...	6 18	6 35	7 37	...	9 34	12 47	1 6	...	...	2 44	3 19	...	...	...	...	5 56	6 59	...	8 0	...	9 19	1019	...	1 14	...	...
Reichenbach......arr	5 50	...	6 33	6 54	7 53	10 4	9 53	1 6	1 18	2 21	2 32	3 3	3 40	4 13	4 0	...	5 23	6 11	7 20	7 48	8 20	...	9 39	1038	...	1 31	2 27	2 35
EGER ....dep	...	a.m.	...		1 a46	7 a47	...	8 a10	...		11 27		11a27	...	...	...	...	2 p25	4 p39	4 p39		...	...		6 p33		10 p0	
Reichenbach......dep	5 55	5 6	6 45	...	7 59	10 12	9 59	1 12	1 24	...	2 35	2,3,4	3 50	4 24	4 8	...	5 28	6 18	7 37	7 54	...	...	9 47	...	11 0	...	2 30	...
Neumark	...	5 20	6 56	a.m.	8 11	...	10 13	1 24	...	...	...	p.m.	4 7	4 35	...	...	...	6 29	7 51	...	...	...	10 0	p.m.	11 10	nght	...	...
Werdau..........arr	...	5 31	7 5	7 14	8 22	10 30	10 24	1 35	1 41	...	2 51	3 1	4 20	4 45	4 28	...	...	6 39	8 2	...	...	A	10 11	1020	11 20	12 9	...	...
Crimmitzschau	...	5 55	7 18	7 32	8 49	10 43	10 54	2 1	1 53	...	3 3	3 23	5 2	4 58	4 43	...	...	6 56	8 35	8 10	...	...	10 48	1031	11 33	12 45	...	...
Gössnitz	...	6 14	7 28	7 51	9 5	10 53	11 12	2 24	2 4	...	...	3 42	5 20	5 9	4 56	...	...	7 6	9 2	...	p.m.	...	11 4	1041	11 47	1 13	...	...
Altenburg	...	6 42	7 43	8 12	9 23	11 8	11 35	2 49	2 18	...	3 23		5 40	5 25	5 13	...	...	7 22	9 22	8 40	9 38	...	11 26	1056	12 1	1 47	3 20	...
Kieritzsch	...	7 8	...	8 36	...	...	12 3	3 13	...	...	...	...	6 5	...	...	...	...	...	9 40	...	10 3	...	11 51	...	...		...	...
Gaschwitz	...	7 28	...	8 54	...	RC	12 22	3 32	...	...	...	...	6 24	...	RC	...	...	...	...	...	1022	...	12 11	1122	...	...	...	...
Leipsic Bayer. B. arr	...	7 41	...	9 12	...	...	12 34	3 47	...	...	...	p.m.	6 36	...	...	...	...	...	10 2	...	1039	...	12 24	...	...	a.m.	...	...
" " dep	...	8 2	...		...	...	1 27		...	...	...	4 26	6 46	...	...	...	...	...	10 6	...		...		...	...	5 44	...	...
" Hauptbahnhof arr	7 16	8 16	8 25	...	10 5	11 50	1 47	...	2 57	...	4 2	4 46	7 5	6 7	5 57	...	6 51	8 3	10 26	9 17	...	9 52	...	1143	12 43	6 4	4 6	...
	Ex 3		Ex 3	1,2,3	1,2,3	Ex 3	1—4		Ex 3			1,2,3	1—4	Ex 3		Ex2	Ex 1		2,3,4	Ex 3		Ex3		2 3 4		1—4	Ex 3	
	a.m.		a.m.	a.m.	a.m.	p.m.	p.m.		p.m.			p.m.	p.m.	p.m.		p.m.	p.m.		p.m.	p.m.		p.m.		a.m.		a.m.	a.m.	
Leipsic Hauptbhf. dep	7 45	...	8 35	8 45	10 55	12 40	1 55	...	3 12	...	...	5 10	7 15	6 25	...	6 45	7 0	...	10 45	9 47	...	9 59	...	1233	...	6 20	4 20	...
Delitzsch	...	...	...	9 7	11 35	12 59	2 36	...	...	...	...	5 48	7 53	...	...	...	...	...	11 21	...	...	...	...	1 6	...	6 58	...	...
Bitterfeld........ arr	...	...	...	9 18	11 47	1 9	2 48	...	3 38	...	...	6 0	8 5	6 52	...	...	...	...	11 35	10 14	...	...	...	1 18	...	7 10	...	...
Bitterfeld........ dep	...	...	...	9 27	12 16	1 10	3 8	...	3 46	...	...	6 12	8 46	6 53	...	...	B	...		10 15	...	A	...	1 28	...	7 17	...	...
Wittenberg	8 41	...	...	10 0	1 46	1 40	Ex2	...	4 19	...	...	6 47	9 19	7 23	...	...	...	...	...	10 45	...	...	...	2 27	...	7 49	...	...
Jüterbog ....dep	...	...	...	10 31	3 0	...		...	...	...	...	7 18	...	...	...	...	...	...	...	...	...	...	...	3 20	...	...	...	...
Berlin Anhaltbhf...arr	9 53	...	10 31	11 30	4 29	2 52	4 49	...	5 42	...	...	8 19	10 38	8 35	...	8 41	9 5	...	...	11 57	...	12 7	...	5 0	...	9 5	6 25	...

Extra.—Plauen to Reichenbach 5.13, 10.18 p.m. RC—Restaurant Car. SC—Sleeping Car in this train.

A—Tyrol-Berlin Express, Luxuszug. **B**—Carlsbad-Marienbad-Berlin Express, Luxuszug, runs only in July and August.

SAXONY STATE RAILWAYS. [Luggage Rates—see page 462.

BERLIN and LEIPSIC to DRESDEN, BODENBACH, and TETSCHEN.

THROUGH CARRIAGES. Berlin to Vienna—in 8.5 a.m. and 8.10 p.m. from Berlin (via Zossen) and 4.30, 6.45 and 11.15 p.m. from Berlin (via Juterbog).

	234				Ex3	234					1—4					1—4			Ex 3
BERLIN—					a.m.	a.m.					a.m.					p.m.			p.m.
Anhalt Bahnhof......dep	...	...	...	...	6 55	5 35	...	...	...	...	6 15	...	...	...	...	1210	...	...	4 30
Jüterbog	...	...	...	...	7 51	6 52	...	...	...	...	8 6	...	...	...	...	1 43	...	...	:
Holzdorf	...	...	...	...	...	7 25	...	...	...	...	8 45	...	...	...	...	2 16	...	...	:
Herzberg	a.m.	...	...	...	...	7 38	...	...	...	...	9 0	...	...	...	...	2 29	...	...	:
Falkenberg	5 50	...	...	...	8 32	7 49	...	...	...	...	10 18	...	...	...	...	2 51	...	...	:
Burxdorf	6 8	...	...	...	...		...	...	...	...	10 37	...	...	...	...	3 10	...	...	:
Röderau	6 27	...	...	...	8 59	...	...	...	...	...	11 3	...	...	...	...	3 37	...	...	:
Priestewitz ....arr		...	...	...	:	...	...	...	...	...	11 27	...	...	...	...	4 0	...	...	:
		1—4	1—4	Ex3	:		1—4	Ex3	Ex 3		:	3 Cl	1—4	Ex 3	1,2,3	:	1—4	Ex3	:
LEIPSIC—			a.m.	a.m.	:		a.m.	a.m.	a.m.		:	a.m.	a.m.	p.m.	p.m.	:	p.m.	p.m.	:
Hauptbahnhof...dep	...	...	5 5	6 20	:	...	7 48	8 43	9 32	...	:	...	1137	1 15	2 22	:	3 22	5 0	:
Borsdorf	...	...	5 24	...	:	...	8 7	...	...	...	:	...	1152	...	...	:	3 37	...	:
Wurzen (184)	...	...	5 48	6 45	:	...	8 28	...	9 58	...	:	10 0	1212	RC	2 48	:	3 57	RC	:
Dahlen	...	...	6 14	...	:	...	8 54	RC	...	...	:	1040	1238	...	...	:	4 23	...	:
Oschatz (190)	...	a.m.	6 26	7 10	:	...	9 5	...	10 21	...	:	1057	1250	1 56	3 16	:	4 35	...	:
Riesa..........arr	...	5 10	6 42	7 23	:	...	9 22	9 35	10 33	...	:	1122	1 7	2 7	3 29	:	4 52	...	:
Priestewitz..........dep	...	5 38	7 16	...	:	...	10 8	...	...	...	11 30		1 42	...	3 50	4 1	5 30	...	:
Coswig	...	6 1	7 37	...	:	...	1028	...	RC	...	11 53	...	2 4	...	4 7	4 23	5 52	...	:
Kötzschenbroda	...	6 8	7 44	...	:	...	1034	...	...	...	11 59	...	...	...	...	...	...	...	:
DRESDEN Neustadt ar	...	6 22	7 58	8 5	9 41	...	1048	1017	11 13	...	12 15	...	2 20	2 48	4 21	4 38	6 8	6 29	6 49
DRESDEN Neustadt dp	...	6 25	8 1	8 7	9 42	...	1050	1020	11 14	...	12 18	...	2 22	2 49	4 23	4 41	6 11	6 30	6 50
" Hauptb'hf arr	...	6 33	8 9	8 13	9 48	...	1058	1026	11 20	...	12 26	...	2 30	2 55	4 31	4 49	6 19	6 36	6 56
		234				1—4			Ex.3	Ex3			1—4			1,2,3			
BERLIN—						a.m.			a.m.	a.m.			a.m.			p.m.			
Anhalt Bahnhof...dep	...	...	...	...	...	6 0	...	...	8 5	9 20	...	...	1010	...	...	1 20	...	...	...
Zossen	...	...	...	...	...	6 37	...	...	RC	...	...	...	1047	...	...	...	...	...	...
Golssen	...	...	...	...	...	7 22	...	...	...	K	...	...	1132	...	...	...	...	...	...
Uckro	...	...	...	...	...	7 44	...	...	9 13	...	...	...	1154	...	...	...	...	...	...
Dobrilugk-Kirch....	...	a.m.	...	...	2 3 4	8 29	...	...	9 39	1053	...	...	1236	...	...	2 55	...	...	...
Elsterwerda	...	4 44	...	...	a.m.	9 5	...	...	10 3	...	...	...	1 14	...	...	3 17	...	...	...
Grossenhain	...	5 20	...	...	7 38	9 36	...	...	10 23	RC	...	...	1 44	...	...	...	...	...	...
Weinböhla	...	5 44	...	...	7 59	10 0	...	...	...	...	...	...	2 5	...	...	...	...	...	...
DRESDEN Neustadt arr	...	...	...	...	8 28	1025	...	...	10 58	1157	...	...	...	...	...	4 7	...	...	...
DRESDEN Haupt ...arr	...	6 30	...	...	8 38	1040	...	...	11 6	12 4	...	...	2 49	...	...	4 15	...	...	...

	1,2,3	1—4	1,2,3	1—4	1,2,3	1,2,3	1—4			Ex.3	Ex3	1,2,3	1,2,3	1—4		1 2 3		1—4		Ex 3
DRESDEN—	a.m.	a.m.	a.m.	a.m.	a.m.	a.m.	a.m.			a.m.	p.m.	p.m.	p.m.	p.m.		p.m.	...	p.m.		p.m.
Hauptbahnhof...dep	5 0	6 0	7 10	6 24	8 30	10 1	1045	...	...	11 30	1210	12 53	2 22	3 15	...	4 40	...	6 30	...	7 5
Pirna	5 35	6 37	7 27	7 2	8 51	1020	1121	...	...	11 48	...	1 15	2 44	3 51	...	5 1	...	6 53	...	...
Pötzscha		6 51	7 37	7 15	9 5	1029	1134	...	...	RC	K	1 28	2 58	4 6	...	5 15	...	7 7	...	...
Königstein	a.m.	7 7	7 51	7 30	9 19	1043	1149	...	...	...	RC	1 44	3 13	4 21	...	5 30	...	7 23	...	...
Schandau 188A	4 41	7 18	7 59	7 37	9 26	1053	1156	...	...	12 10	1245	1 54	3 24	4 28	...	5 39	...	7 30	...	7 38
Schöna	4 58	7 34	8 13		9 45	11 6		...	...	...	...	2 10	3 41		...	5 55	...		...	...
Bodenbach ......arr	5 25	7 58	8 34	...	10 7	1130	...	...	...	12 39	1 7	2 29	4 8	...	...	6 16	...	...	...	7 59
PRAGUE (252A) arr	...	11a5	11a5	...	...	...	...	...	...	3 p17	...	6 p58	...	...	...	...	...	...	...	10p57
VIENNA 243-252a arr	...	6p28	6p28	...	...	...	...	...	...	9 p45	...	...	...	...	...	...	...	...	...	6 a55
Tetschen ....arr	5 25	...	8 35	...	...	1131	...	...	...	12 39	...	...	4 8	...	...	...	...	...	...	...
VIENNA (224)...arr	...	...	...	...	...	...	...	...	...	9 p36	...	...	...	...	...	...	...	...	...	...

K—Carlsbad Express.

FARES.	m.pf.	m.pf.	m.pf.
Berlin to Dresden......	16 20	10 50	6 60
" " Prague	34 50	22 20	13 90
" " Vienna	69 80	43 60	27 40

RC—Restaurant Car attached.

REICHENBACH and EGER.

	2&3	Ex3	1—4	1—4	1—4	Ex3	1—4	Ex3	2&3	1—4	Ex 3	1—4	Ex1	1—4	1—4	1—4	1—4	1,2,3	1—4
LEIPSIC 187......dep	...	1a18	1a18	...	...	...	7a 5	9a57	...	9a57	12p25	1225	2p30	1p50	...	5 p0	...	7p50	9p10
		a.m.	a.m.		a.m.	a.m.	a.m.	a.m.		noon	p.m	p.m.	p.m.	p.m.	p.m.	p.m.		p.m.	p.m.
Reichenbach ...dep	...	3 8	4 45	...	7 1	...	8 58	1150	...	12 3	2 30	2 52	4 1	4 6	5 29	7 18	...	9 48	11 8
Herlasgrün	...	3 21	5 6	...	7 22	...	9 15	...	...	12 22	...	3 14	...	4 25	5 49	...	...	...	11 23
Plauen ....dep	...	3 37	6 5	a.m.	8 0	...	9 41	1218	...	12 53	3 0	4 10	4 27	5 43	7 25	7 55	p.m	10 14	11 47
Weischlitz (184)	...	...	6 22	7 0	8 16	9 4	9 56	RC	...	1 10	3 12	4 26	A	5 59	7 39	8 7	10 2		12 2
Oelsnitz (189A)	...	3 58	6 41	7 15	8 34	9 18	1017	1240	...	1 31	3 26	4 43	...	6 17	7 56	8 22	10 18	...	12 21
Adorf (185)	...	4 14	7 4		8 57	9 35	1044	1256	...	2 15	3 42	5 4	...	6 43	8 18	8 42		...	12 41
Bad Elster	...	4 20	7 12	...	9 3	9 41	1053	1 2	...	2 23	3 50	5 17	5 11	6 51	8 25	8 50	...	...	12 51
Voitersreuth ...... arr	...	4 54	7 54	...		1013	1142	1 37	...	3 6	4 25	6 1	...	7 33		9 29	...	...	1 32
Voitersreuth ...... dep	...	5 9	8 7	...	...	1027	1153	1 51	...	3 18	4 37		...	7 48	...	9 42	...	...	1 42
Franzensbad ......arr	a.m.	5 20	8 17	a.m.	...	1037	12 3	2 1	p.m.	3 28	4 46	1,2,3	5 52	8 1	...	9 52	...	p.m.	1 52
" (197) ...dep	4 50	5 21	8 19	9 18	...	1038	12 4	2 3	2*40	3 30	4 50	6 p0	5 53	8 3	...	9 55	...	11 28	1 53
Eger ....arr	5 5	5 30	8 29	9 30	...	1046	1214	2 11	2 55	3 40	5 0	6 12	6 2	8 13	...	10 5	...	11 40	2 3
MARIENBAD (243A) arr	...	6a31	9a36	1025	...	12p3	...	3 p9	...	5 p7	6 p40	...	6p54	...	...	1050	...	...	...
CARLSBAD (251) ...arr	7 a1	7 a1	1020	...	...	1p29	1p29	4p17	...	5p31	...	8 p4	7p 6	...	...	1143	...	...	...

*—Sunday at 2.18 p.m. A—Berlin-Carlsbad Express, Luxus-Zug, runs until 31st August.

Extra—Franzensbad to Eger, 6.38 a.m., 12.32, 3‡44, 6.30, 9.14 p.m. ‡—Until 15th Sept.

For Continuation of Trains, see next page.

Luggage Rates—see page 462.] SAXONY STATE RAILWAYS.

BERLIN and LEIPSIC to DRESDEN, BODENBACH, and TETSCHEN.

SLEEPING CAR, Berlin to Vienna—in 8.10 p.m. from Berlin. Extra fare, 1st class 12 m., 2nd class 9 m. 50 pf.
¶—Customs Examination of luggage for Vienna by this train may be deferred until arrival at Vienna, at option of passenger.

	1—4			Ex3				1—4		2 3 4	Ex.3
BERLIN—	p.m.			p.m.				p.m.		a.m.	p.m.
Anhalt Bahnhof......dep	4 55	...	...	6 45	...	...	...	7 25	...	...	11 15
Jüterbog	6 45	...	...	...	...	...	...	8 55	...	1225	12 15
Holzdorf	7 18	...	...	RC	...	...	...	9 30	...	1259	...
Herzberg	7 31	...	...	...	...	...	...	9 45	...	1 13	...
Falkenberg	7 52	...	...	8 25	...	...	...	10 4	...	1 25	12 59
Burxdorf	8 9	...	...	...	...	...	...	10 22	...		...
Röderau	8 27	...	...	8 53	...	...	...	10 41	...	...	1 25
Priestewitz......arr		...	...	⋮	...	...	...	11 13	...	...	1 41
	1—4	Ex 3	1,2,3	⋮	1—4	Ex 3	2,3,4	⋮	Ex3	Ex3	⋮
LEIPSIC Hauptbahnhof...dep	p.m. ...	p.m. 6 47	p.m. 7 1	⋮	p.m. 7 30	p.m. 8 40	p.m. 11 0	⋮	p.m. 10 5	ng't 12 0	⋮
Borsdorf	...	...	...		7 46	...	11 21		...	...	
Wurzen (184)	...	...	7 26		8 4	...	11 49		1028	SC	
Dahlen	...	RC	...		8 30	RC	12 15		...	...	
Oschatz (190)	5 50	...	7 53		8 42	...	12 27		1050	1243	
Riesa	6 16	7 40	8 8		9 5	...	12 44		11 2	1255	
Priestewitz......dep	6 43	...	8 26	⋮	9 32	...		11 23	1119	...	1 42
Coswig	7 5	...	8 42	9 26	9 54	...	...	11 44	...	...	...
Kötzschenbroda	7 11	...	...	...	...	...	...	11 51	...	...	...
DRESDEN Neustadt ar	7 27	8 19	8 57	9 40	1013	10 7	...	12 6	1144	1 34	2 9
DRESDEN Neustadt dp	7 30	8 21	8 59	9 42	1015	10 8	...	12 8	1146	1 37	2 10
„ Hauptb'hf arr	7 38	8 27	9 5	9 48	1023	10 14	...	12 16	1152	1 43	2 16
	1—4				1—4		Ex.3	2,3,4			
BERLIN—	p.m.				p.m.		p.m.	nght			
Anhalt Bahnhof...dep	2 25	...	...		7 10	...	8 10	12 5	...	...	
Zossen	3 2	...	...		7 47	...	...	12 42	...	...	
Golssen	3 47	...	...		8 30	...	SC	1 27	...	...	
Uckro	4 10	...	...		8 51	...	...	1 47	...	...	
Dobril-Kirchhain	5 6	...	...		9 47	...	...	2 27	...	...	
Elsterwerda	5 40	...	...		1027	...	...	2 58	...	...	
Grossenhain	6 9	...	...		1055	...	...		...	...	
Weinböhla	6 36	...	...		1117	...	...	...	...	...	
DRESDEN Neustadt arr	6 59	...	...		1139	...	10 39	...	...	...	
DRESDEN Haupt....arr	7 9	...	...		1152	...	10 46	...	...	...	
	1—4		1—4	Ex3	1,2,3		Ex.3			Ex3	
DRESDEN—	p.m.		p.m.	p.m.	ng't		p.m.			a.m.	
Hauptbahnhof.......dep	8 12	...	1110	9 55	1222	...	10 53	...	...	2 30	
Pirna	8 35	...	1146	⋮	1259	...	...	...	...	2 47	...
Pötzscha	8 48	...	1159		1 12	...	...	...	...	...	...
Königstein	9 4	...	1214		1 27	...	...	...	...	3 4	...
Schandau (188A)	9 14	...	1221		1 38	...	11 28	...	...	3 11	...
Schöna	9 30	...			1 51	...	⋮	...	...	...	...
Bodenbach......arr	10 0	...	...		2 18	...	⋮	...	...	3 40	...
PRAGUE (252A)......arr	...	...	...	⋮	5a50	...	⋮	...	...	6a25	...
VIENNA (243 or 252A) arr	...	...	...	¶ ⋮	1248	...	⋮	...	...	12p48	...
Tetschen......arr	10 1	...	...	1052	2 20	...	11 51	...	...	3 41	...
VIENNA (324)......arr	...	...	...	7a22	...	...	8a 0	...	...	...	...

NEUMARK and GREIZ.

Neumark ...dep	4 54	7 35	8 41	1030	1214	1 33	3 32	5 12	6 39	8 18	9 25	1056
Greiz ......arr	5 46	8 4	9 8	11 1	1242	2 1	3 59	5 40	7 9	8 46	9 53	1129
Greiz......dep	6 8	6 16	7 35	9 15	11 15	1248	2 42	4 0	5 50	6 33	7 16	9 24
Neumark ...arr	6 38	7 16	8 6	9 51	11 46	1 19	3 13	4 31	6 21	7 15	7 47	9 55

SCHANDAU and NIEDERNEUKIRCH.

Schandau ......dep	5a58	8a18	1220	3p25	6p34	8 p4	11p33
Kohlmühle	6 12	8 32	1234	3 38	6 48	8 18	11 46
Sebnitz	6 37	8 53	1256	4 3	7 16	8 56	12 10
Neustadt	7 8	1030	1 50	4 32	7 37	9 24	12 32
Niederneukirch ar	7 31	1053	2 13	4 52	...	9 45	...

Niederneukirch...dep	...	...	8a54	1249	3p10	5p50	...	10p35
Neustadt (185)	4a51	6a58	9 21	1 21	3 40	6 24	9p50	11 0
Sebnitz	5 13	7 20	9 57	1 46	4 34	6 49	1015	11 20
Kohlmühle	5 33	7 38	1017	2 7	4 55	7 11	1036	
Schandau (189)...arr	5 46	7 50	1030	2 20	5 8	7 23	1048	...

Kohlmühle.......dep	8a38	12p40	8p21
Hohnstein ....arr	9 27	1 29	9 4

Hohnstein ....dep	6a50	11a40	6 p18	...	...	...	...
Kohlmühle.......arr	7 31	12 22	7 3	...	...	...	...

ELSTERWERDA, RIESA, & NOSSEN.

Elsterwr. Oberlaus B. dep		...	8a19	9a48	1024	1p38	...	4p57	...	...
„ Berl. Dresd. Bhf. dep		5a31	8 29	9 53	1030	1 46	3p20	5 4	6p55	1020
Riesa......arr	a.m.	6 40	9 49		1119	3 1	3 55	6 11	7 37	1121
„ ......dep	4 47	7 8	9 53	...	1 15			6 42	9 38	
Lommatzsch	5 24	7 46	1047	...	1 55	...	...	7 21	1016	...
Ziegenhain	5 47	8 15	1123	...	2 19	...	...	7 42		...
Nossen (183A)......arr	6 14	8 43	1155	...	2 45	...	...	8 7	...	...

Nossen......dep	4a59	...	7 a10	...	1037	...	1p46	6p28	...	...
Ziegenhain	5 25	...	7 43	...	1117	...	2 17	6 54	...	p.m.
Lommatzsch	5 52	...	8 10	...	1155	...	2 44	7 17	...	1040
Riesa......arr	6 29		8 47	p.m.	1238	p.m.	3 24	7 51	p.m.	1119
„ ......dep	6 59	8a58		12 4	1 33	2 21	5 24	8 11	1018	
Elsterwerda Berl. Dr. arr	7 57	9 51	10a10	1 9	2 39	2 58	6 31	8 55	1054	...
Elsterwerda Oberl. B. „	8 8	...	10 15	1 28	3 25	...	...	...	...	...

BAUTZEN and WILTHEN.

Bautzen ......dep	7a20	1047	2 p6	4p39	6p41	8p28	9p41	...
Grosspostwitz	7 35	11 1	2 21	4 53	6 55	8 49	9 55	...
Wilthen ......arr	7 47	1113	2 34	5 5	7 7	...	10 7	...

Wilthen ......dep	8a25	...	12p3	3 p3	5p25	7p25	...	10p24	...
Grosspostwitz ...	8 41	11a48	1214	3 19	5 37	7 36	7p48	10 35	...
Bautzen ......arr	8 54	12 16	1227	3 38	5 50	7 49	8 9	10 48	...

EGER and REICHENBACH.

CARLSBAD 250 dep		1a39	6 a1	...	...	9 a8	9 a8	1125	1145	1219	2p25	...	3p50	3p50	8 p0	8 p0
MARIENBAD 243A		dep	6a32	6a32	6a32	10a1	10a4	12p5	12p5	1 p0	2p52	...	4p49	4p49	8p37	8p37
	1,2,3	1—4	Ex3	1,2,3	1—4	Ex3	1—4	1,2,3	Ex3	1—4	Ex1	1,2,3	Ex3	1,2,3	1,2,3	1—4
	a.m.	a.m.	a.m.	a.m.	a.m.	a.m.	a.m.	p.m.	p.m.	p.m.	p.m.	p.m.	p.m.	p.m	p.m.	p.m.
Eger......dep	5 2	4 43	7 46	8 15	8 10	11 0	1127	1245	1 30	2 24	3 35	4 39	6 33	6 23	9 40	10 0
Franzensbad arr	5 13	4 52	7 54	8 25	8 19	11 8	1137	1255	1 38	2 33	3 42	4 48	6 41	6 34	9 50	10 9
Franzensbad dep		4 54	7 56		8 21	1110	1139		1 40	2 34	3 44	4 49	6 43			1011
Voitersreuth arr		5 7	8 6	...	8 33	1121	1152	...	1 50	2 49	A	4 59	6 53	1—4	...	1024
Voitersreuth dep		5 18	8 19	...	8 46	1136	12 2	...	2 10	3 0	...	5 11	7 6	7p20	1—4	1039
Bad Elster	1—4	6 5	8 52	1—4	9 33	12 8	1245	...	2 45	3 46	4 20	5 57	7 42	8 10	8p36	1130
Adorf	4a45	6 14	8 58	a.m.	9 41	...	1253	...	2 51	3 53	...	6 7	7 49	8 17	8 45	1144
Oelsnitz	5 3	6 33	9 14	7 56	10 0	RC	1 13	...	3 8	4 15	...	6 28	8 5	8 38	9 5	12 5
Weischlitz	5 18	6 50	...	8 11	1016	...	1 30	...	RC	4 33	...	6 45	8 17	8 55	9 20	1222
Plauen ...arr	5 35	7 7	9 36		1032	1249	1 48	...	3 30	4 49	4 56	7 3		9 11	9 37	1239
Herlasgrün	6 19		...	...	11 8	...	2 32	...	...	5 41	...	...	...	1019		1 6
Reichenb'ch	6 34	...	10 4	...	1127	1 18	2 51	...	4 0	6 0	5 23	7 30	...	1038	...	1 23
LEIPSIC (187) arr		...	1150	...	2n57	2p57	5p57	...	5p57	8 p3	6p51	9p17	...	1243		4 a6

Extra—Eger to Franzensbad 5‡45 a.m., 3‡0, 4.9, 5.40, 7‡50 p.m.
A—Carlsbad-Berlin Express, Luxus Zug—Runs until Aug. 31.
‡—Until 15th Sept.

SCHÖNFELD and GEYER.

Schönfeld dep	6a30	9a30	1p20	5 p7	7p50	11p25	...
Geyer ......arr	7 9	1010	1 59	5 47	8 30	12 4	...

Geyer ......dep	4a55	7a48	1224	4 p5	6p35	10p13	...
Schönfeld arr	5 51	8 28	1 4	4 44	7 14	10 52	...

SAXONY STATE RAILWAY. [Luggage Rates—see page 462.

TETSCHEN and BODENBACH to DRESDEN, LEIPSIC, and BERLIN.

VIENNA 224 ....dep	...	...	8p20	...	...	...	9p40	...	...	...	...	...	...	...	...	...	...	...
		Ex3	Ex3				Ex3			1—4	1—4	Ex 3	1,2,3	1—4	1—4	1—4	1—4	
			a.m.				a.m.			a.m.			a.m.		a.m.	p.m.		
Tetschen ....dep	...	...	4 28	...	...	...	6 7	...	...	...	...	...	8 48	...	...	12 7	...	...
VIENNA 243 or 252 dep	...	4p15	⋮	...	...	...	⋮	...	...	...	...	10 p0	10 p0	...	...	...	...	...
PRAGUE 252 ....dep	...	1035	RC	...	...	...	⋮	...	...	...	...	5 a55	5 a55	...	...	7 a31	...	...
Bodenbach ....dep	...	1a20	⋮	...	...	...	⋮	...	...	5 15	...	8 a35	8 48	...	1030	12 8	...	...
Schöna	...	...	⋮	...	...	...	⋮	...	...	5 38	a.m.	...	9 16	...	1052	12 38	p.m.	...
Schandau	...	1 43	⋮	...	...	...	6 32	...	...	5 57	7 55	8 56	9 35	...	1113	12 51	12 57	...
Königstein	...	1 50	⋮	...	...	...	...	...	...	6 5	8 3	9 4	9 43	...	1121	...	1 4	...
Pötzscha	...	...	⋮	...	...	...	...	...	...	6 20	8 18	...	9 58	a.m.	1136	...	1 19	...
Pirna	...	2 8	⋮	...	...	...	...	...	...	6 35	8 38	9 22	10 13	11 16	1150	1 18	1 33	...
DRESDEN Hauptbhof arr		2 25	5 26	...	...	...	7 8	...	...	6 55	9 10	9 39	10 48	11 48	1210	1 40	2 6	...
					2 3 4				1—4	1—4		Ex 3		2 3 4		1,2,3		1—4
			a.m.						a.m.	a.m.		a.m.		p.m.		p.m.		p.m.
DRESDEN Haupt. dep		...	5 36	...	...	...	...	...	6 20	8 5	...	10 0	...	12 5	...	2 12	...	2 42
,, Neustadt dep		...	5 43	...	...	...	...	...	6 33	...	...	10 8	...	12 15	...	2 20	...	2 56
Weinböhla		...	...	...	...	...	...	...	7 0	8 47	...	...	...	12 45	...	...	...	3 25
Grossenhain		...	...	...	a.m.	...	...	...	7 26	9 9	...	10 41	...	1 5	...	...	...	3 51
Elsterwerda		...	...	...	4 35	...	...	...	8 0	1110	...	11 0	...		...	3 10	...	4 23
Dobril.-Kirchhain		...	...	...	5 35	...	...	...	8 32	1145	...	11 21	...	...	...	3 31	...	5 5
Uckro........		...	...	...	6 16	...	...	...	9 10	1224	...	...	...	...	...	3 56	...	5 43
Golssen		...	...	...	6 35	...	...	...	9 28	1242	...	...	...	...	...	...	...	6 1
Zossen		...	...	...	7 21	...	...	...	1014	1 26	...	...	...	...	...	...	...	6 46
BERLIN Anhalt. Bh.ar		...	8 8	...	7 57	...	...	...	1050	2 2	...	12 48	...	...	...	5 1	...	7 22
	1—4	Ex3		1—4	2 3 4	Ex3	Ex3	Ex 3	1—4	1—4	Ex 3	Ex 3	1—4	Ex 3	1—4		1—4	
	a.m.	a.m.		a.m.		a.m.	a.m.	a.m.	a.m.	a.m.	a.m.	a.m.	a.m.	p.m.	p.m.		p.m.	
DRESDEN Hauptbh. dep	2 42	3 41	...	5 45	...	7 15	7 20	8 0	9 32	8 14	10 25	10 35	11 29	1 18	2 18	...	2 25	...
,, Neustadt arr	2 50	3 47	...	5 53	...	7 21	7 26	8 6	9 40	8 22	10 31	10 41	11 37	1 24	2 26	...	2 33	...
,, Neustadt dep	2 54	3 51	...	5 55	...	7 22	7 28	8 8	9 42	8 25	10 33	10 46	11 40	1 25	2 30	...	2 36	...
Kötzschenbroda........	3 9	...	...	...	...	...	...	...	9 57	8 40	...	...	11 55	...	2 41	...	2 51	...
Coswig 2 3 4	3 16	...	...	6 10	...	...	7 44	...	10 3	8 47	...	RC	12 3	...	2 49	...	2 58	...
Priestewitz ....a.m.	3 37	...	...	6 33	...	...	⋮	8 36	1027	9 12	...	...	12 31	...	3 9	...	3 26	...
Riesa ....arr 4 52	⋮	4 29	...	6 56	...	RC	⋮	8 53	1052	9 38	RC	11 29	12 56	RC	⋮	...	3 48	...
Oschatz 5 9	⋮	4 43	...	7 18	...	...	⋮	9 7		10 1	...	11 43	1 19	...	⋮	...	4 17	...
Dahlen 5 23	⋮	...	...	7 31	...	...	RC	...	...	1014	...	...	1 32	...	⋮	...	4 30	...
Wurzen........5 47	⋮	5 5	...	7 55	...	...	⋮	...	...	1037	...	12 8	1 58	...	⋮	...	4 55	...
Borsdorf 6 14	⋮	...	...	8 16	...	...	⋮	...	...	11 0	...	...	2 19	...	⋮	...	...	...
LEIPSIC Haupt. ...6 29	⋮	5 29	...	8 30	...	8 51	⋮	9 53	...	1113	12 5	12 33	2 32	2 55	⋮	...	5 24	...
Priestewitz ....dep	3 38	...	...	...	a.m.	...	⋮	...	...	←1—4 class.→	...	...	...	...	3 12	...	...	...
Röderau	4 5	...	...	...	7 16	...	8 21	...	2 3 4		...	...	...	...	3 52	...	...	...
Burxdorf	4 23	...	...	...	7 35	...	...	...	a.m.		...	...	...	...	4 12	...	...	...
Falkenberg	4 53	...	...	...	8 8	...	8 47	...	9 22		...	...	...	...	4 42	...	...	...
Herzberg	5 5	...	...	...	8 22	...	...	...	9 34		...	...	...	...	4 54	...	...	...
Holzdorf........	5 19	...	...	...	8 38	...	...	...	9 47		...	...	...	...	5 7	...	...	...
Jüterbog........	5 57	...	...	...	9†16	...	9 27	...	10 31		...	...	...	...	5 39	...	...	...
BERLIN Anhalt. Bh. arr	7 25	...	...	...	1118	...	1020	...	11 30	...	...	...	...	...	7 52	...	...	...

For Continuation of Trains, see next page.

CHEMNITZ and WEIPERT.

	a.m.	a.m.	a.m.	a.m.	p.m.	p.m.	p.m.	p.m.	ngt.
Chemnitz dep	4 28	6 42	9 12	1040	1212	3 0	5 20	9 7	12 5
Flöha	4 45	7 3	9 38	1056	1238	3 24	5 44	9 35	1234
Wilischthal........	5 23	7 51	1024	...	1 25	4 10	6 34	1023	1 17
Wolkenstein ...	5 45	8 16	1049	1145	1 49	4 35	7 1	1048	1 41
Schonfeld........	6 7	8 38	1112	...	2 11	4 58	7 23	1112	2 3
Annaberg arr	6 16	8 47	1121	1210	2 20	5 7	7 32	1121	2 12
,, 189A dep	6 19	8 52	1123	1213	2 25	5 20	7 36	1126	2 17
Buchholz	6 32	9 6	1225	1220	2 40	5 34	8 2	1140	2 26
Cranzahl	6 50	9 24	1244		2 58	5 53	8 20	1159	
Weipert 251	7 20	9 54	1 14	...	3 28	6 23	8 51	1229	...

		a.m.	a.m.	a.m.	p.m.	p.m.	p.m.	p.m.	p.m.
Weipert dep	...	5 26	8 15	1113	1 58	...	5 24	6 50	10 1
Cranzahl	a.m.	5 51	8 42	1140	2 25	4 25	5 52	7 12	1027
Buchholz	4 22	6 10	9 3	12 0	2 44	4 38	6 11	7 26	1046
Annaberg arr	4 30	6 18	9 11	12 8	2 53	4 45	6 19	7 34	1054
,, ...dep	4 32	6 20	9 16	1218	2 58	4 47	6 32	7 36	11 0
Schonfeld	4 40	6 28	9 24	1226	3 6	4 56	6 40	7 45	1110
Wolkenstein ...	5 0	6 49	9 45	1246	3 29	5 13	7 3	8 2	1131
Wilischthal........	5 25	7 15	10 9	3 9	3 55	...	7 32	...	1155
Flöha	6 9	8 0	1055	1 56	4 39	6 0	8 10	8 48	1237
Chemnitz arr	6 36	8 22	1120	2 13	5 4	6 17	8 30	9 6	1 2

CHEMNITZ and STOLLBERG.

Chemnitz dep	...	5a40	9 a18	12p23	3 p5	...	7p51	11p20
Wüstenbrand ...	a.m.	6 28	10 0	1 31	4 2	...	8 30	11 57
Neuölsnitz	4 47	7 25	10 44	2 10	4 45	5 p5	9 13	12 44
Stollberg arr	5 2	7 41	10 58	2 22	4 57	5 20	9 27	12 58

Stollberg 185 dp	5a10	8a10	11a12	2p34	5p38	9 p32	...	...
Neuölsnitz	5 28	8 33	11 32	2 54	5 59	9 49	...	...
Wüstenbrand arr	6 5	9 11	12 12	3 31	6 36	10 26	...	...
Chemnitz ...arr	6 44	9 48	12 50	4 23	7 10	11 1	...	...

CHEMNITZ and RÖDERAU.

Chemnitz ...	4a20	6a58	8a34	1230	1p14	3p20	5p46	6p52	9p15	9p45
Mittweida......	4 52	7 16	9 5	1 0	1 32	3 51	6 17	7 10	9 32	1015
Waldheim ...	5 16	7 29	9 26	1 21	1 46	4 14	6 41	7 23	9 45	1037
Döbeln 183A	5 53	7 41	9 49	2 20	1 57	4 41	7 10	7 34	9 55	1111
Riesa arr	6 36	8 5	1028	3 4	2 20	5 20	7 47	7 57	1017	1154
Riesa dep	7 6	8 7	1042	3 10		7 23		7 58	1025	1 3
Röderau arr	7 12	8 12	1048	3 16	...	7 32	...	8 4	1034	1 12

Röderau dp	1a33	4a17	6a28	9 a5	1117	3p34	...	4p15	8p57	9p25
Riesa arr	1 39	4 24	6 34	9 10	1123	3 41	...	4 25	9 2	9 35
Riesa dep	1 55	4 54	7 1	9 11	1147	3 56	4p2	6 30	9 3	1010
Döbeln	2 30	5 49	7 41	9 44	1234	4 22	4 45	7 21	9 29	1111
Waldheim ...	2 46	6 11	8 1	9 56	1257	4 34	5 5	7 42	9 41	1132
Mittweida ...	3 5	6 34	8 23	1011	1 21	4 49	5 30	8 6	9 56	1156
Chemnitz	3 25	7 5	8 54	1030	1 52	5 9	6 4	8 36	1016	1227

Extra.—Riesa to Röderau, 3.45, 8.40, 9.56 a.m., 3.35 p.m. Röderau to Riesa, 8.24, 8.41 a.m., 11.8 p.m.
Chemnitz to Döbeln 5.25, 10.25 a.m. Döbeln to Chemnitz 9.58 a.m., 2.16 p.m.

Luggage Rates, see page 462.] SAXONY STATE RAILWAYS.

TETSCHEN and BODENBACH to DRESDEN, LEIPSIC, and BERLIN.

VIENNA (224 ......dep	...	...	...	...	...	...	8a50	...	...	...	...	...	...	...	...	...
	Ex3		1,2,3	Ex 3	1—4	1,2,3	Ex3			1—4	2,3,4	1,2,3	1—4		1,2,3	1,2,3
			p.m.	p.m.		p.m.	p.m.					p.m.			p.m.	p.m.
Tetschen..............dep	...	...	...	...	...	4 35	5 44	...	...	...	...	7 4	...	...	9 12	10 23
VIENNA (243) ......dep	6a30	...	...	...	...	...	8a25	...	...	...	...	...	...	...	...	...
PRAGUE (252).......dep	1220	...	...	...	...	...	2p56	...	...	...	...	...	p.m.	...	...	...
Bodenbach ....dep	2 55	...	1 45	4 2	...	4 36	5 45	...	...	...	...	7 3	8 31	...	9 12	10 26
Schöna	...	...	2 7	...	p.m.	5 2	...	...	...	p.m.	p.m.	7 31	8 48	...	9 41	10 52
Schandau	3 17	...	2 27	4 23	4 0	5 22	6 15	...	...	6 33	8 10	7 51	9 2	...	10 2	11 12
Königstein................	...	...	2 35	...	4 8	5 30	...	...	...	6 41	8 19	7 59	9 10	...	10 10	11 20
Pötzscha..................	...	...	2 50	...	4 23	5 47	RC	...	...	6 57	8 36	8 16	...	...	10 27	11 35
Pirna......................	...	...	3 8	...	4 48	6 2	...	...	...	7 14	8 52	8 33	9 29	...	10 42	11 49
DRESDEN Hauptbhof arr	3 52	...	3 42	5 0	5 21	6 23	6 53	...	...	7 50	9 29	8 54	9 46	...	11 2	12 9
			2 3 4	Ex 3					1—4				Ex 3			
			p.m	p.m.					p.m.				p.m.			
DRESDEN Haupt. dep	...	...	5 4	5 14	...	...	...	...	7 26	...	...	...	10 3	...	...	...
" Neustadt dep	...	...	...	5 20	...	...	...	...	7 39	...	...	...	10 11	...	...	...
Weinböhla................	...	...	5 53	...	...	...	...	...	8 4	...	...	...	...	...	...	...
Grossenhain..............	...	...	6 15	...	...	...	...	...	8 29	...	...	...	...	...	...	...
Elsterwerda..............	...	...	6 41	...	...	...	...	...	9 0	...	...	...	10 59	...	...	...
Dobril.-Kirchh.	...	...		RC	...	...	...	...	9 35	...	...	...	...	...	...	...
Uckro......................	...	...	...	...	...	...	...	...	10 20	...	...	...	...	...	...	...
Golssen....................	...	...	...	...	...	...	...	...	10 38	...	...	...	...	...	...	...
Zossen	...	...	...	...	...	...	...	...	11 26	...	...	...	...	...	...	...
BERLIN Anhalt. Bh. ar	...	...	...	7 57	...	...	...	...	12 2	...	...	...	12 49	...	...	...
	Ex3	Ex3	2 3 4		1—4	1—4	Ex3	Ex 3		1—4	Ex 3	1—4		Ex3	1—4	1,2,3
	p.m.	p.m.			p.m.	p.m.	p.m.	p.m.		p.m.	p.m.	p.m.		p.m	p.m.	a.m.
DRESDEN Hauptbh. dep	4 0	4 20	...	...	5 57	6 40	7 15	7 10		7 56	8 6	9 54	...	1030	10 53	12 25
" Neustadt arr	4 6	4 26	...	...	6 5	6 48	7 21	7 16		8 4	8 12	10 2	...	1036	11 1	12 33
" Neustadt dep	4 10	4 27	...	...	6 8	6 50	7 23	7 18		8 7	8 13	10 4	...	1040	11 3	12 35
Kötzschenbroda..........	...		...	...	...	7 5	RC	...		8 24	...	...	...	...	11 18	12 50
Coswig.....................	RC		...	...	6 25	7 13		...		8 32	...	10 21	...	...	11 24	12 56
Priestewitz..............	...		p.m.	...	6 48	7 35		...		8 58	...	10 41	...	1110	11 42	1 22
Riesa......................	4 56		5 26	...	7 19	7 53		8 2		9 31	...		...	1129		1 51
Oschatz....................	...		5 44	...	7 38			8 16		9 51	...		...	1142	...	2 9
Dahlen.....................	...		5 57	...	7 51	...		...		10 4	...		...	...		2 21
Wurzen.....................	...		6 21	...	8 16	...		8 40		10 29	...		...	12 6		2 42
Borsdorf...................	...		6 47	...	8 37	...		...		10 50	...		...	...		2 58
LEIPSIC Haupt. ...arr	5 53		7 7	...	8 50	...		9 5		11 5	9 41		...	1231		3 12
Priestewitz............dep	...		...	...	...	...		...		...	...	10 42	...	...		...
Röderau....................	...		...	...	...	...	8 12	...		...	...	11 10	...	...		...
Burxdorf..................	...		...	...	...	p.m.	8 27	...		...	...	11 28	...	...		...
Falkenberg...............	...		...	...	...	7 25	8‡45	...		...	...	11 48	...	...		...
Herzberg..................	...		...	...	...	7 39	8 57	...		...	...	12 0	...	...		...
Holzdorf..................	...		...	...	...	7 54	...	...		...	...	12 14	...	...		...
Jüterbog..................	...		...	...	...	8 28	9 30	...		...	...	12 49	...	...	...	...
BERLIN Anhalt. Bahnhf.	...	6 51	...	...	...	10 21	1026	...		...	...	2 6	...	...	...	...

‡—At Falkenberg connects with train for Magdeburg (arr. 11.42, page 172).

RC—Restaurant Car attached.

SCHONBERG and HIRSCHBERG.

Hirschberg ......dep	4a36	7a33	10a40	1p14	4p3	7p0
Schonberg 187 ...arr	5 33	8 52	11 28	2 3	5 1	7 55
Schonberg ...dep	6a26	9a15	1212	2p43	5p43	8p31
Hirschberg...arr	7 20	10 9	1 1	3 35	6 34	9 24

ROSSWEIN and CHEMNITZ.

	a.m.	a.m.	a.m.	a.m.	p.m.	p.m.	p.m.	p.m.	
Rosswein ....dep	...	6 18	...	10 16	...	3 7	5 28	9 7	...
Hainichen...............	5 20	7 6	8 50	11 5	1 13	3 59	6 18	9 54	...
Niederwiesa............	5 53	7 38	9 21	11 38	1 45	4 31	6 54	10 28	...
Chemnitz.........arr	6 10	7 54	9 37	11 54	2 1	4 47	7 10	10 44	...
Chemnitz ....dep	...	6a50	7 a43	8a45	12 p5	2 p22	6 p21	8 p52	11p20
Niederwiesa............	...	7 6	8 11	9 4	12 22	2 42	6 39	9 8	11 36
Hainichen	5a18	7 46	8 42	9 41	1 1	3 20	7 16	9 42	12 8
Rosswein ....arr	5 58	8 27	...		1 43	4 3	7 57	—	—

ALTENBURG and LANGENLEUBA-OBERHAIN.

	a.m.	a.m.	p.m.	p.m.	
Altenburg............dep	5 3	8 44	2 55	8 1	...
Wiesebach..................	5 38	9 19	3 30	8 37	...
Langenleuba ......arr	6 5	9 46	3 56	9 8	...
	a.m.	a.m.	p.m.	p.m.	
Langenleuba .....dep	7 6	10 54	5 16	10 9	...
Wiesebach..................	7 32	11 21	5 45	1035	...
Altenburg 189A arr	8 4	11 54	6 20	1111	...

CHEMNITZ and LIMBACH.

	a.m.	a.m.	a.m.	a.m.	a.m.	p.m.	p.m.	p.m.	p.m.	p.m.	p.m.	a.m.						
Chemnitz ....dep	6 3	7 12	8 15	10 0	1055	1 26	3 45	5 15	6 12	8 14	11 16	1 26	...	...	...	...	...	...
Wittgensdorf	6 24	7 34	8 42	10 21	1117	1 48	4 6	5 32	6 34	8 35	11 38	1 48	...	...	...	...	...	...
Limbach ....arr	6 38	7 48	8 59	10 35	1131	2 3	4 20	5 47	6 48	8 52	11 52	2 2	...	...	...	...	...	...
	a.m.	a.m.	a.m.	a.m.	p.m.	p.m.	p.m.	p.m	p.m.	p.m.	p.m.	n'gt						
Limbach ....dep	5 35	7 4	9 0	1036	12 5	1 10	2 38	4 50	6 13	6 58	9 46	1220	...	...	...	...	...	...
Wittgensdorf	5 50	7 18	9 15	1051	1224	1 25	2 52	5 5	6 27	7 13	10 2	1234	...	...	...	...	...	...
Chemnitz ....arr	6 10	7 38	9 35	1111	1245	1 45	3 12	5 25	6 47	7 30	10 22	1254	...	...	...	...	...	...

GERA, GOSSNITZ, and GLAUCHAU.

	a.m.	a.m.	a.m.	a.m.	p.m.	p.m.	p.m.	p m.	p.m.	p.m.	p.m.		a.m.	a.m	a.m.	a.m.	p.m.	p m	p.m	p.m.	p.m.	p.m.
Gera ...dep	4 58	6 8	7 51	10 1	1257	...	4 3	5 11	...	7 38	1045	Glauchau	5 34	8 2	8 28	1023	1 31	3 30	4 30	7 40	8 28	1028
Ronneburg	5 28	6 25	8 13	1027	1 20	...	4 27	5 30	...	8 4	11 7	Meerane ...	5 56	8 16	8 48	1040	1 50	3 50	4 52	7 57	8 39	1048
Gössnitz ...	6 28	7 3	9 38	1114	2 3	2 45	5 32	6 6	7 15	9 6	1146	Gössnitz ...	6 25	8 23	9 9	1114	2 27	3 59	5 29	9 14	8 53	1146
Meerane ...	6 39	7 10	9 50	1125	2 14	2 55	5 44	6 16	7 24	9 20	1155	Ronneburg	7 13	8 53	9 52	12 3	3 10	...	6 16	9 56	9 22	1226
Glauchau	6 56	7 22	10 7	1142	2 28	3 13	6 1	6 30	...	9 37	1212	Gera ...arr	7 33	9 9	1011	1221	3 31	...	6 36	1016	9 39	1245

Extra.{ Gössnitz to Meerane 7.32 a.m., 4.16 p.m. Meerane to Gössnitz 7.8 a.m., 2.9, 6.50 p.m.
Gössnitz to Glauchau, 1.12 a.m. Glauchau to Gössnitz, 12.28 a.m.

SAXONY STATE RAILWAYS.

PRIESTEWITZ and GROSSENHAIN

Priestewitz dep	3a46	6a39	7a25	9a23	10a33	11a34	12p35	1p45	3p17	4p4	5p34	6p55	8p23	8p32	9p3	9p38	11p0	11p45
Grossenhain ar	3 58	6 49	7 36	9 33	10 42	11 44	12 45	1 55	3 26	414	5 43	7 5	8 30	8 42	912	9 48	1110	11 52
Grossenhain dep	2a45	6a14	7a0	8a10	9a12	9a50	11a3	12p14	1p17	2p52	3p35	5p8	6p17	7p20	8p6	9p13	10p26	1211
Priestewitz 189	3 0	6 27	710	8 22	9 20	10 0	1119	12 24	1 32	3 2	3 45	518	6 31	7 30	815	9 23	10 36	1221

ZWICKAU and OELSNITZ.

Zwickau ......dep	...	6a51	10a20	2 p8	4p46	7p55	11p20	Oelsnitz.....dep	4a15	6a49	10a15	1p36	4 p52	8 p40	...
Lengenfeld	4a55	7 35	11 9	2 53	5 35	8 38	12 4	Falkenstein ...	5 3	7 43	11 6	2 29	5 42	9 31	...
Falkenstein	5 45	8 18	11 57	3 29	6 20	9 27	12 37	Lengenfeld.....	5 29	8 8	11 32	2 54	6 10	10 4	...
Oelsnitz 188...arr	6 27	9 0	12 35	4 10	7 3	1010	...	Zwickau ...arr	6 10	8 47	12 11	3 34	6 50	10 44	...

GASCHWITZ and PLAGWITZ-LINDENAU.

Gaschwitz ....dep	6 a16	9 a37	1 p8	4p11	5p54	7p20	...	Plagwitz-Lindenau ...dep	4a57	8a 33	11a 3	2p28	5 p6	6 p24
Plagwitz-Lindenau...arr	6 42	10 4	1 35	4 37	6 19	7 45	...	Gaschwitz..................arr	5 23	8 59	11 29	2 54	5 34	6 51

DRESDEN and SCHWEPNITZ.

Dresden N. dep	7a18	11a19	2 p45	5p42	8 p35	11p49	**Schwepnitz** dep	5a40	9 a25	...	3p40	...	9p12
Klotzsche...........	7 33	11 33	2 59	5 56	8 49	12 3	Königsbrück	6 18	9 58	12p28	4 30	7 p3	9 57
Königsbrück	8 33	12 35	3 52	6 53	9 52	12 57	Klotzsche	7 11	10 52	1 23	5 27	8 1	1055
Schwepnitz arr	9 2	1 10	...	7 25	10 20	...	**Dresden N.** ...arr	7 23	11 4	1 36	5 39	8 13	11 7

ALTENBURG and ZEITZ.—MEUSELWITZ and RONNEBURG.

Altenburg dp	6a48	7a51	10a47	1p56	3p48	5p49	7p34	9p30	11p28	Zeitz...... dep	5a22	6a45	8a57	11a18	1p45	3p48	5p50	7p34	9p31
Meuselwitz ...	7 18	8 21	11 21	2 25	4 23	6 22	8 6	10 2	11 58	Meuselwitz ...	5 59	7 12	9 24	11 52	2 16	4 16	6 17	8 0	9 57
Zeitz........arr	7 45	8 46	11 47	2 49	4 48	6 46	8 31	1027	...	**Altenburg** arr	6 30	7 39	9 53	12 24	2 44	4 47	6 48	8 28	1030

Meuselwitz ...dep	4 a45	7 a30	11a51	4p26	6†p22	10 p4	**Ronneburg** ......dep	5 a52	a.m.	9 a55	1 p40	6 p33	8 p8	†
Dobitschen	5 33	8 1	12 22	4 58	6 58	10 36	Dobitschen	6 35	8†29	10 38	2 26	7 17	9 6	Not
Ronneburg 189	6 45	8 45	1 5	5 42	7 45	11 20	**Meuselwitz** ......arr	7 7	9 41	11 9	2 57	7 48	947	Sun.

HERLASGRUN and ZWOTENTAL.

Herlasgrun...dep		6a40	8a24	9 a22	11a10	1p20	3p23	...	6 p1	8p 5	Zwotental..dep	5a35	6a47	9 a16	11a24	1p28	2p58	5 p51	9 p17
Eich	a.m.	7 6	8 49	9 48	1134	1 46	3 48	...	6 26	8 31	Muldenberg......	6 2	7 13	945	11 53	1 56	3 27	6 45	9 56
Falkenstein	5 31	7 25	9 8	10 7	1153	2 5	4 7	6p15	6 45	8 50	Falkenstein dep	6 33	8 27	10 12	12 22	2 27	5 4	7 42	1022
Muldenberg	5 53	8 50	9 37	10 35	1250	2 53	—	6 39	7 46	9 39	Eich..............	6 52	8 48	10 31	12 41	2 47	5 23	8 13	1041
Zwotental ar	6 39	9 15	10 6	11 12	1 18	3 21	...	7 9	...	1022	Herlasgrun arr	7 16	9 10	10 53	1 2	3 10	5 46	8 50	11 4

Extra. { Zwotental......dep 10a13, 7p25; Falkenstein ...arr 11 2, 8 29 | Falkenstein ...dep 5 a21; Herlasgrun ......arr 6 2 | Herlasgrun...dep 11p27 ...; Falkenstein...arr 12 12 ...

Extra.								
Zwotental......dep	10a13	7p25	Falkenstein ...dep	5 a21	Herlasgrun...dep	11p27	...
Falkenstein ...arr	11 2	8 29	Herlasgrun ......arr	6 2	Falkenstein...arr	12 12	...

MOLDAU and BIENENMUHLE.

Moldau ....dep	5a48	10 a5	1 p20	6 p30	9 p50	Bienenmuhle dep	4 a13	8a42	1144	3 p0	8p10
Bienenmuhle (190)...arr	6 35	10 52	2 7	7 17	10 41	Moldau (246) arr	5 10	9 37	1239	3 47	9 11

ZITTAU and HERMSDORF.

Zittau..............dep	6a58	a.m.	10a13	p.m.	1p44	5 p26	8 p21	...	Hermsdorf.i-B. dep	...	8 a11	10a30	2 p7	3 p20	6 p4	...
Reichenau	7 48	10 6	10 58	12 29	2 55	6 20	9 8	...	Markersdorf............	...	8 21	10 40	2 17	3 30	6 14	...
Markersdorf	7 53	10 12	...	12 35	3 1	6 26	...	...	Reichenau	5 a35	8 35	11 2	2 36	3 35	6 37	...
Hermsdorf-i-B. arr	8 3	10 22	...	12 45	3 11	6 36	...	...	Zittau (184) ......arr	6 20	9 23	11 47	3 22	—	7 22	...

LEIPSIC and MEUSELWITZ.

Leipsic-Bayer dep	5a51	7a54	9a44	12p38	1p20	2p45	4p48	6p37	8p30	11p21	Meuselw.	6a12	7a33	9a32	11a55	p.m.	3p1	5p5	6 51	8p9	p.m. 1020
Gaschwitz......	6 12	8 11	10 4	12 57	1 39	3 3	5 6	6 59	8 49	11 42	Groitzsch	6 40	8 8	10 2	12 28	...	3 36	537	7 44	845	1057
Groitzsch	6 38	8 44	1040	1 27	...	3 33	5 36	7 25	9 20	12 5	Gaschwitz	7 11	8 33	1030	1 1	2 25	4 4	6 7	8 15	914	1127
Meuselwitz arr	7 8	9 14	1112	1 59	...	4 5	6 8	7 56	9 52	12 35	Leipsic ar	7 33	8 51	1048	1 23	2 45	4 22	624	8 38	930	1148

OBERRITTERSGRUN and GRUNSTADTEL.

Oberrittersgrün dep	6a25	9a37	12p10	3p12	8p15	Grünstädtel ...dep	7a40	10a57	1p20	5p36	9p35
Grünstädtel ......arr	7 10	1021	12 55	3 58	8 58	Oberrittersgrün arr	8 30	11 43	2 10	6 21	1020

WERDAU and ANNABERG.

†—Weekdays only.

	a.m.	a.m.	a.m.	a.m.	a.m.	a.m.	a.m.	a.m.	a.m.	a.m.	p.m.	p.m.	p.m.	p.m.	p.m.	p.m.	p.m.	p.m.	p.m.	p.m.
Werdau ....dep	4 43	5 43	6 30	7 26	7 30	8 35	9 18	9 58	...	...	12 2	12 45	1 46	3 20	4 29	5 2	6 42	7 20	9 16	1034
Zwickau arr	5 2	6 2	6 47	7 36	7 49	8 53	9 31	1015	...	...	1221	1 4	2 3	3 38	4 42	5 23	7 0	7 41	9 34	1052
Zwickau dep	5 10	6 4	6 52	7 37	7 51	8 58	9 45	1017	...	11 15	1223	1 10	2 57	3 43	—	5 54	7 15	8 30	9 40	1120
Wilkau 185	5 28	6 18	7 8		8 4	9 16	10 1	1030	...	11 31	1240	1 27	3 7	3 59	p.m.	6 10	7 32	8 46	9 56	1134
Niederschlema	6 14	—	7 46	8 9	—	9 56	—	—	1057	12 15	—	2 7	3 39	4 38	7 1	—	8 15	—	10 40	1211
Aue 185 arr	6 21	...	7 52	8 15	...	10 3	...	...	11 5	12 21	...	2 14	3 45	4 44	7 9	...	8 22	...	10 47	1217
Aue 185 dep	6 38	...	8 6	8 19	...	1011	...	...	—	12 24	...	2 33	3 46	4 54	—	...	8 35	...	11 27	1222
Schwarzenberg arr	7 3	...	8 29	8 41	a.m.	10 34	...	...	...	12 47	...	2 56	4 7	5 17	...	...	9 0	...	11 50	1245
Schwarzenberg dep	7 8	...	—	—	8 46	10 42	...	...	...	12 52	...	3 0	—	5 21	...	...	9 18	...	—	—
Grünstädtel	7 18	a.m.	...	...	8 54	10 50	...	...	...	1 2	...	3 8	...	5 29	...	p.m.	9 27	...	...	...
Schlettau	8 1	5†35	...	...	9 46	11 35	...	...	...	1 49	...	3 53	...	6 18	...	8 30	10 12	...	...	...
Annaberg 189 ...arr	8 31	6 18	...	...	1023	12 8	...	...	...	2 23	...	4 25	...	6 54	...	9 4	10 44	...	...	...

						a.m.		a.m.		a.m.				p.m.	p.m.	p.m.			p.m.	p.m.
Annaberg ....dep		...	...	...	...	6 0	...	9 13	...	11 40	...	...	...	2 55	5 13	6 27	...	...	7 54	10 26
Schlettau		...	...	...	...	6 38	...	9 47	...	12 19	...	...	...	3 31	5 49	7 2	...	...	8 31	11 7
Grünstädtel		...	...	...	...	7 19	...	10 30	...	1 0	...	...	...	4 12	...	—	...	...	9 10	11 46
Schwarzenberg arr		a.m.	...	a.m.	...	7 26	...	10 37	...	1 7	...	p.m.	...	4 19	6 32	...	p.m.	p.m.	9 17	11 53
Schwarzenberg dep		4 18	...	6 3	...	7 33	...	10 45	...	1 12	...	3 15	...	4 25	6 40	...	7 52	9 8	9 25	—
Aue arr		4 40	...	6 26	...	7 56	...	11 8	...	1 35	...	3 36	...	4 48	7 3	...	8 15	9 26	9 48	...
Aue dep		5 10	...	6 42	...	8 16	...	11 15	...	1 38	...	3 37	...	5 2	7 5	...	8 25	9 28	9 58	...
Niederschlema.. ...	a.m.	5 18	a.m.	6 49	a.m.	8 28	a.m.	11 24	p.m.	1 47	p.m.	3 44	p.m.	5 11	7 12	p.m.	8 33	...	10 6	p.m.
Wilkau	4†34	5 56	6 23	7 28	8 18	9 10	1048	12 1	1 24	2 24	3 0	4 10	4 35	5 47	7 46	6 52	9 10	...	10 42	11 20
Zwickau arr	4 49	6 11	6 37	7 44	8 34	9 26	11 3	12 17	1 41	2 38	3 16	4 19	4 51	6 2	8 1	7 8	9 26	10 0	10 56	11 34
Zwickau dep	4 52	...	6 41	8 18	9 3	10 0	11 6	1 8	1 52	2 40	3 55	4 23	4 55	6 11	8 50	7 11	9,41	10 3	11 1	11 40
Werdau 187 ...arr	5 15	...	7 0	8 31	9 22	10 19	1126	1 27	2 10	2 58	4 15	4 37	5 14	6 27	9 10	7 30	10 0	1016	11 15	11 59

Johanngeorgenstadt dep	5 a8	6a10	9a53	12p 3	3p15	5p50	8p16	Schwarzenberg	7a34	8a50	10a55	1p12	5p34	9p26	11p58	...
Schwarzenberg.........arr.	5 52	7 3	1037	12 47	4 9	6 28	9 0	Johanngeorgenstadt	8 30	9 29	11 45	2 2	6 26	10 19	12 47	...

Niederschlema	6a28	8a34	10a0	12p35	2p 8	3 p47	5p16	8p38	10p44	Schneeberg ...	5a50	7a58	9a25	10a35	1p20	3 p10	4p14	6p35	9p38
Schneeberg ...	6 49	8 55	1021	12 55	2 28	4 7	5 37	8 58	11 4	Niederschlema	6 9	8 19	9 46	10 55	1 39	3 31	4 32	6 55	9 57

CRANZAHL and OBERWIESENTHAL.

Cranzahl.........dep	9a28	12p47	3p10	5p58	8p30	12a 2	Oberwiesenthal	7a32	10a40	1p20	3p20	6p 0	9p10
Oberwiesenthal arr	1030	1 46	4 22	7 5	9 39	1 6	Cranzahl.........	8 32	11 36	2 19	4 15	7 40	1011

Luggage Rates—see page 462.] **SAXONY STATE RAILWAYS.**

RADEBURG and RADEBEUL.

	a.m.	a.m.	a.m.	p.m.	p.m.	p.m.		a.m.	a.m.	p.m.	p.m.	p.m.	p.m.	
Radeburg ......dep	6 10	8 26	1044	1 23	5 30	9 32	**Radebeul** ...dep	7 18	9 36	12 10	4 8	8 21	11 15	...
Radebeul 188A)arr	7 9	9 24	1142	2 23	6 29	10 30	**Radeburg** ...arr	8 17	1035	1 10	5 9	9 20	12 14	...

‡—On Sun., Mon. Thurs. and Sat. only.]

DÖBELN and MÜGELN (O.)

		a.m.	p.m.	p.m.	p.m.		a.m.	a.m.	n'on	p.m.	p.m.
Döbeln ...dep	6‡45	10 0	1 42	4 45	7 41	**Mügeln** (Osch.) dp	4‡18	8 18	12 0	3 2	5 55
Tronitz............	7 26	10 42	2 19	5 21	8 22	Tronitz................	4 51	8 51	1234	3 36	6 29
Mügeln (O.) ar	8 0	11 16	2 52	5 55	8 56	**Döbeln (189)** arr	5 31	9 31	1 13	4 15	7 6

GEISING-ALTENBERG and MUGELN (Pirna).

Geising-Altenberg...dep	6 a0	10a12	1 p5	4 p9	8 p5	Mugeln...................dep	6 a28	9a43	2p25	5p10	9p12
Mugeln (Pirna) .....arr	8 9	12 17	3 12	6 12	1016	Geising-Altenberg...arr	8 44	11 56	4 40	7 19	1126

ORTMANNSDORF and MOSEL.

	a.m.	a.m.	p.m.	p.m.	p.m.		a.m.	a.m.	p.m.	p.m.	p.m.	
Ortmannsdorf.........dep	4 54	9 40	12 40	3 26	8 10	Mosel......................dep	8 39	11 20	2 2	6 30	10 40	...
Mosel ....arr	5 43	10 30	1 30	4 18	9 4	Ortmannsdorf.........arr	9 30	12 12	2 58	7 29	11 32	...

WILISCHTHAL and GEYER.

Wilischthal ...dep		7a58	...	1p30	4p18	...	1030	**Geyer**...........dep	5a30	7a13	10a14	1115	2 p1	5p51	8p33	1213
Oberherold		8 53	...	2 21	5 4	...	...	Ehrenfriedersdorf	5 49	7 33	10 33	1133	2 19	6 8	8 51	1229
Thum	7a10	9 5	11a49	3 21	5 15	9p33	1136	**Thum**	6 9	7 47	10 47	1154	2 45	6 27	9 5	1243
Ehrenfrieders	7 30	9 20	12 6	3 41	5 30	9 52	1153	Oberherold	6 17	—	—	12 5	2 55	6 36	—	—
Geyer ......arr	7 46	9 36	12 22	3 57	5 46	10 8	12 9	Wilischthal ...arr	7 5	...	...	1254	3 43	7 20	...	...

WERMSDORF and OSCHATZ.

Wermsdorf dp	a.m.	7a29	11a8	2p15	5p13	...	**Oschatz** dp	7a23	10a24	1p27	4p55	7p55	9p58
Mügeln (O.)	4 21	8 15	12 0	3 5	6 22	8p59	Mügeln (O.)	8 20	11 52	2 55	6 0	8 36	10 40
Oschatz 188 ar	5 5	8 55	1244	3 49	7 6	9 40	**Wermsd'f**	8 59	12 31	3 34	6 39	...	...

Oschatz ...dep	9a11	1p32	4 p47	8 p20	10p55	**Strehla** ......dep	6a23	11a57	3 p20	6 p21	9 p7	...	...	...	...
Strehla ...arr	9 52	2 13	5 28	8 58	11 33	**Oschatz** ...arr	7 5	12 39	4 2	7 1	9 45	...	...	...	...

‡—Sun, Wed, & Sat. only. **OBERCUNEWALDE and GROSSPOSTWITZ.**

Obercunewalde dp	7a48	a.m.	12 p4	2p28	7 p0	...	Grosspostwitz dp	...	8a50	11a10	1‡p40	...	5 p5	8p53
Cunewalde	8 5	1018	12 17	2 46	7 18	...	Cunewalde.........	7a23	9 15	11 38	2 3	2 p5	5 34	9 16
Grosspostwitz arr	8 30	1043	12‡41	3 11	7 43	...	Obercunewaldear	7 36	...	11 51	...	2 18	5 47	..

FREIBERG and HALSBRUCKE.

Freiberg ...dep	4a55	8a23	1p48	6p25	10p16	Halsbrücke dep	5a45	9a34	3p14	7p48	10p56
Halsbrücke arr	5 30	8 59	2 25	7 1	10 48	Freiberg......arr	6 17	10 7	3 47	8 24	11 27

BRAND and LANGENAU.

Brand ......dep	8a50	11a11	2p24	7 p2	10p54	Langenau ...dep	5a25	9 a21	11a55	4p40	8p20
Langenau ...arr	9 11	11 32	2 45	7 23	11 13	Brand ....arr	5 45	9 42	12 16	5 0	8 40

FREIBERG and GROSSHARTMANNSDORF.

Freiberg ....dep	6a33	8a18	10a38	1p53	6p30	1022	Grosshartm'dorf dep	5a25	a.m.	9a23	11a55	4p43	8p20
Berthelsdorf...................	6 46	8 32	10 54	2 7	6 45	1037	Brand	5 50	7 10	9 47	12 21	5 8	8 47
Brand	6 58	8 50	11 14	2 25	7 3	1054	Berthelsdorf	6 2	7 27	10 0	12 36	5 22	9 2
Grosshartmannsdorf arr	...	9 13	11 37	2 48	7 26	1117	Freiberg............arr	6 12	7 37	1010	12 46	5 32	9 12

SCHLETTAU and OBERCROTTENDORF.

Schlettau.............dep	6 a39	8a10	12 p2	7 p9	11p46	...	...	Obercrottendorf dep	7a22	9 a0	1 p10	7p48	12a36
Obercrottendorf...arr	7 12	8 43	12 40	7 40	12 21	...	...	Schlettau ....arr	7 57	9 35	1 43	8 21	1 7

LÖBAU and OBERRODERWITZ.

Löbau..............................dep	5a25	8 a32	11a57	3 p10	6 p35	8 p6	...	...	...	...	...
Herrnhut	5 53	9 0	12 26	3 40	7 1	8 39	...	...	...	...	...
Oberoderwitz 185 ......arr	6 6	9 13	12 39	3 54	7 14	8 53	...	...	...	...	...
Oberoderwitz ....dep	7 a34	10a29	1 p45	4 p16	6 p41	8p20	11p31	...	...	...	...
Herrnhut	7 49	10 45	2 0	4 31	7 0	8 38	11 45	...	...	...	...
Löbau (184) ....arr	8 17	11 13	2 28	4 59	7 28	9 6	12 11	...	...	...	...

WOLKENSTEIN and JOHSTADT.

Wolkenstein dp	8a24	2 p0	7 p15	...	...	Jöhstadt ...dep	5a20	11a15	5p30	...	...
Jöhstadt ...arr	9 39	3 15	8 30	...	...	Wolkenstein ar	6 39	12 30	6 50	...	...

SCHONBERG and SCHLEIZ.

Schönberg ....dep	6a28	9a16	12p14	2 p43	5p42	8p30	12a16	Schleiz ....dep	4 a48	7a44	10a46	1 p21	4p15	7 p6	10p40
Schleiz ....arr	7 10	9 59	1 55	3 29	6 26	9 12	12 56	Schönberg 189.........arr	5 31	8 29	11 30	2 6	5 3	7 49	11 22

HERRNHUT and BERNSTADT.

Herrnhut ...dep	9 a7	2 ‡p6	8p45	Bernstadt ...dep	7a 5	11a38	6p11	‡—Sunday
Bernstadt ...arr	9 49	2 47	9 22	Herrnhut ...arr	7 40	12 18	6 52	dep. 2.3 p.m.

DURRHENNERSDORF and TAUBENHEIM.

Durrhennersdorf...dep	9 a32	3 p31	8p32	Taubenheim............dep	7 a3	11a55	5 p45
Taubenheim ....arr	11 19	4 33	9 29	Durrhennersdorf......arr	7 55	12 55	6 51

HETZDORF and EPPENDORF.

Hetzdorf.........dep	9 a8	11a50	5 p34	10p10	Eppendorf ...dep	8 §a6	10a41	3 p30	6 p28	§Sun.dep.
Eppendorf ......arr	9 46	12 28	6 11	10 48	Hetzdorf 190A arr	8 40	11 15	4 5	7 2	6.54 a.m.

PENIG and WALDHEIM.

Penig ....dep	5a51	...	9a32	12p20	3p34	6p57	...	9p49	Waldheim dep	...	6a18	...	10a20	2p41	5p32	...	7p47	10p42
Langenleuba	6 9	6a24	9 55	12 39	4 0	7 19	9p12	1011	Rochlitz ...arr	...	7 25	...	11 24	3 45	6 38	p.m	9 5	11 48
Narsdorf............arr	6 22	6 35	10 8	12 52	4 13	7 32	9 23	1024	„ ...dep	5a56	7 31	9a34	12 20	3 48	—	7 5	1012	—
„ ....dep	6 51	8 24	1035	1 10	4 32	8 34	—	1 6	Narsdorf 184A	6 25	8 3	10 3	12 55	4 17	...	7 35	1042	...
Rochlitz 184 ...arr	7 19	8 52	11 3	1 37	4 58	9 1	...	1 31	„ ...dep	6a53	8 14	1030	1 13	4 46	...	8 57	1 9	9p52
„ ......dep 4 a1	8 7	...	1148	2 39	5 15	—	9p18	...	Langenleuba...	7 4	8 28	1048	1 20	5 2	...	9 12	1 23	10 3
Waldheim...arr 5 5	9 11	...	1252	3 36	6 31	...	1022	...	Penig 184 arr	...	8 45	11 9	1 51	5 19	...	9 29	1 40	...

CHEMNITZ and STOLLBERG. via Harthau.

Chemnitz (Haupt.)dp	6 a41	9a55	2p15	5 p53	8p50	12 p5	...	**Stollberg** ...dep	5a20	8a18	12p45	4p18	7p21	10p22	...
„ (Sud.) dep	6 47	10 2	2 22	5 59	8 58	12 11	...	Harthau................	5 59	8 57	1 24	4 57	8 1	11 2	...
Harthau	7 8	10 22	2 43	6 20	9 19	12 31	...	Chemnitz (Sud.) ...	6 19	9 17	1 44	5 17	8 20	11 22	...
Stollberg ....arr	7 49	11 4	3 24	7 1	10 0	1 12	...	„ (Haupt.)arr	6 25	9 26	1 51	5 24	8 26	11 30	...

MULDA and SAYDA.

Mulda.........dep	8 a24	11a35	2 p50	7 p58	...	Sayda ....dep	6 a0	10a15	1 p20	6p27	...
Sayda ....arr	9 43	12 54	4 9	9 17	...	Mulda 190 arr	7 1	11 16	2 21	7 28	...

NOSSEN, FREIBERG, and BIENENMUHLE.

	a.m.	a.m.	p.m.	p.m.	p.m.	p.m.	p.m.	p.m.		a.m.	a.m.	a.m.	p.m.	p.m.	p.m.	
Nossen ....dep	6 28	9 14	1211	...	4 5	...	8 23	...	**Bienenmühle** dp	4 43	6 50	11 2	2 15	...	7 25	...
Freiberg	7 50	10 47	1253	2 5	4 52	7 15	9 9	1015	Mulda	5 1	7 7	11 24	2 35	...	7 42	...
Lichtenberg	8 7	11 9	—	2 23	—	7 33	—	1032	Lichtenberg	5 8	7 14	11 31	2 42	...	7 53	p.m.
Mulda	8 16	11 20	...	2 33	...	7 43	...	1041	**Freiberg** ....arr	5 24	7 30	11 49	3 0	5 45	8 11	9 52
Bienenmühle ar	8 36	11 40	...	2 55	...	8 3	...	11 2	**Nossen 188A** arr	6 59	8 46	1 32	...	6 20	...	1026

FLOHA and REITZENHAIN.

* Not on Sunday. ‡—Sat. and Sun. excepted.

	a.m.	a.m.	a.m.	p.m.	p.m.	p.m.	p.m.
Chemnitz ......dep	6 21	8 38	10 50	2 14	4 49	5 54	9 25
Flöha, Staats.........dep	6 41	8 53	11 20	2 40	5 19	6 9	9 52
Hetzdorf	6 51	9 1	11 30	2 48	5 29	6 ‡25	10 4
Grünhainichen	7 13	9 21	11 50	3 8	5 52	6 ‡44	10 35
Pockau-Lengefeld dep	7 41	10 0	12 18	3 35	6 24	—	11 4
Marienberg	8 15	10 33	12 51	4 8	6 57	...	11 36
Reitzenhain 251 ...arr	8 51	...	1 27	4 43	7 32	...	12 10

		a.m.	a.m.	p.m.	p.m.	p.m.	p.m.
Reitzenhain...dep	...	5 42	9 34	...	2 19	5 18	8 40
Marienberg	*	6 15	10 7	1248	2 55	5 51	9 14
Pockau-Lengefeld	a.m.	6 50	10 44	1 23	3 31	6 26	9 49
Grunhainichen	5 56	7 14	11 8	1 46	3 54	6 49	10 14
Hetzdorf	6 15	7 34	11 29	2 7	4 14	7 8	10 35
Flöha, Staats ...arr	6 23	7 41	11 37	2 15	4 22	7 16	10 43
Chemnitz...arr	6 49	8 3	12 4	2 42	4 56	7 59	11 10

Neuhausen..............dep	5 a46	9a37	...	2p25	5p23	8 p43
Olbernhau	6 21	10 15	12p56	3 0	5 58	9 20
Pockau-Lengefeld ...arr	6 43	10 37	1 18	3 23	6 20	9 42

Pockau-Lengefeld ......dep	7a48	9a42	12p25	3 p42	6p31	11p11
Olbernhau	8 23	10 12	12 58	4 14	7 3	11 43
Neuhausen ....arr	8 59	...	1 34	4 50	7 39	12 19

AALEN and DILLINGEN.

Aalen..............dep	...	7a32	11†a50	6p15
Ballmertshofen	4a35	9 54	2 25	8 10
Dillingen ......arr	6 1	1047	3 19	8 55

Dillingen ....dep	7 a15	12*p19	5p56	9p53
Ballmertshofen	8 13	1 11	6 54	1038
Aalen..................arr	10 23	3 20	9 26	...

*-Sun. 10.38 a.m. †—11.18 a.m. on Sunday.

WURTTEMBERG RAILWAYS—(WURTTEMBERGISCHE EISENBAHNEN).—

MARBACH and HEILBRONN.

Marbach-a-N. dep	...	5a40	8a18	1 p28	3p46	7*p0	8p14	10p11	...
Kleinbottwar	...	6 4	8 44	1 52	4 10	7 22	8 35	1032	...
Beilstein	4§a37	6 41	9 27	2 29	4 51	7 50	9 8	11 0	...
Ilsfeld	5 0	7 1	9 49	2 49	5 13	—	9 29	—	...
Heilbronn (Sud)ar	5 46	7 47	1043	3 46	6 6	...	1018	...	...

Heilbronn (Sud) dep		5a33	8a37	1p10	4p25	6 p29	10p28
Ilsfeld		6 17	9 32	1 59	5 14	7 23	11 11
Beilstein	4a34	6 44	10 0	2 25	5 39	7 51	11 28
Kleinbottwar	5 1	7 14	1033	2 57	6 12	8 20	—
Marbach 194 arr	5 22	7 35	11 0	3 24	6 41	8 43	...

*—6.0 p.m. on Sundays. §—4.20 a.m. on Sunday.

LAUFFEN and LEONBRONN.

‡—Weekdays only.

Lauffen ...dep	...	6a59	8a36	12 p2	2p50	...	7 p6	8p56	...	...	...	...	...
Brackenheim	5a39	7 30	9 6	12 25	3 25	5‡p50	7 33	9 24	...	...	...	...	...
Guglingen	5 53	7 48	9 26	12 40	3 49	6 4	7 51	9 42	...	...	...	...	...
Leonbronn arr	6 23	8 22	9 59	1 8	4 23	6 33	...	1015	...	...	...	...	...

Leonbronn...dep	4‡a47	a.m.	6a35	8a30	10a14	1p18	p.m.	4‡p55	6p48	10p25	...	...	...	...	...	...	...	...	...
Guglingen	5 16	4 48	7 9	8 58	10 52	1 48	4 41	5 24	7 34	10 54	...	...	...	...	...	...	...	...	...
Brackenheim	5 30	5 5	7 26	—	11 14	2 3	5 1	5 38	7 56	—	...	...	...	...	...	...	...	...	...
Lauffen (193)arr	...	5 31	7 49	...	11 41	2 25	5 28	...	8 22	...	...	...	...	...	...	...	...	...	...

SCHUSSENRIED and BUCHAU

Schussenried dep	8 a8	11a18	3p15	5p23	10p6	...
Buchau ....arr	8 46	11 56	3 53	6 1	1044	...

Buchau..............dep	5a27	10 a5	12p13	4p23	8p26	...
Schussenried (193)arr	6 4	10 42	12 50	5 0	9 3	...

BLAUFELDEN and LANGENBURG.

Blaufelden ...dep	6a20	8a30	11a10	2p38	5p40	7p53
Langenburg arr	6 58	9 8	11 48	3 16	6 18	8 31

Langenburg dep	5 a0	7a34	10a21	1p22	4p42	6p38
Blaufelden ...arr	5 37	8 11	10 58	2 4	5 20	7 15

HEILBRONN, HALL, and CRAILSHEIM.

†—Weekdays only.

	2 3 4	Ex3	2 3 4	2 3 4	Ex1	1,2,3	Ex3	1—4	2 3 4	2 3 4	2,3,4	2 3 4	2 3 4	1,2,3	Ex3	2 3 4	3 &4	2 3 4	3 &4	2 3 4	2 3 4
			a.m.	a.m.	a.m.	a.m.			a.m.		p.m.		p.m.	p.m.		p.m.	p.m.		p.m.	p.m.	p.m.
Heilbronn dep	...	...	5†35	6 10	7 15	8 15	...	...	9 29	...	12 24	...	2 15	4 24	...	5 5	6 24	...	7 32	9 30	11 9
Weinsberg	...	...	5 50	6 24	:	8 25	...	...	9 43	...	12 39	...	2 31	...	...	5 20	6 40	...	7 48	9 44	1124
Bretzfeld	...	...	6 21	6 48	:	...	...	...	1013	...	1 5	...	3 4	...	...	5 46	7 16	...	8 23	10 8	1155
Oehringen	...	...	6 30	6 58	K	8 44	...	...	1023	...	1 15	...	3 18	4 51	...	5 56	7 27	...	8 33	10 18	12 3
Waldenburg	a.m.	...	From 15th Sept.	7 23	:	...	...	a.m.	1047	p.m.	1 44	p.m.	3 49	5 9	...	6 20	7 51	p.m.	—	10 42	—
Hall ....arr	4 28	a.m.		7 45	:	9 12	...	9 36	11 8	1212	2 6	3 50	4 15	5 23	...	6 42	8 15	8 18	...	11 5	...
STUTTGART dep	...	6 0		...	:	...	8a15	...	8a40	...	10a59	...	1246	...	4 p0	4p15	—	6 p5	...	...	...
Hessenthal 191	5 5	...		8 37	:	...	...	9 50	1126	1228	2 27	4 6	4 46	...	5 43	7 8	...	8 47	...	11 28	...
Eckartshausen	5 39	...		9 9	:	...	...	—	1159	—	2 58	—	5 28	...	...	7 44	...	9 25	...	—	...
Crailsheim arr	5 55	7 39		9 23	8 57	9 46	1016	...	1211	...	3 13	...	5 46	5 59	6 12	8 0	...	9 40	...	...	...

	2 3 4	2 3 4	3&4	1—4	2 3 4	2 3 4	Ex 3	1,2,3	2 3 4	2 3 4	2 3 4	2 3 4	2 3 4	2 3 4	1,2,3	2 3 4	2 3 4	Ex1	3 &4	Ex3	2 3 4
				a.m.	a.m.	a.m.	a.m.	a.m.	a.m.		p.m.		p.m.		p.m.		p.m.	p.m.	p.m.	p m	n'gt
Crailsheim dp	...	...	...	5†50	7 0	9 11	9 48	10 0	...	...	1252	...	3 20	...	6 53	...	7 0	7 48	8 33	1117	...
Eckartshausen	...	...	...	5 6	7 19	9 28	...	10 13	...	...	1 9	p.m.	3 40	p.m.	...	p.m.	7 18	:	8 52	...	...
Hessenthal ...arr	...	...	...	6 33	7 48	9 57	...	...	1130	...	1 37	1 52	4 6	5 45	7 17	7 10	7 46	:	9 26	1143	1227
STUTTGART arr	...	...	a.m.	...	1038	...	11a45	...	...	p.m.	...	...	6p56	...	9p53	...	11p12	:	...	1252	
Hall	...	...	4 58	6 45	8 6	1012	—	10 38	1139	1214	2 10	2 0	4 23	5 58	7 27	7 19	8 1	K	9 40	—	1235
Waldenburg	a.m.	a.m.	5 27	—	8 32	—	...	10 58	—	1243	2 42	—	4 56	6 33	7 43	—	8 28	:	—	...	—
Oehringen	4 30	5 ‡5	5 48	...	8 50	...	...	11 11	...	1 1	3 1	...	5 16	7 1	7 56	...	8 58	:	...	...	...
Bretzfeld	4 41	5 15	5 57	...	8 59	...	...	...	...	1 10	3 12	...	5 27	7 12	...	...	9 8	:	...	...	...
Weinsberg	5 13	5 46	6 29	...	9 23	...	...	11 32	...	1 39	3 50	...	5 55	7 46	8 13	...	9 43	:	...	...	...
Heilbronn arr	5 26	6 0	6 42	...	9 35	...	...	11 41	...	1 51	4 5	...	6 7	8 0	8 22	...	9 56	9 15	...	...	...

K—Carlsbad Express runs until 28th September.

WEIKERSHEIM and CREGLINGEN.

	a.m.	a.m.	p.m.	p.m.
Weikersheim......dep	7 32	11 50	4 48	8 8
Röttingen-i-Ufr. 196A ...	7 59	12 18	5 9	8 35
Creglingen ....arr	8 25	12 45	5 30	9 1

	a.m.	a.m.	p.m.	p.m.	
Creglingen ....dep	5 28	8 45	3 28	5 41	...
Röttingen-i-Ufr.	5 55	9 20	4 6	6 10	...
Weikersheim 191 arr	6 23	9 41	4 28	6 42	...

SCHORNDORF and WELZHEIM.

Schorndorf...dep	5a55	8 a4	1‡p59	6 p13	9 p15
Rudersberg	6 27	8 35	2 34	6 52	9 47
Welzheim......arr	7 21	9 19	3 19	7 37	10 33

Welzheim...........dep	4 a31	5 a42	9 a27	1 p48	7 p0
Rudersberg	5 14	6 25	10 5	2 31	7 47
Schorndorf 191...arr	5 45	6 56	10 34	3 0	8 26

‡—Weekdays only.

ULM, AALEN, CRAILSHEIM, and MERGENTHEIM.

†—Weekdays only. *—Arrive 1.21 p.m.

	234	234	234	1,2,3	234	234	2,3,4	234	234	Ex3	234	2,3,4	1,2,3	234
		a.m.	a.m.	a.m.	a.m.	a.m.	a.m.	p.m.	p.m.	p.m.	p.m.	p.m.	p.m.	p.m.
Ulm ....dep	...	4 11	...	7 55	6 36	8 20	11 20	...	2 23	4 10	5 9	7 30	8 53	1030
Sontheim-a-d-B.	...	4 50	6 †9	...	7 24	9 8	12 16	...	3 14	...	5 56	8 18	...	1125
Giengen............	...	5 9	6†23	8 30	7 41	9 26	12 35	1257	3 34	4 48	6 11	8 40	9 26	1143
Heidenheim......	...	5 38	6†46	8 43	8 2	9 49	1 2	2*23	3 59	5 3	6 33	9 8	9 38	12 4
Königsbronn ...	...	5 59	7 †3	...	8 20	10 6	1 19	2 41	4 17	...	6 47	9 25	...	—
Aalen 191 ...arr	...	6 22	7†26	9 3	8 45	1029	1 41	3 5	4 40	5 23	7 8	9 47	9 58	...
NORDLING arr	...	7a55	...	1031	1031	1†20	3 p26	...	6p10	...	8p51	10p43	1043	...
Aalen ....dep	...	6 32	7 52	9 7	—	1052	1 51	3 7	4 53	5 26	7 15	10 7	—	...
Wasseralfingen	...	6 37	7 57	...	...	1057	1 56	3 12	4 58	...	7 20	10 12	...	...
Goldshofe.........	...	6 46	8 9	...	...	1111	2 8	—	5 9	...	7 32	10 23	...	...
Ellwangen	...	7 0	8 25	9 24	...	1128	2 26	...	5 23	5 44	7 49	10 53	...	...
Jagstzell	...	7 11	8 41	...	...	1144	2 43	...	5 34	...	8 4	11 8	...	...
Crailsheim...arr	...	7 34	9 5	9 43	2 3 4	12 7	3 8	...	5 54	6 4	8 25	11 36	...	...
NURNBERG arr	a.m.	9 a0	—	1148	a.m.	2p44	7 p5	...	7p55	7p55	1129	—	...	...
Crailsheim dep	4 53	7†43	...	9 51	1020	1 12	3 25	...	6 49	—	9 44	...	...	...
Roth am See......	5 21	8 †9	...	10 9	1046	1 45	3 51	...	7 13	...	10 8	...	...	...
Blaufelden	5 43	8†28	...	1021	11 4	2 8	4 5	...	7 27	...	1021	...	...	...
Niederstetten ...	6 11	9†31	a.m.	1042	1130	2 35	4 29	...	7 50	...	1042	...	...	...
Weikersheim ...	6 29	1013	1020	1053	1146	2 50	4 45	...	8 4	...	1056	...	...	...
Mergentheim ...	6 50	†	1042	11 5	12 7	3 9	5 8	...	8 26	...	1115	...	...	...
143 WURZBURG	9 a5	...	1245	1245	1p21	4p56	6 p51	...	10p13	...	...	...	...	...

	234	234	234	1,2,3	Ex3	2,3,4	234	1—4	234	Ex3	234	234	2,3,4
WURZBURG dp	...	...	4a30	5†50	...	7 a27	...	9a58	2 p0	...	...	5 p4	8 p37
		a.m.	a.m.	a.m.		a.m.		p.m.	p.m.			p.m.	p.m.
Mergentheim dp	...	...	7 0	8 25	...	9 18	...	1 18	4 6	...	...	6 24	9 58
Weikersheim ...	...	...	7 27	8 38	...	9 47	...	1 40	4 32	...	...	6 50	10 20
Niederstetten	...	5 31	7 52	8 51	...	10 9	...	2 1	4 57	...	...	7 11	10 40
Blaufelden	...	6 9	8 26	9 14	...	11 3	...	2 35	5 33	...	...	7 50	—
Roth am See	...	6 24	8 36	...	...	11 18	...	2 46	5 44	...	...	8 4	...
Crailsheim...arr	...	6 50	9 1	9 36	a.m.	11 44	...	3 10	6 9	...	...	8 25	...
NURNBERG dp	a.m.	...	6 a4	—	7 58	...	...	12p2	—	5 p6	p.m.	...	...
Crailsheim ..dep	5 11	7 16	9 27	...	9 53	12 19	...	3 40	...	6 50	6 57	8 36	...
Jagstzell	5 36	7 41	9 51	...	...	12 42	...	4 5	...	...	7 18	9 0	...
Ellwangen	5 53	8 1	10 2	...	1014	12 58	...	4 22	...	7 10	7 29	9 17	...
Goldshofe	6 12	8 23	1018	...	...	1 17	p.m.	4 43	...	...	7 46	9 39	...
Wasseralfingen	6 20	8 32	1025	...	...	1 26	3 15	4 52	...	...	7 55	9 48	...
Aalen ....arr	6 24	8 37	1029	...	1032	1 30	3 19	4 56	...	7 27	7 59	9 52	...
NORDLGEN dp	4a36	8a13	8a13	...	8a13	12 p5	...	3p56	...	...	...	9p24	...
Aalen ....dep	6 34	9 6	1040	...	1033	1 43	3 26	5 11	...	7 34	8 7	1020	...
Königsbronn	7 2	9 31	11 6	...	...	2 9	3 53	5 37	p.m.	...	8 34	1045	a.m.
Heidenheim......	7 21	9 47	1125	...	1056	2 25	4 13	5 54	6 18	7 56	8 53	11 1	4 49
Giengen............	7 41	10 4	1143	...	11 7	2 43	4 35	6 14	6 49	8 8	9 15	1118	5 8
Sontheim	7 58	...	1158	...	...	2 58	4 53	6 27	7 7	8 17	9 33	—	5 23
Ulm 192 ......arr	8 58	1043	1250	...	1139	3 47	5 51	7 9	8 12	8 46	1026	...	6 15

STUTTGART and HALL.

†—Weekdays only.] A—Berlin-Zurich Express.

	234	Ex3	Ex3	234	234	234	Ex3	234	1—4	234	234	234
Stuttgart	a.m.	a.m.	a.m.	a.m.	a.m.	p.m.	p.m.	p.m.	p.m.	p.m.	p.m.	p.m.
Haupt. dep	4 50	6 0	8 15	8 40	1059	1246	4 0	4 15	6 5	6 48	9 40	1116
Cannstatt	5 0	⋮	8 22	8 48	11 7	1255	4 7	4 25	6 14	6 58	9 47	1124
Waiblingen	5 27	⋮	8 38	9 8	1129	1 33	4 21	4 44	6 35	7 19	10 9	114
Winnenden	5 50	⋮	8 50	9 29	1153	1 56	4 33	5 11	6 59	7 42	1033	12 4
Backnang (194)	6 16	⋮	9 10	9 54	1215	2 22	4 55	5 41	7 24	8 0	1055	1216
Murrhardt	7 3	A	⋮	1026	1247	2 56	5 11	6 12	7 53	—	1125	—
Gaildorf..................	7 31	⋮	⋮	11 0	1 20	3 31	5 29	6 41	8 21	...	1128	...
Hessenthal ...arr	7 51	⋮	⋮	1122	1 44	3 58	5 42	7 3	8 42	...	1220	...
Hall ....arr	8 2	⋮	⋮	1139	2 0	4 19	5 55	7 19	9 7	...	1235	...
HESSENTHAL ...dp	8 37	⋮	⋮	1126	2 27	4 46	5 43	7 8	8 47	...	—	...
CRAILSHM 190A arr	9 23	7 39	1016	1211	3 13	5 46	6 12	8 0	9 40	...	...	...
NURNBERG **204**	...	9 a0	1148	2p44	7 p5	7p55	7p55	1129	...	...	...	...

	234	234	234	234	Ex3	1—4	234	2,3,4	Ex3	234	234	234	Ex 3
NURNBERG 204 dep	...	...	...	...	7a58	...	...	12 p2	5 p6	...	5 p6	...	9 p40
CRAILSH'M 190A dp	...	2†58	...	7 a0	9a48	9 a11	...	3 p20	6p50	...	6p53	7 p0	11p17
HESSENTHAL ...arr	...	4†23	...	7a48	⋮	9 a57	...	4 p6	⋮	...	7p17	7p46	11p43
		a.m.		a.m.	⋮	a.m.	p.m.	p.m.	⋮		p.m.	p.m.	⋮
Hall ....dep	...	4 23	...	7 49	⋮	9 36	1212	3 50	⋮	...	6 45	8 18	⋮
Hessenthal ... dep	...	4 51	...	8 12	⋮	9 59	1236	4 18	⋮	...	7 20	8 43	11 44
Gaildorf	...	5 12	...	8 33	1026	10 35	1257	4 41	⋮	...	7 42	9 4	...
Murrhardt..............	a.m.	5 40	a.m.	8 58	...	11 7	1 25	5 11	⋮	p.m.	8 10	9 28	...
Backnang	4 57	6 24	6 39	9 35	1054	11 58	2 2	5 48	⋮	8 10	8 44	10 0	A
Winnenden	5 21	6 49	6 59	9 55	1115	12 19	2 22	6 6	⋮	8 33	9 6	1019	...
Waiblingen	5 44	7 12	7 25	1014	1126	12 40	2 41	6 27	⋮	8 59	9 26	1042	...
Cannstatt	6 3	7 32	7 48	1031	1137	12 56	2 57	6 46	8 41	...	9 44	1059	...
Stuttgart H. ...arr	6 12	7 40	7 56	1038	1145	1 4	3 6	6 56	8 51	...	9 53	1112	12 52

STUTTGART and NORDLINGEN.

†—Weekdays only.

	234	234	1,2,3	234	234	1,2,3	234	234	1,2,3	234	234	234	234	1,2,3	234
Stuttgart	a.m.	a.m.	a.m.		a.m.	a.m.		a.m.	p.m.	p.m	p.m.	p.m.	p.m.	p.m.	p.m.
Haupt. dep	4 39	3 59	7 21	...	7 31	9 47	...	1110	1 5	2 35	4 5	5 0	7 12	8 39	1116
Cannstatt............	4 47	4 9	7 28	...	7 40	9 54	...	1119	1 12	2 42	4 15	5 9	7 20	...	1124
Waiblingen.........	5 8	4 28	7 42	...	8 1	1013	...	1137	1 29	2 58	4 34	5 24	7 39	...	1143
Schorndorf.........	5 52	4 57	7 58	...	8 47	1042	...	12 8	1 57	3 19	6 16	5 45	8 33	9 12	1214
Lorch		5 23	8 13	...	9 14	11 3	...	1234	2 16	3 45	6 50	6 10	9 0	...	1239
Gmund.....................		5 40	8 24	a.m.	9 31	1114	a.m.	1251	2 28	4 1	7 6	6 25	9 15	9 34	1250
Aalen (191 ....arr		6 25	8 55	9 18	1020	—	1052	1 36	3 3	4 46	8 20	7 10	1029	10 0	—
CRAILSHEIM ....arr		7a34	9a43	...	12p7	...	†	3 p8	—	5p54	1133	8p25	—	1136	...
Goldshofe (191) ...		6 56	⋮	9 35	—	...	1112	2 25	...	5 15	—	7 50	...	...	...
Bopfingen		7 36	⋮	1013	...	...	1245	3 6	...	5 52	...	8 31	...	1031	...
Nördlingen 197A ar		7 55	⋮	1031	...	...	1 20	3 26	...	6 10	...	8 51	...	1043	...
NURNBERG 197B arr		1019	1148	3p33	...	...	4 p0	7p17	...	9p32	...	1235	...	1235	...

		234	234	1,2,3	234	Ex3	234	234	234	234	1,2,3	234	234	234	Ex3	234
NURNBERG dp		...	...	...	...	6 a0	...	...	...	...	...	1p31	...	...	5 p6	7p10
			a.m.			a.m.			a.m.	p.m.		p.m.			⋮	p.m
Nördlingen...dep		...	4 36	...	...	8 13	...	...	9 49	12 5	...	3 56	...	...	⋮	9 24
Bopfingen		...	4 58	a.m.	...	8 28	a.m.	a.m.	1013	1230	...	4 18	...	...	⋮	9 39
Goldshofe		...	5 37	6 12	...	...	8 23	1018	1058	1 9	...	4 53	...	...	⋮	10 5
CRAILSH'M dp		...	...	5a11	...	7a16	7a16	...	9 53	1219	p.m.	3p40	...	p.m.	6p50	8p36
Aalen ......dep		a.m.	5 50	6 30	a.m.	8 59	9 20	1029	1124	1 47	3 30	5 29	p.m.	6 29	7 31	1022
Gmund.....	2 3 4	5 46	—	6 57	7 9	9 22	10 4	—	12 9	2 32	4 4	6 9	6 26	8 15	7 56	11 2
Lorch	a.m.	6 1	...	7 6	7 24	9 31	1016	...	1223	2 45	4 13	6 19	6 41	8 28	...	1113
Schorndorf	4 36	6 34	...	7 19	8 5	9 44	1039	...	1249	3 11	4 32	6 43	7 7	8 56	8 16	1136
Waiblingen	5 27	7 41	...	7 37	8 57	...	11 8	...	1 33	3 43	4 59	7 14	8 49	9 40	...	12 6
Cannstatt...	5 45	8 1	...	7 48	9 17	10 8	1123	...	1 50	4 0	5 13	7 30	9 9	9 58	8 43	1222
Stuttgart	5 54	8 9	...	7 56	9 25	1016	1130	...	1 58	4 8	5 21	7 40	9 18	10 6	8 51	1230

Extra

Stuttgart......dep	1p53	5†p47	6p20	8 p9
Schorndorf...arr	3 10	7 9	7 42	9 33

Schorndorf......dep	3a55	5a37	6p10
Stuttgart..........arr	5 14	7 4	7 34

Aalen ......dep	5a43
Gmund ...arr	6 28

Gmund.......................dep	5 a5	8a30	12p12	2p33	6p30	8 p17	...
Göppingen 192............arr	6 37	10 7	1 25	4 5	8 3	9 28	...

Göppingen.........................dep	5a15	7a25	10a42	2p18	6 p30	8 p10	...	...
Gmund................................arr	6 48	9 15	12 2	3 57	8 7	9 29	...	...

ALTSHAUSEN and PFULLENDORF.

Altshausen	8 a0	11a32	12p42	5p38	10p18	**Pfullendorf**	4 a54	9a20	2 p9	3p43	7p40	...
Ostrach	8 30	12 1	1 32	6 27	10 52	**Ostrach**	5 20	9 46	2 45	4 27	8 13	...
Pfullendorf	8 50	12 37	7	7 11	11 17	**Altshausen**	5 54	1013	3 22	5 15	9 2	...

Luggage Rates—see page 462.] WURTTEMBERG AND BAVARIAN RAILWAYS.

BRUCHSAL, BIETIGHEIM, STUTTGART, ULM, and MUNICH.

Dist. E.M.	Station																		
...	FRANKFORT 136 dep	...	...	10p49	...	...	...	...	...	...	...	...	...	...	...	4a24	...	...	7 a12
...	COLOGNE 122 ...dep	...	...	8 p2	...	...	...	...	...	...	...	...	...	...	...	1a58	...	...	...
...	MAYENCE ....dep	...	...	11p25	...	...	...	...	...	...	...	...	...	...	...	5a30	...	...	6 a15
				Ex 3		Ex3	2&3	2 3 4	Ex.1	1—4	2 3 4	1 2 3	2 3 4	2,3,4	Ex3	Ex3	2 3 4	1,2,3	1—4
				a.m.			a.m.				a.m.			a.m.		a.m.			a.m.
—	**Bruchsal** ....dep	...	...	1 36	...	...	4 47	...	...	...	7 5	...	...	6 0	...	8 5	...	...	9 30
9¾	**Bretten** .... arr	...	...	1 52	...	...	5 15	...	...	...	7 31	...	...	6 24	...	...	...	...	9 54
	Bretten .... dep	...	...	1 53	...	...	5 23	...	...	...	7 37	...	...	6 29	...	...	...	...	9 56
16½	Maulbronn	...	...	...	...	...	5 53	...	...	...	7 58	...	...	6 52	...	...	...	...	10 19
20¼	**Muhlacker** ....arr	...	...	2 9	...	...	6 5	...	Œ	...	8 8	...	...	7 2	...	8 36	...	...	10 29
...	PARIS 64..........dep	...	...	12 0	...	5p15	...	...	7p13	...	...	...	...	...	9 p5	...	...	...	...
...	STRASSBURG 145 dep	...	...	10p58	...	1a45	...	...	3 a44	...	...	...	...	...	5a56	...	...	...	7a18
...	CARLSRUHE 141...dep	...	...	1 a1	...	3a10	...	...	5 a3	a.m.	...	...	...	5 ‡8	7a19	...	...	a.m.	9a43
...	**Muhlacker** ....dep	...	...	2 15	...	4 3	...	...	⋮	6 39	...	...	...	7 5	8 13	8 37	...	10 19	11 5
27	Vaihingen-an-der-Enz ...	...	...	⋮	...	...	...	...	⋮	6 59	...	...	...	7 23	...	...	...	...	11 24
34¾	**Bietigheim** ....arr	...	...	⋮	...	4 24	...	...	⋮	7 21	...	...		7 40	8 33	8 56	...	10 41	11 41
...	BACKNANG......194 arr	...	...	⋮	...	5a59	...	...	⋮	...	...	...	...	...	9 a6	1023	...	11a55	...
...	NURNBERG ....arr	...	...	⋮	...	9 a0	...	a.m.	⋮	...	a.m.	a.m.	a.m.	...	1148		a.m.		...
...	**Bietigheim**..........dep	...	...	⋮	...	4 25	...	4 57	⋮	...	5†30	7 5	7 29	7 48	8 36	8 57	9 1	...	11 44
40½	**Ludwigsburg**	...	...	2 48	...	4 37	...	5 23	⋮	...	6 0	7 25	7 50	8 10	8 46	...	9 22	...	12 6
44¼	Zuffenhausen	...	...	...	...	...	...	5 40	⋮	...	6 15	...	8 6	8 24	...	...	9 36	...	12 20
46½	Feuerbach	...	...	...	...	...	...	5 46	⋮	...	6 21	...	8 11	8 28	...	...	9 41	...	12 25
49¼	**STUTTGART— Hauptbahnhof** arr	...	...	3 4	...	4 52	...	5 55	6 40	...	6 29	7 45	8 20	8 35	9 2	9 19	9 50	...	12 32
				Ex.3		Ex3	2 3 4	2 3 4	Œ Ex.1	1—4	2 3 4	1,2,3	2 3 4	2,3,4	Ex3	Ex3	Ex3	2,3,4	1—4
				a.m.		a.m.		a.m.	a.m.	a.m.	a.m.	a.m.	a.m.	a.m.	a.m.	a.m.	a.m.	a.m.	a.m.
—	**STUTTGART— Hauptbahnhof** dep	...	...	3 15	...	5 0	...	6 6	6 44	5 45	6 50	7 58	8 5	8 45	9 10	9 29	10 6	10 28	11 41
2¾	Cannstatt	...	...	...	...	5 7	...	6 15	...	5 53	6 59	8 5	8 13	8 53	--	...	1013	10 36	11 48
8¾	Esslingen	...	...	3 29	...	...	a.m.	6 41	...	6 17	7 23	8 16	8 33	9 13	RC	...	1024	11 10	12 8
15	Plochingen	...	...	3 41	...	5 24	5 0	7 1	...	6 32	7 50	8 26	8 50	9 56	9 33	...	...	11 32	12 25
26¾	Goppingen	...	...	3 58	...	5 40	5 47		...	7 8	8 50	8 44	9 22	10 34	...	...	1049		1 0
31¾	Sussen	...	...	...	...	...	6 4	...	...	7 32	9 9	...	9 37	11 0	...	...	...	...	
38½	Geislingen	...	...	4 19	...	6 0	6 34	...	7 40	8 0	9 36	9 4	10 3	11 31	1011	1021	11 9	...	...
58½	**Ulm** .... arr	...	...	4 51	...	6 30	7 34	...	8 13	8 58		9 36		12 30	1044	1051	1139	...	...
		Ex2	1,2,3	Ex.3	1,2,3	Ex3		2&3	Ex.1	Ex.3		2&3				Ex3		Ex 3	2 & 3
		a.m.		a.m.		a.m.		a.m.	a.m.			a.m.				a.m.			p.m.
	Ulm .... dep	From Nürnberg dep. 3.42 a.m.	...	4 58	Wurzburg dep. 2.8. ☞	6 37	...	6 20	8 18	Wurzburg dep. 6.10. ☞	...	9 43	...	...	...	11 8	...	Wurzburg dep. 9.26. ☞	1 30
61¼	Neu Ulm		...	5 4		...	...	6 28	...		...	9 52	...	...	...	...	...		1 41
64	Günzburg		...	5 23		...	...	7 12	...		...	1032	...	...	...	RC	...		2 28
67¾	Neu Offingen..............		...	...		...	...	7 22	...		...	1044	...	...	...	...	...		2 40
74	Burgau		...	...		...	...	7 45	...		...	1110	...	...	...	...	...		3 3
97½	Dinkelscherben		...	...		...	...	8 22	...		...	1156	...	...	...	...	...		3 52
111	**Augsburg** .... arr		...	6 19		7 42	...	9 18	9 24		...	1258	...	...	...	1212	2&3		4 47
...	TREUCHTLINGEN 199dep		4a56	|	4a56	...	...	7a18	7 a18	9 a8	...	...	...	...	...	...	p.m.	11a58	12 p5
...	**Augsburg** ......dep 4a50	6 7	6 19	(	6 26	7 45	...	9 43	9 26	10 18	...	...	...	...	...	1214	1 15	1 7	5 0
123½	Mering.....................5 22	...	...	...	...	...	...	1015	...	...	...	...	...	...	...	...	1 46	...	5 30
137½	Maisach 6 1	A	§	...	...	...	...	11 1	...	...	...	...	...	...	...	...	2 22	...	6 7
144¾	Pasing 6 30	...	...	...	...	...	...	1130	...	...	...	...	...	...	...	...	2 55	...	6 30
149½	**MUNICH** Haupt....6 45	7 12	7 14	...	7 20	8 35	...	1143	10 16	11 15	...	...	...	...	...	1 8	3 10	2 0	6 44
244	SALZBURG (300) arr	1050	1050	...	1050	1228	...	...	12p45	3 p30	...	...	...	...	...	4 p5	...	6 p50	12 a8
439½	VIENNA (329A) ...arr	...	...	...	...	6p32	...	...	6 p0	9 p50	...	...	...	...	...	9p50	...	...	8 a10

Œ—Orient Express, from Paris to Vienna ; only takes up if places are vacant.

RC—Restaurant Car in this Train. †—Weekdays only. *–Via Bruchsal.

A—Runs from July 3rd to 16th only. §—In June and September only.

Extra Slow train: Ulm ....dep 3a20; Augsburg dep 7 54; Munich ...arr 9 14.

FARES.

	1 Cl. m.pf.	2 Cl. m.pf.	3 Cl. m.pf.
Stuttgart to Augsburg......	16 20	10 50	6 60
" " **Munich**.........	20 50	13 70	8 50
" " **Salzburg**	32 10	20 60	13 30
" " **Vienna**.........	64 40	40 30	25 90

‡—7.10 p.m. on Sunday.

STUTTGART and HOHENHEIM.

Stuttgart ...dep, Degerloch ...., **Hohenheim** arr — From Stuttgart, 6.15, 7.20, 10.0 a.m., 12.32, 2.0, 3.0, 5.15, 6.15, 6.35, 7‡30, 8.45, 10.45, 11.45 p.m.

Hohenheim ...dep, Degerloch..............., **Stuttgart**.........arr — From Hohenheim, 6.0, 7.0, 9.30 a.m., 12.3, 1.15, 2.43, 4.18, 5 58, 7.2, 8.30, 9.30, 11.30 p.m.

GUNZBURG and MINDELHEIM.

Gunzburg ....dep	...	...	7a14	10a45	...	5 p3	8p27	11p20
Krumbach H.	3a25	...	8 45	12 20	...	6 40	9 45	12 57
Pfaffenhausen 203B	4 30	6a36	9 36	2 9	5p55	8 0		
Mindelheim ......arr	4 56	7 4	9 59	2 36	6 25	8 26	...	...

Mindelheim...dep	...	6a13	7a45	11a55	3p40	7p25	...	9 p0
Pfaffenhausen ...	...	6 42	8 12	12 18	4 13	7 57	...	9 28
Krumbach	3a45	7 55		1 5	5 48		8p16	1013
Gunzburg 192 arr	5 7	9 13	...	2 22	7 18	...	1018	...

Luggage Rates—see page 462.] WURTTEMBERG AND BAVARIAN RAILWAYS.

BRUCHSAL, BIETIGHEIM, STUTTGART, ULM, AND MUNICH.

FRANKFORT 136 dep	7a12	...	...	...	10a29	...	...	12p50	...	1 p58	...	...	...	...	...	5p15	5 p15	...	8 p13
COLOGNE 122 ...dep	...	...	...	...	...	...	...	10 a8	...	11a20	...	...	...	...	...	1p 5	1 p 5	...	3 p38
MAYENCE ....dep	6a15	...	...	...	9 a24	...	...	1 p13	...	2 p32	...	...	...	...	...	4p48	4 p48	...	7 p36
	Ex3	Ex3		1,2,3	1,2,3	2 3 4	2 3 4	1,2,3	1,2,3	Ex 3	2 3 4	2 3 4	Ex2	Ex3		1,2,3	1—4	1,2,3	Ex 3
	a.m.				p.m.	noon	p.m.	p.m		p.m.	p.m	p.m				p.m	p.m.		p.m.
Bruchsal ....dep	10 3	...	...	...	12 50	12 0	2 17	3 20	...	4 58	5 10	6 43	...	...	...	8 6	7 49	...	10 42
Bretten .... arr	...	...	...	...	1 6	1225	2 46	...	...	...	5 46	7 12	...	...	...	8 22	8 15	...	10 58
Bretten dep	...	...	...	...	1 7	1228	2 51	...	...	...	5 51	7 19	...	...	...	8 23	8 29	...	10 59
Maulbronn	...	...	...	...	...	1254	3 16	...	...	...	6 16	7 48	...	...	...	⋮	8 52	...	...
Muhlacker ....arr	1034	...	...	...	1 26	1 4	3 26	3 55		5 30	6 26	7 59	...	...	...	⋮	9 2	...	11 15
PARIS 64 ....dep	9 p5	1015	...	...	10p15	...	...	⋮	...	...	...	...	9 a0	9 a0	...	⋮	...	9 a0	12 0
STRASSBURG 145 dep	7a18	9 a0	...	...	9 a35	...	1217	⋮	1217	1 p22	...	2 3 4	4p57	5p22	...	⋮	4 p57	8p56	8 p45
CARLSRUHE 141...dep	9‡25	1048	...	...	11a30	...	2p38	⋮	2p38	3 p25	...	p.m.	6p13	6p45	...	⋮	6 p24	8p43	10p12
Muhlacker ....dep	1035	1146	...	...	1 30	...	4 4	⋮	3 33	5 31	6 30	5 9	⋮	7 37	...	⋮	9 7	9 42	11 25
Vaihingen-an-der-Enz...	...	...	...	...	...	...	4 25	⋮	...	...	6 50	5 30	⋮	...	...	⋮	9 26	...	...
Bietigheim...........arr	1054	12 9	...	...	1 53	...	4 46	4 19	3 52	5 55	7 12	5 51	7 18	8 1		⋮	9 43	10 2	11 45
BACKNANG..194...arr	1155	...	...	...	...	...	...	4 p51	4 51	7 p20	...	...	...	...	...	⋮	10 35	...	...
NURNBERG............arr	...	...	...	...	...	2 3 4	...	7 55	7p55	...	...	...	...	...		⋮	...	...	...
Bietigheim ....dep	11 0	1210	...	p.m.	1 54	p.m.	4 54	4 21	4 0	5 57	7 24	6 34	7 19	8 2	...	⋮	9 47	10 7	11 46
Ludwigsburg	1112	1226	...	1 56	2 8	2 15	5 21	4 33	4 17	6 12	7 50	7 1	...	8 18	...	9 6	10 9	1026	12 0
Zuffenhausen	RC	...	...	...	...	2 30	5 38	...	...	...	8 6	7 16	...	RC	...	...	10 23	...	...
Feuerbach.......................	...	...	...	...	...	2 34	5 43	...	...	...	8 12	7 22	...	...	...	...	10 28	...	...
STUTTGART— Hauptbahnhof arr	1128	1242	...	2 12	2 24	2 44	5 53	4 47	4 34	6 29	8 21	7 31	7 42	8 35	...	9 21	10 35	1042	12 15
	Ex3	Ex3	2 3 4		1,2,3	2 3 4	2 3 4	1,2,3	1—4	Ex 3	2 3 4	Ex3	Ex2	Ex3	2,3,4	1,2,3		1,2,3	2,3,4
	a.m.	p.m.	p.m.		p.m.	p.m.		p.m.	p.m.	p.m.	p.m		p.m.	p.m.	p.m.	p.m.		p.m	a.m.
STUTTGART— Hauptbahnhof dep	1137	1258	1228	...	2 31	2 58	...	4 55	6 12	6 42	6 56	...	7 53	8 45	8 55	9 36	...	11 6	12 23
Cannstatt	RC	1 3	1236	...	...	3 6	...	5 2	6 20	6 49	7 4	...	...	8 52	9 5	9 42	...	1113	12 30
Esslingen	1151	1 14	1258	...	...	3 30	...	5 15	6 44	6 59	7 29	...	...	9 2	9 29	9 54	...	1124	12 50
Plochingen	...	1 25	1 30	...	2 53	3 51	...	5 27	7 15	7 10	7 54	...	8 15	9 13	10 9	10 4	...	1133	1 9
Goppingen	1216	1 43	2 5	...	3 9	4 26	...	5 46	7 51	7 29	8 35	...	...	9 30	10 48		...	12 4	1 44
Sussen	...	RC	2 24	...	RC	4 46	p.m.	6 0	8 10	...	8 52	From Wurzburg (depart 5.56)	...	...	11 6	...	...	1218	
Geislingen.........................	1238	2 7	2 53	...	3 30	5 12	6 28	6 18	8 58	7 54	9 19		8 51	9 52	11 33	...	...	1241	...
Ulm .... arr	1 12	2 42	3 49	...	4 2	6 12	7 27	6 58	9 57	8 29			9 22	1025		...	...	1 16	...
	Ex3	1,2,3	2&3	1,2,3	2 & 3	2&3	2&3	1,2,3					Ex2	Ex3		2&3			
	p.m.	p.m			p.m.	p.m.	p.m.	p.m.					p.m.	p.m.		p.m.			
Ulm dep	1 17	2 52	...	...	4 12	7 25	6 25	7 17	...	...	...		9 28	1031	...	1115	...	...	...
Neu Ulm	1 22	2 57	...	...	4 20	7 32	6 34	7 24	...	...	...		...	...	Wurzburg dep. 7.22.	1125	...	...	...
Günzburg..........................	1 41	3 16	...	...	4 59	8 [illegible]	7 23	7 43	...	...	...		RC	1052		12 8	...	...	...
Neu Offingen	...	3 22	...	...	5 10	8 19	7 30	7 51	...	...	...		...	...		1215	...	...	...
Burgau	RC	...	...	...	5 33	8 41		...	...	...	...		...	...			...	...	...
Dinkelscherben	...	...	...	...	6 11	9 17	...	8 17	...	...	...		...	...			...	...	...
Augsburg ....arr	2 31	4 9	...	...	6 56	1018	Ex3	8 41	...	...	...		1030	1145		...	...	...	...
TREUCHTLINGEN199dp	...	12p5	3p20	5p36	...	...	p.m.	...	...	...	...	8p29	...	8p36	|	...	...	...	...
Augsburg ....dep	2 35	4 12	6 10	7 0	7 46	1036	7 43	8 44	...	...	...	9 35	1033	1150		...	...	...	...
Mering	...	...	...	...	8 18	11 5	...	...	...	...	...	...	...	...	...	...	...	...	...
Maisach	...	...	...	...	8 59	1140	RC	...	...	...	...	...	...	...	...	...	...	...	...
Passing	...	...	...	...	9 22	12 7	...	...	...	...	...	...	...	...	...	...	...	...	...
MUNICH Hauptbhf. arr	3 25	5 9	7 15	7 55	9 35	1220	8 34	9 40	...	...	...	1025	1123	1240	...	...	...	...	...
SALZBURG 200 arr	6p50	8p55	...	12a8	...	...	...	2a10	...	...	...	2a10	2a10	...	...	...	...	...	...
VIENNA 239A ...arr	...	6 a0	...	8a10	...	...	...	8a10	...	...	...	8a10	8a10	...	...	...	...	...	...

WURTTEMBERG AND BAVARIAN RAILWAYS. [Luggage Rates—see page 462.

MUNICH, ULM, STUTTGART, BIETIGHEIM, AND BRUCHSAL.

THROUGH CARRIAGES {Munich to Paris—in 7.0 a.m., 5.20 p.m., and 10.25 p.m. from Munich. Stuttgart to Frankfort—in 2.19 a.m., 6.0 a.m., 10.3 a.m., 12.22 p.m., & 4.47 p.m. from Stuttgart.

Station																		
VIENNA **239** ....dep	...	...	...	...	...	...	...	...	...	...	8p40	8p40	...	...	...	...	...	...
SALZBURG **200**.........dep	...	...	...	...	...	...	...	...	...	...	3a25	3a25	...	...	5a40	...	...	...
	2 & 3						2 & 3	2 & 3		1,2,3	Ex3	Ex3	2&3		Ex3			
MUNICH— Hauptbahnhof ......dep	p.m. 11 32	...	...	...	...	...	...	...	...	a.m. 5 0	a.m. 7 0	a.m. 7 5	a.m. 6 5	...	a.m. 8 22	...	...	...
Pasing	11 44	...	...	...	...	...	...	...	...	...	...	...	6 21	...	...	...	...	...
Maisach	12 8	...	...	...	...	...	...	...	...	5 37	RC	RC	7 1	...	RC	...	...	...
Mering	12 31	...	...	...	...	...	...	...	...	6 14	...	...	7 57	...	...	...	...	...
Augsburg ....arr	12 48	...	...	...	...	...	...	...	...	6 42	7 49	7 57	8 25	...	9 17	...	...	...
TREUCHTLINGEN **199** arr	...	...	...	...	...	...	...	a.m.	...	8a47	9 a2	9 a2	...	...	...	...	...	...
Augsburg ....dep	...	...	...	...	...	...	...	4 40	...	7 ‡20	7 52	To Wurzburg (arr. 11.25).	...	...	9 20	...	...	...
Dinkelscherben............	...	...	...	...	...	...	...	5 40	...	8 19	...		...	...	...	...	...	...
Burgau............	...	...	...	...	...	...	a.m.	6 18	...	8 57	...		...	...	...	...	...	...
Neu Offingen	...	...	...	...	...	...	4 35	6 39	...	9 21	...		...	...	...	...	...	...
Gunzburg	...	...	...	...	...	...	4 44	6 50	...	9 34	...		...	...	1011	...	...	...
Neu Ulm	...	...	...	...	...	...	5 33	7 35	...	10 20	...		...	...	1032	...	...	...
Ulm ....arr	...	...	...	...	...	...	5 40	7 43	...	10 28	9 3		...	...	1037	...	...	...
			1—4	1—4	2 &3	1—4	2,3,4	1,2,3	2 3 4		Ex3		Ex3	1—4	1,2,3	1—4	2,3,4	1—4
Ulm ....dep	...	...	...	...	a.m. 5 0	a.m. 5 25	a.m. 6 32	a.m. 8 5	a.m. 8 35	...	a.m. 9 10	...	a.m. 1048	...	a.m. 11 0	a.m. 11 15	p.m. 12 15	p.m. ...
Geislingen	...	...	...	...	5 34	6 23	7 34	8 42	9 50	...	9 46	...	RC	...	1136	12 13	1 19	2 20
Sussen	...	...	...	...	5 45	6 38	7 54	...	10 9	...	...	...	...	...	1147	12 28	1 38	2 41
Goppingen	...	...	a.m.	a.m.	5 54	6 54	8 12	9 0	1026	...	10 4	...	1138	a.m.	1156	12 45	1 58	2 57
Plochingen............	...	...	5 49	6 13	6 10	7 32	8 50	9 17	11 7	...	...	...	...	11 35	1213	1 26	2 33	3 32
Esslingen............	...	...	6 9	6 27		7 46	9 0	9 27	1126	...	1028	...	...	12 10	1223	1 42	2 45	3 42
Cannstatt............	...	...	6 30	6 43		8 8	9 21	9 37	1146	...	...	...	...	12 30	1234	2 5	3 4	3 53
STUTTGART— Hauptbahnhof ......arr	...	...	6 38	6 52	...	8 15	9 29	9 45	1154	...	1042	...	1216	12 37	1241	2 14	3 12	4 0
	2,3,4	1,2,3	1—4	Ex 3	1—4		2,3,4	1,2,3		1—4	Ex3	2 3 4	Ex3	2,3,4	1,2,3	2 4	2,3,4	1—4
STUTTGART— Hauptbahnhof ......dep	a.m. 4 8	a.m. 6 0	a.m. 7 15	a.m. 6 58	a.m. 8 1	...	a.m. 9 38	a.m. 10 3	...	a.m. 10 26	a.m. 1052	p.m. 12 5	p.m. 1222	...	p.m. 1248	p.m. 2 26	p.m. 3 40	p.m. 5 12
Feuerbach	4 21	...	7 27	...	8 10	...	9 48	...	...	10 37	...	1216	..	...	...	2 36	3 55	5 26
Zuffenhausen............	4 26	...	7 33	...	8 16	...	9 54	...	...	10 42	RC	1220	RC	...	...	2 42	4 3	5 32
Ludwigsburg	4 41	6 17	7 46	7 14	8 31	...	10 9	10 19	...	10 57	1110	1234	1239	...	1 5	2 57	4 20	5 48
Bietigheim ....arr	4 58	6 28	8 0	7 24	8 47	...	10 21	10 28	...	11 7	1121		1248	...	1 14	3 13	4 37	6 5
NURNBERG ....dep	...	...	...	...	...	...	...	...	...	...	7a5§	...	...	...	...	...	...	...
BACKNANG ....dep	...	4a55	7a13	...	7a13	...	...	...	...	...	1056	...	...	...	1212	2 p19	...	...
Bietigheim ....dep	5 8	6 27	8 8	7 26	8 48	...	...	10 29	...	11 11	1131	...	1250	...	1 16	3 20	...	6 30
Vaihingen-an-der-Enz	5 31	...	8 36	...	...	...	...	...	...	11 29	⋮	...	...	...	..	3 38	...	6 55
Muhlacker ....arr	5 52	6 49	8 57	7 46	9 13	...	...	10 51	...	11 47	⋮	...	1 9	...	1 38	3 54	...	7 15
CARLSRUHE **141** ......arr	7 a49	...	...	8 a32	1026	...	...	11a47	...	1 p47	1236	...	2p25	...	2p25	5 p26	...	...
STRASSBURG **145** ......arr	10 a1	...	...	10 a1	1 p1	...	...	2 p 8	...	...	2 p8	...	4p48	...	4p48	7 p40	...	...
PARIS **65**............arr	...	...	...	4 p39	...	...	...	9 p20	...	...	9p20	...	5 a0	p.m.	5 a0	...	...	...
Muhlacker ....dep	6 54	6 50	...	8 11	9 20	...	...	10 53	...	12 12	...	...	1 10	1 16	...	4 6	...	...
Maulbronn	7 6	...	...	8 23	9 32	...	...	...	...	12 24	...	...	...	1 29	...	4 20	...	...
Bretten ....arr	7 22	...	...	8 38	9 46	...	...	...	...	12 40	...	...	1 27	1 46	...	4 37	...	...
Bretten ....dep	7 25	...	...	8 40	9 47	...	...	...	...	12 42	...	...	1 28	1 50	...	4 44	...	...
Bruchsal 141............arr	7 50	7 22	...	9 1	10 8	...	...	11 25	...	1 4	...	...	1 45	2 16	...	5 12	...	...
MAYENCE ....arr	...	1024	...	12p10	1p57	...	...	2 p23	...	3 p28	...	...	3p59	...	...	8 p52	...	...
COLOGNE (**123B**) ......arr	...	2p17	...	4 p32	6 p5	...	...	6 p5	...	7 p7	...	...	7 p7	...	...	12a55	...	...
FRANKFORT(**126**) ...arr	...	9a31	...	11a40	1239	...	...	2 p2	...	3 p16	...	...	4p25	...	...	8 p20	...	...

‡—2&3 class only. §—Via Bruchsal.

WURTTEMBERG AND BAVARIAN RAILWAYS. [Luggage Rates—see page 462.

MUNICH, ULM, STUTTGART, BIETIGHEIM, AND BRUCHSAL.

SLEEPING CAR—Munich to Nancy, in 10.25 p.m. from Munich.

VIENNA 239 ... dep	...	1055	...	...	...	...	...	...	...	...	8a15	9a25	...	12 0	...	...	1 p0	1 p0
SALZBURG 200 ... dep	...	9 a7	...	...	...	...	...	...	...	12p14	2p25	3p50	...	5p32	5p19	...	7 p20	7 p20
	2 & 3	Ex3		2&3			2&3	Ex 3		Ex 3	Ex3	Ex3	2 & 3	Ex1	2&3	2 & 3	Ex.3	1,2,3
MUNICH—	a.m.	p.m.		a.m.			p.m.	p.m.		p.m.	p.m.	p.m.	p.m.	p.m.	p.m.	p.m.	p.m.	p.m.
Hauptbahnhof ... dep	9 0	1245	...	1115	...	...	1 55	2 50	...	4 25	5 20	6 55	5 30	7 55	8 10	9 0	10 25	10 18
Pasing ...	9 16	...	...	1132	...	...	2 8	...	...	...	...	...	5 45	...	...	9 16	SC	...
Maisach ...	9 51	RC	...	12 0	...	...	2 34	...	...	RC	RC	...	6 13	Œ	8 36	9 52	...	...
Mering ...	10 28	...	...	1238	...	...	3 10	...	...	...	...	...	6 51	...	8 56	10 32	...	...
Augsburg ... arr	10 55	1 37	...	1 6	...	...	3 37	3 42	...	5 14	6 10	7 44	7 18	8 48	9 10	10 55	11 15	11 8
TREUCHTLINGEN 199 arr	1 p27	...	...	5p15	...	...	...	...	...	6 p55	...	...	...	...	1110	12a18	...	12a18
Augsburg ... dep	11 12	1 41	...	2 0	...	...	4 0	3 45	...	To Wurzburg (arr. 8.29).	6 12	Wurzburg arr. 10.55.	7 58	8 49	9 35	...	11 17	Wurzburg arr. 2.41.
Dinkelscherben ...	12 5	...	...	2 57	...	...	4 56	...	...		...		9 15	...	1019	2 & 3	...	
Burgau ...	12 43	...	...	3 39	...	...	5 34	...	...		...		9 56	...	1050	p.m.	...	
N. Offingen ...	1 3	...	...	4 4	...	...	5 56	...	...		...		10 23	...	11 9	8 15	...	
Gunzburg ...	1 13	2 33	...	4 15	...	...	6 8	...	...		7 1		10 36	...	1121	8 25	12 4	
Neu Ulm ...	1 57	2 56	...	5 5	...	...	6 53	5 0	...		...		11 18	...	12 4	9 5	12 24	
Ulm ... arr	2 5	3 1	...	5 12	...	...	7 0	5 4	...		7 24		11 25	9 54	1210	9 13	12 28	
	1—4	Ex3	Ex3		2 3 4	2,3,4		Ex 3	2,3,4	1—4	Ex3	Ex3	2,3,4	Ex1				Ex.3
	p.m.	p.m.	p.m.					p.m.	p.m.	p.m.	p.m.	p.m.	p.m.	p.m.				a.m.
Ulm ... dep	2 10	3 17	3 58	...	...	...	...	5 12	5 26	7 40	7 31	8 55	...	9 59	...	...		12 38
Geislingen ...	3 11	...	4 34	...	...	...	...	...	6 28	8 48	8 6	9 29	9 34	...	...	...		1 12
Sussen ...	3 26	...	...	...	p.m.	...	...	...	6 47	9 7	...	...	9 53	...	...	...	...	...
Goppingen ...	3 39	RC	4 51	...	5 17	p.m.	...	6 1	7 7	9 23	8 24	9 46	10 9	Œ	...	...	...	1 29
Plochingen ...	4 26	...	5 8	...	5 53	7 6	...	...	7 42	10 6	...	10 2	11 10	...	...	...	...	...
Esslingen ...	4 45	...	5 19	...	6 11	7 24	...	6 24	7 56	10 20	8 47	1011	11 30	...	...	...	...	1 52
Cannstatt ...	5 6	...	5 29	...	6 27	7 45	...	6 34	8 15	10 40	8 57	1021	11 51	...	...	...	...	2 2
STUTTGART— Hauptbahnhof arr ...	5 15	4 39	5 36	...	6 36	7 53	...	6 41	8 24	10 48	9 5	1028	11 59	1128	...	...	...	2 9
1—4	3 Cl.	Ex3	Ex3	2 3 4	2 3 4	1—	2&3	Ex 3	2,3,4		Ex3	Ex3		Ex1	1—4		Ex.3	Ex 3
p.m.		p.m.	p.m.	p.m.	p.m.	p.m.		p.m.	p.m.		p.m.	p.m.		p.m.	p.m.		a.m.	a.m.
dep 4 23	...	4 47	5 44	6 13	7 12	8 10	...	6 50	8 56	...	9 17	1038	...	1132	11 0	...	2 19	2 29
Feuerbach ... 4 35	...	⋮	...	6 26	7 25	8 21	...	...	9 8	...	RC	SC	...	⋮	1113	...	SC	...
Zuffenhausen ... 4 40	...	⋮	...	6 32	7 30	8 28	...	...	9 14	...	...	...	...	⋮	1120	...	...	...
Ludwigsburg ... 5 34	...	⋮	6 2	6 48	7 46	8 45	...	7 7	9 29	...	9 35	1054	...	⋮	1135	...	2 33	2 45
Bietigheim ... arr 5 49	...	⋮	6 11	7 5	8 1	9 3	...	7 17	9 51	...	9 44	11 4	...	Œ	1149	...	⋮	⋮
NURNBERG ... dep	...	⋮	...	...	...	5 p6	...	12 p2	...	...	5 p6	...	...	⋮		...	⋮	⋮
BACKNANG ... dep	...	⋮	...	6p18	...	8 p42	...	6 p18	...	...	8p42	...	...	⋮	...	...	⋮	⋮
Bietigheim ... dep	...	⋮	6 13	7 25	8 8	9 56	...	7 19	...	...	9 46	11 5	...	⋮	...	...	⋮	⋮
Vaihingen-an-der-Enz ...	...	⋮	...	7 50	8 30	10 22	...	⋮	...	...	...	...	...	⋮	...	...	⋮	⋮
Muhlacker ... arr	...	5 33	6 37	8 9	8 50	10 41	...	⋮	...	...	10 9	1127	...	⋮	...	...	3 3	3 15
CARLSRUHE (141) ... arr	...	7p11	7p34	1329	1029	12a15	...	8 p28	...	...	11p2	1215	...	1 a1	...	...	4 a2	4 a2
STRASSBURG (145) ... arr	...	8p44	9p54	...	...	...	...	9 p54	...	...	1228	⋮	...	2a25	...	...	5 a34	5a34
PARIS (65) ... arr	...	...	8a25	...	...	...	p.m.	8 a25	...	...	8a25	⋮	...	8a56	...	...	12p16	12p16
Muhlacker ... dep	...	5 37	6 41	8 14	8 53	10 53	6 23	...	...	...	1018	⋮	...	...	...	...	3 4	...
Maulbronn ...	...	...	...	8 26	9 14	11 5	6 36	...	...	...	...	⋮	2 & 3	...	2&3	...	...	...
Bretten ... arr	p.m.	...	6 59	8 42	9 38	11 21	6 52	...	...	...	1035	⋮	a.m.	...	a.m.	...	3 20	...
Bretten ... dep	6 20	...	7 0	8 46	9 41	11 31	7 26	...	...	...	1036	⋮	5 7	...	6 12	...	3 21	...
Bruchsal (141) ... arr	6 54	6 9	7 17	9 10	10 7	11 55	7 50	...	...	...	1053	⋮	5 41	...	6 43	...	3 38	...
MAYENCE ... arr	...	8p52	1028	...	...	...	...	...	...	...	...	2a28	...	...	...	...	5 a56	...
COLOGNE (123B) ... arr	...	1255	5 a9	...	...	...	...	...	...	...	...	5a42	...	...	...	...	9 a50	...
FRANKFORT (136) ... arr	...	8p32	10p0	...	...	...	...	...	...	...	1a16	...	...	...	...	...	5 a44	...

Œ—Orient Express, only takes up if places are vacant.

RC—Restaurant Car in this Train.
SC—Sleeping Car in this Train.

STUTTGART and CALW.

Stuttgart ... dep	5a29	8 a1	8 a22	9a22	12 p5	1p26	3p40	5p12	5p†55	6 †26	7 p2	7p32	9p45	10p0	11p10	11p18	...	...
Feuerbach ...	5 41	8 10	...	9 35	12 16	1 40	3 55	5 26	6 7	6 40	7 16	7 44	...	1013	11 19	...	...	...
Zuffenhausen ... dep	5 49	8 20	8 34	9 42	12 27	1 47	4 10	5 40	6 18	6 48	7 22	7 51	...	1018	11 33	11 28	...	...
Leonberg ...	6 20	8†47	8 56	1013	12 56	2 17	4 41	6 10	6 53	7 24	7 57	8 21	10 17		12 1		...	...
Renningen ...	6 34		...	1026		2 30	4 54	5†26		7 39	8 12	8 34	...	...	12 14		...	...
Schafhausen ...	6 52	...	...	1045	...	2 50	5 5		...	8 2		8 53	10 39	...		...	...	...
Calw (194A) ... arr	7 23	...	9 44	1118	...	3 23	5 45	...	...		...	9 22	11 6	...	...	...	...	...
Calw ... dep	...	a.m.	...	...	6 a5	...	7a43	...	11a47	...	1p58	4p20	...	...	7 p33	9p48	...	...
Schafhausen ...	a.m.	4†56	...	a.m	6 37	...	8 23	...	12 27	...	2 33	5 5	...	p.m.	8 11	10 24	...	...
Renningen ...	4 49	5 21	a.m.	6 8	6 52	...	8 43	a.m.	12 45	p.m.	2 50	5 16	...	7 6	8 34	10 42	...	...
Leonberg ...	5 1	5 34	5 †50	6 21	7 4	7 a26	8 56	11†26	12 57	1 17	3 1	5 27	...	7 23	8 45	10 53	...	...
Zuffenhausen ...	5 26	6 6	6 18	6 55	7 31	8 6	9 23	11 58	1 25	1 45	3 32	5 57	7p16	8 5	9 17	11 19	...	...
Feuerbach ...	5 31	6 11	6 41	7 1	...	8 11	9 28	12 2	1 31	1 50	3 37	6 2	7 22	8 12	9 22	11 24	...	...
Stuttgart ... arr	5 40	6 20	6 50	7 11	7 40	8 20	9 36	12 12	1 40	1 59	3 46	6 11	7 31	8 21	9 31	11 33	...	...

†—Weekdays only.

WURTTEMBERG RAILWAYS.

[Luggage Rates—see page 462.

OSTERBURKEN, HEILBRONN, STUTTGART, and IMMENDINGEN.

BERLIN ......170 dep		...	...	8 p25	...	...	...	...	...	10p50	...	...	...	...	...	8 a20	...	...	...	1 p45
ERFURT ......170 dep		...	...	12a21	...	...	...	...	...	...	...	...	...	...	5 a58	12p26	...	...	...	
RITCSHENH'S N195 dep		...	...	...	...	...	...	...	...	...	5 a4	...	...	...	9 a32	...	...	...	...	
SCHWEINFURT 198 dep		...	...	3 a42	...	...	...	5 a53	...	...	7 a58	...	...	...	12p10	4 p12	...	...	...	
WURZBURG ...143 dep		...	...	4 a30	...	...	...	7 a27	...	9a10	9 a58	...	...	...	2 p0	5p 4	...	...	...	
	2,3,4		1—4	Ex.3	1—4	2,3,4	2,3,4	2,3,4	1,2,3	1,2,3	1—4	1,2,3	2,3,4	1,2,3	2,3,4	Ex.3	2 3 4	2 3 4	2,3,4	Via Nurnberg.
				a.m.	a.m.		a.m.	a.m.		a.m.	p.m.				p.m.	p.m.		p.m.		
Osterburken ...dep	...	...	...	6 10	...	...	7 18	9 47	...	10 45	12 40	...	...	...	4 30	6 40	...	7 41	...	
Möckmuhl	...	...	...	⋮	4 47	...	7 47	10 16	...	11 1	1 7	...	...	...	4 56	⋮	...	8 52	...	
Untergriesheim	...	...	...	⋮	5 23	...	8 18	10 46	...	..	1 36	...	...	...	5 26	⋮	...	9 22	...	
Jagstfeld ....arr	...	...	...	⋮	5 34	...	8 27	10 55	...	11 22	1 46	...	...	...	5 36	⋮	...	9 32	...	
NECKARELZ142dep	...	...	...	⋮	...	5 a42	7 a25	9 a41	11 a9	...	...		2 p5	...	5 p0	⋮	6p31	8p53	p.m.	
Jagstfeld ....dep	...	...	...	⋮	5 36	7 7	8 33	10 57	⋮	11 23	1 47	...	2 46	...	5 48	⋮	7 18	9 35	10 39	
Neckarsulm	...	...	...	⋮	5 50	7 18	8 44	11 9	⋮	...	1 58	...	2 57	...	6 0	⋮	7 29	9 46	10 50	
Heilbronn ... arr	...	...	a.m.	6 53	6 3	7 28	8 56	11 20	11 39	11 34	2 9	p.m.	3 8	p.m.	6 11	7 23	7 40	9 57	11 1	
Heilbronn ... dep	...	...	4 44	6 55	6 15	7 36	9 57	12 13	11 46	—	2 18	3 30	4 34	5 20	6 17	7 25	8 28	10 5	11 ‡6	
Lauffen-a-N. 190A...	...	...	5 7	...	6 35	7 59	10 21	12 33	11 59	—	2 41	3 44	4 56	5 33	6 43	...	8 52	10 29	11 18	
Besigheim	...	...	5 28	...	6 54	8 19	10 41	12 50	...	...	3 1	3 58	5 16	...	7 3	RC	9 13	10 49	11 30	
Bietigheim ... arr	a.m.	...	5 39	7 23	7 3	8 29	10 52	1 1	12 17	...	3 11	4 8	5 26	5 52	7 13	7 53	9 23	11 0	11 39	
Bietigheim ... dep	4 57	...	5 54	7 25	7 5	9 1	11 15	1 7	12 19	...	3 15	4 21	5 29	5 57	7 24	7 54	9 28	11 6	11 46	
Ludwigsburg	5 23	...	6 32	...	7 25	9 22	11 45	1 30	12 32	...	3 38	4 33	5 52	6 12	7 50	8 10	9 53	11 52	12 0	
STUTTGART arr	5 55	...	7 4	7 52	7 45	9 50	12 17	1 59	12 49	...	4 4	4 47	6 20	6 29	8 21	8 26	10 20	12 0	12 15	12 52

STUTTGART Hauptbahnhof	1—4	2,3,4	1,2,3	Ex.3	3 & 4	2,3,4	3 & 4	2,3,4	2,3,4	Ex 3	2,3,4		2,3,4	...	2,3,4		2 3 4			Ex 3
	a.m.	a.m.	a.m.	a.m.		a.m.		p.m.	p.m.	p.m.	p.m.		p.m.		p.m.		p.m.			a.m.
STUTTGART Hauptbahnhof dep	2 58	5 35	7 34	8 3	...	10 50	...	1 10	2 26	3 21	5 15	...	6 48	...	8 56	...	11 17	...	...	12 58
Boblingen	Via Ploch	6 25	8 12	...	...	11 46	...	2 2	3 30	4 9	6 10	...	7 34	...	9 44	...	12 12	...	...	
Herrenberg		6 52	8 28	RC	...	12 13	...	2 29	4 1	4 26	6 38	...	7 53	...	10 10	...	—	...	...	Z
Eutingen194A arr		7 21	8 46	9 9	...	12 43	...	2 57	4 34	4 45	7 8	...	8 13	...	10 38	...	...	...	‡—1,2,3 Class.	Via Tubingen.
Eutingen194A dep	...	8 49	—	9 10	...	12 59	...	3 10	4 56	4 48	7 41	...	8 16	...	10 42	...	...	...		
Horb 194A...... arr	5 51	8 59	...	9 20	...	1 9	...	3 35	5 8	4 57	7 53	...	8 26	...	10 52	...	...	...		
Horb 194A...... dep	5 59	9 35	...	9 25	...	1 25	...	—	5 30	5 0	—	...	8 31	...	10 59	...	...	...		
Sulz-am-Neckar ...	6 19	10 0	...	...	...	1 59	...	...	6 1	5 15	...	...	8 54	...	11 23	...	...	...		
Oberndorf.........	6 37	10 19	...	9 50	...	2 17	...	...	6 25	5 29	...	...	9 12	...	11 40	...	...	...		3 11
Rottweil 194A arr	7 7	10 54	...	10 11	p.m.	2 54	p.m.	...	7 10	5 51	...	...	9 44	...	12 8	...	...	...		3 30
Rottweil 194A dep	7 14	11 1	...	10 13	12 10	3 6	1 12	...	7 25	5 53	...	...	9 52	...	—	...	...	...		3 32
Spaichingen	7 41	11 31	...	...	12 47	3 40	1 47	...	7 56	6 19	...	...	10 19	...	...	...	...	...	...	SC
Tuttlingen 194A ...	8 6	12 9	...	10 50	1 16	4 12	2 19	...	8 20	6 34	...	...	10 46	...	...	...	...	...	...	4 5
Immendingen ...arr	8 22	12 23	...	11 1	—	4 26	3 0	...	8 39	6 45	...	...	11 1	...	...	...	...	...	...	4 16
SINGEN 144 ...arr	9 a7	12 59	...	11a36	...	5 p38	...	...	10p37	7 p26	...	...	1 a0	...	...	...	...	...	...	4 a52
SCHAFFH'N139A ar	11 a0	1 p22	...	12 p1	...	7 p3	...	...	...	7 p59	...	...	...	...	...	...	...	...	...	5 a19
ZURICH 261B...arr	12p40	2 p31	...	1 p8	...	9 p45	...	...	...	9 p12	...	...	...	...	...	...	...	...	...	6 a25
MILAN 269A ...arr	...	10p25	...	8 p40	...	6 a22	...	...	...	6 a22	...	...	...	...	...	...	...	...	...	2 27

Extra									
Jagstfeld ...dep	6 a22	7a56	10 a5	10a21	1p22	3p†38	4p39	5 30	6 p54
Heilbronn...arr	6 44	8 10	10 28	10 42	1 43	4 1	4 59	5 43	7 13

SC—Sleeping Car.
RC—Restaurant Car.

Z—Berlin-Zurich Express, with Sleeping Cars.

ULM and FRIEDRICHSHAFEN.

	4 Cl.	1,2,3	1,2,3	4 Cl.	1—4	1,2,3	2,3,4	Ex3	1,2,3	2,3,4	4 Cl	1,2,3	2,3,4	4 Cl	4 Cl.	1—4	Ex 3	2,3,4	
		a.m.	a.m.	a.m.	a.m.	a.m.	a.m.	a.m.	a.m.	p.m.	p.m.	p.m.	p.m.	p.m.	p.m.	p.m.	p.m.	p.m.	
Ulm.........................dep	...	5 10	6 54	8 ‡6	9 14	9 41	10 5	10 56	11 48	1 0	1‡55	4 12	5 12	6‡30	7 ‡4	7 32	8 54	10 32	...
Erbach	...	...	...	8 34	9 34	...	10 30	...	...	1 17	2 18	...	5 33	6 57	7 26	7 50	...	10 54	...
Laupheim	...	5 31	7 21	9 6	10 7	10 0	11 31	11 15	...	1 35	2 40	4 33	5 54	7 22	7 43	8 10	9 13	11 15	...
Biberach	...	5 48	7 40	9 43	10 37	10 15	12 23	11 30	...	2 5	—	4 49	6 21	—	—	8 41	9 27	11 42	...
Essendorf (Waldsee)	...	...	...	—	11 2	...	12 48	...	...	2 30	...	...	6 48	...	‡—Rail Motor.	9 7	...	—	...
Schussenried 190A.........	...	6 10	8 5	...	11 16	...	1 6	...	...	2 45	...	5 11	7 2	...		9 25	9 47	...	...
Aulendorf 194 ...... arr	...	6 15	8 12	...	11 23	10 39	1 14	11 53	...	2 52	2 3 4	5 16	7 9	...		9 33	9 53	...	...
Aulendorf 194 ...... dep	a.m.	6 17	8 13	a.m.	11 27	10 40	1 20	11 55	...	2 59	p.m.	5 18	7 14	p.m.		10 3	9 55	...	...
Ravensburg.........................	4‡30	6 42	8 33	10‡35	11 58	11 0	2 2	12 15	...	3 35	4 23	5 39	7 46	8‡12		10 39	10 15	...	...
Meckenbeuren	4 49	...	8 43	10 55	12 10	.	2 23	12 25	...	3 54	4 42	5 49	7 58	8 31		10 57	...	...	...
Friedrichs-hafen ... Bahnhof arr	5 9	7 1	8 53	11 16	12 21	11 17	2 44	12 34	1 13	4 8	5 1	5 58	8 8	8 50		11 13	10 31	...	...
Friedrichs-hafen ... Hafen ...arr	5 17	7 8	8 59	11 22	12 26	11 22	3 22	12 47	1 20	4 15	5 6	6 3	8 13	...		...	...	...	...

Laupheim to Schwendi, in 1 hour, 5.40,10.25a.m., 2.19, 6.20 8.18p.m. From Schwendi 4.17, 6.37a.m., 12.25, 3.34,7.9p.m.

Meckenbeuren and Tettnang.—In 16 minutes. Local service connecting with all trains stopping at Meckenbeuren.

Ravensburg and Weingarten.—In 20 minutes. Half-hourly service throughout the day.

BIBERACH and OCHSENHAUSEN.

Biberach ....dep	5a58	7 a58	10a24	1 p38	5p33	9 p31	Ochsenhausen ....dep	4a27	5a41	8 a13	12 0	3 p16	7 p21	...
Sulmingen	6 40	8 39	11 3	2 28	6 39	10 6	Sulmingen	5 8	6 28	9 3	12 45	4 3	8 2	...
Ochsenhausen ....arr	7 26	9 29	11 49	3 15	7 20	10 48	Biberach 193..........arr	5 42	7 8	9 44	1 26	4 38	8 37	...

*—Week-days only.

SUSSEN and WEISSENSTEIN.

Sussen ....dep	8a10	10*a14	12p48	6p35	7*p12	9p10	...	Weissenstein ......dep	4*a47	5a45	9*a2	11a38	3p19	8p15	...
Weissenstein ......arr	8 49	10 56	1 27	7 13	7 50	9 46	...	Sussen ....arr	5 20	6 20	9 32	12 9	4 0	8 47	...

HERRENBERG and TUBINGEN															
Herrenberg...dep	4a25	6a56	9 32	12p35	4p30	6p38	7p54	Tübingen ...dep	5a43	8 a5	10 55	12p25	2p30	6p30	7p45
Tübingen......arr	5 24	7 47	10 37	1 47	5 17	7 28	8 46	Herrenberg arr	6 44	8 57	11 58	1 52	3 55	7 37	8 46

MOCKMUHL and DORZBACH.										
Möckmuhl............dep	7 a57	10a 2	2 p20	6p10	Dörzbach ....dep	5 a16	10a40	2 p18	6 p10	...
Dörzbach ....arr	10 0	12 57	4 35	8 25	Möckmuhl (193)...arr	7 29	12 55	4 33	8 23	...

Luggage Rates, see page 462.] **WURTTEMBERG RAILWAYS.**

IMMENDINGEN, STUTTGART, HEILBRONN, and OSTERBURKEN.

SLEEPING CAR—Stuttgart to Berlin, in 9.39 p.m. from Stuttgart.

MILAN 269A ...dep	4 p0	...	...	...	...	...	...	...	...	...	11p35	...	...	...	...	...	9 a25	...	9 a25	9 a25
ZURICH 261B dep	11p37	...	...	...	...	...	...	...	4 a53	...	8 a25	...	...	10 59	...	...	4 p20	...	4 p20	6 p13
SCHAFFH'N 139A d	12a37	...	...	...	...	...	...	...	7 a1	...	9 a37	...	...	12p25	1 p30	...	5 p27	...	5 p44	7 p34
SINGEN 144 ...dep	1 a12	...	...	...	...	4 a0	...	6 a7	7 a54	...	10a16	10a28	...	1 p0	2 p46	...	6 p5	...	6 p28	8 p7
	Ex.3			2,3,4		2,3,4	2,3,4	2,3,4	3 & 4	2,3,4	Ex 3	3 & 4	2,3,4	2,3,4	2,3,4	3 & 4	Ex.3	3 & 4	2,3,4	1,2,3
	a.m.					a.m.		a.m.	a.m.		a.m.	a.m.	p.m.	p.m.	p.m.	p.m.	p.m.	p.m.	p.m.	p.m.
Immendingen...dep	2 3	...	...	...	...	5 24	...	7 12	8 55	...	11 4	11 58	12 57	1 45	3 30	...	6 46	...	7 32	8 50
Tuttlingen	2 15	...	...	...	...	6 0	...	7 27	9 13	...	11 16	12 17	1 12	2 3	3 50	4 6	6 58	6 17	8 2	9 5
Spaichingen	...	...	...	...	...	6 24	...		9 42	...	11 30	12 47		-2 26		4 39	RC	6 49	8 34	9 25
Rottweil ...... arr	2 45	...	...	a.m.	...	6 44	...	...	10 9	...	11 44	1 11		2 47	...	5 7	7 24	7 16	8 55	9 47
Rottweil ...... dep	2 47	...	...	4 30	...	6 49	...	...	10 14	...	11 46	1 14	...	2 55	...	5 53	7 26		9 4	9 50
Oberndorf	3 13	...	...	4 57	...	7 12	...	...	10 47	...	12 4	1 43	...	3 24	...	6 27	7 44	...	9 33	10 16
Sulz-am-Neckar ...	...	...	...	5 14	...	7 27	...	...	11 7	...	12 17	2 0	...	3 41	...	6 46	...	...	9 49	10 31
Horb .... arr	...	...	...	5 36	...	7 48	...	a.m.	11 36	...	12 30	2 23	...	4 3	...	7 9	8 7	...	10 9	10 47
Horb .... dep	...	...	...	5 59	...	8 7	...	9 45	11 44	...	12 31	2 47	...	4 13	...	7 33	8 9	...	10 17	10 54
Eutingen ...... arr	Z	...	...	6 13	...	8 25	...	10 2	11 59	p.m.	12 46	3 0	...	4 32	...	7 47	8 23	p.m.	10 31	...
Eutingen ...... dep	...	...	...	6 21	...	8 35	...	10 33		12 1	12 52		...	4 52	...		8 25	7 56	10 39	...
Herrenberg	...	...	...	6 52	...	9 5	a.m.	11 1	...	12 34	1 11	...	p.m.	5 23	..	...	...	8 58	11 8	...
Boblingen	...	...	...	7 28	...	9 23	8 45	11 31	...	1 4	1 31	...	4 31	5 56	...	...	...	9 39	11 38	...
STUTTGART arr	5 45	...	...	8 10	...	9 55	9 33	12 9	...		2 3	...	5 21	6 38	...	...	9 27	10 26	12 16	1 13
	Ex 3	1,2,3	1—4		1—4	Ex.3	2,3,4	2,3,4	1,2,3	2,3,4	1,2,3	1—4	Ex 3	Ex 3	2,3,4	2,3,4	Ex.3	1,2,3	2,3,4	2,3,4
Hauptbahnhof	a.m.	a.m.	a.m.		a.m.	a.m.	a.m.	a.m.	p.m.	p.m.	p.m.	p.m	p.m.	p.m.	p.m.	p.m.	p.m.	p.m.		a.m.
dep	6 0	6 0	7 15	...	8 1	10 21	10 26	11 46	12 48	2 41	3 22	5 12	5 44	6 50	7 12	8 56	9 39	11 18	...	4 8
Ludwigsburg	Via Nurnberg.	6 17	7 46	...	8 31	10 40	10 57	12 24	1 5	3 13	3 41	5 48	6 2	7 7	7 46	9 29	9 54	11 40	...	4 41
Bietigheim... arr	⋮	6 26	8 0	...	8 47	10 51	11 7	12 40	1 14	3 29	3 53	6 5	6 11	7 17	8 1	9 51	10 4	11 52	a.m.	4 58
Bietigheim... dep	⋮	6 36	8 4	...	9 0	10 53	11 28	2 0	1 24	3 32	3 57	6 27	6 20	7 27	8 13	10 15	10 6	11 54	4 27	5 5
Besigheim	⋮	6 43	8 12	...	...	RC	11 36	2 9	1 31	3 41	...	6 37	...	7 34	8 24	10 24	...	12 1	4 37	5 14
Lauffen-a-Neckar ...	⋮	6 57	8 33	...	...	...	11 55	2 29	...	3 58	...	6 58	...	7 45	8 48	10 44	...	12 15	5 1	5 36
Heilbronn ... arr	⋮	7 8	8 54	...	9 24	11 17	12 15	2 51	1 52	4 14	4 21	7 20	6 45	7 57	9 9	11 4	10 30	12 30	5 29	5 59
Heilbronn ... dep	⋮	7 10	9 2	...	9 41	11 19	12 57	2 55		4 20	4 33	7 31	6*50	8*27		11 14	10 32		5‡50	6†20
Neckarsulm........	⋮	7 17	9 11	...	9 52	⋮	1 10	3 6	...	4 31	...	7 42	7 1	8 33	...	11 25	⋮	...	5 57	6†31
Jagstfeld 142 ...arr	⋮	7 24	9 18	...	10 2	⋮	1 22	3 16	...	4 41	4 47	7 51	7 11	8 48	...	11 35	⋮	...	6 4	6†41
NECKARELZ ...arr	⋮	9a20	10a38	...	10a38	⋮	...	...	...	5 p23	5 p23	8p27	8 p27	11p39	...	...	⋮	a.m.	6a38	...
Jagstfeld ....dep	⋮	7 25	9 20	...	...	⋮	1 26	...	...	...	5 15	...	...	8 49	...	...	⋮	4 14	†—Weekdays only.	...
Untergriesheim	⋮	...	9 23	...	...	⋮	1 38	...	...	...	5 27	...	...	9 0	...	...	SC	4 31		...
Möckmuhl	⋮	7 47	9 57	...	...	⋮	2 14	...	...	...	6 0	...	...	9 32	...	...	⋮	5 18		...
Osterburken......arr	⋮	8 3	10 26	...	...	12 5	2 44	...	...	...	6 30	...	...	10 2	...	...	11 17	5 50		...
WURZBURG 143arr	⋮	9 a22	12p45	...	...	1 p31	4 p56	...	...	...	10p13	...	...	...	...	...	12a52	...		...
SCHWEINFURT 198	⋮	...	2 p10	...	...	2 p26	7 p21	...	...	...	...	...	...	...	...	...	1 a48	...		...
BITCHENHA'N 195	⋮	...	...	...	...	4p50	...	...	...	...	...	...	...	...	...	...	...	...		...
ERFURT 171 ...arr	⋮	...	...	...	...	6 p21	...	...	...	...	...	...	...	...	...	...	5 a12	...		...
BERLIN 171 ...arr	4 p49	8 p35	...	...	...	10p38	...	...	...	...	...	...	...	...	...	...	9 a5	...	...	...

Extra											
Heilbronn ...dep	3a45	7a42	8a25	10a3	12p27	1p25	4p58	6p16	6p22	10p41
Jagstfeld......arr	4 6	8 2	8 45	1027	12 50	1 46	5 14	6 32	6 48	11 2

RC-Restaurant Car.

*—2, 3, 4 class. ‡—1, 2, 3 class.

Z—Zurich-Berlin Express, with Sleeping Car.

†—Weekdays only.

FRIEDRICHSHAFEN and ULM.

‡—Rail Motor.

	2,3,4	2,3,4	1,2,3	4 Cl.	Ex 3	4 Cl.	2,3,4	2,3,4	2,3,4	Ex 3	Ex.3	2,3,4	1—4	2,3,4	4Cl.	Ex 3	1—4	1,2,3	
Friedrichshafen—		a.m.	a.m.	a.m.	a.m.		a.m.	a.m.	p.m.	p.m.	p.m.	p.m.	p.m.	p.m.	p.m.	p.m.	p.m.	p.m.	
Hafen.........dep	...	...	...	7‡30	8 46	...	9 16	11 33	...	1 35	1 55	2 15	3 38	5 34	6‡20	7 8	8 18	10 10	...
Bahnhof ...dep	...	5 20	6 3	7 35	8 51	...	9 22	11 39	12†38	1 40	2 0	2 23	3 45	5 40	6 32	7 12	8 30	10 16	...
Meckenbeuren	...	5 35	...	7 56	...	...	9 37	11 54	1 10	...	2 10	2 50	3 59	6 1	6 53	...	8 44	...	...
Ravensburg...........	...	5 57	6 23	8 16	9 9	...	9 57	12 16	1 31	...	2 21	3 13	4 22	6 24	7 15	7 29	9 7	10 35	...
Aulendorf 194 arr	...	6 37	6 48		9 35	...	10 35	12 59		...	2 45		5 1	7 8		7 51	9 46	11 2	...
Aulendorf 194 dep	...	7 0	6 50	...	9 36	...	10 40	1 4	...	...	2 47	2 p54	5 6	7 16	...	7 52	9 55	...	...
Schussenried	...	7 10	...	...	...	...	10 50	1 13	...	...	...	3 11	5 14	7 27	...	...	10 5	...	...
Essendorf(Waldsee)	a.m.	7 25	...	...	...	a.m.	11 4	1 25	4 Cl.	...	...		5 27	7 43	...	...	10 17	...	...
Biberach	4 55	7 52	7 15	...	10 2	10‡20	11 31	1 49	p.m.	...	3 12	...	5 52	8 21	...	8 15	10 40	11 29	...
Laupheim	5 23	8 20	7 28	...	10 16	11 48	12 5	2 15	3 ‡6	...	3 26	p.m.	6 18	8 49	...	...	11 6	11 41	...
Erbach..............	5 46	8 38	...	...	...	12 9	12 23	2 31	3 26	...	...	7‡55	6 37	9 10	...	...	11 22	...	...
Ulm ....arr	6 9	9 0	7 48	...	10 35	12 31	12 42	2 46	4 0	3 6	3 46	8 35	6 59	9 35	...	8 45	11 40	12 4	...

GEISLINGEN and WIESENSTEIG.

Geislingen ...dep	6 a38	11a40	2 p14	6 p30	9 p54	**Wiesensteig** dep	4a48	9 a25	12p56	4 p45	8p12
Deggingen............	7 29	12 20	3 3	7 12	10 34	Deggingen............	5 12	9 54	1 20	5 14	8 37
Wiesensteig arr	8 3	12 48	3 33	7 41	11 1	**Geislingen**...arr	5 56	10 46	2 3	6 2	9 10

FRIEDRICHSHAFEN and LINDAU.

	1,2,3	1,2,3	1,2,3	1,2,3	Ex3	1,2,3	1,2,3	1,2,3	1,2,3		1,2,3	1,2,3	1,2,3	1,2,3	1,2,3	1,2,3	Ex3	1,2,3	1,2,3	
Friedrichshafen—	a.m.	a.m.	a.m.	a.m.	p.m.	p.m	p.m.	p.m.	p.m.	**Lindau**	a.m.	a.m.	a.m.	p.m.	p.m.	p.m.	p.m.	p.m.	p.m.	
Hafen ....dep	6 25	8 46	...	1153	...	1 35	5 9	7 33	1010	Bahnh. dep	4 30	7 21	1129	1249	2 18	5 12	6 3	7 47	9 30	...
Bahnhof..............dep	6 37	9 6	1125	1151	1253	1 51	5 15	7 39	1035	**Langenargen**	4 57	7 46	1153	...	2 47	5 42	...	8 13	9 55	...
Langenargen	6 51	9 19	1139	...	...	2 4	5 28	7 52	1048	**Friedrichs-** Bh	5 11	8 0	12 6	1 13	3 2	5 56	6 26	8 26	10 9	...
Lindau Bahnhof...arr	7 16	9 44	12 7	1215	1 19	2 31	5 53	8 19	1113	**hafen** Hafen	5 17	8 10	1247	1 20	3 22	6 3	7 30	...	...	...

BOBLINGEN and DETTENHAUSEN.

Boblingen.........dep	7a12	8a57	2 p5	5p26	7p20	Dettenhausen ...dep	6a17	8 a0	12p20	3 p1	6p20	8p38
Dettenhausen ...arr	7 52	9 57	2 51	6 10	8 11	Boblingen 193...arr	7 5	8 42	1 25	3 59	7 10	9 26

EUTINGEN and SCHILTACH.

*—Not on Sunday.

		a.m.	a.m.	a.m.	a.m.	p.m.	p.m.	p.m.	p.m.		p.m.	p.m.	
Eutingen ......dep	...	...	7 29	8 54	9 32	12 50	1 6	3 5	4 55	...	8 28	10 49	...
Hochdorf	...	...	7 37	9 0	9 40	...	1 14	3 12	5 3	...	8 36	10 57	...
Freudenstadt	a.m.	6 8	8 27	9 26	10 32	1 19	2 13	4 0	5 52	p.m.	9 23	11 43	...
Alpirsbach	5*23	6 31	8 50	9 46	10 57	—	2 36	4 23	6 14	8*12	9 46	—	...
Schiltach 145......arr	5 38	6 43	9 2	9 56	11 9	...	2 48	4 35	6 26	8 25	9 57	...	...

	a.m.	a.m.	a.m.	a.m.	a.m.	p.m.	p.m.	p.m.	p.m.	p.m.	p.m.	p.m.
Schiltach ......dep	...	6 52	9 3	9 40	1110	...	2 49	5 54	...	7 *44	8 55	10 4
Alpirsbach	...	7 10	...	10 9	1128	...	3 10	6 14	...	8 4	9 12	10 24
Freudenstadt	4 35	7 45	9 55	1054	12 2	1 33	3 56	6 50	7 50	—	9 45	11 2
Hochdorf	5 16	8 24	10 21	—	1240	1 57	4 32	7 30	8 16	...	1023	...
Eutingen 193.....arr	5 22	8 29	10 27	...	1246	...	4 37	7 36	8 22	...	1028	...

Freudenstadt ......dep	5a48	8a28	12 p3	4 p4	6 p10	9 p43	...
Kloster-Reichenbach ......arr	6 36	9 21	12 51	4 50	6 58	10 30	...

Kloster-Reichenbach......dep	4a52	6 a50	9 a35	2 p59	5 p3	8 p23	...	...	...	...	...	...	...
Freudenstadt......arr	5 38	7 40	10 26	3 49	5 50	9 12	...	...	...	...	...	...	...

AULENDORF and HERBERTINGEN.

‡—Rail Motor, 4th class only.

	a.m.	a.m.	a.m.	a.m.	a.m.	p.m.	p.m.	p.m.	p.m.	p.m.	p.m.	p.m.	p.m.
Aulendorf ......dep	...	7 11	8 25	9‡49	1050	1210	1 31	3 6	...	4 56	5 20	7 55	9 58
Altshausen (191)	‡	7 32	8 43	10 18	11 5	1236	1 48	3 25	4‡11	5 25	5 37	8 9	1015
Saulgau	5 4	7 55	9 8	10 50	1127	...	2 22	3 47	4 45	—	5 55	8 26	1038
Herbertingen 194A arr	5 25	8 6	9 25	...	1143	...	2 46	3 58	5 28	...	6 6	8 37	1054

	a.m.	a.m.	a.m.	a.m.	a.m.	p.m.	p.m.	p.m.	p.m.	p.m.	p.m.	p.m.	p.m.
Herbertingen dep	5 26	6‡25	7 25	9 45	1049	1 36	2‡47	...	4 13	...	6 15	9 5	10‡9
Saulgau	5 42	7 1	7 39	10 1	11 7	1 56	3 20	...	4 28	...	6 33	9 18	1037
Altshausen	5 59	7 33	7 55	1020	1130	2 16	3 53	4 0	4 45	5 46	6 51	9 37	—
Aulendorf 193 arr	6 12	7 53	8 5	1033	1143	2 29	...	4 22	4 55	6 13	7 3	9 50	...

AULENDORF and MEMMINGEN.

‡-Rail Motor, 4th class only.

	a.m.		a.m	a.m.	p.m.	p.m.	p.m.	p.m.	p.m.	p.m.
Aulendorf ...dep	...	...	7 10	9 ‡56	12 1	...	3 2	5 21	...	10 3
Rossberg	...	...	7 42	10 41	12 28	...	3 34	5 48	6‡49	10 34
Kisslegg	5 28	a.m.	8 7	11 21	12 50	1‡56	4 1	6 11	7 17	10 56
Leutkirch......	5 55	6 16	8 33	11 48	1 11	2 29	4 30	6 40	7 45	11 13
Memmingen arr	—	7 12	9 20	—	1 55	3 32	5 27	7 38	9 2	...

	a.m.	a.m.	a.m.	p.m.	p.m.	p.m.	p.m.	p.m.	p.m.	
Memmingen dep	4 37	...	8 36	...	12 35	2 35	4 ‡0	7 5	9‡20	...
Leutkirch......	5 35	7 ‡29	9 28	12‡24	1 38	3 39	5 36	8 10	10 29	...
Kisslegg	5 57	8 6	9 48	12 49	2 0	4 5	6 8	8 41	10 54	...
Rossberg	6 17	8 42	10 9	—	2 20	4 28	6 34	9 6	—	...
Aulendorf 193 arr	6 40	9 9	10 31	...	2 42	4 51	7 0	9 29	...	...

Rossberg to Wurzach, in half an hour, 8.40 a.m , 12.42, 4.28, 6.37, 10.37 p.m. From Wurzach 5.40, 9.30 a.m., 1.37, 5.12, 8.29 p.m.

KISSLEGG and HERGATZ.

Kisslegg ...dep	5a54	8a19	9 a55	...	12p58	2 p8	4 p4	6p17	8 p50	10p58	...
Wangen......	6 16	8 45	10 31	1141	1 16	2 30	4 26	6 42	9 11	11 18	...
Hergatz ...arr	6 23	8 52	1040	1155	...	2 37	4 33	6 48	9 18	...	...

Hergatz ...dep	...	7 a25	9a10	11a10	...	1p20	...	2p58	5 p21	7 p7	9p40
Wangen	5 a0	7 36	9 28	11 19	12p10	1 30	1p32	3 15	5 35	7 37	10 1
Kisslegg ...arr	5 25	8 0	...	...	1 35	...	1 53	3 45	6 0	8 12	10 26

LEUTKIRCH and ISNY.

Leutkirch......dep	6a10	9 a30	1p35	4 p35	6p32	8 p5	11p18	...
Isny (203C) ...arr	6 52	10 10	2 15	5 24	6 59	8 46	11 51	...

Isny......dep	4a58	7 a46	12p29	2 p54	4 p50	7 p1	9p53	...	...	...	...
Leutkirch ...arr	5 29	8 26	1 0	3 29	5 24	7 43	10 24	...	...	...	...

PLOCHINGEN and OBERLENNINGEN.

§—In July and Aug. depart 8.10 p.m.

Plochingen ......dep	6a22	9 a0	1p28	2p55	6 p9	7p24	8p18	9p16	11p38
Unterboihingen	6 37	9 12	1 41	3 6	6 21	7 39	8 27	9 28	11 51
Kirchheim-u-T. .....arr	6 51	9 29	1 58	3 20	6 35	7 54	9 5	9 46	12 5
: Weilheim-a-d-T. arr	7 39	1013	2 42	...	7 16	—	—	1028	—
Oberlenningen...arr	7 33	1011	2 44	4 1	7 18	...	...	1027	...

Oberlenningen dep	...	6a10	...	10a19	1p16	...	4 p2	...	5p58	7p28	...
: Weilheim-a-d-T. dep	...	6 11	7a57	...	1 26	...	...	...	5 45	7§25	...
Kirchheim	5a35	6 52	8 51	10 52	1 59	2p48	4 34	5p22	6 36	8 7	9p29
Unterboihingen......	5 48	7 8	9 4	11 6	2 17	3 2	4 48	5 40	6 50	8 22	9 46
Plochingen 192...arr	6 2	7 21	9 16	11 18	2 29	3 18	5 0	5 47	7 2	8 34	9 58

STUTTGART, TUBINGEN, and HORB.

*—Weekdays only. [Z—Berlin-Zurich Express.

	Ex3	1—4	1—4	Ex 3	2 3 4	1—4	1—4	1,2,3	1—4	1—4	1—4	1,2,3	2 3 4	1,2,3	1—4	Ex3
	a.m.	a.m.	a.m.	a.m.		a.m.	a.m.	p.m.		p.m.	p.m.	p.m.	p.m.	p.m.	p.m.	n'gt
Stuttgart...dep	3 15	2 58	5 20	8 25	...	9 10	11 41	2 18	...	5 7	6 12	6 42	7 22	9 36	1036	1258
Ploching'n	3 39	3 45	6 15	8 54	...	9 54	12 21	2 55	...	6 2	7 18	7 13	8 18	10 5	1138	:
Nurtingen		4 4	6 39	9 8	...	1018	12 44	3 12	...	6 28	7 43	7 26	8 39	10 19	1159	Z
Metzingen		4 21	7 6	9 25	...	1044	1 7	3 27	...	6 53	8 7	7 42	9 7	10 37	1223	:
Urach ......arr		6 8	8 10	10 5	...	1123	2 16	4 5	p.m.	7 30	8 56	8 56	...	11 13	...	:
Reutlingen		4 36	7 29	9 40	a.m.	1110	1 28	3 40	5 45	7 16	8 27	7 55	9 30	10 51	1242	2 0
Tübingen...194A		5 2	8 12	9 54	1043	1224	1 51	4 2	6 20	7 40	9 6	8 9	9 55	11 5	1 2	2 13
Rottenburg		5 16	8 32	10 24	11 6	1240	2 8	4 18	6 44	—	9 28	8 36	—	11 42	—	:
Niedernau......		5 22	8 38	—	1112	1246	2 15	4 25	6 50	...	9 34	8 44	...	—	...	:
Horb 193 ......arr		5 51	9 6	...	1141	1 15	2 42	4 52	7 21	...	10 2	...	...	...	...	:

		Ex3	2 3 4	1,2,3	2 3 4	1,2,3	2 3 4	1—4	1,2,3	2 3 4	1—4	Ex3	1—4	1,2,3
		a.m.	a.m.	a.m.	a.m.			p.m.		p.m.	p.m.		p.m.	p.m.
Horb......dep		:	5 38	7 52	9 7	...	...	1 17	...	2 30	5 4	...	8 11	1054
Niedernau		Z	6 7	...	9 31	a.m.	...	1 42	...	2 58	5 30	...	8 43	1116
Rottenburg		:	6 14	8 15	9 37	1156	p.m.	1 49	p.m.	3 5	5 37	p.m.	8 50	1122
Tübingen		4 27	6 41	8 27	9 56	1228	1235	2 14	2 37	4 34	5 59	7 45	9 15	1148
Reutlingen		4 45	7 14	8 45	1026	1245	1 16	3 2	2 53	4 58	6 32	8 3	9 47	12 7
Urach ......dep		:	6 30	8 25	1017	1230	1230	2 36	2 36	...	6 10	7 40	9 29	...
Metzingen ...		:	7 30	8 56	1042	1256	1 36	3 21	3 5	5 11	6 48	8 15	10 3	1218
Nurtingen ...	4a43	:	7 53	9 10	11 3	1 9	2 4	3 48	3 19	5 31	7 9	8 29	1024	1232
Ploching'n	5 33	5 17	8 16	9 22	1128	1 21	2 33	4 11	3 32	5 53	7 32	8 42	1043	1245
Stuttgart ...	6 27	5 45	8 56	9 50	12 1	2 14	3 12	5 15	4 0	6 36	8 15	9 12	1121	1 13

Reutlingen ...dep	...	5a10	7a40	9a44	10a35	...	12*14	1p58	3 p0	4p26	5p59	7p18	8p10	11p5
Honau......	...	5 54	8 24	1020	11 56	p.m.	12 53	2 37	3 45	5 20	6 42	7 55	8 54	1142
Münsingen ......arr	4a28	7 8	9 30	1125	—	1236	—	3 45	—	6 25	8 1	—	9 58	—
Schelklingen arr	5 18	8 6	...	1214	...	1 40	...	4 37	...	...	9 0	...	...	...

Schelklingen dep	...	...	5a57	9 a26	...	11a35	...	3p17	...	6 p8	8p24
Münsingen	*	4a47	6 59	10 50	*	12 42	...	4 37	...	7 18	9 27
Honau	5 a5	5 59	8 10	12 9	1p15	1 55	4p14	5 55	7 p4	8 50	1034
Reutlingen .....arr	5 38	6 37	8 42	12 41	1 46	2 28	4 54	6 27	7 51	9 21	11 4

BIETIGHEIM and BACKNANG.

†—Rail Motor.]

	am	am	a.m.	a.m.	pm	pm	p.m.	p.m.	p.m.
Bietigheim... dep	5 2	840	9†14	11 2	1 8	423	4 32	6 12	9 47
Beihingen......arr	513	:	9 29	1113	117	:	4 42	6 24	9 57
Marbach-a-N. ...	530	:	9 43	1129	131	:	4 59	6 53	10 9
Backnang 191 arr	556	9 6	1023	1155	159	451	5 26	7 20	1035

	am	am	a.m.	a.m.	p.m.	pm	pm	pm
Backnang 191 dep	455	713	10†30	1056	1212	219	618	842
Marbach-a-N.	525	739	11 42	...	1237	249	652	9 7
Beihingen-a-N. ar	537	751	12 0	...	1249	3 0	7 1	918
Bietigheim 193 arr	545	759	12 13	1122	1258	3 9	710	927

Ludwigsburg dep	4a50	7a18	1035	1258	3 p0	5p27	6p30	7p49	9p39
Beihingen	5 0	7 28	1035	1 8	3 13	5 38	6 40	8 0	9 49
Marbach a-N arr	5 11	7 37	1048	1 18	3 26	5 48	6 50	8 9	9 59
Marbach-a-N dep	4a44	5a38	7a56	1128	1p25	3p40	5p56	7 p5	8p55
Beihingen	5 1	5 56	8 9	1142	1 39	3 57	6 9	7 20	9 21
Ludwigsburg arr	5 15	6 12	8 21	1154	1 52	4 11	6 22	7 34	9 38

HEILBRONN and EPPINGEN.

K—Carlsbad Express.

Heilbronn ...dep	6 a8	9a40	12p20	3p13	5p25	7 p4	9p20	10p38
Schwaigern	6 29	10 1	12 41	3 34	5 49	7 28	K	10 59
Eppingen (142) ar	6 50	1022	1 2	3 55	6 14	7 55		11 21

Eppingen ...dep	4a30	5†a8	K	7 a18	11a28	3p38	6p40	9p19	...	...
Schwaigern......	5 3	5 37		7 39	11 50	3 59	7 2	9 41	...	...
Heilbronn 193ar	5 29	5 58	7a10	7 58	12 8	4 16	7 20	10 0	...	...

†—Weekdays only.

PFORZHEIM and WILDBAD.

	1—4	1—4	1,2,3	1—4	Ex3	1—4	1,2,3	1—4	1—4	1—4	2 3 4	1—4	1—4	1—4	1—4	
CARLSRUHE......dep	4a10	7a19	7a33	...	1048	1048	11p30	...	3p25	...	...	6p45	...	8p43	10p12	...
	a.m.	a.m.	a.m.	a.m.	a.m.	p.m.	p.m.	p.m.	p m	p.m.	p.m.	p.m.	p.m	p.m.	p.m.	
Pforzheim..........dep	5 35	8 13	9 38	1024	1136	1218	2 5	2 31	4 32	5†57	6†20	7 41	8 2	9 38	11 0	...
Neuenbürg	5 57	8 40	9 54	1049	1152	1245	2 21	2 57	4 54	6 25	6 47	8 7	8 39	10 2	11 22	...
Höfen	6 13	8 55	10 6	11 4	...	1 1	B	3 14	5 10	6 42	7 4	8 25	8 56	1020	11 36	...
Wildbad ....arr	6 26	9 8	1017	1120	1213	1 15	2 42	3 29	5 24	6 56	7 20	8 40	9 9	1035	11 49	..

	1—4	1—4	2 3 4	1—4	1—4	1—4	1—4	1—4	Ex3	1—4	1—4	1—4	1—4	1—4		
	a.m	a.m.	a.m.	a.m.	a.m.	a.m.	a.m.	p.m.	p.m.	p.m.	p.m.	p.m.	p.m.	p.m.		
Wildbad..............dep	4†43	5 12	5†50	7 6	9 16	9 55	11 4	1 28	2 43	3 39	5 56	7 6	8 *12	1010	...	...
Höfen	4 53	5 21	6 0	7 16	9 27	10 6	1118	1 39	...	3 48	6 6	7 17	8 24	1021	...	...
Neuenbürg	5 5	5 36	6 17	7 30	9 39	10 20	1133	1 58	2 56	4 3	6 23	7 32	8 40	1032	...	...
Pforzheim..........arr	5 24	6 56	6 34	7 50	9 57	10 37	1154	2 15	3 8	4 20	6 43	7 52	8 59	1049	...	...
CARLSRUHE141Aarr	...	...	7a49	8a32	...	11a47	1236	3p30	3p50	5p26	7p34	8p28	10p29	1155	...	...

†—Weekdays only.

*—In July and Aug. only.

B—Runs until 15th Sept.

WALDENBURG and KUNZELSAU.

Waldenburg......dep	8 a36	11 a6	1 p55	5 p16	8 p32	10p45	...
Künzelsau ......arr	9 22	11 52	2 41	6 2	9 18	11 30	...

Künzelsau ....dep	6 a32	9 a52	12p50	3 p55	6 p41	9p45	...	...
Waldenburg (190A)arr	7 19	10 39	1 37	4 42	7 28	10 32	...	...

ULM, HERBERTINGEN, and TUTTLINGEN.

†—Weekdays only. *—Rail Motor.

	a.m.	a.m.	a.m.	a.m.	a.m.	a.m.	p.m.	p.m.	p.m.	p.m.	p.m.
Ulm............dep	6*35	5 6	8 22	1033	1056	11*45	1 28	3 12	4 6	6 21	8 51
Blaubeuren	7 16	5 37	9 4	11 3	1114	12 28	2 3	3 29	4 34	6 56	9 16
Schelklingen......	7 28	5 49	9*18	1130	...	12 4	2 17	...	4 44	7 5	9 25
Ehingen	7 49	6 7	9 43	1146	1133	1 9	2 43	3 47	5 1	7 26	9 46
Munderkingen...	—	6 27	10 4	12 5	1145	1 28	3 3	...	5 19	7 43	10 8
Untermarchthal		6 33	1010	1219	...	1 33	3 10	...	5 24	7 48	1015
Rechtenstein..............		6 41	1024	1218	...	1 44	3 18	...	5 32	7 56	1024
Zwiefaltendorf...	a.m.	6 48	1034	1226	...	1 53	3 26	...	5 40	8 3	1036
Riedlingen.........	4 54	7 1	1048	1240	12 5	2 17	3 41	4 16	5 53	8 16	1050
Herbertingen arr	5 16	7 20	—	1258	...	2 45	4 9	...	6 9	8 34	11 9
Herbertingen dep	5 42	7 25	1148	1 4	...	3 0	4 18	...	6 18	8 42	1118
Mengen......arr	5 52	7 33	1156	1 12	...	3 10	—	4 34	6 27	8 50	1128
,, ...dep	5 53	7 36	1159	1 16	...	3 14	...	4 35	6 30	8 55	1131
Sigmaringen arr	6 17	7 58	1223	1 34	1232	3 39	p.m	4 46	6 50	9 15	1154
Sigmaringen dep	6 22	8 51	—	1 38	1235	—	4*10	4 48	7 2	—	—
Inzigkofen	6 40	9 1	...	1 45	...	...	4 19	4 55	7 10	...	...
Gutenstein.........	6 48	9 8	p.m.	1 52	1248	...	4 27	...	7 17	...	p.m.
Beuron	7 16	9 36	1248	2 15	1 8	p.m.	4 59	5 17	7 41	...	9 46
Tuttlingen arr	7 52	1011	1 18	2 41	1 28	6 34	6 2	5 37	8 17	...	1023
Immendin. arr	8 22	1031	...	3 0	1 42	6 45	6 31	5 48	8 39	...	11 1

		a.m.	a.m.	a m.	p.m.		p.m.	p.m.	p.m
Immendingen...dep	...	5 24	7 12	1158	1 45	...	...	7 46	7 56
Tuttlingen dp	...	5 41	8 5	12 9	2 21	...	6 17	7 57	8 25
Beuron	...	6 10	8 32	1228	2 54	...	6 52	...	8 55
Gutenstein	...	6 32	8 54	1247	3 17	...	7 16	...	9 18
Inzigkofen	...	6 38	9 2	...	3 23	...	7 24	..	9 27
Sigmaringen arr	a.m.	6 46	9 8	1257	3 31	p.m	7 31	8 41	9 34
Sigmaringen......dep	4 53	6 51	9 12	1 0	3 42	5 23	8 5	8 43	9 37
Mengen ...arr	5 11	7 9	9 29	1 11	3 59	5 47	8 27	8 54	9 54
,, ...dep	5 12	7 11	9 31	1 13	4 1	5 48	8 30	8 55	9 56
Herbertingen arr	5 20	7 19	9 38	...	4 8	5 57	8 38	9 1	10 3
Herbertingen...dep	5 30	7 30	9 46	...	4 2[illegible]	6 12	8 40	9 3	10 6
Riedlingen	5 51	7 47	10 4	1 31	4 46	6 30	9 *6	9 15	1024
Zwiefaltendorf	6 3	7 59	1016	...	4 58	6 42	—	...	1037
Rechtenstein ...	6 11	8 7	1023	...	5 5	6 49	...	...	1044
Untermarchthal	6 19	8 13	1029	...	5 12	6 56	...	...	1050
Munderkingen	6 26	8 19	1035	1 50	5 18	7 1	...	..	1056
Ehingen	6 47	8 39	1056	2 3	5 39	7 25	p.m.	9 44	1116
Schelklingen ...	7 7	8 56	1130	...	6 0	7 51	9 4	..	1136
Blaubeuren......	7 17	9 6	1139	2 21	6 8	8 4	9 17	10 2	1145
Ulm ....arr	7 48	9 34	12 7	2 38	6 34	8 33	9 48	1019	12 8

Extra—Ulm to Schelklingen 2.9, 5.17, 7.30, 10*42 p.m., Schelklingen to Ulm, 4*33, 5.24, 8.19 a.m., 12.18, 12.50, 1.46, 4*21, 4.43 p.m

ROTTWEIL and VILLINGEN.

[†—Weekdays only.

	a.m.	a m.	a.m.	a.m.	a.m.	p.m.	p.m.	p.m.	p.m.	p.m.
Rottweil dep	...	5 50	7 15	1017	11 5	1 29	2 59	6 1	7 19	9 55
Trossingen	...	6 24	7 39	1039	1143	1 42	3 23	6 27	7 44	1019
Schwenningen	5 15	7 10	7 56	1055	12 9	1 59	3 39	6 41	8 1	1036
Villingen arr	5 35	7 33	8 16	1110	1232	2 19	3 59	6 56	8 21	1053

(144)	a.m.	a.m.	a.m.	a.m.	a.m.	p.m.	p.m.	p m.	p.m	p.m.
Villingen......	5 48	8 25	9 8	1039	1150	1 35	5 49	7 20	8 35	9 2[illegible]
Schwenningen	6 9	8 53	9 50	1057	1215	2 2	6 14	8 0	9 0	9 48
Trossingen......	6 23	9 10	1015	1112	1230	2 18	6 28	8 14	9 15	—
Rottweil193..	6 45	9 39	1050	1138	1256	2 43	6 56	8 40	9 40	...

PFORZHEIM, CALW, and HORB.

†—Weekdays only.] [*-Rail Motor.

(141)	a.m.	a.m.	a.m.	a.m.	a.m.	p.m	p.m	...	p.m.	p.m.	p.m.
Pforzheim dep	...	6 14	8 10	1042	1133	1254	2 27	...	5 13	8 11	11 5
Liebenzell	5 40	6 58	8 55	1119	1154	1 33	3 11	p.m.	5 53	8 54	1143
Calw 192A...arr	6 1	7 15	9 12	1133	12 6	1 53	3 27	4*37	6 12	9 12	1159
,, ...dep	6 11	7 30	9 49	1137	12 7	2 2	3 32	4 43	6 17	9 26	—
Teinach	6 17	7 35	9 55	1143	1212	2 8	3 38	4 58	6 26	9 32	...
Wildberg.........	6 30	7 47	—	1155	...	2 25	3 52	5 21	6 41	9 45	...
Nagold............	6 50	8 4	...	1212	1229	2 46	4 12	—	7 2	10 1	...
Hochdorf	7 20	8 23	a.m.	1232		3 10	4 34	...	7 26	1022	p.m.
Eutingen	7 33	8 49	9 10	1259	1245	—	4 56	...	7 41	1029	1042
Horb 193 ...arr	7 47	8 49	9 20	1 9	...	...	5 8	...	7 53	1039	1052

		a.m.	a.m	* a.m.	p.m.	p.m.		p.m.	p.m.		p.m
Horb...... dep		5 59	9 45	1144	1210	...	...	2*47	4 13	...	7 33
Eutingen......		6 19	1011	1211	1256	...	...	3 5	5 0	...	8 30
Hochdorf		6 28	1022	1243	1 5	2 2	...	3 14	5 8	...	8 39
Nagold		6 50	1046	1 1	1 17	2 14	...	3 34	5 25	...	9 1
Wildberg		7 6	11 2	1 14	...	...	p.m	3 52	5 39	p.m.	9 16
Teinach		7 21	1117	1 26	1 35	2 31	3 13	4 5	5 51	6 27	9 32
Calw .arr	a.m.	7 27	1123	1 32	1 40	2 36	3 2[illegible]	4 11	5 56	6 34	9 37
,, dep	4 55	7 33	1134	—	1 41	2 37	3 28	—	5 59	6 50	9 46
Liebenzl	5 10	7 46	1155	...	1 55	2 49	3 43	...	6 14	7 7	10 2
Pforzh'm	5 45	8 26	1234	...	2 22	3 11	4 23	...	6 52	7 47	1043

Nagold-Bahnhof dep	6a51	8a 29	1p20	4p22	5 p35	9 p3	10p 3
Altensteig .... arr	7 50	9 25	2 10	5 20	6 38	10 1	11 0

Altensteig...dep	5a28	6 a55	9a34	10a55	3p12	5 p54	7p20	...	...	...
Nagold ......arr	6 30	7 58	10 28	11 55	4 2	6 55	7 24	...	...	...

TUBINGEN and SIGMARINGEN.

E.M.			a.m	a.m.	a.m.	p.m	p.m.	p.m.	p.m
—	Tübingen...........dep	...	5 28	8 3	9 58	2 13	4 0	8 12	11 17
15⅓	Hechingen..................	...	6 35	8 38	10 46	3 2	4 53	8 58	11 49
26	Balingen.....................	a.m.	7 11	8 56	11 16	3 36	5 25	9 32	12 9
36¼	Ebingen	5 56	8 9	9 27	11 54	4 18	6 17	10 9	12 38
54	Sigmaringen (194A)	6 38	8 50	10 1	12 33	5 3	7 0	11†45	1 10

		a.m	a.m.	a.m.	p.m.	p.m	p.m.	p.m
Sigmaringen dep		5 7	6 47	9 47	1 45	5 4	7 17	9 20
Ebingen		6 5	7 19	10 44	2 47	5 5[illegible]	7 53	10 10
Balingen..........	a.m.	6 37	7 40	11 14	3 18	6 27	8 13	10 39
Hechingen ..	552	7 12	7 58	11 44	3 54	6 59	8 30	11 7
Tübingen 194	636	7 52	8 22	12 21	4 28	7 35	8 58	11 39

Ebingen ....dep	7a22	9a28	12 5	2p50	4p22	6†20	8 p0	10p15
Onstmettingen ...arr	8 1	9 55	1244	3 17	4 49	6 56	8 27	10 42

Onstmettingen dep	6a†7	8a43	9†57	1p30	3p33	4p54	7p20	9 p3	† Not on
Ebingen...........arr	6 46	9 10	1030	1 57	4 0	5 33	7 47	9 30	Sun.

Balingen......dep	7 a15	11†a23	6 p26	9 p34	...
Schömberg ..arr	8 6	12 18	7 16	10 19	...

Schömberg dep	6 a0	10a20	2‡p25	7 p28	...
Balingen.....arr	6 35	11 5	3 10	8 8	...

†—1.7 p.m. on Sunday.

‡—2.0 p.m. on Sunday.

SCHILTACH and SCHRAMBERG.

†—Not on Sunday.

Schiltach	5†44	6a56	9a41	11a21	1p22	2p53	4p39	6p29	8 p30	10 p5
Schramberg...	6 10	7 27	1012	11 54	1 56	3 23	5 9	6 57	8 59	10 36

Schramberg ...	4†a29	6a20	7a57	10a39	12p36	2p13	3p57	5p21	7p7	9p2[illegible]
Schiltach (194)	4 51	6 44	8 25	11 6	1 8	2 40	4 25	5 49	734	9 54

SCHWEINFURT, KISSINGEN, and MEININGEN.

ASCHAFFENBG 196	...	...	...	1a20	...	7a33	8a19	...	...	1050	1050	...	...	4p28	5p33
WURZBURG dp	1 a2	3a33	...	6 a0	...	10a0	11a7	...	1p27	1p40	1p40	2 p15	...	6p10	7p15
	Ex3	1,2,3	1,2,3	1,2,3	1,2,3	1,2,3	Ex3	Ex3	Ex3	Ex3	1,2,3	1,2,3	1,2,3	1,2,3	1,2,3
	a.m.	a.m.	a.m.	a.m.	a.m.	a.m.	p.m.		p.m.	p.m.	p.m.	p.m.	p.m.	p.m.	p.m.
Schweinfurt dep	1 53	5 30	5 50	7 20	8 0	1057	1 8	...	2 15	2 40	2 49	3 50	5 0	7 35	8 27
benhausen arr	...	5 57	6 13	7 40	8 28	1124	...	...	...	2 59	3 15	4 10	5 30	7 56	8 55
Ebenhausen dp	...	6 14	6 14	7 50	8 30	1135	...	...	...	3 12	...	4 12	5 42	7 57	9 5
Kissingen ...arr	...	6 32	6 32	8 18	8 48	1153	1 44	p.m.	2 50	3 30	...	4 30	6 0	8 15	9 23
" ...dep	SC	5 35	—	7 17	—	11 0	—	1 48	—	...	2 55	—	5 5	—	8 15
Ebenhausen dep	...	5 58	...	7 46	...	1129	...	2 11	...	3 2	3 16	...	5 35	...	9 0
Münnerstadt	...	6 21	...	8 5	...	1151	...	...	...	...	3 37	...	6 1	...	9 24
Neustadt-a-S. ...	...	6 39	...	8 16	...	12 5	...	...	...	3 29	3 51	...	6 19	...	9 40
Mellrichstadt......	...	7 5	...	8 32	...	1231	...	...	...	3 44	4 17	...	6 47	...	10 7
Rentwertshausen	...	7 31	...	8 53	...	1256	...	...	...	:	4 41	...	7 15	...	1034
Ritschenhsen arr	...	7 40	...	9 1	...	1 5	...	...	...	RC	4 50	...	7 25	...	1043
ERFURT 171 arr	5a13	...	...	1152	...	4 p7	...	5p25	...	6p21	7p59	...	1030	...	...
Ritschenhsen dep	...	7 45	...	9 3	...	1 11	...	...	...	:	4 54	...	7 33	...	1045
Meiningen ...arr	3 21	7 54	...	9 11	...	1 20	...	3 17	...	4 16	5 3	...	7 43	...	1054

	Ex3	1,2,3	1,2,3	1,2,3	1,2,3	1,2,3	1,2,3	Ex 3	1,2,3	Ex3	1,2,3	1,2,3	1,2,3	3 Cl.
	a.m.	a.m.		a.m.		a.m.	p.m.	p.m.		p.m.	p.m.		p.m.	ng't
Meiningen 173B dp	2 17	4 50	...	6 40	...	9 13	1247	1 53	...	2 36	5 6	...	7 45	1230
Ritschenhausen ar	...	5 3	...	6 52	...	9 27	1 0	...	...	...	5 18	...	7 59	1249
ERFURT ......dep	1221	...	...	...	...	5a58	1015	11a50	...	1226	2 p32	...	4p48	8p47
Ritschenhausen dp	...	5 4	...	6 53	...	9 32	1 12	...	...	RC	5 25	...	8 7	1 5
Rentwertshausen	...	5 19	...	7 6	...	9 48	1 27	...	...	...	5 38	...	8 23	1 37
Mellrichstadt	...	5 36	...	7 18	...	10 6	1 44	RC	...	3 6	5 53	...	8 41	2 5
Neustadt (195) ...	SC	6 3	...	7 37	...	1034	2 11	...	...	3 19	6 16	...	9 11	3 15
Münnerstadt	...	6 19	...	7 52	...	1051	2 28	...	...	3 30	6 31	...	9 29	3 50
Ebenhausen ...arr	...	6 46	...	8 18	...	1120	2 56	3 3	...	3 51	6 56	...	9 59	4 45
Kissingen ...arr	...	7 8	a.m.	8 48	a.m.	1153	3 30	3 30	p.m.	4 30	7 20	p.m.	1025	5 23
" ...dep	...	5 35	7 17	...	9 45	11 0	1 48	—	2 55	...	6 30	7 36	9 35	...
Ebenhausen arr	...	5 53	7 33	...	10 3	1118	2 5	...	3 12	...	6 48	7 54	9 53	...
Ebenhausen ...dep	...	6 48	7 34	8 20	10 4	1125	3 0	...	3 17	3 52	7 1	7 56	10 8	4 50
Schweinfurt ...arr	3 36	7 8	7 48	8 41	1024	1147	3 21	...	3 31	4 5	7 20	8 10	1030	5 30
WURZBURG 198	4a24	8a52	8 a52	1125	1125	1p25	4p32	...	4p32	4p57	8 p13	9p52	1255	7a15
ASCHAFFENB'G	7a40	1057	10a57	1 p0	1 p0	4p47	8 p5	...	8 p5	8 p5	10p24	1223	3a52	8a52

‡—Weekdays only. SC—Sleeping Car attached. RC—Restaurant Car.

Extra

Kissingen......dep	1 p5	11 p0	Ebenhausen......dep	6a50	7 p2	10p7	Kissingen.........dep	5 p5	8p15
Schweinfurt...arr	1 45	11 38	Kissingen ....arr	7 8	7 20	1025	Ebenhausen......arr	5 23	8 47

BAVARIAN STATE RAILWAYS. [Luggage Rates, see page 467.

REGENSBURG, INGOLSTADT, and AUGSBURG.

	2&3	2&3	2&3	2&3	2&3	2&3	2&3	2&3	
	a.m.	a.m.	a.m.	p.m.	p.m.	p.m.	p.m.	p.m.	...
Regensburg......dep	6 5	5 40	9 30	1 26	2 3	5 40	6 35	1111	...
Sinzing	6 19	5 51	9 41	1 39	2 18	5 51	6 49	1124	...
Abbach	—	6 9	9 59	2 0	—	6 9	—	1145	...
Saal...............	...	6 25	10 9	2 10	...	6 17	...	1154	...
Abensberg.......	...	6 55	10 32	2 40	...	6 41	...	1223	...
Neustadt-a-D.	...	7 4	10 40	2 50	...	6 50	...	1232	...
Ingol- ...arr	a.m.	7 45	11 17	3 30	...	7 33	...	1 14	...
stadt...dep	3 43	8 10	11 29	3 49	...	7 47	...	—	...
Niederarnbach	4 9	8 31	11 52	4 12	...	8 11	...	...	...
Aichach	5 8	9 13	12 46	4 59	...	9 1	...	...	...
Hochzoll	6 1	9 50	1 23	5 45	...	9 42	...	...	...
Augsburg...arr	6 15	9 58	1 31	5 55	...	9 51	...	...	...

	2&3	2&3	3 Cl.	2&3	2&3	2&3	2&3	2&3	2&3	2&3	
				a.m.	a.m.	p.m.		p.m.		p.m.	...
Augsburg ...dep	...	...	...	6 48	9 39	12 5	...	4 20	...	7 27	...
Hochzoll	...	...	a.m.	6 57	9 47	1212	...	4 27	...	7 35	...
Aichach............	...	...	6 2	7 41	1021	1247	...	4 58	...	8 12	...
Niederarnbach	...	...	7 15	8 30	1059	1 23	...	5 35	...	8 54	...
Ingol- ......arr	a.m.	...	7 50	8 51	1118	1 42	...	5 55	...	9 13	...
stadt......dep	5 21	...	—	9 6	—	2 6	...	6 6	...	10 8	...
Neustadt-a-D.	5 57	...	...	9 41	...	2 48	...	6 48	...	1053	...
Abensberg	6 6	...	...	9 50	...	2 57	...	7 0	...	11 6	...
Saal	6 27	...	...	1012	...	3 19	...	7 23	...	1133	...
Abbach	6 35	a.m.	...	1021	...	3 28	p.m.	7 32	p.m.	1144	...
Sinzing	6 53	7 7	...	1033	...	3 45	5 55	7 48	9 12	12 3	...
Regensburg arr	7 4	7 22	...	1050	...	3 56	6 9	7 58	9 27	1214	...

PROBSTZELLA and LICHTENFELS.

	2&3	2&3	2&3	1,2,3	2&3	2&3	1,2,3	Ex3	2&3	Ex3	2&3	Ex3
	a.m.	a.m.	a.m.	a.m.	a.m.	p.m.	p.m.	p.m.	p.m.	p.m.	p.m.	a.m.
Probstzella ...dep	2 40	...	7 50	1012	...	1 17	2 35	3 14	...	6 42	7 36	1 34
Ludwigstadt	3 11	...	8 15	1027	...	1 45	2 51	To Munich.	...	...	8 8	To Munich.
Rothenkirchen ...	4 6	7 11	9 6	...	1045	2 38	3 23	:	6 16	...	9 5	:
Stockheim	4 17	7 23	9 16	11 1	1111	2 51	3 30	:	6 30	7 31	9 20	:
Kronach	4 33	7 41	9 33	1110	1128	3 7	3 39	:	6 48	7 39	9 46	:
Hochstadt............	5 7	8 18	10 4	...	12 0	3 40	3 55	:	7 20	...	1024	:
Lichtenfels ...arr	5 22	8 33	1020	1130	1217	3 55	4 4	:	7 37	8 0	1042	:

	Ex3	2&3	Ex3	2&3	1,2,3	2&3	1,2,3	2&3	2&3	
	a.m.	a.m.	a.m.	a.m.	p.m.	p.m.	p.m.	p.m.	p.m.	
Lichtenfels	:	6 10	1037	1043	2 2	5 8	6 1	8 2	1035	...
Hochstadt ...	:	6 27	...	1058	2 13	5 26	...	8 20	1055	...
Kronach	:	7 3	11 2	1133	2 38	6 3	6 29	8 57	1135	...
Stockheim ...	:	7 22	1113	1152	2 52	6 24	6 41	9 16	1156	...
Rothenkirch	3 3	7 39	1122	1221	3 5	6 59	6 51	9 33	12 8	...
Ludwigstadt	:	8 29	:	1 5	3 53	7 47	7 34	1025	—	...
Probstzella	:	8 46	:	1 21	4 5	8 2	7 45	1040	...	...

INGOLSTADT and NEU-OFFINGEN.

‡—Not on Sunday.

		a.m.	a.m.	a.m.	p.m.	p.m.	p.m.	p.m.	p.m.
Ingolstadt......dep	...	5 32	8 11	9 29	1253	3 47	6 19	7 40	10 8
Neuburg-a-D.	...	6 10	8 46	10 9	1 31	5 28	6 59	8 14	10 46
Rain	...	6 51	—	10 46	2 9	6 52	7 36	—	11 21
Donauworth ...arr	...	7 15	...	11 8	2 29	—	7 57	...	11 40
" (199) dep	...	7 54	...	11 23	2 38	6 p18	9 [illegible]	...	—
Höchstädt-a-D. ...	a.m.	8 28	...	12 0	3 13	6 53	9 35	...	...
Dillingen	3 45	8 46	...	12 21	3 33	7 10	9 52	...	...
Neu-Offingen ...arr	4 13	9 15	...	12 53	4 1	7 40	10 19	...	...
ULM (192A)...arr	5a40	10a28	...	2 p5	5p12	...	11p25	...	...

	a.m.	a.m.		a.m.	p.m.	p.m.		p.m.	p.m.
ULM ....dep	...	4 58	...	9 43	2 52	4 12	...	7 17	11 15
Neu-Offingen...dep	...	6 4	...	1055	3 24	5 21	...	8 33	12 19
Dillingen	...	6 32	...	1124	3 54	5 53	...	9 4	12 45
Höchstädt-a-D. ...	...	6 45	...	1138	4 6	6 7	‡	9 19	—
Donauworth ...arr	...	7 16	...	1210	4 34	6 41	p.m.	9 51	...
" ...dep	5 39	7 27	...	1218	4 40	—	9 1	1015	...
Rain	5 59	7 48	a.m.	1238	4 59	p.m.	9 36	1036	...
Neuburg-a-D.	6 36	8 26	10 36	1 11	5 28	8 39	1046	1111	...
Ingolstadt......arr	7 5	8 58	11 7	1 42	5 57	9 9	...	1142	...

NEUSTADT-A-S. and BISCHOFSHEIM.

	a.m.	a.m.	p.m.	p.m.		a.m.	a.m.	p.m.	p.m.
Neustadt-a-S.dep	7‡20	1040	4 0	9 45	**Bischofsheim ...dep**	4 40	8 45	1250	7 26
Schönau	7 58	1137	4 41	1023	Schönau	5 10	9 30	1 20	7 56
Bischofsheim arr	8 27	1220	5 10	1052	**Neustadt-a-S. 195arr**	5 45	1025	1 55	8 30

‡—6.50 a.m. on Sunday.

IMMENSTADT and OBERSTDORF.

*—Until 15th Sept.

	a.m.	a.m.	a.m.	a.m.	a.m.	p.m.	p.m.	p.m.	p.m.	p.m.	p.m.
Immenstadt dep	5 5	6 30	7 40	9 *8	1035	1 10	2 55	4 25	7 55	9 45	11 25
Sonthofen......arr	5 25	6 50	8 0	9 28	1055	1 30	3 15	4 45	8 15	10 5	11 45
Oberstdorf ...arr	6 7	...	8 37	10 6	1135	2 *11	3 52	5 22	8 52	10*44	...

Oberstdorf dep	...	5 a0	...	7a33	8*a52	11a9	1*p0	...	2p38	5p43	7p47	9*p15	...
Sonthofen dep	4 a5	5 55	7 a5	8 15	9 30	1155	1 33	1p40	3 15	5 20	8 25	10 30	10p35
Immenstadt199	4 25	6 15	7 35	8 35	9 50	1215	...	2 0	3 35	6 40	8 45	...	10 55

Luggage Rates—see page 456.]

BAVARIAN STATE RAILWAYS.

WURZBURG, NURNBERG, REGENSBURG, and PASSAU.

RC—Restaurant Car. SC—Sleeping Car.

COLOGNE 122, 128 dep		11p57	1 a58	...	...	...	...	10a3	10 a3	12p10	...	8 p2
FRANKFORT 196 dp	...	3 a36	6 a26	...	8a25	...	9 a6	2p20	2 p20	4 p36	...	1221
	2&3	Ex 1	Ex.3		Ex.3	2 & 3	2 & 3	2&3	1,2,3	Ex.3	2 & 3	Ex3
	a.m.	a.m.	a.m.		a.m.	a.m.	p.m.	p.m.	p.m.	p.m.	p.m.	a.m.
Wurzburg ......dep	5 15	6 8	9 32	...	10 53	9 45	2 0	4 40	5 0	7 22	9 28	2 51
Rottendorf	5 33	...	...	...	...	10 2	2 18	4 57	...	SC	9 47	...
Kitzingen 198	6 4	A	10 4	...	...	10 32	2 51	5 38	5 30	7 53	10 20	3 20
Mainbernheim	6 16	...	RC	...	...	10 42	3 4	5 50	...	...	10 32	...
Mkt. Einersheim ...	6 34	...	...	...	...	10 58	3 23	6 7	...	...	10 50	...
Mkt. Bibart	7 10	...	10 35	...	RC	11 17	3 46	6 27	5 58	...	11 12	3 50
Langenfeld	7 19	...	...	...	...	11 24	3 56	6 36	...	...	11 22	...
Neustadt-a-A, 203A	7 36	...	10 51	...	...	11 44	4 17	6 54	6 12	8 35	11 41	4 5
Emskirchen	7 57	...	...	...	...	12 15	4 38	7 12	...	...	12 0	...
Siegelsdorf 201	8 22	...	...	...	...	12 39	5 8	7 40	...	...	12 21	...
Furth 197 ...... arr	8 36	7 46	11 27	...	12 28	12 51	5 24	7 53	6 44	9 11	12 41	4 39
dep	8 40	7 47	11 28	...	12 29	12 56	5 42	7 57	6 45	9 12	12 50	4 40
Nurnberg Cent. arr	8 56	7 56	11 39	...	12 41	1 11	5 58	8 10	6 54	9 22	1 7	4 52
BAYREUTH 202 arr	11a6	11 a6	...	...	3p21	5 p24	...	1042	10p42	...	...	...
EGER 202 ......arr	12p5	11 a9	...	...	3p48	8 p24	...	1257	12a57	...	...	...
CARLSBAD 251 arr	1p29	12p21	...	...	5p31	11p43	...	...	...	...	...	...

	2&3	2&3	Ex 1		2 & 3	Ex 3	2 & 3	2 & 3	2&4		Ex.3	2 & 3	1,2,3
Nurnberg—	a.m.	a.m	a.m.		p.m.	p.m.	p.m.	p.m.	p.m.		p.m.	p.m.	a.m.
Central dep	5 1	9 12	8 15	...	12 26	12 51	4 37	6‡42	8 25	...	9 40	11 38	5 30
Feucht 201	5 25	9 39	...	...	12 55	...	5 4	7 6	8 50	...	...	12 2	...
Neumarkt-i-O.	6 27	1029	A	...	2 0	1 30	5 56	8 6	9 51	...	10 34	12 59	6 14
Deining ......dep	6 43	1046	...	...	2 16	...	6 12		10 6	...	...		...
Parsberg	7 10	1112	...	...	2 42	...	6 37	...	1032	...	...	...	6 43
Laaber	7 32	1135	...	...	3 4	...	6 5[illegible]	...	1053	...	...	...	...
Prüfening........	7 55	1159	...	...	3 28	...	7 23	...	1118	...	...	2 & 3	
Regensburg arr	8 1	12 5	10 15	...	3 34	2 27	7 29	...	1125	...	11 38	a.m.	7 12
„ 195, 202 dep	9 15	1220	10 20	...	4 20	2 31	8 10	...		...	11 43	3 35	7 24
Obertraubling	9 28	1235	...	...	4 33	...	8 25	...	...	...	...	3 50	...
Sünching	9 56	1 4	...	...	5 3	...	8 54	...	...	...	...	4 20	...
Radldorf	10 7	1 15	...	...	5 13	...	9 5	...	...	...	...	4 31	...
Straubing 197 arr	1018	1 28	...	...	5 24	3 4	9 17	...	...	...	12 18	4 43	8 0
dep	1024	1 40	...	...	5 30	3 5	9 22	...	...	...	12 20	4 50	8 2
Strasskirchen ...	1041	1 59	...	...	5 47	...	9 37	1,2,3	...	...	...	5 7	...
Plattling 198 arr	1059	2 17	...	...	6 4	3 25	9 52	p.m.	...	...	...	5 24	8 21
dep	1145	2 47	...	...	6 15	3 27	10 14	9 55	...	...	...	6 5	8 24
Vilshofen	1232	3 32	...	...	7 5	3 54	11 3	10 25	...	...	...	6 52	8 54
Passau 239B ¶ arr	1 9	4 7	12 7	...	7 42	4 15	11 42	10 45	...	...	1 25	7 28	9 17
VIENNA 239A arr	...	...	6 p0	...	6 a0	9 p59	7a20	...	...	...	7 a20	...	...

‡—Weekdays only. ¶—Customs Examinations. A—Ostend-Vienna Express.

VIENNA 239 dep	8p30	...	...	...	10p55	...	7a25	...	12 0	...	...	...	...	...	1 p0
	Ex3		1,2,3	2 & 3	2 & 3	2 & 3	Ex 3		Ex1.			2 & 3	2&3	1,2,3	2 & 3
	a.m.		a.m.	a.m.	a.m.	p.m.	p.m.		p.m.			p.m.	p.m.	p.m.	p.m.
Passau ¶ ...dep	2 28	...	8 24	4 0	8 50	12 22	1 35	...	5 17	...	...	4 15	6 20	7 50	8 16
Vilshofen	...	...	8 44	4 42	9 34	1 1	1 55	...	...	...	...	4 55	6 44	8 10	8 59
Plattling arr	...	...	9 12	5 31	10 22	1 46	2 21	...	A	...	...	5 42	7 18	8 37	9 47
dep	...	...		6 5	10 42	2 1	2 22	...	...	...	...	6 11		8 39	10 6
Strasskirchen ...	...	...	...	6 23	11 0	2 18	...	...	...	...	...	6 29	...	...	10 24
Straubing arr	3 48	...	...	6 40	11 16	2 33	2 42	...	...	...	...	6 45	...	8 58	10 40
dep	3 50	...	...	6 48	11 20	2 50	2 43	...	...	...	...	6 53	...	9 0	10 4
Radldorf	...	...	...	7 2	11 33	3 3	...	...	...	...	...	7 [illegible]	...	...	11 2
Sünching........	...	...	...	7 12	11 43	3 12	...	...	...	...	...	7 16	...	...	11 13
Obertraubling	...	...	2 & 3	7 40	12 10	3 37	...	...	...	...	...	7 42	...	...	11 42
Regensberg arr	4 34	...	a.m.	7 53	12 23	3 49	3 17	...	6 50	...	...	7 54	...	9 37	11 55
dep	4 40	...	4 10	9 15	12 58	4 28	3 20	...	6 53	...	...	8 52	...	9 42	
Prüfening........	...	...	4 17	9 21	1 5	4 36	...	...	...	...	...	8 59	...	...	...
Laaber	...	...	4 58	9 53	1 42	5 14	RC	...	...	...	...	9 34	...	...	...
Parsberg	...	...	5 44	10 20	2 10	5 44	...	...	...	...	...	10 1	...	1030	...
Deining........	...	...	6 14	10 45	2 38	6 15	...	...	...	...	...	10 28	...	...	p.m.
Neumarkt........	6 3	...	6 30	10 59	2 54	6 31	4 22	...	...	...	...	10 44	...	11 0	8 20
Feucht	...	...	7 16	11 39	3 44	7 23	...	...	...	...	...	11 17	...	...	9 10
Nurnberg C. arr	6 40	...	7 36	11 56	4 4	7 45	4 55	...	8 30	...	...	11 35	...	1140	9 32
CARLSBAD dep	...	1a39	1a39	6 a1	12p19	...	12p19	1219	4p52	...	...	...	3p50	...	...
EGER ......dep	...	3 a54	3 a54	8 a35	1p55	...	1p55	1p55	6 p7	...	...	...	6p26	...	...
BAYREUTH dp	...	5 a57	5 a57	9 a52	2p33	...	2p33	2p33	5p52	5p52	...	...	7p45	...	...
	Ex3	Ex 3	2 & 3	2 & 3	2 & 3		Ex 3	Ex3	Ex.1	Ex3	2 & 3		2&3	...	2 & 3
Nurnberg—	a.m.	a.m.	a.m.	p.m.	p.m.		p.m.	p.m.	p.m.	p.m.	p.m.		p.m.		a.m.
Central dep	7 0	9 20	9 31	1 25	4 37	...	5 8	6 10	8 49	8 55	9 3	...	1147	...	5 12
Furth ...... arr	7 10	9 29	9 46	1 37	4 49	...	5 16	6 18	8 57	9 4	9 18	...	12 2	...	5 28
dep	7 11	9 30	9 51	1 44	4 53	...	5 17	6 20	8 58	9 5	9 27	...	12 3	...	5 33
Siegelsdorf	...	...	10 11	2 4	5 18	...	...	...	...	SC	9 44	...	1225	...	5 51
Emskirchen	RC	...	10 42	2 34	5 47	...	...	...	A	...	10 11	...	1252	...	6 17
Neustadt........	7 48	10 8	11 1	2 54	6 1	...	...	6 59	...	9 41	10 29	...	1 6	...	6 36
Langenfeld	...	...	11 12	3 5	6 12	...	...	...	...	...	10 41	...		...	6 46
Mkt. Bibart......	8 4	10 24	11 22	3 15	6 22	...	...	7 15	...	...	10 52	...	...	...	6 56
Mkt Einersheim	...	...	11 39	3 32	6 39	...	...	...	...	...	11 10	...	...	...	7 12
Mainbernheim	...	...	11 50	3 44	6 50	...	...	...	...	...	11 23	...	...	...	7 24
Kitzingen........	8 26	10 48	12 2	3 55	7 0	...	...	7 37	...	1016	11 36	...	...	...	7 37
Rottendorf	...	11 10	12 34	4 27	7 33	...	...	...	...	...	12 10	...	...	...	8 8
Wurzburg ...arr	8 58	11 20	12 45	4 38	7 47	...	6 45	8 5	10 30	1048	12 23	...	...	...	8 20
FRANKFT 196B	12 0	2 p5	...	...	11p30	...	8p56	1130	2a46	1a19	5a53	...	...	...	12 3
COLOGNE arr	4p32	6 p8	...	...	...	...	12a55	5a18	4 a35	5a42	...	...	...	...	4 p20

Extra { Neustadt-a-A. ....dep 5a14 ; Nurnberg ....arr 6 46 } Regensburg ....dep 6 a28 ; Passau ....arr 10 36

VILSHOFEN and AIDENBACH.

Vilshofen......dep	7 a0	10a17	1p15	7p10	...	Aidenbach...dep	3a57	8 a5	11a40	5p55	...
Aidenbach ...arr	7 34	10 51	1 49	7 44	...	Vilshofen......arr	4 32	8 40	12 15	6 30	...

Vilshofen to Ortenburg, in half an hour, 7.5, 10.41 a.m., 1.19, 7.15 p.m From Ortenburg 4.0, 7.55, 11.35 a.m., 5.50 p.m.

MELLRICHSTADT and FLADUNGEN.

Mellrichstadt...dep	6 a0	10a15	3p50	10p20	Fladungen.........dep	4a30	7a20	12p25	6 p50
Fladungen.. ......arr	7 9	11 20	4 48	11 19	Mellrichstadt 195 arr	5 25	8 15	1 21	7 53

EICHSTATT and KINDING.

Eichstatt Junction...dep	6a48	1p15	6p40	...	Kinding............dep	5a15	10a15	5p46	...
„ Stadt	7 20	2 10	7 30	...	Walting	6 17	11 19	6 51	...
Walting	8 1	2 51	8 11	...	Eichstatt Stadt ...	6 55	11 58	7 30	...
Kinding ....arr	9 0	3 50	9 10	...	„ Junct. arr	7 30	12 30	8 25	...

Neustadt-a-Aisch to Demantsfurth-Uehlfeld, in one hour, 6.40, 11.42 a.m., 3.25, 9.45 p.m. From Demantsfurth, return, 5*25, 7.46 a.m., 1.35, 5.0 p.m.
*—4.5 a.m. on Mon. and Sat.

Luggage Rates—see page 462.] BAVARIAN STATE RAILWAYS.

FRANKFORT, ASCHAFFENBURG, GEMUNDEN, WURZBURG, TREUCHTLINGEN, and MUNICH.

SLEEPING CARS.—Frankfort to Munich, in 11.13 p.m. from Frankfort. Extra fare, 1st class 10 m., 2nd class 8 m. Frankfort to Vienna, in 4.36 p.m. from Frankfort, extra fare, 1st class 12 m., 2nd class 10m.

Dist.	COLOGNE 122,128 dp	...	11p57	...	...	...	...	1 a58	...	...	...	...	...	...	...	9 a32	10a 3	...
E.M.			Ex 1					Ex.3				Ex.3	2,3,4	2,3,4		1,2,3	Ex 3	
	FRANKFORT—		a.m.					a.m.				a.m.	a.m.	a.m.		p.m.	p.m.	
—	Hauptbahnhof dep	...	3 36	...	...	...	...	6 25	...	...	...	8 29	9 6	10 46	...	2 2	2 23	...
2¾	,, Sud	...	B	...	...	...	...	6 34	...	...	...	...	9 14	10 55	...	2 10		...
6¼	Offenbach	...	...	...	...	...	...	6 43	...	...	...	...	9 26	11 8	...	2 19		...
14	Hanau Ostbahn arr	...	4 *0	...	...	...	...	6 57	...	...	...	8 53	9 47	11 29	...	2 33		...
			Ex.1					Ex.3	2,3,4				2,3,4	2,3,4		1,2,3		2,3,4
	Frankfort—							a.m.	a.m.				a.m.	a.m.		p.m.		p.m.
...	Ostbahnhof...dep	...		...	...	...	...		6 4	...	...		9 12	11 14	...	1 53		2 36
...	Mainkur	...		...	...	...	...		6 13	...	...		9 20	11 22	...	2 0		2 44
...	Wilhelmsbad	...		...	...	...	...		6 30	...	...		9 37	11 40	...	...		3 1
...	Hanau Westbahn	...		...	...	...	...		6 34	...	...		9 44	11 45	...	2 11		3 6
...	Hanau Ostbahn arr	...		...	...	...	...		6 40	...	...		9 48	11 52	...	2 16		3 11
...	Hanau Ostbahn dep	...	4 *1	...	...	...	...	6 58	6 46	...	...	8 55	9 53	11 54	...	2 34		3 25
19	Kahl	...	...	...	...	...	...	7 8	7 16	...	...	...	10 13	12 11	...	...		3 42
21¾	Dettingen	...	...	...	...	...	...	...	7 24	...	...	...	10 21	12 19	...	...		3 50
28¾	Aschaffenburg arr	...	4 22	...	...	...	...	7 24	7 41	...	...	9 17	10 38	12 37	...	2 55	3 7	4 8
...	COLOGNE 122 dep	...	11p57	...	...	...	...	1 a58	...	...	...	...	...	6 a17	...	9 a32	9 a32	...
...	MAYENCE 123 dep	...	2a49	...	...	...	...	5 a54	...	...	...	7 a9	7a51	10a38	...	1 p32	1 p32	...
		3 Cl.	Ex 1	Ex 2	2 & 3	2 & 3	Ex 3	Ex.3		3 Cl.	2 & 3	Ex.3	2 & 3	2 & 3	Ex 3	1,2,3	Ex 3	
			a.m.	From Hamburg dep. 9.27 p.m.	a.m.	a.m.	From Hamburg dep. 11.19 p.m.	a.m.				a.m.	a.m.	p.m.	From Hamburg dep. 7.22 a.m.	p.m.	p.m.	...
...	Aschaffenburg dep	...	4 27		4 10	6 55		7 33	...	...	...	9 19	10 50	1 5		3 18	3 12	...
35¾	Laufach	...			4 45	7 17		7 48	...	...	...		11 12	1 31		3 30		...
40	Heigenbrucken	...			5 3	7 35		8 5	...	...	...		11 30	1 49		...	RC	...
48¾	Partenstein	...	B		5 20	7 52		...	...	a.m.	...	RC	11 48	2 7		...		...
52¾	Lohr (196)	...			5 32	8 0		8 23	...	8 5	...		11 58	2 17		4 3		...
60¾	Gemunden 196A arr	...			5 52			8 35	...	8 27	...		12 17	2 38		4 16		...
93	SCHWEINFURT arr	...			...	...		10a44	...	10a44	...		...	4 p36		...		...
107½	KISSINGEN 195 arr	a.m.		a.m.	...	...	a.m.	11a53	...	11a53	...		...	6 p0	p.m.	...		...
...	Gemunden dep	4 15		5 25	6 4	...	8 33	8 37	...	9 10	...		12 21	2 50	3 54	4 17		...
69¼	Carlstadt	4 39		...	6 27	...	...	8 50	...	9 33	...		12 43	3 13	...	4 29		...
74¼	Retzbach	4 53		...	6 40	...	...	RC	...	9 47	...		12 56	3 27	...	...		...
80½	Veitshochheim	5 22		...	7 0	...	...	...	...	10 11	...		1 17	3 47	...	...		...
84¼	Wurzburg arr	5 40	5 50	5 56	7 15	...	9 5	9 12	...	10 29	...	10 47	1 30	4 0	4 25	4 51	4 36	...
147¾	NURNB'G 195A arr	...	7 a56	...	11a39	...	11a39	11a39	...	...	...	12p41	5 p58	6 p54	6 p54	6 p54	6 p54	...
241¾	EGER 202 arr	...	11 a9	...	3 p48	...	3 p48	3p48	...	...	...	3 p48	...	12a57	12a57	12a57	12a57	...
274	CARLSBAD 251 arr	...	12p21	...	5 p31	...	5 p31	5p31	...	...	...	5 p31	...	...	...	...	...	...
126	KISSINGEN 195 arr	...	8 a18	8 a18	...	...	11a53	11a53	...	1p44	a.m.	1 p44	3 p30	...	...	...	...	...
...	Wurzburg dep	...	Via Nurnberg	6 10	7 52	...	...	9 26	...	...	10 15	Via Nurnberg.	1 45	...	...	...	4 45	...
88¼	Heidingsfeld	...		...	8 7	...	...	...	B—Ostend and Vienna Express.	...	10 30		1 59	...	...	...	...	...
97½	Ochsenfurt 196A	...		...	8 32	...	...	...		...	10 56		2 23	...	...	...	...	...
100¾	Marktbreit	...		...	8 42	...	...	...		...	11 7		2 33	...	...	...	...	...
111½	Uffenheim	a.m.		...	9 23	...	...	...		...	11 47		3 11	...	...	...	...	...
120¼	Steinach 196A	3 30		7 17	9 52	...	...	10 33		...	12 17		3 40	...	...	...	...	...
127½	Oberdachstetten	4 17		...	10 18	...	...	...		...	12 44		4 7	...	...	...	...	...
134½	Lehrberg	4 46		...	10 34	...	...	...		...	1 0		4 23	...	...	...	...	...
139½	Ansbach 204 arr	5 5		7 49	10 44	...	...	11 5		...	1 10		4 33	...	...	...	6 13	...
	Ansbach 204 dep			7 56		...	...	11 10		...	1 24		5 42	...	...	...	6 19	...
156¾	Gunzenhausen 197A arr	...		8 29	...	...	...	11 37		...	2 4		6 25	...	...	...		...
	Gunzenhausen 197A dep	...		8 31	...	...	...	11 38		...	2 9		6 50	...	...	...		...
166¼	Berolzheim	...		...	...	...	...	...		...	2 30		7 14	...	...	...		...
171½	Treuchtlingen arr	...		8 55	...	...	...	11 57	...	...	2 43		7 28	...	...	...		...
...	TREUCHTLINGEN	...		9 8	...	...	...	11 58	...	...	2 49		8 31	...	...	...		...
205¾	INGOLSTADT arr	...		...	...	...	...	...	...	...	3 42		9 p23	...	...	...		...
256½	MUNICH Haupt	...		11§15	...	...	...	2 §p0	...	...	5p2		10p51	...	...	...	8 p55	...
351¾	SALZBURG 200 arr	...		3 p30	...	...	...	...	...	...	8 p55		...	...	...	...	12 a8	...
546¾	VIENNA 239A arr	...	6 p0	9 p50	...	...	...	9p50	...	...	6 a0	9 p50	...	...	...	...	7‡20	...

*—Stops at Hanau in early morn of Sun. and Mon. only.

RC—Restaurant Car.
‡—Via Nurnberg-Passau.

§—Arrives Munich via Augsburg, page 192.

Frankfort and Hanau—frequent Local Service between these towns.

FARES.		m.pf.	m.pf.	m.pf.
	Frankfort to Carlsbad	37 40	24 20	15 20
	,, Kissingen	17 90	11 60	7 30
	,, Munich	33 40	21 50	13 90
	,, Vienna	77 70	48 50	31 10

LOHR and WERTHEIM.

E.M.							
	Lohr dep	6a30	8 a35	12p45	4p10	9p38	...
11¼	Hafenlohr	7 12	9 16	1 27	4 52	1018	...
16¾	Lengfurt-Trennfeld	7 33	9 36	1 47	5 12	1038	...
23½	Wertheim 146 arr	7 56	10 0	2 11	5 36	11 0	...

Wertheim dep	4 a0	6a30	10a25	2 p0	5p25
Lengfurt-Trennfeld	4 24	6 53	10 48	2 23	5 49
Hafenlohr	4 45	7 13	11 8	2 42	6 8
Lohr 196 arr	5 28	7 55	11 51	3 22	6 49

For Continuation of Trains, see next page.

Luggage Rates—see page 462.] **BAVARIAN STATE RAILWAYS.**

FRANKFORT, ASCHAFFENBURG, GEMUNDEN, WURZBURG, TREUCHTLINGEN, and MUNICH.

RESTAURANT CAR.—Frankfort to Vienna, in 4.36 p.m. from Frankfort.

Station													
COLOGNE 122, 128 dep	...	...	11a27	12p10	...	...	...	3 p38	6 p33	8 p2	...	...	...
		2,3,4	Ex 3	Ex 3			2,3,4	2,3,4	1,2,3	Ex.3			
FRANKFORT—		p.m.	p.m.	p.m.			p.m.	p.m.	p.m.	ni'gt			
Hauptbahnhof ...dep	...	3 15	3 36	4 36	...	...	7 33	8 44	11 13	12 21	...	...	...
,, Sud	...	3 24	...	RC	...	...	7 41	8 53	11 21	...	...	...	...
Offenbach	...	3 38	3 49	4 50	...	...	7 56	9 6	11 30	12 35	...	...	...
Hanau Ostbahn ......arr	...	3 58	4 3	5 4	...	...	8 17	9 28	11 44	12 49	...	...	...
		2,3,4	⋮	⋮	2,3,4		2,3,4	2,3,4	1,2,3	⋮			
Frankfort—		p.m.			p.m.		p.m.	p.m.	p.m.				
Ostbahnhof......dep	...	3 21	⋮	⋮	6 30	...	7 36	8 55	11 3	⋮	...	...	...
Mainkur	...	3 29	⋮	⋮	6 40	...	7 46	9 3	11 11	⋮	...	...	...
Wilhelmsbad	...	3 46	⋮	⋮	6 59	...	8 5	9 20	11 28	⋮	...	...	...
Hanau Westbahn......	...	3 51	⋮	⋮	7 6	...	8 11	9 24	11 32	⋮	...	...	...
Hanau Ostbahn ...arr	...	3 58	⋮	⋮	7 10	...	8 17	9 30	11 37	⋮	...	...	...
Hanau Ostbahn ......dep	...	4 9	4 4	5 5	7 15	...	8 25	9 36	11 47	12 51	...	...	...
Kahl	...	4 25	...	...	7 33	...	8 47	9 53	...	...	...	...	...
Dettingen.........	...	4 33	...	...	7 41	...	8 57	10 0	SC	...	...	...	...
Aschaffenburg ......arr	...	4 50	4 26	5 27	7 58	...	9 18	10 17	12 10	1 13	...	...	...
COLOGNE 122 ......dep	...	...	...	...	...	p.m.	...	...	6 p33	...	...	...	...
MAYENCE 123 ......dep	...	2 p15	1 p32	2 p15	...	5 11	...	8 p2	10p34	...	...	...	...
	3 Cl.	2 & 3	Ex 3	Ex 3		2 & 3		2 & 3	1,2,3	Ex 3	2 & 3		
		p.m.	p.m.	p.m.		p.m.		p.m.	a.m.	a.m.			
Aschaffenburg ......dep	...	5 40	4 28	5 33	...	8 2	...	10 26	12 20	1 20	...	...	...
Laufach	...	6 6	⋮	⋮	...	8 31	...	10 51	12 36	⋮	...	...	...
Heigenbrucken	Not on Sunday.	6 25	⋮	⋮	...	8 50	...	11 9	...	⋮	...	...	...
Partenstein		6 44	RC	RC	...	9 8	...	11 26	SC	⋮	...	...	...
Lohr (296).........		6 58	⋮	6 19	...	9 18	...	11 36	1 10	⋮	...	...	...
Gemunden ....arr		7 19	⋮	6 31	...	9 40	...	11 56	1 23	⋮	...	...	...
SCHWEINFURT 196A arr		9 p55	⋮	...	...	...	...	...	6 a0	⋮	...	...	...
KISSINGEN 195......arr	p.m.	...	⋮	...	...	...	...	...	8 a18	⋮	...	...	...
Gemunden ....dep	5 58	7 55	⋮	6 32	...	9 45	...	12 3	1 24	⋮	...	...	...
Carlstadt	6 34	8 17	⋮	...	...	10 9	...	12 25	1 38	⋮	...	...	...
Retzbach		8 30	⋮	...	...	10 24	...	12 38	...	⋮	...	...	...
Veitshocheim.........	...	8 49	⋮	...	...	10 46	...	12 57	...	⋮	...	...	...
Wurzburg ....arr	...	9 2	5 51	7 3	...	11 0	...	1 10	2 1	2 44	...	...	...
NURNBERG 195A...arr	...	1 a7	9 p22	9 p22	...	...	...	...	4 a52	4 a52	...	...	...
EGER 202 ....arr	...	...	...	...	...	...	...	...	...	...	...	...	...
CARLSBAD 251......arr	2 & 3	...	...	...	...	...	2 & 3	...	...	...	...	...	...
KISSINGEN 195......arr	p.m	...	8 p15	9 p23	...	...	p.m.	...	6 a32	6 a32	a.m.	...	...
Wurzburg ....dep	6 40	9 8	5 56	7 22	...	...	11 20	...	2 8	2 51	4 35	...	...
Heidingsfeld	6 57	9 23	...	⋮	...	...	11 36	...	...	...	4 50	...	...
Ochsenfurt	7 32	9 48	6 17	⋮	...	...	12 2	...	...	...	5 15	...	...
Marktbreit	7 43	9 58	6 24	⋮	...	...	12 12	...	...	...	5 24	...	...
Uffenheim	8 23	10 38	6 49	⋮	...	...	12 53	...	...	Via Nürnberg.	6 3	...	...
Steinach 196	8 53	11 5	7 7	⋮	...	...	1 25	...	...		6 31	...	...
Oberdachstetten	9 19		...	⋮	...	...	1 53	...	...		6 57	...	...
Lehrberg	9 36	...	...	⋮	...	...	2 10	...	...		7 13	...	...
Ansbach 204 ...... arr	9 46	...	7 38	⋮	...	...	2 21	...	3 53		7 23	...	...
Ansbach 204 ...... dep	10 10	...	7 43	⋮	...	...	2 31	3 Cl.	4 0		7 31	...	...
Gunzenhausen ... arr	10 52	...	8 8	⋮	...	...	3 17	a.m.	4 28		8 11	...	...
Gunzenhausen ... dep	11 0	...	8 9	⋮	...	...	3 24	6 5	4 29	...	8 15	...	...
Berolzheim	11 23	...	...	⋮	...	...	3 47	6 45	...	...	8 35	...	...
Treuchtlingen.........arr	11 38	...	8 27	⋮	...	...	4 0	7 8	4 49	7 10	8 48	...	...
TREUCHTLINGEN dep	...	...	8 29	⋮	...	...	...	...	4 56	7 13	9 8	...	...
INGOLSTADT.........arr	...	...	...	§	...	...	...	...	...	8 3	§	...	...
MUNICH Haupt...arr	...	...	10§25	12a40	...	...	...	...	7a§20	9 a29	11a15	...	...
SALZBURG 200......arr	...	...	2 a10	...	...	...	...	...	10a50	12p28	3 p30	...	...
VIENNA 239A ......arr	...	...	7a‡20	7a‡20	...	...	...	...	6 p32	6 p32	...	...	...

ASCHAFFENBURG and AMORBACH.

[†—Saturday only.

Station									
Aschaffenburg	6 a5	8 a18	a.m.	1110	...	1p18	5 p40	8†p10	10p36
Wörth	6 51	9 9	...	1154	p.m.	2 2	6 28	8 57	11 20
Miltenberg......	7 15	9 35	9 53	1218	1246	2 25	6 55	9 20	11 51
Amorbach arr	7 40	...	10 17	...	1 9	2 50	7 33	9 50	12 14

Station									
Amorbach.........dep	5a20	8a53	11a42	1p30	...	6 p14	8 p42	10†17	...
Miltenberg	5 55	9 25	12 20	1 53	2 p53	6 42	9 9	10 50	...
Wörth.........	6 24	9 52	12 45	...	3 18	7 7	9 33	11 19	...
Aschaffenburg 196ar	7 15	1040	1 30	...	4 5	7 52	10 18	12 7	...

Station						
Miltenberg ......dep	...	7a25	9a45	2p50	7p10	9p25
Stadtprozelten......	5a45	8 33	1052	3 53	8 5	10 30
Wertheim ......arr	6 20	9 7	1127	4 27	8 33	...

Station						
Wertheim ......dep	4a30	8 a0	10a15	4p53	7p25	...
Stadtprozelten......	4 59	8 29	10 51	5 30	8 1	...
Miltenberg .....arr	5 48	9 18	11 51	6 30	9 0	...

STEINACH and ROTHENBURG.

Station											
Steinach ....dep	5a15	7a20	8a46	10a35	12p23	2p25	5p32	7p44	9p10	1110	...
Rothenburg 204 arr	5 45	7 55	9 16	11 5	1 0	2 55	6 3	8 13	9 40	1140	...

Station											
Rothenburg	4a40	6a0	8a7	9a24	11a45	1p43	4p45	6p35	8p21	10p0	...
Steinach 196	5 7	626	840	9 50	12 11	2 16	5 12	7 1	8 46	1034	...

OCHSENFURT and ROTTINGEN.

Station						
Ochsenfurt ..dep	7 a45	2p30	4p‡20	7p45	...	...
Röttingen ...arr	9 18	4 4	6 50	9 20	...	...

Station						
Röttingen dep	4a52	8a*19	11a10	5p45	...	...
Ochsenfurt arr	6 27	10 33	12 45	7 25	...	...

*—7.50 a.m. on Sunday. ‡—4.10 p.m. on Sunday.

GEMUNDEN and SCHWEINFURT.

Dist E.M.	(196)	3 Cl a.m.	2&3 a.m.	2&3 p.m.	2&3 p.m.	
—	**Gemunden** dep	3 0	9 11	3 7	8 10	...
7¼	Eussenheim	3 43	9 34	3 29	8 38	...
14¾	Müdesheim.........	4 27	9 56	3 51	9 3	...
24½	Waigolsh'n 198	5 31	1028	4 22	9 38	...
31¾	**Schweinfurt**	6 0	1044	4 36	9 55	...
46¾	KISSINGEN 195	8a18	1153	6 p0	...	...

Station						
KISSINGEN dp	...	5a35	11 a0	2p55	7p36	
	3 Cl.	2&3	2 & 3	2&3	3 Cl	
		a.m.	noon	p.m.	p.m.	
Schweinfurt ......dep	...	7 15	12 3	5 0	9 27	...
Waigolshausen	a.m.	7 35	12 24	5 22	1017	...
Müdesheim	3 55	8 2	12 52	5 51	1117	...
Eussenheim ...	4 25	8 18	1 8	6 8	1145	...
Gemunden...	5 0	8 35	1 26	6 27	1219	...

Luggage Rates—see page 462.] **BAVARIAN STATE RAILWAYS.**

MUNICH, TREUCHTLINGEN, WURZBURG, GEMUNDEN, ASCHAFFENBURG, and FRANKFORT.

THROUGH CARRIAGES.—Munich to Cologne, in 7.5 a.m., 9.0 a.m., 4.45 p.m., and 10.18 p.m. from Munich
SLEEPING CARS.—Munich to Frankfort, in 10.18 p.m. from Munich—extra fare, 1st class 10 m., 2nd class 8 m.

	1	2	3	4	5	6	7	8	9	10	11	12	13	14	15	16	17	18	19
VIENNA 239....dep	...	...	...	...	...	8 p30	...	¶—Via Augsburg.	8 p40	...	...	...	...	...	...	7§a25	...	...	7 §25
SALZBURG 200 dep	...	...	...	...	...	:	...		3 a25	5a40	...	...	...	...	...	9 a7	9 a7	...	12p14
MUNICH Haupt	dep	...	...	...	...	:	...		7 a5	9 a0	...	...	...	...	...	12p45	12p45	...	4 p25
INGOLSTADT...dep	...	...	...	...	...	:	...		¶	:	...	...	...	...	...	1 p59	1 p59	...	:
TREUCHTLINGEN	arr	...	...	...	...	:	...		9 2	:	...	...	...	...	...	2 p54	2 p54	...	:
		3 Cl.			2 & 3	:	2&3		Ex.3	Ex 3					2 & 3	Ex 3	2 & 3	2 & 3	1,2,3
							a.m.		a.m.						a.m.	p.m.	p.m.		p.m.
Treuchtlingen...dep	...	...	...	...	...	Via Passau and Nurnberg.	5 22	...	9 6	:	...	...	...	...	11 30	2 57	3 5	...	Via Augsb'g.
Berolzheim	...	...	...	...	...		5 36	...	RC	:	...	...	...	...	11 45		3 17	...	
Gunzen-hausen arr	...	a.m.	...	...	...		6 0	...	9 24	:	...	...	...	...	12 10	...	3 38	p.m.	
Gunzen-hausen dep	...	3 19	...	...	...		6 20	...	9 25	:	...	...	...	...	12 23	...	3 44	5 23	
Ansbach	...	5 15	...	...	...		7 55	...	9 56	:	...	...	...	...	1 32	...	4 43	6 52	7 10
Lehrberg	...	5 33	...	...	...		8 6	...	...	:	...	...	...	...	1 43	...	4 53		...
Oberdachstetten	...	6 1	...	...	a.m.		8 25	...	...	:	...	...	...	...	2 2	...	5 10	...	...
Steinach	...	6 53	...	...	5 30		8 48	...	10 25	RC	...	...	...	...	2 26	...	5 29	...	7 38
Uffenheim	...	7 37	...	...	6 4		9 12	...	10 40	:	...	...	...	...	2 51	...	5 50	...	RC
Marktbreit	...		...	...	6 23		9 41	...	10 58	:	...	...	...	...	3 22	...	6 17	...	...
Ochsenfurt	...	...	...	...	6 32		9 51	...	11 4	:	...	...	...	...	3 32	...	6 25	...	...
Heidingsfeld	...	...	...	...	7 0		10 15	...	...	:	...	...	...	...	3 57	...	6 46	...	...
Wurzburg.........arr	...	...	...	...	7 15		10 30	...	11 25	12 25	...	...	...	...	4 12	6 45	7 0	...	8 29
KISSINGEN 195 dep	...	...	...	...	...	7 a17	...	...	9 a15	9 a45	...	...	11 a0	...	2 p55	...	...	...	6 p30
CARLSBAD 250 dep	...	...	...	...	...	...	...	...	1 a39	1 a39	1 a39	...	1 a39	...	6 a1	12p19	...	...	12p19
EGER 203.......dep	...	...	...	...	...	...	...	...	3 a54	3 a54	3 a54	...	3 a54	...	8 a35	1 p55	...	...	1 p55
NURNBERG 195A dp	...	...	...	...	...	7 a0	...	...	9 a20	9 a20	9 a20	...	9 a31	...	1 p25	5 p8	...	...	6 p10
		2 & 3	3 Cl.	Ex 3	2 & 3	Ex 3		2 & 3	Ex 3	Ex 3	Ex 3		2 & 3		2 & 3	Ex 3		3 Cl.	Ex 3
		a.m.	a.m.	a.m.	a.m.	a.m.		a.m.	a.m.	p.m.	p.m.		p.m.		p.m.	p.m.		p.m.	p.m.
Wurzburg.........dep	...	4 45	5 52	7 20	7 45	9 15	...	10 45	11 37	12 33	12 50	...	1 40	...	5.45	6 50	...	7 10	8 39
Veitschochheim	...	4 59	6 7	...	7 59	...	...	10 59	...	:	...	...	1 53	...	5 49	...	...	7 25	...
Retzbach	...	5 17	6 27	...	8 18	...	...	11 18	RC	RC	...	...	2 10	...	6 17	...	...	7 46	...
Carlstadt	...	5 32	6 41	7 41	8 34	9 38	...	11 32	...	:	1 12	...	2 23	...	6 31	...	...	8 0	...
Gemunden.........arr	...	5 53	7 0	7 53	8 55	9 51	...	11 52	12 6	:	1 26	...	2 42	...	6 52	RC	...	8 20	9 14
KISSINGEN 195 dep	...	...	...	...	5 a35	5 a35	...	...	...	:	Hamburg arr. 10.14 p.m.	...	11 a0	...	2 p55	:	...	...	:
SCHWEINFURT 196A	dep	...	...	...	7 a15	7 a15	2 & 3	...	...	:		...	12 p3	...	5 p0	:	...	...	:
Gemunden ......dep	...	6 0	7 5	7 54	9 10	9 53	a.m.	12 10	12 7	:		...	2 55	...	7 0	:	...	...	To Elm (page 149) and Hamburg (arr. 6.44 a.m.).
Lohr	...	6 26	7 29	8 8	9 33	10 9	8 28	12 34	12 20	:		...	3 28	...	7 33	:	...	...	
Partenstein	...	6 39		...	9 46	...	8 44	12 49	...	:		...	3 43	...	7 48	:	...	...	
Heigenbrucken	...	7 7	...	8 33	10 13	...	9 17	1 19	...	:		...	4 13	...	8 18	:	...	...	
Laufach	...	7 22	...	...	10 26	...	9 32	1 42	...	:		...	4 26	...	8 32	:	...	...	
Aschaffenburg...arr	...	7 40	...	8 52	10 43	10 57	9 50	2 0	1 0	1 48	...	...	4 47	...	8 50	8 5	...	...	
MAYENCE 123A arr	...	10a24	...	...	12p47	12p47	...	3 p28	3 p28	3 p28	...	...	8 p9	...	11p23	...	...	...	
COLOGNE 123B arr	...	...	...	...	...	4 p40	...	7 p7	7 p7	7 p7	...	...	12a55	...	5 a9	...	...	...	
	2,3,4	2,3,4		Ex 3		Ex 3	2,3,4		Ex.3	Ex 3	Ex 2	2,3,4	2,3,4	2,3,4	2,3,4	Ex 3			
	a.m.	a.m.		a.m.		a.m.	a.m.		p.m.	p.m.	p.m.	p.m.	p.m.	p.m.	p.m.	p.m.			
Aschaffenburg dep	5 38	8 13	...	8 57	...	11 7	11 33	...	1 3	1 50	...	2 29	5 3	8 13	9 15	8 6	...	...	
Dettingen	5 57	8 32	...	...	...	...	11 53	...	...	...	...	2 47	5 22	8 33	9 34	...	...	...	
Kahl	6 7	8 40	...	...	...	...	12 2	...	...	...	...	2 55	5 33	8 42	9 42	...	...	...	
Hanau Ost. ....arr	6 26	8 55	...	9 21	...	11 29	12 17	...	1 27	2 10		3 11	5 51	9 0	9 58	8 28	...	...	...
Hanau Ost. ...dep	6 42	9 4	...	...	...	11 37	12 20	...	...	...	2 23	3 24	5 54	9 4	10 18	:	...	...	...
Hanau West.	6 49	9 10	...	...	...	11 42	12 27	...	...	...	...	3 30	6 1	9 12	10 25	:	...	...	...
Wilhelmsbad	6 55	...	...	...	...	...	12 32	...	...	...	...	3 36	6 6	9 18	10 31	:	...	...	...
Mainkur	7 16	9 29	...	...	...	11 54	12 51	...	...	...	...	3 53	6 26	9 37	10 49	:	...	...	...
Frankf't Ost...arr	7 23	9 37	...	...	...	12 0	12 59	...	...	...	2 41	4 0	6 34	9 45	10 57	:	...	...	...
Hanau Ost. ...dep	6 33	9 29	...	9 23	...	11 30		...	1 37	2 13	...	4 0	6 5			8 29	...	...	...
Offenbach	7 2	9 54	...	9 37	...	11 43	...	...	1 52	2 27	...	4 24	6 28	...	...	8 43	...	...	...
Frankfort Sud.	7 17	10 11	...	9 45	...	11 51	...	...	...	...	2 50	4 36	6 41	...	...	...	...	...	...
FRANKFORT— Hauptbahnhof arr	7 25	10 19	...	9 54	...	12 0	...	...	2 5	2 41	...	4 44	6 49	...	...	8 56	...	...	...
COLOGNE 123B 129	12p31	...	...	2 p17	...	4 p32	...	...	6 p8	7 p7	7 p7	9 p30	12a13	...	...	12a55	...	...	...

B—Vienna-Ostend Express, at extra fares.

RC—Restaurant Car attached. †—Weekdays only. §—Via Passau and Nurnberg. ‡—Via Ansbach.

For Continuation of Trains, see next page.

BUCHLOE and MEMMINGEN.

Buchloe ......dep	...	8a10	6a32	...	11a20	...	2p10	4p18	8 p0
Turkheim	...	8 27	6 48	...	11 33	...	2 23	4 34	8 14
Stetten	...	8 55	7 17	...	12 0	...	2 50	5 3	8 40
: Ottobeuren dp	6 a43	...	...	9a10	...	1p10	...	4 45	8 20
Ungerhausen ...	7 12	9 14	7 37	9 47	12 20	1 37	3 10	5 23	9 0
Memmingen 201	7 30	9 24	7 47	10 5	12 30	1 55	3 20	5 33	9 10

Memmingen dep	4a20	8 a5	9a25	11a45	2p35	2p50	4p23	6p10	9 p25
Ungerhausen ...	4 32	8 25	9 36	12 5	2 47	3 10	4 38	6 23	9 36
: Ottobeuren ar	...	9 0	...	12 52	...	3 46	...	7 2	10 12
Stetten	4 55		9 58		3 12		5 4	6 48	10 0
Turkheim	5 25	8 40	1029	...	3 44	...	5 35	7 23	10 28
Buchloe ......arr	5 40	8 56	1043	..	3 59	...	5 50	7 39	10 42

Turkheim to Wörishofen (4 miles).—Depart from Turkheim 5.30, 6.55, 8 35, 10.33 11.40 a.m., 2.30, 3.48. 4.40, 7.30, 8.20, 10.30 p.m. Depart from Wörishofen, 5.0, 6.25 8.18, 10.0, 11.10 a.m., 2.5, 3.15, 4.12, 7.0, 7.55, 10.10 p.m.

Turkheim to Markt Wald (10 miles).—Depart from Turkheim 7.15, 11.40 a.m., 4.48, 8.20 p.m. Depart from Markt Wald 4.36, 9.30 a.m., 1.29, 6.33 p.m.

Luggage Rates—see page 462.] BAVARIAN STATE RAILWAYS.

MUNICH, TREUCHTLINGEN, WURZBURG, GEMUNDEN, ASCHAFFENBURG, and FRANKFORT.

Station												
VIENNA 239 ....dep	7a25	...	12 0	...	...	...	9 a25	...	1 p0	...	...	...
SALZBURG 200........dep		...		1214	...	...	3 p50	...	7 p20	...	...	...
MUNICH Haupt...dep		...		4p45	...	...	6 p55	4 p45	10p18	...	...	...
INGOLSTADT ......dep		...		6 p6	...	...		6 p6	¶	...	...	...
TREUCHTLINGEN arr		...		7 p4	...	...		7 p4	12a18	...	...	...
				Ex3		2 & 3	Ex 3	2 & 3	1,2,3	2 & 3		
				p.m.				p.m.	a.m.	a.m.		
Treuchtlingen ......dep	Via Passau and Nurnberg.	...	Via Passau and Nurnberg.	7 11	...	...		7 45	12 21	12 30	¶—Via Augsburg.	...
Berolzheim		...			...	...	RC	7 59	SC	12 44		...
Gunzenhausen ... arr		...		Via Nurnberg.	...	...	9 6	8 24	12 42	1 8		...
Gunzenhausen ... dep		...			...	p.m.	9 7	8 38	12 43	1 15		...
Ansbach		...			...	8 17	9 40	10 0	1 19	3 0		...
Lehrberg		...			...	8 27	...	10 10	...	3 11		...
Oberdachstetten		...			...	8 45	...	10 28	...	3 29		...
Steinach		...			...	9 6	...	10 49	...	3 53		...
Uffenheim		...			...	9 28	SC	11 14	...	4 17		...
Marktbreit		...			...	9 56	...	11 44	...	4 48	...	...
Ochsenfurt		...			...	10 4	...	11 53	...	4 59	...	...
Heidingsfeld		...			...	10 27	...	12 19	...	5 29	...	...
Wurzburg ....arr		...		1048	...	10 41	10 55	12 34	2 41	5 43	...	...
KISSINGEN 195 ...dep	6 p30	...	7 p36	...	7p36	...	7 p36	9p35	...	...	...	...
CARLSBAD 250......dep	12p19	...	4 p52	...	...	...	...	...	...	...	...	...
EGER 203 ....dep	1 p55	...	6 p7	...	...	...	...	...	...	...	...	...
NURNBERG 195A...dep	6 p10	...	8 p49	...	8p55	...	8 p55	9 p3	...	...	...	...
	Ex 3	3 Cl.	Ex. 1		Ex3	2 & 3	Ex 2	2 & 3	1,2,3			
	p.m.	p.m.	p.m.		p.m.	p.m.	p.m.	a.m.	a.m.			
Wurzburg ....dep	8 45	9 2	10 38	...	11 5	11 25	11 15	1 15	2 50	...	...	...
Veitschochheim...........	RC	9 17		...		11 38	...	1 28		...	...	...
Retzbach	...	9 38		...		11 55	...	1 42		...	...	...
Carlstadt	9 8	9 52		...		12 8	...	1 53		...	...	...
Gemunden ....arr	9 20	10 12		...		12 28	11 49	2 12		...	...	...
KISSINGEN 195......dep	...	...		...		...	Hamburg arr. 8.22a.m.	7 p36		...	...	...
SCHWEINFURT 196A dep	...	...		...		...		9 p27		...	...	...
Gemunden ....dep	9 21	...		...		...		2 16		...	...	...
Lohr	9 36	...		...	1146	...		2 40		...	...	...
Partenstein	...	...	B	...	...	...		2 54		...	...	...
Heigenbrucken	10 4	...		...	SC	...		3 22		...	...	...
Laufach	...	...		...	...	...	...	3 35		...	...	...
Aschaffenburg ......arr	10 24	...	11 55	...	1223	...	...	3 52	4 21	...	...	...
MAYENCE 123A ...arr	12a12	...	1 a37	...	...	...	...	5a56	5 a56	...	...	...
COLOGNE 123B......arr	5 a21	...	4 a35	...	...	...	...	9a50	9 a50	...	...	...
	Ex.3		Ex.1		Ex3			2,3,4	1,2,3			
	p.m.		nght		ng't			a.m.	a.m.			
Aschaffenburg ......dep	10 30	...	12 0	*—Calls at Hanau Sat. & Sun. midnight only.	1229	...	...	4 13	4 55	...	...	...
Dettingen..................	...	...	B		...	...	...	4 34	...	...	...	...
Kahl	...	...	...		SC	...	...	4 46	...	...	...	...
Hanau Ost. ....arr	10 50	...	12*19		1250	...	...	5 6	5 20	...	...	...
Hanau Ost. ....dep		...	...		...	...	...	5 11	...	...	...	...
Hanau West		...	...		...	...	...	5 19	...	...	...	...
Wilhelmsbad		...	...		...	...	...	5 25	...	...	...	...
Mainkur		...	...		...	...	...	5 46	...	...	...	...
Frankfort Ost. ...arr		...	...		...	...	...	5 53	...	...	...	...
Hanau Ost. ....dep	10 55	...	12*20		1251	...	...	5 34	5 22	...	...	...
Offenbach	11 10	...	12 32		1 5	...	...	5 52	5 36	...	...	...
Frankfort Sud.	11 20	...	...		...	...	...	6 4	5 44	...	...	...
FRANKFORT— Hauptbahnhof ...arr	11 30	...	12 46	...	1 19	...	...	6 12	5 53	...	...	...
COLOGNE 123B 129 arr	5 a21	...	4 a35		5a42	...	...	12p31	12p31	...		...

HOF, BAMBERG, NURNBERG, and MUNICH.

Station																			
LEIPSIC 187......dep	...	...	...	...	...	...	...	...	1a10	...	...	1 a10	...	1 a10	...	...	...	7 a5	8a36
DRESDEN 186...dep	...	...	...	...	...	...	...	...	1055	...	...	10p55	...	...	...	...	...	5 a40	7a20
	2&3	1,2,3	Ex 2	Ex3	Ex 3	1,2,3	3 Cl.	2 & 3	1,2,3	Ex3	2 & 3	Ex.3	2 & 3	2 & 3	1,2,3	1,2,3	2&3	2 & 3	Ex3
									a.m.			a.m.		a.m.	a.m.	a.m.		a.m.	a.m.
Hof..................dep	...	...	...	...	...	...	...	...	4 2	...	...	4 12	...	5 42	...	8 0	...	10 42	1158
Oberkotzau dep	...	...	...	...	...	...	...	...	...	...	...	4 21	...	5 53	...	8 9	...	10 51	...
Schwarzenbach......	...	...	...	...	...	...	...	...	4 16	...	...	...	...	6 3	...	8 18	...	11 0	...
Münchberg 203B......	...	...	...	...	...	...	...	...	4 35	...	...	...	...	6 27	...	8 33	...	11 20	1230
Falls	...	...	...	...	...	...	...	...	...	...	...	...	...	6 58	...	9 3	...	11 49	...
Neuenmarkt arr	...	...	...	...	...	...	...	...	5 16	...	...	5 24	...	7 24	...	9 24	...	12 10	1 14
BAYREUTH 203 dep	...	...	...	...	...	...	a.m.	...	4a30	...	...	Arrive Bayreuth 5.55.	...	6 a40	...	8 a38	...	...	1242
Neuenmarkt dep	...	...	...	...	...	...	4 36	...	5 18	...	...		...	7 34	...	9 28	...	...	1 16
Kulmbach	...	...	...	...	...	...	5 3	...	5 31	...	...		...	7 57	...	9 45	...	...	1 32
Burgkundstadt	...	...	...	...	...	...	5 29	...	...	...	...		...	8 23	...	10 7	...	...	1 49
Hochstadt......arr	...	...	...	...	...	...	5 36	...	...	...	...		...	8 31	...	10 14	...	...	1 55
" ......dep	...	...	...	...	...	...	5 37	...	...	...	...		...	8 33	...	10 16	...	...	1 56
Lichtenfels ...arr	...	...	...	...	...	...	5 52	...	6 0	...	...		...	8 48	...	10 30	...	...	2 5
BERLIN 170 ...dep	...	...	8 p15	8p50	9 p50	...	...	...	...	...	...		...	...	...	...	...	...	...
PROBSTZELLA dep	...	...	SC		July and August only.	...	...	...	2a40	...	2 a40		...	...	1012	...	...	...	...
COBURG 173B dep	...	...				...	...	...	4a52	...	4 a52		...	8 a26	1055	...	...	10a55	1p26
Lichtenfels...dep	...	...	A			...	...	...	6 4	...	5 30	...	...	9 5	1136	...	...	12p45	2 8
Breitengussbach 197	...	...				...	...	...	...	...	6 13	...	...	9 47	...	...	...	1 28	...
Bamberg ......arr	...	...	2 40	3 11		...	...	...	6 36	...	6 27	...	...	10 1	12 4	...	...	1 42	2 40
WURZBURG 198 arr	...	...	...	...		...	...	a.m.	8a52	a.m.	8 a52	...	...	1 p25	...	...	...	4 p32	4p32
Bamberg ......dep	...	...	2 41	3 12		...	...	4 34		6 44	7 12	...	...	10 45	1211	...	...	...	...
Strullendorf.......	...	...	...	...		...	...	4 46		...	7 24	...	...	10 58	...	...	...	...	...
Forchheim	...	...	...	...		...	...	5 18	...	7 6	7 56	...	...	11 33	1232	...	...	...	...
Erlangen 197A	...	...	...	...		...	...	5 48	...	7 20	8 29	...	...	12 5	1247	...	...	...	...
Furth..................	...	...	3 25	3 56		...	...	6 21	...	7 35	9 8	A—Runs from July 3rd to 16th only.	...	12 42	1 3	...	...	...	...
Nurnberg ......arr	...	...	3 38	4 7	4 39	a.m.	...	6 38	...	7 45	9 26		p.m.	1 0	1 15	...	...	p.m.	...
" 203,204 dep	...	...	3 42	4 15	4 51	6 0	...	6 48	...	8 2	9 45		12 47		1 31	...	...	3 20	...
Schwabach	...	...	Via Augsburg (Arrive 6.0 a.m.)	...	To Augsburg (arrive 6.44 a.m.)	6 17	...	7 16	...	...	10 13		1 9	...	1 48	...	...	3 45	...
Roth 198	...	...		...		6 29	...	7 38	...	...	10 36		1 30	...	2 0	...	...	4 2	...
Georgensgm'nd 203B	...	...		Via Augsburg in Sept. (arrive 6.18 a.m.).		...	...	7 55	...	...	10 53		1 45	...	...	...	...	4 19	...
Pleinfeld ......arr	...	...				6 48	...	8 15	...	...	11 12		2 4	...	2 19	...	...	4 40	...
" 197A...dep	...	...				6 50	...	8 18	Ex3	...	11 20		2 27	...	2 21	...	...	4 45	...
Weissenburg-a-S....	...	...				7 1	2 & 3	8 37	a.m.	...	11 39		2 44	...	2 33	...	...	5 6	...
Treucht- ......arr	...	a.m.				7 10	a.m.	8 51		8 58	11 54		2 58	...	2 42	...	...	5 20	...
lingen ....dep	...	5 20				7 13	7 21	9 23	9 8		12 4			...	2 49	...	...	5 40	...
Pappenheim	...	5 29				...	7 30	9 32	Via Augsburg. (arr. 10.15 a.m.).	...	12 13		...	...	2 57	...	...	5 50	...
Solnhofen...............	...	5 38				...	7 38	9 41		...	12 22		...	...	...	...	...	5 59	...
Dollnstein	...	5 48				...	7 47	9 51		...	12 32		...	...	...	...	...	6 9	...
Eichstätt	...	6 9				7 40	8 7	10 13		...	12 54		...	...	3 19	...	...	6 31	...
Ingolstadt Nordbhf.	...	6 51				...	8 47	10 55		...	1 36		...	...	...	...	...	7 11	...
Ingol- Haptbhf.arr	a.m.	6 57				8 3	8 53	11 1		...	1 42		...	...	3 42	...	p.m.	7 17	...
stadt 195 ......dep	6 11	7 10				8 5	9 2	11 25		...	1 52		...	...	3 44	...	6 0	7 50	...
Wolnzach...............	6 51	7 45				8 26	9 43	12 5		...	2 32		...	...	4 5	...	6 36	8 20	...
Pfaffenhofen	7 15	8 5		...		8 39	10 5	12 27	...	...	2 56		...	...	4 19	...	6 56	8 39	...
Dachau	8 25	...		...	...	...	11 12	1 32	...	...	4 5	...	...	...	...	...	7 56	9 26	...
Munich Hptbf. arr	8 59	9 21	7 12	7 14	...	9 29	11 40	2 2	1115	...	4 38	...	...	...	5 12	...	8 24	9 53	...

BREITENGUSSBACH and MAROLDSWEISACH.

Breitengussbach..dep	7a48	10*a2	2 p55	7p10	10p36	...	Maroldsweisach dep	4a12	7a50	1155	4*p45	7 p9	...	*—Not on Sunday.
Ebern	8 43	12 16	3 49	8 5	11 28	...	Ebern	5 10	8 45	1250	6 28	8 11	...	
Maroldsweisach ...arr	9 35	1 40	4 42	8 58	12 15	...	Breitengussbach arr	6 3	9 33	1 43	7 35	8 58	...	

STRAUBING and NEUFAHRN.

†—Weekdays only.

Straubing ......dep	5a55	8a23	9†a10	12p17	4p21	5p44	9p23	...	**Neufahrn** ...dep	5a18	7a33	10a45	2p40	6 p0	9p40	...
Geiselhoring............	6 29	8 57	11 29	12 52	4 55	7 0	9 57	...	Neiderlindhart ...	5 37	7 45	10 57	2 52	6 11	9 52	...
Niederlindhart	7 2	9 29	12 28	1 25	5 27	7 59	1030	...	Geiselhoring	6 35	8 18	11 30	3 26	6 45	1025	...
Neufahrn 202 arr	7 12	9 40	12 44	1 35	5 38	8 15	1040	...	**Straubing** ...arr	7 27	8 51	12 3	4 0	7 47	1058	...

LANDSBERG and SCHONGAU.	**Landsberg** ...dep	6a46	10a35	5 p4	10p26	**Schongau** ....dep	4a25	8 a25	2 p2	7p10
	Schongau ......arr	8 0	11 45	6 14	11 36	**Landsberg** ...201 arr	5 38	9 37	3 14	8 22

NEUSTADT-a-S. and KONIGSHOFEN.	Neustadt-a-S. ......dep	7‡a20	4 p0	9 p51	Königshofen-i-Gr. dep	4 a25	12p30	7p15	‡—6.50 a.m. on Sunday.
	Königshofen-i-Gr. arr	8 40	5 6	11 0	Neustadt-a-S. 195 arr	5 44	1 47	8 32	

RENTWERTSHAUSEN and ROEMHILD.	Rentwertshausen dep	7a32	10 a0	1p40	8p30	10‡45	Roemhild dep	6 a15	8a15	12 p5	6p10	9‡50
	Roemhild ....arr	8 3	10 35	2 15	9 5	11 20	Rentwert arr	6 55	8 48	12 45	6 50	1030

‡—Runs until 31st August.

HOF, OBERKOTZAU and EGER.

†—Sunday arr. 2.17] *—Until 15th Sept. Sun. excepted.

	a.m.	a.m.	a.m.	p.m.	p.m.	p.m.	p.m.	a.m.				a.m.	a.m.	a.m.	p.m.	p.m.	p.m.	p.m.
Hof.................dep	4 40	7 20	10 34	...	4 2	6 48	9 35	1 0	...	**Eger**...............dep	...	5 2	5*45	8 15	1245	4 9	6 23	9 40
Oberkotzau	4 54	7 33	10 47	...	4 14	7 1	9 46	1 38	...	**Franzensbad** dep	a.m.	5 15	6 40	8 28	1257	4 21	6 40	9 54
Selb-Plösberg ...	5 43	8 19	11 35	...	5 2	7 52	10 24	3 4	...	**Asch**	2 46	6 15	8 19	9 24	1 53	5 20	7 42	1047
Asch 243	6 7	8 42	11 57	† 44	5 25	8 35	10 57	3 50	...	Selb-Plösberg	3 8	6 27		9 35	2 4	5 31	7 54	1058
Franzensbad arr	6 36	9 18	12 29	2† 3	5 57	9 8	11 27	4 41	...	**Oberkotzau**	4 15	6 59	...	10 6	2 35	6 1	8 25	1129
Eger 203 ......arr	6 50	9 30	12 4	3 0	6 12	9 26	11 40	5 10	...	**Hof 197** ....arr	5 0	7 11	...	1022	2 52	6 15	8 40	1144

Kulmbach and Thurnau (10 miles)—Kulmbach depart 8.10 a.m., 1.45, 7‡27 p.m. Thurnau depart 6§0, 10.30 a.m., 4*29 p.m.
*—8.20 p.m. on Sunday. ‡—10.20 p.m. on Sunday. §—4.47 a.m. on Sunday.

For Continuation of Trains, see next page.

Luggage Rates—see page 462.] BAVARIAN STATE RAILWAYS.

HOF, BAMBERG, NURNBERG, and MUNICH.

LEIPSIC 187 ....dep	...	...	...	9 a40	...	...	9 a40	1225	...	...	...	...	...	7 p50
DRESDEN 186...dep	...	...	...	8 a30	...	...	8 a30	1111	...	...	...	...	...	6 p0
	1,2,3	2 & 3	Ex3	Ex 3	1,2,3	2 & 3	2 & 3	Ex3	Ex2	Ex3	2 & 3	1,2,3	2 & 3	1,2,3
				p.m.			p.m.	p.m.	...			p.m.	p.m.	p.m.
Hof..............dep	...	...	...	12 55	...	...	1 11	3 54	...	...	...	4 37	7 53	11 25
Oberkotzau...dep	...	...	...	...	...	...	1 21	4 2	...	...	...	4 51	8 5	11 33
Schwarzenbach.......	...	...	...	RC	...	...	1 30	4 10	...	...	...	5 2	8 16	11 41
Münchberg 203B......	...	...	...	...	...	...	1 54	4 28	...	...	...	5 26	8 41	11 59
Falls..................	...	...	...	...	...	...	2 25	...	...	...	...	5 58	9 14	...
Neuenmarkt...arr	...	...	...	2 2	...	...	2 48	5 10	...	...	...	6 25	9 40	12 38
BAYREUTH 203 dep	...	...	...	Arrive Bayreuth 2.31.	...	...	1 p57	4p22	...	...	...	5p40	9 p8	11 p7
Neuenmarkt...dep	...	...	...		...	...	2 55	5 12	...	...	...	6 35	9 55	12 39
Kulmbach	...	...	...		...	...	3 16	5 25	...	...	...	6 59	10 13	12 52
Burkunstadt	...	...	...		p.m.	...	3 40	...	...	...	...	7 27	10 36	...
Hochstadt......arr	...	...	...				3 47	...	...	...	...	7 34	10 43	...
,, ...dep	...	...	...		3 55	...	3 58	...	...	...	...	7 36	10 44	...
Lichtenfels....arr	...	...	a.m.		4 4	...	4 13	5 51	...	...	...	7 52	10 56	1 18
BERLIN 170.....dep	...	...	1030		8a20	...	8 a20	...	1p10	...	...	...	...	...
PROBSTZELLA dep	...	...	⋮		2p35	...	2 p35	...	⋮	6p42	...	6p42	7 p36	...
COBURG 173B...dep	...	...	⋮	...	3p39	...	3 p44	5p14	⋮	7 p8	...	7 p8	9 p45	12 30
Lichtenfels ...dep	...	...	⋮	...	4 10	...	5 8	6 53	⋮	8 1	...	8 18	11 10	1 22
Breitengussbach 197	...	...	⋮	...	...	...	5 53	...	⋮	...	...	8 57	11 49	...
Bamberg........arr	...	...	4 47	...	4 40	...	6 7	6 21	⋮	8 27	...	9 7	12 3	1 51
WURZBURG 198 arr	p.m.	p.m.	...	...	...	...	8 p13	8p13	⋮	...	...	1255	...	...
Bamberg........dep	2 55	3 6	4 50	...	5 6	...	7 3	...	⋮	8 28	...	9 49	12 30	1 54
Strullendorf	...	3 17	...	...	...	...	7 16	...	⋮	...	...	9 59	12 42	...
Forchheim..............	3 20	3 49	...	...	5 30	...	7 55	...	⋮	...	...	1025	1 15	2 16
Erlangen................	3 37	4 17	...	...	5 46	...	8 35	...	⋮	9 0	...	1049	1 49	2 31
Furth	3 56	4 57	5 33	...	6 3	...	9 19	...	⋮	9 16	...	1110	2 28	2 48
Nurnberg........arr	4 8	5 15	5 43	...	6 15	p.m.	9 38	...	7 34	9 26	p.m.	1122	2 47	3 0
,, 203, 204 dep	4 20	——	5 49	...	7 10	7 25	——	...	7 40	9 36	10 20	1150	——	3 16
Schwabach.............	4 37	...	⋮	...	...	8 9	...	...	...	Via Augsburg, (arr. 11.29 p.m.)	10 49	1215	...	3 37
Roth 198...............	4 49	...	⋮	...	7 36	8 26	...	...	...		11 11	1246	...	3 50
Georgensgm'nd 203B	4 59	...	RC	...	...	8 41	...	...	...		11 27	1251	...	4 2
Pleinfeld ....arr	5 10	...	Via Augsburg (arrive 7.41 p.m.)	...	7 55	9 2	...	...	...		11 45	1 10	...	4 16
,, 198...dep	5 12	...		...	7 57	9 5	...	...	...		11 47	1 11	...	4 19
Weissenburg-a-S. ...	5 23	...		...	8 8	9 24	...	...	...		12 4	1 28	...	4 35
Treucht-lingen ......arr	5 33	...		...	8 17	9 38	...	...	...		12 18	1 41	...	4 46
......dep	——	...		...	8 31	9 48	...	...	...		——	——	...	4 56
Pappenheim............	...	...		...	...	9 57	...	...	...	⋮	...	...	...	Via Augsburg ... (arrive 6.11 p.m.)
Solnhofen	...	...		...	...	10 5	...	...	...	⋮	...	...	...	
Dollnstein..............	...	...		...	...	10 14	...	...	...	⋮	...	...	...	
Eichstätt	...	...		...	9 0	10 32	...	...	...	⋮	...	...	...	
Ingolstadt Nordbhf..	3Cl.	...		...	...	11 11	...	...	...	⋮	...	2&3	...	
Ingol- Haptbhf.arr	p.m.	...		...	9 23	11 17	...	...	...	⋮	...	a.m.	...	
stadt 195.......dep	8 0	...	⋮	...	9 24	——	...	...	...	⋮	...	3 50	...	
Wolnzach	8 53	...	⋮	...	9 46	...	...	...	...	⋮	...	4 28	...	
Pfaffenhofen...........	10 7	...	⋮	...	9 59	...	...	...	...	⋮	...	4 49	...	
Dachau	1124	...	⋮	...	...	...	...	...	...	⋮	...	5 52	...	
Munich Hptbf. arr	1156	...	8 34	...	1051	...	...	...	10 5	1240	...	6 26	...	7 20

ERLANGEN and HERZOGENAURACH

Erlangen ....dep	5a42	9a41	1p25	6p47	9 p8	...
Herzogenaurach ..arr	6 26	1028	2 7	7 33	9 44	...

Herzogenaurach ...dep	4 a5	6a40	11a13	2 p40	8 p0	...	...	...
Erlangen 197.........arr	4 45	7 18	11 52	3 25	8 46	...	...	...

NEUENMARKT and BISCHOFSGRUN.

Neuenmarkt......dep	8a10	1p30	5p20	10p12	...	...
Berneck	8 49	2 7	5 59	10 51	...	...
Bischofsgrun ...arr	9 35	2 49	6 43	11 35	...	...

Bischofsgrun ...dep	6 a3	10a50	3p33	8 p0	...	...	...	...
Berneck....................	6 38	11 27	4 10	8 43	...	...	...	...
Neuenmarkt 197 arr	7 10	11 59	4 41	9 15	...	...	...	...

FORCHHEIM and HÖCHSTADT-a-AISCH.

Forchheim.........dep	9 a5	4 p37	8p41	...	...	...	...
Höchstadt-a-A. ...arr	10 20	5 47	9 49	...	...	...	...

Höchstadt...........dep	6 a38	12p30	6 p25	...	...	...	...
Forchheim (197) arr	7 53	1 50	7 40	...	...	...	...

NÖRDLINGEN and PLEINFELD.

Nördlingen ...dep	4 a55	8 a17	11a 2	1 p29	3p 55	7 p10	9 p55	10p50	...	...	...	...	...	...	...	...	...	...
Oettingen	5 16	8 30	11 21	1 45	4 16	7 23	10 14	...	...	...	...	...	...	...	...	...	...	...
Wassertrüdingen......	5 39	8 44	11 42	2 1	4 39	7 35	10 33	...	...	...	...	...	...	...	...	...	...	...
Gunzenhausen	6 8	9 6	12 30	2 29	5 10	7 53	11 1	...	...	...	...	...	...	...	...	...	...	...
Pleinfeld 197...arr	6 33	9 25	1 25	2 55	5 38	8 11	11 25	11 41	...	...	...	...	...	...	...	...	...	...
Pleinfeld.........dep	4 a28	6 a58	8 a30	11a53	2p24	6 p10	8 p13	...	...	...	...	...	...	...	...	...	...	...
Gunzenhausen	4 59	7 17	9 15	12 26	2 54	6 50	8 35	8 p46	...	...	...	...	...	...	...	...	...	...
Wassertrüdingen.......	5 25	7 34	9 41	12 53	3 16	7 22	8 54	10 13	...	...	...	...	...	...	...	...	...	...
Oettingen	5 42	7 46	10 0	1 10	3 31	7 42	9 6	11 10	...	...	...	...	...	...	...	...	...	...
Nördlingen 191.arr	6 0	8 0	10 20	1 29	3 48	8 5	9 20	11 45	...	...	...	...	...	...	...	...	...	...

Luggage Rates, see page 462.] **BAVARIAN STATE RAILWAYS.**

MUNICH, NURNBERG, BAMBERG, and HOF.

Dist E.M		2 & 3	2 & 3	1,2,3	Ex3	2&3 a.m.	2&3 a.m.	1,2,3 a.m.	Ex 3 a.m.	2 & 3 a.m.	Ex 2 a.m.	Ex.3 a.m.	Ex3	1,2,3	2 &3	2&3 a.m.	Ex3	1,2,3 p.m.	2 & 3
—	**Munich** Haupt. dep	...	...	...	...	...	4 52	6 45	7 5	6 50	8 15	8 25	...	...	...	9 14	...	1245	...
11	Dachau	...	...	...	...	...	5 18	...	Via Augsburg	7 15	R C	...	...	...	...	9 37	...	...	...
31	Pfaffenhofen	...	...	...	...	...	6 14	7 32	⋮	8 10	⋮	...	...	...	...	1035	...	1 29	...
37½	Wolnzach	...	...	...	...	...	6 32	7 43	⋮	8 25	⋮	...	...	...	...	1051	...	1 38	...
50½	**Ingolstadt**-Hpt. arr	...	...	...	...	...	7 4	8 2	⋮	8 55	⋮	...	...	...	a.m.	1123	...	1 56	...
...	" dep	...	...	...	From Zurich (dep. 11.30 p.m.) and Augsburg (dep 6.50 a.m.)	3 37	7 14	8 5	⋮	—	⋮	...	...	...	9 31	1135	...	1 59	...
52½	Ingolstadt Nordbnhof	...	...	...		3 45	7 22	...	⋮	...	⋮	...	...	...	9 39	1144	...	...	...
67	Eichstätt	...	...	...		4 32	8 10	8 36	⋮	...	⋮	...	...	...	1034	1236	...	2 26	...
73½	Dollnstein	...	...	...		4 47	8 25	...	⋮	...	⋮	...	...	...	1049	1252	...	...	...
77¾	Solnhofen	...	...	...		4 57	8 36	...	⋮	...	⋮	...	...	...	11 0	1 4	...	...	...
81	Pappenheim	...	...	...		5 6	8 45	...	⋮	...	⋮	...	...	...	11 8	1 14	...	...	...
85	**Treuchtlingen** arr	a.m.	...	...		5 15	8 54	9 3	9 2	...	⋮	R C	...	...	1117	1 23	...	2 54	...
...	" dep	4 54	...	...		6 7	1010	9 13	—	...	⋮	...	...	...	1124	1 36	...	2 57	...
90½	Weissenburg-a-S.	5 9	...	...		6 22	1020	9 23		...	⋮	...	...	...	1138	1 52	...	3 6	...
96¼	**Pleinfeld** arr	5 22	...	...		6 36	1033	9 32	...	...	⋮	...	...	...	1150	2 6	...	3 15	...
...	" dep	5 26	...	...		6 43	1038	9 34	...	...	⋮	...	...	...	1154	2 11	...	3 16	...
101¼	Georgensgmund	5 41	...	...		6 57	1049	...	...	...	⋮	...	...	...	12 8	2 27	...	...	...
107¼	Roth	5 55	...	...		7 10	1058	9 50	...	...	⋮	...	...	...	1223	2 43	...	3 32	...
114¼	Schwabach	6 13	...	...		7 30	1111	10 3	...	...	⋮	...	...	...	1247	3 9	...	3 43	...
123½	**Nurnberg** Hpt. arr	6 35	...	a.m.	8 50	7 52	1132	1019	...	...	10 30	10 55	...	p.m.	1 8	3 33	...	4 0	...
...	" dep	—	...	7 35	9 14	—	1240	1039	...	...	10 35	11 0	...	12 3	3 13	—	...	4 15	...
128¾	**Furth**	...	...	7 48	9 24	...	1 2	1049	...	...	⋮	11 10	...	12 14	3 33	...	...	4 27	...
138	Erlangen	...	...	8 7	9 38	...	1 38	11 5	...	...	⋮	...	...	12 31	4 9	...	...	4 44	...
147½	Forchheim	...	...	8 33	...	...	2 11	1119	...	...	⋮	...	...	12 45	4 36	...	...	4 59	...
157½	Strullendorf	...	...	9 0	...	...	2 43	...	...	...	⋮	...	...	...	5 5	...	...	...	...
162¼	**Bamberg** arr	...	...	9 9	10 7	...	2 54	1140	...	...	⋮	11 54	a.m.	1 6	5 15	...	p m.	5 21	...
...	WURZBURG 198 dep	...		6 a0	...	p.m.	1p40	...	...	...	⋮	10 a0	10 0	...	...	...	1 40	...	2p15
...	**Bamberg** dep	...	...	9 27	10 9	1 38	3 47	...	...	...	⋮	11 56	12 2	1 11	...	...	3 37	5 28	6 50
167	Breitengussbach	...	...	9 41	...	1 54	4 2	...	...	...	⋮	⋮	...	...	...	...	..	...	7 7
182	**Lichtenfels** arr	...	...	10 21	1035	2 38	4 43	...	Ex 3	...	⋮	⋮	1232	1 45	...	---	4 7	5 57	7 52
221⅝	PROBSTZEL 195 arr	...	...	1 p21	1p21	...	8 p2	...		...	⋮	⋮	...	4 p5	...	...	7p46	7p46	10p40
436½	BERLIN 171 arr	...	...	...	4p49	...	...	...		...	4 p56	6 p42	...	10p38	1,2,3	...	...	...	...
195	COBURG 173B arr	...	a.m.	11a28	1128	...	5p32	...		...			1p13	2 p40	p.m.	..	5p32	6p53	9 p0
...	**Lichtenfels** dep	...	6 15	10 50	..	...	5 2	...	From Bayreuth 11.8	...	...	...	1234	2 2	1 55	...	4 10	...	8 8
187¼	**Hochstadt** arr	...	6 31	11 7	...	...	5 20	...		...	...	...	1244	2 12	2 7	...	4 19	...	8 25
...	" dep	...	6 33	11 9	...	...	5 22	...		...	...	...	1245	—	2 7	...	4 20	...	8 27
190¾	Burgkundstadt	a.m.	6 43	11 20	...	...	5 31	...		...	...	...	...	...	2 15	...	...	...	8 38
200½	Kulmbach	5 0	7 14	11 52	...	...	6 2	...	a.m.	...	...	...	1 7	...	2 37	...	4 41	...	9 12
208½	**Neuenmarkt** arr	5 24	7 42	12 22	...	...	6 30	...	11 35	...	...	...	1 22	...	2 55	...	4 56	...	9 39
221½	BAYREUTH 203 arr	5 a55	8 a31	1 p16	...	...	7p26	...		...	...	...	1p46	...	3p46	...	5p38		10p46
...	**Neuenmarkt** dep	5 31	7 51	12 31	...	...	6 38	...	11 42	...	...	...	1 27	...	2 59	...	4 57	...	9 58
216	Falls	6 2	8 25	1 2	...	...	7 14	...	...	...	...	...	...	...	3 25	...	...	...	10 30
226¼	Munchberg	6 32	9 1	1 36	...	...	7 50	...	12 28	...	...	...	2 13	...	3 50	...	5 41	...	11 5
234½	Schwarzenbach	6 56	9 24	1 57	...	...	8 12	...	...	...	...	...	...	...	4 6	...	...	...	11 28
237¾	**Oberkotzau** arr	7 3	9 32	2 4	...	...	8 24	...	R C	...	...	...	2 33	...	4 13	...	6 0	...	11 36
241¼	**Hof** arr	7 17	9 45	2 19	...	...	8 35		12 56	...	...	...	2 43	...	4 27	...	6 10	...	11 49
381½	DRESDEN 186 arr	1 p3	5 p0	7 p23	...	...	...	...	5 p0	...	...	...	7p28	...	1047	...	1047	...	5 a45
343½	LEIPSIC 187 arr	11a50	2p57	6 p7	...	...	...	...	4 p2	...	...	...	6 p7	...	8 p3	...	9p17	...	4 a6

For Continuation of Trains, see next page.

MUNICH, MURNAU, OBERAMMERGAU, and GARMISCH-PARTENKIRCHEN.

	a.m.	a.m.	a.m.	a.m.	a.m.	a.m.	a.m.	a.m.	a.m.	a.m.	p.m.	p.m.	p.m.	p.m.	p.m.	p.m.	p.m.	p.m.	p.m.	p.m.	p.m.	p.m.
Munich Central dep	5 15	5 50	6 30	7 45	7 50	8 45	9 45	1045	1050	1130	1250	1 50	2 30	2 50	3 55	4 20	5 20	6 20	6 58	7 30	9 25	1135
Starnberg	6 11	...	7 11	...	8 38	9 18	1018	...	1151	12 3	1 34	2 23	...	3 24	4 33	5 16	5 53	7 3	7 52	8 4	1021	1222
Possenhofen	6 24	...	7 22	..	8 49	9 28	1028	...	12 4	1213	1 46	2 33	..	3 33	4 44	5 28	6 3	7 15	8 4	8 14	1033	1231
Tutzing 203A arr	6 37	6 43	7 34	8 30	9 1	9 40	1040	1130	1219	1225	1 59	2 45	3 16	3 45	4 57	5 41	6 15	7 29	8 18	8 26	1047	1242
Weilheim 197B arr	—	7 9	—	8 47	9 24	—	—	1145	1252	—	—	—	3 30	—	5 24	—	—	7 58	—	8 42	1113	—
Murnau arr	—	8 6	...	9 14	1014	...	...	1213	1 46	...	...	...	3 58		6 21	...	...	8 58	...	9 14	—	...
Murnau dep		8 25	...	9 20	1030	...	...	1223	1 58	...	...	...	4 10	...	6 35	...	...	9 22	...	9 22	...	...
Kohlgrub Ort		8 59	...	9 48	11 4	...	...	1247	2 32	...	...	...	4 44	...	7 9	...	...	9 56	...	9 56	...	...
Oberammergau arr		9 30	...	1019	1135	...	...	1 28	3 3	...	...	...	5 15	...	7 40	...	...	1029	...	1029	...	...
Murnau dep		8 16	...	9 17	1023	...	...	1216	1 56	...	...	...	4 0	...	6 31	...	...	...	...	9 21	...	6a20
Oberau		8 49	...	..	1056	...	...	...	2 30	...	...	...	...	...	7 4	...	...	...	...	9 53	...	6 53
Garmisch-Partenkirch.		9 4		9 49	1111	...	...	1248	2 46	...	...	...	4 32	...	7 19	...	...	...	...	10 7		7 8

Garmisch-Partenkirchen dep	5a30	7a28	10 a2	1p15	2p57	5p40	7p37	...
Griesen 203C arr	5 57	7a55	10 29	1 43	3 24	6 p7	8 4	...

Fares from Munich: To Murnau 5 m. 50 pf., 3 m. 60 pf., 2 m. 40 pf.; to Oberammergau 6 m. 90 pf., 5 m., 3 m. 80 pf.

WEILHEIM and PEISSENBERG.

Weilheim dep	7a20	9a32	11a50	1 p5	3p35	5p38	7p42	8 p58
Peissenberg arr	7 38	9 50	12 8	1 23	3 53	5 56	8 0	9 16

Peissenberg dep	6a40	8a25	10a25	12p33	2p55	4p15	6p54	8p15	...
Weilheim 197B arr	6 57	8 42	10 42	12 50	3 12	4 32	11	8 32	..

Luggage Rates, see page 462.] BAVARIAN STATE RAILWAYS.

MUNICH, NURNBERG, BAMBERG, and HOF.

SLEEPING CAR—Munich to Berlin, in 10.20 p.m. from Munich.

	2 & 3 p.m.	2 & 3	Ex 3 p.m.	2 & 3 p.m.	1,2,3	2 & 3 p.m.	2 & 3 p.m.	1,2,3 p.m.	Ex.3 p.m.	2&3	2 & 3 p.m.	Ex 3	2 & 3	
Munich Haupt. dep	1 17	...	4 45	5 10	...	5 48	7 5	8 45	10 20	...	11 25	From Augsburg, dep. 12.53 a.m. Runs from 2nd July until 1st Sept.	...	...
Dachau	1 45	...	...	5 36	...	6 10	7 34	...	...	...	11 53		...	...
Pfaffenhofen	2 43	...	5 33	6 31	...	6 53	8 33	9 33	SC	...	12 43		...	...
Wolnzach	3 0	...	5 44	6 46	...	7 6	8 49	9 44	...	...	12 56		...	...
Ingolstadt-Hpt. arr	3 31	...	6 3	7 17	...	7 30	9 22	10 3	...	...	1 24		...	...
" dep	3 42	...	6 6		...	7 38	9 31	10 6	...	...			...	...
Ingolstadt Nordbnhof	3 50	...	...	...	...	7 46	9 39	...	...	...			...	...
Eichstätt	4 39	...	6 37	...	...	8 34	10 46	10 42	...	...	...		...	...
Dollnstein	4 53	...	...	...	...	8 49	11 2	...	...	...	...		...	...
Solnhofen	5 4	...	...	...	...	8 59	11 13	...	...	...	...		...	...
Pappenheim	5 12	...	...	...	...	9 8	11 22	...	...	...	...		...	...
Treuchtlingen arr	5 21	...	7 4	p.m.	...	9 17	11 33	11 10	...	...	3 Cl. ng't		...	...
" dep	5 26	...	7 11	7 40	...	9 23		11 20	...	...	12 25		...	...
Weissenburg-a-S.	5 41	...	7 21	7 55	...	9 37	...	11 30	...	...	12 41		...	...
Pleinfeld arr	5 54	...	...	8 8	...	9 49	...	11 39	...	...	12 55		...	...
" dep	6 3	...	...	8 19	...	9 52	...	11 49	...	...	1 1		...	...
Georgensgmund	6 17	...	...	8 33	...	10 4	...	...	...	...	1 16		...	...
Roth	6 32	...	7 45	8 47	...	10 16	...	12 6	...	...	1 31		...	...
Schwabach	6 53	...	7 58	9 8	...	10 33	...	12 19	...	...	1 58	a.m	...	
Nurnberg Hpt. arr	7 17	p.m.	8 15	9 32	...	10 52	...	12 35	12 50	a.m.	2 22	2 40	a.m.	RC—Restaurant Car attached. SC—Sleeping Car.
" dep		7 22	8 34		...	11 54	...	1 5	12 55	1 56		2 46	4 50	
Furth	...	7 37	8 46	...	...	12 8	...	1 18	1 6	2 20			5 6	
Erlangen	...	8 5	9 2	...	...	12 27	...	1 35	...	2 55	...		5 33	
Forchheim	...	8 36	9 17	...	...	12 52	...	1 51	...	3 34	...		6 0	
Strullendorf	...	9 8	...	...	...	1 19	...	...	...	4 2	...		6 29	
Bamberg arr	...	9 18	9 38	...	p.m.	1 28	...	2 13	1 52	4 11	...		6 39	
WURZBURG 198 dep	...	...		...	7 15	☞ From Bayreuth 10.47.	...	9 p15	9 p15	...	...		3 a33	
Bamberg dep	...	...			9 49		...	2 20	1 53	4 41	...		7 0	
Breitengussbach	...	...	...	...	...		...	...		4 58	...		7 16	
Lichtenfels arr	...	...	...	...	10 23		...	2 50		5 43	...		7 58	
PROBSTZEL 195 arr	...	...	...	...	...		...	...		8a46	...		...	
BERLIN 171 arr	...	...	...	...	...		3 Cl.	...	8 a25	...	...	10a 4	...	
COBURG 173B arr	...	...	...	...	12a10		p.m.	3 a48		6a36	...		8 a41	
Lichtenfels dep	...	...	...	...	10 26		10 30	2 53	...	...	...	...	...	...
Hochstadt arr	...	...	...	...	10 35		10 47	...	...	...	...	...	...	...
" dep	...	...	...	...	10 36		10 48	...	...	...	...	...	...	...
Burgkundstadt	...	...	...	...	...		10 58	...	...	...	...	...	...	...
Kulmbach	...	...	...	...	10 57		11 30	3 24	...	...	...	...	...	...
Neuenmarkt arr	...	...	...	...	11 13	Ex.3	11 59	3 39	...	...	...	...	...	...
BAYREUTH 203 arr	...	...	...	...	1 a34	p.m.	1 a34	5 a55	...	...	...	...	...	...
Neuenmarkt dep	...	...	...	...	...	11 23	...	3 42	...	...	...	...	...	...
Falls	...	...	...	...	...	...	...	...	...	...	...	...	...	...
Munchberg	...	...	...	...	...	12 15	...	4 27	...	...	...	...	...	...
Schwarzenbach	...	...	...	...	...	12 31	...	...	...	...	...	...	...	...
Oberkotzau arr	...	...	...	...	...	...	...	4 51	...	...	...	...	...	...
Hof arr	...	...	...	...	...	12 45	...	5 0	...	...	...	...	...	...
DRESDEN 186 arr	...	...	...	...	...	5 a45	...	9 a48	...	...	...	...	...	...
LEIPSIC 187 arr	...	...	...	...	...	4 a6	...	8 a25	...	...	...	...	...	...

GARMISCH-PARTENKIRCHEN, OBERAMMERGAU, and MUNICH.

G.-Partenkirchen dep			...	5a23	...	7a27	...	9a50	...	...	1127	2p33	...	...	3 p0	...	...	5p42	...	7 40	...	8p15
Oberau			...	5 39	...	7 42	...	...	...	...	1142	...	...	...	3 16	...	...	5 58	...	...	...	8 31
Murnau arr			...	6 12	...	8 16	...	1023	...	...	1216	3 6	...	...	3 49	...	...	6 31	...	8 13	...	9 4
Oberammergau dep			...	5 13	...	7 10	...	9 16	...	...	11 5	1 57	...	...	2p49	...	...	5 25	...	7p 8	...	8 p0
Kohlgrub Ort			...	5 45	...	7 42	...	9 48	...	...	1137	2 31	...	...	3 21	...	...	5 57	...	7 40	...	8 32
Murnau arr			...	6 13	...	8 10	...	1016	...	...	12 5	2 59	...	...	3 49	...	...	6 25	...	8 7	...	9 0
		a.m	a.m.	a.m.		a.m.		a.m.			p.m.	p.m.			p.m.			p.m.		p.m.		p.m
Murnau dep	...	...	...	6 22	...	8 24	...	1024	...	...	1226	3 7	...	...	4 2	...	...	6 37	...	8 17	...	9 15
Weilheim	a.m.	5 35	...	7 10	a.m.	9 8	a.m.	1047	a.m.	p.m.	1 8	3 30	p.m.	p.m.	4 45	p.m.	p.m.	7 17	p.m.	8 42	p.m.	9 57
Tutzing	5 20	6 11	6 44	7 45	8 55	9 42	9 50	11 5	1140	1 10	1 41	3 48	3 54	5 10	5 21	6 30	7 25	7 49	8 30	9 0	9 18	1030
Possenhofen	5 36	6 32	7 0	8 2	9 12		10 7	...	1153	1 23	2 0	...	4 11	5 23	5 40	6 43	7 42	8 6	8 43	...	9 35	1047
Starnberg	5 44	6 43	7 8	8 10	9 20	10 0	1015	...	12 0	1 30	2 8	...	4 20	5 30	5 59	6 50	7 51	8 15	8 50	...	9 43	1055
Munich arr	6 23	7 34	7 46	8 46	10 0	1031	11 2	1147	1232	2 1	2 54	4 30	5 6	6 1	6 38	7 22	8 30	9 1	9 21	9 43	1021	1141

Griesen dep	6a47	9a 9	1p52	2p55	4p 2	6p55	8p51	...
Garmisch-Partenkirchen arr	7 13	9 35	2 19	3 22	4 37	7 22	9 17	...

BAVARIAN STATE RAILWAYS.

[Luggage Rates—see page 462.

WURZBURG and BAMBERG.

†—Not on Sunday. ‡—2 and 3 class.

ASCHAFFENB'G dep	1a20	...	7a33	9a19	...	1050	...	...	...	4p28	5p33	5p33	8 a2
HEIDELBERG dep	...	...	6a19	6a19	1010	1010	...	...	...	1240	4 p0	...	9p39
	2&3	1,2,3	Ex3	2&3	Ex3	Ex3	1,2,3	2&3	3 Cl	1,2,3	1,2,3	2&3	Ex3
	a.m	a.m.	a.m.	a.m.	p.m.	p.m.	...	p.m		p.m.	p.m.	p.m.	a.m.
Würzburg.........dep	3 33	6 0	10 0	11 7	1 27	1 40	...	2 15	...	6 10	7 15	9 15	1 2
Rottendorf	3 52	6 17	...	1126	...	...	...	2 34	...	6 28	7 33	9 33	...
Seligenstadt	4 11	6 31	...	1144	...	...	...	2 53	...	6 45	...	9 53	...
Waigolshausen 196A	4 33	6 52	...	12 7	...	...	...	3 18	...	7 7	...	1017	...
Schweinfurt Cen.ar	4 48	7 6	1047	1223	2 10	2 26	...	3 34	...	7 21	8 10	1033	1 48
KISSINGEN (195)ar	6a32	8a18	1153	1p44	2p50	3p30	p.m.	4p30	p.m.	8p15	9p23	...	To Meiningen.
Schweinfurt Cen.dep	5 0	7 24	1055	1238	2 33	...	3 40	4 45	6 20	...	8 25	1048	
Schweinfurt Stadt..	5 7	7 31	...	1246	2 38	...	3 47	4 53	6 26	...	8 31	1058	
Schonungen	5 16	7 41	...	1256	...	...	...	5 1	6 38	...	8 38	11 6	
Hassfurt ...a.m.	5 47	8 13	1117	1 26	2 59	...	4 8	5 32	7 5	...	8 55	1134	
Ebelsbach ...4†20	6 7	8 33	...	1 45	...	...	...	5 52	7†24	...	9 12	1153	
Bamberg ....arr 5 35	6 39	9 7	1147	2 19	3 30	...	4 40	6 25	—	...	9 32	1225	...
HOF (197B)......arr	...	2p19	2p43	...	6p10	...	1149	1149	...	...	1245	5 a0	...

HOF 197..........dep	...	...	...	4 a2	...	5a42	8 a0	1158	...	1158	3p54	3p54	4p37
	Ex3	3 Cl	2&3	1,2,3	1,2,3	2&3	1,2,3	Ex3	Ex3	2&3	Ex3	1,2,3	2&3
	From Meiningen.	a.m.	a.m.	a.m.		a.m.	p.m.	p.m		p.m.	p.m.	p.m	p.m.
Bamberg ....dep		...	5 21	6 45	...	1015	1212	2 51	...	3 7	6 27	6 40	10 0
Ebelsbach		4 15	5 54	7 4	...	1046	...	...	...	3 40	...	7 13	1032
Hassfurt		4 35	6 15	7 20	...	11 7	1239	3 18	...	4 4	6 55	7 33	1053
Schonungen		5 4	6 43	7 36	...	1134	...	...	...	4 32	...	8 1	1116
Schweinfurt Stadt ...		5 18	6 53	7 43	...	1144	...	...	...	4 41	7 14	8 10	1126
Schweinfurt Cent. arr		5 25	7 0	7 49	...	1150	1 2	3 40	...	4 48	7 20	8 17	1132
KISSINGEN 195...dep	a.m.	...	5a35	7a17	9 a45	11a0	...	2p55	2p55	...	6p30	7p36	11p0
Schweinfurt Cent.dep	3 42	5‡53	7 15	7 58	10 30	1210	...	3 50	4 12	5 11	7 30	8 30	1142
Waigolshausen	...	6 18	7 34	8 14	10 45	1232	...	...	...	5 36	...	8 55	12 4
Seligenstadt	...	6 51	—	8 34	11 7	1 2	...	...	...	6 9	...	9 28	1232
Rottendorf	...	7 3	...	...	...	1 14	...	...	...	6 21	...	9 40	1244
Würzburg ....arr	4 24	7 15	...	8 52	11 25	1 25	...	4 32	4 57	6 33	8 13	9 52	1255
HEIDELBERG 143arr	7a50	1156	...	12p8	...	6p46	...	8 p8	8 p8	1140	1140	...	...
ASCHAFFENB'G 196B	7a40	8a52	...	1057	1 p0	4p47	...	8 p5	8 p5	8 p5	1024	1223	3a52

HASSFURT and HOFHEIM.

Hassfurt ....dep	6a35	1p30	7 p40	...	...	...	...	...
Hofheim..........arr	7 30	2 22	8 25	...	...	...	...	...
Hofheim ....dep	4 a45	10a 0	4p25	...	...	...	...	...
Hassfurt (198) ......arr	5 30	10 50	5 12	...	...	...	...	...

ROTH and GREDING.

E.M.										
	Roth........dep	5 a0	8 a6	2 p5	8p30	...	...	...	...	...
10¾	Heydeck	6 15	9 4	2 56	9 23	...	...	...	...	...
24½	Greding... arr	7 46	10 16	4 8	10 29	...	...	...	...	...
	Greding ......dep	5 a8	8 a33	11a40	4 p45	...	...	...	...	...
	Heydeck	6 11	9 37	12 49	6 15	...	...	...	...	...
	Roth (197)...arr	7 4	10 26	1 43	7 25	...	...	...	...	...

AUGSBURG and HAUNSTETTEN.

Augsburg ....dep	5a20	9a50	12p20	2 p52	4 p40	7p37	...	...
Haunstetten ......arr	5 46	10 16	12 46	3 18	5 6	8 3	...	...
Haunstetten ....dep	6a44	11 a5	1p12	3 p25	6 p21	8 p13	...	...
Augsburg..........arr	7 10	11 31	1 38	3 51	6 47	8 39	...	...

ROSENHEIM and LANDAU-a-ISAR.

†—Weekdays only. ‡—Sunday arr. 11.53 p.m.

Rosenheim ....dep	...	5a11	9a15	11a12	4p42	...	9 p10	...
Wasserburg	...	5 51	10 0	12 35	5 21	...	9 46	...
Muhldorf 203B	3a20	7 9	1110	2 38	6 10	p.m.	10 50	...
Neumarkt-a-Rott ...	5†35	7 46	1150	3 36	7 2	7 20	11 15	...
Gangkofen	6†12	8 5	1212	3 57	—	7 41	—	...
Landau-a-Isar ...arr	8†26	9 1	1 13	5 9	...	8 45	...	...

Landau-a-Isar dep	...	...	6a20	7†55	11a53	3p43	8p10
Gangkofen	...	a.m.	7 28	10 58	1 7	4 56	9 23
Neumarkt-a-Rott	a.m.	6 23	7 55	11 49	1 35	5 43	9 51
Muhldorf	5 58	6 43	9 0	12 11	2 33	6 34	10 14
Wasserburg	6 56	—	10 2	—	3 36	7 33	1‡12
Rosenheim .....arr	7 34	...	1038	...	4 12	8 8	...

Landau	7 a0	11a55	7 p0
Arnstorf	8 23	1 p27	8 16
Arnstorf	4a11	9a25	3 p22
Landau...	5 29	1057	4 57

LANDAU and EISENSTEIN.

*—Sundays excepted.

Landau-a-I dep	5a34	9a10	a.m.	a.m.	11a9	1p15	2p26	p.m.	5p26	9 p7	9p35	...	...	...
Plattling	6 9	9 32	9 40	9 50	1149	2 0	2 44	3 40	6 13	9 32	10 0	...	...	...
Deggendorf	6 29	—	9 51	10 6	1211	2 17	—	3 59	6 36	—	1017	...	...	...
Gotteszell	7 20	...	10 26	—	1 7	—	...	4 53	7 27	...	11 6	...	...	...
Regen	7 46	...	10 45	...	1 33	...	...	5 21	7 54	...	1131	...	...	...
Zwiesel	8 7	...	10 58	...	1 56	...	...	5 45	8 14	...	1148	...	...	...
Eisenstein arr	8 40	...	11 19	...	2 30	...	...	6 17	8 47	...	1220	...	...	...

Eisenstein dep	3a50	...	7 a4	...	...	...	1150	...	...	4p10	5 50	...	...	7p50
Zwiesel	4 9	...	7 28	...	...	...	1212	...	...	4 33	6 7	...	...	8 12
Regen	4 25	...	7 45	...	...	...	1228	...	...	4 50	6 21	...	...	8 30
Gotteszell	4 51	...	8 16	...	a.m.	...	1 1	...	...	5 20	6 43	...	p.m.	8 59
Deggendorf	5 19	a.m.	8 49	a.m	1022	a.m.	1 37	p.m.	p.m.	5 50	7 8	p.m.	8 4	9 30
Plattling	5 41	6*30	9 4	9 17	1036	11 9	1 52	2 31	3 10	6 6	7 20	7 29	8 35	9 45
Landau ......arr	6 6	7 24	...	9 33	...	1135	...	2 59	3 40	6 48	...	7 49	...	1027

ZWIESEL and GRAFENAU.

Zwiesel ....dep	8 a15	2 p10	5 p43	8p20	...	...	...	...
Grafenau ....arr	9 40	3 40	7 38	9 45	...	...	...	...
Grafenau ....dep	5 a40	10a20	1p40	6p15	...	...	...	...
Zwiesel 198......arr	7 20	12 0	4 17	7 55	...	...	...	...

KITZINGEN and SCHWEINFURT.

Kitzingen .... dep	...	7a40	12p50	5p35	10p22	...	...
Gerolzhofen	3a55	9 20	2 31	7 18	11 42	...	...
Schweinfurt ......arr	4 50	10 14	3 34	8 10	...	...	...
Schweinfurt.........dep	...	8 a10	1p32	...	4p20	...	8p30
Gerolzhofen	3 a51	9 53	2 27	3 p2	5 14	7p53	9 25
Kitzingen 195A...arr	5 34	11 36	...	4 45	...	9 24	...

LANDSHUT and ROTTENBURG.

Landshut ....dep	6 a40	2p50	8p40	...	...	...	...	...
Rottenburg ....arr	8 5	4 17	10 8	...	...	...	...	...
Rottenburg..........dep	4a50	11a53	5p38	...	...	...	...	...
Landshut ....arr	6 11	1 6	7 15	...	...	...	...	...

ROTTERSHAUSEN and STADTLAURINGEN.

‡—Sunday at 8.15 p.m.

Rottershausen ....dep	6 a50	3 p30	9p55	
Stadtlauringen..........arr	7 50	4 25	1050	
Stadtlauringen ....dep	5a 5	10a 5	5‡p35	...
Rottershausen..........arr	6 0	10 59	6 35	...

KRONACH and NORDHALBEN.

†—9.40 p.m. on Sun. *—7.24 p.m. on Sunday.

Kronach..........dep	7 a42	1 p0	7†p0	
Nordhalben ....arr	8 55	2 13	8 13	
Nordhalben..........dep	5 a26	9 a46	4*p15	...
Kronach ....arr	6 40	10 56	5 25	...

THANN-MATZBACH and HAAG.

Thann-Matzbach ......dep	9 a35	1p35	9p 0	...	...	...	...	...
Haag ....arr	10 40	2 42	10 5	...	...	...	...	...
Haag ....dep	6 a55	11a11	6 p15	...	...	...	...	...
Thann-Matzbach ......arr	8 0	12 10	7 35	...	...	...	...	...

LINDAU to MUNICH, AUGSBURG, and TREUCHTLINGEN. [‡—Via Bregenz.]

Dist. E.M.	Station																			
	ZURICH ....262 dep		11p30	...	...	...	...	...	...	6 a45	8 a54	8 a54	1048	10a48	...	...	2 p55	...	4p15	4p15
	ROMANSH'N stmr 368 dep			...	...	...	...	...	...	9 a0	10a45	10a45	1240	12p40	...	...	4 p35	...	6p40	6p40
	CHUR .... 268A dep		A	...	...	...	...	4 a0	...	6 a5	8 a8	...	1012	10a12	...	...	2 p43	3 p20	...	6p‡7
	RORSCHACH stmr 368 dep			...	...	...	...	6a20	...	9 a17	11a25	...	1p12	1 p12	...	2p15	4 p50	6 p28	...	8 p4
		3 Cl.	Ex.3		3 Cl.	3 Cl	2&3	1,2,3		2 & 3	Ex.3	2 & 3	Ex3	1,2,3	3 Cl.	2&3	Ex 3	Ex 3	2&3	Ex 3
			a.m.			a.m.	a.m.	a.m.		a.m.	p.m.	p.m.	p.m.	p.m.		p.m.	p.m.	p.m.	p.m.	p.m.
—	**Lindau** ....dep	...	3 10	...	...	6 15	4 15	7 30	...	10 20	12 44	12 55	2 25	2 40	...	4 25	6 6	7 38	8 34	9 40
14¼	Hergatz	...	...	...	...	7 19	5 2	8 2	...	11 9	1 19	1 58	...	...	...	5 18	...	...	9 37	...
24	Rothenbach	...	...	...	...	8 5	5 34	8 26	...	11 43	1 47	2 51	...	3 40	...	5 55	RC	RC	1030	...
32	Oberstaufen	...	...	...	a.m.		5 57	8 46	...	12 6	2 7	3 16	...	4 0	...	6 21	...	...	1054	...
42½	Immenstadt(195)...arr	...	4 33	...	8 6	2&3	6 21	9 4	...	12 30	2 24	3 50	...	4 18	...	6 47	...	8 49	1119	10 59
56	**Kempten** ....arr	...	4 57	...	9 0	a.m.	7 0	9 30	...	1 10	2 50	4 30	...	4 42	p.m.	7 30	7 49	...	1158	*
...	" ....dep	...	5 2	1,2,3		4 0	7 25	9 38	...	2 5	2 55		...	4 47	5 4	8 20	7 54	...		
67¾	Gunzach	a.m.	...	a.m.	...	4 37	8 5	10 7	...	2 43	...	p.m.	...	5 14	6 2	9 3	...	...	p.m.	
79	Biessenhofen....	7 20	...	8 2	...	5 5	8 38	...	...	3 12	...	2 1	...	...	6 53	9 41	...	...	7 56	
82½	Kaufbeuren	7 30	5 48	8 12	...	5 16	8 53	1035	2&3	3 24	3 48	2 16	...	5 41	7 8	10 5	...	9 58	8 5	
95	**Buchloe** ....arr		6 5		...	5 45	9 20	1051	p.m.	3 53	4 6		4 53	5 57	7 55	1035	8 53	...		
...	**Buchloe** ...dep 3Cl.	...	6 10	...	...	5 55	9 35	1056	2 20	4 20	4 11	...	4 57	6 5	8†25	11 0	8 58	...	...	Until 31st August.
102¼	**Kaufering**......3 a4	...	...	...	...	6 24	10 5	11 7	2 42	4 46	4 24	...	...	6 17	8 50	1123	...	...	...	
111	Geltendorf 3 43	...	...	...	...	6 53	1041	...	3 14	5 19	...	...	...	...	9 35	1149	...	...	...	
132½	Pasing 5 19	...	...	...	...	8 4	1138	...	4 12	6 22	...	...	...	...	10 38	1248	...	...	...	
137½	**Munich** ......arr 5 35	2 & 3	7 5	2 & 3	Ex 3	8 17	1150	1156	4 25	6 35	5 15	...	5 50	7 5	10 50	1 0	9 55	11 5	...	
		a.m.	a.m.	a.m.	a.m.			a.m.			p.m.		p.m.	p.m.		p.m.	p.m.			
...	**Buchloe** ....dep	4 30	6 12	6 23	From Munich	...	...	11†0	...	...	4 14	...	5 0	6 10	...	1052	9 0	...	...	
105½	Schwabmünchen....	4 54	...	6 44		...	...	1125	...	...	4 31	...	...	6 36	...	11†5	...	...	...	
112¼	Bobingen	5 11	...	6 58		...	...	1140	...	...	4 43	Ex 3	...	6 52	Ex 3	1130	...	1,2,3	2&3	
119¾	**Augsburg**....arr	5 30	6 41	7 14		...	a.m.	1157	...	...	4 56	p.m.	5 33	7 10	p.m.	1146	9 30	p.m.	p.m.	12 47
...	" ....dep	6 0	6 50		7 59	...	11 5	1 20	...	...	5 17	5 40		7 50	7 47		9 37	11 11	1125	12 53
140½	Mertingen	6 57	...	...	...	...	1157	2 16	...	3 Cl.	To Ansbach (arr. 7.4)	...	...	8 43	Ansbach arr. 9.35.	†—2&3 Class.	...	...	1218	...
145	**Donauwörth** ...arr	7 10	7 20	a.m.	8 30	...	12 9	2 28	...	p.m.		6 13	...	8 54			10 11	11 43	1230	...
...	" ...dep		7 22	7 40	8 30	...	1225		...	3 40		6 16	...				10 17	11 44		...
155¼	Fünfstetten			8 19	...	...	1 1	...	...	4 34		...	...	...			10 48	...	...	...
166½	**Treuchtlingen**...arr	...		8 47	9 2	...	1 27	...	...	5 15		6 55	...	...			11 10	12 18	...	...
205	NURNBERG 197B arr	...	8 a50	10a19	10a19	...	3p33	...	...	...	...	8 p15	...	...	...		12a35	2a22	...	2a40

NOTE.—Customs Examination for principal expresses takes place on board Boden See steamers.

* Passengers arrive Kempten 11.31 p.m., changing at Hegge.

SLEEPING CAR—Munich to Zurich, in 11.20 p.m. from Munich.

Station																					
NURNBERG 197...dep	3a16	...	...	4a15	4a51	...	...	6 a0	8 a2	...	...	8 a2	9 a45	...	9a45	1p31	...	4p20	7 p10	7 p10	9 p36
	1,2,3		2&3	Ex3	Ex 3	1,2,3	2 & 3	Ex3	Ex3	2 & 3	Ex3	2&3	Ex 3	Ex3	2&3	2&3	2&3	1,2,3	Ex 3	2 & 3	Ex.3
	a.m.			a.m.	a.m.		a.m.	a.m.	a.m.			a.m.	a.m.		n on	p.m.		p.m.	p.m.	p.m.	p.m.
Treuchtlingen dep	4 56	...	...			...	6 5	7 18	9 8	...	...	9 50	11 58	...	12 5	3 20	...	5 36	8 29	8 36	
Fünfstetten	...	...	...			...	6 48	...	...	...	...	1034	...	...	1 38	4 3	...	...	...	9 16	
Donauwörth ...arr	5 32	...	...			...	7 10	7 48	...	...	...	1056	RC	...	2 16	4 25	p.m.	6 11	8 58	9 38	
" ...dep	5 34	...	...			...	7 56	7 49	...	...	...	1130	...	...	2 36	4 45	8 4	6 13	8 59	10 6	
Mertingen	...	...	...			...	8 10	...	...	...	...	1146	...	...	2 49	4 58	8 19	...	...	10 19	
Augsburg ....arr	6 11	...	a.m.	6 18	6 44	a.m.	9 10	8 23	1015	...	p.m.	1255	1 5	...	4 0	6 0	9 22	6 56	9 33	11 20	11 29
" ....dep		...	5 10		6 50	7 6	9 30	8 28	1025	...	1 10	2 45		...		6 25					11 40
Bobingen		...	5 31	☞		7 22	9 51	...	...	...	1 24	3 7	...	...	...	6 48	...	...	To Munich.	...	...
Schwabmünchen		...	5 49			7 36	10 10	...	...	...	1 37	3 28	...	...	...	7 10	...	...		...	...
Buchloe ....arr		...	6 18			7 55	10 38	9 3	1111	...	1 55	3 58	2 & 3	...	...	7 40	1,2,3	...		2 & 3	12 19
			a.m.			a.m	a.m.	a.m.	a.m.	a.m.	p.m.	p.m.	p.m.	p.m.			p.m.			p.m.	p.m.
Munich—Central ...dep		...	4 10	From 1st September.	Until 31st August.	6 50	8 35	8 10	1020	11 25	1250	1 35	5 5	4 10	...		6 50	...		7 59	11 20
Pasing		...	4 24			...	...	...	...	11 41	RC	1 52	5 22	...	...		...	...	...	8 15	...
Geltendorf		...	5 37			...	9 35	RC	...	12 50	...	3 10	6 37	...	...		...	...	...	9 37	SC
Kaufering		3 Cl.	6 4			7 45	10 6	...	RC	1 18	1 45	3 44	7 8	...	...		7 40	...	...	10 7	12 11
Buchloe ....arr		a.m.	6 21			7 58	10 25	9 1	1117	1 40	1 58	4 5	7 30	...	...		7 53	...	...	10 30	12 24
Buchloe ....dep		3 40	6 46			8 7	11 0	9 11	1125		2 3	4 35		...	p.m.		7 58	...	...	10 50	12 34
Kaufbeuren		4 48	7 33	...		8 32	11 52	...	1146	...	2 26	5 32	5p50	5 25	8 30		8 21			11 37	12 56
Biessenhofen....		5 7	7 53	...		...	12 3	...	...	...	...	5 42	5 59	...	8 40	...	...			11 51	...
Gunzach	2&3	6 5	8 32	...		9 4	12 40	...	...	...	2 54	6 18		...		...	8 48			12 31	...
Kempten ....arr	a.m.	6 52	9 0	...		9 23	1 7	...	12*43	...	3 13	6 45	...	6 6	p.m.	...	9 7	A—Via St. Margrethen.	RC—Restaurant Car attached.	1 0	1 40
" ....dep	4 10	7 †2	9 35	...		9 30	2 10	...		...	3 18	7 0	...	6 11	8 15	...	9 13				1 45
Immenstadt	4 55	7 38	1031	...	8 44	9 57	2 51	1023	1254	...	3 44	7 43	...	...	8 52	...	9 39			...	2 10
Oberstaufen	5 25	8 7	11 1	...	...	1018	3 22	...	...	...	4 6	8 13	p.m.	...		...	9 59			*—Via Hegge.	...
Rothenbach	5 49	8 28	1125	...	...	1034	3 44	...	...	...	4 21	8 39	6 15	...	...	...	1017				...
Hergatz	6 29	8 55	12 0	...	--	1052	4 10	...	...	...	4 39	9 23	6 52	...	...	...	1038	...			...
Lindau ....arr	7 12	9 30	1244	...	9 50	1116	4 45	1125	2 0	...	5 3	1010	7 36	7 42	...	...	11 3	...			3 20
RORSCHACH stmr 369 arr		1055	1p53	...	10a55	1235	...	1235	3 p5	...	7p50	...	...	...	...	...	...	...	...		
CHUR (268) ....arr		2p25	4p53	...	2p25	2p43	...	2p43	5p10	...	1138	...	...	...	...	...	...	...	...		A
ROMANSHORN stmr. 369		1250	...	...	12p50	1250	...	1250	3p30	...	6p25	...	...	9 p5	...	...	...	...	...		
ZURICH (262A) ......arr		2p40	...	...	2p40	2p40	...	2p40	5p23	...	9 p7	-	...	1132	...	...	...	...	...		6 a50

Fünfstetten ....dep	6a55	8a25	1p35	4p40	7 p5	...	...
Monheim....arr	7 10	8 40	1 55	4 55	7 20	...	...
Monheim ....dep	6a20	7a50	12p30	3p35	6p30	...	...	...
Fünfstetten....arr	6 35	8 5	12 50	3 50	6 45	...	...	...

DONAUWORTH and NÖRDLINGEN.

Donauwörth....dep	7 a23	8 a40	12p17	2 p35	6p20	9 p0	12a37	...	...	...	...	...
Nördlingen ....arr	8 8	9 35	1 12	3 30	7 6	9 48	1 26	...	...	...	...	...
Nördlingen....dep	4a40	6 a25	10a35	1 p40	3 p55	7 p7	9 p25	10p50	...	...	...	...
Donauwörth ....arr	5 27	7 15	11 19	2 27	4 37	7 55	9 56	12 20	...	...	...	...

SAAL and KELHEIM.

Saal ......dep	6 a33	8‡a51	10a17	2p12	3p26	6p24	7p33
Kelheim arr	6 46	9 5	10 32	2 27	3 41	6 37	7 48
Kelheim dep	6 a3	9a46	1p46	2p56	5p54	7 p1	8‡p52
Saal ......arr	6 17	10 0	2 0	3 10	6 8	7 15	9 6

‡—Until 15th September.

Luggage Rates, see page 462.]

BAVARIAN STATE RAILWAYS.

RC Restaurant Car.] **MUNICH and SALZBURG.** [SC Sleeping Car.

STUTTGART 192 dp	...	...	...	...	...	3a15	3a15	5 a0	5 a0	6a44	...	...	9a29	9a29	1137	1258	...	2p31	...	4p55	7p53	7p53
	1,2,3	1,2,3	1,2,3	Ex3	1,2,3	Ex3	Ex3	Ex3	Ex3	Ex1	Ex2	1,2,3	Ex3	1,2,3	Ex3	1,2,3	1,2,3	1,2,3	Ex.3	Ex3	Ex3	Ex1
Munich—	a.m.	a.m.	a.m.	a.m.	a.m.	a.m.	a.m.	a.m.	a m.	a.m.	a.m.	p.m.	p.m.	p.m.	p.m.	p.m.	p.m.	p.m.	p.m.	p.m.	p.m.	n'gt
Haupt B'nhf. dep	3‡50	5‡ 0	5 48	7 0	7 5	8 5	8 15	8 45	9 40	1028	1145	12 5	1 30	2 30	4 10	5 40	6 50	8 0	9 30	1040	1140	1238
„ Ostbahnhof dep	4 12	5 13	6 16	7 13	7 19	8 19	8 28	RC	9 54	⋮	...	1240	1 43	3 1	4 22	5 53	7 25	8 22	9 42	1052	...	⋮
Zorneding	4 42	...	6 48	C	...	...	RC	...	...	⋮	RC	1 10	...	3 34	...	...	7 56	...	SC	...	...	⋮
Grafing	4 58	...	7 6	...	7 44	8 45	⋮	...	...	A	...	1 30	...	3 52	...	...	8 22	8 53	⋮	...	SC	B
Ostermünchen	5 20	...	7 30	...	...	...	⋮	...	...	⋮	...	1 51	...	4 16	...	...	8 46	...	⋮	...	...	⋮
Rosenheim arr	5 38	6 0	7 49	7 55	8 8	9 10	⋮	9 45	1040	⋮	1243	2 8	2 26	4 35	5 4	6 37	9 5	9 20	⋮	1134	1232	⋮
KUFSTEIN 200 arr	7 a0	7 a0	...	8a25	9a20	...	Via Muhldorf.	1025	1210	⋮	1p20	3p35	3p35	6 p3	6 p3	7p32	1032	1032	Via Muhldorf.	1215	...	2 a?
INNSBRUCK 235 arr	9a45	9a45	...	1011	...	...		1218	2p48	⋮	3p22	6 p8	6 p8	8p54	8 54	1013	...	...		2a12	...	3a17
INNSBRUCK dep	...	...	4a58	...	...	5a20			7a12	⋮			9a55	1p10	1 10	...	6p19	...			...	
KUFSTEIN ...dep	...	4 a3	6a42	...	6a42	8a15		...	9a52	⋮	...	p.m.	1255	3p38	3p38	5p25	8 p5	...		...	10p15	...
Rosenheim dep	...	6 10	8 24	...	8 13	9 15		...	1047	⋮	...	1250	2 31	5 20	5 10	6 50	9 25	...		...	1234	...
Endorf	...	6 42	8 55	...	...	...		...	...	⋮	...	1 22	...	5 54	...	7 13	9 59	...		...	...	...
Prien 201	...	6 59	9 11	...	8 45	9 49		...	1116	⋮	...	1 38	2 58	6 14	5 37	7 26	1017	...		...	1 3	...
Uebersee 201	...	7 19	9 32	...	9 0	10 2		...	...	⋮	...	1 58	...	6 37	...	7 41	1038	...		2&3	...	...
Bergen	...	7 34	9 48	...	9 13	1014		...	...	⋮	...	2 14	...	6 54	...	7 55	1056	...		a.m.	1 32	⋮
Traunstein	...	7 50	10 3	...	9 25	1027		...	1147	⋮	...	2 29	3 26	7 12	6 7	8 7	1114	...		5 55	...	...
Teisendorf	...	8 13	1033	...	9 42	...		...	...	⋮	...	2 59	...	7 37	...	8 27	1142	...		6 24	...	...
Freilassing	...	8 29	1049	...	9 54	10 55	1039	...	1214	⋮	...	3 16	3 51	7 54	6 34	8 40	12 0	...	11 59	6 39	2 0	...
Salzburg ¶ arr	...	8 45	1117	...	10 6	11 8	1050	...	1228	1245	...	3 30	4 5	8 9	6 50	8 55	1220	...	12 8	6 50	2 10	...
LINZ 239A arr	...	1126	...	...	2p31	...	...	...	3 p8	2p56	...	6p36	6p36	...	...	1253	4a51	...	4 a51	12 0	4a51	...
VIENNA 239A arr	...	...	...	...	5p50	...	...	...	6p32	6 p0	...	9p50	9p50	...	...	6 a0	8a10	...	8 a10	...	8a10	...

Express Fares from Munich To Salzburg 14m. 50pf., 9m. 40pf.

‡—Between Munich and Rosenheim until 14th Sept. only. ¶—Customs Examination. A—Orient Express.
B—Tyrol-Rome Express. C—Runs until 15th September.

VIENNA 239 dep	8p40	...	...	...	...	10p10	10p55	...	...	...	8a15	...	9a25	...	...	...	12 0	...	...	1 p0	...	...
LINZ 239 dep	1213	...	...	...	...	3 a12	3a53	...	...	8a40	1137	...	1 p4	..	...	...	3 p7	...	...	4p30	...	...
	Ex3	3 Cl	Ex3	1,2,3	Ex3	1,2,3	Ex 3		1,2,3	1,2,3	Ex3	1,2,3	Ex3	1,2,3	1,2,3	Ex3	Ex1	1,2,3	Ex3	Ex3	1,2,3	2&3
	a.m.			a.m	a.m.	a.m.	a.m.		a m.	p.m.	p.m.		p.m.	p.m.	p.m.	p.m.	p.m.			p.m.	p.m.	p.m
Salzburg ¶ dep	3 25	...	†—Takes up only.	4 50	5 40	7 10	9 7	...	9 28	1214	2 25	...	3 50	4 10	4 49	5 19	5 32	Until 14th Sept. only.	...	7 20	8 15	1140
Freilassing	3†33	...		5 8	⋮	7 24	9 19	...	9 43	1228	2 39	...	4 4	4 25	5 5	5 27	⋮		...	7 34	8 42	12 2
Teisendorf	3†51	a.m.		5 33	⋮	7 39	...	...	10 7	1253	...	...	...	4 46	5 30	RC	⋮		...	...	9 6	1226
Traunstein	4 20	2 10		6 11	⋮	8 5	9 59	...	10 44	1 28	3 15	...	4 43	5 15	6 20	⋮	A		...	8 9	9 41	1 4
Bergen	...	2 32		6 23	⋮	8 15	...	...	10 55	1 39	...	...	...	5 25	6 32	⋮	⋮		...	...	9 52	
Uebersee	...	2 57		6 34	Via Muhldorf.	3 25	...	...	11 6	1 59	...	...	...	5 36	6 44	Via Muhldorf.	⋮		...	...	10 3	...
Prien	4 49	3 39		6 54		8 38	10 29	...	11 26	2 11	3 41	...	5 10	5 51	7 15		⋮		...	8 34	1022	...
Endorf	...	4 10	...	7 12		8 49	...	...	11 44	2 30	...	...	...	6 4	7 37		⋮		...	...	1040	...
Rosenheim arr	5 16	4 54	...	7 39		9 5	10 57	...	12 10	2 54	4 4	...	5 34	6 20	8 6		⋮		...	8 57	11 5	...
KUFSTEIN 200 arr	7a 0	...	...	9a20		10 25	12 10	...	1 p20	...	6 p3	...	7p32	7p32	1032		⋮	...	...	1032	1215	...
INNSBRUCK 235 arr	9a45	...	...	1218		12 18	2 p48	...	3 p22	Ex2	8p54	...	1013	1013	...		⋮	...	...	...	2a12	Ex3
INNSBRUCK dep	...	1,2,3	4a58	4a58		5 a20	7 a12	1127	...	1 p0	...	1p10	1p10	...	6p19		⋮	4p50	5p19	6p19	8p21	8 21
KUFSTEIN dep	4 a3	4 a3	6a36	6a42	⋮	8 a15	9 a52	1239	...	2p35	...	3p38	3p38	5p25	8 p5	⋮	⋮	7 p8	8 p5	8 p5	1015	9p58
Rosenheim ¶ dep	5 20	5 36	7 3	7 52	⋮	9 13	11 4	⋮	12 25	3 4	4 6	4 52	5 40	6 28	9 4	⋮	⋮	8 15	8 37	9 0	11‡15	1026
Ostermünchen	...	6 1	...	8 21	⋮	...	...	B	12 53	...	...	5 18	...	...	9 30	⋮	⋮	...	...	...	...	...
Grafing	5 50	6 39	...	9 2	⋮	...	...	⋮	1 40	...	...	5 57	...	...	9 57	⋮	⋮	8 48	...	...	1142	C
Zorneding	...	7 1	...	9 25	⋮	...	...	⋮	2 1	...	...	6 19	...	...	1025	⋮	⋮	...	...	...	...	...
Munich Ostbahn'f arr	6 15	7 29	...	9 51	⋮	9 57	11 56	⋮	2 29	...	...	6 45	6 28	7 20	1053	7 45	⋮	9 13	9 24	...	12 8	1114
„ Haupt Bhf. arr	6 30	8 13	7 57	1025	8 2	10 10	12 10	2 5	3 0	4 0	5 0	7 18	6 40	7 35	1120	7 59	7 45	9 30	9 40	10 0	1224	1128
STUTTGART 192A arr	1042	1216	1216	...	1216	-	4 p39	6p41	...	...	9p 5	...	...	...	...	...	1128	...	2 a9	2 a9	...	...

ROSENHEIM and KUFSTEIN.

	1,2,3	Ex3	1,2,3	Ex3	1,2,3	1,2,3	Ex 2	1,2,3	1,2,3	1,2,3	1,2,3	Ex.3	1,2,3	Ex 1	...	...
	a.m.	a.m.	a.m.	a.m.	a.m.	a.m.	p.m.	p.m.	p.m.	p.m.	p.m.	p.m.	p.m.	a.m.	...	...
Rosenheim ...dep	6 7	7‡57	8 20	9 49	9§57	11 10	12 47	2 42	5 11	6 46	9 32	11 36	11 45	⋮	...	...
Brannenburg	6 45	...	9 3	...	10 40	11 53	...	3 21	5 48	7 19	1017	...	12 26	B	...	...
Kufstein ¶ 235 arr	7 0	8 25	9 20	1025	10 57	12 10	1 20	3 35	6 3	7 32	1032	12 15	12 42	2 0	...	...

¶—Customs Examination.

	1,2,3	Ex3	1,2,3	1,2,3	1,2,3	Ex. 1	1,2,3	Ex2	1,2,3	1,2,3	1,2,3	Ex3	Ex 3	1,2,3	...	...	...
	a.m.	a.m.	a.m.	a.m.	a.m.	p.m.	p.m.	p.m.	p.m.	p.m.	p.m.	p.m.	p.m.	p.m.	...	...	...
Kufstein ...dep	4 3	6 36	6 42	8 15	9 52	12 39	1255	2 35	2 38	5 25	7 8	8 5	9 ‡58	10§15	...	...	...
Brannenburg	4 19	...	7 1	8 31	10 8	B	1 14	...	3 57	5 42	7 25	...	...	10 32	...	...	...
Rosenheim arr	4 55	7 2	7 40	9 0	10 42	⋮	1 51	3 2	4 36	6 18	8 0	8 33	10 25	11 7	...	...	...

‡—Runs until 15th Sept §—Until 14th Sept. B—Tyrol-Rome Express.

REICHENHALL, FREILASSING, and SALZBURG.

Reichenhall ...dep	6a50	8a40	10a55	11a45	2p10	3 p35	5 p5	6 p0	7 p0	8 p0	9*p10	11 p0	...	...	...
Freilassing ...arr	7 13	9 3	11 20	12 6	2 32	3 56	5 20	6 22	7 23	8 26	9 31	11 21	...	...	...
Salzburg ...arr	7 33	9 20	11 33	12 19	2 50	4 15	5 30	6 35	7 40	8 40	9 45	11 32	...	...	...
Salzburg ...dep	7 a0	8a30	9a43	10a43	12 p5	1*p30	2p15	3p40	4p35	6p25	8 p35	11 p50	*—In July and August only.		
Freilassing	7 15	8 44	10 2	11 2	12 20	1 41	2 32	3 58	4 48	6 42	8 52	12 7			
Reichenhall ...arr	7 47	9 13	10 35	11 30	12 44	2 10	3 0	4 28	5 20	7 15	9 25	12 35			

REICHENHALL and BERCHTESGADEN.

Reichenhall ...dep	5a30	8 a0	9 a20	11a36	12p55	2*p20	3 p6	4p35	7p22	9p55
Hallthurm	6 10	8 40	9 59	12 15	1 35	3 0	3 48	5 14	8 1	10 15
Berchtesgaden arr	6 40	9 10	10 28	12 45	2 5	3 30	4 20	5 45	8 30	10 45
Berchtesgaden dep	5a35	7a20	10a28	1 p0	2 p25	3 p50	5p45	6 p35	8*p0	9p40
Hallthurm	6 10	7 54	11 3	1 33	2 58	4 25	6 19	7 10	8 34	10 17
Reichenhall 200 arr	6 41	8 25	11 35	2 3	3 28	4 57	6 50	7 45	9 4	10 50

*—In July and Aug. only.

Endorf and Obing (12 miles).—Depart from Endorf 6.47, 9 ‡ 5 a.m., 2.35, 4*30, 7.45 p.m.
Depart from Obing 5.50, 8 ‡ 2, 10.47 a.m., 1.10, 6.20 p.m.
*—Not on Sun. ‡—Sun., Tues., Thurs., and Sat. only.

Luggage Rates—see page 462.]

BAVARIAN STATE RAILWAYS.

MUNICH and SIMBACH.

	2&3	2&3	Ex3	2&3	2&3	2&3	Ex 3
Munich—	a.m.	a.m.	a.m.	no'n	p.m.	p.m.	p.m.
Hauptbhf ......dep	3 55	7 50	8 15	12 0	3 31	7 20	9 30
Sudbhf .... ,,	4 12	8 2	...	1213	3 44	7 35	...
Ostbhf........... ,,	4 27	8 35	8 28	1226	4 0	7 53	9 42
Schwaben...............	5 13	9 9	...	1 4	4 38	8 32	...
Thann Matzbach......	5 40	9 35	...	1 31	5 4	8 58	...
Dorfen	5 57	9 49	...	1 45	5 19	9 13	10 20
Ampfing	6 27	1021	...	2 16	5 47	9 45	...
Muhldorf 201	7 0	1112	9 30	2 48	6 18	1050	10 43
Neuötting...............	7 17	1130	9 43	3 6	6 35	1111	—
Simbach 239B arr	7 55	1210	1012	3 47	7 14	1155	...

	Ex 3	2&3	1,2,3	2&3	2&3	Ex3	2&3	3CL.	2&3
	a.m.	a.m.	a.m.	a.m.	p.m.	p.m.	p.m.	p.m.	a.m.
Simbach ...dep	...	5 25	8 10	9 37	1 5	...	4 44	7 32	1 52
Neuötting............	...	6 10	8 39	1022	1 49		5 37	9 47	2 36
Muhldorf	6 48	6 58	8 54	1116	2 35	6 32	6 45	1030	3 18
Ampfing	...	7 11	—	1129	2 48	...	6 59	—	3 33
Dorfen	...	7 53	...	1210	3 29	6 58	7 41	...	4 17
Thann Matzbach..	...	8 11	...	1227	3 44	...	8 0	...	4 37
Schwaben............	...	8 49	...	1 5	4 24	...	8 39	...	5 21
Munich—Ost. ...	...	9 28	...	1 38	4 59	7 45	9 21	...	6 4
,, Sudbhf	...	9 39	...	1 52	5 13	...	9 35	...	6 26
,, Hauptbhf ...	8 2	9 56	...	2 10	5 27	7 59	9 49	...	6 40

SALZBURG and MUHLDORF.

[‡—6.41 a.m. on Tuesday.

Salzburg..........dep	4 a0	5a40	7 a0	8a58	12p24	3p30	5p19	8p25
Freilassing	4 12	...	7 16	9 16	12 34	3 42	5 27	8 44
Wiesmuhl	5 17	...	8 15	10 9	1 24	4 56	...	9 34
Garching	6 1	...	—	1040	1 58	5 3	...	10 8
Muhldorf 201......arr	6 33	6 46	...	11 4	2 22	6 8	6 27	1035

Mühldorf ....dep	7a11	9a33	9a42	12p21	2p35	6p30	10p46
Garching	7 42	...	1015	12 52	3 3	7 5	...
Wiesmuhl	8 15	...	1048	1 25	3 36	7 39	...
Freilassing ....7a‡23	9 21	1042	1134	2 26	4 25	8 39	11 59
Salzburg ....arr 7 33	9 30	1050	1144	2 40	4 35	9 6	12 8

DORFEN and VELDEN.

Dorfen ....dep	6 a17	9a48	1‡p48	9p17
Velden-a-d-Vils ...arr	7 27	1056	2 50	1027

Velden ......dep	4a48	6 a23	10a56	5p40
Dorfen 201...arr	5 50	7 40	11 58	6 50

‡—12.35 p.m. on Sunday.

WIESMÜHL and TITTMONING.

Wiesmühl......dep	5a20	8a18	10a50	1p30	5p 0	7p40	9p28
Tittmoning......arr	5 35	8 33	11 5	1 45	5 15	7 55	9 53

Tittmoning...... dep	4 a47	7a50	9a42	12p55	3p12	7p12	9 p8	...	...
Wiesmühl.........arr	5 5	8 8	10 0	1 13	3 30	7 30	9 26	...	...

ULM and KEMPTEN.

	a.m.	a.m.	a.m.	p.m.	p.m.	p.m.	p.m.	p.m.
Ulm ....dep	5 30	7 30	1028	1214	4 28	4 53	...	7 31
Neu Ulm	5 37	7 35	10 38	1220	4 33	5 5	6 28	7 37
Senden	5 57	7 46	11 0	1238	4 44	5 23	6 43	7 54
Kellmunz..............	6 45	8 13	11 46	1 19	5 13	6 4	—	8 39
Memmingen	8 0	8 35	12 46	1 50	5 38	6 45	...	9 26
Gronenbach	8 26	...	1 16	2 26	..	7 12	...	9 56
Kempten (199) arr	9 1	9 18	1 57	3 1	6 30	7 48	...	10 35

	a.m.	a.m.	a.m.	p.m.	p.m.	p.m.		p.m.
Kempten ....dep	5 1	7 10	9 50	1 20	1 30	4 46	...	8 0
Gronenbach..............	5 33	7 44	1022	...	2 3	5 18	...	8 41
Memmingen	5 55	8 16	1045	2 1	2 25	5 39	...	9 20
Kellmunz..................	6 23	8 47	1111	2 16	2 50	6 5	p.m.	9 51
Senden	7 6	9 26	1148	2 39	3 27	6 46	8 21	10 36
Neu Ulm	7 24	9 41	12 4	2 51	3 47	7 3	8 49	10 58
Ulm (192A) ....arr	7 55	9 53	1212	2 56	3 53	7 15	...	11 5

KELLMUNZ and BABENHAUSEN.

Kellmunz ...dep	8a49	3p 0	6 p15	9p58
Babenhausen arr	9 24	3 35	6 50	1030

Babenhausen......dep	5a43	12p40	4 p33	7p53	...	...	...
Kellmunz 201......arr	6 18	1 15	5 8	8 28	...	...	...

LANDSBERG, KAUFERING, and AUGSBURG.

†—Weekdays only.

Landsberg.........dep	5a44	7a25	9a41	10a48	12†18	1p25	3p19	4 p7	6 p0	6p48	8p28	9 p38	11 p2	...	...
Kaufering	6 30	7 37	1012	11 0	12 30	1 37	3 30	4 40	6 12	7 0	8 40	10 10	11 14	...	...
Bobingen	7 20	...	11 4	...	...	...	...	5 29	...	...	...	11 1	...	...	...
Augsburg ....arr	7 40	...	1125	...	...	...	...	5 50	...	...	...	11 22	...	...	...

Augsburg.........dep	4a45	...	8 a40	...	...	...	2p33	p.m.	p.m.	p.m.	p m	8 p45	...	...	...
Bobingen	5 10	...	9 4	a.m.	p.m.	p.m.	2 54	...	...	...	...	9 8	a.m.	...	...
Kaufering	6 30	7a53	10 20	1115	12†55	1 50	3 48	4 50	6 25	7 44	8 55	10 10	12 13	...	...
Landsberg ....arr	6 41	8 5	10 31	1127	1 7	2 2	3 59	5 1	6 37	7 56	9 7	10 21	12 25	...	...

UEBERSEE and MARQUARTSTEIN.

Uebersee.........dep	7a20	9a35	11a10	2 p10	5p37	7p50	...
Marquartstein arr	7 49	10 2	11 40	2 40	6 4	8 20	...

Marquartstein dep	6 a0	7a54	10a30	1p12	4p45	6p10	...	...
Uebersee 200 ...arr	6 30	8 21	10 57	1 42	5 15	6 40	...	...

TRAUNSTEIN and GARCHING.

Traunstein.........dep	4 a0	8 a38	1210	4p 3	8 p58	...
Empfing	4 8	8 44	1216	4 9	9 4	...
Trostberg......................	5 20	9 39	1 10	5 0	9 53	...
Garching 201 ......arr	5 51	10 10	1 41	5 30	...	...

Garching ....dep	...	7 a42	10a50	3p 5	...	7p10	...
Trostberg	6 a0	8 20	11 55	3 34	3 p39	7 49	...
Empfing	6 56	9 17	12 52	...	4 47	8 44	...
Traunstein (200)arr	7 2	9 23	12 58	...	4 55	8 50	...

GRAFING and GLONN.

Grafing......dep	7 a15	9a12	2 p0	6p10	8 p57
Glonn.........arr	7 40	9 36	2 25	6 36	9 22

Glonn ....dep	5 a10	8a10	12p42	5 p5	7p15	...
Grafing **200** ...arr	5 39	8 36	1 10	5 33	7 43	...

GRAFING and WASSERBURG-A-INN.

Grafing..............dep	7 a52	9 a10	1 p38	6 p0	8 p55	...
Ebersberg ....arr	8 12	9 29	1 59	6 20	9 16	...
Wasserburg ......arr	9 7	...	2 50	7 14	10 12	...

Wasserburg ....dep	4a25	7 a17	12 p5	...	6p28	...	...
Ebersberg	5 23	8 18	1 1	4 p55	7 28	...	...
Grafing 200 ....arr	5 43	8 38	1 17	5 22	7 45	...	...

NEUMARKT and PFARRKIRCHEN.

[†—Sunday at 5.15 a.m.

E.M.							
	Neumarkt-a-R....dep	2 a55	7 a55	11a53	3 p28	7p35	10p25
8¾	Dietfurt-a-Rott	3 49	8 22	12 21	3 56	8 4	10 53
21½	**Pfarrkirchen 204** arr	5 20	9 3	1 4	4 38	8 46	11 32

Pfarrkirchen ......dep	3 †28	6 a1	10a25	1 p56	5 p28	8 p46
Dietfurt-a-Rott	5 12	6 42	11 10	2 39	6 15	9 28
Neumarkt-a-R 203B ar	6 10	7 10	11 38	3 8	6 45	9 56

FEUCHT and ALTDORF.

Feucht ....dep	5a31	7a30	1 p0	5p10	7p25	10p25
Altdorf....arr	6 8	8 10	1 41	5 50	8 4	11 4

Altdorf ...dep	4a23	6a30	10a48	2p46	6p21	9p4
Feucht.....arr	5 0	7 7	11 25	3 25	7 1	10 20

FEUCHT and WENDELSTEIN.

Feucht.........dep	5a37	7a35	1p0	5p10	7p22	10p26
Wendelstein arr	5 52	7 54	119	5 28	7 41	10 45

Wendelstein dep	4a45	6a50	11a9	3 p6	6p37	9p55
Feucht (195A) arr	5 3	7 5	1127	3 24	6 55	10 13

SINZING and ALLING.

Sinzing......dep	6a20	2 p19	6 p50	...	...
Alling ....arr	6 33	2 32	7 2	...	...

Alling ......dep	6a54	3*p20	5p32	8p58
Sinzing ...arr	7 6	3 37	5 45	9 11

*—1.50 p.m. on Sunday.

SIEGELSDORF and MARKT ERLBACH.

[‡—Sat. at 7.8 p.m.

Siegelsdorf.........dep	6 a42	10a20	2 p17	5‡p25	9 p53	...
Langenzenn	7 3	10 41	2 41	5 47	10 17	...
Wilhermsdorf	7 28	11 8	3 10	6 12	10 41	...
Markt Erlbach ... arr	7 48	11 30	3 32	6 35	11 3	...

Markt Erlbach dep	4 a30	8 a43	11a52	3p47	8p12	...	...	...
Wilhermsdorf	4 58	9 12	12 16	4 18	8 40	...	...	...
Langenzenn.............	5 26	9 44	12 37	4 43	9 7	...	...	...
Siegelsdorf 195A arr	5 45	10 0	12 54	5 0	9 25	...	...	...

ASCHAU and PRIEN.

Aschau ......dep	6 a0	8a 0	9a50	1p30	4p35	6 p38
Prien 200...arr	6 30	8 30	1016	2 0	5 5	7 5

Prien.........dep	7 a0	9a15	11a30	3p 0	5p55	7p35	...
Aschau.......arr	7 30	9 41	12 0	3 30	6 24	8 5	...

BAVARIAN STATE RAILWAYS. [Luggage Rates—see page 462.

MUNICH, REGENSBURG, SCHWANDORF, and HOF.

THROUGH CARRIAGES } **Munich to Berlin, in 9.25 a.m., 12.35 p.m., 7.20 p.m.,** & 11.20 p.m. from Munich.

RC—Restaurant Car. SC—Sleeping Car.

MILAN.....280 dep	...	...	...	...	6p20	6p20	...	...	6p20	...	1125	...	1230	...	1230	...	...	...
VERONA...282 dep	...	...	...	...	9p18	9p18	...	...	9p18	...	4a42	...	4a33	...	4a33	...	...	...
ALA......235A dep	...	...	...	...	1057	1057	...	...	1057	...	6 a3	...	6a30	...	6a30	...	...	...
KUFSTEIN 200 dep	...	4 a3	4 a3	6 36	6a36	6a36	...	8a15	9a52	...	1239	...	2p35	...	3p38	...	8 p5	8 p5
	2&3	2&3	2&3	Ex3	Ex3	Ex3	2&3	2&3	Ex3	2&3	Ex1	2&3	2&3	1,2,3	Ex3	2&3	Ex3	2&3
Munich	a.m.	a.m.	a.m.	a.m.	a.m.	a.m.	a.m.	a.m.	p.m.	p.m.	p.m.	p.m.	p.m.	p.m.	p.m.	p.m.	p.m.	p.m.
Hauptbhf.......dep	4 2	7 0	7 15	8 15	8 25	9 25	9 37	1120	1235	1 30	2 10	2 24	4 50	6 0	7 20	8 20	1120	1135
Feldmoching	4 26	...	7 40	Runs in July and August only.	...	...	10 3	1143		1 53	...	...	5 13	...	...	8 45	...	1159
Lohhof	4 40	...	7 55		RC	RC	1018	1158	RC	2 8	...	...	5 28	...	RC	9 0	SC	1213
Freising 203B.........	5 13	7 36	8 24		...	...	1050	1228	...	2 46	...	3 9	6 0	6 36	...	9 32	...	1242
Moosburg ....2&3	5 40	7 51	9 15		...	...	1117	1256	...	3 13	...	3 29	6 28	6 53	SC	9 58	...	1 1
Landshut { arr a.m. 6 8	6 8	8 7	9 40		9 23	1026	1145	1 24	1 33	3 40	B	3 50	6 56	7 11	8 22	1025	1222	1 23
{ dep 5 0	6 32	8 9	9 54		9 24	1028	12 3	1 45	1 38	3 53	...		8 40	7 19	8 32	1053	1224	
Neufahrn { arr 5 44	7 20	...	1037		...	...	1247	2 29	...	4 34	...		9 25	7 48	...	1140	...	...
{ dep 5 46	7 25	...	1056		...	...	1251	2 33	...	4 38	...	...	9 30	7 49	...	1147	...	...
Eggmuhl.........6 11	7 49	8 49	1120		...	...	1 16	2 58	...	5 0	...	...	9 54	8 5	...	1211	...	...
Obertraubling 6 39	8 18	...	1147		...	...	1 44	3 26	...	5 25	...	...	1022	8 23	...	1238	...	...
Regensburg arr 6 53	8 33	9 11	12 2	10 1	1015	1122	1 59	3 40	2 37	5 37	3 54	...	1036	8 34	9 32	1253	1 24	a.m.
" 195A dep	9 18		1 4	10 6	1020	1127		4 6	2 44	6 35	4 0	...		9 53	9 44	1 38	1 29	5 50
Walhallastrasse ...	9 26		1 12		...	...	...	4 13	...	6 45	...	...	...	10 1	...	1 46	...	5 58
Regenstauf	9 44	...	1 34		...	...	...	4 31	...	7 6	...	...	...	1019	...	2 4	...	6 19
Haidhof	1010	...	2 2		...	...	...	4 53	...	7 31	...	...	...	1045	...	2 29	...	6 45
Schwandorf 204 arr	1034	...	2 27		...	12 5	...	5 17	3 26	7 53	...	...	p.m.	11 9	1027	2 49	...	7 9
" ...dep	1110	...	2 50		...	12 8	...	5 27	3 28	8 3	...	...	1114		1029	2 58	...	7 22
Irrenlohe ... { arr	1119	...	2 57		...	...	...	5 36	...	8 11	...	...	1123	...	...	...	...	7 30
{ dep	1123	...	2 58		...	...	...	5 38	...	8 12	...	...	1125	...	...	...	...	7 34
Nabburg	1145	...	3 13		...	...	...	5 57	...	8 33	B	...	1154	...	...	3 19	...	7 50
Wernberg	12 5	...	3 30		...	...	...	6 18	...	8 51	...	...	1226	...	...	3 36	...	8 8
Weiden ....arr	1239	...	3 57		1130	1248	...	6 52	4 11	9 19	...	...	1 18	...	1111	4 2	...	8 36
BAYREUTH 203 arr	3p34	...	6p50		3p34	3p34	...	9p 0	6p50	..	...	...	...	...	1 a7	6a30	...	1052
Weiden............dep	1 2	...	4 24		1131	1250	...	7 4	4 13	9 37	...	...	1 40	...	1112	4 11	...	8 50
Neustadt-a-W.	1 15	...	4 35		...	...	...	7 16	...	9 48	...	...	1 56	...	...	4 24	...	9 2
Reuth	1 49	...	5 7		...	...	...	7 52	...	1021	...	...	2 47	...	...	4 58	...	9 34
Wiesau ....arr	2 7	...	5 24		...	1 26	...	8 12	...	1038	...	...	3 15	...	...	5 17	...	9 51
EGER 203 ......arr	3p39	...	6p10	1213	...	2p15	...	9 p9	...	...	...	...	...	3 cl	...	6a51	...	1039
Wiesau............dep	2 22	...	5 59	...	...	1 29	...	8 27	...	1046	...	ng't	3 50	a.m.	...	5 26	...	10 0
Mkt. Redwitz	2 53	...	6 54	...	1224	1 54	...	9 10	5 19	1116	...	1215	5 2	9 27	1211	6 14	...	1134
Holenbrunn	3 11	...	7 10	...	...	2 7	...	9 28	...		...	1230	5 15	9 41	...	6 28	...	1149
Kirchenlamitz	3 41	...	7 41	...	...	...	...	10 2	...	...	...	1 2		1012	...	6 59	...	1221
Oberkotzau	4 0	...	8 5	...	...	...	...	1021	...	...	...	1 19	...	1029	...	7 21	...	1240
Hof ....arr	4 10	...	8 18	...	1 5	2 48	...	1032	6 6	...	6 55	1 29	...	1039	1256	7 31	4 28	1250
DRESDEN 186 arr	1047	...	...	...	5 p0	7p28	...	...	1047	...	...	...	...	...	5a45	1 p3	8a35	5 p0
LEIPSIC ...187 arr	8 p3	...	...	...	4 p2	6 p7	...	...	9p17	...	9p52	...	...	...	4 a6	1150	7a16	4 p2
BERLIN ...187 arr	...	...	...	...	8p19	8p35	...	...	1157	...	12a7	...	...	...	6a25	2p52	9a53	8p19

B—Rome-Tyrol-Berlin Express.

Extra.—Weiden to Neustadt 6.0, 9.0 a.m., 1.13, 4.36, and 9.47 p.m. Landshut to Neufahrn 5.12 p.m.

KIRCHENLAMITZ and WEISSENSTADT.

Kirchenlamitz...dep	7 a0	12p53	3p45	7p48	...	Weissenstadt......dep	5a15	11a20	2p15	5p40	...	...
Weissenstadt......arr	7 51	1 44	4 36	8 39	...	Kirchenlamitz ...arr	6 4	12 9	3 0	6 29	...	...

LUDWIGSTADT and LEHESTEN.

Ludwigstadt dep	9 a10	4 p5	8 p15	...	Lehesten ...dep	7 a30	12 0	6 p32
Lehesten ......arr	9 45	4 40	8 50	...	Ludwigstadt arr	8 5	12 35	7 7

WEIDEN and NEUKIRCHEN.

E.M.		a.m.	p.m.	p.m.	p.m.			a.m.	a.m.	p.m.	p.m.	
—	**Weiden** ....dep	6 44	1 17	4 25	7 40	...	**Neukirchen** ...dep	6 30	10 0	4 34	10 5	...
9¼	Rothenbach	7 15	1 48	4 57	8 11	...	Schönlind	6 58	10 28	5 1	10 33	...
17¼	Langenbruck	7 44	2 17	5 29	8 41	...	Langenbruck	7 21	10 51	5 25	10 56	...
23¼	Schönlind...............	8 5	2 38	5 52	9 4	...	Rothenbach-i-O.	7 48	11 18	5 53	11 23	...
32¼	**Neukirchen** ...arr	8 40	3 12	6 30	9 39	...	**Weiden** 203 ......arr	8 18	11 47	6 21	11 52	...

LANDSHUT and LANDAU-a-I.

	a m	a m	a.m.	p.m.	p m	p m	p.m.		a.m.	a.m.	a.m.	p.m.	p m	p.m.	
Landshut......dep	6 38	8 13	9 47	1 40	3 57	7 36	8 47	**Landau-a-I.** dep	6 10	9 35	1143	2 59	6 53	7 51	...
Dingolfing	8 14	8 47	1038	2 10	4 49	8 28	9 17	Dingolfing	6 42	9 51	1213	3 28	7 23	8 13	...
Landau-a-I. arr	9 1	9 6	11 6	2 25	5 18	8 55	9 33	**Landshut** ......arr	7 32	1017	1 4	4 16	8 13	8 46	...

NURNBERG, BAYREUTH, and EGER.

COLOGNE 122, 128 dep	...	...	...	8 p2	1157		...	...	...	1a58		...	...	10a3	10a3	1210
	3Cl.	2&3	2&3	2&3	Ex1	Ex3	Ex3	Ex1	2&3	Ex3		2&3	2 & 3	2&3	Ex3	2&3
Nürnberg—				a.m.	a.m.	a.m.	a.m.	a.m.	a.m.	p.m.		p.m.	p.m.	p.m.	p.m.	p.m.
Hauptbahnhof ...dep	...	...	...	7 0	8 25	9 15	9 20	1029	1130	1 5	...	2 10	5 40	7 22	8 47	1150
Lauf	...	...	...	7 32	:	9 34	9 40	:	12 5	1 24	...	2 42	6 17	8 1	9 9	1225
Schnaittach	...	...	...	7 39	:	...	...	:	1212	..	...	2 51	6 22	8 8	...	1231
Hersbruck..................	a.m.	...	...	7 54	:	9 45	9 53	:	1228	1 36	...	3 7	6 37	8 27	9 21	1245
Ranna.........................	5†20	...	...	8 39	:	...	..	:	1 17	...	...	3 54	7 21	9 19	...	
Schnabelwaid ......arr	6 35	...	a.m.	9 13	:	1033	1045	:	1 57	2 28	...	4 31	7 55	9 59	1014	...
Schnabelwaid ...dep	...	...	6 50	9 18	:	1046	1046	:	...	2 46	...	4 50	8 0	1026	1016	...
Neuenreuth	...	...	7 22	9 38	O	...	..	P	...	3 7	...	5 10	8 15	1047	...	...
Bayreuth ....arr	...	...	7 46	9 52	:	11 6	11 6	:	...	3 21	...	5 24	8 27	11 1	1042	...
Schnabelwaid ......dep	6 55	...	...	9 25	:	1035	...	:	2 7	2 30	2&3	4 44	...	1020	...	...
Kirchenlaibach ...arr	7 55	a.m.	...	9 54	:	...	...	:	2 39	2 48	p.m.	5 14	...	1053	...	
...dep		6 1	...	1015	:	...	...	:		2 50	3 2	5 48	...	1058	...	
Neusorg	...	6 39	...	1053	:	...	...	:	...	...	3 46	6 27	...	1143	...	
Markt Redwitz	...	7 14	...	1111	:	1122	...	:	...	3 21	4 23	7 40	...	1213	...	
Schirnding	...	7 37	...		:	1151	...	:	...	...	4 49	8 3	...	1236	...	
Eger ....arr	...	7 57	...	...	11 9	12 5	...	1259	...	3 48	5 9	8 24	...	1257	...	
CARLSBAD 251......arr	...	9a30	...	...	1221	1p29	...	2 p1	...	5p31	...	1143	...	...	...	...

†—Not on Sunday.

O—Ostend-Carlsbad Express, runs until 16th September.

P—Paris-Carlsbad Express, runs until 28th September.

HAIDHOF and BURGLENGENFELD.

Haidhof....dep	6a50	8a20	10a20	2 p5	6*p10	7p35
Burglengenf'd	7 14	8 48	10 45	2 30	6 39	8 3
Burglengenf'd	5a13	7a38	9a31	10a55	4p12	6*51
Haidhof 202 ar	5 40	8 5	10 0	11 22	4 40	7 18

*—Not on Sunday.

Luggage Rates—see page 462.] **BAVARIAN STATE RAILWAYS.**

HOF, REGENSBURG, and MUNICH.

BERLIN...187 dep	6p30	1050	...	...	...	...	12a30	...	...	7a30	...	10a50	...	3 p5	1245	...
DRESDEN 186 dep	1045	1055	...	...	...	...	5 a40	...	7a20	8a30	...	12p54	...	...	...	...
LEIPSIC 187..dep	9 45	1a10	...	...	...	4a55	7 a5	...	8a36	9a40	...	1p50	...	5p23	5 p0	...
	Ex3	Ex3	2 &3	3 Cl.	2&3	2&3	Ex.3	Ex3	2&3	Ex3	2 & 3	Ex 3	2&3	Ex1	2&3	3 Cl
	a.m.	a.m.		a.m.	a.m.	a.m.	a.m.		p.m.	p.m.	p.m.	p.m.	p.m.	p.m.	p.m.	a.m.
Hof ...dep	2 50	4 7	...	7 40	5 30	9 58	10 30	...	12 5	1259	2 21	4 54	6 10	8 6	10 3	1 0
Oberkotzau	...	...	...	7 52	5 43	10 9	RC	...	1216	...	2 36	...	6 23	...	1020	1 16
Kirchenlamitz	...	...	...	8 22	6 15	1033	...	...	1247	...	3 6	...	6 51	...	1051	2 7
Holenbrunn	...	...	...	8 55	6 51	11 2	11 8	...	1 23	...	3 39	...	7 22	...	1126	3 1
Mkt. Redwitz	...	4 56	...	9 5	7 15	1129	11 20	...	2 0	1 50	4 15	5 39	7 43	...	1212	3 18
Wiesau ...arr	...	...	...	—	7 46	12 0	11 38	...	2 30	2 10	4 49	...	8 14	...	1244	—
EGER 203 ...dep	...	...	...	a.m.	6a58	11a0	11 a0	1p42	1p30	...	4p13	...	7 p3	...	...	...
Wiesau ...dep	...	...	...	6 0	7 55	12 5	11 46	2 24	2 42	2 17	5 18	RC	8 29	...	1249	...
Reuth	...	...	...	6 28	8 8	1218	...	...	2 55	...	5 34	...	8 43	...	1 3	...
Neustadt a. W.N.	...	...	...	7 18	8 37	1246	...	...	3 25	...	6 5		9 13	B	1 31	...
Weiden ...arr	4 17	5 44	...	7 36	8 46	1255	12 17	Runs in July and August only.	3 35	...	6 15	6 27	9 22	...	1 40	...
BAYREUTH 203 dp	...	3a50	a.m.	—	5a14	9a27	9 a27		1p56	RC	4 p30	4 p30	7p35	...	—	a.m.
Weiden ...dep	4 18	5 46	6 20	...	9 8	1 10	12 19		4 10	...	6 45	6 29	9 42	...	...	2 6
Wernberg	...	...	6 50	...	9 40	1 41	...		4 37	...	7 17	...	1012	...	...	2 52
Nabburg	...	...	7 7	...	9 59	1 58	12 45		4 55	...	7 35	...	1030	...	...	3 20
Irrenlohe... arr	...	...	7 24	...	1017	2 15	...		5 12	...	7 52	...	1047	...	...	3 47
Irrenlohe... dep	...	...	7 25	...	1020	2 16	...		5 14	...	7 54	...	1048	...	...	3 49
Schwandorf arr	...	6 24	7 34	...	1029	2 24	1 0		5 22	...	8 2	7 7	1056	...	a.m.	4 0
Schwandorf dep	...	6 26	7 44	...	11 0	2 40	1 2		5 37	...	9 33	7 17	1115	...	4 13	—
Haidhof	...	...	8 12	...	1128	3 9	...	...	6 10	...	10 20	...	1147	...	4 39	—
Regenstauf	...	...	8 30	...	1148	3 28	...	...	6 31	...	10 40	...	12 8	...	4 56	...
Walhallastrasse	...	...	8 47	2 & 3	12 8	3 44	...	...	6 50	...	10 57	...	1225	...	5 14	...
Regensburg arr	5 32	7 5	8 55	a.m.	1216	3 51	1 40	4 13	6 58	4 5	11 6	7 56	1234	1038	5 22	a.m.
Regensburg dep	5 38	7 20	9 5	8 15	1231	4 24	1 45	4 18	8 17	4 10	—	8 1	—	1043	6 8	4 0
Obertraubling	...	...	...	8 28	1245	4 39	...		8 32	...	...	...	...	...	6 23	4 15
Eggmuhl	...	RC	...	9 0	1 18	5 12	...	RC	9 8	...	...	...	...	...	6 55	4 48
Neufahrn... arr	...	...	9 44	9 23	1 42	5 37	...	...	9 32	...	p.m.	...	...	...	7 18	5 12
Neufahrn... dep	...	...	9 45	9 25	1 47	5 43	...	...	9 38	...	10 43	...	...	...	7 24	5 16
Landshut... arr	6 35	8 14	1015	10 6	2 31	6 25	2 44	5 16	1022	5 8	11 25	8 54	a.m.	...	8 7	5 59
Landshut... dep	6 38	8 17	1024	10 34	3 0	6 40	2 47	5 19	1037	5 10	—	8 57	4 50	B	8 28	6 48
Moosburg	...	...	...	11 5	3 32	7 12	...	...	11 9	...	...	...	5 22	...	9 0	7 17
Freising	7 11	...	11 0	11 36	4 5	7 45	3 20	...	1142	...	...	9 30	5 56	...	9 31	7 48
Lohhof	...	...	...	12 9	4 39	8 20	...	...	1225	...	...	...	6 37	...	10 4	8 20
Feldmoching	...	...	...	12 27	4 57	8 39	...		1244	...	...	...	6 55	...	1022	8 38
Munich ...arr	7 50	9 23	1139	12 54	5 26	9 5	3 58	6 22	1 10	6 14	...	10 10	7 22	1233	1047	9 5
KUFSTEIN 200 ar	1025	1210	1p20	3 p35	7p32	1215	7p32	1032	...	1032	...	12a15	...	2 a0	1p20	1210
ALA ...235 arr	6p12	9p20	9p21	...	7a57	8 a8	7a57	8 a8	...	8 a8	...	8 a8	...	8a29	...	...
VERONA 282 arr	...	1055	1055	...	...	10a0	10 a0	10a0	...	10a0	...	10 a0	...	9a41	...	...
MILAN ...280 arr	...	6a10	6a10	...	...	1225	12 25	...	...	1225	...	12 25	...	...	...	...

B—Berlin-Tyrol-Rome Express. RC—**Restaurant Car in this Train.**

Extra.						
Landshut ...dep	1p10	1p21	4p30	8 p26	...	...
Munich ...arr	2 42	3 40	6 59	10 56	...	...

Extra. {Holenbrunn to Markt Redwitz 4.31 a.m. Neustadt to Weiden 5.4, 7.6, 11.34 a.m., 3.12, 7.17 p.m. | Regensburg to Landshut 1.53 p.m.

WIESAU and EGER.

Wiesau ...dep	5a24	8 a0	9a59	A ⁝	1 p35	2p37	5p30	8 p25	...	...	...	...
Waldsassen	6 20	8 51	1025	⁝	2 1	3 15	5 55	8 52	...	...	...	...
Eger ...arr	6 51	*	1039	12 13	2 15	3 39	6 10	9 9	...	...	...	...

E.M. Dist.					A			
	Eger ...dep	6a58	11 a0	1‡p30	1 p42	4p13	7 p3	...
7½	Waldsassen	7 21	11 17	1 47	1 59	4 33	7 27	...
16¾	Wiesau (203)...arr	7 48	11 38	2 9	2 20	5 1	7 55	...

*—Week-days only. A—In July and August only. ‡—From 1st Sept.

EGER and NURNBERG.

CARLSBAD (250)...dep		...	1a39	...	6 a1	...	9 a8	...	1219	...	2 36	...	4 p52	5p50	8p42
		Ex3	2&3	2 & 3	2&3	2 & 3	2&3	Ex3	Ex3	2&3	Ex1	1,2,3	Ex 1	1,2,3	2&3
		a.m.	a.m.		a.m.	...	p.m.		p.m.	p.m.	p.m.	p.m.	p.m.	p.m.	p.m.
Eger ...dep		...	3 54	...	8 35	...	1226	...	1 55	...	3 55	...	6 7	6 26	1040
Schirnding		...	4 14	...	8 51	...	1246	...	...	...	⋮	...	⋮	6 47	1058
Markt Redwitz		...	5 3	...	9 31	...	1 45	...	2 30	...	⋮	5 42	⋮	7 40	1150
Neusorg	2&3	...	5 24	...	9 52	...	2 6	...	...	...	⋮	5 56	⋮	8 1	1211
Kirchenlaibach arr	a.m.	...	5 51	...	1016	...	2 33	...	2 58	...	⋮	6 15	⋮	8 27	1233
" (203) dep	3 50	...	5 57	...	1021	...	2 38	...	3 0	...	⋮	6 17	⋮	8 35	—
Schnabelwaid arr	4 19	—	6 27	a.m.	1051	p.m.	3 13	p.m.	3 20	...	⋮	6 37	⋮	9 10	...
Bayreuth ...dep	...	5 57	5 34	7 49	9 52	12 5	...	2 33	2 2	...	⋮	5 52	⋮	7 45	...
Neuenreuth	...	...	5 52	8 18	1011	12 38	...	..	2 19	...	⋮	6 10	⋮	8 15	...
Schnabelwaid arr	...	6 28	6 17	8 55	1033	1 22	...	3 8	2 42	...	⋮	6 32	⋮	8 55	...
Schnabelwaid dep	4 20	6 31	6 42	...	11 5	...	...	3 9	3 22	3 31	P	6 43	O	9 20	...
Ranna	4 45	...	7 13	...	1132	...	...	...	...	3 59	⋮	7 7	⋮	9 49	...
Hersbruck	5 26	7 11	8 0	...	1220	...	...	3 46	4 6	4 46	⋮	7 44	⋮	1036	...
Schnaittach	5 48	...	8 15	...	1235	...	...	...	..	5 0	⋮	...	⋮	1052	...
Lauf	5 55	...	8 22	...	1243	...	...	...	4 17	5 7	⋮	7 55	⋮	11 0	...
Nürnberg ...arr	6 32	7 35	8 56	...	1 15	...	...	4 10	4 34	5 38	6 6	8 12	8 23	1130	..
COLOGNE (123B, 129)		6 p8	6 p8			...	...	...	-	5a21	..	5a42	4 a35	...	...

P—Carlsbad-Paris Express, runs until 29th September.

O—Carlsbad-Ostend Express, runs until 16th September.

†—Not on Sunday.

NEUENMARKT and WEIDEN.

	2&3	Ex3	2&3	2 & 3	2&3	2&3	Ex3	2&3	Ex3	2 & 3	2&3	2&3	2&3
	a.m.	a.m.	a.m.	a.m.	a.m.	p.m.	p.m.	p.m.	p.m.	p.m.	p.m.	p.m.	n'gt
Neuenmarkt...dep 2&3	...	5 30	6 22	7 50	9 40	1235	1 26	3 5	5 15	6 45	...	10 5	1255
Bayreuth ...arr a.m.	...	5 55	7 38	8 31	1021	1 16	1 46	3 46	5 38	7 26	...	1046	1 34
" ...dep 3 50	5 14	—	—	9 27	—	1 56	—	4 30	—	7 35	1014	—	—
Seybothenreuth ...4 19	5 43	...	...	9 57	...	2 24	...	5 0	...	8 5	1043	...	...
Kirchenlaibach ...4 31	5 55	...	...	10 9	...	2 36	...	5 12	...	8 17	[illegible]	...	...
NURNBERG (203) arr	7a35	...	...	1 p15	...	4p34	...	8p12	...	11p30	—	...	...
Kirchenlaibach ...4 34	6 23	...	...	10 22	p.m.	3 2	...	5 19	...	8 30	...	...	...
Pressath ...5 8	6 59	...	...	10 57	1†55	3 34	...	5 54	...	9 3	...	...	...
Weiden ...arr 5 40	7 31	...	...	11 28	3 4	4 4	...	6 25	...	9 33	...	...	...

	2&3	2&3	Ex3	2 & 3	Ex3	2&3	Ex3	2&3	2&3	2 & 3	Ex3	2&3	2&3
	a.m.	a.m.		a.m.				p.m.	p.m.	p.m.			p.m.
Weiden ...dep	4 33	6 0	...	8 55	...	...	...	1 15	4 31	7 5	...	...	1120
Pressath	5 10	6 59	...	9 33	...	...	...	1 53	5 8	7 43	...	...	1157
Kirchenlaibach...arr	5 47	—	...	10 11	...	...	...	2 31	5 45	8 21	...	...	1235
NURNBERG (202) dep	...	...	...	7 a0	...	...	...	1 p5	2p10	...	...	...	8p47
Kirchenlaibach...dep	6 0	...	...	10 23	...	...	...	3 4	6 20	8 32	...	...	1240
Seybothenreuth ...2&3	6 9	...	...	10 32	...	...	...	3 13	6 29	8 41	...	...	1248
Bayreuth ...arr a.m.	6 30	a.m.	a.m.	10 52	p.m.	p.m.	p.m.	3 34	6 50	9 0	p.m.	p.m.	1 7
" (202) dep 4 30	6 40	8 33	11 8	11 25	1242	1 57	4 22	5 40	—	9 8	1047	11 7	—
Neuenmarkt ...arr 5 13	7 23	9 22	1135	12 8	1 9	2 40	4 48	6 23	...	9 48	1113	1228	...

Pressath to Kirchenthumbach, 7.15 a.m., 3.40, 9.5 p.m. Kirchenthumbach to Pressath, 3.45 a.m., 12.24 6 8 p.m.

MUNICH and DEISENHOFEN.

‡—On Sat., Sun. and Wed. only.

Station																		
Munich Ost..........dep	5a15	6a20	7a19	8a10	11a20	12p32	2 p0	3p15	4p28	5p16	6 p28	7 p26	8p20	9 p50	11‡p20	...	...	...
Deisenhofen..........arr	5 43	6 48	7 47	8 38	11 47	12 58	2 28	3 43	4 55	5 44	6 56	7 54	8 48	10 16	11 44	...	...	...

Station																		
Deisenhofen..........dep	5a53	7a10	8a 2	9 a0	10a35	11a55	1p12	2p35	4p12	5 p0	6p10	7p20	8 p12	9p 0	10p25	11‡p50	...	...
Munich Ost..........arr	6 18	7 37	8 29	9 26	11 1	12 19	1 38	3 1	4 38	5 36	6 36	7 47	8 39	9 26	10 52	12 11	...	...

HOLZKIRCHEN and ROSENHEIM.

Station									
MUNICH..........dep	...	5a50	8 a50	11a50	2p40	...	5p50	8p50	...
	a m	a.m	a.m.	p.m.	p.m.	p.m.	p.m.	p.m.	
Holzkirchen.....dep	...	6 48	9 49	12 50	3 41	...	6 52	9 52	...
Kreuzstrasse 203A...	...	6 57	9 58	12 59	3 51	...	7 2	10 1	p.m.
Aibling..........	4 45	7 28	10 30	1 30	4 24	6 8	7 33	1031	11 0
Rosenheim.......arr	4 58	7 42	10 44	1 44	4 38	6 21	7 47	1045	1112

Station	a.m.	a.m.	a.m.	p.m.	p.m.	p.m.	p.m.	p.m.
Rosenheim.......dep	5 0	8 11	1118	2 12	4 24	5 12	8 15	1010
Aibling..........	5 19	8 29	1135	2 29	4 42	5 30	8 35	1028
Kreuzstrasse..........	6 9	9 13	1216	3 11	—	6 12	9 24	—
Holzkirchen.......arr	6 23	9 26	1229	3 24	...	6 25	9 37	...
MUNICH 203C...arr	7a30	10a7	1 p9	4 p6	...	7p19	10p45	...

Station								
Aibling..........dep	5a55	8 a40	11a45	2p45	4p55	6p22	8p50	...
Feilnbach..........arr	6 28	9 13	12 18	3 18	5 28	6 55	9 23	...

Station									
Feilnbach..........dep	6a44	9 a44	12p44	3p39	5p30	7p50	9p44	...	...
Aibling..........arr	7 15	10 15	1 15	4 10	6 1	8 21	1015	...	...

HOLZKIRCHEN and BAYRISCHZELL.

Station									
Holzkirchen	6a50	8‡a46	9a52	12 2	3p37	5‡p10	6p48	A	9p50
Miesbach ...	7 22	9 8	10 23	1 25	4 12	5 30	7 24	8‡19	1023
Schliersee	7 57	9 30	10 56	2 0	4 47	5 51	8 0	8 40	1046
Bayrischzell	8 41	10 [illegible]	11 41	2 41	5 31	6 27	8 44	9 16	...

Station									
Bayrischzell..........	...	6‡a54	7a37	10a40	1p40	3‡p42	4p52	6‡58	7p40
Schliersee..........	5a30	7 35	8 30	11 34	2 32	4 22	5 47	7 38	8 35
Miesbach..........	5 52	7 47	8 48	11 50	2 48	4 34	6 6	7 49	8 53
Holzkirchen (203A)	6 31	8 13	9 24	12 23	3 21	5 0	6 39	B	9 27

‡—Until 14th Sept. A—Munich dep. 7.10 p.m. B—Munich arr. 8.47 p.m.

MUNICH OST and KREUZSTRASSE.

Station							
Munich Ost.........dep	...	7 a50	10a52	1 p50	5 p27	8 p45	...
Aying..........	5 a40	8 47	11 46	2 44	6 28	9 38	...
Kreuzstrasse 203A arr	5 58	9 5	12 4	3 2	6 46	9 56	...

Station							
Kreuzstrasse.......dep	6 a8	9 a15	12p18	3 p15	7 p5	10 p5	...
Aying..........	6 32	9 35	12 38	3 35	7 25	10 20	...
Munich Ost.........arr	7 29	10 27	1 29	4 27	8 2[illegible]	...	...

STEINACH and WINDSHEIM.

Station					
Steinach......dep	12p25	5 p30	9 p10	...	...
Windsheim...arr	1 10	6 11	9 45	...	...

Station							
Windsheim......dep	5a48	9a35	2 p45	8 p0	...	...	...
Steinach 196...arr	6 20	10 20	3 30	8 45	...	...	...

NEUSTADT and WINDSHEIM.

*—Mon. & Sat.

Station	a.m.	a.m.	a.m.	p.m.	p.m.	p.m.
Neustadt..........dep	5*12	7 55	1142	4 18	7 8	11 42
Windsheim..........arr	5 45	8 36	1223	5 0	7 50	12 25

Station	a.m.	a.m.	a.m.	p.m.	p.m.	p.m.
Windsheim...dep	3*58	5 52	9 17	2 35	5 15	9 48
Neustadt........arr	4 41	6 30	10 4	3 21	5 55	10 27

NEUMARKT-i-OPF. and DIETFURT-a-A.

Station							
Neumarkt-i-O. ....dep	6a35	11 a0	2p10	6 p35	11 p3	...	...
Greisselbach..........	6 56	11 20	2 31	6 55	11 24	...	...
Beilngries..........	7 55	12 20	3 28	7 53	12 27	...	...
Dietfurt-a-A. ....arr	8 23	12 48	3 55	8 20	...	...	...

Station						
Dietfurt-a-A. ....dep	4 a10	8 a33	11a40	4 p0	6p15	...
Beilngries..........	4 41	9 4	12 16	4 32	6 53	...
Greisselbach..........	5 38	10 1	1 10	5 29	9 10	...
Neumarkt-i-O. 195A ...arr	5 55	10 18	1 26	5 46	9 31	...

Station							
Greisselbach.........dep	6a56	11a20	2p33	6p55	...	...	...
Freystadt..........arr	7 26	11 48	3 1	7 23	...	...	...

Station							
Freystadt..........dep	5 a6	9a28	12p36	4 p55	...	...	...
Greisselbach..........arr	5 34	9 56	1 5	5 21	...	...	...

MARKTOBERDORF and KAUFBEUREN.

*—Until 16th Sept.]

Station									
Marktoberdorf dep	4a40	7 a1	7a46	9a57	1p52	3*10	4p49	7p40	9 p7
Biessenhofen..........	5 5	7 20	8 2	10 11	2 7	3 25	5 5	7 56	9 41
Kaufbeuren......arr	5 12	7 30	8 12	10 20	2 16	3 35	5 14	8 5	9 48

Station									
Kaufbeuren...dep	4a48	8a20	8a40	12 p3	2*p45	3p56	5p50	8p30	...
Biessenhofen......	5 5	8 35	8 50	12 14	...	4 6	6 1	8 42	9p45
Marktoberdorf ar	5 54	8 55	9 4	12 28	3 5	4 20	6 15	8 58	10 0

Station							
Marktoberdorf..dep	9 a8	4 p25	9 p8	...	...	...	...
Lechbruck.........arr	10 28	5 32	10 21	...	...	...	...

Station								
Lechbruck..........dep	5 a40	12p25	6p10	...	...	...	...	...
Marktoberdorf......arr	6 54	1 40	7 30	...	...	...	...	...

Station								
Fussen..........dep	6a36	8a51	12p39	2 ‡p1	3p37	6‡p28	7p55	8§p52
Marktoberdorf arr	7 44	9 58	1 47	3 7	4 45	7 36	9 3	9 51

Station								
Marktoberdorf dep	6*a21	7§a44	9 a7	12p31	3‡p7	4p26	6‡p18	9 p3
Fussen..........arr	7 58	8 43	1015	1 39	4 8	5 39	7 26	1011

*—Sunday dep. 6.0 a.m. ‡—Until 15th September. §—Until 14th September.

STRAUBING and CHAM.

Station									
Straubing dep	...	...	6 a0	8 a3	1210	...	4p54	7p55	...
Konzell Süd......	a.m.	...	7 34	1051	1 35	...	6 23	9 23	...
Miltach..........	4 14	5a37	8 20	1218	2 18	4p49	7 21	10 9	...
Cham(204)arr	4 50	6 3	8 48	1 0	2 44	5 14	7 46	1034	...

Station									
Cham..........dep	...	5 a5	7a43	9a38	1p47	3p12	6p52	9p38	...
Miltach..........	...	5 36	8 19	10 8	2 19	3 41	7 23	10 6	...
Konzell Süd..........	4a31	6 18	—	1053	3 1	—	8 8	—	...
Straubing 195A.	6 45	7 31	...	12 5	4 17	...	9 2[illegible]	...	...

AUGSBURG, MERING, and WEILHEIM.

†—Weekdays only. ‡—From 1st July until 10th Sept.

Station									
Augsburg ...dep	4a13	7 a0	...	9 a8	...	1‡p45	1p50	5p15	8p10
Mering..........	4 39	...	a.m.	9 35	...	...	2 16	5 44	8 37
Geltendorf..........	5 33	...	7†10	1034	...	...	3 11	6 35	9 40
Schondorf..........	5 52	...	8 5	1054	p.m.	...	3 31	6 55	10 0
Diessen..........	6 13	...	9 32	1116	1236	2 56	3 55	7 16	1023
Weilheim 197B a	6 41	8 29	1024	1139	1257	3 14	4 19	7 40	1047

Station									
Weilheim..........dep	4a23	7a20	9a10	1p50	3‡49	5p12	8p15	8p50	9†38
Diessen..........	4 45	7 40	9 33	2 15	...	5 35	8 38	9 7	1021
Schondorf..........	5 11	—	10 0	2 42	...	6 1	9 5	...	—
Geltendorf..........	5 43	...	10 33	3 14	...	6 33	9 43	...	...
Mering..........	6 24	...	11 14	3 55	...	7 14	1023	...	...
Augsburg (192)...arr	6 49	...	11 38	4 19	5 7	7 39	1047	1017	...

Extra—Diessen to Weilheim 7.50 a.m., Weilheim to Diessen 12.10 p.m.

JOSSA and WILDFLECKEN.

‡—7.30 p.m. on Sunday.

Station							
Jossa..........dep	...	8a35	10a40	3p33	...	8p15	9 p55
Bad Brückenau..........	...	9 22	11 29	4 20	...	9 3	10 44
Stadt Bruckenau..........	7a15	9 45	11 43	4 32	6p35	9 15	10 53
Wildflecken..........arr	8 15	10 42	12 28	5 17	7 20	10 0	...

Station								
Wildflecken..........dep	6a24	8a43	10a54	1p10	5p35	7‡p50	...	...
Stadt Bruckenau..........	7 3	9 42	11 40	1 50	6 13	8 27	...	...
Bad Brückenau..........	7 10	9 49	—	1 57	6 20	8 34	...	...
Jossa (149)..........arr	7 53	1027	...	2 42	7 0	9 16	...	...

MUHLDORF and BURGHAUSEN.

Station						
Muhldorf ...dep	6 a50	9a15	11a20	2 p45	6p44	10p56
Altotting..........	7 35	10 13	11 55	3 29	7 24	11 26
Burghausen arr	8 29	10 54	12 40	4 19	8 13	12 5

Station								
Burghausen..........dep	5 a15	...	9a26	...	12p45	4 p30	8p50	...
Altotting..........	6 1	8a21	10 21	12p16	1 35	5 25	9 42	...
Muhldorf (198) ...arr	6 33	8 50	10 50	12 48	2 6	5 56	10 21	...

STRULLENDORF and EBRACH.

*—7.36 a.m. on Sunday.

Station				
Strullendorf..........dep	9a*10	3 p28	10 p9	...
Frensdorf..........	9 33	3 47	10 30	...
Schlüsselfeld..........arr	11 3	5 5	11 58	...
Ebrach..........dep	11 9	5 12	12 0	...

Station					
Ebrach..........dep	...	4 a20	12p10	5p57	...
Schlüsselfeld......dep	4a12	4 12	12 15	5 57	...
Frensdorf..........	5 30	5 44	1 49	7 33	...
Strullendorf.........arr	5 51	6 5	2 11	7 56	...

NEUSTADT a. d. NAAB and ESLARN.

E.M	Station						Station							
	Neustadt a.W.N. dp	6a13	9 a14	1p26	4p49	10 p1	Eslarn ...dep	...	4a47	9 a10	12p52	4 p55	8 p0	...
16¼	Vohenstrauss	7 35	10 37	3 0	6 20	11 19	Waidhaus	...	5 12	9 35	1 16	5 19	8 24	...
26	Waidhaus	8 20	11 25	3 45	7 5	12 3	Vohenstrauss	4 a0	6 3	10 29	2 8	6 11	9 7	...
31	Eslarn ...arr	8 40	11 45	4 5	7 25	12 23	Neustadt a.W.N. 202	5 2	7 4	11 31	3 10	7 13	...	...

	Station								Station							
HOF and BAD STEBEN.	Hof ...dep	5a22	8 a4	10a42	1p20	...	4p34	9 p25	Bad Steben	5a57	8a30	11a17	3 p0	4p45	6 p8	9 p7
	Marxgrün	6 50	9 13	12 2	2 26	3p55	5 41	10 43	Marxgrün	6 12	8 45	11 32	3 12	5 1	6 23	9 26
	Bad Steben arr	7 3	9 26	12 14	2 38	4 7	5 53	10 57	Hof (202) arr	7 14	9 46	12 30	...	6 2	7 36	1037

	Station						Station					
DINKELSCHERBEN and THANNHAUSEN.	Dinkelscherben...dep	5a55	8a30	12p20	5 p0	10p20	Thannhausen	4a25	7a15	10a40	1p46	7 p0
	Thannhausen ...arr	6 49	9 24	1 14	5 54	11 14	Dinkelscherben	5 10	8 0	11 34	2 40	8 4

	Station							Station						
FREISING and MAINBURG.	Freising ...dep	9 a6	11a48	1223	3p45	9p14	9p32	Mainburg ...dep	...	5a45	a.m.	12p44	6 p8	...
	Langenbach	9 34	12 56	1238	4 10	10 0	9 46	Enzelhausen		6 9	8 54	1 8	6 32	...
	Enzelhausen	11 3	3 10	—	5 26	1121		Langenbach	7a28	7 40	11 1	2 25	7 55	...
	Mainburg ...arr	1123	3 34	...	5 45	1141	...	Freising (202) arr	7 44	7 59	1121	2 44	8 14	...

	Station						Station						
WOLNZACH and MAINBURG.	Wolnzach dep	7a55	12p17	5p45	9 p50	...	Mainburg ...dep	5 a45	10a43	2p50	7 p15	...	...
	Mainburg arr	9 2	1 27	6 53	10 59	...	Wolnzach 197 arr	7 0	11 50	4 0	8 15	...	...

	Station								Station							
LANDSHUT and MÜHLDORF.	Landshut dep	6a21	8a25	10a31	...	1p40	4p25	9 p4	Mühldorf dep	3 a20	6a58	7a 9	11a10	2p38	6p38	6p58
	Höhenberg	6 58	...	11 7	...	2 17	5 0	9 39	Neumarkt	4 10	7 19	7 56	11 48	3 15	7 25	7 17
	Neumarkt	7 31	...	11 42	1p35	2 52	5 35	1014	Höhenberg	5 16	...	8 33	12 27	3 52	8 2	...
	Mühldorf arr	8 19	9 23	12 11	2 0	...	6 7	1039	Landshut ar	6 17	8 5	9 7	12 59	4 24	8 31	8 0

	Station						Station						
PASSAU and HAIDMÜHLE.	Passau ...dep	4 a42	8 a20	1p30	4p38	8 p34	Haidmuhle...dep	4 a0	7a45	12 p3	..	7p40	...
	Waldkirchen	6 50	10 20	3 31	7 9	10 35	: Freyung	4 45	8 40	12 50	4 p54	8 30	...
	: Freyung ...arr	7 52	11 6	4 20	8 1	11 13	Waldkirchen	5 28	9 34	1 34	5 26	9 10	...
	Haidmuhle 242 arr	8 9	12 3	5 15	9 0	...	Passau ...arr	7 30	11 27	3 44	7 22	1055	...

MUNICH and HERRSCHING.

Station									Station								
Munich Central dep	6a15	8 a0	10a24	1p20	2 p2	4p18	7p20	8p20	Herrsching dep	6a10	7a47	9a20	12 0	3 p5	6 p5	8p25	9 p2
Pasing	6 26	8 10	10 35	1 31	...	4 29	7 30	8 31	Pasing	7 27	...	1020	1 2	4 8	7 10	...	1010
Herrsching ...arr	7 28	8 58	11 37	2 38	2 54	5 31	8 11	9 39	Munich ...arr	7 39	8 41	1031	1 13	4 18	7 21	9 8	1021

	Station						Station					
AUGSBURG and WELDEN.	Augsburg ...dep	7 a0	10a58	2p20	4p35	8p43	Welden ...dep	5 a25	8 a55	12p35	4p25	6p15
	Welden ...arr	8 20	12 17	3 49	5 55	10 0	Augsburg ...arr	6 43	10 15	1 55	5 45	7 35

	Station						Station					
NORDLINGEN and WEMDING.	Nordlingen ...dep	8 a33	2 p0	8 p10	...	...	Wemding ...dep	5 a12	12p25	5 p55	...	...
	Wemding ...arr	9 13	2 44	8 50	...	...	Nordlingen ...arr	5 55	1 10	6 40	...	...

	Station					Station				
INGOLSTADT and RIEDENBURG.	Ingolstadt ...dep	6 a59	11a20	2 p9	7p50	Riedenburg ...dep	4 a37	10a31	3 p3	6p50
	Riedenburg ...arr	9 12	2 13	4 11	9 57	Ingoldstadt ...arr	6 57	12 45	5 47	8 57

	Station					Station				
ROTHENKIRCHEN and TETTAU.	Rothenkirchen dep	9 a15	3 p35	9 p39	...	Tettau ...dep	6 a12	1 p30	7p 35	...
	Tettau ...arr	10 25	4 45	10 46	...	Rothenkirchen arr	7 4	2 22	8 35	...

	Station						Station					
AMBERG and LAUTERHOFEN.	Amberg ...dep	7 a10	1 p15	9 p5	...	...	Lauterhofen ...dep	5 a0	9a25	6 p37	...	...
	Ursensollen	7 54	1 59	9 49	...	...	Ursensollen	6 4	10 31	7 44	...	...
	Lauterhofen ...arr	9 0	3 5	10 53	...	...	Amberg ...arr	6 42	11 10	8 25	...	...

	Station					Station					
BAYREUTH and HOLLFELD.	Bayreuth ...dep	7 a0	1†p55	7p38	† On Sun.	Hollfeld ...dep	3a34	10a30	5 p0	...	...
	Mistelgau	7 54	2 55	8 31	1.20 p.m.	Mistelgau	4 40	11 37	6 7	...	...
	Hollfeld ...arr	9 0	4 1	9 37		Bayreuth ...arr	5 33	12 33	6 59	...	...

	Station						Station					
PASSAU and HAUZENBERG.	Passau ...dep	5a10	10a40	2 p18	6†p7	8 p20	Hauzenberg	5 a23	10a40	2p26	6 p5	†-From or at
	Hauzenberg...arr	6 47	12 12	3 56	7 28	9 57	Passau ...arr	6 55	12 16	3†42	7 39	Innstadt.

	Station					Station				
NABBURG and OBERVIECHTACH.	Nabburg ...dep	7 a55	12p50	6 p5	...	Oberviechtach ...dep	5 a23	10 a8	3 p3	...
	Oberviechtach ...arr	9 34	2 13	7 44	...	Nabburg ... arr	6 55	11 40	4 30	...

	Station					Station					
MERTINGEN and WERTINGEN.	Mertingen dep	8 a15	12 ‡0	3 p0	8 p50	Wertingen ...dep	5 a20	10a27	1p‡15	7 p0	‡—Sun., Tues.,
	Wertingen arr	9 11	12 50	3 58	9 41	Mertingen (199)arr	6 14	11 25	2 5	8 0	Fri. only.

Amberg and Schnaittenbach (in 70 min.) Amberg dep. 8.23 a.m., 1.0, 9.15 p.m. Schnaittenbach dep. 5.36, 10.9 a.m., 7.31 p.m. †—Not on Sunday.

Bamberg and Schesslitz.—Bamberg dep. 7.10, 10†30 a.m., 3.0, 7.0 p.m. Schesslitz dep. 5.15, 9†35 a.m., 12.40 noon, 6.0 p.m.

Bayreuth and Thurnau (1½ hrs.)—Bayreuth dep. 8.13 a.m., 1.47, 8.7 p.m. Thurnau dep. 4.23, 10.10 a.m., 5.51 p.m

Falls and Gefrees (in 15 min.).—Falls dep. 8.30 a.m., 1.10, 3.35, 7.17 p.m. Gefrees dep. 6.30 11.20 a.m., 1.59, 5.25 p.m.

Forchheim & Ebermannstadt (in 40 min.). Forchheim dep. 8.56, 11.40 a.m., 4.45, 8.37 p.m. Ebermannstadt dep. 7.2, 10.16 a.m., 1.4, 6.5 p.m.

Georgensgmund and Spalt (in 20 min.)—Georgensgmund dep. 8.0, 11.0 a.m., 4.30, 8.47 p.m. Spalt dep. 6.28, 10.8 a.m., 1.10, 7.5 p.m.

Holenbrunn and Wunsiedel (in 10 minutes). Holenbrunn dep. 5.25, 7‡33, 9.45, 11.58 a.m., 2.12, 3.45, 7.22, 8.15, 9.30, 11.28 p.m., 12.34 night. Wunsiedel dep. 4.17, 6.10, 8.38, 10.43 a.m., 1.3, 2.50, 4‡25, 6.50, 7.58, 9.10, 11.10 p.m., and 12.16 night. ‡—Not on Sunday.

Memmingen and Legau (in 1 hr). Memmingen dep. 8.39 a.m., 2.30, 6.48 p.m. Legau dep. 6.32 a.m., 12.57, 4.37 p.m.

Munchberg and Helmbrechts (in 30 min.).—Munchberg dep. 6.55, 9.10 a.m., 2.18, 4.35, 8.50 p.m. Helmbrechts dep. 5.45, 7.55, 11.50 a.m., 3.11, 7.10 p.m.

Munchberg and Zell-i-Ofr. (in 40 min.).—Munchberg dep. 6.35, 9‡15 a.m., 2.18, 6†15, 8.45 p.m. Zell dep. 5.0, 8‡0, 11.43 a.m., 4†35, 7.9 p.m.
†—Weekdays only. ‡—Sun., Mon., Wed., Fri. only.

Ochenbruck and Allersberg (in one hour).—Ochenbruck dep. 7.45 a.m., 1.27, 9‡10 p.m. Allersberg dep. 6§10, 11.47 a.m., 5.52 p.m.
‡—7.28 p.m. on Sat. §—5 0 a.m. on Mon.

Pfaffenhausen and Kirchheim (15 min.)—Pfaffenhausen dep. 8.14, 9.40 a.m., 12.20, 2.10, 4.30, 8.2, 9.30 p.m. Kirchheim dep. 6.15, 9.10, 11.45 a.m., 1.32, 3.36, 5.30, 8.40 p.m.

Ranna and Auerbach (in 30 min.).—Ranna dep. 8.50 a.m. 1.30, 4.10, 9.52 p.m. Auerbach dep. 6.31, 10.53 a.m., 3.10, 6.29 p.m.

Reuth and Erbendorf (18 min.)—Reuth dep. 9.40 a.m., 1.55, 5.45, 8.50 p.m. Erbendorf dep. 7.35, 11.50 a.m., 4.35, 7.22 p.m.

Rothenbach and Scheidegg (in 40 min.).—Rothenbach dep. 6.5, 8.40, 11.45 a.m., 3.50, 6.5, 10.40 p.m. Scheidegg dep. 4.50, 7.30, 9.42 a.m., 1.45, 4.55, 9.25 p.m.

Schwaben and Erding (9 miles).—Schwaben dep. 5.25, 9.15 a.m., 1.10, 4.41, 8.50 p.m., 12.26 night. Erding dep. 4.15, 6.3, 8.0, 11.45 a.m., 3.29, 6.40 p.m.

Seligenstadt and Volkach (7 miles).—Seligenstadt dep. 7.0 a.m., 3.5, 10.0 p.m. Volkach dep. 5.36 a.m., 12.0 noon, 8.35 p.m.

Senden and Weissenhorn (in 20 min.). Senden dep. 6.0, 7.52, 11.4 a.m., 12.48, 5.26, 7.57 p.m. Weissenhorn dep. 4.43, 6.37, 8.47 a.m., 12.1, 2.4, 6.11 p.m.

Wolnzach and Geisenfeld (in 20 min.). Wolznach dep. 8.0 a.m., 12.10, 4.20, 7*15 p.m. Geisenfeld dep. 7.0, 10.19 a.m., 1.54, 5.56 p.m. *—9.55 p.m. on Sunday.

MUNICH, HOLZKIRCHEN, and BAD-TOLZ.

E.M																		
	Munich ... dep	5 a10	5 a50	7 a50	8 a12	8 a50	9*a50	11a15	11a50	2 p8	2 p40	4 *15	5 p8	5 p50	7 ‡p0	8 p15	8 p50	...
6½	Grosshesselohe	5 33	...	...	8 35	...	...	11 38	...	2 30	...	...	5 33	...	...	8 37	...	...
11½	Deisenhofen	5 49	...	...	8 52	...	...	11 54	...	2 45	...	...	5 49	...	7 25	8 52	...	...
22½	**Holzkirchen**	6 48	6 40	8 43	9 32	9 40	...	12 31	12 40	3 40	3 30	5 5	6 26	6 40	...	9 48	9 40	...
29¼	Schaftlach (203C)	7 17	...	9 5	—	10 14	10 53	1 14	—	4 7	—	5 25	—	7 17	8 10	10 15	—	...
36	**Bad-Tölz** ... arr	7 32	...	9 16	...	10 29	...	1 29	...	4 22	...	5 36	...	7 32	8 21	10 30	...	...

...	**Bad-Tölz** ... dep	5 a50	...	7 ‡45	8 a39	...	11a47	...	2 p45	...	4 *33	5 p45	...	p.m.	7 p48	8 p58	...	...
...	Schaftlach	6 19	...	8 5	9 7	a.m.	12 15	p.m.	3 13	p.m.	4 53	6 13	p.m.	7 *13	8 8	9 26	p.m.	...
...	**Holzkirchen**	6 42	7 a0	8 18	9 40	9 31	12 40	12 35	3 40	3 32	5 5	6 35	6 48	...	...	9 50	9 32	...
...	Deisenhofen	7 6	7 42	...	10 7	...	1 10	...	4 7	...	...	6 56	7 16	...	...	10 18	...	...
...	Grosshesselohe	7 16	7 53	...	10 17	...	1 21	...	4 17	...	...	...	7 27	...	...	10 28	...	...
...	**Munich** ... arr	7 30	8 16	8 53	10 34	10 5	1 43	1 9	4 39	4 6	5 39	7 19	7 45	7 56	8 52	10 45	10 14	...

*—Until 14th September. ‡—Until 15th September.

SCHAFTLACH and TEGERNSEE.

Schaftlach	7a18	9 a8	10a14	10*56	1p15	4 p7	5*26	7p19	8*11	10p16
Gmund ...	7 38	9 25	10 34	11 13	1 35	4 28	5 43	7 40	8 28	10 33
Tegernsee	7 50	9 36	10 46	11 23	1 47	4 40	5 53	7 51	8 38	10 45

Tegernsee	5a40	7*28	8a25	11a35	2p36	4*19	5p31	6*42	7p30	8p45
Gmund ...	5 54	7 39	8 37	11 49	2 49	4 30	5 46	6 53	7 42	8 59
Schaftlach	6 11	7 59	8 55	12 6	3 6	4 46	6 4	7 9	8 1	9 17

*—Until 14th September.

TUTZING and KOCHEL.

‡—Until 31st August.

E.M									
	Tutzing ... dep	6a50	...	...	9a45	...	2 p2	5p45	8p32
7	Seeshaupt	7 9	...	a.m.	10 4	...	2 21	6 5	8 52
14	Penzberg Pbf.	7 26	...	‡	1020	p.m.	2 38	6 23	9 10
16¾	Bichl	7 38	8 a2	8 49	1032	2 9	2 49	6 35	9 22
22	**Kochel** ... arr	7 57	8 21	9 6	1051	2 29	3 9	6 54	9 42

Kochel ... dep	5a35	8a30	11a30	2p30	5p18	6p15	7‡25	8 p2
Bichl	5 56	8 51	11 49	2 51	5 39	6 34	7 42	8 24
Penzberg Pbf.	6 7	9 2	—	3 3	5 50	—	—	8 36
Seeshaupt	6 23	9 18	...	3 20	6 7	...	...	8 54
Tutzing ... arr	6 41	9 37	...	3 39	6 25	...	...	9 14

TRAUNSTEIN and RUHPOLDING.

Traunstein dep	7a49	11a10	2p35	6‡p25	8 p20
Siegsdorf	8 5	11 31	2 56	6 44	8 41
Ruhpolding arr	8 25	11 53	3 17	7 4	9 2

Ruhpolding ... dep	6*a25	8†a45	12p40	5 p27	7‡p18
Siegsdorf	6 47	9 3	1 4	5 46	7 37
Traunstein ... arr	7 6	9 21	1 23	6 5	7 56

*—5.10 a.m. on Sunday. †—8.35 a.m. on Sunday. ‡—Until 6th September.

TRAUNSTEIN and WAGING.

Traunstein ... dep	7 a55	2 p40	5 p15	...
Weibhausen	8 10	2 56	8 31	...
Waging ... arr	8 32	3 19	8 54	...

Waging ... dep	6 a6	12p30	5 p32
Weibhausen	6 35	12 59	6 0
Traunstein ... arr	6 50	1 14	6 15

EGGMUHL and LANGQUAID.

Eggmuhl ... dep	9 a5	1p23	5 p23	10 p0	...
Langquaid ... arr	9 36	1 54	5 54	10 31	...

Langquaid ... dep	5 a32	10a26	2 p10	7 p32	...
Eggmuhl 202 ... arr	6 0	10 54	2 38	8 0	...

SCHNAITTACH & SIMMELSDORF.

Schnaittach dep	6a13	8a35	3 p0	6 p25	8p20
Simmelsdorf arr	6 50	9 16	3 36	6 59	8 55

Simmelsdorf ... dep	5 a4	7 a6	11a30	4p50	7 p10
Schnaittach 202 arr	5 37	7 36	12 8	5 52	7 52

KEMPTEN and GRIESEN.

Kempten ... dep	...	5 a5	9 a52	...	12p28	1p26	4p56	9p16
Jodbad Sulzbrunn	...	5 34	10 20	...	12 56	2 27	5 24	9 42
Nesselwang	...	6 28	11 12	...	1 44	4 10	6 16	1032
Pfronten ¶	...	6 50	11 32	...	2 3	4 36	6 37	1051
Reutte	5 a25	7 40	12 18	...	2 45	—	7 28	1141
Lermoos	6 10	8 38	1 16	2 p24	3 33	...	8 19	—
Griesen 197B ... arr	6 34	8 57	1 41	2 48	3 [illegible]	...	8 40	...

Griesen ... dep	...	7 a58	10a32	1 p41	3 p26	6 p6	8 p8
Lermoos	...	8 33	11 9	2 9	4 0	6 38	8 40
Reutte	4 a33	9 26	12 34	—	5 6	8 11	9 25
Pfronten ¶	5 23	10 17	1 26	...	5 58	9 7	—
Nesselwang	5 42	10 36	1 45	...	6 17	9 26	...
Jodbad Sulzbrunn	6 28	11 19	2 27	...	7 3	1012	...
Kempten 201 arr	6 51	11 42	2 49	...	7 26	1035	...

¶—Customs Exam.

KEMPTEN and ISNY.

Kempten ... dep	5 a5	10 a5	2p15	6p50	...
Sibratshofen	6 55	11 55	4 5	8 40	...
Isny (194) ... arr	7 20	12 20	4 30	9 5	...

Isny ... dep	6a25	10a15	2p25	7 p8	...	...
Sibratshofen	6 53	10 43	2 53	7 34	...	...
Kempten (203C) ... arr	8 35	12 25	4 35	9 6	...	...

BAYREUTH and WARMENSTEINACH.

Bayreuth ... dep	7 a5	2 p5	9†p10	...
Untersteinach	7 41	2 41	9 46	...
Warmensteinach arr	8 28	3 30	10 33	...

Warmensteinach dp	4a34	11*a8	7p30	...	...
Untersteinach	5 19	11 55	8 15	...	...
Bayreuth 202 ... arr	5 54	12 30	8 50	...	...

*—9.43 a.m. on Thursday and Saturday. †—10.50 p.m. on Sunday.

BODENWOHR and NEUNBURG

Bodenwohr ... dep	8 a40	2 p25	6 p25
Neunburg—v.W. arr	9 12	2 57	6 57

Neunburg v.W. dep	4 a30	7a‡15	12p45	5 p8
Bodenwohr 204 arr	5 2	8 0	1 17	5 40

‡-Weekdays only.

BODENWOHR and NITTENAU.

Bodenwohr ... dep	8a40	2 p35	6 p26	...
Nittenau ... arr	9 8	3 3	6 54	...

Nittenau ... dep	4 a31	1 p0	5p14	...	...	...
Bodenwohr 204 arr	5 2	1 31	5 45	...	...	...

SALZBURG and BERCHTESGADEN.

†—Until 14th September.

	a.m.	a.m.	a.m.	a.m.	a.m.	a.m.	a.m.	p.m.	p.m.	p.m.	p.m.	p.m.	p.m.	p.m.	p.m.	p.m.		
Salzburg ... dep	5 40	7 2	7†51	8 23	9 13	10 15	11†20	12 13	1 28	2†34	3 13	4 34	6 7	7†18	8 16	9†29	...	...
Schellenberg	6 40	8 5	9 5	9 34	9 59	11 19	12 6	1 16	2 35	3 20	4 20	5 42	7 21	8 21	9 19	10 27	...	...
Berchtesgaden ... arr	7 14	8 39	9 40	10 8	10 26	11 53	12 34	1 51	3 9	3 47	4 53	6 22	7 56	8 55	9 52	11 1	...	...

	a.m.	a.m.	a.m.	a.m.	a.m.	p.m.	p.m.	p.m.	p.m	p.m.	p.m.	p.m.	p.m.	p.m.	p.m.	p.m.	p.m.		
Berchtesgaden dep	6 7	7†34	8 7	9 23	10 48	12 17	1†18	2 24	3†50	4 22	5 5	5 50	6 43	7 †7	7 38	8 8	9 †8	...	...
Schellenberg	6 40		8 41	9 57	11 22	12 50	1 50	2 56		4 54	5 38	...	7 18	7 43	8 18	8 41	9 40	...	...
Salzburg ... arr	7 47	8 48	9 51	11 0	12 28	1 54	2 57	4 3	5 5	5 59	6 39	7 6	8 21	7 49	9 20	9 44	1044	..	...

BERCHTESGADEN and KONIGSSEE.

	a.m.					
Berchtesgaden ... dep	5 30	About twice hourly, in the afternoon three times hourly, from 5.30 a.m. to 8.1 p.m.	...	...	...	...
Königssee ... arr	5 46		...	...	...	...

	a.m.					
Königssee ... dep	5 50	About twice hourly, in the afternoon three times hourly, from 5.50 a.m. to 8.47 p.m.	...	...	...	...
Berchtesgaden ... arr	6 3		...	...	...	...

Motor Boat Service on the Königssee.					
Königssee ... dep	7 a10	8 a20	9 a15	10 a0	And about hourly until 7.0 p.m.
Bartholomä	7 45	8 55	9 50	10 30	
Sallet Alpe	8 0	9 15	10 10	10 50	
Königssee ... arr	8 50	10 5	11 0	11 40	

SALZBURG and the GAISBERG.—From Salzburg Lokalbahnhof, 8.34, 9.54, 11.5 a.m., 2.0, 3.19, 4.32 p.m.

ROTHENBACH and WEIL (Algäu).

Röthenbach . dep	6 a10	8 a45	11a50	3‡50	5 p55	10p40	...
Weiler (Algäu) ar	6 30	9 5	12 10	4 10	6 15	11 0	...

Weiler (Algäu) ...dep	5 a5	7a50	10 a5	2p15	5p15	9p45	...	...
Röthenbach 199...arr	5 25	8 10	10 25	2 35	5 35	10 5	...	...

MUNICH (Isar) and BICHL.

Munich ...dep	6 a5	7‡a15	10a15	12p12	2p15	4 p30	7p18	8p55
Wolfratshausen	7 10	8 7	11 14	1 15	3 17	5 30	8 23	9 53
Beuerberg	7 35	8 27	—	1 39	3 40	5§59	8 49	—
Bichl 203A arr	8 0	8 48	...	2 6	...	6§25	9 17	...

Bichl ....dep	6 a6	...	11a51	...	...	6p36	7‡43	8§23
Beuerberg	6 34	...	12 19	4 p2	...	7 4	8 6	8 51
Wolfratshausen	6a25 7 5	9 a15	12 47	4 30	6p10	7 31	8 26	9 18
Munich ...arr	7 32 8 11	10 10	1 46	5 24	7 8	8 30	9 15	1025

‡—Until 1st September. §—In July and August only.

FURTH and CADOLZBURG.

(Extended service on Sundays).

Fürth..................dep	5a55	8a10	9 a8	10a3	11a15	12 12	1p48	2p40	3p48	4p36	6p25	7 p5	8 p10	9p45	...	...	...	...	...
Zirndorf	6 12	8 28	9 24	1019	11 31	12 30	2 4	3 0	4 4	5 53	6 43	7 32	8 27	10 2	...	...	...	...	...
Cadolzburg ....arr	6 33	8 49	...	...	...	12 51	...	3 21	...	5 14	7 4	...	...	1023	...	...	...	...	...

Cadolzburg...........dep	5 a12	...	6a47	...	9 a0	...	...	...	1 p2	...	...	3p45	5p30	...	7p15	..	...	...	...
Zirndorf	5 39	6 a16	7 10	8a40	9 24	10a20	11a34	1 p0	1 26	2p14	3 p2	4 7	5 53	6p44	7 38	9p22	...	...	...
Fürth ....arr	5 50	6 31	7 26	8 56	9 40	10 36	11 50	1 16	1 42	2 30	3 18	4 23	6 9	7 0	7 54	9 38	...	...	...

DEGGENDORF and METTEN.

Deggendorf......dep	8a15	10a15	12p15	3 p45	6 p40	...	...
Metten ....arr	8 30	10 30	12 30	4 0	6 55	...	...

Metten ....dep	7a30	9 a33	11a45	1 p10	5p15	...	...
Deggendorf 198. ...arr	7 45	9 48	12 0	1 25	5 30	...	...

WIESAU and BARNAU-a-d-W-N.

Wiesau...............dep	5 a20	...	7 a55	10a10	2 p40	5 p35	8 p30
Tirschenreuth	5 48	7 a5	8 23	10 40	3 33	6 3	9 3
Bärnau ....arr	...	7 56	...	11 31	4 24	...	9 54

Bärnau..............dep	...	6 a0	8 a25	12 0	...	6 p10
Tirschenreuth	3 a18	6 50	9 15	12 50	4 p32	7 20
Wiesau 202 ....arr	3 46	7 16	9 42	1 18	5 0	7 48

Luggage Rates—see page 462.]

BAVARIAN STATE RAILWAYS.

CRAILSHEIM, NURNBERG, and FURTH.

	2&3	2&3	2&3	Ex3	Ex1	Ex3	2&3	2&3	2&3	Ex3	1,2,3	2&3
STUTTGART 191 dp	...	...	...	6 a0	...	8a15	...	8a40	10a59	4 p0	...	4p15
		a.m.	a.m.	a.m.	a.m.	a.m.		p.m.	p.m.	p.m.		p.m.
Crailsheim ......dep	...	...	6 4	7 44	9 2	1021	...	1216	3 50	6 21	...	8 29
Dombuhl 204	...	4 28	6 45	8 5	...	1045	...	1250	4 45	6 46	...	9 15
Ansbach ....arr	...	5 6	7 17	8 22	...	11 6	...	1 17	5 29	7 8	p.m.	9 48
„ 196......dep	...	5 15	7 35	8 23	P	11 8	...	1 28	5 46	7 10	7‡45	9 58
Wicklesgreuth......	...	5 45	8 2	...	...	...	...	1 54	6 11	...	...	1028
Heilsbronn	...	5 57	8 12	...	...	...	...	2 3	6 21	...	...	1040
Nürnberg Hbf. arr	...	6 42	8 52	9 0	1024	1148	...	2 44	7 5	7 55	8 28	1129
COLOGNE ......dep	8 p2	...	P—Paris-Carlsbad Express, runs until 28th Sept.				1a58		10 a3	‡—Runs in July and August only, and not on Sunday.		
Nürnberg—	a.m.	a.m.		1,2,3			p.m.	p.m.	p.m.		p.m.	
Hauptbahn....dep	4 58	8 4		10a8	...	...	1 35	6 38	8 5		9 0	...
Mögeldorf	5 6	8 16		...	...	...	1 45	6 50	8 14		...	...
Hersbruck............	5 39	9 0		1041	...	...	2 38	7 34	9 4		9 34	...
Pommelsbrünn ...	5 48	9 9		...	...	...	2 49	7 42	9 16		...	...
Etzelwang............	6 10	9 31		...	...	...	3 15	8 3	9 43		...	...
Neukirchen ...arr	6 16	9 37		11 8	3 Cl	3 Cl	3 21	8 9	9 50		10 1	...
„ 202 dep 2&3	6 18	9 38		11 9	no'n	p.m.	3 27	8 12	†—Weekdays only.		10 3	...
Sulzbach ....a.m.	6 35	9 54		1125	12†0	6†41	3 46	8 29	...		1019	...
Amberg 203B 5 38	7 1	10 19		1139	1 51	7 6	4 12	8 54			1038	...
Irrenlohe 6 10	7 31	10 48		...	2 23	—	4 48	9 21			11 0	...
Schwan-202 arr 6 19	7 38	10 55		12 4	2 32	2&3	4 56	9 28			11 6	a.m.
dorf...dep	7 55	—		1220	—	1 p5	5 34	—			1114	4 34
Bodenwöhr............	8 32	...		1240	...	1 40	6 5	...			1140	5 10
Cham 204............	9 34	...		1 11	...	2 27	6 50	...			1222	6 9
Furth-in-W. ...arr	1014	...		1 31	...	2 59	7 24	...			1252	6 48
PRAGUE 243B arr	...	...		5p14	...	8 p5	...	...	...	...	6a55	1p42

	2&3	1,2,3	Ex3	1,2,3	2&3	2&3	Ex3	2&3		1,2,3	2&3	2&3
PRAGUE 243B dep	...	8 p40	...	...	...	...	...	8a11	...	1 p0	1p43	...
		a.m.			a.m.	a.m.		p.m.		p.m.	p.m.	
Furth-i-W. ...dep	...	2 24	...	...	4 22	9 0	...	1258	...	5 2	8 35	...
Cham	...	2 52	...	...	4 55	9 30	...	1 30	...	5 29	9 7	...
Bodenwöhr	...	3 30	...	...	5 42	1010	...	2 14	...	6 5	9 55	...
Schwandorf ...arr	...	3 52	...	...	6 16	1037	...	2 37	...	6 28	1025	p.m.
„ ....dep	...	4 3	...	...	7 30	1044	...	2 46	...	6 30	1114	7 58
Irrenlohe	...	4 11	...	...	7 38	1052	...	2 54	...	...	1124	8 10
Amberg................	...	4 48	...	...	8 11	1127	...	3 29	...	6 57	12 1	8 59
Sulzbach	...	5 10	...	...	8 35	1152	...	3 53	...	7 9	—	9 29
Neukirchen......arr	a.m.	5 29	...	...	8 54	1210	...	4 11	...	7 25	...	9 50
„ ......dep	3†50	5 36	...	...	8 57	1211	...	4 18	...	7 25	...	10 2
Etzelwang	3 56	5 41	...	...	9 3	1217	...	4 24	...	...	...	10 8
Pommelsbrünn ...	4 18	5 58	...	...	9 21	1234	...	4 43	...	...	...	1029
Hersbruck............	4 27	6 7	...	...	9 27	1242	...	4 53	...	7 44	...	1038
Mögeldorf	5 23	6 32	...	...	10 9	...	...	5 42	...	...	...	1128
Nürnberg ......arr	5 30	6 39	...	...	1017	1 15	...	5 50	...	8 11	...	1135
COLOGNE......arr	—	4 p32	...	...	...	...	...	5a21	Ex1	5 a42	Ex3	...
Nürnberg—	a.m.	—	a.m.	a.m.	noon	p.m.	p.m.		p.m.	p.m.	p.m.	p.m.
Hauptbahn....dep	6 4	...	7 58	8‡56	12 2	2 51	5 6	...	6 13	8 17	9 40	1148
Heilsbronn	6 57	...	...	...	1245	3 54	5 35	...	...	9 13	...	1239
Wicklesgreuth......	7 12	2&3	...	...	1259	4 12	5 45	...	...	9 28	...	1253
Ansbach ....arr	7 27	a.m.	8 47	9 51	1 14	4 28	5 55	...	P	9 43	1024	1 7
„ ....dep	7 51	5 21	8 49	—	1 19	4 38	5 57	...	...	9 58	1025	—
Dombuhl	8 32	6 9	9 17	...	2 4	5 19	6 23	...	...	10 58	1050	...
Crailsheim ......arr	9 7	6 50	9 39	...	2 46	5 53	6 44	...	7 43	11 59	1112	...
STUTTGART 191 ar	1145	...	11a45	...	6p56	8p51	8p51	...	...	...	1252	...

Extra { Ansbach dep 10a10, 8p30 — Nürnberg arr 11 38, 9 53 } { Nürnberg dep 8a10, 6p35 — Ansbach arr 9 43, 8 14 }

DOMBUHL and ROTHENBURG-A-D-TAUBER.

E.M.								
	Dombühl ....dep	6 a47	10a49	2 p12	6 p50	10p55	...	...
4¼	Schillingsfürst	7 10	11 11	2 43	7 14	11 19	...	...
16½	Rothenburg 196A ...arr	7 58	12 0	3 49	8 3	12 8	...	...

Rothenburg.........dep	4 a43	7 a58	11a22	3 p9	7 p23	...	...	...
Schillingsfürst	5 42	8 56	12 21	4 9	8 38	...	...	...
Dombühl ....arr	6 0	9 14	12 39	4 28	9 0	...	...	...

NÖRDLINGEN and DOMBUHL.

Nördlingen ......dep	...	6 a6	8*a30	10a35	2p11	7p10	1047	...	*—Not on Sunday	...	...
Fremdingen	a.m.	6 36	9 19	11 9	2 48	7 43	1118	...		...	...
Dinkelsbuhl.........	3 30	7 9	10 14	11 45	3 32	8 17	1148	...		...	...
Feuchtwangen	3 57	7 37	—	12 14	4 4	8 43	—	...		...	...
Dombuhl 204......arr	4 22	8 2	...	12 40	4 30	9 8	...	...		...	...

Dombuhl ....dep	...	6 a7	9a21	2 p0	...	6p50	10p55	...
Feuchtwangen	a.m.	6 34	9 51	2 26	...	7 19	11 22	...
Dinkelsbuhl.........	3 32	7 6	1028	2 51	4*35	8 13	11 49	...
Fremdingen	4 3	7 38	11 8	3 21	5 38	8 47	—	...
Nördlingen ......arr	4 32	8 9	1145	3 50	6 31	9 20	...	...

ANSBACH and BECHHOFEN.

Ansbach......dep	7 a25	1 p45	7†p14	†—Sun. & Sat. at 8.22 p.m.	...
Leutershausen ...	8 11	2 16	7 36		...
Bechhofen arr	9 16	3 17	8 40		...

Bechhofen dep	5 a35	10 a1	4*p9	*—Sunday at 6.17 p.m.	...
Leutershausen ...	6 40	11 9	5 30		...
Ansbach ......arr	7 1	11 30	5 52		...

PFARRKIRCHEN and PASSAU.

Pfarrkirchen ...dep	...	5 a30	9 a15	1p10	4 p44	8p53	...
Pocking	5a38	6 36	10 24	2 17	5 50	9 50	...
Hohenstadt	6 15	7 12	11 0	2 52	6 26	—	...
Passau ....arr	7 11	8 7	11 57	3 45	7 22	...	...

Passau ....dep	...	7 a40	11 a0	2 p2	5 p46	8 p26	...
Hohenstadt	a.m.	8*37	12 1	3 9	6 44	9 24	...
Pocking	4 53	9 20	12 53	3 58	7 31	10 1	...
Pfarrkirchen arr	5 53	10 17	1 51	5 11	8 28	...	...

NURNBERG, ERLANGEN, and GRAFENBERG.

†—Not on Sunday.

Nürnberg (Nordost) ...dep	7 a5	...	11a40	2p15	6 p45	9 p5
Erlangen ....dep	...	8 a58	...	1 7	4 54	8 32
Eschenau	8 5	10 27	12 43	3 8	7 46	10 8
Gräfenberg ....arr	8 36	11 5	1 17	3 40	8 18	10 40

Gräfenberg dep	3†a37	5 a0	9a53	12p50	1p55	5p49	...
Eschenau	4 10	5 33	1026	1 29	2 30	6 27	...
Erlangen......arr	...	7 4	1154	3 6	...	7 53	...
Nürnberg ...arr	5 12	6 36	1127	...	3 35	7 35	...

NEUSORG and FICHTELBERG.

Neusorg......dep	6 a55	11 a5	8 p10	...	...
Fichtelberg arr	8 0	12 5	9 10	...	...

Fichtelberg ...dep	4 a17	8†a38	4 p46	†—On Sunday at 8.20 a.m.
Neusorg (202) arr	5 12	9 42	5 45	

WICKLESGREUTH and WINDSBACH.

Wicklesgreuth dep	5†a49	8a20	2 p0	6 p20	9 p40
Windsbach ......arr	6 20	8 59	2 34	6 54	10 14

Windsbach ....dep	4†a50	6a33	11a28	4p39	8p10	†—Sunday excepted.
Wicklesgreuth 204 arr	5 25	7 5	12 5	5 25	8 47	

CHAM and WALDMUNCHEN.

Cham ....dep	6a35	1p40	7 p 0	...
Waldmunchen...... arr	7 51	2 55	8 15	...

Waldmunchen ...dep	3a40	11a30	4p10	...
Cham 204............arr	4 45	12 42	5 16	...

CHAM and LAM.

[†—4.5 a.m. Saturday.

Cham.......dep	5 a5	7a43	9a38	1 p47	3p12	6 p52	9 p38
Miltach	5 32	8 21	10 10	2 17	3 42	7 20	10 9
Kötzting	—	8 45	10 34	2 45	4 3	7 54	10 33
Lam ......arr	...	9 55	...	—	5 0	8 56	...

Lam..dep	a.m.	a.m.	6 †a5	...	...	10a37	...	3 p9	5p27	...
Kötzting..	3 51	5 10	7 1	7a23	9a36	11 43	1p34	4 28	6 32	...
Miltach ...	4 14	5 37		8 20	10 0	12 18	2 18	4 49	7 21	10p9
Cham 204	4 50	6 3	...	8 48	...	1 0	2 44	5 14	7 46	1034

GEMUNDEN and HAMMELBURG.

‡—Not on Sunday.

E.M.					
	Gemunden...dep	7 a5	10a0	3 p0	8 p28
6¼	Wolfsmunster	7 35	10 24	3 25	8 53
10	Michelaubrück	8 3	10 47	3 47	9 15
17½	Hammelburg arr	8 40	11 22	4 21	9 49

Hammelburg ...dep	7 a0	9‡a10	1 p0	5 p0	...
Michelaubrück..........	7 34	9 54	1 35	5 33	...
Wolfsmunster	7 56	10 25	1 56	5 56	...
Gemunden (196) arr	8 20	10 54	2 20	6 20	...

NURNBERG and FURTH.

Ludwigsbahn—Between Nurnberg and Furth (3¾ miles) half-hourly (during some hours, quarter hourly) from 5.30 a.m. to 12.0 night.

BRUNSWICK and DERNEBURG.

E.M					
	Brunswick (Nordbahnhof) ...dep	7 a50	9a10	1p40	7 p0
2¾	„ (Westbahnhof).........	8 10	9 30	2 0	7 20
7¾	Thiede..............	8 29	9 49	2 19	7 39
17¾	Salder	9 15	10 34	3 9	8 29
27¼	**Derneburg** (166) ....arr	9 58	11 14	3 51	9 11

Derneburg ....dep	5 a55	10a32	3 p3	7 p9	...
Salder	6 38	11 15	3 51	7 50	...
Thiede	7 30	12 2	4 44	8 38	...
Brunswick (Westbahnhof)	7 48	12 20	5 2	8 56	...
„ (Nordbhf.) ....arr	8 24	12 40	5 24	9 15	...

—	Thiede ....dep	a.m.	8 a29	11a43	4 p29	7 p39
1½	Hoheweg..............	7 25	8 38	11 57	4 39	8 32
4	Wolfenbüttel ....arr	7 36	8 49	12 8	4 50	8 47

Wolfenbüttel ....dep	7 a3	8 a22	9a40	2 p10	7 p30	...
Hoheweg	7 20	8 33	9 58	2 28	7 41	...
Thiede ....arr	7 27	...	10 5	2 35	8 37	...

Derneburg ....dep	7 a52	11a24	4 p35	7 p12	9p47	...	...
Bockenen	8 41	11 53	5 10	7 45	10 15	...	...
Gr. Rhüden..............	9 10	12 16	5 35	8 14	—	...	...
Seesen..............arr	9 40	12 43	6 5	8 42	...	...	...

Seesen......dep	...	8 a25	2p30	4 p40	7 p45	...	...	...
Gr. Rhüden...	a.m.	9 2	3 8	5 16	8 20	...	...	...
Bockenen......	5 20	9 30	3 37	5 45	8 42	...	...	...
Derneburg arr	5 50	10 1	4 8	6 16	9 13	...	...	...

Brunswick Nordbahnhof ...dep	7 a5	10a30	1 p54	7 p22	...	...
Fallersleben..............arr	8 8	11 34	2 56	8 26	...	...

Fallersleben ....dep	5 a39	9 a40	12p52	7 p22	...	...
Brunswick Nord ...arr	6 45	10 46	1 54	8 28	...	...

BRUNSWICK, SCHONINGEN, and OSCHERSLEBEN.

		a.m.	a.m.	p.m.		p.m.	p.m.		
Brunswick ...dep	...	7 20	10 12	2 12	...	7 4	9‡40	...	...
Hotzum..............	...	7 53	10 44	2 43	...	7 35	10 19	...	...
Schöppenstedt ...	a.m.	8 37	11 28	3 25	p.m.	8 17	11 13	...	...
Schöningen	5 47	9 15	12 11	4 9	6 22	8 55	12 1	...	...
Ottleben	6 22	9 49	12 53	4 56	6 54	—	—	...	...
Oschersleben ..arr	6 45	10 11	1 19	5 22	7 28	...	...	...	...

		a.m.	a.m.	p.m.	p.m.	p.m.		
Oschersleben dep	...	7 1	10 58	2 54	6 26	8 45	...	...
Ottleben	a.m.	7 25	11 25	3 21	6 53	9 20	...	...
Schöningen........	4 20	8 0	12 7	4 4	7 33	9 56	...	...
Schöppenstedt ...	5 19	8 38	12 49	4 45	8 16	—	...	...
Hotzum	6 14	9 20	1 34	5 29	9 1	...	...	...
Brunswick ...arr	6 51	9 47	2 6	5 56	9 30	...	...	...

‡—On Sun. dep. at 11.16 p.m.

BERLIN (Schöneberg) and JUTERBOG.

Berlin—	a.m.	a.m.	a.m.	p.m.	p.m.	p.m.		
Militar B. dep	5 50	7 51	10 14	12 8	3 0	5 25	...	...
Mahlow	6 10	...	10 36	12 30	3 20	5 45	p.m.	...
Zossen	6 31	8 22	10 57	12 51	3 41	6 6	8 45	...
Sperenberg......	6 51	8 39	11 17	1 11	4 1	6 26	9 5	...
Kummersdorf	6 59	8 47	11 26	1 20	4 9	6 34	9 14	...
Juterbog ...arr	7 39	9 15	12 6	2 0	4 49	7 14	...	...

	a.m.	a.m.	a.m.	p.m.	p.m.	p.m.	p.m.	
Juterbog ......dep	5 38	8 15	10 45	12 50	3 0	5 25	...	...
Kummersdorf ...	6 16	8 46	11 24	1 18	3 38	6 3	8 2	...
Sperenberg.........	6 25	8 54	11 33	1 26	3 47	6 12	8 12	...
Zossen	6 44	9 11	11 52	1 44	4 7	6 31	8 31	...
Mahlow	7 7	...	12 13	...	4 28	6 52	—	...
Berlin..........arr	7 27	9 42	12 34	2 15	4 48	7 12	...	...

*—Until 15th September. **WALHALLA LINE.** †—Not on Sunday.

Stadtamhof ..dep	6 a0	8 a0	9a55	11a50	2 p0	4p30	7 p0	8p30
Donaustauf........	6 43	8 41	10 32	12 35	2 38	5 8	7 45	9 6
Walhalla..........	6 49	8*47	10*38	12 41	2*44	5*14	7 51	—
Worth-a-Donau	7 34	—	—	1 26	—	—	8 52	...

Worth-a-D ......dep	...	5a47	a.m.	a.m.	11a44	p.m.	...	6p55
Walhalla..............	...	6 36	8*50	10*40	12 29	2*46	6*p1	7 39
Donaustauf............	5 a3	6 48	9 5	10 55	12 41	3 5	6 9	7 51
Stadtamhof ...arr	5 40	7 25	9 42	11 32	1 18	3 42	6 46	8 28

HOMBURG i. PFALZ and MUNSTER-am-STEIN.

E.M.		2 3 4	2—4	2—4	2—4	2 3 4	2—4	2—4	2—4	2—4	2—4	2—4	2—4	2—4	2—4	3—4	2—4	2—4
					a.m.	a.m.			a.m.			p.m.			p.m.	p.m.	p.m.	
—	**Homburg**..............dep	...	...	...	6 17	7 40	...	a.m.	10 43	p.m.	...	1 10	...	p.m.	4 34	7 35	8 55	p.m.
13½	Glanmünchweiler..........	...	...	...	6 50	8 14	...	10 56	11 13	1 0	...	1 42	...	2 56	5 7	8 11	9 28	10 12
19¾	Altenglan	a.m.	...	...	7 8	8 35	a.m.	11 18	11 25	1 21	p.m.	1 59	p.m.	3 18	5 25	—	9 47	10 33
31¾	Lauterecken-Grumbach...	4 18	...	a.m.	7 45	—	10 22	—	11 53	—	1 20	2 35	4 42	—	6 3	2,3,4	10 26	—
38	Meisenheim..............	4 39	a.m.	7 50	8 1	...	10 43	...	12 7	...	1 41	2 51	5 3	†—Not on Sun.	6 20	p.m.	10 42	...
43	Odernheim-a-Glan	4 56	7 3	8 8	8 15	...	11 1	...	12 20	...	1 59	3 5	5 21		6 34	8 15	10 56	...
45½	Staudernheim ......arr	5 9	7 10	8 15	...	...	11 8	...	...	...	2 6	...	5 28		6 45	8 22	11 21	...
53½	**Münster-am-Stein** 125arr	5 43	...	...	8 34	...	11 58	...	12 40	...	2 38	3 23	6 †7		6 54	...	11 16	...

	2—4	2—4	2—4	3 & 4	2—4	2—4	2—4	2—4	2 3 4	2 3 4	2—4	2—4	2—4	2—4	2—4	3 & 4	2—4	2—4
		a.m.	a.m.			a.m.	a.m.	a.m.			p.m.	p.m.	p.m.	p.m.			p.m.	p.m.
Münster-am-Stein dep	...	5 23	...	...	...	7 56	10 34	...	...	...	1 46	2 50	5 28	...	...	...	9 11	11 15
Staudernheim ...dep	...	5 28	7 18	...	...	8 30	...	11 37	...	...	2 19	...	5 35	7 24	...	...	9 18	11 48
Odernheim-a-Glan	...	5 42	7 26	...	...	8 38	10 53	11 45	...	...	2 27	3 10	5 49	7 31	...	...	9 35	11 56
Meisenheim..............	a.m.	5 56	7 42	...	...	8 56	11 7	12 3	...	...	2 45	3 24	6 3	7 49	...	...	9 44	12 14
Lauterecken-Grumbach	4 53	6 13	—	a.m.	a.m.	9 16	11 22	12 23	p.m.	p.m.	3 5	3 41	6 19	—	p.m.	...	9 57	12 34
Altenglan..............	5 47	6 54	...	9 3	11 1	—	12 4	—	12 52	3 22	—	4 20	7 1	...	8 10	p.m.	10 20	—
Glanmünchweiler 205...	6 8	7 13	...	9 33	11 22	...	12 22	...	1 14	3 43	...	4 39	7 19	...	8 31	8 35	10 32	...
Homburg 205 ....arr	...	7 48	...	10 9	...	...	12 54	...	...	...	...	5 12	7 50	...	...	9 11	10 55	...

Extra—Glanmünchweiler to Altenglan 5 50 p.m., Altenglan to Lauterecken 7.32 p.m.

‡—Not on Sunday. **NEUNKIRCHEN and HOMBURG i. PFALZ.** §—6.11 a.m. on Sundays.

	a.m.	a.m.	a.m.	a.m.	a.m.	p.m.	p.m.	p.m.	p.m.	p.m.	p.m.	p.m.	p.m.					
Neunkirchen..........dep	5 37	6 36	7 1	9 35	11 3	1 22	3 24	6 39	7 0	8 11	9 7	10 3	11 49	...	...	...	...	...
Bexbach..............	5 51	6 51	7 16	9 48	11 16	1 33	3 37	6 47	7 14	8 24	9 22	10 14	12 1	...	...	...	...	...
Homburg..............arr	6 4	7 5	7 30	10 1	11 29	1 45	3 50	6 58	7 28	8 37	9 35	10 26	12 13	...	...	...	...	...

	a.m.	a.m.	a.m.	a.m.	a.m.	p.m.	p.m.	p.m.	p.m.	p.m.	p.m.	p.m.	p.m.	p.m.	p.m.			
Homburg..............dep	4 43	5‡41	7 §7	7 58	10 42	1 4	1‡14	2 35	5 20	5‡31	7 11	7 57	8 11	10 9	11 3	...	...	...
Bexbach	5 1	5 58	7 22	8 12	10 53	1 21	1 31	2 48	5 36	5 46	7 24	8 13	8 22	10 26	11 14	...	...	...
Neunkirchen 125.....arr	5 15	6 13	7 35	8 23	11 3	1 35	1 45	2 59	5 50	5 59	7 35	8 26	8 31	10 40	11 23	...	...	...

LOWER PALATINE RAILWAY (PFALZISCHE EISENB.).—Luggage Rate, see page 462.

GERMERSHEIM, ZWEIBRUCKEN, and SAARBRUCKEN.

		2 3 4	2 3 4	2 3 4	2 3 4	2 3 4	1,2,3	2 3 4	Ex3	2 3 4
		a.m.	a.m.	a.m.	a.m.	p.m.	p.m.	p.m.	p.m.	p.m.
Germersheim ...dep		4 8	4 28	6 52	9 24	1248	2 37	3 30	6 42	8 30
Hochstadt		4 32	5 3	7 15	9 46	1 13	...	3 54	...	8 54
Landau Haupt. arr		4 46	5 21	7 29	10 0	1 28	2 59	4 8	7 0	9 8
,, (208)......dep		—	5 25	7 37	1012	1 37	3 5	5 42	7 2	9 34
Landau Westbf.		...	5 32	7 43	1019	1 44	RC	5 49	RC	9 40
Annweiler		...	5 58	8 5	1044	2 7	3 20	6 14	7 47	10 3
Wilgartswiesen		...	6 13	8 20	1059	2 22	...	6 30	...	1018
Kaltenbach (Pfalz)..		...	6 34	8 39	..	2 39	...	6 53	...	1036
Biebermühle......arr		...	6 58	8 59	1144	3 2	3 55	7 18	7 50	1059
Pirmasens ......arr		a.m.	7 23	9 19	1225	3 23	4 35	7 54	8 11	1123
,, ...dep		4 58	6 38	8 35	1122	2 35	3 35	6 55	7 12	1026
Biebermühle......dep		5 21	7 4	9 1	1149	3 5	3 57	7 23	7 51	11 4
Zweibrucken ...arr		6 3	7 46	9 37	1231	3 44	4 18	8 5	8 12	1146
,, dep	4 a8	6 20	8 0	9 43	1 8	3 48	4 19	9 1	8 13	—
Bierbach	4 22	6 38	8 24	9 55	1 33	4 1	...	9 15	...	...
St. Ingbert...arr	5 7	7 12	8 59	1029	2 9	4 33	4 45	9 49	8 35	...
Saarbrucken arr	5 41	7 40	9 24	1057	2 36	4 52	5 0	1111	8 53	...

	2 34	Ex3	2 3 4	2 3 4	1,2,3	2 3 4	2 3 4	2 3 4	2 34
	a.m.	a.m.	a.m.	a.m.	p.m.	p.m.	p.m.	p.m.	p.m.
Saarbrucken ...dep	...	7 10	7 55	9 37	12 4	2 26	5 43	6 54	10 0
St. Ingbert.........dep	...	7 26	8 20	1016	1220	2 49	6 7	7 19	1029
Bierbach	...	RC	8 50	1055	...	...	6 36	7 53	11 4
Zweibrucken ......arr	...	7 49	9 1	11 9	1242	3 27	6 47	8 4	1116
,, ...dep	4 44	7 50	9 7	1123	1243	3 31	6 52	8 24	1131
Biebermühle ......arr	5 29	8 11	9 46	12 2	1 4	4 16	7 31	9 3	12 8
Pirmasens ......arr	6 16	8 31	1011	1225	1 27	4 35	7 54	9 25	1230
,, ...dep	4 58	7 50	9 28	1122	1245	3 35	7 12	8 36	—
Biebermühle ......dep	5 36	8 12	9 51	12 7	1 5	4 15	7 36	9 6	...
Kaltenbach (Pfalz)	6 5	...	1013	1229	1 29	4 37	7 59	9 29	...
Wilgartswiesen	6 29	...	1033	1249	...	4 58	8 17	9 47	...
Annweiler	6 43	8 45	1046	1 2	1 40	5 11	8 30	10 0	...
Landau Westbahn ...	7 6	...	11 7	1 25	...	5 32	8 52	1021	3& 4
Landau Hauptb. arr	7 13	8 59	1114	1 30	1 54	5 38	8 58	1028	a.m.
,, ...dep	7 49	9 4	1122	—	2 4	5 46	9 3	—	3 28
Hochstadt	8 5	...	1136	...	...	6 0	9 17	...	3 43
Germersheim......arr	8 31	9 24	1159	...	2 28	6 24	9 41	...	4 13

Extra { Germersheim to Landau 5.32 p.m.
Zweibrucken to Saarbrucken 4.54, 6.21, 9.33, 10.8, 11.2 p.m

Saarbrucken to Zweibrucken 6.25, 11.15 a.m., 3.28, 6.29, 7.41 p.m.
Landau to Germersheim 6.50, 10.11 a.m., 4.14, 7.12 p.m.

Biebermuhle to Waldfischbach 5.55, 7.12, 8.26, 10.0 a.m., 12.10, 1.11, 3.6, 4.22, 7.38 p.m. From Waldfischbach 4.58, 6.43, 7.40, 9.26, 11.22 a.m., 12.41, 2.36, 3.34, 6.44 p.m.

Landau to Herxheim 5‡55, 7.50, 10.12 a.m., 12.43, 4.25, 7.6, 10.35 p.m. From Herxheim 5‡17, 6‡32, 8.28, 11.17 a.m., 2.15, 5.47, 8.0 p.m. ‡—Not on Sunday.

HOMBURG and SAARGEMUND.

		a.m.	a.m.	p.m.	p.m.	p.m.	p.m.	p.m.	p.m.
Homburg ....dep		8 8	10 42	1 9	2 34	5 30	7 12	8 44	11 4
Schwarzenacker ...		8 18	10 51	1 18	2 43	5 39	7 21	8 53	11 13
Einöd ....arr		8 21	10 55	1 22	2 47	5 43	7 25	8 57	11 17
Zweibrücken arr		8 28	11 2	1 28	2 54	5 50	7 32	9 4	11 24
,, ...dep	a32	8 0	—	1 17	3 48	6 29	—	9 8	—
Einöd ....dep	5 39	8 6	...	1 24	3 54	6 36	...	9 15	...
Bierbach ...dep	5 46	8 18	...	1 31	4 0	6 43	...	9 22	...
Bliescastel	5 53	8 25	...	1 38	—	6 50	...	9 29	...
Reinheim	6 22	8 54	...	2 7	...	7 19	...	9 53	...
Saargemünd arr	6 44	9 18	...	2 31	...	7 41	...	10 20	...

		a.m.	a.m.		p.m.	p.m.	p.m.	p.m.
Saargemünd dep	...	6 26	10 16	...	3 0	...	6 58	9 5
Reinheim	...	6 46	10 36	...	2 22	...	7 18	9 30
Bliescastel	...	7 12	11 0	...	2 50	...	7 42	9 57
Bierbach ......dep	...	7 31	11 6	...	2 57	...	7 48	10 3
Einöd..........arr	...	7 36	11 11	...	3 3	...	7 53	10 9
Zweibrücken ar	a.m.	7 42	11 17	p.m.	3 10	...	7 59	10 16
,, dep	7 0	—	11 9	1235	3 55	6 38	8 20	10 8
Einöd..........dep	7 7	...	11 16	1242	4 2	6 45	8 27	10 15
Schwarzenacker	7 12	...	11 21	1247	4 7	6 50	8 32	...
Homburg ......arr	7 20	...	11 25	1255	4 15	6 58	8 40	10 26

Extra								
Homburg......dep	6a10	7a10	11a53	4 p1	4p36	8 p6	10p8	12a21
Zweibrucken arr	6 30	7 30	12 13	4 15	4 56	8 20	1028	12 41
Zweibrucken dep	5a39	9a51	1p25	3p20	4p54	7p26	9p33	11p53
Homburg ...arr	5 59	1011	1 45	3 40	5 14	7 46	9 53	12 13

BERGZABERN and MAXIMILIANSAU.

		a.m.	a.m.	a.m.	a.m.	p.m.		p.m.	p.m.		p.m.
Bergzabern dep		6 20	7 44	9 5	1151	1 56	...	4 24	6 5	...	9 22
Barbelroth-Ob.		6 34	7 58	9 19	12 5	2 10	...	4 38	6 17	...	9 36
Winden arr	a.m.	6 46	8 10	9 31	1217	2 22	p.m.	4 50	6 29	p.m.	9 48
,, dep	5 15	7 15	8 20	9 49	1254	3 23	4 40	5 26	7 32	8 40	10 5
Wörth	5 37	7 52	8 42	1010	1 23	3 46	5 2	6 3	7 54	9 20	1025
Maximilia.	5 41	7 56	8 46	1013	1 27	3 50	5 6	6 7	7 58	9 24	1029

	a.m.	a.m.	a.m.	a.m.	a.m.	p.m.	p.m.	p.m.	p.m.	p.m.
Maximiliansau dep	5 23	6 15	7 37	9 10	1156	3 13	...	6 5	7 5	9 2
Wörth	5 35	6 25	7 49	9 15	12 2	3 18	...	6 10	7 10	9 16
Winden ......arr	5 54	6 45	8 9	9 35	1222	3 43	...	6 30	7 39	9 36
,, ...dep	—	7 8	8 20	9 50	1 2	3 48	5 30	—	7 34	10 8
Barbelroth-Ob.	...	7 21	8 33	10 3	1 15	4 1	5 43	...	7 46	1021
Bergzabern arr	...	7 34	8 46	1016	1 28	4 14	5 56	...	7 58	1034

KUSEL and LANDSTUHL.

E.M.																
	Kusel..............dep	5 a52	6a38	8 a51	10a49	11a44	12p40	3 p9	4 p4	6p45	7p58	...	...	...	...	...
2¾	Altenglan	5 47	6 54	9 3	11 1	12 4	12 52	3 22	4 20	7 1	8 10	...	...	...	...	...
9	Glan-Münchweiler	6 9	7 12	9 26	11 23	12 21	1 15	3 44	4 38	7 18	8 32	...	...	...	...	...
18	Landstuhl 206..arr	6 46	...	10 3	12 0	...	1 52	4 21	...	...	9 [illegible]	...	...	...	...	...
	Landstuhl..............dep	7a36	10a18	...	12p22	p.m.	2p18	...	5p12	9 p34	...	...	...	...	...	...
	Glan-Münchweiler	8 14	10 56	11a13	1 0	1 42	2 56	5 p7	5 50	10 12	...	...	...	...	...	...
	Altenglan	8 36	11 19	12 5	1 22	2 4	3 21	5 29	6 12	10 34	...	...	...	...	...	...
	Kusel..............arr	8 47	11 30	12 16	1 33	2 15	3 32	5 40	6 23	10 45	...	...	...	...	...	...

ROHRBACH and KLINGENMUNSTER							
Rohrbach ...dep	8a42	1p6	4 p0	5p19	7p24	10p7	...
Klingenmünster	9 11	135	4 23	5 48	7 53	1036	...
Klingenmünster	6a16	9a52	2 p0	4p37	6p0	8p2	...
Rohrbach 208 arr	6 50	1021	2 33	5 10	632	831	...

LUDWIGSHAFEN and MANNHEIM.

‡—10.33 p.m. on Sunday.

	a.m.	a.m.	a.m.	a.m.	a.m.	a.m.	a.m.	a.m.	p.m.	p.m.	p.m.	p.m.	p.m.	p.m.	p.m.	p.m.	p.m.	p.m.	p.m.	p.m.	p.m.	p.m.	p.m.	a.m.
Ludwigshafen dep	5 46	6 42	7 46	8 10	9 7	9 34	11 5	11 15	12 40	1 14	1 40	2 45	3 27	3 43	4 34	5 11	6 6	6 41	7 58	8 47	8 59	9 20	1127	12 20
Mannheim	5 [illegible]	6 50	7 55	8 18	9 16	9 42	11 13	11 22	12 48	1 21	1 48	2 54	3 35	3 52	4 43	5 19	6 15	6 48	8 6	8 55	9 7	9 28	1135	12 28

	a.m.	a.m.	a.m.	a.m	a.m.	a.m.	a.m.	a.m.	a.m.	p.m.	p.m.	p.m.	p.m.	p.m.	p.m	p.m.	p.m.	p.m.	pm	p.m	p m	pm	p.m.	a.m.
Mannheim...dep	4 48	6 30	7 7	8 15	8 25	8 58	9 32	1043	1116	1215	1 10	1240	2 10	2 46	3 48	5 11	5 46	7 8	810	8 27	8 46	945	10‡51	12 14
Ludwigshafen ar	4 57	6 39	7 14	8 23	8 33	9 6	9 41	1051	1125	1223	1 17	1248	2 18	2 55	3 56	5 19	5 55	7 16	819	8 35	8 55	953	11 0	12 22

LUDWIGSHAFEN and MECKENHEIM.

†—Not on Sunday.

Ludwigshafen (Brücke)...dep	5a22	6a50	8a35	12p15	1p34	4p17	6†20	6 p42	8 p28	...	...	...	...	...	...	...	...
Dannstadt	6 27	8 3	9 40	1 17	2 50	5 17	7 17	7 48	9 28	...	...	...	...	...	...	...	...
Meckenheim ....arr	6 49	8 25	10 2	1 39	3 13	5 39	7 39	8 10	9 50	...	...	...	...	...	...	...	...
Meckenheim ....dep	3a55	5†20	6 a2	7a40	10 a3	12p54	3p30	4p54	7p39	...	...	...	...	...	...	...	...
Dannstadt	4 25	5 50	6 32	8 12	10 33	1 25	4 0	5 25	8 9	...	...	...	...	...	...	...	...
Ludwigshafen (Brücke) arr	5 20	6 47	7 30	9 11	11 30	2 23	4 56	6 20	9 4	...	...	...	...	...	...	...	...

Luggage Rate—see page 462.]

LOWER PALATINE RAILWAY.

WORMS, LUDWIGSHAFEN, and SAARBRÜCKEN.

	2,3,4	1—4	2 3 4	1,2,3	Ex3	2,3,4	2 3 4	1,2,3	1,2,3	Ex 2	2,3,4	Ex3	2 3 4	Ex3	1,2,3	2 3 4	Ex3	Ex 3	2 3 4	2&3	2 3 4	Ex3
	a.m.	a.m.	a.m.	a.m.	a.m.	a.m.	a.m.		p.m.		p.m.	p.m.	p.m.		p.m.	p.m.		p.m.	p.m.	p.m.	p.m.	a.m.
Worms.............dep	...	4 18	5 50	7 52	...	8 8	9 25	...	1218	...	12 48	2 57	3 20	...	5 38	...	...	8 23	...	1010	1130	1 5
Frankenthal	5 13	4 40	6 18	8 4	...	8 30	9 37	...	1230	...	1 7	3 9	3 38	...	5 50	6 17	...	8 36	...	1028	1147	1 17
Ludwigshafen ...arr	5 31	4 56	6 35	8 14	...	8 49	9 48	a.m.	1241	...	1 23	3 19	3 55	...	6 0	6 38	...	8 48		1045	12 2	1 28
" ...dep	5 37	5 38	6 42	8 32	8 44	9 34	9 51	11 30	1251	...	1 44	3 35	4 3	...	6 10	6 45	...	9 6	1050	1149	—	1 32
Schifferstadt......dep	6 3	5 43	7 7	8 46	...	10 6	10 3	11 44	...	...	2 12	3 50	4 26	...	6 24	7 11	...	9 20	1114	12 6	...	...
Hassloch..................	6 16	...	7 21	...	...	10 21	—	11 54	...	...	2 28	...	4 40	...	...	7 26	...	...	1129	1221	...	...
Neustadt............arr	6 26	6 0	7 35	9 3	9 12	10 32	...	12 4	1 18	...	2 39	4 7	4 51	...	6 40	7 37	...	9 37	1140	1232	Ex3	2 0
							p.m.			p.m.				p.m.			p.m.				a.m.	
Neustadt ....dep		6 2	7 52	...	9 14	10 42	1210	...	1 20	1 56	2 51	...	5 0	5 39	6 42	7 47	8 43	9 40	1147	...	1 14	...
Lambrecht..................		...	8 2	...	9 24	10 54	1221	...	...	:	3 4	...	5 11	:	...	7 59	:	9 51	1158	...	:	...
Hochspeyer ....arr		6 31	:	...	9 46	11 22	1251	...	...	:	3 36	...	5 40	:	...	8 29	:	10 13	1229	...	:	...
MUNSTER-a-S. 206 arr		8a35	9a15	...	1120	...	2p38	...	...	3 p8	5 p51	...	7p45	6p57	...	...	9p54	11p50	...	...	2a23	...
Hochspeyer ....dep		6 32	—	2 3 4	9 47	11 24	1253	...	...	To Bingerbruck (arr. 3.31 p.m.)	3 39	...	5 42	—	...	8 32	—	10 14	1230	...	—	...
Kaiserslautern.........arr		6 44	...	a.m.	9 58	11 41	1 8	...	1 56		3 56	...	5 55	...	7 22	8 59	...	10 26	1245	...	...	...
" 207...dep		6 52	...	9 13	10 0	11 51	—	...	1 58		4 8	...	5 59	...	7 25	8 59	...	10 28	—	...	...	...
Landstuhl 205 ....arr		7 20	...	9 37	1013	12 16	...	...	2 11		4 34	...	6 21	...	7 40	9 25	...	10 41	...	...	...	...
Homburg 205............arr		7 50	...	1010	1031	12 52	...	...	2 29		5 10	...	6 52	...	8 1	9 59	...	10 59	a.m.	a.m.	...	...
" ....dep		7 59	...	—	1033	1 18	...	...	2 31		5 20	...	—	...	8 3	1010	...	11 1	4 39	6 10	...	...
Rohrbach		8 25	...	...	...	1 44	p.m.	...	...		5 45	...	...	...	...	1035	...	...	5 7	7 6	...	...
St. Ingbert......................		9 1	...	...	1057	1 50	2 14	...	2 54		5 52	...	...	...	8 27	1048	...	11 24	5 18	7 18	...	...
Saarbrücken 205......arr		9 24	...	...	1111	...	2 36	...	3 8		6 14	...	...	...	8 41	1111	...	11 38	5 41	7 40	...	...

Extra.—Ludwigshafen to Neustadt, 12.27, 4.40, 6.4, 7.40, 9.15, 9.57 p.m.

†—Weekdays only.]

SAARBRÜCKEN, LUDWIGSHAFEN, and WORMS.

	Ex3	Ex3	2 3 4	1—4	1,2,3	1—4	Ex3	Ex3	1,2,3	2 3 4	2,3,4	1—4	1,2,3	2 3 4	Ex2	2,3,4	2 3 4	Ex3		2 3 4	1,2,3	2,3,4
						a.m.	a.m.			a.m.	a.m.		p.m.			p.m.		p.m.		p.m.	p.m.	p.m.
Saarbrücken.....dep	...	...	...	...	...	5 10	7 0	...	...	7 55	9 37	...	1 17	...	...	2 26	...	6 29	...	7 41	9 53	10 0
St. Ingbert............	...	...	...	...	...	5 35	7 16	...	...	8 20	10 5	...	1 31	...	...	3 17	...	6 45	...	8 2	10 9	10 29
Rohrbach	...	...	...	...	...	5 42	...	...	...	8 27	10 13	...	...	...	...	3 25	...	...	...	8 10	...	10 37
Homburg............arr	...	...	...	...	...	6 6	7 26	...	...	1011	10 37	a.m.	1 49	...	...	3 49	p.m.	7 5	...	8 34	10 26	12‡13
" ....dep	...	...	...	...	...	6 30	7 38	...	...	1016	—	11 35	1 50	...	...	3 58	4 32	7 6	...	8 50	10 31	12 23
Landstuhl	...	...	...	...	...	7 6	7 56	...	...	1048	...	12 7	2 8	...	...	4 31	5 9	7 25	...	9 24	10 48	12 54
Kaiserslautern...arr	A	...	...	a.m.	a.m.	7 31	8 10	...	...	1111	...	12 29	2 22	p.m.	...	4 56	5 34	7 39	...	9 49	11 1	1 18
" ...dep	...	...	...	4 54	6 30	7 43	8 14	...	...	1114	...	12 32	2 23	2 37	...	5 4	—	7 41	...	10 0	11 3	—
Hochspeyer ......arr	a.m.	a.m.	...	5 8	6 44	7 55	8 25	...	a.m.	1125	...	12 43	...	2 51	...	5 18	...	...	...	1014	...	...
MUNSTER-A-S. dep	1 25	1 35	...	...	...	5a50	5a50	...	1022	...	...	10a56	...	...	3p11	3 p46	...	...	...	8p10	...	...
Hochspeyer ......dep	:	:	...	5 9	6 53	7 56	8 26	...	:	1126	...	12 44	...	2 53	:	5 20	...	...	...	1020	...	...
Lambrecht.............	:	:	...	5 34	7 20	8 14	8 43	...	:	1151	...	1 10	...	3 21	:	5 46	...	...	...	1050	11 31	...
Neustadt............arr	2 32	2 42	...	5 42	7 29	8 23	8 51	...	1138	12 0	1,2,3	1 19	2 53	3 30	4 25	5 55	...	8 12	1,2,3	11 0	11 40	2,3,4
			a.m.					a.m.			p.m.						p.m.		p.m.			p.m.
Neustadt ....dep	...	...	4 17	5 45	7 39	8 26	8 56	1030	...	1214	2 2	2 14	2 55	3 35	...	6 4	7 8	8 14	8 46	1110	11 44	9 8
Hassloch	...	...	4 30	5 15	...	8 36	...	...	...	1224	...	2 26	...	3 48	...	...	7 18	...	...	1122	...	9 21
Schifferstadt ...dep	...	...	4 47	6 10	...	8 51	9 14	1047	...	1234	2 19	2 41	3 12	4 10	...	6 21	7 32	8 31	...	1141	11 59	9 37
Ludwigshafen ...arr	...	...	5 12	6 35	8 6	9 17	9 28	11 0	...	1247	2 31	3 5	3 24	4 24	...	6 35	7 54	8 43	9 14	12 5	12 12	10 3
" ...dep	...	...	5 46	7 0	8 45	9 59	—	1117	...	1252	2 36	3 32		4 30	...	6 41	—	9 5	9 25	1227	12 27	10 16
Frankenthal	...	...	6 2	7 18	9 2	10 6	...	1127	...	1 3	2 48	3 48	—	4 49	...	6 52	...	9 16	9 42	1244	12 44	10 36
Worms 209.........arr	...	...	6†45	7 38	9 17	...	...	1137	...	1 14	2 59	4 3	...	5 6	...	7 3	...	9 27	9 59	1 1	1 1	10 52

Extra.—Neustadt to Ludwigshafen, 6.54, 9.58 a.m., 12.40, 4 40, 6.12 p.m.

A—From 2nd July until 1st Sept.

KAISERSLAUTERN and MUNSTER-AM-STEIN.

	Ex3	2 3 4	1,2,3	2,3,4	2 3 4	2 3 4	Ex2	2 3 4	2 3 4	Ex3	1,2,3	Ex 3	2 3 4
		a.m.			a.m.	p.m.		p.m.	p.m.		p.m.		p.m.
Kaiserslautern......dep	...	6 30	...	...	9 28	1246	...	3 5	5 4	...	7 50	...	10 0
NEUSTADT ....dep	1a14	6 a2	7a52	...	9a14	1210	1p56	2p51	5 p0	5p39	6p51	8 p43	9p40
Hochspeyer ....dep	:	6 56	...	a.m.	9 53	1 3	...	3 44	5 45	...	8 9	...	1018
Enkenbach 207...........	:	7 6	8 36	8 42	10 2	1 13	2 31	3 57	6 1	6 13	...	9 16	1027
Langmeil-Munchweil.	:	7 23	...	8 55	1016	1 32	:	4 18	6 35	...	8 24	...	1043
Winnweiler	:	7 29	...	—	1021	1 38	:	4 26	6 41	...	—	...	1049
Rockenhausen	:	7 46	8 53	...	1036	1 53	:	4 48	6 57	...	...	...	11 4
Alsenz	:	8 12	...	...	1059	2 17	:	5 21	7 22	...	...	...	1128
Altenbamberg	:	8 26	...	...	1111	2 29	:	5 40	7 36	...	...	...	1141
Munster-am-Stein arr	2 23	8 35	9 15	...	1129	2 38	3 8	5 51	7 45	6 57	...	9 54	1150
BINGERBRUCK 125 ar	2a46	9a30	9a39	...	1244	3p24	3p31	7p11	8p34	7p20	...	10p17	1a45

	Ex3	Ex3	2 3 4	2 3 4	1,2,3	2 3 4	Ex3	2 3 4	Ex2	2 3 4	2 3 4	2 3 4	1,2,3
	a.m.	a.m.	a.m.	a.m.	a.m.	a.m.	p.m.	p.m.	p.m.	p.m.	p.m.	p.m.	p.m.
BINGERBRUCK ...dep	1259	1 9	5 3	8 45	9 56	10 4	1239	...	2 46	3 3	...	7 10	8 49
Munster-a-Stein dep	1 25	1 35	5 50	9 14	1022	1056	1 4	...	3 11	3 46	...	8 10	9 15
Altenbamberg............	:	:	6 0	9 24	...	11 6	:	...	:	3 55	...	8 20	...
Alsenz	:	:	6 14	9 38	...	1120	:	...	:	4 8	...	8 34	...
Rockenhausen	:	:	6 39	10 3	...	1145	:	...	:	4 32	...	9 1	9 38
Winnweiler	A :	:	6 54	1018	...	12 0	:	...	:	4 47	...	9 18	...
Langmeil-Munchweil	:	:	7 3	1026	...	12 8	:	2 18	:	4 53	7 27	9 25	...
Enkenbach	:	:	7 20	1042	11 6	1224	:	2 34	3 55	5 8	7 43	9 40	9 59
Hochspeyer ....arr	:	:	7 28	1051	...	1232	:	2 43	...	5 17	7 52	9 45	...
NEUSTADT 206 ...arr	2a32	2a42	8a23	1138	1138	1 19	2 p9	...	4p25	5p55	8p40	11 0	1030
Kaiserslautern ...arr	...	...	7 44	11 7	...	1247	...	3 0	...	5 55	8 12	10 6	...

A—Runs from 2nd July until 1st September.

LAMBRECHT and ELMSTEIN.

Lambrecht	8a20	12p41	3p23	7p21	10p7
Elmstein...	9 11	1 32	4 16	8 0	1046
Elmstein...	6‡a0	9a55	1p58	6p12	8p20
Lambrecht	6 50	1045	2 49	6 58	8 57

‡—Mondays dep. 4.38 a.m.

LOWER PALATINE RAILWAY.

[Luggage Rate—see page 462.

SCHIFFERSTADT and LAUTERBURG.

	a.m.	a.m.	a.m.	a.m.	a.m.	a.m.	a.m.	a.m.	a.m.	a.m.	p.m.	p.m.	p.m	p.m.	p.m.	p.m.	p.m.	p.m.	p.m.	p.m.	p.m.
LUDWIGSHAFEN...	5 54	6 42	7 19	8 32	8 37	9 9	9 51	11 4	1130	1145	1 6	2 32	3 23	4 10	6 4	6 29	7 22	8 54	9 57	1050	1140
Schifferstadt ...dep	6 12	7 20	...	8 45	8 51	...	10 4	...	1143	12 6	1 29	2 45	...	4 32	6 17	6 54	7 38	...	10 10	1117	12 8
Speyer ....dep	6 26	7 55	7 40	:	9 2	9 30	1014	11 25	:	1217	1 43	2 58	3 44	4 44	:	7 8	7 52	9 16	:	1131	1221
Germersheim........	6 55	8 20	7 53	:	9 17	:	1028	:	:	1240	2 10	3 20	:	5 8	:	7 34	8 25	9 29	:	—	1246
Worth	7 50	—	:	:	—	:	11 3	:	:	1 24	2 53	—	:	5 52	:	—	9 8	9 51	:	...	—
Lauterburg ...207A	8 17	...	:	:	...	:	1116	:	:	1 49	3 18	...	:	6 17	:	...	9 32	10 2	:	...	...
STRASSBURG ...arr	1047	...	9 a4	11a7	...	10a55	12p8	12p49	2 p9	...	4p48	...	5 p10	7p56	8p30	...	10p50	10p50	12a27	...	...

			a.m.		a.m.	a.m.			a.m.			p.m.	p.m		p.m.	p.m.	p.m.		p.m.		
STRASSBURG dep	...	...	...	...	5 47	7 23	...	...	8 55	...	...	1241	2 14	...	5 25	4 29	7 7	...	7 37	...	...
Lauterburg ...dep	...	...	5 0	...	7 20	8 34	...	...	10 36	...	...	2 15	:	...	:	6 12	:	...	8 51	...	...
Worth	a.m.	a.m.	5 38	a.m.	7 45	8 47	...	a.m.	11 2	p.m.	...	2 40	:	p.m.	:	6 39	:	...	9 10	p.m.	...
Germersheim........	4 15	5 0	6 25	7 3	8 36	9 30	a.m.	10 58	11 43	12 3	p.m.	3 34	3 27	5 32	6 45	7 24	:	p.m.	9 50	10 57	...
Speyer 139A ...arr	4 39	5 29	6 50	7 28	8 59	9 43	1028	11 22	11 59	1229	2 53	3 57	3 41	5 55	6 59	7 47	8 33	9 1	10 6	11 20	...
Schifferstadt ...arr	4 52	5 39	7 3	7 40	9 10	9 53	1042	11 35	12 11	1244	3 7	4 9	...	6 8	...	8 0	...	9 15	1017	11 32	...
LUDWIGSHAFEN	5 22	6a10	7a41	7 55	9a28	10 6	11a0	12 0	12p35	1p30	3 24	4p24	4 2	6 35	7 p20	8p23	8p55	10p3	1034	12 5	...

Frequent local service between Speyer and Schifferstadt.

SPEYER and NEUSTADT a.d. H.

‡—Not on Sunday

Speyer ....dep	5‡a30	9 a12	1 p0	4p35	7p35	...	...	...
Neustadt a.d. H. arr	7 20	11 15	2 35	6 30	9 10	...	...	...

Neustadt a.d. H. dep	5a55	9 a56	1p15	5 p11	...	...	...	...
Speyer ....arr	7 43	12 5	3 45	7 15	...	...	...	...

KAISERSLAUTERN and ALZEY.

‡—Not on Sunday.

	2 3 4	2 3 4	2 3 4	2 3 4	2 3 4	2 3 4	2 3 4	2 3 4	2 3 4
Kaiserslautern...	a.m.	a.m.	a.m.	a.m.	p.m.	p.m.	p.m.	p.m.	p.m
Hauptbahn dep	6 36	8 16	7 54	9 28	1246	3 20	5 54	8 40	10 0
Nordbahn ... ,,	6 42	...	8 0	...	...	3 26	6 0	8 46	...
Eselsfürth	6 51	...	8 9	...	...	3 35	6 7	8 55	...
Enkenbach..........	7 6	8 42	8 22	10 2	1 18	3 57	6 19	9 20	1027
Langmeil ......arr	7 21	8 55	—	1015	1 16	4 14	6 29	9 34	1040
,, ...dep	7 25	8 57	...	1033	1 30	4 58	6 32	9 36	1042
Borrstadt	7 42	9 8	...	1043	1 41	5 8	6 43	9 47	11 3
Gollheim Dreisen	7 52	9 17	p.m.	1051	1 49	5 16	6 51	9 55	1116
Marnheim	8 4	9 29	1 20	1059	2 10	5 26	7 3	10 4	1130
Kirchheim- arr	8 13	9 39	1 30	11 9	2 20	5 36	7 13	1014	1156
bolanden ...dep	—	9 40	—	1121	2 21	5 37	7 17	1016	—
Alzey ....arr	...	10 5	...	1149	2 48	6 4	7 44	1044	...

	2 3 4	1,2,3	2 3 4	2 3 4	2 3 4	2,3,4	2 3 4	2 3 4	2 3 4	2 3 4
	a.m.	a.m.		a.m.	p.m.	p.m.	p.m.	p.m.		
Alzey.........dep	...	7 59	...	1043	1 7	...	3 32	6 8	...	...
Kirchheim- arr	...	8 30	a.m.	1111	1 34	...	4 0	6 36	p.m.	p.m.
bolanden dep	5 48	8 31	9 10	1127	1 35	1 58	4 2	6 39	8 28	9 38
Marnheim arr	5 59	8 40	9 18	1137	1 44	2 7	4 10	6 48	8 37	9 47
Gollheim Dreis.	6 25	8 53	9 52	1146	1 56	—	4 19	7 7	—	—
Borrstadt	6 40	9 0	10 1	1155	2 5	...	4 27	7 16	...	...
Langmeil ...arr	6 55	9 8	1011	12 5	2 16	...	4 35	7 26	p.m.	...
,, ...dep	7 3	9 9	1026	12 8	2 18	p.m.	4 53	7 27	9 25	p.m.
Enkenbach ...	7 21	9 22	1042	1223	2 34	4 0	5 8	7 43	9 41	1013
Eselsfürth	7 32	9 31	...	...	...	4 12	...	...	...	1024
K'lautern Nord	7 38	9 36	...	...	...	4 18	...	...	...	1030
Hauptbahn...	7 44	9 41	11 7	1247	3 0	4 24	5 55	8 12	10 6	1036

Extra.				
Kaiserslautern Hpt. dep.	2 p3	5p30	9 p27	...
Enkenbach ....arr.	2 27	5 58	9 54	...

Enkenbach ......dep	8a39	11 a9	2p38	6p18	9p18	10p3
Kaiserslautern Hpt.	9 2	11 45	3 2	6 41	9 40	1019

Kaiserslautern Hpt.	5 p4
Langmeil ....arr	6 14

NEUSTADT-AN-DER-HAARDT and MARNHEIM.

	2 3 4	2 3 4	2 3 4	2 3 4	2 3 4	2 3 4	2 3 4	2 3 4	2 3 4	2 3 4	2 3 4
		a.m.	a.m.	a.m	p.m.	p.m.	p.m.	p.m.	p.m.	p.m.	p.m.
Neustadt dep	...	5 47	6 55	11 0	1 45	2 18	4 37	6 16	7 43	9 50	1146
Deidesheim...	a.m.	6 4	7 15	1121	2 2	3 16	4 55	6 34	8 2	1010	12 5
Dürkheim ...	5 22	6 24	7 35	1145	2 22	3 36	5 15	6 55	8 22	1030	1219
Freinsheim...	5 41	6 36	7 55	12 2	2 39	3 52	5 37	7 7	8 39	1043	—
Grunstadt ...	5 58	—	8 12	1219	2 56	4 9	5 54	—	8 56	—	...
Eisenberg ar	...	1,2,3	8 51	1 2	...	...	6 31	...	9 38	...	...
Monsheim ar	6 30	a.m.	8 39	1241	3 24	4 35	6 20	...	9 23	p.m.	...
,, dep	7 25	8 27	8 51	1245	3 34	—	6 25	...	9 35	1046	...
Marnh'm arr	7 54	8 47	9 16	1 10	4 0	...	6 50	...	10 0	1111	...

		2 3 4	2 3 4	2 3 4	2,3,4	2 3 4	2 3 4	2 3 4	2 3 4	2 3 4
			a m.		a.m.	a.m.	p.m.		p.m.	p.m.
Marnheim dep		...	6 3	...	9 33	1150	2 18	...	7 8	1010
Monsheim ar		...	6 32	...	10 1	1217	2 43	p.m.	7 38	1036
Monsheim dp		...	7 2	...	10 6	1246	2 59	4 54	7 48	1045
Eisenberg dp		...	6 35	...	...	11 9	2 25	...	7 25	...
Grunstdt	4a17	a.m.	7 26	...	10 30	1 10	3 30	5 20	8 14	1110
Freinsh'm	4 38	6 44	8 0	a.m.	10 49	1 29	3 55	5 40	8 37	1131
Durkheim	4 57	7 2	8 19	9 53	11 8	1 47	4 15	5 59	8 56	1143
Deidesh'm	5 11	7 16	8 33	10 7	11 23	2 1	4 30	6 13	9 11	—
Neustadt	5 29	7 34	8 51	1025	11 41	2 20	4 51	6 31	9 30	...

Extra.—Marnheim to Monsheim, 8.43 p.m. Dürkheim to Neustadt, 12.46, 9.54 p.m. Neustadt to Dürkheim, 9.16 a.m., 12.14 p.m.

FREINSHEIM to FRANKENTHAL (in 25 minutes). Freinsheim dep. 4.38, 5†39, 6.45, 7.54, 10 53 a.m., 12.14, 1.31, 2.48, 3.56, 5.45, 7.12, 7†18, 8.40, 10.49 p.m. Frankenthal dep. 4†3, 6.12, 7.20, 10.14, 11.32 a.m., 12.50, 1.59, 3.17, 5.7, 6†32, 6†40, 7.59, 11.1 p.m. †—Weekdays only.

†—Weekdays only.]

KAISERSLAUTERN and LAUTERECKEN.

Kaiserslautern (Hauptb.)... dep	...	7a50	1p13	4p30	6p52	8p55	...
Katzweiler	...	8 16	1 37	4 56	7 35	9 21	...
Wolfstein.............................	5a33	8 57	2 11	5 34	—	9 59	...
Lauterecken ....arr	5 59	9 21	2 31	5 57	...	1021	...

Lauterecken......dep	6a16	9 a35	2p38	6p23	...	...	...
Wolfstein	6 37	9 58	2 59	6 44	...	...	...
Katzweiler	7 11	10 36	3 33	7 18	...	...	...
Kaiserslautern...arr	7 38	11 4	3 59	7 45	...	...	...

LUDWIGSHAFEN and GROSSKARLBACH.

Ludwigshafen	4a29	6a37	...	1055	11a45	...	4p48	6p38	8 p5
Frankenthal......	6 10	7 39	9a38	12 0	1 6	2p15	7 2	7 40	9 6
Grosskarlbach...	6 57	...	1028	...	...	3 5	7 52	...	9 58

Grosskarlbach	...	...	4a35	7 a3	...	1038	...	3p30	...	8 p0
Frankenthal	4a4	5 a0	6 49	7 50	9a40	12 8	2p52	4 20	6p30	8 50
Ludwigshafen	5 5	6 2	7 50	...	1041	1 27	3 56	...	7 55	...

GRUNSTADT and ALTLEININGEN.

Grünstadt...........dep	8 a25	12p23	6 p0	9 p1
Altleiningen .... arr	9 6	1 4	6 39	9 40

Altleiningen ......dep	6 a35	9a45	2 p5	6p52	...
Grünstadt..........arr	7 16	10 24	2 46	7 31	...

ALSENZ and OBERMOSCHEL.

Alsenz ....dep	6 a30	8a15	9a42	11a24	2p24	4p12	5p24	7p26	8p37
Obermoschel arr	6 38	8 33	10 0	11 42	2 42	4 30	5 42	7 44	8 55

Obermoschel dep	5a50	7a47	9a14	10a36	1p55	3p41	4p57	6p58	8p10
Alsenz ....arr	6 8	8 5	9 32	10 54	2 13	3 59	5 15	7 16	8 28

GRUNSTADT and OFFSTEIN.

Grunstadt...........dep	6 a3	8 a18	1p25	4 p14	6 p58	9 p7	...
Offstein ....arr	6 26	8 43	1 50	4 37	7 23	9 32	...

Offstein.........dep	6 a34	8 a46	1p52	3 p37	7 p25	9 p37	...	...
Grunstadt......arr	6 59	9 9	2 17	4 0	7 50	10 2	...	...

BASLE, MÜLHAUSEN, and BELFORT.—Paris Time at Belfort.

	2–4	1–4	2–4	1,2,3	2 3 4	Ex2	Ex 2	2 3 4	2 3 4	2,3,4	Ex3	2–4	Ex3	1–4	2 3 4	2 3 4	1–4	Ex 2	Ex2	1–4		
	a.m.	a.m.	a.m.	a.m.	a.m.	a.m.	a.m.	a.m.	p.m.	p.m.	p.m.	p.m.	p.m.	p.m.	p.m.	p.m.	p.m.	p.m.	p.m.	p.m.		
Basle ....dep		4 58	6 0	6 33	7 58	9 40	10 41	1041	1215	12 38	1 45	3 19	5 6	...	...	6 17	7 32	9 25	10 0	1011	...	...
Mülhausen ......dep	5 18	6 10	7 8	7 36	9 36	1011	11 15	1140	1 4	2 15	2 45	4 8	5 38	5 44	6 35	7 13	8 48	9 55	1035	1140	...	...
Altkirch................	5 57	6 27	7 46	7 53	10 9	...	11 33	1213	1 38	3 12	3 3	4 49	...	6 17	7 10	7 45	9 2	...	...	1212	...	...
Dammerkirch..........	—	6 41	—	8 4	1023	...	...	1227	1 53	3 26	...	5 16	...	6 32	—	7 59	9 38	...	...	1225	...	...
Alt-Münsterol ...arr	...	6 54	...	8 14	1036	1047	11 52	1240	2 6	3 40	3 19	—	6 8	6 45	...	8 12	9 48	10 27	1113	1237	...	...
BELFORT (69) arr	...	6a37	...	7a53	1033	1017	11a36	1229	1p54	...	3 p6	...	5p54	6 p27	...	8 p0	9p29	10 p2	11p3	1216	...	...
PARIS (69)......arr	...	2p49	...	2p49	...	...	5 p45	9 p0	...	...	...	...	1148	...	...	4a55	6a25	...	6:25	...	...	...

PARIS ....dep	9 p45	9 p45	9p45	...	...	...	...	10p0	...	...	...	...	...	...	8a55	...	...	...	1 p0	...	...	...
BELFORT ....dep	3 a20	3 a20	3a53	...	4a50	...	4a52	6a28	7a55	10 5	10a30	1252	1p33	...	2p45	2p45	4p30	...	6p39	...	8 p3	—
	Ex 2	Ex 2	Ex2	2,3,4	Ex2	2,3,4	1–4	1,2,3	1–4	Ex2	2,3,4	1–4	Ex3	2–4	Ex2	Ex2	2 3 4	2 3 4	Ex3	2 3 4	2 3 4	
(Montreux Vieux	a.m.	a.m.	a.m.	a.m.	a.m.	a.m.	a.m.	a.m.	a.m.	a.m.	p.m.	p.m.	p.m.	p.m.	p.m.	p.m.	p.m.		p.m.	p.m.	p.m.	
Alt-Münsterol...dep	4 38	4 57	5 32	5 53	6 24	...	6 42	8 15	9 41	1139	12 25	2 37	3 13	...	4 23	4 51	6 22	...	8 14	8 25	9 50	...
Dammerkirch	...	...	...	6 6	...	...	6 56	8 24	9 56	...	12 39	2 49	...	3 31	...	...	6 35	p.m.	...	8 38	10 1	...
Altkirch	H	...	...	6 20	K	6 46	7 12	8 34	1012	D	12 55	3 2	3 29	3 58	4 39	C	6 49	7 8	8 30	8 52	1016	...
Mülhausen ....arr	5 9	5 26	6 3	6 48	7 0	7 24	7 40	8 49	1039	12 8	1 23	3 28	3 44	4 36	4 54	5 21	7 12	7 45	8 45	9 19	1045	...
Basle ....arr	5 50	5 58	6 34	7 51	7 58	8 5	—	1010	1115	1242	2 27	4 25	4 33	5 28	5 28	5 54	8 11	8 20	9 20	...	12 8	...

C—Until September 6th runs on Saturdays only. D—Runs on Saturdays only.
H—From 13th July until 17th August. K—From 2nd July until 1st October.

DAMMERKIRCH and BONFOL.

Dammerkirch...dep	6a56	8 a38	12p50	5p18	...	...
Bonfol 266........arr	7 49	9 31	1 42	6 10	...	...
Bonfol ....dep	7a19	11a24	1p50	7p35	...	...
Dammerkirch ...arr	8 18	12 22	2 45	8 30	...	...

ALTKIRCH and PFIRT.

Altkirch dep	6 a0	7a56	10a30	1p42	4p52	6 p5	9p37	...
Pfirt ......arr	7 21	9 17	11 52	3 4	6 13	7 26	105	...
Pfirt ....dep	5a19	6a10	8a44	11a20	2p30	5p40	7 p56	
Altkirch 207A arr	6 43	7 35	10 5	12 46	3 56	7 6	9 22	

SCHLETTSTADT and MARKIRCH.

	a.m.	a.m.	a.m.	a.m.	p.m.	p.m.	p.m.	p.m.	p.m.	p.m	p.m.
Schlettst.	5 10	6 45	8 27	9 52	12 8	1 43	3 32	6 22	7 24	9 20	1140
Weilerthal	5 23	7 0	8 42	10 6	1223	1 58	3 46	6 36	7 38	9 33	1153
Markirch	5 59	7 34	9 16	1040	1 0	2 35	4 20	7 10	8 12	10 6	1227

	a.m.	a.m.	a.m.	p.m.	p.m.	p.m.	p.m.	p.m.	p.m.	p.m.
Markirch	6 25	8 7	1054	1229	2 4	4 58	6 3	7 19	8 21	1015
Weilerthal	6 58	8 40	1127	1 2	2 37	5 30	6 35	7 51	8 52	1046
Schlettst.	7 11	8 53	1140	1 15	2 50	5 44	6 49	8 4	9 5	105

ZABERN, OBERMODERN, and RASTATT.

†—Weekdays only.

Zabern ...dep	4a38	5a48	7 a22	8a48	11a26	3p35	5p13	7p44	10p21
Steinburg	4 47	5 57	7 31	8 57	11 35	3 44	5 26	7 53	10 30
Buchsweiler	5 11	6 19	7 55	9 19	11 57	4 8	5 50	8 16	10 53
Obermodern arr	5 18	6 25	8 3	9 25	12 3	4 15	5 56	8 22	10 59
Obermodern dep	5 27	6 33	8 14	9 34	12 12	4 24	6 3	8 29	11 8
Hagenau arr	5 53	6 58	8 40	9 56	12 36	4 48	6 27	8 53	11 33
Hagenau dep	6 9	7 37	—	10 0	12 41	4 53	—	9 7	—
Röschw'g dep	6 46	8 13	1p51	1030	1 15	5 29	...	9 39	...
Rastatt ...arr	7 7	8 34	2 7	1048	1 36	5 53	...	10 0	...

Rastatt ...dep	†	...	6a34	9a26	...	1p15	2p58	3p15	...	6p52	9p30
Röschwoog ...	5a21	...	6 58	9 52	...	1 38	3 13	3 37	...	7 15	9 53
Hagenau arr	5 56	...	7 30	1023	...	2 10	—	4 9	...	7 47	1025
Hagenau dep	—	6 a1	7 40	1026	1227	2 15	...	4 15	6p24	7 54	1035
Obermodern arr	...	6 27	8 6	1052	1253	2 40	...	4 41	6 49	8 21	11 1
Obermodern dep	...	6 32	8 14	11 3	1259	2 43	...	4 42	6 51	8 30	11 7
Buchsweiler	5a15	6 42	8 24	1114	1 9	2 53	...	4 52	7 1	8 40	1117
Steinburg......	5 38	7 1	8 43	1134	1 28	3 13	...	5 20	7 21	9 1	1139
Zabern ...arr	5 48	7 10	8 52	1143	1 37	3 22	...	5 29	7 30	9 10	1149

BUCHSWEILER and INGWEILER.

‡—Week-days only.

Buchsweiler ......dep	4 a6	6 a1	7‡48	9a23	12 p5	4 p12	8p18	...
Ingweiler............arr	4 18	6 16	8 1	9 38	12 20	4 27	8 31	...
Ingweiler ....dep	7a25	8 ‡8	10a58	1p30	7p41	9 p0	...	...
Buchsweiler 207A ...arr	7 41	8 22	11 11	1 45	7 55	9 15	...	...

DIEDENHOFEN, TETERCHEN, and VOLKLINGEN.

‡—Not on Sunday.

Diedenhofen		...	7 a0	7a58	1034	1p40	4p48	6p12	8 p0	9p55
Metzerwiese		a.m.	7 23	8 11	1054	2 0	5 1	6 33	8 20	1016
Busendorf		6 0	8 8	8 37	1137	2 41	5 27	7 14	9 1	1058
Teterchen......	a.m.	6 20	8 23	8 49	1158	3 0	5 38	7 29	9 18	1116
Hargarten ...	4 29	6 34	8 33	8 55	12 9	3 17	5 46	7 41	9 27	1124
Wadgassen...	5 0	6 59	8 56	9 10	1234	3 41	6 1	8 5	9 52	1149
Bous arr	5 4	...	...	..	1‡35	3 48	...	...	...	...
Völklingen arr		7 9	9 6	9 17	1245	3 55	6 9	8 15	10 3	1159

Völklingen dp	a.m.	7a18	7a41	10a12	1 p2	3p32	5p41	7p11	9p33	12a57
Bous ...dep	5 37	...	...	...	...	...	...	...	...	...
Wadgassen ,,	5 41	7 24	7 51	10 23	1 11	3 40	5 50	7 20	9 43	1 9
Hargarten	6 9	7 42	8 28	10 50	1 42	3 58	6 20	7 58	1011	1 35
Teterchen	6 22	7 51	8 41	11 1	1 53	4 7	6 30	8 9	1020	1 44
Busendorf	6 35	8 1	8 55	11 13	2 11	4 17	6 44	8 28	—	1 56
Metzerwiese ...	7 19	8 28	9 36	11 54	2 55	4 45	7 26	9 12	...	—
Diedenhofn	7 36	8 40	9 53	12 11	3 12	4 57	7 43	9 29	...	...

STRASSBURG, RÖSCHWOOG, and LAUTERBURG.

	2–4	2–4	2–4	Ex3	2–4	1,2,3	Ex3	2–4	Ex3	2–4	Ex3	2–4	2–4
	a.m.	a.m.	a.m.	a.m.	p.m.	p.m.	p.m.	p.m.	p.m.	p.m.	p.m.	p.m.	p.m
Strassburg dep	5 47	7 23	8 55	1126	1241	1 22	2 14	4 29	5 25	6 0	7 7	7 37	8 58
Wanzenau	6 3	7 37	9 11	:	1256	...	:	4 46	:	6 17	:	7 52	9 13
Drusenheim	6 26	7 56	9 34	:	1 19	...	:	5 9	:	6 41	:	8 14	9 35
Röschwoog arr	6 42	8 8	9 49	:	1 34	1 50	:	5 25	:	6 57	:	8 26	9 49
Röschwoog dep	6 49	8 10	10 7	:	1 40	—	:	5 29	:	6 58	:	8 27	9 53
Selz	7 5	8 20	1022	:	1 56	...	:	5 44	:	7 14	:	8 37	10 9
Lauterburg arr	7 18	8 33	1035	:	2 9	...	:	5 57	:	7 27	:	8 50	1022
GERMERSHM arr	8a29	9a22	1141	:	3p18	...	3p26	7p17	6p45	9p49	:	9p43	...
LUDWIGSHN arr	9a28	10a6	1235	1p10	4p21	..	4 p2	8p23	7p20	1034	8p55	1034	...

‡—Sunday dep. 9.41 p.m.

	2–4	Ex3	2–4	Ex3	2–4	Ex3	2–4	1–3	2 3 4	Ex3	2–4	2–4	1,2,3
	a.m.	a.m.			a.m.	a.m.			p.m.			p.m.	p.m.
LUDWIGSHAFN dp	...	7 19	5a54	9 a9	9 51	11 4	...	...	1 6	5p25	4p10	...	8 54
GERMERSHEIM dp	...	7a53	6a55	:	1028	:	p.m.	...	2 9	:	5 p8	...	9‡29
Lauterburg dep	5 52	:	9 17	:	1117	:	1242	...	3 23	:	6 31	9 ‡4	10 3
Selz	6 7	:	9 32	:	1127	:	1257	...	3 38	:	6 46	9 19	1013
Röschwoog arr	6 22	:	9 47	:	1135	:	1 11	p.m.	3 53	:	7 1	9 31	1020
Röschwoog dep	6 24	:	9 52	:	1136	:	1 16	3 15	3 54	:	7 2	9 42	1021
Drusenheim	6 42	:	10 8	:	...	:	1 31	...	4 9	:	7 17	9 57	...
Wanzenau	7 8	:	1031	:	...	:	1 54	...	4 32	:	7 40	1020	...
Strassburg arr	7 25	9 4	1047	1055	12 8	1249	2 10	3 45	4 48	7 5	7 56	1036	1050

Extra Rail Motor

Strassburg...dep	11p10	Lauterburg dep	7a10	4p56
Lauterburg arr	12 33	Strassburg...arr	8 38	6 25

ZABERN, MOLSHEIM, STRASSBURG, and SCHLETTSTADT.

	a.m.	a.m.	a.m.	p.m.	p.m.	p.m	p.m
Zabern(210)dep	4 42	6 42	9 7	1244	4 45	6 24	8 55
Wasselnheim ...	5 17	7 16	9 42	1 18	5 20	6 58	9 30
Sulzbad	5 37	7 36	10 3	1 38	5 40	7 17	9 50
Molsheim 212A	5 45	7 44	1011	1 46	5 48	7 25	9 58
Strassburg dp	5 22	7 54	9 47	1 20	5 12	6 51	9 31
Molsheim..arr	5 59	8 22	1024	1 59	5 52	7 29	10 9
Molsheim...dep	6 3	8 24	1026	2 4	5 58	7 32	1012
Bischofsheim...	6 17	8 36	1040	2 17	6 11	7 45	1025
Barr...............	6 40	9 57	11 2	2 40	6 34	8 7	1046
Schlettstadt ar	7 8	9 25	1130	3 9	7 4	8 35	1114
Schlettstadt dp	4a42	6a45	9 a2	1250	4p44	6p41	9p27
Barr...............	5 15	7 17	9 32	1 22	5 21	7 16	9 58
Bischofsheim...	5 36	7 35	9 51	1 42	5 42	7 36	1017
Molsheim ...arr	5 52	7 47	10 3	1 55	5 57	7 50	1030
Molsheim .dep	6 a0	7 49	10 5	2 1	6 4	7 56	1037
Strassburg arr	6 36	8 19	1031	2 37	6 37	8 28	1110
Molsheim...dep	6 5	8 15	1030	2 7	6 9	8 2	1040
Sulzbad..........	6 13	8 23	1038	2 17	6 17	8 10	1048
Wasselnheim ...	6 36	8 46	11 1	2 45	6 40	8 33	1112
Zabern ......arr	7 8	9 18	1133	3 20	7 12	9 7	1144

ALSACE and LORRAINE RAILWAY. [Luggage Rate—see page 462.

MAYENCE, WORMS, NEUSTADT, WEISSENBURG, STRASSBURG, MULHAUSEN and BASLE.

THROUGH CARRIAGES, 1st and 2nd Class. { Frankfort to Basle—in 6.45 a.m., 7.40 a.m., 9.37 a.m., 4.3 p.m., 11.55 p.m. from Frankfort. Cologne to Basle—in 10.3 a.m., 12.10 p.m., 10.33 p.m. from Cologne.

RC—Restaurant Car.

E.M. Dist.	Cologne 128 ......dep	...	1033	...	...	...	...	...	...	...	1 a58	...	1 a58	...	...	...	...	...	...	...
	Frankfort ....dep	...	1210	...	...	...	...	...	...	...	5a35	...	4a37	6 a35	...	9a37	...	8a30	...	8 a30
			Ex3				Ex 3		2—4	2,3,4	1,2,3	Ex 3	2,3,4	2,3,4	2,3,4	Ex3		Ex3		1—4
	Mayence—		a.m.							a.m.	a.m.		a.m.	a.m.		a.m.		a.m.		a.m.
—	Hauptbahnhof dep	...	1 49	...	...	...	...	...	...	4 10	6 43	...	5 45	7 56	...	⋮	...	9 31	...	9 41
1¼	,, Sud	...	...	...	...	...	...	...	...	4 15	6 51	...	5 50	8 1	...	⋮	...	...	...	9 46
6¾	Bodenheim	...	...	...	...	...	...	...	...	4 32	7 2	...	6 8	8 16	...	⋮	...	...	...	10 0
11¼	Nierstein	...	...	...	...	...	...	...	...	4 47	7 12	...	6 32	8 30	...	⋮	...	9 50	...	10 13
12¾	Oppenheim	...	2 8	...	...	...	...	...	...	4 54	7 17	...	6 37	8 35	...	⋮	...	9 55	...	10 18
19¾	Alsheim	...	...	...	...	...	...	...	...	5 13	...	...	7 1	8 52	...	⋮	...	...	...	10 32
23¾	Osthofen (208	...	...	...	...	...	...	...	...	5 29	7 39	...	7 25	9 5	...	⋮	...	1013	...	10 47
28½	Worms .... { arr	...	2 29	...	...	...	...	...	a.m.	5 39	7 48	...	7 35	9 15	...	1034	...	1022	...	10 57
	{ dep	...	2 33	...	...	...	...	...	4 18	5 50	7 52	...	8 8	9 25	...	1036	...	1024	...	11 8
35½	Frankenthal (207)........	...	⋮	...	...	...	...	...	4 40	6 18	8 4	...	8 30	9 37	...	...	...	1036	...	11 25
42	Ludwigshafen ....arr	...	⋮	...	...	...	...	...	4 56	6 35	8 14	...	8 49	9 48	...	1055	...	1046	...	11 40
44¾	Mannheim (205) ..arr	...	3 a4	...	...	...	...	...	5a53	6 a50	9a16	...	9 a16	...	...	1113	...	11a13	...	...
...	Frankfort ....dep	...	⋮	...	...	...	5 a52	...	...	...	6 a45	7 a40		...	7 a40	...	...		9 a44	10a20
...	Ludwigshafen ....dep	...	⋮	...	...	...	7 19	...	5 30	6 42	8 32	9 9	...	...	9 34	11 4	...	...	11 30	12 27
49½	Schifferstadt (207)...arr	...	⋮	...	...	...	⋮	...	5 42	7 5	8 45	⋮	...	...	9 56	⋮	...	...	11 43	12 47
122½	Strassburg (207A) arr	...	⋮	...	...	...	⋮	...	9a 4	...	...	⋮	...	...	12 p8	⋮	...	...	...	...
...	Schifferstadt ....dep	...	⋮	...	...	...	⋮	...	5 43	7 7	8 46	RC	...	...	10 6	⋮	...	...	11 44	12 48
55	Hassloch........	...	⋮	...	...	...	⋮	...	...	7 24	...	⋮	...	...	10 21	⋮	...	...	11 54	1 0
60½	Neustadt........arr	...	⋮	...	...	...	⋮	...	6 0	7 35	9 3	⋮	...	...	10 32	⋮	...	...	12 4	1 10
		Ex 3	⋮	2—4	2,3,4	2,3,4	⋮	2 3 4	2 3 4	1,2,3	1,2,3	⋮		2,3,4	2,3,4	Ex3			1,2,3	1,2,3
...	Cologne v.Munster dp	10p33	⋮	...	...	...	⋮	...	...	...	12a28	⋮	...	...	...	⋮	...	...	6a17	...
		a.m.						a.m.	a.m.	a.m.	a.m.			a.m.	a.m.				p.m.	p.m.
...	Neustadt ....dep	2 46	Via Carlsruhe, page 140.	...	...	...	Via Lauterburg, page 207A	6 5	6 58	8 30	9 7	Via Lauterburg, page 207A	...	9 25	10 42	Via Lauterburg page 207A	...	...	12 9	1 30
65½	Edenkoben	...		...	...	...		6 18	7 13	8 40	...		...	9 41	10 57		...	...	12 19	1 40
71¾	Landau (205) ...... { arr	...		a.m.	...	...		6 36	7 32	8 52	9 25		...	10 0	11 17		...	...	12 30	1 51
	{ dep	...		4 49	...	...		6 40	7 51		9 27		...	10 10	12 5		...	...	12 33	
76½	Rohrbach	...		5 3	...	...		6 55	8 7	...	...		...	10 25	12 20		...	...	...	...
79¾	Winden (205)	...		5 10	...	...		7 4	8 15	...	9 41		...	10 37	12 30		...	...	12 51	...
83½	Scheidt	...			...	...		7 14		...	...		...	10 46	12 40		...	...	...	...
89½	Weissenburg ...... { arr	...		...	a.m.	a.m.		7 29	a.m.	...	9 59		...	11 1	12 56		...	...	1 9	...
	{ dep	...		...	5 4	6 40		7 41	8 55	...	10 5		...	11 9	1 19		...	...	1 12	...
99¾	Sulz-u-W 2 3 4	...		2,3,4	5 33	7 5		7 58	9 20	...	...		...	11 34	1 44		...	...	...	...
105	Walburg.. .... a.m.	...		a.m.	5 48	7 17		8 8	9 [illegible]	...	...		...	11 47	1 56		...	...	...	...
110	Hagenau (212A) ..... 4†28	...		5 25	6 17	7 33		8 18	9 50	...	10 34		...	12 11	2 7		...	...	1 40	...
114¾	Bischweiler 4 41	...		5 38	6 30	7 45		8 27	10 4	...	10 44		...	12 23	2 19		...	...	1 48	...
120¾	Hördt 4 57	...		5 54	6 45	7 59		...	1020	...	...		...	12 38	2 34		...	...	...	...
125¼	Vendenheim 5 7	...		6 4	6 55	8 7		...	1029	...	...		...	12 48	2 43		...	...	...	...
131	Strassburg.........arr5 20	4 22	5 34	6 17	7 6	8 18	9 4	8 51	1042	...	11 7	10 55	...	1 1	2 54	1249	Ex 3		2 9	Ex 3
...	Brussels 103A ...dep	...	...	...	...	...	11p28	...	...	...	...	...	...	...	...	...	5 a24	|	...	6 a8
...	Luxemburg 210 dep	...	...	...	...	...	5 a3	...	...	...	5 a53	5 a53	2,3,4	9 a42	...	...	10a45	|	...	11a41
...	Metz 202............dep	...	1,2,3	2,3,4	1,2,3	...	6 a13	...	...	...	7 a50	7 a50	7 a57	10 49	2,3,4	...	11a43	Ex3	...	12p50
		a.m.	a.m.	a.m.	a.m.	a.m.	a.m.	a.m.			a.m.	a.m.	p.m.	p.m.	p.m.	p.m.	p.m.	p.m.		p.m.
...	Strassburg..............dep	4 28	6 0	6 10	7 40	8 25	9 14	10 7	...	...	11 13	11 1	12 17	2 24	4 18	1254	2 2	2 15	...	3 26
135½	Grafenstaden	...	...	6 18	...	8 33		1016	...	...	...	...	12 25	2 32	4 26	...	...	A	...	...
143½	Erstein	...	...	6 40	7 57	8 54	RC	1039	...	...	...	...	12 46	2 54	4 48	RC	B	2 32	...	RC
148	Benfeld	...	...	6 52	8 5	9 5	—	1050	...	...	...	...	12 57	3 5	4 59	...	...	2 40	...	...
158	Schlettstadt	...	6 33	7 16	8 21	9 28	9 47	1111	...	...	11 47	...	1 35	3 30	5 23	1 27	...	2 56	...	4 1
164	Rappoltsweiler........	...	6 42	7 30	8 31	9 42	9 56	1125	p.m.	...	11 56	...	1 49	3 44	5 37	...	...	3 5	...	...
172¾	Colmar (211)........	5 18	6 54	7 53	8 46	10 14	10 8	1143	1217	...	12 9	11 52	2 13	4 50	6 18	1 46	2 55	3 18	...	4 22
180½	Rufach	...	...	8 12	8 59	10 34	...		1236	p.m.	...	...	2 32	5 10	6 37	...	...	...	...	...
188	Bollweiller (211)........	...	7 14	8 33	9 12	10 53	10 29	...	1256	1 21	12 30	RC	2 53	5 31	6 57	...	...	3 41	...	4 44
194¾	Lutterbach	...	...	8 51	9 24	11 11	...	...	1 14	1 40	...	...	3 12	5 49	7 16	...	...	...	...	...
196½	Dornach ....2—4	...	...	8 56	...	11 16	...	...	1 19	1 45	...	...	3 17	5 54	7 21	...	...	A	...	...
198½	Mulhausen ... { arra.m.	5 52	7 31	9 0	9 31	11 21	10 44	...	1 23	1 50	12 45	12 26	3 21	5 58	7 25	2 19	3 29	3 58	...	5 1
	{ dep6 16	5 53	7 33	9 59	9 34	11 28	10 45	...	1 30		12 47	12 27	3 35	6 9		2 22	3 30	4 1	...	5 3
208¾	Sierentz 6 39	...	...	10 24	9 49	11 53	...	...	1 55	...	...	...	4 0	6 35	...	...	...	...	...	...
215½	St. Ludwig 6 58	...	7 55	10 41	9 59	12 10	...	...	2 14	...	1 8	...	4 16	6 54	...	...	...	...	...	5 25
219½	Basle ¶........arr7 12	6 24	8 5	10 54	10 10	12 22	11 15	...	2 27	...	1 19	12 58	4 27	7 7	...	2 52	4 0	4 33	...	5 36
274½	Zurich (261) ....arr	8 a35	9a58	1 p13	12 48	3 p29	1 p13	...	...	...	3 p29	3 p29	7 p55	...	...	6 57	...	7p55	...	7 p55
278¾	Lucerne (258) ......arr	8 a59	1048	1 p56	1 p40	3 p49	1 p56	...	6p15	...	3 p49	3 p49	...	...	...	6p15	...	8p15	...	8 p15
451	Milan (269A)........arr	3 p5	7p47	...	...	10p25	8 p40	...	...	...	10p25	10p25	...	...	...	...	...	...	...	6 a22

A—Runs until 30th Sept. B—On Saturday only, until 20th Sept.

St. Ludwig to Leopoldshohe (12 minutes), 6.1, 6.59, 7 59, 10.4 a.m., 12.14, 2.14, 5.36, 7.6, 8.2, 9 2 p.m. From Leopoldshohe, 4.46, 6.26, 7.32, 9.40, 11.3 a.m., 1.36, 3.21, 4.19, 6.44, 8.16, 11.27 p.m.

OSTHOFEN and WESTHOFEN.	E.M																	
		Osthofen...dep	8a‡20	1053	1 p6	3p14	6p40	8p35	9p55	Westhofen ...	6a55	9a50	11a55	2 p0	4 n5	7p35	9p15
	4	Westhofen arr	8 42	1115	1 28	3 35	7 0	8 57	1015	Osthofen 208	7 18	1010	12 15	2 20	4 25	7 55	9 35

‡—8.0 a.m. on Sunday.

Luggage Rate—see page 462.] ALSACE and LORRAINE RAILWAY.

MAYENCE, WORMS, NEUSTADT, WEISSENBURG, STRASSBURG, MULHAUSEN, and BASLE.

SLEEPING CARRIAGES for Basle in 11.55 p.m. from Frankfort (1st cl. 8 m., 2nd cl. 6 m.).
The 3.35 a.m. from Strassburg for Basle has Sleeping Carriages from Ostend.

Station	1	2	3	4	5	6	7	8	9	10	11	12	13	14	15	16	17	18	19	20
COLOGNE (122)......dep	...	6a17	10a3	10 a3	...	1120	...	...	12p10	...	...	1 p5	2 p31	...	3 p38	...	6 p33	...	8 p2	...
FRANKFORT ....dep	...	10a25	1215	12 27	...	1p33	...	...	1 p59	...	...	3 p52	6 p9	6p22	8 p25	7p17	9 p12	1155	...	...
		2,3,4 a.m.	2 3 4 p.m.	Ex.3 p.m.		Ex2 p.m.	2,3,4	Ex 3	1,2,3 p.m.	2,3,4 p.m.	1,2,3	2,3,4 p.m.	2,3,4 p.m.	1,2,3 p.m.	1,2,3	2 3 4 p.m.	2,3,4 p.m.	Ex3	Ex.3 nght	
Mayence—Haupt-bahnhof ....dep	...	11 27	1 18	1 55	...	2 32	...	...	3 48	3 33	...	5 2	6 45	7 36	⋮	8 35	10 13	⋮	12 5	...
,, Sud	...	11 32	1 26	2 0	...	...	...	...	3 53	3 38	...	5 10	6 51	...	⋮	8 40	10 18	⋮	12 10	...
Bodenheim	...	11 46	1 40	...	...	...	...	...	...	3 52	...	5 25	7 7	...	⋮	8 55	10 32	⋮	...	...
Nierstein	...	11 59	1 53	...	...	...	...	...	...	4 5	...	5 39	7 25	...	⋮	9 13	10 44	SC	...	...
Oppenheim	...	12 4	1 58	2 18	...	...	...	...	4 14	4 20	...	5 44	7 30	7 55	⋮	9 20	10 49	⋮	12 28	...
Alsheim	...	12 19	2 14	...	...	...	...	...	...	4 36	...	6 2	7 49	...	⋮	9 40	...	⋮	...	...
Osthofen	...	12 32	2 27	2 36	...	...	...	...	4 30	4 51	...	6 22	8 4	8 12	⋮	9 55	11 11	⋮	12 45	...
Worms .... arr	...	12 42	2 37	2 45	...	3 11	p.m.	...	4 39	5 1	p.m.	6 32	8 14	8 21	9 29	10 5	11 21	1252	12 55	...
Worms .... dep	...	12 48	2 46	2 57	...	3 15	3 20	...	4 40	5 6	5 38	6 40	8 50	8 23	9 31	1010	11 30	—	1 5	...
Frankenthal (207).........	...	1 7	2 59	3 9	...	⋮	3 38	...	4 53	5 23	5 50	7 1	9 11	8 36	9 43	1028	11 47	—	1 17	...
Ludwigshafen ....arr	...	1 23	3 12	3 19	...	⋮	3 55	...	5 6	5 47	6 0	7 17	9 26	8 48	9 53	1045	12 2	...	1 28	...
MANNHEIM (205) ...arr	...	1 p48	3p35	3 p35	...	3p46	4 p43	...	5 p19	6 p15	6 p15	8 p6	...	9 p7	...	1135	12a28	...	...	...
FRANKFORT ....dep	...	11a58	—	12p50	...	⋮	1p58	4 p3	...	...	4 p10	...	...	...	7 p46	...	...	...	10p41	...
Ludwigshafen ....dep	...	1 44	...	3 2	...	To Carlsruhe (arr. 4.39), page 140A.	4 40	5 25	...	...	6 4	...	...	...	9 57	1050	...	...	1 32	...
Schifferstadt (207) ...arr	...	2 8	...	⋮	...		4 57	⋮	...	...	6 17	...	...	...	10 10	1112	...	...	⋮	...
STRASBURG (207A) arr		...	...	⋮	...		...	Via Lauterburg, p. 207A	...	...	...	...	...	...	...	...	...	...	⋮	...
Schifferstadt...........dep	...	2 12	...	⋮	...		4 58		...	...	6 18	...	...	...	10 11	1114	...	...	⋮	...
Hassloch....................	...	2 27	...	⋮	...		5 15		...	...	...	...	...	...	...	1129	...	...	⋮	...
Neustadt.................arr	...	2 38	...	⋮	...		5 30		...	...	6 34	...	...	...	10 29	1140	...	...	2 0	...
	Ex.3		2—4	⋮	Ex.3		2,3,4		2 & 3		1,2,3	2,3,4	2,3,4		1,2,3	2 3 4	2 & 3		Ex.3	Ex 3
COLOGNE v.Munster dep	10 a3	...	...	⋮	12p10		...		...	...	...	...	...	...	5 p56	...	...	...	...	10p22
	p.m.	p.m.	p.m.		p.m.		p.m.		p.m.		p.m.	p.m.	p.m.		p.m.	p.m.	p.m.		a.m.	a.m.
Neustadt...................dep	2 15	3 0	2 25	Via Lauterburg, p. 207A.	4 30		6 15		5 0	...	6 38	8 56	9 43	...	10 36	11 5	11 48	...	2 4	2 36
Edenkoben	...	3 15	2 38		...		6 30		5 16	...	...	9 9	9 58	...	10 45	1120	12 3	...	2 15	...
Landau (205) ...... arr	2 32	3 35	2 55		4 49		6 48		5 36	...	6 56	9 26	10 16	...	10 56	1138	12 22	...	2 26	...
Landau (205) ...... dep	2 33	3 41	2 58		4 50	...	6 52			...	6 58	9 33	—	...	10 57	—	—	...	2 27	...
Rohrbach	...	3 56	3 13		RC	...	7 5		...	...	...	9 48	...	...	...	...	...	...	...	...
Winden (205)	...	4 7	3 21		...	...	7 39		...	...	7 11	10 0	...	...	11 10	...	...	...	SC	...
Scheidt 2 3 4	RC	4 17	—		...	...	7 48		...	...	...	10 9	...	...	...	...	...	...	...	...
Weissenburg arr p.m.	...	4 33	p.m.		5 19	...	8 3		...	...	7 27	10 24	...	...	11 26	...	...	...	2 59	C
Weissenburg dep 4 47	...	—	6 7		5 22	...	8 15		...	...	7 30	—	...	...	11 29	...	...	...	3 2	...
Sulz-u-W 5 12	...	1—4	6 32		...	...	8 40		...	...	7 45	...	...	...	...	...	...	...	...	...
Walburg...................5 24	...	p.m.	6 45		...	...	8 53		...	...	...	...	...	p.m.	...	...	...	...	...	...
Hagenau (212A) 5 58	3 21	4 17	7 0		5 50	...	9 10		...	...	8 1	...	...	11 4	11 57	...	...	...	3 30	...
Bischweiler 6 10	...	4 29	7 12		...	...	9 22		...	...	8 9	...	...	1115	12 6	...	...	...	...	...
Hördt 6 25	...	4 44	7 23		...	...	9 37		...	...	...	...	...	1126	...	...	...	...	...	...
Vendenheim 6 34	...	4 53	7 35		...	...	9 46		...	...	...	...	...	1134	...	...	...	...	...	...
Strassburg.. ......arr 6 47	3 48	5 3	7 48	5 10	6 17	...	9 59	7 5	...	...	8 30	...	...	1145	12 27	...	...	Ex3	3 58	4 10
BRUSSELS 103A......dep	6 a8	...	...	7 a49	7 a49	...	...	10a20	...	...	...	12 10	...	...	...	...	...	6p35	...	...
LUXEMBURG 210 ...dep	11a41	...	...	1 p28	1 p28	...	...	3 p55	...	...	...	6 p50	...	...	...	...	...	1211	...	...
METZ 210 ....dep	12p50	...	...	2 p25	2 p25	1,2,3	...	4 p58	...	2,3,4	...	7 p59	2,3,4	2 3 4	...	...	...	1a 9	...	...
	p.m.			p.m.	p.m.	p.m.		p.m.		p.m.	p.m.	p.m.	p.m.	nigt				a.m.	a.m.	a.m.
Strassburg ....dep	3 53	...	...	5 15	6 20	6 34	...	7 21	...	7 35	8 36	10 55	10 8	12 0	...	...	...	3 35	4 4	4 16
Grafenstaden	...	...	...	...	...	...	...	...	...	7 44	...	...	10 17	12 8	...	...	...	...	...	...
Erstein	...	...	...	RC	...	6 51	...	...	...	8 7	8 53	11 12	10 40	1226	...	...	...	...	...	...
Benfeld	RC	...	...	...	...	6 59	...	RC	...	8 18	9 1	11 20	10 51	1234	...	...	a.m.	SC	...	C
Schlettstadt	...	...	...	5 49	6 54	7 14	...	...	...	8 42	9 16	11 36	11 16	1253	...	...	5 6	...	4 38	...
Rappoltsweiler	...	...	...	5 59	...	7 23	...	...	...	8 50	9 25	11 46	11 30	1 3	...	...	5 20	...	...	...
Colmar (211)	4 43	...	...	6 12	7 15	7 36	...	8 10	...	9 45	9 38	11 59	11 48	1 15	...	...	5 43	4 30	4 57	5 7
Rufach	...	...	...	...	...	7 50	...	...	...	10 4	9 50	12 11	—	—	...	...	6 3	...	...	...
Bollweiler (211)	...	...	...	6 33	RC	8 2	...	...	...	10 25	10 2	12 23	...	...	...	...	6 23	4 51	...	...
Lutterbach	...	...	...	...	...	8 14	...	...	...	10 43	10 13	12 36	...	...	...	...	6 41	...	...	...
Dornach..................	...	...	...	...	...	8 19	...	...	...	10 48	...	...	...	...	...	2 3 4	6 46	...	...	...
Mulhausen .... arr	5 16	...	...	6 51	7 49	8 23	...	8 43	...	10 52	10 19	12 43	...	...	...	a.m.	6 51	5 9	5 32	5 42
Mulhausen .... dep	5 17	...	...	6 53	7 50	—	...	8 44	...	11 15	10 21	—	...	...	...	4 34	6 58	5 11	5 34	5 43
Sierentz..................	...	...	...	...	...	...	...	...	...	11 33	...	...	...	...	...	5 2	7 23	...	...	...
St. Ludwig	...	...	...	...	...	...	...	...	...	11 56	10 44	...	...	...	...	5 24	7 40	...	5 56	...
Basle ¶.....................arr	5 47	...	...	7 22	8 20	...	...	9 13	...	12 8	10 55	...	...	...	...	5 36	7 51	5 43	6 7	6 14
ZURICH (261) ....arr	7 p55	...	...	11p25	11p25	...	...	11p25	...	...	...	...	...	...	...	...	...	8a35	8 a35	8 a35
LUCERNE (258) ......arr	8p15	...	...	9 ; 55	11p42	...	...	11p42	...	...	...	...	...	...	...	...	...	8a59	8 a59	8 a59
MILAN 269A..........arr	6 a22	...	...	6 a22	6 a22	...	...	6 a22	...	...	...	...	...	...	...	...	...	3 p5	3 p5	3 p5

†—Weekdays only. ¶—Customs Examination.
C—Runs from 2nd July until 1st September.

Extra.

Neustadt...dep	12p25	3p35	6p10	8p18
Landau ...arr	1 1	4 11	6 43	8 52

Landau...dep	4p15	5 p0	7 p5
Winden ...arr	4 37	5 22	7 27

WALBURG and LEMBACH.

Walburg ...dep	7a24	11a50	2 p5	5 p34	7 p50	...
Worth............	7 57	12 24	2 42	6 9	8 27	...
Lembach ...arr	8 19	12 46	3 5	6 32	8 50	...

Lembach ...dep	4‡a11	6a10	8 a25	10‡a8	12p53	4 p20	5 p41
Worth............	4 49	6 35	8 49	10 45	1 17	4 45	6 7
Walburg ...arr	5 40	7 8	9 22	11 30	1 51	5 20	6 40

‡—Sundays excepted.

ALSACE and LORRAINE RAILWAY. [Luggage Rate, see page 462.

BASLE, MULHAUSEN, STRASSBURG, WEISSENBURG, NEUSTADT, WORMS, and MAYENCE.

THROUGH CARRIAGES 1st and 2nd class.
- Basle to Berlin—in 9.29 a.m. and 11.48 p.m. from Basle.
- Basle to Ostend—in 10.22 a.m., 7.32 p.m., and 11.40 p.m. from Basle.
- Basle to Vlissingen—in 10.14 a.m. from Basle.
- Basle to Frankfort—in 7.40 a.m., 9.29 a.m. and 11.48 p.m. from Basle.

†—Weekdays only.

RESTAURANT CARS in Trains marked RC

Station																			
MILAN 269A ......dep	...	...	...	...	...	...	...	...	...	...	9p 5	...	...	11p35	...	11p35	11p35	...	...
LUCERNE 258 ......dep	...	...	...	...	...	...	...	...	...	...	5 a5	...	...	7 a0	...	7 a0	7 a0	...	...
ZURICH 261 ......dep	...	...	...	...	...	...	...	...	...	...	4a52	...	...	7 a16	...	7 a16	7 a16	...	...
		2—4	2,3,4	1,2,3	2,3,4	1,2,3	2,3,4	2,3,4	1,2,3	2,3,4	Ex.3	2,3,4	2,3,4	Ex.3	2 & 3	Ex.3	Ex.3	1—4	2,3,4
					a.m.				a.m.	a.m.	a.m.		a.m.	a.m.		a.m.	a.m.		a.m.
Basle ......dep	...	...	...	...	4 58	...	...	...	6 0	6 33	7 40	...	7 58	9 29	...	10 14	10 22	...	9 50
St. Ludwig	...	...	...	...	5 9	...	...	...	6 10	6 44	...	...	8 10	...	...	...	10 32	...	10 2
Sierentz	...	...	...	...	5 26	...	...	...	...	7 1	...	...	8 26	RC	...	RC	RC	...	10 13
Mulhausen arr	...	...	...	...	5 50	...	...	...	6 31	7 24	8 7	a.m.	8 47	9 58	a.m.	10 44	10 54	...	10 33
Mulhausen dep	...	...	...	...		...	...	...	6 33	7 26	8 8	6 40	8 55	9 59	10 6	10 45	10 56	...	11 3
Dornach	...	...	...	...	...	...	...	...	...	7 33	...	6 45	9 0	...	10 12	...	...	...	11 9
Lutterbach	...	...	...	...	...	...	...	...	6 40	7 59	...	6 51	9 6	...	10 18	...	...	...	11 14
Bollweiler	...	...	...	...	...	...	...	...	6 51	7 56	RC	7 8	9 24	...	10 33	...	11 12	...	11 32
Rufach	...	...	a.m.	...	...	...	a.m.	a.m.	7 2	8 13	...	7 25	9 42	...		...	...	...	11 48
Colmar	...	...	6 16	...	...	...	4 53	5 56	7 16	8 30	8 40	7 46	10 5	10 32	...	11 21	11 33	...	12 9
Rappoltsweiler	...	...	6 28	...	...	...	5 12	6 15	7 28		...	8 5	10 24	...	...	...	...	...	12 27
Schlettstadt (207A)	...	...	6 38	...	...	...	5 25	6 45	7 39	...	8 58	8 19	10 57	...	...	...	11 52	...	12 42
Benfeld	...	...	6 53	...	...	...	5 48	7 6	7 53	...	...	8 40	11 18	...	...	...	...	...	1 3
Erstein	...	...	7 1	...	...	...	6 0	7 17	8 1	...	...	8 51	11 29	...	...	...	...	...	1 15
Grafenstaden	...	...	...	...	...	...	6 22	7 37	...	...	...	9 10	11 49	...	...	...	...	...	1 36
Strassburg ......arr	...	...	7 18	...	...	...	6 30	7 45	8 17	...	9 29	9 18	11 57	11 20	...	12 10	12 25	...	1 44
METZ (210) ......arr	...	...	...	...	...	...	10 a0	1 p22	...	...	1 p22	1 p22	...	...	...	...	2 p56	...	4p41
LUXEMBURG (210) arr	...	...	...	...	...	...	11a21	...	...	...	...	...	...	...	...	...	4 p8	...	5 p45
BRUSSELS (103A) ...arr	...	...	...	...	...	...	3 p22	...	...	...	...	...	...	...	...	...	8 p11	...	9 p26
				a.m.	a.m.	a.m.	a.m.	a.m.	a.m.		a.m.	a.m.		a.m.		p.m.		p.m.	p.m.
Strassburg ......dep	...	...	...	6 0	6 9	6 55	7 †2	8 33	8 24	...	9 38	10 35	...	11 26	...	12 17	...	12 50	2 26
Vendenheim ......dep	...	...	...	...	6 22	...	7 16	8 46	...	...		10 47	...		...	...	...	1 3	2 40
Hordt	...	...	...	...	6 30	...	7 24	8 55	...	...		10 56	...		...	...	...	1 11	2 49
Bischweiler	...	...	...	6 22	6 45	7 17	7 40	9 10	8 47	...		11 11	...		...	...	...	1 28	3 5
Hagenau	...	...	...	6 31	7 2	7 26	7 52	9 23	8 57	...		11 25	...		...	12 46	...	1 44	3 17
Walburg	...	...	...	...	7 12	...		9 34	...	...		11 36	...		...	...	...	1 55	
Sulz-u-W.	...	...	...	...	7 23	...	...	9 46	...	...		11 48	...		...	...	...	2 8	...
Weissenburg arr	...	a.m.	...	...	7 47	7 55	a.m.	10 10	9 26	a.m.		12 13	...		...	...	...	2 34	...
Weissenburg dep	...	4 5	...	...		7 58	6 25		9 31	10 18		12 17	...		...	...	...	2 41	...
Scheidt	...	4 21	a.m.	...	...	...	6 40	...	...	10 34		12 33	...		...	...	...	2 58	p.m.
Winden	...	4 31	5 55	...	...	8 14	6 51	...	9 47	10 46	Via Lauterburg, page 207A.	12 45	...	Via Lauterburg, page 207A.	...	...	...	3 10	3 45
Rohrbach	...	4 38	6 2	...	...	...	6 58	...	...	10 56		12 52	...		...	...	2 & 3	3 17	3 53
Landau arr	...	4 50	6 14	7 17	...	8 27	7 10	...	10 1	11 10		1 4	...		...	1 34	p.m.	3 29	4 7
Landau dep	...	4 53	6 16	7 18	...	8 29	7 39	...	10 4	11 20		1 7	...		...	1 35	2 0	3 38	4 17
Edenkoben	...	5 11	6 34	...	...	8 41	7 59	...	10 16	11 38		1 26	...		...	...	2 22	3 59	4 39
Neustadt (206) ......arr	...	5 24	6 47	7 35	...	8 50	8 14	...	10 25	11 51		1 40	...		...	1 52	2 38	4 13	4 55
123B COLOGNE (via Munster)		12p37	12p37	12p37	...	...	...	...	...	...		6 p5	...		...	6 p5	...	...	...
	1—4	2—4	2—4	1,2,3	2—4	Ex3	1—4	1—4	Ex.3			1,2,3	1—4				1—4	2—4	2—4
		a.m.	a.m.	a.m.	a.m.	a.m.			a.m.			p.m.	p.m.				p.m.	p.m.	p.m.
Neustadt ......dep	...	5 45	6 54	7 39	9 58	8 56	...	...	10 30	...		2 2	12 40		...	...	3 35	4 40	6 12
Hassloch	...	5 55	7 4	⋮	10 10	...	...	...	...	...		...	12 52		...	...	3 48	4 52	6 24
Schifferstadt (206) ...arr	...	6 7	7 17	⋮	10 24	9 13	...	...	10 46	...		2 18	1 5		...	...	4 3	5 6	6 37
STRASSBURG ......dep	...	...	...	⋮	7 a23	...	...	...	...	...		...	...		...	...	12p41	12p41	...
Schifferstadt ......dep	...	6 10	7 20	⋮	10 26	9 14	...	...	10 47	...		2 19	1 7		...	...	4 10	5 8	6 40
Ludwigshafen ......arr	...	6 35	7 41	8 6	10 50	9 28	...	...	11 0	...	11 11	2 31	1 30	1 10	...	...	4 24	5 32	7 7
FRANKFORT 136, 139 ar	...	8 a38	9a31	9 a33	12p40	1140	...	...	12p40	...	2 p2	4 p25	4 p25	2 p33	p.m.	1,2,3	6 p25	8 p32	10 p0
MANNHEIM ......dep	4 a48	6 a30		7 a 7	10a43	...	8 a25	9 a32	10a43	...	...	2 p10	...	12p40	1 34	3 p57	3 p48	5 p11	7 p8
Ludwigshafen ......dep	5 3	7 0	...	8 10	11 17	...	8 45	10 9	11 17	...	11 17	2 36	2 10	1 14	⋮	⋮	4 30	5 37	7 33
Frankenthal	5 25	7 18	...	8 20	11 27	...	9 2	10 20	11 27	1—4	11 27	2 47	2 29	...	⋮	⋮	4 49	5 57	7 55
Worms arr a.m.	5 44	7 38	...	8 30	11 37	...	9 17	10 31	11 37	p.m.	11 37	2 59	2 46	...	2 7	4 30	5 6	6 15	8 13
Worms dep 5 9	5 58	7 46	...	8 32	12 8	...	9 24	10 36	11 39	12 53	11 39	3 1	3 21	...	2 12	4 35	5 10	6 22	8 20
Osthofen 5 20	6 10	7 57	...	...	12 21	...	9 35	10 46	11 49	1 5	11 49	3 11	3 33	...	...	4 45	5 22	6 33	8 33
Alsheim 5 33	6 23	8 10	...	...	12 34	...	9 47	10 56	...	1 18	...	...	3 46	...	...	...	5 33	6 46	8 49
Oppenheim 5 51	6 45	8 26	...	8 54	12 52	...	10 3	11 11	12 9	1 35	12 9	3 28	4 4	...	...	5 2	5 51	7 2	9 9
Nierstein 5 57	6 53	8 31	...	...	12 57	...	10 8	11 16	12 14	1 40	12 14	3 33	4 12	...	...	5 7	5 57	7 10	9 15
Bodenheim 6 17	7 13	8 45	...	...	1 13	...	10 22	11 29	...	1 55	...	...	4 26	...	...	...	6 11	7 27	9 35
Mayence Süd 6 34	7 30	8 58	...	...	1 27	...	10 35	11 42	12 31	2 9	12 31	3 50	4 41	...	...	5 23	6 25	7 41	9 50
„ Hauptbahnhof 6 40	7 37	9 3	...	9 13	1 33	...	10 43	11 47	12 37	2 15	12 37	3 54	4 45	2 51	2 51	5 28	6 31	7 47	9 55
FRANKFORT (123)...arr	8 a44	10a14	...	10a14	2 p17	...	12p27	1 p26	1 p36	3 p5	1 36	5 p21	5 p29	...	...	6 p33	7 p41	8 p35	10p44
COLOGNE 123B ......arr	12p37	12p48	...	12 48	6 p5	...	...	5 p45	4 p40	6 p5	4 p10	7 p7	...	6 p5	6 p5	...	10p30	...	...

Extra.

Winden ......dep	2 p28	Weissenburg...dep	6 p6
Landau ......dep	2 48	Winden ......arr	6 30
Neustadt ......arr	...	Neustadt ......arr	7 30

†—Weekdays only.

Luggage Rate, see page 462.] ALSACE and LORRAINE RAILWAY.

BASLE, MULHAUSEN, STRASSBURG, WEISSENBURG, NEUSTADT, and MAYENCE.

SLEEPING CAR
- Basle to Ostend—in 11.40 p.m from Basle. Extra fare 18 fr. 1st cl., 14 fr. 40 c. 2nd cl.
- Basle to Berlin—in 4.59 p.m. from Basle. Extra fare 13 m. 1st cl., 11 m. 2nd cl.
- Basle to Frankfort—in 11.48 p.m. from Basle. Extra fare 6 m, 1st cl., 5 m. 2nd cl.
- Basle to Emmerich—in 9.33 p.m. from Basle. Extra fare, 10 m.

MILAN (269A)........dep	...	...	...	...	...	...	...	...	7 a25	7 a25	...	7 a25	7 a25	9 a35	9 a35	12p40	...	2 p40	2 p40
LUCERNE (258)......dep	...	...	9 a55	1010	...	10a10	1235	...	2 p2	2 p2	...	2 p19	2 p19	4 p57	5 p2	7 p0	7 p0	9 p10	9 p10
ZURICH (261).........dep	9 a45	...	9 a45	1138	...	11a38	1138	...	2 p48	2 p48	...	...	...	...	5 p22	6 p40	...	9 p12	9 p12
	2,3,4	2,3,4	Ex 3	Ex3	Ex.3	2,3,4	Ex3	2,3,4	1,2,3	Ex 3	2 3 4	Ex 3	2,3,4	Ex 3	2 ,34	Ex.3	2,3,4	Ex.3	Ex 3
	p.m.	a.m.	p.m.	p.m.		p.m.	p.m.	p.m.	p.m.	p.m.		p.m.	p.m.	p.m.	p.m.	p.m.	p.m.	p.m.	p.m.
Basle ....dep	12 38	11 6	12 15	1 45	...	2 13	3 19	3 53	4 37	4 59	...	6 10	6 50	7 32	8 23	9 33	10 11	11 40	11 48
St. Ludwig	12 53	11 21	...	1 55	...	2 26	3 28	4 7	4 47	...	...	...	7 4	...	8 37	SC	10 25	SC	11 58
Sierentz	1 10	11 38	RC	RC	...	2 43	...	4 24	...	...	...	A	7 21	...	8 54	...	10 42	...	...
Mulhausen .... arr	1 33	12 0	12 43	2 17	...	3 6	3 49	4 47	5 9	5 27	p.m.	6 42	7 45	8 3	9 17	10 4	11 5	12 10	12 20
Mulhausen .... dep		12 4	12 44	2 19	...	3 13	3 56	6 9	5 11	5 32	4 23	6 45	8 22	8 5	9 27	10 6	11 22	12 11	12 22
Dornach	...	12 9	...	...	...	3 18	...	6 16	...	...	4 29	...	8 28	...	9 33	...	11 28	...	...
Lutterbach	...	12 15	...	...	...	3 24	...	6 23	...	SC	4 35	6 54	8 34	8 13	9 39	...	11 33	...	SC
Bollweiler	...	12 34	...	2 35	...	3 43	RC	6 43	5 26	...	4 54	7 6	8 53	8 26	9 57	...	11 51	...	...
Rufach	...	12 51	...	...	...	4 0	...	7 2	...	...	5 11	...	9 10	...	10 14	...	12 8	...	...
Colmar	...	1 24	1 18	2 55	...	4 40	4 29	7 35	5 47	6 11	6 25	7 28	9 31	8 48	10 47	10 41	12 25	12 45	12 56
Rappoltsweiler	...	1 43	...	...	...	4 59	...	7 54	5 59	...	6 44	7 40	9 50	9 0	11 8	...		...	...
Schlettstadt (207A)	...	1 58	1 36	3 14	...	5 14	...	8 9	6 9	...	6 56	7 50	10 4	9 10	11 22	11 2	...	...	1 15
Benfeld	...	2 19	...	...	...	5 35	...	8 32	...	...	7 19	8 5	10 25	9 25		...	...	...	...
Erstein	...	2 30	...	...	...	5 46	...	8 44	6 28	...	7 29	8 13	10 36	9 33	...	...	...	...	...
Grafenstaden	...	2 52	...	...	...	6 7	...	9 4	...	...	7 48	...	10 55	...	...	...	...	...	...
Strassburg..............arr	...	3 0	2 9	3 46	...	6 15	5 18	9 12	6 44	7 0	7 56	8 30	11 3	9 50	...	11 35	...	1 34	1 48
METZ (210) ....arr	...	6 p16	4 p41	6p16	...	9 p56	...	...	9 p56	9 p56	...	...	...	12a32	...	...	...	3 a58	...
LUXEMBURG (210) arr	...	7 p34	5 p45	7p34	...	...	...	...	...	...	...	...	...	1 a44	...	...	...	5 a1	...
BRUSSELS (103A) ...arr	...	...	...	...	...	...	...	...	...	...	...	...	...	5 a26	...	...	...	8 a28	...
	p.m.	p.m.	p.m.	p m.	p.m.	p.m.	p.m.		p.m.	p.m.	p.m.				p.m.	p.m.	p.m.		a.m.
Strassburg ....dep	4 29	5 53	2 14	3 52	4 4	6 22	5 25	...	6 50	7 7	7 35	...	...	...	10 15	11 41	11 49	...	1 58
Vendenheim............dep	4 40	6 7	Via Lauterburg, page 207A.	...	...	6 33	Via Lauterburg, page 207A.	...	...	Via Lauterburg, page 207A.	7 49	...	...	...	10 29	...	...	...	...
Hordt	4 48	6 16		...	...	6 42		...	...		7 58	...	...	...	10 38	...	12 6	...	...
Bischweiler	5 3	6 32		4 14	4 26	6 58		...	7 12		8 17	...	...	...	10 53	...	12 19	...	...
Hagenau	5 17	6 44		4 23	4 35	7 10		...	7 21		8 35	...	...	...	11 7	...	12 31	...	2 22
Walburg	5 27			...	...	7 42		...	...		8 46	...	...	...	11 17	...		...	...
Sulz-u-W	5 38	...		...	...	7 55		...	...		8 58	...	...	...	11 29	...	...	...	...
Weissenburg ...... arr	6 2	...		...	5 3	8 21		...	7 49		9 23	...	...	...	11 54	-.-	...	...	2 51
Weissenburg ...... dep		...		...	5 8			...	7 52		9 27	...	...	...		SC	...	...	2 55
Scheidt	...	p.m.		...	...	p.m.		...	...		9 42	...	...	...	...	...	...	...	...
Winden	...	8 30		5 3	5 24	6 35		...	...		9 55	...	...	...	...	...	...	...	...
Rohrbach	2—4	8 39		...	...	6 43		...	...		10 3	...	...	...	...	...	...	...	...
Landau............ arr	p.m.	8 54		5 15	5 38	6 57		p.m.	8 16		1016	...	...	...	...	...	...	...	3 18
Landau............ dep	6 22	9 4		5 16	5 43	7 12		7 30	8 17		1033	...	...	...	...	...	...	...	3 19
Edenkoben	6 44	9 22		5 26	...	...		7 52	8 29		1051	...	...	...	...	...	...	...	...
Neustadt (206) ....arr	6 58	9 35		5 35	6 0	7 30		8 8	8 38		11 4	...	...	...	...	1 10	...	...	3 36
123B COLOGNE (via Muns	ter a	rr.		1015	...	...		...	12a55		...	...	...	...	...	5 a21	...	...	...
	2—4				1,2,3			Ex 3	1,2,3		1—4		1,2,3	1,2,3					Ex.3
	p.m.				p.m			p.m.	p.m.		p.m.			p.m.					a.m.
Neustadt.................dep	7 8	...		...	6 4	...		8 14	8 46		1110	...	...	11 42	...	...	...	...	3 40
Hassloch	7 18	...		...	...	...		...			1122	...	...	...	...	...	...	...	
Schifferstadt (206) ...arr	7 30	...		...	6 21	...		8 30			1136	...	...	11 58	...	...	...	...	
STRASSBURG ....dep	...	...		...	...	...		...			7p37	...	...	...	...	...	...	...	
Schifferstadt ....dep	7 32	...		...	6 21	...		8 31			1141	...	...	11 59	...	...	...	...	
Ludwigshafen ....arr	7 54	...	4 2	...	6 35	...	7 20	8 43	9 14	8 55	12 5	...	...	12 12	...	...	...	...	4 10
FRANKFORT 136, 139 ar	10 p0	...	6 p25	...	8 p32	...	3§43	10p25	10p58	10p25	...	...	...	Arrives Mannheim 12.28	...	...	...	...	...
MANNHEIM...........dep	...	...	3 p48	...	5 p46	...	7 p8	...	8 p46	8 p46	1214	...	9 p45		...	...	...	...	...
Ludwigshafen ....dep	...	...	4 8	...	6 41	...	7 23	...	9 20	9 5	1227	...	10 16		...	...	...	Ex 3	4 15
Frankenthal	...	2,3,4	4 19	...	6 52	§—Via Worms.	7 34	...	Via Lampertheim.	9 16	1244	...	10 36		...	2,3,4	...	a.m.	4 27
Worms .... arr	...	p.m.	4 30	...	7 3		7 45	...		9 27	1 1	...	10 52		...	a.m.	...		4 38
Worms .... dep	...	7 15	4 35	...			7 57	...		9 34		...	11 7		...	3 59	...	4 48	4 54
Osthofen	...	7 26	4 45	...	...		8 7	...		9 44	...	...	11 19		...	4 12	...		5 3
Alsheim	...	7 39	...	...	...		...	...		...	...	...	11 32		...	4 25	...		...
Oppenheim	...	7 58	5 2	...	...		8 23	...		10 5	...	...	11 48		...	4 45	...		5 18
Nierstein	...	8 4	5 7	...	...		...	...		...	...	...	11 53		...	4 52	...		5 28
Bodenheim	...	8 19	...	...	...		...	...		...	...	...	12 6		...	5 11	...		...
Mayence Süd	...	8 35	5 23	...	...		8 42	...		10 24	...	...	12 19	...	...	5 26	...		5 39
„ Hauptbahn'f arr	...	8 39	5 28	...	...	...	8 47	...	11 5	10 28	..	...	12 24	2 28	...	5 30	...		5 43
FRANKFORT (123)...arr	...	9 p20	6 p33	...	...	...	10p7	...	...	11p20	...	...	2 a34	...	...	7 a9	...	5 a48	...
COLOGNE (123B)......arr	...	12a55	10p30	...	...	...	1255	...	5 a9	5 a9	...	...	5 a21	...	...	...	...	...	9 a50

A—Runs until 30th September.

SCHLETTSTADT and SUNDHAUSEN.

Schlettstadt...dep	6a43	8a28	12p10	4p25	7p20
Sundhausen ...arr	7 11	8 56	12 40	4 53	7 48

Sundhausen ...dep	7a21	9a33	12p54	5p29	8 p4	...
Schlettstadt ...arr	7 48	10 1	1 22	5 57	8 32	...

ALSACE and LORRAINE RAILWAY. [Luggage Rate see page 462

LUXEMBURG, METZ, SAARBURG, STRASSBURG, and APPENWEIER.

Dist. E.M.	Brussels-Nord dep	...	...	...	...	...	...	1128	...	...	...	...	...	...	...	5§24	...	6 a8	7a49	...	...	...	1020	...	10a20	1210	1210	...	...	6 p35
					3&4		2 3 4	Ex3	1,2,3	1—4	1—4	Ex3	1,2,3	1—4	Ex3	Ex3	1—4	Ex3	Ex.3	1,2,3		1—4	Ex3		1—4	1,2,3	1—4	1—4	1,2,3	Ex 3
								a.m.	a.m.	a.m.	a.m.	a.m.	a.m.	a.m.		a.m.	a.m.	a.m.	p.m.			p.m.	p.m.		p.m.	p.m.	p.m.	p.m.	p.m.	nig't
—	Luxemburg ...dep	...	...	...	...	...	...	5 3	5 53	6 32	7 2	8 14	9 42	8 45	...	1045	1052	11 41	1 28	...	...	2 10	3 55	...	4 54	6 50	7 38	8 44	1010	12 11
7	Bettemburg	...	...	...	...	...	...	...	6 10	6 49	7 17	8 23	9 54	9 2	...	⋮ A	1110	11 55	...	...	...	2 30	4 7	...	5 11	7 3	7 55	9 0	1029	SC
10½	Diedenhofen ...arr	...	...	...	...	...	...	5 33	6 35	—	7 42	8 45	1013	9 28	...	⋮	1134	12 15	1 56	...	...	2 56	4 26	...	5 40	7 22	8 21	—	—	12 39
...	Coblence 124 dep	...	...	...	...	...	...	...	...	...	3 a6	3 a6	...	...	8a38	⋮	8a38	8 a38	8a47	11 a9	...	11a 9	...	...	...	2p50	2p55	4 p40	8p43	8 p43
...	Treves 124.....dep	...	...	...	a.m.	...	...	...	...	...	5a54	5a54	8a27	8a27	1034	⋮	1034	10 34	11 44	1 p17	...	1p17	...	...	2p45	5p11	6p18	8 p16	1053	10p53
...	Diedenhofen ...dep	...	...	...	3 58	...	...	5 35	6 39	2 3 4	7*58	8 47	1015	1024	1138	⋮	1232	12 17	1 57	2 32	...	3 0	4 28	...	5 49	7 24	8 39	10p25	12‡2	1240
16	Ueckingen	...	...	...	4 6	...	...	...	6 47	a.m.	8 6	...	...	1032	...	⋮	1240	...	...	...	...	3 8	...	...	5 58	...	8 47	10 33	...	...
27½	Hagendingen (212A)	...	...	...	4 19	...	...	5 47	6 58	7 15	8 17	9 0	1027	1043	1150	⋮	1251	RC	...	2 44	...	3 19	...	...	6 10	7 36	8 57	10 44	1214	...
33	Metz Nord	...	...	...	4 40	...	...	...	7 20	7 36	8 38	...	...	11 4	...	⋮	1 13	...	...	...	...	3 38	RC	...	6 32	...	9 18	11 2	...	...
38½	Metz Haupt.212 arr	...	...	...	4 49	...	a.m.	6 3	7 29	7 45	8 47	9 17	1046	1113	12 6	1138	1 22	12 44	2 22	3 0	...	3 47	4 54	...	6 41	7 52	9 27	11 11	1230	1 5
	Metz Haupt.212 dep	...	...	...	—	...	5 0	6 13	7 50	7 57	1016	—	1049	1*14	—	1143	—	12 50	2 25	—	...	4*18	4 58	...	7 *17	7 59	—	11*46	—	1 9
46¾	Courcelles..................	...	...	...	...	...	5 18	...	8 6	8 15	1034	...	11 4	1 33	...	⋮	...	...	...	...	...	4 35	...	...	7 38	...	...	12 6	...	SC
52½	Remilly (212)	...	...	...	...	...	5 31	6 35	8 16	8 28	1047	...	1113	1 51	...	⋮	...	...	...	...	...	4 48	...	...	7 54	8 21	...	12 17	...	...
66¼	Mörchingen	...	...	...	...	...	6 5	6 56	8 42	9 2	1120	...	1134	2 25	...	⋮	...	1 33	3 3	...	...	5 24	5 35	...	8 29	8 44	...	12 49	...	1 50
71½	Bensdorf ....arr	...	...	...	...	...	6 16	7 4	8 49	9 12	1131	...	1141	2 35	...	⋮	...	1 42	...	...	...	5 33	5 42	...	8 39	8 52	...	12 58	...	...
...	" ....dep	...	...	...	...	...	6 19	7 5	8 50	9 15	1158	...	1142	2 38	...	⋮	...	1 43	...	...	...	5 54	5 43	...	9 1	8 53	...	—	...	...
85¾	Berthelmingen dep	...	...	...	...	...	6 50	...	9 11	9 45	1227	...	...	3 8	...	⋮	...	...	...	...	...	6 26	...	...	9 32	...	...	...	...	...
93	Saarburg ....arr	...	...	...	...	...	7 8	7 35	9 23	10 2	1244	...	1212	3 24	...	⋮	...	2 15	3 39	...	...	6 44	6 11	...	9 50	9 24	...	...	...	2 25
		Lux	Ex1	Ex3	2 3 4	1,2,3	2 3 4	Ex3						2 3 4		⋮		⋮	Ex 3	Ex.2	2,3,4	2,3,4	⋮	Ex 3		1,2,3			Ex3	⋮
...	Paris 64 ......dep	7p13	7p15	9 p5	9 p5	...	1015	1015	...	...	...	...	...	...	...	A	...	⋮	8 a0	9 a0	...	...	⋮	12 0	...	...	...	...	5p15	⋮
...	Deutsch-	a.m.	a.m.	a.m.	a.m.	a.m.	a.m.	a.m.	a.m.	a.m.	p.m.			p.m.		⋮		⋮	p.m.	p.m.	p.m.	p.m.	⋮	p.m.		p.m.			a.m.	⋮
...	Avricourt dep	2 26	3 13	4 35	4 56	6 23	7 1	7 1	9 1	9 38	1218	...	...	2 54	...	⋮	...	⋮	3 19	3 42	5 10	6 50	⋮	7 20	...	8 45	2 3 4	...	1224	⋮
...	Saarburg arr 2 3 4	⋮	⋮	4 51	5 24	6 43	7 30	7 30	9 19	10 6	1246	...	...	3 22	...	⋮	...	⋮	3 37	⋮	5 58	7 21	⋮	7 37	...	9 12	p.m.	...	1240	⋮
...	Saarburg ...dep 7a13	⋮	⋮	4 52	5 27	6 45	7 58	7 41	9 28	1024	1254	...	1215	4 3	...	⋮	...	2 19	3 44	⋮	5 43	7 44	6 15	7 38	...	9 28	1010	2,3,4	1241	2 29
103½	Lützelburg 7 37	⋮	⋮	..	5 50	7 0	8 25	...	9 43	1049	1 17	...	1231	4 25	...	⋮	...	...	...	⋮	6 7	8 6	...	"	...	9 44	1032	a.m.	...	...
109½	Zabern 207A ...7 50	⋮	⋮	5 15	6 5	7 11	8 43	8 6	9 53	11 3	1 32	...	1241	4 39	...	⋮	...	2 43	4 7	RC	6 44	8 20	6 38	8 2	...	9 54	1047	4 12	1 4	2 52
112½	Steinburg 207A —	Œ	⋮	...	6 13	7 17	8 51	...	...	1111	1 41	...	...	4 48	...	⋮	...	...	...	⋮	6 54	8 28	...	...	...	...	1055	4 21	...	...
123½	Mommenheim............	⋮	K	...	6 40	7 37	9 18	...	...	1138	2 8	...	...	5 17	...	⋮	...	...	...	⋮	7 23	8 55	...	...	...	...	1122	4 52	SC	SC
131	Vendenheim arr	⋮	⋮	...	6 58	...	9 36	...	10 20	1155	2 26	...	...	5 36	...	⋮	...	RC	...	⋮	7 41	9 12	RC	...	...	...	1141	5 12	...	...
	Vendenheim dep	⋮	⋮	...	7 6	...	9 37	...	10 21	1156	2 27	...	...	5 37	...	⋮	...	...	...	⋮	7 42	9 13	...		...	...	1142	5 14	...	...
137	Strassburg ......arr	3 38	4 28	5 50	7 14	8 0	9 50	8 44	10 30	12 9	2 41	...	1 17	5 50	...	1 57	...	3 19	4 41	4 52	7 55	9 26	7 12	8 38	...	1031	1155	5 27	1 39	3 27
...	Basle 208 ......arr	...	...	8a 5	1010	...	...	1115	12 58	2p52	5p36	...	...	8p20	...	4 p0	...	5 p36	7p22	7p22	...	...	9p13	...	...	...	...	...	...	5 a43
			Ex1	Ex3	1—4	2 3 4	2 3 4	1,2,3	2,3,4	1—4	2 3 4		2 3 4	2 3 4				Ex.3		Ex.2	2,3,4	2,3,4	1,2,3	Ex 3		1—4		2,3,4	Ex3	2,3,4
		a.m.	a.m.	a.m.	a.m.	a.m.	a.m.	a.m.	a.m.	p.m.	p.m.		p.m.	p.m.				p.m.		p.m.	p.m.	p.m.	p.m.	p.m.		p.m.		a.m.	a.m.	a.m.
...	Strassburg ......dep	3 44	4 33	5 56	7 17	8 8	10 8	9 0	11 39	1217	2 51	...	1 22	6 21	...	...	...	3 50	...	4 57	8 10	10 5	7 32	8 45	...	1058	...	6 23	1 45	3 58
142	Kehl	⋮	⋮	⋮	7 30	8 23	1021	9 10	11 55	1231	3 4	...	1 35	6 38	...	...	...	4 0	...	⋮	8 30	10 18	7 45	8 55	...	11 9	...	6 35	⋮	4 10
150½	Appenweier......arr	⋮	⋮	⋮	7 44	8 43	1037	9 23	12 15	1250	3 26	...	1 50	7 0	...	...	...	4 13	...	⋮	8 54	10 38	7 53	9 9	...	1129	...	6 55	⋮	4 27
190½	Carlsruhe 141 arr	4a59	5a47	7a11	9 a1	1030*	...	1030	1 p52	2p11	5p19	...	3p15	8p30	...	...	...	5 p30	...	6 p8	...	...	...	10 p6	...	12a20	...	8 a55	3 a1	6 a41

A—Runs on Saturday only until 20th Sept. K—Carlsbad Express, running until 28th Sept.

RC—Restaurant Car attached. SC—Sleeping Car. Œ—Orient Express. *—2—4 class only. ‡—Ex. 3. §—From Quartier Leopold Station.

Extra						
Diedenhofen......dep	2 p5	3 p52	4p40	6p23	6p37	12a10
Metz ....arr	2 53	4 42	5 29	6 51	7 25	12 56

Luxemburg.........dep	8a23	9a29	11a26	2p19	4 p5	6p39
Bettemburg.........arr	8 39	9 46	11 45	2 35	4 21	6 55

Luxemberg...... .dep	6p23	10p47
Diedenhofen ......arr	7 7	11 38

DIEDENHOFEN, FENTSCH (Fontoy), and DEUTSCH-OTH.

[Audun-le-Roman is the French frontier Station.

Metz 210 ....dep	6a26	8a21	8a42	10a10	10a10	12p 2	1248	3p10	4p44	5p32	6p27	7p35	8p53	10p18
Diedenhofen ... dep	7a12	8 55	⋮	10a46	11a42	12 37	1p45	4 p5	5p13	6p26	7 28	8p27	9p47	10p54
Hayingen	7 27	9 10	9 18	11 3	11 57	12 53	2 2	4 20	5 24	6 43	7 51	8 42	10 2	11 9
Algringen	7 54	9 32		11 16	12 14	1 23	2 19	...	5 51	6 55	8 4	8 55	1014	11 30
Fentsch ....arr	7 44	9 41	9 28	—	12 14	1 9	—	4 40	5 41	—	8 7	—	—	11 34
Audun............arr	7 2	...	8 41	...	11 30	...	...	...	4 57	...	...	...	...	...
Mezieres 71 arr	1053	...	1113	...	2 p46	...	...	...	7p39	...	...	...	...	...
Aumetz	8 14	10 6	...	...	...	1 31	...	5 7	...	...	8 29	...	...	11 57
Deutsch-Oth ...arr	8 38	1030	...	...	...	1 55	...	5 32	...	...	8 53	...	...	12 21

Deutsch-Oth dep	...	6a32	...	9 a0	...	12 3	...	...	3p12	6 p0	...	9p13	...
Aumetz................	...	6 59	...	9 26	...	1235	...	...	3 39	6 32	...	9 39	...
Mezieres 71 dep	...	2a59	...	...	...	6 a5	...	1128	...	...	5p52	...	...
Audun	...	5 58	...	...	...	1135	...	2p19	...	...	8 42	...	...
Fentsch.........dep	5a17	7 20	...	9 45	...	1257	...	3 45	3 58	6 51	10 3	1010	...
Algringen	...	7 22	8 a4	9 41	11a42	1253	1p59	3 40	...	6 6	9 15	...	10p22
Hayingen............	5 33	7 35	8 17	9 57	11 55	1 9	2 12	3 57	4 10	7 4	1015	1023	10 33
Diedenhofen arr	5 50	7 48	8 30	10 8	12 8	1 32	2 26	4 10	4 23	7 17	⋮	1035	10 44
Metz 210 ...arr	7a29	8a47	9a17	1046	12 41	2p22	3p 0	4p54	4p54	7p52	1055	2a30	12 30

APPENWEIER, STRASSBURG, SAARBURG, DEUTSCH AVRICOURT, METZ, and LUXEMBURG.

CARLSRUHE 140 dep		...	4a10	...	...	...	4a10	5a36	...	8a38	9 a3	9a42	...	...	1244	...	...	1 p6	1 p6	...	3p24	...	4p48	...	7p21	8p33	8 p12	1045	11p8	...	1 a6
			Ex3				2 3 4	1,2,3		Ex3	1—4	1—4		2&3	Ex3			2 & 3	Ex3	2 3 4	2 3 4	1—4	2 3 4		2 3 4	Ex3	2,3,4	Ex1	Ex3		Ex 1
			a.m.				a.m.	a.m.		a.m.	a.m.	a.m.		p.m.	p.m.			p.m.	p.m.	p.m.	p.m.	p.m.	p.m.		p.m.	p.m.	p.m.	ng't	ng't		a.m.
Appenweier dep		...	5 10	...	...	...	5 18	6 59	...	⋮	1010	1111	...	1226	1 47	...	...	2 14	3‡10	3 38	4 20	4 54	6 10	...	8 45	9 31	10 34	⋮	12 5	...	⋮
Kehl		...	5 25	...	...	...	5 42	7 14	...	9 51	1031	1132	...	1249	...	...	...	2 36	3 24	4 0	4 35	5 17	6 31	...	9 0	9 45	10 55	⋮	1219	...	⋮
Strassburg arr		...	5 34	...	...	...	5 57	7 24	...	10 1	1043	1144	...	1 1	2 8	...	...	2 51	3 33	4 12	4 48	5 30	6 46	...	9 10	9 54	11 8	1212	1228	...	2 25
BASLE 209 dep		...	...	...	...	...	...	...	...	7a40	...	1022	...	...	1215	...	...	12 15	1p45	..	...	...	4p50	4p50	...	7p32	...	...	..	11p40	...
		Ex3	Ex3	2 3 4	Ex3	1—4	2 3 4	1,2,3	2 3 4	Ex3	2 3 4	Ex3	2—4	2 3 4	Ex3	Ex3	Ex3	2,3,4	1,2,3	Ex3	2 3 4	2,3,4	1,2,3	2 3 4	2 3 4	Ex3	2,3,4	Ex1	Ex3	Ex 3	Ex 1
			a.m.		a.m.		a.m.	a.m.	a.m.	a.m.	a.m.	p.m.		p.m.	p.m.			p.m.	p.m.	p.m.	p.m.	p.m.	p.m.	p.m.	p.m.	p.m.	p.m.	n'gt	a.m.	a.m.	a.m.
Strassburg dep		...	5 40	...	5 52	...	6 16	7 30	8 13	10 8	1116	1233	...	1 33	2 18	...	...	3 10	3 58	4 40	4 55	6 23	7 14	7 26	9 20	10 5	11 30	1219	1234	1 40	2 31
Vendenheim arr		...	...	...	...	...	6 26	...	8 26	...	1123	...	...	1 46	...	...	...	3 23	...	...	5 8	6 42	...	7 40	9 33	...	11 42	⋮	...	...	⋮
Vendenheim dep		...	...	...	RC	...	6 27	...	8 27	...	1131	...	...	1 47	...	...	...	3 24	...	...	5 9	6 43	...	7 42	9 34	...	11 43	⋮	...	...	⋮
Mommenheim	2 3 4	...	...	...	...	...	6 47	...	8 48	...	1152	...	...	2 8	RC	...	...	3 40	...	...	5 29	7 2	...	8 2	9 54	...	12 1	K	SC	SC	⋮
Steinburg	a.m.	...	...	...	...	...	7 16	...	9 17	...	1222	...	...	2 37	...	...	...	4 2	...	5 15	5 58	7 30	7 48	8 31	1022	...	12 30	⋮	...	...	⋮
Zabern	5 51	...	6 16	...	6 29	...	7 28	8 9	9 29	1045	1235	1 10	...	3 7	2 56	...	...	4 12	4 34	5 23	6 14	7 40	7 55	8 42	1050	1043	12 39	⋮	1 10	2 18	OE
Lützelburg	6 6	...	...	...	...	...	7 43	8 20	9 44	1057	1251	RC	...	3 23	...	...	...	4 27	...	...	6 30		8 7	8 57	11 6	...		⋮	...	...	⋮
Saarburg arr	6 29	...	6 39	...	6 52	...	8 5	8 35	10 6	1112	1 15	1 35	...	3 48	3 21	...	...	4 47	4 57	5 48	6 53	...	8 24	9 20	1129	11 8	...	⋮	1 33	2 43	⋮
Saarburg dep		...	6 40	...	...	...	8 8	...	1017	1113	1 20	...	...	3 50	3 23	...	...	5 2	...	5 49	6 57	...	8 23	9 28	1133	...		⋮	1 34	⋮	⋮
D. Avricourt arr		...	6 59	...	...	...	8 35	...	1047	1132	1 49	...	...	4 19	3 40	...	...	5 30	...	6 8	7 26	...	8 50	9 56	12 1	...		1 35	1 53	⋮	3 40
PARIS (65) arr		...	1216	...	...	...	...	...	4p39	4p39		...	...	1147	9p20	...	...	11p47	...	1147	...	...	5 a0	5 a0	...	...		7a21	8a25	⋮	8 a56
				a.m.	a.m.		a.m.	a.m.	a.m.			p.m.	p.m.			p.m.		p.m.	p.m.				p.m.	p.m.		p.m.				a.m.	
Saarburg dep		...	...	5 29	6 55	...	8 11	8 39	1117	...	...	1 39	1 49	...	...	3 28	...	5 10	5 0	...	...	...	8 30	9 39	...	1112			...	2 47	...
Berthelmingen dep		...	1—4	5 44	7 7	...	8 23	8 52	1135	...	...	1 51	2 7	...	...	...	...	5 29	...	...	...	...	8 42	9 52	...	1124			...	...	...
Bensdorf arr		...	a.m.	6 14	7 26	...	8 59	9 11	12 5	...	...	2 11	2 37	...	...	...	...	5 59	5 29	...	...	...	9 2	1022	...	1144			...	SC	...
" dep		...	4 15	6 17	7 27	...	9 21	9 12	12 8	...	...	2 12	2 40	...	...	...	...	6 3	5 30	...	...	...	9 3	1023	...	1145			...	...	...
Mörchingen		...	4 28	6 30	7 35	...	9 34	9 20	1221	...	...	2 21	2 54	...	...	4 4	...	6 16	5 38	...	...	...	9 13	1036	...	1154			...	3 23	...
Remilly		...	5 1	7 5	7 54	...	10 6	9 39	1254	...	...	...	3 28	...	...	4 23	...	6 49	5 57	...	...	...	9 34	11 6	...	1213			...	...	...
Courcelles		...	5 16	7 21	...	...	1018	9 48	1 6	1—4	1—4	...	3 42	...	...	...	...	7 2	...	1—4	...	Ex 3	9 44	1118	3&4	...			...	...	...
Metz Haupt arr	1—4	a.m.	5 33	7 40	8 13	a.m.	1034	10 0	1 22	p.m.	p.m.	2 56	3 53	...	...	4 41	p.m.	7 18	6 16	p.m.	...	p.m.	9 56	1134	p.m.	1232			...	3 58	...
Metz Haupt dep	4a55	6 26	6 30	7 53	8 21	9 40		1010	2 30	1248	3 10	3 4	4 58	...	...	4 44	5 26	8 53	6 27	7 35	...	10 18			1159	1237			...	4 0	...
Metz Nord	5 6	6 32	6 41	8 2	...	9 49	...	...	2 40	1257	3 20	...	5 7	...	...	...	...	9 3	...	7 44	...	...	...	...	12 0	...			...	...	...
Hagendingen	5 30	6 45	7 5	8 22	RC	10 9	...	1028	3 1	1 18	3 41	RC	5 28	...	...	...	5 44	9 25	6 46	8 5	...	10 35	...	..	1221	1254			...	...	...
Ueckingen	5 42	...	7 15	8 32	...	1019	...	...	3 11	1 28	3 51	...	5 38	...	...	...	...	9 35	...	8 15	...	...	...	...	1233	...			...	...	...
Diedenhofen arr	5 50	6 56	7 22	8 39	8 49	1026	...	1040	3 19	1 35	3 58	3 29	5 45	...	...	5 8	5 56	9 42	6 57	8 22	...	10 46	...	...	1241	1 5			...	4 25	...
TREVES 124 arr	...	8a10	...	11a4	11a4	...	...	1p19	5p50	...	...	5p50	7 p9	...	...	...	7 p9	11 42	...	...	...	...	...	...	...	...			...	7 a43	...
COBLENCE 124 arr	...	1016	...	2p43	2p43	...	1—4	4p 2	8p 1	...	...	8p 1	9 p4	1—4	...	...	9 p4	2a28	...	...	1—4	...	...	...	...	...			...	...	...
Diedenhofen dep	6 2	...	7 56	9 15	8 51	1050	a.m.	1042	4 14	1 40	p.m.	3 30	5 51	p.m.	...	5 10	...	9 47	6 59	8 25	p.m.	10 48	...	...	...	1 7	...		...	4 26	...
Bettemburg dep	6 40	...	8 32	9 48	...	1124	1155	1110	4 47	2 18	4 7	3 56	6 26	6 35	...	...	...	10 22	...	8 57	1035	11 17	...	...	...	...	...	...	...	...	...
Luxemburg arr	6 56	...	8 47	10 5	9 26	1139	1213	1121	5 2	2 35	4 26	4 8	6 41	6 56	...	5 45	...	10 37	7 34	9 12	1052	11 28	...	...	...	1 44	...	...	...	5 1	...
BRUSSELS 103A arr		...	...	3p22	1255	...	...	3p22	...	7 p7	...	8p11	1238	1238	...	9p26	...	...	...	...	...	...	...	...	...	5a26	...	...	...	8 a28	...

‡—Between Appenweier and Strassburg only until 30th Sept.

K—Carlsbad Express, runs until 30th Sept.

OE—Orient Express. RC—Restaurant Car. SC—Sleeping Car.

Extra					
Metz dep	12 p2	12 p8	5p32	7 p8	...
Diedenhofen arr	12 32	12 58	6 19	7 55	...

Bettemburg dep	5 a22	6 a9	7 a55	8 a58	2 p28	6 p47
Luxemburg arr	5 40	6 25	8 10	9 13	2 45	7 8

BETTEMBURG and REDINGEN.

Bettemburg dep	a.m.	6a54	8a42	9 a50	11a59	2 p36	4p24	6 p59	9 p2	10p32	11p23
Esch	5 50	7 14	9 5	10 15	12 27	2 59	4 49	7 26	9 23	10 52	11 41
Redingen arr	6 10	...	9 29	10 53	12 47	3 18	5 10	7 47	9 39	...	..

Redingen dep	4a31	5a26	7a12	a.m.	10a17	a.m.	1 p45	3 p30	5p43	...	8 p0	9 p55	...
Esch	4 59	5 48	7 37	8 41	10 50	11 34	2 9	3 46	6 11	6 p23	8 24	10 14	...
Bettemburg 210	5 19	6 5	7 53	8 57	11 6	11 50	2 25	4 2	6 31	6 43	8 42	10 30	...

SAARGEMUND and SAARBURG.

		a.m.	a.m.	a.m.	a.m.	a.m.	p.m.	p.m.	p.m.	p.m.	p.m.	p.m.	p.m.
Saargemund dep		5 46	...	...	7 27	1015	1226	1 51	4 24	6 6	6‡20	7 46	1039
Saaralben 211	4a16	6 14	6 18	7‡10	8 1	1042	1253	2 10	4 52	6 33	6 55	8 11	11 7
Saar-Union	4 31	6 34	6 35	7 27	8 18	1059	1 12	2 27	5 9	6 50	7 12	8 27	1123
Berthelmingen	—	7 7	—	—	8 52	1130	1 46	2 58	5 41	7 21	—	8 58	1154
Saarburg 210 arr		7 2[illegible]	...	...	9 9	1149	2 4	3 11	5 59	7 34	...	9 15	1210

		a.m.	a.m.	a.m.	a.m.	a.m.	a.m.		p.m.	p.m.	p.m.	p.m.	p.m.	p.m.	p.m.	p.m.	p.m.
Saarburg dep		5 8	...	6 43	...	8 1	1011	...	1 25	1 39	4 5	6 57	...	8 15	8 30	1053	1112
Berthelmingen		5 27	...	7 1	...	8 15	1028	...	1 55	1 50	4 24	7 17	...	8 46	8 41	1126	1123
Saar-Union	4a39	5 59	6 42	7 33	8 ‡5	8 37	1058	p.m.	2 24		4 55	7 47	8 14	9 15	—	1149	
Saaralben	4 57	6 18	7 1	7 50	8 23	8 49	1118	1 24	2 40	—	5 12	8 4	8 30	9 31	...	12 2	—
Saargemund arr		6 45	7 26	8 15	8 52	9 6	1143	1 45	3 5	...	5 38	8 29	...	9 55	...	1221	...

‡—Weekdays only.

Luggage Rate—see page 462.]

ALSACE and LORRAINE RAILWAY.

COLMAR and METZERAL.

Station																			
Colmar ...dep	5a58	8 a4	9 a4	10a13	12p14	1p53	3 p21	4 p49	6 p22	7p44	10p45	...	...	...	...	...	...	...	...
Türkheim	6 13	8 19	9 17	10 29	12 28	2 6	3 34	5 3	6 35	7 57	10 58	...	...	...	...	...	...	...	...
Münster	6 47	8 51	9 50	11 11	1 0	2 38	4 6	5 35	7 7	8 29	11 29	...	...	...	...	...	...	...	...
Luttenbach	6 52	8 56	9 55	11 16	1 4	2 42	4 11	5 40	7 12	8 33	11 33	...	...	...	...	...	...	...	...
Metzeral arr	7 7	9 11	1010	11 31	1 19	2 57	4 26	5 54	7 27	8 48	11 48	...	...	...	...	...	...	...	...

Station																			
Metzeral dep	6a29	7a28	9a27	10a42	12p36	1p30	3 p4	4p36	6 p6	8 p11	9 p24	...	...	...	...	...	...	...	...
Luttenbach	6 43	7 43	9 41	10 56	12 51	1 46	3 18	4 50	6 19	8 24	9 40	...	...	...	...	...	...	...	...
Münster	6 49	7 50	9 47	11 2	12 59	1 59	3 25	4 56	6 26	8 30	9 48	...	...	...	...	...	...	...	...
Türkheim	7 20	8 21	1015	11 33	1 27	2 29	3 56	5 27	6 56	8 59	10 18	...	...	...	...	...	...	...	...
Colmar ...arr	7 32	8 33	1027	11 45	1 40	2 41	4 9	5 39	7 8	9 11	10 30	...	...	...	...	...	...	...	...

MÜNSTER and SCHLUCHT.

‡—8.35 p.m on Sunday.

Station							
Münster ...dep	6 a52	9 a0	9 a55	11 a40	1 p6	2 p41	5 p40
Stossweier	7 4	9 12	10 7	11 52	1 18	2 53	5 52
Altenberg	7 41	9 49	10 44	12 29	1 55	3 30	6 29
Schlucht (69) ...arr	7 53	10 1	10 56	12 41	2 7	3 42	6 41

Station								
Schlucht ...dep	8 a31	10a35	11a27	12p53	3p45	5 p3	7‡p10	...
Altenberg	8 40	10 44	11 36	1 2	3 54	5 12	7 19	...
Stossweier	9 20	11 24	12 16	1 42	4 34	5 52	7 59	...
Münster ...arr	9 32	11 36	12 28	1 53	4 46	6 4	8 11	...

LAUTENBACH and BOLLWEILER.

Station																		
Lautenbach ...dep	5a39	6 a4	a.m.	7a30	8 a30	9 a40	10a28	p.m.	12p39	1 p53	2p55	p.m.	4p38	5p42	7p13	p.m.	9p14	p.m.
Gebweiler	6 2	6 31	7 35	8 9	8 52	10 7	10 51	12 10	1 4	2 14	3 19	4 24	5 0	6 12	7 37	8 5	9 35	11 29
Bollweiler (209)	6 17	6 46	7 51	8 25	9 7	10 23	11 7	12 25	1 20	2 30	3 36	4 39	5 16	6 27	7 55	8 20	9 49	11 44

Station																		
Bollweiler ...dep	6a28	7a18	8a36	9 a27	10a34	11a15	1 p0	1p25	2p56	3 p53	4 p57	5 p40	6p46	8 p32	9 p0	10 p6	11p57	...
Gebweiler	6 46	7 55	8 54	10 1	10 50	11 35	1 17	2 14	3 15	4 9	5 13	6 12	7 1	8 48	9 16	10 22	12 14	...
Lautenbach ...arr	7 8	8 16	9 14	10 21	...	11 57	1 37	2 34	3 37	...	5 33	6 33	...	9 8	...	10 42	12 35	...

COLMAR and BOLLWEILER

Station															
Colmar ...dep	...	4a37	...	7a55	...	9 ‡a26	...	12p20	...	4 p30	6‡55	...	8p12	‡—Not on Sunday.	...
Ensisheim	5 a2	5 58	7 a29	9 6	10a4	11 34	12 p3	1 31	2 p7	6 5	8 25	8 p29	9 27		...
Bollweiler arr	5 22	6 18	7 50	...	1025	...	12 25	...	2 29	6 26	...	8 49	9 47		...

Station																
Bollweiler dp	5a30	6 a55	9a28	11a17	12p58	3p50	6p45	8 p59	10 p6	...	...	...	...	...	...	...
Ensisheim	6 19	7 15	9 59	11 39	1 31	4 21	7 5	9 23	10 26	...	...	...	...	...	...	...
Colmar ...arr	7 32	...	1115	...	2 47	5 41	...	10 36	...	...	...	...	...	...	...	...

SAARALBEN and CHAMBREY.

Station		a.m.	a.m.	a.m.	p.m.	p.m.	p.m.	p.m.		p.m.							
SAARGEMUND ...dep	...	4 40	7 59	1039	12 10	1 33	4 29	7 21	...	10 34	...	...	...	...	...	...	...
Saaralben ...dep	...	5 23	8 28	1118	12 49	1 58	5 14	8 13	...	11 9	...	...	...	...	...	...	...
Bensdorf (212A) ...arr	...	6 9	9 8	1155	1 31	2 34	5 50	8 49	...	11 42	...	...	...	...	...	...	...
,, ...dep	a.m.	6 20	9 19	1210	—	2 44	6 5	9 6	p.m.	—	...	...	...	...	...	...	...
Château-Salins	6 20	6 53	9 53	1245	...	3 20	6 41	9 18	10 17	...	...	...	...	...	...	...	...
Burthécourt (211)	6 31	7 2	10 3	1256	...	3 32	6 52	9 48	10 28	...	...	...	...	...	...	...	...
Chambrey ...arr	...	7 6	10 8	1 1	...	3 37	6 57	9 52	10 34	...	...	...	...	...	...	...	...

Station		a.m.	a.m.		a.m.	a.m.	p.m.		p.m.		p.m.	p.m.	p.m.				
Chambrey ...dep	...	4 46	...	...	7 52	10 53	1 44	p.m.	4 29	...	6 46	7 52	10§45	†—Week-days only.	§—10.27 p.m. on Sunday.	...	...
Burthécourt	...	4 52	5 24	...	7 57	10 58	1 49	3 1	4 34	...	7 6	7 57	10 53			...	...
Château-Salins	...	5 40	5 35	...	8 12	11 7	1 58	3 14	4 46	...	7 23	8 11	11 5			...	...
Bensdorf ...arr	a.m.	6 13	—	a.m.	8 46	11 38	2 32	—	5 22	p.m.	—	8 48	—			...	...
,, ...dep	4†35	6 21	...	7 51	9 2	12 9	2 43	...	5 24	6 42	...	9 6	...			...	...
Saaralben ...arr	5 40	7 0	...	8 26	9 38	12 48	3 27	...	6 4	7 21	...	9 46	...			...	...
SAARGEMUND ...arr	...	7 33	...	8 52	10a11	1 p26	3p57	...	6 42	7 50	...	1025	...			...	...

Burthecourt and Vic–Dist. 2½ m. Burthecourt dep. 6.35, 7.8, 8.5, 10.11, 11.5 a.m., 1.0, 1.55, 3.45, 4.44, 6.56, 8.2, 9.52, 10.55 p.m. Vic dep. 5.13, 6.49, 7.42, 9.48, 10.45 a.m., 12.42, 1.36, 2.50, 4.21, 6.37, 7.43, 9.35, 10.12 p.m.

METZ and CHATEAU SALINS.

Station						
Metz ...dep	5a33	7a40	1026	1 p6	4p21	8 p3
Liocourt	6 51	9 0	1145	2 27	5 41	9 23
Chateau Salins ...arr	7 40	9 49	1234	3 15	6 29	1011

Station									
Chateau Salins ...dep	5 a6	8 a9	1124	2 p7	4p48	8 p8	...	...	...
Liocourt	5 58	8 59	1216	2 58	5 40	8 58	...	...	...
Metz ...arr	7 17	1012	1 32	4 11	6 54	1014	...	...	...

MULHAUSEN and MULLHEIM.

Dist.	Station																		
	Mülhausen ...dep	4a33	7 a7	7a50	10a15	2 p24	4 p5	5 p5	6p32	8p32	10p6	...	...	...	...	...	...	...	...
9¾	Banzenheim	4 56	7 27	8 11	10 36	2 45	...	5 25	6 55	8 53	10 27	...	...	...	...	...	...	...	...
14¾	**Müllheim 140A** arr	5 12	7 41	8 25	10 50	2 58	4 27	5 39	7 10	9 7	10 42	...	...	...	...	...	...	...	...
...	**Müllheim** ...dep	5 a2	6a14	8 a11	9 a23	12 p2	3 p15	4 p53	6p10	8p36	11p23	...	...	...	...	...	...	...	...
...	Banzenheim	5 16	6 28	8 28	9 36	12 16	3 30	...	6 25	8 52	11 36	...	...	...	...	...	...	...	...
...	**Mülhausen** ...arr	5 37	6 49	8 51	9 54	12 38	3 52	5 18	6 47	9 14	11 57	...	...	...	...	...	...	...	...

SELZ and MERZWEILER.

Station								
Selz ...dep	4 a52	6a16	8a32	...	1 p1	4 p27	7 p51
Walburg arr	5 42	7 8	9 22	...	1 51	5 20	8 41
Walburg dep	5 56	...	9 37	11a50	...	5 32	—
Merzweiler 212A ...arr	6 17	...	9 58	12 12	...	5 54	...

Station								
Merzweiler ...dep	6a45	...	11a12	1 p23	...	6p50	...
Walburg arr	7 6	...	11 33	1 46	...	7 12	...
Walburg dep	7 26	9a37	11 50	2 5	5p31	—	9 p4
Selz 207A ...arr	8 10	1019	12 42	2 55	6 19	...	9 48

METZ, TETERCHEN, and SAARGEMUND.

Station		a.m.	a.m.	a.m.	p.m.	p.m.		p.m.	p.m.
Metz ...dep		5 7	7 34	11 3	1 56	4 29	...	6 24	9 59
Courcelles		5 27	7 52	1118	2 14	4 48	...	6 43	1017
Bolchen		6 8	8 27	1149	2 50	5 22	...	7 18	1050
Teterchen ...	a.m.	6 21	8 40	12 0	3 3	5 35	p m	7 29	1116
Hargarten ...	7 18	6 33	8 57	12 8	3 18	5 47	6 17	7 48	1123
Beningen arr	8 2	7 6	9 25	1241	3 56	6 12	6 49	8 20	—
,, dep	—	7 12	9 26	1258	4 3	6 13	7 3	8 27	...
Saargemund arr		7 50	10 4	1 27	4 41	6 39	7 41	9 6	...

Station			a.m.	a.m.	a.m.	noon	p.m.	p.m.	p.m.	pm	p.m.	p.m.
Saargemund dep		...	5 36	6 49	9 17	12 0	1247	2 39	4 41	6 8	8 33	1124
Beningen arr	a.m.	...	6 15	7 27	9 55	1242	1 30	3 17	5 21	647	9 12	12 2
,, dep	4 52	a m	6 23	7 39	1010	1258	2 37	3 21	5 30	7 3	9 22	1230
Hargarten ...	5 34	6 9	6 58	8 20	1052	1 42	3 13	4 1	6 22	749	1011	1 10
Teterchen ...	—	6 22	—	8 31	11 2	1 50	—	4 11	6 31	8 0	1021	—
Bolchen		6 32	...	8 43	1113	2 0	...	4 21	6 41	812	1031	...
Courcelles		7 7	...	9 19	1149	2 34	...	4 55	7 15	851	—	...
Metz ...arr		7 23	...	9 35	12 5	2 49	...	5 9	7 31	9 7	...	...

Extra.								
Beningen ...dep	6a22	8a20	10a23	3p25	5p16	9 p21	11‡p45	12‡a30
Saargemünd arr	7 0	9 0	11 3	4 5	5 54	10 2	12 35	1 20

Station				
Saargemünd dep	7a32	11a12	7p43	‡—Not on Sunday.
Beningen ... arr	8 12	11 42	8 21	

ALSACE and LORRAINE RAILWAY.

[Luggage Rate—see page 462.

PAGNY, METZ, and SAARBRUCKEN.

French Customs Examination at Pagny, and German at Novéant.

French Time at Pagny.

RC—Restaurant Car. SC—Sleeping Car.

Paris 64 ......dep	9 p5	...	10p15	...	...	...	...	...	...	1235	9 a0	...	...	12 0	12 20	1220	5p15	5p15
Frouard 72 dep	2a15	...	4a39	5 a47	...	7a52	...	9a17	...	1132	1p40	2p13	4p10	5p12	5 p54	7p20	...	1033
	Ex3 a.m.	2 3 4	1—4 a.m.	1—4 a.m.	Ex 3	1—4 a.m.	1—4	1—4 a.m.	2 3 4	1—4 p.m.	Ex3 p.m.	1—4 p.m.	1—4 p.m.	1,2,3 p.m.	1—4 p.m.	1—4 p.m.	Ex3 p.m.	1—4 p.m.
Pagny-Mosel ...dep	2 58	...	5 42	6 47	...	8 23	...	1010	...	1235	2 15	3 31	4 55	6 7	6 55	7 55	1040	1129
Novéant................	4 29	...	7 8	8 7	...	9 44	...	1136	...	1 57	3 45	4 51	6 20	7 36	8 20	9 16	12 7	1254
Ars an der Mosel ...	4 36	...	7 18	8 18	...	9 55	...	1146	...	2 9	3 52	5 1	6 31	7 43	8 31	9 26	...	1 4
Metz (210) ......arr	4 46	...	7 29	8 28	...	10 5	a.m.	1156	a.m.	2 19	4 3	5 11	6 41	7 54	8 41	9 36	1221	1 14
Luxembu'g 210 dep	...	a.m.	5a53	...	8 a14	...	8 45	...	1141	...	2p10	3p55	4p54	6p50	7 p38	...	1047	...
Metz ....dep	4 54	5 41	7*42	8*34	9 25	...	1121	...	1 27	...	4 11	5*35	6*59	8 7	9*42	...	1235	...
Courcelles (211) ...	SC	6 0	7 57	8 53	...	...	1139	...	1 46	2 3 4	RC	5 53	7 18	...	9 59	...	SC	...
Remilly (210)	5 16	6 13	8 7	9 6	9 45	...	1152	...	2 0	p.m.	4 33	6 6	7 31	8 28	10 13	...	1255	...
St. Avold	5 42	6 53	8 45	9 44	10 9	2 3 4	1230	p.m.	2 39	5 30	4 59	6 45	8 10	8 55	10 50	...	1 19	...
Beningen (211)	5 53	7 11	8 58	10 0	10 19	p.m.	1246	4 3	2 54	5 46	5 10	7 1	8 25	9 6	11 4	...	1 29	...
Forbach (125)	6 2	7 25	9 8	10 13	10 28	2 3	1259	4 22	3 7	5 59	5 19	7 14	8 37	9 15	11 17	...	1 37	...
Stieringen	...	7 30	9 13	10 18	...	2 8	1 4	4 29	3 12	6 4	...	7 19	8 42	...	11 22	...	...	...
Saarbrücken......arr	6 12	7 38	9 21	10 26	10 38	2 16	1 12	4 42	3 20	6 12	5 29	7 27	8 50	9 25	11 30	...	1 47	...
Bingerbck 125A ar	9a30	1244	...	...	1 p30	...	3p49	...	...	...	8p34	10p1	...	...	...	...	4a18	...

Bingerbuck dep	...	1 a27	...	...	4 a36	8 a45	...	...	10 a4	1p56	...	...	...	5 p45	...	9 p50
	2 3 4 a.m.	1—4 a.m.	1,2,3 a.m.	2 3 4 a.m.	2,3,4 a.m.	Ex 3 a.m.	2,3,4 p.m.	1—4	2,3,4 p.m.	Ex3 p.m.	2 3 4 p.m.	2 3 4 p.m.	2,3,4 p.m.	Ex 3 p.m.	1—4 p.m.	Ex 3 a.m.
Saarbrücken ...dep	...	5 50	7 16	7 47	9 37	11 28	12 25	...	2 48	5 7	4 17	6 23	7 57	8 59	11 43	12 36
Stieringen ......dep	...	5 59	...	7 56	9 46	RC	12 34	...	2 57	...	4 27	6 32	8 5	...	11 51	SC
Forbach	4 33	6 5	7 26	8 2	9 52	11 38	12 40	...	3 4	5 17	4 33	6 39	8 12	9 9	11 56	12 46
Beningen	4 50	6 20	7 34	8 16	10 7	11 46	12 54	...	3 21	5 26	4 47	6 54	8 26	9 17	12 9	...
St. Avold	—	6 38	7 46	8 32	10 24	11 58	1 11	...	3 39	5 38	4 59	7 12	8 44	9 29	12 24	1 3
Remilly.................	...	7 17	8 13	9 4	11 0	12 22	1 48	...	4 28	6 2	—	7 49	9 21	9 55	12 56	1 26
Courcelles.............	...	7 31	8 22	9 14	11 12	...	2 0	...	4 40	...	...	8 1	9 33	...	...	...
Metz.................arr	1—4	7 48	8 34	9 29	11 28	12 41	2 16	...	4 54	6 22	1—4	8 17	9 50	10 14	1 17	1 45
Luxembu'g 210 arr	a.m.	9 a26	...	1121	2 p35	2 p35	4 p8	p.m.	6 p41	7p34	p.m.	1037	11p28	11p28	...	5 a1
Metz ....dep	6 15	7 54	...	9‡40	11‡34	12 48	3‡10	3 53	5‡18	6 31	7 1	8‡24	10‡27	—	...	1 51
Ars an der Mosel ...	6 26	8 5	...	9 51	11 45	12 59	3 21	4 4	5 29	...	7 12	8 35	10 38	...	...	...
Novéant................	6 47	8 22	...	10 4	11 59	1 10	3 32	4 18	5 44	6 48	7 27	8 47	10 54	...	...	2 8
Pagny-Mosel ...arr	5 55	7 30	...	9 12	11 7	12 17	2 39	3 26	4 52	5 55	6 35	7 54	10 3	...	...	1 15
Frouard (72) arr	7 a6	8 a38	...	...	...	1 p16	3 p40	4 p36	...	7 p0	7p39	9 p5	11 p0	...	...	2 a2
Paris (65)......arr	12p16	...	...	4p39	...	6 p40	9 p20	10p30	11p47	11p47	...	...	5 a0	...	...	8 a25

Extra.—Metz to Novéant, 12.38 night. Metz to Pagny, 2.3 p.m. ‡ 1—4 class. *—2,3,4 Class.

METZ and AMANVILLERS.

E.M. Dist.		a.m.	a.m.	a.m.	p.m.	p.m.	p.m.	p.m.
	Metz.................dep	6 7	7 59	10 34	1 55	4 28	6 26	8 29
9¾	Amanvillers...arr	6 44	8 35	11 11	2 31	5 3	7 1	9 4
...	Chalons 67 ...arr	10a42	...	3 p2	6 p22	9p25	...	...

Chalons.........dep	...	1a50	5 a32	10a28	...	...	3 p49	...
	a.m.	a.m.	p.m.	p.m.	p.m.	p.m.	p.m.	
Amanvillers...dep	6 56	8 45	12 43	4 25	7 2	8 0	10 32	...
Metz..................arr	7 24	9 12	1 9	4 52	7 29	8 27	10 57	...

SAARBURG and ALBERSCHWEILER.

E.M.									
	Saarburg ......dep	5a50	8a10	10a25	11a30	2p22	4p10	7p42	9 p35
3¾	Oberhammer	6 6	8 28	10 40	11 47	2 39	4 26	7 56	9 50
10½	Alberschweiler arr	6 40	9 2	11 14	12 21	3 13	5 0	8 28	10 24

Alberschweiler .....dep	5a30	6a47	9a15	12p46	2 p1	5p21	7p24	8p38
Oberhammer................	6 6	7 22	9 50	1 21	2 35	5 53	7 57	9 10
Saarburg .... arr	6 19	7 35	10 3	1 34	2 48	6 6	8 10	9 23

Oberhammer......dep	6a†16	8a27	11a45	2p37	4p29	7p16	9p50
Dreibrunnen-V. arr	6 42	8 55	12 13	3 8	4 57	7 44	1018

Dreibrunnen-V dep	6 a52	9 a20	12p50	6 p3	8p43	...	...
Oberhammer......arr	7 17	9 45	1 16	6 27	9 7	...	...

†—Weekdays only.

LUXEMBURG and WASSERBILLIG.

	a.m.	a.m.	a.m.	a.m.	p.m.	p.m.	p.m.	p.m.	p.m.	p.m.
Luxemburg dep	6 11	7 2	9 31	1144	1249	1 55	4 20	6 20	7 1	10 14
Wasserbillig ar	7 6	7 41	1031	1239	1 26	2 49	5 16	6 57	7 56	11 9
Treves 125 arr	7 32	8 2	1057	1 9	1 47	3 15	5 40	7 14	8 25	11 35

	a.m.	a.m.	a.m.	a.m	a.m.	a.m.	p.m.	p.m	p.m.	p.m.	p.m.
Treves dep	...	6 0	8 8	8 15	1041	1138	1 27	2 50	5 4	6 29	11 8
Wasserbillig	4 30	6 31	8 26	8 45	1111	1154	1 54	3 16	5 21	6 58	1136
Luxemburg	5 40	7 37	9 10	9 48	1220	1238	2 58	4 18	6 14	8 3	1227

METZ and DILLINGEN.

Metz ....dep	...	5 a38	7a27	11a18	2p24	4p15	8 p2	...	...
Anzelingen	...	6 38	8 20	12 15	3 17	5 8	8 55	...	...
Busendorf	5a13	6 52	8 40	12 30	3 29	5 29	9 9	...	...
Dillingen ....arr	5 45	7 23	9 11	1 7	4 0	5 58	9 40	...	...
Dillingen.........dep	5a59	8 a5	11a40	1p37	4p33	6p50	7p55	9p58	...
Busendorf	6 41	8 39	12 19	2 19	5 5	7 28	8 35	1036	...
Anzelingen	6 53	8 51	12 31	2 30	5 17	—	8 49	—	...
Metz ....arr	7 42	9 42	1 21	3 21	6 5	...	9 45	...	...

LUXEMBURG and WILWERDINGEN.

E.M Dis.		1—4 a.m.	1—4 a.m.	1—4 a.m.	Ex 3 a.m.	1—4 a.m.	1—4 a.m.	2—4	1—4 p.m.	1—4 p.m.	1—4 p.m.	1—4 p.m.	1—4 p.m.
—	Luxemburg...dep	...	7 6	8 22	9 36	9 54	1147	...	12 42	3 3	5 48	7 4	9 16
16	Kruehten	...	7 44	9 1	...	10 32	1224	...	1 19	3 42	6 28	7 42	9 52
19½	Ettelbruck.....arr	5 10	7 55	9 12	10 9	10 44	1236	...	1 31	3 54	6 40	7 54	10 2
21½	Diekirch .....arr	5 18	8 8	9 22	10 21	10 58	1246	...	2 0	4 16	7 4	8 7	10 15
...	Ettelbruck ...dep	—	7 58	—	10 10	10 49	—	...	1 45	4 0	6 49	—	10 4
28½	Kautenbach	2—4	8 22	a.m.	...	11 14	...	p.m.	2 11	4 24	7 14	...	10 28
42½	Ulflingen............	6a11	9 8	9 13	10 56	12 0	...	12 10	2 54	5 9	8 0	...	11 17
45¼	Wilwerdingen arr	6 19	...	9 21	—	—	...	12 18	3 8	—	8 31	...	...
61½	St. Vith 127 arr	7 4	...	10 5	...	...	...	1 3	3 52	...	9 16	...	...

	1—4 a.m.	1—4 a.m.	1—4 a.m.	1—4 a.m.	1—4 a.m.	2—4 a.m.	1—4 p.m.	1—4 p.m.	1—4 p.m.	1—4 p.m.	2—4 p.m.	Ex3 p.m.
St. Vith 127 dep	...	...	...	...	9 25	10 49	...	1 40	5 3	...	9 58	...
Wilwerdingen dep	...	...	...	...	10 14	11 38	...	2 29	5 52	...	10 39	...
Ulflingen	...	...	6 52	...	10 30	11 44	12 15	4 5	6 39	8 49	10 45	1050
Kautenbach.........	...	...	7 28	...	11 14	—	12 49	4 43	7 15	9 25	—	...
Ettelbruck......arr	...	...	7 50	...	11 34	p.m.	1 10	5 13	7 37	9 47	...	1131
Diekirch......dep	4 30	6 26	7 35	9 43	11 17	2 40	1 6	5 5	7 20	9 39	...	...
Ettelbruck ...dep	4 45	6 39	7 55	9 52	11 39	2 51	1 17	5 20	7 40	9 50	...	1132
Kruchten	4 58	6 52	8 8	10 5	11 52	3 4	1 29	5 33	7 53	10 2	...	...
Luxemburg ...arr	5 40	7 34	8 50	10 47	12 34	3 46	2 11	6 15	8 35	10 43	...	12 5

Luggage Rate—see page 462.]

ALSACE and LORRAINE RAILWAY.

STRASSBURG and SAARGEMUND.

	2 3 4 a.m.	2 3 4 a.m.	1,2,3 a.m.	2 3 4 a.m.	Ex3 a.m.	2 3 4 p.m.	Ex3 p.m.	2 3 4 p.m.	1,2,3 p.m.	2 3 4 p.m	2 3 4 p.m.	1,2,3 p.m.
Strassburg dep	4 6	5 26	7 36	8 40	1023	1 40	4 17	5 4	7 50	8 7	9 4	1028
Vendenheim ...	4 20	5 37	...	8 51	...	1 54	...	5 18	...	8 22	9 19	...
Mommenheim	4 40	5 55	7 57	9 9	...	2 16	...	5 38	...	8 42	9 40	...
Obermodern ...	5 2	6 18	8 10	9 30	1057	2 38	4 52	6 0	8 25	9 4	10 2	11 3
RASTATT dep	...	...	6a34	...	9a26	1p15	3p15	...	6p52	...	—	9p30
Obermodern ...	5 4	6 32	8 11	9 32	1058	2 45	4 53	6 2	8 26	9 8	a.m.	11 5
Ingweiler	5 15	6 43	8 19	9 43	11 7	2 56	5 1	6 14	8 34	9 19	4 26	1114
Wingen 212A...	5 31	6 58	8 29	9 58	:	3 11	5 13	6 29	8 45	9 34	4 46	1127
Kalhausen arr	6 25	7 46	8 57	1047	:	4 3	:	7 17	9 12	1023	—	...
Kalhausen dep	...	7 49	9 1	11 2	:	4 10	:	7 46	9 15	1054	...	...
Saaralben arr	...	8 0	9 15	1114	:	4 24	:	8 0	9 29	1115	...	...
METZ 210 arr	...	10a0	...	1p22	:	7p18	:	9p56	1232	...	...	...
Kalhausen dep	6 26	7 47	8 58	1048	:	4 4	:	7 18	9 13	1024	...	...
Saargemund ar	6 50	8 7	9 11	11 7	1156	4 25	5 52	7 37	9 26	1044	...	12 5

	2 3 4 a.m.	2 3 4 a.m.	2 3 4 a.m.	1,2,3 a.m.	1,2,3 a.m.	2 3 4 a.m.	Ex3 p.m.	2 3 4 p.m.	1,2,3 p.m.	2 3 4 p.m.	Ex3 p.m	2 3 4 p.m.
Saargemund	4 40	4 52	6 30	8 32	11 9	1120	1 31	2 38	4 20	6 5	6 50	8 28
Kalhausen arr	5 4	5 12	6 51	8 44	1121	1142	:	3 0	:	6 26	:	8 49
METZ...dep	—	...	...	6a13	7a50	...	:	1049	:	1p14	:	4p58
Saaralben dep	...	4 58	...	8 29	9 39	1124	:	2 40	:	6 5	:	8 30
Kalhausen ar	...	5 10	...	8 41	9 50	1138	:	2 52	:	6 19	:	8 44
Kalhausen dep	a.m.	5 14	6 52	8 45	1122	1143	:	3 1	:	6 27	:	8 50
Wingen	4 59	6 6	7 43	9 12	1149	1234	2 12	3 55	5 4	7 53	7 28	9 40
Ingweiler........	5 13	6 19	7 55	9 21	1159	1246	2 22	4 9	5 14	8 7	7 37	9 52
Obermodern a	5 22	6 28	8 4	9 28	12 6	1255	2 29	4 19	5 21	8 18	7 43	10 1
RASTATT arr	7 a7	8a34	...	1048	1p36	...	...	5p53	...	10p0	...	...
Obermodern d	5 26	6 35	8 12	9 29	12 9	1259	2 30	4 24	5 22	8 26	7 44	10 2
Mommenheim	5 52	6 56	8 33	...	...	1 17	...	4 46	...	8 45	...	1021
Vendenheim ...	6 14	7 21	8 53	...	...	1 37	...	5 8	...	9 5	...	1040
Strassburg arr	6 30	7 36	9 7	10 0	1244	1 50	3 3	5 21	5 58	9 16	8 16	1051

Extra.

Kalhausen......dep	7a14	9a51	1 p4	1 p34	6p20	10p2	...	
Saargemund ...arr	7 33	10 10	1 26	1 53	6 42	1025	...	
Kalhausen dep	5a 6	5a58	11a47	12p32	3 p4	4p54	6p40	...
Saaralben arr	5 20	6 10	11 59	12 43	3 18	5 8	6 54	...
Saaralben...dep	7 a2	12p49	3p41	5p31	9 p47	...	...	
Kalhausen...arr	7 13	1 3	3 55	5 43	10 1	...	...	
Saargemund dep	7 a27	9 a29	10a39	12p10	4p29	7p21	10p34	
Kalhausen ...arr	7 48	9 52	11 1	12 31	4 53	7 45	10 53	

DEUTSCH-AVRICOURT and BENSDORF.

E.M.		a.m	a.m.	a.m.	a.m.	a.m.	p.m.	p.m.	p.m.	p.m.
—	**Deutsch-Avricourt** dep	...	6 43	...	9 0	11 37	3 45	5 34	...	8 55
6¼	Azoudange	...	7 2	...	9 19	11 56	4 3	5 52	...	9 14
13¼	**Dieuze** ....arr	...	7 23	...	9 40	12 17	4 24	6 13	...	9 35
...	" ......dep	5 48	7 25	8 18	11 10	1 12	4 54	6 15	8 21	—
16¼	Vergaville	5 56	7 33	8 26	11 18	1 20	5 2	6 23	8 29	...
21¾	**Bensdorf** 210arr	6 13	7 50	8 44	11 35	1 38	5 20	6 41	8 47	...

			a.m.	a.m.	p.m.	p.m.	p.m.	p.m.	p.m.	p.m.
...	**Bensdorf** ...dep	...	7 30	9 20	12 9	1 47	2 42	6 6	9 7	1140
...	Vergaville	...	7 48	9 38	12 27	2 5	3 0	6 24	9 25	...
...	**Dieuze** ....arr	a.m.	7 55	9 45	12 34	2 12	3 7	6 31	9 32	1211
...	" ....dep	5 37	7 57	10 3	—	2 32	3 42	6 33	—	—
...	Azoudange	5 59	8 19	1025	...	2 54	4 4	6 55	...	...
...	**D.-Avricourt** 64	6 18	8 38	1044	...	3 13	4 22	7 14	...	...

WINGEN and MUNZTHAL.

Wingen...dep	4a49	8a32	11a53	3p14	5p16	9p45	...
Münzthal arr	5 25	9 12	12 42	4 1	5 56	1021	...
Münzthal ......dep	5a30	7*a2	11a10	1p34	4p16	6p24	10p48
Wingen 212A arr	6 2	7 39	11 44	2 8	4 58	7 6	11 22

*—Not on Sunday.

FREIBURG and COLMAR.

Freiburg...	7a24	10a9	12p12	1p39	3p34	4p57	6p35	7p23	8p22	11p4
Breisach ...	7 57	1040	12 43	2 15	3 57	5 29	7 18	7 57	8 51	1137
Colmar 209	8 31	1112	1 13	2 50	4 23	6 3	...	8 37	9 17	12 9
Colmar ...	6 a0	7a21	8a53	10a14	12p18	1p51	4p47	7p39	9 p50	11p16
Breisach	6 42	7 55	9 25	10 42	12 58	2 30	5 27	8 18	10 27	1149
Freiburg	7 18	8 30	10 2	11 11	1 33	3 7	6 0	9 0	11 0	...

STRASSBURG and SAALES.

	a.m.	a.m.	a.m.	a.m.	a.m	p.m.	p.m.	p.m.
Saales ....dep	...	...	6 7	8 27	1148	3 18	5 33	8 15
St. Blaise-Poutay	...	...	6 38	8 58	1219	3 54	6 3	8 46
Rothau...............	4 58	5*58	7 7	9 36	1250	4 40	6 34	9 18
Lutzelhausen	5 21	6 17	7 29	9 54	1 9	5 1	6 55	9 37
Molsheim...... arr	5 50	6 44	8 1	10 21	1 37	5 33	7 25	10 6
Strassburg arr	6 36	7 24	8 39	10 5[illegible]	2 8	6 0	7 56	10 37

*Weekdays only.

	a.m.	a.m.	a.m.	p.m.	p.m.	p.m.	p.m.
Strassburg dep	5 41	7 39	1014	1 49	5 34	7 9	10 9
Molsheim	6 21	8 8	1045	2 24	6 7	7 56	10 38
Lutzelhausen	6 56	8 44	1116	2 56	6 43	8 22	11 13
Rothau	7 27	9 30	1146	3 29	7 15	9 16	11 40
St. Blaise-Po.	7 52	9 55	1221	3 55	7 40	9 41	—
Saales ...arr	8 22	1025	1 0	4 25	8 10	1011	...

HAGENAU and SAARGEMUND.

Dist EM		a.m.	a.m.	a.m.	a.m.	p.m.	p.m.	p.m.	p.m.	p.m.
	Hagenau	5 1	7 1	9 6	1130	1 44	3 26	5 52	7 33	1110
6¾	Merzweiler...	5 16	7 16	9 14	1147	1 56	3 41	6 7	7 48	1125
11¾	Reichshofen	5 34	7 32	9 30	12 6	2 10	3 59	6 26	8 5	1137
13¾	Niederbronn	5 41	7 38	9 36	1214	2 16	4 6	6 32	8 12	1143
23	Bitsch	6 21	8 12	1011	1253	2 45	4 41	7 7	8 49	1216
33½	Lemberg ...	6 36	8 24	1023	1 5	—	4 51	7 19	9 1	—
40¾	Rohrbach ...	6 56	8 43	1049	1 23	...	5 13	7 36	9 20	...
52¾	**Saarg'm** ...	7 19	9 6	11 3	1 46	...	5 36	7 58	9 43	...

	a.m.	a.m.	a.m.	a.m.	p.m.	p.m.	p.m.	p.m	p.m.	p.m.
Saargemund dep	...	5 18	7 37	1114	2 14	...	4 45	6 54	9 12	1035
Rohrbach	...	5 46	8 5	1145	2 41	...	5 12	7 24	9 39	11 3
Lemberg	...	6 6	8 25	12 6	2 59	...	5 32	7 44	9 57	1121
Bitsch	4 55	6 23	8 36	1218	3 9	4 51	5 48	7 57	10 7	1130
Niederbronn	5 29	6 54	9 9	1254	3 38	5 15	6 20	8 29	1033	
Reichshofen...	5 35	7 0	9 16	1 0	3 44	5 21	6 27	8 34	1028	...
Merzweiler ...	5 51	7 15	9 31	1 16	3 59	...	6 41	8 49	1047	...
Hagen. 208	6 5	7 29	9 45	1 31	4 13	5 42	6 55	9 3	11 0	...

MULHAUSEN, SENNHEIM, and KRUT.

	a.m.	a.m.	a.m.	a.m.	p.m.	p.m.	p.m.	p.m.	p.m.	p.m.
Mulhausen dep	5 42	6 53	9 15	11 17	1 38	4 13	5 47	7 5	8 15	10 34
Dornach ...	5 48	6 59	9 21	11 23	1 44	4 19	6 1	7 12	8 21	10 40
Sennheim	6 10	7 22	9 41	11 45	2 7	4 43	6 19	7 32	8 44	11 4
Thann	6 24	7 35	9 54	11 58	2 20	4 56	6 33	7 45	8 58	11 17
Weiler	6 38	7 49	10 7	12 10	2 32	5 8	6 47	7 57	9 10	11 29
Wesserling	7 4	8 25	10 30	12 32	2 54	5 30	7 10	8 15	9 30	11 47
Krüt ...arr	7 19	8 40	10 45	12 46	3 10	5 46	7 23	...	9 45	...

	a.m.	a.m.	a.m.	a.m.	p.m.	p.m.	p.m.	p.m.	p.m.
Krüt.....dep	...	6 29	8 6	10 11	1258	3 17	5 10	6 34	8 35
Wesserling	5 3	6 46	8 35	10 36	1 13	3 34	5 28	6 53	8 55
Weiler	5 17	7 1	8 50	10 51	1 27	3 48	5 43	7 9	9 11
Thann	5 28	7 11	9 1	11 1	1 38	4 0	5 54	7 22	9 22
Sennheim .	5 38	7 22	9 12	11 11	1 49	4 11	6 5	7 35	9 33
Dornach ...	5 56	7 40	9 34	11 29	2 7	3 31	6 23	7 55	9 54
Mulhausen	6 1	7 45	9 40	11 34	2 12	4 37	6 28	8 1	10 0

SENNHEIM and SEWEN.

Sennheim...dep	6 a12	7a28	9 a44	2 p12	6 p22	8 p52	11 p8
Masmünster	7 2	8 25	10 38	3 6	7 15	9 46	11 59
Sewen ....arr	7 33	8 56	11 10	3 38	7 43	10 17	...

Sewen...........dep	...	5 a48	7 a52	12p12	2 p37	6 p2	8 p10	10p27
Masmünster	4a44	6 20	8 19	12 46	3 11	6 36	8 37	10 59
Sennheim... ..arr	5 33	7 11	9 9	1 37	4 2	7 27	9 26	...

GROSS MOYEUVRE and HAGENDINGEN.—In 23 minutes.

Gross Moyeuvre dep. 3.51, 6.15, 6.50, 7.47, 9.4, 9.59, 11.33 a.m. ; 1.4, 2.29, 4.27, 6.15, 6.58, 8.27, 8.58, 10.2, 11.47p.m.
Hagendingen dep. 5.36, 6.16, 7.8, 8.25, 9.25, 10.32 a.m. ; 12.3, 1.45, 3.22, 4.48, 5.33, 7.4, 7.42, 9.28, 10.55 p.m. ; 12.31 night.

WEILER and WEILERTHAL.

Weiler ....dep	6a22	8 a1	10a42	1p56	3p52	6 p0	8p15	10p11
Weilerthal 207A...arr	6 54	8 34	11 20	2 31	4 24	6 32	8 47	10 43
Weilerthal dep	5a28	7 a5	8a46	12p28	2p40	5 p9	6p40	9p35
Weiler 212A arr	6 6	7 37	9 21	1 3	3 13	5 41	7 12	10 5

LUXEMBURG and LONGWY.

*—Greenwich Time.]

Station									
Luxemburg dep	5a45	7a18	9a17	10a11	12p46	2p16	4p45	7p21	10p58
Petange	6 11	7 56	9 43	10 59	1 12	2 52	5 35	8 5	11 35
Mont St. Martin*	5 25	7 11	8 56	10 14	12 21	1416	1650	1920	22 50
Longwy* arr	5 29	7 16	9 0	10 19	12 25	1421	1655	1925	22 55

Station									
Longwy* dep	4 33	...	6 27	9 0	11 28	1351	1555	1834	1953
Mont St. Martin*	4 39	a.m.	6 33	9 6	11 34	1357	16 1	1840	1959
Petange	6 10	6 17	8 8	1034	1 11	3 35	5 35	8 5	9 23
Luxemburg a	6 35	6 51	8 42	11 8	1 45	4 0	6 9	8 39	9 4[illegible]

ESCH and ATHUS.

*—Greenwich Time.]

Station										
Esch dep	...	7a18	9 a6	10a16	12p22	2p58	4p43	7p27	9p30	10p59
Petange	7 a10	8 2	9 37	10 54	12 52	3 33	5 44	8 11	10 1	11 30
Athus* arr	6 30	7 12	...	10 4	12 2	1443	1650	1921	...	...

Station									
Athus* dep	...	6a48	7a40	11a25	12p18	...	1552	17 55	19 39
Petange	5 a7	8 5	1016	12 39	1 33	3p38	5 32	7 p9	9 30
Esch arr	5 41	8 36	1045	...	2 4	4 9	6 4	8 41	10 1

PETANGE and ETTELBRUCK.

Station									
Petange dep	5 a37	7 a58	10a55	3p35	6 p5	7 p40	...	...	...
Kleinbettingen	6 30	8 36	12 3	4 11	6 53	8 21	...	...	...
Hagen	6 33	8 39	12 7	4 14	6 57	8 24	...	...	...
Steinfort	6 38	8 44	12 12	4 19	7 2	8 29	...	...	...
Noerdange	7 5	9 13	12 38	4 42	7 22	8 57	...	...	...
Ettelbruck arr	7 40	9 48	1 13	5 17	...	9 32	...	...	...

Station								
Ettelbruck dep	...	8 a3	10a16	1p38	5p31	7p45	...	...
Noerdange	5 a8	8 40	10 53	2 15	6 8	8 22	...	...
Steinfort	5 36	9 13	11 25	2 40	6 33	8 48	...	...
Hagen arr	5 40	9 17	11 29	2 44	6 37	8 52	...	...
Kleinbettingen	...	9 38	12 3	2 51	6 53	...	...	...
Petange arr	6 7	10 12	12 36	3 24	7 26	9 19	...	...

Station					
Martelange dep	6 a42	8 a51	12p16	2 p32	6 p40
Noerdange arr	8 16	10 30	1 59	4 11	8 14

Station					
Noerdange dep	8 a51	11 a0	2 p30	4 p45	8 p57
Martelange arr	10 28	12 48	4 16	6 22	10 34

DIEKIRCH and GREVENMACHER.—BENONCHAMPS and KAUTENBACH.

Station									
Diekirch	5a19	8 a9	10a24	11a46	2p10	4p25	...	8p10	...
Grundhof	5 55	8 49	10 56	12 21	2 48	5 4	...	8 48	...
Echternach	6 14	9 40	11 15	12 43	4 29	6 6	p.m.	9 12	p.m.
Wasserbillig	7 5	10 27	12 0	2 46	5 23	7 5	7 50	9 52	11 4
Grevenm'her	7 18	10 40	12 13	2 59	5 36	7 18	8 3	...	1117

Station											
Grevenmacher	...	6a25	8 a7	...	11a3	1p39	3 p8	...	6p34	7p32	10p39
Wasserbillig	...	7 11	8 29	p.m.	12 0	1 57	3 24	5p25	6 47	7 58	10 52
Echternach	6 a40	7 57	9 9	1210	1241	2 43	4 8	6 19	—	8 42	12 16
Grundhof	6 59	8 16	9 27	1230	...	3 2	4 27	6 38	...	9 1	—
Diekirch arr	7 34	8 57	9 58	[illegible] 5	...	3 42	5 4	7 15	...	9 38	...

Station						
Grundhof dep	8 a54	12p35	3 p6	5 p9	6 p43	9 p6
Beaufort arr	9 29	1 10	3 41	5 44	7 18	9 41

Station						
Beaufort dep	7 a35	11a40	2 p8	3 p46	5 p58	8 p7
Grundhof arr	8 10	12 15	2 43	4 21	6 33	8 42

Station								
*Benonchamps dep	...	9 a27	12p23	16 51	19 14	p.m.		...
Wiltz	7 a3	10 53	1 50	6 p37	8 p42	8 52	*-Greenwich	...
Kautenbach 212 arr	7 22	11 12	2 9	6 56	...	9 11	Time.	...

Station						
Kautenbach dep	8a26	1130	2 p25	7p20	10p37	...
Wiltz	9 5	12 0	3 5	7 41	10 57	...
*Benonchamps 95 arr	8 30	1125	14 30	19 6	—	...

DIEKIRCH and VIANDEN. E.M. 8½

Station					
Diekirch dep	8a15	11 a5	2p11	8p12	...
Vianden arr	9 2	11 52	2 58	8 59	...

Station						
Vianden dep	6a35	9 a7	12 p5	6p20	...	...
Diekirch (212) arr	7 20	9 52	12 50	7 5	...	...

LUXEMBURG, MONDORF, and REMICH.

Dist. E.M.	Station	a.m.	a.m.	p.m.	p.m.	p.m.	
	Luxemburg dep	7 10	10 2	2 35	4 40	7 37	...
5½	Weiler-la-Tour	7 39	10 31	3 4	5 2	8 5	...
10	**Mondorf** Dorf	8 1	10 53	3 27	...	8 29	...
10½	,, Bad	8 9	11 1	3 35	5 32	8 37	...
16½	**Remich (Nennig)** arr	8 33	11 25	3 59	5 56	9 1	...

Station	a.m.	a.m.	p.m.	p.m.	p.m.		
Remich (Nennig) dep	6 39	10 26	12 37	5 17	7 24	...	...
Mondorf Bad	7 9	10 57	1 7	5 49	7 54	...	...
,, Dorf	7 13	11 1	1 11	5 53	7 58	...	...
Weiler-la-Tour	7 39	11 25	1 36	6 18	8 23	...	...
Luxemburg arr	8 8	11 55	2 5	6 47	8 53	...	...

KRUCHTEN and LAROCHETTE (Fels).

‡—9.20 a.m. on Sunday.

Dist. E.M.	Station	a.m.	p.m.	p.m.	p.m.		
	Kruchten, Bhf. dep	8 20	1 45	5 45	8 0	...	...
0½	,, Dorf	8 23	1 48	5 48	8 3	...	...
7½	Larochette arr	9 0	2 25	6 25	8 40	...	...

Station	a.m.	a.m.	p.m.	p.m.		
Larochette dep	6 40	11 ‡0	4 35	6 55	...	...
Kruchten, Dorf	7 18	11 [illegible]	5 13	7 33	...	...
,, Bhf. (212) arr	7 20	11 40	5 15	7 35	...	...

LUXEMBURG and ECHTERNACH.

Station								
Luxemburg dep	7 a1	10a15	2p10	7 p5	...	...	...	...
Echternach arr	9 6	12 26	4 25	9 22	...	...	...	...

Station								
Echternach dep	6a35	9 a50	1 p0	6 p32	...	...	...	...
Luxemburg arr	8 46	12 4	3 15	8 52	...	...	...	...

LÜTZELBURG and DRULINGEN.

E.M.	Station							
	Lützelburg dep	7a46	8 a29	11 a0	1p20	4p31	6p33	9 p0
3½	Pfalzburg arr	8 16	9 0	11 31	1 51	5 3	7 4	9 32
...	Pfalzburg dep	6 57	...	11 14	...	4 45	...	9 14
13	Drulingen arr	9 11	...	12 32	...	6 2	...	1031

Station									
Drulingen dep	...	5a24	...	9 a18	...	2p39	...	6p26	...
Pfalzburg dep	*	6 39	...	10 29	a.m.	3 57	...	7 41	...
Pfalzburg arr	5a13	6 22	6a57	10 13	1156	3 41	5p31	7 25	...
Lützelburg 210 arr	5 45	6 55	7 26	10 45	1226	4 15	6 0	7 58	...

*—Weekdays only.

COLMAR and SCHNIERLACH

E.M.	Station								
	Colmar dep	6 a0	8 a3	10a12	12p14	2p15	4p45	8 p6	...
6¾	Kaysersberg	6 49	8 51	11 2	1 5	3 8	5 36	8 54	...
12½	**Schnierlach** arr	7 25	9 28	11 39	1 43	3 45	6 14	9 32	...

Station						
Schnierlach dep	6 a8	7 a46	9a58	12p20	4p29	7 p42
Kaysersberg	6 47	8 26	10 36	1 2	5 9	8 22
Colmar (209) arr	7 32	9 12	11 22	1 48	5 56	9 11

Station									
Colmar Haupt dp	6 a3	7a55	12p15	1p12	3 p4	4p47	6p58	10p17	...
Horburg	6 25	8 16	12 38	1 33	3 26	5 8	7 19	10 38	...
Markolsheim arr	7 32	9 29	1 55	...	4 39	6 21	8 26	11 48	...

Station									
Markolsheim	6 a6	7a52	9a36	p.m.	2 p3	4p46	6p54	8 p32	...
Horburg	7 18	9 7	10 50	1 43	3 [illegible]	6 0	8 11	9 45	...
Colmar arr	7 38	9 29	11 9	2 5	3 47	6 20	8 33	10 5	...

Station										
Colmar dep	7a35	8a30	10a35	12p15	2p5	255	4p40	615	7p15	9p10
Winzenheim arr	7 52	8 47	10 52	12 32	222	312	4 57	632	7 32	9 27

Station										
Winzenheim	7a15	8 a0	8 55	11a5	1p35	230	4 10	5 40	6 40	8p45
Colmar	7 32	8 17	9 12	1122	1 52	247	4 27	5 57	6 57	9 2[illegible]

LUBECK and STRASBURG.

SC—Sleeping Car. RC—Restaurant Car.

	1—4	1—4	Ex3	Fx3	Ex3	1,2,3	1—4	1—4	1—4	Ex3	Ex3	1—4	Ex3
HAMBURG 213A dep	...	5a50	8a50	9a13	9a25	Schwerin dep. 1p9.	1030	2 p0	3p54	5p20	7p10	7p30	12 0
		a.m.	a.m.	a.m.	a.m.		p.m.	p.m.	p m.	p.m.	p.m.	p.m.	a.m.
Lübeck dep	...	7 23	9 55	1012	1028		1210	3 38	5 22	6 21	8 10	9 18	1 3
Schönberg	...	7 53	1016	RC	C	A	1241	4 9	5 45	RC	⋮	9 50	SC
Grevesmühlen	...	8 18	1036	...	11 9		1 9	4 35	6 7	...	⋮	1016	...
Kleinen arr	a.m.	8 50	1058	1110	1135		1 42	5 7	6 39	7 23	SC	1050	2 1
,, dep	5 49	9 3	11 3	1116	1143		1 55	——	6 50	7 25	⋮	11 6	2 2
Blankenberg	6 12	9 27	RC	...	⋮		2 18	...	7 14	⋮	⋮	1130	⋮
Bützow arr	6 40	9 57	1136	1150	⋮		2 45	...	7 44	⋮	⋮	1157	⋮
Bützow dep	6 50	10 6	1151	1151	⋮		2 56	...	7 53	⋮	⋮	12 5	⋮
Rostock arr	7 31	1040	1220	1220	1242	2p33	3 36	...	8 32	8‡59	1010	1242	3 2
WARNEMUNDE arr	8a50	1116	1239	1230	1p29	2p55	4p36	...	9p50	9p50	1136	1 a9	3a20
COPENHAGEN arr	...	...	6p41	6p41			...	2 3 4	...	⋮	...	...	9a42
Bützow dep	6 52	10 5	1137	...	...	1—4	2 50	p.m.	7 49	⋮	...	1210	...
Gustrow	7 16	1020	1155	2 3 4	...	12p6	3 11	5 2	8 30	8 22	...	1230	‡—Via Gustrow.
Lalendorf	7 37	——	...	p.m.	...	1225	3 34	5 23	8 58	...	...	1250	
Teterow	7 58	a.m.	...	1254	...	1243	3 51	5 44	9 17	...	...	1 7	
Malchin	8 20	4 59	...	1 15	...	1 2	4 8	6 3	9 37	...	...	1 23	
Neubrandenburg	9 23	6 0	1 13	——	...	1 59	5 9	7 8	1037	9 46	...	——	
Strasburg arr	1047	7 4	⋮	...	...	2 50	5 59	8 20	——	⋮	...	...	...
STETTIN 183 arr	1 p4	8a54	2p45	...	...	4p14	7p36	10p9	...	1122	...	...	...

	Ex3	1—4	Ex3	1—4	1—4	1,2,3	1—4	Ex.3	1—4	Ex3	Ex3	Ex3	1—4	1—4	2 3 4
STETTIN 183 dep	...	...	...		...		6a43	8a28	1048	...	2p24	...	4p25	7p16	8p44
				a.m.		...	a.m.	⋮	p m.		p.m.	...	p.m.	p.m.	p.m.
Strasburg dep	...	...	...	...	...	...	8 35	⋮	1235	...	3 33	...	6 17	8 54	1053
Neubrandenburg	...	...	...	5 10	...	...	9 26	10 8	2 4	...	4 9	...	7 10	9 48	1129
Malchin	...	...	...	6 10	...	...	1020	...	2 59	...	4 54	...	8 13	1045	——
Teterow	...	...	...	6 31	...	...	1039	RC	3 16	...	RC	...	8 34	11 2	...
Lalendorf	...	...	...	6 53	a.m.	...	1057	...	3 36	...	...	...	8 59	1120	...
Gustrow	...	...	...	7 20	9 35	...	1213	11 30	3 54	...	5 44	...	9 28	1140	...
Bützow arr	...	...	...	7 38	9 55	...	1232	⋮	4 8	...	5 58	...	9 42	1154	...
COPENHAGEN dep	8p10	...	...	...	...	...	...	...	...	11a0	11a0	...	...	...	1—4
WARNEMUNDE	2a40	...	5a42	5a42	8a45	10a0	1123	10 a5	2p45	4p59	4p59	5p48	8p15	...	8p15
Rostock dep	3a 0	...	6a56	7 a3	9a25	1027	1149	10‡34	3 43	5p19	5p19	6 8	9 0	...	9 0
Bützow arr	3 30	...	E	7 37	10 2	Schwerin arr. 11.56.	1233	⋮	4 11	5*46	5 46	6 36	9 41	...	9 41
Bützow dep	3 31	...	⋮	7 48	10 7		1242	⋮	4 19	5*46	5 59	6 37	10 1	...	9 53
Blankenberg	SC	...	SC	8 23	1038		1 18	⋮	4 46	...	...	C	1035	...	1024
Kleinen arr	4 8	a.m.	⋮	8 48	11 0	B	1 45	12 24	5 6	6 24	6 39	7 20	1059	...	1048
,, dep	4 11	5 50	⋮	8 59	1112		1 56	12 29	5 13	6 27	6 49	7 25	1110	...	——
Grevesmühlen	...	6 25	⋮	9 29	1139		2 26	...	5 44	...	7 17	...	1141	...	...
Schonberg	...	6 51	⋮	9 53	12 0		2 51	...	6 9	...	7 35	...	12 5	...	...
Lübeck arr	5 8	7 21	8 53	1028	1227		3 21	1 24	6 38	7 22	7 56	8 19	1234	...	...
HAMBURG 213A arr	6a15	9 a3	9a51	1227	2p15		4p55	2 p25	8p12	8p23	9 p7	9p20	...	...	...

*—From 14th September. A—From Leipzig; runs until 30th August.
B—To Leipzig; runs from 2nd July until 31st August. C—Until 15th September.
E—In case of great delay in the arrival of the Sassnitz Ferry steamer this train will not run.

Extra.—Malchin to Teterow, 12.8 p.m.

GREVESMUHLEN and KLUTZ.

Grevesmühlen dep	11a15	2 p35	6‡p15	10p23
Klütz arr	11 55	3 15	6 55	11 3

Klütz dep	7 a25	12p15	4 p52	9‡p20
Grevesmühlen arr	8 5	12 55	5 32	10 0

‡—Until end August.

WAREN and DARGUN.

Waren dep	7 a0	11a16	...	2p11	...	7p20	...	...	...	...	...	...
Malchin	7 55	12 0	1p25	2 54	5 p5	8 4	9 p42	...	...	...	...	...
Dargun arr	9 11	...	2 39	...	6 17	...	10 47	...	...	...	...	...

Dargun dep	4 a57	...	9a27	...	3p25	6p52	...	...	...	...
Malchin	6 4	8 a31	1013	1 p5	5 10	8 25	...	...	...	...
Waren arr	...	9 43	...	1 48	6 20	9 24	...	...	...	...

HAGENOW and SCHWERIN.

E.M.									
	Hagenow dep	7a51	12p40	3 p52	6 p4	9p 3	11p52	..	...
17¾	**Schwerin** arr	8 27	1 15	4 32	6 35	9 42	12 29	...	...

Schwerin dep	7 a0	9 a26	1p10	5 p5	8p11	10p45	...	...
Hagenow 167 arr	7 40	10 2	1 46	5 41	8 48	11 21	...	...

LUDWIGSLUST and WISMAR.

A—To Warnemünde; runs until 20th Aug. B—From Warnemünde; from 2nd July to 21st Aug.

Dist. E.M.		a.m	a.m.	a.m.	non	a.m.	p.m.	p.m.	p.m.		p.m.			
	Ludwigslust dep	3 26	7 29	9 50	...	1140	1233	1 30	5 31	...	9 35	...	...	...
22¼	Schwerin arr	4 25	8 19	1030	...	1226	1 5	2 18	6 14	...	10 19	...	...	...
...	,, dep	5 20	8 32	1035	12 0	1 25	1 9	4 48	6 20	...	10 35	...	...	...
32½	Kleinen arr	5 41	8 53	1057	1219	1 47	⋮	5 8	6 40	p.m.	10 57	...	...	...
...	,, dep	5 52	9 6	1110	——	1 58	A	5 17	6 53	7 30	11 9	...	...	...
42¼	**Wismar** 166A arr	6 10	9 26	1128	...	2 17	⋮	5 36	7 11	7 51	11 27	...	...	...

	a.m.	a.m.	a.m.	a.m.	p.m.	p.m.	p.m.	p.m.	p.m.	p.m.		
Wismar dep	5 20	8 25	⋮	1035	...	1 19	4 40	6 14	6 50	1024	...	...
Kleinen arr	5 42	8 49	B	1059	...	1 45	5 5	6 40	7 15	1048	...	...
,, dep	——	9 1	⋮	1114	1233	1 59	5 16	6 51	7 33	11 6	...	...
Schwerin arr	a.m.	9 22	1156	1132	1255	2 23	5 34	7 12	7 57	1129	...	...
,, dep	7 15	9 38	12 0	1215	——	3 15	5 40	7 20	——	1137	...	...
Ludwigslust arr	8 6	1024	1231	1 4	...	4 7	6 15	8 8	...	1224	...	...

SCHWERIN and PARCHIM.

Schwerin dep	6 a30	11a39	5 p47	10p37	...	...	...	...	...	...
Crivitz	7 15	12 20	6 29	11 17	...	...	...	...	...	...
Parchim arr	7 53	12 56	7 7	11 53	...	...	...	...	...	...

Parchim dep	6a34	11a38	3p23	7p30	...	...	...	...	...
Crivitz	7 13	12 19	4 3	8 10	...	...	...	...	...
Schwerin (213) arr	7 53	12 58	4 43	8 51	...	...	...	...	...

SCHWERIN and RHENA.

Schwerin dep	9 a35	1p30	6 p40	10p32	...	...	...	...	...	...
Gadebusch	10 15	3 21	7 28	11 16	...	...	...	...	...	...
Rehna arr	10 31	3 37	7 44	11 32	...	...	...	...	...	...

Rehna dep	6 a43	10a50	4 p25	9p10	...	...	...	...	...
Gadebusch	7 1	11 8	4 43	9 28	...	...	...	...	...
Schwerin arr	7 53	11 47	5 27	1014	...	...	...	...	...

GUSTROW and MEYENBURG.

E.M.							
	Gustrow dep	...	7a21	12p20	5 p3	7 p6	...
22	Karow	...	8 37	2 22	6 10	8 25	...
32	Ganzlin	6a31	9 10	3 13	7 16	9 10	...
38¼	Meyenburg arr	6 46	9 25	3 32	7 32	9 26	...

Meyenburg dep	7a18	9a55	1p20	6p27	9p27	...
Ganzlin	7 40	1016	1 36	7 2	9 42	...
Karow	8 48	11 3	2 14	8 20	——	...
Gustrow arr	9 52	12 1	3 17	9 21	...	...

Ganzlin dep	10a20	3 p19	9 p47	...	...
Robel arr	11 7	4 20	10 48	...	...

Robel dep	5 a40	12p25	5 p23	...	...	...	...
Ganzlin arr	6 24	1 30	6 38	...	...	...	...

GUSTROW and PLAAZ.

Gustrow dep	7a28	12p10	8 p8	9p30	...
Plaaz arr	7 59	12 33	8 39	9 52	...

Plaaz dep	6 a41	9 a2	4 p10	8p49	...
Gustrow arr	7 4	9 25	4 42	9 10	...

TETEROW and GNOIEN

E.M.								
	Teterow dep	8 a5	12p50	4 p0	9p25	...	...	...
10¾	Poggelow	8 40	1 24	4 35	10 0	...	...	...
16½	**Gnoien** arr	8 58	1 42	4 53	10 18	...	...	...

Gnoien dep	5 a23	9 a42	2 p15	7 p30	...	...	...	...	...
Poggelow	5 42	10 0	2 34	7 49	...	...	...	...	...
Teterow 213 arr	6 20	10 32	3 9	8 23	...	...	...	...	...

LUBECK and HAMBURG.—Distance 39¼ miles.

	Ex3	1—4	1—4	1,2,3	2 3 4	Ex3	1,2,3	1—4	1,2,3	1—4	Ex3	1,2,3	1—4	1,2,3	1—4	1—4	1,2,3	Ex3	Ex3	Ex3	1,2,3	1,2,3	1,2,3
	a.m.	a.m.	a.m.	a.m.	a.m.	a.m.	a.m.	a.m	p.m.	p.m.	p.m.	p.m.	p.m	p.m	p.m.	p.m	p.m.	p.m.	p.m.	p.m	p.m.	p.m.	p.m.
Lübeck dep	5 13	5 50	7 31	8 15	...	9 0	10 0	1052	12 5	1250	1 28	2 17	3 34	4 52	5 50	6 45	7 21	7 28	8 2	8 25	9 0	9 52	1133
Oldesloe	5 35	6 22	8 6	8 36	8 42	...	1026	1129	...	1 22	1 49	2 47	4 6	5 14	6 24	7 17	...	...	8 28	...	9 34	...	12 3
Bargteheide	...	6 39	8 22	...	9 1	...	1039	1146	...	1 38	...	3 2	4 22	...	6 42	7 34	B	...	...	A	9 53	...	1220
Ahrensburg .	...	6 48	8 32	...	9 11	...	...	1156	...	1 47	...	3 12	...	...	6 53	7 43	...	...	...	...	10 3	...	1230
Wandsbek ...	6 7	7 10	8 55	9 5	9 32	...	11 0	1219	1255	2 7	...	3 32	4 47	5 44	7 16	8 4	...	...	8 59	...	1025	1046	1252
Hamburg ..	6 15	7 18	9 3	9 13	9 44	9 51	11 8	1237	1 3	2 15	2 25	3 40	4 55	5 52	7 24	8 12	8 19	8 23	9 7	9 20	1033	1054	1 2

	1—4	1,2,3	1—4	1,2,3	Ex3	Ex3	Ex3	1—4	1,2,3	1,2,3	1—4	1,2,3	1—4	1,2,3	Ex3	1,2,3	2&3	Ex3	1—4	1,2,3	1,2,3	Ex3	1—4
Hamburg	a.m.	a.m.	a.m.	a.m.	a.m.	a.m	a.m.	a.m.	a.m.	p.m.	p.m.	p.m.	p.m.	p.m	p.m.	p.m	p.m.	p.m.	p.m	p.m	p.m.	n'gt	n'gt
Hauptbahnhf	5 50	7 25	7 30	8 38	8 50	9 13	25	1030	1120	1230	2 0	3 12	3 54	4 45	5 20	5 45	6 36	7 10	7 30	9 0	10 0	12 0	1225
Wandsbek.....	6 1	7 33	7 40	8 46	8 59	...	...	1039	1128	1238	2 10	3 20	4 2	4 53	...	5 54	6 49	...	7 39	9 8	10 9	12 8	1235
Ahrensburg...	6 23	...	8 2	...	...	...	A	11 2	...	1258	2 32	...	4 22	...	...	6 16	7 11	...	7 59	...	1029	...	1255
Bargteheide..	6 32	...	8 12	B	...	...	...	1112	...	1 7	2 42	...	4 31	...	...	6 26	7 21	...	8 10	9 30	1038	*	1 4
Oldesloe	6 48	8 5	8 27	...	9 31	...	...	1131	1158	1 23	2 58	...	4 46	5 24	...	6 42	7 35	...	8 31	9 43	1054	...	1 18
Lübeck..arr	7 18	8 31	9 5	9 43	9 51	10 8	1020	12 2	1221	1 50	3 29	4 10	5 13	5 45	6 14	7 12	—	8 4	9 3	10 5	1123	1258	1 45

*—Sleeping Car, Hamburg to Copenhagen (see page 213).

A—Until 15th September. B—In July and August only.

LUBECK and TRAVEMUNDE.

Lubeck ....dep	5a40	7a32	7a57	8a35	9*a47	10a15	10‡a32	12p24	1p45	2 p0	3 p5	4p14	5p20	5 p48	7 p17	8p23	10p9	11p34	...
Travemunde Str,....arr	6 24	8 13	8 25	9 7	10 15	10 48	10 49	1 0	2 23	2 38	3 38	4 41	5 55	6 5	7 47	8 59	1040	12 9	...

Travemunde Str. ....dep	5†a58	6a45	7a43	8 a20	9 a6	11a26	12*36	1p33	4 p0	5 p51	6 p50	7p15	7‡p55	8 p10	9 p40	10§p10	10p50	...
Lubeck ....arr	6 36	7 23	8 10	8 48	9 44	12 1	1 10	2 11	4 38	6 32	7 17	7 52	8 19	8 49	9 47	10 43	11 25	...

*—In July and August only. †—Not on Sunday. ‡—Until 15th Sept. §—Until 31st August.

LUBECK and BUCHEN.

	a.m.	a.m	a.m	a.m.	a.m.	p.m.	p.m	p.m.	p.m	p.m.	p.m.		
Lubeck ....dep	5 35	6 33	8 20	9 3	1042	1 31	2 56	4 48	5 49	8 55	11 30	...	...
Ratzeburg	6 25	6 59	8 51	9 23	11 4	2 1	3 20	5 8	6 19	9 30	11 59	...	...
Mölln.........................	⋮	7 11	9 2	⋮	1115	2 15	3 32	⋮	6 32	9 47	12 10	...	...
Buchen (167)...... ......arr	⋮	7 33	9 23	⋮	1134	2 39	3 51	⋮	6 54	1015	12 31	...	...
Wittenberge 167......arr	9 0	...	...	11 8	...	...	...	6 55	...	...	...	...	...

	a m		a.m.	a.m.	a.m.	p.m.	p.m.	p.m.	p.m.	p.m.	p.m		
Wittenberge ....dep	...	...	...	...	1058	...	2 43	...	...	...	...	...	...
Buchen ....dep	6 27	...	8 16	11 36	⋮	3 5	⋮	4 49	7 11	7 43	1032	...	...
Mölln.........................	6 49	a.m.	8 41	11 59	⋮	3 30	⋮	5 10	7 34	8 4	1053	...	...
Ratzeburg	7 1	7 40	8 58	12 11	1245	3 43	4 20	5 21	7 45	8 16	11 4	...	...
Lubeck ....arr	7 27	8 18	9 24	12 37	1 5	4 9	4 40	5 42	8 11	8 38	1125	...	...

LUBECK and SCHLUTUP.

Lubeck ...dep	7 a40	10a50	2 p0	3p40	6 p45	8p20	11p35
Schlutup arr	8 17	11 18	2 28	4 8	7 13	8 48	12 3

Schlutup...dep	6 a50	10a5	12p55	2p56	5 p55	7p25	10p15
Lubeck ......arr	7 18	1033	1 24	3 24	6 30	7 53	10 43

WISMAR and KAROW.

Wismar............dep	5a15	8a 25	...	...	3p25	...	9p25
Blankenberg (212)...	6 23	9 31	...	2p23	5 10	7p25	1040
Sternberg.............	6 57	9 53	12p45	2 43	5 53	7 56	11 6
Goldberg	7 54	10 35	1 31	—	7 5	8 40	—
Karow (212) ...arr	8 24	10 58	1 55	...	7 43	...	...

Karow ....dep	a.m.	8a40	11a15	2 p20	8p22
Goldberg..................	6 55	9 9	11 45	3 1	8 55
Sternberg	7 44	9 56	12 42	4 3	9 43
Blankenberg..............	8 30	1045	1 8	4 52	1040
Wismar (212) arr	9 29	12 8	...	5 44	1130

LUDWIGSLUST and NEUBRANDENBURG.

Dist. E.M.			a.m.	a.m.	p.m.	p.m.	p.m.
	Ludwigslust ....dep	...	5 33	8 53	12 12	6 26	9 50
5½	Neustadt......................	...	5 48	9 8	12 27	6 41	10 7
16¾	**Parchim** ....arr	...	6 16	9 36	12 54	7 9	1036
...	,, ...dep	...	7 10	9 45	1 2	7 14	1041
25	Lübz	...	7 40	10 14	1 28	7 38	11 5
38	**Karow 213**..............arr	...	8 21	10 53	2 2	8 11	—
...	,, ...dep	...	8 39	11 8	2 15	8 27	...
46	Malchow.......................	a.m.	9 5	11 35	2 43	8 58	...
59½	Waren 213..................arr	6 32	9 42	12 14	3 20	9 46	...
79½	Penzlin	7 34	—	1 22	4 40	11 0	...
88½	Neubrandenburg 181 arr	8 0	...	1 47	5 7	11 27	...

		a.m.	a.m.	p.m.	p.m.	p.m.
Neubrandenburg ....dep	...	5 19	11 10	...	4 14	7 20
Penzlin	...	5 49	11 42	...	4 44	7 50
Waren ....dep	...	7 22	1 0	4 57	7 13	8 45
Malchow	...	8 2	1 39	5 39	7 51	—
Karow ....arr	...	8 23	2 0	6 0	8 12	...
,, ...dep	a.m.	8 37	2 15	6 12	8 28	...
Lübz............................	6 5	9 12	2 55	6 50	9 9	...
Parchim ....arr	6 29	9 34	3 17	7 13	9 31	...
,, ...dep	6 36	9 38	3 21	7 20	9 36	...
Neustadt......................	7 5	10 7	3 52	7 51	10 6	...
Ludwigslust 213 ......arr	7 19	10 21	4 7	8 5	10 20	...

PAULINENAUE and NEU-RUPPIN.

Dist.							
	Paulinenaue dep	7a47	10a45	2p51	6p20	7p30	10p58
17¼	Neu-Ruppin arr	8 50	11 42	3 50	7 8	8 51	11 52

Neu-Ruppin ......dep	6 a0	7 a53	1p20	6p18	9 p20
Paulinenaue **167** arr	7 8	8 47	2 15	7 13	10 30

DOMITZ and LUDWIGSLUST.

Domitz.........dep	7a53	10a28	4 p13	7 p20	9p51
Malliss..................	8 11	10 46	4 31	7 38	10 7
Ludwigslust arr	8 45	11 20	5 7	8 12	...

Ludwigslust dep	8a21	1 p27	4p22	...	8 p37
Malliss..................	9 0	2 2	4 59	7 p39	9 12
Domitz (167) arr	9 16	2 18	5 15	8 0	9 28

MALLISS and LUBTHEEN.

Malliss..................dep	9 a6	2p10	5 p10	10p12
Lübtheen ....arr	9 46	2 58	5 58	10 51

Lübtheen ....dep	7a23	10a0	3p30	6p40
Malliss ....arr	8 4	1040	4 21	7 30

STRASBURG and NEUSTRELITZ.

Strasburg ...dep	5a50	11a20	3p37	6 p17	...
Woldegk..................	6 46	12 22	4 41	6 48	...
Blankensee	7 31	1 38	5 33	7 44	...
Neustrelitz...arr	7 56	2 12	6 0	8 12	...

Neustrelitz ...dep	8 a23	1 p16	2p13	9p19	...
Blankensee	9 3	1 39	3 0	9 51	...
Woldegk	10 16	2 20	5 23	1055	...
Strasburg 213 arr	10 48	2 45	5 56	1128	...

ROSTOCK and TRIBSEES.

*—11.8 p.m. on Sunday.] [‡—11.51 p.m. on Sunday.

Rostock...........dep	8 a27	12p39	5 p13	9*p25	...	...	...
Sanitz	9 5	1 15	5 53	10 5	...	...	...
Tribsees...........arr	9 51	2 0	6 39	10 52	...	...	...

Tribsees ....dep	6a15	10a14	2 p14	7p 4	...	...	...
Sanitz	7 13	11 6	3 4	7 55	...	...	...
Rostock ....arr	7 46	11 41	3 35	8 30	...	...	...

Sanitz ....dep	9 a8	1p18	5p56	10‡p8	...	...	...
Tessin ....arr	9 26	1 36	6 14	10 26	...	...	...

Tessin ....dep	6a 47	10a40	2p35	7 p29	...	...	...
Sanitz.............arr	7 5	10 58	2 53	7 47	...	...	...

Tribsees..............dep	5 a35	10a14	2 p35	6 p50	...	...
Grimmen	6 50	11 13	3 34	7 49	...	...
Greifswald 183...arr	8 52	12 35	5 5	9 55	...	...

Greifswald ....dep	6 a4	10a20	2p30	6 p0	...	...
Grimmen	7 55	1 14	4 6	7 51	...	...
Tribsees...............arr	9 5	2 9	5 5	8 50	...	...

WISMAR and ROSTOCK.

	a.m.				a.m.	a.m.	p.m.							p.m.				
Wismar..............dep	6 20	§	§	...	9 44	11 42	2 30	§	...	§	...	...	...	8 2	...	...	...	...
Neu Buckow	7 6	a.m.	a.m.	a.m.	10 38	12 32	3 17	p.m.	p.m.	p.m.	p.m.	p.m.	p.m.	8 58	p.m.	...	...	...
Doberan......	7 48	9 7	9 49	9 58	11 28	1 15	4 2	2 23	3 2	3 43	4 25	5 34	8 20	9 42	10 25	...	...	...
Rostock 181 ....arr	8 19	9 36	10 17	10 28	11 59	1 43	4 35	2 47	3 30	4 10	4 53	6 0	8 49	10 11	10 53	...	...	...
	a.m.	a.m.	a.m.	a.m.	p.m.	p.m.	p.m.	p.m.	p.m.	p.m.	p.m.	p.m.	p.m.	p.m.				
Rostock ....dep	5 55	8 24	9 §14	10 58	12 40	12§52	1 §44	2 50	3 50	5 0	7 5	7 44	9 12	11 10	...	...	...	...
Doberan................	6 29	8 58	9 42	11 30	1 7	1 21	2 10	3 20	4 34	5 26	7 33	8 19	9 38	11 37	...	...	...	...
Neu Buckow	7 9	9 41	—	12 9	—	—	—	—	5 18	—	—	9 0	—	—	...	...	...	...
Wismar 213A ......arr	7 56	10 25	...	12 58	...	...	...	...	6 0	...	...	9 48	...	...	...	...	...	...

§—Until 15th September.

Doberan ....dep	6 34	From Doberan dep. 6.34, 7.51, 9.6, 9§55, 11.36 a.m., 1.15, 1§30, 2§22, 3.30, 4.35, 5.46, 7§40, 8.24, 9.45 p.m. From Arendsee dep. 6 48, 8.3, 8§52, 10.24 a.m., 12.7, 1§12, 2.6, 2§35, 3.28, 4.36, 6§35, 7.24, 8.40, 9.29 p.m.
Heiligendamm	6 57	
Arendsee ....arr	7 22	

§—Until 15th September

STRALSUND and DAMGARTEN.

Stralsund ....dep	...	7 a22	...	11a30	3 p1	7 p13	9 p28	**Damgarten**.........dep	...	5 a11	10a24	...	...	3 p20	...
Alten-Pleen	...	8 10	...	12 18	3 53	8 1	10 11	Barth	...	7 12	12 3	1 p0	...	5 4	...
Clausdorf ....arr	...	...	...	12 49	...	8 32	...	Clausdorf.........dep	5a28	...	—	...	1 p34	...	...
Barth	6 a0	9 4	11a12	—	5 18	—	10 58	Alten-Pleen	6 0	8 7	...	1 49	2 15	5 53	...
Damgarten ....arr	7 42	...	12 51	...	6 53	...	...	**Stralsund** ....arr	6 47	8 49	...	2 31	2 57	6 35	...

BRILON and SOEST.	**Brilon**..............dep	6 a25	10 a3	1 p25	...	8 p28	...	**Soest** ....dep	6 a3	10 a7	1p15	3 p35	8 p14	...
	Belecke..................	7 12	11 11	2 21	4 p47	9 17	...	Belecke............	7 12	11 15	2 17	4 39	9 20	...
	Soest ....arr	8 14	12 14	3 24	5 56	10 20	...	**Brilon**.........arr	7 55	12 2	...	5 21	10 5	...

LIPPSTADT and NEU BECKUM.

Lippstadt.........dep	...	6a35	...	9 a38	1 p8	3 p25	...	6 p38	8 p32	...	...	...	...	...	...	...	...	...
Beckum	6 a10	7 38	8 a17	10 47	2 10	4 29	6 p20	7 39	10 0	...	...	...	...	...	...	...	...	...
Neu Beckum ...arr	6 21	7 49	8 28	10 58	2 21	4 40	6 40	7 50	10 11	...	...	...	...	...	...	...	...	...
Neu Beckum ...dep	6 a43	8 a1	8 a46	12p15	2 p45	...	5 p29	7 p0	8 p25	10p28	...	...	...	...	...	...	...	...
Beckum	6 58	8 12	9 12	12 28	2 56	3 p25	5 55	7 14	8 39	10 39	...	...	...	...	...	...	...	...
Lippstadt.........arr	7 56	...	10 35	1 24	...	4 22	7 34	...	9 35	...	...	...	...	...	...	...	...	...

MUNSTER and WARENDORF.

Munster ....dep	6 a25	10a30	1 p20	3 p25	...	7 p0	9 p0	**Warendorf** ......dep	...	7 a5	10a13	...	1p42	3 p56	6p36	...
Neu Beckum **160A**	8 39	12 20	2 47	4 32	5p25	8 25	10 10	Neu Beckum	6 a40	8 39	10 58	12p2	2 50	5 0	7 38	8 p25
Warendorf ......arr	9 25	1 2	3 31	...	6 15	9 7	...	Munster..........arr	7 45	9 46	...	1 7	3 56	6 7	...	9 35

BETTEMBURG and DÜDELINGEN

Bettemburg	5a28	7 a0	9a8	9a51	11a16	1159	2p41	5p15	7p7	9p5	10p35	Düdeli.	620	7a39	9a33	10a50	11a38	2p0	3p51	6 p9	8p29	10p10	10p52
Düdelingen	5 38	7 11	918	10 2	11 26	1210	2 52	5 26	718	915	10 45	Bettem.	630	7 48	9 42	11 0	11 48	210	4 1	6 20	8 38	10 19	11 1

NOERZINGEN and OETTINGEN-RUMELINGEN.

Noerzingen......dep	5a17	6 a4	7a10	9 a0	10 a3	11 a4	12p12	2p50	4p35	6p27	7p13	9 p12	10p45	...	...	...	...	...	...	...
Oettingen Rum. arr	5 32	6 19	7 25	9 15	10 18	11 19	12 27	3 5	4 40	6 42	7 28	9 27	11 0	...	...	...	...	...	...	...
Oettingen Rum. dep	4a52	5a39	6a42	8a29	9 a38	10a35	11a25	1p58	3p35	6 p2	6p48	8p16	10p2	...	...	...	...	...	...	...
Noerzingen ......arr	5 7	5 54	6 57	8 44	9 53	10 50	11 40	2 13	3 50	6 17	7 3	8 31	1018	...	...	...	...	...	...	...

WEISSENBURG and LAUTERBURG.

Weissenburg......dep	5 a3	8a27	1 p0	4p11	8 p6	...	...	...	**Lauterburg**......dep	6a51	11a20	2p24	6p22	9p37	...	...	...
Lauterburg........arr	5 48	9 12	1 59	4 52	8 47	...	...	...	**Weissenburg** ...arr	7 36	12 5	3 23	7 6	1021	...	...	...

BISCHWEILER and OBERHOFEN.—In 8 min.-Bischweiler dep. 6.9, 7.20, 9.56, 11.55 a.m., 12.38, 1.32, 4.47, 7.15, 9.4 p.m. Oberhofen dep. 6.21, 7.33, 10.18 a.m., 12.10, 1.18, 2.6, 5.5, 8.7, 10.20 p.m.

ALTENHUNDEM and MESCHEDE.

Altenhundem ......dep	...	7 a15	9 a9	1 p15	3 p30	6 p5	8 p38	Meschede ....dep	...	8 a6	10a21	1 p5	...	6 p50	9 p50
Lenne	...	7 45	...	1 45	4 1	6 36	9 9	Wennemen	...	8 16	10 33	1 21	...	7 7	10 2
Fredeburg	7 a10	8 14	9 57	2 15	4 31	7 7	9 38	Wenholthausen	...	8 33	11 0	1 38	...	7 24	10 21
Wenholthausen	7 50	8 54	10 20	2 56	—	7 44	—	Fredeburg	5 a22	9 18	11 45	2 17	4 p45	8 23	11 2
Wennemen	—	9 12	10 49	3 20	...	8 1	...	Lenne	5 48	9 48	12 13	2 43	5 9	8 51	—
Meschede ....arr	...	9 22	10 58	3 30	...	8 11	...	Altenhundem ......arr	6 17	10 15	12 42	3 10	5 38	9 20	...

FINNENTROP and MESCHEDE.

Finnentrop ....dep	...	6 a55	9 a20	2 p55	5 p41	7 p52	11p10	Meschede .....dep	...	6 a53	10a21	1 p20	3 20	6 p30	7 p50	11p20
Wenholthausen	6 a9	7 55	10 30	3 52	6 41	8 47	12 12	Wennemen	...	7 3	10 33	1 32	3 32	6 45	8 0	11 31
Wennemen	6 30	8 25	10 49	4 10	7 0	9 4	...	Wenholthausen ..	4 a45	7 22	10 52	1 49	3 51	7 4	8 17	11 50
Meschede.............arr	6 40	8 35	10 58	4 19	7 9	9 12	...	Finnentrop ...arr	5 45	8 26	11 57	2 50	4 49	8 7	9 6	...

PREISWITZ and RYBNIK.

Preiswitz...................dep	7 a15	2 p13	5p31	9 p12	...	...	...	Rybnik ....dep	6 a20	8 a10	11a25	5 p24	...	...
Rybnik (219)..............arr	8 0	2 58	6 10	9 57	...	...	...	Preiswitz (220A)..........arr	7 4	8 50	12 8	6 1	...	...

[Luggage Rates, see page 462.

SIEGEN and BETZDORF.

‡—Weekdays only.

Station																						
Siegen 216 ...dep	3a50	...	5 a59	6a23	7‡a30	8a34	9a 0	...	9a29	9a42	11a54	12‡12	2 p11	3‡p45	4p42	5p48	...	6p49	7p15	7p35	9p35	11p34
Eiserfeld	3 57	...	6 6	...	7 38	8 41	9 7	a.m.	...	9 49	12 1	12 20	2 18	3 55	4 51	5 58	p.m.	6 55	...	7 43	9 41	11 40
Kirchen 216	4 21	6a19	6 25	...	7 58	9 1	9 26	9 36	...	10 7	12 18	12 40	2 35	4 17	5 12	6 23	6 51	7 12	...	8 5	9 59	11 58
Betzdorf 133Bdep	4 26	6 24	6 30	6 40	8 3	9 6	9 31	9 41	9 46	1012	12 23	12 45	2 40	4 22	5 18	6 29	6 56	7 17	7 33	8 11	10 4	12 3

Station																							
Betzdorf ....dep	5a49	6a45	6a55	8‡a25	9a27	9a58	10a3	10a13	11a35	12p42	1‡p10	3p 0	4‡43	5p49	6p55	7p58	8 p2	8p16	8p52	1026	1032	1a56	...
Kirchen	5 55	6 50	7 2	8 31	9 37	...	10 8	10 19	11 42	12 49	1 16	3 7	4 50	5 55	7 1	...	8 7	8 23	8 58	...	1040	2 4	...
Eiserfeld	6 16	—	7 21	8 49	10 0	...	—	10 39	12 1	1 9	1 35	3 26	5 9	6 16	7 22	...	—	8 43	9 18	...	11 1	2 24	...
Siegen ....arr	6 23	...	7 28	8 56	10 6	1016	...	10 45	12 8	1 15	1 41	3 32	5 15	6 23	7 29	8 16	...	8 50	9 24	1044	11 7	2 30	...

HAGEN, FINNENTROP, and SIEGEN.

Station	a.m.	a.m.	a.m.	a.m.	a.m.	a.m.	p.m.	p.m.	p.m.	p.m.	p.m.	p.m.	p.m.	n'gt
Hagen ....dep	5 12	6 4	7 33	8 56	1022	1122	1 18	3 52	5 16	6 36	8 27	9 25	1041	1 15
Letmathe	5 47	6 36	7 56	9 29	1056	1154	1 51	4 27	5 41	7 8	9 0	10 0	1117	1 50
Altena...............	6 5	6 53	8 7	9 46	1114	1210	2 9	4 46	5 52	7 25	9 20	1018	1148	2 4
Werdohl..............	6 16	7 5	...	9 57	1125	1222	2 20	4 58	...	7 36	9 32	1030	12 4	—
Finnentrop arr	6 49	7 36	8 37	1030	12 0	1249	2 52	5 32	...	8 9	10 6	11 5	—	...
,, dep	6 51	8 45	8 38	1032	12 2	1250	2 54	5 34	...	8 14	10 8	11 6	...	...
Altenhundem ...	7 13	9 6	...	1054	1223	1 11	3 16	5 57	...	8 35	1031	1129	...	...
Creuzthal.........	8 3	—	9 16	1133	—	1 51	4 2	6 40	7 1	9 14	1113	1211	...	...
Siegen 216 ...arr	8 19	...	9 28	1149	...	2 7	4 21	6 56	7 13	9 30	1129	1227	...	...

Station			a.m.		a.m.	a.m.	a.m.	a.m.	a.m.	p.m.	p.m.	p.m.	p.m.	p.m.	p.m.
Siegen ....dep	...	...	5 19	...	7 48	...	1017	1051	1155	1 22	3 36	...	6 27	8 17	9 28
Creuzthal.........dep	...	...	5 41	...	8 8	...	1031	1117	1216	1 45	3 54	...	6 47	8 30	9 49
Altenhundem	...	...	6 24	...	8 51	1020	...	12 1	1 1	2 30	4 35	6 31	7 30	...	1039
Finnentrop ......arr	...	...	6 41	...	9 8	1040	...	1219	1 20	2 50	4 52	6 51	7 48	9 9	1059
,, ...dep	...	...	6 45	...	9 10	1042	...	1223	1 22	2 56	4 54	6 56	7 53	9 10	11 2
Werdohl	5a10	a.m.	7 19	a.m.	9 43	1116	...	1 0	1 56	3 29	5 24	7 31	8 30	...	1133
Altena	5 54	6 30	7 31	8 58	9 55	1157	1136	1 14	2 8	3 41	5 36	7 45	8 45	9 38	1146
Letmathe	6 14	6 51	7 51	9 14	1014	1215	1156	1 34	2 29	4 1	5 55	8 7	9 5	9 50	12 4
Hagen 216 ...arr	6 45	7 22	8 21	9 38	1044	1247	1218	2 5	3 1	4 32	6 25	8 39	9 38	1011	1234

‡—Weekdays only.

Extra.

Hagen dep	2p54
Altena arr	3 41

Creuzthal .dep	5a39	6‡a30	7‡a11	9a24	10a26	1p25	5p25	6p28	7 p8	8p18	9p32	10p33
Siegen ....arr	5 56	6 46	7 28	9 40	10 48	1 45	5 45	6 44	7 28	8 39	9 52	10 53

Siegen ...	5‡50	6a45	7a32	9 a1	12p15	4p55	5p59	7p32	9 p3	11p14
Creuzthal	6 13	7 8	7 51	9 21	12 37	5 15	6 18	7 52	9 23	11 37

EISERN and SIEGEN.

Station										
Eisern ....dep	5§a40	6‡a45	9a22	2p35	6p40	8 p40	...	...	...	...
Eiserfeld.........................	6 9	7 14	9 51	3 4	7 14	9 9	...	...	...	...
Siegen (Eintracht).........arr	6 30	7 35	10 7	3 20	7 30	9 30	...	...	...	...

Station						
Siegen (Eintracht)......dep	4§a50	5‡a33	8a27	1p30	5p30	7 p45
Eiserfeld	5 10	6 10	8 44	1 48	5 48	8 2
Eisern ....arr	5 33	6 37	9 11	2 16	6 15	8 29

‡—From August 6th.
§—Until August 5th.

FINNENTROP, OLPE, and KIRCHEN.

‡—Weekdays only.

§—On Sunday dep. 7.25 a.m.

Station	a.m.	a.m.	a.m.	a.m.	a.m.	a.m.	a.m.	a.m.	p.m.	p.m.	p.m.	p.m.	p.m.	p.m.	p.m.	p.m.	p.m.	p.m.
Finnentrop ....dep	...	...	...	...	...	7 38	9 18	10 32	...	12 56	...	3 0	...	5 35	...	8 21	9 17	11 18
Olpe	...	4 50	...	...	8 11	8 27	10 12	11 20	1 15	1 45	...	3 50	5 26	6 23	8 33	9 11	10 0	12 8
Rothemühle	...	5 10	‡	...	8 31	—	11 8	—	1 34	—	...	4 20	5 45	7 16	8 53	9 50	—	—
Freudenberg................	5 7	5 36	6 50	7 44	8 55	...	11 30	...	1 58	...	4 18	4 46	6 9	—	9 16	—	...	...
Kirchen ....arr	5 48	6 18	7 30	8 25	9 34	...	12 9	...	2 31	...	5 3	6 ‡18	6 49	...	9 54	...	...	...

Station	a.m.	a.m.	a.m.	a.m.	a.m.	a.m.	p.m.	p.m.	p.m.	p.m.		p.m.	p.m.	p.m.			p.m.	p.m.
Kirchen ....dep	...	...	5 58	7§38	...	10 9	...	1 19	...	3 13	...	...	5 58	8 8	...	...	10 ‡3	10 42
Freudenberg.................	...	...	6 44	8 24	...	10 47	..	2 0	...	3 58	...	...	6 50	8 49	...	p.m.	10 46	11 24
Rothemühle	5‡20	...	7 15	8 50	„	11 7	...	2 24	...	—	p.m.	6 28	7 17	9 12	p.m.	10 0	—	11 46
Olpe	5 38	5 48	7 40	9 8	9 24	11 29	1 53	2 42	3 51	...	5 44	6 53	7 40	9 30	10 11	10 17	...	12 4
Finnentrop ....arr	...	6 39	8 30	—	10 16	12 17	2 44	...	4 44	...	6 35	7 42	...	...	10 59	...	...	...

HAGEN and ALTENVORDE.

Station									
Hagen.....................dep	7a45	12 p8	1 p18	4 p30	6 p53	8 p10	...	...	...
Altenvörde...........arr	8 36	12 58	2 5	5 16	7 48	8 57	...	...	...

Station										
Altenvörde ......dep	6a13	8 a54	1 p23	2p 22	6 p41	8 p14	...	...	...	...
Hagen ....arr	6 59	9 40	2 8	3 13	7 34	9 10	...	...	...	...

LENNEP, MARIENHEIDE, and OPLADEN.

Station															
Lennep...dep	5a13	7a31	8a30	10a33	12p16	1p23	3 p7	3p56	4p17	5p40	6p56	7p50	8 p9	9p52	12a56
Born	5 33	7 40	8 37	10 41	12 24	1 31	3 14	4 3	4 25	5 55	7 9	7 57	8 16	9 59	1 3
Wipperfurth	6 9	8 14	8 57	11 14	12 52	1 56	3 38	4 28	4 50	6 31	7 35	8 22	8 42	1021	1 25
Marienheide	6 37	8 39	9 18	11 41	1 15	...	3 58	4 55	5 17	6 59	...	8 46	9 7	1046	...

Station														
Lennep ....dep	5a21	7 a5	7a38	8 a23	10a20	11a47	12p31	2p23	3 p20	4p40	5 p32	7 p4	7p50	10p5
Born	5 31	7 12	7 46	8 39	10 28	11 56	12 39	2 32	3 29	4 47	5 40	7 15	7 57	1015
Wermelskirch	5 42	7 19	7 53	8 46	10 36	12 5	12 48	2 38	3 37	4 55	5 48	7 25	8 4	1023
Opladen ...arr	6 25	7 54	8 25	9 21	11 15	...	1 29	...	4 17	5 35	6 27	8 12	8 43	11 0

Station															
Opladen	5a42	7 a0	9a18	1056	p.m.	12p34	1p53	2p54	5 p0	6p46	7p20	7p56	9 p2	...	11p45
Wermelsk.	6 26	7 45	9 57	1138	1245	1 18	2 38	3 35	5 45	7 23	8 2	8 37	9 43	1117	12 27
Born	6 34	7 53	10 4	1146	1253	1 27	2 46	3 42	5 54	7 31	8 14	8 44	9 52	1125	12 35
Lennep	6 40	7 59	1010	1152	1259	1 33	2 52	3 48	6 0	7 37	8 20	8 50	9 59	1132	12 41

Station														
Marienhe.	...	6a13	6 a45	...	8 a57	10a29	12p24	2 p27	...	5p35	7 p3	8 p0	...	10p48
Wipperfurth	5a34	6 46	7 8	7a48	9 25	11 9	12 50	3 2	3p52	6 2	7 26	8 31	9p42	11 11
Born	6 17	7 14	7 29	8 18	9 48	11 39	1 16	3 27	4 23	6 27	7 48	8 58	1013	11 33
Lennep ...	6 24	7 20	7 35	8 25	9 54	11 45	1 22	3 33	4 29	6 33	7 54	9 4	1020	11 39

DEUTZ and LINDLAR.

‡—Weekdays only.

Station	a.m.	a.m.	a.m.	a.m.	a.m.	p.m.	p.m.	p.m.	p.m.	p.m.	p.m.	p.m.	p.m.	nigt
Deutz........dep	6 34	7 42	8 41	9 53	1132	1213	1 35	2 45	4 42	6 58	7‡20	8 34	1059	12 5
Mülheim ...dep	6 47	7 54	9 0	10 3	1254	1225	1 51	2 58	4 53	7 9	7 32	8 48	1110	1217
Bensberg	7 37	8 22	9 25	10 29	1 20	1251	2 18	3 23	5 20	7 39	7 59	9 16	1138	1241
Immekeppel...	8 53	9‡17	1049	12 9	...	2 39	...	5 47	...	8 22	9 34	...	...	...
Lindlar......arr	9 29	...	1124	...	...	3 14	...	6 22	...	...	10 9	...	...	...

Station	a.m.	a.m.	a.m.	a.m.	a.m.	a.m.	a.m.	p.m.	p.m.	p.m.	p.m.	p.m.	p.m.	p.m.	p.m.	p.m.
Lindlar dep	...	...	5 54	...	8 20	...	...	...	...	12 53	...	...	...	4 42	...	8 33
Immekeppel	4‡58	...	6 34	...	9 3	...	1131	1227	...	1 33	2 46	...	...	5 28	...	9 13
Bensberg ...	5 49	7 7	7 55	9 1	10 6	11 29	1219	1 22	1 52	2 37	3 39	5 27	5 59	6 55	7 34	10 4
Mülheim arr	6 10	7 26	8 14	9 20	1026	11 48	1239	1 42	2 11	...	3 58	5 46	6 17	7 16	7 53	1026
Deutz ....arr	6 24	7 39	8 26	9 32	1036	12 2	1252	1 54	2 27	...	4 13	5 59	6 33	7 39	8 5	1038

CREUZTHAL and MARBURG.

		a.m.	a.m.	a.m.	a.m.	a.m.	p.m.	p.m.	p.m.	p.m.	p.m.
Creuzthal ...dep	...	...	7 13	8 26	9 26	11 37	2 0	4 7	7 12	9 28	1158
Stift Keppel	...	...	7 36	8 49	9 47	12 0	...	4 27	7 33	9 47	1219
Hilchenbach	...	...	7 44	8 55	9 58	12 16	2 25	4 35	7 41	10 10	1225
Erndtebruck 217	...	6 1	8 25	—	10 36	1 8	3 2	5 20	8 23	10 50	—
Feudingen	a.m.	6 34	8 56	...	11 4	1 42	...	5 51	8 54	11 17	...
Laasphe	4 57	7 0	9 20	...	11 24	2 5	3 47	6 14	9 18	11 37	...
Biedenkopf 131	5 20	7 23	9 44	...	11 49	2 34	4 9	6 41	9 40	12 0	...
Carlshutte	5 38	7 45	10 3	...	12 7	2 54	...	7 0	9 57	—	...
Caldern	5 53	8 1	1020	...	1226	3 14	...	7 15	10 12	...	...
Sarnau	6 12	8 18	1036	...	1243	3 30	4 50	7 30	10 26	...	...
Marburg 156A arr	6 28	8 35	1052	...	1 1	3 47	5 7	7 47	10 41	...	...

				a.m.	a.m.	a.m.	p.m.		p.m.	p.m.	p.m.	p.m.
Marburg...dep		...	...	6 29	9 46	11 45	2 39	...	5 22	7 13	7 36	10 52
Sarnau		...	...	6 46	10 3	12 5	2 56	...	5 39	7 32	7 54	11 8
Caldern		...	...	7 4	10 20	12 27	3 14	...	5 57	...	8 12	11 24
Carlshutte		a.m.	...	7 23	10 35	12 43	3 30	...	6 14	...	8 29	11 39
Biedenkopf		5 7	...	7 47	10 58	1 8	3 55	...	6 38	8 18	8 49	12 4
Laasphe		5 33	...	8 12	11 23	1 32	4 21	...	7 7	8 44	9 17	12 26
Feudingen		5 55	...	8 37	11 46	1 56	4 41	...	7 31	...	9 42	—
Erndtebruck	a.m.	6 36	a.m.	9 18	12 28	2 34	5 19	p.m.	8 24	9 35	10 52	...
Hilchenbach	5 6	7 13	8 28	9 53	1 10	3 12	5 55	7 47	9 0	10 8	11 27	...
Stift Keppel	5 13	7 20	8 35	10 0	1 17	3 19	6 2	7 53	9 6	...	11 34	...
Creuzthal	5 35	7 45	8 56	10 22	1 39	3 41	6 24	8 14	9 27	10 31	11 56	...

FRANKENBERG and BERLEBURG.

Frankenberg...dep	5 a27	9 a52	2 p30	5 p49	9 p40	...	...
Allendorf	5 48	10 13	2 57	6 9	10 1	...	...
Berleburg ...arr	7 15	11 37	4 25	7 35	11 31	...	...

Berleburg ...dep	4 a39	7 a43	1 p51	6 p8	9 p20	...	...
Allendorf	6 18	9 5	3 15	7 42	11 4	...	...
Frankenberg...arr	6 38	9 25	3 35	8 2	11 24	...	...

ERNDTEBRUCK and BERLEBURG.

Erndtebruck ...dep	5†a20	6a40	8a35	9a21	10a38	1 p3	5p23	7†p16	8p32	10p54
Berleburg ... arr	6 0	7 20	9 18	9 57	11 17	1 45	6 2	7 56	9 11	11 36

Berleburg ...dep	5a16	7a37	8a31	9a38	11a45	1p46	4p29	6†p13	7p39	9p45
Erndtebruck (217) arr	5 56	8 16	9 11	1021	1225	2 25	5 7	6 55	8 15	1025

†—Not on Sunday.

TRACHENBERG and HERRNSTADT.

Trachenberg ...dep	7 a30	3p54	9 p30	...	...
Herrnstadt ...arr	8 41	4 41	10 52	...	...

Herrnstadt ...dep	5a25	11a20	5p10	...	...	...	...	...
Trachenberg ...arr	6 41	12 33	6 14	...	...	...	...	...

FREYSTADT and WALTERSDORF.

Freystadt ...dep	6 a17	8a8	11a50	1 p56	5 p40	7p 28
Waltersdorf 220A ...arr	7 3	9 38	12 42	310	6 48	8 43

Waltersdorf ...dep	7a12	9 a54	3p30	7 p0	8 p54	...	...
Freystadt ...arr	8 0	10 42	4 52	8 3	9 50	...	...

BRESLAU and TREBNITZ.

Breslau (Oderthor) dep	6 a33	8a57	11a15	2p43	4p56	6p22	8p46	11p55
Hundsfeld	6 47	9 11	11 29	2 58	5 7	6 33	9 0	12 9
Trebnitz ...arr	7 31	9 53	12 11	3 40	5 40	7 15	9 44	12 54

Trebnitz ...dep	4a35	6a55	7a45	10 a5	12p28	4 p 7	7p30	10p10
Hundsfeld	5 16	7 29	8 28	10 48	1 12	4 50	8 13	10 57
Breslau Oderthor arr	5 29	7 39	8 41	11 0	1 22	5 3	8 26	11 10

GLEIWITZ, KATTOWITZ, and SCHWIENTOCHLOWITZ.

Rail Motor. { Beuthen to Kattowitz, 5.12, 6.55, 10.26, 11.53 a.m., 1.45, 2.28, 3.55, 6.0, 9.30, and 10.30 p.m.
Kattowitz to Beuthen, 1.42, 6.20, 8.58, 10.9, 11.20 a.m., 5.4, 7.50, and 10.10 p.m.

	a.m.		a.m.	a.m.	a.m.	a.m.	a.m.	a.m.		a.m.	p.m.	p.m.		p.m.		p.m.		p.m.	p.m.	p.m.		p.m.		p.m.	p.m.	p.m.	a.m.
Gleiwitz ...dep	2 30	...	5 14	6 2	...	7 16	8 35	9 15	...	10 39	1210	1 1	...	2 29	...	4 48	...	4 57	6 5	7 30	...	8 43	...	10 3	11 5	⋮	1224
Borsigwerk	...	...	5 36	6 23	...	...	8 56	...	...	11 0	...	1 23	...	2 51	...	...	...	5 18	6 26	...	...	...	...	1026	1127	⋮	...
Beuthen O.S. arr	2 51	a.m.	5 48	6 35	...	7 37	9 8	9 36	a.m.	11 11	1233	1 34	...	3 2	...	5 9	p.m.	5 28	6 39	7 55	...	9 4	...	1038	1138	11 52	1245
Beuthen O.S. dep	2 52	5 4	—	6 38	7 55	7 38	9 15	9 37	9 41	—	1235	—	p.m.	3 40	...	5 11	5 18	—	6 52	7 56	...	9 5	p.m	1124	—	11 53	1246
Chorzow	...	5 13	...	6 47	8 4	...	9 25	...	9 49	11a32	...	p.m.	2 21	3 54	p.m.	...	5 31	...	7 1	...	p.m.	...	9 49	1133	...	...	...
Konigshutte ...arr	3 3	5 19	...	6 53	8 10	7 49	9 30	9 48	9 53	11 37	1246	1 5	2 28	3 59	4 40	5 22	5 36	...	7 7	8 8	9 5	9 16	9 54	1139	...	12 4	1257
Kattowitz ...arr	3 13	...	...	...	...	8 0	9 45	9 58	...	...	...	...	...	...	...	5 33	...	...	...	...	...	9 27	...	...	...	12 15	1 7
Schwientochl'z...arr	...	5 28	...	6 59	8 17	...	...	...	9 59	11 44	1256	1 11	2 35	4 6	4 46	...	5 43	...	7 14	8 15	9 11	...	10 2	1145	...	...	1 46

	a.m.	a.m.		a.m.	a.m.	a.m.	a.m.	a.m.	a.m.	noon	p.m.	p.m.	p.m.	p.m.	p.m	p.m.	p.m	p.m.	p.m.	p.m.	p.m.	p.m.	p.m.	p.m.	p.m.	p.m.	nigt	nigt
Schwientochl'z dep	4 0	...	...	5 56	7 16	7 39	8 40	9 27	1015	...	1210	...	1 24	...	3 9	...	4 20	...	4 55	...	6 23	...	8 26	...	9 23	1045	12 3	...
Kattowitz ...dep	...	5 30	...	...	...	...	...	...	...	12 0	...	1 2	...	2 35	...	3 15	...	4 15	...	5 46	...	7 35	...	8 35	...	...	...	1225
Konigshutte ...dep	4 9	5 41	...	6 8	7 23	8 25	8 47	9 34	1050	12 12	1216	1 18	1 35	2 47	3 20	3 31	4 26	4 31	5 2	5 58	6 31	7 48	8 32	8 47	9 31	1053	12 9	1238
Chorzow	4 16	...	...	6 15	7 30	...	8 54	...	1057	...	—	1 25	2 19	...	3 27	3 38	—	4 38	5 22	...	6 38	...	—	...	9 37	11 0	—	...
Beuthen O.S. arr	4 21	5 51	a.m.	6 23	7 38	8 37	9 2	9 47	—	12 22	p.m.	1 32	2 26	2 58	—	3 45	p.m.	4 45	5 29	6 9	6 45	7 59	...	8 57	1034	11 9	...	1249
Beuthen O.S. dep	5 18	5 52	6 30	7 10	—	8 40	—	9 51	1127	12 24	1 0	—	2 31	3 0	...	—	3 55	—	6 15	6 10	7 40	8 1	...	8 59	...	1122	...	1250
Borsigwerk	5 32	⋮	6 43	7 24	...	...	...	...	1140	...	1 13	...	2 44	...	...	...	4 8	...	6 27	...	7 53	...	...	...	...	1135	...	...
Gleiwitz ...arr	5 48	⋮	7 2	7 40	...	8 59	...	1012	1158	12 43	1 32	...	3 3	3 19	...	...	4 26	...	6 42	6 29	8 10	8 20	...	9 19	...	1154	...	1 10

Beuthen to Morgenroth & Kochlowitz.—From Beuthen, 5.13, 6†57, 8†0, 9.33, 11†23 a.m., 12.48, 2†15, 3.57, 5†50, 7†50, 9†0, 9†58, 11†30 p.m., 1†27 night. †—To Morgenroth only. Return from Kochlowitz, 6.36 a.m., 12.45, 3.51, 7.45 p.m. From Morgenroth, 2.18, 6.2, 7.25, 8.40, 10.24 a.m., 12.0 noon, 1.23, 3.5, 4.48, 6.28, 8.22, 9.32, 10.38 p.m., 12.10 night.

OTTMACHAU and PRIEBORN.

Ottmachau ...dep	7a24	12 0	4 p1	7p12	...	...
Prieborn ...arr	8 29	1 52	5 50	8 15	...	...

Prieborn ...dep	5a41	8 a40	3p58	7p38	...	...
Ottmachau ...arr	7 10	10 4	5 2	9 25	...	...

SCHILDBERG and DEUTSCHHOF.

Schildberg ...dep	6a25	10a35	2p52	...	...
Deutschhof ...arr	7 43	12 2	4 19	...	...

Deutschhof ...dep	8a20	12p22	4p48	...	...
Schildberg ...arr	9 49	1 45	6 30	...	...

GOSTYN and KOSCHMIN.

Gostyn ...dep	6 a37	10a45	5 p45	...	...	...	...
Pogorzela	7 12	11 50	7 1	...	...	...	...
Koschmin ...arr	7 42	12 42	7 48	...	...	...	...

Koschmin ...dep	8 a56	1 p36	9 p0	...	...	...	...
Pogorzela	9 34	2 7	9 52	...	...	...	...
Gostyn 218A arr	10 16	2 40	10 50	...	...	...	...

BRESLAU, KANDRZIN, KATTOWITZ, and OSWIECIM.

Extra.—Gleiwitz to Kattowitz—6.18, 8.50 p.m., and 12.28 night.

	2 3 4	Ex3	1—4	1—4	1,2,3	Ex 3	2 3 4	1,2,3	2 3 4	2 3 4	1—4	1—4	Ex3	1,2,3	1—4	1,2,3	1—4	Ex3	2 3 4	1—4	1—4	Ex3	Ex3	2 3 4	Ex 3	1—4
Breslau—		a.m.	a.m.	a.m.		a.m.	a.m.	a.m.	a.m.		noon	...	p.m.	p.m	p.m.	p.m.		p.m.	p m.	p.m.	p.m.	p.m.	p.m.	p.m.	nght	nght
Hauptbahnof dep	...	5 0	...	5 35	...	6 30	8 48	9 50	7 50	...	12 0	...	2 12	2 18	3 33	4 36	...	6 18	5 6	6 37	9 27	9 55	10 2	11 0	12 8	12 20
Ohlau	...	5 23	...	6 15	...	6 56	9 28	...	8 31	...	12 43	From Neisse.	...	2 43	4 17	5 1	...	6 42	5 44	7 19	1030	...	1025	1140	...	1 1
Brieg	...	5 38	...	6 38	...	7 14	9 51	1024	8 53	...	1 7		2 50	2 58	4 41	5 17	...	6 58	6 1	7 47	1049	1029	1040	12 0	...	1 22
Oppeln arr	...	6 8	6 16	7 26	...	7 48	1040	1054	9 45	...	2 1		3 23	3 32	5 30	5 52	...	7 30	—	8 42	1135	11 1	1114	—	1 12	2 22
Gogolin	...	⋮	6 39	7 57	...	8 10	1126	Via Gr. Strehlitz.	—	...	2 36		...	...	6 3	6 13	...	...	...	9 20	12 9	...	1132	...	...	3 3
Kandrzin arr	...	⋮	7 4	8 21	...	8 30	1149		...	...	3 1		4 2	4 9	6 28	6 35	...	8 6	...	9 49	1233	1136	1149	...	1 46	3 39
Oderberg 219 arr	...	⋮	9 a13	9 a30	...	9 a30	1p28		...	...	4 p40		4p55	...	7 p55	7 p55	...	9p39	...	11p50	...	1233	...	...	2a40	5 a50
Vienna (222) arr	...	⋮	...	...	a.m.	3 p10	...		p.m.	...	9 p50	p.m.	9p50	...		...	p.m.	...	p.m.	6 a0	...	6 a0	...	...	8 a7	12p34
Kandrzin dep	...	⋮	7 10	8 46	8 41	2,3,4	1155		1 34	...	3 10	3 38	1—4	4 13	2,3,4	6 49	6 53	8 9	8 22	10 5	1238	2 3 4	1152	...	1 59	4 20
Laband	a.m.	⋮	7 50	9 25	...	a.m.	1234		2 15	p.m.	3 55	4 13	p.m.	...	p.m.	...	7 36	...	9 9	10 50	1 17	p.m.	...	a.m.	...	5 1
Gleiwitz	6 33	7 16	8 0	9 37	9 15	11 13	1246	12 3	2 26	3 20	4 9	4 28	5 0	4 48	6 42	7 24	7 47	8 43	9 26	11 5	1 28	10 3	1224	4 29	2 30	5 12
Morgenroth	7 0	⋮	8 28	10 4	...	11 46	1 14	1225	2 58	3 49	4 42	5 2	5 35	...	7 12	7 46	8 16	⋮	9 57	11 38	1 57	1032	...	4 55	...	5 39
Schwientochlowitz	7 7	⋮	8 37	10 12	...	11 55	1 21	...	3 8	3 57	4 53	5 10	5 47	...	7 20	...	8 24	⋮	10 6	11 49	2 5	1040	...	5 4	...	5 47
Kattowitz arr	7 17	8 0	8 47	10 20	9 58	12 7	1 29	1237	3 18	4 7	5 5	5 20	5 58	5 33	7 30	7 58	8 33	9 27	1015	11 58	2 14	1050	1 7	5 14	3 13	5 55
Kattowitz dep	...	Via Gross Strehlitz, p. 219.	...	10 31	...	...	1 38	1 38	3 45	...	5 54	Until 31st August only.	...	5 54	...	...	9 15	...	...	...	...	1115	...	5 28	...	6 52
Sosnowitz arr	...		...	10 45	...	...	1 54	1 54	4 0	...	6 7		...	6 7	...	...	9 29	...	...	...	...	1129	...	5 43	...	7 8
Warsaw 316 arr	...		...	10p17	...	...	...	...	...	...	...		...	...	...	...	...	...	...	...	...	7a47	...	—	...	6 p52
					a.m.																			a.m		
Kattowitz dep	7 22		9 5	10 25	10 0	12 18	1 33	1240	3 28	4 15	5 40		6 16	5 36	7 35	...	8 38	9 30	1028	12 20	2 19	11 6	1 9	5 5	...	6 2
Schoppinitz	7 34		9 17	10 33	...	12 32	1 41	...	3 38	4 28	5 47		6 27	...	7 43	...	8 46	...	1040	12 28	2 30	1119	...	5 17	...	6 10
Myslowitz arr	7 41		9 23	10 39	10 11	12 40	1 47	1251	3 45	4 35	5 54		6 34	5 46	7 50	...	8 52	9 40	1047	12 34	2 36	1128	1 20	5 23	...	6 16
Cracow 222 arr	...		11a55	...	...	...	4p52	...	...	...	8p10		...	...	...	...	1138	1138	...	...	...	...	3 a7	...	...	...
Myslowitz dep	...		9 25	10 46	...	12 58	1 53	1258	...	4 39	6 4		6 38	...	...	...	9 0	...	...	...	...	1129	...	5 30	...	6 28
Neuberun	...		9 51	11 16	...	1 25	2 24	1 25	...	5 12	6 34		7 12	...	...	...	9 33	...	...	...	...	12 2	...	6 5	...	7 1
Oswiecim arr	...		9 57	11 22	...	1 31	2 30	1 31	...	5 19	6 40	...	7 19	...	...	...	9 40	...	...	...	...	1210	...	6 12	...	7 7
Cracow 222 arr	...	...	11 55	2 p45	...	2 p45	4p52	2p45	...	...	8p10	...	9p45	...	...	...	1138	...	...	...	...	3 a7	...	9a35	...	9a35

	2 3 4	2 3 4	1—4	2 3 4	Ex3	2 3 4	1,2,3	1—4	1—4	Ex3	Ex 3	2,3,4	2—4	1,2,3	2 3 4	1—4	1,2,3	2 3 4	2 3 4	1—4	Ex3	1—4	1,2,3	2—4	1—4	2,3,4	Ex3	1—4
Cracow 222 dep	1250	...	...	3a55	...	...	...	6a52	...	...	...	9 a30	...	...	...	2p25	...	2p35	...	...	...	...	...	6 p0	6p45	...	...	1035
	a.m.	a.m.	a.m.	a.m.				a.m.				a.m.			p.m.	p.m.	p.m.	p.m.	p.m.					p.m.	p.m.			n'gt
Oswiecim dep	4 15	...	...	6 54	...	...	...	8 40	...	...	...	11 42	...	...	2 56	3 55	...	4 42	5 37	...	...	...	...	8 1	8 57	...	...	1230
Neuberun	4 24	...	...	7 2	...	...	...	8 47	...	...	...	11 52	...	...	3 4	4 2	...	4 52	5 45	...	...	...	...	8 9	9 5	...	...	1239
Myslowitz arr	4 57	...	...	7 30	...	...	...	9 14	...	...	...	12 23	...	...	3 32	4 30	...	5 24	6 20	...	...	...	...	8 37	9 34	...	...	1 12
Cracow 222 dep	...	...	...	...	6a52	6a52	...	...	a.m.	a.m.	...	9 a30	p.m.	p m	...	...	...	2p35	...	...	...	p.m.	...	...	6p45	p.m.	...	...
Myslowitz dep	4 59	5 8	6 35	7 32	8 35	9 0	...	9 17	11 6	1145	...	12 34	2 8	2 20	3 39	4 34	5 30	5 45	6 25	...	...	8 4	...	8 42	9 38	11 20	...	1 17
Schoppinitz	5 7	5 15	6 42	7 39	...	9 8	...	9 25	1114	...	...	12 43	2 16	...	3 46	4 41	...	5 53	6 32	...	...	8 12	...	8 50	9 47	11 29	...	1 25
Kattowitz arr	5 17	5 22	6 50	7 46	8 45	9 17	...	9 32	1126	1156	...	12 51	2 24	2 31	3 56	4 50	5 42	6 1	6 43	...	...	8 21	...	8 58	9 56	11 35	...	1 35
Warsaw dep	...	...	1212	...	...	...	...	1257	...	a.m.	...	...	...	...	...	...	...	8a37	...	8a37	...	...	...	...	...	3 p47	n'gt	...
Sosnowitz dep	...	...	6 23	...	...	...	...	9 25	...	1129	...	...	...	...	3p16	...	...	5 25	...	6 46	...	...	...	...	...	10p10	12 0	12 0
Kattowitz arr	...	...	6 37	...	...	...	a.m.	9 41	...	1140	...	...	...	...	3 29	...	...	5 36	...	7 0	p.m.	p.m.	p.m.	...	...	10 25	1212	1212
Kattowitz dep	...	5 24	7 0	8 15	8 47	9 19	9 40	9 48	1134	12 0	...	12 56	2 26	2 35	4 1	4 55	5 46	6 5	6 48	7 25	7 35	8 27	8 35	9 4	10 0	11 42	1225	1 50
Schwientochlowitz	...	5 34	7 13	8 26	...	9 30	...	10 2	1147	⋮	...	1 6	2 40	⋮	4 14	5 8	...	6 16	6 59	7 39	⋮	8 38	...	9 16	1012	11 52	⋮	2 4
Morgenroth	...	5 43	7 21	8 35	...	9 37	9 56	1010	1155	⋮	...	1 17	2 50	⋮	4 24	5 19	...	6 25	7 8	7 49	⋮	8 47	...	9 26	1021	12 0	⋮	2 15
Gleiwitz	...	6 10	7 45	8 59	9 15	9 59	1021	1037	1220	1246	...	1 46	3 11	3 25	4 53	5 49	6 31	6 52	7 32	8 30	8 24	9 13	9 22	9 49	1046	12 20	1 12	2 50
Laband	...	6 18	7 53	—	Via Gr. Strehlitz.	—	...	1045	1228	...	...	1 55	—	...	5 1	5 57	...	7 0	Extra.—Kattowitz to Gleiwitz, 11.50 a.m., 1.40 and 3.40 p.m.	8 39	Via Gross Strehlitz p 219	—	...	—	1055	—	...	3 0
Kandrzin arr	Ex3 2 4	6 55	8 30	Ex3		...	1058	1123	1 7	1 15	...	2 38	...	3 57	5 40	6 36	7 0	7 43		9 17		...	9 51	Ex3	1133	...	1 44	3 51
Vienna dep	1015	1015	1015	...	1040		...	...	...	...	7 a34	7 a34	...	...	...	...	...	1235				...	...	3p55	...	7 p45	7p45	...
Oderberg	3a27	3a27	5a25	...	7a41		...	...	9a48	...	...	12p29	12p59	...	...	3p45	...	...	6p15			...	...	9 p6	1022	1 a4	1 a4	...
Kandrzin dep	4 18	5 8	7 0	...	8 41		...	2 3 4	1131	...	1 18	1 24	2 46	...	4 9	5 49	...	7 5	7 53			...	...	10 1	1150	2 0	1 54	...
Gogolin	...	5 33	7 24	...	8 59		...	a.m.	1155	...	...	...	3 13	...	...	6 17	...	...	8 18			...	...	...	1216	2 24	...	...
Oppeln dep	4 52	6 4	7 58	...	9 18	1017	a.m.	1021	1223	...	1 53	2 0	3 46	p.m.	4 46	6 49	...	7 39	8 47		9 34	...	...	1036	1242	3 12	...	...
Brieg	5 24	6 58	8 53	...	9 51	1049	1034	1110	1 14	...	2 26	2 36	4 39	6 15	5 19	7 40	...	8 14	9 39		1012	...	...	1111	—	4 33	...	...
Ohlau	...	7 19	9 16	...	...	...	1048	1130	1 36	...	2 41	...	5 0	6 33	...	8 1	...	8 28	9 59		1027	...	...	...	...	4 54	...	...
Breslau arr	5 56	7 58	9 55	...	1023	1120	1110	1210	2 15	...	3 4	3 10	5 41	7 10	5 52	8 40	...	8 50	1040		1053	...	...	1148	...	5 35	3 24	...

GLEIWITZ and IDAWEICHE.

Gleiwitz dep	8 a1	10 a0	12p58	...	9 p26	
Kochlowitz 217	8 32	10 38	1 40	5p10	10 2	
Idaweiche 220A arr	8 41	10 48	1 51	5 21	10 11	
Idaweiche dep	6 a23	11a27	2 p18	5 p52	7 p5	11p32
Kochlowitz	6 34	11 38	2 31	6 3	7 15	12 0
Gleiwitz arr	7 11	12 11	3 6	6 37	...	...

GLEIWITZ and POREMBA.

Gleiwitz dep	4a40	7a46	11a15	1 p7	3p50	6p9	11p15
Poremba arr	5 9	8 21	11 45	1 37	4 22	6 49	11 45
Poremba dep	6a33	8a0	10a35	11a57	4p0	6p26	7p42
Gleiwitz 218 arr	7 2	8 26	11 0	12 23	4 30	7 9	8 7

OPPELN and KREUZBURG.

Oppeln dep	5 a35	9 a21	1 p30	3 p49	6 p5	8p52
Jellowa	6 20	10 6	2 8	4 26	6 53	9 28
Kreuzburg arr	7 3	10 50	...	5 8	7 50	10 11
Kreuzburg dep	5 a34	7a32	9 a10	1p30	6p50	...
Jellowa	6 27	8 19	10 3	2 21	7 45	...
Oppeln arr	7 5	8 54	10 42	2 58	8 21	...

Jellowa dep	6 a25	10a10	2 p18	4 p40	9 p36		
Carlsruhe-O.-S.	7 3	10 51	2 59	6 18	10 17		
Namslau arr	7 40	11 32	3 40	7 25	...		
Namslau dep	...	8 a33	12p55	6 p15	9 p56	...	...
Carlsruhe-O.-S.	5a20	9 16	1 38	6 58	10 37	...	...
Jellowa arr	6 7	9 53	2 16	7 36	...	...	...

STARGARD and BRESLAU.

A—From 15th July until 31st August. [Luggage Rates see page 462.

			a.m.	a.m.	a.m.		a.m.	a.m.				a.m.		p.m.	p.m.		p.m.	p.m.	p.m.		p.m.
Stargard ......dep			12 28	...	...	...	...	6 15	...	Neustettin dep. 10.55.	...	10 44	...	1 19	3 29	...	3 34	6 20	8 26	...	9 25
Arnswalde			1 24	...	...	...	...	7 8	...		...	11 29	...	2 13	4 3	...	5 19	7 24	9 4	...	10 17
Kreuz 176 ...... arr			2 38	...	...	a.m.	...	8 18	...		...	12 34	...	3 31	4 56	...	7 28	8 46	10 2	...	11 26
Kreuz 176 ...... dep			2 53	5 10	...	8 55	...	8 28	...		...	12 49	...	5 14	5 4	...	—	—	10 19	...	11 36
Wronke			3 24	5 52	...	10 27	...	9 4	p.m.		...	1 31	p.m.	5 59	5 36	...	p.m.	...	10 52	...	12 17
Rokietnice 182			4 0	6 42	...	12 0	9 13	9 42	12 59	...	p.m.	2 18	5 2	6 50	...	...	8 17	...	11 29	...	1 10
Posen 219 ...... arr			4 17	7 6	...	12 44	9 38	10 0	1 27	2 37		2 46	5 31	7 19	6 28	...	8 39	p.m.	11 47	a.m.	1 37
Posen 219 ...... dep			4 26	7 12	7 18	1 49	10 11	—	—	2 42	2 59	3 17	6 6	—	7 0	...	8 44	9 38	—	12 5	2 8
Czempin 218A			5 1	7 38	7 59	2 31	10 56	...	...	A	...	4 3	6 54	...	...	...	9 28	...	...	12 50	2 49
Kosten 182			5 13	7 49	8 13	2 46	11 11	...	...	3 17	3 32	4 18	7 10	...	7 34	...	9 43	...	...	1 5	3 1
Lissa 218A ...... arr			5 44	8 12	8 47	—	11 46	...	...	3 42	3 56	4 54	7 46	...	7 57	p.m.	1018	10 31	p.m.	1 40	3 33
Lissa 218A ...... dep			5 55	8 16	8 52	*—Until 31st August.	11 51	...	...	3 46	4 1	5 17	—	...	8 2	8 10	—	10 35	10 45	—	3 38
Bojanowo 220A			6 21	...	9 16		12 15	...	...	...	4 20	5 44	...	...	8 21	8 35	...	...	11 26	...	4 1
Rawitsch			6 36	8 43	9 34		12 29	...	...	4 14	4 32	6 0	...	...	8 33	8 50	...	11 2	11 50	...	4 15
Trachenberg 217 ...	a.m.		6 56	8 57	9 55		12 49	p.m.	p.m.	4 28	4 46	6 21	...	p.m.	8 47	9 11	...	11 16	—	...	4 34
Obernigk ..	5†a45	6*54	7 27	...	10 27		1 19	2 38	4 3	...	...	6 52	...	8 10	...	9 43	...	...	...	...	5 4
Breslau arr	6 30	7 19	8 7	9 40	11 10		2 2	3 10	4 49	5 16	5 35	7 33	...	9 0	9 35	10 26	...	12 0	...	...	5 46

		a.m.	a.m.	a.m.	a.m.	a.m.	a.m.	a.m.		a.m.	a.m.	p.m.	p.m.	p.m.	p.m.	p.m.		p.m.	p.m.	p.m.	night
Breslau ......dep		...	...	...	6 13	7 34	7 42	8 33	...	10 42	11 27	1252	1 38	2 36	4 28	3 31	...	6 15	8 14	11 22	1a 25
Obernigk		...	...	...	6 57	...	...	9 12	...	11 28	...	1 32	2 24	3 25	...	4 6	...	7 4	8 59	12 8	...
Trachenberg		...	...	...	7 22	8 16	B	9 35	...	11 51	12 9	—	—	3 52	5 9	—	...	—	9 25	12 31	1 9
Rawitsch	4a33	...	...	...	7 42	8 31	8 39	9 51	...	12 9	12 24	...	...	4 13	5 24	...	...	...	9 47	12 50	1 25
Bojanowo	5 4	...	...	...	7 55	...	...	10 4	...	12 23	...	...	...	4 28	5 37	...	...	...	10 1	1 3	...
Lissa arr	5 41	...	...	...	8 17	8 57	9 8	10 21	a.m.	12 45	12 51	...	...	4 52	5 54	...	...	p.m.	10 25	1 25	1 52
Lissa dep	—	5 53	...	...	8 22	9 1	9 12	—	1149	1 33	12 55	...	...	5 8	5 56	...	...	8 0	10 37	1 29	1 56
Kosten		6 29	...	...	8 57	9 25	...	...	1226	2 7	...	...	...	5 45	6 20	...	...	8 36	11 12	2 0	2 20
Czempin		6 45	...	...	9 11	...	...	...	1242	2 21	...	...	...	6 1	...	...	...	8 52	11 27	2 11	...
Posen ...... arr		7 30	...	...	9 52	9 59	10 9	a.m.	1 27	3 0	1 47	...	p.m.	6 44	6 53	p.m.	p.m.	9 38	12 7	2 48	2 55
Posen ...... dep		—	5 51	6 57	—	10 22	1015	11 40	2 3	—	2 24	...	3 10	—	7 0	7 26	8 50	9 55	12 22	—	—
Rokietnice		...	6 23	7 17	...	10 51	...	12 7	2 29	...	2 45	...	3 36	...	7 26	7 54	9 20	1020	12 50	†-Weekdays only.	B—Until 31st Aug.
Wronke		...	7 13	7 50	...	11 39	Neustettin arr. 2.5	—	—	...	3 19	...	4 21	...	8 10	—	10 8	—	1 38		
Kreuz ...... arr		a.m.	7 57	8 19	...	1220		...	...	...	3 50	...	4 59	...	8 50	...	1052	...	2 18		
Kreuz ...... dep		5 25	8 40	8 30	...	1249		...	...	...	4 5	...	5 13	...	9 3	...	—	...	3 37		
Arnswalde ..	6a44	7 32	10 4	9 25	...	2 8		...	...	...	5 10	...	6 34	...	11 3	...	...	...	4 51		
Stargard arr	7 41	9 0	11 2	9 57	...	2 55		...	...	...	5 46	...	7 30	...	11 51	...	...	...	5 34		

CZEMPIN and JAROTSCHIN.

Czempin ...dep	5a25	8 a5	11 a3	...	4 p10	6p10	9 p35
Schrimm	6 56	9 13	12 7	1p23	5 20	7 24	10 39
Jarotschin arr	8 12	...	...	3 50	...	9 25	12 33

Jarotschin ......dep	...	5 a35	11a54	...	5 10	...	9p47
Schrimm	5a35	8 9	1 21	4p20	7 35	9 p38	1213
Czempin 218A arr	6 39	9 7	2 16	5 28	8 39	10 45	...

LIEGNITZ and KOBYLIN.

		a.m.	a.m.	a.m.	p.m.		p.m.	p.m.
Liegnitz ......dep	...	...	6 57	7 20	1 10	...	5 5	9 20
Steinau a.-O.	a.m.	...	8 6	9 35	2 18	p.m.	6 32	10 24
Rawitsch St. Bhf.	6 5	7 46	9 32	12 34	4 35	5 47	8 34	—
Görchen	6 56	8 10	9 55	1 10	5 5	6 8	9 3	...
Kobylin ......arr	...	9 10	10 35	2 17	5 59	—	9 56	...

	a.m.	a.m.	a.m.	a.m.	p.m.	p.m.	p.m.	
Kobylin ......dep	...	5 6	...	10 42	2 47	...	6 36	...
Görchen	...	6 3	8 34	11 25	3 31	5 7	7 38	...
Rawitsch St. Bhf.	...	6 40	9 6	12 32	4 34	5 37	8 16	...
Steinau a.-O.	5 16	8 24	—	2 26	6 5	—	—	...
Liegnitz ......arr	6 34	9 26	...	3 47	7 32	...	...	...

RADZIONKAU and BEUTHEN.

Radzionkau dep	4a29	7a12	8a27	11a45	1p28	2p34	4p20	...	8p43	p.m.
Scharley	4 45	7 24	8 40	12 0	1 40	2 43	4 32	6p12	8 55	1025
Beuthen ......arr	4 55	7 33	8 50	12 10	1 50	2 53	4 42	6 22	9 5	1035
Beuthen ......dep	5a5	7a48	10a30	12p55	2 p1	3p10	5p20	6p50	9p25	11p25
Scharley	644	7 58	10 43	1 6	2 12	3 21	5 30	7 1	9 35	11 36
Radzionkau arr	657	8 11	10 56	1 18	2 24	3 32	...	7 14	...	11 49

SAGAN to SKALMIERZYCE and KALISZ.

		Ex3	2 3 4	2 3 4	2 3 4	2 3 4	1,2,3	2 3 4	2 3 4	Ex3	2 3 4	1—4
		a.m.	a.m.		a.m.	a.m.	a.m.	p.m.	p.m.		p.m.	p.m.
Sagan ......dep		3 0	3 34	a.m.	5 16	9 10	1156	1210	2 45	...	5 5	8 14
Waltersdorf		...	4 9	7 8	5 56	9 52	...	1248	3 21	...	5 44	8 51
Glogau ...... arr		3 47	4 51	7 52	6 40	1037	1247	1 38	4 3	...	6 29	9 33
Glogau ...... dep		3 48	4 56	—	6 43	1050	1248	2 36	4 8	...	6 45	9 36
Lissa ...... arr		4 25	5 47	...	7 41	1143	1 27	3 38	4 59	p.m.	7 48	1028
Lissa ...... dep		4 33	5 53	...	9 2	1 47	—	—	5 11	7 13	8 26	—
Kobylin	Ex3	...	7 15	...	1039	3 18	...	1,2,3	6 33	...	10 2	...
Krotoschin arr	a.m.	5 31	7 37	...	11 0	3 42	2 3 4	p.m.	6 57	8 18	1028	...
Krotoschin dep	5 29	5 39	7 48	a.m.	11 7	4 0	p.m.	3 51	8 39	8 32	1045	...
Ostrowo	6 0	6 11	8 34	7 0	115	5 57	1 45	4 22	9 23	8 57	1145	...
Skalmierzyce	6 18	6 29	1016	7 28	1226	6 26	2 16	4 40	9 57	9 20	1212	...
Kalisz (316) ...	6 49	6 49	1031	7 48	1246	6 40	...	4 55	...	9 35	—	...

		2 3 4	2 3 4	Ex3	2 3 4	2 3 4	1 2 3	2 3 4	2 3 4	2 3 4	Ex3	Ex3
		a.m.	a.m.	a.m.	a.m.	non	a.m.	p.m.	p.m.	p.m.	p.m.	p.m.
Kalisz ......dep		...	...	6 49	8 43	...	1153	1 45	3 51	...	9 29	9 28
Skalmierzyce dep		7 5	4 58	8 13	9 13	12 1	1248	2 35	4 43	7 9	1026	1038
Ostrowo	2 3 4	7 37	5 29	8 37	10 0	1240	1 10	3 3	5 15	7 40	1050	1058
Krotoschin arr	a.m.	—	6 22	9 5	1043	1 23	1 35	—	5 58	8 23	1115	1122
Krotoschin dep	4 38	...	6 24	9 15	11 6	1 49	—	...	6 7	8 31	1117	1126
Kobylin	5 2	1,2,3	6 46	9 30	1128	2 14	...	1 2 3	6 30	8 53	To Breslau.	...
Lissa ... arr	...	a.m.	8 5	1019	1245	3 41	...	p.m.	7 54	1015		1224
Lissa ... dep	4a50	5 50	9 11	—	1258	5 2	...	4 2	8 10	1039		1229
Glogau arr	5 45	6 26	10 6	...	1 48	5 56	...	4 39	9 5	1135		1 4
Glogau dep	5 50	6 27	1017	...	2 24	6 4	...	4 40	9 35	1148		1 5
Waltersdorf ...	7 16	6 57	11 7	...	3 15	6 54	...	...	1028	1238		...
Sagan ......arr	7 55	7 23	1141	...	3 50	7 30	...	5 31	11 5	1 13		1 56

NEISSE and OPPELN.

Neisse ......dep	5a15	10a5	1 p45	6p46	11 p2	...
Schiedlow ......arr	6 30	11 18	2 45	7 56	12 9	...
Deutsch Leippe ...dep	...	8 1	1 42	...	8 21	...
Schiedlow ......arr	...	9 30	2 33	...	9 38	...
Schiedlow ......dep	6 42	11 20	2 46	7 58	12 10	...
Oppeln (219) ...arr	7 16	11 48	3 13	8 31	12 38	...
Oppeln ......dep	...	5 a0	9a28	12p42	3p55	9 p7
Schiedlow ......arr	a.m.	5 33	9 59	1 11	4 34	9 42
Schiedlow ......dep	4 55	...	11 22	...	5 0	...
Deutsch Leippe ...arr	6 17	...	12 19	...	6 36	...
Schiedlow ......dep	...	5 35	10 0	1 12	4 39	9 44
Neisse (219) ......arr	...	6 47	11 5	2 21	5 58	1049

GLATZ and KUDOVA-SACKISCH.

Glatz Haupt. ...dep	7 a25	9a15	11a50	1p47	4‡p8	5p20	8p51
Rückers	8 15	10 4	12 32	2 31	4 57	6 8	9 41
Reinerz	8 33	1023	12 53	2 50	5 16	6 29	10 1
Kudova S. ......arr	9 17	11 7	1 35	3 34	6 0	7 16	1045
Schlaney ......arr	...	1123	...	3 50	...	...	...
Schlaney ......dep	...	...	11a33	...	4p40	...	...
Kudova S. ......dep	5 a7	9 a35	11 55	1p52	4 55	6p10	...
Reinerz	5 58	10 24	12 48	2 45	5 48	7 8	...
Rückers	6 14	10 40	1 2	3 0	6 6	7 26	...
Glatz Haupt. 219 arr	7 1	11 25	1 40	3 44	6 55	8 15	...

‡—Until 15th August.

LISSA and JAROTSCHIN.

Lissa ......dep	a.m.	6 a9	9 a15	1 p35	6 p0	8p12	10p50
Gostyn 217	3 35	7 13	10 26	3 2	7 14	9 15	11 52
Borek	4 9	7 46	11 1	3 36	7 55	—	—
Jarotschin ......arr	4 46	8 22	11 39	4 14	8 38	...	...
Jarotschin ......dep	...	5 a20	8a45	12p20	4p50	...	9a50
Borek	...	5 59	9 29	1 17	5 38	...	1029
Gostyn	4 a42	6 39	1027	2 50	6 28	9p27	11 1
Lissa ......arr	5 43	7 43	1133	3 54	7 37	1029	...

CAMENZ, NEISSE, and KANDRZIN.

A—Until 31st Aug.

		a.m	a.m	a.m.	a.m	a.m.	p.m.	p.m.			p.m.	p.m.			p.m.	p.m.	...	p.m
Camenz (Schl.) dep	...	4 2	5 30	...	8 29	10 9	1225	...	...	...	4 34	4 40	...	...	...	8 17	p.m.	11 8
Ottmachau	...	4 33	5 54	7 15	8 57	1037	1253	A	p.m.	p.m.	...	5 7	p.m.	p.m.	...	8 45	9 31	1133
Neisse	...	5 2	6 20	7 42	9 27	1115	1 21	1 45	2 28	4 25	5 15	5 37	6 43	7 30	7 58	9 18	10 1	12 7
Deutsch Wette	...	5 30	6 28	8 51	9 45	1134	1 42	2 4	2 43	4 44	5 31	5 56	7 0	7 49	8 14	9 37	—	1226
⋮Ziegenhals	...	5 41	6 55	8 59	10 0	1146	1 52	⋮	2 57	4 55	...	6 13	7 11	...	8 32	1012	...	1244
⋮Langenbruck	...	—	7 9	—	...	1 22	—	⋮	...	—	...	...	—	...	...	...	...	...
Neustadt-o-S.	a.m.	...	7 7	...	1012	12 4	...	2 30	3 5	...	5 51	6 24	...	8 20	8 33	10 7	...	1252
Rasselwitz	5 39	...	7 29	...	1031	1224	...	2 45	3 20	...	6 6	6 43	...	8 51	8 46	1031	...	1 11
Ober Glogau	5 53	a.m.	7 43	a.m.	1043	1237	...	2 59	3 31	p.m.	...	6 59	p.m.	9 6	—	1045	...	—
Cosel Stadt	6 23	7 52	8 11	1043	11 5	1 3	...	3 22	3 53	6 17	6 33	7 26	7 4	9 34	...	1114	...	...
Kandrzin arr	6 35	8 8	8 22	1057	1117	1 14	...	3 33	4 0	6 31	6 40	7 38	7 21	9 45	...	1127	...	...

Kandrzin dep	4a35	6a15	7a30	8a55	9 a5	11a2	...	...	...	1p26	3p10	4p15	5p50	7 p5	8p18	10p0	...	1239
Cosel Stadt	4 49	6 28	8 1	9 7	9 19	11 9	...	...	...	1 39	3 26	4 27	6 4	7 13	8 30	1014	...	1251
Ober Glogau	5 18	6 58	8 30	9 34	—	...	a.m.	...	...	2 8	—	4 50	—	7 35	8 57	—	...	1 13
Rasselwitz	5 35	7 14	8 55	9 51	...	1135	1151	...	...	2 24	...	5 5	...	7 47	9 12	...	...	1 29
Neustadt-o-S.	6 0	7 38	9 12	1017	...	1150	1214	A	...	2 48	...	5 26	...	8 3	9 34	...	...	1 54
⋮Langenbruck	...	7 25	...	...	...	...	...	...	1p38	...	...	...	p.m.	...	...	p.m.	...	...
⋮Ziegenhals	6 10	7 48	9 15	1027	...	1155	1228	1 30	2 29	3 2	...	5 18	7 43	...	9 15	1027	...	2 8
Deutsch Wette	6 30	8 5	9 28	1047	...	12 7	1246	1 42	2 40	3 17	...	5 53	7 55	8 23	9 59	1037	nght	2 27
Neisse ... 5a13	6 52	8 20	9 45	1111	...	12 3	1 3	—	2 58	3 35	...	6 41	8 10	8 40	1015	1057	12 6	2 50
Ottmachau ... 5 40	7 20	...	...	1140	...	...	—	...	3 36	3 57	...	7 9	—	9 2	—	—	12 36	3 21
Camenz arr 6 8	7 48	...	1020	12 8	...	1259	...	...	...	4 24	...	7 36	...	9 28	...	...	1 4	3 52

OPPELN and BEUTHEN.

Oppeln dep	5a10	6a12	8 a0	1056	1p20	3p47	8p54
Gross Strehlitz	6 0	6 42	8 51	1127	2 10	4 36	9 45
Peiskretscham	6 42	...	9 32	...	2 48	5 12	1022
Gleiwitz arr	7 5	7 14	9 54	12 1	3 8	5 35	1045
Beuthen 217 arr	7 26	...	1017	...	3 32	5 54	11 7

Beuthen dep	5a28	8 a5	...	10a0	1p37	6p36	...	9 p7	n'gt
Gleiwitz dep	5 40	8 0	9a15	10 4	1 52	6 57	8p24	9 26	1230
Peiskretscham	6 7	8 53	⋮	1042	2 15	7 19	...	9 45	1248
Gross Strehlitz	6 47	9 38	9 50	1122	2 50	7 54	9 2	1019	—
Oppeln arr	7 28	...	1016	12 9	3 31	8 35	9 30	1058	...

NEUSTADT and GOGOLIN.

Neustadt dep	5 a12	7 a45	...	10a24	12p19	3 p10	...	6 p27
Zulz	5 39	8 10	8a44	10 49	12 42	3 35	4 p0	6 50
Gogolin arr	7 6	...	11 15	...	2 11	...	5 52	8 0
Gogolin dep	...	...	8 a13	...	12 0	3 p22	9 p28	...
Zulz	4 a30	7 a3	9 35	11a16	2 13	4 44	10 53	...
Neustadt arr	4 55	7 27	9 58	11 40	2 38	5 9	...	...

MITTELWALDE, KAMENZ, and BRESLAU.

‡—Until 15th August.

Mittelwal a.m.	a.m	6 a6	10a38	p.m.	2p0	p.m.	2p48	5p52	...	7 p3
Glatz Haup 3 25	7 25	7 35	11 46	1‡55	248	4 11	3 55	7 11	8p20	8 44
Camenz ... 4 1	7 53	8 25	12 25	2 21	313	4 33	4 36	7 54	8 43	9 16
Strehlen ... 4 49	8 28	9 13	1 11	2 56	348	—	5 19	8 55	9 19	—
Breslau H 5 42	9 1	10 1	2 0	3 44	420	...	5 59	9 45	9 56	...

Breslau	...	6a15	7a12	10a1	10a30	...	2p28	3p22	6 p4	7 p0	12a6
Strehlen	a.m.	7 15	7 45	1034	11 19	...	3 14	‡	6 58	7 33	1259
Camenz	6 31	8 13	8 30	1113	12 15	p.m	4 7	4 31	7 56	8 15	1 50
Glatz Ha.	7 14	9 3	8 57	1140	12 49	4‡21	5 9	5 8	8 30	8 38	2 23
Mittelw.	8 32	1012	...	1230	2 47	5 25	6 26	—	9 51	...	...

Extra.—Strehlen to Breslau 5.33 p.m. Breslau to Strehlen 12.23, 4.23, 7.15, and 10.18 p.m.

POSEN and KREUZBURG.

		a.m.	a.m.	a.m	p.m.	p.m	p.m	n'gt
Posen dep		3 20	6 52	1013	1 58	3 3	7 59	1225
Schroda		4 8	7 41	11 1	2 30	3 54	8 50	1 16
Jarotschin		4 56	8 35	1157	3 0	4 48	9 43	2 8
Ostrowo	4a58	5 57	9 46	1 15	3 46	6 0	1144	3 13
Kempen arr	6 2	—	1047	2 15	4 31	7 6	1253	—
Pitschen	6 43	...	1123	2 50	...	7 46	1 31	...
Kreuzburg arr	7 4	...	1143	3 11	5 6	8 8	1 53	...

		a.m.	a.m.	a.m.	p.m.	p.m	p.m.	...
Kreuzburg dep		4 52	8 47	1147	1 20	5 27	8 40	...
Pitschen		5 16	9 11	...	1 44	5 51	9 4	...
Kempen arr		5 50	9 42	1220	2 19	6 24	9 37	...
Ostrowo	4 a0	7 15	1045	1 15	3 31	7 50	11 1	...
Jarotschin	5 7	8 29	1210	1 59	4 50	9 24	1210	...
Schroda	5 49	9 10	1254	2 29	5 35	1010	1254	...
Posen arr	6 38	9 56	1 43	2 59	6 27	1058	1 42	...

Ostrowo dep	6 a0	9a46	1p40	4p35	7p41
Grossgraben arr	7 46	1214	4 0	6 15	9 20

Grossgraben dep	6a33	10a23	2p30	5p23	9p38
Ostrowo arr	8 16	1 2	4 4	7 5	1118

RYBNIK & AN'ABERG

‡—Not on Sunday.

Rybnik	...	8 a23	12p39	2 p4	5p20	6p45	9 p0	...
Loslau	4a52	8 50	1 12	3 4	5 47	7 23	9 37	...
Annab'g	5 29	9 21	1 53	3 49	6 19	...	...	...
Annaberg	4‡a15	5a52	10a3	...	2 p5	...	4p40	6p40
Loslau	4 50	6 34	1041	1p18	2 44	4p25	5 48	7 33
Rybnik 220A	...	7 2	1130	1 48	...	5 0	6 18	8 10

BRESLAU and CHARLOTTENBRUNN.

Breslau dep	...	6a32	8a48	10a40	...	2p35	6p11	8p56
Koberwitz	...	7 1	9 16	11 15	...	3 3	6 39	9 23
Zobten	...	7 34	9 41	11 48	...	3 35	7 12	9 54
Ströbel	...	7 41	9 48	11 54	...	3 41	7 18	10 0
Schweidn N	7a4	8 17	1015	12 30	p.m.	4 15	7 53	1034
Schweidn O	716	8 54	1025	12 54	1 57	4 23	8 16	1039
Croischwitz	724	9 2	1032	1 1	2 5	4 30	8 23	—
Charlotten	819	10 2	1111	1 50	3 0	5 24	9 11	...

Charlottenb	...	5a53	8a34	11a13	1 p2	2 p6	4p34	5p52	7p15	9p47
Croischwitz	...	6 42	9 31	12 0	1 54	2 57	5 22	6 46	8 8	1034
Schweidn. O.	5a30	7 38	9 38	12 10	2 15	3 3	5 38	6 53	8 21	1055
Schweidn. N.	5 35	7 44	—	12 16	2 18	—	5 44	—	8 27	11 2
Strobel	6 7	8 18	...	12 51	2 50	...	6 19	...	9 3	1143
Zobten	6 17	8 24	...	12 57	2 56	...	6 26	...	9 10	1149
Koberwitz	6 49	8 57	...	1 31	3 24	...	7 1	...	9 44	—
Breslau arr	7 16	9 25	...	2 0	3 50	...	7 40	...	1021	...

BRIEG and NEISSE.

Brieg dep	7a17	9a55	1p16	3 p6	5p27	7 p8	7p54	1053
Grottkau	7 48	1027	1 46	3 41	5 58	7 30	8 27	1123
Neisse 219 arr	8 29	11 8	2 24	4 21	6 38	7 55	9 8	12 0

Neisse dep	5a30	8a30	9 a46	11 46	1p21	3 p3	6p14	8p16
Grottkau	6 15	9 14	10 12	12 25	2 0	4 6	6 53	8 55
Brieg 218 arr	6 45	9 43	10 52	12 55	2 29	4 32	7 26	9 24

FRIEDRICHSGRUBE and TICHAU.

Friedrichsgrube dep	8a10	2p 3	8 p0	...
Tichau 220A arr	8 50	2 47	8 48	...
Tichau dep	7 a8	10a55	5 p5	...
Friedrichsgrube arr	7 40	11 38	5 38	...

KANDRZIN and ODERBERG.

‡—Not on Sunday.

Dist E M		a.m	a.m.	a.m.	a.m.	a.m.	a.m.	p.m.	p.m.	p.m.	p.m.	p.m.	p.m.	p.m.	p.m.
	Kandrzin dep	1 50	4 15	5‡40	7 40	8 35	1157	1 25	3 10	4 6	6 48	...	8 12	10 4	1140
14¼	Nensa	...	4 50	6 21	8 16	8 58	1230	1 59	3 43	...	7 14	...	8 44	1049	...
20	Ratibor 220A	2 18	5 12	6 37	8 34	9 8	1250	2 12	4 1	4 34	7 27	7 50	9 5	1110	12 9
32¾	Annaberg	...	5 43	—	9 5	9 24	1 21	—	4 33	...	7 49	8 19	9 34	1143	1227
35¾	Oderberg 222 arr	2 40	5 50	...	9 13	9 30	1 28	...	4 40	4 55	7 55	8 26	9 42	1150	1233

	a.m.	a.m.	a.m.	a.m.	a.m.	a.m.	p.m.	p.m.	p.m.	p.m.	p.m.	p.m	p.m.	p.m.	p.m.
Oderberg dep	1 4	3 27	5 25	6 8	7 41	9 46	...	1229	1259	...	3 45	5 55	6 15	9 6	1022
Annaberg	...	...	5 34	6 16	...	9 54	‡	...	1 8	...	3 54	...	6 24	...	1030
Ratibor	1 24	3 48	6 2	6 41	8 3	1020	1220	1253	1 40	3 9	4 25	6 18	6 55	9 29	1059
Nensa 220A	...	...	6 18	—	8 13	1030	1235	...	1 56	3 24	4 40	...	7 11	...	1113
Kandrzin 218 arr	1 49	4 13	6 48	...	8 56	1057	1 6	1 19	2 33	3 57	5 15	6 44	7 43	9 55	1144

GLATZ and SEITENBERG.

Glatz Haup	7a20	9a10	11a45	1p52	4‡14	5§14
Landeck	8 10	10 0	12 25	2 44	5 11	6 5
Seitenberg	8 20	1010	12 35	2 54	5 23	6 15

Glatz dep	5‡30	8p56
Landeck	6 27	9 48
Seitenberg arr	6 37	10 0

‡—Until August 15th.

Seitenberg	5a57	10a21	1243	2p32	5p47	7p59
Landeck	6 10	10 35	1256	2 48	6 1	7 13
Glatz Haup	6 56	11 33	1 35	3 39	6 50	8 3

§—From August 16th.

OPPELN and TARNOWITZ.

Oppeln dep		5a27	6 a27	8 a33	1p12	2p10	3p53	6p10	8 p49
Vossowska	4a45	6 25	7 7	9 40	2 3	2 50	4 40	7 14	9 42
Tarnowitz	5 56	7 46	...	10 42	3 5	...	5 43	8 18	10 41

Tarnowitz dep	5a16	7 a27	8a33	12 0	1 p51	...	6 p9	8p36
Vossowska dep	6 27	8 24	9 39	1 1	3 15	3 p37	7 16	9 41
Oppeln 218 arr	7 17	9 6	1030	1 46	...	4 27	8 4	1027

Vossowska dep	6a20	9a45	2p10	7p17	9p52	...	...
Kreuzburg arr	7 10	10 40	3 3	8 12	1047	[illegible]	...

Kreuzburg dep	5a14	8a46	1 p10	5p30	8 p41	...	...	...	...
Vossowska arr	6 7	9 33	1 58	6 23	9 30	...	...	...	...

BRESLAU and KATTOWITZ.

	2 3 4	Ex3	2 3 4	2 3 4	1 2 3	2 3 4	2 3 4	1—4	2 3 4	1—4	1—4	1—4	1—4	1—4	2 3 4	2—4	1—4	1—4	Ex 3	2 3 4	2 3 4
Breslau—		a.m.		a.m.				a.m.		a.m.	a.m.	p.m.	p.m.	p.m	p.m.	p.m.	p.m.	p.m.	p.m.	p.m.	n'gt
Hauptbnhf dp	...	3 45	...	5 0	...	...	...	6 8	...	8 26	10 37	1245	1 53	2 7	3 26	4 33	6 0	6 45	8 21	7 48	1212
„ Oderthor dep	...	3 57	...	5 13	...	...	...	6 26	...	8 39	10 51	1 0	2 26	2 19	3 40	4 47	6 15	7 0	8 33	8 6	1226
Hundsfeld	...	...	...	5 27	...	...	...	6 37	...	8 53	11 4	1 16	2 40	...	3 54	5 1	6 28	7 13	...	8 20	1240
Oels (220)......arr	...	4 25	...	5 58	...	...	...	7 8	...	9 23	11 33	1 48	3 10	2 44	4 25	5 32	6 57	7 43	8 59	8 51	1 9
„ ....dep	...		...		...	...	...	7 12	...	9 31	11 36			3 15		5 35	7 2		9 3	9 15	1 11
Namslau (218) ...	...	...	...	...	...	...	...	7 51	...	10 7	1214	...	...	3 58	...	6 11	7 43	...	9 31	9 51	1 53
Kreuzburg ...arr	...	...	...	...	...	...	a.m.	8 41	...	1057	1 3	...	...	5 0	...		8 35	...	10 9		2 45
„ (219) dep	...	...	...	...	...	...	6 0	8 46	...	11 1	1 8	...	...	5 12	...	...	8 40	...	10 15	...	2 52
Rosenberg	...	...	...	...	...	...	6 33	9 17	...	1129	1 39	...	...	5 39	...	...	9 11	...	10 36	...	3 22
Lublinitz...........	...	2 3 4	...	1—4	...	...	7 16	10 0	...	1210	2 20	...	...	6 17	2 3 4	...	9 52	2 3 4	11 3	...	4 10
Tarnowitz ...arr	a.m.	a.m.	a.m.	a.m.	...	a.m.	8 49	10 43	a.m.	1253	3 4	p.m.	...	6 59	p.m.	p.m.	1040	p.m.	11 33	...	4 54
„ ...dep	3 52	4 13	5 10	6 0	...	7 55	8 52	10 46	1125	1257	3 9	4 2	...	7 3	5 47	8 22	1045	9 15	11 34	...	
Radzionkau	4 7	4 29	5 26	6 13	...	8 8	9 5	10 59	1140	1 11	3 23	4 20	2 3 4	7 16	6 1	8 35	1058	9 28	...	2 3 4	...
Beuthen ....arr	4 29	To Scharley.	5 48	6 33	a.m.	8 28	9 23	11 12	12 3	1 32	3 36	4 37	p.m.	7 33	6 22	8 55	1111	9 49	11 52	a.m.	Extra.—Breslau to Oels, 10.35 p.m.
„ ....dep	4 32		6 0	6 43	7 2	8 33	9 27	11 17	1243	1 39	3 40	4 39	5 18	7 36	6 31	9 10	1116		11 53	1251	
Eichenau ......arr	4 58		6 29	7 9	:	8 59	10 2	11 49	1 18	2 6	4 9	5 5	5 53	8 2	6 58	9 35	1143	...		1 17	
Eichenau ...dep	5 15		...	...	:	8 56	10 4	11 53	1 19	...	4 15	5 6	...	...	7 1	...	1150	...	Via Königshütte	...	
Schoppinitz ...	5 23		...	...	:	9 2	10 8	11 58	1 26	...	4 21	5 11	...	...	7 7	...	1156	...		...	
Myslowitz arr	:		...	...	:	...	1016	:	1 34	...	...	5 19	...	...	...	...	...	...		...	
Sosnowitz..arr	6 5	...	...	...	:	...		12 4		...	...		...	...	7 12	...	...	...		...	
Eichenau .....dep	4 59	...	6 30	7 10	:	9 0	...	11 50	...	2 7	4 10	...	5 54	8 3	6 59	9 36	1145	...		1 18	
Kattowitz ....arr	5 11	...	6 43	7 20	7 27	9 10	...	12 2	...	2 20	4 21	...	6 7	8 15	7 11	9 47	1156	...	12 15	1 29	

	1—4	1—4	Ex 3	2 3 4	2 3 4	1—4	2 3 4	1,2,3	1—4	2 3 4	2 3 4	1—4	1—4	1,2,3	2 3 4	2 3 4	2 3 4	1—4	2 3 4	2,3,4	1—4
		a.m.	a.m.	a.m		a.m.			a.m.	p.m.		p.m.	p.m.	p.m.	p.m.	p.m.	p.m.	p.m.		p.m.	ng't
Kattowitz ...dep	...	3 47	5 30	6 4	...	8 45	...	...	1127	1 45	...	3 54	4 46	6 12	6 22	7 5	8 8	9 50	...	10 55	12 2
Eichenau......arr	...	4 0	Via Königshütte	6 16	...	8 55	...	...	1140	1 57	...	4 5	4 59	:	6 35	7 18	8 21	10 3	...	11 7	1214
Sosnowitz dep	...	...		...	a.m.	7 41	a.m.	...	...	...	p.m.	3 31	...	:	...	...	...	...	...	10 35	...
Myslowitz dep	...	...		...	6 58	...	1030	...	...	...	2 30	...	...	:	...	...	...	...	From Scharley.	...	...
Schoppinitz ...	...	...		4 48	7 6	8 20	1043	...	1119	...	2 39	3 49	...	:	6 16	...	...	...		10 52	...
Eichenau...arr	...	...		4 55	7 12	8 28	1049	...	1126	...	2 44	3 54	...	:	6 23	...	...	...		10 58	...
Eichenau .....dep	...	4 1		6 17	7 12	8 56	1050	...	1141	1 58	2 45	4 6	5 1	:	6 36	7 20	8 22	10 4		11 8	1215
Beuthen ....arr	...	4 28	5 51	6 42	7 43	9 21	1118	...	1210	2 26	3 13	4 38	5 29	6 39	7 4	7 50	8 49	10 34	...	11 39	1241
„ ....dep	...	4 32	5 52	6 48	7 52	9 24	1121	...	1238	2 37	3 15	4 50	5 33		7 9	8 ‡3	9 9	10 45	p.m.	11 48	1255
Radzionkau	...	4 53	...	7 11	8 18	9 43	1144	...	1 4	3 1	3 38	5 16	5 53	...	7 35	8 22	9 33	11 8	1150	12 15	1 19
Tarnowitz ...arr	a.m.	5 4	6 9	7 24	8 29	9 51	1155	...	1 16	3 12	3 50	5 28	6 4	...	7 46	8 32	9 45	11 19	12 5	12 27	1 30
„ ...dep	1 37	5 10	6 10			9 56		...	1 27	3 18			6 11	...				11 23			
Lublinitz	2 23	5 59	6 34	...	...	1038	...	...	2 10	4 4	...	...	7 0	...	...	...	‡—3 and 4 cl. only.	12 5	...	...	...
Rosenberg	3 2	6 40	6 57	...	...	1117	...	...	2 49	4 46	...	...	7 43	...	...	...		12 47	...	...	...
Kreuzburg ...arr	3 24	7 6	7 13	...	...	1141	...	...	3 12	5 14	...	...	8 9	...	...	...		1 15	...	...	...
„ ...dep	3 30	7 21	7 15	...	...	1150	...	...	3 17	5 19	...	...	8 17	...	...	...			...	...	...
Namslau	4 22	8 13	7 44	1—4	...	1245	1—4	...	4 10	6 12	1—4	1—4	9 17	...	...	Ex3		...	...	...	2 3 4
Oels ....arr	4 59	8 52	8 6	a.m.	a.m.	1 24	p.m.	p.m.	4 45	6 47	p.m.	p.m.	9 56	...	...	n'ht		...	...	...	a.m.
„ ....dep	5 2	8 57	8 8	8 19	1050	1 28	1254	2 41	4 55	6 51	7 54	8 55	10 0	...	...	1225		...	...	...	5 50
Hundsfeld	5 29	9 23	...	8 45	1119	1 54	1 21	...	5 22	7 17	8 22	9 22	10 26	...	...	...		...	...	...	6 19
Breslau Oder. ...	5 42	9 36	8 31	8 55	1132	2 7	1 34	3 4	5 34	7 30	8 35	9 35	10 39	...	...	1251		...	...	...	6 32
„ Haupt. ar	5 58	9 52	8 41	9 8	1146	2 24	1 48	3 16	5 51	7 45	8 48	9 50	10 53	...	...	1 3		...	...	...	6 47

Vossowska ....dep	...	7a21	9 a42	2p53	4p49	7p17	...
Lublinitz	6a50	8 10	10 40	3 38	6 0	8 1	...
Herby	7 19	8 45	11 15	4 31	...	8 45	...
Czenstochau (Russ)316	9 29	1123	3 1	7 2	...	11 7	...

Czenstochau dep	...	6a32	8a15	9a37	12p55	4 p7	7p51	...
Herby	...	6 55	9 16	1130	1 32	5 25	8 20	...
Lublinitz	5a18	7 29	9 48	12 2	2 30	6 5	8 51	...
Vossowska ...arr	6 7	8 15	...	1256	3 25	7 3	9 36	...

GNESEN and OELS.

Gnesen ......dep	...	6a27	8a40	...	1115	2p56	5p39	...	10p7
Wreschen	a.m.	7 10	9 16	...	1152	3 37	6 18	...	1046
Jarotschin	5 33	8 32	1018	...	1255	4 50	7 33	9p48	1146
Krotoschin arr	6 17	9 10	1057	p.m.	1 15	5 32	8 16	1027	
„ dep	6 28	9 12	11 8	1 38	2 15	6 7	8 29		11p17
Militsch	7 3	9 41	1144	1 59	2 56	6 41	8 56	...	1139
Oels............arr	8 13	1042	1246	2 36	4 35	7 45	9 53	...	1220

Oels ....dep		4a30	6 a4	9a33	1140	1p54	2p49	7 p3	9 p4
Militsch		5 6	7 6	1031	1237	2 59	3 25	7 58	10 5
Krotoschin arr		5 27	7 38	11 0	1 7	3 30	3 46	8 26	1036
„ dep	4a22		7 44	11 8	1 12	3 54		8 32	1041
Jarotschin	5 12	...	8 36	1154	2 15	5 0	...	9 44	1122
Wreschen	6 25	...	9 47	1252	3 33	6 16	...	1045	
Gnesen arr	7 4	...	1025	1 27	4 12	6 53	...	1122	...

BRESLAU and STETTIN.

A—Until 15th August.

Extra.—Stettin to Greifenhagen, 1.25 p.m.

		2 3 4	2,3,4	Ex3	2 3 4	1,2,3	2 3 4	2,3,4	2 3 4	1,2,3
Breslau—Haupt-		a.m.	a.m.	a.m.	a.m.	p.m.	p.m.	p.m.	p.m.	p.m.
Bahnhof...........dep		6 16	8 4	9 12	1116	3 15	3 30	6 53	9 1	1115
Wohlau.....................		7 17	9 8	...	1224	...	4 33	8 4	10 6	1157
Steinau-a-O.		7 37	9 32	...	1250	A	4 56	8 27	1032	1217
Raudten 183A dep		8 0	10 1	...	1 16	...	5 24	8 52	11 9	1235
Glogau 220A ...arr		8 35	10 30	1040	1 47	4 39	5 56	9 25	1142	1 0
„ ....dep		8 40	11 5	1045	1 54	4 43	6 8	9 40		5 7
Beuthen.....................		9 14	11 36	RC	2 24	...	6 43	10 14	...	5 40
Neusalz......................		9 29	11 50	1115	2 37	5 12	7 0	10 31	a.m.	5 55
Grünberg		10 5	12 28	1141	3 9	5 37	7 39	11 3	3 37	6 33
Rothenburg ...arr		1022	12 44	1155	3 22	5 50	7 56	11 30	4 10	6 50
„ (182) ...dep		1030	12 50	12 1	3 40	5 51	8 1			6 54
Baudach		1113	1 32	...	4 23	...	8 41	...	...	7 32
Reppen (182)...arr		1153	2 10	1247	5 8	6 35	9 18	...	...	8 10
FRANKFORT ......arr		1256	3 p23	1p19	6 p4	...	9p55	...	...	8a48
Reppen ....dep		...	2 22	1253	6 46	6 39	9 35	...	...	8 23
Cüstrin N { arr	a.m.	...	3 10	1 22	7 38	7 8	1028	...	...	9 12
Haupt { dep	4 54	...	3 24	1 30	7 53	7 14	1045	...	...	10 3
Jädickendorf	5 47	p.m.	4 25	...	9 10	...	1142	a.m.	a.m.	1057
Greifenhagen......	6 52	3 10	5 31	...	1017	8 31	1249	4 15	8 4	1152
Stettin(183) arr	7 29	3 47	6 9	3 17	1055	8 55	1 21	4 56	8 42	1240

		2—4	2 3 4	2—4	1,2,3	2,3,4	Ex 3	2 3 4	2—4
Stettin		a.m.	a.m.	a.m.	a.m.	a.m.	p.m.	p.m.	p.m.
Berliner Bhf dep		12 7	7 18	6 3	1010	10 47	2 10	2 30	5 40
Greifenhagen		1243	7 54	6 46	...	11 27		3 15	6 23
Jädickendorf				7 50	A	12 34	RC	4 21	7 26
Cüstrin N { arr		...	a.m.	8 40	1144	1 23	3 48	5 8	8 21
Haupt. { dep		...	6 22	9 13	1149	1 29	3 53	5 43	8 27
Reppen ......arr		...	7 15	10 8	1222	2 21	4 25	6 36	9 22
FRANKFORT dep		...	6 a7	11a7	...	1p44	3p58	6p13	9 p7
Reppen ......dep		...	7 30	1135	1230	2 27	4 30	6 43	9 34
Baudach		2 3 4	8 12	1213	...	3 4	...	7 19	10 11
Rothenb'rg arr		a.m.	8 50	1248	1 21	3 37	5 15	7 52	10 44
„ dep		4 44	8 57	1250	1 22	3 43	5 21	7 58	10 45
Grünberg		5 19	9 22	1 8	1 40	4 11	5 39	8 18	11 8
Neusalz		5 55	9 55	1 35	2 1	4 46	6 1	8 50	11 38
Beuthen............	1,2,3	6 11	1010	1 48	...	5 3	...	9 4	11 52
Glogau ...arr	a.m.	6 43	1041	2 17	2 30	5 35	6 32	9 30	12 22
„ ...dep	8 15	7 15	1046	2 23	2 36	6 46	6 38	9 38	
Raudten arr	8 39	7 50	1117	2 54	3 1	7 18	...	10 9	...
Steinau-a-O.	8 57	8 20	1141	3 28	A	7 41	...	1032	...
Wohlau	9 17	8 43	12 4	3 57	...	8 4	...	1055	...
Breslau arr	9 55	9 40	1 10	5 2	4 12	9 0	8 9	1152	...

NEUSALZ and SAGAN.

Neusalz ...dep	5a57	7a20	10a0	11a27	2p41	6 p8	7 p5	8p 53	11p41	...
Freystadt.........	6 14	7 47	1022	11 46	2 57	6 28	7 23	9 12	12 6	...
Sagan 220A arr	7 5	...	1123	...	3 49	7 26	...	...	...	...

Sagan ......dep	...	...	8a10	...	11a58	4p31	...	...	8p48
Freystadt.........	4a58	6a35	9 5	10a46	1 11	5 38	6p29	8p10	9 56
Neusalz ......arr	5 15	7 0	9 19	11 5	1 30	5 57	6 53	8 36	1015

KATTOWITZ and DZIEDITZ.

Extra.—Kattowitz to Pless 8.25 p.m., 12.20 night.

	a.m.	a.m.	a.m.	a.m.	p.m.	p.m.	p.m.	p.m.
Kattowitz dep	5 20	7 35	9 15	11 0	12 45	2 36	5 40	10 30
Idaweiche	5 31	7 43	9 23	11 9	12 54	2 45	5 49	10 39
Emanuelsegen	5 39	7 52	9 32	11 19	1 3	2 54	5 58	10 49
Tichau	5 53	8 6	9 48	11 35	1 17	3 10	6 14	11 4
Pless	6 15	8 28	1014	11 58	1 38	3 36	6 36	11 25
Dzieditz 222 ar	6 27	8 41	1035	12 15	1 52	3 51	6 50	11 39

	a.m.	a.m.	a.m.	a.m.	p.m.	p.m.	p.m.	p.m.	nght
Dzieditz dep	...	6 13	8 10	9 57	1 0	2 29	4 20	7 22	12 30
Pless	4 6	6 37	8 30	1012	1 19	2 46	4 35	7 35	12 43
Tichau	4 34	7 7	8 54	1037	1 46	3 16	4 59	7 57	1 5
Emanuelsegen	4 53	7 29	9 14	1057	2 5	3 34	5 19	8 15	1 23
Idaweiche	5 1	7 38	9 23	11 6	2 14	3 42	5 27	8 23	1 31
Kattowitz arr	5 12	7 48	9 31	1113	2 22	3 49	5 38	8 30	1 38

DEUTSCH-RASSELWITZ & KATTOWITZ.

	a.m.	am		a.m	a.m.	p.m.		p.m.	p.m.	p.m.	p.m.	p.m.	p.m.	p.m.
Dt.-Rasselwitz dep	5 37	...	...	7 30	1035	1230	...	3 28	...	5 14	6 50	9 17	8 47	1041
Leobschutz	6 20	457	a.m.	7 59	1139	1 16	...	3 56	...	5 49	8 2	9 49	9 5	1125
Bauerwitz	—	513		8 15	1156	3 11	p.m.	—	...	6 6	8 21	1015	—	—
Ratibor arr		551	8 53	8 50	1233	3 48	4 37	...	5 35	6 43	8 57	1042	1220	...
Nensa arr		626	9 6	1023	1 13	—	...	...	5 48	7 57	9 50	—	1235	a.m.
Rybnik		719	9 50	1111	1 59	...	5 16	...	6 44	8 50	1035	...	1 20	3 22
Friedrichsgrube 219		748	...	1142	2 28	...	...	p.m.	7 21	9 24	—	...	—	3 59
Orzesche 220A	6a55	8 0	1025	1152	2 40	p.m.	5 41	5 55	7 36	9 39	p.m.	...	...	4 8
Nicolai	7 17	820	1042	1210	2 58	4 45	5 54	6 13	7 54	9 59	9 10	...	...	4 30
Kattowitz 218 arr	7 39	840	11 3	1231	3 19	5 9	6 9	6 35	8 17	1023	9 35	...	...	4 59

Kattowitz dep		...	6 a5	6a55	7a30	9a40	11 a8	3 p6	1p46	4p10	4p55	6p48	...	11p20
Nicolai		...	6 28	7 18	7 46	10 5	11 32	3 28	2 13	4 38	5 19	7 11	...	11 44
Orzesche		...	6 46	7 36	7 57	1027	11 54	—	2 39	4 57	5 44	7 39	...	12 5
Friedrichsgrube		...	6 51	8 7	...	1033	12 0	...	2 45	—	5 50	7 45	p.m.	12 11
Rybnik		5a20	7 25	—	8 18	1113	12 32	...	3 15	...	6 24	8 18	11 5	12 42
Nensa dep	a.m.	6 10	8 5	a.m.	...	1155	1 15	...	3 57	...	7 21	9 3	11 44	—
Ratibor dep	5 20	6 50	8 18	9 22	8 57	12 9	1 38	...	4 42	...	7 39	9 16	11 58	11p20
Bauerwitz	6 5	7 29	—	10 0	—	—	2 18	...	5 20	p.m.	8 22	—	—	11 58
Leobschutz	6 24	7 47	9a20	1018	...	...	2 36	4p38	5 38	7 52	8 41	...	...	12 14
Dt.-Rasselwitz	7 9	8 54	9 44	1129	...	...	3 14	5 0	6 30	8 32	1020	...	...	...

Extra.—Leobschütz to Dt.-Rasselwitz, 5a0; Dt.-Rasselwitz to Leobschütz, 1a28.

Bauerwitz dep	8a20	12 p5	6p15	...
Troppau arr	9 30	1 14	7 32	...

Troppau dep	6 a2	10a50	6p32	...	...
Bauerwitz arr	7 18	11 51	8 11	...	...

Jägerndorf dep	7a24	10a8	1p40	4p2	9p0
Leobschütz arr	7 56	1054	2 25	434	946

Leobschütz dep	6a28	8a25	11a34	2p47	5p4	1010
Jägerndorf arr	7 2	9 21	12 25	3 38	555	11 5

COSEL and BAUERWITZ.

E.M							
	Cosel dep	...	9a20	3p29	10p15	...	...
10	Neukirch-Polnisch	6 a8	10 5	4 25	11 0	...	...
24½	Bauerwitz arr	7 5	1057	5 16	11 53	...	...

Bauerwitz dep	6a10	9a10	4p10	...	8p50	...
Neukirch-Polnisch	7 9	10 7	5 37	6 p0	1010	...
Cosel 219 arr	7 50	1042	...	7 0	...	...

BRESLAU and GNADENFREI.

Breslau dep	...	6 a8	10a21	2p11	5p51	8p27
Koberwitz	...	7 4	11 18	3 5	6 43	9 6
Heidersdorf	...	8 0	12 16	3 56	7 41	9 55
Nimptsch	6 a3	8 25	12 46	4 19	8 3	1014
Gnadenfrei arr	6 32	8 45	1 10	4 46	8 22	...

Gnadenfrei dep	5a18	7 a48	11a34	3p46	7p28	9p10
Nimptsch	5 38	8 6	11 56	4 4	7 47	9 33
Heidersdorf	5 58	8 27	12 25	4 23	8 11	—
Koberwitz	6 46	9 12	1 17	5 8	8 57	...
Breslau	7 43	9 58	2 21	5 50	9 31	...

GLEIWITZ and BADJASTRZEMB.

Gleiwitz dep	6a46	1044	1p50	4p55	6p53	8p47	11p6
Preiswitz	7 12	11 7	2 6	5 11	7 8	9 4	1126
Orzesche	7 35	12 2	2 43	5 47	7 41	9 42	12 6
Sohrau-o-S.	8 30	1235	3 10	6 18	8 7	10 7	1232
Badjastrzemb	9 20	1 25	3 58	7 7	...	...	...

Badjastrz'mb dep		...	6a15	10a20	...	4p10	...	8 p0
Sohrau-o-S.		6a10	7 18	11 14	2 p1	5 5	6p55	8 58
Orzesche	4a12	6 49	8 3	11 55	2 37	5 43	7 34	9 37
Preiswitz	4 40	7 16	8 28	12 20	3 2	6 9	8 2	10 3
Gleiwitz arr	4 58	7 33	8 44	12 36	3 16	6 25	8 17	1022

SAGAN and HANSDORF.

Sagan dep	5a35	7a30	8a28	1156	4p21	5p33	6p44
Hansdorf arr	5 54	7 42	8 47	12 9	4 35	5 45	7 2

Hansdorf dep	7a46	1050	1140	2p15	5 p3	7p30	7p57	...
Sagan arr	8 1	11 9	1151	2 34	5 22	7 45	8 7	...

BOJANOWO and GLOGAU.

[‡—10.20p.m. on Sunday.

Bojanowo dep	...	8 a6	10a10	12p28	...	4p32	6 p3	10p7
Guhrau	5 a8	8 50	10 55	1 3	3p58	5 1	7 55	1051
Glogau arr	6 20	1011	...	2 12	5 44	...	9 12	...

Glogau dep	...	6a50	...	11a17	2p25	...	6p38	9‡p41
Guhrau	5a30	8 36	11a10	1 0	3 44	5 p2	7 48	10 55
Bojanowo arr	6 15	9 6	11 55	...	4 13	5 31	8 17	...

WALTERSDORF and REISICHT.

Waltersdorf dep	4a28	7 a8	8a38	12p51	3p26	7 p6	8 p55
Primkenau	4 51	7 24	9 1	1 8	3 43	7 36	9 14
Kotzenau	5 31	7 55	9 43	1 39	4 16	8 32	—
Reisicht (179) arr	5 49	8 10	10 4	1 54	4 31	8 57	...

Reisicht dep	6 a5	8 a45	2 p8	5 p5	...	...	10p45	...
Kotzenau	6 21	9 1	2 24	5 30	...	...	11 4	...
Primkenau	6 51	9 31	2 54	6 31	8 p10	9 p46	11 41	...
Waltersdorf 218A arr	7 6	9 47	3 10	6 50	8 36	10 11	11 59	...

OTTMACHAU and HEINERSDORF.

Ottmachau dep	7 a26	9 a5	1 p0	5 p11	7 p11
Heinersdorf arr	8 4	9 50	1 35	5 52	7 46

Heinersdorf dep	6 a38	8 a16	10a55	3 p4	6p30
Ottmachau (219) arr	7 12	8 45	11 30	3 51	6 58

GROTTKAU, STREHLEN, BRIEG, and HEIDERSDORF.

Grottkau dep	6 a16	7a51	11a22	2 p2	7 p38	...
Glambach	7 1	8 57	12 27	2 55	8 40	...
Strehlen arr	7 10	9 8	12 40	3 8	8 49	...
Strehlen dep	5 a13	7 a20	9 a15	1 p31	5 p25	7 p40
Glambach	5 25	7 37	9 30	1 44	5 39	7 52
Brieg arr	6 21	8 41	...	2 41	6 44	...
Strehlen dep	7 a20	11a22	3 p17	7 p3	...	...
Heidersdorf arr	7 55	11 58	3 52	7 38	...	...

Brieg dep	5 a42	...	...	11a21	3 p30	7 p44
Glambach	6 38	8 a39	10a54	12 44	4 46	8 40
Strehlen arr	6 49	8 54	11 8	12 59	5 1	8 49
Strehlen dep	5 a0	7 a53	11a23	3 p18	7 p4	...
Glambach	5 14	8 5	11 34	3 31	7 14	...
Grottkau arr	6 9	9 3	12 22	4 28	8 16	...
Heidersdorf dep	8 a32	12p22	4 p30	8 p10	...	
Strehlen arr	9 7	1 6	5 5	8 45	...	

DEUTSCH WETTE and GR. KUNZENDORF.

Deutsch Wette dep	6 a43	11a45	3p20	8 p20
Gr. Kunzendorf arr	7 38	12 33	4 15	9 7

Gr. Kunzendorf dep	5 a55	8 a40	1 p45	6 p55
Deutsch Wette (219) arr	6 25	9 20	2 31	7 38

RATIBOR and TROPPAU.

Ratibor dep	6 a7	9a34	1p46	4p50	6p30	7p47
Kuchelna	6 46	1014	2 26	5 32	7 11	8 26
Troppau 222 arr	7 30	11 5	3 13	6 18	...	9 12

Troppau dep	4a42	7 a45	11a21	4 p40	...	9p26
Kuchelna	5 27	8 34	12 10	5 33	7p49	10 15
Ratibor 220A arr	5 58	9 6	12 45	6 8	8 29	10 50

TRACHENBERG and SULMIERZYCE.

Trachenberg dep	7 a33	12p10	4p47
Przittkowitz arr	8 7	12 44	5 21
Prausnitz arr		1 15	
Militsch 230	10 48	...	8 10
Sulmierzyce arr	12 13	...	9 35

Sulmierzyce dep	5a29	...	...	1p19	...
Militsch	6 53	8 a5	...	2 45	3 p30
Prausnitz dep	...	...	2 p40	...	...
Przittkowitz dep	...	10 41	3 10	...	5 36
Trachenberg 218A arr	...	11 15	3 44	...	6 10

SORAU and GRUNBERG.

‡-Wed, Sat, & Sun. only.

Sorau dep	6 a3	9a14	12 p4	2 p30	5p45	9‡p8
Benau	6 36	9 40	12 35	3 0	6 14	9 40
Christianstadt	7 1	10 6	1 17	3 28	6 40	10 3
Grünberg arr	8 0	11 9	2 44	...	7 35	11 0

Grünberg dep	5 a8	10a7	1p22	...	5p44	8‡p20
Christianstadt	6 4	11 6	2 26	4 p0	6 46	9 16
Benau	6 35	1128	2 58	4 34	7 16	9 41
Sorau arr	7 0	1152	3 25	5 0	7 49	10 11

JAUER and ROHNSTOCK.

Jauer dep	6a37	7a31	10a25	2p57	7p48
Rohnstock arr	7 25	7 55	10 56	3 26	8 28

Rohnstock dep	5a35	9a24	1 p46	6p48	10p55	...	...	...
Jauer arr	6 13	10 6	2 24	7 28	11 26	...	...	...

RC—Restaurant Car.

VIENNA and BRUNN

		1,2,3	Ex3	Ex.3	Ex3	1,2,3	Ex3	1,2,3	Ex3	Ex.3
		a.m.	a.m.	p.m.	p.m.	p.m.	p.m.	p.m.	p.m.	p.m.
Vienna Nord-bahnhof......dep		6 1	7 53	12 35	2 20	2 30	3 55	5 55	7 45	9 20
Wagram		6 35	...	...	...	3 3	...	6 31	...	9 43
Ganserndorf...		6 56	8 27	1 8	2 54	3 26	...	6 52	...	9 57
Durnkrut		7 24	...	...	...	3 54	...	7 13	RC	...
Drosing	1,2,3	7 39	RC	...	...	4 9	...	7 31	...	...
Hohenau	a.m.	7 49	...	...	...	4 19	...	7 40	...	10 28
Lundenb'g	3 15	8 30	9 18	2 2	3 45	4 45	5 14	8 16	9 18	11 0
Saitz	3 43	8 57	...	2 31	...	—	5 43	8 48	...	11 21
Auspitz	3 53	9 6	9 43	2 39	4 10	...	5 51	8 58	9 43	11 29
Branowitz ...	4 13	9 25	...	2 56	...	...	6 9	9 17	...	11 40
Rohrbach	4 27	9 39	10 2	3 9	4 32	...	6 24	9 31	10 2	11 50
Brünn...arr	5 2	1012	1022	3 39	4 52	...	6 55	10 6	1022	12 15

	1,2,3	Ex3	Ex3	Ex3	Ex3	1,2,3	Ex3	1,2,3	1,2,3	Ex3	1,2,3
	a.m.	a.m.	a.m.	a.m.	a.m.	p.m.	p.m.	p.m.	p.m.	p.m.	p.m.
Brünn dep	3 53	6 18	7 8	9 35	1130	1 20	4 12	4 40	6 10	8 5	1115
Rohrbach ...	4 26	6 50	...	10 3	1150	1 51	4 31	5 16	6 46	...	1151
Branowitz...	4 41	7 3	...	1013	...	2 5	...	5 31	7 0	RC	12 6
Auspitz	4 57	7 20	...	1024	12 8	2 22	...	5 52	7 19	8 41	1224
Saitz	5 6	7 29	...	1032	...	2 32	...	6 1	7 28	...	1234
Lundenb	5 38	8 48	8 25	1110	1238	3 18	5 18	6 28	8 40	9 11	2 30
Hohenau ...	6 5	9 13	8 42	...	1256	3 45	...	—	...	...	2 58
Drosing	6 14	9 22	...	...	...	3 55	...	...	...	...	3 8
Durnkrut ...	6 27	9 35	8 56	...	RC	4 9	...	...	...	...	3 19
Gansernd	6 56	10 3	9 16	12 4	1 31	4 40	...	...	...	9 58	3 54
Wagram......	7 16	1022	9 30	...	...	4 59	...	...	...	...	4 13
Vienna arr	7 52	1054	9 52	1234	2 5	5 30	6 28	...	9 50	1030	4 45

Extra.—Lundenburg to Brünn, 5.39 a.m.

LUNDENBURG and ZELLERNDORF.

		a m	a.m.	p.m.	p.m.	p.m.
Lundenburg ....dep		4 40	9 20	12 46	3 55	9 10
Nikolsburg	a.m.	5 25	10 3	1 34	4 41	10 6
Neusiedl-Durnholz ar	3 52	5 42	10 20	1 51	4 58	1018
Grussbach 252...arr	4 10	6 13	10 43	2 13	5 20	—
Neusiedl-Durnholz dp	—	5 50	10 30	2 0	5 10	...
Laa		6 29	11 5	2 36	5 47	...
Kadolz-Mailberg		7 9	11 35	3 9	6 21	...
Zellerndorf 224 ....arr		7 58	12 16	3 50	7 2	...

		a.m.	a.m.	p.m.		p.m.	
Zellerndorf ....dep		5 10	9 38	1 15	...	7 16	...
Kadolz-Mailberg................		5 55	10 28	2 2	...	8 3	...
Laa		6 32	11 22	2 41	...	8 41	...
Neusiedl-Durnholz ......arr		7 4	11 56	3 15	p.m.	9 15	...
Grussbach.........dep.	a.m.	6 50	12 14	3 5	5 38	9 10	...
Neusiedl-Durnholz dep	4 15	7 12	12 35	3 35	6 0	9 33	...
Nikolsburg........................	4 38	7 31	12 54	3 56	6 19	9 56	...
Lundenburg ....arr	5 25	8 10	1 36	4 42	7 2	10 40	...

NEZAMISLITZ and OLMÜTZ.

	a.m.	a.m.	a.m.	p.m.	p.m.	p.m.	p.m.
Nezamislitz dep	5 40	7 44	9 55	2 10	4 15	6 5	8 35
Prossnitz 246......	6 20	8 22	1022	2 48	4 54	6 45	9 14
Olmütz 221 ...arr	6 59	9 0	1050	3 25	5 30	7 22	9 51

	a.m.	a.m.	a.m.	a.m.	p.m.	p.m.	p.m.	p.m.
Olmütz......dep	...	6 8	8 10	1150	1243	4 23	6 28	1145
Prossnitz	3 5	6 51	8 51	1230	1 21	4 53	7 18	1220
Nezamislitz ar	3 35	7 22	9 22	1 1	1 52	5 20	7 50	...

BRUNN and PRERAU.

	a.m.	a.m.	a.m.	p.m.	p.m.	p.m.	p.m.
Brünn ......dep	5 40	8 12	1125	1 50	4 8	6 8	1045
Krzenowitz......	6 22	8 45	12 6	2 42	4 43	6 55	1125
Wischau	7 8	9 22	1251	3 33	5 24	7 44	1210
Nezamislitz......	7 51	9 44	1 22	4 0	5 51	8 24	1235
Kojetein 221 ...	8 13	10 0	1 45	4 20	6 11	8 51	1254
Prerau 222...arr	8 38	10 20	2 10	4 46	6 36	9 17	1 19

	a.m.	a.m.	a.m.	p.m.	p.m.	p.m.	p.m.
Prerau ....dep	2 54	6 30	8 55	1 10	4 48	7 9	1120
Kojetein	3 20	6 56	9 20	1 42	5 9	7 36	1146
Nezamislitz	3 46	7 33	9 42	2 8	5 27	8 9	12 9
Wischau	4 16	8 2	1011	2 38	5 54	8 39	1240
Krzenowitz	4 55	8 46	1050	3 18	6 26	9 21	1 18
Brünn 221 ...arr	5 35	9 25	1124	3 58	6 56	10 0	1 55

PRERAU and OLMUTZ

Prerau dep	1a45	5a25	6a32	9 a0	10a37	12 p5	2p40	3p46	5 p5	7 p6	11 p0	11§p12	§—Until
Olmutz arr	2 17	6 0	7 5	9 32	11 8	12 30	3 18	4 18	5 38	7 38	11 31	12 7	30th Sept.
Olmutz dep	4§15	5a42	8 a0	9a50	11a25	1p25	3 p0	3p56	6 p0	10 p5	10p25	12 a9	3a50 ... ...
Prerau arr	4 38	6 15	8 32	1021	11 57	1 56	3 33	4 34	6 32	10 36	10 50	12 41	4 21 ... ...

VIENNA, GANSERNDORF, and MARCHEGG.

Dist E.M		1,2,3	1,2,3	1,2,3	Ex3	1,2,3	1,2,3	1,2,3
		a.m.	a.m.	a.m.	p.m.	p.m.	p.m.	p.m.
—	**Vienna**.........dep	6 1	8 10	9 18	2 20	3 30	5 55	1040
3¾	Floridsdorf.........	6 11	8 19	9 28	2 28	3 38	6 6	1049
11¾	Wagram	6 35	8 41	9 52	...	3 59	6 31	1111
19¾	**Ganserndorf** arr	6 52	8 59	1010	2 52	4 16	6 48	1130
...	,, dep	7 10	9 25	1020	3 5	—	7 8	1145
31	**Marchegg** ...arr	7 35	9 45	1045	3 25	...	7 33	1210

		1,2,3	Ex3	Ex3	1,2,3	1,2,3	1,2,3
		a.m.	a.m.	a.m.	p.m.	p.m.	p.m.
Marchegg ...dep		5 15	7 55	1135	4 35	6 5	8 45
Ganserndorf arr		5 40	8 20	1155	5 0	6 30	9 10
,, ...dep	5 0	5 59	9 16	12 4	5 15	7 6	9 29
Wagram	5 19	6 17	9 30	...	5 35	7 25	9 47
Floridsdorf...	5 42	6 39	9 44	...	6 1	7 50	1010
Vienna ...arr	5 50	6 47	9 52	1234	6 9	7 58	1018

KOJETEIN and BIELITZ.

		a.m.	a.m.	a.m.	a.m.	p.m.	p.m.
Kojetein ....dep		...	4 55	8 25	1015	2 0	6 15
Kremsier................		3 20	5 20	8 51	1210	2 19	6 38
Hullein ....arr		3 31	5 33	9 2	1220	2 30	6 49
,, ...dep		4 15	6 20	9 45	1 2	3 38	7 20
Holleschau		4 34	6 38	10 2	1 18	3 56	7 38
Wall. Meseritsch ...		5 52	—	1115	2 27	5 12	8 53
Krasna		6 35	...	1126	2 30	5 45	9 2
Hotzendorf		6 54	...	1143	—	6 0	9 18
Wernsdorf	a.m.	7 9	...	1159	p.m.	6 16	9 33
Friedek-Mistek	4 53	8 31	...	1 17	5 23	7 40	1035
Teschen	6 0	9 39	...	2 22	6 51	8 57	—
Golleschau	6 30	10 6	...	2 54	7 15	9 22	...
Bielitz......arr	7 22	11 0	...	3 52	8 6	1015	...

			a.m.	p.m.	a.m.	p.m.	p.m.
Bielitz ....dep		...	6 14	1 53	9 52	3 53	9 2
Golleschau		...	7 8	2 43	10 46	4 50	9 58
Teschen		a.m.	7 45	3 18	12 25	5 33	10 40
Friedek-Mistek		4 42	8 55	4 2	1 27	6 37	11 25
Wernsdorf		5 49	10 7	—	2 43	7 49	—
Hotzendorf	a.m.	6 5	10 24	...	2 59	8 8	...
Krasna	4 10	6 33	10 48	...	3 30	8 28	...
Wall.Meseritsch	4 14	6 39	10 55	p.m.	3 37	8 34	...
Holleschau	5 21	7 50	12 3	2 17	4 53	9 45	...
Hullein ......arr	5 35	8 5	12 17	2 35	5 7	9 59	p.m.
,, ...dep	6 5	8 24	1 0	3 28	5 25	10 12	6 50
Kremsier	6 13	8 45	1 13	3 42	5 38	10 23	7 8
Kojetein 223 ar	6 35	9 2	1 30	...	5 55	...	7 27

Krasna ....dep	7 a12	11a50	5p52	9 p12	...	...
Roznau ....arr	8 12	12 45	6 42	10 3	...	...

Roznau ....dep	5 a30	9a10	2p10	7p12	...
Krasna ....arr	6 24	9 55	3 6	7 56	...

BIELITZ and KALWARYA.

Bielitz...........dep	a.m.	7 a50	11a40	5 p0	8p28
Wadowice	5 15	11 23	3 48	8 41	1022
Kalwarya 245 arr	6 3	12 10	4 35	9 26	...

Kalwarya...dep	a.m.	6a40	12p40	5 p5	9p51	...	...
Wadowice	3 56	7 31	1 31	5 56	10 36	...	...
Bielitz 221 ...arr	5 52	9 28	3 25	7 55	...	...	...

OSTRAU and FRIEDLAND.

Dist.			a.m.	a.m.	p.m.	p.m.	p.m.
E.M.	Mahr. Ostrau.....dep		4 49	7 25	12 3	5 34	9 29
9¼	Paskau...............a.m.		5 26	8 2	1240	6 11	10 2
14¼	Friedek-Mistek..	4 42	6 0	8 55	1 27	6 37	1019
21¼	Friedland......arr	5 3	6 22	9 17	1 10	6 58	...

		a.m.	a.m.	p.m.	p.m.	p.m.	p.m.
Friedland ....dep	...	6 53	7 51	1240	..	6 59	10 15
Friedek-Mistek	5a32	7 15	9 10	1 18	4 12	7 27	10 35
Paskau	5 46	—	9 26	1 32	4 26	7 41	—
Mahr. Ostrau ...arr	6 17	...	10 0	2 4	4 56	8 13	...

CRACOW and PODGORZE.

Cracow ....dep	8a52	12p40	...	...
Podgorze ....arr	9 20	1 8	...	...

Podgorze ....dep	10a30	3p43	...	...	...
Cracow.........arr	10 57	410	...	...	...

Golleschau dp	7a18	10a15	11a40	3p50	10p12
Ustron ...arr	7 35	10 32	11 57	4 7	10 29

Ustron ......dep	5 a56	9a38	11 a0	2p30	8p56
Golleschau 221	6 13	9 55	11 17	2 47	9 13

STAUDING and WAGSTADT.

Stauding ......dep	7 a45	11a40	3 p15	5 p0	9p15
Wagstadt......arr	8 10	12 5	3 40	5 25	9 40

Wagstadt ......dep	5a45	10a 5	2p39	4p15	8p 0	...
Stauding ......arr	6 10	10 30	2 55	4 40	8 25	...

ZAUCHTEL and BAUTSCH.

Zauchtel	4a46	11a55	4p45	9p34
Bautsch	7 28	2 42	7 15	12 8

Bautsch..	3a40	8a10	12p42	5p18
Zauchtel.	5 45	1026	3 17	7 45

ZAUCHTEL and FULNEK.

Zauch.	6a10	8a 3	11a45	3p55	6p18	9p33
Fuln.	6 42	8 35	12 17	4 27	6 50	10 5

Fuln.dep	5 9	7a8	9a50	2p40	5p25	7p10
Zauchtel	540	739	1021	3 11	5 56	7 41

VIENNA to ODERBERG and CRACOW.

	Ex3	1,2,3	Ex.2	1,2,3	1,2,3	Ex3	1,2,3	Ex3	Ex3	1,2,3	1,2,3	Ex3	Ex.3	Ex2	1,2,3	
Vienna—			a.m.	a.m.	a.m.	p.m.	p.m.	p.m.	p.m.	p.m.	p.m.	p.m.	p m.	p.m	p.m.	
Nordbahnhof ......dep	...	...	7 31	8 10	10 30	12 35	1 28	2 20	3 55	4 50	6 35	7 45	9 20	1015	10 40	...
Ganserndorf	...	...	...	9 5	11 21	1 8	2 20	2 54	...	5 46	7 32	...	9 57	...	11 43	...
Drosing	...	...	RC	9 45	12 0	...	2 58	...	...	6 26	8 14	SC	...	SC	12 26	...
Hohenau	...	a.m.	...	9 55	12 9	...	3 7	...	...	6 36	8 24	...	10 28	...	12 36	...
Lundenburg ......arr	...	5 50	8 50	10 20	12 33	1 52	3 30	3 38	5 7	7 0	8 50	9 4	10 45	1127	1 0	...
Göding	...	6 26	...	11 5	1 17	2 29	4 28	—	5 36	7 52	10 3	...	11 16	1157	1 50	...
Rohatetz	...	6 36	...	11 16	1 27	...	4 39	...	...	8 5	10 15	...	...	...	2 1	...
Bisenz-Pisek	...	6 57	...	11 39	1 48	2 40	5 0	...	...	8 32	10 38	...	11 39	...	2 24	...
Ung-Hradisch	...	7 20	...	12 3	2 8	2 54	5 24	...	6 7	8 58	11 2	...	11 55	...	2 47	...
Napajedl 1,2,3	...	7 38	...	12 22	2 25	RC	5 42	...	...	9 18	11 21	...	12 9	...	3 6	...
Otrokowitz ....a.m.	...	7 46	...	12 32	2 33	...	5 50	...	...	9 30	11 30	...	...	...	3 16	...
Hullein 5 45	...	8 16	...	1 4	2 56	3 23	6 16	...	6 35	10 8	11 59	...	12 30	1255	3 43	...
Prerau 221......arr 6 10	a.m.	8 40	10 26	1 30	3 20	3 38	6 40	...	6 50	10 30	12 24	1045	12 46	1 10	4 7	...
" ......dep	4 46	9 10	10 32	2 25	—	3 48	7 10	...	7 5	—	1 37	11 5	12 55	1‡25	4 27	...
Mahr-Weisskirchen	...	9 56	11 0	3 6	...	4 20	7 51	...	7 36	...	2 25	...	1 30	...	5 26	...
Zauchtel	...	10 35	11 20	3 48	...	4 41	8 24	...	7 57	...	3 5	...	1 51	...	6 5	...
Stauding	...	10 55	11 31	4 8	a.m.	4 54	8 4[illegible]	...	...	p.m.	3 30	...	2 4	...	6 25	...
Schönbrunn 223 dep	...	11 24	11 48	4 42	10 8	5 11	9 8	...	8 27	8 8	4 3	1218	2 21	...	6 56	...
Mahr-Ostrau	6 1	11 42	11 56	5 5	10 20	5 20	9 21	...	8 36	8 20	4 24	1228	2 30	2 48	7 14	...
Oderberg ....arr	6 10	11 55	12 5	5 20	10 35	5 30	9 34	...	8 46	8 34	4 40	1236	2 40	2 58	7 28	...
BRESLAU 218........arr	1023	3 p10	3 p10	10p40	...	10p40	...	...	11p48	...	...	3a24	5 a56	5a56	10a23	...
BERLIN 179A.........arr	4 p5	...	8 p16	5 a8	...	5 a8	...	...	5 a8	...	...	7a35	10a50	1050	4 p5	...
Oderberg ....dep	6 28	12 34	12 25	5 46	...	5 40	...	...	8 56	...	5 15	1250	2 50	3 20	7 50	...
Petrowitz	...	12 58	...	6 7	...	...	...	...	9 12	...	5 38	...	...	...	8 11	...
Dzieditz	7 16	2 12	1 15	7 5	...	6 32	...	RC—Restaurant Car.	9 52	...	6 45	1 38	3 43	4 13	9 25	...
Oswiecim ....arr	...	2 42	1 34	7 32	...	6 51	...		10 12	a.m.	7 12	1 57	4 2	4 34	9 59	...
" ....dep	...	2 50	1 40	7 40	...	6 58	...		10 14	5 30	7 18	1 58	4 3	4 35	10 9	...
Chrzanow 247A	...	3 24	...	8 13	...	7 19	...		...	6 2	8 9	...	4 25	...	10 40	...
Trzebinia ....arr	7 58	3 34	2 5	8 21	...	7 26	...		10 41	6 10	8 17	2 23	4 32	5 4	10 48	...
GRANICA 222........arr	...	5 p7	3 p0	9p32	...	9 p32	...		12 0	7 a47	...	...	...	6a32	11a57	...
WARSAW 316........arr	...	...	12a26	...	...	7 a47	...		7 a47	6 p52	...	...	...	2p17	...	...
Trzebinia..........dep	8 4	3 48	2 8	8 45	...	7 32	...		10 58	6 15	8 34	2 29	4 46	5 20	11 0	...
Cracow ....arr	8 40	4 52	2 45	9 45	...	8 10	...		11 38	7 20	9 35	3 7	5 30	6 0	11 55	...
LEMBERG 246A......arr	2p20	...	8 p25	7 a25	...	2 a22	...		8 a45	...	...	8a45	1p25	1p25	...	...
PODWOLOCZ 246A arr	6p 4	...	2 a24	4 p20	...	...	...		...	...	...	4p20	5p55	5p55	...	...
ODESSA 320 ....arr	...	...	6 p58	...	...	...	...	...	...	...	...	9a25	9a25	9a25	...	...

‡—Takes also 3rd class between Prerau and Cracow.

	1,2,3	Ex.3	1,2,3	Ex.3	1,2,3	1,2,3	1,2,3	1,2,3	Ex2	1,2,3	1,2,3	Ex3	Ex 2	Ex3	Ex3	
ODESSA 320 ....dep	...	8 p40	...	10 p5	...	...	...	...	9a55	...	...	...	8 p40	8p40	8p40	...
PODWOLOCZYSKA 246A dep	...	11a45	...	5 p22	...	...	...	...	1a49	...	...	10a9	10a22	1022	1145	...
LEMBERG 246A......dep	...	5 p50	7 p30	12a35	...	...	...	...	8a25	...	8 a32	2 p5	2 p40	2p45	7 p0	...
		a.m.	a.m.	a.m.		a.m.	p.m.		p.m.	p.m.	p.m.	p.m.	p.m.	p.m.	a.m.	
Cracow ....dep	...	3 55	5 20	6 52	...	9 30	1 57	...	2 35	6 0	6 45	7 44	10*15	1035	1250	...
Trzebinia ....arr	...	4 39	6 20	7 32	...	10 33	3 2	...	3 17	6 59	7 47	8 26	11 1	1122	1 32	...
WARSAW 316 ......dep	...	...	...	12a12	...	12a57	...	...	...	8 a37	8 a37	8a37	3 p47	...	...	...
GRANICA 222........dep	...	...	...	6 a20	...	9 a25	2p15	...	2p15	6 p0	6 p0	6 p0	9 p35	...	...	...
Trzebinia..........dep	...	4 44	6 44	7 55	...	10 45	3 31	...	3 23	7 8	7 54	8 34	11 15	1130	1 38	...
Chrzanow	...	4 51	6 54	RC	...	10 57	3 42	...	...	7 16	8 3	...	...	1137	SC	...
Oswiecim ....arr	...	5 9	7 20	8 22	...	11 28	4 20	...	3 45	7 44	8 29	...	11 38	1156	2 1	...
" ....dep	...	5 10	7 25	8 25	...	11 50	4 34	...	3 46	—	8 34	...	11 39	1159	2 2	...
Dzieditz	...	5 40	8 7	8 50	...	12 32	5 30	...	4 10	...	9 20	9 15	12 3	1223	2 25	...
Petrowitz	...	6 24	8 59	...	...	1 21	6 30	...	RC	...	10 14	...	...	...	...	...
Oderberg ....arr	...	6 40	9 17	9 38	...	1 39	6 50	...	4 55	...	10 32	9 58	12 48	1 14	3 8	...
BERLIN 179 ....dep	...	7 p45	12a16	12a16	...	...	8 a54	...	8a54	...	1 p2	1 p2	4 p57	4p57	7p45	...
BRESLAU 218.......dep	a.m.	12a20	6 a30	6 a30	a.m.	8 a48	4 p36	p.m.	2p12	p.m.	6 p18	6p18	9 p55	9p55	12a8	...
Oderberg ....dep	6 10	6 48	10 10	10 0	11 12	1 53	8 8	5 2	5 18	7 42	10 56	1012	1 7	1 28	3 24	...
Mahr Ostrau	6 27	7 3	10 29	10 14	11 29	2 12	8 29	5 20	5 31	8 5	11 15	1023	1 21	1 44	3 36	...
Schönbrunn ......dep	6 40	7 12	10 44	10 23	11 39	2 27	8 42	5 30	5 40	8 20	11 34	...	1 30	1 53	3 44	...
Stauding	7 5	7 32	11 11	10 42	—	2 57	9 7	—	...	8 47	12 0	...	...	2 10	...	...
Zauchtel	7 25	7 49	11 33	10 58	...	3 20	9 28	...	6 7	9 7	12 21	...	SC	2 25	...	...
Mahr-Weisskirchen	7 58	8 14	12 8	11 21	...	3 58	9 59	...	6 29	9 37	12 59	...	...	2 49	...	...
Prerau..........arr a.m.	8 35	8 42	12 45	11 50	p.m.	4 36	10 35	...	6 54	10 14	1 37	1134	2 42	3 18	4 56	...
" ....dep 5 30	9 6	9 0	2 20	12 9	12 25	4 55	11 15	...	7 5	—	1 50	...	2 55	3 30	5 7	...
Hullein 6 1	9 34	9 20	2 51	12 25	12 55	5 30	11 51	...	...	SC—Sleeping Car.	2 14	...	...	3 47	...	...
Otrokowitz 6 23	9 54	...	3 13	...	1 16	5 55	12 13	...	...		2 33	...	...	...	...	...
Napajedl 6 32	10 3	...	3 23	...	1 24	6 5	12 22	...	...		2 41	...	...	4 7	...	...
Ung-Hradisch 6 53	10 20	9 55	3 43	12 54	1 43	6 26	12 44	...	...		3 0	...	...	4 20	...	...
Bisenz-Pisek 7 15	10 40	10 11	4 4	...	2 4	6 47	1 7	...	...		3 21	...	...	4 36	...	...
Rohatetz 7 36	10 58	...	4 24	...	2 24	7 7	1 29	...	...		3 40	...	...	4 51	...	...
Göding 7 50	11 9	10 35	4 37	1 25	2 35	7 20	1 42	...	...		3 51	...	...	5 0	...	...
Lundenburg dep 8 48	11 47	11 10	5 40	1 53	3 18	8 5	2 30	...	8 40		4 45	...	4 40	5 32	6 48	...
Hohenau 9 13	12 12	...	6 11	...	3 45	8 29	2 58	...	...		5 8	...	...	...	...	...
Drosing 9 22	12 21	...	6 21	...	3 55	8 38	3 8	...	...		5 16	...	...	...	...	...
Ganserndorf 10 3	1 2	12 4	7 6	2 38	4 40	9 29	3 54	...	...		5 59	...	...	6 26	...	...
Vienna Nord....arr 1054	1 50	12 34	7 58	3 10	5 30	10 18	4 45	...	9 50	...	6 47	...	6 0	7 7	8 7	...

*—Takes also 3rd Class between Cracow and Oderberg.

DZIEDITZ and ZYWIEC.

‡—Not on Sunday.

	a.m.	a.m.	a.m.	a.m.	p.m.	p.m.	p.m.	p.m.	p.m.	p.m
Dzieditz ....dep	4 25	5 40	6 50	9 18	1 20	2 15	4 15	5 25	7 15	1010
Bielitz	4 45	6 8	7 15	9 51	1 50	2 38	4 40	5 50	8 13	1035
Zywiec ..... arr	...	6 47	...	1031	2 30	...	6 10	7‡45	8 53	1130
Zywiec ......dep	...	5a20	6a15	1052	...	2p52	...	4p10	...	10p10
Bielitz	5 6	6 10	7 37	12 5	1p13	3 40	4p15	6 5	8p35	11 30
Dzieditz 220A	5 28	6 36	7 57	1226	1 40	4 0	5 8	6 24	8 58	11 53

TRZEBINIA, GRANICA, and MYSLOWITZ.

[¶—Customs Examination.

	a.m.	a.m.	a.m.	a.m.	p.m.	p.m	p.m	p.m.	
Trzebinia......dep	5 30	6 42	7 43	1115	2 22	4 10	8 33	1127	...
Szczakowa ...arr	5 52	7 11	8 3	1140	2 42	4 35	8 55	1148	...
Szczakowa dep	6 27	7 40	...	1150	2 55	5 0	9 25	1155	...
Granica ¶ 316	6 32	7 47	...	1157	3 0	5 7	9 32	12 0	...
Szczakowa ...dep	...	7 30	8 4	12 0	...	4 50	9 5	...	...
Mysolwitz 218 arr	...	7 45	8 19	1215	...	5 5	9 20	...	...

	n'gt	a.m.	a.m.	p.m.	p.m	p.m.	
Myslowitz dep	1 30	...	9 30	1 55	6 0	9 48	...
Szczakowa ¶	1 45	...	9 45	2 10	6 15	10 3	...
Granica......	...	6 20	9 25	2 15	6 0	9 35	...
Szczakowa	...	6 25	9 32	2 22	6 7	9 40	...
Szczakowa ...	1 59	6 55	10 5	2 45	6 35	10 14	...
Trzebinia......	2 20	7 18	1030	3 10	7 0	1035	...

SCHONBRUNN and TROPPAU.

Schönbrunn.........dep	12a30	4a30	6a55	7 a30	10a50	11a54	2 p31	5p50	9 p15	...	...	...	...	...
Troppau ....arr	1 5	5 20	7 43	8 20	11 42	12 25	3 15	6 39	10 5	...	...	...	...	...
Troppau ....dep	5a42	9 a8	11a0	1 p32	3 p42	4p32	7p15	10p30	...	...	...	...	...	...
Schönbrunn 222 ...arr	6 30	9 54	1134	2 17	4 30	5 5	8 2	11 15	...		...	...	...	...

TROPPAU and BENNISCH.

Troppau......dep	5 a37	1 p5	7 p52	...	...
Mladetzko	6 35	2 4	8 50	...	...
Bennisch .....arr	7 27	2 56	9 42	...	...

Bennisch ......dep	5 a45	10a42	5 p0	...	...	...	...
Mladetzko	6 32	11 27	5 48	...	...	...	...
Troppau ......arr	7 23	12 23	6 45	...	...	...	...

MAHR.-WEISSKIRCHEN and WSETIN.

M.-Weisskirchen dep	5 a4	8a56	1p45	4p25	...
Krasna	6 42	11 2	3 18	5 58	8p40
Wsetin ....arr	7 45	1218	4 14	6 58	9 45

Wsetin ....dep	5a30	10a0	2p16	4p30	7p16
Krasna	6 37	1) 30	3 17	5 50	8 24
M.-Weisskirch. 222	7 50	1244	...	7 5	9 43

Wsetin ....dep	8a40	2p20	7p12
Gr. Karlowitz arr	1025	4 6	8 57
Gr. Karlowitz dep	6a32	1213	5 p7
Wsetin ....arr	8 7	1 58	6 43

HOLICS and GODING.

E.M.						
	Holics..........dep	7 a28	12p45	3 p56	6 p50	...
3¾	Göding (222)...arr	7 46	1 3	4 14	7 8	...

Göding.............dep	6 a35	11a20	2 p56	5 p40	...	...
Holics (226).......arr	6 52	11 37	3 12	5 57	...	...

SAITZ and GODING.

Saitz............dep	...	8 a20	...	2 p50	...	6 p5
Czeitsch	5 a25	9 35	1225	3 40	6 p25	7 5
Mutenitz............	5 45	10 0	1245	3 59	6 50	—
Goding...(222) arr	6 5	10 20	1 5	4 18	7 10	...

Goding ....dep	...	6 a35	11a35	1 p38	4 p45	7 p55
Mutenitz	...	7 9	12 8	1 59	5 9	8 24
Czeitsch	4 a50	7 40	12 50	2 15	5 25	8 40
Saitz......(221) arr	5 55	8 40	1 50	...	...	...

Czeitsch dep	7a55	2 p25	7p15
Steinitz arr	9 35	4 5	8 55
Steinitz dep	5a45	10a23	4p32
Czeitsch arr	7 30	12 7	6 15

Mutenitz dep	7a10	12 p5	4p 0	8p25
Gaya 253 arr	8 10	1 5	5 1	9 25
Gaya ...dep	4a30	8a55	2p48	5p35
Mutenitz arr	5 25	9 50	3 41	6 35

KOJETEIN and TOBITSCHAU.

Kojetein.........dep	5 a0	6 a57	9 a28	1p55	7 p41
Tobitschau .....arr	5 31	7 26	9 57	2 24	8 10

Tobitschau ....dep	6 a3	7 a36	12p48	5 p22	8p25	...
Kojetein (221).........arr	6 34	8 5	1 19	5 52	8 55	...

BRANOWITZ and POHRLITZ.

Branowitz dep	4a50	7a42	10a20	3 p0	5p35	7p35
Pohrlitz ...arr	5 20	8 12	10 50	3 30	6 5	8 5

Pohrlitz ....dep	5a58	8 a46	1 p35	4p38	6p35	8p30	...
Branowitz 221 arr	6 28	9 16	2 5	5 8	7 5	9 0	...

STAUDING and STRAMBERG.

Stauding..............dep	5a20	7a50	11a43	5 p0	8 p55	...
Stramberg ....arr	6 35	9 0	12 50	6 7	9 59	...
Stramberg...........dep	4a53	9a24	1 p42	3p26	6 p44	...
Stauding..............arr	5 58	10 30	2 49	4 30	7 55	...

ZAUCHTEL and NEUTITSCHEIN.

Zauchtel......dep	3a20	6a30	8 a5	11a30	11a56	4 p0	4p50	6p20	8 p5	9p35	...
Neutitschein arr	3 44	6 54	8 29	11 54	12 20	4 24	5 14	6 44	8 29	9 59	...
Neutitschein...dep	1a50	5a25	7 15	9a55	1045	2 50	3 30	5 30	7 15	8 40	...
Zauchtel 221...arr	2 14	5 49	7 39	1019	11 9	3 14	3 54	5 54	7 39	9 4	...

Stramberg...........dep	9 a35	5 p38	...	...	...	...
Wernsdorf ....arr	9 57	6 0	...	...	...	...

Wernsdorf ....dep	12p10	7 p55	...	...	...	...	...	...
Stramberg ....arr	12 33	8 18	...	...	...	...	...	...

HOTZENDORF and NEUTITSCHEIN.

E.M						
	Hotzendorf dep	7 a0	11a55	3 p10	6 p7	9p35
6¾	Neutitschein arr	7 36	12 30	3 44	6 37	10 9

Neutitschein dep	5a15	9 a33	2 p0	4 p58	6p52	...
Hotzendorf arr	6 0	10 18	2 43	5 43	7 35	...

HULLEIN and ZBOROWITZ.

Hullein (222)dep	6 a5	8a24	3p28	6 p50	...	...
Kremsier ...dep	6 25	9 0	3 54	7 10	...	...
Zborowitz ...arr	7 23	10 5	4 57	8 12	...	...

Zborowitz ...dep	7a48	10a53	5p40	8 p34	...	...	...	...
Kremsier	8 39	11 55	6 28	9 27	11p26	...	...	...
Hullein.........arr	9 2	12 20	6 49	...	11 40	...	...	...

DROSING and ZISTERSDORF.

Drosing ....dep	6a40	9 a55	12p30	4 p25	8 p25
Zistersdorf ....arr	7 21	10 36	1 11	5 6	9 6

Zistersdorf ....dep	5 a27	8a25	11a12	2 p8	6 p10	...
Drosing (222) ......arr	6 5	9 3	11 50	2 46	6 48	...

ROHATETZ and STRASSNITZ.

Rohatetz ...dep	4a57	7 a50	11a25	4 p44	8 p14
Strassnitz...arr	5 35	8 30	12 5	5 25	8 p54

Strassnitz ....dep	5a50	10 a5	3 p23	6 p17	9 p14	...	...
Rohatetz (222) ...arr	6 28	10 48	4 2	6 55	9 52	...	...

ROHRBACH and GROSS SEELOWITZ.

Rohrboch ....dep	5a50	7a30	10a8	3p15	5p25	7p15
Gross Seelowitz ...arr	5 59	7 39	1017	3 24	5 34	7 24

Gross Seelowitz dep	6a35	9a16	1p40	4p12	6p10	7p50
Rohrbach (221) arr	6 45	9 26	1 50	4 22	6 20	8 0

KOLOZSVAR and NAGYBANYA (Szamosvolgyer Eisenbahn).

Dist	(Klausenburg)			a.m.		p.m.	p.m.
E M	Kolozsvar ...dep	...	...	7 48	...	2 30	5 45
7½	Apahida	...	...	8 9	...	2 53	6 9
27½	Szamosujvar	...	a.m.	9 10	...	4 5	7 19
36¼	Dees	...	6 0	9 52	...	4 45	7 43
74	Aranymezo	...	9 33	11 55	...	6 47	—
83¾	Zsibo	†	1030	1 3	†	7 24	...
99¼	Sülelmed	6 a0	—	2 12	8 p25	8 12	...
120½	Nagybanya ...arr	7 32	...	3 33	9 45	—	...

	a.m.		a.m.	a.m.		p.m.
Nagybanya...dep	4†27	...	...	9 40	...	6†34
Sülelmed............	5 34	...	5 48	11 3	p.m.	8 0
Zsibo	—	...	6 38	12 34	3 30	—
Aranymezo..............		a.m.	7 11	1 5	4 38	...
Dees		7 2	9 38	3 38	8 32	...
Szamosujvar............		7 34	10 8	4 4	—	...
Apahida		8 58	1118	5 15	...	...
Kolozsvar 233 ...arr		9 18	1138	5 34	...	...

†—Tuesday and Friday only.

Zsibo	7a10	1 p23
Zilah	8 10	2 22
Zilah	10a18	5p50
Zsibo	11 20	6 56

Dees ....dep	4 a50	10 a2	4p51	7 p58	...	...
Bethien	5 59	10 59	5 43	8 55	...	...
Sajo-Magyaros.........	7 33	11 40	6 25	9 38	...	...
Besztercze 233A	8 35	1 0	7 3	10 16	...	...
Borgó-Besztercze arr	10 25	2 24	...	...	...	...

Borgó Besztercz..dep	...	5 a50	...	...	3 p16	...	...	...	...
Besztercze	4 a42	7 20	7 a24	1 p6	5 28	...	...	...	...
Sajo-Magyaros............	5 18	—	7 58	1 41	6 24	...	...	...	...
Bethlen	6 0	...	8 33	2 22	7 38	...	...	...	...
Dees 323 ....arr	6 52	...	9 19	3 10	8 52	...	...	...	...

Sulelmed ....dep	11a20	2 p40	8p20	...	...	...
Szilagy ....arr	12 13	3 35	8 55	...	...	...

Szilagy ....dep	5a10	9 a30	12p50	...	...	...	...	...	...
Sulelmed ....arr	5 41	10 24	1 44	...	...	...	...	...	...

Bethlen.................dep	6 a44	11a19	9 p4	...	...	...
Oradna ....arr	9 36	3 51	11 46	...	...	...

Oradna ....dep	3 a10	10a36	4 p54	...	...	...	...	...	...
Bethlen ....arr	5 44	2 7	7 28	...	...	...	...	...	...

ESZEK and NOSKOVCI.

E.M							
	Eszek ...dep	6a49	8 a45	1p25	4 p0	7 p20	...
18	Belisce........	8 9	10 20	2 51	5 15	8 33	...
51	Noskovci ar	1019	12 45	5 1	7 31	...	...

Noskovci dep	...	7 a6	11 a5	2p27	5p40	...
Belisce	4a53	9 26	1 18	4 53	7 50	...
Eszek.....arr	6 7	1042	2 37	6 27	8 59	...

Belisce ....dep	8 a37
Prandauovci ....arr	9 30
Prandauovci..........dep	10a20
Belisce..................arr	11 16

MELNIK and ALT PAKA.

Melnik ....dep	...	...	...	9 a30	2 p0	...	4 p2	...	8p18
Lhotka	...	...	...	10 7	2 56	...	4 33	...	9 24
Mscheno	...	5a56	...	11 4	3 33	...	5 17	...	10 6
Sudomer-Skalsko	...	6 32	...	11 44	—	...	5 50	...	—
Jungbunzlau	4a45	7 20	10a4	12 35	...	4p44	6 32	9 p2	...
Unterbautzen ...	5 50	—	1049	1 55	...	5 40	—	9 53	...
Sobotka	6 7	...	1059	2 9	...	5 55	...	10 3	...
Libun	7 5	...	1133	3 0	...	6 37	...	—	...
Alt Paka ......arr	8 10	...	1220	5 20	...	8 12	...	...	...

Alt Paka......dep	...	...	5a37	...	11a22	...	1p20	6p15	...
Libun..................	...	a.m.	6 25	...	12 28	...	2 45	7 6	p.m.
Sobotka	...	5‡31	6 57	...	12 59	...	3 22	7 42	10*6
Unterbautzen	...	5 44	7 9	...	1 8	...	3 33	7 51	1016
Jungbunzlau	...	6 40	8 4	10a46	1 53	...	4 32	8 52	11 8
Sudomer-Skalsko	...	—	—	11 37	—	...	5 46	9 44	—
Mscheno	5a11	...	...	12 22	...	3p56	6 21	1018	...
Lhotka	6 6	...	...	1 1	...	4 31	6 56	—	...
Melnik (224) arr	6 30	...	...	1 25	...	4 54	7 18	...	...

*—Monday and Thursday excepted. ‡—Tuesdays and Fridays only.

Lhotka ...dep	5a44	2p29	8p52
Strednitz arr	5 52	2 41	9 5
Strednitz dep	5a58	2p43	9p10
Lhotka......arr	6 5	2 50	9 18

Sudomer-Skalsko...dep	6a50	6p 2
Unter Cetno...........arr	7 10	6 18
Unter Cetno...dep	10a24	8p43
Sudomer-Skal.arr	10 44	8 59

DEUTSCHBROD and BRUNN.

Deutschbrod dep	...	...	7 a40	2p16	6p20	**Brünn** ... dep	...	6 a39	11a58	5 p17	8p15
Pribislau	...	...	8 23	2 55	7 0	Tischnowitz	...	8 10	1 27	6 47	9 38
Saar in Mähren	...	5a30	9 30	3 45	7 58	Bystritz	4 a5	9 41	2 43	8 6	—
Bystritz	...	6 39	10 58	4 57	9 19	Saar	5 21	11 2	3 55	9 16	...
Tischnowitz	6a10	8 5	12 20	6 14	...	Pribislau	5 59	11 39	4 33	—	...
Brünn ... arr	7 38	9 27	1 44	7 45	...	**Deutschbrod** ... arr	6 32	12 13	5 9	...	...

WEISSBACH and RASPENAU.

Weissbach	6a37	8a17	10 a7	1p35	3p19	5p19	7p28	...	...	Raspenau ...	7a24	8a57	10a52	2 p17	4 p5	6 p10	8p30	...	...	...
Raspenau...	7 0	8 39	10 30	1 57	3 50	5 45	7 50	...	...	Weissbach...	7 54	9 19	11 20	2 41	4 26	6 31	8 51	...	...	...

FRIEDLAND and HERMSDORF.

Friedland dep	7a26	9 a45	2 p25	5p19	8 p23	...	Hermsdorf dep	6 a10	8a17	12p53	3p21	6p46	...
Hermsdorf arr	8 1	10 20	2 59	5 54	8 58	...	Friedland ...arr	6 45	8 52	1 27	3 55	7 21	...

JICIN and TURNAU.

Jicin......dep	4a‡25	7 a41	1p56	7p55	...	‡—4.0 a.m. on	Turnau......dep	6 a10	11a16	5 p25	9p40
Turnau......arr	5 45	9 15	3 56	9 13	...	Monday.	Jicin.........arr	7 34	1 2	7 30	11 0

DEUTSCHBROD and SEIDENBERG.

		Ex3	1,2,3	2&3	1,2,3	1,2,3	1,2,3	2&3	1,2,3
			a.m.		a.m.	a.m.	p.m.		p.m.
Deutschbrod ...dep		...	3 5	...	6 59	9 59	2 10	...	6 10
Chotebor		...	3 33	...	7 27	1029	2 38	...	6 40
Hlinsko		...	4 6	...	8 2	11 4	3 13	...	7 18
Skutsch		...	4 27	a.m.	8 23	1126	3 33	p.m.	7 39
Chrast		...	4 48	6 23	8 42	1146	3 53	5 52	7 58
Chrudim		...	5 9	6 46	9 0	12 7	4 17	6 16	8 20
Rossitz ......arr		...	5 28	7 7	9 19	1226	4 36	6 37	8 39
Pardubitz......arr		...	5 52	7 16	9 28	1235	4 45	6 46	8 52
" ......dep		...	5 30	—	9 52	1 35	4 56	—	8 33
Rossitz ......dep		...	5 40	...	9 58	1 40	5 1	...	8 46
Koniggratz arr	a.m.	...	6 6	...	10 25	2 6	5 27	...	9 12
" dep	3 10	...	6 12	...	10 33	2 20	5 42	...	9 27
Smiritz (255) ...	3 26	...	6 31	...	10 53	2 39	6 1	...	9 46
Josefstadt...arr	3 37	...	6 42	...	11 4	2 50	6 12	...	9 57
" ...dep	3 44	...	6 50	...	11 13	3 9	6 17	...	10 12
Königinhof......	4 9	...	7 18	...	11 40	3 29	6 45	...	10 41
Falgendorf	4 50	...	7 58	...	12 19	4 3	7 26	...	11 21
Alt-Paka ...arr	4 59	...	8 7	...	12 28	4 12	7 35	...	11 30
" (225) dep	5 35	...	8 22	...	12 47	4 17	7 59	...	11 50
Eisenbrod (225)	6 12	...	9 0	1,2,3	1 25	4 51	8 38	Ex3	12 33
Turnau (249) arr	6 31	a.m.	9 19	a.m.	1 44	5 10	8 58	p.m.	12 55
" dep	6 39	8 29	9 26	1128	1 57	5 18	9 24	8 38	1 50
Liebenau	7 2	8 47	9 47	1149	2 18	5 39	9 45	...	2 11
Reichenau	7 17	8 56	9 57	1159	2 32	5 49	10 0	9 3	2 20
Reichenberg arr	7 43	9 16	1019	1230	2 58	6 11	1026	9 24	2 46
" (184) dep	8 16	—	1113	1 29	3 24	7 22	1036	—	5 19
Habendorf	8 22	...	1119	1 35	3 30	7 28	1042	...	5 25
Raspenau	8 53	...	1148	2 6	4 0	8 2	1111	...	5 55
Friedland........	9 3	...	1156	2 16	4 9	8 16	1119	...	6 3
Seidenberg arr	9 28	...	1220	2 41	4 34	8 41	1144	...	6 28
GORLITZ arr	10a20	...	1259	3p22	5 p18	9p27	1230	...	7a12

	123	1,2,3	1,2,3	Ex3	1,2,3	1,2,3	1,2,3	1,2,3	1,2,3	1,2,3
GORLITZ 180 dp	...	...	4a17	...	5 a45	9 a10	...	1240	4p46	7p 6
			a.m.		a.m.	a.m.		p.m.	p.m.	p.m.
Seidenb'g dep	...	...	4 56	...	6 30	9 58	...	1 27	5 30	7 49
Friedland	...	...	5 17	...	6 58	10 26	...	1 56	5 58	8 17
Raspenau	...	...	5 25	...	7 6	10 35	...	2 5	6 8	8 26
Habendorf......	...	...	5 49	...	7 36	11 5	...	2 35	6 38	8 56
Reichen- arr	...	a.m.	5 55	a.m.	7 42	11 11	p.m.	2 41	6 44	9 2
berg ......dep	...	2 48	6 11	6 55	8 22	11 58	2 0	4 2	7 ‡0	9 30
Reichenau......	...	3 20	6 35	7 17	8 58	12 28	2 33	4 34	7 22	10 0
Liebenau	...	3 30	6 44	...	9 7	12 37	2 42	4 43	7 31	10 9
Turnau......arr	...	3 48	7 2	7 40	9 25	12 55	3 0	5 1	7 47	1027
" ......dep	...	3 58	7 6	—	9 33	12 58	—	5 11	8 37	1028
Eisenbrod	...	4 21	7 27	...	9 57	1 22	...	5 34	9 0	1050
Alt-Paka ...arr	...	4 58	8 0	...	10 35	1 55	...	6 10	9 35	1123
" ...dep	...	5 30	8 17	...	11 7	1 58	...	6 36	—	1131
Falgendorf ...	...	5 44	8 29	...	11 19	2 9	...	6 48		1143
Königinhof ...	...	6 22	9 5	...	11 59	2 40	...	7 26	‡—Ex 3.	1221
Josefstadt arr	am	6 45	9 28	...	12 22	2 58	...	7 49		1241
" dep	521	6 54	9 38	...	12 30	3 12	...	8 15		1248
Smiritz..........	538	7 5	9 49	...	12 42	3 23	...	8 27		1259
Konig- arr	6 0	7 23	10 4	...	1 0	3 41	p.m.	8 45		1 14
gratz dep	—	7 34	1010	...	1 12	3 51	5 11	8 56	...	—
Rossitz .....arr	...	8 0	1036	...	1 38	4 17	5 33	9 23	1,2,3	2&3
Pardubitz arr	...	8 5	1041	...	1 45	4 22	5 46	9 28	a.m.	a.m.
" dep	...	10 1	1117	...	2 8	—	5 29	9 46	3 58	5 13
Rossitz.....dep	...	1010	1127	...	2 17	...	5 40	10 0	4 7	5 29
Chrudim	...	1033	1150	...	2 40	...	6 1	1026	4 28	5 52
Chrast...........	...	1054	1213	...	3 1	...	6 21	1047	4 48	6 14
Skutsch	...	1124	—	...	3 33	...	6 50	1115	5 17	—
Hlinsko	...	1154	...	...	4 7	...	7 19	1145	5 45	...
Chotebor.........	...	1224	...	...	4 37	...	7 49	1214	6 15	...
Deutschbrod ..	...	1248	...	...	5 1	...	8 13	1235	6 39	...

Extra.—Turnau to Eisenbrod, 11.15 a.m., Chrudim to Pardubitz, 9.45 a.m., 9.38 p.m., Pardubitz to Chrudim, 8.28 a.m., 7.29 p.m. Josefstadt to Königgratz 5.12p.m.

SEDLETZ-KUTTENBERG and KUTTENBERG STADT.

Sedletz-Kuttenberg dep	6a47	8a26	9 a58	11a23	1p21	2p21	4 p2	6p31	8p20	9p15	11 p7	...	...	...	
Kuttenberg Stadt ...arr	7 0	8 39	10 11	11 36	1 34	2 34	4 15	6 44	8 33	9 28	11 20	...	...	...	
Kuttenberg Stadt ...dep	6 a23	8 a0	9a35	10a53	1 p0	1p38	3p15	6 p8	7p27	8p52	10p42	...	...	...	...
Sedletz-Kuttenberg arr	6 36	8 13	9 48	11 6	1 13	1 51	3 28	6 21	7 40	9 5	10 55	...	...	...	...

KUTTENBERG STADT and ZRUC.

Kuttenberg Stadt....dep	8 a43	12p32	4 p30	Zruc..........dep	5 a55	1 p7	5 p12
Zruc..........arr	10 33	2 24	6 29	Kuttenberg Stadt...arr	7 40	3 0	6 51

STARKENBACH and ROCHLITZ.

Starkenbach ...dep	6 a9	8 a0	12p15	6p40	...	Rochlitz ......dep	6a58	10 a5	3 p40	8 p30	...	...
Rochlitz ....arr	6 53	9 23	2 5	7 55	...	Starkenbach arr	7 41	11 27	5 28	10 0	...	...

ZELLERNDORF and SIGMUNDSHERBERG.

E.M.											
	Zellerndorf......dep	6 a0	9 a7	1p20	7 p6	Sigmundsherberg	3a54	7 a23	11a30	4 p11	7 p9
6¾	Pulkau..........	6 23	9 35	1 48	7 38	Pulkau	4 17	7 48	11 53	4 35	7 34
12½	Sigmundsherberg.	6 50	9 57	2 10	8 0	Zellerndorf ....arr	4 43	8 14	12 19	5 2	8 0

GROSS PRIESEN and WERNSTADT.

Gross Priesen ....dep	7 a10	6 p0	...	Wernstadt..........dep	5 a5	3 p30	...
Loschowitz..........arr	7 48	6 40	...	Auscha ....dep	5 5	3 25	...
Auscha ....arr	8 25	7 22	...	Loschowitz..........dep	5 40	4 10	...
Wernstadt ....arr	8 25	7 12	...	Gross Priesen (224)......arr	6 18	4 50	...

CASLAU and ZAWRATETZ.

‡—1.38 p.m. on Sun.

Dist		a.m.	a.m.	p.m.	p.m.	p.m.		a.m.	p.m.	p.m.	p.m.
—	Caslau (224)...........dep	6 10	11 38	...	4‡25	9 30	Zawratetz-Trem....dep	6 30	1 45	6 50	...
3¾	Skowitz ....arr	6 34	12 2	2 46	4 49	9 54	Skowitz ....arr	7 18	2 39	7 48	...
5½	Wrdy-Butschitz...arr	6 49	12 17	2 57	5 6	10 9	Wrdy-Butschitz ...arr	7 36	2 57	...	...
...	Wrdy-Butschitz...dep	—	11 48	—	4 36	9 40	Wrdy-Butschitz...dep	7 6	2 28	4 36	10 14
...	Skowitz..........dep	...	12 5	...	4 51	9 56	Skowitz..........dep	7 20	2 42	7 50	10 28
10½	Zawratetz-T. ....arr	...	12 56	...	5 50	1045	Caslau..........arr	7 43	3 5	8 13	10 51

DEUTSCHBROD and HUMPOLETZ.

Deutschbrod ....dep	7 a15	2 p15	6 p10	...	...	...	Humpoletz ....dep	5 a22	11a32	3 p54	...	...	...	...
Humpoletz ....arr	8 32	3 28	7 27	...	...	...	Deutschbrod ....arr	6 42	12 52	5 13	...	...	...	...

CASTOLOWITZ and SOLNITZ.

Castolowitz .... dep	5 a35	9 a10	3 p14	7 p0	10p11	...	Solnitz..........dep	4 a18	7 a18	11a17	4 p18	8 p42	...	...
Solnitz ....arr	6 29	9 55	4 3	7 48	10 56	...	Castolowitz (225)......arr	5 0	8 10	12 8	5 1	9 33	...	...

VIENNA, DEUTSCHBROD, NIMBURG, JUNGBUNZLAU, AUSSIG and TETSCHEN.

THROUGH CARRIAGES from Vienna to Dresden and Berlin—in 8.50 a.m. and 9.40 p.m. from Vienna. RC—Restaurant Car. SC—Sleeping Car.

		1,2,3	1,2,3	2&3	1,2,3	Ex.3	Ex3	1,2,3	1,2,3	1,2,3	1,2,3	Ex3	1,2,3	Ex 3
					a.m.	a.m.	p.m.	p.m.	a.m	p.m.	p.m.	p.m.	p.m.	p.m.
Vienna Nord-westbahnhof dep		...	...	...	7 10	8 50	1 22	1 48	11 15	4 55	5 40	8 20	8 50	9 40
Korneuburg		...	...	...	7 30	RC	...	2 21	...	...	7 10	...	9 10	A
Stockerau		...	...	...	7 44	...	...	2 42	11 49	5 29	7 24	SC	9 23	...
Oberhollabrunn		...	...	...	8 22	9 37	2 13	3 26	12 29	6 10	8 6	...	9 54	...
Zellerndorf arr		...	...	a.m.	8 51	...	...	3 53	12 58	6 37	8 46	...	10 23	SC
" 223A dep		...	...	6 24	8 56	...	...	3 56	1 6	6 39	8 48	...	10 24	...
Retz		...	...	6 47	9 7	...	2 42	4 6	1 18	6 51	8 59	...	10 34	...
Znaim arr		...	a.m.	7 36	9 31	10 28	3 1	4 30	1 46	7 15	9 23	9 52	10 58	11 16
" 252 dep		a.m.	6 23	—	9 51	10 33	3 6	4 56	2 15	7 53	—	9 57	11 8	11 22
Mährisch Budwitz		2 53	7 18	1,2,3	1051	11 24	3 48	7 5	3 18	9 0	...	...	12 23	...
Startsch-Trebitsch		4 3	7 48	a.m.	1122	...	...	8 14	3 49	9 31	2&3	...	12 54	...
Okrisko 252		4 21	7 59	7 6	1140	12 4	4 22	8 32	4 7	9 50	p.m	...	1 12	...
Iglau 239B		6 10	8 50	7 40	1 25	12 37	4 56	—	5 6	10 25	1054	1146	1 48	1 21
Polna		6 23	9 4	—	1 38	...	...	...	5 19	—	1118	...	2 19	...
Deutschbrod arr		6 48	9 30	...	2 3	1 2	5 20	...	5 48	—	1158	1211	2 39	1 46
" 223A dep		6 52	9 38	...	2 13	1 8	5 23	...	6 5	...	—	1216	2 49	1 52
Swetla		7 12	10 0	Ex3	2 34	1 25	...	...	6 28	...	1,2,3	...	3 19	...
Goltsch Jenikau		7 51	1046	p.m	3 13	1 55	...	p.m.	7 11	...	a.m.	...	4 4	...
Cáslau 223A		8 6	11 5	1 45	3 30	2 7	6 17	4 18	7 26	...	6 30	...	4 16	2 51
Sedletz-Kutt		8 19	1119	1 56	3 46	2 18	6 28	4 31	7 48	...	6 43	...	4 29	3 2
Kolin 252 arr		8 30	1132	2 7	3 57	2 29	6 38	4 44	8 3	...	6 55	...	4 40	3 13
" dep	Ex3	8 36	1141	2 10	4 4	2 30	6 42	4 52	8 14	Ex 3	5 58	...	4 43	3 14
Gr. Wossek arr	a.m.	8 45	1150	2 19	4 13	2 39	6 51	5 1	8 23	p.m.	7 7	1 35	4 52	3 23
" 225 dep	7 16	9 2	12 3	2 30	4 23	2 47	6 58	5 15	8 48	6 48	7 23	1 40	4 58	3 28
Podebrad	7 27	9 16	1217	2 41	4 36	B	7 9	5 29	9 2	6 59	7 36		5 11	...
Nimburg arr	7 36	9 29	1226	2 50	4 45	3 2	7 18	5 42	9 15	7 8	7 48		5 20	3 43
Nimburg dep	8 23	...	1240	...	4 58	3 10	7 19	...	10 0	7 19	—		6 14	4 2
Jungbunzlau	9 17	...	1 30	...	6 27	3 44	7 49	...	10 41	7 49	...		7 9	4 41
	a.m.	a.m.	p.m.	p.m.	p.m.	p.m.	—	p.m.	p.m.	p.m	a.m.		a.m.	a.m.
Nimburg dep	7 38	9 39	1233	2 52	4 54	3 5	...	5 51	9 20	7 9	...		5 23	3 44
Lissa arr	7 53	10 0	1252	3 7	5 11	3 19	...	6 10	9 39	7 24	...		5 40	3 58
PRAGUE 225	8a36	11a19	1p57	3p50	6p15	4p15	...	7p25	10p40	8 p11	...		6a38	5 a30
Lissa dep	—	—	1 6	—	6 29	3 22	...	—	—	—	4 8		8 10	3 59
Alt-Bunzlau		...	1 21	...	6 44	...	...	...	...	...	4 23		8 26	...
Vsetat-Priv. arr		...	1 36	1,2,3	6 59	3 43	...	...	...	...	4 38	2 29	8 43	...
PRAGUE dep		...	12 2	2p 3	6p18	2 p43	...	...	...	...	...	1a36	7 a30	...
Vsetat-Priv dep		...	1 44	3 56	7 14	3 47	...	...	...	...	4 39	2 36	9 10	...
Melnik 223		...	1 59	4 10	7 27	3 59	...	...	...	...	4 53	...	9 25	...
Leitmeritz		...	2 56	6 40	8 17	4 35	...	...	...	...	5 51	3 22	10 21	5 2
Schreckenst'n arr		...	3 27	7 22	8 52	4 57	...	...	...	...	6 34	3 44	11 1	5 24
Aussig arr		...	3 48	7 36	9 5	5 8	...	...	...	...	6 55	3 55	11 21	5 40
Aussig dep		...	3 17	7 11	9 19	4 45	...	...	...	...	6 22	...	10 41	5 10
Schreckenst'n dep		...	3 37	7 27	9 30	4 58	...	...	...	...	6 45	3 46	11 11	5 26
Gr. Priesen		...	3 49	7 44	9 42	5 8	...	...	...	...	7 3	...	11 25	...
Tetschen ¶ arr		...	4 14	8 20	10 4	5 25	...	...	...	...	7 39	4 10	11 50	5 50
DRESDEN (Hpt) ar		...	6p23	11p2	12a9	6p53	...	...	...	...	1048	5a26	1 p40	7 a8
BERLIN 189 arr		...	1026	...	...	10p26	...	...	...	...	...	8 a8	5 p1	10a20

		1,2,3	1,2,3	Ex3	1,2,3	1,2,3	Ex3	Ex.3	1,2,3	Ex3	1,2,3	1,2,3	1,2,3	Ex 3	Ex 3
BERLIN 188 dep		...	...	...	...	...	...	8 a5	...	...	...	...	...	6 p45	8 p10
DRESDEN (Hpt) "		...	...	...	...	7 a10	...	11a30	10a1	...	...	2 p22	...	9 p55	10p53
			a.m.		a.m.	a.m.		p m.	p.m.			p.m.	p.m.	p.m.	nght
Tetschen ¶ dep		...	4 15	...	6 4	8 44	...	1 0	1222	...	...	5 5	9 20	11 15	12 9
Gr. Priesen		...	4 40	...	6 29	9 8	...	RC	1 0	...	...	5 30	10 0	A	SC
Schreckenst'n arr		...	4 53	...	6 42	9 21	...	1 26	1 15	...	...	5 43	10 15	11 41	12 35
Aussig arr		...	5 4	...	6 55	9 30	...	1 39	1 39	...	...	6 4	10 28	11 58	12 45
Aussig dep		...	4 42	...	6 22	9 5	...	1 12	1 12	...	...	5 43	10 2	11 32	12 23
Schreckenst'n dep		...	5 1	...	6 54	9 26	...	1 28	1 36	...	...	5 58	10 18	11 47	12 36
Leitmeritz		...	5 39	...	7 29	9 59	...	1 51	2 14	...	...	6 34	11 6	12 10	12 59
Melnik		...	6 37	...	8 36	10 57	...	2 27	3 14	...	...	7 32	—		...
Vsetat-Priv. arr		...	6 49	...	8 48	11 9	...	2 37	3 26	...	...	7 44	...		1 43
PRAGUE 249 arr		...	8a50	...	9 a57	12p50	...	3 p49	4p43	...	...	9 p5	...		2 a41
Vsetat-Priv dep		...	6 53	...	9 10	11 12	...	2 40	3 39	...	...	8 0	...		1 46
Alt-Bunzlau		...	7 9	...	9 26	11 28	...	...	3 55	...	...	8 16	1,2,3		...
Lissa arr		...	7 23	...	9 37	11 42	p.m.	3 1	4 9	p.m	p.m.	8 30	p.m.		...
PRAGUE dep		...	7 47	...	8 45	10 50	2 0	2 p0	4p10	6 18	6 33	8 p30	11 30		...
Lissa dep		...	7 48	...	9 46	11 57	2 40	3 2	5 47	6 59	7 32	9 31	12 28		...
Nimburg arr		...	8 3	a.m.	10 3	12 16	2 55	3 16	6 6	7 14	7 51	9 48	12 47	1 27	...
Jungbunzl dep		...	6 46	8 26	...	10 55	2 10	2 10	4 56	...	...	8 50	11 40	11 40	...
Nimburg		a.m.	7 31	8 58	...	11 54	2 44	2 44	5 44	...	...	9 34	12 30	12 30	...
Nimburg dep	6 40	4 25	8 4	9 0	10 10	12 21	3 0	3 17	6 14	7 15	8 0	9 58	12 57	1 28	...
Podebrad	6 54	4 34	8 13	9 9	10 20	12 36	3 9	C	6 27	7 24	8 15	10 6	1 9	...	...
Gr. Wossek arr	7 6	4 45	8 22	9 17	10 31	12 48	3 18	3 31	6 39	7 33	8 27	10 17	1 21	1 42	2 32
Gr. Wossek dep	7 20	4 50	—	9 22	10 38	12 52	3 26	3 36	—	7‡45	8 36	10 27	—	1 49	2 39
Kolin arr	7 30	4 59	...	9 31	10 47	1 1	3 35	3 45	...	7 54	8 45	10 36	...	1 58	...
" dep	7 40	5 2	...	9 43	10 55	1 3	3 37	3 46	1,2,3	7 58	8 56	10 46	...	1 59	...
Sedletz-Kutt.	7 56	5 17	...	9 55	11 12	1 18	3 50	3 58	p.m.	8 13	9 11	11 4	...	2 11	...
Cáslau	8 10	5 32	...	10 6	11 28	1 31	4 0	4 11	4 22	8 28	9 24	11 23	...	2 23	...
Goltsch-Jenik.	—	5 50	...	...	11 46	—	—	4 28	4 40	8 52		11 43	...	...	...
Swetla		6 31	...	...	12 30	...	...	...	5 21	9 27	...	12 33	...	...	...
Deutschbrod arr		6 50	...	11 4	12 49	...	...	5 17	5 43	9 46	...	12 52	...	3 27	4 8
" dep		6 56	...	11 5	1 11	...	...	5 25	5 50	9 50	...	1 6	...	3 33	4 13
Polna	a.m.	7 22	p.m.	...	1 39	...	...	...	6 17	1016	...	1 31	...	...	...
Iglau	5 25	8 34	1 24	1135	2 10	...	...	5 55	6 46	1028	...	1 56	...	4 0	4 40
Okrisko	6 3	9 18	1 59	12 4	2 55	...	...	6 28	7 24	—	...	2 36	...	4 30	...
Startsch-Treb.	6 15	9 30	—	...	3 7	...	...	...	7 36	...	...	2 48	...	...	...
Mährisch Bud.	6 47	10 8	...	1237	3 48	...	1,2,3	7 5	8 6	...	2&3	3 19	...	...	...
Znaim arr	7 35	11 8	...	1 16	4 36	...	p.m.	7 47	8 55	...	p.m.	4 4	a.m.	5 43	6 22
" dep	7 45	1142	...	1 22	4 55	...	7 34	7 52	—	...	1117	4 14	5 12	5 49	6 27
Retz	8 10	1211	...	1 42	5 24	...	7 59	...	...	...	12 8	4 39	5 37	...	...
Zellerndorf	8 18	1220	...	...	5 33	...	8 7	...	...	...	1223	4 47	5 45	...	...
" dep	8 22	1228	...	...	5 41	...	8 8	...	...	...	1245	4 48	5 47	...	...
Oberhollabrn	8 51	1 0	...	2 13	6 11	...	9 6	8 44	...	...	1 45	5 16	6 16	...	...
Stockerau	9 34	1 42	...	...	6 51	...	9 50	...	...	...	2 50	5 46	7 4	...	...
Korneuburg	...	...	...	...	...	...	10 5	...	...	...	3 14	5 58	7 18	...	...
Vienna arr	10 3	2 12	...	3 0	7 20	...	1037	9 36	...	...	4 0	6 17	7 47	7 22	8 0

A—Admits 3rd class passengers travelling not less than 78 miles. | B—From Cáslau to Lissa only admits passengers for stations beyond Lissa. | C—Between Lissa and Cáslau will only take up for beyond Cáslau. | ‡—1,2,3 class. | ¶—Customs Examinations.

Extra. Lissa dep 7a35, Gr.-Wossek arr 8 38 | Gr.-Wossek dep 3a37, Lissa arr 4 25

JOSEFSTADT and LIEBAU.

Dist E.M.		1,2,3	1,2,3	1,2,3	1,2,3	1,2,3	1,2,3	1,2,3	
			a.m.	a.m.		p.m.	p.m.	p.m.	
—	**Josefstadt** ......dep	...	7 30	11 15	...	3 14	6 19	10 9	...
8	Böhm. Skalitz	...	7 52	11 36	...	3 29	6 40	10 30	...
11¾	Starkotsch	...	8 7	11 48	...	3 41	6 53	10 43	...
22¼	Schwadowitz	...	8 38	12 17	...	4 8	7 23	11 13	...
29¾	**Parschnitz** ......arr	a.m.	8 53	12 32	p.m	4 21	7 38	11 28	...
...	,, ...dep	6 0	10 53	12 36	3 30	4 42	7 44	11 32	...
38	Königshan	6 25	11 18	1 0	3 49	5 7	8 9	11 57	...
41	Liebau (182) ......arr	6 31	11 24	1 7	3 55	5 13	8 15	12 3	...

	1,2,3	1,2,3	1,2,3	1,2,3	1,2,3	1,2,3	1,2,3	
	a.m.	a.m.	a.m.	p.m.	p.m.	p.m.	p.m.	
Liebau ....dep	4 1	7 29	10 25	1 21	2 38	6 3	10 35	...
Königshan 225	4 28	7 36	10 32	1 28	2 45	6 11	10 42	...
Parschnitz ......arr	5 2	7 56	10 52	1 48	3 0	6 32	11 2	...
,, ...dep	5 17	8 21	10 57	1 53	—	6 38	—	...
Schwadowitz	5 34	8 37	11 15	2 9	...	6 56	...	...
Starkotsch	6 4	9 1	11 47	2 34	...	7 27	...	...
Böhm. Skalitz........	6 13	9 10	11 56	2 43	...	7 38	...	...
Josefstadt ......arr	6 33	9 25	12 16	3 3	...	7 58	...	...

SCHATZLAR and KONIGSHAN.

Schatzlar ...dep	7a10	10a1	12p36	5 p36
Königshan...arr	7 30	1020	12 55	5 55

Königshan...dep	8 a0	11a50	1p32	5 p8	8p10
Schatzlar......arr	8 22	12 12	1 54	5 29	8 31

CHLUMETZ and PARSCHNITZ.

Prague (225) dep	...	11p30	...	6a22	10a50	2 p0	6 p18
		a.m.	a.m.	a.m.	p.m.	p.m.	p.m.
Chlumetz ....dep	...	4 5	6 48	9 30	1 50	4 35	8 17
Neu-Bidschow..........	...	4 21	7 4	9 47	2 3	4 52	8 34
Smidar	...	4 29	7 12	9 55	2 11	5 0	8 42
Wostromer	...	4 46	7 28	10 13	2 25	5 16	8 59
Belohrad	...	5 1	7 43	10 28	2 38	5 31	9 14
Alt-Paka ....arr	...	5 24	8 6	10 51	3 2	5 55	9 37
,, (223A)...dep	...	5 40	8 25	11 7	3 10	6 19	9 46
Starkenbach.............	...	6 9	8 51	11 37	3 30	6 39	10 14
Pelsdorf	...	6 23	9 4	11 53	3 41	6 50	10 29
Arnau	...	6 37	9 17	12 7	3 54	7 3	10 43
Trautenau.........arr	a.m.	7 5	9 45	12 35	4 18	7 27	11 11
,, (252A)...dep	5 5	8 12	1040	1 35	4 30	7 32	11 16
Parschnitz.........arr	5 12	8 18	1047	1 42	4 37	7 39	11 23
Liebau (225) ...arr	6a31	...	1124	3p55	5p13	8p15	12 a3

Liebau ...dep	...	4 a1	10a25	...	1p21	2p38	6 p3	6 p3	10.35
(225)	a.m.	a.m.	a.m.	p.m.	p.m.	p.m.	p.m.	p.m.	p.m.
Parschnitz dep	...	5 13	10 59	1240	1 54	4 23	6 39	7 40	11 36
Trautenau...arr	...	5 24	11 6	1247	2 0	4 29	6 46	7 46	11 42
,, ...dep	3 24	6 32	11 16	—	2 4	4 39	—	9 48	—
Arnau..................	3 53	7 5	11 39	...	2 27	5 8	...	10 16	...
Pelsdorf..............	4 9	7 23	11 54	...	2 40	5 25	...	10 32	...
Starkenbach.........	4 27	7 43	12 6	...	2 52	5 42	...	10 49	...
Alt-Paka ......arr	4 50	8 8	12 24	...	3 9	6 5	...	11 12	...
,, ...dep	5 10	9 29	12 33	...	3 14	6 20	...	11 35	...
Belohrad	5 32	9 50	12 54	...	3 35	6 41	...	11 56	...
Wostromer	5 50	10 10	1 6	...	3 47	6 59	...	12 13	...
Smidar	6 5	10 24	1 18	...	3 59	7 13	...	12 27	...
Neu-Bidschow......	6 15	10 32	1 26	...	4 7	7 24	...	12 37	...
Chlumetz ...arr	6 30	10 47	1 38	...	4 20	7 39	...	12 52	...
Prague (225)	8a36	1p57	3p50	...	7p25	10p40	...	5 a30	...

Extra.—Trautenau to Parschnitz, 5.45 a.m., 12.22, 3.17, 6.23 p.m. Parschnitz to Trautenau, 7.22, 8.2, 8.58 a.m., 3.6, 11.8p.m.

WOSTROMER and JICIN.

E.M.								
	Wostromer	5a55	7a42	10a20	2p25	5p16	7 p3	9 p5
10½	**Jicin** ...(255)	6 32	8 19	10 57	3 2	5 53	7 40	9 46

Jicin	5 a0	6a44	9a15	12p25	3 p4	4p25	8p18
Wostromer	5 36	7 20	9 51	1 1	3 40	5 4	8 54

PELSDORF and HOHENELBE.

Pelsdorf ...	4a20	6a32	7a30	9a19	12 0	2p45	3p45	5p35	6p55	10p37
Hohenelbe	4 34	6 46	7 44	9 33	12 14	3 2	4 2	5 49	7 8	10 51

Hohenelbe	3a47	5a58	6a58	8 a41	11a23	2p15	3p16	5 p2	6 p28	9 p58
Pelsdorf ...	4 1	6 12	7 12	8 55	11 37	2 33	3 30	5 16	6 42	10 12

EISENBROD and TANNWALD.

Eisenbrod dep	7 a28	11a47	1p49	5p50	9 p0	...
Tannwald...arr	8 24	12 43	2 36	6 46	9 56	...

Tannwald dep	5a12	8 a1	12p20	3 p22	7p30	...
Eisenbrod arr	6 4	8 54	1 10	4 14	8 22	...

TRAUTENAU and FREIHEIT-JOHANNISBAD.

Trautenau dep	5a27	7a14	8a15	11a45	1 p5	2p10	4p44	6p52	8 p9	11p45
Freiheit-Jnsb.a	5 54	7 42	8 46	12 12	1 32	2 37	5 11	7 19	8 36	12 12

Freiheit-J.	2a54	6 a3	7a13	10a0	11a46	2p49	5p46	6p48	8p37	9p15
Trautenau	3 17	6 26	7 45	1023	12 11	3 12	6 9	7 22	9 0	9 38

REICHENBERG and GRÜNTHAL.

Reichenberg dp	6a10	8a20	11a20	1 p3	3p48	7p17	9p40
Gablonz............	7 5	9 14	12 7	1 55	4 38	8 11	1019
Morchenstern ...	7 36	9 46	—	2 29	5 9	8 46	—
Tannwald.........	8 29	1016	...	3 0	5 39	9 18	...
Grünthal ...arr	9 8	1056	...	3 39	6 18	9 57	...

Grünthal...dep	...	5a32	9a25	...	12p27	3p52	6p43	...
Tannwald	4a59	6 23	10 9	...	1 11	4 36	7 26	...
Morchenstern	5 29	6 55	1041	p.m	1 44	5 10	8 1	p.m.
Gablonz	6 2	7 28	1111	1242	2 20	5 42	8 38	1051
Reichenberg...	6 38	8 7	1148	1 12	2 57	6 20	9 17	1125

Morchenstern.........dep	7a42	2 p34	5 p22	8 p52	...
Josefsthal-Maxdorf arr	8 4	2 56	5 44	9 13	...

Josefsthal-Maxdorf...dep	6 a16	1p15	4 p36	7 p15	...
Morchenstern ....arr	6 40	1 38	5 0	7 39	...

§—From or at Prague Franz-Jos. Bhf. **PRAGUE and GEIERSBERG.** **Extra.**—Nimburg to Prague, 6.0 a.m.

		1,2,3	Ex3	1,2,3	1,2,3	Ex3	1,2,3	Ex3	1,2,3	1,2,3	1,2,3
Prague		a.m.	a.m.	a.m.	a.m.	p.m.	p.m.	p.m.	p.m.	p.m	p.m.
(N.West) dep		6 22	7 §7	8 45	1050	2 0	4 40	6 18	6 33	8 30	1130
Vysotschan......		6 39	⋮	9 0	11 6	...	4 56	...	6 47	8 45	1143
Celakowitz......		7 11	⋮	9 29	1139	...	5 31	...	7 16	9 16	1215
Lissa....arr	1,2,3	7 21	7 47	9 38	1149	2 39	5 41	6 58	7 25	9 25	1225
,, ...dep	a.m.	7 35	7 48	9 45	1157	2 40	5 47	6 59	7 32	9 31	1228
Nimburg	4 25	8 11	8 4	1010	1221	3 0	6 14	7 15	8 0	9 56	1257
Podebrad	4 34	8 26	8 13	1020	1236	3 9	6 27	7 24	8 15	10 6	1 9
Gr. Wossek	4 45	8 38	8 22	1031	1248	3 18	6 39	7 33	8 27	1017	1 21
,, dep	5 58	8 49	8 27	—	1257	3 42	7 1	7 42	—	—	1 45
Chlumetz	6 34	9 21	...	...	1 30	4 16	7 37	8 8	2&3	...	2 15
Konig'ätz	7 19	10 0	9 19	...	2 10	5 2	8 28	8 38	p.m.	p.m.	2 48
,, dep	7 32	1050	—	...	2 23	—	—	—	5 52	9 22	3 0
Tynist......	8 9	1122	...	...	3 0	...	Extra.—Prague to Lissa, 1.30 p.m.		6 40	9 54	3 31
Castolo'itz	8 20	1133	...	...	3 11	...			6 57	10 8	3 42
Daudleb ...	8 35	1146	...	...	3 24	...			7 26	1025	3 54
Pottenstein	8 44	1156	...	...	3 33	...			7 44	1034	4 3
Senftenberg	9 13	1225	...	...	3 57	...			8 29	1058	4 27
Geiersberg	9 21	1235	...	...	4 5	...			8 46	11 6	4 35

‡—Ex 3.		1,2,3	1,2,3	1,2,3	1,2,3	Ex3	1,2,3	1,2,3	Ex3	1,2,3	1,2,3
		a.m.		a.m.	a.m.					p.m.	ngt.
Geiersberg...dep		4 15	...	8 11	11 24	...	...	...	...	4 11	12 0
Senftenberg......		4 27	...	8 22	11 35	...	...	...	...	4 22	1213
Pottenstein		4 48	...	8 44	11 56	...	...	...	...	4 43	1237
Daudleb............		4 56	...	8 52	12 5	...	...	...	...	4 53	1248
Castolowitz		5 10	...	9 6	12 17	...	...	...	...	5 8	1 5
Tynist		5 25	...	9 18	12 28	...	...	...	...	5 20	1 20
Koniggrätz arr		5 53	a.m.	9 46	12 56	...	...	p.m.	p.m.	5 48	1 50
,, dep		6‡12	7 29	1037	1 8	...	...	3 48	5 53	6 45	2 13
Chlumetz ...arr		6 38	8 5	1117	1 36	...	...	4 25	...	7 26	2 46
G.Wossek	a.m.	7 11	8 47	1155	2 18	p.m.	p.m.	5 4	6 45	8 30	3 18
,, dep	4 58	7 16	9 2	12 3	2 ‡30	2 47	4 23	5 15	6 50	8 48	3 37
Podebrad...	5 11	7 27	9 16	1217	2 41	...	4 35	5 29	7 1	9 2	3 48
Nimburg...	5 23	7 38	9 39	1233	2 52	3 5	4 54	5 51	7 11	9 20	4 8
Lissa ...arr	5 40	7 53	10 0	1252	3 7	3 19	5 11	6 10	7 27	9 39	4 25
,, ...dep	5 42	7 54	1012	1259	3 8	3 27	5 20	6 18	...	9 44	4 33
Celakowitz	5 53	...	1026	1 10	...	3 38	5 31	6 30	...	9 55	4 44
Vysotschan	6 25	...	11 5	1 44	...	...	6 2	7 12	...	1027	5 17
Prague arr	6 38	8 36	1119	1 57	3 50	4 15	6 15	7 25	8§11	1040	5 30

Daudleb ....dep	5 a0	12p10	5 p5	...	...
Rokitnitz ....arr	6 30	1 32	6 30	...	...

Rokitnitz.............dep	2 a47	10 a0	2 p5	...	...
Daudleb...............arr	3 48	11 3	3 10	...	...

MITTELWALDE and WILDENSCHWERT.

‡—Sunday 9.56 p.m.

	a.m.	a.m.	a.m.	p.m.	p.m.	p.m.	
Mittelwalde ......dep	...	...	10 27	12 49	3 11	10 7	...
Wichstadtl	...	7 13	10 45	1 2	3 33	10 30	...
Gabel	...	7 44	11 4	1 16	3 52	10 49	...
Geiersberg	5 28	8 14	11 27	1 28	4 35	11 18	...
Wildenschwert...arr	6 8	8 39	11 55	1 44	5 3	11 39	...

	a.m.	a.m.	a.m	a.m.	p.m.	p.m.	p.m.	p.m.
Wildenschwert...dep	3 10	...	7 20	9 17	12 45	3 20	8 24	...
Geiersberg	3 49	4 41	8 4	9 39	1 2	3 50	8 54	9 1
Gabel	—	4 57	—	9 54	1 16	4 36	—	9 28
Wichstadtl..................	...	5 36	...	10 16	1 34	5 3	...	10‡30
Mittelwalde ......arr	...	5 46	...	10 26	1 44	5 13	...	10 50

For Fares, see page 233B.]

BUDAPEST, SZABADKA, and BELGRADE.

E.M.	VIENNA 225B, 227 dep	...	...	...	...	1020	...	...	1020	...	...	9a10	9 a10	9a10	...	1 p55	1 p55	1p55	6p51
Dist.		1,2,3	1,2,3	2&3	1 & 2	Ex2	1,2,3	2&3	1,2,3	2&3	1,2,3	1,2,3	Ex 3	Ex2	2&3	2 & 3	1,2,3	1,2,3	Ex1
	Budapest—					a.m.			a.m.	a.m.	p.m.	p.m.	p.m	p.m.	p.m.	p.m.	p.m.	p.m	p.m.
	„ Westbahnhof ...	...	...	...	...	...	...	...	...	...	...	...	...	...	...	...	...	...	1130
—	„ Ostbahnhof	...	...	...	...	7 10	...	...	7 45	10 0	12 20	2 15	2 45	3 20	6 5	6 45	8 5	1115	...
4¼	„ Ferenczvaros ...	...	...	...	...	7 21	...	...	8 2	1013	12 36	2 27	2 56	3 31	6 17	7 5	8 16	1130	...
16¾	Taksony	...	...	...	...	RC	...	...	8 46	1054	1 34	3 3	RC	RC	7 2	7 51	8 40	12 3	B
26	Kiskunlaczhaza	...	...	...	...	...	...	...	9 15	1124	2 2	3 40	3 35	...	7 28	8 19	9 16	1230	...
38	Kunszentmiklós-Tass	...	...	...	...	8 16	...	...	9 49	1148	2 40	4 5	3 54	...	7 52	8 43	9 42	1 7	...
49	Szabadszallas	...	...	...	...	8 34	...	...	1014		3 4	4 29	...	...			10 6	1 31	...
53½	Fülöpszállás	...	...	...	...	8 42	...	...	1035	...	3 13	4 38	4 21	...	...	...	10 15	1 40	...
67	Kis-Körös (225A)...arr	...	...	...	...	9 2	...	...	11 4	...	3 42	5 8	4 44	5 19	...	...	10 44	2 8	1 45
84	Kis-Kun-Halas (225A)	...	...	...	...	9 35	...	...	12 7	...	4 30		5 20	5 55	...	...	11 32	3 11	...
108¾	Szabadka (230)......arr	...	...	...	...	1014	...	...	1 0	...	5 23	...	6 1	6 36	From Brod.		12 24	4 1	2 50
...	SERAJEVO (247B) arr	...	...	...	...	7a14	...	...	...	...	...	...	8a10	...			8p28	...	...
...	Szabadka ....dep	...	...	...	...	1030	...	...	1 44	...	5 35	...		6 48			1 2	5 20	2 57
128½	Topolya	...	...	...	...	11 2	...	...	2 40	...	6 27	...	...	7 22			2 7	6 22	...
138½	Bácsfeketehegy (225A)	...	...	...	...	1123	...	...	3 10	...	6 53	...	...	7 41			2 35	7 3	...
145½	Ujverbasz 226A	...	...	...	...	1137	...	...	3 30	...	7 11	...	...	7 55			2 56	7 25	...
154	Oker	...	...	a.m.	...	1151	...	p.m.	3 49	...	7 30	...	...	...			3 15	7 46	...
171½	Ujvidék	...	...	5 42	...	1225	...	1 54	4 28	...	8 9	...	...	8 44	Ex2		4 8	8 53	4 31
174½	Petervarad	...	...	5 55	...	...	...	2 7	5 3	...		...	...	...	p.m.		4 19	9 6	...
192¾	India (230)..........arr	...	...	6 48	...	1 12	...	3 3	5 54	1,2,3	...	...	...	9 34	10 4	RC SC	5 19	9 57	...
202½	Ujpazua	a.m.	a.m.	7 27	p.m.	...	p.m.	3 38	6 34	p.m.	...	...	...	SC	1023		5 50	1041	...
215½	Zimony (Semlin)	4 25	6 30	8 1	12 50	1 53	2 48	4 14	7 6	8 0	...	...	...	1018	1046	...	6 18	1114	5 44
223	Belgrade..........arr	4 40	6 45	...	1 5	2 14	3 3	...	7 50	8 15	...	...	...	1038	11 9	...	7 0	12 4	5 58
374	NISH (325A) ....arr	...	...	...	...	...	...	...	...	...	...	...	...	...	...	...	...	...	...
474	SOFIA (325A)......arr	...	...	...	...	...	...	...	...	...	...	...	...	...	...	...	...	...	...
881	CONSTANTINOPLE 325A arr			...	...	...	...	...	...	...	...	...	...	...	...	...	...	...	...

RC—Restaurant Car. SC—Sleeping Car.

B—From Budapest on Tuesday, Thursday, Friday, and Sunday only.

CONSTANTINOPLE dep	...	...	...	...	...	...	...	...	...	...	...	...	...	...	...	...	...	...	...
SOFIA (325A)......dep	...	...	...	...	...	...	...	...	...	...	...	...	...	...	...	...	...	...	...
NISH (325A) ......dep	...	...	...	...	...	...	...	...	...	...	...	...	...	...	...	...	...	...	...
	1,2,3	1,2,3	2 & 3	Ex 2	Ex2	Ex 3	1,2,3	1,2,3	1,2,3	2&3	1,2,3	Ex2	1 & 2	1,2,3	2 & 3	1,2,3	1,2,3	Ex 1	1 & 2
			a.m.	a.m.	a.m.			a.m.	a.m.	p.m.	p.m.	p.m.	p.m.	p.m.		p.m.	p.m.	p.m.	p.m.
Belgrade..........dep	...	...	...	5 15	5 41	...	...	7 25	8 0	...	1234	1 57	3 4	3 43	...	8 20	8 43	10 39	11 30
Zimony (Semlin)	...	...	4 43	5 45	6 19	...	...	8 6	8 15	1233	1249	2 52	3 19	4 34	...	8 35	9 21	10 50	11 45
Ujpazua	...	...	5 26	6 7	RC	...	...	8 35		1 8		RC		5 7	...		9 57	...	
India..........dep	...	...	6 13	6 26	7 5	...	...	9 25	...	1 38	...	3 35	...	5 55	...	...	1031	A	...
Petervarad	...	a.m.	7 8	To Brod.	...	...	...	1017	...	2 32	...	...	...	6 44	...	...	1116	...	
Ujvidék..........dep	...	4 27	7 20		7 55	...	...	1040	...	2 44	...	4 29	...	7 22	...	...	1133	12 19	
Oker	...	5 9			...	...	...	1119	...		...	5 1	...	8 10	...	...	12 8	...	
Ujverbasz	...	5 34	...		8 38	...	...	1145	...	...	...	5 16		8 36	...	...	1231	...	
Bácsfeketehegy	...	5 56	...		...	...	...	12 3	...	...	...	5 33		8 58	...	...	1247	...	
Topolya	...	6 26	...		9 7	RC	...	1231	...	...	...	5 51		9 29	...	...	1 14	...	
Szabadka (230)......arr	...	7 24	...	...	9 38	...	...	1 21	...	...	...	6 25		1021	...	...	1 51	2 1	
SERAJEVO (247B) dep	a.m.		...	...	...	8 p30	...	...	...	...	...	1050		2p15	...	...	...	...	
Szabadka..........dep	4 50	...	...	...	9 50	10a15	...	1 55	...	...	...	6 37		1153	...	...	2 51	2 19	
Kis-Kun-Halas	5 50	...	...	...	...	10 56	...	3 1	...	...	p.m.	7 20		1259	...	...	4 3	...	
Kis-Körös ....dep	6 30	...	...	...	11 5	11 30	...	3 48	...	...	6 40	7 58		2 9	...	...	4 53	3 48	
Fülöpszállás	7 2	...	...	...	...	11 53	...	4 38	...	...	7 12	8 24		2 46	...	2 & 3	5 31	...	
Szabadszallas	7 11	...	...	...	...	12 0	p.m.	4 50	...	...	7 22	...		2 58	a.m.	a.m.	5 41	...	
Kunszentmiklós-Tass	7 37	...	...	...	...	12 21	1235	5 20	...	...	7 53	8 52		3 37	4 21	5 26	6 10	...	
Kiskunlaczhaza	8 21	...	...	...	...	12 41	1 5	5 59	...	...	8 22	9 13		4 14	5 0	6 0	6 41	...	
Taksony	8 50	...	...	...	...	...	1 35	6 25	...	...	8 51	...		4 41	5 28	6 29	7 8	...	
Budapest Fren... arr	9 35	...	...	...	1250	1 20	2 24	7 4	...	...	9 31	9 51		5 22	6 6	7 15	7 57	...	
„ Ostbahnhof arr	9 55	...	...	...	1 0	1 30	2 40	7 20	...	...	9 45	10 0		5 45	6§17	7 25	8 10	...	
„ Westbahnhof arr	...	...	...	...	...	...	...	...	...	...	...	...	...	...	...	...	...	6 10	
VIENNA 225B, 227 arr	...	...	...	...	6p40	6 p40	...	...	...	...	7a20	7a20	...	1p50	...	...	1p50	11 a4	...

§—At Budapest Józsefváros.

A—Runs on Monday, Tuesday, Thursday, and Saturday only.

KIS-KUN-HALAS and REGOCZE.

Kis-Kun-Halas dep	4 a8	12p27	5p35	...	...
Bácsalmás	6 48	3 30	7 40	8p55	...
Regocze ....arr	7 55	5 6	...	9 55	...

Regocze..........dep	2a44	9a44	6p20	...	...
Bácsalmás	4 1	12 0	7 39	8p50	...
Kis-Kun-Halas 225A	5 45	2 27	...	1056	...

KUNSZENTMIKLOS and DUNAPATAJ.

Kunszentmiklos ...dep	9 a55	2 p35	8 p57
Dunapataj ....arr	12 9	4 32	10 49

Dunapataj..........dep	5 a 0	1 p50	5 p12	...
Kunszentmiklos 225A arr	7 23	3 46	7 35	...

KISKOROS and KALOCSA.

Kiskörös ......dep	2a40	6a35	11a40	5p13	10p49
Kalocsa.........arr	4 16	7 41	12 57	6 12	11 49

Kalocsa .... dep	5 a0	9 a56	2 p4	6p42	12a17	...
Kiskörös 225A arr	6 8	11 9	3 29	7 43	1 29	...

BÁCSFEKETEHEGY and UJPALANKA.

Bácsfeketehegy..........dep	7 a10	3 p25	7p47	...	...
Kula	7 47	4 10	8 26	...	...
Szepliget	9 21	6 12	9 38	...	...
Ujpalánka 230 ....arr	10 9	6 54	1025	...	...

Ujpalánka ....dep	2 a44	8 a0	1 p30	...	...	...
Szepliget	3 40	9 24	2 47	...	...	...
Kula	5 13	10 47	4 18	...	...	...
Bácsfeketehegy 225A ... arr	5 44	11 17	4 46	...	...	...

UJVIDEK and BEOCIN.

Ujvidék ....dep	10a49	4p36	8p50	...	...
Petervarad	11 5	4 50	9 5	...	...
Beocin ....arr	12 7	5 42	9 57	...	...

Beocin ....dep	6a10	2 p7	6 p5	...	...
Petervarad	7 18	3 14	7 1	...	...
Ujvidék 225A....arr	7 34	3 30	7 15	...	...

For Fares, see page 233B.]

VIENNA, BRUCK, GYOR, and BUDAPEST.

SLEEPING CAR—in 10.20 p.m. from Vienna.

	2&3	1,2,3 a.m.	1,2,3 a.m.	1,2,3 a.m.	Ex3 a.m.	1,2,3 a.m.	Ex2 a.m.	Ex2 a.m.	1,2,3	1,2,3 a.m.	1,2,3 a.m.	Ex2 p.m.	Ex2 p.m.	1,2,3 p.m.	1,2,3 p.m.
Vienna Staats. 253 ...dep		...	...	...	...	6 15	9 10	...	...	...	1155	1 55	...	4 20	1020
Bruck ...arr		...	...	...	...	7 39	...	...	...	...	...	2 40	...	5 40	1141
Bruck ...dep		...	...	5 0	...	7 49	10 8	...	...	1140	1 36	2 46	...	6 1	1156
Pándorfalu		...	...	5 17	...	8 2	...	...	...	1153	1 59	2 55	...	6 27	1212
Hegyeshalom		...	...	6 8	...	8 35	1038	...	...	1229	2 44	3 16	...	7 33	1247
Moson-Magyaróvár		...	...	6 25	...	8 51	1048	...	...	1249	3 8	3 27	...	7 52	1 6
Györ (Raab) 225B ...arr		...	...	7 9	...	9 32	1119	RC	...	1 36	4 12	4 2	...	8 42	1 52
Györ (Raab) ...dep	2&3	3 27	4 55	—	7 25	9 38	1121	1148	...	1 50	4 33	4 5	7 22	—	2 16
Komárom ...arr	a.m.	4 19	5 43	...	8 1	1022	1152	1222	p.m.	2 42	5 20	4 37	7 59	RC—Restaurant Car.	3 9
Komárom ...dep	3 0	4 39	5 50	...	8 7	1029	1159	1229	12 34	2 52	5 32	4 44	8 6		3 26
Almás-Füzitö 225B	3 19	5 1	6 10	...	8 19	1046	...	1241	12 57	3 13	5 52	...	8 19		3†43
Tata-Tóváros	3 33	5 15	6 26	...	8 30	1057	RC	1251	—	3 31	6 8	5 4	8 29		4†1
Bánhida 225B	3 54	5 38	6 51	...	8 44	1117	...	1 4	...	4 2	6 29	RC	8 43		4†17
Bicske 225B	4 44	6†28	7 48	...	9 12	12 3	...	1 32	...	4 59	7†17	5 42	9 14		5 †4
Budapest-Kelenföld	5 43	7 30	8 51	...	9 48	1258	1 25	2 9	...	5 55	8 18	6 18	9 52		6 3
Budapest-Ferencz	5 54	7 49	9 5	...	...	1 9	...	...	...	6 5	8†31	...	...		6†14
Budapest Ostbahnhof arr	6 5	8 0	9 20	...	10 5	1 20	1 40	2 25	...	6 20	8 45	6 35	1010	...	6 25
BELGRADE 225A ...arr		...	...	...	...	...	1038	1038	...	...	12p4	7 a0	...	...	2p14

SLEEPING CAR—in 10.55 p.m. from Budapest. †—Sets down only.

Dist. E.M.			1,2,3 a.m.	1,2,3 a.m.	Ex2 a.m.	Ex2 a.m.	2&3 a.m.	1,2,3 p.m.	Ex2 p.m.	Ex2 p.m.	2&3 p.m.	Ex3 p.m.	1,2,3 p.m.	1,2,3 p.m.	1,2,3 p.m.	1,2,3 p.m.
	BELGRADE (225A) ...dep		...	3p43	3p43	8p43	...	...	5a41	5a41	...	...	...	7a25	1p57	...
—	**Budapest** Ostbahnhof dep		...	6 40	7 20	9 10	1155	1230	1 40	2 5	4 25	5 15	7 20	9 15	1055	1155
4¼	Budapest Ferencz ...dep		...	6 53	RC	RC	12 7	...	RC	RC	4 36	...	7 32	9 27	11 7	1210
12½	Budapest Kelenföld ...dep		...	7 5	7 37	9 27	1217	1252	1 57	2 22	4 47	5 32	7 44	9 44	1122	1225
34¾	Bicske		4 30	8 22	8 17	10 6	1 23	1 37	2 37	...	5 55	6 11	8 47	1056	1220	1 46
51	Bánhida		5 22	9 14	8 46	...	—	2 19	3 6	...	6 56	6 41	9 32	1147	1 2	—
57¼	Tata-Tóváros		5 50	9 38	8 58	1045	a.m.	2 40	3 16	...	7 17	6 53	9 51	1210	1 18	...
62¾	Almás-Füzitö		6 5	9 52	9 8	...	1020	2 51	3 28	...	7 30	7 4	10 3	1224	1 32	...
69½	**Komárom** ...arr		6 22	10 9	9 19	11 4	1043	3 6	3 39	3 53	7 47	7 15	1020	1241	1 46	...
	Komárom ...dep		6 30	1021	9 26	1111	—	3 16	3 44	4 0	—	7 22	1027	1248	2 7	...
93¾	**Györ** (Raab) ...arr	a.m.	7 20	11 9	10 2	1143	...	4 1	4 20	4 32	p.m.	8 0	1115	1 40	2 56	...
	Györ (Raab) ...dep	4 33	7 28	1129	—	1145	...	4 14	—	4 35	8 7	—	—	—	3 21	...
115½	Moson-Magyaróvár	5 30	8 18	1244	...	1218	...	5 15	...	5 7	8 53	...	...	...	4 10	...
122½	Hegyeshalom	6 9	8 36	1 4	...	1228	...	5 31	...	5 18	9 9	...	...	...	4 30	...
137½	Pándorfalu	7 9	9 14	1 50	...	1250	...	6 15	...	...	9 44	...	...	...	5 13	...
141¾	**Bruck** ...arr	7 21	9 24	2 2	...	1258	...	6 24	...	5 48	9 53	...	...	...	5 24	...
—	" ...dep	—	—	...	...	1 14	...	6 45	...	5 52	10 0	...	...	...	5 58	...
167¾	**Vienna** 253 ...arr	...	...	3 45	...	1 50	...	7 55	...	6 40	1120	...	...	...	7 20	...

Komárom ...dep	6a35	12p45	5p28	9p35	...	...	Ersekújvár ...dep	4a25	9a11	2p40	7p50	...
Ersekújvár ...arr	7 34	1 43	6 29	1033	...	...	Komárom ...arr	5 20	10 3	3 34	8 43	...

ALMASFUZITO and ESZTERGOM (Gran).

Almásfüzitö dep	6a15	1 p5	4p40	7p40	...	Esztergom ...dep	3a50	8a12	12p10	4p12	...
Tokod ...	7 47	2 48	6 54	9 27	...	Kenyérmezömajor ...	4 4	8 29	12 25	4 35	...
Kenyérmezö 226A	7 59	3 3	7 13	9 37	...	Tokod ...	4 15	8 39	12 41	4 46	...
Esztergom ...arr	8 11	3 16	7 28	9 50	...	Almásfüzitö 225B ...arr	5 54	1015	2 37	6 42	...

Tokod ...dep	8a45	4p54	...	...	Annavölgyibánya-Sárisáp ...dep	6a52	11a56
Annavölgyibánya-Sárisáp arr	9 25	5 30	...	...	Tokod ...arr	7 34	12 36

FEHRING and GYOR (Raab).

GRAZ 246 ...dep		...	...	6 a0	8a20	...	2 p0	6p20
		a.m.	a.m.	a.m.	a.m.		p.m.	p.m.
Fehring ...dep		...	4 50	8 5	1030	...	3 25	8 40
Gyanafalva		...	5 15	8 16	1045	...	3 36	8 56
Körmend		...	6 49	8 58	1143	...	4 17	10 5
Szombathely arr	a.m.	...	7 35	9 23	1220	p.m.	4 42	1044
Szombathely dep	2 33	4 40	—	9 28	1232	3 49	4 55	1110
Porpácz	3 5	5 0	...	9 45	1256	4 24	...	1135
Sárvár	3 18	5 9	...	9 53	1 10	4 47	5 24	1154
Czell-dömölk arr	4 5	5 35	a.m.	1016	1 42	5 33	5 50	1232
Czell-dömölk dep	4 25	5 43	5 48	1022	1 52	6 25	5 57	1250
Pápa	5 21	6 16	7 5	1049	2 36	7 56	6 25	1 44
Vaszar	5 36	...	—	1057	2 47	8 15	...	1 56
Gyömörö	5 59	6 37	...	11 9	3 6	8 47	...	2 16
Györ ...arr	6 52	7 7	...	1138	3 47	9 51	7 12	3 2

	a.m.	a.m.	a.m.	a.m.	p.m.		p.m.	p.m.
Györ ...dep	2 5	3 37	1012	1139	4 30	...	5 30	8 15
Gyömörö	2 47	4 33	1041	1225	...	...	6 46	8 47
Vaszar	3 5	5 5	1058	1243	...	...	7 10	...
Pápa 225B	3 21	5 47	11 9	1258	5 20	...	7 30	9 10
Czell-dömölk ...arr	4 0	6 44	1135	1 35	5 46	...	8 23	9 39
Czell-dömölk ...dep	4 10	6 56	1141	1 45	5 54	...	8 55	9 45
Sárvár	4 48	7 42	12 5	2 26	6 19	...	9 41	1011
Porpácz	5 6	7 59	1213	2 39	6 28	...	9 56	...
Szombathely ...arr	5 31	8 32	1231	3 5	6 46	p.m	1028	1037
" ...dep	6 1	—	1237	3 24	6 53	7 16	—	—
Körmend 225B	6 45	...	1 5	4 16	7 20	8 8	...	...
Gyanafalva	7 48	...	1 45	5 9	8 1	9 47	...	...
Fehring ...arr	8 4	...	1 56	5 24	8 12	1010	...	...
GRAZ (246) ...arr	10a27	...	3p20	7p45	1015	...	...	...

KORMEND an MURASZOMBAT.

Körmend ...dep	4 a49	7 a20	1 p9	4 p34	Muraszombat ...dep	3 a12	6 a53	12p50	4p12	...
Sal	7 2	9 51	3 11	7 10	Sal	4 26	8 21	1 59	5 35	...
Muraszombat ...arr	8 9	11 8	4 11	8 28	Körmend 225B ...arr	6 30	11 13	4 0	7 56	...

KORMEND and NEMETUJVAR.

Körmend ...dep	7 a15	1 p14	4 p18	8 p24	...	...	Németjúvar ...dep	5 a19	10a14	2 p54	6p 3	...	...	...	...
Németújvar ...arr	8 15	2 8	5 22	9 23	...	...	Körmend ...dep	6 20	11 20	3 50	7 1	...	...	...	...

BANHIDA and PAPA.

Bánhida ...dep	...	4 a25	9 a32	4p37	...	**Pápa** ...dep	3a20	10a58	...	...	5p25	...	...
Kisbér	...	7 4	11 39	6 39	...	Veszprémvarsány ...	5 40	12 51	1 p20	...	7 22	...	...
Veszprémvarsány	6 a0	—	1 25	7 43	...	Kisbér	7 5	—	2 22	6p41	—	...	...
Pápa ...arr	7 32	...	3 10	9 35	...	**Bánhida** 225B arr	8 36	...	3 50	8 37	...	...	...

BICSKE and SARBOGARD.

Bicske ...dep	5 a46	12 p8	...	...	6p16	**Sarbogard** ...dep	...	6 a5	...	11a52	5 p10
Székesfehérvár	9 19	2 7	2p36	7p30	8 19	Börgönd	...	7 38	...	1 21	6 23
Börgönd	9 49	—	2 54	7 50	—	Székesfehérvár	5a15	7 55	9 a10	1 40	6 39
Sárbogárd (231) arr	11 6	...	4 6	9 5	...	**Bicske** 225B ...arr	7 35	...	11 22	5 30	...

POZSONY (Pressburg) and LIPOTVAR.

Pozsony ....dep	6 a5	9 a12	12p50	1 p45	...	6 p44	9 p52
Bazin..............	6 48	9 34	1 36	2 23	...	7 34	10 30
Nagyszombat	7 51	10 4	2 32	3 12	4p52	8 35	11 17
Lipotvár ....arr	8 19	10 21	3 0	3 40	5 28	9 6	11 41

Lipótvar ....dep	2a43	4a15	5 a22	11a20	5 p34	6 p16	9 p12
Nagyszombat	3 37	4 41	6 0	12 0	6 10	6 38	10 6
Bazin	4 43	5 21	6 48	12 46	—	7 7	11 1
Pozsony 227............arr	5 35	5 55	7 25	1 23	...	7 30	11 44

POZSONY-UJVAROS and UJKOMAROM.

Pozsony-Ujv. dep	...	6a33	11a50	2p32	8 p0
Somorja-Uszor ...	...	7 34	1 3	3 32	9 6
Dunaszerdahely...	4a48	8 31	2 5	4 32	10 5
Nagymegyer	6 7	9 27	—	5 30	—
Ujkomárom ...arr	7 32	1031	...	6 41	...

Ujkomárom ...dep	...	4a52	12p50	5p45
Nagymegyer........	...	6 14	2 18	7 6
Dunaszerdahely...	4a40	7 21	3 20	8 9
Somorja-Uszor ...	5 40	8 17	4 18	9 10
Pozsony ....arr	6 32	9 8	5 11	10 3

POZSONY and SZAKOLCZA.

Pozsony .... dep	5 a1	8 a25	1 p30	6 p1	...	...	...
Dévényujfalu............	5 28	8 49	1 56	6 26	...	...	...
Dévénytó	5 37	8 57	2 7	6 37	...	...	...
Zohor 226	5 49	9 11	2 21	6 51	...	...	...
Jókút	6 57	10 17	3 28	8 11	...	...	...
Holics	7 24	10 44	3 54	8 43	...	...	...
Szakolcza ......arr	7 34	10 54	4 5	8 54	...	...	...

Szakolcza ..... dep	5 a15	9 a17	1 p15	4 p59	...	...	...
Holics	5 27	9 29	1 26	5 11	...	...	...
Jókút	5 55	9 55	1 56	5 41	...	...	...
Zohor	6 55	10 59	3 6	6 50	...	...	...
Dévénytó.....................	7 7	11 13	3 18	7 6	...	...	...
Dévényujfalu	7 16	11 20	3 25	7 15	...	...	...
Pozsony ....arr	7 40	11 42	3 48	7 38	...	...	...

Devenyto ...dep	11a20	...
Marchegg ...arr	11 31	...

Marchegg ...dep	1 p45	...
Devenyto ...arr	1 58	...

Devenyto.............. dep	5 a43	7 a25	9 a5	2 p25	7p15	...	...
Stomfa-Mászt ....arr	6 8	7 45	9 30	2 45	7 35	...	...

Stomfa-Mászt ......dep	5 a7	6 a38	10a35	6 p0	...	...
Devenyto...............arr	5 30	6 58	10 55	6 2[illegible]	...	...

Detreköszentmiklós.........dep	4 a7	...	9a15	...	4p46	...
Zohor 226	5 35	7 a11	1043	3p20	6 40	...
Magyarfalu-czukorgyár ...arr	...	7 40	1135	3 56	7 34	...

Magyarfalu-czukorgyár...dep	5 a11	...	10a0	1p41	6 p0	...
Zohor	5 40	7a10	1035	2 30	7 10	...
Detreköszentmiklós ....arr	...	8 45	...	4 5	9 12	...

POZSONY UJVAROS (Pressburg), and SOPRON (Odenburg).

Pozsony-Ujv. dp		5 a38	...	12p22	...	4p40	6p50	...
Pándorfalu		7 5	...	1 55	...	6 20	8 5	...
Nezsider		7 20	...	2 10	...	6 35	—	...
Sérez 226	5a26	8 23	11a37	3 15	5p13	7 35	...	...
Kismarton	6 15	8 42	12 3	3 32	5 28	7 51	...	...
Vulkapordány ..	6 50	9 5	12 38	3 57	5 47	8 22	...	...
Sopron ....arr	7 24	9 42	1 8	4 36	6 19	9 5	...	...

Sopron ....dep	...	4 a0	8 a0	10a50	...	3 p20	7p40	...
Vulkapordány	...	4 45	9 1	11 32	12p45	3 59	8 17	...
Kismarton	...	5 4	9 18	11 53	1 2	4 15	8 33	...
Sércz	...	5 19	9 32	12 9	1 16	4 31	8 47	...
Nezsider	...	6 25	—	1 17	—	5 36	—	...
Pándorfalu	5a12	7 10	...	2 4	...	6 22	...	...
Pozsony 226A arr	6 23	8 18	...	3 17	...	7 36	...	...

Sércz ....dep	9a37	1p17	4p33	8p48	...
Szentmargitbánya-Ruszt...arr	9 58	1 38	4 47	9 7	...

Szentmargitbánya-Ruszt...dep	4a55	11a15	2p50	4p58	...
Sércz ....arr	5 15	11 35	3 9	5 12	...

POZSONY UJVAROS and SZOMBATHELY.

Ponzsony-Ujvaros dep		4a30	7 a9	9a14	11a14	1p20	...	6 p25
Hegyeshalom		5 58	8 20	1024	12 23	2 28	3p35	7 40
Csorna	4a38	7 35	—	1143	—	—	5 7	8 59
Répczelak...........	6 0	8 54	...	1253	...	...	7 25	—
Porpácz	7 1	9 55	...	1 52	...	...	8 34	...
Szombathely arr	7 34	1030	...	2 25	...	...	9 9	...

Szombathely ......dep		...	...	4a15	...	1159	...	2p35	7 p22
Porpácz		...	...	5 3	...	1240	...	3 9	8 0
Répczelak..................		...	...	6 6	...	1 53	...	4 17	9 19
Csorna		4a43	...	7 15	...	2 58	3p21	5 28	10 35
Hegyeshalom arr	4a36	5 57	8a52	10 8	1 p9	—	4 48	7 18	—
Pozsony-Ujv. arr	6 27	7 28	10 8	1215	2 18	...	6 45	8 46	...

NAGYTAPOLCSANY and TRENCSEN.

Nagytapolcsány ...dep	5 a15	12p56	7p37
Nagybossány	5 36	1 14	7 54
Bán	6 45	2 17	8 49
Bercseny	7 25	3 2	9 26
Trencsén 233B ....arr	8 50	4 21	10 38

Trencsén ....dep	7 a40	1 p25	6 p10
Bercseny	9 9	3 15	7 31
Bán	9 45	4 3	8 4
Nagybossány	10 36	5 15	8 55
Nagytapolcsány ......arr	10 52	5 33	9 10

ERSEKUJVAR and NEMETPRONA.

Ersekujvar ......dep	...	4a25	6a50	9a42	1p15	4p52	9 p0
Nagysurány 226	...	4 46	7 21	10 2	1 35	5 8	9 17
Nyitra	...	5 58	8 16	1142	2 28	6 0	1015
Uzbég	...	6 18	8 30	12 6	2 42	6 14	1029
Szomorlovászi	...	6 40	8 59	1225	3 2	6 33	1049
Nagytapolcsány	...	7 24	9 16	1 6	3 28	7 24	1115
Nagybossány...............	...	7 39	—	1 21	—	7 39	—
Nagybélicz	a.m	8 16	...	1 55	...	8 10	...
Privigye-Bajmoczfürdö	6 30	9 49	1p30	3 26	...	9 40	...
Németprona ......arr	6 58	1018	1 58	3 55	...	10 9	...

Németprona ....dep		3a25	7a27	...	12p42	...	2p20	6 p1
Privigye-Bajmoczfürdö..		3 50	7 50	...	1 9	...	2 43	6 30
Nagybélicz....................		5 13	—	...	2 36	3p43	—	8 8
Nagybossány.................		5 39	...	...	3 3	4 46	...	8 39
Nagytapolcsány........	5a30	6 12	9a49	11a14	3 29	5 14	6p20	9 15
Szomorlovászi	5 58	6 42	1017	11 41	3 56	—	7 49	9 43
Uzbég	6 17	7 2	1031	12 1	4 15	...	8 40	10 1
Nyitra..........................	6 35	7 42	1153	12 49	4 49	...	9 2	1021
Nagysurány.................	7 21	8 33	1141	1 36	5 46	...	—	1118
Ersekujvar 227 arr	7 37	8 49	1157	1 52	6 2	...	...	1133

Privigye-Bajmóczfürdö...dep	9 a55	3 p35	9 p45
Nyitrabánya ....arr	10 52	4 24	10 34

Nyitrabánya ....dep	2 a58	12p15	5 p30
Privigye-Bajmóczfürdö...arr	3 39	12 56	6 20

Nyitra...............dep	6a46	9 a5	4 p1	...	...
Uzbég	7 5	9 21	4 19	...	...
Lipótvár ....arr	7 54	10 11	5 18	...	...

Lipótvár............dep	8 a32	11a13	6 p27	...	...
Uzbég	9 22	12 15	7 22	...	...
Nyitra................arr	9 35	12 28	7 35	...	...

Nyitra ...dep	7 a21	12p41	7 p3	...	...
Uzbég.........	7 42	12 58	7 25	...	...
Radosna arr	9 4	2 9	8 36	...	...

Radosnadep	4 a51	10 a0	3 p1	...	...
Uzbég	6 25	11 12	4 24	...	...
Nyitra ...arr	6 45	11 31	4 43	...	...

ERSEKUJVAR and KISTAPOLCSANY.

Ersekujvár.........dep	4a40	9a52	5p20	8p45
Nagysurány	5 8	1023	5 51	9 10
Aranyosmarót	7 20	1233	7 37	1053
Kistapolcsany ...arr	7 31	1245	7 47	11 3

Kistapolcsany ......dep	5a10	9a35	3p53	8p56
Aranyosmarót	5 20	9 47	4 5	9 14
Nagysurány 226	7 7	1126	5 54	11 2
Ersekujvár ....arr	7 27	1146	6 14	1123

Garamkovácsi.........dep	8a40	2p54	7p57	...	...
Aranyosmarót ....arr	9 38	3 54	8 55	...	...

Aranyosmarót..........dep	7a12	12p40	5p20	...	...
Garamkovácsi ....arr	8 11	2 12	6 50	...	...

OBECSE, UJVIDEK, and TITEL.

Obecse ......dep	4a20	9a30	5p26
Vaskapu	6 29	12 34	7 30
Ujvidék ......arr	6 53	1 4	7 52

Ujvidék ...dep	4a32	9a15	4p53
Vaskapu	4 58	9 43	5 19
Obecse (226A)..	6 59	12 27	7 31

Ujvidék......dep	6a54	7p0
Vaskapu	7 18	7 23
Titel..........arr	9 11	8 58

Titel..........dep	3a32	1p56
Vaskapu	5 33	3 23
Ujvidék ......arr	6 0	3 46

SZABADKA and OBECSE.

E.M.						
	Szabadka dep	4a37	1p38	7p10	...	...
24½	Zenta 230A dep	7 5	3 50	9 3	...	...
47¾	**Obecse** ....arr	8 56	5 14	10 35	...	...

Obecse......dep	4a10	7a26	1p0	...	...
Zenta	6 40	9 12	3 37	...	...
Szabadka 230A	8 30	11 4	5 25	...	...

SZEGED-ROKUS and SZABADKA.

Szeged-Rokus dep	2a58	5a45	6a19	8a14	11a30	3p12	4p40	6p53	10p20
Horgos	3 32	6 5	7 0	8 49	12 3	3 46	5 14	7 27	10 56
Szabadka 230...arr	4 13	6 38	7 40	9 27	12 42	4 29	5 51	8 6	11 35

Szabadka dep	2a56	6a15	9a44	10a55	1p30	4p4	6p53	10p26	11p5
Horgos.........	3 32	6 54	1021	11 31	2 10	4 43	7 26	10 56	1149
Szeged-R. 227	3 55	7 25	1048	12 3	2 39	5 12	7 53	11 20	1217

SZABADKA and BATASZEK.

E.M.							
	Szabadka ...dep	5a5	6a57	10a36	2p20	4p43	7p0
16½	Bacs-Almas	5 58	7 29	11 40	3 20	5 33	7 46
37	Baja...............	7 0	8 15	12 41	4 38	6 22	8 51
61½	Bátaszék 231 arr	7 28	8 37	1 14	5 11	6 50	9 20

Bátaszek ....dep	5a16	6a59	9a38	4p8	7p5	8p26
Baja.....................	5 50	7 42	10 24	4 43	7 44	8 51
Bacs-Almas...........	6 53	8 42	11 30	5 37	8 40	9 35
Szabadka 225A...arr	7 45	9 30	12 21	6 27	9 26	10 6

PECS and BATASZEK.

Pecs ....dep	6a9	1p22	4p40	...	...
Bataszek ......arr	9 10	4 47	8 21	...	...

Bataszek...........dep	3a34	9a50	7p0	...	...	...
Pécs (230)..........arr	7 18	1 6	10 21	...	...	...

BAJA and UJVIDEK (Neusatz).

Baja..............dep	...	4a0	...	8a20	1p0	4p50
Regöcze	...	5 9	...	9 39	2 16	5 57
Zombor ... arr	...	6 25	...	11 5	3 23	7 20
Zombor ... dep	2a30	—	6a51	—	3 46	—
Hódság 230	3 55	...	8 10	...	5 7	...
Szépliget.............	5 8	...	9 16	...	6 3	...
Ujvidék 225A arr	6 39	...	10 31	...	7 17	...

Ujvidék ....dep	...	2a7	7a51	...	...	1p30
Szépliget	...	3 45	9 9	...	...	2 57
Hódság	...	4 42	10 2	...	...	3 50
Zombor ... arr	...	6 3	1120	...	...	5 0
Zombor ... dep	3a30	6 45	—	12p30	4p28	—
Regöcze	5 15	8 8	...	2 17	5 53	...
Baja 226A........arr	6 35	9 15	...	3 23	7 6	...

ZOMBOR and OBECSE.

Zombor..............dep	3a10	7a50	4p35	...
Kula	5 10	10 40	6 30	...
Ujverbasz 225A...........	5 38	11 50	6 51	8p0
Turja.........................	6 28	12 53	—	8 59
Obecse 226A ....arr	7 14	1 48	...	9 45

Obecse..............dep	3a44	9a10	1p49	...	...	...
Turja	4 31	10 3	2 33	...	...	...
Ujverbasz.................	5 42	1155	3 45	...	...	...
Kula 225A	6 4	1224	4 25	...	...	...
Zombor 226A ......arr	7 44	2 50	7 0	...	...	...

TORONTAL-SZECSANY and ALIBUNAR.

Torontalszecsany ...dep	5a0	8a0	6p28	...	...
Szamos	5 47	8 46	7 19	...	...
Antalfalva..........arr	6 47	10 12	...	...	...
Alibunar ....arr	...	10 6	8 42	...	...

Alibunar..............dep	4a40	...	...	4p6	...
Antalfalva.........dep	...	7a40	3p0	...	...
Szamos	6 0	8 32	4 3	5 20	...
Torontalszecsany arr	6 53	...	4 53	6 8	...

BELOVAR and VERÖCZE.

Belovár ....dep	5a40	12p5	5p34	...
Misulinovac....................	6 9	12 44	6 6	...
Klostar 231A..................	7 3	1 48	6 58	...
Veröcze....................arr	8 44	4 15	8 25	...

Veröcze....................dep	4a30	9a0	3p0	...
Klostar	6 11	10 21	5 5	...
Misulinovac......................	7 12	11 7	6 10	...
Belovár (231A)..... ...arr	7 35	11 29	6 34	...

Belovar........................dep	5a0	12p30	5p20	...
Velika Pisanica ....arr	6 7	1 37	6 27	...

Velika Pisanica ....dep	6a41	2p2	6p57	...
Belovar ....arr	7 47	3 29	8 3	...

TEMESVAR and NAGYSZENTMIKLOS.

Temesvár Jozsef ....dep	8a0	1p31	3p40
Lovrin	9 47	3 15	6 10
Nagyszentmiklos 226A...arr	10 17	3 46	6 55

Nagyszentmiklos ....dep	4a41	10a40	5p13	...
Lovrin	5 21	11 17	5 56	...
Temesvár 227 ....arr	7 10	12 59	8 5	...

Lovrin...........................dep	3a0	10a10	4p0
Zsombolya ....arr	4 1	11 19	4 57

Zsombolya......................dep	6a44	2p5	6p15	...
Lovrin ....arr	7 42	3 0	7 25	...

NAGY SZT. MIKLOS and HODMEZO VASARHELY.

Nagyszentmiklos......dep	6a30	4p0	...
Apatfalva	7 40	5 14	...
Hodmezo Vasarhely arr	9 40	7 32	...

Hodmezo Vasarhely dep	6a57	4p5	...	...
Apatfalva	9 11	6 29	...	...
Nagyszentmiklós ......arr	10 7	7 30	...	...

TEMESVAR and MARIARADNA.

Temesvár Jozsef ......dep	3a20	11a48	4p0	...
Mariáradna ....arr	7 8	3 7	7 16	...

Mariaradna ....dep	4a0	10a2	3p56	...	...
Temesvár 227..........arr	7 54	1 13	7 25	...	...

BUDAPEST and KECSKEMET.

Budapest Westbf. dep		...	...	6a30	...	11a10	...	2p50	7p40
Kebanya		...	...	6 54	...	11 34	...	3 16	8 8
Inarcs-Kakucs		...	...	8 33	...	1 6	...	4 50	9 44
Lajos-Mizse..............		6a35	...	10 1	...	2 32	...	6 20	11 9
Kisnyir	4a28	7 9	8a28	1036	1p8	3 10	4p6	6 56	—
Kecskemét	5 7	7 45	9 5	1110	1 46	3 48	4 44	7 34	...

Kecskemét...	...	3a6	5a8	5a33	9a58	10a53	2p18	4p45	6p15	...
Kisnyir	...	3 45	5 46	6 10	1035	11 35	2 56	5 27	6 54	...
Lajos-Mizse...	3a1	4 30	6 20	—	—	12 18	—	6 13	—	...
Inarcs-Kak.	4 24	5 54	—	...	...	1 37	...	7 35	...	p.m.
Kobanya......	6 11	7 33	...	...	...	3 21	...	9 13	...	1013
Budapest arr	6 30	7 50	...	...	...	3 40	...	9 30	...	1030

Kisnyir to Kerekegyhaza 6.11, 7.15, 10.40, 11.45a.m., 3.14, 7.0 p.m. From Kerek. 4.5, 6.42, 8.6, 11.11a.m., 12.45, 3.44p.m.

Alkenyer to **Kudsir**, 7.6 a.m., 12.28, 4.49 p.m. From **Kudsir**, 4.15, 10.40 a.m., 2.19 p.m.

KECSKEMET and FÜLOPSZALLAS.

Kecskemét ....dep	4a24	9a26	1p20
Fülöpszállás 225A ...arr	6 45	11 46	3 55

Fülöpszállás ....dep	4a55	10a40	4p43	...	...
Kecskemét 226A ......arr	6 51	12 45	7 25	...	...

KECSKEMET and TISZAUG.

Kecskemét...dep	4a17	12p17	5p0	...
Lakytelek	5 32	1 58	6 27	...
Tiszaug........arr	5 39	2 6	6 34	...

Tiszaug ....dep	5a42	2p11	6p39	...	...
Lakytelek	6 12	2 24	7 14	...	...
Kecskemét 226A arr	7 15	3 26	8 28	...	...

BUDAPEST and ESZTERGOM (Via O-Buda.)

Budapest Westb'hof dep	6a0	9a5	12p30	1p50	2p20	6p40	11p10
Obuda............................	6 39	9 34	1 0	2 22	2 49	7 9	11 40
Piliscsaba.......................	7 34	10 27	1 55	3 11	3 48	7 58	12 26
Kenyérmezömajor 225B ...	8 25	11 8	2 34	3 51	4 29	8 38	1 3
Esztergom (Gran)...arr	8 37	11 22	2 47	4 5	4 42	8 52	1 16

Esztergom dep	3a35	4a52	5a49	7a40	11a48	2p48	7p30
Kenyérmezömajor	3 49	5 7	6 4	7 58	12 1	3 3	7 45
Piliscsaba	4 35	5 52	6 49	8 42	12 46	3 48	8 36
Obuda	5 22	6 43	7 44	9 30	1 37	4 39	9 30
Budapest Wbhf	5 50	7 10	8 15	9 55	2 8	5 5	10 0

KARANSEBES and ORVARALJA.

Karánsebes.........dep	...	7a0	11a30	6p25	...
Bauczar..................	4a8	9 36	2 7	8 33	...
Orváralja 232 ......arr	7 15	...	5 20	...	...

Orvaralja ....dep	...	7a37	...	6p0	...
Bauczar	4a30	11 30	2p40	9 17	...
Karánsebes (227)...arr	6 35	1 40	5 30	...	...

VACZ and IPOLYSAG.

Vácz..............dep	...	6a49	10a42	3p42	8p0	...	...
Diósjenő.............	5a10	8 1	11 54	5 14	9 18	...	...
: Romhány ...arr	5 50	8 59	12 43	6 19	1012	...	...
Ipolyság 232A arr	...	9 42	1 13	6 35	1042	...	...

Ipolysag ....dep	3a40	6a39	9a5	3p51	...	...	...
: Romhány ...dep	4 0	7 10	9 44	4 10	8p26	...	...
Diósjenő..............	5 1	8 2	1044	5 31	9 10	...	...
Vácz 227.........arr	6 2	9 1	1156	6 51	...	...	...

VAGSELLYE and NEGYED.

Vagsellye...... dep	10a20	2p10	8p0	...
Negyed ....arr	11 28	2 57	8 47	...

Negyed...............dep	4a55	12p23	4p36	...	...	...
Vagsellye 227 .....arr	5 42	1 10	5 35	...	...	...

For Fares, see page 233B.] **HUNGARIAN STATE RAILWAYS.**

VIENNA, BUDAPEST, CZEGLED, TEMESVAR, and VERCIOROVA.

Dist. E.M.	Station		1,2,3	1,2,3	1,2,3	Ex2	Ex2	Ex.2	1,2,3	1,2,3	1,2,3	1,2,3	Ex2	Ex2	1,2,3	Ex2		Ex2	Ex1	1,2,3	1,2,3
				a.m.		a.m.		a.m.		a.m.	p.m.	p.m.	p.m.	p.m.	p.m.	p m.			p m.	p.m.	p.m.
—	Vienna Staatsbf. ...dep	...	...	6 40	...	7 45	...	9 25	...	9 32	1215	1 30	2 10	2 55	3 30	4 50	...	...	6 51	7 30	1110
6¾	Stadlau	...	...	7 6	...	7 59	...	...	...	9 53	1236	1 56	...	...	3 51	...	...	...	...	7 51	SC
28½	Marchegg	...	...	8 17	...	8 45	...	10 13	...	1114	1 38	3 18	3 5	3 47	5 0	5 42	...	...	7 43	9 6	1245
32¼	Deveny-Ujfalu	...	...	8 29	...	8 54	...	...	...	1130	—	3 31	...	...	5 26	...	...	...	B	9 17	1257
40½	Pozsony (Pressburg)... arr	...	...	8.58	a.m.	9 9	a.m.	10 45	...	1152	...	3 58	3 29	4 8	5 36	6 3	...	...	8 4	9 40	1 20
	Pozsony (Pressburg)... dep	...	...	—	5 25	—	6 15	10 50	...	1212	...	4 18	3 33	4 12	6 34	6 7	...	...	8 8	1045	1 42
56½	Szencz	...	...	...	6 22	...	6 39	RC	...	1252	...	4 58	...	...	7 30	RC	...	...	...	1127	2 19
66¼	Némétdioszeg	...	...	...	6 45	...	6 54	...	...	1 9	...	5 19	...	...	7 53	...	...	...	...	1150	2 37
70¾	Galanta ...arr	...	...	...	6 56	...	7 1	11 32	...	1 18	Ex3	5 30	RC	...	8 4	6 46	...	a.m.	8 47	12 1	2 46
...	ODERBERG 253A ...dep	...	5p45	1,2,3	1a10	...	1a10	...	...	3a20	9a50	...	...	...		...	...	1045	...	—	5p45
...	ZSOLNA 233B ...dep	...	9p27	a.m.	3a51	...	3a51	...	a.m.	6a53	1227	...	...	...	...	...	...	8p20	...	...	9p27
...	Galanta ...dep	...	2 a1	5 40	7 17	...	7 12	11 33	10 0	1 26	3 54	5 35	...	...	...	6 47	...	6 57	8 48	...	2 55
77¾	Vagsellye	...	2 15	5 56	7 33	...	...	11 44	1023	1 41	...	5 50	...	...	...	...	...	RC	...	...	3 9
90¾	Totmegyer	...	2 49	6 31	8 10	...	RC	12 2	—	2 13	...	6 21	...	...	...	...	...	7 27	B	...	3 40
97	Ersekújvár ... arr	...	3 1	6 45	8 24	...	7 49	12 12	p.m.	2 25	4 31	6 35	4 44	5 24	...	7 20	...	7 37	9 21	p.m.	3 52
	Ersekújvár ... dep	...	3 13	7 0	—	...	7 55	12 18	2 18	2 47	4 37	6 50	4 50	5 30	...	7 26	...	7 43	9 27	8 20	4 10
124¼	Párkány Nána 232A ...	...	4 24	8 40	...	...	8 31	12 56	3 31	3 57	5 12	8 7	5 29	...	...	...	...	8 25	...	9 29	5 15
140½	Nagy-Maros	...	5 10	9 34	...	...	...	...	4 22	4 42	...	9 8	...	...	...	...	...	...	...	1028	6 43
152¼	Vacz 226A	...	5 45	1016	...	...	9 11	1 31	4 55	5 19	5 51	9 45	6 9	...	...	...	...	9 10	...	1056	7 18
172¾	Budapest Westbf. ...arr	...	6 40	1125	...	...	9 40	2 6	5 55	6 10	6 20	1035	6 40	7 10	...	9 5	...	9 45	11 5	1150	8 10
395¾	BELGRADE 225A ...arr	...	...	...	...	...	...	...	...	...	...	...	...	...	...		...	...	5a58	...	...
From Pest.		1,2,3	Ex2	Ex2	1,2,3	1,2,3	Ex3	Ex.2	1,2,3			1,2,3		1,2,3	Ex2	Ex2	Ex2	1,2,3	Ex1	2&3	
		a.m.	a.m.	a.m.	a.m.	a.m.	p.m.	p.m.	p.m.					p.m	p.m.	p.m. SC	a.m.	p.m.	p.m.		
	Budapest Westbf. ...dep	5 40	7 0	8 25	8 40	1120	2 25	2 40	4 30	...	...	...	...	8 5	9 35	1015	1050	1055	1145	...	...
5	Kobanya	5 59	7 12	...	8 58	1142	2 37	...	4 49	...	...	...	...	8 25	9 47	1026	11 2	1112	...	...	...
22¼	Monor	6 51	7 37	RC	9 50	1242	3 3	3 14	5 47	...	...	...	...	9 11	SC	1054	...	12 4	B	...	...
45¼	Czegléd 227B ... arr	7 44	8 9	9 25	1039	1 44	3 35	3 44	6 45	...	...	...	...	10 1	1039	1129	1211	1 10	1256	...	...
	Czegléd 227B ... dep	8 1	—	9 31	1048	2 50	—	3 50	6 55	...	...	...	...	1015	—	1135	—	1 20	1 1	...	...
56	Nagykörös ......a.m.	8 36	...	9 51	1116	3 23	...	4 10	7 25	...	...	...	...	1040	...	1154	...	1 47	...	...	...
65¼	Kecskemét 226A 4 44	9 12	...	10 9	1152	3 52	...	4 27	7 50	...	...	...	...	11 5	...	12 9	...	2 9	1 32	a.m.	...
80¾	Kiskunfelegyhaza 5 39	9 56	2&3	1037	1231	5 20	1,2,3	4 56	8 40	...	...	...	...	1146	...	1233	...	2 46	...	3 21	1,2,3
118	Szeged 230A.. arr 7 37	12 3	p.m.	1141	2 21	7 9	p.m.	6 0	1029	...	...	...	...	1 14	...	1 35	...	—	2 55	5 37	a.m.
	Szeged 230A.. dep —	—	1 19	1156	2 57	—	5 40	6 10	—	...	...	...	...	2 9	—		...	...	3 1	—	4 25
121¾	Szöreg	...	1 33	12 6	3 11	...	5 53	6 19	...	...	...	...	...	2 20	...	...	...	...	...	...	4 41
139¾	Valkany 227A	...	2 40	1237	3 59	...	6 38	6 50	...	...	...	...	...	3 2	...	...	...	...	...	...	5 26
152¼	Nagykikinda 227B	...	3 14	1259	4 39	...	7 24	7 14	...	...	...	...	...	3 41	...	...	...	...	...	...	6 2
164	Zsombolya 227B	...	—	1 20	5 8	...	7 56	7 37	...	...	...	a.m	...	4 19	...	...	...	...	...	...	6 38
188¼	Temesvár 227 ... arr	...	p.m.	2 6	6 6	...	9 10	8 22	...	...	...		—	5 17	...	...	...	...	4 50	...	7 36
	Temesvár 227 ... dep	...	2 21	—	6 40	...	—	8 40	...	...	...	5 49	...	7 55	...	...	...	...	4 55	...	—
191½	Temesvár-Gyarvaros	...	2 37	...	6 52	...	...	8 46	...	...	...	5 57	...	8 5	...	...	...	...	...	...	...
210	Nagytopoly	...	3 30	...	7 59	...	...	SC	...	...	...	6 57	...	8 49	...	...	...	...	...	...	...
225½	Lugos	...	4 38	...	8 46	...	...	9 45	...	...	...	7 49	...	9 42	...	...	...	...	5 58	...	...
249¾	Karansebes 226A	...	6 11	...	9 57	...	...	10 38	...	...	...	9 9	...	1116	...	...	...	...	6 48	...	...
262¾	Temesszlatina	...	6 53	...	—	...	...	...	...	...	...	9 53	...	1156	...	...	...	...	...	...	2&3
274	Porta Orientalis	...	7 40	...	...	...	...	...	...	...	...	1046	...	1242	...	...	...	...	...	...	a.m.
291½	Mehadia	...	8 37	...	...	...	...	...	...	...	...	1142	...	1 47	...	...	...	...	...	...	6 2
294	Herkulesfurdo	...	8 51	...	...	...	...	12 32	...	...	...	1153	...	2 1	...	...	...	...	8 48	...	6 32
305¾	Orsova	...	9 19	...	...	...	...	1 11	...	...	...	1233	...	3 11	...	...	...	...	9 30	...	7 20
308¾	Verciorova ¶ ...arr	...	...	...	...	...	...	1 20	...	...	...	1242	...	3 21	...	...	...	...	9 40	...	...
546	BUCHAREST 324A...arr	...	...	...	...	...	...	11a25	...	...	...	1025	...	7a50	...	...	...	...	6p34	...	...

RC—Restaurant Car. SC—Sleeping Car. ¶—Customs Examination.
B—Sleeping Car Co.'s Express, from Vienna daily; from Budapest on Monday, Wednesday and Saturday only.

TEMESVAR and BAZIAS.

E.M.							
	Temesvar Jos dep	6 a4	11a20	2p30	6 p24	8p48
15	Szephely 227	6 50	12 5	3 14	7 10	9 27
21½	Vejte 227B	7 3	12 18	3 35	7 24	9 42
46½	Versecz	8 18	1 2?	4 38	8 36	1058
59	Karasjeszenö 227	8 51	2 1	6 1	9 11	1135
75½	Báziás ...arr	9 25	2 36	6 28	9 43	1210

Bazias ...dep	3a23	5a48	8a42	12p12	4p26
Karasjeszenö ...dep	4 9	6 32	9 33	12 59	5 15
Versecz	4 46	7 10	1010	1 53	6 10
Vejte ...dep	6 2	8 19	1116	2 59	7 22
Szephely	6 16	8 31	1128	3 13	7 41
Temesvar 227... arr	7 0	9 10	1212	3 55	8 25

SZEPHELY and BOKA.

Szephely ...dep	7a25	3p50	9 p35
Csak	7 53	4 16	9 55
Boka 227B...arr	9 47	5 59	...

Boka ...dep	...	8 a37	5 p0
Csak	5a40	10 39	6 38
Szephely 227arr	6 1	11 0	6 55

Szephely to Liebling, 7.0, 8.45 a.m., 12.23, 3.30, 7.50, 9.36 p.m. From Liebling 5.30, 7.55, 10.47 a.m., 2.34, 6.35, 8.45 p.m.

KARASJESZENÖ and STAJERLAKANINA.

E.M.							
	Karasjeszenö ...dep	...	9a30	2p18	6 p6	...	1131
16¾	Rakasd	a.m.	1015	3 47	6 51	p.m.	1244
23¾	Oraviczabánya 227B	7 50	1048	4 19	7 10	9 0	1 16
34¾	Lissava	9 12	1155	—	—	1018	—
44¾	Stajerlakanina arr	1059	1 29	...	...	12 5	...

Stajerlakanina...dep	...	3a30	...	11a54	5p20
Lissava	a.m.	5 29	...	1 55	7 15
Oraviczábánya	2 25	7 0	11a0	3 17	8 23
Rakasd	2 54	7 31	1129	3 33	—
Karasjeszenö ...arr	4 0	8 38	1237	4 15	...

TEMESVAR and BUZIASFÜRDÖ.

Temesvár ...dep	8 a10	3p29	8p34	...	...
Tesöld	8 23	3 47	8 47	...	...
Buziásfürdö 227 arr	10 1	5 9	10 9	...	...

Buziásfürdö ...dep	5a20	10a50	7p25	...	...	...
Tesöld	7 2	12 10	9 1	...	...	...
Temesvár 227 ...arr	7 15	12 22	9 12	...	...	...

VERSECZ and MAROS ILLYE.

Versecz ...dep	...	3 a15	...	...	8a22	2p18	...
Gatalja	...	5 11	...	8a17	10 8	5 59	...
Buziásfürdö 227...	...	6 34	...	9 38	—	7 24	...
Lugos	4a31	7 39	9a38	1039	4 p25	8 28	...
Marzsina	7 29	—	11 51	—	6 33	—	...
Maros Illye ...arr	9 20	...	1 11	...	7 56	...	...

Maros Illye dep	...	...	...	7 a20	...	...	3p21	...	5p35	...
Marzsina	...	...	3 a30	8 53	...	...	4 53	...	7 48	...
Lugos	...	3a29	5 55	10 49	12p20	...	7 0	7p20	—	...
Buziásfürdö	3a15	4 36	—	—	1 32	...	—	8 42	...	...
Gatalja	5 0	6 12	...	...	2 58	6 p6	...	—	...	...
Versecz ...arr	...	7 50	...	...	4 44	8 16	...	...	...	...

VERCIOROVA, BUDAPEST, MARCHEGG, and VIENNA.

THROUGH CARRIAGE.—Budapest to Berlin in 12.20 p.m. and 6.50 p.m. from Budapest.

	1,2,3	1,2,3	Ex1	1,2,3	1,2,3	1,2,3	Ex2	1,2,3	Ex2			2 & 3	1,2,3	1,2,3	Ex 2	1,2,3	2&3	1,2,3
BUCHAREST 324A dep	...	...	1250	...	9p45	...	...	...	6 p5	...	...	...	...	...	...	...	...	...
			p.m.		a.m.	p.m.			a.m.				a.m.				p.m.	
Verciorova (Passport Exam.) dep	...	...	7 50	...	1155	..	...	...	1 51	...	...	...	...	...	...	...	...	...
Orsova	...	...	8 20	...	1 15	2 45	...	...	3 3	...	...	...	5 16	...	...	...	5 31	...
Herkulesfurdo	...	...	8 51	...	1 57	3 23	...	...	3 36	...	...	...	5 52	...	...	...	7 10	...
Mehadia	...	...	...	...	2 16	3 37	...	...	SC	...	...	...	6 6	...	...	...	7 40	...
Porta Orientalis	...	...	C	...	3 28	4 54	...	...	4 42	...	...	...	7 19	...	...	...	—	...
Temes-Szlatina	a.m.	...	...	...	4 3	5 29	...	...	...	...	...	...	7 58	...	...	...	...	...
Karànsebes	3 46	...	11 7	...	4 59	6 16	...	...	5 43	...	...	...	9 19	...	...	...	...	...
Lugos	4 52	...	1154	...	6 15	7 23	...	...	6 31	...	...	...	1055	...	...	...	...	...
Nagytopoly	5 33	...	...	...	6 47	7 59	...	...	RC	...	...	...	1132	...	...	...	...	...
Temesvár-Gyarvaros	6 34	...	...	...	7 32	8 47	...	...	7 28	...	...	...	1223	...	...	...	1,2,3	...
Temesvár Jos. ... arr	6 41	a.m.	1 2	...	7 39	8 53	...	...	7 34	...	...	...	1230	a.m.	p.m.	p.m.	p.m.	...
Temesvár Jos. ... dep	—	4 23	1 8	...	9 45	/	...	...	7 48	...	...	...	—	9 25	1 11	1 33	4 24	...
Zsombolya	...	5 30	...	...	1047	—	...	...	8 28	...	...	...	...	1028	1 58	2 55	5 37	...
Nagykikinda	...	6 15	...	...	1128	...	...	...	8 48	...	...	...	...	11 8	2 17	3 26	6 9	...
Valkany	...	6 42	...	...	12 5	...	...	...	9 10	...	...	...	...	1145	2 40	3 55	6 52	...
Szöreg	...	7 26	...	...	1246	...	...	...	9 39	...	...	...	...	1232	3 10	4 40	7 36	...
Szegéd arr	...	7 36	2 49	...	1257	a.m.	a.m.	...	9 48	...	...	...	a.m.	1243	3 17	4 52	7 48	p.m.
Szegéd dep	...	—	2 56	a.m.	1 40	4 30	6 5	...	9 59	...	...	...	8 40	1 23	3 23	—	—	5 7
Kiskunfelegyhaza	...	...	C	4 43	3 26	6 19	7 2	...	11 2	...	...	p.m.	1036	3 6	4 24	...	...	7 5
Kecskemét	...	...	...	5 18	3 59	6 58	7 26	...	1129	...	..	1 15	1148	4 2	4 53	...	...	7 49
Nagykörös	...	Ex2	...	5 39	4 31	7 23	7 43	...	1146	Ex3	...	2 4	1219	4 34	5 9	...	Ex2	8 12
Czegléd arr	...	a.m.	4 42	6 0	4 54	7 48	8 0	a.m.	12 4	p.m.	..	2 40	1248	4 56	5 28	...	p.m.	8 37
Czegléd dep	...	6 24	4 47	6 29	5 13	—	8 5	8 10	1210	1224	...	—	1 32	5 12	5 34	...	8 26	8 50
Monor	...	...	...	7 27	6 7	...	8 45	9 24	1244	...	...	...	2 43	6 24	...	...	9 2	9 50
Kobanya	...	7 23	5 57	8 28	7 0	...	9 14	1027	1 13	1 38	...	...	3 48	7 26	...	...	9 27	1046
Budapest Westbhf. arr	...	7 35	6 10	8 40	7 15	...	9 25	1045	1 25	1 50	...	...	4 5	7 45	6 35	...	9 40	11 0
BELGRADE 225A...dep	...	...	1039	...	...	...	...	...	...	...	...	...	...	...	...	...	...	...

	1,2,3	1,2,3	1,2,3	Ex1	Ex2	Ex2	1,2,3	1,2,3	Ex3	Ex2	Ex2	1,2,3	1,2,3	Ex2		Ex 2	1,2,3	1,2,3	1,2,3
	a.m.			a.m.	a.m.	a.m.	a.m.	noon	p.m.	p.m.	p.m.	p.m.	p.m.	p.m.		p.m.	p.m.	p.m.	
Budapest Westb. dp	5 25	...	...	6 50	7 5	7 55	9 15	12 0	1220	2 0	2 30	2 10	2 35	5 15		6 50	8 40	9 30	...
Vacz	6 26	...	...	...	7 39	...	1012	1256	1250	...	3 0	2 46	3 39	...		...	9 34	1023	...
Nagymaros	6 59	...	...	...	...	RC	1043	1 24	...	...	...	3 21	4 13	...		...	10 8	1054	...
Párkány Nana	7 57	...	...	...	8 26	...	1134	2 5	1 32	3 4	...	4 0	5 7	...		7 58	1054	1142	...
Ersekújvár ... arr	8 55	a.m.	...	8 23	9 6	9 31	1233	3 1	2 9	3 38	4 8	—	6 21	6 52		8 34	1153	1240	...
Ersekújvár ... dep	—	3 50	...	8 29	9 12	9 37	1251	3 11	2 15	3 44	4 14	...	7 3	6 58		8 40	12 5	1255	...
Tótmegyer		4 7	a.m.	...	9 23	...	1 4	3 26	...	RC	...	...	7 18	...		RC	1218	1 8	...
Vágsellye		4 44	6 22	...	9 43	...	1 37	3 56	...	...	...	...	7 54	...		...	1252	1 41	...
Galánta arr		4 59	6 45	9 3	9 54	1011	1 49	4 10	2 50	4 17	...	...	8 10	...		9 15	1 5	1 54	...
ZSOLNA 233B arr		...	...	C	1p30	...	6 p2	...	6 p2	...	...	...	12a24	RC		12a24	6a10	SC	...
ODERBERG 253A arr		...	...	...	5 p6	...	8p30	...	8p30	...	...	...	2 a55	...		2 a55	9a30	...	...
Galánta dep		5 3	7 15	9 3	RC	1012	1 59	4 25	—	4 18	4 47	...	—	...		9 23	—	2 2	...
Németdiószeg		5 15	7 27	...		...	2 8	5 5	Restaurant Car.	...	4 53	...	...	...		9 31	...	2 14	...
Szencz		5 43	7 54	...	...		2 27	5 32		...	...	Ex2	...	...		9 47	...	2 38	...
Pozsony (Pressburg) ... arr		6 40	8 50	9 45	...	1051	3 14	6 12		4 57	5 27	p.m	...	8 11		10 14	...	3 15	a.m.
Pozsony (Pressburg) ... dep		7 10	—	9 49	...	1055	3 24	6 28		5 1	5 31	7 34	...	8 15		—	...	3 43	6 0
Dévényujfalu		7 33	a.m.	...	...	...	3 50	6 59		...	...	7 51	...	...			...	4 5	6 20
Marchegg		7 56	1150	1018	...	1125	4 20	7 25		5 30	6 0	8 6	...	8 44		...	...	4 35	6 39
Stadlau		9 1	1252	...	...	...	5 20	8 23	RC	...	...	...	...	...		...	...	5 30	7 32
Vienna Staatsbf. ...arr		9 20	1 15	11 4	...	1214	5 40	8 45		6 20	6 55	9 5	...	9 35	...	...	...	5 50	7 50

Extra.—Szeged to Felegyhaza 2.35, 8.10 p.m.; Galánta to Pozsony 4.50 a.m.

C—Sleeping Car Co.'s Express, from Verciorova on Sun., Wed., and Friday only; from Budapest daily.

VALKANY and TEMESVAR.

E.M								Temesvár dep	...	7 a4	...	1p21	6 p10
	Valkany dep	...	7 a0	12p44	4 p5	7 p0							
15½	Nagyszentmiklós	...	8 20	1 28	5 11	8 10		Sz. Andras	...	7 28	...	1 57	6 43
27¼	Perjámos	4 a15	9 30	—	6 6	9 9		Varjas	3 a0	8 50	...	3 23	8 12
32¼	Varjas	4 40	10 3	...	6 28	9 26		Perjámos	3 27	9 22	p.m.	3 53	8 29
50¼	Sz. Andras	6 20	11 44	...	7 49	—		Nagyszentmiklós	4 24	10 24	1 48	5 2	—
59	Temesvár 227 arr	6 45	12 10	...	8 15	...		Valkány (227)	5 21	11 21	2 33	6 2	...

ASZOD and LOSONCZ.

Aszód dep	4 a1	9 a48	...	4 p0	7 p20	Losoncz dep	...	5a59	...	2 p41	7 p29	...
Galgaguta	5 17	11 7	...	5 11	8 36	Szecseny	...	7 40	...	4 19	9 15	...
Balassagyarmat	6 58	12 32	1 p40	6 45	9 49	Balassagyarmat	4a18	8 50	3 p6	5 19	9 56	...
Szecseny	7 46	—	2 41	7 34	—	Galgaguta	5 47	10 19	4 31	6 48	...	...
Losoncz 232A arr	9 23	...	4 21	9 10	...	Aszód 231 arr	7 3	11 37	5 42	8 9	...	...
Losoncz dep	6 a15	10a20	3 p30	...	...	Gacs dep	7 a20	12p22	5 p2	...	...	...
Gacs arr	6 40	10 45	3 55	...	...	Losoncz arr	7 43	12 45	5 25	...	...	...

MISKOLCZ, TORNA, and KASSA.

E.M																
	Miskolcz dep	...	3a41	6 a0	10a35	1 p36	4 p10	7 p20	Kassa dep	...	...	6 a45	12p17	1 p0	5 p31	9 p36
6¼	Sajo-Ecseg	...	4 8	6 39	10 59	2 12	4 38	7 43	Szepsi	...	6 a8	8 35	1 36	2 33	6 50	11 7
23	Szendro	...	5 24	8 5	12 10	3 40	5 49	8 55	Torna	3a22	6 42	9 54	2 23	3 47	7 30	11 40
42½	Torna	4a29	6 53	10 7	1 37	5 55	7 3	10 29	Szendro	5 23	7 54	11 11	3 30	5 52	8 54	...
47¾	Szepsi	5 4	7 17	10 37	2 5	6 51	...	10 52	Sajo-Ecseg	6 50	9 8	12 20	4 38	7 43	10 ...	...
67½	Kassa (231) arr	6 33	8 39	11 57	3 29	8 46	...	...	Miskolcz 232A	7 25	9 31	12 44	5 0	8 17	10 31	...

Szepsi dep	8 a43	10a40	2 p48	7 p0	11p29	Meczenzef dep	3a53	6 a27	9 a46	12p49	5 p25	...
Meczenzef arr	9 29	11 23	3 37	7 52	12 21	Szepsi arr	4 49	7 10	10 27	1 30	6 10	...

PAPA and CSORNA.

Papa dep	5 a25	3 p20	Czorna dep	8 a42	6p20
Egyed-Rábacsanak	6 38	4 52	Egyed-Rábacsanak	9 8	7 7
Csorna arr	7 3	5 29	Papa 225B arr	10 19	8 49

PETRE and PANCSOVA.

Petre dep	6 a50	11 a3	8 p10	Pancsova dep	3 a44	6 a38	1 p35
Pancsova 227B arr	8 2	12 19	9 22	Petre 227B arr	4 55	7 50	2 55

NYIREGYHAZA and POLGAR.

Nyiregyháza dep	7 a10	10 a4	5 p55	Polgar dep	3 a0	...	1p48
Görögszallas	8 1	10 30	6 46	Tiszalök	4 30	8 a58	3 25
Tiszalök	9 15	11 8	7 47	Görögszallas	5 35	9 42	4 38
Polgar 228 arr	1050	...	9 8	Nyiregyháza arr	6 10	10 3	5 15

E.M								
	Nyiregyháza dep	7 a50	2 p10	7 p57	Nyiradony dep	5 a8	11a30	5 p20
24½	Nyiradony arr	9 25	4 7	9 21	Nyiregyháza arr	6 40	1 11	6 40

VEJTE and BOKSANBANYA.

Station					
Vejte ....dep	7a30	12p30	4p27	9 p58	...
Gátalja	8 12	1 22	5 22	10 42	...
Zsidovin	8 51	2 37	6 14	11 21	...
Boksánbánya...arr	9 22	3 10	6 45	11 53	...

Station						
Boksánbánya...dep	3a30	8a53	12p39	4p51	...	...
Zsidovin	4 23	9 24	1 15	5 20	...	...
Gátalja	5 8	1013	2 7	6 1	...	...
Vejte ....arr	5 45	1046	2 46	6 34	...	...

ORAVICZA and RESICZABANYA.

Station						
Oraviczabánya ...dep	1 a30	...	11a15	3 p5	...	...
Zsidovin	4 41	...	2 20	5 57	...	...
Boksánbánya	5 32	9a40	3 26	7 30	12a19	...
Resiczabanya......arr	6 31	1054	4 46	8 45	1 18	...

Station								
Resiczabanya....dep	2 a8	...	7 a8	...	10a18	3 p26	6p20	...
Boksánbánya	3 2	4 a7	8 19	9a30	11 38	5 16	7 28	...
Zsidovin	—	4 43	—	10 10	—	6 12	—	...
Oraviczabánya 227...	...	7 31	...	1 41	...	8 55	...	...

VERSECZ and KEVEVARA.

Station				
Versecz ....dep	5 a9	8 a35	6 p9	...
Alibunar	6 25	10 20	7 40	...
Petre	6 41	10 58	8 15	...
Kevevara ....arr	...	12 35	10 2	...

Station					
Kevevara ......dep	3a18	...	1p15	...	...
Petre	5 15	8 a0	3 25	...	...
Alibunar	5 32	8 17	3 51	...	...
Versecz ....arr	6 48	9 34	5 3	...	...

TORONTAL-SZECSANY and VERSECZ.

Station				
Torontalszecsany dep	5 a30	8 a11	8a21	6p45
Boka 227	5 49	8 27	8 44	7 2
N.-Margita	7 11	—	10 34	8 28
Versecz ....arr	8 3	...	11 34	9 20

Station					
Versecz ....dep	5 a5	9a18	1p48	...	...
N.-Margita	5 57	1030	2 49	p.m.	...
Boka	7 14	1226	4 27	6 2	...
Torontalszecs. arr	7 30	1246	4 43	6 18	...

SZEGED and NAGY-BECSKEREK.

Station							
Szeged .... dep	1a55	4a51	11a46	12p1	2p29	...	6p15
Tiszaszentmiklós...	3 39	6 40	...	1 58	4 33	...	8 0
Karlova	4 49	7 42	1 50	3 5	5 35	8 p0	8 51
N.-Becskerek ...arr	6 49	9 24	3 11	4 50	7 17	9 21	...

Station								
N.-Becskerek ...dep	...	6a21	7 a10	10a0	11a27	1p13*	7p18	...
Karlova	4a35	7 46	9 6	1142	12 52	3 10	9 40	...
Tiszaszentmiklós ...	5 28	...	9 59	—	...	4 4	10 40	...
Szeged ....arr	7 15	9 41	11 45	...	2 55	5 55	12 34	...

Station							
Karlova ......dep	5a10	7a58	1 p5	3p29	9p35	...	...
Nagy-Kikinda...arr	5 45	8 33	1 40	4 4	1013	...	...

Station						
Nagy-Kikinda...dep	3a46	6a36	11a40	2p25	7p20	...
Karlova ....arr	4 25	7 13	12 14	2 59	7 55	...

Nagy-Kikinda and Nyerö (In 40 minutes). { Nagy-Kikinda dep. 6.40 a.m., 3.36 and 7.40 p.m. Nyerö dep. 5.15, 9.30 a.m., and 4.56 p.m.

†—From or at Nagybecskerekbégapart.] **NAGYBECSKEREK and ZSOMBOLYA.** [A—Via Bégafö.

Station									
Nagybecskerek dep		2†26	3†33	6a25	...	10a59	11†55	4 p0	5†25
Sandorudvar		:	3 52	6 56	...	11 21	:	4 39	:
Torontalszecsany ...		A	4 55	8 20	8 a5	12 54	A	6 35	A
Modos	3a50	:	5 14	8 41	8 44	1 40	:	7 9	:
Zsombolya 227 arr	6 28	6 34	...	...	1159	4 16	4 5	9 30	9 35

Station								
Zsombolya ......dep	...	4a24	4a50	12p10	2p17	...	5p30	5p40
Modos	4a33	:	7 35	:	4 40	...	7 56	:
Torontalszecsany ...	5 10	A	8 2	A	5 9	6p50	—	A
Sandorudvar	6 20	:	9 0	:	6 8	7 55	...	:
Nagybecskerek arr	6†56	8†23	9 28	4 †10	6 40	8†16	...	9†34

MODOS and TEMESVAR.

Station			
Modos ....dep	5a20	2p10	6 p59
Temesvár Jozsef arr	7 21	4 42	9 15

Station			
Temesvár Jozsef...dep	5a31	11 a0	2 p19
Modos ....arr	7 28	1 22	4 15

†—From or at Nagybecskerekbégapart.] **NAGYBECSKEREK and PANCSOVA.**

Station					
Nagybecskerek dep	4 †30	...	8a10	5 p40	...
Sandorudvar	4 56	...	9 2	6 13	...
Antalfalva	6 27	6 a50	10 30	7 33	...
Pancsova 227A ...arr	...	8 18	12 7	9 3	...

Station							
Pancsova ....dep	5a10	12p30	3 p26	...	...	...	...
Antalfalva	6 51	2 38	5 15	...	...	...	...
Sandorudvar	8 9	4 39	6 40	...	...	...	...
Nagybecskerek 227B...arr	8 38	5 †4	7 9	...	...	...	...

CZEGLED and SZOLNOK.

Station	a.m.	a.m.	a.m.	a.m.	p.m.	p.m.	p.m.	p.m.	p.m.	p.m.	nigt
Czegléd	5 26	8 12	8 38	11 5	1 55	3 41	5 40	7 20	9 20	1045	1217
Abony	5 53	8 29	9 1	1132	2 21	3 59	6 4	7 46	9 43	11 2	1234
Szolnok	6 11	8 42	9 18	1150	2 39	4 15	6 22	8 5	10 0	1117	1249

Station	a.m.	a.m.	a.m.	a.m.	a.m.	a.m.	a.m.	p.m.	p.m.	p.m.	p.m.
Szolnok	3 0	4 30	5 5	5 46	6 50	9 42	11 45	1235	4 21	7 44	9 7
Abony	3 20	4 45	5 28	6 1	7 11	10 5	12 0	1255	4 41	8 1	9 27
Czegléd	3 43	5 2	5 51	6 18	7 34	1030	12 17	1 18	5 4	8 18	9 50

KARCZAG and TISZAFURED.

Station			
Karczag ....dep	6a40	2 p40	...
Tisza-Fured ....arr	8 28	5 11	...

Station				
Tisza-Fured ......dep	3a30	11 a0	...	...
Karczag ....arr	5 12	1 3	...	...

SZOLNOK and KISKUNFELEGYHAZA.

Station			
Szolnok ....dep	3a39	12 0	4p40
Lakytelek	5 37	2 29	6 53
Kiskunfélegyháza ...arr	6 39	3 49	8 8

Station			
Kiskunfélegyháza dep	3a35	12p46	5p16
Lakytelek	4 45	1 51	6 42
Szolnok ....arr	6 40	3 34	8 33

KISKUNFELEGY and KISKUNHALAS.

Station				
Kiskunfélegyháza dep	...	7a12	1 p0	8 p45
Kiskunmajsa	4a38	8 30	2 0	9 37
Kiskúnhalas 225A arr	5 30	9 25	2 48	...

Station				
Kiskúnhalas ....dep	...	7 a0	4 p42	7p42
Kiskunmajsa	3 a39	8 16	5 40	8 30
Kiskunfélegyháza.....arr	4 35	9 23	6 43	...

PUSPOKLADANY and SZEGHALOM.

Station			
Püspökladány ....dep	7 a44	1 p55	...
Füzesgyarmat	9 44	3 49	...
Szeghalom ....arr	10 5	4 10	...

Station			
Szeghalom ....dep	10a35	5 p50	...
Füzesgyarmat	11 0	6 17	...
Püspökladány (233) ....arr	1 0	8 49	...

TARACZKOZ and NYERESHAZA. E.M. 9¼

Station			
Taraczkoz ....dep	6a45	12p29	4p31
Nyereshaza ....arr	7 48	1 32	5 29

Station				
Nyereshaza ....dep	8 a8	2p55	5p40	...
Taraczkoz (228) arr	9 2	3 50	6 30	...

UNGVAR and NYIREGYHAZA.

Station									
Ungvar ....dep	4 a5	...	7a49	9a41	12p40	2p13	5 p3	p.m.	8p47
Csap (231)	4 42	6a15	8 28	1123	1 38	2 55	5 34	6 25	9 35
Kisvarda	5 39	7 20	—	1226	2 39	—	—	7 22	—
Nyiregyháza arr	6 53	8 45	...	1 44	4 0	...	...	8 37	...

Station									
Nyiregyháza ...dep		6a55	...	11a12	...	2p20	...	7p20	9p10
Kisvarda	a.m.	8 29	a.m.	12 33	p.m.	3 52	p.m.	8 42	1033
Csap	6 46	9 27	1040	1 30	3 49	4 48	6 30	9 35	1125
Ungvar 231 arr	7 29	1015	1127	2 59	4 42	...	7 1	1033	...

Station				
Nyiregyháza......dep	7a12	10a30	2p43	8p50
Nyirbakta 227B	8 41	12 12	4 10	1023
Vásarosnamény arr	9 40	1 16	5 9	1125

Station				
Vásarosnamény ...dep	3a56	11a10	2 p0	5p52
Nyirbakta	5 1	12 13	3 22	6 54
Nyiregyháza....arr	6 30	1 39	5 20	8 16

Station			
Kisvárda ......dep	9a20	2 p44	8p43
Nyirbakta 227B arr	11 7	4 0	1012

Station			
Nyirbakta......dep	5a44	12p35	4p50
Kisvárda 227B arr	7 0	1 54	6 35

Station				
Nyiregyháza ...dep	7a16	10a25	2p10	7p28
Máriapócs	8 36	11 49	3 28	8 38
Mateszalka ......arr	9 55	1 10	4 48	9 50

Station				
Mateszalka ....dep	3a50	10a29	2p10	4p52
Máriapócs	5 4	11 52	3 26	6 0
Nyiregyháza 227A arr	6 6	1 11	4 39	7 10

MISKOLCZ and MEZOCSAT.

Station				
Miskolcz ....dep	7 a6	...	4 p32	7 p18
Mezönyek Ladhaza	7 47	1 p45	5 2	8 0
Mezöcsát ....arr	8 40	2 35	5 56	8 53

Station				
Mezöcsát ....dep	4a15	6a50	11a51	4 p0
Mezönyek Ladhaza	5 12	7 46	12 45	5 0
Miskolcz 231 ......arr	5 39	8 13	...	5 27

DEBRECZEN and SZERENCS.

Station							
Debreczen dep	5a14	8a51	12 p5	2p21	4p28	7p30	10p42
Ujfehértó	6 12	9 39	12 59	3 35	5 18	8 22	11 56
Nyiregyháza	6 50	10 4	1 20	4 8	5 45	9 6	12 23
Gorogszallas	7 23	1025	—	4 30	6 5	9 37	—
Tokaj	7 53	1052	...	5 0	6 28	1010	...
Szerencs 231	8 21	1117	...	5 27	6 53	1045	...

Station							
Szerencs ...dep	...	5a30	8a50	12p5	...	5p41	7 p9
Tokaj	...	6 0	9 18	1238	...	6 9	7 45
Gorogszallas ...	...	6 26	9 42	1 9	...	6 38	8 16
Nyiregyháza ...	5a42	7 20	1014	2 6	4p47	7 20	9 2
Ujfehértó.......	6 13	7 42	1034	2 31	5 21	7 40	9 25
Debreczen 228	7 26	8 33	1124	3 32	6 39	8 30	1024

PUSPOKLADANY, MARAMAROSSZIGET, and KOROSMEZO.

		1,2,3	1,2,3	1,2,3	1,2,3	Ex2	2&3	1,2,3	Ex2	1,2,3
BUDAPEST 233 dp		9p35	1050	...	...	7 a0	...	8a55	2p25	...
		a.m.	a.m.	a.m.	a.m.	a.m.	p.m	p.m.	p.m.	p.m.
Puspokladány dep		1 32	4 0	6 31	8 0	1040	1 50	2 37	6 10	9 10
Kaba		1 48	4 16	6 51	8 24	1054	2 5	2 51	6 22	9 27
Debreczen dep		2 54	5 16	7 47	10 1	1148	2 58	3 53	7 15	1051
Vámospércs		3 22	5 51	—	1041	1212	—	4 29	7 41	1135
Ermihályfalva		3 56	6 27	...	1125	1239	...	5 11	8 10	1215
Nagykaroly		4 58	7 29	...	1230	1 23	...	6 10	8 52	1 17
Gilvàcs		5 26	7 58	...	1256	1 42	...	6 40	9 13	1 50
Szatmár-Nemeti		6 7	8 38	...	1 38	2 10	1,2,3	7 21	9 40	2 31
Halmi		6 42	9 10	...	2 12	2 35	p.m.	7 52	—	3 5
Királyháza		7 33	9 45	...	2 46	3 6	5 59	8 56	...	4 16
Bustyaháza		8 39	—	...	—	3 46	7 11	9 53	...	5 39
Taraczkoz	2&3	9 12	...	...	...	4 6	7 43	1021	...	6 18
Máramarossziget arr	a.m.	9 50	...	...	p.m.	4 28	8 21	1053	...	7 0
Máramarossziget dep	5 45	10 8	...	...	4 42	—	—	1120	...	—
Nagybocskó	6 28	1034	...	...	5 10	...	...	1154	...	...
Raho	7 57	1151	...	...	6 22	...	...	1 24	...	...
Körösmezo arr	9 13	1252	...	...	7 22	...	...	2 34	...	...

		1,2,3	Ex2	1,2,3	2&3	1 2 3	Ex2	1,2,3	1,2,3	1,2,3
				n'gt	a.m.		a.m.		p.m.	
Korosmezo dep		...	...	12 0	3 32	...	9 34	...	1 35	...
Raho		...	...	2 0	4 56	...	1025	...	2 23	...
Nagybocskó		...	...	3 34	6 39	...	1122	...	3 17	...
Máramaros sziget 228 arr		...	...	4 14	7 20	a.m.	1145	...	3 39	p.m
Máramaros sziget 228 dep		...	...	5 10	—	10 7	1155	...	3 55	6 0
Taraczkoz		...	...	5 40	...	1038	1214	...	4 25	6 36
Bustyaháza		a.m.	...	6 11	...	1112	1234	...	4 51	7 10
Királyháza		1 54	...	7 30	...	12 9	1 22	...	5 54	8 54
Halmi		2 33	a.m.	8 4	...	1 32	1 46	p.m.	6 27	9 3
Szatmár		3 24	6 23	8 44	...	2 42	2 12	3 0	7 12	1015
Gilvàcs		3 58	6 49	9 12	...	—	2 32	3 33	7 43	1049
Nagykaroly		4 43	7 14	9 49	...	...	3 2	4 14	8 20	1129
Ermihályfalva	1,2,3	5 47	7 56	1043	...	2&3	3 38	5 20	9 14	1224
Vamospércs	a.m.	6 21	8 20	1115	a.m.	p.m.	4 0	5 55	9 41	1255
Debreczen arr	6 0	6 59	8 45	1146	1050	3 45	4 23	6 32	10 8	1 29
Kaba	6 49	—	9 34	1 6	1156	4 55	5 23	10 6	1145	2 55
Puspokladány	7 5	...	9 45	1 22	1216	5 16	5 35	1024	12 0	3 14
BUDAPEST 233 arr		...	1p50	7 p0	.s.	...	9p40	5a20	6a15	7a35

M. Sziget dep	7 a3	3p22
Szigetkamara	7 12	3 36
Nagybocsko	7 55	4 22
Nagybocskoigyár arr	8 8	4 35

Nagybocskoigyár dep	8a53	5 p57
Nagybocsko	9 14	6 24
Szigetkamara	9 50	7 2
M. Sziget arr	9 58	7 10

M. Sziget. dep	5a52	1p20	3 p40	6‡42
Aknaszlatina arr	6 10	1 43	4 1	7 16
Aknaszlatina dep	6a31	2‡20	4p20	7p32
M. Sziget arr	6 50	2 40	4 39	7 52

‡—Runs until Sept 1st.

Kaba to Nadudvar 7.0, 9.40, 11.5 a.m., 1.15, 3.5, 5.0, 6.32, 10.15 p.m. From Nadudvar 6.6, 7.44, 10.20 a.m. 12.24, 2.10, 4.15, 5.44, 8.44 p.m.

DEBRECZEN and FUZES-ABONY.

Debreczen dep	...	5a20	11a55	5 p3
Ohat-Pusztakócs arr	...	7 50	2 23	7 37
„ „ ...dep	5 a7	8 0	2 30	7 45
Tisza-Füred	5 54	8 45	3 7	8 22
Fuzés-Abony arr	7 19	1017	4 35	...

Fuzes-Abony dep	...	4 a10	12p22	5 a22
Tisza-Füred	4 a24	6 10	1 48	6 48
Ohat-Pusztakócs arr	5 1	6 47	2 29	7 29
„ „ ...dep	5 9	—	2 40	7 39
Debreczen arr	7 42	...	5 25	10 9

Ohat-Pusztakócs dp	8 a5	3 p5	8 p
Polgár 227A arr	9 51	4 45	9 3
Polgár dep	3 a10	11a45	5p4
Ohat-Pusztakócs arr	4 47	1 19	7 2

DEBRECZEN and TISZA-LÖK.

E.M.								
	Debreczen dep	...	5 a30	8 a13	12p22	2p25	4p35	7 p10
23	Hajdudorog	...	7 6	9 36	1 57	4 16	6 10	8 47
35½	**Büdszentmihaly**	3a43	8 1	—	2 49	5 16	7 2	9 39
41	**Tiszalök** arr	4 0	8 20	...	3 8	5 38	7 22	9 58

Tiszalök dep	4 a25	5a57	...	12p40	3p36	8 p0
Büdszentmihaly	4 45	6 15	...	1 0	3 58	8 18
Hajdudorog	5 40	7 3	10a22	1 58	5 1	9 1
Debreczen 227B arr	7 16	8 29	11 41	3 40	6 45	10 37

DEBRECZEN and NAGYVARAD.

Debreczen dep	4a10	8a50	12p18	2p42	4 p8	7 p5
Sarand	4 37	9 18	12 46	3 12	4 35	7 37
Nagyléta-Vertes arr	5 31	1014	...	4 11	...	8 32
Biharpüspoki	6 56	—	3 13	—	7 5	—
Nagyvarad (230A) arr	7 10	...	3 28	...	7 20	...

Nagyvarad dep	...	3a26	...	...	11a36	...	5p1
Biharpüspoki (228)	...	3 42	...	...	11 52	...	5 2
Nagyléta-Vertes dep	3a46	...	5a59	11a50	...	5 p2	...
Sarand	4 35	5 57	6 56	12 50	2 9	6 0	7 4
Debreczen arr	...	6 27	7 30	1 25	2 39	6 35	8 1

NAGYVARAD and ERMIHALYFALVA.

(230A)	a.m.	p.m.	p.m.	
Nagyvarad dep	7 18	12 18	4 45	...
Biharpüspöki	7 34	12 44	4 59	...
Szekelyhid	9 36	2 24	6 42	...
Ermihalyfalva arr	1030	3 12	7 27	...

(228)	a.m.	p.m.	p.m.	
Ermihalyfalva dep	6 25	1 22	5 25	...
Szekelyhid	7 17	2 17	6 28	...
Biharpüspöki	8 49	3 52	8 21	...
Nagyvarad arr	9 1	4 5	8 35	...

Szekelyhid dep	...	9a24	2p27	6 p4
Margitta	5 a10	1052	3 57	8 4
Szilagy-Som arr	7 19	1 6	6 14	102
Szilagy-Somlyo	3 a0	10a45	1p34	7 p46
Margitta	5 24	12 55	4 25	10 1
Szekelyhid arr	6 39	2 6	5 51	...

GILVACS and NAGYSOMKUT.

Gilvacs dep	5 a40	3 p58	...	...
Károlyierdod	6 32	4 47	...	...
Nagysomkut arr	10 30	8 30	...	...

Nagysomkut dep	3 a17	1 p15	...	...	...
Károlyierdod	6 52	5 11	...	...	...
Gilvacs (228) arr	7 37	6 0	...	...	...

KAROLYIERDOD and SZATMARNEMETI.

Karolyierdod dep	5a47	7a11	...	...	5 p6	...
Erdodvar	5 59	7 19	...	...	5 16	...
Szatmár Lippa	6 17	7 32	10a16	1 p9	5 29	8p54
Szatmarhegypiac	6 28	7 43	10 11	1 4	5 41	8 46
Szatmari gozfuresz	7 35	8 34	10 57	1 48	6 36	9 35
Szatmar-Nemeti arr	8 0	8 59	11 20	2 14	7 1	10 0

Szatmar-Nemeti dep	4a48	8a49	11a49	2p30	6 p7	7p13	...
Szatmari gozfuresz	5 11	9 12	12 12	2 56	6 32	7 38	...
Szatmarhegypiac	6 7	10 3	12 59	3 57	7 23	9 9	...
Szatmár Lippa	6 16	9 57	12 54	4 5	7 17	9 20	...
Erdodvar	6 29	...	...	4 18	—	9 39	...
Karolyierdod arr	6 37	...	...	4 26	...	9 54	...

SZATMAR and MATESZALKA

Szatmar dep	7 a30	2 p31	7 p29	...
Mateszalka arr	10 0	4 45	9 59	...

Mateszalka dep	5 a40	10a40	2 p9	...
Szatmar arr	7 50	12 52	5 10	...

SZATMAR and FELSO BANYA.

Szatmar dep	...	6a18	...	2p47	7p36
Szinyervaralya	...	7 56	...	4 4	8 58
Nagy Banya	6a10	9 37	1p20	5 12	1012
Felso Banya arr	6 51	1014	2 1	5 44	1044

Felso Banya dep	5a38	7a20	10a45	2p50	7 p20
Nagy Banya	6 13	7 54	11 17	3 53	7 50
Szinyervaralya	7 14	—	12 16	5 15	—
Szatmar 228 arr	8 30	...	1 30	6 45	...

Nagy Banya dep	9 a25
Alsofernezely arr	9 54
Alsofernezely dep	10a36
Nagy Banya arr	11 2

SZATMAR and FEHER-GYARMAT.

Szatmar dep	6 a42	2 p50	7 p31	...
Feher-Gyarmat arr	8 31	4 30	9 24	..

Feher-Gyarmat dep	6 a20	11a32	5p12	...	...	...
Szatmar arr	8 18	1 25	6 52	...	...	...

NAGY-KAROLY and CSAP.

Nagy-Karoly dep	5a10	11a12	3p45	...	...	...
Mateszalka	6 42	12 47	4 57	...	...	...
Vasarosnameny	7 36	1 42	6 0	...	...	...
Csap arr	9 18	3 20	7 43	...	...	...

Csap dep	2 a5	9 a28	3p50	...	...	...
Vasarosnameny	4 32	11 1	5 44	...	...	...
Mateszalka	5 32	11 50	6 37	...	...	...
Nagy-Karoly arr	6 58	1 7	7 59	...	...	...

NAGY-KAROLY and ZILAH.

N.-Karoly dep	5a30	...	3p10	6p15	...	...
Sarmasag arr	8 18	9a30	6 0	9 7	...	...
Szilagy Som. arr	...	1017	7 2	1026	...	...
Zilah (223) arr	9 38	...	7 18	1030	...	...

Zilah dep	3 a20	...	8 a24	3 p7	...	...
Szilagy S. dep	...	7a30	...	3 20	8p15	...
Sarmasag	4 31	8 12	9 33	4 18	8 58	...
Karoly 228 arr	7 5	...	12 21	7 8	...	...

MARMAROS-SZIGET to AKNASUGATAG and RONASZEK.

E.M.		a.m.	p.m.	
—	M.-Sziget dep	5 †0	1†15	...
12½	Aknasugatag	6 24	2 39	...

	a.m.	p.m.	
Aknasugatag	6†36	2§51	...
M.-Sziget arr	7 59	4 22	...

E.M.		a.m.	a.m.	p.m.
—	**M.-Sziget** dep	5 *0	9 ‖0	1*15
12½	**Ronászék** arr	6 29	1020	2 44

	a.m.	a.m.	p.m.
Ronászék dep	6*46	10 37	3 *1
M.-Sziget arr	8 9	12 0	4 22

†—Weekdays only.
§—Mon., Tues., Wed., and Fri. only.
*—Mon., Tues., Wed., Fri. excepted.
‖—Thurs., Sat. excepted.

BOBA and CSAKTORNYA.

E.M.							
	Boba (229)...dep		5a33	...	10a49	2p31	6p28
11¼	Ukk ...arr		6 27	...	11 35	3 18	7 14
...	,, ...dep		6 44	...	11 43	3 37	7 22
18	Türje (229) ...		7 23	...	12 13	4 10	7 55
31¾	Zalaszentiván-Kisf....	a.m.	8 34	p.m.	1 14	5 29	9 0
36¾	Zalaegerszeg...	4 36	8 49	1220	1 29	5 54	9 15
67	Rédics ...	6 34	—	2 31	—	8 16	—
85¾	**Csáktornya** 229 arr	7 57	...	3 49	...	9 39	...

Csáktornya...dep	...	6a10	...	1 p4	4p36
Rédics ...	...	7 28	...	2 32	6 7
Zalaegerszeg ...	4a57	9 36	1 p46	4 48	8 [illegible]
Zalaszentiván-Kisf.	5 12	10 0	2 2	5 18	8 57
Türje ...	6 13	1058	3 5	6 31	—
Ukk...arr	6 43	1129	3 36	7 4	...
,, ...dep	6 53	1142	3 46	7 15	...
Boba (229) ...arr	7 40	1234	4 36	8 6	...

Zalaszentiván ...dep	2a42	5 a1	7a39	1 p40	4p11	8 p30	9 p50
Zalaszentiván-Kisf. ...	2 50	5 13	7 55	2 1	4 27	8 36	10 6
Zalaegerszeg...arr	3 9	5 32	8 14	2 20	4 42	9 15	10 25

Zalaegerszeg ...dep	4 a12	6 a10	11a24	2p33	6 p2	8p42	1a50
Zalaszentiván-Kisf....	4 31	6 28	11 47	2 53	6 21	9 10	2 9
Zalaszentiván...arr	4 37	6 34	11 53	3 1	6 27	9 16	2 15

Turje ...dep	4 a9	7 a41	8 p0	...	...
Zalacsány ...	5 15	8 58	9 13	...	...
Balaton Szt. György ...arr	6 14	10 10	10 42	...	...

Balaton Szt. György dep	4 a0	12p38	5 p35	...	...
Zalacsány...	5 8	1 49	6 43	...	...
Turje ...arr	6 6	2 54	7 42	...	...

‡—Until 15th September.

Ukk ...dep	...	...	6a58	...	1150	...	3p42	...	7 p27
Tapolcza ...	...	4a21	8 39	a.m.	1 28	...	5 32	p.m.	9 31
Keszthely	1a20	3a29	5 30	9 49	1145	2 32	5 p4	6 54	8‡15	10 32
Balaton S.	1 46	3 55	5 54	1013	12 9	2 58	5 30	7 18	8 41	10 56

Balaton Sz.Gy	2a15	2a45	5 a4	6a43	11a20	1p10	3p20	5p13	7‡40	8p50	11p40
Keszthely ...	2 44	3 11	5 28	7 6	11 55	1 36	3 58	6 39	8 6	9 14	12 6
Tapolcza ...	4 49	...	...	9 10	1 30	...	5 21	...	...	1013	...
Ukk... arr	6 17	...	...	1050	2 51	...	6 46	...	...	...	...

ZAGRAB and CSAKTORNYA.

Zágráb (Agram)...dep	...	...	...	5 a2	7a13	7a37	10a32	2p42	4p28	...	...
Zapresic ...	...	...	...	5 38	8 36	8 9	11 10	3 16	5 3	p.m.	...
Zabok ...arr	...	...	...	6 31	—	9 5	12 6	4 12	5 50	8 30	...
Krapina ...arr	a.m.	a.m.	a.m.	...	noon	9 56	...	5 4	6 54	9 15	...
Varasd ...	4 0	5 34	7 0	9 33	12 0	—	3 9	—	9 14	—	...
Csáktornya 229 ...arr	4 22	5 56	7 22	9 55	1232	...	3 31	...	9 36	...	...

Csáktornya ...dep	...	5a10	6a35	8 a2	...	1120	1 p0	...	4p40	1116	...
Varasd ...	a.m.	5 47	6 58	8 25	a.m.	1143	1 34	p.m.	5 13	1139	...
Krapina...dep	4 37	...	—	—	1126	—	...	5 5	7 21	—	...
Zabok ...dep	5 21	8 38	...	...	1226	...	4 16	5 46	8 15	...	...
Zapresic ...	6 21	9 27	...	...	1 23	...	5 4	—	9 10	...	...
Zágráb ...arr	6 55	10 1	...	...	1 52	...	5 35	...	9 44	...	...

SOMOGYSZOB and BALATON S. G.

Somogyszob ...dep	7 a50	1 p15	5 p53
Marczali ...	9 43	3 15	8 15
Balaton Szt. György 229 arr	10 46	4 13	9 20
Balaton S. G. ...dep	3 a23	12p45	7 p45
Marczali ...	4 59	2 16	9 3
Somogyszob ...arr	7 0	4 17	10 51

SOMOGYSZOB and BARCS.

Somogyszob ...dep	5 a20	9 a40	6 p9
Barcs ...arr	7 32	12 30	8 45
Barcs ...dep	4 a20	1 p30	9 p25
Somogyszob (229) ...arr	7 10	4 6	11 47

KAPOSVAR and BARCS.

Kaposvar ...dep	4a50	12p18	4 p25	...
Középrigócz ...	7 49	3 21	7 54	...
Barcs 230...arr	8 5	3 47	8 10	...

Barcs ...dep	4 a13	11a20	6 p0	...
Középrigócz ...	4 32	11 41	6 19	...
Kaposvar 231A ...arr	7 33	2 47	9 55	...

VARASD and GOLUBOVEC.

Varasd...dep	8 a32	12p15	5p25	...	...
Golubovec ...arr	10 39	2 40	7 32	...	...
Golubovec...dep	5a22	12p16	6p16	...	...
Varasd ...arr	7 40	2 28	8 34	...	...

SZOMBATHELY and PINKAFO. †—Runs until 15th Sept.

Szombathely dep	...	6a15	...	...	3p20	7 p56
Rohoncz ...	...	7 19	...	...	4 9	8 45
Felsöör ...	7 a8	8 46	12p47	12p52	5 17	9 53
Felsölövö ...arr	7 40	9 28	...	1 23	6 2	10†33
Pinkafö ...arr	...	9 23	1 33	...	5 47	10 23

Pinkafö ...dep	5a37	...	11a56	...	4 p41	6 p43
Felsölövö ...dep	5 26	7 a58	11 44	4 p25	...	6 †35
Felsöör ...	6 4	8 27	12 23	4 54	5 21	7 14
Rohoncz...	7 12	—	1 31	—	—	8 43
Szombathely arr	7 52	...	2 10	...	...	9 32

SZOMBATHELY and RUM.

Szombathely ...dep	5a40	9a28	11a50	12p41	4p15	7p34	...	...
Rum ...arr	6 31	1020	12 45	2 3	5 7	8 27	...	...

Rum ...dep	6a46	10a35	1p16	2p52	5p41	9 p0	...
Szombathely ...arr	7 40	11 27	2 16	4 10	6 36	9 59	...

SZEKESFEHERVAR and CZELLDOMÖLK.

		a.m.		a.m.		p.m.	p.m.	
Székesfehérvár	...	6 0	...	9 20	...	2 14	9 10	...
Hajmáskér ...	...	7 7	...	10 24	...	3 13	10 17	...
Jutas 229 ...	...	7 30	...	10 50	...	3 36	11 33	...
Herend ...	...	7 56	...	11 19	...	4 3	—	...
Ajka ...	...	8 32	...	11 58	...	4 39	...	...
Devecser ...	a.m.	8 50	p.m.	12 17	p.m.	4 56	p.m.	...
Boba 229...	7 43	9 22	12 37	12 51	4 39	5 27	8 10	...
Czelldömölk(229)	8 3	9 35	12 57	1 4	5 0	5 40	8 30	...

		a.m.	a.m.	a.m.	p.m.	p.m	p.m.	p.m.
Czelldömölk	..	5 2	5 10	10 31	2 0	2 10	6 2	6 10
Boba ...	...	5 16	5 30	10 48	2 15	2 30	6 16	6 27
Devecser ...	...	5 55	—	—	2 52	—	6 53	—
Ajka ...	...	6 19	...	...	3 22	...	7 19	...
Herend...	a.m.	6 59	...	...	4 4	...	7 59	...
Jutas ...	4 44	7 27	...	...	4 38	...	8 27	...
Hajmáskér ...	4 59	7 41	...	...	4 51	...	8 41	...
Székesfeh..	5 59	8 40	...	...	5 47	...	9 40	...

Jutas...	7a40	9a10	10a43	11a35	1p4	1p39	3p40	4p40	8p30	9p52	10p38	...
Veszprém	7 55	9 25	10 55	11 48	118	1 54	3 55	4 55	8 45	10 7	10 53	...

Veszprém	3a5	4 a5	7 a5	10a10	11a1	12p37	2p47	4p8	7p51	10p15	...
Jutas...	318	4 18	7 16	10 23	1114	12 48	3 0	420	8 4	10 28	...

CZELLDÖMÖLK and PANDORFALU.

Czelldömölk...dep	...	5 a0	...	2 p0	...
Répczelak ...	...	6 17	...	3 42	...
Eszterháza-Szt. Miklós ...	4 a50	7 14	p.m	5 44	...
Nezsider ...	6 48	—	1218	8 57	...
Pándorfalu 225B ...arr	7 4	...	1240	9 15	...

Pandorfalu ...dep	5 a19	8 a20	2 p30	...
Nezsider ...	5 33	8 38	2 36	...
Eszterháza-Szt. Miklós	7 30	—	5 39	...
Répczelak ...	8 50	...	7 20	...
Czelldömölk 229 arr	9 40	...	8 32	...

GYOR and EBENFURT.

Györ (Raab)...dep	...	6 a25	12p28	4p48	8p23	...
Csorna ...	...	7 25	1 14	5 41	9 4	...
Eszterháza-Szt. Miklos	a.m.	8 26	2 9	6 48	9 44	...
Sopron ...	5 50	9 9	3 10	7 40	1020	...
Vulka-Pordány ...	6 23	10 36	3 39	8 12	—	...
Ebenfurt 240 ...arr	*6 57	11 9	4 12	8 45	...	...

Ebenfurt ...dep	...	8a51	12 p6	...	5p16	9p29
Vulka-Pordány ...	a.m.	a.m.	9 24	12 38	...	5 47	1012
Sopron ...	5 19	6 44	9 56	1 31	4p45	6 32	1034
Eszterháza-Sz. M.	5 51	7 25	—	2 10	5 26	7 14	—
Csorna ...	6 36	8 21	...	3 4	—	8 18	...
Györ (Raab) arr	7 10	9 9	...	3 48	...	9 8	...

SOPRON and SZOMBATHELY.

Sopron ...dep	...	3a13	7a40	...	12p40	...	...	8p34
Köszeg...	3a50	6 47	1047	1p35	3 59	5p46	9p45	12 3
Szombathely	4 30	7 32	1130	2 14	4 43	6 31	1030	1246

Szombathely	2a15	5a58	9a40	1244	3p11	4p51	7p30	11p15
Köszeg...	3 8	6 48	1026	1 41	3 58	5 34	8 13	1159
Sopron ...arr	6 15	9 33	...	4 35	8 22	...	...	...

GYOR and UJDOMBOVAR.

‡—Monday only. *—Saturday only.

Györ (Raab) ...dep	...	2‡a10	3a27	11a50	5p40	...	...
Veszprémvarsány ...	...	3 21	4 57	1 17	7 38	...	...
Jutas ... arr	...	5 15	7 3	3 22	9 47	...	...
Jutas ... dep	4a25	—	7 37	3 45	—	...	...
Lepsény 237...	6 9	...	1010	6 0	...	...	...
Tamási-Majsamiklósvár ...	8 23	...	12 0	7 53	...	...	...
Ujdombóvár 230 ...arr	9 43	...	1 20	9 13	...	...	...

Ujdombóvar ...dep	...	3 a20	...	...	10a30	...	4 p25
Tamási-Majsamiklós.	...	5 5	...	...	12 8	...	5 52
Lepsény...	...	7 6	...	...	2 30	...	7 57
Jutas ... arr	...	9 1	...	*	4 26	...	9 41
Jutas ... dep	3a23	—	11a24	1p25	—	4p56	—
Veszprémvarsány ...	5 33	...	1 12	3 14	...	7 40	...
Györ (Raab) 225B arr	7 1	...	2 32	4 25	...	9 18	...

[For Fares, see page 233B.

BOROVO and RACA.

Borovo ......dep	4 a31	11a20	5 p53
Vukovar	4 44	11 43	6 2
Ilaca	6 10	1 1	7 28
Sid 230	6 40	1 27	7 58
Raca ....arr	8 30	3 13	9 56

Raca.........dep	4 a37	12p30	6 p39
Sid	6 2	1 40	7 59
Ilaca	6 38	2 40	8 34
Vukovar...........	7 48	4 21	10 32
Borovo 230 arr	7 56	4 30	10 41

Frequent service between Borovo and Vukovar.

UJ-DOMBOVAR and DALJA.

RC—Restaurant Car.

Dist. E.M.												
	BUDAPEST 231A dep	1025	...	7 a0	8a25	2p55	...	...	...	...	8p30	...
		1,2,3	1,2,3	1,2,3	1,2,3	Ex2	1,2,3	1,2,3	1,2,3	1,2,3	1,2,3	...
		a.m.	a.m	a.m.	p.m	p.m.					a.m.	
—	**Uj-Dombovar** dep	5 35	6 25	1048	2 15	6 15	...	...	...	...	2 22	...
11¾	Bakocza-Godisa	6 6	7 11	1121	2 45	6 38	...	...	...	...	2 55	...
29¾	Szt. Lörincz 230	6 58	—	1219	3 38	7 17	...	...	...	...	3 53	...
41	**Pécs** (Funfkirchen) arr	7 30	...	1248	4 6	7 43	...	p.m.	...	...	4 25	...
...	**Pécs** (Funfkirchen) dep	7 45	...	1 17	4 20	7 52	...	8 45	...	...	5 1	...
44	**Uszög**	8 12	...	1 30	4 36	RC	...	9 0	...	...	5 16	...
63½	**Villány** 230.........dep	9 41	...	2 25	5 32	8 49	...	9 58	...	...	6 20	...
72	Baranyavár 229	1019	...	2 55	6 0	8 59	...	1026	...	...	7 3	...
91½	**Eszek** .... arr	1116	p.m.	3 33	6 44	9 31	p.m	11 8	a.m.	a.m.	7 46	...
	Eszek .... dep	—	1 30	4 50	7 42	—	10 46	—	2 27	6 47	8 31	...
106½	**Dalja** 230 ....arr	...	2 18	5 46	8 25	...	11 29	...	3 10	7 30	9 11	...

	1,2,3	Ex2	1,2,3	1,2,3	Ex2	1,2,3	1,2,3	1,2,3	1,2,3
	a.m	a.m.	a.m.	a.m.		p.m.	p.m.	p.m.	p.m.
Dalja ....dep	3 33	...	7 49	10 0	...	1 38	6 4	8 58	1154
Eszek .... arr	4 19	...	8 30	1042	...	2 24	6 51	9 37	1238
Eszek .... dep	4 40	6 26	8 48	1119	...	3 34	7 20	—	—
Baranyavár..............	5 26	6 58	9 34	12 6	...	4 44	8 11	...	...
Villány .... dep	6 8	7 22	1013	1239	...	5 39	8 56	...	...
Uszög	7 2	RC	1112	1 32	...	6 47	9 51	...	...
Pécs(Funfkirchen)...... arr	7 13	8 14	1123	1 45	p.m.	7 2	10 2	...	...
Pécs(Funfkirchen)...... dep	—	8 27	1145	2 22	4 25	—	1027	...	...
Szt. Lörincz............	a.m.	8 53	1218	2 58	4 51	...	11 5	...	...
Bakocza-Godisa.........	5 0	9 39	1 10	3 49	5 37	...	1154	...	...
Uj-Dombovar	5 34	10 2	1 39	4 18	6 0	...	1223	...	...
BUDAPEST 231A arr	...	1p55	8p15	9p10	9p35	...	5a30	...	...

SZABADKA and BOSZNA-BROD.

Dist. E.M.											
	BUDAPEST 225A dep	...	...	...	11p15	7a10	7a45	2p45	...	3p20	8 p5
		1,2,3	1,2,3	Ex2	1,2,3	1,2,3	1,2,3	Ex3	1,2,3	1,2,3	1,2,3
				From Belgrade (dep. 5.15)	a.m.	a.m.	p.m.	p.m.		p.m.	ni'gt
...	**Szabadka** ....dep	...	...		5 0	10 25	1 42	6 14	...	6 57	12 43
30½	Nemesmilitics	...	...		6 21	11 51	3 3	7 13	...	8 43	1 49
36¾	Zombor	...	...		6 36	12 18	3 34	7 31	...	9 0	2 16
55¼	Gombos	...	...		8 10	1 10	4 37	8 9	...	—	2 56
66½	**Dalja** (230) ......arr	...	a.m.		8 32	1 30	4 58	8 30	p.m.	...	3 15
...	" .... dep	...	7 40		9 13	2 26	6 10	8 35	8 49	...	3 30
76½	Borovo	a.m.	8 6		10 10	3 3	6 46	8 53	9 22	...	3 53
85¾	**Vinkovcze 230** ...	5 40	8 32	8a47	10 39	3 36	7 19	9 13	9 52	...	4 15
106¼	Strizivojna-Vrpolje ...	6 50	—	9 18	12 13	4 50	—	9 57	1110	...	5 24
126¾	**Brod** (Slav.)... arr	7 51	...	9 51	1 11	5 47	p.m	1035	12 2	a.m.	6 12
...	**Brod** (Slav.)... dep	7 59	...	—	2 26	6 47	9 13	1037	—	4 1	6 16
131	**Boszna-Brod** ...arr	8 10	...	...	2 36	6 56	9 24	1045	...	4 11	6 24
298¼	SERAJEVO 247B arr	8 p28	...	...	...	7 a14	...	8a10	...	2p10	8 p28

SERAJEVO 247B dep	...	8 p30	...	...	10p50	...	...	...	...	2 p15
	1,2,3	Ex.3	1,2,3	1,2,3	1,2,3	1,2,3	Ex2	1,2,3	1,2,3	1,2,3
	a.m.	a.m.		a.m.	a.m.	p.m.	p.m.		p.m	p.m.
Boszna-Brod dep	...	5 30	...	7 35	9 31	1 10	...	...	8 57	11 46
Brod .... arr	...	5 38	...	7 47	9 40	1 21	...	...	9 5	11 56
Brod .... dep	3 44	5 40	...	—	9 52	2 22	6 40	...	9 10	—
Strizivojna-Vrpolje ...	4 40	6 14	...	a.m.	10 59	3 32	7 12	p.m.	9 59	...
Vinkovcze	5 27	6 56	...	8 48	12 15	4 48	7 43	7 49	1052	...
Borovo	6 43	7 19	...	9 20	12 54	5 28	...	8 15	1117	...
Dalja .... arr	7 8	7 39	a.m.	9 48	1 27	5 54	To Belgrade, (arr. 11.9)	8 48	1139	...
" ....dep	—	7 44	9 55	—	2 45	6 43		—	1149	...
Gombos ....dep	a.m.	8 4	10 22	...	3 20	7 23		...	1210	...
Zombor	5 10	8 52	11 36	...	4 18	8 20		...	1258	...
Nemesmilitics	5 34	9 4	11 51	...	4 34	8 43		...	1 11	...
Szabadka ......arr	7 21	10 4	1 13	...	5 58	1013		...	2 17	...
BUDAPEST 225A arr	...	1 p30	7p20	...	10 p0	5a45	...	...	8a10	...

Pecs............dep	7 a46	3p 6	7 p23
Szt. Lörincz ...	8 48	3 50	8 0
Szigetvár	9 24	4 12	8 25
Barcs 229 ...arr	10 22	5 0	9 17

Barcs......dep	4a40	7 a35	12p55	6p25
Szigetvár ...	6 11	8 27	1 51	7 26
Szt. Lörincz	6 58	8 54	2 13	7 56
Pecs 230...arr	7 30	9 23	2 45	8 25

Bakócza-Felso dep	7 a30	11a30	6 p43
Komló ....arr	8 35	12 35	7 44
Komló...........dep	3 a55	10a 0	2p45
Bakócza ....arr	4 50	10 55	3 40

E.M.				
	Eszek...... dep	6a50	1p0	4p58
21¼	Vinkovcze arr	8 42	241	6 46

Vinkovcze ...	5a45	12p45	4p40
Eszek......arr	7 39	2 32	6 41

SZABADKA and GOMBOS.

Szabadka ...dep	4a42	2 p15	...	7p17	...
Cservenka	7 20	4 50	5p26	9 52	...
Hodsag 226A ...	8 15	—	6 15	1036	...
Bacsordas.........	8 37	...	6 39	1053	...
Gombos ......arr	9 4	...	7 0	1118	...

Gombos ......dep	3 a5	11 a3	...	4 p8	...	...
Bacsordas.........	3 31	11 33	...	4 38	...	...
Hodsag	4 0	11 51	...	5 11	...	...
Cservenka	5 0	12 37	1 p4	6 15	...	...
Szabadka ...arr	7 35	...	3 54	8 57	...	...

Gombos......dep	5a41	8a15	8p24
Bacsordas.........	6 13	8 55	9 1
Ujpalanka 225A	7 34	1047	1030

Ujpalanka dep	5a21	1p15	4p25
Bacsordas	6 47	2 41	6 25
Gombos ...arr	7 11	3 5	6 46

Baja ....dep	3a30	1236	5 p2
Zombor ......arr	6 40	3 29	8 21

Zombor......dep	3a26	8a57	5 p5
Baja ....arr	6 55	1223	8 44

Zombor ......dep	7a51	1211	4p30
Szond	9 45	2 35	7 8
Gombos ......arr	9 59	2 50	7 22

Gombos ...dep	4a13	1240	8 p9
Szond	4 29	1 5	8 29
Zombor......arr	6 20	3 10	1036

Eszek ....dep	6 a35	11a50	3p45	...	...
Semeljci-Sirokopolje ...	7 44	1 31	5 11	...	...
Strizivojna-Vrpolje arr	8 55	2 49	6 30	...	...

Strizivojna-Vrpolje...dep	5 a20	12p10	3 p25	...	...
Semeljci-Sirokopolje......	6 23	1 40	5 4	...	...
Eszek ....arr	7 22	3 10	6 37	...	...

Strizivojna-V. dp	10a57	4 p0
Samac ....arr	11 56	4 59

Samac ....dep	3a21	1p40
Strizivojna-Vrpolje	4 18	2 37

ESZEK and UJ-KAPELA.

Eszek ...dep	4a14	...	8a40	11a43	3p38
Prandauovci	5 19	...	9 59	1 7	4 46
Nasic 230......	6 14	a.m.	11 6	2 19	5 24
Pleternica ...	8 27	11 47	1 28	4 42	—
Uj-Kapela-B	9 8	1234	2 15	5 26	...

Uj-Kapela.	2a29	...	11 a0	1p26	6 p4
Pleternica.	3 27	...	11 53	2 11	6 54
Nasic	6 22	9a10	4 47	—	9 24
Prandau....	6 58	9 58	5 39	...	10 5
Eszek arr	8 3	1111	7 0	...	1116

Pleternica dep	9 a0	2p16	6p59	...
Pozega ...arr	9 37	2 53	7 36	...
Pozega ...dep	7a43	10a51	4 p4	...
Pleternica arr	8 16	11 26	4 37	...

SZ. LÖRINCZ and NASIC.

Sz. Lörincz...dep	...	4a15	9 a10	12p38	4 p0
Noskovci............	...	5 49	11 10	2 13	5 35
Slatina	4a13	6 26	12 3	2 49	6 15
Nasic 230 ...arr	5 57	8 24	2 4	4 36	8 3

Nasic ....dep	4a29	10a52	2p50	5p28
Slatina	6 34	12 46	4 55	8 5
Noskovci	7 5	1 14	5 36	8 45
Sz. Lörincz arr	8 34	2 43	7 9	1030

VINKOVCZE and ZUPANJE-SZAVAPART.

Vinkovcze..............dep	6 a0	1 p6	7p57
Zupanje-Szavapart arr	7 59	2 34	9 22

Zupanje-Szavapart dep	3a30	6 a0	2p10
Vinkovcze ....arr	5 0	7 42	3 58

INDIA and VINKOVCZE.

India....................dep	...	6a34	7a15	10a30	6p20	9 p57	...
Ruma 230..................	...	7 1	7 58	11 31	7 1	10 46	...
Mitrovicza .... arr	...	7 20	8 24	12 4	7 25	11 15	...
Mitrovicza .... dep	2a25	7 21	8 36	12 40	7 35	—	...
Sid	3 41	7 58	9 37	1 58	8 41	...	...
Vinkovcze (230) arr	5 15	8 37	1050	3 30	9 47	...	...

Vinkovcze ....dep	...	4a30	5 a50	...	12p20	4p47	7p52
Sid	...	6 3	6 57	...	1 52	6 14	8 33
Mitrovicza .... arr	a.m.	7 17	7 51	...	3 0	7 16	9 9
Mitrovicza .... dep	5 10	—	8 1	p.m.	3 25	7 26	9 10
Ruma..........................	5 47	...	8 32	1220	4 20	8 0	9 30
India (225A) ....arr	6 33	...	9 10	1 30	5 18	8 37	9 56

NAGY-VARAD and SZEGED-ROKUS.

		a.m.			a.m.	a.m.	a.m.	p.m.		p.m.		p.m.
Nagy-Varad (Grosswardein)...dep		1 14	...	...	6 0	8 1	1010	1 15	...	4 40	...	7 52
Nagyszalonta		2 17	...	...	7 6	9 27	1118	2 55	...	6 3	...	9 27
Kotegyan 230A		2 37	...	a.m.	7 26	9 59	1138	3 27	...	6 25	p.m.	9 54
Gyula		3 7	...	5 55	7 54	1039	1218	4 7	...	7 1	8 31	1039
Békéscsaba 232 arr		3 26	a.m.	6 20	8 12	11 4	1237	4 34	...	7 22	8 56	11 6
" ...dep		3 34	4 34	6 48	8 19	1140	1 48	4 43	...	7 37	—	—
Oroshaza 230A	a.m.	4 20	5 40	7 56	9 15	1237	2 49	5 48	p.m.	8 59	...	...
Hodmezö Vásárh	4 32	5 2	6 52	—	10 0	1 53	3 44	7 5	8 50	1012	...	...
Szeged 227...arr	5 27	5 35	7 40	...	1045	2 43	4 22	7 58	9 46	11 1	...	...

Szeged Rokus ...dep	...	3a20	...	...	8a12	.059	2p44	3p50	7p15	8 p0	1p35
Hodmezö Vásárhely	...	4 18	...	a.m.	9 0	1140	3 35	4 55	8 14	8 56	12 6
Oroshaza	...	5 31	...	8 16	10 2	1230	4 28	6 12	—	10 7	12 51
Békéscsaba ...arr	a.m.	6 26	a.m.	9 21	1055	1 18	5 16	7 21	...	1110	1 32
" ...dep	4 35	6 49	8 18	9 34	1140	1 38	5 56	7 39	...	—	1 47
Gyula	5 3	7 12	8 56	9 59	1210	2 1	6 16	8 8	...	...	2 7
Kotegyan	5 45	7 55	9 52	—	1248	2 33	6 49	—	...	...	2 36
Nagyszalonta	6 15	8 31	1022	...	1 9	2 57	7 14	...	...	...	2 58
Nagy-Varad 233 arr	7 29	9 40	12 1	...	2 15	4 0	8 20	...	...	...	3 54

VESZTO and PUSZTAHOLLOD.

Vesztö ...dep	6 a13	10a20	5p 5
Kotegyan 230A ...arr	7 17	11 25	6 12
Kotegyan 230A ...dep	8 1	11 50	6 56
Tenke	10 (	1 36	9 17
Pusztahollód 230A arr	10 42	2 17	1011

Pusztahollód ...dep	4a40	11a34	3p50
Tenke	5 24	12 24	4 31
Kotegyan ...arr	7 19	2 25	6 9
Kotegyan ...dep	8 4	3 32	6 52
Vesztö 254 ...arr	9 18	4 51	7 56

RUMA and KLENAK-SZAVAPART.

Ruma ...dep	11a50	8 p10	...	...	...
Klenak-Szavapart ...arr	1 5	9 38	...	...	...
Klenak-Szavapart ...dep	5 a10	2 p30	...	...	...
Ruma ...arr	6 46	3 50	...	...	...

Vinkovcze dep	5a55	1p20	4p58	...	...	...	...
Brcka ...arr	8 14	3 45	7 28	...	...	...	...
Brcka ...dep	2 a35	5 p15	4p20	...	...	...	...
Vinkovcze ...arr	4 55	7 48	6 51	...	...	...	...
Ruma ...dep	12p15	8p 0	...	...	...	...	
Vrdnik ...arr	1 20	8 58	...	...	...	...	
Vrdnik ...dep	6 a9	5 p0	...	...	...	...	
Ruma ...arr	6 50	5 57	...	...	...	...	

MOHACS and VILLANY.

Mohács ...dep	5 a6	8a‡17	11a40	4p30	7 p45	...
Villány 230 ...arr	5 51	9 20	12 25	515	8 30	...
Villány	6a35	10a‡10	2 p35	5p50	10p18	‡—While ferry is open.
Mohács	7 19	11 20	3 19	634	11 2	

SZOLNOK and HODMEZO—VASARHELY.

Szolnok...dep	...	3 a40	7 a3	9 a38	1 p25	...	4p52
Szajol	...	4 13	7 26	10 1	2 2	...	5 16
Puszta Tenyo	...	4 33	7 39	10 15	2 23	...	5 31
Szentes	4a41	8 29	—	1 35	5 59	6p45	8 23
Vasarhely arr	6 30	10 20	...	3 9	...	8 35	...

Vasarhely dep	4 a0	...	7 a22	...	3p50	9 p0	...	...	...
Szentes	5 30	...	10 49	3 p24	6 0	10 47	...	...	...
Puszta Tenyo	8 16	10a50	2 22	6 17	9 20	—	...	...	...
Szajol	8 31	11 25	2 40	6 32	9 41	...	...	...	...
Szolnok 232 ar	8 55	11 49	3 6	6 55	10 6	...	...	...	...

‡—Runs until 15th Sept.

KISKUNFELEGYHAZA and OROSHAZA.

Kiskunfelegyhaza ...dep		7 a7	...	...	12p51	5 p16	8p35
Csongrad		8 1	...	...	2 7	6 11	9 36
Szentes	3a10	8 36	...	1p21	3 1	6 50	10 4
Fabian	3 50	9 16	‡	2 10	3 58	7 26	—
Gadoros	4 23	9 47	1p57	2 43	4 42	7 55	...
Oroshaza (230A) ...arr	5 10	10 33	2 44	3 30	5 41	8 38	...

Oroshaza ...dep		5a11	5 a46	11a2	1‡p5	3 p31	...	6 p47
Gadoros		5a57	6 54	1158	1 52	4 29	...	7 48
Fabian		6 20	7 29	1231	—	4 53	...	8 12
Szentes	3 a8	6 57	8 30	1 20	...	5 32	6 p39	8 51
Csongrad	3 39	—	9 12	1 56	...	/	7 17	—
Kiskunfelegyhaza	4 30	...	10 16	2 44	...	...	8 10	...

Fabian ...dep	4a30	5 p7	7 p35	...
Arpádhalom ...arr	5 0	5 37	8 5	...

Arpádhalom ...dep	6 a43	6 p30	...	...
Fabian ...arr	7 14	7 3	...	...

NAGYVARAD and PÜSPÖKFÜRDÖ.—Nagyvarad depart 7.49, 9.50 a.m., 2.19, 4.39, and 8.10 p.m. Püspökfürdö depart 8.59, 10.59 a.m., 3.29, 7.11, and 9.29 p.m.

NAGYVARAD and FÉLIKSFÜRDO.—Nagyvarad depart 8.0, 10.1 a.m., 2.30, 4.50, and 8.31 p.m. Féliksfürdö depart 8.40, 10.39 a.m., 3.10, 6.59, and 9.10 p.m.

SZÉKELYKOCSARD and MAROSUJVAR.

	a.m.	a.m.	a.m.	p.m.	p.m.	p.m.	
Székelykocsárd ...dep	7 56	9 40	11 41	3 40	8 57	11 10	...
Marosújvár ...arr	8 8	9 52	11 53	3 52	9 9	11 22	...

	a.m.	a.m.	a.m.	p.m.	p.m.	p.m.	
Marosújvár ...dep	7 9	9 7	10 25	2 41	6 34	10 25	...
Székelykocsárd ...arr	7 21	9 19	10 37	2 53	6 46	10 37	...

NAGY-VARAD and VASKOH.

	a.m.	p.m.	
Nagy-Varad 230A ...dep	2 59	4 28	...
Drág Cséke	5 27	6 43	...
Szombatsag-Venterrogoz ...arr	6 23	7 35	...
Bihardobrosd ...arr	7 45	8 29	...
Pusztahollód (230A)	7 4	7 56	...
Belenyes	9 8	9 44	...
Vaskoh Körösbarafalva ...arr	10 24	1049	...

	a.m.	p.m.		
Vaskóh Körösbarfalva dep	3 53	1248	...	...
Belenyes	5 1	2 1	...	...
Pusztahollód	6 36	3 52	...	...
Bihardobrosd ...dep	5 56	3 18	...	...
Szombatsag-Venterro...dep	6 56	4 19	...	...
Drág Cséko	7 55	5 18	...	...
Nagy-Varad...arr	9 49	7 8	...	...

SZEGED-ROKUS and ZENTA.

E.M.				
	Szeged-Rokus dp	4 a0	12p4	...
11¼	Horgos	4 52	1 2	...
33	Zenta 226A ...arr	6 29	2 55	..

Zenta ...dep	6a30	3p30	...	...	...
Horgos	8 13	5 27	...	...	...
Szeged-R. 230A arr	8 52	6 5	...	...	...

NAGY-VARAD and GYOMA.

Nagy-Varad ...dep		...	6a27	1 p48	5 p5
Ossipuszta		...	6 42	2 2	5 23
Veszto		6 a45	9 48	5 9	8 3
Szeghalom	a.m.	7 22	10 25	5 41	—
Devavanya	6 40	8 32	11 42	6 38	...
Gyoma ...arr	7 21	9 13	12 23	7 18	...

Gyoma ...dep		3 a35	7 a49	10a54	2p39
Devavanya		4 32	8 31	11 47	3 32
Szeghalom		5 29	—	12 37	4 30
Veszto	3a31	6 13	...	1 5	5 16
Ossipuszta	6 10	9 12	...	—	8 14
Nagy-Varad 233	6 26	9 30	...	...	8 30

Kisujszallas dep	5a26	10a40	5p25
Devavanya ...arr	6 32	11 35	6 28
Devavanya ...dep	8a36	3p47	6p52
Kisujszallas ...arr	9 32	5 5	8 1

BUDAPEST and TAPOLCZA.

	1,2,3	Ex 2	1,2,3	1,2,3	1,2,3	1,2,3	1,2,3	1,2,3
Budapest	a.m.	a.m.	a.m.			p.m.		p.m.
Ostbahnhof...dep	5 40	8 5	10 45	...	...	2 55	...	10 25
Adony-Pusztaszabolcs	8 6	9 20	12 40	...	...	4 21	...	1 10
Börgönd	8 42	9 48	1 18	...	...	4 52	...	2 2
Szabadbattyán	9 20	10 4	1 35	...	...	5 8	...	2 30
Alsóörs ...arr	10 39	11 16	2 54	p.m.	p.m.	6 26	p.m.	4 28
: Veszprém ...dep	9 27	9 27	1 20	2 13	4 57	...	8 50	3 50
Alsóörs ...dep	10 47	11 23	3 16	3 9	5 51	6 33	9 57	5 0
Balatonfüred	11 6	11 39	3 34	—	6 8	6 51	10 20	5 34
Tapolcza 229...arr	12 46	1 3	5 10	...	...	8 28	...	7 37

	1,2,3	1,2,3	1,2,3	1,2,3	Ex 2	1,2,3
	a.m.	a.m.	p.m.	p.m.	p.m.	p.m.
Tapolcza ...dep	3 53	8 50	1 14	...	5 30	9 0
Balatonfüred	5 33	10 31	2 52	6 13	6 54	11 20
Alsóörs ...arr	5 52	10 46	3 7	6 32	7 10	11 42
: Veszprém ...arr	7 4	12 32	4 7	7 46	8 24	1 1
Alsóörs ...dep	5 59	10 53	4 21	—	7 20	11 49
Szabadbattyán	7 15	12 32	4 35	...	8 40	1 40
Börgönd	7 34	1 11	5 1	...	8 58	2 6
Adony-Pusztaszabol.	8 5	1 47	5 32	...	9 28	2 50
Budapest Ostbahnh'f	9 35	4 0	8 5	...	11 0	5 30

SATORALJAUJHELY and MEZO LABORCZ.

E.M																
	Satoraljaujhely ...dep	7a10	1 p6	8 p5	Mezo-Laborcz dep	4a12	1p11	3 p9	...	...	...	...	...	...	...	...
10	Legenye- arr	7 44	1 35	8 34	Homonna	5 16	2 7	4 37	...	...	...	...	...	...	...	...
...	Alsómihalyi 231 dep	7 50	1 43	8 39	Nagy-Mihaly.........	5 56	2 44	5 40	...	...	...	...	...	...	...	...
23	Töketerebes	8 37	2 19	9 17	Töketerebes	6 29	3 14	6 37	...	...	...	...	...	...	...	...
35½	Nagy-Mihaly	9 20	2 54	9 54	Legenye- arr	7 4	3 46	7 21	...	...	...	...	...	...	...	...
50¼	Homonna	1014	3 35	1039	Alsómihalyi dep	7 6	3 48	7 26	...	...	...	...	...	...	...	...
75¾	Mezo-Laborcz 247 ...arr	1137	4 45	1150	Satoraljaujhely ar	7 31	4 11	7 59	...	...	...	...	...	...	...	...

Töketerebes ...dep	8 a42	2 p30	7 p 0	...	...	...	...	Varanno.........dep	4 a8	11a42	4 p40	...	...	...	...	...	...
Varanno ....arr	10 34	4 6	9 4	...	...	...	...	Töketerebes ...arr	6 0	1 35	6 20	...	...	...	...	...	...

Homonna ......dep	5 a40	10a20	5 p4	...	...	...	...	Takcsány ......dep	3 a34	8 a10	12p41	...	...	...	...	...	...
Takcsány.........arr	7 7	11 47	6 31	...	...	...	...	Homonna.........arr	4 48	9 24	1 55	...	...	...	...	...	...

EGER and PUTNOK.

Eger............dep	3 a47	7 a28	1p38	...	...	...	...	...	Putnok.........dep	3 a9	12p35	5 p15	...	...	...	...	...	...
Bélapátfalva ...	5 29	9 8	3 27	...	...	...	...	...	Bélapátfalva......	5 30	3 31	8 15	...	...	...	...	...	...
Putnok 232A arr	7 28	11 24	6 20	...	...	...	...	...	Eger 231 ......arr	6 49	5 14	9 52	...	...	...	...	...	...

CSAP and SIANKI.

Csap ......dep	6 a46	9 a44	6 p30	**Sianki** ....dep	6 a20	1 p32	...	
Ungvar	7 29	10 15	7 1	Nagy-Berezna	5a34	8 11	3 30	...
Vajan ...arr	9 45	4 35	9 5	Perecseny ...	6 34	8 50	4 10	..
Perecseny	8 46	11 13	8 2	Vajan dep	5 38	...	12 35	5 p12
Nagy-Berezna	9 35	11 55	8 46	Ungvar.........	7 49	9 41	5 3	6 57
Sianki ...arr	...	2 17	11 8	**Csap** 231arr	8 28	10 15	5 34	9 35

BATYU and KIRALYHAZA.

Batyu............dep	5a17	10a55	3p10	6p25	10p50	...
Tiszaujlak	6 31	12 19	4 37	7 45	12 9	...
Kiralyháza 228arr	7 9	1 2	5 21	8 29	12 51	...
Kiralyháza ...dep	2a30	7 a40	1230	3p20	8 p30	...
Tiszaujlak	3 9	8 25	1 9	3 59	9 9	...
Batyu 231 ......arr	4 27	9 48	2 26	5 20	10 22	...

KISTERENYE and KIS-UJSZALLAS.

Kisterenye .....dep	...	3a35	6a47	12p50	...	...	...	...	Kisujszallas dep	...	5a26	...	1p10	5p29	...	...	...	...
Parad	...	5 14	8 8	2 3	...	...	...	...	Kunhegyes	a.m.	6 25	...	1 54	6 24	...	...	...	...
Kál-Kapolna ...arr	...	6 39	9 15	3 15	...	...	...	...	Heves	5 56	8 27	p.m.	3 26	—	...	...	...	...
Heves	a.m.	7 25	1227	6 14	...	...	...	...	Kál-Kapolna ...	6 34	9 13	1239	4 4	5p37	...	...	...	...
Kunhegyes	3 31	8 56	1 49	—	...	...	...	...	Parad	—	1110	2 16	—	7 16	...	...	...	...
Kisujszallas ...arr	4 19	9 34	2 26	...	...	...	...	...	Kisterenye...arr	...	1218	3 29	...	8 34	...	...	...	...

SARBOGARD and BATASZEK.

Sarbogard.........dep	3a20	9 a0	12p10	5 p4	...	Bataszek......dep	4a20	8 a10	10a20	4p17	8p43	...	...	...	...	...	...
Retszilas	3 45	9 19	12 32	5 23	...	Szekszárd	5 9	8 59	11 40	5 4	9 30	...	...	...	...	...	...
Nagydorog	4 31	1023	1 54	6 23	...	Nagydorog.........	6 27	10 15	1 37	6 18	—	...	...	...	...	...	...
Szekszárd	5 46	1156	4 15	7 57	...	Retszilas...........	7 13	11 1	2 39	7 6	...	...	...	...	...	...	...
Bataszek ....arr	6 24	1241	5 6	8 42	...	Sarbogard ...arr	7 30	11 18	3 0	7 23	...	...	...	...	...	...	...

UJDOMBOVAR and BATASZEK.

Ujdombovár ..dep	4a46	10a30	2p25	5p24	6p50	...	...	Bátaszek ......dep	8a38	11 a5	1p32	7 p7	9 p25	...	...	...	...
Mágocs	5 6	10 52	2 43	5 41	7 5	...	...	Hidas-Bonyhád ...	9 5	11 55	2 17	7 50	9 58	...	...	...	...
Hidas-Bonyhád...	6 15	12 1	3 34	6 30	7 49	...	...	Mágocs	9 43	12 58	3 25	8 49	10 47	...	...	...	...
Bátaszek ......arr	6 52	12 38	4 1	6 55	8 13	...	...	Ujdombóvár...arr	9 56	1 18	3 45	9 7	11 2	...	...	...	...

BUDAPEST, MISKOLCZ, and LAWOCZNE.

RC—Restaurant Car. SC—Sleeping Car.

Dist. E.M.		1,2,3	1,2,3	1,2,3	Ex2	1,2,3	Ex2	1,2,3	Ex2	1,2,3	Ex2	Ex2	1,2,3	1,2,3	2&3	1,2,3	Ex2	1,2,3	1,2,3	1,2,3	
					a.m.	a.m.	a.m.	a.m.	a.m.		p.m.	p.m.		p.m.		p.m.	p.m.	p.m.		p.m.	
—	**Budapest** ....dep	...	...	...	6 45	6 55	7 25	8 10	9 35	...	1 20	2 0	...	5 10	...	8 0	10 0	1025	...	1135	...
5	**Rákos**	...	...	...	RC	...	RC	8 28		...	RC	...	...	...	...	8 17	...	...	...	1157	...
23	Gödöllő	...	...	...	...	7 44	...	9 12	RC	...	2 1	2 42	...	5 59	...	9 11	...	1122	...	1256	...
33	Aszód	...	...	a.m.	...	8 8	...	9 41		...	...	...	...	6 18	...	9 34	SC	1143	...	1 30	...
43	**Hatvan 232A** ....dep	...	...	5 8	8 6	8 55	8 42	1020	1051	...	2 38	3 21	...	6 41	...	10 9	1123	1215	...	2 17	...
56	Vámosgyörk	...	...	5 47	8 29	9 27	9 5	1056	...	...	3 1	3 44	...	7 6	...	1044	1146	1250	...	2 54	...
72	Kál-Kápolna	...	...	6 45	8 57	10 6	9 31	1149	...	...	3 30	4 14	...	7 39	...	1127	...	1 27	...	3 43	...
79½	Füzesabony	...	...	7 22	9 17	1028	9 49	1212	1154	...	3 50	4 39	...	7 59	...	1154	1235	1 54	...	4 18	...
87½	Mezőkövesd	...	...	7 41	9 30	1046	...	1231	...	...	4 4	...	...	8 16	...	1214	...	2 11	...	4 41	...
115	**Miskolcz** ....arr	...	...	8 50	1020	1146	1049	1 29	1256	...	4 55	5 46	...	9 13	...	1 14	1 39	3 12	...	5 54	...
...	KASSA 231 ....arr	...	a.m.	12p2	12p2	2p40	...	...	2p50	p.m.	6p51	9p19	p.m.	...	p.m.	4a13	3a23	6a38	...	9a13	...
...	**Miskolcz** ....dep	...	6 12				1056	1 57		4 25		6 0	6 6	9 50	11 6			3 41	...	7 42	...
139¼	**Szerencs 227B** arr	...	7 12	...	...	...	1136	2 49	...	5 25	...	6 38	6 58	1042	1216	...	...	4 42	...	8 34	...
...	" ....dep	...	7 19	...	...	...	1141	2 55	...		...	6 45	7 4	1055	1237	...	...	5 10	...		...
154	Olaszliszka-T.	...	8 7	...	...	2&3	12 9	3 36	...	...	...	7 11	7 46	1140	1 36	...	...	5 53	...	...	...
167¾	**Sátoralja-** arr	...	8 46	...	...	p.m.	1239	4 10	...	...	...	7 40	8 20	1215	2 20	...	...	6 29	...	...	...
...	**ujhely** ....dep	a.m.		...	...	1 22	1 11	4 33	...	...	...		8 41	1235		...	...	7 39	...	...	...
193¾	**Csap** (231)	4 53	...	...	...	2 51	2 10	5 50	...	...	...	...	10 1	1 57	...	...	...	9 39	...	...	...
203¾	**Bátyu** (231) ....dep	5 28	...	...	...		2 48	6 47	...	p.m.	...	...	1034	2 33	...	...	...	1038	p.m.	...	...
220	**Munkács**	6 17	...	...	...	...	3 27	7 29	...	8 14	...	...	1122	3 22	...	...	...	1129	1230	...	...
236¾	Szolyva-Hársfalva		...	...	...	...	4 10			9 17	...	...	1217	4 19	...	...	...	...	1 44	...	...
270¼	**Lawoczne** ....arr	...	...	...	...	...	6 4		...	11 38	...	...	2 33	6 35	...	...	...	...	4 41	...	...
361⅞	LEMBERG 245 arr	...	...	...	...	...	11p0	...	...	...	...	...	7a20	1140	...	...	...	...	...	...	...

	1,2,3	2&3	1,2,3	Ex.2	Ex2	1,2,3	1,2,3	Ex2	1,2,3	Ex.2	Ex2	2&3	1,2,3	1,2,3	1,2,3	Ex3	Ex2				
LEMBERG ...dep		...	6p50	...	...	...	...	...	...	7 a25	...	...	...	...	...	1p50	...	...	...	...	...
			a.m.			a.m.				p.m.				p.m.		p.m.					
Lawoczne ....dep	...	...	1224	...	...	4 13	...	...	...	12 2	...	...	...	1249	...	7 30	...	...	...	...	...
S-Hársfalva	...	...	2 48	...	...	6 43	a.m.	...	...	1 39	...	...	...	2 52	p.m.	9 14	...	...	...	...	...
Munkács	...	...	4 6	...	...	7 37	8 50	...	...	2 17	...	...	...	4 16	9 31	10 0	...	...	...	...	...
Bátyu ....dep	...	...	4 54	...	...		10 9	...	...	3 3	...	...	...	5 51	1050	1040	...	...	...	...	...
Csap	...	...	5 41	...	...		1038	...	...	3 25	...	...	...	6 32	1121	11 6	...	...	...	...	...
Sátoraujhely arr	...	...	6 58	a.m.	a.m.	...	1149	...	...	4 17	...	...	...	7 47		1210	...	...	...	...	...
" dep	...	...		7 45	7 55	...	12 9	...	...	4 39	...	...	...	8 55	...	1230	...	...	...	...	...
Olaszl.	...	...		8 14	8 33	...	1247	...	...	5 7	...	...	...	9 42	...	1 3	...	...	...	...	...
Szerencs ....arr	...	a.m.	...	8 39	9 15	a.m.	1 29	...	...	5 33	...	p.m.	...	1027	...	1 38	...	...	...	...	...
" ....dep	...	5 10	...	8 46	9 22	1124	1 35	...	...	5 38	...	7 12	...	1121	...	1 45	...	...	...	...	...
Miskolcz ....arr	p.m.	6 50	...	9 26	1021	1214	2 35	p.m.	p.m.	6 18	p.m.	8 4	...	1228	...	2 33	a.m.	...	...	...	...
KASSA ....dep	1142		a.m.	6 a58	8 57	...	...	1 20	1 20	...	5 25	...	...	9p26	...		1 17	...	...	...	...
Miskolcz ....dep	2 25	...	6 10	9 40	1040	1235	2 53	3 6	3 37	6 28	7 8	8 40	...	1257	...	...	3 4	...	...	...	...
Mezőkövesd	3 27	...	7 7	...	1129	1 59	4 12	RC	4 43	RC	7 58	10 0	...	2 15	...	...	...	...	...	...	...
Füzes-Abon	3 52	...	7 32	10 48	1151	2 40	4 40	4 9	5 8	7 36	8 19	1033	...	2 45	...	...	SC	...	...	...	...
Kál-Kápol	4 12	...	7 47	11 1	12 5	3 10	4 59	...	5 27	...	8 33	11 2	...	3 5	...	...	...	...	...	...	...
Vámosgyör	5 12	...	8 21	11 27	1235	4 13	5 43	...	6 14	...	9 2	1159	a.m.	3 49	...	...	4 52	...	...	...	...
Hatvan ....dep	5 59	...	8 50	11 53	1 3	5 20	6 26	5 15	6 57	8 43	9 30	1236	2 22	4 36	...	...	5 18	...	...	...	...
Aszód	6 35	...	9 8	12 10	1 21	5 54	6 49	...	7 26	...	9 47		3 3	5 1	...	...	...	...	...	...	...
Gödöllő	7 5	...	9 31	12 28	1 40	6 29	7 23	...	7 56	...	10 6	...	3 48	5 33	...	...	...	...	...	...	...
Rákos	7 57	...	...	...	RC	7 19	8 1	...	8 36	...	RC	...	4 51	6 32	...	...	...	...	...	...	...
Budapest ....arr	8 15	...	1020	1 5	2 20	7 35	8 20	6 25	8 50	9 55	1045	...	5 10	6 50	...	...	6 0	...	...	...	...

Vamos-Gyork ...dep	4a10	6 a0	9a13	10a58	12p50	4 p10	7 p16	9 p20	12 a3	...	...	...	...	...	...	...	...	...
Gyongyos ....arr	4 45	6 35	9 46	11 34	1 26	4 45	7 49	9 55	12 38	...	...	...	...	...	...	...	...	...

Gyongyos ....dep	3 a6	5a12	7 a43	10a17	11a54	2 p21	5p25	8 p21	10p53	...	...	...	...	...	...	...	...	...
Vamos Gyork ....arr	3 36	5 26	8 10	10 44	12 24	2 51	5 54	8 50	11 22	...	...	...	...	...	...	...	...	...

Füzes Abony ...dep	4a42	7a45	9a30	12p17	2p40	5p12	8p27	12a47	Eger ....dep	3 a0	6a24	9a31	10a50	1p34	3p45	6p39	10p40
Eger ....arr	5 27	8 30	1027	1 2	3 25	5 57	9 12	1 32	Füzes Abony arr	3 40	7 5	10 12	11 31	2 15	4 26	7 20	11 21

MISKOLCZ and KASSA.

Miskolcz ....dep	3a54	6a24	10a31	12 p5	1 p3	5p12	6p42	1a34	1a48
Hidasneméti	5 50	8 25	11 33	1 56	2 17	6 21	8 33	3 27	...
Kassa 253A ...arr	6 38	9 13	12 2	2 40	2 50	6 51	9 19	4 13	3 23
Kassa ....dep	6a58	8a57	12p26	1p20	4p54	5p25	9p26	11p42	1a17
Hidasnémeti	7 38	9 26	1 10	1 46	6 12	5 53	1018	12 22	...
Miskolcz 231 arr	9 16	1030	3 9	2 59	...	6 58	12 9	1 52	2 53

SATORALJA and KASSA.

Satoralja-Ujhely dp	2a40	7 a25	1p16	4p46	8p30	...
Legenye Mihalyi	3 27	8 6	1 45	5 20	9 0	...
Kassa ....arr	6 9	10 0	3 24	6 58	1037	...
Kassa ....dep	4a56	10 a1	12p13	6 p5	...	
Legenye Mihalyi	6 37	11 33	1 41	8 2	...	
Satoralja-Ujhely 231 arr	7 2	12 0	2 6	8 33	...	

SZERENCS and KASSA.

Szerencs ...dep	5a38	11a47	7 p17	...	...	...	...	...	Kassa ....dep	3a24	9a 21	12p44	...	...	...	...	...	...
Hidasnémeti ...	8 25	2 22	10 20	...	...	...	...	...	Hidasnémeti ...	4 23	10 27	2 18	...	...	...	...	...	...
Kassa ....arr	9 13	3 18	11 23	...	...	...	...	...	Szerencs ...arr	6 58	12 53	4 40	...	...	...	...	...	...

SZEKESFEHERVAR (Stuhlweissenburg) & PAKS.

Szekesféhervar ...dep	1a34	7 a1	...	9 a7	12p13	4p17	...
Börgönd	1 51	7 18	...	9 26	12 30	4 34	...
Adony-Szabolcs 231A	—	—	8a25	1042	—	—	6p35
Adony	...	...	8 41	1058	...	...	6 51
Duna Földvar	...	...	1037	1252	...	...	8 49
Paks ...arr	...	...	1116	1 32	...	...	9 26

Paks ...dep		2a46	...	...	12p45	...	4 p6
Duna Földvar		3 33	...	...	1 35	...	4 56
Adony		5 21	...	...	3 35	...	6 53
Adony-Szabolcs		5 58	a.m.	a.m.	3 52	...	8 36
Börgönd	2a12	6 42	8 50	1011	—	5p10	9 23
Székesféhervár	2 28	6 58	9 6	1028		5 26	9 38

For Fares, see page 233B].

BUDAPEST and FIUME.

§—Sleeping Car.

Dist. E M.			1,2,3	Ex2	2&3	1,2,3	1,2,3	1,2,3	Ex. 2	1,2,3	Ex2	Ex2	1,2,3	1,2,3
	Budapest-		a.m.	a.m.			a.m.	p.m.	p.m.	p.m.	p.m.	p.m.	p.m.	p.m.
—	Ostbahnhof dep		5 40	7 0	...	...	8 25	12 45	2 55	3 30	6 15	7 40	8 30	10 25
12½	„ (Kelenföld) dep		6 14	7 18	...	...	8 54	1 15	3 15	3 53	6 37	7 59	9 5	10 55
43	Adony-Szabolcs		7 39	8 8	...	...	1024	2 41	4 4	5 28	7 31	8 55	10 27	12 1
61½	Sarbogard		—	8 48	...	...	1145	3 42	4 44	—	8 12	9 39	11 37	1 §0
87	Hidegkut Gyönk		...	9 26	...	...	1247	4 47	5 28	...	SC	...	12 47	2 1
111	Uj Dombovar 230 arr		a.m.	10 3	...	...	1 47	5 50	6 7	...	9 30	11 0	1 53	2 54
...	„ ...dep		6 30	1011	...	...	2 10	6 12	RC	...	9 40	11 7	—	3 5
113	Dombovar		6 39	RC	...	...	2 23	6 17	—	...	RC	RC	...	3 10
131	Kaposvár 231A		7 56	1048	...	...	3 22	7 8	...	...	1017	1143	...	4 9
156¼	Somogyszob		9 33	1137	...	...	4 50	8 11	...	...	11 6	...	...	5 15
168¾	Csurgo		10 8	1158	...	...	5 24	8 38	...	...	1127	SC	2 & 3	5 42
175¾	Gyekenyes ...arr		1029	1210	a.m.	p.m.	5 46	8 52	...	...	1139	1 2	a.m.	5 55
...	„ ...dep		—	1220	1115	4 30	—	9 10	...	...	1150	1 10	4 6	6 15
185¼	Kaproncza		...	1238	1151	4 59	...	9 30	...	...	12 7	...	4 35	6 36
200¾	Koros		...	1 11	1 20	5 59	p.m.	10 17	...	...	1241	2 1	5 40	7 20
220¼	Dugoselo		...	1 38	2 40	7 7	8 26	11 4	...	...	...	...	6 55	8 4
243½	Zagrab (Agram) arr		p.m.	2 10	3 20	7 45	9 7	11 31	...	...	1 43	2 59	7 33	8 30
...	„ dep	5 a0	2 50	2 30	—	8 22	—	11 55	...	...	1 54	3 9	—	8 50
272¾	Karolyvaros	7 15	5 3	3 28	...	1015	...	1 22	...	...	2 51	4 6	...	10 9
307½	Ogulin	—	7 49	4 45	...	—	...	2 55	...	...	4 5	5 23	...	11 50
326¼	Cameral-Moravicza		9 4	5 32	...	...	...	3 48	...	...	4 52	6 14	...	12 52
344¼	Delnice		—	6 18	...	...	...	4 45	...	...	5 38	7 6	...	1 51
366	Plase		...	7 10	...	...	...	5 59	...	...	6 30	8 1	...	3 7
382	Fiume (234) ...arr		...	7 54	...	...	...	6 55	...	...	7 15	8 50	...	4 5

	1,2,3	1,2,3	2&3	Ex2	1,2,3	2&3	1,2,3	Ex2	Ex 2	Ex 3	1,2,3
				a.m.			p.m.	p.m.	p.m.		p.m.
Fiume (234) ...dep	...	...	...	8 0	...	...	1255	6 0	7 56	...	10 23
Plase	...	...	a.m.	9 13	...	...	2 19	7 13	9 9		11 47
Delnice	...	a.m.	8 25	1017	...	...	3 34	8 15	SC		1 8
Cameral-Moravicz	...	5 8	1021	11 8	...	...	4 35	9 6	11 3		2 10
Ogulin	...	6 22	—	1150	...	...	5 29	9 47	11 45		3 4
Karolyvaros	...	8 25	...	1259	...	...	6 53	1052	12 54		5 2
Zagrab ...arr	a.m.	1024	p.m.	1 58	...	p.m.	8 11	1154	1 53		6 45
„ (Agram) dep	8 35	—	1 8	2 20	...	7 0	8§31	12 7	2 9		7 34
Dugoselo	9 25	...	1 50	2 39	...	7 48	8 59	SC	2 37		8 8
Koros	—	...	3 40	3 16	...	9 10	9 55	1 7	3 15		9 8
Kaproncza	...	...	4 57	3 51	...	1019	1037	...	3 49		9 57
Gyekenyes ...arr	a.m.	...	5 30	4 6	p.m.	1047	1055	1 58	4 5		10 19
„ ...dep	6 48	...	—	4 14	4 25	—	1110	2 6	4 12		10 46
Csurgo	7 7	...	...	4 27	4 48	...	1128	...	4 25		11 6
Somogyszob	7 41	...	...	4 48	5 43	...	1157	...	4 46		11 38
Kaposvár	8 59	Ex2	...	5 38	8 11	...	1 10	3 21	5 35		1 10
Dombovar	9 43	a.m.	1,2,3	RC	9 15	...	1 53	...	...		2 3
Uj Dombovar arr	9 48	RC	p.m.	6 11	9 20	a.m.	1 57	3 54	6 5	SC RC	2 8
„ ...dep		1014	4 30	6 20	—	1234	2 7	4 2	6 13		2 32
Hidegkut Gyonk	—	1057	5 29	...	...	1 31	3 1	RC	6 55	...	3 37
Sarbogard	a.m.	1145	6 31	7 37	p.m.	2 43	3 55	5 12	7 41	a.m.	5 0
Adony-Szabolcs	6 0	1229	7 33	8 18	5 55	3 36	4 48	5 53	8 17	8 22	6 19
B'pest (Kelenf) ar	7 17	1 31	8 48	9 16	7 34	5 3	6 13	6 44	—	9 17	7 52
Budapest-Ost. arr	8 20	1 55	9 10	9 35	8 5	5 30	6 50	7 0	...	9 35	8 15

SC—Sleeping Cars in this train. RC—Restaurant Car.

Kaproncza ...dep	3 a55	10a12	5 p4	...
Klostar 226A ...arr	5 51	12 36	6 50	...

Klostar ...dep	4 a8	10a30	7 p8	...
Kaproncza ...arr	6 16	12 38	9 15	...

ZAGRAB and BOSZNA-BROD.

E M							
	Zagrab (Agram) dep	2a10	8a40	11 a0	2p27	9p15	...
31	Sissek	3 35	9 49	1 27	3 21	1028	...
34½	Caprag	3 46	9 59	1 49	3 30	1039	...
45½	Sunja 231A	4 31	1031	2 50	3 51	1113	...
73½	Novska	5 41	1145	4 39	4 50	1234	...
94½	Ujgradiska	6 34	1242	6 42	5 30	1 39	...
108¾	Uj Kapela-Batrina	7 6	1 17	7 42	5 54	2 22	...
126¾	Brod	7 59	2 1	8 48	6 26	3 9	...
131	Boszna-Brod 247B	8 10	2 36	9 21	6 56	4 11	...

Boszna-Brod dp	7a35	9a31	1p10	5p30	11p46	...
Brod	8 6	10 0	1 35	5 58	12 45	...
Uj Kapela-Bat.	9 18	1034	2 30	6 53	1 43	...
Ujgradiska	1020	11 1	3 13	7 36	2 24	...
Novska	12 9	1143	4 11	8 31	3 17	...
Sunja	2 26	1243	5 50	9 53	4 40	...
Caprag	3 31	1 4	6 22	1020	5 9	...
Sissek	4 11	1 16	6 40	1032	5 26	...
Zagrab (Agram)	6 6	2 7	7 50	1142	6 35	...

Caprag...dep	...	5a19	10a9	3p54	...
Vrginmost	5a40	8 11	1 25	7 40	...
Karolyvaros	7 40	9 55	3 15	...	...

Karolyvaros	7a45	1p10	5p23	...	...
Vrginmost	9 57	3 8	7 26	1a57	...
Caprag...arr	1256	5 48	...	4 52	...

SUNJA and BANJALUKA.

Sunja ...dep	4a15	10a41	3p58
Doberlin ...arr	5 58	12 2	5 19
Novi	7 33	12 41	6 6
Priedor	8 31	2 5	7 18
Banjaluka..arr	1038	4 20	9 25

Banjaluka dep	7 a0	11a45	3p55	...
Priedor	9 20	2 24	5 58	...
Novi	1033	3 46	6 58	p.m.
Doberlin	1111	4 18	7 21	8 13
Sunja 231A arr	1231	5 44	...	9 36

KESZÖHIDEGKUT-GYONK and TAMASI-MAJSAMIKLOSVAR.

Keszöhidegkut-Gyonk ...dep	4a25	1 p0	...
Tamasi-Miklosvar ...arr	5 0	1 38	...

Tamasi-Miklosvar ...dep	10a15	2p35	...	...
Keszöhidegkut-Gyonk arr	10 51	3 12	...	...

DUGOSELO and NOVSKA.

Dugoselo ...dep	5a24	...	9a54	...	2 p50	8 p30	...
Banovajaruga	8 41	10a19	1247	1p20	5 24	11 32	...
Novska (231A) ...arr	9 19	10 57	...	1 58	...	12 10	...

Novska ...dep	3 a25	...	12p19	4 p55	...	...	...
Banovajaruga	4 6	10a33	12 55	5 36	...	...	...
Dugoselo (231) ...arr	6 40	1 24	...	8 9	...	...	...

Banovajaruga ...dep	4 a16	1 p10	5 p50	...	...	...	...
Pakrac ...arr	5 40	2 40	7 28	...	...	...	...

Pakrac ...dep	8 a35	3 p20	10 p7	...	...	...	...	...
Banovajaruga ...arr	9 52	4 52	11 22	...	...	...	...	...

KAPOSVAR and SZIGETVAR.

Kaposvar ...dep	5 a20	11 a2	4p15	...	...	...	...
Mozsgo-Szuliman	7 58	1 26	6 50	...	...	...	...
Szigetvar ...arr	8 18	1 46	7 10	...	...	...	...

Szigetvar ...dep	4 a40	11a55	4p50	...	...	...	...
Mozsgo-Szuliman	5 3	12 22	5 16	...	...	...	...
Kaposvar 231A ...arr	7 24	2 57	7 51	...	...	...	...

KAPOSVAR and SIOFOK.

Kaposvar ...dep	4a40	6a28	1 p5	3p25
Felsomocsolad	6 47	7 30	2 6	4 22
Kapoly	9 28	8 49	3 32	5 42
Siófok ...arr	1145	9 56	4 48	6 58

Siófok ...dep	3a43	8 a3	1p20	5p50
Kapoly	5 4	9 26	4 0	7 15
Felsomocsolad	6 37	11 1	6 22	8 50
Kaposvar 231A..arr	7 29	1153	8 1	9 42

KOROS and BELOVAR.

Koros ...dep	5 a50	9 a20	3 p35	10p25	...
Belovar ...arr	7 41	11 11	5 6	11 53	...

Belovar ...dep	5 a30	11a37	3 p55	7 p4	...
Koros (231A) ...arr	7 8	1 5	5 39	8 53	...

KAPOSVAR and FONYOD.

‡—Until September 15th.

Kaposvar dep	7 a50	11‡a7	12p47	3p30
Fonyod ...arr	10 5	1 4	3 36	6 5

Fonyod ...dep	5a35	12 p1	7 p0	8‡p50
Kaposvar 231A arr	7 49	3 10	9 7	10 46

For Fares, see page 233B.

BUDAPEST, SZOLNOK, ARAD, and TOVIS.

Dist		Ex3	2&3	1,2,3	1,2,3	1,2,3	Ex2	Ex2	1,2,3	1,2,3
E.M	Budapest—	a.m.			a.m.	p.m.	p.m.	p.m.	p.m	p.m.
—	Keleti dep (See also page 233) dep	7 5	...	...	7 50	1220	2 10	5 0	9 30	1125
5	Rákos 231 ...	7 20	...	...	8 7	1238	2 23	5 14	9 53	1147
16¾	Gyömrö	RC	...	...	8 44	1 21	RC	...	SC	1228
34¼	Nagykáta.....	8 19	...	...	9 33	2 23	3 12	6 9	1129	1 31
52¼	Ujszász 232	8 51	...	...	1016	3 15	3 42	6 40	1214	2 17
62¾	Szolnok 233 arr	9 9	...	...	1037	3 41	3 59	6 57	1238	2 39
...	,, ... dep	9 23	...	...	11 0	4 11	4 6	7 12	1 5	3 4
69¾	Szajol	9 38	...	...	1120	4 32	4 19	7 25	1 26	3 26
74¼	Pusztatenyo	...	...	...	1131	4 46	...	7 33	1 39	3 38
88¼	Mezö Tur 232 ...arr	1013	...	...	12 3	5 26	4 50	7 58	2 15	4 15
100	Gyoma 230A	1044	...	...	1239	6 9	5 11	8 25	2 55	5 2
116½	Békés-Földvar	...	...	...	1 15	6 50	5 38	...	3 35	5 44
121¼	: Békés..............arr	...	...	...	2 16	8 37	8 37	...	4 14	7 32
122¾	Csaba 230A............	1127	...	...	2 5	7 29	5 57	9 6	4 24	6 39
133	Kétegyhaza	1146	...	...	2 33	7 58	6 17	9 25	4 54	7 10
158¼	Arad 232 ....arr	1232	p.m.	...	3 31	9 3	6 59	10 9	6 0	8 11
...	,, ...dep	1247	2 15	...	4 6	1115	7 9	—	6 30	—
180¼	Maria Radna........	1 25	3 27	...	5 16	1236	7 49	...	7 37	...
211¼	Soborsin 1,2,3	2 25	4 57	...	7 0	2 30	8 52	...	9 4	...
236	Maros Illye ...a.m.	3 13	—	p.m.	8 14	4 11	9 37	...	1012	...
256¾	Piski 232 ......6 0	4 3	...	4 40	9 24	5 39	1032	...	1125	...
274¾	Alkenyér 6 53	4 40	...	5 45	1020	—	11 9	...	1218	...
284	Alvincz 232 ...7 17	4 58	...	6 21	1047	...	1126	...	1246	...
289½	Gyulafeh- arr7 32	5 10	...	6 36	11 1	...	1137	...	1259	...
...	érvár dep7 33	5 12	...	6 46	11 8	...	1139	...	1 6	...
302	Tovis 233 ...arr8 3	5 33	...	7 20	1135	...	12 0	...	1 32	...

	1,2,3	Ex2	Ex?	1,2,3	1,2,3	Ex3	2&3	1,2,3	1,2,3
	a.m.			a.m.	a.m.	a.m.	p.m.	p.m.	p.m
Tövis ....dep	6 5	...	a.m.	3 51	8 53	1046	5 59	2 5	8 17
Gyula- arr	6 46	...	3 15	4 17	9 22	11 6	6 45	2 30	8 44
fehérvár dep	6 55	...	3 36	4 25	9 27	11 7	—	2 33	8 47
Alvincz	7 16	...	3 37	4 45	9 44	1120	...	2 50	9 4
Alkenyér............	—	...	3 50	5 7	10 7	1136	...	3 11	9 26
Piski............2&3	...	...	SC	6 14	11 1	1244	...	4 17	1041
Maros Illye...a.m.	...	...	4 55	7 15	—	1 26	...	5 13	1148
Soborsin 4 15	...	...	5 36	8 25	...	2 19	...	6 23	1 7
Maria Radna6 6	1,2,3	...	6 28	10 0	...	3 22	...	7 51	2 58
Arad...... arr7 20	a.m.	a.m	7 30	11 0	...	4 1	p.m.	8 52	4 20
,, ...dep	5 0	6 23	8 8	11 42	...	4 15	4 51	9 39	RC Restaurant Car
Kétegyhaza	6 16	7 8	8 20	12 48	...	5 0	6 23	1047	
Csaba	6 38	7 28	9 4	1 32	...	5 25	7 38	1131	
: Békés..........dep	5 18	RC	9 26	12 40	...	5 0	...	1053	
Békés-Földvar ...	6 55	...	...	1 49	...	5 39	8 1	1148	
Gyoma	7 35	8 15	...	2 33	...	6 15	9 3	1233	
Mezö Tur	8 2	8 37	1013	3 7	...	6 36	9 48	1 4	
Pusztatenyo	8 36	9 4	1039	3 42	...	RC	1033	1 39	SC Sleeping Cars in this train.
Szajol	8 48	9 13	RC	3 52	...	7 8	1053	1 50	
Szolnok..........arr	9 5	9 25	1110	4 10	...	7 20	1110	2 7	
,, ...dep	9 40	9 35	1122	4 30	...	7 27	1 50	2 35	
Ujszász	10 5	9 53	1129	4 52	...	7 45	2 20	3 1	
Nagykáta	1054	1024	1147	5 42	...	8 17	3 27	3 54	
Gyömrö	1145	...	1219	6 33	...	...	...	SC	
Rákos	1217	1118	...	7 9	...	9 10	5 3	5 36	
Budapest ......arr	1230	1130	1 14 1 25	7 25	...	9 20	5 20	5 45	

MEZÖ-TUR and TURKEVE.

Mezö-Tur ....dep	5 a50	12p25	5p35	...
Turkeve............arr	6 30	1 5	6 15	...
Turkeve ....dep	7 a7	1p46	6 p50	...
Mezö-Tur (232) ....arr	7 47	2 25	7 30	...

PISKI and VAJDA HUNYAD (10 miles in 40 mins.)—Piski dep. 6.20, 8.55, 11.21 a.m., 12.55, 4.45, 5.5, 8.35, and 10.55 p.m. Vajda dep. 4.11, 7.41, 10.0 a.m., 12.0 noon, 2.55, 3.51, 7.28, and 9.38 p.m.

Vajda Hunyad...dep	8a20	12*p10	3p45
Retyisora ....arr	9 38	1 25	5 0
Retyisora ....dep	6a‡0	5p10	...
Vajda Hunyad...arr	7 15	6 20	...

*—Saturday only. ‡—9.50 a.m. on Sunday.

UJSZASZ and VAMOSGYÖRK.

E.M.					
	Ujszasz ....dep	...	5a41	12 0	7 p0
8¾	Jaszladány	...	6 22	12 42	7 51
20	Jászapáti	3 a6	7 27	2 0	8 55
38½	Vámosgyörk 231arr	4 45	8 55	3 38	...

Vámosgyörk......dep	...	5a50	11a32	7p10	...
Jászapáti	2a55	7 15	1 6	8 43	...
Jászladány	3 38	8 4	2 4	—	...
Ujszász 232 ....arr	4 7	8 30	2 35	...	...

ARAD and TEMESVAR.

Arad 232 ....dep	6a15	12p37	4p33	7p11	10p40	...
Szt-András	7 28	1 53	5 52	8 13	11 52	...
Temesvár 227	7 45	2 11	6 9	8 30	12 9	...
Temesvár.........dep	4a27	8a50	2p24	5 p6	9p28	...
Szt-András	4 47	9 8	2 42	5 26	9 46	...
Arad 232.............	6 5	1022	3 56	6 45	11 0	...

ARAD and NAGY-KIKINDA.

	a.m.	a.m.	p.m.	p.m.	
Arad...... ....dep	...	6 42	1 0	7 24	...
Perjamos...............	3 44	8 54	3 21	9 32	...
Lovrin	4 28	9 34	4 10	—	...
Nagy-Kikinda ...arr	5 30	10 28	5 17	...	...

	a.m.	a.m.	a.m.	p.m.	
Nagy-Kikinda ......dep	...	6 30	11 25	7 30	...
Lovrin	...	7 52	12 31	8 42	...
Perjamos................	3 32	8 45	1 12	9 17	...
Arad ....arr	5 50	11 12	3 15	...	...

PISKI and PETROZSENY.

Piski....................dep	3 a11	6 a25	11a20	4p29	10p50	...
Orvaralja 226A	4 26	7 32	12 27	5 36	12 18	...
Banicza	6 34	9 38	2 29	7 37	2 36	...
Petrozsény...........arr	7 5	10 9	3 0	8 8	3 7	...

Petrozsény ....dep	5 a15	7a46	12p39	5p10	1a16	...	...
Banicza	5 53	8 24	1 17	5 48	1 54	...	...
Orvaralja	7 35	10 4	2 55	7 27	3 32	...	...
Piski (232)...........arr	8 29	1059	3 50	8 22	4 27	...	...

Petrozsény ....dep	3a33	7 a25	10a34	1 p25	3 p15	8p28
Lupeny ....arr	4 40	8 54	11 50	2 59	4 30	9 45
Lupeny ....dep	3a57	5a57	11 a5	3p46	6 p40	11p50
Petrozsény ....arr	5 5	7 24	12 19	4 57	8 5	1 2

MEZOTUR and MEZOHEGYES.

Mezötúr ....dep	...	2a24	8 a25	12p15	5p40	...	...
Szarvas....................	...	3 25	9 11	1 27	6 38	...	...
Kisszénás..................	...	4 16	—	2 19	7 35	...	...
Oroshaza	3a40	5 25	...	3 46	8 40	...	...
Mezohegyes 254.........	5 20	8 21	...	5 40	...	...	...

Mezohegyes ....dep	...	5a55	...	9 a18	...	6p35
Oroshaza	5a55	7 33	...	11 17	6 p7	8 28
Kisszénás	7 32	—	...	12 39	7 26	—
Szarvas....................	8 24	...	11a10	1 26	8 13	...
Mezötúr ....arr	9 58	...	11 57	2 30	9 12	...

Kisszénás ....dep	4 a41	7 a45	2 p37	7‡p45	...
Kondoros ....arr	4 56	8 0	2 52	8 0	...
Kondoros ....dep	6 a50	12 0	6 p51	...	
Kisszénás...................arr	7 5	12 15	7 6	...	

‡—On Sun., Tues., and Fri. only.

NAGYSZEBEN. CAINENI—FOGARAS.

‡—From 1st July.

	a.m.	a.m.	p.m	p.m.	p.m.	p.m.
Nagyszeben ....dep	4 6	4 20	12 56	1 42	4‡42	5 42
Olthid ....arr	4 58	5 18	1 55	2 41	5 34	6 41
: Olthid ....dep	4 59	6 21	1 56	...	5 35	...
: Verestorony *	5 46	6 30	2 43	...	6 22	...
: Caineni (224B)...arr	6 30	...	3 30	...	7 9	...
Olthid ....dep	—	5 21	—	2 42	—	6 43
Felek	...	5 55	...	3 18	...	7 21
Fogaras (233)......arr	...	8 13	...	5 48	...	9 51

*—"Turnu Rosiu" of Roumania—Customs Exam'n.

	a.m	a.m.			p.m.	
Fogaras ....dep	3 33	8 14	...	...	4 42	...
Felek	5 48	10 51	...	...	7 25	...
Olthid ....arr	6 11	11 16	a.m.	p.m.	7 50	p.m.
: Caineni ....dep	...	...	8‡57	12 31	...	7 21
: Verestorony............	5 7	...	10 43	2 32	...	9 17
: Olthid ....arr	5 16	...	10 51	2 40	...	9 25
Olthid ....dep	6 16	11 19	10 52	2 42	7 51	9 26
Nagyszeben 233 ...arr	7 16	11 27	11 50	3 37	8 59	10 27

NAGYSZEBEN and ALVINCZ.

Nagyszeben ......dep	3 a5	7a37	10a35	4p51
Szelistye	4 41	9 9	12 7	6 24
Szerdahely	5 51	10 8	1 18	7 27
Alvincz (232).........arr	7 0	11 9	2 25	8 31

Alvincz ....dep	2a34	7a39	12p51	5 p8	...	...
Szerdahely	3 57	9 4	2 11	6 28	...	...
Szelistye	5 30	1030	3 2'	7 44	...	...
Nagyszeben 233 ...arr	6 40	1139	4 29	8 46	...	...

NAGYSZEBEN and NAGYDISZNOD.

Nagyszeben ....dep	5 a21	7a30	1 p29	9 p13
Nagydisznód............arr	5 57	8 4	2 5	9 49
Nagydisznód.............dep	6a27	12p41	2 p48	10p10
Nagyszeben 233 ....arr	7 0	1 18	3 23	10 44

For Fares, see page 233B.]

BUDAPEST and RUTTKA.

Dist. E.M.		Ex1	2&3	1,2,3	2 & 3	Ex2	2 & 3	1,2,3	1,2,3
		a.m.		a.m.	p.m.	p.m.		p.m.	p.m.
—	**Budapest** ...dep	6 25	Mon. and Thurs. only.	8 35	...	2 20	...	5 55	1110
42¾	**Hatvan**...arr2&3	7 35		1057	...	3 30	...	7 38	1 33
...	,, 231 dep3a32	7 42		11 7	1 25	3 37	...	8 8	1 49
61½	Pásztó 5 38	8 12		12 1	2 57	4 8	...	9 3	2 50
70¾	Kisterenye 231 6 32	8 29		1236	3 48	4 27	p.m.	9 40	3 27
78¼	Salgotarján ...7 18	8 46		1 4	4 22	4 48	5 15	1014	3 58
91¼	**Fulek** 232A...8 45	9 26	p.m.	1 57	—	5 29	6 41	1120	5 9
101½	Losoncz 232A —	9 45	1 10	2 44	...	5 47	7 16	1147	5 48
118¾	Krivány-Gyetva ...	...	2 57	3 41	...	6 28	8 24	1241	6 49
133¾	**Zólyom** 232A dep	1055	3 27	4 50	...	7 5	9 15	1 29	8 35
141¾	Garamberze'cz232A	11 9	—	5 15	...	7 18	—	1 50	8 56
157¾	Körmöczbánya ...	1156	a.m.	6 11	...	8 3	...	2 54	9 50
175¾	Stubnyafürdo	1240	6 39	7 5	...	8 47	...	3 51	1045
194¾	**Ruttka** 253A arr	1 16	8 15	7 50	...	9 23	...	4 43	1138
270½	ODERBERG ...arr	5 p6	...	1230	...	1230	...	9a30	5 p6

	2&3	Ex1	1,2,3	2&3	Ex 2	1,2,3	1,2,3
ODERBERG dep (253A)	...	3a20	4a50	...	10a45	...	5p45
		a.m.	a.m.	a.m.	p.m.	p.m.	p.m.
Ruttka.........dep	...	6 20	9 10	1154	2 40	3 50	1047
Stubnyafürdo	...	7 0	1010	2 4	3 19	4 58	1148
Körmöczbánya ...	...	7 43	1114	—	4 2	6 15	1259
Garamberzencze..	a.m.	8 19	12 4	...	4 36	7 20	1 50
Zólyom ......dep	4 3	8 40	1238	...	5 7	8 28	2 19
Krivány.........1,2,3	5 29	...	1 23	...	5 44	9 27	3 6
Losoncz.........a.m.	6 54	9 45	2 20	...	6 23	1023	3 59
Fulek 4 45	—	10 6	3 10	...	6 46	1119	4 24
Salgótarján ...5 44	...	1040	4 2	...	7 23	1210	—
Kisterenye ...6 4	...	1051	4 24	...	7 34	1232	...
Pasztó 6 33	...	11 7	4 57	...	7 50	1 7	...
Hatvan...arr7 20	...	1135	5 45	...	8 18	1 57	...
,, ...dep7 30	...	1140	6 0	...	8 23	2 22	...
Budapestar9 25	...	1250	7 45	...	9 35	5 10	...

ZÓLYOM and TISZOLCZ.

Zólyom ...dep 2a30	...	6a29	7a51	8a44	11a0	1233	4p55	7p10	9p25
Szliácsfürdö...2 50	...	6 47	8 15	9 1	1116	1252	5 11	7 29	9 48
Beszterczebán3 52	...	7 48	8 58	9 43	1159	1 48	6 5	8 19	1040
Zólyombrézó 5 45	6a59	10 5	—	—	—	3 38	8 22	—	—
Breznóbánya —	7 30	1119	...	...	...	4 38	8 55	...	...
Erdököz	9 15	1230	...	2p30	...	5 19	9 42	...	...
Tiszolcz 232A arr	1150	...	...	4 22	...	7 21	...	...	...

Tiszolcz ......dep	7a16	...	...	12p9	...	...	...	2p58
Erdököz 4a39	9 10	...	10a30	2 26	...	...	...	5 33
Breznóbánya5 15	—	...	11 18	3 28	4p29	...	p.m.	6 41
Zólyombrézó6 10	a.m.	p.m.	1 12	4 22	4 56	p.m.	6 50	—
Beszterczeba7 38	9 55	12 6	3 34	6 4	—	6 52	9 4	1159
Szliácsfürdö 8 15	1033	1252	4 22	6 40	...	7 42	—	1254
Zólyom 232A8 29	1047	1 10	4 40	6 53	...	7 57	...	1 15

BREZNOBANYA and VERESKO.

Breznobánya......dep	8 a10	6 p25	...
Garamszecs	9 43	8 5	...
Vereskö ....arr	11 34	9 56	...

Vereskö ....dep	4 a50	12p36	...	...
Garamszecs	6 43	2 14	...	...
Breznobánya.........arr	7 45	3 5	...	...

MISKOLCZ, BANREVE, DOBSINA, and FULEK.

	a.m.	a.m.	a.m.	p.m.	p.m	p.m.
Miskolcz.............dep	3 27	6 27	1057	3 25	5 50	7 10
Sajóecseg	3 46	6 50	1120	3 47	6 12	7 38
Barczika	4 7	7 9	1140	4 8	6 38	8 4
: Ormospuszta ...arr	5 40	9 22	1 32	5 53	...	...
Putnok	4 35	7 38	12 8	4 36	7 11	8 39
Bánréve 232A ...arr	4 47	7 49	1219	4 48	7 24	8 50
Bánréve ....dep	4 57	8 15	1240	5 3	—	9 10
Pelsocz 232A.........	6 29	9 51	2 20	6 53	...	1055
Rozsnyo	7 21	1049	3 11	7 49	...	1151
Dobsina ....arr	8 44	1210	4 31	9 13	...	1 14
Bánréve ....dep	—	7 54	1227	4 56	...	9 18
Feled 232A	...	8 34	1 5	5 40	...	10 1
Fülek 232A ....arr	...	9 17	1 49	6 26	...	1043

		a.m.	a.m.	p.m.	p.m.	p.m.	ngt	
Fülek...............dep	...	6 12	1025	2 55	5 40	7 12	1232	...
Feled	...	7 7	1118	3 44	6 50	8 20	2 30	...
Bánréve ....arr	...	7 42	1151	4 19	7 34	8 58	3 44	...
Dobsina ......dep	...	4 12	7 40	1225	—	4 50	—	...
Rozsnyo	...	5 31	9 2	1 38	...	6 10	...	...
Pelsocz............	...	6 20	9 54	2 32	...	7 2	...	...
Bánréve ......arr	a.m.	7 36	1116	3 46	...	8 21	...	...
Bánréve ....dep	6 5	7 52	1159	4 24	...	9 14	...	...
Putnok...............	6 19	8 4	12 8	4 36	...	9 27	...	...
: Ormospuszta dep	6 5	...	1048	3 15	6p25	...	...	...
Barczika	6 45	8 30	1234	5 1	7 14	9 56	...	...
Sajóecseg	7 9	8 50	1254	5 21	—	1020	...	...
Miskolcz 231 ...arr	7 33	9 10	1 14	5 41	...	1041	...	...

BANREVE and OZD.

Bánréve.........dep	5 a0	8a20	12p55	5 p0	9p20
Ozd ....arr	6 14	9 0	1 35	5 40	9 59

Odz...............dep	6 a58	10a44	3p22	7p22	...	...
Bánréve......arr	7 37	11 23	4 1	8 1	...	...

Pelsocz and Muranyalja.—Pelsocz dep. 6.45 a.m., 7.20 p.m. Return from Muranyalja 3.56 and 10.50 a.m.

Pelsocz and Nagyszabos.—Pelsocz dep. 7a0, 2p46, 7p30 Return from Nagyszabos 4.15, 11.30 a.m. and 5.4 p.m.

HATVAN and SZOLNOK.

E.M.						
	Hatvan..........dep	4a47	9 a0	1p27	4p57	9p38
16½	Jaszbereny	5 47	9 46	2 14	5 40	1022
33	Ujszasz	6 44	1033	3 0	6 24	11 6
42½	Szolnok (233) ...arr	7 18	1056	3 24	6 49	1129

Szolnok.........dep	4a25	8a36	12p15	5p17	8 p38	...
Ujszasz...............	4 49	9 1	12 42	5 47	9 11	...
Jaszbereny.........	5 40	9 52	1 34	6 42	10 18	...
Hatvan 232A arr	6 22	1034	2 17	7 23	11 8	...

ARANYOSGYERES and TORDA.

Aranyosgyéres...dep	4a54	8a35	10a32	11a51	3 p3	4p18	5p32	7p40	9p12	10p41	12a43
Torda.................arr	5 16	8 57	10 54	12 13	3 25	4 40	5 54	8 2	9 34	11 3	1 5
Torda ....dep	4 a0	6a50	9a37	11a11	2p20	3p43	4p57	7 p4	8 p30	9 p50	11p50
Aranyosgyéres 233	4 20	7 10	9 57	11 31	2 40	4 3	5 17	7 24	8 50	10 10	12 13

FELED and TISZOLCZ.

Dist										
	Feled ......dep	7a12	8a59	1130	1p15	3p51	5p44	7 p5	8p30	1011
7½	Rimaszombat...	8 0	9 42	1216	2 3	4 32	6 11	7 31	8 56	1046
17½	Rimabanya......	8 59	1041	1 12	—	5 28	—	—	—	1143
31	**Tiszolcz** 232A	1021	12 3	2 29	...	6 47	...	...	...	1258

Tiszolcz...dep	4a21	5a46	...	...	12p43	...	5p21	7p30
Rimabanya......	5 33	7 1	a.m.	p.m.	2 0	p.m.	6 56	8 37
Rimaszombat...	6 25	7 50	1012	1225	2 54	4 55	7 45	9 21
Feled 232Aarr	6 55	8 20	1057	1252	3 22	5 20	8 11	9 50

LOSONCZ and RIMAKOKOVA.

Losoncz............dep	10 a0	3 p16	7 p26
Ipolyberzencze...........	10 45	4 3	8 16
Poltar	11 20	4 40	8 50
Rimakokova......arr	12 28	5 48	9 57

Rimakokova ...dep	5 a20	3p10	6p32
Poltar	6 37	4 26	7 48
Ipolyberzencze	7 11	4 58	8 23
Losoncz 232A ...arr	7 52	5 35	9 0

Ipolyberzencze ....dep	11 a0	8p18
Katalinhuta ....arr	11 41	8 59
Katalinhuta...............dep	6a18	4 p11
Ipolyberzencze ....arr	6 52	4 50

GARAM-BERZENCZE and SELMECZBANYA.

Garam-Berzenczedep	9 a4	12p21	5 p18	8 p0
Selmeczbanya......arr	10 53	2 1	7 4	9 45

Selmeczbanya ...dep	6 a32	9 a30	2p59	5 p37
Garam-Berzenczearr	8 0	10 55	4 24	7 6

PARKANY NANA and GARAM-BERZENCZE

Parkany Nana ......dep	5a40	8 a55	...	1 p8	4p28	9p20
Csata	6 37	9 56	...	2 5	5 31	1020
Léva	8 9	11 19	12§p50	3 28	7 2	12 0
Garamkovácsi 226	8 36	12‡24	1 20	—	7 30	—
Garam-Berzencze ..arr	1053	2‡57	3 5	...	9 44	...

Garam-Berzenczedep	...	6 a4	...	12p25	5p25
Garamkovácsi	...	8 17	p.m.	2 49	7 52
Léva	5 a4	8 51	1234	3 45	8 24
Csata........................	6 50	1020	1 58	5 19	9 49
Parkany Nana 232Aar	7 37	11 7	2 45	6 10	1037

‡—Until 15th September. §—From 16th September.

BALASSA-GYARMAT and PARKANY-NANA.

Balassa-Gyarmat....dep	2a55	8a34	2p20	...
Ipolysag	4 40	10 7	3 43	...
Csata.........................	6 25	11 25	5 22	...
Párkány-Náná 232A arr	7 27	12 20	6 21	...

Párkány-Nána	5a50	9 a10	4p18	...
Csata	6 45	10 22	5 26	...
Ipolysag	8 45	12 8	7 10	...
Balassa-G ...arr	1014	1 28	8 23	...

Ipolysag...dep	10a12	7p34	...
Korpona...arr	12 25	10 3	...
Korpona...dep	5a53	1 p30	...
Ipolysag...arr	8 16	3 30	...

For Fares, see page 233B.]

BUDAPEST, KOLOZSVAR, BRASSO, and PREDEAL.

Dist E.M	VIENNA 225B ......dep	...	...	...	1020	...	1020	...	...	9 a10	...	9 a25	...	...	...	1p55	4 p50	...	...
		1,2,3	1,2,3	Ex 2	Ex3	1,2,3	1,2,3	1,2,3	1,2,3	Ex.2	2&3	Ex.3	Ex2	2&3	1,2,3	1,2,3	Ex.2	Ex 2	1,2,3
	Budapest-			a.m.	a.m.		a.m.	a.m.	p.m.	p.m.		p.m.	p.m.		p.m.	p.m.	p m.	p.m.	p.m.
—	Ostbahnhof........dep	...	...	7 ‡0	7 5	...	8 20	8 55	12 20	2 10	...	2‡25	5 0	...	6 15	7 45	9‡35	10‡50	1125
5	Rakos	...	...	⋮	7 20	...	8 39	9 14	12 38	2 23	...	⋮	5 14	...	6 35	8 6	⋮	⋮	1147
34¼	Nagykata	...	...	⋮	8 19	...	1010	1047	2 23	3 12	...	⋮	6 9	...	8 14	9 18	⋮	⋮	1 31
52¾	Ujszasz	...	...	⋮	8 51	...	1055	1131	3 15	3 42	...	⋮	6 40	...	9 1	10 3	⋮	⋮	2 17
62¾	**Szolnok** ....arr	a.m.	...	8 42	9 9	...	1117	1152	3 41	3 59	...	4 15	6 57	...	9 25	1024	11 17	12 49	2 39
...	" ....dep	4 0	...	8 49	9 23	...	1131	1218	4 38	4 6	...	4 25	7 22	...	9 46	1040	11 25	12 57	—
69½	Szajol	4 19	...	9 2	9 38	...	1149	1237	5 3	4 19	...	4 38	7 36	...	10 5	1057	11 39	1 11	...
75¼	Török Sz. Miklos	4 33	...	9 13	⋮	...	12 2	1250	5 23	⋮	...	...	7 47	...	1019	1111	RC	...	...
91¼	Kisújszállás	5 21	...	9 41	⋮	...	1246	1 38	6 40	⋮	...	5 15	8 18	...	11 8	12 0	12 17	1 49	...
102	Karczag 227B	5 46	...	10 0	RC	...	1 14	2 6	7 10	⋮	...	5 33	8 37	...	1135	1224	12 37	2 8	...
111½	**Püspök-Ladány** arr	6 10	a.m.	10 20	⋮	...	1 40	2 25	7 37	⋮	...	5 49	8 54	...	1159	1246	12 56	2 24	...
...	dep	—	5 13	10 35	⋮	...	2 5	—	—	⋮	...	5 56	9 1	...	1225	—	1 3	2 31	...
131¾	Berettyóújfalu	...	6 9	11 14	⋮	...	2 54	...	...	RC	...	6 30	9 37	...	1 13	...	1 39	3 9	...
153¼	**Nagyvarad**.........arr	...	7 17	11 59	⋮	p.m.	3 54	...	...	⋮	...	7 9	1020	p.m.	2 12	...	2 20	3 50	...
...	" 230A...dep	...	7 24	12 5	Via Arad.	1226	4 18	...	...	⋮	...	7 14	—	1118	2 52	...	2 25	4 9	...
168½	Mezőtelegd	...	8 10	12 29	⋮	1 0	4 57	...	...	Via Arad.	...	7 42	...	1221	3 29	...	2 53	4 37	...
182½	Rév	...	9 5	1 2	⋮	1 44	5 35	...	...	⋮	...	8 15	...	1 29	4 9	...	3 28	5 11	...
203¾	Csucsa	...	1028	1 47	⋮	2 53	6 37	...	...	⋮	...	9 3	...	3 6	5 12	...	4 17	5 57	...
217½	Bánffyhunyad	...	1114	2 17	⋮	3 31	7 20	...	...	⋮	...	9 33	...	3 58	5 57	...	4 47	6 29	...
248½	**Kolozsvár 223** arr	...	1252	3 16	⋮	4 43	8 34	...	...	⋮	...	10 32	⌒	6 3	7 22	...	5 47	7 45	...
	dep	...	p.m. 1 15	...	⋮	p.m. 4 55	p.m. 9 4	...	...	⋮	...	...	p.m. 1051	...	...	...	a.m. 6 13	a.m. 8 8	a.m. 8 32
256	Apahida	...	1 37	...	⋮	5 20	9 22	...	...	⋮	...	...	1112	...	...	...	6 28	8 14	8 58
280½	**Aranyosgyéres 232A**	...	2 58	...	⋮	6 34	1031	...	...	⋮	...	...	1233	...	...	...	7 23	9 13	1027
290¾	**Székely-** ....arr	...	3 29	...	⋮	7 3	1055	...	...	⋮	...	...	1 1	...	...	...	7 43	9 34	1057
...	**kocsárd 233A**...dep	...	4 4	...	⋮	7 8	1120	...	...	⋮	...	...	1 16	...	...	...	7 45	—	1117
303¾	Nagyenyed	...	4 56	...	⋮	7 42	1153	...	...	SC	...	2 & 3	1 53	...	...	...	8 12	...	12 6
311¼	**Tövis** 232 ....arr	...	5 20	...	5 33	7 59	12 9	...	...	12 0	...	a.m.	2 14	...	...	...	8 26	...	1232
...	" ....dep	...	—	...	5 55	8 10	1234	...	...	12 20	...	3 1	⌣	...	...	...	8 45	...	1 56
324½	Küküllőszög 233A	...	...	...	6 20	8 44	1 11	...	...	12 45	...	3 51	...	...	...	...	9 10	...	2 39
343	**Kis-Kapus** 233...arr	...	...	...	6 55	9 32	1 57	...	...	1 22	...	5 2	...	...	...	...	9 49	...	3 21
371	NAGYSZEBEN ......arr	...	...	...	8p56	...	3a53	...	...	3 a53	...	7 a12	...	...	...	...	11a49	...	5p18
...	**Kis-Kapus**........dep	...	...	...	7 0	9 42	2 14	...	...	1 27	...	5 17	...	...	...	...	9 51	...	3 41
361	Erzsebetvaros	...	...	...	7 31	1026	3 3	...	...	2 0	...	6 24	...	...	...	...	10 21	...	4 24
374	**Segesvar** 233A ...arr	...	...	...	7 55	1059	3 35	...	...	2 24	...	7 7	...	...	...	...	10 45	...	4 54
380½	Héjjasfalva	...	...	...	8 14	—	4 6	...	...	2 43	...	8 15	...	...	...	...	11 2	...	5 30
407¾	Homoród-Kőhalom	...	...	...	9 10	...	5 31	...	...	3 43	...	10 5	...	...	...	...	12 4	...	6 52
422½	Agostonfalva	...	...	...	9 40	...	6 10	...	...	...	...	10 48	...	...	...	...	12 35	...	7 28
430¾	Apácza	...	...	...	9 58	...	6 42	...	...	4 30	...	11 22	...	...	...	...	12 55	...	7 52
440½	Foldvar	...	...	...	1015	...	7 12	...	...	4 48	...	11 55	...	...	...	...	1 15	...	8 17
454½	**Brassó** 233A ......arr	p.m.	...	...	1043	...	7 53	...	a.m	5 16	a.m.	12 45	...	...	...	...	1 46	...	8 56
...	(Kronstadt).........dep	6 40	...	...	—	...	—	...	2 46	5 26	11 5	—	...	...	...	...	2 1	...	—
464¾	Felsőtömös	7 42	...	...	...	...	...	...	3 35	6 5	1151	...	...	...	...	...	2 41	...	...
473	**Predeal** 324A ¶...arr	8 14	...	...	...	...	...	...	4 5	6 33	1219	...	...	...	...	...	3 9	...	...
563	BUCHAREST 324 arr	...	...	...	...	...	...	...	10a25	11a40	7 p0	...	...	...	...	...	9 p20	...	...

‡—From Westbahnhof via Czegléd, page 227. ¶—Customs Examination.
SC—Sleeping Cars in this train. RC—Restaurant Car.

BANFFYHUNYAD and KISKALOTA.

Bánffyhunyad..........dep	5 a30	8 a48	3 p45	...	...	Kiskalota ....dep	7 a11	1 p5	6 p10	...	...	...
Kiskalota ....arr	6 35	9 50	4 50	...	...	Banffyhunyad (233).......arr	8 8	2 0	7 6	...	...	...

KIS-KAPUS and NAGY-SZEBEN.

E.M																
	Kis-Kapus ....dep	2a24	5a22	10a19	3p36	7p26	...	...	Nagyszeben ......dep	7a27	1 p0	4p33	7p20	11p10	...	...
21¼	Vizaknafürdő	3 29	6 41	11 26	4 50	8 32	...	...	Vizaknafürdő	7 56	1 34	5 3	7 56	11 37	...	...
28	Nagyszeben ......arr	3 53	7 12	11 49	5 18	8 56	...	...	Kis-Kapus 233 ...arr	8 57	2 52	6 4	9 10	12 33	...	...

Extra trains between Vizaknafürdő and Nagyszeben until 15th September.

[For Fares, see page 233B.

PREDEAL, BRASSO, KOLOZSVAR, and BUDAPEST.

BUCHAREST 324 ...dep	...	...	...	...	...	...	...	...	...	...	...	7 a50	...	...	...	9a35	5 p5	...	5 p5
	1,2,3	Ex2	1,2,3	1,2,3	2&3	2 & 3	Ex3	1,2,3	2&3	2&3	Ex2	Ex. 2	2&3	Ex2	2&3	2&3	1,2,3	1,2,3	Ex 2
						a.m.						p.m.				p.m.	p.m.		p.m.
Predeal ¶ ....dep...	...	...	...	...	...	6 34	...	...	...	...	...	12 50	...	...	...	3 49	9 2	...	8 42
Felsötömös..........	...	...	...	...	...	7 4	...	...	...	...	...	1 18	...	...	...	4 22	9 27	...	9 6
Brassó ....arr	...	...	...	...	...	7 48	a.m.	a.m.	...	...	...	2 0	p.m.	...	...	5 10	10 5	p.m.	9 44
(Kronstadt)..........dep	...	...	...	...	...		6 0	6 36	...	...	...	2 40	1 47	...	...			7 41	10 8
Foldvar..........	...	...	...	...	...	...	6 26	7 12	...	...	...	3 8	2 28	...	...	...	...	8 17	10 36
Apácza..........	...	...	...	...	...	...	6 41	7 40	...	...	...	3 26	3 6	...	...	...	...	8 39	10 52
Agostonfalva..........	...	...	...	...	...	...	6 54	8 3	...	...	...	3 42	3 52	...	...	...	...	9 9	...
Homoród-Köhalom..........	...	...	...	...	...	1,2,3	7 23	8 46	...	...	...	4 19	4 50	...	...	...	...	9 48	11 33
Héjjasfalva..........	...	...	...	...	...	a.m.	8 15	10 8	...	p.m.	...	5 28	6 36	...	...	...	...	10 58	12 30
Segesvar ....arr	...	...	...	...	...	7 8	8 27	10 25	...	1 15	...	5 41	6 57	...	...	...	...	11 11	12 42
Erzsebetvaros..........	...	...	...	...	...	7 41	8 54	11 26	...	2 6	...	6 15		...	...	...	...	11 57	1 16
Kis-Kapus..........arr	...	...	...	...	...	8 22	9 26	12 16	...	3 5	...	6 47	...	...	...	...	...	12 37	1 53
NAGYSZEBEN..........dep	...	...	...	...	...	...	7a27	...	...	1 p0	...	4 p33	...	...	...	...	...	11p10	11p10
Kis-Kapus..........dep	...	...	...	...	...	8 37	9 28	12 31	...	3 22	...	6 56	...	...	...	...	...	12 57	1 58
Küküllöszög..........	...	...	...	...	...	9 25	10 2	1 22	...	4 33	...	7 28	...	...	...	1,2,3	...	1 56	2 32
Tövis ....arr	...	...	...	a.m.	a.m.	9 55	1023	1 55	p.m.	5 15	...	7 49	...	...	...	a.m.	...	2 25	3 0
" ....dep	...	...	...	6 29	8 35	10 29	1046	2 19	2 29		...	8 0	...	...	...	1235	...	3 8	3 15
Nagyenyed..........	...	...	...	6 51	9 6	10 46		2 41	3 6	...	...	8 15	...	...	...	1 3	...	3 27	
Kocsárd ....arr	...	...	...	7 34		11 16	RC	3 13	4 3	...	p.m.	8 37	...	...	...	1 43	...	3 57	
" ....dep	...	...	...	7 44	...	11 20		3 30	4 18	...	7 6	8 42	...	...	...	1 56	...	4 15	
Gyéres..........	...	...	...	8 25	...	11 46		4 13	5 27	...	7 35	9 7	...	...	...	2 33	...	4 48	SC
Apahida..........	...	...	...	9 50	...	12 40		5 25	7 30	...	8§46	10 §3	...	...	...	3 55	...	5 52	
Kolozsvar ......arr	...	...	...	1015	...	12 56		5 44	8 5	...	9 3	10 20	2&3	...	...	4 20	Ex3	6 12	
		p.m.			n'on	p.m.		p.m.			p.m.	p.m.	p.m.				a.m.	a.m.	
Kolozsvar ......dep	...	1 13	...	...	12 0	2 19		6 19	...	...	9 23	10 56	1125	...	...		5 20	6 37	
Banffyhunyad..........	...	2 16	...	...	2 26	5 22	Via Arad.	7 56	...	...	1036	12 6	2 20	...	...		6 28	8 22	Via Arad.
Csucsa..........	...	2 46	...	...	3 30			8 33	...	...	11 9	12 39	3 36	...	...	...	6 59	8 58	
Rév..........	...	3 30	...	...	4 45	...		9 25	...	...	1152	1 23	5 7	...	...	...	7 43	9 51	
Mezötelegd..........	...	3 54	...	2&3	5 40	...		10 0	...	...	1220	1 50	6 8	...	...	...	8 10	10 23	
Nagy- ....arr	...	4 17	...	p.m.	6 30	...		10 34	...	...	1246	2 16	6 50	a.m.	a m.	...	8 34	10 53	
varad..........dep	...	4 35	...	2 30		...		11 9	...	...	1254	2 26		6 15	6 42	...	8 41	11 7	
Berettyóújfalu..........	...	5 17	...	3 58	1,2,3	...		12 5	...	...	1 38	3 10	...	6 57	8 26	2&3	9 21	12 1	RC
Püspök- ....arr	p.m.	5 52	...	5 10	p.m.	nght		12 54	...	...	2 15	3 47	...	7 32	9 40	a.m.	9 55	12 48	
Ladany..........dep	1 41	6 2	...	6 28	1110	12 20		1 22	...	...	2 30	3 54	...	7 39		4 50	10 1	1 12	
Karczag..........	2 5	6 20	...	7 14	1134	12 56		1 45	...	...	2 51	4 13	...	7 57	...	5 19	1018	1 39	
Kisújszallas..........	2 37	6 40	...	8 18	1217	1 26		2 18	...	...	3 15	4 35	...	8 17	...	5 53	1037	2 13	
Török Sz. Miklos..........	3 20	7 11	...	9 26	1257	2 14		2 55	...	...	...	5 11	...	8 50	...	6 44	...	2 56	
Szajol..........	3 34	7 23	...	9 52	1 12	2 29	7 8	3 10	...	...	4 0	5 23	...	9 2	...	7 1	1120	3 11	11 10
Szolnok ....arr	3 51	7 35	p.m.	1017	1 27	2 45	7 20	3 27	...	...	4 15	5 36	a.m.	9 15	...	7 21	1133	3 27	11 22
" ....dep	4 2	7 44	7 48		1 50	3 10	7 27	4 0	...	...	4 30	5 46	5 43	9 35	...	9 40	1145	3 44	11 29
Ujszasz..........	4 24	RC	8 12	...	2 20	3 33	7 45	4 25	...	...			6 8	9 53	...	10 5	...	4 4	11 47
Nagykata..........	5 17	...	9 1	...	3 27	4 28	8 17	5 16	...	...			7 0	1024	...	1054	RC	4 48	12 19
Rakos..........	6 44	...	1020	...	5 3	5 56	9 10	6 57	...	...			8 23	1119	...	1217	...	6 1	1 14
Budapest-Ost. ......arr	7 0	9‡40	1035	...	5 20	6 15	9 20	7 20	...	...	6‡50	7 ‡35	8 35	1130	...	1230	1‡50	6 15	1 25
VIENNA 225B ......arr	...	...	...	...	...	3 p45	7a20	1 p50	...	...	...	12p14	...	...	...	6p40	6p20	...	6 p40

‡—Arrives at Budapest Westbahnhof via Czegléd, page 227.
SC—Sleeping Cars in this train.
RC—Restaurant Car.
¶—Customs Examination.
§—Stops until 16th Sept.

BRASSO (KRONSTADT) and FOGARAS.

E.M.							
	Brassó ....dep	4 a8	1 p5	5p25	...	...	...
18	Vledeny	5 47	2 31	6 50	...	...	...
27	Ujsinka..........	6 34	3 16	7 34	...	...	...
44	Fogaras 232 ......arr	7 59	4 32	8 50	...	...	...

Fogaras..........dep	3a13	8 a43	6 p0	...	...	...	...	...
Ujsinka..........	4 51	10 14	7 30	...	...	...	...	...
Vledeny..........	5 40	11 4	8 18	...	...	...	...	...
Brassó 233 ......arr	7 13	12 27	9 36	...	...	...	...	...

SZEKELYKOCSARD and BRASSO (Kronstadt).

Szekelykocsárd ......dep	...	...	...	2 a20	5a50	9a50	...	12 p1	3 p35	8 p18
Marosludas..................	...	...	...	3 0	6 28	10 21	...	12 43	4 15	8 56
Maros-Vásárhely............	...	...	...	4 42	7 39	11 24	11a39	2 6	6 7	10 8
Szászrégen	...	...	...	5 55			12 43	3 21	7 18	
Déda	...	...	...	6 55	...	...	1 32	4 21	8 16	...
Marosheviz	...	...	...	8 29	...	...	2 47	5 55	9 42	...
Gyergyoszentmiklos......	...	6 a27	10a15	10 2	...	...	4 0	7 25	10 45	...
Madefalva 233A...........	4 a20	8 20	10 27	11 40	...	4 p5	5 33	8 56		...
Csikszereda..................	4 33	9 9		12 55	...	11 17	5 50	9 8	...	...
Tusnadfurdo	5 28	10 20	...	2 18	...		6 51		...	...
Malnasfurdo	5 52	10 46	...	2 46	...	...	7 14	...	...	...
Sepsiszentgyörgy 233A	6 47	11 40	...	4 0	...	...	8 8	...	...	...
Brassó 233 ....arr	8 10	1 0	...	5 20	...	...	9 26	...	...	...
Brassó.....................dep	...	...	...	5 a31	...	...	...	11 a0	2 p45	6 p13
Sepsiszentgyörgy	...	...	...	6 46	...	...	...	12 18	3 59	7 30
Malnasfurdo	...	...	...	7 41	...	...	...	1 23	5 14	8 28
Tusnadfurdo................	...	...	...	8 14	...	...	...	1 55	5 41	8 52
Csikszereda	...	...	5 a10	9 52	11a26	...	5 p7	3 36	7 14	9 52
Madefalva	...	...	5 29	10 20	11 39	...	5 20	4 10	7 37	10 5
Gyergyoszentmiklos......	...	4 a20	7 24	12 11		...		6 14	9 10	
Marosheviz	...	5 30	8 38	1 24	...	...	...	7 24		...
Déda	...	6 48	9 52	2 37	...	...	...	8 38	...	...
Szászrégen	...	7 45	10 46	3 30	...	p.m.	p.m.	9 31	...	...
Maros-Vásárhely..........	5 a10	9 4	12 11	4 31	...	5 1	8 36	10 52	...	...
Marosludas..................	6 28	10 26	1 28	...	...	6 8	10 5	12 9	...	...
Szekelykocsárd 233 arr	7 5	11 2	2 5	...	...	6 13	10 45	12 46	...	...

Marosludas ......dep	...	3 a53	10a41
Sajo-Magyaros	5 a36	9 3	3 56
Beszterczo (223) arr	6 27	9 55	4 48
Beszterczo......... dep	6 a47	11a35	6 p10
Sajo Magyaros	7 35	12 27	6 58
Marosludas ......arr	12 38	5 50	...

BRASSO and ZERNEST.

Brassó ....dep	8 a20	2 p48	10p13	...	...	...	...
Zernest ....arr	9 46	4 13	11 33	...	...	...	...

Zernest ....dep	6 a10	12p15	6 p15	...	...	...	...
Brassó (233) ....arr	7 30	1 35	7 27	...	...	...	...

GYULAFEHERVAR and ZALATNA.

Gyulafehervardep	4 a37	9 a30	6 p55	...	...	...
Totfalud...............	5 49	10 42	8 9	...	...	...
Zalatna ....arr	7 33	12 26	9 50	...	...	...

Zalatna ....dep	4 a55	8 a20	3 p50	...	...	...	...	...
Totfalud	6 23	9 51	5 19	...	...	...	...	...
Gyulafehervar 232...arr	7 23	10 53	6 22	...	...	...	...	...

NAGYSZOMBAT and SZERED.

Nagyszombat...dep	6 a5	10a10	1p10	5p40	12a25	...	...
Szered 226.........arr	6 29	10 34	2 0	6 12	12 57	...	...

Szered ....dep	3 a38	7 a5	11a25	3p40	9p37	...	...
Nagyszombat 226...arr	4 12	7 31	11 51	4 19	10 0	...	...

NAGYSZOMBAT and JOKUT.

Nagyszombat...dep	...	8 a0	12p20	6p50	...	...	...
Jabláncz	4a21	9 44	1 49	8 29	...	...	...
⁝ Berezó...........arr	...	1051	3 51		...	...	...
Jókút ....arr	5 46	1131	3 20	...	...	...	...

Jókút..............dep	...	7a10	1 p0	8p20	...	...	...	...
⁝ Berezó ....dep	...	7 45	1 0	...	...	...	...	...
Jabláncz	4a30	8 39	3 5	10 2	...	...	...	...
Nagyszombat ......arr	5 55	9 54	3 42		...	...	...	...

‡—Runs until 15th Sept.]

KUKULLOSZOG and PARAJD.

Küküllöszög ......dep	1 a55	5 a0	9a27	...	3 p4	...
Dicsö-Szt-Marton ...	3 40	7 25	10 45	10‡54	5 10	...
Sovarad	6 36			1 2	8 1	...
Parajd ....arr	7 6	...	...	1 35	8 30	...

Parajd ....dep	4a22	7‡a36	...	1p51	...	...	...	...	...
Sovarad....................	4 51	8 12	a.m.	2 21	...	...	...	...	...
Dicsö-Szt-Marton...	7 33	10 53	1113	4 46	...	...	...	...	...
Küküllöszög 233 arr	9 3	...	1245	6 5	...	...	...	...	...

SEGESVAR and SZEKELYUDVARHELY.

Segesvar................dep	4a55	11 a0	7p30	...	...	...
Hejjasfalva	5 28	11 33	8 24	...	...	...
Szekelyudvarhely ...arr	7 25	1 32	1012	...	...	...

Szekelyudvarhely...dep	4a54	2p30	7p48	...	...	...	...
Hejjasfalva	6 34	4 13	9 32	...	...	...	...
Segesvar 233...........arr	7 2	4 42	10 0	...	...	...	...

SEGESVAR and NAGYSZEBEN (Hermannstadt).

Segesvar.................dep	a.m.	5 a34	...	1 p19	...	...
Szentagota	2 19	10 9	p.m.	5 52	...	...
Hortobagyfalva	5 3	12 53	6 2		...	...
⁝ Vurpod...................arr	6 15	2 1	6 54	...	...	...
Nagyszeben (233)......arr	6 46	2 36	...	...	...	...

Nagyszeben...........dep	...	...	7 a43	4 p8	...	...	...
⁝ Vurpod	4 a4	...	8 16	4 45	...	...	...
Hortobagyfalva..............	4 47	a.m.	9 27	5 51	...	...	...
Szentagota		3 36	12 32	8 45	...	...	...
Segesvar (233A)......arr	...	7 46	4 45	...	...	...	...

SZATMAR-NEMETI and BIKSZAD.

Szatmar-Nemeti.........dep	9 a0	3 p5	7 p26	...
Sárköz	10 23	4 20	8 57	...
Bikszád ....arr	12 50	6 6	11 14	...

Bikszád ....dep	4 a26	10a40	3 p8	...	...	...
Sárköz	6 50	12 28	5 30	...	...	...
Szatmar-Nemeti............arr	8 8	1 35	6 50	...	...	...

SEPSISZENTGYORGY and BERECZK.

Sepsiszentgyörgy dep	6 a55	12p40	4 p9	7p59	...	...
Kézdivásárhely...............	9 9	2 44	6 12	9 56	...	...
Bereczk ....arr	10 23	4 0	7 30	...	...	...

Bereczk ....dep	...	7 a34	12p35	4p39	...	...
Kézdivásárhely.....................	4 a42	9 18	2 0	6 3	...	...
Sepsiszentgyörgy 233A ar	6 34	11 15	3 55	7 42	...	...

MADEFALVA and PALANCA.

Madefalva ....dep	5 a44	11a48	5 p28	...	...	...
Csik-Gyimes	8 29	1 30	7 8	...	...	...
Palanca 324A ......arr	...	2 0	7 40	...	...	...

Palanca..............dep	...	7 a43	...	1 p33	...	...	...	...
Csik-Gyimes.................	5 a20	7 55	8 a30	2 20	...	...	...	...
Madefalva 233A...arr	8 10	...	10 10	4 0	...	...	...	...

SIKLOS and BARCS.

Siklos..................dep	2 a40	8 a35	3 p56	...	...	...
Harkányfürdö	3 7	8 56	4 23	...	...	...
Sellye	5 12	10 42	6 21	...	...	...
Barcs ....arr	7 27	12 51	8 50	...	...	...

Barcs..............dep	2 a40	8 a6	1 p20	...	...	...	...
Sellye	5 20	10 36	3 46	...	...	...	...
Harkányfürdö	7 14	12 19	5 40	...	...	...	...
Siklos 229 ....arr	7 35	12 40	6 2	...	...	...	...

Harkányfürdö ....dep	5 a26	9 a6	12p40	5 p46	...
Miholjac...................arr	6 2	9 42	1 16	6 22	...

Miholjac..............dep	6 a26	11a33	3 p4z	7 p10	...
Harkányfürdö ....arr	7 2	12 9	4 18	7 46	...

ZSOLNA and GALANTA.

THROUGH CARRIAGES { Zsolna to Budapest—in 3.51 a.m., 12.27, 3.20, and 9.27 p.m.
Zsolna to Marchegg—in 12.49 night.

Dist. E.M.														
	ODERBERG (253A)......dep	1 a10	...	...	...	3 a20	4 a50	9 a50	...	10a45	...	...	5 p45	...
		Ex 2	2 & 3	1,2,3	1,2,3	1,2,3	1,2,3	Ex 2	1,2,3	Ex 2	1,2,3	1,2,3	1,2,3	1,2,3
		a.m.	a.m.			a.m.	a.m.	p.m.		p.m.	p.m.		p.m.	nght
—	Zsolna ....dep	3 §51	4 20	...	...	6 53	10 0	12 27	...	3 ‡20	3 33	...	9 27	12 49
37¼	Illava	5 0	6 42	...	...	8 35	11 52	1 36	p.m.	4 33	5 20	...	11 2	2 14
44¾	Hölak-Trencsénteplicz ¶ ...	5 18	7 14	...	...	8 59	12 19	1 54	2 4	4 51	5 47	...	11 26	2 38
49¾	Trencsén (226)..................	5 27	7 29	...	...	9 18	12 32	2 4	2 26	5 1	6 9	...	11 39	2 48
64½	Vágujhely	5 54		...	...	10 1		2 31	3 41	5 30	6 59	...	12 17	3 23
75¾	Pöstyén	6 14	...	a.m.	...	10 32	...	2 52	4 29	5 51	7 47	...	12 41	3 45
87	Lipótvár ....arr	6 32	...	8 50	...	11 4	...	3 10	5 13	6 10	8 24	...	1 4	4 11
126¾	POZSONY (226) ....arr	...	...	...	a.m.	1 p23	...	...	7 p30	7 p30	11p44	a.m.	5 a35	5 a55
97⅓	Szered	6 53	...	9 24	10 35	12 7	...	3 35		6 41		1 2	1 35	
105	Galánta ....arr	7 8	...	9 51	10 52	12 28	...	3 52	...	6 56	...	1 28	1 51	...
207	BUDAPEST (227) ....arr	9 a40	...	...	2 p0	6 p10	...	6 p20	...	9 p45	...	...	6 a40	...

THROUGH CARRIAGES { Budapest to Zsolna—in 9.55 a.m., 2.51, 9.17 p.m., and 1.10 night from Galánta.
Marchegg to Zsolna—in 11.47 p.m. from Lipótvár.

BUDAPEST (227A) ......dep	9 p30	...	...	...	7 a5	...	7 a55	9 a15	12p20	...	6 p50	...	8 p40
	1,2,3	1,2,3	1,2,3	1,2,3	Ex 2	1,2,3	1,2,3	1,2,3	Ex 2	2 & 3	Ex 2	1,2,3	1,2,3
	a.m.	a.m.	a.m.		a.m.		a.m.	p.m.	p.m.		p.m.		a.m.
Galánta ....dep	3 3	...	7 5	...	9 ‡55	...	11 6	2 15	2 51	...	9 §17	...	1 10
Szered	3 30	...	7 33	...	10 10	...	11 24	2 37	3 6	...	9 32	...	1 31
POZSONY (226)...........dep		...	...	6 a5	9 a12	...		1 p45	12p50	p.m.	6 p44	9 p52	...
Lipótvár	...	4 33	8 7	8 24	10 36	...	...	4 6	3 27	6 11	9 53	11 47	2 5
Pöstyén	...	5 10		8 56	10 58	...	...	4 39	3 46	7 8	10 11	12 16	2 34
Vágujhely	...	5 44	...	9 27	11 18	p.m.	...	5 12	4 4	8 2	10 29	12 39	3 3
Trencsén	...	6 35	...	10 16	11 48	1 14	...	5 55	4 29	9 17	10 54	1 17	3 49
Hölak-Trencsénteplicz ¶	...	7 0	...	10 38	12 3	2 0	...	6 27	4 44	9 40	11 8	1 35	4 8
Illava	...	7 21	...	10 57	12 15	2 21	...	6 48	4 56		11 20	1 53	4 28
Zsolna ....arr	...	9 20	...	12 53	1 30	4 21	...	8 38	6 2	...	12 24	3 20	6 10
ODERBERG (253A) ......arr	...	12 p6	...	5 p6	5 p6	...	...	12a30	8 p30	...	2 a55	...	9 a30

‡—Restaurant Car attached.
§—Sleeping Car attached.

¶—Rail Motor Service to Trencsénteplicz-fürdö (25 minutes) in connection with all trains.

Pöstyén...	3a58	7a25	9 a0	11a20	6 p6
Verbó	4 24	7 49	9 24	11 48	6 30

Verbó	5a24	8 a4	9a55	2p14	7p10	...
Pöstyén ...	5 50	8 30	1017	2 40	7 32	...

E.M.					
	Hölak-Trencsén ....dep	7 a36	1p13	6 p15	...
8¾	Vlarapass (253).................arr	8 13	1 55	6 52	...

Vlarapass ....dep	7 a25	10a52	3p27	7 p10	...
Hölak-Trencsén (233B) .....arr	7 56	11 19	4 22	7 50	...

Holak-Trencsén......dep	7 a27	12p20	6 p25	...	...
Ledniczrona..........arr	8 28	1 20	7 45	...	...

Ledniczrona ....dep	5 a52	10a47	3 p13	...	...
Holak-Trencsén......arr	6 52	11 45	4 34	...	...

TABLE OF FARES ON THE HUNGARIAN RAILWAYS.

English Miles.	Quick Trains.			Slow Trains.		
	1 Cl.	2 Cl.	3 Cl.	1 Cl.	2 Cl.	3 Cl.
	k. h.	k. h.	k. h.	k. h.	k. h.	k. h.
¾— 3¼	2.20	1.50	—.90	—.72	—.36	—.24
3¾— 6¼	2.20	1.50	—.90	—.72	—.48	—.30
6¾— 9½	2.20	1.50	—.90	1.08	—.72	—.44
10 — 12½	2.20	1.50	—.90	1.44	—.96	—.60
13 — 16¾	2.88	2.18	1.44	2.04	1.32	—.84
17½— 18¾	3.64	2.54	1.78	2.88	1.92	1.20
19¼— 24¾	4.40	2.90	2.10	3.70	2.50	1.60
25½— 31	5.80	3.70	2.70	4.90	3.20	2.—
31¾— 37¼	6.80	4.40	3.20	5.80	3.80	2.40
38 — 43½	8.20	5.30	3.80	7.—	4.60	2.90
44 — 49¾	9.20	5.90	4.30	7.80	5.20	3.20
50¼— 56	10.50	6.80	5.—	8.90	6.—	3.70
56½— 62¼	11.60	7.50	5.40	9.80	6.50	4.10
62¾— 68¼	12.90	8.40	6.10	10.90	7.30	4.60
69 — 74½	13.90	9.—	6.60	11.80	7.90	4.90
75¼— 80¾	15.30	9.90	7.20	13.—	8.60	5.40
81½— 87	16.30	10.60	7.70	13.80	9.20	5.80
87½— 93¼	17.70	11.40	8.30	15.—	10.—	6.20
93¾— 99½	18.70	12.10	8.80	15.80	10.60	6.60
100 —105¾	20.10	13.—	9.40	17.—	11.30	7.10
106¼—111¾	21.10	13.60	9.90	17.90	11.90	7.40
112½—118	22.40	14.50	10.60	19.—	12.70	7.90
118¾—124¼	23.50	15.20	11.—	19.90	13.20	8.30
125 —130½	24.80	16.10	11.70	21.—	14.—	8.80
131 —136¾	25.80	16.70	12.20	21.80	14.60	9.10
137¼—143	27.20	17.60	12.80	23.—	15.40	9.60
143½—149¼	28.20	18.30	13.30	23.90	16.—	10.—
149¾—155¼	29.60	19.10	13.90	25.10	16.70	10.40
156 —161½	30.60	19.80	14.40	25.90	17.30	10.80
162¼—167¾	31.30	20.20	14.70	26.50	17.60	11.—
168½—174	32.30	20.90	15.20	27.40	18.20	11.40
174½—180¼	33.—	21.30	15.50	28.—	18.60	11.60
80¾—186½	34.—	22.—	16.—	28.80	19.20	12.—
187 —192¾	34.30	22.20	16.20	29.—	19.40	12.10
193¼—198¾	34.70	22.40	16.30	29.40	19.60	12.20
199½—205	35.—	22.70	16.50	29.60	19.80	12.40
205¾—211¼	35.40	22.90	16.60	30.—	19.90	12.50
212 —217½	35.70	23.10	16.80	30.20	20.20	12.60
218 —223¾	36.—	23.30	17.—	30.50	20.40	12.70
224¼—230	36.40	23.50	17.10	30.80	20.50	12.80
230½—236	36.70	23.80	17.30	31.10	20.80	13.—
236¾—242¼	37.10	24.—	17.40	31.40	20.90	13.10
243 —248½	37.40	24.20	17.60	31.70	21.10	13.20
249¼—254¾	37.70	24.40	17.80	31.90	21.40	13.30
255½—261	37.70	24.40	17.80	31.90	21.40	13.30
261½—267¼	38.10	24.60	17.90	32.30	21.50	13.40

Luggage Rates on the Hungarian Railways.

Kilometers.	English Miles.	Fillers per 10 kg.
1—50	¾—31	12
51—100	31¼—62¼	24
101—200	62¾—124¼	48
201—300	124¾—186½	72
301—450=	187—279½	96
451 and beyond.	280½	Charge made pro rata on 50 kg.

VIENNA, BRUCK, GRAZ, PRAGERHOF, ST. PETER, and TRIESTE.

THROUGH CARRIAGE—Vienna to Venice in 7.35 a.m. and 7.20 p.m. from Vienna (also 9.15 p.m., page 241).

Dist		1,2,3	1,2,3	1,2,3	1,2,3	Ex3	Ex.3	1,2,3	1,2,3	1,2,3	Ex3	Ex2	1,2,3	1,2,3	1& 2	Ex3	1,2,3	Ex2	Ex3	Ex3	1,2,3
E M	**Vienna**	a.m.			From July 12 to 14th Sept.	a.m.	a.m.			a.m.	a.m.	a.m.	a.m.	p.m.	p.m.		p.m.	p.m.	p.m.	p.m.	p.m.
—	Südbahnhof dp	6 25	...	...		7 35	8 45	...	...	9 0	9 40	1125	11 50	1 20	3 30	...	4 35	7 20	8 25	9 30	10 30
10	**Mödling**	6 47	...	...		7‡54	...	...	...	9 23	...	...	12 27	...	...	...	4 59	SC	SC	SC	10 54
16¾	Baden	7 2	...	...		8 ‡6	9‡10	...	...	9 38	...	RC	12 52	1‡54	...	...	5 14	...	...	9‡58	11 9
19¼	Voslau	7 10	‡—Takes up only.	...		...	...	...	...	9 47	...	...	1 1	...	B	...	5 22	...	...	...	11 17
21½	Leobersdorf	7 16		...		...	...	...	...	9 53	...	...	1 14	...	...	...	5 28	...	...	...	11 24
30½	**Neustadt** arr	7 38		...		8 26	9 30	...	...	1015	1023	12 7	1 38	2 20	4 15	...	5 45	8 4	9 11	1018	11 41
39	Neunkirchen	...		...	a.m.	8 45	...	...	...	11 2	...	...	2 18	2 49	...	...	6 14	...	...	...	12 26
46½	**Gloggnitz**	8 26		...	7 35	9 7	10 4	...	...	1128	1057	1241	2 45	3 14	4 52	...	6 40	8 38	9 46	1052	12 53
51	Payerbach	8 40		...	7 47	9 19	10 15	...	...	1146	...	1252	3 1	3 28	5 5	...	6 56	8 49	9 57	11 3	1 10
60¼	Klamm	9 9		...	8 18	9 41	...	...	...	1215	...	...	3 29	3 52	5 32	...	7 23	...	...	1125	1 36
69½	Semmering	9 38		a.m.	8 46	10 6	10 58	...	...	1246	1151	1 36	3 57	4 21	5 55	...	7 52	9 31	1040	1148	2 5
80¾	**Mürzzuschlag**	10 3		6 25	9 14	1031	11 28	...	...	1 17	1219	1 59	4 21	4 55	6 19	...	8 24	9 54	11 3	1211	2 36
103¾	Kapfenberg	1145		7 24	10 7	11 8	...	...	...	2 17	RC	...		6 3		...	9 21	...	...	...	3 30
106¼	**Bruck** arr	1152		7 30	10 13	1114	12 6	...	...	2 23	1255	2 37	...	6 9	...	...	9 28	1030	1140	1249	3 36
116¾	LEOBEN 235A arr		...	8a37	10 40	1135	...	...	...	3p28	1p50	3p28	...	8p21	...	...	10p9	...	1229	...	4 a24
124¼	ST. MICHAEL 241 ar		...	9 a6	11 a2	1158	...	...	...	4 p2	...	4p 2	...	9p12	...	...	1036	...	1252	...	4 a54
233	VILLACH 241 arr		...	2p47	—	3p57	...	...	...	1028	...	1028	...	...	...	...	5a30	...	7a19	...	11a10
271½	PONTEBBA 241 arr		...	5p12	...	5p55	...	...	...	...	...	...	...	...	...	...	8 a4	...	9 a6	...	2 p31
398¾	VENICE 285A arr		a.m.	1037	...	1037	...	...	p.m.	...	...	...	p.m.	...	...	p.m.	...	...	2 p5	...	9 p15
...	**Bruck** dep		6 15	7 44	...	1122	12 9	...	1 21	3 3	1258	2 40	6 3	6 46	...	7 44	9 33	1033	1143	1252	4 9
112½	Pernegg		6 27	7 56	a.m.	1134	RC	...	1 32	3 15	...	...	6 15	6 59	1,2,3	...	9 45	...	...	...	4 21
121¾	**Frohnleiten**		6 47	8 17	10 20	1155	12 33	...	1 52	3 35	...	...	6 36	7 19	p.m.	8 10	10 5	...	...	1 16	4 42
126¾	**Peggau**		6 57	8 27	10 34	12 5	12 43	...	2 2	3 45	...	...	6 47	7 29	8 30	8 21	1016	...	...	...	4 52
139¼	**Graz** arr		7 27	8 57	11 16	1235	1 4	...	2 32	4 15	1 47	3 31	7 20	8 0	9 15	8 44	1047	1122	1232	1 44	5 22
...	" dep		8 8	1045	July and Aug. only.		1 16	...	2 39	5 5	1 52	3 36	7 40	9 7	July and August only.		1135	1127	1237	1 49	5 47
161½	Leibnitz		9 4	1141		...	1 48	...	3 32	6 0	...	...	8 33	10 6		...	1226	...	...	2 21	6 41
168½	**Spielfeld**		9 26	12 0		...	2 0	...	3 51	6 29	2 48	...	8 56	1035		...	1244	...	...	...	7 7
180¼	**Marburg** arr	a.m.	9 56	1230		...	2 20	...	4 20	7 1	Runs until 29th September. ☞	4 33	9 27	11 8		...	1 13	1222	1 33	2 50	7 39
...	" dep	5 42	1040			...	2 28	...	4 58	7 30				12 0		...		1227	To Ala.	3 2	8 13
191½	**Pragerhof** dep	6 20	1116	...		...	2 54	...	5 32	8 50		...	...	1 0		...	...	1253		3 28	9 0
200	Pöltschach	6 44	1140	...		...	3 14	...	5 56	9 16		...	...	1 22		...	...	...		3 44	9 24
212½	Grobelno	7 14	12 9	...	...	...	3 36	...	6 25	9 49		...	...	1 50		...	...	...		...	9 54
221¾	Cilli	7 39	1235	...	...	...	3 52	...	6 50	1031		...	...	2 20	...	...	...	1 41	...	4 18	10 23
228	Markt-Tüffer	7 52	1248	...	...	...	4 5	...	7 3	1045		...	...	2 33	...	...		...	...	4*30	10 36
232½	Römerbad	8 2	1258	...	...	...	4 14	...	7 13	1056		...	...	2 43	...	...		...		...	10 46
236¾	**Steinbruck** arr	8 12	1 8	...	...	...	4 24	...	7 23	11 7		...	...	2 53	...	...		2 7		4 48	10 56
...	" dep	8 25	1 13	...	...	...	4 32	...	7 28	1122		...	...	3 15	...	...		2 12		4 53	11 13
257¼	Littai	9 13	2 0	...	...	...	5 14	...	8 15	1212		...	...	4 5		...		...		...	12 4
276½	**Laibach** arr	9 56		...	...	...	5 46	p.m.	8 58	1255	...		...	4 48		...		3 14		5 55	12 47
...	" dep	10 2	...	...	...	...	6 0	8 28		1 20	...		...	5 13		...		3 19		6 3	1 6
300¼	Loitsch	1115	...	...	...	...	6 50	9 42	...	2 35	...		...	6 28		...		4 9		6 53	2 19
316¼	Adelsberg	12 3	...	...	...	...	7 21	1030	...	3 22	...		...	7 36		...		...		7 24	3 5
324¼	**St. Peter** arr	1222	...	...	...	...	7 38	1052	...	3 44	...	RC —Restaurant Car. SC —Sleeping Car.	...	7 57	B—On Weekdays only.	...	*—Stops only in July and August.	4 53	Extra.—Frohnleiten to Graz, 5.37 p.m.	7 39	3 25
363½	FIUME 234 arr	3 p1	...	...	...	...	10p16	1255	...	...	...	...	...	9a46		...	...	...		9a46	...
...	**St. Peter** dep	1227	...	...	...	...	7 49	...	...	4 8	...	...	...	8 20		...	...	4 56		7 53	3 38
339¼	**Divazza**	1258	...	...	...	...	8 18	...	...	4 55	...	...	...	9 4	...	...	...	5 27		8 21	4 17
344¾	Sessana	1 10	...	...	...	...	8 29	...	...	5 7	...	...	...	9 16	...	...	...	...		8 33	4 29
356¾	**Nabresina** arr	1 35	...	...	...	...	8 49	...	...	5 33	...	...	...	9 43	...	...	...	5 57		8 52	4 54
484½	VENICE arr. via C		orm	ons	...	...	...	...	...	...	...	...	...	4p47	...	...	...	...	...	2 p5	10p37
456¾	VENICE arr. via C		ervi	gna	no	...	...	...	...	9a45	...	...	...	...	...	...	...	9a45	...	...	11p18
...	**Nabresina** dep	1 41	...	...	...	...	8 52	...	...	5 43	...	...	...	10 2	...	...	...	6 7	...	8 57	5 5
366	**Trieste** arr	2 10	...	...	...	...	9 10	...	...	6 10	...	...	...	1030	...	...	...	6 25	...	9 15	5 35

Express Fares, Vienna to Trieste: 1st class, 61 kr. 20 h., 2nd class, 45 kr. 90 h., 3rd class, 27 kr. 60 h.

Grobelno to Rohitsch, in 1½ hour, 10.10 a.m., 4.27 p.m. From Rohitsch 7.55 a.m., 12.1 noon.

TRIESTE, NABRESINA, and CORMONS.

Dist E.M		2&3	Ex3	1 2 3	Ex2	Ex3	1,2,3	1 2 3	1,2,3	2&3	1 2 3	Ex3	Ex3	1,2,3
			a.m	a.m.	a.m.	a.m.	a.m.	p.m.	p.m.	p.m.	p.m.	p.m.	p.m.	p.m.
—	**Trieste** dep	...	5 40	6 20	7 50	8 32	9 0	1240	1 10	...	4 10	7 5	8 10	9 40
10½	**Nabresina** dep	...	6 17	7 16	S	9 14	9 52	...	...	4‡48	5 11	...	8 58	...
20½	Monfalcone	a.m.	6 45	7 51	8 28	9 33	1034	1 45	1 56	5 17	5 45	8 0	9 18	1043
34¾	Görz	5 40	7 29	8 46	8 57	10 9	1124	2 29	—	6 5	6 28	8 44	9 59	1130
41¾	**Cormons** arr	6 6	7 46	...	9 10	1022	1146	2 50	...	6 24	6 47	8 59	1012	1150
138	VENICE 285A	...	...	...	1233	2 p5	4p47	9p15	...	...	10p37	...	...	...

	2&3	1,2,3	Ex3	Ex3	1,2,3	1,2,3	1,2,3	1,2,3	1,2,3	Ex3	Ex2	Ex2	1,2,3	...
VENICE 285A	...	...	1130	...	5 a0	...	8a47	...	11a25	2p10	4p10	...	...	...
	a.m.	a.m.	a.m.	a.m.	a.m.	p.m.	p.m.	p.m.	p.m.	p.m.	S	...	p.m.	...
Cormons dep	4‡54	5 18	6 45	8 35	9 12	...	1 55	...	4 50	6 48	7 30	...	9 5	...
Görz	5 25	5 45	7 7	9 8	9 46	...	2 34	...	5 33	7 7	7 45	p.m.	9 34	...
Monfalcone	6 10	6 31	7 44	9 58	1030	1 30	3 23	5 50	6 22	7 39	8 20	8 36	1032	...
Nabresina ar	6 45	7 4	8 10	:	11 2	2 3	:	6 16	6 55	8 4	...	9 1	...	...
Trieste arr	...	7 40	8 45	1040	1148	2 42	4 15	6 55	7 45	8 42	9 0	...	1127	...

‡—Not on Sunday. S—Simplon Express.

GORZ and HAIDENSCHAFT.

Görz dep	8 a11	2 p36	8 p50
Haidenschaft arr	9 57	4 9	10 20
Haidenschaft dep	5 a10	11a26	5 p56
Görz arr	6 31	1 10	7 52

ST. PETER and FIUME

St. Peter dep	8a 8	10a20	1p20	8p40	11 p6
Dornegg-Feistritz	8 34	10 47	1 46	9 6	11 35
Abbazia Mattuglie	9 32	11 52	2 47	10 4	12 41
Fiume arr	9 46	12 6	3 1	1016	12 55

Fiume dep	5a13	7a52	12p56	5 p0	8p10	...
Abbazia Mattuglie	5 45	8 20	1 28	5 33	8 41	...
Dornegg-Feistritz	6 45	9 16	2 34	6 35	9 45	...
St. Peter arr	7 12	9 41	3 11	7 10	1012	...

For Fares, see page 237B].

TRIESTE, ST. PETER, PRAGERHOF, GRAZ, BRUCK, and VIENNA.

RC—Restaurant Car. SC—Sleeping Car.

	Ex3	1,2,3	1,2,3	1,2,3	1,2,3	1,2,3	Ex2	1,2,3	1,2,3	Ex3	Ex3	1 2 3	2&3	1,2,3	1,2,3	1,2,3	1,2,3	1,2,3	Ex2	Ex3	1,2,3
											a.m.					a m	p.m.	p.m.	p.m.	p.m.	p.m.
Trieste ....dep	...	...	...	...	...	...	...	...	...	...	8 10	...	...	...	...	1015	1 50	6 10	6 40	8 45	1155
Nabresina.........arr	...	...	...	...	...	...	...	...	...	...	8 34	...	...	...	...	1050	2 34	6 46	7 4	9 9	1233
VENICE via Cervi	gn.	dep	...	...	...	...	...	...	...	...	RC	...	...	...	...	...	...	2p20	...	...	7p10
VENICE via Corm	ons	dep	...	...	...	...	...	...	...	...	1130	...	...	...	...	5 a0	...	...	...	2p10	...
Nabresina ......dep	...	...	...	...	...	...	...	...	...	...	8 38	...	...	...	...	1115	2 39	7 35	7 14	9 17	1238
Sessana..................	...	...	...	...	...	...	...	...	...	...	9 6	...	...	...	...	1156	3 24	8 16	...	9 46	1 20
Divazza	...	...	...	...	...	...	...	...	...	...	9 24	...	...	...	...	1219	3 46	8 46	7 58	10 7	1 42
St. Peter ....arr	...	...	...	...	...	...	...	...	...	...	9 51	...	...	...	...	1253	4 26	9 21	8 25	1034	2 22
FIUME (234)...dep	...	...	...	...	...	5a13	...	...	...	...	7a52	...	...	...	...	...	1256	5 p0	5 p0	8p10	...
St. Peter ....dep	...	...	...	...	...	7 20	...	...	...	...	9 59	...	...	...	...	1 1	4 31	9 45	8 30	1046	2 31
Adelsberg	...	...	...	...	...	7 42	...	...	...	...	1014	...	...	...	...	1 22	4 52	10 7	8 45	11 1	2 52
Loitsch	...	...	...	...	...	8 17	...	...	...	...	1043	...	...	...	...	1 59	5 28	1047	...	SC	3 31
Laibach......... arr	...	...	...	...	...	9 4	...	a.m.	...	...	1121	...	...	...	...	2 51	6 17	1142	9 50	12 5	4 24
Laibach......... dep	...	...	...	...	...		...	7 30	...	...	1126	...	p m.	...	...	3 11	6 32	1218	9 55	1211	4 38
Littai......................	Coming from Ala.	...	...	...	...	...	...	8 11	...	...	1158	...	2 22	...	...	3 53	7 14	1 0	SC	...	5 22
Steinbruck ... arr		...	...	...	...	...	...	8 55	...	...	1237	...	3 16	...	...	4 41	7 5	1 46	1059	1 15	6 12
Steinbruck ... dep		...	...	...	...	...	...	9 0	...	...	1242	...	3 23	...	...	4 56	8 8	2 17	11 4	1 22	6 29
Römerbad		...	...	...	...	...	...	9 11	...	...	1252	...	3 34	...	...	5 7	8 19	2 28	...	...	6 40
Markt-Tüffer		...	...	...	...	...	...	9 21	...	...	1 1	...	3 44	...	...	5 17	8 29	2 38	...	1*40	6 50
Cilli		...	...	...	...	...	...	9 38	...	...	1 14	...	4 1	...	...	5 40	8 45	3 1	1132	1 53	7 8
Grobelno		July & August only.	...	...	...	...	...	10 1	...	...	1 30	...	4 23	...	...	6 5	9 8	3 25	...	...	7 32
Pöltschach			ng't	...	a.m.	...	...	1032	...	...	1 53	...	4 52	...	...	6 34	9 39	3 54	...	2 29	8 1
Pragerhof ......dep			1240	...	6 22	...	...	11 0	...	...	2 19	...	5 15	...	...	7 11	10 3	4 29	1225	2 50	8 39
Marburg ...... arr	a.m.		1 11	...	6 57	...	p.m.	1130	...	p.m.	2 36	p.m.	5 45	...	p.m.	7 41	1032	4 58	1243	3 7	9 9
Marburg ...... dep	2 47			...	7 2	...	1225	1 2	...	2 14	2 44	4 7		...	6 33	8 5	1130	5 23	1248	3 15	9 47
Spielfeld...............	...		...	...	7 37	...	...	1 36	...	...	3 5	4 38	...	...	7 2	8 43	12 0	5 55	...	...	1017
Leibnitz	...		...	...	7 56	...	RC	1 55	...	...	3 17	4 55	1,2,3	...	7 19	9 2	1217	6 13	...	...	1035
Graz .... arr	3 47	a.m.	a.m.	a.m.	8 54	p.m.	1 26	2 49	...	3 16	3 51	5 50	p.m	p.m.	8 11	9 59	1 12	7 9	1 55	4 24	1130
Graz .... dep	3 55	8 5	6 30	9 10	9 17	1242	1 34	4 6	...	3 24	3 59		2 45	6 10	8 24	1040		7 19	2 3	4 34	1154
Peggau..................	...	9 2	7 2	9 33	9 52	1 15	...	4 38	...	...	4 22	...	3 28	6 41	8 55	1115	...	7 53	...	...	1226
Frohnleiten...........	...		7 13	9 43	10 3	1 27	...	4 50	...	RC	4 32	...	3 42	6 54	9 6	1127	...	8 5	...	5 6	1237
Pernegg	...	...	7 34	...	1023	1 48	...	5 10	...	...	...	...		7 17	9 27	1148	...	8 25	...	...	1257
Bruck ....arr	4 47	...	7 46	10 7	1034	1 59	2 27	5 21	...	4 16	4 56	Ex3	...	7 30	9 38	1159	...	8 36	2 56	5 31	1 8
VENICE 285A dep	...	Weekdays only.	...	...	...	...	...	5 a0	...	...	...	5 a0	...	...	...	5a55	...	...	...	2p10	...
PONTEBBA 241 dep	...		...	...	...	...	...	1052	...	...	...	1052	...	...	...	1p52	...	...	...	7p50	...
VILLACH 241 dep	...		...	...	...	...	6 a0	1226	...	...	...	1226	...	1 p2	...	4p45	...	...	...	1030	6 a0
ST. MICHAEL 241	...		6a42	...	9a38	...	1225	4p45	...	...	...	4p30	...	6p55	...	11p8	...	6a42	...	4a30	1225
LEOBEN 235A dep	...		7a13	...	10a8	...	1p59	5p12	...	...	...	4p54	...	7p14	...	1140	...	7a13	...	5 a2	1250
Bruck...............dep	4 52	1& 2	7§52	...	1054	...	2 32	5 45	...	4 21	5 1	5 16	...	7 46	...	1244	...	8 50	3 1	5 36	1 30
Kapfenberg	...	a.m.	7 59	a.m.	11 4	...	...	5 52	p.m.	...	...	5 23	...	7 53	p.m.	1254	...	8 58	...	5 43	1 37
Mürzzuschlag	5 43	6 15	8 56	7 42	1240	...	3 17	6 56	4 25	5 11	5 52	6 10	...	8 51	9 1	2 8	...	10 7	3 46	6 38	3 30
Semmering............	6 9	6 45	§—From 12th July until 15th Sept.	8 15	1 14	...	3 44	7 29	4 59	5 38	6 19	6 37	...		9 37	2 43	...	1043	4 12	7 7	4 5
Klamm..................	...	7 6		8 36	1 37	...	...	7 50	5 21	...	...	6 53	p.m.	...	9 59	3 3	...	11 7	...	...	4 25
Payerbach	6 40	7 28		8 52	2 1	...	4 15	8 12	5 44	...	...	7 9	8 40	...	1022	3 22	...	1131	4 45	7 41	4 47
Gloggnitz	6 55	7 42		9 15	2 18	...	4 29	8 28	6 1	6 23	7 4	7 23	8 56	...	1034	3 36	...	1150	5 0	7 55	4 58
Neunkirchen	...	...		9 33	2 39	...	...	8 46	6 20	...	...	7 35	9 19	...	From July 12 to Sept. 14.	3 55	a.m.	1211	...	...	5 21
Neustadt..............	7 21	8 8		9 55	3 9	...	4 52	9 12	6 52	6 47	7 28	7 49	1017	...		4 23	4 25	1237	5 25	8 21	5 44
Leobersdorf..........	...	...		1018	3 30	...	...	9 33	7 11	...	...	...	1042	...		...	4 46	1258	...	...	6 8
Voslau	...	...		1024	3 36	...	...	9 41	7 17	...	...	...	1051	...		...	4 52	1 5	...	...	6 17
Baden	...	...		1031	3 43	...	...	9 48	7 24	...	7‡50	8 10	1059	...		...	4 59	1 13	...	8‡43	6 25
Mödling	...	...		1045	3 57	...	...	10 2	7 39	...	...	8 22	1120	...		...	5 18	1 30	...	...	6 42
Vienna Südbhn. ar	8 10	8 55		11 5	4 18	...	5 40	1025	8 2	7 47	8 15	8 40	1150	...		5 38	5 47	1 55	6 25	9 10	7 5

*—Stops only in July and August. ‡—Sets down only.

SPIELFELD and LUTTENBERG.

E.M.																
	Spielfeld.........dep	...	7 a32	10a19	2 p2	3 p55	7 p3	8 p53	Luttenberg......dep	...	6a51	10a28	12p45	...	5p31	7p12
7½	Murek	...	8 1	10 48	2 33	4 24	7 34	9 22	Bad Radein	...	7 29	11 8	1 23	...	6 11	7 50
19¼	Radkersburg...........	5 a35	8 59	11 35	3 23	5 11	8 16	10 4	Radkersburg..........	4 a30	8 4	11 41	1 46	3p16	6 45	8 8
24¼	Bad Radein	5 54	9 18	11 54	3 42	5 30			Murek	5 15	8 52	12 31	2 30	4 25	7 32	
35½	Luttenberg......arr	6 38	9 55	12 31	4 19	6 11	...	...	Spielfeld 234 ...arr	5 45	9 20	1 0	2 58	5 1	8 0	...

LAIBACH and OBERLAIBACH.

Laibach.........dep	7a35	1p18	8p10	...	Oberlaibach...dep	6 a2	10 a0	6p47	...	...
Oberlaibach arr	8 10	1 53	8 45	...	Laibach ....arr	6 38	10 36	7 23	...	...

TRIESTE and VENICE, via CERVIGNANO.

Dist E.M		Ex3	1,2,3	1,2,3	2&3	Ex3	1,2,3		1,2,3	2 & 3	Ex3	1,2,3	1,2,3	1,2,3
		a.m.	a.m.	p.m.	p.m	p.m.	p.m.	VENICE 285A ....dep	...	...	6 a0	9 a10	2 p20	7p10
—	Trieste ....dep	5 40	9 0	1 10	4 10	7 5	9 40		a.m.	a.m.	a.m.	p.m.	p.m.	p.m.
10½	Nabresina...................dep	6 17	10 3	...	5 11	...	...	Cervignano ....dep	5 30	5 45	9 27	12 48	5 0	10 0
20½	Monfalcone..........................	6 40	1028	2 1	6 25	7 55	1048	Monfalcone	6 15	7 10	9 52	1 25	5 34	1025
31½	Cervignano ....arr	7 7	11 1	2 34	7 12	8 20	1122	Nabresina...................arr	7 4	8 10	...	...	6 16	...
...	VENICE 285A..............arr	9a45	...	5p55	...	1118	...	Trieste ....arr	7 40	8 45	1040	2 42	6 55	1127

For Fares, see page 237B].

SOUTHERN RAILWAY.

KUFSTEIN, INNSBRUCK, BOTZEN-GRIES, and ALA.

[For other trains between Worgl and Innsbruck see page 238.]

Dist. E.M.	Station																		
...	MUNICH 200...dep	12a38	8 p0	...	...	...	...	...	5 a0	7 a0	8a45	8 a45	9a40	11a45	1 p30	...	4p10	5 p40	10p40
		Ex 1	1,2,3	1,2,3	Ex3	1,2,3	Ex.3	Ex3	1,2,3	1,2,3	Ex3	1,2,3	1,2,3	Ex.2	1,2,3	1,2,3	1,2,3	1,2,3	Ex.3
		a.m.	p.m.			a.m.			a.m.	a.m.	a.m.	a.m.	p.m.	p.m.	p.m.		p.m.	p.m.	nght
—	Kufstein.....dep	2 8	11 6	...	...	4 25	...	...	7 20	8 50	1055	11 13	1235	1 52	3 55	...	6 36	7 56	12 45
8¾	Worgl.....arr	...	11 30	...	...	4 46	...	...	7 47	9 6	1111	11 36	1256	2 13	4 18	...	7 2	8 16	1 2
	SALZBURG 239 dep	...	—	1010	...	...	12a32	...	12a32	...	7 a0	—	7 a0	RC	...	9 a0	...	3 p55	SC
...	Worgl.....dep	T	...	4a32	...	4 53	6 10	...	7 59	9 8	1115	...	1 2	2 15	4 27	4 45	7 10	8 35	1 3
18	Brixlegg	...	...	4 51	...	5 18	RC	...	8 25	A	...	...	1 28	2 31	4 52	5 11	7 36	9 2	1 22
23½	Jenbach 237A	SC	...	5 3	...	5 36	6 35	...	8 46	9 33	1140	...	1 48	2 44	5 11	5 28	7 55	9 17	1 32
29¼	Schwaz	...	...	5 14	...	5 51	6 44	...	9 0	9 42	1149	...	2 2	2 53	5 23	5 42	8 8	9 30	1 43
40¼	Hall	...	...	5 38	...	6 23	...	...	9 33	10 1	12 8	...	2 34	3 12	5 54	6 14	8 40	10 1	2 2
45¼	Innsbruck.....arr	3 17	a.m.	5 48	a.m.	6 37	7 10	a.m.	9 45	10 11	1218	p.m.	2 48	3 22	6 8	6 25	8 54	10 13	2 12
...	Innsbruck.....dep	3 22	5 §15	—	6 12	7 7	—	7 57	10 30	10 23	1230	1 42	5 15	3 37	7 35	—	—	11 8	2 22
57¾	Matrei	...	6 5	...	6 44	8 5	...	8 42	11 26	11 8	1 15	2 33	6 5	4 22	8 31	—	...	12 4	3 7
61	Steinach in Tyrol...	...	6 15	...	6 50	8 16	...	8 50	11 37	11 16	1 23	2 43	6 15	4 30	8 43	...	...	12 15	3 15
70¼	Brenner	4 46	6 51	...	7 14	9 2	...	9 24	12 38	11 49	1 56	3 21	6 51	5 4	9 30	...	...	12 58	3 48
72¾	Brennerbad	RC	—	...	7 19	9 9	...	9 30	12 45	11 55	2 2	3 28	—	5 10	9 37	...	...	...	...
81¼	Gossensass	...	...	...	7 36	9 32	...	9 46	1 8	12 11	2 18	3 50	...	5 26	10 2	...	...	1 23	4 8
85¼	Sterzing	...	...	...	7 45	10 2	...	9 54	1 22	12 19	2 26	4 0	...	5 34	10 14	...	Ex3	1 35	4 16
97½	Franzensfeste.....arr	5 32	a.m.	a.m.	8 8	10 35	a.m.	1018	1 55	12 41	2 48	4 35	p.m.	5 56	10 50	...	p.m.	2 6	4 38
	Franzensfeste.....dep	5 34	5 40	8 37	—	11 10	10 41	—	3 10	12 51	2 58	—	6 55	6 4	11 10	...	8 38	2 38	4 45
98¾	„ Military Station	...	5 45	8 42	...	11 15	...	...	3 15	A	RC	...	7 0	...	11 15	...	...	2 43	...
104¼	Brixen	5 48	6 4	8 59	...	11 32	10 55	...	3 33	1 6	3 12	...	7 17	6 19	11 31	...	8 53	3 1	5 0
110¼	Klausen	...	6 24	9 18	...	11 52	...	...	3 53	1 20	...	...	7 37	6 33	11 50	...	RC	3 22	5 14
114¼	Waidbruck	T	6 37	9 28	...	12 3	11 16	...	4 6	1 29	3 33	...	7 49	6 42	12 1	...	9 11	3 33	5 23
120	Atzwang	...	6 52	9 43	...	12 18	...	...	4 19	...	...	...	8 4	6 53	12 15	...	...	3 48	...
128¼	Botzen-Gries ...arr	6 33	7 20	1011	...	12 46	11 44	...	4 46	1 57	4 0	...	8 32	7 11	12 42	...	9 41	4 16	5 51
148½	MERAN 237A...arr	8 a39	8 a39	1135	...	3p41	1 p0	...	6 p42	3 p41	5p30	p.m.	9p56	8 p28	—	...	1045	7 a17	7 a17
...	Botzen.....dep	6 45	8 1	—	...	1 30	12 4	...	5 10	—	4 20	10 38	—	7 26	...	...	—	4 40	6 9
141½	Neumarkt	...	8 43	...	...	2 16	12 26	...	5 50	...	4 42	11 14	...	7 48	...	...	...	5 20	6 32
152¼	S. Michele	...	9 16	...	...	2 51	12 46	...	6 20	...	5 2	11 42	...	8 10	...	...	...	5 50	6 53
162¾	Trient 237	7 43	10 0	...	...	3 40	1 15	...	6 43	...	5 24	12 23	...	8 32	...	...	...	6 17	7 15
177¾	Rovereto	...	10 45	...	...	4 24	1 49	...	7 39	...	5 50	1 6	...	8 58	...	...	...	7 29	7 45
180¼	Mori	8 10	10 59	...	...	4 36	1 59	...	7 52	...	6 0	1 17	...	9 8	...	...	...	7 39	7 56
187¾	Ala (Customs Exm.)	8 29	11 19	...	...	4 55	2 11	...	8 10	...	6 12	1 35	...	9 20	...	...	...	7 57	8 8
221¾	VERONA 282 ...arr	9 a44	...	...	...	...	4 p10	...	10p33	...	7p40	...	...	10p55	...	...	...	...	10 a0
293¾	VENICE 280.....arr	...	...	...	...	...	7 p30	...	4 a19	...	1130	...	...	4 a19	...	...	...	...	12p20
315	MILAN 280.....arr	...	...	...	...	...	6 p40	...	6 a10	...	1120	...	...	6 a10	...	...	...	...	12p25
391	FLORENCE 279 arr	3 p33	...	...	...	...	3 a26	...	6 a48	...	3a26	...	...	6 a48	...	...	...	...	5 p18
587½	ROME 279.....arr	9 p0	...	...	...	...	8 a50	...	1 p5	...	8a50	...	...	1 p5	...	...	...	...	10p55

§—Until 8th September.
RC—Restaurant Car attached. SC—Sleeping Car.

A—Runs until 15th September.
T—Berlin-Tyrol-Rome Express, Luxus Zug.

STEINBRUCK and SISSEK.

†—At and from Hungarian State Railway Station.

E.M.		a.m.	a.m.	a.m.	a.m.	p.m.	p.m.	p.m.	p.m.	p.m.	p.m.	p.m.	p.m.	a.m.	
—	Steinbrück.....dep	...	5 0	...	9 10	...	...	1 23	...	5 0	...	...	8 12	...	...
27¼	Rann	...	6 27	...	11 0	...	...	2 44	...	6 24	...	...	10 21	...	...
39	Zapresic	6 21	6 59	9 27	11 46	1 23	...	3 14	5 4	6 56	...	9 10	11 7	...	...
47½	Zagrab (Agram)...arr	6 48	7 †56	10 †1	12 18	1†52	...	3 37	5 28	7†41	...	9 †44	12†17	...	...
...	„ 229.....dep	—	8 †40	11 16	—	—	2†27	3 48	—	—	9†15	—	—	2†10	...
78¾	Sissek 231A.....arr	...	9 44	12 57	...	...	3 16	5 3	...	...	1020	...	...	3 27	...

	a.m.	a.m.	a.m.	a.m.	a.m.	a.m.	p.m.	p.m.	p.m.	p.m.	p.m.	p.m.	p.m.	p.m.	p.m.
Sissek.....dep	...	...	5 26	6 43	...	10 40	...	1 16	...	...	...	4 11	6 40	...	10 32
Zagrab (Agram)...arr	...	...	6†35	7 58	...	12 23	...	2 †7	...	...	...	5 50	7 †50	...	11†42
„ .....dep	4 55	5 †2	7†13	8 13	10 40	—	1 46	—	2†42	3 38	4†28	—	—	9 †50	—
Zapresic	5 30	5 37	8 8	8 38	11 8	...	2 10	...	3 13	4 15	5 1	...	...	11 3	...
Rann	6 20	—	—	9 16	—	...	2 47	...	—	5 10	—	...	...	11 38	...
Steinbrück 234 ...arr	8 2	...	...	1036	...	...	4 1	...	...	7 13	...	...	...	12 58	...

BOTZEN-GRIES and MENDEL.

Botzen-Gries	...	6a13	8 a5	9 a7	1039	1p0	2p11	4p51	6p28	7p51
Kaltern	6 a5	7 4	8 45	9 48	1120	147	2 52	5 34	7 11	8 32
Mendel 237B	6 45	7 44	9 31	1033	1157	227	3 33	6 15	7 49	9 13

Mendel ...dep	6a19	7a35	8a34	10a7	12p1	2p35	3p49	5p18	7p23	8p47
Kaltern	6 56	7 44	9 14	1053	1239	3 15	4 28	6 7	8 3	9 41
Botzen-Gries	7 30	...	9 59	1134	1 19	3 55	5 7	6 46	8 41	1022

BOTZEN and KLOBENSTEIN.

Botzen-Walterplatz	5a38	7 a29	8 a51	9 a51	11 a2	2 p6	3 p17	5 p39	...	...	...	...
Klobenstein	7 1	8 53	10 15	10 20	12 26	3 35	4 46	7 8	...	...	...	...
Klobenstein	7a11	9 a32	12p37	1 p43	4 p5	5p16	6 p27	7 p15	...	...	...	...
Botzen-Walterplatz	8 30	10 52	1 56	3 7	5 29	6 40	7 51	8 34	...	...	...	...

CERVIGNANO and GRADO.

E.M.		a.m.	a.m.	p.m.	p.m.
—	Cervignano.....dep	7 20	11 13	2 50	8 27
4¼	Aquileia	7 38	11 31	3 8	8 45
7¾	Belvedere	7 55	11 48	3 25	9 2
8	Grado.....arr	7 58	11 51	3 28	9 5

	a.m.	a.m.	p.m.	p.m.
Grado.....dep	8 25	11 59	4 0	9 13
Belvedere	8 40	12 6	4 13	9 17
Aquileia	8 54	12 20	4 27	9 31
Cervignano (234A) arr	9 13	12 39	4 46	9 50

MORI and RIVA.

‡—In Sept. only.

	a.m.	a.m.	p.m.	p.m.	p.m.	pm	p.m.	p.m.
Mori.....dep	8 33	11‡11	1230	2 30	4 3[illegible]	621	8 22	9 52
Nago-Torbole	9 18	11 51	1 12	3 10	5 18	7 1	9 5	1031
Arco	9 35	12 12	1 35	3 32	5 40	723	9 27	1053
Riva.....arr	9 50	12 27	1 50	3 47	5 55	738	9 42	11 8

	a.m.	a.m.	a.m.	p.m.	pm	pm	p.m.	p.m.
Riva.....dep	6 18	8‡33	1035	1230	230	438	6 21	7 49
Arco	6 35	8 50	1052	1248	247	455	6 38	8 6
Nago-Torbole	6 56	9 12	1113	1 10	3 9	517	7 0	8 27
Mori (235) arr	7 34	9 50	1152	1 48	347	555	7 38	9 5

SOUTHERN RAILWAY.

[For Fares, see page 237B.

ALA, BOTZEN-GRIES, INNSBRUCK, and KUFSTEIN.

[For other trains between Innsbruck and Worgl see page 238A.]

ROME 279C......dep	...	...	...	...	5p20	2 p40	...	...	...	...	...	9 p5	...	...	...	...	...	...	...	9 a5
FLORENCE 279B dp	...	...	...	...	1045	9 p2C	...	...	...	...	...	2a15	...	...	...	...	...	...	...	2p30
MILAN 280......dep	...	...	...	...	...	12a30	...	...	...	...	...	7 a5	...	...	9a45	9 a45	...	...	...	6p20
VENICE 280 ...dep	...	...	...	...	...	12a10	...	...	...	...	...	8 a0	...	...	9a J	9 a30	...	...	2 p0	6 p10
VERONA 282 ...dep	...	...	...	...	4a42	4 a26	...	...	...	5 a40	...	1010	...	...	1220	12p20	...	3p32	6p35	9 p2
	1,2,3	1,2,3	1,2,3	Ex3	Ex1	Ex 2	1,2,3	1,2,3	1,2,3	1,2,3	1,2,3	Ex2	1,2,3	1,2,3	Ex3	1,2,3	Ex3	1,2,3	1,2,3	Ex 3
		a.m.			a.m.	a.m.				a.m.	a.m.	a.m.			p.m.	p.m.	...	p.m	p.m.	p.m.
Ala ....dep	...	5 25	...	...	6 3	6 30	...	...	...	8 11	10 6	1152	...	...	2 35	3 41	...	5 54	9 30	10 57
Mori	...	5 47	...	...	6 17	6 47	...	...	...	8 36	1037	12 9	...	...	2 52	4 9	...	6 23	9 59	11 13
Rovereto	a.m	5 56	...	...	...	6 58	...	...	...	8 51	1051	1219	...	...	3 2	4 24	...	6 36	10 16	11 21
Trient.........................	5 43	6 34	...	...	6 47	7 43	...	...	...	9 44	1139	1247	...	...	3 30	5 20	...	7 40	11 17	11 47
S. Michele.....................	6 18	——	...	...	T	8 3	...	...	...	10 12	1212	1 8	...	...	3 54	5 53	...	8 14	11 51	12 7
Neumarkt.......................	6 49	...	...	...	...	8 21	...	...	...	10 42	1243	1 26	...	...	4 12	6 21	...	8 41	12 35	12 25
Botzen-Gries ...arr	7 26	...	...	...	7 48	8 45	...	...	a.m.	11 17	1 18	1 50	...	p.m.	4 36	6 56	...	9 16	1 8	12 49
MERAN 237A...dep	——	...	a.m.	6 a0	6a40	7 a37	...	...	1015	10 15	——	1248	12p48	2 14	3p42	5 p50	...	8p58	11p15	11p15
Botzen-Gries ...dep	...	...	6 2	7 2	8 0	9 0	...	...	1250	11 38	...	2 10	2 35	4 25	5 2	7 12	...	12 2	1 33	1 2
Atzwang	...	...	6 31	...	...	...	...	...	1 19	12 7	...	...	3 6	A	...	7 39	...	1232	2 0	SC
Waidbruck	...	...	6 53	7 28	...	9 34	...	...	1 39	12 27	...	2 44	3 26	4 59	5 36	7 55	...	1254	2 21	1 36
Klausen.........................	...	...	7 4	RC	...	9 44	...	...	1 50	12 38	...	RC	3 37	5 10	...	8 5	...	1 6	2 33	...
Brixen	...	...	7 26	7 48	8 52	10 0	...	...	2 12	12 57	...	3 8	4 2	5 25	6 0	8 26	...	1 30	2 54	2 0
Franzfst Mil. Stat'n	...	...	7 49	...	...	...	...	...	2 31	1 17	...	...	4 25	...	..	8 45	...	1 53	3 15	...
Franzensfeste arr	...	...	7 53	8 4	9 13	10 21	...	a.m.	2 38	1 21	...	3 29	4 29	5 46	6 21	8 49	p.m.	1 57	3 19	2 21
Franzensfeste dep	...	...	8 14	——	9 18	10 33	...	1157	——	1 48	...	3 41	6 40	5 53	——	——	8 58	——	4 0	2 36
Sterzing........................	...	...	9 3	——	...	11 5	...	1230	...	2 34	...	4 16	7 25	6 25	...	...	9 26	...	4 42	3 8
Gossensass	...	...	9 19	...	...	11 20	...	1242	...	2 50	...	4 31	7 41	6 40	1,2,3	...	9 37	...	4 59	8 23
Brennerbad......................	...	...	9 53	...	...	11 45	...	...	...	3 20	...	4 59	8 14	7 6	p.m.	...	9 56	...	5 30	...
Brenner.........................	...	...	10 4	...	1036	11 55	...	1 29	...	3 32	...	5 10	8 26	7 16	7 25	...	10 4	...	5 41	3 58
Steinach in Tyrol ...	...	...	1030	...	...	12 14	...	1 58	...	3 57	...	5 29	8 52	7 35	7 54	...	1021	...	6 6	4 17
Matrei	...	...	1038	...	...	12 21	...	2 7	Ex3	4 5	...	5 36	9 0	7 43	8 3	...	1029	...	6 14	4 24
Innsbruck ... arr	a.m.	a.m.	11 9	...	1121	12 45	p.m.	2 43	p.m.	4 36	...	6 0	9 32	8 7	8 38	p.m.	1053	...	6 43	4 48
Innsbruck ... dep	5 20	9 55	——	...	1127	1 0	1 10	3 12	3 40	4 50	...	6 19	9 50	8 21	——	10 25	——	...	7 12	4 58
Hall	5 35	10 6	...	...	⋮	1 10	1 26	3 15	RC	5 4	...	6 29	10 6	8 31	...	10 36	...	...	7 26	5 9
Schwaz..........................	6 6	1035	...	...	⋮	1 27	1 57	3 42	...	5 35	...	6 46	10 35	8 48	...	10 59	...	...	7 57	5 29
Jenbach	6 21	1046	...	...	⋮	1 35	2 13	3 54	4 15	5 49	...	3 57	10 49	8 58	...	11 9	...	...	8 14	5 39
Brixlegg	6 36	11 0	...	...	⋮	1 46	2 28	4 7	...	6 3	...	RC	11 3	A	...	11 21	...	...	8 29	...
Worgl..................arr	6 59	1124	...	...	⋮	2 1	2 51	4 30	4 39	6 26	...	7 20	11 26	9 21	...	11 39	...	...	8 52	6 4
SALZBURG ......arr	1155	4p15	...	...	⋮	RC	...	——	9 p5	...	p.m.	1a12	5 a21	...	...	5 a21	...	...	...	11a55
Worgl..................dep	7 15	1158	...	...	⋮	2 2	2 56	...	——	6 30	4 49	7 25	11 31	9 23	...	11 55	...	...	9 7	6 5
Kufstein..............arr	7 37	1224	...	...	1232	2 16	3 18	...	...	6 52	5 9	7 40	11 53	9 37	...	12 20	...	...	9 29	6 20
MUNICH 200 ...arr	1010	4p 0	...	...	2 p5	4 p0	6p40	...	...	9 p30	7p35	9p40	...	1128	...	...	...	...	12p10	7 a57

Extra. { Brenner.........dep 7§a20 9‖a28; Innsbruck.......arr 8 32 10 38 — §—Until 8th Sept. ‖—From 6th July until 14th Sept.

*—Takes up for beyond Worgl only.

A—Runs until 15th Sept. T—Rome-Tyrol-Berlin Express, Luxus Zug.

RC—Restaurant Car attached.

BRUCK, LEOBEN, and VORDERNBERG.

Dist. E.M.																
		a.m.	a.m	a.m.	a.m.	a.m.	a.m.	a.m.	p.m.	p.m.	p.m.	p.m	p.m.	n gt		
	Bruck ....dep	3 55	6 26	8 10	10 22	1042	11 17	...	1 23	3 0	5 30	7 52	9 49	12 4	...	...
10½	**Leoben**.........arr	4 24	6 54	8 37	10 40	11 9	11 35	...	1 50	3 28	5 57	8 21	10 9	1229	...	...
...	„ (241)dep	——	7 8	9 29	——	——	——	1154	1 55	——	6 12	——	1020	——	...	...
13	Donawitz		7 18	9 37	...	...	...	12 2	2 3	...	6 20	...	1028	...	...	...
23	**Vordernberg 242** arr		7 57	1013	...	...	...	1238	2 41	...	6 55	...	11 5	...	...	...

		a.m.	a.m.	a.m.		p.m.			p.m.			p.m.			
Vordernberg dep	...	6 12	8 35	1029	...	1 8	...	...	4 30	...	...	8 7	...	...	...
Donawitz..............	...	6 44	9 5	11 0	...	1 38	...	...	5 0	...	...	8 39	...	...	...
Leoben ....arr	a.m.	6 52	9 12	11 7	p.m.	1 45	p.m.	p.m.	5 7	p.m.	p.m.	8 47	p.m.	...	...
„ ....dep	5 2	7 13	10 8	1136	1250	...	1 59	4 54	5 12	7 0	7 14	8 53	1140	...	...
Bruck ....arr	5 26	7 38	1032	1156	1 14	...	2 26	5 13	5 37	7 24	7 34	9 19	1210	...	...

JENBACH and ACHENSEE.

Jenbach ....dep	7a55	8a52	11 a0	11a54	1p53	2p52	4p20	6p18	7p28	...	...	...
Achensee.......................arr	8 30	9 27	11 36	12 29	2 28	3 28	5 15	6 54	8 4	...	...	...
SCHOLASTIKA (stmr) arr	local steamer connects with the trains.									...	...	...
SCHOLASTIKA (stmr) dep	...	...	...	...	...	...	...	...	...	...	...	...
Achensee.......................dep	6a48	9a38	12p 5	1 p12	3p 4	4 p0	5p38	6p30	7p40	...	...	...
Jenbach 235 ....arr	7 27	10 17	12 45	1 51	3 43	4 39	6 16	7 8	8 18	...	...	...

TRIESTE and PARENZO.

Trieste S. Andrae		5a50	9a15	2 p40	7 p35
Capodistria		7 10	1039	4 2	8 50
Sicciole		8 24	1154	5 17	10 3
Buje..................	5a50	9 26	1241	6 23	10 50
Montona..............	7 36	11 9	——	8 7	——
Parenzo arr	9 15	1242	...	9 43	...

Parenzo dep	...	6 a 0	...	2p55	6p16
Montona	...	7 37	...	4 36	8 5
Buje	5 a8	9 28	1 p12	6 36	9 55
Sicciole	5 54	10 15	2 2	7 25	——
Capodistria ...	7 9	11 28	3 18	8 46	...
Trieste...arr	8 25	12 46	4 32	10 0	...

LEIBNITZ and PÖLFING BRUNN.

Leibnitz............dep	7 a0	2 p0	6 p9
Pölfing Brunn...arr	8 10	3 23	7 17
Pölfing Brunn...dep	5 a3	9 a13	4 p17
Leibnitz............arr	6 8	10 18	5 48

NEUSTADT, KANIZSA, and BARCS.

	a.m.	a.m.	a.m.	p.m.	p.m.	p.m.	p.m.
Neustadt ....dep	5 28	8 0	11 50	3 55	5 3	6 35	9 59
Mattersdorf	5 59	8 34	12 24	4 36	5 50	6 58	10 36
Sopron	6 29	9 12	12 59	5 9	6 34	7 24	11 16
Szombathely arr a.m.	8 19	10 40	2 31	6 44	—	8 36	12 52
,, dep 6 14	—	10 52	2 41	7 5	...	8 46	1 7
St.Iv.-Zala-Egersz'g 7 33	...	12 10	3 58	8 31	...	9 42	2 27
Nagykanizsa arr 8 42	...	1 22	5 5	9 44	...	10 35	3 40
,, ...dep —	...	3 11	5 35	—	...	10 42	5 3
Zákány	...	3 57	6 22	...	...	11 23	5 56
Gyekenyes	...	4 11	6 26	...	...	11 27	6 4
Vizvár	...	4 52	—	...	...	12 23	6 45
Barcs (236).........arr	...	5 23	...	...	...	12 54	7 17

			a.m.	a.m.		a.m.			p.m.	
Barcs (236) dep	...	...	4 2	9 10	...	11 0	...	...	9 45	...
Vizvár	a.m.	...	4 48	9 44	...	11 34	...	...	1019	...
Gyekenyes	2 40	...	6 1	1040	...	12 32	...	...	1118	...
Zákány	2 44	...	6 17	1044	...	12 36	...	...	1123	...
Nagykanizsa ar	3 20	a.m.	7 30	1125	p.m.	1 17	...	p.m.	12 3	...
,, ...dep	4 5	6 20	—		1242	1 55	...	5 30	1255	...
St.Iv.-Zala-Egrzg	4 58	7 35	...	...	1 35	3 12	...	6 44	2 25	...
Szombathely arr	5 53	8 53	...	...	2 30	4 36	p.m.	8 11	3 45	...
,, ...dep	6 1	9 33	p.m.	...	2 39	4 46	7 0	—	4 3	...
Sopron ......dep	7 15	1129	1 25	...	3 50	7 1	8 43	...	5 57	...
Mattersdorf	7 34	12 6	2 13	...	4 9	7 36	9 16	...	6 31	...
Neustadt ...arr	7 58	1248	3 5	...	4 32	8 14	9 52	...	7 12	...

MARBURG and FRANZENSFESTE.

For Fares, see page 237B.

Dist E.M.		Ex3 a.m.	1,2,3	1,2,3	1,2,3 a.m.	1,2,3 a.m.	Ex3	1,2,3 a.m.	Ex3 p.m.	1,2,3 p.m.	1,2,3 p.m.
—	**Marburg**............dep	1 48	...	...	3 25	6 0	...	10 10	2§56	3 5	7 55
16½	St. Lorenzen............	SC	...	...	4 3	6 46	...	10 53	RC	3 50	8 40
40¼	Unter Drauburg.........	3 4	...	...	4 53	8 0	...	12 0	4 4	4 50	9 39
54¾	Bleiburg............	3 42	...	...	5 36	8 49	...	12 55	4 41	5 39	1026
62¾	Völkermarkt-Kühnsd	...	...	...	5 53	9 9	...	1 15	4 54	6 0	1045
79	**Klagenfurt**............arr	4 19	a.m.	...	6 23	9 44	p.m.	1 50	5 19	6 35	1119
...	,, (237C)...dep	4 27	5 52	Runs until 14th September.	6 47	10 6	3§16	2 14	5 23	6 52	1143
87½	Pörtschach am See ...	4 45	6 14		7 16	1032	3 33	2 41	5 41	7 19	1212
92½	Velden	4 56	6 26		7 31	1049	3 43	2 58	5 52	7 33	1226
103¾	**Villach**............arr	5 16	6 56		7 59	1123	4 1	3 32	6 12	8 2	1254
...	,, (241) ....dep	5 36	7 50		8 24	1156	4 14	4 24	6 22	8 25	1 11
115	Paternion-Feistritz ...	...	8 13		8 50	1223	...	4 50	...	8 51	1 37
125½	**Spittal** (237C)............	6 15	8 35		9 21	1 4	4 51	5 19	6 59	9 19	2 6
131¾	Mollbrücke	6 26	—		9 40	1 20	...	5 34	7 10	9 31	2 21
144¾	Greifenburg	6 47	...		10 16	1 54	...	6 9	7 30	1013	2 58
151	Dellach	...	...		10 30	2 8	...	6 23	...	1027	3 9
156	Ober Drauburg	7 5	...		10 42	2 19	...	6 34	7 48	1039	3 20
164¾	Dölsach	7 20	...	a.m.	11 5	2 38	...	6 53	8 3	1056	3 39
167¾	Lienz	7 34	...	9 14	11 22	3 0	5 58	7 21	8 15	1113	3 52
182	Abfaltersbach	...	...	1013	12 16	3 52	...	8 13	...	12 7	4 44
193¾	Innichen	8 42	...	1053	12 56	4 30	7 5	8 56	9 30	1243	5 24
196½	Toblach	8 49	...	11 4	1 6	4 40	7 12	9 8	9 38	1253	5 35
199½	Niederdorf............	8 56	...	1113	1 15	4 49	...	9 16	9 45	1 1	5 43
207	Olang	...	...	1131	1 33	5 11	...	9 34	...	1 19	6 1
214½	Bruneck (236)	9 34	...	1150	1 50	5 32	7 49	9 51	1017	1 37	6 30
229½	Mühlbach	10 3	...	1228	2 27	6 10	...	10 29	104.	2 12	7 13
233	Franzf. Military Sta...	...	...	1240	2 39	6 22	...	10 41	...	2 21	7 27
234½	**Franzensfeste** ......arr	1013	...	1244	2 43	6 26	8 28	10 45	1057	2 25	7 31
265½	BOTZEN (235)......arr	1144	...	1p57	4 p0	8p32	9p41	12a42	1242	4a16	1011
358½	VERONA (282) ... ,,	4p10	...	...	7 p40	...	...	...	...	10a0	...
386½	INNSBRUCK (235A),,	1245	...	4p36	6 p0	9p32	1053	...	...	4a48	11a9

INNSBRUCK dep		7p35	...	2a22	3a22	6a12	...	7 a57	12p30	3p37	3 p37
VERONA 282 dep		...	...	9 p2	9 p2	...	...	4 a26	10a10	1220	12p20
BOTZEN 235A dp		...	...	1 a2	1a33	7 a2	7 a2	9 a0	2 p10	5 p2	5 p2
		1,2,3 p.m.	1,2,3	1,2,3 a.m.	Ex3 a.m.	Ex3 a.m.	1,2,3 a.m.	1,2,3 a.m.	1,2,3 p.m.	Ex3 p.m.	1,2,3 p.m.
Franzensfeste dp		1058	...	5 10	6 18	8 18	8 28	10 50	3 35	6 39	6 45
,, Military Sta		11 1	...	5 13	...	...	8 31	10 53	3 38	...	6 48
Mühlbach		1116	...	5 29	6 30	RC	8 46	11 8	3 53	6 51	7 3
Bruneck		12 1	...	6 17	7 3	8 59	9 42	12 12	4 41	7 24	7 49
Olang		1229	...	6 47	RC	...	1014	12 42	5 11	SC	8 21
Niederdorf		1 1	...	7 16	7 50	...	1045	1 14	5 39	8 17	8 56
Toblach		1 12	...	7 30	7 58	9 43	11 1	1 27	5 52	8 29	9 12
Innichen.........		1 20	...	7 39	8 4	9 50	1110	1 35	6 0	8 36	9 28
Abfaltersbach ...		—	a.m.	8 15	...	...	1140	2 6	6 38	...	10 0
Lienz		...	5 8	9 19	9 7	1045	1255	2 57	7 18	9 36	10 37
Dölsach		...	5 15	9 26	9 13	...	1 2	3 4	7 25	9 42	Until 14th Sept.
Ober Drauburg...		...	5 32	9 47	9 27	...	1 25	3 23	7 48	9 56	
Dellach		...	5 41	9 58	...	...	1 36	3 34	7 59	...	
Greifenburg		...	5 54	1016	9 45	...	1 54	3 49	8 13	1013	
Mollbrücke.........		a.m.	6 26	1048	10 6	...	2 26	4 26	8 45	1034	
Spittal.........		4 10	6 47	1112	1019	1148	2 45	4 48	9 9	1046	
Paternion-F. 2&3		...	7 11	1136	...	...	3 10	5 13	9 33	...	—
Villach ...arr	a.m.	4 47	7 36	12 2	1051	1220	3 37	5 40	9 59	1118	...
,, ...dep	6 28	5 17	8 15	1251	1058	1232	4 2	6 13	10 22	1128	...
Velden	7 0	5 43	8 47	1 24	1118	1251	4 31	6 41	10 54	1145	...
Pörtschach...	7 17	5 53	9 4	1 37	1128	1 0	4 46	6 54	11 9	1155	...
Klagenfurt arr	7 45	6 16	9 31	2 2	1143	1 14	5 12	7 24	11 35	1210	a.m.
,, dep	—	6 28	10 0	2 45	1149	—	—	7 56	—	1216	1 34
Völkermarkt-Kn		7 0	1037	3 28	1214	...	...	8 33	...	1243	2 9
Bleiburg ......2&3		7 20	11 0	3 54	1232	...	...	8 55	...	1259	2 43
Unter Draub	5a22	8 3	1152	4 46	1 0	...	...	9 43	...	1 31	3 36
St. Lorenzen	6 8	8 49	1244	5 38	...	...	...	10 37	...	...	—
Marburg arr	6 49	9 26	1 25	6 21	2 6	...	...	11 18	...	2 39	...

Extra.						
Klagenfurt...dep	8a32	12 p2	4p15	9p38	...	
Villach.........arr	9 52	1 21	5 30	10 52	...	
Villach ......dep	10a16	2p23	8 p3	...		
Klagenfurt...arr	11 29	3 39	9 15	...		

§—Runs until 29th Sept.

VÖLKERMARKT and EISENKAPPEL.

Völkermarkt...dep	10a50	3 p27	8p35	...	...
Eisenkappel ...arr	11 56	4 24	9 28	...	...

Eisenkappel ...dep	8a14	1p51	5 p2	...	...	...	...
Völkermarkt...arr	9 6	2 50	5 57	...	...	...	...

BRUNECK and SAND.

E.M.								
	Bruneck......dep	4a15	6a39	9 a48	2 p0	4p53	8 p0	...
7	Uttenheim	4 42	7 7	10 17	2 30	5 21	8 29	...
10½	Sand............arr	5 1	7 27	10 37	2 50	5 41	8 49	...

Sand.............dep	5a15	7a49	10a50	3p30	6 p6	8p59	...
Uttenheim............	5 32	8 6	11 7	3 47	6 33	9 16	...
Bruneck 236 ...arr	5 59	8 31	11 32	4 12	6 50	9 41	...

VIENNA, POTTENDORF, and NEUSTADT.

	am	a.m.	a.m.	p.m.	p.m.	p.m.	pm	p.m.	
Vienna ....dep	550	8 0	...	1210	...	3 45	625	9 5	...
Grammat-Neu. dep	6 0	...	8 33	...	2 13	...	6 0	...	...
Wampersdorf	655	8 54	9 8	1 8	2 45	4 51	721	10 7	...
Pottendorf-Land. dep	7 3	9 1	9 22	1 14	2 55	5 1	733	1013	...
Ebenfurth	711	9 8	9 33	1 22	3 5	5 13	743	1020	...
Neustadt 236 ......arr	732	9 28	10 3	1 45	3 34	5 36	8 9	1040	...

	a.m.	a.m.	am	a.m.	a.m.	p.m.	p.m.	p.m.	pm	p.m.	p.m.
Neustadt ......dep	4 23	5 25	6 2	8 29	1114	1214	4 13	4 23	6 0	6 47	8 50
Ebenfurth	...	...	625	8 51	1143	1236	4 37	4 52	622	...	9 13
Pottendorf-Land.	...	...	632	9 1	1151	1243	4 45	5 2	630	...	9 21
Wampersdorf......	...	...	638	9 7	1159	1249	4 52	5 11	636	...	9 27
Grammat-Neu.	...	...	728	...	1230	...	...	5 42	755	...	...
Vienna ....arr	5 38	6 25	740	10 3	...	1 45	5 54	...	740	7 47	1030

BARCS and PAKRACZ-LIPIK.

Dist					
	Barcs ....dep	2a15	8a15	10a50	5p29
15½	Terezovac-Suhopoljearr	3 8	9 19	11 46	6 26
28½	: Slatina ....arr	4 3	11 4	12 41	8 0
...	Terezovac-Suhopoljedep	—	9 39	—	6 35
36¾	Bastaji ....arr	...	1121	...	8 11
46	: Koncanica-Zdenci arr	...	1 0	...	...
...	Bastaji ....dep	...	1134	...	8 19
44	Daruvar	...	1214	...	8 56
59	**Pakracz-Lipik** ...arr	...	1 20	...	10 2

Pakracz-Lipik ...dep	...	5a50	2p50	...
Daruvar	...	7 0	4 3	...
Bastaji ....arr	...	7 40	4 49	...
: Koncanica-Zdenci dep	...	...	2 0	...
Bastaji ....dep	...	7 48	4 53	...
Terezovac-Suhopoljearr	a.m.	9 29	6 33	p.m.
: Slatina ....dep	6 24	7 50	5 17	7 23
Terezovac-Suhopoljedep	7 18	9 40	6 53	8 24
Barcs (236).........arr	8 13	1043	8 5	9 20

PÖLTSCHACH and GONOBITZ.

Pöltschach ......dep	9a28	3 p20	6p37	...	...	...
Gonobitz ....arr	1026	4 18	7 35	...	...	...
Gonobitz ....dep	6a52	12p44	4p50	...	...	...
Pöltschach 234 arr	7 47	1 39	5 45	...	...	...

BUDAPEST and PRAGERHOF.

	2 & 3	1,2,3	1,2,3	Ex 3	1,2,3	1,2,3	1,2,3	1,2,3	1,2,3	Ex 3	1,2,3	1,2,3	2&3	1,2,3
Budapest—	...	a.m.	a.m.	a.m.	p.m.	p.m.	p.m.	p.m.	p.m.	p.m.	p.m.	p.m.		p.m.
Südbahn......dep	...	...	6 30	7 45	12‡25	1 36	2 §30	...	5 0	6 0	6 8	7 5	...	9 15
„ Kelenföld ... „	...	...	6 47	7 54	12 35	1 47	2 37	...	5 11	6 10	6 21	7 19	...	9 34
Nagytétény	...	...	7 9	...	12 57	2 9	...	...	A	...	6 42	...	...	9 59
Székesfehérvár.........arr	...	...	8 36	8 58	2 30	3 37	3 52	...	6 24	7 15	8 12	8 36	...	1125
Székesfehérvár ...dep	...	6 15	...	11 20	...	3 55		...	...	...		9 43	...	...
Kisber	...	7 39	...	1 18	...	5 3	...	...	A	...	...	1127	...	...
Komárom..............arr	...	8 30	...	2 28	...		...	...	...	...	...	1233	...	...
Székesfehérvár ......dep	...		9 16	9 3	2 45	...	...	3 57	6 29	7 19	...	8 42	...	1135
Lepseny (229)	...	...	9 59	9 34	3 30	...	...	4 43	7 1	7 52	...	9 15	...	1220
Sió-Fok	...	...	10 36	10 2	4 19	...	...	5 24	7 33	8 18	...	9 44	...	1258
Balaton Foldvar	a.m.	...	11 0	10 18	4 50	...	...	5 54	7 56	8 *35	...	10*1	...	...
Boglar	3 †35	...	11 41	10 38	5 23	...	...	6 41	8 34	8 54	...	1027	...	1 54
Fonyod	3 51	...	11 53	10*46		...	...	6 52	8 45	9 2	...	1037	...	2 5
Balaton Sz. Gyorgy	5 26	...	12 36	11 10	...	...	2 & 3	7 35	9 46	9 26	...	11 6	...	2 50
Nagykanizsa (236)......arr	7 21	...	1 38	11 51	...	...	p.m.	8 42	1046	10 7	...	1150	...	3 50
„ ....dep		...	2 45	11 58	...	...	5 51			10 16	...	1158	...	4 46
Csaktornya (229)	...	...	4 18	12 53	...	...	8 8	...	...	11 10	...	1 7	a.m.	6 23
Pettau	...	...	5 42	1 43	...	...		...	...	11 56	...	2 0	5 46	7 35
Pragerhof (234) ....arr	...	...	6 10	2 2	...	...	...	...	...	12 15	...	2 20	6 17	8 2

	1,2,3	1,2,3	Ex3	2&3	1,2,3	1,2,3	1,2,3	Ex3	1,2,3	2 & 3	1,2,3
		a.m.	a.m.	a.m.	a.m.		a.m.	p.m.	a.m.	p.m.	p.m.
Pragerhof 234A ......dep	...	1 12	3 42	...	...	...	9 19	3 8	...	...	8 30
Pettau	...	1 36	4 1	...	...	...	9 53	3 28	...	...	9 1
Csaktornya	...	2 39	4 46	4 57	...	A	1111	4 20	...	...	1024
Nagykanizsa ....arr	...	3 48	5 39	7 12	...	a.m.	1220	5 13	...	...	1139
„ .... dep	...	4 0	5 55		9 18	11 30	2 0	5 25	...	7 0	1245
Balaton Sz. Gyorgy	...	4 51	6 37	...	1023	12 34	3 8	6 7	...	8 45	1 51
Fonyod	...	5 23	...	...	1111	1 12	3 48	6*31	...	10 †7	2 27
Boglar	...	5 34	7 12	...	1132	1 23	4 5	6 45	7 ‡0	10†21	2 47
Balaton Foldvar	...	6 5	7*31	...	12 5	1 57	4 40	7 *5	7 40		3 15
Sió-Fok	...	6 33	7 57	...	1239	2 28	5 15	7 31	8 15	...	3 46
Lepseny	...	6 59	8 20	...	1 16	3 0	5 47	7 53	8 44	...	4 15
Székesfehérvár.........arr	a.m.	7 34	8 49	...	2 2	3 42	6 28	8 28	9 28	...	4 56
Komárom ....dep	3 45	...	...	...	1227	...	...	5 35	...	...	...
Kisber	4 44	...	...	...	1 16	...	5 23	6 39	...	...	...
Székesfehérvár......arr	5 55	...	...	...	2 21	...	6 21	8 5	...	...	...
Székesfehérvár ......dep	6 11	7 40	8 59	...	2 32	3 53	6 49	8 38	9 36	...	5 6
Nagytétény	7 39	...	...	...	4 12	5 25	8 28	...	10 52	...	6 38
Budapest Kelen	8 6	8 59	10 5	...	4 33	5 45	8 52	9 47	11 14	...	7 1
„ (Süd) ....arr	8 15	9 10	1015	...	4 45	5 55	9 10	9 55	11 24	...	7 20

*—Stops when required.
†—Between Boglár and Sz-György in July and August only.
‡—Until 31st August.
‖—Runs until 14th Sept.
§—From 1st Sept.
A—Runs until 31st August.

GRAZ and KOFLACH.

	a.m.	a.m.	p.m.	p.m.	p.m.	p.m.	p.m.	
Graz Sudbhf dep	6 15	7 32	1 33	5 0	5 39	7 24	8 51	...
Premstetten-Tobe	6 36	7 53	1 54	5 24	6 1	7 45	9 17	...
Lieboch 237	6 43	8 1	2 4	5 32	6 9	7 52	9 25	...
Söding		8 10	2 16		6 18		9 34	...
Krems	...	8 29	2 35	...	6 37	...	9 53	...
Koflach ......arr	...	8 50	2 56	...	6 58	...	10 13	...

	a.m.			a.m.		p.m.		p.m.
Koflach ......dep	5 36	...	...	1141	...	4 44	...	8 35
Krems	5 53	...	...	1159	...	5 2	...	8 53
Söding	6 16	a.m.	p.m.	1218	p.m.	5 22	p.m.	9 14
Lieboch	6 25	6 47	12 1	1227	4 59	5 33	8 47	9 26
Premstetten	6 37	6 55	12 9	1235	5 7	5 42	8 55	9 35
Graz ....arr	6 57	7 13	1227	1253	5 25	6 3	9 16	9 55

PREDING and STAINZ.

Preding ....dep	7 a25	2p38	6 p8	8 p29	...	...	...
Stainz ....arr	8 0	3 18	6 48	9 10	...	...	...

Stainz ....dep	5a30	10a43	3p45	7p33	...	...	...	...	...
Preding **237** ......arr	6 9	11 12	4 24	8 9	...	...	...	...	...

LIEBOCH and WIES.

Lieboch ......dep	6 a51	2 p7	5 p35	7p53	...	...
Preding W. 237	7 17	2 33	6 0	8 20	...	...
Deutsch Landsberg	7 52	3 6	6 33	8 53	...	...
Wies ....arr	8 28	3 42	7 8	9 28	...	...

Wies ....dep	5a20	10a31	3 p26	7p20	...	...	...	...
Deutsch Landsberg	5 53	11 4	4 3	7 53	...	...	...	...
Preding W.	6 20	11 34	4 33	8 21	...	...	...	...
Lieboch ......arr	6 45	11 59	4 58	8 46	...	...	...	...

TRIENT and PRIMOLANO.

Dist. E.M.		a.m.	a.m.	p.m.	p.m.	p.m.	p.m.	
	Trient ....dep	5 27	9 58	1 31	5 30	7 32	9 18	...
15½	Pergine	6 13	10 44	2 19	6 4	8 14	10 4	...
21¾	Caldonazzo	6 34	11 5	2 38	6 21	8 33	1027	...
24½	**Levico**	6 45	11 14	2 47	6 28	8 41	1039	...
29¾	**Roncegno**	7 6	11 35	3 6	6 44	9 0	1057	...
33	Borgo	7 17	11 47	3 18	6 53	9 10	11 8	...
43½	Grigno	7 48	12 18	3 48	7 20	9 42	1139	...
47½	Tezze	8 1	12 29	4 1	...	9 53	1149	...
49¾	**Primolano** ...arr	8 10	12 38	4 9	7 35	10 2	...	...
...	VENICE 288 ...arr	11a32	4 p0	7 p5	9p45	...	...	...

VENICE ....dep	...	5 a30	9 a20	12p30	4 p40	7 p5	...
	a.m.	a.m.	a.m.	p.m.	p.m.	p.m.	
Primolano ...dep	4 0	8 15	11 55	3 50	7 36	9 16	...
Tezze	4 10	8 25	12 7	4 1	7 48	...	...
Grigno	4 30	8 53	12 32	4 29	8 16	9 48	...
Borgo	5 0	9 25	1 4	5 1	8 50	10 14	...
Roncegno	5 10	9 34	1 13	5 11	9 2	10 23	...
Levico	5 29	9 56	1 33	5 32	9 27	10 39	...
Caldonazzo	5 37	10 4	1 41	5 41	9 37	10 45	...
Pergine	5 57	10 27	2 3	6 4	10 2	11 2	...
Trient (235) ...arr	6 41	11 13	2 45	6 45	10 45	11 35	...

KAPFENBERG and AU-SEEWIESEN.

Kapfenberg Sudbn.	5 a56	9 a6	11a54	2 p23	6 p15	...
Thorl	6 34	10 0	12 41	3 12	7 1	...
Aflenz	6 40	10 6	12 46	3 20	7 7	...
Seebach-Turnau	7 6	10 34	1 11	3 47	7 31	...
Au-Seewiesen...arr	7 18	10 46	1 23	3 59	7 41	...

Au-Seewiesen...dep	5a48	9 a13	11a50	3 p35	7 p31	...	...	...
Seebach-Turnau	5 58	9 23	12 1	3 48	8 0	...	...	...
Aflenz	6 23	9 48	12 29	4 15	8 20	...	...	...
Thorl	6 33	9 56	12 39	4 23	8 30	...	...	...
Kapfenberg 234 arr	7 16	10 23	1 20	5 12	9 9	...	...	...

BOTZEN-GRIES, MERAN, and MALS.

E.M.	All 1 & 3 Class.	a.m.	a.m.	a.m.	a.m.	a.m.	p.m.		p.m.	p.m.	p.m.	p.m.	p.m.
—	**Botzen-Gries (235)**...dep	6 5	7 32	8 58	1030	1158	2 31	...	4 22	5 36	7 23	8 45	9 50
3¾	Sigmundskron	6 17	7 43	9 9	1041	12 9	2 43	...	4 36	5 48	7 35	8 57	...
8	Terlan	6 34	7 58	9 23	1056	1222	2 58	...	4 50	6 2	7 48	9 11	A
10	Vilpian....................	6 43	8 8	9 31	11 4	1230	3 7	...	4 59	6 10	7 56	9 20	...
12½	Gargazon	6 50	...	9 38	1110	...	3 14	...	5 5	6 18	8 2	9 28	...
14¼	Lana-Burgstall	6 59	8 22	9 46	1118	1244	3 23	...	5 12	6 26	8 10	9 38	10 30
18¾	Untermais	7 12	8 34	9 58	1130	...	3 36	...	5 25	6 38	8 23	9 51	...
20	**Meran** ....arr	7 17	8 39	10 3	1135	1 0	3 41	p.m.	5 30	6 42	8 28	9 56	10 45
...	" ....dep	7 38		1013		1 30		3 ‡55		7 10			
33¼	Naturns	8 24	...	11 0	...	2 17	...	4 43	...	7 58	...	...	...
41¾	Latsch	9 0	...	1133	...	2 52	...	5 18	...	8 32	...	...	...
48¼	Schlanders	9 20	...	1153	...	3 12	...	5 41	...	8 53	...	...	...
58¼	Spondinig-Prad	9 59	...	1230	...	3 50	...	6 19	...	9 30	...	...	...
64½	**Mals** ....arr	1019	...	1250	...	4 10	...	6 39	...	9 50	...	...	...

			a.m.		a.m.	a.m.			p.m.		p.m.		
Mals ....dep	...	...	5 8	...	7 46	9 ‡36	...	...	12 52	...	5 55	...	...
Spondinig-Prad..........	...	...	5 25	...	8 5	9 59	...	...	1 14	...	6 18	...	...
Schlanders	...	...	5 54	...	8 35	10 29	...	...	1 46	...	6 48	...	...
Latsch.........................	...	...	6 11	...	8 54	10 46	...	...	2 5	...	7 5	...	...
Naturns	...	...	6 35	...	9 18	11 12	...	...	2 33	...	7 29	...	...
Meran......................arr	a.m.	a.m.	7 13	a.m.	9 57	11 51	p.m.	p.m.	3 14	p.m.	8 8	p.m.	...
" ....dep	6 0	6 40	7 37	8 40	1015		12 48	2 14	3 42	5 50	8 58	11 15	...
Untermais	...	6 46	7 43	8 46	1021	...	12 56	2 20	...	5 55	9 4	...	...
Lana-Burgstall............	6 15	7 0	7 55	8 58	1033	...	1 8	2 33	3 58	6 8	9 18	11 31	...
Gargazon.....................	...	7 8	...	9 6	1040	...	...	2 41	...	6 17	9 27	...	...
Vilpian.........................	...	7 16	8 8	9 13	1048	...	1 22	2 48	4 12	6 24	9 34	...	...
Terlan	...	7 26	8 16	9 23	1057	...	1 30	2 57	4 21	6 33	9 44	11 52	...
Sigmundskron..............	...	7 43	8 30	9 37	1112	...	1 45	3 11	4 37	6 47	10 1	12 6	...
Botzen (235) ....arr	6 54	7 53	8 40	9 48	1124	...	1 56	3 22	4 48	6 58	1012	12 16	...

A—Runs until 29th September. ‡—Until 15th September.

BREGENZ and BEZAU.

Bregenz dep	6 a4	10a31	1p50	3 p53	8 p14	...	...	...	...	...	...	...	...	...	...
Egg	7 25	11 53	3 9	5 16	9 35	...	...	...	...	...	...	...	...	...	...
Bezau ......arr	8 6	12 34	3 50	5 57	10 16	...	...	...	...	...	...	...	...	...	...
Bezau ...dep	5 a26	8 a30	1 p10	4 p35	6 p45	...	...	...	...	...	...	...	...	...	...
Egg	6 7	9 11	1 51	5 16	7 26	...	...	...	...	...	...	...	...	...	...
Bregens 238	7 26	10 23	3 10	6 30	8 44	...	...	...	...	...	...	...	...	...	...

ABBAZIA and LOVRANA.

Abbazia Mattuglie dep	5 a44	9 a36	9 a44	11a44	1p36	2 p48	5p44	10p0	10 p8	...	...	...	...
Volosca	6 6	9 58	10 6	12 6	1 58	3 10	6 6	1022	10 30	...	...	...	...
Abbazia Hafen.............	6 18	10 10	10 18	12 18	2 10	3 22	6 18	1034	10 42	...	...	...	...
Lovrana.....................arr	6 44	...	10 44	12 52	...	3 48	6 41	...	11 8	...	...	...	...
Lovrana ....dep	...	6a48	...	...	12 p8	1 p28	4 p8	7 p4	11p12	...	...	...	...
Abbazia Hafen	4a48	7 14	7a30	10a58	12 34	1 54	4 34	7 30	11 38	...	...	...	...
Volosca	4 58	7 26	7 42	11 10	12 46	2 6	4 46	7 42	11 50	...	...	...	...
Abbazia Mattuglie arr	5 20	7 48	8 4	11 32	1 8	2 28	5 8	8 4	12 12	...	...	...	...

KRAINBURG and NEUMARKTL.

Krainburg...........dep	7a56	12p36	4 p47	7p40	...	...	...	...	...	...	...	...	...
Neumarktl...........arr	8 43	1 24	5 34	8 27	...	...	...	...	...	...	...	...	...

Neumarktl ....dep	5a52	9 a5	2p28	6p20	...	...	...	...	...	...	...	...	...	...
Krainburg (242) ...arr	6 33	9 48	3 11	7 2	...	...	...	...	...	...	...	...	...	...

ZELL-AM-SEE and KRIMML.

‡—Until 31st Aug.

Zell-am-See ....dep	5a40	9a20	12p30	5 p22	7‡p15
Walchen	6 11	..	1 7	5 53	7 44
Mittersill	7 1	1033	2 12	6 44	8 33
Bramberg	7 33	11 4	2 51	7 14	9 4
Neukirchen i. Pinzgau	7 47	1118	3 7	7 28	9 18
Krimml..................arr	8 10	1138	3 30	7 50	9 40

Krimml ....dep	5a30	8 a42	12p12	4p10	8‡20	...	...	...
Neukirchen i. Pinzgau ...	5 51	9 3	12 33	4 33	8 40	...	...	...
Bramberg	6 5	9 17	12 47	4 48	8 53	...	...	...
Mittersill	6 37	9 49	1 18	5 24	9 22	...	...	...
Walchen..........................	7 27	10 39	2 6	6 18	10 8	...	...	...
Zell-am-See 238 arr	7 55	11 7	2 34	6 50	1035	...	...	...

JENBACH and MAYRHOFEN.

Jenbach ......dep	6†a47	9 a0	10‡46	12†p9	2p44	5‡p51	7p54	...
Fugen	7 21	9 42	11 20	12 46	3 12	6 28	8 37	...
Kaltenbach Stumm	7 41	10 7	11 40	1 7	3 43	6 49	9 1	...
Zell-am-Ziller	8 2	1035	12 2	1 29	4 7	7 10	9 30	...
Mayrhofen...arr	8 22	1058	12 24	1 49	4 28	7 33	9 53	...

†—Until 9th Sept.

Mayrhofendep	4‡a39	6 a1	8†a52	11a29	2†p31	4p58	7†p9
Zell-am-Ziller ...	5 0	6 31	9 16	12 1	2 54	5 20	7 31
Kaltenbach Stu.	5 21	6 55	9 37	12 24	3 15	5 41	7 52
Fugen..............	5 41	7 20	9 59	12 49	3 36	6 3	8 11
Jenbach 238 arr	6 13	7 57	10 32	1 27	4 8	6 38	8 44

‡—Until 31st August.

INNSBRUCK and GARMISCH PARTENKIRCHEN.

	a.m.	a.m.	a.m.	a.m.		p.m.	p.m.	p.m.
Innsbruck (Haup) dep	4 55	7 25	8 43	1152	...	2 57	5 10	6 39
,, (Westbhf)	5 0	7 30	8 51	12 0	...	3 5	5 16	6 46
Hochzirl	5 31	...	9 27	1236	...	3 39	...	7 23
Seefeld	5 56	8 20	9 52	1 1	p.m.	4 4	6 6	7 48
Scharnitz ....dep	6 17	8 39	1014	1 21	1 47	4 25	6 26	8 10
Mittenwald	6 28	8 50	1025	1 35	1 59	4 36	6 37	8 22
Garmisch Partenk.	7 2	9 40	1117	2 23	2 50	5 31	7 27	9 15

Garmisch- (197B)	a.m.	a.m.	a.m.	a.m.	p.m.	p.m.	p.m.	p.m	p.m.
Partenkirchen dep	...	7 25	10 0	1122	1259	3 10	4 43	7 35	1014
Mittenwald	5 15	8 12	1036	12 7	1 35	3 57	5 20	8 22	1057
Scharnitz ....arr	5 27	8 24	1047	1219	1 46	4 9	5 31	8 34	11 9
Seefeld	5 56	9 1	1120		2 19	4 47	6 6	9 7	
Hochzirl	6 21	9 28	...	...	2 43	5 12	...	9 32	...
Innsbruck (Westbhf)	6 54	10 2	1210	...	3 15	5 52	6 56	10 6	...
,, 238 (Hpt.) arr	7 0	1010	1215	...	3 20	6 0	7 1	1013	...

TRIENT, ST. MICHELE, and MALE.—All 1 & 3 Class (Rail Motor).

E.M.	Trient—	a.m.		a.m.	a.m		a.m.		p.m.		p.m.			p.m.	p.m.	p.m.	p.m.	p.m.		
—	(TorreVerde) dep	3 50	...	6 58	8 21	...	10 22	...	12 6	...	2 46	...	...	5 30	6‡20	7 0	8 44	10 26	...	...
3	Gardolo	4 6	...	7 12	8 46	...	10 41	...	12 20	...	3 3	...	...	5 50	6 39	7 20	8 58	10 43	...	...
5½	Lavis	4 22	...	7 27	8 56	...	10 57	...	12 34	...	3 21	...	...	6 5	6 54	7 36	9 13	10 59	...	...
8	Nave S. Felice	4 35	a.m.	7 39	9 8	a.m.	11 9	p.m.	12 45	p.m.	3 32	p.m.	p.m.	6 16		7 48	9 25	11 15	n'gt	...
11¾	**St. Michele**	4 55	6 58	8 6	9 27	10 15	11 27	12 14	1 12	2 55	3 56	5 10	5 57	6 34	...	8 15	9 43	11 46	1210	...
12¾	Mezocorona	5 0	7 3	8 11	9 31	10 20	11 31	12 19	1 17	3 0	4 0	5 15	6 2	6 38	...	8 21	9 48	11 50	1214	...
13¾	Mezolombardo	5 16	7 11	8 23	9 48	10 28	11 46	12 27	1 30	3 8	4 10	5 23	6 10	6 51		8 38	10 0	11 58	1222	...
16¾	Rochetta	5 36		8 42	10 7		12 6		1 48		4 28			7 7		8 59	1017			...
26	Tajo	6 23	...	9 21	1054	...	12 56	...	2 29	...	5 13	...	...	7 59		9 51	1057	...	...	...
28	Dermullo 237B	6 31	...	9 29	11 2	...	1 4	...	2 37	...	5 21	...	...	8 7		9 59	11 5	...	...	...
28½	S. Giustina	6 42	...	9 37	1115	...	1 16	...	2 46	...	5 28	...	...	8 18		10 6	1111	...	...	...
32¼	Cles	7 5	...	9 56	1134	...	1 38	...	3 6	...	5 49	...	...	8 39		1025	1129	...	...	...
36¾	Mostizzolo	7 23	...	1010	1150	...	1 55	...	3 22	...	6 7	...	...	8 55	...	1041	1143	...	...	...
39¾	Cassana	7 42	...	1025	12 9	...	2 15	...	3 38	...	6 26	...	...	9 14	...	11 0	12 0	...	...	...
44	**Malé** ......arr	8 4	...	1048	1232	...	2 37	...	3 58	...	6 50	...	...	9 38	...	1123	1220	...	...	...

‡—Not on Sunday.

		a.m.		a.m.		a.m.		a.m.	a.m.		p.m.		p.m.	p.m.	p.m.					
Malé ......dep	...	3 20	...	5 15	...	6 40	...	10 5	1144	...	1 50	...	3 15	5 28	7 38	...	...	...	...	...
Cassana	...	3 43	...	5 35	...	7 3	...	10 28	12 9	...	2 16	...	3 39	5 47	8 2	...	...	...	...	...
Mostizzolo	...	4 2	...	5 52	...	7 23	...	10 44	1228	...	2 39	...	4 2	6 5	8 22	...	...	...	...	...
Cles	...	4 19	...	6 10	...	7 43	...	11 0	1248	...	3 3	...	4 29	6 22	8 46	...	...	...	...	...
S. Giustina	...	4 34	...	6 24	...	7 59	...	11 14	1 4	...	3 20	...	4 48	6 36	9 4	...	...	...	...	...
Dermullo	...	4 42	...	6 33	...	8 9	...	11 21	1 14	...	3 30	...	5 1	6 43	9 14	...	...	...	...	...
Tajo	...	4 50	...	6 41	...	8 18	...	11 29	1 22	...	3 39	...	5 13	6 51	9 24	...	...	...	...	...
Rochetta	a.m.	5 36	a.m.	7 19	a.m.	9 7	a.m.	12 5	2 9	p.m.	4 28	p.m.	5 57	7 29	1018	p.m.	...	...	...	...
Mezolombardo	4 40	5 59	6 32	7 42	8 57	9 40	11 50	12 28	2 32	3 32	4 47	5 33	6 20	7 51	1043	11 20	...	...	...	...
Mezocorona	4 49	6 8	6 41	7 51	9 5	9 49	11 59	12 37	2 41	3 41	4 54	5 42	6 29	8 0	1052	11 29	...	...	...	...
St. Michele 235	4 55	6 14	6 45	7 57	9 9	9 54	12 3	12 48	2 51	3 45	5 4	5 46	6 31	8 14	1056	11 33	...	...	...	...
Nave S. Felice	5 14	6 36		8 14		1012		1 5	3 8		5 21		6 51	8 30	1114		...	...	...	...
Lavis	5 28	6 53	...	8 26	...	1026	...	1 18	3 22	...	5 35	...	7 5	8 43	1128	...	...	...	...	...
Gardolo	5 44	7 12	...	8 41	...	1041	...	1 32	3 38	...	5 50	...	7 21	8 58	1143	...	...	...	...	...
Trient (235) ...arr	6 0	7 28	...	8 55	...	1057	...	1 46	3 54	...	6 6	...	7 37	9 12	1158	...	...	...	...	...

DERMULLO and MENDEL.

	a.m.	a.m.	p.m.	p.m	p.m.		
Dermullo ......dep	6 25	9 25	1 25	5 25	8 25	...	...
Malgolo	6 54	9 54	1 54	5 54	8 54	...	...
Fondo	7 36	1030	2 30	6 26	9 26	...	...
Mendel 235 ......arr	8 12	11 6	3 6	...	...	...	...

	a.m.	a.m.	a.m.	p.m.	p.m.		
Mendel ......dep	...	...	11 10	3 10	6 20	...	...
Fondo	5 10	7 30	11 50	3 50	7 0	...	...
Malgolo	5 41	8 1	12 21	4 21	7 31	...	...
Dermullo 237B ......arr	6 10	8 30	12 50	4 50	8 0	...	...

WEIZELSDORF and FERLACH.

Weizelsdorf...dep	5a10	8a25	10a35	1 p5	2p46	5 p3	8 p8	...
Ferlach ......arr	5 26	8 42	10 57	1 27	3 2	5 20	8 24	...

Ferlach ......dep	5a42	9a43	11a50	2 p10	3p12	6p33	8p34	...
Weizelsdorf 237C...arr	5 58	10 0	12 7	2 26	3 28	6 50	8 51	...

TABLE OF FARES ON THE AUSTRIAN STATE RAILWAYS.

Kilometer.	English miles.	Express Trains. 1 Cl.	Express Trains. 2 Cl.	Express Trains. 3 Cl.	Ordinary Trains. 1 Cl.	Ordinary Trains. 2 Cl.	Ordinary Trains. 3 Cl.	Luggage per 10 kg.
		k. h.	k. h.	k. h.	k. h.	k. h.	k. h.	k. h.
10	6¼	1 30	0 80	0 50	1 00	0 60	0 40	0 04
20	12½	2 40	1 50	0 90	1 80	1 10	0 70	0 08
30	18¾	3 60	2 20	1 40	2 80	1 70	1 10	0 12
40	24¾	4 70	2 90	1 80	3 60	2 20	1 40	0 16
50	31	6 10	3 70	2 40	4 60	2 80	1 80	0 20
80	49¾	9 50	5 80	3 70	7 20	4 40	2 80	0 32
100	62¼	11 90	7 30	4 60	9 0	5 50	3 50	0 40
120	74½	14 20	8 70	5 50	10 80	6 60	4 20	0 48
150	93¼	17 90	10 90	7 0	13 60	8 30	5 30	0 60
180	111¾	21 40	13 10	8 30	16 20	9 90	6 30	0 72
200	124¼	23 70	14 50	9 20	18 0	11 00	7 0	0 80
250	155¼	29 80	18 20	11 60	22 60	13 80	8 80	1 00
300	186½	35 70	21 80	13 90	27 0	16 50	10 50	1 20
400	248½	47 50	29 0	18 50	36 0	22 0	14 0	1 50
500	310¾	58 90	35 80	22 60	44 50	27 0	17 0	1 80
600	372¾	70 30	42 60	26 70	53 00	32 00	20 00	2 10
700	435	80 60	48 30	29 80	60 50	36 00	22 00	2 40
800	497	91 10	54 10	33 00	68 00	40 00	24 00	2 70
900	559¼	10140	59 80	36 10	75 50	44 00	26 00	3 0
1000	621½	11180	65 60	39 20	83 00	48 00	28 00	3 30

TRIESTE, ROSENBACH, ST. VEIT, VILLACH, GASTEIN, and BISCHOFSHOFEN.

THROUGH CARRIAGES { Trieste to Berlin, in 7.40 a.m. and 8.40 p.m. from Trieste.
Trieste to Munich, in 7.40 a.m., 6.0 p.m., and 8.40 p.m. from Trieste.
Trieste to Vlissingen (Flushing), in 8.40 p.m. from Trieste.

For other trains between Schwarzach-St. Veit and Bischofshofen see page 238A.

Canadian Pacific Railway Observation Car on the 7.40 a.m. train from Trieste.—See page ii.

Dist. E.M.		1,2,3	1,2,3	1,2,3	1,2,3	Ex 3	Ex 3	1,2,3	Ex 3		1,2,3	Ex 3	1,2,3	Ex 3	Ex 3	1,2,3	1,2,3
			a.m.			a.m.	a.m.	a.m.	a.m.		p.m.		p.m.	p.m.	p.m.	p.m.	p.m.
—	**Trieste** dep	...	5 40	...	...	7 40	8 45	9 5	11 5	...	12 48	...	4 15	6 0	8 40	7 40	10 39
13¾	Opcina	...	6 19	...	...	8 11	...	9 50	11 42	...	1 32	...	4 57	6 32	9 12	8 23	11 20
34¼	Prvacina	...	7 8	...	...	8 49	...	10 44	...	...	2 22	...	5 40	7 0	...	9 7	12 6
41¾	**Görz** arr	...	7 26	...	a.m.	9 3	10 2	11 3	12 30	...	2 40	...	5 58	7 22	10 0	9 25	12 23
	Görz dep	...	—	...	5 12	9 7	10 8	11 18	12 35	...	2 55	...	6 12	7 28	10 4	—	12 41
79	Podbrdo	...	...	...	6 56	RC	...	12 56	...	...	4 49	p.m.	7 49	SC	...	...	2 19
102½	**Assling** arr	...	a.m.	...	8 0	11 10	12 16	1 58	2 41	...	5 56		8 43	9 33	12 5	...	3 20
	Assling dep	...	5 19	...	9 25	11 14	12 22	2 18	2 45	...	6 14	8 51	9 9	9 36	12 11	...	3 48
111¼	**Rosenbach** arr	...	5 36	...	9 42	11 30	⋮	2 35	3 0	...	6 31	9 7	9 26	9 51	12 27	...	4 5
...	**Rosenbach** dep	...	5 38	...	9 50	...	⋮	3 4	...	...	6 43	9 8	9 56		...	...	...
124¼	Weizelsdorf	...	6 9	...	10 23	...	12 58	3 37	...	...	7 14	..	10 25	...	...	...	...
134¼	**Klagenfurt** arr	...	6 37	a.m.	10 53	...	1 17	4 5	...	...	7 43	9 47	10 55	...	...	...	...
	Klagenfurt dep	...	6 50	8 30	11 5	...	1 27	5 40	...	...	7 53	9 51	11 25	...	...	...	...
145½	**St. Veit** arr	...	7 26	9 7	11 42	...	1 49	6 20	...	...	8 32	10 13	12 0	...	...	...	...
262¼	SELZTHAL 241A arr	...	1 p53		...	...	5 p35	12 34	...	...		2 a25	...	...	...	...	...
410	BUDWEIS 237C arr	...	...	...	...	...	10p33	...	...	...	...	11a33	...	...	...	...	...
515	PRAGUE 243 arr	...	...	...	...	...	1 a22	...	...	...	...	2 p35	...	...	...	...	...
367¼	VIENNA 234A, 241A arr	...	5 p40	...	8 p40	...	8 p40	5 a38	...	...	...	7 a40	9 a10	...	...	...	...
		1,2,3	1,2,3		1,2,3	Ex 3		1,2,3	Ex 3	1,2,3	1,2,3	1,2,3	1,2,3	Ex 3	Ex 3		
		a.m.	a.m.		a.m.	a.m.	§—Via Spittal.	p.m.	p.m.	p.m.	p.m.	p.m.	p.m.	p.m.	nig't		
...	**Rosenbach** dep	4 14	6 30	...	9 56	11 31		2 47	3 6	...	6 39	...	9 32	9 52	12 28	...	...
125½	Bad Villach	4 49	7 13	...	10 35	11 56		3 28	3 37	4 0	7 11	8 38	10 5	10 15	...	...	...
128¾	**Villach** arr	5 6	7 23	...	10 45	12 4		3 38	3 44	4 16	7 20	8 51	10 15	10 22	12 56	...	...
259½	FRANZENSFESTE 236 arr	10a13	2 p43	...	...	6 §26		8 p28	8 p28	10p45	2 a55			...	7 a31	...	...
311¾	INNSBRUCK 235A arr	12p45	6 p0	...	...	9 p32		10p53	10p53	...	4 a48	...	...	...	11 a9	...	...
		1,2,3	1,2,3	Ex 3	1,2,3	Ex.3	1,2,3	1,2,3	Ex 3	1,2,3	1,2,3	1,2,3		Ex 3	Ex 3		1,2,3
		a.m.	a.m.	a.m.	a.m.	p.m.	July 14 to Aug. 31.	p.m.	p.m.	p.m.	p.m.	p.m.		p.m.	a.m.		a.m.
...	**Villach** dep	6 0	7 50	8 50	10 59	12 22		3 55	4 14	4 24	7 30	8 25	...	10 33	1 6	...	1 11
140¼	Paternion Feistritz	6 23	8 13	...	11 23	...		4 18	...	4 50	7 53	8 51†	...	SC	...	...	1 37
150¾	**Spittal** arr	6 45	8 35	9 26	11 47	12 58		4 40	4 47	5 14	8 15	9 15	...	11 9	1 42	...	2 1
	Spittal dep	6 50	8 40	9 30	11 51	1 3		4 52			8 23		...	11 13	1 45	...	
158½	Mühldorf-Möllbrücke	7 11	9 0	...	12 10	...		5 12	...	...	8 47	...	...	...	...	...	...
174	Obervellach	8 0	9 49	...	12 59	...		6 0	...	...	9 42	...	...	...	...	...	1,2,3
179¾	Mallnitz ... a.m.	8 21	10 10	10 51	1 19	2 20	p.m.	6 20	...	...	10 3	...	RC—Restaurant Car.	12 27	2 59	...	a.m.
187¾	Böckstein ... 7 4	8 39	10 27	...	1 36	RC	3 10	6 37	...	...	10 20	...	SC—Sleeping Car.	...	...	...	5 24
190¾	**Bad Gastein** dep 7 15	8 52	10 40	11 18	1 49	2 49	3 23	6 50	...	...	10 32	...		12 48	3 20	...	5 37
197½	Hofgastein Haltestelle 7 32	9 6	10 52	...	2 4	...	3 37	7 2	...	...	10 40	...		12 59	3 31	...	5 51
200¼	Hofgastein ... 7 38	9 12	10 59	11 34	2 10	3 5	3 43	7 9	...	...	10 48	...		...	...	...	5 57
203¾	Dorfgastein ... 7 46	9 20	11 7	...	2 18	...	3 51	7 17	...	...	10 54	Ex 3		...	...	...	6 5
215¾	**Schwarzach St. Veit** arr 8 9	9 45	11 29	11 58	2 40	3 29	4 20	7 39	p.m.	p.m.	11 15	p.m.		1 28	3 59	...	6 28
	Schwarzach St. Veit dep —	10 9	11 47	12 0	2 43	3 39	4 23		7 52	8 43	11 32	11 22		1 34	4 0	...	6 37
218¾	St. Johann in Pongau	1017	11 56	...	2 51	...	4 31	...	8 0	8 51	11 41	11 29		...	...	...	6 45
224¼	**Bischofshofen** arr	1027	12 11	12 17	3 1	3 54	4 41	...	8 12	9 4	11 55	11 39	RC SC	1 50	4 16	...	6 59
257½	SALZBURG 239A arr	1155	1 p30	1 p30	4 p15	4 p58	6 p50	...	...	10p45	1 a12	1 a12		2 a58	5 a21	...	8 a50
...	MUNICH 200 arr	4 p0	5 p0	5 p0	7 p59	7 p59	10 p0	...	...	...	...	...	...	6 a30	8 a2	...	12p10

Extra. { Bad Villach ...dep 5a20, 7a20, 11a25, 12p5, 6p33, 9 p3 | Villach ...arr 5 30, 7 34, 11 35, 1212, 6 43, 9 10. Klagenfurt to St. Veit 12.30, 2.10 p.m. Rosenbach to Klagenfurt 8.21 p.m.

SELZTHAL, LINZ, and BUDWEIS.

ST. VEIT dep	...	...	...	10p24	...	12a23	...	...	...	7 a45	...	...	7 a45	1 p51	...	2 p52
	1,2,3	1,2,3	Ex3	1,2,3	Ex 3	1,2,3	Ex2	1,2,3	1,2,3	Ex 3	1,2,3	Ex 3	1,2,3	Ex 3	1,2,3	1,2,3
	*—Thurs. and Sat. only.			a.m.	a.m.	a.m.			a.m.	p.m.			p.m.	p.m.		p.m.
Selzthal dep	...	...	...	3 30	6 20	7 25	...	...	11 26	12 54	...	...	2 57	5 40	...	8 56
Spital-am-Pyhrn	...	...	...	4 3	6 50	7 54	...	...	11 56	1 18	...	...	3 26	6 7	...	9 30
Windischgarsten		...	...	4 11	7 2	8 2	...	...	12 4	1 25	...	...	3 34	6 15	...	9 40
Klaus		...	...	4 49	7 29	8 38	...	...	12 41	1 50	...	...	4 12	6 40	...	10 18
Kremsmunster		...	...	5 53	8 5	9 40	...	...	1 40	2 24	...	...	5 11	7 13	...	11 6
Rohr (248)		...	...	6 5	8 12	9 59	...	...	1 54	2 35	...	...	5 30	7 19	...	11 16
Traun		...	...	6 43	8 43	10 40	...	...	2 34	...	...	...	6 12	...	...	11 41
Linz arr		...	a.m.	6 58	8 52	10 53	a.m.	p.m.	2 47	3 4	p.m.	p.m.	6 25	7 48	p.m.	11 51
Linz dep		...	6 18	7 55	9 9	—	1132	12 38	—	—	4 21	4 50	—	8 10	9 50	—
St. Georgen		...	...	8 24	...	...	...	1 3	2 & 3	...	4 45	...	...	...	10 15	...
Gaisbach 240 arr		...	...	8 49	RC	...	A	1 30	p.m.	...	5 11	...	...	RC	10 42	...
Gaisbach 240 dep	...	...	...	8 56	...	...	...	2 0	3 25	...	5 30	...	...	...	10 55	...
Prägarten	a.m.	...	6 57	9 8	9 48	...	...	2 13	3 41	...	5 42	5 30	...	...	11 8	...
Freistadt	5 *5	a.m.	7 24	9 47	10 13	...	1238	2 54	4 15	...	6 25	5 54	...	9 14	11 48	...
Summerau	5 22	5 25	...	10 2	...	...	...	3 11	—	...	6 41	...	...	...	12 2	...
Zartlesdorf 239B	—	5 50	7 52	10 26	10 40	...	...	3 36	...	...	7 5	6 27	...	9 41	12 24	...
Weleschin	...	6 32	...	11 16	11 6	...	...	4 16	...	...	7 52	...	...	...	12 57	...
Budweis arr	...	7 25	8 48	11 56	11 33	...	2 0	4 57	...	...	8 33	7 19	...	10 33	1 33	...
WESELI 243 arr	...	9 a46	9a46	1 p7	12p16	...	...	6 p59	...	...	...	8 p4	...	11p15	2 a42	...
PRAGUE 243 arr	...	11a55	1155	5 p18	2 p35	...	...	10p15	...	...	...	10p15	...	1 a22	6 a46	...

A—Runs until 15th Sept.

Bad Hall dep	4 a45	5 a45	7 a55	8 a56	9 a35	11a32	1 p30	2 p18	5 p10	7 p5	8 p30	10§20	11 p0	§—From 1st July.	...
Rohr arr	4 55	5 55	8 5	9 4	9 48	11 42	1 40	2 28	5 20	7 15	8 40	10 30	11 10		...

[For Fares, see page 237B.

BISCHOFSHOFEN, GASTEIN, VILLACH, ST. VEIT, ROSENBACH, and TRIESTE.

For other trains between Bischofshofen and Schwarzach St. Veit see page 238.

Canadian Pacific Railway Observation Car on the 11.22 a.m. train from Salzburg.—See page ii.

MUNICH 200......dep	9 p30	1140	...	...	...	...	...	...	7 a5	...	8 a15	8 a15	9a40	...	11a45	...	...	4p10	...
SALZBURG 239...dep	12a32	2a40	...	...	5 a22	...	...	7 a0	10a35	...	11a22	11a22	1p42	...	3 p55	...	...	7p15	...
	Ex 3	Ex3	2 & 3	1,2,3	1,2,3	Ex 3	1,2,3	Ex3	Ex 3	1,2,3	Ex. 3	1,2.3	1,2,3	1,2,3	1,2,3	1,2,3	Ex 3	1,2,3	Ex 3
	a.m.	a.m.		a.m.	a.m.		a.m.	a.m.	a.m.		p.m.	p.m.	p.m.		p.m.		p.m.	p.m.	
Bischofshofen......dep	1 35	3 46	...	6 0	6 54	...	7 43	8 1	11 42	...	12 26	12 33	3 26	...	5 23	...	7 32	9 5	...
St. Johann in Pongau.....	1 46	SC	...	6 14	7 7	...	7 58	...	...	...	...	12 47	3 40	...	5 36	...	...	9 22	...
Schwarzach St. Veit arr	1 53	4 2	...	6 21	7 14	...	8 5	8 17	11 59	...	12 41	12 54	3 47	...	5 43	...	7 47	9 30	...
Schwarzach St. Veit dep	1 54	4 8	...	6 30	—	...	8 25	—	12 14	...	12 46	1 2	3 54	...	5 52	...	7 55	9 38	...
Dorfgastein.....................	SC	...	...	7 1	...	...	9 1	...	...	...	...	1 33	4 27	...	6 25	...	...	10 9	...
Hofgastein	...	...	...	7 9	...	...	9 12	...	12 48	...	1 22	1 41	4 35	...	6 34	...	8 31	1017	...
Hofgastein Haltestelle ...	2 34	4 47	...	7 17	...	...	9 21	...		...	...	1 50	4 46	...	6 45	...	...	1026	...
Bad Gastein ....arr	2 52	5 2	...	7 37	...	...	9 41	...	1 12	...	1 48	2 11	5 7	...	7 11	...	8 58	1051	...
Böckstein.....................	3 10	5 16	a.m.	7 58	...	...	10 5	...	1 31	...	2 10	2 31	5 30	...	7 34	...	9 16	11 6	...
Mallnitz........................	3 26	5 30	5 40	8 17	...	...	10 22	...	1 47	...	2 26	2 50	5 47	...	7 51	...	9 33	—	...
Obervellach	...	...	5 49	8 27	...	...	10 31	...	RC	...	RC	3 0	6 2	...	8 1	...	...	...	...
Mühldorf-Möllbrücke	...	...	6 18	9 0	...	...	11 1	...		...	...	3 29	6 32	...	8 31	...	10 4	...	...
Spittal .... arr	4 9	6 12	6 37	9 16	a.m.	a.m.	11 18	...	2 35	p.m.	3 8	3 46	6 48	p.m.	8 48	p.m.	10 18	...	p.m.
Spittal .... dep	4 10	6 17	6 47	9 20	11 12	11 48	11 23	...	2 38	2 45	3 12	3 52	6 56	4 48	8 58	9 9	10 20	...	10 46
Paternion Feistritz	...	...	7 11	9 43	11 36	...	11 45	...	--	3 10	...	4 13	7 19	5 13	9 22	9 33	...	...	...
Villach....................arr	4 47	6 50	7 36	1010	12 2	12 20	12 10	...	3 10	3 37	3 48	4 39	7 45	5 40	9 48	9 59	10 55	...	11 18
INNSBRUCK 235......dep	...	...	...	...	...	6 a12	6 a12	...	...	...	...	...	...	7a57	...	...	3 p37	...	
FRANZENSFESTE 236dep	...	...	...	...	...	8 a18	8 a18	...	...	...	8 a28	...	...	1050	...	...	6 p39	...	
	Ex 3	Ex3	1,2,3		1,2,3	Ex 3	1,2,3	1,2,3	Ex 3	1,2,3	Ex 3	1,2,3	1,2,3	1,2,3		1,2,3	1,2,3		
	a.m.	a.m.	a.m.		p.m.	p.m.	p.m.	p.m.	p.m.	p.m.	p.m.	p.m.	p.m.	p.m.		p.m.	p.m.		
Villach ....dep	4 58	7 5	8 8	...	12 25	12 32	12 41	1 48	3 20	2 52	4 0	4 50	8 7	8 13	...	11 0	11 26	...	
Bad Villach....................	...	7 12	8 18	...	12 36	12 39	12 51	2 2	...	3 4	4 8	5 0	8 17	8 24	...	11 9	11 37	...	
Rosenbach ....arr	5 32	7 41	8 52	...	—	1 8	1 28	2 44	3 55	—	4 38	5 39	—	8 58	...	—	12 16	...	
VIENNA ....dep	...	9p15	...	...	...	...	...	...	...	7 a35	...	7 a35	...	...	...	...	11a25	...	
PRAGUE..................dep	...	...	...	...	...	...	...	...	...	2 a57	...	...	...	...	...	...	...	...	
BUDWEIS ....dep	...	...	...	...	...	...	...	...	...	5 a59	...	...	...	...	...	...	6 a44	...	
SELZTHAL................dep	...	2a30	...	...	...	...	2 a38	7a35	...	10a54	...	...	...	...	...	...	2 p28	...	
		Ex3	1,2,3	1,2,3	1,2,3		1,2,3	1,2,3		Ex 3		1,2,3	1,2,3	1,2,3			1,2,3		
		a.m.	a.m.	a.m.	a.m.		a.m.	p.m.		p.m.		p.m.	p.m.	p.m.			p.m.		
St. Veit ....dep	...	6 22	7 1	7 44	9 20	...	11 3	1 28	...	2 45	...	3 0	4 31	6 35	...	...	8 54	...	
Klagenfurt...... arr	...	6 42	7 40	8 18	9 53	...	11 36	2 5	...	3 5	...	3 35	5 5	7 10	...	...	9 28	...	
Klagenfurt...... dep	...	6 55	7 51	—	—	...	11 47	2 12	...	3 13	...	4 20	—	7 32	...	...	11 0	...	
Weizelsdorf..................	...	7 16	8 19	...	...	...	12 18	2 45	...	3 36	...	4 55	...	8 6	...	...	11 32	...	
Rosenbach ....arr	...	7 39	8 55	...	...	...	12 58	3 26	...	3 59	...	5 33	...	8 47	...	...	12 9	...	
Rosenbach ....dep	5 32	7 51	9 5	...	...	1 10	1 43	...	...	4 3	4 39	5 51	...	9 2	...	...	12 35	...	
Assling .... arr	5 48	8 7	9 21	...	...	1 25	2 0	...	...	4 19	4 55	6 8	...	9 19	...	...	12 52	a.m.	
Assling .... dep	5 51	8 12	9 35	...	...	1 28	2 23	...	...	4 23	4 58	6 45	...	—	...	...	1 23	5 5	
Podbrdo 1,2,3	...	RC	10 32	...	...	RC	3 24	...	...	...	...	7 49	...	...	...	...	2 19	6 2	
Görz............. arr a.m.	7 35	10 5	11 52	...	...	3 13	4 44	...	...	6 6	6 45	9 9	...	...	...	...	3 43	7 19	
Görz............. dep 5 40	7 39	10 9	12 7	...	...	3 18	5 0	...	...	6 11	6 51	9 26	...	...	...	...	4 3	8 7	
Prvacina 6 0	...	1023	12 32	...	...		5 19	...	...	...	7 8	9 47	...	...	...	...	4 23	8 28	
Opcina 6 59	8 37	11 6	1 32	...	...	4 16	6 32	...	...	...	7 54	10 48	...	...	...	...	5 31	9 45	
Trieste..................arr 7 23	9 1	1125	2 0	...	...	4 35	7 0	...	...	7 30	8 14	11 16	...	...	...	...	6 5	1010	

Extra. Villach.........dep 5a50 7a25 8a15 4 p6; Bad Villach ...arr 6 1 7 33 8 24 4 14

BUDWEIS, LINZ, and SELZTHAL.

Dist E.M																	
...	PRAGUE ....dep	...	9 p25	2 a57	...	...	6 a50	...	...	...	...	9 a31	1 p35	...	1 p35	4 p20	...
...	WESELI.................dep	...	1 a40	5 a16	...	...	9 a15	...	...	...	...	1 p45	4 p10	...	4 p10	6 p38	...
		1,2,3	1,2,3	Ex 3	1,2,3	Ex 3	Ex 3	1,2,3	1,2,3	Ex 2	2 & 3	1,2,3	Ex 3	1,2,3	1,2,3	Ex 3	Ex 3
			a.m.	a.m.	a.m.		a.m.		a.m.	p.m.		p.m.	p.m.		p.m.	p.m.	
—	**Budweis** ....dep	...	2 57	5 59	6 44	...	9 59	...	10 50	2 3	...	2 58	4 58	...	5 30	7 22	...
16½	Weleschin	...	3 35	...	7 40	...	10 30	...	11 50	...	...	3 52	...	...	6 17	...	...
31	Zartlesdorf	...	4 11	6 58	8 24	...	11 5	...	12 26	A	...	4 33	5 55	...	7 3	...	...
39⅔	Summerau	...	4 34	...	8 47	...	...	...	12 51	...	p.m.	5 3	...	...	7 24	RC	...
45¾	Freistadt in O. Ost.	...	4 51	7 24	9 4	...	11 31	...	1 5	3 21	4 38	5 *24	6 23	...	7 40	8 47	...
58½	Prägarten	...	5 27	...	9 49	...	11 54	...	1 40	...	5 9	—	6 44	...	8 23	...	...
62½	Gaisbach W. 240 ... arr	...	5 37	...	9 59	...	...	...	1 49	...	5 18	...	...	...	8 35	...	...
	Gaisbach W. 240 ... dep	...	5 47	...	10 4	...	...	...	2 10	...	—	...	...	...	8 54	...	...
70½	St. Georgen.....................	...	6 12	...	10 28	...	...	...	2 32	...	...	...	...	...	9 17	...	...
79	Linz 239 .... arr	a.m.	6 40	8 19	10 52	a.m.	12 37	p.m.	2 55	4 16	...		7 23	p.m.	9 42	9 48	p.m.
	Linz 239 .... dep	4 15	7 40	8 32	—	11 20	—	1 15	4 37	—	...		—	7 58	—	—	10 5
84½	Traun	4 27	7 54	RC	...	11 31	...	1 30	4 51	...	...		...	8 12	...	...	10 16
97	Rohr 237C......................	5 1	8 36	9 7	...	11 57	...	2 32	5 31	...	...		...	8 52	...	...	10 39
99½	Kremsmunster	5 9	8 43	9 14	...	12 4	...	2 39	5 38	...	...		...	8 59	...	...	10 48
117½	Klaus 246	5 57	10 8	9 50	...	12 41	...	3 42	6 40	...	...		...	9 51	...	...	11 23
131¾	Windischgarsten	6 39	10 49	10 18	...	1 8	...	4 26	7 29	...	...		...	10 31	...	...	11 51
136	Spital-a-Pyhrn	6 51	10 59	10 27	...	1 19	...	4 36	7 41	...	...	...	...	10 41	...	...	12 1
148	Selzthal ....arr	7 15	11 25	10 49	...	1 41	...	5 0	8 10	...	...	...	...	11 5	...	...	12 24
264¾	ST. VEIT 241......... arr	1 p0	...	2 p35	...	8 p30	...	...	3 a24	...	...	...	...	6 a10	...	...	6 a10

*—Thurs. and Sat. only.

A—Runs until 15th September.

Rohr ....dep	5 a5	6 a10	8 a40	9 a15	10 a5	11a56	1 p52	2 p40	5 p35	7 p25	8p55	10§p42	11p20	...	...	§—From
Bad Hall ....arr	5 15	6 20	8 48	9 25	10 15	12 6	2 2	2 50	5 45	7 35	9 5	10 52	11 30	...	...	1st July.

For Fares, see page 287B.] AUSTRIAN STATE RAILWAY.

SELZTHAL, INNSBRUCK, BUCHS, and BREGENZ.

THROUGH CARRIAGES.—Vienna to Zurich, in 12.35 and 7.50 p.m. from Vienna.

Canadian Pacific Railway Observation Car in 7.20 a.m. from Innsbruck.—See page ii.

	VIENNA 241, 239...dep			...	7 p50	...	9 p15	10p10	...	...	...	10p55	...	8 a0	8 a15	...	9a25	12p35	1235	...	11a35
	AMSTETTEN 241,239 dp			...	10 p8	...	11p45	1 a28	...	...	...	3 a0	6 a0	10 a9	10a31	10a16	1146	2 p51	2p51	...	4 p2
Dist. E.M.				Ex 3	Ex 3	2 & 3	1,2,3	Ex.3	Ex.3	1,2,3	1,2,3	1,2,3	1,2,3	Ex 3	1,2,3	1,2,3	Ex3	Ex 3	Ex3	1,2,3	1,2,3
					a.m.		a.m.					a.m.	a.m.	p.m.		p.m.		p.m.	p.m.	p.m.	p.m.
—	**Selzthal** ...dep			...	12‡49	...	3 20	⋮	...	...	...	7 27	1136	12 56	⋮	2 14	⋮	5 51	5 42	6 27	8 52
11½	**Stainach Irdning** ...			...	1 11	...	3 49	⋮	...	...	...	7 57	1224	1 18	⋮	2 44	⋮	6 12	6 2	6 54	9 27
35½	Schladming ...			...	1 52	...	5 1	⋮	...	...	...	9 4	1 33	2 3	⋮	3 52	⋮	—	6 41	—	10 40
46	Radstadt ...			...	2 14	...	5 35	⋮	...	...	...	9 33	2 0	2 25	⋮	4 24	⋮	...	...	1,2,3	11 9
61	**Bischofshofen** ...arr			...	2 43	...	6 22	⋮	...	...	...	10 16	2 38	2 54	p.m.	5 4	⋮	...	7 27	p.m.	11 47
...	SALZBURG 239 ...dep			...	12a32	...	5 a22	7 a0	...	...	...	9 a0	1250	1 p42	2 15	—	3p55	...	...	7 15	10p10
...	**Bischofshofen** ...dep			...	2 53	...	6 54	8 1	...	...	...	11 22	2 44	3 10	3 58	...	5 10	...	7 32	9 5	12 22
66½	St. Johann in Pongau ...			...	3 4	...	7 7	...	...	...	...	11 40	2 56	...	4 13	...	...	...	...	9 22	12 36
69¾	Schwarzach-St. Veit...			...	3 14	...	7 16	8 21	...	...	...	12 50	3 8	3 38	4 23	...	5 33	...	7 51	9 36	12 56
75¾	Lend ...			...	...	...	7 28	...	...	...	...	1 3	3 23	...	4 35	...	...	...	...	9 48	1 8
80¾	Rauris-Kitzloch ...			...	SC	...	7 41	...	...	...	...	1 14	3 34	...	4 46	...	RC	...	RC	10 1	...
86¼	Bruck-Fusch ...			...	3 48	...	8 3	8 53	...	...	...	1 38	3 55	...	5 8	...	6 6	...	...	10 26	1 35
90	Zell-am-See 237A ...			...	3 56	a.m.	8 12	9 1	...	...	...	1 53	4 6	4 18	5 17	...	6 16	...	8 29	10 41	1 46
98¾	Saalfelden...			...	4 19	4 51	8 36	9 25	...	...	...	2 24	4 25	4 37	5 42	...	6 35	...	8 49	11 0	2 13
103¾	Leogang ...			‡Until 15th Sept.	...	5 6	8 54	...	...	...	...	2 41	—	...	5 55	...	...	...	...		2 30
109¾	Hochfilzen ...				...	5 23	9 12	...	...	...	...	2 59	...	RC	6 16	p.m.	...	...	...	...	2 51
120	St. Johann in Tirol ...				5 6	5 51	9 43	10 9	...	...	...	3 27	...	...	6 47	5 48	...	...	...	...	3 16
126¼	Kitzbühel...				5 19	6 8	10 0	10 21	...	...	...	3 42	...	5 37	7 3	6 6	7 31	...	9 52	...	3 29
131½	Kirchberg ...				...	6 24	10 14	...	...	...	...	3 57	...	...	7 19	6 20	...	...	...	...	3 42
148	**Worgl** ...arr				6 0	7 5	10 52	11 1	...	...	p.m.	4 35	...	...	8 2	6 56	8 14	...	...	p.m.	4 20
...	" ...dep				6 10	7 59		11 6	...	...	1 2	4 45	...	...	—	7 10	8 24	...	...	8 35	4 32
164	Jenbach (237A)...				6 35	8 41	—	11 31	...	...	1 48	5 28	...	6 45	...	7 55	8 50	...	SC	9 17	5 3
179¾	Hall ...				...	9 33	...	...	...	...	2 34	6 14	...	...	...	8 40	9 19	...	...	10 1	5 38
185¼	**Innsbruck** Haupt. arr		1,2,3		7 10	9 45	...	12 5	...	...	2 48	6 25	...	7 20	...	8 54	9 30	...	1130	10 13	5 48
			a.m.	a.m.	a.m.	a.m.	a.m.		p.m.	p.m.	p.m.	p.m.		p.m.				p.m.	p.m.		
...	**Innsbruck** Haupt. dep		5 0	7 5	7 20	11 0	8 0		12 54	1 20	3 55	7 40	...	7 30	...	...	...	10 30	1145	‡—Only admits 3rd class travelling at least 62 miles.	...
186½	Innsbruck W.B. ...		5 10	...	...	11 8	8 13	—	...	1 31	4 4	7 54	...	...	...	...	...	10 39	...		...
194½	Zirl ...		5 36	...	RC	11 35	8 41	...	RC	1 56	4 30	8 25	...	...	...	...	...	11 6	...		...
202	Telfs ...		6 0	...	...	12 2	9 7	...	...	2 22	4 54	8 52	...	...	...	...	...	11 30	...		...
209½	Silz ...		6 23	...	...	12 25	9 33	...	...	2 51	5 17	9 16	...	...	...	...	...	11 50	...		...
213¾	Oetzthal ...		6 36	7 51	8 14	12 39	9 51	...	1 43	3 9	5 35	9 35	...	8 20	...	...	...	12 7	...		...
219¼	Imst ...		6 51	8 2	8 26	12 56	10 8	1,2,3	1 55	3 29	6 0	9 52	...	8 32	...	...	...	12 27	...		...
224¼	Schönwies ...		7 6	...	...	—	10 21	p.m.	...	3 46	6 15	10 5	...	...	...	...	...	12 39	...		...
230¼	**Landeck** ...		7 34	8 26	8 52	...	10 45	1 0	2 21	4 0	6 53	10 38	...	8 56	...	...	...	12 52	1 10		...
235½	Plans ...		7 52	...	...	...	11 1	1 19	...	—	7 9	10 54	...	...	...	...	...	—	...		...
244¼	Flirsch...	1,2,3	8 19	...	...	...	11 25	1 48	...	...	7 32	11 18	...	RC	...	...	...	...	...		...
248	Pettneu ...	a.m.	8 40	...	...	...	11 39	2 2	...	p.m.	7 45	11 31	...	...	...	...	...	...	...		...
253	St. Anton-am-A.	4 48	8 57	9 28	9 45	...	11 55	2 15	3 11	5 12	8 1	11 46	...	9 46	...	...	...	...	2 1		...
262½	Langen...	5 4	9 14	9 45	10 0	...	12 11	—	3 27	5 30	8 17	12 2	...	10 1	...	...	...	...	2 17		...
267½	Dannöfen ...	5 17	9 26	...	...	...	12 23	...	...	5 46	8 30	12 14	...	...	...	...	...	1,2,3	...	...	...
271½	Dalaas ...	5 28	9 37	...	...	...	12 34	p.m.	...	5 59	8 45	12 27	...	...	...	...	...	a.m.	...	a.m.	a.m.
285¼	**Bludenz**...	5 56	1011	10 30	10 41	...	1 18	4 41	4 14	6 45	9 28	1 17	...	10 42	...	...	...	3 50	3 1	6 2	8 18
292	Nenzing ...	—	1028	...	...	1,2,3	1 38	5 2	...	7 6	9 49	1 37	...	...	...	...	1,2,3	4 8	...	6 21	8 37
299	**Feldkirch** ...arr		1045	10 52	11 2	p.m.	1 56	5 24	4 35	7 26	10 6	1 54	...	11 4	...	...	a.m.	4 25	3 26	6 38	8 55
...	**Feldkirch** ...dep		1213	11 0	11 15	4 33	2 22	⋮	5 8	7 55	10 35	⋮	...	⋮	...	...	3 10	⋮	3 43	7 10	9 48
309	Schaan Vaduz...		1241	11 24	11 36	5 4	2 53	⋮	5 27	8 23	11 12	⋮	...	⋮	...	...	3 31	⋮	4 5	7 39	10 16
310½	**Buchs** ¶ 268...arr		1245	11 29	11 40	5 8	2 58	⋮	5 32	8 27	11 20	⋮	...	⋮	Ex 3	...	3 35	⋮	4 10	7 43	10 20
377½	ZURICH 268C arr		4 p47	2 p9	2 p9	8 p22	6 p48	⋮	8 p22	...	⋮	⋮	...	⋮	July and August only.	...	...	⋮	6a56	10a40	...
432½	BASLE 261 ...arr		7p45	4 p12	4 p12	—	10p17	⋮	10p45	...	⋮	⋮	...	⋮		...	...	⋮	9 a3	1 p18	...
759	PARIS 69...arr		...	11p48	11p48	...	...	⋮	7 a28	...	⋮	⋮	...	⋮		...	...	⋮	5p45	...	...
...	**Feldkirch** ...dep		1158	...	11 9	...	2 18	5 29	4 48	7 36	10 27	2 30	...	11 6		...	...	4 34	...	6 41	9 0
309½	Hohenems ...		1231	...	11 28	...	2 54	6 1	...	8 9	10 59	2 57	...	11 23		...	...	5 7	...	7 16	9 33
314½	Dornbirn ...		1246	...	11 38	Ex 3	3 8	6 15	5 12	8 21	11 13	3 9	...	11 32		Ex.3	...	5 22	...	7 30	9 46
319½	Lauterach...		1 3	...	...	p.m.	3 24	6 30	...	8 36	11 30	3 22	...	...	p.m.	a.m.	...	5 41	...	7 47	10 1
321½	**Bregenz** Bahn. arr		1 9	...	11 50	12 5	3 30	6 36	5 25	8 42	11 36	3 28	...	11 45	9 1	2 32	...	5 48	...	7 54	10 7
322½	" Hafen arr		⋮	...	11 55	⋮	3 44	⋮	5 37	...	...	⋮	...	⋮	...	⋮	...	...	...	⋮	10 52
328	LINDAU ...arr		2 9	...	...	12 21	4 2	7 5	5 50	9 6	12 10	4 6	...	12 10	9 17	2 48	...	...	...	8 35	11 19

Extra.—Selzthal to Stainach Irdning, 1.5 p.m.

RC—Restaurant Car. SC—Sleeping Car.

ST. MARGRETHEN and BREGENZ.

‡—Until end of August.

St. Margrethen...dep	2a10	5 a38	7 a0	9 a54	11a42	1p22	2p45	5p18	6p51	6p56	8‡p32	9 p33	11 p5		...
Bregenz ...arr	2 27	5 59	7 22	10 17	12 0	1 44	3 7	5 40	7 8	7 29	8 51	9 55	11 29		...
Bregenz ...dep	3a52	6 a0	7a58	9a‡32	10a18	12p2	2 p0	3p38	5p41	7 p9	8p15	9 p10	11p54	...	...
St. Margrethen...arr	4 9	6 25	8 20	9 53	10 32	1225	2 21	4 1	5 58	7 34	8 31	9 32	12 15	...	...

‡—Until 15th September.

INNSBRUCK and FULPMES.

Innsbruck (Stubai). dep	5a‡0	6 a18	8 a7	9a37	11 a7	12p37	2 p7	3 p37	5 p7	6 p37	8 p7	...	...	...	...	...	...	...
Mutters ...	5 21	6 39	8 28	9 58	11 28	12 58	2 28	3 58	5 28	6 58	8 28	...	...	...	...	...	...	...
Fulpmes ...arr	5 58	7 16	9 5	10 35	12 5	1 35	3 5	4 35	6 5	7 35	9 5	...	...	...	...	...	...	...
Fulpmes ...dep	6 a0	7 a49	9 a19	10a49	12p19	1 p49	3 p19	4 p49	6 p19	7p49	9‡p19	...	...	...	...	...	...	...
Mutters ...	6 38	8 27	9 57	11 27	12 57	2 27	3 57	5 27	6 57	8 27	9 57	...	...	...	...	...	...	...
Innsbruck ...arr	6 58	8 47	10 17	11 47	1 17	2 47	4 17	5 47	7 17	8 47	10 17	...	...	...	...	...	...	...

AUSTRIAN STATE RAILWAY. [For Fares, see page 237B.

BREGENZ, BUCHS, INNSBRUCK, and SELZTHAL.

Canadian Pacific Railway Observation Car on the 2.33 p.m. train from Buchs.—See page ii.

LINDAU ...dep	...	...	...	...	...	3 a32	3 a58	6 a0	...	...	10 a8	10 a0	9 a6	1 p30	12p27	2 p45	5 p17	6 p15	8p40	11p20
	1,2,3	Ex 3	1,2,3	1,2,3	Ex 3	⋮	1,2,3	Ex 3	1,2,3	2&3	Ex.3	1,2,3	1,2,3	Ex.3	1,2,3	1,2,3	⋮	1,2,3	1,2,3	1,2,3
							a.m.	a.m.	a.m.		a.m.		a.m.	p.m.	p.m.	p.m.		p.m.	p.m.	p.m.
Bregenz Hafen ...dep	...	...	...	...	...		...	...	7 51	...			...	1 44	...	3 3		6 32	...	...
„ Bahnhof dep	...	...	...	...	...	3 47	4 26	6 16	8 6	...	10 27	10 15	10 35	1 51	12 55	3 16	5 33	6 41	10 4	11 46
Lauterach	...	...	...	...	...		4 34	...	8 13	...	...	In July and August.	10 42	...	1 4	3 24		6 48	1014	11 53
Dornbirn	...	...	...	...	...	...	4 52	6 31	8 31	...	10 41		10 58	2 6	1 25	3 42	...	7 6	1043	12 6
Hohenems	...	...	...	...	...	...	5 6	6 38	8 44	...	...		11 10	2 15	1 42	3 55	...	7 19	11 4	12 16
Feldkirch ...arr	...	...	...	...	...	...	5 38	6 55	9 14	...	11 5		11 44	2 32	2 17	4 27	Ex.3	7 51	1142	12 40
PARIS 68...dep	...	1 p0	...	...	...	...	...	...	...	...	9 p45			9 p45	...	...	10 p0	...	...	8 a55
BASLE 261...dep	...	9p39	...	...	...	...	...	...	...	...	7 a5			8 a50	...	...	11a30	1 p37	2p26	6 p15
ZURICH 268B...dep	...	11p40	...	...	...	...	...	...	...	7a20	8 a51			11a52	...	...	1 p30	4 p23	5p30	8 p35
Buchs ¶ ...dep	...	2 4	...	...	...	...	5 6	...	...	1010	11 30	...		2 33	...	3 44	4 46	6 50	8 56	11 55
Schaan Vaduz	...	...	...	...	...	...	5 11	...	...	1016	11 36	...		2 39	...	3 49	4 50	6 55	9 5	12 0
Feldkirch ...arr	...	2 24	...	...	...	...	5 37	...	...	1044	11 52	...		2 57	...	4 17	5 7	7 22	9 40	12 24
Feldkirch ...dep	...	2 29	...	...	...	...	5 43	6 58	9 19		11 58	...	12 5	3 10	2 43	4 36	5 10	8 0	1152	12 56
Nenzing	...	...	...	...	...	...	6 3	...	9 41	...	...	...	12 23	...	3 7	5 1	...	8 20	1213	1 16
Bludenz	...	2 56	...	...	...	...	6 28	7 25	9 58	...	12 25	...	12 45	3 42	3 26	5 41	5 34	8 40	1234	1 49
Dalaas	...	...	...	...	...	...	7 8	...		...	...	...	1 32	RC		6 21		9 ‡35		2 34
Dannöfen	...	...	...	...	...	...	7 21	...	...	...	RC	...	1 46	...	...	6 33	...	9 ‡47	...	2 49
Langen	...	3 45	...	...	...	...	7 38	8 14	...	...	1 15	...	2 4	4 41	...	6 48	...	10 ‡2	...	3 4
St. Anton-am-Arlberge	...	4 1	...	...	...	...	7 55	8 31	...	...	1 31	...	2 21	5 0	...	7 5	...	10‡18	...	3 21
Pettneu	...	...	...	...	...	...	8 7	...	...	...	...	...	2 34	...	...	7 18	...		...	3 33
Flirsch	...	...	...	...	...	1,2,3	8 18	...	...	...	...	...	2 50	...	...	7 33	...	...	...	3 46
Pians	...	...	...	...	...	a.m.	8 39	...	...	...	...	...	3 10	...	p.m.	7 51	...	...	...	4 5
Landeck	...	4 43	...	...	...	6 48	9 0	9 22	...	...	2 15	...	3 32	5 42	6 30	8 8	...	...	...	4 27
Schonwies	...	...	...	...	...	7 5	9 14	...	...	p.m.	...	...	3 46	...	6 46	8 21	...	...	...	4 40
Imst	...	...	...	...	...	7 17	9 30	9 40	...	1 8	2 33	...	4 1	6 0	7 2	8 33	...	...	...	5 6
Oetzthal	...	...	...	...	...	7 30	9 43	9 55	...	1 22	2 43	...	4 17	6 12	7 18	8 48	...	...	...	5 22
Silz	...	...	...	...	...	7 46	10 10	...	...	1 36	...	...	4 30	...	7 33	8 57	...	...	...	5 35
Telfs	...	...	...	...	...	8 13	10 35	...	...	2 1	...	...	4 56	...	8 2	9 21	...	...	...	6 1
Zirl	...	...	...	...	...	8 38	11 0	...	...	2 24	...	...	5 20	...	8 28	...	...	...	...	6 24
Innsbruck W.B.	...	...	...	...	...	9 7	11 29	...	...	2 49	...	...	5 47	...	8 56	9 56	...	...	...	6 52
Innsbruck Haupt. arr	...	5 50	...	...	...	9 10	11 32	10 35	...	2 52	3 25	...	5 50	6 55	9 0	10 0	...	...	...	6 55
		a.m.		a.m.	a.m.	a.m.		a.m.	p.m.	p.m.	p.m.	p.m.		p.m.	p.m.	p.m.			a.m.	
Innsbruck Haupt. dep	...	6 10	...	7 12	8 0	9 55	...	10 45	1,10	3 2	3 40	4 50	...	7 10	9 50	10 25	...	...	5 20	...
Hall	...	RC	...	7 26	8 *11	10 6	...	RC	1 26	3 15	...	5 4	...	...	10 6	10 36	...	...	5 35	...
Jenbach	...	...	...	8 14	8 38	10 46	2 & 3	11 21	2 13	3 54	4 15	5 49	...	7 48	10 49	11 9	...	...	6 21	...
Worgl ...arr	a.m.	7 8	a.m.	8 52	9 2	11 24	p.m.	11 45	2 51	4 30	4 39	6 26	...	8 13	11 26	11 39	...	...	6 59	...
„ ...dep	6 15	7 11	7 52		9 9	11 56	3 4	11 49	4 52		4 44	7 8	...	8 19		11 51	...	...		...
Kirchberg	7 2	...	8 41	...	...	12 43	3 57	...	5 50	...	...	8 5	...	...	...	12 38	...	...	...	...
Kitzbühel	7 18	8 3	8 59	...	9 57	12 59	4 13	12 39	6 7	...	5 32	8 22	...	9 13	...	12 52	...	...	...	...
St. Johann in Tirol	7 32	...	9 15	...	...	1 13	4 26	...	6 22	...	5 †43	36	...	9 25	...	1 5	...	...	...	...
Hochfilzen	8 7	...	9 50	...	...	1 45		...	7 0	...	RC	9 14	...	...	...	1 41	...	...	¶—Customs Examination.	...
Leogang	8 20	...	10 3	...	...	1 59	...	...	7 12	...	...	9 27	...	...	...	1 54	...	a.m.		...
Saalfelden	8 39	...	10 20	...	11 8	2 18	...	...	7 27	...	6 38	9 38	...	10 20	...	2 20	...	5 10		...
Zell am See	9 2	9 19	10 42	...	11 26	2 41	...	1 54	7 47	...	6 56		...	10 43	...	2 44	...	5 34		...
Bruck-Fusch	9 10	...	10 51	...	11 33	2 50	...	...	7 57	...	7 3	...	...	10 52	...	2 54	...	5 45		...
Rauris Kitzloch	9 28	...	11 12	...	...	3 9	Ex 3	...	8 18	...	...	...	...	...	Ex 3	3 14	Ex 3	6 4		...
Lend	9 38	...	11 25	a.m.	...	3 22	p.m.	...	8 30	...	...	...	...	...	a.m.	3 29	a.m.	6 16		...
Schwarzach-St. Veit	9 48	10 2	11 47	10 9	12 15	3 48	3 39	2 33	8 43	...	7 45	...	...	11 22	1 34	3 48	4 0	6 37		...
St. Johann in Pongau		...	11 56	10 17	...	3 57	...	...	8 51	...	...	...	...	...	...	3 56	...	6 45		...
Bischofshofen ...arr	...	10 17	12 11	10 27	12 31	4 10	3 54	2 48	9 4	...	8 0	...	...	11 39	1 50	4 10	4 16	6 59		...
SALZBURG 239A ...arr	...	11 55	1 p30	11 55	1 p41	6 p50	4 p58	4 p15	10p45	...	9 p5	...	...	1 a12	2 a58	5 a21	5 a21	8 a50		...
Bischofshofen ...dep	...	10 25		10 47		4 28		3 18	9 22	...		...	...	11 50		4 20		7 10		...
Radstadt	...	...		11 42		5 22	1,2,3	4 3	10 14	...		...	...	12 35	...	5 10		8 2		...
Schladming	a.m.	11 28		12 8		5 49	p.m.	4 23	10 52	...		...	...	12 54	...	5 37		8 29	...	...
Stainach-Irdning	1153	12 9		1 32		7 12	4 38	5 9	11 55	...		...	...	1 39	...	6 45		9 40	...	...
Selzthal ...arr	1216	12 30		1 57		7 38	5 3	5 30	12 20	...		...	...	2 0	...	7 10		10 5	...	...
AMSTETTEN 241...arr	...	3 p12	5 p43	6 p10	5p43	12a30	...	8 p10	...	...	2 a41	...	...	4 a48	...	11a15	10a23	3 p12	...	...
VIENNA 239A...arr	...	5 p25	7 p55	9 p35	7p55	6 a0	...	10p25	...	...	6 a0	...	...	7 a10	...	3 p40	12p55	5 p25	...	...

RC—Restaurant Car. *—Will not take up for Jenbach or Worgl. ‡—On Sun., Wed., and Sat. only.
§—Admits 3rd class only when travelling not less than 62 miles.

BLUDENZ and SCHRUNS.

Bludenz ...dep	6a30	8 a30	10a43	1 p20	3p48	6p50	10p0	**Schruns** ...dep	5a10	7a24	9 a39	11a37	2 p49	4p44	7p58	...
St. Anton in Montafon...	6 54	8 57	11 7	1 44	4 12	7 14	1024	Kaltenbrunnen	5 18	7 35	9 47	11 45	2 57	4 52	8 6	...
Kaltenbrunnen	7 5	9 11	11 18	1 55	4 23	7 25	1035	St. Anton in Montafon...	5 30	7 51	9 59	11 57	3 9	5 4	8 18	...
Schruns ...arr	7 14	9 21	11 27	2 4	4 32	7 34	1044	**Bludenz** ...arr	5 51	8 12	10 20	12 18	3 30	5 25	9 39	...

INNSBRUCK LOCAL LINE.										
Berg Isel ...dep	6 a8	And at 8 min. past the hour until 9.8 p.m.	7 a38	And at 38 min. past hour until 7.38 p.m.	Hall ...dep	6 a4	And at 4 min. past hour until 9.4 p.m.	8a34	And at 34 min. past hour until 7.34 p.m.	...
Wilten	6 13		7 43		Rum	6 18		8 48		...
Maria Theresienstrasse.	6 19		7 49		Dollinger	6 30		9 0		...
Innsteg	6 25		7 55		Innsteg	6 36		9 6		...
Dollinger	6 31		8 1		Maria Theresienstrasse.	6 42		9 12		...
Rum	6 43		8 13		Wilten	6 47		9 17		...
Hall ...arr	6 57		8 27		Berg Isel ...arr	6 53		9 23		...

BERG ISEL and IGLS.—In 26 min. From Berg Isel dep. 7.4, 8.34, 10.4 a.m., 12.4, 2.4, 3.4, 4.4, 5.4, 6.4, 7.4, 8.4, 9.4 p.m.
From Igls 7.32, 9.2, 10.32 a.m., 12.32, 2.32, 3.32, 4.32, 5.32, 6.32, 7.32, 8.32, 9.32 p.m.

For Fares, see page 237B.] **AUSTRIAN STATE RAILWAY.**

VIENNA, LINZ, WELS, ATTNANG, SALZBURG, and BISCHOFSHOFEN.

THROUGH CARRIAGES, 1st and 2nd class. { Vienna to Zurich—in 12.35 p.m. from Vienna. / Vienna to Paris—in 8.15 a.m. and 12.35 p.m. from Vienna.

Canadian Pacific Railway Observation Car on the 9.25 a.m. from Vienna.—See page ii.

E.M.		2&3	2&3	1,2,3	1,2,3	Ex3	1,2,3	1,2,3	Ex3	Ex 3	Ex 3	Ex2	1,2,3	1,2,3	1,2,3	1,2,3	Ex1	Ex 3	2&3
	Vienna						a.m.	a.m.	a.m.	a.m.	a.m.	a.m.	a.m.		a.m.	a.m.	n'on	p.m.	
—	West Bahnhof......dep	...	...	...	...	...	5 30	6 45	7‡25	8 ‡0	8 ‡15	9 25	9 32	...	9 45	1135	12 0	12 35	...
3¾	Hütteldorf-H.	...	...	...	...	...	5 43	6 58	7 36	8 10	8 25	9 36	9 44	...	9 58	1148	...	12 46	...
7½	Purkersdorf	...	...	...	...	...	...	...	RC	...	...	...	...	...	...	1159	O	...	...
15½	Reckawinkl	...	...	...	...	...	6 15	7 32	...	...	...	RC	...	...	...	1238	...	RC	...
24¼	Neulengbach	...	...	...	...	...	6 36	7 55	...	...	...	...	1033	a.m.	1045	1 2	...	...	...
38	S. Pölten (239B)	...	...	...	...	...	7 17	8 31	8 43	...	9 28	1037	11 8	9 35	1122	1 39	...	1 49	...
49	Loosdorf	...	...	...	...	...	7 48		...	...	...	...		10 6	1152	2 36	...	...	...
52¾	Melk	...	a.m.	...	...	...	7 58	...	9 10	RC	RC	11 6	...	1016	12 2	2 46	...	...	...
58½	Pöchlarn (242)	...	3 16	...	...	...	8 12	...	9 21	...	...	...	...	1031	1215	2 59	...	...	...
67	Ybbs-Kemmelbach	...	3 51	...	...	...	8 34	...	9 37	...	...	B	...	1055	1237	3 21	...	...	...
77¾	Amstetten 241 ... arr	...	4 33	...	a.m.	...	9 2	...	9 55	10 4	10 27	1143	...	1123	1 5	3 48	2 1	2 46	...
	Amstetten 241 ... dep	...		...	5 22	...	9 10	...	10 0	10 9	10 31	1146	...	1153	1 20		2 5	2 51	...
90	St. Peter	...	...	...	5 54	...	9 43	...	1024	⋮	...	...	...	1226	1 54	...	...	⋮	...
102½	St. Valentin (240)	...	...	...	6 41	...	1022	...	1045	⋮	...	1227	...	1 13	2 48	...	...	⋮	...
106¼	Enns	...	...	...	6 54	...	1035	...	1053	⋮	...	1235	...	1 26	3 2	...	O	⋮	...
113¾	Kleinmunchen	...	1,2,3	...	7 16	...	1057	...	...	⋮	...	...	...	1 48	3 26	...	...	⋮	...
117½	Linz (248) arr	...	a.m.	...	7 25	a.m.	11 6	...	1111	⋮	11 32	1252	...	1 57	3 35	...	3 7	⋮	p.m.
	Linz (248) dep	...	6 5	...	7 45	8 40	1142	...	1116	⋮	11 37	1 4	...	2 10	3 59	...	3 7	⋮	4 50
133	**Wels**......arr	...	6 46	...	8 29	9 6	1226	...	1142	⋮	⋮	1 30	...	2 54	4 43	...	3 31	⋮	5 40
183¾	PASSAU (239B)......arr	...	...	...	1127	...	3p25	...	1p18	⋮	⋮	...	...	...	8 p0	...	5 pl	Via Selzthal.	...
189	SIMBACH (239B) ...arr	...	...	...	1210	...	4p 8	...	4p 8	⋮	⋮	...	...	...	8p38	...	...	⋮	...
265¼	MUNICH (201) ......arr	...	...	...	5p27	...	7p59	...	7p59	⋮	⋮	...	...	...	...	...	...	⋮	...
...	**Wels**......dep	...	6 47	...	8 42	9 8	1244	...	1148	⋮	⋮	1 31	...	3 6	5 22	...	3 42	⋮	...
141	Lambach (242)......arr	...	7 6	...	9 1	9 23	1 3	...	12 4	⋮	⋮	1 46	...	3 30	5 41	...	...	⋮	...
148	Schwanenstadt	...	7 29	...	9 27	...	1 32	...	1218	⋮	⋮	...	...	3 53	6 12	...	...	⋮	...
151½	**Attnang**......arr	...	7 36	...	9 35	9 43	1 40	...	1225	⋮	12 34	2 6	...	4 1	6 20	...	4 15	⋮	...
179½	ISCHL (240) ...... arr	...	9a25	...	1136	1136	3p37	...	1p57	⋮	1 p57	3p37	...	5p55	8p35	...	...	⋮	...
	ISCHL (240) ...... dep	4 a5	...	a.m.	7a58	7a58	1239	...	1046	⋮	10a46	1239	...	2p47	4p55	...	...	⋮	...
...	**Attnang**......dep	5 29	7 42	8 *6	9 55	9 46	1 54	...	1231	⋮	12 46	2 18	...	4 24	6 52	...	4 16	⋮	...
154	Vöcklabruck (242)	5 44	7 50	8 14	10 4	9 54	2 5	...	1239	⋮	...	2 26	...	4 33	7 3	...	Orient Express.	⋮	...
161½	Redl-Zipf	6 4	8 11		1025	...	2 26	...	...	⋮	...	...	...	4 54	7 25	...		⋮	...
167¼	Frankenmarkt	6 31	8 29	...	1040	...	2 52	...	...	⋮	...	B	...	5 9	7 45	...		⋮	...
179	Steindorf (242)	7 25	9 6	...	1117	...	3 30	...	1 25	⋮	...	...	...	5 47	8 27	...		⋮	...
186½	Seekirchen-Mattsee	7 48	9 28	...	1139	...	3 52	...	1 38	⋮	...	...	...	6 9	8 52	...		⋮	...
195	**Salzburg**......arr	8 14	9 53	Ex3	12 3	11 5	4 17	...	1 52	⋮	2 0	3 33	...	6 33	9 17	...	5 25	⋮	...
290¾	MUNICH (200)......arr	1210	...	C	4 p0	4 p0	7p59	Ex 3	5 p0	⋮	5 p0	6p40	...	10p0	...	...	7p45	⋮	...
861¾	PARIS (65)......arr	...	...	a.m.	8a25	8a25	...	p.m.	8a25	⋮	8 a25		...	...	...	...	8a56	⋮	...
...	**Salzburg**......dep	9 0	...	1035	1250	1122	...	1 42	2 15	⋮	...	3 55	...	...	1010	...	...	⋮	...
206½	Hallein	9 35	...	...	1 25	1142	...	2 5	2 50	⋮	...	4 17	...	...	1041	...	...	⋮	...
228	**Bischofshofen**......arr	1031	...	1137	2 23	1221	...	2 49	3 52	2 54	...	5 0	...	...	1136	...	...	7 27	...
315	INNSBRUCK (238)...arr	6p25	...	...	...	...	...	7 p20	9p30	7 p20	...	9p30	...	...	5a48	...	...	11p30	...
926½	PARIS (69)......arr	...	...	...	...	...	...	...	...	...	...	...	...	...	...	...	...	5 p45	...

RC—Restaurant Car. **SC**—Sleeping Car.

*—In July and August only.

‡—Admits 3rd class travelling not less than 62 miles.

B—Observation Car in this train.

C—Runs from 1st July.

O—Orient Express, and Vienna-Ostend Express; train de Luxe.

AUSTRIAN STATE RAILWAY. [For Fares, see page 237B

VIENNA, LINZ, WELS, ATTNANG, SALZBURG, and BISCHOFSHOFEN.

THROUGH CARRIAGES, 1st and 2nd class. { Vienna to Zurich—in 7.50 p.m. from Vienna. Vienna to Paris—in 7.50 p.m. and 8.40 p.m. from Vienna.

	Ex2	Ex3	1,2,3	1,2,3	1,2,3	Ex3	1,2,3	Ex3	1,2,3	1,2,3	1,2,3	Ex3	Ex3	Ex3	Ex3	2 & 3	1,2,3	1,2,3	1,2,3	
Vienna		p.m.		p.m.	p.m.	p.m.	p.m.			p.m	p.m.	p.m.	p.m.	p.m.	p.m.		p m.	p.m.	p.m.	
West Bahnhof......dep	...	1 ‡0	...	2 45	3 0	3‡45	4 10	...	...	6 15	7 0	7‡50	8 30	8 40	9‡15	...	1010	10 55	1140	...
Hütteldorf-H.	...	1 11	...	2 57	3 13	3 55	4 23	...	...	6 28	7 13	7 59	8 40	8 51	9 25	...	1023	11 9	1153	...
Purkersdorf	...	...	...	3 8	...	...	4 34	...	..	...	...	SC	SC	SC	SC	...	...	...	12 9	...
Reckawinkl	...	...	...	3 34	3 47	...	5 0	...	...	7 4	7 47	...	...	...	...	...	1055	11 42	1236	...
Neulengbach	...	...	...	3 59	4 13	4 37	5 22	...	...	7 29	8 13	...	...	...	...	p.m.	1112	11 58	1 1	...
S. Pölten (239B)	...	2 13	...	4 44	4 54	5 4	5 58	...	...	8 11	8 53	9 3	9 44	9 54	1029	10 45	1146	12 32	1 35	...
Loosdorf	...	...	...	5 14		5 27		...	...	8 41		...	...	...	...	11 9	1214	12 56		...
Melk	...	...	...	5 24	...	5 35	...	...	...	8 52	...	...	...	...	1056	11 20	1224	1 6	...	...
Pöchlarn (242)	...	...	...	5 50	...	5 44	...	...	...	9 6	...	...	...	...	...	11 35	1237	1 19	...	...
Ybbs-Kemmelbach	...	...	...	6 13	...	6 0	...	...	...	9 27	...	...	...	...	1120	11 56	1257	1 38	...	...
Amstetten (241)... arr	...	3 12	...	6 42	...	6 20	...	...	...	9 56	...	10 4	1049	11 0	1140	12 23	1 21	2 2	...	...
Amstetten (241)... dep	...	3 16	...	6 55	...	6 25	...	...	...		...	1010	1053	11 4			1 28	2 8	...	...
St. Peter	...	...	p.m.	7 26	...	6 49	...	...	p.m.	...	...		...	...	To Venice, page 241.	...	1 58	2 36	...	...
St. Valentin (240)	...	3 58	6 10	8 9	...	7 9	...	...	10 4	...	...		1133	...		...	2 27	3 6	...	...
Enns	...	4 6	6 23	8 22	...	7 17	...	...	1017	...	...		...	1150		...	2 37	3 18	...	...
Kleinmunchen	C	...	6 45	8 45	...	...	...	...	1038	...	...		...	...		...	2 54	3 35	...	...
Linz (248) arr	p.m.	4 23	6 54	8 55	...	7 34	...	p.m.	1046	...	...		1155	12 7		...	3 3	3 46	...	...
Linz (248) dep	4 24	4 30	7 2		...	7 46	...	9 58	11 0	...	...		12 0	1213		...	3 12	3 53	...	...
Wels...arr	4 48	4 56	7 43	...	...	8 16	...	1022	1143	...	...		1225	1239		...	3 46	4 24	...	...
PASSAU (239B)......arr	...	8 p0	...	...	...	1119	...	...	...	...	...		1a54	...	...	...	7a19	7 a19	...	...
SIMBACH (239B) ...arr	...	8p38	...	...	...	1135	...	...	...	...	...		...	...	...	...	7a51	7 a51	...	...
MUNICH (201) ......arr	...	...	...	...	...	6a40	...	...	...	...	...		...	...	...	...	2p10	2 p10	...	...
Wels...dep	4 49	4 57	7 48	...	...	8 19	...	1023	...	...	...		...	1241	...	...	3 56	4 28	...	...
Lambach (242)...arr	C	...	8 8	...	...	8 34	...	1039	...	...	...		...	1256	...	...	4 17	4 49	...	...
Schwanenstadt	...	...	8 31	...	...	8 50	...	...	...	...	...		...	...	...	...	4 36	5 7	...	...
Attnang...arr	5 22	5 31	8 39	...	...	8 58	...	11 2	...	...	...		...	1 17	...	...	4 44	5 15	...	...
ISCHL (240) ...... arr	...	8p35	1025	...	...	1025	...	1248	...	...	...		...	4 a4	...	...	7 a8	7 a8	...	...
ISCHL (240) ...... dep	...	3p38	7p 4	p.m.	...	7 p4	...	...	...	...	...		...	1152	...	...	...	...	...	...
Attnang...dep	...	5 41	8 48	9*20	...	9 10	...	11 3	...	...	...	Via Selzthal.	...	1 24	...	...	4 50	...	...	...
Vöcklabruck (242)	...	5 49	8 57	9 28	...	9 18	...	...	...	...	...		...	1 31	...	...	4 59	...	...	...
Redl-Zipf	...	...	9 18		...	9 33	...	...	...	...	...		...	...	...	...	5 17	...	...	...
Frankenmarkt	...	...	9 32	...	...	9 46	...	...	...	...	...		...	...	...	...	5 32	...	...	...
Steindorf (242)	...	...		...	...	...	...	...	...	...	...		...	...	...	Ex 3	6 10	...	...	...
Seekirchen-Mattsee	...	...	...	...	...	1026	...	...	...	...	...		...	...	...	a.m.	6 27	...	...	...
Salzburg...arr	...	6 58	...	...	...	1040	...	1210	...	...	...		...	2 50	...		6 49	...	...	...
MUNICH (200) ......arr	...	10p0	1,2,3	...	...	...	...	...	...	...	...		Ex3	6a30	...		...	...	...	...
PARIS (65)...arr	...	1216	p.m.	...	...	...	...	...	...	...	...		a.m.	9p20	a.m.		...	...	...	...
Salzburg...dep	...	...	7 15	...	...	...	...	1232	...	...	...		2 40	...	5 22	7 0	...	...	...	...
Hallein	...	...	7 53	...	...	...	...	1252	...	...	...		3 2	...	5 56	7 20	...	...	...	...
Bischofshofen...arr	...	...	8 55	...	...	...	...	1 29	...	...	...	2 43	3 40	...	6 49	7 57	...	...	...	...
INNSBRUCK (238)...arr	...	...	...	...	...	...	...	...	...	...	...	7a10	...	...	...	12 p5	...	...	...	...
PARIS (69)...arr	...	...	...	...	...	...	...	...	...	...	...	11p48	...	...	...	7 a28	...	...	...	...

AUSTRIAN STATE RAILWAY. For Fares, see page 233B.

BISCHOFSHOFEN, SALZBURG, ATTNANG, WELS, and VIENNA.

Canadian Pacific Railway Observation Car in the 8.0 a.m. from Innsbruck to Vienna.

PARIS 68......dep	...	...	...	...	...	...	...	...	...		...	...	1 p0	...	...	...	...	...	...
INNSBRUCK dep	...	...	...	...	10p25	10p25	...	...	...	...	...	...	6a10	...	...	...	...		8 a0
	Ex3	1,2,3	1,2,3	1,2,3	Ex 3	1,2,3	1,2,3	1,2,3	1,2,3	Ex2	1,2,3	1,2,3	Ex3	1,2,3	Ex3	Ex1	Ex2		Ex2
	a.m.				a.m.	a.m.						a.m.	a.m.	a.m.					
Bischofshofen dep	1 55	...	...	...	4 21	4 27	...	...	...	Until Sept. 15th.	...	7 12	1025	10 32	...	...	...		...
Hallein	2 35	...	...	...	5 1	5 24	...	...	...		...	8 16		11 26	...	...	...		...
Salzburg ......arr	2 58	...	...	...	5 21	5 58	...	...	...		...	8 50		11 55	...	...	...		...
PARIS 64A...dep	...	...	...	...	...	...	...	...	...		...	...		...	...	7p13	5p15		5p15
MUNICH 200 dep	...	...	...	...	...	...	...	...	...	5 a0	...	7 a5		...	...	1028	9a40		9a40
					a.m.				a.m.	a.m.		a.m.				p.m.	p.m.		p.m.
Salzburg ......dep	...	...	...	...	6 24	...	...	...	7 15	9 10	...	10 27		...	...	1251	1257	...	2 12
Seekirchen-Matt.	...	...	...	...	6 45	...	...	...	7 44	...	...	10 55		...	...	...	...	...	...
Steindorf	...	...	...	a.m.	6 59	...	...	...	8 13	...	...	11 20		...	...	Orient Express	...	...	...
Frankenmarkt ...	...	...	...	4 44	7 23	...	...	...	8 50	...	...	11 56		...	...		RC	...	...
Redl-Zipf	...	...	...	4 58	...	a.m.	...	...	9 6	...	...	12 10		...	...		...	...	...
Vöcklabruck	...	...	...	5 20	7 46	7 *34	...	...	9 29	1020	...	12 31		...	...		2 9	...	
Attnang ....arr	...	...	...	5 27	7 52	7 42	...	...	9 36	1026	...	12 38		...	...	1 57	2 16	...	3 30
ISCHL 240 arr	...	...	...	7 a8	9 a25	...	...	...	11a36	...	...	1p57		...	p.m.	...	3p37	...	5p55
ISCHL 240 dep	...	...	...	4 a5	6 a44	...	...	7a58	7 a58	9a26	...	10a46		...	1239	...	1239	...	2p18
Attnang ......dep	...	...	...	5 35	8 3	...	...	9 45	9 58	1035	...	12 48	Via Selzthal	...	1 50	1 58	2 21	...	3 40
Schwanenstadt ...	...	...	...	5 44	8 10	...	...	9 54	10 8	...	...	12 57		...		...		...	...
Lambach ......arr	...	...	...	6 5	8 23	...	...	1010	10 29	...	...	1 22		...		...		...	3 58
Wels..............arr	...	...	...	6 25	8 35	...	...	1028	10 53	11 3	...	1 40		...		2 23		...	4 10
MUNICH 201 dep	...	...	...	...	...	...	...	...	3 a55	...	...	...		...		...		...	...
SIMBACH 239B dp	...	...	...	3a40	...	...	...	...	8 a18	...	...	...		...		...		...	...
PASSAU 239B dep	...	...	1a57	4 a0	...	...	...	...	8 a17	8a17	...	...		1,2,3		1255		1,2,3	...
			a.m.	a.m.	a.m.	...	a.m.	a.m.	a.m.	a.m.		p.m.		p.m.		p m.		p.m.	p.m
Wels ....dep	...	...	5 0	6 39	8 36	...	...	1029	11 19	11 5	...	1 50		...		2 35		...	4 11
Linz .... arr	...	...	5 40	7 20	8 57	...	...	11 9	12 0	1126	...	2 31		...	2 37	2 56	3 8	...	4 32
Linz .... dep	...	...	5 46		9 3	...	10 0	1139	12 17		...			1 40	2 43	3 0	3 14	3 34	4 43
Kleinmunchen ...	...	...	5 56	...	...	...	1010	1149	12 27	...	...	...		1 51	...	...	...	3 45	...
Enns	...	...	6 18	...	9 24	...	1032	1211	12 49	...	...	...		2 14	...	O	...	4 8	5 1
St. Valentin	...	...	6 37	...	9 33	...	1058	12 9	1 8	...	...	...		2 27	...	...	...	4 29	...
St. Peter	...	...	7 12	...	10 1	...	1129	1 3	1 45	...	...	...			...	...	...	5 7	...
Amstetten arr	a.m.	a.m.	7 42	...	10 23	...	1158	1 31	2 15	...	p.m	...	3 12	...	3 44	3 57	4 14	5 37	5 43
Amstetten dep	5 22	5 30	7 48	...	10 26	...	12 7	1 44	2 28	...	2 35	...	3 17	...	3 48	4 1	4 17	6 22	5 46
Ybbs-Kemmelb'ch	...	5 58	8 15	...	10 43	...	1234	...	...	...	3 5	...	...	...	...	...	...	6 50	...
Pöchlarn	5 50	6 32	8 35	...	10 57	...	1256	...	3 4	...	3 28	...	RC	...	...	...	...	7 14	...
Melk	5 59	6 44	8 47	...	11 8	...	1 8	...	...	...	3 41	...	...	...	...	...	...	7 27	6 23
Loosdorf	...	6 54	8 56	a.m.	11 17	a.m.	1 18	...	...	...	4 4	...	4 17	...	...	...	...	7 39	...
St. Pölten	6 27	7 34	9 28	8 50	11 40	11 54	1 55	3 0	3 50	...	5 25	...	...	...	...	O	5 20	8 50	6 50
Neulengbach	...	8 14	10 3	...	...	12 33	2 34	3†26	4†18	...	6 4	...	...	...	...	...	...	9 40	...
Reckawinkl.........	...	8 37	1025	9 43	...	1 1	3 4	...	...	...	...	...	...	...	...	...	...	10 2	...
Purkersdorf.........	...	...	...	...	...	1 27	...	...	...	...	...	...	...	...	...	...	...	...	...
Hütteldorf-H.......	7†32	9 4	1050	1010	12 47	1 38	3 30	4 10	5 4	...	6 49	...	5†16	...	5‡42	...	6†24	1029	7†46
Vienna West Bhf.	7 40	9 15	11 0	1020	12 55	1 50	3 40	4 20	5 15	...	7 0	...	5 25	...	5 50	6 0	6 32	1040	7 55

For Continuation of trains see next page.

O—Orient and Ostend-Vienna Express, Train de Luxe.

‡—Admits 3rd class travelling not less than 62 miles.
†—Sets down only.

AUSTRIAN STATE RAILWAY. For Fares, see page 233B.

BISCHOFSHOFEN, SALZBURG, ATTNANG, WELS, and VIENNA.

PARIS 68.........dep	...	...	...	...	...	...	...	...	...	...	...	...	9p45	...	...	9 p45	...	9p45	...	...
INNSBRUCK ...dep	...	...	...	8 a0	...	...	...	...	1045	...	...	...	3p40	...	...	7 p10	...	7 p10	...	...
	1,2,3	1,2,3	Ex2	Ex3	1,2,3	Ex.3	Ex3	1,2,3	Ex3	Ex3	1,2,3	1,2,3	Ex3	1,2,3	1,2,3	Ex 3	Ex3	Ex.3		
			p.m.	p.m.	p.m.				p.m.	p.m.	p.m.		p.m.		p.m.	p.m.		nght		
Bischofshofen ...dep	...	...	1222	1234	1246	...	...	...	3 10	3 59	5 13	...	8 3	...	9 11	11‡50	...	12 7	...	...
Hallein	...	...	1 9	1 21	1 50	...	...	...	3 54	4 39	6 14	...	8 44	...	10 9	⋮	...	12 50	...	...
Salzburg ....arr	...	...	1 30	1 41	2 25	...	...	...	4 15	4 58	6 50	...	9 5	SC	1045	⋮	...	1 12	...	...
PARIS 64A.......dep	...	...	C	...	...	...	9 p5	...	...	...	...	...		10p15	...	⋮	...	9a 0	...	...
MUNICH 200...dep	...	9a40	...	...	...	...	1p30	...	...	...	4p10	...		5 p40	...	⋮	...	11p40	...	...
		p.m.				p.m.	p.m.	p.m.		p.m.	p.m.			p.m.		⋮		a.m.		
Salzburg ....dep	...	1 53	...	...	...	3 ‡9	4 20	4 35	...	5 26	7*16	...		9 23	...	Via Selzthal.	...	2 40	...	...
Seekirchen-Matt. ...	...	2 20	...	...	...	3 30	...	5 3	...	...	7 44	...	...	9 49	...	⋮	...	...	...	...
Steindorf	...	2 47	...	...	...	3 44	...	5 26	...	...	8 15	...	...	10 7	...	⋮	...	...	...	...
Frankenmarkt	...	3 24	...	...	...	4 9	...	6 0	...	...	8 56	...	...	10 44	...	⋮	...	...	...	...
Redl-Zipf	...	3 38	...	...	...	4 20	...	6 16	...	...	9 16	p.m.	...	10 58	...	⋮	...	...	...	...
Vöcklabruck	...	4 0	...	...	...	4 33	...	6 46	...	6 38	9 38	8 *39	...	11 16	...	⋮	...	3 52	...	...
Attnang............arr	...	4 7	...	...	...	4 39	5 38	6 53	...	6 44	9 45	8 47	...	11 23	...	⋮	...	3 58	...	...
ISCHL 240 ... arr	...	5p55	...	...	...	...	...	8p35	...	8p35	...	...	...	12a48	...	⋮	...	6a55	...	...
ISCHL 240 ... dep	...	2p47	...	...	...	3 p38	3,38	4p55	...	4p55	...	...	...	9 p40	...	⋮	...	...	...	...
Attnang ....dep	...	4 17	...	...	...	4 51	5 39	7 10	...	6 46	...	...	...	11 31	...	⋮	...	4 0	...	...
Schwanenstadt	...	4 28	...	...	...	4 59	...	7 19	...	...	...	...	...	11 40	...	⋮	...	...	...	...
Lambach ....arr	...	4 47	...	...	...	5 11	...	7 39	...	7 3	...	...	...	11 57	...	⋮	...	...	...	...
Wels.................arr	...	5 7	...	...	...	5 24	6 7	8 3	...	7 15	...	...	...	12 16	...	⋮	...	4 29	...	...
MUNICH 201 ...dep	...	8a15	...	...	...	8 a15	...	1153	...	...	...	...	...	3 p21	...	⋮	...	...	...	...
SIMBACH 239B dep	...	1p34	...	...	...	1 p34	...	4p26	...	...	...	...	...	7 p31	...	⋮	...	...	...	...
PASSAU 239B dep	...	2 p8	...	..	...	2 p8	4p40	5 p2	...	...	...	...	...	8 p2	...	⋮	1a57	1 a57	...	...
		p.m.				p.m.	p.m.	p.m.	...	p.m.				a.m.		⋮	a.m.	a.m.		...
Wels ....dep	...	5 13	...	...	...	5 26	6 16	8 21	...	7 16	...	...	...	12 20	...	⋮	3 24	4 30	...	...
Linz .... arr	...	6 0	...	...	...	5 47	6 36	9 1	...	7 37	...	...	...	12 53	...	⋮	3 45	4 51	.	...
Linz .... dep	...	6 12	...	...	...	5 53	6 40	9 16	...		...	...	...	1 1	...	⋮	3 52	4 56	...	...
Kleinmunchen	...	6 22	...	...	...	RC	RC	9 27	...	...	...	...	...	1 11	...	⋮	SC	...	...	...
Enns	...	6 44	...	...	...	6 12	...	9 49	...	...	...	...	...	1 28	...	⋮	...	...	...	...
St. Valentin	...	7 17	...	...	...	6 22	7 2	1011	...	...	...	...	...	1 42	...	⋮	4 10	...	...	...
St. Peter	...	7 55	...	...	...	6 50	...	1048	...	...	...	Ex 3	...	2 14	...	⋮	...	...	...	...
Amstetten ... arr	p.m.	8 25	...	...	...	7 10	7 38	1117	...	...	...	p.m.	...	2 41	...	4 48	4 59	5 55	...	...
Amstetten ... dep	4 54		...	...	...	7 13	7 42		...	...	...	8 15	...	2 55	...	4 58	5 2	5 59	...	...
Ybbs-Kemmelbach	5 23	...	...	...	...	7 31	...	...	...	...	...	...	...	3 18	...	...	...	...	...	...
Pöchlarn	5 44	...	...	...	...	7 45	...	...	...	...	...	...	...	3 37	...	...	...	...	...	...
Melk	5 57	...	...	...	...	7 57	...	...	...	...	...	...	...	3 49	...	...	...	...	...	...
Loosdorf	6 7	p.m.	...	...	...	...	...	...	...	...	...	...	...	3 58	a.m.	...	...	...	...	...
St. Pölten..............	6 58	8 3	...	...	...	8 24	8 42	...	...	...	...	9 14	...	4 26	5 23	5 55	6 4	6 59	...	...
Neulengbach	7 35	8†29	...	...	...	...	...	...	...	...	...	...	...	5 0	6 0	...	...	...	...	...
Reckawinkl	8 3	...	...	...	...	...	...	...	...	...	...	...	...	5 22	6 28	...	...	...	...	...
Purkersdorf............	...	...	...	...	...	...	...	...	...	...	...	...	...	...	...	...	...	...	...	...
Hütteldorf-H	8 30	9 14	...	...	...	9 †26	9†41	...	...	...	...	10†15	...	5 49	6 53	7 †1	7†11	8 †1	...	...
Vienna Westbahnf	8 40	9 25	...	...	...	9 35	9 50	...	...	...	...	10 25	...	6 0	7 5	7 10	7 20	8 10	...	...

C—Runs until 15th September. RC—Restaurant Car. *—2 & 3 class only.

AUSTRIAN STATE RAILWAY. [Luggage, h.0·4 per 22 lbs. per kilometer.

†—Arrives at Stadt Iglau.]

IGLAU and RAZICE.

Iglau ....dep		...	...	2a58	8a55	1 p5	3p40	7p 5
Wolframs-Cejl		...	...	3 26	9 27	1 29	4 16	7 36
Ober-Cerekwe........arr		...	...	3 52	9 53	1 51	4 42	8 3
„ „ 239B......dep		...	...	5 4	10 1	2 4	4 44	—
Pilgram		...	...	5 40	1038	2 43	5 25	...
Wobratain 239B		...	...	6 28	1128	3 33	6 17	...
Tabor 243 ....arr	a.m.	...	a.m.	7 10	1212	4 21	7 0	...
„ ....dep	4 50	a.m.	1025	—	1257	—	8 41	p.m.
Pisek	6 37	1020	12 6	...	2 43	4p50	1032	9 11
Razice 243A ....arr	6 48	1034	1 15	...	2 54	5 5	1045	9 21

Razice ....dep		...	5 a0	7a15	7a55	...	1p35	3p23	5p30	9p40
Pisek		...	5 16	7 30	8 12	...	1 47	3 38	5 46	9 56
Tabor ....arr		a.m.	7 11	—	10 0	...	3 27	—	7 37	—
„ ....dep		6 5	—	...	1024	...	3 37	...	8 40	...
Wobratain		6 52	...	...	11 7	...	4 22	...	9 27	...
Pilgram		7 51	...	...	1158	...	5 16	...	1023	...
Ober-Cerekwe arr	a.m.	8 25	...	...	1228	p.m.	5 37	...	1045	...
„ „ dep	5 5	8 45	...	...	1230	3 48	5 49	...	11 5	...
Wolframs-Cejl	5 30	9 25	...	...	1253	4 19	6 13	...	1131	...
Iglau 224 ....arr	6 2	9 56	...	...	1 17	4 47	6 40	...	12 0	...

WESELI and OBER-CEREKWE.

Weseli-Mezimosti ......dep	3 a15	6 a40	11a10	1p51	4p12	8 p50
Neuhaus........	3 59	7 33	12 16	2 35	4 54	9 45
Ober-Cerekwe 239B.......arr	4 59	8 36	...	3 42	...	10 52

Ober-Cerekwe ....dep	4 a2	...	10 a5	1 p58	...	8p10	...	...
Neuhaus........	5 25	7 a55	11 22	3 8	6p18	9 38	...	...
Weseli 243........arr	6 7	8 56	12 8	3 51	7 14	1045	...	...

WELS and PASSAU—NEUMARKT and SIMBACH. [O—Ostend-Vienna Express.

	1,2,3 a.m.	1,2,3 a.m.	Ex 3 a.m.	1,2,3 p.m.	Ex 1 p.m.	1,2,3 p.m.	2&3	1,2,3 p.m.	Ex2 n'ht
Wels 239 ....dep	4 33	8 50	11 52	12 47	3 43	5 30	...	8 32	1228
Grieskirchen	5 16	9 29	12 13	1 26	O	6 14	...	9 12	1249
Neumarkt ......arr	5 36	9 47	12 25	1 44	...	6 28	...	9 30	1 1
„ ......dep	5 56	10 4	12 26	2 0	...	6 39	...	9 55	1 2
Riedau	6 16	10 25	12 38	2 21	...	7 0	...	10 16	...
Schärding 240	6 59	11 6	1 2	3 5	...	7 41	...	11 0	1 38
Passau ¶ 195A...arr	7 19	11 27	1 18	3 25	5 1	8 0	...	11 19	1 54
Neumarkt ...dep	5 50	10 14	—	2 13	—	6 44	...	9 50	—
Ried 240........arr	6 27	10 51	2 & 3	2 50	2 & 3	7 21	...	10 27	...
„ ....dep	6 43	11 5	p.m.	2 59	p.m.	7 32	p.m	10 30	...
Braunau-am-I. ...	7 47	12 6	12 48	4 4	4 21	8 34	9 56	11 31	...
Simbach 201...arr	7 51	12 10	12 10	4 8	4 25	8 38	10 0	11 35	...

¶—Customs Exam.	Ex 3	1,2,3 a.m.	1,2,3 a.m.	Ex 1 p.m.	1,2,3 p.m.	Ex 3	1,2,3 p.m.	1,2,3 p.m.
Simbach dep	...	3 40	8 18	...	1 34	...	4 26	7 31
Braunau-am-I	...	3 45	8 24	...	1 41	...	4 34	7 38
Ried.........arr	...	4 45	9 26	...	2 43	...	5 37	8 48
„ ....dep	...	4 46	9 28	...	3 0	...	5 46	8 59
Neumarkt arr	a.m.	5 18	10 2	...	3 32	p.m.	6 20	9 37
Passau ¶ ... dep	1 57	4 0	8 17	12 55	2 8	4 40	5 2	8 2
Schärding	2 14	4 22	8 43	...	2 31	4 58	5 24	8 33
Riedau	...	5 2	9 25	...	3 12	5 24	6 4	9 16
Neumarkt ...arr	2 51	5 21	9 45	O	3 31	5 36	6 23	9 36
„ ...dep	2 52	5 40	10 12	...	3 44	5 38	6 38	9 58
Grieskirchen ...	3 3	5 57	10 29	...	4 3	5 49	6 54	10 20
Wels 239......arr	3 22	6 30	11 2	2 17	4 36	6 8	7 27	10 59

Extra					
Simbach dep	4a35	9a45	1p10	5p46	
Braunau arr	4 39	9 49	1 14	5 51	
Braunau dep	8a26				
Simbach arr	8 30				
Schärding...dep	7a54	12p15	...		
Passau ......arr	8 15	12 36	...		
Passau ......dep	1p19	5p35	...		
Schärding arr	1 40	5 57	...		

NEUMARKT and WAIZENKIRCHEN.

Neumarkt...........dep	5 a50	10a10	1p56	3p45	6p33
Niederspaching ...arr	6 14	10 34	2 20	4 9	6 52
Peuerbach ....arr	6 30	10 55	2 34	4 23	7 2
Waizenkirchen ...arr	6 27	10 47	2 30	4 19	7 0

Waizenkirchen ......dep	5 a0	9a15	12 p5	2p50	5p17
Peuerbach ....dep	5 0	9 17	12 7	2 52	5 18
Niederspaching........	5 10	9 31	12 21	3 3	5 36
Neumarkt 239B ......arr	5 33	10 0	12 50	3 32	6 5

LEOBERSDORF and ST. POLTEN.

Dist E.M				a.m.	a.m.		p.m.	p.m.	p.m.	p.m.			
	Leobersdorf ...dep	...	...	8 0	10 9	...	1 37	4 54	7 31	9 57	...	...	...
1¾	Wittmannsdorf	...	...	8 11	10 15	...	1 45	5 1	7 38	10 6	...	...	...
9¾	Pottenstein	a.m.	a.m.	8 46	10 43	p.m.	2 15	5 31	8 5	10 32	...	...	...
27¼	Hainfeld	5 42	7 35	1010	11 50	1225	3 34	6 50	9 15	11 42	...	...	...
32¼	St. Veit a-d-Gölsen ...	5 57	7 50	1025	—	1240	3 50	7 5	—	—	...	...	...
35¾	Scheibmuhl 242	6 15	8 3	1040	...	1255	4 1	7 20	...	...	...	...	...
47½	**St. Polten** ....arr	6 54	8 36	1114	...	1 32	4 38	7 55	...	...	...	...	...

St. Polten ....dep	...	7a29	8 a55	9 a55	12p10	...	5 p10	9p18	...	...	...	...
Scheibmuhl	...	8 7	9 31	10 37	1 0	...	5 50	9 58	...	...	...	...
St. Veit a-d-Gölsen ...	...	8 18	9 41	10 48	1 12	p.m.	6 4	10 9	...	...	...	...
Hainfeld	5a10	8 49	9 57	11 10	1 53	4§20	6 45	1024	...	...	...	...
Pottenstein	6 18	9 58	—	12 22	3 4	5 32	8 4	—	...	...	...	...
Wittmannsdorf	6 51	1030	...	12 56	3 34	6 8	8 37	...	...	...	...	...
Leobersdorf......arr	6 55	1035	...	1 1	3 39	6 13	8 42	...	...	...	...	...

§—Depart 5.32 p.m. on Sunday.

ARNOLDSTEIN and HERMAGOR.

E.M				
	Arnoldstein......dep	7a56	1 p8	8p55
19¼	Hermagor........arr	9 15	2 39	1015
	Hermagor ....dep	5a15	9a32	6p32
	Arnoldstein 241 arr	6 30	1051	8 0

NEUHAUS and WOBRATAIN.

Neuhaus ....dep	...	7 a38	3 p15	10p0	
Kamenitz........	5a50	9 3	4 30	11 5	
Wobratain 239B arr	6 19	10 44	6 7	...	
Wobratain dep ...		7 a20	11a35	6 p35	...
Kamenitz........	5a50	9 20	1 15	8 18	...
Neuhaus......arr	6 53	10 25	2 18	9 21	...

WITTMANSDORF & GUTENSTEIN.

Wittmannsdorf ...dep	8a16	1 p48	5p10	7p51	...	...	...	...
Steinabrückl	8 34	2 4	5 28	8 8	...	...	...	...
Wöllersdorf	8 42	2 12	5 38	8 17	...	...	...	...
Gutenstein...........arr	9 50	3 20	6 42	9 23	...	...	...	...

Gutenstein ....dep	5a22	8a57	2 p5	6p55	...	...	...
Wöllersdorf	6 23	10 2	3 9	7 57	...	...	...
Steinabrückl	6 32	10 8	3 16	8 7	...	...	...
Wittmannsdorf ......arr	6 47	10 23	3 31	8 22	...	...	...

BUDWEIS & SCHWARZES-KREUZ.

E.M.								
	Budweis ....dep	6a29	1 p22	5 p12	8 p7	...	...	...
12½	Adolfsthal	7 0	2 10	6 1	9 10	...	...	...
19½	Krumau	7 29	2 40	6 30	9 46	...	...	...
22½	Gojau	7 43	2 55	6 43	9 58	...	...	...
28½	Höritz	8 4	3 18	7 5	—	...	...	...
38½	Schwarzbach Stuben......	8 51	4 7	7 55	...	...	...	...
42½	Oberplan........	9 7	4 23	8 11	...	...	...	...
46½	Salnau........	9 32	4 54	8 40	...	...	...	...
57½	Schwarzes-Kreuz 242 arr	10 1	5 38	9 24	...	...	...	...

Schwarzes-Kreuz ...	...	6 a7	11a25	6p35	...	...	...
Salnau	4a30	6 48	12 15	7 21	...	...	...
Oberplan........	4 47	7 5	12 32	7 38	...	...	...
Schwarzbach Stuben	5 3	7 21	12 50	7 54	...	...	...
Höritz	5 40	8 3	1 31	8 34	...	...	...
Gojau	6 9	8 27	1 55	8 58	...	...	...
Krumau	6 21	8 40	2 11	9 12	...	...	...
Adolfsthal	6 45	9 4	2 41	9 40	...	...	...
Budweis (239B) ...arr	7 34	9 49	3 28	1024	...	...	...

LIPPNERSCHWEBE and ZARTLESDORF.

E M									
	Lippnerschwebe dep	...	5a38	8a40	10a55	2 p5	5p28	8p45	...
6¾	Hohenfurth Stift	5 a0	6 13	9 27	11 38	2 44	6 12	9 19	...
14	Zartlesdorf 237C arr	5 44	6 48	1012	12 16	3 25	6 53	...	...

Zartlesdorf.........dep	...	6 a0	8a32	11a12	12p32	3p44	7p15	...
Hohenfurth Stift......	4a55	6 45	9 22	11 49	1 17	4 24	7 54	...
Lippnerschwebe arr	5 29	7 25	9 58	...	1 50	5 5	8 33	...

For Fares, see page 233B.] **AUSTRIAN STATE RAILWAY.** [Luggage, h.0·4 per 22 lbs. per kilometer.

A—Runs until 15th Sept.] **SCHARDING, ISCHL, and STAINACH-IRDNING.** ‡—In July and August only.

	1,2,3	1,2,3	1,2,3	1,2,3	Ex 3	1,2,3	Ex 2	1,2,3	1,2,3	1,2,3	1,2,3	1,2,3	Ex 3	1,2,3
PASSAU (239B) ...dep	...	...	4 a0	...	...	8a17	...	1p19	...	...	...	5p35	...	...
			a.m.			a.m.		p.m.				p.m		
Schärding ....dep	...	...	5 20	...	...	9 46	...	1 48	...	...	...	6 14	...	...
St. Martin	...	...	5 59	...	...	1025	...	2 24	...	...	...	6 55	...	...
Ried (239B) ....arr	...	...	6 24	...	...	1050	...	2 45	...	...	...	7 19	...	...
" ....dep	...	...	6 31	...	...	11 1	...	2 58	...	...	...	7 27	...	...
Holzleithen (240)	...	...	7 5	...	...	1136	...	3 33	...	...	...	8 3	...	...
Attnang ....arr	...	...	7 30	...	...	12 4	...	4 2	...	...	...	8 29	...	...
VIENNA (239)......dep	8p40	10p55	—	...	8 a15	—	9a25	—	...	1 p0	...	—	3p45	...
LINZ (239) ....dep	1213	3 a53	6 a5	8a40	11a37	1142	1 p4	...	2p10	4p30	...	...	7p46	9p58
SALZBURG (239A) dep	...	2 a40	6a24	7a15	10 27	...	1257	...	2p12	4p20	5p26	...	..	9p23
	a.m.	a.m.	a.m.	a.m.	p.m.	p.m.	p.m.		p.m	p.m.	p.m.		p.m.	p.m.
Attnang ....dep	2 45	5 37	8 0	10 3	12 51	2 3	2 26	...	4 19	5 48	7 4	...	9 15	1130
Gmunden (242)............	3 8	6 8	8 29	1039	1 11	2 33	2 48	...	4 56	6 8	7 31	...	9 37	1158
Ebenzweier	3 16	6 16	8 37	1047	1 20	2 41	2 58	...	5 4	6 15	7 42	...	9 44	12 6
Traunkirchen	3 23	6 23	8 44	1054	1 27	2 50	3 5	...	5 11	6 22	7 52	...	9 51	1212
Traunkirchen See	3 28	6 28	8 49	1059	1 32	2 55	3 10	...	5 16	6 27	7 57	...	9 56	1216
Ebensee Landungsplatz	3 35	6 35	8 55	11 5	1 38	3 1	3 16	...	5 22	6 33	8 3	...	10 2	1221
Ebensee	3 39	6 39	8 59	1111	1 41	3 23	...	...	5 28	...	8 9	...	10 7	1225
Langwies	3 50	6 54	9 12	1123	...	3 36	...	...	5 41	...	8 21	...	...	1236
Mitterweissenbach	3 57	7 1	9 19	1130	...	3 45	...	...	5 48	...	8 28	...	...	1242
Ischl (248A)............arr	4 4	7 8	9 25	1136	1 57	3 52	3 37	...	5 55	6 55	8 35	...	1025	1248
" ....dep	4 12	7 23	9 34	1155	2 11	4 9	3 46	...	6 7	7 9	8 47	...	1037	—
Anzenau............	4 26	7 36	9 48	12 8	2 25	4 23	3 57	...	6 21	7 18	9 1	...	104[illegible]	...
Goisern	4 31	7 41	9 53	1215	2 30	4 28	4 2	...	6 26	7 23	9 9	...	1052	...
Steeg	4 38	7 48	10 1	1222	2 37	4 35	4 8	...	6 33	7 30	9 16	...	11 1	...
Hallstatt............	4 51	7 59	1013	1235	2 50	4 48	4 18	...	6 48	7 40	9 29	p.m.	...	...
Obertraun	4 56	8 4	1018	1240	2 57	4 53	4 3	p.m.	6 54	7 45	9 34	A	1116	...
Aussee	5 34	8 35	1040	1 2	3 36	5 43	4 45	7‡37	7 17	8 6	9 56	1055	1138	...
Mitterndorf-Zauchen...	6 13	9 11	1245	—	4 13	6 22	—	8 19	—	—	—	1128	124	...
Stainach-Irdning arr	6 37	9 33	1 9	...	4 36	6 52	...	8 44	...	...	...	1150	1 4	...
SELZTHAL (238A) arr	7a10	10 a5	1p57	...	5 p3	7p38	...		...	...	...	...	2 a0	...

	1,2,3	Ex 3	1,2,3	1,2,3	1,2,3	Ex 3	1 & 2	1,2,3	Ex 3	1,2,3	1,2,3	1,2,3	1,2,3
SELZTHAL (238) dep	...	...	...	...	7a27	...	...	1136	...	...	2p14	6p27	8p52
					a.m.			p.m.	p.m.		p.m.	p.m.	p.m.
Stainach-Irdning	dep	...	...	A	8 0	...	...	1210	1 31	...	3 0	7 4	9 21
Mitterndorf-Zauch.	...	a.m.	a.m.	a.m.	8 37	a.m.		1245	2 13	p.m	3 39	7 41	9 55
Aussee	...	5 45	6 45	8 30	9 25	114	...	1 16	2 42	3 30	5 30	8 26	1019
Obertraun	...	6 2	7 4	8 45	9 42	1155	...	1 32	2 56	3 47	5 47	8 46	1044
Hallstatt	...	6 6	7 10	8 49	9 48	12 0	...	1 37	3 1	3 53	5 53	8 51	1050
Steeg	...	6 16	7 23	8 58	10 1	12 9	...	1 49	3 10	4 9	6 8	9 3	11 2
Goisern	...	6 22	7 29	9 4	10 7	1215	...	1 55	3 16	4 15	6 14	9 9	11 9
Anzenau............	...	6 27	7 36	9 9	1012	1220	...	2 0	3 21	4 23	6 21	9 14	1115
Ischl ....arr	a.m.	6 35	7 48	9 17	1025	1228	p.m.	2 10	3 29	4 35	6 35	9 29	1129
" ....dep	4 5	6 44	7 58	9 26	1046	1239	2 18	2 47	3 38	4 55	7 4	9 40	1152
Mitterweissenbach	4 12	...	8 5	...	1053	...	...	2 54	...	5 3	7 12	9 47	12 0
Langwies	4 18	...	8 12	...	1059	..	...	3 0	...	5 10	7 19	9 54	12 7
Ebensee	4 30	...	8 25	...	1111	1257	2 28	3 19	...	5 23	7 37	10 7	1225
Ebensee Landung.	4 34	7 5	8 29	9 45	1115	1 0	2 38	3 22	3 58	5 32	7 41	1011	1229
Traunkirchen See	4 41	7 13	8 37	9 52	1123	1 8	2 46	3 30	4 5	5 41	7 48	1019	1237
Traunkirchen	4 45	7 17	8 44	9 56	1127	1 12	2 50	3 34	4 9	5 45	7 52	1021	1241
Ebenzweier	4 54	7 26	8 53	10 3	1136	1 20	2 58	3 42	4 16	5 54	8 0	1033	1250
Gmunden	5 2	7 36	9 4	1011	1149	1 29	3 8	3 51	4 26	6 13	8 10	1044	1258
Attnang ....arr	5 22	7 52	9 26	1027	1213	1 45	3 24	4 13	4 41	6 34	8 33	11 7	1 15
SALZBURG 239 arr	8a14	...	11a5	...	1p52	3p33	..	6p33	6p58	9p17	1010	2a50	2a50
LINZ (239A)...arr	7a20	8a57	12 0	1126	2p31	2p37	4p32	5p47	5p47	7p37	—	1253	4a51
VIENNA (239A) arr	...	1255	5p15	5p15	5p50	5p50	7p55	9p35	9p35	..	...	6 a0	8a10
Attnang ....dep	5 30	—	10 0	...	...	—	...	4 44	—	7 27	...	—	—
Holzleithen	6 4	...	1034	...	...	...	...	5 15	...	8 4	...	...	...
Ried ....arr	6 29	...	11 0	...	...	...	...	5 40	...	8 33	...	...	...
" ....dep	6 50	...	11 8	...	...	...	...	5 45	...	8 53	...	...	...
St. Martin............	7 12	...	1130	...	...	...	...	6 5	...	9 18	...	...	...
Schärding ......arr	7 50	...	12 5	...	...	...	...	6 41	...	9 53	...	...	...
PASSAU (239B) arr	8a15	...	1236	...	...	...	...	8 p0	...	1119	...	...	...

Extra, until 15th September { Stainach...dep. 6p13. / Aussee......arr. 7 1.

KLEIN REIFLING and GAISBACH-WARTBERG.

E.M. Dist.		2 & 3	1,2,3	1,2,3	1,2,3	1,2,3	2 & 3	2 & 3	1,2,3	1,2,3	1,2,3	2 & 3	1,2,3	1,2,3
			a.m.	a.m.		a.m.					p.m.		p.m.	p.m.
—	**Klein Reifling** dep	...	4 41	7 21	...	1017	...	...	...	...	3 40	...	4 50	8 0
7½	Gr. Raming	...	5 1	7 41	...	1037	...	...	...	...	3 59	...	5 16	8 18
15½	Losenstein	...	5 21	8 4	...	11 4	...	...	...	...	4 21	...	5 44	8 38
27¼	Garsten (246).........	...	5 52	8 38	a.m.	1138	...	...	p.m.	...	5 2	...	6 28	9 10
29¼	Steyr.........	...	5 59	8 49	10 0	1151	...	...	3 15	...	5 13	...	7 2	9 24
37¼	Ernsthofen	...	6 22	9 14	1024	1214	...	...	3 35	...	5 39	...	7 27	9 47
41¾	**St. Valentin** ...arr	a.m.	6 32	9 25	1033	1224	p.m.	p.m.	3 45	p.m.	5 50	p.m.	7 37	9 57
...	" ...dep	6 50	7 55	—	—	1 10	1 24	2 43	—	4 35	—	7 12	—	10 6
46⅓	Mauthausen	7 4	8 8	...	...	1 24	1 38	2 54	...	4 46	...	7 24	...	1017
54	Gaisbach W. 239B	...	8 37	...	...	1 52	...	3 22	...	5 16	...	...	...	1045

	2 & 3	1,2,3	1,2,3	1,2,3	2 & 3	1,2,3	1,2,3	1,2,3	2 & 3	2 & 3	1,2,3	1,2,3	1,2,3
	a.m.	a.m.		a.m.	p.m.		p.m.		p.m.	p.m.		p.m	
Gaisbach W. ...dep	...	5 49	...	10 5	..	...	1 54	...	5 22	...	...	8 59	...
Mauthausen	5 58	6 11	...	1028	12 9	...	2 16	...	5 41	5 50	...	9 22	...
St. Valentin ...arr	6 12	6 23	a.m.	1041	12 23	p.m.	2 27	p.m.	5 53	6 4	p.m	9 35	p.m.
" (239) dep	—	6 35	9 40	1058	—	1 24	2 42	4 32	—	—	7 17	10 8	11 37
Ernsthofen.........	...	6 45	9 50	11 8	1,2,3	1 35	2 53	4 43	...	...	7 27	1018	11 47
Steyr.........	...	7 8	1019	1132	12p31	1 56	3 21	5 4	...	...	7 53	1042	12 7
Garsten	...	7 13	1024	1136	12 37	—	3 27	—	...	...	8 1	1046	—
Losenstein	...	7 43	11 0	—	1 10	...	4 2	...	...	...	8 38	—	...
Gr. Raming	...	8 3	1120	...	1 28	...	4 21	...	...	...	8 57	...	...
Klein Reifling arr	...	8 20	1138	...	1 44	...	4 39	...	...	...	9 14	...	...

EBENFURTH and WITTMANNSDORF.

Ebenfurth ....dep	7a26	11 a9	4p17	8p47	...	...	...	...	...	...	...
Sollenau.........	7 50	11 28	4 50	9 23	...	...	...	...	...	...	...
Wittmannsdorf ....arr	7 57	...	4 57	9 30	...	...	...	...	...	...	...

Wittmannsdorf ......dep	7 a18	...	a.m.	3p40	p.m.	8 p39	..	...	...	...	...
Sollenau.........	7 25	7a47	1145	3 47	4 52	8 46	9 p8	...	...	...	...
Ebenfurth 229 ....arr	...	8 6	12 4	...	5 11	...	9 27	...	...	...	...

HOLZLEITHEN & THOMASROITH.	E.M.				
		Holzleithen 240 dep	10a55	Thomasroith dep	2p22
	3½	Thomasroith ...arr	11 33	Holzleithen ...arr	3 0

For Fares, see page 233B.]

VIENNA, SELZTHAL, ST. MICHAEL, ST. VEIT, VILLACH; and PONTEBBA.

THROUGH CARRIAGE—Vienna to Venice, in 9.15 p.m. from Vienna (see also page 234)
RESTAURANT CAR—in 12.12 p.m. and 12.22 p.m. from St. Michael, and 6.25 a.m. from St. Veit.
SLEEPING CAR—Vienna to Venice, in 9.15 p.m. from Vienna.

Dist E.M		1,2,3		1,2,3		1,2,3 p.m.	Ex3	Ex 3	1,2,3 a.m.		1,2,3 a.m.	Ex3 a.m.	Ex3	1,2,3 a.m.	Ex3 p.m.	1,2,3	2&3 p.m.	1,2,3 a.m.	Ex3 p.m.	Ex3 p.m.
—	**Vienna** dep	...	...	...	...	1055	...	...	...	...	7 25	8 0	...	9 45	1235	...	2 45	11 35	7 50	9 15
38	St. Polten	...	...	...	...	1232		...	...	...	8 43	...	...	1122	1 49	...	4 44	1 55	9 3	1031
77¾	**Amstetten** dep	...	...	...	...	3 0	Direct Service Berlin—Trieste.	...	6 0	...	10 16	10 9	...	1 50	2 51	...	7 22	4 2	10 8	1145
92¼	Waldhofen a. d. Y.	...	...	...	...	3 46		...	7 20	...	11 0	1035	...	2 47	3 24	...	8 8	4 48	1034	1211
99½	Gaflenz	...	...	...	...	4 19		...	7 50	...	11 29	...	...	3 13	RC	...	8 40	5 19	...	¶
107	**Klein Reifling** arr	...	...	...	...	4 38		...	8 10	...	11 48	1110	...	3 32	4 1	...	9 0	5 40	1119	1247
...	**Klein Reifling** dep	...	...	...	...	4 47		...	8 25	...	12 4	1114	...	3 35	4 5	...		6 0	1113	1253
123	Gross Reifling	...	...	...	...	5 23		...	9 0	...	12 40	...	...	4 12	...	...	...	6 41	...	RC
129¼	**Hieflau** arr	...	...	...	...	5 40		...	9 15	...	12 56	1154	...	4 27	4 45	...	...	6 58	1152	1 33
	Hieflau dep	...	...	...	...	5 53		...	9 17	...	1 1	1158	...	4 29	4 49	...	...	7 7	1156	1 34
143½	Admont	...	...	...	...	6 31	...	...	9 52	...	1 41	1229	...	5 5	5 18	...	...	7 45	1226	2 5
152¼	**Selzthal** arr	...	...	...	...	6 50	a.m.	...	10 8	...	2 0	1245	...	5 24	5 33	...	...	8 4	1242	2 20
...	LINZ 237D dep	...	...	a.m.	...	4a15	8 32	...	...	...	11a20		1p15			1p15	...	4 p37		10 5
...	**Selzthal** dep	...	...	2 38	...	7 35	1054	...	1016	...	2 28	...	5 45	...		6 10	...	8 40	...	2 30
156½	Rottenmann	...	...	2 52	...	7 49	...	...	...	...	2 42	...	...	...		6 28	...	8 58	...	...
162¾	Trieben	...	...	3 5	...	8 3	RC	...	1040	...	2 56	...	...	...	...	6 43	...	9 13	...	...
172¼	Wald	...	...	3 37	...	8 34	...	...	11 5	...	3 29	...	...	...	...	7 17	...	9 48	...	...
191½	**St. Michael** arr	...	...	4 21	...	9 18	12 2	...	1146	...	4 14	...	6 50	...	...	8 6	1,2,3	10 33	...	3 41
...	VIENNA (234) dep	...	M—Rail Motor. Runs until 14th September.	10p30	...	...	7a35	7a35	7a35	...	11a25	...	...	...	...	...	1p20	4 p35	...	...
...	BRUCK 235A dep	...		3a55	...	8a10	1117	11a17	1117	...	3 p 0	...	...	...	...	...	7p52	9 p49	...	...
...	LEOBEN (241) dep	...		4a32	...	8a43	1142	11 55	1155	...	3 p40	...	...	...	...	...	8p51	10p15	...	...
—	**St. Michael** dep	...		5 15	...	9 35	1212	12 22	1235	...	4 50	...	...	...	...	...	9 23	11 12	...	3 44
205	Knittelfeld	...		5 56	...	1012	1239	12 50	1 15	...	5 29	...	...	...	...	...	10 1	11 52	...	4 12
210	Zeltweg	...		6 14	...	1025	...	1 0	1 32	...	5 46	...	...	...	...	...	1013	12 8	...	...
214½	Judenburg	...		6 28	...	1036	...	1 10	1 47	...	5 59	...	...	...	...	...	1024	12 23	...	4 31
226¼	Unzmarkt	...		7 0	...	11 5	RC	1 30	2 18	...	6 30	...	...	...	...	...	1050	12 55	...	...
230¼	Scheifling	...		7 15	...	1119	...	RC	2 33	...	6 45	...	...	...	...	...		1 13	...	...
237¼	Neumarkt-Steier	...		7 41	...	1145	...	2 2	3 0	...	7 11	...	...	...	...	...	...	1 55	...	5 19
249¼	Friesach	...		8 7	...	1210	2 2	2 21	3 27	...	7 38	...	...	...	¶—3rd class passengers must be travelling at least 62 miles.	...	...	2 25	...	5 37
255½	Treibach-Althofen	...		8 26	...	1227	...	...	3 45	...	7 57	...	...	...		...	...	2 44	...	5 49
264	Launsdorf	...		8 49	...	1248	...	...	4 6	...	8 18	...	...	...		...	...	3 12	...	...
268½	**St. Veit-Glan** arr	...		9 0	...	1 0	2 35	2 54	4 18	1,2,3	8 30	...	...	...		...	...	3 24	...	6 10
...	TRIESTE 237D arr	...		...	...	...	7p30	...	...	p.m.	6 a5	...	...	...		...	...	...	...	1125
...	**St. Veit-Glan** dep	...	...	9 30	3 cl.	1 21		3 4	4 43	6 30	9 0	3 cl.	...	...		...	...	4 0	...	6 25
269¾	St. Veit (Stadt)	a.m.	3 cl.	9 34	M	1 24	...	...	4 49	6 34	9 3	M	...	...		...	...	4 4	...	...
284½	Feldkirchen	6 59	M	10 20	a.m.	2 2	...	3 31	5 46	7 12	9 45	p.m.	...	...		...	...	4 45	...	6 52
291	Ossiach	7 17	a.m.	10 42	1125	2 21	...	...	6 7	7 31	10 3	6 54	...	...		...	...	5 4	...	RC
296	Annenheim	7 30	8 43	10 56	1140	2 34	...	3 49	6 20	7 44	10 15	7 0	...	...		...	...	5 16	...	...
300¼	**Villach** Hbf arr	7 43	8 58	11 10	1155	2 47	3 cl.	3 57	6 35	7 57	10 28	7 17	...	...		...	...	5 20	...	7 19
451¼	FRANZFEST 236 arr	2p43	...	6 p26	...	...	M	8 p28	...	2a25	7 a31	...	...	...		...	...	10a13	...	2p43
...	GASTEIN dep	5 a2	...	9 a41	...	...	p.m	1p48	...	5 p7	8 p58	...	...	...		...	...	2 a52	...	5 a2
...	**Villach** Hbf dep	8 15	9 0	12 25	...	2 51	3 25	4 6	6 44	8 7	11 0	7 21	...	...		...	...	5 50	...	7 25
303¼	Bad Villach	8 25	9 15	12 36	...	3 5	3 47	4 14	6 48	8 18	11 9	7 31	...	...		...	...	6 1	...	7 33
310¾	Arnoldstein	8 55		1 5	...	3 35		4 34		8 50	11 35		...	...		...	...	6 33	...	7 52
317½	**Tarvis** arr	9 20	...	1 31	...	4 4	...	4 56	...	9 15	12 0	...	...	...		...	...	7 0	...	8 16
	Tarvis dep	9 25	...	1 35	...	4 9	...	4 58	...	9 20		...	...	...		...	...	7 4	...	8 18
326¼	Uggowitz	9 49	...	2 0	...	4 36	...	...	...	10 3	...	...	...	...		...	...	7 29	...	...
338	**Pontafel** arr		...	2 23	...	5 0	...	5 36	...	1050	...	...	...	...		...	...	7 52	...	8 56
338¾	**Pontebba** arr	...	...	2 31	...	5 12	...	5 55	...	...	...	...	...	...	...	...	...	8 4	...	9 6
466¼	VENICE 285A arr	...		9 p15	...	1037	...	10p37	...	...	...	...	...	...	...	...	...	2 p5	...	2 p5

HUTTENBERG and ST. VEIT-A-D-GLAN.

	a.m.	a.m.	p.m.	p.m.					a.m.	a.m.	p.m.	p.m.		
Huttenberg dep	6 10	11 55	5 0	7 25	...	...	...	**St. Veit-a-d-Glan** dep	7 35	9 15	3 1	8 37	...	...
Launsdorf	7 18	1 2	6 9	8 32	...	...	...	Launsdorf	7 53	9 33	3 18	8 56	...	...
St. Veit-a-d-Glan arr	7 32	1 15	6 23	8 45	...	...	...	**Hüttenberg** arr	9 5	10 45	4 30	1010	...	...

TREIBACH-ALTHOFEN and KLEIN GLODNITZ.							
Treibach-Althofen dep	8 a40	12p50	8 p7	Klein-Glödnitz dep	6 a6	10a40	4 p50
Klein-Glödnitz arr	10 19	3 8	10 0	Treibach-Althofen arr	8 2	12 12	6 50

HIEFLAU and EISENERZ.												
Hieflau dep	5a52	9a30	1p33	4p52	7p17	10 p3	**Eisenerz** dep	8 a3	12p15	2 p41	5p50	9 p3	...
Radmer	6 1	9 41	1 44	5 3	7 28	10 14	Radmer	8 28	12 40	3 6	6 15	9 28	...
Eisenerz 242 arr	6 32	1013	2 16	5 35	8 0	10 50	**Hieflau** arr	8 36	12 49	3 15	6 24	9 37	...

ST. MICHAEL and LEOBEN (Sud-Bahnhof and Staatbahnhof).

St. Michael dep	4a30	6a42	9a38	11a13	12p25	4p30	4p45	6p55	8p15	11 p8	...	...	...
Leoben Staat arr	4 51	6 59	9 53	...	12 40	...	5 1	...	8 31	11 24	...	...	...
,, Sud. arr	4 55	7 3	9 57	11 29	12 44	4 45	5 5	7 10	8 35	11 28	...	...	...
Leoben Sud. dep	4a32	8a43	10a46	11a17	11a42	1155	3p40	6 p5	8p51	10p15	12a32	...	...
,, Staat dep	4 38	8 50	...	11 26	...	12 0	3 46	6 10	8 56	10 20	12 36	...	...
St. Michael arr	4 54	9 6	11 2	11 41	11 58	1216	4 2	6 26	9 12	10 36	12 52	...	...

ZELTWEG and FOHNSDORF.

Zeltweg dep	6 a30	11a30	6 p3	...	...	...	...	Fohnsdorf dep	5 a17	9 a10	2 p13	8 p50	...	...	...	...
Fohnsdorf arr	6 50	11 50	6 23	...	...	...	...	Zeltweg (241) arr	5 36	9 59	2 32	9 9	...	...	...	...

For Fares, see page 233B.]

PONTAFEL, VILLACH, ST. VEIT, ST. MICHAEL, SELZTHAL, and VIENNA.

		1,2,3	3 Cl	3 Cl	Ex3	Ex3	1,2,3	1,2,3	1,2,3	1,2,3	Ex3	Ex3	1,2,3	1,2,3	2&3	2&3	1,2,3	1,2,3	1,2,3	Ex 3
VENICE (285A) ...dep		...	...	...	...	...	...	...	...	...	5 a0	...	...	...	...	...	5 a55	...	1125	2 p10
Pontafel							a.m.		a.m.	a.m.	a.m.						p.m.		p.m.	p.m.
(Customs Exam.) dep		...	...	...	...	...	...	...	5 40	9 0	1052	...	...	...	...	...	1 52	...	6 45	7 50
Uggowitz		...	...	...	...	...	...	...	6 8	9 58	RC	...	...	...	...	...	2 33	...	7 23	¶
Tarvis (242) arr		...	...	...	...	...	...	...	6 30	1027	1133	...	...	...	...	...	2 58	p.m.	7 45	8 31
Tarvis (242) dep		...	...	M	...	...	4 38	...	6 35	1040	1135	...	...	...	...	...	3 13	5 50	7 50	8 35
Arnoldstein (239B)		...	...	a.m.	...	...	4 56	...	6 56	1058	1150	...	...	p.m.	p.m.	p.m.	3 33	6 8	8 10	RC
Bad Villach		...	...	9 56	...	...	5 20	...	7 20	1125	12 5	...	...	1 0	1 43	3 15	4 0	6 33	8 38	9 3
Villach arr		...	...	1010	...	...	5 30	...	7 34	1135	1212	...	...	1 4	1 47	3 19	4 16	6 43	8 51	9 10
GASTEIN 237C ......arr		...	M	...	...	...	...	...	1040	...	2p49	Direct Service Trieste–Berlin.	...	...	...	...	...	1032	1248	12a48
FRANZENSFESTE 236 dep		...	a.m.	...	...	...	...	...	...	...	8a18		...	...	...	...	8 a28	1050	3p35	...
Villach dep		...	8 10	1030	...	...	6 0	...	9 22	...	1226		...	1 12	1 50	3 25	4 45	7 0	1030	9 15
Annenheim		...	8 25	1045	...	...	6 14	...	9 38	...	1236		...	1 25	2 5	3 40	5 0	7 15	1044	SC
Ossiach		...		11 2	...	...	6 26	...	9 51	...	...		...	1 37	2 17	3 58	5 13	7 31	1056	...
Feldkirchen		...	...		...	...	6 52	...	1018	...	1256		...	1 59		4 20	5 38	7 50	1119	9 45
St. Veit on Glan (Stadt)		...	...	...	...	...	7 27	...	1053	...	...		...	2 34	...		6 13	8 25	1153	...
St. Veit on Glan ...arr		...	...	...	...	...	7 30	...	1056	...	1 20	a.m.	...	2 37	...	...	6 16	8 28	1156	10 9
TRIESTE ......dep		...	...	...	...	...	...	...	...	...	...	8 45	...	...	...	...	9a 5		6 p0	4p15
St. Veit (237B) ......dep		...	...	...	...	...	7 45	...	12 0	...	1 30	1 51	...	2 52	...	...	6 45	...	1223	10 24
Launsdorf		...	...	...	...	...	8 2	...	1217	...	...	...	...	3 9	...	...	7 2	...	1240	...
Treibach-Althofen		...	...	...	...	...	8 27	...	1243	...	...	...	...	3 34	...	...	7 24	...	1 5	10 51
Friesach		...	...	...	...	...	8 45	...	1 2	...	2 8	2 29	...	3 52	...	...	7 47	...	1 24	11 3
Neumarkt-in-Steiermark		...	2&3	...	...	...	9 20	...	1 39	...	2 36	...	...	4 27	...	...	8 22	...	2 0	11 33
Scheifling		...	a.m.	...	...	...	9 42	a.m.	2 1	...	...	...	...	4 49	...	...	8 44	...	2 22	...
Unzmarkt (253)		...	5 4	...	...	...	9 55	1015	2 12	...	3 0	RC	...	5 0	...	...	9 0	...	2 37	...
Judenburg		...	5 32	...	...	...	10 18	1042	2 40	...	3 20	...	...	5 28	...	...	9 32	...	3 6	12 18
Zeltweg (248)		...	5 44	...	...	...	10 28	1054	2 55	...	3 30	...	...	5 40	...	...	9 48	...	3 18	...
Knittelfeld		...	6 0	...	...	...	10 40	1111	3 17	...	3 42	3 54	...	5 56	...	...	10 6	...	3 34	12 39
St. Michael ......arr		...	6 32	...	...	...	11 3	1144	3 50	...	4 5	4 17	...	6 28	...	...	10 40	...	4 6	1 2
LEOBEN (241)......arr		...	7 a3	...	...	...	11a29	1244	4p45	...	4p45	4p45	...	7p10	...	...	11p28	...	4a55	...
BRUCK (235A) ...arr		...	7a38	...	...	...	11a56	1p14	5p13	...	5p13	5p13	...	7p34	...	...	12a10	...	5a26	...
VIENNA (234A)...arr		...		1,2,3	...	...	5 p40	5p40	8p40	...	8p40	8p40	...	...	...	...	5 a38	...	9a10	...
		a.m.		a.m.	a.m.		p.m.					p.m.	p.m.	p.m.			p.m.			a.m.
St. Michael ......dep		5 13	...	9 19	1110	...	12 5	...	...	...	...	4 25	4 33	6 51	...	...	10 50	...	...	1 5
Wald		6 12	...	1016	...	...	1 4	...	...	...	...		5 20	7 48	...	...	11 47	...	...	RC
Trieben		6 35	...	1041	...	...	1 27	...	...	...	...	RC	5 39	8 11	...	...	12 9	...	...	...
Rottenmann		6 49	...	11 5	...	...	1 41	...	...	...	...		5 55	8 25	...	...	12 23	...	...	...
Selzthal ......arr		7 1	...	1117	1228	...	1 53	...	...	...	...	5 35	6 7	8 37	...	...	12 34	...	Ex3	2 25
LINZ (237c)......arr		1053	...	2p47	3 p4	p.m.	6 p25	...	...	...	p.m.	7p48	...	1151	...	...		...	a.m.	6a58
Selzthal ......dep		7 42	...	12 5		1246	2 24	...	...	...	5 45		6 17	8 52	...	...	...	...	2 21	2 36
Admont		8 2	...	1229	...	1 3	2 45	...	...	...	6 1	...	6 33	9 12	...	...	...	...	2 32	2 53
Hieflau ......arr		8 35	...	1 0	...	1 28	3 18	...	...	...	6 28	...	7 5	9 44	...	...	...	...	3 3	3 20
" (241) ......dep		8 42	...	1 9	...	1 29	3 26	...	...	...	6 29	...	7 8	9 47	...	...	...	...	3 4	3 22
Gross Reifling	2&3	9 0	...	1 25	...	...	3 42	...	...	...	...	...	7 24	10 6	...	...	...	...	...	...
Klein Reifling arr	a.m.	9 35	a.m.	2 0	...	2 10	4 27	...	...	...	7 10	...	7 55	1040	...	...	...	...	3 46	4 8
Klein Reifling ......dep	6 0	9 48	1152	2 34	...	2 12	4 43	...	...	...	7 12	...	8 14	1048	...	...	...	...	3 50	4 14
Gaflenz	6 23	1011	1214	3 0	...	...	5 6	...	...	...	...	...	8 40	1115	...	...	...	...	...	...
Waldhofen 242	6 53	1035	1235	3 24	...	2 48	5 32	...	...	...	7 46	...	9 5	1149	...	...	...	...	4 24	4 53
Amstetten ......arr	7 35	1115	1 12	4 0	...	3 12	6 10	...	...	...	8 10	...	9 40	1230	...	...	...	...	4 48	5 17
St. Polten	9 25	1 48	3 44	6 48	...	4 15	8 13	...	...	...	9 12	...		4 21	...	...	...	...	5 58	6 25
Vienna ......arr	11 0	3 40	5 15	7 55	...	5 25	9 35	...	...	...	1025	...	...	6 0	...	...	...	...	7 10	7 40

Extra { Bad Villach......dep. 5p34; Villach ......dep. 5 51; Ossiach ......arr. 6 25 }

RC—Restaurant Car. SC—Sleeping Car.

M—Rail Motor; runs until 14th September.

LAIBACH and TARVIS.

E.M								
	Laibach S.B.	5a47	6a54	9 a9	11a30	3p44	6 p35	10 p0
18	Krainburg ...	6 41	7 52	9 58	12 32	4 45	7 30	10 52
24½	Podnart ...	7 1	8 9	1016	12 49	5 4	7 46	11 10
31¾	Lees ...	7 24	8 35	1041	1 15	5 28	8 11	11 36
39¾	Assling ...	7 47	8 58	11 3	1 38	5 52	8 35	12 0
64	**Tarvis** 241 arr	...	1034	...	3 7	7 24	10 43	...

Tarvis ....dep	...	7 a7	...	1237	...	5p 3	8 p0
Assling ...	5a52	8 15	9a37	2 32	4p33	6 30	9 44
Lees ...	6 11	8 34	9 57	2 54	4 49	6 49	10 7
Podnart ...	6 29	8 52	1016	3 18	5 4	7 12	1032
Krainburg ...	6 44	9 8	1032	3 38	5 17	7 29	1049
Laibach arr	7 25	9 52	1114	4 33	5 51	8 16	1131

LAIBACH and STEIN.

E.M.						
	Laibach ....dep	7a32	1150	3p12	7p15	...
8¾	Domschale ...	8 16	1236	3 56	7 57	...
14½	**Stein** ....arr	8 43	1 4	4 24	8 24	...

Stein ....dep	5a30	9a46	1p30	5 p0
Domschale ...	5 59	1016	1 58	5 32
Laibach (242) a	6 42	11 0	2 41	6 15

CERCAN-PISELY and WRAN.

‡—Not on Monday.

Cercan-Pisely ....dep	3a44	5a 5	9 a26	3p40	...	6p37	...
Eule ...	4 56	6 20	10 36	4 56	7 p0	7 36	...
Wran (248) ....arr	5 45	7 ‡9	11 23	5 43	7 47	...	...
Wran ....dep	...	7a25	11a52	6 p0	...	8 p9	...
Eule ...	6a18	8 18	12 50	6 51	7p46	9 7	...
Cercan-Pisely (243) arr	7 15	9 16	1 51	...	8 42	10 9	...

POCHLARN and KIENBERG-GAMING.

Pöchlarn dp	4a44	9 a40	1p10	6 p10	9 p28
Wieselburg ...	5 12	10 7	1 37	6 38	9 56
Scheibbs ...	5 48	10 45	2 13	7 15	10 36
Kienberg ar	6 16	11 15	2 41	7 43	11 4

Kienburg dp	4 a9	6a30	10a38	1p10	5 p32
Scheibbs ...	4 37	7 0	11 7	1 39	6 2
Wieselburg ...	5 13	7 35	11 43	2 17	6 39
Pöchlarn arr	5 38	8 0	12 8	2 42	7 3

KIENBERG and WAIDHOFEN.

‡—From 15th July until 15th Sept.

Kienberg ...dep	...	6a32	11‡a25	2p48	7p53
Lunz ...	...	7 40	12 31	4 7	9 4
Göstling ...	4 a8	8 8	12 55	4 53	9 30
Gro. Hollenstein	4 58	8 57	—	6 0	—
Gstadt ...	6 3	9 51	...	6 52	...
Waidhofen arr	6 24	10 6	...	7 10	...

Waidhofen ...dep	...	6a50	...	12p2	8p12
Gstadt ...	...	7 7	...	1228	8 30
Gross Hollenstein	...	8 1	...	1 47	9 27
Göstling ...	4a25	8 59	1‡p5	2 58	1013
Lunz ...	4 57	9 29	1 30	3 54	—
Kienberg ....arr	6 0	1030	2 31	4 58	...

*—From 15th July until 31st August.

Waidhofen ...dep	7a40	12p40	5*p57	8p25	...
Gstadt ...	7 59	12 59	6 16	8 44	...
Ybbsitz ....arr	8 19	1 19	6 36	9 4	...

Ybbsitz ....dep	6a 0	9a43	4p49	6*p47	...
Gstadt ...	6 20	10 3	5 9	7 6	...
Waidhofen ...arr	6 36	1019	5 25	7 22	...

LAMBACH and GMUNDEN.

Dist					
	Lambach 239 dep	5 a34	9a19	1p25	5p57
9¼	Traunfall ...	6 13	9 52	1 58	6 29
10½	Steyrermühl ...	6 19	9 57	2 3	6 34
17½	**Gmunden** ....arr	6 48	10 26	2 32	7 4

Gmunden ...dep	4a45	9 a0	3p37	9 p0
Steyrermühl ...	5 15	9 31	4 7	9 31
Traunfall ...	5 20	9 36	4 11	9 36
Lambach ...arr	5 49	10 7	4 41	1010

STEINDORF and BRAUNAU-AM-INN.

Steindorf ....dep	7 a2	11a27	2p55	8p35
Friedburg-Lengau	7 10	11 35	3 3	8 43
Mauerkirchen ...	8 1	12 26	3 56	9 34
Braunau (239B)	8 21	12 46	4 17	9 55

Braunau ...dep	4a40	9a50	1p16	5p56	...
Mauerkirchen ...	5 3	1013	1 39	6 27	...
Friedburg-Len.	5 54	11 3	2 30	7 34	...
Steindorf ...arr	6 2	1111	2 38	7 43	...

Steindorf .... dep	8a12	...
Schneegattern arr	9 5	...
Schneegattern dep	10a33	...
Steindorf ....arr	11 24	...

WELS and ASCHACH

‡—Until 31st Aug. §—In September only.

E.M						
	Wels ...dep	5a48	8 a41	1 p1	5p51	8‡p45
5	Haiding ...	6 19	8 58	1 17	6 7	9 2
12¼	Eferding ...	7 18	9 41	1 59	6 48	9 38
17¼	**Aschach** arr	7 41	10 4	2 22	7 12	10 0

Aschach ....dep	5 a0	9 a15	11a53	6§p11	6‡p22
Eferding ...	5 24	9 52	12 21	6 43	6 51
Haiding ...	6 0	10 32	1 4	7 29	7 29
Wels (239B) arr	6 15	10 47	1 20	7 45	7 45

DIVAZZA, POLA, CANFANARO, and ROVIGNO.

E.M								
	Divazza ....dep	...	5a34	...	9 a32	...	5p15	8p59
8	Herpelje-Kozina ...	...	6 1	6a12	10 15	...	6 1	9 25
23	Pinguente ...	...	6 30	7 2	11 0	...	6 47	9 57
31¾	Lupoglava ...	...	6 47	7 32	11 25	...	7 10	1015
40½	Cerovglie ...	...	7 9	8 4	11 52	...	7 38	1037
44¾	Mitterburg-Pisino ...	a.m.	7 21	8 24	12 9	...	7 57	1049
57¾	Canfanaro ....arr	6 15	7 51	9 5	12 43	p.m.	8 31	1117
...	Canfanaro ....dep	...	...	9 12	12 53	3 55	8 43	...
70¾	Rovigno ....arr	...	...	9 54	1 36	4 37	9 25	...
69	Dignano ...	6 48	8 12	9 57	1 16	—	9 7	1139
77	Pola ....arr	7 9	8 27	1020	2 36	...	9 28	1154

Pola ....dep	5a10	7a40	11 a9	2p20	6p42
Dignano ...	5 36	8 12	11 35	2 46	7 2
Rovigno ....dep	5 10	...	11 7	2 22	6 25
Canfanaro ....arr	5 59	...	11 56	3 11	7 14
Canfanaro ....dep	6 11	8 45	12 11	3 24	7 27
Mitterburg-Pisino ...	6 49	—	12 52	4 2	7 56
Cerovglie ...	7 5	...	1 7	4 18	8 9
Lupoglava ...	7 31	...	1 35	4 46	8 31
Pinguente ...	7 52	...	1 56	5 7	8 48
Herpelje-Kozina ...	8 41	...	2 56	6 10	9 27
Divazza ....arr	8 59	...	3 15	6 29	9 42

TRIESTE and HERPELJE-KOZINA.

Trieste (S. Andr.) ...dp	5a 0	7a35	9a10	4p42	8p24
Herpelje-Kozina ...arr	5 49	8 32	10 4	5 36	9 14

Herpelje-Kozina ...dep	6a24	8a51	2 p54	6p17	9p39	...
Trieste (S. Andrae) ...ar	7 10	9 35	3 41	7 5	1026	...

SCHEIBMUHL and KERNHOF.

Scheibmuhl dep	6a12	8a28	10a50	1 p5	6 p1	10p0
Lilienfeld ...	6 27	8 47	11 7	1 21	6 18	1015
Freiland ...	6 43	9 5	11 24	1 39	6 35	1031
St. Egydi ...	7 25	9 52	12 7	2 22	7 19	11 8
Kernhof ....arr	7 43	1010	12 25	2 40	7 37	...

Kernhof ....dep	...	...	8a40	...	1p50	4 p7	5p30	8 p7
St. Egydi ...	5 a0	6a40	9 6	11a25	2 25	4 42	5 56	8 21
Freiland ...	5 34	7 21	9 47	12 5	3 3	5 19	6 34	—
Lilienfeld ...	5 48	7 36	10 5	12 20	3 17	5 34	6 49	...
Scheibmuhl (239B)	6 2	7 50	1021	12 35	3 32	5 48	7 3	...

E.M								
	Freiland ....dep	7a25	9a48	11a25	1p40	3p50	6p40	...
6¼	Türnitz ....arr	8 0	1023	11 57	2 8	4 24	7 10	...

Türnitz ....dep	6a35	8a28	10a45	12p55	2p25	5p50
Freiland ....arr	7 7	9 0	11 14	1 25	2 56	6 20

ST. POLTEN and TULLN.

St. Pölten .... dep	4a56	7a34	11a42	11a56	1p55	5p35	7 p1	8p34	11 p7
Herzogenburg ...	5 24	8 2	12 5	12 22	2 25	6 9	7 24	8 59	11 33
Sitzenberg-Reidling	6 8	8 38	—	1 2	3 2	6 46	—	9 35	—
Tulln (243) ... arr	7 2	9 30	...	1 55	3 56	7 37	...	1026	...

Tulln ....dep	4a50	8a38	11a44	2 p8	5p57	9p35
Sitzenberg ...	5 40	9 28	12 34	3 3	6 47	1025
Herzogenburg	6 25	10 9	1 13	3 44	7 33	11 4
St. Pölten arr	6 51	1034	1 43	4 10	7 59	1138

KREMS and HERZOGENBURG

Krems ....dep	5a15	9a12	12p15	2p38	6p20
Herzogenburg arr	6 13	10 4	1 10	3 35	7 20

Herzogenburg ....dep	5a33	8 a5	12p 7	2p27	7p29	...
Krems (248A) ....arr	6 27	9 0	1 0	3 25	8 23	...

EISENERZ and VORDERNBERG.

Eisenerz ....dep	6a40	11 a0	2p32	6 p7
Vordernberg (235) ...arr	8 30	1 2	4 23	8 2

Vordernberg ...dep	8 a5	12p42	2p54	7 p3
Eisenerz (241) arr	10 4	2 31	4 48	8 53

WODNAN and HAIDMUHLE.

Wodnan ....dep	...	6a31	...	2p30	...	10p15
Prachatitz ...	4a25	7 42	8a15	3 39	4 p5	11 22
Wallern ...	5 47	—	10 9	—	5 57	—
Schwarzes-Kreuz..	6 13	...	1116	...	6 37	...
Haidmühle ....arr	7 0	...	1147	...	7 14	...

Haidmühle ....dep	...	...	9 a30	...	12p20	5p20	9 p20
Schwarzes-Kreuz ...	...	...	10 6	...	12 57	5 50	9 50
Wallern ...	...	5a55	10 28	...	1 40	6 11	10 5
Prachatitz ...	4a10	7 31	—	11a45	3 16	7 39	—
Wodnan (243A) arr	5 17	...	...	12 55	...	8 46	...

STRAKONIC and WALLERN.

Strakonic ...dep	...	7a30	3p45	10 p0	...	...
Winterberg ...	3a20	8 57	5 7	11 22	...	...
Wallern ....arr	5 40	1049	7 31	...	...	...

Wallern ....dep	...	6 a0	...	2p10	...	8 p0
Winterberg ...	5a50	7 52	11a24	4 21	7p15	9 56
Strakonic ....arr	7 10	...	12 44	...	8 36	...

NAKRY-NETOLIC and NETOLIC STADT.

Nakry-Netolic...dep	6a20	2p24	8p46	...
Netolic Stadt ...arr	7 8	3 13	9 35	...

Netolic Stadt ...dep	4a40	12p57	7p22	...	...
Nakry-Netolic...arr	5 29	1 47	8 12	...	...

GOPFRITZ and RAABS.

Göpfritz ....dep	5a30	10a55	7 p40	...	...
Raabs ....arr	6 34	12 11	8 48	...	...

Raabs ....dep	3a26	7 a37	3p38	...	...
Göpfritz ....arr	4 35	8 57	4 56	...	...

VOCKLABRUCK and KAMMER

Vocklabruck	5a51	8a15	10a21	12p43	2p32	4p38	7p11	9p41
Kammer	6 25	8 39	10 55	1 11	2 53	5 12	7 43	1010

Kammer	7 a3	8a52	11a42	1p37	3p17	5p50	8 p8	10p25
Vocklabruck	7 32	9 24	12 13	2 2	3 48	6 24	8 34	10 55

Dist.		1,2,3	Ex3	2&3	2&3	1,2,3	Ex3	Ex3	Ex2	1,2,3	Ex3	1,2,3	1,2,3	1,2,3	1,2,3	Ex3
E.M	Vienna-Kaiser Ferd.	a.m.	a.m.			a.m.	a.m.	a.m.	a.m.	p.m.	p.m.	p.m	p.m.	p.m.	p.m.	p.m.
—	Jos. Bahnhof...dep	5 8	6 30	...	...	6 40	8 25	9 0	1025	12 6	4 15	3 18	7 20	8 30	9 5	1015
13¾	St. Andrä-Wördern ...	5 50	...	...	...	...	...	...	...	...	...	...	...	...	...	...
21¼	Tulln 242	6 7	...	...	...	7 29	RC	...	A	1 1	...	4 10	8 15	9 18	9 50	SC
25½	N.-Aigen-Stetteldorf	6 17	...	...	...	...	...	...	...	1 12	...	4 21	...	9 28	9 59	...
27¼	Absdorf-Hippersdorf ...	6 32	...	...	...	7 46	9 10	RC	RC	1 25	...	4 32	8 35	9 40	1016	11 7
33	Gross-Weikersdorf......	6 47	...	...	...	8 2	...	...	...	1 43	...	4 51	8 50	9 57	1032	...
49	Eggenburg	7 53	...	...	...	8 54	9 53	...	1149	2 42	5 39	6 5	9 44	1055	1125	1155
55½	Sigmundsherberg	8 10	...	a.m.	...	9 17	10 9	...	...	3 15	...	6 30	1013	1117	1144	...
75¾	Göpfritz		...	5 10	...	1014	1046	...	...	4 21	6 29	7 30	1116	1215	1237	1251
86¼	Schwarzenau 246	...	...	5 33	...	1043	11 3	...	...	4 52	6 46	7 53	1152	1242	1 25	1 9
96¼	Pürbach-Schrems......	...	...	5 59	...	1110	1122	...	...	5 22	...	8 20	1220	1 9	1 49	...
102	Gmünd ...arr	2&3	9 2	6 15	...	1123	1132	1147	1 16	5 39	7 12	8 36	1233	1 25	2 2	1 35
283½	EGER 243A ...arr	a.m.	...		a.m.	5p20	5p20	5p20	6p13	...	5a36			7a 6		7 a6
...	Gmünd...dep	4 50	9 7	...	6 30	12 0	1136			5 53	7 21	...	...	1 50	...	
112½	Suchenthal	5 16	...	...	7 4	1226	...	...	...	6 20	...	...	...	2 13	...	...
122½	Wittingau	5 42	...	...	7 46	1252	12 3	...	2&3	6 52	7 49	3Cl.	Ex3	2 40	...	...
129¼	Lomnic	5 56	...	...	8 4	1 6	...	...	p.m.	7 7	...	p.m.	p.m.	2 52	...	...
136	Weseli Mezimosti 243	6 35	9 56	...	8 25	1 42	1227	...	4 0	7 33	8 12	8 40	1119	3 5	...	...
140½	Sobieslau	6 46	...	...		1 53	1234	...	4 10	7 44	...	9 0	...	3 34	...	...
152¾	Tabor 243 ...2&3	7 19	1019	...	...	2 30	1254	...	4 42	8 20	8 36	10 3	1143	4 7	...	...
171	Klein-Herman. S. a.m.	8 14	...	...	...	3 24	...	...	5 36	9 21	...	1145	...	4 59	...	...
176½	Wotic-Weselka ...7 1	8 34	...	...	...	3 38	...	2&3	5 51	9 38	...	1 11	...	5 15	2&3	2&3
182¾	Bistric...7 16	8 52	...	p.m.	p.m.	3 51	...	p.m.	6 5	9 51	...	1 33	...	5 28	a.m.	a.m.
185¾	Beneschau...7 33	9 9	...	1244	1 59	4 11	1 47	4 19	6 21	10 8	9 27	2 0	1234	5 40	4 50	5 54
191½	Cercan-Pisely 242 7 48	9 24	...	1259	2 16	...	...	4 34	6 38	1025	...	2 35	...	...	5 5	6 8
200	Strancic...8 18	9 54	...	1 29	2 46	...	...	5 5	7 9	1056	9 50	3 30	...	...	5 35	6 40
204½	Rican ...8 28	10 4	...	1 39	2 56	...	...	5 15	7§19	11 6	...	3 50	...	...	5 45	6 51
208¾	Ourinoves ...8 37	1014	...	1 48	3 5	...	...	5 25	7§29	1115	...	4 4	...	...	5 55	7 1
216¼	Nusle-Vrsovic 248 9 2	1035	...	2 13	3 29	5 13	...	5 53	7 53	1134	...	4 44	...	6 41	6 22	7 22
217½	Prague...arr 9 9	1042	1155	2 20	3 36	5 18	2 35	6 0	8 0	1141	1015	4 50	1 22	6 46	6 29	7 29
299½	BODENBACH 252 arr	2p32	2p32	5p29	...	...	5p29	...	1257	...	1257	8a15	...	1136	...	...
336½	DRESDEN 189...arr	3p52	3p52	6p53	...	...	6p53	...	...	...	2a25	9a39	...	1p40	...	...

	Ex3	1,2,3	Ex3	1,2,3	2&3	1,2,3	2&3	Ex3	Ex3	2&3	2&3	Ex3	2&3	2&3	2&3	1,2,3	2&3
DRESDEN 188 dep	...	...	2a30	...	...	...	...	...	7a10	...	...	1130	1130	...	1253	...	...
BODENBACH 252A	...	...	4 a5	...	...	...	...	...	8a47	...	...	1257	1257	...	3 p5	...	...
	a.m.		a.m.	a.m.	a.m.	a.m.	a.m.		p.m.	p.m.	p.m.	p.m.	p.m.	p.m.	p.m.	p.m.	p.m.
Prague...dep	2 57	...	6 50	7 3	8 15	9 31	11 5	...	1 35	2 4	3 10	4 20	4 28	5 44	7 25	9 25	1150
Nusle-Vrsovic	...	...	...	7 13	8 27	9 40	1117	...	...	2 16	3 24	...	4 39	6 0	7 39	9 32	1158
Ourinoves	...	...	...	7 35	8 50	10 2	1140	...	...	2 40	3 47	...	5 2	6 24	8 5	9 53	1222
Rican	...	...	...	7 46	9 0	1014	1150	...	...	2 52	3 58	...	5 13	6 36	8 17	10 5	1234
Strancic ...2&3	...	...	...	7 59		1027	12 5	...	2 7	3 5	4 10	RC	5 25	6 49	8 30	1018	1247
Cercan-Pisely a.m.	...	...	...	8 23	...	1050	1231	...	...	3 34	4 36	...	5 52	7 15	8 57	1037	1 14
Beneschau...5 48	3 50	...	7 46	8 43	...	1115	1248	...	2 34	3 59	4 53	...	6 13	7 32	9 15	11 0	1 30
Bistric...5 57	...	...	...	8 52	...	1124		...	...	4 8		...	6 22			11 9	
Wotic-Weselk 6 15	...	...	8 3	9 12	...	1141	...	...	2 51	4 24	...	...	6 41	...	...	1128	...
Kl. Hermanic 6 32	...	a.m.	...	9 30	...	1159	...	...	...	4 40	...	...	6 57	...	...	1145	...
Tabor ...7 18	4 47	5 30	8 42	1022	...	1253	...	...	3 32	5 30	...	6 4	7 49	...	...	1244	...
Sobieslau	...	6 1	9 1	1052	...	1 22	p.m.	...	3 52	5 58	p.m.	...	8 20	...	...	1 12	...
Weseli Mezimosti	5 11	6 28	9 13	11 2	...	1 59	4 13	...	4 4	6 7	7 38	6 33	8 30	...	...	1 22	...
Lomnic		6 45	...		...	2 15	4 35	...	...		7 58	...		...	...	2 18	
Wittingau	...	7 1	9 35	...	...	2 31	4 58	...	4 22	...	8 13	...	...	...	...	2 39	
Suchenthal	...	7 27	...	...	...	2 57	5 34	...	...	...	8 39	...	...	1,2,3	Ex3	3 7	
Gmünd ...arr	...	7 53	10 3	...	Ex2	3 23	6 13	a.m.	4 51	...	9 6	7 20	...	p.m.		3 30	
EGER 243A ...dep	...	...	...	p.m.	9a53	7 a7		1128	1128	...	...	...	...	5 45	1015	1015	
Gmünd ...dep	...	8 2	1010	1235	2 58	4 18	...	4p46	4 57	...	9 30	7 25	...	1a39	3a51	4 1	
Purbach-Schrems.	...	8 23	...	1256	A	4 37	...	...	5 10	...	9 51	...	...	1 56	4 5	4 22	
Schwarzenau	1,2,3	8 50	1039	1 24	...	5 36	...	...	5 29	...	1036	...	...	2 24	4 23	4 50	
Göpfritz	a.m.	9 20	...	1 55	3 46	6 12	p.m.	RC	5 52	...	11 7	...	...	2 55	4 50	5 20	
Sigmundsherberg	8 50	1012	1127	2 53	...	7 12	7 22	...	6 22	...	1212	...	...	3 45	5 22	6 11	
Eggenburg	9 5	1028	1138	3 9	...	7 25	7 41	...	6 31	...	1230	...	...	4 1	5 33	6 26	
Grs.-Weikersdorf.	9 51	1116	...	3 54	...	8 2	8 39	...	...	...	1 19	...	...	4 49	SC	7 13	
Absdorf-Hippersd.	10 8	1138	...	4 15	RC	8 15	9 12	...	...	...	1 38	...	...	5 9	6 10	7 32	...
N.-Aigen-Stetteld	1014	1144	...	4 22	...	...	9 20	...	...	...	1 45	...	...	5 16	...	...	...
Tulln	1027	1157	...	4 35	...	8 29	9 33	...	...	...	1 58	...	...	5 28	...	7 50	...
St. Andrä-Wörd.	1047	...	...	...	...	...	..	...	...	...	2 20	...	...	5 50	...	8 4	...
Vienna ...arr	1135	1240	1248	5 20	5 32	9 10	1021	7 25	7 45	...	3 17	9 45	...	6 25	6 52	8 34	...

Extra.—Beneschau to Prague 8.28 p.m. Prague to Beneschau, 5.57 a.m., 12.30 p.m.

A—Runs until 15th Sept.
§—Not on Sunday.

ASCH and ADORF.

E M												
	Asch ...dep	...	9a25	...	2 p0	5p21	**Adorf** ...dep	7 a6	...	2 p0	...	8p52
1¾	Asch Stadt	4a34	9 44	11a3	2 12	5 36	Rossbach	7 44	12p25	3 1	6p21	9 35
10	Rossbach	5 28	1036	12 5	2 56	6 40	Asch Stadt ...	8 25	1 23	3 59	7 12	1023
18	**Adorf** 188 arr	6 4	...	1245	...	7 23	**Asch** 197 arr	8 32	1 36	5 0	7 28	1031

LAMBACH and HAAG AM HAUSRUCK.
*—7.52 a.m. on Thurs.

Lambach...dep	5a59	1p26	8p42	**Haag** ...dep	3a58	8*a15	5 p3
Gaspoltshofen ...	6 54	2 24	9 31	Gaspoltshofen ...	4 43	9 7	5 55
Haag...arr	7 39	3 16	1010	**Lambach** ...arr	5 25	9 57	6 46

LAMBACH and VORCHDORF-EGGENBERG.

Lambach ...dep	7 a9	1 p35	8 p40	...
Vorchdorf-Eggenberg ...arr	7 58	2 24	9 27	...
Vorchdorf-Eggenberg ...dep	5 a5	9 a40	5 p55	...
Lambach ...arr	5 58	10 29	6 46	...

WOTIC and SELCAN.

Wotic ...dep	5a20	9a20	6 p45	...	...	Selcan ...dep	4 a4	6 a47	1p32	...	...	...	...	...
Selcan ... arr	6 21	1024	7 45	...	...	Wotic ...arr	5 0	7 49	2 39	...	...	...	...	...

TABOR and BECHIN.

Tabor...dep	7 a55	1 p0	4 p25	8 p50
Bechin ...arr	9 20	2 5	5 39	9 56
Bechin ...dep	5 a50	11a32	2 p20	6 p0
Tabor 243 ...arr	7 8	12 41	3 23	7 17

BUDWEIS and WESELI.

Dist		a.m	a.m	a.m.	a.m.	p.m.	p.m	p.m.	p.m.		a.m	a.m.	a.m.	a.m.	p.m.	p.m.	p.m.	p.m.	
E M	**Budweis** ...dep	1 47	5 4	9 3	11 38	12 8	5 49	7 27	10 38	**Weseli** ...dep	1 40	5 16	6 33	9 15	1 45	4 10	6 38	8 38	...
6¼	Zámost	2 2	5 22	...	...	12 26	6 7	...	...	Sevetin	2 3	...	6 57	...	2 9	...	...	9 2	...
13¾	Sevetin	2 21	5 44	...	...	12 45	6 33	...	...	Zámost	2 25	...	7 15	...	2 27	...	...	9 20	...
23½	**Weseli 243** arr	2 42	6 6	9 46	12 16	1 7	6 59	8 4	11 15	**Budweis** ...arr	2 40	5 53	7 30	9 52	2 42	4 50	7 15	9 35	...

KOLIN and CERCAN-PISELY.

Kolin...dep	...	5 a50	10a8	4p32	...	**Cercan-Pisely**...dep	7a47	2 p23	9 p10
Becwar	...	6 53	11 8	5 39	...	Ledecko ...4a43	9 7	3 38	10 20
Ledecko 243	4a52	8 14	1228	7 10	...	Becwar 253...6 2	1026	4 54	
Cercan-Pisely ...	6 3	...	1 37	8 24	...	**Kolin** ...arr 6 50	1118	5 40	...

SWETLA and LEDECKO.

Swetla...dep	...	7 a20	...	2p40	Ledecko ...dep	8a59	1230	3p50	5 p0	7p15
Zruc 223A	...	9 10	...	4 52	Kacow	10 2	1 16	6 17	6 17	8 0
Kacow	3a57	9 43	2p35	5 58	Zruc	1043		7 7	7 7	
Ledecko 243 ...arr	4 40	12 0	3 20	6 45	Swetla ...arr	1224	...	9 9	9 9	...

NEPOMUK and BLATNA.

Nepomuk	6a25	2p38	7p45	Blatna ...dep	4a24	10a0	3 p5
Blatna	7 52	4 17	9 20	Nepomuk (243A)	5 50	1130	4 36

WODNAN and MOLDAUTHEIN.

Wodnan ...dep	6a35	2p35	10p13	Moldauthein dep	4a10	11a38	7 p20
Moldauthein ...arr	7 59	3 59	11 15	Wodnan ...arr	5 15	1 0	8 43

For Fares, see page 233B].

GMUND, PILSEN, AND EGER.

RC—Restaurant Car. SC—Sleeping Car.
B—Runs until 15th September. C—Runs until 31st August.

E.M. Dist	VIENNA 243 ......dep	1015	...	1015	...	...	...	...	9 a0	...	9 a0	10a25	...	12p6	4p15
		Ex3	Ex3	1,2,3	2&3	1,2,3	2&3	Ex2	Ex 3	1,2,3	1,2,3	Ex 2	1,2,3	1,2,3	Ex3
		a.m.		a.m.	a.m.				a.m.		a.m.	p.m.		p.m.	p.m.
—	**Gmünd** ....dep	1 39	...	2 9	6 20	...	...	...	11 50	...	11 56	1 19	...	6 0	7 18
8¾	Gratzen	SC	...	2 26	6 40	...	...	...	---	...	12 16	...	...	6 19	...
18¾	Forbes-Schweinitz......	...	...	2 45	7 7	...	...	...	RC	...	12 41	B	...	6 43	...
31	**Budweis** 239B ...arr	2 28	...	3 14	7 35	a.m.	a.m.	...	12 34	...	1 9	1 59	...	7 11	7 59
...	" ....dep	2 35	...	3 29	—	5 37	9 25	...	12 42	...	1 29	2 21	...	8 8	
44	Nakry-Netolic............	...	...	4 0	...	6 11	9 58	...	...	...	2 10	...	...	8 44	—
49¾	Wodnan-Cicenic	...	...	4 11	...	6 30	1015	...	1 12	...	2 27	---	...	9 1	...
53¾	**Protivin**	3 11	...	4 23	...	6 47	1030	...	1 22	...	2 45	RC	...	9 16	...
59	Razice	...	...	4 36	...	7 1	1044	...	1 32	...	3 11	...	...	9 33	...
67¾	Strakonic	3 33	...	5 0	...	7 29	11 8	...	1 47	...	3 38	3 17	...	9 56	...
78¼	Horazdiowic-Babin ...	3 51	...	5 30	...	8 3	1145	...	2 6	p.m.	4 13	...	...	1028	...
93¾	Nepomuk	...	...	6 14	...	8 47	1230	From 15th July until 15th Sept.	2 33	4 41	4 54	...	...	11 8	...
100¾	Blowic	...	...	6 33	...	9 6	1246		...	4 57	5 10	...	...	1125	...
105	Nezvestic	...	...	6 47	...	9 19	1259		...	5 9	5 20	...	...	1136	...
115½	**Pilsen** ....arr	4 52	...	7 15	...	9 47	1 28		3 5	5 37	5 47	4 24	p.m.	12 1	...
...	" ....dep	4 57	...	7 45	...	1035	2 5		3 18	6 0	6 12	4 28	8 31	1 10	...
129¾	Neuhof	...	...	8 26	...	1124	2 55		...	6 48	7 0	...	9 10	2 13	...
136	Mies-Kladrau	5 34	...	8 41	...	1138	3 10		3 52	7 0	7 15	...	9 23	2 33	...
141¾	Schweissing Tschern	...	...	8 57	...	1152	3 23		...	—	7 29	B	9 35	2 51	...
154¾	Plan	6 8	...	9 32	...	1230	—		4 22	...	8 7	...	10 7	3 46	...
162¼	**Marienbad** ......arr	6 24	...	9 52	Ex3	1250	Ex1		4 38	...	8 28	5 33	1028	4 16	...
200¼	CARLSBAD 243A arr	8 a0	a.m.	1134	p.m.	3 p4	p.m.	p.m.	6 p17	p.m.	10p28	7 p7	...	...	...
...	**Marienbad** ......dep	6 32	9 48	10 4	12 5	1 0	2 52	3 56	4 49	8 6	8 37	5 45	1030	4 32	...
167½	Bad-Königswart	6 43	9 59	1017	1216	1 12	C	4 7	4 59	8 18	8 49	5 54	1043	4 49	...
171	Sandau	...	...	1026	...	1 21	...	...	...	8 27	8 58	...	1052	5 2	...
181½	**Eger** ....arr	7 6	1035	1050	1240	1 45	3 21	4 29	5 20	8 52	9 21	6 13	1115	5 36	...
185¾	FRANZENSBAD 188A	7a54	11a8	11a8	1255	2p33	3p42	4p43	5 p53	9p50	9 p50	6 p34	...	6 a5	

FRANZENSBAD (188) dep		5a21	1a53	6a38	8a19	9a18	...	10a38	2 p3	2 p3	3 p14	4p50	6 p0	6p30	9p55	...
		Ex3	1,2,3	1,2,3	2&3	Ex2	2&3	Ex 3	Ex3	1,2,3	Ex 3	1,2,3	Ex 1	1,2,3	Ex 3	1,2,3
		a.m.	a.m.	a.m.	a.m.	a.m.		a.m.	p.m.	p.m	p.m.	p.m.	p.m.	p.m.	p.m.	p.m
Eger ....dep		5 54	4 30	7 7	8 45	9 53	...	11 28	2 25	2 32	4 32	5 45	6 22	6 55	10 15	1117
Sandau......................		...	5 0	7 39	9 14	B	...	...	...	3 7	...	6 20	C	7 26	SC	1159
Bad-Königswart		6 23	5 12	7 50	9 27	1017	...	11 55	3 1	3 19	4 59	6 31	...	7 37	10 42	1213
Marienbad ......arr		6 31	5 21	7 59	9 36	1025	...	12 3	3 9	3 28	5 7	6 40	6 54	7 46	10 50	1225
CARLSBAD 243A dep		—	...	5 a54	—	8a50	...	10a34	—	1p32	—	3p23	—	—	9p16	...
Marienbad......dep		...	5 23	8 5	...	1035	...	12 13	...	3 38	...	6 44	...	...	10 59	1232
Plan		...	5 40	8 24	...	...	a.m.	12 27	...	3 57	...	7 1	...	...	11 12	1256
Schweissing Tsc.		...	6 15	8 58	...	RC	1155	...	...	4 40	...	7 29	...	...	...	1 38
Mies-Kladrau		...	6 28	9 12	...	...	1210	12 55	...	4 59	...	7 41	...	...	11 40	1 56
Neuhof		1,2,3	6 42	9 25	...	...	1226	...	...	5 12	...	7 54	...	...	...	2 13
Pilsen ....arr		a.m.	7 30	10 2	...	144	1 15	1 25	...	5 51	...	8 30	...	...	12 9	3 6
" ....dep		5 5	—	10 30	...	1150	2 15	1 31	...	6 30	...	8 40	...	...	12 14	—
Nezvestic...................		5 38	...	11 1	...	...	2 50	...	...	7 3	...	9 9	...	...	...	...
Blowic		5 52	...	11 17	...	...	3 8	...	...	7 18	...	9 20	...	...	...	...
Nepomuk...................		6 12	...	11 38	...	B	3 31	2 4	...	7 40	...	9 38	...	...	...	...
Horazdiowic-Babin...		6 54	...	12 25	...	...	4 25	2 31	...	8 33	...	1021	...	...	1 17	...
Strakonic..........	1,2,3	7 24	...	1 8	...	1259	4 57	2 47	...	9 8	...	1046	...	...	1 34	...
Razice	a.m.	7 48	...	1 32	...	...	5 21	3 2	...	9 34	...	11 5	...	...	...	...
Protivin	5 11	8 2	...	1 45	...	1 22	5 36	3 11	...	9 51	...	1116	...	...	1 57	...
Wodnan-Cicenic	5 23	8 16	...	1 59	...	1 30	5 53	...	...	1011	...	1126	...	...	...	...
Nakry-Netolic ...	5 35	8 28	...	2 10	...	...	6 8	...	2&3	1025	...	1137	...	...	...	...
Budweis ...arr	6 7	9 0	a.m.	2 44	...	1 56	6 44	3 45	p.m.	1057	...	12 7	...	...	2 34	...
" ...dep	6 34	9 13	10 5	2 54	...	2 9	—	3 52	5 20	—	...	1222	...	...	2 50	...
Forbes-Schweintz	7 8	...	1039	3 27	...	...	...	...	5 54	...	...	1254	...	...	...	...
Gratzen	7 32	...	11 2	3 48	...	...	...	...	6 19	...	...	1 13	...	...	...	...
Gmünd (243)arr	7 50	9 59	1120	4 6	...	2 55	...	4 40	6 37	...	...	1 29	...	...	3 43	...
VIENNA ......arr	1240	1248	5p20	7 p25	...	5p32	...	7 p25	...	...	...	6a25	...	...	6a52	...

MARIENBAD and CARLSBAD.

Marienbad...dep	6a42	6a59	10‡15	10a31	1p11	4 p59	5 p50	6 p44	7 §32	8p42
Tepl	7 14	7 41	10 47	11 12	1 59	5 31	...	7 25	8 4	9 25
Petschau..................	7 31	8 6	11 8	11 40	2 26	5 50	‡	7 49	8 23	9 51
Schonwehr...............	...	8 15	...	11 48	2 35	...	...	7 57	...	9 59
Carlsbad Cen.arr	8 0	8 44	11 34	12 16	3 4	6 17	7 7	8 23	8 49	1028
Carlsbad Cent....	5a54	7a34	8 a50	10a34	12§34	1 p32	3 p23	6 ‡22	8 p24	9p16
Schonwehr...............	6 33	8 16	...	...	...	2 12	4 3	6 52	9 6	...
Petschau..................	6 45	8 29	‡	11 9	1 9	2 25	4 16	7 1	9 18	9 51
Tepl	7 14	9 0	...	11 32	1 32	2 55	4 47	7 26	9 47	1014
Marienbad ...arr	7 47	9 34	10 14	11 57	1 57	3 28	5 24	7 56	10 22	1039

Schonwehr dep	8a18	4 p7	9p10	...	Elbogen ... dep	7a11	12p50	5p26	...
Elbogen ......arr	9 1	5 6	1015	...	Schonwehr arr	8 1	2 2	6 43	...

§—Runs until 31st Aug. ‡—Runs until 15th Sept.

NEUHAUS and NEUBISTRITZ.

Neuhaus .....dep	8a25	3p25	9p50
Konigseck Tieb'r	9 42	4 35	1056
Neubistritz...arr	1033	5 26	1140
Neubistritz..dep	5 a5	1210	7 p5
Konigseck Tieb'r	6 0	1 5	8 2
Neuhaus 239b arr	7 3	2 9	9 7

DALLWITZ and MERKELSGRUN.

Dallwitz.........dep	11 a5	3p40	8p40	Merkelsgrün...dep	7a38	2p14	7 p9	...
Merkelsgrün ...arr	11 59	4 34	9 33	Dallwitz.........arr	8 30	3 5	8 4	...

CARLSBAD and JOHANNGEORGENSTADT.

Carlsbad Central ....dep	6a50	9a15	12p23	4p49	5p29	8p28	**Johanngeorge.** dep	6a30	9a45	12p4	2p12	7 p0
" Buschterad-Bahnhof dep	7 8	9 35	12 36	5 2	5 44	8 54	Neuhammer	7 38	...	1 13	3 18	8 10
Neurohlau 247B..................	7 34	9 59	1 0	5 27	6 9	9 21	Neurohlau	8 22	...	1 57	4 3	8 52
Neuhammer	8 28	1044	1 57	6 20	7 3	1018	**Carlsbad** Bu.E.B.arr	8 46	1138	2 23	4 28	9 16
Johanngeorgenstadt 189A arr	9 34	1145	3 1	7 21	8 5	1120	" Central Bahnhof arr	9 13	1149	2 34	4 40	9 33

STRAKONIC and BREZNITZ.

Strakonic dep	7a32	3p35	9p58	**Breznitz** ...dep	5a10	11a 4	6p48
Blatna	8 51	4 38	1126	Blatna	6 4	11 55	7 41
Breznitz 245 arr	9 48	5 25	...	**Strakonic** 243A	7 9	12 53	8 42
Breznitz ... dep	6a23	11 a6	6p50	Rozmital	4a28	9a20	4p57
Rozmital ... arr	6 51	11 34	7 18	Breznitz	4 55	9 47	5 24

ST. POLTEN and GUSSWERK.

St. Polten ....dep	...	...	7a37	11a55	...	1p57	5 p23	...	...
Ober-Grafendorf	...	...	8 5	12 24	...	2 25	5 52	...	...
Ruprechtshofen...arr	...	...	1019	2 11	...	...	7 17	...	...
Kirchberg am Pielach	...	...	8 57	1 19	...	3 20	6 48	...	...
Laubenbachmühle ...	...	...	9 50	2 10	...	4 0	7 37	...	...
Mariazell	5a47	9a50	1119	3 40	4p10	—	9 5	...	...
Gusswerk ....arr	6 5	10 8	1233	—	4 29	...	—	...	...

Gusswerk ....dep	...	6a32	11a26	3 p32	5p10	...	...	...
Mariazell	...	7 10	12 30	4 5	5 28	...	...	...
Laubenbachmühle ...	4a40	8 55	2 18	5 50	—	...	...	...
Kirchberg am Pielach	5 23	9 40	3 3	6 35	...	...	...	...
Ruprechtshofen...dep	5 0	...	1 53	5 44	...	...	...	...
Ober-Grafendorf	6 17	1028	3 58	7 29	...	...	...	...
St. Polten 239 ......arr	6 46	1057	4 27	7 58	...	...	...	...

NEUHOF and WESERITZ.

Neuhof..........dep	8 a49	12p40	8 p0	...
Weseritz.........arr	10 10	2 13	9 34	...
Weseritz.......dep	5 a0	10a49	5 p0	...
Neuhof..........arr	6 33	12 15	6 35	...

PRAGUE, PILSEN, and FURTH I. W.

Dist E M		1,2,3	2&3	2&3	1,2,3	1,2,3	Ex3	2&3	1,2,3	2&3	Ex3	1,2,3	2&3	1,2,3	2&3	2&3	Ex3	2&3	1,2,3	2&3	1,2,3	2&3
			a.m.		a.m.	a.m.	a.m.	a.m.	a.m.	p.m.	p.m.	p.m.	p.m.	p.m	p.m.	p.m.	p.m.		p.m.	p.m.	p.m	p.m.
—	**Prague** ....dep	...	...	...	6 10	6 45	8 11	8 33	9 28	...	1 0	1 43	2 25	3 7	4 15	5 20	6 5	...	6 43	7 45	8 40	1049
3	Smichov....................	...	...	...	6 30	7 7	8 23	8 47	9 49	1230	1 9	2 4	2 38	3 28	4 35	5 37	6 15	...	7 2	8 9	8 53	11 7
20	Hinter Treban.........	...	...	a.m.	7 12	8 2	...	9 34	1039	1 17	...	2 54	—	...	5 22	6 24	...	...	7 55	8 56	...	1152
27½	**Beraun 245**	...	...	6 10	7 35	8 32	8 59	9 56	11 3	1 38	1 44	3 20	...	4 32	5 44	6 44	6 51	...	8 21	9 22	9 35	1212
33	**Zdic 245**	...	...	6 26	7 58	8 49	9 14	1012	1133	—	1 59	3 46	...	4 50	6 5	—	7 20	...	—	9 38	9 52	—
45½	Zbirow	...	6 5	—	8 38	—	...	—	12 7	...	...	4 31	...	—	6 50	...	...	...	...	—	1032	...
57½	**Rokitzan**	...	6 41	...	9 17	...	9 54	...	1238	...	2 39	5 5	...	...	7 20	...	7 53	p.m.	...	...	1110	...
64½	**Chrast**	...	7 4	...	9 32	...	...	...	1256	...	...	5 24	...	...	7 39	...	...	9 *0	...	...	1125	...
71½	**Pilsen** ....arr	...	7 22	...	9 47		1014	...	1 11	...	3 0	5 40	...	...	7 56	...	8 13	9 25	...	...	1140	...
137½	**Eger 243A** ......arr	a.m.	1050	...	1p45	|	1p45	...	5p20	...	5p20	9p21	...	...	...	...	1115	...	...	...	5a36	...
—	**Pilsen** ....dep	6 5	...	...	1028		...	...	1 55	...	3 11	6 2	...	...	...	...	...	...	...	...	1215	...
95¾	Stankau	7 15	...	...	1136	...	...	...	3 9	...	3 58	7 15	...	...	...	...	...	...	...	...	1 6	...
107½	Taus 248..................	7 51	...	...	1210	...	...	...	3 40	...	4 20	7 49	...	...	...	...	...	...	...	...	1 33	...
121¾	**Furth-i.-W. 204** arr	8 22	...	...	1241	...	...	...	4 18	...	4 44	8 20	...	...	...	...	...	...	...	...	2 0	...
163½	SCHWANDORF arr	1037	...	...	2p37	...	...	...	...	...	6p28	10p25	...	...	...	...	...	...	...	...	3a52	...
221¾	NURNBERG 204 arr	1p15	...	...	5p50	...	...	...	...	...	8p11	...	...	...	...	...	...	...	...	...	6a39	...

*—Runs until 15th August.

	2&3	1,2,3	2&3	2&3	1,2,3	2&3		1,2,3	Ex3	2&3	1,2,3	1,2,3	1,2,3	1,2,3	Ex3	2&3	Ex3	1,2,3	1,2,3	2&3	2 & 3
NURNBERG 204 dep	...	9 p0	...	...	...	...	...	...	...	...	...	...	...	4 a58	10 a8	...	...	...	...	...	...
SCHWANDORF dep	...	11p14	...	...	...	...	...	...	...	...	...	4a34	...	7 a55	12p20	...	...	...	1 p5	...	...
		a.m.						a.m.				a.m.		a.m.	p.m.				p.m.	p.m.	
Furth-i.-W. ....dep	...	1 25	...	...	...	...	...	5 14	...	...	...	7 15	...	10 52	1 48	...	...	...	3 11	7 45	...
Taus	...	2 5	...	...	...	...	...	5 51	...	...	...	7 57	...	11 32	2 13	...	...	...	3 49	8 26	...
Stankau	...	2 32	...	...	...	...	...	6 21	...	...	...	8 30	...	12 9	2 32	...	...	...	4 24	8 56	...
Pilsen..............arr	...	3 28	...	...	...	...	...	7 35	...	...	...	9 35	...	1 21	3 10	...	...		5 32	9 59	...
Eger 243A...... dep	...	11p17	...	...	...	a.m.	...	...	4a30	...	...	7 a7	...	11a28	1128	...	2p32	|	2p32	...	10p15
Pilsen ....dep	...	3 43	...	...	...	6 46	...	...	8 12	...	...	1019	...	2 25	3 21	...	6 10		6 40	...	12§10
Chrast	...	4 1	...	...	...	7 4	...	...	...	...	...	1038	...	2 50	...	...	...	...	6 59	...	12 31
Rokitzan	...	4 15	...	...	...	7 25	...	...	8 33	...	...	11 0	...	3 9	3 43	...	6 31	...	7 25	...	12 52
Zbirow	a.m.	4 47	...	...	a.m.	8 2	...	...	...	a.m.	a.m.	1133	p.m.	3 44	...	...	...	p.m.	8 3	...	1 30
Zdic	4 45	5 21	a.m.	a.m.	6 31	8 35	...	...	9 19	1025	1136	1210	3 15	4 40	...	p.m.	7 10	7 14	8 42	...	—
Beraun	5 4	5 39	5 50	6 32	6 48	8 52	...	...	9 29	1041	1152	1227	3 32	4 58	4 29	6 10	7 20	7 32	9 2	...	...
H. Treban	5 26	...	6 17	6 56	7 10	9 14	...	...	...	11 2	1212	...	3 53	5 21	...	6 33	...	7 50	9 23	...	...
Smichov	6 14	6 26	7 20	7 46	7 56	1011	...	...	10 7	1150	1 9	1 29	4 47	6 19	5 6	7 25	7 57	8 40	1013	...	...
Prague ....arr	...	6 39	7 34	...	8 9	1024	...	...	1015	...	1 22	1 42	5 0	6 34	5 14	7 38	8 5	8 56	1027	...	...

§—Sun. and Wed. night only.

E M												
	Chrast...dep	7 a7	10a39	2p50	7 p5	...	Radnitz dep	5a40	8a25	11a54	4p14	...	...
10½	Radnitz arr	8 7	11 35	3 57	8 14	...	Chrast...arr	6 45	9 25	12 50	5 20	...	...

KREMS and ST. VALENTIN.

E.M							
			a.m.	a.m.	a.m.	p.m.	p.m.
—	**Krems-a-d-Donau** dep	...	5§10	...	9 15	1 15	7 18
2½	Stein-Mautern	...	5 28	...	9 24	1 24	7 27
4¼	Dürnstein-Oberloiben	...	5 48	...	9 34	1 34	7 38
27¼	Kleinpöchlarn	...	9 57	...	11 1	3 0	9 3
30½	Marbach-Maria Taferl	a.m.	10 18	...	11 10	3 11	9 16
48½	**Grein**	4 46	1 0	1053	12 12	4 26	1030
67	Mauthausen 240	5 58	—	12 9	—	5 50	—
71½	**St. Valentin 239** ......arr	6 12	...	1223	...	6 4	...

		a.m.	p.m.	p.m.	p.m.	p.m.
St. Valentin ....dep	...	6 50	...	1 24	...	7 12
Mauthausen	a.m.	7 5	...	1 39	...	7 25
Grein	4 52	8 23	...	2 55	5 12	8 33
Marbach-Maria Taferl......	5 52	9 46	12§18	—	6 23	—
Kleinpöchlarn	6 1	10 3	12 57	...	6 32	...
Dürnstein-Oberloiben	7 25	11 40	4 1	...	8 1	...
Stein-Mautern	7 35	11 50	4 25	...	8 11	...
Krems 248A..............arr	7 42	11 58	4 35	...	8 18	...

§—Not on Sunday.

BRUX and TSCHISCHKOWITZ.

Station					
Brux dep	3a15	...	9 a9	2p34	5p50
Obernitz	3 27	4 a35	9 30	3 8	6 23
Triblitz	...	6 0	10 41	4 28	7 33
Tschischkowitz arr	...	6 40	11 20	5 10	...

Station			
Tschischkowitz dep	5a19	10a50	6 p45
Triblitz	6 7	11 52	7 51
Obernitz	7 9	1 8	9 7
Brux (246) arr	7 34	1 32	9 26

EISENSTEIN, PILSEN and DUX.

Station											
				a.m.	a.m.	a.m.			p.m.	p.m.	a'gt
Eisenstein dep		...	...	...	6 3	10 20	...	...	2 47	9 4	1227
Grun		...	...	...	6 47	11 4	...	...	3 31	9 50	1 10
Janovic		...	...	5 53	7 18	11 33	...	...	4 2	1021	1 39
Klattau		...	...	6 13	7 50	11 59	...	...	4 23	1039	1 56
Prestitz		...	...	6 57	8 34	12 43	...	...	5 6	1119	2 40
Pilsen 243B arr		...	...	7 31	9 10	1 17	...	...	5 40	1152	3 12
PRAGUE arr		a.m.	...	10 15	1p42	5 p14	p.m.	...	8 p5	—	6a39
Pilsen dep		5 10	...	—	1025	—	3 24	...	6 20	...	—
Mlatz		6 13	...	...	1127	p.m.	4 14	...	7 27	...	...
Pladen		6 43	...	...	1157	3 50	4 36	...	7 59	...	...
Rudig		7 9	...	...	1226	4 18	...	...	8 27	...	...
Kaschitz	a.m.	7 36	...	...	1251	4 45	...	p.m.	8 50	...	...
Saaz (Staats)	5 6	8 3	...	...	1 22	5 13	5 37	6 22	9 18	...	...
Saaz B.E.B.	5 13	8 11	...	...	1 38	—	5 42	6 30	9 34	...	...
Postelberg	5 30	8 27	...	...	2 0	...	5 56	6 51	9 51	...	...
Potscherad	5 42	8 38	a.m.	p.m.	2 15	...	...	7 3	10 2	...	...
Obernitz	6 4	8 58	1115	1 15	2 33	...	6 16	7 32	10 45	...	...
Bilin Hbf	6 24	9 17	1137	1 37	3 21	...	6 30	7 54	11 7	...	...
Dux A.T.Bhf	6 34	9 27	1147	1 48	3 30	...	6 39	8 4	11 17	...	...

Station								
		a.m.	a.m.	a.m.	p.m.	p.m.	p.m.	p.m.
Dux A. T. Bhf. dep	...	5 32	8 18	10 18	1236	2 16	5 40	1013
Bilin Hauptbhf	...	5 42	8 29	10‡28	1246	2 27	5 51	1025
Obernitz dep	...	6 16	8 50	10 39	1 14	3 5	6 20	1048
Potscherad	...	6 33	—	...	1 32	3 23	6 40	11 6
Postelberg	...	6 43	...	10 57	1 43	3 34	6 53	1116
Saaz (B.E.B.) dep	a.m.	7 3	...	11 11	2 14	3 51	7 30	1133
Saaz (Staats)	5 5	7 9	...	11 17	2 20	3 54	7 36	1136
Kaschitz	5 36	7 37	...	...	2 50	—	8 5	—
Rudig	6 2	7 59	...	...	3 14	...	8 26	...
Pladen	6 30	8 30	...	12 14	3 46	...	8 59	...
Mlatz	—	8 58		...	4 14	...	9 27	...
Pilsen arr	...	9 58		1 22	5 15	...	1030	...
PRAGUE dep	a.m.	8a11		—	1p43	6 p5	8p40	...
Pilsen dep	5 59	10 30		...	6 9	8 37	1222	...
Prestitz	6 43	11 15		...	6 54	9 21	1 4	...
Klattau	7 40	12 11		...	7 45	10 6	1 52	...
Janovic	7 56	12 28		...	8 1	1020	2 6	...
Grun	8 44	1 15	...	...	8 47	—	2 50	...
Eisenstein 198 arr	9 38	2 9	...	...	9 41	...	3 43	...

‡—Bilin Stadt Station.

RAKONITZ and MLATZ.

Station				
Rakonitz dep	6 a 5	1 p30	6 p30	...
Kralowitz	8 11	3 25	8 32	...
Mlatz arr	8 45	4 6	9 13	...

Station					
Mlatz dep	6 a20	9 a40	7 p43	...	...
Kralowitz	7 5	10 37	8 45	...	...
Rakonitz arr	8 35	12 22	10 23	...	...

HOHENSTADT and ZOPTAU

Station							
Hohenstadt dep	4a28	7a25	10a55	1p34	5 p0	...	9p35
Blauda	4 46	7 41	11 15	1 53	5 17	p.m.	9 57
Schönberg **244**	5 55	7 58	11 24	2 10	5 33	7 20	1022
Petersdorf	6 15	8 13	11 44	2 28	5 48	7 37	1038
Zoptau arr	6 24	8 21	11 52	2 37	5 56	7 45	1046

Station										
Zoptau dep	...	4a48	7a20	8a36	12p15	2p54	6p20	...	8p33	...
Petersdorf	a.m.	5 3	7 29	8 50	12 23	3 3	6 36	...	8 42	...
Schonberg	3 38	5 40	7 44	10 2	12 45	3 35	6 51	7p36	8 57	...
Blauda	3 49	5 55	—	1013	12 56	3 46	—	7 50	—	...
Hohenstadt	4 5	6 14	...	1030	1 12	4 2	...	8 10	...	...

Station					
Petersdorf dep	6 a20	11a48	2 p32	7 p40	...
Bad Ullersdorf	6 35	12 2	2 43	7 55	...
Winkelsdorf arr	7 14	12 38	3 27	8 30	...

Station				
Winkelsdorf dep	4 a8	7 a56	1p26	5 p23
Bad Ullersdorf	4 43	8 25	2 1	6 10
Petersdorf arr	4 58	8 40	2 15	6 24

OLMÜTZ and ZIEGENHALS.

Station								
	a.m.		a.m.	a.m.		p.m.	p.m.	p.m.
Olmütz dep	2 56	...	9 10	11 30	...	4 42	7 44	1150
Sternberg	3 38	...	9 38	12 2	...	5 15	8 11	1215
Mährisch-Neustadt	4 4	a.m.	10 5	12 27	...	5 42	8 37	—
Schönberg	5 28	7 59	11 6	1 40	...	6 57	9 32	...
Blauda	5 36	8 7	1114	1 51	...	7 9	—	...
Hannsdorf 244 arr	6 13	8 48	1149	2 27	...	7 45	...	...
" dep	6 32	—	1222	2 40	p.m.	7 56	...	a.m.
Nieder-Lindewiese	7 50	10a47	1 51	3 56	6 23	9 17	...	4 48
Freiwaldau-Gräfenberg	8 2	10 58	2 4	4 9	6 34	9 29	...	4 59
Niklasdorf	8 33	11 26	2 35	4 42	7 4	10 0	...	5 28
Ziegenhals 249 arr	8 49	11 42	2 51	4 58	7 20	10 17	...	5 44

Station								
		a.m.	a.m.	p.m.	p.m.	p.m.	p.m.	p.m.
Ziegenhals dep		5 47	9 9	12 26	2 20	3 53	7 49	10 22
Niklasdorf		6 5	9 27	12 43	2 35	4 12	8 6	10 39
Freiwaldau-Gräfenb.		6 35	9 57	1 12	3 1	4 48	8 40	11 8
Nieder-Lindewiese		6 48	10 10	1 25	3 10	5 3	8 50	11 18
Hannsdorf arr		7 59	11 21	2 32	—	6 15	—	—
" dep	6a40	8 9	11 56	2 45	...	6 30	...	...
Blauda	7 18	8 48	12 34	3 25	...	7 8	...	a.m.
Schönberg arr	7 25	8 56	12 42	3 33	...	7 15	...	5 25
Mährisch Neust'dt	—	10 7	1 57	4 37	...	8 34	a.m.	6 17
Sternberg ...		10 38	2 25	5 9	...	9 2	3 22	6 47
Olmutz (221) arr ...		11 2	2 48	5 34	...	9 25	3 45	7 12

Station								
Hannsdorf dep	...	...	8a57	11 54	2p39	...	8 p4	...
Grulich arr	...	...	9 44	12 38	3 20	...	8 52	...
" dep	4a55	6a50	9 55	12 44	3 21	4p43	9 10	...
Wichstadtl-Lich. 225 arr	5 12	7 8	10 4	12 54	3 29	4 53	9 19	...

Station								
Wichstadtl-Lich. dep	5a30	10a47	1p43	3p45	5p17	10p22	...	...
Grulich arr	5 39	10 56	1 52	3 54	5 26	10 32	...	...
" dep	5 44	10 58	1 53	—	5 35	—	...	...
Hannsdorf arr	6 25	11 40	2 34	...	6 17	...	...	...

Station							
Grulich dep	6 a5	9a50	2p0	5p50	9p20	...	...
Mährisch Schildberg arr	7 18	1048	3 5	6 59	1011	...	...

Station							
Mährisch Schildberg dep	4a38	8a25	1125	3p32	7p25	...	...
Grulich arr	5 37	9 30	1232	4 38	8 47	...	...

Station							
Hannsdorf dep	6 a45	12 p2	2 p48	8 p13	...	...	...
Mähr. Altstadt arr	7 20	12 37	3 25	8 50	...	...	...

Station							
Mähr. Altstadt dep	5 a35	10a59	1p49	5 p18	...	...	...
Hannsdorf arr	6 9	11 33	2 23	5 54	...	...	...

SPALATO and KNIN.

E.M.	Station				
	Spalato dep	6 a30	12†0	5p25	...
5	Salona	6 46	1216	5 41	...
13	Castelvecchio-Stari	7 21	1249	6 16	...
39¾	**Perkovic** arr	8 42	—	7 35	...
...	**Perkovic** dep	9 0	...	7 48	...
56½	**Sebenico** arr	9 49	...	8 37	...
...	**Perkovic** dep	8 52	...	7 45	...
65¼	Dernis	10 4	...	8 55	...
67	Siveric	10 24	...	9 1	...
82	**Knin** arr	11 5	...	9 42	...

Station				
Knin dep	...	6 a25	...	5p30
Siveric	...	7 23	...	6 14
Dernis	...	7 29	...	6 20
Perkovic arr	...	8 38	...	7 30
Sebenico dep	...	7 40	...	6 21
Perkovic arr	...	8 33	...	7 14
Perkovic dep	a.m.	8 48	p.m.	7 42
Castelvecchio-St. ...	7†31	10 1	1 †8	8 54
Salona	8 4	10 31	1 41	9 24
Spalato arr	8 17	10 44	1 55	9 37

Station		
	a.m.	p.m.
Spalato dp	1010	6 15
Sinj ...arr	1243	8 50
Sinj ...dep	6 a0	3 p0
Spalato ar	8 4	5 6

†—Mon. and Thurs. only.

HORAZDIOWIC and TAUS.

E.M.	Station							
	Horazdiowic dep	...	5a45	...	8a35	12p35	4p25	10p40
12½	Schüttenhofen	...	6 21	...	9 53	1 23	4 59	11 10
19½	Kolinec	a.m.	6 44	a.m.	1032	—	5 21	—
36¾	Klattau (**244**)	6 20	7 33	10 5	1152	1 p44	6 19	...
41¾	Janovic	6 35	—	1020	—	2 9	6 39	...
61½	**Taus** (**243B**) arr	7 29	...	1114	...	3 30	7 34	...

Station							
Taus dep	...	8a13	...	12p15	4p23	...	8p28
Janovic	...	9 10	p.m.	1 12	5 23	...	9 49
Klattau	...	9 32	1210	1 24	5 36	7p50	10 3
Kolinec	...	1031	1 8	—	—	8 48	—
Schüttenhofen	4a45	1055	1 26	...	7p10	9 11	...
Horazdiowic	5 20	1129	1 55	...	8 0	9 42	...

BENESCHAU and UNTERKRALOWITZ.

E.M.	Station			
	Beneschau dep	8 a0	2 p40	6p25
18¾	Wlaschim	9 26	3 49	7 50
38½	Unterkralowitz arr	10 55	...	9 18

Station					
Unterkralowitz dep	4 a40	...	2p30	...	...
Wlaschim	6 10	11a15	4 21	...	...
Beneschau (243) arr	7 15	12 20	5 34	...	...

SCHWEISSING and HAID.

E.M.	Station				
	Schweissing dep	9 a28	12 p5	7 p38	...
10	Haid arr	10 26	12 59	8 31	...

Station						
Haid dep	7 a59	10a53	3 p50	...	...	...
Schweissing arr	8 45	11 40	4 35	...	...	...

SUCHA and STRYI.

	a.m.		a.m.				p.m.	p.m.	p.m.	p.m.
Sucha ......dep	2 35	...	9 10	...	...	...	1230	1 16	6 5	11 5
Chabówka	3 44	...	9 59	...	...	...	1 45	2 10	7 40	1215
Dobra	4 51	...	—	...	...	p.m.	2 59	—	8 48	1 26
Neu-Sandez	6 50	...	...	a.m.	...	1240	4 35	...	1035	3 15
Stroze.........	7 49	...	...	1025	...	1 44	7 5	10p0	1135	4 35
Zagorzany	—	...	...	11 8	...	4 0	7 46	1038	—	5 15
Jaslo	a.m	...	...	1225	...	4 55	8 44	1123	...	6 15
Neu-Zagórz	2 34	...	...	3 4	...	7 45	1111	—	...	8 45
Chyrów ......arr	4 28	a.m.	p.m	4 58	p.m.	1026	1 1	...	...	1034
,, (247) dep	4 40	8 30	1 3	5 12	8 18	—	1 18	...	...	1042
Sambor	6 19	9 31	2 1	6 30	9 16	...	2 25	...	...	1130
Drohobicz	7 39	1054	3 23	7 51	1038	...	3 45	...	...	—
Stryi ....arr	9 15	1140	4 4	8 37	1125	...	4 32	...	...	...

	a.m.		a.m.	a.m.	a.m.			p.m.	p.m.
Stryi...... dep	1 40	...	5 8	9 17	9 45	...	p.m.	4 5	1034
Drohobicz ...	2 30	...	5 59	10 6	1035	...	1248	4 58	1125
Sambor	—	...	7 22	1131	—	...	2 8	6 20	1 6
Chyrów ....arr		...	8 10	1219	...	...	2 56	7 6	1 53
,, ...dep		...	8 26	1229	...	p.m.	6 6	8 16	2 0
Neu-Zagórz ...	a.m.	...	1018	2 25	...	5 30	7 55	10 5	4 0
Jaslo	2 35	...	1230	4 30	...	8 10	—	—	6 18
Zagorzany......	3 21	...	1 17	5 16	...	8 59	...	...	7 7
Stroze	4 0	...	1 55	5 53	p.m.	9 54	...	a.m.	8 5
Neu-Sandez ...	6 0	...	4 15	8 5	4 48	11 5	...	6 55	9 6
Dobra	—	p.m.	—	—	6 18	1251	...	8 47	1 18
Chabówka		5 43	...	...	7 35	2 5	...	1015	2 35
Sucha (245)....arr		6 30	...	...	8 29	3 2	...	1112	3 35

STRYI and HUSIATYN.

Stryi.....dep	...	5a40	9a37	...	5p35	9 p50	...
Dolina........	...	6 55	1052	...	6 52	10 59	...
Kalusz	...	7 53	1147	...	7 48	11 51	...
Stanis- arr	...	9 18	1 10	p.m.	9 9	1 15	a.m.
lau ....dep	...	1158	—	5 23	—	—	3 14
Chryplin ...	...	12 7	...	5 31	...	...	3 22
Monasterzys	...	2 24	...	7 34	...	...	5 23
Buczacz......	p.m	3 20	...	8 31	a.m.	...	6 13
Biala Czort.	2 18	4 32	p.m.	9 45	7 10	...	7 24
Czortkow ...	2 37	4 45	6 52	1020	7 22	a.m.	7 46
Wygnanka..	2 59	—	7 23	1043	—	7 48	8 9
Kopyczynce	3 22	...	8 30	1128	...	8 15	8 53
Husiatyn ar	4 58	...	9 31	1230	...	...	9 57

Husiatyn dp	1a50	5a50	...	...	2p 5	...	6p40
Kopyczynce	3 5	7 21	7a40	...	3 10	3p50	8 21
Wygnanka..	3 36	8 3	8 8	...	—	4 35	8 52
Czortkow ...	4 16	8 25	—	10a20	...	7 50	9 22
Biala Czort.	4 39	8 46	...	10 43	...	8 12	9 44
Buczacz......	6 12	—	...	12 19	...	9 46	—
Monasterzys	7 9	...	...	1 14	...	1041	...
Chryplin	9 20	...	...	3 16	...	1253	...
Stanis- arr	9 28	a.m.	p.m.	3 23	...	1 1	...
lau.....dep	—	5 23	1212	5 27	...	1 22	...
Kalusz	...	6 50	1 41	6 50	...	2 47	...
Dolina	...	7 51	2 40	7 46	...	3 42	...
Stryi .....arr	...	8 51	3 40	8 43	...	4 42	...

GLEISDORF and WEIZ.

Gleisdorf........dep	7 a4	9a35	2 p47	7p30	9p24
Weiz ....arr	7 40	1015	3 26	8 6	10 0
Weiz..............dep	6 a0	8a25	1p15	5p50	8 p28
Gleisdorf (246) arr	6 36	9 6	1 52	6 26	9 4
Weiz ....dep	8 a5	1 p20	8 p20	...	...
Birkfeld ....arr	9 35	2 45	9 45	...	...
Birkfeld ....dep	6a35	11 a0	6p15	...	...
Weiz (245).......arr	8 0	12 40	7 40	...	...

LEMBERG and LAWOCZNE.

E.M						
	Lemberg .....dep	7a25	1p50	6p50	8 p15	11p25
28	Mikolajow-Dro.	8 43	3 7	8 8	9 36	12 45
46½	Stryi ....arr	9 30	3 53	8 53	10 24	1 30
...	,, ...dep	9 40	4 12	9 21	—	—
70½	Skole	1044	5 22	1030	...	...
91½	Lawoczne ....arr	1152	6 32	1140	...	...

Lawoczne 231 dep	2 a58	...	7 a9	...	6p33
Skole	4 0	...	8 14	3 p2	7 39
Stryi ....arr	4 50	a.m.	9 7	3 55	8 32
,, ...dep	5 13	6 50	9 34	4 14	8 55
Mikolajow-Dro.	5 59	7 38	10 20	4 59	9 41
Lemberg ......arr	7 20	9 0	11 40	6 20	11 0

TARNOW and ORLO.

Dist								
	Tarnow...dep	2a40	...	8a22	1p20	5 p10	...	8p10
13	Tuchow	3 12	...	8 59	1 53	5 44	...	8 42
36	Stroze ...arr	4 12	...	10 0	2 55	6 46	...	9 42
...	,, (245) dep	4 55	8 a5	1010	3 10	7 8	...	9 54
47¾	Ptaszkowa...	5 33	8 41	1042	3 48	7 42	p.m.	1026
61	Neu-Sandez.	6 0	9 6	11 4	4 15	8 5	8 28	1051
84½	Zegiestow ...	7 55	—	1225	6 1	—	9 36	—
100¾	Orlo ....arr	8 47	...	1 10	6 55	...	10 20	...

Orlo ......dep	...	4a50	9 a47	...	...	2p55	8 p0
Zegiestow	a.m.	5 38	10 36	...	p.m.	3 40	8 40
Neu-Sandz.	3 15	6 50	11 38	12p40	5 30	4 50	10 35
Ptaszkowa	3 50	7 28	—	1 19	6 8	5 27	11 13
Stroze...arr	4 15	7 49	...	1 44	6 35	5 48	11 35
,, ...dep	4 25	8 0	...	2 12	—	6 8	11 55
Tuchow ...	5 25	9 2	...	3 14	...	7 5	1 8
Tarnow 246A	5 56	9 31	...	3 44	...	7 36	1 30

LAUN and BERAUN.

Laun ......dep	...	7a43	11a35	4p35	7 p4
Domauschitz ...	...	8 40	12 32	5 34	8 1
Rakonitz	5a27	9 43	1 42	6 25	—
Purglitz	5 56	1012	2 11	7 23	...
Beraun ...arr	6 42	1056	2 54	8 12	...

Beraun ...dep	...	...	7a53	12p2	3p35	9p35
Purglitz..........	...	...	8 41	1247	4 22	1022
Rakonitz	4a35	...	9 34	1 16	4 58	1052
Domauschitz....	5 28	6a39	1028	—	5 52	—
Laun.......arr	6 12	7 28	1116	...	6 36	...

RAKONITZ and PETSCHAU.

Rakonitz..dep		5a15	10a0	2p20	5p55
Pladen....	...	6 55	1233	4 42	7 28
Protiwitz	5a10	8 10	1 31	5 44	9 6
Petschau	7 11	1021	3 34	7 41	...

Petschau..dep	...	8a30	11a56	4p17
Protiwitz......	5a42	1046	2 7	6 22
Pladen	7 5	1232	4 0	8 8
Rakonitz..arr	8 42	2 4	5 20	9 20

Protiwitz	8a15	10a56	2p13	6p28	9p20
Buchau ...	9 18	11 58	3 13	7 30	1022
Buchau ...dep	9a43	12p30	4p27	7 p58	
Protiwitz arr	1039	1 27	5 32	8 54	

PROTIVIN and ZDIC.

Protivin dp	3a23	...	6a55	8a20	12 0	3p50
Pisek	3 44	...	7 11	8 44	12 25	4 14
Cimelic......	4 32	...	...	9 36	1 13	5 2
Breznitz	4 59	...	8 6	10 4	1 45	5 33
Tochovic....	5 8	a.m.	...	1013	1 54	5 42
Pribram	5 38	7 45	8 33	1045	2 22	6 16
Lochowitz.	6 8	8 15	...	1115	2 53	6 46
Zdic 243B	6 22	8 28	9 8	1128	3 6	6 59

Zdic ...dep	...	6a30	9a17	1138	5 p0	7p15	9p54
Lochowitz	...	6 46	9 33	1154	5 16	...	1010
Pribram ...	5a45	7 21	1015	1236	6 7	7 52	1048
Tochovic..	6 11	—	1038	1 1	6 31	...	—
Breznitz...	6 22	...	1051	1 12	6 44	8 18	...
Cimelic....	6 47	...	1118	1 38	7 9	...	...
Pisek	7 35	...	12 9	2 22	7 57	9 10	...
Protivin ar	7 55	...	1231	2 41	8 16	...	...

DOLINA and WYGODA.

Dolina dep	11a12
Wygoda ar	11 42
Wygoda dp	1p45
Dolina arr	2 15

OSWIECIM and PODGORZE.

Oswiecim No'd dp		5a20	7a55	...	1p50	...	...	6p56	...
Spytkowice.........		5 59	8 43	p.m.	2 45	...	...	7 34	p.m.
Skawina	5 a6	7 6	9 42	1 15	3 52	5p56	7p50	8 19	1017
Podgorze	5 41	7 42	1020	1 51	4 29	6 36	8 10	8 53	1050

Podgórze .	4a35	7‡a21	9a45	10 39	1p29	3p38	8p13	12 a8
Skawina..	5 17	7 45	1021	11 13	2 10	4 9	9 5	1 0
Spytkowice	6 7	—	—	—	2 56	—	1017	2 10
Oswiecim	6 44	...	...	...	3 34	...	1118	3 12

JASLO and RZESZOW.

Jaslo...............dep	6a22	1p40	8p50	...
Rzeszow 246A arr	8 14	3 35	1041	...

Rzeszow ....dep	4 a0	9a50	6p15	...	...
Jaslo (245) ......arr	5 50	11 42	8 3	...	...

NIEDER-LINDEWIESE and HEINERSDORF.

Nieder-Lindewiese		4a56	10a13	1p46	5 p8	9p25
Haugsdorf		5 48	11 6	2 35	5 59	1016
Barzdorf	8 a2	6 2	11 20	2 52	6 15	1030
Heinersdorf arr	8 6	6 8	...	2 55	6 19	...

Heinersdorf dep		6a15	8a20	p.m.	3p30	7p58
Barzdorf ...	3a30	6 21	8 25	12 9	3 37	8 2
Haugsdorf ...	3 47	6 41	—	1226	3 54	8 17
Nieder-Lind	4 36	7 37	...	1 15	4 45	9 9

Haugsdorf to Weidenau......5.54, 6.42, 11.10 a.m., 12.42, 4.10, 6.10, 10.20 p.m.
Weidenau to Haugsdorf......5.28, 6.18, 10.42 a.m., 12.11, 3.36, 5.35, 9.58 p.m.

Barzdorf to Jauernig ......6.28, 8.31, 11.23 a.m., 2.51, 3.45, 6.15, 8.10, 10.31 p.m.
Jauernig to Barzdorf ......3.16, 5.35, 7.40, 11.53 a.m., 2.17, 3.22, 5.40, 7.45 p.m.

DROHOBICZ and TUSTANOWICE.

Drohobicz ....dep	2a40	3a55	6 a2	7a12	7a50	11a3	1p31	3p27	5p13	7p59	11p27
Tustanowice .arr	3 8	4 24	6 30	7 47	8 20	1131	2 3	3 56	5 42	8 33	11 55
Tustanowice ....dep	3 a9	5a16	7a49	9a28	12p16	2p44	7p12	9p54	...	...	
Drohobicz ....arr	3 33	5 40	8 19	9 52	12 40	3 13	7 36	1018	...	...	

ZAGORZANY and GORLICE.

	a.m.	a.m.	a.m.	a.m.	p.m.	p.m.	p.m.	p.m.	p.m.	p.m.	
Zagorzany....dep	3 30	5 26	7 20	1115	1 25	4 10	5 26	7 54	9 10	1043	...
Gorlice..........arr	3 46	5 42	7 36	1131	1 41	4 26	5 42	8 10	9 26	1059	...

	a.m.	a.m.	a.m.	a.m.	p.m.	p.m.	p.m.	p.m.	p.m.	p.m.	
Gorlice.........dep	2 50	4 46	6 41	1037	1250	3 28	4 50	7 15	8 30	10 5	...
Zagorzany....arr	3 6	5 2	6 57	1053	1 5	3 43	5 6	7 30	8 46	1020	...

NIKLASDORF & ZUCKMANTEL.

Niklasdorf ...dep	6a10	9a35	12§p48	2p45	4p50	10p45
Zuckmantel ...arr	6 42	1010	1 19	3 16	5 22	11 16

Zuckmantel dep	4a50	7a55	12§0	1p41	3p30	6p10	...
Niklasdorf arr	5 21	8 27	1231	2 16	4 5	6 45	...

§—Runs until 15th September.

BODENBACH and KOMOTAU.

Dist.	Station		a.m.	a.m.	p.m.	p.m.	p.m.
—	**Bodenbach** ......dep	...	6 17	11 58	3 15	6 47	9 23
12	Tyssa-Königswald......	...	6 50	12 30	3 50	7 19	9 59
21¼	Kulm	...	7 18	12 57	4 17	7 45	10 25
24¾	Rosenthal-Graupen ...	a.m.	7 34	1 11	4 30	7 58	10 38
27¼	Teplitz-Waldthor	4 40	7 46	1 22	4 39	8 7	10 46
29¾	Kosten..........	4 48	7 54	1 29	4 46	8 14	—
34¼	Ossegg..........	5 3	8 8	1 44	5 1	8 31	...
...	**Wiesa-** arr	5 15	8 22	1 56	5 13	8 44	...
38¼	**Oberleutensdorf**	5 33	8 33	2 5	5 20	8 55	...
42¾	Obergeorgenthal.........	5 55	8 49	2 20	5 37	9 10	...
56	**Komotau (250)** arr	7 1	9 28	2 54	6 16	9 45	...

Station		a.m.	a.m.	p.m.	p.m.	p.m.
Komotau..........dep		4 28	8 28	1 12	5 0	7 10
Obergeorgenthal		5 3	9 6	1 47	5 37	7 44
Wiesa-Ober- (246) arr	a.m.	5 17	9 19	2 0	5 50	7 58
leutensdorf ...dep	6 29	5 30	9 22	2 8	5 53	8 10
Ossegg	6 47	5 43	9 35	2 21	6 6	8 27
Kosten	7 8	5 58	9 49	2 36	6 20	8 40
Teplitz-Waldthor	7 17	6 7	9 56	2 44	6 28	8 48
Rosenthal-Graupen......	—	6 18	10 6	2 55	6 39	9 0
Kulm		6 34	1020	3 10	6 54	9 14
Tyssa-Königswald		7 3	1043	3 33	7 20	9 41
Bodenbach (252) ...arr		7 34	1112	4 2	7 48	10 12

PRAGUE, BRUX, and MOLDAU.

Station	2 & 3	1,2,3	1,2,3	2 & 3	2 & 3	1,2,3	2 & 3	Ex3	2&3
Prague—K.		a.m.	a.m.	a.m.	p.m.	p.m.	p.m.	p.m.	p.m.
F. J. Bhnf	...	6 10	6 55	11 12	4 15	3 25	6 15	8 20	1059
Smichov........	...	6 36	7 13	11 29	4 46	3 43	6 32	8 29	1116
Dusnik	...	7 7	7 46	12 1	5 20	4 14	7 8	...	1147
Noutonic	a.m.	—	8 18	12 33	—	4 41	7 35	...	1214
Schlan........	5 20	...	9 2	1 14	...	5 27	8 19	9 30	1251
Zlonitz	5 37	...	9 19	1 29	...	5 44	8 36	9 41	—
Peruc	6 2	2&3	9 42	1 52	...	6 7	9 2	9 55	...
Laun	6 37	a.m.	10 13	2 22	p.m.	6 41	9 29	1018	...
Obernitz......	7 22	9 22	10 53	3 4	6 19	7 26	10 48	1036	...
Brüx (250) ar	7 34	9 37	11 5	3 16	6 35	7 38	11 0	1044	...
Wiesa-Oberl.	8 28	—	11 35	4 41	—	8 15	11 23	—	...
Klostergrab ...	8 55	...	12 6	5 7	...	8 46	11 54	...	...
Eichwald	9 20	...	12 31	5 32	...	9 11	—	...	...
Moldau ...arr	9 47	...	1 0	5 57	...	9 36	...	...	...

Station		1,2,3	Ex 3	1,2,3	2 & 3	2 & 3	1,2,3	2 & 3	2&3
				a.m.	a.m.	a.m.	p.m.	p.m.	p.m.
Moldau dep		...	...	7 4	...	10 15	12 50	4 1	...
Eichwald		a.m.	...	7 37	...	10 48	1 20	4 32	...
Klostergrab ...		4 58	...	7 59	...	11 4	1 40	4 50	...
Wiesa-Oberl.		5 24	a.m.	8 30	...	11 30	2 9	5 17	...
Brüx ...	3a15	5 46	6 5	9 9	10 11	11 51	2 34	5 50	1023
Ob'rnitz	3 28	6 19	6 14	9 26	10 28	12 52	2 57	6 18	1039
Laun	4 6	6 59	6 40	10 7	—	—	3 36	7 6	—
Peruc	4 36	7 28	6 56	10 36	...	...	4 6	7 39	...
Zlonitz ...	4 58	7 50	7 11	10 57	...	...	4 27	8 3	...
Schlan......	5 16	8 9	7 23	11 17	...	...	4 47	8 22	1,2,3
Noutonic	5 57	8 48	...	11 54	...	...	5 26	9 2	a.m.
Dusnik ...	6 25	9 16	8 3	12 23	...	...	5 55	9 30	5 41
Smichov ...	6 59	9 47	8 21	12 58	...	...	6 29	10 1	6 26
Prague	7 14	10 0	8 30	1 15	...	...	6 42	10 14	6 39

Station				
Laun..........	4a50	7a29	11a35	7p18
Postelberg (244)	5 25	8 4	12 13	7 54
Postelberg	5a55	1028	2p41	9p53
Laun	6 33	1116	3 18	1032
Dusnik	7 a8	12p30	5p21	7p15
Beraun	7 48	1 10	6 0	7 55
†Beraun	5 a3	1110	4p49	...
Dusnik	5 40	1152	5 33	...

ZLONITZ and RAUDNITZ.
†-From or at Raudnitz Stadt.

Station				
Zlonitz..........dep	5 a39	11a20	...	6p15
Straschkow-Wodochod	6 55	12 37	3p38	8 20
Raudnitz ....arr	7 51	1 21	4†22	9 10
Raudnitz ....dep	8a20	2 p15	5†p33	9p18
Straschkow-Wodochod	9 52	3 8	6 55	10 16
Zlonitz.......... arr	10 49	...	7 56	11 12

JENSCHOWITZ, LIBOCHOWITZ, and LAUN.
†At or from Lib. Stadt.

Station							
Jenschowitz dep	...	...	8a55	2p28	...	8p25	...
Straschkow-Wod.	...	...	10 0	3 36	...	9 13	...
Libochowitz	5a24	8a34	1125	5 24	8p20	10 9	...
Laun..........arr	6 21	9 36	1 8	6 24	9 23	...	...

Station					
Laun ....dep	4a20	7a10	10a16	4p25	7 p2
Libochowitz	5 31	8 32	11 26	5 34	8 5
Straschkow-Wod.	7 0	—	12 48	7 0	—
Jenschowitz ...arr	8 0	...	1 29	7 50	...

POTSCHERAD and WURZMES.

E.M.	Station			
	Potscherad ......dep	7 a0	2 p23	...
11½	Wurzmes ....arr	8 23	4 4	...
	Wurzmes ....dep	11a20	5 p11	...
	Potscherad **244** ...arr	1 0	6 30	...

KORNITZ and PROSSNITZ. [†—Lokalbahnhof—Weekdays only.

Station								
Kornitz..........dep	4a32	...	...	10a20	...	...	4p46	...
Kosteletz	5 57	7a26	10 a8	11 53	2p20	5†p9	6 48	9p54
Prossnitz (221) arr	6 15	7 43	10 18	12 18	2 40	5 22	6 39	10†4
Prossnitz.....dep	7a50	8 a24	12p35	2p52	3p20	4†30	6†42	7p14
Kosteletz (247)	8 11	8 44	12 52	3 11	3 37	4 41	6 54	7 41
Kornitz (252A) arr	...	10 5	...	4 32	...	...	...	9 4

BIERBAUM and NEUDAU.

Station					
Bierbaum......dep	9 a24	12p47	4 p50	7 p0	...
Neudau ....arr	9 52	1 15	5 15	7 24	...
Neudau..........dep	6 a15	11a10	3 p10	6 p5	...
Bierbaum (**246**) ...arr	6 39	11 34	3 34	6 38	...

GRAZ and ASPANG.

Station										
Graz Sud.)......dep		...	6 a0	8a20	10a0	1p10	2 p0	3p40	6p20	8p16
" (Staats) ...dep		...	6 9	8 32	1013	1 20	2 8	3 50	6 34	8 25
Gleisdorf		...	7 1	9 21	11 0	2 9	2 42	4 39	7 27	9 10
Feldbach........	a.m.	...	7 37	10 1	—	2 47	3 5	5 14	8 4	—
Fehring	4a55	a.m.	8 15	1035	...	3 30	3 15	5 47	8 30	...
Fürstenfeld ...	6 8	6 30	9 3	1128	...	4 24	—	6 35	9 20	...
Bierbaum	—	6 51	9 20	1146	...	4 40	...	6 51	—	...
Hartberg	a.m.	8 0	1020	1 11	...	5 40	...	7 53	...	...
Friedberg	5 5	9 0	1115	2 5	...	6 35	...	8 44	...	...
Aspang 248A	5 45	9 45	...	2 45	...	7 15	...	...	...	...

Station									
Aspang dep	...	...	...	...	5a55	9 a56	1p15	...	6p15
Friedberg ...	...	...	5a10	...	7 25	10 45	2 3	4p47	7 7
Hartberg ...	...	...	6 0	...	9 0	11 55	3 0	5 55	8 20
Bierbaum246 ...	...	...	6 50	...	—	12 45	3 56	6 49	9 38
Fürstenfeld ...	...	...	7 9	...	...	1 5	4 26	7 11	10 0
Fehring	5a10	...	8 29	...	1p10	2 7	5 45	8 25	—
Feldbach ...	5 28	a.m.	8 46	a.m.	1 25	2 19	6 3	8 41	...
Gleisdorf	6 14	6 54	9 28	1130	2 5	2 43	6 45	9 20	...
Graz (Staats)	7 1	7 38	1012	1214	2 50	3 14	7 31	10 4	...
" (Sud. ...	7 15	7 52	1027	1226	3 2	3 20	7 45	1015	...

GARSTEN and KLAUS.

Station					
Garsten..........dep	7a23	12p 9	6p31	8 p6	...
Steyrdorf..........	7 36	12 28	6 47	8 25	...
Pergern ....arr	7 50	12 42	7 1	8 39	...
Pergern ....dep	7 59	12 52	...	8 45	...
Bad Hall ....arr	8 50	1 45	...	9 38	...
Pergern..........dep	7 58	12 54	7 4	—	...
Grünburg	8 47	1 53	7 59	...	...
Agonitz	9 38	2 50	8 56	...	...
Klaus 248 ....arr	10 2	3 14	9 20	...	...

Station						
Klaus ....dep	5a58	10a28	...	6 p43	...	...
Agonitz	6 21	10 53	...	7 6	...	...
Grünburg	7 6	11 57	...	7 57	...	...
Pergern ....arr	7 51	12 43	...	8 40	...	...
Bad Hall ....dep	6 56	11 48	6 p8	...	...	...
Pergern ....arr	7 49	12 41	7 0	...	...	...
Pergern ....dep	8 0	12 55	7 3	8 44	...	...
Steyrdorf	8 24	1 19	7 27	9 2	...	...
Garsten 240 ....arr	8 33	1 28	7 36	9 11	...	...

URFAHR and AIGEN.

E.M.	Station			
	Urfahr ....dep	5 a55	1 p0	5p20
33	Haslach	8 18	3 23	7 43
43½	**Aigen-Schlägl** ... arr	9 0	4 5	8 25
	Aigen-Schlägl ...dep	4 a30	11a35	6 p0
	Haslach	5 10	12 15	6 40
	Urfahr..........arr	7 25	2 30	8 55

WOLFRAMS and SCHWARZENAU

Station						
Wolframs Cejl dep	...	...	5a35	9a35	4p28	7p44
Teltsch	...	...	6 44	1120	5 55	9 6
Zlabings	...	...	8 24	1 48	7 52	—
Waidhofen a. d. Thaya	1a48	7a30	9 56	3 11	9 51	...
Schwarzenau ...arr	2 10	7 54	1020	4 7	1015	...

Station					
Schwarzenau ...dep	1a15	3a55	6 a30	11a15	6 p55
Waidhofen a. d. Thaya	1 38	4 31	6 53	11 51	7 25
Zlabings	—	6 12	—	1 25	9 10
Teltsch	3a55	7 59	...	3 2	11 42
Wolframs Cejl arr	5 2	9 5	...	4 6	...

SCHWARZENAU and MARTINSBERG.

E M	Station						
	Schwarzenau ...dep	5a40	8a15	11a15	7 p0	...	...
18	Zwettl	7 6	9 12	12 56	8 25	...	...
44¾	**Martinsberg**......arr	9 12	...	3 7	1022	...	...

Station				
Martinsberg......dep	5a20	...	1p10	6p33
Zwettl	7 7	9a32	3 30	8 34
Schwarzenau ...arr	8 6	1028	4 26	9 38

VIENNA and HEILIGENSTADT.

Station									
Vienna (West)...dep	5a45	8a15	1020	12p30	3 p5	4p55	7p10	9 p5	1135
St. Veit	5 56	8 26	1032	12 42	3 17	5 7	7 21	9 17	1146
Klein Schwechat......	6 38	9 4	1122	1 32	4 10	5 52	8 7	9 55	1223
Heiligenstadt arr	7 36	...	1219	2 31	5 9	6 51	9 4	...	...

Station									
Heiligen.	...	6 a3	7a42	a.m.	1 p0	3p38	5p15	7 p9	p.m.
Schwechat..	6a17	7 5	8 46	1120	2 0	4 40	6 21	8 13	1025
St. Veit	7 0	7 45	9 39	12 0	2 40	5 20	7 4	8 53	11 4
Vienna arr	7 10	7 55	9 50	1210	2 50	5 30	7 15	9 5	1115

For Fares, see page 233B.]

CRACOW, LEMBERG, and PODWOLOCZYSKA.

Extra.—Krasne to Lemberg, 9.29 p.m.

Dist E.M	VIENNA (222)......dep		10p15	10p15	...	...	7a34	...	...	...	1235	12p35	1235	3p55	7p45
		1,2,3 a.m.	Ex3 a.m.	1,2,3 a.m.	Ex3 a.m.	1,2,3 a.m.	Ex2 p.m.	1,2,3 p.m.	1,2,3 p.m.	1,2,3 p.m.	Ex3 p.m.	1,2,3 p.m.	1,2,3 p.m.	1,2,3 nigt	Ex3 a.m.
—	**Cracow** ....dep		6 40	7 50	8 46	10 45	2 51	3 0	5 40	6 55	8 43	9 0	1055	1220	3 13
3	Podgórze		6 48	7 58	...	10 56	...	3 8	5 49	7 6	...	9 11	11 5	1229	...
5½	Bierzanow		RC	8 5	...	11 4	RC	3 15	5 57	7 14	SC	9 21	1113	1236	SC
23½	Bochnia		7 22	8 49	...	11 48	3 24	4 0	6 46	7 59	...	10 4	1154	1 19	...
48½	**Tarnow**	4 32	8 8	10 5	10 0	1 35	4 8	4 53	7 56	8 55	9 55	11 1	1254	2 30	4 20
69	**Debica**	5 55	8 43	10 57	RC	2 33	4 37	—	9 3	—	1028	11 48	1 42	3 36	4 50
98½	Rzeszow	7 32	9 46	12 30	1120	4 5	5 25	...	1016	...	1122	12 59	2 52	4 46	5 40
108¾	Lancut	8 47	10 4	12 54	...	4 29	5 41	...	1047	...	...	1 23	3 13	5 10	5 57
121½	Przeworsk	9 17	10 26	1 25	...	5 12	6 0	...	—	...	1155	1 51	3 43	5 41	6 17
130½	**Jaroslau**	9 39	10 47	1 50	12 9	5 39	6 17	...	...	...	1212	2 14	4 4	6 5	6 33
152¼	**Przemysl** ... arr	1029	11 26	2 41	1242	6 33	6 50	...	...	...	1245	3 2	4 50	6 58	7 6
	" dep	1037	11 34	2 55	1250	7 4	6 56	...	...	...	1253	3 15	4 58	7 22	7 16
180¾	Sadowa Wisznia ...	1146	12 24	4 5	...	8 14	...	...		...	...	4 21	6 4	8 32	...
192¾	Grodek	1219	12 50	4 39	...	8 48	...			...	...	4 55	6 34	9 5	...
212½	**Lemberg** ....arr	1 10	1 25	5 30	2 20	9 40	8 25			...	2 22	5 42	7 25	9 55	8 45
377¾	CZERNOWITZ 246A arr		7 p25	...	7p25	6 a22	6a22			...	7a34	1 p36	—	...	2p10
...	**Lemberg** ....dep	2 55	2 0	8 40	2 45	11 15	—			...	—	6 8	...	1035	—
216¾	" Podzamcze	3 12	2 14	9 2	2 58	11 33	...			...	...	6 25	...	11 0	...
244½	**Krasne** ..... arr	4 11	2 52	10 2	3 36	12 32	...			...	...	7 19	...	1159	...
	" dep	—	2 58	10 12	3 42	12 40	...			...	...	7 24	...	1217	...
259¾	Zloczow		3 29	10 58	4 12	1 26	...			...	...	8 5	...	1259	...
299½	Tarnopol		4 50	1 2	5 27	3 46	...			...	...	9 50	...	3 0	...
308¼	Borki Wielkie		5 7	1 24	...	4 15	...			...	...	10 11	...	3 23	...
321¾	**Podwoloczyska** arr		5 55	2 24	6 24	5 25	...	...	...	...	...	11 20	...	4 20	...
335	WOLOCZYSKA ....arr		6 p18	3 a0	6p57	...	...	...	...	...	...	11a50	...	...	...
674¾	ODESSA (320)....arr		9 a25	6 p58	9a25	...	...	...	...	...	...	7 a34	...	...	...

SC—Sleeping Cars attached.

RC—Restaurant Car in this Train.

	ODESSA (320) ...dep		...	9a55	...	8p40	9 p0	...	...	...	...	10 p5	...
	WOLOCZYSKA ....dep		...	2a15	...	9a48	9 a48	...	9 a48	...	...	4 p56	...
		1,2,3 a.m.	Ex2	1,2,3 a.m.	1,2,3 a.m.	Ex3 a.m.	Ex 3 a.m.	1,2,3	1,2,3 a.m.	Ex3	1,2,3	1,2,3 p.m.	Ex3
	Podwoloczyska dep		...	1 49	6 0	10 9	10 22	...	11 45	...	...	5 22	...
	Borki Wielkie		...	2 48	7 9	...	11 5	...	12 44	...	...	6 21	...
	Tarnopol		...	3 18	7 42	1112	11 25	...	1 22	...	...	6 54	...
	Zloczow		...	5 0	9 21	1222	12 41	...	3 7	...	...	8 32	...
	Krasne .... arr		...	5 28	9 56	1246	1 5	...	3 45	...	...	9 7	...
	" dep		...	5 46	10 2	1252	1 11	...	3 57	...	...	9 12	...
	Lemberg Podzamcze		...	7 1	1111	1 35	2 3	...	5 11	...	...	10 16	...
	Lemberg ....arr		...	7 15	1125	1 47	2 15	...	5 25	...	...	10 30	...
	CZERNOWITZ dep		1135	...	—	7a55	7 a55	p.m	9 a50	1p20	1p20	...	6p54
	Lemberg ....dep	3 35	8a25	8 32	...	2 5	2 45	3 40	5 50	7 0	7 30	11 10	1235
	Grodek	4 26	RC	9 29	...	...	3 17	4 33	6 40	...	8 23	12 1	SC
	Sadowa Wisznia ...	4 54	...	9 57	...	...	3 36	5 1	7 5	RC	8 51	12 29	...
	Przemysl arr	5 55	9 53	1058	...	3 30	4 23	6 2	8 5	8 25	9 52	1 30	2 5
	" dep	6 5	9 59	1158	...	3 35	4 31	6 21	8 40	8 33	10 2	1 38	2 16
	Jaroslau	7 32	1035	1254	...	4 10	5 12	7 18	9 37	9 8	1056	2 34	2 52
	Przeworsk	7 57	1051	1 15	...	...	5 28	7 39	9 58	9 23	1117	3 17	3 7
	Lancut	8 27	1112	1 44	p.m	...	5 50	8 8	10 27	9 43	1146	3 46	...
	Rzeszow	9 8	1142	2 22	6 30	5 7	6 20	8 31	11 0	10 9	1220	4 18	3 52
	Debica	1021	1230	3 29	7 35	...	7 16	—	12 14	1055	1 26	5 32	4 39
	Tarnow	1122	1 8	4 24	8 30	6 27	8 2	...	1 14	1129	2 28	6 31	5 16
	Bochnia	1223	...	5 22	9 28	...	8 44	...	2 21	...	3 40	7 38	5 53
	Bierzanow	1 7	...	6 8	10 9	...	RC	...	3 11	SC	4 35	8 24	...
	Podgórze	1 17	...	6 18	1017	...	9 18	...	3 23	...	4 45	8 35	6 26
	Cracow ....arr	1 24	2 20	6 25	1024	7 36	9 24	...	3 30	1240	4 52	8 42	6 32
	VIENNA 222 arr	9p50	9p50	...	...	6 a0	6 a0	...	...	8 a7	...	...	3p10

RC—Restaurant Car attached.]

LEMBERG, CZERNOWITZ, and ITZKANY.

Dist E.M	CRACOW (245A) dep	8p43	...	9 p0	3 a13	3 a13	8a46	...	...	2 p51
		Ex3 a.m.	1,2,3	1,2,3 a.m	Ex 3 a.m.	1,2,3 a.m.	Ex 3 p.m.	1,2,3 p.m.	1,2,3 p.m.	1,2,3 p.m.
—	**Lemberg** ....dep	2 45	...	6 10	9 10	10 3	2 30	3 12	5 52	11 0
39¾	Chodorow (247)	3 55	...	7 54	10 22	11 43	3 39	4 55	7 46	12 46
62¼	Bursztyn	SC	...	8 47	RC	12 45	RC	5 55	8 47	1 43
69½	Halicz (247)....	4 43	...	9 3	11 11	1 2	4 26	6 13	9 6	2 2
87	**Stanislau** (245)...arr	5 10	a.m.	9 42	11 42	1 41	4 56	6 54	9 53	2 41
...	" ....dep	5 17	5 25	10 4	11 49	1 57	5 3	—	10 3	2 56
90	Chryplin	...	5 32	1012	...	2 4	5 10	...	1010	3 4
121¾	**Kolomea** (247)	6 26	6 58	1141	12 57	3 36	6 12	...	1130	4 22
133¼	Zablotow	6†44	7 25	1211	...	4 7	6 28	...	—	5 2
143¼	Sniatyn-Zalucze	...	7 45	1233	...	4 28	6 43	...	...	5 26
150¼	Nepolokoutz (248A)...	A	7 59	1247	1 46	4 43	6 55	...	...	5 41
156¼	Luzan	...	8 15	1 1	...	4 56	7 10	...	...	5 55
165¼	**Czernowitz**....arr	7 34	8 45	1 36	2 10	5 23	7 25	p.m.	...	6 22
...	" (247) dep	7 46	9 40	2 20	—	5 34	—	10 15	...	6 35
186¼	**Hliboka** (247)....	8 39	1052	3 22	...	6 53	...	11 35	...	7 56
202¼	Hadikfalva (247)	9 18	1146	4 16	...	7 44	1,2,3	12 30	...	8 50
216¼	Hatna	9 41	1219	4 56	...	8 33	p.m.	1 25	a.m.	9 28
221½	**Itzkany** ....arr	9 50	1230	5 8	...	8 45	11 1	1 35	1028	9 40
223	**Burdujeni** ...arr	10 0	...	5 24	...	...	11 6	3 50	1034	11 0
307½	JASSY (324) ....arr	2p45	...	1120	...	...	...	11a15	...	2p45
500¼	BUCHAREST 324 arr	7p45	...	6a55	...	...	...	10p45	...	...

†—Sets down only.

A—Berlin-Constantinople Express (via Constanza). SC—Sleeping Car attached.

BUCHAREST (324)	...	...	...	...	10p5	...	8a35	...	...
JASSY (324) ...dep	...	...	...	...	6 a0	...	1 p15	...	...
	1,2,3 a.m.	Ex3 a.m.	1,2,3 a.m.	Ex 3 p.m.	1,2,3 a.m.	1,2,3 p.m.	Ex.3 p.m.	1,2,3 p.m.	1,2,3 p.m.
Burdujeni dep	4 30	RC	...	...	9 40	...	4 16	5 50	...
Itzkany ....dep	4 37	5 45	6 40	...	1020	2 35	4 45	5 57	8 20
Hatna	—	5 55	6 54	...	1036	2 55	4 57	—	8 48
Hadikfalva....	...	6 21	7 36	...	1117	3 39	5 24	...	9 30
Hliboka	...	6 59	8 38	...	12 2	4 29	6 0	...	1016
Czernowitz...arr	...	7 44	9 38	...	1 0	5 29	6 42	...	1117
" ...dep	...	7 55	9 50	1 20	1 25	5 40	6 54	...	1135
Luzan	...	8 12	1020	...	1 56	6 7	...	...	12 3
Nepolokoutz	...	8 27	1035	1 47	2 12	6 24	A	...	1217
Sniatyn....	...	8 38	1050	RC	2 28	6 44	...	...	1232
Zablotow	a.m.	8 57	1113	...	2 54	7 6	...	...	1257
Kolomea....	5 0	9 29	1154	2 44	3 41	7 44	8 20	...	1 34
Chryplin	6 24	1033	1 20	...	5 11	9 2	...	...	3 3
Stanislau ....arr	6 30	1039	1 26	3 46	5 17	9 8	9 25	a.m.	3 9
" ....dep	6 40	1049	1 42	3 55	5 31	—	9 33	1 20	3 22
Halicz	7 20	1129	2 20	4 27	6 14	...	10 4	2 5	4 8
Bursztyn	7 35	1142	2 38	...	6 30	...	SC	2 26	4 33
Chodorow	8 40	1231	3 49	5 24	7 32	...	10 59	3 48	5 48
Lemberg ....arr	1028	1 45	5 35	6 31	9 26	...	12 7	5 43	7 40
CRACOW 246A arr	...	7p36	1240	12a40	6a32	...	6 a32	2p20	2p20

Extra.—Halicz to Stanislau, 6.58 a.m. Stanislau to Halicz, 8.21 a.m.

ITZKANY and SUCZAWA.

Itzkany ....dep	4a10	6a25	10a15	12p40	3p10	5 p25	8p55	...	...	...
Suczawa ....arr	4 45	6 58	10 48	1 13	3 43	5 58	9 28	...	...	...

Suczawa....dep	4a59	8a59	11a25	1p55	4 p0	7p34	9 p49	...	...
Itzkany ....arr	5 30	9 30	11 56	2 25	4 30	8 5	10 20	...	...

KRASNE and RADZIWILLOW.

	a.m.	p.m.	p.m.	p.m.	
Krasne ....dep	7 34	1235	4 19	1022	...
Brody ....arr	8 27	1 29	5 13	1117	...
" (Customs Ex.)...dep	8 46	—	5 28	...	...
Radziwillow ....arr	9 3	...	5 45	...	...

	a.m.		a.m.	p.m.	p.m.
Radziwillow....dep	...	...	1120	...	8 34
Brody ....arr	...	a.m.	1140	...	8 51
" (Customs Ex.)...dep	4 36	8 35	1139	1 53	8 28
Krasne ....arr	5 30	9 49	1234	2 48	9 23

PRZEMYSL & CHYROW.

Station								
Przemysl ...dep	3a17	7a12	11a8	11a48	3p40	4p47	7 p0	10p5
Chyrow 245 arr	4 21	8 14	1214	12 53	4 47	5 56	8 6	1135

Station								
Chyrow ...	4a48	8a24	10a46	12p41	3p4	5p8	7p16	10p36	1a9
Przemysl...	5 45	9 25	11 47	1 43	4 5	6 9	8 13	11 36	2 6

NEU-ZAGORZ and MEZO-LABORCZ.

Station			
Neu-Zagorz......dep	10a35	8p20	...
Zagorz	10 41	8 25	...
Neu Lupkow	12 6	9 50	...
Mezo-Laborcz 231	12 50	10 35	...

Station			
Mezo-Laborcz dep	5 a0	5p55	...
Neu Lupkow	5 52	6 47	...
Zagorz	7 6	8 2	...
Neu-Zagorz......arr	7 10	8 6	...

Station		
Neu Lupkow ...dep	12p15	7p30
Cisna ...arr	2 32	9 47
Cisna ...dep	8 a0	4 p0
Neu Lupkow ....arr	1016	6 14

Station									
Neu Zagorz dep	4a0	7a15	9a30	10a18	1‡p22	2p25	5p30	8p14	10p20
Sanok ....arr	4 8	7 26	9 41	10 26	1 33	2 33	5 39	8 25	10 31

Station										
Sanok ......dep	7a36	8a24	9a51	1‡p43	2p34	7p35	8p46	10p52	2a13	...
Neu Zagorz arr	7 49	8 33	10 3	1 55	2 45	7 45	8 59	11 1	2 25	...

‡—From 1st September.

‡—Not on Sunday.]

OLMUTZ and KOSTELETZ.

Dist	Station							
	Olmutz (Nord) ...dep	4a18	...	8a20	12p15	...	4p30	8 p0
2½	„ (Stadtbh) „	4 34	...	8 37	12 34	...	4 46	8 20
13¾	Namiescht ... „	5 17	a.m.	9 23	1 27	p.m.	5 31	9 13
21½	Cellechowitz ... „	5 48	7 16	9 56	2 5	4‡58	6 4	9 46
28	Kosteletz 246 ......arr	5 54	7 23	10 2	2 13	5 8	6 10	9 53

Station						
Kosteletz ......dep	5a58	8a47	12p53	3p40	4‡p42	7 p48
Cellechowitz	6 5	8 56	1 1	3 48	4 49	7 55
Namiescht ... „	6 46	9 42	1 41	4 30	——	8 32
Olmutz (Stadt) ...arr	7 34	10 50	2 27	5 24	...	9 30
„ 221 (Nord) „	7 46	11 3	2 38	5 36	...	9 42

JAROSLAU and SOKAL.

E.M.	Station					
	Jaroslau	7 a7	11a20	...	7p30	...
27½	Lubaczów	8 27	12 51	...	9 4	...
54	Rawa Ruska........	10 45	2 44	5p39	10 52	...
79	Belz	12 4	4 4	6 59	12 10	...
93¾	Sokal ....arr	12 50	4 50	7 44	12 58	...

Station						
Sokal ....dep	7a52	11a10	2 p23	11p53	...	...
Belz	8 43	12 0	3 14	1 2	...	...
Rawa Ruska	10 1	1 38	5 35	3 12	...	...
Lubaczów	——	3 23	7 17	4 57	...	...
Jaroslau 246A	...	4 45	8 42	6 20	...	...

DEBICA and PRZEWORSK

Station			
Debica......dep	5 a0	11a5	4p45
Tarnobrzeg	7 26	1 49	7 13
Sobow	7 35	1 58	7 22
Rozwadow	8 26	2 49	8 26
Sarzyna	9 21	3 48	9 30
Przeworsk ar	1010	4 40	1025

Station			
Przeworsk dp	4 a5	1p35	6p12
Sarzyna	4 58	2 28	7 4
Rozwadow	6 4	3 29	8 7
Sobow	6 50	4 14	8 52
Tarnobrzeg	7 21	4 32	9 5
Debica ......arr	9 51	6 56	1130

Station			
Przeworsk	5a25	11a0	6p15
Dynow arr	9 3	1 36	8 51

Station		
Dynow .....dep	5 a0	2p18
Przeworsk .arr	7 36	4 54

CRACOW and WIELICZKA.

Station							
Cracow....dep	8a10	1p30	7p40	9 p0	...	10p55	...
Bierzanow	8 37	1 55	8 4	9 30	10p15	11 25	...
Wieliczkaarr	8 48	2 6	8 15	9 40	10 25	11 35	...

Station							
Wieliczkadep	6 50	10a45	2p58	5p32	8p50	9p10	...
Bierzanow	7 1	10 56	3 11	5 47	9 0	10 9	...
Cracow ....arr	7 20	11 20	3 35	6 14	...	1624	...

TARNOBRZEG and NADBRZEZIE.

Station			
Tarnobrzeg......dep	7a38	1p32	4p45
Nadbrzezie ......arr	8 11	2 5	5 18

Station			
Nadbrzezie ....dep	6a14	12p30	3p33
Tarnobrzeg ....arr	6 48	1 5	4 8

STANISLAU & KOROSMEZO.

Station					
Stanislau ......dep	5a33	9 a52	2p22	5p34	...
Chryplin	5 41	9 59	2 30	5 42	...
Delatyn 247A	7 18	11 34	3 58	7 21	...
Woronienka	8 42	12 50	——	8 45	...
Korosmezo...arr	9 9	1 16	...	9 13	...

Station						
Korosmezo dep	3a48	...	1 p25	7p42	...	...
Woronienka	4 23	...	1 58	8 17	...	...
Delatyn	5 57	11a43	3 18	9 42	...	...
Chryplin	7 21	1 8	4 42	11 7	...	...
Stanislau ......arr	7 29	1 16	4 50	1115	...	...

STRYI and TARNOPOL.

Station				
Stryi ....dep	4 a8	6a16	2 p5	...
Chodorow 246A...	5 28	8 46	3 13	...
Rohatyn	——	9 35	5 51	...
Podwysokie 247	5 a8	1019	6 33	...
Potutory	5 46	1110	7 26	...
Ostrow-Berezow	7 21	1245	9 10	...
Tarnopol arr	7 34	1258	9 24	...

Station			
Tarnopol dep	3a30	2p52	5p34
Ostrow-Berezow	3 44	3 7	5 49
Potutory	5 20	4 54	7 30
Podwysokie	6 6	5 39	8 4
Rohatyn	6 42	6 19	——
Chodorow .. 6a20	7 50	7 41	...
Stryi 245 ar 7 38	9 0	8 45	...

Station	a.m.	p.m.	p.m.
Tarnopol ....dep	4 15	1219	5 17
Ostrow-Berezow.	4 34	1252	5 40
Kopyczynce 245	7 5	3 31	8 6
Kopyczynce dep	3a50	8a39	3p32
Ostrow-Berezow	6 54	1048	5 48
Tarnopol ....arr	7 12	11 4	6 4

TARNOPOL and ZBARAZ.

Station					
Tarnopol..........dep	3 a55	8 a35	2 p51	...	...
Zbaraz ....arr	5 25	10 7	4 20	...	...

Station						
Zbaraz ....dep	6 a 4	11a36	5 p2	...	...	...
Tarnopol ....arr	7 27	1 4	6 30	...	...	...

CZERNOWITZ and NOWOSIELITZA.

Station			
Czernowitz ....dep	8a35	2p28	7p55
Zuczka	8 43	2 44	8 1
Nowosielitza ......arr	9 45	3 58	9 5
„ 330 (Russia) arr	...	...	9 30

Station			
Nowosielitza (Russ) ... dep	5a42	...	...
Nowosielitza (Aust) ... dep	6 10	11 a0	4p 3
Zuczka	7 15	12 34	5 5
Czernowitz 246A ......arr	7 20	12 40	5 10

HATNA and DORNA WATRA BAD.

Station			
Hatna ....dep	1a30	10a42	5 p0
Wama	4 14	12 55	7 21
Kimpolung	5 10	1 43	8 7
Dorna Watra Bad arr	7 25	3 31	9 50

Station			
Dorna Watra Bad dep	4a55	8a45	2p30
Kimpolung	6 32	10 39	4 36
Wama	7 14	11 33	5 30
Hatna ....arr	9 15	2 32	8 28

HLIBOKA and SERETH.

Station			
Hlibokadep	8a50	12p20	7p5
Sereth arr	9 45	1 10	8 0
Sereth dep	5a35	10a35	3p5
Hlibokaarr	6 35	11 35	4 5

WAMA and RUSS-MOLDAWITZA.

Station			
Wama........dep	4a30	...	...
Russ-Moldawitza	6 42	...	...
Russ-Moldaw.	8a37	...	...
Wama......arr	10 50	...	...

HALICZ and PODWYSOKIE.

Station				
Halicz	4a12	9 a7	4p35	...
Podwys	5 0	9 51	5 24	...
Podwys	6 a8	1017	8p11	...
Halicz	6 56	11 3	8 57	...

KOLOMEA and SLOBODA.

Station		
Kolomea dep	3p50	5p10
Nadwornian ...	4 16	5 37
Szeparow. arr	5 2	...
Sopów	...	6 3
Sloboda ...arr	...	...

Station			
Sloboda......dep	...	11a8	...
Sopów	...	1 37	...
Szeparowce dep	...	...	5p12
Nadwornian	8 a14	1 53	6 9
Kolomea (246A)	8 40	2 20	6 34

LEMBERG and SAMBOR.

Station				
Lemberg dep	6a52	9 a5	3p50	10p56
Rudki	8 22	10 29	5 14	12 16
Sambor arr	9 3	11 10	5 55	12 56
Sambor dep	5a38	7a39	11a40	6 p22
Rudki	6 21	8 23	12 24	7 6
Lemberg arr	7 45	9 55	1 48	8 20

Station			
Sambor ......dep	9a42	2p17	6p50
Strzylki	1056	3 31	8 3
Sianki ....arr	1 6	5 42	1012
Sianki ....dep	4 a0	7 a 6	2p59
Strzylki	5 52	9 4	4 56
Sambor........arr	7 5	10 19	6 5

HLIBOKA and BERHOMETH.

Station			
Hliboka	8 a45	1p10	7 p0
Karapcziu ...	9 14	1 45	7 30
: Czudin arr	10 25	...	8 40
Berhom'th...	11 20	5 10	9 40

Station				
Berhom'th ...	4a15	6a35	1p40	...
: Czudin dep	5 0	...	...	4 p0
Karapcziu ...	6 19	11 0	3 44	5 5
Hliboka 246A	6 45	1125	4 10	5 40

LEMBERG and BELZEC.

Station			
Lemberg	7a50	2p35	7p50
Zolkiew	9 16	4 11	9 21
Rawa Ruska	1035	5 56	1027
Belzec......	1140	7 14	...
Belzec ...	...	8a38	3p12
Rawa R'ska	4a26	1028	4 49
Zolkiew ...	5 35	1133	6 4
Lemberg	7 5	1 0	7 38

CZUDIN and KOSZCZUJA.

Station		
Czudin..............dep	10a45	...
Koszczuja ....arr	12 58	...

Station		
Koszczuja ......dep	1 a45	...
Czudin............arr	3 45	

LEMBERG and JAWOROW.

Station					
Lemberg...dep	8a40	6p31	...	...	...
Janow	1015	7 54	...	...	...
Jaworow......arr	1140	9 18	...	...	...

Station			
Jaworow......	5 a0	1p20	...
Janow	6 55	3 9	...
Lemberg...	8 4	4 20	...

HADIKFALVA and BRODINA.

Station						
Hadikfalva	3a30	6a28	9a25	11a55	4p25	7p49
Radautz	4 25	7 11	1018	12 40	5 25	8 28
Karlsberg ...	6 0	——	1158	——	7 10	——
Brodina arr	6 55	...	1 5	...	8 10	...

Station							
Brodinadep	...	4a15	...	12a10	...	6 p0
Karlsberg ...	...	5 10	a.m.	1 0	...	6 58
Radautz	5a20	6 33	10 11	2 28	4p25	8 29
Hadikfalva	6 0	7 15	10 55	3 15	5 10	9 10

Station			
Karlsberg .....dep	4‡a0	1 p5	7p25
Putna ....arr	4 21	1 26	7 46
Putna ....dep	4‡a35	5p50	8p20
Karlsberg .....arr	4 50	6 10	8 35

‡—Mon., Wed., and Fri. only.

CSACZA and SKAWINA.

E.M.					a.m.		p.m.			p.m.
—	Csacza dep	...	...	...	7 18	...	1 20	...	...	7 3
13	Zwardon ...	...	a.m.	...	8 50	...	3 0	...	...	8 0
38	Zywiec	...	4 5	7a20	10 5	...	4 15	...	...	9 16
45½	Jelesnia ...	a.m.	4 29	7 45	1029	p.m.	4 41	...	p.m.	9 43
65¾	Sucha	3 25	5 28	8 35	1117	3 58	5 30	6p43	8 47	1035
84	Kalwarya .	4 23	6 22	—	1224	5 2	—	7 19	9 39	—
97½	Skawina ar	4 59	6 56	...	1 10	5 45	...	7 49	1014	...

			a.m.	a.m	a.m.	p.m.	p.m.	p.m.	p.m.	n gt
Skawina dp	...	...	7 48	1027	11 18	2 18	4 13	...	8 55	1244
Kalwarya..	a.m.	...	8 19	11 9	1153	2 57	4 53	...	9 37	1 22
Sucha	3 30	...	8 57	12 6	1250	3 50	5 45	8 40	1032	2 17
Jelesnia ...	4 28	a.m.	—	—	2 2	—	—	9 39	1147	—
Zywiec......	4 55	6 55	...	...	3 25	...	...	10 0	12 8	...
Zwardon ...	—	8 45	...	...	5 15	...	...	—	—	...
Csacza. arr	...	9 54	...	...	6 24	...	...	...	...	...

DELATYN and ZALESZCZYKI.

		a.m.	a.m.				p.m.
Delatyn ....dep	...	...	5 52	...	...	...	4 6
Kolomea	...	6 35	7 50	...	...	...	6 44
Okno	a.m.	8 38	—	a.m.	p.m.	p.m.	8 28
Stefanowka............	8 50	10 56	...	11 46	5 26	9 53	10 29
Zaleszczyki...arr	9 25	...	...	12 10	6 0	10 25	11 17

	a.m.	a.m.	a.m.		p.m.	p.m.	p.m.
Zaleszczyki.........dep	4 0	5 20	10 45	...	...	2 50	6 35
Stefanowka...............	4 52	5 58	11 20	...	12 40	3 33	7 20
Okno.......................	7 22	—	—	p.m.	3 27	—	—
Kolomea	9 34	...	...	4 54	5 35	...	...
Delatyn (247) ......arr	11 15	...	...	6 46	...	...	...

CZERNOWITZ and ZALESZCZYKI.

Czernowitz dep	5 a20	9 a50	2p18	7p10	...
Zuczka	5 27	9 56	2 27	7 22	...
Luzan	6 25	10 25	3 10	8 0	p.m.
Stefanowka	8 50	11 46	5 26	9 53	1042
Zaleszczyki arr	9 25	12 10	6 0	1025	1117

Zaleszczyki...dep	5a20	10a45	1p10	2p50	6p35
Stefanowka............	6 6	11 22	1 48	3 48	7 30
Luzan	8 15	12 38	—	6 8	9 30
Zuczka	8 41	1 0	...	6 30	9 59
Czernowitz ...arr	8 45	1 5	...	6 36	10 5

Czortkow.........dep	8 a25	9 p22
Zaleszczyki .....arr	10 35	11 42
Zaleszczyki......dep	5 a8	12p20
Czortkow........arr	7 22	2 29

TARNOW and SZCZUCIN.

E.M		a.m.	a.m.	p.m.		
...	**Tarnow** ....dep	6 35	10 20	5 40	...	...
15½	Dabrowa	8 50	11 31	6 47	...	...
30½	**Szczucin** ....arr	10 10	12 30	7 45	...	...

	a.m.	p.m.	p.m.			
Szczucin ....dep	7 5	1 30	3 30	...	...	...
Dabrowa	8 16	2 37	5 55	...	...	...
Tarnow (246A)....arr	9 16	3 37	7 34	...	...	...

CRACOW and KOCMYRZOW.

E.M		a.m.	p.m.	p.m.		
—	**Cracow** ....dep	8 25	1 42	8 0	...	...
5	Czyzyny	8 51	2 12	8 25	...	...
12½	**Kocmyrzow** ......arr	9 41	2 58	9 11	...	...

	a.m.	a.m.	p.m.				
Kocmyrzow ......dep	6 18	11 50	5 57	...	...	...	...
Czyzyny	7 3	12 33	6 40	...	...	...	...
Cracow ....arr	7 35	12 58	7 10	...	...	...	...

Czyzyny ....dep	8 a53	2 p16	...
Mogila ....arr	9 0	2 23	...

Mogila...........dep	6 a50	12p20	...	...
Czyzyny ....arr	6 57	12 27	...	...

BOLECIN and JAWORZNO.

E.M		a.m.	p.m.	p.m.		
—	**Bolecin** ....dep	...	7 5	...	...	...
6¾	Chrzanow.....................	11 20	7 51	8 25	...	...
18	**Jaworzno**...........arr	12 29	...	9 30	...	...

	a.m.	p.m.	p.m.				
Jaworzno...........dep	4 45	2 10	...	...	...	...	...
Chrzanow....................	5 47	3 15	4 0	...	...	...	...
Bolecin 247a ....arr	...	...	4 45	...	...	...	...

SUCHA and SIERSZA Wodna.

E.M		a.m.	p.m.			
—	**Sucha** ....dep	3 42	12 10	...	...	...
16½	Wadowice	4 55	1 46	...	...	...
24¾	Spytkowice.....................	6 10	3 5	...	...	...
38	Bolecin 247a	7 31	4 28	p.m.	...	...
41¾	Trzebinia	8 4	4 57	8 0	...	...
46	**Siersza Wodna**......arr	8 30	5 20	8 25	...	...

	a.m.	p.m.	p.m.				
Siersza Wodna ...dep	5 40	5 25	6 20	...	...	...	...
Trzebinia......................	6 50	5 50	6 37	...	...	...	...
Bolecin	7 24	6 16	—	...	...	...	...
Spytkowice....................	8 55	7 49	...	...	...	...	...
Wadowice	9 55	8 50	...	...	...	...	...
Sucha ....arr	11 25	10 10	...	...	...	...	...

CHABOWKA and ZAKOPANE.

E.M		a.m.	a.m.	a.m.	p.m.	p.m.		
—	Chabowka .....dep	3 50	7 10	10 5	2 27	7 25	...	...
18	Nowy Targ	5 3	8 45	10 56	3 23	8 21	...	...
33	Zakopane ......arr	6 20	1 0	11 44	4 29	9 20	...	...

	a.m.	a.m.	p.m.	p.m.	p.m.	
Zakopane..............dep	6 35	8 0	4 0	5 20	10 0	...
Nowy Targ	7 25	9 3	4 48	6 21	10 57	...
Chabowka 245.........arr	...	10 3	5 38	7 28	11 55	...

Nowy Targ ....dep	7a35	3p30	...	...	...
Szuchahora ....arr	9 0	4 40	...	...	...

Szuchahora ....dep	9a15	4p55	...	...	...
Nowy Targ ....arr	10 34	6 5	...	...	...

KASCHITZ and KAADEN-BRUNNERSDORF.

[‡—Sun. and Thurs. only.

E.M.			a.m.	a.m.	p.m.	p.m.	p.m.	p.m.
	Kaschitz...............dep	a.m.	7 48	...	...	...	2 57	8 53
8	Willomitz	6 10	9 8	...	12‡20	...	4 10	9 48
20½	Kaaden	7 8	10 3	1134	1 18	1 40	5 9	1046
23	**Kaaden-Brunnersdrf**	7 20	1015	1144	...	1 50	6 30	1120

		a.m.	a.m.	p.m.	p.m.	p.m.	p.m	p.m.	p.m.
Kaaden-Brunnersdorf dep		8 7	10 32	...	12 4	2 10	...	7 10	1150
Kaaden.........	5 0	8 16	10 40	...	1212	2 35	...	7 25	1158
Willomitz ...	5 50	9 2	11‡47	12 4	—	3 29	7 11	8 15	—
Kaschitz arr	7 7	—	...	1244	...	...	7 55	...	...

E.M.							
	Willomitz...............dep	9 a8	4 p5	9 p47	...	...	...
13¾	Duppau ....arr	10 25	5 22	11 0	...	...	...

Duppau.....................dep	5 a0	10a46	5p52	...	...	...
Willomitz.................arr	6 1	11 50	6 59	...	...	...

LEMBERG and PODHAJCE.

E.M								
	Lemberg.........dep	...	...	6 a9	...	4p53	...	...
74½	Brzezany	4a31	6 a9	1046	4p20	9 58	...	...
80¼	Potutory 247	4 50	6 33	1111	4 39	1019	...	...
95	**Podhajce**.........arr	..	7 57	12 5	6 0	1115	...	...

Podhajce ....dep	4a24	9a46	3p56	6p35	...	...	...	...
Potutory	5 49	1047	4 55	7 41	...	...	...	...
Brzezany.....................	6 14	1140	5 20	8 0	...	...	...	...
Lemberg ....arr	11 10	...	1020	...	...	...	...	...

LEMBERG and STOJANOW.

E.M							
	Lemberg..............dep	8 a5	6 p0	...	...	...	...
56½	Stojanów...............arr	11 47	9 39	...	...	...	...

Stojanów ....dep	5 a57	2 p42	...	...	...	...	...
Lemberg..............arr	9 50	6 30	...	...	...	...	...

BOSNA BROD and SERAJEVO.

Dist. E.M.							
	BUDAPEST ....dep	...	8 p5	11p15	7a10	2 p45	...
		1—4 a.m.	1—4 a.m.	1—4 p.m.	1—4 p.m.	1,2,3 p.m.	
—	**Bosna Brod** ......dep	4 40	8 40	3 24	7 30	11 5	...
3	Siekovac	4 51	8 51	3 36	7 40	...	...
15½	Dervent	5 27	9 40	4 39	8 24	11 51	...
52¼	**Doboj** .... arr	7 26	11 58	8 0	10 37	1 46	...
	dep	7 46	12 45	—	11 17	1 57	...
67¾	Maglaj	8 34	1 43	...	12 12	2 44	...
118	Zenica .... arr	11 10	4 44	...	3 6	5 19	...
	dep	11 32	5 0	...	3 50	5 44	...
127½	Lasva ....arr	11 57	5 28	...	4 20	6 9	...
148	Visoko	1 7	7 16	...	5 51	7 14	...
152¼	Podlugovi	1 22	7 32	...	6 11	7 23	...
157	Semizovac	1 33	7 52	...	6 36	7 43	...
167½	**Serajévo**	2 10	8 28	...	7 14	8 10	...

	1—4 a.m.	1—4 p.m.	1—4 p.m.	1,2,3 p.m.	1—4 p.m.	
Serajévo ....dep	6 0	2 15	5 10	8 30	1050	...
Semizovac	6 36	2 47	5 50	8 58	1122	...
Podlugovi	6 57	3 3	6 11	9 13	1138	...
Visoko	7 16	3 20	6 32	9 27	1154	...
Lasva	8 36	4 25	7 56	10 23	1255	...
Zenica .... arr	9 4	4 50	8 35	10 46	1 20	...
dep	9 20	5 6	—	11 2	1 45	...
Maglaj	12 6	7 29	...	1 24	4 24	...
Doboj .... arr	1 0	8 15	...	2 8	5 16	...
dep	1 30	8 44	...	2 20	5 48	...
Dervent	3 51	10 40	...	4 18	8 10	...
Siekovac	4 31	11 14	...	...	8 51	...
Bosna Brod230 arr	4 40	11 22	...	5 0	9 0	...
BUDAPEST ....arr	8 a10	...	...	1 p30	10p0	...

Podlugovi dep	7a45	3p10	7p40	Vares ......dep	5 a0	11a20	5p32	...
Vares ....arr	9 35	5 0	9 30	Podlugovi arr	6 46	1 10	7 20	...

Semizovac..dep	8a20	3p10	Cevljanovicdep	5a40	11a50	5p50
Cevljanovic arr	10 0	4 50	Semizovac .arr	7 15	1 25	7 35

SERAJEVO and MOSTAR.

Dist. E.M.		1—4 a.m.	1,2,3 a.m.	1—4 p.m.	1—4 p.m.	1—4 p.m.
—	**Serajévo** ....dep	5 50	9 0	3 0	5 12	9 27
16¾	Tarcin	8 17	10 25	4 30	7 48	11 3
32¼	Konjica ...... arr	10 52	12 16	6 26	—	1 4
	dep	—	12 44	6 50	...	1 27
51½	Jablanica	...	1 49	7 57	...	2 33
81½	**Mostar** ....arr	...	3 23	9 40	...	4 15

	1—4	1—4 a.m.	1,2,3 p.m.	1—4 p.m.	1—4 p.m.
Mostar ....dep	...	7 0	1 42	...	1113
Jablanica	...	8 56	3 23	...	1 3
Konjica .... arr	...	10 0	4 21	...	2 4
dep	a.m.	10 19	4 31	5 50	2 12
Tarcin	5 24	12 21	6 29	8 37	4 10
Serajévo ......arr	7 16	1 46	7 49	1036	5 30

SERAJEVO and VARDISTE.

E.M.						
—	**Serajévo** ....dep		...	8 55 a.m.	...	2 45 p.m.
52¼	Ustipraca-Gorazda		a.m.	12 28	...	6 45
60¼	Megjegje	a.m.	8 56	1 0	p.m.	7 36
69	Visegrad	6 0	9 30	1 30	4 0	8 10
79½	**Vardiste** ...arr	6 44	...	...	4 44	...

	a.m.	p.m.	p.m.	
Vardiste ....dep	6 57	...	5 17	...
Visegrad	7 56	3 25	6 25	...
Megjegje	8 52	4 0	6 59	...
Ustipraca-Gorazda ...	9 35	4 34	—	...
Serajévo ....arr	1 30	7 52	...	...

	p.m.	
Megjegje ...dep	7 20	...
Uvac ....arr	9 10	...
Uvac ....dep	7 a0	...
Megjegje ...arr	8 40	...

SERAJEVO and ILIDZA BANJA—Trains each way almost hourly from 6.12 a.m until 10.42 p.m.

MOSTAR and GRAVOSA.

Dist. E.M.		1—4 a.m.	1,2,3 p.m.	1—4 p.m.	
—	**Mostar** ....dep	4 48	3 38	5 30	...
23	Gabela .... arr	6 16	4 45	7 44	...
	dep	6 26	4 52	—	...
54¾	Ravno	8 23	6 31	...	...
74¼	Hum	9 46	7 40	...	...
79½	Uskoplje	10 6	7 59	...	...
94½	**Gravosa** (Gruz) ...arr	10 50	8 45	...	...

	1—4	1—4 a.m.	1—4 p.m.	
Gravosa (Gruz) ...dep	...	8 15	5 0	...
Uskoplje	...	9 0	5 49	...
Hum	...	9 30	6 26	...
Ravno	...	10 27	7 39	...
Gabela .... arr	a.m.	11 56	9 21	...
dep	6 17	12 2	9 29	...
Mostar ....arr	7 45	1 13	10 53	...

Gabela ....dep	6 a30	10a20	12p10	2 p45	5 p0	7p48	9p35
Metkovic ....arr	6 40	10 30	12 20	2 55	5 10	8 0	9 45

Metkovic ....dep	5 a50	9a40	11a30	2p10	4 p20	8p55
Gabela ....arr	6 0	9 50	11 40	2 20	4 30	9 5

Hum ....dep	9a59	7 p19	7 p59	...	...	...
Trebinje ....dep	10 40	8 4	8 40	...	...	...

Trebinje ....dep	5 a6	8 a20	5 p10	...	...	...	...
Hum ....arr	5 45	9 1	5 51	...	...	...	...

USKOPLJE and ZELENIKA.

E.M.		a.m.	p.m.	p.m.	
—	**Uskoplje** ....dep	10 10	...	8 3	...
24¼	Cavtat (Ragusavecchia) ...	11 35	2 50	9 27	...
45¼	Hercegnovi (Castelnuovo)	1 6	4 30	10 56	...
47½	**Zelenika** ....arr	1 17	4 40	11 6	...

	a.m.	p.m.	p.m.	
Zelenika ....dep	5 30	12 30	2 20	...
Hercegnovi (Castelnuovo)	5 43	12 42	2 33	...
Cavtat (Ragusavecchia) ...	7 17	2 15	4 7	...
Uskoplje ....arr	8 50	...	5 40	...

DOBOJ and TUZLA.

E.M.		a.m.	p.m.	p.m.			
—	**Doboj** ....dep	5 54	1 35	8 50	...	...	...
11¼	Gracanica ....arr	7 0	3 45	10 0	...	...	...
38½	**Tuzla** ....arr	7 35	4 38	11 50	...	...	...

	a.m.	a.m.	p.m.			
Tuzla ....dep	4 40	8 50	7 20	...	...	...
Gracanica ....dep	6 0	10 35	9 5	...	...	...
Doboj ....arr	7 17	11 50	10 22	...	...	...

Tuzla ....dep	7 a5	2p20	4 p43	...	Simin Han......dep	7 a36	2 p50	5 p10	...
Simin Han ......arr	7 20	2 35	4 58	...	Tuzla ....arr	7 50	3 4	5 24	...

LASVA and JAJCE.

E.M.		a.m.	a.m.	p.m.	p.m.	
—	**Lasva** ....dep	6 16	8 35	6 5	8 15	...
19¼	Travnik .... arr	8 2	9 44	7 32	10 0	...
	dep	—	9 52	7 50	—	...
38	Donji Vakuf	...	11 26	9 43	...	...
58½	**Jajce** ....arr	...	12 46	11 20	...	...

	a.m.	a.m.	p.m.
Jajce ....dep	...	6 0	1 30
Donji Vakuf	...	7 50	2 52
Travnik .... arr	...	9 35	4 28
dep	5 0	9 55	4 40
Lasva ....arr	6 0	11 26	5 45

Donji Vakuf ....dep	8 a0	11a50	3p25	10p10	...	...
Bugojno ....arr	8 25	12 15	3 50	10 25	...	...

Bugojno ....dep	6 a50	10a30	2 p0	9 p0	...	...	...
Donji Vakuf ....arr	7 15	10 55	2 25	9 25	...	...	...

ELBOGEN and NEUSATTL.

Elbogen ......dep	4 a37	9 a4	12 p4	3 p16	7 p0	10p35
Neusattl ......arr	5 6	9 28	12 33	4 45	7 29	11 4

Neusattl ...dep	6 a44	10 a5	1 p20	4 p30	9p20	11p25
Elbogen......arr	7 8	10 30	1 45	4 55	9 45	11 50

CHODAU and NEUDEK.

E.M.					
	Chodau (**250**) ....dep	7 a0	10 a7	4 p12	...
4¼	Neurohlau (**243A**)	7 27	10 34	4 39	...
8¾	Neudek ....arr	...	11 0	5 5	...

Neudek ......dep	5 a14	...	3 p0	6 p40	...
Neurohlau	5 43	8 a24	3 30	7 9	...
Chodau ......arr	6 10	8 49	3 57	7 36	...

HINTER TREBAN and LOCHOWITZ.

E.M.				
	Hinter Treban ......dep	7 a20	3 p0	8 p5
24	Lochowitz ....arr	9 23	4 59	10 2

Lochowitz ....dep	5 a0	10a15	5 p38
Hinter Treban ....arr	6 50	12 3	7 30

MÜRZZUSCHLAG and NEUBERG.

Mürzzuschlag dep	6a43	10a37	2 p1	5p13	9 p5
Kapellen	7 19	10 52	2 34	5 28	9 20
Neuberg arr	7 44	11 5	3 5	5 41	9 33

Neuberg dep	5a37	8a45	11a30	3p23	6 p15	...
Kapellen	5 51	9 9	11 44	3 54	6 29	...
Mürzzuschlag arr	6 5	9 37	11 58	4 18	6 43	...

KRIEGSDORF and ROMERSTADT. E.M. 9¼

Kriegsdorf dep	6 a12	9a10	2p14	4p45	8 p0
Römerstadt arr	6 56	10 0	3 0	5 31	8 56

Römerstadt dep	5 a0	7 a30	11a40	3p40	6p15	...
Kriegsdorf 249 arr	5 39	8 14	12 23	4 28	7 11	...

ERBERSDORF and WURBENTHAL.

Erbersdorf dep	7a55	1 p39	4 p21	9 p17
Wurbenthal arr	8 51	2 30	5 20	10 13

Wurbenthal dep	5 a35	11a45	2p32	5 p42	...
Erbersdorf 249 arr	6 30	12 48	3 24	6 50	...

ZELTWEG and CILLI.

Zeltweg dep	...	...	...	6a25	...	1 p 6	6 p0
Wolfsberg	...	...	6a14	8 25	10a0	3 8	8 10
Unter Drauburg	...	5a27	8 6	—	12 5	4 56	9 32
Missling	...	6 23	9 1	...	1 1	6 1	—
Wollan	5a39	—	9 44	...	1 47	7 1	...
Heilenstein-Frasslau	6 22	...	1031	...	2 35	7 51	...
Cilli arr	6 58	...	11 9	...	3 14	8 30	...

Cilli dep	...	...	...	7a44	...	2p47	4p20	6 p0
Heilenstein-Frasslau	...	...	...	8 27	...	1 30	5 3	6 43
Wollan	...	...	...	9 43	...	2 20	5 51	7 45
Missling	...	6a34	...	1022	...	3 2	—	8 25
Unter Drauburg	6 a2	7 30	8 a4	1117	11a57	4 0	5 p0	9 20
Wolfsberg	8 6	—	9 35	—	1 31	—	6 54	—
Zeltweg 241 arr	1010	...	...	...	3 19	...	9 12	...

PRAGUE and DOBRISCH.

E.M.						
	Prague K.F.J.B. dp	6 a5	10a20	2p40	4p37	6 p50
1¾	Nusle-Vrsovic	6 17	10 33	2 55	4 50	7 3
10	Modran	6 55	11 13	3 35	5 31	7 41
15½	Wran	7 33	11 45	3 56	5 52	8 1
41¾	Dobrisch arr	9 8	1 20	—	7 46	...

Dobrisch dep	...	5a40	10 a5	...	4 p5	...
Wran	5 a48	7 26	11 35	4p21	5 53	8 p5
Modran	6 13	7 52	11 57	4 45	6 17	8 25
Nusle-Vrsovic	6 55	8 36	12 41	5 28	6 59	9 5
Prague arr	7 2	8 43	12 48	5 35	7 6	9 12

GROSSLUPP and GOTTSCHEE.

Grosslupp dep	8 a39	2 p44	8 p58	...
Reifnitz	10 1	4 6	10 20	...
Gottschee arr	10 35	4 40	10 54	...

Gottschee dep	5 a48	11a55	6 p8	...	...	...
Reifnitz	6 23	12 31	6 44	...	...	...
Grosslupp arr	7 42	1 50	8 2	...	...	...

LAIBACH and STRASCHA-TÖPLITZ.

Laibach dep	7 a32	1p30	7p46	...
Grosslupp	8 34	2 36	8 51	...
Treffen	10 0	4 4	1017	...
Rudolfswert	10 45	4 54	1056	...
Strascha-Toplitz arr	11 3	5 12	...	...

Strascha dep	...	11a13	5p22	...
Rudolfswert	5 a42	11 46	5 56	...
Treffen	6 28	12 31	6 42	...
Grosslupp 248	8 7	2 7	8 21	...
Laibach arr	8 59	3 0	9 16	...

Treffen dep	10 a5	4 p6	10p20
Johannisthal arr	11 6	5 12	11 15
Johannisthal dep	5 a19	11a18	5 p25
Treffen arr	6 16	12 18	6 29

MAHR-BUDWITZ and JAMNITZ.

Mähr-Budwitz dep	7a20	11a30	9 p3
Jamnitz arr	8 13	12 31	9 54

Jamnitz dep	5 a45	8a59	5p50	...	...
Mähr-Budwitz 224 arr	6 34	9 52	6 48	...	...

TIRSCHNITZ and SCHONBACH. E.M. 15½

Tirschnitz dep	6a25	12p40	6p45	10p17	...
Schonbach arr	7 26	1 42	7 46	11 18	...

Schonbach dep	4a45	9 a13	3p26	7 p49	...
Tirschnitz arr	5 50	10 18	4 30	8 50	...

TAUS and PLAN.

Taus dep	...	...	8 a10	12p23	8 p28	...	...
Ronsperg	...	a.m.	9 6	1 34	9 35	...	...
Haid 244	a.m.	6 8	10 44	4 2	—	...	...
Tachau	4 56	7 25	11 35	5 28	...	...	...
Plan 243A arr	5 30	7 59	12 8	6 2	...	...	...

Plan dep	...	6 a25	10a12	12p48	...	8 p17	...	...
Tachau	...	7 13	10 49	1 25	2 p1	9 5	...	...
Haid	a.m.	8 1	—	—	3 9	10 3	...	...
Ronsperg 248	6 11	10 4	...	...	5 44	—	...	...
Taus 244 arr	7 30	11 9	...	...	7 0	...	...	...

STANKAU and RONSPERG.

Stankau dep	8 a33	12p10	4 p25	7 p25	...
Ronsperg 248 arr	9 44	1 24	5 27	8 39	...

Ronsperg dep	6 a30	10a12	2 p24	5p57	...
Stankau 243B arr	7 50	11 14	3 48	7 0	...

WELS and GRUNAU and ROHR. §—Not on Sunday.

Wels dep	6a50	...	10a35	12p36	3p17	5p33	7 p5	...
Sattledt arr	7 25	...	11 11	1 11	4 2	6 12	7 41	...
Sattledt dep	7 35	9§a16	...	1 16	...	6 21	...	...
Pettenbach	8 15	9 52	...	1 56	...	7 5	...	...
Grunau arr	8 54	10 29	...	2 37	...	7 44	...	...
Sattledt dep	7 30	—	11 13	1 17	4 37	6 19	7 49	...
Rohr 248 arr	8 4	...	11 40	1 47	4 49	6 54	8 25	...

Rohr dep	6a30	9 a50	12p30	...	2p43	5p38	...	7p20	...
Sattledt arr	7 15	10 29	1 3	§	3 21	6 13	...	7 48	...
Grunau dep	6 0	9 11	—	2p38	...	—	...	5 54	...
Pettenbach	6 40	9 52	...	3 22	...	...	...	6 34	...
Sattledt arr	7 16	10 24	...	3 59	...	...	p.m.	7 8	...
Sattledt dep	7 26	10 34	...	—	3 25	...	7 10	7 48	...
Wels arr	8 4	11 13	...	...	4 5	...	7 42	8 16	...

VIENNA, NEUSTADT, and ASPANG.

E.M	Vienna—	a.m.	a.m.	a.m	a.m	p.m.	p.m	p.m.	
—	Aspangbhf ...dep	7 40	8 45	1015	1125	2 30	3 38	7 50	...
11½	Biedermannsdorf	...	9 22	...	1157	3 5	4 0	...	...
15½	Traiskirchen.........	8 11	9 41	11 6	1214	3 22	4 11	8 21	...
25½	Sollenau............	8 31	1019	1136	1244	3 58	4 33	8 42	...
32½	Neustadt............	8 47	—	1154	1 9	—	4 50	9 3	...
40½	Pitten	9 11	...	1211	1 41	...	5 21	9 34	...
54	**Aspang**..........arr	9 48	...	1247	2 25	...	6 4	1016	...

	a.m.	a.m.	p.m	p.m.	p.m.	p.m.	p.m.	p.m	
Aspang ...dep	5 55	10 5	...	2 55	3 5	...	7 30	7 40	...
Pitten..........	6 30	1042	...	3 21	3 44	...	8 1	8 21	...
Neustadt	6 55	1114	...	3 40	4 15	...	8 22	8 55	...
Sollenau	7 14	1140	1248	4 1	4 46	6 55	8 45	9 15	...
Traiskirchen	7 34	1214	1 16	4 25	5 13	7 32	9 5	9 43	...
Biedermanns.	7 45	1229	1 33	...	5 28	7 54	...	9 56	...
Vienna ...arr	8 14	1258	2 3	4 58	5 57	8 30	9 38	1026	...

Sollenau..............dep	8 a33	11a44	1253	4 p39	8 52	...	...	...
Fischau..................	9 8	12 8	1 21	5 10	9 20	...	...	...
Puchberg ....arr	10 11	...	2 23	6 12	1022	...	...	...

Puchberg ....dep	5 a45	11a15	2 p30	7p10	...	...	...
Fischau Bad	6 43	12 16	3 30	8 14	...	...	...
Sollenau.............arr	7 7	12 40	3 52	8 37	...	...	...

Puchberg ....dep	6 a30	10a20	12p30	2 p35	...	...	...
Hochschneeberg ......arr	7 45	11 26	1 41	3 41	...	...	...

Hochschneeberg ....dep	8 a55	10a47	1 p0	3p42	5 p35	...
Puchberg ....arr	10 10	12 24	2 15	4 57	6 50	...

Fischau ....dep	6 a5	8a20	9a44	1 p54	2p49	5p23	8 p0	9p 5	...
Wöllersdorf ...arr	6 15	8 30	9 54	2 4	2 59	5 33	8 10	10 5	...

Wöllersdorf...dep	6a25	8a46	10a10	2 p8	3 p11	5p40	8p20	10p15
Fischau ....arr	6 34	8 56	10 20	2 17	3 20	5 49	8 29	10 24

VIENNA and KREMS.

Vienna	...	a.m.	a.m.	a.m.	a.m.	p.m.	p.m.	p.m.	p.m	p.m.
K.F.J.Bhf....dep	...	5 8	6 40	7 42	1036	1 20	3 18	5 8	7 0	9 5
Klosterneuberg ...	...	5 31	...	...	1054	1 37	...	...	7 19	...
Tulln	...	6 7	7 29	8 19	1140	2 21	4 10	5 54	8 2	9 50
Absdorf............	a.m.	6 28	7 44	8 30	1159	2 43	4 40	6 14	8 22	1011
Hadersdorf	6 53	7 13	8 33	8 59	1246	3 31	5 28	6 52	9 13	1047
Krems ....arr	7 10	7 30	8 50	9 9	1 4	3 50	5 44	7 8	9 30	11 2

	a.m.	a.m.	a.m.	a.m.	p.m.	p.m.	p.m.	p.m
Krems ...dep	6 35	8 10	8 16	1030	1210	3 0	5 10	8 50
Hadersdorf ...	6 59	8 21	8 32	1047	1234	3 18	5 32	9 19
Absdorf dep	7 45	8 50	—	1138	1 20	4 15	6 14	10 4
Tulln	8 3	9 1	...	1157	1 39	4 35	6 32	1021
Klosterneub'g	8 45	...	...	...	2 10	5 5	...	1051
Vienna ...arr	9 0	9 35	...	1240	2 26	5 20	7 15	11 5

Hadersdorf ....dep	...	7a12	9a 0	12p48	...	5p45	9p20
Horn	7a30	8 47	1043	2 23	5p41	7 20	1052
Sigmundsherberg-Hornarr	7 58	9 9	11 5	2 45	6 4	...	1114

Sigmundsherberg-Horndep	4‡a55	6 a35	8a13	10a20	3p28	7 p8
Horn	5 20	7 8	8 46	10 46	3 52	7 33
Hadersdorf.....................arr	6 48	...	...	12 20	5 20	9 3

Absdorf............dep	5a22	7a50	12p7	6 p18	8 p26	...
Stockerau ....arr	6 0	8 35	1245	6 54	9 2	...

Stockerau..........dep	6a41	10a35	2 p0	7 p12	9p12	...
Absdorf ....arr	7 22	11 17	2 36	7 49	9 47	...

‡—Mon. at 4.35 a.m.

VIENNA and LAXENBURG. 11¾ miles, in 45 minutes From the Sudbahnhof at 5.5, 6.0, 6.35, 7.10, 8.5, 9.5, 9.50, 10.25, 11.40 a.m., 12 50, 1.30, 1.50, 2.55, 3.35, 4.10, 4.40, 5.40, 6.10, 6.45, 7.30, 8.0, 8.45 p.m. From Laxenburg, 6.12, 6.46, 7.26, 8.6, 9.10, 9.52, 11.4 a.m., 1.6, 1.47, 3.6, 3.40, 4.20, 5.0, 5.55, 6.28, 7.8, 7.40, 8.18, 9.4p.m. All trains call at Mödling.

NUSSDORF & KAHLENBERG.—From **Nussdorf.**—Service about hourly from 7.50 a.m. until 8.0 p.m

SALZKAMMERGUT LOCAL RAILWAY.

			‡		‡		¶		¶	‡	¶				
Ischl............dep	5a55	7a35	9 a28	11a0	12p35	2p20	3p50	4p40	6 p0	7 p4	8p42	...	...	...	...
Strobl..................	6 28	8 8	9 54	1130	1 7	2 46	4 24	5 15	6 33	7 37	9 14	...	...	...	...
St.Wolfgang	6 40	8 21	10 5	1143	1 16	2 17	4 38	5 28	6 42	7 47	9 25	...	...	...	...
St. Gilgen...........	7 0	8 41	10 23	12 2	—	3 14	4 56	5 48	—	8 6	9 43	...	...	...	...
Scharfling	7 18	8 58	...	1219	...	3 29	—	6 5	...	8 23	—	...	...	...	...
Plomberg	7 25	9 5	10 45	1226	...	3 36	...	6 12	...	8 30	...	...	...	...	...
St. Lorenz ......arr	7 30	9 11	10 50	1231	...	3 41	...	6 17	...	8 35	...	...	...	...	...
Thalgau	7 53	9 37	...	1253	...	3 59	...	6 39	...	8 56	...	...	...	...	...
Eugendorf-Kal. ...	8 23	10 11	...	1 26	...	...	...	7 4	...	9 19	...	...	...	...	...
Salzburg ....arr	8 45	10 34	11 48	1 47	...	4 39	...	7 25	...	9 40	...	...	...	...	...

						§	‡	‡							
Salzburg......dep	...	6a25	8 a0	9 a50	...	12p35	1 p5	2 p30	...	5p10	...	7 p15	...	...	...
Eugendorf-K..........	...	6 46	8 22	...	...	1 1	...	2 55	...	5 32	...	7 42	...	...	...
Thalgau	...	7 9	8 48	10 32	...	1 29	1 47	3 23	...	5 58	...	8 10	...	...	...
St. Lorenz..............	...	7 32	9 12	10 56	...	1 55	2 8	3 48	...	6 21	...	8 36	...	...	...
Plomberg	...	7 37	9 18	11 1	...	2 2	2 13	3 53	...	6 26	...	8 41	¶	...	...
Scharfling.............	a.m.	7 44	9 25	...	...	2 9	...	4 0	¶	6 33		8 48	p.m.	...	...
St. Gilgen	5 40	8 2	9 44	11 24	†	2 30	2 36	4 19	5 p47	6 51	¶	9 5	9 6	...	...
St.Wolfgang..........	5 59	8 23	10 4	11 44	1 p20	2 56	2 56	4 41	6 7	7 11	7p25		9 26	...	...
Strobl	6 9	8 33	10 14	11 54	1 30	3 6	3 6	4 53	6 17	7 21	7 43		9 36	...	...
Ischl ....arr	6 40	9 4	10 42	12 20	2 1	3 34	3 34	5 27	6 50	7 51	8 15	...	10 5	...	...

St.Lorenz ....dep	7 a36	9 a16	12p37	1§p54	2‡p9	3 p50	6p24	8 p41	...	...	...	...	...	...
Mondsee ....arr	7 47	9 27	12 48	2 5	2 20	4 1	6 34	8 52	...	...	...	...	...	...

Mondsee ....dep	7 a17	8 a55	12p19	1§p35	1‡50	3p29	6 p2	8 p16	...	...	...	...	...	...
St. Lorenz ....arr	7 28	9 6	12 30	1 46	2 1	3 40	6 13	8 27	...	...	...	...	...	...

‡—Runs until 15th September.

¶—In July and Aug. only.

§—Runs from 16th September.

†—Until 15th Sept.

‖—From 15th July until 31st August.

St.Wolfgang ...dep	7 a0	9†a0	10a30	12p5	2†p14	3 p25	5‖p50
Schafbergspitze arr	8 0	10 0	11 30	1 5	3 14	4 25	6 50

Schafbergspitzedep	8 a5	10†a15	11a50	1p10	3†p19	5p43	6‖p53
St. Wolfgang ...arr	8 58	11 16	12 50	2 3	4 12	6 36	7 53

BORKI WIELKIE and GRZYMALOW.						
Borki Wielkie...dep	5 a35	11a55	5p17	...	...
Grzymalow ......arr	7 35	1 50	6 49	...	...
Grzymalow ....dep	9 a5	2 p34	8 p30	...	...
Borki Wielkie 246A arr	10 37	4 15	10 10	...	...

BARN-ANDERSDORF and HOF.				
Bärn-Andersdorf ...dep	7 a0	3 p0	7p25	...
Hof in Mähren ....arr	7 46	3 46	8 11	...
Hof in Mähren..........dep	5a45	1p14	6p12	...
Bärn-Andersdorf 249 arr	6 30	2 0	6 58	...

ROWERSDORF and HOTZENPLOTZ.				
Röwersdorf ....dep	8a14	12p26	3 p45	9p42
Hotzenplotz ....arr	9 28	1 40	4 59	1043
Hotzenplotz ....dep	5a 1	9 a48	1p58	6p30
Röwersdorf 249.........arr	6 24	11 11	3 3	7 56

NEPOLOKOUTZ and WIZNITZ.				
Nepolokoutz ....dep	8a50	2 p20	7p 0	...
Wiznitz ....arr	1135	5 5	9 35	...
Wiznitz ....dep	5 a15	9a45	3 p20	...
Nepolokoutz 246A ...arr	7 45	1220	5 50	...

WYGNANKA and IWANIE.

Wygnanka... dep	8 a21	8 p57	...
Teresin	10 5	10 1	...
Iwanie puste ...arr	12 37	12 0	...

Iwanie puste...dep	4 a21	10 a2	...
Teresin	6 36	12 8	12p40
Wygnanka 245 arr	7 41	...	2 43

Teresin ....dep	10a20	10p11	...	...
Skala ....arr	10 53	10 43	...	...
Skala ....dep	6 a 0	11a47	...	...
Teresin ....arr	6 31	12 20	...	...

PRAGUE and GEORGSWALDE

Station		a.m.	a.m.	a.m.	p.m.	p.m.	p.m.	p.m.	p.m.	p.m.
Prague—Kaiser Franz. J. Bhf. dep		1 36	6 0	7 30	12 2	1 24	2 43	5 45	6 18	1025
Neratowitz		...	6 44	8 39	1 6	2 30	...	6 47	7 1	1127
Vsetat-P.	5a14	2 27	6 51	8 48	1 16	2 38	3 34	6 55	7 8	1135
TETSCHEN 224 arr		4a10	...	11a50	4p14	...	5p25	—	10p4	...
Kuttenthal 249	6 30	—	7 17	9 33	—	3 25	—	...	7 37	1217
Jungbunzlau ...	6 58	4a51	7 33	10 1	...	3 54	...	...	8 6	1242
Bakov 249 ...arr		5 9	7 47	10 20	...	4 16	...	...	8 20	1259
„ ....dep		5 21	7 50	10 30	...	4 21	...	...	8 29	—
Weisswasser..........		5 36	8 1	10 46	...	4 35	...	...	8 41	...
Böhm. Leipa arr		6 39	8 43	11 49	...	5 33	...	...	9 27	...
		a.m.		a.m.	p.m		p.m.	...	p.m.	...
Bodenbach dep		5 6	...	9 5	1234	...	5 20	...	8 25	...
Tetschen		5 14	...	9 50	1250	...	5 40	...	8 32	...
Bensen 249		5 35	...	10 9	1 8	...	5 57	...	8 51	...
Politz Sandau......		5 59	...	10 38	1 30	...	6 23	...	9 13	...
Böhm. Leipa ar		6 20	...	11 3	1 47	...	6 41	...	9 30	...
Böhm. Leipa dep		6 51	8 49	12 20	2 30	5 40	...	...	9 33	...
Langenau..............		7 10	9 2	12 39	3 8	5 58	...	...	9 47	...
Röhrsdorf 249		7 36	9 16	1 5	—	6 23	...	...	10 2	...
Tannenberg............		8 2	9 28	1 33	...	6 43	...	...	1015	...
Kreibitz-T. ar	a.m.	8 20	9 42	1 52	p.m.	7 1	...	...	1029	a.m.
„ 249 dep	7 31	8 28	9 43	2 2	1 5	7 13	...	...	1030	5 43
Rumb'g 249	7 55	9 1	10 0	2 40	1 31	7 49	...	...	1045	7 15
Georgswalde ...		9 17	1011	2 57	1 50	8 5	...	...	1055	7 40

Station			a.m.	a.m.	a.m.	p.m.		p.m.	p.m.	p.m.
Georgswalde Ebersbach dep		...	5 16	6 40	9 38	12 14	p.m.	2 8	6 1	6 14
Rumburg		...	5 27	7 2	10 2	12 38	1 32	2 27	6 11	6 41
K.-Teichstatt arr		...	5 42	7 25	1026	1 3	1 58	—	6 27	7 8
„ ...dep		...	5 44	7 32	—	1 13	—	...	6 28	7 26
Tannenberg		...	...	7 53	...	1 34	...	...	6 46	7 46
Röhrsdorf............		...	6 10	8 9	...	1 51	...	...	6 56	8 6
Langenau............		...	6 25	8 27	...	2 13	...	...	...	8 30
Böhm. Leipa arr		...	6 37	8 42	...	2 28	...	...	7 18	8 49
			a.m.	a.m.	p.m.		p.m.		p.m.	...
Böhm-Leipa ...dep		...	6 48	8 52	1228	...	5 38	...	7 32	...
Politz Sandau......		...	7 9	9 14	1247	...	5 55	...	7 52	...
Bensen		...	7 31	9 37	1 8	...	6 13	...	8 13	...
Tetschen		...	7 48	9 50	1 28	...	6 28	...	8 27	...
Bodenbach arr		...	7 53	9 55	1 33	...	6 33	...	9 14	...
Böhm. Leipa dep		...	6 49	8 55	...	2 40	...	...	7 24	9 37
Weisswasser		...	7 37	10 0	...	3 40	...	...	8 10	1039
Bakov ....arr		a.m.	7 49	10 14	...	3 54	p.m.	p.m.	8 22	1052
„ ....dep		4 52	7 55	10 22	...	3 59	1 41	6 22	8 31	11 0
Jungbunzlau		5 17	8 27	10 44	...	4 30	2 3	6 46	8 45	1124
Kuttenthal		5 37	8 42	11 5	p.m.	4 52	2 22	7 9	9 1	—
TETSCHEN dep	4a15	...	6 a4	8 a44	1 0	...	1222	5 p5	...	12a9
Vsetat-Priv.	7 18	6 9	9 7	11 45	2 59	5 26	3 36	7 56	...	1 52
Neratowitz ..	7 36	6 19	...	11 53	...	5 36	3 45	8 5	9 32	...
Prague ...arr	8 50	7 27	9 57	12 50	3 49	6 38	4 43	9 5	1015	2 41

Extra.—Kreibitz to Georgswalde, 11.3 a.m. Georgswalde to Kreibitz, 9.10 p.m.

TURNAU and BAKOV.

Station									
Turnau ...dep	4 a4	7a10	7a45	9a32	1 p5	3p12	5p40	7p54	9p55
Münchengrätz ...	4 32	7 32	8 4	9 59	1 27	3 37	6 7	8 17	1032
Bakov 249 arr	4 45	7 42	:	1012	1 40	3 50	6 20	8 26	1047
Jungbunzlau	...	...	8 22	...	...	...	...	...	...

Station								
Jungbunzlau dep	...	...	a.m.	...	...	7p58	...	...
Bakov ....dep	5a22	7a53	1028	1p56	4p23	:	8p32	1 a4
Müchengrätz.........	5 37	8 4	1043	2 10	4 37	8 17	8 43	1 17
Turnau (223A) arr	6 3	8 25	11 9	2 36	5 4	8 33	9 4	1 43

ROHRSDORF and DEUTSCH GABEL

Station						
Rohrsdorf......dep	...	8a16	9a18	1p53	7 p4	8p10
Zwickau..................	7 a1	8 47	9 32	2 16	7 28	8 24
Deutsch Gabel ar	7 42	9 40	...	3 2	8 13	...

Station					
Deutsch Gabel dep	6a18	8 a1	11a38	...	6p35
Zwickau..................	7 10	8 47	12 39	5p54	7 37
Rohrsdorf.........arr	7 25	9 2	12 54	6 9	7 52

BODENBACH and WARNSDORF.

†—Not on Sunday.		a.m.		a.m.	a.m.	p.m.	p.m.	p.m.
Bodenbach...............dep		6 13	...	9 5	1158	5 20	6†40	8 25
Tetschen ....dep		6 23	...	9 17	12 7	5 33	6 49	8 32
Bensen		6 42	...	9 38	1222	5 46	7 9	8 55
Böhm-Kamnitz.....................		7 12	...	10 4	1254	6 12	7 41	9 25
Tannenberg	a.m.	7 57	a.m.	1038	1 38	6 48	—	10 1
Kreibitz-Teich.	5 45	8 26	9 44	11 1	2 4	7 15	...	1032
Warnsdorf (184) arr	6 8	8 51	10 4	1126	2 29	7 35	...	1049

Station	a.m.	a.m.	a.m.	p.m.	p.m.	p.m.	p.m.	
Warnsdorf dep	5 14	7 4	1020	1234	6 3	6 41	9 34	...
Kreibitz..........	5 36	7 37	1042	1 8	6 24	7 18	10 2	...
Tannenberg	—	7 58	1059	1 29	—	7 38	1035	...
Böhm-Kamnitz ...	5 a0	8 34	1128	1 59	...	8 16	11 3	...
Bensen	5 33	9 1	1152	2 22	...	8 49	1128	...
Tetschen ......arr	5 51	9 15	12 6	2 34	...	9 5	1144	...
Bodenbach arr	6 3	9 25	1215	2 43	...	9 14	1152	...

BOHM-KAMNITZ & STEINSCHONAU

Station				
Böhm-Kamnitz (249)......dep	7 a14	10a6	12p56	6 p16
Steinschönau ....arr	7 30	1022	1 12	6 32

Station				
Steinschönau ....dep	8 a 9	11 a4	1 p36	7 p16
Böhm-Kamnitz ......arr	8 25	11 20	152	7 32

Station					
Böhm-Leipa...........dep	7 a35	12 0	4 p44	9 p45	...
Steinschönau ....arr	9 32	1 33	6 28	11 7	...

Station					
Steinschönau ....dep	5 a5	10 a0	1 p50	6 p50	...
Böhm-Leipa..............arr	621	11 36	3 12	8 25	...

KRALUP and NERATOWITZ.

Station				
Kralup ....dep	4 a10	6 a30	10a55	6 p12
Neratowitz...........arr	5 23	7 12	11 43	6 49

Station					
Neratowitz (249)...dep	7 a38	1 p15	7 p6	9 p36	...
Kralup ....arr	8 15	2 2	8 10	10 23	...

KUTTENTHAL and SUDOMER SKALSKO.

Station				
Kuttenthal ....dep	9 a45	7 p50	...	...
Sudomer-Skalsko arr	10 44	8 49	...	...

Station				
Sudomer-Skalsko dep	7 a8	5 p53	...	...
Kuttenthal..........arr	8 15	6 50	...	...

OLMUTZ and TROPPAU.

Station		a.m.	a.m.	a.m.		p.m.		p.m.
Olmütz Nordb. dep		4 17	7 20	11 18	...	1 0	...	5 56
Domstadtl		5 16	8 20	11 57	...	2 0	...	6 58
Bärn-Andersdorf 248A		5 31	8 35	12 9	...	2 14	...	7 13
Kriegsdorf (248)		6 7	9 6	12 32	...	2 52	...	7 48
Freudenthal		6 23	9 18	12 42	...	3 9	...	8 6
Erbersdorf (248)		6 39	9 31	12 54	...	3 28	...	8 22
Jagerndorf arr	a.m.	6 59	9 51	1 10	p.m.	3 48	p.m.	8 45
„ dep	6 22	7 19	10 2	1 17	3 55	4 5	6 14	9 2
Skrochowitz-B.	6 53	7 41	10 24	1 31	4 8	4 27	6 36	9 24
Troppau Staat Bf.	7 17	8 2	10 45	1 45	4 22	4 48	6 56	9 47
Troppau Nordb	7 38	8 14	10 54	1 52	4 29	4 57	7 6	9 58

(222)		a.m.	a.m.	p.m.	p.m.	p.m.	p.m.	p.m.	p.m.
Troppau Nord. dep		6 10	9 45	1230	1 36	3 20	5 0	7 43	1050
Troppau Staat Bhf....		6 23	9 58	1237	1 49	3 27	5 12	7 52	11 2
Skrochowitz-B.		6 46	10 25	...	2 12	3 40	5 38	8 14	1124
Jagerndorf arr	a.m.	7 6	10 46	1 4	2 33	3 54	6 0	8 35	1145
„ dep	5 12	7 21	1 12	—	—	3 59	6 28	8 51	—
Erbersdorf ...	5 35	7 47	1 36	—	...	4 16	7 1	9 14	...
Freudenthal	5 49	8 6	1 53	...	...	4 28	7 27	9 27	...
Kriegsdorf......	6 5	8 21	2 8	...	...	4 40	7 45	—	...
Bärn-Andersdorf	6 40	9 3	2 41	...	...	5 4	8 23	...	...
Domstadtl	6 50	9 14	2 51	...	...	5 12	8 35	...	...
Olmütz Nord arr	7 47	10 11	3 44	...	...	5 41	9 31	...	...

Station					
Freudenthal ....dep	8 a20	2 p0	8 p15	...	...
Kl. Mohrau ....arr	9 24	3 9	9 17	...	...

Station					
Kl. Mohrau ....dep	4 a46	11a35	6 p2	...	...
Freudenthal............arr	5 41	12 36	7 12	...	...

JAGERNDORF and ZIEGENHALS

Station						
Jagerndorf.........dep	7a35	10a51	1p23	2p41	6p26	9 p5
Rowersdörf 248A	8 8	11 20	1 44	3 11	7 1	9 36
Ziegenhals (244) arr	8 42	11 46	2 12	3 42	7 34	10 6

Station						
Ziegenhals dep	6 a0	9 a7	11a54	3 p4	5 p6	7p36
Rowersdörf	6 35	9 35	12 24	3 31	5 38	8 13
Jägerndorf arr	7 8	10 0	12 51	3 51	6 6	8 40

SCHLACKENWERTH and JOACHIMSTHAL.

Station						
Schlackenwerth	6a51	9a13	11a8	3p30	6 5	8p45
Joachimsthal ...	7 31	9 43	1148	4 0	6 35	9 14

Station						
Joachimsthal.........	6 a4	7a51	10a16	1p16	5 p9	6p52
Schlackenwerth 250	6 33	8 20	10 45	1 45	5 38	7 21

RUMBURG and NIXDORF.

Station						
Rumburg......... dep	7 a4	10 a4	2 p32	7 p42	...	...
Herrnwalde	7 25	10 28	3 2	8 12	...	...
Nixdorf ....arr	7 52	10 59	3 38	8 50	...	...

Station							
Nixdorf ...dep	5a33	8 a8	11a17	4p56	...	...	...
Herrnwalde......	6 25	8 42	12 6	5 44	...	...	...
Rumburg arr	6 48	8 58	12 25	6 4	...	...	...

Station					
Herrnwalde ......dep	6 a29	8a45	12 p9	5 p47	...
Schönlinde ....arr	6 46	9 2	12 26	6 4	...

Station					
Schönlinde ......dep	7 a0	9 a59	2 p30	7 p44	...
Herrnwalde ......arr	7 17	10 16	2 47	8 1	...

RUMBURG and SEBNITZ.

Station						
Rumburg ...dep	5 a44	6 a59	10 a6	2 p44	7 p55	10p48
Nixdorf	6 39	8 4	11 11	3 49	8 57	11 40
Nieder Einsiedel	7 9	8 35	11 46	4 22	9 27	12 0
Sebnitz 188A arr	7 14	8 40	11 51	4 27	9 32	...

Station							
Sebnitz ......dep	...	...	7 a22	10a28	4 p16	8 p46	...
Nieder Einsiedel	4 a6	5 a0	7 35	10 43	4 29	9 1	...
Nixdorf	4 27	5 31	7 59	11 12	4 57	9 28	...
Rumburg ...arr	5 20	6 43	8 54	12 20	6 1	10 26	...

For Fares, see page 237B.]

PRAGUE, KOMOTAU, CARLSBAD, FRANZENSBAD, and EGER.

Dist																			
	VIENNA 252 ....dep		...	...	10p0	10 p0	...	...	...	...	...	...	...	...	...	7a53	...	...	...	2 p20
E.M			1,2,3	Ex 3	Ex3	Ex 3	Ex2	Ex 3	Ex1	Ex1	1,2,3	Ex3	Ex 3	Ex1	2&3	Ex 3	1,2,3	1,2,3	2&3	1,2,3
	Prague—			a.m.	a.m.	a.m.					a.m.	a.m.			p.m.	p.m.		p.m.	p.m.	p.m.
—	„ Staatsbahnhof dep		...	4 52	6 7	7 13	...	...	...	...	8 37	1144	...	...	2 10	3 30	...	5 39	6 50	10 12
1½	„ Bubna .... „		...	...	...	...	...	...	...	...	8 45	...	...	...	2 18	...	...	5 47	6 58	10 21
2¾	„ Sandthorbhf. „		...	...	...	7 26	...	...	...	...	8 57	1156	...	...	2 30	3 42	...	5 59	7 10	10 37
10¼	Hostiwitz		...	...	Via Tuschmitz.	...	...	...	...	...	9 29	...	...	...	3 4	...	...	6 34	7 43	11 7
18¾	**Kladno 250**		...	...		8 1	...	...	...	...	9 50	1231	...	...	3 25	4 22	...	6 56	8 4	11 29
26¼	Lana		...	...		8 18	...	...	...	...	10 17	...	...	...	—	4†14	...	7 23	—	11 56
31	Neustraschitz		a.m.	...		8 27	...	...	...	...	10 30	...	...	...	...	...	...	7 37	...	12 9
39½	**Luzna Lischan 250**		5 8	...		8 41	...	...	...	...	10 49	1 10	...	...	...	5 7	...	7 56	...	12 28
42¼	**Krupa**		5 14	...		8 51	...	...	...	...	11 1	...	...	...	...	...	...	8 8	...	12 39
...	**Krupa** ....dep		...	...		...	...	...	...	Carlsbad-Paris Express; runs until 29th September.	11 10	...	...	...	...	...	...	8 16	...	...
50½	**Kolleschowitz** ...arr		...	...		...	...	...	Carlsbad-Berlin Express; runs until 31st August.		11 54	...	...	Ostend Express; runs until 16th September.	...	...	...	9 0	...	...
57¼	Michelob		5 51	...	...	9 18	...	...			11 42	1 47	...		...	5‡43	...	8 53	...	1 18
64½	**Saaz 244**		6 10	7 0	8 10	9 33	...	...			12 8	2 2	...		...	5 59	...	9 14	...	1 46
73¾	Priesen		6 31	⋮	⋮	...	...	...			12 31	...	...		...	...	...	9 51	...	2 9
79	**Komotau 251** ....arr		6 45	⋮	⋮	10 1	Through Carriage to Frankfort.	...			12 46	2 30	...		1,2,3	6 27	p.m.	10 5	1,2,3	2 24
...	DRESDEN Hpt. 188...dep		2a30	⋮	⋮	...		7 a10			8 a30	...	12 10		1210	12p53	1253	...	7 p5	...
...	AUSSIG 250 ....dep		5a47	⋮	⋮	8 a5		9 a27			11a25	...	1 p56		2 22	4 p5	4 p5	...	9 p8	...
...	**Komotau** ....dep		7 23	Via Tuschmitz.	⋮	10 8		11 5			1 43	2 35	3 23		4 40	6 34	6 45	†—Sets down only. ‡—Stops if required.	1142	2 42
87	Kaaden-Brunnersdorf ...		7 43		⋮	10 23		11 20			2 3	2 50	...		4 58	6 48	7 7		12 0	3 4
90¾	Klösterle		7 53		⋮	10‡30		...			2 14	...	...		5 8	...	7 18		1210	3 15
95¾	Pürstein		8 4		⋮	10‡38		...			2 25	...	RC		5 19	...	7 30		1221	3 27
99½	Hauenstein-Warta		8 13		⋮	...		11 42			2 34	...	...		5 28	...	7 40		1230	3 37
102½	Wickwitz		8 21		⋮	10‡52		...			2 42	3‡18	...		5 36	7‡20	7 49		1233	3 47
107	Schlackenwerth		8 33		9 †8	10‡59		11‡55			2 56	3 26	...		5 47	7 30	8 2		1249	4 2
114¼	Dallwitz	1,2,3	8 53		...	...		...			3 20	...	...		...	...	8 27		...	...
116¼	**Carlsbad** ....arr	a.m.	8 58	8 18	9 25	11 17	a.m.	12 12	p.m.	p.m.	3 25	3 41	4 30	p.m.	6 13	7 49	8 32		1 15	4 31
...	„ ....dep	6 1	9 8	—	—	11 25	1145	12 19	2 25	2 36	3 50	—	—	4 52	—	8 0	8 42		1 39	4 46
123	**Chodau**	6 17	9 24	...	...	...	...	12 33	...	...	4 9	...	...	...	...	8‡13	9 1		1 46	5 5
125½	Neusattl	6 25	9 33	...	...	...	...	12 40	...	...	4 20	...	...	...	...	8 19	9 11	...	1 54	5 16
130¼	**Falkenau 250**	6 37	9 48	...	...	11 55	...	12 50	...	...	4 36	...	...	...	...	8 29	9 25	Extra.—Prague to Krupa, 11.14 p.m.	2 12	5 35
132¼	Zieditz	6 43	9 54	...	...	...	...	12 56	...	...	4 42	...	...	...	...	...	9 31		2 18	5 41
139¼	Königsberg a.d. Eger	7 0	1010	...	...	12 11	...	1 11	...	...	5 0	...	...	...	...	8‡45	9 48		2 35	5 59
145½	**Tirschnitz.** ......arr	7 14	1023	...	...	12 21	...	1 24	...	...	5 15	...	...	...	...	8 55	10 2		2 49	6 15
...	**Tirschnitz** ...dep	7 19	1033	...	...	12 33	...	1 30	...	...	5 24	...	...	...	...	9 4	1015		...	6 23
148½	**Franzensbad** arr	7 30	1044	...	...	12 44	...	1 41	...	...	5 35	...	...	...	...	9 15	1026		...	6 34
...	**Tirschnitz** ......dep	7 16	1026	...	...	12 24	...	1 26	...	...	5 18	...	...	...	...	8 57	10 4		2 50	6 20
148½	**Eger** ....arr	7 26	1035	...	...	12 32	1246	1 35	3 25	3 36	5 29	...	...	5 52	...	9 5	1015		3 0	6 31
167¾	MARIENBAD 243A ar	...	12p3	...	...	3 p9	3 p9	3 p9	5 p7	5 p7	6 p40	...	...	6p54	...	10p50	1225		6a31	7 a59
182¼	OBERKOTZAU 197 arr	...	...	...	...	2 p35	...	...	...	...	8 p25	...	...	...	...	11p29	...		6a59	10 a6
242½	NURNBERG 203 .arr	1p15	...	...	...	4 p34	4p34	4 p34	...	6 p6	11p30	...	...	8p22	...	3 a0	...		7a35	1 p15
243½	BAMBERG 197....arr	...	...	...	...	6 p21	...	...	...	...	...	...	...	...	...	1 a51	...		...	2p40
390¼	FRANKFORT 196B ....arr		...	...	...	8 p56	8p56	8 p56	...	1130	...	...	...	1246	...	12 0	...	...	2 p5	...

FALKENAU and KLINGENTHAL.

Falkenau ....dep	6a41	9 a52	1 p5	5 p7	9p30	...	...
Bleistadt	7 8	10 19	1 32	5 35	9 57	...	...
Ober-Graslitz	7 42	10 46	1 59	6 11	1026	...	...
Klingenthal 185...arr	7 52	10 56	2 9	6 21	1036	...	...

Klingenthal....dep	5 a14	8 a17	10a35	3p12	7 p8	8 p4	...
Ober-Graslitz	5 29	8 37	10 55	3 32	7 28	8 24	...
Bleistadt	5 54	9 2	11 20	3 57	7 53	8 49	...
Falkenau 250 ....arr	6 20	9 28	11 46	4 23	8 19	9 15	...

RAKONITZ and LUZNA LISCHAN.

Rakonitz 245 ....dep	5 a7	8a10	9 a20	2 p14	7p26	...
Luzna Lischan ....arr	5 29	8 36	9 46	2 40	7 52	...

Luzna Lischan 250...dep	1a28	8a46	11a 7	5p12	8p22	...
Rakonitz ....arr	1 48	9 6	11 27	5 32	8 42	...

WICKWITZ & GIESSHUBL.

Wickwitz ....dep	8a26	11a16	2p47	6p12
Giesshubl Sauerbrunn arr	8 55	11 45	3 16	6 41

Giesshubl Sauerb. dep	10a18	1p45	5 p1	7p13
Wickwitz ....arr	10 47	2 14	5 30	7 42

KLADNO and KRALUP.

Dist						
	Kladno 250 ....dep	4 a51	1p32	4 p48	...	...
7½	Buschtehrad	5 14	1 55	5 7	...	...
13¾	Wotwowitz	5 38	2 19	5 35	...	...
17½	**Kralup 252** ....arr	5 49	2 30	5 46	...	...

Kralup ....dep	8a52	3 p45	9 p15	...	...
Wotwowitz	8 44	3 57	9 27	...	...
Buschtehrad......	9 10	4 23	9 53	...	...
Kladno .....arr	9 34	4 47	10 17	...	...

AUSSIG and KOMOTAU.

DRESDEN Hpt. 88	12a22	2a30	...	...	...	...	...	7 a10	8 a30	12p10	12p10	1253	...	...	4p40	7 p5	...	8 p12	...
BODENBACH 252A	2 a30	4a 5	...	...	...	5a45	...	8 a47	10a20	1 p23	1 p23	3p12	...	...	6p48	8 p20	...	10p40	...
	1,2,3	Ex3	1,2,3	Ex3	1,2,3	1,2,3	1,2,3	Ex 3	1,2,3	Ex 3	1,2,3	1,2,3	1,2,3	1,2,3	1,2,3	1,2,3	1,2,3	1,2,3	
	a.m.	a.m.	a.m.	a.m.	a.m.	a.m.	a.m.	a.m.	a.m.	p.m.	p.m.	p.m.	p.m.	p.m.	p.m.	p.m.	p.m.	nght	
Aussig Staat. ...dep	3 57	4 45	...	...	...	6 58	8 5	9 27	11 25	1 56	2 22	4 5	5 20	...	8 5	9 8	10 50	12 47	...
„ A.T.E. ...dep	4 2	...	...	5 47	5 58	7 4	8 9	9 33	11 30	...	2 27	4 10	5 28	6 15	8 10	9 13	10 56	12 53	...
Türmitz	4 8	...	...	...	6 6	7 12	8 15	...	11 36	RC	2 33	4 16	5 35	6 22	8 19	...	11 3	12 59	...
Mariaschein	4 24	...	...	...	6 29	7 32	8 30	9 50	11 52	...	2 50	4 32	5 52	6 42	8 38	9 31	11 21	1 13	...
Teplitz-Schönau	4 33	5 8	...	6 10	6 40	7 42	8 37	9 57	11 59	2 20	3 0	4 40	6 2	6 52	8 48	9 38	11 28	1 20	...
„ ....dep	4 40	5 12	...	6 15	—	7 50	8 42	10 0	12 5	2 24	3 5	4 48	6 12	—	8 55	9 48	11 40	—	...
Settenz	4 45	...	...	...	...	7 56	8 47	10 4	12 11	...	3 11	4 54	6 17	...	9 1	9 54	11 45	...	...
Dux 244 ....dep	4 58	5 25	5 28	6 28	...	8 12	9 1	10 15	12 27	...	3 26	5 11	6 32	...	9 18	10 8	11 59	...	...
Brüx 46	—	—	5 56	6 47	...	8 42	9 27	10 34	1255	...	3 55	5 40	7 2	...	9 45	10 49	12 23	...	...
Wurzmes	...	...	6 18	...	...	9 6	...	...	1 17	...	4 18	6 3	7 25	...	—	11 10	—	...	...
Komotau ....arr	...	...	6 35	7 13	...	9 22	9 54	11 0	1 33	3 18	4 35	6 20	7 42	...	...	11 26	...	...	...
CARLSBAD 250...arr	...	...	8 a58	8a58	...	1117	11a17	12p12	3 p25	4 p30	6 p13	7p49	...	...	...	1 a15	...	...	...

EGER, FRANZENSBAD, CARLSBAD, KOMOTAU, and PRAGUE.

FRANKFORT 196 dep	...	...	4p36	...	4p36	3a36	...	1221	...	...	...	...	8a25	...	...	...	...	...
BAMBERG 197B dep	...	...	2a20	...	2a20	...	...	...	...	...	...	...	...	...	...	...	1p11	3p37
NURNBERG 202 dep	...	...	1 a5	...	1 a5	8a25	...	9a15	...	...	1029	...	1 p5	...	...	...	...	2p10
OBERKOTZAU 197 dep		1 a28	4a54	...	4a54	...	...	...	...	...	...	1047	...	...	...	...	4p14	7 p1
MARIENBAD 243A dep		4 a32	6a32	...	6a32	10a4	...	...	...	...	12p5	1 p0	...	4p49	...	...	4p49	3p37
		Ex 3	1,2,3	Ex3	1,2,3	Ex1	Ex3	Ex3	Ex3	1,2,3	Ex1	1,2,3	Ex3	Ex1	Ex3	Ex3	1,2,3	1,2,3
		a.m.	a.m.		a.m.	a.m.		p.m.			p.m.	p.m.	p.m.	p.m.			p.m.	p.m.
Eger ...dep	...	5 58	8 7	...	8 46	1124	...	1224	...	...	1 4	2 51	4 28	6 12	...	...	6 30	10 0
Tirschnitz ...arr	...	6 4	8 14	...	8 54		...	1230	...	...		2 58	4 34		...	...	6 39	10 7
Franzensbad dep	...	5 48	8 0	...	8 38		...	1217	...	...		2 44	4 18		...	...	6 21	9 59
Tirschnitz ...arr	...	5 58	8 10	...	8 48		...	1227	...	...		2 54	4 28		...	...	6 31	10 9
Tirschnitz ...dep	...	6 6	8 16	...	8 57		...	1234	...	...		3 0	4 38		...	...	6 41	1014
Königsberg a. d. Eger	...	6 16	8 31	...	9 14		...	1244	...	...	RC	3 15	4 48		...	...	6 58	1029
Zieditz	...	...	8 48	...	9 31		...	...	...	...		3 33	...		...	...	7 17	1046
Falkenau	...	6 33	8 55	...	9 40		...	1 2	...	...		3 41	5 5		...	...	7 25	11 5
Neusattl	...	6 44	9 9	...	9 55		...	1*12	...	...		3 56	...		...	...	7 40	1121
Chodau	...	6 50	9 16	...	10 4		...	1*17	...	...		4 3	...		...	...	7 48	1128
Carlsbad ...arr	a.m.	7 1	9 30	a.m.	1020	1221	p.m.	1 29	p.m.	p.m.	2 1	4 17	5 31	7 6	p.m.	p.m.	8 4	1143
„ ...dep	6 20	7 11		9 40	1034	☞	1250		1 37	1 47	☞		5 42	☞	7 29	8 9	8 17	1158
Dallwitz	...	...	...	...	1040		...	...	...	...		...	...		...		8 22	...
Schlackenwerth	6 46	7 29	...	9*58	11 3		...	...	1 55	2 10		...	6 0		7§44		8 41	1226
Wickwitz	6 55	7*36	...	...	1112		...	...	...	2 19		...	6 *7				8 50	1235
Hauenstein Warta	7 3	...	...	...	1120		RC	...	...	2 27		...	...				8 58	1243
Pürstein	7 12	...	...	...	1129		...	...	...	2 35		...	6*21				9 7	1252
Klösterle	7 23	7‡57	...	...	1142		...	...	...	2 45		...	6*29				9 17	1 4
Kaaden-Brunnersdorf	7 34	8 *5	...	1035	1154		...	...	2 29	2 54		...	6 38				9 27	1 17
Komotau ...arr	7 52	8 19	...	1049	1214		1 55	...	2 43	3 12		...	6 53				9 45	1 36
AUSSIG (251) ...arr	1039	10a39	...	1 p5	2p55		3p15	...	4p45	6p55		...	8p30				1120	...
DRESDEN (189) arr	1p40	1 p40	a.m.	3p52	5 p0		5 p0	...	6p53	9p46		p.m.	12a9				2a25	...
Komotau ...dep	...	8 30	8 43	...	1247		...	...	2 48	...		7 13	7 1				1136	1 55
Priesen ...dep	...	...	8 55		1 1		...	...	...	...		7 25	...				1148	2 8
Saaz	...	8 55	9 16		1 33		...	...	3 12	...		7 43	7 26		8 44	9 27	12 8	2 36
Michelob	...	9 13	9 41		1 54		...	...	3 27	...			7*43			...	1229	2 57
Kolleschowitz dp	...	8 52	...		1 46		...	...	...	...		...	...				...	...
Krupa ...arr	2&3	9 37	...		2 32	...	...	...	...	...		...	...	...			...	...
Krupa	a.m.	9*42	1031		2 37	...	...	...	...	...		...	8*10	...			1 11	3 40
Luzna Lischan	5 33	9 52	1050		2 49	...	...	...	4 3	...	...	...	8 20	...			1 8	3 52
Neustraschitz	5 58	...	1114		3 13	...	...	...	...	...	...	2&3	8*36	...				4 16
Lana	6 10	10§16	1126		3 25	...	...	...	...	...	...	p.m.	8*15	...			...	4 28
Kladno	6 35	10 30	1151		3 51	...	...	...	4 42	...	...	8 5	8 59	...			...	4 54
Hostiwitz	7 1	...	1216		4 16	...	...	...	...	...	...	8 28	...	...			...	5 21
Prague Sandthor arr	7 25	11 3	1240		4 41	...	...	...	5 12	...	...	8 54	9 32	...			...	5 46
Prague Bubna ...arr	7 32	11 8	1246		4 48	...	...	...	5 17	...	...	9 2	9 37	...			...	5 53
Prague Staats ...arr	7 40	11 14	1254		4 57	...	...	...	5 22	...	...	9 12	9 43	...	1046	1142	...	6 1
VIENNA (252A) ...arr	...	6 p28	1030	...	...	...	...	...	4a45	...	...	...	6a55	...	6a55	...	...	2 p5

*—Stops when required. ‡—Sets down only.

Ostend Express. Luxus Zug. Runs until 16th September.

§—Stops to take up only.

Paris-Carlsbad Express. Runs until 28th Sept.

Berlin-Carlsbad Express. Runs until 31st August.

Via Tuschmitz. (two columns)

KOMOTAU and WEIPERT

E.M					
	Komotau ...dep	3 a0	10a16	2p15	7p28
20¾	Krima-Neudorf	3 53	11 10	3 9	8 22
...	Krima-Neudorf dep	4 2	...	3 20	...
29¾	**Reitzenhain**...arr	4 48	...	4 10	...
28	Pressnitz-Reischdorf	4 25	11 44	3 41	8 59
36¾	Schmeideberg	5 0	12 18	4 16	9 33
44¾	**Weipert** (189) ...arr	5 21	12 39	4 37	9 54

Weipert ...dep	4 a36	10a16	3p52	7 p0
Schmiedeberg	5 1	10 40	4 17	7 30
Pressnitz-Reisch	5 35	11 14	4 51	8 4
Reitzenh dep	5 19	10 25	...	7 51
Krima-N ...arr	5 58	11 5	...	8 27
Krima-Neudorf	6 6	11 44	5 20	8 35
Komotau ...arr	6 50	12 28	6 4	9 19

TEPLITZ and REICHENBERG.

Teplitz-Schönau dp	...	...	5a53	6a57	10a30	1p15	4p20	7 p2
Settenz	...	...	5 58	7 3	10 36	1 21	4 25	7 8
Auperschin	...	...	6 27	7 19	10 58	1 50	4 45	7 37
Lobositz A. T. E. ...dep	...	5 a20	7 30	8 0	12 1	3 2	5 37	8 48
„ Staats ... „	...	5 26	7 35	8 4	12 7	3 8	5 43	8 53
Czalositz	...	5 36	7 43	...	12 15	3 17	5 51	9 2
Leitmeritz	...	5 53	7 50	8 17	12 25	3 28	6 2	9 8
Auscha	...	6 33		8 45	1 2	4 9	6 37	
Bohm. Leipa, Halt	...	7 30		9 22	1 55	5 6	7 23	9p50
„ A.T.E. ar	...	7 32		9 24	1 57	5 8	7 25	9 52
„ A.T.E. dep	5 a0	7 40		9 28	2 2		7 30	9 54
Niemes	5 34	8 16		9 54	2 35		7 57	1030
Gabel	6 10	8 48		1015	3 7		8 24	
Reichenb'g A.T.E. ar	7 35	10 0		11 2	4 14		9 24	...

Reichenberg ...dep	...	...	6a51	9 a50	2 p0	5 p28	7p10
Gabel	...	...	7 48	10 53	3 7	6 21	8 23
Niemes	...	6 a0	8 15	11 20	3 37	6 43	8 52
Bh. Leipa A.T.E. ar	...	6 33	8 40	11 50	4 9	7 8	9 22
„ A.T.E. dep	...	6 40	8 44	11 55	4 15	7 13	9 23
„ Halte	...	6 55	8 48	12 0	4 20	7 21	9 25
Auscha	a.m.	7 36	9 26	12 45	5 15	7 59	
Leitmeritz	5 26	8 16	9 58	1 20	5 58	8 29	...
Czalositz	5 35	8 23	10 4	1 27	6 6	...	...
Lobositz Staats	5 44	8 31	1016	1 36	6 15	8 41	...
„ A.T.E.	5 50	8 40	1025	1 45	6 28	8 48	...
Auperschin	6 53	9 41	1120	2 43	7 38	9 31	...
Settenz	7 19	10 8	1142	3 6	8 3	9 48	...
Teplitz-Schönau ar	7 23	1012	1146	3 10	8 6	9 52	...

AUSSIG and BILIN.

E.M.					
	Aussig (A.T.E.) ...dep	5a58	...	1 p0	6 p50
3	**Türmitz**	6 13	a.m.	1 11	7 0
12	Auperschin	6 55	1125	1 48	7 43
20	**Bilin** (244) ...arr	7 30	12 2	2 22	8 17

Bilin ...dep	5a50	9 a0	1 p5	6 p57	...	...
Auperschin	6 32	9 34	1 47	7 41	...	...
Türmitz	7 7	...	2 23	8 29	...	...
Aussig (A.T.E.) ...arr	7 14	...	2 30	8 36	...	...

KOMOTAU and AUSSIG.

CARLSBAD 251 ...dep	...	...	...	...	7 a11	9a40	1034	1250	1 p37	...	1 p47	5p42	5p42	8 p17	...	...
	1,2,3	1,2,3	1,2,3	1,2,3	1,2,3	1,2,3	1,2,3	Ex3	1,2,3	1,2,3	1,2,3	Ex 3	1,2,3	Ex 3	1,2,3	
			a.m.	a.m.	a.m.	a.m.	p.m.	p.m.	p.m.		p.m.	p.m.	p.m.	p.m.	p.m.	
Komotau ...dep	...	...	5 25	7 0	8 27	1055	1250	2 0	2 50	...	4 50	6 58	7 10	9 53	1013	...
Wurzmes	...	...	5 41	7 16	8 44	1122	1 6	...	...	...	5 7	...	7 27	...	1033	...
Brüx	...	a.m.	6 14	7 39	9 12	1137	1 30	RC	3 25	...	5 30	7 25	7 52	10 20	1057	...
Dux	...	5 22	6 43	8 5	9 42	1151	1 56	...	3 51	...	5 57	7 45	8 20	10 39	1127	...
Settenz	A	5 35	7 2	8 18	9 58	1220	2 10	...	4 5	...	6 12	...	8 34	...	1141	...
Teplitz-Schönau	a.m.	5 39	7 6	8 22	10 2	1224	2 14	2 50	4 9	p.m.	6 16	7 58	8 38	10 52	1145	...
„ ...dep	3 52	5 42	7 10	8 25	10 8	1230	2 20	2 53	4 15	5 5	6 22	8 2	8 44	10 55	1151	...
Mariaschein	3 59	5 54	7 18	8 35	10 16	1240	2 29	...	4 23	5 15	6 32	8 9	8 54	11 9	1159	...
Türmitz	4 12	6 12	7 34	8 51	10 30	1256	2 46	...	4 36	5 31	6 47	...	9 10	...	1213	...
Aussig (A.T.E.)...arr	4 17	6 17	7 39	8 56	10 35	1 2	2 51	3 12	4 41	5 36	6 52	8 27	9 15	11 20	1218	...
„ Staat ...arr	4 20	6 22	7 42	9 0	10 39	1 5	2 55	3 15	4 45	...	6 55	8 30	9 19	...	1221	...
BODENBACH 252 arr	...	7a40	8a15	...	11a37	2p40	3p49	3p49	5 p29	...	8 p8	...	1010	...	1258	...
DRESDEN Hpt. 189 arr	...	9a39	9a39	...	1 p40	3p52	5 p0	5 p0	6 p53	...	9 p46	...	12a9	...	2a25	...

A—Runs until 8th September.

RC—Restaurant Car.

VIENNA, BRUNN, PRAGUE, and BODENBACH.

THROUGH CARRIAGES, 1st and 2nd class.—Vienna to Berlin—in 2.20 p.m. from Nordbahnhof, and in 10.0 p.m. from Staatsbahnhof.

RC—Restaurant Car. SC—Sleeping Car. *—Not on Sunday.
X—Restaurant Car.

E.M.			1,2,3	Ex 3	2 & 3	1,2,3	Ex 3	1,2,3	1,2,3	Ex. 3	1,2,3	2&3	1,2,3	Ex3	Ex 3	1,2,3	2&3	1,2,3	Ex 3	Ex 3
Dist	**Vienna—**							a.m.	a.m.				a.m.	p.m.		p.m.	p.m.	p.m.		p.m.
—	Staatsbahnhof ....dep		...	...	...	...	...	5 55	7 50	...	...	...	11 35	1 22	...	2 25	4 5	6 10	...	10 0
6¾	Stadlau		...	...	...	...	...	6 17	8 12	...	...	...	11 57		...	2 46	4 25	6 31	...	...
18	Wolkersdorf		...	...	a.m.	...	...	6 52	8 34	...	...	...	12 23		...	3 18	4 57	6 55	...	10 30
34¾	Mistelbach		...	...	4 0	...	...	7 43	9 15	...	...	...	1 18		...	4 16	5 50	7 45	...	11 0
44¾	Enzersdorf 252		...	...	4 34	...	...	8 8	9 33	...	...	...	1 43		...	4 44	——	8 9	...	SC
51½	Laa 221		...	...	4 58	a.m.	...	8 26	9 54	...	...	...	2 1		...	5 9	...	8 32	...	11 28
57¾	**Grusbach 252**		...	...	5 14	5 20	...	8 40	10 7	...	...	...	2 25		...	5 34	...	8 47	...	11 44
76½	Kromau		...	...		6 18	...	9 31	1056	...	...	...	3 11		...	6 30	...	9 50	...	12 19
82	Kanitz Eibenschitz		...	...	——	6 44	...	9 46	1110	...	...	...	3 28		...	6 52	...	10 7	...	12 32
88¾	Strelitz		...	...	...	7 4	...	10 4	1127	...	...	...	3 47		...	7 14	...	10 27	...	...
97	**Brünn** ....arr		...	...	...	7 26	...	10 19	1142	...	...	...	4 2		...	7 36	...	10 42	...	12 59
...	VIENNA Nord ...dep	2&3	...	...	...	2 & 3	...	...	...	7a53	...	...	...		2 p20	...	1,2,3	7p45	...	9 p20
...	BRUNN 221.........arr	a.m	...	a.m.	a.m.	a.m.	...	...	...	10a22	p.m.	p m.	...		4 p52	...	p.m.	10p22	...	12p15
...	**Brünn** .... dep	5 46	...	7 0	7 6	9 2	...	...	1152	10 29	1 55	2 30	5 13	Depart Vienna Nord West Bahnhof.	5 7	8 5	6 15	11 10	...	1 5
111¼	Blansko	6 24	...	X	7 45	9 42	...	...	1227	RC	2 35	3 10	5 53		5 36	8 53	6 57	11 50	...	SC
121¼	Skalitz Boskowitz 252A	6 56	...	7 39	——	10 11	...	...	1247	11 1	3 5	3 59	6 22		5 54	9 28	7 33	12 19	...	1 45
143	Zwittau 252	8 1	...	8 10	...	——	...	...	1 41	11 44	4 21	——	——		6 33	——	8 50	1 20	...	2 24
152¾	**Böhm-Trübau** arr	8 43	a.m.	8 25	...	...	p.m.	...	2 6	12 1	4 57	...	...		6 51	...	9 20	1 43	a.m.	2 41
...	" 254dep	——	6 0	8 35	...	...	2 31	...	2 16	12 6	5 5	...	...		6 55	...	——	2 5	2 0	2 48
159¾	Wildenschwert 225 ...	...	6 18	8 47	1,2,3	...	2 44	1,2,3	2 36	12 21	5 25	...	...		7 7	...	...	2 25	...	3 0
166	Brandeis-a-d-Adler...	...	6 30	8 58	a.m.	...	...	p.m.	2 47	...	5 37	...	...		7 17	...	...	2 36	SC	...
168½	**Chotzen** 252A ...arr	1,2,3	6 37	9 4	8 19	...	3 3	3 46	2 54	12 36	5 41	...	...		7 23	...	...	2 43	...	3 15
189½	**Pardubitz** ....arr	a.m.	7 33	9 35	9 17	...	3 34	4 32		1 7	6 53	...	...		8 0	...	...	3 38	2 54	3 48
...	" 223A dep	6 0	7 37	9 39	10 7	2 & 3	3 38	4 50	...	1 10	7 0	1,2,3	...		8 4	...	2&3	4 1	2 59	3 51
198½	Prelauc 252	6 23	7 53	...	10 36	p.m.	3 53	5 7	...	...	7 23	p.m.	...		8 19	...	a.m.	4 19	...	...
216½	**Kolin 224**	7 18	8 39	10 22	11 40	3 0	4 21	5 48	...	1 49	8 9	4 36	...	6 50	8 49	...	5 40	5 9	...	4 31
225½	Pecek 253	7 50	9 1	...	12 12	3 31	...	6 23	...	...	8 45	5 7	...	...	9 5	...	6 8	5 31	...	4 49
231½	Porican	8 12	...	...	12 28	4 0	...	6 35	...	...	9 19	5 29	...	...	9 15	...	6 22	5 44	...	...
254¾	**Prague 249**........arr	9 27	9 58	11 28	1 51	5 12	5 ‡24	7 34	...	2 48	1031	6 31	...	7‡54	9 57		7 35	6 50	4 40	5 40
...	" ....dep	1110	——	12 20	2 0	——	To Eger.	8 10	...	2 56	——	6 35	...	——	10 35	¶—Customs Examination.	8 45	7 31	——	5 55
271½	**Kralup 252**	12 9	...	12 47	3 40	...		9 1	...	3 25	...	7 43	...	...	11 2		9 59	8 25	...	6 23
279¾	Jenschowitz	1243	...	...	4 14	...		9 22	...	RC	...	8 11	...	...	...		——	8 47	2 & 3	...
296½	Raudnitz	2 13	...	1 28	5 23	...	——	10 2	...	4 10	...	——	2 & 3	...	11 44		‡—Arrives at Franz Josef Station.	9 25	5a28	7 4
303½	Theresienstadt	2 33	...	1 41	5 48	...	...	10 23	...	4 24	...	...	p.m.	...	11 53			9 51	5 50	7 18
307½	Lobositz 252A	2 44	...	1 50	6 17	...	...	10 3	...	4 34	...	...	8 46	...	12 7			10 14	6 8	7 27
321½	**Aussig** ....arr	3 25	Ex 3	2 12	6 59	...	...	11 9	...	4 56	...	...	9 23	...	12 29			10 45	6 45	7 49
333	TEPLITZ 250-1 arr	4p40	p.m	3 p0	8 p48	...	...	...	...	6 p2	...	...	...	...	1 a20			11a59	7a42	8 a37
	TEPLITZ 250-1 dep	2p53	2 53	12p30	6 p22	...	...	8 p44	...	4 p15	...	...	8p44	...	11p51			10 a8	5 a42	7 a1
...	**Aussig** ....dep	3 40	3 20	2 15	7 11	...	...	11 22	...	4 59	...	...	9 27	...	12 34			10 58	6 48	7 52
335½	**Bodenbach** ¶ ...arr	4 21	3 49	2 40	8 8	...	...	12 0	...	5 29	...	...	10 10	...	12 58			11 37	7 40	8 15
374	DRESDEN H. 189 arr	6p23	5 p0	3 p52	9 p46	...	...	2 a25	...	6p53	...	...	12 a9	...	2 a25			1p40	9 a39	9 a39
393½	BERLIN 189........arr	...	7 p57	6 p51	...	...	...	7 a25	...	10p26	...	...	...	...	7 a25		...	5 p1	12p48	12p48

Extra.—Vienna to Grusbach 7.40 p.m. Prague to Kralup, 4.38, 11.47 p.m. Vienna to Mistelbach 9.40 a.m., 11.25 p.m.

PRELAUC and KALK-PODOL.

E.M										
	Prelauc ......dep	...	10a50	4p23	8p25	**Kalk-Podol** dep	...	6 a0	1p40	6p16
8¾	Hermanmestec ...	4 a55	12 16	5 19	9 19	Hermanmestec ...	5a11	6 44	2 44	7 0
13¾	**Kalk-Podol** arr	5 40	1 4	6 0	...	**Prelauc** (252) arr	6 8	...	3 38	7 47

HERMANMESTEC and BOROHRADEK.

Hermanmestec	6a50	...	9 a5	...	2p50	**Borohradek** ......dep	5a30	...	9 a45	3 p16
Chrudim Stadt...	7 34	5a52	9 46	12p30	4 18	**Morawan**............	6 49	...	10 43	4 20
Hrochowteinitz ...	——	6 30	——	12 57	4 56	Hrochowteinitz	7 15	9 a5	——	4 53
Morawan............		7 55	11a15	——	5 40	Chrudim Stadt	8 4	9 30	11a28	5 25
Borohradek (252A) arr		9 3	12 10	...	6 32	**Hermanmestec** (252)	8 47	...	12 10	6 13

Hrochowteinitz...dep	5 a20	4 p55	...	**Chrast**..............dep	6 a25	6p25	...
Chrast ....arr	6 8	5 46	...	Hrochowteinitz...arr	6 56	7 14	...

BRUNN and OKRISKO.

(252)	a.m.	a.m.	p.m.	p.m.	p.m.	p.m	(224)	a.m.	a.m.	p.m.	p.m.
Brünn ......dep	4 20	8 36	1 16	2 46	7 1	9 50	**Okrisko** ......dep	5 0	9 25	2 5	7 44
Strelitz............	4 40	9 2	1 41	3 55	7 21	1030	Gr. Meseritsch dp	4 30	8 55	1 15	7 8
Segen Gottes.....	5 2	9 23	2 2	4 33	7 42	11 5	Studenetz ......a.m.	6 1	10 28	3 8	8 46
Studenetz .....arr	5 59	1020	2 59	——	8 39	——	Segen Gottes 5 4	6 59	11 2	4 6	9 46
Gross Meser. ar	7 20	1151	4 18	...	1010	...	Strelitz 5 32	7 19	11 47	4 26	10 7
Okrisko.....arr	7 1	1121	4 2	...	9 40	...	**Brünn** ...arr 6 0	7 33	12 8	4 50	1030

ENZERSDORF and POYSDORF.

Enzersdorf dep	5 a1	8a10	9 a50	5p10	8p30	Poysdorf ..... dep	6a30	8a47	12p15	7 p23	9p20
Poysdorf ...arr	5 30	8 39	10 20	5 40	9 0	Enzersdorf 252 arr	7 2	9 19	12 47	7 55	9 55

GRUSBACH and ZNAIM.

	a.m.	a.m.	a.m.	a.m.	p.m.	p.m.	p.m.		a.m.	a.m.	a.m.	a.m.	p.m.	p.m.	p.m.
Grusbach	4 17	6 40	9 5	1050	2 21	5p40	9 12	Znaim ...	4 22	5 50	7 47	1131	1 25	4 47	8 2
Hödnitz ...	4 42	7 4	9 29	1115	2 44	6 4	9 35	Hödnitz...	4 41	6 8	8 7	1147	1 42	5 6	8 18
Znaim 224	4 58	7 20	9 45	1130	2 59	6 20	9 50	Grusbach	5 4	6 32	8 32	12 9	2 5	5 30	8 41

ZWITTAU and SKUTSCH.

	a.m.	a.m.	p.m.	p.m.					
Zwittau ......dep	...	9 55	2 25	6 50	...	...	...	...	...
Policka	6 2	1056	3 52	7 56	...	...	...	...	...
Skutsch 223A...ar	8 15	...	6 36	...	...	...	...	...	...

	a.m.	a.m.	p.m.						
Skutsch ...dep	5 15	...	3 36	...	...	...	...	...	...
Policka	7 10	1145	5 30	...	...	...	...	...	...
Zwittau 252 arr	8 4	1245	6 25	...	...	...	...	...	...

KRALUP and STREBICHOVIC.

Kralup......dep	8a38	3p30	6p39	**Strebichovic**	4a20	12p55	5 p2
Svolenoves......	9 32	4 13	7 32	Svolenoves ...	5 0	1 42	5 41
Strebichovic	1011	4 52	8 10	**Kralup 252** ...	5 44	2 24	6 20

KRALUP and WELWARN.

Kralup ...dep	8a50	3p48	7p50	**Welwarn** ...dep	4a48	1p15	5p10
Welwarn arr	9 33	4 30	8 32	**Kralup (252)** arr	5 31	2 0	5 55

For Fares, see page 237B.]

BODENBACH, PRAGUE, BRUNN, and VIENNA

RC—Restaurant Car. SC—Sleeping Car. ‡—From Franz Josef Station. ¶—Customs Examination.

BERLIN (188) ......dep	...	...	...	8 p10	11p15	...	...	...	...	...	...	8 a5	9 a20	...	1p20	4 p30	...	...
DRESDEN Haupt...dep	...	...	...	12a22	2 a30	...	...	7 a10	...	...	8 a30	11a30	12p10	12p53	4p40	7 p5	...	8p12
	1,2 3	2 & 3	2 & 3	1,2,3	Ex 3	Ex 3	2 & 3	Ex 3	1,2,3	1,2,3	2 & 3	Ex 3	Ex 3	1,2,3	1 2 3	Ex.3	Ex 3	2&3
				a.m.	a.m.		a.m.	a.m.			a.m.	p.m.	p.m.	p.m.	p.m.	p.m.		p.m.
Bodenbach ¶ ...dep	...	...	...	2 30	4 5	...	5 45	8 47	...	...	10 20	12 57	1 23	3 12	6 48	8 20	...	1040
Aussig........ ....arr	...	...	...	3 3	4 29	...	6 34	9 11	...	...	11 7	1 20	1 48	3 48	7 33	8 45	...	1130
TEPLITZ (250)... arr	...	...	...	4 a33	5 a8	...	7 a42	9 a57	...	...	11a59	2 p20	2 p20	4 p40	8p48	9 p39	...	1a20
TEPLITZ (250)... dep	...	...	...	...	...	...	5 a42	8 a25	...	...	10 a8	12p30	—	2 p53	6p22	8 p2	...	8p44
Aussig ....dep	...	...	...	3 12	4 32	...	6 44	9 14	...	...	11 18	1 23	...	3 57	7 37	8 49	...	1134
Lobositz	...	...	...	3 43	4 55	...	7 28	9 37	...	...	12 10	1 49	...	4 36	8 15	9 11	...	1214
Theresienstadt	...	...	...	3 56	5 4	...	7 40	9 46	...	...	12 27	1 57	...	4 49	8 26	9 20	...	1227
Raudnitz..........................	...	...	...	4 18	5 18	...	8 2	10 0	...	...	12 58	2 12	...	5 10	8 45	9 37	...	1247
Jenschowitz	...	...	...	4 54	...	...	8 48	...	p.m.	...	2 6	RC	...	5 45	9 23	...	...	
Kralup.........................	...	...	...	5 18	5 57	...	9 22	10 36	12 10	...	2 59	2 49	...	6 16	9 45	10 28	...	...
Prague........... arr	a.m.	...	...	5 50	6 25	a.m.	10 25	11 5	1 11	p.m.	4 2	3 17	p.m.	6 58	1031	10 57	p.m.	...
Prague........... dep	5 25	...	...	7 45	6 35	8 ‡35	—	11 25	—	1 10	4 23	3 25	5 ‡25	7 30	—	11 12	11 52	...
Porican	6 39	...	...	8 43	7 12	...	...	12 5	...	2 27	5 38	...	...	8 34	...	SC	...	...
Pecek	6 52	a.m.	...	8 57	...	...	...	12 15	...	2 42	5 52	...	...	8 47	...	11 58	...	...
Kolin............................	7 19	6 0	...	9 37	7 36	9 33	...	12 33	...	3 24	6 48	4 28	6 40	9 17	...	12 15	SC	...
Prelauc	—	6 53	...	10 18	...	Nord West Bahnhof.	...	...	...	4 16	7 53	...	...	9 57	...	12 43	...	...
Pardubitz arr 1,2,3	...	7 18	...	10 34	8 13		...	1 12	...	4 41	8 20	5 9	7 19	10 13	...	12 58	1 27	...
Pardubitz dep a.m.	...	7 23	...	10 46	8 17		...	1 16	...	4 45	9 0	5 13	7 23	10 23	...	1 2	1 31	...
Chotzen 6 41	...	8 23	...	11 41	8 53		...	1 53	..	6 14	10 0	5 52	7 59	11 25	...	1 40	...	...
Brandeis-a-d-Adler 6 52	...	8 31	...	11 49	9 1		...	...	...	6 22	—	...	8 7	11 33	...	...	...	...
Wildenschwert......7 12	...	8 43	...	12 3	9 11		...	2 13	...	6 42	...	6 8	8 18	11 48	...	1 56	...	...
Böhm-Trübau arr 7 37	a.m.	9 5	a.m.	12 21	9 23		...	2 28	p.m.	7 0	...	6 21	8 33	12 6	...	2 9	2 29	...
Böhm-Trübau dep —	4 10	—	6 15	12 30	9 27		...	2 37	2 45	—	2 & 3	6 23	8 42	12 18	...	2 16	—	...
Zwittau	4 48	a.m.	6 54	12 55	9 46		a.m.	2 56	3 20	2 & 3	p.m.	6 42	9 4	12 44	...	2 35	...	...
Skalitz-Boskowitz	5 59	6 21	8 6	1 42	10 27		11 50	...	4 30	5 p7	7 24	7 16	9 49	1 32	...	...	...	...
Blansko	6 22	6 53	8 37	2 2	10 46		12 23	...	5 0	5 39	8 1	...	10 8	1 52	...	...	...	...
Brünn ....arr	6 56	7 30	9 18	2 35	11 13		1 10	4 4	5 39	6 23	8 49	7 57	10 39	2 24	...	3 45	...	...
BRUNN ....dep	...	...	1,2,3	...	11a30		...	4 p12	6 p10	...	...	8 p5	11p15	3 a53	2 &3	...	...	...
VIENNA Nord 221 arr	...	...	p.m.	...	2 p5		...	6 p28	9 p50	...	...	10p30	4 a45	7 a52	nigt	...	...	...
Brünn ....dep	7 4	...	12 9	2 46	...	Arrive Vienna	...	...	6 0	7 *7	...	...	...	2 36	12 0	3 50	...	...
Strelitz..........................	7 26	...	12 34	3 5	...		...	...	6 22	7 32	...	...		2 54	1243	...	...	...
Kanitz Eibenschitz......	7 46	2 & 3	12 56	3 25	...		...	...	6 48	7 52	...	...		3 14	1 17	4 21	...	2&3
Kromau	8 2	p.m.	1 15	3 41	...		...	...	7 4	8 11	...	...		3 30	1 42	4 35	...	a.m.
Grusbach	8 50	12 18	2 18	4 29	...		...	...	7 52	9 4	...	...		4 18	2 55	5 15	...	6 35
Laa	9 5	12 35	2 35	4 44	...		...	...	8 7	—	...	...		4 33	—	5 27	...	6 52
Enzersdorf....................	9 23	12 55	2 57	5 4	...		...	...	8 25	...	...	...		4 51	...	..	a.m.	7 12
Mistelbach....................	9 48	1 21	3 28	5 29	...		...	...	8 49	...	...	...		5 15	...	5 53	6 2	7 42
Wolkersdorf	10 33	2 11	4 19	6 9	...		...	...	9 38	...	...	...		5 55	...	...	6 58	8 35
Stadlau	10 57	2 42	4 57	6 32	...		...	...	10 8	...	...	...		6 19	...	..	7 22	9 8
Vienna (Staats) ...arr	11 15	3 5	5 20	6 48	...	3 0	...	...	10 30	...	...	...	...	6 35	...	6 55	7 40	9 30

*—1,2,3 class. §—Not on Sunday.

Extra.—Kralup to Prague, 4§50, 6.28 a.m., 6.28, 8.55 p.m. Prague to Porican, 2.23 and 5.45 p.m. Blansko to Brünn, 8.0 a.m. Mistelbach to Vienna, 11.52 a.m. Prague to Kolin, 6.46 p.m., 12.0 night.

CHOTZEN and MITTELSTEINE.

E.M.		a.m.	a.m.	a.m.	p.m.	p.m.	
—	**Chotzen** ....dep	3 30	4 35	9 15	3 10	8 4	...
7½	Cerma-a.d.Adler	3 46	4 57	9 31	3 26	8 20	...
10½	**Borohradek**	3 54	5 6	9 39	3 34	8 28	...
15	**Tynist**	4 5	5 23	9 49	3 41	8 39	...
24¾	Opocno	4 27	5 56	10 11	4 6	9 1	p.m.
34¼	**Wenzelsberg**	5 0	6 45	10 45	4 38	9 33	1057
38	Nachod	5 13	7 2	11 0	4 50	9 45	1110
51½	Wekelsdorf	5 53	7 59	11 41	5 29	10 26	—
56½	**Halbstadt** ....arr a.m.	6 9	8 17	11 58	5 45	10 45	...
...	,, 180 ...dep 7 0	6 19	8 53	12 20	6 0	10 53	...
62½	Braunau..................7 36	6 51	9 22	12 48	6 30	11 25	...
71½	**Mittelsteine** 182A ...arr	7 26	9 57	1 23	7 5	12 0	...

	a.m	a.m.	a.m.	p.m	p.m.	p.m.
Mittelsteine ...dep	...	7 47	10 55	3 22	7 48	9 20
Braunau	5 25	8 25	11 35	3 59	8 25	9 57
Halbstadt ......arr	5 57	8 52	12 5	4 27	8 50	1026
,, ...dep	6 10	9 0	12 25	4 38	8 55	—
Wekelsdorf	6 28	9 18	12 43	4 55	9 12	...
Nachod 5a24	7 5	9 55	1 34	5 33	9 46	...
Wenzelsberg 5 37	7 16	10 6	1 47	5 45	9 56	...
Opocno .... —	7 44	10 33	2 26	6 14	1023	...
Tynist.....................	8 8	10 54	3 0	6 36	1044	...
Borohradek (252)...	8 19	11 4	3 14	6 46	1054	...
Cerma-a.d.Adler...	8 27	11 12	3 25	6 54	11 2	...
Chotzen 252......arr	8 43	11 28	3 41	7 12	1118	...

OPOCNO to DOBRUSKA (in 20 mins.)
Opocno dep. 6.13, 7.53, 10.43 a.m., 4.13, 6.23 p.m.
Dobruska dep. 5.35, 7.15, 9.40 a.m., 1.55, 5.40 p.m.

TRAUTENAU and WEKELSDORF.

Trautenau ....dep	7a10	9 a35	1 p6	7p18	...	...	...
Radowenz......................	8 1	10 28	2 11	8 40	...	...	...
Wekelsdorf (252A) arr	9 1	11 27	3 29	9 42	...	...	...

Wekelsdorf ....dep	7a13	9a35	1 p9	5p45	...	...
Radowenz..........................	8 27	1053	2 41	7 14	...	...
Trautenau (225) ...arr	9 15	1135	3 33	8 4	...	...

LOBOSITZ and LIBOCHOWITZ.

E.M.	(252)	a.m.	a.m.	a.m.	p.m.	
...	**Lobositz** ......dep	5 1	7 38	1020	6 20	...
3	Tschischkowitz	5 15	7 53	1043	6 40	...
8½	**Libochowitz** arr	..	8 21	1117	7 12	...

	a.m	a.m.	a.m.	p.m.	p.m.			
Libochowitz dep	6 16	8 46	...	3 11	...	...	...	...
Tschischkowitz	6 56	9 15	1121	3 44	5 16	...	...	...
Lobositz ....arr	7 8	9 26	1136	3 56	5 31	...	...	...

TRIEBITZ and SKALITZ-BOSKOWITZ.

E.M.						
	Triebitz........................dep	3a15	8 a26	3 p15	7p30	...
23	Kornitz..............................	4 36	10 12	4 50	8 50	...
29¾	Gross Opatowitz	5 6	10 43	5 45	...	...
46	**Skalitz-Boskowitz** (252) ...arr	6 6	11 40	6 59	...	...

Skalitz-Boskowitz ...dep	8 a12	1p55	7 p38	...	...
Gross-Opatowitz...... ...	9 26	3 38	8 41	...	...
Kornitz (246)...........4 a3	10 16	4 37	9 24	...	...
Triebitz (254) ... arr 5 21	11 33	5 52	10 44	...	...

VIENNA and BRUCK (Hungarian Station).

Vienna (Staatsbahnhof)	1,2,3 a.m.	1,2,3 a.m.	Ex 2 a.m.	1,2,3 a.m.	1,2,3 a.m.	Ex 2 p.m.	1,2,3 p.m.	1,2,3 p.m	1,2,3 p.m.	1,2,3 p.m.	1,2,3 p.m.
Vienna (Staatsbahnhof) ......dep	6 15	7 21	9 10	10 45	1155	1 55	2 30	4 20	6 25	8 25	10§20
Simmering	6 24	7 28	...	10 52	12 3	...	2 37	4 28	6 36	8 34	1027
Lanzendorf............	6 38	7 42	...	11 6	1221	...	2 51	4 43	6 50	8 51	1042
Himberg	6 49	7 49	9 2	11 15	1228	...	2 57	4 51	6 58	9 4	1051
Gramat-N. ......arr	7 0	8 0	9 36	11 26	1237	...	3 7	5 1	7 8	9 16	11 1
Götzendorf............	7 13	8 16	...	11 40	12 0	...	3 20	5 15	7 22	9 32	1115
Trautmannsd'rf......	7 20	8 23	...	11 51	1258	...	3 27	5 22	7 29	9 39	1122
Bruck.............arr	7 39	8†45	10 0	12†12	1 20	2 38	3†49	5 40	7†51	10†0	1138
PESTH 225B ...arr	1p20	...	1p40	...	...	6p35	...	...	...	...	6a25

	1,2,3	1,2,3	1,2,3		Ex 2	1,2,3	1,2,3	Ex 2	1,2,3	1,2,3	1,2,3
BUDAPEST ...dep	...	10p55	...	...	9a10	9a10	...	2 p5	...	...	...
	a.m.	a.m.	a.m.	p.m.	p.m.	p.m.	p m.	p.m.	p.m.	p.m.	p.m.
Bruck ....dep	5† 0	5 55	7†36	12†15	1 6	2 20	3†50	5 56	6 34	7†27	10 0
Trautmannsdorf ...	5 24	6 17	8 8	12 38	...	2 45	4 13	...	6 53	7 54	1017
Götzendorf............	5 33	6 26	8 18	12 48	...	2 53	4 23	...	7 1	8 3	1025
Gramat-N.	5 45	6 38	8 29	12 59	...	3 8	4 36	...	7 12	8 15	1037
Himberg	5 58	6 50	8 40	1 10	...	3 18	4 50	...	7 24	8 27	1050
Lanzendorf............	6 6	6 57	8 47	1 18	...	3 24	4 59	...	7 33	8 34	1057
Simmering	6 23	7 13	9 2	1 33	...	3 39	5 17	...	7 49	8 51	1113
Vienna .... arr	6 30	7 20	9 9	1 40	1 50	3 45	5 25	6 40	7 55	9 0	1120

†—At and from Bruck Localbahnhof. §—Sleeping Cars in this Train.

BRUCK and HAINBURG.

Bruck Localbhf......dep	5a45	8 a51	12p20	8 p0	...
Hainburg ....arr	7 45	9 55	1 25	9 3	...
Hainburg ....dep	6 a25	10a55	6 p15	...	...
Bruck (253) ....arr	7 28	11 55	7 15	...	...

KLEIN-SCHWECHAT and MANNERSDORF.

E.M.									
	Klein-Schwechat	...	6a50	7a35	11a11	2p35	...	...	6p20
7½	Fischamend..............	...	7 32	8 20	11 52	3 18	...	...	6 59
10	Klein-Neusiedl..........	a.m.	7 44	—	12 9	3 40	...	p.m.	7 12
14½	Götzendorf	6 41	8 10	...	1 4	4 15	5p25	7 25	7 39
18¾	**Mannersdorf** ...arr	7 8	8 56	...	1 30	...	5 51	7 52	8 33

Mannersdorf ...dep	4a10	5a45	7a25	11a53	3p37	4p30	6p28
Götzendorf	4 50	6 11	8 20	12 53	4 26	5 20	6 54
Klein-Neusiedl	5 21	—	8 52	1 19	5 0	5 46	8 33
Fischamend..............	5 40	...	9 6	1 31	5 13	5 56	8 54
Klein-Schwechat	6 16	...	9 42	2 5	5 48	...	9 30

BRUNN and VLARAPASS.

		a.m.	a.m.	a.m.	p.m.	p.m.	p.m.
Brunn ....dep	...	4 49	8 23	11‡30	1 17	5 40	8 50
Austerlitz	...	5 49	9 23	12 9	2 14	6 36	9 52
Gaya	5a50	6 57	1033	1 1	3 16	7 43	—
Bisenz-Stadt	6 21	7 30	11 5	1 19	3 40	8 10	...
Wessely-a-M. (252)	—	7 51	1137	1 35	4 0	8 41	...
Kunowitz	4a54	8 22	1222	1 57	4 33	9 17	...
Ungarisch Brod	5 31	8 55	1252	2 17	5 3	9 47	...
Aujezd Luhatschow	5 38	9 5	1258	2 22	5 12	9 54	...
Boikowitz...............	6 5	9 33	—	—	5 40	1021	...
Vlarapass 233B ar	7 16	1042	...	...	6 51	1130	...

‡—Runs until 15th Sept.

		a.m.	a.m.	p.m.	p.m.		p.m.	
Vlarapass dep		3 20	8 23	...	2 10	...	7 0	...
Boikowitz...........		4 30	9 34	...	3 24	...	8 10	...
A. Luhatschow		4 54	10 1	1‡51	3 53	...	8 35	...
Ungarisch Brod		5 3	1011	1 57	4 3	...	8 43	...
Kunowitz		5 39	1048	2 20	4 40	p.m.	9 16	...
Wessely-a-M. ...		6 13	1123	2 43	5 15	6 23	—	...
Bisenz-Stadt ...		6 30	1152	2 57	5 33	7 5	...	...
Gaya	a.m.	6 53	1216	3 18	6 1	7 42	...	...
Austerlitz ...	5 50	8 10	1 23	4 9	7 15	9 15	...	...
Brunn 252	6 49	9 7	2 20	4 49	8 11	1024	...	...

BRANDEIS-a-E. and CELAKOWITZ.

	a.m.	a.m.	p.m.	p.m.	p.m.		
Brandeis-a-E.......dep	6 0	9 40	1232	3 0	8 30	...	...
Celakowitz ...225.arr	6 27	1010	12 59	3 27	8 57	...	...

	a.m.	a.m.	p.m.	p.m.	p.m.		
Celakowitz ....dep	7 22	1150	2 23	5 43	9 20	...	...
Brandeis-a-E.......arr	7 49	1217	2 50	6 10	9 47	...	...

PECEK and BECWAR.

Pecek ....dep	7a 0	12p28	2 p50	9 p11	...	...
Boschitz.........arr	7 51	1 32	3 41	10 1	...	...
Kaurim .....arr	8 4	1 47	3 52	10 11	...	...
Kaurim .....dep	8 20	1 57	4 0	10 18	...	...
Boschitz........dep	8 35	2 10	4 23	10 30	...	...
Zasmuk ....arr	9 9	2 35	5 3	10 54	...	...
Becwar 243 ...arr	9 22	...	5 16	...	...	...

Becwar ....dep	6 a30	9a45	...	6p 0	...	...
Zasmuk.........dep	6 47	10 7	2 p46	6 20	...	...
Boschitz ....arr	7 10	10 30	3 9	6 43	...	...
Kaurim .....arr	7 23	10 43	3 52	6 56	...	...
Kaurim.....dep	7 33	10 53	4 0	7 6	...	...
Boschitz........dep	7 52	11 4	4 12	7 20	...	...
Pecek (252).....arr	8 46	11 55	5 14	8 10	...	...

BISENZ-STADT & BISENZ-PISEK.

Bisenz-Stadt dp.	4 a5	6a35	9a45	11a11	1 p34	3p46	6p14	8p16
Bisenz-Pisek ar.	4 16	6 46	9 56	11 22	1 45	3 57	6 25	8 27
Bisenz-Pisek dep	4a40	7a17	10a46	11a38	2p19	5 p0	6p50	8p44
Bisenz-Stadt arr	4 51	7 28	10 57	11 49	2 30	5 11	7 1	8 55

Wessely-a-M. ....dep	8 a5	4 p1	...	...	...
Skalitz ....arr	9 11	4 54	...	...	...
Skalitz ....dep	10a15	5 p15	...	...	...
Wessely-a-M. ....arr	11 11	6 14	...	...	...

Kunowitz ...dep	3a50	5a45	8a35	11a 0	12p30	2p25	4p43	9p24
Ung. Hradischar	4 5	6 43	9 40	11 20	12 45	2 40	4 58	9 42
Ung.Hrad'h	4a30	7a30	10a27	12 p4	1p20	4 p5	8p58	...
Kunowitz...	4 48	8 10	10 42	12 19	1 45	4 20	9 13	...

UNZMARKT and MAUTERNDORF.

E.M.						
	Unzmarkt-Frauenburg dep	7a20	11a24	3p20	6p50	...
16½	**Murau**	8 47	1 2	4 53	8 3	...
35½	Ramingstein-Thomathal	1032	2 44	6 42	—	...
47¾	**Mauterndorf** .... arr	1133	3 45	7 48	...	...

Mauterndorf........... dep	5a53	9a18	...	4p37	...	...
Ramingstein-Thomathal	6 54	1018	p.m.	5 40	...	...
Murau................................	8 33	12 1	1 33	7 25	...	...
Unzmarkt-Frau. 241 arr	9 40	1 10	2 40	8 35	...	...

POPRAD-FELKA and TATRA-LOMNICZ.

*—In July and August only. ‡—Until 15th September only.

Poprád-Felka ...	6a54	8*a40	10‡50	1*p5	3p26	5‡p35	7*p10	10*p44
Tarpatak	7 16	9 1	11 11	1 25	3 47	5 54	8 1	11 4
Tátra-Lomnicz...	7 36	9 22	11 32	1 45	4 10	6 1[illegible]	8 22	11 25

Tátra-Lomnicz ...	5*a2[illegible]	7*a42	9‡a40	12*p5	2 p0	4‡p30	6*p35	8p45
Tarpatak	5 42	8 3	10 1	12 26	2 22	4 52	6 56	9 9
Poprád-Felka 253A	6 1	8 21	10 20	12 45	2 43	5 11	7 15	9 23

Poprád	6a38	8a30	10a40	1 p5	2p20	3p15	5p35	7p36	9p47	...
Tátrafüred...	7 18	9 10	11 20	1 45	3 0	3 55	6 15	8 16	1027	...
Tátraszéplak	7 30	9 23	11 32	2 7	3 2[illegible]	4 10	6 [illegible]6	8 27	1038	...

Tátraszéplak	5a28	7a35	9a26	11a36	1p44	4p16	6p15	8 p30	9 p22	...	...
Tátrafüred...	5 40	7 48	9 40	11 48	2 0	4 36	6 30	8 42	9 38	...	...
Poprád	6 16	8 24	1016	12 24	2 36	5 12	7 6	9 18	10 14	...	...

Electric line also connects Tátra-Lomnicz and Tátrafüred.

KRALOVAN and SZUCHAHORA.

‡—Until 15th Sept.

Kralován ....dep	5a35	9a55	1p17	3p15	5p32	8p35
Alsó-Kubin	6 27	1047	2 10	4 6	6 25	9 18
Arvavaralja	6 57	1115	2 40	4 30	6 55	9‡47
Szuchahora 247A arr	8 55	...	4 41	...	...	...

Szuchahora	...	9a25	...	...	5 p5	...
Arvavaralja	7 a6	11 17	2p35	5p40	6 56	10‡p0
Alsó-Kubin	7 40	11 50	3 9	6 16	7 26	10 30
Kralován	8 25	12 30	3 52	7 0	8 10	11 12

BRANDEIS-a-d-E. and NERATOWITZ.

Brandeis-a-d-Elbe...dep	6 a25	10a45	4 p31	...
Neratowitz...............arr	7 20	11 46	5 27	...
Neratowitz..............dep	8 a42	1 p13	7 p20	...
Brandeis-a-d-Elbe ...arr	9 38	2 15	8 15	...

RC—Restaurant Car.

ODERBERG and KASSA (Kaschau).

Breslau ....dep		9p55	...	...	12 a8	...	1220	...	6 a30	...	...	...	...	8a48	...	2p12	...	...	4p36
		Ex3	Ex3	1,2,3	1,2,3	1,2,3	1,2,3	1,2,3	Ex 3	1,2,3	1,2,3	1,2,3	1,2,3	1,2,3	1,2,3	1,2,3	1,2,3	1,2,3	1,2,3
		a.m.			a.m.	a.m.	a.m.	a.m.	a.m.		a.m.	p.m.		p.m.		p.m.	p.m.	p.m.	p.m.
Oderberg ....dep		1 10	...	...	3 20	4 50	6 20	7 50	9 50	...	1045	1230	...	2 50	...	5 10	5 45	7 0	9 0
Karwin 253A		1 33	...	...	3 46	5 21	7 2	8 25	10 12	a.m	1115	1 8	...	3 30	...	5 34	6 12	7 39	9 36
Teschen 221...........		1 53	...	...	4 7	5 45	7 53	8 57	10 30	1118	1146	1 40	...	4 20	...	5 55	6 49	8 15	1053
Trzynietz		2 4	...	...	SC	5 57	8 10	—	RC	1135	RC	2 26	...	4 37	...	6 6	6 57	—	1111
Jablunkau		2 23		...	4 35	6 20	8 34	...	10 57	1156	1220	2 50	...	5 0	...	6 23	7 30	...	1135
Csacza		2 52	a.m.	a.m.	5 2	6 56	—	...	11 23	—	1253	—	p.m.	—	p.m.	6 52	8 6	...	—
Zsolna 226 ....arr		3 24	3 40	4 8	5 37	7 45	...	...	11 56	...	1 35	...	2 55	...	6 28	7 25	8 55	...	...
Ruttka...............arr		⋮	4 2	4 35	6 10	8 52	...	...	12 24	...	2 21	...	3 23	...	6 56	7 54	1010	...	...
Budapest 232A ar		9*40	...	...	12p50	...	...	...	6 *20	...	9p35	...	5a10	...	...	...	6*40	...	...
Ruttka ....dep		SC	4 5	4 50	—	9 14	...	...	12 28	...	2 32	...	3 40	...	7 6	7 58	—	...	...
Kralován 253		—	4 26	5 26	...	9 50	...	...	12 50	...	2 59	...	4 18	...	7 43	8 21	...	...	
Rózsahegy		...	4 48	6 8	...	1033	...	...	1 12	...	3 21	...	5 5	...	8 23	8 45	...		
Liptó-Szt. Miklós....		...	5 15	6 55	...	1122	...	...	1 40	...	4 0	...	5 55	...	9 0	9 15	...		
Liptó Ujvár...........		...	A	7 14	Ex 2	1142	...	...	1 52	...	4 14	...	6 16	...	—	9 27	...		
Csorba		...	6 4	7 58	A	1230	...	...	2 29	...	5 0	...	7 5	...	...	10 4	...		
Poprád Felka ...arr		...	6 26	8 22	a.m.	1255	...	...	2 52	...	5 20	...	7 30	...	...	1026	...		
Tatra Lomni.dep		5a20		7a42	9 40	12p5	...	...	2 p0	...	4p30	...	6p35	...	...	8p45	...		
Poprád Felka ...dep		6 34	—	8 34	10 45	1 20	...	...	3 0	...	5 43	...	7 48	...	...	1040	...		
Igló	4a35	7 8	...	9 29	11 20	2 18	...	...	3 33	...	6 43	...	8 49	...	...	1115	...		
Szepesolaszi ..	5 24	7 35	...	10 3	11 46	2 52	...	...	3 59	...	7 20	...	9 24	...	...	1142	...		
Margitfal. 253A	6 6	7 59	...	1037	12 10	3 23	...	...	4 24	...	7 57	...	9 58	...	...	12 8	...		
Abos	7 12	8 32	...	1132	12 49	4 22	...	...	4 57	...	8 46	...	1052	...	...	1246	...	...	
Kassa ....arr	7 40	8 50	...	1155	1 7	4 50	...	...	5 15	...	9 5	...	1115	...	...	1 5	...	...	...
Miskolcz 231	1030	1030	...	3 p9	2p59	6p58	...	...	6 p58	...	12a9	...	1a52	...	...	2a53	...	...	...

A—Runs until 15th Sept.

*—Via Pöstyen, page 233B.

Miskolcz ....dep			...	...	1 a48	...	...	1 a48	3 a54	...	6a24	1031	...	12p5	1 p3	...	...	5 p12	...
			1,2,3	1,2,3	Ex 3	1,2,3	1,2,3	1,2,3	1,2,3	2&3	1,2,3	Ex3	1,2,3	Ex2	1,2,3	1,2,3	Ex3	Ex 3	
					a.m.			a.m.	a.m.		a.m.	p.m.		p.m.	p.m.	p.m.		p.m.	
Kassa (Kaschau)...dep			...	...	3 40	...	...	4 35	7 10	...	1050	1230	...	3 0	3 55	5 16	...	7 5	...
Abos			...	...	4 4	...	...	5 4	7 38	...	1122	1250	...	3 19	4 26	5 45	...	7 24	...
Margitfalva			...	...	4 43	...	...	5 46	8 23	...	12 9	1 25	...	3 54	5 10	6 37	...	7 58	...
Szepesolaszi			...	...	5 15	...	...	6 22	8 58	...	1242	1 49	...	4 19	5 46	7 18	...	8 22	...
Igló			...	...	5 47	...	...	7 6	9 36	...	1 23	2 23	...	4 48	6 31	7 56	...	8 54	...
Poprád-Felka ......arr			...	...	6 20	...	...	7 52	10 15	...	2 12	2 56	...	5 20	7 20	—		9 25	...
Tat. Lomnicz 253arr			...	...	7 a36	...	...	9 a22	11a32	...	...	4p10	...	6 15	8 p22	...	p.m.	11p25	...
Poprád-Felka ......dep			...	...	6 28	...	...	8 4	10 30	...	2 30	3 7	...	A	7 35	...	9 35	—	...
Csorba			...	...	6 52	...	...	8 35	11 0	...	3 15	3 37	...	—	8 5	...	10 3	...	...
Liptó Ujvár			a.m.	...	7 31	...	...	9 18	11 41	...	4 31	4 13	...	...	8 47	...	A	...	...
Liptó-Szt. **Miklós**			6 0	...	7 47	...	...	9 45	11 58	...	5 1	4 29	...	...	9 11	...	1050		...
Rózsahegy..................			6 40	...	8 14	...	...	10 28	12 25	...	5 44	4 56	...	...	9 47	...	1115		...
Kralován			7 17	...	8 38	...	...	11 7	12 52	...	6 26	5 18	...	1,2,3	10 14	p.m.	1137		...
Ruttka ....arr			7 47	...	9 0	...	...	11 34	1 17	...	6 54	5 38	...	p.m.	10 40	SC	1157		...
Budapest ....dep			...	8*40	RC	...	...	...	7 *a5	...	...	12*20	...	2 20	...	6*50	...		...
Ruttka..................dep			7 55	5a20	9 6	...	...	11 51	1 28	...	7 20	5 45	...	9 36	11 5	⋮	12 1		...
Zsolna	2&3	2&3	8 24	6 25	9 40	...	...	12 20	2 14	...	8 20	6 20	...	1010	11 35	1243	1223		...
Csacza	a.m.	a.m.	—	7 14	10 20	a.m.	p.m.	—	2 58	p.m.	9 16	6 56	...	1044	—	1 17			...
Jablunkau ...	3 53	6 50	...	7 49	10 54	1130	2 25	...	3 34	5 28	9 52	7 26	...	1115	...	1 47	—	SC	...
Trzynietz......	4 17	7 17	...	8 9	11 8	1156	2 54	...	3 53	6 5	1014	7 40	p.m.	1131	...	2 3	...		...
Teschen	4 45	7 32	...	8 25	11 20	1230	3 29	...	4 10	6 39	1050	7 52	8 45	1146	...	2 16	...	...	...
Karwin..........	5 20	—	...	8 58	11 40	1 6	4 3	...	4 35	7 16	1117	8 9	9 17	12 4	...	2 33	...	...	...
Oderberg arr	5 55	...	...	9 30	12 6	1 40	4 35	...	5 6	7 50	1145	8 30	9 50	1230	...	2 55	...	...	...
Breslau 218 arr		...	...	2p15	3 p10	...	...	...	10 40	...	3a24	1148	...	3a24	...	5a56	...	...	...

SC—Sleeping Car in this train.

SZEPESOLASZI and SZEPESVARALJA.

Szepesolaszi ....dep	7 a46	10a15	3 p5	5 p55	9p35	...	...
Szepesváralja ....arr	8 10	10 40	3 30	6 20	10 0	...	...
Szepesváralja ....dep	5 a50	8a25	1 p10	5 p0	6p35	...	...
Szepesolaszi ....arr	6 15	8 49	1 35	5 25	7 0	...	...

IGLO and LOCSE.

Igló ....dep	7 a22	9 a42	2p26	3p52	6p47	9 p2
Löcse ....arr	7 55	10 15	2 50	4 25	7 20	9 35
Löcse ....dep	6 a15	8 a40	12p35	3 p0	5p35	7p55
Igló ....arr	6 48	9 13	1 8	3 24	6 8	8 28

ZSOLNA and RAJECZ.

Zsolna dep	8a45	1‡p40	3 p38	6§p23	9 p35	Rajecz ...dep	5a50	11a50	2‡p33	5§p0	8 p0
Rajecz arr	10 5	2 23	4 45	7 6	10 38	Zsolna253A arr	6 47	1 8	3 15	5 43	9 7

‡—Until 15th September.
§—Until 31st August.

KASSA, ABOS, and ORLO.

‡—Until 15th September.

Kassa ......dep	3a40	4a58	6a48	...	10a50	12p12	4p23	7 p5	10p51
Abos ......dep	4 7	5 32	7 14	8a44	11 28	12 34	5 1	7 28	11 19
Eperjes ...arr	4 30	6 3	7 40	9 15	11 54	12 59	5 26	7 54	11 45
Nagysáros ...	5 6	—	8 7	—	—	1 25	6 0	8§42	—
Kisszeben ...	5 30	...	8 30	...	...	1 46	6 23	9 §9	...
Héthárs	5 55	...	8 55	...	...	2 6	6 50	9§36	...
Orló 245 ...arr	...	...	9 35	...	...	2 45	7 30	...	...

Orlo ......dep	...	...	...	9 a0	...	1p22	...	...	7p55	§	...
Hethárs	...	...	6a25	9 44	...	2 5	...	...	8 43	1020	...
Kisszeben ..	...	...	6 51	10 8	...	2 30	...	...	9 8	1050	...
Nagysáros	a.m.	a.m.	7 14	1028	p.m.	2 52	p.m.	...	9 29	1117	a.m.
Eperjes	4 31	6 30	7 52	1048	12 4	3 25	6 40	8 p4	10 0	1134	12 1
Abos......arr	4 58	7 1	8 23	1113	1230	3 51	7 11	8 30	1025	—	1230
Kassa ...arr	5 30	7 40	8 50	1145	1 ‡7	4 20	...	9 5	1050	...	1 5

E.M.												
	Eperjes ....dep	6a18	10*50	1p14	5p36	Bártfa ....dep	5a30	9*a45	1p20	7p50	...
28	Bártfa ....arr	8 30	12 50	3 15	7 30	Eperjes 253A ...arr	7 20	11 46	3 10	9 40	...

*—In July and August only.
§—Mon., Wed., and Sat. only.

KARWIN and PETROWITZ.

Karwin.........dep	7a12	11a50	5p10	8p15	...	...	Petrowitz..........dep	5a50	9a16	1p42	6p50	...	...	...
Petrowitz......arr	7 55	12 46	6 0	9 5	...	...	Karwin 253A ...arr	6 40	10 1	2 40	7 45	...	...	...

ROZSAHEGY and KORYTNICZAI-FURDO.

Rózsahegy ....dep	6‡a10	8a25	3p40	...	...	Korytniczai-fürdö dep	8a40	10a50	6p40	...	...	...
Korytniczai-fürdö arr	7 40	10 0	5 15	...	...	Rózsahegy ....arr	1012	12 15	8 10	...	...	...

‡—Until 31st August.

MARGITFALVA and SZOMOLNOKHUTA.

E.M.																		
	Margitfalva ......dep	6 a8	8a39	1p29	5p18	8 p9	10 p9	...	**Szomolnokhuta**	...	5 a50	9 a35	1p15	...	7p35	...
5	Gölniczbánya	6 32	9 10	1 55	5 45	8 30	10 30	...	Gölniczbánya	5 a15	7 32	11 24	2 55	7p15	9 15	...
20½	**Szomolnokhuta** arr	8 5	1045	3 25	7 15	...	...	...	**Margitfalva 253A**	5 36	7 50	11 45	3 12	7 36	9 36	...

‡—From September 16th.]

POPRAD-FELKA and PODOLIN.

[§—Until September 15th.

Poprád-Felka ....dep	6a39	8a55	...	3p12	5p52	7‡p53	8§40	10p31	Podolin.............................dep	5a55	8a35	12p45	5p15	7p40
Késmárk............................	7 24	9 53	2 p0	3 55	6 41	8 42	9 31	11 6	Szepesbéla-Barlangliget dep	6 10	8 45	12 56	5 30	7·50
Elágazás.............................	7 39	10 9	2 15	4 10	6 56	8 57	9 46	—	Elágazás..................................	6 30	9 5	1 15	5 50	8 10
Szepesbéla-Barlangliget arr	8 0	1030	2 27	4 30	7 12	9 18	10 5	...	Késmárk 5a40	6 56	9 26	1 40	6 18	8 33
Podolin.......................arr	8 10	1045	...	4 42	7 28	9 30	1016	...	**Poprád-Felka 253A** ......arr 6 14	7 41	10 5	2 18	7 0	9 13

ARAD and SZEGED.

Dist. E.M.		2 & 3	2 & 3	1 & 2	1,2,3	2 & 3	2 & 3	1 & 2	2 & 3	1,2,3	2&3	2 & 3		
				a.m.	a.m	a.m.	a.m.	a.m.	p.m.	p.m.	p.m.	p.m.		
—	**Arad** ...dep	...	...	6 16	6 40	8 45	11 5	11 48	2 25	4 11	5 35	7 10	...	...
21¼	Battonya	...	...	7 3	7 52	9 58	12 13	12 35	3 35	5 29	6 52	8 15	...	...
24¾	Tompapuszta	...	a.m	...	8 3	10 8	12 23	...	3 44	5 40	7 5	8 29	...	...
31¾	**Mezöhegyes 254**	...	5 44	7 27	8 46	10 34	1 15	1 1	4 11	6 24	7 28	8 51	...	...
43¼	Nagylak	...	6 16	7 52	9 24	11 12	1 57	1 28	4 44	7 8	—	—	...	...
49¾	Apatfalva	a.m.	6 33	8	9 46	11 33	2 17	1 42	5 4	7 34	...	...	...	...
54¼	Mako	4 12	6 50	8 2	10 27	11 53	2 34	1 56	5 21	8 15	...	...	...	...
70¾	Szoreg	5 6	7 36	9 4	11 21	12 46	3 26	2 32	6 13	9 16	...	...	...	...
74	**Szeged** ...arr	5 19	7 49	9 14	11 35	12 59	3 40	2 42	6 26	9 31	...	...	...	...

		2 & 3	1,2,3	2 & 3	2 & 3	1,2,3	1 & 2	1,2,3	2 & 3	2 & 3	1 & 2	2 & 3		
			a.m	a.m.		a.m.	p.m.	p.m.	p.m.	p.m.	p.m.	p m.		
...	**Szeged** ...dep	...	3 6	6 10	...	10 40	12 34	1 56	3 22	5 6	6 33	7 25	...	...
...	Szoreg	...	3 20	6 24	...	10 54	12 49	2 10	3 37	5 22	6 42	7 42	...	...
...	Mako	...	4 27	7 17	...	11 51	1 27	3 2	4 44	6 20	7 17	8 46	...	...
...	Apatfalva	...	4 44	7 33	...	12 7	1 43	3 18	5 11	6 39	7 31	—	...	...
...	Nagylak	a.m.	5 6	7 52	a.m.	12 27	1 57	3 37	5 40	7 3	7 45	...	...	...
...	**Mezöhegyes**	4 0	6 5	8 27	11 38	1 2	2 27	4 21	6 40	7 40	8 12	...	...	...
...	Tompapuszta	4 21	6 31	8 47	12 2	1 24	...	4 46	7 4	—	...	...	...	...
...	Battonya	4 35	6 43	9 0	12 14	1 35	2 51	5 0	7 16	...	8 36	...	...	...
...	**Arad (232)** ...arr	5 48	8 4	10 10	1 25	2 43	3 37	6 15	8 27	...	9 20	...	...	...

MEZOHEGYES and KETEGYHAZA.

E.M.		a.m	a.m.	a.m.	p.m.	p.m.	p.m.	p.m.		a.m.	a.m.	a.m.	a.m.	a.m.	p.m.	p.m.
—	**Mezöhegyes** ...dep	4 5	7 30	8 40	1 6	4 31	6 30	8 56	**Ketegyháza** ...dep	4 15	5 14	6 32	9 41	11 50	2 38	6 50
8	Mezökováczháza	4 33	7 56	9 7	1 32	4 58	7 11	9 23	Medgyesegyhaza	4 39	5 50	6 58	10 8	12 11	3 0	7 16
16¾	Medgyesegyhaza	5 19	8 27	9 44	2 3	5 34	8 0	9 59	Mezökováczháza	5 9	6 40	7 34	1044	12 35	3 30	7 46
24¾	**Ketegyháza** ...arr	5 49	8 50	1010	2 25	6 0	8 31	1025	**Mezöhegyes 232** ...arr	5 34	7 13	8 2	1110	12 53	3 55	8 8

ARAD and KETEGYHAZA.

Kétegyháza dep	4a25	5a10	7 a16	10a42	12p10	3 p0	6p35	...	**Arad** ...dep	5a10	8 a23	11a53	...	4p20	5p16	7p29	...
Kisjenö-Erdöhegy	5 25	6 29	8 9	11 45	1 30	3 57	7 29	...	Ujszentanna	6 32	9 23	12 44	3 p0	4 55	6 20	8 35	...
Ujszentanna	6 14	7 22	8 48	12 34	2 22	4 42	8 13	...	Kisjenö-Erdöhegy	7 23	10 11	1 30	3 56	5 40	7 40	9 21	...
Arad ...arr	7 15	7 59	11 0	1 33	3 42	5 51	9 8	...	**Kétegyháza 254** arr	8 20	11 8	2 23	4 50	6 32	9 9	1015	...

ARAD and BRAD.

		a.m.	a.m.	a.m.	a.m.	p.m.	p.m.	p.m.	p.m.	p.m.
Arad ...dep		5 10	6 11	6 35	8 23	1240	3 0	4 20	5 16	7 29
Uj-Szt-Anna		6 0	6 52	7 28	9 15	1 24	3 52	4 53	6 1	8 19
Pankota	a.m.	6 40	7 23	8 15	9 54	2 3	4 31	5 22	6 46	8 58
Borosjeno	5 0	7 33	7 55	9 11	1044	2 55	5 21	5 54	7 33	9 44
Bokszeg	5 29	—	8 13	9 41	1112	3 21	5 45	6 13	8 0	—
Borossebes	6 5	a.m.	8 35	1014	1139	3 52	6 15	6 37	8 26	...
Honcztö	6 56	5 24	9 10	1113	1227	4 46	7 12	7 10	—	...
Brad ...arr	—	7 35	1049	1 19	2 43	7 12	9 17	...	...	...

	a.m.	a.m.	a.m.	a.m.	a.m.		p.m.	p.m.	p.m.	p.m.	p.m.
Brad ... dep	...	...	3 0	5 40	...	...	12 7	2 15	...	2 50	5 2
Honczto	...	5 6	5 16	7 21	9 22	...	1 50	3 58	4 8	4 48	6 58
Borossebes	4 0	5 42	6 7	8 3	10 20	...	2 35	—	4 41	5 32	—
Bokszeg	4 30	6 3	6 39	8 31	10 54	p.m.	3 3	...	5 2	6 13	...
Borosjeno	4 55	6 24	7 13	9 2	11 20	1 18	3 30	...	5 20	6 45	...
Pankota	5 39	6 56	7 59	9 40	12 3	2 5	4 15	...	5 51	7 33	...
Uj-Szt-Anna	6 18	7 27	8 53	1016	12 42	2 52	5 2	...	6 21	8 23	...
Arad ...arr	7 15	7 59	9 53	11 0	1 33	3 42	5 51	...	6 53	9 8	...

BOROSSEBES and MENYHAZA.

Borossebes ...dep	10a18	6‡p45	...	**Menyhazafurdö** ...dep	4‡a30	3p10	...	...
Dezna	11 2	7 22	...	**Dezna**	4 59	3 58	...	...
Menyhazafürdö ... arr	11 33	7 52	...	Borossebes ...arr	5 35	4 35	...	...

‡—Runs until 31st August.

BOROSJENO and CSERMO.

Borosjeno ...dep	9 a3	11a20	3 p2	6p40	...	Csermo ...dep	5 a34	10 a6	12p37	4p33	...
Csermo ...arr	9 36	11 54	3 35	7 13	...	Borosjeno arr	6 9	10 36	1 7	5 8	...

TOT KOMLOS and BEKESCSABA.

Tot Komlos ...dep	4 a0	9 a18	1 p38	5 p2	Bekescsaba ...dep	4a50	9 a40	2 p0	6 p4	...
Klemi-major	...	...	...	...	Klemi-major	...	...	...	...	...
Bekescsaba ...arr	6 24	12 1	4 20	7 39	Tot Komlos ...arr	7 21	12 24	4 32	8 39	...

Mezökováczháza...dep	9 a20	1p38	5 p5	...	Tot Kolmos ...dep	6a28	9a18	1p38	5 p2
Tot Komlos ...arr	12 24	4 32	8 39	...	Mezökováczháza...arr	7 22	12 23	4 32	8 40

Bekescsaba ...dep	7 a4	11a30	1p46	7p40	...	Veszto ...dep	4 a0	6a15	10a30	5 p4	...
Veszto ...arr	9 27	2 10	4 8	1010	...	Bekescsaba arr	6 20	8 53	1 7	7 23	...

PORICAN and NIMBURG.

Porican dep	7a20	12p30	3p50	6p47	9p27
Nimburg ar	7 53	1 13	4 30	7 18	1012
Nimburg dep	5a14	7a21	11a8	4p54	8p41
Porican arr	6 9	7 55	1152	5 22	9 10

Wenzelsberg and Starkotsch.

Wenzelsberg...dep	5a15	7 a33	10a50	1 p58	6 p8	10p8
Starkotsch ...arr	5 52	7 40	10 57	2 5	6 15	1015
Starkotsch ...dep	6 a20	9a10	11a55	3p50	7 p35	10p45
Wenzelsberg..arr	6 34	9 24	12 9	4 4	7 49	10 53

Chotzen and Leitomischl.

Chotzen ...dep	6a45	9a25	3p51	8p10
Leitomischl arr	8 0	1047	5 9	9 30
Leitomischl dep	5a20	9a47	11a21	4p12
Chotzen ...arr	6 31	1112	12 21	5 29

OLMUTZ and BOHM. TRUBAU.

‡—Until 30th Sept.

Dist E.M								
	Olmütz ...dep	6a14	9a43	12p40	3p51	8 p0	11p40	12a12
13	Schwarzbach	6 41	1011	1 2	4 18	8 35	12 5	...
28	**Hohenstadt**	7 20	1048	1 33	4 56	9 28	12 41	1 3
44¾	Rudelsdorf	8 0	1128	2 5	5 41	1021	1 20	‡
49¾	Triebitz (252A)	8 13	1144	2 17	6 0	1037	1 33	...
54	**Böh. Trübau 253**	8 22	1152	2 24	6 8	11 0	1 41	1 55

Böhm. Trübau dep	2a55	5a14	9 a36	12p33	2p55	7p15	8p37	2a33
Triebitz	3 10	5 27	9 49	12 43	3 10	7 26	...	...
Rudelsdorf	3 27	5 40	10 2	12 54	3 26	7 39	...	‡
Hohenstadt	4 15	6 25	10 51	1 35	4 14	8 25	9 29	3 25
Schwarzbach	4 57	7 7	11 35	2 7	4 57	9 10	...	...
Olmütz (331) ...arr	5 30	7 38	12 8	2 35	5 28	9 42	1021	4 12

Schwarzbach to Littau (1⅝ miles, in 8 min.), 7.15, 10.20, 11.40 a.m., 1.10, 2.12, 4.22, 5.5 p.m.; ret., 6.25, 9.55, 11.15 a.m., 12.45, 1.50, 4.0, 4.40 p.m.

Rudelsdorf to Landskron (3 miles in 14 min.), 5.46, 8.6, 10.11, 11.36 a.m., 3.31, 5.46, 7.46, 10.26 p.m.; return, 5.20, 7.34, 9.40, 11.3 a.m., 1.40, 5.15, 7.15, 9.52 p.m.

NIMBURG and JICIN.

E.M						
—	**Nimburg** (St. E.G)	4a36	8a17	1p27	4p55	7p27
10	**Krinec** ....arr	5 17	8 52	2 7	5 39	8 1
19½	**Konigstadtl** ,,	...	9 57	5 20	...	9 15
...	**Krinec**..........dep	5 22	8 55	2 11	5 50	8 6
18¾	Kopidlno	6 10	9 31	2 58	7 24	8 44
28½	**Jicin (225)** ......arr	7 4	1017	3 55	8 15	9 30

Jicin ....dep	5a19	8a30	2p45	6p38
Kopidlno	6 9	9 30	3 37	7 29
Krinec ......arr	6 39	10 5	4 7	7 59
Konigst. dep	5 28	...	2 38	6 40
Krinec ......dep	6 43	10 9	4 11	8 2
Nimburg ...arr	7 17	1047	4 45	8 36

Konigstadtl ...dep	5 a40	12p35	6 p24
Chlumetz ......arr	6 21	1 22	7 5
Chlumetz ......dep	7 a20	1 p53	8 p16
Konigstadtl ...arr	7 59	2 29	8 52

KOPIDLNO and BAKOV.

Kopidlno ......dep	7 a15	3 p45	7 p39	...
Detenic	7 41	4 22	8 10	...
: Taxis-Dobrovic ...	9 9	5 39	...	...
Bakov (249) ...arr	9 31	...	9 58	...

Bakov ......dep	6 a5	...	4p35	...	...	...	...
: Taxis-Dobrov.	...	10a0	..	6p30	...	...	...
Detenic	8 4	1120	6 27	7 46	...	...	...
Kopidlno 255	8 32	1158	6 58	8 18	...	...	...

KONIGGRATZ and WOSTROMER.

Koniggratz ......dep	...	7 a30	10a7	2 p15	...	6 p25	...	9 p18
Smiritz 223A dep	...	7 12	...	1 10	...	6 5	...	...
Sadowa ....arr	...	8 2	...	2 0	...	6 55	...	...
Sadowa ....dep	...	8 19	11 7	3 16	...	7 24	...	10 4
Horic	5 a7	9 13	1211	4 7	6p10	8 10	9p42	
Wostromer 225 arr	5 30	9 36	1237	4 30	6 33	8 45	10 5	

Wostromer ...dep	4a20	5a51	10a28	1p20	5p20	6 p58	9 p5
Horic....................	4 52	6 20	11 5	2 10	5 49	7 30	9 34
Sadowa..........arr	5 29	—	11 44	2 51	—	8 7	—
Sadowa......dep	5 33	...	11 47	3 42	...	...	...
Smiritz.......arr	6 23	...	12 37	4 32	...	...	...
Koniggratz 223A	6 28	...	12 38	3 44	...	8 52	...

SMIDAR and HOCHWESSELY.

Smidar...........dep	10a35	5 p5	8p50	...	...	...
Hochwessely arr	11 11	5 41	9 26	...	...	...
Hochwessely	5a20	12p33	6 p25	...	...	...
Smidar 225 ...	5 54	1 7	6 49	...	...	...

ROKITZAN and NEZVESTIC.

Rokitzan .....dep	..	7a35	10a0	3p45	5 p5	8 p5	...
Miroschau	5a35	8 13	1031	4 14	5 36	8 36	...
Nezvestic 243A arr	6 40	...	...	5 15	...	...	...
Nezvestic ....dep	...	7a10	...	...	7 p8	...	...
Miroschau	6a52	8 17	2 p4	5p57	8 10	...	...
Rokitzan ......arr	7 20	8 46	2 32	6 25	...	...	...

SWISS RAILWAYS.

NEUCHATEL and MORTEAU.

	a.m	a.m	a.m	a.m		p.m	p.m	p.m	p.m	p.m.		p.m	p.m.	p.m.
Neuchâtel ......dep	5 40	7 51	9 54	1045	...	1217	2 10	3 9	4 16	6 13	...	6 52	8 14	1117
Chambrelien........	6 10	8 21	1019	1115	...	1247	2 40	3 32	4 45	6 43	...	7 15	8 45	1144
Hauts-Geneveys ...	6 36	8 48	1040	1142	...	1 15	3 8	3 53	5 12	7 11	...	7 37	9 14	12 7
Convers...............	6 48	9 1	1049	1155	...	1 28	3 21	...	5 25	7 24	...	...	9 27	...
Chaux-de-Fonds ar	6 54	9 7	1056	12 1	p.m.	1 34	3 28	4 8	5 32	7 30	...	7 52	9 34	1222
,, ...dep	7 8	9 14	11 0	12 5	1 1	1 40	3 34	4 12	5 38	7 38	p.m	7 58	9 51	1225
Locle ....arr	7 24	9 30	1111	1223	1 19	1 57	3 50	4 23	5 54	7 54	8 38	8 9	10 7	1241
Morteau 52......arr	8 32	—	—	1 8	—	2 39	—	—	6 46	—	9 22	—	—	—
BESANCON....arr	1024	...	...	...	...	4p43	...	...	8p55	...	...	...	...	...

BESANCON ...dep	...	...	...	4a37	...	...	...	9 a8	...	...	...	3 p4	...	6p28
	a.m.	a.m.	a.m.	a.m	a.m.	p.m.	p.m.	p.m	p.m	p.m	p.m.	p.m	p.m.	p.m.
Morteau ....dep	..	.	...	8 40	.	...	...	1 14	.	5 7	...	7 10	...	1017
Locle	5 57	7 24	8 48	9 38	10 17	1227	1 39	2 24	4 29	6 10	7 11	7 54	9 25	1052
Chaux-de-Fonds ar	6 15	7 42	9 6	9 56	10 36	1245	1 55	2 42	4 48	6 28	7 27	8 12	9 43	1111
,, dep	6 19	7 47	9 11	—	10 42	1252	2 1	2 47	4 53	6 35	7 36	8 28	9 50	—
Convers	6 27	7 55	9 19	...	10 51	1 2	...	2 55	5 1	6 43	7 46	8 38	9 58	...
Hauts-Geneveys ...	6 40	8 5	9 29	...	10 59	1 13	2 16	3 6	5 11	6 59	7 56	8 50	10 8	...
Chambrelien	7 5	8 26	9 51	...	11 20	1 37	2 36	3 27	5 33	7 13	8 17	9 15	1030	...
Neuchâtel ......arr	7 26	8 44	10 9	...	11 38	1 56	2 52	3 46	5 50	7 34	8 35	9 33	1048	...

Extra.

Chaux-de-Fonds dep	6a36	8a24	10a18	11a46	2 p2	4p30	6p54	...	...	...	...
Locle ....arr	6 53	8 42	10 34	12 2	2 19	4 48	7 11	...	...	...	...
Locle..............dep	5 a32	6§a34	11a14	12p7	1 p3	3p50	6p35	...	...	...	...
Chaux-de-Fonds arr	5 50	6 54	11 33	1227	1 23	4 9	6 54	...	...	...	...

§—Not on Sunday.

LOCLE and BRENETS.—In 15 minutes. Depart from Locle, 7.0, 7.55, 9.36 a.m., 12 26 2 0 4.27, 6.15, 8.12, 9.24, 10.20 p.m. From Brenets, 6.35, 7.35, 9.15 a.m., 12 0 noon, 1.38, 3.25, 5.40, 7.33, 9.5, 10.0 p.m.

‡—2.20 p.m. on Sunday. **NEU SOLOTHURN and LANGNAU.** §—7.41 p.m. on Sun. *—7.5 p.m. on Sun.

	am	a.m.	a.m.	p.m.	pm	p.m	pm	pm	p.m.	p.m
Neu Soloth'rn	5 0	7 28	9 15	1238	...	3‡28	439	538	7§45	8 56
Burgdorf ...arr	541	8 12	9 54	1 16	...	4 12	521	617	8 32	9 35
BERNE ...dep	5a0	7a10	9a37	1233	214	—	5p5	6p0	—	8p40
Burgdorf...dep	559	8 15	1033	1 37	314	...	538	652	...	9 53
Hasle-Rüegsau	614	8 29	1055	1 53	329	...	553	712	...	10 9
Ramsei	624	8 39	11 9	2 4	339	...	6 4	727	...	1020
Langnau ...arr	642	8 55	1129	2 23	356	...	620	746	...	1037

	a.m.	am	a.m.	a.m.	p m	pm	p.m.	pm	pm	p.m.	p.m.	p.m
Langnau dep	4 40	...	7 28	9 9	1233	...	2 46	...	432	...	7*10	8 46
Ramsei	4 56	...	7 47	9 26	1252	...	3 7	...	451	...	7 30	9 5
H.-Rüegsau	5 7	...	7 59	9 36	1 2	...	3 27	...	5 2	...	7 42	9 15
Burgdorf arr	5 22	...	8 15	9 51	1 18	...	3 42	...	516	...	8 0	9 30
BERNE arr	6a33	...	9a12	1027	2 p0	...	5p18	...	6p0	...	9 p5	10‡30
Burgdorf dep	5 55	724	8 38	1019	1 30	3 2	...	439	536	6 55	9 11	10 20
Neu Soloth.	6 37	815	9 32	1057	2 8	344	...	517	616	7 44	9 50	11 0

SOLOTHURN and MOUTIER.

Neu Solothurn ...dep	6a59	9a35	10a59	2p13	5p39	9 p0
Lommiswil	7 16	9 59	11 15	2 31	5 57	9 18
Moutier (Münster)arr	7 49	1047	11 48	3 4	6 30	9 54

Moutier ....dep	5a52	9a23	1 p1	4p15	5p50	7p54
Lommiswil............	6 25	9 57	1 34	4 50	6 31	8 27
Neu Solothurn arr	6 41	1012	1 50	5 5	6 48	8 42

BASLE and RODERSDORF.

Basle..................dep	5a45
Binningen	5 51
Oberwil	6 2
Fluh	6 24
Rodersdorf ......arr	6 35

And from Basle at 6†51, 7.50, 8†50, 9.50, 10†50, 11.50, 1.50, 2†50, 3.45, 4†50, 5.50, 6†18, 6†50, 7.18. 8.18, 9†30.
†—Not go beyond Fluh.
Frequent service between Basle and Oberwil.

FRAUENFELD and WIL.

Frauenfeld-Stat. dp	6a50	8 a0	...	...	3p57	7 p0	...
,, Town dep	6 57	8 8	11a11	1p12	4 2	7 10	8p16
Mazingen	7 15	8 26	11 29	1 30	4 20	7 28	8 34
Rosenthal	7 34	8 45	11 48	1 49	4 39	7 47	8 54
Wil 268 ....arr	7 55	9 8	12 10	2 12	5 0	8 10	9 16

Wil ....dep	5 5	8a20	10a10	1 p12	3p18	5p52	8p32
Rosenthal..................	5 47	8 44	10 34	1 34	3 42	6 13	8 53
Mazingen	6 6	9 3	11 2	1 54	4 3	6 31	9 13
Frauenfeld-Town arr	6 24	9 20	11 30	2 12	4 21	6 49	9 31
,, Station arr	6 30	...	...	...	...	6 54	...

GENEVA (Place Molard) and **TREIZE ARBRES** on Mont Saleve. calling at Etrembières, Bas Mornex, Haut Mornex, and Monnetier. From Geneva 7.15, 9.55, 12.55, 15*15, 16.15, 17.55. From **Treize Arbres** 9.30, 12.38, 14.50, 15.55, 17.0, 18.45. Also from **Geneva** (Cours de Rive) to **Treize Arbres**, calling at Veyrier and Monnetier. **From Geneva**, 6.15, 7.30, 9.0, 10.15, 12.30, 13.15. 14.15, 16.30. From **Treize Arbres**, 7.40, 10.40, 12.38, 14.50, 15.55, 17.0, 18.45.

*—To Monnetier.

GENEVA and ST. JULIEN (40 min.)—Departures from Geneva and St. Julien, almost hourly.

RIGIBAHN—Rigi Line.

Single fr. c.	Return fr. c.												
		LUCERNE Stmr. dep	5a25	7a45	8a40	9a35	10a10	11 a0	12 45	2 p0	2p30	4p30	6p15
		FLUELEN „ dep	...	6a10	8a25	8a25	8 a25	10a20	11§50	1 p0	1 p0	3p35	5 0
			a.m.	a.m.	a.m.	a.m.	a.m.	no'n	p.m.	p.m.	p.m.	p.m	p.m.
—	—	Vitznau ....dep	6 30	8 45	10 2	10 35	10*47	12 0	1 40	3 10	3‖40	5 30	7*25
2 70	...	Freibergen	6 58	9 13	10 30	11 3	11 15	12 27	2 8	3 37	4 8	5 58	7 53
3 40	...	Romiti Felsenthor ...	7 7	9 22	10 39	11 12	11 24	12 36	2 17	3 46	4 17	6 7	8 2
4 50	...	Kaltbad ...... arr	7 18	9 33	10 50	11 23	11 35	12 47	2 28	3 57	4 28	6 18	8 13
		Kaltbad ...... dep	7 20	9 35	10 52	11 25	11 37	12 49	2 30	3 59	4 30	6 20	8 15
5 6	...	Staffelhöhe	7 25	9 40	10 57	11 30	11 42	12 54	2 35	4 4	4 35	6 25	8 20
6 6	...	Staffel	7 34	9 49	11 6	11 39	11 51	1 2	2 44	4 13	4 44	6 34	8 29
7 0	10 50	Rigi Kulm ......arr	7 44	9 59	11 16	11 49	12 1	1 13	2 54	4 23	4 54	6 44	8 39

*—Until 15th Sept. ‖—Until 31st August.

fr. c.		a.m.	a.m.	a.m.	p.m.	p.m.	p.m.	p.m.	p.m.	p.m.
—	Rigi Kulm ....dep	6 35	8 35	10 25	12 10	1 24	3 25	3*30	5 20	7*30
0 50	Staffel	6 45	8 45	10 35	12 20	1 34	3 35	3 40	5 30	7 40
1 0	Staffelhöhe	6 54	8 54	10 44	12 29	1 43	3 44	3 49	5 39	7 49
1 25	Kaltbad .... arr	6 59	8 59	10 49	12 34	1 48	3 49	3 54	5 44	7 54
	Kaltbad .... dep	7 1	9 1	10 56	12 36	1 50	3 51	4 20	5 46	7 56
1 80	Romiti Felsenthor ...	7 12	9 12	11 7	12 47	2 1	4 2	4 31	5 57	8 7
2 15	Freibergen	7 21	9 21	11 16	12 56	2 10	4 11	4 40	6 6	8 16
3 50	Vitznau ....arr	7 48	9 49	11 44	1 24	2 37	4 39	5 8	6 34	8 44
...	FLUELEN Stmr. arr	10a10	1 p7	1 p45	3 p15	4p50	6 55	6 55	8p55	...
...	LUCERNE „ arr	8 a55	11a10	12 50	2 p30	3p35	5p35	6 45	7p40	9p45

ARTH-GOLDAU and RIGI-KULM.

‡—Sunday only until 31st August.

Up-w'rd fr. c.	Return fr. c.										
		LUCERNE ......dep	6a40	7a50	7a50	9 a47	11a0	12p35	2p30	3p59	5 p5
5 20	7 10	Arth-Goldau dep	7*40	8 35	9 ‡6	10*25	1140	1*26	3 20	4 37	6*20
...	...	Rigi-Klösterli	8 27	9 22	9 53	11 13	1226	2 12	4 7	5 24	7 7
...	...	Wölfertschen-First	8 35	9 30	10 4	11 22	1235	2 21	4 15	5 32	7 15
7 10	9 70	Rigi-Staffel	8 42	9 37	1011	11 29	1242	2 28	4 22	5 39	7 22
8 00	11 00	Rigi-Kulm ...arr	8 50	9 45	1019	11 37	1250	2 36	4 30	5 47	7 30

*—Until Sept. 15.

Rigi-Kulm ...dep	7*a3	8*58	9a50	10‡24	12*0	1p50	2‡42	4 35	6p20	...
Rigi-Staffel	7 10	9 5	9 57	10 32	12 8	1 57	2 50	4 42	6 27	...
Wölfertschen-First	7 16	9 11	10 4	10 38	1215	2 3	2 56	4 48	6 33	...
Rigi-Klösterli	7 25	9 22	1013	10 47	1225	2 14	3 5	4 57	6 42	...
Arth-Goldau arr	8 13	1013	11 0	11 34	1 10	3 0	3 52	5 45	7 30	...
LUCERNE ......arr	9a37	...	...	...	...	4p35	4p35	6p50	8p20	...

	a.m.	a.m.	a.m.	a.m.	a.m.	a.m.	a.m.	p.m	p.m.	p.m.	p.m.	p.m.	p.m.	p.m.	p.m.	p.m.
Arth-See	5 28	7 11	7 59	8 35	10 2	1049	1122	1251	2 20	2 55	3 40	4 13	5 39	7 16	9 3	9 50
Arth-Gold	5 43	7 26	8 14	8 50	1020	11 4	1136	1 6	2 35	3 9	3 55	4 28	5 45	7 31	9 18	10 4

	a.m.	a.m.	a.m.	a.m.	a.m.	a.m.	a.m.	p.m.	p.m.	p.m.	p.m.	p.m.	p.m.	p.m.	p.m.	p.m.	
Arth-G	6 8	7 38	8 18	9 5	1030	11 8	1150	1 25	2 40	3 20	3 58	4 40	5 55	7 45	9 36	11 2	...
Arth-S	6 21	7 51	8 31	9 21	1043	1120	12 3	1 38	2 53	3 32	4 11	4 53	6 8	7 58	9 48	11 15	...

Sing fr. c.	Ret. fr. c.		†	‡							
		Rigi-Kaltbad ...dep	7 a25	9 a40	11a50	2 p35	4 p5	6 p25	...	...	...
0 50	0 75	Rigi-First	7 33	9 46	11 56	2 41	4 11	6 33	...	...	...
1 30	2 0	Rigi-Unterstetten...	7 40	9 52	12 0	2 47	4 17	6 40	...	...	...
2 50	3 60	Rigi-Scheideck...arr	8 5	10 15	12 25	3 10	4 40	7 5	...	...	...

	†					‡
Rigi-Scheideck dep	8 a15	10a20	1 p15	3 p15	5 p10	7 p15
Rigi-Unterstetten...	8 35	10 39	1 34	3 34	5 29	7 35
Rigi-First	8 44	10 45	1 40	3 40	5 35	7 44
Rigi-Kaltbad ...arr	8 50	10 50	1 45	3 45	5 40	7 50

†—From 10th July until 10th Sept. ‡—Until 10th Sept.

WINKELN and APPENZELL.

‡—Not on Sunday. *—7.16 p.m. on Sundays in July & August.

E.M.		a.m.	a.m.	a.m.	a.m.	p.m.	p.m.	p.m.	p.m.	p.m.	p.m.	p.m.	p.m.
—	Winkeln dep	7 16	7‡45	8 40	1036	1 20	2 27	...	4 0	4 43	6 41	8 6	9 50
2¼	Herisau	7 38	8 15	9 19	1050	1 34	2 37	3 21	4 10	4 55	6 55	8 18	1010
5¼	Waldstatt	7 50	8 36	9 32	11 2	1 46	—	3 36	—	5 7	7 7	8 52	—
9¼	Urnasch	8 5	9 7	9 47	1117	2 1	...	3 51	...	5 22	7 22	9 7	...
11¼	Jakobsbad ...	8 15	9 19	9 57	1127	2 11	...	4 1	...	5 32	7 32	9 17	...
12¾	Gonten	8 20	9 33	10 2	1132	2 16	...	4 6	...	5 37	7 37	9 22	...
14	Gontenbad ...	8 25	9 38	10 7	1137	2 21	...	4 11	...	5 42	7 42	9 27	...
15¾	Appenzell ar	8 33	9 46	1015	1145	2 29	...	4 19	...	5 50	7 50	9 35	...

		a.m.	a.m.	a.m.	p.m.			p.m.	p.m.	p.m.	p.m.	p.m
Appenzell dp	...	6 33	9 15	1117	1215	...	...	2 50	4 50	5 58	8 5	8*57
Gontenbad ...	...	6 44	9 26	1128	1226	...	...	3 0	5 1	...	8 16	9 8
Gonten	...	6 49	9 31	1133	1232	...	...	3 5	5 6	6 10	8 21	9 13
Jakobsbad ...	...	6 54	9 36	1138	1237	...	...	3 10	5 11	...	8 26	9 18
Urnasch	...	7 4	9 46	1148	1250	...	...	3 20	5 21	6 23	8 36	9 28
Waldstatt ...	a.m.	7 19	10 1	12 3	1 9	p.m.	p.m.	3 35	5 36	6 35	8 51	9 43
Herisau	6 58	8 17	1020	1220	1 25	2 9	3 20	3 50	6 0	6 58	9 6	9 54
Winkeln 268	7 8	8 27	1030	1230	...	2 19	3 30	4 0	6 0	7 8	9 16	...

RORSCHACH and HEIDEN.

‡—In July and August only.

					‡			
Rorschach Hafen .dep	7 a7	9 a6	11a19	2 p3	3‡p5	4p31	7 p7	8p54
Rorschach Bahnhof...	7 18	9 22	11 27	2 12	3 18	4 44	7 17	9 2
Wienachten	7 39	9 43	11 48	2 33	3 37	5 5	7 39	9 23
Schwendi	7 45	9 49	11 54	2 39	3 43	5 11	7 45	9 29
Heiden ....arr	7 55	9 59	12 4	2 49	3 53	5 21	7 55	9 39

					‡			
Heiden ....dep	5a28	8 a5	10a18	12p15	2p15	3 p54	5 p44	7 p23
Schwendi	5 39	8 16	10 29	12 26	2 26	4 5	5 55	7 34
Wienachten	5 45	8 22	10 35	12 32	2 33	4 11	6 1	7 40
Rorschach Bhf.	6 5	8 42	10 55	12 52	2 56	4 30	6 22	8 0
Rorschach Hafen..arr	6 16	8 49	11 2	1 2	3 3	4 43	6 30	8 12

WINTERTHUR and WALD.

						‡		
Winterthur dep	6a24	8a31	1040	1p27	4p9	6‡33	7p2	9p18
Sennhof-Kyburg	6 42	8 49	1057	1 46	426	7 0	720	9 36
Zell	6 58	9 3	1111	2 3	440	7 19	735	9 51
Wyla	7 8	9 13	1121	2 15	450	7 36	745	10 2
Bauma (256)	7 26	9 31	1140	2 39	5 6	7 53	8 6	1015
Gibswil	7 50	9 54	12 3	3 1	528	...	828	—
Wald 268A ...arr	8 1	10 5	1215	3 13	540	...	840	...

									‡
Wald ....dep	...	5a50	...	8a51	1220	2p35	4p25	639	8p10
Gibswil	a.m.	6 5	am	9 6	1233	2 50	4 39	653	8 34
Bauma	4 55	6 26	814	9 33	1252	3 11	5 3	712	9 10
Wyla	5 8	6 38	827	9 47	1 5	3 24	5 16	723	—
Zell	5 18	6 48	836	9 57	113	3 33	5 25	735	...
Sennhof-Kyburg	5 34	7 3	850	1013	1 25	3 45	5 39	752	...
Winterthur 262	5 52	7 21	9 6	1032	1 39	3 59	5 54	8 7	...

‡—Not on Sat. and Sun.

BAUMA and UERIKON.

Bauma ....dep	...	6a40	9a29	11a37	2p36	5 p4	6p35
Hinwil	5a49	7 10	9 58	12 13	3 5	5 34	7 4
Bubikon	6 14	7 28	1010	12 30	3 17	5 47	7 22
Uerikon 262B arr	6 45	7 56	1029	12 49	3 36	6 6	7 44

Uerikon ....dep	7 a5	8a13	10a45	1 p8	3p49	7p15	8p11
Bubikon	7 28	8 38	11 13	1 38	4 14	7 43	8 34
Hinwil	7 44	8 54	11 33	2 0	4 30	8 3	8 49
Bauma (256) arr	8 13	9 24	12 5	2 33	5 0	8 35	...

CHAUX DE FONDS and LES PONTS.

Chaux de Fonds ...dep	7 a7	9 a20	2 p5	5 p15	7 p38	9p55
Sagne	7 42	9 55	2 40	5 50	8 13	1030
Les Ponts ....arr	8 1	10 14	2 59	6 9	8 32	1049

Les Ponts ....dep	5 a20	8a12	1 p0	3 p32	6p31	8p50	...
Sagne	5 41	8 33	1 21	3 53	6 52	9 11	...
Chaux de Fonds 265 arr	6 14	9 6	1 54	4 26	7 25	9 44	...

St. GALLEN and APPENZELL.

St. Gallen...dep	7 a3	8a52	10a58	1p19	2 p13	4 p7	6p11	7 p5	8p16	10 p5
Teufen	7 33	9 27	11 33	1 49	2 48	4 40	6 46	7 48	8 51	10 39
Gais §	7 59	9 56	12 2	2 15	3 17	5 5	7 14	8 20	9 20	11 6
Appenzell ..arr	8 16	10 14	12 20	2 32	3 35	5 22	7 32	...	9 38	...
Appenzell ....dep	...	6 a27	9 a3	...	12p32	1 p52	3p50	...	5p45	8 p1
Gais §	5a45	6 50	9 24	10a47	12 55	2 17	4 13	5 p3	6 6	8 25
Teufen	6 12	7 18	9 50	11 15	1 23	2 46	4 41	5 30	6 29	8 53
St. Gallen (268)	6 42	7 48	1020	11 43	1 53	3 16	5 11	6 6	6 58	9 23

§—Electric line from Gais to Altstatten.

Sissach and Gelterkinden.

(In 15 minutes). FARES, 40c., 25c.

From Sissach 6.10, 7.10, 8.11, 8.55, 11 20 a.m. 1.10, 3.38, 5.8, 6.7, 6.54, 7.44, 8.20, 9.17 p.m.

From Gelterkinden 5.45, 6.42, 7.50, 8.30, 10.25 a.m., 12.19, 2.52, 4.38, 5.45, 6.28, 7.21, 8.1, 8.56 p.m.

WADENSWEIL and ARTH-GOLDAU.—Schweizerische Sudostbahn.

Wadensweil dep	6 a5	7 a8	9a50	11a52	1 p9	3 p8	4p15	6p12	8p11
Samstagern	6 24	7 24	1011	12 10	1 25	3 24	4 34	6 29	8 29
Schindellegi	6 32	7 32	1019	12 18	1 33	3 32	4 42	6 38	8 37
Biberbrücke arr	6 39	7 39	1027	12 25	1 41	3 40	4 50	6 45	8 45
Einsiedeln arr	6 57	8 2	1050	12 44	1 55	3 55	5 3	6 59	9 0
Einsiedeln dep	6 26	7 25	9 38	12 10	1 28	3 20	—	6 33	—
Biberbrücke dep	6 41	7 40	1029	12 28	1 42	3 42	...	6 48	...
Rothenthurm ...	6 59	7 58	1047	12 46	2 1	4 1	...	7 6	...
Sattel-Aegeri ...	7 11	8 10	11 0	12 58	2 13	4 13	...	7 18	...
Steinerberg	7 23	8 22	1112	1 10	2 26	4 26	...	7 30	...
Arth-Goldau arr	7 30	8 29	1120	1 17	2 33	4 33	...	7 37	...

Arth-Goldau dp	...	7a46	9 a3	11a39	1p23	3p28	...	6p19	7p48
Steinerberg	...	7 55	9 11	11 47	1 32	3 36	...	6 27	7 57
Sattel-Aegeri ...	...	8 11	9 24	11 59	1 45	3 49	...	6 39	8 11
Rothenthurm ...	...	8 24	9 37	12 11	2 0	4 2	...	6 51	8 26
Biberbrücke ar	...	8 41	9 54	12 28	2 17	4 18	...	7 8	8 44
Einsiedeln ar	a m	8 58	10 50	12 44	2 35	4 35	p m	7 30	9 0
Einsiedeln dp	5 45	8 20	10 14	12 10	2 2	4 5	5 18	6 33	8 30
Biberbrücke dep	5 57	8 42	10 36	12 32	2 18	4 19	5 31	7 9	8 45
Schindellegi ...	6 5	8 50	10 48	12 40	2 26	4 27	5 39	7 17	8 53
Samstagern	6 22	8 59	11 4	12 48	2 34	4 35	5 47	7 25	9 1
Wadensweil arr	6 40	9 15	11 20	1 2	2 50	4 50	6 3	7 40	9 18

Rapperswil ...dep	6a52	9a38	11a35	12p29	2p52	5p33	8 p0	...	...	...	...
Pfaffikon	7 1	9 50	11 45	12 48	3 2	5 48	8 9	...	...	...	...
Samstagern	7 24	1011	12 4	1 13	3 24	6 18	8 29	...	...	...	...
Biberbrücke ...arr	7 39	1027	12 18	1 31	3 40	6 37	8 45	...	...	...	...
Biberbrücke...dep	5a57	...	8a42	9a55	12p32	2p25	4p19	7 p9	8 p45	...	...
Samstagern	6 12	a.m.	8 58	10 10	12 49	2 41	4 37	7 26	9 2	...	...
Pfaffikon	6*32	6 38	9 18	10 33	1 13	3 4	5 4	7 49	9 25	...	...
Rapperswil ...arr	..	6 46	9 26	10 41	1 21	3 12	5 12	7 57	9 33	...	...

*—Runs until 31st August.

INTERLAKEN, LAUTERBRUNNEN, MURREN, and GRINDELWALD.

(Berner Oberland Bahnen.)

E.M		a.m.	a.m.	a.m.	a.m.	a.m.	a.m.	p.m.	p.m.	p.m.	p.m.	p.m.
	Interlaken (Bahnhof) ...dep	6 40	7 57	8 39	10*8	10 38	11 37	12§45	2 2	3 45	6 18	8§22
—	Interlaken (Ost)	7 4	8 10	9 10	1023	10 50	11 50	12 55	2 14	4 6	6 30	8 33
2	Wilderswyl	7 13	8 19	9 19	...	10 59	12 0	1 3	2 23	4 15	6 39	8 42
5	Zweilütschinen .... arr	7 26	8 32	9 33	...	11 13	12 14	1 16	2 37	4 28	6 53	8 55
	Zweilütschinen .... dep	7 29	8 34	9 37	...	11 15	12 17	1 19	2 40	4 31	6 58	8 58
7¾	Lauterbrunnen ....arr	7 45	8 50	9 54	1057	11 31	12 34	1 35	2 55	4 48	7 15	9 14

*—July and August only.

§—Runs until 15th Sept.

		a.m.	a.m.	a.m.	a.m.	a.m.	a.m.	p.m.	p.m.	p.m.	p.m.	p.m.	p.m.	p.m	p.m.		
...	Lauterbrunnen ....dep	6 34	8 2	9 13	...	10 18	11§55	12 54	...	3 10	4 58	...	...	6 33	8 35	...	...
...	Zweilütschinen .... arr	6 50	8 19	9 30	...	10 35	12 12	1 10	...	3 26	5 15	...	...	6 50	8 50	...	...
	Zweilütschinen .... dep	6 56	—	—	9 35	10 42	12 16	1 16	2 38	3 29	—	5§18	5 28	6 56	8 56	...	...
...	Wilderswyl	7 11	...	...	9 53	10 57	12 32	1 30	2 52	3 45	...	5 31	5 41	7 13	9 11	...	...
...	Interlaken (Ost) ....arr	7 18	...	...	10 0	11 4	12 39	1 37	3 0	3 52	...	5 38	5 48	7 21	9 18	...	...
...	Interlaken (Bahnhof) ...arr	7 30	...	...	10 30	11 20	1 7	1 52	3 23	4 13	...	6 7	6 7	7 35	9 29	...	...

	a.m.	a.m.	a.m	a.m.	p.m.	p.m.	p.m.	p.m.	p.m.
Zweilütschinen dep	7 32	8 37	9 40	11§18	1220	2 43	4 34	7 1	9 *1
Lütschenthal.........	7 44	8 48	9 52	1129	1231	2 54	4 45	7 13	9 12
Burglauenen.........	8 0	9 4	10 9	1145	1248	3 10	5 2	7 29	9 28
Grindelwald......arr	8 19	9 24	1028	12 3	1 7	3 29	5 20	7 49	9 46

	a.m.	a.m.	a.m	p.m.	p.m	p.m.	p.m	p.m
Grindelwald ...dep	6 8	8*40	9 50	1228	1 52	4 35	5 58	8 9
Burglauenen	6 28	9 1	1012	1249	2 11	5 0	6 21	8 28
Lütschenthal	6 42	9 15	1026	1 3	2 25	5 14	6 35	8 42
Zweilütschinen arr	6 53	9 27	1038	1 13	2 35	5 25	6 47	8 52

E.M.																		
	Lauterbrunnen......dep	6a10	7§a0	8 a0	9 a5	10a13	11§a10	11a40	12p45	1p50	3 p5	3*p35	5p10	7p30	...	...	...	...
3½	Murren...............arr	7 0	7 50	8 55	10 0	11 5	12 5	12 35	1 35	2 45	3 55	4 25	6 0	8 20	...	...	...	...
...	Murren ....dep	5a40	7§a25	8 a0	9 a5	10§a40	11a40	1p50	2*p55	3*p30	4 p0	5p35	7 p0	...	...	...	...	...
...	Lauterbrunnen ......arr	6 30	8 20	8 55	10 0	11 30	12 35	2 45	3 55	4 25	4 50	6 25	7 50	...	...	...	...	...

E.M																			
	Lauterbrunnen dep	6 a40	...	7 a54	9 a6	10 a7	11*a3	...	11a37	...	12p40	...	1§p56	3 p3	4p55	6p30	7p23	...	...
2¼	Wengen	7 13	...	8 27	9 44	10 42	:..	...	12 10	...	1 15	...	2 30	3 37	5 28	7 0	7 53	8*p0	...
5¼	Wengernalp	7 51	...	9 1	10 24	11 23	...	...	12 44	...	1 56	...	3 19	4 11	6 8	*	—	8 38	...
6½	Scheidegg...	8 7	8 a31	9 17	11 1	11 39	12 15	12p40	1 0	1§p41	2 12	3 p1	3 35	4 35	6 24	—	...	8 54	...
11¾	Grindelwald ......arr	...	9 48	...	12 11	..	...	1 49	...	2 51	...	4 19	...	5 52	7 58	...	...	...	...

Grindelwald ....dep	...	6a50	*	8 a24	...	...	9 a30	...	10a43	..	1p30	2p55	4p26	..
Scheidegg	...	8 9	7a33	9 43	8 a43	9 a21	10 50	11a7	12 2	1p40	3 3	5 5	5 44	7p10
Wengernalp	...	—	7 50	—	9 0	9 38	—	1124	—	1 57	3 29	5 22	—	7 27
Wengen	6 a0	...	8 23	8 a33	9 36	10 14	...	12 7	...	2 32	4 8	5 58	...	8 2
Lauterbrunnen........arr	6 30	...	...	9 3	10 6	10 39	...	1237	...	3 2	4 38	6 28	...	8 32

*—In July and Aug. only.

§—Until 15th Sept.

SCHYNIGE PLATTE RAILWAY.

	a.m	a.m.	a.m	a.m.	a m	p.m	p.m.	p.m.
Interlaken Ost...dep	7 *4	8 10	9 10	10§50	1150	2 14	4 6	6*30
Wilderswyl-Gsteig ..	7 15	8 20	9 20	11 0	12 1	2 25	4 16	6 40
Breitlauenen	8 3	9 6	10 8	11 47	1249	3 9	5 4	7 28
Schynige Platte..arr	8 25	9 27	1030	12 9	1 11	3 30	5 26	7 50

	a.m.	a.m.	a.m.	p.m.	p.m.	p m.	p.m.	p.m.
Schynige Platte dep	8*43	9 45	11§25	1220	2 40	4 30	6 3	8 *6
Breitlauenen	9 9	1011	11 50	1246	3 5	4 58	6 29	8 29
Wilderswyl-Gsteig	9 53	1057	12 32	1 30	3 45	5 41	7 13	9 11
Interlaken Ost...arr	10 0	11 4	12 39	1 37	3 52	5 48	7 21	9 18

*—July and August only. §—Runs until 15th September.

JUNGFRAU RAILWAY.

[A—In July and August only.

	a.m.	a.m.	a.m.	a.m.	a.m.	p.m.	p.m.	p.m.	p.m.	p.m.	p.m.	p.m.	p.m.					
Scheidegg ....dep	8 16	9 22	9 45	10 57	11 45	12 20	12 24	1 5	2 15	3 40	4 30	5 49	7 15	...	...	...	...	...
Gletscher	8 35	9 37	10 3	11 15	12 5	...	12 39	1 25	2 32	3 58	4 48	6 4	7 30	...	...	...	...	...
Eigerwand	9 0	—	10 28	11 41	12 29	A	—	1 48	2 54	4 20	5 10	—	—	...	...	...	...	...
Eismeer ....arr	9 10	...	10 38	11 51	12 39	1 2	...	1 58	3 4	4 30	5 20	...	...	...	...	...	...	...
Jungfraujoch.........arr	9 35	...	11 0	12 14	1 0	1 45	...	2 18	3 24	4 48	5 40	...	...	...	...	...	...	...

			a.m.	a.m.		p.m.	p.m.	p.m.	p.m.	p.m.	p.m.	p.m.						
Jungfraujoch ......dep	...	...	9 50	11 12	...	12 15	1 2	1 47	2 50	3 52	5 10	6 5	...	...	...	...	...	...
Eismeer	...	...	10 9	11 31	...	12 41	1 17	2 7	3 15	4 10	5 32	6 22	...	...	...	...	...	...
Eigerwand	a.m.	a.m.	10 21	11 42	p.m.	12 53	—	2 18	3 27	4 21	5 43	6 33	...	...	...	...	...	...
Gletscher	8 0	10 5	10 39	12 1	12 42	1 12	...	2 37	4 13	4 46	6 5	6 51	...	...	...	...	...	...
Scheidegg ....arr	8 15	10 20	10 54	12 16	12 57	1 36	...	2 52	4 28	5 1	6 20	7 6	...	...	...	...	...	...

HERZOGENBUCHSEE, SOLOTHURN, and LYSS.

Herzogenbuchsee ...dep	...	6a18	8a35	10a20	1p10	4p10	5p50	8p20
Subigen	...	6 32	8 51	10 34	1 24	4 25	6 4	8 36
Derendingen	...	6 38	8 57	10 41	1 29	4 30	6 9	8 41
Neu-Solothurn arr	a.m.	6 44	9 4	10 47	1 35	4 36	6 14	8 47
Neu-Solothurn dep	4 40	7 6	—	11 35	1 55	—	6 18	9 38
Buren	5 16	7 38	...	12 7	2 26	...	6 48	1010
Busswyl	5 31	7 50	...	12 21	2 38	...	6 59	1023
Lyss (265) ...arr	5 42	7 55	...	12 26	2 43	...	7 4	1028

Lyss ...dep	...	6 a4	9 a6	...	1 p6	3p47	...	7 p22	8p40
Busswyl	...	6 10	9 11	...	1 12	3 53	...	7 27	8 48
Buren	...	6 22	9 22	...	1 25	4 4	...	7 39	9 4
Neu Solothurn arr	a.m.	6 50	9 49	p.m.	1 55	4 31	...	8 8	9 38
Neu Solothurn dep	5 15	7 8	1022	1210	2 18	4 36	6p23	8 58	—
Derendingen	5 21	7 14	1028	1216	2 24	4 42	6 30	9 4	...
Subingen	5 26	7 19	1033	1222	2 30	4 47	6 36	9 9	...
Herzogenb. 257 arr	5 40	7 32	1046	1237	2 46	5 0	6 51	9 22	...

BERNE and AARAU.

	2&3	1,2,3	2&3	1,2,3	2&3	1,2,3	1,2,3	1,2,3	1,2,3	2&3	1&2	1,2,3	2&3	1,2,3	1,2,3	2&3	2&3	1,2,3	1,2,3	2&3	2&3	2&3
		a.m.	a.m.	a.m.	a.m.	a.m.	a.m.	a.m.	p.m	p.m.	p.m.	p.m.	p.m.	p.m.	p.m.	p.m.	p.m	p.m.	p.m.	p.m.	p.m	p.m.
Berne ...dep	...	5 0	5 5	6 50	7 10	9 22	9 37	1045	1222	1233	1 40	2 14	3 55	5 5	5 40	6 0	7 †3	8 20	8 40	...	9 5	11*22
Zollikofen	...	...	5 18	7 2	7 21	...	9 49	RC	...	1246	...	2 26	4 8	...	...	6 15	7 15	8 32	...	...	9 28	11 35
Schonbuhl	...	...	5 25	...	7 33	...	9 56	...	RC	1253	...	2 33	4 16	...	...	6 21	7 22	...	...	...	9 38	11 41
Burgdorf	...	5 28	5 47	7 19	7 59	...	1018	1112	...	1 21	...	2 55	4 38	5 31	...	6 44	7 40	8 51	9 8	...	1015	12 0
Herzogenbuchsee	a.m.	5 45	6 15	7 36	8 31	...	1048	1129	A	1 50	RC	3 21	5 5	5 48	RC	7 9	—	9 8	9 26	...	1049	
Langenthal	5†38	5 55	6 32	7 46	8 54	...	11 5	1138	...	2 7	...	3 37	5 20	5 58	...	7 24	...	9 20	9 37	9†43	11 7	*—On Sun. and Wed. only.
Murgenthal	5 51	...	6 44	...	9 6	...	1117	...	...	2 19	...	3 49	5 32	6 6	...	7 37	...	...	...	9 59	1124	
Aarburg	6 6	...	6 58	8 3	9 21	...	1132	...	...	2 35	...	4 3	5 47	6 16	...	7 52	1,2,3	9 40	9 54	10 21	1146	
Olten (258) arr	a.m. 6 13	6 18	7 5	8 9	9 28	1029	1139	12 0	1 30	2 41	2 50	4 10	5 54	6 22	6 48	7 59	p.m.	9 46	10 0	10 30	1155	
,, ...dep 5 5	—	6 35	7†25	8 23	9 37	1037	1144	12 9	—	...	3 2	4 20	6†18	6 30	6 58	8 10	9 38	—	1010	10 43	...	
Aarau ...arr 5 35	...	6 52	7†59	8 41	9 59	1051	12 3	1224	...	...	3 16	4 36	6†39	6 47	7 12	8 32	9 53	...	1024	11 5	...	
ZURICH **262** arr 7a34	...	8 a2	...	9a52	1136	1143	1 p3	1p20	...	...	4 p8	5p44	7p46	7p46	8 p5	1050	1050	...	1118	...	...	

Extra.—Olten to Aarau, 6†0, 9.0, 11.55 a.m., 12†25, 1.12, 4.42, 5†35, 7.12, 8†55 p.m.

A—Until 30th September between Olten and Berne. RC—Restaurant Car attached.

	2&3	2&3	2&3	1,2,3	1,2,3	1,2,3	2&3	1,2,3	1,2,3	2&3	1&2	1&2	1,2,3	2&3	1,2,3	2&3	1,2,3	1,2,3	2&3	2&3	1,2,3	1,2,3
ZURICH ...dep	...	...	4a52	6a27	7 a5	7a23	8 a22	1055	...	...	...	1p45	...	1p59	3p24	4p10	5p55	6p15	...	7p36	9 p20	1157
	a.m.	a.m.	a.m.	a.m.	a.m.	a.m.	a.m.	a.m.		p.m.	p.m.	p.m	p.m.	p.m.	p.m	p.m.	p.m.	p.m.		p.m.	p.m.	ngt
Aarau ...dep	...	...	6 29	7 44	7 58	8 14	9 52	1149	...	12†15	...	2 36	...	3 30	4 16	6 0	7 1	7 12	...	9 10	10 17	1250
Olten ...arr	...	...	6 50	8 5	8 12	8 30	10 15	12 5	p.m.	1 0	...	2 50	...	3 52	4 30	6 23	7 17	7 30	p.m.	9 36	10 33	1 4
,, ...dep	4 25	4 55	7 0	8 10	8 20	8 53	10 35	1217	12 25	1 40	2 43	3 2	3 10	4 52	4 46	6‡30	7 28	7 38	8 13	—	10 47	1 15
Aarburg	4 33	5 5	7 9	...	...	9 0	10 43	...	12 31	1 47	...	...	3 18	5 0	...	6 37	...	7 45	8 21	...	10 54	1 22
Murgenthal	4 48	5 26	7 24	...	...	9 11	10 59	...	12 41	2 1	...	...	3 32	5 15	...	6 51	A	7 55	8 36	...	11 4	...
Langenthal	5 5	5 49	7 42	...	...	9 23	11 18	...	12 53	2 16	A	...	3 48	5 32	...	7 8	7 54	8 7	8 52	...	11 15	1 42
Herzogenbuchsee	5 19	6 7	7 57	...	...	9 35	11 34	RC	1 3	2 30	...	...	4 2	5 46	...	7 20	8 4	8 17	9 6	...	11 24	1 51
Burgdorf	5 53	6 50	8 30	...	...	9 59	12 8	...	1 28	3 1	...	...	4 34	6 20	5 34	—	8 26	8 38	9 42	...	11 43	2 10
Schonbuhl	6 13	7 13	8 51	...	...	...	12 32	...	...	3 23	...	...	4 55	6 42	...	...	...	RC	10 7	...	...	...
Zollikofen	6 21	7 22	9 0	...	...	...	12 42	...	1 49	3 32	...	...	5 5	6 51	...	...	...	8 55	1017	...	...	...
Berne (265) ...arr	6 33	7 35	9 12	9 20	9 32	1027	12 55	1 32	2 0	3 44	3 55	4 12	5 13	7 3	6 0	...	8 53	9 5	1030	...	12 8	2 35

Extra—Aarau to Olten, 5.57, 11.20 a.m., 2.4, 5†45 p.m. †—Weekdays only. ‡—Not on Sat. nor Sun.

BERNE and THUN.

*—Sun. only. ‡—On Sun. only. §—From the opening of the Lotschberg line.

Dist		a.m.	a.m.	a.m.	a.m	a.m.	a.m	a.m.	a.m.	a.m.	a.m.	p.m	p.m.	p.m.	p.m.	p.m.	p.m	p.m.	p.m.	p.m.	ng't	
—	**Berne** ...dep	5‡15	5 20	6 17	6‡45	7 22	8 0	8 50	9 32	9 50	1040	1 0	1 53	2 22	4 26	5 45	6 18	7 23	8 33	9 38	1215	...
4¾	Gumlingen	...	5 35	...	...	7 37	...	9 2	...	...	1055	...	...	2 37	...	6 0	...	...	8 48	9 53	...	...
9½	Munsingen	5 37	5 51	A	7 5	7 51	...	9 11	...	...	11 9	§	...	2 51	...	6 15	...	7 44	9 3	10 10	§	...
13¾	Kiesen	...	6 4	...	...	8 1	...	...	...	...	1120	...	...	3 2	...	6 28	...	...	9 15	10 22	...	...
18½	**Thun**	6 2	6 30	6 55	7 28	8 15	8 38	9 28	1010	1027	1134	1 37	2 25	3 16	5 7	6 40	6 55	8 2	9 27	10 37	1253	...
19½	**Scherzligen** ...arr	...	6 34	...	7 31	8 47	...	9†36	...	1030	1145	...	2 33	3 25	5 10	7 8	...	8 11	9†36	...	...	...
35¾	INTERLAKEN 267 arr	6 50	7 52	7 35	8 28	10 0	9 28	10 2†	1055	1123	1240	...	3 25	4 36	5 58	8 15	7 45	9 5	10†43	...	...	...

	a.m.	a.m.	a.m.	a.m	a.m.	a.m	a.m	a.m.	p.m.	p.m	p.m	p.m	p.m.	p.m	p.m.	p.m.	p.m.	p.m.	p.m.	p.m.	p.m	p.m.
INTERLAKEN ...dep	...	...	...	6 35	7 40	10 5	1043	11 35	1 30	2 0	3 38	...	5 0	5 58	6 3	6 15	...	7 45	...	...	9 40	1030
Scherzligen ...dep	...	...	...	7 38	8 25	11 18	...	12 25	...	3 6	4 27	...	6 6	...	...	7 1	...	8 39	...	...	...	...
Thun	5 23	5§55	6 35	7 50	8 33	11 45	11*4	12 35	2 35	3 16	4 36	5 0	6 15	6 50	7 0	7 10	7*47	8 47	9 12	9 46	1023	1125
Kiesen	5 36	...	6 50	8 3	...	11 58	RC	...	...	3 29	...	...	6 31	...	...	...	8 1	...	9 24	...	...	...
Munsingen	5 48	...	7 1	8 18	8 50	12 11	B	...	...	3 40	...	§	6 46	†	‡	...	8 12	...	9 34	§	A	‡
Gumlingen	6 3	...	7 15	8 35	...	12 28	...	...	...	3 54	...	...	7 3	...	...	...	8 26	...	9 49	...	...	...
Berne ...arr	6 17	6 28	7 30	8 50	9 7	12 42	12 8	1 8	3 8	4 7	5 12	5 32	7 18	7 23	7 35	7 43	8 40	9 20	10 3	1018	1057	1157

A—Train de Luxe, runs from 9th July until 15th Sept. B—Until 30th Sept. †—Until 15th Sept.

AARAU and ZOFINGEN.

†—Weekdays only.

	a.m.	a.m.	a.m.	p.m.	p.m.	p.m	p.m.	p.m.
Aarau ...dep	7 1	7†20	1020	12 6	2 52	6 23	7 6	1033
Suhr	7 11	7 52	1033	1217	3 3	6 35	7 17	1043
Entfelden	7 17	8 25	1040	1225	3 10	6 42	7 23	1049
Kölliken	7 23	8 46	1046	1231	3 16	6 48	7 29	1054
Zofingen 258 arr	7 41	9 31	11 5	1248	3 37	7 6	7 48	1113

	a.m.	a.m.	a.m.	p.m.	p.m.	p.m.	p.m.	
Zofingen dep	5 45	7 57	1142	1 7	4 32	7 57	9 31	...
Kölliken	6 7	8 15	12 2	1 28	4 49	8 15	9 48	...
Entfelden	6 12	8 21	12 8	1 33	4 54	8 20	9 53	...
Suhr	6 19	8 27	1215	1 40	5 0	8 26	9 59	...
Aarau 257 arr	6 27	8 37	1222	1 50	5 8	8 34	10 7	...

AARAU and ARTH-GOLDAU.

†—Weekdays only.] *—Earlier on Sunday.

	2&3	2&3	2&3	2&3	1,2,3	2&3	2&3	2&3	1,2,3	2&3
	a.m.	a.m	a.m	a.m	p.m	p.m.	p.m.	p.m.	p.m	p.m.
Aarau ...dep	4 50	7 0	8†12	9 36	1 10	2 2	3 24	5 22	8 37	1031
Rupperswell	5 1	7 8	8 23	9 45	1 19	2 14	3 32	5 31	8 46	1040
Lenzburg arr	5 8	7 3	8 34	9 50	1 25	2 26	3 37	5 37	8 53	1045
Lenzburg dep	5 10	7 15	8 41	9 52	1 28	2 37	3 42	5 39	8 55	1046
Hendschiken	5 17	7 21	8 50	9 58	1 35	2 48	3 49	5 45	9 1	1051
Wohlen arr	5 31	7 32	9 6	10 9	1 46	3 3	4 0	5 55	9 12	11 1
Wohlen dep	5 36	7 37	9 15	10 12	1 56	3 19	—	6 0	9 15	—
Muri	5 58	7 53	9 39	10 28	2 11	3 40	...	6 17	9 30	...
Rothkreuz ...arr	6 40	8 23	1020	11 3	2 41	4*24	...	6 49	10 4	...
LUCERNE (260) arr	7a33	9 a8	...	11a42	3p14	4p52	...	7p35	11p12	...
Rothkreuz ...dep	6 4	8 26	1030	11 6	2 51	4*36	...	6 53	1110	...
Immensee	7 0	8 39	1049	11 16	3 4	4*55	...	7 5	1123	...
Arth-Goldau 259 arr	7 18	8 51	1110	11 27	3 17	5*16	...	7 17	1135	...

		2&3	1,2,3	2&3	2&3	2&3	2&3	1,2,3	2&3	2&3
		a.m.	a.m.	a.m.	a.m.	p.m.	p.m.	p.m	p.m.	p.m.
Arth-Goldau dp		4†42	6 3	8 3	9 12	1210	2 †2	4 2	5 18	8 35
Immensee		4 57	6 14	8 16	9 27	1223	2 22	4 14	5 38	8 46
Rothkreuz arr		5 11	6 23	8 26	9 41	1234	2 38	4 25	5 50	8 54
LUCERNE dep		...	5a55	7a35	...	1142	2p16	4 p5	5p17	8p20
Rothkreuz dep		5 13	6 25	8 28	9 45	1237	2 53	4 31	6 3	9 0
Muri ...2&3		5 59	6 54	8 57	1027	1 9	3 39	4 58	6 52	9 29
Wohlen arr	a.m.	6 16	7 6	9 10	1044	1 22	3 56	5 9	7 11	9 41
Wohlen dep	5 50	6 20	7 9	9 12	1048	1 25	4 0	5 11	7 20	9 43
Hendsch'en	6 1	6 36	7 19	9 23	11 8	1 36	4 15	5 21	7 39	9 53
Lenzburg arr	6 6	6 44	7 23	9 28	1110	1 40	4 22	5 26	7 47	9 57
Lenzburg dep	6 7	6 50	7 24	9 29	1118	1 42	4 27	5 27	8 *0	9 58
R'p'swell	6 18	6 58	7 29	9 34	1126	1 46	4 34	5 32	8 *8	10 3
Rau (257)	6 21	7 10	7 36	9 42	1140	1 55	4 45	5 40	8*22	1010

MARTIGNY and ARGENTIERE.

Greenwich Time between Valorsine and Argentière.

	a.m.	a.m.	a.m.	a.m.	p.m.	p.m.	p.m.	p.m.
Martigny-Gare ...dep	6 45	9 7	9 28	1158	2 35	4 58	5 15	9 ‡5
" **Ville**........	6 50	9 12	9 33	12 3	2 40	5 3	5 20	9 10
Vernayaz..................	7 7	...	9 50	1218	2 57	...	5 37	9 25
Salvan	7 42	...	1025	1253	3 32	...	6 11	9 58
Les Marécottes	7 50	...	1033	1 1	3 40	A	6 19	10 6
Finhaut	8 13	...	1056	1 23	4 3	...	6 43	1028
Le Chatelard-Trient	8 45	1036	1150	1 44	4 44	6 34	7 40	1045
Valorsine......... arr	8 56	1047	12 1	1 55	4 55	6 45	7 51	—
Valorsine......... dep	8 11	9 57	1120	1 20	4 12	5 57	7 5	...
Montroc	8 30	1017	1139	1 39	4 31	6 16	7 24	...
Argentière ....arr	8 42	1029	1154	1 51	4 43	6 28	7 36	...
CHAMONIX 61B arr	9 10	1059	1224	2 22	5 13	6 58	8 10	...

A—Until 15th September.

CHAMONIX ...dep	4a26	...	...	6a55	9a15	11a0	12 0	...	3 p0	4p11
	A	a.m.	a.m.	a.m.	a.m.	a.m.	p.m.		p.m.	p.m.
Argentière ...dep	5 0	...	...	7 26	9 45	1130	1231	...	3 31	4 44
Montroc	5 12	A	...	7 38	9 57	1142	1243	...	3 43	4 56
Valorsine ... arr	5 29	...	...	7 55	1015	1159	1 0	p.m.	4 0	5 13
Valorsine ... dep	—	6 37	...	9 10	1130	1 10	—	2 10	5 10	6 23
Le Chatelard-T. ...	...	6 47	6 52	9 33	12 0	1 40	...	2 49	5 50	7 0
Finhaut	...	—	7 10	9 52	1218	1 58	...	...	6 11	7 18
Les Marécottes......	...	...	7 31	1013	1239	2 19	...	A	6 32	7 39
Salvan	a.m.	...	7 39	1022	1250	2 27	...	...	6 41	7 47
Vernayaz	6 20	...	8 10	1053	1 21	2 58	...	...	7 12	8 18
Martigny-Ville ...	6 35	...	8 25	1111	1 37	3 16	...	4 14	7 28	8 34
" Gare arr	6 39	...	8 29	1115	1 41	3 20	...	4 18	7 32	8 38

‡—In July and August only.

ST. MORITZ and PONTRESINA.

		a.m.		a.m.	a.m.		a.m.	a.m.	a.m.			a.m.	a.m.	p.m.	p.m.	p.m.	p.m	p.m.			
St. Moritz ....dep	...	6 45	...	8 15	8‡30	...	9 5	10‡10	1050	...	...	11‡20	11 55	12‡25	1 5	2 20	2‡45	3 5	...	...	...
Celerina	...	6 50	...	8 20	8 35	...	9 10	10 15	1055	...	...	11 25	12 0	12 30	1 10	2 25	2 50	3 11	...	...	...
Samaden .... arr	a.m.	6 54	a.m.	8 24	8 39	a.m.	9 14	10 19	1059	a.m.	a.m.	11 29	12 4	12 34	1 14	2 29	2 54	3 15	p.m	p m.	...
Samaden .... dep	5 5	7 11	8 ‡6	8‡27	—	8 53	9 31	—	—	11‡2	1118	—	12‡19	12 48	1 37	2 47	—	3‡17	3§26	3‡38	...
Punt Murail	5 10	7 16	8 11	8 32	...	8 58	9 36	...	...	11 7	1124	...	12 24	12 53	1 42	2 52	...	3 22	3 31	3 43	...
Pontresina ....arr	5 15	7 20	8 15	8 37	...	9 2	9 40	...	...	1112	1129	...	12 28	12 57	1 47	2 56	...	3 27	3 36	3 48	...

		p.m.		p.m.	p.m.	p.m.			p.m	p.m.											
St. Moritz...................arr	...	4 30	...	6‡15	6 40	7 15	...	...	9 40	1035	...	...	...	...	...	...	...	...	...	...	...
Celerina	...	4 36	...	6 20	6 45	7 20	...	...	9 45	1040	...	...	...	...	...	...	...	...	...	...	...
Samaden .... arr	p.m.	4 40	p.m.	6 24	6 49	7 25	p.m.	p.m.	9 50	1045	...	...	...	...	...	...	...	...	...	...	...
Samaden .... dep	4 ‡9	4 48	6 0	6 29	7 2	—	9 6	9 24	1011	—	...	...	...	...	...	...	...	...	...	...	...
Punt Mureil	4 14	4 53	6 5	6 34	7 7	...	9 11	9 29	1016	...	...	...	...	...	...	...	...	...	...	...	...
Pontresina ....arr	4 18	4 58	6 9	6 38	7 12	...	9 15	9 34	1020	...	...	...	...	...	...	...	...	...	...	...	...

		a.m.			a.m.	a.m.	a.m.	a.m.		a.m.		a.m.	p.m.	p.m.	p.m.	p.m.	p.m.			p.m.
Pontresina ....dep	...	6 40	...	...	8 15	8‡26	8‡43	9 8	...	1045	...	11‡20	12‡20	12‡34	1 4	2§20	2‡35	...	...	3 7
Punt Murail	...	6 45	...	...	...	8 31	8 48	9 13	...	1050	...	...	12 25	12 39	1 9	2 25	2 40	...	p.m.	3 12
Samaden .... arr	a.m.	6 49	a.m.	a.m.	8 23	8 36	8 53	9 17	a.m.	1054	a.m.	11 28	12 30	12 43	1 13	2 30	2 44	p.m.	A	3 17
Samaden .... dep	6 15	7 35	8 5	8‡29	8 55	—	—	—	10‡30	—	1119	12 16	—	12 45	1 35	—	—	3 ‡7	3 15	—
Celerina	6 20	7 40	8 10	8 34	9 0	...	...	...	10 35	...	1124	12 21	...	12 50	1 40	...	...	3 12	3 20	...
St. Moritz	6 25	7 45	8 15	8 40	9 5	...	...	...	10 40	...	1130	12 25	...	12 55	1 45	...	...	3 17	3 25	...

			p.m.	p.m		p.m.	p.m.	p.m.	p.m.	p.m.	p.m.	p.m	p.m.	
Pontresina ....dep	...	...	4‡18	4 27	...	5§37	6‡14	6 38	6‡48	8 40	9 23	9 55	1030	...
Punt Murail	...	...	4 23	4 32	...	5 42	6 19	6 43	6 53	8 45	9 28	10 0	1035	...
Samaden .... arr	p.m.	p.m.	4 27	4 37	p.m.	5 47	6 23	6 48	6 58	8 49	9 33	10 5	1040	...
Samaden .... dep	3§24	4‡10	—	4‡40	5‡30	6 4	6 30	—	—	9 5	—	1010	—	...
Celerina	3 30	4 15	...	4‡45	5 35	6 10	6 35	...	...	9 10	...	1015	...	...
St. Moritz...................arr	3 35	4 20	...	4‡50	5 40	6 15	6 40	...	...	9 15	...	1020	...	...

‡—Until 15th September.

§—From 16th September.

A—July and August only.

Muottas-Murail Cable Railway.—In 25 minutes.—Service about half hourly from 7.50 a.m. until 6.45 p.m.

ST. MORITZ, PONTRESINA, POSCHIAVO, and TIRANO (Bernina Railway). All 2&3 Class.

*—Runs until 15th September. §—From 16th September.

e—Stops at these stations from 16th September only.

	a.m.	a.m.	a.m.	a.m.	a.m.	a.m.	p.m.	p.m.	p.m	p.m.	p.m.	p.m.	p.m.	p.m.	p.m.	p.m.	p.m.	
St. Moritz...............dep	5 3	7 30	8*38	9*15	9 48	11 18	1223	1*35	2 5	2 53	3 55	4 45	5*47	6 35	7 20	7 *50	9 10	...
Celerina	5 8	7 35	8 43	9 20	9 53	11 23	1228	1 40	2 10	2 58	4 0	4 50	5 52	6 40	7 25	7 55	...	...
Punt Murail.......................	...	7 40	8 48	9 25	9 58	11 28	1233	1 45	2 15	3 3	4 5	4 55	5 57	6 45	7 30	8 0	...	...
Pontresina 257A	5 22	7 51	8 55	9 35	1010	11 35	1245	1 53	2 25	3 8	4 10	5 8	6 2	6 50	7 39	8 5	9 23	...
Sanssouci...........................	5 27	7 56	9 0	9 40	1015	11*40	1250	1 58	2 30	3*19	4*26	5 13	—	—	7 44	—	—	...
Morteratsch.......................	5 39	8 8	9 12	9 53	1029	11*51	1 2	2 13	2 45	3*34	4*37	5 25	...	...	7 56	...	...	...
Bernina Hospitz	6 12	8 41	9 45	1027	11 5	12*24	1 35	2 47	3 27	4*10	—	6 0	...	...	8 30	...	...	...
Alp Grüm...........................	6 26	8 58	9 58	1040	1126	12*37	1 53	3 0	3 46	4*23	...	6 14	...	...	8 44	...	...	...
Cavaglia	6 47	9 19	—	—	1147	—	2 14	—	4 7	—	...	6 35	...	...	9 5	...	...	...
Cadera	7 5	9 37	...	...	12 5	...	2 32	...	4 25	...	...	6 53	...	...	9 23	...	...	...
Poschiavo	7 26	10 0	...	...	1231	...	2 53	...	4 45	...	...	7 15	...	...	9 42	...	...	...
Le Prese	7 38	1012	...	...	1243	...	3 5	...	4 55	...	...	7 27	...	...	—	...	...	...
Brusio	7 58	1032	...	...	1 3	...	3 25	...	5 14	...	...	7 47	...	...	...	...	...	...
Campo Cologno (Ital. Frontier) ...	8 13	1055	...	...	1 19	...	3 40	...	5 28	...	...	8 1	...	...	...	...	...	...
Tirano.........................arr	8 27	11 9	...	...	1 33	...	3 51	...	5 37	...	...	8 15	...	...	...	...	...	...

	a.m.	a.m.	a.m.	a.m.	a.m.	a.m.	a.m.	p.m	p.m.	p.m.	a.m.	p.m.	p.m.	p.m.	p.m.	p.m.	p.m.	p.m	p.m.	p.m.	p.m.
Tirano ....dep				5 31	...	6 34	9 13	...	...	...	11*43	...	12 56	...	...	2 45	...	...	...	5 16	7 38
Campo Cologno.................				5 51	...	6 56	9 35	...	...	...	12 7	...	1 18	...	...	3 9	...	...	...	5 39	8 [illegible]
Brusio				6 7	...	7 17	9 51	...	...	...	...	...	1 34	...	...	3 25	...	...	...	5 55	8 16
Le Prese				6 28	...	7 38	10 12	...	...	...	12 43	...	1 55	...	...	3 46	...	...	...	6 16	8 37
Poschiavo				6 45	...	8 40	10 27	...	...	...	12 56	...	2 12	...	...	4 6	...	...	...	6 33	8 4[illegible]
Cadera				7 5	...	9 0	10 47	...	...	...	...	...	2 32	...	...	...	...	...	...	6 53	—
Cavaglia				7 24	...	9 19	11 6	...		...	...	...	2 51			...		...		7 12	...
Alp Grüm...........................				7 45	...	10 5	11 29	...	1*20	...	...	...	3 12	3*55	4*35	5 e4	5*41	...	6*13	7 33	...
Bernina Hospitz				8 3	...	10 25	11 46	...	1 38	...	2 9	...	3 30	4 11	4 51	5 22	5 58	...	6 29	7 51	...
Morteratsch.......................				8 32	...	10 54	12 15	...	2 9	...	2 42	...	3 59	4 40	5 24	5e49	6 29	...	6 58	8 20	...
Sanssouci..........				8 43		11 5	12 26		2 20		2 53		4 10	4 51	5 35	5e59	6 41		7 9	8 31	...
Pontresina..........	6 25	7*45	8*20	8 53	10 3	11 14	12 38	1 50	2 25	2 27	2 58	3 8	4 20	5 0	5 43	6 8	6 50	6§55	7 16	8 41	...
Punt Murail..........	6 30	7 50	8 25	8 58	10 8	11 19	12 43	1 55	—	2 32	—	3 13	4 25	5 5	5 48	6 13	6 55	7 0	7 21	8 46	...
Celerina..................	6 34	7 54	8 29	9 2	1012	11 23	12 47	1 59	...	2 36	...	3 17	4 29	5 9	5 52	6 17	6 59	7 4	7 25	8 50	...
St. Moritz.........arr	6 40	8 0	8 35	9 8	1018	11 29	12 53	2 5	...	2 42	...	3 23	4 35	5 15	5 58	6 23	7 5	7 10	7 31	8 56	...

OLTEN and BIEL.

†—Weekdays only. ‡—Sunday only.

E.M.																		
			a.m.	a.m.	a.m.	a.m.	p.m.	p.m.	p.m.	p.m.	p.m.	p.m.		p.m.	p.m.	p.m.	p.m.	
—	Olten 258	...	5 35	8 35	8 47	10 24	12 20	1233	1 †40	1 ‡40	4 45	4 50	...	6 20	7 28	8 15	10 43	...	...
3¾	Hagendorf	...	5 51	...	9 1	10 38	12 37	1248	2 0	1 52	...	5 5	...	6 38	...	8 30	10 57	...	...
6	Egerkingen	...	5 58	RC	9 7	10 44	12 43	1254	2 9	1 58	RC	5 11	...	6 45	RC	8 36	11 3	...	...
10¾	Oensingen	...	6 16	...	9 21	10 58	Saturday only.	1 8	2 32	2 9	...	5 25	...	Not on Saturday or Sunday.	7 49	8 51	11 14	...	...
15½	Wangen-a-A.	...	6 31	...	9 34	11 11		1 21	3 0	2 22	...	5 39	...		7 59	9 6	11 25	...	...
21½	Neu Solothurn ...arr	a.m.	6 48	9 12	9 51	11 27		1 37	3 23	2 40	5 23	5 57	p.m.		8 9	9 25	11 40	...	...
...	" 257 ...dep	5 20	6 53	9 14	9 54	11 31		1 44	3 47	4 2	5 25	6 0	7†16		8 12	9 32	—	...	...
22	Alt Solothurn	5 26	6 58	...	9 58	11 35		1 50	3 54	4 7	...	6 5	7 15		...	9 38	...	...	...
28½	Grenchen (Granges)	5 45	7 15	...	10 16	11 52		2 11	4 19	4 25	...	6 24	7 31		8 27	9 57	...	...	...
31½	Pieterlen	5 56	7 25	...	10 26	12 2		2 21	4 33	4 37	...	6 34	7 41		...	10 7	...	...	...
37	Biel (Bienne) ...arr	6 10	7 38	9 45	10 40	12 15	...	2 34	4 55	4 55	5 50	6 47	7 55		8 43	10 20	...	...	...
55	NEUCHATEL 264A...arr	7a20	10 a7	1031	11a39	1 p45	...	3p55	6 p34	6 p34	6p34	8 p37	...	...	9 p37	11p47	...	...	...

NEUCHATEL (264) dep	...	5 a5	...	7 a45	9 a53	11a10	1 p5	2 p0	4p15	4p15	5 p2	...	7p47	8p10	...	...	...	...	...
		a.m.	a.m.	a.m.	a.m.	p.m.	p.m.	p.m.	p.m.	p.m.	p.m.	p.m.	p.m.	p.m.					
Biel (Bienne) ...dep	...	6 10	8 †2	9 35	10 40	12 40	1 42	3 5	4 55	5 2	6†20	7 25	8 25	9 30	...	...	...	...	...
Pieterlen	...	6 25	8 16	9 49	...	12 55	...	3 21	...	5 15	6 35	7 40	...	9 45	...	...	...	...	...
Grenchen (Granges)	...	6 35	8 25	9 58	10 56	1 5	RC	3 32	...	5 24	6 46	7 49	RC	9 56	...	...	...	...	...
Alt Solothurn	...	6 56	8 44	10 16	...	1 26	...	3 52	...	5 42	7 5	8 9	...	1015	...	...	...	...	...
Neu Solothurn ...arr	a.m.	6 59	8 47	10 19	11 9	1 30	2 10	3 56	5 25	5 44	7 8	8 12	8 53	1018	...	...	...	...	...
" ...dep	5 5	7 3	—	10 25	11 12	1 37	2 11	4 17	5 27	5 47	7 15	8 16	8 55	—	...	...	...	...	...
Wangen-a-A.	5 23	7 21	...	10 43	11 23	1 53	...	4 40	...	6 5	7 58	8 33	...	...	...	...	...	...	...
Oensingen	5 40	7 37	...	11 0	11 34	2 8	...	5 5	...	6 20	8 19	8 49	...	...	...	...	...	...	...
Egerkingen	5 57	7 52	...	11 14	...	2 20	...	5 20	...	6 33	—	9 3	...	...	...	...	...	...	...
Hagendorf	6 7	7 58	...	11 20	...	2 26	...	5 26	...	6 39	...	9 10	...	...	...	...	...	...	...
Olten (258) ...arr	6 22	8 11	...	11 33	11 51	2 40	2 48	5 40	6 10	6 52	...	9 24	9 33	...	...	...	...	...	...

RC—Restaurant Car attached.

SULGEN and ST. GALLEN.

Sulgen ...dep	6a10	7a26	9†a0	...	9 *a0	12p20	3p32	5p58	8 p5
Sitterthal	6 24	7 39	9 13	...	9 34	12 33	3 46	6 13	8 19
Bischofszell	6 31	7 46	9 2[illegible]	...	9 53	12 40	3 53	6 22	8 27
Arnegg	6 51	8 4	9 38	a.m.	10 38	1 0	4 13	6 42	8 47
Gossau	6 57	8 10	9 44	9 50	10 48	1 7	4 20	6 49	8 54
Winkeln	7 9	8 20	—	10 0	11 8	1 19	4 31	7 0	9 6
St. Gallen 262	7 20	8 31	...	1012	11 30	1 30	4 42	7 12	9 17

St. Gallen ...dep	4a54	7a14	9*a10	10a25	12p43	3p23	6p24	8p30
Winkeln	5 6	7 27	9 32	10 40	12 55	3 35	6 38	8 44
Gossau	5 15	7 40	9 52	10 46	1 7	3 48	6 49	8 54
Arnegg	5 22	7 48	10 8	11† 0	1 14	3 56	6 56	9 1
Bischofszell	5 36	8 4	10 46	11†14	1 30	4 12	7 12	9 17
Sitterthal	5 42	8 10	11 3	11†20	1 36	4 19	7 18	9 23
Sulgen (262) ...arr	5 54	8 23	11 26	11†32	1 48	4 31	7 30	9 35

†—Sunday only. *—Weekdays only.

EMMENBRUCKE and WILDEGG.

†—Until end of August.

		2&3	2&3	2&3	2&3	2&3	2&3	2&3	2&3	2&3
LUCERNE ...dep		6a32	8a12	1048	1227	2p25	4 p8	5p20	6p24	8p37
(258)		a.m.	a.m.	a.m.	p.m.	p.m.	p.m.	p.m.	p.m.	p.m.
Emmenbrucke dep		6 43	8 25	1059	1238	2 36	4 19	5 30	6 35	8 48
Eschenbach		7 7	8 48	1118	1 1	3 3	4 40	...	6 56	9 8
Ballwyl		7 13	8 53	1123	1 6	3 9	4 46	...	7 2	9 14
Hochdorf		7 22	9 6	1131	1 13	3 17	4 55	5 56	7 11	9†21
Gelfingen		7 37	9 14	1145	1 26	3 32	5 10	...	7 26	9†35
Hirtzkirch-R. 2&3		7 41	9 17	1149	1 29	3 36	5 14	...	7 30	9†39
Mosen	a.m.	7 53	9 25	1156	1 37	3 45	5 22	...	7 39	9†48
Beinwyl	5 55	8 7	9 36	12 5	1 45	3 55	5 33	6 21	7 54	9†56
Boniswyl-See	6 13	8 24	9 56	1220	2 1	4 12	5 50	...	8 10	—
Seon	6 24	8 35	1010	1231	2 13	4 23	6 2	...	8 20	...
Lenzburg	6 47	8 47	1040	1243	2 27	4 37	6 25	6 51	8 31	...
Wildegg (262)	6 59	8 57	1051	1252	2 39	4 48	6 37	6 58	8 44	...

	2&3	2&3	2&3	2&3	2&3	2&3	2&3	2&3	2&3
	a.m.	a.m.	a.m.	a.m.	a.m.	a.m.	p.m.	p.m.	p.m.
Wildegg ...dep	...	5 20	7 9	7 30	9 37	11 6	1 26	3 15	5 29
Lenzburg	...	5 29	7 17	7 41	9 49	1118	1 37	3 31	5 48
Seon	...	5 41	...	7 53	1011	1132	1 49	3 56	6 1
Boniswyl-Seengen	...	5 52	...	8 4	1023	1145	2 0	4 11	6 13
Beinwyl	4†45	6 8	7 45	8 22	1040	12 4	2 17	4 30	6 34
Mosen	4†53	6 15	...	8 30	1048	1213	2 25	4 38	6 42
Hirtzkirch-R.	5† 1	6 22	...	8 38	1056	1223	2 33	4 46	6 50
Gelfingen	5† 5	6 26	...	8 42	11 0	1227	2 37	4 50	6 54
Hochdorf	5 21	6 40	8 11	8 59	1115	1247	2 52	5 6	7 9
Ballwyl	5 28	6 47	...	9 5	1122	1255	2 58	5 12	7 15
Eschenbach	5 34	6 53	...	9 10	1128	1 2	3 4	5 17	7 21
Emmenbrucke arr	6 0	7 18	8 39	9 34	1151	1 25	3 28	5 42	7 45
LUCERNE ...arr	6 a8	7a26	8a47	9a42	12 0	1p33	3p37	5p50	7p53

Extra.—Wildegg to Beinwyl, 7.2, 9.0 p.m. Beinwyl to Wildegg, 6.57 p.m.

Beinwyl ...dep	6 12	7 46	8 21	9 37	10 41	12 5	1 49	2 20	4 29	5 32	6 33	7 55	10 1
Reinach ...arr	6 19	7 53	8 28	9 44	10 48	12 12	1 58	2 27	4 36	5 41	6 45	8 2	10 8
Menziken	6 25	8 5	8 34	9 49	10 54	12 18	...	2 33	4 42	5 44	6 49	8 8	10 13
Münster ...arr	6 37	...	8 45	...	11 6	12 30	...	2 45	4 52	5 53	7 0	8 20	...

Münster ...dep	...	5 33	7 21	...	9 12	...	11 34	1 21	...	3 32	5 3	5 59	...	7 28	...
Menziken	5 43	5 55	7 30	7 56	9 22	10 24	11 44	1 31	...	3 42	5 13	6 8	6 43	7 37	...
Reinach ...dep	5 46	5 58	7 33	7 58	9 25	10 29	11 47	1 34	2 7	3 45	5 16	6 11	6 46	7 40	...
Beinwyl ...arr	5 54	6 6	7 42	8 5	9 34	10 36	11 56	1 43	2 16	3 54	5 26	6 19	6 55	7 49	...

SURSEE and TRIENGEN.

Sursee ...dep	6a20	9 a0	11 a0	1p32	3 p5	5p55	8p48	...
Triengen ...arr	6 40	9 20	11 32	1 52	3 25	6 15	9 8	...

Triengen ...dep	5a36	7a17	9a45	12p30	2p18	5 p4	8p18	...
Sursee 258 ...arr	5 56	7 50	10 5	12 50	2 38	5 24	8 38	...

LUGANO and TESSERETE.

Lugano ...dep	6a15	7a40	9 a40	11a50	2 p0	2‡p36	3 p15	4 p40	6 p20	7 p45	9p21	10*p45
Canobbio	6 31	7 56	9 56	12 6	2 16	2 52	3 31	4 58	6 36	8 1	9 37	11 1
Tesserete ...arr	6 45	8 10	10 10	12 20	2 30	3 6	3 45	5 10	6 50	8 15	9 51	11 15
Tesserete ...dep	5a45	6 a50	8 a30	10a40	1p28	2‡p4	2 p40	4 p0	5 p30	7 p0	8 p50	10*p10
Canobbio	5 57	7 2	8 42	10 52	1 40	2 16	2 52	4 12	5 42	7 12	9 2	10 22
Lugano ...arr	6 11	7 16	8 56	11 6	1 54	2 30	3 6	4 26	5 56	7 26	9 16	10 36

‡—Sun. only; daily in Sept.
*—Sunday only.

LUGANO and PONTE TRESA.

Lugano ...dep	6 a43	7a57	9a15	10a51	12p10	1p58	3 p7	4p25	5p38	6 p49	7p45	10p20	...	...	...	...	...	...	...
Ponte Tresa ...arr	7 13	8 25	9 43	11 21	12 38	2 26	3 37	4 55	6 6	7 17	8 13	10 48	...	...	...	...	...	...	...
Ponte Tresa ...dep	5 a50	7a21	8a30	10a15	11a29	1p22	2p31	3p46	5 p2	6 p12	6p55	9p40	...	...	...	...	...	...	...
Lugano ...arr	6 19	7 50	8 59	10 44	11 58	1 51	3 0	4 15	5 31	6 41	7 24	10 9	...	...	...	...	...	...	...

BASLE (Swiss Station), OLTEN, and LUCERNE.

THROUGH CARRIAGES—Basle to Milan, in 7.0 a.m., 12.2, 1.50 p.m., and 9.45 p.m. from Basle. RC—Restaurant Car. SC—Sleeping Car.

Dist.																														
...	BRUSSELS 103A dep	...	...	...	...	6 p35	6p35	6p35	6 p35	6 p35	...	...	11p28	11p28	...	...	...	...	...	...	...	...	...	6 a8	6 a8	...	7a49	1020	...	...
...	PARIS 68 ......dep	...	...	...	7 p47	9 p45	9p45	9p45	9 p45	9 p45	9p45	10 p0	10 p0	...	...	...	...	...	...	...	...	...	...	8a55	8a55	...	...	1 p0	...	...
		2 & 3	2 & 3	1,2,3	1 Cl.	2 & 3	1 &2	1,2,3	1,2,3	1,2,3	1,2,3	1,9,3	1,2,3	2 &3	2 & 3	1 &2	1& 2	2&3	1,2,3	2 & 3	1,2,3	2&3	2&3	1,2,3	1,2,3	2&3	1,2,3	1,2,3	,2,3	1,2,3
E.M.	Basle—		a.m.	a.m.	a.m.	a.m.	a.m.	a.m.	a.m.	a.m.	a.m.	a.m.	p.m.	p.m.	p.m.	p.m	p.m.		p.m.	p.m.	p.m	p.m.	p.m.	p.m.	p.m.	p.m	p.m.	p.m.	p.m.	n'gt
—	Swiss Station..dep	...	5 0	5 42	5 52	6 25	7 0	7 15	7 30	7 40	8 25	10 40	12 2	1215	1 8	1 42	1 50	...	2 50	3 10	3 40	4 21	5 22	6 10	6 20	7 25	7 55	9 45	1120	12 0
5¼	Pratteln	...	5 14	...	...	6 41	...	...	...	7 51	...	10 51	...	1230	1 22	...	...	...	3 5	3 26	...	4 36	5 38	...	...	7 40	...	...	...	1212
7½	Nieder Schönthal...	...	5 20	...	...	6 47	...	...	...	...	...	10 57	...	1237	1 29	...	...	...	3 12	3 34	...	4 44	5 45	...	...	7 47	...	...	...	...
9	**Liestal 266**	...	5 24	5 57	A	6 51	RC	7 31	...	7 57	8 41	11 3	RC	1243	1 33	...	...	...	3 17	3 39	...	4 50	5 51	...	6 37	7 54	D	SC	SC	1221
13	Sissach	...	5 40	6 8	...	7 9	...	...	...	8 8	8 51	11 17	...	1257	1 47	...	...	...	3 35	3 55	...	5 5	6 6	...	6 50	8 10	...	...	...	1232
19¼	Läufelfingen	...	6 0	6 24	...	7 29	...	...	...	8 28	...	11 37	...	1 18	2 8	...	...	...	3 57	S	...	—	6 30	...	...	8 30	...	...	...	...
24½	**Olten** ....arr	...	6 12	6 36	6 46	7 41	7 53	8 7	8 22	8 40	9 19	11 49	12 56	1 30	2 20	2 35	2 43	...	4 10		4 33	...	6 43	7 4	7 20	8 42	8 52	1038	1213	1 0
66	BERNE 257......arr	a.m.	9 a12	9a12	9 a12	9 a20	9a20	9a20	10a27	10a27	1255	1 p32	3 p44	3p44	3 p55	3p55	4p12	...	6 p0	...	6 p0	p.m.	8p53	8p53	8 p53	...	...	12a8	2a35	2a35
...	**Olten** ....dep	5 6	6 55	6 38	6 50	...	7 56	...	8 25	...	9 22	12 3	1 0	1 46	Sunday only.	Runs until 30th Sept.	2 53	...	4 38	...	...	6‡25	...	7 9	7 50	...	8 55	1043	1216	...
26¾	Aarburg	5 14	7 3	...	...	...	...	...	8 31	...	9 29	12 10	...	1 54			...	...	4 45	...	...	6 32	...	7 15	7 58	...	...	...	...	...
29½	**Zofingen**	5 22	7 13	6 49	...	...	...	...	8 38	...	9 36	12 18	...	2 4			...	...	4 53	...	...	6 43	...	7 22	8 7	...	...	1054	...	...
33	Reiden	5 33	7 24	Sunday only.	...	...	...	...	...	...	9 45	12 28	...	2 15			...	...	5 4	...	...	6 53	...	...	8 17	...	D	...	...	...
36½	Nebikon	5 43	7 34		...	...	...	...	...	...	9 55	12 38	...	2 25			...	...	5 14	...	...	—	...	...	8 27	...	...	...	...	...
39¼	Wauwyl	5 50	7 42		...	...	...	...	...	...	10 2	12 45	...	2 32			...	...	5 21	...	...	...	...	...	8 34	...	...	...	...	...
43	Sursee 257B......2&3	6 1	7 55		...	2 & 3	...	2&3	...	2 & 3	1010	12 51	...	2 44	...		...	...	5 31	...	2&3	...	2&3	7 45	8 43	...	...	...	...	...
49	Sempach ....a.m.	6 19	8 13		...	a.m.	...	a.m.	...	a.m.	1026	1 12	...	3 3	p.m.		...	p.m.	5 47	p.m.	p.m.	...	p.m.	...	8 58	...	...	...	...	...
56	Emmenbrucke 6 0	6 40	8 32		...	7 18	...	8 39	...	9 34	1041	1 31	...	3 23	1 25	...	...	4 24	6 7	3 28	5 42	...	7 45	...	9 17	...	...	...	...	...
59	**Lucerne** .....arr 6 8	6 48	8 40	7 38	7 50	7 26	8 59	8 47	9 28	9 42	1048	1 40	1 56	3 31	1 33	...	3 49	4 22	6 15	3 27	5 50	...	7 53	8 15	9 26	...	9 55	1142	1 12	...
199	CHIASSO 259 ...arr	1 p10	1 p54	1p10	...	...	1p54	...	3p20	...	5p52	...	7p19	...	...	...	9 p0	...	...	...	...	...	...	...	...	...	...	5 a5	7a20	...
231¼	MILAN 269A ...arr	2 p27	3 p5	2p27	...	...	3 p5	...	4p40	...	7p47	...	8p40	...	...	...	1025	...	...	...	...	...	...	...	...	...	...	6a22	8a53	...

Extra.—Basle to Sissach 8.0 a.m., 2.12, 6.45, 8.38, and 9.53 p.m. Sissach to Basle, 5§10, 7§12 a.m. Olten to Zofingen, Saturday only, 12.30 p.m.

‡—Sat. & Sun. excepted. §—Weekdays only. A—Train de Luxe, runs from 2nd July until 15th Sept. D—Until 30th Sept.

MILAN 269A ...dep	...	9 p5	...	9 p5	11p35	...	...	...	...	...	...	...	...	...	...	...	...	7a25	7a25	...	9a35	...	9 a35	...	...	...	12p40	...	12p40	2p40	...
CHIASSO 259A dep	...	10p50	...	10p50	1 a5	...	...	...	...	...	...	...	...	...	...	...	...	8a50	8a50	...	1110	...	11a10	...	...	...	1 p54	...	1 p54	4 p4	...
	2 & 3	1,2,3	1,2,3	2 & 3	1,2,3	2&3	2&3	2 & 3	2&3	2&3	1,2,3	1,2,3	2&3	2&3	1,2,3	2&3	1& 2	1&2	1,2,3	2 & 3	1,2,3	2&3	1,2,3	2&3	2&3	1,2,3	1,2,3	2&3	1,2,3	1,2,3	1Cl.
		a.m.		a.m.	a.m.	a.m.		a.m.	a.m.	a.m.	a.m.	a.m.	a.m.	p.m.	p.m.	p.m.		p m.	p.m.	p.m.	p.m.	p.m.	p.m.	p.m.	p.m	p.m	p.m.	p.m.	p m.	p.m.	p.m.
Lucerne ....dep	...	5 5	...	5 28	7 0	6 32	†—Sunday dep. 5.17 a.m.	8 0	8 12	9 11	9 55	10 10	1048	1227	1235	1243	...	2 2	2 19	2 25	4 57	4 8	5 2	6 24	5 20	6 50	7 0	8 37	8 0	9 10	1013
Emmenbrucke	...	...	...	5 38	...	6 40		8 12	8 21	9 19	...	10 20	1056	1235	...	1252	...	...	2 28	2 33	...	4 16	5 12	6 32	5 28	Sunday only.	...	8 45	8 9	...	...
Sempach	...	...	...	6 0	...	—		8 39	—	—	...	10 40	—	—	...	1 13	...	...	2 48	—	...	—	5 32	—	—		...	—	8 29	...	...
Sursee	...	SC	...	6 17	...	...		8 58	...	...	...	10 56	...	...	...	1 30	...	...	3 5	...	5 27	...	5 52	...	...		...	...	8 45	...	...
Wauwyl	...	...	...	6 26	...	...		9 8	...	...	...	11 5	...	...	...	1 40	...	...	3 14	...	...	...	6 2	...	...		...	...	8 55	...	A
Nebikon	...	...	...	6 34	...	...		9 16	...	...	...	11 12	...	...	D	1 48	...	...	3 21	...	RC	...	6 10	p.m.	...		RC	...	9 3	...	...
Reiden	...	...	...	6 46	...	...	a.m.	9 28	a.m.	...	...	11 24	...	...	...	2 1	...	...	3 33	...	...	...	6 23	§	...		...	...	9 15	...	...
Zofingen	...	...	...	6 58	7 49	...	6 †8	9 41	9 8	...	...	11 35	...	...	...	2 12	...	...	3 45	...	5 50	...	6 37	7 28	...	7 43	7 54	...	9 28	...	...
Aarburg	...	...	...	7 6	...	1,2,3	6 17	9 48	9 21	...	...	11 43	...	...	...	2 20	...	...	3 52	...	...	...	6 46	7 38	...	...	...	...	9 35	...	...
Olten ....arr	...	6 5	a.m.	7 13	7 58	a.m.	6 23	9 55	9 28	1,2,3	1051	11 50	a.m.	p.m.	1 35	2 28	p.m.	2 57	3 58	...	5 59	1,2,3	6 53	7 45	...	7 52	8 3	p.m	9 41	10 5	1112
BERNE 257.....dep	a.m.	...	5 0	5 a5	...	6 50	...	7 a10	...	9a22	...	10a45	1045	S	1222	...	1 40	1p40	2p14	...	3p55	5 p5	5 p40	...	...	...	6 p0	6 0	8 p20	8p40	...
Olten ....dep	5 25	6 13	6 28	7 31	8 1	8 17	...	10 6	...	1039	1054	12 12	1225	2 35	1 45	...	3 3	3 12	4 18	...	6 2	6 32	7 5	...	...	7 57	8 7	8 35	9 54	1010	1115
Läufelfingen	5 45	...	...	7 51	...	8 36	a.m.	10 27	...	...	...	...	1246	2 54	...	p.m.	...	...	4 39	p.m.	...	6 51	7 25	p.m.	...	...	...	8 57	10 13	...	...
Sissach	6 4	...	7 1	8 10	...	8 49	9 30	10 45	...	1111	...	12 44	1 8	3 10	...	3 12	...	...	4 58	6 10	6 33	7 5	7 41	7 54	...	...	...	9 17	10 26	...	...
Liestal	6 16	...	7 8	8 24	...	8 56	9 43	10 58	...	1118	...	12 53	1 22	—	D	3 24	...	...	5 11	6 22	6 41	7 15	7 50	8 10	...	8 36	8 44	9 33	10 34	...	A
Nieder Schönthal ...	6 21	...	...	8 28	...	...	9 48	11 3	...	...	...	...	1 27	...	...	3 29	...	...	5 16	6 27	...	...	...	8 17	...	...	...	9 38	...	...	...
Pratteln	6 27	...	...	8 34	...	9 3	9 55	11 10	...	...	...	1 2	1 34	...	...	3 35	...	...	5 22	6 33	...	7 23	...	8 24	...	...	...	9 45	10 42	...	...
Basle ....arr	6 41	7 10	7 25	8 43	8 57	9 13	1010	11 25	...	1135	1147	1 12	1 50	...	2 38	3 50	3 57	4 6	5 36	6 50	6 58	7 35	8 7	8 38	...	8 53	9 0	10 0	10 53	11 3	1210
PARIS 69 ......arr	...	...	...	...	5 p45	5p45	...	...	...	...	...	...	...	...	...	...	1148	11p48	4a55	...	...	...	...	...	...	...	6 a25	...	...	7a28	8a42
BRUSSELS 103B arr	...	...	...	...	8 p11	8p11	...	...	...	9p26	9p26	...	...	...	...	...	...	...	...	...	5a26	...	...	...	...	...	8 a28	...	...	8a28	...

BRUGG and BREMGARTEN.

Brugg ....dep	6a55	8 a6	9a27	1p16	5p12	7p28	8p35	...	...
Othmarsingen	7 10	8 23	9 43	1 35	5 30	7 46	8 50	...	...
Wohlen ....arr	7 32	8 39	10 0	1 53	5 46	8 3	9 5	...	...
Bremgarten .....arr	7 57	9 4	11 5	2 18	6 24	8 27	10 3	...	...

Bremgarten .....dep	5a54	6a40	8a40	10a57	1p 0	2 p57	6p14	8p40	...	...	...
Wohlen	6 40	7 9	9 19	11 47	2 10	4 20	6 35	9 49	...	...	...
Othmarsingen	6 57	7 30	9 40	12 9	2 29	4 37	6 52	10 6	...	...	...
Brugg 262 ....arr	7 10	7 46	9 54	12 25	2 43	4 50	7 5	1019	...	...	...

LUCERNE, AIROLO, BELLINZONA, LUGANO, and CHIASSO.
THROUGH CARRIAGES—BASLE to MILAN in 7.0 a.m., 12.2 p.m., and 9.45 p.m. from Basle.

Dis. Eng. Miles	...	...	...	BASLE Swiss258dp	...	...	...	...	...	...	...	7 a0	7a30	...	8 a25	...	...	12p2	12 p2	1 p50	...	...	3p40	6p10	7 p55	9 p45	11p20
	1 Cl.	2 Cl.	3 Cl.		3 Cl.	2&3	1,2,3	2&3	1,2,3	1,2,3	1,2,3	1&2	1,2,3	3 Cl.	1,2,3	1,2,3	1,2,3	1,2,3	1,2,3	1&2	1,2,3	2&3	1,2,3	1,2,3	1,2,3	1&2	1,2,3
	fr. c.	fr. c.	fr. c.					a.m.	a.m.	a.m.		a.m.	a.m.		a.m.	p.m.		p.m.	p.m.	p.m.		p.m.	p.m.	p.m.	p.m.	p.m.	a.m.
—	—	—	—	**Lucerne**......dep	...	...	...	5 8	6 40	7 48	...	9 8	9 47	...	11 0	12 30	...	2 22	2 42	4 0	...	5 6	6 55	8 30	10 10	11 52	1 22
6¾	1 15	0 80	0 60	Meggen	...	...	...	5 22	6 56	8 1	...	:	...	...	11 13	12 46	...	...	2 57	...	...	5 21	7 12	8 47	10 27	...	...
10	1 80	1 25	0 90	Küssnacht	...	...	...	5 30	7 6	8 8	...	:	...	...	11 20	12 55	...	RC	3 6	...	...	5 30	7 22	8 56	10 36	SC	SC
12	2 10	1 45	1 5	Immensee	...	...	...	5 36	7 13	8 13	...	RC	...	...	11 25	1 2	...	...	3 12	...	...	5 37	7 30	9 3	10 42	...	...
17¼	2 95	2 5	1 45	**Arth-Goldau** arr	...	...	...	5 48	7 25	8 23	...	:	1017	...	11 35	1 15	...	2 53	3 24	4 29	...	5 50	7 43	9 15	10 55	12 22	1 52
...	...	...	...	ZURICH 260 ...dep	...	...	...	...	5 a58	7a25	7a30	:	9 a5	...	10 a0	...	12p25	1p45	1 p45	3 p22	3p22	...	5 p51	8 p8	9 p30	11p15	12a30
...	...	...	...	ZUG 259B ......dep	...	...	...	5 a5	7 a5	8 a6	8a31	:	9a53	...	11 a0	12 20	1 p15	2p31	2 p31	4 p5	4 p5	5 p2	7 p10	9 p4	10 33	12 0	1a20
...	...	...	...	**Arth-Goldau** dep	...	...	...	5 52	7 43	8 34	9 0	:	1027	...	11 47	1 29	1 47	3 5	3 35	4 37	4 43	6 10	7 57	9 37	11 8	12 32	2 2
20½	3 45	2 40	1 75	Steinen	...	...	...	6 0	7 52	RC	9 10	:	...	...	11 55	1 38	1 55	...	3 43	RC	4 51	6 21	8 7	9 46	11 16	...	...
22¼	3 75	2 65	1 90	Schwyz-Seewen	...	...	...	6 7	8 0	8 44	9 18	:	...	...	12 1	1 44	2 2	...	3 50	...	4 57	6 30	8 15	9 52	11 22	...	...
24½	4 20	2 95	2 10	Brunnen	...	...	...	6 14	8 10	8 50	9 27	:	1041	...	12 8	1 52	2 11	...	3 59	...	5 3	6 40	8 25	9 58	11 29	...	...
28¼	4 80	3 35	2 40	Sisikon	...	...	...	6 25	8 20	...	9 3[illegible]	:	...	...	12 17	2 3	2 22	...	4 11	...	5 14	6 52	8 37	10 9	11 38	...	...
31¾	5 45	3 80	2 70	Fluelen	...	...	...	6 34	8 31	9 4	9 46	:	1056	...	12 27	2 13	2 33	3 31	4 22	5 4	5 24	7 2	8 50	1019	11 47	...	...
33¾	5 75	4 5	2 90	Altdorf	...	...	...	6 41	8 40	9 9	9 52	:	...	a.m.	12 33	2 20	2 40	...	4 31	...	5 31	7 9	8 58	1026	11 53	...	...
37½	6 35	4 45	3 20	Erstfeld	...	...	...	6 55	8‖50	9 22	10 0	1013	1112	11*23	12 48	2 38	2 50	3 46	5†47	5 19	5 40	7 18	9 7	1035	12 10	1 12	2 47
40¾	7 20	5 5	3 60	Amsteg	...	...	...	7 6	9 46	...		...	...	11 38	12 59	2 51		...	5 58	...			9 16		12 21	...	...
45¼	8 55	6 0	4 30	Gurtnellen	...	...	...	7 26	10 5	...	...	...	...	12 9	1 18	3 10		...	6 18	...	...	...	9 48	...	12 40	...	...
50¾	9 90	6 95	4 95	Wassen	...	...	...	7 46	10 24	...	...	...	...	12 36	1 37	3 29		...	6 38	...	...	...	10 9	...	1 0	...	...
55½	11 15	7 80	5 60	**Göschenen** arr	...	...	...	8 5	10 40	1011	...	11 2	12 7	1 0	1 52	3 45		4 34	6 55	6 9	...	...	10 28	...	1 16	2 5	3 47
				dep	...	...	...	8 15	11 26	1016	...	11 7	1231		1 57	3 50		4 38	7 0	6 13	...	...	10 33	...	1 21	2 10	3 52
65¼	17 35	9 65	6 90	**Airolo** arr	...	...	a.m.	8 35	11 46	1034	...	...	1250	...	2 16	4 10		...	7 22	...	...		10 55	...	1 40	...	4 11
				dep	...	...	5 40	8 37	11 48	1035	...	...	1251	...	2 17	4 13		...	7 27	...	...			...	1 42	...	4 13
69¼	14 90	10 45	7 45	Ambri-Piotta	...	...	5 52	8 49	12 0	...	...	...	...	...	2 28	4 25		...	7 40	...	...		...	...	...	...	...
72½	15 75	11 0	7 90	Rodi-Fiesso	...	...	6 1	8 58	12 9	...	...	...	...	...	2 36	4 34		...	7 49	...	...		...	...	...	...	...
77½	17 10	11 95	8 55	Faido	...	...	6 17	9 12	12 23	1057	...	...	...	...	2 48	4 48		RC	8 4	...	...		...	...	2 9	...	4 40
81¾	18 25	12 75	9 15	Lavorgo	...	...	6 29	9 24	12 35	...	...	...	...	...	2 59	5 0		...	8 17	...	...		...	...	...	...	...
86¼	19 40	13 60	9 70	Giornico	...	...	6 42	9 37	12 48	RC	...	...	...	...	3 10	5 13		...	8 31	...	...		...	...	...	...	...
89¼	20 35	14 25	10 15	Bodio	...	...	6 52	9 48	12 58	...	...	...	...	...	3 19	5 23	...	...	8 42	...	...		...	...	2 35	...	...
93¾	21 35	14 95	10 70	Biasca	...	...	7 8	10 2	1 10	1125	...	...	...	...	3 29	5 47	...	5 41	8 58	...	...			...	2 46	...	5 16
101	22 60	15 85	11 30	Claro	...	...	7 27	1019	1 27	...	...	...	...	...	3 44	6 4	...	...	9 15	...	...			...	...	...	...
103½	23 5	16 15	11 50	Castione	...	...	7 34	1025	1 33	...	...	...	...	...	3 50	6 10	...	...	9 21	...	...			...	...	...	...
105½	23 35	16 35	11 70	**Bellinzona** ...arr	...	...	7 40	1030	1 38	1142	...	1225	1 53	...	3 55	6 15	...	5 57	9 26	7 33	...	...		...	3 5	3 33	5 35
130	...	...	...	LUINO 259B ...arr	...	...	10 a3	1152	3 p10	...	...	3p10	3p10	...	5 p23	7 p40	...	7p40	...	9 p40	...	...		...	...	5 a20	6 a45
234¼	...	...	...	TURIN 269 ...arr	...	...	3 p25	...	...	...	...	...	7p15	...	9 p45	11p50	...	1150	...	...	...	...		...	...	9 a50	12p35
260½	...	...	...	GENOA 270 ...arr	...	...	5 p25	...	...	...	...	...	10p5	...	11p25	...	...	...	...	...	...	...		...	...	12p15	2 p35
571¾	...	...	...	ROME 270 ...arr	...	a.m.	...	...	...	...	...	...	8a40	...	9 a30	...	...	...	...	...	...	...		...	...	11p50	...
...	...	...	...	**Bellinzona** ...dep	...	6 10	8 3	1041		1149	...	1230	1 59	...	4 5	6 32	...	6 3	9 40	7 44	...	...		...		3 45	5 50
107½	23 75	16 65	11 90	Giubiasco	...	6 17	8 11	1048		...	...	...	...	...	4 11	6 41	...	...	9 48	...	...	...		...		...	...
114¼	25 55	17 90	12 75	Rivera-Bironico	...	6 42	8 36	1112		...	...	RC	2 24	...	4 33	7 8	...	...	10 15	RC	...	...		...		...	...
119¾	27 10	18 95	...	Taverne	...	6 56	8 48	1125		...	...	...	2 37	2 & 3	4 46	7 22	2 & 3	...	10 31	...	...	...		...		...	...
124	27 70	19 40	13 85	**Lugano** arr	a.m.	7 7	8 58	1135		1232	...	1 17	2 45	p.m.	4 56	7 32	p.m.	6 44	10 41	8 26	...	...		...		4 26	6 35
				dep	5 36	7 21	9 4	1146		1235	...	1 20	2 48	2 57	5 5	7 39	6 *3	6 47	10 46	8 30	...	...		...		4 31	6 40
128½	28 45	19 90	14 25	Melide	5 51	7 31	9 14	1157		...	...	...	...	3 8	5 15	7 49	6 17	...	10 56	...	...	...		...		...	...
130½	28 85	20 20	14 45	Maroggia	6 2	7 38	9 21	12 5		...	...	...	...	3 16	5 22	7 57	6 27	...	11 3	...	...	...		...		...	...
132¾	29 20	20 45	14 60	Capolago	6 13	7 44	9 28	1211		...	...	...	3 5	3 23	5 28	8 3	6 38	...	11 11	...	...	...		...		...	...
135¼	29 60	20 70	14 80	Mendrisio	6 31	7 53	9 38	1222		1 0	...	...	...	3 33	5 38	8 13	6 52	...	11 22	...	...	...	...	...	...	...	7 8
140	29 90	20 95	15 0	**Chiasso** ......arr	6 50	8 6	9 52	1235		1 10	...	1 54	3 20	3 46	5 52	8 26	7 10	7 19	11 35	9 0	...	...		...	...	5 5	7 20
143	30 0	21 5	...	COMO 269A ...arr	7 a51	8a21	10a27	...		1p33	...	2p11	3p44	5 p2	6 p22	9 p24	...	7p46	...	9 p24	...	...	...	...	...	5 a26	7 a51
172¾	35 70	25 0	...	MILAN 269A arr	8 a53	9a55	12 0	...	...	2p27	...	3 p5	4p40	6 p31	7 p47	10p25	...	8p40	...	10p25	...	...	...	...	...	6 a22	8 a53
266¼	54 55	38 25	...	GENOA 269A arr	12p30	...	5 p25	...	...	...	...	6p45	8p20	...	12a10	...	...	1210	...	...	...	...	...	...	...	9a20	12p30
577½	116 60	81 65	...	ROME 270......arr	...	...	...	...	...	6a45	...	6a45	8§40	...	8a50	...	...	8a50	...	1 p5	...	...	...	...	...	6p55	10p55

(‖—Dep. at 9.33 a.m.)

On Sunday only.

†—Arrives Erstfeld 4.42 p.m.

RC—Restaurant Car attached. SC—Sleeping Car.

*—Weekdays only. §—Via Genoa.

"Table d'Hote" at Göschenen for 9.47 a.m. from Lucerne.
Customs Examination at Chiasso and Luino.

CHIASSO, LUGANO, BELLINZONA, AIROLO, and LUCERNE.

Station		1	2	3	4	5	6	7	8	9	10	11	12	13	14	15	16	17	18	19	20
Rome 279B...dep		...	...	...	...	...	...	6 p5	...	9 r5	9 p5	9 p5	...	...	1150	11p50	...	...	...	...	9 a5
Genoa 269A dep		...	...	...	...	...	--	2 a40	2a40	5a50	5a50	5 a50	8 a20	...	1110	11a10	...	2 p35	2p35	5 p40	7p45
Milan 269A dep		...	...	...	...	...	4 a25	7 a25	7a25	9a25	9a35	10a35	12p40	...	2p40	2 p40	4 p0	6 p10	7p20	9 p5	11p35
Como 269A ...dep		...	...	...	...	...	6 a7	8 a26	8a26	1017	10a42	12p10	1 p36	...	3p42	3 p42	5 p0	7 p27	8p57	10p27	12a37
		2&3	2 & 3	1,2,3	2 & 3	2 & 3	1,2,3	1 & 2	1,2,3	1,2,3	1,2,3	2 & 3	1 & 2	2 &3	1,2,3	1,2,3	1,2,3	1,2,3	1,2,3	1,2,3	1 & 2
					a.m.	a.m.	a.m.	a.m.	a.m.	a.m.	a.m.	p.m.	p.m.	p.m.	p.m.	p.m.	p.m.	p.m.	p.m.	p.m.	a.m.
Chiasso ....dep		...	...	...	4 *55	7 *25	6 30	8 50	9 0	1040	11 10	12 57	1 54	2*15	4 4	4 15	5 26	8 0	9 40	10 50	1 5
Mendrisio..............		...	...	...	5 19	7 52	6 49	...	9 20	..	11 24	1 16	RC	2 39	...	4 33	5 40	8 16	9 58	11 5	...
Capolago		...	...	...	5 33	8 1	6 58	RC	9 30	1056	...	1 25	...	2 49	...	4 40	...	8 24	10 6	...	SC
Maroggia		...	...	...	5 42	8 13	7 4	¶	9 37	RC	...	1 33	¶	3 0	...	4 47	RC	8 31	1013	...	...
Melide		...	...	...	5 52	8 30	7 10	...	9 44	..	...	1 40	...	3 9	...	4 54	...	8 38	1021	...	...
Lugano...... arr		...	...	a.m.	6 10	8 47	7 21	9 22	9 55	1113	11 46	1 52	2 26	3 25	4 35	5 5	6 3	8 49	1032	11 27	1 39
Lugano...... dep		...	...	4 26	6 35		7 26	9 26	10 2	1117	11 52	1 57	2 29	3 36	4 38	5 13	6 7	8 56		11 32	1 42
Taverne..................		...	...	4 36	6 54	...	7 37	...	1014	...	...	2 8	¶	3 59	...	5 25	...	9 9	...	...	...
Rivera-Bironica ...		...	...	4 50	7 22	...	7 53	...	1031	...	...	2 26	...	4 31	...	5 44	...	9 25	...	SC	...
Giubiasco..............		...	...	5 5	7 48	...	8 12	...	1050	...	...	2 45	...	4 56	...	6 4	...	9 43	...	...	...
Bellinzona ...arr		...	...	5 10	7 55	...	8 18	10 2	1056	1153	12 30	2 51	3 5	5 4	5 14	6 10	6 44	9 48	...	12 12	2 22
Rome 271......dep		...	...	...	...	...	...	2 p0	6p15	6p15	6 p15	9 p0	9 p0	...	...	...	...	...	...	...	...
Genoa 271 ...dep		...	...	...	...	...	...	2 a30	5 a0	5 a0	5 a0	6a55	6 a55	...	8a30	8 a30	8a30	...	...	...	5p40
Turin 269...dep		...	...	...	...	...	...	4 a0	6a35	6a35	6a35	8 a54	8 a54	...	1125	11a25	1125	3 Cl.	...	...	8 p0
Luino 259B dep		...	...	...	...	...	6 a25	8 a57	1035	1035	11 a2	1 p24	1 p24	...	4 p8	4 p8	4 p8	p.m.	...	...	12a15
Bellinzona ...dep		...	...	5 18	...	...	8 30	10 10	1225	12 0	12 55	3 25	3 13	...	5 19	6 56	6 50	8*35	...	12 22	2 30
Castione		...	...	5 24	...	...	8 36	...	1232	...	...	3 32	...	...	...	7 3	...	8 45	...	...	...
Claro		...	...	5 30	...	a.m.	8 42	...	1239	...	...	3 40	...	...	...	7 10	RC	8 55	...	...	...
Biasca		...	...	5 50	...	7 §10	9 5	10 32	1257	1221	1 16	4 10	3 35	...	5 40	7 36	7 12	9 22	...	12 45	2 53
Bodio..................		...	...	6 0	...	7 28	9 16	...	1 35	...	...	4 23	...	...	...	7 49	...		...	...	...
Giornico		...	...	6 13	...	7 49	9 31	...	1 50	...	...	4 41	...	...	...	8 6	...	...	...	...	...
Lavorgo		...	...	6 27	...	8 21	9 49	...	2 8		...	5 2	...	...	...	8 25	...	...	...	...	...
Faido..................		...	...	6 39	...	8 45	10 8	11 10	2 26	1259	1 54	5 25	4 14	...	...	8 43	7 51	...	...	1 34	3 42
Rodi-Fiesso..........		...	...	6 56	...	9 19	10 30	...	2 48	..	...	5 49	...	...	...	9 4	...	...	...	...	...
Ambri-Piotta..........		...	...	7 4	...	9 34	10 40	...	2 58	RC	...	6 0	...	...	...	9 14	...	...	...	...	...
Airolo ...... arr		...	...	7 16	...	9 47	10 55	11 40	3 14	1 29	2 24	6 18	4 44	...	6 46	9 30	8 22	...	...	2 12	4 20
Airolo ...... dep		...	...	7 18	1,2,3	10 0	12 15	11 42	3 17	1 31	2 26	6 22	4 46	1,2,3	6 48	9 38	8 24	...	...	2 15	4 23
Göschenen arr		a.m.	a.m.	7 36	a.m.	10 28	12 36	12 0	3 36	1 48	2 44	6 45	5 4	p.m.	7 5	10 3	8 42	...	...	2 33	4 41
Göschenen dep		4 56	6 0	7 38	8 58	10 31	12 41	12 5	3 43	1 50	2 49	7 31	5 9	5 20	7 20		8 47	...	...	2 38	4 46
Wassen..................		5 9	6 18	...	9 11	10 48	12 54	...	3 57	...	...	7 45	...	5 34	...	...	...	...	...	...	...
Gurtnellen	1,2,3	5 23	6 38	...	9 24	11 9	1 8	RC	4 11	...	...	8 0	...	5 48	...	...	...	...	...	...	...
Amsteg	a.m.	5 37	6 56	...	9 37	11 27	1 22	...	4 25	...	...	8 15	RC	6 2	...	...	...	...	...	...	...
Erstfeld..............	4 45	5 53	7 19	8 15	9 55	11 43	1 35	...	4 42	2 26	3 21	8 30	...	6 20	...	...	...	...	...	3 20	...
Altdorf	4 54	6 3	7 33	8 23	10 6	11 52	1 44	...	4 53	2 34	3 29	8 40	...	6 31	...		9 26	...	...	3 28	...
Fluelen..............	5 0	6 10	7 42	8 29	10 14	12 2	1 50	12 46	5 2	2 40	3 31	8 47	...	6 39	...		...	...	...	...	...
Sisikon	5 10	6 23	7 57	...	10 24	12 16	2 2	...	5 12	...	...	8 58	...	6 50	...		...	...	...	...	...
Brunnen	5 19	6 33	8 13	8 44	10 39	12 28	2 12	1 1	5 22	2 54	3 51	9 7	6 1	7 0	...	*—Weekdays only.	9 43	...	...	3 48	...
Schwyz-Seewen	5 26	6 40	8 22	8 50	10 48	12 37	2 20	...	5 29	3 0	3 57	9 14	...	7 8	...		9 49	...	...	...	5 45
Steinen	5 32	6 46	8 30	...	10 55	12 44	2 26	...	5 35	...	...	9 20	...	7 15	...		...	...	...	...	...
Arth-Goldau	5 41	6 55	8 44	9 0	11 5	12 55	2 36	1 16	5 45	3 10	4 9	9 29	6 16	7 25	8 24		10 1	...	...	4 4	5 58
Zug 259B......arr		7a56	9 a36	9 a36	11a47	1 p43	3 p33	1 p43	6p20	3p33	...	10 p9	6 p43	8p11	8p49		1027	...	2&3	4 a45	6 a28
Zurich (260)arr		9a36		10a30	12p49	2 p19	4 p10	2p19	7p22	4p10	...	11p10	7 p30	9p15	9p32		1110	...	a.m.	5 a55	7 a28
Arth-Golddep	5 46	7 3	7 36	9 8	11 27	...	2 45	1 21	5 49	...	4 13	9 31	6 20	7 41	8 30		1010	...	4 28	4 17	6 10
Immensee	5 58	7 15	7 48	9 19	11 39	...	2 57	...	6 1	...	..	9 43	...	7 53	...		...	...	...	...	...
Küssnacht	6 4	7 22	7 54	9 25	11 46	...	3 4	...	6 7	...	4 26	9 49	...	7 59	...		...	...	4 44	...	...
Meggen........ ...	6 12	7 30	8 3	9 32	11 55	...	3 13	...	6 16	...	...	9 57	...	8 7	...	...	...	...	4 53	...	...
Lucerne 258	6 25	7 45	8 17	9 45	12 10	...	3 28	1 51	6 30	...	4 44	10 10	6 50	8 20	9 0	...	1040	...	5 8	4 50	6 40
Basle Swiss...arr		1125	...	11 47	2 p38	...	6 p58	4 p6	9 p0	...	6 p58	...	9 p0	11p3	11p3	...	...	...	...	7 a10	8 a57

Table d'Hote at Goschenen for 11.16 a.m. and 4.4 p.m. from Chiasso.

Extra { Chiasso...dep 6p15 / Lugano ...arr 7 6 }

§—Biasca to Erstfeld 3rd class only, and not on Sundays.

¶—Customs Examination of Luggage by 8.50 a.m. and 1.54 p.m. from Chiasso is made between Chiasso and Bellinzona in the train. RC—Restaurant Car attached. SC—Sleeping Car attached.

MONTE SALVATORE RY.—Dep. from station at Paradiso (on the Lake) for Pazzallo and Salvatore, 8.20, 9.0, 10.20, 11.40 a.m., 2.20, 3.0, 4.20, 5.40 p.m.; and from Salvatore to Paradiso at the same times. In about 30 min. Fares, 2 fr. 40 c. up, 1 fr. 60 c. down; return, 3 fr. 20 c.

*—In July and August only. **MONTE GENEROSO RAILWAY.** ‡—Until 14th September.

fr. c.	Retn											
		Capolago—Lake dep	9 a37	*	2 p50	6‡p46	**Generoso** ....dep	8§a12	1 p34	4*p3	5 p39	
—	fr. c.	Capolago—Gothard	9 43	10a57	2 54	6 51	Bella Vista	8 35	1 55	4 36	5 48	§—Until
5 85	7 80	Bella Vista	10 34	11 47	3 43	7 40	Capolago—Gothard ...	9 24	2 44	5 25	6 36	15th September.
7 50	10 0	**Generoso** ....arr	10 54	12 7	4 3	8 0	**Capolago**—Lake arr	9 27	2 47	...	6 39	

BRUNNEN—MORSCHACH (AXENFELS and AXENSTEIN).

Brunnen	7 a8	7a45	8a29	9 a7	9a42	10a17	11 a2	11a38	11§48	12p30	1 p0	1p49	2p14	3p16	3p37	4§p6	4 p20	4p52	5 p17	5*p27	6§p47	7p23	8§p4
Morschach	7 19	7 56	8 40	9 18	9 53	10 28	11 13	11 49	11 59	12 41	1 11	2 0	2 25	3 27	3 48	4 17	4 31	5 3	5 28	5 38	6 58	7 34	8 15
Axenstein	7 24	8 1	8 45	9 23	9 58	10 33	11 18	11 54	12 4	12 46	1 16	2 5	2 30	3 32	3 53	4 22	4 36	5 8	5 33	5*43	7 3	7 39	8 20
Axenstein	6a50	7a26	8a11	8a46	9a24	9a59	10a34	...	11p19	11a58	12p23	1 p17	2*p7	2p59	3 p9	3p47	4p30	4p45	5 p10	5*p37	6p11	6§23	7 p5
Morschach	6 56	7 32	8 17	8 52	9 30	10 5	10 40	11§15	11 25	12 4	12 29	1 23	2 13	3 5	3 15	3 53	4 36	4 51	5 16	5 43	6 17	6 29	7 11
Brunnen	7 6	7 42	8 27	9 2	9 40	1015	10 50	11 25	11 35	12 14	12 39	1 33	2 23	3 15	3 25	4 3	4 46	5 1	5 26	5 53	6 27	6 39	7 21

Extra.—Brunnen to Axenstein, 2*39, 2.49, 5.54, 6.30, 8§45 p.m. Axenstein to Brunnen, 2.32, 3§59, 7§43, 8§22 p.m. Morschach to Brunnen, 2.2 p.m. *—In July and August only. §—Runs until 10th September.

BIASCA and ACQUAROSSA.

Biasca ....dep	7 a10	9a10	10a50	1 p20	4 p5	5 p47	7 p30	Acquarossa ....dep	6 a29	9 a11	11a47	2 p45	5 p0	6 p36	8 p19
Acquarossa..................arr	7 49	9 50	11 34	1 59	4 49	6 26	8 1	Biasca..........................arr	7 0	9 46	12 18	3 20	5 31	7 7	8 50

BELLINZONA and LOCARNO

All 1,2,3 Class.	a.m.	a.m.	am	a.m.	p.m.	pm	pm	p.m.	pm	p.m.
Bellinzona dep	3 38	5 55	820	11 7	12 46	240	411	6 8	738	9 48
Giubiasco	3 44	6 1	826	1114	12 53	247	417	6 14	744	9 54
Cadenazzo ...	3 52	6 10	835	1127	1 2	256	430	6 22	753	10 5
Gordola	4 6	6 25	850	1143	1 18	311	445	6 36	8 8	1021
Locarno ...arr	4 12	6 32	857	1150	1 25	318	452	6 42	815	1028

	a.m.	a.m.	a.m.	a.m.	p.m.	p.m.	p.m.	p.m.	p.m.	p.m.
Locarno......dep	4 30	7 10	9 13	11 5	1 7	4 10	5 20	7 0	8 40	11 2
Gordola	4 37	7 18	9 20	1113	1 16	4 17	5 28	7 8	8 48	1111
Cadenazzo ...dep	4 51	7 33	9 35	1130	1 31	4 34	5 42	7 23	9 2	1128
Giubiasco	4 59	7 42	9 44	1139	1 42	4 43	5 50	7 33	9 11	1139
Bellizonna 259	5 4	7 47	9 49	1144	1 48	4 48	5 55	7 38	9 16	1145

Customs Examination at Luino.]

BELLINZONA and LUINO.

[*—Sunday only. §—Not on Sunday.

Dist E.M	LUCERNE 259 dep	11p52	1a22	...	5 a8	9a47	11 a0	2 p22	4 p0	4 p0
		1,2,3	1,2,3	1,2,3	1,2,3	1,2,3	1,2,3	1,2,3	1,2,3	2 & 3
		a.m.	a.m.	a.m.	a.m.	p.m.	p.m.	p.m.	p.m.	p.m.
	Bellinzona dp	4 12	5 40	8 55	1047	2 4	4 20	6 25	7*50	7§52
2	Giubiasco	4 19	5 47	9 2	1053	2 11	4 26	6 32	7 56	8 4
5¼	Cadenazzo	4 28	5 56	9 11	11 2	2 20	4 35	6 44	8 5	8 19
10	Magadino	4 39	6 8	9 22	1113	2 32	4 46	6 55	8 17	8 41
12¼	St. Nazzaro	...	6 14	9 29	1119	2 38	4 52	7 4	8 23	8 51
14¼	Ranzo-Gera ...	4 50	6 20	9 36	1125	2 44	4 58	7 11	8 29	9 0
16¾	Pino	4 58	6 27	9 43	1133	2 51	5 5	7 18	8 36	9 10
21	Maccagno	5 10	6 36	9 53	1143	3 1	5 14	7 30	8 48	9 26
24½	**Luino 269 arr**	5 20	6 45	10 3	1152	3 10	5 23	7 40	8 58	9 40
...	TURIN ......arr	9 a50	1235	3 p25	...	7p15	9 p45	11p50	...	...

TURIN 269 dep	...	4 a0	6a35	...	8a54	1125	...	3 p5	8 p0
	1,2,3	1,2,3	1,2,3	2 & 3	1,2,3	1,2,3	2&3	1,2,3	1,2,3
	a.m.	a.m.	a.m.	a.m.	p.m.	p.m.	p.m.	p.m.	a.m.
Luino ......dep	6 25	8 57	1035	11 2	1 24	4 8	6§15	8 14	1215
Maccagno	6 37	9 6	1044	11 17	1 35	4 17	6 30	8 25	1224
Pino	6 48	9 16	1054	11 34	1 47	4 27	6 46	8 37	1235
Ranzo-Gera ...	6 56	9 23	11 1	11 45	1 55	4 34	6 56	8 45	1242
St. Nazzaro	7 3	9 28	11 6	11 53	2 2	4 39	7 6	8 53	...
Magadino	7 10	9 34	1112	12 2	2 9	4 45	7 25	9 0	1253
Cadenazzo	7 22	9 44	1122	12 19	2 22	4 55	7 52	9 13	...
Giubiasco	7 32	9 52	1130	12 32	2 32	5 3	8 6	9 24	1 12
Bellinzona ar	7 38	9 57	1135	12 40	2 38	5 8	8 14	9 30	1 17
LUCERNE 259A	1p51	1p51	4p44	4p44	6p50	9 p0	...	4a50	6a40

ZUG and ARTH-GOLDAU.

§—Not on Sunday.
‡—Sunday only.

	a.m.	a.m.	a.m.	a.m.	a.m.	a.m.	p.m.	p.m.	p.m.	p.m.	p.m.	p.m.	p.m.	p.m.	ng't	a.m.
Zug ....dep	5 §5	7 5	8 6	8 31	9 53	11 0	12§20	1‡15	2 31	4 5	5 2	7 10	9 4	1033	12 0	1 20
Walchwyl	5 26	7 19	...	8 45	...	1113	12 50	1 31	2 44	...	5 24	7 26	9 20	1046	...	...
Arth-Goldau 259 arr	5 43	7 30	8 25	8 54	10 14	1123	1 9	1 42	2 54	4 25	5 43	7 37	9 32	1056	1220	1 45
Arth-Goldau ...dep	4a24	6 a8	7a32	9 a10	1125	1p24	3p13	5p55	6p22	7‡40	7p48	8p32	9p34	10p7	...	...
Walchwyl	4 33	6 17	7 43	9 22	1135	1 32	3 22	6 6	...	...	7 59	...	9 49	...	...	...
Zug (260) ....arr	4 45	6 28	7 56	9 36	1147	1 43	3 33	6 20	6 43	7 58	8 11	8 49	10 9	1027	...	...

VALLORBES and LE BRASSUS.

Vallorbes......dep	8 a 5	11a17	3p35	8 p5	...
Day	8 15	11 27	3 44	8 12	...
Le Pont	8 42	11 58	4 12	8 40	...
Lieu	8 54	12 11	4 24	8 52	...
Sentier-Orient	9 10	12 28	4 40	9 8	...
Le Brassus ...arr	9 18	12 36	4 48	9 16	...

Le Brassus...dep	5a51	9a35	1p45	5 p52	...	...	...
Sentier-Orient	5 59	9 43	1 58	6 0	...	...	...
Lieu	6 14	9 58	2 16	6 15	...	...	...
Le Pont	6 26	10 10	2 37	6 27	...	...	...
Day	6 46	10 31	3 0	6 47	...	...	...
Vallorbes 263B ar	6 56	10 42	3 12	6 57	...	...	...

A—Until 10th Sept.

STANSSTADT and ENGELBERG.

‡—Until 10th Sept.

	a.m.	a.m.	a.m.	a.m.	a.m.	p.m	p.m.	p.m.	p.m	p.m.
Stansstadt...dep	6 0	8 40	1012	1020	1140	2 2	A	3 20	6 25	8 ‡0
Stans	6 14	8 54	1023	1034	1154	2 14	2 16	3 35	6 39	8 21
Dallenwyl	6 29	9 9	...	1049	12 9	—	2 31	3 49	6 54	8 36
Wolfenschiessen	6 39	9 19	A	1059	1219	—	2 41	4 0	7 4	8 45
Grafenort	6 55	9 35	...	1115	1235	...	2 57	4 16	7 20	—
Engelberg.....arr	7 36	1015	1131	1156	1 16	...	3 38	4 59	8 1	...

	a.m.	a.m.	a.m.	a.m.		p.m.	p.m.	p.m.	p.m.
Engelberg......dep	6 35	8 25	9‡57	10 34	...	2 15	3 55	5 47	7 1
Grafenort	7 15	9 6	...	11 16	p.m.	2 56	4 36	6 27	7 42
Wolfenschies.	7 30	9 22	...	11 32	1 ‡5	3 11	4 51	6 42	7 57
Dallenwyl ...	7 40	9 32	...	11 41	1 14	3 21	5 0	6 53	8 7
Stans	7 56	9 49	11 1	11 56	1 30	3 36	5 16	7 9	8 23
Stansstadt arr	8 8	10 1	1111	12 8	1 42	3 48	5 28	7 21	8 35

STANSERHORN RAILWAY.

Stansstadt ....dep	6 a0	7 a28	8a40	...	10a20	11a40	12p47	2 p2	3 p2	3 p20	4 p10	5 p38	6p25	...
Stans ....dep	6 15	7 58	8 58	9 a51	10 41	11 58	1 32	2 15	3 20	3 50	4 25	6 0	6 51	...
Stanserhorn ....arr	7 5	8 47	9 48	10 39	11 31	12 45	2 20	3 3	4 10	4 39	5 15	6 50	7 39	...
Stanserhorn ....dep	6 a48	8 a55	10 a4	10a22	12p28	1 p10	2 p46	4 p22	4 p58	5 p40	6p15	7 p22	...	...
Stans.......................arr	7 38	9 45	10 55	11 10	1 18	2 0	3 34	5 12	5 48	6 30	7 5	8 10	...	...
Stansstadt ....arr	8 8	10 1	11 19	12 8	1 42	2 32	3 48	5 28	6 7	...	7 21	8 35	...	...

BERNE and NEUCHATEL via Kerzers.

Dist E.M		2&3	1,2,3	1,2,3	1,2,3	1,2,3	2 & 3	1,2,3	1,2,3	1,2,3	1,2,3	2&3	1 & 2	1 Cl						
		a.m.	a.m.	a.m.	a.m.	p.m.	p.m	p.m.	p.m	p.m.	p.m.	p.m	p.m.	p.m.						
—	**Berne ....dep**	5 33	6 40	9 19	1045	2 10	2 30	4 12	5 40	7 8	8 20	9 25	10 0	11 5	...	...	...	...	...	...
10¼	Gummenen	6 7	6 59	9 43	1117	2 32	3 0	4 40	6 0	7 36	8 46	9 58	...	...	...	...	...	...	...	...
13¾	Kerzers.....................	6 23	...	9 56	1130	2 42	3 11	4 51	6 6	7 51	8 57	1010	...	A	...	...	...	...	...	...
18½	Ins	6 40	7 11	10 7	1147	2 51	3 25	5 5	6 15	8 7	9 12	1024	10 40	...	...	...	...	...	...	...
24	St. Blaise..................	6 58	...	10 21	12 4	...	3 42	5 21	...	8 24	9 26	1040	...	...	...	...	...	...	...	...
26¾	**Neuchatel........arr**	7 12	7 25	10 28	1212	3 7	3 52	5 30	6 31	8 34	9 34	1049	11 0	12 0	...	...	...	...	...	...
59¼	PONTARL'E 266 ...arr	7a41	7a41	11 36	...	3p28	...	7p40	7 p40	1040	10p40	1125	11 25	1218	...	...	...	...	...	...
146½	DIJON 52A ....arr	9a49	9a49	4 p44	...	6p46	...	1117	11p17	...	1 a39	...	2 a10	2a30	...	...	...	...	...	...
342	PARIS 51 ....arr	2p25	2p25	...	...	11p0	...	4a55	4 a55	...	6 a20	...	6 a45	7a15	...	...	...	...	...	...

...	PARIS ....dep	...	7 p45	...	1015	1015	10p50	...	10p50	...	...	8a30	8 a30	2 p20	...	...	...
...	DIJON ....dep	...	12 28	...	3 a4	3 a4	3 a47	...	4 a20	5 a44	5a44	1246	12p46	6 p42	...	...	...
...	PONTARLIER......dep	...	3 a8	...	5a20	5a20	6 a50	...	9 a40	12 35	1235	3p28	4 p40	9 p2	...	...	...
		1,2,3	1 Cl	2 & 3	1 &2	1,2,3	1,2,3	1,2,3	1,2,3	1,2,3	1,2,3	1,2,3	1,2,3	1,2,3			
		a.m.	a.m.	a.m.	a.m.	a.m.	a.m.	a.m.	p.m.	p.m.	p.m.	p.m.	p.m.	p.m.			
...	**Neuchatel........dep**	5 0	5 15	6 10	7 42	7 50	9 29	1155	2 4	3 58	4 30	5 55	8 42	11 13	...	...	...
...	St. Blaise.................	5 9	...	6 18	...	7 59	9 36	12 3	2 12	4 5	4 40	...	8 49	...	...	...	...
...	Ins	5 34	A	6 35	7 58	8 17	9 48	1219	2 30	4 16	5 1	6 13	9 8	11 27	...	...	...
...	Kerzers.....................	5 50	...	6 47	...	8 35	9 57	1233	2 49	4 26	5 20	6 22	9 25	...	...	...	...
...	Gummenen	6 5	...	7 2	...	8 53	10 8	1247	3 2	4 38	5 38	6 34	9 39	...	...	...	...
...	**Berne ....arr**	6 40	6 8	7 35	8 35	9 32	10 32	1 18	3 31	5 0	6 13	6 55	10 15	12 1	...	...	...

A—Luxus-Zug runs from 9th July until 15th September

GUMMENEN and FLAMATT.

Gümmenen dep	7 a3	9a43	12p47	2p32	...	5p35	6p40	7p37	8p48
Laupen	7 34	9 53	12 56	2 44	4 p0	5 45	6 49	7 46	8 57
Flamatt ...arr	8 0	10 9	1 13	3 5	4 20	6 0	...	8 3	...

Flamatt ...dep	6a15	8a15	11a36	1p30	3p18	4p55	6p10	...	8p13	...
Laupen	6 40	6 38	12 18	2 5	3 35	5 14	6 24	7p10	8 30	...
Gümmenen arr	6 52	8 48	12 30	2 17	...	5 23	6 32	7 20	8 38	...

FRIBOURG and INS.

Fribourg dep	6 a0	8a34	10a39	1218	1p45	4p44	7 p5	8 p8	9p18	...
Murten	6 46	9 24	11 25	2 40	3 28	5 45	7 48	8 44	10 8	...
Ins 259B ..arr	7 0	9 42	11 43	3 18	3 44	6 4	8 4	8 58	1027	...

Ins........dep	6a16	8 a0	10a7	12p22	2p50	4p20	6p18	9p10	11p28	...
Murten	6 39	8 19	1030	12 45	3 11	5 4	6 25	9 26	11 43	...
Fribourg arr	7 30	9 3	1113	1 38	4 4	6 38	7 26	10 5	12 18	...

ZURICH, ZUG, and LUCERNE.

		1,2,3	1,2,3	1,2,3	1,2,3	1,2,3	1,2,3	1,2,3	1,2,3	1,2,3	1,2,3	2&3	1,2,3	1,2,3	1,2,3	1,2,3	2&3	1,2,3	1,2,3	1,2,3	1 & 2	1,2,3
MUNICH 193...dep		...	11p20	11p20	...	...	...	...	...	...	...	...	6a50	6a50	o.m	...	...	...	1020	12p50	...	...
ROMANSH'N 262A		dep	...	...	...	7 a4	...	...	...	1112	1112	1112	1 p2	1 p2	3 6	3 p6	...	...	4 p8	7 p15	...	...
		a.m.	a.m.	a.m.	a.m.	a.m.	a.m.	no'n	p.m	p.m.	p.m.	p.m.	p.m	p.m	o.m.	p.m.			p.m.	p.m.	p.m.	ng't
Zurich ....dep		5 58	7 12	7 25	7 30	9 5	10 0	...	1 13	1 45	2 8	2 36	3 14	3 22	5 5	5 51	...	...	8 8	9 30	11 15	1230
Enge		6 6	7 20	7 33	7 40	9 14	10 8	...	1 24	1 53	2 16	2 46	3 21	3 29	5 12	6 2	...	...	8 17	9 37	11 23	...
Thalweil ..dep		6 20	7 31	7 43	7 57	9 26	10 23	...	1 45	2 4	2 28	3 5	3 32	3 40	5 25	6 15	...	...	8 29	9 55	...	...
Horgen-Oberd.		6 31	...	...	8 7	...	10 34	...	1 59	...	...	3 19	...	...	...	6 26	...	...	...	10 6	11 42	...
Sihlbrugg		6 38	...	RC	8 14	...	10 41	...	2 8	RC	A	3 27	...	...	...	6 34	...	...	...	10 13	...	...
Zug ....arr		6 50	7 53	8 5	8 26	9 49	10 53	...	2 21	2 28	2 50	3 43	3 57	4 3	5 48	6 47	p.m.	p.m.	8 59	10 25	11 58	1 15
Zurich ......dep		4 52	⋮	...	6†58	⋮	9 33	12 0	⋮	⋮	⋮	2 15	⋮	...	⋮	5 15	6*10	7 13	⋮	9†25	...	...
Altstetten		5 5	⋮	...	7 8	⋮	9 43	12 6	⋮	⋮	⋮	2 23	⋮	...	⋮	5 22	6 21	7 23	⋮	9 32	...	...
Birmensdorf		5 38	⋮	...	7 32	⋮	10 2	1222	⋮	⋮	⋮	2 42	⋮	...	⋮	5 41	6 48	7 41	⋮	9 48	...	...
Bonstetten		5 55	⋮	...	7 41	⋮	10 12	1230	⋮	⋮	⋮	2 53	⋮	...	⋮	5 52	7 2	7 50	⋮	9 56	...	...
Affoltern		6‡12	⋮	...	7 53	⋮	10 24	1241	⋮	⋮	⋮	3 6	⋮	...	⋮	6 5	7 18	8 2	⋮	10 7	...	...
Mettmenstetten		6‡21	⋮	...	7 59	⋮	10 31	1247	⋮	⋮	⋮	3 13	⋮	...	⋮	6 11	7 28	8 9	⋮	10 13	...	...
Knonau.......dep		‡28	⋮	...	8 3	⋮	10 36	1251	⋮	⋮	⋮	3 18	⋮	3 Cl	⋮	6 16	7 35	8 15	⋮	10 17	...	...
Zug ......arr a.m.		6 47	⋮	...	8 15	⋮	10 49	1 2	⋮	⋮	⋮	3 31	⋮	p.m	⋮	6 30	7 54	8 30	⋮	10 29	...	...
Zug ....dep	5 45	6 53	7 55	...	8 28	9 57	10 58	1 3	2 33	┘	2 52	4 5	3 59	5 32	5 49	6 50	—	8 40	9 1	10 32	...	...
Cham	5 57	7 0	...	...	8 35	...	11 6	1 10	2 40	...	...	4 13	...	5 42	...	6 58	...	8 49	9 9	10 39	...	...
Rothkreuz ar	6 8	7 7	...	...	8 42	...	11 14	1 17	2 47	...	...	4 22	...	5 52	...	7 6	...	8 57	...	10 46	...	...
„ dep	—	7 8	...	...	8 43	...	11 16	1 18	2 49	...	...	4 28	...	—	...	7 8	...	8 58	...	10 47	...	...
Gisikon		7 14	...	...	8 49	...	11 23	1 24	2 55	...	...	4 34	...	...	...	7 15	...	9 4	...	10 53	...	...
Ebikon		7 21	...	...	8 56	...	11 30	1 31	3 3	...	...	4 41	...	...	...	7 23	...	9 12	...	11 10	...	...
Lucerne.......arr		7 33	8 25	...	9 8	1030	11 42	1 43	3 14	...	3 22	4 52	4 29	...	6 19	7 35	...	9 23	9 35	11 12	...	...
BERNE 265......arr		9 a45	...	...	...	1p45	...	3p50	...	...	...	8 p0	8 p0	...	9p10	11p17	...	...	...	...	...	...

†—2&3 class between Zurich and Zug. *—Weekdays only. RC—Restaurant Car in this train. SC—Sleeping Car.
A—Runs until 31st August.

LUCERNE, ZUG, and ZURICH.

	1,2,3	2&3	1,2,3	1,2,3	1,2,3	1,2,3	2&3	1,2,3	1,2,3	1,2,3	1,2,3	1&2	2 & 3	1 & 2	1,2,3	1,2,3	1,2,3	1,2,3	1,2,3	1,2,3	1,2,3
BERNE 265 ....dep	...	...	...	...	6a55	7a48	*	...	1050	...	1 p45	...	2 p8	2 p8	...	...	5p12	...	5p12	6p52	6 p52
			a.m.	a.m.	a.m.	a.m.	a.m.	p.m.	p.m.		p.m.		p.m.	p.m.	p.m.		p.m.		p.m.	p.m.	p.m.
Lucerne ......dep	...	...	5 55	7 35	9 15	11 5	1142	1 20	2 16	...	4 5	...	5 17	6 20	7 13	...	7 57	...	8 20	9 43	10 0
Ebikon	...	...	6 6	7 47	...	1117	12 2	...	2 30	...	4 17	...	5 33	⋮	...	...	...	...	8 33	9 55	...
Gisikon	...	...	6 13	7 57	...	1124	1224	...	2 39	...	4 24	...	5 47	⋮	...	...	...	...	8 43	10 3	...
Rothkreuz ...arr	...	...	6 18	8 3	...	1129	1232	...	2 45	...	4 28	...	5 55	⋮	B	...	...	...	8 50	10 8	...
„ ...dep	...	...	6 19	8 6	...	1130	1252	...	2 47	...	4 29	...	6 5	⋮	...	...	...	...	8 57	10 9	...
Cham	...	...	6 27	8 14	...	1138	1 5	1 46	2 57	...	4 37	...	6 17	⋮	...	...	...	...	9 8	1016	...
Zug ....arr	...	a.m.	6 34	8 20	9 47	1144	2 3	1 52	3 3	...	4 44	...	6 27	6 50	7 45	...	8 27	...	9 14	1022	10 32
Zug ....dep	...	5 8	6 51	8†38	⋮	1234	—	2†28	⋮	...	4†50	...	6 55	⋮	...	...	⋮	...	9†20	⋮	...
Knonau	...	5 24	7 3	8 51	⋮	1250	...	2 42	⋮	...	5 4	...	7‡16	⋮	...	...	⋮	...	9 37	⋮	...
Mettmenstetten	...	5 31	7 8	8 57	⋮	1256	...	2 48	⋮	...	5 10	...	7‡26	⋮	...	...	⋮	...	9 44	⋮	...
Affoltern	...	5 39	7 15	9 4	⋮	1 3	...	2 55	⋮	...	5 17	...	7‡41	⋮	...	...	⋮	...	9 54	⋮	...
Bonstetten	...	5 54	7 27	9 17	⋮	1 17	...	3 9	⋮	...	5 31	...	8‡10	⋮	...	...	⋮	...	1010	⋮	...
Birmensdorf	...	6 2	7 33	9 24	⋮	1 24	...	3 17	⋮	...	5 40	...	8‡20	⋮	...	...	⋮	...	1018	⋮	...
Altstetten	...	6 16	7 44	9 38	⋮	1 37	1,2,3	3 30	⋮	...	5 53	...	8‡43	⋮	...	...	⋮	...	1032	⋮	...
Zurich .....arr	a.m.	6 23	7 50	9 45	⋮	1 45	p.m.	3 37	⋮	p.m.	6 0	p.m.	8 50	⋮	...	p.m.	⋮	p.m.	1040	⋮	...
Zug ....dep	4 50	...	6 40	8 26	9 49	1153	1 44	1 54	3 6	3 34	4 47	6 47	6 58	6 52	7 47	8 3	8 30	8 50	9 17	1031	10 37
Sihlbrugg	5 9	...	6 57	8 47	...	12 9	...	...	3 25	...	5 3	...	7‡34	...	...	B	...	...	9 39	RC	...
Horgen-Oberdorf	5 15	...	7 3	8 52	...	1214	RC	2 13	3 31	RC	5 8	...	7‡41	...	B	8 22	...	9 8	9 45	...	...
Thalweil ....arr	5 24	...	7 9	9 0	10 10	1221	...	2 20	3 40	3 53	5 17	...	7‡53	7 12	8 9	8 29	8 51	9 15	9 57	1053	10 59
Enge ....arr	5 46	...	7 21	9 24	10 23	1240	...	2 30	3 56	..	5 32	...	8‡25	7 24	8 18	8 41	9 7	9 26	1014	11 3	11 9
Zurich 262......arr	5 55	...	7 28	9 36	10 30	1249	2 19	2 38	4 4	4 10	5 40	7 22	8§29	7 30	...	8 50	9 15	9 32	1024	1110	11 15
ROMANSHORN arr	8a48	...	10a30	1210	12 33	3p49	...	4 p28	6p16	6p16	...	...	...	10p47	...	...	...	...	...	...	⋮
MUNICH 199 ...arr	...	...	5 p15	7 p5	7 p5	...	...	9 p55	...	...	...	...	...	...	...	...	...	...	...	...	7 a5

‡—Earlier departures from these stations on Sunday. §—Zurich-Wiedikon. B—Sunday only.

WETTINGEN and OERLIKON.

All 2 & 3 class.	a.m.	a.m.	a.m.	p.m.	p.m.	p.m.	p.m.
Wettingen ....dep	5 20	7 0	9 12	12 50	5 32	6‡30	7 38
Buchs-Dällikon	5 38	7 19	9 33	1 10	5 51	6 49	7 57
Regensdorf-Watt	5 44	7 25	9 40	1 16	5 57	—	8 3
Seebach	5 57	7 36	9 54	1 30	6 10	...	8 15
Oerlikon ....arr	6 0	7 39	9 58	1 33	6 14	...	8 18
ZURICH ....arr	6 a12	7 a50	1015	1 p48	6 28	...	8 30

‡—Weekdays only

ZURICH ....dep	6 a0	8 a0	11 a5	2 p26	...	6 p31	8p54
	a.m.	a.m.	a.m.	p.m.		p.m.	p.m.
Oerlikon ....dep	6 12	8 12	11 24	2 42	...	6 48	9 15
Seebach	6 16	8 16	11 30	2 47	...	6 52	9 19
Regensdorf-Watt	6 28	8 28	11 46	3 0	p.m.	7 4	9 31
Buchs-Dällikon	6 34	8 34	11 54	3 7	6‡53	7 10	9 37
Wettingen ....arr	6 50	8 52	1217	3 26	7 11	7 27	9 55

BIEL and MAGGLINGEN (Macolin).—Fare, 80c. upward, 50c. downward: return, 1fr. Trains in each direction, from 7.20 a.m. until 9.30 p.m., hourly service (in afternoon half-hourly).

BIEL and LEUBRINGEN (Evilard).—Fare, upward 50c., downward, 30c.; return 65c. Trains in each direction, twice every hour, from 6.0 a.m. to 10.50 p.m.

KRIENS (Lucerne) and SONNENBERG in 10 minutes. Trains in each direction every 12 minutes from 6.12 a.m. until 9.48 p.m.

RORSCHACH and SCHAFFHAUSEN.

		a.m.	a.m.	Until 15th Sept.	a.m.	a.m.	p.m.	p.m.	p.m.	p.m.	p.m.		*—Week days only.	
Rorschach Bahnhof...dep		4 55	6 13	...	7 50	9 55	12 14	3 16	5 55	6 33	8 33	...	...	...
,, Hafen ...... ,,		5 0	6 18	...	7 58	10 0	12 20	3 22	6 1	6 41	8 41	...	...	...
Arbon		5 12	6 23		8 12	1013	12 33	3 35	6 10	6 55	8 56	...	...	...
Romanshorn...arr		5 24	6 41		8 24	1025	12 46	3 47	6 19	7 8	9 8	...	...	...
,, ...dep		5 30	6 44		8 30	1037	12 54	3 54	6 24	7 38	9 15	...	...	...
Guttingen		5 45	...		8 45	1052	1 9	4 8	...	7 52	9 31	...	...	...
Munsterlingen		5 56	6 59		8 56	11 3	1 19	4 19	6 39	8 3	9 42	...	...	...
Kreuzlingen		6 3	7 5		9 2	1110	1 26	4 25	6 45	8 10	9 49	...	...	...
Constance ... arr		6 10	7 7	a.m.	9 5	1113	1 29	4 28	6 52	8 13	9 52	...	...	...
Constance ... dep		6 15		7 11	9 12	1220	1 33	4 32	6 56	8 25	—	...	...	...
Emmishofen-Kreuz.		6 21	...	7 15	9 21	1223	1 41	4 40	7 0	8 38	...	...	...	...
Ermatingen		6 34	...	7 23	9 34	1232	1 53	4 51	7 9	8 49	...	...	...	...
Mannenbach		6 39	...	...	9 39	...	1 58	4 56	...	8 54	...	...	...	...
Berlingen		6 44	...	...	9 44	...	*2 2	5 0	...	8 59	...	...	...	...
Steckborn		6 51	...	7 33	9 50	1243	2 8	5 6	7 1	9 5	...	...	...	...
Mammern	a.m.	7 0	...	7 41	9 59	1251	2 16	5 14	7 27	9 13	...	...	...	...
Stein-a-Rhein	5 28	7 12	...	7 48	10 11	1258	2 25	5 23	7 34	9 22	...	...	...	...
Etzwellen	5 40	7 23	...	...	10 24	1 4	2 32	5 31	7 41	9 32	...	...	...	...
Diessenhofen	5 53	7 34	...	8 1	10 36	1 12	2 43	5 42	7 50	9 43	...	...	...	...
Feuerthalen	6 11	7 50	...	...	10 53	...	2 57	5 56	...	9 57	...	...	...	...
Schaffhausen	6 15	7 54	...	8 13	10 57	1 24	3 0	6 0	8 2	10 0	...	...	...	...

		a.m.	a.m.		a.m.	p.m.	Until 15th Sept.	p.m.	p.m.	p.m.	p.m.	p.m.	
Schaffhausen dep	...	4 48	6 57	...	9 42	1225	...	1 30	4 26	6 31	7 16	9 35	...
Feuerthalen	...	4 53	7 1	...	9 47	1230	...	1 35	4 30	6 36	...	9 40	...
Diessenhofen	...	5 10	7 13	...	10 4	1246	...	1 53	4 43	6 54	7 29	9 56	...
Etzwellen	...	5 23	7 25	...	10 22	1 2	...	2 12	4 58	7 8	7 39	10 8	...
Stein-a-Rhein	...	5 29	7 30	...	10 28	1 7	...	2 18	5 4	7 13	7 45	1013	...
Mammern	...	5 38	7 40	...	10 37	1 16	...	2 28	5 13	—	7 54	1022	...
Steckborn	...	5 46	7 48	...	10 46	1 24	...	2 37	5 21	...	8 2	1030	...
Berlingen	...	5 51	7 53	...	10 53	1 29	...	2 43	5 26	...	8 7	1035	...
Mannenbach	...	5 55	7 57	...	10 58	1 34	...	2 48	5 31	...	8 11	1040	...
Ermatingen	...	6 0	8 2	...	11 5	1 39	...	2 54	5 36	...	8 16	1045	...
Emmis.-Kreuzlingen	...	6 12	8 13	...	11 18	1 50	...	3 6	5 47	...	8 27	1056	...
Constance ... arr	a.m.	6 20	8 20	a.m.	11 21	1 52	p.m.	3 14	5 50	...	8 30	1058	...
Constance ... dep	4 52	6 26	8 25	9 26	11 30	☞	1 58	3 20	5 54	...	8 35	—	...
Kreuzlingen	4 56	6 30	8 29	9 33	11 39		2 3	3 24	6 4	...	8 41	...	...
Munsterlingen	5 2	6 36	8 35	9 45	11 45		2 7	3 30	6 10	...	8 50	...	...
Guttingen	5 13	6 46	8 43	10 3	11 56		2 23	3 41	6 20	...	9 0	...	...
Romans-horn arr	5 27	7 0	8 52	1030	12 10		2 37	3 54	6 34	...	9 13	...	...
Romans-horn dep	5 37	7 7	8 55	1038	12 19		2 43	4 1	6 42	...	9 23	...	...
Arbon	5 54	7 21	9 4	1052	12 35		2 57	4 15	6 58	...	9 39	...	...
Rorschach Hf. arr	6 5	7 32	9 11	11 3	12 46	...	3 8	4 26	7 9	...	9 50	...	...
,, Bahnhof arr	6 13	7 40	9 17	1110	12 55	...	3 16	4 34	7 15	...	9 57	...	...

§—Sunday only.

SINGEN and WINTERTHUR.

		a.m.	a.m.	a.m.	p.m.	p.m.	p.m.	p.m.	p.m.	p.m.	p.m.
Singen dep	...	5 *0	6 50	9 56	12 8	1*25	1§45	4 30	6*15	7 9	8 50
Ramsen	...	5 17	7 3	10 9	1235	1 50	1 58	4 41	6 30	7 22	9 6
Etzwellen	...	5 41	7 26	10 27	1255	2 9	2 9	5 32	6 42	7 45	9 30
Stammheim	a.m.	5 51	7 33	10 35	1 13	2 56	2 44	5 39	—	7 56	9 41
Thalheim	5*34	6 22	7 55	10 59	1 34	3 50	3 8	6 0	...	8 27	10 9
Ober Winterthur	5 51	6 45	8 11	11 16	1 49	4 31	3 25	6 17	...	8 50	1029
Winterthur arr	5 56	6 54	8 17	11 22	1 55	4 39	3 31	6 23	...	8 58	1037

* Weekdays only.

		a.m.	a.m.			a.m.	a.m.	p.m.	p.m.	p.m.	p.m.	
Winterthur dep	...	6 25	8 35	...	...	10*8	11§58	1 12	4 5	6 33	8 29	...
Ober Winterthur	...	6 31	8 42	...	...	1019	12 5	1 18	4 11	6 40	8 36	...
Thalheim	...	6 47	8 58	...	...	1058	12 20	1 35	4 26	7 0	8 53	...
Stammheim	a.m.	7 9	9 20	a.m.	a.m.	1147	12 44	1 57	4 48	7 24	9 15	...
Etzwellen	5*37	7 27	9 33	10§30	10*30	12 5	1 10	2 33	5 35	7 42	9 34	...
Ramsen	5 48	7 37	9 44	10 41	10 50	1 33	1 22	2 46	5 46	7 51	9 48	...
Singen 144 arr	6 1	7 48	9 56	10 52	11 10	1 55	1 35	3 0	5 58	8 1	10 5	...

All 2 and 3 class.]

AARAU and WETTINGEN.

Dist.											
	Aarau dep	4*a50	...	6a10	9*a3	9§a19	11a25	1§p50	1*p50	4p50	7p40
2½	Suhr	‡	...	6 24	9 20	9 33	11 40	2 6	2 7	5 6	7 52
7¼	Lenzburg (257)	5 8	5a15	6 47	9 57	9 57	11 55	2 19	2 28	5 26	8 7
10	Othmarsingen	—	5 25	6 56	10 9	10 5	12 7	2 28	2 40	5 35	8 15
13½	Mellingen	...	5 38	7 7	1028	10 18	12 19	2 38	2 56	5 46	8 26
17	Baden Oberstadt	...	5 56	7 20	1049	10 30	12 34	2 50	3 13	5 59	8 40
18	**Wettingen 262** arr	...	6 0	7 23	1054	10 35	12 38	2 53	3 17	6 2	8 43

Wettingen dep	6a10	9a8	1022	1p 2	3*p28	4§p48	6p15	7*16	9 pl	...
Baden Oberstadt	6 14	9 12	1029	1 6	3 40	4 52	6 24	7 21	9 5	...
Mellingen	6 27	9 26	1046	1 20	4 12	5 5	6 39	7 34	9 18	...
Othmarsingen	6 40	9 42	11 3	1 34	4 40	5 16	6 51	7 47	9 30	...
Lenzburg	6 52	9 53	1115	1 43	5 20	5 28	7 1	8 0	9 58	...
Suhr	7 13	10 11	1135	2 1	5 45	5 45	7 19	...	...	...
Aarau arr	7 23	10 20	1144	2 10	5 54	5 54	7 30	8‡22	10‡10	...

*—Weekdays only. ‡—Via Ruppersweil. §—Sunday only.

All 2 and 3 class.]

BADEN and BULACH.

§—Sunday dep. 10.56 a.m.

E.M.											
	Baden dep	7 a44	12p10	3 p58	8 p32	...	...	...	...	...	...
1¼	Wettingen	7 54	12 20	4 18	9 0	...	...	...	...	...	...
3¾	Würenlos	8 3	12 34	4 31	9 11	...	...	...	...	...	...
7¾	Buchs	8 21	12 57	4 53	9 30	...	...	...	...	...	...
13	Niederglatt	8 38	1 19	5 11	9 46	...	...	...	...	...	...
16½	**Bulach 261B** arr	8 46	1 29	5 22	9 55	...	...	...	...	...	...

Bulach dep	5 a4	9 a43	2 p18	7 p8	...	...	...	...	...	...
Niederglatt	5 12	10 2	2 30	7 20	...	...	...	...	...	...
Buchs	5 28	10 26	2 51	7 39	...	...	...	...	...	...
Würenlos	5 41	10 45	3 6	7 56	...	...	...	...	...	...
Wettingen	5 55	11 §3	3 32	8 17	...	...	...	...	...	...
Baden (262) arr	6 0	11 8	3 37	8 21	...	...	...	...	...	...

CONSTANCE and WIL.

	a.m.	a.m.	a.m.	a.m.	p.m.	p.m.	p.m.	p.m.	
Constance dep	...	6 2	8 5	10 37	1 5	3 52	6 39	8 47	...
Emmishofen-Kreuz.	...	6 13	8 14	10 41	1 9	3 56	6 49	8 52	...
Weinfelden	5 30	7 9	9 11	11 34	2 14	4 54	7 49	9 40	...
Marwil	5 47	7 26	9 28	11 51	2 31	5 12	8 6	—	...
Wil (268) arr	6 12	7 51	9 53	12 16	2 56	5 39	8 32	...	...

	a.m.	a.m.	a.m.	a.m.	p.m.	p.m.	p.m.	p.m.	
Wil dep	...	6 24	8 23	10 50	1 18	5 7	6 52	8 40	...
Marwil	...	6 46	8 46	11 13	1 41	5 26	7 13	9 3	...
Weinfelden	5 8	7 10	9 10	11 33	2 15	5 47	7 48	9 19	...
Emmishofen-K.	5 56	7 58	9 57	12 22	3 3	6 33	8 42	—	...
Constance arr	5 59	8 1	10 0	12 25	3 6	6 36	8 45	...	...

SCHAFFHAUSEN and OBERWIESEN-STUHLINGEN.

Schaffhausen dep	7a24	9a50	11a35	1p20	1p45	3p20	6p25	8p39
Oberwiesen Stuhlingen arr	8 38	11 3	1 4	2 35	2 58	4 33	7 40	9 52

Oberwiesen-Stuhlingen dep	5a30	6a53	9a22	11a41	1p40	4 p3	5p53
Schaffhausen arr	6 46	8 6	1046	12 51	2 51	5 21	7 6

BASLE, BRUGG, and ZURICH.

STRASSBURG dep	...	...	4a28	4a28	4a28	4a28	6 a0	6 a0	7a40	9a14	9 a14	11a1	11a13	1113	1254	3p53	3p53	3p53	5p15	7p21	...
	1Cl.	2&3	1,2,3	1,2,3	1,2,3	1,2,3	1 &2	1,2,3	1,2,3	1,2,3	2 & 3	1,2,3	1,2,3	2 &3	1,2,3	1,2,3	1,2,3	1,2,3	2&3	1,2,3	2&3
Basle—	a.m.	a m.	a.m.	a.m.	a.m.	a.m.	a.m.	a.m.	a.m.	a.m.	p.m.	p.m.	p.m.	p.m	p.m.	p.m.	p.m.	p.m.	p.m.	p.m.	
Swiss Bahnhof dep	5 10	5 30	6 45	7 5	7 10	7 20	8 20	8 50	1034	1130	12‡15	1 18	1 37	2 26	4 12	6 15	6 25	6 38	8 *1	9 39	...
Muttenz	...	5 38	...	...	...	7 28	...	...	1041	...	12 24	...	...	2 35	4 20	...	6 32	...	8 19	...	...
Pratteln	...	5 44	6 55	...	...	7 34	...	...	1047	RC	12 32	1 28	...	2 41	4 26	RC	6 37	...	8 29	9 50	...
Augst	...	5 49	...	...	...	7 39	...	...	1053	...	12 39	...	...	2 47	4 31	...	6 42	...	8 36	...	...
Rheinfelden	...	5 58	7 7	...	7 31	7 48	...	9 9	11 2	1149	12 50	1 38	1 56	2 57	4 40	...	6 49	7 0	8 48	10 0	...
Möhlin	...	6 4	...	...	...	7 54	...	...	11 9	...	12 59	...	...	3 3	4 46	...	6 54	...	8 57	...	...
Mumpf	...	6 14	...	...	...	8 4	...	...	1120	...	1 13	...	...	3 14	4 56	...	7 3	...	9 13	...	...
Stein-Säckingen	...	6 22	7 22	...	7 47	8 13	...	...	1127	...	1 21	1 53	2 12	3 28	5 3	...	7 7	7 17	9 32	1015	...
Eiken	...	6 28	...	...	Via Bulach.	8 21	...	...	1132	...	1 30	To Winterthur.	...	3 36	5 9	...	To Winterthur.	7 23	9 42	...	...
Frick	E	6 35	...	...		8 30	...	...	1138	...	1 40		...	3 44	5 16	...		7 30	9 53	1025	...
Hornussen	...	6 45	...	...		8 41	A	...	1147	...	1 57		...	3 55	5 26	...		7 39	1012	...	...
Effingen	...	6 54	...	...		8 52	...	...	1155	...	2 14		...	4 6	5 35	...		7 51	1044	SC	...
Schinznach Dorf	...	6 59	...	...		8 57	...	...	1159	...	2 21		...	4 12	5 40	...		7 56	1051	...	...
Brugg arr a.m.	...	7 8	7 57	...		9 7	...	9 59	12 7	1235	2 33		2 48	4 22	5 49	...		8 7	11 6	1050	p.m.
262 dep 7 20	...	8 12	7 58	...		9 12	...	10 0	12 9	1236	3 2		2 50	4 26	5 55	...		8 11	—	1051	1056
Turgi ...7 26	...	8 18	...	...	...	9 18	...	...	1215	...	3 9		...	4 33	6 3	...		8 18	...	...	11 2
Baden ...7 36	6 22	8 30	8 11	...	...	9 27	9 35	10 14	1225	1248	3 19	...	3 3	4 43	6 14	7§31	...	8 28	...	11 3	1112
Altstetten ...	...	9 6	...	...	...	...	...	...	...	...	3 50	...	...	5 15	6 49	...	...	...	...	...	1142
Zurich ...arr 8 2	6 45	9 14	8 35	8 42	9 31	9 52	9 58	10 37	1248	1 13	3 57	...	3 29	5 23	6 57	7 55	...	8 58	...	1125	1150

ZURICH, BRUGG, and BASLE.

	2 & 3	1,2,3	2 & 3	1,2,3	1,2,3	1,2,3	1,2,3	1,2,3	1,2,3	1,2,3	1 & 2	1 2 3	2&3	2&3	1,2,3	1,2,3	1,2,3	1,2,3	1,2,3	1,2,3	1Cl.
	a.m.	a.m.		a.m.	a.m.	a.m.	a.m.	p.m.	p.m.	p.m.	p.m.	p m	p.m.	p.m.	p.m.	p.m.		p.m.	p.m.	p.m	p.m.
Zurich ...dep	4 52	6 27	...	7 16	8 25	9 45	1138	12 6	...	1 59	2 30	2 48	Sunday only.	Weekdays only.	5 22	6 40	...	7 36	9 5	9 12	10 5
Altstetten	4 59	6 34	...	...	Via Bulach.	9 52	RC	1214	...	2 7	...	...			...	RC	...	7 44	...	...	...
Baden	5 31	7 2	...	7 41		1020	12 1	1251	...	2 41	2 55	3 12			5 52	7 5	...	8 17	...	9 36	1028
Turgi	5 38	7 9	a.m.	...		1027	...	1 0	...	2 50	...	...			5 59	...	...	8 25	...	...	...
Brugg arr a.m.	5 43	7 14	†	7 50		1032	1211	1 5	...	2 55	3 5	3 21	...		6 5	7 15	...	8 30	9 28	9 45	...
dep 4†40	5 54	—	7 23	7 51		1033	1212	—	1 11	—	3 6	3 23	3 30	3 30	6 8	7 16	...	8 39	9 29	9 47	...
Schinznach D 4 56	6 9	...	7 42	...		1045	...	...	1 25	...	...	...	3 45	3 51	6 25	...	...	8 53	...	...	E
Effingen ...5 3	6 15	...	7 50	...		1050	...	...	1 30	...	...	...	3 51	3 59	6 31	...	...	9 0	...	...	...
Hornussen ...5 11	6 22	...	7 59	...		1056	...	...	1 36	...	...	...	3 59	4 8	6 37	...	...	9 7	...	...	...
Frick ...5 20	6 29	a.m.	8 7	8 20		11 2	...	...	1 42	...	...	...	4 7	4 18	6 44	...	C	9 14	...	...	...
Eiken ...5 27	6 35	C	8 33	...		11 7	...	p.m.	1 47	p.m.	...	...	4 13	4 26	6 50	...	p.m.	9 20	...	...	...
Stein-Säckin. 5 38	6 45	7 21	8 39	8 29		1114	...	1253	1 55	3 25	...	3 56	4 20	4 38	6 56	7 49	8 4	9 26	...	1021	...
Mumpf ...5 45	6 50	7 26	9 31	...		1119	...	...	2 0	...	...	...	4 26	4 45	7 1	...	8 9	9 31	...	...	...
Möhlin ...6 0	7 0	7 36	9 47	...		1128	...	...	2 11	3 37	...	...	4 37	4 59	7 11	...	8 18	9 41	...	...	...
Rheinfelden 6 12	7 6	7 42	9 54	8 44	10 6	1133	...	1 7	2 17	3 42	3 52	4 11	4 43	5 10	7 17	8 7	8 23	9 47	...	1037	...
Augst ...6 24	7 15	7 50	10 24	...	...	1139	...	...	2 26	...	...	...	4 50	5 20	7 25	...	8 30	9 56	...	...	...
Pratteln ...6 32	7 21	7 55	10 32	8 54	...	1144	...	C	2 32	C	...	...	4 56	5 28	7 32	...	8 36	10 2	...	...	...
Muttenz ...6 38	7 27	8 0	10 39	...	...	1149	...	...	2 38	...	...	...	5 2	5 35	7 37	...	8 41	10 8	...	...	...
Basle 209 ar 6 50	7 35	8 8	10 55	9 3	1025	1156	1 18	1 25	2 45	4 2	4 12	4 29	5 10	5 50	7 45	8 28	8 48	1017	1045	1058	1145
STRASSBURG 9a29	9a29	1120	2 p9	11a20	2 p9	2 p9	3p46	3p46	5p18	6p44	6 p44	6p44	...	9p50	11p35	11p35	11p35	1a34	1a34	1a34	...

A—Runs until 15th September.
C—From Winterthur.
SC—Sleeping Car.
E—Engadine Express, runs from 2nd July until 15th September.
RC—Restaurant Car.

*—On Sunday dep. Basle 8.15 p.m., arr. Brugg 9.44 p.m., with earlier departures from intermediate stations.
†—Weekdays only.
§—Stops to set down only.
‡—On Sunday at 1.0 p.m.

LOCARNO and BIGNASCO.

Locarno-Gothard dep	5 a5	a.m.	9a23	11a55	1p30	3p23	5p27	7 p0	...
,, St. Ant. dep	5 15	7 43	9 32	12 10	1 43	3 32	5 36	7 17	...
Pontebrolla	5 26	7 54	9 43	12 20	1 54	3 43	5 47	7 28	...
Maggia	5 52	8 22	10 9	—	2 21	4 9	6 13	7 54	...
Bignasco ...arr	6 34	9 2	1048	...	3 1	4 49	6 53	8 34	...

Bignasco ...dep	5a46	7a43	9a32	...	1p42	3p34	5p36	7p16	...
Maggia	6 23	8 19	10 8	p.m.	2 19	4 10	6 12	7 53	...
Pontebrolla	6 46	8 44	1031	1226	2 41	4 33	6 35	8 16	...
Locarno St.A. arr	6 56	8 52	1041	1236	2 51	4 43	6 45	8 26	...
,, Gothard B.	7 5	9 6	1057	1246	3 1	4 52	6 56	8 34	...

BELLINZONA and MESOCCO.—Electric Rly.

‡—Until 15th Sept.

	a.m.	a.m.	a.m.	p.m.	p.m.	p.m.	p.m.
Bellinzona ...dep	6 21	8 4	10 30	12 9	2 12	5 42	8 25
Castione	6 30	8 17	10 40	12 18	2 29	5 52	8 34
Lostallo	7 15	9 11	11 25	1 ‡4	3 20	6 40	9 19
Mesocco ...arr	7 46	9 42	11 55	1 ‡34	3 52	7 9	9 48

	a.m.	a.m.	a.m.	a.m.	p.m.	p.m.	p.m.
Mesocco ...dep	4 55	6 10	8 10	10 5	12 ‡2	2 5	5 47
Lostallo	5 20	6 35	8 40	10 30	12‡27	2 33	6 12
Castione	6 4	7 22	9 33	11 15	1 10	3 28	6 58
Bellinzona ...arr	6 13	7 31	9 45	11 25	1 21	3 38	7 8

AARAU and MENZIKEN.—Electric Tramway.

	a.m.	a.m.	a.m.	p.m.	p.m.	p.m.	p.m.	p.m.
Aarau ...dep	6 58	8 45	10 9	12 50	2 37	4 4	6 19	7 41
Suhr Ausweiche	7 12	8 59	10 23	1 4	2 51	4 18	6 35	7 55
Menziken arr	8 20	9 59	11 28	2 9	3 56	5 23	7 44	9 0

	a.m.	a.m.	a.m.	a.m.	p.m.	p.m.	p.m.	p.m.
Menziken ...dep	5 6	6 19	7 9	9 55	12 36	3 7	5 24	8 20
Suhr Ausweiche	6 10	7 25	8 18	11 0	1 41	4 17	6 34	9 28
Aarau ...arr	6 25	7 39	8 32	11 14	1 55	4 31	6 50	9 4[illegible]

AARAU and SCHÖFTLAND.

	a.m.		
Aarau ...dep	6 57	...	From 7.59 a.m. to 10.29 p.m. Ten trains daily, extra on Sunday.
Schöftland ...arr	7 42	...	

	a.m.		
Schöftland ...dep	5 56	...	From 6.53 a.m. to 8.44 p.m. Ten trains daily, extra on Sunday.
Aarau ...arr	6 43	...	

LUGANO and DINO.

Lugano dep	5a30	6a52	8a30	10a30	12 p2	2p10	4p10	6p30	8p48	...
Pregassona	5 46	7 8	8 48	10 48	12 20	2 28	4 28	6 47	8 58	...
Dino ...arr	6 2	7 24	9 4	11 4	12 36	2 45	4 45	7 3	9 14	...

Dino ...dep	6 a8	7a30	9a10	11a10	1 p0	3 p0	5p10	7p10	9p20	...
Pregassona	6 23	7 45	9 25	11 25	1 15	3 15	5 25	7 25	9 35	...
Lugano arr	6 39	7 59	9 40	11 39	1 30	3 30	5 39	7 40	9 50	...

ALLAMAN and GIMEL—Electric Railway.

Allaman	6a23	7a37	8a42	1036	1p40	3p27	5p10	7p40	9p15	...
Aubonne	6 33	7 55	9 0	1050	1 52	3 40	5 23	7 52	9 25	...
Gimel ...	6 57	8 22	9 27	1117	2 19	4 7	5 50	8 19	9 52	...

Gimel	6a57	8a33	9a40	12p51	2p40	4p21	6 p10	8p58	10p19
Aubonne...	7 21	9 8	1010	1 23	3 9	4 50	6 40	9 30	10 48
Allaman...	7 31	9 18	1020	1 33	3 19	5 0	6 50	9 40	10 58

Service between Allaman and Aubonne almost half-hourly.

ROLLE and GIMEL—Electric Railway.

Rolle Port dep	7a16	10 a1	1p17	3 p6	5 p7	7 p34	9p25	...
Mont Eglise......	7 49	10 21	1 37	3 21	5 25	7 56	9 45	...
Gimel ......arr	8 23	10 55	2 11	3 55	5 59	8 30	10 19	...

Gimel ......dep	6a42	8a24	11a49	2p12	4 p9	6 p1	8p34	...
Mont Eglise......	7 16	8 58	12 23	2 46	4 43	6 35	9 8	...
Rolle Port arr	7 36	9 13	12 38	3 5	5 2	6 54	9 23	...

GLAND and BEGNINS (Electric Railway).—In 17 mins. Gland dep. 6.49, 7.55, 9.3, 10.1, 11.2 a.m., 1.21, 3.11, 4.42, 5.28, 6.33, 8.25, 9.42, 10.42 p.m. Begnins dep. 6.4, 7.20, 8.38, 9.38, 10.39 a.m., 12.52, 2.35, 4.20, 5.5, 6.10, 7.35, 9.18, and 10.10 p.m.

All 2 & 3 class. **BURGDORF and THUN.**

Dist. E.M.		a.m.		a.m.	a.m.	a.m.	a.m.	a.m.	p.m		p.m.	p.m.	p.m.	p.m.	p.m.	p.m.			
	Burgdorf ....dep	4 53	...	6 52	7 24	...	8 27	10 0	12 7	...	1 45	3 14	4 48	6 26	8 46	9 43	...	...	...
4	Hasle-Rüegsau.........	5 7	...	7 6	7 35	...	8 41	10 14	12 21	...	1 59	3 27	5 2	6 41	8 58	9 57	...	...	...
10	Walkringen..........	5 26	a.m.	7 26	...	...	8 58	10 33	12 40	p.m.	2 18	3 56	5 22	7 2	9 14	1016	...	...	...
16	**Konolfingen** 265	5 45	7 24	7 46	8 6	8 35	9 18	10 53	1 0	1 20	2 38	4 16	5 42	7 22	9 33	1035	...	...	...
19	Oberdiessbach	6 3	7 34	8 1	8 15	8 47	9 39	11 10	1 12	1 31	2 53	4 43	6 1	7 42	9 43	1055	...	...	...
25	**Thun** ....arr	6 24	...	8 24	8 31	9 8	10 0	11 30	1 31	1 52	3 14	5 4	6 22	8 3	10 0	1115	...	...	...
25¾	SCHERZLIGEN...arr	6 34	...	...	...	9 38	9 38	11 43	2 37	...	3 25	...	6 38	8 11	...	...	...	...	...

	a.m.	a.m.	a.m.	a.m.	a.m.	a.m.	p.m.	p.m.	p.m.	p.m.	p m.	p.m	p.m.	p.m.	p.m.				
SCHERZLIGEN..dep	...	...	...	7 45	8 45	...	12 25	...	3 7	...	6 7	...	...	...	9 0	...	...	...	...
Thun ....dep	5 20	6 43	...	7 52	9 28	1050	12 34	2 4	3 54	5 9	6 44	...	7 26	8 45	10 5	...	...	...	...
Oberdiessbach.........	5 42	7 5	7 39	8 14	9 50	1111	12 56	2 26	4 16	5 30	7 4	...	7 43	9 6	10 27	...	...	...	...
Konolfingen.........	6 13	7 15	7 49	8 36	10 11	1133	1 13	2 46	4 35	5 49	7 14	7 35	7 54	9 20	10 46	...	...	...	...
Walkringen...............	6 34	—	—	8 57	10 32	1155	1 34	3 7	4 56	6 9	—	7 56	...	9 39	11 5	...	...	...	...
Hasle-Rüegsau.........	6 52	...	...	9 16	10 51	1210	1 59	3 27	5 13	6 26	...	8 13	...	9 57	11 22	...	...	...	...
Burgdorf 257...arr	7 6	...	...	9 30	11 5	1223	2 13	3 42	5 26	6 40	...	8 27	8 38	10 10	11 35	...	...	...	...

BURGENSTOCK RAILWAY.—Fares, up 1fr. 50c., and 1fr.; down 1fr. and 50c.
From the Pier (Kehrsiten) to the Burgenstock, and from Burgenstock to the Pier, 7.15, 7.35, 7.55, 8.15, 8.40, 9.5, 9.25, 9.47, 10.30, 10.45, 11.10 a.m., 12.0 noon, 12.15, 12.42, 1.10, 1.45, 2.10, 2.25, 2.45, 3.15, 3.38, 3.55, 4.10, 4.35, 4‡55, 5.15, 5.30, 5.45, 6.10, 6.35, 7.20, 7.45 p.m. ‡—Until 10th September.

TRAVERS to ST. SULPICE and BUTTES. ‡—3.8 p.m. on Sunday.

Travers..............dep	...	7 a2	8 a9	9 a0	11a32	1p15	3‡p15	3p55	...	6p25	7p40	9p35	10p50
Fleurier	5a48	7 32	8 34	9 25	11 55	1 40	4 12	4 20	5p55	6 54	8 5	10 0	11 15
Buttes ....arr	5 55	7 39	...	9 57	12 7	1 53	...	4 32	6 2	7 5	8 17	...	11 45

Buttes ....dep	6 a0	...	7a44	10a8	12p12	1p58	...	4p37	6p12	7p10	8p25	...	11p50
Fleurier	6 10	7a31	8 20	1025	12 22	2 10	2p40	4 52	6 23	7 17	8 45	10p12	11 57
Travers 265........arr	6 35	7 56	8 44	11 8	12 47	2 35	3 40	5 17	6 48	...	9 15	10 37	...

Fleurier..............dep	5a28	8a 0	9a30	12 p2	1p20	4p26	5p35	8p12	11p18	...	...	...
St. Sulpice..........arr	5 33	8 5	9 35	12 7	1 25	4 31	5 40	8 17	11 23	...	...	...

St. Sulpice ....dep	5a38	8a10	9a40	12p12	1p59	4p36	5p45	8p25	11p28	...	...	...	...
Fleurier ....arr	5 43	8 15	9 45	12 17	2 4	4p41	5 50	8 30	11p23	...	...	...	...

UETLIBERG RAILWAY.

‡—Until 15th Sept.
*—Sunday only.

(The Zurich Station is at Selnau, 15 min. from Hauptbahnhof).
From Zurich, 6‡30, 9.30, 11.0 a.m., 1*0, 2.0, 3.15, 4.35, 6.10, 7.20, 9‡0 p.m.
From Uetliberg, 7‡40, 10.15, 11.30 a.m., 1*30, 2.30, 3.45, 5.15, 6.40, 8.10, 9‡30 p.m.
FARES: Zurich to Uetliberg 3 fr. 50 c. and 2 fr.; Uetliberg to Zurich, 2 fr. 50 c. and 1 fr. 20 c.; return fare, 5 fr. and 3 fr.

ZURICH and SIHLBRUGG.

Zurich-Selnau dp	5a45	7a53	10a5	1210	2p25	3p50	5p25	6p30	7p16	9p30
„ -Giesshübel	5 48	7 57	10 8	1213	2 29	3 55	5 28	6 34	7 50	9 33
„ -Manegg ...	5 56	8 5	1016	...	2 37	4 3	5 36	6 43	7 58	...
Adliswell............	6 7	8 14	1025	1230	2 47	4 12	5 46	6 54	8 7	9 50
Langnau Gattikon	6 16	8 23	1034	1239	2 56	4 21	5 55	7 4	8 17	9 59
Sihlwald	6 23	8 31	1041	1246	3 3	4 28	6 2	7 11	8 24	—
Sihlbrugg 260 arr	6 32	8 41	...	1255	3 14	4 38	6 13	7 22	...	...

Sihlbrugg dep	...	6a43	8a59	...	1 p5	3p42	5p16	6p42	7p57
Sihlwald	5a33	6 52	9 8	11a5	1 14	3 51	5 29	6 53	8 7
Langnau Gatt.	5 41	6 59	9 15	1113	1 22	4 0	5 36	7 2	8 16
Adliswell......	5 51	7 9	9 25	1123	1 32	4 12	5 47	7 11	8 26
Zurich-Maneg	6 2	7 18	...	1132	...	4 21	5 56	...	8 35
„ -Giesshüb	6 12	7 26	9 46	1140	1 49	4 31	6 6	7 29	8 45
„ -Selnau...	6 15	7 29	9 50	1143	1 52	4 34	6 9	7 32	8 48

CHAUX-DE-FONDS and SAIGNELEGIER.

Chaux-de-Fonds ...dep	6a58	9a11	11 a1	2 p1	5p36	7p40
Le Boechet	7 51	10 1	11 54	2 59	6 29	8 35
Saignelégier ....arr	8 20	1030	12 23	3 35	6 58	9 4

Saignelégier ......dep	5a35	8a49	11 a0	2p 8	5p43	7p50
Le Boechet	6 5	9 19	11 37	2 38	6 14	8 20
Chaux-de-Fonds arr	6 58	10 9	12 35	3 30	7 7	9 12

SAIGNELEGIER and GLOVELIER.

Saignelégier dep	6a35	8a23	10a33	1p43	4p50	7 p2
Glovelier ......arr	7 32	9 25	11 25	2 55	5 47	8 0

Glovelier ...dep	7a46	9a50	1250	4p15	6p43	8p20
Saignelégier arr	8 46	1055	1 52	5 36	7 45	9 22

WETZIKON and MEILEN.

Wetzikon.....dep	5 a58	8 a17	10a42	11a50	1 p10	3 p44	6 p12	7 p36
Langholz..........	6 41	9 1	11 26	12 33	2 8	4 29	7 2	8 35
Meilen ....arr	7 14	9 38	12 3	1 5	2 48	5 4	7 36	9 5

Meilen ......dep	7 a55	10a21	12p34	2 p0	3 p38	5 p55	7 p52	10 p3
Langholz.........	8 33	11 0	1 15	2 37	4 20	6 31	8 30	10 36
Wetzikon ...arr	9 19	11 45	1 57	3 21	5 14	7 17	9 15	...

Langholz ......dep	4a55	6a43	9 a5	11a35	2p10	4p32	6p45	8p35
Uster ....arr	5 37	7 27	9 50	12 20	2 52	5 27	7 30	9 17

Uster ....dep	5a50	8a10	10a5	12p50	3p30	5p56	7p48	9p24
Langholz ...arr	6 34	8 56	1051	1 52	4 16	6 41	8 29	1010

WINTERTHUR and STEIN SACKINGEN.

*—Weekdays only. §—Sunday only.

		a.m.	a.m.	a.m.	a.m.	a.m.		a.m.		p.m.			p.m.	p.m.		p.m.	p.m.	p.m.	p.m.
Winterthur ....dep	...	5 2	*	7 *4	8 26	8 31	...	11 14	...	1 21	...	...	2*50	2 §57	...	5 6	6 6	6*41	8 25
Pfungen	...	5 17	...	7 28	...	8 46	a.m.	11 29	...	1 36	p.m	...	3 14	3 14	...	5 21	6§16	6 57	8 39
Bulach	...	5 38	6 34	7 48	8 46	9 3	9*58	11 42	...	1 50	2 47	p.m.	3 32	3 28	...	5 42	6 30	7 11	8 52
Eglisau	...	5 55	7 0	—	9 0	9 16	1032	11 52	...	2 4	2 55	3 *2	—	3 46	...	5 54	6 48	—	9 0
Weiach-Kaiserstuhl	...	6 8	7 16	...	:	9 29	11 7	...	*	2 15	—	3 23	...	3 57	...	6 7	6 57	...	9 10
Reckingen	a.m.	6 21	7 29	...	:	9 44	1136	...	p.m.	2 28	—	3 49	p.m.	4 10	p.m.	6 21	...	...	9 21
Koblenz	5*20	6 39	8 16	...	:	1011	12 8	12 23	1227	2 43	...	4 19	4*50	4 24	5 §27	6 37	7 23	...	9 34
Leibstadt	5 37	6 50	8 30	...	:	1026	—	...	1249	2 52	...	—	5 18	—	5 39	—	7 36	...	9 44
Etzgen	5 50	6 59	8 43	...	:	1038	...	...	1 6	3 2	...	...	5 51	...	5 50	...	7 45	...	9 53
Laufenburg	6 3	7 8	8 55	...	9 43	1049	...	12 43	1 28	3 11	...	...	6 25	...	5 59	...	7 53	...	10 1
Stein Sackingen 261 arr	6 20	7 20	9 18	...	A	11 5	...	12 52	1 46	3 23	...	...	6 44	...	6 12	...	8 3	...	1012

			a.m.	a.m.	a.m.		a.m.	a.m.		a.m.	p.m.	p.m.		p.m.	p.m.	p.m.			
Stein Sackingen......dep	...	...	5 48	6*43	7 48	...	8§11	8*32	...	1132	1 54	3 33	...	5*5	7 8	10 25	...	...	...
Laufenburg	...	...	6 4	7 9	7 58	...	8 23	8 59	...	1147	2 5	3 50	...	5 33	7 20	10 39	...	...	...
Etzgen	...	...	6 14	7 22	...	...	8 31	9 14	...	1157	...	4 0	...	5 58	7 28	10 48	...	...	...
Leibstadt	...	a.m.	6 26	7 36	...	a.m.	8 41	9 32	...	12 9	...	4 12	...	6 17	7 37	10 59	...	...	...
Koblenz	...	5 0	6 42	7 52	8 17	8*27	8 52	10 5	...	1238	2 26	4 37	...	6 50	7 48	11 10	...	...	...
Reckingen	...	5 16	6 59	—	...	8 48	9 6	1040	...	1254	...	4 55	...	7 31	8 2	—	...	...	...
Weiach-Kaiserstuhl	...	5 32	7 15	...	...	9 10	9 19	1114	a.m.	1 8	...	5 12	...	7 59	8 14	...	...	...	...
Eglisau	a.m.	5 58	7 31	...	8 52	9 33	9 33	1136	1149	1 23	2 55	5 31	p.m.	—	8 26	p.m.	...	...	...
Bulach	5*30	6 18	7 52	...	9 2	9 54	9 46	—	12 1	1 38	3 3	5 48	7 *36	...	8 38	9 *25	...	...	...
Pfungen	5 44	6 33	8 6	...	...	1012	10 0	...	—	1 51	3 15	6 4	7 57	...	8 51	10 2	...	...	...
Winterthur ....arr	6 0	6 49	8 22	...	9 24	1032	10 15	...	...	2 5	3 24	6 22	8 18	...	9 5	10 40	...	...	...

A—To Basle (arrive 10.25).

ZURICH, BULACH, and SCHAFFHAUSEN.

	2&3	1,2,3	1,2,3	1,2,3	1,2,3	1,2,3	1,2,3	1,2,3	1,2,3	1,2,3	1,2,3	2&3	2&3	1,2,3	2&3	1,2,3				
		a.m.	a.m.	a.m.	a.m.	p.m.		p.m.	p.m.	p.m.	p.m.	p.m.	p.m.	p.m.	p.m.	p.m.				
Zurich (Haupt.) dep	...	4 53	8 0	8 25	1059	1255	...	3 0	4 20	4 53	6 13	6*20	6 45	8 0	9 54	1137	...	...	...	...
Oerlikon	...	5 4	8 11	...	11 9	1 5	...	3 10	RC	5 6	...	6 31	6 55	8 10	10 5	SC	...	...	...	...
Oberglatt	...	5 21	8 29	...	1122	1 22	...	3 24	...	5 23	...	6 47	7 10	8 25	1021	...	...	...	...	...
Bulach ....arr	a.m.	5 33	8 40	8 50	1132	1 34	p.m.	3 33	...	5 34	6 36	6 59	7 24	8 35	1033	1159	...	...	...	...
,, **260A** ......dep	5*21	5 48	9 10	8 51	1133	1 42	2 47	3 34	4 44	5 36	6 37	—	7 27	8 38	—	12 0	...	...	...	...
Eglisau	5 33	6 3	9 35	9 2	1142	2 5	3 0	3 44	4 45	5 47	6 45	...	7 36	8 48	...	...	...	...	...	...
Rafz	5 46	6 16	9 46	...	1151	2 16	...	3 53	...	5 58	...	...	—	8 59	...	...	...	...	...	...
Neuhausen(Rheinf'l)	6 7	6 40	10 10	9 26	1212	2 40	3 21	4 14	5 13	6 23	7 6	...	...	9 21	...	...	...	...	...	...
Schaffhausen .....arr	6 12	6 45	10 15	9 30	1217	2 45	3 26	4 19	5 18	6 28	7 10	...	...	9 25	...	1230	...	...	...	...
SINGEN 139A ....arr	...	7a35	11a41	9a56	1246	3p24	...	...	5p46	8 p2	8 p2	...	...	10p13	...	1257	...	...	...	...
STUTTGART 193A ar	...	...	...	2 p3	6p38	...	...	...	9p27	1a13	1a13	...	...	...	...	5a45	...	...	...	...

STUTTGART 193 dep	...	...	1258	...	...	...	2 a58	8 a3	...	...	...	...	...	...	...	3 p21	...	...	...	...
SINGEN 139A ...dep	...	...	4a59	6a13	7a46	...	10a25	1141	...	1 p3	...	2p46	5p30	...	6p22	7 p40	...	...	...	...
	2&3	2 &3	1,2,3	1,2,3	1,2,3	2&3	1,2,3	1,2,3	3 Cl.	1,2,3	2&3	1,2,3	1,2,3	2 & 3	1,2,3	1,2,3	3 Cl.			
		a.m.	a.m.	a.m.	a.m.	a.m.	a.m.	p.m.	p.m.	p.m.		p.m.	p.m.	p.m.	p.m.	p.m.	p.m			
Schaffhausen.....dep	...	4 55	5 28	7 0	8 18	...	11 8	12 6	12*17	1 32	...	4 7	6 5	6*30	7 32	8 11	8*37	...	...	...
Neuhausen(Rheinf'l)	...	5 0	SC	7 5	8 23	...	11 13	1211	12 28	1 37	...	4 13	6 11	6 35	7 38	8 16	8 43	...	...	...
Rafz	...	5 26	...	7 29	8 43	...	11 38	RC	1 30	...	...	4 38	6 34	7 1	8 4	...	9 23	...	...	...
Eglisau	...	5 41	5 53	7 39	8 58	9 33	11 49	...	1 50	1 58	...	4 49	6 44	7 13	8 15	8 37	9 40	...	...	...
Bulach ....arr	a.m.	5 54	...	7 50	9 7	9 48	12 1	1240	—	2 6	p.m.	5 1	6 56	7 27	8 26	8 45	—	...	...	...
,, ...dep	5 33	6 18	...	7 52	9 8	9 52	12 3	1241	...	2 7	2 12	5 4	6 59	—	9 6	8 46	...	...	...	...
Oberglatt	5 46	6 35	...	8 7	...	10 4	12 15	...	...	...	2 34	5 21	7 14	...	9 19	...	...	...	...	...
Oerlikon	6 4	6 56	...	8 24	...	1019	12 31	...	...	...	2 55	5 37	7 32	...	9 36	...	...	...	...	...
Zurich ....arr	6 12	7 6	6 25	8 34	9 31	1026	12 40	1 8	...	2 31	3 4	5 46	7 41	...	9 45	9 12	...	...	...	...

RC—Restaurant Car attached. SC—Sleeping Car attached. *—Weekdays only.

Oberglatt ....dep	6a36	8a33	10a12	1p27	3p26	5 p30	7p23
Dielsdorf	6 46	8 43	10 24	1 37	3*47	5 41	7 33
Niederweningen ...arr	7 1	9 0	10 44	1 56	4 14	6 0	7 50

Niederweningen dep	5 a57	7 a34	9 a15	11a40	2 p4	4 p43	6 p36
Dielsdorf	6 15	7 50	9 48	11 58	2 21	5 1	6 53
Oberglatt ....arr	6 25	8 0	10 0	12 8	2 30	5 11	7 3

*—Sunday dep. 3.36 p.m.

ZÜRICH and RAPPERSWIL (via Uster).

Dist E.M.		a.m.	a.m.	a.m.	a.m.	a.m.	p.m.	p.m.	p.m.	p.m.	p.m.	p.m.			p.m.	p.m.	p.m.		
	Zürich ....dep	5 0	7 22	8 33	9 22	1054	12*3	12‖10	1 13	2 26	5 17	6 § 6	...	...	6 31	8 40	10‡30	...	...
5½	**Wallisellen**	5 16	7 38	8 51	9 38	1113	1221	12 52	1 32	2 43	5 33	6 33	...	...	6 48	8 57	10 46	...	...
7¼	Dubendorf	5 21	7 43	8 57	9 43	1118	1225	12 58	1 37	2 48	5 38	6 38	...	...	6 53	9 2	10 51	...	...
11	Nanikon-Greifensee	5 32	7 55	9 8	9 53	1129	—	1 11	1 47	3 0	5 49	6 49	*	...	7 4	9 12	11 2	...	...
13	Uster	5 39	8 2	9 14	9 59	1135	...	1 16	1 52	3 7	5 55	6 55	p.m.	...	7 12	9 19	11 8	...	...
17¼	**Wetzikon**	5 54	8 17	9 29	10 13	1149	...	—	2 5	3 25	6 9	—	6 48	...	7 31	9 38	11 22	...	...
21	Bubikon	6 3	8 26	9 37	10 21	1158	...	...	2 12	3 33	6 17	...	6 59	p.m.	7 40	9 47	11 30	...	...
22½	**Ruti 268**	6 9	8 32	9 45	10 28	12 4	...	...	2 17	3 39	6 22	...	7 4	7 11	7 47	9 52	11 35	...	...
26¾	**Rapperswil**........arr	6 18	8 40	9 54	10 37	1212	...	...	2 24	3 48	6 30	...	...	7 20	7 55	10 0	11 44	...	...

		a.m.	a.m.	a.m.	a.m.	a.m.	a.m.		p.m.	p.m.	p.m.	p.m.	p.m.		p.m.	p.m.	p.m.	
Rapperswil ....dep	...	5 18	...	6 50	8 15	10 9	11 39	...	1231	1 55	3 52	4 55	6 7	p.m.	6 58	7 35	9 7	...
Ruti	...	5 32	...	7 4	8 30	10 25	11 53	...	1243	2 16	4 5	5 10	6 19	6*21	7 13	7 47	9 21	...
Bubikon	*	5 39	*	7 10	8 37	10 32	11 59	...	1249	2 23	4 12	5 16	—	6 29	7 20	—	9 28	...
Wetzikon	a.m.	5 52	6 44	7 22	8 50	10 42	12 14	...	1258	2 40	4 24	5 29	...	6 42	7 34	...	9 40	...
Uster	5 43	6 4	6 57	7 35	9 3	10 54	12 26	§	1 7	2 54	4 36	5 42	...	—	7 48	...	9 53	...
Nanikon-Greifensee	5 49	6 9	7 3	7 42	9 9	10 59	12 31	p.m.	...	3 1	4 41	5 48	...	...	7 55	...	9 58	...
Dubendorf	6 0	6 20	7 14	7 55	9 20	11 9	12 42	12 55	1 18	3 13	4 52	5 58	...	...	8 7	...	10 8	...
Wallisellen	6 5	6 25	7 19	8 0	9 25	11 14	12 47	12 59	1 23	3 19	4 57	6 3	...	...	8 14	...	1013	...
Zürich ....arr	6 20	6 40	7 38	8 15	9 40	11 31	1 2	...	1 37	3 35	5 13	6 28	...	...	8 30	...	1028	...

‖—Saturday only *—Weekdays only. ‡—Runs 45 mins. later on Fridays. §—Saturday and Sunday excepted.

AARAU and ZURICH.—ZURICH, WINTERTHUR, SCHAFFHAUSEN, ROMANSHORN, and RORSCHACH.

BERNE 257 ......dep		...	...	5 a0	...	...	6a50	7a10	9a22	...	...	9a37	10a45	...	10a45	...	1p40	2 p14	2 p14	...	...	5 p5	5 p40	5 p40	...	...	8 p40	...	...
		2&3	2&3	1,2,3	2&3	2&3	1,2,3	2&3	1,2,3	2&3	2&3	1,2,3	1,2,3	2&3	1,2,3	2&3	1&2	1,2,3	2&3	2&3	2&3	1,2,3	1,2,3	1,2,3	2&3	1,2,3	1,2,3	2&3	2&3
		‖—From Baden Oberstadt.	a.m.	a.m.			a.m.	a.m.	a.m.	a.m.		p.m.	p.m.		p.m.	p.m.	p.m.	p.m.	p.m.	p.m.		p.m.	p.m.	p.m.		p.m.	p.m.		p.m.
Aarau ......dep			5 43	6 55	...	...	8 45	10 3	1052	1158	...	1212	12 26	...	12 39	2 27	3 18	4 39	5 11	6 2)	...	6 49	7 14	7 37	...	9 56	10 26	...	11 9
Rupperswell			5 54	...	...	...	...	1011	:	12 7	...	:	:	...	12 48	2 37	:	...	5 19	6 32	...	...	:	7 46	...	:	...	...	1117
Wildegg			6 2	7 8	...	...	8 59	1016	:	1212	...	:	:	...	12 55	2 44	:	4 50	5 26	6 40	...	7 1	:	7 52	...	:	...	...	1122
Schinznach Bad...... A			6 11	...	...	...	9 5	1023	:		...	:	RC	...	1 2	2 52	:	4 56	5 34	6 50	...	...	RC	7 58	...	:	...	...	1129
Brugg ......arr	2&3		6 21	7 19	...	...	9 11	1029	:	...	a.m.	:	:	a.m.	1 9	3 0	:	5 2	5 42	7 0	...	7 11	:	8 4	...	:	10 44	...	1135
BASLE **261** ...dep	a.m.		...	5a30	...	6a45	7a20	8a50	:	...	*	:	:	1130	11a30	1p37	:	2 p26	4 p12	...	...	...	:	6 p38	...	:	...	9p39	...
Brugg ......dep	5 5		6 31	7 20	...	8 12	9 12	1031	:	...	1120	:	:	1258	1 13	3 2	:	5 3	5 55	...	...	7 12	:	8 11	...	:	10 45	1056	...
Turgi	5 12	a.m.	6 39	7 26	...	8 18	9 18	1039	:	...	1140	:	:	1 4	1 20	3 9	:	5 9	6 3	...	...	...	:	8 18	p.m.	:	...	11 2	...
Baden	5 24	5‖56	6 50	7 36	...	8 30	9 27	1052	1121	...	1210	:	12 56	1 13	1 31	3 19	3‡45	5 17	6 14	...	p.m.	7 24	7 43	8 28	8 32	10 26	10 56	1112	...
Wettingen	5 30	6 4	6 56	...	a.m.	8 37	...	11 0	:	a.m.	1215	:	:	1 18	1 36	3 25	:	...	6 20	p.m.	6 58	...	...	...	8 48	...	...	1117	...
Dietikon	5 47	6 19	7 13	...	8 2	8 52	9 40	1115	:	1153		:	:	1 31	1 50	3 40	:	5 31	6 36	6 5	7 10	...	...	8 42	9 3	...	...	1131	...
Schlieren	5 54	6 25	7 20	...	8 8	8 59	...	1122	:	1159	...	:	:	1 37	1 56	3 45	:	...	6 42	6 12	7 16	...	...	...	9 10	...	...	1137	...
Altstetten	6 2	6 31	7 26	...	8 13	9 6	...	1123	:	12 4	...	:	:	1 43	2 2	3 50	:	...	6 49	6 18	7 21	...	...	...	9 17	...	...	1142	...
Zurich ......arr	6 10	6 38	7 34	8 2	8 20	9 14	9 52	1136	1143	1211	...	1 3	1 20	1 50	2 9	3 57	4 8	5 44	6 57	6 25	7 28	7 46	8 5	8 58	9 25	10 50	11 18	1150	...

‡—Sets down only.

Dist. E.M.																															
		2&3	2&3	1,2,3	2&3	2&3	1 2 3	1,2,3	1,2,3	2&3	1,2,3	2&3	1,2,3	2&3	1 2 3	1,2,3	1,2,3	2&3	1,2,3	1,2,3	1,2,3	1,2,3	1,2,3	2&3	1,2,3	1,2,3	1,2,3	2&3	1,2,3	1,2,3	2&3
		a.m.	a.m.	a.m.	a.m.	a.m.	a.m.	a.m.	a.m.	a.m.	a.m.	a.m.	p.m.	p.m.	p.m.	p.m.	p.m.	p.m.	p.m.	p.m.	p.m.	p.m.	p.m.	p.m.	p.m.	p.m.	p.m.	p.m.	p.m.	p.m.	p.m.
—	**Zurich** ......dep	5 55	5 7	6 45	7 5	7 40	8 43	8 54	9 40	10 0	10 48	11 5	1210	1 8	1 35	2 55	3 10	3 44	4 15	4 25	5 53	6 0	6 6	7 8	7 23	8 17	8 30	8 55	9 45	11 30	11 42
3¼	Oerlikon	6 7	5 18	6 55	7 15	7 58	...	...	9 52	1011	...	11 16	1220	1 19	...	...	3 21	3 54	...	...	RC	...	6 16	7 19	7 35	...	...	9 10	9 55	...	11 51
9	Bassersdorf ...arr	6 23	...	...	...	8 19	...	...	...	1026	...	...	...	...	...	...	...	4 9	...	...	...	...	...	7 36	...	...	...	9 32	...	...	...
5¼	Wallisellen	...	5 25	7 0	7 21	...	8 57	...	10 0	...	...	11 23	1226	1 25	...	...	3 27	...	...	RC	6 6	B	6 24	...	7 39	...	8 43	...	10 0	SC	11 57
10¾	Effretikon	6 36	5 42	...	7 37	8 37	...	...	1020	1038	...	11 40	1243	1 43	2 0	...	3 44	4 21	...	...	6 19	...	6 42	7 46	7 58	...	8 56	9 48	...	...	12 13
13	Kemptthal	6 43	5 48	...	7 43	8 45	...	...	1027	1045	...	11 47	1248	1 49	...	...	3 51	4 28	...	...	...	...	6 48	7 53	8 4	...	...	9 56	...	...	12 18
16¾	**Winterthur** ...arr	6 52	5 56	7 21	7 51	8 56	9 20	9 28	1036	1054	11 24	11 56	1256	1 58	2 11	3 29	4 0	4 37	4 50	4 57	6 29	6 35	6 57	8 2	8 12	8 48	9 8	10 7	1024	12 5	12 26
...	**Winterthur** ...dep		6 7	...	8 26	...	...		...	...	...	12 8	...	...	2 18	...	...	...	5 5	...	6 35	...	...	...	8 27	...	9 14	...	...	Via St. Gallen and Bregenz.	...
22½	Henggart		6 21	...	8 41	...	...		...	...	...	12 24	...	...	2 32	...	...	...	5 21	...	6 52	...	...	...	8 40	...	9 28	...	...		...
24¾	Andelfingen		6 28	...	8 48	...	...		...	...	...	12 31	...	...	2 39	...	...	...	5 28	...	7 0	...	...	...	8 46	...	9 35	...	...		...
32¼	Dachsen		6 44	...	9 8	...	...		...	...	...	12 50	...	...	2 57	...	...	...	5 47	...	7 19	...	...	...	9 3	...	9 54	...	...		...
34	Neuhausen (Rheinfall)		6 49	...	9 14	...	...		...	...	...	12 56	...	...	3 3	...	...	...	5 52	...	7 25	...	...	...	9 8	...	10 0	...	...		...
35½	**Schaffhausen** ...arr		6 53	...	9 18	...	...		...	...	...	1 0	...	...	3 8	...	...	...	5 56	...	7 30	...	...	...	9 12	...	10 4	...	...		...
47½	SINGEN **130A** ...arr		7 a35	...	9 a56	...	...		...	...	...	2 p4	...	...	3p47	...	...	...	8 p2	...	8 p2	...	...	...	1013	...	10 34	...	...		...
66½	IMMENDINGEN **144**		8 a£9	...	10a40	2&3	...		2&3	...	...	3 p8	...	...	5p25	...	2&3	...	8p43	...	8p43	...	2&3	...	1138	...	11p38	...	...		...
158	STUTTGART **(193A)**		...	...	2 p3	a.m.	...		§	...	...	...	...	...	9p27	...	p.m.	...	1a13	...	1a13	...	p.m.	...	...	...	5a45	...	...		...
...	**Winterthur** dep	2&3	6 6	7 29	8 *4	9*37	9 31		1039	...	11 28	...	1 2	2 14	...	3 31	4 15	...	4 55	...	...	6 39	6 47	...	...	...	9 17	...	1030		...
20¼	Wiesendangen	a.m.	6 18	7 37	8 27	10 2	...	...	1049	...	...	...	1 14	2 25	...	...	4 31	...	...	...	...	...	6 59	...	...	...	9 28	...	1041		...
26¼	Frauenfeld	5 20	6 36	7 52	9 5	1040	9 50	...	11 5	...	11 48	...	1 32	2 43	...	3 50	4 52	...	5 14	...	...	6 58	7 17	...	...	...	9 45	...	1056		...
32¾	Mullheim-Wigolt ...	5 36	6 54	8 5	9 39	1117	...	...	1121	...	...	...	1 50	3 0	...	...		...	5 23	...	...	...	7 35	...	...	...	10 1	...			...
37½	Weinfelden	5 48	7 6	8 17	10 13	1148	10 7	...	1136	...	12 6	...	2 2	3 12	...	...	...	...	5 42	...	...	...	7 47	...	...	...	10 13	...	...		...
41¼	Sulgen **257B**	6 0	7 19	8 28	10 33	12 9	...	...	1146	...	12 15	...	2 14	3 24	...	...	...	...	5 53	...	...	...	8 0	...	...	...	10 24	...	...		...
47¼	Amrisweil	6 17	7 37	8 41	12 2	1 12	1023	...	12 3	...	12 26	...	2 30	3 41	...	...	...	...	6 9	...	...	...	8 17	...	...	...	10 40	...	...		...
51¼	**Romanshorn** arr	6 25	7 45	8 48	12 15		1030	...	1210	...	12 33	...	2 38	3 49	...	4 28	...	...	6 16	...	...	7 34	8 25	...	...	...	10 47	...	...		...
59	FRIEDRICHSHAFEN arr		8 a37	...	1 p30	...	1123	...	1p30	...	1 p30	...	...	...	...	5p18	...	...	7 p2	...	...	...	10p0	...	...	...	...	...	...		...
65¾	LINDAU **368** ......arr		...	1010	...	...	12p5	...	1p50	...	1 p50	...	...	...	...	5p45	...	...	8 p0	...	...	...	...	...	...	...	...	...	...		2 & 3
203	MUNICH **199** ......arr		...	...	...	...	5p15	...	7 p5	...	7 p5	...	...	...	...	9p55	...	...	...	...	...	...	...	p.m.	...	...	...	...	a.m.	7 a5	a.m.
...	**Romanshorn** dep	7 7	7 51	8 55	12 19	...	1038	...	1219	...	12 50	...	2 43	4 1	...	...	...	...	6 42	...	...	7 40	...	9 23	...	...	10 57	...	5 37	...	6*30
46½	Arbon	7 21	8 22	9 4	12 35	...	1052	...	1235	...	1 25	...	2 57	4 15	...	...	...	...	6 58	...	...	7 49	...	9 39	...	...	1110	...	5 54	...	6 45
60¼	**Rorschach** Hafen	7 32	8 48	9 11	12 46	...	11 3	...	1246	...	1 49	...	3 8	4 26	...	...	...	...	7 9	...	...	7 56	...	9 50	...	...	11 21	...	6 5	...	6 56
61	" Bahnhof	7 40	8 53	9 17	12 55	...	1110	...	1255	...	1 56	...	3 16	4 34	...	...	...	...	7 15	...	...	8 2	...	9 57	...	...	11 25	...	6 13	...	7 3
71½	LINDAU **368** ......arr		10 a5	10a5	...	...	1225	...	2 p3	...	...	...	...	5 p40	...	...	...	...	...	...	...	9 55	...	...	...	...	...	...	...	...	...

A—On Sunday dep. Brugg at 4.50 a.m. B—Restaurant Car Zurich–St. Margrethen in July and August.
*—Weekdays only. §—Sunday only. RC—Restaurant Car. SC—Sleeping Car.

RORSCHACH, SCHAFFHAUSEN, WINTERTHUR, ZURICH.—ZURICH & AARAU.

Station		1,2,3	1,2,3	2&3	1,2,3	1,2,3	2&3	1,2,3	1,2,3	1,2,3	1,2,3	2&3	1,2,3	1,2,3	2&3	1,2,3	1,2,3	2&3	1,2,3	1,2,3	1,2,3	2&3	1,2,3	2&3	1,2,3	1,2,3	1,2,3	1,2,3	2&3
LINDAU 368 ....dep		...	...	...	...	...	...	...	...	7 a40	...	...	...	...	...	10 a5	1253	...	...	...	2p15	...	...	...	...	...	...	6 p15	...
				a.m.	a.m	a.m.		a.m.		a.m.	a.m.					p.m.	p.m.				p.m.			p.m.		p.m.	p.m.	p.m.	p.m
Rorschach Bahnhof dep		...	‡—Earlier on Sunday from these stations.	4 55	6 13	6†28	...	7 50	...	9†24	9 55	...	...	...	...	12 14	2 8	...	...	...	3 16	...	...	5 42	...	5 55	6 33	8 33	10 33
" Hafen ...dep		...		5 0	6 18	6 34	...	7 58	...	9 32	10 0	...	...	...	...	12 20	2 14	...	...	...	3 22	...	...	5 47	...	6 1	6 41	8 41	10 39
Arbon........		...		5 12	6 29	6 45	...	8 12	...	10 50	1013	...	...	...	...	12 33	2 29	...	...	...	3 35	...	...	6 0	...	6 10	6 55	8 56	10 52
Romanshorn ....arr		p.m.		5 24	6 41	—	...	8 24	...	11 7	1025	...	...	...	...	12 46	2 43	...	...	...	3 47	...	...	6 12	...	6 19	7 8	9 8	11 5
MUNICH 199 ....dep		1120		...	...	...	...	...	...	...	...	...	...	6 a50	...	...	...	...	1020	...	...	...	...	...	...	1250	12p50	...	...
LINDAU 368 ....dep		Via Bregenz and St. Gallen.		...	...	...	...	6a45	...	...	...	...	...	11a40	...	...	...	...	2p20	...	...	5p15	...	...	...	5p15	5 p15	7 p55	...
FRIEDRICHSHAFEN dep				...	6 a0	...	...	7a30	...	...	9a20	...	...	11a35	...	...	2 p0	...	2 p0	...	...	6 p8	...	...		...	6 p8	8 p18	...
Romanshorn ....dep				5 38	7 4	...	...	8 32	...	...	1112	...	...	1 2	...	1 25	3 6	...	3 52	...	4 8	7 36	...	...	*—3rd class and weekdays only.	6 41	7 15	9 18	...
Amrisweil........				5 49	7 14	...	...	8 42	...	...	1122	...	...	...	...	1 36	3 16	...	...	...	4 19	7 46	...	...		6 52	7 25	9 29	...
Sulgen (257B)				6 8	7 24	...	...	8 58	...	...	1138	...	...	...	...	1 54	3 29	...	...	...	4 37	8 2	...	...		7 11	7 36	9 46	...
Weinfelden			...	6 19	7 32	...	...	9 9	...	...	1149	...	...	...	...	2 7	3 38	...	...	...	4 50	8 13	...	...		7 25	7 45	9 57	...
Mullheim-Wigolt			a.m.	6 31	...	...	...	9 21	...	...	12 0	...	...	...	...	2 19	...	...	...	...	5 2	8 25	...	p.m.		7 37	...	10 7	...
Frauenfeld (255)			5 34	6 49	7 50	...	...	9 37	...	...	1216	...	...	1 41	...	2 39	3 58	...	4 30	...	5 22	8 40	...	6 12		8 10	8 2	10 23	...
Wiesendangen			5 53	7 8	...	...	...	9 54	...	...	1235	...	...	...	...	2 57	...	...	...	...	5 41	—	...	6 33		8 28	...	10 38	...
Winterthur ....arr			6 4	7 19	8 10	...	...	10 5	...	...	1246	...	...	2 2	...	3 8	4 19	...	4 48	...	5 51	...	...	6 46		8 40	8 21	10 47	...
STUTTGART 193 dep			...	...	1258	...	...	...	12a58	...	2a58	...	...	...	...	8 a3	...	...	...	...	...	...	...	...	10a50	3p21	...	†—Weekdays only.	...
IMMENDINGEN 144 dp			...	...	4a20	...	...	...	5 a56	...	8a31	...	...	...	...	1 p0	...	...	...	...	...	...	...	...	4 p55	7 p2	...		...
SINGEN 139A......dep			...	...	6a13	...	...	...	8 a44	...	1025	...	...	...	...	2 p46	...	...	...	...	...	...	p.m.	...	5 p30	7p40	...		...
Schaffhausen dep			5 a0	...	7 5	...	...	...	9 30	...	1142	...	...	...	...	3 10	...	...	...	...	...	...	4 45	...	6 18	8 18	...		...
Neuhausen (Rheinfall)			5 5	...	7 10	...	...	...	9 36	...	1148	...	...	...	...	3 15	...	...	...	...	...	...	4 50	...	6 24	8 23	...		...
Dachsen........			5 10	...	7 16	...	...	...	9 42	...	1154	...	...	...	...	3 20	...	...	...	...	...	...	4 55	...	6 29	8 28	...		...
Andelfingen........			5 29	...	7 35	...	...	...	10 3	...	1216	...	...	...	...	3 37	...	...	...	...	...	...	5 15	...	6 46	8 45	...		...
Henggart			5 36	...	7 43	...	...	...	10 13	...	1226	...	...	...	...	3 44	...	...	...	...	...	...	5 23	...	6 53	8 53	...		...
Winterthur ......arr			5 51	...	7 58	a.m.	a.m	...	10 30	p.m.	1242	p.m.	p.m.	...	p.m.	3 56	...	p.m.	...	p.m.	...	p.m.	5 39	...	7 6	9 6	...		1,2,3 p.m.
Winterthur......dep	4a40	6 17	6 23	7 26	8 22	8 34	9†12	1010	10 36	12 8	1257	1 3	1 47	2 5	2 16	4 6	4 24	4†30	4 52	5 2	5 57	6 10	6 29	7 11	8 18	9 15	8 29	10 56	10 34
Kemptthal	4 50	...	6 32	7 35	...	8 43	9 24	...	10 46	12 17	...	1 12	...	...	2 26	4 15	...	4 44	...	...	...	6 19	6 38	7 20	...	9 25	...	11 5	...
Effretikon (262A) ...	5 0	...	6 39	...	...	8 51	9 35	1024	10 56	12 24	RC	1 20	...	...	2 35	4 24	...	4 58	...	...	...	6 28	6 46	7 28	...	9 37	8 43	...	...
Wallisellen	5 17	...	...	...	8 46	9 3	...	...	11 9	...	...	1 33	2 10	...	...	4 38	...	...	...	5 27	...	6 41	6 58	...	...	9 52	8 53	...	...
Bassersdorf ......dep	...	...	7‡ 2	...	...	...	9 46	...	...	12 31	...	...	...	...	2 44	...	...	5 10	...	...	...	...	...	7 35	...	...	...	...	...
Oerlikon	5 25	...	7‡22	...	...	9 10	10 5	...	11 15	12 47	...	1 39	...	...	3 0	4 44	...	5 37	...	...	...	6 47	7 4	7 50	...	10 0	8 59	11 24	...
Zurich ....arr	5 34	6 50	7‡32	8 3	8 58	9 20	1015	1045	11 25	12 56	1 30	1 48	2 21	2 40	3 10	4 52	4 58	5 46	5 23	5 40	6 34	6 57	7 14	7 59	8 54	10 10	9 7	11 32	11 5

Station	2&3	2&3	1,2,3	1,2,3	1,2,3	2&3		1,2,3	2&3	1,2,3	2&3	1,2,3	1&2	2&3	1,2,3	2&3	2&3	1,2,3	1,2,3	2&3	2&3	2&3	2&3	1,2,3	2&3	1,2,3	1,2,3	
	a.m.	a.m.	a.m.	a.m.	a.m.	a.m.		a.m.	a.m.	a.m.	a.m.	p.m.	p.m.	p.m.	p.m.	p.m.	p.m.	p.m.	p.m.	p.m.	p.m.	p.m.	p.m.	p.m.	p.m.	p.m.	p.m.	
Zurich ....dep	4 52	...	6 27	7 5	7 23	7 38	...	8 22	9 52	10 55	11 18	12 6	1 45	1 59	3 24	4 10	5 9	5 55	6 15	6 20	6†48	7 36	8 27	9 20	9 45	1137	11 57	§—Takes up only. *—Arrives at Baden Oberstadt.
Altstetten	4 59	...	6 34	...	...	7 45	...	8 29	9 59	...	11 25	1214	...	2 7	...	4 18	5 16	...	...	6 27	7 1	7 44	8 35	...	9 53	1145	...	
Schlieren	5 5	...	6 39	...	...	7 50	...	8 35	10 5	...	11 31	1219	...	2 13	...	4 24	5 22	...	...	6 32	7 9	7 50	8 40	...	9 58	1150	...	
Dietikon	5 11	...	6 44	...	RC	7 55	...	8 41	10 11	...	11 36	1226	...	2 19	...	4 30	5 27	...	RC	6 38	7 17	7 56	8 46	...	10 3	1155	...	
Wettingen (260A)	5 25	5 55	6 57	...	...	—	...	8 57	10 25	...	—	1245	...	2 35	...	4 46	—	...		6 50	7 39	8 11	9 1	...	10 6	12 8	...	
Baden (260A)	5 31	6 28	7 2	7 27	7 46	...	...	9 3	10 30	11 18	11a33	1251	2 §8	2 41	3 48	4 52	...	6 21	6 40	—	7 45	8 17	9 *4	9 44	1021	1212	12§20	
Turgi ....arr	5 37	6 36	7 8	7 32		...	...	9 9	10 36	...	11 43	1258		2 48		5 0	...	...		...	7 54	8 23	—	...	1027	1219	...	
Brugg ....arr	5 43	6 44	7 14	7 37		...	2&3	9 17	10 43	11 28	12 0	1 5		2 55		5 8	...	6 32		...	8 2	8 30	...	9 54	1033	1224	12 29	
BASLE (261)........arr	7a35	...	9 a3	9 a3		...	a.m.	1156	...	1 p18	...	2p45		4p12		7p45	...	8p28		...		1017	...	...	...	...	...	
Brugg ....dep	5 46	6 48	7 15	7 38		...	8†45	9 19	10 46	11 29	...	1 7		2 57		5 14	...	6 33		...	†—Weekdays only.	8 33	...	9 55	...	...	12 30	
Schinznach Bad	5 54	6 55	7 22	...		...	8 54	26	10 53	...	p.m.	1 15		3 5		5 21	...	6 40		...		8 41	...	...	...	...	...	
Wildegg........	6 1	7 1	7 29	...		...	9 4	9 33	11 1	...	12 57	1 23		3 12		5 29	...	...	7 0	...		8 49	...	...	...	...	...	
Rupperswell........	6 7	7 7	7 35	...		...	9 12	9 39	11 8	...	1 7	1 30		3 18		5 38	...	...	...	...		8 56	...	...	...	...	...	
Aarau........arr	6 15	7 15	7 42	7 56	8 13	...	9 23	9 47	11 16	11 47	1 18	1 40	2 34	3 26	4 14	5 49	...	6 57	7 10	...		9 4	...	1015	...	...	12 48	
BERNE (257) ......arr	9a12	9a20	9a20	9a32	10a27	...	...	1255	1 p32	1 p32	...	4p12	4p12	6 p0	6 p0	...	...	8p53	9 p5	...		...	...	12p8	...	...	2 a35	

EFFRETIKON and HINWIL.

E.M.	Station											
	Zurich......dep	6 a0	...	7a40	10 a0	1p35	...	3p44	6 p6	8p30	...	...
	Effretikon dep	6a41	...	8a53	10a40	2 p2	...	4p34	6p47	8p58	...	...
7	Pfäffikon	7 2	...	9 23	11 4	2 25	...	5 5	7 10	9 21	...	...
11¼	Wetzikon........	7 25	8a19	9 47	11 21	2 44	3p35	5 31	7 36	9 41	...	...
14	**Hinwil**........arr	7 35	8 28	9 57	11 31	2 54	3 45	5 40	7 45	9 50	...	...

Station										
Hinwil...dep	4a52	6a33	8a 0	9a15	12 p6	3p15	5p11	7p14	...	...
Wetzikon	5 0	6 42	8 8	9 31	12 30	3 28	5 33	7 53	...	...
Pfäffikon	5 17	7 1	—	9 48	12 47	3 45	5 51	8 11	...	...
Effretikon.	5 36	7 21	...	1013	1 12	4 8	6 15	8 30	...	...
Zurich arr	6 6	7 50	...	1045	1 54	4 52	6 57	9 7	...	...

TURGI and WALDSHUT.

†—Not on Sunday.

E.M.	Station									Station									
	Turgi ......dep	5a58	7a38	9a32	10a45	1p25	3p17	6p19	8p27	**Waldshut** dep	6a31	8a20	9a49	12p29	2p20	4p25	7†12	7 p8	...
8¼	Koblenz	6 43	7 58	10 4	11 44	1 49	3 52	6 44	8 48	Koblenz	6 44	8 35	10 0	12 36	2 27	4 34	7 18	7 49	...
10½	**Waldshut** arr	6 49	8 4	1011	11 53	1 56	4 0	6 52	8 53	**Turgi 262** arr	7 4	9 0	1022	12 57	2 47	4 57	...	8 9	...

ZURICH, MEILEN, RAPPERSWIL, GLARUS, and LINTHAL.

[For other trains between Zurich and Ziegelbrucke see page 268B.]

E M Dist			1,2,3	1,2,3	2&3	1,2,3	2&3	1,2,3	1,2,3	1,2,3	1,2,3	1,2,3	1,2,3	1,2,3	1,2,3	1,2,3	1,2,3	1,2,3	2&3	1,2,3	1,2,5	2&3	1,2,3
	Zurich—		a.m.	a.m.	a.m.	a.m.	a.m.	a.m.	a.m.	a.m.	a.m.	a.m.	a.m.	p.m.	p.m.	p.m.	p.m.	p.m.	p.m.	p.m.	p.m.	p.m.	p.m.
—	Hauptbahnhof...dep		5 5	5 55	7 12	7 20	8 20	8 27	8 51	9 27	1054	1152	1159	1 20	2 32	4 15	4 23	5 5	6 7	7 8	8 35	9 20	1137
1¾	Letten		5 11	6 2	7 18	...	8 26	Via Wadenswell p. 268b.	Via Wadenswell p. 268b.	9 33	Via Uster.	Via Wadenswell p. 268b.	12 5	1 26	2 39	4 21	Via Wadenswell p. 268b.	5 11	6 13	7 14	Via Wadenswell, p. 268b.	9 26	1143
3½	Stadelhofen		5 17	6 9	7 24	...	8 31			9 40			1210	1 31	2 46	4 26		5 18	6 20	7 21		9 33	1149
5	Tiefenbrunnen		5 22	6 14	7 28	...	8 35			9 46			1215	1 35	2 52	4 30		5 23	6 25	7 26		9 38	1154
7¼	Küsnacht		5 31	6 24	7 37	...	8 44			9 55			1224	1 44	3 2	4 39		5 32	6 35	7 35		9 47	12 3
8¼	Erlenbach		5 35	6 28	7 41	...	8 48			9 59			1228	1 48	3 6	4 43		5 36	6 40	7 39		9 51	12 7
12	Meilen		5 46	6 40	7 52	...	8 58			1011			1238	1 58	3 18	4 53		5 48	6 51	7 49		10 3	1217
16½	Stäfa		6 0	6 55	8 6	...	9 12			1026			1254	2 12	3 33	5 7		6 4	7 7	8 4		1018	1231
18	Uerikon		6 5	7 1	8 12	...	9 17			1032			1259	2 16	3 38	5 12		6 10	7 14	8 9		1024	1236
22¼	**Rapperswil** arr		6 16	7 14	8 25	...	9 28			1043			1 12	2 26	3 50	5 23		6 22	7 27	8 20		1037	1247
	Rapperswil dep		6 28	7 35	8 47	...				1053	1215		1 23	2 28	4 5	5 27		6 38		8 25			
28½	Schmerikon		6 44	7 48	9 1	...	...			11 8	1229		1 37	2 40	4 21	5 39		6 50	...	8 41		...	...
30¼	Uznach		6 52	8 3	9 10	...	...			1120	1235		1 41	2 45	4 30	5 43		6 56	...	8 48		...	...
32¼	Benken		6 58	8 10	9 15	...	...			1126	1241			2 50	4 36			7 1	...	8 54		...	...
36¼	Schänis	1,2,3	7 9	8 20	9 25	...	...			1136	1251		...	2 58	4 45	...		7 9	...	9 3		...	...
38	**Ziegelbrücke** arr	a.m.	7 14	8 25	9 29	...	...	1029		1141	1256		...	3 2	4 50	...		7 14	...	9 8	9 52	...	...
	Ziegelbrücke dep	5 20	7 25		9 30	8 28	...	1031		1155	1 3		...	3 9	5 5	...		7 20	...	9 13	9 58	...	...
39¾	**Weesen** arr	5 25	...	...	9 34	8 35	...	...	10 6	...	...	1255	...	3 14	...	p.m.	5 29	...	...	9 18	...	...	...
	Weesen dep	5 47	...	...	9 42	...	...	...	1016	...	...	1 14	...	3 16	...	4*20	5 33	...	...	9 22	...	...	...
39	Urnen	...	7 29	...	...	8 40	...	1036	...	12 0	1 8	...	...	...	5 10	...	...	7 24	...	...	10 2	...	...
40¾	Näfels-Mollis	5 55	7 36	...	9 51	8 46	...	1041	1024	12 6	1 14	1 23	...	3 24	5 16	4 29	5 40	7 30	...	9 30	10 8	...	...
43	Netstal	6 2	7 43	...	9 59	8 54	...	1049	1031	1213	1 20	1 27	...	3 31	5 24	4 37	5 47	7 37	...	9 37	1015	...	...
45	**Glarus** arr	6 7	7 48	...	10 5	9 0	...	1054	1036	1218	1 26	1 31	...	3 36	5 30	4 43	5 53	7 42	...	9 42	1020	...	...
	Glarus dep	6 15	8 2	...			...		1041	1224			...	3 45			5 58	7 47	...		1024	...	...
45½	Ennenda	6 19	8 6	...	...	...	...	...	1045	1228	...	...	...	3 50	...	...	6 2	7 50	...	...	1027	...	...
47¼	Mitlödi	6 25	8 12	...	...	...	...	...	1051	1234	...	...	...	3 58	...	...	6 8	7 56	...	...	1034	...	...
48¼	Schwanden	6 30	8 19	...	...	...	...	...	1056	1239	...	...	...	4 4	...	...	6 14	8 1	...	...	1039	...	...
49½	Nidfurn-Haslen	6 35	8 25	...	...	...	...	...	11 1	1244	...	...	...	4 10	...	...	6 20	8 6	...	...	1044	...	...
51¼	Luchsingen-Hätz.	6 42	8 32	...	...	...	...	...	11 7	1250	...	...	...	4 17	...	...	6 26	8 12	...	...	1050	...	...
52¾	Diesbach-Betsch	6 48	8 39	...	...	...	...	...	1113	1256	...	...	...	4 25	...	...	6 32	8 19	...	...	1056	...	...
53¾	Rüti (Glarus)	6 53	8 45	...	...	...	...	...	1118	1 1	...	...	...	4 32	...	...	6 38	8 25	...	...	11 1	...	...
54¾	**Linthal** arr	6 58	8 50	...	...	...	...	...	1122	1 5	...	...	...	4 37	...	...	6 43	8 30	...	...	11 5	...	...

Extra.—Zurich to Meilen. 6‡33 p.m. *—Runs until 15th September.

‡—Weekdays only.

LINTHAL, GLARUS, and ZURICH.

	2&3	1,2,3	2&3	1,2,3	1,2,3	1,2,3	1,2,3	1,2,3	1,2,3	1,2,3	1,2,3	1,2,3	1,2,3	1,2,3	1,2,3	1,2,3	1,2,3	1,2,3	1,2,3	1,2,3	1,2,3	1,2,3
				a.m.		a.m.		a.m.			a.m.				p.m.		p.m.	p.m.			p.m.	p.m.
Linthal dep	...	...	...	4 38	...	7 15	...	9 25	...	...	1150	...	...	...	1 51	...	3*10	3§40	...	...	6 50	7 57
Rüti (Glarus)	...	...	...	4 41	...	7 19	...	9 29	...	...	1153	...	...	...	1 55	...	3 14	3 44	...	...	6 54	8 1
Diesb'h-Betschwanden	...	...	...	4 44	...	7 23	...	9 33	...	...	1156	...	...	...	1 59	...	3 18	3 48	...	...	6 58	8 5
Luchsingen-Hätzing'n	...	...	...	4 49	...	7 29	...	9 38	...	...	12 1	...	...	...	2 5	...	3 23	3 54	...	...	7 3	8 11
Nidfurn-Haslen	...	...	...	4 55	...	7 35	...	9 43	...	...	12 7	...	...	...	2 11	...	3 29	4 0	...	...	7 9	8 17
Schwanden	...	...	...	4 59	...	7 41	...	9 47	...	...	1211	...	...	...	2 16	...	3 33	4 6	...	...	7 14	8 21
Mitlödi	...	...	...	5 3	...	7 45	...	9 51	...	...	1215	...	...	...	2 20	...	3 37	4 10	...	...	7 18	8 25
Ennenda	...	...	...	5 8	...	7 50		9 56	...	...	1220	...	...	...	2 25	...	3 43	4 16	...	...	7 23	8 30
Glarus arr	...	a.m.	a.m.	5 10	...	7 53	a.m.	9 59	a.m.	a.m.	1222	p.m.	...	...	2 28	...	3 45	4§19	p.m.	p.m.	7 26	8 33
Glarus dep	...	4 49	6 55	5 16	...		8 47	10 5	9 38	1123	1226	1232	...	...	2 35	...	3 50	4 30	5 2	6 27	7 32	8 37
Netstal	...	4 55	7 1	5 21	...	...	8 53	1010	9 45	1129	1231	1238	...	...	2 41	...	3 55	4 36	5 8	6 32	7 38	8 42
Näfels-Mollis	...	5 2	7 8	5 28	...	...	9 0	1016	9 52	1136	1237	1244	...	...	2 48	...	4 1	4 43	5 15	6 39	7 46	8 49
Urnen	...	5 7	...	...	...	...	9 6	1021	...	...	...	1250	...	...	2 53	...	...	4 48	...	...	7 52	...
Weesen arr	...	...	7 16	5 35	...	a.m.	...	...	10 0	1143	1244	...	...	...	...	...	4 7	...	5 21	6 46	...	8 57
Weesen dep	...	...		5 37	...	7 18	...	...	1148	1153		...	...	...	...	...	4 14	...		7 0	...	9 9
Ziegelbrücke arr	...	5 10	...	5 42	...	7 23	9 10	1025	1152	1157	...	1254	p.m.	...	2 56	...		4 52	...	7 5	7 56	9 13
Ziegelbrücke dep	...	5 15	...	5 51	...	7 27	9 21	1033	1153	12 0	...	1 1	1 6	...	3 7	...		5 8	...	7 7	8 7	9 14
Schänis	...	Via Wadenswell p. 268c.	...	5 56	...	7 32	9 26	1039	1158	Via Wadenswell p. 268c.	...	Via Wadenswell p. 268c.	1 12	...	3 12	...		5 14	...	Via Wadenswell p. 268c.	8 12	Via Wadenswell p. 268c.
Benken	...		...	6 5	...	7 42	9 36	1050	12 6		...		1 22	p.m.	3 21	p.m.		5 24	p.m.		8 22	
Uznach	...		...	6 12	...	9 7	9 43	11 1	1211		...		1 30	2 33	3 27	4 32		5 32	6 54		8 37	
Schmerikon	...		...	6 17	2&3	9 12	9 48	11 7	1216		2&3		1 36	2 39	3 32	4 37		5 38	7 0		8 42	
Rapperswil arr	a.m.		a.m.	6 28	a.m.	9 23	10 0	1122	1227		p.m.		1 48	2 50	3 43	4 50		5 50	7 15		8 56	
Rapperswil dep	4‡20		5 22	6 49	7 50	9 28	1015	1137	Via Uster		1244		1 55	2 54	3 50	5 0		5 56	7 34		9 5	
Uerikon	4 35		5 35	7 2	8 3	9 41	1034	1150			1258		Va Uster.	3 7	4 4	5 13		6 9	7 47		9 19	
Stäfa	4 41		5 40	7 7	8 7	9 46	1041	1155			1 3			3 12	4 9	5 19		6 14	7 52		9 24	
Meilen	5 0		5 59	7 22	8 22	10 1	11 0	1210			1 18			3 27	4 25	5 35		6 28	8 7		9 39	
Erlenbach	5 16		6 9	7 32	8 32	1011	1114	1221			1 29			3 38	4 36	5 47		6 39	8 19		9 50	
Küsnacht	5 21		6 13	7 36	8 36	1015	1119	1225			1 33			3 42	4 40	5 51		6 43	8 23		9 54	
Zurich-Tiefenbrun	5 32		6 22	7 44	8 44	1023	1131	1234			1 43			3 50	4 48	6 0		6 52	8 32		10 3	
" Stadelhofen	5 40		6 27	7 49	8 49	1028	1137	1239			1 49			3 55	4 53	6 5		6 57	8 37		10 9	
" Letten	5 47		6 33	7 55	8 54	1033	1144	1245			1 55			4 0	4 58	6 12		7 3	8 43		1015	
" Hauptbhf. arr	5 53	6 30	6 38	8 0	9 0	1038	1150	1250	1 37	1 40	2 0	2 9	3 35	4 5	5 3	6 18	5 30	7 8	8 49	8 22	1020	1032

§—Between Linthal and Glarus runs only from 16th September.

Schwanden and Elm, 8½ miles in 30 minutes. Depart from Schwanden 6.45, 8.22, 11.0 a.m., 1.20, 4.15, 6.25, 8.5 p.m. Depart from Elm 6.33, 8.46, 10.48 a.m., 1.8, 3.5, 6.13, 7.24 p.m.

BULLE and CAILLER FABRIQUE.

Bulle	6a10	7a42	9a15	10a17	12p38	2p50	4p56	7p10	8p45
Broc	6 22	7 54	9 27	10 29	12 50	3 2	5 8	7 22	8 57
Cailler Fabrique	6 25	7 57	9 30	10 32	12 53	3 5	5 11	7 28	9 0

Cailler Fabrique	6a32	8a12	9a35	12 p2	1p44	4p20	6p20	8p12	9 p3
Broc	6 36	8 16	9 39	12 6	1 48	4 24	6 24	8 16	9 7
Bulle	6 48	8 28	9 51	12 17	2 0	4 36	6 36	8 28	9 19

MONTREUX, LES AVANTS, CHATEAU d'OEX, and ZWEISIMMEN.—Electric Railway.

		2 & 3	2 & 3	3 Cl.	1,2,3	2 & 3	2 & 3	1 & 2	1,2,3	2 & 3	2 & 3	2 & 3	1,2,3	2 & 3	2 & 3	2&3	2 & 3	2 & 3
			a.m.	a.m.	a.m.	a.m.	a.m.	a.m.	a.m.	a.m.	p.m.	p.m.	p.m.	p.m.	p.m.	p.m.	p.m.	p.m.
Montreux ......dep		...	5 †57	5 ‡59	7 51	8 41	9 22	9 42	10 28	11 1	12 3	1 51	2 17	2 *42	3 ‖20	4 5	6 11	8 15
Châtelard		...	6 5	6 7	...	8 49	9 29	...	...	11 9	12 11	B	RC	2 50	3 27	5 4	6 19	8 23
Fontanivent		...	6 9	6 11	...	8 53	9 32	A	...	11 13	12 16	2 3	2 28	2 56	3 31	5 9	6 23	8 27
Chernex		...	6 12	6 15	8 5	8 57	9 36	...	RC	11 17	12 20	2 7	2 32	3 0	3 35	5 13	6 27	8 31
Sonzièr......		...	6 16	6 20	...	9 2	9 41	...	...	11 22	12 25	...	...	3 5	3 40	5 18	6 31	8 35
Chamby		...	6 21	6 31	8 16	9 13	9 57	...	10 52	11 29	12 31	2 17	2 43	3 11	3 47	5 25	6 39	8 43
Les Avants		...	6 34	6 51	8 30	9 36	9 59	...	11 5	11 43	12 43	2 31	2 57	3 23	4 2	5 37	6 57	9 2
Montbovon		...	7 9	7 36	9 5	10 17	—	10 48	11 41	12 20	—	3 4	3 33	—	4 45	A	7 34	9 41
Rossinière	2&3	a.m.	7 24	8 0	9 19	10 35	...	...	...	12 36	...	3 19	3 48	...	4 59	—	7 52	9 55
Chateau d'Oex	a.m.	7 ‡20	7 37	8 35	9 33	11 3	...	RC	12 9	12 50	...	3 34	4 3	...	5 15	...	8 13	10 7
Saanen	5 28	7 50	8 3	9 18	9 58	11 51	...	...	12 33	1 17	...	4 2	4 30	...	5 41	...	8 40	—
Gstaad	5 40	8 0	8 11	9 33	10 5	12 3	...	...	12 41	1 28	...	4 11	4 38	...	5 50	...	8 49	...
Zweisimmen 267...arr	6 25	8 45	8 55	10 29	10 45	12 55	...	12 26	1 25	2 12	...	5 0	5 22	...	6 33	...	9 32	...
SPIEZ (267) ......arr	7a51	...	10a15	11a57	11a57	2 p31	...	1 p22	2 p31	3 p50	...	6 p36	6 p36	...	8 p10	...	...	...
INTERLAKEN 267 arr	9a28	...	10a55	12p40	12p40	3 p0	...	1 p42	3 p0	4 p36	...	7 p6	7 p6	...	9 p5	...	...	...

	2 & 3	2 & 3	2 & 3	2 & 3	2&3	2 & 3	1,2,3	3 Cl.	1 & 2	1,2,3	2 & 3	1,2,3	2 & 3	2 & 3	2 & 3
INTERLAKEN ..dep	...	...	...	...	6a52	...	8 a50	...	11 a5	11a35	...	2 p35	3 p35	5 p0	...
SPIEZ......dep	...	...	...	...	7a30	...	9 a20	...	11a27	12p17	...	3 p10	4 p15	5 p45	...
		a.m.	a.m.		a.m.		a.m.	a.m.	p.m.	p.m.		p.m.	p.m.	p.m.	p.m.
Zweisimmen .....dep	...	5 54	7 †54	...	9 12	...	10 52	11 ‡32	12 26	2 11	...	4 30	6 2	7 18	10 25
Gstaad	...	6 46	8 42	...	10 4	...	11 44	1 0	...	3 5	...	5 19	6 50	8 6	11 14
Saanen	a.m.	6 53	8 17	...	1010	...	11 49	1 23	A	3 11	...	5 24	6 56	8 11	11 18
Chateau d'Oex	5 34	7 23	9 14	...	1036	...	12 12	2 12	...	3 35	...	5 49	7 23	8 33	—
Rossinière	5 48	7 35	9 26	...	1047	...	12†21	2 40	RC	3 49	p.m.	6 0	7 34	8 50	
Montbovon......	6 12	7 54	9 41	a.m.	11 6	p.m.	12 36	3 18	1 57	4 5	A	6 17	7 52	9 6	
Les Avants......	6 47	8 33	10 16	10 37	1143	12 58	1 11	4 8	...	4 40	6 4	6 51	8 27	9 41	
Chamby	7 1	8 48	10 30	10 54	12 1	1 12	1 26	4 25	2 42	4 55	6 17	7 6	8 41	9 56	
Sonzièr......	7 7	...	10 35	11 2	...	1 17	...	4 31	...	5 †0	6 22	RC	8 47	10 2	RC —Restaurant Car.
Chernex	7 13	8 58	10 41	11 9	1211	1 22	RC	4 37	...	5 †5	6 27	7 16	8 51	10 7	
Fontanivent......	7 17	9 2	10 45	11 12	1215	1 26	...	4 41	...	5 8	6 31	7 20	8 55	10 11	
Châtelard......	7 21	9 6	10 49	11 16	...	1 30	...	4 45	...	RC	6 35	...	8 59	10 15	
Montreux ......arr	7 30	9 14	10 57	11 24	1227	1 38	1 51	4 53	3 5	5 20	6 43	7 32	9 7	10 23	

*—From 16th September.
†—Sun. only.
‡—Weekdays only.
‖—Restaurant Car between Montbovon and Zweisimmen attached.
A—Until 15th Sept.
B—From 20th July to 10th Aug.

‡—Sunday only.

ZWEISIMMEN and LENK.

	a.m.	a.m.	a.m.	a.m.	p.m.	p.m.	p.m.	p.m.	p.m.	p.m.	p.m.	p.m.
Zweisimmen ...dep	6 35	7 ‡55	9 10	10 50	12*22	12§32	1 31	2 20	4 33	6 5	7 21	10 26
Blankenburg	6 41	8 1	9 16	10 56	12 30	12 38	1 37	2 26	4 39	6 11	7 27	10 32
Stöckli......	6 48	8 8	9 23	11 3	12 39	12 45	1 44	2 33	4 46	6 18	7 34	10 39
St. Stephan	6 54	8 14	9 29	11 11	12 50	12 51	1 50	2 43	4 52	6 26	7 40	10 45
Matten......	7 1	8 21	9 36	11 18	12 59	12 58	1 57	2 50	5 0	6 33	7 47	10 52
Boden	7 8	8 28	9 43	11 25	1 8	1 5	2 4	2 57	5 7	6 40	7 54	10 59
Lenk ......arr	7 13	8 33	9 48	11 30	1 15	1 10	2 9	3 2	5 12	6 45	7 59	11 4

	a.m.	a.m.	a.m.	a.m.	a.m.	a.m.	p.m.	p.m.	p.m.	p.m.	p.m.	p.m.
Lenk ......dep	5 53	7‡22	8 24	10 15	11*35	11§54	12 49	1 37	3 53	4 50	6 12	9 43
Boden	5 56	7 25	8 27	10 18	11 40	11 57	12 52	1 40	3 56	4 54	6 15	9 46
Matten......	6 1	7 30	8 32	10 23	11 47	12 2	12 59	1 45	4 1	4 59	6 20	9 51
St. Stephan	6 6	7 35	8 37	10 28	11 54	12 7	1 8	1 51	4 6	5 4	6 25	9 56
Stöckli......	6 10	7 39	8 41	10 32	12 1	12 11	1 12	1 55	4 10	5 8	6 29	10 0
Blankenburg	6 16	7 45	8 47	10 38	12 9	12 17	1 18	2 1	4 16	5 14	6 35	10 6
Zweisimmen 267arr	6 20	7 49	8 51	10 42	12 15	12 21	1 23	2 5	4 20	5 18	6 39	10 10

*—From 16th Sept. §—Until 15th Sept.

CLARENS and BLONAY.

	a.m.	
Clarens......dep	6 48	***
Pont de Tavel	6 50	
Baugy	6 54	
Chailly	6 58	
Fontanivent 262c	7 5	
Brent	7 8	
Blonay ......arr	7 16	

***—Frequent service throughout the day between Clarens and stations to Blonay, from 6.48 a.m. until 9.34 p.m.; not all the trains run as far as Blonay.

PALEZIEUX and MONTBOVON.—Electric Railway.

Palezieux...dep	...	6a56	8 a56	11 a3	1p31	2‡40	3 p58	5 p23	7 p13	9 p21	11p15	...	...	...
Chatel St. Denis	...	7 19	9 22	11 28	1 54	3 20	4 19	5 50	7 36	9 50	11 34	...	...	...
Bulle	6a13	8 10	10 13	12 32	2 41	4 43	—	6 42	8 25	10 39	—	...	...	...
Montbovon arr	7 5	9 2	11 5	1 24	3 30	6 0	...	7 33	9 38	...	...	...	...	...
Montbovon dep	...	6 a6	7a55	9 a10	11a15	1p30	...	4 p4	6p18	7 p51	9 p42	...	...	...
Bulle	...	6 58	9 9	10 50	12 18	2 23	...	4 55	7 12	8 58	10 32	...	...	...
Chatel St. Denis	6a29	8 0	1020	12 17	1 11	3 22	4p24	5 56	8 15	9 49	...	10p35	...	...
Palezieux...arr	6 48	8 19	1041	12 38	1 27	3 41	4 45	6 15	8 34	...	...	10 54	...	...

‡—Dep. 3.42p.m. on Sunday.

VEVEY and CHEXBRES.

Vevey......dep	5 a0	8a12	10a9	11a57	2p22	6 p0	8p20	10p20
Puidoux Chexbres arr	5 25	8 36	1032	12 20	2 45	6 28	8 45	10 45
Puidoux Chex dp	7a13	9 a2	11a22	1p47	4p10	6p48	9 p7	11p13
Vevey ......arr	7 35	9 24	11 44	2 10	4 36	7 10	9 30	11 36

VEVEY and CHATEL ST. DENIS.

Vevey ......dep	5§a37	6 a15	8 a39	10a45	1 p5	2p32	4 p50	6p52	8p49	...	...	...
Monts de Corsier	5 58	6 39	9 0	11 7	1 27	2 54	5 14	7 14	9 11	...	...	...
Chatel St. Denis......arr	6 18	7 0	9 20	11 27	1 47	3 14	5 34	7 34	9 31	...	...	...
Chatel St. Denis......dep	6§23	7 a54	10 a5	1 p10	1 p55	3p25	5 p50	8 p8	10 p0	...	...	...
Monts de Corsier	6 38	8 9	10 20	1 26	2 11	3 41	6 6	8 24	10 16	...	...	...
Vevey ......arr	6 55	8 28	10 37	1 42	2 30	4 2	6 25	8 43	10 35	...	...	...

§—Weekdays only.

VEVEY and CHAMBY.

Vevey ......dep	7a40	8 a32	10 a5	11a24	12 p6	1 p45	3 p0	4p10	6 p0	7 p20	9 p17	...	...	...
Chamby ......arr	8 15	9 10	10 42	12 0	12 42	2 21	3 39	4 48	6 37	7 58	9 55	...	...	...
Chamby ......dep	7 a1	8 a47	9 a54	10a51	12p15	1 p32	2 p49	4 p0	4p58	7 p20	8 p42	9 p57	...	...
Vevey ......arr	7 32	9 22	10 30	11 20	12 49	2 9	3 24	4 38	5 33	7 46	9 12	10 29	...	...

‡—Until Sept. 15th.

VEVEY and LES PLEIADES (Electric Railway).

E.M.								
	Vevey ......dep	7a40	10a5	11a24	1p45	3 p0	6 p0	...
3½	Blonay 262c	8 1	1030	11 49	2 9	3 27	6 25	...
6¼	**Les Pléiades**...arr	8 55	1120	12 36	2 58	4 15	7‡16	...

Les Pléiades...dep	9a20	11a40	12p58	4p25	5p15	8 ‡5	...
Blonay	10 7	12 29	1 46	5 11	6 5	8 52	...
Vevey 262c......arr	1030	12 49	2 9	5 33	6 29	9 12	...

GENEVA, LAUSANNE, FRIBOURG, and BERNE.

Dist.	1 Cl.	2 Cl.														
...	...	...	LYONS 53 ......dep	...	...	...	...	...	...	...	...	...	...	...	...	...
...	...	...	AMBERIEU 60 dep	...	...	...	...	...	...	...	...	...	...	...	...	...
				2&3	1 2 3	2 & 3	1,2,3	1,2,3	2 & 3	1,2,3	2&3	1& 2	1&2	2 & 3	2&3	2&3
E.M.	fr. c.	fr. c.		a.m.	a.m	a.m.	a.m.	a.m.	a.m.		a.m.	a.m.	a.m.		a.m.	p.m.
—	From	Geneva.	**Geneva** ....dep	4 55	5 30	5 52	6 50	7 12	8 5	...	9 13	1010	1047	...	1140	1210
3½			Genthod................	5 7	...	6 4	...	...	8 17	...	9 24	...	...	...	1152	1222
5¼	0 95	0 65	Versoix	5 13	...	6 10	...	...	8 23	...	9 30	...	RC	...	1158	1228
8¼	1 45	1 5	Coppet	5 25	...	6 22	...	...	8 35	...	9 38	...	...	...	1210	1240
13½	2 30	1 60	Nyon	5 42	5 53	6 40	7 14	7 34	8 53	...	9 52	...	...	...	1240	1257
16½	2 80	2 0	Gland 261A		6 1	6 48	...	7 42	9 1	...	10 0	...	...	...	1248	
21	3 55	2 50	Rolle ....2&3	...	6 12	7 1	7 28	7 51	9 14	...	1013	...	...	...	1 1	...
24	4 5	2 85	Allaman ....a.m.	...	6 23	7 10	7 37	8 0	9 23	...	1024	...	...	...	1 10	...
29¾	5 0	3 50	Morges ....6§18	...	6 36	7 26	7 49	8 10	9 38	...	1039	...	...	...	1 27	...
34½	5 85	4 10	Renens 6 33	...	6 47	7 42	...	8 23	9 53	...	1052	...	1143	...	1 43	...
37½	6 35	4 45	**Lausanne** arr6 40	...	6 55	7 49	8 5	8 30	10 0	...	11 0	1110	1150	...	1 50	...
157¼	25 10	17 60	BASLE 264 ...arr	...	...	...	1 p3	1*p3	...	...	...	3p57	3*57	...	...	...
153¼	...		263B DOMODOSSOLA arr	...	...	...	1 p0	1 p0	...	...	...	4p32	4p32	...	...	...
226½	...	...	MILAN 274 ...arr	...	...	...	3 p45	3p45	...	...	...	7p45	7p45	...	...	...
...	...	...	MILAN.........dep	...	...	...	11p45	...	...	...	...	...		...	...	...
...	...	...	D'OSSOLA ...dep	a.m.	...	...	2 a35	...	...	a.m.	...	...	...	p.m.	...	...
Fr. L	ausa	nne.	**Lausanne** ......dep	5 0	...	...	8 17	...	...	10 12	...	1124	...	12 10	...	...
2½	0 55	0 40	Conversion	5 9	...	...	...	...	...	10 21	...	...	...	12 19	...	...
5¼	0 95	0 65	Grandvaux	5 19	...	...	...	...	...	10 31	...	RC	...	12 29	...	...
7½	1 35	0 95	Puidoux-Chexbres	5 28	...	a.m.	8 41	...	...	10 40	...	...	...	12 39	...	...
12¾	2 20	1 55	Palezieux ....arr	5 42	...	6 50	8 54	...	...	10 52	...	...	...	12 53	...	...
15	2 60	1 85	Oron	5 53	...	7 3	...	...	...	11 0	...	...	...	1 3	...	...
19	3 25	2 30	Vauderens..............	6 5	...	7 24	...	...	...	11 11	...	...	...	1 16	...	...
25	4 30	3 0	**Romont** 265 { arr	6 22	...	7 48	9 19	...	...	11 24	...	...	...	1 32	...	...
			{ dep	6 27	...	8 10	9 20	...	...	11 27	...	...	...	1 36	...	...
31	5 20	3 65	Chenens.............2&3	6 46	...	8 40	...	...	...	11 41	...	...	...	1 52	...	...
41	6 90	4 85	**Fri-** { arr a.m.	7 25	...	9 38	9 47	...	a.m.	12 10	...	1251	...	2 25	...	...
			bourg { dep 5 15	7 37	...		9 50	...	10 34	12 15	...	1254	1,2,3	2 32	...	...
44¾	7 60	5 35	Dudingen 5 28	7 47	...	...	...	...	10 47	12 25	...	...	p.m.	2 44	...	...
52¼	8 85	6 20	Flamatt 5 57	8 9	...	...	10 12	...	11 15	12 44	...	...	1 22	3 10	...	...
57¾	...	...	Bumplitz 6 15	8 23	...	...	...	...	11 36	12 58	...	...	1 39	3 28	...	...
60½	10 20	7 15	**Berne**.........arr6 25	8 30	...	...	10 27	...	11 47	1 5	...	1 25	1 47	3 37	...	...
119½	...	...	LUCERNE 265 arr	1p48	...	...	1 p48	...	...	3 p43	...	3p43	...	7 p45	...	...
126½	...	...	BASLE 258 ...arr	1135	...	...	1p12	...	...	3p57	...	3p57	...	6 p58	...	...

LYONS 53 ......dep	7 a0	...	...	...	...	1230	12p30	...	...	...	...	2p45	...	7p16
AMBERIEU 60 dep	8 a13	...	...	...	...	1p30	1 p30	...	...	...	...	4 p1	...	8p40
	1,2,3	1,2,3	1,2,3	2 & 3	2&3	1,2,3	1,2,3	2&3	1,2,3	2&3	2&3	1,2,3	1,2,3	1,2,3
	p.m.	p.m.	p.m.	p.m	p.m.	p.m.	p.m.		p.m.	p.m.	p m.	p.m.	p.m.	a.m.
Geneva ....dep	12 49	1 30	2 10	3 45	4 25	5 5	5 23	...	5 43	6 15	7 27	9 0	10 0	1 0
Genthod................	...	...	2 21	3 57	4 37	...	...	...	5 54	6 27	7 39	...	10 10	...
Versoix	...	...	2 27	4 3	4 43	...	RC	...	6 0	6 33	7 45	...	10 15	...
Coppet	...	...	2 35	4 15	4 55	...	...	...	6 8	6 45	7 57	...	10 21	...
Nyon	1 12	1 52	2 50	4 33	5 12	5 27	...	...	6 24	7 2	8 16	9 22	10 33	1 22
Gland 261A	1 20	...	2 58	4 41		...	...	...	6 32		8 24	...	10 40	...
Rolle ....2&3	1 29	...	3 11	4 54	...	...	...	...	6 46	...	8 37	9 37	10 51	1 35
Allaman ....a.m.	1 38	...	3 22	5 3	...	...	...	p.m.	6 53	...	8 46	9 46	11 1	...
Morges ....6§18	1 49	2 2)	3 38	5 18	...	5 55	...	6†50	7 17	...	9 2	9 56	11 14	1 52
Renens 6 33	2 2	...	3 52	5 33	...	...	6 20	7 5	7 32	...	9 18	10 8	11 23	...
Lausanne arr6 40	2 10	2 35	4 0	5 40	...	6 10	6 28	7 12	7 40	...	9 25	1015	11 30	2 10
BASLE 264 ...arr	7 p35	7p35	...	10p53	...	1053	10*53	...	...	...	...	...	...	...
263B DOMODOSSOLA arr	8 p15		...	...	...	10p3	10 p3	...	...	...	...	...	3 a40	...
MILAN 274 ...arr	...	...	...	...	...	1215	12a15	...	...	...	...	...	6 a25	...
MILAN.........dep	5 a0	...	8 a0	...	...	1050	...	...	10a50	...	...	3p25	...	...
D'OSSOLA ...dep	8 a20	...	10a55	...	...	1p42	...	...	1 p42	...	...	6p22	...	...
Lausanne ......dep	2 23	...	4‡35	...	...	6 20	...	...	8 33	...	...	1034	...	2 25
Conversion	...	...	4 45	...	...	...	...	...	8 43	...	...	1043	...	...
Grandvaux	...	Weekdays only.	4 55	...	...	...	...	...	8 53	...	...	...	...	...
Puidoux-Chexbres	2 50		5 5	...	...	6 44	...	...	9 4	...	...	11 0	...	...
Palezieux ....arr	3 3		5 19	...	...	6 57	...	...	9 19	...	...	1112	...	...
Oron	3 13		5 30	...	...	...	...	...	9 31	...	...	...	...	...
Vauderens..............	3 25		5 43	...	...	...	...	...	9 43	...	...	...	...	...
Romont 265 { arr	3 40		5 59	...	...	7 22	...	...	10 0	...	...	1134	...	...
{ dep	3 42		6 2	...	...	7 23	...	...	10 1	...	...	1135	...	...
Chenens.............2&3	...		6 19	...	...	...	...	3 Cl.	10 21	...	...	...	...	...
Fri- { arr a.m.	4 9		6 53	...	...	7 49	...	p.m.	10 50	...	...	12 1	...	4 1
bourg { dep 5 15	4 13	2&3	7 0	...	...	7 52	...	8§50	10 55	...	...	12 3	...	4 4
Dudingen 5 28	...	p.m.	7 12	...	...	...	...	9 6	11 4	...	...	...	...	...
Flamatt 5 57	4 37	6 55	7 35	...	...	8 12	...	9 46	11 26	...	...	...	...	...
Bumplitz 6 15	...	7 10	7 51	...	...	...	...	1010	11 41	...	...	...	...	...
Berne.........arr6 25	4 52	7 18	8 0	...	...	8 27	...	1022	11 48	...	...	1233	...	4 40
LUCERNE 265 arr	7 p45	...	10p52	...	...	1052	...	...	...	...	...	...	...	8a32
BASLE 258 ...arr	7 p35	...	10p53	...	...	11p3	...	...	...	...	...	...	...	7a25

*—Change at Renens for Basle.
RC—Restaurant Car.

Extra.					
Geneva......dep	1p40	8p28	11p45	...	...
Nyon.........arr	2 27	9 15	12 32	...	...

†—From 1st July dep. 7.53 p.m.
‡—2 & 3 Class. §—Not on Sunday.

NYON and DIVONNE.

	a.m.	a.m.	p.m.	p.m.	p.m.	p.m					
Nyon ....dep	8 10	10 15	1 30	3 57	5 40	9 53	...	...	...	...	...
Crassier	8 31	10 38	1 51	4 18	6 3	10 12	...	...	...	...	...
Divonne ....arr	8 37	10 44	1 57	4 24	6 9	10 18	...	...	...	...	...

	a.m.	a.m.	p.m.	p.m.	p.m.	p.m.					
Divonne ....dep	6 30	9 10	12 4	2 13	4 48	7 28	...	...	...	...	...
Crassier	6 41	9 26	12 20	2 29	5 4	7 44	...	...	...	...	...
Nyon ....arr	6 55	9 40	12 34	2 43	5 18	7 58	...	...	...	...	...

BERNE and SCHWARZENBURG.

	a.m.	a.m.	p.m.	p.m	p.m.	p.m.
Berne Hauptbahnhof dep	6 50	10 50	2 5	4 17	6 33	8 42
Fischermätteli	6 58	11 0	2 14	4 25	6 42	8 52
Schwarzenburg ......arr	7 53	11 55	3 9	5 23	7 40	9 51

	a.m.	a.m.	p.m.	p.m.	p.m.	p.m
Schwarzenburg ......dep	5 20	8 8	12 7	3‡35	5 45	8 13
Fischermätteli	6 13	9 1	1 2	4 58	6 40	9 8
Berne Hauptbahnhof...arr	6 20	9 8	1 10	5 6	6 47	9 15

‡ 4.8 p.m. on Sunday.

SIERRE and MONTANA.

Sierre ....dep	8a10	11a49	3 p5	4 p2	...	5 p0	5 p35	6p33	7p20	8p25	...
St. Maurice de Laques	8 38	12 17	3 33	4 30	5 p8	5 23	6 5	7 2	7 58	8 48	...
Montana-Vermala arr	9 0	12 40	3 55	4 52	5 30	...	6 28	7 25	8 20	...	...

Montana-Vermala dep	6a32	8a38	10a30	11a24	12p17	1p42	2p37	3p33	5 p8	6 p5	7 p2	7p58	...
St. Maurice de Laques	7 0	9 5	10 56	11 49	12 46	2 10	3 5	4 2	5 35	6 33	7 30	8 25	...
Sierre 263B ....arr	7 23	9 28	11 19	12 14	...	2 33	3 28	4 25	5 58	6 56	7 53	8 48	...

BERNE, FRIBOURG, LAUSANNE, and GENEVA.

*—Weekdays only. ‡—2nd & 3rd class. §—Weekdays only, 3rd class. RC—Restaurant Car.

Extra. {Berne......dep 11 p0 / Fribourg arr 12 3}

Basle 258 ...dep	...	...	...	...	...	...	...	...	...	7 a15
Lucerne 265 dep	...	...	...	...	...	...	...	...	...	7 a38
	2&3	2&3	1,2,3	2 & 3	2&3	1,2,3	1,2,3	2 & 3	1,2,3	1,2,3
					a.m.	a.m.		a.m.		a.m.
Berne ......dep	...	...	...	...	5 15	6 55	...	7 45	...	9 56
Bumplitz	...	...	...	...	5 35	...	...	7 54	...	...
Flamatt	...	...	...	...	6 3	...	...	8 13	...	...
Dudingen	...	...	...	...	6 45	...	...	8 40	...	...
Fribourg ......arr	...	...	...	a.m.	7 0	7 32	...	8 52	...	10 34
" 263A dep	...	...	...	5 20	—	7 35	...	9 14	...	10 37
Chenens	...	...	...	6 0	...	...	...	9 58	...	...
Romont 265 arr	...	...	...	6 17	...	8 3	...	10 14	...	11 6
" ......dep	...	...	...	6 22	...	8 5	...	10 19	...	11 8
Vauderens	...	...	...	6 39	...	...	...	10 41	...	...
Oron	...	a.m.	...	6 48	...	...	a.m.	10 53	...	...
Palezieux 264A	...	6 17	...	6 58	...	8 28	8 45	11 2	...	...
Puidoux-Chexbres	...	6 28	...	7 12	...	8 39	9 0	11 19	...	...
Grandvaux	...	6 35	...	7 20	...	...	9 9	11 27	...	...
Conversion	...	6 43	...	7 29	...	...	9 18	11 35	...	...
Lausanne 263B ar	...	6 50	...	7 37	...	8 53	9 25	11 43	...	11 55
Domodossola arr	...	1055	...		...	1 p0	...	4 p32	...	4 p32
Milan 274......arr	...		p.m.	...	...	3 p45	...	7 p45	...	7 p45
Milan ......dep	...	...	1145	...	...	...	...	...	...	...
D'Ossola......dep	...	...	2a35	...	...	...	...	...	...	...
Basle 264A dep	a.m.	...	a.m.	...	a.m.	...	...	...	7a30	7 a30
Lausanne ......dep	5 20	...	7 0	...	8 2	9 17	9 55	...	1150	12 10
Renens	5 29	...	7 7	...	8 9	...	10 5	...	12 2	...
Morges	5 42	...	7 17	...	8 24	9 31	1018	...	...	12 24
Allaman	6 0	...	7 32	...	8 41	9 43	1035	...	...	...
Rolle ......2&3	6 11	...	7 41	...	8 49	9 50	1046	...	RC	RC
Gland ......a.m.	6 26	a.m.	7 54	a.m.	9 2	...	11 1	...	...	...
Nyon 5 55	6 36	7 0	8 1	8 5	9 12	10 4	1111	...	...	12 52
Coppet 6 11	6 51	7 16	...	8 21	9 28	...	1125	...	...	...
Versoix 6 22	7 0	7 27	...	8 32	9 39	...	1134	...	...	...
Genthod 6 27	7 6	7 32	...	8 37	9 44	...	1139	...	...	...
Geneva ......arr 6 40	7 18	7 45	8 20	8 50	9 57	10 25	1150	...	1252	1 13
Amberieu 61 arr	...	...	...	...	2p12	2 p12	...	...	3p33	3 p33
Lyons 53 ..... arr	...	...	...	...	4 p1	4 p1	...	...	4p32	4 p32

Basle 258 ...dep	...	...	7 a40	...	...	10a40	...	10a40	1 p42	1p59
Lucerne 265 dep	...	...	7 a52	...	...	10a54	...	10a54	1 p56	1p56
	3 Cl	2 & 3	1,2,3	1,2,3	2 & 3	1 2 3	2&3	2 & 3	1 & 2	1& 2
			a.m.	p.m		p.m.		p.m.	p.m.	p.m.
Berne ......dep	...	...	11 10	1213	...	2 15	...	2 45	4 3	4 22
Bumplitz	...	...	11 19	1220	...	...	...	2 54	...	...
Flamatt	...	...	11 34	1233	...	...	...	3 14	...	...
Dudingen	...	a.m.	11 56	1§35	...	...	...	3 39	...	...
Fribourg ......arr	...	*	12 5	1§55	...	2 52	...	3 50	4 40	4 59
" 263A dep	...	11 40	12 10	—	...	2 55	...	4 17	4 43	5 1
Chenens	*	1 25	12 43	...	...	...	...	4 55	...	...
Romont 265 arr	a.m.	1 53	12 56	...	p.m.	3 24	...	5 5	...	...
" ......dep	1121	—	12 58	...	2 20	3 26	...	5 42	...	...
Vauderens	12 2	...	1 15	...	3 2	...	...	6 1	...	...
Oron	1224	...	1 23	...	3 23	...	...	6 11	...	...
Palezieux 264A	1 5	...	1 30	...	3 38	3 53	...	6 19	...	...
Puidoux-Chexbres	1 20	...	1 44	...	3 51	4 6	...	6 33	...	...
Grandvaux	1 28	...	1 51	...	3 58	...	...	6 40	...	...
Conversion	1 36	...	1 58	...	4 6	...	...	6 48	...	...
Lausanne 263B ar	1 43	...	2 5	...	4 13	4 23	...	6 55	5 55	6 14
Domodossola arr	...	...	8 p15	...	...	...	...	...	10 p3	10p3
Milan 274......arr	...	...	...	...	...	...	...	...	12 15	1215
Milan ......dep	...	...	5 a0	8 a0	...	...	...	...	10a50	1050
D'Ossola......dep	...	...	8 a20	1055	...	...	...	...	1 p42	1p50
Basle 264A dep	...	7 a30	7 a45	7a45	...	8a25	p.m.	...	...	1044
Lausanne ......dep	...	12 15	2‡10	2 55	...	4 40	4 46	...	6 5	6 29
Renens	...	12 22	2 17	...	...	...	4 53	...	...	...
Morges	...	12 37	2 32	3 12	...	4 56	5 8	...	...	...
Allaman	...	12 54	2 49	3 25	...	5 8	5 25	...	...	...
Rolle ......2&3	2&3	1 2	2 57	3 32	...	5 16	5 33	...		...
Gland ......a.m.	p.m.	1 15	3 10	3 43	p.m.	5 27	5 46	p.m.	From 1st July.	...
Nyon 5 55	1 5	1 23	3 20	3 52	4 15	5 37	5 54	7 10		...
Coppet 6 11	1 21	1 39	3 36	4 1	4 31	...	6 10	7 26		...
Versoix 6 22	1 32	1 50	3 47	4 9	4 42	...	6 21	7 37	...	...
Genthod 6 27	1 37	1 55	3 52	...	4 47	...	6 26	7 42	...	...
Geneva ......arr 6 40	1 50	2 8	4 5	4 20	5 0	6 0	6 39	7 55	6 55	7 22
Amberieu 61 arr	...	6 p17	...	...	...	9p40	...	...	...	1014
Lyons 53 ..... arr	...	8 p39	...	...	...	1112	...	...	...	1112

Basle 258 ...dep	...	...	...	...	3p40	3p40	...	6p20	12 0
Lucerne 265 dep	...	...	...	2 p13	2p13	...	5p14	7p10	8 p25
	2 & 3	1,2,3	2&3	1,2,3	1,2,3	2&3	2&3	1,2,3	1,2,3
				p.m.	p.m.	p.m.	p.m	p.m.	a.m.
Berne ......dep	...	...	...	5 37	6 13	7 40	8 38	9 30	2 47
Bumplitz	...	...	...	5 46	...	7 50	8 52	...	...
Flamatt	...	...	...	6 2	...	8 11	9 12	...	...
Dudingen	...	...	...	6 27	...	8 38	9 42	...	...
Fribourg ......arr	...	...	...	6 38	6 50	8 50	9 56	10 7	3 24
" 263A dep	...	...	...	7 3	6 53	8 58	—	10 10	3 29
Chenens	...	...	...	7 44	...	9 40	...	...	...
Romont 265 arr	...	...	...	7 58	...	9 57	...	10 38	...
" ......dep	...	...	...	8 3	...	10 0	...	10 39	...
Vauderens	...	...	...	8 20	...	1019	...	...	...
Oron	...	...	...	8 29	...	1029	p.m.	...	...
Palezieux 264A	...	...	...	8 37	...	1037	10 2	11 1	...
Puidoux-Chexbres	...	...	...	8 51	...	1051	1016	11 11	...
Grandvaux	...	...	...	8 57	...	1057	1024	...	...
Conversion	...	...	...	9 4	...	11 4	1032	...	...
Lausanne 263B ar	...	...	...	9 10	8 7	11 10	1038	11 27	4 44
Domodossola arr	...	...	...	...	...	...	...	3 a40	10a55
Milan 274......arr	...	...	...	...	...	...	1,2,3	6 a25	1 p3
Milan ......dep	...	...	...	...	...	...	3p25	...	...
D'Ossola......dep	...	...	...	...	...	...	6p22	...	...
Basle 264A dep	10a44	3 p40	3p40	...	...	...	6p44	6 p44	...
Lausanne ......dep	7 0	7 53	8 30	9 30	8 20	...	1052	11 43	5 5
Renens	7 7	8 7	8 41	9 38	...	...	11 5	11 51	...
Morges	7 21	...	8 56	9 51	...	...	1115	12 1	5 19
Allaman	7 38	...	9 14	10 7	...	...	1127	12 16	...
Rolle ......2&3	7 46	RC	9 20	10 18	...	...	1134	12 23	...
Gland ......a.m.	7 59	...	9 41	10 33	...	p.m.	...	12 34	...
Nyon 5 55	8 7	8 40	9 50	10 43	...	9 30	1149	12 41	5 47
Coppet 6 11	8 23	...	10 5	10 57	...	9 46	...	12 50	...
Versoix 6 22	8 34	...	1014	11 5	...	9 57	...	12 57	...
Genthod 6 27	8 39	...	1020	11 10	...	10 2	...	...	...
Geneva ......arr 6 40	8 52	9 0	1032	11 20	9 15	1015	12 8	1 8	6 10
Amberieu 61 arr	...	11p19	...	...	...	...	...	...	9 a7
Lyons 53 ..... arr	...	1 a17	...	...	...	...	...	...	10a15

BIERE and MORGES.

Bière ......dep	6a15	9a20	12p30	6 p3	...	...
Ballens	6 23	9 28	12 39	6 12	...	...
Apples	6 34	9 39	12 50	6 21	...	...
Yens	6 46	9 51	1 2	6 43	...	...
Morges ......arr	7 7	1012	1 23	7 4	...	...
Apples ......dep	8 a19	11a25	3p30	8p12	...	...
L'Isle ......arr	8 45	11 51	3 56	8 38	...	...

Morges ......dep	7a35	10a42	2p47	7p30	...	...
Yens	8 1	11 8	3 13	7 56	...	...
Apples	8 17	11 24	3 27	8 10	...	...
Ballens	8 32	11 37	3 39	8 22	...	...
Bière ......arr	8 40	11 45	3 47	8 30	...	...
L'Isle ......dep	6 a 5	9a10	12p20	6 p0	...	...
Apples ......arr	6 30	9 35	12 45	6 25	...	...

FRIBOURG and YVERDON. All 2 & 3 cl.

Fribourg dep	...	6a25	9a52	1p0	2p46	5p16	7p37	1058
Grolley	...	6 44	1014	121	3 18	5 37	7 58	1117
Corcelles	...	7 8	1036	146	4 16	6 1	8 21	1141
Payerne arr	a.m.	7 12	1040	150	4 21	6 5	8 26	1145
" ...dep	5 0	7 22	1053	2 2	4 26	6 13	8 43	—
Estavayer	5 16	7 39	1113	218	4 41	6 29	9 1	...
Yverdon arr	5 42	8 10	1145	244	5 4	6 54	9 30	...

Yverdon dep	...	6a27	9a42	1 p0	3p35	6 p0	7p40	11p8
Estavayer	...	6 58	1017	1 28	4 4	6 28	8 9	1138
Payerne arr	...	7 15	1035	1 44	4 20	6 44	8 25	1155
" ...dep	5a33	7 25	1050	2 0	4 30	6 52	8 40	—
Corcelles	5 43	7 29	1054	2 4	4 34	6 56	8 45	...
Grolley	6 43	7 56	1119	2 30	5 0	7 21	9 13	...
Fribourg arr	7 15	8 15	1137	2 46	5 16	7 37	9 33	...

YVERDON and STE. CROIX.—

No Train Service on Sunday.

Yverdon ......dep	6 a5	9 a10	12p46	3 p45	7 p30
Ste. Croix ......arr	7 9	10 16	1 52	4 51	8 46
Ste. Croix ......dep	7 a20	11 a0	2p12	5 p30	9 p9
Yverdon ......arr	8 17	12 0	3 9	6 33	10 5

PONTARLIER, LAUSANNE, BRIG, and DOMODOSSOLA.

SIMPLON TUNNEL LINE. ☞ Greenwich Time between Pontarlier and Vallorbes.

Dist.	1 Cl.	2 Cl.	Station																			
...	...	...	PARIS 48 ......dep		7 p45	9p30	...	9p30	...	...	1050	1050	...	...	...	...	8 a30	...	...	...	...	2p20
...	...	...	DIJON 53......dep		12a28	1a48	...	1a48	...	...	3a47	4a20	...	...	5a44	...	12p46	...	...	...	...	6p42
Dist.	1 Cl.	2 Cl.			1 Cl.	1& 2		1,2,3			1,2,3	2&3		2 & 3	2&3		1 & 2	2&3	2 &3	2 & 3	2 & 3	1 &2
E.M. Fr. P	fr. c. Ponta	fr. c. rlier			a.m.	a.m.		a.m.			a.m	a.m		a.m.	p.m.		p.m.		p.m.	p.m.		p.m.
			Pontarlier ...dep		3 13	4 22	...	4 40	...	...	7 0	8 32	...	9 30	1 0	...	3 32	...	9 52	4 35	...	9 10
2¾	0 55	0 40	Frambourg		B	...	...	4 48	...	...	...	8 39	...	9 45	1 8	...	...	...	10 1	4 44	...	...
10¼	1 90	1 30	Hopitaux-Jougne...		...	...	...	5 12	...	...	...	9 0	...	10 30	1 30	...	...	...	1028	5 9	...	...
15¾	2 95	2 0	Vallorbes ¶ ... arr		3 49	5 0	...	5 25	...	...	7 40	9 12	...	10 50	1 43	...	4 10	...	1045	5 25	p.m.	9 45
			Vallorbes ¶ ... dep		5 1	6 17	...	6 43	...	...	8 55	1027	...	12 22	2 58	...	5 25	...		6 43	8 45	11 0
17½	...	...	Day 259B		...	...	...	6 50	...	...	...	1034	...	12 30	3 6	...	...	...	...	6 51	8 52	...
23½	4 30	2 95	Croy		...	...	...	7 2	...	...	...	1046	...	12 53	3 18	...	...	...	...	7 1	9 6	...
27¼	4 90	3 35	Arnex		...	...	...	7 11	...	...	...	1054	...	1 9	3 27	...	...	...	...	7 10	9 17	...
30¼	5 40	3 75	La Sarraz............		...	...	...	7 18	...	...	...	11 2	...	1 22	3 34	...	...	...	...	7 17	9 25	...
35½	6 25	4 30	Cossonay		...	...	...	7 31	...	...	...	1113	...	1 45	3 47	...	...	...	...	7 31	9 40	...
40	7 0	4 85	Bussigny		...	...	...	7 44	...	...	...	1123	...	2 1	4 0	...	...	...	...	7 44	9 55	...
41¾	7 30	5 5	Renens		...	7‡ 2	...	7 49	...	...	...	1128	...	2 10	4 5	...	...	...	...	7 49	10 2	11‡47
44¾	7 70	5 35	**Lausanne** ......arr		5 50	7 10	...	7 57	...	...	9 48	1135	...	2 18	4 13	...	6 15	...	...	7 57	10 10	1154
...	...	...	BERNE 263A dp	2a47	...	...	...	...	6 a55	6a55	...	9a56	9 a56	11a10	2p15	...	4 p23	4p23	6p13	...	9 p30	9p30
...	...	...	GENEVA 263 dp	1 a0	...	5a30	5 a30	6a50	7 a12	7a12	8 a5	1047	10 47	12p49	2p10	3 p45	5 p5	5p23	5p43	9 p0	10 p0	10p0
Dist.	1 Cl.	2 Cl.		1,2,3	1 Cl.	1&2	1,2,3	1,2,3	1,2,3	1,2,3	1,2,3	1,2,3	1,2,3	1,2,3	1,2,3	1,2,3	1,2,3	1,2,3	1,2,3	1,2,3	1,2,3	1 &2
E.M. Fro	fr. c. Lau	fr. c. san		a.m.	a.m.	a.m.	a.m.	a.m.	a.m.	a.m.	a.m.	p.m.	p.m.	p.m.	p.m.	p.m.	p.m.	p.m	p.m.	p.m	p.m.	nigt
			Lausanne dep	5 1	6 0	7 20	7 28	8 20	9 10	9 33	1040	1215	12 22	2 25	4 55	6 5	6 30	6 48	8 15	10 22	11 40	1210
3¼	0 65	0 45	Lutry	5 11	...	...	7 38	8 30	...	...	1051	...	12 33	2 34	5 5	6 15	...	...	8 25	10 29	11 50	...
5¼	0 95	0 65	Cully	5 17	B	...	7 47	8 39	...	9 45	11 0	RC	12 42	2 40	5 14	6 23	RC	7 2	8 34	10 35	11 56	...
8¾	1 45	1 5	Rivaz............	5 25	...	...	7 57	8 49	...	...	11 9	...	12 51	2 48	5 24	6 32	...	...	8 44	10 42	12 4	...
11½	2 0	1 40	Vevey	5 36	6 18	7 39	8 10	9 2	9 29	9 58	1125	1235	1 6	2 58	5 38	6 55	6 49	7 19	9 0	10 51	12 12	1229
12¼	2 10	1 50	LaTour-de-Peilz	5 40	...	...	8 14	9 6	...	...	1130	...	1 10	3 2	5 42	6 59	...	...	9 4	...	12 16	...
13¾	2 30	1 60	Burier	...	...	...	8 18	9 10	...	...	1134	...	1 14	...	5 47	7 3	...	...	9 8	...	...	...
14¼	2 50	1 75	Clarens	5 46	...	...	8 23	9 15	...	10 5	1139	...	1 18	3 8	5 53	7 7	...	7 27	9 13	11 0	12 21	...
15¼	2 60	1 85	**Montreux** arr	5 49	6 26	7 47	8 26	9 18	9 37	10 8	1142	1243	1 20	3 11	5 56	7 10	6 57	7 30	9 16	11 3	12 24	1237
16	2 80	2 0	Territet-Glion...	5 58	6 31	...	8 34	9 25	9 44	1016	1152	1251	1 27	3 18	6 6	7 19	...	7 40	9 26	11 9	12 30	...
16¾	2 95	2 5	Veytaux-Chillon	6 1	...	...	8 38	9 28	...	...	1157	...	1 31	3 21	6 10	7 23	...	...	9 30	11 12	...	...
18¼	3 15	2 20	Villeneuve	6 6	...	RC	8 44	9 32	...	1024	12 4	1256	1 35	3 26	6 16	7 27	...	7 46	9 36	11 17	12 35	...
21	3 55	2 50	Roche	6 14	...	...	8 52		...	1031	1213	...		3 33	6 25		...	...	9 45	11 24		...
24¼	4 20	2 95	Aigle	6 28	6 44	...	9 7	...	9 58	1042	1228	1 9	...	3 43	6 40	...	...	8 0	10 1	11 35	...	...
27	4 60	3 25	St. Triphon	6 35	...	...	9 14	...	...	1049	1236	...	...	3 49	6 48	...	...	..	10 9	11 41	...	...
29½	5 0	3 50	Bex............	6 44	...	...	9 24	...	10 10	1059	1246	1 21	...	3 59	6 58	...	...	8 13	1022	11 50	2 & 3	...
32	5 40	3 80	**St. Maurice** arr	6 50	6 57	8 15	9 30	...	10 16	11 6	1252	1 27	...	4 5	7 5	...	7 24	8 20	1029	11 56	a.m.	1 4
			St. Maurice dep	7 7	6 58	8 17		...	10 18	1120		1 32	...	4 18		...	7 26	8 30			4 55	1 6
36	6 5	4 25	Evionnaz.........	7 18	...	...	...	...	...	1131	...	...	...	4 30	...	...	...	8 42	...	...	5 8	...
38½	6 45	4 55	Vernayaz.........	7 25	...	...	...	...	...	1140	...	1 46	...	4 37	...	...	...	8 50	...	...	5 16	...
41¼	7 0	4 90	**Martigny**	7 33	7 13	8 36	...	...	...	1148	...	1 52	...	4 45	...	...	...	8 58	...	...	5 25	...
46¾	7 90	5 55	Saxon-les-Bains	7 51	...	...	...	...	...	12 6	...	...	...	5 3	...	...	...	9 17	...	...	5 45	...
49½	8 35	5 85	Riddes	7 59	...	...	...	...	...	1213	...	...	...	5 10	...	...	...	9 25	...	...	5 53	...
53	8 95	6 30	Ardon............	8 9	...	...	...	...	...	1222	...	...	...	5 19	...	...	...	9 35	...	...	6 3	...
57½	9 70	6 80	Sion arr	8 18	7 37	9 0	...	...	10 59	1230	...	2 21	...	5 27	...	...	8 6	9 45	...	...	6 12	1 45
			(Sitten) dep	8 25	7 38	9 2	...	2&3	11 1	1235	...	2 24	...	5 31	...	...	8 8	9 55	...	...	6 19	1 47
63¼	10 60	7 45	Granges............	8 40	...	...	...	a.m.	...	1252	...	...	...	5 45	...	...	...	1010	...	...	6 34	...
67¼	11 35	7 95	Sierre 263	8 51	7 55	...	...	7 12	11 18	1 3	...	2 43	...	5 55	...	...	...	1023	...	...	6 45	...
69¾	11 75	8 25	Salgesch	9 1	...	...	...	7 23	...	1 13	...	...	...	6 5	...	...	...	1033	...	...	6 55	...
73	12 30	8 65	Leuk	9 13	...	...	...	7 35	11 34	1 25	...	2 59	...	6 17	...	...	...	1045	...	...	7 7	...
76	12 80	9 0	Turtman	9 20	...	...	...	7 44	...	1 32	...	...	...	6 24	...	...	...	1053	...	...	7 14	...
78	13 10	9 20	Gampel	9 26	...	...	...	7 52	...	1 38	...	...	...	6 30	...	C	...	1059	...	...	7 20	...
80¾	13 55	9 50	Raron............	9 34	...	...	...		...	1 45	...	...	...	6 37	...	p.m.	...	11 6	...	...	7 28	...
85	14 25	10 0	Visp (Viège)......	10 5	8 26	9 52	...	...	11 53	1 55	...	3 20	...	6 50	...	7 §27	...	1118	...	...	7 40	...
90½	15 20	10 65	**Brig** (Brigue) ar	1017	8 35	10 2	...	...	12 2	2 7	...	3 30	...	7 0	...	7 38	9 5	1130	...	...	7 52	2 43
...	...	...	PARIS (Est)......dep		...	...	9 p0	...	9 p45	...	...	...	...	10 p0	...	§—From the opening of the Lötschberg line.	8 a0	...	...	...	...	1 p0
...	...	...	,, (P.L.M.) dep		...	...	...	...	10p15	...	...	1050	...	...	...		...	...	...	...	...	2p20
...	...	...	BERNE 267......dep		...	5a20	8 a0	...	9 a32	...	2&3	1 p0	...	2 p22	...		6 p18	...	...	3 Cl.		1215
...	...	...	SPIEZ 268F......dep		...	7a25	9 a0	...	10a30	...	p.m.	1p57	...	4 p12	...		7 p16	...	a.m.	a.m.		1a14
...	...	...	**Brig** ....dep		8 40	10 7	10§43	...	12 7	...	1 0	3 40	...	7 8	...		9 15	...	6 0	8 7	RC—Restaurant Car	2 53
104	20 5	14 10	Iselle di Trasquera		...	...	11 10	...	12 38	...	1 52	4 7	...	7 49	...		...	...	6 30	9 17		...
108	20 70	14 55	Varzo		...	...	11 19	...	...	...	2 8	4 16	...	7 58	...		...	...	6 42	9 32		...
113½	21 70	15 20	Preglia		...	...	11 30	...	...	...	2 27	...	...	8 9	...		...	...	6 57	9 51		...
115¾	22 40	15 70	**Domodossola** ar		9 32	1055	11 36	...	1 0	...	2 38	4 32	...	8 15	...		10 3	...	7 3	10 0		3 40
137½	...	...	BAVENO 274...arr		10a30	1148	12 33	...	2 p0	...	...	5p42	...	...	...		10p45	...	8a45	11a19	RC	a28
140	...	...	STRESA 274 ...arr		10a37	1155	12 39	...	2 p7	...	...	5p48	...	...	...		10p51	...	8a53	11a26		a34
150½	...	...	ARONA 274 ...arr		10a55	1213	12 56	...	2 p25	...	...	6p15	...	...	...		11 p6	...	9a21	11 55	...	a53
192½	38 30	26 40	MILAN 274 ...arr		12p12	1p30	2 p10	...	3 p45	...	...	7p45	...	...	...		12a15	...	1115	3 p8	...	[illegible]

‡—Sets down only. ¶—Customs Examination. B—Train de Luxe, Simplon Express. C—Runs until 15th Se[pt.]

†—6.26 p.m. on Sundays.

BOUVERET and ST. MAURICE.

‡—Sunday excepted.

Bouveret......dep	6a25	9a35	12p42	3p30	4p†50	7p53	...
Vouvry............	6 36	9 45	12 53	3 41	5 25	8 2	...
Monthey	6 52	10 0	1 10	3 59	6 22	8 17	...
St. Maurice...arr	7 2	10 10	1 20	4 10	6 37	8 25	...

St. Maurice dep	7 a5	9a45	12 p5	1‡p45	1§p45	4 p55	8p45	§-Sunday only
Monthey	7 20	9 58	12 17	2 25	1 57	5 6	8 57	
Vouvry............	7 37	1013	12 32	3 12	2 12	5 19	9 12	
Bouveret 61A...	7 48	1023	12 42	3 30	2 22	5 28	9 22	

VEVEY, CHARDONNE, MONT PELERIN.—(Funicular Railway). Departures from Vevey and Pèlerin, 6.15, 7.15, 8.15, 9.15, 10.15, 11.15, 11.45 a.m., 12.15, 1.15, 1.45, 2.15, 2.45, 3.15, 3.45, 4.15, 5.0, 5.45, 6.10, 6.30, 6.50, 7.30, 8.0, 9.15 p.m.

DOMODOSSOLA, BRIG, LAUSANNE, and PONTARLIER.

MILAN 274......dep	...	...	...	...	...	5 a0	...	8 a0	...	8a15	...	10a50	...	...	...	2p20	3p25	4 p30	5 p25	11p45
ARONA 274......dep	...	...	...	...	...	6a35	...	9 a22	...	9a39	...	12p16	...	...	...	3p41	4p55	5 p57	7 p5	1 a13
STRESA 274 ...dep	...	...	...	...	...	7 a4	...	9 a41	...	10a9	...	12p40	...	...	...	4 p1	5p16	6 p21	7 p36	1 a33
BAVENO 274 ...dep	...	...	...	...	...	7a11	...	9 a48	...	1016	...	12p47	...	...	...	4 p8	5p23	6 p27	7 p43	1 a39
	2&3	2&3	1,2,3	3 Cl.	1,2,3	1,2,3	1,2,3	1,2,3	1,2,3	1,2,3	1,2,3	1,2,3	1,2,3	1,2,3	1,2,3	1,2,3	1 &2	1 Cl.	2 & 3	1 & 2
				a.m.	a.m.	a.m.		a.m.		a.m.	p.m.	p.m.				p.m.	p.m.	p.m.	p.m.	a.m.
Domodossola dp	...	...	...	5 50	...	8 20	...	10 55	..	1122	1218	1 42	...	...	...	5 7	6 22	7 15	8 57	2 35
Preglia	...	...	...	6 3	...	8 28	...	...	...	...	1223	...	...	...	...	5 16	...	...	9 7	...
Varzo	...	...	...	6 41	...	8 47	...	RC	...	§	1246	2 9	...	...	...	5 35	RC	C	9 28	...
Iselle di Trasquera	...	...	...	7 12	...	9 4	...	11 34	...	12 1	1 3	2 26	...	...	...	5 52	...	...	9 47	...
Brig ....arr	...	...	...	7 56	...	9 35	...	12 7		1233	1 38	2 58	...	...	...	6 23	7 33	8 30	10 22	3 48
SPIEZ 268F ......arr	...	...	...	...	...	1158	...	2p11	..	2p11	..	4 p36	...	...	...	8p15	9p20	...	...	5a30
BERNE 267 ......arr	...	...	...	...	...	1 p8	...	3 p8	...	3 p8	...	5 p32	...	...	...	9p20	1018	...	...	6a28
PARIS P.L.M...arr	...	...	...	...	...	11p0	...	...	...	...	...	4 a55	p.m.	...	...	6a45	...	...	...	2 p25
,, Est ......arr	a.m.	...	...	...	...	...	a.m.	11p48	...	1148	...	6 a25	§	...	p.m.	7a28	7a28	...	...	2 p49
Brig ....dep	4*15	...	...	...	6 45	9 42	1017	12 11	...	...	1 45	3 5	3 33	...	5 0	6 33	7 43	8 43	10 27	3 58
Visp (Viège)	5 15	...	...	...	7 2	9 57	1033	12‡22	...	...	1 58	3 17	3 44	...	5 15	6 45	7 52	8 56	10 39	...
Raron	5 45	a.m.	...	...	7 12	...	1043	...	...	...	2 7	...		...	5 27	...	...	...	10 50	...
Gampel	6 0	6 15	...	...	7 19	...	1049	...	...	...	2 14	...	...	...	5 35	...	...	C	10 58	...
Turtman		6 21	...	...	7 25	...	1055	...	...	...	2 20	...	...	...	5 42	...	...	...	11 5	...
Leuk		6 29	...	...	7 34	1022	11 4	...	...	...	2 28	...	...	...	5 53	7 7	...	...	11 14	...
Salgesch	..	6 37	...	...	7 42	...	1111	...	...	...	2 36	...	...	...	6 4	...	...	...	11 23	...
Sierre (Siders)	...	6 45	...	...	7 50	1038	1120	...	...	...	2 46	3 48	...	...	6 15	7 19	...	9 25	11 31	...
Granges	...		...	2 & 3	7 59	...	1130	...	...	...	2 55	...	...	...	6 26	...	...	...	11 41	...
Sion (Sitten)... arr	...	...	...	a.m.	8 13	1055	1145	12 59	...	...	3 8	4 3	...	...	6 42	7 35	8 34	9 42	11 57	4 44
Sion (Sitten)... dep	...	...	...	5 20	8 18	1059	1153	1 1	...	...	3 13	4 5	...	...	6 49	7 40	8 36	9 45		4 46
Ardon	...	...	...	5 30	8 28	...	12 4	...	...	...	3 22	...	...	...	7 1	...	...	...	...	...
Riddes	...	...	...	5 39	8 37	...	1214	...	...	...	3 30	...	...	...	7 12	...	...	...	...	...
Saxon	...	...	...	5 49	8 45	1121	1223	...	...	...	3 37	...	...	...	7 22	...	...	...	...	...
Martigny	...	...	...	6 7	9 3	1135	1242	...	...	...	3 54	4 32	...	...	7 42	8 9	9 3	...	...	...
Vernayaz	...	...	...	6 17	9 13	1144	1253	...	...	...	4 4	...	...	...	7 52	8 18	...	...	...	...
Evionnaz	...	1,2,3	...	6 25	9 20	...	1 1	...	...	...	4 11	...	...	...	8 0	...	...	...	1,2,3	...
St. Maurice arr	...	a.m.	a.m.	6 35	9 27	11 57	1 12	1 37	p.m.	...	4 20	4 47	p.m.	p.m.	8 10	8 30	9 18	10 23	p.m.	5 22
St. Maurice dep	...	5 38	6 43		9 34	1210		1 40	2 3	...	4 28	4 52	5 17	6 42		8 36	9 20	10 26	9 25	5 24
Bex	...	5 47	6 52	...	9 42	1219	...	...	2 13	...	4 36	...	5 25	6 52	...	8 44	...	...	9 33	...
St. Triphon	...	5 55	6 59	...	9 48	1226	...	...	2 20	...	...	...	5 33	7 0	...	...	...	...	9 41	...
Aigle	1,2,3	6 5	7 10	1,2,3	9 56	1234	1,2,3	...	2 30	...	4 48	...	5 42	7 11	...	8 55	...	10 40	9 51	...
Roche	a.m.	6 16	7 21	a.m.	10 4	1242	p.m.	...	2 40	p.m.	...	...	5 53	7 23	...	...	...	...	10 2	...
Villeneuve	5 17	6 25	7 30	9 22	1011	1250	1220	...	2 49	4 10	4 59	...	6 2	7 33	...	9 5	...	...	10 12	...
Veytaux-Chillon	5 22	6 30	7 35	9 27	...	...	1225	...	2 55	4 15	...	...	6 7	7 38	...	...	...	...	10 17	...
Territet-Glion	5 26	6 34	7 39	9 31	1019	1257	1229	...	2 59	4 19	5 7	5 21	6 12	7 42	...	9 14	...	10 54	10 21	...
Montreux	5 32	6 41	7 46	9 38	1027	1 5	1235	2 9	3 10	4 26	5 14	5 29	6 21	7 50	...	9 21	9 52	11 0	10 28	5 52
Clarens	5 37	6 46	7 51	9 44	1032	1 10	1240	...	3 14	4 31	...	...	6 26	7 55	...	9 26	...	...	10 33	...
Burier	...	6 50	7 56	9 49	...	...	1244	...	3 19	4 35	...	...	6 30	7 59	...	...	...	...	10 37	...
La Tour-de-Peilz	5 45	6 55	8 1	9 54	...	...	1248	...	3 23	4 39	...	...	6 34	8 3	...	...	...	...	10 41	...
Vevey	6 7	7 0	8 9	10 3	1042	1 21	1254	2 20	3 30	4 45	5 25	5 41	6 42	8 10	...	9 35	10 2	11 10	10 47	6 2
Rivaz Saphorin	6 17	7 11	8 18	10 14	...	...	1 5	...	3 38	4 56	...	...	6 50	8 21	...	...	...	...	10 55	...
Cully	6 28	7 23	8 27	10 26	...	1 35	1 17	...	3 47	5 8	...	...	6 59	8 33	...	...	...	...	11 4	...
Lutry	6 36	7 32	8 35	10 36	...	...	1 26	...	3 54	5 18	...	...	7 6	8 43	...	...	...	...	11 11	...
Lausanne ......arr	6 48	7 44	8 45	10 48	11 2	1 48	1 38	2 40	4 7	5 30	5 45	6 0	7 15	8 55	...	9 56	1021	11 29	11 20	6 20
GENEVA 263A...arr	8a20	9a57	1025	12p52	1252	4 p5	4 p5	4p20	6 p0	7p22	7p22	7 p22	9 p0	1120	...	12a8	12a8	1 a8	1 a8	8 a20
BERNE 263 ......arr	...	1027	1 p5	1p25	1p25	4p52	4p52	...	8 p0	8p27	8p27	8 p27	1148	...	...	1233	1233	...	4 a40	10a27
	2&3		2&3				2&3	1 & 2	2&3			1,2,3		1,2,3			1 &2	1 Cl.		1 & 2
	a.m.		a.m.				p.m.	p.m.	p.m.			p.m.		p.m.			p.m.	p.m.		a.m.
Lausanne......dep	6 55	...	10 0	...	...	...	2 15	3 0	5 20			6 53	...	9 42	...	...	1047	11 39	...	6 42
Renens	7 2	...	10 8	...	...	...	2 23	...	5 35			...	...	9 49	...	...	...	...	...	6‖49
Bussigny	7 7	...	1013	...	...	...	2 28	...	5 42			...	...	9 54	...		...	...	...	...
Cossonay	7 20	...	1027	...	...	...	2 42	...	6 0			...	...	10 5	...		...	C	...	...
La Sarraz	7 33	...	1041	...	...	...	2 55	...	6 17			7 18	...	1017			...	...	...	...
Arnex	7 43	...	1052	...	...	...	3 6	...	6 30			...	...	...	...		...	...	...	...
Croy	7 55	...	11 6	...	...	...	3 20	...	6 46			7 37	...	1038	...		...	...	...	...
Day	8 14	...	1127	...	...	...	3 41	...	7 8			...	...	...	...		...	...	2 & 3	...
Vallorbes ...... arr	8 20	...	1133	...	...	...	3 47	3 58	7 15			7 58	...	11 0	...		1147	12 35	a.m.	7 42
Vallorbes ...... dep	7 40	...	1050	...	...	...	3 35	3 6	6 25			7 10	...	1010	...		1058	11 47	4 25	6 50
Hopitaux-Jougne	8 3	...	1115	...	...	...	3 58	...	6 52			...	...	...	...		...	...	4 48	...
Frambourg	8 23	...	1137	...	...	...	4 18	...	7 17			...	...	...	...	...	...	...	5 12	...
Pontarlier ¶...arr	8 32	...	1145	...	...	...	4 25	3 44	7 25	...	...	7 48	...	1050	...	...	1138	12 25	5 20	7 28
DIJON 52..........arr	1247	...	4p44	...	...	...	9p12	6p46	11p17	...	...	11p17	...	1a39	...	...	2a10	2 a30	..	9 a49
PARIS 51..........arr	6 p8	...	...	...	...	...	...	11 p0	4a55	...	...	4 a55	...	6a20	...	...	6a45	7 a15	...	2 p25

‡—Stops at Visp only until 15th September.

§—From the opening of the Lötschberg line.

RC—Restaurant Car.

☞ **Greenwich Time between Vallorbes and Pontarlier.** ¶—Customs Examination.
*—Weekdays only. ‖—Takes up only. C—Train de Luxe, Simplon Express.

MARTIGNY and ORSIERES.

Martigny—Gare dep	7a43	9a10	12p15	2p10	5 p0	8‡p20	9 p5
Sembrancher	8 23	9 50	12 55	2 50	5 40	9 0	9 45
Orsières ....arr	8 40	10 7	1 12	3 7	5 57	9 17	10 2

Orsières ....dep	6a23	7a34	10 a20	12p34	3p20	6p55	7‡p49
Sembrancher	6 42	7 53	10 30	12 53	3 39	7 14	8 8
Martigny—Gare ...arr	7 20	8 31	11 17	1 31	4 17	7 52	8 46

‡—Saturdays and Sundays only until 15th September.

LAUSANNE, NEUCHATEL, BIEL (BIENNE), DELEMONT, and BASLE.

		3 Cl.	2 & 3	1,2,3	2 & 3	1,2,3	1,2,3	1,2,3	2 & 3	1 &2	1,2,3	1,2,3	1,2,3	2 & 3	1,2,3	1,2,3	1&2	1,2,3	2 & 3	2 & 3
GENEVA (263) ...dep		...	...	...	...	5a30	7 *12	...	9a13	10*47	...	12*49	1p30	...	2p10	5 *23	...	5 p23	...	9* 0
					a.m.	a.m.	a.m.		a.m.	a.m.	...	p.m.	p.m.		p.m.	p.m.	...	p.m.	p.m.	p.m.
Lausanne ...dep		...	...	...	4 55	7 10	8 15	...	11 10	1135	...	1 55	2 50	...	4 30	6 13	...	6 43	7 5	10 3
Renens		...	...	...	5 3	7 18	8 27	...	11 17	1147	...	2 4	...	...	4 38	6 26	...	...	7 14	10 11
Bussigny		...	...	...	5 8	7 23	...	...	11 22	...	...	2 9	...	...	4 43	...	...	...	7 19	10 16
Cossonay		...	...	...	5 24	7 39	8 40	...	11 36	RC	...	2 19	...	...	4 58	RC	...	RC	7 36	10 28
Eclépens		...	...	...	5 35	7 50	...	...	11 46	...	...	...	...	...	5 12	...	...	...	7 48	10 40
Chavornay-Orbe		...	...	...	5 47	8 0	...	...	11 55	...	...	2 36	...	...	5 24	...		...	7 58	10 48
Yverdon ...arr		...	...	...	6 2	8 15	9 4	a.m.	12 10	1220	...	2 48	3 28	...	5 40	7 0		7 23	8 13	11 3
„ (263A)...dep		...	...	...	6 7	8 20	9 7	9†13	12 30	1222	...	2 51	3 30	...	5 50	7 2		7 25	8 18	11 7
Grandson		...	...	...	6 14	8 26	...	9 22	12 38	...	...	2 57	...	...	5 56	...		...	8 25	11 13
Onnens Bonvillars		...	...	...	6 22	8 34	...	...	12 46	...	...	3 4	...	...	6 4	...		...	8 33	11 20
Concise		...	...	...	6 28	8 40	...	9 39	12 52	...	...	3 9	...	...	6 10	...	Interlaken—Calais Express, runs until 15th September.	...	8 39	11 25
Vaumarcus-Vernéaz		...	...	...	6 36	8 47	...	...	12 59	...	...	...	...	...	6 17	...		...	8 46	11 32
Gorgier St. Aubin		...	...	...	6 44	8 53	...	9 57	1 5	...	...	3 18	...	...	6 24	...		...	8 52	11 37
Bevaix		...	...	...	6 53	9 1	...	10 12	1 13	...	...	3 26	...	...	6 32	...		...	9 0	11 45
Boudry		...	...	...	7 1	9 8	...	10 24	1 20	...	...	3 33	...	...	6 41	...		...	9 8	11 52
Colombier		...	...	...	7 6	9 12	...	10 31	1 24	...	...	3 37	...	...	6 47	...		...	9 12	11 56
Auvernier		...	...	...	7 12	9 18	...	10 40	1 30	...	...	3 42	...	...	6 52	...		...	9 17	12 1
Neuchâtel ...arr		...	a.m.	...	7 22	9 26	9 48	10 55	1 40	1 2	...	3 50	4 10	p.m.	7 2	7 43		8 6	9 27	12 10
„ (265)...dep		...	5 5	...	7 45		9 53	11 10	2 0	1 5	...	3 55	4 15	5 2	7 12	7 47		8 10	9 37	
St. Blaise		...	5 12	...	7 52	...	...	11 17	2 7	...	...	4 2	...	5 9	7 19	...		...	9 44	...
Cressier		...	5 23	...	8 2	...	...	11 28	2 17	...	...	4 13	...	5 20	7 30	...		...	9 55	...
Landeron		...	5 27	...	8 7	...	...	11 33	2 22	...	...	4 17	...	5 25	7 35	...		...	9 59	...
Neuveville		...	5 33	...	8 12	...	10 12	11 39	2 27	...	...	4 22	...	5 32	7 40	...		...	10 4	...
Twann		...	5 44	...	8 22	...	...	11 51	2 37	...	...	4 30	...	5 44	7 51	...		...	10 14	...
Biel (Bienne) ...arr		...	5 57	...	8 35	...	10 30	12 6	2 50	1 36	...	4 40	4 48	5 58	8 5	8 18		8 41	10 27	...
OLTEN (257B) ...arr		...	8 a11	...	11a33	...	11a51	2p40	5 p40	2p48	...	6 p10	6 p10	9 p24	9p33	9 p33	☞	...	...	...
BASLE (258) ...arr		...	9 a13	...	1p12	2 & 3	1 p12	3p57	6 p58	3p57	...	7 p35	7 p35	10p53	1053	10p53		...	...	1,2,3
ZURICH (262) ...arr		a.m.	9 a52	a.m.	1 p3	a.m.	1 p 3	4 p8	7 p46	4 p8	p.m.	7 p46	7 p46	10p50	1050	10p50	p.m.	...		p.m.
Biel (Bienne) ...dep		4†50	6 28	7 19	8 38	10 0	10 45	1 40	...	...	3 57	5 21	...	...	...	9 ‡27	8 22	8 52		11 21
Reuchenette		5 20	6 46	⋮	8 58	10 22	...	2 0	...	...	⋮	5 39	...	...	...	9 48	⋮	...		⋮
Sonceboz ...arr		5 35	6 56	⋮	9 9	10 33	11 13	2 12	...	...	⋮	5 50	...	...	...	10 0	⋮	9 19		⋮
CHAUX DE FONDS 265		...	5 a55	⋮	...	9a12	10a13	12p53	...	...	⋮	4 p20	...	...	...	8p59	⋮	8 p18		⋮
Sonceboz ...dep		5†42	7 0	⋮	...	10 41	11 16	2 20	...	...	⋮	5 53	...	...	...	10 8	⋮	9 21	A—Runs from 2nd July until 15th September.	⋮
Tavannes (264)		6 12	7 19	⋮	...	11 0	11 32	2 38	...	...	⋮	6 12	...	...	...	10 29	⋮	9 37		B
Malleray-Bevilard		6 40	7 32	⋮	...	11 11	...	2 49	...	...	⋮	6 24	...	...	...	10 44	⋮	...		⋮
Court		7 3	7 42	⋮	...	11 21	...	2 59	...	...	⋮	6 34	...	...	...	10 54	⋮	...		⋮
Moutier		7 20	7 57	⋮	...	11 34	11 55	3 13	...	...	⋮	6 48	...	...	...	11 7	⋮	9 59		⋮
Roches		7 27	8 2	⋮	...	11 39	...	3 18	...	...	⋮	6 54	...	...	...	11 12	⋮	...		⋮
Choindez		7 35	8 8	⋮	...	11 45	...	3 25	...	...	⋮	7 0	...	...	...	11 17	⋮	...		⋮
Courrendlin		7 41	8 13	⋮	...	11 50	...	3 30	...	...	⋮	7 5	...	...	...	11 22	⋮	...	...	⋮
Delemont ...arr		7 48	8 18	8 29	...	11 56	12 8	3 35	1,2,3	...	5 17	7 10	...	...	...	11 27	9 32	10 12	1 Cl.	12 32
PARIS (68)...dep	9 p0	...	9 p45	...	...	10p 0	10p 0	...	8 a0	...	...	8 a55	...	...	...	...		1 p0	7p47	...
BELFORT (68) dep	2a42	2 & 3	4 a26	...	3 Cl.	6 a52	6 a52	11a55	1p37	2&3	...	3 p25	2 & 3	2 & 3	...	...		6‖39	1a28	
DELLE (266) dep	4a15	a.m.	6 a15	...	a.m.	10 a3	10 a3	1 p55	3p10	p.m.	...	5 p18	6 p40	6p40	...	...		9 ‖0	3 a3	
Delemont ...dep	5 23	6 23	8 37	...	9†25	12 35	12 13	3 50	4 25	5 32	...	7 16	8§35	8†35	...	...		10 17	⋮	...
Soyhieres	...	6 30	8 43	...	9 43	12 41	...	3 57	...	5 38	...	7 23	8 43	8 43	...	...	B—Runs from day of opening of the Lœtschberg Line.	...	A	
Liesberg	...	6 39	8 51	...	10 18	12 50	...	4 7	...	5 47	...	7 31	8 53	8 53	†—Sunday excepted.	§—Sunday only.		...	⋮	‖—From day of opening of the Lötschberg line.
Barschwyl	...	6 47	8 57	...	10 30	12 56	...	4 14	...	5 53	...	7 37	9 0	9 0				...	⋮	
Laufen	...	6 55	9 2	...	10 48	1 4	12 33	4 23	...	6 0	...	7 44	9 7	9 7				10 36	⋮	
Zwingen	...	7 1	9 7	...	11 0	1 9	...	4 30	...	6 5	...	7 50	9 12	9 14				...	⋮	
Grellingen	...	7 10	9 15	...	11 32	1 18	...	4 40	...	6 13	...	7 58	9 20	9 26				...	⋮	
Aesch	...	7 18	9 22	...	11 48	1 25	...	4 47	...	6 20	...	8 5	9 26	9 36				...	⋮	
Dornach-Arles	...	7 24	9 27	...	12 2	1 30	...	4 52	...	6 25	...	8 10	9 31	9 45	...	...		10 52	⋮	
Mönchenstein	...	7 30	9 32	...	12 24	1 35	...	4 58	...	6 30	...	8 15	9 36	9 54	...	...		...	⋮	
Basle ...arr	6 7	7 40	9 40	...	12 40	1 44	1 3	5 7	5 15	6 40	...	8 23	9 45	10 10	...	...		11 2	4 45	...
ZURICH (261)...arr	8a35	...	12p48	...	...	5 p23	3 p29	7 p55	7p55	...	...	11p25	...	...	...	...		...	6a45	...
LUCERNE (258) arr	8a59	10 48	1 p40	...	...	3 p49	3 p49	8 p15	8p15	...	...	11p42	...	...	...	...		1 a12	...	...

*—Train from Geneva connects at Renens. ‡—2 & 3 class only.
RC—Restaurant Car.

Extra		
Delemont...dep	5a10	2p25
Basle ...arr	6 25	3 36

TRAMELAN and TAVANNES.

Tramelan ...dep	6 a5	9a20	1p10	4 p12	7 p17	9 p0
Tavannes (264) arr	6 33	9 48	1 32	4 40	7 45	9 28
Tavannes dep	7a27	11 a5	2p50	6 p9	7p55	10p24
Tramelan arr	7 55	11 33	3 18	6 37	8 23	10 52

ORBE and CHAVORNAY.—In 14 minutes. { Orbe depart 5.27, 7.40, 9.0, 11.35 a.m., 12.42, 2.13, 3.26, 5.2, 7.34, 10.28 p.m.
Chavornay depart 6.4, 8.5, 9.22, 11.58 a.m., 1.6, 2.39, 3.47, 5.28, 8.3, 10.51 p.m.

LAUSANNE, MOUDON, and SAVIGNY.

Lausanne dep	5a22	...	6a50	7a12	7a58	9a7	10a2	11a12	12p8	1p37	2p11	2p38	4p2	4p8	5p18	5p58	6p15	6p38	7p12	7p18	8p3	9p38	10p16
En Marin	5 49	...	7 17	7 40	8 25	935	1029	11 40	1236		2 39	3 6	430	436	5 46	6 26	6 39	7 6	7 39	7 46	831	10 6	10 43
Mézières	⋮	5a42	7 50	...	8 59	⋮	11 3	⋮	⋮	2 28	⋮	—	5 2	⋮	⋮	—	7 7	—	⋮	—	9 3	⋮	11 12
Moudon arr	⋮	6a10	8 18	...	9 27	⋮	1131	⋮	⋮	2 54	⋮	...	530	⋮	⋮	...	7 33	...	⋮	...	931	⋮	—
Savigny ...arr	6 6	...	...	8 2	...	957	...	12 2	1253	...	3 1	...	...	458	6 8	...	...	...	8 1	...	...	1023	...

Savigny ...dep		6 a6	6a54	8 a2	...	...	10 a6	..	12p10	1p10	...	...	3 p4	...	..	5 p3	6 p16	...	...	8 p8	...	10p25
Moudon dep		⋮	6 20	⋮	8a33	..	⋮	10a1	⋮	⋮	1 p3	...	...	...	...	4 32	⋮	6 p 9	...	⋮	8p28	⋮
Mézières	5a54	⋮	6 54	⋮	9 0	a.m.	⋮	1035	⋮	⋮	1 38	...		...	...	4 59	⋮	6 42	p.m	⋮	9 1	⋮
En Marin	6 23	6 23	7 23	8 25	9 26	10 19	10 29	11 5	12 26	1 29	2 8	2p39	3 26	3 p59	4c39	5 27	6 39	7 14	7 59	8 31	9 30	10 43
Lausanne	6 50	6 50	7 51	8 54	9 51	10 47	10 58	1131	12 55	1 58	2 35	3 7	3 55	4 27	5 7	5 51	7 7	7 40	8 27	9 9	9 57	11 11

BASLE, DELEMONT, BIEL, NEUCHATEL, and LAUSANNE.

Station																				
LUCERNE 258 dep	...	...	...	...	5 a5	5 a5	5 a5	...	7 a0	9a55	...	10a10	2 p2	2p19	4 p57	...	7 p0	9p10	9p10	1013
ZURICH 261 ...dep	...	...	...	...	...	...	4 a52	...	8a25	9a45	...	11a38	2 p30	2 p48	...	...	6p40	9p12	9p12	10p5
	2 & 3	1,2,3	1& 2	2 & 3	1,2,3	1,2,3	1,2,3	1,2,3	1,2,3	2&3	1,2,3	2 & 3	2 & 3	1,2,3	2 & 3	1,2,3	1,2,3	1,2,3	1 & 2	1Cl.
				a.m.	a.m.	a.m.	a.m.		a.m	p.m.		p.m.	p.m.	p.m.	p.m.		p.m.	p.m.	p.m.	ng't
Basle Station...dep	...	...	Runs until 15th September. ☞	5 2	7 25	7 35	7 45	...	10 44	1216	...	2 10	4 17	6 44	7 13	...	9 15	1133	1145	1230
Mönchenstein	...	...		5 17	...	...	7 53	...	10 55	1225	...	2 20	4 25	...	7 23	...	9 25	...	...	:
Dornach-Arlesheim	...	...		5 26	...	...	7 58	...	11 2	1231	...	2 26	4 30	...	7 30	...	9 32	...	...	:
Aesch	...	...		5 36	...	...	8 3	...	11 8	1236	...	2 32	4 35	...	7 36	...	9 38	...	...	:
Grellingen	...	...		5 57	...	...	8 10	...	11 16	1244	...	2 40	4 41	...	7 43	...	9 45	...	...	:
Zwingen	...	...		6 10	...	...	8 18	...	11 25	1253	...	2 48	4 49	...	7 51	...	9 53	...	...	:
Laufen	...	...		6 20	7 54	...	8 22	...	11 32	1 1	...	2 56	4 54	...	7 57	...	10 0	...	...	:
Barschwyl	...	...		6 29	...	...	8 27	...	11 38	1 6	...	3 1	4 59	...	8 2	...	10 5	...	...	:
Liesberg	...	...		6 40	...	...	8 33	...	11 44	1 12	...	3 7	5 5	...	8 8	...	1011	...	...	:
Soybières	...	...		6 53	...	...	8 42	...	11 54	1 22	...	3 16	5 13	...	8 17	...	1022	...	...	:
Delémont......arr	...	...		7 2	8 13	8 25	8 48	...	12 [illegible]	1 28	...	3 22	5 20	7 28	8 23	...	1028	1218	1229	:
DELLE 266 ...arr	...	...		9a27	9 27	9a27	10a31	...	1p38	...	...	5p18	...	9 p0	10p25	...	...	1a13	1a33	2a16
BELFORT 69 arr	...	...		9 a7	9 a7	9 a7	10a24	...	1p24	...	...	6 p0	...	9 p4	10 p0	...	...	1254	...	2a29
PARIS 69 .....arr	a.m.	a.m.	a.m.	2p49	2p49	2p49	5 p45	...	9 p0	...	p.m.	11p48	...	6a25	6 a25	p.m.	...	7a28	...	8a42
Delemont......dep	5 0	5 45	6 36	...	8 18	...	8 55	...	12 32	...	4 15	3 35	...	7 33	8 32	1012	...			
Courrendlin	5 7	:	:	...	...	...	9 2	...	12 39	...	:	3 42	...	...	8 39	:	...			
Choindez	5 12	:	:	...	...	...	9 6	...	12 44	...	:	3 47	...	...	8 44	:	...			
Roches	5 18	:	:	...	...	...	9 12	...	12 50	...	:	3 53	...	...	8 50	:	...			
Moutier (Munster)...	5 25	:	:	...	8 36	...	9 18	...	12 57	...	:	4 0	...	7 50	8 57	:	...			
Court	5 40	:	:	...	...	...	9 33	...	1 13	...	:	4 15	...	...	9 13	:	...			
Malleray-Bevilard	5 50	:	:	...	...	...	9 42	...	1 24	...	:	4 24	...	...	9 23	:	...			
Tavannes	6 5	:	:	...	...	...	9 55	...	1 45	...	:	4 38	...	...	9 36	:	...			
Sonceboz ......arr	6 16	:	:	1,2,3	9 10	...	10 7	...	2 0	1,2,3	:	4 48	...	8 29	9 48	:	...			
CHX. FOND. 265A arr	8 a21	:	:	a.m.	10a13	...	11a41	...	3 p30	p.m.	:	7 p13	...	9 p46	11 p0	:	...			
Sonceboz......dep	6 20	:	:	8 50	9 12	...	10 12	...	2 12	4 2	:	4 10	...	8 31	10 0	:	...			
Reuchenette	6 29	:	:	9 2	...	...	10 23	...	2 24	4 16	:	5 1	...	...	10 11	:	...			
Biel (Bienne) ...arr	6 42	6 57	7 50	9 15	9 32	...	10 35	...	2 37	4 30	5 21	5 15	...	8 51	10 24	1121	...			
ZURICH 262A dep	...	...	...	...	...	7 a23	7 a23	8 a22	10a55	...	3 p24	3 p24	...	5 p55	6 p15	☞	...			
BASLE 258......dep	...	...	...	...	...	7 a30	7 a40	8 a25	10a40	...	3 p40	3 p40	...	6 p20	...		...			
OLTEN 257B ...dep	2 & 3	...	...	...	...	8 a35	8 a47	10a24	12p33	...	4 p45	4 p50	...	7 p28	8 p15		...			
	a.m.	a.m	a.m.	2 & 3	a.m.	a.m.	a.m.	p.m.	p.m.	p.m.	p.m.	p.m.		p.m.	p.m.		...			
Biel (Bienne)...dep	6 24	7 0	9 0	†—Not on Sunday.	9 40	9 55	10 48	12 45	3 3	4 48	5 58	7 55	...	9 0	10 43	Runs from day of opening of the Lœtschberg Line.	...			
Twann	6 37	...	9 16		...	...	11 0	12 59	3 16	5 5	...	7 50	...	...	10 58		...			
Neuveville	6 49	...	9 31		...	...	11 10	1 12	3 26	5 18	...	8 3	...	9 16	11 11		...			
Landeron	6 54	...	9 37		RC	RC	11 15	1 18	3 31	5 24	RC	8 9	...	RC	11 17		...			
Cressier	6 59	...	9 43		...	...	11 19	1 23	3 36	5 29	...	8 14	...	...	11 23		...			
St. Blaise......2 & 3	7 13	...	9 59		...	...	11 31	1 37	3 48	5 43	...	8 28	2 & 3	...	11 38		...			
Neuchâtel arr a.m.	7 20	7 35	10 7	a.m.	10 16	10 31	11 39	1 45	3 55	5 50	6 34	8 37	p.m.	9 37	11 47		...			
dep 4 30	7 47	7 38	§—For Geneva change at Renens.	9 †2	10 20	10 35	11 43	2 5	4 8	6 0	6 37	8 55	10†10	9 40	RC—Restaurant Car between Biel and Lausanne.		...			
Auvernier 4 41	7 58	7 47	...	9 19	...	...	11 53	2 17	4 18	6 12	...	9 7	10 28	...			...			
Colombier.........4 47	8 4	...	...	9 30	...	...	11 58	2 23	4 23	6 18	...	9 13	10 36	...			...			
Boudry 4 51	8 8	...	...	9 38	...	...	12 2	2 28	4 27	6 22	...	9 18	10 41	...			...			
Bevaix 4 59	8 16	...	...	9 48	...	...	12 9	2 36	4 33	6 31	...	9 26	10 54	...			...			
Gorgier St. Aub. 5 6	8 24	...		9 56	...	...	12 15	2 43	4 39	6 38	...	9 34	11 3	...			...			
Vaumarcus 5 12	8 30	...		10 7	...	...	12 20	2 50	4 44	6 44	...	9 42	11 12	...			...			
Concise 5 20	8 39	...		10 18	...	...	12 26	2 58	4 50	6 52	...	9 50	11 24	...			...			
Onnens Bonv.....5 26	8 46	...		10 28	...	...	12 32	3 5	4 55	6 58	...	9 57	11 34	...			...			
Grandson 5 34	8 54	...		10 40	...	...	12 39	3 14	5 2	7 7	...	10 6	11 45	...			...			
Yverdon arr 5 40	9 0	8 20		10 50	10 58	11 18	12 44	3 20	5 7	7 12	7 21	10 12	11 55	10 20			...			
263A dep 5 45	9 4	8 22			11 0	11 20	12 47	3 28	5 9	7 35	7 23	10 32		10 22		...	...			
Chavornay Orbe 6 3	9 20	...		...	...	...	1 3	3 46	5 25	7 56	...	10 50	...	...		...	...			
Eclépens 6 12	9 29	...		...	...	...	1 12	3 55	5 34	8 6	...	10 59	...	...		...	...			
Cossonay 6 24	9 39	...		...	...	...	1 21	4 5	5 43	8 18	...	11 11	...	...		...	...			
Bussigny 6 36	9 51	...		...	...	...	1 31	4 17	5 53	8 32	...	11 21	...	...		...	...			
Renens 6 42	9 58	...	...	...	...	11 58	1 36	4 22	5 58	8 38	8 1	11 27	...	11 0		...	...			
Lausanne arr 6 50	10 6	9 2	...	...	11 40	12 5	1 43	4 30	6 5	8 47	8 7	11 35	...	11 7	...	...	...			
GENEVA 263A 8a20	11§50	1025	...	...	12 52	12§52	4 p5	6 p0	7 p22	10p32	9§ 0	1 a8	...	12§a8	...	...	...			...

NEUCHATEL to BOUDRY.—Local line.—From Neuchatel (Place Purry), to Serrieres, Auvernier, Colombier, Cortaillod, and Boudry. Dep. Neuchatel 6.50, 7.10, 7.50, 8.10 a.m., and about every 20 minutes until 10.30 p.m. also at 11.0 p.m.

Runs from 2nd July until 15th September. ☞

Extra {Basle ......dep 6p 2 / Delemont ...arr 7 16}

LAUSANNE, PAYERNE, MURTEN, and LYSS.

[†—Not on Sunday.

Dist E.M		a.m.	a.m.	a.m.	p.m.	p.m.	p.m.	p.m.
	Lausanne ...dep	5 0	8 28	11 55	2 32	4 18	6 28	8 45
7½	Puidoux-Chexbres	5 28	8 56	12 24	3 0	4 47	6 57	9 16
12¾	Palezieux	5 54	9 12	12 40	3 16	5 5	7 12	9 33
23½	Moudon	6 32	9 48	1 13	3 45	5 35	7 45	1013
36¼	**Payerne** arr a.m.	7 13	10 27	1 48	4 16	6 7	8 20	1053
	dep 5 5	7 35	10 48	1 57	4 25	6 50	8 34	
37¾	Corcelles 5 11	7 40	10 53	2 1	4 30	6 55	8 38	...
43	Avenches 5 32	7 57	11 10	2 16	4 46	7 12	8 53	...
47¼	**Murten** arr 5 47	8 10	11 22	2 27	4 58	7 24	9 4	...
	dep 5 57	8 15	11 30	2 34	5 2	7 30	9 6	...
52¾	Kerzers 6 38	8 34	11 46	2 48	5 16	7 50	9 22	...
54½	Fraeschels......6 49	8 39	11 52	2 53	5 21	7 57	9 27	...
59½	Aarberg 7 16	8 52	12 8	3 6	5 34	8 14	9 40	...
62½	**Lyss 265** arr 7 28	8 59	12 15	3 13	5 41	8 22	9 47	...

	a.m.	a.m.	a.m.	p.m.	p.m.	p.m.	p.m.	p.m.
Lyss ....dep	5 54	9 15	10†20	12 45	2 55	4 51	7 17	9 55
Aarberg	6 3	9 25	10 45	12 53	3 5	4 59	7 26	10 3
Fraeschels	6 16	9 42	11 17	1 6	3 18	5 12	7 39	1017
Kerzers	6 25	9 58	12 2	1 11	3 25	5 18	7 48	1025
Murten ... arr	6 38	10 11	12 25	1 24	3 38	5 33	8 1	1040
dep	6 43	10 13		1 26	3 41	5 36	8 3	1043
Avenches	6 57	10 27	...	1 38	3 55	5 49	8 15	1056
Corcelles	7 13	10 44	...	1 53	4 11	6 4	8 30	1113
Payerne arr a.m.	7 17	10 48	...	1 57	4 15	6 8	8 34	1117
dep 5 2	7 27	11 0	...	2 15	4 28	6 52	8 45	
Moudon 5 38	8 5	11 43	...	2 57	5 6	7 42	9 21	...
Palezieux 6 17	8 45	12 27	...	3 38	5 58	8 37	10 2	...
Puidoux-Chex 6 28	9 0	12 44	...	3 51	6 13	8 51	10 16	...
Lausanne ...6 50	9 25	1 8	...	4 13	6 35	9 10	10 38	...

PONTARLIER, NEUCHATEL, BIEL (BIENNE), and BERNE.

Dist E.M	Station	1 cl.	2&3	1,2,3	2&3	1&2	1,2,3	1&2	1,2,3	2&3	2&3	2&3	1,2,3	1,2,3	1,2,3	2&3	1,2,3	1,2,3	2&3	1,2,3	1,2,3	1,2,3
...	PARIS (48) ...dep	7p45	...	...	...	...	9p30	1015	1050	...	...	1050	...	...	...	...	8a30	8a30	...	...	2p20	...
...	DIJON (52) ...dep	1228	...	...	...	...	1a48	3a 4	3a47	...	...	4a20	...	...	5a44	...	1246	1246	...	...	6p42	...
		a.m.				Until 15th Sept.	a.m.	a.m.	a.m.	a.m.		a.m.			p.m.		p.m.	p.m.		p.m.	p.m.	Runs from day of opening of the Loetschberg Line.
—	**Pontarlier**...dep	3 8	...	...	...	...	4 28	5 20	6 50	6 20	...	9 40	...	...	1235	...	3 28	4 40	...	6 55	9 2	
7	Verrières de Joux	...	...	...	...	...	4 48	...	...	6 40	...	10 9	...	...	1254	...	...	4 59	...	7 15	...	
8	Verrières ¶ arr	3 23	...	...	...	...	4 52	5 35	7 7	6 45	a.m.	1015	...	...	1258	...	3 43	5 3	...	7 20	9 17	
...	Swiss. dep	4 28	...	...	...	...	6 10	6 50	8 25	—	8 52	12 3	...	...	2 15	...	5 0	6 23	...	8 45	1025	
10¼	Les Bayards	...	...	...	...	...	6 17	...	...	...	9 0	1211	...	...	2 22	...	...	6 33	...	8 53	...	
14¼	Boveresse	A	...	...	...	...	6 27	...	...	...	9 12	1226	...	...	2 32	...	...	6 42	...	9 6	...	
16¼	Couvet	...	...	...	...	...	6 33	...	...	...	9 19	1236	...	...	2 38	...	...	6 48	...	9 13	...	
18½	Travers (261A)	...	...	...	...	...	6 40	...	8 50	...	9 30	1252	...	...	2 45	...	5 21	6 58	...	9 25	1045	
21¼	Noiraigue	...	...	...	...	...	6 47	...	8 57	..	9 38	1 3	...	...	2 53	...	...	7 6	...	9 34	...	
29¼	Auvernier	...	...	...	...	...	7 8	...	9 12	...	10 2	1 35	...	...	3 16	...	...	7 30	...	10 0	...	
32½	**Neuchâtel** ...arr	5 10	...	...	...	...	7 17	7 35	9 20	1,2,3	10 13	1 47	...	...	3 28	...	5 46	7 40	...	1010	11 9	
59½	BERNE 259B ..arr	6 a8	a.m.	...	...	...	8a35	8a35	1032	a.m.	1 p18	3p31	...	...	5 p0	p.m.	6p55	1015	p.m.	—	12 1	
...	**Neuchâtel** ...dep (See also p. 264)	—	5 5	...	...	...	7 45	—	—	9 53	11†10	2 0	...	...	3 55	5 2	—	8 10	9 37	...	—	
40¼	Landeron	...	5 27	...	...	...	8 7	...	†—1st, 2nd & 3rd cl.	...	11 33	2 22	...	...	4 17	5 25	...	...	9 59	...	...	
41¾	Neuveville	...	5 33	...	...	...	8 12	...		1012	11 39	2 27	...	...	4 22	5 32	...	...	10 4			
45¼	Twann	...	5 44	...	...	...	8 22	...		...	11 51	2 37	...	...	4 30	5 44	...	...	1014			
50¾	**Biel** ...arr	...	5 57	...	...	...	8 35	...		1030	12 6	2 50	...	...	4 40	5 58	...	8 41	1027			
87¾	OLTEN 257B...arr	1,2,3	8a11	...	...		1133	1,2,3		1151	2 p40	5p40	...	...	6p10	9p24	...	...	...			
126¾	ZURICH 262 ...arr	a.m.	9a52	a.m.	a.m.	a.m.	1 p3	a.m.	a m.	1p20	4 p8	7p46	p.m.	p.m.	7p46	1050	...	...	...			p.m.
...	**Biel** ...dep	5 30	—	7 0	7 43	7 55	8 50	9 38	1057	...	12§18	...	2 58	5 24	5 30	6 52	...	9 35	1040			1123
55½	Busswyl	5 43	...	...	7 57	...	...	...	1110	...	12 32	...	3 12	...	5 4	7 5	...	...	1054			...
57	**Lyss 264A** arr	5 48	...	...	8 2	...	9 3	...	1114	...	12 37	...	3 17	...	5 45	7 10	...	9 49	1058			...
	dep	5 52	...	...	8 7	...	9 5	...	1118	...	12 43	...	3 20	...	5 47	7 14	...	9 50	11 5			...
59¼	Suberg	6 0	...	...	8 16	...	...	...	1125	...	12 50	...	3 28	...	5 53	7 22	...	...	1112			...
61¾	Schüpfen	6 9	...	...	8 26	...	...	...	1133	...	12 58	...	3 36	...	6 0	7 32	...	...	1120			...
65¼	Münchenbuchsee	6 19	...	...	8 36	...	...	...	1143	...	1 6	...	3 45	...	6 8	7 43	...	...	1129			...
67	Zollikofen	6 26	...	...	8 43	...	9 27	...	1150	...	1 11	...	3 50	...	6 12	7 52	...	1012	1134			...
71½	**Berne 265** ...arr	6 38	...	7 40	8 55	8 35	9 37	1020	12 2	...	1 22	...	4 2	6 5	6 23	8 5	...	1023	1145			12 2

§—2 & 3 Class. ¶—Customs Examination.
A—Train de Luxe runs from 9th July to 15th Sept.
A—Until Sept. 30th.

BERNE and LUCERNE.

Station		2&3	1,2,3	1,2,3	2&3	1,2,3	1&2	1,2,3	2&3	1,2,3	2&3	1,2,3	2&3
		a.m.	a.m.	a.m.	a.m.	a.m.	p.m.	p.m.		p.m.	p.m.	p.m.	p.m.
Berne ...dep		5 28	6 55	7 48	9 0	10 50	1 45	2 8	...	5 12	6 52	8 48	9 57
Ostermundigen		5 38	...	7 57	9 18	10 59	...	2 16	...	...	7 1	...	10 7
Gümlingen		5 44	...	8 3	9 35	11 5	...	2 21	...	5 24	7 7	...	10 13
Worb		5 54	...	8 12	9*49	11 14	...	2 28	...	5 33	7 16	...	10 23
Tagertschi		6 2	...	8 20	9 59	11 22	...	2 35	...	5 40	7 23	...	10 32
Konolfingen 261A		6 11	7 22	8 30	10 22	11 31	A	2 42	...	5 47	7 31	9 19	10 42
Zäziwyl		6 18	...	8 37	10 39	11 38	...	2 48	...	5 53	7 38	...	10 50
Signau	2&3	6 31	...	8 49	11 1	11 51	...	2 59	...	6 5	7 50	...	11 4
Emmenmatt	a.m.	6 38	...	8 55	11 12	11 58	...	3 5	p.m.	6 10	7 57	...	11 12
Langnau	4 45	6 52	7 42	9 8	11*22	12 10	2 30	3 13	2†30	6 22	8 8	9 40	11 20
Trubschachen	4 55	7 2	...	9 20	†—Sunday excepted.	12 22	...	3 22	3 3	6 31	8 20	...	*—Sun. dp. Worb 9.45, Langnau arr. 10a38.
Wiggen	5 5	7 13	...	9 30		12 33	...	3 31	3 43	6 40	8 29	...	
Escholzmatt	5 15	7 23	...	9 38		12 44	...	3 39	4 12	6 48	8 37	...	
Schüpfheim	5 26	7 35	...	9 49		12 56	A	3 50	4 40	6 59	8 48	...	
Entlebuch	5 36	7 46	...	9 58		1 5	...	3 59	5 2	7 7	8 56	...	
Wolhusen	5 52	8 4	...	1010		1 20	...	4 12	5 48	7 18	9 8	...	
Malters	6 6	8 14	...	1021		1 31	...	4 23	6 10	7 28	9 19	...	
Littau	6 17	8 23	...	1029		1 39	...	4 31	6 28	7 36	9 28	...	
Lucerne ...arr	6 28	8 32	8 53	1038		1 48	3 43	4 40	6 40	7 45	9 38	1052	
ZURICH 260 arr	9a36	10a30	1030	1249	...	4 p4	5p40	7 p30	9p15	9p15	11p10	...	

Station	2&3	2&3	2&3	1,2,3	1,2,3	2&3	1,2,3	1&2	1,2,3	1,2,3	1,2,3	2&3
ZURICH (260) dep		...	...	5a58	5a58	...	9 a5	12 0	12 0	3 p14	5 p5	5 p51
		a.m.	a.m.	a.m.	a.m.		a.m.	p.m.	p.m.	p.m.	p.m	p.m.
Lucerne ...dep	...	5 20	...	7 38	7 52	...	10 54	1 56	2 13	5 14	7 10	8 25
Littau	...	5 30	5†47	...	8 3	...	11 4	...	2 24	5 25	...	8 36
Malters	...	5 39	6 7	...	8 13	...	11 13	...	2 34	5 35	...	8 46
Wolhusen	...	5 55	6 48	8 5	8 29	...	11 28	...	2 52	5 51	...	9 6
Entlebuch	...	6 14	7 14	...	8 43	...	11 44	A	3 10	6 7	...	9 23
Schüpfheim	...	6 26	7 33	...	8 53	...	11 54	...	3 21	6 17	...	9 33
Escholzmatt	...	6 44	8 4	...	9 7	...	12 9	...	3 38	6 33	...	9 49
Wiggen	...	6 52	8 20	...	9 13	†	12 15	...	3 44	6 39	...	9 55
Trubschachen	a.m.	7 1	8 39	...	9 21	a.m.	12 23	...	3 51	6 47	...	10 3
Langnau	5 15	7 15	8 49	9 2	9 34	9 52	12 38	3 10	4 1	6 58	8 28	10 13
Emmenmatt	5 22	7 23	—	...	9 40	10 3	12 44	...	4 7	7 4	...	10 19
Signau	5 31	7 32	...	...	9 48	1018	12 52	...	4 14	7 11	...	10 26
Zäziwyl	5 43	7 46	...	...	9 59	1034	1 3	...	4 24	7 22	...	10 37
Konolfingen	5 55	7 58	...	9 22	10 7	1056	1 10	A	4 31	7 29	...	10 44
Tagertschi	6 4	8 4	...	...	10 13	11 4	1 16	...	4 37	7 34	...	10 50
Worb	6 13	8 11	...	...	10 19	1117	1 23	...	4 43	7 40	...	10 56
Gümlingen	6 23	8 18	...	...	10 27	1129	1 31	...	4 51	7 47	...	11 4
Ostermundigen	6 30	8 24	...	...	10 33	1139	1 37	...	4 57	7 52	...	11 19
Berne ...arr	6 43	8 30	...	9 45	10 40	1154	1 45	3 50	5 5	8 0	9 10	11 17

‡—Weekdays only.]

BIEL (Bienne) and CHAUX-DE-FONDS.

Dist E.M	Station	a.m.	a.m.	a.m.	a.m.	a.m.	a.m.	p.m.	p.m.	p.m.	p.m.	p.m.	p.m.	p.m.	p.m.
	Biel (Bienne) ...dep	5 20	6 28	7 50	8 40	10 0	1055	...	1 40	3 18	5 21	6 7	8 0	8 52	9 8
9	Sonceboz ...arr	5 50	6 55	8 18	9 12	1033	1127	...	2 12	3 50	5 50	6 35	8 31	9 19	9 43
...	" 264 ...dep	5 55	7 10	8 19	9 15	1038	1132	12‡51	2 18	3 55	5 58	6 37	8 35	—	9 53
14	Courtelary	6 12	7 26	...	9 29	1053	1148	1 6	2 35	4 14	6 18	...	8 52	...	10 8
16¾	Villeret	6 23	7 37	...	9 38	11 4	1159	1 17	2 46	4 26	6 29	...	9 4	...	1019
17¾	St. Imier	6 30	7 45	8 40	9 44	1110	12 6	1 24	2 54	4 34	6 37	6 59	9 11	...	1026
19½	Sonvillier	6 36	7 54	...	9 50	1116	1212	1 30	3 1	4 42	6 44	...	9 19	...	1033
21¾	Renan	6 45	8 3	...	9 58	1124	1221	1 39	3 12	4 52	6 55	...	9 28	...	1042
27½	Chaux de Fonds arr	7 3	8 21	9 5	1013	1141	1237	1 57	3 30	5 10	7 13	7 25	9 46	...	11 0

Station	a.m.	a.m.	a.m.		a.m.	a.m.	a.m.	p.m.	p.m.	p.m.	p.m.	p.m.	p.m.	p.m.
Chaux de Fonds dep	5 55	7 36	7 48	...	9 12	10 13	11‡41	1253	2 57	4 20	6 40	8 18	8 59	10 12
Renan	6 13	...	8 4	...	9 28	10 29	11 55	1 11	3 12	4 36	6 56	...	9 14	10 27
Sonvillier	6 20	...	8 11	...	9 35	10 36	12 2	1 18	3 19	4 43	7 4	...	9 20	10 34
St. Imier	6 27	8 0	8 17	...	9 42	10 42	12 8	1 26	3 26	4 50	7 11	8 42	9 26	10 40
Villeret	6 32	...	8 21	...	9 46	10 46	12 12	1 30	3 30	4 55	7 16	...	9 30	10 44
Courtelary	6 40	...	8 30	...	9 54	10 54	12 20	1 40	3 39	5 4	7 25	...	9 38	10 53
Sonceboz ...arr	6 56	8 19	8 47	a.m.	10 9	11 10	12 34	1 56	3 55	5 20	7 42	9 1	9 53	11 9
" dep	7 4	8 20	8 50	9 12	10 12	11 27	12 38	2 12	4 2	5 25	7 45	9 2	10 0	11 11
Biel (Bienne) 265 arr	7 33	8 40	9 15	9 32	10 35	11 52	1 17	2 37	4 30	5 52	8 14	9 24	10 24	11 37

BULLE and ROMONT.
All 2&3 class.

Station						
Bulle ...dep	5a35	7a20	10a5	[illegible]p12	5 p0	9p21
Sales	5 52	7 38	1030	3 0	5 17	9 38
Vuisternens	5 59	7 45	1045	3 8	5 24	9 45
Romont arr	6 9	7 55	11 0	3 20	5 36	9 55

Station						
Romont dep	6a30	8a25	11a35	3p48	8 p6	10p43
Vuisternens	6 45	8 41	12 0	4 5	8 21	10 58
Sales	6 54	8 51	12 10	4 14	8 30	11 7
Bulle ...arr	7 7	9 7	12 30	4 30	8 43	11 20

BERNE. BIEL, NEUCHATEL, and PONTARLIER.

	2&3	2&3	1,2,3	1,2,3	1,2,3	2&3	1,2,3	1,2,3	1,2,3	2&3	1,2,3	2&3	2&3	1,2,3	1,2,3	1,2,3	1&2	1,2,3	1&2	2&3	2&3	1,2,3
		a.m.		a.m.	a.m.	a.m.	a.m.	p.m.		p.m.	p.m.		p.m.		p.m.	p.m.	p.m.	p.m.			p.m.	p.m.
Berne...dep	...	5 10	...	6 38	7 3	7 17	9 27	12 8	...	2 0	3 18	...	4 12	...	5 18	6 23	7 43	8 7	...	...	10 10	1038
Zollikofen	...	5 22	...	...	...	7 30	9 42	1220	...	2 13	...	...	4 24	...	5 29	6 34	...	...	...	...	10 22	...
Münchenbuchsee	...	5 27	...	...	...	7 36	9 49	1225	...	2 18	...	...	4 29	...	...	6 40	...	...	...	...	10 27	...
Schüpfen	...	5 34	...	...	...	7 45	10 0	1232	...	2 26	...	...	4 37	...	...	6 47	C	...	...	...	10 34	...
Suberg	...	5 40	...	...	...	7 53	10 7	1238	...	2 32	...	...	4 43	...	...	6 53	...	8 34	...	...	10 40	...
Lyss arr	a.m.	5 45	...	...	7 31	7 58	1012	1243	...	2 37	...	...	4 48	...	5 47	6 58	...	8 35	...	...	10 45	...
Lyss dep	6†18	5 48	...	...	7 32	8 2	1015	1250	...	2 40	...	...	4 50	...	5 50	7 2	...	...	...	...	10 50	...
Busswyl	6 24	5 53	...	...	...	8 8	1020	1256	...	2 45	...	...	4 55	...	...	7 7	...	...	...	...	10 55	...
Biel (Bienne) arr	6 38	6 6	...	7 16	7 43	8 22	1032	1 10	...	2 58	3 54	...	5 8	...	6 2	7 19	8 20	8 47	...	p.m.	11 8	1118
ZURICH (262A) dep		...	...			...	7a23		8a22	1055		...		3p24		3p24		5p55	...	6 15		☞
OLTEN (257B) dep	...	...	...	...	...	5a35	8a47	...	1024	1233	...	p.m.	...	4p45	...	4p50	...	7p28	...	8 15	...	
Biel ...dep (See also p.264a)	...	6 24	...	...	...	9 0	1048	...	1245	3 §3	...	4 48	...	5 58	...	7 35	...	9 0	...	1043	...	
Twann	..	6 37	...	...	...	9 16	11 0	...	1259	3 16	...	5 5	...	...	...	7 50	...	...	...	1058	...	
Neuveville	...	6 49	...	...	...	9 31	1110	...	1 12	3 26	...	5 18	...	...	...	8 3		9 16	...	1111	...	
Landeron	...	6 54	...	...	2&3	9 37	1115	2&3	1 18	3 31	...	5 24	...	...	2&3	8 9		...	...	1117	1 Cl.	
Neuchâtel ... arr	2&3	7 20	a.m.	...	a.m.	10 7	1139	a.m.	1 45	3 55	...	5 50	...	6 34	p.m.	8 37		9 37	p.m.	1147	p.m.	
BERNE (259B) dep	a.m.	6 40	6 40	...	9 19		...	1045	2p10	...	...	5p40	...		8 20				9 25		11 5	
Neuchâtel ...dep	5 15	7§30	8 0	...	1040	...	1143	1‡22	3 13	4 8	...	6 43	...	...	9 53			...	11 7		12 5	
Auvernier	5 35	...	8 11	...	1050	...	1153	1 36	...	4 18	...	6 54	...		10 4	...		...	...		...	
Noiraigue	6 27	...	8 43	...	1120	...		2 32	...		...	7 24	...		1034	...		...	...		...	
Travers	7 11	8 3	8 55	...	1130	...	...	3 3	3 47	...	...	7 35	...		1044	...		...	...		B	
Couvet	7 22	...	9 3	...	1137	...		3 16	...	...	...	7 43	...		1051	...		...	...		...	
Boveresse	7 35	...	9 11	...	1145	...		3 29	...	...	...	7 51	...		1058	...		...	...		...	
Les Bayards	7 55	...	9 25	...	1158	...		3 48	...	...	...	8 5	...		1111	...		...	...		...	
Verrières Switz. arr a.m.	8 3	8 25	9 30	...	12 3	...		3 55	4 11	p.m.	...	8 10	...		1116	...		...	12 3		1 1	
Verrières Switz. dep 5 35		7 27	8 38	...	1115	...			3 14	5 †3	...	7 20	...		1021	...	...	...	1110		12 4	
Verrières-de-J. 5 43	...	...	8 42	...	1120	...		...	...	5 10	...	7 24	...		1025	...	...	...	...		...	
Pontarlier 6 8	...	7 41	8 58	...	1136	...	...	...	3 28	5 35	...	7 40	...	...	1040	...	...	...	1125		12 18	
DIJON (53) ...arr	...	9a49	1247	...	4p44	...	...	...	6p46	...	...	1117	...	...	...	...	...	...	2a10		2a30	...
PARIS (51) ...arr	...	2p25	6 18	...	...	...	...	...	11p0	...	...	4a55	...	...	...	...	...	...	6a45		7a15	...

‡—2.16 p.m. on Sunday.

†—Weekdays only. §—1,2,3 class.

C—From 2nd July until 15th September.

B—Train de Luxe, runs from 9th July until 15th Sept.

☞ Runs from day of opening of the Loetschberg Line.

DELLE and DELEMONT.

BELFORT 68 ...dep	1a28	2a42	2a53	...	3a55	4a26	6a52	1150	1p37	3p25	...	7p29	7p36				
	1Cl.	1 2 3	1 2 3	2&3	1&2	1,2,3	1,2,3	1,2,3	1,2,3	1,2,3	2&3	1 2 3	1 2 3				
	a.m	a.m.	a.m.	a.m.	a.m.	a.m.	a.m.	p.m.	p.m	p.m.	p.m.	p.m	p.m.				
Delle ...dep	3 3	4 15	4 35	...	5 30	6 15	10 3	1 55	3 10	5 18	6 40	9 0	9 45	...	...	...	...
Porrentruy ...arr	3 17	4 30	4 50	...	5 44	6 39	1030	2 19	3 23	5 44	7 4	9 13	1012	...	...	...	...
Porrentruy ¶ ...dep	3 19	4 45	5 5	5 15	5 59	7 8	1055	2 35	3 38	6 3	7 28	9 28	1013	...	...	...	...
Courgenay	⋮	...	...	5 27	...	7 20	11 7	2 45	...	6 14	7 40	..	1041	...	...	...	...
St. Ursanne	⋮	...	...	5 40	...	7 31	1119	2 55	...	6 25	7 52	D	1052	...	...	...	...
Glovelier	A	...	...	5 53	C	7 43	1130	3 5	...	6 36	8 4	...	11 2	...	...	...	...
Courfaivre	⋮	...	...	6 6	...	7 55	1141	3 16	...	6 48	8 15	...	1114	...	...	...	...
Delémont ...arr	⋮	5 20	5 40	6 18	6 35	8 5	1151	3 25	4 12	6 58	8 25	10 5	1123	...	...	...	...
BASLE 264 ...arr	4a45	6a 7	...	7a40	...	9a40	1 p3	5p 7	5p15	8p23	1010	11a2	...	...	...	...	...
BIEL 264A...arr	...	6a57	6a57	...	7a50	9a32	2p37	...	5p21	8p51	1024	1121	...	...	...	...	...
BERNE 265 arr	...	7a40	7a40	...	8a35	1020	4 p2	...	6 p5	1023	1145	12a2	...	...	...	...	...

BERNE 266 dep	...	...	6a38	...	..	12p8	3 18	...	4p12	7p13	...	...	10D38	...	...	...	...
BIEL 264...dep	...	...	7a19	...	10 45	1p40	3p57	...	5p21	8p22	...	...	11D21	...	...	...	...
BASLE 264...dep	1230	...	7a35	7 a45	10a44	2p10	4p17	4p17	6p44	7p13	9p15	1133	1145	...	...	...	...
¶—Customs Exam.	1Cl.	2&3	1,2,3	1,2,3	1,2,3	1,2,3	1,2,3	1,2,3	1,2,3	1&2	2&3	1,2,3	1&2				
	a.m.	a.m.	a.m.	a.m.	p.m.	p.m.	p.m.	p.m.	p.m	p.m.	p.m.	n'gt	a.m.				
Delémont ...dep	⋮	5 5	8 35	9 10	12 15	3 45	5 25	5 34	7 40	9 35	1035	1220	1240	...	...	...	...
Courfaivre	⋮	5 35	...	9 22	12 27	3 57	...	5 50	7 52	...	1047	...	...	...	...	...	...
Glovelier	B	5 56	...	9 37	12 40	4 12	...	6 9	8 5	C	11 1	...	...	...	...	...	...
St. Ursanne	⋮	6 16	...	9 47	12 49	4 23	...	6 26	8 15	...	1111	...	...	...	...	...	...
Courgenay	⋮	6 35	...	9 58	...	4 35	...	6 43	8 26	...	1121	...	...	...	...	...	...
Porrentruy ...arr	2 1	6 45	9 12	10 5	1 7	4 42	6 3	6 55	8 33	1010	1128	1256	1 17	...	...	...	...
Porrentruy ...dep	2 3	7 20	9 15	10 10	1 16	4 57	6 7	7‡ 5	8 40	1012		1 0	1 20	...	...	...	...
Delle ¶ ...arr	2 16	7 47	9 27	10 31	1 38	5 18	6 20	7‡45	9 0	1025	...	1 13	1 33	...	...	...	...
BELFORT 69...arr	2a29	7a43	9 a7	10a24	1 p21	6 p0	6 p0	...	9 p4	10p0	...	1254	1a13		...	...	...

‡—Weekdays only.

A—Runs from 2nd July until 15th Sept.

B—Runs from 3rd July until 16th Sept.

C—Until 15th Sept.

D—From the day of opening of the Lœtschberg Line.

PORRENTRUY and PFETTERHAUSEN.

Porrentruy ...dep	5 a0	6a52	10a57	1p21	4p50	7 p8	9 p0
Pfetterhausen arr	5 43	7 30	11 36	2 1	5 37	7 46	9 44

Pfetterhausen dep	5a50	7a38	9a19	11a55	1p31	5p59	7p56	10p14
Porrentruy ...arr	6 35	8 25	10 8	12 55	2 29	6 45	8 37	10 52

VISP and ZERMATT.

Dist E.M.	fr.c.	fr.c.		a.m.	a.m.	a.m.	p.m.	p.m.	p.m.	p.m.
	—	—	Visp ...dep	7 43	8 †32	1030	1 *0	2‡ 0	3 50	7§20
4½	3 55	2 25	Stalden	8 7	8 56	1054	1 24	2 34	4 14	7 44
6¾	4 90	3 5	Kalpetran	8 22	9 12	11 9	1 39	2 49	4 29	7 59
10	7 55	4 75	St. Niklaus	8 46	9 40	1133	2 6	3 14	4 53	8 23
16	11 55	7 25	Randa	9 21	10 18	12 8	2 42	3 51	5 29	8 59
18¼	13 35	8 35	Taesch	9 32	10 28	1218	2 52	4 2	5 40	9 9
21¾	16 0	10 0	Zermatt...arr	9 50	10 44	1236	3 10	4 20	5 58	9 27

	a.m.	a.m.	a.m.	p.m.	p.m.	p.m.	p.m.
Zermatt...dep	7 40	9§15	11‡35	1 55	4 25	5*20	6 †32
Taesch	7 53	9 34	11 53	1 13	4 44	5 38	6 50
Randa	8 8	9 44	12 6	1 23	4 54	5 48	7 0
St. Niklaus	8 43	1020	12 42	2 0	5 32	6 23	7 35
Kalpetran	9 5	1042	1 4	2 22	5 54	6 45	7 57
Stalden	9 19	11 0	1 21	2 36	6 10	7 0	8 12
Visp 263B...arr	9 39	1120	1 41	2 56	6 30	7 20	8 32

‡—From 15th July until 31st August.

§—Until 31st August.

†—On Sunday only from opening of the Lœtschberg until 31st August.

*—Until 15th Sept.

ZERMATT and GORNERGRAT.

Zermatt ...dep	7†a0	8 a0	10‡a8	10a32	1p50	3p45	6*20
Riffelalp	7 36	8 36	10 45	11 9	2 27	4 23	6 55
Riffelberg	7 58	8 58	11 7	11 31	2 49	4 45	
Gornergrat ..arr	8 23	9 23	11 32	11 56	3 14	5 10	...

Gornergrat .dep	8†53	10a42	2 p0	2 ‡22	3p36	5p26
Riffelberg	8 59	11 8	2 26	2 48	4 2	5 52
Riffelalp	9 21	11 31	2 49	3 11	4 26	6 15
Zermatt ...arr	9 56	12 6	3 24	3 46	5 1	6 50

†—Until 31st August.

‡—From 15th July until 31st August.

BERNE, THUN, INTERLAKEN, and BONIGEN.

*—1, 2, 3 Class. ‡—Not on Sunday. [Between Berne and Thun see also page 257.]

Dist. E.M.	Station	2&3	1,2,3	1,2,3	1Cl.	1,2,3	2&3	1,2,3	1,2,3	1,2,3	1,2,3	1,2,3	2&3	1,2,3	1&2	2&3	1,2,3
		a.m.	a.m.	a.m.	a.m.	a.m.	a.m.	a.m.		a.m.	a.m.	a.m.	a.m.	a.m.		p.m.	p.m.
—	Berne Haupt. ...dep	5 0	5 15	5 20	6 17	6 45	7 0	8 0	...	8 50	9 32	9 50	1034	1040	...	‡	1 0
3¼	Berne Weissen.	5 11	:	:	:	:	7 11	:	...	:	:	:	1044	:	...	1215	:
7¾	Belp	5 28	:	:	:	:	7 29	:	...	:	:	:	1058	:	...	1230	:
13¼	Thurnen	5 47	A	A	A	A	7 48	A	...	A	A	A	1114	A	...	—	A
...	Burgistein-Wat.	5 53	:	:	:	:	7 54	:	...	:	:	:	1119	:	...	...	:
18½	Utendorf	6 6	:	:	:	:	8 8	:	...	:	:	:	1130	:	...	...	:
	Thun arr	6 14	5 55	6 18	6 50	7 21	8 18	8 33	...	9 28	10 5	1022	1138	1134	...	...	1 32
21	Thun	—	B	a.m	a.m.	B	—	a.m.	a.m.	a.m.	a.m.	a.m.	—	a.m.			D
	Thun dep	...	6 2	6 30	6 55	7 28	...	8 38	8 43	9 33	1010	1027	...	1142	...	...	1 37
21¾	Scherzligen	...	...	6 39	...	7 35	...	...	8 52	9†35	...	1034	...	1148	...	...	...
23¾	Gwatt	...	...	6 48	C	...	...	...	9 0	...	...	...	...	1153	p.m.	...	...
28	Spiez 268F ...arr	...	6 18	7 6	7 12	7 55	...	8 56	9 17	9 53	1026	1052	...	12 7	1†23	...	1 53
29½	Faulensee	...	...	7 25	...	...	...	...	9 23	...	...	...	...	1216	...	...	—
33¼	Leissigen	...	B	7 36	...	...	...	...	9 43	...	...	...	...	1227	...	...	...
35½	Darligen	...	...	7 45	...	...	...	...	9 51	...	...	...	...	1233	...	...	...
38	Interlaken arr	‡	6 50	7 52	7 35	8 28	1,2,3	9 28	10 0	1020	1055	1123	...	1240	1 42	...	2&3
	Interlaken	a.m.	a.m.	a.m.	—	—	a.m.	—	a.m.	a.m.	—	a.m.		p.m.	—	p.m.	p.m.
	Interlaken dep	6 40	6 53	7 57	...	...	8 30	...	10 8	1038	...	1137	...	1245	...	2 2	2 37
39¾	Interlaken Ost.	7 2	7 2	8 4	...	...	8 37	...	1015	1048	...	1148	...	1252	...	2 9	2 48
40½	Bonigen ...arr	7 9	7 9	...	...	...	...	...	...	1055	...	1155	...	...	...	...	2 55

Station	1,2,3	2&3	1,2,3	2&3	1,2,3	1,2,3	1,2,3	2&3	1,2,3	1,2,3	2&3	1,2,3	1,2,3	1,2,3	2&3	1&2
		p.m.	p.m.	p.m	p.m.		p.m.	p.m.	p.m		p.m	p.m.		p.m	p.m.	n'gt
Berne Haupt. ...dep	...	1 18	1 53	1 52	2 22	...	4 26	5 12	6 18	...	6 28	7 23	...	8 33	8 33	1215
Berne Weissen.	...	1 28	:	2 2	:	...	:	5 23	:	...	6 40	:	...	:	8 44	:
Belp	...	1 43	:	2 20	:	...	:	5 40	:	...	7 3	:	...	:	9 1	:
Thurnen	...	2 0	A	2 39	A	...	A	5 58	A	...	7 23	A	...	A	9 20	A
Burgistein-Wat.	...	2 5	:	2 45	:	...	:	6 6	:	...	7 32	:	...	:	9 27	:
Utendorf	...	2 15	:	2 58	:	...	:	6 21	:	...	7 45	:	...	:	9 41	:
Thun arr	...	2 22	2 25	3 6	3 16	...	5 0	6 30	6 50	...	7 52	8 2	...	9 27	9 50	1249
Thun	...	B	p.m	p.m.		...	p.m.	—	p.m	p.m.	—	p.m.	...	p.m	—	n'gt
Thun dep	...	—	2 33	3*21		...	5 7	...	6 55	7 4	...	8 8	...	9†32	...	1253
Scherzligen	...	...	2 38	3 31	—	...	5 13	1,2,3	...	7 14	...	8 13	...	9 40	...	...
Gwatt	p.m.	...	...	3 37	...	p.m.	...	p.m.	...	7 20	...	8 19	p.m.	9 46	...	D
Spiez 268F ...arr	2 34	...	2 57	3 56	...	4 48	5 31	6 41	7 12	7 36	...	8 36	9 28	10 2	...	1 10
Faulensee	...	...	...	4 10	...	...	...	...	...	7 46	...	...	...	...	...	:
Leissigen	2 47	...	...	4 21	...	D	...	6 54	...	8 0	...	8 53	D	1025	...	:
Darligen	2‖53	...	...	4 28	...	...	...	...	...	8 7	...	8 59	...	1035	...	To Brig.
Interlaken arr	3 0	...	3 25	4 36	2&3	5 13	5 58	7 6	7 45	8 15	...	9 5	9 52	1043	...	
Interlaken	—		p.m.	p.m.	p.m.	—	p.m	—	p.m	p.m		—	—	—		
Interlaken dep	.	...	3 45	4 53	5 16	...	6 17	...	7 53	8 22	...	...	...	...	...	
Interlaken Ost.	...	...	3 52	5 0	5 28	...	6 25	...	8 0	8 32	...	...	...	...	...	
Bonigen ...arr	...	...	...	...	5 35	...	6 32	...	...	8 39	...	...	...	...	...	

Station		1&2	2&3	1,2,3	1,2,3	2&3	1,2,3	1,2,3	1,2,3	1,2,3	1&2	1,2,3	2&3	1,2,3	1,2,3	1,2,3
						a.m.				a.m.		a.m.	p.m.	p.m.	p.m.	p.m.
Bonigen ...dep		...	...	...	...	7 15	...	...	...	...	...	11 3	12 5	...	...	...
Interlaken Oststation ...		...	...	...	...	7 23	...	...	...	1023	...	1113	1213	1 0	1 45	2 20
Interlaken—Bahnhof arr		...	...	...	...	7 30	...	...	...	1030	...	1120	1220	1 7	1 52	2 27
				a.m.	a.m.	—	a.m.	a.m.	a.m.	a.m.	a.m.	a.m.	—	p.m.	p.m.	p.m.
Interlaken—Bahnhof dep		...	...	6 35	7 40	...	8 28	8 50	10 5	1043	11†5	1135	...	1 30	2 0	2 35
Darligen		D	...	6 43	...	...	D	...	1014	...	...	...	...	...	2 8	...
Leissigen		...	...	6 50	...	...	8 39	...	1022	...	...	...	...	...	2 15	...
Faulensee		a.m.	...	7 4	...	...	...	...	1036	...	...	...	...	...	2 29	...
Spiez		5 34	...	7 15	8 7	...	8 54	9 13	1052	1115	1126	12 7	...	2 15	2 40	3 0
Gwatt		...	...	7 29	...	...	—	—	11 6	...	—	...	...	...	2 55	—
Scherzligen		...	...	7 38	8 25	...	...	...	1118	...	...	1225	...	...	3 6	...
Thun arr	2&3	5 49	...	7 42	8 28	...	...	...	1122	1129	...	1229	...	2 30	3 10	2&3
Thun	a.m.	a.m.	a.m.	a.m.	a.m.	a.m.			a.m.			p.m.	p.m.	p.m.	p.m.	p.m.
Thun dep	5 12	5 55	6 32	7 50	8 33	8 45	...	...	1145	1134	...	1235	1237	2 35	3 16	3 28
Utendorf	5 20	:	6 40	:	:	8 54	...	...	:	:	2&3	:	1245	:	:	3 36
Burgistein-Watten.	5 31	:	6 52	:	:	9 7	...	...	:	:	p.m.	:	1257	:	:	3 49
Thurnen	5 37	A	7 0	A	A	9 13	...	...	A	A	‡	A	1 3	A	A	3 55
Belp	5 58	:	7 26	:	:	9 32	...	...	:	:	1236	:	1 21	:	:	4 14
Berne Weissenbühl	6 19	:	7 44	:	:	9 55	...	...	:	:	1252	:	1 40	:	:	4 36
Berne Haupt. ...arr	6 30	6 28	7 55	8 50	9 7	10 5	...	...	1242	12 8	...	1 8	1 52	3 8	4 7	4 45

Station	1,2,3	1,2,3	2&3	1,2,3	1&2	1,2,3	1,2,3	1,2,3	2&3	1,2,3	1,2,3	1,2,3	2&3	1,2,3	1Cl.	1,2,3
	p.m		p.m.	p.m.			p.m.		p.m.			p.m.	p.m.			
Bonigen ...dep	3 3	...	...	...	...	...	5 43	...	6†37	Sun. only from 1st July to 14th Sept.	...	...	8 50	...	...	...
Interlaken Oststation ...	3 16	...	4 6	4 40	...	...	6 0	...	6 45		...	7 28	8 57	...	...	B
Interlaken—Bahnhof arr	3 23	...	4 13	4 47	...	...	6 7	...	6 52		...	7 35	9 29	...	...	...
	p.m	...	—	p.m.	p.m.	p.m	p.m.	p.m.	—		Sunday only.	p.m.	—		p.m.	p.m.
Interlaken—Bahnhof dep	3 38	...	...	5 0	5†58	6 3	6 15	6 44	...			7 45	...	...	9 40	1030
Darligen	...	...	...	5 8	...	...	...	..	...			7 52	...	...	...	...
Leissigen	3 49	D	...	5 15	...	B	...	D	...			7 58	...	...	C	1040
Faulensee	...	p.m.	...	5 29	...	...	...	...	...			...	...	p.m.	...	...
Spiez	4 10	4 40	...	5 41	6 28	6 30	6 44	7 8	...			8 20	...	9 25	10 2	11 3
Gwatt	...	...	...	5 55	...	...	...	—	...	p.m.	p.m.	8 30	...	D	...	B
Scherzligen	4 27	...	...	6 6	...	...	7 1	...	...	7 37	8†20	8 39	...	...	...	...
Thun arr	4 30	4 55	...	6 9	6 45	6 55	7 4	...	...	7 40	8 24	8 42	B	9 41	1018	1118
Thun	p.m.	p.m	p.m	p.m.	p.m	p.m	p.m.		p.m.	p.m.	p.m.	p.m	p.m.	p.m.	p.m.	p.m
Thun dep	4 36	5 0	5 45	6 15	6†50	7 0	7 10	...	7 13	7 47	8†35	8 47	8 55	9 46	1023	1123
Utendorf	:	:	5 52	:	:	:	:	...	7 21	:	:	:	9 3	:	:	:
Burgistein-Watten.	:	:	6 4	:	:	:	:	...	7 35	:	:	:	9 15	:	:	:
Thurnen	A	A	6 10	A	A	A	A	...	7 41	A	A	A	9 23	A	A	A
Belp	:	:	6 28	:	:	:	:	...	8 0	:	:	:	9 42	:	:	:
Berne Weissenbühl	:	:	6 50	:	:	:	:	...	8 20	:	:	:	10 0	:	:	:
Berne Haupt. ...arr	5 12	5 32	7 0	7 18	7 23	7 38	7 43	...	8 33	8 40	9 14	9 20	10 10	1018	1057	115

†—Until 15th Sept. ‖—In July and August only. A—Via Munsingen page 257. B—Sundays only.
C—Luxus Zug, runs from 9th July until 15th Sept. D—From the day of opening of the Lœtschberg line for traffic.

SPIEZ and ZWEISIMMEN.

*—Not on Sunday. ‡—Sunday only. A—Until 15th September.

Station	2&3	2&3	1,2,3	2&3	1&2	2&3	1,2,3	2&3	2&3	2&3	
INTERLAKEN ...dep	...	6 a35	8a50	...	11 a5	11a35	2p35	3 p38	5 p0	7 p45	...
	a.m.	a.m.	a.m.	a.m.	a.m.	p.m.	p.m.	p.m.	p.m	p.m.	
Spiez ...dep	6 ‡32	7 30	9 20	1040	11 27	12 17	3 10	4 15	5 45	8 50	...
Wimmis	6 40	7 41	9 28	1050	...	12 27	3 17	4 25	5 53	9 0	...
Oey-Diemtigen	6 51	7 51	9 39	11 1	...	12 38	3 29	4 36	6 4	9 10	...
Erlenbach	6 58	7 58	9 50	1110	...	12 45	3 34	4 46	6 13	9 20	...
Därstetten	7 11	8 12	...	1125	A	1 2	...	5 0	6 25	9 33	...
Weissenburg	7 16	8 17	10 5	1130	...	1 8	3 48	5 6	6 30	9 37	...
Boltigen	7 31	8 37	1022	1149	...	1 30	4 4	5 27	6 51	9 57	...
Zweisimmen 262c ...arr	7 50	9 0	1040	12 8	12 21	1 55	4 23	5 45	7 11	10 20	...

Station	2&3	2&3	2&3	2&3	2&3	1&2	1,2,3	2&3	1,2,3	2&3
	a.m.	a.m.	a.m.	a.m.	a.m.	p.m.	p.m.	p.m.	p.m.	p.m.
Zweisimmen ...dep	5 *40	6 ‡0	6 35	9 0	10 50	12 32	1 30	2 35	5 27	6 48
Boltigen	5 59	6 17	6 53	9 18	11 6	...	1 48	2 53	5 45	7 9
Weissenburg	6 16	6 31	7 8	9 36	11 21	...	2 1	3 11	6 0	7 2
Därstetten	6 20	6 35	7 13	9 40	11 26	...	...	3 15	6 4	7 31
Erlenbach	6 33	6 45	7 28	9 52	11 34	A	2 11	3 26	6 14	7 44
Oey-Diemtigen	6 39	6 50	7 33	9 56	11 40	...	2 16	3 31	6 18	7 50
Wimmis	6 49	6 59	7 42	10 6	11 49	...	2 24	3 40	6 27	8 0
Spiez ...arr	7 0	7 8	7 51	10 15	11 57	1 22	2 31	3 50	6 36	8 10
INTERLAKEN (267) ...arr	7 a52	7 a52	9 a28	10a55	12p40	1 p42	3 p0	4 p36	7 p6	9 p5

LUCERNE, BRUNIG, and BRIENZ.

	1,2,3	1,2,3 a.m.	1,2,3 a.m.	1 & 2 a.m.	1,2,3 a.m.	1,2,3 a.m.	1,2,3 p.m.	1 & 2 p.m.	3 Cl. p.m.	1,2,3 p.m.	1,2,3 p.m.	1,2,3 p.m.
Lucerne ......dep	...	5 55	7 50	9 20	9 53	11 22	1250	2 19	2 53	4 20	6 24	9 10
Hergiswyl		6 14	8 9	A	1013	11 41	1 10	A	3 36	4 40	6 43	9 30
Alpnach-Stad		6 24	8 19	9 46	1028	11 53	1 22	2 45	3 45	4 51	6 53	9 40
Alpnach-Dorf		6 30	8 25	...	1034	11 59	1 28	...	4 5	4 57	6 59	9 46
Kerns-Kägiswil		6 39	8 35	...	1044	12 8	1 38	...	4 19	5 7	7 8	9 55
Sarnen		6 47	8 42	10 3	1053	12 15	1 47	3 1	4 40	5 14	7 15	10 1
Sachseln		6 53	8 48	...	1059	12 21	1 55	...	4 55	5 20	7 21	10 7
Giswyl ......arr		7 5	9 2	1017	1114	12 35	2 8	3 16	5 13	5 32	7 33	1020
,, ...dep		7 12	9 10	1023	1123	12 45	2 14	3 21		5 40	7 40	
Lungern		7 44	9 41	1049	1155	1 18	2 43	3 49		6 8	8 10	...
Brunig ......arr	...	8 5	10 2	11 9	1215	1 40	3 3	4 9		6 28	8 31	...
,, ...dep	A	8 18	1017	1132	1245	2 8	3 29	4 22		6 37	8 39	...
Meiringen ......arr	a.m.	8 45	1043	1158	1 12	2 35	3 43	4 48		7 3	9 5	a.m.
,, ...dep	8 0	8 55	1051	12 5	1 22	2 44	3 56	4 58		7 9	—	5 20
Brienz ......arr	8 23	9 20	1114	1225	1 45	3 8	4 18	5 18		7 32	...	5 43
INTERLAKEN 363 arr	9a56	11a2	1234	2 p0	3 p9	4 p33	5p50	6 p38		9 p8	...	7a15

A—Until 15th September. 3 Cl. train (Sarnen 4 40 – Giswyl 5 13): Weekdays only.

	1,2,3	1,2,3	1,2,3	1 & 2	1,2,3	1,2,3	1 & 2	1,2,3	1,2,3	1,2,3	1,2,3	1,2,3
INTERLAKEN ......dep	...	...	5a40	8 a9	8a44	10a25	1150	12p58	2p35	4 p0	5 p6	8 p5
		a.m.	a.m.	a.m.	a.m.	a.m.	p.m	p.m.	p.m.	p.m	p.m.	p.m.
Brienz ......dep	...	...	7 18	9 20	1028	11 43	1 2	2 22	4 18	5 30	6 47	9 25
Meiringen ......arr	...	...	7 40	9 40	1051	12 5	1 22	2 44	4 41	5 52	7 9	9 47
,, ...dep	...	5 50	7 48	9 47	1056	12 10	1 28	2 50	4 48	A	7 15	
Brunig ......arr	...	6 21	8 18	10 17	1126	12 40	1 58	3 20	5 18	—	7 41	...
,, ...dep	...	6 27	8 24	10 27	1136	12 52	2 6	3 30	5 26	...	7 51	...
Lungern	...	6 48	8 45	10 47	1157	1 14	2 26	3 50	5 47	...	8 11	...
Giswyl ......arr	a.m.	7 12	9 10	11 9	1225	1 37	2 48	4 14	6 12	...	8 35	...
,, ...dep	4 40	7 18	9 18	11 14	1235	1 44	2 55	4 20	6 17	...	8 40	...
Sachseln	4 52	7 30	9 30	...	1248	1 56	A	4 35	6 29	...	8 53	...
Sarnen	4 59	7 36	9 37	11 32	1255	2 3	3 12	4 42	6 35	...	8 59	...
Kerns-Kägiswil	5 4	7 41	9 42	...	1 0	2 8	...	4 47	6 40	...	9 4	...
Alpnach-Dorf	5 13	7 49	9 52	A	1 9	2 17	...	4 56	6 48	...	9 13	...
Alpnach-Stad	5 19	7 57	10 1	11 50	1 19	2 24	3 27	5 3	6 56	...	9 21	...
Hergiswyl	5 29	8 8	1012	...	1 29	2 34	...	5 13	7 6	...	9 31	...
Lucerne ......arr	5 50	8 27	1032	12 17	1 49	2 53	3 54	5 33	7 28	...	9 50	...

LAUSANNE and BERCHER.

Dist.										
	Lausanne ......dep	7 a30	9 a45	2 p0	4 p0	6p15	8p15	...	...	...
4½	Cheseaux		10 15	2 30	4 30	6 45	8 45	...	...	...
8¾	Echallens	8 24	10 39	2 49	4 54	7 4	9 14	...	...	...
14¼	**Bercher** ......arr	8 51	11 6	...	5 21	...	9 44	...	...	...

Bercher ......dep	5 a40	...	9 a22	12p23	...	6 p28	...	...	...	...
Echallens	6 12	8 a22	9 54	12 55	4p11	7 5	...	...	...	...
Cheseaux	6 31	8 41	10 15	1 14	4 30	7 25	...	...	...	...
Lausanne ......arr	7 0	9 10	10 44	1 43	4 59	7 54	...	...	...	...

ST. GALLEN and TROGEN.

St. Gallen dep	7 a2	7a59	9a12	10a50	12p7	1p46	2p37	4p18	5p24	6p13	7p17	8p16	10p6
Trogen ....arr	7 44	8 41	9 54	11 32	1249	2 28	3 19	5 0	6 6	6 55	7 59	8 58	1048

Trogen ...dep	6a10	7 a7	8 a0	9a13	10a50	12p24	1p13	2p38	4p5	4p48	6p14	7p9	8p21
St. Gallen arr	6 52	7 49	8 42	9 55	11 32	1 6	1 55	3 20	4 47	5 25	6 56	7 51	9 3

MONT PILATUS RAILWAY.

§—Until 10th Sept.

Alpnach-Stad dep	6§30	8a20	10a25	11a55	1p30	3p27	5p10	6§p55
Pilatus-Kulm arr	7 50	9 45	11 50	1 20	2 55	4 50	6 35	8 15

Pilatus-Kulm dep	6§30	8a20	10a25	1155	1p30	3p25	5p10	6§55
Alpnach-Stad arr	7 50	9 40	11 45	1 15	2 55	4 45	6 35	8 15

BRIENZ and the ROTHHORN.—FARE, 8 frs. upward, 4 frs. downward. Return, 10 fr.

E.M.								
	Brienz ......dep	7 a15	9‡23	10a31	11a35	2p17	5p25	...
4¾	Rothhornkulm arr	8 25	1033	11 41	12 45	3 27	6 35	...

Rothhornkulm ...dep	7a53	10 a1	12p45	2p57	4‡20	5 p25	...
Brienz ......arr	8 58	11 6	1 50	4 2	5 25	6 30	...

‡—Until 15th September.

BEX & CHESIERES.—Electric Railway.—

*—Until 10th Sept. ‡—From 15th July until 31st Aug.

Bex ......dep	7a10	...	10a30	11a‡31	1 p46	...	4p45	7p10	8p50
Bevieux	7 27	...	10 47	11 53	2 3	*	5 2	7 27	9 7
Gryon	8 11	9a35	11 31	12 40	2 50	3p50	5 50	8 11	9 51
Villars	8 30	9 54	11 50	1 4	3 9	4 9	6 9	8 30	1010
Chesières ...arr	8 37	10 1	11 57	1 11	3 16	4 16	6 16	8 37	1017

Chesières dep	7a43	9*a0	10a15	2p‡16	2 p31	4p29	6p54	9p23
Villars	7 50	9 7	10 26	2 26	2 43	4 39	7 4	9 30
Gryon	8 11	9 28	10 47	2 50	3 4	5 3	7 27	9 51
Bevieux	8 54	—	11 30	3 33	3 47	5 47	8 10	1039
Bex ......arr	9 10	...	11 46	3 49	4 3	6 3	8 27	1055

Extra.

Gryon ......dep	11*a40	5*p40
Chesières ......arr	12 6	6 6

Chesières ......dep	11*a0	1*p47	3*p20	5*p0
Gryon ......arr	11 28	2 8	3 48	5 28

AIGLE and LEYSIN.

Aigle ...dep	6 a50	9a10	10 a5	1 p17	4 p3	8p10
Leysin arr	7 54	10 16	11 10	2 20	5 12	9 14

Leysin dep	6 a4	8a40	11a20	1 p22	3 p33	5p55	7p20	9 p26
Aigle ...arr	7 4	9 43	12 20	2 24	4 35	6 55	8 25	10 25

AIGLE, MONTHEY, and CHAMPERY.

‡—Until 31st August.

Aigle ......dep		6a50	10 a4	10a50	9 a6	1p30	2p45	3p55	...	...	5 p0	6p58	8 p5	...	10 p0
Ollon		7 1	10 16	11 2	9 17	1 42	2 56	4 7	...	...	5 12	7 10	8 17	‡	10 12
St. Triphon Gare		7 11	10 25	11 12	—	1 52	—	4 17	...	...	5 35	7 20	8 27	9 p45	10 22
Collombey		7 19	10 32	11 20	a.m.	2 0	...	4 25	‡	...	5 43	7 28	8 35	9 53	10 30
Monthey	5a54	7 40	10 44	11 27	1154	2 25	...	4 32	4p37	5p20	5 50	7 35	8 42	10 0	10 37
Val d'Illiez	6 52	8 32	11 34	—	1247	3 17	...	—	5 29	6 20	—	—	10 3	—	—
Champéry ...arr	7 10	8 50	11 52	...	1 5	3 35	...	...	5 47	6 38	...	...	10 21	...	...

Champery ......dep	...	5a37	...	7 a40	...	10a27	12 0	...	2 p25	...	5 p10	6p50	7‡46
Val d'Illiez	...	5 54	...	7 57	...	10 44	12 15	...	2 40	...	5 27	7 5	8 3
Monthey	6 a3	6 45	7 a50	8 55	...	11 40	1 26	...	3 50	5p12	6 20	8 0	9 0
Collombey	6 11	—	7 58	9 3	...	11 48	1 34	...	3 58	5 20	6 28	8 8	9 8
St. Triphon Gare	6 19	...	8 6	9 11	a.m	11 56	1 42	...	4 6	5 35	6 36	8 16	9 15
Ollon	6 29	...	8 16	9 21	10 18	12 6	1 52	3 p9	4 16	5 45	6 46	8 26	—
Aigle ......arr	6 40	...	8 27	9 32	10 29	12 17	2 3	3 20	4 27	5 56	6 57	8 37	...

LAUSANNE and OUCHY—Departures from Lausanne and Ouchy every 15 minutes from 6.45 a.m. until 10.45 p.m.

TERRITET and NAYE.

Territet ...dep	6*a15	8 a5	8a56	10a37	12 p9	1p54	3 p3	3p53	6p20	7 p45	...
Glion	6 25	8 15	9 6	10 47	12 19	2 4	3 13	4 3	6 30	7 55	...
Caux	6 43	8 33	9 24	11 5	12 37	2 22	2 31	4 21	6 4[illegible]	8 13	...
Jaman	7 26	9 15	—	11 48	1 20	3 5	—	5 4	7 31	...	...
Naye ......arr	7 40	9 30	...	12 2	1 34	3 19	...	5 18	7 45	...	...

Naye ......dep	5*a55	7a46	...	10a59	1p34	...	3p31	4p44	...	7p45	...
Jaman	6 11	8 2	...	11 15	1 50	...	3 47	5 0	...	8 1	...
Caux	6 45	8 36	9a26	11 49	2 24	3p33	4 21	5 34	8 p35	8 35	9p40
Glion	7 5	8 56	9 46	12 9	2 44	3 53	4 41	5 54	8 55	8 55	10 0
Territet ...arr	7 13	9 4	9 54	12 17	2 52	4 1	4 49	6 2	9 3	9 3	10 8

*—Sunday only.

MONTREUX and GLION.—From Montreux (Gare Centrale), 6§57, 7.53, 8.43, 9.26, 9.56, 10.27, 11.0, 11.50 a.m., 12.49, 1.42, 2.12, 2.52, 3.36, 5.30, 6.5, 7.34, 8.27, 9.25 p.m.; from Glion, 7.19, 8.16, 9.3, 9.48, 10.19, 10.50, 11.22 a.m., 12.11, 1.15, 2.4, 2.44, 3.58, 4.44, 5.55, 6.35, 7.55, 8.56, and and 10.2 p.m.

§—Sunday at 6.1 a.m.

WINTERTHUR, ST. GALLEN, RORSCHACH, and CHUR.

ZURICH (262) ......dep	...	...	...	5 a7	6 a45	...	7 a5	...	8 a54	...	...	10a48	...	...	1p35	2p55	...	...	4p25	4 p25	5 p53	6 p0	8 p17	8 p30	11p30
	1,2,3	1,2,3	1,2,3	2 & 3	1,2,3	2&3	1,2,3	1,2,3	1,2,3	2 & 3	1,2,3	1,2,3	1,2,3	2&3	1,2,3	1,2,3	1,2,3	2&3	1,2,3	1,2,3	1,2,3	1,2,3	1,2,3	1,2,3	1,2,3
				a.m.	a.m.	a.m.	a.m.		a.m.			a.m.			p.m.	p.m.			p.m.	p.m.	p.m.	p.m.	p.m.	p.m.	nght
Winterthur ......dep	...	...	...	6 11	7 25	...	8 28	...	9 34	...	...	11 30	...	...	2 19	3 37	...	...	4 59	5 8	6 34	6 39	8 50	9 22	12 8
Elgg	...	...	...	6 28	...	...	8 45	...	...	...	...	11 48	...	...	2 36	...	...	...	...	5 25	6 ‡49		...	9 40	...
Aadorf	...	...	...	6 34	...	...	8 51	...	...	...	...	11 54	...	...	2 42	...	...	...	...	5 31	6 54		...	9 46	...
Eschlikon	...	...	...	6 42	...	...	8 59		...	...	...	12 3	...	...	2 50	...	...	...	...	5 39	7 2		...	9 55	...
Sirnach	...	...	...	6 48	7 51	...	9 5		...	...	...	12 9	...	...	2 56	...	...	...	...	5 45	7 8		...	10 1	...
Wil (268) ...... arr	...	a.m.	...	6 53	7 56	...	9 10		10 4	...	...	12 15	...	...	3 1	4 7	...	...	...	5 50	7 13		9 19	10 6	SC
Wil (268) ...... dep	...	5 45	...	6 58	8 0	8 *6	9 16		10 6	...	...	12 23	...	...	3 5	4 9	...	...	...	5 58	7 17		9 20	10 11	...
Schwarzenbach	...	5 51	...	7 3	...	8 15	9 22		...	...	...	12 29	...	...	3 10	...	...	...	...	6 3	7 23		...	10 16	
Utzwyl	...	6 2	...	7 13	...	8 30	9 31		...	...	...	12 39	...	p.m.	3 20	...	...	...	...	6 13	7 32		...	10 25	
Flawyl	...	6 12	...	7 24	...	8 51	9 41		...	a.m.	...	12 50	...	1 *24	3 31	...	...	...	...	6 23	7 41		...	10 35	
Gossau (257B)	...	6 20	...	7 33	8 24	9 10	9 50		...	11 *0	...	12 58	...	1 33	3 41	...	...	...	...	6 30	7 47		...	10 42	
Winkeln (256)	...	6 31	...	7 41	8 32	9 25	10 0		10 35	11*15	...	1 7	...	1 41	3 49	4 42	...	...	...	6 38	7 55		9 48	10 50	
Bruggen	...	6 37	...	7 46	...	9 31	10 5		...	11*22	...	1 15	...	1 46	3 54	...	...	...	...	6 46	8 2		...	10 54	...
St. Gallen 256 ...... arr	a.m.	6 45	a.m.	7 52	8 40	9 40	10 12	a.m.	10 44	11*30	p.m.	1 21	p.m.	1 52	4 0	4 50	p.m.	p m	6 1	6 52	8 8		9 56	11 0	1 15
St. Gallen 256 ...... dep	5 45	6 50	7 24	8 6	8 49		10 30	1020	10 50	11 40	1211	1 35	2 45		4 9	5 10	5 30	6*15	6 5	7 17	8 18		10 2	11‡10	1 18
St. Fiden	5 50	6 55	...	8 13	...	...	10 36	...	...	11 45	1216	1 42	2 50	...	4 14	5 16	5 36	6 20	...	7 23	8 23		10 7	11‡15	...
Mörschwil	5 59	7 4	...	8 26	...	...	10 45	...	...	11 54	1227	1 51	...	...	4 23	5 25	5 45	6 31	...	7 33	8 32		10 16	11‡24	...
Goldach	6 6	7 11	...	8 38	...	...	10 53	...	...	12 2	1234	1 58	...	...	4 30	5 32	5 52	6 40	...	7 41	8 40		10 23	11‡31	...
Rorschach Bahnhof ......arr	6 10	7 15	7 43	8 45	9 9	...	10 58	1040	11 10	12 7	1238	2 3	3 7	...	4 35	5 37	5 57	6 45	6 25	7 46	8 45	8 2	10 27	11‡35	1 39
Rorschach Hafen ......arr	6 16	7 20	7 53	8 57	9 14	...	11 7	1048	11 19	12 17	1244	2 11	3 13	...	4 43	5 45	6 10	6 54	6 36	7 52	8 52	7 56	10 36	11‡40	...
LINDAU (368) ......dep	5 a10	...	...	...	7 a40	...	10 a5	...	10 a5	...	1145	12 53	2p15	2 p15	...	...	...	...	...	...	6 p45	6p45	...	...	
FRIEDRICHSHAFEN dep	...	...	5 a55	...	7 a28	...	9 a20	9a20	9 a20	...	1132	...	1p50	1 p50	...	...	...	...	...	...	6 p40	6p40	...	...	
CONSTANCE (260A)...dep	4 a52	...	6 a26	...	8 a25	...	9 a26	...	9 a26	...	1130	...	1p58	1 p58	3p20	...	...	...	...	...	5 p54	...	8p35	...	
ROMANSHORN (260A) dep	5 a37	...	7 a7	...	8 a55	...	10a38	...	10a38	...	1219	...	2p43	2 p43	4 p1	...	...	...	...	...	6 p42	...	9p23	...	
Rorschach Hafen ...dep	6 10	...	7 37	...	9 14	...	11 13	1035	11 7	...	1252	2 0	3 19	3 19	4 31	...	5 58	6*57	6 22	...	8 45	7 59	10 22	...	...
" Bahnhof dep	6 20	...	7 48	...	9 20	...	11 24	1045	11 14	...	1258	2 10	3 26	3 42	4 42	...	6 7	7 5	6 28	...	8 57	8 4	10 33	...	1 40
Staad	6 25	...	...	...	9 24	...	11 30	...	...	...	...	2 15	...	3 50	4 48	...	6 12	7 13	...	...	9 2	...	10 38	...	...
Rheineck	6 34	...	7 57	...	9 31	...	11 40	1055	...	1,2,3	1 7	2 24	3 35	4 6	4 57	...	6 22	7 27	...	...	9 11	A	10 45	...	...
St. Margrethen ......arr	6 40	...	8 2	...	9 36	...	11 46	11 0	11 27		1 12	2 30	3 40	4 15	5 3	1,2,3	6 28	7 37	6 40	...	9 17	8 16	10 50	...	1 55
BREGENZ (238) ......arr	7 a22	...	...	...	10a17	...	1p44	12 0	12 0		1p44	3 p7	5p40	5 p40	5p40	p.m.	7p29	...	7p29	...	9 p55	8p51	11p30	...	2 a27
St. Margrethen ......dep	6 43	...	8 3	...	9 38	...	11 49	11 6	...	1 14		2 32	3 41	4 21	...	6 32	...	...	...	...	9 20	...	10 52	...	...
Heerbrugg	6 56	...	8 12	...	9 48	...	12 2	...	...	B		2 44	3 49	4 35	...	6 46	...	...	...	...	9 33	...	11 3	...	...
Altstatten ¶	7 10	...	8 20	...	10 0	...	12 17	1120	...	1 28		2 57	3 57	4 50	...	7 3	...	...	...	...	9 47	...	11 14	...	...
Oberriet	7 19	...	...	...	10 8	...	12 26	...	...	...		3 5	...	4 59	...	7 12	...	...	...	...	9 56	...		...	...
Saletz (Sennwald)	7 36	...	...	...	10 22	1,2,3	12 44	...	...	...		3 20	...	5 16	...	7 30	...	...	...	...	10 11	...	2 & 3	...	1,2,3
Buchs (238) ...... arr	7 50	a.m.	8 42	...	10 34	non	12 58	1147	...	1 50		3 32	4 19	5 30	...	7 45	...	...	...	...	10 23	...	a.m.	...	a.m.
Buchs (238) ...... dep	7 57	6 25	8 46	1,2,3	10 36	1215	1 5	1152	...	1 52		3 37	4 20	5 50	...	7 51	...	...	...	...	10 27	...	4 *10	...	4 40
Sargans 268B ...... arr	8 20	6 47	9 1	a.m.	10 57	1230	1 30	12 9	p.m.	2 8		3 53	4 35	6 13	...	8 14	...	...	...	...	10 50	...	4 55	...	5 3
Sargans 268B ...... dep	8 30	6 57	9 4	10 50	11 0		1 42	1212	1 22	2 10		4 12	4 37	6 18	...	8 22	...	...	...	...	10 58	...		...	
Ragaz (Pfäfers)	8 40	7 6	9 12	10 59	11 9	...	1 52	1220	1 31	2 18		4 21	4 45	6 27	...	8 31	...	...	...	...	11 7	...	...	...	...
Maienfeld	8 45	7 11	...	...	11 14	...	1 57	...	1 36	...		4 26	...	6 32	...	8 36	...	...	...	...	11 12	...	...	...	...
Landquart ......arr	8 51	7 18	9 19	11 7	11 20	...	2 3	1228	1 42	2 26		4 32	4 53	6 38	...	8 42	...	...	...	...	11 18	...	...	...	...
DAVOS PLATZ (268D) arr	12p15	...	12p15	2p10	2p10	...	5 p2	2p42	5 p2	5 p2		7 p35	7p35	9 p25	...	...	...	...	...	...	...	...	...	...	...
Landquart ......dep	8 58	7 21	9 21	11 9	11 22	...	2 7	1230	1 47	2 28		4 35	4 55	6 42	...	8 45	...	...	...	...	11 21	...	...	...	...
Zizers	9 5	7 28	...	...	...	...	2 14	...	1 54	...		4 42	...	6 49	...	...	...	...	...	...	11 27	...	...	...	...
Chur (Coire) ......arr	9 16	7 40	9 37	11 25	11 37	...	2 25	1245	2 5	2 43		4 53	5 10	7 2	...	9 0	...	...	...	...	11 38	...	...	...	...

Printed across the columns, where the table has no times:
- 1,2,3 train from Zurich (no departure time given), the fourth 1,2,3 column: Runs until 15th September.
- 6 p0 from Zurich: RC—In July and August.
- 11p30 from Zurich: To Munich.
- The second 1,2,3 column after 8 a54 from Zurich: B—Between St. Margrethen and Chur only runs until 15th Sept.

Extra.								
Gossau ......dep	6a59	8a12	1p10	4 p22	6 p52	8 p58	St. Gallen...dep	7 p58
St. Gallen ...arr	7 20	8 31	1 30	4 42	7 12	9 17	Rorschach...arr	8 36

A—Between Rorschach and St. Margrethen runs until 31st August only.

*—Weekdays only. ‡—Sun. only. ¶—Altstatten and Gais—Electric railway connects these places.

NESSLAU and WIL.

Nesslau-Neu St. Johann dep	...	6a25	8 a0	10a23		1p40	3p40	5p45	7p40	8 p52	...	...	...	...
Ebnat Kappel	5 a33	6 42	8 18	10 43	11a23	1 58	3 58	6 5	7 58	9 8	...	...	...	...
Wattwil	5 42	6 54	8 30	10 50	11 37	2 12	4 14	6 19	8 5	9 20	...	...	...	...
Lichtensteig	5 48	7 0	8 37		11 42	2 19	4 22	6 26		9 25	...	...	...	...
Wil 268 ......arr	6 18	7 38	9 8	...	12 12	2 55	4 58	7 0	...	9 55	...	...	...	...
Wil ......dep	5 a12	8 a3	10a10	...	1p16	3p15	5p55	7p25	...	10p16	...	...	...	...
Lichtensteig	5 46	8 39	10 47	...	1 58	3 57	6 28	8 3	...	10 51	...	...	...	...
Wattwil	5 55	8 48	11 0	11a39	2 13	4 13	6 37	8 11	9p23	11 0	...	...	...	...
Ebnat Kappel	6 5	8 59	11 8	11 49	2 24	4 24	6 49	8 20	9 32	11 7	...	...	...	...
Nesslau-Neu St. Johann arr	6 25	9 20	...	12 10	2 45	4 45	7 10	8 40	9 52	...	...	...	...	...

CHUR, RORSCHACH, ST. GALLEN, and WINTERTHUR.

Station		1,2,3 (☞ From Munich.)	1,2,3 a.m.	1,2,3	...	1,2,3 a.m.	1,2,3 (Until 31st August only. ☞)	1,2,3	1,2,3 a.m.	1,2,3 a.m.	1,2,3	1,2,3 p.m.	1,2,3 p.m.	1,2,3 (B—Between Chur and St. Margrethen runs until 15th Sept. only.)	1,2,3 p.m.	...	...	1,2,3 p.m.	1,2,3 p.m.	1,2,3 p.m.	1,2,3 p.m.
Chur (Coire) ......dep		...	4 0	...	...	6 5	...	...	8 8	10 12	...	12 45	2 43		3 20	...	...	5 22	6 47	7 37	10 7
Zizers		...	...	...	...	6 17	...	...	8 20	...	...	12 56	B		...	...	...	5 34	...	...	10 16
Landquart ......arr		...	4 12	...	...	6 23		...	8 26	10 24	...	1 1	2 55		3 33	...	...	5 39	7 0	7 50	10 24
DAVOS PLATZ (268D) dep		...	...	...	...	...		...	5 a45	8 a10	...	10a45	1 p5		1 p5	...	...	3 p32	4p50	5 p55	6 p50
Landquart ......dep		...	4 14	...	...	6 26		...	8 30	10 27	...	1 4	2 57		3 37	...	...	5 45	7 2	7 52	10 30
Maienfeld		...	4 20	...	...	6 33		...	8 37	...	...	1 10	3 3		3 43	...	...	5 51	...	7 58	10 39
Ragaz (for Pfäfers)...1,2,3			4 24	...	...	6 38		...	8 42	10 35	...	1 15	3 7		3 48	...	...	5 56	7 10	8 3	10 46
Sargans arr	a.m.		4 31	...	...	6 45		a.m.	8 50	10 42	p.m.	1 22	3 14		3 55	...	...	6 3	7 17	8 10	10 57
Sargans dep	1 26		4 35	...	...	6 55		1057	9 16	10 47	1 45	1 30	3 15		4 9	...	...	6 13	7 18	8 23	11 5
Buchs arr	1 42		4 55	...	...	7 17		1117	9 37	11 3	2 3	1 52	3 30		4 31	...	...	6 35	7 32	8 44	11 27
Buchs dep	—		4 56	...	...	7 20		—	9 40	11 6	—	1 55	3 32		4 34	...	...	6 39	7 33	8 46	—
Saletz (Sennwald)			5 8	...	...	7 34		...	9 54	...	2 & 3	2 8	B		4 46	...	...	6 53	...	8 59	...
Oberriet			5 22	a.m.	...	7 50		...	10 10	11 26	p.m.	2 22	...		5 0	...	...	7 10	...	9 13	...
Altstatten			5 30	6 20	...	8 0		...	10 20	11 34	12 13	2 30	3 58		5 8	...	...	7 19	8 0	9 22	...
Heerbrugg			5 40	6 39	...	8 21		...	10 34	11 42	12 25	2 42	...		5 19	...	...	7 38	...	9 35	...
St. Margrethen ......arr			5 49	6 43	...	8 26	a.m.	...	10 46	11 49	12 35	2 51	4 11	...	5 29	...	...	7 42	8 13	9 45	...
BREGENZ (238) ......dep		3 a52	...	6 a0	...	7 a58	10 18	...	10a18	...	12 p2	2 p0	|	3p38	...	5p41	...	7 p9	...	9 p10	8 p15
St. Margrethen ......dep		4 23	5 51	6 47	...	8 30	11 0	...	10 50	11 51	12 38	2 54		4 15	5 32	6 16	...	7 45	8 16	9 48	8 45
Rheineck		...	5 57	6 55	...	8 38	...	...	10 57	11 57	12 46	3 1	—	4 23	5 39	...	...	7 53	8 22	9 56	...
Staad		...	6 4	7 3	...	8 45	RC	...	11 4	...	12 54	3 8	...	...	5 46	...	...	8 0	...	10 3	...
Rorschach Bahnhof arr		4 35	6 8	7 "	...	8 49	11 12	...	11 8	12 5	12 58	3 12	...	4 32	5 50	6 28	...	8 4	8 30	10 7	8 57
„ Hafen ...arr		⋮	6 16	7 20	...	8 57	11 19	...	11 19	12 17	1 9	3 19	...	4 43	5 58	6 26	..	8 15	8 36	10 15	9 6
ROMANSHORN 260A arr		⋮	6a41	8 a21	...	10a25	|	...	...	12p46	...	3 p47	...	6 p19	6p19	7 p8	...	9 p8	9 p8	11 p0	...
CONSTANCE 260A ...arr		⋮	7 a7	9 a5	...	11a13	|	...	...	1 p29	...	4 p28	...	6 p52	6p52	8p13	...	9 p52	9p52	...	...
FRIEDRICHSHAFEN...arr		⋮	...	8 a36	2 &3	10a35	|	...	...	1 p23	...	5 p53	...	5 p53	7p20	8p23	2 &3	...	9p50	...	...
LINDAU 269 ......arr		⋮	7 a10	...	a.m.	10 a5	|	a.m.	12p25	2 p8	2 p9	...	p.m.	5 p40	...	...	p.m.	9 p55	9p55	...	...
Rorschach Hafen ...dep		⋮	6 10	7 7	7 37	8 47		11 7	11 13	12 5	1 2	3 13	3 19	4 31	5 58	6 22	6 57	8 4	8 22	10 5	8 45
„ Bahnhof dep		4 36	6 18	7 15	7 53	8 57	...	1118	11 30	12 13	1 12	3 20	3 27	4 41	6 12	6 34	7 10	8 11	8 34	10 14	8 59
Goldach		...	6 25	7 22	8 5	9 5	...	...	11 38	...	1 20	...	3 34	4 49	6 21	...	7 18	8 19	...	10 22	...
Mörschwil		...	6 36	7 36	8 24	9 17	...	...	11 53	...	1 31	...	3 46	5 1	6 32	...	7 31	8 31	...	10 33	...
St. Fiden ......2&3		...	6 49	7 47	8 41	9 30	...	...	12 8	...	1 45	...	3 58	5 14	6 45	...	7 44	8 43	...	10 44	...
St. Gallen arr	a.m.	5 3	6 54	7 52	8 48	9 35	...	1144	12 13	12 39	1 50	3 48	4 2	5 20	6 50	7 0	7 48	8 48	9 0	10 45	9 25
St. Gallen dep	5 25	5 10	7 2	8 22	—	10 25	...	1150	12 24	12 43	2 10	3 55	4 15	6 12	7 24	7 7	8 30	9 7	—	11 10	9 30
Bruggen	5 32	...	...	8 28	...	10 31	...	...	...	12 49	2 17	...	4 21	6 19	7 31	...	8 37	9 14	...	11 16	...
Winkeln	5 38	...	7 12	8 36	...	10 40	...	...	12 34	12 55	2 24	4 4	4 28	6 26	7 38	7 16	8 44	9 21	...	11 21	...
Gossau	5 46	5 22	7 18	8 44	...	10 50	...	...	12 40	1 1	2 32	...	4 35	6 34	7 47	...	8 50	9 28	...	11 26	...
Flawyl	5 55	...	7 26	8 53	...	10 58	...	...	12 48	—	2 41	...	4 43	6 42	7 56	...	—	9 37	...	11 33	...
Utzwyl	6 5	...	7 34	9 2	...	11 7	...	...	12 56	...	2 51	...	4 52	6 51	8 6	...	...	9 45	...	—	...
Schwarzenbach	6 14	...	...	9 10	...	11 15	...	...	...	...	2 59	...	...	6 59	8 14	...	...	9 53	...	...	...
Wil arr	6 20	5 45	7 45	9 16	...	11 20	...	1223	1 6	...	3 5	4 32	5 4	7 5	8 20	7 43	...	9 58	...	...	10 4
Wil dep	6 28	5 46	7 49	9 22	...	11 24	...	1225	1 8	...	3 11	4 33	5 10	7 13	—	7 46	...	10 13	...	...	10 6
Sirnach	6 34	...	...	9 28	...	11 29	...	...	1 12	...	3 17	...	5 16	7 19	...	...	...	10 18	...	...	...
Eschlikon	6 41	...	...	9 34	...	11 35	...	...	1 17	...	3 23	...	5 22	7 26	...	...	...	10 24	...	...	...
Aadorf	6 50	...	...	9 41	...	11 42	...	...	1 24	...	3 31	...	5 30	7 35	...	...	...	10 31	...	...	...
Elgg	6 57	...	...	9 47	...	11 47	...	...	1 29	...	3 36	...	5 35	7 48	...	...	...	10 36	...	...	...
Winterthur ......arr	7 16	6 11	8 15	10 3	...	12 3	...	1251	1 43	...	3 53	4 59	5 49	7 51	...	8 13	...	10 5)	...	...	10 32
ZURICH 262A ...arr	8 a3	6 a50	8a58	10a45	...	12p56	...	1p30	2 p21	...	4 p52	5 p40	6 p34	8 p54	...	8p54	...	11p32	...	..	11 p5

Extra—St. Gallen to Gossau 4.54, 7.14, 9*10a.m., 12*10, 3.23 and 6.24p.m. *—Weekdays only.

RUTI and WALD.

‡—Not on Sunday.

Ruti dep	5a34	6a15	7a15	8a34	10a32	12p5	2p18	4 p7	6p23	7p50	9p53
Wald arr	5 48	6 30	7 31	8 48	10 52	1219	2 33	4 21	6 37	8 4	10 8

Wald	5a12	5a48	6a46	8 a4	10 a8	11a30	12p19	1p‡45	3p15	5p43	6p54	8p45
Ruti	5 24	6 2	6 59	8 17	10 20	11 44	12 34	2 0	3 28	5 58	7 8	9 0

RAPPERSWIL and ROMANSHORN.

†—Sunday only.

Station		a.m.	a.m.		a.m.		a.m.	a.m.		p.m.		p.m.		p.m.		p.m.	p.m.			p.m.
Rapperswil ......dep	...	...	5 52	...	7 35	...	...	10 45	...	...	...	1 23	...	3 18	...	5 27	...	...	...	8 25
Uznach	...	...	6 17	...	7 58	...	...	11 3	...	...	...	1 42	...	3 40	...	5 45	...	...	...	8 52
Wattwil	...	5 44	6 51	...	8 33	...	...	11 35	...	...	...	2 9	...	4 11	...	6 15	6 44	...	...	9 22
Lichtensteig	...	5 52	6 56	a.m.	8 40	a.m.	...	11 41	p.m.	...	...	2 14	p.m.	4 16	p.m.	6 21	6 50	p.m.	...	9 27
Herisau	...	6 35	7 33	8 30	9 20	1025	11 20	12 23	1 11	1 35	...	2 52	3 49	4 55	5 50	6 50	7 31	9 7	...	10 4
St. Gallen arr	a.m.	6 48	7 45	8 43	9 33	1040	11 35	12 36	1 23	1 48	p.m.	3 4	4 2	5 8	6 3	7 0	7 44	9 20	p.m.	10 16
St. Gallen dep	6 0	—	7 54	—	9 46	—	12 7	—	—	—	2 †0	3 9	—	5 34	—	7 6	8 25	—	9 40	—
St. Fiden	6 5	...	7 58	...	9 51	...	12 12	...	...	...	2 †5	3 14	...	5 40	...	7 11	8 31	...	9 55	...
Romanshorn ......arr	6 39	...	8 28	...	10 23	...	12 44	...	...	...	2†40	3 45	...	6 14	...	7 31	9 5	...	1050	...

Station		...	a.m.		a.m.		a.m.		a.m.		p.m.	p.m.	p.m.	p.m.	p.m.		p.m.	p.m.	p.m.		p.m.	...
Romanshorn ......dep		...	5‡32	...	7 3	...	8 56	...	1045	...	...	1255	...	2 55	4 15	...	6 †0	6 38	7 5	...	9 16	...
St. Fiden		...	6 38	...	7 43	...	9 38	...	1152	...	...	1 36	...	3 35	5 5	...	6 41	7 6	7 50	...	9 56	...
St. Gallen arr	a.m.	a.m.	6 44	a.m.	7 47	a.m.	9 42	a.m.	1158	p.m.	...	1 40	...	3 40	5 10	p.m.	6 45	7 10	7 55	p.m	10 0	p.m.
St. Gallen dep	4 55	6 23	—	7 18	7 57	8 58	10 0	1030	—	12 8	1 14	2 0	3 4	4 20	5 30	6 20	—	7 16	—	8 20	10 5	1115
Herisau	5 13	6 36	...	7 45	8 11	9 13	10 18	1045	...	1223	1 33	2 15	3 24	4 35	5 49	6 35	...	7 33	...	8 35	1022	1128
Lichtensteig	5 48	—	...	8 29	8 37	—	10 50	—	...	—	2 5	—	3 59	—	6 23	—	...	8 5	...	—	1054	—
Wattwil	5 58	...	...	8 33	8 46	...	10 56	...	...	...	2 12	...	4 8	...	6 34	...	...	8 13	p.m.	...	1058	...
Uznach	6 21	...	...	—	9 7	...	11 17	...	...	...	2 33	...	4 32	...	6 54	...	...	8 31	8 37	...	—	...
Rapperswil ...arr	6 43	...	...	...	9 23	...	11 33	...	...	...	2 50	...	4 50	...	7 15	...	...	...	8 56	...	...	...

Rheineck and Walzenhausen.—(in 13 min.)—From 6.11 a.m. until 10.51 p.m., about every twenty minutes.

ZURICH, ZIEGELBRUCKE, SARGANS, and CHUR.

THROUGH CARRIAGES.—Basle to Innsbruck, in 7.5 a.m. and 9.39 p.m. from Basle.

[For other Trains between Zurich and Ziegelbrucke see page 262B.]

Basle (261)...........dep		...	...	5a10	...	...	...	7 a5	7a10	7a20	8 a20	8 a50	...	11a30	...	1p37	2p26	...	4 p12	6p15	9p39
		1,2,3	2&3	1 Cl	2&3	1,2,3	1,2,3	1,2,3	1,2,3	1,2,3	1 & 2	1,2,3	2 & 3	1,2,3	1,2,3	1,2,3	1,2,3	1,2,3	1,2,3	1,2,3	1,2,3
		a.m.	a.m.	a.m.	a.m.	a.m.	a.m.	a.m.	a.m.	a.m.	a.m.	a.m.	noon	p.m.	p.m.	p.m.	p.m.	p.m.	p.m.	p.m.	p.m.
Zurich Hauptbahn'f dep		5 5	6 17	7 0	7 12	7 20	8 27	8 51	9 40	10 0	10 10	11 52	12 0	1 30	2 48	4 23	5 30	6 12	7 20	8 35	1140
Enge		5 16	6 27	:	:	7 27	8 38	...	9 53	10 8	...	...	12 12	1 38	2 59	:	5 38	6 23	7 28	8 43	:
Wollishofen		5 21	6 31	:	:	...	8 42	...	9 57	...	B	...	12 16	...	3 3	R	...	6 28	...	...	:
Kilchberg		5 27	6 36	:	:	...	8 47	...	10 4	...	...	...	12 22	...	3 9	:	...	6 35	7 35	...	SC
Ruschlikon		5 31	6 40	:	:	...	8 51	...	10 9	...	...	RC	12 26	...	3 14	:	...	6 40	7 39	...	:
Thalweil		5 38	6 44	:	Via Meilen.	7 38	9 10	9 7	10 19	1017	10 31	...	12 32	1 49	3 20	:	5 50	6 45	7 44	8 54	:
Oberrieden		5 43	6 49	:	:	...	9 14	...	10 23	—	...	...	12 36	1 53	3 25	:	...	6 49	...	...	:
Horgen		5 49	6 54	:	:	...	9 20	...	10 28	—	...	...	12 41	1 58	3 32	:	5 58	6 55	7 53	...	:
Au		5 56	7 1	:	:	...	9 27	...	10 35	...	...	...	12 48	2 5	3 40	:	...	7 2	...	...	:
Wädensweil		6 7	7 10	:	:	7 54	9 34	9 22	10 40	...	...	12‡20	12 56	2 12	3 53	:	6 10	7 9	8 9	9 10	:
Richtersweil		6 19	7 22	:	:	...	9 40	...	10 56	...	...	...	1 3	2 19	4 2	:	6 17	7 15	8 15	9 16	:
Pfäffikon		6 31	7†50	:	:	...	9 51	9 34	11 8	...	...	...	1 24	2 28	4 15	:	6 30	7 25	8 25	9 24	:
Lachen		6 46	8†16	:	:	...	10 1	...	11 17	...	...	...	1 33	2 36	4 24	:	6 39	—	8 34	9 33	:
Siebnen (Wangen)		6 54	8†34	E	:	8 11	10 9	...	11 24	...	...	...	1 38	2 42	4 32	:	6 46	...	8 42	...	:
Bilten	2&3	7 12	8†54	:	:	...	1025	...	11 39	...	...	...	—	2 55	4 49	:	7 2	...	8 58	...	:
Ziegelbrucke ...arr	a.m.	7 17	8†59	:	9 29	8 28	1029	...	11 44	...	...	...		3 0	4 54	:	7 7	...	9 2	9 52	:
" 262B dep	5 20	7 23	9 †0	:	9 30	8 30	—	...	11 57	...	...	...	...	3 4	5 1	:	7 18	...	9 4	9 55	:
Weesen 262B ... arr	5 25	7 28	9 †6	:	9 34	...	...	10 6	12 1	...	11 20	12 55	...	3 8	5 6	5 29	7 23	...	9 9	9 59	:
Weesen 262B ... dep	5 42	7 30	9 38	:	—	...	...	10 8	12 15	...	11 21	12 56	...	3 10	5 8	5 30	7 25	...	—	10 0	:
Mühlehorn	5 52	7 40	9 48	:	...	8 42	...	...	12 25	...	...	...	...	3 21	5 18	:	7 34	...	...	10 9	:
Murg	5 59	7 46	9 54	:	...	...	...	...	12 31	...	...	...	...	3 27	5 24	:	7 39	...	...	1015	:
Unterterzen	6 6	7 53	10 0	:	...	8 51	...	...	12 38	...	...	...	...	3 33	5 30	:	7 44	...	...	1020	:
Wallenstadt	6 15	8 1	10 8	:	...	...	...	...	12 51	...	B	...	...	3 41	5 37	:	7 51	...	...	1027	:
Flums	6 24	8 8	1015	:	...	...	...	...	12 58	...	...	...	...	3 48	5 44	:	7 57	...	...	1033	:
Mels	6 37	8 20	1027	:	...	...	...	...	1 9	...	...	...	...	3 58	5 55	:	8 7	...	...	1043	:
Sargans ....arr	6 42	8 25	1033	:	...	9 13	...	10 44	1 15	...	11 57	1 35	...	4 3	6 0	6 7	8 12	...	...	1047	1 20
Buchs 268A ...arr	7a17	9 a37	11a3	:	...	9 a37	...	11 a3	1 p56	...	...	2 p3	...	4p31	6 p35	6p35	8p44	...	...	1127	1a42
Feldkirch 238A...arr		10a44	1152	:	1,2,3	10a44	...	11a52	2 p57	...	...	2 p57	1,2,3	5 p7	7 p22	7p22	9p40	...	...	1224	2a24
Innsbruck 238A... arr		3 p25	3p25	:	a.m.	3 p25	a.m.	3 p25	6 p55	...	...	6 p55	p.m.	...	...	...	...	...	...	6a55	5a50
Sargans ....dep	6 57	8 30	...	:	9 4	9 15	11 0	10 50	1 22	...	11 58	1 42	4 37	4 12	6 18	6 10	8 22	...	...	1058	...
Ragatz (Pfäfers)	7 6	8 40	...	8 59	9 12	9 23	11 9	10 59	1 31	...	12 7	1 52	4 45	4 21	6 27	6 19	8 31	...	...	11 7	...
Maienfeld	7 11	8 45	...	...	...	...	1114	...	1 36	...	...	1 57	...	4 26	6 32	...	8 36	...	...	1112	...
Landquart ....arr	7 18	8 51	...	9 7	9 19	9 31	1120	11 7	1 42	...	12 15	2 3	4 53	4 32	6 38	6 27	8 42	...	...	1118	...
Davos Platz 268D arr		12p15	...	1215	1215	12 15	2p10	2p10	5 p2	...	2 p42	5 p2	7 p35	7 p35	9 p25	9p25	...	...	...	...	...
Landquart ....dep	7 21	8 58	...	9 10	9 21	9 23	1122	11 9	1 47	...	12 17	2 7	4 55	4 35	6 42	6 32	8 45	...	...	1121	...
Zizers	7 28	9 5	...	...	...	...	...	...	1 54	...	...	2 14	...	4 42	6 49	...	...	...	...	1127	...
Chur (Coire)......arr	7 40	9 16	...	9 25	9 37	9 48	1137	11 25	2 5	...	12 32	2 25	5 10	4 53	7 2	6 47	9 0	...	...	1138	...
St. Moritz 268B ar	11 30	12p55	...	1225	1255	12p55	3p17	3p17	6p15	...	4 p20	6 p15	9p15	9p15	10p20	1020	...	...	...	...	...

Extra						
Zurich Haupt.	11a4	4p30	6p46	8p13	10p10	11p45
Richtersweil	1210	5 27	7 50	9 8	11 7	12 35

†—Earlier at these stations on Sunday.
‡—Stops to take up only.

B—Runs until 15th September. **E**—Engadine Express, Luxus Zug, runs from 2nd July until 15th Sept.

R—Restaurant Car in this train until 15th Sept.

CHUR, THUSIS, DAVOS, SAMADEN, PONTRESINA, and ST. MORITZ.

Zurich..............dep	...	...	7 a0	7 a20	7 a20	8 a51	8 a51	8 a51	10a10	10a10	...	11a52	11a52	1 p30	4 p23	...	5 p30	...
	1,2,3	1,2,3	1 Cl.	1,2,3	1,2,3	1,2,3	1,2,3	1 & 2	1 & 2	1,2,3	1,2,3	1,2,3	1,2,3	1,2,3	1,2,3	2 & 3	1,2,3	
	a.m.	a.m.	a.m.	a.m.	a.m.	a.m.	p.m.	p.m.	p.m.	p.m.		p.m.	p.m.	p.m.	p.m.		p.m.	
Chur ....dep	5 20	7 45	9 35	9 55	10 8	11 55	12 15	12 28	1 20	1 37	...	2 38	3 0	5 35	7 18	...	9 10	...
Felsberg	5*27	...	...	...	...	A	B	...	...	...	...	B	A	...	...	...	9 18	...
Reichenau-Tamins	5 38	8 1	9 52	10 12	10 25	12 12	12 32	12 45	1 37	1 54	...	2 54	3 16	5 52	7 34	...	9 37	...
Bonaduz	5 47	8 10	...	...	10 34	12 21	12 41	...	...	...	...	3 3	3 25	6 1	7 43	...	9 46	...
Rhäzüns	5 51	8 14	E	...	10 38	...	...	...	...	...	...	3 7	3 29	6 5	7 47	...	9 50	...
Rothenbrunnen	5 59	8 22	...	A	10 46	12 30	12 50	C	A	C	...	3 15	3 37	6 13	7 55	...	9 58	...
Rodels-Realta	6 6	8 29	...	...	10 53	12 37	12 57	...	...	...	...	3 22	3 44	6 20	8 2	...	10 5	...
Cazis	6 11	8 34	...	...	10 58	...	...	...	...	...	...	3 27	3 49	6 25	8 6	p.m.	10 10	...
Thusis	6 24	8 47	10 29	10 47	11 9	12 51	1 13	1 23	2 11	2 28	...	3 38	4 1	6 38	8 13	8 38	10 17	...
Sils	6 30	8 53	...	...	11 15	12 57	1 19	...	...	...	...	3 44	4 7	6 44	...	8 45	—	...
Tiefencastel	6 54	9 17	...	11 10	11 39	1 17	1 39	...	2 35	2 53	...	4 8	4 33	7 8	...	9 12	...	...
Alvaneu	7 12	9 34	...	11 21	11 55	1 29	1 51	...	...	3 6	p.m.	4 24	4 51	7 24	...	9 30	...	...
Filisur ....arr	7 21	9 43	...	11 28	12 3	1 37	1 58	...	2 54	3 14	3 21	4 32	5 0	7 32	...	9 40	...	...
Davos Platz 268D arr	9 a3	10a40	...	12p48	12p48	...	3 p25	...	4 p44	4p44	A	6 p42	6 p42	8 p52	...	—	...	...
Stuls	7 39	10 2	...	..	12 25	...	...	...	...		...	4 50	5 18	7 52	...	...	...	...
Bergün	7 51	10 16	...	11 52	12 35	2 7	2 24	C	3 18	...	3 44	5 0	5 28	8 2	9 19	...	...	...
Preda	8 27	10 51	...	A	1 8	A	B	...	A	...	4 16	5 34	6 2	8 35	...	...	...	...
Bevers	8 47	11 12	12 11	12 38	1 28	3 0	3 15	3 6	4 4	...	4 33	5 54	6 23	8 56	10 4	...	...	...
Samaden ....arr	8 50	11 15	12 14	12 41	1 31	3 3	3 19	3 9	4 7	...	4 36	5 58	6 26	9 0	10 7	...	...	...
Pontresina 257A arr	9 a2	1'a29	12 28	12p57	1 p47	3 p27	3p43	3 p27	4 p18	...	4 p58	6 p9	6 p38	9 p15	10p20	...	...	...
Celerina Rh.B.	9 0	11 24	12 21	12 50	1 40	3 12	3 30	3 20	4 15	...	4 45	6 10	6 35	9 10	10 15	...	...	...
St. Moritz ....arr	9 5	11 30	12 25	12 55	1 45	3 17	3 35	3 25	4 20	...	4 50	6 15	6 40	9 15	10 20	...	...	...

*—Sunday only. **A**—Runs until 15th Sept. **B**—From 16th Sept.

C—In July and August only. **E**—Engadine Express, runs until 15th Sept.

CHUR, SARGANS, ZIEGELBRUCKE, and ZURICH.

Station		1,2,3	1,2,3	1,2,3	3 Cl	2&3	1,2,3	1,2,3	1,2,3	1,2,3	1,2,3	1,2,3	1,2,3	1,2,3	1,2,3	1& 2	1,2,3	1,2,3	1,2,3	1,2,3	1,2,3	1 Cl	1,2,3
ST. MORITZ ......dep		...	...	...	...	...	...	...	...	6a45	6 a45	8a30	...	9 a5	9 a5	1120	...	...	2p20	2p20	3 p5	4p30	4p30
		a.m.					a.m.	a.m.	a.m.	a.m.	a.m.	a.m.		p.m.	p m	p.m.	p.m.		p.m.	p.m.	p.m.	p.m.	p.m.
Chur (Coire) ......dep		4 0	...	...	...	...	6 5	7 50	8 8	1012	10 20	1137	...	1245	1 20	3 5	3 20	...	5 42	6 2	6 20	7 30	7 37
Zizers		...	...	...	...	...	6 17	...	8 20	...	...	§	...	1256	1 32	B	...	...	...	6 14	B	...	...
Landquart ....arr		4 12	...	...			6 23	8 2	8 26	1024	10 32	1150	...	1 1	1 37	3 17	3 33	...	5 54	6 20	6 32	7 43	7 50
DAVOS PLATZ dep		...	...	...	Week days only.	Sunday only. ☞	...	5a45	5 a45	8a10	8 a10	10a5	...	1045	[illegible]	1 p5	1 p5	...	3p32	...	4p50	5p55	5p55
Landquart ....dep		4 14	...	...			6 26	8 5	8 30	1027	10 34	1153	...	1 4	1 42	3 20	3 37	...	5 56	6 27	6 38	7 46	7 52
Maienfeld		4 20	...	...			6 33	...	8 37	...	...	12 0	...	1 10	1 48	...	3 43	...	...	6 33	...	...	7 58
Ragaz (Pfäfers)		4 24	...	...			6 38	8 15	8 42	1035	10 43	12 5	...	1 15	1 54	3 29	3 48	...	6 4	6 38	6 46	7 55	8 3
Sargans ....arr		4 31	...	...			6 45	8 22	8 50	1042	10 50	1212	...	1 22	2 2	3 35	3 55	...	6 10	6 45	6 52	⋮	8 10
INNSBRUCK 238dep		...	...	11p45			...	...	...	...		7a20	7 a20	...	...	...	8 a0	1254	☞	...	1254	⋮	...
FELDKIRCH 238dep		...	...	3 a43			2&3	7a10	7 a10	9a48		11a15	11a15	...	...	...	2p22	5 p8		...	5 p8	⋮	...
BUCHS 268 ......dep		...	a.m.	4 a40	4a10	a.m.	6a25	7a57	8 a46	1036		1152	12 15	...	1 p5	1p52	3p37	5p50		...	5p50	⋮	7p51
Sargans ....dep		4 35	4 40	5 10	5 0	7 20	6‡52	8 26	9 13	11 2	—	1220	12 35	...	2 12	3 37	4 *3	6 22	From 16th Sept.	7 1	6 53	⋮	8 21
Mels		...	4 46	...	5 17	7 26	7 7	...	9 20	11 7	—	...	...	...	2 17	...	4 9	...		7 7	...		8 26
Flums		...	4 56	...	5 39	7 36	7 28	8 39	9 30	1115	...	...	...	...	2 26	...	4 18	...		7 17	...		8 34
Wallenstadt		...	5 3	...	5 58	7 43	7 44	8 45	9 37	1120	...	RC	B	...	2 32	...	4 25	...		7 24	B		8 40
Unterterzen		...	5 11	...	6 18	7 51	8 7	...	9 46	1127	...	...	...	...	2 39	...	4 33	...		7 32	RC	E	8 47
Murg.....................		...	5 17	...	6 39	7 56	8 24	...	9 53	1133	...	...	...	...	2 44	...	4 39	...		7 38	...		8 52
Mühlehorn..............		...	5 23	...	6 55	8 1	8 41	...	9 59	1138	...	...	..	...	2 50	...	4 45	...		7 44	...		8 58
Weesen .... arr		...	5 32	5 42	7 7	8 9	8 55	9 7	10 8	1146	a.m.	1254	1 11	...	2 58	4 12	4 54	6 58	...	7 53	7 25		9 7
Weesen .... dep		...	5 50	5 43	7 18	8 11	—	9 9	10 15	1148	11 53	1255	1 12	...	3 0	4 14	4 56	7 0	...	7 55	7 27		9 9
Ziegelbrucke .. arr		5 14	5 55	5 47	7 23	8 16	...	9 14	10 20	1152	11 57	1259	1 16	...	3 4	...	5 1	7 5	...	8 0	...		9 13
Ziegelbrucke .. dep		5 15	5 57	5 48	7 54	8 18	...	9 18	10 29	1153	12 0	1 1	1 17	2&3	3 6	...	5 6	7 7	...	8 5	...		9 14
Bilten		...	6 2	...	8 4	8 25	...	...	10 35	⋮	12 6	...	...	p.m.	3 11	...	5 11	...	...	8 10	...		...
Siebnen (Wangen)...		...	6 19	...	8 52	8 41	...	...	10 52	⋮	12 26	...	...	2 8	3 25	B	5 28	...	...	8 26	...		...
Lachen	1,2,3	5 34	6 26	...	9 14	8 47	...	9 41	11 0	⋮	12 35	...	RC	2 15	3 31	...	5 35	...	p.m.	8 33	...		...
Pfäffikon	a.m.	...	6 36	...	10 2	8 56	a.m.	9 49	11 10	Via Uster.	12 44	...	...	2 27	3 38	...	5 45	...	7 38	8 43	...		9 40
Richtersweil	5 55	...	6 50	...	1020	9 7	9 12	...	11 20	⋮	12 54	...	...	2 43	3 49	...	6 1	...	8 5	8 58	...		9 48
Wädensweil......	6 2	5 51	6 56	6†22	—	—	9 21	10 1	11 26	⋮	1 4	1 34	1 49	2 52	3 58	...	6 8	7 43	8 12	9 24	8 5		9 53
Au	6 8	...	7 2	...	...	...	9 28	...	11 32	⋮	...	...	...	2 58	4 3	...	...	...	8 18	9 30	...		...
Horgen	6 15	...	7 11	...	2&3	...	9 35	...	11 40	⋮	1 15	...	...	3 5	4 10	...	6 19	...	8 25	9 38	...		10 4
Oberrieden	6 20	...	7 18	...	p.m.	...	9 40	...	11 47	⋮	...	...	...	3 10	4 16	...	...	...	8 31	9 44	...		...
Thalweil	6 25	6 10	7 25	6 40	1 ‡3	...	9 46	1020	11 54	⋮	1 23	1 51	2 7	3 16	4 21	5 10	6 29	8 0	8 37	9 50	8 24		1012
Ruschlikon	6 29	...	7 29	...	1 7	...	9 50	...	11 58	⋮	...	...	...	3 20	4 25	...	...	...	8 41	9 54	...		...
Kilchberg..........	6 33	...	7 34	...	1 11	...	9 54	...	12 2	⋮	...	...	...	3 24	4 29	...	...	...	8 45	9 58	...		...
Wollishofen.......	6 38	...	7 40	...	1 16	...	9 59	...	12 8	⋮	...	...	...	3 28	4 34	...	...	...	8 51	10 3	...		...
Enge	6 41	...	7 44	...	1 19	...	10 4	1033	12 14	⋮	1 33	2 1	2 17	3 32	4 38	5 22	6 40	8 14	8 56	10 7	8 35	⋮	1024
Zurich ....arr	6 51	6 30	7 55	6 56	...	...	1013	1040	12 23	1 37	1 40	2 9	2 24	3 41	4 47	5 30	6 48	8 22	9 5	1016	8 42	9 54	1032
BASLE(261)arr	9 a3	9 a3	10a25	9 a3	...	...	...	1p18	...	4p12	4 p12	4p12	4 p12	...	7p45	8p28	1017	1045	1058	...	1045	1145	...

Extra.					
Richtersweil..........dep	5 a1	8 a0	1 p2	5 p27	6 p15
Zurich ....arr	6 8	9 0	1 59	6 27	7 13

***—2 & 3 class only.** †—Stops to set down only. **‡—Week-days only.** **RC—Restaurant Car attached.**
B—Until 15th September.
E—Engadine Express, Luxus Zug, runs from 2nd July until 15th Sept. §—Restaurant Car until 15th Sept.

ST. MORITZ, PONTRESINA, SAMADEN, DAVOS, THUSIS, and CHUR.

Dist. E.M.	Station	2 & 3	1,2,3	1,2,3	1,2,3	1,2,3	1,2,3	1 & 2	1,2,3	1,2,3	1,2,3	3 Cl	1,2,3	1,2,3	1,2,3				
			a.m.	a.m.	a.m.	a.m.	a.m.	a.m.	p.m.	p.m.	p.m.		p.m.	p.m.	p.m.				
—	**St. Moritz** ....dep	...	6 45	8 15	8 30	9 5	10 50	11 20	1 5	2 20	2 45	...	3 5	4 30	6 40	...	...	...	...
1½	Celerina Rh. B.	...	6 50	8 20	8 35	9 10	10 55	11 25	1 10	2 25	2 50	...	3 11	4 36	6 45	...	...	...	...
...	PONTRESINA ....dep	...	6 a40	8 a15	8 a26	9 a8	10a45	11a20	1 p4	...	2 p35	...	3 p7	4p27	6 p38	...	...	...	...
3¼	**Samaden**..............dep	...	6 58	8 25	8 44	9 20	11 1	11 34	1 17	2 34	2 56	...	3 22	4 44	6 53	...	...	...	...
4½	Bevers..........................	...	7 5	8 29	8 48	9 27	11 8	11 38	1 25	2 40	3 4	...	3 31	4 48	7 1	...	...	...	...
10¾	Preda	...	7 24	9 9	...	9 47	11 28	A	1 44	B	...	...	A	...	7 20	...	...	...	...
18½	Bergün	...	7 48	⋮	9 30	10 11	11 53	12 19	2 8	3 22	3 45	...	4 12	5 29	7 44	...	...	...	...
20½	Stuls............................	...	7 56		A	10 19	...	...	2 15	3 30	...	...	...	...	7 51	...	...	...	...
...	DAVOS PLATZ ......dep	a.m	6 a40	To Davos. Arr. 9.57 a.m.	9 a3	9 a3	A	...	1 p0	2 p45	A	p.m.	2 p45	5 p7	6 p55	...	...	...	...
24	Filisur	5 35	8 10		9 48	10 31	12 10	12 40	2 31	3 47	4 2	4§ 4	4 32	5 49	8 3	...	...	...	...
26¼	Alvaneu	5 43	8 17		...	10 38	...	12 47	2 38	3 55	...	4§12	4 39	...	8 10	...	...	...	...
30½	Tiefencastel	5 58	8 32		10 6	10 52	To Davos and Landquart.	1 0	2 52	4 10	To Davos and Landquart.	4§35	4 51	6 7	8 24	...	...	...	...
37¼	Sils	6 20	8 54		...	11 14		...	3 13	4 32		5§ 1	...	...	8 46	...	...	...	...
38¼	**Thusis** ....dep	6 25	9 0		10 32	11 22		1 24	3 20	4 37		5 45	5 17	6 32	8 52	...	...	...	...
40	Cazis	6 31	9 6	...	...	11 28		...	3 26	4 43		5 53	...	...	8 58	...	...	...	...
41½	Rodels-Realta	6 36	9 11	...	...	11 33		...	3 31	4 48		6 1	A	...	9 3	...	...	...	...
43½	Rothenbrunnen	6 43	9 18	...	A	11 40		A	3 38	4 55		6 12	5 33	...	9 10	...	...	...	...
46	Rhäzüns.........................	6 52	9 27	...	...	11 49		...	3 46	5 4		6 23	...	...	9 19	...	...	...	...
46¾	Bonaduz.........................	6 56	9 31	...	...	11 53		...	3 50	5 8		6 30	...	...	9 23	...	...	...	...
49¼	Reichenau-Tamins ...arr	7 3	9 38	...	11 3	11 59	...	1 55	3 58	5 15	...	6 37	5 49	7 2	9 29	...	...	...	...
53	Felsberg.........................	...	...	...	...	...	...	...	4 13	5 28	...	6 58	...	...	...	...	...	...	...
55¼	**Chur**.......................arr	7 20	9 55	...	11 18	12 15	...	2 10	4 20	5 35	...	7 5	6 5	7 18	9 45	...	...	...	...
123	ZURICH (268C)......arr	10a40	1 p37	...	2 p9	4 p47	...	5 30	...	8 p22	...	...	8 p42	9‡54	...	...	...	...	...

A—Runs until 15th Sept. B—From 16th Sept.
§—Weekdays only. ‡—The arrival at Zurich is of the Engadine Express when running.

CHUR, LANDQUART, DAVOS, and FILISUR.

A—Runs until 15th September. B—From 16th September.

Dist.		1,2,3	1,2,3	3Cl.	1,2,3	1,2,3	1,2,3	1,2,3	1,2,3	1,2,3	1,2,3	1,2,3	1,2,3	1,2,3	1,2,3	1,2,3	3 Cl	1,2,3
E.M.			a.m.	a.m.	a.m.	a.m.	a.m.		p.m.		p.m.	p.m.		p.m.	p.m.	p.m.	p.m.	p.m
—	**Chur** dep	...	5 50	6 10	7 33	9 5	11 0	...	12 20	...	12 32	1 55	...	4 30	5 16	6 15	7‡40	10 0
6	Zizers	...	6 9	6 30	7 55	9 24	11 20	...	12 39	p.m.	12 52	2 14	...	4 49	5 35	6 34	8 6	10 19
8½	**Landquart** arr	...	6 17	6 38	8 3	9 32	11 28	...	12 47	A	1 0	2 22	...	4 57	5 43	6 42	8 15	10 27
	Landquart dep	...	6 25	Weekdays only.		9 42	11 37	...	A	12 52	B	2 35	...	5 5		6 51		
12½	Seewis-Valzeina	...	6 40		...	9 56	11 51	...		...		2 48	...	5 19	...	7 7	...	...
15½	Schiers	...	6 53		...	10 9	12 4	...	...	...	...	3 1	...	5 31	...	7 21	...	...
19¾	Fideris	...	7 10		...	10 26	12 21	...	...	...	...	3 18	...	5 48	...	7 38	‡—On Sunday Chur dep. 7.36 p.m.	...
21¾	Kublis	...	7 22		...	10 37	12 33	...	...	1 29	...	3 30	...	6 0	...	7 50		...
28¾	**Klosters** dep	...	8 5		...	11 25	1 18	p.m.	p.m.	2 1	...	4 12	...	6 45	...	8 33		...
35½	Wolfgang	a.m.	8 41		...	12 1	1 50	A	B	...	...	4 48	p.m.	7 21	...	9 9		...
37¾	Davos-Dorf	6 30	8 53	...	...	12 10	2 6	12 50	1 10	2 38	...	4 58	6 45	7 30	...	9 21		...
39½	**Davos-Platz** arr	6 35	8 57	...	...	12 15	2 10	12 55	1 15	2 42	...	5 2	6 50	7 35	...	9 25		...
	Davos-Platz dep	6 40	9 3	...	...			1 0	1 20	2 45	...	5 7	6 55		...			...
41½	Frauenkirch	6 47	9 10	...	...	...	...	1 6	1 26	...	...	5 14	7 1	...	...	...		...
43¼	Glaris (Davos)	6 54	9 15	...	...	...	...	1 12	1 32	...	...	5 20	7 7	...	...	...		...
45¾	Schmelzboden	7 2	9 23	...	...	...	...	1 20	1 40	...	...	5 28	7 15	...	...	...		...
48½	Wiesen	7 13	9 33	...	...	...	...	1 3)	1 50	...	...	5 38	7 24	...	...	...	...	...
51½	**Filisur** arr	7 22	9 42	...	...	...	...	1 39	1 59	3 18	...	5 47	7 33	...	...	...	...	...
72¼	SAMADEN (268B) arr	8 a50	11a15	...	...	...	...	3 p3	3 p19	4 p36	...	...	9 p0	...	...	...	...	...

FILISUR, DAVOS, LANDQUART, and CHUR.

		3 Cl	1,2,3	1,2,3	1,2,3	1,2,3	1,2,3	1,2,3	1,2,3	1,2,3	1,2,3	3 Cl	1,2,3	3 Cl.	1,2,3	1,2,3	1,2,3	1,2,3	1,2,3	1,2,3	1,2,3
SAMADEN dep		...	...	...	...	...	6a58	6 a58	8 a25	8a44	...		...		11a1	1p17	2p56	...	...	4p44	6p53
							a.m.	a.m.		a.m.			p.m.		p.m.	p.m.	p.m.			p.m.	p.m.
Filisur dep		...	...	...	...	...	8 9	8 9	⋮	9 52	...	Weekdays only.	12 5	Weekdays only.	1215	2 38	4 8	...	...	5 55	8 5
Wiesen		...	...	...	...	...	8 20	8 22		10 3	...		12 15		1226	2 50	...	...	...	6 6	8 16
Schmelzboden		...	...	...	...	...	8 31	8 34		1014	...		12 25		1237	3 2	A	...	...	6 17	8 27
Glaris (Davos)		...	...	...	...	...	8 41	8 46		1024	...		12 34		1246	3 11	...	...	...	6 27	8 37
Frauenkirch		Weekdays only.	...	...	...	...	8 49	8 57		1033	...	p.m.	12 42	p.m.	1254	3 19	...	...	...	6 36	8 46
Davos-Platz arr			a.m.	...	...	a.m.	8 55	9 3	9 57	1040	a.m.	A	12 48	B	1 0	3 25	4 44	...	p.m.	6 42	8 52
Davos-Platz dep			5 45	...	...	8 10	8 57	9 5	10 5	A	1045	1235	B	12 55	1 5	3 32	4 50	...	5 55	6 50	8 55
Davos-Dorf			5 52	...	...	8 16	9 2	9 10	10 10		1051	1245		1 5	1 10	3 38	4 55	...	6 1	6 56	9 0
Wolfgang			6 1	...	...	8 25	Sunday only. ☞	Weekdays only.	...	...	11 0	1254	...	1 14	A	3 47	...	...	...	7 5	
Klosters dep			6 30	...	...	8 57			10 45	...	1132	1 26	...	1 48	1 45	4 19	5 30	...	6 37	7 36	...
Küblis			7 1	...	...	9 29			...	...	12 4	2 15	...	2 25	2 9	4 51	5 54	...	7 1	8 8	...
Fideris			7 9	...	...	9 37			...	...	1212	2 24	...	2 34	...	4 59	...	...	...	8 16	...
Schiers			7 25	...	...	9 53			...	...	1228	2 47	...	3 0	A	5 15	A	...	7 20	8 32	...
Seewis-Valzeina	1,2,3	...	7 36	a.m.	a.m.	10 5			...	...	1240	3 5	...	3 17	...	5 27	...	...	...	8 43	...
Landquart arr	a.m.	a.m.	7 50	A	B	1017			11 45	...	1252	3 24	p.m.	3 32	2 43	5 39	6 31	p.m.	7 40	8 57	...
Landquart dep	4 25	6 55	7 55	9 5	9 22	1023			11 50	...	1 0		2 6		2 50	5 48		6 42	7 48	9 5	...
Zizers	4 34	7 8	8 4	9 14	9 31	1032			...	...	1 9	...	2 15	...	2 59	5 57	...	6 51	7 57	9 14	...
Chur arr	4 55	7 33	8 25	9 33	9 49	1050		...	12 12	...	1 30	...	2 33	...	3 20	6 15	...	7 9	8 15	9 35	...

§—Until 15th Sept.

CHUR, ILANZ, and DISENTIS.

E.M.		a.m.	a.m.	a.m.	a.m.	a.m.	a.m.	p.m.	p.m.	p.m.	p.m.	p.m.								
—	**Chur** dep	5 5	7 35	9§42	9 ‡55	11§42	11‡52	2 ‡29	2§48	5‡20	5§20	7 5	...	...	...	...	...	...	...	...
2½	Felsberg	5 14	7 43	9 59	10 2	11 49	12 0	2 36	2 55	5 27	5 27	7 12	...	...	...	...	...	...	...	...
4	Ems	5 22	7 48	9 56	10 7	11 54	12 5	2 41	3 0	5 32	5 32	7 18	...	...	...	...	...	...	...	...
6½	Reichenau-Tamins	5 33	8 4	1014	10 14	12 9	12 13	2 50	3 8	5 33	5 54	7 37	...	...	...	...	...	...	...	...
11¾	Versam-Safien	5 54	8 23	1033	10 33	12 28	12 32	3 9	3 27	5 57	6 12	7 56	...	...	...	...	...	...	...	...
14½	Valendas-Sagens	6 4	8 31	1041	10 41	12 36	12 40	3 17	3 35	6 5	6 20	8 4	...	...	...	...	...	...	...	...
18¼	**Ilanz**	6 27	8 48	1058	10 58	12 58	12 58	3 40	3 51	6 20	6 35	8 24	...	...	...	...	...	...	...	...
23¾	Waltensburg	6 46	9 3	1113	11 13	1 13	1 13	3 55	4 7	6 35	6 48	8 39	...	...	...	...	...	...	...	...
25½	Travanasa-B.	6 58	9 12	1122	11 22	1 22	1 22	4 4	4 16	6 44	6 57	8 48	...	...	...	...	...	...	...	...
29¼	Truns	7†14	9 25	1135	11 35	1 35	1 35	4 17	4 29	6 57	7 10	9 1	...	...	...	...	...	...	...	...
31¼	Rabius	7†26	9 35	1145	11 45	1 45	1 45	4 27	4 39	7 7	7 20	9 11	...	...	...	...	...	...	...	...
32¾	Somvix	7†35	9 43	1153	11 53	1 53	1 53	4 35	4 47	7 15	7 28	9 18	...	...	...	...	...	...	...	...
36¾	**Disentis** arr	7 55	10 0	1210	12 10	2 10	2 10	4 52	5 4	7 32	7 45	9 36	...	...	...	...	...	...	...	...

	a.m.	a.m.	a.m.	p.m.	p.m.	p.m.	p.m.													
Disentis dep	5 25	8 5	1025	1225	2 45	5 27	7 53	...	...	...	...	...	...	...	...	...	...	...	...	...
Somvix	5 39	8 19	1039	1239	3 2	5 41	8 7	...	...	...	...	...	...	...	...	...	...	...	...	...
Rabius	5 45	8 25	1045	1245	3 10	5 47	8 13	...	...	...	...	...	...	...	...	...	...	...	...	...
Truns	5 52	8 32	1052	1252	3 20	5 54	8 20	...	...	...	...	...	...	...	...	...	...	...	...	...
Travanasa	6 3	8 43	11 3	1 3	3 33	6 5	8 31	...	...	...	...	...	...	...	...	...	...	...	...	...
Waltensburg	6 12	8 52	1112	1 12	3 43	6 14	8 40	...	...	...	...	...	...	...	...	...	...	...	...	...
Ilanz	6 30	9 9	1129	1 29	4 5	6 32	8 57	...	...	...	...	...	...	...	...	...	...	...	...	...
Valendas-Sagens	6 44	9 23	1143	1 43	4 21	6 45	9 10	...	...	...	...	...	...	...	...	...	...	...	...	...
Versam-Safien	6 52	9 31	1151	1 51	4 31	6 53	9 18	...	...	...	...	...	...	...	...	...	...	...	...	...
Reichenau-Tamins	7 11	9 50	1210	2 11	4 52	7 13	9 36	...	...	...	...	...	...	...	...	...	...	...	...	...
Ems	7 17	9 56	1216	2 17	4 58	7 19	9 42	...	...	...	...	...	...	...	...	...	...	...	...	...
Felsberg	7 22	10 1	1221	2 22	5 3	7 24	9 47	...	...	...	...	...	...	...	...	...	...	...	...	...
Chur arr	7 29	10 8	1228	2 29	5 10	7 31	9 54	...	...	...	...	...	...	...	...	...	...	...	...	...

†—Earlier departures on Sunday from these stations. ‡—Runs from 16th September.

ST. MORITZ and SCHULS-TARASP.

E.M.		a.m.	a.m.	a.m.	a.m.	p.m.	p.m.	p.m.	p.m.	p.m.	p.m.	p.m.	p.m.				
...	**St. Moritz** ....dep	6‡35	6§50	8 30	10 50	12§25	1 10	2§45	3 ‡5	4§20	5‡40	6§15	8 40	...	...	...	...
...	Celerina	6 41	6 55	8 35	10 55	12 30	1 15	2 50	3 11	4 25	5 45	6 20	8 45	...	...	...	...
...	**Samaden** ....arr	6 45	6 59	8 39	10 59	12 34	1 20	2 54	3 15	4 29	5 49	6 24	8 50	...	...	...	...
...	,, ...dep	6 51	7 1	8 40	11 1	12 35	1 24	2 56	3 19	4 30	5 50	6 26	8 52	...	...	...	...
...	Bevers	6 58	7 7	8 53	11 12	12 40	1 35	3 7	3 27	4 37	5 57	6 34	9 0	...	...	...	...
...	Ponte-Campovasto........	7 7	7 15	9 1	11 20	...	1 43	3 15	3 35	...	6 5	6 42	9 8	...	...	...	...
...	Zuoz........	7 20	7 23	9 9	11 28	12 54	1 51	3 23	3 43	4 51	6 13	6 50	9 16	...	...	...	...
...	Scanfs	7 27	7 28	9 14	11 33	...	1 56	3 28	3 48	...	6 18	6 55	9 21	...	...	...	...
...	Zernez	8 5	7 55	9 40	11 59	1 21	2 21	3 54	4 14	5 19	6 44	7 21	9 47	...	...	...	...
...	Süs	8 19	8 7	9 52	12 11	...	2 33	4 5	4 25	...	6 55	7 32	9 58	...	...	...	...
...	Ardez	8 44	8 27	10 12	12 31	...	2 53	4 25	4 45	...	7 15	7 51	10 18	...	...	...	...
...	Fetan	8 55	8 37	10 22	12 41	...	3 3	4 35	4 55	...	7 25	8 1	10 28	...	...	...	...
...	**Schuls-Tarasp** ....arr	9 0	8 42	10 27	12 45	2 0	3 7	4 40	5 0	5 58	7 30	8 5	10 33	...	...	...	...
		a.m.	a.m.	a.m.	a.m.	a.m.	p.m.	p.m.	p.m.	p.m.	p.m.						
...	**Schuls-Tarasp** ....dep	5 15	6§50	7 40	9§30	11 0	12 50	2 §0	3 7	5 10	7 30	...	...	...	...	...	...
...	Fetan	5 22	...	7 47	...	11 8	12 57	...	...	5 17	7 37	...	...	...	...	...	...
...	Ardez	5 35	...	8 0	...	11 23	1 10	...	...	5 30	7 50	...	...	...	...	...	...
...	Süs	5 55	...	8 20	...	11 47	1 31	...	3 41	5 51	8 11	...	...	...	...	...	...
...	Zernez	6 7	7 34	8 32	10 14	12 5	1 43	2 44	3 53	6 3	8 23	...	...	...	...	...	...
...	Scanfs	6 38	...	9 2	...	12 44	2 14	...	...	6 34	8 54	...	...	...	...	...	...
...	Zuoz........	6 43	8 7	9 8	10 47	12 53	2 19	3 14	4 24	6 39	8 59	...	...	...	...	...	...
...	Ponte-Campovasto........	6 51	...	9 16	...	1 3	2 27	...	...	6 47	9 7	...	...	...	...	...	...
...	Bevers	7 4	8 22	9 24	11 4	1 14	2 37	3 30	4 40	6 56	9 16	...	...	...	...	...	...
...	**Samaden** ....arr	7 8	8 25	9 27	11 8	1 17	2 41	3 33	4 44	6 59	9 19	...	...	...	...	...	...
...	,, ...dep	7 10	8 29	9 30	11 10	1 20	2 46	3 35	4 46	7 0	9 20	...	...	...	...	...	...
...	Celerina	7 15	8 34	9 35	11 15	1 25	2 51	3 40	4 51	7 5	9 25	...	...	...	...	...	...
...	**St. Moritz** ....arr	7 20	8 40	9 40	11 20	1 30	2 55	3 45	4 55	7 10	9 30	...	...	...	...	...	...

‡—From 16th September. §—Until 15th September.

WALDENBURG and LIESTAL.

Dist.																
	Waldenburg ....dep	6a14	7a19	10a1	11a48	2 p0	4p15	8p40	Liestal ....dep	7a35	9 a5	11a20	1 p0	3p25	6p48	8p13
6¼	Bubendorf	6 52	8 5	1039	12 26	2 38	4 53	7 19	Bubendorf	7 46	9 16	11 31	1 11	3 36	6 59	8 24
8½	Liestal (258)........arr	7 3	8 16	1050	12 37	2 50	5 5	7 30	Waldenburg........arr	8 28	9 55	12 11	1 50	4 14	7 40	9 3

LANGENTHAL and WOLHUSEN.

Langenthal ....dep	...	6 a8	8*10	9 a26	11a41	1p10	3p53	6p13	8‡20	9 p41	...	...	...	...	...	...	...
Huttwil	4a40	6 57	8 57	10 8	12 24	2 39	4 39	7 32	8 58	10 18	...	...	...	...	...	...	...
Wolhusen 265 ....arr	5 38	7 54	...	11 10	1 18	4 7	5 44	8 35	...	...	...	...	...	...	...	...	...
Wolhusen........dep	...	5a58	...	8 a40	11a30	...	3 p0	4§32	6 p5	...	9p13	...	...	...	...	...	...
Huttwil ‡........	5 a0	6 54	8 a1	10 12	12 19	1p58	4 14	6 7	7 20	8p41	10 16	...	...	...	...	...	...
Langenthal ....arr	5 35	7 34	8 45	10 52	12 47	3 12	4 47	...	8 0	9 13	...	...	...	...	...	...	...

*—7.56 a.m. on Sunday. ‡—Sunday at 8.13 p.m. §—Sunday at 4.22 p.m.

HUTTWIL and RAMSEI.

Huttwil ....dep	...	6a52	...	10‡50	12p28	2 p8	...	4p40	...	7p15	9 p6	...	...	...	...	...	...
Affoltern-Weier-i-E........	...	7 17	...	11 19	12 52	2 34	...	5 12	...	7 41	9 32	...	...	...	...	...	...
Sumiswald-Grünen	6 a6	7 32	9 a9	12 29	1 40	2 49	4p35	5 25	6p55	7 54	9 44	...	...	...	...	...	...
Ramsei ....arr	6 17	7 43	9 20	12 40	1 53	3 0	4 46	5 51	7 7	9 1	...	...	...	...	...	...	...
Ramsei ....dep	a.m.	6a27	8a41	11a12	12p56	2§p15	3 p40	5 p0	6 p5	7p35	10p23	...	...	...	...	...	...
Sumiswald-Grünen	5 45	6 41	9 6	11 26	1 10	2 31	3 52	5 14	6 19	7 50	10 37	...	...	...	...	...	...
Affoltern-Weier-i-E.	6 2	...	9 25	11 47	1 32	3 6	...	...	6 39	8 11	...	...	...	...	...	...	...
Huttwil ....arr	6 27	...	9 54	12 12	1 55	3 35	...	...	7 4	8 35	...	...	...	...	...	...	...

Sumiswald-Grünen ...dep	6a44	7a42	1141	3p54	5p35	8 p5	...	Wasen-i-E........dep	7a10	8a44	12p9	4p16	6 p3	8p30	...
Wasen-i-E. ....arr	7 2	8 0	1159	4 11	5 53	8 23	...	Sumiswald-Grünen ...arr	7 27	9 1	1226	4 33	6 20	8 47	...

‡—10.10 a.m. on Sunday. §—2.7 p.m on Sunday.

LANGENTHAL and OENSINGEN.

	a.m.	a.m.	a.m.	a.m.	a.m.	p.m.	p.m.	p.m.	p.m.	p.m.	p.m.	p.m.	p.m.				
Langenthal ....dep	5 18	6 33	7 55	9 26	11 42	1 15	2 14	3 56	5 10	6 10	7 35	8 10	9 40	...	...	...	...
Niederbipp	6 2	7 10	8 33	10 20	12 21	1 53	2 50	4 34	5 48	6 45	8 12	8 48	10 17	...	...	...	...
Oensingen........arr	6 9	7 18	8 41	10 28	12 29	2 1	...	4 42	5 56	...	...	8 56	...	...	...	...	...
	a.m.	a.m.	a.m.	a.m.	p.m.	p.m.	p.m.	p.m.	p.m.	p.m.	p.m.	p.m.	p.m.				
Oensingen........dep	6 44	8 25	10 12	11 52	1 12	2 40	...	5 0	6 17	...	...	9 16	...	...	...	...	...
Niederbipp	6 53	8 34	10 21	12 3	1 21	2 50	4 0	5 14	6 26	7 20	8 47	9 25	10 18	...	...	...	...
Langenthal 257 ....arr	7 30	9 10	10 57	12 41	1 57	3 26	4 36	5 50	7 5	7 56	9 24	10 1	10 51	...	...	...	...

*—Weekdays only.

SPIEZ and BRIG.

Lœtschberg Tunnel Line.

The opening of the line for traffic between Frutigen and Brig is expected during July.

PARIS P.L.M. ......dep	...	...	...	...	...	1015	1015	...	10p50	...	...	...	...	...	...	...	...	8a30	2 p20
PARIS Est. ....dep	...	...	...	9 p0	...	9p45	9p45	...	...	...	...	10 p0	...	...	...	8 a"	8 a0	...	1 p0
BASLE ....dep	...	...	...	...	...	...	7a15	7a15	7 a40	8 a25	...	10a40	10a40	2 p2	...	3 p40	3p40	...	9 p45
BERNE ....dep	...	5 a20	...	8 a0	...	8a50	9a32	9a50	10a40	1 p0	...	1 p53	2 p22	4p26	...	6 p18	6p18	7p23	12a15
	1,2,3 a.m.	1,2,3 a.m.	3 Cl. a.m.	1,2,3 a.m.	2&3 a.m.	3Cl. a.m.	1,2,3 a.m.	2&3 a.m.	1,2,3 p.m.	1,2,3 p.m.	2&3 p.m.	2 & 3 p.m.	1,2,3 p.m.	3Cl. p.m.	3Cl. p.m.	1,2,3 p.m.	2&3 p.m.	2&3 p.m.	1 & 2 a.m.
Spiez ....dep	6 22	7 25	8 9	9 0	9 7	9 58	1030	1113	12 15	1 57	2 11	3 5	4 12	5 48	6 45	7 16	7 45	8 49	1 14
Heustrich-Emdthal	...	7 34	8 18	...	9 14	10 6	...	1122	12 23	...	2 19	3 13	4 22	5 57	6 54	...	7 55	9 1	...
Mülenen-Aeschi	6 30	7 38	8 21	...	9 18	1010	...	1126	12 27	...	2 23	3 17	4 29	6 1	6 57	...	8 1	9 5	...
Reichenbach	6 33	7 43	8 24	...	9 22	1015	...	1129	12 31	...	2 27	3 21	4 34	6 6		...	8 6	9 11	...
Frutigen	6 42	7 55	8 33	9 16	9 30	1024	1046	1138	12 43	2 12	2 38	3 30	4 50	6 15	☞	7 32	8 20	9 22	...
Kandergrund	...	8 4		...	9 39		...		12 51	...	2 46		4 58		Until 15th September.	...	8 28	9 32	...
Blausee-Mittholz	6 57	8 13	...	...	9 48	...	...	...	1 0	...	2 55	...	5 7	...		...	8 37	9 41	...
Kandersteg	7 12	8 30	...	9 43	10 5	...	1112	...	1 18	2 39	3 10	...	5 24	...		8 2	8 55	9 56	...
Goppenstein	7 30	8 50	...	...		...	...	...	1 33	...		...	5 43	...		8 23			...
Hothen	...	9 0	...	...	...	...	...	...	1 48	...	...	...	5 53	...		8 31	...	...	...
Ausserberg	...	9 12	...	...	...	...	...	...	2 0	...	...	...	6 4	...		8 41	...	...	...
Lalden	...	9 23	...	...	...	...	...	...	2 11	...	...	...	6 14	...		8 50	...	...	...
Brig ....arr	7 57	9 33	...	10 33	...	...	1157	...	2 22	3 25	...	...	6 25	...	...	8 58	...	...	2 38
DOMODOSSOLA 263B..	9 a32	10a55	...	11a36	...	...	1 p0	...	...	4 p32	...	...	8 p15	...	...	10 p3	...	...	3 a40
MILAN 274 ....arr	12p12	1 p30	...	2 p10	...	...	3p45	...	...	7 p47	...	...	12a15	...	...	12a15	...	...	6 a25

MILAN ....dep	11p45	...	...	...	...	5 a0	...	...	8 a15	...	...	10a50	...	...	...	...	2p20	3 p25	4 p30
DOMODOSSOLA ...dep	2 a35	...	...	...	...	8a20	...	...	11a22	...	12p13	1 p42	...	...	...	...	5 p7	6 p22	7 p15
	1 & 2 a.m.	2 & 3	1,2,3 a.m.	3Cl.	2 & 3	1,2,3 a.m.	1,2,3 a.m.	2&3	1,2,3 p.m.	3Cl.	1,2,3 p.m.	1,2,3 p.m.	1,2,3	2 & 3	3Cl.	2&3	1,2,3 p.m.	1,2,3 p.m.	1,2,3 p.m.
Brig ....dep	4 3	...	5 50	...	...	9 43	1013	...	12 41	...	2 27	3 9	...	...	Until 15th September.	...	6 38	7 48	9 25
Lalden	...	...	6 1	...	...	...	1025	...	...	...	2 37	...	...	...		...	6 47	...	...
Ausserberg	...	...	6 12	...	...	...	1034	...	...	...	2 48	...	...	...		...	6 56	...	...
Hothen	...	...	6 24	...	...	...	1045	...	...	...	3 1	...	...	...		...	7 7	...	...
Goppenstein	...	a.m.	6 35	...	a.m.	...	1054	p.m.	...	...	3 15	...	p.m.	p.m.		...	7 16	...	10 2
Kandersteg	...	6 0	6 55	...	9 25	1034	1113	1257	1 33	...	3 40	4 1	4 10	5 22		...	7 33	8 42	10 20
Blausee-Mittholz	...	6 18	7 13	...	9 47	...	1124	1 15	...	...		...	4 30	5 38		...	7 45	...	...
Kandergrund	...	6 27	7 22	a.m.	9 56	...	1131	1 24	...	p.m.	...	...	4 41	5 47	☞	p.m.	7 52	...	...
Frutigen	...	6 37	7 32	8 38	10 5	1058	1138	1 33	1 56	3 35	...	4 23	4 54	5 57		7 40	8 0	9 6	10 44
Reichenbach	...	6 46	7 41	8 46	10 13	...	1146	1 41	...	3 43	...	...	5 6	6 8	p.m.	7 48	...	...	...
Mülenen-Aeschi	...	6 51	7 45	8 49	10 17	...	1149	1 45	...	3 47	...	...	5 12	6 12	6 59	7 52	...	...	...
Heustrich-Emdthal	...	6 55	7 49	8 52	10 21	...	1152	1 49	...	3 51	...	...	5 17	6 16	7 2	7 57	...	...	...
Spiez ....arr	5 30	7 4	7 57	9 0	10 30	1111	1158	1 57	2 11	4 0	...	4 36	5 28	6 26	7 10	8 6	8 15	9 20	11 0
BERNE 267 ....arr	6 a28	8 a50	9 a7	...	12p42	12p8	1 p8	...	3 p8	5p12	...	5 p32	7p18	7 p23	...	...	9p20	10p18	...
BASLE ....arr	9 a13	11a35	11a35	...	3 p57	2p38	3p57	...	6 p40	8 p7	...	8 p7	...	10p53	...	...	...	...	...
PARIS Est. ....arr	2 p49	...	...	...	...	...	1148	...	11p48	...	...	...	...	7 a28	...	...	...	...	...
PARIS P.L.M. ......arr	2 p25	...	...	...	...	...	11p0	...	...	...	...	4 a55	...	6 a20	...	...	6a45	...	...

THUN, BEATENBUCHT, and INTERLAKEN.—Electric Railway.

	am	a.m.	a.m.	a.m.	a.m.	a.m.	a.m.	a.m.	a.m.	a.m.	p.m.	pm	p.m.	p.m.	pm	p.m.	pm	p.m.	p.m.	p.m.	p.m.	p.m.	p.m.	p.m.	p.m.
Thun ...dep	516	6 22	6 44	7‡28	8 34	8 56	9‡40	1024	1046	1152	1236	142	2 4	2 26	248	3 32	354	4 16	5 22	6 28	6 50	7 12	7 34	8§18	9 46
Hilterfingen	534	6 40	7 2	7 46	8 52	9 14	9 58	1042	11 4	1210	1254	2 0	2 22	2 44	3 6	3 50	412	4 34	5 40	6 46	7 8	7 30	7 52	8 36	10 4
Oberhofen...	537	6 43	7 5	7 49	8 55	9 17	10 1	1045	11 7	1213	1257	2 3	2 25	2 47	3 9	3 53	415	4 37	5 43	6 49	7 11	7 33	7 55	8 39	10 7
Gunten	548	6 54	7 16	8 0	9 6	9 28	1012	1056	1118	1224	1 8	214	2 36	2 58	320	4 4	426	4 48	5 54	7 0	7 22	7 44	8 6	8 50	
Merligen ...		7 5	7 27	8 11	9 17	9 39	1023	11 7	1129	1235	1 19	225	2 47	3 9	331	4 15	437	4 59	6 5	7 11	7 33	7 55	8 17	9 1	...
Beatenbucht ¶		7 10	7 32	8 16	9 24	9 44	1030	1112	1136	1242	1 24	232	2 52	3 14	338	4 20	444	5 4	6 12		7 40	8 0	8 22	9 6	...
Nachtstall			7 38	8 22	9 28		1034		1140	1246		236			342		448		6 16	...	7 44				...
Beatushöhle ...		...	7 45	8 29	9 35	...	1041	...	1147	1253	...	243	...	...	349	...	455	...	6 23	...	7 51	...	...	...	...
Interlaken arr		...	8 6	8 50	9 56	...	11 2	...	12 8	1 14	...	3 4	...	...	410	...	516	...	6 44	...	8 12	...	...	...	...

			a.m.	a.m.		a.m.		a.m.	p.m.		p.m.			pm		p.m.		p.m.		p.m.			p.m.		
Interlaken dep		...	8 16	9 ‡0	...	10 6	...	11‡12	1218	...	1 24	...	...	314	...	4 20	...	5 26	...	6 54	...	...	8 22	...	...
Beatushöhle ...		...	8 37	9 21	...	1027	...	1133	1239	...	1 45	...	...	335	...	4 41	...	5 47	...	7 15	...	...	8 43	...	...
Nachtstall		a.m.	8 44	9 28	a.m.	1034	a.m.	1140	1246	p.m.	1 52	pm	p.m.	342	pm	4 48	p.m.	5 54	...	7 22	p.m.	p.m.	8 50	p.m.	...
Beatenbucht ¶		7 22	8 50	9 34	9 56	1040	1122	1146	1252	1 36	1 58	3 4	3 26	348	432	4 54	5 16	6 0	p.m.	7 28	8 12	8 34	8 56	9§18	...
Merligen ...	am	7 27	8 55	9 39	10 1	1045	1129	1151	1257	1 41	2 3	3 9	3 31	353	437	4 59	5 21	6 5	7 11	7 33	8 17	8 39	9 1	9 23	...
Gunten	548	7 38	9 6	9 50	1012	1056	1140	12 2	1 8	1 52	2 14	320	3 42	4 4	448	5 10	5 32	6 16	7 22	7 44	8 28	8 50	9 12	9 34	p.m.
Oberhofen...	559	7 49	9 17	10 1	1023	11 7	1151	1213	1 19	2 3	2 25	331	3 53	415	459	5 21	5 43	6 27	7 33	7 55	8 39	9 1	9 23	9 45	10 7
Hilterfingen	6 2	7 52	9 20	10 4	1026	1110	1154	1216	1 22	2 6	2 28	334	3 56	418	5 2	5 24	5 46	6 30	7 36	7 58	8 42	9 4	9 26	9 48	1010
Thun .....arr	620	8 10	9 38	1022	1044	1128	1212	1234	1 40	2 24	2 46	352	4 14	436	520	5 42	6 4	6 48	7 54	8 16	9 0	9 22	9 44	10 8	1028

‡—Until 15th September. §—From 9th July until 15th September.

¶—**St. Beatenberg Climbing Railway.**—Fares Upward 2 fr. 50 c., Downward 1 fr., Return 3 fr.
From Beatenbucht—Two or three times hourly from 7.20 a.m. to 8.16 p.m.
From St. Beatenberg—Two or three times hourly from 6.52 a.m. to 7.42 p.m.

TABLE OF FARES ON ITALIAN RAILWAYS.

Chilo metri	Eng. Miles.	Express Trains. 1 Cl. L. C.	2 Cl. L. C.	3 Cl. L. C.	Ordinary Trains. 1 Cl. L. C.	2 Cl. L. C.	luggag per 100 chilo. L. C.	Chilo metri.	Eng. Miles.	Express Trains. 1 Cl. L. C.	2 Cl. L. C.	3 Cl. L. C.	Ordinary Trains. 1 Cl. L. C.	2 Cl. L. C.	luggag per 100 chilo. L. C.
5	3	0.65	0.45	0.30	0.60	0.45	0.70	45	28	5.75	4.5	2.65	5.25	3.70	2.10
7	4¼	0.90	0.65	0.45	0.85	0·60	0·70	50	31	6.40	4.50	2.90	5.80	4.10	2.35
10	6¼	1.30	0.90	0.60	1.20	0.85	0.70	55	34¼	7.5	4.95	3.20	6.40	4.50	2.60
15	9¼	1.95	1.35	0.90	1.75	1.25	0.70	60	37¼	7.70	5.40	3.50	7.0	4.90	2.80
20	12½	2.60	1.80	1.20	2.35	1.65	0.95	65	40½	8.30	5.85	3.80	7.55	5·30	3.5
25	15½	3.20	2.25	1.45	2.90	2.5	1.20	70	43½	8·95	6·30	4.10	8.15	5.70	3.25
30	18¾	3.85	2.70	1.75	3·50	2.45	1.40	75	46½	9.60	6·70	4.35	8·70	6.10	3.50
35	21¾	4.50	3.15	2.5	4·10	2.85	1.65	80	49¾	10.25	7.15	4.65	9.30	6.50	3.75
40	24¾	5.15	3.60	2.35	4.65	3.25	1.90	85	52¾	10.85	7.60	4.95	9.90	6.95	3.95

Chilo metri.	Eng. Miles.	Express Trains. 1 Cl. L. C.	2 Cl. L. C.	3 Cl. L. C.	Ordinary Trains. 1 Cl. L. C.	2 Cl. L. C.	luggag per 100 chilo. L. C.	Chilo metri.	Eng. Miles.	Express and Ordinary Trains. 1 Cl. L. C.	2 Cl. L. C.	3 Cl. L. C.	luggag per 100 chilo. L. C.
90	56	11.50	8.5	5.25	10.45	7.35	4.20	275	171	33.25	23.10	14.95	11.20
95	59	12.15	8.50	5.55	11.5	7.75	4.45	300	186½	35.85	24.85	16.10	12.10
100	62¼	12.80	8.95	5.80	11.60	8.15	4.65	400	248½	45.15	30.85	19.95	15.20
125	77¾	15.95	11.20	7.25	14.50	10.15	5.80	500	310¾	53.40	35.80	23.00	17.90
150	93¼	19.15	13 40	8.70	17.40	12.20	7.0	600	372¾	60.40	40.05	25.70	20.10
175	108¾	22.30	15.60	10.10	20.30	14.25	7.80	700	435	66.15	43.55	27.95	21.90
200	124¼	25.50	17.85	11.55	23.20	16.25	8.70	800	497	70.95	46.60	29.95	23.10
225	139¾	28.10	19.55	12.70	26.10	18.30	9.50	900	559½	74.85	49.25	31.85	24.00
250	155¼	30.65	21.30	13.80	29.0	20.30	10.40	1000	621½	78.60	51.70	33.45	24.60

LUINO, MORTARA, MILAN, and ALESSANDRIA.

E.M		Station											
		Luino (Customs Exam.)	...	...	5 55	7 25	10 58	...	...	15 32	17 38	...	1955
9¼		Laveno	...	...	6 17	7 51	11 25	...	...	15 55	18 5	...	2015
22¼		Sesto Calende	...	...	6 50	8 31	12 2	...	...	16 27	18 40	...	2046
31¾		Oleggio	...	5 35	7 19	9 8	12 34	1255	...	16 52	19 14	19 4	21 8
42¼		Novara ...arr	...	5 58	7 37	9 30	12 56	1313	...	17 10	19 36	19 22	2126
104¼		Turin 269 ...arr	...	...	9 50	12 35	15 25	1525	...	19 15	21 45	21 45	2350
...		Arona 274a ...dep	...	5 0	6 50	9 32	...	1225	13 8	15 52	—	18 35	—
...		Novara ...dep	5 15	6 5	8 1	10 44	...	1318	14 25	17 20	...	19 53	...
49¾		Vespolate	5 36	...	8 18	11 1	...	...	14 45	17 40	...	20 11	...
57¼		Mortara ...arr	5 56	6 29	8 34	11 17	...	1342	15 4	18 0	...	20 27	...
—	—	Milan—Centrale dep	4 30	...	7 13	9 20	...	...	13 20	16 15	17 17	18 55	...
...	5	,, —P.Ticinese ...	4 57	...	7 38	9 50	...	...	13 50	16 47	17 35	19 23	2020
...	18	Abbiategrasso	5 32	...	8 2	10 31	...	...	14 32	17 22	17 58	19 53	2055
...	24¼	Vigevano	5 48	...	8 16	10 50	...	...	14 51	17 38	18 12	20 7	2113
...	32¼	Mortara ...arr	6 5	...	8 31	11 9	...	...	15 10	17 55	18 27	20 22	2130
...		Mortara ...dep	...	6 33	8 45	11 22	...	1345	15 19	18 6	18 35	20 31	2136
71½		Torreberetti	...	7 7	9 13	11 53	...	...	15 50	18 40	...	20 56	2210
75¼		Valenza 273	...	7 21	9 24	12 6	...	1413	16 4	18 51	19 6	21 7	2221
84		Alessandria ...arr	...	7 40	9 41	12 25	...	1430	16 23	19 10	19 23	21 24	2240
130½		Genoa 270 ...arr	...	9 35	12 15	14 35	...	1725	18 30	22 5	22 5	23 25	...

Station										
Genoa 271 ...dep	2 30	5 0	5 15	6 55	8 30	11 15	...	15 5	1740	20 0
Alessandria ...dep	4 55	6 55	7 54	8 56	11 15	13 40	...	17 15	2030	22 0
Valenza	5 17	7 12	8 11	9 18	11 36	14 2	...	17 37	2053	22 18
Torreberetti	5 28	7 21	...	9 29	11 47	14 13	...	17 46	21 4	22 27
Mortara ...arr	5 59	7 49	8 38	10 0	12 18	14 44	...	18 17	2136	22 53
Mortara ...dep	6 5	8 1	8 43	10 25	12 30	15 25	...	18 28	2141	...
Vigevano	6 20	8 18	8 58	10 46	12 50	15 46	...	18 45	2159	...
Abbiategrasso	6 34	8 34	9 12	11 6	13 9	16 6	...	19 1	2215	...
Milan—P.Ticinese arr	7 5	9 5	9 34	11 45	13 50	16 47	...	19 36	2246	...
,, Centrale ...arr	7 30	9 25	9 53	12 15	...	17 20	...	20 0	2310	...
Mortara ...dep	6 10	7 54	...	10 10	12 24	14 49	...	18 40	2146	22 58
Vespolate	6 28	8 10	...	10 28	12 42	15 7	...	19 2	22 3	...
Novara ...arr	6 44	8 25	...	10 44	12 58	15 23	...	19 20	2220	23 23
Arona 274a ...arr	8 52	9 17	...	11 50	14 16	16 21	...	21 12	...	0 26
Turin 269 ...dep	4 0	6 35	...	8 54	11 25	12 0	15 5	17 35	20 0	...
Novara ...dep	6 50	8 43	...	11 11	13 32	15 28	17 5	20 5	2225	23 35
Oleggio	7 21	9 9	...	11 39	14 6	15 53	17 33	20 35	2252	24 0
Sesto Calende	7 50	9 27	...	12 4	14 34	—	18 2	—	2310	—
Laveno	8 23	9 55	...	12 35	15 8	...	18 35	...	2334	...
Luino (Customs Exam) arr	8 47	10 13	...	13 0	15 32	...	19 12	...	2355	...

TURIN and MILAN.

Frequent extra trains between Turin and Chivasso.] [‡—Stops at Chivasso from 15th July until 15th Sept.

Dist E.M	Turin—	1,2,3	1,2,3	1,2,3	1,2,3	1 & 2	1,2,3	1,2,3	1,2,3	1,2,3	1,2,3	1,2,3	1,2,3
	Porta Nova dep	4 0	5 34	6 35	8 54	11 25	12 0	13 0	15 5	16 20	17 35	18 25	20 0
3¾	,, Porta Susa...	4 15	5 50	6 50	9 10	11 39	12 15	13 13	15 20	16 35	17 50	18 40	20 15
10½	Settimo 289	4 33	6 8	...	...	RC	12 33	...	...	16 53	RC	18 58	...
18	Chivasso ...arr	4 49	6 24	7 10	9 31	11‡58	12 49	13 33	15 40	17 9	18 10	19 14	20 37
...	,, 274A dep	4 53	6 27	7 11	9 34	11‡59	12 53	13 36	15 43	17 16	18 12	19 17	20 39
36¾	Santhia ...arr	5 41	7 18	7 38	10 4	12 24	13 44	14 3	16 11	18 9	18 39	20 5	21 9
...	,, ...dep	5 52	7 56	7 41	10 7	12 26	13 47	—	16 14	—	18 42	20 12	21 13
40½	San Germano	6 0	8 4	...	...	...	13 55	RC Restaurant Car attached.	...	...	18 50	20 20	...
49	Vercelli ...arr	6 14	8 20	7 58	10 24	12 43	14 11		16 31	...	19 5	20 36	21 32
...	,, 273...dep	6 16	8 21	8 0	10 26	12 44	14 27		16 35	...	19 8	20 39	21 35
52¼	Borgo Vercelli	6 24	8 33	...	...	...	14 36		...	...	19 17	20 48	...
62¼	Novara ...arr	6 45	8 55	8 22	10 48	13 5	14 56		16 57	...	19 37	21 8	21 59
104½	Luino 269 ...arr	8 47	...	10 13	13 0	15 32	...		19 12	...	...	—	23 55
...	Novara...dep 5 30	7 4	9 23	8 25	10 52	13 9	15 3		17 2	...	19 42	...	22 4
68¼	Trecate ...5 43	7 16	9 36	...	...	...	15 16		...	...	19 54	...	...
75¾	Magenta ...6 3	7 33	9 54	...	11 15	...	15 34		17 24	...	20 11	...	22 29
84½	Rho ...6 27	7 53	1015	...	11 30	...	15 56		17 41	...	20 31	...	...
93¾	Milan ...arr 6 46	8 8	1030	9 10	11 45	13 55	16 15		17 55	...	20 45	...	22 57

Station	1,2,3	1,2,3	1,2,3	1,2,3	1,2,3	1 & 2	1,2,3	1,2,3	1,2,3	1,2,3	1& 2	1,2,3
Milan ...dep	4 0	...	7 5	7 25	9 45	12 50	...	13 55	16 20	18 5	19 0	20 50
Rho	4 17	...	...	7 43	10 2	...	...	14 13	16 37	18 22	...	21 7
Magenta	4 36	...	...	8 3	10 16	...	...	14 33	16 51	18 44	RC	21 25
Trecate	4 53	...	...	8 21	...	...	...	14 51	...	19 2	...	21 42
Novara ...arr	5 5	...	7 54	8 32	10 38	13 36	...	15 3	17 13	19 14	1947	21 54
Luino ...dep	...	...	5 55	...	7 25	10 58	...	...	15 32	17 38	1738	19 55
Novara ...dep	5 9	...	7 57	8 38	10 42	13 39	...	15 8	17 17	20 2	1951	21 58
Borgo Vercelli	5 31	...	...	9 1	...	...	...	15 31	...	20 25	...	...
Vercelli ...arr	5 38	...	8 17	9 8	11 2	13 59	...	15 38	17 37	20 32	2011	22 18
,, ...dep	5 41	...	8 19	9 12	11 6	14 2	...	15 42	17 40	20 36	2014	22 21
San Germano	5 56	...	...	9 28	...	...	...	15 58	...	20 52	...	...
Santhia ...arr	6 4	...	8 39	9 36	11 25	14 20	...	16 6	17 59	21 0	2033	22 40
,, ...dep	6 10	6 49	8 41	9 41	11 28	14 23	1617	16 27	18 3	21 4	2036	22 43
Chivasso ...arr	6 59	7 21	9 7	10 30	11 54	14‡48	1643	17 16	18 32	21 53	...	23 10
,, ...dep	7 5	7 25	9 9	10 34	11 57	14‡49	1644	17 30	18 34	21 57	...	23 11
Settimo	7 22	...	...	10 51	...	...	...	17 47	...	22 14	...	...
Turin Por. Susa	7 40	7 51	9 34	11 10	12 21	15 10	17 8	18 6	19 0	22 33	2130	23 35
Turin Por. Nova	7 55	8 5	9 50	11 25	12 35	15 25	1723	18 20	19 15	22 48	2145	23 50

☞ Italian Railway Time—See Note on page 272. ☜

CHIASSO, COMO, MILAN, PAVIA, and GENOA.

Dist. E.M.	Station																	
	Basle 258 ......dep	...	...	9 p45	...	...	...	11p20	...	...	...	...	...	...	...	...	7 a0	7 a0
	Lucerne 259...dep	...	...	11p52	...	...	...	1 a22	...	...	...	...	...	...	...	7a48	9 a8	9 a8
			1,2,3	1,2,3	1,2,3	1,2,3	1,2,3	1,2,3		1,2,3	1,2,3	1,2,3	1,2,3		1,2,3	1,2,3	1 & 2	1,2,3
—	Chiasso ¶ ....dep	...	...	5 20	...	...	6 5	7 45	...	8 18	9 5	...	1020	...	11 57	1327	14 5	14 25
3	Como 287 ...... arr	...	...	5 26	...	...	6 12	7 51	...	8 24	9 11	...	1027	...	12 4	1333	14 11	14 32
	Como 287 dep	...	...	5 29	...	...	6 20	7 56	...	8 36	9 18	...	1035	...	12 14	1335	14 13	14 37
6¼	Albate Camerlata...	...	...	...	...	...	6 32	...	...	8 47	...	...	1047	...	12 26	...	...	14 48
10½	Cantu Asnago..........	...	...	5 47	...	...	6 45	...	...	9 0	...	...	11 0	...	12 41	...	...	15 1
15	Camnago 287	...	...	...	...	...	6 56	...	...	9 12	A	...	1112	...	12 53	...	R C	15 13
18¾	Seregno 275... arr	...	...	S C	...	...	7 4	8 26	...	9 19	...	...	1120	...	13 2	...	...	15 21
	Seregno 275 dep	...	5 25	...	...	...	7 6	8 28	...	9 20	...	...	1122	...	13 4	...	...	15 23
20½	Desio	...	5 32	...	...	...	7 11	...	...	9 26	...	...	1128	...	13 10	...	...	15 29
24¼	Monza .... arr	...	5 45	...	...	...	7 22	8 38	...	9 37	9 58	...	1139	...	13 21	1412	...	15 40
	Monza dep	...	5 47	...	...	...	7 24	8 40	...	9 39	10 0	...	1141	...	13 24	1413	...	15 42
32¼	Milan Central arr	...	6 10	6 22	...	...	7 45	8 53	...	9 55	1015	...	12 0	...	13 45	1427	15 5	16 0
		1,2,3		1 & 2				1,2,3	1,2,3				1,2,3	1,2,3			1,2,3	1,2,3
	Milan Central dep	4 35	...	6 40	7 10	...	...	9 15	9 50	...	...	11 30	12 5	13 20	...	...	15 35	16 20
36¾	Rogoredo	4 46	...	...	7 19	...	...	...	10 1	...	...	...	1216	...	...	...	...	16 31
41¾	Locate	4 57	...	...	7 33	...	...	...	10 18	...	...	R C	1232	...	...	...	...	16 46
49¾	Certosa	5 15	...	...	7 50	...	...	9 44	10 40	...	...	...	1252	...	...	...	...	17 5
54¾	Pavia 273 ...... arr	5 25	...	...	8 0	...	...	9 54	10 52	...	...	12 5	13 2	13 55	...	...	16 10	17 15
	Pavia 273 dep	5 30	...	...	8 5	...	...	9 57	12 15	...	...	12 8	13 7	13 57	...	...	16 13	17 45
62¾	Bressana Bottar 274	5 50	...	...	8 23	...	...	...	12 37	...	...	...	1326	...	...	...	...	18 3
70¾	Voghera 269A arr	6 8	...	...	8 40	...	...	10 22		...	A—Until 30th September.	12 36	1344	14 22	...	...	16 38	18 22
	Voghera 269A dep	6 33	...	...	8 46	...	...	10 28	...	...		12 41		14 27	...	...	16 44	18 32
81½	Tortona ...... arr	6 54	...	...	9 3	...	...	10 45	...	...		12 58	...	14 47	...	...	17 1	18 54
	Tortona dep	6 57	...	...	9 5	...	...	10 47	...	...		12 59	...	14 49	...	...	17 3	19 2
90	Pozzolo	7 20	...	...	...	...	...	...	...	...		...	...	15 9	...	...	...	19 27
92½	Novi 270 ...... arr	7 28	...	...	9 27	...	...	11 9	...	...		13 19	...	15 17	...	...	17 25	19 35
	Novi 270 dep	7 31	...	...	9 32	10 53	...	11 14	...	...		13 21	...	15 25	...	...	17 28	19 59
101½	Arquata..................	7 52	...	...	...	11 12	...	...	...	...		...	...	15 46	...	...	...	20 22
108¾	Ronco	8 23	...	...	10 12	11 36	...	11 54	...	...		13 53	...	16 10	...	...	18 9	20 50
124¼	Sampierdarena 272 arr	8 59	...	9 12	10 40	12 4	...	12 22	...	...	...	14 47	...	17 8	...	...	18 37	22 3
	Sampierdarena 272 dep	9 4	...	9 14	10 44	12 9	...	12 24	...	...	...	14 52	...	17 19	...	...	18 39	22 9
126¼	Genoa P. Principe arr	9 10	...	9 20	10 50	12 15	...	12 30	...	...	...	14 58	...	17 25	...	...	18 45	22 15
437½	Rome 270 ......arr	1915	...	19 15	...	...	...	23 50	...	...	...	...	...	...	...	...	7 0	8 40

GENOA, PAVIA, MILAN, COMO, and CHIASSO.

Station																		
Rome 271 ......dep	...	14 0	...	...	18 15	18 15	...	...	21 0	...	21 0	...	...	...	2355	...	...	...
		1,2,3	1,2,3	1,2,3	1,2,3	1,2,3		1,2,3	1&2	1,2,3	1,2,3			1,2,3	1,2,3	1,2,3		1,2,3
Genoa Piazza Principe ....dep	...	2 40	...	...	5 15	5 50	...	...	6 55	...	8 20	...	...	...	1110	...	...	...
Sampierdarena ar	...	2 46	...	...	5 21	5 56	...	...	7 1	...	8 26	...	...	...	1116	...	...	...
Sampierdarena dp	...	2 51	...	...	5 24	5 58	...	...	7 3	...	8 31	...	...	...	1118	...	...	...
Ronco......................	...	3 55	...	...	6 26	6 49	...	...	7 48	...	9 26	...	...	...	...	...	...	...
Arquata....................	...	4 15	...	...	6 46	...	...	...	...	...	...	...	...	...	...	...	...	...
Novi .... arr	...	4 34	...	...	7 5	7 15	...	...	8 14	...	9 56	...	...	...	...	...	...	...
Novi dep	...	4 40	...	5 30		7 23	...	...		8 25	10 0	...	...	...	R C	...	...	...
Pozzolo....................	...	...	...	5 37	...	...	...	...	...	8 32	...	...	...	...	...	...	...	...
Tortona ...... arr	...	5 0	...	5 57	...	7 41	...	...	...	8 51	10 18	...	...	...	...	...	...	...
Tortona dep	...	5 2	...	6 0	...	7 43	...	...	...	8 54	10 21	...	...	...	...	...	...	...
Voghera ...... arr	...	5 19	...	6 20	...	7 59	...	...	...	9 14	10 37	...	...	...	1258	...	...	...
Voghera dep	...	5 24	...	6 36	...	8 3	...	...	...	9 20	10 46	...	...	...	13 0	...	...	...
Bressana Bottar......	...	...	6 31	6 55	...	...	...	9 14	...	9 39	...	...	...	...	...	1321	...	...
Pavia........... arr	...	5 51	6 50	7 13	...	8 29	...	9 33	...	9 57	11 11	...	...	...	...	1341	...	...
Pavia dep	...	5 57		7 27	...	8 31	...		...	10 1	11 15	...	...	1228	...	1348	...	...
Certosa	...	6 8	...	7 38	...	...	...	...	...	10 12	11 26	...	...	1242	...	14 3	...	...
Locate	...	6 26	...	7 57	...	...	...	...	...	10 31	...	...	...	13 3	...	1426	...	...
Rogoredo	...	6 40	...	8 11	...	...	...	...	...	10 45	...	...	...	1318	...	1443	...	...
Milan Centrale ... arr	...	6 50	...	8 20	...	9 5	...	...	...	10 55	11 55	...	...	1330	1355	1455	...	...
	1,2,3	1,2,3	1,2,3			1,2,3	1,2,3	1,2,3				1 & 2	1,2,3		1,2,3		1,2,3	1,2,3
Milan Centrale dep	4 25	7 25	7 42	...	...	9 25	9 35	10 35	...	...	...	12 40	13 20	...	1440	...	16 0	16 10
Monza .... arr	4 43	7 39	8 4	...	...	...	9 50	10 56	...	...	...	...	13 38	...	1454	...	...	16 32
Monza dep	4 46	7 41	8 7	...	...	...	9 52	10 58	...	...	...	...	13 40	...	1456	...	...	16 34
Desio	5 0	...	8 22	...	...	...	...	11 12	...	...	...	...	13 54	...	...	...	...	16 49
Seregno......... arr	5 6	...	8 28	...	...	R C	10 6	11 18	...	...	...	...	14 0	...	...	...	...	16 55
Seregno dep	5 9	...	8 30	...	...	...	10 7	11 20	...	...	...	...	14 2	...	...	...	...	
Camnago	5 19	...	8 41	...	...	...	...	11 29	...	...	...	R C	14 12	...	...	...	...	...
Cantu Asnago..........	5 33	...	8 55	...	...	...	...	11 42	...	...	...	...	14 26	...	...	...	...	...
Albate Camerlata ...	5 48	...	9 10	...	...	...	...	11 56	...	...	...	...	14 42	...	...	...	...	...
Como .... arr	5 56	8 20	9 18	...	...	10 14	10 35	12 5	...	...	...	13 32	14 50	...	1537	...	1655	...
Como dep	6 7	8 26	9 25	...	...	10 17	10 42	12 10	...	...	...	13 36	15 2	...	1542	...	17 0	...
Chiasso .... ¶ arr	6 15	8 35	9 35	...	...	10 25	10 50	12 18	...	...	...	13 44	15 10	...	1550	...	17 8	...
Lucerne 259A arr	...	1 51	...	...	...	4 p44	4 p44	6 p50	...	...	...	6 p50	9 p0	...	9 p0	...	1040	...
Basle 258 ......arr	...	4 p6	...	...	...	6 p58	6 p58	9 p0	...	...	...	9 p0	11 p3	...	11p3	...	...	...

Voghera and Salice, in 30 minutes. Voghera dep. 5*0, 6.30, 8.53, 10.48, 12.50, 14.50, 16.50, 20.5. Salice dep. 5*45, 7.15, 9.43, 11.40, 13.40, 15.50, 17.40, 20.45. *—Sunday, Tuesday, and Friday only.

For Continuation of Trains and Notes, see next page.

Fares and Luggage Rates, see page 269.]

CHIASSO, COMO, MILAN, PAVIA, and GENOA.

Basle 258 ......dep	7a30	...	...	...	...	8 a25	12 p2	...	1 p50	...	...	...	...	...	...	...	...	...
Lucerne 259..dep	9a47	...	...	...	...	11 a0	2 p22	...	4 p0	...	...	...	...	...	...	...	...	...
	1,2,3				1,2,3	1,2,3	1,2,3	1,2,3	1,2,3									
Chiasso ¶ ....dep	1538	...	...	...	16 55	18 15	19 40	20 5	21 18	...	...	...	...	...	...	...	...	...
Como 287 ...... arr	1544	...	...	...	17 2	18 22	19 46	20 12	21 24	...	...	...	...	...	...	...	...	...
Como 287 ...... dep	1547	...	...	...	17 10	18 28	19 48	20 22	21 28	...	...	...	...	...	...	...	...	...
Albate Camerlata...	...	...	...	...	17 21	18 39	...	20 34	...	...	...	...	...	...	...	...	...	...
Cantu Asnago........	...	...	...	...	17 34	18 51		20 50	...	...	...	...	...	...	...	...	...	...
Camnago 287	...	...	...	...	17 46	19 3	RC	21 3	...	...	...	...	...	...	...	...	...	...
Seregno 275 ... arr	...	...	...	...	17 54	19 11	...	21 12	...	...	...	...	...	...	...	...	...	...
Seregno 275 ... dep	...	...	...	...	17 56	19 13	...	21 14	...	...	...	...	...	...	...	...	...	...
Desio	...	...	...	...	18 2	19 19	...	21 20	...	...	...	...	...	...	...	...	...	...
Monza .... arr	1625	...	...	...	18 13	19 30	...	21 31	22 8	...	...	...	...	...	...	...	...	...
Monza .... dep	1626	...	...	...	18 15	19 32	...	21 34	22 10	...	...	...	...	...	...	...	...	...
Milan Central arr	1640	...	...	...	18 31	19 47	20 40	21 55	22 25	...	...	...	...	...	...	...	...	...
	1,2,3	1,2,3	1,2,3	1,2,3			1,2,3											
Milan Central dep	17 0	...	18 15	19 0	...	...	20 55	...	...	...	...	...	...	...	...	...	...	...
Rogoredo	...	...	18 28	...	...	...	...	...	...	...	...	...	...	...	...	...	...	...
Locate	...	...	18 44	...	...	...	21 13	...		...	...	...	...	...	...	...	...	...
Certosa	...	...	19 5	...	...	...	...	...		...	...	...	...	...	...	...	...	...
Pavia 273...... arr	1733	...	19 16	RC	...	...	21 36	...		...	...	...	...	...	...	...	...	...
Pavia 273...... dep	1735	...		...	...	...	21 39	...		...	...	...	...	...	...	...	...	...
Bressana Bottar 274	...	...	...	...	...	...	...	...		...	...	...	...	...	...	...	...	...
Voghera 269A arr	18 2	...	...	19 56	...	...	22 4	...		...	...	...	...	...	...	...	...	...
Voghera 269A dep	...	...	...	20 0	...	...	22 11	...		...	...	...	...	...	...	...	...	...
Tortona ...... arr	1819	...	...	...	...	...	22 28	...		...	...	...	...	...	...	...	...	...
Tortona ...... dep	1821	...	...	...	...	...	22 31	...		...	...	...	...	...	...	...	...	...
Pozzolo	...	...	...	...	...	...	...	...		...	...	...	...	...	...	...	...	...
Novi 270 ...... arr	1841	...	...	...	...	...	22 52	...		...	...	...	...	...	...	...	...	...
Novi 270 ...... dep	1844	20 50	...	...	...	...	22 56	...		...	...	...	...	...	...	...	...	...
Arquata	...	...	...	...	...	...	...	...		...	...	...	...	...	...	...	...	...
Ronco.....................	1916	21 23	...	...	...	...	23 29	...		...	...	...	...	...	...	...	...	...
Sampierdarena 272 arr	2010	21 54	...	21 36	...	...	23 57	...		...	...	...	...	...	...	...	...	...
Sampierdarena 272 dep	2014	21 59	...	21 39	...	...	0 4	...		...	...	...	...	...	...	...	...	...
Genoa P. Principe arr	2020	22 5	...	21 45	...	...	0 10	...	...	...	...	...	...	...	...	...	...	...
Rome 270 ......arr	8 40	8 40	...	8 40	...	...	...	...	...	...	...	...	...	...	...	...	...	...

¶—Customs Examination.
RC—Restaurant Car attached.

GENOA, PAVIA, MILAN, COMO, and CHIASSO.

Rome 271 ......dep	...	23 55	...	...	...	...	...	...	...	...	...	9 0	...		...	...	...	...
		1,2,3	1,2,3	1,2,3		1,2,3	1,2,3	1,2,3	1,2,3	1 & 2	1,2,3	1,2,3						
Genoa Piazza Principe.........dep	...	11 50	...	14 35	...	...	15 5	...	17 0	17 40	18 30	19 45	...		...	...	...	...
Sampierdarena ar	...	11 53	...	14 41	...	...	15 11	...	17 6	17 46	18 36	19 51	...		...	...	...	...
Sampierdarena dp	...	12 1	...	14 46	...	...	15 16	...	17 8	17 48	18 41	19 54	...		...	...	...	...
Ronco.....................	...	13 7	...	15 41	...	...	16 11	...	18 4	18 34	19 46	20 38	...		...	...	...	...
Arquata	...	13 27	...	15 56	...	...	...	...	18 27	RC	20 6	...	...		...	...	...	...
Novi .... arr	...	13 46	...	16 13	...	...	16 37	...	18 45	19 0	20 24	21 7	...		...	...	...	...
Novi .... dep	...	13 51	...	16 15	...	...		17 55		19 3		21 10	...		...	...	...	...
Pozzolo.................	...	13 58	...	...	...	...	...	18 2	...	...	...	...	...		...	...	...	...
Tortona ...... arr	...	14 17	...	16 33	...	...	...	18 21	...	19 21	...	21 23	...		...	...	...	...
Tortona ...... dep	...	14 20	...	16 35	...	...	...	18 24	...	19 23	...	21 30	...		...	...	...	...
Voghera ...... arr	...	14 40	...	16 51	...	...	...	18 44	...	19 39	...	21 46	...		...	...	...	...
Voghera ...... dep	...	14 48	...	16 56	...	17 6	...	18 54	...	19 45	...	21 52	...		...	...	...	...
Bressana Bottar......	...	15 7	16 45	...	...	17 26	...	19 15	19 33	...	...	...	...		...	...	...	...
Pavia........... arr	...	15 25	17 5	17 21	...	17 44	...	19 35	19 55	20 10	...	22 17	...		...	...	...	...
Pavia........... dep	...	15 33		17 23	...	17 50	...	20 23		20 13	...	22 20	...		...	...	...	...
Certosa	...	15 45	...	...	...	18 2	...	20 35	...	...	...	...	...		...	...	...	...
Locate	...	16 7	...	...	...	18 21	...	20 56	...	...	...	...	...		...	...	...	...
Rogoredo	...	16 20	...	...	...	18 35	...	21 10	...	...	...	...	...		...	...	...	...
Milan Centrale ... arr	...	16 30	...	18 0	...	18 45	...	21 20	...	20 50	...	22 55	...		...	...	...	...
	1,2,3	1,2,3			1,2,3	1,2,3				1,2,3		1,2,3						
Milan Centrale ... dep	17 0	17 25	...	...	18 10	19 20	...	...	...	21 5	...	23 35	...		...	...	...	...
Monza .... arr	...	17 46	...	...	18 25	19 38	...	...	...	21 20	...	23 50	...		...	...	...	...
Monza .... dep	...	17 48	...	...	18 27	19 40	...	...	...	21 22	...	23 51	...		...	...	...	...
Desio	...	18 2	...	...	...	19 54	...	...	...	21 36	...	...	...		...	...	...	...
Seregno......... arr	A	18 8	...	...	18 42	20 0	...	...	...	21 42	...	...	...		...	...	...	...
Seregno......... dep	...	18 10	...	...	18 43	20 2	...	...	...	21 43	...	...	...		...	...	...	...
Camnago	...	18 19	...	...	...	20 12	...	...	...	21 52	...	SC	...		...	...	...	...
Cantu Asnago	...	18 32	...	...	19 0	20 26	...	...	...	22 2	...	...	...		...	...	...	...
Albate Camerlata...	...	18 47	...	...	19 11	20 42	...	...	...	22 14	...	...	...		...	...	...	...
Como............ arr	17 50	18 55	...	...	19 19	20 50	...	...	...	22 22	...	0 34	...		...	...	...	...
Como............ dep	17 52	19 2	...	...	19 27	20 57	...	...	...	22 27	...	0 37	...		...	...	...	...
Chiasso ....¶ arr	18 0	19 10	...	...	19 35	21 5	...	...	...	22 35	...	0 45	...		...	...	...	...
Lucerne 259A arr	...	...	...	...	...	4 a50	...	...	...	4 a50	...	5 a40	...		...	...	...	...
Basle 258 ......arr	...	...	...	...	...	7 a10	...	...	...	7 a10	...	8 a57	...		...	...	...	...

A—Until 30th September.
SC—Sleeping Cars in these trains.

[Fares and Luggage Rates, see page 269.

MODANE, TURIN, GENOA, SPEZIA, PISA, and ROME.

SLEEPING CARS { **Pisa to Rome, in 0.5 from Pisa.** **Turin to Rome, in 20.10 from Turin.**

E.M.	Station																			
...	PARIS (48) ......dep	...	...	...	...	...	...	...	14 20	...	...	...	...	...	...	...	...	22 15	...	...
E.M.		1,2,3	1,2,3	1,2,3	1,2,3	1,2,3	1,2,3 (Until 31st October only.)	1,2,3	1 & 2	1,2,3	1,2,3	1,2,3	1,2,3	1,2,3	1,2,3	1,2,3	1,2,3	1 & 2	1,2,3	1,2,3
Dist.	**MODANE**.........dep	...	...	...	...	...	...	...	3 15	...	...	...	5 15	...	...	8 5		11 30	...	...
5	Bardonecchia..........	...	...	...	...	...	...	...	3 55	...	...	...	6 0	...	...	8 48		12 10	...	...
11¾	Oulx	...	...	...	...	...		...	4 12	...	...	...	6 20	...	...	9 8		12 27	...	...
15½	Salbertrand	...	...	...	...	...		...	4 22	...	...	...	6 30	...	...	9 18	RC	12 37	...	...
30½	Bussoleno (**273**).....	...	...	...	...	...		...	5 2	...	6 0	...	7 12	...	...	10 0		13 17	...	...
43½	Avigliana	...	...	...	...	...		...	5 24	...	6 38	...	7 51	...	...	1037		13 39	...	...
58½	**TURIN** Porta Nova { arr	...	...	...	...	...		...	5 50	...	7 15	...	8 27	...	...	1115		14 5	...	...
	TURIN Porta Nova { dep	...	...	...	...	...		4 10	6 25	7 15	7 30	8 45		9 10	11 0	...	12 10	1,2,3 15 0	...	...
66¼	Trofarello (**272A**)...	...	...	...	...	...		4 31	...	...	7 51	...		9 33	RC	...	12 30	...	...	...
68¾	Cambiano	...	...	...	...	...		4 37	...	...	7 57	...	...	9 40	...	...	12 36	...	...	...
83¾	Villafranca	...	...	...	...	...		5 9	...	...	8 30	...	...	10 16	...	...	13 8	...	...	...
93	**Asti** (**274A**)..........	...	...	...	...	...		5 37	7 16	8 9	8 59	9 40	...	10 46	11 51	...	13 34	15 55	...	...
105½	Felizzano	...	...	...	...	...		6 10	...	8 28	9 31	...	...	11 19	...	...	14 6	...	...	...
115	**Alessandria** ...arr	...	...	...	...	...		6 30	7 45	8 42	9 51	1014	...	11 40	12 20	...	14 26	16 29	...	...
...	„ (**273**)...dep	...	...	...	...	...		6 40	7 58	8 45		1022	11 15		12 33	...	14 42	16 38	...	1750
120½	Frugarolo (**287**) ...	...	...	...	...	...		6 54	...	9 2	...	...	11 32	...	...	...	14 56	...	...	18 4
128	**Novi** (**269A**).........	...	...	...	...	5 20	6 35	7 31	8 27	9 32	...	1053	11 52	...	12 58	...	15 25	17 13	1728	1844
144	Ronco (**270A**).........	...	...	...	...	6 12	7 28	8 23	8 59	10 12	...	1136		...	...	...	16 10	17 52	18 9	1916
159¼	Sampierdarena	...	...	...	...	6 54	8 9	9 4	9 29	10 44	...	12 9	...	...	14 29	...	17 19	18 24	1839	2014
161½	**Genoa** P. Principe	...	...	...	...	7 0	8 15	9 10	9 35	10 50	...	1215	...	...	14 35	...	17 25	18 30	1845	2020
...	MILAN (269A) dep	...	...	...	...	...	...	6 40	6 40	...	...	9 15	...	11 30	...	...	13 20	15 35	...	...
...	**Genoa** P. Principe	...	...	4 15	6 15	8 10	...	10 0	9 45	...	...	1250	14 15	16 0	...	1710	17 55	19 10	1950	...
163¼	**Genoa** P. Brignole	...	...	4 25	6 23	8 18	...	10 8	9 57	...	...	13 0	14 25	16 10	...	1718	18 6	19 23	20 0	...
167½	Quinto	...	...	4 40	...	8 36	...	10 24	...	...	...	...	14 40	16 25	...	...	18 27	...	2015	...
168¾	Nervi	...	...	4 47	6 39	8 44	...	10 30	10 9	...	...	1314	14 49	16 32	...	.733	18 40	19 39	2022	...
170	Bogliasco	...	...	4 52	...	8 51	...	10 35	...	...	...	...	14 54	16 37	...	1738	18 47	...	2027	...
174¼	Recco	...	...	5 12	6 55	9 15	...	10 53	...	...	...	1330	15 14	16 55	...	1757	19 10	19 56	2045	...
178¾	Sta. Margherita	...	...	5 28	7 11	9 36	...	11 8	...	...	...	1342	15 29	17 10	...	1814	19 30	20 12	21 2	...
180	Rapallo	...	...	5 35	7 19	9 44	...	11 14	...	...	...	1348	15 36	17 17	...	1820	19 39	20 19	21 9	...
182¾	Zoagli	...	...	5 45	7 28	9 53	...	11 23	...	...	...	...	15 45	17 27	...	1829	19 48	...	2118	...
185¾	Chiavari	...	...	6 4	7 38	10 6	...	11 35	10 49	...	...	14 4	15 59	17 42	...	1843	19 58	20 37	2133	...
190	Sestri Levante.........	...	...	6 23	7 53	11 7	...	11 59	...	...	...	1417	16 18	18 1	...	19 0		20 54	2151	...
196¾	Moneglia	...	...	6 43	...	11 26	...		...	...	...	...	16 37	18 19	...		...	...	22 9	...
204½	Levanto	...	5 27	7 12	8 24	11 58	...	...	...	...	...	1451	17 8	18 46	...	...	...	21 31	2242	...
217¼	**Spezia** (**275**) { arr	...	6 25	7 53	8 51	12 37	...	...	11 53	...	...	1521	17 50	19 30	...	...	...	22 0	2325	...
	Spezia (**275**) { dep	6 10			8 59	13 0	...	...	12 8	...	...	1531	18 5	19 50	...	...	...	22 10		...
227¼	**Sarzana** (**275**)......	6 40	...	...	9 25	13 29	...	...	...	...	...	1554	18 36	20 21	...	...	...	22 30	...	...
233½	**Avenza** (**275**)	6 58	...	...	9 38	13 48	...	...	RC	...	...	16 9	18 52	20 40	...	...	...	22 42	...	...
237¾	Massa.....................	7 8	...	...	9 50	14 1	...	...	...	...	...	1620	19 5	20 51	...	...	...	22 53	...	...
244¾	Pietra Santa	7 24	...	...	10 6	14 18	...	...	...	...	...	1633	19 22	21 8	...	...	...	23 6	...	...
251	Viareggio (**274A**) ...	7 38	...	...	10 21	14 38	...	...	...	...	...	1650	19 39	21 24	...	...	...	23 21	...	...
264	**Pisa** Centrale ...arr	8 7	...		10 45	15 9	...	...	13 19	...	...	1714	20 11	21 53	...	...	...	23 44	...	...
...	FLORENCE 270A arr	10 23	...		13 50	17 33	...	...	15 12	...	...	1910	23 11	1 50	...	...	...	1 50	...	...
...	**Pisa** Centrale...dep	9 20	...	11 5	12 0	...	...	...	13 33	...	...	1735	20 40	22 7	...	1920	...	0 5	...	...
276½	**Leghorn** (Central) { arr	9 45	...	1127	12 25	...	...	...	13 55	...	...	1758	21 7	22 31	...	1942	...	0 28	...	...
	Leghorn (Central) { dep	9 ‡50	...		12 32	...	...	...	14 2	...	...	18 3			...	1950	...	0 35	...	...
294	Vada	10‡41	...	...	13 14	...	...	...	...	...	...	1838	...	...	...	2035	...	SC	...	...
297¾	**Cecina** (**275**) ...arr	10‡50	...	...	13 22	...	...	...	...	...	...	1846	...	...	...	2044	...	1 15	...	...
319½	Campiglia Mar. 271A		...	...	14 20	...	...	...	15 8	...	...	1926	...	...	...	2150	...	1 51	...	...
330	Follonica	...	...	...	14 48	...	...	...	...	...	...	1945	...	...	...	2219	...	2 10	...	...
339¼	Gavorrano (Potassa)	...	...	...	15 13	...	...	...	...	...	...	RC	...	...	...	2242	...	2 31	...	...
348½	Montepescali...........	...	...	...	15 36	...	...	...	...	...	...	2019	...	...	...	23 5	...	...	...	...
356	**Grosseto** (**275**) ...	...	...	...	16 36	...	...	...	16 17	...	...	2039	...	...	...	2320	...	3 10	...	...
379¾	Orbetello ...... { arr	...	...	...	17 35	...	...	...	...	...	...	2117	...	...	...		...	4 1	...	...
	Orbetello ...... { dep	...	...	...	17 43	...	...	...	...	...	...	2119	...	...	...	...	...	4 4	...	...
400¾	Montalto................	...	...	...	18 30	...	...	...	RC	...	...	...	...	...	...	...	...	4 46	...	...
410	Corneto	...	1 &3	1 &3	18 50	...	...	...	...	...	...	...	...	...	...	...	...	5 3	...	1 &3
422¼	Civita Vecchia.........	...	10 50	1617	19 24	...	...	...	17 52	...	...	2227	...	...	...	...	...	5 30	...	5 46
434¼	Santa Severa...........	...	11 5	1642	19 50	...	...	...	...	...	...	...	...	...	...	...	...	...	...	6 12
443	Palo	...	11 38	17 2	20 13	...	...	...	...	...	...	...	...	...	...	...	...	...	...	6 33
447½	Palidoro	...	11 48	1712	20 23	...	...	...	...	...	...	...	...	...	...	...	...	...	...	6 43
459¼	Ponte Galera **275**)...	...	12 12	1736	20 47	...	...	...	...	...	...	...	...	...	...	...	...	...	...	7 8
464¼	Magliana	...	12 22	1746	20 57	...	...	...	...	...	...	...	...	...	...	...	...	...	...	7 19
467¼	**ROME** { Trastevere	...	12 30	1754	21 5	...	...	...	18 57	...	...	...	...	...	...	...	...	6 41	...	7 27
470¼	**ROME** { Tuscolana.	...	12 44	18 9	21 22	...	...	...	...	...	...	...	...	...	...	...	...	...	...	7 43
472¾	**ROME** { Termini ...	...	12 55	1820	21 35	...	...	...	19 15	...	...	2350	...	...	...	...	...	7 0	...	7 55

For Continuation of Trains, see next page.

ALESSANDRIA and OVADA.	E.M.												
		Alessandria ...dep	6 58	11 5	15 0	19 41	...	Ovada ....dep	7 15	11 15	15 15	19 10	...
	21½	Ovada (273)......arr	8 18	12 22	16 18	21 1	...	Alessandria (270)...arr	8 25	12 25	16 20	20 12	...

FOLLONICA and MASSA MARITTIMA.										
Follonica ....dep	7 10	10 50	15 50	19 55	**Massa Marittima**...dep	5 38	8 30	1255	17 20	...
Massa Marittima ...arr	8 23	12 10	17 2	21 0	**Follonica** (270) ......arr	6 30	9 23	1356	18 12	...

LEGHORN and COLLE SALVETTI.															
Leghorn...dep	5 40	11 30	16 30	18 40	...	...	...	C. Salvetti dep	7 10	15 10	17 48	19 50	...	...	...
C. Salvetti arr	6 10	12 0	17 0	19 10	...	...	...	Leghorn ...arr	7 42	15 42	18 20	20 22	...	...	...

MODANE, TURIN, GENOA, SPEZIA, PISA, and ROME.

PARIS.....dep	...	...	...		...	...	...	8 40	...
	1,2,3	1,2,3	1,2,3	1,2,3	1 & 2		1,2,3	1,2,3	
MODANE ......dep	...	...	...	16 5	...	1815	19 6	2137	...
Bardonecchia	1240	...	...	1647	...	...	1947	2217	...
Oulx	13 0	...	...	17 7	...	...	20 7	...	...
Salbertrand	1310	...	...	1717	...	...	2017	...	...
Bussoleno (273)	1352	...	...	1759	...	...	21 0	2320	...
Avigliana	1429	...	...	1833	...	...	2142	...	...
TURIN Porta Nova arr	15 5	...	...	19 7	...	2049	2220	0 5	...
TURIN Porta Nova dep	1630	18 45	18 35	...	20 10	2115	...	...	...
Trofarello (272A)	1651	19 6	...	...	...	...	...	...	...
Cambiano	1657	19 12	SC	...	SC	...	...	...	...
Villafranca	1729	19 44	...	...	...	...	...	...	...
Asti (274A)	1756	20 15	19 30	...	21 5	...	...	...	...
Felizzano	1827	20 47	...	...	...	...	...	...	...
Alessandria ......arr	1847	21 7	20 4	...	21 39	2244	...	...	...
„ (273)...dep	1918		20 20	...	21 47	P. & O. Express to Piacenza, runs on Saturday only.	...	...	...
Frugarolo (287)	1933	...	...	...	...		...	...	...
Novi (269A)	1959	22 56	20 50	...	22 15		...	...	...
Ronco (270)	2050	23 29	21 23	...	22 48		...	...	...
Sampierdarena	22 9	0 4	21 59	...	23 19		...	...	...
Genoa P. Principe arr	2215	0 10	22 5	...	23 25		...	...	...
MILAN (269A) ......dep	...	...	19 0	...	19 0		2055	...	...
Genoa P.Principe dep	...	...	22 25	...	23 40		0 25	...	...
Genoa P. Brignole	...	...	22 35	...	23 47		0 33	...	...
Quinto	...	...	...	...	...		...	...	...
Nervi	...	...	22 48	...	0 3		0 50	...	...
Bogliasco	...	...	...	...	...		...	...	...
Recco	...	...	...	...	SC		1 9	...	...
Sta. Margherita	...	...	23 15	...	...		1 24	...	...
Rapallo	...	...	23 22	...	...		1 30	...	...
Zoagli	...	...	...	...	...		1 39	...	...
Chiavari	...	...	23 37	...	0 44		1 52	...	...
Sestri Levante	...	...	23 47	...	...	...	2 7	...	...
Moneglia	...	...	SC	...	...	...	2 25	...	...
Levanto	...	...	0 23	...	...	...	2 54	...	...
Spezia (275)...... arr	...	...	0 50	...	1 50	...	3 31	...	...
Spezia (275)...... dep	...	...	0 55	...	1 56	...	3 45	...	...
Sarzana (275)	...	...	1 22	...	2 15	...	4 10	...	...
Avenza (275)	...	...	1 34	...	...	...	4 23	...	...
Massa	...	...	1 45	...	2 34	...	4 37	...	...
Pietra Santa	...	...	...	...	...	...	4 54	...	...
Viareggio (274A)	...	...	2 4	...	2 54	...	5 12	...	...
Pisa Centrale ......arr	...	...	2 28	...	3 17	1,2,3	5 43	...	...
FLORENCE (270A) arr	...	...	...	...	5 44	...	8 7	...	...
Pisa Centrale ......dep	...	...	2 35	...	3 26	5 0	5 55	7 0	...
Leghorn (Central) arr	...	...	2 57	...	3 48	5 25	6 20	7 25	...
Leghorn (Central) dep	...	...	3 2	...	3 52	5 32		7 32	...
Vada	...	...	...	...	...	6 14	..	8 14	...
Cecina (275) ......arr	...	...	3 34	...	4 25	6 22	...	8 22	...
Campiglia Mar. (271A)	...	...	4 10	...	5 1	7 19	...	9 25	...
Follonica	...	...	...	...	5 20	7 43	...	9 50	...
Gavorrano (Potassa)	...	...	...	...	...	8 6	...	1013	...
Montepescali	...	...	...	...	...	8 29	...	1036	...
Grosseto (275	...	...	5 21	...	6 19	8 44	...	1128	...
Orbetello ...... arr	...	...	5 57	...	6 55		...	1218	...
Orbetello ...... dep	...	...	5 58	...	6 56	...	...	1223	...
Montalto	...	...	6 33	...	...	...	...	13 6	...
Corneto	...	...	6 49	...	...	...	...	1325	...
Civita Vecchia	...	...	7 14	...	8 5	..	...	14 0	...
Santa Severa	...	...	...	...	...	...	...	1427	...
Palo	...	...	...	...	...	...	...	1449	...
Palidoro	...	...	...	...	...	...	...	1457	...
Ponte Galera (275)	...	...	...	...	...	...	...	1521	...
Magliana	...	...	...	...	...	...	...	1530	...
ROME Trastevere arr	...	...	8 22	...	9 12	...	...	1537	...
ROME Tuscolana.. „	...	...	...	...	...	...	...	1553	...
ROME Termini..... „	...	...	8 40	...	9 30	...	...	16 5	...

‡—Until 15th September.

SC—Restaurant Car. SC—Sleeping Car.

FLORENCE and LEGHORN.

Dis. S.M.		1,2,3	1,2,3	1,2,3	1,2,3	1,2,3	1 & 2	1,2,3	1,2,3	1,2,3	1,2,3	1,2,3	1,2,3	1,2,3
	Florence ...dep	3 50	6 10	7 30	8 50	9 35	...	1150	1425	17 25	18 25	20 15	2125	2355
6¼	S. Donnino	...	6 24	...	9 4	...	...	...	1439	...	18 39	...	2139	...
9¼	Signa	4 8	6 32	...	9 11	...	...	12 8	1446	17 43	18 47	20 32	2146	0 16
21¾	**Empoli** ......arr	4 34	7 2	8 6	9 40	1011	...	1233	1514	18 9	19 16	20 53	2213	0 42
...	„ (275) dep	4 39	7 8	8 8	9 44		...	1240	1522	18 17	19 21	20 57	2225	0 50
30	S. Romano	5 0	7 29	...	10 5	...	...	1259	1541	18 36	19 42	21 15	2249	1 12
36¾	Pontedera	5 17	7 47	8 36	1022	...	...	1317	1558	18 51	20 0	21 31	23 9	1 30
45	Navacchio	5 36	8 6	...	1041	...	...	1336	1617	...	20 19	...	2336	1 51
49	**Pisa** ......arr	5 46	8 18	8 55	1051	...	...	1346	1627	19 11	20 29	21 50	2340	2 1
...	GENOA 271 arr	1035	...	...	...	...	...	1840	2225	1 40	2 9	2 9	4 15	5 50
...	**Pisa** ......dep	5 55	8 30	9 0	11 5	...	1333	1355	1640	19 20	20 40	22 7	2348	2 15
62¾	**Leghorn** S.M. a	6 20	8 55	9 22	1127	...	1355	1420	17 5	19 42	21 7	22 31	0 11	2 39

	1,2,3	1,2,3	1 & 2	1,2,3	1,2,3	1,2,3	1,2,3	1,2,3	1 & 2	1,2,3	1,2,3	1,2,3	1,2,3	1 & 2
Leghorn ...dep	3 0	5 5	7 30	7 45	1110	13 5	...	14 50	1715	1745	20 25	2120	2330	2353
Pisa ......arr	3 24	5 29	7 51	8 10	1134	1326	...	15 15	1736	18 6	20 49	2141	2351	0 14
GENOA 270 dp	2340	0 25	...	...	6 15	9 45	...	...	1250	...	14 15	16 0	1910	
Pisa ......dep	3 42	6 2	7 56	8 16	1145	1336	14 0	15 25	1746	1813	21 0	2215	0 23	...
Navacchio	3 53	6 14	...	8 27	1155	...	14 15	15 36	...	...	21 12	2240	...	...
Pontedera	4 12	6 33	8 16	8 47	1215	1356	14 38	15 56	18 6	1838	21 34	2320	0 44	...
S. Romano	4 30	6 51	...	9 5	1233	...		16 14	...	1853	21 54		...	...
Empoli ...arr	4 50	7 11	8 42	9 25	1253	1426	...	16 35	1832	1911	22 15	...	1 10	...
„ ...dep	4 56	7 17	8 44	9 32	13 0	1431	16 8	16 43	1834	1918	22 22	...	1 12	...
Signa	5 26	7 47	...	10 2	1330	1457	...	17 14	...	1945	22 52	...	1 35	...
S. Donnino	5 33	7 54	...	10 9	1337	...	...	17 21	...	...	22 59	...	...	...
Florence arr	5 44	8 7	9 20	1023	1350	1512	16 45	17 33	1910	20 0	23 11	...	1 50	...

Extra

Pontedera ......dep	19 5	...
Pisa ......arr	19 42	...

Pisa ...... dep	2 35	3 26	5 0	7 0	9 20	12 0	1531	1735	22 7	0 5
Leghorn arr	2 57	3 48	5 25	7 25	9 45	1225	16 0	1758	2231	0 28

Leghorn dep	2 20	5 24	6 20	8 30	9 22	1745	...
Pisa ......arr	2 40	5 45	6 41	8 51	9 44	18 6	...

PISA and CECINA.

Pisa (Centrale) ......dep	5 55	9 14	11 52	16 40	19 16	...	...	...	...	...
Colle Salvetti	6 19	9 41	12 15	17 12	19 36	...	...	...	...	...
Vada	7 9	10 30	13 4	18 16	20 25	...	...	...	...	...
Cecina 270 ......arr	7 17	10 38	13 12	18 27	20 33	...	...	...	...	...

Cecina ......dep	6 0	8 28	13 52	16 35	20 19	...	...	...	...	...	...
Vada	6 8	8 37	14 1	16 44	20 28	...	...	...	...	...	...
Colle Salvetti	7 2	9 38	14 55	17 39	21 19	...	...	...	...	...	...
Pisa (Centrale) 270 ....arr	7 25	10 0	15 18	18 0	21 40	...	...	...	...	...	...

‡—Until 31st October.

GENOA and RONCO.

Genoa P.P. dep	2 30	2 40	5 15	8 20	8 30	1115	1150	14 35	15 5	16 30	17‡30	1830	...
Busalla	3 26	3 43	6 15	9 16	9 33	1211	1256	15 31	16 1	17 38	18 33	1935	...
Ronco ......arr	3 35	3 52	6 24	9 24	9 42	1219	13 5	15 39	16 9	17 50	18 45	1944	...

Ronco ......dep	6 15	7‡30	8 20	10 17	...	1353	16 10	1815	1916	20 50	...	...	...	...
Busalla	6 34	7 48	8 34	10 32	1344	14 8	16 24	1830	1931	21 6	...	...	...	...
Genoa P.P....arr	7 35	8 45	9 30	11 30	1435	1458	17 25	1930	2020	22 15	...	...	...	...

Fares and Luggage Rates, see page 269.]

ROME, PISA, SPEZIA, GENOA, TURIN, and MODANE.

SLEEPING CARS—in 18.15, 21.0, and 23.55 from Rome; and in 20.0 from Genoa.

	1,2,3	1,2,3	1,2,3	1,2,3	1,2,3	1,2,3	1,2,3	1 & 3	1,2,3	1,2,3	1,2,3	1,2,3	1 & 2	1,2,3	1,2,3	1,2,3	1,2,3	1,2,3
ROME Termini dep	...	...	...	...	...	...	...	6 10	...	...	...	9 0	...	...	...	9 10	...	...
„ Tuscolana „	...	...	...	...	...	...	...	6 20	...	...	...	...	...	...	...	9 20	...	...
„ Trastevere „	...	...	...	...	...	...	...	6 31	...	...	...	9 15	...	...	...	9 33	...	...
Magliana	...	...	...	...	...	...	...	6 40	...	...	...	...	...	...	...	9 42	...	...
Ponte Galera	...	...	...	...	...	...	...	6 51	...	...	...	RC	...	...	...	9 53	...	...
Palidoro	...	...	...	...	...	...	...	7 14	...	...	...	...	...	...	...	10 16	...	...
Palo	...	...	...	...	...	...	...	7 24	...	...	...	...	...	...	...	10 26		...
Santa Severa	...	...	...	...	...	...	...	7 43	...	...	...	...	...	...	...	10 45		...
Civita Vecchia	...	...	...	...	...	5 0	...	8 5	...	...	...	10 22	...	...	...	11 19		...
Corneto	...	...	...	...	...	5 31	...		...	...	...	10 42	...	...	...	11 41		...
Montalto	...	...	...	...	...	5 56	...	...	...	...	...	...	...	...	...	12 0		...
Orbetello arr	...	...	...	...	...	6 52	...	...	...	...	...	11 23	...	...	...	12 41		...
Orbetello dep	...	...	...	...	...	7 2	...	...	...	...	...	11 24	...	...	...	12 46		...
Grosseto	...	...	...	...	...	8 13	...	...	5 50	...	...	12 5	...	10 50	...	13 45		...
Montepescali	...	...	...	...	...		...	...	6 9	...	...	...	...	11 9	...	14 1		...
Gavorrano (Pot)	...	...	...	...	...	...	...	...	6 34	...	...	...	...	11 33	...	14 24		...
Follonica	...	...	...	...	...	...	...	...	6 58	...	...	...	...	11 54	...	14 46		...
Campiglia Maritt	...	...	...	...	...	5 4	...	...	7 26	...	...	13 7	...	12 32	...	15 22		...
Cecina	...	...	...	...	...	6 15	...	...	8 18	...	...	13 42	...	13 19	...	16 25	18 50	...
Vada	...	...	...	...	...	6 25	...	...	8 27	...	...	...	...	14 1	...	16 35	19 0	...
Leghorn arr	...	...	...	...	...	7 9	...	...	9 8	...	...	14 17	...	⋮	...	17 23	19 50	...
Leghorn dep	...	...	...	3 0	8 30	7 30	...	...	9 22	...	...	14 21	...	⋮	14 50	17 45		20 25
Pisa (Centrale)..arr	...	...	...	3 24	8 51	7 51	...	...	9 44	...	...	14 41	...	15 18	15 15	18 6	...	20 49
FLORENCE 270A dep	...	...	...	23 55	7 30	...	...	...	8 50	11 50	...	11 50	...	...	14 25	17 25	...	18 25
Pisa dep	...	...	...	4 0	9 5	...	...	...	12 15	14 10	...	14 55	...	...	16 37	19 30	...	20 50
Viareggio	...	...	...	4 34	9 39	...	...	...	12 50	14 36	...	15 21	...	...	17 8	20 6	...	21 29
Pietra Santa	...	...	...	4 49	9 53	...	...	...	13 4	14 48	...	...	...	...	17 21	20 21	...	
Massa	...	...	...	5 8	10 11	...	...	...	13 23	15 2	...	15 42	...	...	17 38	20 41	...	...
Avenza	...	...	...	5 20	10 23	...	...	...	13 36	15 13	...	15 53	...	...	17 49	20 55	...	...
Sarzana	...	...	...	5 39	10 41	...	...	...	13 57	15 29	...	16 7	...	...	18 6	21 19	...	...
Spezia arr	...	...	...	6 9	11 10	...	...	...	14 29	15 50	...	16 25	...	...	18 35	21 48	...	...
Spezia dep	...	...	4 45	6 30	11 24	...	12 40	...		16 0	...	16 35	...	18 0	18 45	22 0	...	...
Levanto	...	...	5 32	7 16	12 0	...	13 25	...	...	16 29	...	17 5	...	18 46	19 31	22 45	...	...
Moneglia	...	...	5 58	7 42	12 18	...	13 51	...	...	...	...	...	...		19 57	23 11	...	...
Sestri Levante	...	5 40	6 18	8 2	12 35	...	14 11	...	...	17 0	...	17 37	...	18 10	20 16	23 29	...	...
Chiavari	3 55	6 2	6 42	8 29	12 54	...	14 34	...	...	17 19	...	17 52	...	18 30	20 38	23 53	...	...
Zoagli	4 4	6 12	6 52	8 38	13 3	...	14 43	...	...	17 28	...	...	...	18 39	20 47	0 3	...	...
Rapallo	4 12	6 22	7 4	8 48	13 11	...	14 53	...		17 36	...	18 9	...	18 49	20 57	0 15	...	...
Sta. Margherita	4 21	6 32	7 14	8 56	13 18	...	15 1	...		17 44	...	18 16	...	18 51	21 5	0 24	...	...
Recco	4 39	6 53	7 33	9 12	13 33	...	15 16	...		18 0	...	...	...	19 15	21 23	0 48	...	...
Bogliasco	5 2	7 15	7 53	9 32	...	...	15 34	...		...	...	...	...	19 35	21 43	...	...	...
Nervi	5 9	7 22	8 0	9 39	13 48	...	15 41	...		18 15	...	18 45	...	19 42	21 52	1 11	...	...
Quinto	5 16	7 30	8 5	9 44	...	...	15 46	...		...	...	...	...	19 47	21 58	...	...	...
Genoa P. Brignole	5 29	7 48	8 18	9 57	13 58	...	15 59	...		18 28	...	18 55	...	20 0	22 13	1 25	...	...
Genoa P. Principe	5 40	8 0	8 35	10 10	14 10	...	16 11	1 & 2		18 40	...	19 10	...	20 15	22 25	1 40	...	...
MILAN (269A) arr	9 5	11 55	...	13 55	18 0	...	20 50	...	1,2,3	22 55	...	22 55	...	...	...	6 50	...	...
Genoa P. Prin. 2 30	...	8 30	...	...	...	15 5	17 0	17 40	17 45	...	19 45	...	20 0	...	...	...	...	...
Sampierdarena 2 41	...	8 41	...	...	...	15 16	17 8	17 48	17 58	...	19 54	...	20 11	...	...	...	...	...
Ronco 3 38	...	9 45	...	...	...	16 11	18 4	18 34	18 55	...	20 38	...	20 56	...	...	...	...	...
Novi 4 11	...	10 30	...	...	...	16 39	18 51	19 14	19 33	...	21 7	...	21 24	...	...	...	...	...
Frugarolo 4 27	...	10 47	...	...	...	16 53	19 7	...		...	21 57	...	...	...	...	...	...	...
Alessandria (269) arr 4 40	...	11 0	...	...	...	17 5	19 20	19 35	...	...	22 10	...	21 47	...	...	...	...	...
Alessandria (269) dep	5 15	11 10	14 15	...	17 35	17 24			...	19 44		...	21 55	22 50	...	...	...	...
Felizzano	5 36	...	14 39	...	17 56	...	...	...	...	19 58	...	...	...	...	...	...	...	...
Asti	6 9	11 44	15 21	...	18 28	18 0	...	...	...	20 22	...	...	22 28	23 22	...	...	...	...
Villafranca	6 34	...	15 49	...	18 51	...	...	...	...	20 42	...	...	...	...	...	...	...	...
Cambiano	7 14	...	16 31	...	19 31	...	...	...	...	RC	...	...	SC	...	...	...	...	...
Trofarello	7 20	...	16 39	...	19 38	18 44	...		...	...	...	...	...	...	...	...	...	...
TURIN Porta Nova arr	7 40	12 40	17 0	...	19 58	19 0	...		...	21 29	...	...	23 25	0 16	...	...	...	...
TURIN Porta Nova dep	...	14 15	17 50	...	...	...	19*30		...	23 40	...	...	0 30	...	...	...	...	...
Avigliana	...	14 42	18 31	...	...	...	20 15		...	0 25	...	...	1 0	...	...	...	...	...
Bussoleno	...	15 50	19 12	...	...	...	21 6		...	1 41	...	...	1 29	...	...	...	...	...
Salbertrand	...	16 30	19 51	...	...	...	21 46		...	2 35	...	...	2 8	...	...	...	...	...
Oulx	...	16 43	20 3	...	...	...	21 57		...	2 47	...	...	2 19	...	...	...	...	...
Bardonecchia	...	17 11	20 29	...	...	...	22 31		...	3 15	...	...	2 44	...	...	...	...	...
MODANE (61) ¶arr	...	17 40	20 58	...	...	...	23 0		...	3 46	...	...	3 15	...	...	...	...	...
PARIS (51) arr	...	...	...	...	...	...	...	...	...	...	...	...	14 25	...	...	...	...	...

Until 15th Sept. only. (printed vertically in the seventeenth column, Palo to Campiglia Maritt)

Until 31st October. (printed vertically in the ninth column, Levanto to Genoa, with a sleeping-car sign)

*—Runs until 30th Sept. only. (printed vertically in the eighth column, Trofarello to Modane)

For Continuation of Trains and Notes see next page.

TURIN and TORRE PELLICE.	Dis.								
		Turin dep	5 30	7 25	8 30	1250	16 5	18 0	19 55
	15½	Airasca	6 20	8 6	9 15	1335	1657	1836	20 40
	23½	Pinerolo arr	6 46	8 28	9 40	14 0	1722	1856	21 5
	29½	Bricherasio	7 21	...	1014	1425	1752	1922	21 36
	34½	T. Pellice arr	7 46	...	1038	1448	1816	1945	22 0

TURIN and TORRE PELLICE.							
Torre Pellice dep	5 10	6 55	8 45	1220	1550	1919	...
Bricherasio	5 28	7 17	9 6	1242	1610	1939	...
Pinerolo	6 0	7 43	9 40	1314	1637	2010	...
Airasca	6 24	8 3	10 5	1340	17 3	2035	...
Turin arr	7 5	8 35	1047	1423	1745	2120	...

BRICHERASIO and BARGE.						
Bricherasio dep	7 35	10 18	14 28	17 56	21 40	
Barge arr	7 55	10 47	15 1	18 25	22 10	
Barge dep	6 34	8 30	12 0	15 30	18 45	...
Bricherasio arr	7 7	8 59	12 33	16 3	19 15	...

ROME, PISA, SPEZIA, GENOA, TURIN, and MODANE.

	1,2,3	1 & 3	1 & 2	1,2,3	1 & 2	1,2,3	1,2,3
ROME Termini ...dep	14 0	16 45	18 15	18 30	21 0	...	2355
„ Tuscolana „	...	16 55	...	18 40	...	...	...
„ Trastevere „	14 18	17 7	18 30	18 52	21 15	...	...
Magliana	14 27	17 16	...	19 1	SC	...	SC
Ponte Galera	...	17 27	...	19 11	...	...	...
Palidoro	...	17 50	...	19 34	...	...	...
Palo	15 3	18 0	...	19 43	...	...	...
Santa Severa	...	18 19	...	20 2	...	...	...
Civita Vecchia	15 43	18 42	19 47	20 34	22 29	...	1 16
Corneto	16 5		...	20 56	...	...	...
Montalto	16 21	...	...	21 1	...	...	...
Orbetello arr	16 55	...	20 45	21 50	23 27	...	2 19
Orbetello dep	16 57	...	20 46	21 55	23 28	...	2 20
Grosseto	17 45	...	21 33	22 40	0 10	...	2 59
Montepescali	18 3	...	...		...	...	...
Gavorrano (Pot)	18 27	...	RC	...	...	...	...
Follonica	18 50	...	...	...	...	...	3 46
Campiglia Maritt	19 21	...	22 40	...	1 10	...	4 8
Cecina	20 9	...	23 13	...	1 43	...	4 41
Vada	20 18	...	SC	...	...	...	...
Leghorn arr	21 0	...	23 48	...	2 14	...	5 19
Leghorn dep	21 20	...	23 53	...	2 20	...	5 24
Pisa (Centrale) ...arr	21 41	...	0 14	...	2 40	...	5 45
FLORENCE 270A dep	20 15	...	21 25	...	23 55	...	3 50
Pisa ...dep	22 5	...	0 27	...	2 56	...	6 5
Viareggio	22 30	...	0 51	...	3 18	...	6 29
Pietra Santa	22 42	...	1 3	...	...	...	6 42
Massa	22 55	...	1 15	...	3 39	...	6 59
Avenza	23 6	...	1 25	...	3 49	...	7 11
Sarzana	23 21	...	1 39	...	4 1	...	7 26
Spezia arr	23 38	...	1 57	...	4 18	...	7 48
Spezia dep	23 45	...	2 7	...	4 25	...	7 53
Levanto	0 14	...	2 39	...	...	...	8 26
Moneglia	...	...	...	...	...	...	...
Sestri Levante	0 44	...	...	...	...	...	8 56
Chiavari	0 56	...	3 15	...	5 33	...	9 13
Zoagli	...	...	...	...	...	...	...
Rapallo	1 14	...	...	...	5 53	...	9 31
Sta Margherita	1 22	...	...	...	...	...	9 41
Recco	...	...	...	...	SC	...	...
Bogliasco	...	...	...	...	...	...	...
Nervi	1 48	...	...	...	6 21	...	10 8
Quinto	...	...	...	...	...	...	...
Genoa P. Brignole	1 58	...	4 5	...	6 35	...	1023
Genoa P. Principe arr	2 9	...	4 15	...	6 45	...	1035
MILAN (269A)...arr	6 50	...	9 5	...	10 55	...	1355
Genoa P. Principe dep	...	5 50	5 0	...	6 55	5 15	1115
Sampierdarena	...	5 58	5 8	...	7 3	5 24	1126
Ronco	...	6 49	5 52	...	7 48	6 26	1221
Novi	...	7 15	6 22	...	8 16	7 20	1254
Frugarolo	...	7 34	...	...	...	7 34	13 8
Alessandria (269) arr	...	7 46	6 45	...	8 39	7 46	1320
Alessandria (269) dep	...		7 10	7 20	8 47	9 15	1335
Felizzano	...	...	...	7 41	...	9 36	...
Asti	...	...	7 44	8 16	9 20	10 12	1413
Villafranca	...	...	...	8 39	...	10 36	‡
Cambiano	...	...	...	9 19	...	11 17	RC
Trofarello	...	...	...	9 25	10 4	11 24	...
TURIN Porta Nova arr	...	...	8 41	9 45	10 20	11 45	1512
TURIN Porta Nova dep	5 40	7 5	9§10				16 5
Avigliana	6 24	7 48	9 38	...	...	...	1637
Bussoleno	7 6	8 28	10 6	...	...	...	1711
Salbertrand	7 47		10 45	...	...	...	1750
Oulx	8 0	...	10 56	...	...	...	18 4
Bardonecchia	8 31	...	11 19	...	...	...	1829
MODANE (61) ¶ arr	9 0	...	11 48	...	...	...	19 0
PARIS (51)...arr	...	...	23 0	...	...	...	6 45

RC Restaurant Car.
¶—Customs Examination.
‡—Restaurant Car from Genoa to Chambéry.
§—1,2,3 class.

FLORENCE, PISTOJA, PISA, and LEGHORN.

	1,2,3	1,2,3	1,2,3	1,2,3	1 & 3	1 & 2	1,2,3	1 & 2	1,2,3	1,2,3	1,2,3	1,2,3	1,2,3	1 & 2	1,2,3
Florence ...dep	See also p. 279B.	5 15	6 20	7 50	8 40	10 50	11 55	14 30	15 40	17 45	18 45	21 20	...	23 39	2350
Sesto Fiorentino		5 33	...	8 2	8 58	11 1	12 13	...	15 58	18 0	19 3	...	...	...	0 8
Prato		5 52	6 44	8 15	9 16	11 14	12 30	14 50	16 15	18 16	19 21	21 42	...	23 57	0 23
Montale Agliana		6 3	...	...	9 28	...	12 41		16 26	18 27	19 32	...	...	...	0 44
Pistoja ...arr		6 13	7 1	8 32	9 40	11 30	12 51	...	16 36	18 37	19 42	21 58	...	0 11	
„ (279) ...dep	...	6 33	7*15	8 37		11*53	12 58	...	16 50	18 43	19 50	22* 6	2230	0*25	...
Pieve Monsummano	...	6 53	7*48	8 55	...	12*25	13 15	...	17 8	18 58	20 8	22*38	2256	0*51	...
Montecatini	...	7 5	7*53	9 2	...	12*30	13 24	...	17 22	19 5	20 14	22*43	23 2	0*56	...
Altopascio	...	7 40		9 32	...		13 58	...	17 57	19 31	20 44		2340		...
Lucca (274A)	6 5	8 20	...	1014	1212	...	14 36	...	18 25	19 50	21 20	...	0 10	...	...
Ripafratta	6 20	8 36	...	1025	1229	...	14 50	...	18 39	...	21 34	...	...	...	...
S. Giuliano	6 34	8 50	...	1038	1246	...	15 3	...	18 51	20 §9	21 46	...	0 33	...	...
Pisa-Centrale ...arr	6 50	9 7	...	1052	13 1	...	15 18	...	19 3	20 21	21 58	...	0 50	...	...
„ (271) ...dep	7 0	9 20	...	11 5	1333	...	15 31	...	19 20	20 40	22 7	...	2 15	...	...
Leghorn ...arr	7 25	9 45	...	1127	1355	...	16 0	...	19 42	21 7	22 31	...	2 39	...	...
Extra. Montecatini ...dep						1*48	11*48	15*45	20*45	23* 5	...				
Extra. Pistoja ...arr						2 35	12 32	16 32	21 32	23 52	...				

	1 & 2	1,2,3	1,2,3	1,2,3	1,2,3	1 & 3	1,2,3	1,2,3	1,2,3	1,2,3	1,2,3	1,2,3
Leghorn ...dep		3 0	6 20	...	8 30	...	11 10	1421	16 0	18 50	2120	2330
Pisa-Centrale arr		3 24	6 41	...	8 51	...	11 34	1441	16 25	19 14	2141	2351
„ ...dep		4 15	6 49	...	9 10	...	12 33	15 5	16 45	19 35	2220	0 35
S. Giuliano		4 27	7 2	...	9 23	...	12 47	1522	16 59	19 48	2237	0 55
Ripafratta		4 39	...	...	9 35	...	13 0	1536	17 12	20 0	2251	1 9
Lucca		5 5	7 21	...	9 53	...	13 19	1556	17 52	20 35	23 5	1 20
Altopascio		5 28	7 37	...	10 16	...	13 42	1622	18 15	20 59		
Montecatini		6 5	8 8	...	10 49	...	14 23	1712	18 51	21 37	...	...
Pieve Monsumma		6 11	8 13	...	10 54	...	14 29	1718	18 57	21 42	...	...
Pistoja ...arr		6 33	8 31	...	11 14	...	14 51	1749	19 19	22 5	...	...
„ ...dep	6 7	6 48	8 36	9 22	11 25	13 4	15 10	18 0	19 45	22 26	...	4 40
Montale A. ...		7 2	...	9 33	11 35	13 16	15 21	1815	19 56	22 37	...	4 53
Prato	6 27	7 17	8 56	9 46	11 46	13 29	15 36	1827	20 9	22 51	...	5 7
Sesto Fioren. ...		7 33	...	10 0	12 0	13 46	15 52	1842	20 25	23 5	...	5 23
Florence arr	6 48	7 50	9 15	1017	12 18	14 4	16 10	19 0	20 42	23 16	...	5 40

*—Runs until 30th September.

ROME and TERRACINA.

Rome—Termini..dep	6 50	9 20	12 45	17 45	21 30	...
Ciampino	7 13	9 43	13 8	18 8	21 53	...
Cecchina	7 46	10 16	13 41	18 41	22 26	...
Velletri	8 12	10 37	14 7	19 7	22 47	...
Cisterna	8 50		14 45	19 45		...
Piperno	10 4	...	15 59	20 59	...	...
Terracina ...arr	10 43	...	16 38	21 38	...	...

Terracina ...dep	...	5 20	11 5	...	16 54	...
Piperno	...	6 3	11 48	...	17 37	...
Cisterna	...	7 24	13 9	...	18 58	...
Velletri	6 21	8 17	14 2	18 11	19 51	...
Cecchina	6 46	8 41	14 26	18 36	20 16	...
Ciampino	7 11	9 6	14 51	19 1	20 41	...
Rome—Termini...arr	7 30	9 25	15 10	19 20	21 0	...

CAMPIGLIA and PIOMBINO.

Campiglia ...dep	5 52	7 25	9 20	1235	1432	1515	1930	2245
Piombino ...arr	6 36	8 3	10 1	1313	1513	1553	2012	2324
Piombino ...dep	3 20	6 26	8 23	1144	1330	1420	1829	2148
Campiglia 270 arr	4 0	7 6	9 5	1225	14 9	15 0	19 9	2230

STATE RAILWAYS—(continued).

ITALIAN RAILWAY TIME.

Italian Railway Time is reckoned from Midnight to Midnight. The morning hours are reckoned in the same manner as in other parts of Europe, but after 12.0 noon the hours are numbered 13 o'clock, 14 o'clock, and so on to 24 o'clock, which is Midnight. The first hour of the day is written 0.5, 0.10, 0.30, equivalent to 5 minutes past midnight, etc.

ITALIAN RECKONING.

0 5	0 30	1 0	2 0	3 0	4 0	5 0	6 0	7 0	8 0	9 0	10 0	11 0	12 0	13 0	14 0	15 0	16 0	17 0	18 0	19 0	20 0	21 0	22 0	23 0	24 0
USUAL RECKONING.																									
a.m. 12 5	a.m. 12 30	a.m 1 0	a.m. 2 0	a.m. 3 0	a.m. 4 0	a.m. 5 0	a.m. 6 0	a.m. 7 0	a.m. 8 0	a.m. 9 0	a.m. 10 0	a.m. 11 0	no'n 12 0	p.m. 1 0	p.m. 2 0	p.m. 3 0	p.m. 4 0	p.m. 5 0	p.m. 6 0	p.m. 7 0	p.m. 8 0	p.m. 9 0	p.m. 10 0	p.m. 11 0	nigt 12 0

For Fares and Luggage Rates, see page 269.

VENTIMIGLIA, SAVONA, and GENOA.

...	MARSEILLES (54)...dep	...	1850	...	...	...	...	...	0 46	...	...	...	7 20	...	9 40	...	...	...	...
Dist			1,2,3	1,2,3	1,2,3	1,2,3	1,2,3	1,2,3	1,2,3	1,2,3	1& 2	1,2,3	1,2,3	1,2,3	1,2,3	1,2,3			
E.M	**Ventimiglia**............dep	...	2 30	...	4 45	...	6 30	7 55	9 30	11 0	1255	...	1610	1720	18 45	20 35	...	...	...
3	Bordighera	...	2 39	...	4 54	...	6 42	8 9	9 40	1113	13 5	...	1621	1731	18 55	20 49	...	...	...
6¾	Ospedaletti	...	2 48	...	5 3	...	6 51	8 20	9 50	1123	1316	...	1631	1742	19 6	21 1	...	...	...
10	San Remo ¶ ....arr	...	2 56	...	5 11	...	6 59	8 28	9 58	1131	1324	...	1639	1750	19 14	21 9	...	...	...
24¼	Porto Maurizio	...	3 37	...	5 51	...	7 51	9 21	10 37	1220	14 3	...	1728	—	19 55	21 53	...	...	...
25½	Oneglia........................	...	3 43	...	5 57	...	7 57	9 29	10 44	1228	14 9	...	1735	...	20 2	22 2	...	...	...
28½	Diano Marina..................	...	3 51	...	6 5	...	8 6	9 38	10 52	1237	1417	...	1744	...	20 11	22 11	...	...	...
33½	Andora	...	4 5	...	6 15	...	8 21	9 51	...	1250	...	...	1757	...	...	22 24	...	...	...
36	Laigueglia	...	4 12	...	...	...	8 28	9 58	...	1257	...	...	18 4	...	...	22 31	...	...	...
38	Alassio	...	4 18	...	6 27	...	8 36	10 8	11 14	13 4	1439	...	1811	...	20 34	22 38	...	...	...
41½	Albenga	...	4 32	5 56	6 40	...	8 50	1016	11 27	1320	1452	...	1825	...	20 48	22 56	...	...	...
47½	Loano	...	4 50	6 15	...	...	9 10	—	11 40	1340	...	...	1845	...	...	23 13	...	...	...
49	Pietraligure..................	...	4 56	6 21	...	...	9 17	...	...	1348	...	...	1852	...	RC	23 20	...	...	...
51	Borgio Verezzi	...	5 2	6 27	...	...	9 25	...	...	1355	...	...	1859	...	...	23 26	...	...	...
52¾	Finalmarina	...	5 9	6 34	7 9	...	9 33	...	11 56	14 4	1519	...	19 9	...	21 17	23 34	...	...	...
57½	Noli	...	5 23	6 49	...	...	9 47	...	...	1420	...	...	1923	...	...	23 47	...	...	...
59½	Spotorno	1,2,3	5 29	6 56	...	...	9 54	...	...	1427	...	...	1930	...	...	23 54	...	...	...
67	**Savona (272)**	4 20	5 52	7 19	7 40	8 45	10 17	...	12 24	1451	1550	1813	1955	...	21 48	0 15	...	...	...
74½	Varazze	4 45	6 29		8 9	9 11	10 49	...	12 50	1551	1614	1836	2032	...	22 14	0 53	...	...	...
78	Cogoleto	4 56	6 40	—	8 20	9 22	10 59	...	...	16 3	...	1846	2043	...	...	1 4	...	...	...
80¾	Arenzano......................	5 3	6 47	...	8 27	9 30	11 6	...	13 5	1612	...	1853	2051	...	...	1 12	...	...	...
85	Voltri..........................	5 22	7 4	...	8 42	9 44	11 18	...	13 18	1625	1646	19 5	21 6	...	22 39	1 27	...	...	...
88	Pegli	5 35	7 16	...	8 56	9 58	11 31	...	13 30	1637	1656	1917	2118	...	22 49	1 41	...	...	...
90	Sestri Ponente	5 42	7 23	...	9 2	10 5	11 38	...	13 35	1643	...	1923	2125	...	22 54	1 48	...	...	...
91¼	Cornigliano..................	5 47	7 28	...	9 8	1011	11 43	...	...	1648	...	1928	2131	...	...	1 54	...	...	...
91¾	Sampierdarena	5 59	7 34	...	9 19	1024	11 52	...	13 44	1659	1714	1934	2144	...	23 4	2 4	...	...	...
93¾	**Genoa P.Principe** .....arr	6 5	7 40	...	9 25	1030	11 58	...	13 50	17 5	1720	1940	2150	...	23 10	2 10	...	...	...
196¼	PISA (270) ....arr	1045	1319	...	1319	...	17 14	...	20 11	2344	2344	...	2 28	...	3 17	...	...	...	...
405	ROME (270)............arr	...	1915	...	1915	...	23 50	...	...	7 0	7 0	...	8 40	...	9 30	...	...	...	...

¶—Customs Examination at San Remo of luggage to that place.

RC—Restaurant Car in this train.

TURIN, BRA, and SAVONA.

	1,2,3	1,2,3	1,2,3	1,2,3	1,2,3	1,2,3	1,2,3	1,2,3
Turin ....dep	5 50	8 10	1040	1328	16 15	...	19 20	17 50
Trofarello	6 10	8 26	11 1	1348	...	...	19 41	18 10
Carmagnola 272A	6 31	8 44	1123	1410	16 46	...	20 2	18 40
Bra (273) ......arr	7 1	9 9	1153	1440	17 11	...	20 32	19 22
,, ...dep	7 5	9 13	12 0	1447	17 13	1723	20 41	—
Narzole	7 27	9 35	1223	1510	...	1746	21 3	...
Carru	7 54	10 1	1250	1539	17 49	1812	21 32	...
Bastia (273)	8 11	1014	13 4	1554	18 1	1827	21 48	...
Ceva (273)	8 47	1042	1340	1630	18 29	1857	22 27	5 15
S. Giuseppe...arr	9 37	1132	1432	1720	19 16	—	23 16	6 11
di Cairo(273) dp	9 42	1134	1436	1722	19 21	...	23 20	6 27
Santuario	1011	12 2	15 5	1751	19 49	...	23 49	7 6
Savona 272)..arr	1022	1213	1516	18 2	20 0	...	24 0	7 20

	1,2,3	1,2,3	1,2,3	1,2,3	1,2,3	1,2,3	1,2,3	1,2,3
Savona.........dep	3 20	5 16	6 15	8 50	13 10	...	17 7	20 5
Santuario	3 36	5 33	6 31	9 6	13 26	...	17 22	20 19
S. Giuseppe...arr	4 12	6 8	7 4	9 42	13 59	...	17 55	20 49
di Cairo ...dep	4 16	—	7 8	9 50	14 1	...	18 1	20 51
Ceva	5 13	...	8 3	10 48	15 0	1730	18 57	21 45
Bastia	5 43	...	8 34	11 18	15 31	1759	19 26	22 8
Carru	5 54	...	8 43	11 28	15 41	1811	19 35	22 17
Narzole	6 20	...	9 8	11 54	16 7	1837	20 0	...
Bra..............arr	6 48	...	9 33	12 20	16 33	19 5	20 26	23 1
,, ...dep	7 2	...	9 37	12 25	16 41	—	20 32	23 6
Carmagnola	7 34	...	10 3	12 57	17 12	...	21 4	23 29
Trofarello	7 55	...	...	13 19	17 34	...	21 26	...
Turin............arr	8 15	...	1034	13 40	17 55	...	21 46	24 0

STATE RAILWAYS—(continued).

GENOA, SAVONA, and VENTIMIGLIA.

ROME (271) ....dep	...	...	1815	...	21 0	...	...	23 55	23 55	...	...	...	...	9 0	...	...	...	...
PISA (271) ....dep	16 37	...	0 27	...	2 56	...	...	6 5	6 5	9 5	...	...	1410	14 55	...	...	...	...
	1,2,3	1,2,3	1,2,3	1,2,3	1,2,3	1,2,3	1,2,3	1,2,3	1,2,3	1,2,3	1,2,3	1,2,3	1,2,3	1,2,3				
Genoa Piazza P. dep	0 20	...	4 30	6 10	7 10	9 5	9 45	10 50	12 40	1520	17 10	17 35	1850	20 10	...	...	...	...
Sampierdarena	0 32	...	4 40	6 19	7 18	9 16	9 55	11 1	12 50	1530	17 21	17 48	19 0	20 20	...	...	...	...
Cornigliano	0 36	...	4 44	6 23	...	9 20	...	11 5	12 54	1534	...	17 53	19 4	...	...	...	...	...
Sestri Ponente	0 42	...	4 49	6 29	...	9 26	RC	11 11	13 0	1540	17 29	18 0	1912	20 27	...	...	...	...
Pegli	0 48	...	4 55	6 36	7 32	9 33	10 9	11 19	13 8	1547	17 35	18 9	1919	20 32	...	...	...	...
Voltri	1 1	...	5 6	6 50	7 41	9 46	10 18	11 32	13 22	16 0	17 43	18 23	1931	20 40	...	...	...	...
Arenzano	1 14	...	5 21	7 5	...	9 59	...	11 45	13 35	1615	...	18 37	1944	20 52	...	...	...	...
Cogoleto	1 22	...	5 28	7 13	...	10 6	...	11 53	13 42	1623	...	18 45	1952	...	...	...	...	...
Varazze	1 33	...	5 39	7 24	8 7	10 18	10 48	12 4	13 53	1635	18 12	18 57	20 3	21 8	...	...	...	...
Savona	2 8	...	6 6	7 45	8 34	10 41	11 9	12 32	14 35	1713	18 36	19 39	2025	21 29	...	...	...	...
Spotorno	2 29	...	6 30		8 58		...	12 57	15 0	1740	...	20 4		...	...	...	...	...
Noli	2 35	...	6 36	...	9 4	...	...	13 3	15 6	1747	...	20 10	...	...	...	...	...	...
Finalmarina	2 50	...	6 54	...	9 20	...	11 38	13 18	15 21	18 3	19 11	20 26	...	22 2	...	...	...	...
Borgio Verezzi	...	...	7 1	...	9 26	...	...	13 24	15 27	18 9	...	20 32	...	...	...	...	...	...
Pietraligure	3 0	...	7 7	...	9 32	...	...	13 30	15 35	1816	...	20 39	...	...	...	...	...	...
Loano	3 7	...	7 14	...	9 38	...	...	13 37	15 42	1823	...	20 46	...	22 14	...	...	...	...
Albenga	3 27	6 15	7 38	...	10 0	...	12 7	14 0	16 7	1841	19 37	21 13	...	22 30	...	...	...	...
Alassio	3 37	6 25	7 49	...	1010	...	12 16	14 11	16 18		19 47	21 23	...	22 39	...	...	...	...
Laigueglia....................	3 43	6 31	7 55	...	1016	...	...	14 17	16 24	...	19 53	21 29	...	...	...	...	...	...
Andora	3 52	6 39	8 3	...	1024	...	...	14 26	16 33	...	20 0	21 37	...	...	...	...	...	...
Diano Marina	4 6	6 52	8 18	...	1037	...	...	14 39	16 47	...	20 12	21 52	...	22 59	...	...	...	...
Oneglia	4 16	7 1	8 27	...	1047	...	12 44	14 49	16 58	...	20 21	22 3	...	23 7	...	...	...	...
Porto Maurizio	4 23	7 7	8 33	...	1054	...	12 50	14 56	17 5	...	20 27	22 10	...	23 13	...	...	...	...
San Remo	5 11	7 51	9 20	...	1138	12 43	13 28	15 41	17 54	...	21 11	22 55	...	23 49	...	...	...	...
Ospedaletti	5 22	8 1	9 32	...	1148	12 52	13 37	15 51	18 5	...	21 20	23 6	...	23 58	...	...	...	...
Bordighera	5 35	8 12	9 44	...	12 0	13 3	13 48	16 2	18 17	...	21 31	23 17	...	0 8	...	...	...	...
Ventimiglia ¶ ...arr	5 45	8 20	9 55	...	1210	13 10	13 55	16 10	18 25	...	21 40	23 25	...	0 15	...	...	...	...
MARSEILLES 55 ...arr	11 25	1813	...	...	...	19 20	19 55	...	...	...	...	...	...	5 38	...	...	...	...

¶—Customs Examination. RC—Restaurant Car in this train.

TURIN, SAVIGLIANO, SALUZZO, and CUNEO.

E.M. Dist.																
	Turin ....dep	...	6 0	9 0	10 40	14 20	17 50	19 50	**Cuneo** ....dep	5 0	6 20	9 5	12 50	15 5	17 5	20 0
8	Trofarello	...	6 21	9 20	11 1	14 41	18 10	20 13	Maddalena	5 25	6 45	9 27	...	15*26	17 31	20 26
12½	Villastellone.........	...	6 31	9 30	11 11	14 51	18 20	20 24	Fossano	5 36	6 55	9 38	13 19	15 35	17 45	20 37
18	Carmagnola	...	6 42	9 41	11 25	15 3	18 32	20 38	**Savigliano** ....arr	5 52	7 12	9 52	13 33	15 49	18 1	20 53
23½	Racconigi	...	6 52	9 53	11 35	15 15	18 44	20 50	**Saluzzo**............dep	5 20	...	9 20	12 58	...	...	20 20
28	**Cavaller- (273) arr**	...	7 2	10 3	11 45	15 25	18 54	21 0	**Savigliano** ......arr	5 49	...	9 49	13 27	...	...	20 49
...	**maggiore**.....dep	6 25	7 4	10 5	11 46	15 32	18 56	21 4	**Savigliano** ....dep	5 55	7 14	9 56	13 35	15 51	18 10	20 55
32½	**Savigliano** ......arr	6 35	7 14	10 15	11 56	15 42	19 6	21 14	**Cavaller-** ....arr	6 4	7 23	10 5	13 44	16 0	18 19	21 4
...	**Savigliano** ...dep	...	7 19	10 20	...	15 55	...	21 20	**maggiore** ....dep		7 25	10 7	13 46	16 2	18 31	21 7
41½	**Saluzzo 274A arr**	...	7 49	10 49	...	16 25	...	21 49	Racconigi	...	7 35	10 17	13 56	16 12	18 43	21 17
...	**Savigliano**......dep	6 38	7 16	10 18	11 57	15 49	19 8	21 16	Carmagnola (272) ...	...	7 48	10 29	14 8	16 24	18 57	21 30
39¾	Fossano (289)........	6 59	7 35	10 35	12 13	16 13	19 25	21 36	Villastellone	...	7 59	10 40	14 19	16 35	19 8	21 41
44	Maddalena.............	7 9	7 45	10 45	...	16 22	...	21 46	Trofarello	...	8 10	10 50	14 29	16 46	19 19	21 52
54½	**Cuneo** ....arr	7 40	8 15	11 13	12 48	16 53	20 0	22 16	**Turin** ....arr	...	8 30	11 10	14 50	17 6	19 39	22 12

*—Tuesdays and Fridays only.

CUNEO and SALUZZO.												
	Cuneo ....dep	5 35	14 30	17 52	...	**Saluzzo**............dep	7 54	10 54	20 5	...	...	...
	Busca........................	6 4	14 59	18 24	...	Verzuolo......................	8 7	11 8	20 19	...	...	...
	Verzuolo.....................	6 27	15 21	18 46	...	Busca (272A)	8 31	11 32	20 44	...	...	...
	Saluzzo (274A)....arr	6 37	15 31	18 56	...	**Cuneo** ....arr	8 56	11 58	21 10	...	...	...

E.M.										
	Busca...........dep	8 36	15 42	20 50	...	Dronero..................dep	5 30	14 25	17 47	...
8	Dronero.........arr	9 4	16 10	21 18	...	Busca 272A ....arr	5 56	14 51	18 13	...

CUNEO & VIEVOLA.														
	Cuneo ....dep	8 26	11 25	17 30	20‡32	...	...	**Vievola** .....dep	4‡50	7 ‡25	13‡30	18 20	...	...
	Robilante...........	9 1	12 0	18 8	20 59	...	...	Limone	5 10	7 46	13 50	18 40	...	...
	Limone	9 35	12 33	18 45	21 35	...	...	Robilante...........	5 40	8 17	14 20	19 10	...	...
	Vievola ......arr	9 50	12 48	19 0	21 50	...	...	**Cuneo 273** arr	6 11	8 50	14 51	19 43	...	...

‡—Until 30th September.

Milan to Monza, 4.25, 5.15, 6.30, 7.30, 7.42, 8.15, 9.35, 9.42, 10.35, 11.20, 13.10, 13.20, 16.10, 16.35, 17‡15, 17.25, 17.32, 18.10, 18.15, 18.40, 19.20, 19.30, 21.5, 21.15, 22.25. **Monza to Milan,** 5.47, 6.18, 7‡6, 7.24, 7.51, 8.15, 8.40, 8.51, 9.15, 9.39, 10.0, 11.5, 11.41, 12.50, 13.24, 14,13, 14.19, 15.42, 16.5, 16.26, 17.32, 18.15, 18.20, 18.56, 19.32, 19.51, 21.34, 22.19.

‡—Until 30th September.

E.M.																	
	Turin P.N. dep	5 35	7 50	9 48	11 30	15 45	18 56	21 20	**Chieri** ....dep	5 15	7 15	9 15	13 25	1540	1812	21 20	...
8	Trofarello	6 2	8 13	10 8	11 58	16 9	19 22	21 46	Trofarello (270)	5 33	7 32	9 31	13 42	1552	1827	21 38	...
13½	**Chieri** ....arr	6 20	8 30	10 21	12 16	16 26	19 39	22 4	**Turin** P.N. arr	6 0	7 55	9 55	14 8	1612	1850	22 7	...

ALESSANDRIA and PIACENZA.

Dis. E.M		1,2,3	1,2,3	1,2,3	1,2,3	1,2,3	1,2,3	1,2,3	1,2,3	P.&O.Ex.
	TURIN (270) ...dep	...	4 10	7 15	11 0	...	15 0	1835	2010	21 15
—	**Alessandria** dep	4 20	7 0	8 55	1240	1355	1735	2015	2155	22 50
8¾	S. Giuliano	4 42	7 24	...	...	1416	1756	...	...	
13¾	Tortona (269A)......	5 10	7 50	9 20	13 5	1430	1812	...	2220	
24¼	Voghera (269A) ...	6 8	8 28	9 41	1326	1455	1849	2055	2245	
29¾	Casteggio	6 23	8 43	9 53	1338	15 8	19 4	...	2257	
37¼	Broni	6 44	9 4	10 7	1351	1526	1923	...	2312	
39¾	Stradella (274A) ...	6 52	9 13	1015	1358	1535	1931	...	2320	
46½	Castel S. Giovanni...	7 10	9 34	1028	1410	1551	1950	...	2333	
60¼	**Piacenza** ......arr	7 45	1012	1050	1432	1623	2025	2150	2355	0 28
151¾	BOLOGNA 279 ar	1012	...	1324	18 7	19 0	2341	012	2 49	3 2

	1,2,3	1,2,3	1,2,3	1,2,3	1,2,3	1,2,3	1,2,3
BOLOGNA...dep	2 55	2 55	5 33	8 0	1017	1438	18 8
Piacenza...dep	5 30	5 40	8 15	1110	1320	1735	20 45
CastelS.Giovanni	...	6 13	8 52	1133	14 4	1812	21 8
Stradella............	...	6 31	9 11	1146	1427	1831	21 21
Broni	...	6 39	9 19	1153	1436	1839	21 29
Casteggio	...	6 48	9 39	12 6	15 1	1859	21 42
Voghera	6 25	7 15	9 59	1222	1525	1922	21 59
Tortona	...	7 40	1023	1245	1555	1948	22 18
S. Giuliano.........	...	7 51	1035	...	16 8	20 0	...
Alessandria ar	7 0	8 10	1055	13 6	1630	2020	22 40
TURIN 271 arr	8 41	1020	1240	1512	19 0	2325	0 16

ALESSANDRIA and CAVALLERMAGGIORE.

E.M.									
—	**Alessandria** dp		6 10	8 0	1125	...	1650	...	20 0
5	Cantalupo		6 22	8 13	1138	...	17 3	...	20 13
18½	Nizza Monferrato		7 10	9 30	1229	...	1754	...	21 23
27½	S. Stefano Belbo		7 37	10 3	1257	...	1822	...	21 52
...	**Castagnole** arr		7 57	1022	1318	A	1843	...	22 10
33½	„ dep		8 5	1034	1325	...	1852	...	22 16
41½	Alba	5 20	8 28	11 6	1356	1555	1923	...	22 37
52½	**Bra (272)**...	6 0	9 38	1145	1455	1650	20 4	2036	——
60½	**C.Maggiore**	6 19	9 57	...	1514	17 9	...	2055	...

C.Maggiore dp	...	6 30	1010	13 49	...	...	16 5	1824	21 9
Bra	...	7 8	1034	14 8	14 10	14 50	17 18	1850	21 35
Alba	4 35	7 43	11 9	A	14 43	15 22	17 57	1922	22 8
Castagnole ar	4 58	8 5	1133	——	15 3	——	18 19	——	22 29
„ dep	5 8	8 10	1135	...	15 5	...	18 24	...	22 30
S. Stefano Belbo	5 30	8 30	1156	...	15 23	...	18 47	...	22 48
Nizza Monferrato	6 12	9 1	1228	...	15 52	...	19 16	...	23 13
Cantalupo	6 59	9 44	1316	...	16 35	...	19 59	...	——
Aless'ndria ar	7 10	9 55	1328	...	16 46	...	20 10	...	...

A—On Tues., Fri. and Sat. only. **Extra.**—Alba to Bra 6.25. Bra to Alba 9.18.

Dist.						
	Asti ....dep	7 19	9 42	12*30	16 10	21 7
13	Castagnole ...arr	7 59	10 29	13 13	17 25	21 52

*—Wed. and Sat. only.

Castagnole ......dep	5 3	8 11	10*49	13 23	18 50	...	...
Asti ....arr	5 44	8 52	11 30	14 5	20 0	...	...

ALESSANDRIA and VERCELLI.

Alessandria dep	...	6 15	8 56	1130	...	18 0	1950
Valenza ......arr	...	6 35	9 16	1153	...	1820	2013
„ (269)dep	...	6 37	9 27	1157	...	1823	2016
Casale ....arr	...	7 9	10 0	1230	...	1856	2047
„ (274A)dep	4 49	7 28	10 10	13 0	15 36	1922	21 5
Vercelli 269 ar	5 32	8 11	10 55	1345	16 20	20 4	2148

Vercelli......dep	...	6 34	9 20	1120	14 25	1747	1925	22 25
Casale.........arr	...	7 19	10 5	12 5	15 12	1832	2010	23 10
„ ....dep	4 50	7 30	——	1242	16 20	——	2027	——
Valenza ......arr	5 24	8 2	...	1313	16 52	...	21 0	...
„ (273)dep	5 30	8 5	...	1316	16 54	...	21 7	...
Alessandria arr	5 49	8 24	...	1335	17 13	...	2124	...

ALESSANDRIA and SAVONA.

E.M.									
—	Alessandria dep	...	6 55	8 50	11 45	1415	1640	1930	21 50
5	Cantalupo........	...	7 7	9 2	11 57	1427	1652	1942	22 2
10	Sezzè...............	...	7 25	9 16	12 13	1443	17 8	1958	22 18
21	Acqui...............	4 20	8 0	9 44	12 53	1512	1742	2026	22 48
29½	Ponti	4 50	8 24	——	13 17	——	18 5	2115	——
45½	Dego	5 53	9 13	...	14 7	...	1853	2230	...
52	S. Giuseppe......	6 18	9 32	...	14 27	...	1912	2258	...
61½	Santuario	7 6	1011	...	15 5	...	1949	2349	...
65½	Savona 272 arr	7 20	1022	...	15 16	...	20 0	24 0	...

Savona .....dep	...	...	5 16	8 50	1310	...	17 7
Santuario	...	...	5 33	9 6	1326	...	1722
S. Giuseppe........	...	...	6 18	9 52	1412	...	1815
Dego..................	...	...	6 38	10 16	1432	...	1835
Ponti	...	...	7 21	11 7	1515	...	1918
Acqui	5 45	7 0	7 54	12 0	16 5	18 0	1946
Sezzè	6 15	7 26	8 23	12 34	1633	1834	2016
Cantalupo..........	6 33	...	8 39	12 53	1650	1852	2034
Alessandria arr	6 44	7 44	8 50	13 4	17 1	19 3	2045

ALESSANDRIA and PAVIA.

Dist. E.M.						
	Alessandria ......dep	5 10	10 20	15 12	18 10	...
8½	**Valenza (269)**.........	5 40	10 49	15 41	18 37	...
13	Torreberetti	5 51	11 2	15 55	18 51	...
21	Lomello	6 18	11 27	16 20	19 17	...
26½	Sannazzaro	6 38	11 44	16 37	19 35	...
35½	Cava Carbonara	7 11	12 12	17 5	20 4	...
40½	**Pavia (269A)**......arr	7 22	12 23	17 16	20 15	...

Pavia ....dep	4 25	8 15	14 20	18 15	...	...
Cava Carbonara	4 38	8 26	14 31	18 29	...	...
Sannazzaro	5 8	8 53	14 58	19 2	...	...
Lomello	5 26	9 8	15 13	19 21	...	...
Torreberetti	5 54	9 32	15 35	19 50	...	...
Valenza (273).........	6 13	9 46	15 49	20 10	...	...
Alessandria ......arr	6 35	10 8	16 10	20 31	...	...

VERCELLI and PAVIA.

E.M					
—	**Vercelli** ......dep	5 5	8 38	14 16	19 18
10½	Robbio	5 37	9 10	14 48	19 52
17½	**Mortara** ......arr	5 58	9 31	15 9	20 14
...	„ ......dep	6 40	11 45	15 30	20 35
28½	Garlasco..............	7 15	12 20	16 8	21 15
37½	Cava Carbonara...	7 44	12 50	16 38	21 44
41½	**Pavia** (274A)..arr	7 56	13 2	16 50	21 56

Pavia ......dep	4 35	8 46	14 8	18 32	...
Cava Carbonara	4 48	8 59	14 19	18 45	...
Garlasco	5 19	9 24	14 44	19 15	...
Mortara ...arr	5 52	9 53	15 14	19 48	...
„ ...dep	6 55	10 5	16 30	20 32	...
Robbio	7 21	10 25	16 53	20 55	...
Vercelli ...arr	7 54	10 52	17 21	21 26	...

ROCCHETTA and AVELLINO.

Rocchetta ...dep	...	6 10	9 4	1320	1537
Monteverde	...	6 38	9 32	...	16 2
S. Angelo del Lomb	4 20	8 21	11 18	1456	1746
Paternopoli............	5 46	9 53	——	16 4	1914
Avellino........arr	7 1	11 16	...	1658	2034

Avellino ....dep	...	5 55	9 15	9 44	1541
Paternopoli............	...	7 36	10 14	11 12	1655
St. Angelo del Lomb	6 22	9 44	11 23	12 49	1821
Monteverde............	8 1	11 47	12 48	——	1957
Rocchetta.....arr	8 25	12 14	13 9	...	2021

‡—Until 31st October.

ASTI and GENOA.

Asti ....dep	...	...	6 10	9 43	1414	1810	2025
Montegrosso	...	...	6 41	1015	1444	1842	2055
Nizza Monferrato......	...	6 ‡7	7 9	1041	15 7	1918	2122
Acqui .... arr	...	6 47	7 49	1123	1547	20 1	22 2
Acqui .... dep	5 30	6 52	8 5	1150	1552	2035	2212
Ovada..........................	6 6	7 26	8 42	1235	1628	2113	2250
Acquasanta	7 4	8 19	9 40	1336	1722	2214	——
Sampierdarena	7 38	8 48	1013	1413	1753	2253	...
Genoa ....arr	7 45	8 55	1020	1420	18 0	23 0	...

Genoa ....dep		5 5	8 50	1315	1715	18‡0	20 25
Sampierdarena............		5 15	9 0	1326	1726	1811	20 35
Acquasanta		6 0	9 41	14 7	18 8	1853	21 16
Ovada........................	4 45	7 9	1039	15 6	19 9	1951	22 13
Acqui...... arr	5 18	7 48	1115	1540	1949	2022	22 45
Acqui...... dep	5 25	8 10	1135	16 0	2031	——	——
Nizza Monferrato	6 14	9 6	1232	1647	2116	...	...
Montegrosso	6 39	9 31	1257	1712	2141	...	...
Asti ....arr	7 6	10 0	1323	1740	2210	...	...

BUSSOLENO and SUSA.

Bussoleno dep	7 13	8 33	1011	15 45	19 17	21 11
Susa ......arr	7 27	8 47	1025	15 59	19 31	21 25

Susa.........dep	5 45	6 48	9 38	13 31	1738	20 38
Bussoleno arr	5 55	6 58	9 48	13 41	1748	20 48

CEVA and ORMEA.

E.M.					
	Ceva ....dep	8 55	11 0	19 5	...
11½	Priola	9 34	11 38	19 43	...
22½	**Ormea**...............arr	10 16	12 20	20 25	...

Ormea ....dep	6 35	9 15	17 5	...
Priola	7 13	9 54	17 43	...
Ceva (272) ....arr	7 50	10 30	18 20	...

CUNEO and BASTIA.

Cuneo......dep	...	6 50	9 2	...	1132	...	1630	...	2015
Mondovi	5 20	7 50	9 53	1055	1240	15 5	1735	19 5	2120
Bastia 272 arr	5 35	8 5	10 8	1110	1255	1520	1750	1920	2135

Bastia ...dep	5 50	8 37	1017	1120	1312	16 0	1810	1935	2212	...
Mondovi.......	6 18	9 0	1035	1144	1330	1625	1828	1953	2230	...
Cuneo 272A..	7 21	9 56	...	1240	...	1722	...	21 8	...	...

[Fares and Luggage Rates, see page 269.

MILAN, ARONA, and DOMODOSSOLA.

Dist.		1,2,3	1 & 3	1,2,3	1,2,3	1,2,3	1,2,3	1,2,3	1,2,3	1,2,3	1 & 2	1 Cl.	1,2,3	1,2,3	1,2,3	1,2,3	1 & 2	...
E.M.	**Milan** ......dep	5 0	5 50	7 ‡20	8 0	8 §15	8 55	10 50	12 35	1420	15 25	16 30	16 35	...	17 25	20 5	23 45	...
18	Legnano	...	6 35	7 55	RC	..	9 29	RC	13 10	...	...	...	17 9	...	17 55	20 40	SC	...
25¼	**Gallarate** ......arr	5 44	6 55	8 13	8 42	8 57	9 48	11 32	13 30	15 3	16 7	17 14	17 28	...	18 11	21 0	0 27	...
	Gallarate ......dep	5 46	6 57	8 15	8 44	8 59	9 52	11 34	13 35	15 4	16 9	17 16	17 30	...	18 13	21 2	0 28	...
36	Sesto Calende	6 16	7 29	8 49	9 5	9 20	10 28	11 59	14 7	1525	16 30	A	18 0	...	18 49	21 32	0 49	...
41⅝	**Arona** ......arr	6 27	7 43	9 0	9 16	9 31	10 42	12 10	14 18	1536	16 40	17 48	18 14	...	19 0	21 46	1 0	...
...	GENOA ......dep	...			5 0	5 0	...	6 55	8 30	...	11 1	...		...	...	15 5	20 0	...
...	**Arona** ......dep	6 35	...	...	9 22	9 39	10 55	12 16	14 25	1541	16 55	17 57	...	18‡20	19 5	22 0	1 13	...
47¼	Belgirate	6 56	...	...	...	10 0	11 17	...	14 47	...	...	...	...	18 41	19 26	22 24	...	...
52¼	**Stresa**	7 4	...	...	9 41	10 9	11 25	12 40	14 57	16 1	17 16	18 21	...	18 49	19 36	22 34	1 33	...
54¾	**Baveno**	7 11	...	...	9 48	10 16	11 33	12 47	15 5	16 8	17 23	18 27	...	18 56	19 43	22 44	1 39	...
57¾	Pallanza-Fondo Toce...	7 20	...	...	9 57	10 25	11 43	12 55	15 14	1616	17 32	18 34	...	19 4	19 53	22 53	1 46	...
59¾	Mergozzo	7 26	...	...	...	...	11 49	...	15 20	...	...	...	...	...	20 0	22 59	...	...
66¼	Premosello	7 41	...	...	...	10 42	12 9	...	15 36	1632	...	...	...	...	20 15	23 16	...	...
68¼	Vogogna	7 47	...	...	10 19	...	12 15	...	15 41	...	...	...	...	...	20 20	23 22	...	...
76½	**Domodossola** ...arr	8 5	...	...	10 37	11 2	12 35	13 26	16 0	1650	18 5	19 5	...	19 38	20 40	23 42	2 16	...
101¾	BRIG 263C ......arr	9 a35	...	...	12 p7	12 33	2p58	2 p58	6 p23	6p23	7 p33	8 p30	...	...	10p23	...	3 a48	...
192¼	LAUSANNE 263C ...arr	1 p48	...	...	2 p40	...	6 p0	6 p0	9 p56	9p56	10p21	11p29	...	...	...	...	6 a20	...

...	LAUSANNE ......dep	12a10	...	...	...	...	6 a0	...	7 a20	...	9 a10	...	12p15	...	...	6 p30	...	...
...	BRIG ......dep	2 a55	...	...	...	6 a0	8 a40	...	10 a7	10a43	12p 7	...	3 p40	..	...	9 p15	...	...
		1 & 2	1 & 3	1,2,3	1,2,3	1,2,3	1 Cl.	1,2,3	1 & 2	1,2,3	1,2,3	1 & 3	1,2,3	1,2,3	1,2,3	1,2,3		
...	**Domodossola** ...dep	3 52	...	5 0	6 ‡15	7 47	9 50	10 18	11 10	11§55	13 26	14 5	16 50	...	19 20	22 14	...	...
...	Vogogna	...	...	5 19	6 35	8 7	...	10 38	...	...	...	14 24	17 7	...	19 39	...	...	...
...	Premosello	SC	...	5 23	6 40	8 12	...	10 44	RC	RC	...	14 30	17 12	...	19 45	...	...	...
...	Mergozzo	...	...	5 40	6 56	8 28	A	11 1	...	...	...	14 46	17 27	...	20 2	...	...	...
...	Pallanza-Fondo Toce...	4 20	...	5 47	7 3	8 35	10 22	11 8	11 40	12 25	13 52	14 53	17 34	...	20 9	...	...	...
...	**Baveno**	4 28	...	5 56	7 13	8 45	10 30	11 19	11 48	12 33	14 0	15 3	17 42	...	20 18	22 45	...	...
...	**Stresa**	4 34	...	6 4	7 21	8 53	10 37	11 26	11 55	12 39	14 7	15 11	17 48	...	20 26	22 51	...	...
...	Belgirate	...	...	6 13	7 30	9 2	...	11 36	...	...	...	15 21	17 56	...	20 36	...	...	...
...	**Arona** ......arr	4 52	...	6 32	7 49	9 21	10 55	11 55	12 13	12 56	14 25	15 40	18 15	...	20 55	23 6	...	...
...	GENOA (270) ......arr	9 35	...	12 15	...	14 35	...	...	17 25	18 30	...	22 5	23 25	...	...	...	...	...
...	**Arona** ......dep	5 10	5 38	6 43	7 58	9 36	11 1	13 13	12 18	13 1	14 30	16 12	18 24	18 36	21 18	23 9	...	...
...	Sesto Calende	5 21	5 54	6 55	8 10	9 51	...	13 26	12 29	13 12	14 40	16 29	18 42	18 55	21 31	...	...	...
...	**Gallarate** ......arr	5 44	6 29	7 30	8 43	10 25	11 34	14 2	12 53	13 33	15 4	17 4	19 5	19 33	22 5	...	...	...
...	**Gallarate** ......dep	5 45	6 31	7 32	8 46	10 27	11 36	14 4	12 54	13 34	15 5	17 8	19 7	19 35	22 8	...	...	...
...	Legnano	...	6 48	7 52	...	10 45	...	13 21	..	...	...	17 27	...	19 55	22 28	...	...	...
...	**Milan** ......arr	6 25	7 25	8 25	9 30	11 15	12 12	15 8	13 30	14 10	15 45	18 5	19 45	20 25	23 5	0 15	...	...

‡—Until 30th September. §—From the day of opening of the Lötschberg line.
A—Treno di Lusso, Simplon Express. RC—Restaurant Car. SC—Sleeping Car.

PALLANZA—FONDO TOCE and PALLANZA.

Pallanza Fondo Toce dep	1 49	4 26	5 55	7 25	8 43	10 5	10 34	11 18	11 50	12 38	13 2	14 0	1519	1623	1739	1839	20 14	23 0	...
Pallanza Lago ......arr	2 11	4 48	6 17	7 47	9 5	1027	10 56	11 40	12 16	13 0	1324	1422	1542	1645	18 1	19 1	20 36	2322	...
Pallanza Lago ......dep	1 10	3 43	5 8	6 40	8 0	9 8	9 39	10 27	1056	1145	1216	1314	1412	15 30	1647	18 3	19 1	22 7	...
Pallanza Fondo Toce arr	1 32	4 5	5 30	7 2	8 22	9 30	10 1	10 52	1118	1210	1238	1336	1434	15 55	17 9	1825	19 25	22 29	...

MILAN, GALLARATE, LAVENO, and LUINO.

☞ Some Trains do not carry luggage.

E.M									
	Milan (Centrale) dep	5 5	7 10	8 20	1040	1335	17 0	1755	20 30
18	Legnano	5 44	...	8 59	...	14 6	...	...	21 4
25¼	Gallarate ......arr	6 1	8 3	9 20	1120	1423	17 43	1829	21 23
40¼	Besozzo	6 48	8 44	10 3	12 9	15.4	18 22	19 7	22 5
45½	Laveno ......arr	7 0	8 55	1014	1220	1515	18 32	1916	22 16
54¾	**Luino** ......arr	7 25	9 20	1040	13 0	1551	18 57	1940	22 40

Luino ...dep	5 40	6 40	7 45	9 24	1237	16 5	18 8	2125
Laveno	6 10	7 6	8 9	9 50	13 2	16 30	1832	2149
Besozzo	6 26	7 21	8 23	10 5	1316	16 45	1846	22 4
Gallarate	7 7	8 2	9 2	10 43	1358	17 26	1924	2243
Legnano	7 24	...	9 20	...	1413	17 45	...	...
Milan (C) arr	7 55	8 48	9 50	11 25	1440	18 15	20 5	2323

MILAN, GALLARATE, PORTO CERESIO, Electric Ry.

☞ Some Trains do not carry luggage.

Milan Centrale ...dep	5 25	6 10	7 0	...	7 45	8 25	8 50	9 25	10 0	11 3	1140	1215	13 17	1345	14 35	14 55	15 45	16 8	1650	17 20
Gallarate	6 8	7 14	7 42	7 50	8 27	9 26	9 35	10 6	11 4	...	1332	1258	14 0	1449	15 16	15 59	16 51	16 43	1737	...
Varese	6 28	7 43	8 0	8 20	8 50	—	9 56	1026	1133	12 0	14 1	1316	14 20	1518	15 34	16 28	17 20	17 1	18 2	18 13
Porto Ceresio ......arr	6 54	...	8 26	...	9 16	...	...	1052	...	...	...	1342	14 46	...	16 0	...	...	17 27	...	...

Milan (Centrale)...dep	17 45	...	18 15	18 20	18 45	18 50	19 30	19 45	21 10	2130	22 40	...	...	...	...	...	...	...
Gallarate	18 23	18 32	...	19 21	19 29	19 51	20 12	20 49	21 55	2232	23 24	...	...	...	...	...	...	...
Varese	18 41	18 58	19 12	—	19 50	—	20 38	21 18	22 20	—	23 50	...	...	...	...	...	...	...
Porto Ceresio ......arr	19 10	...	...	...	20 20	...	21 7	...	...	...	...	...	...	...	...	...	...	...

Porto Ceresio ......dep	...	...	...	...	6 44	...	7 2	...	7 56	...	...	9 25	...	...	1230	...	1354	...	15 4	...	...
Varese	4 50	5 15	...	5 50	6 45	7 5	7 33	8 0	8 30	...	9 20	9 56	1035	1135	13 0	1330	1425	1450	1535	1545	1640
Gallarate	5 18	5 51	6 8	6 19	...	7 26	7.55	8 22	8 53	9 10	9 41	1019	11 6	1157	1319	1358	...	1516	1554	1616	17 0
Milan (Cent.) ......arr	6 14	6 35	7 0	7 10	7 35	8 0	8 35	9 5	9 35	1012	1020	11 0	12 7	1245	14 0	1440	1515	16 5	1635	1717	1740

Porto Ceresio ......dep	...	...	17 50	...	19 28	...	20 27	...	...	...	...	...	...
Varese	17 20	...	18 20	19 14	20 2	20 10	21 0	21 25	22 40	...	...	...	...
Gallarate	17 48	18 0	18 39	19 47	...	20 41	21 20	21 53	23 2	...	...	...	...
Milan (Centrale)...arr	18 36	19 2	19 20	20 40	20 52	21 40	22 0	22 46	23 45	...	...	...	...

VARESE and LUINO.

‡—In July and August only.

E.M										
	Varese ......dep	5 28	6 58	8 34	1045	1231	1435	1610	1830	20‡4
8¾	Cunardo	6 21	7 51	9 27	1138	1324	1528	17 3	1923	2057
15½	Luino 274 ...arr	6 50	8 20	9 56	12 7	1353	1557	1732	1952	2126

Luino ......dep	5 33	7 3	8 39	1050	1236	1440	1629	1835	19‡59
Cunardo	6 7	7 37	9 18	1124	1310	1514	17 4	19 9	20 33
Varese 274 arr	6 55	8 25	10 1	1212	1358	16 2	1751	1957	21 21

NOVARA and ARONA.
[Fares and Luggage Rates see page 269.

Dist.																		
	Novara 269 dep	5 17	7 45	8 30	1058	1310	15 28	1717	20 5	2335	**Arona** ...dep	5 0	6 50	9 32	1125	13 8	1552	18 35	2112
10½	Oleggio	5 58	8 17	8 54	1126	1343	15 54	1749	2037	0 2	Borgo Ticino	5 16	7 6	9 49	...	1324	1610	...	2129
17	Borgo Ticino...	6 19	8 41	...	...	14 5	...	1813	2055	...	Oleggio	5 35	7 29	1011	1255	1345	1635	19 4	2150
23	**Arona** ......arr	6 30	8 52	9 17	1150	1416	16 21	1824	2112	0 26	**Novara** ...arr	5 58	7 52	1036	1313	1410	1658	19 22	2212

‡—Until 30th Sept.

NOVARA and VARALLO.

Dist.													
	Novara ....dep	5 43	8 15	14 15	17‡35	19 55	**Varallo** ....dep	4 55	8 20	13 40	1720	20‡10
2¾	Vignale	5 50	8 22	14 22	...	20 2	Borgosesia	5 23	8 51	14 12	1748	20 34
11¾	Fara	6 21	8 52	14 52	18 1	20 32	Romagnano.	6 0	9 30	14 55	1820	21 1
18½	Romagnano	7 2	9 21	15 32	18 22	21 3	Fara	6 22	9 54	15 19	1842	21 18
26¾	Borgosesia	7 36	9 56	16 8	18 47	21 38	Vignale.............................	6 50	1023	15 48	1910	...
34½	**Varallo** ....arr	8 6	10 25	16 38	19 10	22 7	**Novara (269)**...........arr	6 56	1029	15 54	1916	21 46

NOVARA and DOMODOSSOLA.

Dist.																
	Novara ....dep	5 10	9 0	14 5	17 27	20 21	...	...	**Domodossola** ...dep	3 15	7 17	12 35	16 39	16 50	18 45
19½	Borgomanero............	6 4	10 3	15 14	18 24	21 31	...	...	Piedimulera	3 39	7 39	13 1	17 1	⋮	19 4
22½	Gozzano	6 13	10 12	15 24	18 33	21 40	...	...	Premosello............	3 56	7 53	13 18	17 15	17 11	19 18
27½	Orta Miasino	6 31	10 29	15 42	18 51	21 58	...	...	Gravellona Toce ...	4 22	8 16	13 44	17 38		19 42
37½	Gravellona Toce	7 1	10 58	16 17	19 27	22 30	...	...	Orta Miasino..........	5 3	8 55	14 29	18 17		20 25
44¾	Premosello (274).........	7 23	11 26	16 42	19 52	22 51	...	...	Gozzano................	5 22	9 13	14 48	18 34	...	20 37
49	Piedimulera..............	7 40	11 37	17 0	20 12	23 8	...	...	Borgomanero	5 42	9 31	15 12	18 43	...	20 52
56	**Domodossola** ......arr	8 2	11 59	17 23	20 35	23 30	...	...	**Novara (269)** ...arr	6 31	10 18	16 3	19 29	...	21 36

GOZZANO and ALZO.													
	Gozzano (St. F. S.) .....dep	6 25	10 15	15 27	1835	...	Alzo ....dep	8 30	14 0	17 40	19 20	...	...
	Alzo ....arr	6 57	10 47	15 59	19 7	...	Gozzano ...arr	9 2	14 32	18 12	19 52	...	...

ASTI and MORTARA.
[A—Not on Sunday.

Asti...........dep	...	5 53	...	7 25	11 7	16 0	...	20 30	**Mortara** ...dep	...	6 20	8 58	11 25	15 21	18 32	...	20 33
Moncalvo	...	6 37	...	8 10	11 56	1645	...	21 23	Terranova..........	...	7 1	9 42	12 6	16 2	19 4	...	21 21
San Giorgio.......	...	7 7	...	8 40	12 26	1712	...	21 59	**Casale** ....arr	...	7 13	9 55	12 18	16 14	19 17	A	21 35
Casale 273 ar	...	7 17	...	8 51	12 37	1723	...	22 10	„ ......dep	5 1	7 25		12 37	16 25		1928	
„ ......dep	4 55	A	7 35	9 3	13 40	1730	20 30		San Giorgio	5 13	7 37	...	12 49	16 37	...	1940	...
Terranova	5 10	...	7 48	9 16	13 55	1743	20 46	...	Moncalvo	5 47	8 8	...	13 22	17 10	...	2014	...
Mortara 269	5 55	...	8 24	9 56	14 40	1823	21 31	...	**Asti (273)**...arr	6 33	8 53	...	14 4	17 51	...	2056	...

PAVIA and STRADELLA.

Dist.																
	Pavia ....dep	5 38	8 35	12 15	14 14	17 55	...	...	**Stradella** ...dep	5 45	8 30	12 30	16 0	18 45	...	...
8¾	Bressana Bottar'e	5 59	8 57	12 39	14 35	18 14	...	...	Bressana Bottar'e	6 31	9 14	13 21	16 45	19 33	...	...
19¾	**Stradella 273**	6 41	9 40	13 25	15 17	18 55	...	...	**Pavia (281)** arr	6 50	9 33	13 41	17 5	19 55	...	...

*—Wed. & Sat. only.

AIRASCA and SALUZZO.

Dist.																
	Airasca (271)....dep	6 25	9 20	13*42	18 40	20 45	...	...	**Saluzzo** ..dep	5 *0	6 42	12 20	15 41	19 2	...	...
7½	Vigone	6 49	9 45	14 6	19 5	21 12	...	...	Moretta..........	5 32	7 13	12 49	16 11	19 38	...	...
13	Moretta	7 10	10 7	14 24	19 30	21 50	...	...	Vigone...........	5 52	7 33	13 7	16 29	20 2	...	...
22½	**Saluzzo (272A)** arr	7 36	10 33	14 50	19 56	22 16	...	...	**Airasca** ...arr	6 15	7 56	13 30	16 52	20 26	...	...

Moretta ....dep	5 45	9 20	20 0	...	...	...	**Cavallermaggiore**...dep	6 33	15 35	21 13	...	...	...
Cavallermaggiore ...arr	6 18	9 53	20 33	...	...	...	**Moretta** ....arr	7 5	16 6	21 45	...	...	...

‡—From 15th July until 15th Sept.

CHIVASSO and AOSTA.

E.M.																			
	TURIN ...dep	4 15	8 33	12 0	14 23	15 5	18 0	18 25	2030	**Aosta** ...dep	...	4 40	7 15	9‡26	12 10	...	16 22	18 ‡5
—	**Chivasso** dep	5 17	9 14	12 57	15 ‡1	1545	18‡46	19 27	2132	Chatillon	...	5 26	7 51	9 58	12 54	...	17 5	18 39
20½	Ivrea	6 21	10 3	14 0	15 44	1641	19 33	20 32	2230	**S. Vincent** ...	...	5 31	7 56	10 3	12 59	...	17 10	18 44
32½	Donnaz	7 2	...	14 42	...		...	21 12		Verrès	...	5 50	8 9	1017	13 17	...	17 26	1 58
38½	Verrès............	7 24	10 46	15 4	16 24	...	20 13	21 34	...	Donnaz.........	...	6 8	...		13 34	...	17 43	...
45½	S. Vincent	7 45	11 2	15 25	16 39	...	20 28	21 55	...	Ivrea	4 40	6 56	8 48	1054	14 20	1616	18 23	19 36
46½	Chatillon	7 56	11 10	15 33	16 47	...	20 35	22 4	...	**Chivasso** arr	5 36	7 52	9 29	1132	15 16	1711	19 4	20 17
62	**Aosta** ......arr	8 45	11 46	16 22	17 24	...	21 11	22 53	...	TURIN ...arr	6 41	8 50	10 12	1215	16 15	1820	19 50	21 0

Extra	TURIN ...dep	7 11	9 55	...	...	Ivrea ......dep	1125	20 52	...	...
	Chivasso ...dep	8 12	10 51	...	...	Chivasso ...arr	1220	21 48	...	...
	Ivrea ......arr	9 11	11 50	...	...	TURIN ...arr	1315	22 48	...	...

CHIVASSO and CASALE.
[*—Wed., Thurs., and Sat. only.

Dist.														
	Chivasso..............dep	5 18	8 4	13*45	17 24	19 23	**Casale** ....dep	5 20	7 *40	10 20	16 3	20 15	...
11½	Crescentino	5 55	8 36	14 13	17 56	19 56	Trino	5 52	8 9	10 51	16 32	20 47	...
20¾	Trino	6 30	9 4	14 36	18 24	20 26	Crescentino	6 20	8 34	11 18	16 56	21 15	...
30¾	**Casale (274A)** ......arr	7 5	9 33	15 2	18 53	20 56	**Chivasso (269)** ....arr	6 50	9 1	11 48	17 24	21 46	...

CHIVASSO and ASTI.	E.M.											
		Chivasso......dep	6 0	9‡43	13 47	1915	Asti............dep	5 50	1013	14‡15	18 5	‡—Until 31st Oct.,
	32½	Asti.............arr	7 51	1136	15 43	20 6	Chivasso......arr	7 44	1210	16 8	20 1	and not on Sunday.

COMO and LECCO.	E.M.												
		Como ....dep	5 40	8 26	14 27	18 0	20 35	**Lecco** ....dep	5 35	8 5	11 20	14 10	19 2
	3	Albate Camerlata	5 51	8 36	14 37	18 10	20 50	Oggiono	6 3	8 32	11 47	14 48	19 29
	7½	Cantu	6 8	8 52	14 55	18 26	21 12	Merone-Pontenuovo	6 30	8 57	12 13	15 19	19 51
	13¾	Merone-Pontenuovo.....	6 33	9 18	15 24	18 50	21 43	Cantu	6 57	9 24	12 42	15 55	20 16
	18¾	Oggiono	6 52	9 36	15 46	19 11	22 13	Albate Camerlata ...	7 12	9 37	12 56	16 15	20 30
	26	**Lecco** ....arr	7 14	9 57	16 10	19 33	22 50	**Como (269A)** arr	7 20	9 46	13 5	16 26	20 38

VIAREGGIO and LUCCA.

E.M.																
	Viareggio.........dep	6 30	7 50	10 30	14 42	17 5	19 46	24 0	Lucca ....dep	5 25	8 30	12 0	14 30	16 0	18 30	21 27
14½	Lucca 274A ......arr	7 6	8 30	11 10	15 23	17 45	20 27	0 37	Viareggio 270 ...arr	6 8	9 13	12 43	15 7	16 37	19 7	22 10

LUCCA and CASTELNUOVO DI GARFAGNANA.

E.M.																
	Lucca ....arr	5 37	8 19	13 46	18 12	...	...	Castelnuovo di G. ...dep	5 27	7 54	12 21	17 48	...	...
12½	Borgo a Mozzano...........	6 15	8 57	14 24	18 50	...	...	Bagni di Lucca.........arr	6 17	8 44	13 11	18 38	...	...
15	Bagni di Lucca.........arr	6 22	9 4	14 31	18 57	...	...	„ „ ......dep	6 22	8 50	13 17	18 45	...	...
...	„ „ .... dep	6 28	9 10	14 39	19 4	...	...	Borgo a Mozzano	6 28	8 56	13 23	18 51	...	...
28½	Castelnuovo di G. ...arr	7 18	10 0	15 29	19 54	...	...	Lucca 271A ....arr	7 7	9 35	14 2	19 30	...	...

E.M.																
	Monzone ....dep	7 33	10 18	14 8	19 20	...	...	Aulla ....dep	6 33	9 10	12 50	17 35	...	...
10½	Aulla 275 ....arr	8 13	10 58	14 48	20 25	...	...	Monzone ....arr	7 13	9 50	13 30	18 40	...	...

‡—Until 15th Sept.]

EMPOLI, SIENA, and CHIUSI.

Dist E.M		1,2,3	1,2,3	1,2,3	1,2,3	1,2,3	1,2,3	1,2,3	
	Empoli ....dep	5 7	8 12	10 13	...	1519	1840	22 18	...
13	Ponte a Elsa	5 15	8 20	...	...	1527	1848	22 25	...
10½	Castel Fiorentino ...	5 34	8 38	10 34	...	1545	19 7	22 43	...
15½	Certaldo	5 46	8 51	10 45	...	1556	1920	22 54	...
23¾	Poggibonsi (288)......	6 14	9 19	11 2	...	1618	1946	23 17	...
39¾	Siena 5 5	7 1	10 5	11 45	14 5	17 6	2043	23 58	...
59	**Asciano (275)** ...6 17	8 42	—	—	15 2	18 3	2143	—	...
62¾	Rapolano	9 4	...	...	15‡20	1827	22 3	...	...
70¾	Lucignano	9 22	...	...	...	1845	2219	...	...
74½	Sinalunga	9 31	...	...	15 42	1856	2228	...	...
78¾	Torrita	9 41	...	...	...	19 6	2237	...	...
83¾	Montepulciano	9 53	...	...	15 56	1918	2248	...	...
94½	**Chiusi (279)** ......arr	1019	...	...	16 14	1942	2311	...	...

	1,2,3	1,2,3	1,2,3	1,2,3	1,2,3	1,2,3	1,2,3
Chiusi ......dep	2 53	...	7 12	...	...	1332	17 35
Montepulciano	3 18	...	7 38	...	...	1358	18 2
Torrita	3 28	...	7 49	...	...	14 9	18 14
Sinalunga	3 35	...	8 0	...	...	1420	18 27
Lucignano	3 46	...	8 10	...	...	1430	18 42
Rapolano	4 3	...	8 26	...	...	1447	19 1
Asciano	4 16	...	8 45	...	...	1510	19 21
Siena	5 28	7 50	9 52	10 52	1430	1718	20 36
Poggibonsi......	6 8	8 29	—	11 37	1512	1759	21 15
Certaldo	6 26	8 49	...	11 56	1530	1818	21 33
Castel Fiorent.	6 37	9 0	...	12 8	1544	1831	21 44
Ponte a Elsa ...	6 54	9 17	...	12 26	...	1849	22 1
Empoli ......arr	7 1	9 23	...	12 34	16 5	1855	22 7

AVENZA and CARRARA.

E.M.															
	Avenza dep	4 28	5 25	7 23	10 35	14 0	16 20	19 0	21 0	2310	1 43	...	...	...	...
3	**Carrara** arr	4 46	5 43	7 41	10 53	14 18	16 38	19 18	21 18	2328	2 1	...	...	...	...
...	**Carrara** ...dep	3 20	4 52	6 32	9 15	13 12	14 52	1722	20 17	22 17	1 5	...	...	...	...
...	**Avenza** ...arr	3 33	5 5	6 45	9 28	13 25	15 5	1735	20 30	22 30	1 18	...	...	...	...

ROME and FRASCATI.

§—21.50 on Sunday. †—Not on Sunday.

Dist. E.M.								
	Rome ......dep	6 30	9 35	12 15	15 50	17†10	18 55	20§15
8½	Ciampino	6 53	9 58	12 37	16 13	17 33	19 18	20 38
15	**Frascati** ...arr	7 14	1017	12 58	16 32	17 52	19 39	20 57

Frascati ...dep	6 29	7 29	9 †7	14 17	18 4	2012	21 52
Ciampino	6 51	7 51	9 26	14 36	18 26	2031	22 11
Rome ....arr	7 10	8 10	9 45	14 55	18 45	2050	22 30

ASCIANO and GROSSETO.

E.M.					
—	**Asciano** ....dep	6 40	9 ‡0	...	18 8
7¾	S. Giovanni d'Asso ...	7 2	9 22	...	18 29
13	Torrenieri	7 12	9 32	...	18 39
20½	Monte Amiata	7 41	9 55	...	19 3
51½	Montepescali	8 55	11 6	2019	20 36
59¾	**Grosseto (270)** arr	9 8	11 19	2043	20 50

Grosseto ....dep	6 10	12 25	16 25
Montepescali	6 24	12 39	16 41
Monte Amiata............	7 44	14 0	18 10
Torrenieri.................	8 9	14 25	18 38
S. Giovanni d'Asso ...	8 20	14 36	18 49
Asciano ....arr	8 38	14 55	19 8

SICIGNANO and LAGONEGRO.

E.M.				
	Sicignano ......dep	4 5	11 12	16 0
25½	Sala Consilina	5 40	12 35	17 33
28½	Sassano Tegiano	5 54	12 49	17 47
48½	**Lagonegro** ......arr	7 4	13 55	18 55

Lagonegro ....dep	7 25	12 50	17 0	...
Sassano Tegiano	8 47	13 55	18 5	...
Sala Consilina	9 1	14 6	18 16	...
Sicignano (277) ...arr	1035	15 31	19 40	...

SPEZIA and PARMA.

Spezia..................dep	...	...	5 40	8 30	11 58	16 45	18 15
S. Stefano di Magra arr	...	...	6 0	8 47	12 15	17 2	18 35
Sarzana..........dep	4 10	...	5 48	...	12 0	16 40	18 14
S. Stefano di M. ...arr	...	...	6 2	...	12 13	16 53	18 27
S.Stefano di Magra dep	...	...	6 8	8 48	12 22	17 5	18 37
Aulla.........................	...	...	6 24	9 0	12 37	17 20	18 56
Pontremoli	4 20	5 10	7 18	9 40	13 25	18 7	19 44
Borgotaro	4 58	5 43	7 54	1019	14 1	18 43	—
Valmozzola	5 29	...	8 21	...	14 28	19 10	...
Fornovo	6 4	...	8 54	11 2	14 57	19 39	...
Parma (279).arr	6 40	6 57	9 29	1128	15 33	20 13	...

Parma ....dep		5 25	8 55	12 10	1640	18 10	2257
Fornovo		6 3	9 25	12 49	1723	18 49	...
Valmozzola		6 41	...	13 24	18 2	19 25	...
Borgotaro		7 21	10 20	14 0	1844	20 2	0 11
Pontremoli..............	5 8	7 55	10 43	14 30	1915	20 30	0 35
Aulla	5 44	8 29	11 9	15 4	—	21 5	...
S. Stefano di M. arr	5 58	8 43	11 19	15 18	...	21 17	...
S.Stefano di M. dp	6 13	8 55	...	15 24	...	21 37	...
Sarzana......arr	6 26	9 15	...	15 37	...	21 53	1 19
S. Stefano di M. dep	6 0	8 47	11 20	15 19	...	21 18	...
Spezia (270) arr	6 20	9 6	11 39	15 38	...	21 40	...

SEREGNO and BERGAMO.

E.M.							
	Seregno ......dep	7 30	13 16	18 20	...	...	...
8¾	Usmate Carnate ...	8 16	13 55	18 57	...	...	...
19¾	Ponte S. Pietro	8 54	14 38	19 32	...	...	...
24½	**Bergamo (281)**	9 5	14 50	19 43	...	...	...

Bergamo ....dep	6 30	12 45	16 10	...	...	...
Ponte S. Pietro	6 45	12 59	16 24	...	...	...
Usmate Carnate	7 55	13 57	17 21	...	...	...
Seregno (269A) arr	8 21	14 23	17 50	...	...	...

SANTHIA and ARONA.

Santhia ....dep	6 9	7 53	8 12	14 6	1623	2010
Romagnano Sesia	6 59	8 34	9 26	1447	1723	21 2
Borgomanero	7 21	8 52	10 1	15 6	1750	2126
Arona... ....arr	7 42	9 11	1025	1525	1814	2147

Arona ....dep	5 12	6 48	9 30	1433	1832	21 2
Borgomanero	5 38	7	10 2	15 3	19 7	2125
Romagnano Sesia	6 2	7 42	1027	1525	1933	2154
Santhia ....arr	6 41	8 27	1113	1610	2024	2230

ROME and FIUMICINO.

E.M.					
	Rome (Termini) ...dep		9 10	16 45	18 30
5½	„ (Trastevere)	5 4	9 33	17 7	18 52
14½	Ponte Galera (**270**)	5 37	10 0	17 40	19 15
21½	**Fiumicino** ......arr	5 59	10 18	17 58	19 33

Fiumicino ......dep	6 28	14 54	18 44	20 38
Ponte Galera	7 8	15 21	20 47	21 5
Rome (Trastevere)	7 27	15 37	21 5	21 32
„ (Termini) arr	7 55	16 5	21 35	...

ROME and TIVOLI—Steam Tramway.

EM Dis.	**Rome-**								
	S.Lorenzo ......dep	6 0	9 30	11 30	15 15	18 30	...	...	...
6¾	Settecamini	6 29	9 58	12 9	15 52	18 57	...	...	...
12½	Bagni ....arr	6 52	1018	12 38	16 22	19 20	...	...	...
...	„ ....dep	6 56	1023	12 43	16 26	19 22	...	...	...
15½	Villa Adriana	7 10	1036	13 0	16 43	19 35	...	...	...
18	**Tivoli** ....arr	7 26	1052	13 17	17 1	19 51	...	...	...

Tivoli dep	5 45	7 50	1215	16 30	17 50	...	...
Villa Adriana	6 1	8 3	1229	16 44	18 5	...	...
Bagni......arr	6 20	8 18	1243	16 55	18 24	...	...
„ ...dep	6 25	8 19	1246	16 58	18 27	...	...
Settecamini..	6 56	8 38	13 8	...	18 58	...	...
Rome ...arr	7 35	9 5	1340	17 40	19 40	...	...

MILAN, USMATE-CARNATE, and BERGAMO.

Milan Centrale......dep	5 15	7 30	9 42	13 10	16 35	18 15	21 15
Monza	5 37	7 49	9 58	13 30	16 51	18 34	21 36
Usmate-Carnate... arr	5 58	8 9	10 16	13 50	17 9	18 52	21 56
Usmate-Carnate... dep	6 8	8 16	10 52	13 55	17 18	18 57	22 4
Ponte S. Pietro-Locate	6 47	8 54	11 30	14 38	17 54	19 32	22 43
Bergamo ....arr	6 59	9 5	11 42	14 50	18 5	19 43	22 55

Bergamo ....dep	4 55	6 30	9 40	1245	1610	1740	2055
Ponte S. Pietro-Locate	5 9	6 45	9 54	1259	1624	1752	21 9
Usmate-Carnate... arr	5 46	7 24	1031	1337	17 1	1826	2147
Usmate-Carnate... dep	5 58	7 32	1048	1356	1715	1832	22 1
Monza	6 18	7 51	11 5	1419	1732	1856	2219
Milan Centrale.......arr	6 40	8 10	1118	1440	1745	1920	2338

CECINA and VOLTERRA.

Dist.						
	Cecina ....dep	7 31	1055	13 50	1852	2056
18¾	**Volterra** ...arr	9 20	1248	15 31	2037	2239

Volterra dep	4 20	6 27	1132	14 15	1813	...
Cecina......arr	5 53	7 58	1311	15 38	1946	...

[Fares and Luggage Rates, see page 269.

ROME and NAPLES.

Dist.	Station																			
...	FLORENCE (279)...dep	...	...	...	...	23 45	...	...	3 34	...	7 10	...	...	8 20	8 20	1335	...	17 30	...	...
Dist.		1,2,3	1,2,3	1,2,3	1,2,3	1,2,3	1,2,3	1,2,3	1 &2	1,2,3	1,2,3	1,2,3	1,2,3	1,2,3	1,2,3	1 &2	1,2,3	1,2,3		
E.M.	**Rome**-Termini ...dep	...	...	...	6 5	7 30	...	8 30	10 0	...	13 50	...	16 0	18 0	18 20	20 0	22 30	0 25	...	...
8¾	Ciampino	...	...	...	6 28	...	...	8 53	...	...	...	...	16 23	...	...	...	22 55	B	...	...
23	Palestrina	...	...	...	7 11	...	...	9 37	...	...	B	...	17 6	...	...	...	23 45	...	...	...
28½	Valmontone	...	...	...	7 25	...	...	9 49	...	...	...	...	17 20	...	19 15	...	23 56	SC	...	...
33½	Segni arr	...	...	...	7 35	...	...	9 58	RC	...	14 58	...	17 30	...	19 23	...	0 6	1 40	...	...
...	Segni dep	...	...	...	7 40	F	...	10 3	...	...	15 0	...	17 35	...	19 24	...	0 11	1 42	...	...
39	Anagni	...	...	...	7 52	...	...	1013	...	...	15 10	...	17 47	F	19 34	...	0 23	...	...	...
48½	Ferentino	...	...	...	8 15	...	...	1035	...	...	...	...	18 11	...	...	...	0 45	...	...	...
53½	Frosinone	...	...	...	8 27	9 2	...	1050	...	...	15 34	...	18 22	...	19 55	...	1 1	2 21	...	...
57¼	Ceccano	...	...	...	8 36	...	...	1059	...	...	15 42	...	18 31	...	20 3	...	1 10	...		...
68¾	**Ceprano** arr	...	...	...	8 59	9 26	...	1121	...	...	15 59	...	18 54	...	20 19	...	1 33	2 49		...
...	**Ceprano** dep	...	...	...	9 0	9 27	...	1122	...	...	16 0	...	18 55	...	20 20	...	1 35	2 51		...
70	Isoletta	...	...	...	9 5	...	...	1127	...	...	16 5	...	19 0	...	...	...	1 40	...		...
75	**Roccasecca** (277A)	...	...	5 5	9 17	9 41	...	1213	...	...	16 18	1656	19 12	...	20 31	...	1 58	3 8		...
78	Aquino	...	...	5 15		...	...	1220	...	...	...	17 4		...	20 37	...	2 5	...		...
85½	Cassino	...	...	5 45	...	10 5	...	1240	1223	...	16 40	1728	...	2021	20 53	2215	2 30	3 35		...
96	Mignano	...	...	6 18	...	...	...	13 8	...	...	B	1758	...	...	21 19	...	3 4	...		...
101	Tora Presenzano	...	...	6 37	...	...	...	1323	...	...	..	1815	...	...	21 33	...	3 24	...		...
105½	**Calanello**	...	...	6 52	...	10 42	1052	1335	...	...	17 17	1832	...	...	21 43	...	3 36	4 40		...
109¾	Riardo	...	...	7 2	...	...	11 1	1344	...	...	...	1843	...	...	21 52		3 46	B		...
113	Teano	...	...	7 12	...	...	1110	1353	...	...	17 28	1855	...	RC	22 0	SC	3 56	5 4		...
118	Sparanise	...	...	7 30	...	11 1	1123	14 7	...	16 7	17 37	1914	...	...	22 11	...	4 11	5 21		...
121½	Pignataro	...	...	7 39	...	...	1136	1415	...	1616	...	1923	...	...	22 19	...	4 20	...		...
127½	**Capua**	6 5	6 45	7 57	9 25	...	1148	1431	...	1630	17 53	1942	...	...	22 30	...	4 38	5 46		...
130½	Santa Maria	6 15	6 55	8 7	9 35	...	1157	1440	...	1639	18 2	1952	...	...	22 38	...	4 48	5 58		...
134¼	**Caserta** arr	6 25	7 5	8 18	9 46	11 26	12 5	1448	1337	1648	18 10	20 1	...	2133	22 46	2327	4 58	6 10		...
...	**Caserta** dep	6 27	7 8	8 26	9 48	11 31	1210	1452	1340	1651	18 18	20 5	...	2135	22 49	2329	5 3	6 15		...
138	Maddaloni	6 36	7 18	8 36	9 58	...	1219	15 1	...	17 0	...	2014	...	...	22 57	...	5 13	...		...
141¾	**Cancello** arr	6 44	7 27	8 44	10 7	11 42	1227	15 8	...	17 8	..	2022	...	...	23 4	...	5 21	6 31		...
146	Acerra	7 3	7 49	9 2	1027	...	1243	1532	...	1725	...	2043	...	...	23 15	...	5 37	...		...
148	Casalnuovo	7 12	7 57	9 9	1034	...	1250	1539	...	1733	...	2050	...	...	23 21	...	5 44	...	...	...
154¾	**Naples** Centrale arr	7 39	8 15	9 25	1052	12 5	13 5	1555	1410	1750	18 53	21 5	...	22 5	23 35	24 0	6 0	6 55	...	...
157¾	**Naples** Porto arr	...	...	...	...	...	...	...	...	...	...	...	...	2235	...	...	...	...	...	...
285½	VILLA S. GIOVAN 277A arr	...	...	...	...	...	...	...	...	...	7 40	...	...	...	11 11	...	...	22 58	...	...
290¼	MESSINA 277A arr	...	...	...	...	...	...	...	...	...	8 35	...	...	...	12 0	...	...	2 50	...	...
435	PALERMO 290 arr	...	...	...	...	...	...	...	...	...	...	...	...	8§30	17 45	...	...	...	...	...

SC—Sleeping Cars in these trains.
RC—Restaurant Car attached.

Station																	
PALERMO dep	...	...	...	20§30	...	...	...	...	...	...	...	...	...	...	...	...	0 20
MESSINA dep	1627	...	...	...	...	...	...	...	...	...	...	...	...	...	...	...	9 55
VILLA S. GIOVANNI dep	1722	...	...	...	...	...	...	...	...	...	...	...	...	...	...	...	1045
	1 &2	1,2,3	1,2,3	1,2,3	1,2,3	1,2,3	1,2,3	1,2,3	1 &2	1,2,3	1,2,3	1,2,3	1,2,3	1,2,3	1,2,3	1,2,3	1,2,3
Naples Porto dep	...	...	...	6 55	...	...	...	...	...	...	...	...	...	...	...	...	SC
Naples Centrale dep	4 20	5 35	7 0	7 45	8 30	9 55	10 10	1235	1345	15 10	...	1635	18 0	1820	1930	1945	2350
Casalnuovo		5 51	7 16	...	8 46	...	10 26	1251	...	...	...	1651	...	1838	RC	20 4	0 7
Acerra		5 58	7 22	...	8 52	...	10 33	1257	...	...	...	1657	...	1846	...	2012	0 13
Cancello dep		6 10	7 40	8 7	9 3	10 17	10 44	1314	...	15 34	...	1720	A	19 0	1952	2028	0 27
Maddaloni		6 20	7 49	...	9 12	...	10 53	1324	...	...	...	1730	...	1911	...	2040	0 37
Caserta arr		6 28	7 57	8 19	9 20	10 30	11 1	1333	1416	15 47	...	1738	1832	1920	20 4	2050	0 46
Caserta dep		6 34	7 59	8 20	9 22	10 32	11 5	1341	1417	15 54	...	1742	1837	1924	2010	2055	0 51
Santa Maria		6 45	8 3	...	9 31	10 40	11 15	1353	...	16 3	...	1753	1845	1935	...	21 7	1 2
Capua arr		6 52	8 15	8 31	9 38	10 46	11 22	14 0	...	16 9	...	18 0	1851	1942	...	2115	1 9
Pignataro		7 8		F	9 52	...	11 37	1453	...	16 22	...		...		...	2134	1 25
Sparanise		7 21	...	...	10 2	11 5	11 50	15 5	...	16 31	...	...	1919	...	...	2150	1 38
Teano		7 34	...	...	1014	...	12 3		...	16 42	...	...	1930		...	22 8	1 53
Riardo		7 44	...	...	1024	...	12 15	...	...	16 51	...	...	...		...	2219	2 4
Calanello		7 59	...	...	1039	11 30	12 33	...	...	17 3	...	...	1948		2054	2230	2 20
Tora Presenzano		8 9	...	...	1049	...	12 44	...	...	17 12	...	...	...		...		2 33
Mignano	SC	8 22	...	...	11 2	...	12 58	...	...	17 23	...	...	...		...	...	2 52
Cassino		8 51	...	9 39	1130	12 5	13 28	...	1535	17 48	...	...	2025		2127	...	3 25
Aquino		9 13	...	...	1150	...	13 48	...	...	18 5	...	...	...		...	...	3 51
Roccasecca		9 20	6 58	9 59	1157	RC	13 58	...	...	18 12	18 25	...	2047		...	...	4 2
Isoletta			7 10	...		...	14 10	...	...	...	18 37	...	...		...	...	4 15
Ceprano arr		...	7 14	...	...	12 34	14 14	...	...	18 24	18 41	...	2059		...	...	4 19
Ceprano dep		...	7 16	...	...	12 35	14 15	...	...	18 25	18 42	...	21 0		...	...	4 20
Ceccano		...	7 41	...	...	12 53	14 40	...	...	18 44	19 7	...	...		...	...	4 48
Frosinone		...	7 52	...	...	13 3	14 54	...	...	18 54	19 18	...	2127		...	...	5 3
Ferentino		...	8 3	...	...	...	15 5	...	...	...	19 29	...	...		...	...	5 16
Anagni		...	8 26	...	...	...	15 28	...	...	19 16	19 52	...	...		...	...	5 42
Segni arr		...	8 37	11 2	...	...	15 39	...	...	19 26	20 3	...	2156		...	...	5 56
Segni dep		...	8 42	11 3	...	...	15 44	...	...	19 28	20 8	...	2157		...	...	6 1
Valmontone		...	8 58	...	...	...	15 57	...	...	...	20 21	...	...		...	...	6 19
Palestrina		...	9 14	...	...	...	16 16	...	...	C	20 39	...	...		...	...	6 41
Ciampino		...	9 46	...	...	...	16 52	...	...	...	21 11	...	...		...	...	7 19
Rome arr	8 20	...	10 5	1155	...	14 25	17 10	...	1745	20 25	21 30	...	2250		2335	...	7 40
FLORENCE (279B) arr	1419	...	...	...	...	20 52	...	...	2328	2 8	...	...	5 58		5 58	...	...

§—By direct steamer service between Naples and Palermo.

A—Will not take 3rd class locally between Naples and Capua.
B—Will not take 3rd class locally between Roccasecca and Naples.
C—Will not take 3rd class locally between Rome and Roccasecca.
F—Will not take 3rd class locally between Naples and Rome.

[Fares and Luggage Rates, see page 269.

NAPLES, METAPONTO, and BRINDISI.

Dist E.M	ROME 276 ...dep	...	0 25	...	...	7 30	...	10 0	10 0	...	...	13 50	13 50	...	20 0	20 0
		1,2,3	1,2,3	1,2,3	1 &3	1,2,3	1 & 3	1,2,3	1,2,3	1,2,3	1 & 3	1,2,3	1,2,3	1 &3	1 & 2	1,2,3
—	**Naples**...........dep	5 35	7 50	8 45	10 10	12 20	13 10	14 40	15 35	17 0	17 25	19 15	19 50	2030	0 15	0 35
7¼	Torre del Greco	6 4	A	9 13	10 43	...	13 43	...	16 5	...	17 54	...	...	21 3	...	...
12¾	Torre Annunziata...	6 33	8 18	9 34	11 14	12 51	14 14	15 6	16 30	17 30	18 16	19 51	20 18	2132	...	1 §1
14½	Pompei	6 39	...	9 40	11 21	...	14 20	...	16 35	...	18 21	...	...	2137	...	...
14¾	Valle di Pompei......	6 44	...	9 45	11 28	...	14 26	...	16 40	...	18 25	...	SC	2142	...	...
22¾	Nocera(277A) arr	7 12	8 35	10 11	12 0	13 11	14 58	15 23	17 8	17 50	18 50	20 13	20 38	2211	...	1 27
	Nocera(277A) dep	7 18	8 41	10 16		13 17		15 29	17 14	17 55	18 56	20 19	20 46	2217	...	1 32
27¾	Cava dei Tirreni ...	7 55	9 6	10 44	...	13 44	...	15 51	17 45	18 23	19 27	20 42	21 13	2247	...	1 54
30½	Vietri......................	8 6	...	10 53	...	13 53	...	...	17 54	18 33	19 37	20 51	21 22	2256	...	...
33½	**Salerno**...... arr	8 16	9 24	11 3	1,2,3	14 3	...	16 6	18 4	18 43	19 47	21 1	21 32	23 6	1 37	2 9
	Salerno...... dep	8 25	9 32	11 10	5 32	14 12	...	16 13		18 51		21 9	21 42		1 45	2 16
45¼	**Battipaglia** ...arr	8 57	9 58	11 41	6 1	14 38	...	16 36	...	19 21	...	21 33	22 5	...		2 43
...	REGGIO(277A)arr		23 55		...	...	...	2 35	...	...	...	...	9 4	...		...
...	**Battipaglia** ...dep	...	10 5	...	6 6	14 43	...	16 45	...	19 26	...	21 37		...		2 48
49¼	**Eboli**	...	10 16	...	6 17	14 54	...	16 55	...	19 35	...	21 46	...	...		3 0
65¼	Sicignano (275).......	...	11 2	...	7 20	15 42	...		...		...	22 31	...	...		3 52
70¾	Ponte San Cono......	...	...	...	7 45	16 2	...	...	...	...	...	...	...	...		...
74½	Romagnano............	...	11 33	...	8 3	16 14	...	...	...	...	...	23 1	...	...		4 23
85	Baragiano	...	12 12	...	8 55	16 53	...	...	...	...	...	23 35	...	...		5 4
96½	Tito......................	...	13 0	...	9 45	17 41	...	...	...	...	...	0 21	...	...		5 53
103	**Potenza** ... arr	...	13 16	...	10 0	17 56	...	...	...	...	...	0 36	...	...		6 8
	Potenza ... dep	...	13 29	...		18 4	...	...	...	...	...	0 42	...	...		6 19
116¾	Trivigno	...	14 10	...	...	18 45	...	...	...	...	...	...	...	...		7 1
132½	Grassano-Garaguso	...	15 0	...	...	19 32	...	...	...	...	...	2 2	...	...		7 52
146	Ferrandina	...	15 32	...	...	20 1	...	...	...	...	...	2 29	...	...		8 26
169½	**Metaponto** ...arr	...	16 23	...	...	20 50	...	...	...	...	...	3 17	...	...		9 14
...	„ (278) dep	13 45	16 35	...	...	21 20	...	...	...	23 1	...	3 31	...	...		9 29
186½	Chiatona	14 30	...	...	...	22 5	...	...	...	23 45	...	4 10	...	...		10 9
196½	**Taranto** 285B arr	14 53	17 21	...	...	22 26	...	...	...	0 8	...	4 30	...	1,2,3		1028
...	„ ....dep		17 29	...	...		...	...	...		...	4 38	...	8 3		1056
217	Francavilla Fon	...	18 21	...	...	...	...	...	...	...	...	5 34	...	8 57		1157
220½	Oria	...	18 29	...	...	...	...	...	...	...	...	5 43	...	9 7		12 7
231	Mesagne	...	18 49	...	...	...	...	...	...	...	...	6 4	...	9 32	...	1232
239½	**Brindisi** ....arr	...	19 4	...	...	...	...	...	...	...	...	6 20	...	9 50	...	1250

1 & 2 train (20 0 from Rome): To Villa S. Giovanni (arr. 11,11) and Syracuse (arr. 16.30).

Station	1 &3	1,2,3	1,2,3	1 & 3	1,2,3	1,2,3	1 &3	1,2,3	1 & 3	1,2,3	1,2,3	1,2,3	1& 2	1,2,3	1,2,3
Brindisi ....dep	...	...	...	...	...	...	...	7 11	...	1326	...	10 50	...	17 19	...
Mesagne	...	...	...	...	...	...	...	7 30	...	1348	...	11 10	...	17 42	...
Oria	...	...	...	...	...	...	...	7 53	...	1415	...	11 34	...	18 12	...
FrancavillaFontana	...	...	...	...	...	...	...	8 8	...	1429	...	11 47	...	18 36	...
Taranto ..... arr	...	...	...	...	...	...	...	8 54	...	1519	...	12 35	...	19 30	...
Taranto ..... dep	...	...	...	...	2 11	...	...	9 4	...	1529	...	12 43	...	19 46	2145
Chiatona	...	...	...	...	2 31	...	...	...	...	1552	...	13 2	...	20 10	...
Metaponto arr	...	...	...	...	3 9	...	...	9 55	...	1635	...	13 40	...	20 54	2240
Metaponto dep	...	...	...	...	3 24	...	...	10 7	...		...	13 50	...		23 0
Ferrandina	...	...	...	...	4 19	...	...	1057	...	...	...	14 53		...	2351
Grassano-Garaguso	...	...	...	...	5 10	...	...	1138	...	...	...	15 41		...	0 25
Trivigno	...	...	...	...	6 6	...	...	1232	...	...	...	16 40		...	...
Potenza ... arr	...	...	...	...	6 55	...	...	1315	...	...	...	17 32		...	1 51
Potenza ... dep	...	...	...	...	7 5	8 50	...	1327	...	...	...	17 56		...	1 57
Tito......................	...	...	...	...	7 27	9 13	...	1353	...	...	...	18 18		...	2 19
Baragiano	...	...	...	...	8 1	9 47	...	1432	...	...	...	18 52		...	2 51
Romagnano............	...	...	...	...	8 37	10 23	...	15 6	...	...	...	19 28		...	3 21
Ponte S. Cono.........	...	...	...	...	8 49	10 35	...	..	...	...	...	19 40		...	...
Sicignano...............	...	...	...	...	9 11	10 57	...	1547	...	...	...	20 8		...	3 54
Eboli .... arr	...	...	...	...	9 52	11 38	...	1625	...	...	...	20 50		...	4 27
Eboli .... dep	...	...	6 45	...	9 55	11 41	...	1627	...	19 0	...	20 53		...	4 29
Battipaglia ...arr	...	...	6 55	...	10 5	11 50	...	1635	...	1910	...	21 1		...	4 38
REGGIO ....dep	...	2020	...	...	...	...	...	...	...	5 20	9 55	...		...	...
Battipaglia ...dep	...	7 5	7 20	...	10 10	11 55	...	1640	...	1921	20 40	21 6		...	4 41
Salerno...... arr	...	7 27	8 0	...	10 36	12 24	...	17 7	...	1948	21 1	21 36		...	5 10
Salerno...... dep	6 10	7 35	8 10	...	10 42	12 30	1410	1715	17 30	1954	21 7	21 43		4 35	5 18
Vietri.....................	6 24	7 48	8 27	...	10 55	12 43	1423	...	17 44	20 7	...	21 56		4 48	...
Cava dei Tirreni......	6 37	8 0	8 42		11 7	12 56	1436	1738	17 57	2020	21 30	22 8		5 0	5 44
Nocera dei Pagani...	7 6	8 21	9 15	9 26	11 29	13 20	15 5	1759	18 21	2043	21 40	22 35		5 23	6 6
Valle di Pompei......	7 35	...	...	9 55	11 47	13 45	1534	A	18 50	21 5	...	...		5 45	...
Pompei	7 40	...	...	10 0	11 51	13 49	1540	...	18 55	21 9	A	...		5 49	...
Torre Annunziata...	7 50	8 38	9 41	10 7	11 56	13 55	1547	...	19 6	2122	22 7	22 55		5 55	6 30
Torre del Greco	8 10	...	9 58	10 27	...	14 14	16 7	...	19 26	2139	...	...		6 12	...
Naples ....arr	8 38	9 5	10 18	10 55	12 25	14 40	1635	1843	19 55	22 2	22 34	23 25	4 10	6 35	7 0
ROME (276) ...arr	...	1425	...	...	17 45	20 25	...	...	...	...	7 40	7 40	8 20	...	1155

1& 2 train (Naples arr. 4 10): From Villa S. Giovanni (dep. 17.22) and Syracuse (dep. 11.45).

‡—Sleeping cars in these trains. §—At Torre Annunziata Città.
A—Will not admit 3rd class locally between Naples and Battipaglia.
B—At Naples will take up 3rd cl. for Villa San Giovanni and beyond.

FRANCAVILLA and LECCE.

Station					
Francavilla Fontana ....dep	5 36	8 58	...	18 31	...
Novoli	7 5	10 30	15 52	20 5	...
Lecce ....arr	7 30	10 49	16 10	20 26	...

Station						
Lecce.....................................dep	6 5	13 15	16 10	20 40	...	...
Novoli	6 28	13 35	16 33	21 3	...	...
Francavilla Fontana ....arr	8 0	...	18 10	22 42	...	...

Station				
Novoli ....dep	7 15	16 35	21 5	...
Nardo Centrale ....arr	8 14	17 25	21 51	...

Station				
Nardo Centrale ....dep	5 9	14 52	19 10	...
Novoli ....arr	6 8	15 45	20 3	...

NARDO and MAGLIE.

E.M	Station						
	Nardo..................dep	...	8 25	15 20	20 20	...	...
30½	Gagliano Leuca	4 40	11 15	17 7	22 32	...	...
37¼	Tricase..........................	5 15	11 55	17 36		...	...
53½	**Maglie** 285...........arr	6 33	13 20	18 38	...	...	...

Station						
Maglie............dep	...	8 20	15 10	20 15	...	...
Tricase.....................	...	10 16	16 17	21 37	...	...
Gagliano Leuca ...	4 24	11 8	16 46	22 8	...	...
Nardo 277 ......arr	6 23	13 23	18 38	...	...	...

BATTIPAGLIA and REGGIO.

[Fares and Luggage Rates, see page 269.

Station									
NAPLES (277) ......dep	0 15	...	...	7 50	12 20	1440	17 0	19 50	...
Battipaglia.........dep	:	...	6 17	10 30	14 50	1641	1930	22 10	...
Pæstum (Pesto)........	:	...	6 58	11 7	15 27	...	2012	...	...
Agropoli	:	...	7 20	11 27	15 49	1720	2030	22 50	...
Castelnuovo Vallo	:	...	8 15	12 21	16 52	18 3	—	23 43	...
Pisciotta	:	...	8 50	12 52	17 26	...	...	0 13	...
Policastro del Golfo......	SC	...	—	13 51	18 34	...	...	SC	...
Sapri............	5 8	5 25	...	14 20	19 12	1946	...	1 32	...
Praia-Aieta ....dep	...	6 5	...	15 6	19 52	...	...	...	...
Belvedere Marittimo ...	...	7 13	...	16 25	—	2111	...	2 49	...
Cetraro	...	7 37	...	16 49	...	2129	...	...	...
Paola	7 9	8 20	...	17 38	...	22 5	...	3 38	...
Amantea	...	8 59	...	18 18	...	2232	...	4 6	...
S. Eufemia .... arr	...	9 47	...	19 5	...	23 8	...	4 45	...
S. Eufemia .... dep	...	10 10	...	19 25	...	2314	...	5 0	...
Pizzo............	...	10 52	...	20 2	...	2342	...	5 30	...
Monteleone	...	10 59	...	20 10	...	2348	...	5 36	...
Ricadi	RC	11 51	...	20 59	...	...	...	...	...
Nicotera	...	12 17	17 20	21 21	...	0 43	4 35	6 41	...
Gioia Tauro Petrace	...	12 50	17 48	21 49	...	1 7	5 4	7 5	...
Bagnara	...	13 34	18 31	22 26	...	1 39	5 44	7 39	...
Scilla	...	13 53	18 49	22 43	...	...	6 2	7 56	...
Villa S. Giovanni ...	11 11	14 10	19 3	22 58	...	2 0	6 17	8 10	...
MESSINA Porto ...arr	12 0	15 5	20 5	2 50	...	2 50	7 5	9 0	...
GIAR.-TAORMINA..arr	13 23	16 53	...	4 35	...	4 35	...	10 39	...
PALERMO ....arr	17 45	23 55	7 50	8 45	...	8 45	...	15 10	...
Reggio Centrale arr	12 10	15 7	20 0	23 55	5 10	2 35	7 13	9 4	...
Reggio Porto.....arr	13 0	15 10	...	...	5 25	...	8 45	...	...
MESSINA..............arr	14 5	16 35	22 20	...	8 15	...	...	...	...

Station										
MESSINA..............dep		...	...	5 0	8 30	1155	...	1425	17 25	...
Reggio Porto.....dep		...	...	6 5	...	...	...	1530	18 32	...
Reggio Centrale dep		...	5 20	7 40	9 55	1315	...	1610	20 20	...
PALERMO ....dep		...	20 0	...	0 30	...	1045	...	14 15	...
GIAR.-TAORMINA..dep		...	1 53	...	8 20	...	15 9	1215	18 36	...
MESSINA.. ....dep		...	5 0	7 25	9 55	1315	1627	16 5	20 25	...
Villa S. Giovanni ...		...	6 19	8 26	10 45	1415	1722	1735	21 20	...
Scilla............		...	6 35	8 41	...	1432	...	1755	21 31	...
Bagnara		...	7 3	9 8	11 14	15 0	...	1825	21 49	...
Gioia Tauro Petrace		...	7 39	9 45	11 47	1546	...	19 7	22 20	...
Nicotera		...	8 9	1018	12 13	1625	...	1940	22 48	...
Ricadi		...	8 30	—	...	1648	RC	—	...	...
Monteleone		...	9 18	...	13 18	1744	...	...	23 47	...
Pizzo		...	9 25	...	13 25	1752	...	...	23 54	...
S. Eufemia .... arr		...	10 5	...	13 58	1836	...	...	0 23	...
S. Eufemia .... dep		...	10 30	...	14 11	1910	...	...	0 38	...
Amantea		...	11 19	...	14 42	1958	...	...	1 9	...
Paola		5 58	12 13	...	15 18	2037	2118	...	1 47	...
Cetraro		6 36	12 46	...	15 41	—	:	...	...	...
Belvedere Marittimo ...		7 7	13 15	...	15 58	...	:	...	2 22	...
Praia-Aieta	5 5	8 35	14 21	...	...	...	:	...	...	...
Sapri	6 25	9 20	15 10	...	17 30	...	SC	...	3 50	...
Policastro del Golfo	6 44	—	15 30	...	...	...	:	...	...	...
Pisciotta	7 46	13 25	16 34	...	18 34	...	:	...	...	...
Castelnuovo Vallo ...	8 20	14 12	17 16	...	19 3	...	:	...	5 40	...
Agropoli	9 5	15 18	18 20	...	19 44	...	:	...	6 20	...
Pæstum (Pesto)......	9 20	15 44	18 35	...	...	...	:	...	...	...
Battipaglia ...arr	9 55	16 23	19 15	...	20 35	...	:	...	7 0	...
NAPLES 277 ...arr	1225	18 43	22 2	...	22 34	...	4 10	...	9 5	...

RC—Restaurant Car between Paola and Reggio Centrale.
SC—Sleeping Car attached.

GAETA and SPARANISE.

Station				
Gaeta-Elena...dep	5 10	8 40	14 5	1648
Formia............	5 31	8 59	1425	17 8
Sessa Aurunca	6 28	10 0	1521	18 4
Sparanise 276 arr	7 5	1038	1558	1841

EM	Station				
	Sparanise dep	7 45	12 0	1645	1930
11¼	Sessa Aurunca	8 30	1244	1729	2014
31¾	Formia	9 29	1339	1824	21 9
37½	**Gaeta**.........arr	9 45	1355	1840	2125

CAIANELLO and ISERNIA.

Station					
Caianello ....dep	4 41	11 40	17 50	...	...
Roccaravindola	5 34	12 37	18 39	...	...
Isernia 283............arr	6 22	13 25	19 20	...	...

Station								
Isernia ....dep	9 15	14 57	19 20	...	...	...	...	...
Roccaravindola	9 45	15 29	19 50	...	...	...	...	...
Caianello ....arr	10 26	16 17	20 34	...	...	...	...	...

NAPLES and BENEVENTO.

[*—Mon., Tues., and Fri. only.

E.M	Station									
	Naples ......dep	...	6 10	8 30	...	12 35	...	16 35	19 45	23 50
13¾	Cancello	...	6 49	9 10	...	13 13	...	17 13	20 50	0 23
21¼	Nola	...	7 5	9 27	...	13 30	...	17 32	21 9	0*44
30¼	Sarno............	...	7 27	9 51	...	13 54	...	17 58	21 36	1 *6
35¼	Codola (277A)	...	7 40	1012	...	14 8	...	18 16	21 53	1*19
40¼	Mercato S. S.	...	8 1	1043	...	14 30	...	18 43	22 15	1*36
52¼	Solofra	...	8 41	1130	...	15 10	...	19 23	22 55	—
59	Avellino ....arr	...	9 0	1150	...	15 29	...	19 42	23 14	...
...	,, 273...dep	7 19	9 16	—	1210	16 0	18 0	19 55	—	...
68¼	Altavilla	7 45	9 45	...	1240	16 30	1832	20 21	...	...
77½	**Benevento**..arr	8 15	1015	...	1312	17 0	19 5	20 50	...	...

Station							
Benevento dep	4 15	6 10	8 55	11 50	...	15 55	19 50
Altavilla	4 45	6 40	9 28	12 23	...	16 27	20 20
Avellino ....arr	5 12	7 9	9 57	12 53	...	16 55	20 48
,, ...dep	5 18	7 21	—	—	13 5	17 10	20 54
Solofra	5 44	7 48	...	...	13 31	17 37	21 20
Mercato S.Sev.......	6 16	8 31	11*15	...	14 4	18 12	21 51
Codola	6 32	9 1	11 33	...	14 20	18 30	22 6
Sarno	6 43	9 18	11 45	...	14 31	18 42	22 17
Nola	7 8	9 50	12 10	...	14 55	19 8	22 40
Cancello	7 36	10 16	12 32	...	15 20	19 32	23 6
Naples ....arr	8 15	10 52	13 5	...	15 55	20 5	23 35

CODOLA and NOCERA.

Station						
Codola..............dep	6 50	9 0	1253	1435	1835	22 20
Nocera de'Pagani...arr	7 0	9 8	13 3	1445	1845	22 30

Station						
Nocera de'Pagani ...dep	6 15	7 23	9 50	1335	18 0	21 12
Codola..............arr	6 25	7 33	10 3	1348	1811	21 22

ROCCASECCA and AVEZZANO.

Station					
Roccasecca ......dep	5 8	12 10	18 19	...	...
Sora	6 25	13 40	19 32	...	...
Avezzano 282 arr	8 20	15 49	21 21	...	...

Station					
Avezzano ....dep	6 58	12 8	17 30	...	...
Sora	8 30	13 49	19 8	...	...
Roccasecca (276) arr	9 23	14 59	20 7	...	...

VELLETRI and SEGNI-PALIANO.

Station				Station			
Velletri ....dep	9 0	14 10	16 10	Segni-Paliano dep	6 17	11 52	1935
Segni-Paliano...arr	9 37	14 47	17 20	Velletri ....arr	7 2	13 8	2035

CANCELLO and BENEVENTO CITTA.

Station						
Cancello..............dep	7 0	9 10	1320	1615	18 35	...
S. Felice-Arienzo	7 9	9 19	1340	1625	18 46	...
Arpaia-Airola	7 42	9 50	1437	17 2	19 24	...
S. Martino V. Caudina	7 57	10 4	1513	1720	19 44	...
Apollosa-S. Leucio ...	8 13	1020	1540	1739	20 3	...
Benevento Città...arr	8 22	1029	1553	1750	20 14	...

Station						
Benevento Citt dep	5 0	7 14	10 0	1529	1828	...
Apollosa-S. Leucio...	5 13	7 26	1019	1541	1841	...
S. Martino............	5 36	7 45	1053	16 0	19 4	...
Arpaia	5 58	7 59	1125	1614	1926	...
S. Felice	6 31	8 29	12 9	1646	20 0	...
Cancello 277A ...arr	6 41	8 38	1220	1655	2010	...

Italian Railway Time—See Note on page 272.

[Fares and Luggage Rates, see page 269

METAPONTO and REGGIO.

NAPLES (277)......dep	...	...	19 15	0 35	...	7 50	12 20	...	...	...	...	...
	1,2,3	1,2,3	1,2,3	1,2,3	1,2,3	1,2,3	1,2,3	1,2,3				
Metaponto ....dep	...	...	3 30	10 5	...	16 50	21 10	...	...	...	...	...
Montalbano-Jonico ...	...	...	3 51	10 28	...	17 12	...	...	...	...	...	...
Policoro....................	...	...	3 59	10 37	...	17 20	...	...	...	...	...	...
Nova Siri	...	...	4 12	10 51	...	17 34	21 44	...	...	...	...	...
Sibari (278)...... arr	...	...	5 27	12 13	...	18 46	22 41	...	...	...	...	...
Sibari (278)...... dep	...	...	7 12	12 30	...	19 5	22 47	...	...	...	...	...
Rossano....................	...	...	7 43	13 4	...	19 39	23 19	...	...	...	...	...
Cariati	4 10	...	8 35	13 54	...	20 35	...	...	...	...	...	...
Cotrone............ arr	5 31	...	9 59	15 10	...	22 0	1 7	...	...	...	...	...
Cotrone............ dep	5 43	...	10 10	15 28	19 53	—	1 16	...	...	...	...	...
Isola Capo Rizzuto ...	5 53	...	10 20	15 37	20 4	...	...	...	...	...	...	...
Catanzaro Marina** arr	7 21	...	11 53	16 58	21 30	...	2 30	...	...	...	...	...
Catanzaro Marina** dep	7 37	...	12 22	17 22	—	...	2 40	...	...	...	...	...
Squillace	7 51	...	12 34	17 36	...	...	...	...	...	...	...	...
Soverato	8 11	...	12 53	17 55	...	...	3 6	...	...	...	...	...
Badolato	8 31	...	13 14	18 18	...	...		...	...	...	...	...
Monasterace..............	8 54	...	13 38	18 42	...	...	3 35	...	...	...	...	...
Roccella Ionica	9 30	...	14 12	19 20	...	...	4 6	5 0	...	...	...	...
Gerace	10 4	...	14 50	19 56	...	...	4 34	5 33	...	...	...	...
Bianconovo	10 36	...	15 24	20 29	...	...	...	6 7	...	...	...	...
Condofuri.................	11 35	...	16 28	21 28	...	...	...	7 10	...	...	...	...
Melito.......................	11 47	...	16 43	21 41	...	...	5 53	7 23	...	...	...	...
Reggio-Centrale ...arr	12 35	1455	17 35	22 35	5 10	...	6 32	8 15	...	...	...	...
„ Porto ......arr	13 0	1510	1[illegible] 5	...	5 2[illegible]	...	7 5	8 45	...	...	...	...

	1,2,3	1,2,3	1,2,3	1,2,3	1,2,3	1,2,3	1,2,3	1,2,3	1,2,3	
Reggio										
Porto ......dep	...	...	6 5	10 20	...	13 30	15 30	18 32	21 20	...
Centrale...dep	...	...	6 32	10 50	...	13 46	15 55	18 58	21 50	...
Melito	...	...	7 25	11 45	...	—	16 45	19 55	22 32	...
Condofuri.........	...	...	7 42	12 3	...	...	17 0	20 15	...	...
Bianconovo......	...	...	8 41	13 1	...	...	18 0	21 13	...	...
Gerace	...	...	9 19	13 39	...	...	18 45	21 53	23 58	...
Roccella Ionica	5 40	...	10 4	14 20	...	...	19 30	22 30	0 42	...
Monasterace ...	6 10	...	10 32	14 52	...	...	20 8	—	1 12	...
Badolato	6 36	...	10 56	15 17	...	...	20 33	...	1 31	...
Soverato	7 1	...	11 20	15 38	...	...	21 3	...	1 48	...
Squillace	7 20	...	11 39	15 56	...	...	21 21	...	...	...
Catanzaro** arr	7 38	...	11 54	16 10	...	...	21 35	...	2 13	...
Catanzaro** dep	7 56	6 20	12 30	16 30	...	19 10	—	...	2 30	...
Isola C. Rizzuto	9 48	7 53	14 3	17 57	...	20 50	...	...	...	...
Cotrone arr	9 58	8 1	14 11	18 5	...	21 0	...	...	3 51	...
Cotrone dep	10 30	8 17	14 24	18 13	...	21 11	...	...	4 4	...
Cariati	12 9	9 40	16 19	19 28	...	22 36	...	...	5 25	...
Rossano............	—	10 34	17 36	20 20	...	—	...	...	6 20	...
Sibari ... arr	...	11 5	18 20	20 50	...	...	...	...	6 51	...
Sibari ... dep	...	11 30	18 50	—	21 11	...	...	...	7 24	...
Nova Siri	...	12 45	20 19	...	...	...	...	...	8 37	...
Policoro	...	12 57	20 33	...	...	...	...	...	8 49	...
Montalbano......	...	13 5	20 42	...	...	...	...	...	8 57	...
Metaponto arr	...	13 25	21 6	...	22 37	...	...	...	9 17	...
NAPLES 277 ar		23 25	...	...	7 0	...	...	...	18 43	...

** Catanzaro Marina to Catanzaro Sala (5½ m. in 25 min.)—2.45, 7.50, 9.40, 12.17, 17.13, 21.55; return, 1.50, 5.41, 7.6, 11.43, 15.57, 20.56.

S. EUFEMIA and CATANZARO SALA.

S. Eufemia...........dep	5 15	1020	14 20	1920	2320	...	...
Marcellinara.............	6 27	1116	15 28	2023	0 11	...	...
Catanzaro Sala......arr	6 59	1141	15 56	2051	0 31	...	...
Catanzaro Sala......dep	3 17	8 19	12 37	1736	2230	...	...
Marcellinara	3 51	8 59	13 9	1811	23 7	...	...
S. Eufemia ....arr	4 35	9 50	13 49	1857	24 0	...	..

TORRE ANNUNZIATA and CASERTA.

T. Annunziata dep	6 42	10 9	13 58	19 5	2025	...	...
Ottajano	7 29	11 1	14 43	19 50	21 8	...	...
Cancello 276	8 0	11 45	15 15	20 21	—	...	...
Caserta 276......arr	8 19	12 7	15 47	21 14		...	...
Caserta ....dep	...	6 27	9 12	12 50	1651	...	...
Cancello	...	6 51	9 40	13 16	17 8	18 5	...
Ottajano	4 50	7 32	10 25	14 4	—	18 52	...
Torre A. 277 ...arr	5 20	8 5	10 58	14 42	...	19 26	...

SIBARI and PIETRAFITTA.

Dist						
	Sibari 278 ....dep	5 40	7 10	12 26	15 35	19 0
10	Spezzano Castrovillari	6 0	7 35	12 49	16 10	19 23
18½	San Marco Roggiano...	6 21	8 2	13 11	16 40	19 45
32¼	Acri-Bisignano...........	6 59	8 51	13 52	17 40	20 28
42¾	**Cosenza** ....arr	7 28	9 34	14 25	18 24	21 0
...	„ ....dep	5 30	10 25	16 45	—	—
48½	**Pietrafitta** ...arr	6 15	...	11 6	17 26	...

Pietrafitta.........dep	...	6 30	1130	...	...	17 40
Cosenza...............arr	...	7 0	12 0	...	...	18 15
„ ....dep	5 6	9 10	—	13 0	16 0	19 24
Acri-Bisignano	5 32	9 39	...	13 28	16 31	...
San Marco Roggiano...	6 20	10 28	...	14 28	17 33	...
Spezzano Castrovillari	6 40	10 52	...	15 1	18 4	20 37
Sibari..................arr	7 0	11 15	...	15 25	18 28	20 55

NAPLES and GRAGNANO.

Naples ....dep	5 35	7 15	8 10	9 20	10 10	11 30	13 10	15 0	15 35	17 50	18 35	19 15	...	20 30	22 30	...	...
Portici	5 53	7 30	8 28	...	10 31	11 48	13 31	15 16	15 54	18 8	18 52	...	...	20 51	22 46	...	...
Torre del Greco	6 4	7 39	8 39	...	10 43	11 59	13 43	15 26	16 5	18 19	19 2	...	...	21 3	22 56	...	...
Torre Annunziata......	6 34	7 57	9 1	9 55	11 10	12 19	14 9	15 49	16 32	18 42	19 20	19 44	20 26	21 28	23 16	...	...
Castellammare di Stabia...	6 54	8 5	9 10	10 15	11 19	12 40	14 30	16 11	16 53	19 0	19 40	...	20 36	21 50	23 25	...	...
Gragnano ....arr	7 9	...	...	10 30	...	12 55	14 45	16 26	17 8	19 15	19 55	...	...	22 6	...	...	...

E.M.																		
	Gragnano ....dep	...	5 42	...	7 10	8 35	...	10 35	11 40	...	12 55	15 49	...	18 24	...	20 43	...	...
3	Castellammare di Stabia...	5 13	6 5	...	7 32	8 58	9 25	10 58	12 3	12 31	13 1[illegible]	16 13	17 0	18 47	19 30	21 6	...	...
6¾	**Torre Annunziata**......	5 25	6 30	7 17	7 50	9 7	9 41	11 9	12 14	12 40	13 27	16 23	17 11	19 6	19 43	21 22	...	...
13¾	Torre del Greco	5 47	...	7 36	8 10	...	9 58	11 30	12 34	—	13 46	...	17 30	19 26	20 7	21 39	...	...
15¼	Portici............................	5 59	...	7 46	8 21	...	10 7	11 41	12 45	...	13 56	...	17 40	19 37	20 19	21 48	...	...
20¼	**Naples** ....arr	6 15	7 0	8 0	8 38	9 40	10 18	12 0	13 0	...	14 10	16 55	17 55	19 55	20 35	22 2	...	...

ROME and VITERBO.

Rome Trastevere ...	...	6 40	9 41	15 30	1844
Bracciano	...	7 59	11 0	16 47	20 1
Capranica...........arr	6 45	8 31	1132	17 19	2033
Ronciglione......arr	7 1	8 54	1156	17 58	2056
Viterbo 283 ...arr	...	9†16	12 7	18 †2	21 8

Viterbo..............dep	6 0	...	10†46	1659	19†47
Ronciglione.........dep	6 15	8 10	11 10	17 0	20 10
Capranica	6 39	8 26	11 32	1739	20 33
Bracciano	7 13	—	12 5	1812	21 6
Rome Trastevere arr	8 19	...	13 13	1920	22 12

†—At or from P. Fiorentina.

SALERNO and MERCATO S. SEVERINO.

Salerno ....dep	5 15	1044	1250	1716
Mercato S. Severino arr	6 5	1146	1340	18 0

Mercato S. Severino dep	6 55	9 0	14 55	18 45
Salerno ....arr	7 40	9 55	15 42	19 30

☞ Italian Railway Time—See Note on page 278 ☜

Fares and Luggage Rates, see page 269.]

MILAN, PIACENZA, BOLOGNA, FLORENCE, AND ROME.

SLEEPING CAR.—Florence to Rome—in 23.45 from Florence.
RESTAURANT CAR—in 10.0 from Milan, and 17.30 from Florence.

Dist E.M																			
	BASLE (258)......dep	...	...	...	...	...	...	...	9 p45	9p45	...	...	...	11p20	...	...	...	...	11p20
						1,2,3		1,2,3	1,2,3	1 & 2	1,2,3			1 & 2		1,2,3			1,2,3
	MILAN—																		
—	Centrale .dep	...	...	...	...	...	...	5 20	6 30	7 0	7 45	...	...	10 0	...	...	...	...	10 10
4¼	Rogoredo	...	...	...	...	...	...	...	...	...	7 56	...	...	...	...	...	...	...	...
11	Melegnano	...	...	...	...	...	...	5 39	...	...	8 13	...	...	RC	...	...	...	...	10 33
20	Lodi	...	...	...	...	...	...	5 57	7 6	...	8 40	...	...	10 31	...	...	...	...	10 52
32¾	Casalpusterlengo	...	...	...	...	...	...	6 19	...	...	9 11	...	...	...	...	...	...	...	11 17
35¼	Codogno (281)	...	...	...	...	...	...	6 29	7 29	...	9 24	...	...	...	...	...	...	...	11 26
37¾	S. Stefano	...	...	...	...	...	...	6 35		...	9 31	...	...	...	...	...	...	...	...
42¾	**Piacenza** ....arr	...	...	...	...	...	...	6 45	...	7 58	9 43	...	...	11 2	...	...	...	...	11 41
...	TURIN (270) ......dep	...	...	...	...	...	...	...	...	...	...	...	...	7 15	...	...	...	...	...
...	ALESSANDRIA (273) dep	...	...	...	...	...	...	...	4 20	4 20	...	...	...	8 55	...	...	...	...	...
...	**Piacenza** ....dep	...	...	...	...	3 45	...	6 50	8 12	8 ‡0	...	...	...	11 10	...	...	...	...	11 55
48½	Pontenure	...	...	...	...	4 1	...	...	8 26	...	...	...	...	...	...	...	...	...	12 11
64½	Borgo S.Donnino 279B	...	...	...	...	4 41	...	7 32	9 6	...	...	...	...	11 45	...	...	...	...	12 54
70½	Castelguelfo	...	...	...	...	4 54	...	7 43	9 18	...	...	...	...	...	...	...	...	...	13 5
78¼	**Parma (281)** ...arr	...	...	...	...	5 13	...	7 57	9 33	8 51	...	...	...	12 5	...	...	...	...	13 23
...	" ....dep	...	...	...	...	5 20	...	8 2	9 39	8 56	...	...	...	12 10	...	...	...	...	13 40
95¾	Reggio (286)	...	...	...	...	6 0	...	8 37	10 12	...	...	...	...	12 35	...	...	...	...	14 22
111¼	**Modena (282)** arr	...	...	...	...	6 31	...	9 6	10 41	...	...	...	...	12 57	...	...	...	...	14 53
...	" ....dep	...	...	...	...	6 39	...	9 9	10 46	...	...	...	...	13 3	...	1318	...	...	15 1
123	Samoggia	...	...	...	...	7 3	...	...	11 10	...	...	...	...	...	...	1340	...	...	15 28
128	Lavino	...	...	...	...	7 16	...	...	11 23	...	...	...	...	...	...	1349	...	...	15 41
134¼	**Bologna** ....arr	...	...	...	...	7 28	...	9 50	11 35	10 12	...	...	...	13 34	...	14 0	...	...	15 55
261	ANCONA (285) arr	...	...	...	...	1455	...	14 55	19 43	14 55	...	...	...	19 43	...	1943	...	...	...
607	BRINDISI (285) arr	...	...	...	...		...			...	...	...	...	...	...		...	...	...
...	VENICE (279A)...dep	...	...	...	...	...	...	...	...	7 0	...	...	...	10 15	...	...	...	10 15	...
		1,2,3	1,2,3	1,2,3	1,2,3	1,2,3	1,2,3		1,2,3	1 & 2	1,2,3	1,2,3	1,2,3	1 & 2	1,2,3		1,2,3	1,2,3	1,2,3
...	**Bologna**......... dep	...	...	...	...	...	6 10	...	8 5	10 24	...	...	...	14 3	From Perugia. Does not run on Sundays.	...	...	14 21	17 45
158½	Vergato	...	...	...	...	...	7 13	...	9 8	...	...	...	...	...		...	...	15 33	18 51
170¾	Porretta Bagni	...	...	...	...	...	7 51	...	9 45	11 38	...	...	...	15 27		...	...	16 27	19 23
180	Pracchia	...	...	...	...	...	8 31	...	10 25	12 5	...	...	...	16 1		...	...	17 8	
195¾	**Pistoja (271A)**...arr	...	...	...	...	...	9 13	...	11 7	12 47	...	...	...	16 39		...	...	17 50	...
...	" ....dep	...	...	...	6 48	8 36	9 22	...	11 25	12 52	13 4	15 10	...	16 45		...	...	18 0	19 45
205½	Prato	...	...	...	7 17	8 56	9 46	...	11 46	RC	13 29	15 36	...	17 1		...	...	18 27	20 9
211¾	Sesto	...	...	...	7 33	...	10 0	...	12 0	...	13 46	15 52	...	...		...	...	18 42	20 25
216¾	**FLORENCE** Piazza Santa Maria Novella arr	...	...	...	7 50	9 15	10 17	...	12 18	13 25	14 4	16 10	...	17 18		...	...	19 0	20 42
...	" dep	...	5 50	...	8 20	...	10 40	...	...	13 35	14 10	...	...	17 30		...	18 20	...	...
219¾	**Florence** Marte dep	...	5 58	...	8 30	...	10 49	...	...	...	14 20	...	...	§		...	18 33	...	...
229¾	Pontassieve	...	6 23	...	8 57	...	11 9	...	...	...	14 48	...	...	RC		...	19 3	...	...
233	S. Ellero (288)	...	6 32	...	9 6	...	...	...	...	14 †9	14 57	...	...	18 †3		...	19 13	...	...
246½	S. Giovanni	...	7 10	...	9 44	...	11 48	...	...	...	15 34	...	...	...		...	19 54	...	...
271¼	**Arezzo (289)**...arr	...	8 17	...	1048	...	12 34	...	...	15 15	16 38	...	...	19 11		...	21 5	...	...
...	" ....dep	5 25		...	1111	...	12 41	...	...	15 18	16 50	...	...	19 15		...	21 10	...	...
282¾	Castiglion Fiorentino	5 51	...	...	1136	...	13 4	...	...	...	17 11	...	...	...		...	21 40	...	...
288¾	Cortona	6 9	...	...	1154	...	13 16	...	...	...	17 25	...	...	...		...	21 58	...	...
292	**Terontola** ......arr	6 19	...	...	12 3	...	13 24	...	...	15 53	17 33	...	...	19 47		...	22 7	...	...
...	" (283)...dep	6 22	...	...	1217	...	14 12	...	...	15 55	18 7	...	...	19 50		...	22 11	...	...
303½	Panicale	6 47	...	...	1240	...	14 40	...	...	...	18 29	...	...	...		...	22 38	...	...
310¾	**Chiusi (275)**......arr	7 5	...	...	1257	...	14 57	...	...	16 20	18 45	...	...	20 14		...	22 54	...	...
...	" ....dep		...	5 10	13 7	...		...	...	16 26	19 0	...	...	20 20		...	23 16	...	...
321	Ficulle	...	...	5 33	1329	...	...	...	...	...	19 40	...	...	...		...	23 39	...	...
335½	**Orvieto**	...	...	6 7	14 2	...	...	...	...	17 3	21 9	...	...	20 56		...	0 8	...	...
347	Alviano	...	...	6 35	1429	...	...	...	...	...	21 49	...	...	...		...		...	...
352¾	Attigliano (283)	...	...	6 48	1442	...	14 18	...	...	...	22 10	...	...	...		...	...	19 46	...
361½	**Orte (283)** ......arr	...	...	7 7	15 0	...	14 40	...	...	17 39	22 38	...	...	21 32	22 52	...	...	20 8	...
...	ANCONA (283)...dep	23 40	...	...	...	7 20	...	...	...	...	...	...	11 35	...	17*30	...	..	15 6	...
...	**Orte**.............dep	5 40	6 10	8 4	1510	13 2	...	...	...	17 41	...	...	18 9	21 34	22 56	...	...	21 55	...
369½	Civita Castellana	...	6 28	8 22	1529	1315	...	...	...	...	...	...	18 26	...	...	...	...	22 9	...
390	Fara Sabina	...	7 9	9 1	16 9	1352	...	...	...	...	...	...	19 3	...	...	...	...	22 47	...
396¾	Monte Rotondo	...	7 22	9 14	1623	14 5	...	...	...	...	...	...	19 16	...	...	...	...	23 0	...
413¼	**ROME** Termini ...arr	7 5	8 0	9 50	17 5	1435	...	...	...	18 55	...	...	19 50	22 55	0 10	...	...	23 30	...

For Continuation of Trains, see next page.

†—Stops at San Ellero only in July, August, and Sept. §—From Florence forward takes also 3rd class.
RC—Restaurant Car attached. SC—Sleeping Car. *—Mon., Wed., and Fri. only.
‡—Will not take locally between Piacenza and Bologna.

MODENA and VIGNOLA.														
Modena...dep	7 29	12 0	14 30	18 45	...	...	Vignola......dep	5 40	8 15	12 46	17 5	...	...	...
Vignola...arr	8 46	13 17	15 47	20 2	...	...	Modena......arr	6 56	9 27	14 2	18 21	...	...	...

MODENA and MARANELLO.														
Modena..........dep	5 20	7 45	13 10	16 25	...	...	Maranello..........dep	6 30	9 0	14 35	1755	...	...	...
Maranello ...arr	6 20	8 45	14 10	17 25	...	...	Modena...............arr	7 30	10 0	15 35	1855	...	...	...

MILAN, PIACENZA, BOLOGNA, FLORENCE, ROME.

SLEEPING CARS—Milan to Rome—in 21.0 and 22.50 from Milan.

Basle (258)..........dep	...	...	7 a0	7 a30	7 a30	7a30	8a25	12p2	...	...	1 p50	...
	1,2,3	1,2,3	1 & 2	1,2,3	1,2,3	1,2,3	1,2,3	1 &2		1,2,3	1,2,3	
MILAN—												
Centrale ......dep	13 0	13 15	15.30	16 50	17 35	1840	20 0	21 0	...	...	22 50	...
Rogoredo	...	...	...	17 1	...	1851	...	...	...	...	SC	...
Melegnano	...	13 34	...	17 16	...	19 6	...	...	...	...	23 8	...
Lodi	...	13 51	16 1	17 37	...	1929	20 31	SC	...	...	23 23	...
Casalpusterlengo	...	14 13	...	18 2	...	1957	...	...	...	...	23 41	...
Codogno (281)	...	14 27	...	18 12	18 30	2011	20 53	...	...	...	23 49	...
S. Stefano	...	14 33	...	18 19		2018	...	...	...	...	...	...
Piacenza ....arr	1358	14 43	16 32	18 30	To Mantua.	2030	21 6	2158	...	...	0 2	...
Turin (270)..........dep	...	11 0	...	...		...	15 0	1835	...	...	20 10	21 15
Alessandria 273 dep	...	12 40	13 55	...		...	17 35	2015	...	...	21 55	22 50
Piacenza ....dep	14 0	14 50	16 38	18 50		...	21 14	22 0	...	...	0 12	0 40
Pontenure	...	15 4	...	19 6		...	...	...	...	...	...	P. & O. Express. Sun. morn. only
Borgo S. Donnino 279A	1435	15 42	17 13	19 46		...	21 52	...	...		0 49	
Castelguelfo	...	15 53	...	19 59		...	...	...	...		...	
Parma (281) ......arr	1455	16 7	17 32	20 17	...	...	22 12	2250	...	From Ala.	1 12	
,, ...dep	15 2	16 13	17 37	20 26	...	...	22 17	2255	...		1 17	
Reggio (286)	1528	16 48	18 2	21 15	...	...	22 43	...	...		1 47	
Modena (282)......arr	1550	17 15	18 24	21 49	...	...	23 5	...	...		2 11	
,, ...dep	1553	17 20	18 27	21 56	...	...	23 9	...	...	1 37	2 13	
Samoggia	...	17 44	...	22 26	...	...	...	...	...	...	...	
Lavino	...	17 54	...	22 37	...	...	...	...	...	...	...	
Bologna..........arr	1625	18 7	19 0	22 50	...	...	23 41	0 12	...	2 15	2 49	3 2
Ancona (285)......arr	2025	23 13	23 13	...	...	...	...	3 42	...	7 44	7 44	6 35
Brindisi (285) ...arr	Until 30th Sept. ☞	11 50	11 50	...	...	...	...	1430	...	21 27	21 27	17 54
Venice (279A)......dep		—	14 25	...	...	...	...	2120	21 20	...	23 8	—
		1 & 3	1,2,3					1& 2	1,2,3		1,2,3	
Bologna ....dep		...	19 42	...	...	...	...	0 31	0 53	...	3 20	...
Vergato		...	20 34	...	...	...	...	...	2 12	...	4 10	...
Porretta Bagni		...	21 10	...	...	...	...	1 46	2 54	...	4 50	...
Pracchia		...	21 40	...	...	...	...	...	3 40	...	5 22	...
Pistoja (271A)......arr		...	22 16	...	...	...	...	2 52	4 27	...	6 1	...
,, ...dep		...	22 26	...	...	...	...	2 55	4 40	...	6 7	...
Prato	...	...	22 51	...	...	...	...	...	5 7	...	6 27	...
Sesto	...	...	23 5	...	...	...	...	...	5 23	...	...	...
FLORENCE Piazza Santa Maria Novella arr	...	...	23 16	...	...	...	...	3 26	5 40	...	6 48	...
			SC									
FLORENCE Piazza Santa Maria Novella dep	...	21 0	23 45	...	...	...	...	3 34	...	...	7 10	...
Florence Marte ...dep	...	21 14	23 55	...	...	...	...	...	...	...	7 18	...
Pontassieve	...	21 48	0 15	...	...	...	...	...	...	...	7 38	...
S. Ellero (288)	...	21 59	...	...	...	...	...	...	...	...	7†46	...
S. Giovanni	...	22 51	0 57	...	...	...	...	...	...	...	8 15	...
Arezzo (289) ......arr	...	—	1 55	...	...	...	...	5 13	...	...	9 5	...
,, ...dep	...	...	2 1	...	...	...	...	5 15	...	...	9 15	...
Castiglion Fiorentino	...	...	2 20	...	...	...	...	...	...	...	9 36	...
Cortona	...	...	2 34	...	...	...	...	...	...	...	9 50	...
Terontola ....arr	...	...	2 43	...	...	...	...	5 43	...	...	9 59	...
,, (283) ....dep	...	...	2 57	...	...	...	...	5 45	...	...	10 1	...
Panicale	...	...	...	...	...	...	...	...	...	...	10 18	...
Chiusi (275) ....arr	...	...	3 32	...	...	...	...	6 10	...	...	10 30	...
,, ...dep	...	...	3 40	...	...	...	...	6 19	...	...	10 36	...
Figulle	...	...	...	...	...	...	...	...	...	...	RC	...
Orvieto	...	...	4 23	...	...	...	...	...	...	...	11 12	...
Alviano	...	...	...	...	...	...	...	...	...	...	...	...
Attigliano (283)	...	...	4 53	...	...	...	...	...	...	10 59	11 38	...
Orte 283)..........arr	...	...	5 8	...	...	...	...	7 29	...	11 21	11 51	...
Ancona (283)......dep	...	...	...	...	...	...	...	2340	...	...	...	...
Orte ....dep	...	...	5 13	...	...	...	...	7 32	...	...	11 53	...
Civita Castellana	...	...	...	...	...	...	...	...	...	...	...	...
Fara Sabina	...	...	...	...	...	...	...	...	...	...	...	...
Monte Rotondo	...	...	...	...	...	...	...	...	...	...	...	...
ROME Termini ......arr	...	...	6 45	...	...	...	...	8 50	...	...	13 5	...

FERRARA and RIMINI.

‡—Until 30th September.

Dist. E.M.													
—	**Ferrara** ....dep	442	9*20	12 36	13 0	1712	**Rimini**......dep	...	7 34	1355	16 30	18§28	2255
15	Portomaggiore	521	9 56	13 6	13 40	1749	Cesenatico	...	8 9	1437	17‡2	19 6	2333
25¾	Lavezzola...arr	548	1021	...	14 8	1814	Classe	...	8 44	1520	B	19 42	0 11
34¼	Alfonsine	615	1042	A	14 35	1834	**Ravenna** ...arr	...	8 51	1530	17 36	19 51	0 20
45¼	**Ravenna** ...arr	642	1110	13 58	15 4	19 2	,, ...dep	430	9 3	1550	17 40	20 5	—
...	,, ...dep	811	1120	14 2	15 12	19 9	Alfonsine	458	9 30	1632	...	20 37	...
48¼	Classe	819	1128	...	15 21	1917	Lavezzola dep	519	9 52	1713	...	21 1	...
63¾	Cesenatico	851	12 2	14‡34	16 8	1950	Portomaggiore	546	1020	1747	18 37	21 32	...
77	**Rimini 285**.arr	923	1235	15 5	16 46	2021	**Ferrara** 279A ar	620	1055	1826	19 7	22 9	...

*—Daily until 15th Sept.; from 16th Sept. on Tues., Thurs., and Sat. only.
§—Daily until 15th Sept.; from 16th Sept. on Mon., Wed., Fri. and only.
A—Runs on Mon., Wed., and Fri. only.
B—Runs on Tues., Thurs., & Sat. only.
Extra. { Portomaggiore dep 7 55 Mon. and / Ferrara ....arr 8 33 Fri. only.

RC—Restaurant Car in this train.]

VENICE, PADUA, and BOLOGNA.

‡—Until 30th Sept.

Dist E M			1,2,3	1,2,3	1,2,3	1& 3	1 & 2	1,2,3	1,2,3	1,2,3	1,2,3	1 & 2	1,2,3	
—	**Venice**...dep	See	...	5 15	7 0	8 0	10 15	1120	14 25	17 0	1835	21 20	23 8	...
5½	**Mestre**	also	...	5 27	7 12	8 11	10 27	1134	14 37	17 14	1850	21 31	2321	...
11¼	Marano	p.	...	—	...	...	RC	1146	...	17 26	19 2	...	...	...
23	**Padua** 280	280	6 3	...	7 46	8 43	10 59	1225	15 14	18 2	1945	22 1	2357	...
29	Abano..........	1,2,3	6 16	...	...	8 59	11‡9	1238	15‡24	18 18	1950	...	...	...
37¼	Monselice 279C	...	6 39	...	8 9	9 26	11 26	13 1	15 44	18 46	2020	...	0 25	...
50¼	**Rovigo 282** ...	3 30	7 15	...	8 35	1030	11 52	1337	16 12	19 20	2053	22 41	0 53	...
55¼	Arquà..........	3 43	7 26	...	...	1043	...	1349	...	—	21 3	...	...	...
59	Polesella	3 52	7 34	...	8 49	1053	12 5	1358	16 26	...	2111	SC	...	...
67½	P'telagoscuro	4 23	8 0	...	9 7	1123	12 22	1427	16 44	...	2135	...	...	...
70¼	**Ferrara** 279A	4 31	8 12	...	9 18	1131	12 32	1444	16 57	...	2147	23 16	1 31	...
84½	S. Pietro in Cl.	6 40	8 45	...	...	—	12 55	1522	17 28	...	2219	...	1 57	...
99½	**Bologna**...arr	7 20	9 20	...	10 3	...	13 16	1559	17 58	...	2254	23 57	2 20	...
182	FLORENCE 279 arr		1325	...	1325	...	17 18	...	23 16	...	...	3 26	6 48	...

	1,2,3	1,2,3	1,2,3	1&3	1,2,3	1& 3	1,2,3	1,2,3	1,2,3	1,2,3	1 & 2	1,2,3	1&3	
FLORENCE dep	2120	...	23 50	2 15	...	...	6 20	...	10 50	1155	14 30	...	...	...
Bologna..........dep	1 30	...	4 45	5 55	8 10	...	10 28	...	14 25	1710	18 30	...	2130	...
S. Pietro in Casale	1 55	...	5 23	...	8 46	...	10 52	...	15 2	1747	18 51	...	2211	...
Ferrara..........	2 26	...	6 2	6 40	9 26	...	11 21	13 30	15 42	1822	19 16	19 27	23 3	...
Pontelagoscuro ...	...	...	6 9	...	9 34	...	11 28	13 39	15 49	—	RC	19 35	2312	...
Polesella	...	...	6 35	...	10 0	...	11 46	14 14	16 15	...	19 37	20 4	2344	...
Arquà..........	...	...	6 43	...	10 8	...	...	14 25	16 23	...	...	20 13	2353	...
Rovigo	3 4	5 33	7 25	7 14	1025	11 7	12 5	14 58	16 39	...	19 54	20 35	0 5	...
Monselice	3 30	6 11	7 57	...	1056	1147	12 32	15 40	17 10	...	20 18	21 10	—	...
Abano	...	6 36	8 18	...	1117	1212	12‡53	16 6	17 31	...	20‡34	21 33	...	...
Padua	3 58	7 4	8 40	7 55	1143	1230	13 10	16 40	17 53	...	20 49	22 0	...	...
Marano	...	7 35	9 12	...	...	13 5	...	17 15	18 22	...	...	22 33	...	...
Mestre	4 25	7 47	9 24	8 20	12 8	1319	13 37	17 29	18 34	...	21 17	22 48	...	...
Venice 285A ...arr	4 40	8 0	9 40	8 33	1220	1335	13 50	17 45	18 50	...	21 27	23 0	...	...

ROME, FLORENCE, BOLOGNA, PIACENZA, AND MILAN.

SLEEPING CARS. { Rome to Milan—in 18.5 and 21.5 from Rome. Rome to Bologna—in 23.50 from Rome.

RESTAURANT CAR—in 9.5 and 18.5 from Rome.

THROUGH CARRIAGE—Rome to Berlin in 9.5 from Rome. Rome to Munich in 9.5 and 14.40 from Rome.

	1,2,3	1,2,3	1,2,3	1,2,3	1,2,3	1,2,3	1 & 2	1,2,3	1,2,3	1,2,3	1,2,3	1& 2	1,2,3	1 & 3	1,2,3	1,2,3	1,2,3	1,2,3	1,2,3
ROME—																			
Termini ....dep	...	...	...	...	...	...	...	...	...	5 50	8 25	9 5	...	...	...	9 15	1210	...	14 40
M. Rotondo	...	...	...	...	...	...	...	...	...	6 24	...	...	...	...	...	9 52	1236	...	...
Fara Sabina...........	...	...	...	...	...	...	...	...	...	6 37	...	...	...	...	...	10 6	1248	...	...
Civita Castellana ...	...	...	...	...	...	...	...	...	...	7 15	...	RC	...	...	...	10 46	1322	...	...
Orte...............arr	...	...	...	...	...	...	...	...	...	7 31	9 38	1018	...	...	...	11 3	1334	...	15 49
ANCONA **283** arr	...	...	...	...	...	...	...	...	...	13 22	14*27	...	...	...	...	...	1840	...	...
Orte...............dep	...	...	...	...	...	5 45	...	...	5 58	8 13	9 43	1024	...	...	...	11 13	...	16 10	15 55
Attigliano	...	...	...	...	...	6 6	...	...	6 18	8 33		...	...	...	...	11 36	...	16 30	16 11
Alviano..................	...	...	...	...	...	6 18	...	...				...	...	...	...	11 48	...		...
Orvieto	...	...	...	...	...	6 51	...	4 0	...	...		11 7	...	...	...	12 22	...	...	16 40
Ficulle	...	...	...	...	...	7 25	...	4 36	...	...		...	...	...	...	13 0	...	...	17 8
Chiusi ....arr	...	...	...	...	...	7 47	...	4 58	...	...		1147	...	...	...	13 22	...	...	17 25
" ....dep	...	...	...	...	...	7 58	...	5 8	...	...		1153	...	...	...	13 35	...	...	17 33
Panicale.................	...	...	...	...	...	8 11	...	5 23	...	...		RC	...	...	...	13 50	...	...	17 48
Terontola......arr	...	...	...	...	...	8 34	...	5 45	...	...		1217	...	...	...	14 12	...	...	18 6
" ......dep	...	...	...	...	...	8 42	...	5 55	...	...		1219	...	...	...	14 18	...	15 54	18 16
Cortona	...	...	...	...	...	8 51	...	6 8	...	...	To Perugia. Does not run on Sundays.	...	...	...	...	14 28	...	16 4	18 25
Castiglion Fiorentin	...	...	...	...	...	9 7	...	6 24	...	...		...	...	...	...	14 44	...	16 19	18 39
Arezzo ....arr	...	...	...	...	...	9 31	...	6 51	...	...		1255	...	...	...	15 9	...	16 43	18 59
" ....dep	...	5 13	...	...	...	9 37	...	7 5	...	...		1257	...	...	...	15 17	...	17 0	19 11
S. Giovanni	...	6 12	...	...	...	10 28	...	8 12	...	...		...	...	13 57	...	16 19	...	18 5	19 58
S. Ellero.................	...	6 48	...	...	...	11 0	...	8 48	...	...		13‡56	...	14 40	...	16 54	...	18 41	RC
Pontassieve	...	7 0	...	...	...	11 8	...	8 58	...	...		...	...	14 50	...	17 3	...	18 54	20 28
Florence Marte...	...	7 28	...	...	...	11 33	...	9 21	...	...		...	...	15 19	...	17 29	...	19 23	20 45
FLORENCE { ar	...	7 35	...	...	...	11 40	...	9 30	...	...		1419	...	15 27	...	17 36	...	19 30	20 52
Piazza Santa Maria Novella { dp	...	...		7 50	8 40	...	10 50	...	11 55	...		1430	15 40	...	17 45	...	1845	...	21 20
Sesto	...	...		8 2	8 58	...	11 1	...	12 13	...		...	15 58	...	18 0	...	19 3	...	...
Prato	...	...	Until 30th September.	8 15	9 16	...	11 14	...	12 30	...	*—Tues., Thurs., and Sat. only.	1450	16 15	...	18 16	...	1921	...	21 42
Pistoja ....arr	...	...		8 32	9 40	...	11 30	...	12 51	...		15 5	16 36	...	18 37	...	1942	...	21 58
" ....dep	...	...				...	11 38	...	13 10	...		1511		...	18 48	...		...	22 16
Pracchia	5§52	...		...	...	...	12 37	...	14 13	...		16 4	...	...	19 58	...	...	...	23 12
Porretta Bagni	6 18	6 30		...	...	...	13 10	...	14 50	...		1634	...	...	20 31	...	...	...	23 37
Vergato..................		6 54		...	...	...	13 34	...	15 16	...		...	...	...	20 56	...	...	...	23 57
Bologna.........arr	...	7 52		...	...	...	14 15	...	16 22	...		1739	...	...	22 0	...	...	...	0 39
VENICE **279A** arr	...	12 20		...	...	...	18 50	...	...	...	...	2127	...	...	...	...	...	...	4 40
BRINDISI 285A dep	...	...		...	17 25	...	...	...	...	...	...	...	...	...	...	...	6 35	...	6 35
ANCONA 285A dep	...	...	4 40	...	5 15	...	8 55	...	...	...	...	13 0	13 0	15 18	...	...	2045	...	20 45
					1,2,3		1,2,3	1,2,3				1 &2	1,2,3	1,2,3			1,2,3		1,2,3
Bologna ....dep	...	...	9 25	...	11 40	...	14 38	15 45	...	...	...	18 8	18 25	21 39	...	...	1 0	...	1 20
Lavino	...	...	...	...	11 53	...	...	15 57	...	...	...	...	18 38	21 57	...	...	...	...	...
Samoggia	...	...	...	...	12 6	...	...	16 7	...	...	...	...	18 51	22 11	...	...	...	...	...
Modena ....arr	...	...	9 58	...	12 31	...	15 13	16 32	...	...	...	1841	19 15	22 46	...	...	1 37	...	1 55
" ....dep	...	...	10 0	...	12 40	...	15 16	16 38	...	...	...	1844	19 23	23 12	...	...		...	1 58
Reggio	...	...	1024	...	13 17	...	15 45	17 13	...	...	...	19 9	19 54	0 5	...	...	...	...	2 26
Parma ....arr	...	...	1050	...	14 0	...	16 14	17 48	...	...	...	1937	20 33	0 51	...	...	...	...	2 56
" ....dep	...	...	1055	...	14 7	...	16 20	17 53	...	...	...	1942	20 38		...	...	...	...	3 2
Castelguelfo	...	...	...	...	14 26	...	...	18 9	...	...	...	...	20 56	...	...		...	...	...
Borgo S. Donnino ...	...	...	1119	...	14 40	...	16 45	18 22	...	...	...	20 4	21 9	...	...		...	...	3 28
Pontenure	...	...	...	...	15 19	...	...	19 3	...	...	...	RC	21 49	...	...		...	...	...
Piacenza 273 arr	...	...	1155	...	15 32	...	17 20	19 15	...	...	...	2034	22 0	...	...		...	...	4 10
ALESSANDRIA arr	...	...	...	...	...	...	20 20	22 40	...	...	...	2240	...	...	...		...	...	7 0
TURIN .....**271** arr	...	...	...	...	...	...	23 25	0 16	...	...	...	01 6	...	...	...		...	...	8 41
Piacenza ....dep	...	...	12 0	...	15 45	...	17 30	19 25	...	...	...	2039	22 13	...	...		...	...	4 25
S. Stefano	...	...	...	...	15 56	...	...	19 36	...	...	...	...	22 24	...	...		...	...	...
Codogno..................	...	...	...	...	16 7	...	17 49	19 46	...	...	...	2052	22 40	...	...		...	...	4 44
Casalpusterlengo	...	...	...	...	16 16	...	17 57	19 56	...	...	...	...	22 48	...	...	RC—Restaurant Car. SC—Sleeping Car.	...	...	4 52
Lodi	...	...	...	...	16 42	...	18 18	20 22	...	...	...	2115	23 14	...	...		...	...	5 15
Melegnano	...	...	...	...	17 4	...	18 34	20 44	...	...	...	...	23 34	...	...		...	...	5 34
Rogoredo	...	...	...	...	17 20	...	...	21 0	...	...	...	...	23 50	...	...		...	...	5 50
MILAN Centrale...	...	...	13 5	...	17 30	...	18 55	21 10	...	...	...	2145	24 0	...	...		...	...	6 0
BASLE ....**258** arr	...	...	...	...	...	...	7 a10	8 a57	...	...	...	8a57	...	...	...	...	...	...	4 p6

For Continuation of Trains see next page.

BORGO S. DONNINO and SALSOMAGGIORE.

Borgo S. Donnino dep	6 36	9 14	12 15	15 36	1720
Salsomaggiore......arr	7 11	9 49	12 50	16 6	1755
Salsomaggiore.........	7 31	10 49	1345	1611	19 7
Borgo S. Donnino 279	8 6	11 24	1420	1641	1942

☞ Italian Railway Time—See Note on page 272. ☜

Fares and Luggage Rates, see page 269.]

ROME, FLORENCE, BOLOGNA, PIACENZA, AND MILAN.

THROUGH CARRIAGE—Rome to Vienna in 14.40 and 23.50 from Rome.

	1,2,3	1,2,3		1,2,3	1 & 2	1,2,3	1&2	1,2,3	1,2,3			
ROME—												
Termini ....dep	15 30	1545	...	...	18 ‡5	18 40	21 5	22 20	23 50	...	...	...
M. Rotondo	...	1624	...	...	RC	19 15	...	22 48	...	...	...	...
Fara Sabina	...	1639	...	...	SC	19 28	SC	23 1	SC	...	...	...
Civita Castellana	...	1725	...	...	...	20 8	...	...	...	...	...	...
Orte ....arr	16 47	1744	...	...	19 18	20 25	2218	23 50	1 6	...	...	...
ANCONA **283** ...arr	22 32	...	...	...	...	...	...	5 24	...	...	...	...
Orte ....dep	...	...	...	...	19 24	20 33	2224	...	1 12	...	...	...
Attigliano	...	...	...	...	19 40	20 54	...	...	1 29	...	...	...
Alviano	...	...	...	...	...	21 6	...	...	...	...	...	...
Orvieto	...	...	...	...	20 9	21 40	...	...	2 0	...	...	...
Ficulle	...	...	...	...	RC	22 16	...	...	...	...	...	...
Chiusi ....arr	...	...	...	...	20 51	22 38	2344	...	2 45	...	...	...
„ ....dep	...	...	...	21 7	20 57	—	2350	...	2 51	...	...	...
Panicale	...	...	...	2123	...	...	...	...	...	...	...	...
Terontola ....arr	...	...	...	2151	21 21	...	...	...	3 20	...	...	...
„ ....dep	...	...	...	22 7	21 24	...	...	...	3 31	...	...	...
Cortona	...	...	...	2217	...	...	...	...	3 39	...	...	...
Castiglion Fiorentino	...	...	...	2237	...	...	...	...	3 51	...	...	...
Arezzo ....arr	...	...	...	23 4	21 59	...	0 43	...	4 9	...	...	...
„ ....dep	...	...	...	—	22 6	...	0 45	...	4 17	...	...	...
S. Giovanni	...	...	...	...	...	...	...	...	4 59	...	...	...
S. Ellero	...	...	...	...	...	...	...	...	...	...	...	...
Pontassieve	...	...	...	...	...	...	...	...	5 34	...	...	...
Florence Marte	...	...	...	...	...	...	...	...	5 51	...	...	...
FLORENCE Piazza Santa Maria Novella arr	...	...	...	...	23 28	...	2 8	...	5 58	...	...	...
„ dep	23 50	...	...	...	23 39	5 15	2 15	...	6 20	...	...	...
Sesto	0 8	...	...	...	...	5 33	...	...	...	...	...	...
Prato	0 23	...	...	...	23 57	5 52	...	...	6 44	...	...	...
Pistoja ....arr	0 44	...	...	...	0 11	6 13	2 47	3 Cl.	7 1	...	...	...
„ ....dep	0 55	...	...	...	0 16	—	2 53	5 0	7 11	...	...	...
Pracchia	2 15	...	...	...	...	...	...	7 0	8 1	...	...	...
Porretta Bagni	2 46	...	...	...	1 40	...	4 12	7 39	8 25	...	...	...
Vergato	3 13	...	...	...	...	...	...	—	8 48	...	...	...
Bologna ....arr	4 17	...	...	...	2 42	...	5 15	...	9 34	...	...	...
VENICE **279A** ...arr	8 33	...	...	...	8 33	...	8 33	...	13 50	...	...	...
BRINDISI 285A...dep	—	...	...	...	12 5	...	...	...	...	17 25	...	...
ANCONA 235A ...dep	...	...	...	...	23 5	...	...	...	...	5 15	...	...
		1,2,3	1,2,3	1,2,3	1 & 2	1,2,3	1 &2			1,2,3		
Bologna ....dep	...	4 57	...	5 50	2 55	8 0	5 33	...	...	10 17	...	...
Lavino	...	5 11	...	...	...	8 11	...	...	...	...	...	...
Samoggia	...	5 21	...	...	...	8 20	...	...	...	...	...	...
Modena ....arr	...	5 49	...	6 29	3 27	8 40	6 4	...	...	10 52	...	...
„ ....dep	...	6 25	...	—	3 29	8 46	6 7	...	...	10 58	...	...
Reggio	...	6 59	...	...	3 53	9 13	6 32	...	...	11 26	...	...
Parma ....arr	...	7 40	...	...	4 19	9 40	6 59	...	...	11 53	...	...
„ ....dep	4 55	7 50	...	...	4 25	9 46	7 5	...	...	12 0	...	...
Castelguelfo	5 10	8 10	...	...	...	...	...	...	...	...	...	...
Borgo S. Donnino	5 22	8 26	...	...	4 46	10 8	7 28	...	...	12 23	...	...
Pontenure	5 59	9 8	...	...	...	...	...	...	...	...	...	...
Piacenza 273 ...arr	6 10	9 20	...	...	5 20	10 44	8 0	...	...	13 0	...	...
ALESSANDRIA ...arr	...	13 6	...	...	7 0	13 6	1055	...	...	16 30	...	...
TURIN **271** ....arr	...	1512	...	...	8 41	15 12	1240	...	...	19 0	...	...
Piacenza ....dep	6 15	9 43	...	...	5 25	10 54	8 5	...	...	13 5	...	...
S. Stefano	6 26	9 54	...	...	...	...	...	1,2,3	...	...	...	...
Codogno	6 50	10 5	9 19	...	...	11 10	...	13 3	...	13 21	...	...
Casalpusterlengo	6 58	1015	9 27	...	...	11 18	...	...	...	13 29	...	...
Lodi	7 24	1042	9 46	...	...	11 41	...	13 30	...	13 50	...	...
Melegnano	7 45	11 4	...	...	...	11 56	...	...	...	...	...	...
Rogoredo	8 1	1120	...	...	...	...	...	...	...	...	...	...
MILAN Centrale arr	8 10	1130	1020	...	6 45	12 15	9 10	14 5	...	14 25	...	...
BASLE **258** ....arr	6 p58	...	...	...	4 p6	9 p0	6 p58	11 p3	...	11 p3	...	...

§—Runs until 15th September only.
†—Stops at S. Ellero in July, August, and September only.
‡—Admits also 3rd class between Rome and Florence.

FERRARA and S. GIOVANNI IN PERSICETO.

‡—Wed. & Sat. only.

E.M.								
	Ferrara ....dep	6 42	10 0	...	14 45	18 27	...	...
20	Cento	8 0	11 12	12 20	15 56	19 27	...	...
28	**S. Giovanni in P. 282** ...arr	8 26	...	12 46	16 20	19‡50	...	...

S. Giovanni in P. ....dep	...	8 50	13 30	...	16 40	19‡58	...	...	...	...	...
Cento	6 33	9 28	13 56	14 30	17 45	20 22	...	...	...	...	...
Ferrara 279A ....arr	7 35	10 38	...	15 38	19 5	...	...	...	...	...	...

CREMONA and BORGO S. DONNINO.

E.M.									
	Cremona ....dep	5 57	10 17	15 45	20 25	...	...	...	...
13	Busseto	6 48	10 53	16 34	21 17	...	...	...	...
21½	**Borgo S. Donnino (279)** ...arr	7 13	11 14	17 0	21 40	...	...	...	...

Borgo S. Donnino ....dep	5 50	9 8	17 16	20 20	...	...	...	...	...
Busseto	6 16	9 31	17 43	20 45	...	...	...	...	...
Cremona (282) ....arr	7 3	10 7	18 27	21 32	...	...	...	...	...

MANTUA and MONSELICE.

E.M.								
	Mantua ....dep	5 5	7 20	...	14 40	17 7	†—Thurs. and Sat. only.	...
15½	Nogara (282)	5 47	8 5	...	15 20	17 42		...
25	Cerea	6 11	8 27	...	15 40	18 3		...
28½	**Legnago (282)** ....dep	6 39	9 1	11†53	16 0	18 34		...
37	Montagnana	7 7	9 31	13 26	16 24	18 59		...
52	**Monselice (279A)** ...arr	7 49	10 21	15 30	17 0	19 37		...

Monselice ....dep	...	7 25	9 ‡46	13 15	17 14	20 22	...	‡—Mon., Thurs., and Sat. only.	...
Montagnana	...	8 11	12 42	14 9	17 56	21 4	...		...
Legnago ....dep	5 38	8 52	13 31	15 5	18 28	21 28	...		...
Cerea	5 49	9 6	—	15 21	18 42	—	...		...
Nogara	6 9	9 27	...	15 45	19 3	...	...		...
Mantua (282) ...arr	6 50	10 8	...	16 30	19 44	...	...		...

PADUA and PIAZZOLA.

E.M.							
	Padua B.M. ....dep	8 0	11 30	15 30	19 15	...	...
10½	**Piazzola sul Brenta** arr	8 35	12 5	16 5	19 50	...	...

Piazzola sul Brenta dep	6 25	9 50	14 0	17 25	...	...	...
Padua B.M. ....arr	7 0	10 25	14 35	18 0	...	...	...

☞ Italian Railway Time—See Note on page 273.

[Fares and Luggage Rates, see page 269.

MILAN, BRESCIA, VERONA, PADUA, and VENICE.

Dist.	TURIN (269) ...dep	...	...	...	...	...	...	...	6 35	6 35	...	...	1125	11 25	...	1125	12 0	15 5	...	20 0	...
E.M.	**Milan**—	1,2,3	1,2,3	1,2,3	1,2,3	1,2,3	1,2,3	1,2,3	1 & 2	1,2,3	Lus	1,2,3	1,2,3	1,2,3	1,2,3	1,2,3	1,2,3	1,2,3	1,2,3	1,2,3	1,2,3
—	Central Station dp	...	...	...	5 15	7 5	7 35	7 50	9 45	9 55	1225	...	14 5	14 40	...	1515	1655	18 20	19 30	23 25	0 30
11¾	Melzo	...	...	...	5 49	...	...	8 21	...	10 27	...	...	...	...	...	1547	...	...	20 0	SC	0 52
16¼	Cassano	...	...	...	6 4	...	...	8 35	...	10 41	...	...	...	...	...	16 1	...	RC	20 15	...	1 1
20	**Treviglio 281** arr	...	...	...	6 12	...	8 3	8 43	RC	10 49	...	...	1432	...	...	16 9	1724	18 49	20 24	23 54	1 9
...	" ...dep	...	...	...	6 15	...	8 5	8 52	...	10 55	...	...	1435	...	...	1614	1729	18 51	20 30	23 57	1 11
28	Romano di Lombard	...	...	...	6 37	C	...	9 15	...	11 17	S	...	1449	...	...	1636	1745	19 5	20 52	...	1 26
36½	Chiari	...	...	...	6 57	...	8 32	9 37	...	11 37	...	...	15 6	...	...	1656	18 2	19 21	21 13	...	1 42
40¾	**Rovato**	6 55	...	...	7 7	...	8 42	9 47	1043	11 46	...	1053	1515	...	13 36	17 7	1812	19 31	21 23	...	1 51
51	**Brescia** ...arr	7 21	...	...	7 33	8 18	8 58	1010	1059	12 8	...	1117	1530	15 51	14 2	1730	1830	19 48	21 45	0 43	2 8
...	" (281)...dep		...	5 35	8 30	8 20			11 3	12 18	...			15 55		1738	1840	19 53	21 54	0 48	2 13
56	Rezzato	...	...	5 48	8 42	...	...	...	...	12 31	...	...	...	...	...	1750	1852	...	22 6	...	...
65	Lonato	...	...	6 9	9 4	...	...	...	...	12 53	...	...	...	...	...	1813	1915	...	22 28	...	2 37
68¼	Desenzano	...	...	6 18	9 13	8 47	...	...	1131	13 5	...	...	...	16 22	...	1820	1928	20 24	22 40	...	2 46
77	Peschiera	...	...	6 40	9 34	...	...	...	1145	13 26	...	...	...	16 35	...		1951	20 39	23 1	C	3 3
79½	Castelnuovo	...	...	6 49	9 43	...	...	...	...	13 35	...	...	...	...	...	...	20 1	...	23 10	...	...
83¾	Sommacampagna	...	...	7 0	9 54	...	...	...	...	13 46	...	...	...	...	...	...	2013	...	23 21	...	...
91¼	**Verona** P.N.	...	...	7 13	10 7	9 19	...	...	12 9	14 2	...	...	...	16 59	...	...	2027	21 7	23 37	1 55	3 30
93¼	**Verona** P. Ves. arr	...	...	7 21	10 15	9 25	...	...	1214	14 8	1440	...	...	17 6	...	...	2035	21 12	23 43	2 0	3 35
118¾	ALA (282) arr	...	...	...	11 30	1130	...	...	14 7	17 28	...	...	...	20 49	...	...	2232	22 32	...	5 40	5 40
	ALA (282) dep	...	...	5 40	8 18	...	...	9 0	...	...	...	...	...	14 23	...	...	...	18 21	...	21 30	...
							1 & 3														
...	**Verona** Porto Vescovo ...dep	5 0	...	7 40	10 27	9 33	...	1127	1223	...	1446	1535	...	17 15	...	1920	2145	21 25	...	2 15	3 50
96½	S. Martino	5 9	...	7 49	...	...	...	1136	...	...	...	1544	...	...	...	1930	2159	...	...	...	...
100¼	Caldiero	5 21	...	8 1	...	...	...	1148	...	...	...	1556	...	...	...	1943	2216	...	...	SC	...
105½	Sambonifacio	5 32	...	8 12	...	...	...	12 3	RC	...	...	1610	...	17 36	...	1956	2233	...	...	C	4 11
113	Montebello	5 50	...	8 31	...	C	...	1221	...	...	...	1629	...	...	...	2017	23 4	...	...	...	...
123	**Vicenza (288)** arr	6 11	...	8 53	11 9	1014	...	1243	13 4	...	S	1651	...	18 9	...	2040	2335	22 11	...	3 1	4 42
...	" ...dep	6 14	7 50	8 58	11 13	1018	...	1318	13 8	...	...	1657	...	18 14	...	2055		22 15	...	3 5	4 46
132¼	Pojana	6 35	8 13	9 19	...	...	...	1339	...	...	...	1720	...	...	...	2118	...	...	...	...	...
141½	**Padua** ...arr	6 55	8 34	9 39	11 39	1044	...	1358	1334	...	...	1740	...	18 43	...	2140	...	22 43	...	3 34	5 14
...	" ...dep	7 4	8 40	9 45	11 43	1048	12 30	14 5	1338	...	...	1753	...	18 48	19 10	22 0	...	22 49	...	3 38	5 20
145¼	Ponte di Brenta	7 13	8 50	9 54	...	...	12 40	1414	...	...	...	18 2	...	...	19 20	22 9	...	...	...	...	5 29
154	Marano	7 35	9 12	1014	...	...	13 5	1433	...	...	...	1822	...	...	19 46	2233	...	...	...	...	5 51
159¾	**Mestre** ...arr	7 47	9 24	1026	12 8	1113	13 19	1444	14 3	...	1620	1834	...	19 16	20 0	2246	...	23 17	...	4 5	6 2
...	" ...dep	7 49	9 27	1029	12 10	1115	13 21	1449	14 5	...	1630	1839	...	19 19	20 2	2243	...	23 19	...	4 8	6 6
164¾	**Venice** ...arr	8 0	9 40	1040	12 20	1125	13 35	15 0	1415	...	1640	1850	...	19 30	20 15	2348	...	23 30	...	4 19	6 17

	1,2,3	1,2,3	1,2,3	1,2,3	1,2,3	1&2	1,2,3	1,2,3	1 &3	1,2,3	Lus	1,2,3	1 & 2	1,2,3	1,2,3	1,2,3	1,2,3	1,2,3	1,2,3	1,2,3	1,2,3
Venice ...dep	...	4 50	5 15	...	7 5	8 0	...	...	8 40	9 30	12 0	12 15	14 0	13 15	17 0	...	18 10	18 35	20 10	2130	0 10
Mestre ...arr	...	5 2	5 25	...	7 17	8 10	...	...	8 54	9 40	12 10	12 27	14 10	13 29	1712	...	18 20	18 47	20 24	2142	0 21
" ...dep	...	5 4	5 27	...	7 20	8 11	...	...	8 56	9 44	12 21	12 30	14 12	13 31	1714	...	18 22	18 50	20 25	2145	0 26
Marano	...	5 16	...	...	7 32	...	...	...	9 10	...	...	12 42	...	13 45	1726	...	...	19 2	20 39	2153	...
Ponte di Brenta	...	5 38	...	...	7 54	...	...	...	9 36	...	...	13 4	...	14 11	1748	...	...	19 24	21 5	2217	...
Padua ...arr	...	5 47	5 56	...	8 3	8 37	...	...	9 45	10 13	...	13 13	14 37	14 20	1757	...	18 51	19 33	21 15	2226	0 56
" ...dep	...	6 15	6 0	...	8 8	8 41	...	...		10 18	S	13 22	14 42		18 3	...	18 55	19 42	21 21	2235	1 2
Pojana	...	6 36	...	...	8 28	...	...	...	...	...	...	13 42	...	...	1823	...	...	20 2	21 46	...	SC
Vicenza arr	...	6 56	6 29	...	8 48	9 7	...	...	...	10 47	...	14 2	15 8	...	1843	...	19 24	20 22	22 10	23 8	1 33
Vicenza dep	...	7 0	6 32	...		9 9	...	11 1	...	10 51	...	14 8	15 13	...	1848	...	19 27	20 32		2316	1 39
Montebello	...	7 23	...	...	...	...	...	11 24	...	...	...	14 32	...	...	1912	...	...	20 55	...	...	...
Sambonifacio	...	7 39	...	...	...	...	...	11 40	...	11 25	...	14 49	15 45	...	1929	...	RC	21 13	...	2349	...
Caldiero	...	7 50	...	...	...	...	...	11 51	...	...	...	15 0	...	...	1940	...	...	21 28	...	...	...
S. Martino	...	8 2	...	...	...	...	...	12 3	...	...	...	15 12	...	...	1949	...	...	21 41	...	...	...
Verona P.V. arr	...	8 10	7 19	...	...	9 50	...	12 11	...	11 46	14 0	15 20	16 5	...	1957	...	20 15	21 50	...	0 12	2 30
ALA 282 arr	...	...	...	...	...	1130	...	14 7	...	14 7	...	17 28	20 49	...	...	...	22 32	...	...	...	5 40
ALA 282 dep	...	...	5 40	...	...	8 18	...	9 0	...	9 0	...		14 23	14 23	...	...	18 21	...	...	2130	21 30
Verona Porto Vescovo...dep	5 0	...	7 30	...	...	10 0	...	12 43	...	12 3	14 5	...	16 15	16 25	...	18 5	20 25	...	...	1 5	2 45
Verona P.N. ...	5 7	...	7 36	...	...	10 6	...	12 50	...	12 11	...	...	16 23	16 36	...	18 13	20 32	...	...	1 13	2 53
Sommacampagna	5 21	...	7 50	...	...	...	...	13 7	...	...	...	...	...	16 51	...	18 29	...	...	...	...	...
Castelnuovo	5 30	...	8 0	...	...	...	...	13 19	...	...	...	...	...	17 1	...	18 40	...	...		...	SC
Peschiera	5 38	...	8 7	...	...	1029	...	13 27	...	12 39	...	...	...	17 9	...	18 48	20 59	...		1 43	...
Desenzano	6 2	7 10	8 29	...	...	1045	...	13 56	...	12 58	...	...	16 59	17 34	...	19 14	21 18	...		2 11	3 34
Lonato	6 13	7 21	8 39	...	...	...	...	14 9	...	RC	...	...	...	17 45	...	19 25	RC	...		2 24	...
Rezzato	6 32	7 43	8 55	...	...	...	...	14 31	...	13 22	...	...	...	18 5	...	19 46	...	...		...	...
Brescia ...arr	6 42	7 55	9 5	...	...	1113	...	14 43	...	13 33	S	18 3	17 27	18 14	...	19 57	21 48	...		2 50	4 6
" ...dep	6 48	8 2	9 10	9 30	10 15	1117	13 5	15 35	1450	13 38	...	18 28	17 32	18 20	...	20 6	21 53	...		3 30	4 10
Rovato	7 12	8 27	...	9 55	10 40	...	1328	16 6	1515	13 58	...		...	18 40	...	20 31	22 13	...		4 1	4 34
Chiari	7 20	8 36	...	10 5		...	1338	16 17		14 6	...	...	...	18 48	...	20 40	22 21	...		4 12	4 44
Romano di Lom.	7 38	8 56	...	1025	...	...	1356	16 40	...	14 21	...	...	...	19 3	...	21 1	22 36	...		4 35	5 5
Treviglio ...arr	7 56	9 17	...	1040	...	...	1410	17 3	...	14 34	...	...	...	19 16	...	21 22	22 49	...		5 0	5 25
" ...dep	8 1	9 23	...	1050	...	...	1415	17 15	...	14 36	...	...	...	19 24	...	21 32	22 50	...		5 47	5 32
Cassano	...	9 31	...	11 0	...	...	...	17 27	...	...	...	...	...	19 33	...	21 41	...	...	...	5 59	...
Melzo	...	9 43	...	1111	...	...	...	17 43	...	...	...	...	...	19 43	...	21 55	...	...	...	6 16	...
Milan Cent. arr	8 32	1010	1025	1135	...	1225	1450	18 20	...	15 7	16 25	...	18 40	20 5	...	22 25	23 20	...	...	6 55	6 10
TURIN 269 arr	1235	...	...	...	...	1525	...	21 45	...	19 15	...	...	21 45	23 50	...	...	...	...	...	9 50	9 50

RC—Restaurant Car.
SC—Sleeping Car.

C—Will not take 3rd Class locally between Milan and Venice.
S—Simplon Express, Treno di Lusso.

MILAN, TREVIGLIO, and BERGAMO.

Milan											
Centrale	515	720	750	9 55	1230	14 5	1720	1750	1930	2125	2325
Melzo	549	...	821	1027	13 2	...	...	1819	20 0	2159	...
Treviglio	633	751	848	1056	1332	1440	1749	1843	2032	2254	2354
Verdello	649	...	9 6	1113	1349	1457	...	19 0	2051	2313	0 18
Bergamo	7 5	815	920	1130	14 6	1512	1815	1916	2110	2332	0 35

Bergamo dep	543	749	850	1010	1230	1335	1643	1815	1847	2036	2158
Verdello	557	8 2	9 4	1024	1244	1351	1656	1829	19 1	2053	2212
Treviglio	630	816	923	1050	1256	1415	1715	1851	1924	2132	2225
Melzo	656	831	943	1111	1326	...	1743	...	1943	2155	...
Milan ... arr	730	850	1010	1135	14 0	1450	1820	1915	20 5	2225	2320

MILAN and SONDRIO.

‡—Until 30th Sept. [A—Until 15th Sept.

Milan											
Centrale...dep		...	5 15	7 15	7 30	...	9 42	1310	1635	...	1930
Monza		...	5 37	...	7 49	...	9 58	1330	1651	...	1949
Usmate Carnate		...	6 1	A	8 11	...	1017	1353	1712	...	20 8
Calolzio		...	6 42	...	8 52	...	1048	1434	1741	...	2038
Lecco		5 10	7 21	8 32	9 15	1010	1113	1457	18 2	1840	21 5
Mandello		5 26	7 38	...	9 29	1026	1127	1513	1817	1857	2121
Lierna		5 38	7 50	...	9 38	1038	1136	1526	1826	19 9	2133
Varenna		5 52	8 4	9 2	9 49	1052	1147	1540	1836	1923	2146
Bellano		6 3	8 14	9 8	9 58	11 2	1156	1549	1844	1933	2156
Dervio		6 12	8 22	...	10 6	1110	12 4	1557	1852	1942	22 4
Colico ...arr		6 32	8 41	9 28	1020	1130	1218	1616	19 6	20 1	2223
,, ...dep	5 37	6 50	8 46	9 32	1026	1221	—	1619	1910	—	2225
Morbegno	6 7	7 22	9 16	9 53	1054	1250	—	1650	1936	...	2255
Ardenno M.	6 21	7 36	9 30	...	11 5	13 3	...	17 4	1946	...	23 9
Sondrio arr	6 47	8 3	9 56	1027	1125	1327	...	1730	20 6	...	2335

Sondrio dp	3 58	5 35	7 10	9 56	1327	...	1558	1750	1845	20 6
Ardenno M	4 25	...	7 37	1023	1353	...	1622	1817	19 6	...
Morbegno	4 39	6 6	7 52	1037	14 7	...	1633	1831	1917	2035
Colico arr	5 8	6 30	8 22	11 6	1435	...	17 0	19 0	1943	2056
,, dep	5 10	6 34	8 29	1120	1437	1510	17 7	19 6	1949	2058
Dervio	5 30	6 49	8 46	1144	1457	1525	1722	1926	20 6	A
Bellano	5 39	6 57	8 54	1155	15 6	1533	1731	1934	2014	2118
Varenna	5 50	7 5	9 6	12 4	1514	1543	1742	1946	2022	2124
Lierna	6 3	7 15	9 17	1217	1527	1553	1753	1959	2032	...
Mandello	6 15	7 24	9 28	1229	1539	...	18 3	2011	2041	...
Lecco	6 40	7 47	10 2	1255	1554	1625	1835	2026	21 7	22 0
Calolzio	6 56	7 59	1015	1312	—	1639	1855	—	2122	...
Usmate C.	7 32	8 34	1048	1356	...	1715	1933	...	22 1	...
Monza	7 51	8 51	11 5	1419	...	1732	1951	...	2219	...
Milan C.	8 10	9 5	1118	1440	...	1745	2010	...	2238	23 1

Extra.—Milan to Lecco 17‡15, 18.15, 22.25. Lecco to Milan 5.0, 5‡55.

SONDRIO and TIRANO.

*-Until 30th Sept. §-From 16th Sept.

Sondrio ...dep	7 20	10*29	11§44	13‡35	17 50	2020
Ponte	7 46	10 49	12 6	13 56	18 21	2041
Tresenda	8 8	11 4	12 26	14 15	18 40	2057
Tirano ...arr	8 30	11 21	12 46	14 35	19 0	2115

Tirano dep	5 45	8 40	12 5	16‡20	17§45	19 ‡8	...
Tresenda	6 6	9 1	12 27	16 39	18 3	19 24	...
Ponte	6 29	9 24	12 50	17 1	18 22	19 41	...
Sondrio arr	6 46	9 41	13 7	17 18	18 38	19 56	...

CHIAVENNA and COLICO.

E.M.								
	Chiavenna dep	5 27	7 31	1018	1330	1421	18 0	20 6
8¼	Novate	6 0	8 1	1051	14 4	...	1833	‡
16¾	Colico (281) arr	6 24	8 19	1115	1428	15 5	1857	2050

Colico ...dep	6 48	8 48	9 30	1030	1225	17 3	1917	2230
Novate	7 33	9 13	‡	1050	1250	1728	1936	2255
Chiavenna arr	8 22	9 45	1015	1117	1322	18 0	20 3	2327

‡—From 1st July until 15th Sept.

BRESCIA and LECCO.

E.M.		1,2,3	1,2,3	1,2,3	1,2,3	1,2,3	1,2,3	1,2,3
—	**Brescia** ...dep	4 10	6 48	1015	14 50	18 3	1820	20 6
7½	Ospitaletto	...	7 2	1031	15 6	18 19	...	20 21
11½	Rovato ...arr	4 31	7 10	1040	15 15	18 28	1839	20 29
...	,, ...dep	4 36	7 17	1048	15 18	18 44	—	20 37
18	Palazzolo	4 55	7 37	1110	15 37	19 3	...	20 58
24½	Gorlago	5 17	8 0	1132	15 58	19 25	...	21 21
31	**Bergamo** arr	5 38	8 22	1155	16 19	19 46	...	21 45
...	,, dep	6 2	8 42	1210	16 30	19 57	...	—
36	Ponte Pietro	6 15	8 57	1223	16 44	20 10	...	...
38½	Mapello	6 25	9 7	1233	16 54	20 20	...	...
47½	Calolzio	6 53	9 37	13 2	17 25	20 48	...	...
51½	**Lecco 281** arr	7 10	9 53	1320	17 40	21 0	...	...

	1,2,3	1,2,3	1,2,3	1,2,3	1,2,3	1,2,3
Lecco ...dep	4 20	8 0	10 49	1430	...	18 45
Calolzio	4 40	8 16	11 5	1449	...	19 4
Mapello	5 15	8 49	11 39	1524	...	19 36
PonteS.Pietro	5 24	9 4	11 48	1533	...	19 45
Bergamo arr	5 37	9 19	12 0	1545	...	19 57
,, dep	5 47	9 30	12 14	16 3	1822	20 10
Gorlago	6 11	9 53	12 40	1625	1844	20 33
Palazzolo	6 35	1015	13 5	1646	19 5	20 56
Rovato ...arr	6 53	1032	13 23	17 2	1923	21 13
,, ...dep	6 55	1053	13 36	17 7	1931	21 23
Ospitaletto	7 5	11 3	13 46	1716	...	21 32
Brescia arr	7 21	1117	14 2	1730	1948	21 45

PAVIA, CREMONA, and MANTUA.

‡—Wed and Sat. only.

		1,2,3	1,2,3	1,2,3	1,2,3	1,2,3	1,2,3	1,2,3	1,2,3
Pavia ...dep		...	4 55	9 38	12 30	15‡28	...	18 0	...
Motta S. Damiano		...	5 9	9 52	12 46	15 52	...	18 17	...
Ospedaletto		...	6 6	10 51	13 49	17 28	...	19 26	...
Casalpust- arr		...	6 15	11 1	13 59	17 38	...	19 36	...
erlengo dep		...	6 32	11 5	14 1	17 46	...	19 42	...
Codogno ar 1,2,3		...	6 39	11 12	14 8	17 55	...	19 50	...
,, dep	6 55	...	7 36	11 31	14 25	—	18 37	20 58	2358
Pizzighettone	7 8	...	...	11 43	14 39	...	18 49	21 10	...
Acquanegra	7 21	...	...	11 56	14 53	...	19 2	21 23	...
Cremona ar	7 38	...	8 9	12 13	15 11	...	19 20	21 40	0 32
,, ...dep		5 10	8 15	12 20	15 17	...	19 30	21 46	—
Gazzo Pieve S. G.		5 34	8 38	12 44	15 40	...	19 53	22 8	...
Piadena		6 2	9 12	13 15	16 5	...	20 18	22 31	...
Mantua 282 arr		6 57	10 0	14 10	16 59	...	21 7	23 20	...

	1,2,3	1,2,3	1,2,3	1,2,3	1,2,3	1,2,3	1,2,3	1,2,3
Mantua ...dep	4 0	7 5	8 17	10 25	15 5	...	1955	...
Piadena	4 52	7 54	9 15	11 22	16 3	...	2050	22 0
Gazzo Pieve S.	5 13	8 15	9 36	11 46	16 24	...	2111	22 34
Cremona arr	5 35	8 37	9 58	12 7	16 45	...	2133	23 2
,, dep	5 41	8 42	1011	12 13	16 51	1955	2140	—
Acquanegra	5 59	...	1029	12 31	17 9	2014	2158	...
Pizzighettone	6 12	...	1043	12 44	17 23	2027	2211	...
Codogno arr	6 24	9 14	1055	12 56	17 35	2040	2223	...
,, dep	6 38	—	1123	14 0	18 20	—	—	...
Casalpust. arr	6 46	...	1131	14 9	18 29	...	...	...
,, dep	6 47	...	1132	14 22	18 32	...	...	...
Ospedaletto	6 57	...	1143	14 35	18 45	...	...	...
Motta S. Damia	7 45	...	1247	15 43	19 53	...	...	...
Pavia ...arr	7 57	...	13 0	15 57	20 7	...	...	...

BRESCIA and PARMA.

*—Tues., Wed., and Sat. only.

Brescia ...dep	4 15	7 35	11*25	...	1420	20 0
S. Zeno Folzano	4 26	7 46	11 36	...	1431	2011
Calvisano	5 3	8 21	12 16	...	15 8	2038
Piadena 281	5 58	9 25	13 9	1320	16 8	2130
Casalmaggiore	6 21	9 50	—	1350	1633	2155
Parma 279 ...arr	7 0	1030	...	1436	1713	2232

Parma 288 ...dep	4 56	8 3	1445	20 50
Casalmaggiore	5 34	8 42	1525	21 28
Piadena	6 6	9 17	16 9	21 57
Calvisano	7 0	10 7	17 0	22 46
S. Zeno Folzano	7 45	1045	1746	23 16
Brescia ...arr	7 57	1056	1758	23 28

CREMONA and BRESCIA.

Cremona dep	6 5	9 15	13 5	17 40	...
Olmeneta	6 23	9 33	1323	17 59	...
Verolanuova	6 46	9 56	1347	18 21	...
S. Zeno Folzano	7 24	10 35	1430	18 59	...
Brescia ...arr	7 35	10 46	1441	19 10	...

Brescia 281 ...dep	6 50	1025	17 35	22 0	...	...
S. Zeno Folzano	7 0	1035	17 46	22 10	...	...
Verolanuova	7 35	1115	18 23	22 45	...	...
Olmeneta	7 55	1133	18 45	23 7	...	...
Cremona ...arr	8 10	1150	19 0	23 22	...	...

BRESCIA and EDOLO.

Brescia ...dep	5 12	8 48	11 30	15 5	18 25	...	...
Paderno Franciacorta	5 41	9 17	11 59	15 34	18 54	...	...
Rovato ...dep	5 11	9 5	...	15 30	18 20	...	...
Iseo ...dep	6 17	9 53	12 32	16 11	19 35	...	...
Pisogne	7 8	10 39	—	17 3	20 20	...	...
Darfo	7 34	11 3	...	17 28	20 45	...	...
Breno	8 9	11 39	...	18 3	21 15	...	...
Cedegolo	8 41	12 11	...	18 35	—	...	...
Edolo ...arr	9 14	12 44	...	19 8	...	...	...

Edolo ...dep	...	...	5 53	10 14	16 30	...
Cedegolo	...	...	6 27	10 48	17 13	...
Breno	...	5 4	6 59	11 20	17 45	...
Darfo	...	5 39	7 35	11 55	18 20	...
Pisogne	...	6 5	8 4	12 20	18 46	...
Iseo ...arr	5 21	6 56	8 52	13 5	19 34	...
Rovato ...arr	...	7 36	9 39	13 44	20 15	...
Paderno Franciacorta	5 55	7 37	9 31	13 45	20 16	...
Brescia ...arr	6 24	8 6	10 0	14 14	20 45	...

ALA and VERONA.

[Fares and Luggage Rates, see page 269.

	1,2,3	1,2,3	Lus.	1,2,3	1,2,3	1,2,3	1 & 2	1,2,3	1 & 2
INNSBRUCK 235 dep	...	2a22	3 a22	...	7a32	...	12 30	...	3 p32
Ala ...dep	5 40	8 18	8 38	9 0	1423	...	18 21	20 31	21 30
Peri	6 23	9 6	8 56	1014	15 9	1715	18 51	21 12	22 8
Domegliara	6 54	9 29	...	1041	1535	1743	...	21 45	...
Verona P.Nuova arr	7 25	9 52	A	1110	16 3	1813	19 32	22 20	22 46
,, P. Vescovo ,,	7 35	10 0	9 41	1120	1610	1823	19 40	22 33	22 55
FLORENCE ...arr	...	1718	15 33	...	3 26	...	3 26	6 48	6 48

	1 & 2	Lus.	1 & 2	1,2,3	1,2,3	1,2,3	1,2,3
FLORENCE ...dep	21 20	22 45	2 15	...	6 20	1050	1430
Verona P.V. (282)...dep	4 26	4 42	1010	12 20	1532	1835	21 2
,, P.N. ,,	4 33	—	1017	12 30	1540	1847	2118
Domegliara	...	A	...	13 3	1613	1929	2143
Peri	5 24	5 38	1114	13 44	17 5	2023	2210
Ala (Customs Ex.)...arr	5 40	5 57	1130	14 7	1728	2049	2232
INNSBRUCK (235A) arr	12p45	11a21	6 p0	...	...	4a48	4a48

Extra.		
Verona P.V. ...dep	5 40	...
Ala ...arr	7 50	...

A—Berlin-Tyrol Express; until 30th Nov.
N—Nord-Sud Express.

VERONA, MANTUA, and MODENA.

Dist E.M.	Verona—	1,2,3	1,2,3	1,2,3	1,2,3	1,2,3	1,2,3	1,2,3	1,2,3	
—	P. Vescovo dp	...	5 48	8 15	1018	1320	17 32	20 34	23 35	...
1¾	P. Nuova	...	5 56	8 23	1026	1328	17 42	20 42	23 42	...
6¾	Dossobuono	...	6 7	8 36	1036	1340	17 58	20 52	...	...
11¼	Villafranca	...	6 18	8 47	1045	1351	18 12	21 1	23 59	...
18	Roverbella	...	6 36	9 6	...	1410	18 32	21 18	...	...
25½	**Mantua (281)**	4 30	7 2	9 24	1113	1434	19 5	21 38	0 26	...
32¼	Borgoforte	4 50	7 22	—	1128	1456	19 27	...	...	...
37¼	Suzzara (288)	5 3	7 38	...	1139	1511	19 50	22 3	0 46	...
54	Carpi	5 38	8 15	...	1213	1553	20 45	22 33	1 14	...
63½	**Modena**...arr	6 2	8 41	...	1230	1620	21 12	22 51	1 32	...
168¾	FLORENCE 279	...	1325	...	1718	2316	3 26	3 26	6 48	...

FLORENCE	1,2,3	1,2,3	1,2,3	1,2,3	1,2,3	1,2,3	1,2,3	1,2,3		
dep	2120	...	2 15	...	6 20	1050	1430	14 30	...	...
Modena dep	1 48	...	6 36	9 20	13 3	1520	1855	19 35	...	...
Carpi	2 7	...	7 3	9 46	13 27	1549	1913	20 6	...	...
Suzzara	2 38	...	7 40	1023	14 3	1626	1942	20 50	...	...
Borgoforte	...	...	7 53	1036	14 16	1638	...	21 3	...	...
Mantua	3 7	7 3	8 15	11 7	14 42	17 8	20 7	21 34	...	...
Roverbella	...	7 22	8 31	1123	14 58	1724	...	21 55	...	...
Villafranca	3 32	7 42	8 48	1140	15 16	1742	2028	22 16	...	...
Dossobuono	...	7 54	9 0	1150	15 26	1753	...	22 28	...	...
Verona P.N.	3 49	8 5	9 9	1159	15 35	18 2	2042	22 39	...	...
,, Vescovo	3 57	8 14	9 18	12 6	15 44	1810	2050	22 47	...	...

VERONA and ROVIGO.

‡—Tues., Fri., and Sun. only.] [*—Mon., Wed., and Sat. only.

E.M.									
	Verona (280)...dep	...	6 0	7 ‡24	...	11 5	17 2	20 55	...
6¾	Dossobuono	...	6 19	7 43	...	11 26	17 21	21 21	...
29¼	Cerea	...	7 11	8 37	...	12 21	18 13	22 18	...
33¼	Legnago (279C)	5 30	7 25	8 52	8 57	12 36	18 28	22 33	...
51½	Lendinara	6 32	8‡32	—	9 51	13 39	19 22	—	...
62¾	**Rovigo (279A)**...arr	7 5	9 ‡1	...	10 20	14 12	19 48	...	...

Rovigo (282) ...dep	4 *7	...	7 20	...	13 35	16 52	21 0	
Lendinara	4 38	...	7 52	*	14 3	17 27	21 34	
Legnago	5 30	5 58	9 5	1310	14 55	18 38	22 30	
Cerea	—	6 12	9 24	1326	15 11	18 54	—	
Dossobuono	...	7 11	10 35	1428	16 6	19 49	...	
Verona (282)...arr	...	7 27	10 55	1449	16 27	20 6	...	

TREVIGLIO and CREMONA.

*—Wed. and Sat. only.]

E.M.							
	Treviglio ...dep	6 17	9 8	11*10	1338	1740	2139
9¼	Casaletto-Vaprio	6 42	9 38	1140	14 5	18 5	22 4
13¾	Crema	6 54	9 54	1155	1416	1816	2214
24¼	Soresina	7 17	1021	1224	1439	1840	2237
33½	Olmeneta	7 38	1046	1251	1459	19 2	2257
40½	**Cremona** ...arr	7 50	11 1	13 5	1512	1915	2310

Cremona 281 dep	5 55	8 50	1215	15*15	1710	19 28
Olmeneta	6 10	9 6	1231	15 31	1727	19 47
Soresina	6 32	9 30	1254	15 55	1752	20 14
Crema	6 57	9 59	1322	16 24	1821	20 45
Casaletto-Vaprio	7 7	10 10	1333	16 35	1833	20 59
Treviglio ...arr	7 30	10 35	1357	17 0	19 0	21 24

ROVIGO and CHIOGGIA.

E.M.					
	Rovigo (282) dep	7 30	13 40	17 16	20 54
15¼	Adria	8 18	15 4	18 22	21 42
35¼	**Chioggia** ...arr	9 15	16 30	19 43	22 39

Chioggia dep	5 20	9 15	1217	1657
Adria	6 21	10 17	1343	1826
Rovigo ...arr	7 6	10 59	1448	1933

TREVISO and BELLUNO.

‡—Until 15th Sept.

Dist. E.M.							
	Treviso (288) dep	5 49	9 44	11‡40	15 0	1815	2020
12½	Montebelluna	6 36	1038	12 16	15 46	1844	21 6
17½	Cornuda	6 49	1053	...	15 58	1856	2118
34	Feltre	7 42	1151	13 9	16 50	1940	22 9
42¾	Sedico Bribano	8 15	1222	13 33	17 20	2010	2240
53¼	**Belluno**...arr	8 34	1242	13 53	17 40	2030	23 0

Belluno...dep	5 17	7 57	1110	15 2	18 0	20‡53
Sedico Bribano	5 34	8 17	1127	1520	1818	21 10
Feltre	6 3	9 5	1152	1551	1846	21 35
Cornuda	6 47	10 0	1229	1638	1930	...
Montebelluna	7 1	1024	1247	1656	1944	22 24
Treviso (283) arr	7 35	11 3	1312	1730	2018	22 46

BELLUNO and LONGARONE-ZOLDO.

E.M.						
	Belluno ...dep	8 44	12‡57	14 *5	18 *5	20 40
12¼	Longarone-Zoldo ...arr	9 30	13 50	14 49	18 50	21 25

Longarone-Zoldo ...dep	7 0	10 0	17 4	19*55
Belluno (282) ...arr	7 46	10 42	17 48	20 37

*—From 15th July until 15th Sept. ‡—Until 14th July and from 16th Sept.

BOLOGNA and NOGARA.

E.M.						
	Bologna ...dep	6 15	7 52	1250	1540	19 6
13	S. Giovanni in P. 279C	7 3	8 45	1323	1634	1954
18¼	Crevalcore	7 22	9 4	1335	1654	2013
26¾	S. Felice	7 48	9 35	1357	1723	2041
31	Mirandola	8 5	9 52	14 8	1740	2058
37¼	Poggio Rusco	8 26	1014	1423	18 1	2120
41	Revere	8 39	1028	1434	1814	2134
43½	Ostiglia	8 54	1038	1450	1829	2144
52¼	Nogara (279C) ...arr	9 14	...	1511	1850	...

Nogara ...dep	...	6 15	11 0	...	18 0	...
Ostiglia	4 30	6 43	1127	1415	1824	...
Revere	4 41	6 58	1142	1432	1835	...
Poggio Rusco	4 54	7 12	1152	1451	19 5	...
Mirandola	5 14	7 32	12 6	1511	1925	...
S. Felice	5 35	7 54	1221	1532	1946	...
Crevalcore	5 [illegible]9	8 18	1242	1558	2012	...
S. Giovanni in P.	6 25	8 39	1257	1635	2034	...
Bologna ...arr	7 11	9 24	1328	1725	2120	...

PALAZZOLO and PARATICO.

E.M.								
	Palazzolo (281) dep	7 40	11 21	13 15	16 50	21 14	...	...
6¼	Paratico ...arr	8 3	11 45	13 55	17 14	21 37	...	...
...	Paratico ...dep	6 7	9 40	12 16	15 9	20 25	...	...
...	Palazzolo ...arr	6 30	10 3	12 50	15 32	20 47	...	...

MANDELA and SUBIACO.

Mandela ...dep	9 43	20 25	...	...	...	...	...
Subiaco ...arr	10 37	21 19	...	...	...	...	...
Subiaco ...dep	7 10	17 13	...	...	...	...	...
Mandela ...arr	8 4	18 7	...	...	...	...	...

ROME and CASTELLAMMARE (ADRIATICA).

Dist. E.M.									
	Rome ...dep		5 45	6§35	7 50	...	12 55	18 35	19 50
13	Bagni		6 21	7 1	8 26	...	13 32	19 11	...
24¾	Tivoli		7 0	—	9 7	...	14 17	19 51	20 54
33½	**Mandela**		7 28	...	9 38	...	14 48	20 20	...
41	Arsoli		8 4	...	10 14	...	15 24	20 56	21 44
57¼	Tagliacozzo		9 6	...	11 18	...	16 26	22 0	22 36
67	**Avezzano (277A)**...arr		9 30	...	11 42	...	16 59	22 24	22 56
...	,, ...dep		—	5 54	11 48	...	16 56	—	23 1
82	Pescina		...	6 46	12 39	...	17 47	‡—Until 15th September.	23 39
106¾	**Sulmona (285B)** ...arr		...	8 7	14 1	...	19 8		0 34
...	,, ...dep	5 0	...	8 16	14 9	...	19 16		0 40
116¾	Popoli	5 23	...	8 40	14 33	...	19 41		1 0
129¾	S.Valentino-Carama	5 55	...	9 18	15 8	...	20 16		1 25
140¼	Chieti	6 22	7‡26	9 45	15 36	1826	20 44		1 43
148½	Pescara	6 40	7 45	10 5	15 55	1852	21 2		1 58
149	**Castellammare** ..arr	6 43	7 49	10 8	15 58	1856	21 5		2 1

Castellammare dep		2 48	...	7 7	11 48	17 0	2016	2140
Pescara		2 53	...	7 12	11 56	17 5	2021	2149
Chieti		3 10	§—Until 31st August.	7 29	12 14	17 22	2040	2210
S.Valentino-Carama		3 32		7 58	12 43	17 51	21 7	—
Popoli		4 8		8 44	13 28	18 35	2148	...
Sulmona ...arr		4 31		9 11	13 55	19 2	2215	...
,, ...dep		4 37		9 19	14 1	19 8	—	...
Pescina		6 10		11 5	15 42	20 45	...	...
Avezzano ...arr		6 47		11 48	16 23	21 30	...	...
,, ...dep	5 10	6 52		11 54	16 31	21 35	...	...
Tagliacozzo	5 38	7 14		12 22	17 0	21 57	...	...
Arsoli	6 33	8 0	...	13 17	17 57	22 43	...	...
Mandela	7 1	8 21	...	13 42	18 25	...	...	...
Tivoli	7 30	8 42	...	14 11	18 57	23 20	...	6 8
Bagni	7 [illegible]8	9 9	10§54	14 39	19 26	...	...	6 36
Rome ...arr	8 30	9 35	11 25	15 15	20 10	0 5	...	7 15

Fares and Luggage Rates, see page 269.] **STATE RAILWAYS—(continued).**

ANCONA, FOLIGNO, and ORTE.

	1,2,3	1,2,3	1,2,3	1,2,3	1,2,3	1,2,3	1,2,3	1,2,3	1,2,3 SC
Ancona..dep	...	...	7 20	...	11 35	15 6	17 30	19 10	23 40
Falconara......	...	...	7 38	...	11 51	15 22	17 43	19 33	23 56
Albacina	...	...	8 53	...	13 24	16 50	A	21 13	1 17
Fabriano ...	...	4 0	9 13	...	13 46	17 11	19 12	21 33	1 42
Fossato 289	...	4 33	9 43	...	14 22	17 48	19 46	—	2 18
Nocera Umbra	...	5 8	1011	...	14 59	18 24	20 20	...	2 49
Foligno arr	...	5 35	1038	...	15 26	18 51	20 45	‡	3 14
,, (**283**) dp	...	5 45	1046	1533	15 48	19 8	—	20 57	3 25
Spoleto	...	6 28	1124	16 5	16 34	19 54	...	21 35	4 4
Terni 285B	6 30	7 25	1225	1658	17 31	20 42	...	22 21	5 3
Narni	6 56	7 39	1239	1714	17 45	21 30	...	22 35	5 13
Orte (279)...	7 20	7 58	1258	1730	18 4	21 50	...	22 51	5 35
ROME ...arr	8 50	9 50	1435	1855	19 50	23 30	...	0 10	7 5

	1,2,3	1,2,3	1,2,3	1,2,3	1,2,3	1,2,3	1,2,3	1,2,3	1,2,3 SC
ROME 279B dep	...	...	5 50	8‡25	...	12 10	1530	1840	22 20
Orte.........dep	...	5 55	7 36	9 43	...	13 37	1652	2038	23 54
Narni	...	6 46	7 56	10 2	B	13 54	1715	21 0	0 14
Terni	4 7	7 6	8 28	10 26	...	14 13	1739	2133	0 39
Spoleto	5 10	—	9 25	11 20	...	15 4	1836	2233	1 40
Foligno ...arr	5 45	...	9 57	11 46	...	15 33	19 8	23 8	2 11
,, dep	5 53	...	10 6	—	1154	15 39	1915	—	2 17
Nocera Umbra..	6 26	...	10 39	...	...	16 7	1951	...	2 50
Fossato.........	7 3	...	11 16	...	1247	16 41	2030	...	3 24
Fabr'no 283	7 33	...	11 45	...	1315	17 14	21 2	...	3 53
Albacina	7 45	...	11 56	...	1325	17 24	2112	...	4 4
Falconara	8 57	...	13 8	...	1418	18 30	2222	...	5 14
Ancona ...arr	9 8	...	13 22	...	1427	18 40	2232	...	5 24

Extra.

Orte ....dep	11 28	18 4
Terni ....arr	12 25	19 3

‡—Sunday excepted.
A—Monday, Wednesday, and Friday only.
SC—Sleeping Car attached.
B—Tuesday, Thursday, and Saturday only.

FABRIANO and MACERATA.

Dist.								
—	**Fabriano (283)** dep	4 3	6 5	8 35	17 30	...	...	...
5¼	Albacina	4 14	6 20	9 0	17 44	...	...	...
13¾	Matelica..................	4 37	6 47	9 43	18 10	...	...	...
18	Castelraimondo	4 54	7 6	10 8	18 28	...	...	...
25½	S. Severino Marche ...	5 20	7 35	10 48	18 57	...	...	...
42½	**Macerata (285)** arr	6 16	8 38	12 21	19 57	...	...	...

Macerata ...dep	5 38	10 31	...	13 30	22 50	...	...
S. Severino Marche	6 37	11 37	...	15 4	23 51	...	...
Castelraimondo ...	7 7	12 8	...	15 46	0 21	...	...
Matelica.............	7 22	12 24		16 17	0 37	...	...
Albacina	7 42	12 45	1650	17 41	0 56	...	...
Fabriano......arr	7 59	13 2	17 6	18 9	1 13	...	...

FABRIANO and URBINO.

Fabriano ....dep	4 15	9 30	17 40	...
Pergola	5 25	10 39	18 49	...
Urbino.................arr	7 5	12 19	20 30	...

Urbino ....dep	4 20	14 5	17 40	...
Pergola	6 9	15 56	19 31	...
Fabriano ....arr	7 13	17 0	20 35	...

TERONTOLA, PERUGIA, and FOLIGNO.

Terontola ....dep	333	643	1015	1330	1610	18§14	...	20 5	2225
Passignano	353	7 5	1037	1347	1633	18 33	...	2028	2245
Magione	4 6	721	1053	1359	1650	18 45	...	2044	2258
Perugia ......arr	437	759	1132	1427	1729	19 15	...	2121	2328
,, ...dep	443	9 0	—	1432	1743	—	19‡42	—	0 30
Ponte S. Giovanni	446	914	...	1446	18 1	...	...	...	0 49
Bastia	5 8	926	...	1458	1817	...	20 8	...	1 5
Assisi...................	515	933	...	15 6	1827	...	20 15	...	1 15
Spello....................	529	947	...	1520	1845	...	...	...	1 33
Foligno (282) ar	537	955	...	1528	1855	...	20 37	...	1 44

Foligno ....dep	330	6 5	...	12‡0	...	1552	1916	2317
Spello	338	6 14	...	12 8	...	16 1	1924	2327
Assisi	351	6 30	...	1221	...	1615	1937	2344
Bastia	357	6 37	...	1227	...	1621	1943	2351
Ponte S. Giovanni ...	4 9	6 52	...	1239	...	1634	1955	0 7
Perugia............arr	427	7 13	...	1257	...	1654	2013	0 30
,, ...dep	437	7 25	1056	13 7	15§0	1659	2019	1 50
Magione..................	5 4	7 54	1129	1335	...	1727	2045	2 20
Passignano..............	517	8 8	1145	1348	...	1740	2057	2 35
Terontola (279) ar	535	8 26	12 5	14 6	1544	1758	2113	2 52

‡—Not on Sunday. §—From 1st September until 30th November.

CASTELBOLOGNESE and RAVENNA.

Dist E.M.								
—	Castelbolognese dep	7 4	9 55	1120	1325	1538	1727	2025
8½	Lugo (283)..............	7 26	1017	1147	1347	16 3	1749	2048
15½	Russi	7 43	1034	12 8	...	1622	...	21 5
26	Ravenna (279A) arr	8 4	1055	1233	...	1644	...	2126

Ravenna ....dep	5 25	7 2	1119	...	1537	...	18*12	2132
Russi........................	5 51	7 25	1147	...	16 0	...	18 45	22 0
Lugo........................	6 13	7 45	12 9	14 5	1620	18 0	19 16	2224
Castelbolognese (285)	6 33	8 5	1231	1425	1639	1820	19 40	2246

*—On Tuesday, Thursday, and Saturday only.

TREVISO and MOTTA DI LIVENZA.

Dist. E.M.							
	Treviso (282) ...dep	5 50	9 35	15 10	20 29	...	...
11¼	Ponte Piave	6 30	10 6	15 52	21 12	...	...
21½	**Motta di Livenza** ar	7 5	10 33	16 28	21 47	...	...

Motta di Livenza dp	5 21	9 5	1315	19 15	...	...	...
Ponte Piave	5 57	9 36	1352	19 44	...	...	...
Treviso ....arr	6 35	10 10	1430	20 15	...	...	...

LUGO and LAVEZZOLA.

Dist. E.M.							
	Lugo ....dep	4 25	8 0	16 22	...	...	...
5¼	Massalombarda	4 44	8 24	16 41	...	...	...
14¼	**Lavezzola 279**A	5 9	8 52	17 8	...	...	...

Lavezzola......dep	6 15	14 50	18 25	...	...	...	...
Massalombarda	6 49	15 38	18 57	...	...	...	...
Lugo (283) ...arr	7 3	15 58	19 11	...	...	...	...

SULMONA and ISERNIA.

Sulmona.........dep	4 41	9 20	14 15	19 25	...	...	...
Palena.....................	6 35	11 40	16 18	22 12	...	...	...
Castel di Sangro	7 38	12 46	17 21	23 21	...	...	...
Isernia (277A**)** arr	9 10	14 47	19 13	...	...	...	...

Isernia ....dep	...	7 18	13 33	19 25	...	...	...
Castel di Sangro	5 1	9 56	16 2	21 21	...	...	...
Palena	6 34	11 39	17 35	22 47	...	...	...
Sulmona ....arr	7 54	12 57	18 53	23 54	...	...	...

CASARSA and PINZANO.

E.M.					
	Casarsa ....dep	9 20	14 20	18 40	21 30
11¾	Spilimbergo	10 11	15 28	19 33	22 16
18	Pinzano.........................arr	10 38	15 56	20 0	...

Pinzano ....dep	...	7 43	12 22	16 50	
Spilimbergo	6 6	8 9	12 56	17 16	...
Casarsa **225**A.......................arr	6 50	8 53	13 45	18 1	...

ATTIGLIANO and VITERBO.

Dist.						
	Attigliano (**279**) ...dep	6 28	8 43	16 40	...	...
24¼	Viterbo ....arr	7 52	10 12	18 5	...	...

Viterbo ....dep	9 25	12 38	18 8	...
Attigliano .....arr	10 49	14 8	19 32	...

☞ Italian Railway Time—See Note on page 272. ☜

Fares and Luggage Rates, see page 269.

BOLOGNA, ANCONA, FOGGIA, BRINDISI, and GALLIPOLI.

Dist E.M.															
...	TURIN 273 ....dep	...	...	...	20 10	...	...	...	...	7 15	...	...	11 0	1835	21 15
	MILAN 279 ....dep	...	...	...	22 50	...	...	7 0	...	10 6	13 0	...	15 30	21 0	‡
	VENICE 279A ......dep	...	...	...	23 8	...	...	7 0	...	10 15	1120	11 20	14 25	2120	...
		1,2,3	1,2,3	1,2,3	1,2,3	1,2,3	1,2,3	1,2,3	1,2,3	1,2,3	1,2,3	1,2,3	1,2,3	1 &2	...
—	Bologna Centrale...dep	...	...	...	3 25	5 55	8 31	10 25	...	14 25	1640	17 45	19 25	0 30	3 18
14¾	Castel S. Pietro..........	...	...	...	...	6 32	9 6	10 51	...	15 2	...	18 20	...	SC	...
21¾	Imola	...	...	...	4 1	6 47	9 19	11 4	...	15 17	A	18 35	19 58	...	...
26	Castel Bolognese 283...	...	...	...	...	7 5	9 33	11 14	...	15 32	...	18 49	20 7	...	...
31	Faenza 286................	...	...	...	4 23	7 23	9 45	11 24	...	15 46	...	19 5	20 16	...	
39¾	Forli 286	...	...	...	4 42	7 47	10 3	11 41	...	16 6	...	19 23	20 33	...	
57½	Cesena	...	...	...	5 6	8 18	1028	12 6	...	16 31	...	19 47	20 52	...	Sunday only.
68¾	Rimini ....arr	...	...	...	5 44	9 4	11 9	12 44	§	17 12	1823	20 28	21 20	2 5	
...	„ 279A ....dep	...	6 50	...	5 50	9 30		12 56	1513	17 25	1834	20 36	21 26	2 11	
90	Pesaro	...	8 1	...	6 33	10 23	...	13 44	1555	18 19	1916	21 24	22 9	...	
97½	Fano	...	8 27	...	6 47	10 39	...	13 59	16 9	18 35	1930	21 42	22 22	...	...
111¼	Senigallia	...	9 0	...	7 10	11 10	...	14 25	1635	19 4	1954	22 14	22 44	...	...
121	Falconara	...	9 29	...	7 34	11 37	...	14 45	1653	19 29	2015	22 38	23 3	...	...
126¾	Ancona ....arr	...	9 46	...	7 44	11 49	...	14 55	17 3	19 43	2025	22 50	23 13	3 42	6 35
...	„ 283 ....dep	5 45		...	8 3	12 45	...	15 12	18 0	20 32			23 29	3 55	6 54
136¼	Osimo	6 18	...	...	8 33	13 17	...	15 41	1840	21 2	...		23 52	...	...
141½	Loreto	6 31	...	...	8 44	13 29	...	15 52	1856	21 13	...	...	0 1	...	...
144	Porto Recanati..............	6 40	...	...	8 51	13 36	...	15 59	19 6	21 20	...	...	0 8	...	...
153¼	Porto Civitanova..........	7 14	...	...	9 13	14 0	...	16 20	1933	21 42	...	...	0 23	...	...
163¼	Porto S. Giorgio	7 36	...	...	9 35	14 23	...	16 41		22 8	...	...	0 39	...	...
176¼	Grottammare................	8 6	...	...	10 4	14 53	...	17 10	...	22 39	...	...	1 3	...	...
179¾	Sambenedetto 286	8 13	4 50	...	10 17	15 5	...	17 23	...	22 52	...	...	1 16	5 39	...
182¾	Porto d'Ascoli		5 0	...	10 26	15 15	...	17 32	...	23 2	...	...	...	...	...
194¼	Giulianova	...	5 32	...	10 51	15 47	...	17 59	...	23 29	...	...	1 44	6 3	...
205½	Atri-Mutignano	...	5 57	...	11 15	16 11	...	18 22	...	23 54	...	...	2 3	...	...
217½	Castellammare ....arr	...	6 24	...	11 42	16 37	...	18 49	...	0 21	...	...	2 24	6 44	9 46
...	„ 282...dep	...	7 1	...	11 56	16 50	...	19 0	2122			...	2 41	6 53	9 56
218½	Pescara	...	7 8	...	12 2	16 56	...	19 5	2131	...		...	2 46	...	...
223½	Francavilla a Mare ...	...	7 18	...	12 12	17 7	...	19 15	2143	...		...	2 55	...	...
231	Ortona	...	7 38	...	12 31	17 27	...	19 29	22 5	...		...	3 10	...	...
257¼	Vasto............................	...	8 45	...	13 34	18 39	...	20 21	2316	...		...	3 58	...	...
273¼	Termoli 286............arr	...	9 19	...	14 5	19 13	...	20 47	2353	...		...	4 21	...	...
...	„ ....dep	5 25	9 25	...	14 11	19 23	...	20 52		...		...	4 26	...	...
277¾	Campomarino	5 35	9 35	...	14 20	19 33	...	...	...	...		...	...	...	...
309¼	S. Severo......................	7 8	10 55	...	15 30	20 56	...	21 57	...	...		...	5 32	...	...
327¼	Foggia ....arr	7 48	11 29	...	16 0	21 30	...	22 23	...	...		...	6 0	1010	13 25
...	NAPLES 285B .. ...dep	...	6 0	...	11 10	...	1420	17 20	...	...		23 10		6 0	...
...	Foggia ....dep	8 30	12 15	1435	16 35	...	2025	22 40	...	...		6 45		1035	13 38
349	Cerignola 285	9 17	13 5	1542	17 14	...	2142	23 15	...	...		7 25		...	...
362	Ofantino 287 1,2,3	9 48	13 38	1623	17 40	...	2219	...	...	...		7 52	...	...	...
369¼	Barletta 285......arr 6 12	10 3	13 54	1642	17 53	...	2250	23 48	...	...		8 5	...	1136	...
378½	Trani 6 35	10 28	14 27	1719	18 12	...		0 7	...	...		8 31	...	1153	...
383	Molfetta 7 9	10 53	14 54	1752	18 34	...	...	0 28	...	...		8 57	...	...	...
392¼	Giovinazzo...........7 21	11 3	15 5	18 4	18 43	...	...	0 36	...	...		9 6	...	...	...
403¾	Bari 285B ....arr 7 55	11 31	15 30	1838	19 4	...	...	0 54	B	...		9 28	...	1230	15 47
...	„ ....dep	14 8	16 10		19 14	...	...		1 4	4 5		9 39	...	1246	15 55
415¼	Mola di Bari	14 38	16 41	...	19 38	...	...	...	1 36	4 32		10 3	...	...	Sunday only.
429	Monopoli	15 14	17 15	...	20 5	...	...	...	2 12	5 6		10 30	...	RC	
437	Fasano..........................	15 38	17 38	...	20 22	...	...	...	2 38	5 25		10 48	...	...	
449½	Ostuni	16 16	18 10	...	20 48	...	...	...	3 15	5 52		11 13	...	...	
472¾	Brindisi Town ....arr	17 9	18 58	...	21 27	...	...	...	4 10	6 35		11 50	...	1430	17 54
...	Brindisi Town ...dep		19 15	...	...	...	...	...		10 10		...	...		
...	Brindisi Port ......arr	...	19 21	...	...	...	...	...	...	10 16		...	...		...
...	Brindisi Town ......dep	...	19 10	...	21 37	...	...	4 20	...	6 50		11 58	14 40		...
483½	S. Pietro Vernotico......	...	19 40	.	21 58	...	...	4 51	...	7 20		12 19	15 8		...
496¼	Lecce ....arr	1 & 3	20 20	1 &3	22 24	...	...	5 30	1 &3	8 0		12 50	15 45		...
	Lecce ....dep	18 46		2035		...	...		6 35			13*25			...
502¼	S. Donato	19 7	...	2052	...	...	...	...	6 55	...		13 41	...		...
508¼	Zollino 285	19 54	...	2116	...	...	...	...	7 27	...		14 10	...		...
517½	Galatone......................	20 20	...	2146	...	...	...	...	8 2	...		14 37	...		...
519½	Nardo	20 28	...	2158	...	...	...	...	8 20	...		14 47	...		...
530	Gallipoli ....arr	21 5	...	2237	...	...	...	...	9 0	...	...	15 24	...	...	...

‡—"P. & O. Brindisi Express," from London 9.0 p.m. on Friday.

§—Mon., Wed., and Fri. only, between Rimini and Ancona.

*—1 & 3 class only.

A—Until 30th September. B—From 1st September until 31st October.

GIULIANOVA and TERAMO.

Giulianova ......dep	3 8	6 7	11 0	18 3	23 32	...
Teramo ....arr	4 9	7 21	12 2	19 4	0 33	...

Teramo.................dep	0 33	8 45	14 30	16 25	21 20	...	...
Giulianova ....arr	1 30	9 44	15 36	17 22	22 19	...	...

PORTO CIVITANOVA and MACERATA.

‡—Wed., Thurs., and Sat. only.

Porto Civitanova ......dep	4 30	9 20	11‡48	16 30	21 44	...	...	...
Macerata ....arr	5 28	10 18	12 47	17 30	22 41	...	...	...

Macerata......................dep	6 23	10 35	13 ‡0	18 0	20 4	...	...	...
Porto Civitanova ....arr	7 8	11 25	13 51	18 52	2050	...	...	...

PORTO S. GIORGIO and AMANDOLA.

Porto S. Giorgio......dep	7 40	1135	19 0	...	...
Amandola ....arr	1040	1428	2153	...	...

Amandola...................dep	5 55	1210	1531	...	...	...
Porto S. Giorgio ....arr	8 50	15 6	1823	...	...	...

CERIGNOLA and CERIGNOLA CITTA.

E.M.							
	Cerignola ....dep	7 40	9 30	13 20	16 0	18 0	22 0
4½	Cerignola Citta...arr	7 55	9 45	13 35	16 15	18 15	22 20

Cerignola Citta dep	6 48	8 53	10 8	1413	1614	21 3	...
Cerignola ....arr	7 5	9 10	10 25	1430	17 2	21 20	...

ZOLLINO and OTRANTO.

E.M.							
	Zollino......dep	7 30	1430	19 50	21 25	...	...
6¼	Maglie............	7 59	1459	20 16	21 51	...	...
18	Otranto ...arr	8 45	1544	21 0	22 35	...	...

Otranto......dep	3 30	6 0	1248	18 0	...	...
Maglie	4 18	6 47	1338	18 52	...	...
Zollino ....arr	4 40	7 8	14 1	19 15	...	...

BARLETTA and SPINAZZOLA.

Barletta ....dep	8 12	15 5	18 45	...
Canne..........................	8 34	15 29	19 8	...
Canosa di Puglia	8 56	15 46	19 28	...
Spinazzola 285B......arr	10 22	17 24	21 7	...

Spinazzola ....dep	4 5	1115	15 40	...
Canosa di Puglia	5 25	1239	17 5	...
Canne..........................	5 40	1255	17 20	...
Barletta 285...........arr	6 0	1315	17 40	...

Fares and Luggage Rates, see page 269.]

GALLIPOLI, BRINDISI, ANCONA, BOLOGNA.

SLEEPING CARRIAGE—in 12.5 from Brindisi.

	1,2,3	1,2,3	1,2,3	1,2,3	1 & 3	1,2,3	1,2,3	1 &2	1,2,3	1,2,3	1,2,3
Gallipoli ....dep	...	...	...	...	3 41	...	6 *0	...	...	12*47	18*20
Nardo	...	...	...	...	4 16	...	6 39	...	...	13 37	19 8
Galatone	...	...	...	...	4 24	...	6 45	...	...	13 44	19 14
Zollino	...	...	...	...	4 51	...	7 22	...	...	14 25	19 56
S. Donato	...	...	...	...	5 7	...	7 42	...	...	14 50	20 17
Lecce arr	...	...	...	...	5 20	...	7 58	...	...	15 11	20 33
Lecce dep	...	...	*—1st and 3rd class only between Gallipoli and Lecce.	...		5 30	8 38	1055	12 15	16 20	20 55
S. Pietro Vernotico	...	...		...		5 58	9 12	1132	12 52	16 53	21 36
Brindisi Town arr	...	...		...	...	6 17	9 33	1155	13 13	17 13	22 3
Brindisi Port dep	...	...		...	...	6 6	...	...	...	16 31	
Brindisi Town arr	...	...		...	...	6 15	...	...	...	16 40	...
Brindisi Town dep	...	...		...	...	6 35	9 58	12 5	13 25	17 25	23 25
Ostuni	...	...		...	...	7 16	10 46	...	14 20	18 12	0 41
Fasano	...	...		...	...	7 38	11 9	...	14 48	18 35	1 18
Monopoli	...	...		...	...	7 53	11 29	...	15 9	18 50	1 44
Mola di Bari	...	...		...	...	8 18	11 55	...	15 40	19 17	2 25
Bari arr	...	...		...	...	8 49	12 18	1349	16 6	19 40	2 58
Bari dep	3 12	...		5 1	...	9 0	12 33	14 5	16 18	19 52	In Sept. and Oct. only.
Giovinazzo	3 31	...		5 2"	...	9 22	13 3	...	16 48	20 15	
Molfetta	3 39	...		5 36	...	9 30	13 13	...	16 58	20 24	
Trani	3 58	...	...	5 59	...	9 49	13 36	1447	17 22	20 47	
Barletta	4 14	...	...	6 26	...	10 4	13 55	15 0	17 53	21 5	
Ofantino	...	...	...	6 43	...	...	14 11	...	18 7	...	
Cerignola	4 50	...	...	7 22	...	10 40	14 52	...	18 47	21 45	
Foggia ....arr	5 24	...	...	8 7	...	11 15	15 37	16 5	19 30	22 20	
NAPLES 285B arr	1110	...	...	...	1,2,3	16 30	...	2050	1,2,3	7 10	
Foggia ....dep	...	5 41	...	...	7 5	12 5	17 3	1630	14 43	...	22 40
S. Severo	...	6 15	...	...	7 51	12 44	17 43	...	15 38	...	23 12
Campomarino	...	...	...	...	9 9	13 51	18 55	...	17 17	...	...
Termoli arr	...	7 10	...	...	9 21	14 1	19 5	SC	17 31	...	0 18
Termoli dep	...	7 15	...	4 48	9 29	14 10	19 15	...		...	0 23
Vasto	...	7 38	...	5 22	10 7	14 46	19 51	...	...	...	0 49
Ortona	...	8 30	...	6 25	11 19	15 50	21 1	...	...	...	1 38
Francavilla a Mare	...	8 43	...	6 44	11 39	16 8	21 20	...	...	...	1 52
Pescara	...	8 53	...	6 57	11 52	16 19	21 33	...	...	...	2 3
Castellamare arr	...	8 57	...	7 1	11 56	16 23	21 37	1954	...	...	2 6
Castellamare dep	4 0	9 7	☞ Tues., Thurs., and Sat. only.		12 50	16 37	21 57	20 5	...	...	2 24
Atri-Mutignano	4 31	9 36		...	13 20	17 5	22 28	...	...	...	...
Giulianova	4 59	10 2		...	13 4	17 30	22 57	...	...	...	3 0
Porto d' Ascoli	5 29	10 27		...	14 17	17 55	23 25	...	...	...	...
Sambenedetto	5 59	10 39		...	14 33	18 7	23 32	2117	...	19 25	3 31
Grottammare	6 10	10 47		...	14 42	18 16		...	...	19 36	3 38
Porto S. Giorgio	6 47	11 17		...	15 21	18 48	...	...	1,2,3	20 20	4 1
Porto Civitanova	7 17	11 40		...	15 58	19 14	...	SC	5 25	20 55	4 17
Porto Recanati	7 39	12 0		...	16 22	19 35	...	...	5 52	21 22	4‡32
Loreto	7 47	12 7		...	16 30	19 43	...	...	6 2	21 32	4 39
Osimo	8 1	12 18		...	16 45	19 55	...	...	6 16	21 48	4 49
Ancona arr	8 30	12 45	...	...	17 14	20 20	...	2248	6 54	22 22	5 5
Ancona dep	8 55	13 0	1435	1518	18 8	20 45	4‡40	23 5	7 3		5 15
Falconara	9 10	13 13	1446	1537	18 38	21 0	4 52	...	7 27	...	5 26
Senigallia	9 33	13 33	15 3	16 4	19 2	21 20	5 10	...	7 54	...	5†53
Fano	10 3	14 2	1529	1638	19 39	21 47	5 38	...	8 31	...	6†19
Pesaro	1020	14 19	1542	1657	20 3	22 5	5 53	...	8 52	...	6†37
Rimini arr	11 5	15 1	1621	1751	21 1	22 44	6 35	0 45	9 58	...	7†20
Rimini dep	1114	15 12	1630	18 0	21 11	22 51	6 42	0 52		4 45	7†30
Cesena	12 1	15 59	To Ferrara.	1849	21 59	23 23	7 25	...	...	5 34	8†13
Forli	1226	16 23		1917	22 25	23 42	7 49	...	...	6 2	8†26
Faenza	1249	16 41		1939	22 47	23 59	8 8	...	...	6 26	8†37
Castel Bolognese	13 5	16 56		1955	23 2	...	8 22	...	8 7	6 40	9† 5
Imola	1317	17 7		20 7	23 13	...	8 32	...	8 17	6 52	9†18
Castel S. Pietro	1333	17 22		2025	23 28	...	8 47	...	8 32	7 7	9†33
Bologna ....arr	14 7	17 52		21 1	24 0	0 45	9 11	2 35	8 57	7 42	9 57
VENICE 279A...arr	1850	21 27	...	...	...	4 40	...	8 33	...	12 20	13 50
MILAN 279B ...arr	1855	21 45	...	...	...	6 0	...	6 45	...	12 15	14 25
TURIN 278......arr	2325	0 16	...	...	...	8 41	...	8 41	...	15 12	19 0

‡—Until 30th Sept. †—Sets down only.

VENICE, UDINE, CORMONS, and PONTEBBA.

¶—Customs Examination.

	1,2,3	1,2,3	1,2,3	1,2,3	1,2,3	1,2,3	1,2,3	1 &2	1,2,3	1,2,3	1,2,3	1,2,3
Venice ....dep	5 0	5 55	7 10	8 47	1055	11 25	14 10	1610	...	1720	19 22	23 30
Mestre ....arr	5 10	6 7	7 24	8 59	11 5	11 37	14 20	1621	...	1730	19 35	23 44
" ....dep	5 15	6 9	7 27	9 1	11 8	11 40	14 26	1638	...	1734	19‡40	23 50
Treviso 282 ...arr	5 37	6 49	8 3	9 30	1130	12 10	14 52	RC	...	1758	20 10	0 26
" ....dep	5 43	6 55	8 9	9 39	☞ From 15th July until 15th September.	12 16	14 58		...	18 4	20 25	0 36
Conegliano 288	6 14	7 38	8 55	1021		12 58	15 31		...	1840	21 9	1 24
Pordenone	6 48	8 29		1110		13 46	16 4		...	1913	21 58	2 9
Casarsa	7 6	9 10	...	1132		14 11	16 23	18 6	...	1931	22 20	2 28
Udine ....arr	7 51	9 57	...	1220		14 58	17 3	1843	...	2011	23 7	3 20
Udine ....dep	8 19	...	...	13 0		15 45	17 58	1853	20 6	...	...	5 46
Buttrio	8 31	...	...	1314		16 2	18 9	...	20 21	...	...	6 1
Cormons ...arr	8 55	...	...	1340		16 33	18 32	1920	20 48	...	...	6 26
TRIESTE 234 arr	1148	...	...	4p15		7 p45	8 p42	9 p0	11 27	...	...	8a45
Udine..........dep	3 10	1014	...	...	...	15 50	17 15	...	...	1855	...	6 5
Gemona Ospedaletto	8 53	1124	...	...		16 46	17 52	...	...	20 1	...	7 10
Carnia	9 13	1154	...	...		17 9	18 9	...	...	2028	...	7 40
Chiusaforte	9 47	1243	...	...		17 49	1843	...	...	2113	...	8 31
Pontebba 241 arr	1018	1320	...	...	...	18 20	19 14	...	...	2146	...	9 5
VIENNA..........arr	8p40	5a38	...	...	...	...	7 a40	...	...	...	...	8 p40

	1,2,3	1,2,3	1,2,3	1 &2	1,2,3	1,2,3	1,2,3	1,2,3	1,2,3	1,2,3	1,2,3
VIENNA 241 ...dep		...	...	...	9p15	...	...	...	...	7 a35	...
Pontebba ¶...dep		...	5 45	...	9 31	10 55	...	...	14 55	18 20	1840
Chiusaforte		...	6 7	...	9 48	11 18	...	...	15 17	18 38	19 8
Carnia		...	6 46	...	10 8	11 47	...	...	15 49	18 59	1939
Gemona Ospedaletto		...	7 5	...	10 22	12 6	...	...	16 9	19 11	20 0
Udine ....arr		...	7 57	...	11 0	12 55	...	...	17 0	19 46	2057
TRIESTE 234 dep		...	...	7a50	8 a32	9 a0	...	...	12 40	4p10	8p10
Cormons ¶ dep		...	6 37	9 25	10 35	12 5	...	...	15 7	18 57	2230
Buttrio		...	7 14	...	10 56	12 35	...	...	15 32	19 26	2257
Udine ....arr		...	7 33	9 51	11 7	12 50	...	...	15 45	19 41	2311
Udine ......dep	4 26	6 55	8 20	1010	11 25	13 10	...	1535	17 22	20 11	
Casarsa	5 11	7 37	9 9	1043	12 2	13 56	...	1620	18 12	20 48	...
Pordenone	5 30	7 54	9 32	...	12 18	14 17	...	1637	18 35	21 4	...
Conegliano	6 17	8 32	10 24	RC	12 55	15 6	4 40	1712	19 26	21 37	...
Treviso ...arr	6 54	9 6	11 0	...	13 23	15 45	5 21	1740	20 6	22 1	...
" ...dep	7 2	9 12	11 12	...	13 28	15 50	5 27	1748	20 28	22 5	1830
Mestre......arr	7 42	9 37	11 52	1211	13 50	16 31	6 9	1815	20 58	22 25	1920
" ...dep	7 44	9 39	11 54	1222	13 55	16 35	6 15	1817	21 3	22 27	1926
Venice 279A arr	7 55	9 50	12 5	1233	14 5	16 47	6 27	1828	21 15	22 37	1940

Extra.—Venice to Treviso, 18.25, 21.35. Treviso to Venice, 7.50.

VENICE, CERVIGNANO, and CASARSA.

Venice..........dep	6 0	9 10	14 20	1610	17 25	19 10
Mestre	6 14	9 29	14 32	1638	17 43	19 25
S. Donà di Piave	7 8	10 26	15 6	...	18 46	19 58
Portogruaro..........arr	7 45	11 4	15 32	1738	19 28	20 25
Portogruaro.........dep	7 50	11 13	15 41	...	19 35	20 30
S. Giorgio di Nogaro	8 42	12 10	16 24	...	20 45	21 10
Cervignano..........arr	8 57	12 26	16 38	...	...	21 25
TRIESTE 234A ...arr	10a40	2p42	6p55	...	...	11p27
Portogruaro..........dep	8 29	13 5	15 42	1739	20 44	20 44
Casarsa ....arr	9 5	13 48	16 15	18 3	21 21	21 21

Casarsa..........dep	5 14	7 40	9 30	1043	...	14 48	21 4
Portogruaro ....arr	5 50	8 21	10 4	11 8	...	15 22	21 45
TRIESTE 234A ...dep	...	5a40		...	9 a0	1 p10	7 p5
Cervignano..........dep	...	7a12	...	...	11 6	14 39	20 32
S. Giorgio di Nogaro	...	7 50	8 46	...	1135	15 12	20 48
Portogruaro..........arr	...	8 24	9 59	...	1211	16 1	21 53
Portogruaro..........dep	5 53	8 31		11 9	1218	16 10	22 0
S. Donà di Piave	6 36	8 57	...	...	1258	16 50	22 31
Mestre ....arr	7 36	9 29	...	1211	1354	17 43	23 4
Venice..........arr	7 50	9 45	...	1233	1410	17 55	23 18

Fares and Luggage Rates, see page 269.]

GALLIPOLI, BRINDISI, ANCONA, BOLOGNA.

SLEEPING CARRIAGE—in 12.5 from Brindisi.

	1,2,3	1,2,3	1,2,3	1,2,3	1 & 3	1,2,3	1,2,3	1 &2	1,2,3	1,2,3	1,2,3
Gallipoli ......dep	...	...	...	...	3 41	...	6 *0	...	...	13*47	18*20
Nardo	...	...	...	...	4 16	...	6 39	...	...	13 37	19 8
Galatone	...	...	...	...	4 24	...	6 45	...	...	13 44	19 14
Zollino	...	...	...	...	4 51	...	7 22	...	...	14 25	19 56
S. Donato	...	...	*—1st and 3rd class only between Gallipoli and Lecce.	...	5 7	...	7 42	...	...	14 50	20 17
Lecce ......arr	...	...		...	5 20	...	7 58	...	...	15 11	20 33
Lecce ......dep	...	...		...		5 30	8 38	1055	12 15	16 20	20 55
S. Pietro Vernotico	...	...		...		5 58	9 12	1132	12 52	16 53	21 36
Brindisi Town arr	...	...		...	...	6 17	9 33	1155	13 13	17 13	22 3
Brindisi Port dep	...	...		...	...	6 6	...	...	...	16 31	
Brindisi Townarr	...	...		...	...	6 15	...	...	...	16 40	...
Brindisi Town dep	...	...		...	...	6 35	9 58	12 5	13 25	17 25	23 25
Ostuni	...	...		...	...	7 16	10 46	...	14 20	18 12	0 41
Fasano	...	...		...	...	7 38	11 9	...	14 48	18 35	1 18
Monopoli	...	...		...	...	7 53	11 29	...	15 9	18 50	1 44
Mola di Bari	...	...		...	...	8 18	11 55	...	15 40	19 17	2 25
Bari ......arr	...	...		...	...	8 49	12 18	1349	16 6	19 40	2 58
Bari ......dep	3 12	...		5 1	...	9 0	12 33	14 5	16 18	19 52	[In Sept. and Oct. only.]
Giovinazzo	3 31	...		5 2	...	9 22	13 3	...	16 48	20 15	
Molfetta	3 39	...		5 36	...	9 30	13 13	...	16 58	20 24	
Trani	3 58	...	...	5 59	...	9 49	13 36	1447	17 22	20 47	
Barletta	4 14	...	...	6 26	...	10 4	13 55	15 0	17 53	21 5	
Ofantino	...	...	...	6 43	...	...	14 11	...	18 7	...	
Cerignola	4 50	...	...	7 22	...	10 40	14 52	...	18 47	21 45	
Foggia ......arr	5 24	...	...	8 7	...	11 15	15 37	16 5	19 30	22 20	
NAPLES 285B arr	1110	...	...	...	1,2,3	16 30	...	2050	1,2,3	7 10	
Foggia ......dep	...	5 41	...	...	7 5	12 5	17 3	1630	14 43	...	22 40
S. Severo	...	6 15	...	...	7 51	12 44	17 43	...	15 38	...	23 12
Campomarino	...	...	...	...	9 9	13 51	18 55	...	17 17	...	...
Termoli ......arr	...	7 10	...	...	9 21	14 1	19 5	SC	17 31	...	0 18
Termoli ......dep	...	7 15	...	4 48	9 29	14 10	19 15	...		...	0 23
Vasto	...	7 38	...	5 22	10 7	14 46	19 51	...	...	...	0 49
Ortona	...	8 30	...	6 25	11 19	15 50	21 1	...	...	...	1 38
Francavilla a Mare	...	8 43	...	6 44	11 39	16 8	21 20	...	...	...	1 52
Pescara	...	8 53	...	6 57	11 52	16 19	21 33	...	...	...	2 3
Castellamare ......arr	...	8 57	...	7 1	11 56	16 23	21 37	1954	...	...	2 6
Castellamare ......dep	4 0	9 7	Tues., Thurs., and Sat. only.		12 50	16 37	21 57	20 5	...	...	2 24
Atri-Mutignano	4 31	9 36		...	13 20	17 5	22 28	...	...	...	...
Giulianova	4 59	10 2		...	13 4	17 30	22 57	...	...	...	3 0
Porto d' Ascoli	5 29	10 27		...	14 17	17 55	23 25	...	...	...	...
Sambenedetto	5 59	10 39		...	14 33	18 7	23 32	2117	...	19 25	3 31
Grottammare	6 10	10 47		...	14 42	18 16		...	...	19 36	3 38
Porto S. Giorgio	6 47	11 17		...	15 21	18 48	...	...	1,2,3	20 20	4 1
Porto Civitanova	7 17	11 40		...	15 58	19 14	...	SC	5 25	20 55	4 17
Porto Recanati	7 39	12 0		...	16 22	19 35	...	...	5 52	21 22	4‡32
Loreto	7 47	12 7		...	16 30	19 43	...	...	6 2	21 32	4 39
Osimo	8 1	12 18		...	16 45	19 55	...	...	6 16	21 48	4 49
Ancona ......arr	8 30	12 45	...	...	17 14	20 20	...	2248	6 54	22 22	5 5
Ancona ......dep	8 55	13 0	1435	1518	18 8	20 43	4‡40	23 5	7 3		5 15
Falconara	9 10	13 13	1446	1537	18 38	21 0	4 52	...	7 27	...	5 26
Senigallia	9 33	13 33	15 3	16 4	19 2	21 20	5 10	...	7 54	...	5†53
Fano	10 3	14 2	1529	1638	19 39	21 47	5 38	...	8 31	...	6†19
Pesaro	1020	14 19	1542	1657	20 3	22 5	5 53	...	8 52	...	6†37
Rimini ......arr	11 5	15 1	1621	1751	21 1	22 44	6 35	0 45	9 58	...	7†20
Rimini ......dep	1114	15 12	1630	18 0	21 11	22 51	6 42	0 52		4 45	7†30
Cesena	12 1	15 59	To Ferrara.	1849	21 59	23 23	7 25	...	...	5 34	8†13
Forli	1226	16 23		1917	22 25	23 42	7 49	...	...	6 2	8†26
Faenza	1249	16 41		1939	22 47	23 59	8 8	...	...	6 26	8†37
Castel Bolognese	13 5	16 56		1955	23 2	...	8 22	...	8 7	6 40	9† 5
Imola	1317	17 7		20 7	23 13	...	8 32	...	8 17	6 52	9†18
Castel S. Pietro	1333	17 22		2025	23 28	...	8 47	...	8 32	7 7	9†33
Bologna ......arr	14 7	17 52		21 1	24 0	0 45	9 11	2 35	8 57	7 42	9 57
VENICE 279A...arr	1850	21 27	...	...	...	4 40	...	8 33	...	12 20	13 50
MILAN 279B ...arr	1855	21 45	...	...	...	6 0	...	6 45	...	12 15	14 25
TURIN 273......arr	2325	0 16	...	...	...	8 41	...	8 41	...	15 12	19 0

‡—Until 30th Sept. †—Sets down only.

VENICE, UDINE, CORMONS, and PONTEBBA.

¶—Customs Examination.

	1,2,3	1,2,3	1,2,3	1,2,3	1,2,3	1,2,3	1,2,3	1 &2	1,2,3	1,2,3	1,2,3	1,2,3
Venice ......dep	5 0	5 55	7 10	8 47	1055	11 25	14 10	1610	...	1720	19 22	23 30
Mestre ......arr	5 10	6 7	7 24	8 59	11 5	11 37	14 20	1621	...	1730	19 35	23 44
" ......dep	5 15	6 9	7 27	9 1	11 8	11 40	14 26	1638	...	1734	19 40	23 50
Treviso 282 ...arr	5 37	6 49	8 3	9 30	1130	12 10	14 52	RC	...	1758	20 10	0 26
" ......dep	5 43	6 55	8 9	9 39	[From 15th July until 15th September.]	12 16	14 58		...	18 4	20 25	0 36
Conegliano 288	6 14	7 38	8 55	1021		12 58	15 31		...	1840	21 9	1 24
Pordenone	6 48	8 29		1110		13 46	16 4		...	1913	21 58	2 9
Casarsa	7 6	9 10	...	1132		14 11	16 23	18 6	...	1931	22 20	2 28
Udine ......arr	7 51	9 57	...	1220		14 58	17 3	1843	...	2011	23 7	3 20
Udine ......dep	8 19	...	...	13 0		15 45	17 58	1853	20 6	...	...	5 46
Buttrio	8 31	...	...	1314		16 2	18 9	...	20 21	...	...	6 1
Cormons ...arr	8 55	...	...	1340		16 33	18 32	1920	20 48	...	...	6 26
TRIESTE 234 arr	1148	...	...	4p15		7 p45	8 p42	9 p0	11 27	...	...	8a45
Udine ......dep	3 10	1014	...	...		15 50	17 15	...	...	1855	...	6 5
Gemona Ospedaletto	8 53	1124	...	...		16 46	17 52	...	...	20 1	...	7 10
Carnia	9 13	1154	...	...		17 9	18 9	...	...	2028	...	7 40
Chiusaforte	9 47	1243	...	...		17 49	1843	...	...	2113	...	8 31
Pontebba 241 arr	1018	1320	...	...	...	18 20	1914	...	...	2146	...	9 5
VIENNA ......arr	8p40	5a38	...	...	...	...	7 a40	...	...	...	...	8 p40

		1,2,3	1,2,3	1 &2	1,2,3	1,2,3	1,2,3	1,2,3	1,2,3	1,2,3	1,2,3
VIENNA 241 ...dep		...	...	...	9p15	...	...	...	...	7 a35	...
Pontebba ¶...dep		...	5 45	...	9 31	10 55	...	...	14 55	18 20	1840
Chiusaforte		...	6 7	...	9 48	11 18	...	...	15 17	18 38	19 8
Carnia		...	6 46	...	10 8	11 47	...	...	15 49	18 59	1939
Gemona Ospedaletto		...	7 5	...	10 22	12 6	...	...	16 9	19 11	20 0
Udine ......arr		...	7 57	...	11 0	12 55	...	...	17 0	19 46	2057
TRIESTE 234 dep		...	...	7a50	8 a32	9 a0	...	...	12 40	4p10	8p10
Cormons ¶ dep		...	6 37	9 25	10 35	12 5	...	...	15 7	18 57	2230
Buttrio		...	7 14	...	10 56	12 35	...	...	15 32	19 26	2257
Udine ....arr	1,2,3	...	7 33	9 51	11 7	12 50	...	...	15 45	19 41	2311
Udine ......dep	4 26	6 55	8 20	1010	11 25	13 10	...	1535	17 22	20 11	
Casarsa	5 11	7 37	9 9	1043	12 2	13 56	...	1620	18 12	20 48	...
Pordenone	5 30	7 54	9 32	...	12 18	14 17	...	1637	18 35	21 4	...
Conegliano	6 17	8 32	10 24	RC	12 55	15 6	4 40	1712	19 26	21 37	...
Treviso ...arr	6 54	9 6	11 0	...	13 23	15 45	5 21	1740	20 6	22 1	...
" ...dep	7 2	9 12	11 12	...	13 28	15 50	5 27	1748	20 28	22 5	1830
Mestre ......arr	7 42	9 37	11 52	1211	13 50	16 31	6 9	1815	20 58	22 25	1920
" ...dep	7 44	9 39	11 54	1222	13 55	16 35	6 15	1817	21 3	22 27	1926
Venice 279a arr	7 55	9 50	12 5	1233	14 5	16 47	6 27	1828	21 15	22 37	1940

Extra.—Venice to Treviso, 18.25, 21.35. Treviso to Venice, 7.50.

VENICE, CERVIGNANO, and CASARSA.

Venice ......dep	6 0	9 10	14 20	1610	17 25	19 10
Mestre	6 14	9 29	14 32	1638	17 43	19 25
S. Donà di Piave	7 8	10 26	15 6	...	18 46	19 58
Portogruaro ......arr	7 45	11 4	15 32	1738	19 28	20 25
Portogruaro ......dep	7 50	11 13	15 41	...	19 35	20 30
S. Giorgio di Nogaro	8 42	12 10	16 24	...	20 45	21 10
Cervignano ......arr	8 57	12 26	16 38	...	...	21 25
TRIESTE 234A ...arr	10a40	2p42	6p55	...	...	11p27
Portogruaro ......dep	8 29	13 5	15 42	1739	20 44	20 44
Casarsa ......arr	9 5	13 48	16 15	18 3	21 21	21 21

Casarsa ......dep	5 14	7 40	9 30	1043	...	14 48	21 4
Portogruaro ......arr	5 50	8 21	10 4	11 8	...	15 22	21 45
TRIESTE 234A ...dep	...	5a40		...	9 a0	1 p10	7 p5
Cervignano ......dep	...	7a12	...	...	11 6	14 39	20 32
S. Giorgio di Nogaro	..	7 50	8 46	...	1135	15 12	20 48
Portogruaro ......arr	...	8 24	9 59	...	1211	16 1	21 53
Portogruaro ......dep	5 53	8 31		11 9	1218	16 10	22 0
S. Donà di Piave	6 36	8 57	...	...	1258	16 50	22 31
Mestre ......arr	7 36	9 29	...	1211	1354	17 43	23 4
Venice ......arr	7 50	9 45	...	1233	1410	17 55	23 18

NAPLES and FOGGIA.

[Fares and Luggage Rates, see page 269.

		1,2,3	1,2,3	1—4	1,2,3	1,2,3	1,2,3	1,2,3	1,2,3
Naples ......dep		4 55	6 0	7 55	11 10	1420	17 2[illegible]	1735	23 10
Casoria		5 11	...	8 13	11 25	1438	17 36	1754	23 25
Fratta Grumo		5 1[illegible]	...	8 22	11 32	1446	17 43	18 2	23 33
S. Antimo		5 22	...	8 27	...	1450	...	18 7	23 38
Aversa		5 30	6 25	8 35	11 40	1459	17 52	1815	23 46
Caserta 276 ...arr		5 52	6 41	8 58	12 0	1521	18 12	1841	0 9
Frasso-Dugenta		6 35	...	9 46	12 43	16 9	18 51	1936	0 53
Telese		6 52	7 ‡28	10 8	12 58	1631	19 8	20 1	1 11
Solopaca		6 5[illegible]	...	10 18	13 5	1639	19 15	2012	1 19
S. Lor. Maggiore		...	...	10 28	...	1649	...	2025	...
Casalduni-Ponte		7 14	...	10 37	13 18	1658	19 28	2035	1 36
Vitulano	1,2,3	7 24	...	10 49	...	17 9	...	2048	...
Benevento 286	5 0	8 22	8 6	11 0	13 41	1729	19 52	21 2	2 4
Paduli	5 15	8 32	...		...	1739	...		...
Apice	5 30	8 42	...	...	...	1749	20 11	...	2 25
Montecalvo	6 3	9 11	...	...	14 23	1818	20 33	...	2 58
Ariano	6 40	9 40	...	...	14 51	1846	21 4	...	3 29
Savignano-G.	7 10	10 2	...	...	15 11	19 7	21 25	...	3 53
Bovino	7 55	10 31	...	...	15 34	1937	21 50	...	4 26
Giardinetto	8 6	10 41	...	...	15 43	1946	...	...	4 37
Cervaro	8 31	...	...	...	...	20 6	...	...	5 0
Foggia 285 arr	8 44	11 12	10 22	...	16 10	2018	22 25	...	5 12
BRINDISI ...arr		18 58	14 30	...	21 27	...	...	...	11 59

		1,2,3	1,2,3	1,2,3	1,2,3	1,2,3	1,2,3	1,2,3	1,2,3	1,2,3
BRINDISI dp		...	...	...	6 35	...	6 35	12 5	12 5	1725
Foggia ...dep		...	6 16	8 18	11 34	...	1210	1621	16 44	2340
Cervaro		...	...	...	...	...	1232	...	16 58	...
Giardinetto		...	...	...	12 5	...	1320	...	17 23	0 30
Bovino		...	6 57	9 19	12 19	...	1352	...	17 38	0 53
Savignano		...	7 32	10 4	12 49	...	1519	...	18 21	1 52
Ariano		...	7 51	1027	13 10	...	16 4	...	18 44	2 25
Montecalvo		...	8 8	1048	13 27	...	1634	...	19 4	2 51
Apice		...	8 24	11 6	...	...	17 0	...	19 22	3 15
Paduli		...	8 33	1117	...	...	1716	...	19 33	3 29
Benevento		6 5	8 50	1126	14 11	1550	1729	1845	20 10	3 58
Vitulano		6 17	...		...	16 4		...	20 28	...
Casalduni-P.		6 27	9 7	...	14 29	1616	...	...	20 31	4 18
S. Lor. Mag.		6 35	...	...	...	1625	...	...	...	...
Solopaca		6 45	9 21	...	...	1638	...	...	20 49	4 34
Telese		6 55	9 28	...	14 46	1648	...	...	20 57	4 43
Frasso-Dug.		7 16	9 43	...	15 0	1713	...	...	21 20	5 7
Caserta	5 5	8 6	10 20	14 8	15 40	1816	...	20 9	22 0	6 0
Aversa	5 37	8 37	10 41	1431	16 0	1844	...	2025	22 25	6 23
S. Antimo	5 48	8 45	...	1438	...	1853	...	...	22 32	6 37
Fratta-G.	5 58	8 51	10 50	1445	16 9	1859	...	...	22 38	6 45
Casoria	6 13	9 1	10 57	1454	16 17	19 9	...	...	22 47	6 56
Naples ar	6 28	9 15	11 10	15 8	16 30	1925	...	2050	23 0	7 10

‡—Until 30th September.

Extra.—Naples to Caserta, 20.20.

FOGGIA and POTENZA.

Dist.					
	Foggia ......dep	...	6 50	11 45	1820
5½	Cervaro	...	7 6	12 1	1836
31	Rocchetta S. Venere	...	8 42	13 43	2033
41½	Melfi	6 0	9 38	14 37	2127
47½	Rionéro-Atella-Ripacand.	6 32	10 12	15 13	2156
74	Potenza di Basilicata arr	8 15	11 55	16 55	...

Potenza ......dep	6 14	1020	18 5
Rionéro-Atella-Ripacand.	7 48	12 8	1938
Melfi	8 9	1237	1959
Rocchetta S. Venere	8 44	1348	2030
Cervaro	9 53	15 3	2127
Foggia ......arr	10 5	1515	2139

ROCCHETTA and GIOIA DEL COLLE.

E.M.						
	Rocchetta ......dep	...	8 45	13 23	20 40	...
21½	Venosa	...	9 45	14 23	21 43	...
35	Spinazzola 285 ......arr	...	10 27	15 5	22 25	...
...	" ......dep	4 0	10 37	15 20	—	...
65½	Altamura	5 26	11 53	16 46	...	...
87	Gioia del Colle 285B arr	6 20	12 43	17 40	...	...

Gioia del Colle ......dep	...	7 52	...	15 35	22 0
Altamura	...	9 6	...	16 41	23 3
Spinazzola ......arr	...	10 37	...	18 3	0 25
" ......dep	6 20	—	11 5	18 30	—
Venosa	7 3	...	1152	19 14	...
Rocchetta (273) ......arr	8 0	...	1258	20 13	...

FOGGIA and LUCERA.

E.M.						
	Foggia ......dep	6 32	9 0	13 0	1810	...
12½	Lucera ......arr	7 15	9 37	13 37	1853	...

Lucera ......dep	4 51	9 56	1315	1540	...
Foggia (285) ......arr	5 29	1028	1417	1618	...

FOGGIA and MANFREDONIA.

E.M.						
	Foggia (285) dep	6 10	9 2	1230	1740	...
10	Amendola	6 43	9 32	13 0	1817	...
22½	Manfredonia arr	7 22	10 8	1336	19 0	...

Manfredonia dep	7 39	1023	1435	2045	...
Amendola	8 20	11 1	1513	2134	...
Foggia ......arr	8 50	1128	1542	22 3	...

‡—Until 30th September.

TERNI, AQUILA, and SULMONA.

E.M.							
	Terni ......dep	5 10	8‡30	...	14 15	19 15	0 ‡2[illegible]
16¾	Greccio	6 23	9 33	...	15 16	20 31	...
25½	Rieti	6 50	10 4	...	15 40	21 3	2 30
31	Citta Ducale	7 5	10 22	...	15 54	21 22	2 46
40½	Antrodoco	7 42	11 2	...	16 35	21 56	3 25
64½	Aquila ......arr	9 42	12 45	...	18 15	—	5 25
...	" ......dep	1145	—	1650	—	19 45	6 8
77¾	Fagnano Campagna	1225	...	1737	...	20 25	6 48
102	Sulmona (282) ......arr	1335	...	1850	...	21 35	7 57

Sulmona ......dep		5 20	9 25	...	1425	19 27
Fagnano Campagna		6 47	10 45	...	1545	20 52
Aquila ......arr		7 26	11 20	...	1621	21 31
" ......dep		7 48	—	13‡25	1630	23 25
Antrodoco	5 0	9 54	...	15 19	1839	1 36
Citta Ducale	5 32	1023	...	15 53	19 8	2 12
Rieti	5 55	1043	...	16 12	1926	2 37
Greccio	6 22	11 7	...	16 35	1949	...
Terni (283) ......arr	7 15	1157	...	17 25	2035	3 50

BARI and TARANTO.

E.M.						
	Bari ......dep	5 0	10 0	13 28	1626	20 3
6¾	Modugno	5 20	1025	13 51	1646	2024
33½	Gioia del Col. 285B	6 35	1231	15 16	18 0	2149
47¾	Castellaneta	7 8	1335	...	1832	2220
71¾	Taranto (277) ......arr	7 57	1451	...	1924	2316

Taranto ......dep	...	6 0	10 55	1555	19 42
Castellaneta	...	7 6	12 7	17 7	21 3
Gioia del Colle	6 30	7 49	12 50	1755	21 57
Modugno	7 33	8 40	13 49	1848	23 16
Bari ......arr	7 46	8 53	14 0	19 0	23 31

BARI and LOCOROTONDO.

Bari ......dep	7 5	12 15	15 40	20 10
Conversano	8 22	13 18	16 56	21 13
Putignano	9 10	13 58	17 43	21 50
Locorotondo ......arr	10 7	14 46	18 40	22 38

Locorotondo ......dep	6 0	8 14	13 0	16 18
Putignano	6 53	9 19	14 7	17 13
Conversano	7 19	9 54	1445	17 42
Bari (285) ......arr	8 13	11 0	16 0	18 42

BARI and PUTIGNANO.

—	Bari ......dep	643	12 5	15 30	20 20
14¼	Casamassima	743	12 54	16 22	21 19
25¾	Putignano ......arr	840	13 42	17 9	22 16

Putignano ......dep	6 58	9 29	14 25	17 40
Casamassima	7 41	1021	15 17	18 23
Bari ......arr	8 25	1114	16 12	19 7

NAPLES, POMPEI, and SARNO.

‡—On Weekdays only—"Vettura Salon."

E.M.																							
	Naples ......dep	6 0	7 0	8 0	9 0	9‡48	10 0	1030	11 0	12 0	13 0	1330	14 0	15 0	16 0	1630	1718	1730	18 0	1830	19 0	20 0	21 0
6½	Pugliano	635	735	8 35	9 35	10 9	1036	11 7	1135	1235	1335	14 5	1435	1536	1635	17 5	1740	18 7	1835	19 5	1935	2035	2135
13	Torre Annunziata	7 0	8 0	9 0	10 0	1028	11 0	1130	12 0	13 0	14 0	1430	15 0	16 0	17 0	1730	18 0	1830	19 0	1930	20 0	21 0	22 0
16¾	Valle di Pompei	718	820	9 20	1020	1042	1120	1147	1220	1320	1420	1447	1520	1620	1720	1747	1813	1847	1920	1947	2020	2120	2217
21¾	Poggiomarino	740	843	9 43	1043	...	...	...	1243	...	1443	...	...	1643	1743	...	1830	...	1943	...	2043	2143	...
27¼	Sarno ......arr	758	9 2	10 2	11 2	...	...	...	13 2	...	15 2	...	...	17 2	18 2	...	1843	...	20 2	...	21 2	22 2	...

Sarno ......dep	...	5 10	...	6 10	...	7 5	8 2	...	8 40	9 40	1040	...	1240	...	...	1440	...	...	1640	1740	...	1940
Poggiomarino	...	5 35	...	6 35	...	7 37	8 18	...	9 5	10 5	11 5	...	13 5	...	...	15 5	...	...	17 5	18 5	19 5	20 5
Valle di Pompei	5 23	5 53	6 23	6 53	7 23	7 53	8 32	8 53	9 23	1023	1123	1223	1323	1423	15‡3	1523	1623	1653	1723	1823	1923	2023
Torre Annunziata	5 43	6 13	6 43	7 13	7 43	8 13	8 48	9 13	9 43	1045	1143	1243	1343	1443	1518	1543	1643	1713	1743	1843	1943	2043
Pugliano	6 9	6 39	7 9	7 39	8 9	8 39	9 7	9 39	10 8	11 9	12 9	13 9	14 9	15 9	1537	16 9	17 9	1739	18 9	19 9	20 9	21 9
Naples ......arr	6 40	7 10	7 40	8 10	8 40	9 10	9 28	1010	1040	1140	1240	1340	1440	1540	1556	1640	1740	1810	1840	1940	2040	2140

TERMOLI and BENEVENTO.

Dist. E.M.								
	Termoli ......dep	...	6 24	9 40	...	16 5	...	...
10	S. Martino	...	6 50	10 6	...	16 33	...	...
23	Larino	...	7 47	11 3	...	17 40	...	...
33½	Bonefro	...	8 36	1152	...	18 30	...	...
54½	Campobasso **286**	5 5	10 37	1314	16 50	19 52	0 40	...
62½	Vinchiaturo	5 37	11 9	—	17 19	—	1 11	...
80½	Morcone	6 33	12 6	...	18 19	...	2 16	...
86½	Campolattaro	6 57	12 30	...	18 41	...	2 41	...
92½	Pescolamazza	7 16	12 49	...	18 59	...	3 3	...
107	**Benevento 285B**	7 58	13 31	...	19 38	...	3 45	...

Benevento ...dep	2 10	8 20	...	14 10	...	20 5	...
Pescolamazza	3 8	9 11	...	15 0	...	20 55	...
Campolattaro	3 34	9 33	...	15 22	...	21 17	...
Morcone	4 1	9 59	...	15 47	...	21 42	...
Vinchiaturo	5 11	11 5	...	16 54	...	22 45	...
Campobasso	5 52	11 35	1545	17 18	20 10	23 9	...
Bonefro	7 14	—	17 7	—	21 32	—	...
Larino	7 51	...	1744	...	22 9	...	...
S. Martino	8 31	...	1824	...	22 49	...	...
Termoli ......arr	9 0	...	1853	...	23 18	...	...

CAMPOBASSO and ISERNIA.

Campobasso ......dep	6 0	12 15	16 25
Vinchiaturo	6 28	12 46	17 0
Carpinone	7 55	14 23	18 49
Isernia ......arr	8 17	14 47	19 13

Isernia ......dep	6 32	8 18	16 15	...
Carpinone	7 9	9 0	16 56	...
Vinchiaturo	8 38	10 38	18 28	...
Campobasso ......arr	9 10	11 11	19 0	...

SAMBENEDETTO and ASCOLI.

E.M						
	Sambenedetto (285) ......dep	5 50	8 25	1034	17 42	23 14
13	Offida-Castel di Lima	6 41	9 17	1126	18 36	0 10
20½	**Ascoli-Piceno** ......arr	7 6	9 42	1151	19 1	0 35

Ascoli-Piceno ......dep	3 50	8 50	12 38	16 23	23 39	...
Offida-Castel di Lima	4 16	9 15	13 8	16 49	0 6	...
Sambenedetto ......arr	5 9	10 3	13 57	17 41	0 54	...

FLORENCE and FAENZA.

A—Tues., Fri., and Sun. only.]

Florence (S.M.N.) ......dep	...	6 15	9 5	11 45	15 45	18 38
Vaglia	...	7 2	10 10	12 27	16 28	19 20
Borgo S. Lorenzo	...	7 27	10 41	12 52	16 51	19 42
Marradi	5 12	8 46	...	14 12	18 9	21 2
Fognano	5 42	9 11	A	14 37	18 34	21 27
Faenza ......arr	6 9	9 32	...	15 0	18 55	21 48

Faenza ......dep	4 35	...	10 0	12 55	17 0	20 20
Fognano	5 0	A	10 25	13 20	17 25	20 54
Marradi	5 40	...	11 4	14 5	18 4	21 39
Borgo S. Lorenzo	7 0	8 45	12 25	15 18	19 21	—
Vaglia	7 24	9 18	12 50	15 39	19 42	...
Florence (S.M.N) ...arr	8 0	1020	13 29	16 15	20 18	...

PADUA and VENICE.—(Steamer between Venice and Fusina.)

Dist E.M				
	Padua (S. Sofia) ...dep	5 0	...	and hourly until 21.0.
6½	Stra	5 28	...	
11¾	Dolo	5 45	...	
21¾	Fusina	6 30	...	
26	**Venice (R.S.)** arr	7 0	...	

Venice (Riva Schiavoni) dep	...	...	6 30	and hourly at 30 minutes past the hour until 21.30.
Fusina	...	...	7 5	
Dolo	5 46	6 46	7 46	
Stra	6 3	7 3	8 3	
Padua ......arr	6 30	7 30	8 30	

PADUA and BAGNOLI.

E.M						
	Padua (S. Sofia) dep	7 10	1130	15 40	19 5	...
9¼	Cagnola	7 49	12 9	16 33	19 58	...
17¼	**Bagnoli** ......arr	8 25	1245	17 20	20 45	...

Bagnoli ......dep	5 20	8 40	13 0	17 35	...
Cagnola	6 7	9 15	13 47	18 10	...
Padua ......arr	7 0	9 55	14 40	18 50	...

PADUA and PIOVE.

Padua S. Sofia ......dep	5 0	7 0	11 20	17 0	19 40
Piove ......arr	6 0	7 45	12 20	17 45	20 40

Piove ......dep	6 5	7 53	12 30	18 0	21 0	...
Padua ......arr	6 50	8 38	13 30	19 0	22 0	...

NAPLES and BAIANO.

EM								
	Naples ...dep	5 30	8 0	10 0	12 5	15 28	1750	20 20
16¾	Nola	6 59	9 20	1113	13 29	16 35	1916	21 34
23¾	**Baiano** ...arr	7 31	9 52	...	14 1	17 7	1948	...

Baiano ...dep	6 0	...	8 0	1120	...	1435	...	18 45	...	...
Nola	6 42	7 29	8 36	1155	1357	1514	1644	19 20	...	...
Naples ...arr	7 59	8 42	9 39	1311	1510	1631	18 4	20 33	...	...

FORLI and RAVENNA.

‡—7.10 on Monday.

Forli ......dep	5 20	8 0	12 40	1640	19 40
Coccolia	5 52	8 33	13 12	1712	20 13
Ravenna (P.A.) ......arr	6 49	9 29	14 9	18 9	21 9

Ravenna (P.A.) ...dep	5 35	9‡40	12 15	16 55	18 22
Coccolia	6 33	1038	13 13	17 53	19 21
Forli (P.V.E.) ......arr	7 4	11 9	13 44	18 24	19 53

FORLI and MELDOLA.

Forli (286) ......dep	5 50	9 0	12 40	16 40	19 40
Meldola ......arr	6 34	9 44	13 24	17 24	20 24

Meldola ......dep	4 30	6 55	10 45	14 50	18 25	...
Forli ......arr	5 14	7 39	11 29	15 34	19 9	...

SASSUOLO and GUASTALLA.

E.M						
	Sassuolo ......dep	6 15	7 25	1145	16 50	...
6¼	Scandiano	6 44	8 25	1220	17 20	...
14¼	Reggio	7 30	9 0	1251	17 46	...
19¼	Bagnolo ......arr	7 48	9 55	1343	18 34	...
31	: Carpi ......arr	8 40	11 10	1434	19 26	...
32¼	**Guastalla (288)** arr	8 55	11 31	1449	19 26	...

Guastalla dep	6 10	7 49	1140	...	1645	...
: Carpi ......dep	6 15	...	1149	1340	1642	...
Bagnolo	6 58	9 10	1242	1457	1733	...
Reggio (279)	7 15	10 5	13 0	1512	1750	...
Scandiano	8 20	1055	14 9	—	1857	...
Sassuolo ...arr	8 50	1132	1440	...	1921	...

NAPLES (Monte Santo) and TORRE GAVETA.

Naples M. Sant. dep	5 58	6 24	7 7	7 44	8 19	8 56	9 27	10 6	1036	1119	1230	1325	1425	1520	1617	1652	1728	18 4	1835	1935	2011	2118
,, Corso V.E.	6 6	6 32	7 15	7 52	8 27	9 4	9 35	1014	1044	1127	1238	1333	1433	1528	1625	17 0	1736	1812	1843	1943	2019	2126
Fuorigrotta	6 12	6 38	7 21	7 58	8 33	9 9	9 41	1020	1050	1133	1244	1339	1439	1534	1631	17 6	1742	1818	1849	1949	2025	2131
Bagnoli	6 25	6 55	7 34	8 9	8 46	9 22	9 54	1033	11 3	1146	1257	1352	1452	1547	1644	1719	1756	1831	19 2	20 2	2038	2143
Pozzuoli	6 42	7 9	7 48	8 22	9 0	9 40	10 8	1047	1119	12 0	1313	14 9	15 6	16 3	17 0	1746	1815	1844	1918	2017	2052	2156
Baia	7 3	—	—	8 40	—	9 57	—	—	1136	—	1330	1426	—	1620	1710	—	1833	—	1935	2033	—	—
Torre Gaveta...arr	7 10	...	...	8 47	...	10 4	...	...	1143	...	1337	1433	...	1627	1716	...	1840	...	1942	2040	...	...

Torre Gaveta ...dep	...	6 10	...	7 21	...	...	9 8	...	1022	...	1150	...	1346	1440	...	1636	1721	...	...	1850	1951	...
Baia	...	6 19	...	7 35	...	...	9 17	...	1031	...	1159	...	1354	1449	...	1645	1731	...	...	1859	20 0	...
Pozzuoli	6 9	6 41	7 17	7 53	8 29	9 8	9 36	1019	1049	1128	1216	1311	1411	15 6	16 1	17 2	1743	1817	1850	1920	2019	21 0
Bagnoli	6 24	6 57	7 33	8 9	8 45	9 24	9 52	1035	11 5	1144	1232	1327	1427	1522	1617	1718	1758	1833	19 4	1937	2036	2116
Fuorigrotta	6 37	7 11	7 47	8 23	8 59	9 39	10 6	1049	1120	1158	1246	1341	1441	1536	1631	1732	18 8	1847	1918	1951	2050	2128
Naples Corso V.E.	6 43	7 17	7 53	8 29	9 5	9 45	1012	1055	1126	12 4	1252	1347	1447	1542	1637	1738	1814	1853	1924	1957	2056	—
,, Monte Santo	6 49	7 23	7 59	8 35	9 11	9 51	1018	11 1	1132	1210	1258	1353	1453	1548	1643	1744	1820	1859	1930	20 3	21 2	...

VESUVIUS RAILWAY.

E.M.							
	Pugliano ......dep	7 10	10 5	14 10	17 5	18 15	...
1¾	San Vito	7 16	10 11	14 16	17 11	18 21	...
3	Eremo	7 30	10 34	14 30	17 34	18 44	...
5	Funicolare	7 52	10 47	14 52	—	—	...
6¼	Cratere ......arr	8 10	11 5	15 10	...	...	...

Cratere ......dep	...	...	8 58	11 53	...	15 58	...	...
Funicolare	...	...	9 14	12 9	...	16 14	...	...
Eremo	...	8 20	9 25	13 35	16 30	17 40	...	...
San Vito	6 54	8 39	—	13 54	16 49	17 59	...	...
Pugliano ......arr	7 0	8 45	...	14 0	16 55	18 5	...	...

MILAN and INCINO-ERBA.

A—From 10th July.

Dist. E.M.	Station																	
...	**Milan**—Nord ......dep	5 30	6 41	7 38	9 28	10 6	13 6	13 51	16 25	17 8	17 25	18 25	18 42	19 36	20 12	...	...	...
3	Bovisa	5 38	6 51	7 45	9 39	10 14	13 15	13 58	16 35	17 14	17 32	18 32	18 56	19 48	20 19	...	...	...
7½	Paderno Dugnano	6 0	7 12	7 59	10 4	10 26	13 34	14 13	16 55	A	17 45	18 46	19 19	20 12	20 32	...	...	...
13¾	Seveso S. Pietro	6 25	7 34	8 20	10 28	10 40	13 57	14 34	17 16	17 36	18 5	19 3	19 44	20 37	20 51	...	...	...
17½	Mariano Comense	6 40	—	8 33	—	10 55	—	14 50	—	...	18 19	19 17	—	—	21 9	...	...	...
24¾	Merone Pontenuovo ...	7 10	...	8 59	...	11 24	...	15 22	...	18 5	18 47	19 51	...	...	21 40	...	...	...
27¼	**Incino-Erba** ......arr	7 16	...	9 5	...	11 30	...	15 28	...	18 11	18 54	19 58	...	...	21 46	...	...	...
...	**Incino-Erba**......dep	5 40	...	6 48	7 20	7 40	...	9 48	12 24	...	...	1646	...	20 12	...	...	...	...
...	Merone Pontenuovo ...	5 48	...	6 55	7 27	7 47	...	9 55	12 33	...	...	1654	...	20 19	...	...	...	...
...	Mariano Comense	6 18	...	7 23	...	8 7	...	10 21	13 2	...	...	1722	...	20 47	...	...	...	...
...	Seveso S. Pietro	6 36	6 43	7 34	7 59	8 21	8 28	10 38	13 17	13 35	16 20	1741	18 43	21 6	...	...	...	...
...	Paderno Dugnano	6 52	7 4	7 49	8 14	A	8 51	10 56	13 33	14 1	16 46	18 1	19 8	21 30	...	...	...	...
...	Bovisa	7 7	7 24	8 8	8 28	8 44	9 13	11 22	13 48	14 23	17 9	1816	19 29	21 52	...	...	...	...
...	**Milan**..................arr	7 14	7 33	8 15	8 34	8 50	9 20	11 30	13 56	14 34	17 20	1822	19 38	22 1	...	...	...	...

MILAN and CAMNAGO.

Dist. E.M.	Station						
...	**Milan**-Nord dep	...	6 41	10 6	16‡25	18 42	‡—After
13¾	Seveso S. Pietro...	5 10	7 40	10 41	17 41	19 47	10th July
15	**Camnago** ...arr	5 15	7 45	10 46	17 46	19 52	depart
26¾	COMO ....arr	7 3	9 17	11 52	19 14	...	17.8.

Station						
COMO ....dep	...	...	11 59	17 12	...	§—After
Camnago ...dep	6 15	8 10	13 5	18 35	2043	10th July
Seveso S. Pietro...	6 20	8 15	13 10	18 40	2048	arrive
Milan ....arr	7 14	9§20	13 56	19 38	22 1	8.50.

MILAN and COMO (Riva Lago).

‡—From 10th July.

Station																					
Milan-Nord dep	6 20	7 20	8 44	10 20	13 0	14 24	15 52	16‡45	17 15	18 2	18 10	20 45	...	...	...	...	...	...	...	...	...
Saronno ...	6 52	7 46	9 11	10 49	13 27	14 48	16 15	17 13	17 36	18 23	18 36	21 27	...	...	...	...	...	...	...	...	...
Como arr	7 52	8 36	10 8	11 44	14 24	15 40	17 7	18 0	18 25	19 5	19 34	22 30	...	...	...	...	...	...	...	...	...
Como dep	5 2	6 35	7 0	7 52	9 18	1015	12 10	1350	15‡56	1615	18 16	19 40	21‡38	...	...	...	...	...	...	...	...
Saronno......	6 3	7 26	8 0	8 36	10 4	1114	13 12	1449	16 43	1714	19 17	20 44	22 34	...	...	...	...	...	...	...	...
Milan ...arr	6 25	7 51	8 28	8 58	10 26	1140	13 37	1514	17 5	1738	19 38	21 9	22 59	...	...	...	...	...	...	...	...

MILAN and LAVENO.

‡—From 10th July. *—Until 9th July.

Station												
Milan ...dep	...	5 34	7 2	8 20	10 0	1248*	13‡20	1620	1720	17‡52	1820	2045
Saronno ...	...	6 20	730	8 48	1028	1317	13 41	1652	1745	18 16	1846	2125
Varese Nord	542	7 26	827	9 43	1140	1429	14 29	1758	1830	19 22	1953	2235
Casbeno	548	7‡36	833	9 49	1147	1435	14 35	18 4	1836	—	1959	—
Gavirate......	6 7	7‡53	850	10 7	12 5	1452	14 52	1820	1853	...	2017	...
Laveno arr	628	8‡14	911	1023	1227	1513	15 13	1840	1912	...	2035	...

Station										
Laveno dp	545	...	646	743	9 32	11 5	1316	1548	1815	19‡40
Gavirate ...	6 6	...	7 6	8 4	9 54	1127	1338	1610	1839	20 2
Casbeno	625	...	723	822	1012	1145	1355	1627	1854	20 21
VareseNord	630	640	730	829	1022	1153	14 5	1634	19 4	20 32
Saronno ...	...	741	818	916	1127	1253	15 8	1723	20 7	21 21
Milan...arr	...	810	840	938	1149	1318	1530	1745	2035	21 46

Extra—Milan to Varese 12‡24, 17‡0, 17.20 Varese to Milan 5.5, 7.8, 7‡46, 16.50, 21‡0.

COMO and VARESE.

‡—From 10th July.

Dist. E.M.	Station							
...	**Como** (Lago) ...dep	5 ‡2	7 0	8 26	10 22	1255	1642	1833
5	Civello	...	7 25	8 53	10 44	1321	17 8	1859
18	**Varese** ....arr	7 26	8 9	9 31	11 23	14 4	1748	1941

Station							
Varese ....dep	6 33	8 36	10 27	14 26	16 39	19 23	20‡32
Civello................	7 13	9 18	11 7	15 7	17 19	20 12	...
Como ....arr	7 39	9 40	11 29	15 30	17 40	20 36	22 30

SASSUOLO to MIRANDOLA and FINALE.

E.M	Station								
...	Sassuolo......dep	...	...	6 7	8 30	...	12 8	15 10	1742
10½	Modena ......arr	...	...	6 55	9 14	...	12 54	15 58	1830
...	,, 282 dep	...	6 40	—	—	1110	14 0	17 40	—
21¾	Solara-Camp ...	...	7 29	...	...	12 1	14 48	18 29	...
26	Cavezzo..........	7 0	7 48	...	1120	1222	15 9	18 48	...
38½	⁝ Finale ...arr	...	8 46	...	⁝	1330	16 18	19 53	...
29¾	Mirandola ...arr	7 15	8 13	...	1135	1242	15 30	19 9	...

Station								
Mirandola dep	...	6 45	7 27	1036	...	1155	14 49	1745
⁝ Finale dep	...	6 0	...	9 50	...	...	14 0	17 5
Cavezzo	...	7 6	7 42	1056	...	1210	15 9	18 6
Solara-Camp...	...	7 27	—	1116	...	—	15 31	1827
Modena......arr	...	8 12	...	12 2	...	...	16 20	1912
,, ...dep	7 20	—	11 0	—	13 30	...	16 40	—
Sassuolo ...arr	8 6	...	11 51	...	14 19	...	17 26	...

BERGAMO and CLUSONE.

Station							
Bergamo (281) ...dep	5 53	8 30	10 20	13 0	14 50	16 20	18 33
Albino	6 30	9 7	11 0	13 40	15 32	17 1	19 10
Ponte della Selva......	7 21	9 58	11 51	14 31	...	17 55	20 1
Clusone .... arr	7 35	10 12	12 5	14 45	...	18 9	20 15

Station								
Clusone ....dep	5 31	7 47	1032	13 25	...	16 32	18 55	...
Ponte della Selva.	5 45	8 1	1046	13 39	...	16 46	19 9	...
Albino	6 32	8 46	1132	14 32	16 25	17 32	1955	...
Bergamo ......arr	7 16	9 17	12 2	15 10	17 0	18 7	2026	...

Station						
Bergamo......dep	5 50	9 20	...	13 5	17 30	...
Romano...........	7 25	10 45	1120	14 30	18 55	19 20
Soncino ....arr	8 44	...	1239	16 20	...	20 40

Station							
Soncino.........dep	5 40	9 0	...	1252	...	1730	...
Romano	7 20	10 20	10 50	1412	15 0	19 9	...
Bergamo ....arr	8 50	...	12 20	...	16 30	2045	...

BERGAMO and SAN GIOVANNI BIANCO.

Station							
Bergamo..............dep	6 25	6 55	8 30	1016	1245	1631	1830
Villa d'Almè..............	6 57	7 25	9 1	1048	1316	17 3	19 2
Zogno	7 18	—	9 22	11 9	1334	1724	1923
S. Pellegrino Terme ...	7 32	...	9 36	1123	1351	1741	1937
S. Giovanni Bianco arr	7 43	...	9 47	1134	1359	1749	1948

Station									
S. Giovanni Bianco	6 9	...	8 1	1042	1416	1657	1952	...	...
S. Pellegrino Terme	6 21	...	8 13	1054	1428	17 9	20 4	...	...
Zogno....................	6 35	...	8 27	11 8	1442	1723	2018	...	...
Villa d'Almè	6 56	7 59	8 48	1129	15 0	1744	2039	...	...
Bergamo	7 27	8 30	9 17	12 0	1530	1815	2110	...	...

OFANTINO and MARGHERITA.

E.M	Station			
...	Ofantino (285) ....dep	8 10	14 20	18 20
3	Margherita di S.........arr	8 27	14 37	18 37

Station			
Margherita di S.......dep	6 13	13 8	17 13
Ofantino ....arr	6 30	13 25	17 30

BASALUZZO and FRUGAROLO.

E.M.	Station					
...	Basaluzzo ......dep	5 25	6 55	10 5	12 25	18 5
5½	Frugarolo (270)arr	5 50	7 20	10 30	12 50	18 30

Station					
Frugarolo ......dep	6 15	9 10	1135	15 0	19 35
Basaluzzo ......arr	6 40	9 35	12 0	1525	20 0

NOVARA and SARONNO.

Station								
Novara ...dep	5 5	7 58	11 40	...	15 50	18‡2	19 40	...
Busto Arsizio...	5 51	8 44	12 33	14 10	16 37	1849	20 35	...
Castellanza......	5 56	8 49	12 39	14 16	16 42	1851	20 41	...
Cairate ...arr	7 14	10 9	...	...	18 44	...	21 42	...
Saronno arr	6 15	9 9	13 4	14 14	17 1	1913	21 7	...
Saronno...dep	6 30	9 20	13 15	...	17 25	...	...	...
Seregno ...arr	7 4	9 54	13 49	...	17 48	...	...	...

Station								
Seregno.........dep	...	8 37	...	10 30	...	1437	1820	...
Saronno.........arr	...	9 0	...	11 6	...	1510	1843	...
Saronno ......dep	6 18	9 12	1030	11 57	14 53	1745	2044	...
Cairate ....dep	5 11	8 6	...	...	...	16 5	20 2	...
Castellanza............	6 37	9 31	1059	12 18	15 13	18 7	21 5	...
Busto Arsizio........	6 45	9 39	11 5	12 29	15 20	1815	2113	...
Novara ....arr	7 27	1025	...	13 14	16 8	19 5	22 0	...

VERONA, GARDA, and CAPRINO.

Station						
Verona ......dep	6 50	9 20	1430	17 0	...	...
Affi....................	8 4	1034	1544	1814	...	...
Garda ......arr	8 32	11 2	1612	1842	...	...
Caprino......arr	8 26	1056	16 6	1836	...	...

Station						
Caprino ....dep	6 33	9 23	14 13	1728	...	...
Garda............dep	6 25	9 15	14 6	1720	...	...
Affi	6 55	9 45	14 35	1750	...	...
Verona ....arr	8 9	10 59	15 53	19 4	...	...

VENICE and PRIMOLANO.

Venice dep	5 30	9 20	1230	16 40	19 5	...	...
Mestre	5 43	9 35	1245	16 58	1918	...	...
Castelfranco Veneto (288)	6 35	1025	1340	17 53	1957	...	...
Bassano (288) arr	7 5	1055	1413	18 27	20 20	...	...
Carpané Valstagna	7 33	1120	1512	18 58	2041	...	...
Primolano arr	7 56	1143	1537	19 23	21 1	...	...
TRIENT 237 arr	11a13	2p45	6p45	10p45	1135	...	...

TRIENT dep	...	5a27	9 a58	1p31	5 p30	...	...	...
Primolano dep	5 20	8 40	13 15	1625	19 50	...	...	...
Carpané Valstagna	5 42	9 4	13 42	1649	20 9	...	...	...
Bassano	6 6	9 40	14 14	1720	20 27	...	...	...
Castelfranco Veneto	6 37	1023	14 48	1755	20 51	...	...	...
Mestre	7 27	1117	15 44	1850	21 31	...	...	...
Venice arr	7 40	1132	16 0	19 5	21 45	...	...	...

TREVISO and VICENZA.

E.M							
	Treviso dep	4 30	7 0	12 47	1630	20 30	...
15¼	Castelfranco	5 15	7 44	13 42	1723	21 20	...
23	Cittadella (288)	5 44	8 9	14 16	1754	21 44	...
37½	Vicenza (280) arr	6 25	8 51	14 57	1835	22 25	...

Vicenza dep	4 53	7 13	13 14	17 1	19 0	...
Cittadella	5 43	8 2	14 17	1749	19 54	...
Castelfranco	6 6	8 24	15 0	1810	20 21	...
Treviso arr	6 45	9 5	15 44	1849	21 5	...

PADUA and BASSANO.

‡—From 15th July until 15th Sept.

E.M.									
	Padua dep	4 45	7 0	8 42	11 ‡0	1318	1355	1644	1856
11¾	Camposampiero	5 17	7 34	9 17	11 25	1350	1431	1718	1928
29¼	: Montebelluna arr	6 31	...	1017	12 5	...	1531	1835	2043
20½	Cittadella (288)	5 48	8 8	10 1	—	1415	—	1751	1951
29¾	Bassano arr	6 15	8 35	1030	...	1441	...	1818	2017

Bassano dep	5 10	7 30	9 33	1330	1717	2045	...
Cittadella	5 54	8 6	10 0	1411	1747	2112	...
: Montebelluna dp	5 35	7 14	...	13 0	1653	1951	22‡30
Camposampiero	6 25	8 28	1022	1434	18 9	2133	23 9
Padua arr	6 58	8 58	1053	15 8	1842	2154	23 30

SCHIO and ARSIERO—SCHIO and TORREBELVICINO.

E.M.						
	Schio dep	7 40	12 0	16 30	20 2	...
6½	Rocchette	8 25	12 40	17 10	20 42	...
11¾	Arsiero arr	8 50	13 5	17 35	21 7	...

Arsiero dep	6 0	10 30	14 37	18 10	...
Rocchette	6 35	11 0	15 10	18 40	...
Schio arr	7 10	11 35	15 45	19 15	...

E.M					
	Schio dep	8 22	12 25	16 30	...
2½	Torrebelvicino arr	8 40	12 49	16 46	...

Torrebelvicino dep	9 13	13 20	17 10	...	...	...
Schio arr	9 35	13 45	17 28	...	...	...

VICENZA and SCHIO

Vicenza dep	7 3	9 30	1117	13 25	1522	19 5	22 30
Thiene	7 49	10 7	12 4	14 20	1611	19 46	23 14
Schio arr	8 5	1020	1220	14 38	1625	19 59	23 30

Schio dep	5 20	6 55	9 50	11 44	14 5	15 50	19 20
Thiene	5 34	7 11	10 5	12 0	14 25	16 5	19 42
Vicenza arr	6 8	7 44	1038	12 39	15 1	16 36	20 16

Thiene dep	7 50	12 8	14 25	16 15	...	19 50	...	...
Rocchette	8 16	12 34	14 53	16 41	17 25	20 16	...	...
Asiago arr	10 8	...	...	...	19 7	...	...	...

Asiago dep	5 0	...	...	13 40	...	...	...
Rocchette	6 35	11 19	13 40	15 23	18 48	...	...
Thiene arr	7 0	11 44	14 7	15 50	19 15	...	...

PARMA and SUZZARA.

E.M							
	Parma dep	5 42	10 0	14 8	18 20	...	...
12	Brescello	6 21	10 43	14 50	18 53	...	...
20	Guastalla	6 47	11 10	15 18	19 16	...	...
27½	Suzzara arr	7 16	11 37	15 45	19 26	...	...

Suzzara dep	5 25	9 5	16 13	19 51	...
Guastalla	5 53	9 36	16 35	20 23	...
Brescello	6 19	10 5	16 58	20 53	...
Parma arr	6 50	10 49	17 28	21 36	...

PORTOMAGGIORE AND BOLOGNA S. VITALE.

Portomaggiore dep	6 36	10 27	13 42	1840
Bologna S. Vitale arr	8 10	11 58	15 13	2026

Bologna S. Vitale dep	7 8	11 0	16 0	19 5
Portomaggiore 282 arr	8 53	12 31	1731	21 0

AREZZO and PRATOVECCHIO STIA.

E.M					
	Arezzo dep	5 50	11 0	16 15	19 20
19¼	Bibbiena	6 58	12 0	17 28	20 22
28	**Pratovecchio S.**	7 26	12 28	18 0	20 49

Pratovecchio S.	5 25	8 5	15 20	19 20	...
Bibbiena	5 52	8 32	15 48	19 51	...
Arezzo (279) arr	6 49	9 28	16 46	21 1	...

ROME and NETTUNO.

‡—Weekdays only.

Rome Termini dep	6 25	6 50	...	8 55	9 20	11 ‡0	12 20	1245	16 30	16 55	18 45	1910	...	...	...	...	...
Marino	7 6	:	...	9 34	:	11 39	12 59	:	17 2	17 36	19 24	:	...	...	...	...	...
Albano Laz.	7 25	:	8 34	9 58	:	11 51	13 18	:	17 25	18 12	19 40	:	...	...	...	...	...
Cecchina	7 40	7 50	8 49	1013	1020	—	13 33	1314	17 40	18 27	19 55	20 5	...	...	...	...	...
Nettuno arr	...	8 46	...	...	1117	...	...	1441	18 33	...	...	21 9	...	...	...	...	...

Nettuno dep	...	6 41	...	...	...	...	1228	...	...	17 26	...	...	...	20 57	...	...
Cecchina	...	7 51	7 48	8 57	9 38	10 25	1336	13 37	...	18 36	18 42	...	22 17	22 21	...	...
Albano Laz.	6 54	:	8 6	9 12	9 55	10 40	:	13 55	17 21	:	19 10	21 1	22 32	:	...	...
Marino	7 7	:	8 19	—	10 8	—	:	14 8	17 34	:	19 23	21 14	—	:	...	...
Rome Termini arr	7 45	8 35	8 55	...	1045	...	1415	14 45	18 10	19 20	20 0	21 50	...	23 0	...	...

POGGIBONSI and COLLE D'ELSA.

Poggibonsi (275) dep	6 16	9 24	11 45	16 20	19 43
Colle d'Elsa arr	6 33	9 41	12 2	16 37	20 0

Colle d'Elsa dep	5 40	8 0	10 35	14 40	17 30
Poggibonsi arr	5 57	8 17	10 52	14 57	17 47

BOLOGNA and MASSALOMBARDA.

Bologna S. Vitale dep	5 20	9 0	14 15	17 33
Massalombarda arr	6 40	1030	15 33	18 55

Massalombarda dep	5 47	8 22	13 46	1658
Bologna arr	7 8	9 36	15 28	1835

‡—Not on Sunday.

CIVIDALE and PORTOGRUARO.

Cividale dep	6 22	...	9 0	12 24	15 2	19 2	21 25
Udine	7 0	8 0	9 28	13 50	16 10	20 14	21 53
S. Giorgio di Nog	7 40	8 40	...	14 47	17 12	21 5	...
Portogruaro	8 24	9 59	...	16 1	18 38	21 53	...

Portogruaro	...	...	7 50	...	11 13	1541	...	...	19 35	20 30
S. Giorgio di Nog	...	6 23	8 45	...	12 7	1621	1640	...	20 45	21 14
Udine	5 20	8 7	9 33	11 15	13 30	...	1745	20 15	...	21 58
Cividale arr	5 48	8 35	...	11 46	13 58	...	1816	20 43	...	...

LODI and BRESCIA.

E.M								
	Lodi dep	...	...	7 21	...	1218	1523	1821
8¾	Crema	...	...	8 32	...	1330	1633	1934
14¼	Soncino arr	4 36	7 15	9 37	1224	1436	1738	2039
34¾	**Brescia** arr	6 38	8 55	...	1428	...	1946	...

Brescia dep	...	4 50	...	9 2	1240	...	18 0
Soncino	5 25	6 54	8 5	1130	1444	17 6	20 4
Crema	6 40	—	9 18	1245	—	1818	—
Lodi arr	7 43	...	1021	1348	...	1921	...

MILAN, BINASCO, and PAVIA.

‡—Weekdays only.

Milan Porta Lodovica dep	5 30	7 30	9 30	11 32	14 0	16 16	17 37	19 49	...	...	...	...	...
Binasco	6 38	8 38	10 31	12 40	15 8	17 24	18 35	20 50	...	...	...	...	...
Torre Mangano (Certosa)	7 3	9 3	10 54	13 5	15 33	17 49	19 1	21 13	...	...	...	...	...
Pavia Piazza Petrarca arr	7 28	9 28	11 16	13 30	15 58	18 14	19 23	21 33	...	...	...	...	...

Pavia Piazza Petrarca dep	...	5 54	7 40	9 40	11 50	14 10	16 30	18 16	19 55	...	...	...	...
Torre del Mangano	...	6 15	8 6	10 6	12 11	14 36	16 56	18 42	20 21	...	...	...	...
Binasco	4 ‡54	6 40	8 34	10 34	12 36	15 4	17 24	19 10	20 49	...	...	...	...
Milan Porta Lodovica arr	6 0	7 38	9 40	11 40	13 36	16 10	18 30	20 16	21 55	...	...	...	...

FERRARA and SUZZARA.

Ferrara dep	...	6 55	1017	13 3	16 50
Sermide	6 5	8 11	1140	14 16	18 1
Suzzara arr	7 34	...	1317	15 57	19 35

Suzzara dep	5 25	8 10	...	1530	19 50
Sermide	7 9	9 50	13 35	1728	21 29
Ferrara arr	8 8	10 56	15 24	1845	...

FERRARA and COPPARO.

Ferrara dep	7 49	11 25	15 58	19 20	...	...
Copparo arr	8 25	12 5	16 34	20 0	...	...

Copparo dep	5 45	9 4	13 50	17 25	...	...
Ferrara arr	6 21	9 40	14 26	18 5	...	...

S. ELLERO and SALTINO.

S. Ellero dep	9 15	15 0	...	...	...
Saltino arr	10 15	16 0	...	...	...

Saltino dep	13 35	17 35	...	...	...	...	...
S. Ellero 279 arr	14 35	18 35	...	...	...	...	...

CONEGLIANO and VITTORIO.

Dist								
	Conegliano dep	6 35	10 30	13 10	15 40	18 45	2140	...
8¾	Vittorio arr	7 5	11 0	13 40	16 10	19 15	2210	...

Vittorio dep	5 40	8 0	12 20	14 24	16 38	2030	...	...
Conegliano (285A) arr	6 6	8 26	12 46	14 50	17 4	2056	...	...

TURIN and RIVOLI.

Turin ...dep	5 25	6 45	7 35	9 0	11 0	12 0	13 30	14 25	16 25	1720	18 30	19 40	20 30	...	...	...	...	...
Regina Margherita ...	5 44	7 4	7 54	9 19	11 19	12 19	13 49	14 44	16 44	1739	18 46	19 59	20 49	...	...	...	...	...
Rivoli ...arr	6 0	7 20	8 10	9 35	11 35	12 35	14 5	15 0	17 0	1755	18 58	20 15	21 5	...	...	...	...	...

Rivoli ...dep	5 28	6 48	7 38	9 3	11 3	12 3	13 33	14 28	16 28	1723	18 35	19 43	20 33	...	...	...	...	...
Regina Margherita ...	5 4	7 6	7 56	9 21	11 21	12 21	13 51	14 46	16 46	1741	18 48	20 1	20 51	...	...	...	...	...
Turin ...arr	6 3	7 23	8 13	9 38	11 38	12 38	14 8	15 3	17 3	1758	19 3	20 18	21 8	...	...	...	...	...

TURIN and LANZO.

Turin...dep	...	...	...	...	...	...	...	...	...
Caselle...	...	...	...	...	...	...	...	...	...
Cirie...	...	...	...	...	...	...	...	...	...
Lanzo...arr	...	...	...	...	...	...	...	...	...

Lanzo...arr	...	...	...	...	...	...	...	...	...
Cirie ...	...	...	...	...	...	...	...	...	...
Caselle...	...	...	...	...	...	...	...	...	...
Turin ...arr	...	...	...	...	...	...	...	...	...

‡—Until 1⁵th Oct. §—Until 15th Sept.

TURIN and SUPERGA.

*—Until 1st Sept. †—From 1st Sept.

Turin (P.C.)dep	7 0	8 8	...	10 40	...	14 8	15 38	17 10	18 18	19 35	...	...	...	...	...	...	...	...	...
Sassi ...	7 22	8 40	10 5	11 10	1335	14 35	16 5	17 40	18 40	19 56	...	...	...	...	...	...	...	...	...
Superga...arr	7‡50	9 9	10 25	11 30	1355	14 55	16 25	18 [illegible]	19 ‡5	20§20	...	...	...	...	...	...	...	...	...

Superga ...dep	6*12	...	7 †0	...	8‡10	...	9 40	10 35	13 10	15 40	17 10	18 20	19‡35	...	21§10	...	...	...	...
Sassi ...	6 32	6 36	7 20	7 25	8 30	8 36	10 0	11 5	13 35	16 10	17 40	18 45	19 55	19 58	21 42	...	...	...	...
Turin (P.C.) arr	...	6 58	...	7 47	...	9 0	...	11 27	13 58	16 34	18 4	19 7	...	20 20	22 6	...	...	...	...

FOSSANO and VILLANOVA.

Fossano dep	7 41	10 35	...	16 50	...	...	...	...
Mondovi ...	9 15	12 10	15 0	18 10	...	...	...	...
Villanova arr	9 35	12 30	1520	19 30	...	...	...	...

Villanova dep	6 10	11 10	14 0	18 20	...	...	...	...	...
Mondovi...	7 10	11 53	14 22	18 50	...	...	...	...	...
Fossano ...arr	8 30	13 11	...	20 10	...	...	...	...	...

AREZZO and FOSSATO.

E.M.								
	Arezzo (279)...dep	...	5 20	11 20	...	15 20	19 20	...
24½	Anghiari ...	...	7 27	13 0	...	17 37	21 13	...
38	Città di Castello ...	5 40	8 30	13 54	1555	18 35	22 10	...
52¾	Umbertide ...	6 50	9 32	14 45	17 2	—	—	...
70¼	Gubbio ...	8 19	11 0	15 49	1832	...	...	...
83¼	**Fossato** (283)...arr	9 20	12 0	16 32	1930	...	...	...

Fossato ...dep	...	4 40	10 0	1255	17 15	...	...	...
Gubbio ...	...	5 40	11 1	1344	18 28	...	...	...
Umbertide ...	...	6 52	12 17	1447	19 48	...	...	...
Città di Castello	5 30	7 55	13 45	1550	20 50	...	...	...
Anghiari ...	6 35	8 55	14 46	1649	—	...	...	...
Arezzo...arr	8 32	10 45	16 43	1825	...	...	...	...

SETTIMO and CASTELLAMONTE.

Dist. E.M.	Turin								
	Porta Susa dep	5 38	8 15	11 4	14 15	17 35	19 0	...	...
7½	**Settimo**...dep	6 1	8 39	1130	14 38	17 56	19 24	...	...
16¾	Bosconero ...	6 25	9 2	1154	15 2	...	19 46	...	...
21½	Rivarolo ...arr	6 39	9 16	12 8	15 16	18 29	20 0	...	...
23½	Ozegna ...	6 49	9 27	1219	15 28	18 39	20 10	...	...
26¾	**Castellamonte**	6 58	9 35	1228	15 36	18 47	20 18	...	...

Castellamon.	5 51	7 42	1033	1425	1631	19 40	...	...
Ozegna ...	6 1	7 52	1043	1435	1641	19 50	...	...
Rivarolo ...dep	6 10	8 0	1052	1445	1649	20 1	...	...
Bosconero ...	6 26	8 15	11 6	15 1	17 4	20 16	...	...
Settimo...arr	6 51	8 38	1128	1524	1727	20 40	...	...
Turin P.S.arr	7 14	9 0	1150	1547	1751	21 3	...	...

E.M.									
	Rivarolo ...dep	6 41	9 20	12 10	1519	18 31	20 4	...	...
6¾	Cuorgnè ...	7 5	9 44	12 34	1543	18 53	2028	...	...
10⅓	Pont...arr	7 15	9 54	12 45	1554	19 3	2038	...	...

Pont ...dep	5 32	7 24	10 14	14 5	1612	19 21	...	...
Cuorgnè ...	5 45	7 36	10 27	1419	1625	19 33	...	...
Rivarolo ...arr	6 6	7 57	10 48	1440	1646	19 55	...	...

REZZATO and VOBARNO.

Rezzato...dep	8 50	12 45	19 8	...	...	...	...
Tormini Châlet ...	9 58	13 53	20 10	...	...	...	...
Vobarno...arr	10 16	14 11	20 27	...	...	...	...

Vobarno ...dep	4 52	7 13	1140	16 20	...	...	...
Tormini Châlet ...	5 10	7 33	11 59	16 33	...	...	...
Rezzato ...arr	6 9	8 39	13 6	17 50	...	...	...

Tormini ...dep	6 22	10 23	12 41	15 49	19 55	...	...	...
Vestone ...arr	7 45	11 29	14 4	17 12	21 1	...	...	...

Vestone ...dep	5 11	8 26	1131	14 21	18 27	...	...	...
Tormini ...arr	6 17	9 49	1237	15 44	19 50	...	...	...

ISEO and CHIARI.—(Steam Tramway).

Iseo...dep	5 30	11 30	16 20	...	...	...	...
Rovato...	6 17	12 17	17 7	...	...	...	...
Chiari ...arr	6 51	12 51	17 41	...	...	...	...

Chiari ...dep	7 35	14 30	17 55	...	...	...	...	...
Rovato ...	8 10	15 5	18 30	...	...	...	...	...
Iseo ...arr	8 56	15 51	19 16	...	...	...	...	...

SANTHIA and BIELLA.

Santhia ...dep	6 12	8 4	8 50	10 10	12 29	14 31	1632	18 45	21 15
Biella ...arr	7 9	9 1	9 51	11 3	13 26	15 32	1733	19 42	22 16

Biella ...dep	5 1	6 48	7 53	1042	13 4	1510	1710	1916
Santhia (269)...arr	5 47	7 34	8 34	1121	14 0	1557	1757	20 4

BIELLA and VALLEMOSSO, BALMA, and MONGRANDO.

Biella (F.S.B.)...dep	7 20	11 13	15 41	19 48	...	...
Biella (F.E.B.) ...dep	7 25	11 18	15 46	19 53	...	...
Cossato ...	8 1	11 55	16 23	20 30	...	...
Vallemosso...arr	8 40	12 38	17 2	21 13	...	...

Vallemosso ...dep	5*14	5‡45	9 10	13 5	17 45	...
Cossato ...	5 53	6 24	9 49	13 45	18 24	...
Biella (F.E.B.) ...	6 34	7 5	10 26	14 25	19 0	...
Biella (F.S.B.) ...arr	6 39	7 10	10 31	14 31	19 5	...

Biella (F.S.B.) ...dep	7 20	11 13	15 41	19 48	...	...
Biella (F.E.B.)...dep	7 29	11 22	16 45	19 57	...	...
Miagliano ...	7 59	11 52	17 15	20 27	...	...
Andorno ...	8 5	11 58	17 21	20 33	...	...
Balma ...arr	8 27	12 20	17 43	20 55	...	...

Balma ...dep	5*37	6 ‡8	8 47	13 28	18 3	...
Andorno ...	5 58	6 29	9 8	13 49	18 24	...
Miagliano...	6 4	6 35	9 14	13 55	18 30	...
Biella (F.E.B.) ...arr	6 30	7 1	9 40	14 21	18 56	...
Biella (F.S.B.) ...arr	6 39	7 10	10 37	14 31	19 5	...

Biella (F.E.B.)...dep	7 26	11 19	14 27	17 45	...	...
Biella Vernato ...	7 32	11 25	14 33	17 51	...	...
Mongrando ...arr	7 50	11 49	14 57	18 15	...	...

Mongrando ...dep	8 5	13§36	15 2	18 21	...	...
Biella Vernato ...	8 30	14 1	15 27	18 46	...	...
Biella (F.E.B.) ...arr	8 35	14 6	15 32	18 51	...	...

*—Until 31st August. ‡—From 1st September. §—Sunday dep. 13.8.

CARNIA and VILLA SANTINA.

Carnia...dep	7 41	9 44	12 5	17 10	19 5	...	...
Villa Santina ...arr	8 23	10 14	12 49	17 52	19 46	...	...

Villa Santina...dep	6 0	8 50	10 54	14 50	18 14	...	...
Carnia 285A...arr	6 40	9 30	11 36	15 34	18 53	...	...

☞ **Italian Railway Time—See Note on page 272.** ☜

MESSINA, CATANIA, and SYRACUSE.

Dist. M.		1,2,3	1,2,3	1,2,3	1,2,3	1,2,3	1,2,3	1,2,3	1,2,3	1,2,3	1,2,3	1,2,3	1,2,3	1,2,3	1,2,3	1,2,3			
	VILLA GIOVANNI...dep	2 15	...	...	...	...	8 25	...	1125	...	...	...	...	...	...	...	...	...	...
—	REGGIO ....dep	SC	...	...	...	...	7 25	...	9 40	...	...	...	...	...	...	...	...	...	...
—	**Messina** Porto ....dep	3 5	...	...	...	...	9 25	...	1215	...	...	...	...	...	...	...	...	...	...
½	,, Centrale ...dep	3 30	...	4 50	7 45	...	9 40	11 40	1227	...	13 35	15 30	16 35	17 25	18 0	19 45	...	...	...
11¾	**Scaletta**	3 56	...	5 0	8 30	...	RC	12 16	...	...	14 19	16 5	17 15	...	18 46	20 32	...	...	...
30½	Giardini-Taormina	4 35	5 10	6 29	—	...	10 39	13 47	1328	...	—	16 53	—	18 29	20 5	21 35	...	...	...
41	Giarre-Riposto	5 13	5 51	7 16	...	9 20	11 15	14 38	...	...	...	17 34	...	19 12	20 47	...	...	...	...
51	Acireale	5 43	6 28	7 54	...	9 58	11 43	15 14	...	...	...	18 7	...	19 37	21 26	...	...	...	...
59¾	Catania .... arr	6 5	6 55	8 20	...	1025	12 0	15 40	1432	...	...	18 30	...	19 55	21 55	...	...	...	...
	Catania .... dep	6 45	...	...	...	...	12 25	...	1437	16 5	...	18 55	...	...	...	...	...	...	...
64½	Bicocca	7 3	...	...	...	...	12 39	...	...	16 34	...	19 13	...	...	...	...	...	...	...
74	Valsavoja	7 33	...	...	...	...	13 3	...	...	17 6	...	19 43	...	...	...	...	...	...	...
77¾	Lentini	7 42	...	...	...	...	13 12	...	C	17 17	...	19 53	...	...	...	...	...	...	...
94½	Augusta	8 31	...	...	...	...	13 53	...	...	18 7	...	20 42	...	...	...	...	...	...	...
103¼	Priolo	8 55	...	...	...	...	14 14	...	...	18 32	...	21 6	...	...	...	...	...	...	...
113¾	Syracuse Centrale...arr	9 20	...	...	...	...	14 35	...	1620	19 0	...	21 30	...	...	...	...	...	...	...
115	,, Porto ......arr	...	...	...	...	...	14 55	...	1630	...	...	...	...	...	...	...	...	...	...

	1,2,3	1,2,3	1,2,3	1,2,3	1,2,3	1,2,3	1,2,3	1,2,3	1,2,3	1,2,3	1,2,3	1,2,3	1,2,3	1,2,3		
Syracuse Porto ...dep	...	...	...	...	...	...	...	11 45	...	...	14 20	...	...	...	...	...
,, Centrale ...dep	...	...	...	4 10	...	...	9 40	11 55	...	...	14 40	...	...	19 55	...	...
Priolo	...	...	...	4 36	...	...	10 8	...	...	...	15 1	...	...	20 20	...	...
Augusta........................	...	...	...	4 59	...	...	10 36	...	...	...	15 23	...	...	20 46	...	...
Lentini	...	...	...	5 45	...	...	11 26	...	...	...	16 4	...	...	21 33	...	...
Valsavoja	...	...	...	6 0	...	...	11 41	D	...	...	16 18	...	...	21 49	...	...
Bicocca	...	...	...	6 25	...	...	12 8	...	...	...	16 35	...	...	22 14	...	...
Catania .... arr	...	...	...	6 40	...	...	12 25	13 50	...	...	16 45	...	SC	22 30	...	...
Catania .... dep	...	...	4 40	7 0	...	10 0	12 45	13 55	...	16 0	17 15	17 35	2025	0 25	...	...
Acireale........................	...	...	5 18	7 28	...	10 38	13 19	...	...	16 32	17 42	18 10	2058	0 55	...	...
Giarre-Riposto	...	...	5 52	7 51	...	11 13	13 47	...	...	17 1	18 7	18 41	2127	1 20	...	...
Giardini-Taormina	...	5 30	6 38	8 20	...	12 15	—	15 9	...	17 42	18 36	19 30	22 6	1 53	...	...
Scaletta........................	6 1	6 39	7 40	...	10 55	13 15	...	...	17 2	18 36	RC	20 33	2251	2 37	...	...
Messina Cent. ......arr	6 50	7 35	8 30	9 27	11 40	14 0	...	16 5	17 50	19 15	19 40	21 20	2325	3 10	...	...
,, Porto ......arr	...	...	...	9 42	...	...	...	16 15	...	...	20 3	...	...	...	...	...
REGGIO ....arr	...	...	...	12 45	...	...	...	18 15	...	...	21 5	...	...	...	...	...
VILLA GIOVANNI arr	...	...	...	10 30	...	...	...	17 2	...	...	21 0	...	...	...	...	...

RC—Restaurant Ca[r] attached.

C—On Tuesday, Thursday, and Saturday is in connection with steamer for Tripoli. At Messina will not take up for Catania

D—On Tuesday, Thursday, and Friday is in connection with steamer from Tripoli. Takes up for Naples and Rome only.

MESSINA and PALERMO.

[‡—Sleeping Cars attached.

Dist. E.M.														
	VILLA GIOVANNI dep	...	2 15	...	...	...	8 25	11 40	...	...	...	...	...	...
	REGGIO ....dep	...	...	...	...	...	7 25	9 40	...	...	...	16 15	...	...
		1,2,3	1,2,3	1,2,3	1,2,3	1,2,3	1,2,3	1,2,3	1,2,3	1,2.3	1,2,3	1,2,3	1,2,3	
—	**Messina**, Porto...dep	...	3 5	...	...	...	9 35	12 40	...	13 40	...	...	‡	...
½	,, Centrale dep	...	3 40	...	5 15	7 50	9 55	12 49	...	14 40	16 30	18 10	0 10	...
13¾	Rometta	...	4 22	...	6 25	9 9	1037	SC	...	15 19	17 21	19 16	1 8	...
23	Milazzo........................	...	4 38	...	7 26	9 50	1056	13 48	...	15 38	17 58	19 59	1 39	...
28½	Barcellona	...	4 50	...	7 51	—	11 9	13 59	...	16 38	18 15	20 17	1 51	...
43½	Patti	...	5 23	...	9 2	...	1146	14 32	...	17 33	19 3	21 10	2 44	...
58½	Naso Capo d'Orlan.......	...	5 49	...	10 5	...	1211	...	...	17 55	19 47	—	3 25	...
66½	S. Agata di Militel.......	...	6 7	6 45	1033	...	1231	15 10	16 0	—	20 20	...	4 0	...
84	S. Stefano Camast.......	...	6 38	7 42	—	...	13 7	15 44	16 52	...	21 2	...	4 44	...
103¼	Cefalu	...	7 17	8 58	...	...	1343	16 22	17 50	...	21 55	...	5 38	...
121¾	Termini........................	5 44	7 57	1025	...	...	1422	17 0	18 52	...	22 48	...	6 35	...
136¾	Bagheria	6 30	8 28	1134	...	...	1454	...	19 22	...	23 33	...	7 24	...
144¾	**Palermo** ....arr	7 0	8 45	12 0	...	...	1510	17 45	19 40	...	23 55	...	7 50	...

	1,2,3	1,2,3	1,2,3	1,2,3	1,2,3	1,2,3	1,2,3	1,2,3	1,2,3	1,2,3	1,2,3			
Palermo ....dep	...	4 15	7 25	1045	...	1415	...	1635	18 0	20‡0	0 30	...	...	...
Bagheria	...	4 38	7 53	RC	...	1431	...	17 3	1827	2021	0 53	...	...	...
Termini	...	5 23	8 55	1130	...	15 2	...	1751	19 7	21 4	1 33	...	...	...
Cefalu	...	6 12	10 2	12 4	...	1539	...	1847	—	2150	2 13	...	...	...
S. Stefano Camastro ...	...	7 4	11 9	1239	...	1622	...	1949	...	2240	2 52	...	...	...
S. Agata di Militello......	5 5	7 43	1155	1315	...	1655	1535	2035	...	2323	3 26	...	...	...
Naso Capo d'Orlando......	5 29	8 6	—	...	...	1710	1615	—	...	2347	3 46	...	...	...
Patti	6 16	8 54	...	1356	...	1742	1755	...	...	0 27	4 33	...	...	...
Barcellona	6 59	9 37	...	1426	...	1817	19 4	...	...	1 9	5 24	...	...	...
Milazzo........................	7 11	9 52	...	1436	1620	1830	1928	...	...	1 22	5 41	...	...	...
Rometta	7 48	1032	...	...	17 3	1852	2030	...	...	1 59	6 30	...	...	...
Messina, Cent. ......arr	8 40	1122	...	1542	18 2	1935	2130	...	...	2 45	7 30	...	...	...
,, Porto ......arr	...	...	...	1553	...	20 3	...	...	...	...	...	...	...	...
REGGIO ....arr	...	...	...	...	...	21 5	...	...	...	...	...	...	...	...
VILLA GIOVANNI...arr	...	...	...	1640	...	21 0	...	...	...	...	...	...	...	...

PORTO EMPEDOCLE and ROCCAPALUMBA.

E.M.									
	Porto Empedocle dp	3 50	4 20	7 20	10 0	1330	1525	18 5	2015
5¼	Girgenti	4 23	4 52	7 55	1030	14 0	16 2	1840	21 4
11¾	**Aragona-Caldare** 290	4 55	5 15	8 17	1138	1428	1625	19 1	2135
27¼	Acquaviva......................	5 50	—	—	1235	1514	—	20 9	—
41¾	Lercara	6 45	...	...	1328	16 1	...	21 1	...
46½	**Roccapalumba**...arr	7 0	...	...	1343	1615	..	2117	...

Roccapalumba dep	...	6 10	9 5	...	11 50	...	...	181
Lercara	...	6 42	9 29	...	12 20	...	...	18
Acquaviva.....................	...	7 27	1010	...	13 9	...	...	19
Aragona-Caldare	5 15	8 33	11 7	11 40	14 25	16 40	1917	20
Girgenti	5 49	9 4	1132	12 7	14 54	17 9	1942	21
Porto Empedocle	6 15	9 25	1150	12 25	15 15	17 30	20 0	213

[Mid Europe Time—See page lxix.]

SYRACUSE and LICATA.

Syracuse dep	...	...	6 20	9 50	15 5	19 30	...	...
Avola	...	...	7 14	10 44	15 58	20 23	...	...
Noto	...	...	7 32	11 3	16 16	20 41	...	...
Pozzallo	...	...	8 36	12 5	17 21	21 40	...	...
Modica	...	5 40	1041	14 30	18 38	22 50	...	...
Ragusa Sup	...	6 40	1143	15 32	19 35	—	...	...
Vittoria	...	8 15	1316	17 13	20 53	...	...	...
Terranova	3 50	9 15	1425	18 15	—	...	...	...
Licata arr	4 46	1012	1530	19 20	...	...	...	...

Licata dep	...	...	6 15	11 50	1455	1950	...	...
Terranova	...	...	7 16	12 50	1556	2045	...	...
Vittoria	...	5 10	8 20	13 54	17 0	—	...	...
Ragusa Sup	...	6 43	9 59	15 29	1838	...	...	...
Modica	5 20	7 35	10 56	16 20	1920	...	...	...
Pozzallo	6 22	8 38	12 7	17 22	—	...	...	...
Noto	7 27	9 49	13 15	18 27	...	...	...	...
Avola	7 42	10 4	13 29	18 42	...	...	...	...
Syracuse arr	8 30	1055	14 17	19 30	...	...	...	...

CATANIA and CALTAGIRONE.

E.M.						
	Catania dep	6 25	13 25	17 25	...	...
15	Valsavoja	7 10	14 12	18 11	...	...
23½	Scordia	7 42	14 44	18 43	...	...
35½	Mineo	8 48	15 50	19 49	...	...
56½	**Caltagirone** arr	10 7	17 10	21 10	...	...

Caltagirone dep	4 30	9 5	16 5	...	...
Mineo	5 56	10 39	17 36	...	...
Scordia	6 39	11 28	18 19	...	...
Valsavoja	7 5	12 0	18 45	...	...
Catania arr	7 50	12 37	19 25	...	...

S. CATERINA and ARAGONA-CALDARE.

E.M.								
	S. Caterina (Xirbi) dp	...	8 30	1130	13 35	16 21	2019	21 42
4¼	Caltanisetta	5 35	8 59	1158	13 56	16 47	2040	22 5
22¼	**Canicatti**	7 0	10 15	1310	—	18 6	—	—
33	Racalmuto	7 49	10 56	1348	...	18 41	...	...
40½	**Aragona-Caldare** ar	8 21	11 28	1414	...	19 7	...	...

Aragona-Cald.	...	5 21	8 35	11 5	...	16 35
Racalmuto	...	6 1	9 10	1138	...	17 15
Canicatti	...	6 50	10 0	1218	...	18 15
Caltanisetta	4 35	7 57	11 5	1313	15 50	19 25
S. Caterina Xirbi	4 49	8 10	11 17	1323	16 2	19 54

CANICATTI and LICATA.

Licata dep	4 51	7 45	1025	1540	...	...
Campobello	6 3	9 5	1132	1655	...	...
Canicatti arr	6 38	9 40	12 3	1730	...	...

Canicatti dep	7 20	10 5	1315	18 5	...	...
Campobello	7 59	10 40	1350	18 40	...	...
Licata arr	9 5	11 40	1450	19 41	...	...

CANICATTI and CAMASTRA.

E.M.						
	Canicatti dep	10 0	13 20	18 20	...	...
9¼	Naro	1043	13 11	19 11	...	...
12½	Camastra arr	1055	13 24	19 24	...	...

Camastra dep	5 17	1116	16 10	...
Naro	5 38	1133	16 33	...
Canicatti 290A arr	6 25	1211	17 20	...

PORTO EMPEDOCLE and SICULIANA.

E.M.						
	Porto Empedocle dep	5 0	9 40	17 40	...	...
8¾	Siculiana arr	5 57	10 37	18 37	...	...

Siculiana dep	6 12	12 20	18 0	...	...	...
Porto Empedocle 290 arr	7 8	13 16	19 56	...	...	...

PARTANNA and SELINUNTE.

[In July and August only.

E.M.						
	Partanna dep	...	6 32	9 30	12 30	15 20
6¾	Castelvetrano 289A	5 30	7 0	9 58	13 15	15 48
15	**Selinunte** arr	6 4	...	10 50	13 49	16‡37

Selinunte dep	6 21	...	...	12 21	...	15 15	19‡55	...
Castelvetrano	6 55	8 51	10 15	12 55	13 16	15 49	20 29	20 36
Partanna arr	...	9 20	10 44	...	13 45	...	...	21 5

ASSORO and VALGUARNERA.

E.M.					
	Assoro dep	1020	15 20	19 26	...
14	Valguarnera arr	1113	16 13	20 20	...

Valguarnera dep	5 10	13 7	17 57	...	...
Assoro arr	6 3	14 0	18 50	...	...

CATANIA and PALERMO.

RC—Restaurant Car attached.

E.M.								
	Catania dep	...	4 0	7 20	...	12 40	...	16 45
5	Bicocca	...	4 17	7 37	...	12 54	...	17 3
28½	Catenanuova	...	5 33	8 46	...	13 47	...	18 24
43	Assoro 290A	...	6 17	9 26	...	14 23	...	19 15
49	Leonforte	...	6 43	9 48	...	14 48	...	19 45
56	Castrogiovanni	...	7 18	10 21	...	15 17	...	20 21
72	S. Caterina arr	...	8 20	11 20	...	16 10	...	21 30
...	(Xirbi) 290A dep	5 2	8 28	11 32	...	16 20	...	—
91¼	Vallelunga	6 14	9 34	12 46	...	17 19	...	...
107½	**Roccapalumba**	7 19	1046	13 52	1625	18 6	...	21 30
119¼	Sciara	8 0	1126	14 27	1659	RC	...	22 5
128	Termini	8 50	12 4	14 57	1727	18 52	1930	22 48
143	Bagheria	9 56	13 6	15 44	18 7	19 22	2020	23 33
151	**Palermo** arr	10 25	1320	15 53	1830	19 40	2050	23 55

Palermo dep	...	3 30	7 10	9 40	11 5	1520	1630
Bagheria	...	3 53	7 25	9 57	1137	1545	17 0
Termini	...	4 37	7 58	10 28	1228	1632	1749
Sciara	...	5 3	8 19	RC	1254	17 0	1824
Roccapalumba	...	6 5	9 20	11 40	1350	18 5	1922
Vallelunga	...	7 3	1015	12 28	—	19 3	—
S. Caterina arr	...	8 8	1115	13 20	...	20 9	...
,, (Xirbi) dep	5 0	8 20	—	13 32	...	2017	...
Castrogiovanni	6 15	9 30	...	14 32	...	2130	...
Leonforte	6 50	9 55	...	14 53	...	2153	...
Assoro	7 6	10 9	...	15 6	...	22 6	...
Catenanuova ...5 10	7 56	10 48	...	15 39	1555	2245	...
Bicocca ...6 45	9 22	11 56	...	16 24	1849	2354	...
Catania arr 7 0	9 40	12 10	...	16 35	1950	24 0	...

Spanish Railways.

[Greenwich Time—See page lxix.]

MEDINA DEL CAMPO and ZAMORA.

E.M.				
	Medina del Campo dep	5 43	13†54	18‡58
10½	**Nava del Rey**	6 26	14 28	19 40
24¼	Castro Nuno	7 27	15 24	20 43
36	Toro	8 14	16 3	21 30
56	**Zamora 298A** arr	9 14	16 56	22 30

Zamora dep	5*30	9†40	14§25	18 45	...	...	...	...
Toro	6 41	10 47	15 36	19 58	...	...	...	...
Castro Nuno	7 30	11 34	16 27	20 49	...	...	...	...
Nava del Rey	8 36	12 39	17 34	21 57	...	...	...	...
M. Campo 291 arr	9 9	13 12	18 7	22 30	...	...	...	...

‡—On Thurs. and Sat. only. *—Sat. only. †—Tues. only. §—Thurs. only.

MEDINA and SALAMANCA.

E.M.						
	VALLADOLID 291A dep	1 19	2 25	8 20	...	1738
...	**Medina Campo** dep	2 20	5 20	9‡17	13§55	1858
13¾	Carpio	2 56	6 2	...	14 37	1916
20½	Cantalapiedra	3 20	6 42	10 3	15 11	1939
33	Pedroso	3 53	7 29	...	15 58	2015
47¾	**Salamanca 299** arr	4 33	8 25	11 1	16 58	21 0
132¼	BARCA D'ALVA arr	11*20	...	...	...	1 54

BARCA D'ALVA 299	...	5 45	...	16†15	‡		
Salamanca dep	5§30	11 2	15 0	22 10	23 11		
Pedroso	6 41	1151	16 3	22 52	...	...	†—Mon.,
Cantalapiedra	7 37	1231	1653	23 29	0 12	...	Wed., &
Carpio	8 3	1253	1716	23 49	...	...	Fri.,
Medina Campo arr	8 45	1331	1754	0 23	0 55	...	dep. 17.54.
VALLADOLID 291 arr	...	1432	1948	2 58	1 58	...	

*—Arrive 8.28 on Tues., Thurs., and Sat. ‡—Sud Express. §—Tuesday, Thursday, and Sunday only.

NORTHERN RAILWAY COMPANY—(Caminos de Hierro del Norte).

MADRID, VALLADOLID, BURGOS, SAN SEBASTIAN, IRUN, and HENDAYA.

Dist E.M	Madrid—	1,2,3	1,2,3	1 &2	1,2,3	1,2,3	1,2,3	1,2,3	1,2,3	1 Cl.	1,2,3
—	Paseo de San Vicente......dep	7 54	7 0	9§15	10 0	1040	13 5	1450	1535	16 0	1717
5½	Pozuelo	8 7	7 16	B	1013	1057	1319	15 5	1549	RC	...
18¾	Torrelodones......	8 41	8 0	...	1046	1143	1354	1541	1623	H	...
23½	**Villalba (291)**	8 53	8 16	10 4	1057	1158	14 7	1554	1634	16 50	18 7
31¾	**El Escorial** ...	—	8 55	Via Segovia.	1118	Via Segovia.	1433	—	1657	Via Segovia.	1832
36¾	Robledo		9 30					...	1730		1856
47¾	Las Navas		1019		...		...	...	1812		1933
70¾	**Avila**		1244		1& 2		...	...	1922		21 3
79½	Mingorria		13 7				...	...			...
90	San Chidrian		1344				...	...	...		2140
102½	Arévalo		1427				...	...	...		22 4
124¼	**Medina 290A**...arr		1531	1346		18 4	...	...	...	20 38	2245
...	Lisbon **300** ...dep		...	1855	On Tues., Thurs., & Sat. only.	...	...	...	...	...	...
...	Salamanca 290Adp		...	11 2		15 0	...	...	...	...	...
...	**Medina** ....dep		1553	1348		1824	...	...	...	20 42	2251
134¼	Matapozuelos		1628	...		19 0	...	...	...	...	...
139¼	Valdestillas		1642	B		1914	...	...	...	SC	...
142¼	Viana		1652	...		1924	...	...	...	21 15	...
150¼	**Valladolid** ......arr		1716	1432		1948	...	...	...	21 30	2340
...	„ **297A**...dep		1746	1441	1459	2013	...	...	...	21 37	2350
169¾	Dueñas		1845	§	...	21 8	...	...	...	...	...
173¾	**Venta de Baños** arr		1856	1516	1539	2119	...	...	...	22 17	0 30
316¼	Santander 292 arr		...	...	21 5	...	...	...	...	...	...
523	Corunna 293...arr		...	...		22 9	...	...	...	11 59	1535
...	**Venta de B.** ...dep		1934	1520	...	...	...	...	...	...	...
186½	Torquemada		20 9	...	...	...	...	...	...	...	...
193¼	Quintana		2030	1555	...	...	...	...	...	...	...
199½	Villodrigo		2051	16 9	...	...	...	...	...	...	...
220	Quintanilleja		2150	...	...	...	...	...	...	...	...
225½	**Burgos**		2228	17 3	...	...	...	...	...	...	...
236	Quintanapalla		23 2	...	...	...	...	...	...	...	...
255¼	Bribiesca		0 7	18 1	...	...	...	...	...	...	...
269	Pancorbo		0 50	1827	...	...	...	...	...	...	...
281½	**Miranda** ....arr		1 25	1853	...	...	...	...	...	...	...
...	Bilbao 292......arr		8 41	21‡33	...	...	...	...	...	1,2,3	...
...	**Miranda** ....dep		1 55	19 8	‡—Arrive Bilbao on Mon., Wed., and Fri. only.	1936	...	On Sun., Wed., and Sat. only.	...	15 5	...
302	Vitoria....................		3 15	1952		2128	...		...	16 21	...
317	Salvatierra.............		4 4	...		23 5	...		...	17 6	...
328¾	**Alsasua** ....arr		4 44	2040		0 20	...		...	17 45	...
...	Barcelona 292dep		...	...		...	...		...	...	...
...	Saragossa 292 dep		...	...		...	...		...	...	...
...	**Alsasua**...........dep		4 58	2042		...	...		...	18 1	...
347¼	Zumarraga		6 12	2120		...	...		...	19 15	...
356	Beasain		6 55	2139		...	...	1732	...	20 2	...
366	Tolosa	6 13	7 44	22 0		16 8	1658	1833	...	20 46	1958
373½	Andoain..............	6 31	8 8	...		1626	1716	1848	...	21 11	2016
381½	**San Sebastian**	7 0	8 52	2237		1656	1751	1916	1926	22†48	2051
385¼	Pasajes	7 9	9 5	...		17 5	18 0		1939	23 1	21 0
385¾	Lezo-Renteria ...	7 13	9 11	...	...	17 9	18 4	...	1945	23 7	21 4
392	**Irun**............arr	7 26	9 28	23 0	...	1722	1817	...	20 2	23 24	2117
...	„ ....dep	7 29	9 36	23 3	...	1724	1819	...	2012	23 34	2119
393¼	**Hendaya** ...arr	7 32	9 40	23 6	...	1727	1822	...	2016	23 38	2122
...	Hendaya ......dep		...	0 22	...	...	...	...	...	0 22	...
538	Bordeaux **45** arr		...	5 17	...	...	...	...	...	5 17	...
903½	Paris (**35**) ......arr		...	1415	...	...	...	...	...	14 15	...

Dist E.M	Madrid—	1,2,3	1,2,3 C	1,2,3 A	X	1,2,3	1 &3	1,2,3	1,2,3	1,2,3	12 3	1 &3
—	Paseo de San Vicente......dep	1735	1810	1850	20 0	1823	21 0	1930	2012	...	2150	...
5½	Pozuelo	...	...	SC	...	1837	...	1944	2028	...	22 5	...
18¾	Torrelodones	...	1850	...	...	1912	...	2019	2115	...	2244	...
23½	**Villalba (291)**	1825	19 1	1940	2050	1929	2150	2036	2136	...	2256	...
31¾	**El Escorial**	Via Segovia.	1927	Via Segovia.	2113	1946	2215	2053	Via Segovia.	...	2329	...
36¾	Robledo		1949		...		SC			...	0 1	...
47¾	Las Navas		2024		...	...	...	...		...	0 50	...
70¾	**Avila**		2128		2316	...	0 18	...		...	2 18	...
79½	Mingorria		...		...	...	0 33	...		...	2 40	...
90	San Chidrian		...		...	...	0 53	...		...	3 12	...
102½	Arévalo		2254		...	...	1 16	...		...	3 47	...
124¼	**Medina 290A**...arr	23 9	2338	0 5	0 52	...	1 56	...	3 49	...	4 42	...
...	Lisbon **300** ...dep	...	...	...	1130	...	2155	...	...	...	...	...
...	Salamanca 290Adp	...	...	...	2311	...	2210	...	...	...	...	...
...	**Medina** ....dep	2320	2345	0 9	1 14	...	2 10	...	4 9	...	5 2	...
134¼	Matapozuelos	...	...	...	...	...	...	...	...	...	5 31	...
139¼	Valdestillas	...	...	...	...	...	SC	...	...	...	5 44	...
142¼	Viana	...	...	...	...	...	...	...	...	...	5 52	...
150¼	**Valladolid** ......arr	0 9	0 34	0 57	1 58	...	2 58	...	5 15	...	6 11	...
...	„ **297A**...dep	0 21	0 41	1 3	2 3	...	3 8	...	5 45	...	6 31	...
169¾	Dueñas	...	...	...	...	...	...	...	6 29	...	7 23	...
173¾	**Venta de Baños** arr	1 1	1 21	1 43	2 39	...	3 48	...	6 40	...	7 32	...
316¼	Santander 292 arr	8 0	8 0	...	...	...	...	...	...	...	1728	...
523	Corunna 293...arr		...	...	...	...	...	...	...	...	...	...
...	**Venta de B.** ...dep	...	...	1 47	2 42	...	3 55	...	...	...	7 57	...
186½	Torquemada	...	...	...	...	...	...	...	...	...	8 31	...
193¼	Quintana	...	...	...	...	...	...	...	...	...	8 49	...
199½	Villodrigo	...	...	...	...	...	SC	...	...	...	9 6	...
220	Quintanilleja	...	...	...	...	...	...	...	...	...	9 58	...
225½	**Burgos**	...	...	3 25	4 20	...	5 37	...	...	...	1026	...
236	Quintanapalla	...	...	3 47	...	...	...	...	...	...	1051	...
255¼	Bribiesca	...	...	4 24	...	...	6 38	...	...	...	1155	...
269	Pancorbo	...	...	4 51	...	...	...	...	...	...	1230	...
281½	**Miranda** ....arr	...	...	5 13	6 3	...	7 26	...	...	...	13 1	...
...	Bilbao 292......arr	...	...	...	...	...	1040	...	...	...	1639	...
...	**Miranda** ....dep	...	...	5 27	6 9	...	7 42	...	...	...	1334	...
302	Vitoria	...	...	6 11	6 52	...	8 25	...	...	...	1437	...
317	Salvatierra	...	...	6 38	...	...	...	...	...	...	1517	...
328¾	**Alsasua** ....arr	...	...	6 59	7 41	J	9 15	...	...	...	1547	...
...	Barcelona 292dep	...	...	...	...	17 4	7 15	...	7 15	...	1840	...
...	Saragossa 292 dep	...	...	...	...	2 37	2040	...	2040	...	5 42	1613
...	**Alsasua**...........dep	...	...	7 14	7 42	8 37	9 20	...	9 34	...	16 1	23 1
347¼	Zumarraga	...	...	7 56	8 20	9 19	10 4	...	1044	...	1658	2340
356	Beasain	...	...	8 17	8 39	9 40	1026	...	1120	1325	1727	0 2
366	Tolosa	1020	...	8 41	8 58	10 0	1049	1132	12 8	1412	18 4	0 23
373½	Andoain	1038	...	8 56	...	1015	11 4	1150	1232	1435	1825	0 40
381½	**San Sebastian**	1058	...	9 50	9 28	1040	1132	1220	1322	15 5	19 3	1 8
385¼	Pasajes	—	...	9 59	...	1049	1142	1229	1336	1514	1913	1 17
385¾	Lezo-Renteria	...	...	10 3	...	1053	1147	1233	1343	1518	1918	1 21
392	**Irun**............arr	...	...	1016	9 51	11 2	12 0	1246	1359	1531	1933	1 33
...	„ ....dep	...	...	1026	9 53	11 5	1210	1248	1414	1533	1951	—
393¼	**Hendaya** ...arr	...	...	1030	9 56	11 8	1213	1251	1418	1536	1955	...
...	Hendaya ......dep	...	...	...	1021	...	1315	1315	1442	...	...	...
538	Bordeaux **45** arr	...	...	...	1358	...	1821	1821	1853	...	...	...
903½	Paris (**35**) ......arr	...	...	...	2054	...	4 56	4 56	4 56	...	...	...

FARES from MADRID.

[For Notes see next page.

	1st Class. P.	1st Class. C.	2nd Class. P.	2nd Class. C.	3rd Class. P.	3rd Class. C.
To El Escorial...	6	40	4	80	2	90
„ Medina.........	25	0	18	75	11	25
„ Burgos	45	40	34	5	20	45
„ Hendaya	79	15	59	35	35	65
„ Bordeaux......	105	25	76	95	47	15
„ Paris	171	10	121	40	76	10

Extra

Madrid...dep	8 35	Tolosa ......dep	...	15 23
El Escorial	10 9	San Sebastian	1410	16 15
Avila... ..arr	1226	Hendaya ...arr	1441	16 42
Villalba.........dep	12 15	...		
El Escorial.....arr	12 32	...		

VILLALBA, SEGOVIA, and MEDINA DEL CAMPO

Madrid 291 ...dep	7 54	9 15	1040	1450	16 0	1735	18 50	2012
Villalba ....dep	8 59	10 8	12 6	16 4	16‡54	1829	19 45	2136
Espinar..................	1014	1113	1328	1722	...	1939	20 54	23 8
Segovia ....arr	1055	1150	1423	18 4	18 34	2019	21 39	0 7
„ ....dep	—	1158	1441	1812	18 39	2050	22 4	0 28
Ortigosa-S. M. de N.	...	1240	16 9	1955	19 33	2153	22 57	1 53
Coca	...	13 3	1645	2037	19 55	...	...	2 31
Olmedo..................	...	...	1725	2116	...	2242	23 41	3 11
Medina.............arr	...	1346	18 4	2158	20 38	23 9	0 5	3 49

‡—Runs on Sun., Tues., and Thurs. only.

Medina ....dep	2 44	4†23	...	6 1	1112	...	1825	22 5
Olmedo	3 13	...	...	6 26	1154	...	1849	2248
Coca.........................	3 36	5 6	...	6 47	1237	...	19 9	2337
Ortigosa-S. Maria de N.	4 3	...	...	7 8	1317	...	1932	0 14
Segovia ....arr	5 2	6 16	...	7 59	1435	...	2024	1 43
„ ....dep	5 16	6 28	7 0	8 15	1457	1730	2034	1 59
Espinar	6 13	7 24	7 51	9 13	1614	1832	2123	3 13
Villalba ....arr	7 14	8 21	8 58	10 7	1743	1944	2216	4 28
Madrid (**291A**) arr	8 8	9 12	10 1	1059	1916	2045	2258	5 39

†—Runs Sun., Wed., and Fri. only.

NORTHERN RAILWAY—(continued).

IRUN, SAN SEBASTIAN, BURGOS, VALLADOLID, and MADRID.

Station																					
PARIS 34 ....dep	14 0	14 0	1938	1938	...	...	...	...	2210	2210	...	...	...	...	...	...	...	...	...	2344	1216
BORDEAUX 45...dep	23 45	2345	4 0	4 0	...	...	...	...	8 23	8 23	...	...	...	...	...	1047	...	...	...	1420	1919
HENDAYA 45 ...arr	5 30	5 30	8 1	8 1	...	...	...	...	1231	1231	...	...	...	...	...	1715	...	...	...	20 0	2255
IRUN 45 ....arr	5 47	5 47	8 10	8 10	...	...	...	...	1241	1241	...	...	...	...	...	1732	...	...	...	2017	23 5
	1 & 3	1 2 3	1,2,3	1 &2	1,2,3	1,2,3	1,2,3	1,2,3	1,2,3	1& 3	1,2,3	1,2,3	1,2,3	1,2,3	1,2,3	1,2,3	1,2,3	1,2,3	1,2,3	1,2,3	X
									L												
Irun ....dep	6 15	7 10	8 18	8 42	10 4	1136	1115	1240	14 0	1435	...	1340	14 52	17 0	1511	1810	1850	1910	1948	2136	2340
Lezo-Renteria	6 28	7 26	8 31	...	1019	1156	1128	1255	1413	1451	...	1355	15 7	1715	1532	1825	19 5	1925	20 3	2159	...
Pasajes..................	6 32	7 31	8 35	D	1023	12 2	1132	1259	1417	1456	...	1359	15 12	1719	1540	1829	19 9	1929	20 7	2231	...
S. Sebastian arr	6 40	7 40	8 43	9 3	1031	1212	1140	13 7	1425	15 4	...	14 7	15 20	172	1550	1837	1917	1937	2015	2241	0 2
S. Sebastian dep	6 50	7 57	8 46	9 7	1036	1235	1154	1312	1435	1519	...	1412	15*33	1732	1618	1842	1925	20 7	2020	23 7	0 7
Andoain	7 10	8 23	9 8	9 23	1058	13 5	1215	1333	1454	1538	...	1433	15*54	1754	1651	19 4	1952	2027	2041	2336	...
Tolosa	7 28	8 47	9 26	9 38	1116	1341	1233	1351	1511	1555	...	1451	16*18	1813	1727	1922	2019	2044	2059	0 10	0 37
Beasain	7 52	9 20		9 58		1431			1536	1621	...		16*43		1823		2050	2113		1 13	0 56
Zumarraga **294A** ...	8 24	9 59	...	1027	...	1522	...	...	16 9	1654	...	...		...	1916	...		2146	...	2 6	1 28
Alsasua ....arr	9 11	1055	...	1110	...	1634	...	...	17 0	1747	...	...	...	...	2028	...	...	2233	...	3 28	2 15
SARAGOSSA **292** arr	15 53	...	...	2028	...	...	...	...	2332	5 40	...	...	...	...	...	...	...	...	...	...	...
BARCELONA 292 arr		...	...	7 37	...	...	...	...	8 57	2037	...	...	...	...	...	...	...	...	...	...	...
Alsasua ....dep	...	1119	...	1111	...	...	...	...	...	1753	...	...	...	...	2055	...	...	2235	...	3 53	2 17
Salvatierra	...	1152	...	RC	...	...	...	...	...	...	...	...	...	...	2142	...	...	2259	...	4 47	...
Vitoria	...	1227	...	12 6	...	...	1740	...	...	1851	...	...	...	...	2243	...	...	2329	...	6 10	3 7
Miranda ....arr	...	1311	...	1250	...	...	1850	...	...	1935	...	...	...	...	2346	...	...	0 8	...	7 17	3 46
BILBAO ....dep	...	...	...	10‖2	...	...	...	...	...	1553	...	...	...	...	1835	...	...	...	...	...	...
Miranda ....dep	...	14 0	...	1310	...	...	...	...	...	20 7	...	...	...	...	0 37	...	...	0 22	...	8 20	3 55
Pancorbo.................	...	1446	...	1339	...	...	...	...	...	2039	☞ Until 15th October.	...	...	...	1 37	...	...	0 52	...	9 18	4 23
Bribiesca.................	...	1529	...	14 8	...	...	...	...	...	2112		...	...	...	2 31	...	...	1 22	...	1010	...
Quintanapalla	...	1639	...	...	...	...	...	...	...	...		...	...	...	3 49	...	...	...	...	1124	...
Burgos	...	1717	...	1516	...	...	...	...	...	2224		...	...	...	4 35	...	...	2 35	...	1216	6 2
Quintanilleja...........	...	1733	...	1528	...	...	...	...	...	...		...	...	...	4 53	...	...	...	...	1235	...
Villodrigo	...	1828	...	16 8	...	...	...	...	...	...		...	...	...	5 52	...	...	3 29	...	1343	6 49
Quintana.................	...	1845	...	1620	...	...	...	...	...	SC		...	...	...	6 11	...	...	...	...	14 4	...
Torquemada	...	19 3	...	...	...	...	...	...	...	...		...	...	...	6 31	...	...	...	...	1425	...
Venta de Baños arr	...	1933	...	1652	...	...	...	...	...	2357		...	...	1Cl.	7 4	...	...	4 18	...	15 0	7 37
CORUNNA 293...dep	...	...	...	...	1&2	1947	...	...	...	...		...	9 0	1130	...	...	...	...	...	...	...
SANTANDER 292 dep	1,2,3	...	...	...	9 54	...	...	...	...	...		1640	...	...	...	...	...	...	...	...	...
Venta de B......dep	19 8	20 3	...	1654	1630	22 2	...	...	...	0 2	0 32	0 50	1 35	2 44	7 50	...	...	4 20	1355	1540	7 39
Duenas.....................	...	2016	...	...	K	2216	...	...	...	...	...	G	...	F	8 4	...	...	...	1411	1555	...
Valladolid ......arr	20 2	21 3	...	1729	1710	2310	...	...	...	0 42	1 12	1 30	2 15	3 24	8.57	...	...	5 0	1519	1650	8 15
" ......dep	20 32	2128	...	1738		2340	...	...	...	0 52	1 19	1 43	2 25	3 29	9 22	...	...	5 5	16 0	1748	8 20
Viana	...	2149	...	...		0 5	...	...	...	...	...	...	...	...	9 48	...	...	...	1634	1813	...
Valdestillas	...	2158	...	...	...	0 17	...	...	...	...	...	...	...	SC	9 58	...	...	...	1651	1823	...
Matapozuelos...........	...	2213	...	...	...	0 36	...	...	...	...	...	...	...	...	1014	...	...	5 37	1715	1841	...
Medina 290A ...arr	21 39	2242	...	1821	...	1 13	...	...	...	1 42	2 11	2 35	3 17	4 19	1047	...	...	5 50	18 0	1917	9 7
SALAMANCA 290A arr	...	...	...	21 0	...	4 33	...	...	...	4 33	4 33	...	8 25	8 25	...	...	...	...	...	...	11 1
LISBON **300** ......arr	...	...	...	1431	...	2353	...	...	...	2353	23 53	...	...	...	...	...	...	...	...	...	2252
Medina ....dep	22 5	2310	...	1825	...	2 31	...	...	...	1 57	2 17	2 44	3 25	4 23	1112	1130	...	6 1	...	1942	9 30
Arévalo	...	0 13	...		...	3 48	...	...	...	2 43	3 8		4 14	RC		1255	...		...	21 2	...
San Chidrian	...	0 54	...		...	4 50	...	...	...	3 10	...		4 40			1342	...		...	2156	1040
Mingorria	...	1 38	...		...	5 28	...	...	...	SC	...		...			1431	...		...	2246	...
Avila	...	2 21	...	Via Segovia.	...	6 9	8 16	...	...	4 3	4 2'	Via Segovia.	5 29	Via Segovia	Via Segovia.	15 0	...	Via Segovia.	16 0	2349	1128
Las Navas	...	3 44	...		...	7 43	9 30	...	...	5 4	5 29		6 36				...		1724	1 30	...
Robledo	...	4 14	...		1,2,3	8 24	10 4	...	...	...	5 56		7 3			...	...		18 4	2 15	...
El Escorial ...1,2,3	...	4 41	7 42		8 44	9 1	1036	1335	...	5 57	6 21		7 26			17 2	...		1848	2 50	1316
Villalba............5 31	4 30	5 4	8 2	2217	9 5	9 26	1059	1359	...	6 16	6 39	7 17	7 43	8 27	1754	1726	1947	1013	1915	3 16	1331
Torrelodones 5 48	4 47	5 20	8·15	...	9 17	9 44	1115	1413	...	...	...	7 30	..	...	1814	1742	20 0	1025	1931	3 33	...
Pozuelo 6 30	5 24	5 55	8 47	...	9 49	1028	1148	1446	...	...	7 18	...	8 22	9 1	19 1	1815	2033	...	...	4 15	...
Madrid ......arr 6 45	5 39	6 8	8 59	2258	10 1	1043	12 0	1458	...	7 0	7 30	8 8	8 34	9 12	1916	1827	2045	1059	2011	4 30	1412

Extra.						
Irun...............dep	16 10	21 5	23 0	Villalba ......dep	20 16
S. Sebastian ...arr	16 37	21 32	23 27	Madrid.........arr	21 42

RC—Restaurant Car.

SC-**Sleeping Cars by this Train.**

A-Sleeping Car attached on Monday Wednesday, and Friday.

B—**On Monday, Wednesday, and Friday takes for Bilbao; on Tuesday, Thursday, and Saturday for Santander.**

C—Runs until 15th October only.

D—**Takes 2nd class travelling not less than 62 miles, or those coming off branch lines.**

F—Runs on Sunday, Wednesday, and Friday only. At Venta de Banos admits 1st class coming from the lines of Asturias and Galicia.

G—**At Venta de Baños takes up 1st, 2nd, and 3rd class from the lines of Asturias and Galicia.**

H—Runs on Sunday, Tuesday, and Thursday only.

J—Wed., Fri., and Sun. only from Alsasua, but daily from San Sebastian.

K—Runs on Monday, Wednesday, and Friday only.

L—Daily between Irun and San Sebastian; from San Sebastian forward on Tues., Thurs., and Sat. only, commencing July 12th.

X—**Sud Express**; take tickets in advance of Sleeping Car Co.

*—On Wed., Sat., and Sun. only.

§—**Wagon Restaurant attached supplementary fares charged. Does not take 2nd cl. passengers travelling less than 62 miles. Exceptionally admits 2nd class between Burgos and Hendaya, or those for branch lines.**

‖—**From Bilbao on Tuesday, Thursday, and Saturday only.**

†—Arrives San Sebastian 21.40.

BARCELONA and SARAGOSSA.

*—Mon., Wed., and Fri. only.

Dist		1,2,3	1,2,3	1,2,3	1,2,3	1,2,3		1,2,3	1 Cl	1,2,3	1,2,3
E.M	**Barcelona** dep	4 34	6 25	7 15	8 22	9 48	...	1416	17 4	1733	1840
6¾	Moncada	5	6 50	7 39	...	1014	...	1442	A	1756	19 2
14¼	Sabadell	5	7 15	8 9	9 3	1039	...	15 9	1742	1820	1929
31¾	Monistrol **293**	6 36	8 13	9 12	9 53	1136	...	1611	1831	1913	2028
40½	**Manresa 290**	7 5	8 38	9 47	1016	12 1	...	1637	1858	1935	2114
62¼	Calaf	—	—	11 4	A—Runs from 10th July on Tues., Thurs., & Sat. only.	—	From Jaca, dep. 10.1.	1815	20 5	—	2218
69½	San Guim		...	1126		...		1837	2024	...	2239
78¼	Cervera		...	1157		...		19 8	2043	...	23 3
99¼	Mollerusa		...	13 7		...		2015	...	...	2357
113¾	**Lerida 293** arr		...	1343		...		2051	2153	...	0 28
...	„ dep		10 0	14 8		4 0		‡—Tues., Thurs., and Sat. only.	2218	...	0 40
128¾	Almacellas		1038	1457		4 49			2252	...	1 22
151½	**Selgua 293**		1142	1618		6 4	1 &3		2351	...	2 25
171½	Sarinena		1235	1727		7 14	‡		0 39	...	3 18
195	**Tardienta 293**		1325	1838		8 17	1350		1 25	...	4 11
211¼	Zuera		—	1927		9 39	1424		1 58	...	4 48
227½	**S'gossa** Arrabal arr		...	2011		1026	1454		2 29	...	5 22
231¼	„ Sepulcro arr		...	...		...	1530		2 50	...	...
443	MADRID (**297**) arr		...	7 50	...	...	2245	...	1015	...	1955

MADRID 297 dep		...	...	1945	...	9 25	...	...	...
		1,2,3	1,2,3	1,2,3	1,2,3	1,2,3	1,2,3	1,2,3	1 Cl
Saragossa- Sepulcro dep		B—Runs from 12th July on Tues., Thur., & Sat. only.	...	6 40	*	16 30	...	..	...
Arrabal dep			...	7 10	1638	17 3	...	20 53	2342
Zuera			...	8 2	1712	17 51	...	21 31	0 17
Tardienta	2&3		...	8 59	1740	18 35	1745	22 6	0 47
Sarinena	3 42		...	10 7	To Jaca, arr. 21.11.	—	1838	23 0	1 36
Selgua	5 31		...	1111		17 45	1927	23 55	2 27
Almacellas	7 29		...	1227		19 47	2027	1 0	3 24
Lerida arr	8 37		...	1314		21 53	2059	1 37	3 56
„ dep	—		6 45	1344		—	—	1 50	4 4
Mollerusa			7 23	1425		...	...	2 23	B
Cervera			8 38	1543	—	...	...	3 30	5 30
San Guim			9 6	1612	...	...	...	3 56	5 53
Calaf	1,2,3		9 30	1640	...	...	...	4 18	6 12
Manresa	6 33	8 46	11 3	18 5	1326	16 6	1948	5 25	7 12
Monistrol	6 58	9 13	1135	1832	1353	16 30	2027	5 48	7 34
Sabadell	7 53	1014	1238	1939	1453	17 20	2133	6 49	8 22
Moncada	8 15	1039	13 3	20 8	1518	...	22 2	7 15	...
Barcelona	8 37	11 4	1328	2037	1543	18 1	2228	7 37	8 57

MOLLERUSA and BALAGUER.

E.M.					
	Mollerusa dep	7 45	15 0	20 30	...
9¼	Menarguens-Empalme	8 40	1548	21 6	...
16¼	**Balaguer** arr	9 14	1617	21 30	...

Balaguer dep	6 0	1115	1815	...	...	...
Menarguens-Empalme	6 27	1149	1854	...	...	...
Mollerusa arr	7 0	1232	1944	...	...	...

SARAGOSSA and ALSASUA.

	1 Cl	1,2,3	1,2,3	1,2,3	1 &3	1,2,3	
Saragossa Arrabal dep	2‡37	5 42	...	11 5	1613	2040	...
Las Casetas arr	2 55	6 6	...	1134	1633	21 9	‡—On Sun., Wed., and Fri. only, from 11th July
„ dep	2 57	6 20	...	1145	1637	2110	
Alagon	3 10	6 39	...	1211	1652	2235	
Cortes (292)	3 54	7 41	...	1351	1742	0 16	
Tudela (293)	4 20	8 22	...	1446	1810	1 8	
Castejon (292) arr	4 38	8 45	...	1510	1828	1 32	
„ dep	4 48	9 2	...	1540	1853	2 7	
Caparroso	...	9 54	...	1657	1937	3 27	
Tafalla	5 52	1035	...	18 2	2014	4 32	
Pamplona (295A) arr	6 56	12 5	...	1947	2124	6 31	
„ dep	7 6	1327	1410	—	2134	7 21	
Huarte-Araquil	...	1434	1622	...	2224	8 31	
Alsasua (291) arr	8 16	15 7	17 9	...	2247	9 7	...

		1,2,3	2&3	1& 3	1,2,3	1 Cl	1,2,3	
Alsasua dep		...	7 37	9 26	1140	1716	18 5	...
Huarte-Araquil		...	8 30	9 10	1213	§	1843	...
Pamplona arr		...	1018	1042	1322	1834	20 3	...
„ dep		5 0	§-On Tue, Thur, & Sat. only, from 12th July.	1052	14 0	19 4	2042	...
Tafalla		6 43		12 7	1535	2017	2249	...
Caparroso		7 23		1236	1610	...	2336	...
Castejon arr	2&3	8 18		1315	17 3	2113	0 41	...
„ dep	3 50	8 46		1340	1732	2123	1 36	...
Tudela	4 26	9 16		14 0	18 8	2145	2 13	...
Cortes	5 8	9 57		1428	1843	2212	3 3	...
Alagon	6 41	1122		1516	1938	23 1	4 32	...
Las Casetas arr	7 7	1144		1530	1953	2312	4 52	...
„ dep	7 16	1152		1533	20 5	2313	5 7	...
Saragossa arr	7 52	1225		1553	2028	2332	5 40	...

CORTES and BORJA.

E.M.					
	Cortes dep	8 0	15 25	...	...
11¼	Borja arr	9 1	16 37	...	...
	Borja dep	9 4	16 50	...	...
	Cortes **293** arr	10 2	17 48	...	...

BILBAO and CASTEJON.

Dist E.M			1 &3	1,2,3	1,2,3	1 &2	1,2,3	1,2,3	1,2,3
—	**Bilbao** dep		6 47	11 6	8 45	10 3	14 48	15 46	17 15
6¼	Arrigorriaga		7 7	1128	9 13	1024	15 13	16 13	17 52
21¼	Amurrio		7 49	1218	10 3	A	16 10	16 59	18 52
25½	Orduna		8 4	1232	10 26	1116	16 24	17 15	19 36
34¼	Lezama		8 31	—	11 1	1143	—	17 45	20 22
43½	Izarra		9 3	...	11 39	1213	...	18 19	21 23
64½	**Miranda** arr		9 44	...	12 30	1250	...	19 0	22 25
...	„ (291) dep		9 56	8 1	13 37	—	...	19 58	2 8
77¾	Haro		1018	8 40	14 6	...	...	20 35	2 59
82	Briones		1029	8 58	14 19	...	...	20 52	3 24
92½	Cenicero	1,2,3	1052	9 34	14 46	...	...	21 25	4 11
107½	Logrono	5 30	1128	1016	15 26	...	...	22 31	5 0
138	Calahorra	7 24	1237	—	16 40	...	...	0 8	—
151½	Alfaro	8 7	13 6	...	17 10	...	...	0 47	...
155¼	**Castej'n**	8 17	1312	...	17 17	...	...	0 55	...

(292)		1,2,3	1,2,3	1,2,3	1,2,3	1 & 2	1 &3
Castejon dep		1 57	9 8	...	15 30	Mon., Wed., and Fri. only.	1855
Alfaro		2 7	9 18	...	15 45		19 3
Calahorra		2 58	9 52	...	17 12		1931
Logrono		5 7	11 21	16 16	20 8		2049
Cenicero		5 51	11 53	17 4	21 40		2121
Briones		6 27	12 20	17 43	22 32		2143
Haro		6 48	12 36	18 11	23 15		2155
Miranda	1,2,3	7 17	12 59	18 45	23 54		2216
„ dep	2 39	7 52	13 45	—	—	19 18	2226
Izarra	5 17	8 41	14 39	...	...	19 59	23 8
Lezama	6 7	9 6	15 4	...	...	20 23	2330
Orduna	7 16	9 32	15 35	12 50	18 15	20 43	2351
Amurrio	7 31	9 44	15 49	13 3	18 28	...	0 1
Arrigor'aga	8 19	1025	16 32	13 47	19 20	21 22	0 35
Bilbao arr	8 41	1042	16 51	14 8	19 42	21 38	0 50

A—Takes for Miranda and beyond only; runs on Tues., Thur., and Sat. only.

SANTANDER and VENTA DE BANOS.

Dist. E.M.		1,2,3	1,2,3	1 &2	1,2,3	1,2,3	1,2,3
	Santander dep	...	7 33	9‡54	1145	16 40	1816
12½	Renedo	...	8 21	1030	1226	17 21	1859
17½	Torrelavega	...	8 50	1047	1245	17 46	1915
21¾	Las Caldas	...	9 9	1058	1259	18 2	1929
29¼	Las Fraguas	...	9 43	1122	1326	18 28	1956
34¼	Barcena	...	10 24	1145	1346	18 55	2017
55¼	Reinosa	...	12 27	1312	—	20 49	—
72	Quintanilla	6 46	14 5	1354	...	21 39	...
86¼	Alar San Q.	7 43	15 2	1424	...	22 16	...
120	Pina	9 47	16 56	...	...	23 39	...
136	**Palencia** arr	1032	17 42	1559	...	0 15	...
...	„ (293) dep	...	17 57	1612	...	0 28	...
143	**V. Baños** arr	...	18 16	1626	...	0 42	...
316¼	MADRID 291A	...	...	2258	...	8 8	...

‡-Runs on Mon., Wed., Fri. only. §-Runs on Tues., Thur., Sat. only.

MADRID 291	1810	...	2150	...	9 15	...	...
	1,2,3	1,2,3	1,2,3	1,2,3	1 & 2	1,2,3	
Venta de Baños dep	1 26	...	8 0	...	15§40	...	...
Palencia arr	1 40	...	8 18	...	15 53	...	...
„ dep	1 49	...	8 33	...	16 0	17 1	...
Pina	2 26	...	9 21	...	...	1748	...
Alar San Quc.	3 47	...	1118	...	17 38	1942	...
Quintanilla	4 23	...	12 5	...	...	2023	...
Reinosa	5 15	...	1335	...	18 49	—	...
Barcena	6 10	8 13	1453	1732	19 40	...	...
Las Fraguas	6 30	8 38	1518	1758	19 55	...	...
Las Caldas	6 51	9 6	1548	1825	20 12	...	...
Torrelavega	7 13	9 25	1621	1845	20 23	...	...
Renedo	7 28	9 43	1643	19 3	20 38	...	...
Santander ar	8 0	1020	1728	1943	21 5	...	...

TARRAGONA and LERIDA.

E.M.						
—	Tarragona dep	9 0	7 35	1229	16 36	1925
10	Reus (295)	9 35	8 22	13 6	17 59	2030
21¼	Plana-Picamoixons	—	9 14	—	19 0	2148
27¼	Montblanch		9 40	...	19 41	2219
39¼	Vinaixa	7 58	1020	...	20 39	23 5
48¼	Borjas	8 28	1046	...	21 17	2338
64	Lerida arr	9 13	1122	...	22 3	0 22

Lerida dep			5 30	8 29	15 0	1727
Borjas			6 32	9 29	1544	1920
Vinaixa			7 27	1021	1617	2027
Montblanch			8 32	1124	1657	—
Plana-Picamoixons			9 10	1153	1726	...
Reus	7 38	1235	9 57	14 8	18 8	...
Tarragona	8 11	13 7	1030	1443	1835	...

SELGUA and BARBASTRO.

Selgua dep	11 20	1635	...
Castejon del P.	11 40	1655	...
Barbastro arr	12 11	1726	...
Barbastro dep	9 43	15 0	...
Castejon del P.	10 24	1540	...
Selgua 292 arr	10 40	1556	...

TARDIENTA and JACA.

Tardienta dep	4 30	9 4	17‡59	1842
Huesca	5 43	9 47	18 30	1918
La Pena	8 25	1123	...	2044
Jaca arr	1119	13 4	21 11	2215

Jaca dep	5 20	10 §1	1358	14 11
La Pena	6 49	...	1541	17 0
Huesca	8 14	13 8	1725	20 22
Tardienta arr	8 42	13 39	1758	21 15

‡—Mon., Wed., and Fri. only. §—Tues., Thurs., and Sat. only.

NORTHERN RAILWAY—continued.

VENTA DE BANOS, LEON, and CORUNNA.

E.M.			1,2,3	1,2,3	1,2,3	1,2,3	1,2,3	1,2,3	1 Cl.
...	MADRID (291) dep		1717	18 10	2150	...	...	10 40	16 0
—	Venta de Banos dep		0 43	1 42	8 25	...	15 40	21 40	22 32
6¾	Palencia ....arr		0 58	1 56	8 43	...	15 53	21 58	22 46
...	,, ...dep		1 5	2 2	9 1	...	16 40	22 29	22 51
20	Paredes		...	2 32	9 52	...	17 36	23 39	23 18
35½	Villada		2 6	3 7	1055	...	18 37	0 43	0 2
44¾	Sahagun		2 31	3 32	1134	...	19 18	1 26	0 26
72	Palanquinos		3 26	...	13 2	...	20 44	2 56	B
83¼	Leon 293 ...... arr		3 46	4 47	1330	...	21 12	3 25	1 40
	Leon 293 ...... dep		4 1	—	—	1640	—	4 33	1 55
115½	Astorga 298A		5 20	...	...	1845	...	6 43	3 4
132¼	Branuelas		6 2	...	...	20 0	...	8 11	...
146	Torre		6 35	...	...	2050	...	8 59	...
162¾	Ponferrada		7 22	...	...	2213	...	10 5	4 52
172	Toral de los Vados...		7 43	...	...	2252	...	10 37	5 9
182¾	Quereno		8 7	...	...	2325	...	11 7	...
192	Barco de Valdeorras		8 28	...	...	0 5	...	11 41	5 49
205	Montefurado		8 55	...	...	0 54	...	12 24	...
231¼	Monforte ....arr		10 4	...	...	2 45	...	14 7	7 19
...	,, 294A...dep		1029	...	...	3 43	...	14 40	7 34
247¼	Oural		1114	...	...	4 58	...	15 51	B
253½	Sarria		1133	...	...	5 27	...	16 18	8 33
275½	Lugo ....dep		1234	...	...	6 55	...	17 43	9 24
292¾	Bahamonde		1317	...	...	7 51	...	18 45	9 59
323¾	Cesuras 1,2,3		1436	18 57	...	9 48	13 30	20 37	11 7
333	Betanzos	6 58	15 3	19 39	8 0	1032	14 6	21 22	11 28
346¾	Corunna ......arr	7 56	1535	20 40	8 50	1123	14 56	22 9	11 59

		1,2,3	1,2,3	1 Cl	1,2,3	1,2,3	1,2,3
Corunna dep	7 6	9 28	9 0	1130	16 6	1947	1836
Betanzos	8 6	1031	9 44	12 8	17 9	2110	1929
Cesuras	8 42	11 8	10 19	A	1743	2154	—
Bahamonde	—	—	11 51	1355	—	2350	...
Lugo ....dep		...	12 41	1439	...	0 57	...
Sarria		...	13 39	1529	...	2 16	...
Oural		...	14 2	1550	...	2 50	...
Monforte ...arr		...	14 39	1624	...	3 42	...
,, ...dep		...	15 4	1638	...	4 13	...
Montefurado		...	16 20	...	...	5 46	...
Barco		...	16 55	1818	...	6 31	...
Quereno		...	17 21	1843	...	7 6	...
Toral de Vados		...	17 50	19 8	...	7 49	...
Ponferrada		...	18 19	1957	...	8 31	...
Torre		...	19 13	2048	...	9 47	...
Brañuelas		...	19 55	2129	...	1036	...
Astorga		...	20 40	22 7	...	1143	...
Leon ...... arr		...	21 48	23 9	...	1320	...
Leon ...... dep		1012	22 13	2326	1434	1634	2116
Palanquinos		1044	22 36	...	15 0	17 8	...
Sahagun		12 9	23 41	0 53	1623	1841	2240
Villada		1246	0 3	1 16	1653	1922	23 4
Paredes		1341	0 38	...	1737	2017	2340
Palencia .....arr		1426	1 4	2 19	1813	21 2	0 6
,, ...dep		1439	1 11	2 21	1818	2118	0 12
Venta de B. arr		15 0	1 25	2 35	1836	2137	0 26
MADRID 291A		2258	8 34	9 12	5 39	8 8	7 30

A—Runs on Tues., Thurs., and Sat. only. B—Runs from Venta de Banos on Sun., Tues., & Thurs. only.

MONISTROL and MONSERRAT.

‡—From 15th July to 21st Sept.

E.M.						
	Monistrol ....dep	8 22	10 0	11 45	16 35	19‡20
5	Monserrat........... arr	9 22	11 0	12 45	17 35	20 20

Monserrat ....dep	8 7	10 22	15 7	17 12	19 ‡2	...
Monistrol 292 ....arr	9 2	11 20	16 5	18 10	20 0	...

TORAL de los VADOS and VILLAFRANCA del BIERZO.

Toral de los Vados ....dep	8 20	18 20	0 20	...
Villafranca del Bierzo ...arr	8 40	18 40	0 40	...

Villafranca del Bierzo ...dep	6 50	17 13	22 0	...	...
Toral de los Vados .... arr	7 10	17 30	22 20	...	...

LEON and GIJON.

†—Mon., Wed., and Fri. only. §—Tues., Thurs., and Sat. only.

	1 Cl	1,2,3	1,2,3	1,2,3	1,2,3	1,2,3	1 2 3	1,2,3
Leon ....dep	2 †1	...	...	5 0	6 15	...	1355	1718
La Robla	...	...	...	5 38	7 39	...	1443	1847
Busdongo	3 20	...	...	6 35	9 50	...	1611	21 9
Navidiello	...	...	...	7 9	—	...	1651	—
Puente los Fierros	4 37	...	5 57	7 54	...	15 46	1749	...
Pola de Lena	4 59	...	6 31	8 19	...	16 30	1819	...
Ujo	5 15	...	6 53	8 35	...	17 3	1840	...
Mieres	5 24	...	7 11	8 50	...	17 21	19 1	...
Soto de Rey 297A...	5 46	...	7 49	9 15	...	18 4	1944	1850
Oviedo 293 ...arr	6 2	...	8 15	9 33	...	18 31	2012	1932
,, ...dep	6 10	7 30	8 30	9 44	1345	18 39	2027	—
Lugones	...	7 41	8 44	9 54	1356	18 51	2040	...
Villabona 293	6 34	8 5	9 13	1013	1420	19 15	21 6	...
Gijon 293 ......arr	7 0	8 43	9 53	1044	1458	19 57	2146	...

	1,2,3	1,2,3	1,2,3	1,2,3	1 Cl	1 2 3	1,2,3
Gijon ....dep	7 12	9 31	1328	1440	17§11	1820	2155
Villabona	8 17	1016	1414	1522	17 47	19 8	2321
Lugones	8 42	1034	1432	1537	18 0	1927	2347
Oviedo ...... arr	8 55	1046	1444	1546	18 9	1940	0 6
,, ... dep	9 15	12 0	—	1556	18 14	1952	0 26
Soto de Rey	9 45	1234	...	1615	18 36	2024	1 3
Mieres	1020	13 5	...	1637	18 56	2057	1 45
Ujo	1042	1326	...	1652	19 7	2123	2 15
Pola de Lena	11 5	1359	...	17 9	19 24	2153	3 18
Puente los Fierros	1152	1432	...	1742	20 20	2226	4 6
Navidiello ...1,2,3	13 8	—	...	1846	21 21	—	—
Busdongo......7 54	14 6	...	...	1934	22 8	...	...
La Robla 294A 9 1	1525	...	...	2020	22 45	...	...
Leon 293 arr 9 44	16 9	...	...	2051	23 13	...	...

Villabona ...dep	6†35	8 27	9 14	10 22	14 18	15 30	1918	2120
S. Juan de Nieva	7 33	9 31	1016	11 24	15 23	16 26	2026	2227

S. Juan de N. dep	6 35	8 40	1238	1349	15§56	1728	1915
Villabona ...arr	7 54	10 0	1355	15 7	17 35	1850	2055

OVIEDO and SAN ESTEBAN de PRAVIA.

Dist					
	Oviedo...........dep	8 0	1116	1430	1820
11¼	Trubia	8 38	1153	15 5	19 0
35½	San Esteban ...arr	9 45	13 3	1614	20 7

San Esteban...dep	7 30	1110	1423	1818	...
Trubia	8 39	1221	1532	1927	...
Oviedo............arr	9 18	1259	1610	20 6	...

Oviedo to Trubia via San Claudio (in 40 minutes.)
Oviedo depart 7.31, 9.50, 16.0, 20.35. Trubia depart 6.31, 8.25, 12.51, 18.51.

OVIEDO and UJO-TARUELO

Oviedo.........dep	8 57	1215	1526	19 20
Ujo-Taruelo arr	10 6	1322	1635	20 29

Ujo Taruelo dep	7 30	1028	14 1	17 53	...
Oviedo .... arr	8 39	1137	15 9	19 0	...

ANDALUSIAN RAILWAY COMPANY—(COMPANIA DE LOS FERRO-CARRILES ANDALUCES). [30 kilogr. (66lbs.) of luggage allowed free.]

ALICANTE and MURCIA.

Dist E.M								
	Alicante ....dep	6 30	16 5	...	...	...	...	...
13	Elche	7 16	1651	...	...	...	...	...
24¼	Albatera-Catral	7 54	1729	...	...	...	...	...
33	Orihuela	8 27	18 2	...	...	...	...	...
40¾	Alquerias	9 5	1832	...	...	...	...	...
47¼	Murcia ....arr	9 30	1850	...	...	...	...	...
—	Albatera-Catral ...dep	10 40	19 35	...	...	...	...	
16¾	Torrevieja ....arr	11 40	20 35	...	...	...	...	

Murcia ....dep	9 5	1755	...	...	...	...
Alquerias	9 28	1823	...	...	...	...
Orihuela	10 2	1857	...	...	...	...
Albatera-Catral ...	1034	1929	...	...	...	...
Elche	1117	2012	...	...	...	...
Alicante 296......arr	1155	2050	...	...	...	...
Torrevieja ....dep	6 30	16 15	...	...	...	
Albatera-Catral ... ..arr	7 30	17 15	...	...	...	

BONANZA and JEREZ.

Bonanza ......dep	7 0	...	...	...	...
San Lucar	7 35	14 0	16 31	...	...
Las Tablas	8 3	14 24	...	...	...
Jerez (294) ...arr	8 35	14 51	17 15	...	...

Jerez ....dep	11 20	12 30	18 50	...	...
Las Tablas	...	12 57	19 23	...	...
San Lucar Bar ...	12 0	13 18	20 6	...	...
Bonanza.........arr	...	...	20 15	...	...

TUDELA and TARAZONA.

Dist.				
	Tudela 292...dep	9 35	14 55	18 30
13¾	Tarazona ......arr	10 45	16 5	19 42
...	Tarazona......dep	6 38	12 26	16 26
...	Tudela ....arr	7 40	13 32	17 30

GIJON and LAVIANA.

Dis. E M	(293)			
	Gijon ....dep	8 5	12 40	18 38
10	Florida	8 47	13 22	19 21
13¾	Norena	9 29	13 55	20 0
24¼	Sama	10 13	14 38	20 44
32¼	Laviana ......arr	10 39	15 0	21 12

Laviana...dep	8 0	14 15	18 37	...
Sama	8 30	14 37	19 7	...
Norena	9 21	15 26	19 58	...
Florida	9 54	15 59	20 31	...
Gijon ......arr	1031	16 38	21 8	...

CORDOBA and BELMEZ.

Cercadilla (Cordova) dep	3 0	8 0	1630
Obejo	421	10 2	1740
Alhondiguilla	512	1115	1823
Espiel	535	1149	1844
Belmez ...arr	630	1255	1920

Belmez dep	7 50	1430	20 0
Espiel	8 26	1557	2117
Alhondigui	8 41	1626	2151
Obejo	9 19	1754	2316
Cercadilla..	1010	1933	0 45

CADIZ to JEREZ and SEVILLE.

Dist		1,2,3	1,2,3	1&2	1,2,3				
E.M	Cadiz..............dep	7 30	13 5	1620	18 25	...	...	...	...
8¾	San Fernando	7 57	13 42	1639	18 55	...	...	...	...
15½	Puerto Real	8 14	14 1	1653	19 14	...	...	...	...
21¼	Puerto Sta. Maria	8 35	14 27	17 7	19 37	...	...	...	...
30½	Jerez 293	9 10	15 9	1731	20 5	...	...	...	...
43	Cuervo	9 37	15 39	1755	—	...	...	...	...
50¼	Lebrija..................	9 56	16 0	1810	...	...	...	...	...
61	Las Cabezas	10 21	16 31	1830	...	...	...	...	...
67¾	Las Álcantarillas...	10 38	16 51	...	...	...	...	...	...
75¾	Utrera 294 ......arr	10 55	17 15	1858	...	...	...	...	...
103¼	MARCHENA ...arr	12 24	19 14	...	...	...	...	...	...
165¼	CORDOBA 294 arr	15 40	1 5	...	...	...	...	...	...
...	Utrera ....dep	11 5	17 45	19 4	...	...	...	...	...
95	Seville ....arr	11 47	18 45	1940	...	...	...	...	...
177	CORDOBA 296A ar	15 50	1 35	2255	...	...	...	...	...

	1,2,3	1,2,3	1&2	1,2,3			
CORDOBA ...dep	...	2 45	6 15	11 10	...	...	...
Seville ....dep	...	8 17	9 11	15 24	...	...	...
Utrera............arr	...	9 25	9 45	16 13	...	...	...
CORDOBA 294 dep	...	2 35	2 35	11 30	...	...	...
MARCHENA...dep	...	8 18	8 18	15 0	...	...	...
Utrera ....dep	...	1010	9 50	16 30	...	...	...
Las Alcantarillas	...	1037	...	16 50	...	...	...
Las Cabezas	...	1057	1020	17 9	...	...	...
Lebrija	...	1125	...	17 34	...	...	...
Cuervo	...	1147	...	17 54	...	...	...
Jerez ....dep	9 1	1234	1118	18 32	...	...	...
Puerto Sta. Maria	9 33	13 5	1139	18 59	...	...	...
Puerto Real.........	9 50	1323	1152	19 15	...	...	...
San Fernando......	1013	1348	12 7	19 36	...	...	...
Cadiz ....arr	1040	1415	1225	20 0	...	...	...

A—Tues., Thurs., and Sat. only.

LA RODA and SEVILLE.

Dist E.M		1,2,3	1,2,3	1,2,3	1,2,3	1,2,3	1 &2
	GRANADA 294 ...dep	...	...	8 10	...	...	1610
	BOBADILLA 294 dep	...	...	12 15	...	...	1956
—	La Roda ....dep	...	6 10	13 5	...	...	2035
7¼	Pedrera....................	...	6 29	13 26	...	...	2055
22¼	Osuna	...	7 17	14 10	...	...	2136
34¼	Los Ojuelos................	...	7 45	14 36	...	...	...
41¾	Marchena 294... arr	...	8 3	14 52	...	...	2213
...	Marchena 294... dep	...	8 18	15 0	...	...	2218
50¼	Arahal	...	8 45	15 26	...	...	...
59	Moron Junction ...arr	...	9 8	15 46	...	...	A
...	„ 294 ...dep	7 40	9 16	15 48	1642	...	...
69	Utrera .... arr	8 4	9 40	16 10	1710	...	2316
	Utrera .... dep	8 19	10 0	16 28	1745	1925	2324
79	Dos Hermanas...........	8 47	1033	16 52	1823	2019	...
87½	Seville ....arr	9 5	1055	17 10	1845	2050	24 0

	1,2,3	1,2,3	1,2,3	1 & 2	1,2,3	1,2,3
Seville ....dep	6 30	8 17	10 0	15 24	16 25	18 0
Dos Hermanas	7 16	8 50	10 26	15 49	16 56	1822
Utrera .... arr	7 53	9 25	10 50	16 13	17 20	1849
Utrera .... dep	—	9 55	11 15	16 20	17 50	1910
Moron Junction arr	...	1023	11 37	A	18 17	1937
Moron Junction dep	...	—	11 41	...	18 24	—
Arahal	...	...	12 2	...	18 50	...
Marchena ...... arr	...	...	12 24	17 12	19 14	...
Marchena ...... dep	...	...	12 36	17 17	19 24	...
Los Ojuelos	...	...	12 53	...	19 43	...
Osuna	...	...	13 24	17 57	20 13	...
Pedrera......................	...	...	14 14	...	20 57	...
La Roda..............arr	...	...	14 31	18 56	21 15	...
BOBADILLA 294 arr	...	...	15 18	19 40	...	...
GRANADA 294 ...arr	...	...	19 45	23 20	...	...

Moron Junct. ......dep	1033	1945
Moron ....arr	1130	2030

Moron..............dep	7 0	1545
Moron Junct. ......arr	7 32	1630

MALAGA and CORDOBA.

E.M			1,2,3	1,2,3	1,2,3	1 & 2
—	Malaga ....dep		9 30	1235	1625	18 0
11¼	Cartama		9 59	13 4	17 4	...
23½	Alora		10 39	1343	1752	18 46
35½	Gobantes		11 34	1444	1854	...
42¾	Bobadilla ....arr		11 55	15 5	1915	19 31
...	„ 294 ...dep		12 15	—	2015	19 56
58½	La Roda 294 ......arr		12 54	...	21 5	20 27
...	„ dep	1,2,3	13 4	...	2130	20 32
72¾	Puente Genil 294	6 20	13 50	...	2233	21 4
75¼	Campo Real......	6 46	14 1	...	2249	...
115½	Valchillon	9 46	15 39	...	0 56	...
119¼	Cercadilla	10 0	15 52	...	1 17	...
120	Cordoba......arr	—	15 55	...	1 20	22 39
302	ALCAZAR 296A arr		2 35	...	15 0	5 55
395½	MADRID 296 ...arr		7 10	...	21 0	9 0

	1,2,3	1&2	1,2,3	1,2,3	1&2	1,2,3
MADRID 296 dep	7 20	2020	...	21 0	...	...
ALCAZAR 296 dp	14 0	2325	...	1 35	...	...
Cordoba ......dep	2 25	6 20	...	11 15	From Seville.	...
Cercadilla	2 30	...	...	11 20		1840
Valchillon	2 42	...	...	11 31		1856
Campo Real......	4 54	...	...	13 24		2210
Puente Genil ...	5 11	7 57	...	13 41		2220
La Roda ......arr	6 4	...	...	14 26	...	—
„ ......dep	6 14	...	...	14 41	19 6	...
Bobadilla ...arr	6 57	8 51	...	15 18	1940	...
„ ......dep	7 7	8 56	12 20	15 38	20 2	...
Gobantes	7 27	...	12 39	15 56	...	...
Alora	8 15	9 35	13 15	16 32	A	...
Cartama..............	8 49	10 0	13 47	17 2	...	...
Malaga.........arr	9 20	1022	14 15	17 30	2125	...

A—Tues., Thurs., and Sat. only.

MALAGA and VELEZ. 1 & 2 cl. only.

Malaga ....dep	8 30	13 15	18 30
Benagalbon	9 21	13 58	19 15
Torre del Mar	10 11	14 35	19 55
Velez................arr	10 23	14 45	20 6

Velez.................dep	5 45	11 0	16 0
Torre del Mar	6 2	11 15	16 15
Benagalbon	6 45	11 52	16 49
Malaga..............arr	7 38	12 40	17 31

BOBADILLA and GRANADA.

A—On Tues., Thurs., and Sat. only—Through 1st Class carriage between Malaga and Granada.

	1,2,3	1& 2	1,2,3	1,2,3	1& 2
MALAGA 294 dep		...	9 30	12 35	18 0
CORDOBA 294 dep		6 20	...	11 15	...
Bobadilla ...dep	...	9 ‡ 8	12 16	15 40	20 3
Antequera	...	9 30	12 45	16 13	2025
Archidona	...	10 7	13 25	16 54	21 2
Las Salinas	...	1038	14 2	17 24	...
Loja	8 35	...	14 54	18 11	A
Tocon...............	9 11	...	15 32	18 44	...
Illora...............	9 30	1159	15 52	19 1	...
Atarfe-Santa Fé	10 2	...	16 24	19 29	...
Granada......arr	10 20	1233	16 40	19 45	2320

		1,2,3	1,2,3	1& 2	1,2,3
Granada.........dep		8 10	11 15	1610	17 5
Atarfe-Santa Fé...		8 25	11 31	1623	17 21
Illora		8 54	12 1	...	17 53
Tocon		9 9	12 18	...	18 9
Loja		9 39	12 52	B	18 40
Las Salinas		10 37	13 58	...	—
Archidona.......	1,2,3	11 3	14 27	1843	...
Antequera	6 50	11 33	15 0	1910	...
Bobadilla arr	6 50	11 54	15 25	1930	...
CORDOBA 294 arr		15 55	22 39	2239	...
MALAGA 294 arr		14 15	17 30	2125	...

B—On Mon., Tues., Thurs., Fri. and Sat. ‡—On Mon. and Fri. only.

Travellers are warned to enquire as to running of these trains.

PUENTE GENIL and LINARES All 1,2,3 class.

E.M.				
	Puente Genil ...dep	8 15	14 0	22 45
16¼	Lucena	1046	14 59	0 20
23	Cabra	12 0	15 26	1 3
62¾	Martos	—	17 33	4 12
78¾	Jaen	...	18 24	5 18
98¼	Espeluy 296A..........	...	19 16	6 15
111¾	Linares 297 ......arr	...	20 30	8 5

Linares ....dep	7 0	...	21 0
Espeluy........................	7 55	...	22 10
Jaen	9 10	...	23 27
Martos	10 5	...	0 44
Cabra............................	12 3	17 58	3 35
Lucena	12 26	18 50	4 6
Puente Genil 294.......arr	13 10	20 15	4 50

E.M.				
	Linares ....dep	8 28	14 0	20 55
10½	Guarroman	9 28	15 18	22 16
18	La Carolina........arr	10 2	16 10	23 5

La Carolina.........dep	8 0	11 0	17 15
Guarroman	8 47	11 47	17 50
Linares ....arr	10 5	13 6	18 56

MARCHENA and CORDOBA.

Dist E.M		1,2,3	1,2,3	1,2,3
	CADIZ ....dep	7 30	...	13 5
	UTRERA......dep	11 15	...	1750
—	Marchena......dep	12 30	15 30	20 0
27¼	Ecija	13 53	18 42	22 5
41	La Carlota	14 35	20 5	2313
57¾	Valchillon	15 21	21 32	0 29
61¼	Cercadilla	15 37	21 50	1 2
62¼	Cordoba.........arr	15 40	...	1 5

	1,2,3	1,2,3	1,2,3				
Cordoba ....dep	2 35	...	1130	...	...	...	...
Cercadilla	3 3	4 25	1143	...	...	...	...
Valchillon	3 19	4 47	12 0	...	...	...	...
La Carlota	4 34	6 26	13 0	...	...	...	...
Ecija	5 37	8 0	1344	...	...	...	...
Marchena.........arr	7 45	10 40	1455	...	...	...	...
UTRERA 294 ...arr	9 40	...	1610	...	...	...	...
CADIZ 294 ......arr	12 25	...	20 0	...	...	...	...

VIGO, ORENSE, and MONFORTE.

Station					
Vigo ...dep	7 55	11*10	1430	19 0	22 35
Redondela ...	8 23	11 31	15 8	1939	22 59
Guillarey ...arr	9 10	12 15	1621	2039	23 45
Guillarey ...dep	...	12 20	...	...	24 0
Tuy ...	...	12 35	...	...	0 25
Valença de Miño...	...	12 43	...	...	0 33
OPORTO 301...arr	...	16 43	...	...	8 57
Guillarey ...dep	9 17	12 17	...	2054	...
Salvatierra...	9 43	12 39	...	2130	...
Arbo...	1016	13 8	...	2217	...
Ribadavia ...	1122	14 6	...	2345	...
Orense ...arr	1211	14 45	...	0 43	...
Los Peares...	1312	15 18	...	1 46	...
Monforte 293...arr	1413	16 10	...	2 59	...

Station					
Monforte ...dep	...	3 55	7‡45	1045	...
Los Peares...	...	4 56	8 30	1136	...
Orense ...dep	...	5 49	9 7	1232	...
Ribadavia ...	...	6 51	9 58	1327	...
Arbo...	...	8 11	10 51	1434	...
Salvatierra...	...	8 51	11 22	15 7	...
Guillarey ...arr	...	9 16	11 43	1527	...
OPORTO 301...dep	...	...	...	...	1421
Valença de Miño...	...	...	11 0	...	1750
Tuy ...	...	...	11 23	...	1818
Guillarey ...arr	...	...	11 28	...	1823
Guillarey ...dep	6 50	9 28	11 45	1532	1833
Redondela ...	8 12	1038	12 34	1630	1927
Vigo ...arr	8 40	11 0	12 50	1649	1950

*—Tuesday, Thursday, and Saturday only. ‡—Monday, Wedneeday, and Friday only.

VIGO and PONTEVEDRA.

Station						
Vigo ...dep	6 20	...	1010	12 10	16 5	...
Redondela ...	6 46	8 30	1050	12 40	16 40	...
Pontevedra ...arr	7 28	9 12	1135	13 15	17 15	...

Station					
Pontevedra...dep	7 30	10 45	1410	1820	2020
Redondela...	8 5	11 30	15 4	1927	2114
Vigo ...arr	...	11 50	1525	1950	2135

Pontevedra to Marin, in 30 minutes, 6.15, 8.30, 10.45, 12,45, 16.45, and 19.0. From Marin, 7.30, 9.30, 12.0, 15.30, 17.45, and 20 15.

SANTIAGO and PONTEVEDRA.

E.M	Station			
	Santiago (Cornes) dep	4 40	7 40	17 5
13¾	**Padron**...	5 31	8 37	18 2
26	**Carril** ...	6 12	9 27	18 52
46½	**Pontevedra**...arr	7 20	10 38	20 3

Station			
Pontevedra...dep	8 0	13 40	17 30
Carril...	9 26	14 56	18 47
Padron...	1018	15 38	19 29
Santiago (Cornes) arr	1114	16 27	20 18

BILBAO and SAN SEBASTIAN.

‡—Sunday excepted.

E.M	Station								
	Bilbao ...dep	5 40	8 40	9 40	12 0	15 0	1640	1845	1943
14½	**Amorebieta** ...	6 20	9 30	1019	1242	1543	1721	1934	2027
20½	**Durango** ...	6 44	9 55	1037	1258	16 5	1741	1955	2045
33½	**Malzaga** ...	7 43		1134			1844		
44	**Deva** ...4 55	8 16	...	12 4	...	...	1917	...	...
51	**Zumaya**...5 23	8 41	...	1223	...	...	1942	...	...
55¼	**Zarauz** ...5 42	8 55	...	1237	1413	1816	1957	...	...
71½	**SanSebastian**6 49	9 43	...	1322	15 6	19 9	2046	...	...

Station										
San Sebastian dep	...	5 40	9 50	1030	1434	1620	...	19‡45	...	...
Zarauz ...	...	6 30	1030	1121	1525	17 0	...	20 42	...	...
Zumaya...	...	6 44	1042			1714	...	20 57	...	...
Deva ...	...	7 9	11 4	...	...	1740	...	21 28	...	...
Malzaga ...	...	7 48	1137	...	...	1822	...		...	...
Durango ...	7 40	8 47	1226	14 5	1640	1917	1835	...	...	...
Amorebieta ...	8 1	9 9	1242	1424	17 2	1936	1857	...	...	...
Bilbao ...arr	8 49	9 47	1320	15 9	1743	2014	1942	...	...	...

E.M	Station				
	Malzaga ...dep	8 5	11 45	18 55	...
6¼	**Vergara** ...	8 33	12 20	19 31	...
16¾	**Zumarraga** ...arr	9 10	13 3	20 15	...

Station				
Zumarraga...dep	6 0	10 10	17 5	...
Vergara...	6 49	10 55	17 49	...
Malzaga ...arr	7 14	11 20	18 13	...

E.M	Station					
	Amorebieta ...dep	6 18	9 32	15 45	19 36	...
9¼	**Guernica** ...	7 1	10 17	16 30	20 17	...
15½	**Pedernales** ...arr	7 26	10 44	16 57	20 41	...

Station						
Pedernales ...dep	4 10	7 48	13 2	17 37	...	...
Guernica ...	4 50	8 20	13 34	18 7	...	...
Amorebieta ...dep	5 31	9 0	14 14	18 47	...	...

E.M	Station					
	Durango...dep	9 55	16 6	1955	...	...
6¼	**Elorrio** ...	10 18	1629	2018	...	...
16¾	**Arrázola**...arr	...	17 0	...	...	...

Station							
Arrázola ...dep	...	...	1820	...	...	...	...
Elorrio ...	8 20	13 40	1850	...	...	...	...
Durango ...arr	8 47	14 5	1917	...	...	...	...

BILBAO and PORTUGALETE.

Bilbao...dep, **Zorroza**..., **Luchana** ..., **Desierto** ..., **Sestao** ..., **Portugalete** arr — Departures from Bilbao and from Portugalete at 5.20, 6.0, 7.0, 8.0, 8.30, and half-hourlyuntil 19.30, also at 20.15 and 21.5. — **Portugalete** dep, **Sestao** ..., **Desierto** ..., **Luchana** ..., **Zorroza**..., **Bilbao**...arr

E.M	Station				
	Desierto ...	8 28	12 28	15 28	19 28
10	**San Julian**	8 59	12 59	15 59	19 59

Station					
San Julian	7 30	9 30	14 30	18 30	...
Desierto ...	8 1	10 1	15 1	19 1	...

E.M	Station								
	Bilbao ...dep	9 †5	12†10	15 5	16 55	19†45	...	...	...
15½	**Aranguren** ...	9 52	12 55	1552	17 35	20 39	...	...	...
21¾	**Valmaseda** ar	10 6	13 9	16 7	17 49	20 53	...	...	...

Station									
Valmasedadep	7†35	...	11 0	12 20	13 35	17 0	1825	...	...
Aranguren ...	7 54	9 1	11 25	12 54	13 52	17 34	1844	...	...
Bilbao...arr	8 43	9 50	12 3	...	14 34	...	1929	...	...

†—May not run.

E.M	Station							
	Luchana ...dep	6†46	12†18	15 24	18 28	...	...	...
10	**Munguia**...arr	7 40	13 14	16 17	19 23	...	...	...

Station					
Munguia...dep	4†50	7 55	13†26	16 24	...
Luchana...arr	5 50	8 51	14 20	17 20	...

†—May not run.

E.M	Station					
	Traslaviña ...dep	8 †45	13 23	16 20	19†40	...
14¼	**Castro-Urdiales** ...arr	9 44	14 36	17 18	20 39	...

Station						
Castro-Urdiales...dep	7 30	9 26	13†55	18†20	...	...
Traslaviña ...arr	8 25	1043	14 55	19 20	...	...

†—May not run.

BILBAO and LAS ARENAS (7½ miles).—Departures from Bilbao and Las Arenas, 6.0, 7.0, 8.0, 8.30, 9.0, 9.30, 10.0, 10.30, 11.0, 11.30, 12.0, 12.45, 13.10, 14.0, 14.30, 15.0,15.30, 16.0, 16.30, 17.0,17.30, 18.0,18.30, 19.0, 19.30, 20.0, 20.30, 21.0.

VITORIA and SALINAS de LENIZ

E.M	Station				
	Vitoria ...dep	8 45	16 0	18 0	...
11¾	**Salinas de Leniz** ...arr	9 29	16 44	1844	...

Station						
Salinas ...dep	10 0	17 0	20 0	...	...	...
Vitoria ...arr	1046	17 46	2046	...	...	...

SANTANDER and LIERGANES.

E.M	Station						
	Santander...dep	8 55	1155	14†50	19†20	...	...
17½	**Lierganes**...arr	9 52	1255	15 54	20 31	...	...

Station							
Lierganes dep	7†35	8†30	10 25	11†40	13 50	18 †5	...
Santander arr	8 38	9 35	11 21	12 37	14 58	19 3	...

†—May not run.

QUINTANILLA and BARRUELO.

E.M	Station				
	Quintanilla dep	7 5	14 10	20 43	...
8¾	**Barruelo** ...arr	8 6	15 16	21 20	...

Station							
Barruelo ...dep	6 0	11 5	19 0	...	...	...	...
Quintanilla arr	6 28	11 48	19 48	...	...	...	...

LA ROBLA and BILBAO.

E.M	Station					
	La Robla ...dep	...	7 45	16 3	...	...
34¼	**Cistierna** ...	...	9 33	1842	...	...
102½	**Mataporquera**...	...	14 0		...	...
148½	**Espinosa** ...	7 7	1627	...	...	...
176¾	**Valmaseda** ...	8 39	18 1	...	...	...
198¾	**Bilbao** ...arr	9 42	1859	...	...	...

Station						
Bilbao ...dep	...	8 0	1550	...	...	...
Valmaseda ...	...	9 6	1658	...	...	...
Espinosa ...	...	10 39	1833	...	...	...
Mataporquera ...	...	14 10		...	...	...
Cistierna ...	12 0	17 55	...	...	...	...
La Robla 293...arr	14 30	19 39	...	...	...	...

GERONA and SAN FELIU DE GUIXOLS.

E.M.							
	Gerona .... dep	7 20	9 25	12‡15	15 55	18 5	...
24¾	San Feliu de Guixols arr	9 15	1115	14 5	17 50	19 50	...

San Feliu de Guixols dep	3 45	6 40	8 ‡45	1320	1515	...
Gerona 295 ....arr	5 30	8 35	10 40	1510	1710	...

‡—Monday, Thursday, and Saturday only.

GERONA and OLOT.

Gerona.................dep	5 40	9 42	15 26	18 15	...	...	...
San Esteban de Bas ...	8 18	11 48	18 4	20 23	...	...	...
Olot ....arr	8 41	12 8	18 27	20 43	...	...	...

Olot.......................dep	2 45	5 18	11 42	14 38	...	...
San Esteban de Bas ...	3 5	5 43	12 8	14 59	...	...
Gerona ....arr	5 13	8 22	14 31	17 4	...	...

PUEBLA DE HIJAR and ALCANIZ.

Puebla de Hijar...dep	9 0	18 52	...	...	...	...
Alcaniz..................arr	10 9	20 1	...	...	...	...

Alcaniz ....dep	5 §30	16 0	...	...	...	...	...	...
Puebla de Hijar295arr	6 39	17 9	...	...	...	...	...	...

§—May not run.

MARTORELL and IGUALADA.

Martorell ....dep	6 0	9 37	13 30	18 55	...	...	...
Vallbona....................	7 32	10 54	14 48	20 13	...	...	...
Igualada ....arr	8 8	11 38	15 28	20 54	...	...	...

Igualada ....dep	5 0	10 25	12 35	16 50	...	...	...
Vallbona....................	5 52	11 8	13 19	17 29	...	...	...
Martorell 295.........arr	7 13	12 7	14 33	18 32	...	...	...

SANTANDER and ONTANEDA.

E.M.							
	Santander ....dep	8†30	11 0	14†25	18 †0	...	...
5½	Astillero......................	8 55	11 25	14 47	18 22	...	...
15	La Cueva (Penilla)......	9 39	12 9	15 31	19 6	...	...
27¼	Ontaneda ....arr	10 33	13 3	16 25	20 0	...	...

Ontaneda ....dep	7 †28	11 †9	14 31	18 †4	...	...
La Cueva (Penilla)......	8 12	11 53	15 15	18 48	...	...
Astillero.......................	8 54	12 38	15 56	19 29	...	...
Santander ....arr	9 15	12 59	16 17	19 50	...	...

†—May not run.

VALLADOLID and RIOSECO.

Dist. E.M.						
	Valladolid— S. Bartolomé......dep	8 30	17 35	...	...	...
15½	La Mudarra	9 45	18 49	...	...	...
25½	Rioseco ....arr	10 25	19 29	...	...	...

Rioseco ....dep	7 55	14 35	...	...	...	...	...
La Mudarra................	8 44	15 23	...	...	...	...	...
Valladolid ....arr	10 2	16 40	...	...	...	...	...

PAMPLONA and SANGÜESA (Electric Rail).

E.M.									
	Pamplona ....dep	7 ‡15	14 3	...	...	...	...	...	...
18¾	Aoiz Junction	8 30	15 45	...	...	...	...	...	...
21¼	⋮Aoiz	8 53	16 8	...	...	...	...	...	...
35½	Sangüesa ....arr	9 49	17 4	...	...	...	...	...	...

Sangüesa ....dep	7 14	14 29	...	...	...
⋮ Aoiz	8 17	15 32	...	...	...
Aoiz Junction	8 36	15 51	...	...	...
Pamplona 292.........arr	10 41	17‡ 8	...	...	...

‡—From or at Pamplona, Paseo de Sarasate.

ISLAND OF MAJORCA.

PALMA and MANACOR.

E.M.								
	Palma............dep	7 40	14 0	14 3	14 40	18 15	...	...
9¼	Sta. Maria............	8 24	14 44	14 46	15 24	19 10	...	...
11¾	Consell	8 35	14 55	—	15 35	19 21	...	...
18	Inca	9 1	15 21	...	16 1	19 47	...	...
21¼	Son Bordils.........	9 16	15 32	...	16 11	20 2	...	...
39¾	Manacor.........arr	10 10	16 26	...	...	21 40	...	...

Manacor.........dep	2 30	6 30	...	...	17 15	...	...
Son Bordils	4 30	7 34	12 50	...	18 19	...	...
Inca	5 15	7 48	13 4	...	18 33	...	...
Consell	6 18	8 16	13 32	...	19 1	...	...
Sta. Maria............	6 33	8 25	13 41	14 46	19 10	...	...
Palma ....arr	7 30	9 0	14 20	15 24	19 45	...	...

Sta. Maria............dep	8 24	14 47	19 19	...	...	...	...
Felanitx ....arr	10 4	16 27	21 27	...	...	...	...

Felanitx..............dep	6 40	12 15	17 0	...	...	...	...
Sta. Maria ....arr	8 20	14 32	19 5	...	...	...	...

Son Bordils ....dep	9 16	16 12	20 2	...	...	...	...
La Puebla ....arr	9 44	16 40	20 41	...	...	...	...

La Puebla..............dep	6 55	12 0	17 25	...	...	...	...
Son Bordils ....arr	7 25	12 45	18 10	...	...	...	...

MADRID, SARAGOSSA, and ALICANTE RAILWAY.

MADRID, ALCAZAR, and ALICANTE.

Dist. E.M.	1 Cl. P. c.	2 Cl. P. c.	3 Cl. P. c.	Madrid—		1,2,3	1,2,3	1 &3	1 & 3	1,2,3	1,2,3	1,2,3	1,2,3	1Cl.	1,2,3	1,2,3
				Puerta de Atocha ......dep		...	7 20	9 30	10 0	10 20	13 0	17 30	1920	2020	20 35	21 0
8¾	1 75	1 35	0 85	Getafe		...	7 51	C	RC	10 50	13 35	17 55	A	B	E	21 25
16¾	3 50	2 75	1 70	Valdemoro		...	8 20	...	...	11 20	14 8	18 20	1953	...	...	21 49
30½	6 15	4 75	2 95	**Aranjuez 297A**		...	9 20	1021	10 46	12 20	16 50	19 0	2027	2113	21 38	22 27
40½	8 15	6 35	3 90	**Castillejo** ......arr		...	9 53	1038	11 3	12 53	17 34	20 15	2051	2130	21 58	22 55
46	9 25	7 20	4 40	Villasequilla		...	10 15	RC	...	13 12	18 37		...	...	...	23 11
63½	12 75	9 90	6 10	Tembleque		...	11 32	1123	11 46	14 10	20 5	...	...	...	...	0 2
75¼	15 15	11 75	7 30	Villacanas		...	12 31	1146	12 9	14 49	21 0	...	2212	...	...	0 34
84	16 90	13 10	8 5	Quero		...	13 3	...	...	15 13	21 34	...	...	...	...	0 53
92½	18 65	14 45	8 85	**Alcazar** ......arr		...	13 25	1215	12 38	15 35	22 5	...	2245	2310	23 45	1 10
275¼	...	...	...	CORDOBA 296A ......arr		...	2 5	...	18 55	...	...	...	...	6 0	...	10 30
356	...	...	...	SEVILLE 296A ...arr	1,2,3	...	7 40	...	21 40	...	...	...	...	9 0	...	15 0
...	...	...	...	**Alcazar** ......dep	3 30	6 25	...	1225	...	16 5	...	...	23 0	...	23 58	...
116¼	23 40	18 15	11 15	Socuéllamos	4 30	7 52	...	RC	...	17 19	...	...	2356	...	...	...
126¾	25 50	19 80	12 15	Villarrobledo	5 0	8 36	...	1338	...	18 1	...	...	0 20	...	1 7	...
151½	30 50	23 65	14 50	La Roda	5 58	1010	...	1425	...	19 12	...	...	1 11	...	1 56	...
173¼	34 90	27 5	16 60	Albacete ......arr	6 45	1125	...	15 5	...	20 10	...	...	1 54	...	2 39	...
...	...	...	...	,, ...dep	6 55	12 0	17 40	1510	...	20 33	...	...	2 16	...	2 51	...
185¼	37 25	28 90	17 70	**Chinchilla** ......arr	7 26	1256	18 49	1536	...	21 20	...	...	2 45	...	3 20	...
286½	...	...	...	MURCIA 297A ......arr		...	...	C	...	4 45	...	...	8 25	...	8 25	...
326¼	...	...	...	CARTAGENA 297A ...arr		...	...	...	...	7 50	...	...	1035	...	10 35	...
...	...	...	...	**Chinchilla** ......dep	7 38	1310	19 35	1538	...	21 50	...	...	3 0	...	...	...
210	42 25	32 75	20 10	Alpera	8 41	1512	22 11	...	...	23 18	...	...	4 0	1,2,3	...	...
223	44 90	34 80	21 35	Almansa	9 15	1615	23 0	1653	...	0 15	...	...	4 33	5 0	...	...
234¼	47 15	36 55	22 40	**La Encina** ......arr	9 45	1657		1715	...	0 51	...	...	5 0	5 43	...	...
304½	...	...	...	VALENCIA 298 ..arr	1440	...	...	20 3	...	7 5	...	...	8 30	...	...	...
...	...	...	...	**La Encina** ......dep	1010	1735	...	Mon., Wed., and Fri.	...	2 0	...	...	5 25	6 1	...	...
246¾	49 65	38 50	23 65	**Villena 297A**	1045	1826	...		...	2 55	...	...	6 5	7 0	...	...
261	52 50	40 70	24 95	Monóvar	1131	1929	...		...	3 54	...	...	6 56	8 5	...	...
264	53 15	41 20	25 25	Novelda	1143	1948	...		...	4 40	...	...	7 13	8 24	...	...
277¾	55 90	43 35	26 55	San Vicente	1222	2047	...		...	5 29	...	...	7 49	9 21	...	...
282¾	56 90	44 10	27 5	**Alicante** ......arr	1235	21 5	...		...	5 45	...	...	8 0	9 40	...	...

	1,2,3	1,2,3	1Cl.	1,2,3	1,2,3	1,2,3	1,2,3	1,2,3	1 & 3	1& 3	1,2,3	1,2,3	1,2,3	1,2,3	
Alicante ......dep	...	...	...	...	...	...	...	6 30	10 10	...	1430	1740	20 0	22 10	...
San Vicente	...	...	...	...	...	...	...	6 49	10 31	...	1445	18 4	20 14	22 33	...
Novelda	...	...	...	...	...	...	...	7 47	11 41	...	1529	1913	20 54	23 40	...
Monóvar	...	...	...	...	...	...	...	8 2	11 57	...	1541	1933	21 5	23 58	...
Villena	...	...	...	...	...	...	...	9 0	13 0	...	1630	21 0	21 53	1 12	...
La Encina ......arr	...	...	...	...	...	...	...	9 40	13 40	...	17 0	2147	22 25	1 58	...
VALENCIA 298 ......dep	...	...	...		...	...	...	...	On Tues., Thurs., and Sat. only.	11 9	12 0	...	19 0	20 10	...
La Encina ......dep	...	...	...	...	...	...	...	9 55		1420	1717	22 7	22 55	3 0	...
Almansa	5 45	...	...	...	...	...	...	1115		1443	1753	2250	23 28	3 55	...
Alpera	6 50	...	...	...	...	...	...	1217		1510	1828		0 1	4 45	...
Chinchilla ......arr	8 55	...	...	...	...	...	...	1355		16 1	1934	...	1 0	6 7	...
CARTAGENA ......dep	...	16 45	...	...	...	...	...	...		D	1130	...	16 45	19 0	...
MURCIA 297A ......dep	...	19 5	...	...	...	...	...	2 20		...	1355	...	19 5	22 5	...
Chinchilla ......dep	9 15	0 40	...	...	...	...	...	1417		16 2	20 4	...	1 15	6 48	...
Albacete ......arr	10 0	1 3	...	...	...	...	...	15 0		1625	2032	...	1 40	7 22	...
,, ...dep		1 13	...	...	...	...	...	1645		1630	2050	...	1 55	7 55	...
La Roda	...	2 0	...	...	...	...	...	18 6		1711	2144	...	2 40	9 3	...
Villarrobledo	...	2 49	...	...	...	...	...	1940		1757	2246	...	3 31	10 18	...
Socuéllamos	...	...	...	...	...	...	...	2018		RC	2311	...	3 52	10 47	...
Alcazar ......arr	...	3 55	...	...	...	...	...	2140	...	19 0	0 20	...	4 50	11 55	...
SEVILLE 296A ......dep	12 10	...	2010	...	...	...	20 50	...	9 25	...	...	...	...	...	...
CORDOBA 296A ......dep	16 15	...	2310	...	...	...	2 10	...	12 12	...	...	...	...	...	...
Alcazar ......dep	3 0	4 10	6 10	...	5 40	...	15 40	RC—Restaurant Car attached.	18 46	1910	...	...	5 15	12 40	...
Quero	3 19	...	...	...	6 35	...	16 4		RC	RC	...	...	A	13 5	...
Villacanas	3 42	F	...	...	7 12	...	16 32		19 16	1940	...	...	5 50	13 31	...
Tembleque	4 13	...	B	...	8 5	...	17 9		19 39	20 3	...	...	...	14 8	...
Villasequilla	4 54	...	...	...	9 29	...	17 59		...	D	...	...	...	14 59	...
Castillejo ......dep	5 10	5 52	7 43	...	10 15	...	18 25		20 20	...	...	...	7 0	15 25	...
Aranjuez	5 39	6 18	8 4	8 10	10 55	12 10	19 10		20 38	21 9	...	...	7 24	16 10	...
Valdemoro	6 22	...	...	8 58		13 8	20 3		...	...	...	...	7 58	17 3	...
Getafe	6 47	...	...	9 26	...	13 43	20 33		...	...	...	...	...	17 33	...
Madrid ......arr	7 10	7 30	9 0	9 50	...	14 15	21 0	...	21 30	22 0	...	...	8 35	18 0	...

A—Sleeping Cars in this train—from Madrid for Valencia daily except Tues. and Sat.; for Alicante on Tues. and Sat. From Valencia to Madrid daily except Sun. and Wed.; from Alicante on Sun. and Wed.

B—Expreso de Lujo, Restaurant and Sleeping Cars; daily service between Madrid and Seville; leaving Madrid as the Morocco Express on Tuesday and Saturday, running to Algeciras, page 299, for Tangier; returning from Tangier on Monday and Thursday, arriving at Madrid on Tuesday and Friday.

C—This train leaves Madrid for Valencia on Monday, Wednesday, and Friday.

D—Runs on Tuesday, Thursday, and Saturday from Valencia

E—Sleeping Car attached on Mon., Wed., and Fri. F—Sleeping Car attached on Tues., Thurs., and Sat.

MADRID and TOLEDO.

‡—21.15 on Sun.

Dist. E.M.	Madrid—	1,2,3	1,2,3	1,2,3	1,2,3
	Puerta de Atocha dep	8 5	12 0	17‡0	19 0
13¾	Parla	8 41	12 50	1745	1938
29¾	Pantoja y Alameda	9 19	13 47	1830	2018
38	Algodor	9 42	15 1	19 0	2050
47¼	**Toledo** ......arr	10 0	15 25	1920	2110

	1,2,3	1,2,3	1,2,3	1,2,3
Toledo ......dep	6 55	12 10	13 50	17 45
Algodor	7 28	12 36	14 54	18 9
Pantoja y Alameda	7 51	13 1	15 28	18 31
Parla	8 40	13 52	16 31	19 11
Madrid ......arr	9 20	14 35	17 25	19 50

Toledo ......dep	6 55	8 35	16 25	2015
Algodor	7 30	9 6	17 1	2036
Castillejo...arr	7 54	10 15	18 25	2057
Castillejo dep	7 51	10 25	1845	20 19
Algodor	8 8	11 1	1921	20 50
Toledo ......arr	8 25	11 25	1945	21 10

MADRID, SARAGOSSA, and ALICANTE RAILWAY.—continued.

SEVILLE, CORDOBA, and ALCAZAR.

Dist	1 Cl	2 Cl	3 Cl		1,2,3	1,2,3	1,2,3	1 & 3	1,2,3	1,2,3	1,2,3	1 Cl.	1,2,3	
E.M	P.c.	P.c.	P.c.	**Seville** ....dep	...	6 45	7 10	9 25	12 10	...	1655	20 10	20 50	...
3	0 65	0 50	0 30	Seville Junction.........	...	6 53	7 19	...	12 30	...	17 3	20 21	21 10	...
13¾	2 75	2 10	1 25	Brenes	...	7 19	7 45	...	12 55	...	1728	B	21 45	...
21¾	4 40	3 30	2 0	**Tocina 297**	...	7 50	8 15	10 8	13 22	...	1751	21 0	22 25	...
25½	5 15	3 85	2 35	Guadajoz 296A	...	8 5		...	13 35	...	18 3	...	22 42	...
34¾	7 0	5 25	3 15	Lora del Rio	...	8 32	...	10 36	14 2	...	1820	21 28	23 16	...
49	9 90	7 45	4 45	Palma	...	9 5	...	11 3	14 36	...	19 5	21 55	24 0	...
67	1365	1025	6 15	Almodóvar	...	9 49	...	11 41	15 20	...	1954	...	0 56	...
80¾	1640	1230	7 40	**Cordoba** ....arr	...	1020	...	12 6	15 50	...	2025	22 55	1 35	...
...	...	...	...	MALAGA 294 ......dep	...	...	...	...	9 30	...	...	18 0	16 25	...
...	...	...	...	**Cordoba** ....dep	9 30	...	...	12 12	16 15	1820	...	23 10	2 10	...
100	2015	1520	9 15	El Carpio..................	1150	...	...	RC	17 5	1919	...	...	3 11	...
115	2315	1755	1060	Villa del Rio	1346	...	...	13 19	17 53	2010	...	0 17	4 10	...
123¾	2490	1890	1145	Marmolejo..................		...	...	13 35	18 18	2033	...	0 33	4 40	...
130½	2625	1995	1210	Andujar	...	...	...	13 55	18 44	21 0	...	0 53	5 16	...
144¼	29 0	2210	1340	**Espeluy 294**	...	...	...	14 23	19 50	2140	...	...	6 50	...
160¼	3225	2460	1495	**Baeza** ....arr	...	...	...	14 57	20 35		...	1 53	7 57	...
...	...	...	...	GRANADA 298A...dep	...	...	...	9 15	13 30	...	...	...	...	...
...	...	...	...	MOREDA 298A ...dep	...	...	...	11 32	16 35	...	...	...	...	...
...	...	...	...	**Baeza** ....dep	...	...	...	14 58	21 0	...	...	1 58	8 20	...
166	3340	2550	1545	Vadollano 297	...	...	...	15 17	21 25	...	...	2 17	8 59	...
190¾	3840	2935	1785	Venta de Cárdenas......	...	...	...	...	23 5	...	...	...	10 54	...
207½	4175	3195	1945	Santa Cruz..................	...	...	...	17 7	23 56	4 30	...	4 9	12 0	...
216¼	4350	3335	2030	Valdepenas 297A.........	...	...	...	17 22	0 20	5 30	...	4 26	12 27	...
233¾	47 0	36 5	2195	Manzanares 297 { arr	...	...	...	17 49	1 0	6 25	...	4 55	13 10	...
				{ dep	...	...	...	17 50	1 30	7 10	...	4 57	13 35	...
248	4990	3825	2330	Argamasilla................	...	...	...	18 14	2 6	8 53	...	5 28	14 16	...
263½	5315	4080	2485	**Alcazar** ....arr	...	...	...	18 40	2 35	9 50	...	5 55	15 0	...
356	7165	5510	3365	MADRID 296........arr	...	...	...	21 30	7 10	...	...	9 0	21 0	...

MADRID 296 ......dep	10 0	7 20	1020	20 20	...	21 0	...	...	...	...	...	...	...
	1& 3	1,2,3	1,2,3	1 Cl.	1,2,3	1,2,3	1,2,3	1,2,3	...	...	...	...	...
Alcazar ....dep	1244	14 0	1620	23 25	...	1 35	...	...	...	...	...	...	...
Argamasilla	RC	14 53	1823	23 57	...	2 12	...	...	...	...	...	...	...
Manzanares..... { arr	1333	15 30	1912	0 23	...	2 40	...	...	...	...	...	...	...
{ dep	1335	15 50	2020	0 25	...	3 0	...	...	...	...	...	...	...
Valdepènas.................	14 3	16 37	2244	0 56	...	3 41	...	...	...	...	...	...	...
Santa Cruz..................	1418	17 15	2315	1 12	...	4 10	...	...	...	...	...	...	...
Venta Cárdenas	...	18 16		1 50	...	4 55	...	...	...	...	...	...	...
Vadollano	16 0	20 0	...	3 1	...	6 17	...	...	...	...	...	...	...
Baeza ....arr	1612	20 15	...	3 13	...	6 30	...	...	...	...	...	...	...
MOREDA 298A......arr	1950	...	...	...	...	12 10	...	...	...	...	...	...	...
GRANADA 298A...arr	2155	...	...	...	...	15 20	...	...	...	...	...	...	...
Baeza ....dep	1613	20 40	...	3 18	...	6 50	...	...	...	...	...	...	...
Espeluy	...	22 0	6 5	B	...	7 45	...	...	...	...	...	...	...
Andujar........................	1715	22 55	6 47	4 21	...	8 22	...	...	...	...	...	...	...
Marmolejo.....................	1731	23 33	7 11	4 37	...	8 43	...	...	...	...	...	...	...
Villa del Rio................	1748	0 18	7 36	4 53	...	9 4	...	...	...	...	...	...	...
El Carpio.....................	RC	1 12	8 30	...	...	9 46	...	...	...	...	...	...	...
Cordoba ....arr	1855	2 5	9 25	6 0	...	10 30	...	...	...	...	...	...	...
MALAGA 294 ......arr	...	9 20	...	10 22	...	17 30	...	...	...	...	...	...	...
Cordoba ....dep	19 0	2 45	...	6 15	7 25	11 10	...	1725	...	...	...	...	...
Almodóvar....................	...	3 26	...	...	7 57	11 42	...	1757	...	...	...	...	...
Palma	20 2	4 25	...	7 16	8 44	12 29	...	1843	...	...	...	...	...
Lora del Rio.................	2033	5 12	...	7 46	9 23	13 5	...	1919	...	...	...	...	...
Guadajoz	...	5 45	...	8 4	9 49	13 32	...	1943	...	...	...	...	...
Tocina	2058	6 15	...	8 12	10 7	13 49	19 3	1953	...	...	...	...	...
Brenes..........................	...	6 44	...	...	1029	14 11	1926	2015	...	...	...	...	...
Seville Junction.........	...	7 15	...	8 47	1052	14 35	1951	2040	...	...	...	...	...
Seville ....arr	2140	7 40	...	9 0	11 0	15 0	20 0	2048	...	...	...	...	...

B—Expreso de Lujo. RC—Restaurant Car.

GUADAJOZ and CARMONA.

Guadajoz ......dep	8 11	10 11	13 56	18 10	22 46	Carmona ......dep	5 0	9 10	1235	1720	19 5	...
Carmona 297A arr	8 45	10 45	14 30	18 44	23 20	Guadajoz 296A arr	5 29	9 39	13 4	1749	1934	...

VILLACANAS and QUINTANAR DE LA ORDEN.

E.M	Villacañas......dep	7 0	15 20	...	...	Quintanar ......dep	10 15	17 30	...	...	...
15½	Quintanar......arr	8 30	16 50	...	...	Villacañas 296 arr	11 45	19 0	...	...	...

MADRID, CIUDAD-REAL, and BADAJOZ.

Dist.	Madrid—	1,2,3	1,2,3	1,2,3	1,2,3	1,2,3	
E.M	Puerta deAtocha dep	...	...	...	12 0	19 0	...
8¾	Getafe	...	...	...	1234	19 26	...
38	**Algodor (296)**...arr	...	...	...	1415	20 39	...
...	" ...dep	...	...	...	1435	20 47	...
56	Mora	...	...	...	1558	21 48	...
65¼	Yévenes	...	...	...	1635	22 16	...
93¾	Malagon 6 16	...	...	...	1826	23 34	...
107½	**Ciudad-Real** arr 7 15	...	...	...	1915	0 10	...
...	" (297) dep	5 10	...	8 25	1940	0 25	...
131¾	Puertollano	6 50	...	1150	2125	1 34	...
143½	Veredas	7 26	...	1313	22 4	2 3	...
168½	Almadenejos y Alma.	8 49	...	1538	2328	3 9	...
190¾	Belalcazar	1013	...	1818	0 54	4 12	...
205	**Almorchon (297)** arr	1115	...	2020	2 0	5 0	...
...	" ...dep	1140	1620		2 30	5 15	...
238	Magacela	1333	1840	...	4 20	6 48	...
247½	Don Benito	1415	20 7	...	5 0	7 21	...
262¾	Guarena	1514	2138	...	6 0	8 13	...
280½	**Merida (297)**...arr	1610	2255	...	7 0	9 0	...
...	" ...dep	1625		...	7 20	9 20	...
284	Aljucen	1640	...	...	7 35	9 36	...
294½	Montijo	1711	...	...	8 16	10 10	...
305¾	Talavera	1736	...	...	8 52	10 35	...
317	**Badajoz (300)** arr	18 0	...	...	9 25	11 0	...
383½	TOR. VARGENS...arr	21 4	...	...	...	16 24	...
491½	LISBON (300)...arr	1 13	...	...	...	...	...

LISBON (300) ......dep	...	21 55	...	...	...
TORRE VARGENS dp	...	3 17	...	...	...
	1,2,3	1,2,3	1,2,3	1,2,3	...
Badajoz ......dep	...	8 25	16 20	18 45	...
Talavera	...	8 54	16 46	19 20	...
Montijo	...	9 25	17 15	19 57	...
Aljucen	...	10 5	17 51	20 38	...
Merida ......arr	...	10 15	18 0	20 50	...
" ......dep	5 5	10 40	18 25	21 15	...
Guarena	6 54	11 44	19 17	22 25	...
Don Benito	9 9	12 45	20 12	23 29	...
Magacela	1025	13 29	20 50	0 13	...
Almorchon arr 1,2,3	1350	15 40	22 25	2 25	...
" dep 5 35		15 55	22 40	3 0	...
Belalcazar 7 26	...	16 49	23 24	4 11	...
Almadenejos y A. 1035	...	18 19	0 39	5 40	...
Veredas 1319	...	20 10	2 1	7 30	...
Puertollano 15 5	...	20 44	2 31	8 15	...
Ciudad-Real ar 1810	...	22 10	3 40	9 45	...
" dep	...	22 50	3 55	10 10	...
Malagon	...	0 2	4 37	11 4	...
Yévenes	...		5 58	12 53	...
Mora	...	...	6 30	13 34	...
Algodor ......arr	...	...	7 17	14 34	...
" ......dep	...	...	7 28	14 54	...
Getafe	...	...	8 53	16 50	...
Madrid-Atocha ...arr	...	...	9 20	17 25	...

MERIDA, ZAFRA, TOCINA, and SEVILLE.

Dist		1,2,3	1,2,3	1,2,3	
...	BADAJOZ 297 ...dep	...	8 25	16 20	...
E.M.	**Merida** ......dep	...	11 0	19 10	...
18¾	Almendralejo	...	12 4	20 30	...
41	**Zafra** 297A...... arr	...	13 13	22 0	...
	dep	...	13 46	22 30	...
65¾	Llerena	6 0	15 6	0 20	...
74	Fuente del Arco 298A	6 55	15 35	1 5	...
89½	Alanis	8 45	16 32	2 25	...
107	Pedroso	11 0	17 36	3 50	...
127½	**Tocina** 296 ... arr	13 0	18 57	5 45	...
	dep	1349	19 3	6 15	...
146¾	Seville Junct. (Emp.)	1452	19 52	7 31	...
149½	**Seville** ......arr	15 0	20 0	7 40	...

	1,2,3	1,2,3	1,2,3		
Seville ......dep	7 10	1210	2050	...	...
Seville Junction ...	7 19	1230	2110	...	...
Tocina ...... arr	8 7	1316	2210	...	...
dep	8 15	14 0	2235	...	...
Pedroso	10 0	1655	0 55	...	...
Alanis	11 8	1850	2 26	...	...
Fuente del Arco	12 12	21 0	3 48	...	...
Llerena	12 41	2140	4 25	...	...
Zafra ...... arr	13 45		5 50	...	...
dep	14 10	...	6 5	...	...
Almendralejo	15 17	...	7 35	...	...
Merida ......arr	16 5	...	8 40	...	...
BADAJOZ 297 arr	18 0	...	11 0	...	...

MADRID and SARAGOSSA.

E.M	**Madrid**—Puerta	1,2,3	1 & 3	1,2,3	1,2,3	1 Cl.	1,2,3
—	de Atocha ......dep	7 10	9 25	9 55	1330	18 50	19 45
6¾	Vicalvaro	7 35	...	1021	1355	...	20 11
21½	Alcalá de Henares	8 15	RC	11 0	1440	A	20 53
28½	Azuqueca	8 36	...	1121	15 2	...	21 11
35½	Guadalajara ...... arr	8 50	1032	1135	1520	19 51	21 25
	dep	9 11	1037		16 5	19 56	21 42
65½	Jadraque	1029	...	...	1811	...	22 55
87	Siguenza	1138	1213	...	2030	21 48	0 5
97	**Torralba** ...... arr	1215	1237	...	2118	...	0 36
	dep	1250	1238	...	2126	...	0 44
103¼	Salinas de M.	13 6	...	...	2148	...	1 4
113	Arcos	1345	1314	...	23 5	22 50	1 32
119¼	St. Maria de Huerta	14 0	...	...	2323	...	1 45
128	**Ariza** 297A	1430	1338	...	0 5	...	2 15
136	Alhama	1455	1353	...	0 47	23 27	2 37
144¼	Ateca	1520	...	...	1 34	...	3 1
152¼	Calatayud ...... arr	1540	1421	...	2 0	23 55	3 20
	dep	16 5	1423	7 0	3 0	23 58	3 35
174½	Ricla	17 6	...	8 5	4 58	...	4 30
203¾	Las Casetas ...... arr	1825	1544	9 34	6 40	1 19	5 40
	dep	1835	1547	9 37	6 55	1 22	6 0
212	**Saragossa**-Sepul. arr	1855	16 0	10 0	7 20	1 35	6 20
425¾	BARCELONA 295 arr	1327	2336	...	...	9 2	17 40

BARCELONA dep	15 4	...	8 25	...	9 23	19 50
Saragossa—	1,2,3	1,2,3	1 & 3	1,2,3	1,2,3	1 Cl.
Sepulcro...dep	7 25	10 0	16 0	1915	21 0	3 25
Las Casetas arr	7 45	1030	16 13	1942	2120	3 38
dep	7 55	1055	16 16	20 0	2140	3 40
Ricla	9 29	1321	...	22 0	2253	...
Calatayud... arr	10 35	1511	17 43	2320	2345	5 7
dep	11 5	1545	17 46	0 30	0 0	5 10
Ateca	11 37	1620	...	1 1	0 25	...
Alhama	12 8	17 4	18 19	1 40	0 49	5 44
Ariza	12 55	1746	...	2 25	1 25	A
S. Maria de Huerta	13 25	1817	RC	2 51	1 46	...
Arcos	13 55	1925	19 6	3 35	2 15	6 35
Salinas de M.	14 30	2027	...	4 24	2 52	...
Torralba arr	14 50	21 0	19 48	4 50	3 12	...
dep	15 0	2120	19 49	5 5	3 22	...
Siguenza	15 35	2230	20 9	6 0	3 54	7 44
Jadraque	16 32		20 51	7 32	4 52	...
Guadala- arr	17 50	...	21 41	9 55	6 0	9 10
jara ...... dep	18 5	2020	21 43	1035	6 20	9 13
Azuqueca	18 22	2035	...	1057	6 35	...
Alcalá de Henares	18 45	2055	...	1128	6 56	...
Vicalvaro	19 35	2137	...	1223	7 33	...
Madrid ......arr	19 55	2155	22 45	1245	7 50	10 15

Extra. {Madrid ......dep 1655, 20 10; Guadalajara...arr 1835, 2222} | Guadalajara...dep 8 0, 16 0; Madrid ......arr 9 40, 1740 | Saragossa dep 18 0, ...; Calatayud arr 21 25, ...

RC—Restaurant Car attached. A—Expreso de Lujo.

SEVILLE and HUELVA.

Seville ......dep	6 35	9 30	17 0	...
San Lucar	7 39	10 25	1751	...
La Palma	9 13	11 51	19 19	...
Niebla	9 43	12 18	19 46	...
S. Juan del Puerto...	10 17	12 47	20 14	...
Huelva 297A ...arr	10 35	13 5	20 30	...

Huelva ...dep	7 0	16 0	17 55
S. Juan Puerto	7 22	16 23	18 23
Niebla	7 47	16 48	18 49
La Palma	8 15	17 16	19 20
San Lucar	9 41	18 49	21 7
Seville ......arr	1035	19 40	22 5

Caceres and Merida.

E.M	**Cáceres** dep	7 40	14 45
24¼	Carmonita ...	8 46	15 52
45¾	**Merida** ...arr	9 40	16 45
	Merida (297) dep	9 55	17 30
	Carmonita	10 59	18 48
	Cáceres ......arr	12 10	20 15

MANZANARES & CIUDAD-REAL. (297)

Manzanares ...dep	3 5	6 45	16 0	...
Daimiel	3 38	7 30	1639	...
Almagro	4 17	8 28	1726	...
Ciudad-Real ...arr	4 50	9 15	18 5	...

Ciudad-Real ......dep	1045	1740	2235
Almagro	1129	1835	2313
Daimiel	1216	1930	2352
Manzanares 296A...arr	1250	2010	0 20

ALMORCHON and BELMEZ.

Almorchon dep	5 30	16 0
Peñarroya	7 24	1925
Belmez 293 arr	7 35	1945
Peñarroya...dep	7 55	2035
Pozoblanco......	1036	2337
Conquista ...arr	1218	...

Belmez ...dep	7 0	1950
Peñarroya......	7 43	2014
Almorchon arr	1045	22 0
Conquista dep	...	1435
Pozoblanco ...	4 8	1642
Peñarroya arr	7 1	19 5

VADOLLANO and LINARES (5½ miles).

From Vadollano at 6.28, 9.8, 20.8, and 21.38. From Linares 5.20, 7.45, 18.50, and 20.45.

MADRID, SARAGOSSA, and ALICANTE RAILWAY—(continued)

CHINCHILLA and CARTAGENA.

MADRID 296 ......dep	20 35	21 0	...	...	10 20	...
	1,2,3	1,2,3	1,2,3	1,2,3	1,2,3	
Chinchilla.........dep	3 ‡40	7 50	...	1440	21 45	...
Tobarra	4 53	9 3	...	1711	23 15	...
Agramon	5 37	9 48	...	1854	0 33	...
Cieza	6 44	10 54	...	2054	2 32	...
Archena................	7 23	11 37	...	2158	3 27	...
Alcantarilla...... arr	7 55	12 10	...	23 4	4 15	...
Alcantarilla...... dep	8 15	12 19	19 20	2329	4 31	...
Murcia (293)... arr	8 25	12 30	19 32	2345	4 45	...
Murcia (293)... dep	8 40	12 55	20 0	—	5 10	...
Alquerias	8 58	13 16	20 27	...	5 36	...
Balsicas................	9 55	14 18	21 44	...	6 57	...
Cartagena ....arr	10 35	15 0	22 30	...	7 50	...

Dist. E.M.		1,2,3	1,2,3	1,2,3	1,2,3	1,2,3
	Cartagena.........dep	...	6 10	1130	16§45	19 0
16¼	Balsicas................	...	7 2	1218	17 32	20 2
34¼	Alquerias	...	8 4	1313	18 22	21 13
40½	**Murcia** .... arr	...	8 23	1330	18 40	21 35
	Murcia .... dep	2 20	8 33	1355	19 5	22 5
45¼	Alcantarilla ... arr	2 36	8 45	14 7	19 16	22 19
	Alcantarilla ... dep	3 1	—	1420	19 30	22 35
57¼	Archena................	4 10	...	15 7	20 13	23 35
71½	Cieza	5 50	...	1556	21 2	0 43
98¼	Agramon	7 58	...	1712	22 13	2 22
115½	Tobarra................	10 34	...	1810	23 10	4 6
141	**Chinchilla**.........arr	12 30	...	1925	0 25	5 50
326¼	MADRID 296.........arr	...	...	...	7 30	18 0

‡—Sleeping Car in this train on Mon., Wed., and Fri. §—Sleeping Car in this train on Tues., Thurs., and Sat.

Cartagena.........dep	5 40	13 20	18 20	...
Los Blancos ......arr	6 38	14 18	19 20	...
Los Blancos.........dep	6 48	14 28	19 30	...
Cartagena............arr	7 45	15 21	20 30	...

ARANJUEZ and CUENCA.

E.M.					
	Aranjuez.........dep	9 40	13 0	19 30	...
10½	Ocana	10 35	14 31	20 12	...
37¼	Tarancon	12 40	16 50	21 19	...
52¾	Vellisca	13 34	—	21 57	...
67	Caracenilla	14 32	...	22 36	...
94½	**Cuenca** ....arr	16 10	...	23 50	...

Cuenca ....dep	...	6 0	14 15	...	...
Caracenilla	...	7 33	15 32	...	...
Vellisca	...	8 27	16 18	...	...
Tarancon	5 0	9 27	17 0	...	...
Ocana	6 33	11 3	18 4	...	...
Aranjuez 296 arr	7 10	11 40	18 35	...	...

VALLADOLID and ARIZA.

Dist. E.M.					
	Valladolid (Norte) ...dep	6 50	17 0	24 0	...
	" (M.Z.A.)...dep	7 10	17 7	0 20	...
12½	Tudela de Duero	7 54	17 37	1 8	...
37¼	Penafiel................	9 55	18 42	3 10	...
49¾	Roa de Duero	10 51	19 16	4 11	...
62½	Aranda	11 30	19 45	4 50	...
95	Osma	—	21 43	7 43	...
126¾	Almazan 299	...	23 18	10 7	...
159	**Ariza** ....arr	...	1 0	1220	...
243½	SARAGOSSA 297.........arr	...	6 20	16 0	...

SARAGOSSA (297).........dep	21 0	...	7 25	...	...
Ariza ....dep	2 35	...	15 45	...	...
Almazan	4 42	...	18 40	...	...
Osma................	6 12	...	21 0	...	...
Aranda	7 50	16 0	23 25	...	...
Roa de Duero	8 20	16 51	0 17	...	...
Penafiel................	8 58	17 55	1 20	...	...
Tudela de Duero	9 57	19 38	3 8	...	...
Valladolid (M.Z.A.) ...... arr	10 23	20 10	3 40	...	...
Valladolid Norte 291 arr	10 30	20 20	4 0	...	...

MURCIA and LORCA.

E.M.					
	Murcia................dep	8 33	19 5	...	...
5	Alcantarilla.......... arr	8 45	19 16	...	...
	Alcantarilla.......... dep	9 10	20 0	...	...
40½	**Lorca** (297A) ....arr	10 55	22 9	...	...

Lorca ....dep	5 0	17 5	...	...
Alcantarilla.......... arr	7 6	18 41	...	...
Alcantarilla.......... dep	8 15	19 20	...	...
Murcia (297A).........arr	8 25	19 35	...	...

LORCA and BAZA.

E.M.				
	Lorca ....dep	11 20	1715	...
15	Almendricos	12 21	1851	...
26	Huercal	12 55	—	...
52¼	Purchena	14 33	...	...
83½	**Baza** ....arr	16 15	...	...

Baza ....dep	...	12 0
Purchena	...	13 29
Huercal	...	15 6
Almendricos	8 19	15 49
Lorca.........arr	9 20	16 25

Almendricos dep	12 23	15 58	19 10
Aguilas..........arr	13 35	17 10	20 40
Aguilas.........dep	6 10	10 30	14 15
Almendricos arr	7 58	11 51	15 33

SOTO DE REY and CIANO SA. ANA.

E.M.					
	Soto de Rey ...dep	8 1	9 50	1625	2032
13¾	Ciana Sa. Ana arr	9 8	11 4	1715	2132

Ciano Sa. Ana......dep	6 24	8 15	1438	16 57	...
Soto de Rey 292 arr	7 28	9 1	1558	18 28	...

ZAFRA and HUELVA.

Dist E.M.						
	Zafra...........................dep	...	...	1415	...	...
14¼	Valencia del Ventosa	...	...	1514	...	...
29¾	Fregenal	...	...	1615	...	...
54¾	Jabugo-Galaroza	...	9 39	1751	...	...
59	Almonaster	...	1020	1815	...	...
70¼	Valdelamusa	6 10	1130	19 0	...	...
81½	Calañas................	7 31	1239	1948	...	...
103¾	Gibraleon	9 19	1419	21 4	...	...
111¾	**Huelva** (Zafra Co. Sta.)arr	9 50	1450	2130	...	...

Huelva—(Zafra Stat.) ......dep	5 30	11 40	17 0	...	...	...
Gibraleon	6 1	12 17	1737	...	...	...
Calañas................	7 30	14 16	1945	...	...	...
Valdelamusa	8 20	15 28	2050	...	...	...
Almonaster	9 14	17 7	—	...	...	...
Jabugo-Galaroza	9 32	17 49	...	...	...	...
Fregenal	1120	—	...	...	...	...
Valencia del Ventoso...	1219	...	...	...	...	...
Zafra (297).........arr	1315	...	...	...	...	...

SEVILLE and CARMONA.

Dist.					
	Seville San Bernardo ...dep	7 0	12†50	1730	22 †0
9¼	Alcala de Guadaira...........	7 45	1 25	1815	22 31
16¾	Mairena........................	8 17	—	1847	—
19¼	Viso........................	8 31	...	19 1	...
26¾	Carmona 296A ....arr	9 0	...	1930	...

Carmona ...dep	...	9 20	...	1950	...
Viso	...	9 51	...	2021	...
Mairena	...	10 5	...	2035	...
Alcala de G. ...	5†15	10 47	15†10	2110	...
Seville ......arr	5 50	11 22	15 41	2145	...

†—May not run.

RIO TINTO and HUELVA.

E.M.				
	Rio Tinto Pueblo ...dep	5 0	13 50	...
36	Niebla	7 50	16 50	...
52¾	**Huelva**....................arr	8 50	17 50	...

Huelva...................dep	11 30	18 50	...	...
Niebla	12 44	19 55	...	...
Rio Tinto Pueblo arr	15 50	22 45	...	...

VILLENA and MURO.

E.M.				
—	Villena ...dep	3 55	6 20	1645
31¾	Muro 298A arr	6 41	8 33	1923

Muro.........dep	7 30	1940
Villena 296arr	1028	2140

VILLENA and JUMILLA.

E.M.				
—	Villenadep	6 20	16 45	2210
31¾	Jumillaarr	8 13	18 50	0 17

Jumilla...dep	1 30	8 35	19 25
Villena 296arr	3 25	1028	21 35

THARSIS and LA PUNTA (Huelva).

E.M.			
	Tharsis ...dep	8 *16	...
28½	La Punta arr	10 29	...

La Punta dep	15*31	...
Tharsis ...arr	17 44	...

*—Not on Sunday.

VALDEPENAS and PUERTOLLANO.

E.M.				
	Valdepeñas..............dep	7 0	15 0	...
26¾	La Calzada de Calatrava	9 15	17 15	...
47½	Puertollano ....arr	11 15	19 15	...

Puertollano ....dep	7 22	15 20	...
La Calzada de Calatrava	9 30	17 30	...
Valdepeñas 296A ......arr	11 30	19 30	...

PUERTOLLANO and SAN QUINTIN.

E.M.				
	Puertollano................dep	8 25	21 30	...
5	Almodovar del Campo	8 59	21 54	...
16½	**San Quintin**...............arr	10 27	...	...

San Quintin................dep	...	17 53	...
Almodovar del Campo	6 0	19 36	...
Puertollano (297) ....arr	6 24	20 0	...

MADRID and VALENCIA DE ALCANTARA.

Dist. E.M.		1,2,3	1,2,3	1,2,3	1,2,3	1,2,3	1Cl.	1& 2
	Madrid—							
—	Principe Pío...dep	...	...	...	...	...	2345	...
...	Atocha ....dep	...	...	...	...	...	2359	...
...	Delicias........dep	7 20	8 15	13 5	17 30	19 50	...	...
3¾	Villaverde	7 31	8 26	13‡25	17 42	20 1	...	...
8¾	Leganes	7 47	8 40	13 51	17 56	20 16	B	...
18	Grinon	8 16	9 11	14 43	18 31	20 48	0 53	...
24¼	Illescas	8 31	9 28	15 15	18 46	21 5	SC	...
31	Villaluenga........	8 50	9 54	16 10	19 5	21 29	...	...
44¾	Villamiel	—	10 37	17 45	—	22 14	...	...
53½	Torrijos........	...	11 4	18 45	...	22 44	2 3	...
61	S. Olalla-Carmena	...	11 22	19 25	...	23 4	...	...
84	**Talavera** ... arr	...	12 19	21 14	...	0 4	3 1	...
	Talavera ... dep	...	12 45	22 20	...	0 16	3 9	...
105¾	Oropesa........	...	13 40	0 10	...	1 12	3 51	...
125	Navalmoral	...	14 27	1 22	...	2 1	4 34	7 30
144¼	La Bazagona	...	15 15	—	...	2 52	5 19	9 20
157¾	Plasencia........	11 15	15 54	16 10	...	3 48	5 51	1018
177¾	Canaveral	12 10	—	17 43	...	4 47	6 42	—
205¾	**Arroyo** ....arr	13 28	...	19 35	...	6 5	7 47	...
...	**Arroyo** ......dep	13 53	22 20	19 45	...	6 38	...	...
216¼	**Cáceres 297** arr	14 28	23 0	20 25	...	7 13	...	...
...	**Arroyo** ....dep	13 51	...	...	...	6 19	7 54	...
228¾	Herreruela	15 30	...	...	...	7 16	8 47	...
250½	**Valencia de A.** ar	17 0	...	...	...	8 14	9 40	...
486	OPORTO **300** arr	...	...	...	...	21 3	21 3	...
408¼	LISBON **(300)** arr	1 13	...	...	...	18 8	1445	...

	1,2,3	1,2,3	1,2,3	1,2,3	2&3	1,2,3	1& 2
							A
LISBON 300 ......dep	...	...	2155	...	...	11 36	17 2
OPORTO 300 ......dep	...	...	1548	...	...	8 35	...
V. Alcantara ¶ dep	...	...	8 45	...	...	19 52	2232
Herreruela	...	...	1025	...	...	20 58	2323
Arroyo........arr	...	...	1146	...	...	22 0	0 14
Cáceres ....dep	5 20	6 55	—	1235	...	21 0	SC
Arroyo........arr	6 0	7 34	...	13 6	...	21 40	...
Arroyo ....dep	—	7 48	...	1331	...	22 14	0 19
Canaveral	...	9 45	...	15 6	...	23 52	1 28
Plasencia........	...	11 1	1126	16 0	1611	1 7	2 15
La Bazagona........	...	—	1210	—	1720	1 50	2 51
Navalmoral........	...	1 54	13 0	...	1915	2 44	3 35
Oropesa........	...	4 25	1343	...	2044	3 30	4 13
Talavera ...... arr	...	6 26	1434	...	2219	4 21	4 52
Talavera ...... dep	...	7 0	1444	...	—	4 31	4 57
S. Olalla-Carmena ...	...	9 12	1549	...	...	5 34	5 51
Torrijos........	...	10 1	1610	...	...	6 17	6 7
Villamiel	...	1045	1633	...	...	6 41	A
Villaluenga........	9 25	1210	1710	1940	...	7 25	...
Illescas	9 49	1256	1732	2015	1,2,3	7 52	...
Grinon	10 6	1322	1752	2046	5 40	8 12	7 26
Leganes	10 33	1425	1819	2126	6 26	8 42	...
Villaverde	10 45	1445	1831	2143	6 45	8 55	...
Madrid-Delicias arr	10 55	15 0	1841	2156	7 0	9 5	...
Atocha........arr	...	...	...	...	...	...	8 17
Principe Pío ......arr	...	...	...	...	...	...	8 20

A—From Lisbon on Mon., Wed. & Sat. only. B—On Sun., Tues., and Thurs. night only. SC—Sleeping Car attached.

VALENCIA and TARRAGONA.

Dist E.M		1,2,3	1 & 3	2 & 3	1,2,3	1,2,3	
	Valencia......dep	8 4	9 42	13 10	17 31	20 34	...
18	Sagunto........	9 26	10 25	14 23	18 24	21 33	...
36	Burriana	10 32	11 4	15 21	19 9	22 22	...
43	Castellon	11 46	11 26	15 52	19 40	22 56	...
91½	Vinaroz........	14 32	13 10	—	21 23	1 4	...
119½	Tortosa	16 13	14 12	...	—	2 21	...
159¼	Cambrils	18 22	15 35	...	...	4 5	...
171	**Tarragona**...arr	18 58	15 59	...	...	4 36	...

	1,2,3	1,2,3	1 & 3	2 & 3	1,2,3			
Tarragona...dep	...	8 56	10 57	...	23 40	...	...	...
Cambrils	...	9 34	11 26	...	0 16	...	...	...
Tortosa	...	11 44	12 51	...	2 12	...	...	...
Vinaroz........	6 0	13 8	13 57	...	3 36	...	...	...
Castellon	7 58	16 0	15 53	17 25	6 4	...	...	...
Burriana	8 21	16 38	16 13	17 59	6 32	...	...	...
Sagunto	9 15	17 53	16 52	19 16	7 32	...	...	...
Valencia ......arr	10 1	18 59	17 30	20 20	8 26	...	...	...

E.M.							
	Castellon........dep	6 40	8 20	1115	1340	18 0	...
5	Villa Real........	7 33	9 5	12 8	1433	18 53	...
11¾	Grao Burriana...arr	8 15	9 55	1250	1515	19 35	...
13¾	Onda ....arr	8 24	...	1259	1524	19 44	...

Onda ....dep	6 34	...	11 9	1334	1754	...	...	...
Grao Burriana...dep	6 45	8 25	1120	1345	18 5	...	...	...
Villa Real	7 34	9 10	12 9	1434	1854	...	...	...
Castellon ....arr	8 19	9 55	1254	1519	1939	...	...	...

VALENCIA and CALATAYUD.

E.M.							
	Valencia ....dep	...	7 12	13 20	18 58	...	...
—	Sagunto	...	8 9	13 59	19 51	...	...
25½	Segorbe........	...	9 23	15 8	21 28	...	...
27¼	Jerica........	...	10 9	15 44	22 4	...	...
46	Barracas........	...	11 38	16 59	—	...	...
85¼	Teruel	5 25	13 55	19 34	...	...	...
120½	Monreal del Campo ...	7 54	—	21 4	...	...	...
144¾	Daroca........	9 19	...	22 6	...	...	...
167¾	Calatayud........arr	1025	...	23 3	...	...	...

Calatayud ....dep	...	3 55	...	15 55	...	...
Daroca	...	5 10	...	17 20	...	...
Monreal del Campo........	...	6 17	...	18 45	...	...
Teruel	...	7 54	1416	20 36	...	...
Barracas	...	9 55	17 1	—	...	...
Jerica........	5 38	10 48	18 7	...	...	...
Segorbe........	6 18	11 20	1844	...	...	...
Sagunto	7 54	12 21	2010	...	...	...
Valencia ....arr	8 30	12 52	2048	...	...	...

†—Tues., Thur., and Sat. only.]

VALENCIA and LA ENCINA.

§—Mon., Wed., and Fri. only.

Dist E.M		1,2,3	1,2,3	1,2,3	1 &3	1,2,3	1,2,3	1& 2	1,2,3
	Valencia...dep	...	6 31	8 46	11†9	12 0	16 9	19 0	20 10
8	Silla 298A	...	6 54	9 9	1127	12 28	1634	19 2	20 41
23	Alcira........	...	7 33	9 49	1156	13 18	1714	20 0	21 43
24¾	Carcagente 298	5 40	7 44	10 0	12 3	13 37	1725	20 10	22 2
34¾	Játiva........	6 52	8 12	1027	1231	14 29	1754	20 42	23 4
51	Mogente........	8 10	—	—	1318	15 42	—	21 35	0 18
70¼	La Encina 296	9 26	...	...	14 8	16 59	...	22 30	1 35
304½	MADRID arr	...	...	...	22 0	...	...	8 35	18 0

MADRID dep	1020	1920	...	21 0	...	...	...	9 30
	1,2,3	1& 2	1,2,3	1,2,3	1,2,3	1,2,3	1,2,3	1 & 3
La Encina dep	2 30	5 12	...	10 5	...	16 8	...	17§25
Mogente	3 37	5 59	...	11 6	...	17 7	...	18 8
Játiva	4 49	6 50	8 14	12 27	15 35	17 59	18 7	18 47
Carcagente	5 33	7 23	8 50	13 10	16 11	—	18 38	19 11
Alcira	5 46	7 31	8 59	13 24	16 21	...	18 46	19 17
Silla	6 37	8 9	9 37	14 14	16 59	...	19 24	19 47
Valencia ...arr	7 5	8 30	9 59	14 40	17 20	...	19 45	20 3

E.M.						
	Játiva........dep	8 31	15 5	18 15	18‡59	20 50
39¾	Alcoy ....arr	11 22	20 10	20 35	23 2	23 22

Alcoy ....dep	4 6	6 0	7 0	15 5
Játiva ....arr	6 26	7 59	12 10	17 50

‡—Mon., Wed., and Fri. only.

CARCAGENTE and DENIA.

E.M.				
	Carcagente 298...dep	7 54	17 34	20 15
22¼	Gandia	9 54	19 9	22 15
41¾	**Denia** ....arr	11 17	20 6	23 22

Denia ....dep	4 3	6 0	15 2	...	...
Gandia	5 27	7 10	16 42	...	...
Carcagente arr	6 58	8 37	18 15	...	...

VALENCIA and LIRIA.

E.M.	Via						
	Manises.	Valencia...dep	6 0	8	1410	18 0	...
18¾		Liria ....arr	7 23	9 53	1537	1940	...
	Paterna.	Valencia ...dep	7 0	10 0	14 0	17 0	...
18		Liria ....arr	8 35	1132	1532	18 35	...

Liria........dep	6 5	8 20	1155	18 0	...	...
Valencia ...arr	7 30	10 8	1325	1947	...	...
Liria........dep	7 42	9 49	12 8	16 40	...	
Valencia ...arr	9 11	11 11	13 38	18 11	...	

VALENCIA and UTIEL.

E.M.					
	Valencia (298) ...dep	6 25	8 52	16 34	...
26	Buñol........	8 50	10 13	18 21	...
54¾	**Utiel** ....arr	10 40	12 0	20 21	...

Utiel ....dep	6 0	15 57	16 40	...	...	...	...	...
Buñol	7 55	17 33	18 45	...	...	...	...	...
Valencia ....arr	9 21	18 40	21 10	...	...	...	...	...

BAEZA and ALMERIA.

E.M.	Station					
	MADRID (296) ...dep	21 0	10 0	...	...	...
	ALCAZAR ....dep	1 35	12 44	...	...	...
—	**Baeza** ....dep	8 15	16 30	...	...	...
24¼	Jodar	9 24	17 31	...	...	...
33¾	Quesada	9 59	...	...	...	...
38½	Larva	10 18	18 18	...	...	...
60¼	Alamedilla	11 32	19 18	...	...	...
73¼	**Moreda** ....arr	12 10	19 50	...	...	...
109¼	GRANADA 298A arr	15 20	21 55	...	...	...
...	**Moreda** ....dep	12 40	——	2030	...	...
88¾	Guadix	13 35	...	2130	...	...
111¼	Abla	14 43	...	2245	...	...
138	Sta. Fe y Alhama	16 9	...	0 12	...	...
150¼	**Almeria** ....arr	16 45	...	0 50	...	...

Station						
Almeria ....dep	4 50	...	1140	...	...	...
Sta. Fe y Alhama	5 40	...	1229	...	...	...
Abla	7 33	...	1415	...	...	...
Guadix	9 40	...	1535	...	...	...
Moreda ....arr	1040	...	1625	...	...	...
GRANADA (298A)dep	——	9 15	1330	...	...	...
Moreda ....dep	...	11 32	1635	...	...	...
Alamedilla	...	12 10	1717	...	...	...
Larva	...	13 4	1817	...	...	...
Quesada	...	...	1831	...	...	...
Jodar	...	13 38	1859	...	...	...
Baeza ....arr	...	14 35	20 0	...	...	...
ALCAZAR 296A arr	...	18 40	2 35	...	...	...
MADRID......296 arr	...	21 30	7 10	...	...	...

MOREDA and GRANADA.

‡—Guadix dep. 19.55. §—Arr. Guadix 8.55

E.M.	Station					
	Moreda...dep	13 0	1650	‡	20 15	...
16¼	Iznalloz	14 1	1823	20 58	21 2	...
32¼	Albolote	15 5	1945	21 55	21 46	...
36	Granada arr	15 20	20 0	23 0	21 55	...

Station					
Granada ...dep	5 45	9 15	13 30	...	...
Albolote	5 58	9 26	13 45	...	...
Iznalloz	7 3	10 16	14 52	...	...
Moreda ......arr	§	11 5	15 58	...	...

E.M.	Station		
	Guadix ....dep	9 20	13 40
10½	Gor	10 4	14 45
31¾	Baza ....arr	1130	16 35
...	Baza ....dep	1045	17 0
...	Gor	1438	18 43
...	Guadix ....arr	1520	19 20

Baeza to Linares (5 miles) at 20.18. In 20 minutes. Linares to Baeza at 7.20.

PUERTO de SANTA MARIA and SANLUCAR de BARRAMEDA.

E.M	Station					
	Puerto de Santa Maria......dep	9 45	14‡37	19 45	...	...
23	Sanlúcar de Barrameda ...arr	1110	15 57	21 10	...	...

Station						
Sanlúcar de Barrameda ...dep	6 45	11‡30	17 10	...	...	...
Puerto de Santa Maria. ....arr	8 15	12 44	18 33	...	...	...

‡—Express 1 & 2 class; runs on Monday, Wednesday, and Saturday only.

PLASENCIA and ASTORGA.

Dist.	Station						
	Plasencia Junction dep	3 55	1145	16 7	...	...	...
10½	,, Town...........	4 30	1245	16 42	...	...	...
34¾	Hervas	6 0	1521	18 12	...	...	...
47¼	Béjar	6 56	1630	19 8	...	...	...
65¾	Guijuelo	7 58	——	20 10	...	...	...
86¼	Alba de Tormes	9 4	...	21 12	...	...	...
101½	**Salamanca 299** arr	9 53	...	22 0	...	...	...
	dep	1010	...	22 30	...	...	...
122½	Cubo	1136	...	23 44	...	...	...
142¼	**Zamora 290A** ... arr	1245	...	0 42	...	...	...
	dep	1311	...	0 56	...	...	...
178¼	Benavente	1552	...	3 0	...	...	...
216½	**Astorga** (Norte) 293 arr	1820	...	5 2	...	...	...

Station							
Astorga (Norte) ....dep	6 50	2145	...	...	...	...	...
Benavente	9 47	0 20	...	...	...	...	...
Zamora .... arr	12 10	2 11	...	...	...	...	...
dep	12 46	2 26	...	...	...	...	...
Cubo	14 32	3 46	...	...	...	...	...
Salamanca .... arr	15 50	5 0	...	...	...	...	...
dep	16 14	5 20	...	...	...	...	...
Alba de Tormes	17 17	6 10	...	...	...	...	...
Guijuelo	18 44	7 21	...	...	...	...	...
Béjar	20 15	8 30	1134	...	...	...	...
Hervas	21 22	9 17	1241	...	...	...	...
Plasencia Town..............	23 25	1040	1453	...	...	...	...
,, Junction 298 arr	0 2	11 8	1535	...	...	...	...

ALCOY and GANDIA.

Dist.	Station					
	Alcoy....................dep	6 58	8 20	19 5	...	...
6¾	Muro	7 20	8 56	19 45	...	...
33½	**Gandia** ....arr	...	10 53	21 40	...	...

Station					
Gandia ....dep	5 25	...	17 5	...	...
Muro	7 34	8 48	19 43	...	...
Alcoy ....arr	8 8	9 20	20 18	..	...

SALAMANCA and PENARANDA.

E.M.	Station			
	Salamanca ....dep	17 12	...	...
25½	Peñaranda ....arr	18 30	...	...

Station				
Peñaranda....................dep	8 10	...	...	...
Salamanca... (299) ...... arr	9 30	...	...	...

SILLA and CULLERA.

E.M	Station					
	Silla.................dep	7 50	10 51	17 31	...	...
16½	Cullera ....arr	9 2	12 3	18 43	...	...

Station					
Cullera ....dep	6 25	9 38	16 18	...	...
Silla 298 ....arr	7 37	10 50	17 30	...	...

PENARROYA and FUENTE del ARCO.

E.M.	Station				
	Peñarroya ....dep	8 0	9 45	20 25	...
26	Azuaga.........................	10 19	12 29	22 59	...
43	**Fuente del Arco** 297	11 40	13 55	0 25	...

Station				
Fuente del Arco dep	4 0	14 0	16 0	...
Azuaga.......................	5 23	15 56	17 21	...
Peñarroya ....arr	7 8	18 19	19 4	...

BILBAO and SANTANDER.

†—May not run.

E.M.	Station							
	Bilbao ....dep	...	7 40	12†10	16†55	18†20	...	...
11½	Sodupe	...	8 9	12 41	17 23	18 48	...	...
15	Aranguren	...	8 21	12 54	17 34	19 4	...	...
20	Traslaviña	...	8 39	13 15	17 52	19 40	...	...
37½	Gibaja	7†30	9 31	14 8	18 45	——	...	...
43	Marron	7 51	9 50	14 27	19 4	...	...	...
63½	Orejo	8 58	1053	15 31	20 8	...	...	...
74	**Santander** ....arr	9 35	1121	16 2	20 37	...	...	...

Station							
Santander......dep	...	8†15	1220	16†55	17†20	...	...
Orejo	...	8 43	1248	17 25	17 55	...	...
Marron	...	9 48	1351	18 23	18 57	...	...
Gibaja	...	10 6	14 9	18 46	——	...	...
Traslaviña	8 40	11 4	15 7	19 38	...	...	...
Aranguren	9 1	1125	1528	19 56	...	...	...
Sodupe	9 15	1134	1538	20 6	...	...	...
Bilbao ....arr	9 50	12 3	16 5	20 35	...	...	...

BILBAO and LEZAMA.

E.M.	Station					
	Bilbao ....dep	7 5	9 45	13†0	1515	19†15
9¼	Lezama 293 arr	749	10 27	1336	1553	19 54

Station					
Lezama ...dep	5 15	8 20	11†20	14†20	17†50
Bilbao ....arr	6 0	8 58	11 57	14 57	18 29

†—May not run.

BILBAO and PLENCIA.

E.M.	Station						
	Bilbao...dep	6 0	9 0	12 0	15 0	18 0	...
16¾	Plencia arr	7 43	10 7	13 9	16 9	19 9	...

Station								
Plencia ...dep	6 0	8 20	1118	1420	1810	...	...	...
Bilbao.......arr	7 29	9 23	1225	1530	1926	...	...	...

SANTANDER and LLANES.

E.M.	Station						
	Santander..................dep	8 0	11‡55	13‡30	14 51	17‡30	19‡15
16¾	Torrelavega....................	8 57	12 50	14 16	15 50	18 27	20 15
28½	Cabezon de la Sal............	9 39	13 28	14 51	16 33	19 8	20 54
42¼	S. Vicente de la Barquera	10 19	——	15 30	——	19 50	——
62¾	**Llanes**.....................arr	11 24	...	16 30	...	20 55	...

Station						
Llanes......................dep	7 ‡45	...	13 ‡6	...	17 30	‡—May not run.
S. Vicente de la Barquera	8 46	...	14 2	...	18 25	
Cabezon de la Sal. ...7 15	9 36	13‡48	14 49	17‡15	19 9	
Torrelavega..............8 4	10 17	14 34	15 25	18 1	19 50	
Santander........arr 9 6	11 9	15 31	16 14	19 1	20 42	

LLANES and OVIEDO.

E.M.	Station						
	Llanes ....dep	...	7 5	11 56	16 42	...	...
18¾	Ribadesella	...	7 59	12 52	17 35	...	...
29¼	Arriondas	...	8 32	13 24	18 5	...	...
43	Infiesto	7 57	9 9	14 0	18 40	...	...
63½	Noreña	9 21	1020	15 22	19 58	...	...
71½	**Oviedo** (293)........arr	9 43	1041	15 46	20 20	...	...

Station							
Oviedo ....dep	8 55	13 30	16 15	19 30	...	...	...
Noreña	9 26	13 55	16 39	19 59	...	...	...
Infiesto	10 38	15 8	17 50	21 8	...	...	...
Arriondas	11 12	15 45	18 27	——	...	...	...
Ribadesella...............	11 40	16 18	18 59	...	...	...	...
Llanes ....arr	12 30	17 13	19 54	...	...	...	...

Station								
Arriondas.........dep	8 35	11 20	1545	1830	...	...	...	...
Covadonga........arr	9 40	12 25	1650	1935	...	...	...	...

Station									
Covadonga...........dep	7 15	9 55	1425	1655	...	...	...	...	...
Arriondas............arr	8 20	11 0	1530	18 0	...	...	...	...	...

SALAMANCA, VILLAR FORMOSO, and BARCA D'ALVA.

E.M.							
	MEDINA (290A)......dep	2 20	2 20	...	9 17	...	18 38
—	**Salamanca**..........dep	4 ‡45	5 5		11 6	16 30	21 15
35½	S. Estéban..........	6 1	6 44	7 4	12 31	18 56	23 20
57½	Ciudad Rodrigo	...	...	8 14	13 18	20 49	0 27
77¾	Fuentes de Onoro	...	...	9 32	14 8	—	1 35
79	**Villar Formoso (301)**...	...	...	9 36	14 11	...	1 39
...	S. Estéban ....dep	6 10	7 27	...	A	...	23 15
63½	Lumbrales..........	7 17	9 32	...	...	...	0 39
84½	**Barca d'Alva (301)** arr	8 28	11 20	...	...	...	1 54
210¾	OPORTO ....arr	13 33	19 38	...	...	...	...

OPORTO **301** dep	...	...	...	8 27	13 3	...
Barca d'Alva dep	...	5 45	...	16 15	17 54	...
Lumbrales..........	...	7 17	...	18 9	19 25	B
S. Estéban ....arr	...	8 55	...	19 37	20 31	...
Villar Formoso ...	...	6 23	1646	...	...	1951
Fuentes de Onoro	...	7 15	1725	...	*	2012
Ciudad Rodrigo	6 0	8 3	1827	...	...	2053
S. Estéban..........	7 22	9 12	1931	20 1	20 44	2151
Salamanca.........arr	...	1037		21 37	21 57	23 7
MEDINA **290A** arr	...	1331	...	0 23	...	0 55

A—Sud Express. B—Sud Express.

‡—1st & 2nd Cl., on Tues., Thurs., and Sat. only. *—1st & 2nd Cl., on Mon., Wed., and Fri. only.

MADRID and ALMOROX.

†—May not run.

E.M.					
	Madrid (Goya) dep	6 30	11†30	20 0	...
20	Navalcarnero..........	8 6	13 38	2135	...
38½	Villa del Prado......	9 35	15 35	23 5	...
46	**Almorox** ....arr	1010	16 10	2340	...

Almorox ......dep	4 20	10†50	16 50	...	...
Villa del Prado...	5 0	11 35	17 30	...	...
Navalcarnero......	6 30	13 39	19 2	...	...
Madrid ....arr	8 0	15 30	20 30	...	...

MADRID and COLMENAR.

§—May not run.

E.M.					
	Madrid (N.J.) dep	8 0	12 §0	19 0	...
10	Montarco..........	8 47	12 55	19 48	...
17½	Arganda	9 30	13 52	20 31	...
29	Tajuna	10 34	15 8	21 34	...
39¾	**Colmenar**......arr	11 20	16 0	22 20	...
	Tajuna ....dep	10 40	21 40	...	...
	Orusco..........arr	11 46	22 46	...	...

Colmenar ...dep	6 13	12 40	17 15	...	...
Tajuna..........	7 6	13 37	18 8	...	...
Arganda	8 13	15 1	19 15	...	...
Montarco..........	8 50	15 42	19 52	...	...
Madrid ....arr	9 33	16 35	20 35	...	...
Orusco ....dep	5 44	16 45	...	...	...
Tajuna ....arr	6 50	17 51	...	...	...

MANRESA and GUARDIOLA BAGA.

E.M.								
	Manresa (N) dp	5 25	8 50	10 25	12 55	17 9	19 50	...
11¾	Sallent	6 29	9 53	11 20	14 3	18 14	20 59	...
23½	Puigreig	7 54	1118	12 35	15 21	19 34	—	...
31	Olvan..........	8 54	1210	13 30	16 18	20 30		...
44	**Guardiola B.**	1015	1335	14 45	17 36	21 47	...	...

Guardiola B. dep	...	8 50	5 35	11 30	12 50	16 5	...
Olvan	...	5 13	7 1	12 52	14 23	17 34	...
Puigreig	...	6 9	8 0	13 43	15 20	18 29	...
Sallent	5 28	7 27	9 47	14 58	16 38	19 57	...
Manresa (293) arr	6 26	8 23	10 47	15 51	17 37	20 55	...

SAN JUAN and ZALAMEA.

†—Sunday only.

E.M.					
	San Juan del P....dep	...	7 56	16 30	20 †8
22½	Valverde	4 38	10 28	18 40	22 23
36	Zalamea ....arr	5 56	11 48	...	23 37

Zalamea ....dep	3†20	6 18	12 26
Valverde	4 48	7 40	13 48
San Juan del P. 297 arr	7 0	9 50	16 0

SARAGOSSA and CARINENA.

E.M.					
	Saragossa......dep	9 0	17 15	...	...
28½	**Carinena** ......arr	11 3	19 18	...	...

Carinena ....dep	6 35	1445	...	...
Saragossa ....arr	8 38	1648	...	...

SARAGOSSA and UTRILLAS-MONTALBAN.

E.M.			
	Saragossa ....dep	7 30	...
38½	Lécera	10 14	...
78¼	Utrillas-Mont. ......arr	13 17	...

Utrillas-Mont.......dep	13 52	...	...
Lécera..........	16 48	...	...
Saragossa ....arr	19 21	...	...

BOBADILLA, RONDA, and ALGECIRAS.—[30 kilogr. (66 lbs. of luggage allowed free.]

Dist E.M.					
...	MADRID 296.......dep	...	2020	20 20	21 0
...	ALCAZAR 296A ....dep	...	2325	23 25	1 35
	CORDOBA 294.......dep	...	6 20	6 20	11 15
—	**Bobadilla** ....dep	...	9 25	12 40	16 9
8¾	Campillos	...	9 43	13 0	16 32
13¾	Teba	...	B	13 11	16 46
26	Cañete	A	1032	13 50	17 34
44	**Ronda**	7 0	1110	14 33	18 29
62¼	Jimera de Libar	8 14	1210	15 26	19 47
84	Jimena	9 46	13 4	16 27	20 54
97	Almoraima	1032	1330	16 59	21 28
101¼	San Roque	1050	1340	17 13	21 42
110½	**Algeçiras** (Pier) ...arr	1120	14 0	17 40	22 10
116¼	GIBRALTAR (stmr) arr	12 0	1435	18 30	23 0

			C	D	
GIBRALTAR (stmr) dep	5 50	8 10	1420	1450	...
Algeçiras ....dep	6 30	9 5	15 5	1530	...
San Roque	7 0	9 38	1528	16 8	...
Almoraima..........	7 10	9 49	1536	1622	...
Jimena..........	7 45	10 29	16 8	1712	...
Jimera de Libar	8 51	11 46	17 9	1851	...
Ronda	9 49	13 4	1758	20 5	...
Cañete	1031	13 51	1836	—	...
Teba	11 1	14 28	19 5	...	...
Campillos..........	1113	14 42	1915	...	...
Bobadilla..........arr	1130	15 0	1931	...	...
CORDOBA 294 ......arr	1555	22 39	2239	...	...
ALCAZAR 296A ...arr	2 35	5 55	5 55	...	...
MADRID 296 ......arr	7 10	9 0	9 0	...	...

Sleeping Cars for Madrid in 15.5 from Algeçiras.
A—On Tues., Thurs., Fri., and Sat. only.
B—On Wed. and Sun. only.
C—On Mon. and Thurs. only.
D—On Tues., Wed., Fri., and Sat. only.

TORRALBA and SORIA.

E.M.				
	Torralba ......dep	2 51	13‡18	...
31¾	Almazan **297A** ...	4 48	15 39	...
58½	**Soria** ....arr	6 45	17 40	...

Soria..........dep	15*30	21 30	...	...	...
Almazan	17 17	23 9	...	...	...
Torralba ....arr	19 31	1 10	...	...	...

‡—On Monday, Wednesday, and Friday only. *—On Tuesday, Thursday, and Saturday only.

VALENCIA and BETERA.

E.M.							
	Valencia dep	6 12	8 0	9 0	1235	1535	1835
6½	Moncada........	6 52	8 44	9 46	1315	1615	1912
11¾	**Betera** ....arr	7 12	...	...	1335	1635	...

Betera ....dep	...	7 35	..	14 5	...	17 5	...
Moncada.........	6 28	7 58	1123	1428	1528	1728	1828
Valencia arr	7 11	8 36	1211	1511	1611	1811	1911

VALENCIA and RAFELBUNOL.

E. M.										
	Valencia..dep	5 0	6 0	8 0	10 0	12 0	14 0	16 0	18 0	...
8¾	Rafelbuñol ar	5 39	6 39	8 39	1039	12 39	1439	1639	1839	...

Rafelbuñol dep	6 0	7 0	9 0	11 0	13 0	15 0	17 0	19 0
Valencia......arr	6 39	7 39	9 39	1139	1339	1539	1739	1939

VALENCIA and ALBERIQUE.

E.M.					
	Valencia ....dep	6 0	9 50	14 45	18 10
10½	Picasent	6 57	10 54	15 35	19 7
29¾	**Alberique**.........arr	8 30	12 36	17 0	20 40

Alberique..........dep	6 37	9 20	1340	17 30
Picasent	8 15	10 58	1544	19 8
Valencia..........arr	9 7	11 35	1629	20 0

VILLAODRID and RIBADEO.

E.M.					
—	**Villaodrid**..........dep	10†30	17 0	...	...
20½	**Ribadeo** (E.).........arr	12 0	18 31	...	...

†—May not run.

Ribadeo..........dep	8 30	15 0	...	...
Villaodrid ....arr	9 56	16 26	...	...

MINAS DE CALA and SAN JUAN DE AZNALFARACHE

E.M.						
	Minas de Cala.....dep	5 †3	14 48	...	...	...
24¾	Ronquillo (E.)	7 1	16 42	...	...	...
60½	**San Juan** ....arr	9 57	19 23	...	...	...

San Juan de Aznalfarache...dep	6 50	16†55	...	...	...
Ronquillo	9 49	20 12	...	...	...
Minas de Cala..........arr	11 49	22 13	...	...	...

E.M.			
	Ronquillo (E.)..........dep	9 54	20†17
9½	**Minas del Castillo de las Guardas**....arr	10 41	21 7

Minas del Castillo..........dep	5 †55	15 42	...
Ronquillo..........arr	6 43	16 34	...

†—May not run.

LISBON and VILLA REAL S. ANTONIO

30 kilogr. (66 lbs.) of luggage allowed free.
The Railway Terminus is at Barreiro, on south side of the Tagus, the connecting Railway Steamer departs from and arrives at the Quay, Praca do Commercio.

Eng. Mls fr Barr'o	1 Cl. Reis Fro	2 Cl. Reis m L	3 Cl. Reis bon		2&3	1,2,3	1,2,3	2&3	1,2,3	1,2,3
				Lisbon Steamer...dep	...	...	8 35	...	1630	2040
	200	160	110	**Barreiro** dep	...	...	9 30	...	1722	2132
3¾	320	290	220	Alhos Vedros...	...	...	9 43	...	1736	2144
10	530	450	320	Pinhal Novo ...	...	...	10 2	...	1756	2158
26	1 020	830	600	Pegoes	...	...	10 37	...	1842	2226
35½	1 310	1 060	760	Vendas Novas	...	...	11 9	...	1913	2246
56½	1 950	1 560	1 100	Casa Branca ...	...	8 5	12 0	...	2016	2333
69	2 330	1 850	1 320	Vianna..........	...	8 47	12 30	...	—	2354
77¾	2 590	2 060	1 470	Alvito	...	9 20	12 49	...	...	0 11
85¾	2 840	2 250	1 610	Cuba............	...	9 44	13 4	...	...	0 25
95¾	3 140	2 480	1 780	Beja	7 40	10 20	13 45	...	...	1 19
111¼	3 620	2 850	2 040	Figueirinha ...	8 53	—	14 13	...	...	1 55
125	4 030	3 180	2 270	Casevel	10 3	...	14 39	...	...	2 26
151	4 830	3 800	2 710	Odemira	1215	...	15 42	...	...	3 54
187¾	5 950	4 670	3 340	Tunes	1456	...	17 11	2020	...	5 54
201¼	6 370	4 990	3 570	Loulé	—	...	17 42	2130	...	6 37
211¼	6 670	5 230	3 740	Faro	...	...	18 8	2220	...	7 9
217¾	6 860	5 370	3 840	Olhao	...	...	18 24	2239	...	7 26
223¾	7 050	5 520	3 950	Fuzeta	...	...	18 39	23 1	...	7 44
231¼	7 270	5 700	4 070	Tavira	...	...	19 4	2333	...	8 10
238¾	7 500	5 880	4 200	Cacella	...	...	19 22	0 1	...	8 30
246	7 730	6 050	4 320	**V.R.S.Anton.**	...	...	19 40	0 25	...	8 50

	1,2,3	1,2,3	2&3	1,2,3	2&3
Villa Real S. Antonio dep	...	9 20	...	17 0	20 0
Cacella..........	...	9 39	...	1721	2024
Tavira	...	9 58	...	1746	2056
Fuzeta	...	10 20	...	18 5	2122
Olhao	...	10 37	...	1829	2147
Faro	...	10 56	...	1851	22 0
Loulé	...	11 16	...	1922	—
Tunes	...	11 52	17 5	2022	...
Odemira..........	...	13 13	1940	2211	...
Casevel	...	14 17	2154	2334	...
Figueirinha ...	...	14 44	23 4	0 7	...
Beja	8 40	15 40	0 8	1 15	...
Cuba.............	9 4	16 4	—	1 40	...
Alvito	9 19	16 18	...	1 58	...
Vianna	9 43	16 37	...	2 23	...
Casa Branca ...	1021	17 7	...	3 5	...
Vendas Novas	1124	17 58	...	4 16	...
Pegoes...........	1146	18 15	...	4 37	...
Pinhal Novo ...	1227	18 57	...	5 20	...
Alhos Vedros...	1242	19 11	...	...	...
Barreiro......	13 5	19 35	...	6 0	...
Lisbon ...arr	1340	20 15	...	6 35	...

BEJA and MOURA.

Beja ....dep	1 0	13 50	...
Serpa	2 10	15 3	...
Moura.........arr	3 15	16 10	...
Moura ...dep	6 0	13 0	...
Serpa	7 8	14 2	...
Beja..........arr	8 20	15 15	...

CASA BRANCA and VILLA VIÇOSA.

E.M								
—	**Casa Branca** ......dep	1020	12 5	1712	2038	23 45	...	...
16¼	**Evora**	1110	13 3	1750	2135	0 23	...	...
31	Valle do Pereiro ...	—	13 56	—	2226	—	...	...
52¾	Estremoz	...	15 28	...	2350	...	...	...
63¾	**Villa Viçosa** arr	...	16 0	...	0 20	...	...	...

Villa Viçosa dep	...	6 30	...	...	2310
Estremoz	...	7 9	...	...	2346
Valle do Pereiro...	...	8 21	...	...	1 0
Evora	7 0	9 16	16 15	2230	1 56
Casa Branca arr	7 55	9 58	16 55	2316	2 42

Evora.............dep	13 8	21 40	...	...
Mora ....arr	15 3	23 57	...	...
Mora ....dep	6 30	14 0	...	...
Evora ....arr	8 47	16 0	...	...

PINHAL NOVO and SETUBAL.

Lisbon ......dep	8 35	11 20	1445	1630	18 0	2040	...	...
Pinhal Novo	9 50	12 29	1558	1733	1919	22 0	...	...
Setubal ......arr	1010	12 47	1618	1751	1940	2219	...	...

Setubal ...dep	8 48	10 50	14 0	1713	18 30	21 5	...	...
Pinhal Novo	9 12	11 6	14 23	1734	18 57	21 27	...	...
Lisbon ......arr	1030	12 10	15 40	1840	20 15	22 45	...	...

TUNES and PORTIMAO.

Tunes ......dep	5 49	11 49	17 9	...	...	...
Silves	6 31	12 28	17 48	...	...	...
Portimao ...arr	6 53	12 50	18 10	...	...	...

Portimao...dep	10 30	15 35	18 40	...	...	...	...	...	...	...
Silves	10 54	16 5	19 6	...	...	...	...	...	...	...
Tunes.........arr	11 31	16 45	19 47	...	...	...	...	...	...	...

LISBON and ALFARELLOS.

E.M.							
	Lisbon Rocio......dep	8 10	...	...	13 30	1623	1955
3¾	Bemfica	...	...	...	13 57	...	2019
10¾	Cacem....................	8 39	...	...	14 30	1653	2051
20¾	Mafra	9 8	...	...	15 10	1721	2134
39¾	Torres Vedras ......arr	9 59	...	...	16 33	1815	23 2
65¼	Caldas da Rainha.......	11 30	...	1230	18 30	1945	1 0
81	Vallado	12 18	...	14 4	—	2056	—
99¾	Leiria....................	13 15	...	1559	...	2229	...
127¼	Amieira .... arr	14 26	...	1756	...	0 7	...
	Amieira .... dep	—	14 46	1826	...	0 24	...
137½	**Alfarellos** ....arr	...	15 17	19 0	...	0 52	...

Alfarellos ....dep	...	3 35	...	1739	...	2036	...
Amieira .... arr	...	4 3	...	1812	...	21 9	...
Amieira .... dep	...	4 18	...	—	18 20	2129	...
Leiria....................	...	6 24	...	...	19 34	0 24	...
Vallado	...	7 40	...	...	20 21	2 20	...
Caldas da Rainha	4 40	8 54	13 22	...	21 11	3 42	...
Torres Vedras ......dep	6 19	10 4	15 9	...	22 23	—	...
Mafra	7 58	11 7	16 50	...	23 23	...	...
Cacem	8 48	1132	17 34	...	23 51	...	...
Bemfica	9 22	...	18 7	...	0 17	...	...
Lisbon Rocio......arr	9 37	1158	18 23	...	0 32	...	...

FIGUEIRA DA FOZ and ALFARELLOS.

Figueira da Foz.........dep	2 20	3 25	6†50	7 20	8*25	10 20	11 25	14 5	17 40	19 35	20 33	23 30	23 43	...	...	...	...	...
Amieira..............	...	3 46	7 23	...	9 6	...	...	14 46	18 1	...	21 9	...	0 4	...	...	...	...	...
Alfarellos ....arr	2 57	...	...	8 7	...	10 55	12 9	15 17	...	20 9	21 40	23 59	...	...	...	...	...	...

Alfarellos ....dep	3 35	8 16	...	...	12 9	...	16 22	17 44	...	22 10	...	0 55	...	...	...	...	...
Amieira	4 15	...	8 †59	10 *59	...	14 44	...	18 22	21 20	...	0 23	...	...	...	...	...	...
Figueira da Foz ......arr	4 36	9 4	9 18	11 18	12 47	15 5	17 12	18 44	21 41	22 50	0 44	1 34	...	...	...	...	...

*—Until 31st October. †—Until 30th September.

ESPINHO-PRAIA and AVEIRO (VOUGA).

Espinho-Praia...dep	...	8 20	...	17 35	20 25	...	...
Oliveira d'Azemeis	...	9 58	...	19 17	21 49	...	...
Albergaria Velha ...arr	...	10 56	...	20 19	—	...	...
" ...dep	6 35	11 5	14 50	—	...	...	...
Aveiro (Vouga) ...arr	8 31	12 45	16 46	...	...	...	...

Aveiro (Vouga)...dep	...	...	9 40	15 0	19 15	...
Albergaria Velha ...arr	...	...	11 36	16 40	21 11	...
" ...dep	...	7 20	—	16 50	—	...
Oliveira d'Azemeis......	5 35	8 36	...	17 53	...	...
Espinho-Praia ...arr	7 5	10 2	...	19 25	...	...

LISBON and VALENCIA D'ALCANTARA (for Madrid).

¶—Customs Examination.

	1,2,3	1 &2	1,2,3		1,2,3	1 Cl.	1,2,3	1 &2 §	1,2,3	1,2,3	1,2,3	1,2,3
Lisbon Rocio dep	7 25	8 30	9 25	1130	1136	17 2	17 8	1855	...	20 5	2135	2155
,, Prata dep	7 46	...	9 54	...	12 1	:	1730	...	1912	2034	2155	2212
Sacavem	7 57	RC	10 5	...	1212	:	1740	...	1925	2046	...	...
Alhandra	8 20	...	10 30	...	1236	:	18 2	...	1959	2111	...	...
Carregado	8 36	...	10 47	...	1252	:	1817	...	2022	2129	...	...
Azambuja	8 52	...	11 3	C	13 7	:	1832	...	2038	2147	...	...
Setil arr	9 6	...	11 17	...	1321	A	1845	...	2054	22 1	2247	23 4
Santa Anna	9 43	...	11 31	...	1328	:	19 1	...	2117	2224	...	...
Santarem	1020	9 37	11 55	...	1349	:	1920	1955	2159	2249	2322	2337
Valle de Figueira	1040	...	12 8	...	14 2	:	—	...	2217	23 3	...	...
Torres Novas	1120	...	12 32	...	1427	:	...	...	2255	2332	...	...
Entroncamento arr	1128	10 3	12 38	1254	1433	18 44	...	2019	23 3	2338	2359	0 14
Entroncamento dep	—	—	—	—	15 4	18 50	...	—	—	—	1 0	0 27
Praia	...	...	...	...	1524	...	...	...	...	...	1 25	0 54
Abrantes	...	...	...	...	1549	19 25	...	...	...	...	1 51	1 33
Torre das Vargens arr	...	...	...	...	1643	20 12	...	...	...	...	—	2 52
Torre das Vargens dep	...	...	...	...	1653	20 17	...	...	...	...	...	3 40
Pezo	...	...	...	...	1737	...	...	...	...	...	...	5 9
Castello de Vide	...	...	...	...	18 9	...	...	...	...	...	...	6 9
Marvão	...	...	...	...	1846	21 48	...	...	...	...	...	7 20
Valencia Alcant.¶ arr	...	...	...	...	1910	22 10	...	...	...	...	...	8 0
,, dep	...	...	...	...	1952	22 32	...	...	...	...	...	...
MADRID (298) arr	...	...	...	...	9 5	8 17	...	...	...	...	...	...

	1,2,3	1,2,3	1,2,3	1& 2	1,2,3	1 Cl	1,2,3	Sud Express daily.	1 &2	1,2,3	1,2,3
MADRID (298) dep	...	...	...	...	1950	2359	...	...	...	...	...
VALENCIA D'A. arr	...	...	...	...	8 14	9 40	...	...	...	...	...
Valencia d'Alcantara dep	...	...	...	...	8 30	9 48	...		...	1730	...
Marvão ¶	...	...	...	...	9 14	1022	...		...	1842	...
Castello de Vide	...	...	...	...	9 44	...	...		...	1925	...
Pezo	...	...	...	...	10 9	...	...		...	20 5	...
Torre das Vargens arr	...	...	...	...	1042	1136	...		...	21 0	...
Torre das Vargens dep	...	...	...	...	1052	1141	...		...	2116	...
Abrantes	...	...	...	...	1153	1223	...		...	2218	...
Praia	...	...	...	...	1215	...	...		...	2240	...
Entroncamento arr	...	*	...		1236	1255	...	...	...	2258	...
Entroncamento dep	3 32	4 31	7 20	1248	1450	13 1	1655	2123	22 6	2315	2340
Torres Novas	3 41	4 38	7 27	...	15 7	:	17 6	...	...	...	0 5
V. Figueira	4 6	5 5	7 55	...	1532	:	1733	...	RC	...	0 39
Santarem	4 19	5 18	8 12	1317	1544	:	1747	...	2235	2348	1 15
Santa Anna	4 40	5 38	8 34	...	16 4	:	18 8	...	...	...	1 52
Setil	4 53	5 47	9 3	...	1615	B	1819	...	2252	...	2 22
Azambuja	5 9	6 4	9 24	...	1634	:	1837	...	...	...	2 44
Carregado	5 22	6 17	9 39	...	1646	:	1850	...	...	...	3 1
Alhandra	...	6 33	9 57	...	17 3	:	19 9	...	...	...	3 25
Sacavem	...	7 2	1026	...	1727	:	1937	...	...	...	4 2
Lisbon P. arr	...	7 13	1037	...	1738	:	1946	...	...	...	4 16
,, Rocio arr	6 25	7 39	11 5	1431	18 8	1445	2017	2252	2353	1 13	5 0

A—Madrid Express, 1st class and Carriages de Luxe, will run only on Mon., Wed., and Sat. from Lisbon.
B—Madrid Express, 1st class and Carriages de Luxe, arrives Lisbon on Mon., Wed., and Fri. only.
C—Sud Express, from Lisbon daily. §—Oporto Express; Restaurant Car attached. *—May not run.

Extra { Santarem .... 22 5 / Lisbon Rocio 0 25

Setil dep	5 40	9 12	19 11
Vendas Novas arr	9 30	11 4	22 21

Vendas Novas dep	5 20	12 7	19 32	...
Setil arr	8 36	15 40	21 42	...

LISBON, ENTRONCAMENTO, and OPORTO.

	1,2,3	1 &2	To Villar Formoso, page 301.	1,2,3	1,2,3	1& 2	1,2,3	1,2,3	
LISBON-Rocio (300) dep	...	8 30	11 30	9 25	1136	1855	2155	2155 *	...
Entroncamento dep	...	10 5	12 55	1325	1620	2021	0 36	1 2	...
Payalvo (Thomar)	...	1019	...	1351	1643	2033	0 59	1 28	...
Chão de Maçãs	...	...	...	14 7	1657	...	1 15	1 44	...
Caxarias	...	...	D	1420	1711	2054	1 32	1 58	...
Pombal	...	...	...	1510	18 4	...	2 25	3 1	...
Alfarellos	8 15	1142	...	1557	1840	2154	3 17	3 59	...
Coimbra Junction arr	8 55	1159	14 31	1632	1954	2211	3 43	4 37	...
Coimbra Town arr	9 12	12 9	14 40	1645	2017	2225	4 5	5 10	...
Coimbra Town dep	8 45	1145	14 15	1620	1930	2155	3 20	4 30	...
Coimbra Junction dep	9 5	12 2	14 32	1649	20 5	2214	3 55	4 49	...
Pampilhosa	9 58	1218	14 45	1736	2039	2230	4 33	5 22	...
Aveiro	11 8	1257		1845	2139	23 9	5 36	6 37	...
Ovar	1148	RC		1926	2221		6 20	7 21	...
Espinho 299A	1211	1336		1951	2243	2348	6 45	7 49	...
Villa Nova de Gaia	1239	1359		2038	2320	0 11	7 25	8 34	...
Oporto Campanhá arr	1250	14 7		2052	2330	0 19	7 35	8 44	...
Oporto arr	1258	1419		21 3	2341	0 32	7 56	9 38	...

*—May not run.

	1,2,3	1& 2	1,2,3		1,2,3	1 &2	1,2,3	1,2,3	
Oporto dep	7 4	8 35	1129	...	1548	1754	1957	*	...
,, Campanha dep	7 15	8 48	1140	...	16 0	18 5	2030	2127	...
Villa Nova de Gaia	7 28	8 59	1156	...	1611	1816	2042	2140	...
Espinho	7 55	9 18	1221	...	1636	1835	21 4	22 8	...
Ovar	8 19	...	1244	...	17 2	...	2127	2232	...
Aveiro	9 10	9 54	1324	...	1743	1911	22 2	2322	...
Pampilhosa 301	1050	1035	1445	19 8	1922	1952	2325	0 47	...
Coimbra Junct arr	11 9	1048	15 6	1922	1939	20 5	2346	1 9	...
Coimbra Tn. arr	1130	1058	1530	1952	1952	2017	0 10	1 25	...
Coimbra Tn. dp	11 8	1035	15 0	1915	1930	1930	2339	0 55	...
Coimbra Junct. dep	1122	1052	1523	1925	1951	20 9	0 3	1 14	...
Alfarellos arr	1152	11 9	16 7	...	2015	2030	0 33	1 42	...
Pombal	1258	...	—	...	2120	...	1 46	2 30	...
Caxarias	1356	...	...	D	2211	...	2 41	3 31	...
Chão de Maçãs	14 8	...	...	2053	2224	...	2 54	3 46	...
Payalvo (Thomar)	1422	1232	...	...	2237	2150	3 7	4 5	...
Entroncam'to arr	1439	1246	...	2121	2252	22 4	3 22	4 23	...
LISBON-R. (300) arr	18 8	1431	...	2252	1 13	2353	6 25	7 39	...

D—Sud Express, Train de Luxe.

COIMBRA and LOUZA.

Coimbra dep	5 25	12 20	16 48
Louza arr	6 54	13 43	18 3

Louza dep	7 10	1450	1818
Coimbra arr	8 39	16 7	1927

ABRANTES and GUARDA.

E.M			
—	**Abrantes** dep	2 1	1610
39¾	Villa Velha Rodam	4 4	18 4
58¼	Castello Branco	5 25	1930
91½	Fundao	7 14	2117
102¼	Covilha	8 16	2213
131¼	**Guarda** 301 arr	10 2	2350

Guarda dep	4 55	1545
Covilha	6 35	1711
Fundao	7 10	1745
Castello Branco	9 2	1934
Villa Velha de Rod.	9 50	2022
Abrantes arr	1128	22 0

TORRE DAS VARGENS and BADAJOZ.

E.M					
	LISBON (300) dep	2155	11 36	17‡2	17‡2
108¼	**Torre das Vargens**	3 17	17 10	2032	2114
114¼	Chança	3 40	17 39	2051	2132
134¼	Portalegre	5 5	19 20	2147	2234
164¼	Elvas	7 13	21 46	2253	2348
174¼	**Badajoz** (297) arr	7 40	22 14	2314	0 10

Badajoz dep	6 45	8 48	11 25	18 24
Elvas (Port. Cust. ex.)	7 45	9 18	12 27	19 9
Portalegre	9 6	A	14 44	20 12
Chança	10 8	...	16 5	20 52
Torre das Vargens arr	1023	1126	16 24	21 4
LISBON (300) arr	1431	1445	...	1 13

‡—Mon., Wed., and Sat. only. A—Seville and Lisbon Express, on certain days only.

†—Weekdays only.

OPORTO and VALENCA.

Oporto ....dep	5 33	7†47	8 45	10 3	14 21	...	1650	1859	...
„ Campanha	5 48	7 55	9 0	1013	14 30	...	1657	1914	...
Ermezinde	6 19	8 10	9 24	1034	14 47	...	1712	1939	...
Trofa	6 53	...	9 48	11 8	15 6	...	1730	20 7	...
Famalicao 301 ...	7 20	8 41	1010	1133	15 20	...	1744	2030	...
Nine	7 36	8 50	1030	1153	15 29	...	1755	2045	...
Vianna	9 34	—	1155	1339	16 31	1644	19 0	2235	...
Caminha	—	...	1235	†	17 0	1756	—	2320	...
Valenca ....arr	...	...	1321	—	17 31	1929	...	0 9	...
VIGO 294A...arr	...	...	...	...	19 50	...	...	...	...

VIGO 294A ...dep	2235	...	...	...	7 55	...	...	...	...
Valenca ....dep	3 35	6 3	7 55	...	1321	1440	16 40	...	...
Caminha	4 30	7 7	9 18	...	1355	1526	17 44	...	...
Vianna	5 25	8 10	1015	10†25	1431	1612	19 11	...	...
Nine	7 5	9 18	—	12 18	1534	1755	21 10	...	...
Famalicao	7 24	9 31	...	12 30	1545	1813	21 33	...	...
Trofa	7 43	9 44	...	12 44	1558	1829	21 55	...	...
Ermezinde	8 22	10 6	...	13 3	1620	1857	22 36	...	...
Oporto Campanha	8 42	1023	...	13 19	1635	1914	22 57	...	...
„ ....arr	8 57	1030	...	13 26	1643	1928	23 12	...	...

Nine ......dep	7 43	8†54	9 17	10 38	15 34	18 0	21 3	...
Braga ...arr	8 19	9 15	9 48	11 12	16 2	18 31	21 37	...

Braga dep	6 27	8 44	10 0	11†55	15 1	17 18	20 21	...	...
Nine ...arr	7 0	9 9	10 28	12 14	15 25	17 45	20 52	...	...

A—On Mon., Wed., and Fri. only.] **OPORTO and BARCA D'ALVA.** [B—On Tues., Thurs., and Sat. only.

Oporto Central dep		6 14	8 27	13 3	15 42	1848	...
„ Camp....dep		6 29	8 42	1311	15 50	19 5	...
Ermezinde		7 3	9 7	1326	16 7	1927	...
Penafiel		8 28	10 8	14 6	16 59	2036	...
Livraçao		9 12	1043	A	17 27	2117	...
Ermida..................		1027	1144	1513	18 20	23 5	...
Regoa	6 16	1153	1232	1539	19 2	0 3	...
Pinhao................	7 24	—	1318	1611	19 47	—	...
Tua (301)	8 16	...	1355	1634	20 14	...	...
Pocinho	10 1	...	1455	1713	—	...	...
Barca ....arr	11 1	...	1541	1744	...	...	...
SALAMANCA 299arr		...	2137	2157	...	...	...

SALAMANCA 299 dep	...	...	4 45	5 5	...	...	...	...	...
			B						
Barca d'Alva ...dep	...	...	8 41	12 9	...	1744	...	...	...
Pocinho....................	...	...	9 13	1258	...	1851	...	...	...
Tua	...	4 7	9 57	1414	...	2038	...	...	...
Pinhao	...	4 35	1016	1443	...	2128	...	...	...
Regoa........................	3 15	5 23	1048	1538	1745	2224	...	...	...
Ermida	4 36	5 59	1119	1623	1919	—	...	...	...
Livraçao	7 53	6 51	B	1726	2031	...	...	...	...
Penafiel	8 36	7 24	1230	18 5	2125	...	...	...	...
Ermezinde	9 42	8 15	1311	19 7	2244	...	...	...	...
Oporto Campanha...	10 3	8 31	1325	1924	23 9	...	...	...	...
„ ....arr	1015	8 39	1333	1938	2324	...	...	...	...

Livraçao...........dep	10 50	17 36	...	...	...	...
Amarante ....arr	11 24	18 10	...	...	...	...

Amarante............dep	6 1	16 35	...	...	...	...	...	...	...	...
Livraçao..............arr	6 35	17 9	...	...	...	...	...	...	...	...

REGOA and VIDAGO

Regoa ...dep	5 28	13 5	19 7	...	...	...
Villa Real...	7 5	14 26	20 30	...	...	...
Vidago ..arr	9 38	16 35	...	...	...	...

Vidago ..dep	...	10 58	17 35	...	...	...	...	...
Villa Real...	4 0	13 17	20 31	...	...	...	...	...
Regoa ...arr	5 10	14 24	21 47	...	...	...	...	...

OPORTO and LEIXOS.—In 29 min. Depart from Oporto, 6.0, 6.50, 7.50, 8.20, 8.45, 9.10, 10.10, 11.10, 12.10, 13.10, 14.35, 15.45, 16.35, 17.35, 18.40, 20.0. Depart from Leixos, 6.45, 7.40, 8.35, 9.0, 9.30, 10.25, 11.25, 12.25, 13.30, 14.30, 15.30, 16.25, 17.25, 18.25, 19.25, 20.40.

‡—Weekdays only. **OPORTO and FAMALICAO.**

Oporto Boa Vista dep	...	6 25	9 10	10 40	1445	17 5	19 15	...	...
Pedras Rubras ...	...	6 52	9 38	11 13	1513	1737	19 46	...	...
Villa do Conde ...	...	7 30	1018	11 52	1552	1816	20 27	...	...
Povoa................	5 25	8 3	1026	12 0	1615	1824	20 35	...	...
Fontainhas	6 12	8 46	—	—	1655	—	—	...	...
Famalicao...arr	6 50	9 20	...	...	1729	...	...	...	...

Famalicao		...	7 35	...	...	16 0	1825	...	...	...
Fontainhas ...		...	8 13	‡	...	1641	19 8	...	...	...
Povoa	5 0	7 40	9 15	1210	16 0	1735	1947	...	...	...
Villa do C.	5 9	7 52	9 26	1220	1610	1746	—	...	...	...
Pedras R...	5 54	8 38	10 9	13 0	1655	1830	...	...	...	...
Oporto...	6 22	9 7	1030	1328	1722	19 0	...	...	...	...

TUA and BRAGANÇA.

*-On Mon., Wed., & Fri. only.

Tua ....dep	...	14 30	20‡20	...
Mirandella..........	7*15	17 2	22 25	...
Macedo...............	8 46	18 14	—	...
Sendas	9 30	18 49	...	...
Rossas	10 14	19 23	...	...
Braganca ......arr	11 10	20 10	...	...

Bragança ......dep	...	8 10	14*40	‡—On Tues., Thurs., and Sat. only.	...
Rossas	...	8 58	15 39		...
Sendas	...	9 28	16 15		...
Macedo	...	10 1	16 54		...
Mirandella	7‡15	1127	18 6		...
Tua (301) ......arr	9 44	1330	...		...

TROFA and FAFE.

Trofa ....dep	8 5	9 58	1511	17†35	20‡28	...
Guimaraes.....	9 44	11 34	1649	18 51	22 11	...
Fafe ....arr	...	12 28	1744	...	23 5	...

Fafe.............dep	4 50	...	9†43	15 35	...
Guimaraes	5 54	8†16	1049	16 41	...
Trofa (301) ...arr	7 23	9 30	1223	18 12	...

†—Sunday excepted. ‡—20.12 on Sunday.

FIGUEIRA DA FOZ and VILLA FORMOSO.

Dis. E M							
	Figueira da Foz ...dep	...	7 40	...	...	1450	2010
22¼	Cantanhede	...	9 11	...	...	1618	2130
31¾	**Pampilhosa** ....arr	...	9 46	...	A	1654	22 5
...	LISBON ....dep	2155	...	8 30	1130	—	1855
...	**Pampilhosa** ....dep	5 0	1040	1240	1452	A—Sud Express.	2315
37¾	Luso-Bussaco	5 28	1057	13 6	15 8		2337
53¾	Sta. Comba Dao	6 51	1146	1410	1549		0 38
80¼	Mangualde.....................	9 7	13 6	—	1659		2 12
128¾	Guarda **(300)**..................	1254	1536	...	1855		4 58
157¼	**Villar Formoso** ......arr	...	1646	...	1951		6 23
236¼	SALAMANCA **(299)**...arr	...	2137	...	23 7		1037

SALAMANCA 299dep	...	2115	5 5	11 6	...	...
				A		
V. Formoso ...dep	...	2 15	10 6	1426	...	...
Guarda	...	3 38	1140	1524	...	16 0
Mangualde	...	6 20	1412	17 4	...	1852
Sta. Comba Dao.........	...	8 4	1547	18 3	1820	2046
Luso-Bussaco	...	9 8	1645	1845	1919	2144
Pampilhosa ...arr	...	9 25	17 0	1858	1935	22 0
LISBON **(300)**...arr	...	1431	2353	2252	2353	6 25
Pampilhosa ...dep	4 30	1050	1730	—	—	—
Cantanhede...............	5 8	1126	18 6	...	...	...
Figueira da Fozarr	6 37	1253	1934	...	...	...

SANTA COMBA DAO and VIZEU.

E.M.				
	Santa Comba Dao .....dep	7 0	14 15	...
31	Vizeu ....arr	8 57	16 22	...

Vizeu...............................dep	13 16	18 20
Santa Comba Dao**(301)**...arr	15 19	20 11

LISBON and CASCAES

Lisbon Caes do Sodre	11 20	Frequent service, about hourly, from 6.0 until 0.55 night.
Belem..............................	11 33	
Alges	11 42	
Paco d'Areos	11 57	
Mont Estoril	12 26	
Cascaes	12 28	

*—Until 31st October. **LISBON** (Rocio **and CINTRA.**

Lisbon, Queluz, Cacem..., Cintra — Depart from Lisbon 0*40, 1.0, 7.17, 8.36, 9*19, 10.5, 11.0, 12.25, 12.58, 14*33, 15.0, 16*8, 17.15, 17.27, 18*12, 18.25, 19*1, 19.30, 21.0, 22.24, 23.40.

Cintra, Cacem..., Queluz, Lisbon — Depart from Cintra 5.30, 7.5, 7.55, 8.28, 9.23, 10*18, 11.21, 13*15, 13.22, 15.0, 15.19, 16.14, 17*5, 18.3, 18.12, 19.28, 20*2, 21*27, 21.34, 22.33, 23*21.

COPENHAGEN, KORSŒR, NYBORG, and FREDERICIA.

SLEEPING CARRIAGES (1st and 2nd class) { Copenhagen to Frederikshavn, in 8.30 p.m. from Copenhagen. Copenhagen to Hamburg, in 12.0 night from Copenhagen. Extra fare, 1st class 8 kr. 90 ö.

THROUGH CARRIAGE, on Mon., Tues., Wed., and Sat., from Copenhagen to Esbjerg in 8.20 a.m. from Copenhagen.

Dist.			2&3	1,2,3	1,2,3	2&3	2&3	1,2,3	2 & 3	2&3	2&3	2&3	1,2,3	1,2,3	2 & 3	1,2,3
E.M.	**Copenhagen—**		a.m.	a.m.	a.m.	a.m.	p.m.	p.m.	a.m.	p.m.	p.m.	p.m.	p.m.	p.m.	p.m.	nght
—	Personbanegaard	...	7 10	8 20	9 5	1123	1230	12 55	11 45	1 11	3 35	6 58	7 50	8 30	11 20	12 0
2½	Valby	...	7 19	...	...	...	...	...	11 54	1 21	3 45	...	...	...	11 29	...
19½	**Roskilde**......arr	...	8 2	8 55	9 40	1158	...	1 25	12 42	2 5	4 35	7 33	8 24	9 5	12 23	...
...	„ (**302**) dep	...	8 12	8 59	9 44	12 3	...	1 27	—	2 20	4 46	7 39	8 29	9 7	12 41	...
31¼	Borup	...	8 39	...	...	1227	...	...	...	3 7	5 15	8 3	...	SC	1 7	SC
40	Ringsted	...	9 3	...	...	1251	...	1 56	...	3 59	5 47	8 26	...	...	1 38	...
49	Soro	...	9 24	...	...	1 13	...	2 11	...	4 43	6 13	8 48	...	...	2 4	...
58	Slagelse (**302A**) ...	...	9 49	10 3	...	1 41	...	2 27	...	5 34	6 48	9 14	9 29	...	2 34	...
68½	**Korsœr** ......arr	...	1014	1022	11 1	2 6	2 14	2 44	...	6 15	7 14	9 36	9 46	1024	2 57	1 39
...	KORSŒR Stm. dep	...	...	...	...	...	...	2p54	...	...	...	...	10 p0	...	...	...
152¾	KIEL......arr	...	...	...	...	...	...	8p25	...	...	...	...	4 a55	...	...	...
222	HAMBURG **168** arr	...	...	...	...	2&3	...	11 p4	2 & 3	...	...	...	7 a27	...	...	...
		2&3	2&3	a.m.	a.m.	p.m.	p.m.		p.m.	...	p.m.		p.m.	p.m.	a.m.	a.m.
...	**Korsœr** Ferry dep	...	...	1032	11 11	...	2 25	2 & 3	3 40	...	7 32	Sleeping Car.	9 57	1036	3 15	1 55
84½	**Nyborg** Ferry dep	a.m.	a.m.	1153	12 29	...	3 45	p.m.	5 15	...	9 0		11 18	1156	4 37	3 16
85	**Nyborg** Sta. ...dep	7 33	9 5	1210	12 41	1 10	3 59	4 21	5 48	...	9 35		11 35	1213	5 22	3 36
103	**Odense** ......dep	8 38	1035	1251	1 16	2 17	4 35	5 12	7 33	...	1041		12 10	1251	6 36	4 7
112¼	**Tommerup** ...arr	9 3	11 9	1 11	...	2 46	4 55	5 36	8 10	...	11 9		...	...	7 15	...
118	Aarup	9 23	1133	...	1 46	3 14	...	5 53	8 50	...	1128		...	1 20	7 34	...
133¾	Middelfart ......arr	10 3	1228	...	2 12	4 6	5 30	6 32	9 53	...	1214		...	1 46	8 31	...
136½	**Strib** ...... { arr	1013	1243	1 59	2 20	4 20	5 38	6 41	10 10	...	1225	SC	1 0	1 54	8 40	5 1
	{ dep	1020	1252	2 7	2 27	4 29	5 46	6 48	10 22	...	1234		1 7	2 3	8 47	5 6
138¼	**Fredericia**......arr	1033	1 10	2 25	2 45	4 47	6 4	7 6	10 40	...	1252	...	1 25	2 21	9 5	5 24
158½	LUNDERSKOV arr	...	...	3§26	3 p54	6p29	7p23	9 p46	12 34	...	...	...	2 a31	4a20	11a34	6 a21
162½	VAMDRUP **303** ar	...	...	...	4p16	6p50	7p54	10p16	1 a5	...	...	...	3 a0	4a48	12 p2	6 a29
324	HAMBURG **168** ar	...	...	...	10p40	1a53	...	.	...	...	...	...	8 a44	1117	7 p58	11a31
193	ESBJERG **303A**...	...	...	4§22	5 p35	8p51	8p51	11 58	...	...	...	...	3 a34	...	3 p20	7 a53
...	ESBJERG ...dep	...	...	4p45 }	From Esbjerg on Mon., Tues., Wed., and Sat.						§-On Mon., Tues., Wed., and Sat. only.					
...	HARWICH ...arr	...	...	3 p0 }												

AARHUS and GRENAA.

Aarhus ......dep	5 a34	8 a45	11a40	3 p10	7 p0	...	...	...
Ryomgaard	7 0	10 10	2 13	5 44	8 25	...	...	...
Trustrup	7 32	10 50	3 10	6 40	8 54	...	...	...
Grenaa ......arr	7 48	11 6	3 34	7 4	9 10	...	...	...
Grenaa ......dep	5 a33	8 a14	12p10	3 p45	7p15	...	...	...
Trustrup	5 53	8 39	12 50	4 24	7 39	...	...	...
Ryomgaard	6 30	9 21	1 54	5 30	8 20	...	...	...
Aarhus ......arr	7 46	10 41	3 54	7 43	9 29	...	...	...

COPENHAGEN, MASNEDSUND, and GJEDSER.

THROUGH CARRIAGES—(1st, 2nd, and 3rd class) Copenhagen to Berlin in 11.0 a.m. from Copenhagen.
SLEEPING CARRIAGES—(1st and 2nd class) Copenhagen to Berlin in 8.10 p.m. from Copenhagen. Extra fare 6 kr. 10 ö

E.M.		2 & 3	2 & 3	2 & 3	2&3	1,2,3	1,2,3	1,2,3	1,2,3	2 & 3	2&3	1,2,3	1,2,3	2&3	2&3
Dist.	**Copenhagen—**		a.m.	a.m.	a.m.	a.m.	a.m	a.m.		a.m.	p.m.	p.m.	p.m.		p.m
—	Personbanegaard...dep	...	5 48	7 43	9 40	1018	11 0	11 7	...	11 23	2 30	7 30	8 10	...	9 16
2½	Valby	...	5 57	7 53	9 50	...		From July 5th until Aug. 18.	...	...	2 40	...		...	9 26
19½	**Roskilde 302**	...	6 43	8 30	1032	1055			...	12 6	3 42	8 6		...	1022
33¼	**Kjöge**	...	7 24	9 10	—	1120			...	12 45	4 30	8 33	SC	...	11 0
46½	Haslev	...	8 0	9 45	...	1144			...	1 22	5 10	8 58		...	1134
57¾	Nestved **302A**	...	8 32	10 19	...	12 6			...	1 55	5 53	9 20		...	1210
74¾	Vordingborg	...	9 19	11 1	...	1234			...	2 40	6 55	9 51		...	1 14
75¾	**Masnedsund** ......arr	a.m.	9 24	11 6	...	1239			...	2 45	7 0	9 56		...	1 20
...	MASNEDSUND Stm. dp	5 0	9 29	11 9	*—Station. †—Ferry.	—	1 ‡2	1‡19	...	2 57	7 5	—	10‡25	...	‡-From Masnedo
79¼	OREHOVED......arr	5†39	10 4	11 41		...	1 19	1 36	p.m.	3 37	7 42	Sleeping Car.	10 42	p.m.	
79½	**Orehoved** ......dep	6*0	10*20	11†53		...	1†37	—	1†43	4*45	7*57		11 † 2	11†8	
93¼	Nykjöbing ...... { arr	7 17	11 3	12 39		...	...	...	2 18	6 14	8 47		...	1142	
	{ dep	7 35	...	12 50		...	...	...	2 24	6 25	9 30		...	...	
107½	**Gjedser** ......arr	8 23	...	1 49		...	2 18	...	3 1	7 20	1026		11 51	...	
107¾	GJEDSER Stmr. ...dep	...	...	...	...	...	2 38	...	...	...	...	SC	12a14	...	...
134	WARNEMUNDE stm. ar	...	...	...	...	...	4p38	...	...	...	...		2 a14	...	...
264	HAMBURG **213**......arr	...	...	...	...	...	8p23	...	...	...	...		6 a15	...	...
214½	NEU STRELITZ **178B**	arr	...	...	...	...	7 p7	...	...	...	...		4 a55	...	...
278½	BERLIN **181**......arr	...	...	...	...	...	8 p55	...	...	...	...		6 a38	...	...

‡—1.50 p.m. on Sundays.

RANDERS and RYOMGAARD.

Randers ......dep	5a22	7a54	11a50	2p55	7p11
Uggelhuse	5 45	8 19	12 22	3 34	7 36
Auning	6 8	8 48	12 59	4 27	7 59
Ryomgaard arr	6 25	9 13	1 30	5 0	8 15
Ryomgaard dep	6a55	10a10	2p15	5 p35	8p29
Auning	7 14	10 28	2 52	6 10	8 49
Uggelhuse	7 39	10 55	3 41	6 53	9 15
Randers ......arr	8 3	11 20	4 21	7 35	9 40

COPENHAGEN and FREDERIKSSUND. *—Weekdays only

Copenhagen ...dep	7a27	10 a2	12 p5	3p17	6p13	8p15	10p17	**Frederikssund** dep	*	6a27	8a28	12 p5	2‡57	5 p0	8p2
Valby	7 39	10 14	12 17	3 29	6 26	8 25	10 30	Ballerup	5 a5	7 7	9 9	12 49	3 39	5 40	9 1
Ballerup	8 9	10 48	12 52	4 2	6 59	8 57	11 3	Valby	5 35	7 36	9 40	1 20	4 9	6 10	9 4
Frederikssund arr	8 48	11 32	1 35	4 44	7 40	...	11 41	**Copenhagen** ...arr	5 46	7 46	9 50	1 30	4 19	6 20	9 5

COPENHAGEN and KALLUNDBORG.

Copenhagen ......dep	7 a55	10a10	1 p11	4 p28	9 p53	...	**Kallundborg** ......dep	5 a30	8 a5	1 p3	4 p40	5 p53	...
Roskilde	8 50	10 47	2 14	5 28	10 39	...	Holbaek	6 39	9 33	2 22	5 33	7 17	...
Holbaek	9 55	11 27	3 23	6 40	11 42	...	Roskilde ......arr	7 36	10 38	3 24	6 18	8 21	...
Kallundborg ......arr	11 1	12 12	4 36	7 58	12 50	...	**Copenhagen** ......arr	8 39	11 35	4 5	6 53	9 25	...

TOMMERUP and ASSENS.

Tommerup 302 ...dep	7a41	1p16	4p59	9‡p5		**Assens** ......dep	5 a5	9a53	1p22	6*32	...	...	
Glamsbjerg	8 17	1 41	5 28	9 42	‡ 1115 p.m.	Glamsbjerg	6 12	10 41	2 9	7 23	...	...	* 9.0 p.m.
Assens ......arr	9 11	2 28	6 12	1036	on Sun.	**Tommerup** ......arr	6 51	11 7	2 33	8 12	...	...	on Sun.

AARHUS and HOU.

Aarhus ......dep	6 a10	9 a10	12p38	3 p30	6 p35	10p18	...	**Hou** ......dep	6 a0	8a45	12p15	3p45	5p50	8p25	...	...
Hou ......arr	8 15	11 0	2 12	5 25	8 10	11 45	...	**Aarhus 303** ...arr	7 48	1020	2 20	5 15	7 45	10 6	...	...

FREDERICIA, NYBORG, KORSŒR, and COPENHAGEN.

SLEEPING CARRIAGE, 1st and 2nd Class, in 12.18 a.m. from Esbjerg to Copenhagen.

HARWICH ...dep	...	9p45	From Harwich on Monday, Wednesday, Friday, and Saturday in about 22 hours.													
ESBJERG......arr	...	8 p0														
ESBJERG 303A dep	10p30	1218	1218	...	...	...	...	4a30	...	...	9a16	1240	12p40	...	1251	4p35
HAMBURG 168 dep	5 p21	...	9 p0	...	...	1110	1110	...	...	...	5a38	...	8 a38	...	..	1p24
VAMDRUP 303 dep	11p53	...	1a50	...	...	4a57	4a57	7 a2	...	...	12p8	...	1 p49	...	2p35	6p28
LUNDERSKOV dep	12a11	1a22	1a22	...	...	5 a6	5 a6	7a36	...	...	1228	1p45	2 p1	...	3p 1	7 p5
	1,2,3	1,2,3	1,2,3	1,2,3	2&3	1,2,3	2&3	2&3	2&3	2&3	2&3	1,2,3	1,2,3	2&3	2&3	2&3
	a.m.	a.m.	a.m.			a.m.	a.m.	a.m.	a.m.		p.m.	p.m.	p.m.	p.m	p.m.	p.m.
Fredericia......dep	1 50	2 22	2 43	...	...	5 55	6 20	9 26	1110	...	1 53	2 30	3 2	3 9	6 23	8 40
Strib .... arr	2 5	2 37	2 58	...	...	6 10	6 35	9 41	1125	...	2 8	2 45	3 17	3 29	6 38	8 55
Strib .... dep	2 21	2 53	3 14	...	...	6 22	6 53	9 53	1137	...	2 21	2 57	3 29	3 41	6 50	9 5
Middelfart.........dep	2 29	...	...	...	...	6 32	7 23	10 3	1145	...	2 30	...	...	3 50	7 6	9 15
Aarup..................	3 1	SC	SC	...	...	7 17	9 0	1054	...	p.m.	...	A	...	4 33	8 15	10 1
Tommerup ...arr	...	..	...	...	...	7 34	9 40	1115	1220	2 47	...	...	...	4 50	8 44	1018
Odense 303A arr	3 26	3 45	4 6	...	...	8 14	1023	1144	1237	3 9	3 26	3 53	4 25	5 11	9 24	1040
Nyborg Sta. ...arr	4 2	4 15	4 38	...	...	8 56	1158	1245	1 9	—	4 5	4 28	4 57	5 55	1051	1129
Nyborg Ferry dep	4 6	4 35	4 55	...	...	9 10	—	—	1 20	...	4 17	4 44	5 7	6 10	—	1253
Korsœr ....arr	—	5 50	6 13	...	...	1028	...	...	2 40	...	5 35	6 2	6 25	7 28	...	2 18
HAMBURG 168 dep	...	...	...	1110	...	...	...	...	7 a5	...	...	...	...	...	...	...
KIEL Steamer dep	...	...	...	1a32	...	...	...	...	9a15	...	...	...	...	...	...	...
KORSŒR ....arr	2 & 3	1,2,3	...	7a30	...	...	...	...	2p38	2&3	...	...	...	...	...	...
	a.m.	a.m.	a.m.	a.m.	a.m.	a.m.	a.m.	p.m.	p.m.	p.m.	p.m.	p.m.	p.m.	p.m.		a.m.
Korsœr ....dep	6 37	6 10	6 28	8 3	8 15	1033	1140	3 11	3 0	5 0	5 50	6 16	6 38	7 43	...	2 58
Slagelse..................	7 3	...	...	8 25	9 14	11 0	1227	3 48	...	5 24	6 14	6 39	7 1	8 16	...	3 57
Soro......................	7 23	...	...	8 42	9 56	...	1250	4 12	1,2,3 Class.	5 43	...	...	...	8 43	...	4 26
Ringsted	7 41	...	...	8 57	1035	...	1 12	4 34		5 59	...	A	...	9 10	...	4 54
Borup....................	8 1	...	...	...	11 6	...	1 33	4 55		...	...	...	...	9 37	...	5 16
Roskilde ... arr	8 23	...	...	9 29	1146	1157	1 57	5 21		6 31	7 15	6 36	7 58	10 3	a.m.	5 51
Roskilde ... dep	8 28	...	...	9 33	12 5	1159	2 4	5 33		6 34	7 18	7 40	8 1	1012	4 48	6 10
Valby.....................	9 8	...	...	...	1248	...	2 42	6 20	...	...	...	...	...	1056	5 26	7 8
Copenhagen arr	9 16	7 54	8 12	10 4	1256	1230	2 50	6 28	4 48	7 5	7 51	8 11	8 32	11 4	5 34	7 17

A—Runs from 5th July until 17th August.

KJÖGE, STUBBERUP, and FAXE.

Kjöge..........dep	a.m.	9a25	2p30	8p36	...	...	...	...
Haarlev	6 20	9 58	3 9	9 6	...	...	...	...
Rödvig ....arr	7 18	1051	4 13	10 0	...	...	...	...
Stubberup	7 17	1044	4 12	9 52	...	...	...	...
Faxe ....arr	...	1059	...	...	...	...	...	...

Faxe ....dep	a.m.	7a25	11a23	p.m.	4p45	...	...	...
Stubberup	5 20	7 40	11 48	2 5	5 0	...	...	...
Rödvig ....dep	5 10	7 30	11 38	...	4 50	...	...	...
Haarlev	6 15	8 25	1 3	2 50	5 45	...	...	...
Kjöge (302) ....arr	6 56	8 58	1 43	...	6 16	...	...	...

GJEDSER, MASNEDSUND, and COPENHAGEN.

BERLIN 181 ....dep	...	...	11p15	...	...	...	...	...	8 a49	...	...	...	...	...	...	...	...
NEU STRELITZ 178B dep	...	...	1 a3	...	...	...	...	...	10a35	...	...	...	...	...	...	...	...
HAMBURG 213 ......dep	...	...	12 0	...	...	...	...	...	9 a13	...	...	...	...	...	...	...	...
WARNEMND. Stm. dep	...	...	3 a45	...	...	...	...	...	1 p2	...	...	...	...	...	...	...	...
GJEDSER Stmr.......arr	...	...	5 a45	...	...	...	...	...	3 p2	...	...	...	...	...	...	...	...
	2 & 3	2&3	1,2,3	1,2,3	2 & 3	2 & 3	1,2,3	1,2,3	1,2,3	1,2,3	2&3	2&3	2 & 3				
		a.m.	a.m.		a.m.	a.m.	p.m.		p.m.		p.m.	p.m.	p.m.				
Gjedser ....dep	...	...	6 6	...	6 18	8 55	2 31	...	3 †20	...	4 0	...	8 †20	...	...	...	...
Nykjöbing .... arr	...	...	...	...	7 7	9 55	3 9	...	⋮	...	5 5	...	9 9	...	...	...	...
Nykjöbing .... dep	...	6 2	SC	...	7 23	10 18	3 20	...	⋮	...	5 30	5 55	9 38	...	...	...	...
Orehoved ....arr	...	6†39	6 †48	...	8 †3	11*31	3 †55	p.m.	4 †2	...	6*56	7†33	10*28	...	...	...	...
OREHOVED Stmr. dep	...	—	6 58	...	8 12	11 51	—	3 59	4 12	...	—	7 43	10 55	...	...	...	...
MASNEDSUND Stm. arr	a.m.	...	7 ‡32	a.m.	8 45	12 30	...	4 ‡22	4 ‡45	p.m.	p.m.	8 16	11 37	...	...	...	...
Masnedsund ......dep	5 15	...	...	7 48	8 48	12 40	...	From July 5 until Aug. 18	⋮	5 4	5 31	8 23	—	...	...	...	...
Vordingborg	5 22	...	...	7 53	8 56	12 48	...		⋮	5 9	5 43	8 30		...	...	...	...
Nestved	6 10	...	...	8 28	9 46	1 46	...		⋮	5 42	6 34	9 17	...	...	...	...	...
Haslev	6 41	...	...	8 49	10 14	2 15	...		⋮	6 3	7 8	9 51	...	...	...	...	...
Kjöge	7 22	...	...	9 15	10 48	2 54	...		⋮	6 27	7 56	1031	...	...	...	...	...
Roskilde	8 9	...	...	9 44	11 40	3 40	...		⋮	6 55	8 52	1117	...	...	...	...	...
Valby........................	8 47	...	...	...	12 8	4 26	...	...	⋮	...	9 39	1157	...	...	...	...	...
Copenhagen.........arr	8 55	...	9 42	10 15	12 16	4 34	...	6 35	6 41	7 26	9 47	12 5	...	...	...	...	...

*—Station. †—Ferry. ‡—From Masnedo.

FREDERIKSHAVN and SKAGEN.

Frederikshavn ...dep	10 a0	4 p15	8 p15	...
Skagen ....arr	11 50	5 50	10 15	...

Skagen ....dep	7 a0	2p15	7 p0	...
Frederikshavn ......arr	9 0	3 55	9 0	...

KALLUNDBORG and NESTVED.

Kallundborg dep	...	5 a50	11a10	4 p52	7p30	...	...
Værslev..................	...	6 12	11 36	5 4	7 48	...	...
Slagelse .... arr	...	8 19	1 32	6 8	9 9	...	...
Slagelse .... dep	7 a13	10 22	2 30	7 15	9 40	...	...
Dalmose..................	7 41	11 24	3 30	7 52	1012	...	...
Nestved 302...arr	8 17	12 34	4 36	8 34	1054	...	...

Nestved	...	6a35	8 a32	10a20	1 p51	6 p42	...	...
Dalmose....................	...	7 38	9 12	11 35	3 0	7 26	...	...
Slagelse ...... arr	...	8 14	9 38	12 18	3 39	7 58	...	...
Slagelse ...... dep	7a 5	—	10 2	—	4 10	9 38	...	...
Vaerslev....................	8 23	...	11 45	...	6 9	11 31	...	...
Kallundborg..arr	8 33	...	11 59	...	6 23	11 45	...	...

Dalmose......dep	7 a51	9a21	11a33	3p31	7p56	10p18	...	...
Skælskor .....arr	8 20	9 44	12 2	4 8	8 23	10 41	...	...

Skælskor... dep	6 a55	8a42	10a27	2 p7	6 p51	9p38	...	...	...
Dalmose ......arr	7 27	9 8	11 3	2 39	7 17	10 4	...	...	...

HILLEROD and GILLELEJE.

Hilleröd ... ..dep	9 a35	1 p35	7 p0	...	...
Graested	10 28	2 48	8 10	...	...
Gilleleje ......arr	11 0	3 0	8 25	...	...

Gilleleje ....dep	5 a45	11a10	3p45	...	...
Graested	6 9	11 29	4 9	...	...
Hilleröd ....arr	7 15	12 40	5 15	...	...

Soro to Vedde. 9.32 a.m., 1.25, 5.48, 9.0 p.m. Return from Vedde 7.40, 11.35 a.m., 4.12, 7.41 p.m.

NYKJOBING, NAKSKOV, RODBY, and BANHOLM.

Nykjöbing............dep	7 a38	11a20	2 p30	7 p0	11p55
Maribo	8 30	12 13	3 17	7 58	12 33
Nakskov.................arr	9 23	1 5	4 2	9 5	1 10

Nakskov ......dep	6 a0	7 a25	1 p25	4p25	7 p8	10 p0
Maribo	6 37	8 45	2 18	5 45	8 17	10 49
Nykjöbing......arr	7 15	9 40	3 5	6 40	9 12	11 32

Maribo ....dep	8 a52	12p55	3 p28	8 p21	12a45
Rodby.......................arr	9 30	1 45	4 0	9 0	1 5

Rodby.....................dep	6 a0	7 a30	1p 20	4p30	7 p5
Maribo ....arr	6 22	8 8	2 0	5 21	7 45

Maribo ....dep	6 a34	9 a 2	3 p28	8p 30	...
Banholm ....arr	6 46	9 22	4 0	8 50	...

Banholm ......dep	7 a38	12p20	6 p45	10 p0	...	...
Maribo ....arr	7 58	12 40	7 5	10 15	...	...

COPENHAGEN and HELSINGBORG.

Copenhagen	a.m.	a.m.	a.m.	a.m.	a.m.	a.m.	a.m.	a.m.	a.m.	p.m.	p.m.	p.m.	p.m	p.m.	p.m.	p.m.	p.m.	p.m	p.m.	p.m.	p.m.	p.m.	p.m.	p.m.	p.m.	p.m.	p.m.	p.m.	p.m.	p.m.	p.m.	p.m.	n'gt	n'gt
Osterbro ...dep	6 8	...	...	...	8 10	...	9 48	...	...	12 5	...	2 34	...	3 0	3 31	...	3 58	...	...	4 46	5 12	5 41	...	6 27	6 44	7 25	...	8 40	...	...	...	1036	12 0	...
" Nord...dep	...	6 35	7 0	7 12	...	8 33	...	1010	1055	...	1222	...	2 56	...	...	3 30	...	4 10	4 43	...	...	...	6 0	...	...	...	7 20	...	9 5	9 20	10 6	...	...	1214
Hellerup	6 17	...	...	...	...	...	9 58	...	...	1215	...	2 43	...	...	3 41	3 44	...	...	...	4 55	...	5 51	...	6 35	...	7 35	7 35	8 49	...	...	...	1044	1210	...
Holte	...	...	...	7 35	...	9 0	...	1036	...	...	1248	...	3 19	...	...	4 6	...	...	5 7	...	...	...	6 26	...	...	...	7 58	...	...	9 46	...	...	...	1238
Hillerod	...	...	...	8 2	...	9 31	...	11 7	...	...	1 19	...	3 47	...	...	4 34	...	...	5 36	...	...	...	6 57	...	...	...	8 30	...	...	1020	...	...	...	1 2
Fredensborg	...	...	...	8 14	...	9 46	...	1118	...	...	1 32	...	3 59	...	...	—	...	...	5 48	...	...	...	7 11	...	...	...	8 43	...	...	1035	...	...	...	1*13
Klampenborg	6 30	...	...	...	...	...	1011	...	...	1228	...	2 57	...	...	3 54	...	...	...	...	5 . 8	...	6 4	...	6 44	6 58	7 48	...	9 2	...	...	1023	1053	1220	...
Rungsted	6 55	7 4	...	...	8 43	...	1038	...	...	1255	...	3 22	...	3 33	4 19	...	4 27	4 38	...	5 33	5 45	6 29	...	7 4	7 13	8 16	...	9 27	...	...	1048	1112	1239	...
Elsinore Station arr		7 37	7 46	8 34	9 19	1010	1116	1138	1147	1 33	1 56	—	4 20	4 11	—	...	4 59	5 10	6 9	—	6 21	—	7 36	—	7 42	8 52	9 6	—	10 4	11 0	1126	—	1 15	1*33
Elsinore Ferry...dep			8 0			1030			12 2		2 1	...			...	...				...	6 26	...		...	7 55			...	1020		1139	...		
Helsingborg 311arr		...	8 22	...	...	1052	...	...	1224	...	2 23	...	...	...	...	...	...	...	...	...	6 48	...	...	...	8 17	...	...	...	1042	...	12 1	...	...	...
GOTHENBURG 309A		...	1p42	...	...	...	...	...	6p34	...	...	...	...	...	...	...	...	...	...	...	...	...	...	...	...	...	...	...	4a20	...	...	...	...	...
CHRISTIANIA 304A ar		...	9p43	...	...	...	...	...	...	...	...	...	...	...	...	...	...	...	...	...	...	...	...	...	...	...	...	...	12 0	...	...	...	...	...

CHRISTIANIA ...dep		...	...	...	5p45	...	...	...	...	...	...	...	...	...	...	...	...	...	...	...	...	...	...	...	...	...	...	...	7a44	...	...	...	...	...
GOTHENBURG...309A		...	...	...	1a33	...	...	...	...	...	...	...	...	...	...	...	...	...	10a0	...	...	...	...	...	...	...	...	...	3p33	...	...	...	...	...
		a.m.	a.m.	a.m.	a.m.	a.m.	a.m.	a.m.	a.m.	a.m.	a.m.	a.m.	a.m.	a.m.	p.m.	p.m.	p.m.	p.m	p.m.	p.m.	p.m.	p.m.	p.m.	p.m.	p.m.	p.m.	p.m.	p.m.	p.m.	p.m.	p.m.	p.m.	p.m.	p.m.
Helsingborg ...dep		...	...	...	7 3	...	...	...	...	...	8 45	...	...	1123	...	1 8	...	...	3 57	...	...	...	...	...	7 3	...	...	...	8 57	...	...	...	...	...
Elsinore Ferry arr	a.m.	...	...	...	7 25	...	...	...	...	...	9 7	...	...	1145	...	1 30	...	...	4 19	...	...	...	...	...	7 25	...	...	...	9 19	...	...	...	...	...
Elsinore Station dep	5 39	6 24	6 39	...	7 40	...	7 45	7 52	7 58	...	9 23	9 32	1020	1157	12 5	1 52	1 58	...	4 39	4 51	...	4 59	...	7 0	7 37	...	...	8 58	9 35	9 49	...	10 7	1049	...
Rungsted	...	7 6	...	7 27	...	8 12	...	...	8 30	8 51	...	1010	11 2	1235	...	...	2 38	3 37	...	...	5 7	5 40	5 53	...	8 15	8 29	9 18	...	...	1021	1026	...	1128	1136
Klampenborg ... A		...	...	7 52	...	...	...	...	...	9 15	...	1035	1127	1 0	...	...	3 4	4 3	...	...	5 32	...	6 19	...	...	8 53	9 44	...	...	...	1051	...	...	1158
Fredensborg	6 7	...	7 4	...	...	...	...	8 16	...	...	9 47	...	...	...	1234	2 18	...	...	...	5 15	...	...	...	7 33	...	...	...	9 22	...	...	...	1033	...	...
Hillerod	6 24	...	7 20	...	...	...	...	8 29	...	...	10 2	...	...	...	1254	2 35	...	...	...	5 33	...	...	...	7 50	...	...	...	9 37	...	...	...	1047	...	...
Holte	6 48	...	7 50	...	...	...	...	8 52	...	...	1025	...	...	...	1 24	2 59	...	...	...	6 2	...	...	...	8 19	...	...	...	10 2	...	...	...	1110	...	...
Hellerup	...	...	...	8 5	...	8 37	...	...	...	9 29	...	1046	1138	1 11	...	...	3 15	4 14	...	...	5 44	...	6 31	...	...	9 2	9 55	...	...	...	11 2	...	...	12 8
Copenhagen Nord	7 9	7 50	8 14	...	8 29	...	...	9 14	8 58	...	1045	...	...	...	1 48	3 20	...	...	5 33	6 26	...	...	...	8 43	...	...	...	1023	1029	...	...	1130	12 4	...
Copenhagen Osterbro arr	...	...	...	8 12	...	8 43	8 50	...	...	9 36	...	1053	1145	1 18	...	...	3 22	4 21	...	...	5 51	6 9	6 38	...	8 44	9 8	10 2	...	...	1051	11 9	...	...	1214

Extra. { Copenhagen Osterbro...dep 5a38, 7a39, 4p16, 11p46; Rungsted ...arr 6 26, 8 28, 4 59, 12 32 } | Rungsted ...dep 6a44, 7a43, 6p39; Copenhagen O. ...arr 7 30, 8 22, 7 21 |

A—Between Elsinore and Hillerod on Mon., Wed., and Sat. only.
*—Tuesday and Friday night only.

VAMDRUP, FREDERICIA, and FREDERIKSHAVN.

	1,2,3	1,2,3	2&3	1,2,3	2&3	2&3	2&3	2&3	2&3	1,2,3	2&3	2&3	1,2,3	2&3	1,2,3
ALTONA 168 dep	...	9p19	...	11p33	...	...	...	6 a0	...	9 a0	...	...	1p44	...	5p43
	a.m.	a.m.	a.m.	a.m.		a.m.	a.m.	p.m.	p.m.	p.m.	p.m.		p.m.	p.m.	p.m.
Vamdrup ...dep	SC	1 50	2 0	4 57	...	7 2	9 34	12 8	...	1 49	2 35	...	6 28	...	1153
Lunderskov ...dep	1 22	...	2 11	5 6	...	7 36	9 54	1228	1 45	2 1	3 1	...	6 40	7 5	1211
Kolding	1 38	2 11	—	5 20	...	8 15	1022	1258	2 3	2 24	4 3	...	7 3	7 45	1231
Fredericia ...arr	2 0	2 30	...	5 40	...	8 57	1057	1 38	2 26	2 43	4 55	...	7 32	8 19	1 0
NYBORG 302 ...arr		4a38	...	8 a56	...	1245	1 p9	4 p5	...	4p57	1051	...	...	1129	4 a2
COPENHAGEN 302 arr		8a12	...	12p30	a.m.	4p48	4p48	7p51	...	8p32	...	p.m.	...	7a17	—
Fredericia ...dep	2 20	2 50	...	6 2	5 0	—	1112	—	3 20	3 6	5 43	6 35	7 47	—	...
Veile	2 49	3 17	a.m.	6 31	6 54	...	1159	...	4 7	3 39	7 35	7 5	8 30	p.m.	...
Horsens ...arr	3 24	3 51	5 43	7 7	8 17	...	1251	p.m.	5 2	4 19	9 2	7 40	9 18	9 46	...
Skanderborg ...arr	4 1	4 23	6 40	7 45	9 40	...	1 50	1235	5 52	5 1	—	8 20	10 7	1110	...
Aarhus 302 ...arr	4 31	4 51	7 39	8 16	11 4	...	2 29	1 41	6 34	5 35	...	8 54	1046	1240	a.m.
" ...dep	4 44	5 3	—	8 26	1125	...	—	—	6 43	5 44	...	9 5	1120	—	5 16
Langaa ...arr	5 27	5 45	...	9 40	1 41	...	...	a.m.	7 58	6 33	...	9 51	1234	...	6 21
Randers 302 ...arr	5 43	6 0	...	10 11	2 42	...	...	1142	8 13	6 53	...	1021	1254	...	6 44
Hobro	—	6 44	a.m.	11 20	4 43	...	...	1 8	9 45	7 33	...	11 7	—	...	7 38
Aalborg ...arr		7 34	8 15	12 42	7 6	...	...	3 38	1135	8 30	...	1156	...	...	8 55
Nörre Sundby		...	8 26	1 6	8 19	...	...	4 20	—	8 53	...	—	...	...	9 31
Hjörring		8 37	9 31	2 26	1113	...	...	6 40	...	9 55	...	...	...	...	1146
Frederikshavn ...arr		9‡10	1017	3 16	1248	...	...	3 5	...	1010	...	...	...	...	1 10

		2&3	2&3	2&3	2&3	1,2,3	1,2,3	1,2,3	2&3	2&3	2&3	2&3	1,2,3	1,2,3
				a.m.	a.m.	Mon., Tues., Wed., and Sat. only (daily July 5 to Aug. 17).		a.m.	a.m.				p.m.	p.m.
Frederikshavn ...dep		...	...	5 30	...		...	6*33	9 45	...	...	...	4 35	6 47
Hjörring		...	...	6 26	...		...	7 11	1127	...	...	...	5 39	7 26
Nörre Sundby		...	...	7 33	...		a.m.	7 53	1 47	...	...	...	6 51	8 9
Aalborg ...dep		...	...	7 42	5 25		5 50	8 16	2 23	...	...	...	7 14	8 31
Hobro		a.m.	a.m.	—	6 18		7 45	9 12	4 53	a.m.	...	...	8 48	9 26
Randers 302A ...dep		6 3	5 4	...	7 3		9 4	9 56	6 16	1025	...	p.m.	9 49	10 7
Langaa 303A ...dep		6 19	5 45	...	7 18		9 44	10 13	7 1	11 4	...	9 45	10 5	1026
Aarhus ...arr		—	7 55	a.m.	8 6		1046	10 56	8 34	1233	p.m.	1032	1056	1117
" ...dep		...	8 35	4 53	8 17		1144	11 6	—	2 32	5 0	1048	11 9	1128
Skanderborg 303A arr		...	9 34	5 40	8 48		1227	11 37	p.m.	3 18	5 46	1120	1140	12 0
Horsens 303A ...dep		...	1110	6 48	9 28		1 10	12 15	1 55	4 20	6 41	12 0	1219	1241
Veile		...	—	8 2	10 6		2 2	12 58	4 3	5 21	7 40	1238	1258	1 23
Fredericia ...arr		1,2,3	...	8 52	1035		2 36	1 27	5 0	6 11	8 25	1 6	1 26	1 55
COPENHAGEN dep		12 0	2&3	...	—	8a20	9 a5	...	...	1230	...	—	7p50	7p50
NYBORG ...dep	a.m.	3a36	a.m.	5a22	...	1210	1241	...	1p10	3p59	...	p.m.	1135	1135
Fredericia ...dep	3 24	5 a41	6 15	10 0	...	2 50	3 12	1 41	5 12	6 29	8 42	11 1	1 47	2 13
Kolding	3 58	6 4	7 23	11 3	...	3 11	3 38	2 5	6 1	7 5	9 24	12 3	2 15	2 36
Lunderskov ...arr	4 20	6 21	8 0	1134	...	3 26	3 54	2 22	6 29	7 28	9 46	1234	2 31	...
Vamdrup ...arr	4 48	6 29	8 22	12 2	...	—	4 16	2 33	6 50	7 54	1016	1 5	...	3 0
ALTONA 168 ...arr		11a14	4 p1	7p35	...	...	1018	7 p35	1a25	...	...	...	...	8a17

Extra.—Vamdrup to Fredericia, 9.38 p.m. Randers to Aarhus, 8.45 p.m. Aarhus to Horsens, 8.15 p.m. Aarhus to Fredericia, 5.50 p.m. Frederikshavn to Aarhus 6.50 a.m.

*—In connection with stmr. from Christiania on Wed. and Sat. ‡—Stmr. to Christiania (arr. 11.0 p.m.), every Mon. and Thurs.

LANGAA and SILKEBORG.																				
	Langaa ...dep	10a18	2 p10	7 p18	...	...	...	...	...	Silkeborg ...dep	7 a32	3 p30	8p40	...	...	...	...	...	...	...
	Silkeborg ...arr	11 39	4 58	9 25	...	...	...	...	...	Langaa (303) ...arr	9 25	5 59	10 0	...	...	...	...	...	...	...

[Mid Europe Time—See page lxix.]

BOGENSE and ODENSE.

Bogense ....dep	6 a0	9 a0	2 p5	6 p0	9 p0
Odense (302).....arr	7 50	1035	3 25	7 35	10 35

Odense ....dep	6a30	9a15	2p10	5p55	9p25
Bogense ...arr	8 10	1050	3 25	7 25	11 5

SKANDERBORG and SKJERN.

	a m	a.m.	p.m.	p.m.	p.m.	p.m.
Skanderborg ......dep	6 0	9 56	1243	6 15	8 30	1150
Silkeborg	7 2	1053	2 44	7 32	9 51	1250
Herning.........	8 32	1217	5 20	9 21	—	—
Skjern ......arr	9 48	1 45	7 4	1033	...	...

	a m	a.m.	a.m.	p.m.	p.m.	p.m.
Skjern .....dep	5 13	...	1110	2 40	...	7 44
Herning	6 26	8 53	1 10	4 30	5 25	9 5
Silkeborg	7 37	11 7	3 31	...	8 1	1021
Skanderb..arr	8 40	1222	4 55	...	9 31	1117

SKIVE and NYKJÖBING

Skive ....dep	8 a31	2 p50	5p45	8 p30
Roslev	9 15	3 50	6 45	9 11
Glyngore............	9 55	4 35	7 30	9 46
Nykjöbing ....arr	10 20	5 5	8 0	10 16
Nykjöbing ....dep	5 a10	8 a5	10a50	5 p35
Glyngore	5 47	8 40	11 27	6 11
Roslev................	6 21	9 16	12 6	6 39
Skive (303A)...arr	7 10	10 8	1 5	7 23

LUNDERSKOV, ESBJERG, and LANGAA.

COPENHAGEN 302	7p50	...	12 0	...	...	9 a5	9 a5	1230	...
FREDERICIA 303dp	1a47	...	5a41	6a15	10a0	2p50	3p12	6p29	8p42
	a.m.	a.m.	a.m.	a.m.	p.m.	p.m.	p m.	p.m.	p.m.
Lunderskov .....dep	2 36	3 10	6 30	8 21	1223	3§29	4 0	7 33	10 2
Bramminge	3 16	5 29	7 31	1033	2 39	...	5 13	8 30	1128
Esbjerg .... arr	3 34	6 1	7 53	11 9	3 20	4 22	5 35	8 51	1158
Esbjerg .... dep	3 45	—	8 5	1131	3 41	—	5 47	9 3	—
Varde ....arr	4 5	...	8 30	12 8	4 20	...	6 9	9 35	...
Skjern....................	5 4	a.m	10 1	2 22	6 36	...	7 21	—	...
Ringkjöbing	5 32	5 48	1050	3 33	7 25	...	7 56	...	...
Vemb......................	6 7	7 3	1143	4 43	—	...	8 33	...	...
Lemvig...........arr	...	...	...	6 35	p.m.	...	1020	...	...
Holstebro	6 27	7 49	1230	5 46	5 10	...	9 6	...	...
Struer ....arr	6 53	8 20	1256	6 24	5 36	...	9 28	...	...
Skive ....arr	7 37	1022	2 26	7 30	6 50	...	—	a.m.	...
Viborg	8 30	12 0	4 19	8 44	8 12	...	...	4 35	...
Langaa ....arr	9 23	1 48	6 17	9 30	9 4	...	...	5 35	...

	p.m.	a.m.	a.m.		a.m.	p m.	p.m.	p.m.
Langaa ....dep	1030	6 34	...	...	1016	2 15	6 53	7 5
Viborg	1141	7 32	...	...	12 6	3 58	7 42	8 14
Skive (303A) ......arr	—	8 18	...	...	1 26	5 16	8 15	9 3
Struer (303A)	...	9 17	9 39	...	3 30	7 12	9 5	10 15
Holstebro...........arr	...	9 37	1015	...	4 9	7 47	9 28	10 40
Lemvig ....dep	...	...	10 0	...	3 30	7 40	...	—
Vemb	a.m.	9 59	1117	...	4 57	8 49	9 49	...
Ringkjöbing ......arr	4 12	1035	1229	...	6 17	9 55	1014	...
Skjern (303A)	5 23	11 8	2 6	...	7 40	—	1047	...
Varde..................arr	7 10	12 6	3 37	...	9 21	*	1139	...
Esbjerg......... arr	8 4	1231	4 20	p.m	1011	nigt	12 4	a.m.
Esbjerg......... dep	8 15	1240	4 35	7 10	1030	1218	—	4 30
Bramminge	8 42	1259	5 9	8 0	1059	1237	...	5 25
Lunderskov.......arr	9 48	1 42	6 26	10 0	12 4	1 17	...	7 16
FREDERICIA (303)	1057	2p26	7p32	...	1 a0	2 a0	...	8 a57
COPENHAGEN 302	4p48	8p32	...	...	...	7a54	...	4 p48

Bramminge.........dep	5a35	7 a35	10a34	1p35	5 p24	8p35	11p21	...
Ribe	6 9	8 8	11 3	2 22	6 17	9 4	11 58	...
Vedsted (Hvidding) ar	6 19	9 18	11 12	2 34	6 30	9 13	...	...

Vedsted ......dep	...	...	7 a40	9 a37	1140	3p14	6 p55	9 p38
Ribe	4a40	6 a41	7 51	9 47	12 2	4 3	7 15	10 16
Bramminge arr	5 16	7 12	...	10 14	1240	4 45	7 53	10 51

Extra.

Esbjerg ....dep	9 a16	12p51
Lunderskov ....arr	11 44	2 51

*—Sleeping Cars, 1 & 2 Class, from Esbjerg Havn on Sunday, Tuesday, Thursday, and Saturday nights.
§—Monday, Tuesday, Wednesday, and Saturday only, (daily from 5th July to 17th August.)

Holstebro to Herning, 6.35 a.m., 12.27, 7.15 p.m. Return from Herning 8.55 a.m., 3.45, 9.27 p.m.

STRUER and THISTED.

Struer (303A) ....dep	6a54	9a22	3p25	7 p0	9 p33
Oddesund (South) ......arr	7 26	9 55	4 7	7 37	10 9
,, (North)......dep	7 49	1016	4 32	8 3	10 29
Hördum	9 19	1235	6 38	9 53	11 59
Thisted ....arr	10 2	1 32	7 41	1044	12 42

Thisted ....dep	5a20	8 a20	3 p6	5p52	7 p10
Hördum	6 3	9 17	3 56	6 38	8 8
Oddesund (North)...arr	7 51	11 38	5 39	8 13	10 31
,, (South)..dep	8 14	12 3	6 4	8 34	10 54
Struer ....arr	8 50	12 44	6 34	8 58	11 31

ODENSE and SVENDBORG.

E.M.							
	Odense(Sudbhf)dp	6a30	9 a35	12p35	2p30	4p50	9p35
13	Ringe ....arr	7 20	10 50	1 4	3 39	5 34	1040
31½	Faaborg ......arr	8 25	12 25	1 50	...	6 30	1155
29	Svendborg......arr	8 25	12 40	1 40	5 15	6 20	1155

Svendborg dep	6a10	10 a5	11a15	3 p0	5p35	9 p45
Faaborg dep	6 0	9 40	...	2 45	4 0	9 30
Ringe ....dep	7 27	11 12	1 10	3 42	7 20	10 56
Odense ......arr	8 20	11 50	2 5	4 15	8 30	11 40

*—Not on Sun.]

HORSENS and JUELSMINDE.

E.M.					
	Horsens ....dep	8a10	3 p0	5p30	9p55
19	Juelsminde arr	9 10	4 0	6 30	1055

Juelsminde...dep	5a45	7*a40	10a0	12*p20	5*45	...
Horsens ......arr	6 45	8 40	11 0	1 20	6 45	...

Herning dep	5a40	...	1 p0	6 p0
Viborg	7 34	1210	4 16	8 40
Aalestrup arr	8 56	1 48	6 1	10 2
Aalestrup dep	6 a2	10 a4	2 p9	6 p32
Viborg	7 25	11 49	3 45	7 56
Herning arr	10 9	2 56	...	10 28

HOBRO and LOGSTOR.

E.M					
	Hobro............dep	7 a55	1 p0	4 p50	8 p52
15	Aalestrup....	9 4	2 19	6 28	10 10
41½	Lögstör ....arr	10 35	4 25	8 36	11 38

Lögstör ....dep	4a23	7 a55	11a55	4 p50	...
Aalestrup............	6 8	10 0	2 15	6 34	...
Hobro 303 ...arr	7 3	11 2	3 21	7 30	...

RANDERS and HADSUND.

E.M.						
	Randers (303) dep	6a25	8 a30	4 p0	9 p0	...
25½	Hadsund ....arr	8 10	11 10	6 10	10 50	...

Hadsund.........dep	5a40	8a30	11a50	6 p40	...
Randers ....arr	7 50	1015	2 20	8 30	...

CHRISTIANIA, EIDSVOLD, and TRONDHJEM (DRONTHEIM).

Dist E.M	1 Cl. k.o.	2 Cl. k.o.	3 Cl. k.o.			2&3	1,2,3	2&3	2 & 3	2&3	2 & 3	2 & 3	1,2,3	2&3	1,2,3	2&3	2&3
						a.m.	a.m.		a.m.	a.m.	p.m.	p.m.	p.m.	p.m.	p.m.	p.m.	p.m.
—	—	—	—	**Christiania O.** ...dep		7 25	7 50	...	9 15	9 40	2 35	4 35	3 25	5 20	6 5	6†25	7 40
2½	...	0 40	0 20	Bryn		...	...	...	9 27	9 54	2 45	4 47	...	5 32	...	6 35	...
13	2 70	1 90	1 20	Lillestrom arr		8 0	8 17	...	10 2	1033	3 20	5 21	3 53	6 15	6 40	7 10	8 15
				Lillestrom dep		—	8 18	...	10 12	—	3 26	—	3 54	6 25	—	—	8 22
22¼	3 60	2 60	1 70	Kloften	3 Cl.	...	8 37	...	10 44	...	3 57	p.m.	...	7 0	...	...	8 53
42¼	5 80	4 20	2 70	**Eidsvold**	a.m.	...	9 20	...	11 54	...	—	1 †0	4 51	8 13	...	...	9 52
63½	8 70	6 15	4 10	Tangen	7†23	...	...	...	12 55	...	3 Cl.	4 0	...	9 27	...	...	—
78¼	10 75	7 60	5 5	**Hamar** arr	8 30	...	1035	a.m.	1 40	...	a.m.	5 45	6 7	1015	...	...	...
				Hamar dep	—	...	—	1050	2 10	...	11† 0	7 46	6§33	—	...	...	...
98¼	13 50	9 50	6 30	Elverum		...	...	1147	3 35	...	12 43	9 20	7 39	...	...	...	...
118	16 20	11 30	7 40	Rena arr		...	...	1231	4 34	...	—	—	8 23	...	...	...	...
				Rena dep		...	...	1237	4 41	...	...	...	8 34	...	...	...	...
153½	21 0	14 50	9 40	Koppang arr		...	...	2 5	6 34	...	...	...	10 5	...	...	...	...
				Koppang dep		...	...	2 23	6 46	...	...	...	1016	...	...	...	...
177	24 30	16 60	10 80	Hanestad	2&3	...	...	3 21	7 59	...	...	...	1121	...	...	...	...
201¼	27 40	18 60	12 0	Lilleelvedal	a.m.	...	...	4 21	9 16	...	...	...	1227	...	...	...	...
215½	29 20	19 70	12 70	Tonset	6 3	...	...	4 56	9 54	...	...	...	1 3	...	...	...	...
248	33 30	22 20	14 30	Roros dep	9 9	...	...	6 23	—	...	...	...	2 32	...	...	...	...
275¼	36 70	24 30	15 60	Eidet	1127	...	...	7 33	...	...	...	3 Cl.	3 46	...	...	...	...
298¼	39 60	26 10	16 70	**Singsaas** dep	1 30	...	3 Cl	8 41	...	...	...	a.m.	4 53	...	...	...	...
317	41 90	27 50	17 60	Storen	3 0	...	p.m.	9 28	...	...	...	6 †3	5 52	...	...	...	...
336¼	44 30	29 0	18 50	Melhus	4 39	...	8 57	1019	...	...	...	7 29	...	...	...	...	...
348¾	45 90	30 0	19 10	**Trondhjem** ...arr	5 50	...	1010	11 3	...	...	...	8 33	7 30	...	†—Weekdays only.	...	§—Sleeping Car (1st Cl.).

	2&3	2 & 3	2&3	3 Cl	2&3	1,2,3	2 & 3	2&3	3 Cl	2&3	3 Cl.	3Cl.	3 Cl.	2 & 3	3 Cl.	1,2,3
					a.m.		a.m.		p.m.				p.m.		p.m.	p.m.
Trondhjem ...dep	...	...	...	...	7 30	...	8 50	...	2†10	...	...	...	6 3	...	11 10	8 15
Melhus	...	...	...	...	...	...	10 0	...	3 1	...	...	...	7 5	...	12 *5	§
Storen	...	...	...	...	9 2	...	11 32	...	—	...	...	...	8 24	...	1 3	9 57
Singsaas ...dep	...	...	...	...	10 5	...	1 7	...	...	...	...	...	—	...	2 0	10 58
Eidet	...	...	...	...	1118	...	2 58	...	...	...	...	...	...	...	—	12 10
Roros ...dep	...	...	...	a.m.	1240	...	5 15	...	...	...	a.m.	...	...	...	...	1 37
Tonset	...	...	...	6†40	2 0	...	7 20	...	...	...	6 23	...	...	...	...	2 59
Lilleelvedal	...	...	...	7 45	2 31	...	8 1	...	...	...	7 0	...	...	...	...	3 32
Hanestad	...	...	...	9 17	3 29	*—Stops if required.	9 8	...	...	...	8 3	...	...	...	...	4 29
Koppang arr	...	...	...	1045	4 20		10 16	...	...	a.m.	9 1	...	...	...	...	5 21
Koppang dep	...	...	...	1110	4 38		—	...	...	6 0	9 14	...	...	...	...	5 33
Rena arr	...	...	...	2 3	5 54		...	...	...	7 54	10 39	...	...	...	...	6 50
Rena dep	...	a.m.	...	2 35	5 59		...	...	...	8 0	10 45	p.m.	...	...	...	6 55
Elverum	...	6†30	...	4 50	6 43		...	...	...	9 15	11 43	2†15	2 & 3	...	...	7 45
Hamar arr	...	8 26	...	6 53	7 35	p.m.	...	a.m.	...	1035	12 39	4 15	p.m.	...	p.m.	8 40
Hamar dep	...	—	...	—	—	7 46	...	6 20	...	1150	—	—	2 20	...	5 10	9 5
Tangen	a.m.	...	...	...		8 *25	...	7 25	...	1258	...	...	3 14	...	6 36	9 54
Eidsvold	5 45	...	...	...	...	9 17	...	8 57	...	2 16	...	...	4 29	...	—	10 35
Kloften	7 0	...	...	...	...	9*56	...	10 3	...	3 17	...	2&3	5 34	...	...	...
Lillestrom arr	7 32	a.m.	a.m.	...	...	10*15	a.m.	1034	...	3 46	...	p.m.	6 2	p.m.	p.m.	11 27
Lillestrom dep	7 40	8 8	9 40	...	...	10 15	9 53	1042	...	3 53	...	6 18	6 5	8 45	9 55	11 28
Bryn	8 21	8 51	1012	...	...	...	...	1121	...		...	6 59	...	9 17	...	...
Christiania O. ...arr	8 30	9 0	1019	...	...	10 42	10 30	1130	...	4 30	...	7 8	6 43	9 25	10 27	11 55

Extra.						
Christania...dep	6a50	1215	3p45	7p20	9p20	11p30
Lillestrom ...arr	7 35	1 0	4 30	8 5	10 5	12 15

Lillestrom ......dep	7 a0	10a5	2p20	4 p5	7p10	10p35
Christania ......arr	7 40	1045	3 0	4 45	7 50	11 15

NARVIK and RIKSGRANSEN.

E.M.		a.m.	a.m.	a.m.	p.m.	p.m.	p.m.	p.m.
—	**Narvik**	6†38	8 30	9†40	12†10	4 3	6§20	6†44
24½	**Riksgränsen**	8 52	1010	12 9	2 52	6 38	7 48	9 10

	a.m.	a.m.	a.m	p.m.	p.m.	p.m.	p.m.
Riksgränsen	6†33	9§11	9†33	12†26	3†10	4 †6	8 33
Narvik	8 23	1038	11 49	2 51	5 29	6 14	10 7

From Riksgransen into Sweden, page 311A. †—Weekdays only. May not run.

§—On Mon., Wed., and Sat. only, until 30th August.

TRONDHJEM (DRONTHEIM) and STORLIEN.

‡—Runs until 17th Aug.

Dist. E.M.		2&3	2&3	3Cl.	3 Cl	2 & 3	3 Cl	2&3	3 Cl
		a.m.	a.m.	p.m.	p m	p.m.	p.m.	p.m.	p.m.
—	**Trondhjem** d	8 10	8 33	1†10	2 13	2‡50	3 †0	6 20	8 5
14¼	Hommelvik	9 0	9 28	1 53	3 2	3 33	4 25	7 14	8 54
20	Hell	9 14	9 53	2 7	3 16	3 51	4 54	7 30	9 8
26	Hegre	—	1013	—	—	4 5	5 24	8 †0	—
44¾	Gudaa		1117	...	...	4 58	6 55	—	...
50¾	Meraker		1143	...	...	5 22	7 32	...	...
65¾	**Storlien** (309) arr		1250	...	...	6 30	9 0	...	...
...	OSTERSUND arr		6p18	...	...	11p49	...	...	...
532	STOCKHOLM arr		7a50	...	...	8p20	...	...	...

†—Weekdays only.

		3 Cl	2&3	‡	3Cl.	3Cl.	2&3	2&3	3 Cl.
STOCKHOLM 309 dep		...	...	9 a0	...	...	...	9p20	...
OSTERSUND ...dep		...	...	5a40	...	...	...	1115	...
		a.m.		a.m.				p.m.	
Storlien ...dep		5 30	...	1047	...	...	...	4 31	...
Meraker		6 50	...	1139	...	...	...	5 22	...
Gudaa	a.m	7 21	...	1153	...	...	...	5 41	...
Hegre	6†45	8 41	a.m.	1233	p.m.	p.m.	p.m.	6 33	p.m.
Hell	7 21	10 0	9 46	1247	2 41	3 55	6 27	6 57	10 16
Hommelvik	7 38	1031	10 0	1 2	3 1	4 15	6 43	7 16	10 34
Trondhjem arr	8 32	1145	1040	1 50	4 0	5 8	7 20	8 3	11 33

HELL and SUNNAN.

†—Sunday excepted.

E.M		a.m.	a.m.	p.m.
—	Hell......dep	...	9 20	7 36
52½	Levanger...	6†30	11 3	9 20
78¼	Stenkjær ...	9 4	1224	1038
85½	Sunnan arr	9 34	1246	11 0

	a.m.	a.m.	p.m.
Sunnan dep	6 12	10†25	2 44
Stenkjær ...	6 36	11 10	3 6
Levanger...	7 58	1 42	4 36
Hell......arr	9 38	...	6 25

*—5.0 p.m. on Sunday. †—Sunday excepted.

TRONDHJEM and LOKKEN.

§—11.15 p.m. on Sunday.

k. o.	k. o.		a.m.	a.m.	p.m.	p.m.
—	—	**Trondhjem**—Steamer dep	...	9 45	...	6§30
1 25	0 75	Thamshavn ...arr	...	1130	...	8 15
...	...	„ Rail ...dep	7†20	1142	3†55	8 27
3 65	1 70	Svorkmo	8 40	1227	5 12	9 15
4 65	2 10	**Lokken** ...arr	9 0	1245	5 30	9 35

	a.m.	a.m.	p.m.	p.m.	
Lokken ...dep	5 30	9 35	2 *15	6†20	...
Svorkmo	5 50	10 0	2 35	6 45	...
Thamshavn ...arr	6 34	10 50	3 19	7 37	...
„ Steamer...dep	6 40	—	3 25	—	...
Trondhjem ...arr	8 25	...	5 10	...	...

CHRISTIANIA, FREDRIKSHALD, and KORNSJO, FOR COPENHAGEN.

THROUGH CARRIAGES—Christiania to Copenhagen and Hamburg in 6.45 p.m. from Christiania.

SLEEPING CARS in 6.45 p.m. from Christiania. ‡—Stops if required to take up only.

Dist E.M	1 Cl. k.o.	2 Cl. k.o.	3 Cl. k.o.		2&3	2 & 3	1,2,3	2 & 3	2 & 3	2 & 3	2&3	2 & 3	1,2,3	2 & 3	2 & 3	2&3	2 & 3	2 & 3	2 & 3
					a.m.		a.m.	a.m.	a.m.	p.m.	p.m.	p.m.	p.m.	p.m.	p.m.	p.m.	p.m.	p.m.	p.m.
—	—	—	—	**Christiania O.** dep	7 0	...	7 44	8 20	9 35	1 †30	2 7	3 10	5 45	6 10	6 45	7 2	7 47	10 20	11 15
5	...	...	...	Lian	7‡16	...	RC	8 ‡35	9 52	1 ‡46	*	...	...	...	7 ‡0	7 19	...	10‡36	11‡35
15	2 90	2 0	1 30	**Ski (304A)**	7 52	a.m.	8 ‡18	9 6	10 26	2 36	2 58	3 57	SC	6 57	7 30	7 53	8 33	11 10	12 17
37¼	5 20	3 80	2 45	Moss	—	5 40	8 59	10 7	—	3 53	—	—	7 6	—	8 32	—	—	—	1 23
58½	8 0	5 55	3 80	Fredrikstad		6 54	9 37	11 12	...	5 14	...	...	7 46	...	9 33	...	...	...	—
67¾	9 30	6 55	4 40	**Sarpsborg (304A)**		7 40	9 59	11 41	...	6 3	...	...	8 8	...	10 8	...	...	...	...
85½	11 65	8 25	5 50	**Fredrikshald** arr		8 30	10 32	12 25	...	7 1	...	...	8 41	...	10 52	...	...	...	...
				Fredrikshald dep		—	10 40	12 31	...	7 11	...	...	8 50	...	11 7	...	...	...	...
105	14 40	10 10	6 70	**Kornsjo** arr		...	11 27	1 53	...	8 30	...	...	9 37	...	12 18	...	...	...	...
145¼	19 50	13 40	8 90	MELLERUD 306 arr		...	1 p5	5 p5	...	...	...	...	1112	...	...	...	...	...	...
221¾	28 90	18 80	12 50	GOTHENBURG 306 arr		...	3 p20	8 p59	...	...	...	...	1a21	...	...	...	...	...	...
407¾	50 70	32 10	...	COPENHAGEN 303 arr		...	10p29	...	...	...	...	...	8a29	...	...	...	...	...	...

	2 & 3	2&3	2 & 3	2 & 3	2 & 3	1,2,3	2 & 3	2 & 3	2&3	2 & 3	2 & 3	2 & 3	1,2,3	2 & 3	2 & 3	2 & 3	2 & 3	
COPENHAGEN 303 dep	...	...	...	...	...	9 p5	...	...	...	...	...	...	7 a0	...	...	...	...	...
GOTHENBURG 306 dep	...	...	...	...	...	4a32	...	...	...	...	...	8 a40	1p54	...	...	...	...	...
MELLERUD 306 dep	...	...	...	...	...	6a43	...	...	...	...	...	12 0	4p10	...	...	...	...	...
						a.m.	a.m.			p.m.		p.m.	p.m.			p.m.	p.m	
Kornsjo dep	...	...	...	...	...	8 16	8 31	...	...	...	...	2 40	5 51	...	...	...	9 45	...
Fredrikshald arr	...	...	...	a.m.	...	8 57	9 42	...	...	...	...	4 10	6 32	...	...	...	11 0	...
Fredrikshald dep	...	...	...	6 50	...	9 5	10 32	...	...	...	...	4 45	6 42	...	...	8 41		...
Sarpsborg	...	...	...	7 38	...	9 41	11 40	...	...	...	...	5 34	7 20	...	...	9 48	...	...
Fredrikstad	...	a.m.	...	8 9	...	10 2	12 18	...	...	12*26	...	6 7	7 44	...	...	10 31	...	...
Moss	a.m.	6 5	a.m.	9 21	a.m.	10 42	—	p.m.	p.m.	1 49	p.m.	7 12	8 25	p.m.	p.m.	11 39	...	...
Ski	5 50	7 32	7*55	10 26	10 37	...	...	12 23	2*37	3 10	4 41	8 18	RC	8 39	9 18	...	...	...
Lian	6 29	8 17	8 36	...	11 §7	...	...	12 59	...	3 46	5 14	8 §43	...	9§11	9 §53	...	...	...
Christiania arr	6 50	8 35	8 53	11 0	11 20	12 0	...	1 15	3 24	4 0	5 31	8 55	9 43	9 26	10 8	...	...	...

§—Sets down only.

*—Weekdays only. †—Weekdays only between Christiania and Frederikstad. RC—Restaurant Car.

Ski and Sarpsborg via Mysen

Ski dep	†	8 a2	3†p8	7 p3	8p†50
Mysen	7a15	9 43	4 36	8 16	10 27
Rakkestad	8 1	10 19	5 8	8 47	—
Sarpsborg 304A arr	8 58	11 9	5 57	9 31	...

Sarpsborg dep	...	7a47	11†a28	6p20	8 †55
Rakkestad	...	8 35	12 25	7 11	10 6
Mysen	5 a50	9 9	1 6	7 51	10 43
Ski 304A arr	7 47	10 34	2 30	9 13	...

†—Weekdays only.

CHRISTIANIA and CHARLOTTENBERG, FOR STOCKHOLM.

SLEEPING CARS to Stockholm in 6.5 p.m. from Christiania.

Dist. E.M.	1 Cl. k.o.	2 Cl. k.o.	3 Cl. k.o.		2 & 3	2 & 3	2 & 3	2 & 3	1,2,3	2 & 3	2 & 3						
					a.m.	a.m.	p.m.	p.m.	p.m.	p.m.	p.m.						
—	—	—	—	**Christiania O.** dep	7 25	9 40	12 15	4 35	6 5	6†25	7 20	...	...	...	...	...	...
13	2 70	1 90	1 20	Lillestrom arr	8 0	10 33	1 0	5 21	6 40	7 10	8 5	...	...	...	...	...	...
...	...	...	...	Lillestrom dep	8 5	10 45	1 5	5 29	6 44	7 20	—	...	...	...	...	...	...
23	...	1 85	1 25	Sorumsanden	8 31	11 19	1 32	5 57	SC	7 56	...	...	...	...	...	...	...
36	5 10	3 70	2 40	Aarnæs	9 7	12 10	2 5	6 39	7 32	8 43	...	...	...	...	...	...	...
62¼	8 50	6 0	4 0	Kongsvinger	10 18	2 25	—	7 56	8 34	—	...	...	...	...	...	...	...
75¾	...	6 10	3 80	Eidskogen	10 47	3 10	...	8 27	...	...	...	...	...	...	...	...	...
88¼	12 10	8 50	5 65	**Charlottenberg** arr	11 17	3 58	...	8 58	9 22	...	...	...	...	...	...	...	...
214½	26 60	17 20	11 45	LAXA (308) arr	4 p38	...	...	...	1 a50	...	...	...	...	...	...	...	...
375¾	37 60	23 80	15 85	STOCKHOLM (308) arr	9 18	...	...	...	7 a8	...	...	...	...	...	...	...	...

STOCKHOLM 309 dep	...	...	9p35	...	...	8 a38												
LAXA (308) dep	...	...	2a58	...	5 a4	1 p18	...	...	...	...	...	...	...	...	...	...	...	...
	2&3	2 & 3	1,2,3	2 & 3	2 & 3	2 & 3	...	...	...	...	...	...	...	...	...	...	...	...
		a.m.	a.m.		p.m.	p.m.												
Charlottenberg dep	...	6 10	7 18	...	12 30	6 39	...	...	...	...	...	...	...	...	...	...	...	...
Eidskogen	...	6 43	...	...	1 28	7 11	...	...	...	...	...	...	...	...	...	...	...	...
Kongsvinger	a.m.	7 23	8 17	p.m.	2 35	7 50	...	...	...	...	...	...	...	...	...	...	...	...
Aarnæs	6 20	8 32	...	2 59	4 20	8 55	...	...	...	...	...	...	...	...	...	...	...	...
Sorumsanden	7 20	9 8	...	3 33	5 26	9 26	...	...	...	...	...	...	...	...	...	...	...	...
Lillestrom arr	7 56	9 32	9 48	3 57	6 6	9 50	...	...	...	...	...	...	...	...	...	...	...	...
Lillestrom dep	8 8	9 40	9 53	4 5	6 18	9 55	...	...	...	...	...	...	...	...	...	...	...	...
Christiania arr	9 0	10 19	10 30	4 45	7 8	10 27	...	...	...	...	...	...	...	...	...	...	...	...

†—Weekdays only.

SORUMSANDEN and SKULERUD.

Sorumsanden dep	8 a50	3‡p37	6‡p20	9*p25	...	...
Bjorkelangen	10 35	5 40	8 0	11 0	...	...
Skulerud arr	12 0	...	9 30	12 20	...	...

Skulerud dep	...	9§a13	1‡p40	6 *p0
Bjorkelangen	5‡a20	11 18	3 23	7 35
Sorumsanden arr	7 0	1 20	5 0	9 0

‡—Sun. excepted. §—5.30 a.m. on Sun. and Thurs. *—Sun. only.

KONGSVINGER and ELVERUM.

Kongsvinger dep	...	10a20	2*p20	8 p35
Flisen	5*a50	12 0	5 51	9 58
Elverum arr	8 20	1 23	7 29	11 3

Elverum dep	5 a40	9*a25	4 p0	8*p0
Flisen	6 55	11 50	5 39	9 19
Kongsvinger arr	8 10	2 20	7 18	...

*—Weekdays only.

CHRISTIANIA and SKIEN.

Dist. E.M.	2 Cl. k. o.	3 Cl. k. o.		2 & 3 a.m.	2 & 3	2 & 3 a.m.	2&3 a.m.	3 Cl.	2 & 3 p.m.	2&3 p.m.	2&3 p.m.	2&3 p.m.	2&3 p.m.
—	—	—	**Christiania V....dep**	6 0	...	8 0	1025	...	3 18	4 19	5 5	8 20	1130
14¼	...	...	Asker	7 20	...	...	1128	...	4 5	...	6 2	9 10	SC
28½	3 10	2 0	Lier	8 19	...	9 15	1215	...	4 52	5 38	7 4	9 59	...
33	3 45	2 25	**Drammen ....arr**	8 38	...	9 30	1233	p.m.	5 8	5 55	7 23	1016	1 0
...	...	...	,, (305)...dep	—	...	9 40	1245	1 ‡15	5 18	—	7 40	—	1 10
53½	5 20	3 45	Holmestrand	...	a.m.	10 44	1 49	3 20	6 25	...	9 24	...	2 6
62½	6 0	4 0	**Skoppum**	...	6 6	11 13	2 19	4 23	6 57	...	10 9	...	2†29
71½	6 90	4 60	Tonsberg	...	7 10	11 47	2 52	5 40	7 37	...	1047	...	2 58
86¼	8 35	5 60	Sandefjord	...	8 12	12 31	3 35	7 46	8 31	...	—	...	3 39
98¼	9 50	6 30	**Larvik** arr	...	8 56	1 1	4 5	9 25	9 5	...	...	...	4 9
			Larvik dep	...	9 20	1 7	4 10	10 10	9 18	...	...	...	4 15
119¼	11 40	7 50	Eidanger	...	10 45	2 9	5 16	11 49	10 30	...	...	...	5 20
121¼	11 50	7 60	Porsgrund	...	11 3	2 17	5 27	12 12	10 38	...	...	...	5 27
126¾	11 90	7 90	**Skien ....arr**	...	11 20	2 30	5 40	12 29	10 51	...	...	...	5 45

	2&3	2&3	2 & 3	2&3 a.m.	3 Cl. a.m.	2 & 3 a.m.	2&3	2&3 p.m	2&3	2&3 p.m.	3Cl, p.m.	2 & 3 p.m.	2&3 p.m.	
Skien ....dep	...	...	...	4 25	...	7 35	...	1240	...	3 25	5 45	...	8 20	...
Porsgrund	...	...	...	4 57	...	7 52	...	1 5	...	3 41	6 1	...	8 43	...
Eidanger	...	...	...	5 5	5 ‡14	8 1	...	1 16	...	3 48	6 7	6 17	8 51	...
Larvik arr	...	...	a.m.	—	6 42	9 4	...	2 39	...	4 48	—	7 11	9 59	...
Larvik dep	...	...	5 35	...	7 7	9 10	...	2 49	...	4 53	...	7 17	—	...
Sandefjord	...	a.m.	6 11	...	8 19	9 48	...	3 39	...	5 29	...	7 50	...	...
Tonsberg	...	5 25	6 57	...	9 54	10 36	...	4 40	...	6 15	...	8 30	...	...
Skoppum	...	6 3	7 35	...	11 44	11 13	...	5 17	...	6 52	...	9 0	...	...
Holmestrand	...	6 36	8 12	...	12 46	11 46	...	—	...	7 24	...	9 29	...	...
Drammen ....arr	a.m.	7 43	9 17	...	2 45	12 45	p.m.	...	p.m.	8 25	...	10 20	...	...
,, ...dep	6 15	7 53	9 40	...	—	12 55	3 30	...	5 18	8 35	...	10 30	...	...
Lier	6 40	8 18	9 58	...	...	1 13	3 54	...	5 37	8 52	...	...	...	...
Asker	7 48	9 24	10 47	...	...	2 3	5 5	...	6 26	9†32	...	...	...	...
Christiania V....arr	8 50	1013	11 29	...	...	2 50	6 11	...	7 8	1012	...	12 4	...	...

†—Sets down only. ‡—Weekdays only. SC—Sleeping Car, 2nd cl. in this train.

LIER and SVANGSTRAND.

	a.m.	p.m.
Lier ....dep	9 20	6 *0
Svangstrand arr	10 25	7 10

	a.m.	p.m.
Svangstrand dep	6 40	4 15
Lier ....arr	7 55	5 28

*—On Sunday dep. 5.50 p.m

Skoppum & Horten, in 15 minutes.—Skoppum depart 6.10, 7.34, 11.20 a.m., 2.25, 4†45, 5.23, 7.0, 9.5, 10.10 p.m. Horten depart 5.40, 7.4, 10.45 a.m., 1.52, 3†43, 6.23, 8.38, 9.40 p.m.

†—Weekdays only.

HOLMESTRAND and VITTINGFOSS.

Holmestrand...dep	1†p15	7p45
Hillestad	2 1	8 33
Vittingfoss......arr	3 8	9 40
Vittingfoss......dep	7 a30	4p15
Hillestad	8 21	5 10
Holmestrand ...arr	9 20	6 6

†—12.0 noon on Sunday.

LILLESAND and FLAKSVAND.

Lillesand ......dep	7 a45	3 p0
Flaksvand ......arr	8 45	4 0
Flaksvand ......dep	9 a15	6p30
Lillesand.........arr	10 15	7 30

SKIEN and BREVIK.

‡—Weekdays only.

Skien...............dep	...	6 a0	8a50	...	11a‡35	1p38	2p30	4p43	5p45	7p15	10 p2	...	...
Eidanger	5a18	6 29	9 21	10a50	12 4	2 12	2 59	5 15	6 18	7 46	10 34	...	...
Brevik .... arr	5 37	6 51	9 43	11 12	12 26	2 34	3 21	5 37	6 40	8 8	10 56	...	...

Brevik ....dep	...	7 a35	8 a54	10a20	11a26	12‡p34	3 p22	4 p15	5 p55	...	7 p3	10p10
Eidanger	5 a20	8 2	9 20	10 44	11 51	12 59	3 50	4 40	6 14	6 p17	7 31	10 38
Skien ....arr	5 45	8 31	9 50	...	12 19	1 28	4 18	5 27	...	6 46	8 1	11 12

TONSBERG and EIDSFOS.

Tonsberg ......dep	12* 5	8 p5
Eidsfos ....arr	3 6	1045
Eidsfos..........dep	6a20	4p15
Tonsberg ......arr	9 35	7 7

*—On Sun. 11.0 a.m.

DRAMMEN and RANDSFJORD.

†—Weekdays only.

E.M.								
	Drammen dep	6a20	8a10	9 a50	3 p0	6 p15	10p30	...
10½	**Hougsund** arr	6 49	8 48	10 18	3 39	6 50	11 2	...
16¾	Skotselven	7 9	—	10 41	4 10	7 17	—	...
26¾	**Vikesund** ...arr	7 35	...	11 7	4 48	7 50	...	...
43	Kroderen ...arr	...	...	12 27	...	9 12	...	...
36	Skjærdalen ...dep	8 3	...	11 12	5 30	8 26	...	...
44	Hönefoss 304	8 24	...	11 57	5 59	8 50	...	...
55½	**Randsfjord** arr	...	...	12 40	6 43	9 26	...	...

Randsfjord ...dep	...	5 a53	...	2 p5	...	7 p3	...
Hönefoss	...	6 36	10a10	3 0	...	8 0	...
Skjærdalen	...	7 0	10 36	3 21	...	8 27	...
Kroderen ....dep	...	6 0	...	2 25	...	...	...
Vikesund ....dep	...	7 35	11 7	3 47	...	8 57	...
Skotselven	a.m.	8 17	11 40	4 11	p.m.	9 28	...
Hougsund ......dep	6 55	8 49	12 3	4 33	6 52	9 49	...
Drammen.........arr	7 28	9 20	12 38	5 0	7 30	10 20	...

Hougsund dep	9 a0	10a30	2†p50	7 p2	11 p4
Kongsberg arr	10 40	11 27	5 0	8 2	12 0

Kongsberg dep	5a50	7 a38	11†a36	3p25	5 p45
Hougsund...arr	6 48	8 40	1 30	4 22	6 45

NOTODDEN and RJUKAN.

		a.m.	a.m.		p.m.	
Notodden ....dep	...	7 40	11 15	...	7 15	...
Tinnoset .... arr	...	9 10	12 15	...	8 15	...
Steamer connection	a.m.	—	p.m	p.m.	p.m.	
Rollag .... dep	7 30	...	2 50	6 30	11 10	...
Rjukan ....arr	8 0	...	3 20	7 0	11 40	...

	a.m.	a.m.		p.m.	p.m.	
Rjukan ....dep	6 35	11 10	...	5 20	1015	...
Rollag .... arr	7 5	11 40	...	5 50	1045	...
Steamer connection	a.m.	—	p.m.	p.m.	—	
Tinnoset .... dep	9 40	...	12 30	8 55	...	...
Notodden ....arr	10 40	...	1 30	9 55	...	...

CHRISTIANSAND and BYGLANDSFJORD.

E.M.		a.m.	a.m.	a.m.	p.m.	p.m.	p.m.	
—	**Christiansand**...dep	6 †0	9 10	10†40	2*10	4 40	7 15	...
9¼	**Vennesla**	6 40	9 43	11 19	2 54	5 23	7 56	...
27¼	**Haegeland**	—	11 1	—	—	7 3	—	...
48½	**Byglandsfjord**...arr	...	12 10	...	...	8 35	...	...

		a.m.			p.m.	
Byglandsfjord...dep	...	6 0	...	...	2 50	...
Haegeland	a.m.	7 36	p.m.	p.m.	4 7	p.m.
Vennesla	7†38	9 16	12 †8	3§45	5 22	8 38
Christiansand ...arr	8 15	9 50	12 45	4 25	5 55	9 15

*—1.25 p.m. on Sunday. †—Weekdays only. §—2.32 p.m. on Sunday.

A—Until 31st August only.]

CHRISTIANIA, FAGERNAES, and GJOVIK.

		2 & 3 a.m.	2 & 3 a.m.	2&3 a.m.	2 & 3 p.m.	2&3 p.m.	2 & 3 p.m.	2 & 3 p.m.
Christiania O. dep		7 35	8 5	1050	2 †15	3 50	6 15	7 25
Grefsen ....dep		7 53	8 24	11 9	2 37	4 7	6 34	7 43
Hakedal ....2&3		8 38	9 11	1216	3 39	A	7 23	8 32
Roa ....arr	6†50	9 17	9 59	1 16	4 35	...	8 11	
Jaren ....arr	7 26	RC	10 28		5 13	5 44	8 40	...
Roikenvik arr	7 46		10 50	...	6 5	6 5	9 3	...
" dep		...	10 10	...	4 0	4 0	8 20	...
Jaren ....dep		...	10 36	...	6 12	5 50	8 48	...
Eina ....arr		...	11 35	...	7 31	6 43	9 46	...
Eina ....dep		3 Cl.	11 40	...	7†45	6 49	...	...
Odnes		a.m.	1 5	...	9 57	8 0	...	...
Dokka		8 †0	1 30	...	10 15	8 23	...	...
Tonsaasen ......2&3		10 25	2 48	...		9 27	...	...
Fagernaes ¶ arr		12 5	3 55	...	...	1020	...	...
Eina ....dep	8 a0	...	11 39	...	...	6 50	9 48	...
Reinsvold	8 16	...	11 51	...	...	7 0	9 59	...
Gjovik ...arr	8 50	...	12 22	...	...	7 31	10 30	...

		2&3 a.m.	2&3 a.m.	2 & 3	2&3 p.m.	2&3 p.m.	
Gjovik ....dep	...	7 30	1030	...	5 50	9†10	...
Reinsvold	...	8 19	1116	...	6 36	9 56	...
Eina ....arr	...	8 30	1127	...	6 47	10 7	...
			a.m.	a.m.	p.m.		
Fagernaes ¶ ...dep	...	...	5 †0	8 0	2 30	...	...
Tonsaasen	...	...	6 48	9 4	3 45	...	...
Dokka	...	...	8 25	10 5	4 58	...	...
Odnes	...	...	8 48	10 19	5 15	...	...
Eina ....arr	...	...	1110	11 30	6 45	...	...
Eina ....dep	...	8 32	1142	11 35	6 53	...	...
Jaren ....arr	2&3	9 16	1241	12 15	7 37	...	...
Roikenvik ....arr	a.m.	9 38	1 5	1 5	7 58	RC	...
" ....dep	5†23	8 57	1210	11 50	7 20	...	...
Jaren ....dep	5†45	9 25	1248	12 19	7 43	2&3	p.m.
Roa ....dep	6 45	10 2	1 35	...	8 19	p.m.	8 55
Hakedal	7 37	1042	2 31	A	8 59	8 40	9 28
Grefsen ....arr	8 38	1128	3 27	1 50	9 43	9 21	10 5
Christiania O. ...arr	8 58	1141	3 45	2 1	9 56	9 36	1018

RC—Restaurant Car.

¶—At Fagernaes are motors and horsed carriages for Lærdal, on the Sogne Fjord. †—Weekdays only.

REINSVOLD and SKREIA.										
Reinsvold...dep	8‡a25	1155	7 p5	10 p2	**Skreia** ....dep	6 a35	10a20	5p20	8p55	‡—8.15 a.m. on Sunday.
Skreia ......arr	9 40	1251	7 55	10 52	Reinsvold ... arr	7 54	11 10	6 25	9 45	

†—Week-days only.]

CHRISTIANIA AND DOMBAAS.

Dist. E.M.	2 Cl. k.o.	3 Cl. k.o.		3Cl.	3Cl.	1,2,3 a.m.	2&3 a.m.	2&3 p.m.	2&3 p.m.
—	—	—	**Christiania O.** dep	...	...	7 50	9 15	3 25	...
13	1 90	1 20	Lillestrom ....dep	...	a.m.	8 18	1012	3 54	...
78¼	7 60	5 5	**Hamar**..............dep	...	5†55	10 50	2 10	6 20	6†33
96¾	9 10	5 90	**Moelven**	a.m.	7 31	11 48	3 13	7 18	8 8
114¼	10 30	6 70	**Lillehammer**	6 30	8 50	12 43	4 14	8 3	9 13
133	11 70	7 50	**Tretten**	8 50		1 32	5 11		
151	12 90	8 30	**Ringebu**..............	1027	...	2 20	5 59	...	...
165	14 0	9 0	**Vinstra**	1148	...	3 4	6 43	...	...
184½	15 30	9 80	**Otta**.............. arr	1255	...	3 46	7 25	...	a.m.
...	...		**Otta** dep		...	3 52	7 34	...	7†25
...	...	☞	Brennhaugen	...	...	4 38	8 20	...	8 50
...	...		Dovre	...	...	4 53	8 35	...	9 25
...	...		**Dombaas**..........arr	...	...	5 18	9 0	...	1010

	2&3	3 Cl	2&3 a.m.	3Cl.	2&3 p.m.	3Cl. p.m.
Dombaas ......dep	...	...	5 55	...	1 0	1 15
Dovre	...	...	6 17	...	1 16	1 55
Brennhaugen	...	...	6 39	...	1 36	2 30
Otta .... arr	...	...	7 16	...	2 8	3 33
Otta .... dep	...	...	7 30	...	2 20	4 0
Vinstra..............	...	a.m	8 25	...	3 9	5 20
Ringebu	...	6†45	9 18	...	3 57	6 45
Tretten..............	a.m.	7 37	1010	p.m.	4 40	8 0
Lillehammer	6 30	8 50	1130	2†10	5 38	9 20
Moelven	7 19	10 0	1235	3 50	6 27	
Hamar .... arr	8 28	1116	1 50	6 15	7 26	...
Lillestrom......arr	1127	3 46	6 2		1015	...
Christiania arr	1155	4 30	6 43	...	1042	...

☞ Opening of line between Otta and Dombaas not yet announced.

CHRISTIANIA, GULSVIK, VOSS, and BERGEN.

Dist E.M	2 Cl. k.o.	3 Cl. k.o.			2&3 a.m.	3 Cl ...	2&3 a.m.	2 & 3 a.m.	2 & 3 p.m.	2&3 p.m.	2&3 p.m.	2&3 p.m.
—	—	—	**Christiania O.**		8 5	...	7‡35	10 50	12‡40	2†15	6 15	1052
4¼	0 40	0 25	Grefsen		8 24	...	7 53	11 9	...	2 37	6 34	§
36	3 70	2 40	Roa		1010	...	9 18	1 30	A	4 50	8 25	..
56	5 40	3 60	Honefoss 305...		11 5	...	1015	3 15	3 0	6 5	9 21	1 12
87½	8 50	5 65	Gulsvik			...	1135	5 35	4 8			2 20
125½	12 0	7 90	Gol			a.m.	1 9	8 40	5 35	...	...	3 45
157¼	14 80	9 70	Gjeilo			8 50	2 48		7 0	A—Runs until	31st August only.	5 9
171¼	16 10	10 50	Haugastol			9 55	3 28	...	7 38			5 47
187¾	17 50	11 40	Finse		2&3	11 5	4 14	...	8 20			6 24
208¾	19 20	12 40	Myrdal ...	3 Cl	a.m.	1225	5 6	...	9 10			7 12
239¼	21 50	13 80	Voss	a.m.	6 15	3 0	6 27	...	10 22			8 22
287¾	20 70	12 90	Garnes ...	6 0	9 33	5 56	8 28	...	...			*
305¾	26 70	17 10	**Bergen** ...	7 24	1035	7 0	9 15	...	1 0			11 0
			BERGEN ......dep		...	...	...	...	...	...	...	1p0¶
			NEWCASTLE...arr		...	...	...	...	...	...	...	...
			BERGEN ...dep		...	...	...	...	...	...	...	12 0
			HULL.........arr		...	...	...	...	...	...	...	●

¶—From Bergen on Mon., Wed., Sat.—passage about 32 hours.

●—From Bergen on Saturday at noon, arrive Hull Mon. early morn.

‡—Restaurant Car in this train. †—Weekdays only.

NEWCASTLE dep	From Newcastle Tues., Th., Sat. midnight—passage about 36 hrs.	12 0
BERGEN ......arr		12 0
HULL ......dep	From Hull every Thur. aft. or even.	...
BERGEN ...arr		...

		2&3	2&3 a.m.	2&3 a.m.	1,2,3 a.m.	2&3 p.m.	2&3 p.m
Bergen............dep		...	6 40	8 15	11‡45	4 5	6*40
Garnes		...	7 42	‡	A	5 10	§
Voss		...	1041	11 8	2 30	8 3	9 28
Myrdal		...		1 10	4 13		11 9
Finse		...	...	2 24	5 18	...	1215
Haugastol		...	...	2 58	5 50	...	1248
Gjeilo		...	a.m.	3 33	6 19	...	1 17
Gol	2&3	...	6 53	4 48	7 30	...	2 24
Gulsvik	a.m.	a.m.	9 38	6 26	8 59	p.m.	3 52
Honefoss	5†15	8 40	12 3	7 56	10 20	6 52	5 4
Roa	6 45	10 2	1 35	8 55	...	8 19	...
Grefsen	8 43	1128	3 30	10 6	A	9 43	...
Christiania arr	8 58	1141	3 45	1018	12 35	9 56	7 15

*—Restaurant Car, Voss-Bergen.

§—Sleeping Car (1st class) in this train.

Bergen to Nesttun, calling at **Fjosanger**, 6.25, 7.45, 8.30, 9*11, 11.5 a.m., 12.20, 1.25, 2.10, 3.35, 4.45, 5.50, 7.20, 8.20, 10.0, and 11.30 p.m. Return from **Nesttun** 7.48, 8.32, 9.13, 10*29, 11.42 a.m., 12.49, 2.12, 3.9, 4.5, 5.14, 6.36, 7.51, 9.0, 10.34 and 11.54 p.m. In 20 minutes. *—Not on Sunday.

Nesttun to Os, 15½ miles, in 1½ hours. From Nesttun 9.0 a.m., 2.37, 7.57 p.m. From Os 6.50 a.m., 12.40, 6.20 p.m.

STAVANGER and FLEKKEFJORD.

	a.m.	a.m.	p.m.	p.m.	p.m.
Stavanger ......dep	5†40	9 0	1 50	3†30	5 50
Sandnæs	6 35	9 27	2 18	4 18	6 35
Nærbo	8 7	1016	3 17	5 50	7 40
Egersund	1010	1134	5 0	7 50	9 10
Flekkefjord......arr	...	2 15	8 15	...	...

	a.m.	a.m.	a.m.	p.m.	p.m.
Flekkefjord ...dep	...	...	8 30	...	1 30
Egersund	5†30	7 30	11 25	2 †0	4 50
Nærbo	8 0	9 12	12 39	3 53	6 26
Sandnæs	9 45	10 9	1 22	5 17	7 30
Stavanger ......arr	1020	1040	1 47	5 47	8 0

†—Week-days only, 3rd class.

*—Dep. 10.10 a.m. on Sunday.

ARENDAL and AAMLI.

‡—On Sunday dep. 1.0 p.m.

Arendal.........dep	8 a30	12*10	5 p15
Rise	9 14	12 45	5 55
Froland	9 36	1 8	6 18
Aamli ....arr	11 21	...	8 2

Aamli ....dep	6 a55	...	3p46
Froland	8 39	2p‡36	5 25
Rise	9 8	3 9	5 54
Arendal ....arr	9 40	3 40	6 26

Rise ....dep	9a20	3†p5	6 p0
Grimstad ....arr	1029	3 58	6 53
Grimstad ......dep	8 a0	2†p0	4p30
Rise ....arr	8 53	2 53	5 40

†—Sat. only.

GOTHENBURG and BORAS.

‡—Not on Sunday. *—Until 10th Sept. on Weekdays only.

Gothenburg......dep	8 a10	12p45	2*p35	3p‡23	5p25	7 p20	...
Landvetter	8 48	1 22	3 12	4 0	6 9	8 4	...
Boras..................arr	10	2 35	4 26	...	7 25	9 20	...

Boras ....dep	a.m. 8 6	8 a37	12p25	3 p1	5p55	10p27	...
Landvetter	8 6	9 57	1 40	4 18	8 5	...	...
Gothenburg...arr	8 46	10 34	2 17	4 55	8 57	11 50	...

STOCKHOLM & NYNASHAMN.

‡—Not on Sunday.

Stockholm C.dep	6‡a45	9a19	1152	3p23	4‡p10	5p22	9p22
Elfsjo..................	7 8	9 41	1219	3 45	4 26	5 38	9 47
Nynashamn arr	8 29	1058	1 37	5 2	5 14	7 11	1055

Nynashamn dep	6a0	7a40	8‡a42	10a44	2p50	5p45	8p15
Elfsjo	812	9 19	9 30	12 7	4 6	6 57	9 36
Stockholm arr	834	9 41	9 46	12 33	4 22	7 21	10 4

FALUN, MELLERUD, and GOTHENBURG.

*—1,2,3 Class.

Dist E M		(times set in station column)										
...	GEFLE (306) ....dep		...	...	...	...	...	7a45	...	...	2p10	...
			2&3	2&3	1,2,3	2&3	2 & 3	2&3	2&3	2&3	2&3	2&3
							a.m.	a.m.	p.m.	p.m.	p.m.	p.m.
—	Falun ....dep		...	...	...	...	7 15	1015	1225	3 15	4 45	7 20
10½	Ornäs		...	...	...	...	7 48	1035	1258	3 39	5 40	7 53
14¼	Borlänge .... arr		...	...	...	...	8 8	1047	1 18	3 52	6 20	8 13
	Borlänge dep		...	...	...	...	—	1049	—	4 1	—	8 23
32¼	Rämshyttan.........................		...	...	...	a.m.	...	1126	...	4 43	...	9 49
43½	Ludvika (B's.) 310A		...	...	...	4 30	...	1215	...	5 30	...	1035
58½	Hörken (B s.)		...	...	...	5 43	...	1250	...	6 9	...	—
65¾	Ställdalen (B's.)......... arr		...	...	...	6 3	...	1 2	...	6 25	...	...
	Ställdalen dep		...	...	...	6 4	...	1 4	...	6 27	...	...
94½	Grythyttehed (311)................		...	...	...	7 55	...	2 2	...	7 31	...	...
108	Herrhult		...	a.m.	...	8 45	...	2 31	...	8 3	...	...
115	Daglosen		...	7 58	...	9 15	...	2 52	...	8 27	...	...
133	Molkom................................		...	8 36	...	1025	...	3 31	...	9 8	2&3	...
152¾	Kil (308) .... arr		a.m.	9 16	...	1145	...	4 11	...	9 51	p.m.	...
	Kil dep		5 35	9 35	...	12 0	...	4 19	...	—	8 8	...
172¾	Segmon................................		6 20	1016	...	1 30	...	5 0	...	...	8 53	...
195	Amal		7 19	11 2	...	3 0	...	5 47	...	...	10 6	...
220½	Mellerud........................arr		8 15	1152	...	4 31	...	6 36	...	...	11 0	...
...	CHRISTIANIA 304A......dep		...	...	7 a44	...	...	8a20	2&3	...	5p45	...
...	FREDRIKSHALD 306dep	2&3	...	...	10a40	...	...	1231	p.m.	...	8p50	...
...	Mellerud .... dep	a.m.	8 25	1155	1 9	p.m.	...	6 38	6 47	...	11*16	...
246	Oxnered (306)	6 35	9 45	1256	1 56	4 40	...	7 25	7 50	...	12 0	3Cl.
252¼	Trollhattän	6 48	10 0	1 10	2 8	4 55	...	7 38	8 4	...	1210	a.m.
270¼	Nygard	7 27	1038	1 49	...	5 40	...	...	8 46	...	...	6 0
281½	Nol	7 56	11 4	2 20	...	6 11	...	...	9 12	...	...	6 39
297	Gothenburg ....arr	8 38	1143	3 1	3 20	6 53	...	8 59	9 50	...	1 21	7 36
483½	MALMO 309A................arr		...	9p31	9 p31	...	...	...	...	...	7a36	...
503	COPENHAGEN 303 ...arr		...	10p29	10p29	...	...	...	...	...	8a29	...

	(times set in station column)									
COPENHAGEN 303 dep		9 p5	...	...	...	...	7 a0	...	...	10a55
MALMO...... 309A dep		1016	...	...	...	...	7a40	...	...	10a32
		1,2,3	2 & 3	2&3	2&3	2&3	1,2,3	2 & 3	2&3	2 & 3
		a.m.	a.m.	...	a.m.	a.m.	p.m.	p.m.	p.m.	p.m.
Gothenburg............dep		4 32	7 40	...	8 40	1110	1 54	2 30	5 30	8 5
Nol		...	8 20	...	...	1150	...	3 11	6 12	8 49
Nygard		...	8 46	...	...	1213	...	3 39	6 42	9 23
Trollhattän		5 46	9 27	...	10 0	1 8	3 9	4 23	7 36	10 7
Oxnered		6 0	9 46	...	1020	1 21	3 27	4 45	7 55	10 20
Mellerud 306...........arr		6 39	10 47	...	1059	—	4 6	5 42	8 45	—
FREDRIKSHALD ...arr		8a57	...	...	4p10	...	6p32	...	...	...
CHRISTIANIA 304A arr		12 0	...	...	8p55	...	9p43	...	...	...
Mellerud ....dep		6 52	...	p.m.	11 2	...	...	5 46	8 47	...
Amal		7 49	...	1212	1153	...	...	6 38	9 43	...
Segmon		8 38	...	1 32	1236	...	...	7 21	1033	...
Kil .... arr		9 24	a.m.	2 58	1 15	...	...	8 0	1118	...
Kil dep		—	7 30	3 18	1 25	...	...	8 11	—	...
Molkom........................		...	8 16	4 42	2 5	...	...	8 49	...	...
Daglosen		...	9 4	6 15	2 48	...	...	9 26	...	...
Herrhult		...	9 17	6 43	3 2	...	...	—	...	...
Grythyttehed		...	9 48	7 50	3 30	...	...	...	...	...
Ställdalen (B's.)... arr		...	10 54	9 19	4 26	...	...	...	...	...
Ställdalen dep		...	10 56	9 24	4 28	...	...	...	...	...
Hörken B s.)...........	2&3	...	11 16	9 52	4 43	...	...	...	...	...
Ludvika (B's.)..........	5a30	...	11 50	1042	5 29	...	...	...	...	...
Rämshyttan	6 36	2&3	12 42	—	5 54	...	...	...	...	...
Borlänge ...... arr	7 57	a.m.	1 20	p.m.	6 29	p.m.	...	...	...	...
Borlänge dep	8 9	1010	1 27	3 53	6 31	8 30	...	...	...	...
Ornäs..........................	8 33	1035	1 40	4 14	6 43	8 45	...	...	...	...
Falun ....arr......	9 10	11 6	2 4	4 45	7 4	9 14	...	...	...	...
GEFLE (306) ....arr		2p54	...	...	9p40	...	...	...	...	...

GOTHENBURG and SKARA.

		a.m.	p.m.	p.m.	p.m.	
Gothenburg dep	...	8 35	3 5	5 10	7 10	
Grabo	...	9 19	3 45	5 54	8 5	
Sollebrunn.........	...	1036	5 2	7 5	—	
Tumleberg ...	a.m.	1116	5 45	7 48	...	
Vara	6 15	1135	6 0	8 4	...	
Skara ......arr	8 0	1235	—	9 5	...	

	a.m.	a.m.	a.m.	p.m.	p.m.
Skara ......dep	...	8 20	...	5 7	9 7
Vara	5 35	9 26	9 42	6 15	1040
Tumleberg ...	5 50	9 50	1010	6 37	—
Sollebrunn ...	6 42	1035	1126	7 18	a.m.
Grabo..............	8 4	1154	1 35	8 29	6 29
Gothenburg ar	8 50	1240	2 50	9 15	7 40

Hakantorp dep	9a21	1 p35	6p 9
Tumleberg arr	9 44	2 5	6 32
Tumleberg dep	11a13	3 p0	7p45
Hakantorp arr	11 36	3 30	8 8

FREDRIKSHALD and MELLERUD (for SUNNANA).

Dist E.M							
	CHRISTIANIA ......dep	...	7a44	...	8a20	5p45	...
			a.m.	p.m.	p.m.	p.m.	
—	Fredrikshald .....dep	...	1040	...	1231	8 50	...
20	Kornsjö....................	...	1131	2 42	2 26	9 42	...
25½	Mon	a.m.	1148	3 0	3 15	10 0	...
33	Ed	8 20	1210	3 32	4 8	1018	...
60½	Mellerud 306......arr	9 40	1 5	5 5	6 19	1112	...

	a.m.	a.m.	no'n	p.m.	p.m.	p.m.	
Mellerud ....dep	6 43	8 20	12 6	4 10	6 40	...	...
Ed	7 44	11 0	1 45	5 17	8 5	8 30	...
Mon	8 2	1230	2 12	5 35	(curve)	9 2	...
Kornsjö.....................	8 12	1246	2 25	5 45	—	9 16	...
Fredrikshald ......arr	8 57	...	4 10	6 32	...	11 0	...
CHRISTIANIA 304A arr	12 0	...	8p55	9p43	...	...	...

UDDEVALLA and HERRLJUNGA.

E.M							
	Uddevalla......dep	6 a5	8a50	12p45	...	6p43	8p30
14½	Oxnered	6 50	9 45	1 55	3 p30	7 55	9 20
16½	Wenersborg.........	7 8	10 0	2 15	3 55	8 5	9 35
39½	Hakantorp	8 18	1114	3 40	6 20	—	1043
57½	Herrljunga ...arr	9 10	1235	4 35	7 50	...	1130

Herrljunga ...dep	5a15	...	7a15	10a10	1p40	5p15
Hakantorp	5 57	...	9 50	11 40	2 29	6 20
Wenersborg..........	7 15	9a25	1145	1 35	3 52	7 35
Oxnered	7 28	9 45	1155	1 55	4 40	7 55
Uddevalla ... arr	8 15	1032	...	2 45	5 30	8 40

GEFLE, FALUN, and ORSA.

Gefle.................dep	7a45	a.m.	...	12p45	2p10	...	5p50	8p30
Storvik (309)	8 43	1012	...	1 50	3 12	...	6 59	1020
Falun (306) arr	10 0	1 15	...	—	4 25	...	8 25	—
Falun (306) dep	1010	—	2 p15	...	5 0	7p16	—	...
Rattvik	1146	...	4 34	...	6 40	8 47	...	...
Mora Noret	1255	...	6 25	...	...	10 8	...	...
Orsa ....arr	1 17	...	6 55	...	...	1030	...	...

Orsa ....dep	...	...	6a45	...	...	a.m. 1155	...	4 p5
Mora Noret	...	...	7 24	a.m.	...	1224	...	4 35
Rattvik	...	...	8 32	1045	...	1 33	...	5 42
Falun ... arr	...	a.m.	10 3	1217	...	3 5	...	7 15
Falun ... dep	a.m.	7 5	—	1245	...	—	3p35	7 25
Storvik	6 25	8 44	...	2 4	3p20	...	6 40	8 48
Gefle ....arr	8 22	9 45	...	2 54	4 25	...	—	9 40

Orsa.................dep	1 p50	...	...
Sveg ....arr	6 20	...	...

Sveg.................dep	7 a30	...	...
Orsa ....arr	11 30	...	...

NORA and BREDSJO.

	a.m.	p.m.			a.m.	p.m.
Bredsjo ......dep	6 50	2 0	...	**Nora** ......dep	9 50	3 15
Striberg..............	8 43	4 50	...	Gyttorp	10 18	3 35
Gyttorp..............	9 10	5 26	...	Striberg	10 56	4 3
Nora (311)...arr	9 20	5 36	...	**Bredsjo** arr	1 20	6 24

STENSTORP and LIDKOPING.

	a.m.	a.m.	p.m.	p.m.		a.m.	p.m.	p.m.	p.m.
Stenstorp	6 55	11 5	3 50	7 40	**Lidko.**	7 7	1 0	3 45	8 21
Skara	8 20	1245	5 10	9 12	Skara...	8 18	1 49	5 6	9 10
Lidkoping	9 15	1 45	5 55	9 59	**Stens.**	9 43	2 57	6 30	1020

‡—Not on Sun.

TINGSTADE and BURGSVIK.

Tingstade	...	8 a0	2p30	**Burgsvik** .	6a30	...	...	4 p0
Visby.........	8a25	9 0	3 45	Hafdhem .	7 10	...	...	4 30
Roma.........	9 15	...	6 24	Roma	9 15	12 ‡0	...	6 40
Hafdhem ...	11 20	...	8 55	Visby	1015	12 55	5 p0	7 35
Burgsvik ar	11 55	...	9 30	**Tingstade**	12 0	...	6 15	...

KARLSTAD and FILIPSTAD.

Karlstad ...dep	6a45	1215	5p37	**Filipstad** dep	5 a0	3p55	...
Deje..................	7 58	1 45	6 46	Finshyttan	5 20	4 5	...
Munkfors	9 0	3 6	7 48	Nordmark	6 40	4 42	...
Sjögränd	9 52	4 10	8 39	Hagfors......4a55	9 40	7 5	...
Hagfors............	1025	4 35	9 0	Sjögränd ...5 27	10 6	7 31	...
Nordmark.........	12 2	7 30	—	Munkfors ..6 39	11 0	8 23	...
Finshyttan	1238	8 51	...	Deje 7 58	12 4	9 34	...
Filipstad	1245	9 0	...	**Karlstad** 9 12	1 11	1035	...

BORLANGE and INSJON.

Borlange.........dep	8 a30	3 p57	**Insjon** ....dep	5a35	12p15	...
Repbäcken............	8 58	4 8	Repbäcken	7 30	1 6	...
Insjön ....arr	10 35	4 58	Borlange.........arr	7 48	1 16	...

BORLANGE and KRYLBO.

Borlange ...	8a30	1p27	8p25	...	**Krylbo** dep	...	1p57	5 p4	...
Kullsveden	10 2	2 12	9 18	...	**Kullsveden**	6a57	3 1	6 52	...
Krylbo	1158	3 10	...	...	**Borlange** ...	7 55	3 45	8 15	...

NASSJÖ and HALMSTAD.

		a.m.	a.m.	p.m			a.m.	a.m.	p.m	p.m.
Nässjö dep	...	6 55	9 45	5 15	**Halmstad**	...	5 5	9 20	4 8	6 28
Vaggeryd	...	8 10	1219	6 54	Kinnared	a.m.	7 30	1022	5 17	8 58
Hörle	...	8 54	2 33	7 51	Landeryd	5 35	8 14	1036	5 39	9 28
Vernamo...	...	9 8	2 40	8 22	Reftele ...	6 33	9 52	—	6 15	—
Reftele ...	...	9 54	5 16	9 24	Vernamo...	8 0	1238	...	7 3	...
Landeryd ..	5a30	1036	7 25	1014	Hörle	8 15	1 0	...	7 16	...
Kinnared .	6 8	1051	8 3	1032	Vaggeryd	9 38	2 40	...	8 12	...
Halmstad..	8 48	1159	10 5	1135	Nässjö .arr	1135	4 50	...	9 25	...

WISLANDA and HALMSTAD.

Wisl'nda	...	9a26	2p20	6p55	**Halmsd**	5a30	a.m.	2 p0	5p20	...
Ljungby arr	5a50	1034	3 57	8 30	Bolmen...	7 36	9 50	5 0	9 35	...
Bolmen dep	6 25	11 9	5 10	...	Ljungby	8 8	1115	5 30	—	...
Halmst'd	9 20	1 13	9 5	...	**Wislan**	9 15	1253	6 35	...	...

WALSKOG and OXELOSUND

Walskog dep	5a44	...	8a32	...	12p57	...	4p15	6p22	...	...
Kolback dep	...	7a42	...	10a52	...	3p41	...	...	6p15	9p15
Rekarne.........	6 39	8 21	9 29	11 31	1 32	4 5	5 9	7 21	7 14	9 41
Eskilstuna arr	7 5	8 43	9 56	11 56	1 48	4 20	5 35	7 48	8 31	9 56

Oxelösund dp	...	8a12	9a24	2p55	5p10	7p40
Nyköping	...	8 34	10 0	3 18	5 44	8 10
Flen	5a50	1034	1240	4 58	7 40	9 37
Eskilstuna ...arr	7 0	1134	2 8	5 58	10 8	...

Eskilstuna ......dep	...	8a57	1036 3p42	6 p8	8p45	...	...
Flen	6 a5	1037	1244 5 0	8 42	9 55	...	...
Nyköping...............	7 32	1156	2 45 6 19	1041	—	...	...
Oxelösund ...arr	7 53	1215	3 15 6 38	1110	...	...	...

Eskilstuna	6a11	7a20	10a27	12p45	2p18	3p38	4p45	6p10	7p20	8 p5	...
Rekarne...	6 46	7 42	10 43	12 59	2 41	4 5	5 15	6 27	8 0	8 38	...
Kolback	...	8 21	...	1 25	...	4 43	...	6 53	8 58	...	...
Walskog	7 42	...	11 18	...	3 35	...	6 7	...	...	9 34	...

GARDSJO and SKARA.

Gardsjo......dep	4a30	...	...	8 a25	noon	2 p0	...	5 p25	...
Moholm...dep	...	5 a42	9 a5	⋮	12 0	⋮	3 p42	6 1	...
Mariestad	6 25	6 30	9 48	10 20	12 45	3 17	4 25	6 43	...
Forshem	—	7 16	—	11 56	—	4 7	—	7 31	...
Skara.........arr	...	8 10	...	1 25	...	5 0	...	8 45	...

Skara ....dep	...	9 a0	...	12p45	2 p0	...	9 p15	...
Forshem	...	10 3	...	1 45	3 35	...	10 17	...
Mariestad ....arr	8 a0	10 50	1 p52	2 30	4 48	5 p0	10 59	...
Moholm	8 45	11 41	2 35	...	...	5 43	11 44	...
Gardsjo ....arr	...	12 15	...	4 0	7 5	...	...	...

CHRISTINEHAMN and MORA.

Christinhmn	6a25	8a45	...	4 p5	7p30	Mora-Nor. dep	...	1253	p.m.
Herrhult	9 30	1019	...	8 4	9 15	Mora...............	...	1258	1 6
Nyhyttan......	10 7	1045	p.m.	8 50	9 43	Brintbodarne ...	a.m.	—	2 28
Persberg	1021	1115	1225	9 4	9 56	Vansbro	4 30	...	3 45
Oforsen	—	1229	3 51	—	—	Oforsen .....a.m	7 24	p.m.	5 32
Vansbro	...	2 20	6 49	...	7a30	Persberg ...6 1	1150	1 0	7 20
Brintbodarne	p.m.	3 2	—	...	8 46	Nyhyttan ...6 35	12 6	1 24	7 35
Mora	1210	4 19	...	...	1127	Herrhult ...7 50	1233	2 35	8 4
Mora-Nor.ar	1215	4 30	...	...	...	Christinh'n 1114	2 17	6 15	9 33

Nyhyttan.......dep	6a36	1050	12p7	7p38	9p44	Finshyttan	5a45	1010	11a27	6p58	9 p7
Filipstad 307	6 59	11 7	1224	7 53	10 6	Filipstad...	6 0	1024	11 37	7 13	9 14
Finshyttan 307 arr	7 4	1112	1229	7 58	1011	Nyhyttan...	6 14	1036	11 49	7 25	9 26

MALARBADEN and SODERTELJE.

Malarbaden	6a41	11a39	5p28	**Sodertelje** ...	8 a0	1p42	7p21
Eskilstuna ...	7 17	1 14	6 12	Saltskog	21	2 4	7 40
Akers Styck.	8 44	2 27	7 30	Laggesta......	9025	3 0	8 45
Laggesta	8 57	2 37	7 41	A. Styckebr'k	1040	3 9	9 0
Saltskog	10 7	3 48	8 51	Eskilstuna ...	1153	4 18	1015
Sodertelje ...	1012	3 53	8 56	**Malarbaden**	1255	4 52	1048

ANNEFORS and HORKEN.

Annefors......dep	7‡a25	Horken.........dep	1p‡0
Gravendal	8 25	Strömsdal	3 0
Strömsdal..	9 25	Gravendal	3 35
Horken (B's) arr	10 55	Annefors ......arr	4 30

‡—Weekdays only.

Akers Styckebruk to Strengnas, 8.45, 10.48 a.m., 3.10, 7.25, 9.5 p.m. Return from Strangnas 7.47, 9.50 a.m., 1.50, 6.15, 8.10 p.m. In half an hour.

Boras to Herrljunga, 7.53 a.m., 12.2, 3.20, 5.40, 10.33 p.m. Return from Herrljunga 5.25, 7.0, 11.45 a.m., 5.13, 7.55 p.m. In 1½ hours.

Boras to Warberg, 7.12, 9.5, 10.40a.m., 2.40, 7.30 p.m. Return from Warberg 4.50, 9.2, 10.36 a.m., 12.26, 3.34, 7.30 p.m. In 3 hours.

Brintbodarne to Limedsforsen, 3.12 p.m. Return from Limedsforsen 10.55 a.m. In 3 hours.

Dannemora to Hargshamn, 12.47, 9.32 p.m. Return from Hargshamn 5 50 a.m., 2.31 p.m. In 2 hours.

Filipstad to Daglosen, 7.40, 8.40 a.m., 2.15, 5.35, 8.0 p.m. Return from Daglosen 9.15 a.m., 2.50, 6.10, 8.30, 9.30 p.m. In quarter hour.

Hillared to Axelfors, 10.54 a.m., 3.40 p.m. Return from Axelfors 12.5, 5.45 p.m.

Hörby to Hör, 11.10 a.m., 5.10 p.m. Return from Hör 12.15, 7.50 p.m. In 40 min.

Jönköpings Hamn to Vaggeryd, 6.50, 9.20 a.m., 5.0, 7.0 p.m. Return from Vaggeryd 6.25, 9.30 a.m., 2.50, 8.15 p.m. In 1½ hours.

Kinnared to Atran, 11.5 a.m., 5.20 p.m. Return from Atran 9.5 a.m., 3.30 p.m. In 1 hour.

Lidkoping to Forshem, 8.50 a.m., 12.39, 2.20, 9.14 p.m. Return from Forshem 7.16, 10.15 a.m., 4.5, 7.30 p.m. In 1 hour.

Lidkoping to Hakantorp, 7.0, 8.19, 11.55 a.m., 5.10 p.m. Return from Hakantorp 8.35, 11.37 a.m., 3.50, 8.10 p.m. In 1 hour.

Mora to Elfdalen, 1.5, 6.40 p.m. Return from Elfdalen 9.55 a.m., 2.55 p.m. In 2 hours.

Morshyttan to Nas, 7.50 a.m., 1.15, 6.10 p.m. Return from Nas 5.40 a.m., 12.0 noon, 3.15 p.m. In 40 minutes.

Roma to Klintehamn, 9.30 a.m., 6.45 p.m. Return from Klintehamn 7.55 a.m., 4.45 p.m. In 1 hour.

Roma to Slite, 9.35 a.m., 6.35 p.m. Return from Slite 7.25 a.m., 4.25 p.m. In 1½ hours.

Sjögränd to Edeback, 5.32, 10.10 a.m., 4.12, 8.47 p.m. Return from Edeback 5.0, 9.30 a.m., 3.40, 7.5 p.m. In quarter hour.

Svensbro to Hjo, 6.10, 11.11 a.m., 3.21, 8.1 p.m. Return from Hjo 8.35 a.m., 1.25, 5.25 p.m. In 1 hour. (Steamer from Hjo to Hastholmen 12.40, 5.15 p.m., in 1½ hours; Hastholmen to Hjo 4.5 p.m.)

Svensbro to Stenstorp, 9.32 a.m., 2.22, 6.22 p.m. Return from Stenstorp 5.15, 10.50 a.m., 3.0, 7.40 p.m. In 20 minutes.

Svensbro to Tidaholm, 11.13 a.m., 3.23, 8.2 p.m. Return from Tidaholm 8.25 a.m., 1.35, 5.30 p.m. In half an hour.

STOCKHOLM, CATHRINEHOLM, and MALMO.

SLEEPING CARS. 1st and 2nd Class. Stockholm to Gothenburg and Christiania—in 9.7 p.m. from Stockholm. Stockholm to Malmo—in 8.30 p.m. and 10.0 p.m. from Stockholm. Extra fare, 1st Class Kr. 10.70, 2nd Class Kr. 5.35.

Dist		2&3	2&3	2&3	2&3	2 & 3	Ex.3	2&3	Ex3	2&3	2&3	2&3	2 & 3	Ex3	Ex3	2&3	Ex3	Ex3	1,2,3	2&3
E.M	**Stockholm**			a.m.	a.m.	a.m.	a.m.	a.m.	p.m.	p.m.	p.m.	p.m.	p.m.	p.m.	p.m.	p.m.	p.m.	p.m.	p.m.	p.m.
—	Central Station.dep	...	...	7 23	8 38	9 51	10 27	1056	1247	3 16	5 30	6 16	6 26	8 3	8 30	8 38	9 7	9 35	10 0	1130
5	Elfsjo	...	...	7 40	...	10 7	...	1113	...	3 33	5 47	...	6 43	...	§	8 55	...	SC	SC	1146
14¼	Tumba	...	...	8 2	...	10 30	RC	1137	RC	3 57	6 11	...	7 7	SC	:	9 17	SC	A	10 42	12 9
23	Saltskog...arr	...	...	8 23	9 18	10 51	...	12 0	...	4 20	6 34	...	7 31	...	:	9 38	...	1019	11 3	1230
23½	Soedertelje...arr	...	...	8 33	9 28	10 57	...	1212	...	4 32	6 40	...	7 42	...	:	9 45	...	1026	11 10	1236
...	Saltskog...dep	...	...	8 26	9 20	—	11 9	12 4	1 31	4 24	—	6 59	—	8 48	:	—	10 5	1021	11 5	—
41	**Gnesta** arr	...	...	9 0	...	...	11 39	1240	...	5 1	...	7 32	...	...	:	...	...	...	11 43	...
	dep	...	...	9 4	...	...	11 39	1245	2 0	5 9	...	7 33	...	9 18	:	...	1038	1058	11 48	...
69	Flen (307)	...	...	10 4	1030	...	12 25	1 50	2 46	6 11	...	8 31	...	10 4	SC	...	1128	1147	12 49	...
83¼	**Cathrineholm**...arr	...	...	1037	1053	...	12 48	2 21	3 9	6 41	...	8 59	...	1028	:	...	1152	1214	1 18	...
284½	GOTHENBU'G 309 arr	...	a.m.	...	7 p5	...	...	...	9 p8	...	...	...	...	...	:	...	7 a2	...	1 p24	...
...	**Cathrineholm**...dep	...	5 21	...	11 5	...	12 52	3 25	...	6 52	...	9 20	...	1033	:	...	...	...	1 25	...
113	**Norrköping** arr	...	6 39	a.m.	1211	p.m.	1 39	4 39	...	7 58	...	1021	...	1121	‡	...	...	A—Runs until 31st August.	2 19	...
	dep	...	6 50	9 44	1218	2 27	1 44	—	...	8 3	...	1026	...	1127	1148	...	...		2 27	...
125	Kimstad	...	7 25	1023	1250	3 10	2 7	...	...	8 32	...	1057	...	...	:	...	...		SC	...
127½	**Norsholm** (310) arr	...	7 31	1029	1255	3 16	2 13	...	...	8 37	...	11 3	...	1151	:	...	...		2 56	...
	dep	a.m.	7 36	1030	1 1	3 18	2 15	...	...	8 39	...	11 4	...	1151	‡	...	...		2 59	...
142½	**Linköping** (309A)	5 22	8 51	11 6	1 39	4 0	2 44	...	...	9 18	...	1154	...	1220	1251	...	...		3 28	...
162¼	**Mjölby** (309A) arr	6 24	9 47	—	2 31	4 54	3 18	...	...	1010	...	1243	...	1254	:	...	...		4 8	...
	dep	6 45	9 51	...	2 48	—	3 25	...	...	1016	...	—	...	1 4	:	...	...		4 38	...
185¼	Tranas	8 6	1045	...	3 34	...	4 3	...	...	—	...	...	...	1 41	:	...	...		5 24	...
202½	Aneby	9 12	1130	...	4 12	...	RC	...	...	...	...	...	...	SC	:	...	...		6 4	...
217½	**Nässjö** (309A) arr	10 4	12 6	...	4 42	...	5 1	...	...	...	...	...	...	2 37	:	...	...		6 38	a.m.
	dep	1042	—	...	5 23	...	5 8	...	...	...	...	...	...	2 44	:	...	...		6 59	9 39
235	Säfsjö (310A)	1148	...	...	5 58	3 Cl.	5 34	...	...	...	...	...	...	...	:	...	2&3		7 35	1029
271	**Alfvesta** (311) arr	1 32	...	...	7 11	p.m.	6 22	...	...	...	...	...	...	3 59	:	...	a.m.		8 49	—
	dep	1 46	...	...	—	4 11	6 30	...	...	...	...	...	...	4 6	:	...	6 42		9 3	...
279½	**Wislanda** (311)	2 18	...	...	...	4 33	6 48	...	...	...	...	...	...	4 22	:	...	6 58		9 22	...
300¾	**Elmhult**	3 23	...	...	...	5 17	7 21	...	...	...	...	...	...	4 51	:	...	7 37	...	9 59	...
320¾	Hästveda (311)	4 20	...	...	3 Cl	7 11	...	3Cl.	...	...	...	...	3 Cl.	5 23	:	...	8 18	...	10 38	...
332½	**Hessleholm** 310 arr	4 50	...	...	p.m	7 35	8 5	p.m.	...	...	...	...	a.m.	5 40	:	...	8 40	...	11 0	...
...	dep	5 12	...	...	2 43	—	8 12	8 30	...	...	...	...	6 34	5 47	6 13	...	8 50	...	11 7	...
350½	**Hör** (307)	6 5	3Cl.	2&3	3 23	2 & 3	...	9 10	...	3 Cl	...	...	7 13	...	:	3 Cl	9 26	...	11 47	...
363	**Eslöf** (310) arr	6 41	a.m.	p.m.	3 52	p.m.	8 58	9 39	...	a.m.	...	...	7 41	6 30	:	a.m.	9 48	...	12 12	p.m.
	dep	6 49	1130	4 55	3 55	8 29	9 0	9 41	...	6 40	...	...	7 42	6 33	:	9 10	9 59	...	12 15	1 42
373½	**Lund**	7 30	1158	5 20	4 23	8 55	9 20	10 8	...	7 19	...	...	8 10	6 55	:	9 37	1026	...	12 41	2 10
384	**Malmö**...arr	8 8	1225	5 41	4 50	9 22	9 36	1035	...	7 45	...	...	8 36	7 15	7 30	10 4	1049	...	12 58	2 37
...	MALMO ferry...dep	...	...	...	...	...	10 p0	...	...	...	...	...	...	8a15	8a15	...	...	...	1 p15	...
404	COPENHAGEN...arr	...	...	...	...	...	11p30	...	...	...	...	...	...	9a45	9a45	...	...	...	2 p45	...
404	TRELLEBORG...arr	...	...	...	...	...	10p33	...	...	...	...	...	...	8a31	8a31	...	...	...	...	...
470½	SASSNITZ ferry arr	...	...	...	...	...	2 a50	...	...	...	...	...	...	1251	1251	...	...	...	...	...
670	HAMBURG 213A arr	...	...	...	...	...	9 a51	...	...	...	...	...	...	8p23	8p23	...	...	...	...	...
642¾	BERLIN (181)...arr	...	...	...	...	...	8 a35	...	...	...	...	...	...	6p34	6p34	...	...	...	...	...

Extra—Stockholm to Soedertelje, 12.54, 4.35 and 7.15 p.m.

§—Takes 3rd class for Germany only. ‡—Takes up for Germany only. RC—Restaurant Car. SC—Sleeping Car.

Malmo and Copenhagen Ferry Steamer Service.											
Malmö	dep	8a10	8a15	11a15	1p15	1p40	3p30	5p50	6p 0	10p0	10p2
Copenhagen (Frihavn)	arr	9 40	...	...	...	3 10	...	7 20	...	...	1127
,, (Osterbro)	arr	9 55	...	...	...	3 20	...	7 30	...	...	1137
,, (Havnegade)	arr	...	9 50	12 50	2 50	...	5 5	...	7 35	1135	...

LAXA and CHARLOTTENBERG.

Dist.	STOCKHOLM 309 dep	9p35	...	...	...	8 a38	...	12p47	...	...	...	...	...	...	...	...	...	...	...	...
E.M.		a.m.	a.m.	a.m.		p.m.		p.m.	p.m.											
—	**Laxa**...dep	2 58	5 4	6 19	...	1 18	...	5 1	7 19	...	...	...	...	...	...	...	...	...	...	...
21½	**Degerfors**	SC	5 59	8 5	...	2 5	p.m.	5 48	8 30	...	...	...	...	...	...	...	...	...	...	...
23½	Strömtorp	3 40	6 7	8 32	...	2 11	3 48	5 54	8 44	...	...	...	...	...	...	...	...	...	...	...
38	**Christin'hamn** 307	4 11	6 58	9 34	p.m.	2 45	4 36	6 29	9 26	...	...	...	...	...	...	...	...	...	...	...
63¾	**Karlstad**	5 2	8 39	1126	2 12	3 49	—	7 38	—	...	...	...	...	...	...	...	...	...	...	...
75¼	**Kil (306)**	5 32	9 34	1153	3 10	4 34	...	8 15	...	...	...	...	...	...	...	...	...	...	...	...
105	Arvika	6 27	11 11	—	—	5 48	...	9 31	...	...	...	...	...	...	...	...	...	...	...	...
126¼	**Charlottenberg** arr	7 10	12 9	...	...	6 31	...	1017	...	...	...	...	...	...	...	...	...	...	...	...
214½	CHRISTIANIA 304A	1030	7 p8	...	...	10p27	...	...	...	...	...	...	...	...	...	...	...	...	...	...

CHRISTIANIA...dep	...	...	...	...	7a25	...	...	...	...	9a40	6 p5	...	...	...	...	...	...	...	...	...
		a.m.			a m.					p.m.	p m.									
Charlottenberg dep	...	7 25	...	...	1127	...	...	...	...	5 16	9 42	...	...	...	...	...	...	...	...	...
Arvika	...	8 14	...	p.m.	1213	p.m.	...	p.m.	...	6 24	1027	...	...	...	...	...	...	...	...	...
Kil	...	9 40	...	1213	1 34	1 49	p.m.	4 25	p.m.	8 20	1123	...	...	...	...	...	...	...	...	...
Karlstad	a.m	10 24	p.m.	1238	2 4	2 47	3 48	4 59	6 48	8 50	1150	...	...	...	...	...	...	...	...	...
Christinehamn	6 3	11 33	1218	—	3 15	—	6 22	—	8 10	—	1241	...	...	...	...	...	...	...	...	...
Strömtorp	6 41	12 3	2 6	...	3 46	...	7 22	...	8 45	...	1 9	...	...	...	...	...	...	...	...	...
Degerfors	6 49	12 9	—	...	3 52	...	7 34	...	8 51	...	SC	...	...	...	...	...	...	...	...	...
Laxa...arr	7 44	12 56	...	...	4 38	...	8 49	...	9 37	...	1 50	...	...	...	...	...	...	...	...	...
STOCKHOLM...arr	...	6p21	...	...	9p 8	...	...	...	...	...	7 a8	...	...	...	...	...	...	...	...	...

MALMO, CATHRINEHOLM, and STOCKHOLM.

SLEEPING CARS, 1st and 2nd Class, Malmo to Stockholm—in 3.0 p.m. and 10.12 p.m. from Malmo. Extra fare, 1st Class Kr. 10.70, 2nd Class Kr. 5.35.

	Ex3	Ex3	3 Cl.	2&3	2&3	2&3	2&3	2&3	Ex3	2&3	3 Cl	3 Cl	2 & 3	2&3	1,2,3	2&3	2&3	2&3	Ex3	Ex 3
Berlin 181 ......dep	...	...	...	...	...	...	...	...	8p15	...	...	...	...	...	...	...	...	...	11a9	11 a9
Hamburg ......dep	...	...	...	...	...	...	...	...	7p10	...	...	...	...	...	...	...	...	...	9a13	9 a13
Sassnitz ferry dep	...	...	...	...	...	...	...	...	2a17	...	...	...	...	...	...	...	...	...	4p56	4 p56
Trelleborg..dep	...	...	...	...	...	...	...	...	6a34	...	...	...	...	...	...	...	...	...	9p13	9 p13
Copenhagen ferry dep		...	...	...	...	...	...	...	5a40	...	...	...	...	...	11a5	...	...	...	8 p0	8 p0
Malmo..............arr	...	...	...	...	...	...	...	...	7a10	...	...	...	...	...	12p35	...	...	...	9p30	9 p30
Malmö ....dep	...	...	...	...	a.m. 6 10	...	...	...	a.m. 7 32	a.m. 7 36	a.m 8 40	p.m. 1 10	...	...	p.m. 3 0	p.m. 3 10	p.m. 6 0	p.m. 7 10	p.m. 1012	p.m. 10 22
Lund..................arr	...	...	...	...	6 50	...	...	...	7 52	8 4	9 7	1 38	...	...	3 24	3 38	6 28	7 35	§	10 43
Eslöf .... arr	...	...	...	...	7 43	...	...	...	8 13	8 34	9 37	2 8	...	...	...	4 8	7 0	8 5	SC	11 5
Eslöf .... dep	...	...	...	...		...	...	...	8 15	8 39	9 43	2 13	...	...	3 52		7 10		⋮	11 7
Hör	...	...	...	...	...	...	...	...	8 35	9 16	1013	2 43	...	...	4 18	...	7 37	...	⋮	11 27
Hessleholm...... arr	...	...	a.m.	...	...	...	...	...	9 4	10 8	1052	3 22	...	...	4 52	...	8 11	...	⋮	11 57
Hessleholm...... dep	...	...	6 25	...	...	...	...	...	9 11	1030			...	...	5 4	...	8 27	...	⋮	12 2
Hästveda	...	...	6 52	...	...	...	...	...	...	1110	...	...	...	...	5 27	...	8 53	...	⋮	...
Elmhult....................		...	7 40	...	...	...	...	...	10 1	1213	...	...	...	...	6 8	...	9 31	...	⋮	12 51
Wislanda		...	8 27	...	...	...	...	...	1033	1 22	...	2&3	...	...	6 50	...	1010	...	⋮	1 22
Alfvesta .... arr		...	8 43	...	...	...	...	a.m.	1047	1 42	...	p.m.	...	...	7 5	...	1025	...	⋮	1 35
Alfvesta .... dep		...		...	...	...	a.m.	9 27	1054		...	2 2	...	...	7 31	...		...	⋮	1 42
Säfsjö		...	...	...	...	...	8 23	1055	1149	...	2&3	4 7	...	...	8 58	...	...	...	⋮	...
Nässjö .... arr		...	...	...	...	...	9 9	1138	1219	...	p.m.	5 4	p.m.	...	9 39	...	...	...	⋮	3 9
Nässjö .... dep		...	...	...	...	...	9 30		1226	...	1238		5 30	...	1027	...	...	...	⋮	3 16
Aneby.....................	B—Runs until 1st September.	...	...	...	a.m.	...	10 1	...	RC	...	1 13	...	6 4	...	11 1	...	...	...	⋮	SC
Tranas		...	...	...	7 20	...	1044	...	1 18	...	1 56	...	6 50	...	1141	...	...	...	⋮	4 4
Mjölby .... arr		...	...	a.m.	8 12	...	1132	...	1 55	...	2 47	...	7 41	p.m.	1233	...	...	...	⋮	4 38
Mjölby .... dep		...	...	6 29	8 21	...	1139	...	2 5	p.m.	2 58	...	8 15	1011	1255	...	...	...	⋮	4 45
Linköping...............		...	...	7 22	9 35	...	1227	...	2 39	6 39	3 57	...	9 13	11 8	1 33	...	...	...	4‡41	5 20
Norsholm .... arr	...	...	...	7 55	1012	...	1 0	...	3 1	7 13	4 34	...	9 45		1 58	...	...	...	⋮	5 45
Norsholm .... dep	...	...	...	7 56	1014	...	1 6	...	3 2	7 15	4 36	...	9 50	...	2 1	...	...	...	⋮	5 46
Kimstad.....................	...	...	...	8 3	1022	...	1 13	...	3 9	7 22	4 43	...	9 58	...	SC	...	...	...	⋮	...
Norrköping ..... arr	...	...	...	8 34	1057	...	1 43	...	3 31	7 52	5 17	...	10 25	...	2 26	...	...	...	5‡35	6 12
Norrköping ..... dep	...	...	...	8 39		...	2 0	...	3 36	7 59	5 23	Ex3	10 45	...	2 36	...	...	...	⋮	6 18
Cathrineholm ......arr	...	p.m.	...	9 46	...	...	3 3	...	4 22	9 10	6 36	p.m.	11 54	...	3 34	...	...	...	⋮	7 4
Gothenburg 309 dep	a.m.	10 6	...	...	...	p.m.	7a24	...	...	...	...	1214	...	p.m.	...	...	...	...	⋮	...
Cathrineholm ......dep	4 20	5 8	...	9 56	...	1249	3 25	...	4 27	...	...	6 44	...	7 11	3 46	...	...	...	⋮	7 9
Flen	4 46	5 37	...	1028	...	1 29	4 1	...	4 52	...	...	7 9	...	7 48	4 17	...	...	...	⋮	7 33
Gnesta .... arr	...	...	a.m.	...	...	...	...	...	5 34	...	...	...	...	...	5 6	...	...	...	⋮	...
Gnesta .... dep	5 46	6 33	6 50	1121	...	2 53	5 2	...	5 34	...	...	7 55	...	8 56	5 15	2&3	...	2&3	⋮	8 17
Saltskog ....arr	6 18	SC	7 27	1158	p.m.	3 31	5 38	...	6 3	...	p.m.	8 24	...	9 40	5 48	a.m.	a.m.	a.m.	⋮	8 50
: **Soedertelje** ......dep	6 10	6 50	7 31	1150	1 22	3 27	5 31	...	...	...	6 2	8 11	...	9 32	5 45	6 31	8 49	9 57	⋮	8 43
Saltskog ....dep	6 19	7 8	7 40	12 1	1 32	3 41	5 40	...	RC	...	6 9	8 25	...	9 42	5 56	6 38	8 56	10 6	⋮	8 51
Tumba	B	...	8 2	...	1 54	4 5	...	...	...	...	6 32	RC	...	10 4	6 16	7 0	9 18	1028	⋮	...
Elfsjo	...	...	8 26	...	2 16	4 28	...	...	...	...	6 55	...	...	1026	6 40	7 22	9 40	1051	⋮	...
Stockholm Central arr	7 8	7 55	8 42	1240	2 32	4 45	6 21	...	6 46	...	7 11	9 8	...	1043	6 58	7 38	9 56	11 7	8 49	9 33

Extra.—Soedertelje to Stockholm—7.31, and 8.41 p.m Malmö to Eslof—10.10 a.m., 12.10, 10.27, and 11.30 p.m.

§—Admits 3rd class coming from Germany ‡—Sets down passengers from Germany only.

Copenhagen and Malmö Ferry Steamer Service.														
Copenhagen (Havnegade) dep	...	6 a5	8a15	...	11a15	3 p0	...	5 p0	...	8 p0	...	...	...	...
" (Osterbro)......dep	5a35	...	...	11a0	...	...	3p30	...	7p40	...	...	...	...	...
" (Frihavn) ....dep	5 40	...	...	11 5	...	...	3 35	...	7 50	...	...	...	...	...
Malmö ....arr	7 10	7 50	9 50	1235	12 50	4 35	5 5	6 35	9 20	9 35	...	...	...	...

*—Not on Sunday.

GOTHENBURG and STROMSTAD.

	a.m.	a.m.	a.m.	p.m.	p.m.	
Gothenburg......dep	...	7 55	9*50	3 26	7 20	...
Uddevalla	5 30	10 40	1 48	5 34	9 44	...
Tanum	8 18	12 13		7 8		...
Stromstad ....arr	9 35	1 2	...	7 56	...	...

	a.m.	a.m.	a.m.	p.m.				
Stromstad ...dep	...	6 23	11 0	4 14	...	...	...	...
Tanum	...	7 12	12 18	5 3	...	...	...	...
Uddevalla	5 50	9 10	2 59	6 50	...	...	...	...
Gothenburg..arr	8 44	11 35	5 31	9 14	...	...	...	...

FALKÖPING and LANDERYD.

E.M.		a.m.	a.m.	a.m.	a.m.	a.m.	p.m.
—	**Falköping** ....dep	...	6 1	...	...	11 5	7 13
11¼	Asarp (308A)	...	6 49	...	...	12 16	7 39
29¼	Ulricehamn	5 0	8 15	8 25	11 40	1 55	8 21
47¾	Limmared	7 15		9 14	1 22		9 3
81½	**Landeryd** ....arr	10 5	...	...	5 10	...	10 13

	a.m.	a.m.	a.m.	p.m.	p.m.	p.m.
Landeryd..............dep	...	...	10 41	12 20	...	7 0
Limmared...................	...	9 19	12 20	3 30	...	9 30
Ulricehamn.................	7 15	10 13	1 5	6 0	7 0	10 35
Asarp.........................	8 41		1 41		8 52	
Falköping..............arr	9 35	...	2 8	...	9 50	...

BORAS and ALFVESTA.

	a.m.	a.m.	p.m.	p.m.		
Boras.....................dep	...	10 17	2 55	7 40	...	...
Hillared	...	10 54	3 32	8 25	...	...
Limmared (310A)............	...	11 17	3 57	9 0	...	...
Vernamo..........................	6 10	12 36	5 15		...	...
Alfvesta (308) ......arr	8 40	1 38	6 16	...	...	...

	a.m.	a.m.	a.m.	p.m.	p.m.	
Alfvesta..........................dep	...	5 41	11 0	...	7 15	...
Vernamo	...	9 12	12 8	...	8 13	...
Limmared...............................	6 55	1 11	1 36	2 35	9 27	...
Hillared	7 34		2 2	3 55	9 49	...
Boras ....arr	8 22	...	2 36	5 15	10 20	...

ASARP and TIDAHOLM.

Asarp ....dep	...	...	2 p16	...	...	...
Wartofta	6a45	10a40	3 6	7 p40	...	...
Tidaholm (307) ......arr	8 15	11 21	4 0	8 20	...	...

Tidaholm ....dep	8 a50	12p30	6 p0	...	...	...
Wartofta (309A)	9 40	1 42	6 45	...	...	...
Asarp (308A)...........arr	...	2 4	...	...	...	...

§—Weekdays only.

STOCKHOLM, UPSALA, OSTERSUND, and STORLIEN.

Dist E.M				2&3	2&3	2&3	2&3	2&3	2&3	Ex3	2&3	Ex 3	2&3	2&3
	Stockholm		...	a.m.	a.m.	a.m.	a.m.	p.m.	p.m.	p.m.	p.m.	p.m.	p.m.	p.m.
—	Central Station ......dep		...	7 45	9 0	10 20	1120	1 22	3 35	6 33	7 0	9 20	8 15	11 30
19¾	Rosersberg		...	8 38	...	...	1213	2 1	4 16	SC	...	SC	9 10	12 22
41	**Upsala** ......arr		...	9 28	10 6	11 29	1 3	2 49	5 6	7 39	8 6	10 26	10 0	1 10
...	GEFLE 309A ......arr		...	—	...	1 p52	8§30	8 §30	—	...	1046	...	—	—
...	**Upsala** ......dep		...	...	10 13	11 37	—	2 56	...	7 45	8 13	10 32	...	...
79½	**Sala** 310A ...... arr		...	...	11 29	1 0	...	4 15	...	8 54	9 34	11 46	...	...
	dep		...	...	11 31	1 3	...	4 17	...	8 55	9 45	11 47	...	...
100	**Krylbo** 307 ...... arr		...	a.m.	12 11	1 45	...	4 58	...	9 33	1130	12 24	...	...
	dep		...	7 11	12 26	—	...	5 25	...	9 48	—	12 31	...	...
111½	**Morshyttan** 307 ......arr		...	7 37	12 55	...	...	5 53	...	1015	...	...	...	...
118	Byvalla 310A		...	7 57	1 18	...	...	6 13	...	1036	...	...	...	...
136	**Storvik** 306 ...... arr		...	8 35	1 55	...	...	6 51	...	1111	...	1 42	...	...
	dep		...	8 §40	2 15	...	...	7 13	...	1118	...	1 49	a.m.	...
159½	Ockelbo 309A		...	10§58	3 12	...	...	8 12	p.m.	12 6	...	2 37	5 19	...
186½	Kilafors 309A		...	—	4 13	...	...	9 8	10 15	1258	...	3 28	7 34	...
196¾	**Bollnas** ...... arr		...	...	4 33	...	...	9 31	10 53	1 19	...	3 49	8 0	...
	dep		...	...	4 56	...	...	9 42	—	1 25	...	4 0	8 26	**Extra.**—Stockholm (Central Station) to Upsala, 5.45 p.m.
236	**Ljusdal** 309A ...... arr		...	...	6 26	...	...	11 5	...	2 36	...	5 20	10 3	
	dep		...	...	6 42	...	...	—	...	2 43	...	5 30	1026	
266	Ramsjö		...	...	7 49	...	...	...	...	...	...	6 35	12 1	
...	Ostavall		...	...	8 39	...	‡—Runs until 17th August.	...	...	...	...	7 34	1 6	
300½	**Ange** 309A ...... arr		...	...	9 8	...		...	...	4 58	a.m.	8 0	1 42	
	dep		...	...	9 26	...		...	...	5 8	8 23	—	2 20	
319¾	**Bracke** ......arr	2&3	...	...	10 8	...		...	...	5 48	9 2	SC—Sleeping Cars attached.	3 27	
532¼	VANNAS 311A ...arr	a.m.	...	p.m.	...	...		...	...	2p26	...		...	
...	**Bracke** ......dep	7 17	...	8 22	10 18	a.m.		...	...	—	9 20		3 53	
363¾	**Ostersund** ... arr	9 57	p.m.	10 13	11 57	SC		...	a.m.	...	11 0		7 35	
	dep	—	3 40	—	—	5 ‡40		...	7 30	...	1115		—	
...	Tang		4 10	...	...	5 58		...	8 12	...	1134		...	
393	Trangsviken		5 48	...	...	6 54		...	10 58	...	1235		...	
...	Mattmar		6 20	...	...	7 11		...	11 45	...	1253		...	
406½	Morsil		6 53	...	...	7 36		...	12 31	...	1 17		...	
412¾	Järpen		7 31	...	...	7 58		...	2 5	...	1 40		...	
429½	Dufed		8 58	...	...	8 58		...	4 35	...	2 41		...	
464½	**Storlien** ......arr		—	...	...	10 22		...	6 52	...	4 6		...	
530¾	TRONDHJEM 304 ......arr		...	...	...	1 p50		...	...	...	8 p3		...	...

		2&3	2&3	2&3	2&3	2&3	2&3	2&3	2&3	2&3	Ex 3	Ex3	2&3
TRONDHJEM ...dep		...	...	...	...	...	...	...	...	8 a33	...	...	2 p50
								a.m.	a.m.	p.m.			p.m.
Storlien ......dep		...	...	...	...	...	...	...	6 0	1 21	...	...	7 ‡5
Dufed		...	...	...	...	...	...	5 0	8 12	2 40	...	...	8 23
Järpen		...	...	...	...	...	...	6 15	1023	3 44	...	...	9 25
Morsil		...	...	...	...	...	...	6 39	1055	4 19	...	...	9 55
Mattmar		...	...	...	...	...	...	7 11	1137	4 38	...	...	10 14
Trangsviken		...	...	...	...	...	...	7 46	1240	5 0	...	...	10 31
Tang		...	...	...	...	...	...	9 12	2 54	6 0	...	...	11 31
Ostersund arr		...	...	...	...	a.m.	a.m.	9 39	3 30	6 18	...	...	11 49
dep		...	...	...	...	7 0	5 38	10 5	4 10	6 33	...	...	—
Bracke ......arr		...	...	...	...	8 47	7 16	12 48	9 13	8 12	...	...	...
VANNAS ......dep		...	...	...	...	—	...	...	—	...	...	3p15	...
Bracke ......dep		...	...	...	...	...	7 25	1 11	...	8 29	...	1149	...
Ange arr		...	...	...	...	...	8 7	2 8	...	9 6	p.m.	1222	...
dep		...	...	...	...	...	8 27	3 25	...	—	9 30	1228	...
Ostavall		...	...	...	...	...	8 57	4 11	...		10 1	...	...
Ramsjö		...	...	...	...	...	9 47	5 14	**Extra.**—Upsala to Stockholm 10.45 a.m., 6.5 p.m.	...	10 45	SC	...
Ljusdal ... arr		...	...	...	a.m.	...	1054	6 41		...	11 45	2 27	...
dep		...	...	...	6 0	...	11 9	6 52		...	11 52	2 38	...
Bollnas ...... arr		...	...	a.m.	7 23	...	1238	8 21		...	1 12	3 43	...
dep		...	...	5 15	7 30	...	1245	8 34		...	1 21	3 51	...
Kilafors		...	...	5 39	8 5	...	1 11	9 2		...	1 43	4 12	...
Ockelbo		...	...	—	9 12	...	2 12	—		...	2 37	5 0	...
Storvik ...... arr		...	...	...	10 9	...	3 2	p.m.		...	3 23	5 43	...
dep		...	...	...	1029	...	3 11	7 3		...	3 30	5 50	...
Byvalla		...	...	...	1110	...	3 53	7 41		...	SC	6 29	...
Morshyttan		...	...	3 Cl	1128	...	4 13	7 59		...	...	6 45	...
Krylbo ...... arr		...	...	a.m.	1156	p.m.	4 42	8 25		...	4 41	7 10	...
dep		...	...	5 58	1218	3 32	5 2	—		...	4 48	7 17	...
Sala ...... arr		a.m.	...	7 37	1259	4 14	5 43	...		...	5 24	7 51	...
dep		6 30	...	8 42	1 2	4 18	5 46	...		...	5 25	7 52	...
Upsala ......arr		7 51	a.m.	1235	2 21	5 33	7 5	p.m.		...	6 31	8 53	...
GEFLE ......dep	a.m.	...	6 20	—	...	3 p5	...	6 30	...	...	...	6a20	...
Upsala ......dep	6 57	8 0	9 8	4 p0	2 28	5 41	7 12	9 35	...	...	6 38	9 0	...
Rosersberg	7 51	8 51	10 3	4 51	3 19	...	...	10 26	...	...	...	...	...
Stockholm ar	8 44	9 44	1040	5 39	3 55	6 53	8 20	11 16	...	...	7 50	10 8	...

Dist E.M			2&3	3Cl.	2&3	2&3	2&3	2&3	Ex3	3Cl.	3Cl.	2&3	Ex3	Ex3
	STOCKHOLM ...dep		...	10p0	...	...	8a38	1056	1247	...	...	6p16	9 p7	9p35
—				a.m.			a.m.	p.m.	p.m.			p.m.	n'gt	n'gt
83¾	**Cathrineholm** ...dep		...	4 32	...	...	11 5	2 27	3 14	...	...	9 15	12 0	1222
...	Kilsmo		...	6 7	...	...	1152	3 16	...	...	...	9 59	...	A
115½	**Palsboda** 310		...	6 33	...	...	12 4	3 30	RC	...	...	1012	1253	1 17
123½	**Hallsberg** 309A...arr		...	7 0	a.m.	...	1217	3 44	4 12	p.m.	p.m.	1025	1 8	1 31
...	" ...dep		...	—	7 11	...	1230	—	4 17	5‡45	7 38	—	1 14	1 36
142¼	**Laxa** 308......arr		...	...	7 45	...	1 6	...	4 50	7 2	8 30	...	1 49	2 13
...	" ......dep		...	...	7 47	...	1 28	...	4 57	7 32	—	3Cl.	2 2	SC
156	Gardsjö 307		...	a.m.	8 16	a.m.	1 58	...	5 24	9 22	...	p.m.	SC	A—Until 31st August.
170½	Töreboda		...	5 11	8 44	11 0	2 27	...	5 46	10 9	...	7 0	3 5	
178¾	Moholm 307		...	5 43	8 57	1146	2 42	...	5 59	—	...	7 55	3 20	
194¾	Skofde 309A		...	7 29	9 35	1251	3 22	...	6 27	...	...	9 57	3 50	
204¼	Stenstorp 307		...	8 26	9 57	1 26	3 46	...	6 50	...	2&3	1054	4 11	
213½	**Falkoping** 309A arr		a.m.	8 59	1016	1 56	4 4	...	7 7	...	p.m.	1127	4 28	
...	" ...dep		6 a0	—	1036	2 20	4 15	...	7 14	...	7 22	—	4 35	
234½	**Herrl-** " ......arr	2&3	6 55	...	1120	2 50	4 59	...	7 44	...	8 16	...	5 9	
...	**junga** 307 dep	a.m.	7 3	...	1126	2 52	5 7	p.m.	7 48	...	8 23	...	5 16	
255¾	**Alingsas**	7 ‡9	8 2	...	1215	3 23	5 56	4‡29	8 20	...	9 20	...	5 54	
272	Lerum	7 56	8 47	...	1257	...	6 35	5 11	...	...	10 7	...	6 29	
284½	**Gothenb'rg** arr	8 32	9 28	...	1 24	4 10	7 5	5 45	9 8	...	1048	...	7 2	...

CATHRINEHOLM and GOTHENBURG.

SC—Sleeping Cars in these trains.

[‡—Weekdays only.]	3Cl.	3Cl.	2&3	2&3	3 Cl	2&3	Ex3	3 Cl	2&3	2&3	2&3	Ex.3	2&3
				a.m.		a.m.	p.m.		p.m.	p.m.	p.m	p.m.	o.m.
Gothenburg ......dep	...	...	...	7 21	...	1017	1214	...	3 50	5‡20	7 37	10 6	1035
Lerum	...	...	...	7 56	...	1058	RC	...	4 25	5 46	8 5	10 38	1117
Alingsas	...	...	...	8 36	...	1150	1 5	...	5 12	6 27	8 54	11 12	1155
Herrljunga ...... arr	...	...	...	9 20	...	1250	1 39	...	5 58	—	9 43	11 51	—
dep	...	...	...	9 21	...	1259	1 43	...	6 6	...	9 50	11 56	...
Falkoping ...... arr	...	a.m.	...	1013	a.m.	2 4	2 20	p.m.	6 55	p.m.	1051	12 36	...
dep	...	6 15	...	1029	1113	—	2 32	2 48	7 16	7‡50	—	12 43	...
Stenstorp	...	6 56	...	1046	1144	...	2 50	3 44	7 37	8 10	...	12 59	...
Skofde	...	7 38	...	1111	1250	RC—Restaurant Car in this train.	3 15	4 36	8 2	—	...	1 19	B—Runs until 1st September.
Moholm	a.m.	9 0	...	1145	—		3 39	5 59	8 37	...	...	1 44	
Töreboda	5 55	9 24	...	12 1	...		3 54	6 29	8 55	...	Ex3	2 1	
Gardsjö	7 4	—	...	1228	...		4 19	—	9 22	...	B	SC	
Laxa ...... arr	7 46	a.m.	...	1253	...		4 41	...	9 48	...	a.m.	2 54	
dep	7 57	6 20	...	1 8	...		4 55	...	9 55	...	2 22	3 4	
Hallsberg ...... arr	8 55	7 5	a.m.	1 42	...		5 26	...	1029	p.m.	2 56	3 37	
dep	—		8 36	2 2	...		5 36	...	—	7 36	3 3	3 50	
Palsboda	...	—	8 50	2 18	...		5 54	...	...	7 54	3 20	4 10	...
Kilsmo	...	...	9 1	2 30	...		...	...	...	8 13	SC	...	...
Cathrineholm ...arr	...	...	9 45	3 13	...		6 39	...	...	9 14	4 11	5 1	...
STOCKHOLM 308 arr	...	...	1240	6p21	...		9 p8	...	...	...	7 p8	7 a55	...

GOTHENBURG and MALMO.

SC—Sleeping Car in this train.

Dist E.M	Station			2&3	2&3	1,2,3	Ex3	2&3	2&3	Ex3	2&3	2&3	3 Cl	Ex.3
...	CHRISTIANIA ......dep			...	...	...	...	...	...	7a44	...	...	...	5 p45
...	FREDRIKSHALD...dep			...	...	...	...	...	...	1040	...	...	...	8 p50
...	MELLERUD ....dep			...	...	...	...	...	...	1p 5	...	...	...	11p12
						a.m.	a.m.		p.m.	p m.	p.m.	p.m	p.m.	a.m.
—	Gothenburg ....dep			...	...	8 0	10 0	...	1212	3 33	5 12	7 38	1115	1 33
17½	Kongsbacka			...	...	8 46	1029	...	1 13	4 6	6 21	8 45	1221	SC
47¾	Warberg 307 ....arr			a.m.	...	9 49	1115	...	2 37	4 52	7 52	9 53	—	2 47
	Warberg 307 ....dep			5 38	...	9 56	1122	...	2 44	4 59	8 8	10 0	...	2 55
67	Falkenberg.... ....2&3			6 28	...	1042	12 7	...	3 44	5 32	9 16	1048	p.m.	3 27
93¾	Halmstad 307 arr		a.m.	7 38	...	1153	1255	...	5 12	6 20	1054	1151	‡	4 13
	Halmstad 307 dep		5 27	7 45	...	12 8	1 19	...	5 19	6 25	—	—	1117	4 18
105¾	Veinge		6 3	8 19	...	1242	1 44	...	6 0	RC	...	...	1151	...
109¼	Laholm		6 13	8 29	...	1251	1 53	...	6 12	6 54	...	...	12 0	4 48
118¾	Bastad		6 42	8 56	p.m.	1 18	2 14	p.m.	6 45	7 14	p.m.	a.m.	—	5 8
134¾	Engelholm arr a.m.		7 28	9 43	1215	2 3	2 50	3 0	7 38	7 47	8 17	5§20	‡—Runs on Sun. Wed. Sat.	5 46
143½	Astorp ....2&3		8 22	10 7	1252	—	—	3 25	—	8 14	8 45	6 26		6 17
149¼	Billesholms ...	6 3	8 48	1018	1 15	...	...	3 40	p.m.	8 24	9 5	6 53		6 29
165¼	Teckomatorp	7 14	9 46	1049	2 42	...	...	4 24	6 53	8 55	10 5	—		7 0
171	Kjeflinge	7 36	10 1	11 2	3 4	...	...	4 44	7 8	9 6	1028	...		7 11
186½	Malmo.......arr	8 25	1031	1127	3 54	...	...	5 27	7 45	9 31	1120	...		7 36
206½	COPENHAGEN arr		1245	2p45	...	...	...	7p30	9p45	1130	...	...		9 a45

Station		2&3	3Cl.	2&3	Ex3	2&3	Ex3	2&3	2&3	2&3	2&3	2&3	2&3	2&3	Ex.3
COPENHAGEN.....dep		...	...	6 a5	5a45	...	...	...	1110	...	...	3 p0	...	...	8 p0
		a.m.		a.m.	a.m.	a m.			p.m.	p m.	p.m.	p.m.		p.m.	p.m.
Malmo ....dep		5 39	...	9 1	7 40	1032	...	...	1252	3 26	3 55	6 4	...	8 17	10 16
Kjeflinge		6 32	...	9 32	8 8	1121	...	...	1 44	3 53	4 49	6 39	...	9 7	10 44
Teckomatorp		7 11	...	9 42	RC	1140	...	...	2 10	4 6	5 6	6 55	p.m.	10 3	10 55
Billesholms		8 5	...	—	8 48	1224	...	...	3 1	4 38	—	7 46	9 1	1048	11 24
Astorp.......................		8 25	...	a.m.	9 1	1251	p.m.	p.m.	3 25	4 49	...	8 19	9 40	—	11 36
Engelholm 311............		8 50	...	6 54	9 31	1 9	1 34	2 10	3 48	5 3	...	8 57	1019	...	12 4
Bastad.......................		—	a.m.	7 49	10 8		2 14	2 57	—	6 5	...	9 50	—	...	12 40
Laholm.......................		...	6§35	8 27	1025	—	2 33	3 23	...	6 35	...	1023	...	...	12 59
Veinge.......................		...	6 50	8 39	1036	...	2 44	3 33	...	6 49	...	1035	...	...	SC
Halmstad ....arr		a.m.	7 30	9 18	1056	p.m.	3 5	4 5	...	7 21	...	1110	...	...	1 29
Halmstad ....dep		5 53	—	9 41	11 1	1 50	3 28	4 18	...	7 36	...	—	...	...	1 34
Falkenberg..........2&3		7 26	...	1119	1148	3 6	4 18	5 33	...	8 52	...	...	...	§—Weekdays only.	2 23
Warberg 307 arr	a.m.	8 24	...	1 2	1218	3 56	4 55	6 16	...	9 40	...	...	...		2 54
Warberg 307 dep	5 2	8 34	a.m.	1 11	1225	—	5 5	6 33	...	—	...	...	...		3 2
Kongsbacka	6 36	9 58	1127	2 42	1 11	...	6 2	7 37	...	...	...	...	...		...
Gothenburg ....arr	7 49	1056	1234	3 49	1 42	...	6 34	8 21	...	...	...	...	...		4 20
MELLERUD 306 ...arr		...	...	...	4p10	...	...	...	...	...	...	...	...	...	6 a43
FREDRIKSHLD 304arr		...	...	...	6p32	...	...	...	...	...	...	...	...	...	8 a57
CHRISTIANIA 304arr		...	...	...	9p43	...	...	...	...	...	...	...	...	...	12 0

FALKOPING and NASSJÖ.

Station	a.m.		a.m.	a.m.	p.m.	p.m.		
Falkoping dp	4 37	...	5 40	1020	2 26	7 17	...	...
Wartofta......	4 51	...	6 20	1034	2 42	7 35	...	...
Mullsjö	5 14	a.m.	8 0	11 3	3 18	8 11	...	...
Jonkoping...	5 56	7 46	9 51	1137	4 1	8 55	...	...
Tenhult	6 15	8 22	1025	...	4 20	9 14	...	...
Nässjö ..arr	6 46	9 16	1133	1215	4 54	9 48	...	...

Station	a.m.	a.m.	p.m.	p.m.	p.m.			
Nässjö...dep	6 53	1014	1228	5 10	10 2	...	...	...
Tenhult......	7 27	1112	1255	5 36	1036	...	...	...
Jonkoping	7 50	1144	1 13	5 54	11 0	...	...	...
Mullsjö	9 1	1250	...	6 26	1140	...	...	...
Wartofta ...	9 49	1 40	2 3	6 56	1210	...	...	...
Falkopingar	1011	2 0	2 15	7 11	1227	...	...	...

RINGSTORP and ODESHOG.

*—6.10 a.m. on Sats.

Station					
Ringstorp dep		6a46	...	1236	7 p0
Linkoping ...		8 22	11a42	3 56	7 53
Fogelsta	7a15	1040	2 23	5 20	1050
Wadstena	8 0	1116	2 50	5 43	1110
Hastholm	9 35	1249	3 51	6 37	—
Odeshog	10 5	1 16	4 20	6 50	...

Station				
Odeshog dep	...	8*a30	1 p30	6 p0
Hastholmen	...	8 43	1 53	6 27
Wadstena ...	6a25	10 0	3 0	7 20
Fogelsta	7 3	10 42	3 33	7 40
Linkoping ...	8 57	12 17	5 35	9 8
Ringstorp ar	1038	3 32	6 18	...

KRYLBO and MJOLBY.

*—Sunday depart 7.16 a.m.

Station				a.m.				p.m.	
Krylbo.........dep		...	...	7 52	...	...	...	5 40	...
Vestanfors		...	...	8 49	...	...	...	6 38	...
Krampen	a.m.	...	a.m.	9 42	p.m	...	p.m.	7 31	p m.
Frovi	5 0	...	8 *0	10 46	1223	...	5 12	8 34	1042
Ervalla	5 43	a.m.	8 22	11 1	1235	p.m.	5 25	8 48	1054
Orebro	7 57	6 5	8 56	11 30	1 15	4 49	6 33	9 30	1116
Hallsberg dp	8 31	7 15	1143	12 24	1 50	5 39	7 31	1034	1 0
Lerbäck	—	7 52	—	12 47	—	6 3	—	1056	—
⁝ Askersund ...arr		8 44	a.m.	1 43	...	6 55	...	...	...
Motala..................		10 2	6 42	2 7	...	7 24	...	12 9	...
Fogelsta 309A		1037	7 32	2 21	...	7 43	...	1222	...
Mjolby (308) arr		1133	8 15	2 42	...	8 8	...	1243	...

Station		a.m.		a.m.		p.m.	p.m.	p.m.
Mjolby...dep		4 55	...	10 0	...	3 10	4 5	1015
Fogelsta......		5 17	...	1028	...	3 31	5 19	1049
Motala............		5 30	...	1042	...	3 44	6 0	11 6
⁝ Askersund dep		...	...	1055	...	4 0	7 35	—
Lerbäck		6 45	a.m.	12 1	p.m.	5 1	8 37	p.m.
Hallsb'g	4a25	7 26	9 1	1230	2 14	5 43	9 10	6 57
Orebro......	6 20	8 28	11 1	2 0	2 59	6 25	1043	9 5
Ervalla ...	6 43	8 56	1133	2 40	4 59	6 49	—	1056
Frovi	6 54	9 16	1148	2 56	5 11	7 6	...	1119
Krampen	—	1010	3 52	—	—	7 59	...	—
Vestanfors......		11 5	6 46	...	...	8 48	...	...
Krylbo ...arr		1155	9 6	...	...	9 34	...	...

Station					
Orebro...dep	5 a15	10a0	1 p56	6p18	...
Svarta ...arr	7 5	1217	3 57	8 5	...

Station					
Svarta ...dep	5a40	7a39	2 p15	5p38	...
Orebro ...arr	7 35	9 34	4 19	7 28	...

ANGE and SUNDSVALL.

Station				
Ange.....dep	5a10	8a25	2p50	9p25
Torpsham'r	6 57	9 25	5 6	1030
Matfors dep	8 0	10 5	6 15	...
Wattjom.....	8 33	1029	6 48	1129
Sundsvall ar	9 15	11 0	7 30	1159

Station				
Sundsvall dep	5a20	1010	1p50	6p10
Wattjom.........	5 51	1055	2 47	6 46
Matfors arr	...	11 8	3 5	7 5
Torpshamm'r	6 57	1226	4 40	7 51
Ange 309...arr	8 5	1 57	...	9 3

LJUSDAL and HUDIKSVALL.

Station			
Ljusdal ...dep	5a35	11a12	6p45
Hudiksvall ar	8 20	2 35	8 24

Station			
Hudiksvall	8a35	2p50	9 p0
Ljusdal arr	1020	6 20	1135

Station		
Bergsjo......dep	6a 0	2p15
Hudiksvall arr	8 18	4 30

Station			
Hudiksvall dep	9a25	5p30	...
Bergsjo......arr	11 20	7 54	...

KILAFORS and STUGSUND.

‡—Not on Sunday.

Station					
Kilafors...	6‡a10	8 a0	1p15	4p15	9p15
Bergvik ...	7 0	9 23	1 55	4 42	9 42
Söderham.	7 45	1046	2 48	5 20	1017
Stugsund	7 53	1054	2 56	5 25	1022

Station				
Stugsund ...	6a10	1120	2p43	7p22
Söderhamn ...	6 20	1137	3 0	7 39
Bergvik.........	6 49	1221	3 30	8 23
Kilafors...ar	7 20	1 0	4 0	9 3

GEFLE and UPSALA.

†—At or from Gefle Södra.

E.M	Station				
	Gefle (Central) dep	6a20	10†a0	3 p5	6†p30
28	Orrskog..................	7 22	12 18	4 6	7 40
33	Tierp	7 33	12 52	4 17	7 52
44	Orbyhus	7 58	1 57	4 41	8 23
68½	Gamla Upsala........	8 49	3 43	...	9 18
70¼	Upsala (309)...arr	8 55	3 53	5 30	9 25

Station						
Upsala ......dep	6a45	11a37	2p54	8p14	...	...
Gamla Upsala ...	6 52	...	3 4	8 20	...	...
Orbyhus	7 58	12 23	4 50	9 11	...	...
Tierp	8 22	12 45	5 39	9 35	...	...
Orrskog	8 37	12 56	6 ‡4	9 45	...	...
Gefle (Central) ar	9†50	1 52	8‡40	10 46	...	...

E M	Station								
	Orbyhus ....dep	8 a30	12p26	5 p5	9p12	...	...	...	...
5½	Dannemora (307) ... ...arr	8 52	12 42	5 27	9 28	...	...	...	...

Station							
Dannemora dep	7 a35	11a43	4 p15	7p25	...	...	...
Orbyhus......arr	7 53	12 5	4 35	7 48	...	...	...

Station									
Ockelbo...................dep	6‡a30	9 a7	2p22	8p15	...	...	...	...	...
Gefle Central ....arr	8 56	1022	3 38	9 50	...	...	...	...	...

Station					
Gefle Central ....dep	7 a0	10‡a55	1p44	6p30	...
Ockelbo......................arr	8 35	1 24	2 59	7 55	...

‡—Not on Sunday.

E M	Station				
	Orrskog dep	8§a32	1 p2	4p25	9p46
5½	Soderfors arr	9 2	1 20	4 49	1010

Station				
Soderfors dep	7§a0	12p28	3p45	9 p0
Orrskog ...arr	7 18	12 49	4 1	9 21

§—Sun., Wed., and Sat.

Station				
Skofde ...dep	5a20	11‡15	3p25	8 p4
Carlsborg arr	7 55	12 27	4 34	9 16

Station				
Carlsborg dep	8 a4	10‡20	1 p45	5 p5
Skofde ...arr	9 16	12 36	2 57	6 17

‡—Not on Sunday.

Station			
Linghed dep	5a‡10	3‡p36	‡ Week-
Ockelbo	9 15	8 20	days
Norrsundet	10 42	9 50	only.

Station			
Norrsundet dep	7a10	...	12‡p30
Ockelbo	8 39	9‡a10	3 28
Linghed ......arr	...	12 50	7 17

NASSJO and OSKARSHAMN. §—Not on Sun.

Nässjo ...dep	7 a3	1030	1240	§	5p12	6p20	9p55
Eksjö	7 36	1124	1 27	1p35	5 44	7 15	1025
Ingatorp	8 19	—	—	3 41	6 28	—	—
Hultsfred 310 arr	9 8	...	...	5 45	7 16	...	..
Hultsfred 310 dep	9 22	2p30	...	—	7 23	...	...
Berga 310	1024	5 15	5p53	...	8 22	...	...
Oskarshamn ...arr	11 5	...	7 13	...	9 0	...	...

Oskarshamn dep	...	...	5a30	8a10	...	5 p5	...
Berga	...	§	6 56	8 58	...	5 52	...
Hultsfred arr	...	a.m.	—	9 55	...	6 55	...
Hultsfred dep	...	4 30	...	10 7	...	7 17	...
Ingatorp	a.m.	6 20	...	1056	p.m.	8 10	...
Eksjö	6 0	7 34	...	1141	4 7	8 59	...
Nässjo (309A) arr	6 33	9 11	...	1212	4 40	9 30	...

Wimmerby ...dep	8 a27	6 p2	6§p52	...	...	...
Hultsfred ...arr	9 2	6 35	8 10	...	...	...

Hultsfred ...dep	10a25	7 p26	7§p55	...
Wimmerby 310A arr	10 58	8 0	9 16	...

§—Not on Sundays.

KALMAR and BERGA. ‡—Not on Sunday.

Kalmar ...dep	6a30	8‡a55	3 p0	5 p15
Alem	7 33	10 53	4 12	7 18
Berga (310) arr	8 53	1 25	5 44	9 48

Berga ...dep	6 a0	10a30	2‡p30	8 p23
Alem	7 56	11 55	5 29	9 40
Kalmar ...arr	9 35	1 0	7 35	10 40

SPANGENAS and WIMMERBY.

Spangenäs ...dep	8 a11	5 p51
Wimmerby ...arr	8 55	6 35
Wimmerby ...dep	9 a35	7 p15
Spangenäs (310) arr	10 25	8 5

NORSHOLM and HULTSFRED.

Norsholm ...dep	...	5 a51	...	8 a0	3p20	5p20	...
Ringstorp	...	6 16	...	8 43	3 51	6 21	...
Atvidaberg	...	7 12	...	1040	5 7	7 49	...
Ofverum	...	8 32	...	1 49	6 32	—	...
Jenny ...arr	...	9 29	...	4 3	7 27	...	...
Westervik ...arr	a.m.	9 38	p.m.	4 35	7 35	...	...
,, ...dep	6 35	—	1250	4 15	—	...	...
Jenny ...dep	...	...	1 8	4 25	...	...	...
Ankarsrum	7 24	...	2 38	5 8	...	...	...
Spangenäs (310)	8 5	...	3 50	5 47	...	...	...
Hultsfred ...arr	9 3	...	5 10	6 40	..	...	...

Hultsfred ...dep	...	4 a20	10 a0	...	7p25	...
Spangenäs	...	5 54	10 47	...	8 16	...
Ankarsrum	...	7 22	11 25	...	8 58	...
Jenny ...arr	...	8 42	12 6	...	...	...
Westervik arr	..	9 6	12 15	p.m.	9 45	...
,, dep	...	8 45	11 30	5 20	—	...
Jenny ...dep	...	8 55	12 7	...	...	...
Ofverum	a.m.	9 56	2 15	6 31	...	...
Atvidaberg	5 0	11 28	5 5	8 7	...	...
Ringstorp	6 36	12 27	6 45	9 4	...	...
Norsholm ...arr	7 11	12 52	7 35	9 28	...	...

OREBRO and NORRKÖPING.

Orebro ...dep	...	...	6a 0	7 a25	...	...	2p22	6 p15	...
Palsboda (309)	...	...	7 33	8 40	9 a0	...	3 40	7 47	...
Finspong	6a32	7a10	—	10 50	1 0	1p35	7 8	—	...
Kimstad	7 32	8 56	...	11 36	1 57	3 25	7 55	...	...
Norrköping ...arr	8 6	10 4	...	12 16	...	4 35	8 33	...	...

Norrköping dep	...	6 a10	9 a3	1 p25	...	...	4 p 0	9 p8
Kimstad	...	7 11	9 43	2 30	...	3p30	4 46	9 59
Finspong	...	9 36	1026	3 15	...	4 45	5 39	1041
Palsboda	8a35	1 50	—	—	4p40	—	8 0	—
Orebro ...arr	9 52	3 20	...	...	5 40	...	8 57	...

TRELLEBORG and KJEFLINGE.

Trelleborg...dep	...	6 a0	...	9 a0	...	2p 0	3p45	...	8p22
Svedala	...	6 39	...	9 38	...	2 34	4 50	...	9 3
Lund	6a10	7 40	9 a5	1046	1 p2	3 30	6 4	8p38	9 50
Kjeflinge...arr	6 28	7 58	9 25	11 4	1 35	3 48	6 30	8 58	1026

Kjeflinge...dep	...	7a37	8a18	10a6	11a23	3 p5	4p50	7 p9	9p13	1040
Lund	5 a55	7 57	8 41	1027	12 0	4 0	5 21	7 29	9 31	1058
Svedala	7 19	—	9 34	—	12 49	4 51	—	9 1	—	—
Trelleborg ...arr	8 8	...	10 6	...	1 19	5 23	...	9 33	...	...

LANDSCRONA and SJOBO.

Landscrona dep	6a45	9a10	2p15	3p25	6p27	9p35
Kjeflinge	7 40	9 54	3 2	4 36	7 10	1019
Ortofta	8 22	—	4 8	—	8 10	—
Harlösa	9 7	...	4 49	...	9 31	...
Sjöbo ...arr	9 40	...	5 20	...	1010	...

Sjöbo ...dep	...	6 a0	...	1055	...	5p50
Harlösa	...	7 7	...	1130	...	6 36
Ortofta	...	8 30	a.m.	1256	pm	8 41
Kjeflinge	6a40	9 33	1125	1 45	640	9 9
Landscrona arr	8 0	1015	1230	2 35	715	9 55

MALMO and YSTAD

E.M.						
	Malmo dep	9 a0	12p15	4p15	8 p25	...
13	Svedala	9 36	12 51	4 51	9 5	...
17¾	Börringe	9 46	1 1	5 1	9 15	...
39	Ystad ...arr	10 40	1 58	5 55	10 10	...

Ystad ...dep	5a15	8a25	12p55	1 p9	7p45	...	...
Börringe	6 25	9 23	1 54	4 10	8 46	...	...
Svedala	6 38	9 35	2 4	5 0	9 2	...	...
Malmo ...arr	7 16	10 6	2 35	6 23	9 35	...	...

Borringe ...dep	9a50	5p 5	9 p18	...	...
Ostratorp ...arr	1055	6 12	10 28	...	...

Ostratorp ...dep	8a10	12p45	7 p30	...	...	...
Borringe ...arr	9 13	1 48	8 40	...	...	...

YSTAD and ESLOF. ‡-Not on Sunday.

Ystad ...dep	5a25	7a35	1p35	...	6p50
Tomelilla	5 57	8 10	2 8	3p25	7 24
Eslof (308) ...arr	7 32	9 38	3 36	6 34	8 51

Eslof ...dep	4a45	9a20	12p35	4 p15	9p15	...
Tomelilla	8 8	1053	2 7	5 47	1044	...
Ystad ...arr	9 6	1121	2 35	6 15	1112	...

Ystad ...dep	7a10	3p25	6p50
Brosarp arr	8 55	4 51	8 34
Brosarp	6a20	9a16	5p12
Ystad	9 6	1045	6 38

Ystad ...dep	8a25	1 ‡9	7p45	
Skifarp arr	10 7	2 16	8 30	
Skifarp	8a40	1p10	4p45	...
Ystad	9 23	1 58	5 55	...

ESLOF and HELSINGBORG.

Eslof ...dep	6a35	a.m.	9a52	1p35	4p50	p.m.	9p10
Teckomatorp	7 2	9 44	10 19	2 10	5 18	6 53	9 37
Billeberga ...arr	7 11	9 51	10 28	2 21	5 27	7 0	9 46
Landskrona arr	7 30	...	10 50	2 45	5 50	7 25	10 5
,, dep	6 30	...	10 5	2 0	4 55	6 25	9 25
Billeberga ...dep	7 14	9 51	10 31	2 28	5 31	7 0	9 49
Helsingborg ...arr	8 0	1027	11 15	3 25	6 15	7 35	1035

Helsingborg	6 a0	8a55	9a40	1p35	4p10	6 p5	9 p0	...
Billeberga ...arr	6 46	9 29	1025	2 22	5 18	6 41	9 45	...
Landskrona arr	7 30	...	1050	2 45	5 50	7 25	10 5	...
Landskrona dep	6 30	...	10 5	2 0	4 55	6 25	9 25	...
Billeberga ...dep	6 49	9 29	1030	2 25	5 28	6 41	9 48	...
Teckomatorp	7 3	9 37	1050	2 37	7 0	6 48	10 3	...
Eslof ...arr	7 30	...	1120	3 5	7 40	7 40	1030	...

HESSLEHOLM and VEINGE.

Hessleholm dp	...	7a24	11a10	5p22	8p28
Markaryd	6a30	9 10	12 32	7 33	9 40
Veinge ...arr	8 13	1028	1 38	...	1034

Veinge ...dep	...	6a51	9a15	1p50	6 p1	...
Markaryd	5 a0	8 27	11 2	3 14	6 58	...
Hessleholm arr	7 1	10 4	...	4 40	8 8	...

LANDSCRONA and BILLESHOLM.

Landscrona ...dep	7a17	11a34	2p12	5 p0	8p10	...
Billesholm ...arr	8 2	12 19	2 57	7 23	8 55	...

Billesholm ...dep	7 a1	8 a48	1p12	3p42	9 p3	...	...
Landscrona ...arr	7 47	9 33	3 12	4 27	9 48	...	...

ASTORP and VERNAMO.

Astorp ...dep	a.m.	7a37	9a50	2p14	8 p5
Markaryd	5 0	9 56	1 48	4 0	1020
Stromsnas	6 10	1048	2 35	4 26	1050
Ljungby	8 45	1211	—	5 30	—
Vernamo ...arr	1056	...	...	6 45	...

Vernamo dep	...	9a25	...	...	1p10	...
Ljungby	...	1037	1p40	...	4 2	...
Stromsnas	5 a0	1143	2 57	3p50	6 10	...
Markaryd	5 31	12 9	3 56	4 55	6 53	...
Astorp ...arr	7 48	1 57	6 40	8 23	...	...

KOPING and RIDDARHYTTAN. ‡—Not on Sunday.

Koping 311 dep	...	8 a10	11a10	1‡p10	4 p2
Uttersberg	6‡a20	10 50	1 5	3 15	6 22
Riddarhyttan	7 20	...	1 40	4 32	...

Riddarhyttan	5a35	9 ‡a0	...	4 p50
Uttersberg	6 35	10 5	3p35	5 50
Koping ...arr	7 58	12 58	6 15	...

HESSLEHOLM and HELSINGBORG. ‡—Weekdays only.

Hessleholm ..dep	am	6a17	...	11a10	...	p.m	5p25	8p20
Klippan	525	7 16	a.m.	1220	pm	1‡20	6 45	9 21
Astorp 310	620	7 36	9 7	1240	2 0	2 30	7 10	9 39
Bjuf	636	7 45	9 19	1250	211	2 46	7 22	9 48
Billesholm .arr	8‡6	...	1010	...	...	...	8 2	...
Helsingborg ..arr	753	8 15	1010	1 20	240	4 25	8 0	1015

Helsingborg ...dep	6a50	9 a2	1p28	2p45	5p30	7 p0	9p35
Billesholm...dep	6‡15	8 50	1 ‡35	...	...	...	...
Bjuf ...dep	7 21	9 45	1 57	3 13	6 4	7 41	10 2
Astorp	7 33	10 8	2 11	3 24	6 20	7 53	1012
Klippan	7 50	1030	—	3 43	6 50	...	1028
Hessleholm 308 arr	8 47	...	...	4 45	7 51	...	1125

Klippan...dep	7 a51	10a44	3 p45	6p44	...	...	...
Eslof ...arr	8 54	12 5	6 10	8 0	...	...	...

Eslof ...dep	9 a0	10a35	4p12	8p20	...	...	...
Klippan ...arr	1014	12 12	6 10	9 19	...	...	...

NORRKOPING and VALDEMARSVIK. †—Not on Sunday. §—Until 31st August.

Norrköping dp	6†a0	8 a7	1p15	4p§2	6p10	8p35	...	...
Söderköping	6 50	8 40	2 9	4 35	6 46	9 15	...	...
Valdemarsvik	8 45	...	4 30	...	8 5	...	...	...

Valdemarsvik	...	6a30	11a15	...	6 p0	...
Söderköping	6a50	8 40	12 40	5p25	8 25	...
Norrköping ar	7 30	9 20	1 14	6 8	9 5	...

MALERAS and LESSEBO.

Maleras ...dep	6 a45	2p35	...
Lessebo 311 ...arr	8 29	4 19	...

Lessebo ...dep	8 a56	5p40	...	...
Maleras ...arr	10 30	7 23	...	...

Astorp ...dep	7a40	9 a0	12p59	2p14	3p54	8p11
Kattarp	8 9	9 36	1 36	2 40	4 30	8 45
Höganäs ...arr	8 55	1015	2 16	...	5 12	9 28

Höganäs dep	6a19	7 a1	8a46	...	2 p0	...	6p49	...
Kattarp	6 59	7 54	9 36	1p33	2 48	4p29	7 32	8p51
Astorp arr	7 25	8 19	10 4	2 5	3 15	5 16	8 0	9 23

FROVI and LUDVIKA.

E.M.						
	Frovi dep	6 a58	9a20	11a55	5p16	7 p10
1¼	Vanneboda	7 5	10 8	12 20	5 26	7 55
13	Lindesberg	7 44	11 0	12 50	5 57	8 36
22¼	Stora	8 17	1140	1 15	6 21	9 10
34¼	**Banghammar**	9 0	1223	2 46	6 52	9 52
35½	Kopparberg	9 9	1232	2 33	6 56	9 57
40½	Ställdalen	9 30	1250	2 53	7 29	—
62¼	**Ludvika (306)** arr	11 18	...	4 40	...	...

Ludvika dep	...	...	12p25	...	...	5p45	...
Ställdalen	...	9 a35	2 15	4p33	6p52	7 37	...
Kopparberg	5a10	10 25	3 26	4 55	7 10	8 5	...
Banghamm'r	...	10 29	3 30	5 0	—	8 11	...
Stora	5 53	11 0	4 3	5 45	...	9 5	...
Lindesberg	6 22	11 26	4 27	6 22	...	9 41	...
Vanneboda	7 8	12 15	5 3	7 8	...	1020	...
Frovi 309A arr	7 12	12 19	5 7	8 5	...	1038	...

UDDEVALLA and BENGTSFORS.

Uddevalla dep	5 a45	10a35	12p55	5 p35
Bäckefors	9 37	12 32	4 3	7 38
Bengtsfors arr	10 48	2 5	6 8	8 40

Bengtsfors dep	5 a20	7 a15	11‡a15	3p 0	...
Bäckefors	6 28	9 37	12 31	4 10	5p10
Uddevalla 306 arr	8 45	12 40	...	6 30	8 20

‡—Not Sun.

SALA and GEFLE.

Sala dep	5 a0	11a35	4p19
Gysinge	7 2	2 25	5 31
Hagastrom	8 50	4 50	6 40
Gefle arr	9 0	5 0	6 48

Gefle dep		10a25	3 p0	6p20
Hagastrom		10 38	3 20	6 40
Gysinge	5a30	11 45	5 40	8 10
Sala arr	7 40	12 53	8 0	...

BOLLNAS and ORSA.

Bollnas dep	8a 5	12p50	5p15
Voxna	9 45	4 16	7 2
Orsa arr	1145	...	9 0

Orsa dep	a.m.	8a50	1p22	...
Voxna	7 ‡0	1055	3 14	5p 0
Bollnas arr	9 50	1228	4 47	8 27

‡—5,5 a.m. on Tuesday and Friday.

NORRKOPING and ARKOSUND.

Norrkoping dep	7 a0	12 45	5 p40	...
O. Husby	8 16	2 20	6 47	...
Arkosund arr	9 10	3 30	7 40	...

Arkosund dep	6 a15	9 a45	4p30	...
O. Husby	7 17	10 45	5 52	...
Norrkoping arr	8 35	11 45	7 20	...

ENGELSBERG and KARRGRUFVAN.

Engelsberg dep	8a15	3 p51	9 p28	...	...
Snyten	8 27	3 58	9 37	...	...
Karrgrufvan 310A	9 0	4 25	10 13	...	...

Karrgrufvan dep	7 a0	12p20	5 p40	...
Snyten	7 43	1 6	6 16	...
Engelsberg arr	7 52	1 15	6 23	...

SALA and TILLBERGA.

E.M.					
	Sala dep	6 a30	7 a55	1 p35	6 p10
17½	**Tillberga** arr	7 18	9 6	2 14	7 28

Tillberga dep	6 a27	10 a5	2 p40	8p20	...
Sala arr	7 15	11 16	3 19	9 43	...

KRYLBO and KARRGRUFVAN.

E.M.				
	Krylbo dep	5 a45	1 p50	...
11¾	**Karrgrufvan** arr	6 55	2 55	...

Karrgrufvan dep	10a15	4 p26	...
Krylbo arr	11 15	4 58	...

TILLBERGA and LUDVIKA.

Tillberga dep	6 a23	9a54	2p45	8 p17	...
Engelsberg	8 27	1048	3 49	9 27	...
Vestanfors	8 51	11 4	4 5	9 43	...
Ludvika arr	10 24	12 0	5 10	10 52	...

Ludvika dep	6 a30	12 p5	5p28	5p40	...
Vestanfors	7 41	1 7	6 27	7 7	...
Engelsberg	8 1	1 22	6 43	7 38	...
Tillberga arr	9 9	2 24	7 37	9 10	...

Ludvika dep	7a35	12p20	5p40	...
Björbo	1025	1 23	7 15	...
Vansbro arr	12 3	2 15	8 24	...

Vansbro dep	9 a5	1p20	3p15	...
Björbo	1024	3 17	4 11	4p42
Ludvika arr	1150	...	5 15	7 27

KARLSKRONA and CHRISTIANSTAD.

Karlskrona dep	...	...	7a15	10 a0	1 p5	3p20	6p45	8p15
Nettraby	...	a.m.	8 2	10 24	1 35	4 6	7 14	8 55
Ronneby	...	5 45	9 10	11 0	2 15	5 5	7 55	9 45
Karlshamn arr	a.m.	8 20	11 0	12 15	3 40	7 5	9 20	—
Karlshamn dep	6 55	8 55	1130	12 23	3 50	7 20	—	...
Sandback	7 32	9 53	1220	12 57	4 26	8 5	...	...
Olofström arr	...	...	2 0	2 0	6 0	...	...	...
Solvesborg	8 15	1055	—	1 27	5 2	8 50	...	...
Christianstad arr	9 20	1245	...	2 25	6 0	9 55	...	...

Christianstad dep		...	6a10	10a55	...	1p30	3 p0	6p35
Solvesborg		a.m.	7 35	12 0	...	3 40	4 25	7 40
Olofström dep		6 45	...	...	...	3 5	...	...
Sandback		7 35	8 7	12 25	...	4 30	5 0	8 7
Karlshamn arr		8 25	8 50	12 55	p.m.	5 23	5 42	8 41
Karlshamn dep	a.m.	—	9 5	1 0	2 15	5 45	—	8 48
Ronneby	6 55	...	10 55	2 20	4 55	8 0	...	1015
Nettraby	7 55	...	11 35	2 51	6 8	9 0	...	1049
Karlskrona 311	8 35	...	12 4	3 15	6 40	9 40	...	1115

Nettrabyhamn dep	8 a5	2p50	7 p0
Nettraby 310A	8 16	3 4	7 15
Eringsboda	10 15	5 14	9 7
Elmeboda arr	11 11	6 10	...

Elmeboda dep	4 ‡15	...	7 §30	...	3p12
Eringsboda	5 11	5a16	8 26	8a30	4 13
Nettraby	—	7 26	—	1025	6 13
Nettrabyhamn arr	...	7 33	...	1032	6 20

‡—Tuesdays and Saturdays only. §—Tuesdays and Saturdays excepted.

Wexio dep	6 a15	10 a5	3 p25
Tingsryd	7 50	12 0	6 0
Ronneby arr	9 30	2 0	8 25

Ronneby dep	...	6 a0	2 p25	5p30
Tingsryd	5 a5	8 0	4 5	8 10
Wexio arr	7 33	9 50	5 30	...

LINKOPING and WIMMERBY.

Linkoping dep	5a30	9 a20	3 p0	7 p5
Kisa	7 24	1 51	4 52	10 19
Wimmerby arr	8 24	5 ‡35	5 58	...

Wimmerby dep	...	11 a2	8 p3	...
Kisa	5a20	12 24	9 10	...
Linkoping arr	8 35	2 15	10 52	...

‡—Not on Sunday.

ELMHULT and SOLVESBORG.

Elmhult dep	5 a0	7 p25	...
Olofström	7 45	9 12	...
Solvesborg arr	9 5	10 15	...

Solvesborg dep	5 a15	2 p10	...	...
Olofström	6 58	3 37	...	...
Elmhult arr	9 25	5 47	...	...

CHRISTIANSTAD and ESLOF.

Christianstad dep	...	8a10	2p50	6p25	...
Karpalund	...	8 17	2 58	6 33	...
Tollarp	...	8 43	3 26	7 1	...
Hörby	6a30	9 21	4 7	7 43	...
Eslof arr	7 33	9 50	4 45	8 19	...

Eslof dep	8a44	9a54	4p18	8 p20	...	...
Hörby	9 21	1055	4 53	8 54	...	...
Tollarp	10 4	—	5 32	9 35	...	...
Karpalund	1028	...	5 55	9 58	...	...
Christianstad arr	1035	...	6 2	10 5	...	...

YSTAD and ST. OLOF.

Ystad dep	5 a57	2 p40	7p25	...	...
Garsnas	7 16	3 54	8 39	...	...
St. Olof arr	7 44	4 15	9 1	...	...

St. Olof dep	6 a20	10a50	5p42	...	...	...
Garsnas	6 46	11 22	6 4	...	...	...
Ystad arr	8 0	12 30	7 15	...	...	...

SAFSJO and HVETLANDA.

Dist					
	Säfsjö dep	7 a50	12 0	6p10	9 p0
18¾	**Hvetlanda** arr	9 10	1 25	7 30	10 20

Hvetlanda dep	5 a50	9 a20	4*p0	6 p55
Säfsjö arr	7 15	10 45	5 28	8 20

*—1p40 on Tues.

KARLSKRONA and BERGQVARA.

Karlskrona dep	8a10	2p50	7p10	9p10
Gulberna	8 21	3 7	7 20	9 20
Torsas	10 0	5 10	8 59	—
Bergqvara arr	1016	5 26	9 15	...

Bergqvara dep	...	8a 0	10a45	5p45
Torsas	...	8 37	11 25	6 30
Gulberna	7a30	10 9	1 15	8 28
Karlskrona arr	7 40	10 19	1 25	8 38

KALMAR & TORSAS.

Kalmar	7a20	10a0	2p35	5p10
Torsas	8 35	1122	4 45	6 25
Torsas	6 a0	9a53	1150	5p22
Kalmar	8 35	1110	1 15	6 48

BYVALLA and LANGSHYTTAN.

Byvalla dep	8 a0	1p23	4p25	7p45
Langshyttan arr	9 18	2 32	5 37	9 0

Langsh'n	5 a5	11a15	2p32	4p45
Byvalla	6 18	12 30	3 45	6 0

JONKOPING and VIREDA.

Jonkoping dep	9 a0	3 p45	9*p5
Vireda arr	11 40	6 25	11 30

*—Wed. and Fri. only.

Vireda dep	3 ‡a0	6 a50	5 p3	...
Jonkoping arr	5 40	9 30	7 39	...

‡—Thurs. & Sat. only.

FALKENBERG and LIMMARED.

Falkenberg dep	...	7 a28	12p10
Axelfors	5 a47	11 32	3 7
Limmared arr	6 48	12 16	3 54

Limmared dep	10a12	4 p50	9 p30	...	...	...
Axelfors	11 32	5 41	10 19	...	...	...
Falkenberg arr	3 25	8 45	...	...	...	...

BRACKE and BODEN.

Dist E.M.				a.m.		a.m.	p.m.	
	Bracke ......dep	...	...	5 58	...	9 22	4 0	...
41¾	Hasjö	...	...	7 27	...	11 22	7 40	...
57¾	Bispgarden	...	...	8 1	...	12 8	9 42	...
81½	Langsele ...... arr	...	a.m.	8 55	...	1 21	1131	...
	Langsele ...... dep	...	3 25	9 15	...	1 47	—	...
138	Mellansel ...... arr	...	7 37	11 24	...	5 18	...	...
	Mellansel ...... dep	...	7 55	11 31	...	5 44	...	...
188¼	Nyaker	...	12 6	1 30	...	9 4	...	...
212½	Vannas ...... arr	a.m.	1 50	2 26	p.m.	10 21	...	...
	Vannas ...... dep	6 30	—	2 36	4 0	—	...	...
...	Bastuträsk (311A)	10 30	...	5 17	9 15	...	a.m.	...
302½	Jorn	1145	...	6 7	1023	...	4 20	...
362¼	Elfsby	2 51	...	8 23	—	...	8 20	...
390¾	**Boden** ......arr	4 10	...	9 22	...	...	1010	...

				a.m.	a.m.	p.m.	
Boden ......dep	...	...	...	8 23	11 38	4 20	...
Elfsby	...	...	a.m.	9 29	1 2	6 35	...
Jorn	...	...	4 0	11 51	4 20	1050	...
Bastuträsk	...	...	5 26	12 36	5 47	—	...
Vannas ...... arr	...	a.m.	10 5	3 5	9 42	...	...
Vannas ...... dep	...	6 43	11 40	3 15	—	...	...
Nyaker	...	8 21	1 40	4 11	...	...	...
Mellansel ...... arr	...	11 28	5 43	6 8	...	...	...
Mellansel ...... dep	...	11 50	6 37	6 20	...	...	...
Langsele ...... arr	a.m.	3 21	10 55	8 30	...	...	...
Langsele ...... dep	4 53	3 52	—	8 48	...	...	...
Bispgarden	7 4	5 10	...	9 42	...	...	...
Hasjö	8 46	6 8	...	10 19	...	...	...
Bracke 309 ......arr	1210	8 0	...	11 44	...	...	...

Langsele ......dep	9a13	1 p53	3 p59	8 p46	11p46	...
Solleftea ......arr	9 37	2 17	4 23	9 10	12 14	...
Sollefteа ......dep	4 a5	8 a15	12p43	2 p53	7 p45	
Langsele ......arr	4 35	8 48	1 16	3 26	8 18	

Mellansel ......dep	7 a57	11a40	6 p25	...	...	...
Ornskoldsvik arr	9 30	12 40	7 30	...	...	...
Ornskoldsvik dep	5a40	10a 5	4 p20	...	...	...
Mellansel ......arr	7 29	11 14	5 31	...	...	...

HERNOSAND and SOLLEFTEA.

Hernosand ......dep	7 a45	12p40	4 p5		
Nyland	10 27	3 55	6 20		
Sollefteа (311A) ...arr	12 30	...	7 35		
Sollefteа ......dep	...	9 a50	4p35	...	...
Nyland	6a30	11 6	6 26	...	...
Hernosand ......arr	9 45	1 15	8 45	...	...

LULEA and RIKSGRANSEN.

Dist. E.M.		a.m.			a.m.		a.m.	p.m.	p.m.		
	Lulea ......dep	6 52	...	...	7 36	...	10 37	2 26	8 10	...	...
22¼	**Boden** ......arr	8 2	...	...	8 12	...	11 28	3 45	1014	p.m.	p.m.
...	" ......dep	—	...	...	8 40	...	12 27	—	—	10 20	10 20
59¾	Lakaträsk	a.m.	a.m.	p.m.	1018	p.m.	3 22	...	...	A	C
127¼	Gellivare ......arr	6 0	9 0	1210	1 21	5 10	8 37	...	...	4 59	2 2
...	Malmberget ...arr	6 20	9 25	1235	2 10	5 35	9 22	...	...	SC	SC
189½	Kiruna	—	—	—	4 35	—	—	...	...	7 45	5 54
269¾	**Riksgränsen** ......arr	...	...	...	8 15	...	...	...	...	—	8 47
294	**Narvik 304** ...arr	...	...	..	10p7	...	...	...	...	...	10a38

Narvik ......dep		...	...	...	...	...	8 a30	...	...	...	6 p20
							a.m.			p.m.	p.m.
Riksgränsen ...dep		...	...	...	...	...	10 33	...	...	...	8 16
Kiruna		...	a.m.	a.m.	a.m.	p.m.	2 15	p.m.	...	10 0	11 25
Malmberget ...dep		...	6 21	8 15	10 45	1 0	4 10	7 10	...	B	D
Gellivare ......dep		...	6 58	8 35	11 5	1 15	5 0	7 30	...	1231	2 56
Lakaträsk		...	1240	—	—	—	7 49	—	...	SC	SC
Boden ......arr	a.m.	a.m.	3 25	p.m.	...	...	9 13	...	p.m.	6 15	6 15
" ......dep	6 47	1059	—	4 35	...	...	9 23	...	9 43	—	—
Lulea ......arr	8 50	1219	...	5 26	...	...	10 9	...	1044	...	...

SC—Sleeping Car attached.

A—Runs from Boden on Tuesday and Friday night from 31st August.
B—Runs from Kiruna on Wednesday and Saturday night from 1st September.
C—Runs on Sunday, Tuesday, and Friday, until 30th August.
D—Runs on Monday, Wednesday, and Saturday, until 31st August.

Gellivare ......dep	11a10	1 p47	5 p15	...
Koskullskulle ......arr	11 30	2 7	5 35	...
Koskullskulle ......dep	12p35	3p50	6 p45	...
Gellivare ......arr	1 5	4 20	7 15	...

BASTUTRASK and KALLHOLMEN.

E M						
	Bastuträsk ......dep	...	...	12p50	5p25	...
9¼	Finnfors	...	...	1 29	5 54	...
13¾	Krängfors	...	...	1 47	6 7	...
29¼	Skellefteå	8a35	1140	3 22	7 15	8 p6
39¾	Kallholmen arr	9 9	1214	4 3	7 45	8 40
	Kallholmen ......dep	7a13	9a30	12p46	5 p43	9 p0
	Skellefteå	8 25	10 4	2 1	6 17	9 34
	Krängfors	9 24	—	3 26	—	—
	Finnfors	9 39	...	3 48	...	...
	Bastuträsk 311A arr	10 9	...	4 32	...	...

VANNAS and UMEA.

[*—Sats. only.

Vannas ......dep	8*a20	10a26	3p17	10p35	...	...	...
Umea ......arr	9 12	11 45	4 9	11 40	...	...	...
Umea ......dep	5 a10	1 p28	2*p42	6p23	...	...	...
Vannas ......arr	6 13	2 24	3 39	7 50	...	...	...

BODEN and KARUNGI.

Boden ......dep	8a18	...	...	...
Morjärv	11 59	...	...	...
Lappträsk	1 38	...	...	...
Karungi ......arr	2 14	...	...	...
Karungi ......dep	3 p3	...	...	...
Lappträsk	3 47	...	...	...
Morjärv	5 54	...	...	...
Boden ......arr	9 10	...	...	...

FALUN and BJORBO.

Falun ......dep	6 a10	4 p40	...	...	...	...
Repbäcken (307)	8 7	5 54	...	...	...	...
Björbo (310A) ......arr	10 15	7 10	...	...	...	...
Bjorbo ......dep	5 a15	4 p15	...	...	...	...
Repbäcken	7 35	5 32	...	...	...	...
Falun ......arr	9 0	6 40	...	...	...	...

MALMÖ and SIMRISHAMN.

‡—Not on Sunday.

E.M		a.m.		a.m.		a.m.	p.m.	p.m.	p.m.	p.m.	p.m.
—	Malmö ......dep	5 ‡0	...	8 20	...	1142	1 17	3 15	7 10	8 10	9 55
9¼	Staffanstorp	6 50	...	8 56	...	1216	1 50	3 53	7 43	8 45	1028
15	Dalby ......arr	7 27	a.m.	9 13	...	1231	2 5	4 8	7 58	9 0	1043
26¾	Sjöbo 310	—	5 55	10 4	...	—	2 46	5 0	8 37	—	—
43	Tomelilla 310	a.m.	7 50	1052	p.m.	p.m.	3 24	6 11	9 15	...	...
46	Gärsnäs 310A	7 10	9 1	1117	1223	4‡28	3 52	6 58	9 40	...	...
59¾	Simrishamn arr	7 34	9 55	1138	1255	4 58	4 13	7 30	10 1	...	...

		a.m.	a.m.	a.m.	noon	p.m.	p.m.	p.m.
Simrishamn dep		6 15	6 35	1050	12 0	5 30	6 33	8 0
Gärsnäs		6 43	7 8	1115	1222	5 55	6 56	8 38
Tomelilla	a.m.	—	7 44	—	1249	—	7 27	9 17
Sjöbo	5 50	a.m.	8 27	...	1 25	p.m.	8 12	10 2
Dalby ...dep	6 33	7 39	9 14	9a50	2 6	6 8	9 3	—
Staffanstorp	6 51	7 58	9 33	10 9	2 22	6 27	9 19	...
Malmö 308	7 23	8 28	10 6	1038	2 50	6 55	9 49	...

Dalby ......dep	5a50	9a16	12p33	4p13	9 p5
Harlösa 310	7 20	9 44	12 59	4 40	9 32
Bjärsjölagard ...arr	8 1	10 3	1 18	4 59	9 51
Bjärsjölagard ...dep	6a49	9 a0	11 a0	5p20	8p10
Harlösa	7 10	9 20	11 57	5 39	8 29
Dalby ......arr	7 36	9 47	1 5	6 5	8 55

ÖSTERSUND and ULRIKSFORS.

E.M.		a.m.	a.m.	p.m.			
—	**Östersund** ......dep	...	11 30	3 35	...	...	...
23½	Häggenäs	...	1 1	5 37	...	...	...
49¾	Jämtlands Sikås	6 45	2 39	7 35	...	...	...
55¼	¦Hammerdal	7 4	3 4	8 11	...	...	...
71½	**Ulriksfors** ......arr	...	3 59	9 14	...	...	...

	a.m.	p.m.	p.m.		
Ulriksfors ......dep	5 0	1 17	...	...	...
¦Hammerdal	5 58	2 8	7 13	...	...
Jämtlands Sikås	6 43	2 42	7 32	...	...
Häggenäs	8 48	4 42	—	...	...
Östersund 30 ......arr	10 44	5 58	...	...	...

ST. PETERSBURG and HELSINGFORS.

E M	St. Petersburg **				a.m.		a.m.	a.m.	p.m.	p.m.	p.m.		p.m.	n'gt	a.m.
—	**St. Petersburg**.........dep	...	...	...	8 0	...	9 45	9 55	1 45	4 30	6 5	...	8 20	12 0	1 0
20	Valkeasaari.........	...	...	...	9 0	...	1021	1044	2 37	5 15	6 53	...	9 12	1241	2 11
30½	**Terijoki**	...	...	a.m.	9 35	...	1043	1125	3 14	5 49	7 33	...	9 53	1 11	2 54
80¼	**Viborg**	...	...	8 1	1141	...	12 9	1 40	5 30	8 5	9 52	...	1210	2 57	6 25
105	Simola	...	...	9 7	—	...	...	2 43	6 50	9 27	1059	...	1 18	3 50	—
141¾	**Kaipiais**	a.m.	...	10 18	...	...	A	3 48	8 16	—	1211	...	2 35	SC	...
155¼	**Kouvola**	8 6	...	11 0	...	...	2 4	4 54	8 46	...	1 3	...	3 22	5 35	...
193¾	Lahti	10 8	p.m.	1 10	p.m.	p.m.	3 13	6 46	—	...	3 4	a.m.	5 21	7 9	a.m.
230½	**Riihimaki**	12 1	1 0	3 8	4 29	6 16	4 16	8 40	...	...	5 0	6 19	7 10	8 35	9 10
...	TOIJALA 312 arr	...	...	—	...	...	5p14	1131	...	...	...	...	9 a0	1 p2	...
...	ABO 312 ......arr	...	...	...	...	...	8 p9	...	...	...	...	...	1 p7	5 p3	..
238	Hyvinkaa............	1221	1 33	...	4 50	6 37	—	9 0	...	...	5 22	6 39	7 31	8 52	9 30
256¾	**Kerava**	1 10	2 58	...	5 37	7 25	...	9 46	...	...	6 10	7 32	8 18	9 27	1018
274¾	**Helsingfors** ...arr	1 53	4 44	...	6 20	8 6	...	1028	...	...	6 53	8 47	9 0	10 0	11 0

					a.m.	a.m.	p.m.	p.m.	p.m.	p.m.	p.m	p.m.	p.m.	p.m.	nig't
Helsingfors ...dep	...	...	...	...	8 38	1015	1 10	2‡50	2 55	3 45	6 50	7 15	9 40	1125	12 0
Kerava	...	...	...	...	9 24	11 3	1 40	3 22	3 42	4 35	7 36	8 1	10 27	12 3	1 34
Hyvinkaa............	...	...	...	...	1013	1152	2 11	3 53	4 32	5 23	8 32	8 57	11 17	1241	2 48
ABO ....dep	...	...	...	...	...	...	1030	1210	...	—	2p20	...	...	...	...
TOIJALA......dep	...	...	...	a.m.	...	9a38	1 p4	2p45	...	...	6p14	...	...	...	...
Riihimaki	...	...	...	6 27	1031	1228	2 40	4 25	5 14	...	9 6	9 15	11 50	1 5	3 11
Lahti	...	a.m.	...	9 10	—	2 12	3 50	5 35	7 6	...	1052	—	1 40	2 25	—
Kouvola	...	6 38	...	1141	...	4 20	4 57	6 42	8 44	...	1246	...	4 15	3 52	...
Kaipiais	...	7 33	...	1241	...	5 16	...	...	—	...	1 42	...	5 13	SC	...
Simola	...	9 3	p.m.	2 39	p.m.	6 56	6 46	...	...	...	3 21	...	6 42	6 2	...
Viborg	a.m.	1033	2 45	3 58	4 50	8 7	7 35	9 20	...	...	4 40	...	8 10	7 5	...
Terijoki............	8 4	1242	5 1	—	7 9	10 8	A	A	...	...	6 41	...	10 14	...	...
Valkeasaari.........	8 48	1 35	5 53	...	8 10	1059	9 25	1120	...	...	7 36	...	11 8	9 20	...
St. Petersburg ...	9 40	2 29	6 40	...	9 4	1150	10 0	1158	...	...	8 30	...	11 54	10 0	...

‡—May not run. A—Runs in connection with Stockholm steamer. SC—Sleeping Car.
** St. Petersburg Time between St. Petersburg and Kaipiais; Helsingfors Time between Kaipiais and Helsingfors.

ABO and TOIJALA.

E.M.						
	Abo (Harbour) ...dep	...	10a30	12‡10	...	...
1¾	,, (Town)	8a40	10 40	12 20	2p20	8 p0
36	Mellilä............	1010	A	A	3 42	9 24
51½	Toijala ....arr	1217	12 59	2 39	5 40	1120

Toijala ....dep	9a30	1p10	5p48	7p20
Mellilä	1139	3 41	A	9 25
Abo (Town) ......arr	1 7	5 3	8 0	1046
,, (Harbour)...arr	...	...	8 9	...

‡—May not run. A—Runs in connection with Stockholm steamer.

VALKOMI and NIEMI.

	a.m.	a.m.	p.m.	p.m.	
Valkomi ....dep	...	8 §20	2 40	6 †0	...
Lovitza	4 25	9 0	3 15	6 40	...
Lahti 312............	9 15	12 45	6 20	10 26	...
Niemi ....arr	9 30	1 30	6 35	11 15	...

	a.m.	p.m.	p.m.		
Niemi ....dep	5 5	1 50	6 45	...	...
Lahti	5 40	2 30	7 15	...	...
Lovitza	9 30	6 30	11 20	...	...
Valkomi ....arr	9 50	6 50	...	...	...

†—Until 31st August (N.S.) §—From 1st Sept. until 15th October (N.S.)

TORNEA and SEINAJOKI.

Dist. E.M.			a.m.	p.m.	p.m.	p.m.
	Tornea ....dep	...	7 18	12 6	...	6 0
16¼	Kemi	...	8 15	1 20	4 0	6 52
81½	Uleaborg	...	11 25	—	8 10	—
140½	Oulainen	a.m.	2 15	...	—	...
157¾	Ylivieska	4 0	3 2	...	...	...
182	Kannus	6 10	4 23	...	...	...
207	Gamlakarleby	8 31	5 29	...	...	...
227½	Bennas	11 19	6 29	...	...	...
266½	Kauhava	3 5	8 23	...	...	...
289½	**Seinäjoki** ......arr	5 5	9 26	...	...	...

				a.m.
Seinäjoki ......dep		...	...	8 20
Kauhava		...	...	9 32
Bennas		...	...	11 22
Gamlakarleby............		...	...	12 25
Kannus............		...	...	1 51
Ylivieska		a.m.	...	2 58
Oulainen		3 50	a.m.	3 46
Uleaborg	a.m.	9 10	9 30	6 40
Kemi	9 0	—	3 0	9 48
Tornea ...arr	9 52	...	4 10	10 40

Kemi ....dep	7 a35	3 p20	...
Rovaniemi............arr	12 0	8 0	...

Rovaniemi.........dep	8 a5	4 p30	...
Kemi ....arr	12 55	8 53	...

HELSINGFORS and ABO.

‡—May not run.

Helsingfors dep	8a10	11a3	...	2p40	3p25	6 p5
Kyrkslätt.........	9 0	12 7	...	3 35	4 58	6 57
Karis............	1035	1 27	...	4 48	6 26	8 35
Salo 8 a2	1219	—	5 p9	6 19	—	1012
Abo ......arr 9 31	1 47	...	6 46	7 22	...	1137

Abo ....dep	7a15	11a20	12‡28	...	5p20	8p20
Salo............ ...	8 53	12 35	1 41	p.m.	6 52	9 56
Karis 6a42	1050	2 2	3 8	5 13	8 50	—
Kyrkslätt ..8 13	12 8	3 7	4 23	6 34	10 9	...
Helsingfors 9 33	1 0	4 0	5 45	7 25	11 0	...

HAAPAMAKI and SUOLAHTI.

Haapamaki ......dep	4a53	11a25	6 p8	...
Jyvaskyla	8 52	3 10	9 25	...
Suolahti ....arr	1033	4 51	10 58	...

Suolahti ....dep	5 a45	11a55	7 p5	...	...
Jyvaskyla	7 30	1 48	9 11	...	...
Haapamaki.........arr	10 35	5 30	1235	...	...

KOUVOLA and KUOPIO.

Kouvola dep	...	3 a50	4 p57
St. Michel......	...	7 22	9 2
Pieksämäki ...	4a30	9 26	—
Suonenjoki ...	7 1	10 38	...
Kuopio arr	9 30	12 0	...

Kuopio ....dep	...	5a30	4 p8	...
Suonenjoki	...	8 47	5 44	...
Pieksämäki	a.m.	10 58	6 53	...
St. Michel............	1115	3 15	9 2	...
Kouvola (312)...arr	3 32	9 15	1219	...

Kouvola ....dep	6 a5	5 p0	8 p55	...
Kotka ....arr	8 16	7 10	10 50	...

Kotka............dep	6 a0	1 p55	10 p5	...	...
Kouvola ....arr	7 54	4 0	12 13	...	...

Kuopio ....dep	...	5‡a30	12p23	4‡p15
Iisalmi	4‡a45	9 30	3 9	8 20
Kajana ....arr	8 46	...	5 25	...

Kajana............dep	...	5‡a0	10a45
Iisalmi	4‡a0	8 58	1 18
Kuopio............arr	8 0	...	3 44

‡-Week-days only.

NIKOLAISTAD and HELSINGFORS.

Dist. E.M.								a.m.			p.m.		p.m.
	Nikolaistad ...dep		...	...	...		...	5 35	...	...	1250	...	7 30
46	**Seinäjoki** ....arr		...	...	...		...	7 37	...	...	5 1	...	9 32
...	,, ...dep		...	...	...		...	7 52	...	...	—	...	1020
98¾	Myllymaki		...	...	...		...	1017	...	...	...	...	1258
119¼	Haapamaki.........	a.m.	a.m.	...	...		...	1 11	...	p.m.	...	p.m.	1 59
164	Orihvesi	7 50	6 40	a.m.	A	‡	...	1 18	p.m.	3 50	p.m.	1020	4 12
190¼	Tammerfors......	9 55	8 30	1150	p.m	p.m.	...	2 48	4 57	6 22	8 30	1153	5 40
215	Toijala	—	9 38	1254	1 4	2‡45	...	3 59	6 14	—	1030	—	6 53
239¼	Tavastehus		1042	—	1 48	3 29	p.m.	5 2	7 21	...	—	...	8 0
262¼	Riihimaki		12 1	...	2 26	4 7	4 29	6 16	8 18	p.m.	...	...	9 10
269¾	Hyvinkää		1221	...	—	—	4 50	6 37	—	8 35	...	...	9 30
288¼	Kerava		1 10	...	...	...	5 37	7 25	...	9 17	...	...	1018
306¼	**Helsingfors** ...arr		1 53	...	...	...	6 20	8 6	...	10 2	...	...	11 0

‡—May not run.

				a.m.			p.m.	p.m.	p.m.
Helsingfors...dep	...	...	...	8 38	...	...	2 55	3 45	7 15
Kerava	...	...	...	9 24	...	A	3 42	4 35	8 1
Hyvinkää............	...	a.m.	...	10 13	...	p.m.	4 32	5 23	8 57
Riihimaki	...	7 6	...	10 47	...	4 26	5 10	—	9 30
Tavastehus	a.m.	8 3	...	11 46	...	5 2	6 7	...	10 29
Toijala	6 14	9 0	a.m.	1 2	p.m.	5 44	7 17	...	11 31
Tammerfors.........	8 10	1034	11 0	2 30	5 30	—	8 20	...	1 10
Orihvesi	—	—	1 15	3 43	7 9	...	10 40	...	2 15
Haapamaki.........	...	...	4 36	6 2	—	...	—	...	4 24
Myllymaki	...	...	—	7 1	...	...	...	...	5 25
Seinäjoki ......arr	...	a.m.	p.m.	9 10	...	...	...	...	7 33
,, ...dep	...	5 0	2 20	9 40	...	...	...	...	8 10
Nikolaistad ...arr	...	9 20	6 50	11 41	...	...	...	...	10 12

A—Runs in connection with Stockholm steamer.

HANGO and HYVINKAA.

	a.m.	a.m.	p.m.	p.m.
Hango ......dep	5 10	9 5	3 44	7 10
Karis	6 35	1030	5 20	8 30
Hyvinkaä...arr	9 20	...	8 17	...

	a.m.	a.m.	a.m.	p.m.
Hyvinkää...dep	...	...	10 25	5 38
Karis	7 0	10 56	1 32	8 43
Hango ...arr	8 38	12 20	2 52	10 2

BENNAS and JAKOBSTAD.

Bennas.........dep	7‡a25	11a25	6p30	...
Jakobstad ...arr	7 50	11 50	6 55	...

Jakobstad ......dep	10a20	3‡p10	5p55	...
Bennas (312) ...arr	10 45	3 35	6 20	...

‡—Weekdays only.

E.M								
	Simola ....dep	3a35	9 a0	2p30	6p40	9 p8	1 a0	...
12	Willmanstrand......arr	4 10	9 35	3 5	7 15	9 38	1 35	...

Willmanstrand ...dep	6 a0	8 a5	1p35	5p45	9 p55	2a10	...
Simola (312) ....arr	6 30	8 40	2 10	6 20	10 30	2 45	...

KERAVA and BORGA.

Kerava ....dep	...	...	...	...
Borga ....arr	...	...	...	...

Borga ....dep	...	...	...	...	...
Kerava (312) ...arr	...	...	...	...	...

VIBORG and LIEKSA. ‡—Runs until 13th Sept.

				a.m.	p.m.	p.m.	p.m.	p.m.
Viborg ....dep	...	...	...	8 0	2 10	3 45	7‡20	7 53
Antrea	...	...	a.m.	9 25	3 40	5 25	8 28	9 18
Elisenvara	...	...	4 20	12 2	6 15	—	—	11 35
Jaakima	...	...	6 0	12 49	7 1	p.m.	...	—
Sordavala..................	a.m.	...	8 10	2 13	8 10	8 20	...	...
Vartsila......................	5 0	a.m.	—	4 23	—	1220	...	...
Joensuu	8 37	11 35	...	6 40	...		...	...
Lieksa ....arr	...	4 49	...	9 46	...	...	...	...

					a.m.	a.m.	p.m.
Lieksa..........dep	...	...	...	...	8 27	8 40	...
Joensuu	...	a.m.	...	...	1153	1 47	4 25
Vartsila	...	4 30	...	a.m.	2 7	—	8 30
Sordavala	...	8 20	...	9 55	4. 6	...	—
Jaakima	...	—	a.m.	1111	5 26	...	...
Elisenvara	a.m.	...	4 48	1212	6 28	...	...
Antrea	6 15	...	8 4	2 50	8 57	...	...
Viborg ....arr	7 46	...	9 44	4 5	10 2	...	...

VIBORG and VUOKSENNISKA. ‡—Runs until 13th Sept.

Viborg ....dep	7 a30	12p10	5p‡17	7 p53
Antrea	8 54	1 26	6 33	9 15
Imatra.....................	9 49	2 21	7 26	10 8
Vuoksenniska ...arr	10 1	2 33	7 38	10 20

Vuoksenniska dep	7a12	12‡30	4 p31	6 p20	7‡55
Imatra	7 32	1 0	4 51	6 50	8 14
Antrea	8 25	2 23	5 40	8 25	9 6
Viborg ....arr	9 54	4 5	7 0	10 2	1020

Elisenvara......dep	5 a0	12p15
Neishloti ....arr	9 8	2 35
Neishloti........dep	6a50	3 p15
Elisenvara .....arr	11 25	5 47

TAMMERFORS and BJÖRNEBORG.

Tammerfors ....dep	...	2p45	6 p5	8 p35
Tyrvaa	4 a10	4 47	8 22	10 29
Peipohja..........................	6 5	6 16	—	11 49
Björneborg ....arr	7 52	7 19	...	12 49

Björneborg ....dep	...	7 a5	12 p5	3p20
Peipohja........................	...	8 20	1 20	6 10
Tyrvaa	6a40	9 46	2 45	8 6
Tammerfors.........arr	8 57	1140	4 38	...

Björneborg......dep	9 a0	2 p45	7 p30	...
Mantyluoto ......arr	9 46	3 30	8 16	...

Mantyluoto ......dep	6 a10	11 a5	5p35	...
Björneborg ......arr	6 54	11 50	6 20	...

TABLE OF FARES on the RUSSIAN RAILWAYS.

For any distance up to 6 versts (4 miles 27 kopecks, 1st class; 16 kopecks, 2nd class; 9 kopecks, 3rd class beyond 6 versts as under:—

Versts	Eng Mile	1 Cl	2 Cl	3 Cl	Versts	Eng Mile	1 Cl	2 Cl	3 Cl	Versts	Eng Mile	1 Cl	2 Cl	3 Cl	Versts	Eng Mile	1 Cl	2 Cl	3 Cl
		r. k.	r. k.	r. k.			r. k.	r. k.	r. k.			r. k.	r. k.	r. k.			r. k.	r. k.	r. k.
7	4¾	0 28	0 17	0 11	30	20	1 13	0 68	0 45	53	35¼	2 00	1 20	0 80	80	53	3 00	1 80	1 20
8	5¼	0 30	0 18	0 12	31	20½	1 18	0 71	0 47	54	35¾	2 03	1 22	0 81	90	59½	3 38	2 03	1 35
9	6	0 35	0 21	0 14	32	21¼	1 20	0 72	0 48	55	36½	2 08	1 25	0 83	100	66½	3 75	2 25	1 50
10	6¾	0 38	0 23	0 15	33	22	1 25	0 75	0 50	56	37	2 10	1 26	0 84	110	73	4 13	2 48	1 65
11	7¼	0 43	0 26	0 17	34	22½	1 28	0 77	0 51	57	37¾	2 15	1 29	0 86	120	79½	4 50	2 70	1 80
12	8	0 45	0 27	0 18	35	23¼	1 33	0 80	0 53	58	38½	2 18	1 31	0 87	130	86¼	4 88	2 93	1 95
13	8½	0 50	0 30	0 20	36	23¾	1 35	0 81	0 54	59	39	2 23	1 34	0 89	140	92¾	5 25	3 15	2 10
14	9¼	0 53	0 32	0 21	37	24½	1 40	0 84	0 56	60	39¾	2 25	1 35	0 90	150	99½	5 63	3 38	2 25
15	10	0 58	0 35	0 23	38	25¼	1 43	0 86	0 57	61	40½	2 30	1 38	0 92	160	106	6 00	3 60	2 40
16	10½	0 60	0 36	0 24	39	25¾	1 48	0 89	0 59	62	41	2 33	1 40	0 93	170	112¾	6 25	3 75	2 50
17	11¼	0 65	0 39	0 26	40	26½	1 50	0 90	0 60	63	41¾	2 38	1 43	0 95	180	119¼	6 50	3 90	2 60
18	12	0 68	0 41	0 27	41	27¼	1 55	0 93	0 62	64	42½	2 40	1 44	0 96	190	126	6 75	4 05	2 70
19	12½	0 73	0 44	0 29	42	27¾	1 58	0 95	0 63	65	43	2 45	1 47	0 98	200	132½	7 00	4 20	2 80
20	13¼	0 75	0 45	0 30	43	28½	1 63	0 98	0 65	66	43¾	2 48	1 49	0 99	210	139¼	7 25	4 35	2 90
21	14	0 80	0 48	0 32	44	29¼	1 65	0 99	0 66	67	44½	2 53	1 52	1 01	220	145¾	7 50	4 50	3 00
22	14½	0 83	0 50	0 33	45	29¾	1 70	1 02	0 68	68	45	2 55	1 53	1 02	230	152½	7 75	4 65	3 10
23	15¼	0 88	0 53	0 35	46	30½	1 73	1 04	0 69	69	45¾	2 60	1 56	1 04	240	159	8 00	4 80	3 20
24	16	0 90	0 54	0 36	47	31¼	1 78	1 07	0 71	70	46½	2 63	1 58	1 05	250	165¾	8 25	4 95	3 30
25	16½	0 95	0 57	0 38	48	31¾	1 80	1 08	0 72	71	47	2 68	1 61	1 07	260	172¼	8 50	5 10	3 40
26	17¼	0 98	0 59	0 39	49	32½	1 85	1 11	0 74	72	47¾	2 70	1 62	1 08	270	179	8 75	5 25	3 50
27	18	1 03	0 62	0 41	50	33¼	1 88	1 13	0 75	73	48½	2 75	1 65	1 10	280	185½	9 0	5 40	3 60
28	18½	1 05	0 63	0 42	51	33¾	1 93	1 16	0 77	74	49	2 78	1 67	1 11	290	192¼	9 25	5 55	3 70
29	19¼	1 10	0 66	0 44	52	34½	1 95	1 17	0 78	75	49¾	2 83	1 70	1 13	300	198¾	9 50	5 70	3 80

From 301 versts to 400 versts there are 4 zones of 25 versts each. — For each zone, irrespective of length, the charge is the same—65 kopecks, 1st class; 40 kopecks, 2nd class; 25 kopecks, 3rd class.

,,	401	,,	500	,,	,,	4	,,	25	,,
,,	501	,,	710	,,	,,	7	,,	30	,,
,,	711	,,	990	,,	,,	8	,,	35	,,
,,	991	,,	1510	,,	,,	13	,,	40	,,
,,	1511	,,	2860	,,	,,	30	,,	45	,,
,,	2861	,,	3010	,,	,,	3	,,	50	,,

With charge for each zone of 50 kopecks, 1st class; 30 kopecks, 2nd class; 20 kopecks, 3rd class.

,,	3011	,,	9030	,,	,,	86	,,	70	,,

With charge for each zone of 1 rouble 1st class; 60 kopecks, 2nd class; 40 kopecks, 3rd class.

There are a few express trains for which it is necessary to pay a small supplementary fare.

The length of time for which tickets are available varies according to distance; validity is reckoned from midnight of day of issue; the passenger may break his journey anywhere and as often as he wishes provided the whole journey be completed within the time specified on the ticket; the ticket must be presented at the booking offices to be stamped.

Up to 200 versts, valid 1 day.
201 — 500 ,, ,, 2 days.
501 — 800 ,, ,, 3 ,,

801 to 1100 versts, valid 4 days.
1101 — 1500 ,, ,, 5 ,,
1501 — 1900 ,, ,, 6 ,,
1901 — 2300 ,, ,, 7 ,,

And 1 day extra for every additional 400 versts.

Luggage is charged according to distance.

Passports.—*Travellers entering Russia must be provided with Passports.*

ST. PETERSBURG, DVINSK, VILNA, and EYDTKUHNEN.

St. Petersburg Time.

SLEEPING CARS, between St. Petersburg and Wirballen—in 11.0 p.m. from St. Petersburg; extra fares, 1st class 5r. 2k., 2nd class 4r. 18k.

Dist. E.M.		1,2,3	1,2,3	1,2,3	1 & 2	1,2,3	1,2,3	1 Cl.	1,2,3	1,2,3	1,2,3	1,2,3	1,2,3	1,2,3
		a.m.	a.m.	p.m.	p.m.	p.m.	p.m.	p.m.	p.m.	p.m.	p.m.		p.m.	p.m.
—	St. Petersburg dp	9 0	11 25	3 30	6 45	7 5	7 25	7 45	8 5	8 25	11 0	...	11 45	1125
27¾	Gatschina	10 5	12 47	4 31	7 29	7 49	8 9	8 29	8 49	9 10	11 54	...	1 9	1232
53	Divenskaja	11 13	2 4	5 38	...	...	...	A	...	...	SC	...	2 16	1 41
86	Luga	12 30	3 36	6 52	8 47	9 8	9 28	9 48	10 8	10 36	1 30	...	3 38	3 0
128	Strugi	2 18	5 38	8 37	...	...	...	...	...	...	...	...	5 38	4 50
170	Pskov (313A)	4 2	7 28	1010	10 54	1116	11 36	11 59	1217	12 45	3 59	...	7 31	6 38
203	Ostrow	5 5	8 50		...	...	...	...	...		...	...	8 48	7 40
249	Korsowka		10 59	...	12 59	1 22	1 42	2 9	2 28		6 16	a.m.	11 3	
276	Reshitza	...	12 16	...	1 38	...	...	...	...		7 2	6 10	12 17	...
288	Antonopol	...	12 57	...	...	...	...	...	...		...	6 40	12 53	...
329	Dvinsk (317) arr	...	2 36	...	2 58	3 17	3 37	4 9	4 25		8 29	8 9	2 28	...
467	Riga ......arr	...	...	...	...	...	...	...	...	7 a50	1 p5	...	...	...
		a.m.	a.m.		a.m.	a.m.	a.m.	a.m.	a.m.		a.m.	a.m.	p.m.	p.m.
...	Dvinsk ‡ ......dep	2 22	4 0	...	3 5	3 25	3 47	4 17	4 35	...	8 41	8 58	2 43	6 30
333	Kalkuhnen (317)	2 37	4 59	...	3 19	...	...	...	...	...	8 58	9 17	3 5	6 50
388	Swentsiany	6 46	7 12	...	...	...	...	...	6 4	...	10 25	1153	5 21	9 28
430	Vileiskaya	8 28	8 50	...	...	5 53	6 15	...	7 10	...	11 35	1 52	7 5	1125
436	Vilna (317) ...arr	8 45	9 5	...	5 46	6 4	6 26	6 58	7 21	...	11 50	2 10	7 20	1140
			a.m.		a.m.		...					p.m	p.m	
...	Vilna ......dep	...	9 45	...	5 54		...		...	...		5 0	8 5	...
447	Landwarowo	...	10 18	...	...		...		...	...		5 42	8 47	...
485	Orani (313A)	...	11 45	...	...		...		...	...		7 22	10 28	...
514	Poretsche	...	12 56	...	...		...		...	...		8 45	11 45	...
534	Grodno	...	1 49	...	8 26		...		...	...		9 42	12 43	...
586	Bialostock arr	...	3 57	...	9 48		...		...	...		1210	3 0	...
670	Brest 320 ar	a.m.	8 p33	...	...		...		...	...		...	8 a10	...
...	Bialostock dep	7 30	4 27	...	9 50		...		...	...		1246	3 50	...
601	Lapy	8 7	5 5	...	10 25		...		...	...		1 38	4 36	...
641	Malkin	9 46	6 47		...		...		...	...		4 12	6 25	...
693	Warsaw ...arr	12 15	8 55		12 47		...		...	...		7 15	8 45	...
			a.m.			a.m.		a.m.			p.m.	p.m.		a.m.
...	Vilna ......dep	...	10 5	SC—Sleeping Car in this train.	...	6 14	...	7 8	...	...	12 15	3 40	...	1220
447	Landwarowo	...	10 40		...	...	...	...	...	...	...	4 13	...	1257
478	Koschedari ...arr	...	11 51		...	7 15	...	...	...	...	1 36	5 25	...	2 15
...	Riga ......dep	...	...		...	8p50	...	A	...	...	...	...	...	...
...	Koschedari ...dep	...	12 1		...	7 25	...	...	...	...	1 38	5 35	...	2 30
500	Kovno	...	1 6		...	8 6	...	9 8	...	...	2 31	6 34	...	3 26
554	Wirballen ......arr	...	3 39		...	9 25	...	10 40	...	...	4 20	8 44	...	5 45
...	" ......dep	...	4 15		...	1010	...	11 20	...	...	5 25	9 24	...	6 29
555	Eydtkuhnen 177 ar	...	4 p20		...	1015	...	11a25	...	...	5 p30	9p29	...	6 34
...	¶ Eydtkuh'n dp	...	5 p52	...	...	10a7	...	11 a0	...	...	5 p52	...	...	...
649½	Konigsb'g ar	...	8 p18	...	...	1156	...	1 p17	...	...	8 p18	...	...	...
1016¼	Berlin ...arr	...	5 a42	...	...	7p25	...	10p38	...	...	5 a42	...	...	...

		1 Cl.	1,2,3	1,2,3	1 & 2	1,2,3	1,2,3	1,2,3	1,2,3	1 & 2	1,2,3	1,2,3	1,2,3
Berlin ...dep		7 a58	...	8a30	...	9 a57	...	...	11p30	...	...	...	...
Konigsb'g dep		3 p56	...	4p19	...	...	...	...	8 a6	...	...	...	...
Eydtkuh'n ar		5 p50	...	6p27	...	10 p8	...	...	10a15	...	...	...	...
		p.m.		p.m.		p.m.		a.m.	a.m.		p.m.		
Eydtkuhnen dep		6 56	...	7 48	...	11 25	...	7 52	11 31	...	1 8	...	...
Wirballen ¶ arr		7 1	...	7 53	...	11 30	...	7 58	11 36	...	1 13	...	...
" (Russ.) dep		7 46	...	8 40	...	1 15	...	8 58	2 30	...	3 15	...	...
Kovno		9 12	...	10 8	...	6 15	...	11 11	4 20	...	5 47	...	...
Koschedari ...arr		...	...	1043	...	7 10	...	12 15	5 8	...	6 47	...	...
Riga 317 ...arr		B	...	8a51	...	6 p0	...	...	...	...	...	...	...
Koschedari ...dep		...	...	1051	...	7 16	...	12 17	5 10	...	6 59	...	...
Landwarowo		...	...	...	...	8 38	...	1 40	SC	...	8 28	...	...
Vilna ......arr		10 48	...	1152	...	9 4	...	2 6	6 28	...	8 55	...	...
					p.m.	p.m.	nig't					a.m.	p.m.
Warsaw ...dep			...		5 50	9 40	12 55			...		10 35	7 30
Malkin			...		...	12 14	3 13			...		12 51	1010
Lapy			...		8 17	2 3	4 58			...		2 34	1154
Bialostock arr			...		8 40	2 36	5 31			...		3 7	1225
Brest 320 dep			...		...	10p47	...			...		9 a13	
Bialostock dep			...		8 42	2 58	5 47			...		3 27	
Grodno			...		1010	5 22	8 6			...		5 42	
Poretsche			...		...	6 16	8 55			...		6 28	
Orani			...		...	7 32	10 6			...		7 35	
Landwarowo			...		...	9 12	11 59			...		9 5	
Vilna ......arr			...		1240	9 40	12 3			...		9 23	
		p.m.	p.m.	a.m.	n'gt	a.m.	p.m.	p.m.	p.m.		p.m.	p.m.	
Vilna ......dep		10 58	1145	12 2	1250	10 6	12 33	2 56	6 55	...	9 20	10 6	
Vileiskaya		...	1158	1214	...	10 30	1 0	3 30	7 19	...	9 45	10 28	
Swentsiany		...	...	1 22	...	12 12	2 39	5 30	8 37	...	11 29	12 25	
Kalkuhnen		...	...	2 41	3 23	2 28	4 48	7 44	...	...	2 2	3 55	
Dvinsk ......arr		1 41	2 30	2 52	3 35	2 40	5 6	7 56	10 14	...	2 14	4 12	
Riga 317 dep		...	...	...	8p10	...	10a16	...	6 p5	11p20	...	...	
		a.m.	a.m.	a.m.	a.m.		p.m.	p.m.	p.m.			a.m.	
Dvinsk ‡ ......dep		1 49	2 40	3 0	3 43	...	5 30	8 18	10 34		...	4 54	
Antonopol		...	...	...	...	...	7 14	10 6	SC		...	6 38	
Reshitza	1,2,3	...	...	...	5 7	...	7 55	10 35	12 7		...	7 20	
Korsowka	p.m.	4 0	4 48	5 8	5 57	p.m.	9 4		12 58		...	8 27	
Ostrow	6 50	...	...	...	...	3 15	11 7	...	...	a.m.	...	10 24	
Pskov	10 0	6 21	7 2	7 25	8 9	4 28	12 28	...	3 23	6 4	...	11 43	
Strugi	1216	...	...	...	...	6 28	2 22	...	...	...	...	1 34	
Luga	2 15	34	9 22	9 42	1022	8 17	4 10	...	5 57	8 17	...	3 22	
Divenskaja	3 54	...	...	...	...	9 35	5 37	...	...	...	...	4 52	
Gatschina	5 24	9 50	1036	1056	1136	10 56	6 47	...	7 28	9 32	...	6 18	
St. Petersb'g	6a25	10 30	11a15	1135	1215	11p45	7 a45	...	8 a15	10a12	...	7 p15	

Extra.						
Malkin...dep	6 a2	1p47		Warsaw .dep	9 a0	1p30
Warsaw..arr	8 10	4 2		Malkin ...arr	1112	3 47

*—Arrives at or departs from Praga Station at Warsaw.

A—Nord Express, special service of Sleeping Car Co., leaving St. Petersburg for Eydtkuhnen and Berlin on Wed. and Sat. only.

B—Nord Express, from Eydtkuhnen on Sun., and Thurs. night only.

☞—A tax of 5 roubles 55 kopecks imposed upon each passenger between Wirballen and St. Petersburg by express trains. It is collected direct from the passenger en route.

¶—**Customs Examination**—entering Russia, at Wirballen; coming from Russia, at Eydtkuhnen.

‡ Dvinsk, St. Petersburg Line...dep	4a56	8a38	2p56	6p15	10p40	...	Dvinsk, Orel-Riga Line ......dep	1a43	8a15	2p25	5 p0	11p18
‡ Dvinsk, Orel-Riga Line ......arr	5 3	8 45	3 3	6 22	10 47	...	Dvinsk St. Petersburg Line . arr	1 50	8 22	2 32	5 7	10 25

☞ **Luggage.**—Travellers are advised to be careful to see that all their luggage arrives at the Russian frontier station in the same train as themselves, is examined in their presence, and leaves in the same train as themselves.

ST. PETERSBURG, GATSCHINA, RIGA, REVEL, and BALTISCHPORT.

‡—Until 31st August. SC—Sleeping Car.

	1,2,3 a.m.	1,2,3 a.m.	1,2,3 p.m.	1,2,3 p.m.	1—4	1,2,3 p.m.	1,2,3 p.m.	1,2,3	1,2,3 p.m.	1,2,3 p.m.	2 & 3	1,2,3	1,2,3
St. Petersburg dep	9 35	...	3 30	3 45	...	7 55	8 25	...	8 50	11 55	...	...	...
Krasnoe Selo ...	1028	...	⋮	...	p.m.	8 43	⋮	...	9 39	SC	...	...	...
Gatschina	1120	10 45	⋮	...	8 20	9 36	⋮	...	10 30	1 17	...	...	...
Tosno ......arr	...	12 15	⋮	...	9 50	...	B	...	...	...	...	...	...
Wolosowo	1235		⋮	6 31		11 0	⋮	...	11 53	2 27	...	...	...
Narwa	2 49	...	B	8 38	...	1 13	⋮	...	2 7	4 33	...	...	...
Jewe	4 1	...	⋮	9 33	...	2 30	⋮	...	3 19	5 42	...	...	...
Taps ....arr	6 32	...	⋮		...	5 29	SC	p.m.	6 5	8 5	p.m.	...	...
Taps.........dep	...	...	⋮	...	...	...	⋮	1028	6 28	...	12 5	...	...
Dorpat (Yurief	...	...	⋮	...	...	...	⋮	1 4	9 46	...	4 55	...	...
Valk	...	...	2 14	...	...	...	4 3	4 25	12 35	...	8 55	...	...
Bendeni.........	...	...	4 39	...	...	...	5 43	6 30	2 54	...		‡	...
Riga ....arr	...	...	7a15	a.m.	...	...	7 a50	9 5	5 35	...	...	a.m.	...
Taps...........dep	6 40	...		5 20	...	5 50				8 15	...	1020	‡
Revel...... arr	8 50	p.m.	...	7 20	...	8 10	...	...	...	10 0	...	1215	p.m.
Revel...... dep		9 40	...		...		...	...	...	11 30	...		3 30
Baltischportarr	...	11 43	...	...	...	...	...	...	...	1 25	...	...	5 23

	1,2,3 a.m.	1,2,3	1,2,3 a.m.	2 & 3	1,2,3	1,2,3	1,2,3 p.m.	1,2,3	1,2,3	1,2,3	1,2,3	1,2,3	1,2,3 p.m.
Baltischport.....dep	5 50	...	...	...	...	...	4 30	...	...	...	...	...	10 ‡0
Revel........... arr	7 50	...	...	...	...	p.m.	6 25	...	...	...	p.m.	p.m.	11 50
Revel........... dep		...	9 5	...	...	4‡35	7 45	...	...	...	8 20	1120	
Taps ....arr	...	...	1137	...	a.m.	6 37	10 2	p.m.	p.m.	p.m.	1018	1 20	...
Riga..............dep	...	...	...	...	10 0		...	6 30	8 35	1120		SC	...
Bendeni..............	...	...	...	a.m.	1 4	...	...	9 28	1124	1 33	...	...	...
Valk (313A).........	...	...	...	6 0	3 8	...	...	1131	1 7	2 59	...	...	...
Dorpat (Yurief)...	...	...	...	1228	6 10	...	...	1 56		SC	...	...	...
Taps ....arr	...	...	...	5 50	9 25	p.m.	...	5 8	...	⋮	...	...	...
Taps...............dep	...	a.m.	1147			9 47	10 35		...	⋮	...	1 32	...
Jewe	...	8 31	2 29	...	...	1245	1 38	...	...	⋮	...	4 14	...
Narwa	...	9 40	3 51	...	...	2 10	3 3	...	...	B	...	5 31	...
Wolosowo............	a.m.	12 0	6 29	...	...	4 42	5 33	...	...	⋮	...	7 49	...
Tosno ....dep	8 15	...	4 55	...	...	...	...	...	...	⋮	...	...	...
Gatschina	9 40	1 8	8 4	...	...	5 57	6 50	...	...	⋮	...	9 0	...
Krasnoe Selo		1 38	8 49	...	...	6 40	7 33	...	...	⋮	...	...	...
St. Petersburg...arr	...	2p15	9p30	...	...	7a20	8 a12	...	...	1012	...	10a5	...

B—Via Pskov, p. 313.

Frequent local service between St Petersburg and Gatschina.

PSKOV and VALK.	E.M									
	89	**Pskov** ....dep	7a55	10p25	12a55	...	**Valk** ....dep	3a10	3p30	1a17	...
		Valk 313A......arr	1215	2 4	3 53	...	**Pskov** 313 ......arr	5 54	8 5	5 2[illegible]	...

VALK and PERNOVI.										
Valk...........dep	2a45	5 a0	4 p5	...	**Pernovi**.........dep	5a25	4p35	7 p0	...
Moizekuli	6 21	8 49	7 59	...	Moizekuli..............	8 30	7 40	10 8	...
Pernovi......arr	9 0	1125	1040	...	**Valk**..................arr	1150	1057	1 35	...

MOIZEKULI and REVEL.							
Moizekuli...dep	9 a0	8 p20	...	**Revel** ....dep	8 a45	9 p30	...
Allenkuli...........	2 28	2 3	...	Allenkuli	2 9	3 4	...
Revel ....arr	7 p0	7 a30	...	**Moizekuli** ....arr	7 p10	8 a2	...

PSKOV and BOLOGOE. ‡—Until 31st August.								
Pskov...............dep	‡	8 a15	8p15	...	**Bologoe**.........dep	6 a25	‡	8 p55	...
Dno	8 a10	12p31	11p6	...	**Staraya Russa** ...	12p52	8 p45	2 a25	...
Staraya Russa	9 5	3 29	1 a5	...	Dno	4 p10	10 40	4 a46	...
Bologoe..............arr	...	10p40	8a10	...	**Pskov**..............arr	7 p10	...	7 p2[illegible]	...

E.M.		
	St. Petersburg dep	**ST. PETERSBURG and ORANIENBAUM.**
18	Peterhof	Service each way at about half hourly intervals from 7.0 a.m.
24½	**Oranienbaum** arr	until 12.40 night.

ORANI and SUBALKI.

Orani......dep	12p12	11§p16	**Subalki** ...dep	1p10	11‡p50	Subalki....dep	8a*10	7 p0	Grodno...dep	8a35	6p*45
Patarani	1 55	1 18	**Patarani**	5 22	5 22	Grodno ....arr	12 55	11 20	Subalki...arr	1244	11 25
Subalki ...arr	6 20	7 10	**Orani** ...... arr	7 0	7 20						

*—Monday and Friday only. ‡—Wednesday and Saturday only. §—Sunday and Thursday only.

OCHTA and BORISOVA-GRIVA.

Ochta ....dep	9 a5	5 p45	8 p50	...	...	**Borisova-Griva**dep	7 a45	4 p20	8 p40	...	...
Poligoni	...	...	...	...	...	Poligoni	...	...	10 42	...	...
Borisova-Grivaarr	11 23	8 3	11 12	...	...	**Ochta** ....arr	10 7	6 49	11 16	...	...

Ochta ....dep	10†10	7 p45	...	Sheremetevka ...dep	6 a40	3†p30	...	†—Until 15th
Sheremetevka ...arr	12 27	10 10	...	Ochta ....arr	9 0	6 0	...	September.

BARANOVITSCHI and BIALOSTOCK.

E.M.											
	Baranovitschi 314, 315 dep	4 a52	6 a2	5 p32	...	**Bialostock**...........dep	5 a50	4p33	6 p26	...	...
34	Slonim	6 45	8 50	7 26	...	Bagrationov	9 34	8 58	10 7	10p47	...
79	Bagrationov	9 30	1 57	10 16	...	Slonim	12 38	—	12 30	3 24	...
136	**Bialostock** 313)..........arr	12p29	7p13	1 a44	...	**Baranovitschi**......arr	2 p52		2 a28	6 a29	...

ST. PETERSBURG and PAFLOVSK.

‡—Until 8th September.] [*—Weekdays only.

St. Petersburg dep	7 a0	8*a0	9a0	9a15	10 a0	11 a0	12 0	1 p0	2 p0	2‡p30	2p50	3p20	4p18	4p30	4*p45	5 p0	5p25	5p35	6 p0	6‡40	7‡p0	7p20	8p15	8p35	9p15	10p15	11p25	11p45	12a45	1a30
Tsarskoe-Selo ...	7 29	8 31	929	9 48	10 26	11 31	12 26	1 30	2 26	2 56	3 14	3 51	4 47	5 2	5 14	5 29	5 49	6 4	6 29	7 6	7 26	7 49	8 44	8 59	9 44	10 44	11 49	12 14	1 11	2 1
Paflovsk.........arr	7 35	8 37	935	9 55	10 32	11 37	12 32	1 40	2 32	3 5	3 20	3 57	4 56	5 9	5 20	5 38	5 55	6 13	6 38	7 12	7 35	7 55	8 53	9 5	9 53	10 50	11 55	12 53	1 17	2 10
Paflovsk ......dep	6a39	7a15	7a54	8*a0	8a30	8*55	9*12	9a25	10 a0	10a19	11 a0	12 0	1 p0	2 p0	3 p0	3 ‡55	4p30	5p15	5p45	6 p0	6p19	7 p0	8 p0	9 p0	10p0	10‡30	11 p0	11‡20	11p45	12a45
Tsarskoe-Selo......	6 52	7 25	8 0	8 10	8 40	9 5	9 18	9 32	10 10	10 27	11 10	12 7	1 7	2 7	3 7	4 2	4 37	5 22	5 52	6 7	6 30	7 7	8 7	9 7	10 7	10 37	11 7	11 27	11 52	12 52
St. Petersburg arr	7 30	7 55	8 22	8 40	9 10	9 30	9 40	9 57	10 40	10 55	11 38	12 35	1 35	2 32	3 37	4 27	5 2	5 52	6 17	6 35	7 0	7 35	8 32	9 37	1032	11 2	11 37	11 52	12 20	1 20

St. PETERSBURG and MOSCOW.

Dist E.M		1,2,3 a.m.	1 & 2 a.m.	1 & 2 a.m.	1,2,3 p.m.	2&3	1,2,3 p.m.	1,2,3 p.m.	1,2,3 p.m.	1&2 p.m.	2&3 p.m.	1 & 2 p.m.	1,2,3 p m.	1,2,3 n'ht
—	St. Petersburg......dep	8 30	9 45	10 0	3 30	...	5 30	7 0	8 30	9 30	9 50	11 0	1155	1215
16	Kolpino..........	9 7	B	RC	4 6	...	6 1	SC	SC	SC	...	...	...	1258
33	Tosno	9 45	...	...	4 47	...	6 42	...	...	...	1053	SC	SC	1 42
52	Ljuban	1031	1059	11 14	5 35	...	7 33	8 45	1018	1051	1145	12 28	1 48	2 33
74	Tschudovo 314...	1118	...	...	6 29	...	8 22	9 23	1056	RC	1 4	...	2 36	3 23
101	Malaji Wisch....	1251	1214	12 29	7 35	...	9 26	1022	1215	12 8	2 6	1 48	3 42	4 31
155	Okulovka	2 57	RC	...	9 50	...	1118	12 6	2 0	1 40	4 6	3 22	5 36	7 17
167	Uglovka	3 22	...	...	1019	...	1140	1228	2 22	...	4 29	...	5 0	7 47
199	Bologœ	4 24	2 37	2 53	1120	...	1235	1 19	3 13	2 42	5 27	4 27	6 55	9 0
227	Wisc. Wolotsc...	5 30	...	...	1257	...	1 35	2 13	4 11	...	6 37	...	7 56	1036
247	Spirovo	6 20	...	...	1 25	a.m.	2 20	2 56	4 55	4 4	7 30	5 51	8 44	1143
274	Lichoslavl 314...	7 11	...	...	2 20	2 44	3 a5	3 40	5 40	...	8 31	...	9 32	1255
300	Tver	8 9	5 8	5 24	3 12	3 37	—	4 27	6 30	5 24	9 33	7 12	1027	2 7
349	Klin	9 46	...	...	4 56	5 20	...	5 57	8 4	6 41	1120	8 33	12 1	4 15
392	Chimki	...	...	...	6 31	6 52	...	...	...	...	...	...	...	6 3
404	Moscow Nicolas	1130	...	...	7 a0	7a20	...	7a40	...	...	1p15	10 a0	...	6p30
...	,, Kursk Stat'n	...	7 42	8 p0	...	...	...	...	9a55	8a10	...	...	1p55	...

Moscow—	1,2,3 a.m.	1& 2 a.m.	2 &3 p.m.	1,2,3	1,2,3	1.2,3 p.m.	1,2,3 p.m.	1,2,3 p.m.	1,2,3 p.m.	1,2,3 p.m.	1 & 2 p.m.	1&2 p.m.	1 &2 p.m.	1,2,3 night
Kursk Stat	...	10 0	...	...	...	...	5 0	SC	8 20	...	...	1135	1155	...
Nicolas Sta	8 0	...	3 0	...	...	4 0	6 0	8 0	9 30	10 0	11 30	B	...	1210
Chimki	8 34	...	3 22	...	...	4 34	6 26	...	...	10 25	SC	SC	...	1249
Klin............	1020	...	4 55	...	...	6 15	8 5	9 51	1123	11 59	1 3	1 18	1 35	2 44
Tver...........	12 2	1240	6 37	p.m.	...	7 58	9 49	1118	1251	1 39	2 21	2 38	2 53	4 37
Lichoslavl...	1 22	...	7 35	8 10	...	8 57	10 38	12 3	1 38	3 38	RC	...	..	5 45
Spirovo	2 22	...	—	9 13	...	9 59	11 41	1257	2 34	4 39	3 49	4 6	4 21	6 56
W. Wolotsc.	3 5	...	...	9 57	p.m.	1041	12 21	1 31	3 9	5 18	...	...	...	7 48
Bologœ 314	4 10	3 15	...	11 5	1130	1155	1 30	2 25	4 5	6 18	5 10	5 27	5 42	9 5
Uglovka......	5 16	...	...	12 8	1235	1259	2 27	3 17	4 58	7 26	...	...	...	1022
Okulovka ...	5 46	...	...	1239	1 5	1 30	2 56	3 45	5 28	7 58	6 22	6 39	6 54	1058
Malaji Wisc.	7 42	5 37	...	2 35	3 1	3 26	4 40	5 20	7 5	9 57	7 47	8 4	8 19	1 11
Tschudovo...	8 38	...	...	3 38	4 1	4 26	5 31	6 9	7 54	10 56	...	...	...	2 17
Ljuban	9 35	6 48	...	4 38	4 57	5 18	6 21	6 55	8 40	11 59	9 10	9 25	9 40	3 25
Tosno	1017	...	...	5 22	5 39	6 0	6 59	7 29	...	12 39	...	...	...	4 17
Kolpino	1051	...	...	6 0	6 16	6 35	7 27	...	...	1 11	...	...	...	5 0
St. Petersb'g	11p30	8 p0	...	6a40	6a55	7a10	8 a0	8a30	1110	1 p45	10a30	1045	11a0	5p45

Extra							
St. Petersburg dep	5 p0	8 p0	11 p6	Bologœ ....dep	2 a57	1 a0	...
Bologœ ....arr	12 a5	2a18	6 10	St. Petersburg arr	8 55	7 a40	...

RC—Restaurant Car. SC—Sleeping Car.

B—Black Sea Express (Sleeping and Restaurant Cars), leaves St. Petersburg for Novorossiisk on Friday only; from Moscow to St. Petersburg, on Tuesday only.

LICHOSLAVL AND VIASMA.

E.M.		a.m.	a.m.	p.m		a.m.	p.m.	p.m.	
—	**Lichoslavl** ...dep	3 30	9 45	7 45	**Viasma** .....dep	3 0	1 0	8 10	...
21¼	Torschok	4 26	1125	8 39	Rschevo	7 45	4 15	11 17	...
59	Staritza..............	6 3	1 46	1010	Staritza	9 18	5 21	12 20	...
85	Rschevo	7 20	4 7	1115	Torschok............	1131	6 52	1 48	...
162	**Viasma (315)** arr	10 25	8p30	2 15	**Lichoslavl**...... (314)	1235	7 40	2 35	...

TSCHUDOVO AND STARAYA RUSSA.

E.M		a.m.	p.m.			a.m.	p.m.
—	**Tschudovo (314)**........dep	4 35	2 25	...	**Staraya Rus.**	8 0	7 0
46	Novgorod	7 38	6 22	...	Novgorod.........	2 15	11 0
104	**Staraya Russa** (313A)...arr	11 0	11 45	...	**Tschudovo**	6 10	1 a40

SEDLETZ and BOLOGOE.

			p.m.		a.m.	p.m.
Sedletz ......dep	12a40	...	3 30	**Bologoe**............dep	6 30	5 0
Bagrationov 9a50		...	10 12	Ostaschkov	9 37	9 31
Mosti 1110		...	11 8	Velikiye-Luki..............	3 p10	—
Lida 2p21		...	1 a15	Nevel........................	4 p55	...
Molodetschno 7p32		10 p0	4 31	Polozk........................	8 p48	12 a8
Polozk	—	6 a36	10 30	Molodetschno	2 a8	10a48
Nevel........................		—	1 p14	Lida	6 a18	5 p50
Velikiye-Luki		...	2 45	Mosti	8 a10	9 p13
Ostaschkov		11a30	8 p18	Bagrationov	9 a1	10p37
Bologoe (314)...arr		3 p30	11p10	**Sedletz (315)** ...arr	4 p7	7 a30

Mosti......dep	10a50
Grodna ...arr	12p40
Grodna...dep	6p19
Mosti ......arr	8 12

ST. PETERSBURG and SHLOBIN.

St. Petersburg dep	9 a15	4p30	10p30	12a10	...	...	Shlobin ....dep	4a47	...	9 a0	...	4 p10
Dno.....................	3 p45	1050	4 a40	8 a10	...	...	Orscha	1020	...	3 p15	...	10p10
Novo Sokolniki ...	—	3 a5	9 a0	1 23	...	...	Vitebsk	1230	12p50	5 p50	...	1 a0
Vitebsk	...	7 a5	1 0	5 p35	...	...	Novo Sokolniki...	—	5 p33	10p17	...	5 a32
Orscha	...	9 23	3 p25	7 p53	...	...	Dno....................	...	11p15	2 a33	4a50	11 58
Shlobin (317)...arr	...	2 30	8 p40	1 a35	...	...	St. Petersburg arr	...	7 a30	8 a10	1055	7 p0

ROVNO and VILNA.

E.M		p.m.	p.m.	p.m.	a.m.		a.m.	a.m.	p.m.	p.m.
—	**Rovno** ....dep	...	1 57	5 8	12 47	**Vilna** ....dep	6 40	7 33	2 46	7 37
55	Sarni..........................	3 5	4 3	7 43	3 44	Lida	8 38	9 31	5 36	11 20
121	Luninez (314) ...arr	4 59	6 0	10 36	6 16	Baranovitschi arr	1043	11 38	8 15	2 26
...	,, ...dep	5 9	6 8	10 51	6 53	,, dep	1053	11 48	9 16	2 46
194	Baranovitschi 312A ar	7 21	8 20	2 15	9 58	Luninez ....arr	1259	1 53	12 7	5 59
...	,, ...dep	7 31	8 30	2 53	10 55	,, ...dep	1 7	2 1	12 22	6 19
259	Lida	9 40	10 38	6 10	1 49	Sarni	3 12	4 p0	3 19	9 50
318	**Vilna (313)** ......arr	1129	12p26	9 a50	4 p40	**Rovno 320** arr	5 p4	...	5 a52	12p27

E.M	BREST-LITEWSKI and KHOLM.					
71	Brest-Litewski dep	10a42	2a37	Kholm ....dep	6 p0	1a40
	Kholm (316A) ...arr	2 30	6 54	Brest-Lit. (315) arr	9 55	7 20

BREST-LITEWSKI and BRIANSK.

Dist E.M	(315)	a.m.	nght		a.m.		p.m.
—	**Brest-Litewski**	9 25	12 10	**Briansk** dp	3 52	...	3 32
16	Jabinka (315)..........	1023	1 0	Unecha	8 22	...	7 32
105	Pinsk	3 42	4 46	Gomel ...arr	12 4	...	11 0
142	Luninez (314)...arr	5 15	6 0	,, ...dep	1 p10	...	12 0
...	,, ...dep	6p19	7 a45	Mosyr.........	5 31	...	5 a48
252	Mosyr.......................	1237	12p57	Luninez arr	10p13	a.m.	11 42
329	Gomel (317) ......arr	5 37	5 6	,, dep	12a40	7 33	1 10
...	,, ...dep	7 10	6 0	Pinsk.........	2 11	9 33	3 2
416	Unecha	1056	10 8	Jabinka ...	6 14	—	7 33
502	**Briansk (318)** arr	2p35	2 a12	**Brest-L.**	6 a56	...	8 p20

BOLOGOE and RYBINSK.

E.M.										
—	**Bologœ** 314 dep	2 a30	9a15	12a20	...	**Rybinsk** dep	9 a50	4 p5	7 p45
38	Udomlya	3 51	11 4	2 4	...	Rodionowo...	12 36	6 13	9 33
70	**Maksaticha**	5 0	1223	3 25	...	Sonkovo	1 44	7 16	10 13
102	**Beshezk**	6 15	1 50	4 53	...	Beshezk	2 45	8 11	11 0
120	Sonkovo	7 1	2 51	5 57	...	**Maksaticha**...	4 18	9 34	12 7
138	Rodionowo	7 38	3 38	6 43	...	Udomlya......	6 2	11 4	1 a19
186	**Rybinsk** ......arr	9 10	5p25	8 a40	...	**Bologœ** arr	8 p0	12a42	2a45

UGLOVKA and BOROVITCHI.

E.M		a.m.	p.m.		
...	Uglovka ......dep	7 55	11 20	...	...
19	Borovitchi ...arr	8 50	12 25	...	...
		a.m.	p.m.		
...	**Borovitchi** ...dep	5 50	8 30	...	...
...	**Uglovka** 314...arr	7 10	9 45	...	...

MOSCOW, SMOLENSK, and BREST LITEWSKI.

Dist. E.M.		2&3 a.m.	1 Cl a.m.	1 & 2 p.m.	1 & 1 p.m.	1,2,3 p.m.	1,2,3 p.m.	1,2,3 p.m.	2,3,4 nght
—	**Moscow** dep	8 40	10 45	1 0	2 0	6 0	8 35	9 45	12 15
15	Odinzowo	9 21	C	A	...	RC	...	10 36	1 19
40	Kubinka	1025	11 49	2 14	3 4	7 36	1018	11 52	2 51
68	Moschaisk	1144	12 42	3 13	4 3	8 41	1123	1 14	4 47
76	Borodino	12 2	RC	3 25	4 16	8 54	1141	1 33	5 14
112	Gjatsk	1 47	1 53	4 24	5 14	10 2	1 14	3 24	7 29
151	Viasma 319	3 24	2 53	5 30	6 20	1113	2 40	5 6	9 42
...	,, dep	—	2 59	5 36	6 26	1119	3 2	5 31	10 42
180	Isdeschkowo		...	...	RC	12 9	4 5	6 43	12 24
197	Dorogobush		4 15	6 52	7 42	1243	4 49	7 32	1 26
221	Jarzewo		4 54	7 35	8 22	1 33	6 0	8 41	2 59
260	Smolensk 317 arr		5 p52	8 p35	9 p20	2a40	7a43	10 30	5 p30
643	RIGA arr		...	...	1 p5	8p50	...	7 a0	...
...	Smolensk dep		5 p58	8 p41	9 p26	2a46	8a12	12 p1	6 p30
302	Krasnoi		6 59	9 42	10 27	4 5	9 53	1 46	8 50
334	Orscha		7 50	10 39	11 24	5 5	1117	3 30	11 49
376	Slawjany		8 53	11 42	12 27	6 23	1 0	5 21	2 10
416	Borissow		10 10	1 5	1 50	7 38	2 39	7 8	4 26
467	Minsk arr		11 43	2 38	3 23	9 29	4 49	9 10	7 14
587	VILNA 317 arr		SC	...	1 p7	6p56	1053	5a31	...
...	Minsk dep		11 57	2 52	3 37	9 49	5 1	10 5	8 25
512	Stolbzy		1 25	4 20	5 5	1134	6 57	12 6	12 7
554	Baran'itschi 314		2 49	5 44	6 29	1 13	9 6	2 2	2 59
618	Pogodino		4 50	7 45	8 30	3 20	1131	5 28	6 19
650	Tewli		...	A	...	4 22	1245	6 43	7 56
664	Jabinka (314)		...	...	...	...	1 14	7 10	8 37
679	**Brest Lite.** arr		6 a43	9 a38	10a23	5p20	1a50	7 a50	9 p25
811	WARSAW (315)		10a50	1 p50	2 p25	9p40	8a52	12p15	7 a37

		1,2,3	2 3 4	1,2,3	1 & 2	1,2,3	1,2,3	1 Cl
WARSAW dep		8 p57	1a17	9a52	3 p25	6 p55	4 p37	8p30
Brest		a.m.	a.m.	p.m.	p.m.	p.m.	p.m.	ngt
Litewski dep		3 5	8 49	2 10	7 25	10 46	11 16	1230
Jabinka		3 39	9 30	RC	...	...	11 50	B
Tewli		4 6	1010	3 6	SC	A	12 17	...
Pogodino		5 23	1157	4 14	9 22	12 43	1 34	2 27
Baranovitschi		8 3	3 44	6 32	11 19	2 40	4 19	4 23
Stolbzy		9 49	6 8	8 6	12 41	4 2	6 8	5 45
Minsk arr		11 47	8 50	9 54	2 12	5 33	8 9	7 15
VILNA dep		6a27	...	...	6 p43	...	12a14	...
Minsk dep		12 12	1043	1014	2 23	5 44	9 4	7 31
Borissow		2 24	1 22	1213	4 3	7 24	11 9	9 11
Slawjany		4 5	3 32	1 28	5 14	8 35	12 52	1022
Orscha		6 17	6 50	2 43	6 26	9 47	3 18	1128
Krasnoi		7 38	8 25	3 42	7 10	10 31	4 36	1210
Smolensk arr		9 p15	1035	4a55	8 a17	11a38	6 p20	1p10
RIGA dep		...	...	1016	6 p5	...	11p55	...
Smolensk dep		10 p4	1150	5 a1	8a28	11a49	7 p20	1p16
Jarzewo		11 50	2 12	6 11	9 30	12 51	9 9	2 14
Dorogobush		12 58	4 5	7 2	10 15	1 36	10 30	2 59
Isdeschkowo	2&3	1 38	5 22	7 30	RC	A	11 21	...
Viasma arr	p.m.	2 35	7 22	8 19	11 25	2 46	12 32	4 9
,, dep	1256	3 8	9 0	8 25	11 31	2 52	1 0	4 15
Gjatsk	2 41	4 39	1133	9 44	12 33	3 51	2 55	5 15
Borodino	4 33	6 16	1 51	1047	1 38	4 59	5 0	...
Moschaisk	5 3	6 50	2 28	11 8	1 58	5 19	5 34	6 34
Kubinka	6 16	8 1	4 17	1210	2 43	6 4	7 0	7 17
Odinzowo	7 29	...	5 57	...	...	...	8 13	...
Moscow arr	8 p5	9 a40	6a50	1p25	3 p41	7 p10	9 a0	8p18

A—*Travellers are warned to enquire as to this train.*
B—Train de Luxe, Wednesday only. Arrives at Kursk Station, Moscow, 8.52 p.m.
C—Train de Luxe, on Friday only.

WARSAW, TERESPOL, and BREST LITEWSKI.—(St. Petersburg Time.)

Dist E.M.		1,2,3 a.m.	1 &2 p.m	1,2,3 p.m.	1,2,3 p.m.	1,2,3 p.m.	1 &2 p.m.	F p.m	1,2,3 p.m.	1,2,3 a.m.
—	Warsaw dep	9§52	3§25	3 47	4 5	4 37	6§55	8 30	8 57	1 17
23	Novo Minsk	...	...	RC	RC	5 48	A	...	10 6	2 34
56	Sedletz (315)	1140	5 7	5 28	5 53	7 29	8 37	10 8	11 36	4 17
73	Lukow (316A)	1220	5 44	6 8	6 32	8 18	9 14	1047	12 23	5 7
105	Biela	1 10	...	6 57	...	9 28	...	...	1 35	6 31
128	Lobatchev	...	RC	...	...	1015	...	...	2 24	7 25
132	Brest Litewski	1 53	7 10	7 41	8 10	1026	1038	1220	2 35	7 3[illegible]
811	Moscow 315 arr	1p25	3p44	...	...	9 a0	7p10	8p18	9 a40	6a50
E.M	Sedletz dep	8 a0	3p45	12 a7	...	...	...	...	...	...
42	Malkin (315) arr	1120	6 6	2 30	...	...	...	...	...	...

	1,2,3		1,2,3	1,2,3	1,2,3	1 & 2	1 &2	1,2,3	1,2,3
Moscow dep	8p35	1045	9 p45	9p45	1 p0	2 p0	...	6 p0	12a15
Brest	a.m.	a.m.	a.m.	a.m.	a.m.	a.m.	a.m.	p.m.	nght
Litewski dep	2 6	5 55	8 30	8 45	10 0	10 37	1057	5 35	12 40
Lobatchev	2 19	...	RC	9 0	RC	...	A	...	12 59
Biela	3 24	E	...	9 51	1046	...	RC	6 20	1 59
Lukow	5 23	8 44	10 13	1124	1150	12 17	1237	7 23	3 51
Sedletz	6 7	9 17	10 44	1 4	1221	12 47	1 8	7 57	4 49
Novo Minsk	7 51	...	...	2 33	...	...	...	...	6 26
Warsaw arr	8 52	1050	12 15	3 32	1 50	2§25	2§52	9§40	7 37
Malkin dep	6a32	4 p0	12a38	...	...	...	...	...	...
Sedletz 314 arr	9 0	7 2[illegible]	3 0	...	...	...	...	...	...

A—*Travellers are warned to enquire as to this train.*
§—Warsaw Kovel Station. F—Tues. only, Train de Luxe. E—Sat. only; Train de Luxe. RC Restaurant Car.

MOSCOW and NIJNI-NOVGOROD.—(St. Petersburg Time.)

Dist. E.M.		1,2,3 a.m.	1,2,3 p.m.	1,2,3 p.m.	1,2,3 p.m.	1,2,3 p.m.	1,2,3 p.m.
—	**Moscow** dep	10 7	7 0	7‡35	9 21	1030	11§30
42	Pawlowo	1147	8 51	9 23	11 5	1211	1 6
77	Petuschki	1 12	1020	1054	1230	1 32	2 23
119	Vladimir	2 44	12 0	1234	2 3	3 2	3 48
149	Novki (316A)	3 48	1 17	1 42	3 18	4 7	4 45
158	Kovrov (322)	4 15	1 44	2 11	3a37	4 34	5 12
196	Viasniki	5 42	3 18	3 47	—	6 1	6 34
225	Gorochowez	6 46	4 26	4 57	...	7 5	7 35
273	**Nijni-Nov.** arr	8p28	6a20	6a48	...	8a46	9 10

	1,2,3 a.m.	1,2,3 p.m.	1,2,3 p.m.	1,2,3 p.m.	1,2,3 p.m	1,2,3 p.m.
Nijni-Novgorod dep	8 32	...	7‡15	7 40	9 38	10§29
Gorochowez	1019	...	9 12	9 40	1124	12 9
Viasniki	1125	...	10 27	10 52	1231	1 13
Kovrov	1251	1134	11 59	12 21	1 56	2 33
Novki	1 13	12 3	12 23	12 54	2 21	2 52
Vladimir	2 23	1 15	1 42	2 9	3 31	3 58
Petuschki	4 0	2 48	3 15	3 47	5 2	5 24
Pawlowo	5 23	4 13	4 41	5 16	6 22	6 40
Moscow arr	6p58	5a50	6 a18	7 a0	7a57	8 a10

‡—From 9th July until 8th September. §—From 11th July until 4th September.

OSTROLENKA and PILJAVA.

Ostrolenka dep	5a58	4 p26
Tluszcz	8 24	7 15
Novo Minsk	9 25	8 20
Piljava arr	1048	9 20
Piljava dep	6 a55	4p45
Novo Minsk	8 0	6 2
Tluszcz	9 35	7 40
Ostrolenka arr	1 20	9 48

Ostrolenka dep	6a10	10p5
Malkin arr	9 22	1153
Malkin dep	3a31	6p58
Ostrolenka arr	5 41	10 1

Ostrolenka dep	6a35	1 30	10p3
Lapy arr	9 55	4 45	1232

Lapy dep	2a54	10a30	5p50
Ostrolenka arr	5 45	4 14	9 22

MOSCOW, YAROSLAV, and KOSTROMA.

Dist. E.M.			a.m.		p.m.	p.m.	p.m.	n'gt
	Moscow dep	...	9 20	...	6 40	9 20	1015	1210
44	Sergievo	...	1114	...	8 47	1051	1233	3 37
70	Alexandrov	...	1227	...	1028	1229	1a34	5 36
139	Rostov	...	3 26	...	1 44	3 40	—	9 45
174	**Yaroslav** arr	p.m.	4p55	p.m.	3a20	5a15	...	1137
	,, dep	1225	—	7 57	—	5 55	...	—
205	Nerekta	1 47	...	1015	...	7 17	...	...
231	**Kostroma** arr	3p12	...	1152	...	8a47	...	...

	a.m.	p.m.			p.m	
Kostroma dep	5 30	2 11	...	...	8 38	...
Nerekta	7 22	3 37	...	...	9 40	...
Yaroslav arr	9 23	4 57	p.m.	...	11 27	a.m.
,, dep	1140	—	6 5	...	11 55	1 40
Rostov	1 13	p.m	8 10	a.m.	1 43	3 30
Alexandrov	4p31	6 30	1226	3 31	4 5	7 10
Sergievo	5 41	7 46	2 45	4 50	6 30	8 27
Moscow arr	7 p5	10 p0	6 a0	6 50	8 45	10a30

YAROSLAV and ARCHANGEL.

E.M.			
	Yaroslav (Urotchi)	4 a15	5 p50
41	Danilov	7 15	8 45
99	Grjasowez	10 17	11 46
127	Vologda 319 arr	11 40	1 a10
...	Vologda 319 dep	5 p10	—
220	Voshega	10 22	...
312	Njandoma	4 a5	...
441	Obozerskaya	10 33	...
522	**Archangel** arr	2 p27	...

Archangel dep	...	3 p7
Obozerskaya	...	7 26
Njandoma	...	2 a22
Voshega	...	7 39
Vologda arr	...	12p40
Vologda dep	3 a42	5 p2
Grjasowez	5 14	6 38
Danilov	8 19	9 53
Yaroslav (Urotchi)	10 50	12a30

Yaroslav dep	6 a10	5 p25	...	...
Rybinsk arr	8 28	7 30	...	...
Rybinsk dep	9 a30	8 p52	...	...
Yaroslav arr	11 35	11 10	...	...

Alexandrov dep	5a20	4 p40	...
Kirshatch arr	6 39	6 4	...
Kirshatch dep	2 p37	10p14	...
Alexandrov arr	4 0	12 10	...

Alexandrov dep	1 a54	10a30
Ivanovo arr	8 a0	4 p43
Ivanovo dep	11a52	9 p5
Alexandrov arr	6 p10	3 a9

WARSAW and GRANICA.—St. Petersburg Time.

Warsaw Time is 37 minutes earlier than St. Petersburg Time.

Dist. E.M.		1,2,3 a.m.	1,2 3 a.m.	1,2,3 a.m.	1,2,3 a.m.	1,2,3 p.m.	1,2,3 p.m.	2&3 p.m	1,2,3 p.m.	2&3 p.m.	1,2,3 p.m.	1 & 2 nght	1,2,3 ngt.
—	**Warsaw**..............dep	...	8 10	8 37	1112	2 32	3 47	...	5 32	6 32	8 27	12 12	1257
27	Zyrardow	...	9 0	9 55	1241	...	...	...	6 27	7 39	9 17	...	2 8
42	Skierniewice	8 0	9 32	1034	1 22	3 41	5 1	...	6 59	8 19	9 31	1 21	2 46
66	Koluski (316) ......dep	9 4	10 30	1144	2 40	4 50	5 47	...	7 54	9 23	11 7	2 10	3 57
90	Petrikau	10 7	—	1255	3 55	5 50	6 33	7 0	—	1026	12 12	2 56	4 59
118	Radomsk	11 18	...	2 5	5 14	—	7 22	8 24	...	1141	—	3 47	6 11
143	Czenstochau 316	12 26	...	3 14	6 35	...	8 12	9 45	...	1256	...	4 41	7 24
182	Zabkowice...........arr	1 58	...	4 49	8 14	...	9 21	1145	...	2 31	...	5 50	9 1
...	Zabkowice ......dep	2 23	...	5 0	8 24	...	9 37	12 5	...	2 36	...	6 5	9 11
186	Golonog	2 31	...	5 8	8 31	...	9 44	1212	...	2 43	...	6 12	9 18
187	Dombrowo	2 39	...	5 16	8 39	...	9 52	1220	...	2 49	...	6 19	9 26
193	Sosnowitz (218) arr	3 0	...	5 37	9 0	...	10 13	1240	...	...	...	6 38	9 47
198¼	KATTOWITZ ...arr	3p29	...	5p36	...	...	10p25	1212	...	...	...	6 a37	9a41
214½	BRESLAU (218) ,,	8p40	...	8p50	...	...	...	3a24	...	...	...	10a23	2p15
...	Zabkowice ....dep	2 8	...	5 5	8 34	...	9 27	1212	...	...	...	6 12	9 16
191	**Granica** (222) ......arr	2 29	...	5 27	8 55	...	9 42	1232	...	...	...	6 27	9 37
202¾	TRZEBINIA........arr	3p10	...	7 p0	...	...	10p35	...	...	...	...	7 a18	1030
435¼	VIENNA (222) ... ,,	9 p50	...	...	...	...	6 a0	...	...	...	...	3 p10	...
227	CRACOW (222)... ,,	4 p52	...	8p10	...	...	11p38	...	...	...	...	9 a35	1155

	1,2,3 a.m.											
CRACOW (222) dep		...	3a55	...	5 a20		9 a30	...	...	2p35	7p44	10p35
VIENNA (222)... ,,		...	1015	...	10p15	...	...	7a34	...	...	1235	3 p55
TRZEBINIA ...... ,,		...	5a30	...	6 a42	1,2,3	11a15	2p22	...	4p10	8p33	11p27
		1,2,3	1,2,3 a.m.	2 & 3	1,2,3 a.m.	...	1,2,3 p.m.	1,2,3 p.m.	1,2,3	2&3 p.m.	1,2,3 p.m.	1 & 2 a.m.
Granica ....dep		...	8 32	...	9 42	...	2 7	5 7	...	7 12	1130	2 0
Zabkowice ....arr		...	8 49	...	10 6	...	2 31	5 31	...	7 40	1153	2 17
BRESLAU.........dep		...	...	...	12a20	...	6 a30	9a50	...	...	4p36	6 p18
KATTOWITZ ...dep		...	5a28	...	6 a52	...	10a31	1p38	...	3p45	9p15	11p15
Sosnowitz ....dep		a.m.	7 45	...	9 14	...	1 44	4 40	...	6 52	1135	1 28
Dombrowo		4 26	8 9	...	9 38	...	2 8	5 4	...	7 16	1159	1 49
Golonog		4 34	8 17	...	9 47	...	2 16	5 12	...	7 24	12 7	1 57
Zabkowice ....arr		4 42	8 25	...	9 55	...	2 24	5 20	...	7 32	1215	2 5
Zabkowice ....dep		4 47	8 55	...	10 19	...	2 41	5 40	...	7 51	1225	2 29
Czenstochau		6 25	10 9	...	12 5	...	4 31	7 16	...	9 54	2 13	3 43
Radomsk		7 26	1053	p.m.	1 14	...	5 36	8 15	...	1110	3 21	4 27
Petrikau	7 24	8 38	1144	12 47	2 34	p.m.	6 50	9 22	p.m.	1227	4 43	5 15
Koluski	8 47	9 45	1227	2 15	3 51	7 9	8 3	1033	1015	—	6 30	5 58
Skierniewice	9 43	11 0	1 12	3 8	4 53	7 54	9 3	1122	1110	...	7 43	6 42
Zyrardow	1011	1132	...	3 35	5 31	...	9 31	—	1137	...	8 18	...
Warsaw ....arr	11 0	1250	2 17	4 31	6 52	8 59	10 17	...	1226	...	9 31	7 47

☞ **Luggage.**—Travellers are advised to be careful to see that all their luggage arrives at the Russian frontier station in the same train as themselves, is examined in their presence, and leaves in the same train as themselves.

CZENSTOCHAU and HERBY.

Czenstochau.........dep	6a32	9 a37	12p55	4 p7	7p51	...
Herby	7 7	10 12	1 29	4 42	8 25	...
Herby (Prussia) 220 arr	7 40	11 5	2 17	5 37	9 8	...

Herby (Prussia) dep	8a23	9a50	12p19	5p34	9p49	...
Herby (Russia) dep	9 2	1053	2 31	6 35	1037	...
Czenstochau 316 ar	9 29	1123	3 1	7 2	11 7	...

KOLUSKI & LODZ. (In 40 min.). †—Until 6th Sept.

Koluski dep. 4.16, 6.47, 8†27, 9.7, 10.37 a.m., 12.35, 2†42 4.35, 5†52, 8.0, 9.47, 10.57 p.m. **Lodz** dep. 7.57, 8†42, 10.37 a.m., 1.27, 2 27, 4.32, 5†27, 6.22, 7 20, 8†10, 9.22 p.m., 12.52 night.

WARSAW and ALEXANDROVO.—St. Petersburg Time.

Dist E.M.	2&3	1,2,3 a.m.	1,2,3 a.m.	A p.m.	2&3 p.m.	2 & 3	2&3 p.m.	1,2,3 p.m.	1,2,3 p.m.	2&3 p.m.	1 &2 p.m.	1—4 a.m.	p.m
—	**Warsaw**..........dep	5 57	9 32	1222	1255	...	4 2	5 12	7 47	9 42	1152	1 20	...
27	Zyrardow	7 13	1049	...	2 39	p.m.	5 9	6 1	8 49	11 8	...	2 42	...
42	Skierniewice	7 50	1128	1 31	3 15	4 14	5 39	6 37	9 31	1141	1 5	3 21	...
83	Kutno	9 28	1 19	2 37	—	6 1	—	8 3	1125	—	2 24	5 55	...
117	Wloclawek	1046	2 41	...	...	7 48	...	9 8	1247	...	3 24	7 44	...
140	**Alexandrovo** ...arr	1136	3 32	4 10	...	8 47	...	9 52	1 40	...	4 2	8 50	...
151¼	THORN...........arr	1155	5 p5	4p13	...	...	...	1037	...	...	4a27	9a32	...
239	POSEN (178) ... ,,	3p12	1119	6p48	...	...	...	1a51	...	...	...	—	...
397	BERLIN (179A) ,,	7p12	...	1038	...	...	...	5a51	...	...	11a10	...	...

	1 &2 a.m.	2 & 3	2 & 3	1—4 a.m.	1,2,3 a.m.	2 & 3 a.m.	1,2,3 p.m.	B p.m.	1,2,3 p.m.	1,2,3	1,2,3 nigt		
BERLIN ......dep	7p35	...	...	...	11p21	...	...	7a52	9a57	...	2p43	...	...
POSEN ...... ,,	...	...	...	...	3a13	...	5a56	1132	1p59	...	7 p3	...	...
THORN ...... ,,	1a12	...	...	...	5a56	...	1156	1p35	4p20	...	10p2	...	...
Alexandrovo dep	4 4	...	...	5 30	8 52	10 12	2 47	3 33	7 25	...	1255	...	...
Wloclawek	4 44	...	...	6 41	9 34	11 21	4 4	...	8 22	...	1 59	...	...
Kutno	5 47	a.m.	a.m.	8 28	1041	1 10	5 55	5 5	9 49	p.m.	3 43	...	...
Skierniewice	7 2	7 17	8 17	1023	12 9	2 52	8 8	6 11	1142	10 0	5 3[illegible]	...	...
Zyrardow	...	7 48	8 51	1059	1236	—	8 40	...	1214	10 39	6 7	...	...
Warsaw.........arr	8 7	9 7	10 8	1221	1 22	...	9 55	7 14	1 29	12 0	7 20	...	...

§—Sleeping Cars between Warsaw and Berlin in these trains. **A**—Nord Express–Saturday only. **B**—Nord Express—Tuesday only.

ALEXANDROVO and CIECHOCINEK.

Alexandrovo dep	1a57	6a37	12p7	4 p2	5 p32	7p37	10p22	...	...
Ciechocinek arr	2 9	6 52	1222	4 17	5 47	7 52	10 37	...	...

Ciechocinek dep	7a54	11 a4	2p12	2p37	4p49	6p34	9 p9	11p59	...	...	...	...
Alexandrovo arr	8 12	11 22	2 30	2 52	5 7	6 52	9 27	12 17	...	...	...	...

WARSAW and KALISZ.

E.M.			a.m.	p.m.	p.m.	p.m.	
—	**Warsaw** ....dep	...	9 0	1 0	3 46	11 52	...
37	Sochaczew	...	10 28	2 35	...	1 24	...
50	Lowicz	a.m.	11 14	3 24	5 17	2 9	...
87	Lodz	8 32	1 1	5 16	6 50	3 49	...
123	Sieradz	10 30	2 30	7 1	8 10	5 19	...
156	**Kalisz** ....arr	11 47	3 52	8 32	9 10	6 40	...
298	SAGAN (218A) arr	5 p31	11 p5	...	1 a56	...	...
416	BERLIN (179A) arr	8 p16	3 a57	...	5 a8	...	...

BERLIN (179)......dep	12 a8	...	...	...	...	...	...	...	...	...	...
SAGAN (218A) ...dep	3 a0	...	5 a16	9 a10	...	...	...	...	...	...	...
	a.m.	a.m.	p.m.	p.m.	nig't						
Kalisz ....dep	9 9	9 47	2 57	7 7	12 5	...	...	...	...	...	...
Sieradz	10 15	11 26	4 31	8 50	1 3[illegible]	...	...	...	...	...	...
Lodz	11 38	1 11	6 7	10 27	3 8	...	...	...	...	...	...
Lowicz	12 51	2 47	7 56	—	4 41	...	...	...	...	...	...
Sochaczew	...	3 32	8 46	...	5 19	...	...	...	...	...	...
Warsaw ....arr	2 15	5 2	10 17	...	6 43	...	...	...	...	...	...

DOMBROWA-GORNAYA and LUKOW.

E.M	Station						
	Dombrowa-Gornaya dep	8a22	...	9 a17	6 p27	1 a10	...
4	Golònog	8 43	...	9 38	6 50	1 30	...
8	Strshemeschiz arr	8 58	...	9 51	7 5	1 43	...
...	Sosnowitz dep	—	8a18	8 a18	6 p15	12a30	...
...	Granica dep	...	8a56	9 a35	6 p50	1 a51	...
...	Strshemeschiz dep	...	9a10	10 15	7 p33	2 a17	...
101	Kelze	...	1220	3 3	12 2	6 33	...
129	Skarshisko (316A)	...	1 18	4 41	1 33	7 50	...
154	Radomi	...	2 4	5 54	2 46	8 54	...
189	Ivangorod arr	...	3 9	7 p24	4a15	10a17	...
253	WARSAW (316A) arr	...	5 p8	11p40	8a30	1p32	...
...	Ivangorod dep	...	3 35	—	6 2	—	...
227	**Lukow** arr	...	5 18	...	8 48	...	...
286	BREST (315) arr	...	7p10	...	...	...	...

Station							
BREST dep	...	...	10a37	5p35	...	...	...
Lukow dep	...	...	12p45	7p22	...	...	...
Ivangorod arr	...	...	2 32	9 2	...	...	...
WARSAW dep	11p35	7a30	1 p20	5p37	...	...	...
Ivangorod dep	4 a0	1040	3 15	9 22	...	...	...
Radomi	5 47	1229	4 25	11 6	...	...	...
Skarshisko	7 14	1 58	5 21	1224	...	...	...
Kelze	8 38	3 36	6 21	1 50	...	...	...
Strshemeschiz arr	1 16	8 33	9 21	6 9	...	...	...
Granica arr	1 55	9 11	9 34	6 36	...	...	...
Sosnowitz arr	2 32	...	10 9	7 12	...	...	...
Strshemeschiz dep	1 45	9 43	—	6 25	...	...	...
Golonog arr	2 0	9 58	...	6 40	...	...	...
Dombrowa arr	2 p26	1019	...	7 a3	...	...	...

SKARSHISKO and KOLUSKI.

Station						
Skarshisko...dep	...	7 a58	3 p9	...	2 a8	...
Tomaschew	7 a0	10 38	6 26	9p12	4 58	...
Koluski (316) arr	8 4	11 38	7 30	10 14	5 53	...

Station									
Koluski dep	2 a37	9 a54	4p46	8 p20	11 p5	...	...	...	...
Tomaschew	3 30	10 42	5 38	9 15	12 5	...	...	...	...
Skarshisko arr	6 20	1 6	...	11 36	...	...	...	...	...

Station					
Skarshisko dep	8 a10	2p36	6 p8	...	...
Ostrowez arr	9 50	4 15	7 57	...	...

Station					
Ostrowez dep	11 a0	2 p0	9 p27	...	...
Skarshisko arr	12 50	4 8	11 20	...	...

MLAVA, WARSAW, IVANGOROD, and KOVEL.

Dist E.M	Station											
	MARIENBURG ...dep	...	...	...	...	...	...	9a40	...	5 p23	...	...
				a.m.				p.m.		p.m.	nght	
—	**Mlava** dep	...	...	8 5	...	...	...	4 2	...	9 41	12 52	...
15	Gonssozin	...	...	9 32	...	...	...	5 32	...	...	3 35	...
79	**Warsaw** (Praga) arr	...	...	1154	...	...	...	7 39	...	...	6 45	...
81	**Warsaw** (Kovel arr	a.m	a.m.	12 2	p.m.	p.m.	p.m.	7 47	p.m.	12 10	6a57	...
...	" Bahnhof) dep	7 30	9 42	—	1†20	4 37	5†37	—	11†35	1 0	—	...
115	Piljava 315	9 9	11 16	...	...	6 17	7 10	...	1 48	2 51	...	...
145	Ivangorod **316A**	10 25	12 43	...	3 20	7 52	8 35	...	3 22	4 44	...	...
191	Lublin	—	2 56	...	4 43	10 7	—	...	—	7 15	...	...
234	Kholm **314**	...	4 58	...	—	1211	...	...	...	9 46	...	...
290	**Kovel 320** arr	...	7 10	...	...	2 25	...	...	...	12 0	...	...

	Station											
				a.m.			p.m.		p.m.			
...	**Kovel** dep	...	...	5 8	...	...	12 13	...	7 37	...	...	...
...	Kholm	...	...	7 48	p.m.	...	2 41	...	1016	...	...	...
...	Lublin	a.m.	a.m.	1013	1 23	...	4 53	p.m.	1 7	...	...	...
...	Ivangorod	5 20	1030	1244	3 22	...	7 5	7 59	3 40	...	...	...
...	Piljava	6 57	12 2	2 17	...	...	8 42	9 48	5 31	...	...	...
...	**Warsaw** (Kovel) arr	8†30	1†32	3 42	5 †8	p.m.	10 7	1140	7 12	...	...	...
...	" (Bahnhof) dep	—	—	4 32	—	5 45	—	1250	8 47	...	...	...
...	**Warsaw** (Praga) dep	...	...	...	...	5 54	...	1 1	8 56	...	...	...
...	Gonssozin	...	...	1050	...	8 18	...	3 38	1050	...	...	...
...	**Mlava 174A** arr	...	...	12 1	...	9 37	...	5 10	12 1	...	...	...
...	MARIENBURG ...arr	...	...	...	...	...	...	8a53	3p40	...	...	...

†—From or at Warsaw Brest Station.

Station			
Lukow dep	5 a30	2 p50	...
Lublin arr	9 20	8 0	...
Lublin dep	7 a 5	4p49	...
Lukow arr	11 1	7 59	...

SASANKA (Saratov), ASTRAKAN, and URALSK.

E.M.	Station					
	Saratov dep	11 a0	6 p25	...	...	...
55	**Sasanka** dep	1 p0	8 p30	...	...	...
76	Urbach arr	3 34	11 p1	3 a50	...	...
170	Krasnié-Kut	4 44	—	4 45	...	...
266	Aleksandrov-Gai	...	...	12p45	...	...
	Verchny-Baskuntschak	3 a0	...	—	...	...
419	**Astrakan** arr	11a25	...	...	...	...

Station									
Astrakan dep	4 p40	...	...	...	...	...	...	...	...
Verchny-Baskuntschak	1 a10	...	...	...	...	...	...	...	...
Aleksandrov-Gai	...	1 p40	...	...	...	...	...	...	...
Krasnié-Kut	10 a8	10 p0	...	...	...	...	...	...	...
Urbach	11a20	10 55	3a45	...	...	...	...	...	...
Sasanka arr	1 p40	—	6 15	...	...	...	...	...	...
Saratov (318) arr	3 p5	...	7a30	...	...	...	...	...	...

E.M.	Station		
	Urbach dep	11p31	...
58	Ershov	2 a40	...
116	Nikolaevsk ...arr	8 a10	...
215	Uralsk arr	1 p0	...

Station			
Uralsk dep	2 p0	...	...
Nikolaevsk	5 p15	...	...
Ershov	12a11	...	...
Urbach arr	3 a15	...	...

Station				
Baskuntchak dep	4 p5	...	...	...
Vladimirovskaya...arr	7 25	...	...	...
Vladimirovskaya..dep	4a55	...	...	...
Baskuntchak 318...arr	8 0	...	...	...

†—Until 31st August.

LGOV and RODAKOVO.

E.M.	Station							
				a.m.		a.m.		
—	**Lgov** dep	...	...	11 10	...	12 55	...	...
37	Sudsha	...	...	12 48	...	2 44	...	...
76	Gotnya	...	...	2 39	...	4 47	...	...
158	**Kharkov** arr	p.m.	p.m.	6 p33	p.m.	8 a42	...	...
...	" dep	12 20	4†30	—	10 31	—	...	...
273	Liman	5 20	8 16	...	4 16	...	...	...
290	: Slaviansk arr	6p40	9 0	...	5 a20	...	...	...
304	Nyrkovo	7 7	—	...	5 52	...	...	...
327	Sentianovka	8 9	...	...	6 54	...	...	...
343	**Rodakovo** arr	8 p45	...	...	7 a30	...	...	...

Station							
		a.m.		p.m.			
Rodakovo dep	...	7 55	...	10 35	...	...	...
Sentianovka	...	8 35	...	11 18	...	...	...
Nyrkovo	a.m.	9 48	...	12 39	...	...	...
: Slaviansk dep	6†40	9a50	...	12a20	...	...	...
Liman	7 24	11 14	...	2 14	...	...	...
Kharkov arr	11 10	4 p15	p.m.	7 a30	...	...	...
" dep	—	—	8 47	10a25	...	...	...
Gotnya	...	...	1 4	2 29	...	...	...
Sudsha	...	...	2 53	4 7	...	...	...
Lgov 318 arr	...	...	4a30	5 p30	...	...	...

NOVKI and KINESCHMA.

Station				
	a.m.	a.m.	p.m.	
Novki dep	4 30	...	3 55	...
Schuja	6 35	9 22	5 52	p.m.
Ivanovo	7 30	1015	6 45	7 48
Ermolino	9 19	1154	7 40	8 36
Kineschma	1140	...	...	1058

Station					
	a.m.	a.m.	p.m.	p.m	
Kineschma	5 56	...	...	5 9	...
Ermolino	8 27	9 27	5 33	7 45	...
Ivanovo	9 11	1020	6 50	8 50	...
Schuja	...	1118	7 36	9 51	...
Novki 315 arr	...	1 3	...	1140	...

Station			
Ermolino dep	12 p4	7 p50	...
Nerekta arr	1 50	9 36	...
Nerekta dep	7 a30	3 p31	...
Ermolino arr	9 20	5 22	...

 For FARES see p. 312A.

RIGA and TUKUM.

E.M.												
	Riga ......dep	8 a12	12 0	4 p25	11p55	...	**Tukum** ...dep	5a42	11a15	2 p50	8 p35	...
14½	Maiorengof	9 3	12 58	5 26	12 54	...	Kemmern.........	6 18	11 50	3 33	9 9	...
27¼	Kemmern.........	9 47	1 45	6 16	1 44	...	Maiorengof	7 10	12 37	4 32	9 56	...
39¾	**Tukum** ...arr	10 20	2 20	6 50	2 20	...	**Riga (317)** arr	8 10	1 30	5 30	10 49	...

RIGA and MOSCHEIKI.

	Dist. E.M.		a.m.	p.m.	p.m.		a.m.	p.m.	p.m.	
RIGA and MOSCHEIKI.		**Riga** ....dep	9 31	3 36	8 50	**Moscheiki**dep	4 45	2 16	7 35	...
	27	Mitau..............	10 38	4 52	10 10	Autz	5 59	3 26	8 35	...
	61	Autz	12 17	6 30	12 9	Mitau............	7 40	4 58	9 59	...
	80	**Moscheiki**arr	1 10	7 25	1 15	**Riga (317)** arr	8 51	6 0	11 0	...

RIGA and OREL.

	1,2,3 a.m.	1,2,3 p.m.	1,2,3 p.m.	1,2,3 p.m.	1,2,3 p.m.		1,2,3	1,2,3 a.m.	1,2,3 p.m.	1,2,3 p.m.	
Riga ....dep	10 16	6 5	7 10	8 10	11 55	**Orel**..............dep	...	11 15	4 55	11 34	From Moscow (dep. 10.0 a.m.)
Stockmannshof ...	1 12	8 12	9 50	10 57	2 34	Karatschew	...	1 30	7 21	1 58	
Kreuzburg 317......	1 42	8 37	10 10	11 29	3 4	**Briansk 314**	...	2 50	8 38	3 55	
Dvinsk 313......arr	3 36	10 8	To Moscow (arr. 5.45 p.m.)	1 23	4 55	Shukovka	...	4 14	10 10	5 45	
" ......dep	4 0	11 0			5 25	Roslavl	...	6 19	12 22	8 22	
Kreslawka...........	5 11	12 6		...	6 35	Potschinok...........	...	7 45	1 48	10 6	
Drissa	6 32	1 17		...	7 57	**Smolensk** 315arr	...	9 p10	3 a12	11a30	
Polozk...............	8 20	2 42		...	9 50	" ....dep	...	9 p53	3 a32	12p20	
Sirotino	10 12	3 54		...	11 25	Rudnja	...	11 47	5 17	2 43	
Vitebsk ....arr	11p30	4 a44		...	12p35	**Vitebsk**........arr	...	1 a24	6 a55	4 p40	
" 314...dep	12a19	4 a59		...	1 p35	**314** ......dep	...	1 a54	7 a20	5 p34	
Rudnja	2 7	6 32		...	3 48	Sirotino	...	3 2	8 34	6 59	
Smolensk ...arr	3 a43	7 a57		...	5 p50	Polozk..............	...	4 24	10 12	8 48	
" ....dep	4 a3	8 a47		...	6 p50	Drissa	...	5 51	11 49	10 27	
Potschinok..........	5 39	10 11		...	8 27	Kreslawka...........	...	7 10	1 15	11 57	
Roslavl	7 23	11 42		...	10 17	**Dvinsk** ....arr	a.m.	8 a5	2 p15	1 a0	
Shukovka	9 23	1 31		...	12 28	" 313........dep	5 35	8 a55	3 p20	1 a20	
Briansk	11 12	3 25		...	2 55	Kreuzburg..........	7 52	10 38	5 39	3 47	5a35
Karatschew	12 22	4 34		...	4 14	Stockm'nnshof......	8 19	11 0	6 7	4 13	6 0
Orel 318, 322 ...arr	2 p35	6 p45		...	6 a40	**Riga** ....arr	11 a5	1 p5	8p50	7 a0	8 40

STOCKMANNSHOF and VALK.

STOCKMANNSHOF and VALK.	Stockmannshof dep	7 a0	1 p55	Valk ....dep	6 a10	4p40	...	...
	Marienburg	2 p50	6 a58	Marienburg	10a30	9 p5	...	...
	Valk ....arr	7 p34	11a15	Stockmannshofarr	5p34	10a30	...	...

LIBAU and VILNA.

	Dist. E.M.		a.m.	p.m.	p.m.		a.m.	p.m.	p.m.	
LIBAU and VILNA.		**Libau** ....dep	11 15	5 2	10 40	**Vilna** ....dep	6 20	1 25	8 48	...
	57	Moscheiki ......arr	1 52	7 20	1 20	Landwarowo	6 43	1 49	9 27	...
	...	" (317) dep	2 20	7 40	1 40	Koschedari......arr	7 40	2 47	10 35	...
	105	Schaul	4 28	10 7	3 40	" ......dep	7 50	3 2	11 0	...
	117	Radziwilischkiarr	4 57	10 38	4 6	Keidani...............	9 15	4 28	12 27	...
	...	" (317) dep	5 56	11 2	4 17	Radziwilischkiarr	10 42	5 54	1 51	...
	158	Keidani.............	7 48	12 31	5 38	" dep	10 52	6 4	2 a0	...
	196	Koschedari......arr	9 19	2 2	7 6	Schaul	11 24	6 38	2 30	...
	...	" (313) dep	9 56	3 3	7 42	Moscheiki ......arr	1 5	8 17	4 13	...
	226	Landwarowo	11 11	4 54	9 1	" ......dep	1 25	8 35	4 50	...
	237	**Vilna (313)** arr	11p35	5 a20	9a25	**Libau** ....arr	3p44	11p 3	8 30	...

RADZIWILISCHKI and KALKUHNEN.

		a.m.	a.m.	p.m.	(313)	a.m.	p.m.
RADZIWILISCHKI and KALKUHNEN.	**Radziwilischki** dep	2 5	6 30	6 55	**Kalkuhnen** ...dep	10 0	5 0
	Ponevesh	3 54	8 22	9 6	Ponemunok...........	12 49	7 20
	Ponemunok..............	6 15	1030	11 33	Ponevesh	3 20	9 13
	Kalkuhnen ....arr	8 40	1 0	2 0	**Radziwilischki**	5 3	10 36

PONEVESH and BERESVETCH.

			a.m.	p.m.				a.m.	
PONEVESH and BERESVETCH.	**Ponevesh** ......dep	...	8 50	3 ‡40	**Beresvetch** ......dep	...	...	8 45	p.m.
	Ootzyani	...	1 p45	8 40	Postayi	...	...	12 5	‡4 0
	Swentsiany ....arr	a.m.	4 30	11 20	Swentsiany ...arr	a.m.	p.m.	4 p0	7 50
	" ....dep	7 50	6 10		" ...dep	2‡10	12 30		
‡—Monday and Thursday only.	Postayi	12 10	10 0	...	Ootzyani	5 35	3 40	...	...
	Beresvetch ......arr	3 p15	...	...	**Ponevesh** ...arr	11 12	8 20	...	...

VILNA, WILEISKAJA, BACHMATSCH, and ROMNEY.

Dist. E.M.		a.m.	a.m.	p.m.	a.m.			a.m.		p.m.	p.m.	
	Vilna ....dep	6 27	11 5	6 43	12 14	...	**Romney**...dep	2 39	...	2 59	8 0	...
5	Vileiskaya ......arr	6 41	11 20	6 57	12 28	...	Bachmatsch arr	4 42	...	4 p52	10p42	...
...	" (313) dep	6 49	11 45	7 10	12 55	...	Kiev ......dep	12 a5	...	12p30	7 p25	...
58	Salessje..............	8 40	1 45	9 6	3 29	...	Bachmatsch dep	6 a1	...	5 p20	12a40	...
120	Minsk (315) ...arr	11 3	4 p0	11 23	7 a0	...	Snowskaja	9 18	...	8 17	3 52	...
...	" ....dep		4 16	11 43	9 a10	...	Gomel..............	12p47	...	11 16	6 a12	...
186	Ossipowitschi......	...	6 28	2 a1	11 48	...	Shlobin	3 30	...	1a49	8 27	...
213	Bobruisk	...	7 24	2 58	12 53	...	Bobruisk	5 22	...	3 33	10 9	...
253	Shlobin **314**	...	8 59	4 33	2 p35	...	Ossipowitschi ...	6 31	...	4 38	11 16	...
306	Gomel (314)	...	11 34	7 0	5 48	...	**Minsk** ....arr	9 p2	p.m.	7 10	1 p50	p.m.
369	Snowskaja	...	1 53	9 28	8 37	...	" ....dep		10 40	7 55	2 p25	5 50
428	Bachmatsch ...arr	...	4 a42	12 0	11p17	...	Salessje............	...	2 42	10 36	4 47	8 21
549	Kiev (318) arr	...	9 a30	5 p0	5 a40	...	Vileiskaya ...arr	...	4 56	12 41	6 35	1016
...	Bachmatsch ..dep	...	6 a21	12p47	12a40	...	" ...dep	...	5 16	12 53	6 42	1033
476	**Romney 321**arr	...	8 a15	2 p41	3 a20	...	**Vilna 313** arr	...	5 a31	1 7	6 p56	10p53

RYLISK and SUDSHA.

RYLISK and SUDSHA.	Rylisk ....dep	5 20	...	2a30	Sudsha ....dep	8 a20	...	...	...
	Korenevo 318........	6 40	1 a55	3 45	Korenevo...........	10 0	7 a20	11p0	...
	Sudsha ....arr	...	3 35	...	Rylisk ....arr	...	8 35	1215	...

MOSCOW and VINDAU.

E M		a.m.		p.m.		p.m.	p.m.	
—	**Moscow**.........dep	10 0	...	11 20	**Vindau** ....dep	5 20	11 50	...
146	Rschevo.................	3 p53	a.m.	7 a55	Tukum	8 p22	6 a55	p.m.
315	Novo Sokolniki......	10p25	8 55	5 p30	Mitau..................	10p 3	9 a18	2 40
434	Ryashitza..............	3 a16	6p14	11p 6	Kreuzburg.........arr	2 a 4		9 p13
493	Kreuzburg.........arr	5 a20		3 a20	" ....dep	3 a0	...	10p25
...	" 317...dep	10a15	...	3 a50	Ryashitza	7 a54	...	12a41
578	Mitau..................	5 p 8	a.m.	8 a 0	Novo Sokolniki	1 p40	...	5 a27
613	Tukum	7 p40	3 5	10a40	Rschevo	11p40	...	11a52
680	**Vindau**.........arr	...	7 40	1 p25	**Moscow** ....arr	7 a 0	...	5 p45

KONOTOP and DNIPRI-KRASNOE.

Konotop ....dep	5 a30	7p25	...	**Dnipri-Krasnoe**...dep	3p10	10p15
Bachmatsch	6 30	8 25	...	Zolotonoscha	4 20	11 40
Itchnya	7 50	9 49	...	Grebenka......................	6 25	3a10
Grebenka........................	11 17	12 30	...	Itchnya........................	9 30	6 30
Zolotonoscha	1 10	5 30	...	Bachmatsch	10 50	7 55
Dnipri-Krasnoe......arr	2 p10	6 a30	...	**Konotop (318)** ......arr	11p30	8a35

Itchnya.........dep	...	10a35	...	10p45	Tschernigov dep	...	8 a0	...	6p40
Kruti................	7a15	11 55	5 p5	12 a5	Kruti	4 a5	11 35	5 p3	10 19
Tschernigov...ar	10 40	...	8 30	...	Itchnya ......arr	5 33	...	6 30	...

MOSCOW, OREL, and KURSK.

RC—Restaurant Car.   SC—Sleeping Car.

	1 & 2	1,2,3	2&3	1,2,3	1,2,3	1,2,3	1 & 2	1 & 2	1 &2	1,2,3	1 2 3
	a.m.	a.m.	a.m.	p.m.	p.m.	p.m.	p.m.	p.m.	p.m.	p.m.	n'ht
Moscow......dep	8 18	10 10	1130	2 20	5 30	6 13	7 50	8 8	9 10	9 37	1210
Tsaritsino..........	RC	RC	12 4	RC	...	6 42	B	...	...	10 14	1244
Serpuchov	10 0	12 25	2 12	4 35	7 48	8 38	9 32	9 50	1052	12 22	2 52
Tula 319 ......arr	11 35	2 29	4 48	6 40	9 58	10 49	11 7	11 25	1227	2 59	5 29
,, ...dep	11 43	2 44	4 58	6 55	—	...	11 15	11 33	1237	3 14	5 47
Gorbatschevo	1 10	4 43	7 17	8 55	...	To Yeletz.	12 42	1 0	To Far East, p. 319A Mon. & Wed. only.	5 38	8 10
Skuratovo	1 24	5 1	7 35	9 13	...		12 56	1 14		5 58	8 28
Mzensk..............	2 4	5 57	8 38	10 9	...		1 36	1 54		7 2	9 31
Orel ....arr	2 57	7 2	9 52	11 15	...		2 29	2 47		8 15	1045
SMOLENSK 317dp	4 a3	8 a47	...	SC	...		...	...		6 p50	...
Orel..... ....dep	3 5	7 17	10 2	11 35	...		2 37	2 55		8 35	11 0
Smievka	...	8 12	11 7	12 31	...	...	...	SC		9 39	12 5
Ponuiry.............	4 34	9 10	1215	1 30	...	...	4 6	4 24		10 49	1 14
Kursk ....arr	5 42	10p30	1a45	2 a51	...	...	5 a14	5 a32		12 18	2p44
KHARKOV **321**	10 p1	4 a50	...	9 a20	...	...	9 a35	9 a52		7 p39	9p25

	1,2,3	1,2,3	1,2,3	1,2,3	1 & 2	1 & 2	1,2,3	1,2,3	1,2,3	1 &2	1 & 2
KHARKOV ......dep		9p28	1 a27	...	9 a23	9 a43	...	9a58	...	From the Far East; on Wed. & Fri. only.	7 p54
		a.m.	a.m.	a.m.	p.m.	p.m.	p.m.	p.m.			nght
Kursk ....dep		4 5	7 43	8 0	1 50	2 10	3 3	5 35	...		12 20
Ponuiry		5 34	9 11	9 46	3 7	3 27	4 52	7 22	...		1 37
Smievka		6 28	10 4	1051	RC	RC	6 0	8 28	From Yeletz.		...
Orel ....arr		7 18	10 53	1146	4 25	4 45	6 56	9 23			2 55
SMOLENSK(317)arr		...	9 p10	...	B	3 a12	...	1130			...
Orel ....dep		7 38	11 8	1156	4 33	4 53	7 16	9 43			3 3
Mzensk		8 46	12 15	1 15	5 23	5 43	8 35	11 1			3 53
Skuratovo		9 54	1 23	2 33	6 17	6 37	9 56	1220			4 47
Gorbatschevo ...	1,2,3	10 6	1 35	2 45	6 25	6 45	1011	1234			4 55
Tula ....arr	a.m.	1158	3 25	4 53	7 47	8 7	1226	2 43	a.m.	a.m.	6 17
,, ...dep	6 33	12 8	3 40	5 3	7 55	8 15	1246	2 58	2 16	5 41	6 25
Serpuchov	8 56	2 26	5 59	8 8	9 40	10 0	3 40	5 44	4 42	7 34	8 10
Tsaritsino	...	...	RC	1013	...	...	5 38	7 41	6 26	...	...
Moscow ...arr	11 5	4p32	8 p5	1042	11p15	11p35	6 a7	8a12	6a55	9a10	9 a45

B—Black Sea Express,—from Moscow on Friday only: from Kursk on Tuesday only.

MOSCOW, KONOTOP, and KIEV.

					p.m.	p.m.	p.m.	nght	
Moscow.........dep	...	...	...	...	1230	8 5	9 10	12 5	...
Malo-Jaroslawetz...	...	...	...	...	4 58	1059	1 26	4 35	...
Tichanowa-Pustin	...	...	...	...	6 34	1211	3 10	6 55	...
Suchinitsch (322) ...	...	...	...	...	9 55	2 30	6 40	10 10	...
Sukevo	...	...	...	...	1151	4 11	8 48	12 6	...
Briansk (314) arr	...	...	a.m.	...	1a38	5 41	10 30	1 p50	...
Briansk (314) dep	a.m.	a.m.	6 15	a.m.	—	5a52	—	3 p35	p.m.
Konotop (318).........	4 29	5 10	3p25	1040	...	1148	...	10 36	1115
Bachmatsch	5 14	5 59	—	1124	...	1240	...	11 45	1 5
Kruti	6 8	6 59	...	1227	...	1 38	...	1 7	2 50
Kiev ....arr	9 30	1040	...	4p20	...	5 p0	...	5 a40	7 a0

		p.m.	p.m.	p.m.	p.m.	p.m.	nigt
Kiev ......dep	...	1230	1 0	6 55	7 25	10 45	12 5
Kruti............	...	4 2	4 58	1031	11 8	3 41	4 39
Bachmatsch...	...	5 8	6 5	1143	1230	5 27	6 5
Konotop	...	5 50	6 40	1216	1 a4	6 a3	6 56
Briansk arr	a.m.	11 33	...	...	...	...	2 p0
Briansk dep	3 55	11p43	...	4 p0	...	...	6 p0
Sukevo	5 43	1 25	...	6 4	...	...	8 5
Suchinitsch...	7 30	2 59	...	8 12	...	...	10 4
Tichanowa-P.	1020	5 20	...	12 5	...	...	1 28
Malo-Jarosla.	1148	6 32	...	1 39	...	...	3 8
Moscow arr	3p45	9a20	...	6a10	...	...	7a30

KONOTOP and KURSK.

Konotop dep	...	6a30	6p50	12a31
Voroshba	...	9 10	8 59	3 15
Korenevo	...	1049	1037	4 39
Briansk ...dep	3a53	...	3p55	...
Lgov 316A.........	9 42	1215	1152	5 43
Kursk.......arr	1140	2p20	1a50	7 25
Kursk ......dep	3a50	3 p50	4p55	10p45
Lgov................	5 51	6 2	6 44	12 28
Briansk ...arr	1p35	...	1a35	...
Korenevo (317)	7 6	7 20	—	1 31
Voroshba (321)	8 46	9 15	...	2 52
Konotop arr	1030	11 3	...	4 a19

MOSCOW and RIASAN.

RC—Restaurant Car.

Dist E.M.		1,2,3	1,2,3	1,2,3	1,2,3	1,2,3	1,2,3	1,2,3	1,2,3	2&3	1,2,3
		a.m.	a.m.	p.m.	p.m.	p.m.	p.m.	p.m.	p.m.	p.m.	n'gt
—	**Moscow** ......dep	9 45	11 35	3 20	5 22	5 55	7 0	10 30	11 10	1145	12 30
42	Faustovo	11 30	12 56	RC	RC	7 32	9 1	...	12 51	1 26	2 47
56	Voskresensk	12 5	1 25	...	...	8 7	9 32	...	1 26	2 9	3 24
70	Yegorievsk...arr	...	3 45	...	...	...	1045	...	...	...	7 0
73	Golutvin	1 12	2 15	5 22	7 21	9 10	—	12 30	2 28	3 7	4 36
85	Luchovizy	1 41	2 43	...	...	9 40	...	...	3 3	3 40	5 5
102	Saraisk ......arr	...	4 45	...	...	...	...	...	...	...	7 25
123	**Riasan** ....arr	3 p30	4 p10	6 p14	8p41	11p25	...	2 a7	4 a40	5a15	7 a40
255	KOSLOV 322 arr	...	9 p40	...	1249	7 a0		7 a25	...	1p35	...

	1,2,3	1,2,3	1,2,3	1,2,3	1,2,3	1,2,3	1,2,3	1,2,3	1,2,3	2&3	
KOSLOV......dep	...	10p15	1015	3 a0	...	5a47	...	...	...	2 p0	...
	a.m.	a.m.	a.m.	a.m.	a.m.	a.m.		p.m.	p.m.	n'gt	
Riasan ......dep	...	3 25	4 3	7 16	1052	1125	...	3 20	1015	1232	...
Saraisk......dep	...	...	...	RC	RC	1115	...	...	...	1130	...
Luchovizy	3 10	...	5 49	...	...	1255	...	5 21	1238	2 15	...
Golutvin	4 18	4 57	6 31	8 48	1227	1 32	...	6 2	1 27	2 56	...
Yegorievsk...dep	4 40	...	...	...	...	1210	p.m.	5 40	...	...	...
Voskresensk	5 55	...	7 29	...	...	2 11	2 25	7 8	2 44	3 52	...
Faustovo	6 52	...	8 13	...	...	2 43	3 3	8 1	3 38	4 35	...
Moscow ......arr	8 45	6 55	9 50	10 41	2 28	3 55	4 40	9 50	5 50	6 20	...

KOSLOV and SARATOV.

E.M.						
	Koslov ....dep	4 a8	7a15	3 p0	...	10 p0
45	**Tambov** ....arr	5a33	9 13	7 35	...	11 32
...	,, ...dep	5a41	9 28	—	...	11 42
88	Inokovka ....arr	7 4	1119	...	...	1 a20
104	Kirsanov	7 42	12 8	...	...	1 59
145	Vertunovskaya 318	9 11	1 52	...	...	3 23
162	Rtischtschevo	9 43	3 7	...	1a20	4 13
223	Atkarsk	1154	6 0	...	4 36	6 38
280	**Saratov** (316A arr	2 p2	8p37	...	7 57	8 a57

Saratov...dep	7a27	1 p37	6p17	7 p27	...	...
Atkarsk	1024	4 3	8 58	10 53	...	...
Rtischtschevo	1 42	6 21	1128	1 47	...	...
Vertunovskaya	2 25	6 55	12 6	...	...	...
Kirsanov	4 15	8 24	1a42	...	...	...
Inokovka	4 58	8 56	2 16	...	...	...
Tambov......arr	6 40	10 16	3 45	...	...	...
,, dep	6 55	10 26	3 55	...	...	...
Koslov ...arr	8p55	11p52	5a26	...	...	...

Vertunovskaya...dep	3 p30	...	Bekovo ....dep	11a50	...
Bekovo..................arr	4 10	...	Vertunovskaya 318 arr	12 30	...

E.M.						
	Tambov ......dep	10a15	9 p0	**Kamyschin**...dep	10p30	...
129	Balaschov	7 p25	6 a30	Balaschov	9 a0	10 p0
295	**Kamyschin**...arr	5 a15	...	**Tambov**.........arr	5 p20	7 a0

Balaschov ...dep	12p35	7 p55	...	**Pensa** ....dep	4a15	6 p40	...
Tavolskanka	1 31	8 55	...	Serdobsk	8 22	11 0	...
Rtischtschevo	5 p44	2 a44	...	Rtischtschevo ...	1030	2 a50	...
Serdobsk	7 23	4 20	...	Tavolskanka	2 11	6 21	...
Pensa	11p20	8 a15	...	**Balaschov** arr	3p10	7 a29	...

Atkarsk ......dep	9p30	Privolsky	5 p0	Atkarsk	7 a0	Balanda dp	4p15
Privolskaya arr	7 14	Atkarsk	5a45	Balanda	1055	Atkarsk arr	8 10

GRIAZI and ZARIZYN.

E.M.									
	Griazi..........dep	2 a20	11a30	...	...	**Zarizyn** dep	6 a20	1 p50	...
48	Mordovo	5 a5	2 p29	...	...	Ilovlia	8 49	4 35	...
83	Sherdevka	6 55	4 35	...	...	Artscheda	10 37	6 40	...
131	Borissoglebsk......	9 55	7 p50	...	...	Sobrjakovo ...	12 4	8 12	...
164	Alexikovo	11 50	9 36	...	...	Philinovo	1 p54	10 8	...
186	Urjupino......arr	5 p15	1 a25	...	...	Urjupino dep	10a15	7 p50	...
200	Philinovo	1 p53	11p20	...	...	Alexikovo	3 p25	11p42	...
245	Sebrjakovo	3 45	1 20	...	...	Borissoglebsk	5 p10	1 a32	...
278	Artscheda.............	5 21	3 1	...	...	Sherdevka	8 13	4 53	...
317	Ilovlia	7 10	4 58	...	...	Mordovo	10 p6	7 0	...
375	**Zarizyn** ......arr	9 p40	7 a35	...	...	**Griazi 322** ar	12a45	9 a55	...

 For FARES, see p. 312A

VIASMA and BATRAKI.

Dist. E.M.		1,2,3 a.m.	1,2,3 a.m.	1,2,3	1 & 2	1,2,3 p.m.
—	**Viasma** ....dep	5 21	10 40	...	...	5 15
64	Miatlevskaya	8 5	1 p22	...	...	8 20
103	Kaluga	10 18	3 5	...	A	10 33
146	Alexin	12 15	4 46	...	...	12 33
181	Protopopovo	1 58	6 14	...	...	2 21
185	Tula ....arr	2 p10	6 25	...	...	2 a33
...	MOSCOW 318 dep	10a10	5 p30	8 p8	9 p10	9 p37
...	Tula ....dep	3 p45	10p12	11p57	12a37	3 a36
216	Youzlovia	5 50	12 7	1 a45	2 a17	5 49
249	Klekotki	7 1	1 12	To Yeletz.	...	7 9
263	Kremlevo	7 31	1 44		...	7 42
307	**Riaschk** ......arr	9 p20	3 a32		5 a12	9 a42
...	MOSCOW 318 dep	11a35	5 p55		...	11p45
...	RIASAN 322 dep	4 p30	11p55		...	5 a45
		p.m.	a.m.		a.m.	a.m.
...	**Riaschk** ......dep	9 54	4 17	...	5 22	10 45
347	Verda	11 34	5 50	...	6 a30	12 39
387	**Morschansk** arr	1 2	7 13	...	7 a41	2 p25
...	,, dep	1 17	8 5	...	7 a51	2 50
419	Vernadovka	2 35	9 21	...	...	4 25
465	Patschelma	4 38	11 8	...	10a32	6 47
500	Voeikovo	6 6	12 25	...	11a40	8 29
526	Simanschtscha ...	7 6	1 p17	...	A	9 35
555	Pensa	8 45	2 38	...	1 p23	12 10
599	Tschaadaewka ...	10 38	4 26	...	2 p57	2 a11
629	Kusnetzk	12 1	5 41	...	4 p2	3 33
649	Nikulino	12 40	6 19	...	...	4 20
711	**Sysran** ....arr	3 p21	8 p44	...	6 p40	6 59
...	,, ...dep	4 0	9 9	...	6 p50	7 45
719	**Batraki** 319A arr	4 p25	9 p34	...	7 p10	8 a12

	1,2,3 a.m.	1 & 2 a.m	1,2,3 p.m.	1,2,3	1,2,3 p.m.
Batraki ......dep	5 38	10 21	2 19	...	6 20
Sysran ....arr	6 4	10 45	2 45	...	6 48
,, ...dep	6 34	11 2	3 25	...	7 48
Nikulino	9 4	A	5 59	...	10 48
Kusnetzk	9 56	1 p57	7 0	...	11 50
Tschaadaewka ...	11 7	2 59	8 12	...	1 a9
Pensa	1 p10	4 p43	10 18	...	4 40
Simanschtscha ...	2 10	...	11 23	...	6 1
Voeikovo	3 5	6 23	12 21	...	7 12
Patschelma	4 28	7 34	1 a47	...	8 59
Vernadovka	6 5	...	3 29	...	11 16
Morschansk ar	7 19	9 59	4 45	...	12 45
,, dep	7 29	10 13	4 55	...	1 p25
Verda	9 0	11 32	6 32	From Yeletz.	3 26
Riaschk ......arr	10p25	12a31	8 a2		5 p26
RIASAN 322 arr	3 a5	...	11 a0		12 a5
MOSCOW 318 ar	6 a55	...	3 p55		6 a20
	p.m.	nght	a.m.		p.m.
Riaschk ......dep	11 19	12 41	8 35		7 50
Kremlevo	1 12	A	10 23		10 3
Klekotki	1 a43	...	10 53	p.m.	10 41
Youzlovia (319)	3 5	3 38	12 9	1150	12 21
Tula ....arr	4 a48	5 a10	1 p55	1 52	2 a18
MOSCOW 318 arr	11 a5	9 a10	8 p5	6a55	8 a12
Tula ....dep	12p10		4 p15		3 a20
Protopopovo	12 29	...	4 34	...	3 40
Alexin	1 p59	...	6 11	...	5 22
Kaluga	3 56	...	8 21	...	7 23
Miatlevskaya	5 33	...	10 10	...	9 14
Viasma 315 arr	7 p58	...	12a40	...	11a58

Extra {Tula......dep 8 a45 / Riaschk arr 6 p59} | Riaschk dep 5 a35 / Tula...... arr 5 p25 | Tula.........dep 6 p55 / Youzlovia arr 9 3 | Youzlovia dep 8 a37 / Tula.........arr 11 0

A—The trains marked "A" are special trains, running twice a week each way. The train leaves Moscow on Mon. and Wed., arrives Irkutsk (see next page) on Sun. and Tues.

VIATKA and CHELIABINSK.

...	ST. PETERSB'G dep	8 p55	2 ‡55	10a15
E M	Viatka ....dep	7 a55	3 p17	8 p33
129	Glasow	1 p40	7 p49	1 a23
297	**Perm** (Zaimki)...arr	9 p50	3 a0	8 a45
301	Perm (Town)...arr	10p55	...	9 a24
...	Perm (Zaimki)...dep	10p52	3 a15	9 a3
534	Ekaterinburg ...arr	10 a8	12p26	7 p22
...	**Tumen** ....dep	4 p12	...	12a30
...	Poklevskaya	8 p50	...	5 a13
...	Bogdanowitsch ...	2 a29	...	10a38
...	**Ekaterinburg** arr	6 a55	...	3 p2
...	**Ekaterinburg** ...dep	10a46	12p40	7 p42
687	**Cheliabinsk** ......arr	7 p20	8 p16	3 a53

‡—Special weekly train for Far East: leaves St. Petersburg on Sat., Viatka on Sun.

Cheliabinsk ......dep	8a§50	9 a27	11p30
Ekaterinburg ...arr	4 p17	6 p13	7 a29
Ekaterinburg dep	...	8 p0	1 p30
Bogdanowitsch ...	...	12a28	5 p57
Poklevskaya	...	5 a27	11p18
Tumen ....arr	...	9 a38	3 a35
Ekaterinburg ...dep	4 p31	6 p48	7 a51
Perm (Zaimki)...arr	1 a34	5 a59	5 p54
Perm (Town) dep	12 a3	5 a40	5 p30
Perm (Zaimki) dep	1 a51	6 a46	6 p19
Glasow	9 a21	3 p38	2 a16
Viatka (319) ......arr	1 p51	9 p12	7 a2
ST. PETERSB'G arr	2 p15	9 a20	6 p15

§—From Far East, arrival on Mon. at St. Petersburg.

E.M			
	Bogdanowitsch dep	2a35	...	...	...
23½	Sinarskaja ......arr	3 55	...	...	...
...	Sinarskaja ....dep	10p30	...	...	...
...	Bogdanowitsch **319** arr	11 50	..	...	...

PERM and EKATERINBURG (via Nijni Tagil).

E.M	Perm (Zaimki)...dep	9 a12	10p45	1 a28	...
79	**Chussovskaya** ...arr	3 p5	2 a58	8 a19	...
...	Chussovskaya dep	4 p35	4 a5	...	...
209	Solevarni ....arr	5 a12	4 p35	...	...
...	**Chussovskaya**...dep	...	3 a16	8 a55	...
140	Biser	...	7 a3	2 p23	...
...	Nadeschdinsk dep	...	...	7 a30	...
193	Goroblagodatskaja	...	10 a1	7 p8	...
222	Nijni Tagil	...	11a38	9 p33	...
311	**Ekaterinburg** ...arr	...	3 p40	4 a10	...

Ekaterinburg ...dep	...	12p45	9 p55	...
Nijni Tagil	...	5 p14	4 a37	...
Goroblagodatskaja	...	6 p35	6 a40	...
Nadeschdinsk..arr	...	...	8 p40	...
Biser	...	10p12	12p36	...
Chussovskaya...arr	...	1 a18	5 p16	...
Solevarni ....dep	9 p34	11a50	...	...
Chussovskaya arr	10a16	12a24	...	...
Chussovskaya...dep	11a52	1 a33	5 p46	...
Perm (Zaimki)...arr	5 p42	5 a50	12a15	...

VIATKA and KOTLAS.

E.M.					
	Viatka ....dep	7 a40	**Kotlas** ...dep	4 a57	...
74	Muraschi	12p52	Pinjug	10a26	...
150	Pinjug	5 p40	Muraschi	3 p22	...
238	**Kotlas** ....arr	10p30	**Viatka** .....arr	7 p53	...

YOUZLOVIA & YELETZ.

E.M.			
	Youzlovia 319 dep	1a59	9p13
38	Volovo	4 4	1131
121	Yeletz 322 ......arr	8 45	4a35
...	Yeletz ....dep	4a50	12a15
...	Volovo	9 51	6 a2
...	Youzlovia(319)arr	1140	8 a22

SAMARA and TASHKEND.

E.M	Samara (319A) dep	1 p38	7 p0	8 p59
26	Kinel	3 p2	8 p59	10p10
108	Busuluk	7 p58	4 a4	1 a38
174	Novo Sergievka....	12a21	9 a33	4 a56
261	Orenburg.... {arr	4 a38	2 p42	7 a52
...	{dep	5 a18	3 p56	8 a12
429	Aktyubinsk..........	2 p11	3 a3	2 p35
657	Tschelkar..........	3 a20	4 p49	11p17
872	Kasalinsk	3 p0	8 a53	7 a17
1071	Perovsk	11p49	7 p51	1 p44
1313	Turkestan	7 a9	4 a46	8 p8
1411	**Tashkend** 323A arr	4 p40	3 p59	3 a36

Tashkend ....dep	5 a0	7 a56	9 a55	...
Turkestan	11 a3	4 p41	8 p59	...
Perovsk	4 p53	12 a1	6 a4	...
Kasalinsk	11a36	8 a28	4 p32	...
Tschelkar..........	7 a46	8 p57	6 a16	...
Aktyubinsk	4 p26	10a10	10p16	...
Orenburg ...... {arr	10p40	7 p27	8 a41	...
{dep	11 p0	8 p19	9 a39	...
Novo Sergievka	2 a23	12a30	3 p11	...
Busuluk	5 a43	6 a15	8 p50	...
Kinel	9 a7	10a57	3 a27	...
Samara (319A) ...arr	10 a5	12p14	4 a50	...

ST. PETERSBURG and VOLOGDA.

E.M		a.m.	p.m.	p.m.	nght
—	**St. Petersburg** dep	10 15	2 ‡55	8 55	12 35
124	Tichvin	3 p46	6 p59	2 a0	6 a7
294	Tscherepovetz..........	10p47	12a11	8 a58	1 p25
371	**Vologda** (315) arr	2 a4	2 a26	12p15	4 p40

	a.m.	a.m.	p.m	p.m.	
Vologda ....dep	2 36	3 0	1 55	5 1	...
Tscherepovetz	5 a6	6a38	5p34	8 p22	...
Tichvin	10 23	1 p6	1a57	3 a28	...
St. Petersburg arr	2 p15	6p15	7a50	9 a20	...

*—Arrives St. Petersburg Mon. only. ‡—From St. Petersburg on Sats. only.

VOLOGDA and VIATKA.

	a.m.	a.m.	p.m.
Vologda ......dep	2†41	3 3	1 15
Bui	5 a11	6 a12	4 p37
Galitsch	...	7 a30	6 p2
Kotelnitsch	...	5 p14	4 a18
Viatka (319) arr	2 p55	7 p31	6 a40

	a.m.	p.m.	p.m.
Viatka ....dep	8 *12	2 15	10 40
Kotelnitsch	10 45	...	1 a26
Galitsch	9 p20	...	11a37
Bui	10p41	11p59	12p57
Vologda ....arr	1 a50	2 a21	4 p11

†—From Vologda Sun. morning. *—From Viatka Sun. afternoon.

SYSRAN and CHELIABINSK.

Dist. E.M.		a.m.	a.m.	p.m.	A		p.m.
	Sysran.........dep	7 45	8 10	4 0	6 p50	...	9 9
—	**Batraki**.........dep	8 a20	9 a45	4p33	7 p18	...	9 p42
...	Maituga	9 a56	12 p7	6p10	8 p45	...	11p15
77	**Samara**...... arr	11a57	2 p55	8 p7	10 p6	p.m.	12a55
	dep	1 p12	4 p35	—	10p14	10 35	1 a25
103	Kinel	2 p41	7 p15	...	11 p7	11p58	2 a33
126	Krotovka	3 p45	8 p53	...	11p55	1 a1	3 a26
176	Pochvistnevo	5 p55	12a38	...	1 a38	3 a21	5 a33
248	Abdulino	9 p32	7 a25	...	4 a21	7 a9	8 a54
283	**Belebei-Aksako**.	11p26	11 a5	...	5 a51	9 a0	10a39
331	**Raevka**	1 a30	2 p8	...	7 a28	10a56	12p33
402	Ufa............ arr	4 a36	6 p55	...	9 a51	2 p10	3 p20
	dep	5 a6	7 p50	...	10 a1	2 p30	3 p35
524	Viasovaya............	11a23	4 a51	...	2 p41	8 p30	8 p57
569	Berdiaush............	1 p20	7 a50	...	4 p14	11p16	10p38
601	**Slatoust**	3 p1	10a31	...	5 p33	12a57	12 a6
700	**Cheliábinsk** ...arr	7 p5	5 p5	...	8 p50	5 a5	3 a50

	a.m.	A		a.m.	p.m.	nght
Cheliábinsk dep	5 48	8 a20	...	8 40	11 35	12 30
Slatoust	3 p10	12 p7	...	1 p14	3 a48	5 a52
Berdiaush.........	5 p35	1 p6	...	2 p35	4 a57	7 a10
Viasovaya	8 p35	2 p35	...	4 p23	6 a34	8 a57
Ufa......... arr	4 a48	7 p2	...	9 p57	11a34	2 p25
dep	5 a58	7 p12	...	10p17	11a49	2 p45
Raevka	11 a5	9 p52	...	1 a34	2 p57	6 p22
Belebei-Aksako	3 p7	12 a1	...	4 a11	5 p29	9 p3
Abdulino	5a48	1 a18	...	5 a51	6 p53	10p49
Pochvistnevo ...	11p17	3 a59	...	9 a12	9 p54	2 a20
Krotovka	2 a39	5 a41	...	11a20	11p53	4 a41
Kinel	4 a40	6 a22	...	12p26	12a48	5 a42
Samara... arr	6 a15	7 a11	a.m.	1 p30	1 a43	6 a45
dep	8 a30	7 a19	1035	2 p30	2 a13	—
Maituga	11a32	8 a52	1241	4 p42	4 a3	...
Batraki ......arr	1 p45	10a13	2p11	6 p12	5 a30	...
Sysran......arr	3 p55	10a45	2p45	6 p48	6 a4	...

CHELIABINSK and NOVO-NIKOLAIEVSK.

E.M			A		
	Cheliabinsk ....dep	5 a30	9 p20	10 p0	...
160	Kurgan............	12p42	3 a33	6 a40	...
325	Petropavlovsk	7 p42	9 a35	3 p12	...
495	Omsk............	3 a5	3 p47	12a20	...
695	Kainsk	11a28	11 p9	9 a55	...
883	Novo-Nikolaievsk arr	8 p34	6 a15	9 p5	...

			A		
Novo-Nikolaievsk	7 a55	9 a34	10p38	...	...
Kainsk	4 p18	7 p14	5 a52	...	...
Omsk	12a39	5 a36	1 p22	...	...
Petropavlovsk	8 a2	1 p55	7 p33	...	...
Kurgan	3 p8	9 p55	1 a34	...	...
Cheliabinsk .....arr	10p15	6 a10	7 a45	...	...

NOVO-NIKOLAIEVSK and TANKOI.

E.M.		A			
	Novo-Nikolai'vskdp	6 a15	8 p34	9 p5	...
142	Taiga............	11a41	3 a21	4 a44	...
234	**Mariinsk**	3 p44	8 a2	10a39	...
358	**Atschinsk**............	8 p41	1 p58	5 p52	...
469	**Krasnoyarsk** arr	1 a28	7 p27	12a30	...
	dep	1 a43	7 p52	2 a20	...
551	Klükvennaya.........	5 a14	12a14	7 a25	...
620	Kansk	8 a1	3 a38	11a21	...
691	Klütchi............	A	7 a28	3 p49	...
982	Sima	10p46	9 p30	8 a7	...
1137	**Irkutsk**......... arr	5 a10	6 a30	5 p45	...
	dep	6 a9	8 a9	8 p19	...
1178	**Baikal**...........arr	7 a36	9 a58	10p21	...
1305	**Tankoi** ....arr	12p48	4 p28	4 a49	...

		A			
Tankoi ....dep	10a21	2 p8	11p14	...	...
Baikal..............dep	4 p41	7 p33	5 a59	...	...
Irkutsk.......... arr	6 p19	8 p54	7 a49	...	...
dep	7 p50	10p20	10a10	...	...
Sima'............	4 a10	5 a26	8 p15	...	...
Klütchi............	7 p31	...	12p46	...	...
Kansk	11p20	8 p40	5 p7	...	...
Klükvennaya............	2 a56	11p36	9 p24	...	...
Krasnoyarsk... arr	7 a8	2 a56	2 a17	...	...
dep	7 a43	3 a12	3 a34	...	...
Atschinsk............	1 p49	8 a11	10a25	...	...
Mariinsk..	7 p56	1 p3	5 p27	...	...
Taiga............	12a41	4 a56	11p24	...	...
Novo-Nikolaievskarr	7 a30	10p20	8 a24	...	...

E.M.							
	Taiga ...dep	5a55	12p30	5 p55	12a50	...	...
54	**Tomsk** ...arr	9 5	4 30	9 50	4 35	...	...

Tomsk ...dep	7 a30	12p30	5p40	10p45	...	...
Taiga......arr	11 10	4 15	9 55	2 30	...	...

RUDNITSA and OLVIOPOL.

E.M.				
	Rudnitsa..............dep	8 a48	...	6 p15
17	Dochno	10 10	...	8 2
48	Gaivoron....................	1 22	p.m.	10 50
117	Podgorodnaya	6 58	7 40	—
121	Olviopol ....arr	...	8 0	...

Olviopol ....dep	...	9a25	...	...
Podgorodnaya	...	9 45	11 a5	...
Gaivoron	6 a40	—	4 p7	...
Dochno	10 11	...	8 27	...
Rudnitsa..............arr	11 43	...	9 p50	...

TANKOI and MANCHURIA.

E.M.		B		
—	**Tankoi** dep	4 a58	12p58	4 p36
138	Verkneydin	11a48	5 p34	10p27
259	Tolbaga ...	5 p59	10p11	4 a56
394	Mogzoni ...	12a39	3 a18	11a20
482	Tchita	5 a46	6 a59	4 p18
544	**Karim-** arr	10a53	9 a45	7 p50
	skaya dep	12p44	9 a48	8 p11
606	**Aga**	6 p4	12p41	1p38
698	Borsia	1 a18	4 p11	4 a3
777	**Manch'ria***	6 a54	7 p24	8 a4

	B		
Manchuria *dep	7 a4	4 p59	6 p4
Borsia	10a20	8 p53	12a53
Aga............	...	1 a2	7 a50
Karim- ......arr	4 p37	4 a38	1 p37
skaya ......dep	4 p40	5 a10	3 p41
Tchita	7 p28	9 a9	8 p33
Mogzoni	11p24	2 p34	2 a6
Tolbaga	4 a22	8 p50	8 a34
Verkneydinsk......	9 a4	3 a31	2 p59
Tankoi ....arr	1 p28	9 a19	9 p54

A—The trains marked "**A**" are special Trains, running three times a week each way. The train leaves Moscow on Mon., and Wed., and St. Petersburg on Sat., arrives Irkutsk on Sun., Tues., and Fri. Returns from Irkutsk on Tues., Thurs., and Sat.

B—From Irkutsk to Manchuria on Sun., Tues., and Fri. Leaves Manchuria for Irkutsk on Mon., Wed., and Fri. only.

*—Local Time at Manchuria.

There is river communication during Summer between Sretensk and Kabarovsk (head of line in table below); duration of steamer journey. about a week.

KARIMSKAYA and SRETENSK.

E.M.			
	Karimskaya......dep	2p14	9 p11
121	Nertchinsk............	8p34	3 7
176	**Sretensk** ....arr	1119	5 a44

Sretensk ....dep	2 a49	7 p29
Nertchinsk	5 48	10 20
Karimskaya.........arr	11 56	4 a14

VLADIVOSTOCK and KABAROVSK.

E.M.			
	Vladivostock .....dep	9 a35	...
68	Nikolsk Ussuri.	4 p15	...
149	Yevgenevka............	8 p40	...
217	Ussuri............	12 a8	...
257	Iman	2 a35	...
330	Bikin	6 a35	...
475	**Kabarovsk** ....arr	2 p55	...

Kabarovsk ......dep	6 a15	...
Bikin	3 p11	...
Iman	7 p26	...
Ussuri	9 p49	...
Yevgenevka............	2 a7	...
Nikolsk Ussuri.	6 a35	...
Vladivostock ...arr	12p50	...

GAIVORON and CHOLONEVSKAYA.

E.M.							
	Gaivoron..............dep	...	...	...	5 a40	...	4 p47
...	Ziatkovtsi	...	...	...	9 54	...	8 35
...	Gumennoe	...	...	...	5 p50	...	4 a10
...	: Vinnitza ....arr	...	...	...	7 p15	...	5 a5
...	Kalinovka	5 a33	8 a45	5 p45	8 p0	11 p0	6 25
146	Cholonevskaya......arr	6 15	9 27	6 3[illegible]	...	11 50	...

Cholonevskaya......dep	4 a50	...	11 a0	7 p13	8 p48	1 a30
Kalinovka	5 32	6a27	11 48	7 55	9 30	2 12
: Vinnitza ....dep	—	7a25	—	—	11p55	—
Gumennoe	...	8 40	...	...	1 a5	...
Ziatkovtsi	...	6 26	...	...	9 50	...
Gaivoron ....arr	...	9 35	...	...	12p47	...

E.M.							
	Cholonevskaya ......dep	10a 0	1 a20	...	...	...	...
36	Berditschev...........arr	1 0	5 0	...	...	...	...

Berditschev...........dep	5 p15	1 a20	...	...	...	...
Cholonevskaya ......arr	8 7	4 31	...	...	...	...

E.M.					
	Berditschev ....dep	7 a0	5 p8	1 a15	...
33	Shitomir ....arr	9 32	7 28	4 0	...

Shitomir ....dep	10a30	7 p35	1 a15	...
Berditschev...........arr	12 50	9 56	3 55	...

	1,2,3	1,2,3	1 & 2	1,2,3	1,2,3	1,2,3	1,2,3	1,2,3
	a.m.	p.m.	p.m.	p.m.	p.m.	p.m.	p.m.	ngt.
Odessa Grav. ...dep	9 55	3 0	8 40	9 0	9 10	9 40	10 5	1220
Rasdelnaya 320 arr	11 45	4 56	10 3	10 32	11 3	11 47	12 7	2 38
" ......dep	11 53	5 6	10 11	10 40	11 11	12 5	12 37	—
Birsula 320	2 46	8 12	12 30	1 15	2 a5	4 a5	3a54	4a24
Slobodka 320	3 39	8 58	1 2	1 50	—	5 5	—	5 27
Rudnitsa	5 15	1036	2 9	3 0	...	6 54	...	7 23
Vapniarka 320	6 5	1139	2 56	3 51	...	8 5	...	8 40
Schmerinka 320 arr	8 5	1 36	4 30	5 a26	...	10 23	...	11 8
" ......dep	8 27	2 11	4 40	5 36	...	10 53	...	1143
Vinnitza	9 54	3 30	5 33	6 34	...	12 29	...	1 23
Kalinovka	10 30	4 3	5 56	7 4	...	1 11	...	2 7
Kasyatin ...arr	11 30	4 58	6 35	7 47	...	2 15	...	3p15
Brest Lit. 320 ar	...	...	10p20	—	a.m.	7 a49	...	7a49
Kasyatin ...dep	12 14	5 13	6 45	...	7 14	2 58	...	4 30
Faustova	3 52	7 20	8 21	...	9 19	5 6	...	7 40
Kiev ...arr	6 a20	8a45	9 a35	...	10a48	6 p49	...	9p30

	1,2,3	1 2 3	1,2,3	1,2,3	1 & 2	1,2,3	1,2,3	1,2,3
	a.m.	a.m.		p.m.	p.m.	p.m.		a.m.
Kiev ...dep	9 0	1050	...	...	9 0	9 30	...	12 50
Faustova	11 18	1 0	...	7 52	10 18	11 16	...	3 28
Kasyatin ...arr	2 14	3 9	...	9 33	11 40	1 42	...	6 49
Brest Litew. dep	11 p7	11p7	...	8 a48	8 a48	...	8 p32	8 p32
Kasyatin ...dep	2 55	3 55	...	11 13	11 52	2 3	7 a0	7 23
Kalinovka	4 5	5 3	...	11 52	12 30	2 53	7 55	8 24
Vinnitza	4 49	5 43	...	12 18	12 58	3 25	8 30	9 1
Schmerinka ...arr	6 32	7 20	...	1 21	1 48	4 46	9 43	10 30
" ...dep	7 2	7 48	...	1 31	1 58	5 15	10 6	10 42
Vapniarka	9 40	1018	...	3 9	3 35	7 22	11 54	12 44
Rudnitsa	10 51	1128	...	3 52	4 16	8 15	12 38	1 37
Slobodka	12 53	1 22	a.m.	4 57	5 24	9 44	1 52	3 2
Birsula	2 4	2 36	4 15	5 33	6 8	10 39	2 35	3 58
Rasdelnaya ...arr	5 17	5 44	7 4	7 40	8 2	1 18	5 11	6 39
" ...dep	5 34	6 4	7 13	7 48	8 12	1 28	5 19	6 47
Odessa Gravnaya arr	7 a34	8 a5	8a58	9 a10	9 a25	3p19	6 p58	8 p30

SCHMERINKA and WOLOCZYSKA.

Dist E.M.				
	Odessa ...dep	8 p40	10 p5	9a55
		a.m.	a.m.	p.m.
—	**Schmerinka** ...dep	5 24	11 52	8 55
62	Proskurow	7 45	2 37	12 0
100	**Woloczyska** ...arr	8 58	3 55	1 30
103	Podwoloczyska ar	9 a58	5 p11	2a30
222½	Lemberg 246A ...arr	1 p47	10p30	7a15

Lemberg ...dep	8 p40	6 a8	2 p0	...	...
Podwoloczyska dp	3 a48	12p41	7 p11	...	...
	a.m.	p.m.	p.m.	...	...
Woloczyska ...dep	5 10	2 8	9 34	...	...
Proskurow	6 47	3 40	11 0	...	...
Schmerinka 320 ...arr	9 31	6 12	1 21	...	...
Odessa ...arr	6 p58	7a34	9 a25	...	...

ODESSA and UNGHENI.

E.M.		a.m.	a.m.	p.m.	nght
—	**Odessa** ...dep	...	9 55	6 10	12 20
45	Rasdelnaja	8 12	3 7	7 49	3 0
74	Tiraspol	9 30	4 24	8 59	4 45
82	Bender 320	10 7	5 16	9 25	5 32
119	Kischinev	11 53	6 58	10 50	7 54
164	Korneschti	1 56	9 9	—	10 24
186	**Ungheni** ...arr	3 p1	10p16	...	11a46
201	Jassy 324 ...arr	5 p25	...	...	5 p25

Jassy ...dep	...	...	12 p5	12 p5
		a.m.	p.m.	p.m.
Ungheni ...dep	...	5 32	2 11	7 17
Korneschti	a.m.	7 1	3 44	9 3
Kischinev	8 0	9 41	5 51	11 56
Bender	9 34	11 22	7 43	2 16
Tiraspol	9 57	12 16	8 9	2 54
Rasdolnaja	1115	2 44	9 43	4 48
Odessa ...arr	1245	6 p58	...	7 a18

SNAMENKA and BIRSULA.

	a.m.	a.m.	p.m.	p.m.
Snamenka ...dep	5 56	6 39	1 56	6 14
Elisavetgrad	7 35	7 59	3 35	7 46
Novo Ukrainka	—	9 29	5 35	9 42
Podgorodnaya	...	10 51	7 31	11 22
Holta	...	11 16	8 8	11 58
Ljubaschewka	...	12 39	9 51	1 41
Balta	...	1 48	11 18	3 11
Birsula 320 ...arr	...	2 16	11 52	3 45
Odessa ...arr	...	6 p58	7 a34	8 a58

Odessa ...dep	9 p10	10 p5	9 a55	...
	a.m.	a.m.	p.m.	
Birsula ...dep	2 35	6 11	3 52	...
Balta	3 15	6 47	4 28	...
Ljubaschewka	4 33	8 1	5 37	...
Holta	6 10	9 33	7 4	...
Podgorodnaya	6 57	10 16	7 33	...
Novo Ukrainka	8 45	11 59	9 3	p.m.
Elisavetgrad ...arr	10 40	1 41	10 33	9 35
Snamenka 321 ...arr	12p25	3 p26	12 0	1131

SCHMERINKA and OKNITZA.

Schmerinka dp	5a36	11a26	8p24
Moghilew Podol	9 55	2 52	1225
Oknitza ...arr	1129	4 18	1a55
Oknitza ...dep	4 a7	1p55	6 p38
Moghilew Podol	5 33	3 10	8 13
Schmerinka arr	9 44	6 42	1 10

SLOBODKA and NOVOSELIZY.

Slobodka ...dep	5a25	4p37
Rybnitza	6 47	6 6
Bialitzy	11 0	1040
Oknitza	4p42	2a20
Novoselizy 247 ar	8p30	6a13

Novoselizy dep	8 a45	11p23
Oknitza	1 p13	4 a28
Bialitzy	6 54	7 4
Rybnitz	10 52	1131
Slobodka 320	12a31	1 p21

KIEV and KOVEL via Sarni.

	a.m.	p.m.	p.m.	nght
Kiev ...dep	9 20	2 40	10 10	12 10
Korosteni	12 11	7 p42	1 a1	4a43
Sarni	2 p47	11p31	3a47	8 35
Kovel arr	...	3 a5	6 a52	11a48

	a.m.	p.m.	p.m.	
Kovel dep	5 15	...	7 31	10 38
Sarni	9 a45	4 15	10p50	1a46
Korosteni	1 32	6 59	2 51	4 37
Kiev ...arr	6 p0	9 p42	7 a15	7a20

BENDER and RENI.

Dist. E.M.		a.m.	p.m.
—	**Bender** ...dep	11 46	10 1
36	Kainary	1 29	12 21
91	Kulmskaia	4 33	5 4
135	Trajan's Wall	6 15	8 13
178	**Reni** ...arr	7 p50	11a10

	a.m.	p.m.
Reni ...dep	8 33	8 24
Trajan's Wall	10 24	11 40
Kulmskaia	12 16	2 57
Kainary	3 5	6 46
Bender ...arr	4 p43	8 a41

KIEV and BREST-LITEWSKI.

	1,2,3	1,2,3	1,2,3	1,2,3	1,2,3	1,2,3	1,2,3	
	a.m.	a.m.	p.m.	p.m.	p.m.	nght	nght	
Kiev ...dep	9 0	10 50	...	7 30	1010	12 25	12 50	...
Faustova	11 18	1 0	...	9 14	:	2 40	3 28	...
Kasyatin arr	2 11	3 9	...	11 23	:	5 29	6 49	...
Kasyatin dep	3 37	4 1	9 55	11 53	:	5 59	7 59	...
Berditschew	4 40	5 2	1028	12 48	:	6 52	8 36	...
Scheptowka	8 43	9 12	1 6	4 38	:	10 43	11 39	...
Sdolbunow ...arr	10 57	11 33	2 29	6 51	:	12 55	1 27	...
Sdolbunow dep	...	...	SC	8 a5	Via Sarni.	5 p54	RC	...
Radziwillow ar	...	...	...	10 32		8 12	...	...
Sdolbunow ...dep	11 15	11 45	2 36	7 3		1 12	1 35	...
Rovno 314	12 1	12 28	2 52	7 47		1 59	1 54	...
Kiwerzy	2 1	2 28	4 13	9 43		4 7	—	...
Kovel 316A ...arr	3 53	4 21	5 28	11 21	6 52	6 11	...	...
Maloryto	6 37	6 37	7 16	—	8 45	8 59	...	...
Brest 315 ...arr	7 a49	7 a49	8 a8	...	9 38	10p20	...	...
Warsaw ...arr	12p15	12p15	12p15	...	1p50	7 a37	...	...

Warsaw ...dep	1 a17	...	9 a52	3 p47	4 p5	4 p37	4 p37	
	1,2,3	1,2,3	1,2,3	1,2,3	1,2,3	1,2,3	1,2,3	
	a.m.		p.m.	p.m.	p.m.	p.m.	p.m.	
Brest ...dep	8 48	...	3 28	8 1	8 32	11 7	11 7	...
Maloryto	10 12	...	4 58	8 58	9 29	12 22	12 22	...
Kovel ...dep	12 42	...	7 33	10 38	11 11	2 45	3 26	...
Kiwerzy	2 54	p.m.	9 19	:	12 34	4 42	5 17	...
Rovno	5 18	5 6	11 2	:	1 44	6 43	7 25	...
Sdolbunow ...arr	5 41	5 26	11 21	:	1 59	7 4	7a46	...
Radziwillow dep	10a37	...	8 p15	:	...	...	...	...
Sdolbunow ...arr	12 53	RC	10 52	Via Sarni.	SC	...	...	...
Sdolbunow ...dep	5 53	5 p34	11 35	:	2 7	7 19	8 a4	...
Scheptowka	8 27	7 30	1 50	:	3 36	9 39	10 29	...
Berditschew	12 44	10 24	5 31	:	6 5	1 31	2 28	...
Kasyatin arr	1 35	11 1	6 18	:	6 35	2 17	3 15	...
Kasyatin dep	2 30	12 14	7 14	:	6 45	2 58	4 30	...
Faustova	5 32	3 52	9 19	:	8 21	5 6	7 40	...
Kiev 318 ...arr	7 p35	6 a20	10a48	7 a20	9 a35	6 p49	9 p30	...

Kiwerzy ...dep	5a40	10a14	4 p21	9p31	...	...
Luzk ...arr	6 16	10 40	4 47	9 57	...	...

Luzk ...dep	8a50	2 p5	7p25	11p45	...	...
Kiwerzy ...arr	9 16	2 31	8 0	12 11	...	...

KASYATIN and UMAN.

Kasyatin dep	2a10	7a55	...	4p20
Christinovka	8 17	1 10	4p27	9 38
Uman ...arr	8 45	...	5 5	1025

Uman ...dep	7a35	12p48	...	9.0
Christinovka	8 12	1 34	4p22	100
Kasyatin 320 arr	1 45	...	9 20	435

VAPNIARKA and ZWETKOVO.

Vapniarka 320 ...dep	8 a59	6 p20
Demkovka	9 50	6 59
Trostyanez-P. ...arr	11 43	8 50
Zlatkovtsi	11 48	8 24
Christinovka	1 p54	9 48
Zwetkovo 323 ...arr	7p31	2 a0

Zwetkovo ...dep	3 a45	10a10
Christinovka	8 19	4 p32
Zlatkovtsi	9 31	6 13
Trostyanez-P. ...dep	8 50	6 0
Demkovka	10 54	8 4
Vapniarka ...arr	11a35	8p58

BREST-LITEWSKI and GRAJEWO.

	a.m.	p.m.
Brest-Litewski d	9 13	1047
Cheremka	1048	12 9
Bjelsk	1152	1 2
Bialostock 313 arr	1p35	2a30
Bialostock 313 dep	4p40	3a18
Grajewo 174A arr	7 12	6 23
Prostken ...arr	7p57	7a10

Prostken dep	8a46	11p13
	a.m.	a.m.
Grajewo ...dep	10 0	12 22
Bialostock arr	1p35	3 a15
Bialostock dep	4p40	4 a0
Bjelsk	6 18	5 40
Cheremka	7 17	6 44
Brest-Litewski	8 33	8 a10

Dist. E.M.			a.m.	a.m.	a.m.	p.m.	p.m.	p.m.	p.m.	p.m.
	Kursk (318)...dep		2 10	3 15	5 23	12 38	3 2	4 40	5 50	10 55
48	Kleinmichelevo.		5 35	5 13	6 43	2 50	5 6	7 2)	7 10	12 50
99	Bjelgorod	5a45	8 39	7 10	8 11	5 5	7 10	9 31	8 37	2 42
127	Kasatschja	7 11	10 4	8 22	A	6 33	8 25	10 52	RC	3 53
152	**Kharkov** arr	8 29	11 10	9 20	9 35	7 39	9 25	12 1	10 1	4 50
...	(321) dep	1040	11 30	1015	9 43	8 9	10 25	12 35	10 11	5 a10
167	Merefa	1131	12 19	1055	...	8 58	11 8	1 27	SC	5 50
207	Likatchevo	1 41	2 16	1236	1119	10 51	1 1	3 30	11 48	7 31
244	**Lozovo 321** arr	3 25	3 52	2 1	1218	12 35	2 31	5 a6	12 47	8 a58
			p.m.	p.m.		a.m.	a.m.		nght	a.m.
...	**Lozovo**.........dep		4 17	2 31	...	1 20	3 1	...	12 59	9 12
281	Pawlograd.........		5 48	3 51	...	2 55	4 28	...	1 56	10 42
304	**Senelnikovo**......		7 23	5 17	...	4 47	5 a45	...	2 53	12 20
351	**Alexandrovsk** ...		9 42	7 16	...	7 14		...	4 16	2 p40
421	Melitopol		1 a12	1013	...	10 57	...	...	6 20	6 0
478	Novo Aleksievka		3 42	1225	...	1 27	...	...	7 48	8 36
504	Taganasch.........		5 0	1a25	...	2 44	...	...	...	9 52
516	**Djankoi**		5 33	1 53	...	3 17	...	...	8 52	10 25
573	Simferopol.........		9 17	5 30	...	6 50	...	...	10 55	2 45
585	Alma		9 53	6 7	...	7 26	...	...	...	3 25
593	Bachtschissaray		10 27	6 41	...	8 0	...	...	11 41	4 4
621	**Sebastopol** ...arr		11a55	8 a0	...	9 p26	...	...	12p45	5 a40

		p.m.	a.m.		p.m.	p.m.	p.m.		p.m.
Sebastopol ......dep		...	7 27	...	6 50	7 27	11 0	...	1145
Bachtschissaray ...		...	9 16	...	8 5	9 11	12 36	...	1 30
Alma.....................		...	9 50	...	RC	9 47	1 a10	...	2 7
Simferopol.............		...	1056	...	9 0	10 42	2 5	...	3 13
Djankoi		...	1p32	...	1036	1 20	4 32	...	5 56
Taganasch		...	2 6	...	SC	2 a0	5 1	...	6 30
Novo Aleksievka ...		...	3 32	...	1141	3 29	6 10	...	7 57
Melitopol...............		...	6 12	...	1a19	6 14	8 50	...	1050
Alexandrovsk..........		p.m.	9 50	...	3 21	9 29	11 50	...	2 30
Senelnikovo		1140	1251	...	4 59	12 10	2 15	...	5 30
Pawlograd.............		1233	1a55	...	5 37	1 6	3 9	...	6 31
Lozovo ....arr		2 21	3 49	...	6 42	2 p55	4 p45	...	8 25
	a.m.	a.m.	a.m.	a.m.	a.m.	p.m.	p.m.	p.m.	p.m.
Lozovo ......dep	1 29	2 46	4 23	6 34	6 54	3 20	5 17	5 5	9 31
Likatchevo......	3 20	4 25	6 12	7 40	8 0	5 7	6 52	6 11	11 6
Merefa............	5 13	5 55	8 3	B	A	6 44	8 13	...	1228
Kharkov ...arr	6 0	6 35	8 50	9 13	9 33	7 28	8 53	7 44	1 7
,, ...dep	6 20	7 18	9 58	9 23	9 43	9 45	9 28	7 54	1a27
Kasatschja	7 32	8 23	1111	...	...	11 12	10 32	...	2 30
Bjelgorod	8 57	9 45	1243	10 55	1115	12 55	11 50	9 26	3 42
Kleinmichelevo	1125	1257	3 18	12 24	1244	3 a50	2 3	1054	5 52
Kursk (318) arr	1p20	2p43	5p15	1 p40	2 p0	5 a55	3 a40	1210	7a28

Extra.

Kursk ......dep	5 a40	...	...	...
Kharkov...dep	10 a0	6p15	11p40	...
Lozovo ......arr	12p37	1042	4 a5	...

Lozovo ......dep	7 a5	1p25	1 a0	...
Kharkov ...arr	11 17	6 0	5 30	...

A—Black Sea Express—Saturday only.
B—Black Sea Express—Tuesday only.

Djankoi ......dep	2 a40	4 p10
Vladislavovka...	5 27	7 0
Feodosia ......arr	6 10	7 55

Feodosia.........dep	8a45	12a12	...
Vladislavovka ...	9 47	1 5	...
Djankoi ....arr	1230	3 45	...

Feodosia ....dep	4 a40	6p36
Vladislavovka	6 0	7 45
Kertch ....arr	9 0	1047

Kertch.............dep	6 a0	9p25
Vladislavovka	9 2	1227
Feodosia ....arr	10 7	1a27

KHARKOV and NIKOLAIEV.

Dist. E.M.		a.m.	a.m.	p.m.	p.m.	p.m.
	Kharkov (321) dep	6 51	1011	1235	10 58	1142
15	Lubotin..................	7 53	1054	1 37	11 41	1246
42	Vodyanaya	9 7	1148	2 54	12 33	2 3
88	Poltava	11 18	1 p0	5 10	1 53	4 25
126	Kobeljaki	1 6		7 1	...	6 15
160	Krementschug (321)	2 50	...	9 0	4 17	8 10
201	Koristowka	4 37	...	1047	5 38	9 59
224	Snamenka (320) arr	5 42	...	1155	6 29	11 8
...	,, ...dep	6 p18	...	1235	6 59	
274	Dolinskaja	9 2	...	3 7	9 5	...
306	Novyi (Bug)...........	10 20	...	4 25	10 4	...
371	**Nikolaiev** ......arr	12a48	...	7 a1	12 a5	...

		a.m.		p.m.	p.m.
Nikolaiev dep	...	5 2	...	6 0	9 40
Novyi (Bug).......	...	7 58	...	8 16	1241
Dolinskaja	...	9 51	...	9 42	2 46
Snamenka...arr	...	12 0	p.m.	11 38	4 56
,, ...dep	...	12 50	6 55	12 16	5a38
Koristowka.......	...	1 46	8 0	1 8	6 36
Krementschug	...	3 44	10 0	2 35	8 28
Kobeljaki.........	p.m.	5 16	1138	...	10 6
Poltava...........	4 20	7 22	1a59	5 10	1232
Vodyanaya	6 0	9 33	4 12	6 48	2 55
Lubotin..........	6 47	10 47	5 27	7 32	4 11
Kharkov arr	7 10	11p31	6a10	7 55	4p55

VOROSHBA and KUTOR MICHAELOVSK.

	a.m.
Voroshba..............dep	10 0
Glukovi	3 2
Kutor Michaelovsk arr	5 15

	a.m.
Kutor Michaelovsk dep	1130
Glukovi	1 57
Voroshba (318) ......arr	6 40

NIKOLAIEV and KHERSON.

E. M.				
	Nikolaiev.........dep	7 a26	1 p40	...
38½	Kherson...........arr	9 2	3 16	...
...	Kherson ....dep	7 a29	4 p11	...
...	Nikolaiev.........arr	8 58	5 40	...

KIEV and LOZOVO.

Kiev ....dep	7 a45	8 p0	...	11p15
Romodan	12p55	2 a17	...	6 a35
Poltava	4 p5	6 a15	6 a35	10a50
Constantinograd...	10 4		9 26	
Lozovo (322) arr	12a47	...	12p17	...

Lozovo.........dep	5 a25	...	...	5 p10
Constantinograd...	8 17	...	...	8 16
Poltava	10 38	1 p12	6 p30	11p20
Romodan		4 p31	11 30	4 a3
Kiev............arr	...	9 p40	6 a30	11a10

KHARKOV and VOROSHBA.

E.M.				
	Kharkov 321 ...dep	12 p5	9 p5	12a11
15	Lubotin	1 7	9 50	1 12
71½	Kirikovka	4 4	11 57	4 4
85	Smorodino	4 43	12 25	4 41
98	Baromlya	5 38	1 2	5 31
115	Basye	6 27	1 35	6 20
121	Sumy	6 53	1 55	6 45
155	**Voroshba** 318...arr	8 p28	3 a5	8 a19

Voroshba ......dep	3 a15	9 a28	9 p38
Sumy	4 32	11 12	11 22
Basye	4 46	11 34	11 40
Baromlya	5 35	12 38	12 44
Smorodino	6 1	1 14	1 18
Kirikovka	6 28	1 57	1 59
Lubotin	8 42	5 1	5 2
Kharkov 322 ...arr	9 a11	5 p45	5 a46

	a.m.	a.m.
Basye ......dep	1155	1 50
Bjelgorod arr	4p40	8 0

	a.m.	p.m.
Bjelgorod dep	1145	9 35
Basye ......arr	5p10	4 a5

KREMENTSCHUG and ROMNEY.

Krementschug	8a35	8 p2
Romodan	11 53	11 38
Romney (317)	2p40	2 a24

Romney ...dep	3 a35	2 p55
Romodan.........	6 43	5 46
Krement. 321...	9 47	8 45

MEREFA and LUBOTIN.

EM				
	Merefa......dep	6 a0	Lubotin dep	5 p45
11	Lubotin 321 arr	7 23	Merefa arr	6 37

MARIUPOL and SVIEREVO.

Dist E M		a.m.		p.m.	n'gt	p.m.	
	Mariupol ...dep	1057	...	6 49	...	1135	...
46½	Volnovakha.........	1 22	...	9 6	1230	2 22	...
66	Elenovka	2 19	p.m.	9 52	1 24	3 23	a.m.
91½	Yassinovataya 321	3 45	4 29	1110		5 0	6 48
122	Chatsepetovka ...		6 38		...		9 10
130	Debaltsevo 321... arr		7 2	...	...	...	9 32
	dep		8 40	...	...	...	1040
162	Shterovka..............		1017	...	...	...	1224
167	Kolpakovo		1033	...	...	...	1240
226	**Svierevo** 322......arr		1a25	...	...	...	3p37

			a.m.		p.m.	
Svierevo dep	...	...	5 22	...	1 50	...
Kolpakovo	...	...	8 18	...	5 12	...
Shterovka........	...	...	8 34	...	5 33	...
Debaltsevo arr	...	...	10 0	...	7 4	...
Debaltsevo dep	...	...	1044	...	8 58	...
Chatsepetovka	...	a.m.	1111	p.m.	9 25	a.m.
Yassinovataya	a.m.	6 36	1 10	1 45	1126	1220
Elenovka	3 48	7 48		3 8		1 52
Volnovakha......	4 46	8 43	...	4 9	...	3 7
Mariupol arr	...	1025	...	6 5	...	5 10

MILLEROVO and KUPYANSK.

Millerovo (322) ......dep	a.m.	...	10a25	p.m.
Lugansk	6 47	...	3 15	9 15
Rodakovo (316A)	7 40	...	4 17	10 8
Debaltsevo.....................	10 50	p.m.	8 3	
Popasnaja	1 24	5 25	10 57	...
Lisitchansk		6 55	12 26	...
Kupyansk (322) ......arr	...	11p14	4 a23	...

Kupyansk.........dep	3 a50	...	1 a33	...
Lisitschansk	8 18	p.m.	5 a35	...
Popasnaja	10 43	3 0	7 40	a.m.
Debaltsevo...............		7 30	10 21	11 20
Rodakovo	7 a50	9 29		1 43
Lugansk...................	8 30	9 58	...	2p57
Millerovo ....arr	...	...	...	6p20

BJELGOROD and KUPYANSK.

Bjelgorod ...dep	11a17	9 p38
Voltchansk	12 40	11 4
Kupyansk......arr	4 p5	2 a45

Kupyansk ...dep	12p15	12 a6	...
Voltchansk	4 28	4 1	...
Bjelgorod......arr	5 50	5 a20	...

NIKITOVKA and DEBALTSEVO.

(322)	a.m.	p.m.		a.m.	p.m.
Nikitovka dep	7 20	5 50	Debaltsevo dp	1044	9 20
Debaltsevo ar	8 25	7 2	Nikitovka arr	1146	1013

CONSTANTINOVKA and YASSINOVATAYA.

	a.m.	a.m.	p.m.		
Constantinovka......dep	3 25	1035	9 10	...	...
Yassinovataya........arr	5 24	1234	1115	...	...

	a.m.	p.m.	p.m.		
Yassinovataya.......dep	5 38	5 40	1136	...	...
Constantinovka ......arr	7 24	7 19	1 15	...	...

LOZOVO and NIKITOVKA.

§—Black Sea Express—Sats. only. †—Black Sea Express—Tues. only.

	a.m.	a.m.	a.m.	p.m.	p.m.	p.m.	p.m.
Lozovo 321...dep	4 25	5 39	9 13	12§27	1247	4 7	1057
Slaviansk	7 28	8 42	1145	2 17	2 38	7 19	1 52
Kramatorskaya	8 2	9 16	12 8	2 31	2 52	7 55	2 16
Constantinovka	9 14	1028	1 1	3 8	3 31	9 5	3 15
Nikitovka ...arr	1030	1145	2 10	3 54	4 17	1022	4 36

	a.m.	a.m.	p.m.	p.m.	p.m.	p.m.	a.m.	
Nikitovka dep	3† 3	6 55	1 32	4 32	6 32	6 52	1248	...
Constantinovka	3 37	7 52	2 6	5 13	7 30	7 51	1 38	...
Kramatorskaya	4 8	8 57	2 39	6 1	8 31	9 0	2 31	...
Slaviansk	4 28	9 36	2 59	6 30	9 5	9 34	3 0	...
Lozovo ...arr	6 24	1255	4 55	9 16	12 14	1248	6 7	...

Kramatorskaya dep	9 a35	9 p10	...	...	...	...
Bachmut	11 50	11 26	...	...	...	...
Popasnaja ...arr	1 47	1 22	...	...	...	...

Popasnaja ...dep	4 a40	3 p23	...	...	...	...
Bachmut	6 25	5 9	...	...	...	...
Kramatorskaya arr	8 30	7 15	...	...	...	...

KOSLOV, VORONESCH, and ROSTOV.

Dist E.M.		a.m.		a.m.	p.m.	p.m.	nght	
	Koslov ...dep	7 55	...	8 15	2 10	11 25	1‡ 4	...
40	Griazi (318)...arr	9 25	...	10 10	4 8	1 9	2 13	...
...	,, ...dep	9 39	...	10 45	4 23	1 29	2 25	
86	Grafskaja	1131	...	1 10	6 45	4 0	3 43	
111	Voronesch 323 arr	1240	...	2 25	8 2	5 13	4 29	
...	,, ...dep	1p 0	...	3 33	8 44	5 a45	4 44	
172	Liski	3 37	...	7 10	11 58	9 0	6 37	
213	Saguni	5 34	...	9 40	—	11 13	8 6	
243	Evstratovka	6 46	...	11 17	...	12 48	9 4	
315	Tschertkowa	1015	...	3 40	...	5 10	11 48	
356	Millerovo	12 1	...	6 2	...	7 32	1 p16	
386	Glubokaja	1a20	...	7 27	...	9 20	2 31	
400	Kamenskaia	1 59	...	8 28	...	10 10	3 6	
415	Lichaja (322)	2a59	3 a30	9 31	...	11 30	3 49	
430	Svierevo (321)	3 45	4 27	10 36	...	12 28	4 27	
442	Sulin	4 15	5 4	11 15	...	1 a11	4 50	
459	Schaktnaja	5 12	6 8	12p20	...	2 17	5 36	...
485	Novotscherkask	6 23	7 37	1 55	...	3 47	6 24	...
517	**Rostov** (323)arr	8a 0	9a40	3 p50	...	5 a40	7 p35	...

‡—Sleeping and Restaurant Cars in the trains.

	a.m.		a.m.	p.m.	p.m.	p.m.
Rostov ...dep	8 ‡15	...	11 0	8 10	9 45	11 20
Novotscherkask	9 28	...	1 6	1017	1132	1 12
Schaktnaja	10 19	...	2 39	1150	1247	2 a41
Sulin	11 5	...	3 42	1257	1a47	3 44
Svierevo	11 38	...	4 47	1 51	2 32	4 36
Lichaja	12 7	...	5 36	2a33	3 9	5 18
Kamenskaia	12 40	...	6 29	—	3 50	6 0
Glubokaja	1 21	...	7 28	...	4 36	6 46
Millerovo	2 26	...	9 20	...	6 1	8 32
Tschertkowa	4 p2	...	1148	...	7 58	11 0
Evstratovka	6 38	...	3 58	...	1114	2p45
Saguni	7 35	a.m.	5 26	...	1231	4 7
Liski	9 3	3 5	8 5	...	2p39	6 30
Voronesch...arr	10 56	6 13	11 3	...	5 8	9 15
,, ...dep	11 11	6 49	12 7	...	5 28	9 41
Grafskaja	12 4	8 16	1 40	...	6 35	11 0
Griazi ...arr	1 19	1020	3 53	...	8 12	12 50
,, ...dep	1 31	1040	4 28	...	8 24	1 55
Koslov 322 arr	2 a40	1240	6p35	...	9p50	3 a40

OREL and GRIAZI.

Dist. E.M.		p.m.	p.m.
	Orel ...dep	3 30	11 40
39	**Salegoschtsch**	5 33	1 a57
...	Marmishi...dep	6 a25	4 p25
...	Livni	1 p0	9 p30
57	**Werschowje**	6 p35	3 a10
122	**Yeletz (319)**	9 p44	6 a29
170	**Lipetzk**	11 59	8 49
192	**Griazi (322)**...arr	12a57	9 a50

	a.m.			a.m.
Griazi ...dep	10 50	...	...	3 0
Lipetzk	12 1	...	...	4 16
Yeletz	2 27	a.m.	a.m.	6 a45
Werschowje	5 31	3 12	3 30	9 a57
Livni	12a25	...	7 0	...
Marmishi ...arr	4 a25	...	10a30	...
Salegoschtsch	6 52	4 43	—	11 9
Orel (318) ...arr	9 p0	8 a10	...	1 p15

Yeletz ...dep	2 a20	3 p0
Kastornaja	8 34	9 0
Valuiki ...arr	6 p30	6 a5
Valuiki ...dep	2 a4J	7 p20
Kastornaja	1 p42	5 a25
Yeletz ...arr	7 p5	10a 5

KHARKOV and BALASCHOV.

E.M.				
	Kharkov (Osnov.) dp	11a32	7 p55	9 p 5
84	**Kupyansk**	4 p22	12 7	1 18
131	**Valuiki**	7 5	2 a33	—
229	**Liski**	12a46	8 a55	...
290	Talovaya	4 5	12 0	...
418	**Balaschov** ...arr	11a35	6p55	...

Balaschov dep	8 a10	...	4 p10	...
Talovaya	2 p55	...	10 55	...
Liski	7 p19	...	2 a40	...
Valuiki	12a53	...	8 a29	...
Kupyansk	3 52	4 a50	11 20	...
Kharkov...arr	8a35	9 30	4p15	...

Talovaya...dep	4 a50	3p15	...
Kalatch ...arr	9 15	7 40	...
Kalatch ...dep	7 a15	5p40	...
Talovaya...arr	11 40	10 5	...

RIASAN and KOSLOV.

E.M.						
	Riasan ...dep	2a27	5 a45	4 p30	8 p58	11p55
30	Staroschil	3 43	7 28	5 50	9 52	1 40
72	Riaschk (319) ...arr	5 7	9 30	7 17	10 59	3 37
...	,, ...dep	5 17	10 20	7 27	11 7	4 12
105	Bogoyavlensk	6 33	12 17	8 48	12 4	5 55
132	Koslov (322)...arr	7 25	1 35	9 40	12 49	7 0

Koslov ...dep	3 a0	5 a47	2 p0	7p40	1015
Bogoyavlensk	3 48	6 50	3 55	9 9	1113
Riaschk ...arr	4 44	7 56	5 40	1035	1218
,, ...dep	4 52	8 15	7 10	1057	1228
Staroschil	6 4	9 52	9 48	1 8	2 1
Riasan (318) ...arr	6 56	11 0	12 5	3 33	3 5

MOSCOW and KOSLOV.

Moscow ...dep	9a10	5 p0	6 p5	7p10
Kashira	1250	9 13	8 55	1027
Michailov	4 55	1213	1112	1 10
Kremlevo	7 3	1 43	1219	2 35
Paveletz	7 22	2 6	1238	3 2
Troekurovo	—	3 51	1 49	4 40
Ranenburg	...	4 28	2 23	—
Bogoyavlensk...	...	5 8	2 58	...
Koslov...arr	...	6a 6	3a49	...

			p.m.	nght
Koslov ...dep	2a35	...	9 35	12 18
Bogoyavlensk	4 40	...	10 39	1 10
Ranenburg	5 38	p.m.	11 17	1 45
Troekurovo	6 38	10 5	11 55	2 22
Paveletz	10 6	1152	2 5	3 39
Kremlevo	1026	12 3	2 19	3 49
Michailov	1220	1 45	3 50	4 54
Kashira	5 7	4 35	7 25	7 8
Moscow ...arr	8p15	7a50	10a45	9 a45

BOGOYAVLENSK and SMOLENSK.

Bogoyavlensk...dep	1a40	8 a0	...
Ranenburg	3 5	8 42	...
Astapovo	5a30	10 16	10p5
Volovo (319)	—	2 p21	3a40
Gorbatschevo	...	4 p33	7 28
Suchinitsch (318)	7a40	10p10	—
Smolensk ...arr	6p10	7 a0	...

			p.m.
Smolensk ...dep	...	10a50	1010
Suchinitsch	...	9 p30	6a35
Gorbatschevo	8p20	—	1144
Volovo	1140	...	1p59
Astapovo	4 a0	9 p2	6 6
Ranenburg	...	10 16	7 20
Bogoyavlensk ...arr	...	11p 2	7p55

E.M.			
	Troekurovo ...dep	4 a45	...
18	**Astapovo**	6 6	...
88	**Yeletz** ...arr	9 45	...

Yeletz ...dep	5 p0	...
Astapovo	9 12	...
Troekurovo ...arr	10 0	...

RIASAN and KAZAN.

Dist E.M			
	Riasan dep	5 a10	7p 4
114	Sasowo	11 26	11 59
131	Kustarevka	12 48	12 37
206	Arapowo	4 44	3 55
260	Rusaevka	7 p25	6 a 3
294	Timiryasevo	1 a40	6 p30
374	Alatyr	4 a48	10p17
497	Svijaschsk	9 a44	4 a17
526	**Kazan** arr	12p 8	7 a31

Kazan ...dep	3 p55	7 p25
Svijaschsk	6 p41	10 54
Alatyr	11p38	4 a55
Timiryasevo	2a41	£a26
Rusaevka	7 a10	11p55
Arapowo	9 54	2 a4
Kustarevka	1 p41	5 10
Sasowo	2 50	5 56
Riasan ...arr	9p40	10a32

Riasan...dep	6 a15	...
Vladimir...arr	9 p25	...
Vladimir...dep	3 a5	...
Riasan ...arr	6 37	...

PENSA and TIMIRYASEVO.

	p.m.	a.m.
Pensa ...dep	2 20	12 55
Rusaevka	8 30	7 0
Timiryasevo arr	10 1	8 34

	a.m.	p.m.
Timiryasevo dep	4 44	6 5
Rusaevka	7 20	8 40
Pensa ...arr	12 10	1 a30

MOSCOW and TIMIRYASEVO.

E.M.					
	Moscow ...dep	11a 5	9 p30	...	...
13	Lübertzy	11 30	10 11	...	...
54	Kurovskaya	12p59	12 30	...	...
179	Murom	5 31	7 38	...	...
...	: Nijni Novgorod..dep	...	8 a10	7 p20	...
259	Arzamas	8 50	12 33	11p36	...
367	Timiryasevo 322 ...arr	1 a22	5 p47	4a32	...

Timiryasevo ...dep	2 a58	8 a54	...	10p13
Arzamas	7 48	2 p31	3 p35	3a21
: Nijni Novgorod 315 arr	...	6 p26	...	7 a16
Murom	10 56	...	8 p 0	...
Kurovskaya	3 p17	...	2 a18	...
Lübertzy	4 43	...	4 43	...
Moscow ...arr	5 p10	...	5a30	...

E.M			
	Kovrov...dep	3 a45	4 p24
68	Murom ...arr	6 47	7 47
...	Murom...dep	9 a 8	8 p25
...	Kovrov 315 arr	12 34	11 26

LICHAJA and ZARIZYN.

Lichaja ...dep	3 a20	6 p10
Krivomusginskaya	1 p30	5 a10
Zarizyn ...arr	4 p15	7 a42
Zarizyn ...dep	1p25	6 p0
Krivomusginskaya	4p13	8 p5,
Lichaja (322) ...arr	2a50	8 a25

RUSAEVKA and SYSRAN.

E.M.			
	Rusaevka dep	6a45	8p15
70	Insa ...arr	9 31	1141
...	Insa ...dep	10a 0	3a20
172	Simbirskarr	3p14	8a48
...	Insa ...dep	9 a51	12 3
190	**Syzran** ...arr	2 p41	6a20

Sysran ...dep	3p42	8 p30
Insa ...arr	8p25	2 a45
Simbirsk dep	3p 0	...
Insa ...arr	8p23	...
Insa ...dep	8p45	3 a5
Rusaevka arr	11p30	6 a25

ROSTOV and VLADIKAVKAS.

B—Black Sea Express, Saturday only.

	p.m.	a.m	p.m.	p.m.	p.m.	p.m.	p.m.	p.m.
Rostov dep	1040	8 40	4 30	8 †0	8 40	9 20	10 0	1110
Kayala	1147	9 46	5 38	8 50	9 40	B	1054	1220
Krylowskay	2 0	1153	7 48	1035	1135	12 2	1240	2 35
Tichorez- arr	3a30	1p20	9p17	1140	1250	1 a7	1a50	4a20
kaia 323 dep	—	1 40	9 32	1145	1255	—	1 55	4 45
Kavkaskaya ...		3 30	1122	1a16	2a30	...	3 30	6 52
Armawiri.........		5 20	1a10	2a44	4a15	...	5 5	8 54
Nevinnomyska.		7 25	3 15	4 30	6 6	...	6 56	11 3
Mineralnya-V.		9 53	5 44	6a32	8 17	...	9 2	1p40
Neslobnaja		1110	7 5	—	9 24	...	1022	3 16
Prochladnaya ...		1a10	9 14	...	1112	...	1210	5 30
Beslani ......arr		3 40	1150	...	1 28	...	2p25	8 5
Vladikavkas arr		5 a0	1p10	...	2p40	...	3p55	9p38

†—Until 20th September.

		a.m.	p.m.		p.m.	p.m.	a.m.	
Vladikavkas dep		8 40	2 0	...	5 15	7 30	1 20	...
Beslani ......dep		9 43	2 53	...	6 0	8 40	2 20	...
Prochladnaya...		12 6	4 52	...	8 6	8 5	4 38	...
Neslobnaja		2p14	6 41	p.m.	9 50	1a11	6 35	...
Mineralnya Vod		3 31	8 4	9†20	11 0	2 35	7 48	...
Nevinnomyskay		6 26	1025	1130	1a21	5 31	1032	...
Armawiri.........		8 30	1155	1258	2 55	7 35	1226	...
Kavkaskaya ...		1036	1a20	2 22	4 20	9 25	2p10	...
Tichorezkaia arr		1214	2 50	3 48	5 48	11 0	3 44	p.m.
,, dep	1a45	1245	2 55	3a55	5a55	1120	4 4	5 56
Krylowskay	3 23	2 38	4 13	5 13	7 16	1256	5 32	7 8
Kayala	5 28	4 51	6 0	7 0	9 5	2 58	7 29	C
Rostov 322	6a30	6 a0	6a55	7a55	10a0	4 p0	8p30	7p30

C—Black Sea Express, Monday only.

E.M					
	Kavkazkaya ......dep	7 a0	3 p50	11p40	...
96	**Stavropol** ....arr	12 30	8 55	6 10	...

Stavropol ....dep	8 a45	5 p3	11p55	...	...
Kavkazkaya ......arr	1 30	10 5	6 a30	...	...

Mineralnya V. to Kislowodsk } Trains in connection with
Kislowodsk to Mineralnya V. } main line Service.

E.M						
	Rostov ......dep	9 p20	10p40	11p10	8 a40	...
		a.m.	a.m.	a.m.	p.m.	p.m.
—	**Tichorezkaia** dep	1 21	3 50	4 55	2 15	5 55
84	Ekaterinodar	4 13	7 10	9 5	6 25	11 50
138	Krumskaya.........	A	...	11 32	8 42	3 28
161	**Novorossiisk**...arr	7 25	10 38	1 20	10 32	6 0

	a.m.	a.m.	p.m.	p.m.	p.m.
Novorossiisk dep	6 30	11 35	4 0	6 45	1150
Krumskaya	8 13	A	5 53	8 16	2 35
Ekaterinodar ...	10 37	2 56	8 18	10 20	6 17
Tichorezkaia arr	2 10	5 45	12 10	1 a20	11 5
Rostov ......arr	8 p30	9 p30	6 a0	6 a30	4 p0

Ekaterinodar dep	11a30	6 p30	11p55
Kavkazkaya arr	3 7	11 0	5 0

Kavkazkaya ...dep	1 a15	7 a10	2p30
Ekaterinodar...arr	6 10	12 0	6 5

A—Black Sea Express—Weekly.

VLADIKAVKAS and BAKU.

E.M		a.m.	a.m.	p.m.	p.m.	
—	**Vladikavkas** dep	2 50	11 15	2 0	7 30	...
14	**Beslani** ...dep	3 55	12 7	2 40	8 35	...
46	**Sliptzovsk** ...	5 11	1 24	3 48	9 55	...
82	Grossnoje......	6 46	3 20	5 12	1134	...
129	**Kasavi Jurti**...	8 43	5 33	6 54	1a46	...
180	**Petrovsk**	11 0	9 30	8 55	4 10	...
261	Derbent.........	2p35	1 a25	12 1	7 52	...
404	Balatschari ...	8 55	7 51	5 30	2 30	...
414	**Baku** ......arr	9p30	8 a30	6 a5	3p47	...

	a.m.	p.m.	p.m.	p.m.	
Baku ....dep	7 30	12 45	10 50	11 55	...
Balatschari	8 7	2 5	11 27	12 40	...
Derbent..............	2 p23	8 55	4 a47	7 a55	...
Petrovsk	5 56	12 35	7 55	12 0	...
Kasavi Jurti	8 19	3 a15	10 0	2 p42	...
Grossnoje...........	10 30	5 42	11 54	5 0	...
Sliptzovsk	12 27	7 42	1 23	6 56	...
Beslani ....arr	2 a5	9 a15	2 p38	8 p35	...
Vladikavkas...arr	3 a32	10a51	3 p55	9 p38	...

VLADIKAVKAS and TIFLIS.—Motor Car Service—in 10 hours.

Vladikavkas ....dep	8 a0
Tiflis ....arr	6 p0

Tiflis.......................dep	7 a0
Vladikavkas ....arr	5 p0

Daily Service until October 15th.

BATOUM and BAKU.—[Tiflis Time.]

‡—Until 14th Sept.

E.M.		a.m.	a.m.		p.m.	nght
—	**Batoum**....dep	6 12	7 2	...	6 30	12‡20
66	**Samtredi**...arr	8 51	1025	...	9 55	3 42
...	,, ...dep	9 1	1040	...	10 10	3 54
85	**Rion** ....arr	9 47	1140	p.m.	11 12	4 53
...	**Kutais**...dep	9 16	11a5	4 7	10 37	4 a20
...	**Rion** ......arr	9 36	1125	4 27	10 57	4 40
...	**Rion** ....dep	9 54	1155	4 39	11 31	5 3
103	Kwirilla.........	10 46	1251	5 49	12 34	6 11
106	Sharopani	10 59	1 p9	5 57	12 52	6 29
143	Michailovo......	2 p3	4 30	—	4 a5	9 42
170	Gori	3 7	5 51	...	5 18	11 3
217	**Tiflis** ....arr	4 p56	8p18	p.m	7 a42	1 p31
...	,, ...dep	5 31	9 18	2 37	9 18	—
269	Akstafa	8 0	1220	5 23	11 44	...
334	Elisavetopol ...	10 37	3a35	8 10	2 p14	...
404	Udsharry........	1 a13	6 52	11 4	4 43	...
480	Adshi-Kabul...	3 52	10 8	2 6	7 18	...
558	**Baku** ....arr	6 a55	2p33	5 a40	10p15	...

	a.m.		p.m.	p.m.		p.m.
Baku ....dep	6 40	...	1 55	4 28	...	10 0
Adshi-Kabul ...	9 50	...	6 35	8 26	...	1 59
Udsharry	12 28	...	9 55	1144	...	5 a8
Elisavetopol.....	3 p41	...	2 a1	3a38	...	8 50
Akstafa	6 9	...	5 4	6 31	...	1150
Tiflis............arr	8 p37	...	8 a3	9a30	a.m.	2p55
,, ...dep	9 32	...	8 53	—	10‡30	3 42
Gori	12a13	...	1135	...	1 14	6 25
Michailovo	1 45	a.m.	1p14	...	2 50	8 3
Sharopani........	4 24	7 10	4 1	...	5 39	1052
Kwirilla	4 41	7 25	4 19	...	6 1	1110
Rion ....arr	5 28	8 13	5 7	...	6 49	1156
Rion ....dep	5 50	8 21	5 45	...	7 16	1216
Kutais .....arr	6 10	8 41	6 5	p.m.	7 36	1236
Rion ....dep	5 38	—	—	4 0	7 4	12 8
Samtredi ....arr	6 31	...	...	4 54	7 57	1 2
,, ...dep	6 41	...	...	—	8 10	1 19
Batoum ....arr	10 a1	...	...	...	11p30	4a42

Michailovo dep	4‡a20	11‡a28	3 p0	4‡p54	7 p0
Borshomi arr	5 24	12 33	4 4	5 59	8 4

Borshomi dep	2‡a38	11a22	1‡p18	4‡p48	12 a6	...
Michailovo arr	3 40	12 26	2 21	5 52	1 10	...

Poti............dep	5a32	8 a4	3p54	7p44	...
Samtredi ...arr	7 37	10 10	6 2	9 47	...

Samtredi......dep	6a51	10a55	5 p10	8 p13	...
Poti ....arr	8 57	1 1	7 18	10 17	...

Sharopani	4a35	1111	6p12
Sachkeri	7 39	2 11	9 6

Sachkeri	4a26	10 a6	7p36
Shorap.	7 0	12 44	1014

Borshomi	6*a34	1†p50
Bakuriani	9 52	5 6

Bakuriani	10*a27	6†p25
Borshomi	1 2	9 3

*—Until 13th Sept. daily; from 14th Sept. on Sun. and Wed. only. †—Until 31st August.

Baku ....dep	4a27	6a36	10a0	1p36	5p36	11p20
Surachany...arr	5 22	7 31	1050	2 29	6 27	12 10

Surachany...dep	5 a34	8a10	11a25	3 p5	6p55	12a25
Baku (323)...arr	6 23	9 0	12 16	4 6	7 50	1 16

TIFLIS, ERIVAN, DZULIFA, and KARS.

E.M					
	Tiflis.....................dep	...	11a53	7 p10	11p48
69	Sanain	...	5 5	12 18	5 8
137	Alexandropol ....arr	...	10p50	5 a59	10a52
225	Ulukanlu	1a27	4 a42	11a40	—
234	**Erivan** ....arr	2 10	6 a3	12p35	...
343	**Dzulifa** ....arr	...	10a44	...	...

Dzulifa.........dep	...	...	...	7p36
Erivan.......dep	...	4 a26	3 p45	12a30
Ulukanlu	...	4 52	4 23	1 a36
Alexandropol	8 p49	—	12 a9	8a53
Sanain...................	1 a54	...	5 a18	1p55
Tiflis ....arr	6 a30	...	9 a52	6p34

E.M				
	Alexandropol......dep	11 a7	12a30	...
48	Kars ....arr	2 20	4 40	...

Kars ....dep	5 a28	5 p43
Alexandropol......arr	8 18	8 34

BOBRINSKAJA and TSCHERKASY.

Bobrinskaja ...dep	4 a8	9 a30	4p55	10 p0
Tscherkasy ......arr	5 50	11 12	6 16	11 17

Tscherkasy ....dep	7 a10	12 0	7 p10	12a30
Bobrinskaja 323 ......arr	8 49	1 19	8 44	1 44

KIEV and SNAMENKA.

Kiev ....dep	...	11a20	7 p50	11p30
Faustova..................	9 a0	1 39	9 38	1 33
Belaja-Zerkow..........	9 41	2 42	10 21	2 42
Olshanitza	10 43	4 22	11 26	4 14
Korsun	12 8	6 32	1 3	6 26
Zwetkovo (**330**) ...	1 8	8 6	2 21	8 7
Bobrinskaja (**323**)	1 53	9 5	3 7	9 9
Funduklejewka	2 52	10 22	4 6	10 27
Snamenka 321 arr	3 p55	11p47	5 a7	11a54

Snamenka ...dep	6 a45	12p48	7 p10	12a30
Funduklejewka......	8 3	1 48	8 29	1 33
Bobrinskaja	9 25	2 43	9 53	2 37
Zwetkovo	10 34	3 29	11 13	3 43
Korsun	11 59	4 24	12 55	4 46
Olshanitza	2 1	5 51	3 8	6 27
Belaja-Zerkow	3 34	6 49	4 51	7 38
Faustova 320 ......arr	4 29	7 p35	5 47	8 22
Kiev ....arr	6 p30	...	7 a55	10 a0

TICHOREZKAIA and ZARIZYN.

	a.m.	p.m.	nght
Tichorezkaia ....dep	4 50	2 40	12 30
Velikoknyasheskaya	9 40	7 25	5 45
Simovinki	12 10	10 0	—
Kotelnikowo	2 45	12 24	...
Shutowo	4 24	2 a2	...
Sarepta	7 35	5 0	...
Zarizyn ....arr	8 p30	5 a50	...

	a.m.	p.m.	
Zarizyn ....dep	8 25	10 5	...
Sarepta....................	9 35	11 7	...
Shutowo	12 39	2 1	...
Kotelnikowo	2 28	3 47	...
Simovinki...............	4 48	6 0	p.m.
Velikoknyasheskaya..	7 20	8 30	3 5
Tichorezkaia ......arr	12a15	1 p13	8 58

VORONESCH and KURSK.

Voronesch ......dep	7 a15	3 p45	1 a0
Kastornaja	10 18	6 18	4 30
Marmishi	11 45	7 38	6 2
Schigri	1 6	8 54	7 26
Okochevka	1 33	9 17	7 58
Kursk 318........arr	2 p40	10p17	9a10

Kursk ....dep	7 a50	3 p25	2 a40
Okochevka	9 7	4 45	3 57
Schigri	9 35	5 14	4 26
Marmishi................	10 51	6 41	5 52
Kastornaja..............	12 10	8 2	7 16
Voronesch 323 arr	2 p35	10p50	10a10

A—Black Sea Express, Monday only

ROSTOV and NIKITOVKA.

RC—Restaurant Car.

	a.m.	a.m.	a.m.	a.m.	p.m.	p.m	p.m.	p.m.
Rostov..........dep	7 5	7 40	1025	10 35	4 20	8 55	9 52	1033
Sinyavskaya	...	RC	RC	11 45	5 34	...	A	1145
Taganrog ....arr	8 32	9 4	12 1	12 33	5 29	1018	1114	1238
,, ...dep	8 42	9 19	1216	12 46	6 49	1025	1122	1258
Iloviskaya	1123	1153	2 59	3 59	1038	1254	1 42	4 45
Harzysskaya arr	1136	12 9	3 16	4 16	1057	1 8	1 57	5 5
SENELNIKOVO arr	5 p9	...	...	12a10	7a41	6a10	...	1p57
Harzysskaya dep	—	1221	3 24	4 54	1111	—	2 5	5 17
Nikitovka ......arr	...	1p20	4p26	6 p22	1235	...	a58	6a40

		a.m.	p.m	p.m.	p.m.	p.m.		p.m.
Nikitovka..........dep	...	4 55	12 5	2 20	4 0	4 22	...	10 35
Harzysskaya ...arr	...	6 10	1 24	3 19	4 52	5 15	p.m	11 48
SENELNIKOVO ...dep	1029	11p2	...	...	B	...	12 18	4 p37
Harzysskaya ...dep	3a39	6 40	1 56	3 31	5 2	5 22	5 51	12 30
Iloviskaya	4 2	7 0	2 16	3 50	5 17	5 37	6 15	1 0
Taganrog ....arr	6 1	10 4	5 5	6 18	7 29	7 49	8 32	4 2
,, ...dep	6 33	10 24	5 23	6 33	7 40	7 56	8 42	4 22
Sinyavskaya	...	1118	6 9	RC	...	RC	...	5 15
Rostov..........arr	8 a9	1224	7 10	8 5	9 5	9 25	10 15	6 a2

B—Black Sea Express, Saturday only.

HARZYSSKAYA and DOLINSKAYA,

			a.m.			a.m.	p.m.		p.m	p.m.
Harzysskaya dep		...	5 33	...	...	11 37	4 36	...	1152	1 9
Yassinovataya ...arr		...	6 26	...	...	12 15	5 28	...	1259	1 42
,, ...dep		...	7 41	...	...	12 25	6 10	...	1 2	1 50
Ocheretino		...	8 31	...	...	1 3	6 56	...	2 10	2 24
Grischino		a.m.	9 29	...	...	1 45	7 49	...	3 21	3 4
Chaplino		4 41	11 38	...	...	3 25	9 53	...	5 23	4 31
Ulyanovka		5 1	11 59	...	...	...	10 16	...	5 47	...
Senelnikovo arr	a.m.	6 57	1 p57	p.m.	...	5 9	12 10	a.m.	7 41	6 10
,, ...dep	6 37	7 17	2 30	7 25	...	5 24	12 30	3 0	7 55	6 17
Ekaterin'slav arr	7 40	8 30	3 47	8 52	p.m.	6 22	1 a44	4 18	9 a8	7 11
,, ...dep	—	—	5 50	—	1050	6 35	2 14	—	10 0	7 27
Verchovzevo arr		...	7 58	...	1245	8 p8	4 10	...	12p4	8 a49
,, dep		...	8 17	...			4 14	...		
Dolginzevo ......arr		...	11 14	...	...	...	6 52	...	...	...
,, ...dep		...	11 36	...	...	...	7 2	...	...	...
Dolinskaya ...arr		...	1 a42	...	...	...	8 a54	...	...	...

			a.m.					p.m.
Dolinskaya...dep		...	4 0	...	...	...	...	9 35
Dolginzevo ......arr		...	6 10	...	...	...	...	11 21
,, ...dep		...	6 55	...	...	...	...	11 31
Verchovzevo ......arr		a.m	9 31	...	p.m.	p.m.	...	2a10
,, ...dep		9 16	9 47	...	7 51	6 12	...	2 14
Ekaterinoslav arr	a.m.	1043	11 55	...	9 9	7 53	p.m.	3 59
,, ...dep	9 18	1053	2 p30	5p38	9 19	9 27	10 7	4 28
Senelnikovo arr	1130	12 3	4 8	7 13	1019	10 52	1120	6 1
,, dep	—	1218	4 37	7 40	1029	11 2	—	6 26
Ulyanovka		...	6 23	9 22	...	12 47	...	8 10
Chaplino		2 8	7 2	9 51	1215	1 25	...	8 46
Grischino		3 44	9 15	—	1 41	3 27	...	10 49
Ocheretino		4 32	10 17	...	2 26	4 27	...	11 50
Yassinovataya ...arr		5 4	11 0	...	2 55	5 10	...	12 34
,, ...dep		5 14	11 25	...	3 5	5 37	...	12 54
Harzysskaya arr		5p50	12a20	...	3a38	6 a27	...	1 p40

CHAPLINO and BERDIANSK.

Chaplino..........dep	9 a46	10p20	...
Berdiansk ......arr	10p31	5 a2	...

Berdiansk......dep	8 a17	8 p36	...	...	...	...	...
Chaplino ......arr	9 p10	4 a2	...	...	...	...	...

VERCHOVZEVO and DOLGINZEVO (via Pyatikatka).

Verchovzevo dep	8 a50	12 p8	...	8 p9	12a49	...
Pyatikatka ....arr	9 42	1 10	...	9 5	1 55	...
,, ...dep	10 16	—	5p46	—	4 25	...
Dolginzevo ......arr	12 54	...	12a10	...	7 5	...

Dolginzevo......dep	...	...	5 a50	...	3 p51	10p37	...
Pyatikatka..........arr	...	...	12 45	...	6 32	1 50	...
,, ...dep	4 a20	8 a19	—	5 p5	7 0	—	...
Verchovzevo ...arr	5 27	9 15	...	6 7	7 50	...	...

PYATIKATKA and SNAMENKA.

Pyatikatka ...dep	9 a50	1 p27	9 p15	2 a0	...	...	...
Snamenka .....arr	12 38	5 p10	12 15	5 45	...	...	...

Snamenka ......dep	5a20	1 p20	4 p5	12a40	...	...
Pyatikatka ......arr	8 10	4 49	6 52	4 5	...	...

DOLGINZEVO and VOLNOVAKHA.

Dolginzevo ....dep	10 a5	1 p14	...	...
Alexandrovsk (321)...	4 p50	9 p40	...	...
Pologi	8 p17	3 a5	...	...
Volnovakha 321...arr	12a12	7 a0	...	...

Volnovakha..........dep	5 a2	9 p14	...	...	...
Pologi	8 a33	2 a45	...	...	...
Alexandrovsk..........	12p50	7 a16	...	...	...
Dolginzevo 323A......arr	7 p40	3 p31	...	...	...

KRASNOVODSK, MERV, and TASHKEND.

Dist E.M		p.m.	p.m.
	Krasnovodsk...dp	3 15	6 p2
163	**Kasandjik**	11 38	3 a25
309	**Kisil Arvad** ...dep	2 a20	6 50
345	**Askabad** ...... arr	8 51	2 p33
...	,, ... dep	9 18	3 9
451	**Dushak**	2 p37	7 45
558	**Merv** ....arr	6 p56	11p56
...	,, (323A)...dep	7 p21	12a10
709	Chardish..........arr	1 a38	6 14
783	Kagan (323A)	5 a10	9 a21
939	Samarcand......arr	2 p6	4 p16
...	,, ...dep	2 20	4 30
1009	Dshisak..........	5 42	7 42
1065	Chernievo 323A arr	8 p17	9 55
...	,, ...dep	8 45	10 17
1159	**Tashkend** 319 arr	2 a46	3 a51

Restaurant Car attached.

	a.m.	p.m.
Tashkend ......dep	6 6	6 25
Chernievo ......arr	11 18	11p18
,, ...dep	11 45	11p50
Dshisak..........	2 p27	2 a51
Samarcand......arr	6 9	7 a12
,, ...dep	6 p29	8 a0
Kagan	12a52	3 p4
Chardish	3 58	6 p44
Merv ....arr	10a13	1 p30
,, ...dep	10a25	1 p53
Dushak	2 p44	6 a49
Askabad ...... arr	7 17	11a24
,, ...dep	7 51	11a47
Kisil Arvad	2 a14	6 p6
Kasandjik	4 50	8 p22
Krasnovodsk arr	12p21	4 a30

Restaurant Car attached.

CHERNIEVO and ANDISHAN.

E.M.		a.m.	a.m.	p.m.		p.m.
—	**Chernievo** ......dep	3 32	1149	1 29	...	1154
119	Kokand..........	11 5	7 p6	1146	3p12	6 48
203	**Andishan** ....arr	...	12a2	6 a1	8p58	1150

		a.m.	p.m.	p.m.	p.m.	n'gt
...	**Andishan** ....dep	8 20	...	3 15	1059	1252
...	Kokand	1p33	2 45	9 3	3a53	7a55
...	**Chernievo** ......arr	8 p4	10p8	...	1 55	4 p0

MERV and KOOSHK.

E.M		p.m.		
—	**Merv**..........dep	4 14	...	...
105	Sari-Jasi	10 36	...	...
195	**Kooshk** ......arr	3 p47	...	...

	p.m.		
Kooshk ......dep	12 25	...	...
Sari-Jasi	5 p40	...	...
Merv ....arr	11p28	...	...

KAGAN and BOKHARA.

E.M.		a.m.	a.m.	p.m.	p.m.	p.m.	a.m.			
—	**Kagan**......dep	6 5	9 47	12 27	3 3	5 20	1 2	...	...	...
8	**Bokhara**...arr	6 35	10 17	12 57	3 33	5 50	1 32	...	...	...

	a.m.	a.m.	a.m.	p.m.	p.m.	p.m.	
Bokhara...dep	4 45	8 37	1115	2 0	3 43	1155	...
Kagan ......arr	5 15	9 7	1145	2 30	4 19	1225	...

BUCHAREST, JASSY, and UNGHENI.

Dist.		1,2,3	1 & 2	1 & 2	1 & 2	1,2,3	1,2,3	1 & 2	1,2,3	1 & 2	1 & 2	1,2,3	1,2,3	1,2,3	1,2,3
E.M.	Bucharest	a.m.	a.m.	a.m.	a.m.	a.m.	a.m.	p.m.	p.m.	p.m.	p.m.	p.m	p.m.	p.m.	p.m.
—	North Station...dep	6 55	7 50	8 35	9 20	9 35	11 15	2 55	3 10	5 5	6 20	6 50	9 5	10 5	11 10
6¼	Chitila	7 14	8 4	RC	...	9 51	11 35	RC	3 26	5 19	6 33	7 7	9 20	10 22	11 28
37¼	Ploesci ...arr	8 38	8 58	9 33	10 26	11 10	1 12	3 53	4 40	6 14	7 18	8 24	10 18	11 23	12 38
90	PREDEAL 324A arr	12 p4	12 p4	...	...	3 p26	...	...	8p30	9 p0	...	...	...	...	...
108¾	BRASSO 233 ...arr	...	2 p0	...	...	5 p10	...	...	9p44	10p 5	...	...	...	...	...
...	Ploesci ...dep	9 6	...	9 42	10 36	...	1 41	4 0	...	...	7 26	8 40	10 28	11 33	12 50
79½	Buzeu ...arr	11 16	...	10 48	11 44	...	3 39	5 2	...	...	8 28	10 25	11 47	12 54	2 17
162¼	GALATZ (324) ...arr	3 p40	...	3 p40	3 p40	...	8 p20	...	...	...	11 35	...	SC	...	6 a20
...	CONSTANZA ...dep	...	a.m.	5 ‖55		...	...	...	...	...	RC	2p25	...	SC	SC
...	Buzeu ...dep	11 39	6 55	11 0	...	...	4 16	5 17	...	...	...	10 45	12 1	1 9	...
100¾	Rimnicu Sarat	12 32	8 19	11 34	...	...	5 18	5 51	...	...	...	11 37	12 43	1 55	a.m.
123¾	Focsani	1 37	9 54	12 10	...		6 39	6 28	...	...	...	12 41	1 33	2 51	7 0
135½	Marasesci 324A arr	2 4		12 28	...		7 10	6 46	...		a.m.	1 16	1 58	3 16	7 45
	dep	3 37		12 34	...		8 26		...		3 46			3 31	8 51
151½	Adjud	4 25		1 3	...		9 9	...	...		4 24	...	a.m.	4 16	9 39
187¾	Bacau ...dep	6 18		2 12	...		11 2	...	...			...	8 15	6 6	11 35
215	Roman arr	7 28		2 57	...		12 5	...	...		...	...	9 58	7 13	12 45
	dep	7 40		2 59				...	...		...	...	10 25	7 27	
239¾	Pascani ...arr	8 43		3 41			...	...	...		...	...	11 54	8 27	...
279	ITZKANI (324B) arr	11p50		5 p20			...	...	...		...	...	...	10a45	...
500¼	LEMBERG (246A) arr	...		12 a7			p.m.	...	...		...	...	...	9 p26	...
...	Pascani ...dep	9 14		4 2			12 50	...	...		...	...	...	9 10	...
259	Tergul-Frumos	10 14		4 58			1 45	...	p.m.		...	...	...	10 9	...
272¾	Podul-Iloei	10 48		5 32			2 18	1,2,3	9 39		...	...	...	10 43	...
287	Jassy 324A arr	11 20		6 p 0			2 45	a.m.	10 20		...	...	...	11 15	p.m.
	dep							6 25			...	...	...		12 5
300¼	Ungheni ¶ ...arr	...		...			...	7 35	...		...	...	...	...	12 52
488	ODESSA (320)...arr	...		...	...		...	...	...	...	...	...	...	...	7 a18

RC—Restaurant Car. ‖—Sun., Wed., and Fri. only. SC—Sleeping Cars in these trains. ¶—Customs Examination.

Extra. Bucharest ...dep 1 p50; Ploesci ...arr 3 10 | Ploesci ...dep 7 a48, 4 p6; Bucharest ...arr 8 55, 5 40

	1,2,3	1,2,3	1,2,3	1 & 2	1 & 2	1,2,3	1,2,3	1 & 2	1 & 2	1,2,3	1,2,3	1,2,3	1 & 2	1,2,3	1,2.3
ODESSA ...dep	...	...	...	...	...	...	...	...	...	...	...	...	...	...	12a35
										a.m.	a.m.	a.m.			p.m.
Ungheni ...dep	...	...	...	...	...	...	...	...	...	...	9 18	...	...	...	4 38
Jassy ¶ arr	a.m.	...	...	...	...	...	...	...	...	...	10 5	...	...	p.m.	5 25
dep	5 5	...	...	...	...	...	...	...		6 0		10 15	...	1 15	6 5
Podul-Iloei	5 48	...	...	...	...	...	...	...		6 34	...	10 46	...	1 45	6 39
Tergul-Frumos		...	...	...	...	...	...	...		7 15	...	11 21	...	2 20	7 17
Pascani ...arr	...	...	...	...	...	...	...	...		8 20	...	12 18	...	3 17	8 22
LEMBERG ...dep	...	...	...	...	...	...	...	...		2 p30	...	2 a45	...	...	9 a10
ITZKANI ...dep	...	...	...	...	...	...	...	...		3 a44	...	9 a56	...	...	5 p20
Pascani ...dep	...	...	...	...	...	...	...	...		8 48	...	12 42	...	4 12	9 3
Roman arr	...	...	...	...	...	a.m.	...	...		9 54	...	1 24	p.m.	5 44	9 57
dep	...	...	...	...	...	4 35	...	...		10 4	...	1 26	3 30	6 9	10 3
Bacau ...depa.m.	...	...	...	...	...	5 47	...	...		11 31	...	2 17	4 56	7 50	11 16
Adjud ...1233	SC	...	...	...	...	7 17	...	...	...	1 20	...	3 14	6 45		12 46
Marasesci. arr1 7	a.m.	a.m.	...	...	...	7 50	...	...	...	1 57	...	3 36	7 20	p.m.	1 19
dep	2 54	4 0	...	...	...	8 53	...	...	...	3 6	p.m.	3 42	7 42	8 32	1 34
Focsani	3 25	4 37	...	...	...	9 28	...	...	...	3 45	6 35	4 5	8 4	9 15	2 7
Rimnicu Sarat	4 23	5 43	...	...	...	10 37	...	...	...	5 17	8 50	4 43	8 42		3 9
Buzeu ...arr	5 1	6 30	...	...	...	11 26	...	...	...	6 12	10 5	5 16	9 12	...	3 49
CONSTANZA 324A arr	...	2 p10	...	RC	...	...	...	...	...	...	...	10‡35	...	SC	SC
GALATZ ...dep	...	...	...	5 a55	...	7 a20	...	12p50	...	12p50	...	12p50	4 p55	10 p0	10 p0
Buzeu ...dep	5 15	6 45	...	9 6	...	12 14	...	5 4	...	6 36	...	5 30	9 20	2 a20	4 7
Ploesci ...arr	6 40	8 33	...	10 16	...	2 21	...	6 10	...	8 32	...	6 40	10 26	4 1	5 31
BRASSO ...dep	...	2 a46	...	5 a26	5 a26	...	11 a5	...	2 p1	...	...	...	...	...	...
PREDEAL ...dep	...	6 a0	a.m.	8 a11	8 a11	...	2 p19	...	5 p29	...	...	...	7 p30	...	...
Ploesci ...dep	6 50	8 48	9 15	10 27	10 48	2 42	5 29	6 18	8 15	9 0	...	6 49	10 35	4 32	5 41
Chitila (324)	7 52	10 10	10 40	11 27	11 43	4 0	6 46	...	9 7	10 30	...	RC	RC	5 46	6 42
Bucharest ...arr	8 5	10 25	10 55	11 40	11 55	4 13	7 0	7 15	9 20	10 45	...	7 45	11 30	6 0	6 55

‡—Sun., Tues., and Thurs. only.

BUCHAREST and GIURGIU.

Bucharest	a.m.	p.m.	p.m.
Northern Station dep	7 35	1 10	5 45
Comana	8 58	2 34	7 13
Giurgiu ...arr	9 57	3 35	8 15
RUSTCHUCK stm...arr	11 a0	...	...
SOFIA (326) ...arr	10 p4	...	...

SOFIA ...dep	...	...	7a30
RUSTCHUCK ...dep	6 a30	2p15	5p43
	a.m.	p.m.	p.m.
Giurgiu ...dep	7 41	3 10	7 10
Comana	8 53	4 18	8 19
Bucharest ...arr	10 15	5 35	9 40

Pitesti ...dep	10a47	9 p38
Curtea de Arges arr	11 50	10 40
Curtea de Arges dep	6 a0	6 p5
Pitesti ...arr	6 50	6 55

E.M.			
	Giurgiu ...dep	10a25	8 p40
26	Videle ...arr	1 55	12 10

Videle ...dep	3a35	2p55
Giurgiu (324) ...arr	7 15	6 35

E.M.				
	Podul-Iloei...dep	6a36	11 a0	6p45
26	Harlau ...arr	9 10	1 30	9 15

Harlau ...dep	7a50	2p40	6p30
Podul-Iloei (324) arr	1016	5 6	9 7

BUZEU and GALATZ.

[§—Sleeping Cars in these trains.

Dist. E.M.	BUCHAREST dep	...	9 a20	11a15	2 p55	...	6 p20	11p10
		a.m.	a.m.	p.m.	p.m.	p.m.	p.m.	a.m.
—	Buzeu ...dep	7 5	11 59	4 11	5 37	...	8 38	2 §35
25½	Faurei 324B	8 14	1 3	5 17	6 24	8 1	9 27	3 40
62¾	Braila	10 20	2 43	7 17	A	9 45	10 48	5 14
75	Barbosi arr	10 54	3 13	7 49		10 17	11 14	5 41
...	dep	11 6	3 17	7 56	...	10 31	11 18	5 55
82¾	Galatz ...arr	11 30	3 40	8 20	...	10 55	11 35	6 20

	a.m.	a.m.		a.m.	a.m.	p.m.	p.m.	p.m.
Galatz ...dep	4 45	5 55	...	7 20	...	12 50	4 55	10 §0
Barbosi arr	5 9	6 17	...	7 44	...	1 13	5 19	10 22
dep	5 21	6 20	a.m.	7 49	1055	1 16	5 34	10 36
Braila	6 19	6 55	B	8 39	1125	2 2	6 20	11 24
Faurei	7 56	8 8	9 47	1022		3 41	8 2	1 3
Buzeu ...arr		8 56	10 35	1130	...	4 39	9 6	2 0
BUCHAREST 324	...	1140	...	4p13	...	7 p15	11p30	6 a0

A—Sun., Tues., and Thurs. only, daily from 14th July. B—Sun., Wed., and Fri. only, daily from 14th July.

E.M.					
	Galatz ...dep	6 a45	4 p20	...	...
49	Berescl	9 8	6 43	...	...
69	Bârlad (324A)...arr	9 55	7 30	...	...

Bârlad ...dep	6 a10	6 p20	...	...
Beresci	7 28	7 34	...	...
Galatz ...arr	9 30	9 35	...	...

BUCHAREST and VERCIOROVA.

Dist.		1,2,3	1 & 2	1,2,3	1,2,3	1 Cl.	1,2,3	1 & 2	1,2,3	1,2,3	1,2,3	1,2,3	
E.M	**Bucharest**	a.m.	a.m.	a.m.	a.m.	p.m.	p.m.	p.m.	p.m.	p.m.	p.m.	p.m.	
—	North Stat. ......dep	...	6 40	7 12	8 10	12 50	2 5	6 §5	6 35	9§45	10 45	11§50	...
6¼	Chitila	...	6 57	7 32	8 28	...	2 22	6 22	6 51	10 10	11 8	12 14	...
30¾	Titu	...	7 43	8 44	9 36	1 42	3 19	7 11	7 49	11 18	12 23	1 26	...
62¾	Golesci 324B	...	8 37	10 22	11 3	A	4 33	8 17	9 13	12 45	1 51	2 57	...
67¾	**Pitesci** ......dep	...	8 49	10 35	11 36	2 48	5 7	8 33	9 25	1 15	2 27	3 40	...
80¾	Costesci 324B	...	9 22		12 20	...	5 54	9 7		1 58	3 16	4 31	...
117½	Slatina	...	10 38	...	2 4	4 31	7 45	10 38	...	3 44	5 22	6 20	...
128	Piatra O. 324B	7 35	11 5	...	2 53	4 52	8 29	11 3	...	4 13	6 8	6 45	...
156	Craiova 324B ...... arr	8 50	11 54	...	4 9	5 44	9 45	11 58	...	5 25	7 28		...
	dep		12 6	...	4 50	5 52		12 7	...	5 43	8 0	...	...
177¾	Filiasi 324B	...	12 52	...	5 50	6 36	...	12 50	...	6 45	8 57	...	...
226¼	Turn-Severin	...	2 35	...	8 29	8 20	...	2 36	...	9 2	11 11	...	...
237¼	**Verciorova** ......arr	...	2 55	...	8 55	8 40	...	2 56	...	9 28	11 35	...	...
546	BUDAPEST 227A ...arr	...	...	...	...	6 a10	...	1 p25	...	7 a15	...	...	...
718¾	VIENNA ......arr	...	...	...	...	11 a4	...	6 p20	...	12p14	...	...	...

VIENNA ......dep	...	9 a25	...	...	6 p51	...	...	...	...	...	4 p50	...	...
BUDAPEST ......dep	...	2 p40	...	...	11p45	...	...	...	...	...	10p15	...	...
	1,2,3	1 & 2	1,2,3	1,2,3	1 Cl.	1,2,3	1 & 2	1,2,3	1,2,3	1,2,3	1,2,3		
		a.m.	a.m.	a.m.	a.m.		p.m.			p.m.	p.m.		
Verciorova ¶	...	2§58	...	6 45	10 50	...	2 8	...	...	5 5	7§35		...
Turn-Severin	...	3 22	...	7 25	11 14	...	2 32	...	...	5 36	8 17		...
Filiasi	...	5 5	...	9 45	12 55	...	4 12	...	...	7 49	10 36		...
Craiova ...... arr	...	5 42	...	10 42	1 32	...	4 49	p.m.	...	8 35	11 33		...
dep	...	5 51	8 15	11 55	1 39	...	5 1	7 55	p.m.	10 20	12 10		...
Piatra O.	...	6 54	9 49	1 31	2 35	...	6 8	9 10	11 §5	12 3	1 38		...
Slatina	...	7 21	10 34	2 9	3 0	...	6 35		11 42	12 53	2 20		...
Costesci	a.m.	8 46	12 26	4 25	4 17	p.m.	7 53	...	1 49	3 1	4 15		...
Pitesci ......dep	6 57	9 22	1 39	5 28	4 49	7 10	8 28	...	2 46	3 53	5 5		...
Golesci	7 18	9 32	1 57	5 41	C	7 33	8 41	...	2 58	4 5	5 17		...
Titu	8 48	10 32	3 22	7 19	5 45	8 59	9 33	...	4 25	5 27	6 37		...
Chitila 324	9 45	11 14	4 16	8 16	...	9 56	10 13	...	5 25	6 26	7 35		...
Bucharest ......arr	10 0	11 25	4 30	8 30	6 34	10 10	10 25	...	5 40	6 40	7 50		...

¶—Customs Examination. §—Sleeping Car attached.

A—Sun., Wed., and Fri. only. **C**—Tues., Thurs., and Sun. only.

PLOESCI and SLOBOZIA.

E.M										
	Ploesci ......dep	5a36	9 a19	5p30	...	Slobozia ......dep	7 a5	2p50	7p46	...
34¼	Urziceni	7 6	10 56	7 4	...	Urziceni	8 54	4 41	9 35	...
72¾	Slobozia 324B ...arr	8 40	12 35	8 40	...	Ploesci 324 ...arr	1029	6 15	1110	...

BUCHAREST and OLTENITZA.

Bucharest ......dep	7a40	5 p15	...	...	Oltenitza ......dep	7 a15	4 p50	...	...
Obor	8 22	5 49	...	...	Tanganu	9 12	6 22	...	...
Tanganu	9 8	6 23	...	...	Obor	10 15	7 6	...	...
Oltenitza ......arr	10 55	7 50	...	...	Bucharest 324 arr	10 40	7 30	...	...

BUCHAREST and CONSTANZA (KUSTENDJE).

Dist. E.M		1,2,3	1,2,3	1,2,3	1 & 2	1 Cl.	1,2,3
			a.m.	p.m.		p.m.	p.m.
—	**Bucharest** ......dep	...	7 25	4 30	...	6 47	11 0
33¼	Sarulesci	...	8 51	5 41	...	7 45	12 29
68¾	Ciulnitza	...	10 34	6 58	C	8 47	2 29
91¼	**Fetesci** ......arr	...	11 28	7 43	p.m.	9 26	3 30
...	PASCANI ......dep	...	RC	...	12 42	...	...
...	BUZEU ......dep	a.m.	7 a5	RC	5 p37	B	SC
...	Fetesci ......dep	5 50	11 51	7 49	8 35	9 28	3 55
107½	Saligny	8 5	12 42	8 28	9 10	10 0	4 48
144¾	**Constanza** *⁎* ......arr	11 0	2 10	9 50	10 35	11 5	6 15
361	CONSTANTINOPLE stm arr	...	...	...	12 0	12 0	
...	ALEXANDRIA ......stm arr	...	...	...	¶	¶	

ALEXANDRIA ......dep	*	...	*	...	...	...
CONSTANTINOPLE dp	3 p0	...	3 p0	...	...	...
	1 & 2	1,2,3	1 Cl.	1,2,3	1,2,3	1,2,3
	a.m.	a.m.	a.m.	p.m.	p.m.	p.m.
Constanza ......dep	5 55	5 50	8 0	2 25	6 50	10 0
Saligny	7 21	7 58	9 23	4 4	10 5	11 45
Fetesci 324B ......arr	7 51	8 35	9 52	4 56	11 25	12 34
BUZEU 324 ......arr	10 35	RC	A	9 p6		SC
PASCANI 324 ......arr	3 p41	...	...	RC		
Fetesci ......dep	...	8 45	9 54	5 17		1 13
Ciulnitza	D	9 45	10 36	6 29		2 46
Sarulesci	...	11 4	11 37	8 11		4 43
Bucharest ......arr	...	12 20	12 35	9 35		6 15

⁎—Steamer leaves Constanza on Tuesday night for Piræus and Alexandria, and on Sunday, Tuesday, and Thursday night for Constantinople.

¶—Arrive Alexandria Monday morning. *—From Alexandria Friday, 4.0 p.m.

A—Orient Express, Sun., Wed., and Fri. only. **B**—Orient Express, Sun., Tues., and Thurs. only.

C—Sun., Tues., and Thurs., arriving at Constantinople on Mon., Wed., and Fri. at noon; daily from 14th July.

D—Sun., Wed., and Fri.; daily from 14th July. **RC**—Restaurant Car. **SC**—Sleeping Car.

PLOESCI and PREDEAL.

¶—Customs Examination. ‡—Until 30th Sept.

E.M	BUCHAREST ......dep	...	7 a50	9 a35	1 p50	3 p10	5 p5	6 p50
		a.m.	a.m.	a.m.	p.m.	p.m.	p.m.	p.m.
—	**Ploesci** ......dep	6 55	9 10	11 40	3 ‡20	5 0	6 23	8 ‡45
22¼	Campina	7 59	10 6	12 53	4 14	6 4	7 10	9 39
41	Sinaja	9 35	11 20	2 29	5 29	7 36	8 18	10 52
52¾	**Predeal** ¶ ...arr	1030	12 4	3 26	6 15	8 30	9 0	11 35

	a.m.	a.m.	a.m.	p.m.	p.m.	p.m.	p.m.
Predeal ¶ ......dep	5‡20	6 0	8 11	1 ‡0	2 19	5 29	7 30
Sinaja	6 4	6 52	8 55	1 50	3 13	6 13	8 19
Campina	6 54	7 55	9 41	2 52	4 21	7 3	9 17
Ploesci ......arr	7 38	8 43	10 23	3 44	5 11	7 47	10 5
BUCHAREST 324 arr	8 55	10 25	11 40	5p40	7 p0	9 p20	11p30

GALATZ and MARASESCI.

E.M									
	Galatz ......dep	...	5a15	9 a5	10a40	...	4p30	...	11p40
7½	**Barbosi** ......dep	a.m.	5 53	9 34	11 19	...	5 2	...	12 12
52¼	**Tecuci**	2 12	8 6	1131	1 30	2p29	6 55	7p41	2 44
64	**Marasesci** ...arr	2 42	8 38	1159	3 1	3 1	7 37	8 11	3 14

Marasesci ...dep	1a36	2a11	8 a3	2p26	p.m.	3 p2	3p47	6p50	7p38
Tecuci	2 26	2 38	8 45	2 56	3 14	3 31	4 21	7 12	8 24
Barbosi	4 33		1036		5 22		6 6		1027
Galatz ......arr	5 10	...	11 5	...	6 0	...	6 35	...	11 5

MARASESCI and JASSY (IASI).

E.M							
	Marasesci ......dep	2 a11	...	8 a3	3 p2	6 p50	7p38
12¼	**Tecuci**	2 53	...	8 47	3 51	7 17	8 30
43¾	**Barlad**	4 15	5a45	10 21	5 20	8 19	9 45
65½	**Crasna 324B**	5 10	7 24	11 25	6 31	9 2	
75¾	**Vaslui**	5 44	8 20	12 1	7 12	9 27	...
117¼	**Jassy 324** ......arr	7 50	11 45	2 15	9 35	11 10	...

Jassy ......dep	...	7 a20	1 p40	3p15	4p40	9 p5
Vaslui	...	10 8	4 1	5 6	8 10	11 23
Crasna	a.m.	10 47	4 30	5 25	9 5	11 48
Barlad	6 40	12 12	5 28	6 14	10 20	12 50
Tecuci ......arr	7 50	1 24	6 40	7 8		1 57
Marasesci ......arr	8 38	2 24	...	7 37	...	2 42

CORABIA and VERESTORONY (Turnu Rosiu).

A—Until Sept. 30th

		a.m.			a.m.	p.m.	p.m.
Corabia ...dep	...	4 15	...	...	8 45	3 0	8 5
Caracal	a.m.	5 41	...	...	11 18	4 30	9 34
Piatra O. 324A ...arr	A	6 37	...	a.m	12 50	5 35	10 30
,, ...dep	4 24	7 5	...	11 13	3 7	—	—
Dragasani	5 28	8 11	p.m.	12 14	4 12	p.m.	...
Riureni	7 10	9 54	12 6	...	5 50	9 11	...
R. Valcei	7 33	10 24	12 20	1 38	6 10	9 25	...
Jiblea (Calimanesti)	8 21	11 8	—	2 0	6 47	—	...
Caineni	9 57	12 14	...	—	7 51	...	...
Verestorony ...arr	11 3	2 37	...	...	9 27	...	...
NAGYSZEBEN 232 ...arr		3 p37	...	...	10p27	...	...

NAGYSZEBEN ...dep		...	4 a6	...	...	12 56	...
			a.m.			p.m.	p.m.
Verestorony (TurnuR.) dep		...	5 46	...	...	2 43	A
Caineni		...	8 20	...	p.m.	5 30	8 49
Jiblea (Calimanesti)		a.m.	9 31	p.m.	3 0	6 45	10 2
R. Valcei		6 45	10 5	2 30	3 26	7 35	10 35
Riureni		6 58	10 22	2 43	...	7 51	10 49
Dragasani		—	12 15	—	5 0	9 43	12 24
Piatra O. ...arr	a.m.	a.m.	1 10	...	5 49	10 35	1 15
,, ...dep	7 15	11 10	3 0	...	—	11 10	—
Caracal	8 33	12 10	4 50	...	...	12 10	...
Corabia ...arr	9 40	1 15	6 40	...	...	1 15	...

Riureni ...dep	7 a18	10a39	2 p53	5 p55	7 p 5	...
Ocnita ...arr	7 45	11 5	3 20	6 21	8 20	...

Ocnita ...dep	9 a15	11a40	5 p15	7 p6	8 p45	...
Riureni ...arr	9 37	11 59	5 37	7 28	9 4	...

PASCANI and ITZKANI.

E.M		a.m.		p.m	p.m.		p.m.
—	Pascani ...dep	8 47	...	1236	3 48	p.m.	9 10
13¾	Dolhasca (324B)	9 19	...	1 46	4 13	...	9 52
28½	Veresti ...arr	9 51	n 'on	2 39	4 40	...	10 30
...	Veresti ...dep	10 6	12 0	...	4 50	8 15	10 45
46½	Leorda	10 49	1 13	...	5 33	9 42	11 29
56½	Botosani ...arr	11 10	1 45	...	5 55	1015	11 50
...	Veresti ...dep	10 1	—	3 5	4 43	—	10 50
37¼	Burdujeni	10 40	...	3 30	5 16	...	11 41
39¼	Itzkani 246A ...arr	10 45	...	...	5 20	...	11 50

	a.m.		a.m.			p.m.
Itzkani ‡ ...dep	3 44	...	9 56	...	...	5 20
Burdujeni ...arr	4 50	...	11 0	p.m.	...	6 24
Burdujeni ...dep	6 15	...	11 30	1 0	...	7 4
Veresti ...arr	6 36	a.m.	11 44	1 23	p.m.	7 20
Botosani ...dep	4 50	7 30	10 15	...	2 25	6 10
Leorda	5 18	8 13	10 44	...	3 8	6 33
Veresti ...arr	6 9	9 30	11 29	...	4 25	7 18
Veresti ...dep	6 56	—	11 47	1 45	—	7 38
Dolhasca	7 47	...	12 14	2 54	...	8 14
Pascani (324) ...arr	8 24	...	12 35	3 37	...	8 39

‡—Departure from Itzkani is by Mid Europe time.

E.M				
	Ploesci ...dep	9 a23	6 p55	...
28	Slanic ...arr	10 55	8 25	...

Slanic ...dep	7 a0	3 p30	...
Ploesci ...arr	8 20	4 47	...

Bacau ...dep	6 a14	11a43	2 p33	6 p20	11p24
Piatra-Neamta ...arr	7 45	1 30	4 20	9 10	12 55

E.M				
	Campina ...dep	6 a20	12p57	7 p12
3¾	Doftana ...arr	6 43	1 20	7 35

Doftana ...dep	7 a20	3 p35	8 p45
Campina ...arr	7 43	3 58	9 8

Piatra-Neamta ...dep	4 a5	8 a40	12p10	3 p0	9 p25
Bacau 324 ...arr	5 30	11 1	1 46	4 32	10 50

TITU and PETROSITA.

Titu ...dep	8 a51	3 p30	7 p53	...	...
Tergovist	9 57	4 43	8 56	...	...
Puciosa	11 10	6 40	10 10	...	...
Petrosita ...arr	12 5	7 50	11 10	...	...

Petrosita ...dep	5a25	10 a5	3 p35	...	...
Puciosa	6 38	12 10	5 7	...	...
Tergovist	7 30	2 4	5 55	...	...
Titu 324A ...arr	8 18	2 57	6 48	...	...

ADJUD and PALANCA.

Adjud ...dep	4 a36	9 a45	4 p40	9 p15	...
Tirgul Ocna	6 13	11 29	7 46	10 59	...
Comanesci	7 16	12 52	9 35	11 58	...
Palanca 233A ...arr	8 23	2 13	11 35	1 45	...

Palanca ...dep	3 a5	6 a0	...	3 p35	9 p15
Comanesci	4 36	8 28	a.m.	4 37	10 21
Tirgul Ocna	5 30	9 40	10 25	5 25	11 13
Adjud 324 ...arr	6 51	...	12 35	6 35	12 23

Comanesci ...dep	4 a49	7 a49	12p44	4 p59	10p14	12 a4	...
Moinesci ...arr	5 15	8 15	1 10	5 25	10 40	12 30	...

Moinesci ...dep	3 a55	6 a25	11a50	4 p5	8 p50	11p15	...
Comanesci ...arr	4 15	6 45	12 10	4 25	9 10	11 35	...

ROSIORI and ZIMNICEA.

Rosiori ...dep	7 a2	9 a20	3 p30	8 p40	...	...
Alexandria	8 1	11 0	5 14	9 38	...	...
Smardiosa	8 27	12 8	6 22	10 4	...	...
Zimnicea ...arr	9 15	1 15	7 30	10 50	...	...

Zimnicea ...dep	6 a35	9 a35	4 p15	8 p20	...	...
Smardiosa	7 23	10 57	5 38	9 13	...	...
Alexandria	7 58	12 17	6 57	9 49	...	...
Rosiori ...arr	8 50	1 39	8 15	10 42	...	...

FAUREI and FETESCI.

Faurei ...dep	8 a30	1 p10	6 *32	9 p30	1 a14	...
Ciora	9 43	2 53	7 28	10 54	2 18	...
Fetesci ...arr	11 10	4 58	8 30	12 54	3 42	...

Fetesci ...dep	3 a50	7 †55	11a48	5 p22	12a56	...
Ciora	6 15	9 1	2 0	6 50	2 27	...
Faurei 324 ...arr	7 45	9 45	3 25	7 42	3 20	...

*—Sun., Tues., and Thurs.; daily from 14th July. †—Sun., Wed., and Fri.; daily from 14th July.

CALARASI and SLOBOZIA.

Calarasi dep	5a15	8 a20	5 p5	12a50
Ciulnitza	6 19	10 52	6 2	2 59
Slobozia ...arr	6 54	11 30	7 36	3 35

Slobozia dep	8a49	5 p20	8p50	1 a25
Ciulnitza ...	9 25	5 58	9 25	2 1
Calarasi arr	1140	8 0	1030	3 45

CRAIOVA and CALAFAT.

Craiova ...dep	7 a50	5 p20
Calafat ...arr	10 45	8 30

Calafat ...dep	7 a20	6 p40
Craiova 324A arr	10 30	10 0

FOCSANI and ODOBESCI.

Focsani ...dep	4 a55	10a15	12p25	4 p10	9 p30
Odobesci ...arr	5 35	10 55	1 5	4 50	10 10

Odobesci ...dep	6 a15	11a30	2 p55	5 p40	10p45
Focsani ...arr	6 43	11 58	3 23	6 8	11 13

JASSY and DOROHOI.

Jassy ...dep	5 a35	8 a25	5 p40	...	...
Cucuteni	5 55	8 54	6 0	...	...
Todireni	7 33	11 44	7 55	...	...
Dorohoi ...arr	9 25	3 0	9 55	...	...

Dorohoi ...dep	6 a20	1 p30	7 p43	...	...
Todireni	8 12	4 57	9 46	...	...
Cucuteni	9 45	7 26	11 19	...	...
Jassy 324 ...arr	10 0	7 50	11 35	...	...

Dorohoi ...dep	6 a45	9 a40	12p15	4 p20	5 p35	8 p35	10p20
Leorda ...arr	7 44	10 27	1 3	5 19	6 22	9 33	11 10

Leorda ...dep	5 a15	8 a15	10a58	3 p10	5 p35	6 p43	10 p8
Dorohoi ...arr	6 0	9 16	12 0	3 55	6 20	7 28	11 10

GOLESCI and CAMPU-LUNG.

E.M					
	Golesci ...dep	10a20	4 p40	9 p9	...
18½	Stalpeni	11 15	5 29	10 4	...
34¼	Campu-Lung arr	12 12	6 25	11 0	...

C.-Lung ...dep	5 a25	12p13	5 p30	...
Stalpeni	6 14	12 58	6 19	...
Golesci 324A ...	7 8	1 47	7 14	...

FILIASI and TIRGU-JIU.

Filiasi ...dep	7 a0	9 a50	1p10	6 p5
Carbunesci	8 46	12 10	3 3	7 48
Tirgu-Jiu ...arr	9 30	1 5	3 45	8 30

Tirgu-Jiu...dep	6 a15	1p25	2 p10	7p45
Carbunesci	7 6	2 17	3 22	8 39
Filiasi 324A arr	8 35	3 50	5 30	1010

DOLHASCA and FALTICENI.

Dolhasca ...dep	9 a30	12p50	4 p23	9 p56
Falticeni ...arr	10 39	2 0	5 20	11 5

Falticeni ...dep	6 a25	11a10	2 p55	6 p50
Dolhasca ...arr	7 29	12 1	3 59	7 54

COSTESCI and TURNU MAGURELE.

Costesci ...dep	4 a36	...	12p50	6 p17	9 p13	...
Rosiori	6 56	9 a15	3 25	8 44	11 14	...
Turnu Magurele ...arr	8 12	11 10	4 41	10 0	12 30	...

Turnu Magurele...dep	5 a10	7 a40	12p13	6 p10	9 p30	...	...
Rosiori	6 43	9 30	1 53	8 10	11 7	...	...
Costesci 324A ...arr	8 35	11 57	4 8	...	1 20	...	...

Turnu Magurele ...dep	8 a30	11a28	4 p58	...	...
Port ...arr	8 45	11 40	5 10	...	...

Port ...dep	11a45	5 p35	8 p55	...	...
Turnu Magurele ...arr	11 59	5 49	9 10	...	...

CRASNA and HUSI.

Crasna ...dep	5 a31	11a30	6 p33	9 p25	11p53
Husi ...arr	7 20	1 30	8 35	11 25	1 55

Husi ...dep	3 a0	8 a35	2 p20	6 p50	9 p25	...
Crasna 324A ...arr	4 50	10 25	4 10	8 39	11 13	...

PIRÆUS, ATHENS, CORINTH, PATRAS, PYRGOS, & OLYMPIA.

Dist E.M	Station			a.m.	a.m.	a.m.	p.m.	
	Piræus	dep	...	5 40	6 15	7 20	12 10	...
5½	**Athens**	arr	...	6 10	6 45	7 50	12 40	...
		dep	...	6 30	7 5	8 20	1 0	...
22¼	Eleusis		...	7 30	8 7	9 50	2 1	...
34¾	Megara		...	8 11	8 46	1035	2 41	...
56	Kalamaki		...	9 15	9 45	12 5	3 40	...
62¼	**Corinth**	arr	...	9 40	10 8	1230	4 3	p.m.
		dep	...	—	1025	—	4 18	5 10
82¾	Xylocastron		a.m.	...	1143	...	5 22	7 25
110	Diacofto		6 2	...	1 22	...	6 39	—
118¾	Æghion		7 2	...	2 0	...	7 9	...
143	**Patras**	arr	9 0	a.m.	3 35	p.m.	8 25	...
		dep	—	6 30	3 45	5 15	—	...
156	Achaja		a.m.	7 42	4 48	6 50	...	...
179	Lechaina		6 0	9 4	6 2	8 20	...	...
183¼	Cavassila		6 28	9 22	6 20	—	...	...
184½	Gastouni		6 43	9 29	6 27	...	...	...
190¾	Amalias		7 15	9 52	6 48	...	...	...
204½	**Pyrgos**	arr	8 20	1032	7 35	...	...	a.m.
		dep	...	1110	7 45	...	...	7 30
217½	**Olympia**	arr	...	12 5	8 40	...	...	8 25

Station				a.m.	a.m.	p.m.		p.m.
Olympia	dep	...	...	5 30	8 45	1 45	...	...
Pyrgos	arr	...	...	6 15	9 35	2 35	...	...
	dep	...	...	6 30	—	2 45	...	3 40
Amalias		...	...	7 18	...	3 25	...	4 49
Gastouni		...	...	7 38	...	3 45	...	5 14
Cavassila		...	...	7 43	...	3 50	p.m.	5 19
Lechaina		...	...	8 6	...	4 13	5 0	5 40
Achaja		...	...	9 28	...	5 31	6 34	—
Patras	arr	a.m.	...	1030	p.m.	6 40	8 0	...
	dep	7 30	...	1140	4 20	—	—	...
Æghion		9 16	...	1 0	7 15	...	...	...
Diacofto		9 46	...	1 21	7 46	...	...	a.m.
Xylocastron		1138	...	2 50	—	...	...	6 55
Corinth	arr	1252	p.m.	3 48	...	p.m.	...	8 45
	dep	1 10	2 5	4 4	...	5 5	...	—
Kalamaki		1 35	2 45	4 27	...	5 28	...	...
Megara		2 45	4 10	5 26	...	6 26	...	...
Eleusis		3 35	5 0	6 11	...	7 11	...	...
Athens	arr	4 40	6 15	7 5	...	8 5	...	...
	dep	4 55	6 35	7 15	...	8 15	...	...
Piræus	arr	5 20	7 5	7 40	...	8 40	...	...

Athens and **Piræus.**—A service every 15 mins. from 5.30 a.m. until 12.0 night.
On days when trains connect at Patras with steamers to and from Brindisi and Trieste, Saloon carriages are attached at 20 per cent. increase on fare.

PYRGOS, KYPARISSIA, and ZEVGALATIO.

E.M	Station							
	Pyrgos ...dep	...	6a20	...	10a55	...	...	...
35½	Kalonero	5a40	8 30	9a57	12 50	4p40	8 p0	...
39¼	**Kyparissia** ...arr	...	8 50	1010	1 35	...	8 12	...
53¼	**Zevgalatio** ...arr	6 50	...	...	2 20	5 50	...	...
...	**Zevgalatio** ...dep	...	8a25	...	3p10	6p45	...	...
...	**Kyparissia** ...dep	5a20	9 20	1235	4 0	...	...	...
...	Kalonero	5 32	9 45	1247	4 30	7 53	...	...
...	**Pyrgos** ...arr	...	1145	...	6 30	...	...	...

CAVASSILA and CYLLENE.

Station				
Cavassila ...dep	6a35	9a30	6p25	...
Vartholomio	6 50	9 50	6 45	...
Cyllene (Port) arr	...	1010	7 10	...

Station					
Cyllene (Port) dep	5a30	...	2p10	...	...
Vartholomio	6 0	7a20	2 40	...	...
Cavassila ...arr	6 15	7 35	2 55	...	...

CORINTH and CALAMATA

E.M.	dr. l.	dr. l.	Station			From Kyparissa dep. 5.20 a.m.	a.m.	p.m.
—	—	—	**Corinth**	dep	...	...	9 55	4 55
20	...	...	Nemee		...	...	11 28	6 35
26¾	5 60	4 40	Mycenæ		...		11 48	6 55
33	6 50	5 20	Argos	arr	a.m.		12 8	7 15
39	...	...	Myli		6 30		12 33	8 10
75	14 0	11 50	**Tripolis**	arr	9 35		3 10	—
...	...	...		dep	10 0		3 25	...
102	19 40	14 70	Bilali		12 1		4 58	...
105	...	...	Megalopolis	arr	12 35		5 30	...
123¾	...	...	Diavolitsi		2 20		6 24	...
126¾	21 80	14 70	Zevgalatio		2 34	6 55	6 42	...
133½	...	...	Tsepheremini		4 7	7 50	7 14	...
143½	...	...	Asprochoma		5 3	8 35	7 46	...
146¾	...	...	Nissi	arr	5 17	8 52	8 2	...
146¾	21 80	14 70	**Calamata**	arr	5 15	8 50	8 0	...

Station			a.m.	p.m.	p.m.
Calamata	dep		7 0	12 5	4 0
Nissi	dep		6 55	12 5	4 0
Asprochoma			7 15	12 23	4 17
Tsepheremini			7 47	1 10	5 9
Zevgalatio			8 17	2 2	5 57
Diavolitsi			8 37	3 5	6 15
Megalopolis	dep		9 45	4 30	—
Bilali			10 14	5 15	...
Tripolis	arr	a.m.	11 55	7 15	...
	dep	6 30	12 15	—	...
Myli		9 0	2 25	...	...
Argos	dep	9 45	2 50	...	...
Mycenæ		10 6	3 11	...	...
Nemee		1048	3 46	...	...
Corinth	arr	1225	4 53	...	...

ARGOS & NAUPLIA, in 20 min. From Argos dep. 7.40, 9.50 a.m., 12.20, 2.55, 7.35 p.m.
From Nauplia dep. 7.5, 8.50, 11.30 a.m., 2.10, 6.0 p.m.

DIACOFTO and KALAVRYTA.

Station	
Diacofto ...dep	1 p35
Kalavryta ...arr	4 5
Kalavryta ...dep	10 a0
Diacofto ...arr	12 35

ATHENS and KEPHISIA.—Departures from Athens almost hourly from 5.0 a.m. until 10.0 p.m. Departures from Kephisia for Athens almost hourly from 5.55 p.m. until 8.55 p.m., also at 10.30, 11.25 p.m., and 12.20 night.

ATHENS and LAURIUM.

Station		
Athens ... dep	6 a50	3 p50
Herakleion	7 14	4 14
Liopesi	7 57	4 57
Kalyvia	8 37	5 37
Laurium arr	9 32	6 32

Station		
Laurium dp.	6 a45	4 p15
Kalyvia	7 45	5 14
Liopesi	8 25	5 55
Herakleion	9 6	6 36
Athens ...arr	9 27	6 57

PIRÆUS, ATHENS, LARISSA, and SYNORA (Turkish Frontier).

E.M	Station				a.m.	p.m.
...	**Piræus**	dep	...	...	6 20	2 10
6¼	**Athens**	arr	...	...	6 40	2 30
		dep	...	...	7 0	2 50
24¾	Kiourka		...	...	8 12	4 13
44	Skimatari	arr	...	...	9 5	5 22
...	Skimatari	dep	...	...	9 15	5 30
102	**Chalchis**	arr	...	...	9 50	6 5
...	Skimatari	dep	...	...	9 13	5 35
62¼	Thebes		...	...	10 4	6 53
88¼	Livadia		...	...	11 19	8 30
92½	Chæronea		...	...	11 30	—
112½	Dadi		...	...	12 47	...
120½	Bralo	arr	...	...	1 20	...
138	Lianokladi **325**	arr	a.m.	...	2 26	...
188¼	Demerle **325**		8‡20	a.m.	6 5	...
216¾	**Larissa 325**	arr	9 57	10 5	7 25	...
244¾	**Synora** (Turkish Frontier)	ar	...	1142	...	...

‡—Wed., Fri., and Sun. only.

Station			a.m.	noon
Synora (Turkish Frontier)	dep	...	...	12 5
Larissa	dep	...	6 55	4 10
Demerle		...	8 19	6 ‡46
Lianokladi		...	11 55	—
Bralo	dep	...	1 18	...
Dadi		...	2 0	...
Chæronea		a.m.	2 55	...
Livadia		5 30	3 16	...
Thebes		7 8	4 32	...
Skimatari	arr	8 6	5 16	...
Chalchis	dep	7 25	4 25	...
Skimatari	arr	8 10	5 10	...
Skimatari	dep	8 16	5 24	...
Kiourka		9 38	6 36	...
Athens	arr	1035	7 30	...
	dep	1050	7 45	...
Piræus	arr	1110	8 5	...

VOLO and LARISSA.

E.M	Station			
	Volo ...dep	4a50	10a0	4p55
11¾	Velestino (**325**)	5 28	1043	6 0
19¼	Gherly	5 49	11 4	6 30
38	**Larissa** ...arr	6 40	1155	7 40

Station			
Larissa	6a50	2p25	7 p40
Gherly	8 5	3 18	8 32
Velestino	8 40	3 46	8 54
Volo arr	9 30	4 22	9 30

Station				
Volo ...dep	6 a4	1025	2p25	4p45
Agria	6 33	1056	2 56	5 19
Lechonia	6 53	1112	3 17	5 35
Gatzéa	7 15	—	3 39	—
Milièś ...arr	8 0	...	4 24	...

Station				
Milièś ...dep	8a10	...	...	6 p0
Gatzéa	8 57	...	...	6 47
Lechonia	9 23	7 a8	1135	7 23
Agria	9 41	7 26	1154	7 34
Volo ...arr	1013	8 0	1225	8 5

VOLO and KALABAK.

E.M	Station			
	Volo ...dep		7a40	3p 5
11¾	Velestino		8 47	3 47
28	Aivaly		1037	4 57
41¾	Pharsala		1147	5 42
49	Demerle	a.m.	1219	6 2
69	Karditza	6 28	1 54	7 19
87	Trikkala	8 0	3 32	8 14
100¾	**Kalabak**	8 45	4 17	9 5

Station			
Kalabak dp	5a20	9 a55	5p 0
Trikkala	6 12	11 3	6 10
Karditza	7 16	12 35	7 18
Demerle	8 26	1 59	—
Pharsala	8 51	2 45	...
Aivaly	9 30	4 0	...
Velestino	1044	5 56	...
Volo ...arr	1120	6 46	...

LIANOKLADI and STYLIS.

E.M.	Station	
	Lianokladi .dep	2p40
3⅜	**Lamia**	2 55
14¼	**Stylis** ...arr	4 10

Station	
Stylis ...dep	10a45
Lamia	11 35
Lianokladi (325) arr	11 45

PYRGOS and CATACOLO (Dist. 5½ miles, time 30 min. Fares 1 dr. 60 lep., 1 dr. 40 lep., 85 lep.; return 2.70, 2.20, 1.60.)—**Pyrgos** dep. 6.30, 9.45 a.m., 1.45, 4.45 p.m. **Catacolo** dep. 8.15, 11.30 a.m., 3.15, 6.30 p.m.

KRIONERI and AGRINION.

E.M									
	PATRAS (Steamer)...........dep	7 a10	4 p5	...					
		a.m.	p.m.		**Agrinion** ....dep	a.m. 6 0	p.m. 2 40	...
—	**Krioneri** ....dep	9 10	6 5	...	Missolonghi................................	7 49	4 40	...
10¼	Missolonghi................................	9 59	6 48	...	**Krioneri**..............................arr	8 25	5 20	...
38½	**Agrinion**...........................arr	11 55	8 35	...	PATRAS (Steamer) ....arr	10a45	8 p15	...

BELGRADE, SOFIA, and CONSTANTINOPLE.

Time.—Between Belgrade and Tzaribrod trains run according to Mid Europe Time; onward from Tzaribrod East Europe Time is observed. See page lxix.

	Dist. E.M		1 Cl.				
	...	VIENNA ....dep	6 p51	...	...	...	...
	...	BUDAPEST ......dep	11p30	...	...	...	...
Servia.	—	**Belgrade**.........dep	a.m. 7 55	...	...	...	...
	21¾	Ralja	O	...	...	...	...
	49	Palanka	...	...	...	...	...
	56	Velika Plana	...	...	...	...	...
	68¼	Lapowo	...	...	...	...	...
	92	Chupria	...	...	...	...	...
	133	Alexinatz	...	...	...	...	...
	151¼	**Nish** .... arr	4 p44	...	...	...	...
		dep	5 p25	...	...	...	...
	179	Bela-Palanka	...	...	...	...	...
	196¼	Pirot................arr	...	...	...	...	...
Bulgaria.	212	**Tzaribrod** ......arr	8 17	...	...	...	...
	...	**Tzaribrod** ......dep	p.m. 10 0	...	...	...	...
	234½	Slivnitza	...	...	...	...	...
	251	**Sofia 326** ...... arr	11 52	...	...	...	...
		dep		...	...	...	...
	275½	Vakarel	...	...	...	...	...
	308¾	Bellova	...	...	...	...	...
	315	**Sarembey** .... arr	...	...	...	...	...
		dep	...	...	...	...	...
	325¾	Tatar-Bazardjik ...	...	...	...	...	...
	348	Philippopoli	...	...	...	...	...
	356	Katunizza-Stanimaka	...	...	...	...	...
	366½	Papasly	...	...	...	...	...
	410¾	Tirnova-Seymenli	...	...	...	...	...
	420	Harmanly	...	...	...	...	...
Turkey.	437½	Moustapha-Pacha	...	...	...	...	...
	459¾	**Adrianople**... (326) arr	...	...	...	...	...
		dep	...	...	...	...	...
	481½	Kouleli-Bourgas ...	...	...	...	...	...
	...	Uzun-Keupri	...	...	...	...	...
	514¾	Baba Eski	...	...	...	...	...
	...	Lulé-Burgas	...	...	...	...	...
	562	Tchorlou	...	...	...	...	...
	577	Tcherkesskeui	...	...	...	...	...
	604½	Kabadjé	...	...	...	...	...
	613¾	Tchataldje	...	...	...	...	...
	...	Hademkeuï	...	...	...	...	...
	644	Kutchuk-Tchekm	...	...	...	...	...
	646	St. Stefano	...	...	...	...	...
	649	Makri-Keui	...	...	...	...	...
	...	Kum-Kapou	...	...	...	...	...
	658	**Constantinople**arr	...	...	...	...	...

	1 Cl.			
Constantinople ...dep	...	...	...	...
Kum-Kapou	...	...	...	...
Makri-Keuï	...	...	...	...
St. Stefano	...	...	...	...
Kutchuk Tchekm.	...	...	...	...
Hademkeuï	...	...	...	...
Tchataldjé	...	...	...	...
Kabadjé	...	...	...	...
Tcherkesskeui	...	...	...	...
Tchorlou	...	...	...	...
Lulé-Burgas	...	...	...	...
Baba Eski	...	...	...	...
Uzun-Keupri	...	...	...	...
Kouleli-Bourgas	...	...	...	...
Adrianople......... arr	...	...	...	...
dep	...	...	...	...
Moustapha Pacha	...	...	...	...
Harmanly	...	...	...	...
Tirnova Seymenli	...	...	...	...
Papasly	...	...	...	...
Katunizza Stanimaka	...	...	...	...
Philippopoli	...	...	...	...
Tatar-Bazardjik	...	...	...	...
Sarembey .... arr	...	...	...	...
dep	...	...	...	...
Bellova.................dep	...	...	...	...
Vakarel	P	...	...	...
Sofia .... arr	a.m.	...	...	...
dep	7 0	...	...	...
Slivnitza	...	...	...	...
Tzaribrod ....arr	8 48	...	...	...
Tzaribrod ....dep	a.m. 8 29	...	...	...
Pirot	...	...	...	...
Bela-Palanka	...	...	...	...
Nish .... arr	11 15	...	...	...
dep	12 5	...	...	...
Alexinatz	...	...	...	...
Chupria	...	...	...	...
Lapowo	...	...	...	...
Velika Plana	...	...	...	...
Palanka	...	...	...	...
Ralja	...	...	...	...
Belgrade ....arr	8 20	...	...	...
BUDAPEST **225A** ...arr	6 a10	...	...	...
VIENNA...............arr	11 a4	...	...	...

O—Orient Express, from Belgrade on Monday, Wednesday, and Friday.
P—Orient Express, from Sofia three times weekly—enquire as to days.

NISH, USKUB, and SALONICA. [Mid Europe Time.]

Nish ....dep	...	...	...	...
Leskovatz	...	...	...	...
Vrania	...	...	...	...
Zibeftché (Ristovatz) arr	...	...	...	...
dep	...	...	...	...
Koumanova	...	...	...	...
Uskub ....arr	...	...	...	...
,, ...dep	...	...	...	...
Keuprulu	...	...	...	...
Krivolak	...	...	...	...
Demir-Kapou	...	...	...	...
Mirowce	...	...	...	...
Ghevgheli	...	...	...	...
Karasuli	...	...	...	...
Salonica.......................arr	...	...	...	...

Salonica........................dep	...	...	...	...
Karasuli	...	...	...	...
Ghevgheli	...	...	...	...
Mirowce	...	...	...	...
Demir-Kapou	...	...	...	...
Krivolak	...	...	...	...
Keuprulu	...	...	...	...
Uskub (325A)..............arr	...	...	...	...
,, ...dep	...	...	...	...
Koumanova	...	...	...	...
Zibeftché (Ristovatz) arr	...	...	...	...
dep	...	...	...	...
Vrania	...	...	...	...
Leskovatz	...	...	...	...
Nish ....arr	...	...	...	...

SALONICA and MONASTIR.—Mid Europe Time.

Salonica ....dep	...	...	...	**Monastir** ....dep	...	...
Kerdjelar	...	...	...	Ekchisou	...	...
Agoustos	...	...	...	Ostrovo	...	...
Vodena	...	...	...	Vodena	...	...
Ostrovo	...	...	...	Agoustos	...	...
Ekchisou	...	...	...	Kerdjelar	...	...
Monastir ....arr	...	...	...	**Salonica**...............arr	...	...

USKUB and MITROWICA. Mid Europe Time.

E.M						
	Uskub......dep	...	...	Mitrowica dep	...	...
22¼	Orhanié........	...	...	Pristina	...	...
33¾	Verisovitz ...	...	...	Verisovitz	...	...
59	Pristina.........	...	...	Orhanié	...	...
74	Mitrowicaarr	...	...	Uskub 325Aarr	...	...

SOFIA and GUECHEVO.

Sofia ....dep	...	...	Guechevo ...dep	...	...
Radomir	...	...	Kustendil ...dep	...	...
Kustendil......arr	...	...	Radomir..........	...	...
Guechevo......arr	...	...	Sofia ....arr	...	...

E.M					
	Velika Plana............dep	2 ‡a45	12p10	...	‡—Runs only during suspension of navigation.
27½	Semendria ....arr	5 10	2 35	...	
...	Semendria ....dep	7 a0	9‡p30	...	...
...	Velika Plana ....arr	9 39	12 4	...	...

Lapowo ....dep	1 p0	2 a50	...
Kragouyevatz ....arr	2 54	4 37	...
Kragouyevatz ....dep	7 a30	11 p0	...
Lapowo ....arr	8 57	12 25	...

ADRIANOPLE and DEDEAGH.

Dist E.M							
	Adrianople ...dep	...	...	Dedeagh...dep	...	...
21¾	Kouleli-Bourgas	...	...	Bidikili	...	...
31¼	Demotika	...	...	Demotika	...	...
62¼	Bidikili	...	...	Kouleli-Bour	...	...
92	Dedeagh ....arr	...	...	Adrianople ar	...	...

SALONICA and DEDEAGH.

Salonica ....dep	12 0	...	Dedeagh............dep	12a23	...
Doiran	2 p15	...	Drama	7 a5	...
Drama	6 p54	...	Doiran	11 33	...
Dedeagh............arr	12a52	...	Salonica....... ....arr	1 p30	...

HAIDAR-PACHA and ESKI-CHEHIR.

(Constantinople)	a.m.	p.m.			a.m.
Pont Karakeuy dep	8 0	1 25	Eski-Chehir ......dep	...	7 0
Haïdar-Pacha...dep	8 40	2 0	Bilédjik......................	...	9 50
Pendik	9 42	3 18	Mékédjé........................	a.m.	11 8
Ismid	11 57	6 3	Arifié	6 5	12 30
Arifié	1 12	7 23	Ismid	7 40	1 48
Mèkédjé....................	2 39	—	Pendik	1049	4 1
Bilédjik....................	4 20	...	Haïdar-Pacha	1220	5 5
Eski-Chehir ......arr	7 15	...	Pont Karakeuy arr	1249	5 25

Arifié.........dep	1p25	7p35	...	Ada Bazar dep	5a37	11a47	...
Ada Bazar arr	1 43	7 53	...	Arifié.........arr	5 55	12 5	...

MOUDANIA and BROUSA.

Moudania.........dep	7 30	...	Brousa ....dep	2 0	...
Brousa ....arr	9 0	...	Moudania.........arr	3 30	...

KONIA and KARA-POUNAR.

Konia ....dep	6a30	Kara-Pounardep	7a40
Karaman	9 35	Eregli	1 20
Eregli.................	1250	Karaman	3 51
Kara-Pounar ...	5p35	Konia ....arr	6 35

MAMOURE and DORAK.

...	Mamoure...............dep	6a30	Dorak...............dep	2 p0
...	Toprak Kalé	7 10	Yénidjé	2 45
...	Djihan	8 10	Adana (New Station)	4 0
...	Adana (New Station) 326..	9 30	Djihan	5 30
...	Yénidjé	1055	Toprak Kalé	6 30
...	Dorak ....arr	1125	Mamouré ....arr	7 0

PHILIPPOPOLI and BOURGAS.

Philippopoli	...	...	...	Bourgas (Port)	...	...
Tchirpan	...	...	...	Zimnitza	...	...
Yeni Saghra...	...	...	...	Jamboli............	...	...
Jamboli.........	...	...	...	Yeni Saghra......	...	...
Zimnitza	...	...	...	Tchirpan	...	...
Bourgas (P) ar	...	...	...	Philippopoli ...	...	...

Zimnitza dep	12p50	5p14	...	Sliven...dep	11a0	3p32	...
Sliven......arr	1 35	5 59	...	Zimnitza ar	1143	4 15	...

TIRNOVA and YENI SAGHRA.

	a.m.			a.m.	
Tirnova ......dep	9 15	...	Yeni Saghra dep	6 6	...
Radné-Mahalessi	10 16	...	Radné-Mahalessi	7 10	...
Yeni Saghra arr	11 14	...	Tirnova 326...arr	8 15	...

ESKI-CHEHIR and KONIA.

	a.m.		a.m.	
Eski-Chehir.........dep	5 0	Konia............dep	5 0	...
Alayund	7 33	Ilghin	9 3	...
Afion-Karahissar 326A	11 1	Ak-Chehir	10 53	...
Ak-Chehir	2 16	Afion-Karahissar	2 13	...
Ilghin	4 8	Alayund	5 42	...
Konia ....arr	8 0	Eski-Chehir...arr	8 0	...

Alayund......dep	7 a35	5 p45	Kutahia ......dep	6 a38	4 p32
Kutahia ......arr	7 55	6 5	Alayund ......arr	6 58	4 52

ESKI-CHEHIR and ANGORA.

Eski-Chehir......dep	7 a0	Angora ....dep	8 a0	...
Sarikeuy	10 9	Polatli	1116	...
Polatli	1 3	Sarikeuy	2 1	...
Angora ....arr	4 0	Eski-Chehir ......arr	5 0	...

MERSINA, TARSUS, and ADANA.

E.M		a.m.	p.m.		a.m.	p.m.
	Mersina...dep	7 30	4 27	Adana.....dep	7 40	4 5
16½	Tarsus	8 28	5 13	Tarsus	8 53	5 40
41½	Adana......arr	9 53	6 22	Mersina..arr	9 38	6 30

SOFIA and VARNA.

East Europe Time.

E.M.			a.m.	p.m.	p.m.	p.m.	
—	Sofia	dep	7 33	1 44	7 45	10 0	...
54¾	Mezdra-Vr.		9 29	3 57	11 7	12 16	...
120	Plevna........................	arr	11 52	6 40	—	2 55	...
		dep	12 0	7 10	...	3 3	...
149¼	Levski (326)		1 12	8 57	...	4 32	...
182¾	Gornia-Orehovitza	arr	2 22	10 57	...	6 7	...
...	Gornia-Orehovitza	dep	2 26	...	...	7 30	...
254¼	Rustchuck...............	arr	5 43	...	...	1 10	...
...	GIURGIU steamer......	arr	6 30	...	...	2 p50	...
...	BUCHAREST (324)......	arr	9 p40	...	...	5 p35	...
...	Gornia-Orehovitza	dep	2 35	11 35	...	6 22	...
220	Poppovo		4 13	2 8	...	8 24	...
270¼	Choumla	arr	5 58	4 24	...	10 28	...
		dep	6 4	4 36	...	10 37	...
285¼	Kaspitchan	arr	6 32	5 7	...	11 8	...
		dep	6 48	5 22	...	11 22	...
33 6	Varna..........................	arr	8 p46	7 a33	...	1 p29	...

		a.m.		p.m.	p.m.	
Varna	dep	7 55	...	4 10	11 12	...
Kaspitchan	arr	9 55	...	6 18	1 27	...
	dep	10 5	...	6 33	1 33	...
Choumla	arr	10 36	...	7 6	2 6	...
	dep	10 45	...	7 12	2 14	...
Poppovo......................		12 36	...	9 16	4 43	...
Gornia-Orehovitza	arr	2 13	...	11 5	7 14	...
BUCHAREST	dep	7 a35	...	...	...	...
GIURGIU stmr.	dep	10a30	...	p.m.	...	...
Rustchuck	dep	11 a5	...	3 45	...	...
Gornia-Orehovitza ...	arr	2 18	...	10 0	...	...
Gornia-Orehovitza	dep	2 33	...	11 20	7 35	...
Levski.........................		3 49	...	12 48	9 34	...
Plevna	arr	4 56	...	1 59	10 58	...
	dep	5 4	a.m.	2 7	11 53	...
Mezdra-Vr.		7 30	2 0	5 0	2 43	...
Sofia (325A)...............	arr	9 p38	6 50	7 a32	5 p25	...

Gornia-Orehovitza...dep	7a25	2p40	11p30	...	...	...	...
Tirnovo	8 0	3 15	12 7	...	...	...	...
Platchkovtzi ....arr	1137	6 42	...	...	...	...	...

Platchkovtzi dep	...	9a30	7p15	...	...	...	...	...
Tirnovo	5a40	1 0	1020	...	...	...	...	...
Gornia-O.......arr	6 15	1 38	1058	...	...	...	...	...

Levski...dep	5 a0	4p10	Sistov ...dep	10a45	10p0
Sistov ...arr	7 7	6 8	Levski ...arr	12 40	12 0

PLEVNA and SOMOVIT.

Plevna......dep	7 a0	7 p5	Somovit dep	10 a0	10p0
Somovit ...arr	8 30	8 35	Plevna...arr	11 26	1130

RUSTCHUCK and VARNA.

BUCHAREST ....dep	7 a35	...
GIURGIU (stm.)...dep	10a30	...
	p.m.	...
Rustchuck Quai dep	...	p.m.
„ Town ...	1 20	6 30
Kaspitchan	6 10	1238
Varna..................arr	8 46	...

	a.m.	a.m.
Varna ....dep	...	7 55
Kaspitchan	5 30	11 15
Rustchuck Town ar	1140	3 35
„ Quai arr	...	...
GIURGIU (stm.)...arr	2p50	6 p30
BUCHAREST (324) arr	5p35	9 p40

MONTENEGRO.—ANTIVARI and VIR.

E.M						
	Antivari.........dep	9a10	...	Vir-Pazar......dep	1p50	...
...	Vir-Pazar ......arr	12 0	...	Antivari ....arr	5 0	...

VARNA and DOBRITCH.

Varna......dep	12 0	7p18	Dobritch...dep	5a16	12p15	...
Valtchi Dol...	3 43	10 3	Valtchi Dol...	6 37	2 12	...
Dobritch...arr	5 27	1122	Varna ......arr	8 58	5 30	...

SMYRNA and DINAIR.

Dist E.M.			Not on Sunday.		a.m.		p.m.		
	Smyrna (L.Pointe) dep		...	...	7 0	...	1 0	...	...
30	Turbali			...	8 41	...	4 0	...	...
47½	⋮ Baïndir			...	...	...	5 20	...	...
68½	⋮ Odemish arr			...	...	...	6 45	...	...
48	Ayasoulouk (Ephesus)			a.m.	9 45	p.m.	—	...	...
61¾	Balachik	a.m.		7 35	10 56	2 50	...	...	...
80¾	Aidin	5 40	a.m.	9 25	12 14	4 35	...	...	...
108¾	Nazli	8 5	5 55	11 40	2 9	6 55	...	...	...
143½	Seraikeuy	1040	8 10	—	4 19	—	...	...	...
...	Gondscheli	1125	9 13	...	4 57	...	...	...	...
161¾	Denizli	1150	...	...	5 22	...	...	...	...
221½	Sutledj	...	2 0	...	—	...	...	...	...
234	**Dinair** arr	...	2 42	...	...	...	...	...	...

			a.m.	a.m.		p.m.		
Dinair dep	...	...	...	9 53	...	...	...	...
Sutledj	...	...	...	1037	...	...	...	...
Denizli	...	...	7 0	...	...	1235	...	...
Gondscheli	...	...	7 23	3 24	...	1 10	...	...
Seraikeuy	...	a.m.	8 9	4 15	p.m.	2 10	...	...
Nazli	...	5 40	10 11	6 18	12 33	4 47	...	...
Aidin	...	8 17	12 13	Not on Monday.	3 20	7 7	...	...
Balachik	...	10 50	1 38		5 30	—	...	...
Ayasoulouk	a.m.	—	2 48		—	...	...	...
⋮ Odemish dep	5 45	...	...		...	...	...	...
⋮ Baïndir	7 30	...	...		...	...	...	...
Turbali	8 55	...	3 44	...	...	...	...	...
Smyrna arr	1120	...	5 40	...	...	...	...	...

E.M.							
	Dinair dep	2*p43	...	...	Koule Eunu dep	7†a12	
43	Koule Eunu arr	5 46	...	...	Dinair arr	9 50	

*—Sunday 6.26 p.m.
†—Monday 6.43 a.m.

Balachik dep	10a50	5 p30	...	**Sokia** dep	6 a0	12p20	...
Sokia arr	11 40	6 25	...	**Balachik** arr	6 55	1 20	...

Sutledj dep	2 p10	...	**Chivril** dep	7a40	...
Chivril arr	3 25	...	**Sutledj** arr	9 20	...

SMYRNA and AFION KARAHISSAR.

Dist. E.M.					
	Smyrna dep	7 a0	11a20	...	...
20	Menemen	8 1	12 57	...	...
41	Magnesia	9 5	2 35	...	...
58½	Cassaba	9 57	3 52	...	...
77	Sardes	...	5 7	p.m.	...
82	Salihli	1111	5 24	5 ‡39	...
105	Alascheir	1250	—	7 5	...
178½	Ouchak	6 20	5a35	—	...
222½	Toumlou Pounar	—	8 33	...	...
261	**Afion Karahissar** S.C.P. arr		10 30	...	...
262½	„ „ C.F.O.A. arr		10 45	...	...

				p.m.
Afion C.F.O.A. dp		...	...	2 35
Karahis. S.C.P. dp		...	...	2 40
Toumlou Pounar		...	...	5 19
Ouchak	a.m.	...	7a50	8 0
Alascheir	6*20	...	1 20	—
Salihli	7 45	8 a0	2 46	...
Sardes	—	8 21	...	...
Cassaba		9 53	4 0	...
Magnesia		11 30	5 0	...
Menemen		1 10	6 3	...
Smyrna arr		2 40	7 10	...

Dist.			
...	**Magnesia** dep	3 p5	...
31¾	**Akhissar**	5 17	...
57½	**Soma** arr	7 0	...
...	**Soma** dep	7 a0	...
...	**Akhissar**	9 0	...
...	**Magnesia** arr	11 5	...

***—On Weds. and Sats. only.**
‡—On Tues. and Fri. only.

JAFFA and JERUSALEM.

E.M	1 Cl. P	2 Cl P		a.m.	p.m.		a.m.	p.m.
—			Jaffa dep	8 5	2 0	Jerusalem dep	7 40	2 20
12½	16 10	6 0	Lydda	8 47	2 40	Bittir	8 7	2 48
14¼	18 30	7 0	Ramleh	8 59	2 53	Deir Aban	9 19	4 2
24¾	32 20	12 0	Sejed	9 43	3 36	Sejed	9 44	4 30
31¾	41 20	15 0	Deir Aban	1015	4 5	Ramleh	10 23	5 10
47¼	61 30	22 0	Bittir	1128	5 18	Lydda	10 32	5 20
54	70 20	25 0	Jerusalem arr	12 0	5 50	Jaffa arr	11 10	6 0

1st class Return Tickets are issued, Jaffa-Jerusalem or Jerusalem-Jaffa, fare 95 piastres = 16s. valid three days.
The fares are shown in Medjidie Piastres; 20 piastres equal about 3s. 4d. 119 piastres = £1.

BEYROUT and DAMASCUS.

E.M.	1 Cl. fr. c.	2 Cl. fr. c.	3 Cl. fr. c.		a.m.	p.m.	p.m.	
—				**Beyrout** (Port) dep	7 20	...	10 50	...
—	—	—	—	„ (Station) dep	7 33	...	11 8	...
15	4 11	2 74	1 37	Aley	9 41	...	1 50	...
31	8 52	5 68	2 84	Jedideh-Shtora	1151	...	4 22	...
36½	10 2	6 68	3 34	Zahleh-Mallakah	1225	6 1	4 50	...
42¾	11 76	7 84	3 92	**Rayak** arr	1245	6 23	5 10	...
62½	17 31	11 54	5 77	Zebdani	2 46	8 45	7 20	...
78¾	21 69	14 46	7 23	Ain-Figeh	3 50	9 43	8 21	...
89½	25 20	16 80	8 40	**Damascus** Beramkieh arr	4 47	10 45	9 30	...
91¼	25 70	17 15	8 57	„ Meidan arr	5 0	10 58	9 a43	...

	a.m.	p.m.	p.m.	
Damascus Meidan dep	6 55	12 40	11 20	...
„ Beramkieh dep	7 30	1 10	11 55	...
Ain-Figeh	8 23	2 19	1 4	...
Zebdani	9 32	3 57	2 39	...
Rayak dep	11 20	6 30	5 20	...
Zahleh-Mallakah	11 50	7 0	5 40	...
Jedideh-Shtora	12 21	7 27	—	...
Aley	2 36	9 47	...	...
Beyrout (Station) arr	4 0	11 10	...	...
„ (Port) arr	4 10	11 20	...	...

RAYAK and ALEPPO.

E.M.	fr. c.	fr. c.	fr. c.		a.m.	p.m.	
—	—	—	—	**Rayak** dep	5 50	1 ‡10	...
16¾	3 60	2 62	1 42	Baalbec	7 4	2 20	...
81¼	17 25	12 0	6 74	Homs	10 46	—	...
117¼	24 84	17 30	9 77	Hama	12 45	...	...
206¾	...	...	...	**Aleppo** arr	5 20	...	...

	a.m.	a.m.
Aleppo dep	...	6 0
Hama	...	1048
Homs	...	1 20
Baalbec	9 ‡40	5 8
Rayak arr	10 40	5 55

‡—Enquire whether running.

E.M			
	Homs dep	2 p0	...
...	El-Hadideh	3 35	...
63½	Tripoli arr	6 0	...
...	Tripoli dep	6 a0	...
...	El-Hadideh	8 33	...
...	Homs arr	10 0	...

BEYROUT and MAMELTEIN.

E M						
	Beyrout (Port) dep	8 a5	11a25	2p40	6 p0	...
...	„ (Station) ... „	8 20	11 41	2 56	6 16	...
...	Debayeh	8 48	12 9	3 24	6 44	...
...	Nahr-el-Kelb (Dog River)	8 53	12 14	3 29	6 49	...
...	Antura	8 59	12 20	3 35	6 55	...
14¼	**Mameltein** arr	9 20	12 40	4 0	7 15	...

Mameltein dep	6a20	9a40	1 p0	4p20	...
Antura	6 39	9 58	1 20	4 38	...
Nahr-el-Kelb	6 46	10 5	1 27	4 45	...
Debayeh	6 58	1016	1 38	4 56	...
Beyrout (Station) arr	7 24	1040	2 2	5 20	...
„ (Port) ... „	7 42	1055	2 20	5 35	...

DAMASCUS and MZERIB.

E.M.	fr. c.	fr. c.	fr. c.		
				Damascus Meidan dep	7 a0
34	9 36	6 24	3 12	Sanamen	9 18
51	14 22	9 48	4 74	Shekh Meskin	10 35
64	17 82	11 88	5 94	**Mzerib** arr	11 30

On Sun., Tues., Thurs., and Sat. only.

Mzerib dep	12p30
Shekh Meskin	1 37
Sanamen	3 1
Damascus Meidan arr	5 30

On Sun., Tues., Thurs., and Sat. only.

DAMASCUS, HAIFA, and MECCA.

Dist. E.M.		a.m.	a.m.
	Damascus dep	7 30 Mon, Wed, Sat.	6 35
77	Deraa arr	12p23 „ „ „	11 10
...	Deraa dep	... ——	11a40
123	Samach (Tiberias)	... ——	2 52
154	El Fule (Nazareth)	... ——	4 42
177	**Haifa** arr	... ——	6 0
...	Deraa	12p55 Mon, Wed, Sat.	...
138½	Aman	5 p37 „ „ „	...
286	Mahan	3 a59 Tues, Thur, Sun.	...
809½	Medina	2 p51 Wed, Fri, Mon.	...
...	**Mecca** arr	In construction.	

		a.m.
Mecca dep	...	... ——
Medina	...	8 36 Tues, Thurs, Sat.
Mahan	...	6 p45 Wed, Fri, Sun.
Aman	...	4 a21 Thur, Sat, Mon.
Deraa arr	a.m.	8 a6 „ „ „
Haifa dep	6 0	... ——
El Fule (Nazareth)	7 17	... ——
Samach (Tiberias)	9 13	... ——
Deraa arr	12 29	... ——
Deraa dep	12p56	9 a50 Thurs, Sat, Mon.
Damascus arr	5 25	3 p10 „ „ „

ALEXANDRIA and CAIRO.

[No free allowance of Luggage.

SLEEPING CAR in 11.30 p.m. from Alexandria and in 11.30 p.m. from Cairo. RC—Restaurant Car attached.

Dist E.M	Alexandria—	1,2,3	1,2,3 a.m.	1,2,3 a.m	1,2,3	1,2,3	1,2,3 a.m.	1,2,3 a.m.	1,2,3	1,2,3 a.m.	1 & 2 noon	1,2,3	1,2,3 p.m	1,2,3 p.m.	1,2,3 p.m.	1,2,3 p.m.	1,2,3	1,2,3 p.m	1,2,3 p.m.
...	Rab-el-Ghedid dep	...	5 25	7 0	...	...	7 20	9 0	...	10 0	12 0	...	1 50	3 0	4 0	6 0	...	7 0	11 30
4¼	Sidi-Gabir	...	5 39	7 10	...	...	7 34	9 10	...	1014	12 10	...	2 4	3 10	4 10	6 10	...	7 14	11 45
18¾	Kafr-Dawar	...	6 16	...	...	...	8 10	...	...	1050	...	...	2 40	...	4 31	RC	...	7 51	12 20
42¼	Damanhour	...	7 13	7 58	...	...	9 7	9 58	...	1147	12 58	...	4 15	...	5 3	6 58	...	8 48	1 20
59	Teh-el-Baroud	...	7 50	8 22	...	...	9 43	...	...	1223	RC	...	4 54	...	5 27	...	...	9 25	2 3
70¾	Kafr-Zayat	...	8 17	8 41	...	...	10 9	1036	...	1249	...	...	5 22	...	5 46	7 36	...	9 52	2 34
82¾	**Tanta** arr	a.m.	8 40	8 58	a.m.	a.m.	1032	1053	...	1 12	1 48	p.m.	5 45	4 43	6 3	7 53	...	1015	3 0
...	,, dep	6 0	—	9 2	9 15	1040	1115	1057	p.m.	2 30	1 51	RC	6 20	4 46	6 7	7 57	p.m.	—	3 10
109¼	**Benha**	7 5	...	9 41	1014	1119	1225	1136	1216	3 35	2 28	4 23	7 22	5 23	6 46	8 36	1016	...	4 20
129¾	Calioub or Kalyub	7 53	...	...	11 3	...	1 12	...	...	4 23	...	...	8 13	...	...	...	RC	...	5 8
139¼	**Cairo** arr	8 15	...	1020	1125	12 0	1 35	1215	1255	4 45	3 5	5 0	8 35	6 0	7 25	9 15	1055	...	5 30

	1,2,3	1,2,3 a.m.	1,2,3 a.m.	1,2,3 a.m.	1,2,3 a.m.	1,2,3 a.m.	1,2,3 a.m.	1,2,3 a.m.	1 & 2 noon	1,2,3 p.m.	1,2,3 p.m.	1,2,3 p.m.	1,2,3 p.m.	1,2,3 p.m.	1,2,3 p.m.	1,2,3 p.m.	1,2,3 p.m.
Cairo dep	...	6 0	7 0	7 15	7 30	8 20	9 30	11 0	12 0	12 10	3 0	3 10	4 15	6 15	6 35	7 20	1130
Calioub	...	6 23	...	...	...	8 44	...	RC	...	12 34	...	3 35	...	RC	RC	7 46	1155
Benha	...	7 13	7 38	7 56	8 12	9 34	1012	1138	12 41	1 20	3 41	4 27	4 57	6 53	7 17	8 38	1247
Tanta arr	a.m.	8 7	—	8 30	8 46	1030	1046	—	1 15	2 15	4 15	5 23	5 36	—	7 51	9 35	1 49
,, dep	5 50	8 12	...	—	8 50	11 0	1050	...	1 18	2 25	4 18	5 50	5 40	...	7 55	—	1 56
Kafr-Zayat	6 15	8 38	...	...	9 9	1125	11 9	...	...	2 50	...	6 15	5 59	...	8 14	...	2 26
Teh-el-Baroud	6 41	9 38	...	...	9 27	1151	...	...	RC	3 15	...	6 41	6 17	...	8 32	...	2 56
Damanhour	7 19	1016	...	...	9 53	1230	1148	...	2 10	3 53	...	7 20	6 43	...	8 58	...	3 40
Kafr-Dawar	8 15	1113	...	...	...	1 26	...	...	...	4 49	...	8 16	...	...	...	...	4 36
Sidi-Gabir	8 52	1151	...	...	1041	2 2	1236	...	2 57	5 26	5 52	8 52	7 31	...	9 46	...	5 17
Alexandria arr	9 5	12 5	...	...	1050	2 15	1245	...	3 5	5 40	6 0	9 5	7 40	...	9 55	...	5 30

FARES FROM CAIRO.

	1st Class.	2nd Class.
To Alexandria	£0 18 0	£0 9 0
,, Port Said	£0 19 6	£0 9 9
,, Luxor	£2 2 2	£1 1 2
,, Shellal	£2 13 4	£1 6 8

CAIRO, WASTA, ASSIOUT, and LUXOR.

Dist E.M		1,2,3	1,2,3	1,2,3	1,2,3	1,2,3 a.m.	1,2,3 a.m.	1,2,3 a.m.	1,2,3 p.m.	1,2,3 p.m.	1,2,3 p.m.	1,2,3 p.m.	1,2,3 p.m.	1,2,3 p.m.	
—	**Cairo** dep	...	...	...	...	7 0	8 30	9 30	2 0	2 30	5 30	6 35	8 0	9 30	...
8¾	Ghizeh	...	...	...	...	7 30	...	9 59	2 22	3 1	5 52	7 3	...	...	...
20½	Bedresheyn	...	...	...	...	8 5	...	1035	2 41	3 38	...	7 38	A	...	...
36¾	Ayat	...	...	...	a.m.	8 45	...	1115	3 5	4 18	6 30	8 19	...	...	...
57¼	**Wasta**	...	...	...	6 40	10 8	9 54	12 7	3 33	5 11	7 4	9 5	9 24	10 55	...
77	Benisouef	...	...	...	7 32	11 0	1029	1259	—	6 2	7 38	—	10 0	11 31	...
111¾	Megaga	...	...	...	9 0	1229	1125	2 19	...	7 30	8 46	...	1057	12 28	...
134¼	Kolossana	...	a.m.	a.m.	10 5	1 33	...	3 18	...	8 34	...	...	...	...	...
153½	Minieh	...	5 30	8 10	11 5	2 28	1234	4 55	...	9 20	10 5	...	12 9	1 39	...
177	Rodah	...	6 30	9 14	1213	3 33	1 27	5 58	...	—	—	...	...	...	...
194½	Deyrout	...	7 16	9 58	1 0	4 20	2 11	6 46	...	...	...	...	1 37	3 29	...
215½	Manfalout	a.m.	8 10	1043	1 53	5 9	3 7	7 38	...	...	...	...	A	4 8	...
233	**Assiout**	5 10	8 51	1120	2 50	5 50	3 46	8 15	...	...	...	...	2 50	4 40	...
259¾	Tema	6 15	9 55	—	3 55	6 54	4 45	—	...	...	...	...	3 42	—	...
270	Tahta	6 43	1021	...	4 23	7 21	5 8	...	...	...	...	...	4 3	...	...
290	Sohag	7 34	1113	...	6 15	8 5	5 53	...	...	...	...	...	4 47	...	...
312	Ghirgueh	8 31	1216	...	7 10	—	6 38	...	...	...	...	...	5 31	...	...
322	Baliana	8 59	1242	...	7 38	...	7 0	...	...	...	...	...	5 51	...	...
344	Nagh-Ham.	10 4	1 38	...	8 35	...	7 48	...	...	...	...	...	6 38	...	...
359	Dechena	1045	2 22	...	—	...	8 28	...	...	...	...	...	7 10	...	...
378	Keneh	1133	3 12	...	...	...	9 14	...	...	...	...	...	7 50	...	...
417	**Luxor** arr	1255	4 45	...	...	...	1030	...	...	...	...	...	9 10	...	...

	1,2,3	1,2,3	1,2,3	1,2,3	1,2,3	1,2,3	1,2,3 a.m.	1,2,3 a.m.	1,2,3	1,2,3 a.m.	1,2,3 p.m.	1,2,3	1,2,3 p.m.	
Luxor dep	...	...	...	...	...	...	...	7 20	...	11 0	3 25	...	6 10	...
Keneh	...	...	...	...	...	...	...	8 43	...	1226	4 49	...	7 28	...
Dechena	...	...	...	...	...	...	...	9 27	...	1 13	5 32	...	8 5	...
Nagh-Hamadi	...	...	...	...	...	...	7 30	10 7	...	2 3	6 9	...	8 41	...
Baliana	...	...	...	...	...	...	8 32	1054	...	2 57	7 4	...	9 25	...
Ghirgueh	...	...	...	...	...	a.m.	9 2	1118	...	3 22	7 38	...	9 48	...
Sohag	...	...	...	...	...	6 0	10 5	12 7	...	4 19	8 37	...	1035	...
Tahta	...	...	...	...	...	6 45	1057	1245	...	5 9	9 20	...	B	...
Tema	...	...	...	...	a.m.	7 13	1126	1 10	p.m.	5 38	9 46	p.m.	1133	...
Assiout	...	...	...	...	7 0	10 0	1235	2 5	4 0	6 56	1045	11 15	1227	...
Manfalout	...	...	...	...	7 39	10 40	1 16	...	4 38	7 35	—	11 51	...	...
Deyrout	...	...	...	...	8 29	11 30	2 8	3 18	5 30	8 24	...	12 33	1 39	...
Rodah	...	a.m.	a.m.	...	9 15	12 16	2 52	...	6 26	9 11	...	...	...	...
Minieh	...	5 15	6 50	...	1025	2 30	5 0	4 52	7 25	1010	...	2 22	3 12	...
Kolossana	...	6 4	...	...	1116	3 21	5 48	...	—	—	...	...	B	...
Megaga	...	7 9	8 5	...	1224	4 27	6 52	5 58	...	...	...	3 26	4 16	...
Benisouef	a.m.	8 36	9 12	p.m.	2 0	5 56	8 19	6 55	...	...	...	4 23	5 12	...
Wasta	6 25	10 0	9 46	3 15	3 30	7 45	9 5	7 31	...	...	...	4 59	5 46	...
Ayat	7 17	1053	1016	3 46	4 23	8 35	—	...	...	...	...	...	...	...
Bedresheyn	7 59	1136	...	4 10	5 6	9 15	...	...	...	...	...	...	...	...
Ghizeh	8 37	1215	...	...	5 46	9 52	...	...	...	...	...	...	...	...
Cairo arr	9 5	1245	1115	4 45	6 15	10 20	...	8 50	...	...	...	6 20	7 5	...

A—Sleeping and Restaurant Cars attached on Mon., Wed., and Sat.

B—Sleeping and Restaurant Cars on Sun., Tues., and Thurs.

LUXOR and CHALLAL (Philae).

*-Mon, Wed, Fri. only. ‡-Sun, Tues, Thur. only.

	1,2,3	1,2,3	1,2,3	1,2,3 a.m.	1,2,3 A a.m.	1,2,3 p.m.	
Luxor dep	...	...	...	5 30	10 0	3‡10	...
Armant	...	...	...	6 17	1036	3 56	...
Esneh	...	a.m.	...	7 46	1140	5 20	...
Edfou	...	5 *0	...	9 47	1 7	7 0	...
Khattara	a.m.	8 27	a.m.	1 26	3 42	—	...
Assouan Town	7 0	9 15	1030	2 5	4 9	...	...
Challal Phil. arr	7 22	...	1052	2 52	4 40	...	...

§-Tues. Thurs., and Sat. only.

	1,2,3	1,2,3 a.m.	1,2,3 B a.m.	1,2,3 a.m.	1,2,3 no'n	1,2,3 p.m.	1,2,3 p.m.	
Challal Philae dep	...	...	8 20	9 40	12 0	...	6 15	...
Assouan Town	...	5 15	8 50	10 2	12 22	3 *0	6 37	...
Khattara	a.m.	5 54	9 20	—	—	3 41	—	...
Edfou	5 §40	9 34	1155	...	...	7 5	...	...
Esneh	7 38	1137	1 22	...	...	—	...	...
Armant	8 58	1258	2 25	...	...	...	...	...
Luxor arr	9 40	1 40	3 0	...	...	...	...	...

A — Restaurant Car on Tues., Thurs., and Sat.

B — Restaurant Car on Sun., Wed., and Fri.

Challal and Wadi Halfa—Between these two places the travel is by Steamer, see page 361.

PORT SAID to CAIRO, via BENHA.

Through Carriages on Wednesday to Suez Docks in 11.0 a.m. from Cairo.

Dist E.M	Port Said—	1,2,3	1,2,3	1,2,3	1,2,3 a.m.	1,2,3	1,2,3 p.m.	1,2,3	1,2,3 p.m.	1,2,3 p.m.
	Gare Maritime	¶	...	...	...	...	...	...	...	...
—	Town Station dep		...	...	8 5	...	1 0	...	4 30	6 40
28	**Kantara**	...	...	...	9 3	...	RC	...	5 32	...
$47\frac{3}{4}$	**Ismailia** arr	...	a.m.	...	9 43	...	2 22	p.m.	6 15	7 57
	Ismailia dep	...	6 20	...	9 49	...	2 26	3 0	—	8 5
$64\frac{1}{2}$	**Mahsame**	...	6 58	...	10 25	...	...	3 39	...	8 36
$78\frac{1}{4}$	Tel-el-Kebir	...	7 31	...	10 54	...	...	4 12	...	RC
$85\frac{1}{4}$	Abu Hamad	...	7 51	...	11 7	...	...	4 28	...	...
97	**Zagazig** arr	a.m.	8 16	a.m.	11 31	p.m.	3 44	4 54	...	9 29
	Zagazig dep	6 0	8 22	10 10	11 35	2 35	3 48	5 2	...	9 35
148	**Benha** arr	6 55	9 20	11 10	12 11	3 30	4 19	6 0	...	10 11
$157\frac{1}{2}$	CAIRO arr	8 a15	10a20	12 15	12p55	4p45	5 p0	7 p25	...	10p55

		1,2,3	1,2,3	1,2,3	1,2,3	1,2,3	1,2,3	1,2,3	1,2,3
CAIRO dep		7 a0	7 a30	9 a30	11 a0	12p10	4 p15	6 p15	6 p35
		a.m.	a.m.	a.m.	a.m.	p.m.	p.m.	p.m.	p.m.
Benha dep		7 42	8 25	10 30	11 46	1 25	5 10	7 0	7 30
Zagazig arr	...	8 19	9 25	11 24	12 18	2 20	6 3	7 37	8 30
Zagazig dep	...	8 23	—	11 32	12 24	—	6 22	7 42	—
Abu Hamad	...	8 48	...	11 59	...	...	6 49	RC	...
Tel-el-Kebir	...	9 3	...	12 15	RC	...	7 10	...	...
Mahsame	1,2,3	9 30	...	12 44	...	...	7 40	8 37	...
Ismailia arr	a.m.	10 4	...	1 18	1 43	...	8 20	9 6	...
Ismailia dep	6 50	10 11	...	—	1 51	...	—	9 12	...
Kantara	7 36	10 55	...	...	...	...	...	9 48	...
Port Said arr	8 40	11 50	...	...	3 10	...	...	10 35	...

RC—Restaurant Car attached.

[Europe bound Steamers often pass through Canal earlier than advertised. Their arrival at Suez is telegraphed to Cairo, where hour of stop at Ismailia and Port Said may be ascertained.]

¶—Connecting carriages from the Gare Maritime, alongside steamer landing place, as announced on board.

SUEZ and ISMAILIA.

	a.m.	noon	p.m.		
Suez Docks dep	7 25	...	5 †40	...	...
„ Rue Colmar	7 40	12 0	5 58	...	...
Faid	8 45	12 54	7 4	...	...
Nefische	9 18	1 24	7 38	...	...
Ismailia arr	9 25	1 30	7 45	...	...

	a.m.	p.m.	p.m.		
Ismailia dep	10 15	2 35	9 30	...	...
Nefishe	10 22	2 44	9 39	...	...
Faid	10 54	3 20	10 15	...	...
Suez Rue Colmar	11 45	4 22	11 17	...	...
„ **Docks** arr	...	4 40	11 35	...	...

†—On Sats. Through Carriages to Cairo.

EDFINA and ALEXANDRIA.

Edfina dep	4a55	2p45	**Alexandria**	7a30	3p20
Rosetta	5 57	3 45	Ramleh	7 53	3 46
Aboukir	7 50	...	Aboukir	...	4 24
Ramleh	8 23	5 46	Rosetta	9 48	6 2
Alexandria arr	8 45	6 15	**Edfina** arr	1050	7 0

CAIRO and MANSOURAH.

		a.m.	a.m.	a.m.	p.m.		p.m.
Cairo dep	...	5 45	7 40	11 10	2 40	...	5 15
Calioub	...	6 11	8 4	11 34	3 4	...	5 38
Shibin-el-Kanater	...	6 39	8 32	12 2	3 32	...	6 5
Bilbés	...	7 28	9 14	12 48	4 14	...	6 46
Bordein	...	7 42	9 28	1 2	4 32	...	7 0
Zagazig arr	a.m.	7 55	9 41	1 15	4 45	p.m.	7 13
Zagazig dep	6 35	—	9 46	1 25	5 0	7 30	7 54
Abou Kebir	7 13	...	10 21	2 2	5 34	8 2	8 30
Mansourah arr	8 35	...	11 40	3 30	7 0	...	10 0

		a.m.	a.m.	p.m.	p.m.	p.m.	p.m.
Mansourah dep	...	5 50	9 0	1235	4 10	...	8 0
Abou Kebir	...	7 15	10 24	2 0	5 34	8 40	9 38
Zagazig arr	a.m.	7 45	10 55	2 30	6 5	9 10	10 25
Zagazig dep	6 0	8 40	11 45	4 15	6 15	—	—
Bordein	6 15	8 55	12 0	4 30	6 29	...	...
Bilbés	6 30	9 16	12 14	4 45	6 45	...	...
Shibin-el-Kanater	7 11	9 59	12 56	5 30	7 25	...	...
Calioub	7 38	10 28	1 24	6 7	7 53	...	...
Cairo arr	8 0	10 50	1 45	6 30	8 15	...	...

El Merg dep	5a10	7a40	11a10	2p10	5 p10	7 p10
Shibin-el-Kanater **328** arr	5 50	8 20	11 50	2 50	5 50	7 50

Shibin-el-Kanater dep	6a20	10a20	1p20	4p20	6p20	8 p20	...
El Merg **328**A arr	7 0	11 0	2 0	5 0	7 0	9 0	...

CAIRO, BARRAGE, and TANTA.

Cairo dep	5 a10	7 a5	9 a10	10a45	1 p30	4 p0	...
Calioub	5 33	7 26	9 33	11 12	1 54	4 28	...
Barrage (New St.)	5 48	7 42	9 50	11 37	2 13	4 43	...
Achemoun	6 28	8 23	10 33	12 29	3 5	5 30	...
Menouf	7 19	9 10	11 29	1 35	3 56	6 27	9p30
Scibin-el-Com	7 54	9 53	12 4	2 13	4 31	7 0	10 5
Tanta arr	8 35	10 35	12 45	3 5	5 20	7 40	1045

Tanta dep	...	6 a0	9 a10	11a10	2 p30	4 p45	6 p15	8p 5
Scibin-el-Com	...	6 47	9 55	12 2	3 16	5 27	7 3	8 50
Menouf	...	7 23	10 30	12 38	3 57	6 0	7 39	9 20
Achemoun	6 a0	8 20	11 24	1 28	4 53	6 49	8 25	—
Barrage	6 45	9 0	12 5	2 15	5 38	7 30	—	...
Calioub	6 59	9 14	12 19	2 29	5 53	7 44	...	...
Cairo arr	7 20	9 35	12 40	2 50	6 15	8 2	...	...

Extra { Cairo to Barrage (Old Station) 7.55 a.m., 12.55, 5.40, 8.0 p.m.
Barrage (Old Station) to Cairo 8.40 a.m., 4.45, 6.35, 9.31 p.m.

CAIRO and TEH-EL-BAROUD.

Cairo—Sabtieh dep	6 a0	1p40	5 p0	...	...
Manachi	6 44	2 25	5 46	...	...
Kafr-Daoud	7 57	3 37	7 12	...	...
Teh-el-Baroud arr	9 0	4 40	8 20	...	...

Teh-el-Baroud dep	6a50	9 a50	5 p30	...	...
Kafr-Daoud	7 54	11 1	6 36	...	...
Manachi	9 6	12 21	7 49	...	...
Cairo-Sabtieh arr	9 50	1 5	8 30	...	...

WASTA and ABOUXA.

Wasta dep	6a50	10a20	3 p40	7p40	9 p35	...
Fayoum	8 0	11 16	4 30	9 0	10 25	...
Abouxa arr	8 40	1 15	...	9 40	...	...

Abouxa dep	...	6 a45	10a0	...	3 p20	...	...
Fayoum	5 a30	8 18	1050	2 p10	5 49	...	...
Wasta arr	6 20	9 15	1150	3 7	6 45	...	...

BENHA and MITBEREH.

Benha dep	6a15	8a25	12p50	5p30	7 p25
Mitbereh arr	6 35	8 45	1 15	5 50	7 45

Mitbereh dep	6a40	9 a0	2 p40	6 p0	7 p55
Benha arr	7 0	9 20	3 5	6 20	8 15

ABOU-KEBIR and SALHIEH.

Abou-Kebir dep	7a25	10a40	2p15	5 p45	8p45	...
Facous	7 50	11 7	2 42	6 12	9 12	...
Salhieh arr	8 22	11 40	3 15	6 45	9 45	...

Salhieh dep	5a50	8 a55	12p25	4 p0	7 p10	...
Facous	6 26	9 33	1 3	4 38	7 58	...
Abou-Kebir	6 47	9 55	1 25	5 0	8 20	...

SHIRBIN and KALLINE.

Shirbin dep	...	8a10	9a20	1p15	3p30	5p35	8p30
Belcas	a.m.	8 36	9 44	1 39	3 59	5 59	8 59
Bielah	5 15	8 56	10 0	1 58	4 20	6 15	9 15
Morabein	6 6	9 47	—	—	5 16	—	—
Kalline arr	7 10	1215	...	...	6 20	...	...

Kalline dep	...	...	10a25	...	2 p20	...	7p35
Morabein	a.m.	a.m.	11 25	...	3 22	p.m.	8 37
Bielah	7 0	1010	12 19	2p36	4 17	7 0	9 30
Belcas	7 18	1028	12 36	2 53	4 35	7 18	—
Shirbin arr	7 40	1050	1 0	3 15	5 0	7 40	...

DAMIETTA and TANTA.

Damietta dep	...	6 a30	9 a45	2 p0	4 p0	...	...
Shirbin	a.m.	7 55	11 0	3 22	5 23	7p50	...
Mansourah	7 10	9 0	11 45	4 0	6 0	8 25	8p35
Samanhood	7 40	9 34	12 19	4 29	6 34	—	9 40
Mehallet Roh	8 14	10 8	12 50	5 2	7 10	...	1050
Tanta arr	8 35	10 30	1 8	5 20	7 30	...	1115

Tanta dep	5a30	...	9 a8	11a 5	2 p0	...	6p15	8p10	...
Mehallet Roh	5 54	...	9 30	11 24	2 20	...	6 34	8 32	...
Samanhood	6 32	...	10 8	11 54	2 52	...	7 10	9 5	...
Mansourah	7 16	8 a40	10 40	12 30	3 21	4p50	7 46	9 35	...
Shirbin	7 54	9 10	—	1 6	—	5 30	8 24	—	...
Damietta arr	9 15	...	...	2 30	...	6 55	9 40	...	...

MIT-GHAMR and TANTA.

Mit-Ghamr .....dep	7 a0	8 a50	11a55	p5	5 p40	...	...
Zifte	7 10	9 0	12 5	3 15	5 50	...	...
Santa	7 27	9 17	12 27	3 30	6 7	...	...
Mehallet Roh	8 5	9 58	1 2	4 5	6 54	...	...
Tanta 328A ......arr	...	...	...	...	7 15	...	...

Tanta 328A ....dep	6a15	...	...	...	...	...	...
Mehallet Roh..............	6 45	9a35	11a45	2 p22	6 p50	...	...
Santa..........................	7 26	1020	12 25	2 58	7 30	...	...
Zifte	7 41	1039	12 44	3 19	7 49	...	...
Mit-Ghamr ....arr	7 50	1045	12 50	3 25	7 55	...	...

TANTA and DAMANHOUR.

	a.m.	a.m.	a.m.		a.m.	p.m.	p.m.	
Tanta ....dep	...	6 50	...	...	1115	2 10	6 0	...
Mehallet-Roh	...	7 12	9 33	...	1137	2 32	6 35	...
Kalline	6 0	8 9	10 20	a.m.	1230	3 27	7 29	...
Dessouk	6 31	8 46	—	11 0	1 5	4 0	8 1	...
Damanhour ...arr	7 5	9 20	...	11 38	1 40	4 35	8 35	...

		a.m.	a.m.	a.m.	p.m.	p.m.	p.m.	
Damanhour ......dep		8 10	10 5	11 10	2 15	5 15	9 0	...
Dessouk	a.m.	8 50	10 40	11 48	2 51	5 53	9 40	...
Kalline	7 15	9 25	—	12 25	3 26	6 28	10 10	...
Mehallet-Roh ...	8 4	1022	...	1 14	4 14	7 24	—	...
Tanta ....arr		1040	...	1 35	4 35	7 45	...	...

FAYOUM and SENNOURES.

Fayoum ...dep	8a30	11a55	4p35	9p10	...	...	...
Sennourès ...arr	9 0	12 25	5 0	9 40	...	...	...

Sennourès......dep	6a45	9a30	1p10	5p10	...	...	...	...	...
Fayoum ....arr	7 15	10 0	1 40	5 35	...	...	...	...	...

CAIRO and EL MERG.

Cairo Pont Limoun...dep	6 a0
Kubbeh......................	6 15
Metariyeh (Heliopolis)........	6 23
El Merg ....arr	6 31

From Cairo at 5.0, 5.30, 6.0, 6.30, and half hourly until 10.0 p.m.; **also at 10.45 p.m. 12.0 and 1.30 night. Maintaining relatively the times shewn in the column.** Return from El Merg 5.38, 6.8, 6.38, and half hourly until 10.38 p.m.; **also at** 9.2, 11.23 p.m., 12.38 and 2.8 night.

ALEXANDRIA and RAMLEH (San Stefano).—**Trains run at frequent intervals from 5.45 a.m.** until 12.0 night.

CAIRO (Bab-el-Louk) **and HELOUAN.** {Bab-el-Louk, Tourah ......, Helouan ...} **Trains run about hourly, from 6.0 a.m. until midnight.**

KHARTOUM, HALFA, PORT SUDAN, and SUAKIN. Sudan Government Railways.

Circular Tickets are obtainable for the round trip from Cairo to Khartoum and back via the Nile and Red Sea.

Dist. E.M.		Daily.	A	Tues. only.	Fri. only.	Sun. and Thur.
		a.m.	a.m.			
	Khartoum Central ......dep	7 30	11§20			
	,, North ....dep	7 58	11 33			
104	Shendi	1 p40	3 p30			
191	Atbara Junction ....arr	5 p55	6 p20	6 p30	7 p15	8p30
216	Berber		7 p26	7 p36	8 p20	10p3
345	Abu Hamed ....arr		12a10	1 a40	...	6 a5
575	**Halfa** ....arr		9 a50	12p30	...	...

	D	B	Daily.	G	
	p.m.	p.m.		p.m.	
Halfa ....dep	1 0	4 §0		...	...
Abu Hamed..........................	12a35	2 a35		2 5	...
Berber	6 a30	7 a15	...	10a10	...
Atbara Junction	7 a30	8 a20	8a40	11p30	...
Shendi	—	11a30	1p25	—	...
Khartoum North ....arr	...	3 p6	6p36	...	...
,, Central ......arr	...	3 p20	6p57	...	...

A—From Khartoum on Sunday and Thursday only.
B—From Halfa on Thursday and Saturday only.
D—From Halfa on Monday only.
G—On Sunday and Friday only.
§—Dining and Sleeping Cars.

Fares: Khartoum to Halfa, 1st cl. £E 5·850, 2nd cl. £E 4·095, 3rd cl. £E 2·050.

	F	
	a.m.	
Khartoum Central dep	11 20	...
,, North...dep	11 33	...
Shendi........................	3 p30	...
Atbara Junction ......arr	6 p20	...
Port Sudan ....arr	11a30	...

	H	
	p.m.	
Port Sudan ......dep	12 40	...
Atbara Junction	8 a20	...
Shendi	11a30	...
Khartoum North arr	3 p6	...
,, Central arr	3 p20	...

‡—Port Sudan Town Station.
H—From Port Sudan on Saturday and Thursday only.
F—From Khartoum on Saturday and Thursday only.

	a.m.	a.m.	p.m.	
Port Sudan Town ...dep	7 †30	9 ‡25	4 *15	...
Sallom	8 40	10 40	5 28	...
Suakin (Shata).........arr	9 52	11 44	6 40	...
	a.m.	p.m.	p.m.	
Suakin (Shata) ......dep	7 *30	12§30	5 ¶30	...
Sallom	9 0	2 5	7 0	...
Port Sudan Town......arr	9 50	2 53	7 50	...

*—Wednesday only.
‡—Mon. and Fri. only.
§—Thurs. and Sat. only.
¶—Friday only. †—Saturday only.

Fares: Khartoum to Port Sudan, 1st cl. £E 5·020, 2nd cl. £E 3·515, 3 cl. £E 1·755.

Abu Hamed ....dep	7 0 a.m. Mon. and Fri.
Kareima ....arr	4 45 p.m ,, ,,

Kareima ....dep	11 0 a.m. Thurs. and Sat.
Abu Hamed..................arr	8 30 p.m. ,, ,,

Dongola Reach Steamboat Service. {Kareima ....dep, Dongola ...., Kerma ....arr, Dongola ....dep, Kareima ....arr} Post Boat Service from Kareima about twice a month.

Khartoum Central..............dep	8 a0	...
Turabi	11 9	...
Wad Medani ....arr	2 p55	...
Wad Medani ....dep	3†p15	...
Sennar	7 8	...
Kosti ....arr	11 20	...

Wad Medani......................dep	9 a0	...
Turabi..................................	12p57	...
Khartoum Central ....arr	3 p55	...
	p.m.	
Kosti..................................dep	10‡30	...
Sennar	5 a0	...
Wad Medani ....arr	8 a25	...

‡—Tuesday and Saturday only.
†—Wednesday and Saturday only.

Kosti ....dep	4a†0	...
Um Ruaba	10a55	...
El Obeid ....arr	4p45	...

El Obeid ....dep	9a‖0	...
Um Ruaba..................	2p39	...
Kosti ....arr	9p20	...

†—Thursday and Sunday only.
‖—Tuesday and Saturday only.

NICOSIA and FAMAGUSTA.—Cyprus.

E.M	1 Cl.	2 Cl.	3 Cl.		a.m.	p.m.			
—	s. d.	s. d.	s. d.	**Nicosia** ....dep	7 0	3 0	...	...	...
14	2 3	1 1½	0 7	Angastina	8 15	3 50	...	...	...
36	6 0	3 0	2 0	**Famagusta** ....arr	10 5	5 2	...	...	...

	a.m.	p.m.		
Famagusta.........dep	8 35	2 0	...	...
Angastina	9 51	3 52	...	...
Nicosia ....arr	10 37	5 2	...	...

30 Kilog. (66 lbs.) of Luggage allowed free.

ALGIERS and ORAN.

	1,2,3	1,2,3	1,2,3	1,2,3	1,2,3	1,2,3	1,2,3	1,2,3	1,2,3
Algiers ......dep		6 7	...	...	8 0	10 0	1250	1720	21 §0
Hussein-Dey ...	...	6 23	...	...	RC	1017	13 8	1739	21 14
Maison Carrée...	...	6 34	...	...	8 22	1028	1314	1748	21 21
Boufarik	...	7 18	...	...	8 56	1118	14 0	1834	21 56
Blidah ......arr	...	7 45	...	...	9 18	1147	1429	19 3	22 19
„ 329) dep	...	8 0	...	...	9 28	12 3	1410	1920	22 28
La Chiffa	...	8 15	...	...	...	1218	1455	1937	22 38
El-Affroun	...	8 32	...	...	9 52	1251	1512	2010	22 53
Bou Medfa	...	—	...	...	1029	1335	—	2054	...
Miliana Marg'te	...	...	...	...	1110	1422		2143	...
Affreville arr	...	...	...	...	1126	1439		22 0	0 18
„ dep	5 5	...	...	...	1135	1513		—	0 27
Lavarande	5 15	...	...	...	1142	1525			...
Les Attafs.........	7 34	...	...	...	1248	1728			...
Pontéba...........	9 13	...	...	...	1329	1850			...
Orleansville	9 23	...	...	...	1336	19 0			2 6
„ dep	—	...	4 50	...	1344	—			2 14
Oued-Sly	...	...	5 19	...	14 3	...			...
Oued-Riou	...	...	6 39	...	1444	...	...		3 8
Djidiouïa	...	...	7 3	...	1456	...	...		...
Relizane ...arr	...	...	8 21	...	1531	...	...		3 53
„ ...dep	...	6 30	9 1	...	1538	...	...	RC	4 1
Oued-Malah...	...	7 43	10 46	...	1632	...	...		...
Perrégaux.........	...	8 22	11 15	1158	1657	19 4	...	...	5 14
St-Denis-du-S...	...	9 23	—	1256	1729	20 6	...	...	5 44
Ste-Barbe-du-T	7 45	10 44	...	1416	1813	2131	...	...	6 23
Valmy	8 13	11 10	...	1447	1831	2159	...	...	...
Oran ....arr	8 35	11 31	...	1513	1850	2220	...	...	6 58

§—Sleeping Car attached.

RC—Restaurant Car attached.

	1,2,3	1,2,3	1,2,3	1,2,3	1,2,3	1,2,3	1,2,3	1,2,3
Oran ....dep	...	5 30	...	...	10 5	13 10	17 20	21‡20
Valmy	...	5 49	...	...	10 21	13 31	17 39	21 36
Ste-Barbe-du-T.	...	6 30	...	...	10 47	14 18	18 20	22 0
St-Denis-du-S. ...	...	7 26	...	...	11 24	15 31	19 13	22 32
Perrégaux	...	8 14	8 34	...	12 2	16 19	20 4	23 5
Oued-Malah	...	—	9 13	...	RC	—	20 34	...
Relizane ...arr	...	...	10 42	...	13 11	...	21 50	0 11
„ ...dep	...	4 55	—	...	13 20	...	—	0 17
Djidiouïa...........	...	6 2	...	...	13 58	...		...
Oued-Riou	...	6 32	...	...	14 12	...		1 3
Oued-Sly...........	...	7 52	...	...	14 56	...		...
Orleansvillear	...	8 24	...	...	15 13	...		1 57
„ dep	...	—	5 25	8 54	15 22	...		2 7
Pontéba	...	...	5 37	9 6	15 30	...		...
Les Attafs	...	...	7 27	10 32	16 15	...		...
Lavarande	...	...	10 12	12 51	17 34	...		...
Affreville ...arr	...	...	10 25	13 0	17 41	...		3 57
„ ...dep	...	6 12	—	13 45	17 51	...	...	4 2
Miliana-Marguer	...	6 43	...	14 20	18 19	...	...	4 22
Bou-Medfa	...	7 21	...	14 58	18 51	...	...	...
El-Affroun	5 23	8 9	11 6	15 44	19 21	...	...	5 10
La Chiffa...........	5 43	8 34	11 24	15 4	19 36	...	...	...
Blidah ....arr	6 3	8 59	11 49	16 24	19 53	...	...	5 36
„ ....dep	6 18	9 19	12 4	16 41	20 3	...	...	5 45
Boufarik	6 40	9 41	12 26	17 5	20 24	...	...	6 1
Maison-Carrée ...	7 29	10 25	13 10	17 49	21 3	...	...	6 35
Hussein Dey	7 38	10 33	13 18	17 57	21 10	...	...	...
Algiers ......arr	7 54	10 47	13 36	18 15	21 25	...	...	6 52

‡—Sleeping Car attached.

EL AFFROUN and CHERCHELL.

E.M.					
	El Affroun ....dep	8 50	15 35	20 15	...
30½	Cherchell ....arr	11 31	18 26	22 56	...

Cherchell............dep	5 10	12 40	16 10	...	...
El Affroun ....arr	7 51	15 21	18 51	...	...

BLIDAH and BOGHARI.

E.M.							
	Blidah.................dep	7 55	14 45	1930	...	...	...
28	Lodi..............................	9 41	16 47	2130	...	...	...
30½	Medea............................	10 0	17 14	2144	...	...	...
51½	Berrouaghia	11 23	18 51	—	...	...	...
77 ●	Boghari ....arr	12 55	20 30	...	...	...	...

Boghari ....dep	...	5 50	13 40	...	...	...	...
Berrouaghia	...	7 46	15 35	...	...	...	...
Medea	6 45	9 26	17 18	...	...	...	...
Lodi	6 58	9 42	17 30	...	...	...	...
Blidah (329) ....arr	8 48	11 25	19 10	...	...	...	...

STE.-BARBE-DU-TLELAT and LALLA MAGHNIA.

E.M							
—	**Ste-Barbe-du-Tlélat**.........dep	6 35	1056	1420	1830	...	...
10	Lauriers-Roses	7 9	1138	1455	19 4	...	...
22¼	Les Trembles	7 44	1217	1529	1939	...	...
32¼	Sidi-bel-Abbés	8 20	1247	1610	2029	...	...
46½	Tabia..........................	9 3	—	1656	2114	...	...
67	Lamoricière	10 2	...	18 4	2210	...	...
86¼	Tlemcen	11 3	...	1920	23 0	...	...
123	**Lalla Maghnia** arr	1252	...	2114	...	...	...

Lalla-Maghnia ...dep	...	...	...	6 0	...	...	1425	...	...
Tlemcen	...	6 11	...	8 29	1232	...	1630	...	...
Lamoricière	...	7 6	...	—	1339	...	1728	...	...
Tabia......................	...	7 59	7 20	...	1444	1632	1824	...	...
Sidi-bel-Abbés	5 42	8 50	8 0	1210	16 0	1730	1929	...	...
Les Trembles	6 11	9 18	—	1241	1630	—	21 0	...	...
Lauriers-Roses	7 5	9 59	...	1332	1721	...	2050	...	...
Ste.-Barbe (329) arr	7 35	1028	...	14 2	1750	...	2120	...	...

Tabia ....dep	9 20	1718
Bedeau	12 7	20 5
Raselma Crampel arr	12 24	...

Raselma C. dep	...	1355	...
Bedeau	5 25	1418	...
Tabia ......arr	7 18	1626	...

Lalla-Maghnia dep	8 30	15 0
Zoudj-el-Beghal	8 51	1521

Zoudj-el-Beghal ......dep	9 15	16 0
Lalla Maghnia arr	9 31	1616

MOSTAGANEM and TIARET.

E.M.						
	Mostaganem ....dep	...	9 33	...	17 5	20 58
13	Ain Tedelis	...	10 24	...	17 58	21 45
29¼	Mekalia	...	11 24	...	18 59	...
47¼	Relizane (329)............arr	...	12 25	...	19 59	23 38
...	„ ....dep	4 50	13 30	15 54	—	—
83¼	Djilali-ben-Omar	6 52	15 36	18 2	...	...
122½	Tiaret ....arr	9 35	18 15	20 40	...	...

Tiaret ....dep	...	6 34	10 10	15 20	...	...
Djilali-ben-Omar	...	9 12	12 46	18 0	...	...
Relizane ....arr	...	11 26	15 2	20 13	...	...
„ ....dep	4 25	12 50	15 50	—	...	...
Mekalia	5 28	13 55	16 54	...	...	...
Ain Tedelis.........................	6 26	14 57	17 57	...	...	...
Mostaganem ....arr	7 13	15 43	18 44	...	...	...

LA MACTA and MOSTAGANEM.

E.M.						
	La Macta ....dep	8 19	15 15	19 31	...	...
18¾	Mostaganem ....arr	9 26	16 24	20 38	...	...

Mostaganem ....dep	4 35	11 6	16 3	...	...	...	...
La Macta (329A) ....arr	5 42	12 13	17 12	...	...	...	...

ALGIERS and AIN-TAYA.

E.M.						
	Algiers ....dep	6 9	13 29	17 49	...	...
20	Ain-Taya ....arr	8 21	15 37	19 57	...	...

Ain Taya ....dep	5 37	12 53	17 13	...	...	...	...
Algiers (329).................arr	7 45	15 5	19 25	...	...	...	...

ORAN to SAIDA and COLOMB-BECHAR.

E.M.								Tues., Thurs., and Sat. only.
—	**Oran** ... dep	...	...	5 45	...	12 40	17‡18	
17½	St. Cloud ...	...	...	6 46	...	13 42	18 15	
26	Damesme ... arr	...	...	7 20	...	14 14	18 49	
29¼	Arzew ... arr	...	...	7 41	...	14 35	19 10	
36¾	La Macta 329 ...	...	...	8 14	...	15 5	19 26	
55¼	**Perregaux 329** ...	...	6 15	9 26	1213	16 17	20 25	
85¾	Tizi ...	...	8 43	—	1428	—	22 33	
129¾	**Saïda** ... arr	...	1130	...	1718	...	0 59	...
...	,, ... dep	7 18	—	...	—	...	—	1‡10
157½	Kralfallah ...	9 24	...	...	...	...	...	2 48
192	El Kreider ...	1144	...	...	...	...	...	4 19
242¼	Mecheria ...	1447	...	...	...	...	...	6 29
305¾	Ain-Sefra ...	1837	...	...	...	...	...	9 38
379	Duveyrier ...	—	...	...	...	...	...	13 55
395¾	Béni-Ounif de Figu	...	...	...	...	...	...	14 57
433¾	Ben Zireg ...	...	...	...	...	...	...	16 35
465½	Colomb-Béchar arr	...	...	...	...	...	...	18 0

					Sun., Wed. & Fri. only.	
Colomb-Béchar ... dep	...	...	...	...	7‡33	...
Ben Zireg ...	...	...	...	...	9 3	...
Béni-Ounif de F.	...	...	...	...	10 53	...
Duveyrier ...	...	...	...	...	11 46	...
Ain-Sefra ... dep	...	...	4 53	...	16 16	...
Mecheria ...	...	...	8 44	...	19 8	...
El Kreider ...	...	...	11 55	...	21 14	...
Kralfallah ...	...	...	14 8	...	22 50	...
Saïda ... arr	...	...	16 2	...	0 18	...
,, ... dep	6‡0	11 1	—	1650		0 33
Tizi ...	8 56	14 19	...	1955		3 5
Perrégaüx ... dep	11 11	16 18	...	2156		4 59
La Macta ...	12 24	17 25	...	—		5 54
Arzew ... dep	12 44	17 46	...	...		6 14
Damesme ...	13 8	18 4	...	...		6 33
St. Cloud ...	13 43	18 41	...	...		7 11
Oran ... arr	14 43	19 40	...	...		8 10

‡-Restaurant Car attached.

E.M						
	Tizi ... dep	3 15	8 58	14 33	20 1	22 28	...
7½	Mascara ... arr	3 42	9 27	15 2	20 30	22 55	...

Mascara ... dep	2 30	8 0	13 35	19 10	21 45	...
Tizi ... arr	2 58	8 30	14 5	19 40	22 13	...

ORAN and AIN TEMOUCHENT.

E.M						
	Oran (Karguentah) ... dep	6 35	12 55	17 32	...	...
4½	La Senia ...	6 52	13 16	17 43	...	...
29¾	Lourmel ...	8 5	14 36	18 50	...	...
47¾	**Ain Temouchent** ... arr	9 9	15 50	19 39	...	...

Aïn Temouchent ... dep	6 35	1240	17 0	...	...	...
Lourmel ...	7 25	1354	18 7	...	...	...
La Senia ...	8 36	1518	19 23	...	...	...
Oran (Karg.) ... arr	8 49	1532	19 37	...	...	...

ALGIERS and ROVIGO.

E.M.					
—	**Algiers (RueWaïsse)** dep	5 ‡9	6 29	13 9	17 29
23	**Rovigo** ... arr	7 52	8 48	15 28	19 48

Rovigo ... dep	5 50	9 ‡4	12 30	17 10
Algiers RueWaïsse arr	8 5	11 45	14 45	19 25

‡—On Sun., Wed., and Fri. only.

ALGIERS, COLEA, and CASTIGLIONE.

E.M.																	
	Algiers ... dep	4 59	6 42	8 59	11 7	12 42	14 15	15 42	17 15	18 42	20 7	...	...	...	...	...	...
10	Guyotville ...	6 4	7 45	10 4	12 12	13 45	15 21	16 47	18 18	19 47	21 20	...	...	...	...	...	...
27½	**Colea** ... arr	—	9 34	—	—	15 34	—	—	20 7	—	...	...	...	...	...	...	...
29¼	**Castiglione** ... arr	...	9 22	...	...	15 22	...	...	19 55	...	23 35	...	...	...	...	...	...
...	**Castiglione** ... dep	2 20	...	6 0	...	...	12 0	...	...	16 33	...	...	...	...	...	...	...
...	**Colea** ... dep	...	...	5 48	...	...	11 48	...	...	16 21	...	...	...	...	...	...	...
...	Guyotville ...	4 40	6 24	7 37	10 33	12 43	13 37	16 9	17 16	18 10	20 14	...	...	...	...	...	...
...	**Algiers** ... arr	5 53	7 27	8 40	11 36	13 53	14 40	17 18	18 27	19 13	21 18	...	...	...	...	...	...

DELLYS and BOGHNI.

E.M.				
	Dellys ... dep	5 2	14 46	...
19¼	Camp du Marechal ...	6 51	16 35	...
42¼	**Boghni** ... arr	11 20	18 49	...

Boghni ... dep	4 45	14 55	...	...	...
Camp du Marechal ...	9 35	21 35	...	...	...
Dellys ... arr	11 14	23 14	...	...	...

ALGIERS and CONSTANTINE.

SC—Sleeping Car attached.] [RC—Restaurant Car.

		RC					SC	
Algiers ... dep	6 27	7 27	9 15	1315	1812	...	2018	23 15
Maison Carré ...	6 46	7 47	9 54	1341	1838	...	2038	23 44
Ménerville ...	8 9	9 1	12 9	1521	20 7	...	2151	1 19
Palestro ...	8 48	9 36	—	16 5	—	...	2225	1 58
Bordj-Bouïra ...	1015	11 1	...	1753	...	...	2350	3 47
Beni-Mancour ...	—	1212	...	—	...	...	0 57	5 13
El-Achir ...	...	1355	...	...	...	...	2 37	7 56
Sétif ...	...	16 0	...	1620	...	...	4 37	10 25
El-Guerrah ...	...	1830	...	1947	2140	6 39	7 10	14 4
BISKRA 329A ... arr	...	...	...	...	...	...	...	21 10
Ouled-R. ...	...	1849	1930	2028	2155	6 54	7 31	14 31
Khroub ...	1742	19 6	1948	2057	2213	7 11	7 51	14 57
DUVIVIER 329B arr	...	...	...	...	...	...	1226	...
TUNIS ... 329B arr	...	...	...	...	...	...	2224	...
Constantine .. arr	1820	1930	2013	2139	2239	7 36	8 15	15 25

			RC					SC	
Constantine ... dep	...	6 5	6 44	7 22	1240	1330	1833	2031	24 0
TUNIS ... dep	...	...	...	...	...	...	...	8 16	...
DUVIVIER dp	...	...	...	...	...	...	...	1613	...
Khroub ...	...	6 32	7 12	7 50	1327	14 2	19 9	2058	0 33
Ouled-Rham'n	...	6 53	7 30	8 7	1353	1433	1929	2115	1 3
BISKRA dep	...	...	...	—	...	7 24	...	...	...
El-Guerrah ...	...	7 9	7 50	...	1413	15 8	1945	2137	1 33
Sétif ...	...	—	1047	...	—	19 8	—	0 32	5 33
El-Achir ...	...	...	1252	...	...	—	...	2 38	8 0
Beni-Mancour	...	...	1413	...	...	...	...	3 56	1020
Bordj-Bouïra	...	...	1536	...	6 5	...	16 9	5 19	1154
Palestro ...	...	...	1642	...	7 20	...	1726	6 24	13 9
Ménerville ...	5 55	...	1722	...	8 10	1018	1815	7 6	1358
Maison C. ...	7 19	...	1824	...	9 32	1223	1931	8 13	1521
Algiers ... arr	7 43	...	1839	...	9 50	1255	1949	8 28	1545

Extra.—Khroub to Constantine 11.41. Constantine to Khroub 10.40, 16.23.

MENERVILLE and TIZI-OUZOU.

E.M.					
	Ménerville ... dep	8 13	1526	2012	...
22½	Camp du Marechal ...	9 20	1634	2120	...
33	**Tizi-Ouzou** ... arr	9 55	1711	2155	...

Tizi-Ouzou ... dep	6 21	12 13	1630	...	...
Camp du Marechal	6 51	12 43	17 0	...	...
Ménerville ... arr	8 0	13 52	18 8	...	...

EL-GUERRAH and BISKRA.

Dist. E.M.						
	CONSTANTINE ... dep	6 5	12 40	18 33	...	...
	El-Guerrah ... dep	7 18	14 28	19 53	...	...
29¾	Aïn-Yagout ...	8 25	16 4	21 11	...	...
50¼	Batna ...	9 22	17 40	22 16	...	...
90¾	El-Kantara ...	—	19 44	—	...	...
125½	**Biskra** ... arr	...	21 10	...	...	...

Biskra ... dep	...	7 24	...	...	...	...	...	...
El-Kantara ...	...	9 10	...	...	...	...	...	...
Batna ...	4 40	1145	19 30	...	...	...	...	...
Aïn-Yagout ...	5 32	1247	20 23	...	...	...	...	...
El-Guerrah ... arr	6 34	14 3	21 25	...	...	...	...	...
CONSTANTINE ... arr	7 36	1525	22 39	...	...	...	...	...

BOUGIE and BENI-MANCOUR.

E.M.				
	Bougie ... dep	8 46	10 50	17 23
29¾	Takriets ...	10 19	12 24	19 0
55¼	**Beni-Mancour** arr	11 45	13 50	20 30

Beni-Mancour 329A ... dep	5 10	12 19	14 16	...
Takriets ...	6 29	13 31	15 28	...
Bougie ... arr	8 2	14 57	16 54	...

OULED-RHAMOUN and KHENCHELA.

E.M				
	Ouled-Rhamoun ... dep	8 12	14 35	...
58	Ain-Beida ...	11 45	18 18	...
91	Khenchela ... arr	13 42	20 22	...

Khenchela ... dep	...	14 18	19 5
Ain-Beida ...	4 13	16 15	21 2
Ouled-Rhamoun ... arr	6 46	19 19	...

PHILIPPEVILLE and CONSTANTINE.

E.M.																
	Philippeville...dep	6 2	8 26	12 5	1610	...	...	**Constantine** ...dep	6 19	8 49	12 50	1625	...	...	...
11¾	St. Charles	6 38	9 4	13 6	1646	...	...	Condé-Smendou	7 21	9 51	14 17	1722	...	...	...
18¾	Robertville	7 2	9 29	13 46	1710	...	...	Robertville	8 30	1054	16 17	1821	...	...	...
37¼	Condé-Smendou	8 22	1055	16 1	1831	...	...	St. Charles (329B)	8 58	1118	16 58	1846	...	...	...
54	**Constantine**...arr	9 12	1150	17 38	1920	...	...	**Philippeville**...arr	9 30	1150	17 40	1918	...	...	...

BONA and ST. CHARLES.

E.M.															
—	**Bona**...dep	4 30	11 15	17 45	...	...	**St. Charles**...dep	...	9 20	17 0	...	...	...	...
20½	Aïn Mokra	5 50	12 37	19 10	...	...	Aïn Mokra	6 30	13 16	20 3	...	...	...	...
61½	**St. Charles** 329B arr	8 30	16 15	...	...	...	**Bona**...arr	8 0	14 45	21 20	...	...	...	...

BONA and RANDON.	E.M.											
	—	Bona...dep	9 30	18 2	...	...	Randon...dep	5 40	15 7	...	...	...
	16½	Randon...arr	10 54	19 16	...	...	Bona...arr	7 1	16 29	...	...	...

BONA and LA CALLE.	E.M.											
	—	**Bona**...dep	6 55	16 0	...	...	**La Calle**...dep	4 50	15 40	...	...	...
	25¼	Lac des Oiseaux	8 45	17 49	...	...	Lac des Oiseaux	7 3	17 46	...	...	...
	54¾	**La Calle**...arr	10 50	19 53	...	...	**Bona**...arr	8 47	19 30	...	...	...

BONA and KHROUB.

[‡—Restaurant Car attached.

Dist																		
	Bona...dep	...	4 56	14‡34	1643	...	...	...	**Khroub**...dep	...	8 ‡7	1332	1711	...	...	...
34½	Duvivier	...	6 39	16 13	1848	...	...	...	Oued-Zenati	...	9 44	1517	1920	...	...	...
55½	Guelma	4 29	7 38	17 10	20 0	...	...	...	Hammam M.	...	10 57	1632	2014	...	...	...
67	Hammam-Meskoutine	5 12	8 14	17 46	—	...	...	...	Guelma	5 31	11 37	1720	2123	...	...	...
93¾	Oued-Zenati	7 1	9 47	19 9	...	...	...	...	Duvivier	6 32	12 26	1815	—	...	...	...
126¼	**Khroub 329A**...arr	8 59	1131	20 44	...	...	...	...	**Bona**...arr	8 31	14 23	2029	...	...	...	...

BONA and TUNIS.

[‡—Mon., Wed. and Fri. only.

E.M																			
—	**Bona**...dep	...	...	...	...	4 56	11 0	1434	1643	**Tunis**...dep	...	6 35	...	8§16	12 0	13 0	1625	17 8
15	Mondovi	...	...	...	...	5 37	1139	1513	1734	Djedeida	...	7 11	...	8 56	12 51	1354	1711	1754
25½	Saint-Joseph	...	...	...	...	6 5	12 7	1541	1811	Medjez el Bab	...	—	...	10 2	—	1525	1843	1919
...	ALGIERS dep	...	...	...	...	...	2018	...	...	Pont-de-Trajan	...	...	...	11 9	...	1735	—	2114
...	KHROUB...dep	...	...	...	...	...	8 7	...	1332	Souk-el-Arba	...	...	...	1228	...	1951	...	2255
34¼	**Duvivier**	...	...	...	...	6 46	1240	1625	19 0	Ghrardimaou ¶	...	...	8‡26	1238	...	21 2	...	—
49	Aïn-Affra	...	...	...	...	7 58	1329	1722	2012	Sidi-Bader	...	...	1014	1346	...		...	...
66½	**Souk-Ahras.**	...	...	5 ‡5	...	9 16	1429	1822	2130	**Souk-Ahras.**	4 42	10 4	11 4	1425	16 6	...	...	...
77	Sidi-Bader	...	...	5 49	...	—	1458	—	—	Aïn-Affra	5 45	11 25	—	...	17 19	...	...	...
103¼	Ghrardimaou ¶	...	...	7 15	8 41	...	16 3	...	...	**Duvivier**	6 31	12 24	...	16 0	18 13	...	...	...
123¾	Souk-el-Arba	...	5 20	—	10 3	...	1818	...	...	KHROUB 329B	11 31	...	...	2044	...	...	...	...
154	Pont-de-Trajan	...	7 13	...	1224	...	1938	...	...	ALGIERS 329A	...	...	...	8 28	...	...	...	...
179½	Medjez el Bab	...	9 0	...	1417	...	2044	...	5 30	Saint-Joseph	7 11	13 6	...	1635	19 9	...	...	...
205	Djedeida	8 5	1034	...	16 7	1833	2146	...	7 12	Mondovi	7 44	13 39	...	17 3	19 42	...	...	...
220½	**Tunis**...arr	8 47	1130	...	17 6	1858	2224	...	8 2	**Bona**...arr	8 31	14 23	...	1740	20 59	...	...	...

¶—Customs Examination. Mid Europe time between Ghrardimaou and Tunis.
§—Restaurant Car between Tunis and Ghrardimaou.

E.M,													
	Pont-de-Trajan...dep	11 15	17 13	21 12	...	...	Béja...dep	6 38	11 56	19 3	...	...	...
8¾	Béja...arr	11 39	17 37	21 36	...	...	Pont-de-Trajan...arr	6 59	12 17	19 24	...	...	...

SOUK-AHRAS and TEBESSA.	E.M.											
		Souk-Ahras...dep	4 48	9 28	15 3	Tebessa...dep	8 8	12 59	21 50	...	...	...
	42¼	Clairfontaine	8 16	12 53	18 32	Clairfontaine	1046	15 14	0 22	...	...	...
	79½	Tebessa...arr	10 40	15 2	20 45	Souk-Ahras...arr	14 5	18 42	4 8	...	...	...

TUNIS and BIZERTA.	E.M													
		Tunis...dep	6 35	12 0	1625	20 †0	Bizerta...dep	6 4	13 15	1629	20*46	...	*—Sat. only.
	61	Bizerta...arr	9 7	15 45	1858	22 16	Tunis...arr	8 47	17 0	1858	23 2	...	†—Wed. only.

Tunis............
Goletta............
Kram............
Carthage............
Marsa............

} Tramway service about every half hour.

TUNIS and KALAA DJERDA.

Station					
Tunis ....dep		6 45	14 10	17 23	20 15
Depienne..................		8 39	16 41	19 53	22 41
Pont du Fahs.........		9 12	17 25	20 30	23 21
Gaffour..............	6 20	11 33	19 57	—	2 2
Les Salines	8 39	13 21	—	...	4 21
Fedj-et-T. (330)	1035	14 47	...	...	6 30
Oued Sarrath..	1121	15 25	...	...	7 20
Kalaa Djerda	1149	15 49	...	...	7 48

Station					
Kalaa Djerda dcp		...	4 40	9 15	19 45
Oued Sarrath		...	5 12	9 47	20 22
Fedj-et-Tameur ...		...	6 24	10 31	21 45
Les Salines		...	8 7	12 18	23 28
Gaffour		5 11	10 26	14 8	2 0
Pont du Fahs...	2 24	7 58	—	16 8	4 48
Depienne	3 6	8 40	...	16 39	5 28
Tunis.........arr	5 30	10 56	...	18 20	7 50

E.M.	Station			Station				
	Oued Sarrath ....dep	7 40	1531	Kalaat-es-Senam...dep	7 19	1820	...	...
18¾	Kalaat-es-Senam ...arr	9 15	17 3	Oued Sarrath.........arr	9 5	1959	...	

E.M.	Station			Station				
	Fedj-et-Tameur ....dep	6 31	14 50	Slata ....dep	8 25	19 28	...	...
18	Slata ....arr	7 53	16 32	Fedj-et-Tameur 330 arr	10 24	21 30	...	...

Station					Station					
Tunis............dep	8 55	14 26	18 21	...	La Laverie ...dep	5 7	12 18	16 15	...	...
La Laverie ...arr	1042	16 1	20 0	...	Tunis............arr	6 58	14 3	17 52	...	...

Station			
Le Kef................dep	11 0	22 0
Les Salines ....arr	12 10	23 10

Station		
Les Salines...........dep	4 31	13 23
Le Kef ....arr	5 45	14 34

Station		
Zaghouan ....dep	4 45	16 0
Depienne...............arr	5 19	16 29
Depienne..............dep	8 45	19 56
Zaghouan ....arr	9 19	20 25

E.M.	Station																					
	Tunis ....dep	5 50	7 0	8 40	1115	11 45	13‡35	1358	1455	1615	1715	1814	1922	23 5	...	...	...	...	...	...	...	...
10½	Hammam-el-Lif	6 21	7 30	9 10	1145	12 15	14 ‡7	1431	1525	1645	1756	1845	1952	2335	...	...	...	...	...	...	...	...
...	Hammam-el-Lif	5 16	6 42	7 57	9 30	1054	1315	1353	1540	1648	17‡58	1·47	20 46	2230	...	...	...	...	...	...	...	...
...	Tunis ....arr	5 48	7 13	8 34	10 0	1127	1345	1423	1610	1720	18‡28	1917	21 16	23 0	...	...	...	...	...	...	...	...

E.M.	Station						Station						
	Fondouk-Djedid ....dep	7 30	14 †3	18 49	...	...	Menzel-bou-Zalfa ...dep	6 30	12†10	17 20	...	...	...
8¾	Menzel-bou-Zalfa .. ...arr	8 6	14 39	19 25	...	...	Fondouk-Djedid ......arr.	7 5	12 42	17 55	...	...	...

†—Thursday only. ‡—Sundays only.

‡—On Friday dep. Sfax 2.59, arr. Susa 6.25.

TUNIS, SUSA, and SFAX.

†—Thursday only.

E.M.	Station							
	Tunis ....dep	6 25	..	13 58	1715	...	...	...
10½	Hammam-Lif.....	6 55	13†24	14 32	18 1	...	...	...
18	Fondouk-Djedid	7 20	13 54	14 58	1834	...	...	...
37¼	Bir-bou-Rekba...	8 21	—	16 1	1950	...	...	...
62¼	Enfidaville	9 23	...	17 7	—	...	...	...
93¾	**Susa** (330)......arr	10 55	...	18 38	...	...	...	...
...	,, ...dep	11 4	...	19 3	...	...	...	...
136	El Djem	13 34	...	21 37	...	...	...	...
176	**Sfax** (330)......arr	15 7	...	23 30	...	...	...	...

Station							
Sfax ....dep	...	...	5‡20	...	10 9	...	...
El Djem	...	...	7 38	...	12 10	...	...
Susa .... arr	...	...	1024	...	14 15	...	...
,, ...dep	...	6 35	—	...	14 25	...	...
Enfidaville	...	8 16	...	...	16 0	...	...
Bir-bou-Rekba ..	6 4	9 28	...	...	17 10	...	...
Fondouk-Djedid	7 21	10 29	...	12†44	18 10	...	...
Hammam-Lif......	7 57	10 54	...	13 10	18 33	...	...
Tunis ....arr	8 34	11 27	...	...	19 2	...	...

Station								Station					
Bir-bou-Rekba ....dep	8 36	1952	...	...	...	...	...	Nabeul ....dep	5 19	15 8	...	...	...
Nabeul........................arr	9 19	2035	...	...	...	...	...	Bir-bou-Rekba...........arr	5 58	15 51	...	...	...

SUSA and HENCHIR-SUATIR.

E.M	Station				
	Susa.............. dep	5 6	...	12 9	18 7
5	Kalaâ-Srira	5 22	...	1227	1851
30½	Ain-Ghrasesia	6 55	...	1414	2028
106	Sbeitla..................	—	6 52	1915	1 14
184	Henchir-Suatir arr	...	1222	...	6 4

Station				
Henchir-Suatir	...	...	1317	20 0
Sbeitla	6 53	...	1945	0 58
Ain-Ghrasesia ...	12 3	1613	—	5 9
Kalaâ-Srira	1359	1744	...	7 0
Susa	1417	18 0	...	7 16

Station				
Ain-Ghrasesia ...dep	5 19	7 0	1412	2033
Kairwan ....arr	5 44	7 22	1434	2058
Kairwan ....dep	4 34	1133	1550	1951
Ain-Ghrasesia arr	4 59	1155	1612	2016

SUSA and MEHDIA.

E.M.	Station							Station							
	Susa.....................dep	6 45	1430	...	...	...	...	Mehdia....................dep	6 0	1530	...	...	...	...	...
23	Moknine	9 2	1644	...	...	...	...	Moknine	7 11	1641	...	...	...	...	...
39¼	Mehdia ....arr	10 8	1750	...	...	...	...	Susa ....arr	9 23	1850	...	...	...	...	...

SFAX and REDEYEF.

E.M.	Station						
—	**Sfax** ....dep	...	6 48	...	...	21' 0	...
39½	Graiba	...	9 5	...	...	23 19	...
127½	Gafsa	5 18	15 47	16 16	2053	5 0	...
151	Metlaoui	6 43	—	17 36	22 7	—	...
177	**Redeyef**.....................arr	9 15	...	—	...	...	...

Station					
Redeyef ....dep	...	...	15 25	...	...
Metlaoui..........................	7 30	12 30	18 46	...	...
Gafsa	9 40	14 30	20 54	...	...
Graiba.............................	16 42	—	2 51	...	...
Sfax ....arr	18 56	...	4 54	...	...

LONDON AND SOUTH WESTERN RAILWAY—Week Days.

	a.m.	a.m.	a.m.	a.m.	a.m.	a.m.	a.m.	a.m.	a.m.	p.m.	p.m.	p.m.	p.m.	p.m.	p.m.	p.m.	p.m.	p.m.	p.m.		Sundays. a.m.	a.m.	a.m.	p.m.	p.m.	p.m.	
London—Waterloo ......dep	6 10	6 35	8 50	9 25	1050	11*0	1110	11†15	1140	12*50	1 0	2 10	2 45	3 30	3 50	5 50	6 55	8 15	9 50	...	8 27	10 0	1115	12 30	5 45	6 40	...
Salisbury ....arr	8 8	9 34	11 2	1212	1221	1233	1243	1 13	2 44	2 23	2 54	4 32	4 44	5 4	6 54	7 51	9 43	1056	2D17	M	11 33	1 37	1 46	2 10	8 51	9 27	...
Yeovil .... ,,	9 23	1130	1218	—	...	...	...	2 33	—	...	4 7	—	—	6 30	8 33	9 8	D	—	4D14	M	1 39	D	—	3 23	11 27	D	...
Exeter...................... ,,	1019	1250	1 8	...	2 9	2 17	2 24	4 4	...	4 15	5 10	...	...	6 55	—	10 0	—	...	...	...	—	—	...	4 10	—	—	...
Ilfracombe .... ,,	1 11	—	3 44	...	...	—	4 26	—	...	—	7 42	...	...	9 28	...	...	...	...	...	...	...	...	...	6 16	...	...	...
Devonport .... ,,	1157	...	3 0	...	3 37	...	4 47	...	...	...	6 51	...	...	8 30	...	11 48	...	...	...	...	...	...	...	5 50	...	...	...
Plymouth (North Road) ,,	12 3	...	3 5	...	3 45	...	4 52	...	...	...	6 57	...	...	8 36	...	11 53	...	...	...	...	...	...	...	5 58	...	...	...

D—Via Eastleigh.

	a.m.	a.m.	a.m.	a.m.	a.m.	a.m.	a.m.	a.m.	a.m.	a.m.	p.m.	p.m.	p.m.	p.m.	p.m.	p.m.		Sundays. a.m.	a.m.	a.m.		p.m.	
Plymouth (North Road) dep	...	...	...	...	8 29	...	10 8	...	...	10 58	...	1218	...	2 28	4 11	...	...	...	...	10 57	...	2 41	...
Devonport .... ,,	...	...	...	...	8 35	...	1014	A	...	11 4	...	1224	...	2 34	4 16	...	...	...	...	11 4	...	2 46	...
Ilfracombe .... ,,	...	...	...	...	7 20	...	9 10	9 49	10 45	A	...	1145	...	1 37	3 15	...	...	...	...	8 12	...	2 28	...
Exeter .... ,,	...	7 20	...	...	1017	...	12 0	1145	12 55	1 48	...	2 10	...	4 15	6 2	...	...	...	...	1 27	...	4 30	D
Yeovil...................... ,,	5 45	8 20	8 31	...	1045	11 10	...	...	1 50	...	...	3 2	...	5 5	6 55	...	...	6 10	...	3 0	p.m.	5 25	p.m.
Salisbury .... ,,	7 34	9 31	10 7	1023	1215	12 31	1 43	1 28	2 54	3 35	2 20	4 12	5 3	6 28	8 25	9 5	...	8 0	9 5	5 8	5 50	6 50	7 8
London—Waterloo ......arr	1011	11 3	12 8	1 31	1 47	2 35	3 15	3 0	4 38	5 9	5 16	6 5	8 10	8 7	1034	12 4	...	11 4	12 4	7 47	8 6	8 30	1040

*—From July 18th,
†—Until July 18th,
A—From July 19th,
M—Not Monday mornings, but Sundays.

	a.m.	a.m.	a.m.	a.m.	a.m.	a.m.	a.m.	a.m.	a.m.	p.m.	p.m.	p.m.	p.m.	p.m.	p.m.	p.m.	p.m.	p.m.	p.m.	p.m.	p.m.	p.m.	p.m.	Sundays. a.m.	a.m.	a.m.	noon	p.m.	p.m.	p.m.
London—Waterloo dep	5 50	6 10	6 35	8 57	9 25	10 15	1035	1115	1140	1230	1240	1250	2 0	2 10	2 20	2 55	4 10	4 50	5 0	6 0	6 55	8 15	9 50	9 20	10 0	10 15	12 0	5 45	6 40	9 15
Winchester ....arr	7 29	8 17	...	10 23	1110	...	1244	...	1 11	...	...	3 2	...	3 39	3 59	5 1	...	6 13	6 42	8 6	8 20	10 6	1133	11 7	1220	...	1 25	7 57	8 9	1136
Portsmouth .... ,,	...	10 6	...	11 43	...	12 44	...	...	2 24	...	A	...	...	...	5 1	6 35	...	...	...	...	9 28	1125	1247	...	1 44	...	...	...	9 22	1249
Southampton Docks ,,	7‡54	8 53	...	10‡49	1147	11‡59	1‡15	1‡40	1 44	2‡10	2‡20	3 36	...	4‡0	4‡27	5 34	...	6‡33	7 20	8 40	9 ‡2	1042	12 7	11‡33	1256	11‡52	1‡50	8 32	8‡35	12 8
Bournemouth (Cen.) ,,	8 45	1057	11§31	11 42	...	12 46	2 27	2 38	...	3 5	3 52	...	4 6	...	5 47	6 57	6 10	7 29	...	...	9 44	12 0	1 48	12 42	...	12 42	2 44	...	9 31	1 48
Weymouth .... ,,	9 51	1233	12 33	...	...	2 3	...	...	...	4 13	5 0	...	...	6 12	...	...	7 16	8 59	...	...	11 2	...	...	...	...	1 43	4 35	...	1056	2 53

*—a.m.	a.m.	am	a.m.	a.m.	am	am	a.m.	a.m.	a.m.	a.m.	a.m.	a.m.	p.m.	p.m.	pm	pm	pm	p.m.	p.m.	pm	pm	p.m.	p.m.	p.m.	p.m.	Sundays. a.m.	a.m.	p.m.	p.m.	p.m.	p.m.	p.m.	p.m.
Weymouth ....dep	...	...	...	...	...	8 0	...	...	8 45	...	10 3	...	...	1255	...	...	...	...	2 10	...	410	...	6 0	7 20	9 50	6 20	...	2 25	4 40	...	5 12	...	9 50
Bournemouth (Cent) ,,	...	...	...	8 0	...	9 8	...	9 17	1011	1025	11 19	11 31	...	2 0	...	2 9	...	...	3 56	...	515	...	7 11	8 45	1110	8 3	...	3 53	5 48	...	6 43	6 58	1110
Southampton Docks ,,	6 3	645	7 45	8‡47	848	...	9 48	10 0	11‡1	1115	12‡10	12‡23	1230	...	143	3‡0	310	3‡22	4‡50	515	6‡2	6 22	8 ‡2	9‡48	1 *0	9 5	9 35	5‡18	...	5 50	7‡26	8 ‡0	1 *0
Portsmouth .... ,,	...	610	...	...	748	...	...	...	...	...	10 55	...	...	...	...	...	...	...	...	420	...	...	...	8 55	1220	...	8 55	4 50	...	...	...	...	1220
Winchester .... ,,	6 38	724	8 20	9 11	926	...	1027	1057	1123	1156	12 33	12 51	1 8	...	223	323	345	3 59	...	552		7 3	8 33	1021	1 37	...	102[illegible]	6 7	...	6 30	...	...	1 37
London—Waterloo arr	8 45	934	1011	1035	114	118	12 8	1230	1245	1 31	2 1	2 35	2 45	4 0	5 7	446	539	5 52	6 45	731	740	9 29	10 5	12 4	3 37	11 4	1246	8 6	8 13	8 49	9 5	9 39	3 37

	a.m.	a.m.	a.m.	a.m.	a.m.	a.m.	a.m.	a.m.	p.m.	p.m.	p.m.	p.m.	p.m.	p.m.	p.m.	p.m.	p.m.	p.m.	p.m.	p.m.	p.m.	p.m.	Suns. a.m.	a.m.	a.m.	a.m.	p.m.	p.m.	p.m.	p.m.
London—Waterloo dep	5 15	6 0	6 20	7 10	8 55	9 10	9 39	11 8	1245	1 5	1 17	2 20	2 35	3 5	3 45	4 30	4 55	5 45	5 30	6 40	7 10	1030	8 40	9 5	9 35	1150	2 20	5 25	6 10	1040
Portsmouth ¶ ....arr	7 52	...	9 21	...	1148	1110	...	1 55	2 34	...	3 54	5 1	5 29	...	5 55	6 49	7 4	8 12	...	8 26	10 0	1 0	1146	...	1156	...	4 55	7 56	9 1	1257
Southampton Docks f ,,	...	9 9	...	1016	...	...	1 4	...	...	4 27	...	...	...	6 27	...	...	...	...	8 20	...	...	...	...	1238	...	1 38	...	...	9 21	...

Week Days.																				Suns. a.m.		a.m.	p.m.	p.m.	p.m.		p.m.	p.m.
Southampton Docks f dep	...	...	6 55	...	...	8 55	...	...	11 57	...	1 57	...	3 50	...	...	...	6 22	...	9 10	...	7 10	...	...	...	...	6 20	...	...
Portsmouth ¶ .... ,,	6 53	7 55	...	8 55	9 41	...	1014	12 6	...	2 51	...	3 7	...	4 20	5 51	7 6	...	8 p0	9 8	7 15	...	8 25	2 45	6 5	6 55	...	8 23	8 45
London—Waterloo ... arr	9 34	9 55	1013	1133	1139	1213	1 12	2 20	3 7	4 50	5 32	6 18	7 6	7 31	8 3	9 6	9 29	11 2	12 4	1028	1039	1042	6 34	8 36	9 36	9 31	1025	1145

§—Bournemouth, West Station. f—Via Farnham. ‡—Southampton West Station. ¶—Via Guildford.

SOUTH EASTERN AND CHATHAM RAILWAYS.—Week Days. (Sunday service much restricted).

§—From or at London Bridge Station.

	a.m.	a.m.	a.m.	a.m.	a.m.	a.m.	a.m.	a.m.	a.m.	a.m.	p.m.	p.m.	p.m.	p.m.	p.m.	p.m.	p.m.	p.m.	p.m.	p.m.	p.m.	p.m.	p.m.	p.m.	p.m.	p.m.	p.m.	p.m.
London. Charing Cross ...dep	7 0	..	9 0	9 3	...	9§37	10 0	...	...	11 0	...	1 0	2 5	...	3 25	...	4 25	4 30	...	...	5 34	6 b0	7 15	...	...	...	9 0	9 45
Victoria .... ,,	...	7 45	...	...	9 15	...	...	1045	11 0	...	12 40	...	...	2 50	...	4 20	...	...	5 0	...	...	...	...	8 15	8 30	8 45	...	...
Holborn Viaduct ,,	...	7 40	...	...	9 10	...	...	...	...	...	12 37	...	...	...	...	4 15	...	...	...	5 10	...	...	...	8 10	8 25	...	...	...
St. Pauls .... ,,	...	7 42	...	...	9 13	...	...	...	...	...	12 39	...	...	...	...	4 17	...	...	...	5 12	...	...	...	8 12	8 26	Friday only.	...	...
Cannon Street ... ,,	7 13	...	...	9 §9	...	...	...	...	...	11 9	...	1 8	...	...	...	...	4 33	...	...	...	5 43	6 7	7 26	...	...		...	10 0
Herne Hill.......... ,,	...	7 55	...	...	9 27	...	...	1056	...	...	12 53	...	...	3 2	...	4 30	...	...	...	...	...	...	...	8 26	8 40		...	...
Folkestone Harbour arr	10 c0	...	...	11 26	...	12 c8	1150	...	...	1c28	...	3 18	3 45	4c52	5 c0	...	6 c2	...	7 8	...	8c23	7c31	9c16	...	1015		1057	1230
Dover Town.......... ,,	...	...	1035	11 28	...	...	...	...	12 40	1 48	...	3 22	3 54	...	...	...	6 15	...	...	...	8 45	7 45	9 36	...	...		1035	1230
,, Harbour ...... ,,	10 20	1029	...	...	1136	12 20	...	1 15	...	...	3 17	...	...	5 7	5 32	6 56	...	...	6 59	7 32	...	...	...	1038	...	...	1125	...
,, Pier .... ,,	...	...	1040	...	...	...	...	...	12 45	...	...	...	3 59	...	...	...	...	6 0	...	...	...	...	...	...	...	1028	1040	...

Dover Pier ......dep	...	...	...	...	...	...	8 20	...	...	...	...	...	...	...	...	...	...	...	...	...	3 20	...	...	...	5 20	...	...	7 55	...
,, Harbour ,,	...	3 45	...	...	...	8 †5	...	8 27	9 0	9 5	...	9 50	10 20	10 50	...	12 0	...	...	1 10	...	...	3 40	...	...	...	5 55	7 12	...	...
,, Town ... ,,	1 45	...	...	5 10	6 30	...	...	...	...	...	9 15	...	...	...	1140	...	12 35	...	...	2 50	3 24	...	4 15	4 40	5 24	...	...	8 0	...
FolkestoneHarb. ,,	...	...	6 ‡0	...	7*c0	8 0	...	...	9c15	...	9 15	...	10 c40	11c5	1125	...	12c51	1‡40	4 8	8c 1	...	...	4c30	4c57	...	...	...	8c15	9 ‡5
London. Herne Hill...arr	...	...	7 35	...	...	...	...	10 43	...	1129	...	...	...	1 2	...	2 30	...	...	...	...	...	6 3	...	...	...	8 22	9 44	...	...
Cannon Street,,	3 50	...	...	8 27	8§47	10 0	...	...	...	...	11 40	...	12 4	...	2 16	...	3 9	...	...	...	...	...	6 48	...	...	...	...	...	...
St. Pauls ... ,,	...	...	7 45	...	...	...	...	10 55	...	1142	...	...	...	...	...	2 44	...	...	4 25	...	...	6 17	...	...	...	8 39	9 57	...	...
Holborn Viaduct ...	...	...	7 48	...	...	...	...	10 57	...	1144	...	...	...	...	...	2 46	...	...	4 27	...	...	6 20	...	...	...	8 41	10 0	...	...
Victoria ...... ,,	...	...	7 48	...	...	...	...	10 52	11 0	1138	...	...	...	1 11	...	2 40	...	...	4 18	...	...	6 10	...	...	7 5	8 32	9 53	...	...
Charing Cross,,	...	5 43	...	8 33	...	10 8	10 15	...	...	...	11 51	1 12	12 12	...	2 28	...	...	3 25	...	5 35	5 10	...	6 58	7 29	...	...	...	10 0	10 45

*—6.55 a.m. on Mons. ‡—From Folkestone Pier. c-Folkestone Central.
A—On Monday only. †—8.0 a.m. on Mon.

GREAT WESTERN RAILWAY.—Service from July 12th.

e—From July 19th. s—From July 18th. t—Not after July 18th.

	Week Days.																									Sundays.						
	a.m.	a.m.	a.m.	a.m.	a m	a.m.	a.m.	a.m.	a.m.	p.m.	p.m.	p.m.	p.m.	p.m.	p.m.	p.m.	p.m.	p.m.	pm	p.m.	p.m.	p.m.	p.m.	p.m.	nght	a.m.	a.m.	p.m.	pm	p.m.	p.m.	p.m.
London—(Paddington)...dep	5 30	7 30	9 0	1030	1035	11 0	1110	1150	1155	1240	1 5	1 10	1 30	2 28	3 0	3 30	4 15	4 30	5 0	5 15	6 40	8 5	9 15	9 50	12G0	1230	9 20	1240	245	4 30	4 55	9 50
Bath ....arr	8 5	9 50	1137	...	...	1248	s	...	2 17	...	...	3 50	4 26	4 55	5 27	...	6 6	6 38	...	8 6	8 32	1043	Sept'mber only.	1228	2 33	3 3	1155	2 54	6 1	...	...	1228
Bristol (Temple M.) ,,	8 28	1015	12 0	...	...	1 0	...	...	2 39	...	3 5	4 10	4 53	5 22	5 47	...	6 25	7F2	...	8 31	8 52	11 5		1 0	2 57	3 27	1218	3 15	...	6 30	10 0	1 0
Exeter (St. David's) ,,	1038	1225	—	1 30	e	2 33	2 15	2 50	—	...	—	—	4 52	—	—	6 30	8 7	—	...	—	1015	—		2 55	4 53	5 23	2 32	—	555	8 2	—	2 55
Plymouth (Millbay) ,,	1210	2*11	...	2*37	...	3*50	3 33	4 59	...	...	...	...	6 28	...	...	7*56	9 50	...	...	...	1230	...		4*28	6 56	7 28	4 51	...	720	9 35	...	4*28
Falmouth............. ,,	2 57	—	...	4 50	...	6 40	6 0	8 30	...	...	...	...	9 4	...	...	1055	—	...	...	...	...	...		7 3	10 6	1035	—	...	...	—	...	7 3
Weymouth ...... ,,	1223	...	...	1t50	1 55	...	—	3e30	...	4 23	...	...	5 41	...	...	6 40	...	...	910	...	1120	...	2 a5	...	...	...	...	...	615	...	...	...

	a.m.	a.m.	a.m.	a.m.	a.m.	non	a.m.	a.m.	p.m.	p.m.	p.m.	a.m.	p.m.	p.m.	a.m.	p.m.	a.m.	pm	pm	p.m.	p.m.	p.m.	p.m.	p.m.	am	a.m.	a.m.	p.m.	pm	p.m.	p.m.	ng't
Weymouth ......dep	...	...	...	8 55	...	...	1025	...	...	1220	...	...	2e23	...	...	...	...	430	...	...	...	6 10	6S15	...	...	9 20	...	4 0	...	...	...	...
Falmouth .... ,,	...	...	...	...	...	...	...	7 9	...	...	...	10 15	...	...	1130	...	11 5	...	...	1 30	...	...	5 20	9§20	...	...	...	1125	...	...	5 20	...
Plymouth (Millbay) ,,	...	...	...	...	8 30	...	...	1030	...	...	...	12*32	...	...	2*10	...	1*48	...	...	4 *0	...	...	8*23	12§12	...	7 5	1030	2 20	...	...	8*23	1212
Exeter (St. David's) ,,	...	...	7 0	...	1015	...	...	12 5	...	...	1222	1 45	e	...	3 27	...	3 12	...	...	5 25	5 43	...	10 13	1§52	...	9 15	12 6	3 51	...	...	1014	1 52
Bristol (Tple. Meads) ,,	7 45	9 10	9 35	...	...	12 0	...	...	1212	1 0	2 11	...	2 25	3 0	s	3 46	5 5	...	550	...	7 50	...	12 20	3§45	9 0	1215	1 40	...	548	6 0	1220	3 45
Bath.................. ,,	8 3	9 30	9 56	...	...	...	1134	...	1236	1 22	2 35	...	2 49	3 20	...	4 8	...	521	610	...	8 10	...	12 42	4 §6	919	1237	...	...	6 9	6 27	1242	4 6
London (Pad'ton) ...arr	1015	1125	1218	1250	1 30	2 0	2 35	3 10	3 20	4 10	4 30	4 45	5 42	6 0	6 45	6 55	7 5	821	830	8 40	1033	1150	3 30	6§45	120	3 15	3 40	7 35	815	9 35	3 30	6 45

	Week Days.																							Sundays.			
	a.m.	a.m.	a.m.	a.m.	a.m.	a.m.	a.m.	a.m.	p.m.	p.m.	p.m.	p.m.	p.m.	p.m.	p.m.	p.m.	p.m.	p.m.	nght					a.m.	a.m.	p.m.	p.m.
London (Paddington) ....dep	5 30	5 42	6 30	8 50	9 10	9 50	1020	11 5	1 0	1 40	2 35	4 0	4 45	4 55	6 5	6 15	7 30	8 0	12 17	...	...	...	...	10 20	1110	2 15	4 0
Worcester (Shrub Hill) ....arr	...	1022	...	1141	12 25	1254	2 12	...	...	3 55	...	...	6 54	8 12	...	9 16	1040	...	9H42	...	...	...	...	2 5	...	...	7 40
Leamington Spa.......................... ,,	8 45	9 30	9 45	—	10 44	1213	—	1239	2 32	—	4 9	5 34	—	7 7	7 39	—	—	9 32	3 8	...	...	...	...	—	1 2	3 49	6 26
Birmingham (Snow Hill)................ ,,	9 52	—	1034	...	11 10	1248	...	1 5	3 0	...	4 35	6 0	...	7 50	8 5	...	...	10 0	3 48	...	...	...	...	...	1 38	4 20	7 5
Wolverhampton (Low Level).......... ,,	1040	...	11 0	...	11 34	—	...	1 34	3 35	...	4 59	6 24	...	—	8 28	...	...	10 45	4 17	...	...	...	...	...	2 5	4 55	7 37
Shrewsbury .... ,,	—	...	—	...	12 17	...	...	2 4	—	...	5 43	7 19	...	...	9 10	...	...	12 0	5 5	...	...	...	...	...	2 55	—	9 5
Chester .... ,,	...	...	...	...	1 23	...	...	3 20	...	...	7 3	8 30	...	...	1023	...	...	—	6 23	...	...	...	...	...	4 22	...	—
Liverpool (Landing Stage)............. ,,	...	...	...	...	2 10	...	...	4 10	...	...	8 0	9 30	...	...	11 0	...	...	...	7 20	...	...	...	...	...	5 23	...	...

	a.m.	a.m.	a.m.	a.m.	a.m.	a.m.	a.m.	a.m.	n 'on	p.m.	a.m.	p.m.	p.m.	p.m.	p.m.	p.m.	p.m.	p.m.	p.m.			a.m.	a.m.	a.m.	p.m.	p.m.
Liverpool (Landing Stage) ....dep	...	...	...	...	6 0	7 50	...	8 50	...	...	11 30	...	12 40	...	2 20	...	4 20	...	...	...	...	...	...	8 20	3 0	...
Chester .... ,,	...	...	...	...	6 45	8 43	...	9 42	...	...	12 15	...	1 30	...	3 5	...	5 10	...	...	...	...	...	...	9 40	3 46	...
Shrewsbury .... ,,	...	...	7 0	...	8 10	10 0	...	11 0	...	...	1 33	...	2 33	...	4 28	...	6 28	...	...	...	...	8 20	...	11 40	5 5	...
Wolverhampton (Low Level) .... ,,	...	6 48	8 30	...	9 0	10 51	...	11 48	...	...	2 18	...	3 27	4 15	5 21	...	7 21	...	...	...	...	10 30	...	12 54	6 5	...
Birmingham (Snow Hill) .... ,,	...	7 30	8 55	...	9 25	11 20	...	12 15	...	...	2 50	...	4 0	4 50	5 50	...	8 0	...	...	...	...	11 0	...	1 43	6 40	...
Leamington Spa.............................. ,,	...	8 8	9 24	...	9 55	11 48	...	12 44	...	...	3 19	...	4 29	5 19	6 19	6 25	8 29	...	...	...	...	11 29	1141	2 45	7 16	...
Worcester (Shrub Hill).................. ,,	6 25	...	...	8 55	...	...	1020	...	12 0	2 0	...	2 50	...	...	...	5 45	...	6 45	8 20	...	...	...	1023	...	...	6 0
London (Paddington).....................arr	9 50	9 56	1055	1110	11 45	1 26	2 10	2 15	3 5	4 15	4 50	5 52	6 0	6 55	7 50	8 58	10 0	1050	3 30	...	...	1 0	2 20	5 45	9 0	9 42

	Week Days.																							Sundays.								
London	a.m.	a.m.	a.m.	a.m.	a.m.	a.m.	a.m.	a.m.	a.m.	a.m.	a.m.	p.m.	p.m.	p.m.	p.m	p.m.	p.m.	p.m.	p.m.	p.m.	p.m.			a.m.	a.m.	a.m.	a.m.	p.m.	p.m.	pm	p.m.	p.m.
(Paddington) dep	1‡0	5 30	5 42	7 30	8 45	9 0	9 10	9 50	1050	1130	1155	1 10	1 40	3 15	3 35	4 30	4 45	6 10	6 40	8 45	9 15	...	...	1 0	1020	1045	1145	1250	2 25	4 0	4 30	9 15
Gloucester ......arr	3 59	...	9 10	1031	...	12 6	...	...	1 43	...	3 11	4 33	4 42	5 50	...	...	8 1	8 53	...	...	12 26	...	...	4 1	...	...	3 20	...	7 34	833	...	1226
Hereford ... ,,	8 35	...	1058	1153	...	...	1 33	2 20	3 20	...	—	...	4 57	7 27	...	...	8 4	1020	...	...	...	...	...	...	7 50	...	—	...	9 7	—	...	...
Cardiff........... ,,	5 28	1014	11 3	—	1135	1 56	—	—	—	2 22	...	4 39	—	—	6 30	8 3	—	9 15	1115	1135	2 21	...	...	5 57	—	2 17	...	4 5	—	...	8 13	2 21
Swansea (H.St.),,	7 22	1220	—	...	1248	—	...	...	...	4 0	...	7 20	...	...	7 55	9 32	...	1040	—	1248	4 15	...	...	7 40	...	—	...	5 45	...	...	—	4 15
Fishguard Har. ,,	12†0	—	...	...	2 15	...	...	...	...	6M35	...	—	...	...	—	1115	...	—	...	2 15	10dH13	...	...	—	...	...	...	...	...	...	...	10d13

	a.m.	a.m.	a.m.	a.m.	a.m.	a.m.	a.m.	a.m.	a.m.	a.m.	p.m.	p.m.	a.m.	p.m.	p.m.	a.m.	p.m.	p.m.	p.m.	p.m.	p.m.	p.m.	p.m.	p.m.	a.m.	a.m.	a.m.	p.m.	p.m.	p.m.
Fishguard Harbour dep	3‡25	...	...	...	...	6 c0	...	...	...	...	...	...	7d5	...	...	10d35	...	...	...	4 0	...	...	...	5 35	3 25	6 30	...	...	...	...
Swansea (High St.)... ,,	5‡0	...	...	...	...	7c50	8 35	...	...	...	...	...	11 40	...	...	1 30	...	3‖35	...	5 35	...	...	...	8 55	5 0	8 38	1038	3 10	...	8 55
Cardiff .... ,,	6‡16	...	...	7 45	7 50	9c18	10 0	1019	...	...	...	...	1 27	...	...	3 8	3 17	5 ‖6	...	6 45	...	...	...	1042	6 16	10 21	1227	4 45	...	1042
Hereford .... ,,	...	6 20	7 30	...	...	...	...	...	8 44	9 56	...	1250	...	1 0	...	...	...	4 12	4 21	...	...	5 10	6 20	9 3	...	10 23	...	...	4 30	...
Gloucester.............. ,,	...	7 40	...	...	9 40	...	...	...	...	1155	12 3	...	...	2 27	2 45	...	...	5 49	...	...	6 50	...	8 10	1225	...	12 2	1 55	...	6 5	1225
London (Pad'ingt'n) arr	9‡ 5	1035	1110	1125	1218	12c40	1 0	2 0	2 10	2 35	3 20	4 15	4 20	4 55	6 0	6 10	7 5	8 30	8 58	9 35	1033	1050	1150	3 30	9 5	3 0	6 5	8 5	9 35	3 30

*—North Road. †—Fishguard and Goodwick. ‡—Mondays excepted. §—Sat. nights & Sun. morn. excepted. ‖—Arrive London 8.10.
a—Landing Stage. c—Tues., Thurs., and Sats. only. d—Fishguard and Goodwick, and Rail Motor Car, one class only. F—Stapleton Road.
G—For Sat. night (Sun. morn.) times, see first column Suns. H—Sun. morn. excepted. M—Rail Motor Car—one class only. S—Saturdays only.

Week Days—Service from July 12th.

London—	a.m.	a.m.	a.m.	a.m.	a.m.	a.m.	a.m.	a.m.	a.m.	a.m.	a.m.	a.m.	a.m.	a.m.	a.m.	p.m.	p.m.	p.m.	p.m.	p.m.	p.m.	p.m.	p.m.	p.m.
Euston .... dep	5 0	7 10	8 30	8 35	8 40	9 20	9 55	10 0	10 5	1010	1030	1040	11 0	1125	1150	1210	1215	1 20	1 30	2 0	2 30	2 40	2 45	4 0
Cambridge .... arr	...	1038	...	...	...	...	...	...	...	1 22	...	...	...	...	...	...	3 50	...	...	...	...	...	6 8	...
Northampton ...... ,,	6 18	9 3	...	1021	...	1048	...	...	...	1142	...	1217	...	...	J	...	1 43	...	...	...	...	...	4 19	...
Leamington .... ,,	8 32	...	I	1144	...	1147	...	...	...	1 9	...	...	...	...	...	...	2 54	...	4 23	4 35	...	...	5 28	6 7
Birmingham ...... ,,	8 3	1012	...	...	1045	1130		...	...	1 20	...	...	...	...	1 50	...	3 5	...	4 2	...	4 30	...	6 2	...
Leicester .... ,,	8 25	1022	...	1219				...	...	2 2	...	...	2 2	...		...	3 45	...	4 55	...		...	6 55	...
Shrewsbury .... ,,	9 47	1117	...	1 52	...	...		...	...	2 35	...	...	2 35	...	...	...	...	4 55	...	...	...	5 56		...
Manchester L. R. ,,	10 0	1210	1233		...	...	Runs until 16th August.	...	...	3 18	2 5	...		...	...	3 50	4 45	...	6 5	...	...	6 23	...	8 15
Rochdale .... ,,	1114	...	1 52	...	...	...		...	...	4 48	2 55	...	...	...	...	4 48	5 54	...	7 20	...	...	7 20	...	9 28
Huddersfield ...... ,,	1111	...	2 13	...	...	...		...	...	...	3 8	...	...	...	...	4 45	5 39	...	7 48	...	...	7 48	...	9 28
Liverpool L. S. ... ,,	1020	1213	1233	...	...	...		...	...	3 18	2 20	...	...	...	...	4 5	5 25	...	6 35	...	...	6 35	...	
Chester .... ,,	9 55	12 1	1215	...	...	...	...	1 45	...	...	...	2 55	...	...	...	3 46	5 27	...	5 55	...	...	6 16	...	...
Dublin, North Wall ,,	...	...	5‡30	...	...	...	...	...	...	...	...		...	...	...	...	...	10‡20	...	...	...	...	...	...
Warrington .... ,,	9 52	1136	1 0	...	...	...	...	...	...	2 39	...	...	...	2 59	...	4 15	4 41		...	...	...	6 25	...	...
Carlisle .... ,,	1237	3 7	...	...	...	...	3 48	4 0	4 22	...	...	...	...	5 38	...	...	...	...	...	8 8	...	...	...	...
Glasgow .... ,,	3 5	6 0	...	...	...	...	...	6 15	...	...	...	...	...	7 55	...	...	...	...	...	1020	...	...	...	...
Edinburgh .... ,,	3 5	5 50	...	...	...	...	6 10	6r15	...	...	...	...	...	7 55	...	...	...	...	...	1030	...	...	...	...
Perth .... ,,	5 40	...	...	...	...	...	...	...	8 0	...	...	...	...	...	...	...	...	...	...	1235	...	...	...	...
Aberdeen .... ,,	9 15	...	...	...	...	...	...	...	10 20	...	...	...	...	...	...	...	...	...	...	3 20	...	...	...	...
Inverness .... ,,	...	...	...	...	...	...	...	...	...	...	...	...	...	...	...	...	...	...	...	4i56	...	...	...	...

London—	p.m.	p.m.	p.m.	p.m.	p.m.	p.m.	p.m.	p.m.	p.m.	p.m.	p.m.	p.m.	p.m.	p.m.	p.m.	p.m.	p.m.	p.m.	nght	ng't	ng't		
Euston .... dep	4 5	4 30	4 45	5 20	5 30	5 35	5 55	6 5	6 55	7 0	7 45	8 0	8 45	8 50	9 0	10 0	1015	1145	12 0	12 5	1215	...	...
Cambridge .... arr	...	...	...	¶	...	8 25	...	...	...	...	...	...	...	...	...	...	...	...	...	...	...	...	...
Northampton ...... ,,	5 27	5 49	...	...	...	7 12	...	...	...	8 22	...	...	...	...	10 26	...	1145	...	...	...	2 5	...	...
Leamington .... ,,	...	7 22	...	8 5	...	8 27	...	...	...	9 21	...	...	I	...	12§15	...	...	...	...	C	3 48	...	...
Birmingham ...... ,,	...	7 3	6 45	7 40	...	8 41	...	...	8 55	9 39	...	D	...	11 14	11 55	...	...	...	...	...	3 7	...	...
Leicester .... ,,	7 37				8 32	9 28	...	...	...		...	...	...	...	12v25	2 52	...	...	...	...	...	...	...
Shrewsbury .... ,,	...	...	...		9 5	...	...	...	1125	...		...	...	...	3 0	3 0	...	...	...	...	...	...	...
Manchester L. R. ,,	9 0	...	...	Saturdays excepted.	...	1047	...	9 35		...	Saturdays excepted.	1 10	1A10	...	...	3 0	...	...	...	5 32	...	...	...
Rochdale .... ,,	1032	...	...		...	...	...	1032	...	...		...	...	...	...	...	...	...	...	9f51	...	...	...
Huddersfield ...... ,,	9 50	...	...		...	...	...	1059	...	...		1 55	1A55	...	...	...	...	...	...	6e55	...	...	...
Liverpool L. S. ... ,,	8 40	...	...		...	1051	9 30		...	...		1240	...	...	...	3 10	...	...	...	6A3	5 55	...	...
Chester .... ,,	8 33	...	...		9 2	...		...	...	...		...	12 34	...	...	2 32	...	...	...	...	5 30	...	...
Dublin, North Wall ,,	...	...	...	...	...	...	...	...	...	...	...	...	6 ‡0	...	...	...	7 30	...	...	...		...	...
Warrington .... ,,	8 28	...	...	...	9 0	1035	...	...	...	...	...	...	...	...	...	...	...	3 13	...	5 15	...	...	...
Carlisle .... ,,	...	...	...	...	...	...	...	...	...	...	1 35	2 0	...	3 50	4 22	5 23	...	5 36	5 50	8 52	...	...	...
Glasgow .... ,,	...	...	...	...	...	...	...	...	...	...	...	...	...	6 15	7 0	...	...	...	8 0	1235	...	...	...
Edinburgh .... ,,	...	...	...	...	...	...	...	...	...	...	...	...	...	...	6 50	...	...	7f45	8A0	1230	...	...	...
Perth .... ,,	...	...	...	...	...	...	...	...	...	...	4 45	5 20	...	...	8f45	...	...	9 0	...	3 0	...	...	...
Aberdeen .... ,,	...	...	...	...	...	...	...	...	...	...	...	7 15	...	...	...	...	...	1155	...	6 0	...	...	...
Inverness .... ,,	...	...	...	...	...	...	...	...	...	...	8 35	9 35	...	...	...	...	...	1 50	...	7 42	...	...	...

	p.m.	p.m.	p.m.	p.m.	p.m.	p.m.	p.m.	p.m.	a.m.	a.m.	a.m.	a.m.	a.m.	a.m.	a.m.	a.m.	a.m.	a.m.	a.m.	a.m.	a.m.	a.m.	a.m.	p.m.
Inverness .... dep	...	...	...	3 50	...	...	5 0	...	...	...	...	...	...	...	...	...	...	...	...	...	...	...	...	...
Aberdeen .... ,,	...	...	...	5 45	...	...	...	7 55	...	...	...	...	...	...	...	...	...	...	...	...	...	...	...	...
Perth .... ,,	...	...	...	8 10	...	...	9 40	10 5	...	...	...	...	...	...	...	...	...	...	...	...	...	...	...	...
Edinburgh .... ,,	...	9 5	9 10	...	...	1050	...	...	...	...	...	...	...	...	...	...	...	...	...	...	...	...	...	...
Glasgow .... ,,	...	9 5	9 5	...	...	1045	...	...	...	...	...	...	...	...	...	...	...	...	...	...	...	...	...	...
Carlisle .... ,,	...	1142	1210	12 15	...	1 0	1 20	1 50	...	...	...	...	...	...	...	...	...	...	...	...	...	...	...	...
Warrington .... ,,	...	...	3 34	3 1	...	...	...	...	...	...	...	...	...	...	8 10	...	...	...	...	...	9 36	...	...	...
Dublin, North Wall ,,	7‡50	...	...	...	9 20	...	...	...	...	...	...	...	...	...	...	...	...	...	...	...	...	...	...	...
Chester .... ,,	2 7	...	...	...	...	...	...	...	...	...	...	6 45	...	...	...	...	...	...	...	...	9 53	1023	...	...
Liverpool L. S. ... ,,	...	...	2 35	2 35	...	2*35	...	...	...	...	...	...	...	...	8 0	...	...	...	...	...	9 45	10 0	...	...
Huddersfield ...... ,,	...					...			...			...	...	...	...	6 52	...	...	8 37	...	...	9 20	...	...
Rochdale .... ,,	...					...			...			...	...	...	...	7 25	...	...	8 52	...	...	8 52	...	...
Manchester L. Rd. ,,	...	Mondays excepted.	Mondays only.	Monday except.	Mondays excepted.	...	Mondays excepted.	Mondays excepted.	...	Saturdays excepted.	Mondays excepted.	...	...	...	...	8 30	...	...	9 45	...	9 25	1015	...	...
Shrewsbury .... ,,	...					...			...	...		...	...	...	7 25	...	...	...	...	...	1010	1010	...	...
Leicester .... ,,	...					...			6 20	...		...	...	...	...	9 0	...	9 50	...	...	...	...	...	...
Birmingham ...... ,,	I			...		...			7 30	8 20	8 40	E	8 45	9 30	...	...	10 5	...	...	1125	...	...	1145	...
Leamington .... ,,	...	...	...	...	...	...	...	...	7 35	7 57	...	...	8 52	9 46	...	...	1010	...	...	...	...	...	1150	1240
Northampton ...... ,,	...	...	6 29	6 23	6 7	...	...	...	...	...	...	...	...	...	...	...	1120	...	...	...	...	...	...	...
Cambridge .... ,,	...	...	...	...	...	...	...	...	...	B	...	...	...	7 40	9 42	...	...	...	...	...	...	...	...	J
London, Euston ... arr	6 10	6 35	8 0	7 50	7 30	7 10	7 45	8 5	9 55	1035	1040	1050	1110	1145	12 0	1225	1210	1 5	1 15	1 25	1 40	2 10	2 25	2 40

	a.m.	a.m.	a.m.	a.m.	p.m.	p.m.	a.m.	a.m.	p.m.	a.m.	p.m.	a.m.	p.m.	p.m.	noon	p.m.	p.m.	p.m.	p.m.	p.m.	p.m.	a.m.	a.m.	p.m.
Inverness .... dep	...	...	...	...	...	...	...	...	...	...	...	...	...	...	...	...	...	...	...	...	...	8 40	11 5	...
Aberdeen .... ,,	...	...	...	...	...	...	...	...	...	...	...	6 45	...	...	...	...	...	...	...	...	...	10 5	1 10	...
Perth .... ,,	...	...	...	...	...	...	...	...	...	...	...	9 5	...	...	...	...	...	...	...	...	...	1215	4 4	
Edinburgh .... ,,	...	...	...	...	...	...	...	...	...	10 5	...	...	...	...	12 0	...	...	...	...	...	...	2 0	6 0	
Glasgow .... ,,	...	...	...	...	...	...	...	I	...	10 0	...	...	...	...	12 0	...	...	...	...	...	...	2 0	5 55	Mondays excepted.
Carlisle .... ,,	6 30	...	...	8 30	...	...	...	...	...	1210	...	1258	...	...	2 20	...	...	...	...	...	...	4 12	8 44	
Warrington .... ,,	1020	...	...	1158	...	...	...	...	...	...	...	...	4 5	...	4 50	...	5 14	...	...	...	...	...	1134	
Dublin, North Wall ,,	...	...	...	...	...	...	...	8 ‡0	...	...	...	...	...	...	...	...	...	...	...	1‡10	...	...	...	...
Chester .... ,,	1130	...	...	...	...	...	1145	1 55	...	2 15	...	...	4 20		...	5 0	...	...	...	7 15	...	6 20	11 2	...
Liverpool L. S. ... ,,	11 0	...	...	...	...	...	12 0	...	2 0	...	...	...	4 5		...	...	5 20	...	...	...	5 25	6 15	1045	1155
Huddersfield ...... ,,	10 5	...	1120	...	...	...	...	11j51	1222	...	...	2 8	2 53		...	...	...	4s10	4 42	4 42	4s10	...	9 12	1119
Rochdale .... ,,	...	...	1122	...	...	...	...	...	1255	...	...	1255	3 33		...	...	...	4 8	...	...	4 8	...	9 57	...
Manchester L. R. ,,	1040	...	1210	...	...	...	1150	12t55	2 10	...	...	2 45	4 10	Saturdays excepted.	...	...	...	5 30	6 15	6 28	5 35	...	1045	1155
Shrewsbury .... ,,	...	1140	...	1145	...	...	1230	...	...	...	2 40	...	...		...	4 50	...	...		...	5 43	...	10 8	...
Leicester .... ,,	...	1145	...	...	...	...	12†15	2 †10	...	...	...	4 25	...		...	5 55	...	...		...	6 37	6 37	...	1115
Birmingham ...... ,,	...	...	...	...	2 5	2 45	...	...	3 40	...	5 0	...	5 30	6 20	...	...	...	7 0		...	...	8 15	1250	...
Leamington .... ,,	...	1 3	...	...	1 30	...	1 30	2 55	3 15	...	...	...	5 50	...	...	...	...	7 14	Saturdays excepted.	...	...	7 55	10k50	...
Northampton ...... ,,	...	...	...	...	3 11	...	3 40	...	4 23	...	...	...	...	...	...	7 40	...	...		...	9 20	...	...	3 57
Cambridge .... ,,	...	...	...	...	...	...	1 50	...	...	...	...	...	...	...	...	...	...	7 8		...	...	...	...	...
London, Euston ... arr	3 10	3 20	4 0	4 20	4 30	4 45	5 20	5 40	6 10	6 20	7 0	7 10	8 10	8 20	8 30	9 5	9 15	9 50	10 0	11 0	1125	1045	3 50	5 50

FOR SUNDAY TRAINS AND NOTES SEE NEXT PAGE.

LONDON AND NORTH WESTERN RAILWAY.—*Continued.*

Sundays.

London—	a.m.	no n	p.m.	p.m.	p.m	p.m.	p.m.	p.m.	p.m.	p.m.	p.m.	ng't	ng't		
Euston ....dep	10 0	12 0	1230	4 30	5 20	6 10	8 0	8 45	8 50	10 0	1145	12 0	12 5	...	...
Cambridge ....arr	1 17	...	...	...	...	...	...	...	...	...	...	...	...	...	...
Northampton ..... „	1142	...	...	6 13	...	...	...	...	1016	...	...	...	1 37	...	...
Leamington......... „	2 30	...	3 40	8 20	...	...	...	I	...	...	...	...	3 48	...	...
Birmingham ...... „	1 53	...	2 40	8 0	7 25	...	...	...	1145	...	...	...	3 3	...	...
Leicester .... „	3 5	...		8 18		...	...	...	...	2 52	...	...	...	...	...
Shrewsbury .... „	3 32	...	...	...	...	...	...	...	...	3 0	...	...	...	...	...
Manchester L.R. „	4 20	4 45	...	9 47	...	10 5	...	1 28	...	3 0	...	...	5 50	...	...
Rochdale .... „	7 2	7 2	...	...	...	...	...	...	...	...	...	...	9 51	...	...
Huddersfield ...... „	8 5	8 5	...	...	...	...	...	2 0	...	...	...	...	8 11	...	...
Liverpool L. S. ... „	4 5	4 55	...	9 55	...	1020	...	...	...	3 10	...	...	6 10	...	...
Chester .... „	...	4 35	...	9 55	...	9 55	...	1234	...	2 32	...	...	8 13	...	...
Dublin,NorthWall „	...	...	...	...	...	...	...	6 ‡0	...	...	...	...	...	...	...
Warrington......... „	3 20	5 0	...	10 5	...	10 5	...	...	...	...	3 13	...	5 15	...	...
Carlisle .... „	8 25	...	...	...	...	...	2 0	...	4 22	5 23	5 36	5 50	8 52	...	...
Glasgow .... „	...	...	...	...	...	...	...	...	6 50	...	...	8 0	1235	...	...
Edinburgh .... „	...	...	...	...	...	...	...	...	6 50	...	7 45	...	1230	...	...
Perth .... „	...	...	...	...	...	...	5 20	...	8 35	...	9 0	...	3 0	...	...
Aberdeen .... „	...	...	...	...	...	...	7 15	...	...	...	1155	...	6 0	...	...
Inverness.......... „	...	...	...	...	...	...	9 8	...	...	...	1 50	...	7 42	...	...
	p.m.	p.m	p.m.	p.m.		a.m.	a.m.	a.m.	a.m.	p.m.	a.m.	p.m.	p.m.	a.m.	p.m.
Inverness...........dep	...	3 50	...	...	Saturday.	...	...	...	...	...	...	...	...	1010	...
Aberdeen........... „	...	5 45	...	7 55		...	...	...	...	...	...	...	...	1 10	...
Perth .... „	...	8 10	...	10 5		...	...	...	...	...	...	...	...	4 5	...
Edinburgh .... „	9 5	...	1050	...		...	...	...	...	...	...	...	...	6 0	...
Glasgow .... „	9 5	...	1045	1115		...	...	...	...	...	9 55	...	...	5 50	...
Carlisle .... „	1142	1215	1 0	1 55	...	...	...	...	...	...	1240	...	...	8 44	I
Warrington......... „	...	3 1	...	...	...	...	9 21	...	1015	...	4 5	...	...	1137	...
Dublin,NorthWall „	...	...	...	...	...	...	...	...	...	...	8 ‡0	...	...	...	7‡45
Chester .... „	...	...	...	...	...	...	9 10	...	9 45	...	4 12	...	...	11 2	2 7
Liverpool L. S. ... „	...	2 35	2 35	...	...	...	8 40	...	9 20	1250	4 5	...	...	11 0	...
Huddersfield ..... „	...	...	...	...	...	...	...	...	7 35	...	1 2	...	1 2	8 44	...
Rochdale .... „	...	...	...	...	...	...	...	...	...	...	...	...	3 15	...	...
Manchester L. R. „	...	...	...	...	...	...	...	...	9 0	1 0	...	...	4 25	1045	...
Shrewsbury .... „	...	...	...	...	...	...	...	...	...	...	...	...	4 15	10 8	...
Leicester .... „	...	...	...	...	...	...	...	...	1135	...	...	...	5 45	...	...
Birmingham ...... „	...	...	...	...	...	8 30	...	1130	1255	...	...	6 25	...	1250	...
Leamington......... „	...	...	...	...	...	8 45	...	...	1225	...	...	5 55	...	8 40	...
Northampton...... „	...	6 23	...	...	...	1023	...	...	2 57	4 10	...	...	...	...	...
Cambridge .... „	...	...	...	...	...	...	8 45	...	...	...	...	...	...	...	...
London, Euston...arr	6 35	7 50	7 10	8 5	...	1150	1255	1 35	4 20	5 45	8 20	8 35	9 0	3 50	6 10

*—Mondays excepted.
†—Leaves at 1.40 p.m.on Sats.
‡—Dublin, Westland Row.
§—To Leamington on Thursday and Saturday only.
¶—From Broad Street (City) at 5.25 p.m.
A—Sunday morning only.
B—Arrives Broad Street (City).
C—Not beyond Liverpool and Manchester on Saturday night,
D—Scotch Express; does not run on Saturday night.
E—Belfast Boat Express—Mondays excepted.
e—Arrive Huddersfield 11.28 on Sunday mornings.
f—Sunday mornings excepted.
I—Irish Mail.
i—No connection on Sunday mornings.
j—Saturday excepted.
k—From Leamington on Tues., Thurs. and Sat. only.
l-8.18 a.m. on Sunday.
r—From 18th August.
s—4.2 p.m. on Saturday.
t—On Sats. leaves at 12.40 p.m.
v—Saturday only.

GREAT CENTRAL RAILWAY.—Marylebone Station.

Service from July 14th. — **Sundays.**

London—	F a.m.	a.m.	a.m.	a.m.	n'on	p.m.	p.m.	p.m.	p.m.	p.m.			a.m.	a.m.	a.m.	p.m.	p.m.		
Marylebone ....dep	12 40	2 40	8 45	10 0	12 15	3 15	4 45	6 20	8 25	10 0	...	...	12 40	9 30	1115	5 30	11 45	...	...
Leicester (Central)..............arr	2 45	4 30	10 59	12 9	2 31	5¶4	7 4	8 14	1022	12 15	...	...	2 45	1247	1 22	7 44	2 4	...	...
Nottingham (Victoria)......... „	3 22	4 59	11 34	12 38	3 6	5¶50	7 38	8 43	1051	12 50	...	...	3 22	1 49	1 59	8 15	2 44	...	...
Hull (Corporation Pier) ...... „	...	10‖12	2‖29	5 2	7 40	9¶35	...	1‖32	...	7S50	...	...	...		10 5	...		...	...
Grimsby Town .... „	...	10 15	...	4E22	6t32	8¶13	...	...	...	5S2	...	...	...	...	9 28	...	...	...	...
Sheffield (Victoria) .... „	4 15	5 53	12 28	1 32	4 1	6 12	8 47	9 36	1230	1 52	...	...	4 15	...	2 53	9 8	...	...	...
Huddersfield .... „	...	10 18	1 41	2 22	5 18	7 29	...	10 29	Sats. only.	...	...	...		...	8 4	1034	...	...	...
Halifax .... „	F	11 10	2 17	3 5	6 24	8 1	...	11B10		...	...	...	...	...	9 27	1037	...	...	...
Bradford .... „	...	10 55	2 21	2 51	6 3	8 32	...	11 2		...	...	...	...	...	1012	11 0	...	...	...
Liverpool (Central G.C.)...... „	9 20	10A35	2 45	4 32	6 50	8 15	...	12 43		5 15	...	...	...	...	6 50	1135	...	...	...
Manchester (London Road) „	7 47	9 53	1 38	3 25	5 18	7 a25	10 21	10 58		3 28	...	...	...	...	4 10	1025	...	...	...

	a.m.	a.m.	a.m.	a.m.	D	a.m.	C	p.m.	p.m.	p.m.	p.m.		a.m.	a.m.	p.m.	p.m.			
Manchester (London Road) dep	1 45	...	...	7 40	a.m.	10 0	11 25	2 15	3 40	5 0	10 25	...	...	6 50	1235	5 a35	...	...	...
Liverpool (Central G.C.)...... „	...	...	...	6 15	...	8 30	10 30	12 30	2 30	4 0	9 30	...	...	...	1040	4 30	...	...	...
Bradford .... „	...	...	...	6 38	...	10 0	...	1 35	2.43	5 0	9 17	...	...	...	...	4 0	...	...	...
Halifax .... „	...	...	...	6 12	...	9 44	...	1 20	2 48	4 47	8 55	...	...	...	...	4 28	...	...	...
Huddersfield....................... „	...	...	...	7 37	...	10 33	...	2 13	3 30	5 27	9 54	...	...	7 40	...	5 0	...	...	...
Sheffield (Victoria) .... „	3 15	5 30	6 50	8 48	1112	11 21	12 50	3 25	4 55	6 21	11 57	...	...	9 50	1 55	6 43	...	...	...
Grimsby Town .... „	...	...	...	6 40	...	8 0	9 9	1 33	...	2 52	7 38	...	...	...	8 55	...	...	...	...
Hull (Corporation Pier) ...... „	...	...	...	6‖20	...	8‖20	10‖52	12 40	2‖55	...	7‖30	...	...	...	7 45	11‖40	...	...	...
Nottingham (Victoria)......... „	5 18	7 35	8 12	9 40	12 6	12 14	1 52	4 18	5 59	7 14	12‡53	...	...	1130	2 52	7 37	...	...	...
Leicester (Central) .... „	6 12	8 11	9 0	10 9	1235	12 50	2 28	4 47	6 34	7 46	1‡32	...	6 20	1210	3 31	8 11	...	...	...
London—Marylebone ......arr	9 48	10 27	11 55	12 3	2 40	3 0	4 35	6 46	8 50	9 55	3‡47	...	10 3	2 28	5 40	10 17	...	...	...

‡—Runs on Sundays but not on Mondays.
‖—Paragon Station. ¶—Slip Carriage for Leicester, etc.
A—On Mondays, arrives Liverpool (Central) at 9.40 a.m. **a**—Central Station.
B—Arrives at 11,39 p.m. on Saturdays. **C**—Thursdays and Saturdays only.
D—Thursdays and Saturdays only, and not on August 2nd.
E—On Saturdays until August 30th arrives at 3,41 p.m.
F—Fridays only. **S**—Sunday morning excepted.
t—From July 19th to September 6th inclusive arrives at 6,5 p.m.

GREAT NORTHERN RAILWAY.—Week Days only.

LONDON—			E			E	E	E		E	E	E	E	E		E			E	E	E		S				S	S	
	a.m.	a.m.	a.m.	a.m.	a.m.	a.m.	a.m.	a.m.	a.m.	p.m.	p.m.	p.m.	p.m.	p.m. Thurs. & Sats. only.	p.m.	p.m.	p.m.	p.m.	p.m.	p.m.	p.m.	p.m.	p.m. Saturdays excepted.	p.m.	p.m.	p.m.	p.m.	p.m. Sats. excepted	
King's Cross dep	3 0	5 5	7 15	8 45	9 50	10 0	10 10	1035	1145	1230	1 5	1 30	1 40	2 0	2 0	2 20	3 25	4 0	5 30	5 45	6 5	7 55	8 15	8 45	10 30	1045	11 30	11 45	...
Lincoln.........arr	...	8 14	10 25	1211	...	...	...	1B48	...	3 50	...	...	...		...	5H20	...	7 4	...	...	9 7	...	...	...	...	...	...	...	...
Nottingham ... ,,	7 54	8 6	10 12	1223	...	...	12 51	2‖25	...	3 31	...	...	4F52		X	5 18	6 20	7 8	8 6	...	9 34	...	...	1142	2 *5	...	5Y37	5 37	...
Sheffield......... ,,	6 59	9 0	10 50	1 55	...	...	...	3 44	...	4 16	...	X	...		5 25	...	7 19	7 47	...	...	9F18	...	...	...	...	2 53	...		...
Manchester L.R.,,	9 53	10 15	12 18	3 25	...	...	...	5 18	...	5e55	...	...	...		7 e25	...	9e16	9e16	...	...	10F21	...		...	...	4e20	...		...
Liverpool....... ,,	10 35	12d15	1d15	4 32	...	...	...	6 50	...	7d15	...	...	...		8 15	...	10 15	10 15	...	...	12K5	...		...	...	5 15	...		...
Southport........ ,,	...	2 25	2 25	5 43	...	...	...	7 13	...	...	...	...	9d33		...	...	...	12d25	...	...	...	...		...	...	8c35	...		...
Wakefield........ ,,	6 33	9 0	10 55	...	...	...	1 35	2F41	...	...	...	4F51	...		...	...	7C11	7 44	...	9 15	10 10	...		...	...	3 10	...		...
Leeds.............. ,,	6 59	9 22	11 15	...	...	...	1 56	3F7	...	...	...	5F12	...		...	7D13	...	8 5	...	9 35	10 42	...		...	...	3 34	4D35	4D35	...
Bradford......... ,,	7 47	9 42	11 28	...	...	...	2 10	3F23	...	...	...	5 26	...		...	...	...	8 20	...	10 4	11 16	...		...	...	4 3	...	...	...
Halifax........... ,,	8 26	10 53	12 29	...	...	...	2 25	4F11	...	...	...	5F38	...		...	...	8 15	8 48	...	10 8	11raB10	...	...	...	...	4j16	...	...	...
Keighley......... ,,	8B48	11 1	12 52	...	...	...	...	4F8	...	...	...	6 21	...		...	...	...	9 42	...	1158	...	...	...	...	...	5j44	...	...	...
York............... ,,	6 55	9 18	12 35	1 20	1 36	1 45	2B9	3 2	4 35	...	...	...	5 38		...	6 3	7 35	...	9 5	10 5	10 20	...	1150	1 5	2 56	...	3 5	3 20	...
Hull................ ,,	8 14	9 50	11 57	2 0	...	...	2 29	3 35	4 59	...	...	5 29	6 12	6 q5	...	...	8 32	...	...	...	10 12	...	...	1 32	4 42	...	...	...	...
Newcastle .... ,,	10 12	11 7	2 45	...	3 18	3 32	5B7	5 25	...	...	6 55	...	7 55	...	...	8 3	...	...	10 48	...	12 32	...	1 28	2 58	5 58	...	5 0	5 0	...
Edinburgh .... ,,	...	1 32	...	...	6 5	6 15	...	8 46	...	...	...	...	...	...	...	10 45	...	...	...	...	...	...	4 0	5 55	...	...	7 15	...	...
Glasgow .... ,,	...	3 26	...	...	...	7 35	...	1030	...	...	...	...	...	...	...	...	...	...	...	...	...	...	5 35	7T23	...	...	9T5	...	...
Aberdeen......... ,,	...	6 30	...	...	...	10 5	...	...	...	...	...	...	...	...	...	...	...	...	...	...	...	...	7 22	...	...	...	11 32	...	...
Inverness......... ,,	...	7 42	...	...	...	...	...	4Y56	...	...	...	...	...	...	...	...	...	...	...	...	...	8M35	9 8	...	...	...	1 50	...	...

Inverness.dep	...	...	...	...	...	...	...	...	...	...	...	...	...	...	10R50	...	...	...	...	...	...	8 40	...	...	...	11s5	3W50	5 0	...	...	...
Aberdeen... ,,	...	...	B	...	...	...	...	...	...	...	...	...	...	...	6 20	...	...	...	...	...	...	10 20	...	...	...	3 30	5W45	7 35	...	...	...
Glasgow ... ,,	...	...	...	...	...	...	...	...	...	...	...	...	...	...	8 45	...	...	...	...	11 0	...	1 0	...	...	...	6s 0	9 35	...	...	...	...
Edinburgh ,,	...	...	...	...	...	...	...	...	...	...	7 45	...	...	...	10 0	10 10	...	...	1025	1228	...	2 20	2 50	...	...	7 45	10 50	1115	...	...	...
Newcastle.. ,,	...	...	...	...	E	8 0	...	...	...	...	1028	...	...	...	1239	12 50	...	...	2 0	3 17	2 40	5 4	7 20	...	...	1119	1V42	1 52	...	...	...
Hull .... ,,	...	...	6 20	7 20	9q10	...	9 43	...	...	11m30	1130	...	...	B	...	...	1 43	2 55	3 20	...	5 5	6 12	9 20	...	...	11w25	...	...	...	...	...
York......... ,,	3 U53	...	6 35	8 12	Runs Mon. & Fri. only.	9 47	...	10 3	...	12m2	1215	...	...	...	2 24	2 39	...	2 52	4 10	...	4 37	6 50	9 50	...	...	1 32	3 27	3 45	...	...	...
Keighley ... ,,	...	...	6 25	7 50		...	...	8 58	...	1010	...	...	...	1150	...	...	1 45	E	...	...	4 15	...	...	8N42	...	...	...	...	...	...	...
Halifax...... ,,	...	...	6 42	7 57		...	...	9 30	...	1036	...	...	...	1 15	...	...	1 58	...	3 16	...	4 45	5 48	...	9 10	...	...	...	...	...	...	...
Bradford... ,,	...	...	7 25	8 40		...	...	9 45	...	1053	1056	...	...	1 37	...	...	2 35	...	3 12	...	5 10	6A0	...	10 5	...	...	...	W	...	...	...
Leeds .... ,,	...	...	7 50	9 0		...	...	1015	...	1120	1130	...	...	2 0	...	...	2 55	B	3 50	...	5 30	6 30	...	10 20	...	...	...	2D48	...	...	...
Wakefield ,,	...	...	8 10	9 21		E	E	1034	...	1141	1158	...	...	2 20	E	E	3 17	...	4 9	...	5 51	6 49	...	10 46	...	...	...	...	...	...	...
Southport.. ,,	...	...	...	...		...	...	...	...	7 50	...	...	10d10	...	...	...	...	1d25	1d25	...	...	2 50	4 d5	...	9 d 0	S	...	...	...	...	...
Liverpool . ,,	...	...	...	6 15		...	...	E	E	8 30	...	...	10u30	...	...	...	...	2d30	2d30	...	...	4 0	6d30	...	9d 30	...	...	...	...	...	...
Man. (L R) ,,	1 U45	B	...	7 40		...	...	...	...	10 0	...	...	1230	...	...	...	...	3 40	3e20	...	E	5 0	7 B20	...	10e55	...	...	S	...	...	...
Sheffield.... ,,	3U 5	...	8 18	8 57		...	...	...	...	1148	E	...	1 50	E	...	...	...	4 50	4 37	...	...	6 9	...	11 0	12 29	...	...	...	...	...	...
Nottingh'm ,,	...	7 50	8‡35	1010		...	11B0	...	...	1150	...	...	2 8	...	...	3B25	...	4 55	...	...	6 15	7 5	11 0	...	...	...	...	...	...	...	...
Lincoln...... ,,	...	7 23	E	9 15		1010	1010	...	11B22	...	...	1 B0	1 50	...	...	2K50	...	4 30	...	...	6 20	6 30	11H0	...	W	...	...	...	...	...	...
King's C. arr	9 50	1040	1130	1 5	1 20	1 30	1 35	1p55	2 15	3 55	4 10	4 45	5 15	5 25	6 15	6 25	7 0	7 48	8 35	9 0	9 25	10 45	2 40	3 24	4 37	5 50	7 10	7 35	...	...	...
	a.m.	a.m.	a.m.	p.m.	p.m.	p.m.	p.m.	p.m.	p.m.	p.m.	p.m.	p.m.	p.m.	p.m.	p.m.	p.m.	p.m.	p.m.	p.m.	p.m.	p.m.	p.m. E	a.m.	a.m.	a.m.	a.m.	a.m.	a.m.			

NOTES.

*—Arr. Nottingham Low Level Station

‡—Mondays only. Arrive King's Cross 11 50 a.m. on other days.

‖—On Thursdays & Saturdays arrives Nottingham 1.33 p.m.

a—Due Halifax 11.39 p.m. on Sats.

c—On Sunday mornings is due Southport 10.57.

d—Via Manchester (Central).

e—Central Station, Manchester.

j—Sunday morning excepted, via Leeds.

k—Fridays only.

m—Arrives King's Cross 3.58 p.m.

p—On Bank Holidays arrives King's Cross 2.15 p.m.

q—Hull (Riverside Quay).

r—Via Sheffield and Penistone.

s—On Sundays leaves Inverness at 10.10 a.m. and Glasgow at 5.5 p.m.

t—Via Manchester (Central and London Road Stations.)

u—Leaves 11.10 a.m. commencing July 14th.

A—Leaves Bradford 5.50 p.m. Sats. and Bank Holidays.

B—Bank Holidays excepted.

C—Kirkgate Station.

D—Via York, arrives at and departs from Leeds (N.E. Station).

E—Breakfast, Luncheon, or Dining Cars (1st and 3rd class) are attached to these trains.

F—Arrives later on Bank Holidays.

H—Sats. only.

K—Via Manchester, London Rd. and Central Stations. Passengers find their own way across Manchester. On Saturdays arr. Liverpool 11.42 p.m.

M—Saturdays excepted commencing July 8th.

N—Via Bradford.

R—Not on Saturday nights.

S—Sleeping Car Express.

T—Arrives later on Sundays.

U—On Mon. arr. King's Cross 8.5 a.m.

V—Leaves Newcastle 1.36 a.m. Mon.

W—Sunday nights and Monday mornings excepted.

X—On Bank Holidays, leaves King's Cross at 1.40 p.m.

Y—Sunday mornings excepted.

MIDLAND RAILWAY.—Week Days.

	a.m.	a.m.	a.m.	a.m.	a.m.	a.m.	a.m.	a.m.	a.m.	a.m.	noon	p.m.	p.m	p.m.	p.m.	p.m.	p.m.	p.m.	p.m.	p.m.	p.m.	p.m.	p.m.	p m.	p.m.	p.m.	p.m.	p.m.	ngnt	ng't	ng't
London— (St. Pancras) ......dep	2 40	4 50	8 0	9 30	9 45	10 0	10 5	1025	1130	1150	12 0	12 7	1215	1 30	1 50	2 5	2 30	3 30	3 40	4 30	4 55	5 35	6 0	6 30	7 10	8 15	8 40	9 30	12 0	12†5	1215
Leicester .... arr	4 25	7 5	10 50	1122	1130	1145	1215	1255	1 20	...	1 55	...	2 40	3 22	3 35	...	4 15	...	6 10	6 25	7 20	7 27	...	8 27	...	10 0	11 15	...	1 53	2 25	2 43
Burton .... „	6 30	8 17	11 30	12 8	...	...	1 22	240	...	...	...	...	3 53	...	...	...	5 40	...	...	7 46	8H30	8 30	...	10 0	K	...	1W 0	1 c 0	...	...	...
Nottingham .... „	...	7 50	10 40	1220	...	...	...	1252	2 12	...	...	2 25	...	...	...	4 35	...	5 45	7 15	...	7 18	8 20	8 30	9 35	...	1037	...	11 50	2 40	...	...
Derby .... „	5 7	7 57	11 10	1230	...	...	1257	1 58	...	...	...	3 22	3 30	...	...	...	4 55	...	...	7 5	...	8 23	...	9 5	9 28	...	12 10	12N35	...	3 10	3 30
Buxton .... „	...	9 20	12H40	...	...	...	2 15	...	...	...	...	3 55	4 50	...	...	...	6 10	...	...	8 46	9 45	9 45	...	10 6	Saturdays excepted.	Saturdays excepted.	...	...	...	...	...
Manchester (Cen) „	6 35	9 52	12 40	...	...	1 40	2 38	...	...	...	3 50	...	5 20	...	...	...	6 25	...	...	8 40	10 12	9 22	...	1035			...	2N40	...	...	5 25
Manchester (Vic.) „	...	10 10	...	...	...	...	2 50	...	...	...	...	4 35	5e38	...	...	...	6 52	...	...	9 5	...	...	...	...			...	...	...	...	5 35
Bolton .... „	...	10 38	...	...	...	...	3 18	...	...	...	...	5 32	6 42	...	...	...	7 43	...	...	9 57	...	...	...	...			...	...	...	...	6g41
Blackburn .... „	...	11z12	...	...	...	...	4 12	...	...	...	...	6 28	7 33	...	...	...	8 55	...	...	1048	...	...	...	...			...	...	...	...	7g33
Liverpool (Cen.) ......„	8 25	10 40	1 42	...		2 25	3 50	...	...	...	4 40	...	6 15	...	...	...	7 0	...	...	9 30	10 10	1015	...	12 5			...	5 15	...	...	6 5
Sheffield .... „	6†35	8 55	12 2	...	1254	☞ Saturdays excepted.	...	1 52	...	...	...	3 48	...	...	4 50	5 47	6 30	6 45	7 50	...	8 20	☞ Saturdays excepted.	9 10	1115	1115	1140	1W50	1 c50	...	4 25	...
Hull .... „	...	11 27	...	...	...		...	4 10	...	...	...	6 40	...	...	6 56	...	...	1012	...	...	10 25		...	...		...	4W42	4 c42	...	6 50	...
York .... „	9 †7	10 42	2 27	...	3 0		...	3 54	...	...	...	5 35	...	...	7 27	...	7 45	...	...	...	10 5		1136	...	K	...	3W31	3 c31	...	8g15	...
Newcastle-on-T. „	11†7	1 57	5 7	5 25	5 25		...	...	6 42	...	...	7 55	...	...	...	9 25	...	1048	...	...	12 32		1g16	...	...	...	5W58	5 c58	9c16	...	...
Leeds .... „	9†10	9 55	1 13	1 28	1 45		...	3 0	3 20	...	...	4 52	...	5 25	...	6 57	...	7 45	...	...	9 15		10 3	...	11 5	1235	...	1 40	4 3	5 47	...
Bradford .... „	9†56	10B33	2 0	...	2 16		...	3 42	4 3	...	...	5 30	...	6 20	6 6	7 34	...	8D 0	...	...	9 50		1040	...	12 2	...	...	2 55	4 48	6g50	...
Morecambe .... „	...	12 40	...	...	4 5		...	...	5 50	...	...	6 44	...	8 20	...	...	...	1025	...	...	...		...	...	...	...	...	...	...	9 g0	...
Carlisle .... „	...	12 25	...	3 50	4. 5		...	...	...	5 55	...	...	...	7 53	...	...	...	...	...	...	...		...	...	1 25	2 55	...	4 15	6 25	...	...
Glasgow (St. E.) ...... „	...	3 0	...	...	6 45	...	...	...	...	8 35	...	...	...	10 20	...	...	...	...	...	...	...	...	...	...	...	6 10	...	7g 15	9 0	...	...
Edinburgh (Wav.) „	...	3 0	...	6 10	...	...	...	...	...	8 42	...	...	...	10 30	...	...	...	...	...	...	...	...	...	...	3 45	...	...	7 0	12c10	...	...
Dundee .... „	...	4 34	...	8 3	...	...	...	...	...	1110	...	...	...	...	...	...	...	...	...	...	...	...	...	...	5 29	...	...	9 20	4 c0	...	...
Aberdeen .... „	...	6 30	...	10 5	...	...	...	...	...	-	...	...	...	...	...	...	...	...	...	...	...	...	...	...	7 22	...	...	11 32	6c30	...	...
Inverness .... „	...	10 15	...	...	...	...	...	...	...	4c55	...	...	...	...	...	...	...	...	...	...	...	...	...	...	9 8	...	...	1 50	7c42	...	...

	p.m.	a.m.	p.m.	p.m		p.m.	a.m.	a.m.	a.m.	a.m.	a.m.	a.m.	a.m.	a.m.	a.m.	a.m.	a.m.	a.m.	a.m.	a.m.	p.m.	p.m	a.m.	p.m.	p.m.	a.m.	p.m.	p.m	p.m.	a.m.	p.m.	a.m.
Inverness ....dep	...	1010	3 50	...	Will not apply until night of July 15th.	5 0	...	...	...	...	...	...	...	...	...	...	...	...	...	...	...	10d50	-	...	...	...	...	...	...	8 40	...	11 5
Aberdeen .... „	...	3 30	5 35	...		7 35	...	...	...	...	...	...	...	...	...	...	...	...	...	...	...	...	6 20	...	...	...	...	...	...	1020	...	1 20
Dundee .... „	...	5 32	7 49	...		9 25	...	...	...	...	...	...	...	...	...	...	...	...	...	...	...	6 30	8 18	...	...	...	...	...	...	1222	...	3 39
Edinburgh (Waverley)... „	...	10 0	10 0	...		1130	...	...	...	...	...	...	...	...	...	...	...	...	...	...	...	9 30	1030	...	...	1030	...	...	...	2 20	...	6 0
Glasgow (St. Enoch)...... „	9 15	...	9 30	11 0		..	...	...	...	...	...	...	...	...	...	...	...	...	...	...	...	...	...	9 20	...	11 0	...	...	1 30	...	...	5 30
Carlisle .... „	12 7	1237	1237	1 35		1 47	...	...	...	...	...	...	Saturdays excepted.	...	...	...	...	...	8 35	...	...	1145	1 10	12 5	...	1 30	..	...	3 58	4 45	...	8 50
Morecambe .... „	...	...	...	...		...	...	...	...	5T55	...	...		7 55	...	...	...	...	1012	...	...	1130.	...	...	...	1257	...	...	2 55	4 20	6 30	...
Bradford .... „	1 55	1 55	1 55	...		...	...	...	...	7 30	7 38	...		9 40	...	...	1045	...	1212	...	...	1 30	2 25	1 30	...	3 24	...	...	5D52	6 22	9 5	1045
Leeds .... „	2 38	2 58	2 58	3 55		4 13	...	...	...	8 8	8 22	...		1015	...	...	1120	...	1 0	...	...	2 15	3 40	2 30		4 2	...	4 20	6 27	7 18	10 0	12†5
Newcastle-on-Tyne ... „	...	...	...	1119		..	..	...	...	...	1‡52	...		...	...	...	8 45	...	...	1028	...	...	1230	...	1220	1230	...	...	2 40	4 50	7 8	9 16
York .... „	...	...	...	1 50		1 50	1 50	...	...	...	7 30	...		...	...	...	10 5	...	...	1222	...	...	...	...	2 5	3 0	...	...	4 40	6 35	9 40	...
Hull .... „	...	...	...			...	...	...	...	...	6 5	...	...	...	...	...	9 36	...	...	11 0	...	...	...	...	1230	2 5	...	3 20	...	5 14	8 40	11 0
Sheffield .... „	3 35	4 0	4 0	Monday mornings excepted.		...	4 25	7 20	...	9 0	9 27	...	...	11 8	...	...	1218	...	...	1 56	...	...	...	2 40	3 17	5 0	...		7 20	...	1129	...
Liverpool (Central) ...... „	...	...	Mon. morn. excepted.			Mondays excepted.	...	...	6 15	...	7 45	8 30	9 15	...	9H15	1125	...	...	...	...	1255	...	...	...	3V30	2 35	3 30	5 R0	...	...	6 30	1130
Blackburn .... „	...	...					...	...	...	...	...	...	8 11	...	8H11	...	9m38	...	...	...	12F15	...	...	...	...	...	2 47	...	...	...	5 20	10x27
Bolton .... „	...	...					...	...	...	...	...	...	9 0	...	9H 0	...	9 58	...	...	...	12F48	...	...	...	...	...	3 25	3 54	...	...	6 3	10x59
Manchester (Victoria)... „	SM	SM					...	...	...	...	...	...	9 40	...	...	...	1045	...	...	...	1 15	...	...	...	...	...	4 2	...	...	...	7 10	1155
Manchester (Central) ... „	...	...					...	...	7 30	...	8 30	9 20	1010	...	1015	12 0	...	...	...	1220	1 50	...	...	...	4V15	3 25	4 20	5 50	...	...	7 25	12 0
Buxton .... „	...	...					...	...	7 58	...	8 45	9 50	...	...	1045	...	...	1125	...	1 10	1 35	...	...	...	...	4 5	...	5 35	...	...	8 15	...
Derby .... „	...	3 18	3 18	4 50		...	5 50	8 §5	8 55	9 2	9 50	1054	...	...	12 0	1217	1245	1 42	...	2 20	3 22	...	...	3 27	4 24	5 35	6 3	7 18	7 24	8 37	1255	2†25
Nottingham .... „	...	5 12	4 28	5 10		6 3	6E35	8 25	8 30	9 25	1040	...	1128	...	11J52	1228	1 30	...	...	3 3	...	3 55	...	3 22	5 0	5 13	...	6 53	7 42	8 22	1245	...
Burton .... „	...	2 45	2 45	...		...	4†40	...	8 27	8 32	8M58	1018	...	1120	...	...	12 5	1259	...	1 40	2 40	...	...	3 15	3 47	4 58	5 29	6 28	...	7 49	1220	...
Leicester .... „	5 3	...	...	6 5		...	7 18	8§50	9 37	1020	...	1132	...	1225	1245	2 2	...	2 20	...	3J5 4	4 0	...	...	4 35	6V10	6 30	6 50	7 55	...	9 27	1 50	3†10
London (St. Pancras) ...arr	7 5	7 35	7 35	8 5		8 15	9 20	1040	1132	12 5	1 15	1 25	1 57	2 10	3 0	3 47	4 0	4 35	4 45	5 25	6 5	6 15	7 20	6 30	7 45	8 15	9 10	10 0	1025	1115	4 20	5†45

†—Monday mornings excepted.
‡—1.36 a.m. on Mondays.
§—Arrive St. Pancras 10.55.
A—4.25 p.m. on Thursdays.
B—11.1 a.m. on Saturdays.
c—Not on Sundays.
D—Bradford Exchange (L. & Y.).
d—Sat. nights excepted.

E—5.52 a.m. on Saturdays.
e—Fri. and Sat. only, until 6th Sept.
F—Blackburn 10.47 a.m. and Bolton 12.30 p.m. on Sats.
g—Later on Sundays.
H—Saturdays only.
J—Thursdays and Saturdays excepted.
K—Will not run until July 14th.
M—9.25 a.m. on Mondays.
m—9.1 a.m. on Sats.

N—Derby 1.17 and Manchester 3.10 a.m. on Sundays.
R—4.30 p.m. on Saturdays.
SM—Sunday nights and Monday mornings only.
T—Mondays excepted, via Heysham.
V—Sats. excepted, and arrives St. Pancras at 7.55 p.m.
W—Sunday mornings only.
x—Leaves Blackburn 9.30, & Bolton 10.35 p.m. on Sats.
z—12.3 p.m. on Saturdays.

ALPHABETICAL LIST OF STEAMERS TO AND FROM FOREIGN PORTS.

AFRICA (SOUTH AND EAST).

TO CAPE TOWN—

from **Antwerp.**—Deutsche Ost-Afrika Linie. July 28th. See p. 728.
" **Boulogne.**—Deutsche Ost-Afrika Linie. July 12th. See p. 728.
" **Hamburg.**—Deutsche Ost-Afrika Linie. July 10th and 25th. See p. 728.
" **Southampton**—Deutsche Ost-Afrika Linie. July 29th. See p. 728.—Union Castle Mail Steamship Co. Saturday.

TO MOMBASSA AND ZANZIBAR—

from **Genoa and Leghorn**—Società Nazionale. Monthly.
" **London**—British India Steam Navigation Co., Ltd. July 25th.—Union Castle Mail Steamship Co.
" **Marseilles**—Messageries Maritimes de France. July 24th. See p. 730.—Union Castle Mail Steamship Co.
" **Naples.**—Società Nazionale. Monthly.—Union Castle Mail Steamship Co.
" **Southampton.**—Union Castle Mail Steamship Co.

TO PORT ELIZABETH, EAST LONDON, DURBAN, AND DELAGOA BAY—

from **Antwerp.**—Deutsche Ost-Afrika Linie. July 28th. See p. 728.
" **Boulogne.**—Deutsche Ost-Afrika Linie. July 12th. See p. 728.
" **Hamburg.**—Deutsche Ost-Afrika Linie. July 10th and 25th. See p. 728.
" **Southampton**—Deutsche Ost-Afrika Linie. July 29th. See p. 728—Union Castle Mail Steamship Co. Saturday.

TO ZANZIBAR, AND EAST AFRICAN PORTS, (BEIRA)—

from **Antwerp.**—Deutsche Ost-Afrika Linie. July 1st and August 1st. See p. 728.
" **Hamburg.**—Deutsche Ost-Afrika Linie. July 14th and 29th. See p. 728.
" **Naples.**—Deutsche Ost-Afrika Linie. July 13th and 29th. See p. 728.
" **Rotterdam.**—Deutsche Ost-Afrika Linie. July 17th. See p. 728.
" **Southampton**—Deutsche Ost-Afrika Linie. July 2nd, 18th, and August 2nd. See p. 728.

ALGERIA.

TO ALGIERS—

from **Amsterdam.**—Nederland Royal Mail Line. See page 729.
" **Cette.**—Cie de Navigation Mixte. Saturday, 10.0 p.m. See p. 730.
" **Genoa.**—Norddeutscher Lloyd. See p. 721.—Nederland Royal Mail Line. See p. 729.
" **Gibraltar.**—Norddeutscher Lloyd. See p. 721.—Adria Line. July 9th and 23rd. See p. 731.—Moss Line. See p. 726.
" **Liverpool.**—Moss Line. See p. 726.—Papayanni and Ellerman Lines.
" **Malaga.**—Adria Line. July 11th and 25th. See p. 731.
" **Marseilles.**—Cie. Générale Transatlantique. Sun., Tues., Wed., Fri., 1.0 p.m. See p. 729.—Cie. de Navigation Mixte. Mon., 6.0 p.m., and Thurs., 11.45 a.m. See p. 730.—Société Générale de Transports Maritimes. Wednesday and Saturday, 6.0 p.m.
" **Oran.**—Adria Line. July 13th and 27th. See p. 731.
" **Palermo.**—Austro Americana Steamers.
" **Port Vendres.**—Cie. de Navigation Mixte. Sunday, 1.30 p.m. See p. 730
" **Southampton.**—Norddeutscher Lloyd. July 1st, 7th, 15th, 29th, and August 4th. See p. 721.—Nederland Royal Mail Line. See page 729.
" **Tangier.**—Adria Line. July 8th, 22nd, and August 5th. See p. 731.—Nederland Royal Mail Line. See p. 729.
" **Tunis.**—Adria Line. July 7th, 21st, and August 4th. See p. 731.

TO BONA—

from **Ajaccio.**—Cie. Gen. Transatlantique. Monday, 11.0 p.m. See p. 729.
" **Marseilles.**—Compagnie Générale Transatlantique. Direct, Tuesday, 5.0 p.m. and, calling at **Philippeville,** Saturday, noon. See p. 729.—Compagnie Mixte, Thurs. noon. See p. 730.—Société Générale de Transports Maritimes. Tuesday and Saturday, 6.0 p.m.

TO BOUGIE—

from **Marseilles.**—Compagnie Générale Transatlantique. Tuesday, 12.0 noon. See p. 729.—Société Générale de Transports Maritimes. Saturday, 6.0 p.m.

TO ORAN—

from **Algiers.**—Adria Line. July 9th and 23rd. See p. 731.
" **Cartagena.**—Cie. Gen. Transatlantique. Tuesday, 8.0 p.m. See p. 729.
" **Cette.**—Cie de Navigation Mixte. Thursday, 10.0 p.m. See p. 730.
" **Malaga.**—Adria Line. July 11th and 25th. See p. 731.
" **Marseilles.**—Cie. Générale Transatlantique. Thursday and Saturday, 5.0 p.m. See p. 729.—Cie. de Navigation Mixte. Wednesday, 6.0 p.m. See p. 730.—Paquet et Cie. See p. 730.—Société Générale de Transports Maritimes. Tuesday, 5.0 p.m.
" **Port Vendres.**—Cie. de Navigation Mixte. Friday, 1.30 p.m. See p. 730.
" **Tangier.**—Cie de Navigation Mixte. Wednesday, 5.0 p.m. See p. 730.—Adria Line. July 8th, 22nd, and August 5th. See p. 731.

ALGERIA—*Continued.*

TO PHILIPPEVILLE—
from **Marseilles.**—Compagnie Générale Transatlantique. Direct, Saturday noon; and, calling at **Bona**, Tuesday, 5.0 p.m. See p. 729.—Compagnie de Navigation Mixte. See p. 730. —Société Générale de Transports Maritimes. Saturday, 6.0 p.m.

AMERICA (NORTH).

TO BOSTON—
from **Genoa.**—White Star Line. See p. 718.
" **Hamburg.**—Hamburg-Amerika Linie. **About twice monthly.**
" **Liverpool.**—Cunard Line. See p. 717.—**White Star Line. See p.** 718.
" **Naples.**—White Star Line. See p. 718.

TO NEW YORK—
from **Algiers.**—Austro-Americana Steamers.
" **Antwerp.**—Red Star Line. See p. 719.
" **Boulogne.**—Norddeutscher Lloyd. See p. 721.
" **Bremen.**—Norddeutscher Lloyd. See p. 721.
" **Cadiz.**—Compania Trasatlantica. See p. 729.
" **Cherbourg.**—White Star Line. See p. 718.—**Norddeutscher Lloyd. See p.** 721.—American Line. See p. 718.—Royal Mail S.P. and Pacific S.N Cos. See p. 728.
" **Dover.**—Red Star Line. See p. 719.
" **Fiume.**—Cunard Line. See p. 717.
" **Genoa.**—White Star Line. See p. 718.—Norddeutscher Lloyd. See page 721.—Navigazione Generale Italiana.
" **Hamburg.**—Hamburg-Amerika Linie.
" **Havre.**—Compagnie Générale Transatlantique. **Saturday. See p.** 719
" **Liverpool.**—Cunard Line. See p. 717.—**White Star Line. See p.** 718 —Leyland Line.
" **London.**—Atlantic Transport Line. See p. 720.
" **Naples.**—White Star Line. See p. 718.—Norddeutscher Lloyd. See p. 721.—Cunard Line. See p. 717.—Navigazione Generale Italiana.
" **Palermo.**—Norddeutscher Lloyd.—See p. 721.—Cunard Line. See p. 717.—Austro-Americana Steamers.
" **Patras.**—Austro-Americana Steamers.
" **Queenstown**—White Star Line. See p. 718.—**Cunard Line. See p. 717.**
" **Rotterdam.**—Holland-Amerika Linie.
" **Santander.**—Compañia Trasatlantica. See p. 729.
" **Southampton.**—White Star Line. See p. 718.—**American Line, See p. 718—Norddeutscher Lloyd.** See p. 721.—**R.M.S.P. and P.S.N. Cos.** See p. 728.—**Hamburg-Amerika Linie.**
" **Trieste.**—Cunard Line. See p. 717.—**Austro-Americana Steamers.**

TO PHILADELPHIA—
from **Antwerp.**—Red Star Line. See p. 719.
" **Liverpool.**—American Line. See p. 718.—Leyland Line.

TO QUEBEC AND MONTREAL—
from **Liverpool.**—Canadian Pacific Rly. Co.'s Steamers. See p. 717.—White Star Line. See p. 718.

TO ST. JOHN (N.B.)—
from **Liverpool**, calling at **Belfast.**—Canadian Pacific Rly. Co.'s Royal Mail Steamers. See p. 717.

AMERICA (CENTRAL).

TO COLON—
from **Bordeaux.**—Compagnie Générale Transatlantique. See p. 729.
" **Havre.**—Compagnie Générale Transatlantique. See p. 729.
" **St. Nazaire.**—Compagnie Générale Transatlantique. See p. 729.
" **Southampton.**—The Royal Mail Steam Packet and P.S.N. Cos. See p. 728.

TO VERA CRUZ—
from **Cadiz.**—Compañia Trasatlantica. See p. 729.
" **St. Nazaire.**—Compagnie Générale Transatlantique. See p. 729.
" **Santander.**—Compañia Trasatlantica. See p. 729.—Cie. Gen. Transatlantique. See p 729.

AMERICA—WEST INDIA ISLANDS.

TO ANTIGUA, BARBADOS, DOMINICA, and TRINIDAD—
from **Copenhagen.**—The East Asiatic Co., Ltd.
" **London.**—The East Asiatic Co., Ltd.
" **Rotterdam.**—The East Asiatic Co., Ltd.
" **Southampton.**—The Royal Mail Steam Packet and P.S.N. Cos. See p. 728.

TO CUBA—from **St. Nazaire.**—Cie. Gén. Transatlantique. See p. 729.

TO GRENADA, MONTSERRAT, NEVIS, ST. KITTS, ST. LUCIA, ST. VINCENT—
from **Southampton.**—The Royal Mail Steam Packet and P.S.N. Cos. See p. 728.

AMERICA (WEST INDIA ISLANDS).—*Continued.*

TO GUADELOUPE AND MARTINIQUE—
from **Bordeaux.**—Compagnie Générale Transatlantique. See p. 729.
" **Havre.**—Compagnie Générale Transatlantique. See p. 729.
" **St. Nazaire.**—Compagnie Générale Transatlantique. See p. 729.

TO HAYTI—
from **Bordeaux.**—Compagnie Générale Transatlantique. See p. 729.
" Havre.—Compagnie Générale Transatlantique. See p. 729.

TO JAMAICA—
from **Southampton** to **Kingston.**—The Royal Mail S.P. and P.S.N. Cos. See p. 728.

TO PORTO RICO—
from **Bordeaux.**—Compagnie Générale Transatlantique. See p. 729.
" **Havre.**—Compagnie Générale Transatlantique. See p. 729.

TO ST. THOMAS—
from **Bordeaux.**—Compagnie Générale Transatlantique. See p. 729
" **Copenhagen.**—(also to **St. Croix**). The East Asiatic Co., Ltd.
" **Havre.**—Compagnie Genérale Transatlantique. See p. 729.
" **London.**—(also to **St. Croix**). The East Asiatic Co., Ltd.
" **Rotterdam** (also to **St. Croix**). The East Asiatic Co., Ltd.

AMERICA (SOUTH).

TO BUENOS AYRES—
from **Almeria.**—Austro-Americana Steamers.
" **Amsterdam.**—Royal Holland Lloyd. See p. 725.
" **Antwerp.**—Lamport & Holt Line. See p. 727A.—Norddeutscher Lloyd. See p. 721.
" **Barcelona.**—Cia. Trasatlantica. See p. 729.—Austro-Americana Steamers.—Navigazione Generale Italiana.
" **Boulogne.**—Royal Holland Lloyd. See p. 725.—Norddeutscher Lloyd. See p. 721.
" **Cadiz.**—Cia.Trasatlantica. Monthly. See p. 729.
" **Cherbourg.**—Royal Mail Steam Packet and P.S.N. Cos. See p. 728.—Lamport & Holt Line. See p. 727A.
" **Dover.**—Royal Holland Lloyd. See p. 725.
" **Genoa.**—Nav. Gen. Italiana.
" **Glasgow.**—Lamport & Holt Line. See p. 727A.
" **Las Palmas.**—R.M.S.P. and P.S.N. Cos. See p. 728.—Austro-Americana Steamers.
" **Lisbon.**—The Royal Mail Steam Packet and Pacific S.N. Cos. See p 728.——Royal Holland Lloyd. See p. 725.—Lamport & Holt Line. See p. 727A.—Norddeutscher Lloyd. See p 721.
" **Liverpool.**—Lamport & Holt Line. See p.727A —R.M.S.P. and Pacific S.N. Cos. See p. 728.
" **London.**—Lamport & Holt Line. See p. 727A.
" **Malaga.**—Compania Trasatlantica. Monthly. See p. 729.
" **Oporto (Leixoes).**—The Royal Mail Steam Packet and P.S.N. Cos. See p. 728 —Norddeutscher Lloyd. See p. 721.—Lamport & Holt Line. See p. 727A.
" **Southampton.**—Royal Mail Steam Packet and P.S.N. Cos. See p. 728.—Lamport and Holt Line. See p. 727A.
" **Trieste.**—Austro-Americana Steamers.
" **Vigo.**—The Royal Mail Steam Packet and Pacific S.N. Cos. See p. 728.—Norddeutscher Lloyd. See p. 721.—Royal Holland Lloyd. See p. 725.—Lamport & Holt Line. See p. 727A.

TO CEARA—
from **Havre.**—Booth Steamship Co., Ltd. See p. 727.
" **Liverpool.**—Booth Steamship Co., Ltd. See p. 727.

TO DEMERARA, TRINIDAD, LA GUAYRA, AND PUERTO COLOMBIA—
from Liverpool.—Leyland Line.
" St. Nazaire.—Compagnie Générale Transatlantique. See p. 729.
" **Southampton.**—The Royal Mail Steam Packet and P.S.N. Cos. See p. 728.

TO DEMERARA and PARAMARIBO—
from **Copenhagen.**—The East Asiatic Co., Ltd.
" **London.**—The East Asiatic Co., Ltd.
" **Rotterdam.**—The East Asiatic Co., Ltd.

TO MANAOS, PARA AND MARANHAM—
from **Havre, Lisbon, Liverpool,** and **Oporto.**—Booth Steamship Co, Ltd. See p. 727.

TO PERNAMBUCO—
from **Liverpool.**—Royal Mail Steam Packet and Pacific S.N. Cos. See p. 728.
" **Southampton.**—The Royal Mail Steam Packet and P.S.N. Cos. See p. 728.

AMERICA (SOUTH).—*Continued*

TO RIO DE JANEIRO AND SANTOS—

from **Almeria.**—Austro-Americana Steamers.
„ **Amsterdam.**—Royal Holland Lloyd. See p. 725.
„ **Antwerp.**—Lamport & Holt Line. **See p. 727A.—Norddeutscher Lloyd. See p. 721**
„ **Boulogne.**—Royal Holland Lloyd. See p. 725. Norddeutscher Lloyd. See p. 721.
„ **Cherbourg.—The Royal Mail Steam Packet and P.S.N. Cos. See p. 728.**
„ **Dover.**—Royal Holland Lloyd. See p. 725.
„ **Fiume.**—Adria Line. See p. 731.
„ **Glasgow.—Lamport & Holt Line.** See p. 727A.
„ **Las Palmas.**—R.M.S.P. and P.S.N. Cos. See p. 728.—**Austro-Americana Steamers.**
„ **Lisbon.—The Royal Mail Steam Packet and P.S.N. Cos. See p. 728.—Norddeutscher Lloyd.** See p. 721.—**Royal Holland Lloyd.** See p. 725.—**Lamport & Holt Line.** See p. 727A.
„ **Liverpool.**—Lamport & Holt Line. See p. 727A.—**R.M.S.P. and Pacific S.N. Cos. See p. 728.**
„ **London.—Lamport & Holt Line. See p. 727A.**
„ **Manchester.**—Lamport & Holt Line. See p. 727A.
„ **Oporto.**—Norddeutscher Lloyd. See p. 721.—**The Royal Mail Steam Packet** and Pacific S.N. Cos.—See p. 728.
„ **Southampton.—The Royal Mail Steam Packet and P.S.N. Cos. See p. 728.**
„ **Trieste.**—Adria Line. See p. 731.—Austro-Americana Steamers.
„ **Vigo.**—Lamport & Holt Line. See p. 727A.—**Royal Holland Lloyd.** See p. 725.—R.M.S.P. and Pacific S.N. Co. See p. 728.

TO ROSARIO—

from **Glasgow, Liverpool, Antwerp, and London.—Lamport & Holt Line. See p. 727A.**

TO VENEZUELA—

from **Havre.—Compagnie Générale Transatlantique. See p. 729.**
„ **Southampton.—The Royal Mail Steam Packet and P.S.N. Cos. See p. 728.**

TO WEST COAST OF SOUTH AMERICA—(Valparaiso, Antofagasta, Iquique, Mollendo. Callao, Guayaquil, and Panama.)

from **Glasgow and Liverpool.—Lamport & Holt Line. See p. 727A.**
„ **Liverpool.**—Royal Mail Steam Packet and Pacific S.N. Cos. See p. 728.
„ **Southampton. Cherbourg, Vigo, and Lisbon.—Royal Mail Steam Packet and P.S.N.** Cos. **See p. 728.**

AUSTRALIA.

TO ADELAIDE, MELBOURNE, and SYDNEY, calling at FREMANTLE—

from **Antwerp.**—Norddeutscher Lloyd. July 6th and August 3rd. See p. 721.
„ **Brindisi.**—Peninsular and Oriental Co. July 6th, 20th, and August 3rd. See p. 726.
„ **Genoa.**—Norddeutscher Lloyd. July 15th. See p. 721.
„ **London—Tilbury.**—Peninsular and Oriental Co. July 11th and 25th. See p. 726.—Orient Line. July 4th, 18th, and August 1st. See p. 725.
„ **Marseilles.**—Peninsular and Oriental Co. July 4th, 18th, and August 1st. **See p. 726**—Messageries Maritimes de France. July 23rd. See p. 730.
„ **Naples.**—Norddeutscher Lloyd. July 16th. **See p. 721.—Orient Line.** July 12th and 26th. See p. 725.
„ **Port Said.—Peninsular and Oriental Co.** July 8th, 22nd, and August 5th. See p. 726—**Messageries Maritimes de France.** July 27th. See p. 730.—Norddeutscher Lloyd. July 20th. See p. 721.—Orient Line. July 2nd, 16th, and 30th. See p. 725.
„ **Southampton.—Norddeutscher Lloyd.** July 7th and August 4th. See p. 721.
„ **Taranto.**—Orient Line. July 13th and 27th. See p. 725,
„ **Toulon.**—Orient Line. July 10th and 24th. See p. 725.

TO BRISBANE AND SYDNEY—

from **Vancouver.—Canadian Pacific Railway Steamers. See p. 717.**

AUSTRIA AND HUNGARY.

TO FIUME—

from **Ancona.—Hungarian State Rly Steamers.**

Ancona depart Thursday, 7.0 a.m., Tuesday and Saturday, 8.30 p.m.
Fiume arrive Thursday, 5.0 p.m.. Wednesday and Sunday, 6.30 a.m.

„ **Catania.—Adria Line.** Thursday, 6.0 p.m. **See p. 731.**
„ **Malta.—Adria Line.** Wednesday, 6.0 p.m. **See p. 731.**
„ **Marseilles.—Adria Line. Wednesday, 6.0 p.m. See p. 731.**
„ **Ravenna.—Hungarian State Railway Steamers. Friday, 5.0 p.m.**
„ **Venice.—Hungarian State Rly. Steamers, Monday 7.15 a.m, Tuesday, Wednesday, Thursday, Friday, and Saturday, 8.15 p.m.**

AUSTRIA AND HUNGARY—*Continued.*

TO TRIESTE—

from **Aden.**—Austrian Lloyd. July 3rd, 8th, 9th, 25th, and August 3rd. See p. 722.
" **Alexandria.**—Austrian Lloyd. Thursday, 3.0 p.m. and Saturday, 2.0 p.m. See p. 722.
" **Algiers.**—Adria Line. See p. 731.—Austro-Americana Steamers.
" **Athens (Piræus).**—Austrian Lloyd. Sun., 7.0 p.m. See p. 722.
" **Barcelona**—Austro-American Steamers.
" **Bari.**—Adria Line. Thursday, 6.0 p.m. See p. 731.
" **Brindisi.**—Austrian Lloyd. Wed., 6.0 a.m. and 7.0 a.m., Thurs., 4.30 a.m., and Sat., 6.0 p.m. See p. 722.
" **Catania.**—Adria Line. Tuesday, 6.0 p.m. See p. 731.
" **Constantinople.**—Austrian Lloyd. Saturday, 10.0 a.m. See p. 722.
" **Malta.**—Adria Line. July 4th, 18th, and August 1st. See p. 731.
" **Naples.**—Adria Line. See p. 731.—Austro-Americana Steamers.
" **Patras.**—Austrian Lloyd, Monday and Tuesday, 11.0 p.m. See p. 722. Austro-Americana Steamers.
" **Port Said.**—Austrian Lloyd. July 3rd, 9th, 13th, 16th, 17th, and August 3rd. See p. 722.
" **Smyrna.**—Austrian Lloyd. Saturday, 4.0 p.m. See p. 722.
" **Venice** (6 hours).—Austrian Lloyd. Fares. 12kr. 40h. and 8kr. 40h. Monday, Wednesday, and Friday, 12.0 night. Also Friday, 8.0 a.m. See p. 722.

Trieste to Dalmatia (Pola, Zara, Spalato, Ragusa, Cattaro) and Albania.—Austrian Lloyd. Trieste dep. Tues., Thurs., and Sat., 8.0 a.m.; Spalato arr. Tues., Thurs. and Sat., 11.45 p.m. Gravosa (Ragusa) arr. Wed., Fri., and Sun. 7.15 a.m.; Cattaro arr. Wed., Fri., and Sun. 11.30 a.m. Also Trieste dep. Mon. 8.0 a.m. and Wed. 3.0 p.m.; Spalato arr. Tues. and Thurs.; Gravosa (Ragusa) arr. Thurs. and Fri.; Cattaro arr. Thurs. 5.0 p.m. and Friday 7.30 a.m. Fares to Spalato, 25kr. 50h., 17kr. 50h., to Gravosa (Ragusa), 41kr., 27kr to Cattaro, 49kr., 32kr. 50h. See p. 722.

BELGIUM.

TO ANTWERP—

from **Goole**—Lancashire and Yorkshire Railway Co. Mon., Wed., and Sat.
" **Grimsby** (20 hrs).—Great Central Railway Co. Monday, Wednesday, & Saturday, 7.0 p.m. See p. 735.
" **Harwich.**—Great Eastern Railway Co. See Advertisement first page after cover.
" **Hull** (22 hours).—Wilson Line. Saturday. See p. 736.
" **Leith.**—G. Gibson & Co. Tuesday and Friday.
" **London** (via Harwich).—Great Eastern Railway Co. See Advt. first page after cover.
" **Newcastle** (28 hours).—The Tyne-Tees Steam Shipping Co. Every Saturday.

TO BRUGES—

from **Goole**—Lancashire and Yorkshire Railway Co. Saturday.

TO GHENT—

from **Goole**—Lancashire and Yorkshire Railway Co. Wed. and Sat.
" **Hull.**—Wilson Line. Saturday. See p. 736.
" **Leith.**—G. Gibson & Co. Saturday.

TO OSTEND—

from **Dover** (3 hours).—Belgian Mail Steamers. See pages 714, 715.

TO ZEE-BRUGGE—

from **Hull** (12 hrs.)—Lancashire & Yorkshire and North Eastern Railway Companies. until October 3rd on Tues., Thurs., and Sat., 6.0 p.m. See p. xiii., in front part of Guide.

CANARY ISLANDS.

TO CANARY ISLANDS (LAS PALMAS AND TENERIFFE)—

from **Almeria.**—Austro-Americana Steamers.
" **Antwerp.**—Deutsche Ost-Afrika Linie. July 28th. See p. 728.
" **Barcelona.**—Compañia Trasatlantica. See p. 729.—Austro-Americana Steamers.
" **Boulogne.**—Deutsche Ost-Afrika Linie. July 12th. See p. 728.
" **Cadiz.**—Compañia Trasatlantica. See p. 729.
" **Hamburg.**—Deutsche Ost-Afrika Linie. July 10th and 25th. See p. 728.
" **Liverpool.**—R.M.S.P. and P.S.N. Cos. July 10th and 24th. See p. 728.
" **London.**—The Royal Mail Steam Packet Co. ———— See p. 728.—New Zealand Shipping Co. July 3rd and 31st. Shaw, Savill, and Albion Co. July 17th. Aberdeen Line. July 17th.—Union Castle Line. Weekly.
" **Southampton.**—Deutsche Ost-Afrika Linie. July 29th. See p. 728.—Union Castle Line. Weekly.
" **Spalato** (or **Gravosa**).—Austro-Americana Steamers.
" **Trieste.**—Austro-Americana Steamers.

DENMARK.

TO AALBORG—

from **Copenhagen.**—"**Cimbria,**" **Monday, Wednesday and Friday, 8.0 p.m.,** "Limfjorden, Saturday, 4.0 p.m.; "**Jyden,**" **Friday, 3.0 p.m.**

TO AARHUS—

from **Copenhagen.**—"Aarhus" or "**Koch,**" daily (Sunday excepted), **11.0 p.m.**
" **Kallundborg.** (4½ hrs.)—"**Kureren,**" "**Prior,**" **daily, 11.35 a.m.**

TO COPENHAGEN—

from **Abo**.—**Finland Steamship Co. Friday afternoon.**
" **Christiania.**—"Melchior," Friday, 3.30 p.m., also (until 13th August) Tuesday, 3.30 p.m., "Kong Haakon," "Dronning Maud," Wednesday and Saturday, 2.0 p.m.
" **Frederikshavn**.—"Baldur," Monday, 5.30 a.m. "Melchior," Saturday, 5.0 a.m., also (until 13th August) Wednesday, 5.0 a.m.
" **Goole.**—Lancashire and Yorkshire Ry. Co. Wednesday.
" **Gothenburg.**—**Swedish Mail Steamers. 3 or 4 times weekly.** "**Odin,**" **etc., Monday,** and Friday, 6.0 p.m.
" **Hangö** (36 hours).—**Finland Steamship Co. Wednesday and Saturday. 4.0 p.m.**
" **Helsingborg** (2 hours).—Oresund Co. 9.15 a.m. and, (until 31st August), 8.30 p.m.
" **Helsingfors.**—Finland Steamship Co. Tuesday, 7.0 p.m.
" **Hull.**—**Finland Line, John Good & Sons, Ltd., Agents.** Every Wednesday and Saturday. See p. 734.—Wilson Line. Wednesday. See p. 736.
" **Leith.**—Leith, Hull, and Hamburg Co. Thursday. See p. 727.
" **Lübeck.**—Hallandsche Steamers. Daily, 6.35 p.m.
" **Newcastle.**—Wilson Line. Thursday. See p. 736.
" **Stettin**—"Odin" and "Ydun," Tuesday and Friday, 4.0 a.m. "**Kong Haakon,**" and "Dronning Maud," Sunday and Wednesday, 4.0 a.m. "**Rudolf.**" Sunday. "Thyra," &c. Friday, 3.0 p.m.
" **Stockholm.**—"Aeolus," Friday, 1.0 p.m. "**Skandia,**" etc., Tuesday, 4.0 p.m. "Dania," etc., ———.

TO ELSINORE—

from **Helsingborg** (20 mins.)—**Daily, 7.3, 8.45, 11.23 a.m., 1.8,** 2.38, **3.57,** 7.3, **8.57, and 11.0** p.m.

TO ESBJERG—

from **Grimsby.**—**The United Steamship Co. of Copenhagen. Every Monday and Thursday.**
" **Harwich.**—**The United Shipping Co. Ltd. Every Monday, Wednesday, Friday, and** Saturday, 9.45 p.m. See p. 735.

TO FREDERIKSHAVN—

from **Christiania** (12 hours).—"Melchior," Tuesday and Friday, 3.30 p.m.
" **Christiansand.**—Mail Steamer, daily, 4.0 a.m.
" **Copenhagen.**—"Melchior," Sunday, 8.0 p.m., and (until 13th August) Wednesday, 8.0 a.m., "Baldur," Friday, 4.0 p.m.
" **Gothenburg** (4½ hours).—"Oluf Bager," "Fiona," daily, 12.0 night.

TO GJEDSER—

from **Warnemünde.**—**Mecklenburg and Danish State Railways, Steamers twice daily.**

TO KORSŒR—

from **Kiel** (5 hours).—**German Mail Steamers, and Danish Steamers.** **See p. 732.**
" **Nyborg.**—**Daily, 12.55, 4.35, 4.55, 9.10 a.m., 1.20, 4.17, 5.7, 6.10 p.m.**

TO NYBORG—

from **Korsœr** (1½ hours).—**Daily 1.55, 3.15, 10.32, 11.11 a.m., 2.25, 3.40, 7.32, 9.57, 10.36 p.m.**

Iceland and Faroe Islands.—Danish Mail Steamers.

Copenhagen dep	July 8	July 13	July 26	Aug. 1	—	Reykjavik...dep	July 3	July 15	July 24	Aug. 2	—
Leith ....dep	,, 12	,, 17	,, 30	,, 4	—	Thorshavn...dep	,, 18	—	,, 26	—	—
Thorshavn ..dep	,, 14	—	—	—	—	Leith ....dep	—	,, 20	,, 29	,, 6	—
Reykjavik ..dep	,, 16	,, 21	Aug. 10	,, 9	—	Copenhagen arr	,, 24	,, 23	Aug. 1	,, 9	—

EGYPT.

TO ALEXANDRIA—

from **Ancona.**—Società Nazionale. July 14th and 29th.
" **Athens (Piræus).**—**Khedivial Mail S.S. Co.** Thursday, 4.0 p.m. **See p. 724.**—Rumanian State Line. Saturday, 4.0 p.m. See p. 723.—**Russian Steam Nav. Co.** Tuesday.
" **Bari.**—Società Nazionale. July 15th and 30th.
" **Beyrout.**—**Khedivial Mail Steamship Co.** **See p. 724.**—**Austrian Lloyd.** Saturday, 11.0 p.m. See p. 722.—**Società Nazionale.** Monday, 10.0 a.m.—**Cie des Messageries Maritimes.** See p. 730.—Russian Steam Navigation Co. Tues., 10.0 a.m.
" **Brindisi.**—**Società Nazionale.** July 1st, 16th, and 31st. **1.0 p.m.** Austrian Lloyd. See p. 722.—

Brindisi ......dep.	Tues. 12.30 p.m.	Sat. 1.0 p.m.	Cairo (rail) ...dep.	Thurs. 9.30 a.m.	Sat. 9.30 a.m.
Alexandria ...arr.	Fri. 3.30 p.m.	Mon. 2 0 p.m.	Alexandria ...dep.	Thurs. 3.0 p.m.	Sat. 2.0 p.m.
Cairo (rail) arr.	Fri. 9.15 p.m.	Mon. 6.0 p.m.	Brindisi .... arr.	Sat. 4.0 p.m.	Wed. 5.30 a.m.

EGYPT—*Continued.*

TO ALEXANDRIA—*Continued.*

from **Catania**—Società Nazionale. Friday, 5.0 p.m.
„ **Constantinople.**—**Khedivial Mail Steamship Co. Tuesday, 3.0 p.m. See p. 724.—Russian Steam Navigation Co.** Sunday, 2.0 p.m.—**Rumanian State Line.** Thursday, 2.30 p.m. See p. 723.
„ **Constanza** (Kustendje)—**Rumanian State Line. Tuesday, 11.30 p.m. See p. 723.**
„ **Cyprus (Larnaca and Limassol).**—Khedivial Mail Steamship Co. Thursday or Friday. See p. 724.—Austrian Lloyd. See p. 722.
„ **Genoa.**—Società Nazionale. Monday, 10 0 **p.m.**
„ **Glasgow.**—Moss Line. See p. 727.
„ **Jaffa.**—Khedivial Mail Steamship Co. **See p. 724.—Messageries Maritimes de France.** July 8th, 22nd, and August 5th. See p. 730.—**Austrian Lloyd.** Sunday, 6.0 **p.m.** See p. 722.—Società Nazionale. July 10th and 26th.
„ **Leghorn.**—Società Nazionale. Tuesday, 6.0 p.m.
„ **Liverpool.**—Moss Line. See p. 727.—**Papayanni and Ellerman Lines.**
„ **Marseilles.**—Messageries Maritimes de France. **Every Friday. See p.** 730.—Norddeutscher Lloyd. July 2nd, 9th, and 16th. See p. 721.
„ **Mersina.**—Khedivial Mail Steamship Co. See p. 724.—**Austrian Lloyd.** Wednesday, 2.30 p.m. See p. 722.—Società Nazionale. Alternate Saturday, 5.0 p.m.
„ **Naples.**—Norddeutscher Lloyd. July 11th. **See p. 721.**—Società Nazionale. Thursday, 4.0 p.m.
„ **Odessa.**—**Russian Steam Navigation Co. Thursday, 11.0 a.m.**
„ **Port Said.**—Khedivial Mail Steamship Co. Tuesday, 3.0 p.m. See p. 724.—Austrian Lloyd. See p. 722.—Cie. des Messageries **Maritimes.** See p. 730.—**Società Nazionale.** July 11th and 27th.
„ **Smyrna.**—**Khedivial Mail S.S. Co.** Wednesday, 5.0 p.m. **See p. 724—Russian Steam** Nav. Co. Mon. 6.0 p.m.
„ **Swansea.**—Moss Line. See p. 727.
„ **Trieste.**—Austrian Lloyd. **Sunday and Friday, 1.0 p.m. See p. 722.**
„ **Tripoli (Syria).**—Austrian Lloyd. Friday, 1.0 p.m. See p. 722.—**Khedivial** Mail Steamship Co. See p. 724.—Società Nazionale. Sunday, 10.0 **a.m.**
„ **Venice.**—Società Nazionale. July 13th and 28th.

The Nile.—**See p. 361.—Messrs. Cook and Son's Steamers.**

TO PORT SAID—

from **Alexandria.**—**Messageries Maritimes de France. See p. 730.—Khedivial Mail Steamship** Co., Saturday, 4.0 p.m. See p. 724.—**Russian Steam Navigation Co. Friday**, 4.0 p.m.—Austrian Lloyd. Monday, 5.0 p.m. See p. 722.—**Società Nazionale.** July 6th and 21st.
„ **Alexandretta.**—**Khedivial Mail Steamship Co., Friday 4.0 p.m. See p. 724.**
„ **Amsterdam.**—Nederland Royal Mail Line. See p. 729.
„ **Ancona.**—Società Nazionale. July 14th and 29th.
„ **Antwerp.**—Norddeutscher Lloyd. See p. 721.—Deutsche Ost-Afrika Linie. See p. 728.—East Asiatic Co.
„ **Bari.**—Società Nazionale. July 15th and 30th.
„ **Beyrout.**—Messageries Maritimes de France. Monday or Wednesday. **See p. 730.**—Khedivial Mail Steamship Co. Sun. 10.0 a.m. **See p. 724.—Russian Steam Navigation** Co. Tuesday, 10.0 a.m.—**Austrian Lloyd.** Monday, 5.0 p.m. **See p. 722**—Società Nazionale. July 9th and 25th.
„ **Brindisi.**—Peninsular & Oriental Co. **Sunday midnight. See p.** 726.—Società Nazionale. July 1st, 16th, and 31st.
„ **Copenhagen.**—East Asiatic Co.
„ **Cyprus (Larnaca and Limassol).**—Khedivial Mail Steamship Co. See p. 724.
„ **Genoa.**—Norddeutscher Lloyd. See p. 721.—**Nederland Royal Mail Line. See p. 729.**—Società Nazionale. July 17th.
„ **Hamburg.** — Deutsche Ost-Afrika Linie. July 14th and 29th. **See p. 728.**
„ **Jaffa.**—Messageries Maritimes de France. July 8th, 22nd, and August 5th. See p. 730.—Khedivial Mail Steamship Co. Monday, 4.0 p.m. See p. 724.—Austrian Lloyd. Monday, 4.0 p.m.—Società Nazionale. July 10th and 26th.—**Russian Steam** Navigation Co., Wednesday, 5.0 p.m
„ **Leghorn.**—Società Nazionale.
„ **Liverpool.**—Bibby Line. July 10th and 24th. **See p. 726.**
„ **London.**—Bibby Line. See p. 726.—**British India Steam Navigation Co.—Shire Line**—Union Castle Mail S.S. Co.
„ **London—Tilbury.**—**Peninsular & Oriental Co.** Friday. **See p. 726.**—Orient Line. July 4th, 18th, and August 1st. **See p. 725.**

EGYPT—*Continued.*

TO PORT SAID—*Continued.*

from **Marseilles.**—Peninsular & Oriental Co. Friday. See p. 726.—Messageries Maritimes de France. See p. 730.—Bibby Line. July 4th, 18th, and August 1st. See p. 726.—Deutsche Ost-Afrika Linie. July 11th and 27th. See p. 728.—Union Castle Mail S.S Co.

" **Mersina.**—Khedivial Mail Steamship Co. See p. 724.—Austrian Lloyd. Wednesday, 2.30 p.m.

" **Middlesbrough.**—East Asiatic Co.

" **Naples.**—Orient Line. July 12th and 26th. See p. 725.—Norddeutscher Lloyd. July 11th, 16th, and 25th. See p. 721.—Deustche Ost-Afrika Linie. July 13th and 29th. See p. 728.—Società Nazionale. July 18th.—Union Castle Mail S.S. Co.

" **Odessa.**—Russian Steam Navigation Co. Saturday.

" **Rotterdam.**—Rotterdam Lloyd Royal Mail Line. Fortnightly. See p. 727A.—Deutsche Ost-Afrika Linie. See p. 728.

" **Smyrna.**—Russian Steam Navigation Co. Thursday afternoon.

" **Southampton.**—Norddeutscher Lloyd. July 1st, 7th, 15th, 29th, and August 4th. See p. 721.—Deutsche Ost-Afrika Linie. July 2nd, 18th, and August 2nd. See p. 728.—Nederland Royal Mail Line. See p. 729.—Rotterdam Lloyd Royal Mail Line. Fortnightly. See p. 727A.

" **Taranto.**—Orient Line. July 13th and 27th. See p. 725.

" **Toulon.**—Orient Line. July 10th and 24th. See p. 725.

" **Trieste.**—Austrian Lloyd. July 1st, 5th, 10th, 20th, 30th, August 1st, and 5th. See p. 722.

" **Venice.**—Società Nazionale. July 13th and 28th.

TO PORT SUDAN and SUAKIM—
from **Suez.**—Khedivial Mail Steamship Co. Wednesday, 5.0 p.m. See p. 724.

TO RED SEA PORTS and ADEN—
from **Genoa, Leghorn, and Naples**—Società Nazionale. Monthly.
" **Suez.**—Khedivial Mail S. S. Co. See p. 724.

TO SUEZ—
from **Suakim.**—Khedivial Mail Steamship Co. Tuesday, 12.0 noon and alternate Saturday, 2.0 p.m. See p. 724.

FRANCE.

TO BORDEAUX—
from **Liverpool.**—Moss Line. Weekly. See p. 726.

TO BOULOGNE—
from Amsterdam (calling at **Dover**).—Royal Holland Lloyd. See p. 725.
" **Folkestone.**—(1 hr. 20 min.).—South Eastern Railway Co. See pages vii to x, in front part of Guide.
" **Leith.**—G. Gibson & Co.
" **London** (9 hours).—Fares, Single, 12s.; Return, 20s. 0d. The Bennett Steamship Company. Three times a week, from Chamberlain's Wharf.

TO CAEN—
from **Havre.**—Daily, according to tide.
" **Newhaven.**—London, Brighton, and South Coast Ry. Co. See p. 713.

TO CALAIS—
from **Dover** (60 to 80 minutes).—South Eastern & Chatham Mail Steamers. See pages vii to x, in front part of Guide.

TO CETTE—
from **Algiers.**—Compagnie de Navigation Mixte. Wednesday. 12.0 noon. See p. 730.
" **Oran.**—Cie de Navigation Mixte. Monday, 12.0 noon. See p. 730.

To CHERBOURG—
from **Lisbon.**—The Royal Mail S.P. and P. S. N. Cos. July 2nd, 9th, 16th, 23rd, and 30th. See p. 728.
" **Madeira.**—The Royal Mail S. P. and P. S. N. Cos. July 7th, 14th, 21st, 28th, and August 4th. See p. 728.
" **New York.**—American Line. See p. 718.—Norddeutscher Lloyd. See p. 722.—Hamburg Amerika Linie.
" **Southampton.**—London & South Western Railway Co. See p. 716.—White Star and American Lines, Every Wednesday and Saturday. See p. 718.

FRANCE—*Continued.*

TO DIEPPE—

from **Newhaven** (3½ hours).—London, Brighton & South Coast Railway Co. See p. 718.

TO DUNKIRK—

from **Goole**—Lancashire and Yorkshire Ry. Co. Tuesday.
" **Hull** (20 hours).—Wilson Line. Tuesday. See p. 736.
" **Leith.**—G. Gibson & Co. Weekly.

TO GRANVILLE—

from **Jersey.**—London & South Western Railway Co. See p. 716.

TO HAVRE—

from **Caen.**—Fares, 5fr. 50c. and 3fr. 50c. Daily, according to tide.
" **Honfleur** (30 minutes).—Fares, 2fr., 1fr. 20c., 70c. Twice daily, according to tide.
" **Lisbon.**—Booth Line. See p. 727.
" **Liverpool.**—Booth Line. See p. 727.—R.M.S.P. and P.S.N. Cos. See p. 728.
" **Morlaix**, Wednesday; from Havre, Saturday.
" **Southampton.**—London & South Western Railway Co. See p. 716.
" **Trouville.**—Daily according to the tide; 3fr. 25c., 1fr. 70c., 90c.

TO MARSEILLES—

from **Ajaccio.**—Cie. des Messageries Maritimes. See p. 730.
" **Alexandria.**—Messageries Maritimes de France Cie. Weekly. See p. 730.—Norddeutscher Lloyd. July 2nd, 9th, 16th, and 23rd. See p. 721.
" **Algiers** (direct, 24 hours).—Compagnie Générale Transatlantique. Sun., Tues., Thurs., & Fri., 12.30 p.m. See p. 729.—Compagnie de Navigation Mixte. Saturday, 12.0 noon. See p. 730.—Société Générale de Transports Maritimes. Wednesday and Saturday, 5.0 p.m.
" **Athens (Piræus).**—Messageries Maritimes de France Cie. July 4th, 13th, 18th, 27th, and August 1st. See p. 730.
" **Bastia.**—French steamer.
" **Bizerta.**—Cie. Générale Transatlantique. Wednesday, 10.30 p.m. See p. 729.
" **Bona.**—Compagnie Générale Transatlantique, (direct), Tuesday, 11.0 p.m. calling at **Philippeville**, Thursday, 6.0 p.m. See p. 729.—Cie. de Navigation Mixte. Sunday, 12.0 noon. See p. 730.—Société Générale de Transports Maritimes. Thursday, 5.0 p.m.
" **Bougie.**—Compagnie Générale Transatlantique, Saturday, 12.0 noon. See p. 729.—Société de Transports Maritimes à Vapeur. Tues. 6.0 p.m.
" **Cette.**—Soc. Générale de Transports Maritimes.
" **Constantinople.**—Messageries Maritimes de France Cie. July 1st, 5th, 10th, 15th, 19th, 24th, 29th, and August 2nd. See p. 730.—Paquet et Cie. Fortnightly. See p. 730.
" **Fiume.**—Adria Line. Saturday, 8.0 p.m. See p. 731.
" **Genoa.**—Adria Line. Friday, 10.0 a.m. See p. 731.
" **Gibraltar.**—Peninsular and Oriental Co. Weekly. See p. 726.
" **Hamburg.**—Deutsche Ost-Afrika Linie. July 14th and 29th. See p. 728.
" **Liverpool.**—Bibby Line. July 10th and 24th. See p. 726.
" **London.**—P. & O. Co. Friday. See p. 726.
" **Malta.**—Compagnie Générale Transatlantique. Thursday, 5.0 p.m. See p. 729.—Adria Line. Tuesday, 6.0 p.m. See p 731.
" **Morocco Ports (Mogador, Mazagan, Casablanca, Tangier).**-Paquet et Cie. See p. 730.
" **Naples.**—Messageries Maritimes de France Cie. July 1st, 15th, and 29th. See p. 730.—Norddeutscher Lloyd. July 5th and 19th. See p. 721.—British India Steam Navigation Co.—Adria Line. Saturday, 4.0 p.m., Tuesday, 6.0 p.m. See p. 731.—Deutsche Ost-Afrika Linie. July 2nd, 16th, and August 1st. See p. 728.
" **Oran** (direct).—Compagnie Générale Transatlantique. Monday and Wednesday, 5.0 p.m. See p. 729.—Compagnie de Navigation Mixte. Saturday, 10.0 a.m. See p. 730.—Société Générale de Transports Maritimes à Vapeur. Tuesday, 8.0 a.m, and Saturday, 5.0 p.m.
" **Palermo.**—Adria Line. Monday, 3.0 p.m. See p. 731.
" **Palma (Majorca).**—Islena Maritima Co. Sunday, 9.0 a.m.
" **Patras.**—Messageries Maritimes de France Co. July 10th and 24th. See p. 730.

GERMANY—*Continued.*

TO HAMBURG—

from **Bergen.**—Bergenske and Nordenfjeldske Cos. Monday, Thursday, Friday, and Saturday.
" **Christiania**—Sondenfj. Norske, Co., or Jelö Line. Tuesday and Saturday.
" **Christiansand.**—Bergenske and Nordenfjeldske Cos. Sunday.
" **Goole** (36 hours).—Lancashire & Yorkshire Rly. Co. Mons., Wed., Thurs., and Sat.
" **Gothenburg** (36 hours)..—"Svenska Lloyd." Wednesday and Saturday.
" **Grimsby** (30 hours).—Great Central Railway Co. Daily (Sunday excepted), 7.0 p.m. See p. 735.
" **Harwich.**—General Steam Navigation Co.'s Steamers. Every Wednesday and Saturday.
" **Heligoland (via Cuxhaven).**—Daily, 12.30 p.m.
" **Hull.**—Wilson Line. Every Tuesday and Saturday. See p. 736.
" **Leith.**—Leith, Hull, and Hamburg Co. Every Mon., Wed., and Sat. See p. 727,
" **Lisbon.**—Deutsche Ost-Afrika Linie. July 10th and 24th. See p. 728.
" **Newcastle** (36 hours).—The Tyne-Tees Steam Shipping Co. Fares 30s. and 16s. 6d. return, available for 3 Months, 35s. and 25s. 6d. Every Saturday.

TO HELIGOLAND—

from **Cuxhaven** (42 miles, 3 hours).—Daily, 12.20 p.m.
" **Hamburg.**—Daily, 8.0 a.m.

TO HOLTENAU—

from **London.**—United Shipping Co., Ltd. See p. 723.

TO KIEL—

from **Korsœr** (5 hours).—Impl. German Mail Steamers, and Danish State Railways Steamers. See p. 732.

TO LUBECK—

from **Copenhagen** (15 hours).—Hallandsche Steamers. Daily, 4.0 p.m.
" **Malmö.**—Hallandsche Steamers. Daily, 11.15 a.m.
" **Riga** (50 hours).—"Alexandra," etc. Saturday, 11.0 a.m. (during the season).
" **Stockholm (Via Calmar).**—The "Gauthiod," "Swithiod," etc. (during the season). See p. 734.

TO NORDERNEY—

from **Norddeich (Norden) 1 hour.**—Frequent service in both directions daily.

TO SASSNITZ—

from **Trelleborg.**—Prussian and Swedish State Railways Ferries. **Daily, 8.46 a.m. & 10.45 p.m.**

TO STETTIN—

from **Christiania.**—"Kong Haakon," "Dronning Maud." Wednesday and Saturday, 2.0 p.m.
" **Copenhagen.**—"Kong Haakon" and "Dronning Maud." Sunday and Thursday, 5.0 p.m. "Odin" &c., Tues. & Sat., 5.0 p.m.
" **Gothenburg**—"Odin," etc., Monday and Friday, 6.0 p.m.—**(Via Malmö).**—"Temis" etc. Friday during the season.
" **Helsingfors.**—Finland Steamship Co. Saturday, 1.0 p.m.
" **Hull**—Wilson Line. Friday. See p. 736.
" **Riga** (45 hours).—"Ostsee" or "Regina. Saturday during the season.
" **St. Petersburg** (60 hours).—Sunday and Thursday, 2.0 p.m., during the season.
" **Stockholm via Visby.**—"Carolus," etc. Wednesday 1.0 p.m. during the season; also, via Revel or Norrkoping, "Alexandra," "Lena." Saturday.

TO WARNEMÜNDE—

from **Gjedser** (2 hrs.). — Mecklenburg and Danish State Railways Steamers, "Friedrich Franz IV," "Mecklenburg," etc., twice daily.

GREAT BRITAIN.

TO DOVER—

from **Calais** (65 to 80 minutes).—South Eastern and Chatham Railway Co.'s Mail Steamers. See pages vii to x, in front part of Guide.
" **Lisbon** (calling at **Vigo**).—Royal Holland Lloyd. See p. 725.
" **Ostend** (3 hours).—Belgian Mail Steamers. See pages 714, 715.

TO DUNDEE—

from **Rotterdam.**—Geo. Gibson & Co. Saturday.

TO FOLKESTONE—

from **Boulogne** (1 hour 40 minutes).—South Eastern Co. See pages vii to x, in front part of Guide.
" **Flushing** (6 hours).—Zeeland Steamship Co. Daily, 12.10 night in connection with the South Eastern and Chatham Railway. See page ix in front part of Guide.

GREAT BRITAIN—*Continued.*

TO GOOLE—

from **Amsterdam.**—Lancashire and Yorkshire Railway Co. **Every Tuesday and Saturday.**
" **Antwerp.**—Lancashire and Yorkshire Railway Co. Tues., Thurs., and Sat.
" **Bruges.**—Lancashire and Yorkshire Railway Co. Wednesday.
" **Copenhagen.**—Lancashire and Yorkshire Railway Co. **Thursday.**
" **Delfziel**—Lancashire and Yorkshire Railway Co. Saturday.
" **Dunkirk.**—Lancashire and Yorkshire Railway Co. Saturday.
" **Ghent.**—Lancashire and Yorkshire Railway Co. Wednesday and Saturday.
" **Hamburg.**—Lancashire and Yorkshire Railway Co. Mon., Wed., Fri., and Sat.
" **Rotterdam.**—Lancashire and Yorkshire Railway Co. Tues., Thurs., and Sat.

TO GRIMSBY—

from **Antwerp** (20 hours).—**Great Central Railway Co. Tues., Thurs., and Sat.,** 7.0 p.m. See p. 735.
" **Christiania.**—Wilson Line. July 4th, 18th, and August 1st. See p. 736.
" **Christiansand**—Wilson Line. July 5th, 19th, and August 2nd. See p. 736.
" **Esbjerg.**—United Steamship Co. of Copenhagen. Tuesday and Friday.
" **Gothenburg.**—Wilson Line. Wednesday, 9.0 a.m. See p. 736.
" **Hamburg** (30 hours).—**Great Central Railway Co. Daily, Sundays excepted,** 9.0 p.m. See p. 735.
" **Malmo.**—Wilson Line. Tuesday. See p. 736.
" **Rotterdam** (12 hours.)—Great Central Railway Co. **Tues., Thurs., and Sats.,** 9.0 p.m. See p. 735.

TO GUERNSEY—

from **Jersey.**—London & South Western Ry. Co. See p. 716.—Gt. **Western Ry. Co.** **See p.** 716. —s.s. Devonia, Thursday, 4.0 p.m.
" **Southampton.**—London & South Western Ry. Co. **See p. 716.**
" **Weymouth.**—**Great Western Ry. Co.** **See p. 716.**

TO HARWICH—

from **Antwerp.**—**Great Eastern Ry. Co. See Advert. first page after cover.**
" **Esbjerg.**—The United Shipping Co., Ltd. Mon., Tues., Wed., and Sat., 4.45 p.m. See p. 735.
" **Hamburg.**—**General Steam Navigation Co., in connection with Great Eastern Railway Co. Every Wednesday and Saturday.**
" **Hoek van Holland** (7½ hours).—**Great Eastern Ry. Co. See Advert. first page after cover.**

TO HULL—

from **Aalesund.**—Wilson Line. Friday, 3.0 p.m. See p. 736.
" **Abo.**—**Finland Line, John Good & Sons, Ltd., Agents.** **See p. 734.**
" **Amsterdam.**—**Hull and Netherlands Steam Ship Co. Ltd.** **See p. 731.**
" **Antwerp** (22 hours).—Wilson Line. Tuesday. See p. 736.
" **Bergen.**—Wilson Line. Saturday, 12.0 noon. See p. 736.
" **Bremen.**—Argo Steamship Co. Tuesday, Thursday and Saturday.
" **Christiania.**—Wilson Line. Wednesday, 1.0 p.m. and alternate Friday, 7.0 p.m. See p. 736.
" **Christiansand.**—Wilson Line. Wednesday, 12.0 night and alternate Saturday, 9.0 a.m. See p. 736.
" **Christiansund.**—Wilson Line. Friday, 8.0 a.m. See p. 736.
" **Copenhagen.**—**Finland Line, John Good & Sons, Ltd., Agents.** **See p. 734.**—**Wilson** Line. Thursday. See p. 736.
" **Drontheim**—Wilson Line. Thursday, 10.0 p.m. See p. 736.
" **Dunkirk.**—Wilson Line. Saturday, 12.0 noon. See p. 736.
" **Ghent.**—Wilson Line. Wednesday. See p. 736.
" **Gothenburg.**—Wilson Line Monday, 9.0 a.m. and Friday, 10.0 p.m. See p. 736.
" **Hamburg.**—Wilson Line. Tuesday and Saturday. See p. 736.
" **Hango.**—**Finland Line, John Good & Sons, Ltd., Agents.** **See page 734.**
" **Harlingen.**—**The Hull and Netherlands Steam Ship Co., Ltd.** **See p. 731.**
" **Helsingfors.**—**Finland Line, John Good & Sons, Ltd., Agents.** **See p. 734.**
" **Libau.**—Wilson Line. See p. 736.
" **Riga.**—Wilson Line. Wednesday, 12.0 noon. See p. 736.
" **Rotterdam** (17 hours).—**Hull and Netherlands Steam Ship Co., Ltd.** **See p. 731.**
" **St. Petersburg** (4½ days).—Wilson Line. Tuesday, 12.0 noon. See p. 736.
" **Stavanger.**—Wilson Line. Saturday, 10.0 p.m. See p. 736.
" **Stettin.**—Wilson Line. Saturday, 12.0 noon. See p. 736.
" **Stockholm.**—**John Good and Sons, Ltd., Steamers.** **See p. 734.**
" **Zee-Brugge.**—**Lancashire and Yorkshire and North Eastern Railway Companies.** until October 3rd, on Sunday, Wednesday, and Friday, 7.0 **p.m.** See p. xiii., in front part of Guide.

GREAT BRITAIN—*Continued.*

TO JERSEY—

from **Carteret to Gorey.**—Daily, in one hour.
" **Granville.**—London & South Western Ry. Co. **See p. 716.**
" **Guernsey.**—S.S. Devonia. Tuesday, 8.0 a.m.
" **St. Malo.**—London & South Western Ry. Co. **See p. 716.**
" **Southampton.**—London and South Western Ry. Co. **See p. 716.**
" **Weymouth.**—Great Western Ry. Co. **See p. 716.**

TO LEITH—

from **Christiansand.**—Leith, Hull, and Hamburg Co. Friday. See p. 727.
" **Copenhagen.**—Leith, Hull, and Hamburg Co. Thursday. See p. 727.
" **Hamburg.**—Leith, Hull, & Hamburg Co. Monday, Wednesday, **and Friday.** See p. 727.

TO LIVERPOOL—

from **Algiers**—Moss Line. See p. 726.—**Papayanni and Ellerman Lines.**
" **Bordeaux.**—Moss Line. See p. 726.
" **Constantinople.**—Papayanni and Ellerman Lines.
" **Corunna.**—Pacific S.N. and R.M.S.P. Cos. July 4th, 18th, and August 1st. **See p. 728.**
" **Gibraltar.**—Moss Line. See p. 726.—**Papayanni and Ellerman Lines.**
" **Lisbon.**—Booth Line. **See p. 727.—Pacific S. N. and R. M. S. P. Cos.** July 2nd, 4th, 16th, and 30th. **See p. 728.—Lamport and Holt Line. See p. 727A.—Papayanni and** Ellerman Lines.
" **Madeira.**—Booth Line. See p. 727.
" **Vigo.**—Lamport and Holt Line. See p. 727A.—Pacific S.N. and R.M.S.P. Co.'s. See p. 728.

TO LONDON—

from **Amsterdam** (16 to 18 hours).—**Holland Steamship Co. Wed. and Sat., 5.0 p.m.**
" **Boulogne.**—The Bennett Steamship Co.
" **Bremen** (36 hours).—Argo Steamship Co. Monday, **Tuesday,** Wednesday, **Thursday,** and Saturday.
" **Canary Islands (Las Palmas).**—**The Royal Mail Steam Packet Co.** See p. 728.—**Union** Castle Line. Weekly.
" **Gothenburg.**—Thule Steamship Co. See p. 733.
" **Hamburg.**—**Kirsten's Line. Tues., Wed., Fri., and Sat. evening.—General Steam** Navigation Co. (via Harwich). Every Wed. and Sat.
" **Madeira.**—The Royal Mail Steam Packet Co. See p. 728.
" **Malta.**—Peninsular and Oriental Co. **See p. 726.**
" **Marseilles.**—Bibby Line. **Fortnightly. See page 726.—British India Steam** Navigation Co.
" **Oporto.**—Coverley and Westray.
" **Rotterdam.**—" Batavier Line." See p. 731.
" **St. Petersburg.**—The United Shipping Co., Ltd. See p. 727.
" **Stockholm** (via Gothenburg and Harwich).—**British and Northern Shipping Agency,** Ltd. See p. 733.
" **Tangier.**—The Royal Mail Steam Packet Co. See p. 728.
" **Teneriffe.**—The Royal Mail Steam Packet Co. See p. 728.

TO LONDON—TILBURY—

from **Gibraltar.**—**Peninsular and Oriental Co. Weekly.** See p. 726.—**Orient Line.** July 1st, 15th, and 29th. See p. 725.
" **Marseilles.**—**Peninsular and Oriental Co. Weekly.** See p. 726.
" **Naples.**—Orient Line. July 11th and 25th. See p. 725.
" **Port Said.**—**Peninsular and Oriental Co. See p. 726.—Orient Line.** July 8th, 22nd, and August 5th. See p. 725.
" **Toulon**—Orient Line. July 13th and 27th. See p. 725.

TO NEWCASTLE—

from **Antwerp** (28 hours).—**The Tyne-Tees Steam Shipping Co. Fares, 20s. and 11s. 6d.** Wednesday.
" **Bergen.**—**Bergenske and Nordenfjeldske Cos. Monday, Wednesday, and Saturday,** 1.0 p.m.
" **Christiania** (calling at **Larvik and Arendal**).—"**Sterling,**" and "**Bessheim.**" **Leaves** Larvik on Friday evening.
" **Copenhagen.**—Wilson Line. **Thursday,** 10.0 p.m. See p. 736.
" **Drontheim.**—**Bergenske Co.** Monday, **Wednesday,** and **Saturday,** 9.0 p.m.

GREAT BRITAIN—*Continued.*

TO NEWCASTLE—*Continued.*

from **Hamburg** (36 hrs).—The Tyne-Tees Steam Shipping Co. Fares, 30s. & 16s. 6d. Tuesday.
" **Rotterdam** (24 hours).—The Tyne-Tees Steam Shipping Co. Fares, 20s. and 11s. 6d. Saturday.
" **Stavanger.**—Bergenske Co. Monday and Wednesday, 11.0 p.m.

TO NEWHAVEN—

from **Caen.**—London, Brighton, and South Coast Ry. Co. See p. 713.
" **Dieppe** (3½ hours).—London, Brighton, and South Coast Ry. Co. See p. 713.

TO PLYMOUTH—

from **Naples.**—Orient Line. July 11th and 25th. See page 725.
" **Toulon.**—Orient Line. July 13th and 27th. See page 725.

TO QUEENBORO'—

from **Flushing** (6 hours).—Zeeland Co. in connection with South Eastern and Chatham Ry. See p. ix, in front part of Guide.

TO QUEENSTOWN—

from **Cherbourg.**—White Star Line. Every Wednesday. See page 718.

TO SOUTHAMPTON—

from **Canary Islands.**—Deutsche Ost-Afrika Linie. See p. 728.—Union Castle Line, Weekly.
" **Cherbourg.**—London & South Western Ry. Co. See p. 716.—White Star & American Lines. Every Wednesday and Saturday. See page 718.—Royal Mail S. P. and P. S. N. Cos. See p. 728.
" **Genoa.**—Norddeutscher Lloyd. See p. 721.—Nederland Royal Mail Line. See p. 729.
" **Gibraltar.**—Rotterdam Lloyd Royal Mail Line. Fortnightly. See p. 727A.
" **Guernsey.**—London & South Western Ry. Co. See p. 716.
" **Hamburg.**—Deutsche Ost-Afrika Linie. July 10th, 14th, 25th, and 29th. See p. 728. Norddeutscher Lloyd. See p. 721.—Hamburg-Amerika Linie.
" **Havre.**—London & South Western Ry. Co. See p. 716.
" **Jersey.**—London & South Western Railway Co. See p. 716.
" **Lisbon.**—The Royal Mail S. P. and P. S. N. Cos. July 2nd, 9th, 16th, 23rd, and 30th. See p. 728.—Deutsche Ost-Afrika Linie. July 10th and 24th. See p. 728.—Nederland Royal Mail Line. See p. 729.—Rotterdam Lloyd Royal Mail Line. Fortnightly. See p. 727A.
" **Madeira.**—The Royal Mail Steam Packet and P.S.N. Cos. See p. 728.—Union-Castle Mail Steamship Co. Weekly.
" **Marseilles.**—Rotterdam Lloyd Royal Mail Line. Fortnightly. See. p. 727A.
" **St. Malo.**—London & South Western Ry Co. See p. 716.
" **Tangier.**—Rotterdam Lloyd Royal Mail Line. Fortnightly. See p. 727A—Deutsche Ost-Afrika Linie. July 9th and 23rd. See p. 728.
" **Vigo.**—The Royal Mail S. P. and P. S. N. Cos. July 3rd, 10th, 17th, 24th, and 31st. See p. 728.

TO WEYMOUTH—

from **Guernsey.**—Great Western Ry. Co. See p. 716.
" **Jersey.**—Great Western Ry. Co. See p. 716.

GREECE.

TO ATHENS (PIRÆUS)—

from **Alexandria.**—Khedivial Mail S.S. Co. Wednesday, 4.0 p m. See page 724.—Rumanian State Line. Friday, 4.0 p.m. See p. 723.—Russian Steam Nav. Co. Tues., 4.0 p.m.
" **Brindisi.**—Austrian Lloyd. Tuesday, 1.30 a.m. and Wednesday, 11.30 p.m.. See p. 722. —Società Nazionale. Sunday, 12.0 night, and Friday, 7.0 p.m.
" **Constantinople.**—Khedivial Mail Steamship Co. Tuesday, 3.0 p.m.. See page 724.—Messageries Maritimes de France. July 1st, 10th, 15th, 24th, and 29th. See p. 730.—Hellenic and Panhellenic Cos. Twice weekly.—Austrian Lloyd. Saturday, 10.0 a.m. See p. 722.—Rumanian State Line. Thursday, 2.30 p.m. See p. 723.—Russian Steam Navigation Co. Sunday, 2.0 p.m.—Società Nazionale. Wednesday, 5.30 p.m., and Friday, 8.0 p.m.
" **Constanza (Kustendje)**—Rumanian State Line. Tuesday, 11.30 p.m. See p. 723.
" **Genoa.**—Società Nazionale. Tuesday, 10.0 p.m.
" **Marseilles.**—Messageries Maritimes de France. July 5th, 10th, 19th, 24th, and August 2nd. See p. 730.
" **Salonica.**—Austrian Lloyd. Alternate Wed., 5.0 p.m. See p. 722.—Società Nazionale. Alternate Saturday, 4.0 a.m.

GREECE—*Continued.*

TO ATHENS (PIRÆUS)—***Continued.***
from **Smyrna**—**Messageries Maritimes de France.** July 3rd, 11th, 17th, 25th, and 31st. See p. 730.—**Khedivial Mail Steamship Co. Wednesday, 5.0 p.m.** **See p. 724.**—**Austrian** Lloyd. Saturday, 4.0 p.m. See p. 722.—**Società Nazionale,** Alternate Saturday, 9.0 a.m. —Russian Steam Navigation Co. Monday, 6.0 p.m.
" **Trieste.**—**Austrian Lloyd. Tuesday, 2.0 p.m.; also Sunday, 10.0** a.m., **and Friday** 5.30 p.m. See p. 722.
" **Volo.**—**Austrian Lloyd. Alternate Thursday, 1.0 p.m. See p. 722.**

TO CALAMATA—
from **Trieste.**—Austrian Lloyd. Sunday, 10.0 a.m. See p. 722.

TO CHALCIS—
from **Volo.**—**Greek steamer, Weekly.**

TO CORFU and PATRAS—

Trieste......dep	———	———	Sun. 10†0a.m.	Tues. 2†0p.m.	———	———
Brindisi ...dep	Sun. 12*0 night	Mon. 11‡0p.m.	Tues.1 30a.m	Wed.11 30p.m.	Fri. 7 *0p.m.	Sat. 11‡0p.m.
Corfu ......arr	———	Tues.10 0a.m.	Tues.1 30p.m.	Thur.10 30a.m.	Sat. 7 15a.m.	Sun. 10 0a.m.
Patras ......arr	Mon. 8 0p.m.	Wed.4 0a.m.	Wed.5 0a.m.	Fri. 4 0a.m	Sat. 9 45p.m.	Mon.5 0a.m.
Athens(rail) ar	A	Wed.4 40p.m.	Wed.4 40p.m.	Fri. 4 40p.m	B	Mon.4 40p.m.

*—Società Nazionale steamers. †—Austrian Lloyd, see p. 722. ‡—Greek Steamer.
A—Steamer arrives Piræus Tuesday 7.0 a.m. B—Steamer arrives Piræus Sunday 9.15 a.m.

TO PATRAS—
from **Naples.**—Austro-Americana Steamers.
" **Spalato** (or **Gravosa**).—Austro-Americana Steamers.
" **Trieste.**—Austrian Lloyd. See p. 722.—Austro-Americana Steamers.

TO ISLANDS—Kephalonia, Zante (Ionian Is.), from Patras.—Austrian Lloyd. Wednesday.— Syra, Samos, Chios, from **Piræus.—Austrian Lloyd. Friday.—from Trieste — Austrian Lloyd. Sunday, 10.0 a.m. See p. 722.**

HOLLAND.

TO AMSTERDAM—
from **Goole.**—Lancashire and Yorkshire Ry. Co. **Every Wednesday and Saturday.**
" **Harlingen** (6 hours).—Wednesday and Saturday, 8.0 a.m.
" **Hull.**—The Hull and Netherlands Steam Ship Co. **See p. 731.**
" **Leith.**—Geo. Gibson & Co. Monday and Friday.
" **Lisbon.**—Nederland Royal Mail Line. See p. 729.—**Royal Holland Lloyd.** **See p. 725.**
" **London.**—**Holland Steamship Co. Sunday and Wednesday, 8.0 a.m**

TO DELFZIEL—
from **Goole.**—Lancashire and Yorkshire Ry. Co. **Tuesday.**

TO FLUSHING—
from **Breskens.**—**Flushing and Breskens (30 minutes).—Departures from Flushing, 5.20, 7.50,** 9.50 a.m., 12.10 (Sundays excepted), 3.43 p.m., and 6.35 p.m. **Departures from Breskens** 5.50, 8.20, 10.30 a.m., 12.40 (Sundays excepted), 4.10, and 7.5 p.m.
" **Folkestone** (5½ hours)—Zeeland Steamship Co. Daily, 10.35 p.m., in connection with the South Eastern and Chatham Railway. See p. ix, in front part of Guide.
" **Queenboro'** (6 hours).—Zeeland Steamship Co. Daily, 11.30 a.m., in connection with the South Eastern and Chatham Railway. **See p. ix, in front part of Guide.**

TO HARLINGEN—
from **Hull**—**The Hull and Netherlands Steam Ship Co.** See p. 731.
" **Leith.**—Geo. Gibson & Co. Tuesday.

TO HOEK van HOLLAND—
from **Harwich** (7½ hours).—Great Eastern Ry. Co. See Advert. first page after cover.

TO ROTTERDAM—
from **Dundee.**—Geo. Gibson & Co. Monday.
" **Gibraltar.**—Rotterdam Lloyd Royal Mail Line. Fortnightly. See p. 727A.
" **Goole.**—Lancashire and Yorkshire Ry. Co. **Monday, Wednesday, and Saturday.**
" **Grimsby** (12 hours).—**Great Central Ry. Co. Tuesday, Thursday, and Saturday, 7.0 p.m** See p. 735.
" **Hull**—Hull & Netherlands Steam Ship Co. Ltd. **Daily (Sunday excepted).** **See p. 731.**
" **Leith**—Geo. Gibson & Co. Tuesday and Friday.
" **Lisbon.**—Rotterdam Lloyd Royal Mail Line. Fortnightly. See p. 727A.
" **Liverpool.**—**Cork Steamship Co., from Trafalgar Dock.** Friday and alternate Wednesday.
" **London—Tilbury.**—**Batavier Line. Daily, Sunday excepted.** See p. 731.
" **Marseilles.**—Rotterdam Lloyd Royal Mail Line. Fortnightly. See p. 727A.
" **Newcastle** (24 hours).—The Tyne-Tees Steam Shipping Co. Fares, 20s. and 11s. 6d. return 30s. and 18s. Tuesday.
" **Tangier.**—Rotterdam Lloyd Royal Mail Line. **Fortnightly. See p. 727A.**

INDIA, CHINA, AND JAPAN.

TO BANGKOK—

from **Antwerp, Copenhagen, and Middlesbrough—East Asiatic Co.**

TO BOMBAY—

from **Brindisi.—Peninsular and Oriental Co. Sunday midnight. See p. 726.—Società** Nazionale. July 16th.

" **Genoa.**—Società Nazionale. July 17th.

" **Gibraltar.**—Peninsular and Oriental Co. Tuesday. See p. 726.

" **London—Tilbury.**—Peninsular and Oriental Co. **Friday. See p. 726.**

" **Marseilles.**—Peninsular and Oriental Co. **Friday. See p. 726.—Messageries Maritimes** de France. July 23rd. See p. 730.

" **Naples.**—Società Nazionale. July 18th.

" **Port Said.**—Peninsular and Oriental Co. See p. 726.—**Messageries Maritimes de France.** July 27th. See p. 730.—Austrian Lloyd. July 5th, 16th, and August 5th. See p. 722.—Società Nazionale. July 23rd.

" **Trieste.—Austrian Lloyd.** July 1st, 10th, and August 1st. See p. 722.

TO CALCUTTA—

from **Colombo.—Peninsular & Oriental Co.** July 3rd and 31st. See p. **726.—Messageries Maritimes de France.** July 2nd and 30th. See p. 730.

" **Liverpool.**—City Line. See p. 733.

" **London.—British India Steam Navigation Co. Ltd.**

" **London—Tilbury**—P. and O. Co. July 5th and 19th. See p. 726.

" **Malta.**—Peninsular and Oriental Co. July 13th and 27th. See p. 726.

" **Marseilles.—Messageries Maritimes de France.** July 13th. See p. 730.

" **Port Said.—Peninsular and Oriental Co.** July 17th and 31st. See p. 726.—Austrian Lloyd. July 11th and 27th. See p. 722.—**Messageries Maritimes de France.** July 17th. See p. 730.—**British India Steam Nav. Co., Ltd.**

" **Trieste.—Austrian Lloyd. July 5th, 20th, and August** 5th. **See p. 722.**

TO COLOMBO—

from **Amsterdam.—Nederland Royal Mail Line. See p. 729.**

" **Antwerp.—Norddeutscher Lloyd.** July 6th, 14th, 28th, and August 3rd. Se p. 721.— East Asiatic Co.

" **Brindisi.—Peninsular and Oriental Co.** July 6th, 20th, and August 3rd. See p. 726.

" **Copenhagen.—East Asiatic Co.**

" **Genoa.—Norddeutscher Lloyd.** July 10th, 15th, and 24th. See p. 721.—**Nederland** Royal Mail Line. See p. 729.

" **Gibraltar.**—Peninsular and Oriental Co. July 1st, 15th, and 29th. See p. 726.—**Orient** Line. July 8th, 22nd. and August 5th. See p. 725.—**Norddeutscher Lloyd.** July 5th, 19th, and August 2nd. See p. 721.

" **Liverpool.**—Bibby Line. July 10th and 24th. **See p. 726.—City Line.** See p. 733.

" **London.**—Shire Line.—**British India Steam Navigation Co. Ltd.**

" **London—Tilbury.**—Peninsular and Oriental Co. July 5th, 11th, 12th, 19th, 25th, and 26th. See p. 726.—**Orient Line.** July 4th, 18th, and August 1st. See p. 725.

" **Malta.—Peninsular and Oriental Co.** July 6th, 13th, 20th, 27th, and August 3rd. See p. 726.

" **Marseilles.—Peninsular and Oriental Co.** July 4th, 18th, and August 1st. See p. 726.— **Messageries Maritimes de France.** July 13th, 23rd, and 27th. **See p. 730.—Bibby** Line. July 4th, 18th, and August 1st. See p. 726.

" **Middlesbrough.**—East Asiatic Co.

" **Naples.**—Orient Line. July 12th and 26th. **See p. 725.—Norddeutscher Lloyd.** July 11th, 16th. and 25th. See p. 721.

" **Port Said.—Peninsular and Oriental Co. See p. 726.—Messageries Maritimes de France.** July 3rd, 17th, 27th, and 31st. See p. 730.—Bibby Line. July 2th and 23rd. See p. 726. Norddeutscher Lloyd. See p. 721.—Orient Line. July 2nd, 16th, and 30th. See p. 725. British India Steam Navigation Co., Ltd.—Austrian Lloyd. July 5th, 11th, 16th, 27th, and August 4th. See p. 722.—Nederland Royal Mail Line. See p. 729.

" **Rotterdam.**—Rotterdam Lloyd Royal Mail Line. Fortnightly. See p. 727A.

" **Southampton.—Norddeutscher Lloyd.** July 1st, 7th, 15th, 29th, and August 4th. See p. 721.—Nederland Royal Mail Line. See p. 729.—Rotterdam Lloyd Royal Mail Line. Fortnightly. See p. 727A.

" **Taranto.—Orient Line.** July 13th and 27th. See p. 725.

" **Toulon.**—Orient Line. July 10th and 24th. See p. 725.

" **Trieste.—Austrian Lloyd. July 5th, 10th, 20th, 30th, and August 5th. See p. 722.**

INDIA CHINA, AND JAPAN—*Continued.*

TO HONG KONG (for MANILA), and SHANGHAI (for JAPAN)—

from **Antwerp.**—Norddeutscher Lloyd. July 14th and 28th. **See p. 721.**—East Asiatic Co.
" **Brindisi.**—Peninsular & Oriental Co. July 6th, 20th, and August 3rd. **See p. 726.**
" **Copenhagen.**—East Asiatic Co.
" **Genoa.** —Norddeutscher Lloyd. July 10th, and 24th. **See p. 721.—Società Nazionale.**
" **Gothenburg.**—East Asiatic Co.
" **London.**—Shire Line.
" **London—Tilbury.**—**P. and O. Co.** July 11th, 12th, 25th, and 26th. **See p. 726.**
" **Marseilles.**—Peninsular and Oriental Co. July 4th, 18th, and August 1st. See p. 726.—Messageries Maritimes de France. July 13th, and 27th. **See p. 730.**
" **Naples.**—Norddeutscher Lloyd. July 11th and 25th. See p. 721.—**Società Nazionale.**
" **Port Said.**—Peninsular and Oriental Co. July 8th, 10th, 22nd, 24th, and August 5th. See p. 726.—Messageries Maritimes de France. July 3rd, 17th, and 31st. See p. 730.—Norddeutscher Lloyd. See p. 721.—Austrian Lloyd. July 5th, 16th, and August 4th. See p. 722.—Società Nazionale.
" **Southampton.**—Norddeutscher Lloyd. July 1st, 15th, and 29th. See p. 721.
" **Trieste.**—Austrian Lloyd. July 10th and 30th. See p. 722.
" **Vancouver.**—Canadian Pacific Railway Steamers. **See p. 717.**

TO JAPAN, calling at Singapore, and Hong Kong—

from **Antwerp.**—Nippon Yusen Mail Steamship Co., Ltd. July 13th, and 27th. See p. 726.—Norddeutscher Lloyd. July 14th, and 28th. **See p. 721.—East Asiatic Co.**
" **Copenhagen.**—East Asiatic Co.
" **Gothenburg.**—East Asiatic Co.
" **London.**—Nippon Yusen Kaisha (Japan Mail Steamship Co., Ltd.) July 5th, 19th, and August 2nd. See p. 726.—P. and O. Co. July 12th and 26th. **See p. 726.—Shire Line.**
" **Marseilles.**—Messageries Maritimes de France. July 13th, and 27th. **See p. 730.**—Nippon Yusen Kaisha (Japan Mail Steamship Co., Ltd.) July 12th and 26th See p. 726.
" **Southampton.**—Norddeutscher Lloyd. July 1st, 15th, and 29th. **See p. 721.**
" **Trieste.**—Austrian Lloyd. July 10th. See p. 722.
" **Vancouver** (direct)—Canadian Pacific Railway Steamers. **See p. 717.**

TO JAVA, calling at Sumatra—

from **Rotterdam.**—Rotterdam Lloyd Royal Mail Line. Fortnightly. See p. 727A.
" **Southampton.**—Rotterdam Lloyd Royal Mail Line. Fortnightly. See p. 727A.

TO KURRACHEE—

from **Port Said.**—Austrian Lloyd. July 11th, 16th, and 27th. **See p. 722.**
" **Trieste.**—Austrian Lloyd. July 5th, 10th, 20th, and August 5th. **See p. 722.**

TO MADRAS—

from **Liverpool.**—City Line. See page 733.
" **London.**—British India Steam Navigation Co., Ltd.
" **Port Said.**—Austrian Lloyd. July 11th and 27th. See p. 722.
" **Trieste.**—Austrian Lloyd. July 5th, 20th, and August 5th. See p. 722.

TO MANILA (PHILIPPINE ISLANDS)—
from **Barcelona.**—Compañia Trasatlantica. **Monthly. See p. 729.**

TO PENANG AND SINGAPORE (for BATAVIA)—

from **Amsterdam.**—Nederland Royal Mail Line. See p. 729.
" **Antwerp.**—Norddeutscher Lloyd. July 14th and 28th. **See p. 721.** (To Singapore only)—East Asiatic Co.
" **Brindisi.**—Peninsular and Oriental Line. July 6th, 20th, and August 3rd. See p. 726.
" **Copenhagen.**—(To Singapore only)—East Asiatic Co.
" **Genoa.**—Norddeutscher Lloyd. July 10th and 24th, **See p. 721.—Società Nazionale.** —Nederland Royal Mail Line. See p. 729.
" **London—Tilbury**—P. and O. Co. July 11th, 12th, 25th, and 26th. **See p. 726.**
" **Marseilles.**—Peninsular and Oriental Co. July 4th, 18th, and August 1st. **See p. 726.**—Messageries Maritimes. (To Singapore only). July 13th, and 27th. **See p. 730.**
" **Middlesbrough.**—(To Singapore only)—East Asiatic Co.

INDIA CHINA AND JAPAN—*Continued.*

TO PENANG AND SINGAPORE (for BATAVIA)—*Continued.*

from **Naples.**—Norddeutscher Lloyd. July 11th and 25th. See p. 721.—**Società Nazionale.**
" **Port Said.**—**Peninsular and Oriental Co.** July 8th, 10th, 22nd, 24th, and August 5th. See p. 726.—Messageries Maritimes de France. (To Singapore only). July 3rd, 17th, and 31st. See p. 730.—Norddeutscher Lloyd. See p. 721.—**Austrian** Lloyd. July 5th, 16th, and August 4th. See p. 722.—Nederland Royal Mail Line. See p. 729. —Società Nazionale.
" **Southampton**—Norddeutscher Lloyd. July 1st, 15th, and 29th. See p. 721.—Nederland Royal Mail Line. See p. 729.
" **Trieste.**—Austrian Lloyd. July 10th and 30th. **See p. 722.**

TO RANGOON—

from **Liverpool.**—**Bibby Line.** July 10th and 24th. See p. 726.
" **Marseilles.**—Bibby Line. July 4th, 18th, and August 1st. See p. 726.
" **Port Said.**—**Bibby Line.** July 9th and 23rd. **See p. 726.**—Austrian Lloyd. July 11th and 27th. See p. 722.
" **Trieste**—**Austrian Lloyd.** July 5th, 20th, and August 5th. **See p. 722.**

ITALY.

TO ANCONA—

from **Brindisi.**—Società Nazionale. Wednesday, 12.0 night.
" **Fiume.**—**Hungarian State Rly. Steamers.**
Fiume depart Wednesday, 7.45 a.m., Monday and Friday, 8.25 p.m.
Ancona arrive Wednesday, 5.45 p.m., Tuesday and Saturday, 6.25 a.m.
" **Venice.**—Società Nazionale. Tuesday, 6.0 p.m.

TO BRINDISI—

from **Alexandria**—Società Nazionale. July 1st, 15th, and August 1st. **Austrian Lloyd.** Thursday, 3.0 p.m. and **Saturday**, 2.0 p.m. See p. 722.
" **Athens (Piræus).**—Austrian Lloyd. Sunday, 7.0 p.m. See p. 722.—Società Nazionale. Monday, 10.0 a.m. and Friday, 9.0 a.m.
" **Corfu and Patras.**—

Athens (rail) dep	Mon. 1 0p.m	Mon. 1 0p.m.	Tues. 1 0p.m.	Tues. 1 0p.m.	Thrs. 1 0p.m.	Fri. 7 5 a.m.
Patras	Mon. 10*0p.m	Mon. 11† 0p.m.	Tues. 9 ‡0p.m	Tues. 11†0p.m.	Thrs. 9 ‡0p.m.	Fri. 7*3 p.m.
Corfu	Tues. 2 0p.m.	Tues. 4 0p.m.	Wed. 4 0p.m	Wed. 2 30p.m	Fri. 4 0p.m.	———
Brindisi ......arr	Wed. 4 0a.m.	Wed. 3 0 a.m.	Thur. 4 0a.m.	Thrs. 2 30a.m.	Sat. 4 0a.m.	Sat. 3 30p.m.
Trieste.........arr	———	Thur. 1 0p.m.	———	Fri. 6 0p.m	———	———

*—Società Nazionale steamers. †—Austrian Lloyd, see page 722 ‡—Greek Steamer.

from **Port Said.**—**P. and O. Co.** See p. 726.—Società Nazionale. July 11th and 27th.
" **Trieste.**—Austrian Lloyd. Tuesday, 2.0 p.m. and Friday, 1.0 p.m. See p. 722.
" **Venice.**—Società Nazionale. Tuesday, 6.0 p.m.

TO CATANIA—

from **Alexandria.**—Società Nazionale. Thursday, 2.0 p.m.
" **Athens (Piræus).**—Società Nazionale. Sunday, 4.0 p.m.
" **Malta**—Adria Line. Monday and Wednesday, 6.0 p.m. See p. 731.
" **Naples.**—Adria Line. Monday, 2.0 p.m., and Thursday, 5.0 p.m. See p. 731.—Società Nazionale.—Navigazione dello Stato. ————.

TO CIVITA VECCHIA—

from **Golfo Aranci (Sardinia).**—Navigazione dello Stato. **Daily, 9.30 p.m.**

TO GENOA—

from **Alexandria.**—Società Nazionale. Thursday, 2.0 p.m.
" **Algiers.**—Norddeutscher Lloyd. July 6th, 12th, 20th, and August 3rd. See p. 721.—Nederland Royal Mail Line. See p. 729.
" **Amsterdam.**—Nederland Royal Mail Line. See p. 729.
" **Boston (U.S.)**—White Star Line. See p. 718.
" **Cagliari.**—Società Nazionale. Wednesday, 7.0 p.m.
" **Constantinople.**—Società Nazionale. Wednesday, 5.30 p.m
" **Leghorn.**—Società Nazionale.
" **Marseilles.**—Adria Line. **Sunday, 10.0 a.m. and Wednesday, 6.0 p.m. See p. 731.**
" **Naples.**—**Norddeutscher Lloyd. See p. 721.—Adria Line. Tuesday, 6.0 p.m. See p. 731.** Società Nazionale.
" **New York.**—**Norddeutscher Lloyd. See p. 721.**
" **Port Said.**—**Norddeutscher Lloyd. See p. 721.—Nederland Royal Mail Line. See p. 729.**
" **Southampton.**—**Norddeutscher Lloyd.** July 1st, 7th, 15th, 29th, and August 4th. **See p. 721.— Nederland Royal Mail Line. See p. 729.**
" **Tunis.**—**Società Nazionale. Tuesday, 4.0 p.m.**

ITALY—*Continued.*

TO LEGHORN—

from **Bastia.**—Società Nazionale. **Monday,** 10.0 a.m.
" **Genoa.**—Società Nazionale.
" **Naples.**—Società Nazionale. Monday, 4.0 p.m., Thursday, 3.0 a.m., and Saturday, 8.0 a.m.
" **Portoferraio** (Elba).—Navigazione Toscano.

Leghorn ......dep. Mon. and Fri.	8 0 a.m.	Wed. 10 0 a.m.	Portoferraio dep. Wed. and Sun.	8 0 a.m	Sat. 8 0 a.m.
Portoferraio arr. " " "	4 35 p.m	" 2 25 p.m.	Leghorn ......arr. " " "	4 45 p.m	" 12.25 p.m.

from **Porto Torres.**—Società Nazionale. Sunday, 5.0 p.m., and Wednesday, 8.0 a.m.

TO MESSINA—

from **Malta.**—Adria Line. See p. 731.—Società Nazionale. Saturday, 9.0 p.m.
" **Naples.**—Adria Line. See p. 731.—Società Nazionale.—Navigazione dello Stato. ————————.
" **Reggio.**—Navigazione dello Stato. ————————.

TO NAPLES—

from **Alexandria.**—Norddeutscher Lloyd. July 2nd and 16th, See p. 721.—Società Nazionale. Thursday, 2.0 p.m.
" **Algiers.**—Austro-Americana Steamers.
" **Barcelona.**—Austro-Americana Steamers.
" **Boston (U.S.)**—White Star Line. See p. 718.
" **Cagliari.**—Società Nazionale. Wednesday, 12.0 noon.
" **Capri.**—Compagnia Napoletana. Daily :—

Naples ....dep	4 0 p.m.	Capri ....dep	6 30 a.m.	Naples ....dep	9 0 a.m.
Vico	5 10 "	Massa	7 5 "	Sorrento ....arr	10 0 "
Eque	5 20 "	Sorrento	7 30 "	Capri ....arr	11 0 "
Meta	5 30 "	Piano Sorrento	7 45 "	Capri ....dep	4 0 p.m.
Piano Sorrento	5 40 "	Meta	7 55 "	Sorrento ....arr	4 40 "
Sorrento	5 55 "	Eque	8 5 "	Naples ....arr	6 0 "
Massa	6 15 "	Vico	8 25 "		
Capri ....arr	6 45 "	Naples ....arr	9 30 "		

from **Catania**—Adria Line. See p. 731.—Navigazione dello Stato. ————————. Società Nazionale.
" **Constantinople.**—Messageries Maritimes de France. See p. 730. Società Nazionale. Wednesday, 5.30 p.m.
" **Genoa.**—Norddeutscher Lloyd. See p. 721.—Adria Line. Tues. and Sat. 6.0 p.m. See p. 731.—Società Nazionale.
" **Hamburg.**—Deutsche Ost-Afrika Linie. July 14th and 29th. See p. 728.
" **Leghorn.**—Società Nazionale.
" **London.**—Orient Line. July 4th, 18th, and August 1st. See p. 725.
" **Malta.**—Adria Line. See p. 731.—Società Nazionale. Sat. 9 0 p.m.
" **Marseilles.**—Messageries Maritimes de France. July 10th and 24th. See p. 730.—Norddeutscher Lloyd. July 9th. See p. 721.—Adria Line. Sunday, 10.0 a.m. and Wednesday, 6.0 p.m. See p. 731.—Deutsche Ost-Afrika Linie. July 11th and 27th. See p. 728.
" **Messina.**—Adria Line. See p. 731.—Navigazione dello Stato. ————————. Società Nazionale.
" **Palermo.**—Società Nazionale. Thursday, 7.0 p.m.—Navigazione dello Stato. Daily, 8.30 p.m—Adria Line. Monday, 3.0 p.m. See p. 731.
" **Port Said.**—Orient Line. July 8th, 22nd, and August 5th. See p. 725.—Norddeutscher Lloyd. See p. 721.—Deutsche Ost-Afrika Linie. July 12th and 28th. See p. 728.—Società Nazionale.—British India Steam Navigation Co., Ltd.
" **Reggio**—Società Nazionale. Tuesday, 10.0 a.m.—Navigazione dello Stato. ————————.
" **Southampton.**—Norddeutscher Lloyd. July 1st, 7th, 15th, 29th, and August 4th. See p. 721.—Deutsche Ost-Afrika Linie. July 2nd, 18th, and August 2nd. See p. 728.
" **Toulon.**—Orient Line. July 10th and 24th. See p. 725.
" **Tunis.**—Società Nazionale. Wednesday, 9.0 p.m.

TO PALERMO—

from **Marseilles.**—Adria Line. See p. 731.
" **Naples.**—Navigazione dello Stato. Daily, 10.45 p.m.—Società Nazionale.—Adria Line. See p. 731.—Norddeutscher Lloyd. See p. 721.
" **Pantellaria.**—Società Nazionale. Monday, 8.0 a.m. From Palermo to Pantellaria, Thursday, 10.0 a.m.
" **Trieste.**—Austro Americana Steamers.
" **Tunis.**—Società Nazionale. Wednesday, 9.0 p.m., and Sunday, 8.0 p.m.
" **Ustica.**—Società "Sicania."

Palermo...dep. Sun. & Thurs. 1.0 a.m.	Tues. & Sat. 6.30 a.m.	Ustica...dep Sun. & Thurs	12 0 noon,	Tues. & Sat. 2.0 p.m.
Ustica.....arr. " " 4.40 a.m.	" " 10.10 a.m.	Palermo arr. " "	3.40 p.m.,	" " 5.40 p.m.

ITALY—*Continued.*

TO PIOMBINO.—Navigazione Toscano.

Piombino ....dep. 10 30 a.m.	4.30 p.m	Portoferraio..........dep. 8‡30 a.m.	12.30 p.m.	‡ Sunday
Portoferraio........arr. 12 0 noon	6. 0 p.m.	Piombino ....arr. 10.0 a.m.	2. 0 p.m.	6.30 a.m.

TO PORTO EMPEDOCLE—
from **Lampedusa** and **Linosa**, Tuesday. From Porto Empedocle to Linosa and Lampedusa, Thursday, 1.30 a.m. Società "Sicania".

TO RAVENNA—
from **Fiume.**—Hungarian State Railway Steamers. Thursday, 7.0 p.m.

TO REGGIO—from Malta.—Adria Line. See p. 731.—Società Nazionale.
from **Naples.**—Navigazione dello Stato. ————————.

TO SPEZIA—from Porto Torres, calling at Maddalena.—Società Nazionale. Wednesday, 8.0 a.m.

TO SYRACUSE—
from **Bengasi.**—Società Nazionale. Tuesday, 7.0 p.m. and Thursday 6.0 p.m.
" **Malta.**—Adria Line. Daily, Wednesday excepted, 3.0 a.m. See p. 731.—Società Nazionale. Saturday, 9.0 p.m..
" **Tripoli.**—Società Nazionale. Mon. & Thurs. 10.0 a.m.; also Fri. 11.0 a.m.

TO VENICE—
from **Alexandria.**—Società Nazionale. July 1st and 15th.
" **Ancona.**—Società Nazionale. Friday, 9.0 p.m.
" **Brindisi.**—Società Nazionale. Wednesday, 12.0 night.
" **Fiume.**—Hungarian State Railway Steamers. Monday, 7.45 a.m., Tuesday, Wednesday Thursday, Friday, and Saturday, 8.25 p.m.
" **Trieste.**—Austrian Lloyd. Tuesday, Thursday, and Saturday, 12.0 night, also Thursday, 2.0 p.m. See p. 722.

Venice (Riva Schiavoni) to **Chioggia.**—6.0, 8.0, 10.0 a.m., 12.0 noon, 2.0, 4.0, 6.0, and 8.0 p.m. Return 5.0, 7.0, 9.0. 11.0 a.m., 1.0, 3.0, 5.0, and 7.0 p.m.

Venice (Station) to **Lido.**—5.30, 7.0, 9.35, 11.0 a.m., 2.20, 7.0, 11.25 p.m. Return 3.25, 6.10, 7.45, 10.15 a.m., 1.10, 5.0, 10.0 p.m.

MADEIRA.

TO MADEIRA—
from **Cherbourg.**—The Royal Mail S.P. and P.S.N. Cos. July 4th, 11th, 18th, 25th, and August 1st. See p. 728.
" **Lisbon.**—Booth Line. See page 727.—The Royal Mail S.P. and P.S.N. Cos. July 8th, 14th, 21st, 29th, and August 4th. See p. 728.—Norddeutscher Lloyd. July 14th and 28th. See p. 722.
" **Liverpool.**—Booth Line. See p. 727.
" **London.**—The Royal Mail Steam Packet Co. See p. 728.
" **Southampton**—The Royal Mail Steam Packet and P.S.N. Cos. July 4th, 11th, 18th, 25th, and August 1st. See p. 728.—Union Castle Mail Steamship Co. Saturday.

Lisbon to Madeira, calling at the Azores.—Empresa Insulana de Navegacao. 5th of every month for St Michael's, Terceira, Graciosa, St. Jorge, Pico, Fayal, and Flores; 20th of every month for Madeira, St. Mary's, St. Michael's (in 4½ days), Terceira, and Fayal.

Lisbon to Madeira, St. Vincent (Cape de Verde), St. Iago (Cape de Verde), Principe, St. Thomas, Ambriz, Loanda, Benguella, Mossamedes.—Portuguese Steamers.—To Madeira the 1st and 7th, to Cape Verde the 7th and 22nd of each month.

MEDITERRANEAN ISLANDS.

TO BALEARIC ISLANDS.—"La Maritima" and "Islena Maritima" Companias. From Barcelona to **Port Mahon,** Tues. and Sat., 6.30 p.m., returning Sun. and Thurs., 5.0 p.m. **Barcelona** for **Alcudia, Ciudadela,** and **Mahon,** Thurs., 4.0 p.m., Returning from **Port Mahon** to **Barcelona** Tues. 9.0 a.m. **Barcelona** to **Palma,** Tues. and Fri., 10.0 p.m., Mon., Wed., and Sat., 6.30 p.m. **Alicante** to **Iviza** and **Palma,** Sun., 12.0 noon. **Valencia** to **Palma,** Thurs. 4.0 p.m. **Palma to Barcelona,** Sun. and Wed., 10.0 p.m., Mon., Thurs., and Sat., 6.30 p.m. **Palma to Iviza** and **Alicante,** Fri., noon. **Palma to Valencia,** Tues., 5.0 p.m.
from **Marseilles to Palma,** Wednesday, 8.0 a.m. **Palma to Marseilles,** Sunday, 9.0 a.m.

TO CORSICA—
from **Bona** to **Ajaccio.**—Cie. Gen. Transatlantique. Alternate Wednesday, 9.0 p.m. Also, calling at **Porto Torres,** alternate Wednesday, 11.0 p.m. See p. 729.
" **Leghorn** to **Bastia & Porto Torres.**—Società Nazionale. Thurs., 11.0 a.m.
" **Marseilles** to **Ajaccio and Bastia.**—French Steamer.
" **Nice** to **Ajaccio and Bastia.**—French Steamer.

TO CRETE—
from **Athens** (Piræus) to **Canea.**—Austrian Lloyd. Alternate Friday, 12.0 noon. See p. 722. Società Nazionale. Sunday, 4.0 p.m.
" **Trieste** to **Canea** and **Candia.**—Austrian Lloyd. Friday, 5.30 p.m. See p. 722.

MEDITERRANEAN ISLANDS—*Continued.*

TO CYPRUS (Larnaca)—

from **Alexandria.**—Khedivial Mail Steamship Co. Tuesday, 4.0 p.m. See page 724.
„ **Beyrout.**—**Messageries Maritimes de France.** July 22nd. See p. 730—**Società** Nazionale. Alternate Thursday, 12.0 night.
„ **Mersina.**—Austrian Lloyd. Wednesday, 2.30 p.m. See p. 722.
„ **Port Said.**—Khedivial Mail Steamship Co. Wednesday, 11.0 a.m. See page 724.

TO MALTA—

from **Alexandria.**—Moss Line. See p. 726—Papayanni and Ellerman Line.
„ **Fiume.**—Adria Line. July 1st, 15th, and 29th. See p. 731.
„ **Liverpool.**—Moss Line. See p. 726.—Papayanni and Ellerman Line.
„ **London.**—P. and O. Co. July 5th, 12th, 19th, and 26th. See p. 726.
„ **Marseilles.**—Cie. Generale Transatlantique. Monday, 12.0 noon. See p. 729.—Adria Line. See p. 731.
„ **Naples.**—Adria Line. Monday, 2.0 p.m. See p. 731.—Società Nazionale. Sunday, 4.30 p.m.
„ **Port Said.**—Peninsular and Oriental Co. See p. 726.
„ **Reggio.**—Società Nazionale. Tuesday, 9.30 a.m.
„ **Syracuse** (9 hours).—Adria Line. Daily, Wednesday excepted, 3.0 p.m. See p. 731.—Società Nazionale. Wednesday, 12.0 night.
„ **Tripoli (Africa).**—Società Nazionale. Friday, 11.0 a.m.
„ **Tunis.**—Compagnie Générale Transatlantique. Wednesday, 3.0 p.m. See p. 729.

TO RHODES—

from **Smyrna.**—Messageries Maritimes de France. July 4th and August 1st. See p. 730.—Khedivial Mail Steamship Co. Alternate Monday, 5.0 p.m. See p. 724.

TO SARDINIA—

from **Civita Vecchia to Golfo Aranci.**—Navigazione dello Stato. Daily, 8.0 p.m.
„ **Naples to Cagliari.**—Società Nazionale. Saturday, 10.0 a.m.
„ **Palermo to Cagliari.**—Società Nazionale. Saturday, 10.0 a.m.
„ **Tunis to Cagliari.**—Società Nazionale. Tuesday, 4.0 p.m.

MOROCCO.

TO CASABLANCA, MAZAGAN, and SAFFI—

from **Gibraltar.**—The Royal Mail Steam Packet Co. July 1st. See p. 728.—Paquet et Cie. See p. 730.—Adria Line. July 12th and 26th. See p. 731.
„ **London.**—The Royal Mail Steam Packet Co. ———— See p. 728.
„ **Marseilles.**—Paquet et Cie. See p. 730.
„ **Tangier.**—The Royal Mail Steam Packet Co. See p. 728 —Paquet et Cie. See p. 730.—Adria Line. July 13th and 27th. See p. 731.

TO CEUTA—Daily between **Ceuta, Gibraltar, and Tangier.**

from **Algeciras.**—Daily; also Sun. and Wed., 3.0 p.m. in connection with the "Morocco Express."

TO MOGADOR—

from **Gibraltar.**—Paquet et Cie. See p. 730 —The Royal Mail Steam Packet Co. July 1st. See p. 728.—Adria Line. July 12th and 26th. See p. 731.
„ **London.**—The Royal Mail Steam Packet Co. ———— See p. 728.
„ **Marseilles.**—Paquet et Cie. See p. 730.
„ **Tangier.**—Paquet et Cie. See p. 730.—The Royal Mail Steam Packet Co. July 2nd. See p. 728.—Adria Line. July 13th and 27th. See p. 731.

TO TANGIER—

from **Algeciras.**—Daily (Monday and Tuesday excepted), 7.0 a.m.; also Sunday and Wednesday, 3.0 p.m.
„ **Algiers.**—Adria Line. See p. 731.—Nederland Royal Mail Line. See p. 729.
„ **Amsterdam.**—Nederland Royal Mail Line. See p. 729.
„ **Cadiz.**—Daily (Sunday and Thursday excepted), 7.0 a.m.
„ **Fiume.**—Adria Line. July 1st, 15th, and 29th. See p. 731.
„ **Gibraltar** (2¼ hrs.)—Almost daily.—Compagnie de Navigation Mixte. See p. 730.—The Royal Mail Steam Packet Co. See p. 728.—Paquet et Cie. See p. 730.
„ **Hamburg.**—Deutsche Ost-Afrika Linie. July 14th and 29th. See p. 728.
„ **Liverpool.**—Papayanni-Ellerman Line. About weekly.
„ **London.**—The Royal Mail Steam Packet Co. ———— See p. 728.
„ **Marseilles.**—Paquet et Cie. See p. 730.—Cie de Navigation Mixte. Wednesday, 6.0 p.m. See p. 730.—Deutsche Ost-Afrika Linie. July 6th, 20th, and August 5th. See p. 728.
„ **Oran.**—Cie de Navigation Mixte. Saturday, 12.0 night. See p. 730.—Adria Line. July 11th and 25th. See p. 731.
„ **Rotterdam.**—Rotterdam Lloyd Royal Mail Line.—Fortnightly. See p. 727A.—Deutsche Ost-Afrika Linie. July 17th. See p. 728.
„ **Southampton.**—Deutsche Ost-Afrika Linie. July 2nd, 18th, and August 2nd. See p. 728.—Nederland Royal Mail Line. See p. 729.—Rotterdam Lloyd Royal Mail Line. Fortnightly. See p. 727A.
„ **Tunis.**—Adria Line. July 7th, 21st, and August 4th. See p. 731.

NORWAY.

TO AALESUND—
from **Hull.**—Wilson Line. Thursday. See p. 736.
" **Newcastle, via Bergen** (58 hours).—B. & N. Line. Tues., Thurs., & Sat., 12.0 night.

TO BERGEN—
from **Christiania via Christiansand** (54 hours).—"Kong Sverre," "Arendal" &c. Daily, 11.0 p.m.—Bergenske Co. Almost daily.
" **Copenhagen.**—"Thyra," etc., Wednesday, 8.0 a.m.
" **Drontheim.**—Bergenske and Nordenfjeldske Cos. Daily.
" **Hamburg.**—(calling at **Christiansand** and **Stavanger**)—Bergenske and Nordenfjeldske Cos. Tuesday and Thursday, 9.0 p.m, Saturday, 12.0 night. Fares, 50 and 33 m.
" **Hull.**—Wilson Line. Every Thursday. See p. 736.
" **Newcastle.**—B. & N. Line. Via **Stavanger** (36 hours).—Tues., Thurs., & Sat. 12.0 night.
" **Stavanger.**—Wilson Line. Saturday. See p. 736.—Bergenske Co. Almost daily.

TO CHRISTIANIA—
from **Bergen, via Christiansand** (51 hours).—Bergenske and Nordenfjeldske Cos. Almost daily.—"Kong Sverre," etc., daily, 7.0 p.m.
" **Christiansand.**—Bergenske and Nordenfjeldske Cos. Sunday, Monday, Tuesday, and Wednesday. "Kong Sverre" (calling at **Arendal** and **Larvik**), etc.. daily, 2.0 a.m.
" **Copenhagen.**—"Melchior," Sunday, 8.0 p.m. and (until 13th August) Wednesday, 8.0 a.m. "Kong Haakon," "Dronning Maud," Monday and Thursday, 12.0 noon.
" **Frederikshavn.**—"Melchior," Monday and Thursday, 9 30 a.m.
" **Gothenburg.**—"Sodra Sverige," or "Birger Jarl." Saturday, 6.0 p.m. "Göteborg,' etc. Sunday and Wednesday, 7.45 a.m.
" **Grangemouth.**—"Norway" or "Scotland," every Wednesday calling at **Christiansand** and **Arendal.**
" **Grimsby.**—Wilson Line. July 9th and 23rd. See p. 736.
" **Hamburg**, calling at **Christiansand.**—Sondenfj.-Norske Co. or Jelö Line. Fares, 40, 25, and 15 kr. Wednesday and Saturday.—"Courier," "Elben," Friday.
" **Hull.**—Wilson Line. Saturday, 6.30 p.m. and alternate Wednesday. See p. 736.
" **Newcastle** (Tyne Dock), calling at **Arendal.**—"Bessheim" and "Sterling." **Every Friday.**
" **Stettin.**—"Kong Haakon" and "Dronning Maud." Sunday and Wednesday, 4.0 a.m.

TO CHRISTIANSAND—
from **Frederikshavn** (11 hours).—Mail Steamer. Daily, 9.45 a.m.
" **Grimsby.**—Wilson Line. July 9th and 23rd. See p. 736.
" **Hull.**—Wilson Line. Saturday, 6.30 p.m. and alternate Wednesday. See p. 736.
" **Leith.**—Leith, Hull, and Hamburg Co. **Every Thursday.** See p. 727.

TO CHRISTIANSSUND—
from **Hull.**—Wilson Line. Thursday. See p. 736.
" **Newcastle, via Bergen** (65 hours).—B. & N. Line. Tues., Thurs., & Sat., 12.0 night.

TO DRONTHEIM (Trondhjem)—
from **Bergen.**—Bergenske and Nordenfjeldske Cos. Daily.
" **Hull.**—Wilson Line. Every Thursday. See p. 736.
" **Newcastle, via Bergen** (72 hours).—B. & N. Line. Tues., Thurs., & Sat., 12.0 night.
" **Tromsö.**—Bergenske and Nordenfjeldske Cos. Daily.

TO MOLDE—
from **Newcastle, via Bergen** (62 hours).—B. & N. Line. Tues., Thurs., & Sat., 12.0 night.

TO NORTH CAPE—
from **Drontheim.**—Tourist steamer "Kong Harald" or "Vega" 9.0 p.m. every Tuesday and Thursday, until 24th July.

TO STAVANGER—
from **Hull.**—Wilson Line. **Every Thursday.** See p. 736.
" **Newcastle.**—(26 hours).—B. & N. Line. **Tuesday, Thursday, and Saturday.** 12.0 night.

Trondhjem to Norway Coast Ports.—Bergenske and Nordenfjeldske Co.'s Steamers :—

	EXPRESS BOATS.				
Bergen ......dep	Mon., Wed., Fri.................10 0 p.m.	Mon. 11 0 p.m.	Tues. 10 0 p.m.	Thurs. 11 0 p.m.	Sat. ...10 0 p.m.
Molde..............	Tues., Thurs., Sat. .... 3 30 p.m.	Tues....9 0 p.m.	—	Fri. ...10 0 p.m.	Sun.... 6 0 p.m.
Trondhjem arr	Wed., Fri, Sun. .... 5 0 a.m.	Wed. 12 0 n'on	Thurs. 12 0noon	Sat. ... 4 0 p.m.	Mon....10 0 a.m.
" ...dep	Wed., Fri., Sun. .... 9 0 a.m.	Thurs 12 0 n'on	Sat. ...12 0n'on	Tues. 12 0n'on	Tues... 9 0 a.m.
Bodo	Thurs., Sat., Mon. .... 1 30 p.m.	Sun. 1 0 a.m.	Tues... 2 0 p.m.	Thurs. 4 0 p.m.	Wed... 1 30 p.m.
Narvik ... arr	—	Sun.....8 0 p.m.	—	Friday 9 0 a.m.	—
Tromso	Fri., Sun., Tues. 12 0noon	Tues...12 0n'on	Thurs. 12 0n'gt.	Sat. ...12 0n'gt.	Thurs. 11 0 a.m.
Hammerfest arr	Fri., Sun., Tues. ....11 30 p.m.	Wed. morn	Fri. ...12 0 n'on	Sun. afternoon	Thurs. 11 30 p.m.
" dep	Sat., Mon., Wed. .... 2 0 a.m.	—	Fri. ...12 0 n'gt.	Sun. ...12 0n'gt.	—
Vardo..............	Sat., Mon., Wed................ 9 0 p.m.	—	Sun. ... 8 0 a.m.	Tues...12 0n'gt.	—
Vadso ....arr	Sun., Tues., Thurs.............. 3 0 a.m.	—	Sunday morn.	Wed.... 4 0 a.m.	—

PORTUGAL.

TO LISBON—

from **Amsterdam.**—Nederland Royal Mail Line. See p. 729.—Royal Holland Lloyd. See p. 725.
" **Boulogne.**—Royal Holland Lloyd. See p. 725.—Norddeutscher Lloyd. See p. 721.
" **Dover.**—Royal Holland Lloyd. See p. 725.
" **Hamburg.**—Deutsche Ost-Afrika Linie. July 14th and 29th. **See p. 728.**
" **Havre.**—Booth Line. See p. 727.
" **Liverpool.**—Booth Line. See p. 727.—R.M.S.P. and **Pacific Steam Navigation Cos.** July 4th, 10th, 18th, 24th and August 1st. See p. 728.—Lamport and Holt Line. See p. 727A.
" **Rotterdam.**—Rotterdam Lloyd Royal Mail Line.—Fortnightly. See p. 727A.
" **Southampton.**—The Royal Mail Steam Packet and P. S. N. Cos. July 4th, 11th, 18th, 25th, and August 1st. See p 728.—Deutsche Ost-Afrika Linie. July 2nd, 18th, & Aug. 2nd. See p. 728.—Nederland Royal Mail Line. See p. 729.—Rotterdam Lloyd Royal Mail Line.—Fortnightly. See p. 727A.—Lamport and Holt Line. See p. 727A.

TO OPORTO—

from **Liverpool.**—Booth Line. See p. 727.—R.M.S.P. and **Pacific Steam Navigation Cos.** See p. 728.
" **London** (4 days).—" Douro" and "Tagus." Coverley and Westray.
" **Southampton.**—The Royal Mail Steam Packet and P. S. N. Cos. See p. 728.

RUMANIA.

TO CONSTANZA (Kustendje)—

from **Alexandria**—Rumanian State Line. Friday, 4.0 p.m. See p. 723.
" **Athens (Piræus)**—Rumanian State Line. Sunday, 3.0 p.m. **See p. 723.**
" **Constantinople.**—Rumanian State Railway Steamers. See p. 723.

Constantinople dep. Tues., Thurs., and Sat., 2.30 p.m.
Constanza ......arr. Wed., Fri., and Sun., 5.0 a.m.

Austrian Lloyd. Friday or Saturday, 4.0 p.m. See p. 722.—Società Nazionale. Wednesday, 12.0 night.
" **Odessa.**—Austrian Lloyd. Alternate Monday, 1.0 p.m.
" **Smyrna**—Rumanian State Line. ———— See p. 723.

RUSSIA.

TO ABO—

from **Copenhagen.**—Finland Steamship Co. Tuesday, 12.0 noon.
" **Hull.**—Finland Line, John Good and Sons, Ltd., Agents. Every Saturday. **See p. 734.**
" **Stockholm.**—"Bore," and "Oihonna." Daily, 7.30 p.m. See p. 734.

AZOV (SEA OF) SERVICE.—Russian Steam Nav. Co.—**Kertch to Berdiansk, Mariupol, Taganrog, and Rostov.**

TO BATOUM—

from **Constantinople.**—(calling at **Armenian Ports.**)—Paquet et Cie. July 1st, 15th, and 29th. See p. 730.—**Austrian Lloyd. Saturday, 2.0 p.m. See p. 722.—Russian Steam** Nav. Co. Friday, 2.0 p.m.—Cie des Messageries Maritimes. See p. 730.
" **Marseilles.**—Paquet et Cie. July 9th and 23rd. **See p. 730.**—Cie des Messageries Maritimes. See p. 730.

BLACK SEA—[Service liable to modification].

Odessa ......dep	Mon. 4 0p.m.	Tues., Sun. 12 0noon	Thurs , Sat. 7 0p.m.	
Sebastopol...dep	Tues. 2 30p.m.	Wed., Mon. 2 30 p.m.	Fri., Sun. 2 30p.m.	—
Yalta ....arr	Tues. 10 0p.m.	Wed., Mon. even.	Fri., Sun. 11 0p.m.	—
Feodosia......dep	Wed 7 0a.m.	Thur.,Tues. 10 0a.m.	Sat , Mon. 8 0a.m.	—
Kertsch ......arr	— —	Thur.,Tues. 12 0n'gt	Sat., Mon. 6 0p.m.	—
Novorossisk arr	Wed. 5 0p.m.	Fri., Wed. 9 0 a.m.	Sun., Tues. 5 0a.m.	—
Poti ....dep	— —	Sun., Fri. 4 0 p.m.	Mon., Wed. 5 30p.m.	—
Batoum ......arr	Fri. 5 0a.m.	Sun., Fri. 8 0 p.m.	Mon., Wed. 8 30p.m.	—
Batoum ......dep	Sat. 12 0n'gt	Mon., Sat. 2 0p.m.	Tues., Thur.12 0n'gt	—
Poti	— —	Mon., Sat. 8 0p.m.	Wed., Fri. 7 0a.m.	—
Novorossisk ...	Mon. 1 0p.m	Wed., Mon. —	Thurs., Sat. 9 0p.m.	—
Kertsch............	— —	Thurs., Tues. morn.	Fri., Sun. 1 0p.m.	—
Feodosia	Tues. 1 0a.m.	Thurs., Tues. even.	Fri., Sun. 11 0p.m.	—
Yalta	Tues. 10 0a.m.	Fri., Wed. 9 0a.m.	Sat., Mon. 10 0a.m.	—
Sebastopol	Tues. 5 0p.m.	Fri., Wed. 5 0 p.m.	Sat., Mon. 5 0p.m.	—
Odessa	Wed. 8 0a.m.	Sat.. Thurs. 12 0noon	Sun., Tues. 11 0a.m.	—

CASPIAN SEA.

Astrakan ......dep	9 0 a.m	—	—	Enzeli ...dep	—		Sun. & Thurs., 5.0 p.m.	—
Petrovsk	2 0 p.m	—	—					
Derbent	—	—	—	Astara	—		—,	Sat. 11 0 a.m.
Baku ....dep	4 0 p.m.	Mon. & Thurs. 6 30 p.m.	Tues. & Fri., 6 30 p.m.	Lenkoran ...	—		—	Thurs. & Sun. 8 0a.m.
Lenkoran	—	Tues. and Fri. 9 30 a.m.	—	Baku ......arr	12 30p.m.	Wed. excepted.	Mon. & Fri., 11.0 a.m.	Wed. and Sat. 5 0p.m.
Astara	—	Fri.... 1 0 p.m.	—	Derbent	—		—	—
Enzeli (Reshd)arr	—	—	Wed. & Sat., 12.30 p.m.	Petrovsk	5 0p.m.		—	—
				Astrakan arr	9 0p.m.		—	—

Teheran (about 200 miles from Reshd).

RUSSIA—*Continued.*

CASPIAN SEA—*Continued.*

Meschedesser ....depart	Thursday, 3.0 p.m.	Astrakan ....depart	Friday, 9 0 a.m.
Krasnovodsk ....arrive	Saturday, 2.45 p.m.	Alexandrovsk ....depart	Saturday, 2.0 p.m.
Alexandrovsk ....arrive	Tuesday, 3.0 p.m.	Krasnovodsk ....depart	Tuesday, 12.0 noon.
Astrakan ....arrive	Wednesday, 9.0 p.m.	Meschedesser ....arrive	Thursday, 9.0 a.m.

Baku ....depart Krasnovodsk ....arrive	8 15 p.m. 11 45 a.m. } daily.	Krasnovodsk ....depart Baku ....arrive	3 15 p.m. 6 45 a.m. } daily.

TO HANGO—

from **Hull.**—Finland Line, John Good and Sons, Ltd., Agents. See p. 734.
" **Stockholm.**—Finland Steamship Co. Tuesday, Wednesday and Thursday, 6.0 p.m.

TO HELSINGFORS—

from **Copenhagen.**—Finland Steamship Co., Saturday, 12.0 noon.
" **Hull.**—Finland Line, John Good and Sons, Ltd., Agents. Wednesday. See p. 734.
" **Stettin.**—Finland Steamship Co. Wednesday, 1.0 p.m.
" **Stockholm**—Finland Steamship Co. Tuesday, Wednesday, Thursday and Saturday, 6.0 p.m.

TO LIBAU—

from **Hull.**—Wilson Line. Weekly. See p. 736.
" **Lubeck.**—Fortnightly during the season.
" **Stettin** (28 hours).—"Curonia." July 5th, 19th, and August 2nd.

TO ODESSA—(see also under "Black Sea").

from **Constantinople.**—Messageries Maritimes de France Cie. July 7th, 21st, and August 4th. See p. 730.—Russian Steam Navigation Co. Monday, 10.0 a.m., and Thursday. or Saturday, 4.0 p.m.—Austrian Lloyd. Saturday, 4.0 p.m. See p. 722.—Società Nazionale. Friday, 5.0 p.m.
" **Kherson.**— {Odessa.........dep / Kherson ....arr} Daily. | Kherson......dep / Odessa.........arr} Daily.
" **Nikolaiev.**—Russian Steam Navigation Co.

TO RIGA—

from **Hull.**—Wilson Line. Friday. See p. 736.
" **Lubeck** (50 hours).—"Alexandra," etc., during season. Saturday, 10.30 a.m.
" **Stettin** (45 hours)—"Ostsee" or "Sedina," Saturday, (during the season).

TO ST. PETERSBURG—

from **Hull** (4½ days).—Wilson Line. Every Monday, during the season. See p. 736.—Via Finland, John Good and Sons, Ltd. Every Wednesday and Saturday. See p. 734.
" **London** (Millwall Dock).—Via the Kiel Canal, every Friday (in winter to Riga). The United Shipping Co., Ltd. See p. 723.
" **Lubeck.**—Hanseatic Co. Wednesday and Saturday during the season.
" **Stettin** (60 hours).—Wednesday and Saturday, 2.0 p.m.
" **Stockholm.**—

Stockholm dep	Tues, Wed., Thurs., and Sat., 6.0 p.m	St. Petersburg dep.	Mon., Wed., Friday, 4.0 p.m. Saturday, 6.0 p.m.
Hangö ......arr	Wednesday, Thursday, and Friday, 11.0 a.m.	Helsingfors dep	Tuesday, Thursday, Saturday, and Sunday, 11.30 a.m.
Helsingfors dep	Wed., Thurs., Fri. 10.0 p.m., and Sunday, 8.0 p.m.	Hangö ......dep	Tuesday, Thursday, Saturday, and Sunday, 6 0 p.m.
St. Petersburg arr	Thurs., Fri., Sat., & Mon., 12.0 noon.	Stockholm arr.	Wednesday, Friday, Sunday, and Monday morn.

" —(via Abo and Helsingfors)—"Bore," etc., Daily, 7.30 p.m. See p. 734.

TO TREBIZOND—

from **Batoum.**—Messageries Maritimes de France Cie. July 9th and 23rd. See p. 730.—Austrian Lloyd. Friday, 12.0 night. See p. 722.—Paquet et Cie. July 3rd, 17th, and 31st. See p. 730.—Russian Steam Navigation Co. Thursday or Friday, 10.0 p.m.—Società Nazionale. Alternate Wednesday, 6.0 p.m.
" **Constantinople.**—(calling at Ineboli, Samsoun, or Kerasund).—Paquet et Cie. See p. 730.—Austrian Lloyd. Saturday, 2.0 p.m. See p. 722—Messageries Maritimes de France Cie. See p. 730.—Russian Steam Navigation Co. Friday, 2.0 p.m.

SPAIN.

TO ALGECIRAS—

from **Ceuta.**—Daily; also Monday and Thursday, 12.0 noon, in connection with the "Morocco Express."
" **Gibraltar** (25 min.).—5.50, 8.10 a.m., and (Sun., Mon., and Thurs. excepted) 2.50 p.m., also Mon. and Thurs., 2.20 p.m. in connection with the "Morocco Express." Fares, 1st cl. 1 p. 50 c., 2nd cl., 1 p.
" **Tangier.**—Daily (Sunday and Monday excepted), 1.0 p.m., also Monday and Thursday, 11.0 a.m., in connection with the "Morocco Express."

TO ALMERIA—

from **Trieste.**—Austro-Americana Steamers.

TO BARCELONA—

from **Fiume.**—Adria Line. See p. 731.
" **Genoa.**—Adria Line. See p. 731.
" **Las Palmas.**—Austro-Americana Steamers.
" **Marseilles.**—Adria Line. See p. 731.
" **Naples.**—Adria Line. See p. 731.—Austro-Americana Steamers.

TO CADIZ—

from **Alicante.**—Compania Trasatlantica. See p. 729.
" **Barcelona.**—Compañia Trasatlantica. See p. 729.
" **Canary Islands (Las Palmas and Teneriffe).**—Compania Trasatlantica. See p. 729.
" **Valencia.**—Compania Trasatlantica. See p. 729.

TO CARTAGENA—

from **Oran.**—Compagnie Générale Transatlantique. Monday, 11.0 p.m. See p. 729.

TO CORUNNA—

from **Amsterdam and Dover.**—Royal Holland Lloyd. See p. 725.
" **Boulogne.**—Norddeutscher Lloyd. See p. 721.—Royal Holland Lloyd. See p. 725.
" **Liverpool.**—R.M.S.P. and Pacific Steam Navigation Cos. July 4th, 10th, 18th, 24th, and August 1st. See p. 728.
" **Southampton.**—The Royal Mail Steam Packet & P.S.N. Cos. ———— See p. 728.

TO GIBRALTAR—

from **Algeciras.**—11.30 a.m. (Sunday, Monday, and Wednesday excepted), 6.0, and 10.30 p.m. also Sunday and Wednesday, 2.5 p.m., in connection with the "Morocco Express."
" **Algiers.**—Adria Line. July 9th and 23rd. See page 731.—Norddeutscher Lloyd. See page 721.
" **Liverpool.**—Moss Line. See p. 726.
" **London.**—Peninsular and Oriental Co. Weekly. See p. 726.—Orient Line. July 4th, 18th, and August 1st. See p. 725.—The Royal Mail Steam Packet Co. —— See p. 728.
" **Malta.**—Adria Line. July 5th, 19th, and August 2nd. See p. 731.
" **Marseilles.**—Cie de Navigation Mixte. Alternate Wednesday, 6.0 p.m. See p. 730.
" **Oran.**—Adria Line. July 11th and 25th. See p. 731.—Compagnie de Navigation Mixte. See p. 730.
" **Rotterdam.**—Rotterdam Lloyd Royal Mail Line. Fortnightly. See p. 727A.
" **Southampton.**—Rotterdam Lloyd Royal Mail Line. Fortnightly. See p. 727A.
" **Tangier** (2 hrs.)—Almost daily.—Adria Line. See p. 731.

TO MALAGA—

from **Gibraltar.**—Adria Line. July 9th and 23rd. See p. 731.
" **Tangier.**—Adria Line. July 8th, 22nd, and August 5th. See p. 731.

TO VALENCIA—

from **Fiume.**—Adria Line. Saturday, 8.0 p.m. See p. 731.
" **Marseilles.**—Adria Line. Saturday, 8.0 p.m. See p. 731.
" **Naples.**—Adria Line. Tuesday, 6.0 p.m. See p. 731.

TO VIGO—

from **Amsterdam and Dover.**—Royal Holland Lloyd, See p. 725.
" **Boulogne.**—Norddeutscher Lloyd. See p. 721.—Royal Holland Lloyd. See p. 725.
" **Liverpool.**—Booth Line. See p. 727.—R.M.S.P. and Pacific Steam Navigation Cos. July 4th, 10th, 18th, 24th, & Aug. 1st. See p. 728.—Lamport & Holt Line. See p. 727A.
" **Southampton.**—R. M. S. P. and P. S. N. Cos. July 4th, 11th, 18th, 25th, & August 1st. See p. 728.—Lamport and Holt Line. See p. 727A.

SWEDEN.

TO GOTHENBURG—

from **Christiania.**—"Göteborg," &c., Wednesday and Saturday, 12.0 noon. "Birger Jarl," etc., Tuesday, 4.0 p.m.
" **Copenhagen.**—"Odin," &c. Wednesday and Saturday, 6.0 p.m. Swedish Mail Steamers (26½ hrs.) Three or four times weekly. Fares, 12 kr. 50 öre, and 7 kr. 75 öre.
" **Frederikshavn.**—"Oluf Bager," or "Fiona," daily, 10.50 a.m.
" **Granton.**—Thule Steamship Co. See p. 733.

SWEDEN—*Continued.*

TO GOTHENBURG—*Continued.*

from **Grimsby** (35 hours).—Wilson Line. Every Saturday. See p. 736.
" **Hamburg** (40 hours).—"Svenska Lloyd." Tuesday and Friday.
" **Harwich.**—The British and Northern Shipping Agency, Ltd. (In Summer only). See p. 733.
" **Hull** (35 hours).—Wilson Line. Thursday, 6.30 p.m. See p. 736.
" **London (Tilbury).**—The British and Northern Shipping Agency, Ltd. See p. 733.
" **Lubeck.**—Swedish Mail Steamers. Three or four times weekly.
" **Stettin.**—"Odin," "Ydun," Tuesday and Friday, 4.0 a.m.
" **Stockholm.**—Through the Götha and Trolhatta Canals. Sun., Tues., Wed., Fri., and Sat., 10.0 a.m. Fares: 35 kr., 20 kr., 12 kr.: and 8 kr.; return ticket at 20 per cent. reduction.—*Via* **Calmar** and **Malmö.**—"Kolga" &c., Monday, 2.0 p.m. "Birger Jarl," &c., Wednesday, 12.0 noon. "Hyperion," &c., Thursday and Saturday, 4.0 p.m.

TO HELSINGBORG—

from **Copenhagen** (2 hours).—Daily, 4.0 p.m, also (until 31st August) 8.30 p.m.
" **Elsinore.**—Daily, 8.0, 10.30 a.m, 12.2, 2.1 (Sunday, 1.46 p.m.), 3.15, 6.26, 7.55, 10.20, and 11.39 p.m., in 20 mins.

TO MALMO—

from **Grimsby.**—Wilson Line. Tuesday. See p. 736.
" **Lübeck.**—Hallandsche Steamers. Daily, 6.35 p.m.

TO SLITE (Gothland)—

from **Hull.**—John Good & Sons, Ltd. Saturday. See p. 734.

TO STOCKHOLM—

from **Abo.**—"Bore" and "Oihonna." Daily, 8.20 p.m. See p. 734.
" **Gothenburg.**—**Via Götha Canal.** Mon., Tues., Wed., Fri., and Sat., 12.0 noon. Fares: 35 kr., 20 kr., 12 kr., and 8 kr.; 20 per cent. reduction for return ticket.—**Via Malmö** and **Calmar.**—"Kolga," etc., Mon., Wed., Thurs., and Sat., 6.0 p.m.
" **Hangö.**—Finland Steamship Co. Sun., Tues., Thurs., and Sat., 6.0 p.m.
" **Helsingfors.**—Finland Steamship Co. Sun., Tues., Thurs., and Sat., 11.30 a.m.
" **Hull.**—(Via Copenhagen), John Good & Sons, Ltd. Every Wed. and Sat. See p. 734.
" **Jönköping.**—Through the **Götha Canal.** Tues., Thurs., and Sat., 11.0 p.m.
" **London** (via Harwich and Gothenburg).—British and Northern Shipping Agency, Ltd. See p. 733.
" **Lubeck.**—The "Gauthiod," "Swithiod," etc. See p. 734.

TO TRELLEBORG—

from **Sassnitz.**—Prussian and Swedish State Rlys. Ferries. 2.17 a.m. and 4.56 p.m.

Stockholm and Gulf of Bothnia.—To Sundsvall, Umea, Pitea, Lulea, and Haparanda, The "Lulea," "Njord," "Pitea," "Norra Sverige," etc. Fares to Lulea, 20 kr. and 15 kr., to Haparanda, 26 kr. and 21 kr. Return tickets 10 per cent. reduction.

TO VISBY—

from **Kalmar and Vestervik.**—Service almost daily.
" **Nynäshamn.**—Daily, 11.0 p.m. (connecting with the 9.22 p.m. from Stockholm Central Station).
" **Stockholm.**—"Hansa." Daily.

TRIPOLI.

TO BENGASI.—

from **Syracuse.**—Società Nazionale. Sunday, 12.0 night, and Friday, 6.0 p.m.

TO TRIPOLI (Africa)—

from **Bengasi.**—Società Nazionale. Tuesday, 4.0 a.m.
" **Malta.**—Società Nazionale. Friday, 9.0 a.m.
" **Syracuse**—Societá Nazionale. Tuesday and Saturday, 5.0 p.m., also Wednesday, 12.0 night.
" **Tunis.**—(calling at coast ports).—Società Nazionale. Saturday, 5.0 p.m.—Compagnie de Navigation Mixte. Friday, 7.0 p.m. See p. 730.

TUNIS.

TO BIZERTA—

from **Marseilles.**—Cie. Générale Transatlantique. Friday, 12.0 noon. See p. 729.

TO TUNIS—

from **Cagliari.**—Società Nazionale. Thursday, 7.0 p.m.
" **Genoa.**—Società Nazionale. Monday, 12.0 night.
" **Malta.**—Adria Line. July 5th, 19th, and August 2nd. See p. 731.
" **Marseilles.**—

Marseilles dep	Mon. † noon.	Wed.*12 0 n'n	Thurs. 4 †0 p.m.	Fri. 12 †0 noon.	Sat.* 12 0 n n
Tunis ......arr	Tues. 7 30p.m.	Fri. 3 15a.m.	Sat. 5 0 a.m.	Sun. 5 0 a.m.	Mon. morn.
Sfax.........arr	—— ——	Sun. 8 30a.m.	—— ——	Alt. Mon. 12 0 noon	—— ——
Susa.........arr	—— ——	Sat. 7 30a.m.	—— ——	Alt. Tues. 5 0 a.m.	—— ——
Malta.....arr	Thurs. 9 0a.m.	—— ——	—— ——	—— ——	—— ——

†—Cie Générale Transatlantique, see page 729. *—Cie. de Navigation Mixte see page 730.

TUNIS—*Continued.*

from **Naples.**—Società Nazionale. Monday, 7.0 p.m.

" **Palermo.**—Societa Nazionale. Tuesday, 1.0 p.m. and Thursday, 10.0 a.m.

" **Tripoli (Africa)**—(calling at coast ports).—Compagnie de Navigation Mixte. Tuesday, 4.0 p.m. See p. 730.—Società Nazionale. Friday, 4.0 p.m.

TURKEY (including ASIA MINOR and SYRIA).

TO BEYROUT—

from **Alexandria.**—

	M	A	K	R	N
Alexandria ...dep	Wednesday	Monday 5 0p.m.	Saturday 4 0 p.m.	Fri. 4.0 p.m.	Wed.12 0noon.
Port Said ...... "	Alternate Fri.	Tuesday 6 0p.m.	Sunday 5 0 p.m.	Sat.	——
Jaffa .... arr	Alternate Sat.	Friday 0a.m.	Monday 7 0 a.m.	Sun. 7.0 a.m.	——
Haifa .... "	——	Saturday 1 30a.m.	Monday 6 0 p.m.	Mon. morn.	——
Beyrout......... "	Friday or Sun.	Wednesday 3 0p.m.	Tuesday 6 0 a.m.	Mon. 4.0p.m.	Thur. 3 0p.m.
Tripoli (Syria) "	——	Sunday 4 0p.m.	Tues. 4.0p.m.or Wd.2.0p.m.	Wed. morn.	Sat. or Sun.
Alexandretta "	——	Alternate Mon. 6 0a.m.	Wed. or Friday morn.	Thurs. morn.	——

	M	A	K	R	N
Alexandretta dep	——	Alternate Thurs. 5 0p.m.	Friday 4 0p.m.	Sun.	——
Tripoli (Syria) "	——	Friday 1 0p.m.	Sat. 10 0 a.m.	Mon. morn.	Sun. 10 0a.m.
Beyrout......... "	Monday or Wed.	Monday 5 0p.m.	Sun. 10 0 a.m.	Tues. 10.0 a.m.	Mon. 10 0a.m.
Haifa .... "	——	Saturday 11 30p.m.	Sun. 10 0p.m.	Tues.	——
Jaffa .... "	Alternate Tuesday	Sunday 6 0p.m.	Mon. 4 0p.m.	Wed. 5.0 p.m.	——
Port Said ...... "	Alternate Wed.	Wednesday 4 0p.m.	Tues. 3 0p.m.	Thurs.	——
Alexandria ...arr	Thursday	Thursday 7 0a.m.	Wed. 7 0 a.m.	Fri. 8.0 a.m.	Tues. 2 0p.m.

M—Messageries Maritimes de France. Weekly. See page 730. A—Austrian Lloyd. Weekly. See p. 722. K—Khedivial Mail Steamship Co. Weekly. See page 724. R—Compagnie Russe. Weekly. N—Società Nazionale. Weekly.

from **Cyprus (Larnaca).**—Messageries Maritimes de France. July 12th. See p. 730.—Austrian Lloyd. Alternate Thursday, 11.0 a.m. See p. 722.—Khedivial Mail Steamship Co. See p. 724.—Società Nazionale.

" **Marseilles.**—Messageries Maritimes de France. See p. 730.

Marseilles.........dep	July	4th.	July	11th.	July	18th.	July	25th.	August	1st.
Alexandria ......arr	"	8th.	"	15th.	"	22nd.	"	29th.	"	5th.
Port Said ....arr	"	11th.	——		"	25th.	——		"	8th.
Jaffa ....arr	"	12th.	——		"	26th.	——		"	9th.
Beyrout ....arr	"	13th.	"	18th.	"	27th.	August	1st.	"	10th.
Beyrout............dep	July	2nd.	July	7th.	July	16th	July	21st.	July	30th.
Jaffa ....arr	——		"	8th.	——		"	22nd.	——	
Port Said ....arr	——		"	9th.	——		"	23rd.	——	
Alexandria ......dep	"	5th.	"	12th.	"	19th.	"	26th.	August	2nd.
Marseilles ......arr	"	9th.	"	16th.	"	23rd.	"	30th.	"	6th.

from **Rhodes.**—Messageries Maritimes de France. July 5th and August 2nd. See p. 730.—Khedivial Mail Co. See p. 724.

TO CONSTANTINOPLE—

from **Alexandria.**—Khedivial Mail Steamship Co. Wednesday, 4.0 p.m. See p. 724.—Rumanian State Line. Friday, 4.0 p.m. See page 723.—Russian Steam Navigation Co. Tuesday and Friday, 4.0 p.m.

" **Athens (Piræus).**—Khedivial Mail Steamship Co. Friday, 4.0 p.m. See p. 724.—Messageries Maritimes de France. July 10th, 14th, 24th, and 28th. See p. 730.—Austrian Lloyd. Saturday, 6.0 p.m. See p. 722.—Rumanian State Line. Sunday, 3.0 p.m. See page 723.—Società Nazionale. Sunday, 2.0 p.m. and 5.0 p.m.—Russian Steam Navigation Co. Thursday afternoon.—Hellenic and Panhellenic Co.

" **Batoum.**—Messageries Maritimes de France. July 9th and 23rd. See p. 730.—Paquet et Cie. July 3rd, 17th, and 31st. See p. 730.—Austrian Lloyd. Friday, 12.0 night. See p. 722.—Società Nazionale.—Russian Steam Navigation Co, Thursday or Friday, 10.0 p.m.

" **Brindisi.**—Austrian Lloyd. Weds., 11.30 p.m. See p. 722.—Società Nazionale.

" **Constanza (Kustendje).**—Rumanian State Steamers. See p. 723.

Constanza dep. Tuesday, Thursday, and Sunday, 11.30 p.m.
Constantinople arr. Wednesday, Friday, and Monday, 12.0 noon.

—Austrian Lloyd. Tuesday or Wednesday. See p. 722.—Società Nazionale. Thursday, 4.0 p.m.

" **Galatz.**—Austrian Lloyd. Tuesday morning. See p. 722.—Società Nazionale.

" **Gallipoli.**—Austrian Lloyd. Alternate Tuesday, 6.0 p.m. See p. 723.

" **Genoa.**—Società Nazionale. Tuesday, 10.0 p.m.

" **Liverpool.**—Moss Line. See p. 726.

TURKEY—*Continued.*

TO CONSTANTINOPLE—

from **Marseilles.**—Messageries Maritimes de France. Saturday and alternate Thursday. See p. 730.—Paquet et Cie. July 9th and 23rd.
,, **Messina.**—Società Nazionale. Wednesday, 2.0 a.m.
,, **Mitylene.**—Khedivial Mail Steamship Co. Saturday, 11.0 p.m., and alternate Monday, 10.0 p.m. From **Constantinople** to **Mitylene**, Tuesday, 3.0 p.m., and alternate Saturday, 4.0 p.m. See p. 724.—Austrian Lloyd. See p. 722.
,, **Naples.**—Messageries Maritimes de France. July 12th and 26th. See p. 730.—Società Nazionale. Saturday, 3.0 p m.
,, **Novorossisk.**—Paquet et Cie. Fortnightly. See p. 730.
,, **Odessa.**—Russian Steam Navigation Co. Thursday, 11.0 a.m., and Saturday, 10.0 a.m. or 4.0 p.m.—Austrian Lloyd. Monday, 1.0 p.m., or Wednesday, 5.0 p.m. See p. 722.—Società Nazionale. Sunday, 5.0 p.m.
,, **Salonica.**—Messageries Maritimes de France. July 5th, 19th, and August 2nd. See page 730.—Austrian Lloyd. Monday, 2.0 p.m. See p. 722.—Società Nazionale. Alternate Tuesday, 4.0 p.m.
,, **Smyrna.**—Messageries Maritimes de France. July 1st, 8th, 11th, 15th, 21st, 25th, 29th, and August 5th. See p. 730.—Khedivial Mail Steamship Co. Saturday, 4.0 p.m. and alternate Monday, 4.0 p.m. See p. 724.—Russian Steam Navigation Co., Friday, 6.0 p.m. Also Monday, 5.0 p.m.—Austrian Lloyd. Monday, 5.0 p.m. See p. 722.—Rumanian State Line. ———— See p. 723.—Società Nazionale.
,, **Swansea.**—Moss Line. See page 726.
,, **Trieste.**—Austrian Lloyd. Tues., 2.0 p.m., Fri., 5.30 p.m., Sun., 10.0 a.m. See p. 722.
,, **Varna.**—Austrian Lloyd. Alternate Wednesday, 4.0 p.m. See p. 722.
,, **Venice.**—Società Nazionale. Tuesday, 6.0 p.m.

TO GALLIPOLI—

from **Constantinople.**—Austrian Lloyd. Alternate Monday, 4.0 p.m. See p. 722.—Khedivial Mail Co. See p. 724.

TO HAIFA—

from **Beyrout.**—Austrian Lloyd. Thursday, 6.0 p.m. See p. 722.—Khedivial Mail Steamship Co. Sun. 10.0 a.m. See p. 724.—Società Nazionale.

TO JAFFA—See also **"To Beyrout."**

from **Beyrout.**—Austrian Lloyd. Thursday, 6.0 p.m. See p. 722.—Khedivial Mail Steamship Co. Sun. 10.0 a.m. See page 724.—Società Nazionale.

TO SALONICA—

from **Athens (Piræus).**—Austrian Lloyd. Friday, 5.0 p.m. See p. 722.—Società Nazionale. Alternate Sunday, 2.0 p.m.
,, **Chalcis (calling at Volo).**—Greek Steamer. Weekly.
,, **Constantinople.**—Messageries Maritimes de France. July 5th, 19th, and August 2nd. See p. 730.—Austrian Lloyd. Monday or Saturday, 4.0 p.m. See p. 722.—Russian Steam Navigation Co. Alternate Monday, 4.0 p.m.—Societá Nazionale.
,, **Smyrna.**—Russian Steam Navigation Co. Alternate Monday, 5.0 p.m.

TO SMYRNA—

from **Alexandria.**—Khedival Mail S.S. Co. Wednesday, 4.0 p.m. See p. 724.
,, **Athens (Piræus).**—Messageries Maritimes de France. July 10th, 14th, 24th, and 28th. See p. 730.—Austrian Lloyd. See p. 722.—Khedivial Mail Steamship Co. Friday, 4.0 p.m. See p. 724.—Società Nazionale.
,, **Constantinople.**—Khedivial Mail Steamship Co. Tuesday, 3.0 p.m. and alternate Saturday 4.0 p.m. See p. 724.—Russian Steam Navigation Co. Sunday, 2.0 p.m.; Monday or Tuesday, 4.0 p.m.—Austrian Lloyd. Monday. See p. 722.—Messageries Maritimes de France. See p. 730.—Rumanian State Line. ———— See p. 723.—Società Nazionale.
,, **Constanza (Kustendje)**—Rumanian State Line. ———— See p. 723.
,, **Liverpool.**—Moss Line. See p. 726.—Papayanni & Ellerman Lines.
,, **Marseilles.**—Messageries Maritimes de France. July 5th, 10th, 19th, 24th, and August 2nd. See p. 730.
,, **Mitylene.**—Khedivial Mail Steamship Co. Wednesday, 9.0 a.m., and alternate Sunday, 11.0 p.m. From **Smyrna** to **Mitylene**, Saturday, 4.0 p.m. and alternate Monday, 4.0 p.m. See p. 724.—Austrian Lloyd. See p. 722.
,, **Rhodes.**—Messageries Maritimes de France. July 20th. See p. 730.—Khedivial Mail Steamship Co. Alternate Sunday, 10.0 a.m. See p. 724.
,, **Trieste.**—Austrian Lloyd. Sunday, 10.0 a.m. See p. 722.

Bi-Monthly Almanac and Tide Table.

7th Mo. (JULY), 1913.

DAY.	Sun Rises.	Sun Sets.	Moon's Age.	Moon Rises MORN	Moon Sets. AFT.	High Water London Bridge. MORN	High Water London Bridge. AFT.
	H.M.	H.M.	DAYS.	H.M.	H.M.	H.M.	H.M.
1 Tuesday	3 49	8 19	27	0 51	6 13	11 23	11 53
2 Wednesday	3 49	8 18	28	1 21	7 30	...	0 21
3 Thursday	3 50	8 18	29	2 7	8 33	0 47	1 12
4 Friday	3 51	8 17	●	3 16	9 18	1 36	2 0
5 Saturday	3 51	8 17	1	4 40	9 49	2 24	2 47
6 **Sunday**	3 52	8 16	2	6 11	10 11	3 10	3 33
7 Monday	3 53	8 16	3	7 44	10 27	3 57	4 21
8 Tuesday	3 54	8 16	4	9 14	10 40	4 45	5 8
9 Wednesday	3 55	8 15	5	10 40	10 53	5 32	5 56
10 Thursday	3 56	8 14	☽	Aft.	11 5	6 21	6 46
11 Friday	3 57	8 13	7	1 31	11 18	7 12	7 38
12 Saturday	3 58	8 12	8	2 57	11 36	8 4	8 32
13 **Sunday**	3 59	8 11	9	4 22	11 59	9 3	9 38
14 Monday	4 1	8 11	10	5 43	Morn.	10 15	10 52
15 Tuesday	4 2	8 10	11	6 54	0 31	11 29	...
16 Wednesday	4 3	8 9	12	7 49	1 19	0 4	0 35
17 Thursday	4 4	8 8	13	8 29	2 20	1 3	1 29
18 Friday	4 5	8 7	○	8 56	3 31	1 54	2 16
19 Saturday	4 7	8 5	15	9 14	4 48	2 36	2 55
20 **Sunday**	4 8	8 4	16	9 28	6 5	3 14	3 33
21 Monday	4 9	8 3	17	9 41	7 18	3 51	4 8
22 Tuesday	4 11	8 1	18	9 51	8 29	4 24	4 40
23 Wednesday	4 12	8 0	19	9 59	9 38	4 56	5 12
24 Thursday	4 13	7 59	20	10 9	10 48	5 28	5 45
25 Friday	4 15	7 57	21	10 20	11 58	6 3	6 21
26 Saturday	4 16	7 56	☾	10 32	Aft.	6 39	6 59
27 **Sunday**	4 17	7 55	23	10 50	2 30	7 21	7 45
28 Monday	4 18	7 54	24	11 16	3 49	8 12	8 43
29 Tuesday	4 20	7 52	25	11 54	5 6	9 20	10 0
30 Wednesday	4 21	7 51	26	Morn.	6 17	10 40	11 8
31 Thursday	4 23	7 49	27	0 51	7 11	11 54	....

8th Mo. (AUGUST), 1913.

DAY.	Sun Rises	Sun Sets.	Moon's Age.	Moon Rises MORN	Moon Sets. AFT.	High Water London Bridge. MORN	High Water London Bridge. AFT.
	H.M.	H.M.	DAYS.	H.M.	H.M.	H.M.	H.M.
1 Friday	4 24	7 48	28	2 10	7 47	0 28	0 58
2 Saturday	4 26	7 46	●	3 40	8 13	1 25	1 50
3 **Sunday**	4 27	7 45	1	5 14	8 32	2 13	2 36
4 Monday	4 29	7 43	2	6 49	8 46	2 59	3 21
5 Tuesday	4 30	7 42	3	8 20	8 58	3 43	4 5
6 Wednesday	4 32	7 40	4	9 48	9 10	4 27	4 49
7 Thursday	4 34	7 38	5	11 17	9 24	5 11	5 32
8 Friday	4 35	7 36	6	Aft.	9 41	5 53	6 15
9 Saturday	4 36	7 34	☽	2 10	10 2	6 38	7 1
10 **Sunday**	4 38	7 32	8	3 34	10 32	7 26	7 54
11 Monday	4 40	7 30	9	4 47	11 14	8 27	9 5
12 Tuesday	4 41	7 29	10	5 47	Morn.	9 48	10 32
13 Wednesday	4 43	7 27	11	6 30	0 10	11 15	11 55
14 Thursday	4 45	7 25	12	6 59	1 19	...	0 31
15 Friday	4 46	7 22	13	7 21	2 35	1 0	1 24
16 Saturday	4 48	7 20	○	7 35	3 49	1 46	2 6
17 **Sunday**	4 50	7 18	15	7 49	5 5	2 24	2 40
18 Monday	4 52	7 16	16	7 59	6 17	2 55	3 11
19 Tuesday	4 54	7 14	17	8 6	7 26	3 26	3 41
20 Wednesday	4 55	7 12	18	8 16	8 37	3 57	4 12
21 Thursday	4 56	7 10	19	8 26	9 47	4 26	4 40
22 Friday	4 58	7 8	20	8 39	10 58	4 54	5 8
23 Saturday	4 59	7 6	21	8 54	Aft.	5 23	5 38
24 **Sunday**	5 0	7 4	22	9 16	1 30	5 55	6 14
25 Monday	5 2	7 2	☾	9 46	2 47	6 34	6 57
26 Tuesday	5 4	7 0	24	10 33	4 0	7 23	7 55
27 Wednesday	5 6	6 58	25	11 41	5 0	8 34	9 20
28 Thursday	5 7	6 56	26	Morn.	5 43	10 8	10 55
29 Friday	5 8	6 54	27	1 5	6 14	11 38	...
30 Saturday	5 10	6 52	28	2 37	6 35	0 15	0 44
31 **Sunday**	5 12	6 50	●	4 12	6 50	1 9	1 33

NORWAY STEAMERS.

*—Until 6th Sept. and not on Sun. ‡—7.30 a.m. on Sun.

SKIEN and DALEN.

Skien ....dep	6a30	2*p50	**Dalen** ...dep	6‡a0	6*a30
Ulefos	9 0	4 50	Laurdal	6 30	7 0
Kirkebjo	2 30	...	Kirkebjo......	8 15	...
Laurdal............	5 30	10 15	Ulefos	1 45	12 15
Dalen ....arr	6 30	10 45	**Skien**......arr	4 0	2 30

†—Not on Sunday. ‡—4.0 p.m. on Sunday,

SKIEN and NOTODDEN.

Skien ......dep	6 a50	2 †50	Notodden	12 †0	6‡20
Notodden......	10 45	6 0	**Skien**.........arr	5 20	9 30

BREVIK and CHRISTIANSAND.

Brevik ....dep	6 a0	...	**Christiansand dep**	2 a0	5 a30
Kragero	8 0	10a30	Arendal	7 30	10 30
Arendal	12 15	3 30	Kragero	11 30	2 30
Christiansand arr	5 0	8 15	**Brevik** ....arr	...	4 30

RANDSFJORD and ODNÆS.

Randsfjord...dep	2 †p0	...	**Odnæs** ....dep	7 *a0	...
Roikenvik	5 50	...	**Roikenvik**	11 0	...
Odnæs ....arr	9 50	...	**Randsfjord** ...arr	1 20	...

Service until 31st August.

‡—Tues. Thurs. and Sat. *—Mon. Wed. and Fri.

LAKE OF MJOSEN.

Lillehammer .....dep	2†p15	2 p45	**Eidsvold** ....dep	...	9 a22
Gjovik	5 25	4 40	**Gjovik**....................	6 a30	12 45
Eidsvold ....arr	...	9 0	**Lillehammer** ...arr	9 40	2 35

Service until 31st August.

†—1 30 p.m. on Sunday.

HARDANGER FJORD.

Service until 4th September.

Bergen dep, Eide ...., Vik ...., **Odde**......arr — From Bergen—Sun., Tues., Wed., Thurs., Fri., Sat., 8.0 a.m.; Mon., 9.0 a.m.; Wed., 10.0 p.m; Sat., 1.0 p.m. From Odde—Daily, 7.0 a.m.; Sun., 3.0 p.m.; Tues., Thurs., Fri. 6.0 p.m.

Stavanger dep, **Eide** ...., **Vik** ...., **Odde** ....arr — From Stavanger—Sun., 6.0 p.m.; Wed., 9.0 p.m. From Odde—Tues., 1.0 a.m.; Fri., 7.15 a.m.

SOGNE FJORD.

Service until 14th September.

Bergen ...dep, **Vadheim** ......, Balholm ......, Laerdal ...., **Skjolden** . arr — From Bergen—Sun., Tues., Fri., and (to Laerdal only) Sat., 8.0 a.m.; Wed., 2.0 a.m. From Skjolden—Mon. and Thurs., 8.0 p.m.; Wed., 2.30 a.m.; Sat., 5.30 p.m.

Balholm..................dep, **Gudvangen** ....arr; **Gudvangen** ....dep, **Balholm**..................arr — Service in both directions almost daily.

ROMSDALS FJORD.

Service until 7th September.

Molde ....dep, **Aandalsnaes**...arr — Daily.

Aandalsnaes...dep, Molde ....arr — Daily.

ERIS FJORD. Service until 7th Sept.

Molde ....dep, **Alfarnäs**......, **Nöste** ......arr — On Sun., Tues., Wed., Thurs., & Fri.

Nöste ......dep, **Alfarnäs**........, **Molde** .. ...arr — On Mon., Wed., Thurs., Fri., and Sat.

TRONDHJEM FJORD.

Trondhjem dep, **Levanger** ...., **Stenkjaer** ...arr — From Trondhjem—Mon. Wed. Thurs. and Sat., 8.0 a.m; Tues. and Fri., 12.0 noon. From Stenkjaer—Wed. and Sat., 9.0 a.m.; Sun., 12.30 p.m.; Tues., 5.0 a.m.; Thurs., 8.0 a.m.; Fri., 4.0 a.m.

ROTTERDAM and MANNHEIM.

Single 1st m.pf	Single 2nd m.pf	Return (60 Days) 1st m.pf	Return (60 Days) 2nd m.pf		Cologne and Dusseldorf Company															Nederland Co.		
						Express.			Express.		Until 14th Sept.	Express.							Until 24th Aug.	Until 12th Sept. ☞		Until 17th Sept.
—	—	—	—	**Rotterdam** dep	...	...	a.m. 7 0	...	...	...		...	...	...	...	...	...	...		a.m. 8 0	...	
3 50	2 10	4 70	2 80	**Arnhem**	...	...	2p30	...	...	...		...	...	...	...	...	...	...		...	...	
4 50	2 70	6 —	3 60	Emmerich	...	...	7 0	...	...	...		...	...	...	...	...	...	...		11 p0	...	
5 30	3 10	7 10	4 25	Wesel	...	...	10 0	...		...			...	...	...	...	...	...		2 a0	...	
6 50	3 85	8 80	5 15	Duisburg	...	...	1230	...		...			...	...	a.m.	...	...	noon		6 a0	...	
7 50	4 45	10 —	5 90	**Düsseldorf**	...	A	4 a0	...		...			...	...	8 30	...	...	12 0		10 0	...	
8 90	5 30	12 —	7 10	Mülheim	...			...		...			...	...	C	...	...	4 p0		3 0	...	
9 20	5 50	12 40	7 30	**Cologne** arr	...		...	...		...			...	...	1215	...	...	4 30		4 p0	...	
							a.m.	...	a.m.	a.m.	a.m.	a.m.	a.m.	noon	p.m.	p.m.	p.m.	p.m.	p.m.		p.m.	a.m.
...	...	...	...	**Cologne** dep	...		2 0	...	6 30	6 50	8 30	8 45	10 15	12 0	1 0	3 0	...	6 0	9 0	...	10 30	7
10 70	6 30	14 20	8 40	Bonn	...		5 0	...	8 45	9 20	11 0	1050	12 45	2 30	3 30	5 30	6‖30	8 30	1130	...	1 30	9
11 10	6 55	14 70	8 70	Godesberg	...	a.m.	5 30	...	9 10	9 50	1130	...	1 15	3 0	4 0	6 0	7 0	9 0	...		...	..
11 20	6 60	14 80	8 90	Königswinter	...	6 15	5 45	...	9 25	10 5	1145	...	1 30	3 15	4 15	6 15	7 15	9 15	1210		2 15	10
11 40	6 70	15 10	9 —	Rolandseck	...	6 35	6 15	a.m.	9 45	1030	1210	...	2 0	3 45	4 45	6 45	7 45	9 40			...	..
11 70	6 90	15 50	9 25	Remagen	...	7 0	6 45	8 25	1010	11 0	1240	...	2 30	4 15	5 15	7 15	8 15	10 5	...		...	..
12 —	7 10	15 90	9 50	Linz	...	7 15	7 0	8 40	1025	1115	1255	...	2 45	4 30	5 30	7 30	8 30		...		3 30	11
13 —	7 70	17 60	10 30	Andernach	...	8 25	8 15	9 55	1135	1230	2 10	...	4 0		6 45	8 45		...	...		5 0	12
13 30	7 80	18 —	10 50	Neuwied	...	8 45	8 45	1015	1155	1250	2 30	...	4 20	...	7 5	9 5	...	...	...		5 30	12
14 20	8 50	19 20	11 20	**Coblence** arr	a.m.	10 0	1015	1130	1 10	2 10	3 50	2 45	5 40	p.m.	8 25	1025	...	...	...	a.m.	7 15	2
...	...	...	...	,, dep	7 15	1015	1045	1140	1 15	2 15	3 55	2 50		5 45			...	...	...	8 0	7 30	2
14 60	8 70	19 80	11 60	Oberlahnstein	7 50	1045	1130	1215	...	2 50	4 30	...	...	6 20	...	...	...	...	...	8 35	8 5	2
15 70	9 10	20 70	12 10	Boppard	8 50	1135	1230	1 15	2 35	3 50	5 30	...	...	7 20	...			...	...	9 35	9 15	3
16 50	9 60	21 80	12 80	St. Goar arr	9 50	1235	1 40	2 15	3 30	4 50	6 30	...	...	8 20	...			...	a.m.	10†40	10†30	4
...	...	...	...	,, dep	9 55	1240	1 45	2 20	3 35	4 55	6 35	...	p.m.		...			a.m.	6 30	...	...	..
18 30	10 70	24 20	14 40	Bingen	1210	2 45	...	4 35	5 40	7 15	8 50	7 0	7¶50	...	...			7 †0	8 45	12 55	1 10	6
18 30	10 70	24 20	14 40	Rüdesheim	1225	3 0	...	4 50	5 55	7 25	9 0	...	8 5	...	...			7 15	9 0	1 5	1 30	7
19 30	11 30	25 50	15 20	Eltville	1 35	4 5	...	6 0	7 0	8 35		...	9 15	...	...			8 25	1010	2 15	3 0	8
19 80	11 60	26 20	15 60	Biebrich	2 10	4 35	6 15	6 35	7 30	9 10	...	8 40	9 50	...	...			9 0	10 15	2 50	3 50	8
19 80	11 60	26 20	15 60	**Mayence** arr	2 35	5 0	6 40	7 0	7 55	9 35	...	9 0	10 15	a.m.	...			9 25	1110	3 15	5 0	9
...	...	...	...	,, dep	3 30						...			4§30	...							1
21 20	12 40	28 40	16 70	Worms	7 5	...	...	...	...	...	...	...	...	8 15	...			...	...	...	...	4
21 80	12 80	29 20	17 20	**Mannheim** arr	8 20	...	...	...	...	...	...	...	...	9 30	...	...	...	...	...	...	...	7

§—Weekdays only. ¶—Until 10th Aug.

MANNHEIM and ROTTERDAM.

	Cologne and Dusseldorf Company.																Nederland Co.			
						From 26th July. ☞	Ex-press	Ex-press.			Ex-press								Until 12th September. ☞	Until
Mannheim dep	...	...	...	...	...	...			a.m. 5 45	...		...	B	...	a.m. 1140	...	...	p.m. 1 0	...	...
Worms	...	...	...	...	...	...		...	6 30	...		...	...	...	1225	...	...	2 0	...	...
Mayence arr	...	...	...	a.m.	a.m.	...	a.m.	a.m.	9 20	a.m.	a.m.	p.m.	p.m.	p.m	3 10	p.m.	a.m.	5 0	a.m.	p.m
,, dep	...	...	...	6 ‡0	8 10	...	9 5	9 30		10 0	11 0	1230	1 0	3 *0	4 0	6 ‖0	6 0		9 20	3
Biebrich	...	...	...	6 20	8 30	...	9 25	9 50	...	1020	1120	1250	1 30	3 20	4 20	6 20	6 20		9 35	3
Eltville	...	...	...	6 45	8 55	...	...	1010	...	1045	...	1 15	2 5	3 45	4 45	6 45	6 50	...	10 0	4
Rüdesheim	...	...	...	7 35	9 45	...	...	1055	...	1135	1230	2 5	3 0	4 35	5 35	7 35	8 0	...	10 50	5
Bingen	...	...	...	7 50	10 0	...	...	1110	...	1150	1245	2 20	3 20	4 45	5 50	7 45	8 30		11 5	5
St. Goar	...	...	...	9 5	1115	...	...	1215	...	1 5	...	3 35	4 35		7 5		9†55	†—At St. Goarshausen.	12†15	6†
Boppard	...	...	...	9 50	1150	...	...	1250	...	1 45	...	4 15	5 15	...	7 45	...	1035		12 50	7
Oberlahnstein	...	...	...	1030	1230		...	1 20	...	2 25	...	4 55	5 55	...	8 25	...	1125		1 30	7
Coblence arr	a.m.	...	a.m.	1050	1250		1255	1 40	...	2 45	3 0	5 15	6 25	...	8 45	...	12 0		1 55	8
,, dep	5 0	...	9 0	1055	1255		1 0	1 45	...	2 50	3 5	5 20		...	8 50	...	1230		2 30	
Neuwied	6 20	a.m.	9 45	1140	1 40		...	2 30	...	3 35	...	6 5	...	...	9 35	...	1 30		3 15	
Andernach	6 35	7 25	10 0	1155	1 55		...	2 45	p.m.	3 50	...	6 20	...	...	9 50	p.m.	1 50		3 30	
Linz	7 35	8 10	1045	1240	2 40		...	3 25	4‖35	4 35	...	7 5	...	...		9 ‖0	2 20		4 0	
Remagen	7 50	8 25	11 0	1255	2 55		...	3 40	4 50	4 50	4 45	7 25	...		...	9 15	...		...	
Rolandseck	8 20	8 40	1115	1 10	3 15		...	3 55	5 5	5 10	...	7 50	...			9 30	...		...	
Königswinter	8 35	8 55	1130	1 25	3 35		...	4 10	5 25	5 30	5 15	8 10	...			9 45	3 20		5 0	
Godesberg	8 45	9 5	1140	1 35	3 45		...	4 20	5 35	5 40	...	8 20				9 55	...		...	
Bonn	9 20	9 30	12 5	2 0	4 10		3 30	4 40	5 55	6 5	5 45	8 50				1020	4 0	...	5 30	
Cologne arr	1045	1050	1 25	3 30	5 45	p.m.	4 45	6 0		7 30	7 5	1015				1135	5 30	p.m.	6 50	
,, dep			2 15			6 0			...									8 0		...
Mülheim	...	...	3 0	...	...	...	...	...	...	...	...	...				...	...	8 15		...
Düsseldorf arr	...	...	5 15	...	...	8 30	...	...	p.m	...	...	...				...	...	11 20		...
,, dep	...	...		...	...		...	...	11 0	...	...	...				...	...	11 30		...
Duisburg	..	...	...	...	...	...	...	...	1230	...	...	...				...	...	1 0		...
Wesel	...	...	...	..	...	...	...	...	2 30	...	...	...				...	...	3 0		...
Emmerich	...	...	...	...	...	...	...	...	6 0	...	...	...				...	...	6 0		...
Arnhem	...	...	...	...	...	...	...	...	8 0	...	...	...		...	...	...	...	...		...
Rotterdam arr	...	...	...	...	...	...	...	...	3 p0	...	...	...	...	...	...	...	...	3 p15		

C—From 27th July. *—Sunday only.
‖—Until 17th August. ‡—Until 15th Sept.
After 18th August one hour earlier. ☞
A—Between Konigswinter and Coblence. runs until 31st Aug. only.
B—One hour later on Sunday.
Express Boats at Express Fares are "Borussia," "Kaiserin Auguste Victoria," "Blücher," "Kaiser Wilhelm II," "Barbarossa," and "Elsa." They run in Summer only.

COBLENCE, TRARBACH, and TREVES.

Coblence dep	9.0 a.m.	Daily.		...	...
Cochem	...			...	...
Zell	...	6.0 a.m.		...	...
Traben-Trarbach arr		...	Daily.		...
,, dep		...			...
Berncastel		...			...
Treves arr		...			...

Treves dep	7 0 m'rn	Daily.
Berncastel	...	
Traben-Trarbach	...	
Zell	...	
Cochem	...	
Coblence arr	...	

THUNER and BRIENZERSEE (Lakes of Thun and Brienz).

	a.m.		a.m.	a.m.	a.m.	a.m.	a.m.	a.m.	a.m.	a.m.	p.m.	p.m.	p.m.	p.m.	p.m.	p.m.	p.m.	p.m.	p.m.			
Thun Hofstetten ...dep	...	...	6 15	7 33	...	8 35	...	9 22	10 15	11 30	A	1 40	...	2 20	3 10	4 6	5 0	6 56	8 0	...	...	...
Scherzligen ....dep	...	...	6 39	7 38	...	8 51	A	9 40	10 34	11 48	1 0	1 50	...	2 37	3 30	A	5 14	7 12	8 14	...	...	...
Oberhofen	6 10	...	6 54	7 52	...	9 6	9 49	9 55	10 49	12 3	1 18	2 7	...	2 52	3 45	4 24	5 29	7 27	8 29	...	...	...
Gunten	6 26	...	7 9	8 6	...	9 20	...	10 10	11 3	12 17	1 33	2 22	...	3 7	4 0	4 38	5 43	7 41	8 43	...	...	...
Spiez	6 51	...	7 19	8 44	...	9 30	10 9	10 20	11 13	12 27	1 42	2 34	...	3 17	4 10	4 48	5 53	7 51	8 55	...	...	...
Beatenbucht	—	...	7 39	8 23	...	9 50	—	10 39	11 32	12 46	2 3	2 54	...	3 33	4 30	5 5	6 8	8 11	—	...	...	...
Interlaken—Pier...arr	...	a.m.	8 25	A	10 8	10 33	...	11 20	12 15	1 23	2 19	3 40	...	4 17	5 8	6 5	6 50	8 50	...	...	...	...
,, Station Rail dep	...	7 57	8 30	—	10 15	10 38	...	11 37	12 45	2 2	—	3 45	...	4 53	5 16	6 17	7 53	—	...	...	...	...
,, Oststation ...arr	a.m.	8 4	8 37	...	10 25	10 45	...	11 44	12 52	2 9	...	3 52	...	5 0	5 23	6 24	8 0	...	...	...	...	...
,, Brienz Lake dep	5 41	8 9	8 44	...	...	—	...	11 50	12 58	2 35	...	—	4 0	5 6	—	—	8 5	...	...	...	...	...
Bonigen	6 1	A	9 2	...	...	...	...	A	1 16	2 53	...	...	...	5 24	...	...	...	...	...	...	...	...
Giessbach ¶	6 59	8 51	9 55	...	11 15	...	...	12 32	2 0	3 50	...	...	4 50	6 17	...	...	9 7	...	...	...	...	...
Brienz—Town ......arr	...	...	10 5	...	...	...	...	...	...	4 0	...	...	A	C	...	...	...	...	...	...	...	...
,, Station ...arr	7 12	9 9	1018	...	11 30	...	...	12 50	2 14	4 10	...	...	5 12	6 35	...	...	9 20	...	...	...	...	...

				a.m.				a.m.	a.m	a.m.		a.m			p.m.	p.m		p.m.	p.m	p.m.		p.m	p.m
Brienz—Station ...dep		...	...	5 48	...	...	...	8A28	...	9 30	...	11 24	...	...	12 35	1 55	...	3 18	4 30	...	...	5 28	7 40
,, Town ......dep		...	...	...	...	...	...	8 31	...	9 33	...	...	...	...	A	...	...	...	...	...	...	A	7 43
Giessbach ¶		...	...	5 58	...	...	...	8 43	...	9 45	...	11 34	...	...	12 45	2 5	...	3 28	4 42	...	...	5 38	7 55
Bonigen		...	...	6 55	...	...	...	9 36	...	10 42	...	12 14	...	...	1 38	...	...	...	5 28	...	...	...	8 48
Interlaken—Pier ...arr		...	...	7 15	...	...	...	9 56	...	11 2	p.m	12 34	...	p.m.	2 0	2 49	p.m.	4 33	5 50	...	...	6 38	9 8
,, Oststation Rail dp		...	...	7 23	...	A	...	10 23	...	11 13	12 13	1 0	...	1 45	2 20	3 9	4 6	4 40	6 0	...	...	6 45	9 22
,, Station ....arr		...	a.m.	7 30	a.m.	a.m.	a.m.	10 30	...	11 20	12 20	1 7	...	1 52	2 27	3 16	4 13	4 47	6 7	..	p.m.	6 52	9 29
,, Thun Lake...dep		...	6 40	—	A	8 35	9 10	—	1040	—	12 35	1 23	p.m.	2 21	—	3 23	4 18	5 10	—	6 12	6 45	—	—
Beatenbucht	a.m.	a.m.	7 17	...	8 24	9 17	10 8	...	1117	A	1 13	2 0	2 37	3 18	...	—	4 56	5 52	...	..	7 35	...	...
Spiez	5 51	6 52	7 37	...	8 45	...	10 28	...	1135	12p15	1 34	2 17	3 1	3 39	...	...	5 16	6 12	...	7 26	7 52	...	...
Gunten	...	7 2	7 47	...	8 55	9 35	10 38	...	1145	12 26	...	2 27	3 11	3 49	...	...	5 26	6 22	...	A	8 3	...	...
Oberhofen	6 10	7 16	8 1	...	9 10	9 49	10 53	...	1159	12 40	1 52	2 41	3 26	4 4	...	...	5 40	6 36	...	7 44	8 17	...	...
Scherzligen............arr		7 33	8 18	...	..	...	11 10	...	1218	12 58	...	3 0	A	4 21	...	...	5 59	6 55	...	8 0	8 33	...	...
Thun Hofstet. ......arr		7 40	8 24	...	9 30	..	11 16	...	1224	...	2 12	3 6	3 46	4 27	...	...	6 5	7 1	..	8 6	8 39	...	...

A—Until 15th September.

¶—**Giessbach Railway.**—From the Pier to the Falls upon arrival of Steamer. From the Falls to the Pier 10 minutes before departure of Steamer. Return fare 1 fr. Runs during season only.

LAKE OF SCUTARI (Montenegro).

Scutari ......dep	...	...	...
Plavnitza..........	...	...	...
Vir-Pazar..........	1 p30	...	...
Rijeka ....arr	2 50	...	...
Rijeka ....dep	11 a0	...	...
Vir-Pazar	12 20	...	...
Plavnitza..........	—	...	...
Scutari ......arr	...	...	...

ZUGERSEE (Lake of Zug).

Zug (Stadt).........dep	8 a15	1 p 0	...	...	...	...
,, (Bahnhof) ... ,,	8 25	1 10	4 p 5	...	...	...
Immensee............ ,,	9 20	2 5	4 52	...	...	...
Walchwyl .... ,,	9 35	2 20	5 6	...	...	...
Arth ....arr	9 51	2 36	5 20	...	...	...
Arth ....dep	10 a0	2 p40	5 p25	...	...	...
Walchwyl .... ,,	10 15	3 15	5 41	...	...	...
Immensee............ ,,	10 30	3 0	5 56	...	...	...
Zug (Bahnhof) ...arr	11 25	3 47	6 45	...	...	...
,, (Stadt)	11 30		6 55	...	...	...

*—Arrival only.

STEAMERS ON THE LAKES OF NEUCHATEL and MURTEN.

fr. c.	fr. c.							
		Neuchâtel ...dep	6a15	8a25	10a30	2p10	5p30	8†p0
1 0	0 80	Cudrefin	6 40	8 50	10 55	2 35	5 55	8 30
1 80	1 30	Sugiez	—	9 50	—	3 40	7 0	—
2 0	1 50	**Murten** ....arr	...	1015	...	4 0	7 45	...

Murten ......dep	...	6 a0	...	2p10	5p45	...
Sugiez	...	6 40	...	2 50	6 5	†
Cudrefin	6a50	7 40	11a0	3 55	7 5	8p30
Neuchâtel...arr	7 15	8 5	1125	4 25	7 35	9 0

†—Until 31st August.

Neuchâtel ...dep	7 a40	7a50	1p30	2p15	6p25	...	...
Auvernier	...	8 10	1 50	...	...	...	...
Cortaillod	...	8 30	2 10	...	...	...	...
Chez-le-Bart ...	8 55	8 55	2 35	...	...	...	...
Chevroux	8 20	...	...	3 0	7 10	...	...
Estavayer ...arr	9 25	...	3 0	3 30	7 45	...	...

Estavayer ...dep	5 a30	9 a45	11 a0	5 p0	6 p45
Chevroux	6 0	10 10	...	5 25	...
Chez-le-Bart ...	...	...	11 25	...	7 10
Cortaillod	...	...	11 50	...	7 35
Auvernier	...	...	12 10	...	7 55
Neuchâtel ...arr	6 50	11 0	1 30	6 15	8 15

*-Tues., Thurs. and Sats. only.

ZURICH and RAPPERSWIL.

§—Not on Sunday.

Zurich—	a.m.	a.m.	a.m	p.m.	p.m.	p.m.	p.m.	p.m	p.m.	p.m	p.m		
Bahnhofstrasse dp	7 45	9 14	10 5	12 3	2 8	2 30	4 15	4 50	6 15	6 42	7 2	...	...
Seefeldquai	...	...	...	...	...	2 35	...	...	...	...	...	...	...
Kusnacht	8 10	9 39	...	12 30	...	2 54	4 43	...	6 43	7 6	...	...	...
Thalweil	...	9 50	10 35	...	2 45	...	...	5 22	6 54	...	8 11	...	...
Horgen	8 41	10 9	10 51	12 59	3 5	...	5 14	6 3	7 12	...	8 48	...	...
Meilen	8 53	10 22	11 2	—	3 17	3 25	5 26	6 14	7 24	7 38	8 37	...	...
Männedorf	...	10 39	11 21	...	3 34	...	5 50	—	...	7 54	—	...	...
Wädensweil.........	9 16	...	11 31	...	3 45	3§48	6 8	...	7 44	8 5	...	...	...
Stafa	...	10 50	11 43	...	...	4 0	6 34	...	8 4	...	...	...	...
Rapperswil .arr	...	...	12 8	...	...	4 27	...	...	...	...	...	...	...

	a.m.	a.m.	p.m.	p.m.	p.m.	p.m.	p.m.	p.m.	p.m.	p.m.	p.m.		
Rapperswil dep	...	...	...	12 27	...	...	...	...	5 30	...	...	...	...
Stafa	6 31	8 52	...	12 52	12 54	...	5 1	...	5§58	6 34	8 45	...	...
Wädensweil..........	7 12	9 25	...	1 6	...	4 5	4 48	...	6 10	6 48	8*31	...	...
Männedorf	7 23	...	...	...	1 4	4 16	5 11	...	...	6 58	8 56	...	...
Meilen	7 40	9 45	...	1 25	1 26	4 33	5 28	6 15	6§31	7 15	9 20	...	...
Horgen	7 52	9 57	1 0	...	1 37	4 45	5 42	...	6 42	7 26	...	...	...
Thalweil	...	10 15	1 17	...	2 17	...	6 2	...	6 59	7 44	9*50	...	...
Kusnacht...............	8 30	...	...	1 54	...	5 15	6 18	6 47	...	8 0	9 51	...	...
Zurich-Seefeld arr	...	...	...	...	...	...	...	...	7 26	...	...	...	...
,, Bahnhofstr. ar	8 56	10 50	1 55	2 12	2 52	5 40	6 39	7 31	7 30	8 22	10 15	...	...

GENEVA and BOUVERET.

*—From or at Quai du Mt. Blanc.

				a.m.	a.m.	a.m.	a.m.			a.m.	a.m.	a.m.	a.m.		p.m.	p.m.	p.m.	p.m.	p.m.	p.m.	p.m.	p.m.		p.m.
Geneva— (Jardin Anglais) ...dep	...	...	...	6 40	6 45	7 50	8 35	...	...	9*25	11 0	1120	11*40	...	1*30	2 5	2 0	3 10	3 15	5 0	5*10	5 15	...	7 0
Versoix	...	...	...	...	7 14	...	...	...	...	...	11 29	...	...	...	...	2 38	...	3 42	...	5 30	...	...	...	...
Anières	...	...	...	7 28	...	...	9 25	...	...	...	...	1210	...	...	...	...	2 49	...	4 4	...	B	6 5	...	7 50
Coppet (Divonne)	...	...	...	...	7 28	...	...	a.m.	...	...	11 43		...	...	..	2 55	...	4 0		5 45	...	...	p.m.	
Nyon ,,	...	...	...	...	7 55	8 45	10 5	10 25	...	1018	12 10	...	...	...	2 27	3 25	3 30	4 30	...	6 15	6 5	...	7 45	...
Nernier	...	...	...	8 8	...	...		10 45	...	...	...	...	...	...	...		3 50	...	...	6 35	...	6 45	...	...
Rolle	...	a.m.	...	...	8 27	9 15	...		...	...	12 42	...	...	p.m.	...	...	...	5 6	...		6 35	...	8 5	...
Thonon	a.m.	7 0	a.m.	8 58	...	...	...	...	...	11 5	...	...	...	1 35	3 20	...	4 45	...	...	...	...	7 30		...
Evian-les-Bains	6 20	...	7 42	9 35	...	...	...	...	...	1140	...	...	...	2 15	3 55	...	5 30	...	...	...	...	8 5	...	...
Morges	...	7 37	...	...	9 10	9 52	...	...	a.m.	...	1 25	...	...	...	...	...	...	5 52	...	...	7 12	...	...	...
Ouchy (Lausanne)	7 15	8 5	8 30	...	9 45	10 30	...	...	11‡50	1220	2 0	...	1 45	3 0	4 35	...	...	6 30	...	...	7 45	8 40	...	...
Cully	7 43		...	...	10 12	...	...	...	12 18	...	2 28	...	...	...	...	...	...	6 58	...	...	...		...	...
Vevey (Gd. Hotel)	8 10	...	...	...	10 38	11 10	...	...	12 45	...	2 55	...	...	...	...	...	...	7 25	...	p.m.	B	...	...	...
Vevey (Marché)	8 15	...	9 18	...	10 43	11 15	...	...	12 50	1 5	3 0	...	2 30	...	5 20	...	...	7 30	...	7 50	8 30	...	...	...
Vevey (La Tour)	8 20	...	9 23	...	10 48	11 20	...	...	12 55	1 10	3 5	...	...	...	5 25	...	...	7 35	...	...	8 35	...	...	...
Clarens	8 35	...	9 38	...	11 3	11 35	...	...	1 10	1 23	3 20	...	...	...	5 40	...	...	7 50	...	C	8 50	...	...	...
Montreux	8 40	...	9 43	...	11 8	11 40	...	...	1 15	1 30	3 25	...	2 48	...	5 45	...	...	7 55	...	...	8 55	...	...	...
Chillon (Territet)	8 47	...	9 50	...	11 15	11 46	...	...	1 22	1 36	3 32	...	2 55	...	5 55	...	...	8 2	...	...	9 1	...	...	...
Villeneuve	8 57	...	10 0	...	11 25	11 55	...	...	1 32	1 45	3 42	...	3 5	...	6 5	...	...	8 12	...	..	9 10	...	...	...
Bouveret ...arr	9 20	...	10 20	1040	11 47	12 15	...	...	1 55	2 25	4 5	...	3 25	3 58	6 45	...	6 33	...	...	8 25	...	...	...	...

		a.m.		a.m.	a.m.		a.m.		a.m.	a.m.	p.m.		p.m.	p.m.	p.m.	p.m.	p.m.		p.m.	p.m.		p.m.	
Bouveret ...dep	...	5 40	...	..	B	...	7 54	...	9 35	10 30	1235	...	1258	2 35	2 55	4 10	4 12	...	5 0	5 35	...	6 50	...
Villeneuve	...	...	...	6 30	7 20	...	8 32	...	1016	...	1255	...	1 18	...	3 15	...	4 32	...	5 20	6 15	...	...	...
Chillon (Territet)	...	...	...	6 41	7 29	...	8 42	...	1026	...	1 4	...	1 29	...	3 25	...	4 41	...	5 30	6 25	...	7 15	...
Montreux	...	...	...	6 48	7 33	...	8 50	...	1035	...	1 11	...	1 37	...	3 32	...	4 48	...	5 37	6 32	...	7 22	...
Clarens	...	...	...	6 53	7 41	...	8 55	...	1040	...	1 16	...	1 42	...	3 37	...	4 53	...	...	6 37	...	7 27	...
Vevey (La Tour)	...	...	...	7 8	7 55	...	9 10	...	1055	...	1 30	...	1 57	...	3 52	...	5 8	...	...	6 53	...	7 45	...
Vevey (Marché)	...	6 16	...	7 13	8 0	...	9 15	...	11 0	...	1 35	...	2 2	...	3 57	...	5 13	...	5 57	6 58	...	7 50	...
Vevey (Gd. Hotel)	...		...	7 18	...	...	...	...	11 5	...	...	...	2 7	...	...	...	5 18	...	...	7 3	...	...	...
Cully	...	...	a.m.	7 45	...	...	...	...	1132	...	...	...	2 33	...	...	...	5 44	p.m.	...	7 31	...	...	...
Ouchy (Lausanne)	...	...	7 3	8 18	8 45	...	10 5	...	12 3	...	2 20	...	3 5	...	4 50	6 10	6 17	6 43	6 45	8 5	...	8‡35	...
Morges	...	...	...	8 48	...	...	...	...	1233	...	...	...	3 26	...	5 25	...	6 45	...	...	...	...		...
Evian-les-Bains	...	...	7 48	...	...	...	10 40	...	...	11 30	...	...	...	3 40	6 0	5 10	...	7 18	...	8 40	...	...	...
Thonon	...	...	8 26	...	...	...	11 15	...	...	12 5	...	...	...	4 20	...		...	7 55	...		..	...	...
Rolle	...	a.m.	...	9 30	...	a.m.	...	...	1 16		...	...	4 22	...	...	...	7 23		...	...	...	...	...
Nernier	...	6 40	9 19	...	B	10 45	...	...	..	...	...	p.m.	...	5 19	..	7 p25	...	...	...	...	...	...	...
Nyon (Divonne)	..	7 0	...	10 2	...	11 15	12 5	...	1 48	...	3 40	3 27	4 55	5 40	6 45	7 44	7 52	...	...	...	...	...	...
Coppet ,,	a.m.	-	...	10 24	...	..	...	p.m.	2 18	...	...	...	5 25	...	7 ‡5		8 17	...	...	...	p.m.	...	...
Anières	6 10	7 40	10 0	...	...	11 55	...	1 3	...	...	...	4 9	...	6 2.	...	...	...	...	...	...	7 40	...	...
Versoix	.	...	...	10 50	...	...	...	...	2 33	...	...	...	5 40	...	7‡17	...	8 29	...	...	...	‡	...	...
Geneva Jardin Angl.arr	7 0	8 28	10 50	11 22	10*45	12 40	1 *0	1*55	3 *5	...	4*35	5 1	6 10	7 15	7*45	...	9 3	...	8 45	...	8 30	...	...

Extra { Vevey (Marché) ....dep | 6 16 a.m.
St. Gingolph..............arr | 6 42 a.m.

B—Runs until 21st September. **C**—Not on Sunday. ‡—Sunday only.

BOUVERET and OUCHY.

Bouveret...dep	5a40	...	7a54	9a35	10a30	11a47	...	...	2p35	...	4p10	5p35
St. Gingolph	5 53	6a43	8 5	9 48	10 40	12 0	...	...	2 48	...	4 20	5 50
Meillerie		7 5			...		...	...	3 9	...	...	
Tourronde	...	7 20	...	...	11 15	a.m.	p.m	p.m	3 24	p.m.	...	p.m.
Evian	6a20	7 35	7a42	9a45	11 30	11 40	1 0	2 15	3 40	3 55	5 10	8 5
Ouchy ...arr	6 53	...	8 15	1020	...	12 15	1 35	2 50	...	4 30	6 10	8 40

Ouchy ...dep	7 a3	8a46	...	10a5	1218	...	2p21	4p50	...	...	6p43	8 p5
Evian	7 38	9 20	...	1040	1253	...	2 55	5 25	5p30	...	7 18	8 40
Tourronde			9a50			...	3 10		5 45	...		
Meillerie	...		10 5	...	p.m.	...	3 25		6 0	C	...	...
St. Gingolph	...	...	1025	...	1240	2p10	3 45	6p32	6 20	8p15	...	...
Bouveret arr	...	...	1040	...	1255	2 25	4 0	6 45	6 33	8 25	...	...

STEAMERS on LAKE COMO.

Como ....dep	...	4 55	...	...	6 30	...	...	8 10	8 55	1045	12 25	1225	...	...	...	...	...	1555	16 20	1720	18 15	1915
Cernobbio	...	5 8	...	...	6 43	...	...	8 23	9 8	1058	12 38	...	...	...	...	...	...	...	16 33	...	18 28	1929
Torno	...	5 35	...	...	6 55	...	...	8 50	...	1117	12 50	...	...	...	...	...	...	...	16 45	...	18 57	1957
Carate	...	5 46	...	...	7 2	...	...	9 3	9 27	1141	12 58	...	...	...	...	...	...	...	16 53	...	19 5	
Torriggia	...		...	...	7 10	...	...	9 26	...		13 5	...	...	...	...	...	...	1654	17 1	...	19 12	...
Argegno	...	...	...	...	7 34	...	...	9 59	10 0	...	13 33	1352	...	...	...	...	...	1733	17 29	1815	19 49	...
Lezzeno	...	...	...	...	7 54	...	...	1034	...	...	...	1426	...	...	...	...	...	18 4	...	...	20 16	...
Campo	...	...	...	...	...	...	...	...	1016	...	13 49	...	...	...	...	...	...	...	17 52	...	20 26	...
Lenno	...	...	...	...	8 2	...	...	1046	...	...	13 59	...	...	...	...	...	...	...	18 2	...		...
Tremezzo	...	5 26	6 56	...	8 9	...	...	...	1029	...	14 7	...	--	...	15 38	...	...	...	18 14	...	...	...
Cadenabbia	5 20	5 35	7 15	7 47	8 18	...	...	1115	1042	...	14 18	...	15 0	1515	15 45	...	1634	...	18 26	1845	18 48	...
Bellagio ....arr	5 28	5 43	:	8 4	8 31	...	...	1123	1050	...	14 31	1458	15 8	1531	15 54	...	1650	1830	18 34	...	19 6	...
,, ...dep	5 32	5 47	:	8 8	8 40	...	...	1126	1058	11 2	14 39	15 4	15 10	1535	15 58	1610	1354	1836	18 43	...		...
Menaggio (Stat.) arr	...	6 1	:	8 22	8 54	...	...	:	1111	:	14 51		:	:	16 12	:	17 6	:	18 57	19 5	...	...
Lierna	5 52	:	7 35	:	:	...	...	:	:	1120	:	...	:	:		1630	:	:	:		...	...
Limonta	6 2	:	7 45	:	:	...	...	:	:	1130	:	...	:	:	...	1640	:	:	:	...	...	...
Onno	6 22	:	8 5	:	:	...	...	:	:	1150	:	...	:	:	...	1658	:	:	:	...	...	...
Mandello	6 31	:	8 15	:	:	...	...	:	:	1158	:	...	:	:	...	17 6	:	:	:	...	...	...
Abbadia	6 40	:	8 25	:	:	...	...	:	:	12 6	:	...	:	:	...	1716	:	:	:	...	...	...
Lecco ....arr	7 0	:	8 45	:	:	...	...	:	:	1226	:	...	15 25	:	...	1736	:	:	:	...	...	...
Menaggio (Stat.) dep		6 8		8 26	8 58	9 10	...	:	1115		14 55	...		:	...		1710	:	19 8	...	...	...
,, (L. Cavour)	...	6 18	...	8 31	9 0	9 16	9 46	1144	...	...	15 1	...	...	:	...	...	...	:	19 14	...	...	...
Varenna	...	6 36	...	8 44		9 32	10 0	12 0	1130	1210	15 15	...	...	1550	15 57	...	1722	1852	19 37	...	...	...
Bellano	...	6 54	...		...	9 48				1226		...	...		16 14	...			19 52	...	...	...
Acquaseria	...	7 4	...	...	...	9 58	...	...	...	1237	...	...	...	...	16 25	...	...	...	20 3	...	...	...
Dervio	...	7 23	...	...	...	1015	...	...	...	1254	...	...	...	...	16 44	...	...	...	20 23	...	...	...
Dongo	...	7 55	...	...	...	1047	...	...	...	1327	...	...	...	...	17 20	...	...	...	20 51	...	...	...
Gravedona	...	8 9	...	...	...	11 1	...	...	...	1341	...	...	...	...	17 34	...	...	...	21 5	...	...	...
Domaso	...	8 17	...	...	...	11 9	...	...	...	1349	...	...	...	...	17 42	...	...	...	21 13	...	...	...
Colico ....arr	...	8 30	...	...	...	1136	..	...	...	1415	...	...	...	...	18 3	...	...	...	21 27	...	...	...

Colico............dep		...	...	4 50	...	6 50	...	...	...	...	...	9 35	...	...	...	1315	...	...	...	...	...	...	17 25
Domaso		...	...	5 3	...	7 3	...	...	...	...	...	9 48	...	...	...	1341	...	...	...	...	...	...	17 38
Gravedona		...	...	5 11	...	7 11	...	...	...	...	...	9 56	...	...	...	1348	...	...	...	...	...	...	17 46
Dongo		...	...	5 25	...	7 25	...	...	...	...	...	1010	...	...	...	14 2	...	...	...	...	...	...	18 0
Dervio		...	...	5 48	...	7 49	...	...	...	...	...	1044	...	...	...	1437	...	...	...	...	...	...	18 33
Acquaseria		...	...	...	...	8 9	...	...	...	...	...	11 2	...	...	...	1454	...	...	...	...	...	...	18 51
Bellano		...	...	6 9	...	8 24	...	...	...	...	...	1118	...	...	...	15 9	...	...	...	...	...	...	19 6
Varenna		...	...	6 25	...	8 41	9 16	...	10 6	...	12 2	1215	...	...	15 30	1523	1550	16 0	1756	...	1855	19 40	20 35
Menaggio (L. Cavour)		4 39	...	6 42	...	...	:	...	...	1058	...	1231	...	1435	15 47		:	1617	1812	...	...	19 57	...
Menaggio (Stat.) arr		:	...	:	...	8 54	:	...	1020	11 1	...	1233	...	1437	15 49	...	:	1619	1814	...	19 8	:	20 47
Lecco ....dep		:	...	:	7 30	:	:	9 20	:	:	...	:	13 0	:	:	...	:	:	...	1810	:	:	:
Abbadia		:	...	:	7 50	:	:	9 40	:	:	...	:	1320	:	:	...	:	:	...	1830	:	:	:
Mandello		:	...	:	7 58	:	:	9 48	:	:	...	:	1328	:	:	...	:	:	...	1838	:	:	:
Onno		:	...	:	8 7	:	:	9 58	:	:	...	:	1337	:	:	...	:	:	...	1847	:	:	:
Limonta		:	...	:	8 26	:	:	10 18	:	:	...	:	1356	:	:	...	:	:	...	19 5	:	:	:
Lierna		:	...	:	8 36	:	:	10 28	:	:	...	:	14 6	:	:	...	:	:	...	1915	:	:	:
Menaggio (Stat.) dep		:	...	:	To Menaggio (L.C.) arr. 9.0.	9 8	:	To Menaggio (L.C.) arr. 10.55	1023	11 6	...	1240	To Menaggio (L.C.) arr. 14.30.	1442	15 55	...	:	1624	1817		1912	:	20 50
Bellagio ....arr		4 52	...	6 56		9 20	:		1056	1119	1220	1253		...	16 7	...	16 5	1637	1830	To Varenna, arr. 19.34.	1925	20 14	21 3
,, ...dep		4 54	...	7 1		9 23	:		...	1121	1255	1259		...	16 12	...	1610	1644	1833		1929	...	21 5
Cadenabbia		5 14	...	7 13		9 44	9 43		1036	1129	...	1312		1458	16 25	...		17 4	1841		1945	20 22	21 15
Tremezzo		5 21	...	7 19		9 50	...				...	1318		15 2	16 31	...	...	...					21 20
Lenno		5 34	...	7 27		9 58	...		...	...	...	1331			16 43	...	...	...	...		...	...	
Campo		5 45	5 55	7 36		10 8	...		...	...	...	1341		...	16 53	...	...	...	...		...	...	...
Lezzeno		5 56	...	...		...	10 4		...	...	1326	...		...	17 3	...	...	...	...		...	...	...
Argegno		6 23	6 22	7 58		10 35	1034		...	...	14 3	14 5		...	17 45	...	...	1740	...	...	...	...	...
Torriggia		6 52	6 45	...		11 0	...		...	...	...	...		...	18 10	...	...	...	...	...	...	...	...
Carate	5 50	6 59	..	8 25		11 7	...		1145	...	...	1435		...	18 18	...	...	...	...	...	...	...	...
Torno	6 0		7 13	8 33	...	11 15	...	...	12 8	...	...	1444	...	...	18 27	...	...	1833	...	...	...	...	...
Cernobbio	6 27	7 23	...	8 45	...	11 35	...	...	1224	...	...	15 4	...	...	18 47	...	...	...	...	...	...	...	...
Como ...... arr	6 40	7 36	7 36	8 58	...	11 48	1153	...	1237	...	1526	1518	...	...	19 0	...	...	19 0	...	...	...	...	...

STEAMERS on LAGO DI GARDA.

Riva ....dep	...	...	4 35	...	7 35	1140	1530	16 0	...	...	...	...
Torbole	...	...	4 50	...	7 45	1210	1545	...	...	...	...	...
Limone	...	...	5 25	...	8 10	1240	...	1632	...	...	...	...
Malcesine	...	5 50	5 45	...	8 35	13 0	1625	...	...	...	...	...
Tremosine	...	..	6 0	...	8 52	1315	...	...	...	...	...	...
Assenza	...	6 10	...	...	...	...	1645	...	...	...	...	...
Castelletto	...	6 30	6 45	...	...	...	17 5	...	...	...	...	...
Gargnano	...	...	7 15	...	9 40	14 0	1730	1730	...	...	...	...
Bogliaco	...	...	7 25	...	9 48	1410	:	1738	...	...	...	...
Maderno	6 5	...	8 0	8 5	1015	1440	:	18 5	...	...	...	...
Gardone-Riviera	6 20	...	8 15	...	1035	1455	:	1820	...	...	...	...
Salò	6 35	...	8 30	...	1050	1510	:	1835	...	...	...	...
Desenzano ...arr	8 5	...	10 0	...	1225	1630	:	1955	...	...	...	...
Garda		7 30		9 5			1830		...	...	...	...
Bardolino	...	7 40	...	9 20	...	...	1845	...	...	...	...	...
Peschiera .....arr	...	8 25	...	1010	...	...	1935	...	...	...	...	...

Peschiera ...dep	...	6 0	...	1050	...	...	1730	...	...	...
Bardolino	...	6 40	...	1130	...	...	1810	...	...	...
Garda	...	6 55	...	1140	...	...	1825	...	...	...
Desenzano ...dep	6 0	:	9 50	...	1430	1720	...	1840	...	...
Salò	7 20	:	11 0	...	1545	1840	...	20 0	...	...
Gardone-Riviera	7 35	:	1115	...	16 0	1855	...	2015	...	...
Maderno	8 0	7 50	1138	...	1625	1920	...	2035	...	...
Bogliaco	8 25		1153	...	1650	1940	...		...	...
Gargnano	8 35		12 3	...	17 0	1950	1935	...	...	...
Castelletto	9 0	...	...	1255	1725	...	...	...	...	...
Assenza	...	...	...	1315	1745	...	2020	...	...	...
Tremosine	9 45	...	...	...	...	2035	...	...	...	...
Malcesine	10 0	...	...	1330	18 0	2050	2045	...	...	...
Limone	1025	...	1315	...	...	2110		...	...	...
Torbole	...	...	...	1410	1845	2140	...	...	...	...
Riva ....arr	11 5	...	1350	1425	1910	2150	...	...	...	...

STEAMERS ON LAGO D'ISEO.

Lovere ....dep	3 0	5 0	6 50	...	11 0	14 30	17 30
Pisogne	3 15	5 15	7 5	...	11 14	14 45	17 45
Iseo ....arr	4 55	6 43	8 40	10 5	12 48	16 10	19 25
Paratico-Sarnico ....arr	5 35	7 25	9 15	10 40	13 50	17 25	20 15

Paratico-Sarnico ...dep	4 15	5 55	8 5	9 25	12 0	15 20	18 22
Iseo ....dep	4 55	6 35	8 40	10 5	12 50	16 20	19 40
Pisogne	...	8 10	—	11 2	...	18 0	21 15
Lovere ....arr	6 35	8 25	...	11 40	14 23	18 15	21 30

STEAMERS on LAKE MAGGIORE.

Arona...dep	...	...	4 50	...	8 0	9 55	1245	1435	...	17 0	1840
Angera	...	...	4 55	...	8 5	10 5	1250	1440	...	17 5	1845
Meina	...	...	5 10	...	8 20	1020	13 5	1455	...	1720	19 0
Lesa	...	...	5 30	...	8 45	1045	1325	1515	...	1740	1920
Belgirate ...	...	...	5 35	...	8 50	1055	1335	1520	...	1745	1925
Stresa	...	...	6 0	...	9 15	1120	14 0	1545	1620	1810	1950
Isola Bella...	...	...	6 10	...	9 20	1130	1410	1555	1630	1815	1955
Baveno	...	...	6 25	8 25	9 35	1145	1425	16 5	1645	1825	2010
Suna......	...	...	6 40	...	9 50	12 0	1440	...	17 0	...	2025
Pallanza ...	5 0	6 0	6 50	8 40	10 0	12 5	1450	1620	1710	1840	2030
Intra	5 20	6 20	7 15	9 0	1020	1225	1515	1640	1730	19 0	2050
Laveno	5 40	6 40	7 45	9 30	1050	1250	1545	...	1750	1930	2110
Ghiffa	6 0	—	8 5	9 55	1110	1315	1610	...	—	1950	—
Portovaltra..	...	...	8 25	...	1130	...	...	1715	...	...	...
Oggebbio ...	6 15	...	8 40	1010	1145	1330	1625	...	...	20 5	...
Cannero	6 30	...	8 55	1025	12 0	1345	1640	...	...	2020	...
Luino	7 0	...	9 15	1040	1220	14 5	17 5	1750	...	2040	...
Maccagno I.	7 15	...	...	—	1235	1420	1710	18 5	...	...	...
Maccagno S.	...	...	9 35	...	1245	...	1730	...	...	...	...
Cannobbio...	7 30	...	9 50	...	13 0	1435	1740	1820	...	21 5	...
Brissago	7 50	...	1015	...	1325	1455	—	1845	...	2125	...
Ascona	...	...	1035	...	...	...	...	19 5	...	...	...
Magadino ...	8 30	...	...	...	...	...	...	...	...	...	...
Locarno ...	8 50	...	11 0	...	14 5	1555	...	1930	...	22 0	...

Locarno dep	...	...	5 15	7 10	9 15	...	1210	1440	...	1730
Magadino ...	...	...	...	7 30	...	...	1230	...	...	1750
Ascona	...	...	5 40	...	...	...	...	15 0	...	...
Brissago	...	...	6 0	8 10	9 50	...	1310	1520	...	1830
Cannobbio ...	4 45	...	6 20	8 35	1010	...	1330	1545	...	1855
Mac- Sup....	...	...	6 30	...	...	...	...	1555	...	...
cagno Inf....	5 0	...	6 40	...	1025	...	1345	16 5	...	1910
Luino	5 20	...	7 0	9 5	1050	11 5	14 5	1625	...	1930
Cannero	5 40	...	7 30	9 25	...	1125	1425	1650	...	1950
Oggebbio	5 55	...	7 50	9 45	...	1140	1440	17 5	...	20 5
Portovaltra ...	...	...	8 5	...	...	1155	...	...	...	...
Ghiffa	6 10	...	8 25	10 0	...	1215	1455	1720	...	2020
Laveno	6 45	7 25	9 20	1040	...	1250	1530	1750	1850	2030
Intra	7 10	7 45	9 45	11 5	1140	1315	1555	1810	1910	2110
Pallanza	7 30	8 5	10 5	1125	12 0	1335	1615	1830	1925	2130
Suna	7 35	...	1010	...	...	1345	1620	...	1930	—
Baveno	7 50	8 20	1027	1142	1217	14 2	1637	1847	1947	...
Isola Bella	8 0	—	1040	1150	1230	1415	1645	19 0	20 0	...
Stresa	8 10	...	1050	12 0	1245	1425	1655	1915	20 5	...
Belgirate	8 30	...	1110	—	1310	1445	1715	1935	—	...
Lesa	8 35	...	1115	...	1315	1450	1720	1940	...	...
Meina	8 55	...	1135	...	1335	1515	1740	20 5	...	...
Angera	9 5	...	1145	...	1350	1525	1755	2020	...	...
Arona ...arr	9 15	...	1155	...	14 0	1535	18 5	2030	...	...

STEAMERS on the ATTER SEE and MOND SEE.

Kammer ...dep	...	a.m. 6‡50	a.m. 7 †0	...	...	a.m. 8 †45	a.m. 11†45	...	...	...	...	p.m. 3 15	...	...	p.m. 5†25	...
Weyregg	...	7 7	7 17	...	...	9 2	12 2	...	...	...	...	3 32	...	...	5 42	...
Attersee	...	7 20	7 30	...	...	9 15	12 15	...	...	...	...	3 45	...	...	5 55	...
Nussdorf	...	7 40	7 48	...	...	9 35	12 33	...	p.m.	...	...	4 3	...	...	6 13	...
Weissenbach	...	8 35	8 40	...	...	10 30	1 21	...	2 35	...	...	4 51	...	...	7 1	...
Unterach ...arr	a.m.	8 55	9 0	a.m.	a.m.	10 50	1 40	p.m.	2 55	p.m.	p.m.	5 10	p.m.	p.m.	7 20	p.m.
UNTERACH dep	7†55	—	—	9 25	10 30	12 †5	—	1 50	—	3 †35	4 30	5 13	5 55	6*25	—	7§21
SEE ......arr	8 9	...	...	9 39	10 44	12 19	...	2 4	...	3 49	4 44	5 27	6 20	6 39	...	7 31
See ......dep	a.m. 8†20	...	...	a.m. 9 45	a.m. 10 55	p.m. 12†25	...	p.m. 2 10	...	p.m. 3 †55	—	p.m. 5 30	—	p.m. 6*45	...	p.m. 7§32
Scharfling	...	...	...	10 9	11 19	12 49	...	2 34	...	4 23	...	...	...	7 9	...	...
Plomberg	9 6	...	...	10 34	11 44	1 2	...	2 59	...	4 48	...	6 12	...	7 34	...	8 3
Mondsee ...arr	9 29	...	...	10 57	12 7	1 25	...	3 22	...	5 11	...	6 34	...	7 58	...	8 17

Mondsee...dep	...	a.m. 7 †0	a.m. 7†50	a.m. 9 35	...	...	a.m. 11†10	...	p.m. 1250	...	p.m. 2†30	...	...	p.m. 5 *25	p.m. 6 §2	...
Plomberg	...	7 26	8 14	9 59	...	...	11 34	...	1 14	...	2 54	...	...	5 49	6 28	...
Scharfling	...	7 51	8 39	1024	...	...	11 59	...	1 39	...	3 19	...	...	6 14	6 53	...
See... ......arr	...	8 15	9 3	1048	...	...	12 23	...	2 3	...	3 43	...	p.m.	6 38	7 17	...
SEE ......dep	...	8 20	9 5	1050	...	...	12 25	...	2 10	...	3 55	...	4 52	6 45	7 35	...
UNTERACH arr	...	8 34	9 19	11 4	...	...	12 39	...	2 24	...	4 9	...	5 6	6 57	7 49	...
Unterach dep	a.m. 5 †0	...	a.m. 9†25	...	a.m. 11†10	a.m. 11‡20	...	p.m. 1 30	...	p.m. 3 †5	...	p.m. 5‡20	p.m. 5†45	...	p.m. 7i50	...
Weissenbach	5 18	...	9 44	...	11 32	11 39	...	1 50	...	3 28	...	5 39	6 4	...	8 9	...
Nussdorf	6 0	...	1032	...	12 25	12 27	...	—	...	4 21	...	6 27	6 52	...	—	...
Attersee	6 17	...	1050	...	12 45	12 45	...	...	...	4 41	...	6 45	7 10	...	...	...
Weyregg	6 27	...	11 3	...	12 58	12 58	...	...	...	4 54	...	6 58	7 23	...	...	...
Kammer ...arr	6 45	...	1120	...	1 15	1 15	...	...	...	5 10	...	7 15	7 40	...	...	...

*—Until 31st August.

†-Until 15th September.

‡-From 16th September.

§—Until 8th September.

i—From 13th July until 18th August.

STEAMERS on the WOLFGANGSEE

Strobl ......dep	8‡a20	10‡55	1‡p20	2‡p55	3‡p50	5‡p28	...	6†p45
St. Wolfgang ...	8 50	11 17	1 42	3 17	4 15	5 48	5‖p52	7 7
Lueg......	9 22	11 50	...	3 49	4 46	—	6 25	7 40
St. Gilgen...arr	9 42	12 10	2 15	4 9	5 6	...	6 45	8 0

St. Gilgen...dep	9‡a25	11‡a5	1‡p20	2‡p20	4‡p12	5‖p30	...	7†p0
Lueg	9 50	11 30	1 40	2 45	4 33	5 50	...	7 22
St. Wolfgang ...	10 25	12 2	2 12	3 19	5 5	6 19	6‡p20	7 55
Strobl ......arr	10 45	12 22	2 32	3 39	5 25	...	6 40	8 15

†—Until 20th August. ‡—Until 15th September. ‖—From 21st August until 15th September.

STEAMERS on the LAKE of ANNECY.

Annecy ......dep	5 15	8 ‡20	10 §0	11 10	12‡30	13§50	14 10	15‡25	16 §0	16 30	17§40	19§25	...	...
Menthon	5 39	8 48	10 34	11 36	12 54	14 24	14 37	15 50	16 34	16 57	18 15	19 53	...	...
Talloires	5 54	9 8	10 50	11 55	13 13	:	14 57	16 10	:	17 15	:	20 10	...	...
Lathuille ......arr	6 12	9 30	:	12 15	13 30	:	15 17	16 30	:	17 32	:	:	...	...
Lathuille ......dep	6 15	9 35	:	12 20	13 35	:	15 20	16 35	:	17 35	:	:	...	...
Talloires	6 35	9 55	10 51	12 40	13 56	:	15 40	16 55	:	17 55	:	20 24	...	...
Menthon	6 55	10 13	11 8	12 55	14 16	14 25	15 55	17 15	16 35	18 14	18 16	20 40	...	...
Annecy ......arr	7 25	10 45	11 45	13 25	14 50	15 5	16 20	17 50	17 10	18 50	18 50	21 10	...	...

‡—Until 30th September.

§—From 10th July until 15th September.

STEAMERS on the LAC DE JOUX.—Service until 1st September.

Rocheray-Le-Sentier......dep	7a45	10a0	1p35	3p20	5p25	...	...
L'Abbaye	8 20	1035	2 10	3 50	6 0	...	...
Le Pont ......arr	8 35	1050	2 25	4 5	6 15	...	...

Le Pont ......dep	8a50	12 0	2p30	4p15	6p45	...	...
L'Abbaye	9 5	12 15	2 40	4 30	7 0	...	...
Rocheray-Le-Sentier arr	9 40	12 50	3 15	5 5	7 25	...	...

DRESDEN, SCHANDAU, TETSCHEN (BODENBACH), AUSSIG, and LEITMERITZ.

Frequent additional Sailings between Dresden, Loschwitz, Blasewitz, N. Poyritz, Pillnitz, and vice versa.
[Service until 24th August]. *—Until 23rd August, Weekdays only.

Dresden—						a.m.	a.m.	a.m.	a.m.	a.m.	a.m.	a.m.	noon	p.m.	p.m.	p.m.	p.m.	p.m.	p.m.	p.m.	p.m.	p.m.	p.m.	p.m.
Altstadt ...dep	...	...	...	...	...	6 0	7 0	8 0	8 15	9 0	10 0	1120	12 0	1 30	2 30	3 0	3 30	4 0	5 0	5 30	6 0	6 30	7 30	8 30
Neustadt... ,,	...	...	...	...	...	6 7	7 7	8 5	8 22	9 7	10 7	1125	12 7	1 37	2 37	3 7	3 37	4 7	5 7	5 37	6 7	6 37	7 37	8 37
Loschwitz	...	...	...	...	...	6 30	7 35	...	8 45	9 30	1035	...	1235	2 5	3 5	3 35	4 5	4 35	5 35	6 5	6 35	7 5	8 5	9 0
Blasewitz	...	...	...	...	...	6 35	7 40	8 30	8 50	9 35	1040	1150	1240	2 10	3 10	3 40	4 10	4 40	5 40	6 10	6 40	7 10	8 10	9 5
Niederpoyritz	...	...	...	...	...	6 50	7 55	...	9 5	9 50	1055	...	1255	2 25	3 25	3 55	4 25	4 55	5 55	6 25	6 55	7 25	8 25	9 20
Pillnitz	...	...	...	...	a.m.	7 20	8 25	9 10	9 35	1020	1125	1230	1 25	2 55	3 55	4 25	4 55	5 25	6 25	6 55	7 25	7 55	8 55	9 50
Pirna	...	...	...	...	5 50	8 10	9 25	9 55	1025	1115	1225	1 15	2 30	4 0		5 25		6*15	7 15			8 45		
Wehlen	...	...	...	...	6 25	8 45	10 0	1025	11 0	1150	1 0	1 45	3 5	4 35	...	6 0	...	7* 5		...	...		...	...
Rathen	...	...	...	...	6 50	9 10	1025	1045	1125	1215	1 25	2 5	3 30	5 0	...	6 25	...	7*30	...	...	...	...	...	...
Königstein	...	...	...	a.m.	7 30	9 50	11 5	1125	12 5	1255	2 5	2 45	4 10	5 40	...	7 5	...	8*15	...	...		...	...	...
Schandau	...	...	...	5 45	8 20	1035	1150	1210	1250	1 45	3 0	3 30	4 45	6 35	...	7 40	...	8*50	...	...		...	...	...
Herrnskretschen	...	...	a.m.	6 30	9 0	1120	1235	1245	1 35	2 30	3 45	4 5		7 20	...		...		...	...		...	...	...
Tetschen	...	a.m.	6 2	8 7	1022	1247	1 50	2 7	3 2	4 12	5 17		...	8 35	...	...	...	...	...	...		...	...	...
Aussig	a.m	7 0	9 30	1115	1 45	4 0		4 30	6 20	6 55	8 0	...	...		...	...	...	...	...	...		...	...	...
Lobositz	6 0	9 5	1135	1 20	3 50	6 5	...		8 25	9‡20		...	...	...	...	...	...	...	...	...	...	...	...	...
Leitmeritz ...arr	6 40	9 45	1215	2 0	4 30	6 45	...	...	9 ‡5	...	...	...	...	...	...	...	...	...	...	...	...	...	...	...

‡—Until 27th July.

								a.m.			a.m.			a.m.					p.m.	p.m.	p.m.	p.m.		
Leitmeritz ...dep	...	...	...	...	...	...	...	6 0	...	...	8 30	...	...	11 0	...	...	...	...	1 30	3 0	5 0	7‡15	...	...
Lobositz	...	...	...	...	...	a.m.	...	6 25	a.m.	...	8 55	...	...	1125	p.m.	...	...	...	1 55	3 25	5 25	7 40	...	...
Aussig	...	...	...	...	...	7 0	...	9 30	1110	...	1115	...	...	1245	1 40	...	...	...	3 30	5 15	7 0	9 0	...	...
Tetschen ...arr	...	...	...	a.m.	...	8 55	...	1127	1230	...	1 0	...	p.m.		3 25	...	...	...	5 17	7 0	8‖45		...	...
,, ...dep	...	...	...	6 45	...	9 0	...	1130	1235	...	1 5	...	2 35	...	3 30	p.m.	...	...	5 25	7 5		...	...	...
Herrnskretschen	...	...	a.m.	7 30	...	9 45	...	1215	1 10	...	1 50	...	3 30	...	4 20	5 5	p.m.	...	6 15	7 50	...		...	...
Schandau	...	...	6 0	8 20	...	1040	...	1 5	1 50	...	2 40	...	4 15	...	5 10	5 45	6 10	...	7 5	8 25	...		...	...
Königstein	...	...	6 30	8 45	...	11 5	...	1 30	2 10	...	3 5	...	4 40	...	5 35	6 5	6 35	...	7 30		...		...	...
Rathen	...	...	6 50	9 5	...	1125	...	1 50	2 30	...	3 25	...	5 0	...	5 55	6 25	7 0	...	7 55	...	...		...	...
Wehlen	a.m.	...	7 5	9 20	...	1140	...	2 5	2 45	...	3 40	...	5 15	...	6 10	6 40	7 15	...	8 10	...	...		...	...
Pirna	5 35	a.m.	7 50	10 0	a.m.	1220	p.m.	2 50	3 6	p.m.	4 20	p.m.	5 50	p.m.	6 50	7 6	7 50	p.m.	8 50	...	...		...	...
Pillnitz	6 15	7 25	8 30	1040	1135	1 0	2 25	3 30	3 40	4 0	4 55	6 0	6 30	7 0	7 30	7 45	8 30	9 0	9 30	...	...		...	...
Niederpoyritz	6 35	7 45	8 50	11 0	1155	1 20	2 45	3 50	...	4 20	...	6 20	6 50	7 20	7 50	...	8 50	9 20	9 50	...	...		...	...
Blasewitz	6 48	7 58	9 3	1113	12 8	1 33	2 58	4 3	4 5	4 33	5 18	6 33	7 3	7 33	8 3	8 10	9 3	9 33	10 3	...	...		...	...
Loschwitz	6 50	8 0	9 5	1115	1210	1 35	3 0	4 5	...	4 35	5 20	6 35	7 5	7 35	8 5	...	9 5	9 35	10 5	...	...		...	...
Dresden, N.	7 5	8 15	9 20	1130	1225	1 50	3 15	4 20	4 25	4 50	5 35	6 50	7 20	7 50	8 20	8 30	9 20	9 50	1020	...	...		...	...
Altstadt ...arr	7 15	8 25	9 30	1140	1235	2 0	3 25	4 30	4 30	5 0	5 45	7 0	7 30	8 0	8 30	8 35	9 30	10 0	1030	...	...	...	...	...

‖—Until 17th August only.

Steamers on Lago di Lugano from PORLEZZA to LUGANO and PONTE TRESA.

RAIL. Menaggio ...dep	...	...	...	...	6 10	9 5	...	...	...	1120	...	...	3 18	...	4 35	7 30	...	...
RAIL. Piano	...	...	...	...	6 48	9 43	...	...	...	12 0	...	...	3 56	...	5 15	8 5	...	...
RAIL. Porlezza ...arr	...	...	...	...	7 0	9 55	...	...	...	1215	...	...	4 10	...	5 30	8 20	...	...
Porlezza ...dep	...	...	...	...	7 10	10 0	...	...	...	1225	...	...	4 20	...	5 40	8 25	...	...
Osteno	...	...	A	...	7 25	1015	...	...	...	1245	...	...	4 40	...	6 0	8 40	...	...
Oria	...	...	...	...	7 45	...	...	...	...	1 5	...	...	5 0	...	6 20	9 0	...	...
Sta. Margherita ¶	...	...	6 25	...	7 53	1035	...	...	...	1 13	...	...	5 8	...	6 28	9 8	...	...
Gandria	...	...	6 35	...	8 0	...	...	...	...	1 20	...	...	5 15	...	6 35	9 15	...	...
Lugano-Centrale arr	...	...	6 50	...	8 20	11 0	...	...	...	1 35	...	...	5 35	...	6 55	9 30	...	...
Lugano-Centrale dep	5 0	5 45		7 0	8 30	11 5	11 15	1 5	1 40	1 45	2 45	4 30	5 40	6 20	7 10	9 35	...	...
Paradiso	5 5	5 50	...	7 5	8 35	1110	11 0	1 10	1 45	1 50	2 50	4 35	5 45	6 25	7 15	9 40	...	...
Campione	5 20	6 5	...	7 15	8 50		11 30	...	2 0	...	3 5	4 50		...	7 30		...	...
Bissone	...	6 15	...	...	...	...	11 40	...	2 10	...	3 20	5 0	...	...	...	...	...	...
Melide	5 35	6 25	...	7 25	9 0	...	11 50	...	2 19	2 20	3 30	5 10	...	...	7 40	...	...	...
Morcote	5 50	6 45	...	7 40	...	...	12 10	...		2 35	3 50	5 25	...	...	8 0	...	...	...
Porto Ceresio	5 58	7 0	...	7 50	9 25	...	12 30	1 45		2 55	4 10	5 40	...	7 10	8 10	...	...	...
Brusimpiano		7 25	...		9 40	...	12 50			3 10	4 30	5 55	...			...	...	...
Ponte Tresa (Station)...arr	...	7 55	...	...	9 55	...	1 10	...	To Capolago.	3 25		6 30	...	...	...	...	...	...
RAIL. Ponte Tresa (Rail) dep	...	8 5	...	...	10 0	...	1 15	...		3 30	...	6 40	...	...	...	...	...	...
RAIL. Luino ...arr	...	8 43	...	...	...	...	...	...		...	...	...	...	...	...	...	...	...
RAIL. ,, (Lake) ...arr	...	8 45	...	...	1040	...	1 55	...		4 10	...	7 20	...	...	...	...	...	...

RAIL. Luino (Lake)...dep	...	...	...	7 15	...	...	9 15	...	1230	...	2 45	...	...	6 0	...	...	...	...
RAIL. ,, (Stat.)...dep	...	...	...	7 17	...	...	...	...	...	...	...	...	...	...	...	...	...	...
RAIL. Ponte Tresa ...arr	...	...	...	7 55	...	...	9 55	...	1 10	...	3 25	...	...	6 35	...	...	...	...
Ponte Tresa Stat. ...dep	...	...	...	8 0	...	...	10 5	...	1 15	...	3 30	...	...	6 40	...	...	...	...
Brusimpiano	...	...	6 35	8 15	...	...	1035	...	1 30	...	3 50	...	5 10	6 55	...	...	...	...
Porto Ceresio	...	...	7 0	8 40	9 25	...	11 0	...	1 50	2 55	4 10	...	5 40	7 15	7 15	8 25	...	...
Morcote	...	...	7 10	8 50	...	...	1110	...	2 0	...	4 20	...	5 50	...	7 25	8 33	...	...
Melide	...	...	7 30	9 5	...	...	1130	...	2 20	...	4 35	...	6 10	...	7 45	8 45	...	...
Bissone	...	...	7 40	9 13	...	...	...	...	2 30	...	4 45	...	6 23	...	7 55	...	...	...
Campione	...	...	7 55	9 20	...	...	1140	...	2 40	...	5 0	...	...	...	8 5	8 55	...	...
Paradiso	5 45	...	8 10	9 35	10 5	1010	1155	1 30	2 55	3 35	5 15	6 35	6 35	7 50	8 15	9 5	...	...
Lugano-Centrale arr	5 50	A	8 15	9 40	1010	1015	12 0	1 35	3 0	3 40	5 20	...	6 40	7 55	8 20	9 10	...	...
Lugano-Centrale dep	5 55	6 0	8 30			1025		1 45		3 45		6 30					...	...
Gandria	6 10	...	8 50	...	...	1040	...	2 5	...	4 0	...	6 50	...	...	...	...	...	...
Sta. Margherita ¶	6 18	6 20	3 58	...	...	1048	...	2 13	...	4 8	...	6 58	...	...	...	...	...	...
Oria	6 25		9 5	...	...	1055	...	2 20	...	4 15	...	7 5	...	...	...	...	...	...
Osteno	6 45	...	9 25	...	...	1115	...	2 40	...	4 35	...	7 25	...	...	...	...	...	...
Porlezza ...arr	7 5	...	9 45	...	...	1135	...	3 0	...	4 55	...	7 45	...	...	...	...	...	...
RAIL. Porlezza ...dep	7 10	...	9 55	...	...	1145	...	3 5	...	5 0	...	7 50	...	...	...	...	...	...
RAIL. Piano	7 22	...	10 7	...	...	12 0	...	3 20	...	5 15	...	8 5	...	...	...	...	...	...
RAIL. Menaggio ...arr	8 0	...	1045	...	...	1235	...	4 0	...	5 50	...	8 40	...	...	...	...	...	...

A—Runs in July and August only.

¶—Funicular Railway from Sta. Margherita up to Belvedere at Lanzo d'Intelvi, in 20 minutes.

Capolago ...dep	9 a40	2 p48	6 p50	...	...
Maroggia	9 54	3 0	7 5	...	...
Paradiso ...arr	10 35	3 35	7 45	...	...
Lugano-Centrale	10 40	40	7 50	...	...

Lugano-Centrale	8 a35	1 p40	5 p45	...
Lugano-Paradiso	8 40	1 45	5 50	...
Maroggia	9 21	2 29	6 31	...
Capolago ...arr	9 35	2 45	6 45	...

		a.m.			p.m.	*—One hour earlier from 1st Sept.	
Passau............dep	...	5 *0	...	...	3 0		...
Linz ....arr	...	9 20	a.m.	a.m.	6 35		...
,, ...dep	a.m.		9 *0	10 30			...
Grein ....dep	5 45	...	11 5	12 27	...		...
Melk ....dep	8 10	...	1255	1 58	...		...
Krems...............dep	10 0	...	2 47	3 16	...		...
Vienna, Praterquai	...	...	6p15	6 p0	...		...

1 Cl. k. h.	2 Cl. k. h.							
				a.m.		a.m.	p.m.	
		Vienna ....dep	...	...	...	7 †0	10 0	...
2 80	2 0	Krems..............dep	...	10 0	...	12 42	4 45	...
4 0	2 80	Melk	...	1 30	...	3 22	8 a0	...
4 40	3 10	Grein	...	8p37	...	6 36	11 50	...
4 70	3 40	Linz ....arr	a.m.		p.m.	11 0	4 p30	...
Fr'm	Linz	,, ...dep	5 30	...	1 §0			...
3 60	2 70	**Passau** ....arr	1 40	...	9 45	...	...	...

§—Until 31st August.

	a.m.			p.m.			
Vienna—Weissgärber or Prater Quai......dep	8 0	Daily to Semlin.	...	5 *0	...	...	From Semlin Sun., Tues., Fri. only.
Deutsch-Altenburg dep	10 5		...	6 50	...	...	
Pozsony ....dep	10 55		...	7 50	...	...	
Komárom ....dep	2 55		Wed., Thur., Sat., and Monday only.	...	...	...	
Budapest ....arr	8 p0			...	...	...	
		p.m.			noon		
Budapest ....dep	*—One hour earlier from 1st September.	10 0		...	12 0	...	
Mohacs	...	8 a30		...	9p25	...	
Bezdan ....dep	...	9 35		Thur., Fri., Sun., and Tuesday only.	Fri., Sat., Mon., and Wednesday only.	From Galatz, Tuesday morn., in Constantinople, Thursday.	
Gombos ....dep	...	12p25			...	...	
Vukovar....................dep		1 55					
Ujvidek ....dep		5 40					a.m.
Zimony (Semlin) ...dep		9 50					4 0
Belgrade ....arr		10p10	a.m.				4 20
,, ...dep		Between Semlin & Belgrade Tu., Wed., Fri., Sun. only.	5 0				5 a0
Baziás ....dep			10 0				10 a0
Orsova			4 p0				4 p0
Turn Severin...........arr			6 p0				6 p0
,, ...dep			6p15				6p15
Widdin ....arr				a.m.			...
,, ...dep	...			12 55			...
Rustschuck	...		...	2p45			2p45
Giurgiu ....arr	...		...	2 50	...		2p50
,, ...dep	...		...	3 0	a.m.		3 p0
Cernavoda..................dep	...		...		12 30		12a30
Braila ....dep	...		...	...	6 30		6a30
Galatz ....arr	...		...	...	7 20	...	7a20
Galatz ....dep	...		...	...		a.m.	...
Constantinople arr	...		...	...		8 0	...

				Sat. Sun. Tues Thu.	p.m.	p.m.	
Constantinople dep	...	Mon., Tu., Thr., and Sat. only.	Sn. Mn. Wd. & Fri. only.		4 0	...	...
Galatz ....arr	Tues., Wed., Fri., and Sun. only.					...	...
Galatz ....dep				2 p0		2 0	...
Braila ....dep				3p20	...	3p20	...
Cernavoda ....arr				11 5	...	11 p0	...
,, ...dep			11p10		From Constantinople, every Friday, in Galatz Monday.	11p10	...
Giurgiu ....dep			10a30			1 p0	...
Rustschuck ....dep		a.m.	1 45	...		1p45	...
Widdin ....dep		7 55		...		...	...
Turn-Severin.............arr		4 p5		...		4 p5	...
,, ...dep		4p30	...	...		4p30	...
Orsova.......................arr		5p30	...	...		5p30	...
,, ...dep	6 a0		...	...		6 a0	...
Baziás ....dep	2p45	...	...	...		2p45	...
Belgrade ....arr	9p15	...	...	...		...	...
,, ...dep	9p30	...	...	...		9p45	...
Zimony (Semlin) ...dep		5 a45	...	...		10p30	...
Ujvidek ....dep	...	11a45	...	...		From Galatz, Mon., Wed., Fri.	...
Vukovar......................dep	...	4 p40	...	...			...
Gombos ....dep	...	6 p40	...	...			...
Bezdan ....dep	noon	10p20	...	...			...
Mohacs ....dep	12 0	11p40	2 a0	...			...
Budapest ....arr	2 a5		2 p50	...			...
				p.m.			
Budapest ....dep	...	...	...	7 0	...		...
Komárom ....dep	...	a.m.	...	2 a25	...		...
Pozsony ....dep	...	6 0	...	9 45	...		...
Deutsch-Altenburg arr	...	7 40	...	11 15	...		...
Vienna-Prater Quai ar	...	11 40	...	3 p15	...		...

Szeged ....dep	...	5 a†0	...
Titel	5 a30	3 p0	...
Semlin (Zimony) arr	8 15	6 p0	...

Semlin (Zimony) ...dep	1 p0	11†p0	...	...
Titel	5 0	2 a15	...	...
Szeged ....arr	...	2 p15	...	...

†—Sun., Wed., & Fri. only.

Belgrade...dep	9‡a30	...
Sabac.........arr	4 p0	...

Sabac.........dep	9§a30	...
Belgrade...arr	3 0	...

‡—Tues., Thurs., and Sat. only.
§—Mon., Wed., and Fri. only.

Raca (Bosnia)...dep	11a20	...
Mitrovicza	2 p0	...
Sabac (Servia)...arr	4 p30	...

Sabac ......dep	4 a0	...
Mitrovicza	7 30	...
Raca........arr	10 50	...

Service daily, Mondays excepted.

‡—Until 22nd Sept.]

THE MEUSE.

Namur ......dep	14‡30	...
Rivière...............	16 15	...
Yvoir..................	16 55	...
Dinant ......arr	18 0	...

Dinant ......dep	9‡15	...	...
Yvoir	10 10	...	...
Rivière	11 0	...	...
Namur ......arr	12 30	...	...

Dinant ......dep	9 15	14 30	...	...	...	...	...
Hastière ...arr	10 50	16 0	...	...	...	...	...
Hastière ...dep	11 0	17 0	...	...	...	...	...
Dinant ......arr	12 30	18 30	...	...	...	...	...

THE VOLGA.—Three Lines of Steamers.

FARES. r. k.	r. k.		"KAVKAS," etc. Daily.	"SAMOLET," etc., daily.	"RUS."	
			noon			
—	—	**Nijni-Novgorod** dep	12 0	2 p0	4 p0	Daily except Monday.
5 25	2 65	**Kazan** ....arr	7 a0	9a30	2 p0	,, ,, Tuesday.
		dep	10 a0	1 p0	7 p0	,, ,, ,,
9 60	6 0	**Simbirsk**	8 p0	12a30	5 a30	,, ,, Wednesday.
12 35	7 90	**Samara** ....arr	6 a30	11 a0	5 p30	,, ,, ,,
		dep	10a30	1 p0	8 p30	,, ,, ,,
14 15	9 10	**Sysran**	4 p0	7 p0	4 a30	,, ,, Thursday.
16 95	10 85	**Voliski**	12 0	8a30	1 p30	,, ,, ,,
18 5	11 55	**Saratov** ......arr	7 a30	10a30	8 p0	,, ,, ,,
		dep	1 p0	1 p0	10p30	,, ,, ,,
20 80	13 35	**Kamyschin**	11 p0	12 0 night	10a30	,, ,, Friday.
23 10	14 85	**Zarizyn** ....arr	7 a0	8 a0	7 p0	,, ,, ,,
		dep	11 a0	1 p0	11 p0	,, ,, ,,
27 75	17 80	Astrakan ....arr	7 a0	10 p0	10 p0	,, ,, Saturday.

LAKE OF CONSTANCE (BODENSEE).

Lindau ...dep	5a10	7a40	10 a5	11a45	1253	2p15	6p45	...	...
Rorschach arr	6 0	8 40	10 55	12 35	1 53	3 5	7 50	...	...

Rorschach...dep	6a20	9 a17	11a25	1p12	2p15	4p50	8p55	...	...
Lindau ......arr	7 10	10 5	12 25	2 8	3 15	5 40	9 55	...	...

Friedrichshafen...dep	6 a0	7a30	9a20	11a35	2 p0	6 p8	8a18
Romanshorn ......arr	6 50	8 15	1010	12 22	2 45	6 53	8 58

Romanshorn ....dep	5 a32	7 a52	10a40	12p50	4p33	6 p24	9 p18
Friedrichshafen ...arr	6 16	8 37	11 23	1 30	5 18	7 2	10 0

Friedrichshafen...dep	5 a55	7 a28	9 a20	11a32	1p50	6 p40
Rorschach...............arr	6 55	8 35	10 20	12 37	3 0	7 45

Rorschach ....dep	7 a36	9 a25	12p25	4 p48	6p15	8 p45	...
Friedrichshafen......arr	8 36	10 35	1 23	4 53	7 20	9 50	...

Lindau......................dep	6 a45	11a40	2 p20	5 p15	7 p55	...
Romanshorn ....arr	8 10	12 50	3 30	6 25	9 5	...

Romanshorn ....dep	9 a0	10a45	12p40	4 p35	6 p40	...	...
Lindau ....arr	10 10	12 5	1 50	5 45	8 0	...	...

LUCERNE and FLUELEN.

1Cl. fr. c	2Cl. fr. c	Lucerne	a.m.	a.m.	a.m.		a.m.		a.m.	a.m.	a.m.			p.m.		p.m.	p.m.			p.m.	p.m.	p.m.	p.m.
		Right Bank	...	...	...	...	...	...	9 20	9 55	1040	...	...	...	...	1 50	...	...	...	...	...	...	...
...	...	,, Bahnhof	5 25	7 0	7 45	...	8 45	...	9 40	1010	11 0	...	...	1245	...	2 10	2*50	...	...	4 35	5 35	6 30	8 25
1 20	0 60	Hertenstein ...	5 50	...	8 10	...	...	...	10 5	A	1125	...	...	1 10	...	2 35	...	...	...	5 0	6 15	6 55	8 50
1 60	0 80	Weggis	6 0	7 45	8 20	...	9 15	...	1015	...	1135	n on	...	1 20	p.m.	2 45	3 20	...	...	5 10	6 25	7 5	9 0
2 0	1 0	Vitznau(Rigi)	6 15	8 2	8 35	a.m.	9 30	a.m.	1035	1050	1152	12 0	p.m.	1 35	2 42	3 5	3 35	p.m.	p.m.	5 25	6 43	7 20	9 15
2 40	1 20	Buochs	6 40	8 30	...	9 15	...	1035	...	...	...	1225	1 35	...	3 5	...	...	4 40	5 15	...	...	7 40	9 35
2 40	1 20	Beckenried ...	6 55	8 45	8 55	9 30	...	1052	1055	...	1210	—	1 50	1 55	3 22	3 25	...	4 55	5 42	5 45	...	7 55	9 50
2 70	1 40	Gersau	7 10		9 10	9 45	9 50	—	1110	...	1225	...	—	2 10	—	3 40	...	—	—	6 0	7 ‡5	8 10	10 5
2 80	1 60	Treib Seelisbg	7 25	—	9 25	—	...	...	1125	...	1240	...	...	2 25	...	3 55	...	...	...	6 15	7‡20	8 25	10‡20
2 95	2 10	Brunnen	7 35	...	9 35	...	1010	...	1130	1135	1250	...	...	2 35	...	4 5	4 15	...	...	6 20	7‡30	8 35	10‡30
3 10	2 20	Rüttli..........	7 45	...	9 45	...	...	...	...	1150	1 5	p.m	...	2 45	...	...	...	...	...	...	—	...	—
3 50	2 50	Tellsplatte ...	...	...	10 0	...	...	...	1150	12 0	1 25	1 5	...	3 0	...	4 25	...	...	...	6 40	...	...	...
3 80	2 70	**Fluelen** ...arr	8 20	...	1015	...	1045	...	1210	1215	1 40	1 20	...	3 15	...	4 45	4 50	...	...	6 55	...	9 10	...

*—Until 31st August. §—From 16th September. ‡—Until 10th September.

		a.m.				a.m.			a.m.	n on		p.m.	p.m.		p.m.		p.m.		p.m.	p.m.	p.m.	p.m.
Fluelen ....dep	...	6 10	...	...	...	8 35	...	...	1025	12 0	...	1230	1 0	...	2 45	...	3 45	...	4 10	5 5	5*30	7 5
Tellsplatte	...	6 20	...	...	...	...	...	...	1035	1210	...	1 5	1 10	...	...	...	3 55	...	...	5 15	...	7 15
Rüttli..........................	...	...	a.m.	...	...	9 0	...	...	...	1225	...	—	1 25	...	3 5	...	...	...	4 40	5 25	...	...
Brunnen	...	6 40	8 ‡0	...	...	9 15	...	...	11 0	1235	...	...	1 40	...	3 20	...	4 20	...	4 55	5 40	6 0	7 40
Treib-Seelisberg	a.m.	6 50	8 5	...	...	9 22	a.m.	...	1110	1245	...	...	1 50	...	...	...	4 30	...	5 5	5 45	...	7 45
Gersau	5 0	7 5	8 20	...	a.m.	9 40	9 52	a.m.	1125	1 0	...	p.m.	2 5	p.m.	...	...	4 45	p.m.	5 20	6 5	...	8 0
Beckenried	5 15	7 20	...	...	8 57	9 55	10 5	11 0	1140	1 15	...	1 57	2 20	3 30	...	p.m.	4 58	5 0	5 35	6 20	...	8 15
Buochs	5 30	7 35	...	a.m.	9 12	...	1020	1115	...	A	p.m	2 12	...	3 45	...	A	...	5 15	...	6 35	...	8 30
Vitznau.....................	5 55	8 0	8 40	8 42	—	1015	—	1145	1155	1 30	1 32	2 35	2 40	—	4 0	4 45	5 15	—	5 55	6 55	6 40	8 50
Weggis	6 10	8 15	—	8 55	...	1030	...	—	1215	—	1 45	—	2 55	...	4 15	5 0	5 30	...	6 10	7 10	...	9 5
Hertenstein	6 15	8 25	...	9 5	...	1040	...	...	1225	...	1 55	...	3 5	...	...	5 10	5§40	...	6 20	7 20	...	9 15
Lucerne ....arr	6 43	9 0	...	...	...	1120	...	...	1255	...	2 40	...	3 35	...	4 45	5 40	6 10	...	6 45	7 45	7 25	9 45

A—Until 15th September.

†—Until 10th Sept.]

LUCERNE, STANSSTAD, and ALPNACH.

Lucerne	a.m.	a.m.	a.m.	a.m.	a.m.	a.m.	a.m.	a.m.	p.m.	n on	p.m.	p.m.	p.m.	p.m.	p.m.	p.m.	p.m.	p.m.	p.m.	p.m.	p.m.	
Bahnhof dep	5 10	6 45	7 0	7 42	...	9 15	10 35	11 30		12 0	1†15	2 10	3 0	.	4 †20	.	5 30	5 35	6 50	7 †0	8 25	...
Burgenstock ...	...	...	7 30	8 15	9 20	9 40	11 0	12 10	12 30	...	1 40	2 40	3 30	3 32	4 50	5 55	...	6 5	7 30	7 35	...	...
Stansstadt	5 45	7 25	—	8 35	9 40	9 55	11 20	—	12 45	1250	2 0	3 0	4 10	3 50	5 10	6 12	6 15	—	—	7 55	9 10	...
Rotzloch	—	7 35	...	—	9 50	...	...	...	—	1 0	...	...	4 20		—	—	6 25	...	...	8 0	—	...
Alpnach arr	...	7 50	...	...	10 5	1020	11 45	...	...	1 15	2 25	3 25	4 35	...	...	...	6 40	...	...	8 20	...	...

	a.m.	a.m.	a.m.	a.m.	a.m.	a.m.		a.m.	p.m.	p.m.	p.m.	p.m.	p.m.	p.m.	p.m.	p.m.	p.m.	p.m.	p.m	p.m.	p.m.	
Alpnach dep	...	7 56	...	...	1010	10†50	...	1155	1 22	...	...	2 30	3 35	...	...	5 10	...	...	7 0	...	8†25	*
Rotzloch	...	8 5	...	...	1020	.	...	...	1 35	...	..	2 40	...	...	†	...	...	...	7 10	...	...	p.m.
Stansstad	5 50	8 15	9 15	...	1031	11 15	p.m.	1220	1 45	...	1 40	2 55	4 0	4 12	5 33	5 35	...	6 20	7 25	...	8 45	9 15
Burgenstock ...	...	8 35	9 45	1050	11 8	...	12 20	1240	2 0	2 5	2 15	3 35	4 20	4 30	...	6 0	6 35	...	7 43	7 45	...	...
Lucerne arr	6 35	9 5	...	1120	1150	11 50	1 5	1 10	2 45	2 40	...	4 10	4 45	...	6 5	6 30	7 5	7 15	8 10	8 30	9 40	9 52

*—From 11th Sept.

Fares: Lucerne to Stansstad, 1 fr 50 c., and 80 c.; to Alpnach, 2 fr 40c., & 1 fr. 20 c.

*—From Right Bank.

LUCERNE and KUSSNACHT.

‡—Until 15th Sept.

fr.c.	fr.c.							
		Lucerne Bhf.........dep	6*a15	7‡a45	10a40	2 p10	4‡p15	6 p5
—	—	Seeburg	...	7 55	10 50	2 20	...	6 15
20	0 60	Hinter Meggen	6 40	8 20	11 10	2 40	...	6 35
0	1 0	**Kussnacht** ....arr	7 10	8 52	11 40	3 10	5 0	7 5

Kussnacht...dep	7a15	8‡a55	12 0	3 p15	5 ‡p5	7p10	...
Hinter Meggen......	7 35	9 25	12 20	3 35	5 25	7 30	...
Seeburg	8 0	9 55	12 45	...	...	7 55	...
Lucerne Bhf.arr	8 15	10 10	1 0	4 10	5 55	8 10	...

‡—Until 10th Sept.

ALPNACH and VITZNAU.

Alpnach...dep	..	7 a56	10a10	1 p22	3 p35	5 p10	...	...	...
Burgenstock ..	7 a30	9 45	11 8	2 0	4 30	6 0	...	...	...
Vitznau ...arr	8 0	10 23	11 48	2 50	5 5	6 43	...	...	...

Vitznau .....dep	8 a42	10a15	12 p2	1 p32	3 p0	5 p20	6 p0	6‡p55	...
Burgenstock.....	9 20	11 0	12 30	2 40	3 32	5 55	6 32	7 35	...
Alpnach .....arr	10 5	11 45	1 15	3 25	4 35	6 40	..	8 20	...

LAKE OF CONSTANCE (BODENSEE).

			a.m.	a.m.		a.m.	a.m.	a.m.			p.m.	p.m.		p.m.	p.m.	p.m.
Constance......dep		...	5 40	7 15	...	9 50	1025	1130	...	...	2 0	3 25	...	4 35	6 0	8 28
Meersburg		...	6 10	7 43	...	1020	...	12 0	...	...	2 25	§	...	5 2	6 28	8 55
Friedrichs- arr		...	7 20	8 40	...	1120	...	1 0	p.m.	...	3 28	4 35	p.m.	6 3	7 23	9 58
hafen ....dep		...	7 30	9 5	...	1126	...	1 5	1 35	...	3 35	4 45	5 23	6 10	7 28	—
Langenargen......		...	8 0	9 35	...	1150	...	...	2 5	...	4 0	...	5 50	...	7 55	...
Lindau.arr	a.m.	a.m.	8 55	1040	a.m.	1250	1220	2 12	3 5	p.m.	5 5	5 50	6 50	7 20	8 55	...
,, ...dep	5 30	7 25	9 10	1050	1130	1 15	1230	2 30	3 20	4 15	5 20	6 0	7 0	7 35	9 5	...
Bregenzarr	5 50	7 50	9 35	1115	1150	1 35	1250	2 55	3 40	4 40	5 40	6 25	7 25	7 55	9 25	...

	a.m.	a.m.	a.m.	a.m.	a.m.	a.m.	p.m.	p.m.	p.m.	p.m.	p.m.	p.m	p.m.	p.m.	p.m.	
Bregenz dp	6 15	5 35	6 50	9 10	9§25	1055	1210	1 35	2 55	3 55	4 30	5 45	6 0	7 40	8 30	...
Lindau arr	6 35	5 55	7 10	9 35	9 45	1120	1235	1 55	3 20	4 15	4 55	6 5	6 25	8 5	8 50	...
,, ...dep	—	6 5	7 30	9 50	9 58	1135	1250	2 35	3 30	—	5 10	6 15	6 40	—	—	...
Langenargen	...	6 55	8 30	1045	...	...	1 45	3 35	4 30	...	...	...	7 40	...	...	...
Friedrichs- a	a.m.	7 25	9 0	1125	1058	1245	2 10	4 5	4 55	...	...	7 25	8 8	...	...	...
hafen ...dep	5 20	7 30	9 10	1130	11 2	1252	2 20	—	5 12	...	...	7 35	—	...	...	...
Meersburg ...	6 20	...	1012	1232	...	...	3 22	...	6 15	...	...	8 45	...	...	...	...
Constance	6 50	8 45	1040	1 0	1210	2 2	3 50	...	6 45	...	7 10	9 15	...	...	...	...

§—Until 15th Sept.

CONSTANCE & SCHAFFHAUSEN

	a.m.	a.m.	p.m.	p.m.	p.m.
Constance dp	6 25	9 30	2 15	4 0	5‡50
Gottlieben ...	6 45	...	2 35	4 20	6 5
Ermatingen	7 0	9 58	2 50	4 35	6 20
Reichenau ...	7 20	10 9	3 11	4 55	6 40
Berlingen	7 30	...	3 21	5 5	6 50
Steckborn ...	7 45	1030	3 36	5 20	7 5
Mammern ...	8 5	...	3 58	5 42	7 25
Stein	8 30	1110	4 20	6 5	7 50
Diessenhofen	9 0	1140	—	6 35	—
Schaffhausen	9 35	1215	...	7 10	...
Schaffhausen	...	7a15	9a55	1‡50	3§30
Diessenhofen.	a.m.	8 5	1045	2 40	4 20
Stein	6 0	9 0	1140	3 35	5 20
Mammern......	6 20	9 20	12 0	3 55	5 40
Steckborn......	6 43	9 40	1222	4 15	6 2
Berlingen......	6 58	9 55	1237	4 30	6 18
Reichenau ...	7 9	1010	1250	4 40	7 0
Ermatingen...	7 30	1030	1 10	5 0	7 20
Gottlieben ...	7 47	1047	1 27	5 20	7 37
Constance arr	8 10	1110	1 50	5 45	8 0

‡—Until 13th Sept.

	a.m.	a.m.	a.m.	p.m.		p.m	p.m.	p.m.
Ludwigshafendep	...	...	...	...	...	...	...	...
Ueberlingen	5 50	8†30	10†45	1 †0	p.m.	3†45	6†40	6†45
Unteruhldingen...	6 40	9 0	11 15	1 30	3*15	4 15	...	7 15
Meersburg	7 20	9 40	11 55	2 10	...	4 55	...	7 55
Constance ......arr	7 50	1010	12 25	2 40	3 55	5 25	7 35	8 25

	a.m.	a.m.	a.m.	p.m.	p.m.	p.m.	p.m.	p.m.			
Constance......dep	6 35	9 15	10 40	2§10	2*30	2 55	4 45	8 20	...	...	...
Meersburg	7 10	9 45	11 15	2 40	...	3 30	5 25	8 50	...	...	...
Unteruhldingen...	7 45	10 10	11 50	...	3 10	4 5	5 50	9 25	...	...	...
Ueberlingen	8†15	10†30	12†25	3†30	—	4†40	6†20	10 5	...	...	...
Ludwigshafenarr	...	...	...	...	...	...	...	...	...	...	...

†—From or at Ueberlingen Town. *—In August only. §—Sunday dep. 1.5 p.m.

FRANCE.

Bourg d'Oisans—

Bourg d'Oisans ...	10a30	5‡p30
Briançon ......arr	5 p0	11a30
Briançon ...... dep	8a45	2‡p30
Bourg d'Oisans ...	2p45	6 40

40½ miles; fare 18 fr.
‡—Until 15th September.

Briançon—Fare 8 fr.

E M			
	Briançon dep	7 a30	2 p40
16½	Oulx ......arr	9 30	4 30
...	Oulx ......dep	10 a0	5 p15
...	Briançon arr	12 0	7 15

Service until 15th Sept.

Evian— Service until 15th Sept.

fr.c.						
	Evian ....dep	8 a0	...	Le Fayet......dep	2p25	...
2 50	Thonon	8 30	...	Sallanches	2 45	...
11 0	Taninges	1040	...	Cluses...............	3 30	...
12 0	Col de Châtillon	1050	...	Col de Châtillon	3 50	...
13 50	Cluses...............	1110	...	Taninges	4 0	...
17 50	Sallanches	12 0	...	Thonon	6 15	...
20 0	Le Fayet......arr	1220	...	Evian ....arr	6 50	...

Le Fayet— Service until 15th Sept.

fr. c.							
	Le Fayet ...dep	9a20	2p15	Thones......dep	9 a20	2p50	...
1 50	St. Gervais.....	9 40	2 35	Col des Aravis	12 0	4 30	...
12 0	Col des Aravis	1 30	4 45	St. Gervais.....	1 55	6 20	...
16 0	Thones ......arr	2 50	6 0	Le Fayet ...arr	2 15	6 40	...

fr. c.					
	Le Fayet ...dep	3 p35	Albertville dep	8 a20	Service
1 50	St. Gervais......	3 55	St. Gervais	10 35	until
14 0	Albertville arr	6 30	Le Fayet ...arr	10 55	15th Sept.

MOUTIERS SALINS and PETIT ST. BERNARD.

[In Summer only.]
‡—From 10th July until 15th September.

fr. c.								
	Moutiers ....dep	...	7‡10	10a0	2p15	7p12	11p20
8 0	Bourg St. Maurice { arr	a.m.	8 20	2 0	6 15	1142	3 20
	Bourg St. Maurice { dep	6 0	...	...	...	...	...
20 0	Petit St. Bernard.....arr	9 45	1040	...	...	...	...
...	Petit St. Bernard ....dep	...	...	...	2‡30	...	3 p30
...	Bourg St. Maurice { arr	a.m.	a.m.	p.m.	...	...	7 15
	Bourg St. Maurice { dep	3 30	7 30	1 30	3 10	4 0	
...	Moutiers ....arr	7 30	1130	5 30	5 10	8 0	...

Briançon— Service until 15th Sept.

fr. c.							
	Briançon dep	...	8 a0	Nice.........dep	...	7 a0	...
47 80	Barcelonnette	7a30	7 p0	Annot...........	...	1045	...
74 90	Annot...........	2 50		Barcelonnette	7 a0	6 p0	...
10040	Nice ....arr	6p30	...	Briançon arr	6p30	...	...

Grenoble—

fr. c				
	Grenoble.......................dep	9 a0	10†a 0	...
10 0	La Grande Chartreuse arr	11 0	12 0	...
...	La Grande Chartreuse dep	2p30	4†p0	
...	Grenoble ....arr	4 30	6 0	

†—Until 15th Sept.

St. Laurent du Pont— †—Until 15th Sept.

fr. c.						
	St. Laurent du Pont ...dep	8a30	10a15	11 a0	11†a20	2†p20
3 50	La Grande Chartreuse arr	9 10	11 0	11 40	12 0	3 0
...	La Grande Chartreuse dep	9a30	1 p0	12p45	4†p20	...
...	St. Laurent du Pont ...arr	1010	1 40	1 25	5 0	...

Luz St. Sauveur—

Luz ....dep
Barèges ...arr
Barèges ...dep
Luz ....arr
Luz ....dep
Gavarnie...arr
Gavarnie...dep
Luz ....arr

Conveyances run in connection with the train service at Luz.

Fares: Luz to Bareges 2 fr., Luz to Gavarnie 2 fr. 50c.

Rumilly—

Service until 15th October.

E.M.			
	Rumilly ...dep	1p30	...
10½	Seyssel .....arr	3 45	...
...	Seyssel ....dep	5p20	...
...	Rumilly ...arr	7 35	...

Fare 2 fr. 50 c.

Mont Dauphin—

fr. c.			
	Mont Dauphin	7a45	1p45
8 0	Abries ......arr	10 0	4 0
	Abries............dep	10a10	4p30
	Mont Dauphin arr	1 10	7 15

St. Jean de Maurienne—

St. Jean de M. dep	9 a5	...
Le Lautaret......arr	2 p40	...
Le Lautaret......dep	2 p40	...
St. Jean de M....arr	6 45	...

Fare 23 fr.
Service until 15th Sept.

AUSTRIA.

Arco—

Arco.............dep	6 a25	3 p50
Sarche............arr	7 30	5 2
Sarche............dep	9 a15	6 p35
Arco...............arr	10 32	7 54

10 miles; fare 3 k 50 h.

Au Seewiesen—

Au Seewiesen dep	11 a0	2 p0
Mariazell.........arr	5 5	7 40
Mariazell ......dep	5 a30	9 a35
Au Seewiesen...arr	11 30	3 10

23 miles fare 5 k.

Banjaluka—

	a.m.	a.m.
Banjaluka ... dep	6†55	9 30
Bocac ...... { arr	8 44	11 19
Bocac ...... { dep	8 59	11 29
Jajce .... arr	10 29	12 59
Jajce .... dep	7 a†0	1 p5
Bocac ...... { arr	8 30	2 35
Bocac ...... { dep	8 45	2 45
Banjaluka ... arr	10 37	4 34

45¼ miles; fare 10 k.
†—Until 30th Sept.

Caldonazzo—

E.M			
	Caldonazzo dep	6†50	11a5
10½	Lavarone ...arr	1045	2 20
...	Lavarone ...dep	7a50	6†p0
...	Caldonazzo arr	10 50	9 20

Fare 2 kr. 40 h.
†—Until 15th Sept.

Gleichenberg—

Gleichenberg ...dep	4 a0	11a45
Feldbach ....arr	5 25	1 10
Feldbach ....dep	7a30	3p15
Gleichenberg ...arr	9 5	4 55

10 miles. Fare 1 k. 60 h.

Dölsach— *-Until 15th Sept. †-From 16th Sept. §—Until 31st August.

k. h.			a.m.	a.m.	a.m.	a.m.	a.m.	p.m.
...	Dölsach dep	...	4 *0	6 §0	7§45	9†45	10*15	6 †0
2 40	Winklern { arr	...	6 30	8 50	11 0	1215	12 45	8 25
...	Winklern { dep	a.m.	6 50	9 0	11 0	3 30	1 15	
4 0	Döllach	6 †0	9 0	1215	1 30	5 30	3 25	...
6 40	Heiligenblut	8 0	11 0	1 50	3 0	...	5 25	...

			a.m.	a.m.	a.m.	a.m.	a.m.	p.m.
...	Heiligenblut dep	...	8 §0	8 *0	8 §0	8†30	9 †0	12*10
...	Döllach.............	...	9 0	9 55	9 15	9 45	1130	2 5
	Winklern...{ arr	a.m.	11 30	11 40	12 30	12 0	1 30	3 50
...	Winklern...{ dep	5†35	11 30	12 10	1 30	1 0	...	4 10
...	Dölsach ......arr	8 0	2 15	2 25	2 30	3 0	...	6 15

Fusch Bad— Service until 30th Sept.

E.M					
	Fusch Bad ......dep	6p30	...	Bruck im Pinzg. dep	3p30
7½	Bruck im Pinzgau	8 40	...	Fusch Bad.........arr	5 40

Fare, 3 kr. 60 h.

Ischl—Fare 6 k.

Ischl ......dep	8†a0	2*p20	3†p0
Unterach arr	1025	3 53	5 25
Unterach dp	10†a30	4*p10	5†30
Ischl ......arr	11 35	5 50	6 35

*—6th July until 14th Sept.
†—24th July until 30th Sept.

Jenbach—

E M		
	Jenbach ....dep	10a15
10½	Scholastica...........	1 2[illegible]
11½	Achenkirch .....arr	1 4[illegible]
...	Achenkirch ....dep	5 a0
...	Scholastica..........	5 25
...	Jenbach ....arr	7 30

Lienz—

	a.m.	a.m.	p.m.
Lienz.........dep	6 †0	9 45	6 0
Huben	9 15	1 15	9 0
Windisch Mat.	10 0	2 45	...

	a.m.	p.m.	noon
Windisch Mat.	6 †0	...	12 0
Huben	7 5	1 30	2 0
Lienz ....arr	10 0	4 0	5 0

†—Until 15th Sept.

Huben ....dep	2 p0
St. Jakob in Defereggen	7 0

Fare: 3 kr.

St. Jakob-in-Def ....dep	8a30
Huben ....arr	12 0

Imst— *—Until 31st July and from 1st Sept. †—Until 10th Sept. §—In Aug. only.

E M	k,h.		a.m.	a.m.	a.m.	p.m.	p.m.
...	...	Imst Bhf...dep	...	8†30	9 45	2 40	6 †5
2¼	0 60	„ Stadt......	6†10	8 55	10 5	3 5	6 25
10	3 0	Nassereit	7 5	9 50	11 0	4 0	7 10
22½	6 50	Lermoos Bhf a	8 40	1120	1255	5 30	8 25

	a.m.	a.m.	p.m.	p.m.	p.m.	p.m.
Lermoos Bhf d	5†55	9 20	1§25	1*25	3†20	5†40
Nassereit	7 15	1115	3 35	4 15	5 5	7 15
Imst Stadt arr	8 5	12 5	4 25	5 5	5 55	8 5
„ Bhf.. arr	8 20	1 25	5 0	5 40	...	...

Lofer— *—Until 15th Sept. ‡—Until 7th Sept. §—From 8th Sept.

E M	k.h.												
		Lofer ....dep	6a40	8‡a5	9§a55	10‡a0	12*p20	1p45	3‡p10	5‡p0	6 p0	7 p25	...
17	4 80	Bad Reichenhall...arr	8 0	9 25	11 15	11 10	1 40	3 5	4 30	6 10	7 20	8 45	...
...	...	Bad Reichenhall dep	6‡a0	8a20	9‡a40	12 0	1‡p20	2 p5	3p30	4‡p55	7p40	...	...
...	...	Lofer ....arr	7 25	9 45	10 50	1 25	2 30	3 30	4 55	6 5	9 5	...	...

Male—

E.M	k. h.			
		Male ....dep	5p30	
7½	1 60	Rabbi Bad arr	8 5	
...		Rabbi Bad dep	5 a0	...
...		Male .... arr	7 0	...

Service until 15th Sept.

E.M	k. h.						
		Lofer ....dep	6 a40	12p25	2*p45	4 p30	...
16½	3 20	Saalfelden.........arr	8 25	2 5	4 25	6 10	...
...	...	Saalfelden ......dep	6 a20	9 a25	2 p20	4*p40	...
...	...	Lofer ....arr	8 0	11 5	0	6 30	...

E M	k. h.						
		Lofer.......................dep	7 a30	11a10	3*p3	5 p5	...
16	3 0	St. Johann-in-Tirol...arr	8 55	12 35	5 0	6 30	...
...	...	St. Johann-in-Tirol dep	6 a30	10a20	2 p30	5*,55	...
...	...	Lofer ....arr	7 55	11 45	3 55	7 20	...

AUSTRIA—*Continued.*

Male—*Continued.*

E.M			
	Male ....dep	8 a15	3 p30
7½	Mezzana........	9 50	5 5
12½	Fucine ....arr	10 30	5 45

Fare 2 k.

Fucine ......dep	5a45	3 p40
Mezzana........	6 45	4 15
Male ....arr	8 0	5 40

E.M			
	Fucine ......dep	5†a30	12 *0
6½	Tonale ......arr	9 0	3 30

Tonale ......dep	9†a0	4*p30
Fucine ......arr	1030	6 0

†—From 15th July until 31st Aug. *—Until 30th Sept.

Neuberg—

E M			
	Neuberg ...dep	11a30	5p50
8	Mürzsteg...arr	12 50	7 10

Mürzsteg ......dep	10 a0	4 p15
Neuberg ....arr	11 20	5 35

Fare: 1 k. 60 h.

Mürzsteg ......dep	1 p10	...
Frein..............arr	2 30	...

Frein ....dep	11a40	...
Mürzsteg.........arr	1 0	...

Fare: 1 k. 80 h.

Riva—

	a.m	o.m
Riva ....dep	7 0	5 0
Piove di Ledro.....	8 21	6 21
Tiarno di Sopra ...	8 54	6 54
Storo	9 49	7 49
Condino ....arr	10 14	8 14

Condino...........dep	5a30	3 p30
Storo	6a30	4 0
Tiarno di Sopra ...	7 4	5 4
Pieve di Ledro......	7 40	5 40
Riva ....arr	8 50	6 50

Niederdorf—

k. h.			
	Niederdorf dep	8a15	2 p15
1 20	Alt Prags arr	9 30	3 30

Alt Prags......dep	5 a30	10a30
Niederdorf ...arr	6 30	11 30

k.h.									
	Niederdorf ...dep	7a35	9‡15	9‡30	10a‡0	1p20	5§45	6‡30	8‡p10
1 0	Neu Prags	8 50	1025	1040	10 30	2 55	6 55	7 0	9 20
2 20	Pragser Wildsee	9 40	11 5	1120	11 0	3 45	7 45	7 30	10 0

Pragser Wildsee ...dep	...	6 a0	6‡a30	11a‡35	2‡p0	2§p30	5 p30
Neu Prags	5‡a0	6 30	6 55	12 5	2 25	3 5	6 0
Niederdorf ....arr	6 0	7 20	7 30	1 0	2 50	4 0	7 10

§-From July 15 until Sept. 15. ‡-From July 4 to Sept. 4.

Pinzolo—

Pinzolo ....dep	6 a0	1135	3p40
M. di Campiglio arr	8 45	1240	4 45

Madonna di Campiglio ...dep	7a30	1p30	7 p0
Pinzolo ....arr	8 35	2 35	8 30

8¾ miles. Fare: 6 kr.

Rovereto—

Rovereto dep	4a30	...
Lavarone	12 0	3 ‡p0
Asiago......arr	...	7 30

Asiago ...dep	5 ‡a0	...
Lavarone	11 30	2 p0
Rovereto ...arr	...	7 45

‡—Until 15th July and from 16th Sept. on Mon., Wed. and Sat only; daily from 15th July until 15th Sept.

Rovereto—

Rovereto ....d·ǝ	8§20	2‡p50
Raossi in Vallarsa	9 20	3 50
Albergo Dolomiti...	1020	4 35
Valli.......................	11 0	5 30
Schio	1135	6 10
Recoaro...........arr	12 0	6 30

Recoaro ....dep	8‡a0	2§p15
Schio	8 20	2 25
Valli	9 0	3 20
Albergo Dolomiti	1020	4 40
Raossi in Vallarsa	11 0	5 20
Rovereto .. ..arr	12 0	6 15

‡—Until 30th September.
§—From 10th July until 9th September.

Tione—

E.M	k. h.							
		Tione ....dep	10a25	...	7 p50	...	...
16¾	4.50	Condino	12 11	...	9 36	...	...
23	6.50	Ponte Caffaro	12 49	3 p30	10 14	1 a30	...
...	...	Anfo ....arr	...	4 30	...	2 30	...

...	...	Anfo ....dep	...	10a25	...	12ngt0	...
...	...	Ponte Caffaro	4a?0	11 25	1p45	1 a0	...
...	...	Condino	5 14		2 39		...
...	...	Tione ....arr	6 45	...	4 10	...	...

Trient (Bahnhof)—

E.M.	k. h.						
		Trient Bhf............dep	5 a45	10a10	3p30	...	...
13¾	5.10	Sarche	7 45	12 5	5 35	...	...
29¼	10. 0	Tione	10 0	2 9	7 50	...	...
39¾	13.80	Pinzolo ....arr	11 14	3 23	9 4	...	...

...	...	Pinzolo ....dep	5a30	8 a55	3p 0	...	...
...	...	Tione	7 14	10 24	4 35	...	...
...	...	Sarche	9 13	12 16	6 34	...	...
...	...	Trient ....arr	10 47	1 50	8 8	...	...

Waidbruck—

E.M	k.h.							
		Waidbruck.........dep	7a30	9§45	1p25	1*40	...	4p30
9¼	2 60	Kastelruth	9 45	...	3 55	4 25	§	6 45
12½	3 30	Seis	10 20	...	4 30	5 5	7p40	7 30
13½	3 70	Salegg ....arr	10§35	1245	4 40	...	7 55	...

Salegg ....dep	...	6§a50	...	8a35	9§a45	p.m.	7p10	§
Seis	...	...	8*a45	8 50	10 5	1245	7 35	9p40
Kastelruth	4 a0	...	9 35	9 35		1 40		1015
Waidbruck ......arr	5 20	8 40	11 0	11 0	...	3 0	...	...

§—Until 15th Sept. *—Until 20th Sept.

SPONDINIG-PRAD and SULDEN.

*—Until 15th Sept.

E.M		a.m.	a.m.	a.m.	p.m.	p.m.	p.m.
	Spondinig-Prad ....dep	...	*	1 5	1‡15	4 0	4*20
...	Neuspondinig	7 0	7 10	10 3⁵	1 30	4 20	...
1¾	Prad	7 15	7 30	1º 50	1 55	4 35	...
6¼	Gomagoi	8 55	8 50	12 30	3 0	6 15	...
*12¼	St. Gertraud in Sulden......	11 20	11 0	2 ⁵5	5 20	8 40	...
‡13¾	Hotel Sulden ....arr	11 35	...	3 40	6 40	8 55	8 50

	a.m.	a.m.	a.m.	p.m.	p.m.	
Hotel Sulden ....dep	8 ?0	9 10	...	2*30	..	...
St. Gertraud in Sulden ...	6 45	9 25	9*30	2 45	3 *0	...
Gomagoi	8 10	10 50	11 0	4 20	4 30	...
Prad	9 0	11 40	12 45	5 10	5 55	...
Neuspondinig..................	9 15	11 55	1 0	6 5	6 5	...
Spondinig-Prad ....arr	...	...	...	6 10		..

SPONDINIG and STILFSERJOCH.

*—Until 15th Sept.
‡—Until 20th Sept.

E.M			a.m.			p.m.	p.m.	p.m.
	Spondinig-Prad	...	*	...	‡	1‡15	...	...
—	Neuspondinig ...	...	7 10	...	a.m	1 30	4‡40	6‡30
1⅞	Prad	...	7 25	a.m	1035	1 50	...	...
6¼	Gomagoi	...	8 40	8 15	...	3 0	7 0	...
8⅞	Trafoi	a.m.	9 40	9 15	2 25	4 10		8 50
9¼	Trafoi-Hotel......	7‡30	10 30	9 45	...	4 20	...	9 0
13⅞	Franzenshöhe...	9 45	1 40		4 55		...	
18	Stilfserjoch arr	1 20	3 50	..	7 0	...	...	...

			p.m.	p.m.	p.m.
Stilfserjoch ...dep	‡	...	12*55	...	3*30
Franzenshöhe ...	a.m	...	2 20	...	5 0
Trafoi-Hotel	6 0	a.m.	3 20	4 ‡0	6 0
Trafoi........... ...	6 15	7‡35	3 40	...	
Gomagoi......... ...	6 45	...	4 20	...	..
Prad	7 20	...	5 25	...	...
Neuspondinig ...	7 40	9 25	5 50	5 30	...
Spondinig-P. ...arr	7 45	..	...	...	...

Extra (until 15th Sept.)

Spondinig-Prad Bhf. dep	8a10	10a10	1p20	4 p0	6p25
Trafoi Hotel ....arr	10 0	12 5	3 15	5 55	8 15

Trafoi Hotel ....dep	6a25	8 a0	10a15	2 p0	4p30
Spondinig-Prad Bhf. arr	7 55	9 40	12 20	3 30	6 0

STILFSERJOCH and BORMIO BAD.

*—Until 15th Sept. ‡—Until 20th Sept.

E.M.							
	Stilfserjoch..................dep	7‡a30	1‡p30	3 ‡p0	4*p0	...	...
1¾	Sta Maria IV Cantoniera ...	8 0	3 0	3 30	4 30	...	...
11¾	Bormio Bad................arr	10 0	5 0	5 30	6 50	...	...

Bormio Bad..................dep	7*a0	7‡a45	8‡a15	...	...
Sta Maria IV Cantoniera ...	12 10	11 20	12 25	...	...
Stilfserjoch ....arr	12 55	12 0	1 25	...	...

LANDECK and TRAFOI.

E.M	k.h.		a.m	a.m.	a.m.	a.m.	p.m.	p.m.	p.m	
—	—	Landeck dep	7 ‡0	7*10	8 0	10*30	12§30	2 *0	3*30	...
10	3 0	Ried	8 5	8 15	9 5	11 25	1 25	3 5	4 35	...
18½	7 50	Pfunds	9 10	9 10	1010	12 20	2 20	4 0	5 35	...
26½	1060	Nauders	10 5		11 5	1 50	3 25		6 25	...
36½	12 0	St. Valentin	1115	...	1245	2 55	4 30	...	7 35	...
42¼	17 0	Mals	1145	...	1 20	3 35	5 5	...	8 5	...
47¾	1920	Neuspondinig		...	1 50	4 5	5 35	...		...
56½	2270	Trafoi ... arr	...	...	3 25	5 25	7 10	...	...	...

			a.m.	a.m	a.m.		p.m		
Trafoi......dep	...	...	6*35	9§55	11†20	...	1250	...	...
Neuspondinig	a.m.	...	8 0	1120	12 45	...	2 25	p.m	...
Mals	7 30	...	8 30	1150	1 40	...	2 55	3 ‡0	...
St. Valentin...	8 20	...	9 20	1240	2 30	...	3 45	3 50	...
Nauders	9 30	a.m.	10 20	2 5	3 40	p.m.	4 55	5 0	...
Pfunds	1015	10*30	11 5	2 50	4 30	5 *0	5 45	5 50	...
Ried	1110	11 25	11 45	3 30	5 25	5 55	6 40	6 45	...
Landeck...arr	1210	12 25	12 40	4 25	6 25	6⁰55	7 40	7 45	...

*—Until 15th Sept. †—From 21st Sept. ‡—Until 20th Sept. §—Until 31st August.

MALS and MUNSTER.

E.M.	fr. c.						
		Mals ....dep	6a30	12†p30	1*p30	5 *p0	...
5	2 0	Taufers	8 40	2 55	3 0	7 0	...
6⅝	2 40	Munster ...arr	9 0	3 15	3 30	7 20	...

Munster dep	7*a0	9 a30	3†p40	5*p0	...	...	...
Taufers	7 20	9 50	4 0	5 20	...	...	...
Mals .....arr	9 0	11 30	5 50	6 50	...	...	...

*—Until 15th September. †—From 16th September.

DOLOMITE REGION.

*—Until 15th Sept. †—1 hour earlier from 15th August. §—Until 31st August. ‖—Until 10th Sept.

	a.m.	a.m.	a.m.	p.m.	p.m.
Longarone dep	6 32	1046	1045	3 40	4 15
Tai arr	8 11	1225	12 0	5 20	5 30
Pieve di Cadore arr	8 18	1232	...	5 30	...
Pieve di Cadore dep	...		...	...	...
Tai dep	...	...	1 0	...	6 0
Borca	9 26	...	1 40	6 36	6 40
S. Vito Cadore arr	9 45	...	1 55	6 55	6 55

S. Vito Cadore dep	5 a30	8a55	1 p0	4p10	...
Borca	5 45	9 5	1 15	4 20	...
Tai arr	6 48	9 45	2 18	5 0	...
Pieve di Cadore arr	...	...	...	...	p.m.
Pieve di Cadore dep	6 54	...	2 24	...	7 0
Tai dep	...	10 0	...	5 30	...
Longarone arr	8 38	1115	4 8	6 45	8 50

Pieve di Cadore dep	8a35	1 p0	...	...
Calalzo	8 55	1 20	...	...
Lozzo Cadore	1015	2 40	...	...
S. Stefano Cad. arr	1245	5 10	...	...

S. Stefano Cad. dep	7 a0	2p35	...
Lozzo Cadore	9 20	4 55	...
Calalzo	1045	6 20	...
Pieve di Cadore arr	11 5	6 40	

Lozzo Cadore dep	10a25	3p40	...
Auronzo arr	11 45	4 10	...

Auronzo dep	7a55	3p30	...	...
Lozzo Cadore arr	9 5	4 40	...	...

Auronzo dep	...	...	...	...
Misurina arr	...	...	...	...

Misurina dep	...	...	...
Auronzo arr	...	...	...

	a.m.	p.m.
Belluno dep	9 5	6 30
Vena d'Oro arr	1040	8 0

	p.m.	p.m.
Vena d'Oro dep	4 0	9 45
Belluno arr	5 35	1115

Toblach dep	7 a0	10a0	2 p0	5 p0	...	...
Schluderbach	8 5	11 5	3 5	6 5	...	...
Cortina arr	9 0	12 0	4 0	7 0	...	...

Cortina dep	6 §a0	10 a0	2 r0	4p30	...
Schluderbach	7 10	11 15	3 15	5 45	...
Toblach arr	7 50	12 0	4 0	6 30	...

Schluderbach dep	8*a0	8§a30	10*20	5 p
Misurina arr	9 30	11 0	11 50	6 30

Misurina dep	*a0	2 p45
Schluderbach arr	8 15	4 0

Karersee dep	...	7‖20	‖	...	2p‖0	*	3‖p0	...	...
Vigo di Fassa	...	8 0	10a30	1140	2 40	2p50	3 40	4p30	6p40
Canazei	7a50	8 40	11 10	1 30	3 20	3 35	—	6 50	7 15
Pordoi Pass	8 30	9 15	11 50	2 10	3 55	4 15	...	—	—
Pieve di Livinallongo	1030	11 0	1 55	4 10	5 40	6 15	...	...	...
Cortina d'Ampezzo arr	1 0	1 0	3 45	6 40	7 40	9*30	...	...	...

Cortina d'A dep	..	*	...	7‖20	8 a0	2‖p0	2p10	4*30
Pieve Liv.	...	7a30	...	9 10	1035	3 50	4 45	7 0
Pordoi Pass	...	9 30	...	1055	1235	5 35	6 45	—
Canazei	7a45	1030	a.m.	1135	2 10	6 15	7 25	...
Vigo di Fassa	8 25	11 5	11‖5	12 5	2 50	6 45	—	...
Karersee arr	...	...	1145	*1255	...	7 35	...	...

Predazzo dep	10‖a20	10a40	1*p50	5p40	7 p0	...
Vigo di Fassa arr	11 0	11 40	2 45	6 40	9 35	...

Vigo di Fassa dep	2a30	8a25	9 a0	11*10	2p50	3‖p45
Predazzo arr	4 50	9 20	11 0	12 5	3 45	4 30

Borca dep	9a26	1p40	6p40	...
Vito Cadore	10 0	1 55	6 55	...
Cortina arr	1130	2 30	7 30	...

Cortina dep	7 a0	8a15	3p30	...
Vito Cadore	8 15	8 55	4 10	...
Borca arr	...	9 0	4 15	...

Botzen dep	7 a0	9*a30	1p30	2 p0	...	...
Cavalese	9 40	12 10	4 10	4 40	...	...
Predazzo	1020	12 50	4 50	5 20	...	...
Rolle Pass	12 5	—	6 35	—	...	...
San Martino di Castrozza arr	1240	...	7 10	...	...	...

San Martino dep	7a30	...	2 p10	...	...	...	...	...
Rolle Pass	8 15	*	2 55	...	...	...	...	...
Predazzo	9 45	12p45	4 30	...	...	...	...	...
Cavalese	10 30	1 30	5 15	...	...	...	...	...
Botzen arr	1 0	4 0	7 45	..	...	...	...	...

	a.m	p.m.
Belluno dep	8 40	5 30
Mas	9 50	7 0
Agordo arr	1 20	1030

Agordo dep	5 a0	1p55
Mas	8 0	4 55
Belluno arr	9 0	6 5

Agordo dep	6 a0	1p40
Cencenighe arr	7 15	3 0

Cencenighe dep	1210	5 p0
Agordo arr	1 10	6 0

Cencenighe dep	7a30	3p15
Alleghe	9 15	5 0
Caprile	10 0	6 0
Rocca Pietore arr	1045	6 30

Rocca Pietore dep	8a40	1p45
Caprile	9 25	2 30
Alleghe	1010	3 15
Cencenighe arr	1140	4 45

E.M	k.h.							
		Botzen dep	6a45	8*a30	1 p40	...	...	...
12	3 60	Birchabruck	10 5	12 30	4 15	...	...	...
16	4 80	Welschnofen	1140	2 0	5 30	...	...	...
21	6 40	Karersee arr	1 10	4 0	7 0	...	...	...
...	...	Karersee dep	6 a0	10*15	4 †p0	...	...	...
...	...	Welschnofen	7 0	11 15	4 55	...	...	...
...	...	Birchabruck	8 0	12 20	5 50	...	...	...
...	...	Botzen arr	10 0	2 30	7 50	...	...	...

THE BLACK FOREST.

Feldberg—(7½ miles).

m. pf					
	Feldberg dep	8*a0	12p30	3*45	6p15
0	Titisee arr	8 45	1 15	4 30	7 0

Titisee dep	6*50	9§a15	10*40	2p25	5*10
Feldberg arr	7 35	10 0	11 25	3 20	5 55

*—Until 15th September.
§—From 16th September.

Griesbach—

E.M	m. pf				
		Griesbach dep	6a10	1p40	8p30
7½	1 20	Oppenau arr	7 40	3 5	9 55
...	...	Oppenau dep	8 a5	3p30	6 p55
...	...	Griesbach arr	9 50	5 15	8 40

Nordrach— Fare 1 m.

E.M			
	Nordrach dep	5 a40	1p20
6¼	Zell (Harmersbach) arr	6 35	2 15
...	Zell (Harmersbach) dep	6 a45	4 p0
...	Nordrach arr	7 50	5 5

Rippoldsau Bad-Fare 2m. 20 pf.

E.M				
	Rippoldsau B. dep	8a10	3§p30	5‡30
14	Wolfach arr	9 20	4 30	6 30
...	Wolfach dep	6‡a50	2p45	5§50
...	Rippoldsau B. arr	8 5	4 5	7 10

‡—Until 15th Sept.
§—Until 10th September.

St. Blasien—

St. Blasien dep	7a20	12c10	3 ‡10	6p30
Schluchsee	7 45	12 40	3 35	7 0
Titisee arr	8 30	1 30	4 20	7 50

Titisee	6‡50	9§a15	10‡40	2p40	6p30
Schluchsee	7 30	9 55	11 15	3 20	7 5
St. Blasien	8 10	10 35	12 0	4 0	7 40

Fare: St. Blasien to Titisee 4 m. 50 pf.

E.M	m.pf			
		St. Blasien dep	5‡p50	...
...	4 50	Titisee	7 10	...
...	8 0	Freiburg arr	8 20	...
...	...	Freiburg dep	9a‡20	...
...	...	Titisee	10 40	...
...	...	St. Blaisen arr	12 0	...

‡—Until 15th Sept. §—From 16th Sept.

E.M				
	St. Blasien dep	6‡a50	10§40	2‡p20
15½	Waldshut arr	8 0	11 50	3 30
...	Waldshut dep	9‡a10	4p50	...
...	St. Blasien arr	10 30	6 10	...

Fare 4 m 50 pf.

St. Blasien dep	9‡a0	2§p0	4‡p30	...
Menzenschwand arr	1015	3 15	5 45	...

Menzenschwand dep	6‡a10	9§a15	1‡p15
St. Blasien arr	7 25	10 30	2 30

‡—Until 15th Sept. §—From 16th Sept.

E.M.	m. pf			
		St. Blasien dep	8a30	4p10
...	2 50	Todtmoos arr	9 15	4 55
...		Todtmoos dep	11a 0	5p30
...		St. Blasien arr	11 45	6 15

Service until 15th Sept.

Peterstal— Fare 1 m.

E.M.				
	Peterstal dep	6a45	2p15	9 p5
5	Oppenau arr	7 40	3 10	10 0
...	Oppenau dep	8 a5	3 30	6 p55
...	Peterstal arr	9 5	4 30	7 55

Schluchsee—

E.M	m. pf.				
		Schluchsee dep	6 a30	...	...
21	3 40	Thiengen arr	11 45	...	...
...		Thiengen dep	8 a40	...	...
...		Schluchsee arr	2 25	...	...

Schluchsee dep	10a40	2p30	5p15	6*35
Titisee arr	11 15	3 5	5 50	7 10
Titisee dep	7a45	12p10	4 p0	5*30
Schluchsee arr	8 20	12 45	4 35	6 5

*—Until 31st August.

Schönwald—

E.M	m. pf.				
		Triberg dep	7 a20	5p20	
4½	0 70	Schönwald arr	8 45	6 45	
...		Schönwald dep	5a 0	6 p25	...
...		Triberg arr	5 55	7 20	...

Todtmoos—

m.pf.					
	Wehr dep	8 a0	11‡a0	3 p5	8p30
1 70	Todtmoos arr	9 15	12 15	4 20	9 45

Todtmoos dep	6a15	9‡20	1 25	6p50
Wehr arr	7 30	10 35	2 40	8 5

‡—Until 15th September.

GERMANY.

Alexandersbad—[In Summer only].

E.M.	m pf						
		Alexandersbad......dep	8 a55	10a45	12p45	4p35	6p40
4	0 90	Markt Redwitz......arr	9 20	11 10	1 10	5 0	7 5

Markt Redwitz.........dep	7a15	11a40	3p35	5p45	...	...	...
Alexandersbad.........arr	7 40	12 5	4 0	6 15	...	...	...

Bad Tölz—

E.M									
	Bad Tölz...dep	6a35	7‡a35	9 a30	10‡a0	1 p5	2‡p15	4p35	7‡p25
8¾	Bichl	7 28	...	10 23	...	1 58	...	5 28	8 18
14¼	Kochel	7 55	8 25	10 50	10 50	2 25	3 5	5 55	8 45
34¼	Mittenwaldarr	1025	10 0	12‡30	12 30	5 0	4 45	9 30	...

Mittenwald...dep	...	6a24	9‡a0	10a40	1‡p45	...	...	6‡p45
Kochel	7a10	8 30	1035	2 p20	3 20	5p10	7 p25	8 20
Bichl	7 40	9 0	..	2 50	...	5 40	7 55	..
Bad Tölz ......arr	8 25	9 45	1125	3 40	4 10	6 25	8 45	9 10

‡—Until 7th Sept.

E.M									
	Bad Tölz dep	7a45	9*20	10a40	1p35	4p25	5*p40	7§p40	8*p25
6½	Lenggries arr	8 20	9 55	11 15	2 10	5 0	6 15	8 15	9 0

Lenggries dep	6*a50	7§a40	8 *50	10a50	1p45	3*p40	5 p5	6*p50	7§p55
Bad Tölz arr	7 25	8 15	9 25	11 25	2 20	4 15	5 40	7 25	8 20

*—Until 15th Sept. §—From 16th Sept, and not on Sunday.

E.M									
	Bad Tölz (Postamt) dep	6a30	8a40	10a10	12‡p55	1p50	4‡15	5p50	...
13¾	Tegernsee (Bhf.)......arr	7 40	9 30	11 20	1 45	3 0	5 5	7 0	...

Tegernsee dep	8a10	9‡a5	11a30	1‡p20	3p10	6‡p25	7p30	...
Bad Tölz arr	9 20	9 55	12 40	2 10	4 20	7 15	8 40	...

Bertrich Bad—

E.M.	m.pf.								
		Bertrich B.dep	8a15	11a20	2p15	3 p5	6p15	8p55	...
7	1 10	Bullay.......arr	8 45	11 50	2 45	3 35	6 45	9 25	...

Bullay ......dep	9a50	12p15	3p15	3p55	7p10	10p10	...	...	...
Bertrich B...arr	1020	12 45	3 45	4 25	7 40	10 40	...	...	...

Friedrichroda—

E.M		
	Friedrichroda...dep	9 a0
7½	Inselsberg ......arr	12 0
...	Inselsberg ......dep	3 p15
...	Friedrichroda...arr	6 30

Fare 1 m. 20 pf.
In Summer only.

Kissingen—

E.M				
	Kissingen ......dep	9a40	3p37	6*p35
6¾	Bocklet Bad ...arr	10 23	4 20	7 18
...	Bocklet Bad...dep	11a30	5p30	7*p25
...	Kissingen ......arr	12 13	6 15	8 8

Fare: 1 m. 40 pf.

E.M					
	Kissingen ....dep	7*a40	9a45	3 p0	7 p
0½	Brückenau Bad arr	9 35	11 40	4 55	8 5
...	Brückenau Bad dep	7*a20	10 a0	4 p5	7 p0
...	Kissingen ....arr	9 15	11 55	6 0	8 55

Fare: 3 m. 30pf. *—In July & Aug. only.

Kochel—

E.M					
	Kochel ......dep	8 a5	11†a10	2p35	7 p0
10½	Murnau ......arr	9 10	12 15	3 40	8 5

Murnau......dep	6a40	9a25	1†p0	4 p5
Kochel ......arr	7 40	1025	2 0	5 5

†—Until 31st Aug.

Kreuth Bad—

E.M	m. pf.											
		Kreuth Bad ....dep	6a§30	7*a15	10 a5	1 p10	3‡p15	4 p25	6‡p25	7p50	...
8	1 30	Tegernsee..................arr	7 5	8 0	10 50	1 55	4 0	5 10	7 10	8 35	...
...	...	Tegernsee.....................dep	8 a5	9‡a45	11 a5	2 p5	4 p55	6 ‡5	8 p0	...	...
...	...	Kreuth Bad ....arr	8 55	10 35	11 55	2 55	5 45	6 55	8 50	...	...

*—From 16th Sept. ‡—Until 8th Sept. §—Until 15th Sept.

Oberammergau—

E.M	m. pf											
		Oberammergau ......dep	6 a10	8 a35	10a15	1 p45	2 p30	6 p20	7 p5	...	...	...
6¾	1 10	Oberau ....arr	6 45	9 10	10 50	2 20	3 5	6 55	8 20	...	...	...
...	...	Oberau ....dep	7 a0	7 a50	10a30	3 p25	6 p5	8 p40	...	...	...	...
...	...	Oberammergau.........arr	7 45	8 35	11 15	4 10	6 52	9 25	...	...	...	...

Oberdorf Bad—

E.M	m.pf					
		Oberdorf Bad dep	7 a0	9a55	2 p5	7 p0
5¼	0 70	Sonthofen ......arr	8 0	1055	3 5	8 0

Sonthofen.....dep	5a40	8a20	11a20	3p40	5p10
Oberdorf Bad arr	6 40	9 20	12 20	4 40	6 10

Tegernsee—

‡—Until 7th September.

E.M		‡	‡		‡		‡	‡			‡
—	Tegernsee...dep	5a15	7 a0	8 a0	9a40	11a0	11a30	1p55	2p0	4p50	6p0
20½	Achenkirch ...	7 20	9 5	10 5	...	1 5	...	...	4 5	6 55	...
22½	Scholastika arr	7 30	9 15	1015	1130	1 15	1 20	3 45	4 15	7 5	7 50

	‡		‡		‡		‡	‡		‡
Scholastika dep	5a50	7a45	9a40	10a35	11a30	1p50	3p35	4p30	4p45	6p15
Achenkirch ...	6 0	7 55	...	10 45	...	2 0	...	...	4 55	6 25
Tegernsee ...arr	8 5	10 0	1125	12 50	1 15	4 5	5 50	6 15	7 0	8 30

E.M.										
	Tegernsee dep	6a55	8‡30	9a55	12p55	2‡p0	3p30	4‡p45	6 p45	...
10	Schliersee arr	7 45	9 20	1045	1 45	2 50	4p20	5 35	7 35	...

Schliersee dep	8a30	10‡a0	11a30	2p30	3‡p30	4‡p30	5p45	7p45	...
Tegernsee arr	9 20	10 50	12 20	3 20	4 20	5 20	6 35	8 35	...

ITALY.

Aosta—

Aosta ....dep	...	...	...	...	...	...	...	...	...	...
Villeneuve	...	...	...	...	...	...	...	...	...	...
Pré St. Didier......	...	...	...	...	...	...	...	...	...	...
Courmayeur ...arr	...	...	...	...	...	...	...	...	...	...
Courmayeur ...dep	...	...	...	...	...	...	...	...	...	...
Pré St. Didier......	...	...	...	...	...	...	...	...	...	...
Villeneuve	...	...	...	...	...	...	...	...	...	...
Aosta ....arr	...	...	...	...	...	...	...	...	...	...

Aosta ....dep	...	...	...
St. Remy.........arr	...	...	...
Gd.St.Bernard arr	...	...	...
Gd.St.Bernard dep	...	...	...
St. Remy ......dep	...	...	...
Aosta ....arr	...	...	...

Courmayeur ....dep	...	...
Petit St. Bernard.....arr	...	...
Petit St. Bernard....dep	...	...
Courmayeur ....arr	...	...

Arsiero— 21½ miles.

Arsiero ...dep	...	...
Lavarone.. arr	...	...

Lavarone ...dep	...	...
Arsiero .. ...arr	...	...

Biella—

E.M	fr. c.						
		Biella ....dep	7 a30	9 a15	1 p30	2 p0	7p3
6	2 50	Oropa ....arr	8 30	10 5	2 20	3 0	8 3
...		Oropa ....dep	10a30	11 a0	3 p20	...	...
...		Biella ....arr	11 10	12 0	4 0	...	—

Chatillon—

Chatillon ....dep	9 a0	...	...	...	...	...
Antey S. Andre	10 30	...	...	...	...	...
Valtournanche...arr	1 0	...	...	...	...	...
Valtournanche...dep	2 p30	...	...	...	...	...
Antey S. Andre	3 50	...	...	...	...	...
Chatillon ....arr	5 0	...	...	...	...	...

ITALY—*Continued.*

Edolo—

Edolo. ....dep	10 a0	2 p0	...
Ponte di Leg	11 30	3 30	...
Ponte di Leg	8 a0	3 p0	...
Edolo...... arr	9 15	4 15	...

Ponte di Legno dep	5a45	...
Dogana di Tonale...	8 0	...
Dogana di Tonale ...	9a30	...
Ponte di Legno dep	1030	...

Piedimulera—

Piedimulera ......dep	1a30	...
Bannio	4 5	...
Ceppomorelli ...arr	6 0	...
Ceppomorelli ...dep	4a30	...
Bannio	5 35	...
Piedimulera ......arr	7 30	...

Rimini—

Rimini ......dep	9a15	3 p0	5p30
San Marino arr	1030	4 15	6 45
San Marino dep	7 a0	7a30	3 p0
Rimini ......arr	8 15	8 45	4 15

Tirano—

Tirano ....dep	9a10	2 p0	...
Bormio	3 0	7 40	...
Bagni di Bormio ...arr	...	...	...
	a.m.	no'n	
Bagni di Bormio ...dep	...	...	...
Bormio............	6 30	12 0	...
Tirano ....arr	11 0	4 30	...

Tresenda—

Tresenda ....dep	9a20	12p50
Edolo ....arr	1135	3 5
Edolo ....dep	9a45	4 p0
Tresenda ....arr	1140	6 5

Varallo—

	a.m.	p.m
Varallo ....dep	5 0	1230
Balmuccia	6 30	2 0
Mollia	9 20	4 50
Alagna ....arr	10 45	6 15
Alagna............dep	2a4ᶜ	12 0
Mollia...	3 45	1 0
Balmuccia	6 15	3 30
Varallo ....arr	7 30	4 45

Varallo ....dep	12 0	...
Balmuccia	1 45	...
Rimasco ....arr	4 30	...
Rimasco ....dep	4a45	...
Balmuccia	6 15	...
Varallo ....arr	7 30	...

Vietri—

	a.m	p.m.
Vietri (Station) dep	8 30	2 0
Maiori	10 0	3 30
Amalfi ....arr	11 0	4 30
	a m	p.m.
Amalfi ....dep	2 40	2 20
Maiori..................	3 35	3 25
Vietri (Station) arr	5 40	5 20

Vievola—

Vievola ...dep	10a0	1p10	...
Tenda	1020	2 0	...
S. Dalmazzo di Tenda	1040	2 15	...
Ventimiglia ar	1 5	4 50	...
Ventimiglia dp	9 a20	1p35	...
S. Dalmazzo...	12 5	4 25	...
Tenda............	12 26	4 50	...
Vievola ...arr	12 50	5 15	...

SWITZERLAND.

Albisbrunn Bad—

Albisbrunn dep	7a50	11a10	4p15
Sihlbrugg arr	8 35	1155	4 50
Sihlbrugg dep	9 a0	2p20	6p45
Albisbrunn arr	10 5	3 25	7 50

4½ miles ; fare 90 c.

Berne—

Berne ....dep	6a 0	10a40	5p 0
Frieswil ....arr	7 14	11 54	6 14
Frieswil ...dep	7a37	12p17	6p37
Berne.........arr	8 50	1 30	7 50

9½ miles; fare 1 fr. 85 c.

Biel (Bienne)—

Biel ....dep	8a40	1p15	7p15
Täuffelen ...arr	10 5	2 40	8 45
Täuffelen...dep	6a25	1p15	7p10
Biel ....arr	7 40	2 30	8 25

6 miles. Fare 1 fr. 20 c.

Bignasco—

Bignasco dep	6a50	11a 0	3p20
Fusio ......arr	1030	2 40	7 0
Fusio ......dep	5a30	1 p25	4p50
Bignasco arr	7 25	3 20	6 45

Fare 1 fr. 80 c. ; 11 miles.

Bremgarten—

E.M.	Bremgart'n dp	5a20	3p55
7	Mellingen arr	7 0	5 35
...	Mellingen dep	9a35	6p45
...	Bremgart'n ar	1120	8 30

Fare, 1 fr. 15 c.

Broc—

Broc ...dep	8a20	1p10	5p25	9p10
Charmey	9 35	2 25	6 45	1025
Jaun...arr	1110	...	8 15	...
Jaun...dep	5a30	...	...	5p10
Charmey	6 55	1040	3 p5	6 35
Broc...dep	7 55	1140	4 5	7 35

11½ miles; 3 fr. 5 c.

Chaux de Fonds—

Chaux de Fonds ......dep	4p15
Maiche ....arr	9 45
Maiche ....dep	6 a5
Chaux de Fonds ......arr	1130

19 miles; fare 3fr. 70c.

Cossonay—

E.M.	Cossonay...dep	8a35	6p30
7	L'Isle ....arr	9 55	8 0
...	L'Isle ....dep	6a50	5p35
...	Cossonay...arr	8 15	6 45

Fare 1 fr. 15 c.

Couvet—

E.M.	Couvet ...dep	8 a45	7p20
7	Brévine...arr	11 15	9 55
...	Brévine ...dep	5 a0	5p15
...	Couvet......arr	6 40	6 55

Fare 1 fr. 45 c.

Croy—

E.M.	fr. c.	Croy.........dep	8a 0
4	0 80	Orbe ....arr	8 45
...	...	Orbe..........dep	6p10
..	...	Croy..........arr	7 30

Croy ....dep	8 a5	3p25	7p45
Vaulion ......arr	9 45	5 5	9 0
Vaulion .....dep	5a45	2 p0	5p50
Croy ....arr	6 55	3 10	6 40

5½ miles ; Fare 1 fr.

Delemont—

E.M	Delemont ..dep	9 a0	4p15
8½	Bourrignon arr	1125	6 40
...	Bourrignon dep	6a10	4p35
...	Delemont ...arr	8 5	6 30

Fare 1 fr. 45 c.

Delemont dep	9 a5	12p25	7p40
Montsevelier ar	11 5	2 25	9 40
Montsevelier dp	6a15	10a0	4p55
Delemont...arr	8 5	1150	6 45

9 miles ; fare 1 fr. 55 c.

Domodossola—

Domodossola dep		6 a0	1 ꞅ45
S. Maria Maggiore		9 0	4 50
Camedo 5 a0		10 50	6 25
Pontebrolla ar 6 30		12 20	7 55

Fare from Domodossola to Pontebrolla, 6 fr. 10 c.

	a.m.	p.m.	pm
Pontebrolla...dep ...	8 0	3 50	6 0
Camedo............ ...	1030	6 20	820
S. Maria Mg...6a0	1 40	8 10	...
Domodossola ar.740	3 20	...	...

Echallens—

Echallens.........dep	8 a55	5p35
Moudon.............arr	11 20	8 0
Moudon.............dep	7 a10	4p 5
Echallens.........arr	9 30	6 35

12 miles. Fare 1 fr. 95 c.

Echallens.........dep	6 a15	5p15
Yverdon ....arr	7 55	8 10
Yverdon ....dep	9 a20	4 p5
Echallens.........arr	12 35	6 25

13 miles. Fare 2 fr. 10 c.

Fribourg—

Fribourg ....dep	7 a5	4 p0
Plaffeien	9 40	6 40
Schwefelberg Bad	...	...
Schwefelberg Bad	...	...
Plaffeien	7a 0	5p40
Fribourg ....arr	9 0	7 40

Fare: To Plaffeien, 2 fr. 90 c.
To Schwefelberg, ———

E.M	Fribourg ...dep	6 a0	4p40
8	Farvagny	7 50	6 35
17½	Bulle .... arr	9 50	8 30
...	Bulle ....dep	6 a0	4p40
...	Farvagny	8 10	6 50
...	Fribourg ...arr	9 50	8 30

Fare, 4 fr. 80 c.

E.M	Fribourg ...dep	6 a0	4p20
10	La Roche	8 30	6 55
18	Bulle ....arr	10 0	8 25
...	Bulle ....dep	6a40	4p40
...	La Roche	8 10	6 15
...	Fribourg ...arr	1020	8 2ˢ

Fare, 4 fr. 85 c.

Frick—

E M	Frick ...dep	6a40	4p20
10½	Aarau ...arr	9 10	6 45
...	Aarau ...dep	7 a0	4p20
...	Frick ......arr	9 10	6 35

Fare 2 fr.

E M	Frick......dep	8 a10	3 p30
6	Oberhof...arr	9 45	5 5
...	Oberhof dep	9 a50	5 p25
...	Frick ......arr	11 15	6 50

Fare 80 c.

Glovelier—

E M	fr. c	Glovelier...dep	9a40
8¾	1 70	Bellelay ...arr	1210
...	...	Bellelay ...dep	4 p0
...	...	Glovelier...arr	5 30

Grandson—

Service until 15th September.

E.M	fr. c	Grandson...dep	8 a35
7¾	1 50	Mauborget arr	1135
...	...	Mauborget dep	3p 0
...	...	Grandson ...arr	4 40

Herisau—

E M	Herisau... dep	5a 0	...
9	Lustmühle ar	7 29	...
...	Lustmühle dp	4 p35	...
...	Herisau ...arr	6 50	...

Fare 1 fr. 75 c.

Herzogenbuchsee—

Herzogenbuchsee ...dep	7 p25
Koppigen ....arr	8 40
Koppigen ....dep	6 a15
Herzogenbuchsee ...arr	7 25

6¼ miles; fare 1 fr. 5 c.

Herzogenb 8 a5	11a50	3p25	9p30
Wangen... 8 5	12 50	4 20	1030
Wangen...6a25	11a50	4 25	5p45
Herzogenb 7 25	12 50	5 25	6 45

4¾ miles ; fare 80 c.

Langenthal—

Langenthal 8a25	1p30	6p30	8p20
Melchnau..9 20	2 25	7 25	9 15
Melchnau. .6a25	9a45	4p 0	7p30
Langenthal 725	1045	5 0	8 30

4¼ miles ; fare 70 c.

Leuk—

Leuk.........dep	10a30	3p10	...
Leukerbad arr	2p30	7 10	...
Leukerbad dep	7 a10	4p10	...
Leuk.........arr	9 5	6 5	...

10 miles; fare 3 fr. 95 c.

Locarno—

E M	Locarno .. dep	5 a0	2p40
18¼	Sonogno ...arr	1010	7 50
...	Sonogno...dep	4 a0	2p 0
...	Locarno ...arr	7 50	5 45

Fare, 2 fr. 95 c.

SWITZERLAND—*Continued.*

Locle—

E M	fr. c.						
		Locle ....dep	8 a20	10a20	2 p30	6 p30	8 p30
$4\frac{1}{2}$	0 95	Chaux du Milieu........	9 25	:	3 35	:	9 35
$9\frac{3}{4}$	1 90	Brévine..............arr	10 30	12 25	4 40	8 35	10 40
7	1 40	Les Ponts.............arr	10 15	...	4 25	...	10 25
...	...	Les Ponts.............dep	6 a20	...	11a40	...	8 p45
...	...	Brévine.............dep	6 10	7a15	11 30	5 p45	8 35
...	...	Chaux du Milieu........	7 15	:	12 35	:	9 40
...	...	Locle ....arr	8 5	9 0	1 25	7 30	10 30

Moutiers—

E.M			
	Moutiers dep	8 a45	5 p0
$6\frac{1}{2}$	Souboz.........	10 50	7 5
$11\frac{1}{2}$	Bellelay..arr	12 10	8 25
...	Bellelay dep	5 a20	4 p0
...	Souboz.........	6 30	5 10
...	Moutiers arr	7 40	6 20

Fares from Moutiers: to Souboz 1 fr. 25c., to Bellelay 2 fr. 20c.

Muri—

E.M.		
	Muri ....dep	4p55
$7\frac{1}{2}$	Bremgarten ...arr	6 30
...	Bremgarten ...dep	8 a15
...	Muri..............arr	9 55

Fare 1 fr. 20 c.

Nyon—

E M	fr. c.							
		Nyon Station ......dep	7a20	3p30	5p45	...	...	...
$8\frac{3}{4}$	3 25	St. Cergues ....arr	9 50	6 0	8 30	...	...	...
$13\frac{1}{2}$	5 10	La Cure ....arr	1055	7 5		...	...	...
$24\frac{1}{2}$	7 20	Le Brassus ......arr	1 20	...	...	...	...	...
$20\frac{3}{4}$	8 0	Morez ....arr	1120	7 25	...	...	...	...
	...	Morez ....dep	...	7a30	2p40	...	...	...
...	...	Le Brassus ......dep	...	...	3 15	...	...	...
...	...	La Cure...............dep	...	10 40	5 55	...	...	...
...	...	St. Cergues ....dep	7a35	1130	6 45	...	...	...
...	...	Nyon ....arr	8 40	1235	7 55	...	...	..

Olten—

Olten ....dep	8a40	4p20
Lostorf Dorf ......arr	9 40	5 20

Lostorf Dorf......dep	7a25	2p55
Olten ....arr	8 20	3 50

$4\frac{1}{4}$ miles. Fare 85 c.

Orbe—

E.M									
	Orbe.........dep	6a35	7a 5	10a15	2p30	5p5	6p40	...	...
2	Arnex ......arr	7 0	7 30	10 40	2 55	6 20	7 5	...	...
...	Arnex ......dep	7a20	7a50	11 a0	3p30	6p35	7p15	...	...
...	Orbe ....arr	7 40	8 10	11 20	3 50	6 55	7 35	...	...

Fare 40c.

E.M			
	Orbe.........dep	8a30	6p15
$7\frac{1}{4}$	Ballaigues arr	1030	8 15
...	Ballaigues dep	6 a0	1050
...	Orbe ....arr	7 10	12 0

Fare 1 fr. 40c.

E.M				
	Orbe ...dep	8a30	1p35	6p15
5	Baulmes arr	9 40	2 45	7 25
...	Baulmes dep	6a30	11 0	4p45
...	Orbe ......arr	7 30	12 0	5 45

Fare 95c.

Payerne—

E.M			
	Payerne ...dep	8 a5	5 p5
$7\frac{1}{2}$	Gletterens arr	9 45	6 50
...	Gletterens dep	5a40	2p20
...	Payerne ...arr	7 5	3 45

Fare 1 fr. 10 c.

Rapperswil—

Rapperswil ......dep	7a30	8p25
St. Gallenkappel ar	9 15	1010
St. Gallenkappel dp	4a45	5p20
Rapperswil ......arr	6 20	6 50

$7\frac{1}{2}$ miles. Fare 1 fr. 45c.

Rheinfelden—

Rheinfeldendp	7a55	3 p5	7p20
Maisprach arr	8 55	4 5	8 20
Maisprach dep	6a30	12 0	5p35
Rheinfelden ar	7 25	1255	6 25

4 miles. Fare 70 c.

St. Gallen—

St. Gallen dep	8a10	3p20	7p10
Rehetobel arr	1025	5 35	9 25
Rehetobel dep	6 a5	1115	4p15
St. Gallen arr	7 50	1 0	6 0

8 miles Fare 1 fr. 55 c.

Sarnen—

E M		a.m.	p.m
...	Sarnen ...dep	9 0	5 30
$4\frac{1}{2}$	St. Niklausen	10 20	6 50
$7\frac{1}{2}$	Melchthal arr	11 10	7 40
		a.m.	p.m.
...	Melchthal dep	7 10	3 0
...	St. Niklausen	7 40	3 30
...	Sarnen......arr	8 30	4 15

Fares from Sarnen: to St. Niklausen, 1fr. 25c. to Melchthal 2 fr. 25 c.

Schwyz—

Schwyz ...	6a45	9a10	1 p0	5p15
Muotathal	8 20	1045	2 35	6 50
Muotathal	6a20	9a10	12p50	5p30
Schwyz ...	7 30	1020	2 0	6 40

$6\frac{1}{4}$ miles. Fare 1 fr. 25 c.

Sion—

E.M.	fr. c.								
		Sion ....dep	6 a0	11‡a45	3p‡30	...	...	...	...
$15\frac{1}{4}$	5 50	Evolène.........	11 10	4 55	8 40	...	...	...	...
$18\frac{1}{4}$	6 50	Haudères...arr	11 50	5 35	9 20	...	...	...	...
...	...	Haudères dep	6a‡0	9‡a35	1 p45				...
...	...	Evolène.........	6 40	10 15	2 25				...
...	...	Sion ......arr	10 15	1 50	6 0				...

‡—Until 15th September.

Sissach—

Sissach ....dep	8a10	1p10	6p10
Eptingen...arr	9 25	2 25	7 25
Eptingen dep	7 a0	11 a40	5 p0
Sissach ..arr	7 55	12 35	5 55

$5\frac{3}{4}$ miles; fare 95 c

Spiez—

Spiez dep	7a20	1215	4p10	7p20
Faulensee	7 55	1250	4 45	7 55
Aeschi ar	8 40	1 35	5 30	8 40
Aeschi dp	6a10	11 a0	1p30	5p40
Faulensee	6 40	11 30	2 0	6 10
Spiez..arr	7 0	11 50	2 20	6 30

$1\frac{1}{4}$ miles. Fares from Spiez: to Faulensee-Bad 65 c.; to Aeschi 1 fr. 40 c.

Sursee—

Sursee (S.)	7a45	1025	2 p5	8p50
Willisau a	9 0	1140	3 20	10 5
Willisau..	7a30	1130	3p30	7p20
Sursee arr	8 50	1245	4 55	8 35

8 miles. Fare 1 fr. 50 c.

Tavannes—

Tavannes...dep	7a30	1145	6p15
Les Genevezarr	9 25	1 40	8 10
Les Genevez dp	4a45	8a25	3p20
Tavannes...arr	5 55	9 35	4 30

$7\frac{1}{4}$ miles. Fare 1 fr. 40 c.

Thun—

E.M	fr. c.		
		Thun ......dep	4 p0
$9\frac{1}{4}$	1 80	Linden......arr	6 50
...	...	Linden ...dep	6a15
...	...	Thun ......arr	8 20

Travers—

Travers .....dep	8a 5	3p50	7p35
Les Ponts...arr	9 50	5 40	9 20
Les Ponts...dep	7a20	1p15	7p55
Travers ......arr	8 40	2 35	9 15

$7\frac{1}{2}$ miles; fare 1 fr. 40 c.

Treib

Treib dep	7a35	11a30	4p 5	7‡50
Sonnenb'g	8 50	12 45	5 20	9 5
Sonnenb'g	6 a5	10a25	3p10	7 ‡0
Treib arr	6 40	11 0	3 45	7 35

$3\frac{1}{2}$ miles. Fare 1 fr. 70 c.
‡-Until Sept. 15th.

Vallorbes—

Vallorbes dep	8a30	4 p5	7p30
Ballaigues arr	9 30	5 5	8 30
Ballaiguesdep	5a45	1p55	5p45
Vallorbes arr	6 30	2 45	6 30

$3\frac{3}{4}$ miles; fare 75 c.

Verrières—

Verrières.........dep	8 a30	5 p5
Chaux-du-Mil...arr	12 30	9 35
Chaux-du-Mil..dep	3 p40	...
Verrières ....arr	8 0	...

15 miles; fare 2 fr. 90 c.

Verrières ....dep	7 a30	5 p5
Côte-aux-Fées..arr	9 10	6 45
Côte-aux-Fées..dep	10a20	6p30
Verrières ....arr	11 50	8 0

6 miles; fare 1 fr. 20 c.

Villeneuve—

E.M			
	Villeneuve dep	9a45	6p35
$5\frac{1}{2}$	Vouvry ......arr	11 0	7 50
...	Vouvry ......dep	8 a0	3p25
...	Villeneuve arr	9 15	4 40

Fare 90 c.

Wohlen

Wohlen ...dep	7a40	1p50	9 p5
Meister-schwandenarr	9 5	3 15	1035
Meister-schwanden dep	5a55	12p5	3p50
Wohlen......arr	7 10	1 20	5 10

$6\frac{1}{2}$ miles; fare 1 fr. 25 c.

Yverdon—

E.M			
	Yverdon ...dep	3p40	...
8	Orbe ....arr	5 10	...
...	Orbe ....dep	7a10	...
...	Yverdon ...arr	8 40	...

Fare 1 fr. 60 c.

E.M			
	Yverdon ...dep	6 p0	...
$10\frac{1}{2}$	Thierrens...arr	9 10	...
...	Thierrens...dep	5a20	...
...	Yverdon ...arr	7 50	...

Fare 2 fr. 5 c.

Zurich—

E.M			
	Zurich ......dep	5p50	...
$7\frac{1}{2}$	Maur ....arr	7 30	...
...	Maur.........dep	7 a0	...
...	Zurich ......arr	8 40	...

Fare 1 fr. 45c.

SWITZERLAND—*Continued.*

PILLON ROUTE.

‡—Until 15th Sept.

E.M.	Coup	Int.								
—	fr. c.	fr. c.				a.m.		a.m.		p.m.
Fro	m A	igle.	**Aigle** ......dep	...	...	7 35	...	11 0	...	4 15
6¾	2 75	2 20	Sepey	‡	...	1010	...	2 0	...	6 45
13¼	5 35	4 25	**Diablerets arr**	a.m.	...	1140	...	3 30	p.m.	8 15
...	...	...	Diablerets dep	6 35	a.m.		p.m.		4 ‡0	
21	...	7 35	Gsteig	8 35	8 45	...	3 20	...	6 10	...
27¼	...	8 60	Gstaad ......arr	...	9 50	...	4 25	...	7 15	...

		a.m.			p.m.	p.m.
Gstaad ......dep	...	10 15	...	...	3‡15	6 55	...
Gsteig	...	11 40	...	...	4 40	8 20	...
Diablerets arr	a.m.	1‡45	p.m	p.m.	6 55		...
Diablerets dep	7 0		1 50	6 0		...	...
Sepey	8 30	...	3 20	7 30	...	...	...
Aigle ......arr	9 30	...	4 25	8 35	...	...	...

E.M.	fr.c.		a.m.	a.m.	p.m.	
—	—	Aigle ....dep	7‡25	11 0	4 10	...
6¾	2 20	Corbeyrier(Hotel)ar	9 35	1 10	6 20	...

	a.m.	p.m.	p.m.			
Corbeyrier (Hotel) dep	8 5	2 45	7‡15	...	...	‡—Until
Aigle ....arr	9 20	4 0	8 30	...	...	15th September.

LES MOSSES ROUTE.

E.M	fr. c		a.m.	p.m.				
—	—	**Sepey**..................dep	10 20	6 40	...	...	...	...
3½	1 10	**Comballaz**	11 40	8 0	...	...	...	...
5	1 60	**Mosses**	12 10	8 30	...	...	...	...
14¾	4 75	**Chateau d'Oex**......arr	2 50		...	...	...	...

	a.m.	a.m.			
Chateau d'Oex......dep	...	9 45	...	...	...
Mosses	7 20	1 5	...	...	...
Comballaz	7 40	1 25	...	...	...
Sepey ....arr	8 15	2 0	...	...	...

ORSIERES and GRAND ST. BERNARD.

‡—Until 15th Sept. §—From 16th Sept.

E.M	fr. c.		a.m.	a.m.	p.m.		
		Orsières (Gare)..............dep	...	8 50	6 10	...	...
8	3 25	Bourg St. Pierre	7 ‡0	12 20	9 25	...	...
16	6 50	**Grand St. Bernard**.........arr	10 30	5 ‡0	...	...	...

	a.m.	a.m.	p.m.	p.m.	
Grand St. Bernard ...dep	§	11‡20	§	5‡30	...
Bourg St. Pierre	8 40	1 40	5 10	7 10	...
Orsières (Gare) ....arr	10 10	3 10	6 40	8 40	...

SEMBRANCHER and LOURTIER.

‡—Until 31st August.

E.M	fr.c.		a.m.	p.m.	p.m.	p.m.
—	—	**Sembrancher** (Gare) ......dep	8 40	1 0	5 55	9 50
3¾	0 90	Le Chable	9 30	1 50	6 45	10 40
7½	1 80	**Lourtier** ....arr	11 25	4‡10	8‡ 3	...

	a.m.	a.m.	a.m.	p.m.	p.m.	p.m.
Lourtier ....dep	...	8‡20	...	1‡20	...	4 50
Le Chable....................	5 50	9 25	9 45	2 25	2 50	5 15
Sembrancher (Gare) ......arr	6 30	...	10 25	...	3 30	7 0

SIMMENTHAL.

‡—Until 15th Sept.

E.M	fr. c.						
		Oey-Diemtigen......dep	7a55	3‡p35	...	...	...
5½	2 15	**Zwischenfluh**	9 40	5 20	...	...	...
8½	3 40	**Grimmialp Hotel**...arr	10 30	6 10	...	...	...

Grimmialp Hotel...dep	5‡a45	4p25	...	...	...	...	...	...
Zwischenfluh	6 20	5 0	...	...	...	...	...	...
Oey-Diemtigen......arr	7 20	6 0	...	...	...	...	...	...

(Service liable to suppression after opening of Lötschberg Rly.

E.M	fr. c.		a.m.	p.m.	p.m.
—	—	**Frutigen** ......dep	8 5	1 15	5 0
2½	0 70	**Kandergrund** ...	8 35	1 50	5 30
4½	1 40	**Blau See**............	8 5	2 10	5 50
8	2 55	**Kandersteg arr**	10 20	3 35	7 15

	a.m.	a.m.	p.m.
Kandersteg dep	5 20	1125	3 50
Blau See	6 20	1225	4 50
Kandergrund ...	6 35	1240	5 5
Frutigen......arr	7 15	1 20	5 45

E.M	fr. c.		a.m.	a.m.	p.m.	p.m
—	—	**Frutigen** ...dep	5	9‡40	1 15	5 0
10	3 25	**Adelboden**arr	10 50	12 25	4 5	7 4[illegible]

			a.m.	a.m.	p.m.	p.m
...	...	**Adelboden** dep	5 15	9 20	1‡20	3 45
...	...	**Frutigen** ...arr	7 15	1120	3 20	5 45

‡—Until 15th Sept.

SIMPLON PASS.

E.M.	fr. c.					
		Brig ....dep	6a50	p.m.	...	...
14	5 50	Simplon Kulm	11 50	1 40	...	...
19½	7 95	Simplon Dorf..............		2 35	...	...
29½	11 80	**Iselle** ....arr	...	3 55	...	...

Iselle........................dep	7 a5	...	...	...	...	...
Simplon Dorf	10 35	...	...	...	...	...
Simplon Kulm	12 30	1p55	...	...	...	...
Brig........................arr	...	4 20	...	...	...	...

KLAUSEN PASS.

‡—From 16th Sept. §—Until 15th Sept.

E.M	Coup	Int.			a.m.	p.m.	p.m.	
...	fr. c.	fr. c.	**Altdorf** (Post Office) dep	...	9§35	2§40	2‡40	...
8½	4 20	3 50	**Unterschächen**..............	...	11 55	4 55	5 0	...
11	5 25	4 35	**Urigen**..............	a.m.	1 55	6 0	6 5	...
22	10 50	8 75	**Urnerboden**	7§20	4 45	8 40		...
31	14 95	12 45	**Linthal** ....arr	8 50	6 10	...	...	...

			a.m.	p.m.	
Linthal...............dep	...	...	8§55	2§30	...
Urnerboden	a.m.	...	1 0	5 30	...
Urigen..............	7 50	a.m.	4 0	8 15	...
Unterschächen..............	8 5	8 10	4 20		...
Altdorf...............arr	...	9 25	5 35	...	...

E.M	Coup	Int.																	
—	fr. c.	fr. c.																	
Fro	m N	essla	u.	a.m.		a.m.	a.m.	p.m.	p.m.		p.m.								
5	...	...	Nesslau ....dep	...	...	6 45	9 40	12 25	3 5	...	7 30	...	...	...	...	...	...	...
12¼	2 35	1 75	**Unterwasser**	4 50	...	8 10	11 10	1 50	4 30	...	8 55	...	...	...	...	...	...	...
14½	3 10	2 30	**Wildhaus**..............	5 35	a.m.	8 50	11 55	2 35	5 15	p.m.	9 35	...	...	...	...	...	...	...
20	4 90	3 65	**Gams**	6 35	8 45		12 55	3 35	6 15	7 55		...	...	...	...	...	...	...
24	6 10	4 55	**Buchs Bahnhof** ...arr	7 10	9 20	...	1 30	4 10	6 50	8 30	...	...	...	...	...	...	...	...

					a.m.		a.m.	a.m.	p.m.	p.m.	p.m.							
...	...	...	**Buchs Bahnhof** .....dep	...	6 15	...	8 5	10 50	3 45	4 40	6 50	...	...	...	...	...	...	...
...	...	...	**Gams**	a.m.	6 50	a.m.	8 45	11 30	4 25	5 20	7 25	...	...	...	...	...	...	...
...	...	...	**Wildhaus**	4 40		8 35	11 45	1 50	6 45	7 40		...	...	...	...	...	...	...
...	...	...	**Unterwasser**..................	5 0	...	9 0	12 10	2 15	7 25	8 0	...	...	...	...	...	...	...	...
...	...	...	**Nesslau** ....arr	6 10	...	10 10	1 20	3 25	8 35	...	...	...	...	...	...	...	...	...

SWITZERLAND—*Continued.*

SPLUGEN and ST. BERNARDINO ROUTE.

‡—Until 15th September. *—From 16th September.

E.M	Coup fr. c.	Int. fr. c.				a.m.	p.m.	p.m.
—			**Thusis** (Postb.) dep	...	...	7 10	1 45	4 30
8	3 90	3 25	Andeer	...	...	9 0	3 35	6 20
16¾	8 5	6 70	**Splügen** arr	a.m.	...	1115	5 50	8 35
...	...	...	„ dep	7 ‡0	...	1145	...	—
41½	20 10	16 75	**Chiavenna** arr	1230	a.m.	5 15	...	...
...	...	...	**Splügen** dep	—	6 ‡0	1150	6 0	...
23	11 20	9 30	Hinterrhein	a.m.	7 10	1 0	7 5	...
33¼	16 15	13 45	S. Bernardino	8‡20	10 0	3 50	9‡45	...
42	20 45	17 0	**Mesocco** arr	9 50	11 30	5 20	...	...

		a.m.		a.m.		p.m.	p.m.
Mesocco dep	...	‡	...	8 10	...	1 ‡0	4‡15
S. Bernardino arr	a.m.	7 55	...	1115	...	4 15	7 20
Hinterrhein dep	6*20	10 20	...	2 10	...	6 40	—
Splügen arr	7 15	11 15	...	3 5	p.m.	7 35	...
Chiavenna dep	—	—	...	6a45	1‡35	—	...
Splügen arr	a.m.	...	noon	2 50	9 25	...	...
„ dep	7 20	...	12 0	3 15	—	...	...
Andeer	8 45	...	1 25	4 40	...	...	...
Thusis (Postb.) arr	1010	...	2 50	6 5	...	...	...

OBERALP ROUTE.

§—From 16th Sept. ‡—Until 15th Sept.

E.M			a.m.		a.m.		p.m.	p.m.
—	**Disentis** (Postb.) dep		t‡15	...	10§30	...	12‡45	5 35
5	Sedrun		7 35	...	11 50	...	2 5	6 55
7	Rueras		7 50	...	12 5	...	2 20	7 10
9¾	Tschamut	a.m.	8 40	a.m.	—	p.m.	3 10	—
19¾	**Andermatt** arr	6 55	11 0	11 10	...	4 25	5 25	...
23¼	**Göschenen** arr	7 25	...	11 40	...	4 55	6 0	...

		a.m.	a.m.		p.m.	p.m.	p.m.	
Göschenen dep		6‡15	10 20	...	2 10	...	6 20	...
Andermatt		7 25	11 20	...	3 10	3‡20	7 20	...
Tschamut	a.m.	10 10	—	p.m.	—	6 0	—	...
Rueras	6§20	10 35	...	3 50	...	6 25	...	...
Sedrun	6 35	10 50	...	4 5	...	6 40	...	...
Disentis (Postb.)	7 30	11 45	...	5 0	...	7 35	...	...

REICHENAU and FLIMS.	E.M.	fr. c.									
			Reichenau Station dep	8 a10	12p25	6 p0	...	Waldhaus bei Flims dep	7 a40	2 p45	7 p25
	7½	3 0	**Flims**	10 35	2 50	8 25	...	**Flims**	8 0	3 5	7 45
	8½	3 45	Waldhaus bei Flims...arr	11 0	3 15	8 50	...	**Reichenau** Station arr	9 30	4 35	9 15

ILANZ and FLIMS.	E.M.	fr. c.									
			Ilanz dep	9 a25	4 p30	...	**Flims** dep	9 a15	4 p40	...	...
	6½	2 55	Waldhaus bei Flims	11 20	6 25	...	Waldhaus bei Flims...	9 35	5 0	...	...
	7½	3 5	**Flims** arr	11 35	6 40	...	**Ilanz** arr	10 35	6 0	...	...

ILANZ and VALS PLATZ.	E.M.	fr. c.										
			Ilanz dep	7 a0	11‡a45	4 p40	...	**Vals-Platz** dep	6 a0	12‡c30	3 p45	...
	7½	2 60	Furth dep	8 35	1 20	6 15	...	Furth	7 15	1 50	5 0	...
	14	5 30	**Vals-Platz** arr	10 15	3 0	7 55	...	**Ilanz** arr	8 15	2 50	6 0	...

‡—Until 15th Sept.

WALTENSBURG and BRIGELS.	E.M.	fr. c.											
	5¼	2 10	**Waltensburg** dep	9 a15	4§p15	...	**Brigels** dep	7a25	2p20	...	...	...	...
			Brigels arr	11 20	6 20	...	**Waltensburg** arr	8 35	3 30	...	...	...	...

§—10 minutes earlier from 16th Sept.

ILANZ and VRIN.	E.M.	fr. c.											
	14	5 65	Ilanz dep	7 a5	4 p35	...	Vrin dep	5 a35	3 p15	...	...	...	...
			Vrin arr	11 5	8 35	...	Ilanz arr	8 20	6 0	...	...	...	...

CHUR and AROSA.	E.M.	fr. c.											
			Chur dep	6 a0	11 a0	3p20	**Arosa** (Inner) dep	5 a50	10a10	4 p30	...	...	...
	13½	5 35	Langwies	10 5	3 20	7 25	Langwies	7 10	11 30	5 50	...	...	...
	19	7 70	**Arosa** (Inner)...arr	12 5	5 20	9 25	**Chur** arr	9 40	2 0	8 20	...	...	...

RAGAZ and VATTIS.	E.M.	fr. c.								
			Ragaz dep	10‡a0	3 p0	...	**Vattis** dep	7 a0	3‡p30	‡—Until 15th Sept.
	2¾	1 15	Pfäfers	11 5	4 5	...	Pfäfers	8 30	5 0	
	9¾	3 90	**Vattis** arr	12 35	5 35	...	**Ragaz** arr	9 0	5 30	

VERSAM and SAFIEN PLATZ.	E.M	fr. c.											
	12	3 90	Versam dep	6a10	3†p35	...	Safien Platz dep	6 a50	4 p10	...	...	...	...
			Safien Platz arr	9 55	7 20	...	Versam arr	9 15	6 35	...	...	...	...

†—From 16th Sept. 20 mins. earlier.

DAVOS and SCHULS.—Service liable to suppression since opening of Bevers-Schuls line.

‡—Until 14th Sept. §—Until 15th Sept.

Dist. E.M.	Coup fr. c.	Int. fr. c.				a.m.	p.m.		p.m.
			Davos-Platz dep	...	...	8 45	12 10	...	9‡35
1½	0 80	0 65	**Davos-Dorf** dep	...	...	9 20	12 45	...	1010
18	8 70	7 25	Süss arr	...	a.m.	1 30	4 50	p.m.	2a40
...	...	...	**Samaden** dep	a.m.	7 10	9 40	—	1 40	—
...	...	...	Süss arr	§	1045	1 15	...	5 15	...
...	...	...	Süss dep	2 50	1055	2 0	...	5 25	...
25	12 10	10 5	Ardez dep	4 0	12 0	3 5	...	6 30	...
29¼	14 20	11 80	Tarasp Kurhaus dep	5 5	1255	4 0	...	7 25	...
31	15 0	12 50	**Schuls** arr	5 20	1 10	4 15	...	7 40	...

	a.m.	a.m.		p.m.	p.m.		
Schuls dep	6 0	1015	...	2 5	9‡40	...	...
Tarasp Kurhaus arr	6 15	1030	...	2 20	9 55	...	...
Ardez arr	7 40	1155	...	3 45	1135	...	...
Süss arr	8 45	1 0	...	4 50	1250	...	...
	a.m.	p.m.		p.m.			
Süss dep	8 55	1 45	...	5 0	⋮	...	...
Samaden arr	1 25	5 50	p.m.	9 5	⋮	...	...
Süss dep	9 a0	—	1 30	—	1 0	...	...
Davos-Dorf arr	1 35	...	5 40	...	5 20	...	...
Davos-Platz arr	1 55	...	6 10	...	5 45	...	...

FURCA ROUTE.

§—From 16th Sept. †—Until 15th Sept.

Dist. E.M.				a.m.		a.m.	p.m.	p.m.	p.m.	
	Göschenen dep	...	...	6 55	...	10 20	1†15	2§10	6 20	...
3½	**Andermatt**	...	...	8 10	...	11 25	2 30	3 15	7 25	...
5¼	Hospenthal	...	...	8 25	...	11 40	2 45	3 30	7 40	...
23	Gletsch arr	a.m.	...	1 35	...	—	7 55	—	—	...
...	(Rhone Gl.) dep	6†40	a.m.	2 20	a.m.	...	—	...	...	...
27	Oberwald	7 5	7 10	2 45	2 50	...	...	...	...	...
32½	Munster	—	8 15	—	3 55	...	...	...	...	...
42¼	Viesch	...	10 0	...	5 40	...	...	...	...	...
53¾	**Brig** (Stadt.) arr	...	1155	...	7 30	...	...	...	...	...

				a.m.		p.m.	
Brig (Stadt.) dep	...	...	...	6 20	...	1 5	...
Viesch „	...	...	...	9 20	...	4 5	...
Munster „	...	...	...	1140	p.m.	6 25	p.m.
Oberwald arr	...	...	...	1230	12 35	7 15	7 20
Gletsch arr	...	...	a.m.	—	2 0	—	8 45
Rh. Glacier dep	a.m.	a.m.	6†45	p.m.	2 50	...	—
Hospenthal	6 35	10§50	11 25	4 5	7 30	...	...
Andermatt arr	6 55	11 5	11 40	4 20	7 45	...	...
Göschenen arr	7 25	11 40	12 20	4 55	8 25	...	...

GRIMSEL.	E.M.	Coup	Int.										
				Meiringen dep	6‡a0	11a15	12‡p50	5 p0	Gletsch dep	...	6‡a30	...	2‡p45
	3½	1 0	0 70	Innertkirchen	6 45	12 5	1 35	5 50	Grimsel Hospice	...	8 25	...	4 40
	9¼	4 45	3 70	Guttannen	8 45	—	3 35	—	Guttannen	a.m.	10 0	p.m.	6 15
‡—Until 15th Sept.	16¾	8 10	6 75	Grimsel Hospice	1215	...	6 35	...	Innertkirchen	7 40	10 55	2 40	7 10
	23	11 20	9 30	Gletsch arr	1 50	...	8 10	...	Meiringen arr	8 30	11 45	3 30	8 0

SWITZERLAND—*Continued.*

MALOGGIA (Maloja) ROUTE (Engadine).

(Service liable to modification since opening of Bevers-Schuls line.)

Dist. E.M.				a.m.	p.m.	p.m.	p.m.							
	Chiavenna ......dep	...	...	6 40	1220	3 0	6 25	...	...	...	...	...	...	...
8½	Promontogno	...	a.m.	9 10	2 50	5 30	8 50	...	...	...	...	...	...	...
12	Vicosoprano	a.m.	7 0	10 40	3 55	6 30	9 50	...	...	...	...	...	...	...
20½	Maloggia	6 10	9 40	1 20	6 35	—	—	...	...	...	...	...	...	...
27¾	Silvaplana ......arr	7 35	11 5	2 45	8 0	...	...	...	...	...	...	...	...	...
...	" ......dep	7 40	11 15	2 55	8 10	...	...	...	...	...	...	...	...	...
29¼	Campfer	7 55	11 20	3 10	8 25	...	...	...	...	...	...	...	...	...
30½	St. Moritz baths ...	8 10	11 50	3 30	8 45	...	...	...	...	...	...	...	...	...
31¾	" village	8 25	12 5	3 45	9 0	...	...	...	...	...	...	...	...	...
35½	**Samaden** ......arr	—	1 0	4 40	9 55	...	...	...	...	...	...	...	...	...

		a.m.	a.m.	p.m.									
Samaden ....dep	...	5 45	9 25	1 40	p.m.	...	...	...	...	...	...	...	...
St. Moritz village......	...	6 55	10 30	2 45	7 25	...	...	...	...	...	...	...	...
" baths	...	7 15	10 50	3 0	7 40	...	...	...	...	...	...	...	...
Campfer............... ...	...	7 30	11 5	3 15	7 55	...	...	...	...	...	...	...	...
Silvaplana ....arr	...	7 45	11 20	3 30	8 10	...	...	...	...	...	...	...	...
" ....dep	...	7 55	11 35	3 35	8 15	...	...	...	...	...	...	...	...
Maloggia	a.m.	9 30	1 10	5 10	9 45	...	...	...	...	...	...	...	...
Vicosoprano	7 25	11 25	2 50	6 45	—	...	...	...	...	...	...	...	...
Promontogno	8 0	12 0	3 25	7 20	...	...	...	...	...	...	...	...	...
Chiavenna ....arr	9 40	1 45	5 10	9 5	...	...	...	...	...	...	...	...	...

LUKMANIER (Lucomagno) ROUTE.

E.M.	Fr. c.				p.m.	
—	—	Acquacalda......dep	...	...	2 ‡20	...
3¾	1 50	Santa Maria	a.m.	p.m.	3 15	...
11	4 45	Platta	7 0	1 45	4 25	...
12	4 85	Curaglia	7 10	1 55	4 35	...
16	6 40	Disentis..............arr	7 55	2 45	5 20	...

	a.m.	p.m.	p.m.
Disentis... ....dep	8‡20	12 5	5 30
Curaglia	9 35	1 15	6 35
Platta	9 55	1 35	6 55
Santa Maria............	12 0	—	—
Acquacalda ......arr	1240	...	...

‡—Until 15th September.

E.M	fr. c.					
		Acquarossa.......dep	9 a0	11a40	2p30	6p30
6¼	1 80	Olivone	9 50	12 30	3 20	7 20
14¾	5 25	Acquacalda ....arr	...	...	...	...

Acquacalda......dep	...	...	...	...
Olivone	8 a0	10a30	1p30	4 p0
Acquarossa......arr	8 50	11 20	2 20	4 50

SCHULS and PFUNDS.

E.M	Fr. c					
...	...	Schuls ....dep	6 a30	1 p40	4 p55	...
11	5 30	Martinsbruck ...arr	8 15	3 25	6 40	...
18½	8 95	Pfunds...............arr	9 35	4 55	...	...

Pfunds...............dep	...	10 a0	5 p15	...
Martinsbruck ...arr	7 a40	11 50	5 55	...
Schuls ....arr	9 50	1 50	9 5	...

CHUR AND TIEFENCASTEL.

E.M.	Coup Fr.c.	Int. Fr.c.		a.m.	a.m.	a.m.	p.m.	p.m.
—			**Chur** ....dep	...	6 20	10 45	2 40	6 10
6¾	3 25	2 70	Churwalden	...	8 25	12 50	4 45	8 15
11¼	5 50	4 55	Lenzerheide	5 45	9 40	2 5	6 0	9 30
18½	8 70	7 25	**Tiefencastel** (Stn) arr	7 0	10 40	...	7 15	...

	a.m.	a.m.	p.m.	p.m.	p.m.
Tiefencastel (Stn) dep	...	8 15	...	4 40	6 50
Lenzerheide	5 25	10 30	2 45	6 55	9 5
Churwalden	6 30	11 35	3 50	8 0	—
Chur ....arr	7 30	12 35	4 50	9 0	...

JULIER ROUTE.

*—Until 15th September. ‡—From 16th September.

E.M.	Coup Fr.c.	Int. Fr.c.			a.m.	p.m.	p.m.	p.m.
—	—	—	**Tiefencastel** (Stat.) dep	...	7 0	1*20	1‡45	7 10
6¼	3 5	2 55	Savognin	...	8 50	3 10	3 35	9 0
12¼	5 95	4 95	Mühlen ....arr	a.m.	1015	4 35	5 0	10 25
...	...	...	" ....dep	7 0	1050	4 40	5 5	—
17	8 25	6 85	Bivio	8 20	12 5	6 0	6 25	...
21¾	10 55	8 80	Julier Hospiz	9 55	1 40	—	—	...
27	13 5	10 90	**Silvaplana** ....arr	1055	2 40	...	...	...

		a.m.		p.m.
Silvaplana ....dep	...	8 10	...	3 45
Julier Hospiz	a.m.	9 55	...	5 30
Bivio	5 30	10 45	...	6 20
Mühlen ....arr	6 15	1130	p.m.	7 5
" ....dep	6 20	1220	3 50	—
Savognin	7 15	1 15	4 45	...
Tiefencastel ....arr	8 25	2 25	5 55	...

OFEN ROUTE.—(Service liable to modification since opening of Bevers-Schuls line).

E.M.	Fr.c.		a.m.	a.m.	p.m.		
...	...	**Zernetz** .... dep	...	10 40	2 55	...	...
9¼	3 70	Ofenberg (Fuorn)... arr	...	12 55	5 10	...	...
...	...	Ofenberg (Fuorn)... dep	...	1 30	5 15	...	...
17½	7 0	Cierfs ....dep	8 0	3 25	7 10	...	...
22¼	8 95	Sta. Maria Munsterthal...	8 55	4 20	8 5	...	...
24½	9 85	**Münster** ....arr	9 15	4 40	8 25	...	...

	a.m.	a.m.	p.m.		
Munster ....dep	6 25	10 25	5 30	...	...
Sta. Maria **Munsterthal**...	7 5	11 5	6 10	...	...
Cierfs ....dep	8 30	12 30	7 30	...	...
Ofenberg (Fuorn)...... arr	1040	2 40	—	...	...
Ofenberg (Fuorn)...... dep	1050	2 50	...	...	...
Zernetz .... arr	1215	4 15	...	...	...

E.M.	Fr. c				
		Sta. Maria Munsterthal......dep	7a‡30	...	...
8½	4 10	**Sta. Maria IVa Cantoniera**......	11 10	...	...
10½	5 20	**Stilfserjoch**..........................arr	12 0	...	...

Stilfserjoch ....dep	4‡p0	...
Sta. Maria IVa Cantoniera	4 30	...
Sta. Maria Munsterthal ..... arr	6 0	...

‡—Until 20th September.

BERNINA ROUTE.

E.M	Fr.c		p.m.			
—	—	Bernina-Hospitz dep	1 45	...	...	...
4	...	La Rösa	2 30	...	...	...
11½	1 90	Poschiavo ....arr	3 40	...	...	...

	a.m.		
Poschiavo ....dep	8 5	...	...
La Rösa	11 10	...	...
Bernina-Hospitz...arr	12 35	...	...

ROUND ROUTE (Rundreise) TICKETS.

Rundreise Tickets must be arranged in the manner of a tour, though it is not required that the tour shall end at its starting point. A tour in Holland and Belgium, provided it is at least 400 kilomètres (249 Eng. miles) in length, may be commenced at Flushing, and end at Hoek van Holland, or Rotterdam, or Amsterdam, or Antwerp, or Ostend, or commence at any one of these ports, and end either at the point of starting or at any of the other ports mentioned. In the case of a tour confined to Belgium the only condition is that the journey must include a complete circuit of 250 kilomètres (155 miles).

The coupons are issued all the year round in the countries belonging to the Rundreise system, viz: France, Luxemburg, Holland, Belgium, Germany, Switzerland, Austria, Hungary, the Balkan States, Turkey, Italy, Denmark, Norway, Sweden, and Finland; tickets can be issued either for a straight return or a circular journey, the only proviso being a minimum distance of 600 kilomètres (373 miles), when the validity is 60 days; if 3,000 kilomètres (1,865 miles), 90 days; and if over 5,000 kilomètres (3,107 miles), 120 days. Further, provided always the distance of 600 kilomètres (373 miles) is travelled, Rundreise tickets can be issued for any route for a wholly German tour, either straight return or circular, but it must end at the starting point.

The coupons are available by all ordinary trains. Only luggage that can be conveniently taken in the carriage is allowed, excess must be paid for.

When it is intended to begin the "Round Route" travel in England, the coupons may be obtained from the Continental Traffic Managers of the Railway Companies operating Continental services, or from the principal tourist agents. The official representatives of the Rundreise Union in England are the Belgian Mail Steam Packet Co., 53, Gracechurch Street, and 72, Regent Street, London; Thomas Cook & Son, Ludgate Circus; the Netherlands State Railways (Zeeland Steamship Company), 33, Cockspur Street, E.C.; and the North Eastern Railway Co., York (Continental Department); from all of whom the tickets may be obtained on application.

The subjoined Lists, abridged from the official lists, include almost all those parts visited for pleasure.

AUSTRIA, BELGIUM, DENMARK, GERMANY, HOLLAND, NORWAY, and SWEDEN.

	Kil.	1 Cl mpf	2 Cl mpf	3 Cl mpf
Aix-la-Chapelle	to			
Cologne	71	5 20	3 50	2 30
Elberfeld	117	8 60	5 70	3 80
Jeumont	184	1430	9 70	5 90
Louvain	125	9 60	6 50	4 0
Neuss	81	6 0	3 90	2 60
Amsterdam to				
Arnheim	93	5 30	4 00	2 70
Cleve	128	8 50	6 70	4 30
Cologne	248	1730	1240	8 10
Emmerich	124	7 50	5 90	3 70
Antwerp to				
Budel	84	6 50	4 40	2 60
Esschen	33	2 60	1 80	1 10
Ghent	69	5 40	3 70	2 20
Louvain	47	3 70	2 50	1 50
Malines	24	2 0	1 30	0 80
Appenweier to				
Baden-Baden	37	2 80	1 80	1 20
Heidelberg	120	8 80	5 80	3 90
Offenburg	9	0 70	0 50	0 30
Strassburg	34	2 50	1 70	1 10
Arlon to				
Bettingen or Sterpenich	10	0 80	0 60	0 40
Libramont	47	3 70	2 50	1 50
Arnheim to				
Cleve	47	4 00	3 20	2 10
Cologne	165	1270	8 80	5 80
Emmerich	32	2 90	2 40	1 50
The Hague	118	6 70	5 00	3 40
Salzbergen	115	7 50	6 0	3 80
Utrecht	57	3 30	2 50	1 70
Aschaffenburg	to			
Darmstadt	43	3 30	2 20	1 50
Eger	343	2510	1650	1100
Furth-i-W.	353	2580	17 0	1130
Gemünden	52	3 80	2 50	1 70
Mayence	77	5 70	3 80	2 50
Munich	367	2680	1770	1180
Nürnberg	192	1410	9 30	6 20
Passau	410	3000	1970	1320
Würzburg	90	660	4 40	2 90
Augsburg to				
Ingolstadt	67	...	3 30	2 20
Lindau	193	1410	9 30	6 20
Munich	62	4 60	3 0	2 00
Nürnberg	138	1010	6 70	4 50
Ulm	85	6 30	4 10	2 80
Basel to				
Bingen	349	2550	1680	1120
Frankfort	347	2540	1670	1120
Mayence	347	2540	1670	1120
Schaffhausen	103	7 00	4 70	3 10
Strassburg	143	1050	6 90	4 60
Bayreuth to				
Eger	77	...	3 70	2 50
Hof	74	5 50	3 60	2 40
Nürnberg	94	6 90	4 60	3 10
Berlin to				
Bremen	384	2810	1850	1230
Breslau	348	2550	1680	1120
Cassel	394	2880	1900	1270
Cologne	596	4360	2870	1910
Dresden	185	1360	8 90	6 00
Düsseldorf	565	4130	2720	1810
Erfurt	276	2020	1330	8 90
Frankfort-a-M.	576	4210	2770	1850
Halle	162	1190	7 80	5 20
Hamburg	297	2170	1430	9 60
Hanover	274	2000	1320	8 80
Leipsic	164	1200	7 90	5 30
Magdeburg	142	1040	6 90	4 60
Neustrelitz	101	7 40	4 90	3 30
Probstzella	330	2410	1590	1060
Stralsund	236	1730	1140	7 60
Wittenberg	95	7 00	4 60	3 10
Bremen to				
Cologne	335	2450	1610	1080
Düsseldorf	295	2160	1420	9 50
Hamburg	119	8 70	5 80	3 90
Magdeburg	284	2080	1370	9 10
Münster	173	1270	8 40	5 60
Osnabrück	123	9 00	6 00	4 00
Breslau to				
Görlitz	185	1360	8 90	6 00
Hirschberg	125	9 20	6 10	4 10

Brussels to	Kil.	1 Cl mpf	2 Cl mpf	3 Cl mpf
Aix-la-Chapelle	155	1190	8 0	4 90
Bettingen or Sterpenich	208	1590	1080	6 40
Esschen	74	5 80	3 90	2 30
Ghent	58	4 50	3 0	1 80
Louvain	30	2 40	1 70	1 0
Malines	21	1 70	1 20	0 70
Mons	69	5 40	3 70	2 20
Mouscron	102	7 90	5 40	3 20
Namur	62	4 80	3 30	1 90
Bruges to				
Ghent	45	3 50	2 40	1 50
Brunswick to				
Frankfort-a.-M.	385	2810	1850	1240
Hamburg	213	1560	1030	6 90
Magdeburg	87	6 40	4 20	2 80
Soest	243	1780	1170	7 80
Budapest to				
Bruck or Marchegg	228	2310	1500	6 80
Trieste	612	5780	4060	2780
Carlsbad to				
Eger or Franzensbd	52	5 70	3 80	2 40
Cassel to				
Halle	218	1600	1050	7 00
Hanover	175	1280	8 40	5 60
Leipsic	264	1950	1290	8 60
Magdeburg	250	1830	1200	8 00
Charlottenberg to				
Kongsvinger	36	3 30	2 00	1 40
Chemnitz to				
Dresden	83	6 10	4 0	2 70
Hof	146	1070	7 10	4 70
Leipsic	83	6 30	4 10	2 80
Christiania to				
Lillestrom	21	2 0	1 20	0 80
Moss	60	5 40	3 30	2 20
Coblence to				
Bullay	60	4 40	2 90	2 0
Ems	18	1 40	0 90	0 60
Frankfort-a-M.	137	1010	6 60	4 40
Giessen	117	8 60	5 70	3 80
Metz	212	1550	1020	6 80
Coburg to				
Eisenach	131	9 60	6 30	4 20
Lichtenfels	21	1 60	1 10	0 70
Cologne to				
Bonn	34	2 50	1 70	1 10
Cassel	289	2110	1390	9 30
Düsseldorf	44	3 30	2 20	1 50
Elberfeld	46	3 40	2 30	1 50
Frankfort-a-M.	229	1680	1100	7 40
Leipsic	563	4140	2720	1820
Magdeburg	452	3300	2170	1450
Münster	172	1260	8 30	5 60
Neuss	37	2 80	1 80	1 20
Oberhausen	72	5 30	3 50	2 40
Soest	132	9 70	6 40	4 30
Treves	193	1410	9 30	6 20
Utrecht	224	1600	1130	7 40
Constance to				
Schaffhausen	50	3 30	2 30	1 60
Copenhagen to				
Elsinore	58	...	3 00	1 80
Gjedser	178	1450	9 10	5 40
Korsoer	111	9 10	5 70	3 40
Lubeck	273	1350	8 50	...
Malmo	30	1 60	1 60	1 10
Diez to				
Ems	31	2 30	1 50	1 0
Langenschwalb'ch	31	2 30	1 50	1 0
Limburg	4	0 30	0 20	0 20
Donaueschingen to				
Neustadt	40	3 00	2 00	1 30
Dresden to				
Bodenbach	64	4 80	3 20	2 10
Eger	253	1850	1220	8 10
Franzensbad	253	1850	1220	8 10
Görlitz	105	7 70	5 10	3 40
Hof	228	1670	1100	7 30
Leipsic	118	8 70	5 70	3 80
Reichenbach	154	1130	7 40	5 00
Tetschen	64	4 80	3 20	2 10

	Kil.	1 Cl mpf	2 Cl mpf	3 Cl mpf
Dusseldorf to				
Elberfeld	28	2 10	1 40	0 90
Leipsic	541	3950	2600	1740
Neuss	11	0 90	0 60	0 40
Eger to				
Franzensbad	7	0 60	0 40	0 30
Leipsic	191	1440	9 50	6 30
Munich	285	2090	1370	9 20
Nürnberg	152	1110	7 30	4 90
Elsinore to				
Helsingborg	10	0 50	0 50	0 30
Emmerich to				
Oberhausen	61	4 50	3 00	2 0
Wesel	35	2 60	1 70	1 20
Engelholm to				
Halmstad	66	4 70	2 80	1 90
Helsingborg	27	1 90	1 20	0 80
Flushing (Vlissingen) to				
Boxtel	138	7 80	5 90	3 90
Breda	99	5 60	4 30	2 90
Rotterdam (Delft, or Beurs)	133	7 50	5 70	3 80
Venlo	210	1190	8 90	6 00
Frankfort-am-Main to				
Göttingen	257	1880	1240	8 30
Hamburg	547	4000	2630	1760
Hanover	365	2670	1760	1170
Homburg	20	1 50	1 0	0 70
Leipsic	433	3200	2100	1400
Magdeburg	452	3300	2170	1450
Mannheim	81	6 00	3 90	2 60
Mayence	37	2 80	1 80	1 20
Saarbrücken	208	1520	1000	6 70
Strassburg	231	1690	1110	7 40
Wiesbaden	37	2 80	1 80	1 20
Franzensfeste to				
Innsbruck	84	7 80	5 90	3 80
Toblach	61	6 10	4 60	3 00
Fredrikshald to				
Kornsjo	32	3 0	1 80	1 20
Moss	76	6 90	4 20	2 80
Freiburg (Breisgau) to				
Neustadt	47	3 50	2 30	1 60
Offenburg	63	4 60	3 10	2 10
Friedrichshafen to				
Constance	35	2 60	1 70	1 20
Lindau	25	1 90	1 20	0 80
Romanshorn	12	1 20	1 20	0 80
Rorschach	19	1 80	1 80	1 20
Gemunden to				
Schweinfurt	52	3 80	2 50	1 70
Gera to				
Weimar	68	5 00	3 30	2 20
Ghent to				
Louvain	79	6 10	4 20	2 50
Gjedser to				
Warnemünde	42	4 50	4 50	3 00
Görlitz to				
Hirschberg	91	6 70	4 40	3 00
Görz to				
Assling	99	1000	6 20	3 90
Trieste	67	6 10	3 70	2 10
Gothenburg to				
Mellerud	123	1020	6 10	4 10
Varberg	77	5 50	3 30	2 20
The Hague to				
Amsterdam	63	3 60	2 70	1 90
Salzbergen	235	1420	11 0	7 20
Utrecht	61	3 50	2 60	1 80
Halmstad to				
Varberg	74	5 30	3 20	2 10
Hamburg to				
Hanover	185	1360	8 90	6 0
Kiel	109	8 00	5 30	3 50
Lubeck	64	4 70	3 10	2 10
Magdeburg	265	1940	1280	8 50

	Kil.	1 Cl mpf	2 Cl mpf	3 Cl mpf
Hanover to				
Gottingen	109	8 00	5 30	3 50
Magdeburg	159	1170	7 70	5 10
Salzbergen	188	1380	9 10	6 10
Hausach to				
Offenburg	34	2 50	1 70	1 10
Singen	116	8 50	5 60	3 80
Heidelberg to				
Bretten	49	3 60	2 40	1 60
Mayence	95	7 00	4 60	3 10
Würzburg	160	1170	7 70	5 20
Hoek van Holland to				
Amsterdam	97	5 60	4 20	2 80
Dordrecht	48	2 80	2 10	1 40
The Hague	43	2 50	1 90	1 30
Roosendaal	87	5 00	3 80	2 50
Rotterdam	32	1 90	1 40	1 00
Salzbergen	259	1560	1200	7 90
Homburg to				
Friedberg	22	...	1 10	0 80
Immendingen to				
Singen	31	2 30	1 50	1 00
Kiel to				
Korsör	136	9 0	9 0	5 0
Neumünster	31	2 30	1 50	1 0
Kissingen to				
Meiningen	74	5 50	3 60	2 40
Schweinfurt	24	1 80	1 20	0 80
Kongsvinger to				
Lillestrom	79	7 20	4 30	2 90
Kornsjo to				
Mellerud	65	6 20	3 80	2 50
Kufstein to				
Ala	302	3040	2280	1490
Lalendorf to				
Rostock	44	3 30	2 20	1 60
Waren	36	2 70	1 80	1 30
Leipsic to				
Franzensbad	191	1440	9 50	6 30
Magdeburg	119	8 70	5 80	3 80
Probstzella	165	1220	8 00	5 40
Lindau to				
Bregenz	11	1 20	0 70	0 50
Linz to				
Passau	106	1070	6 50	4 20
Salzburg	125	1260	7 70	4 90
Vienna	189	1940	12 0	7 60
Luxemburg to				
Bettingen or Sterpenich	19	1 40	1 0	0 70
Metz	63	4 0	3 10	2 20
Strassburg	222	1630	1070	7 20
Meiningen to				
Eisenach	61	4 50	3 00	2 0
Schweinfurt	78	5 70	3 80	2 50
Mons to				
Feignies	16	1 30	0 90	0 60
Quievrain	21	1 70	1 20	0 70
Munich to				
Augsburg	62	4 60	3 0	2 00
Kufstein	99	7 30	4 80	3 20
Lichtenfels	293	2140	1410	9 40
Lindau	221	1620	1070	7 10
Nürnberg	199	1460	9 60	6 40
Probstzella	356	2600	1710	1140
Ulm	147	1080	7 10	4 80
Würzburg	278	2030	1340	8 90
Neuss to				
Vlodrop (Dalheim)	43	3 20	2 10	1 40
Neustrelitz to				
Waren	34	2 50	1 70	1 20
Nurnberg to				
Crailsheim	91	6 70	4 40	3 00
Hof	175	1280	8 40	5 60
Ostend to				
Bruges	23	1 80	1 30	0 80
Dover	98	9 20	7 30	...
Pforzheim to				
Carlsruhe	31	2 30	1 50	1 0
Wildbad	23	1 70	1 20	0 80

	Kil.	1 Cl mpf	2 Cl mpf	3 Cl mpf
Pilsen to				
Prague	115	1160	7 10	4 50
Taus	59	6 0	3 70	2 40
Pontebba to				
Tarvis	34	3 50	2 10	1 40
Prague to				
Bodenbach or Tetschen	137	1380	8 40	5 40
Brunn	254	2570	1570	10 0
Eger or Franzensbad	245	2250	1380	8 80
Roermond to				
Budel	35	2 00	1 60	1 30
Dalheim	14	0 90	0 70	0 50
Roosendaal to				
Esschen	8	0 60	0 40	0 30
Rostock to				
Warnemünde	14	1 10	0 70	0 50
Rotterdam to				
Amsterdam	73	4 20	3 20	2 10
Arnheim	110	6 30	4 70	3 20
Boxtel	88	5 00	3 80	2 50
Cologne	268	1840	1320	8 60
Emmerich	141	8 60	6 70	4 20
Nymegen	120	6 80	5 10	3 40

	Kil.	1 Cl mpf	2 Cl mpf	3 Cl mpf
Roosendaal	58	3 30	2 50	1 70
Salzbergen	227	1380	1070	6 90
Utrecht	53	3 10	2 30	1 60
Venlo	160	9 00	6 90	4 50
Saarbrücken to				
Metz	80	5 90	3 90	2 60
Salzburg to				
Ulm	300	2200	1450	9 70
Sassnitz to				
Stralsund	53	3 90	2 60	1 70
Trelleborg	102	10 0	10 0	6 0
Stockholm to				
Charlottenborg	439	2930	1760	1170
Gothenburg	458	3040	1830	1220
Malmo	618	3770	2370	1510
Strassburg to				
Deutsch Avricourt	92	6 80	4 50	3 00
Stuttgart to				
Bretten	64	4 70	3 10	2 10
Crailsheim	109	8 00	5 30	3 50
Friedrichshafen	198	1450	9 60	6 40
Immendingen	160	1170	7 70	5 20
Ulm	94	6 90	4 60	3 10

	Kil.	1 Cl mpf	2 Cl mpf	3 Cl mpf
Taus to				
Furth-i-W.	24	2 50	1 50	0 90
Treves to				
Bullay	53	3 90	2 60	1 70
Metz	100	7 30	4 80	3 20
Trelleborg to				
Malmo	31	2 20	1 40	0 90
Vienna to				
Bregenz or Buchs	744	6320	3940	2550
Bruck	46	5 00	3 00	2 00
Brunn	144	1520	9 30	6 0
Eger	456	4610	2820	1790
Marchegg	46	5 0	3 0	2 0
Prague	350	3570	2190	14 0
Triesto	589	5200	3650	2350
Villach to				
Assling	41	4 20	2 60	1 70
Tarvis	28	2 80	1 70	1 10
Toblach	151	1520	1140	7 40
Wiesbaden to				
Langenschwalb'ch	24	1 80	1 20	0 80
Rudesheim	36	2 70	1 80	1 20

FRANCE.

The minimum round route must be 300 kilomètres (186 miles), or same distance when route is broken at a frontier station to be resumed on return at another frontier station—for example, this permits entering Italy from France at Modane and returning by Ventimiglia, or vice versa.

	Kil.	1 Cl fr.c.	2 Cl fr.c.	3 Cl fr.c.
Aix-les-Bains to				
Chambéry	15	1 40	1 0	0 65
Geneva	101	8 50	6 15	4 0
Lyons	117	9 90	7 15	4 65
Macon	141	1190	8 65	5 65
Amiens to				
Paris	131	1075	7 75	5 15
Angers to				
Le Mans	95	8 0	5 75	3 75
Nantes	88	7 50	5 50	3 65
Paris	306	2575	1865	1215
Annemasse to				
Bellegarde	39	3 40	2 40	1 65
Geneva	6	0 50	0 40	0 25
Avignon to				
Marseilles	121	1025	7 40	4 90
Belfort to				
Delle	13	1 15	0 90	0 65
Geneva	374	3150	2265	1475
Lyons	345	29 0	2090	1365
Paris	443	3775	2725	1775
Petit Croix	12	1 15	0 90	0 65
Bordeaux to				
Gannat	447	3815	2750	1790
Paris	588	5015	3600	2350
Toulouse	257	2165	1565	1025
Boulogne to				
Calais	42	3 65	2 65	1 75
Paris	254	1965	1475	9 90
Briançon to				
Grenoble	219	1850	1325	8 75
Caen to				
Cherbourg	132	1115	8 0	5 25
Granville	131	1115	8 0	5 25
Paris	239	2015	1450	9 50
Calais to				
Laon	277	2365	1665	1090
Paris	295	2275	17 0	1140

	Kil.	1 Cl fr.c.	2 Cl fr.c.	3 Cl fr.c.
Cannes to				
Marseilles	194	1640	1175	7 75
Nice	31	2 65	1 90	1 25
Cette to				
Marseilles	160	1350	9 75	6 40
Toulouse	223	1875	1350	8 90
Chambéry to				
Lyons	123	1040	7 50	4 90
Chamonix to				
Geneva	108	9 15	5 90	4 40
Lyons	280	2365	1625	1115
Paris	700	5890	4165	2765
Delle to				
Dijon	190	16 0	1150	7 50
Laon	434	37 0	2665	1740
Paris	456	3890	28 0	1825
Deutsch Avricourt to				
Paris	411	35 0	2525	1650
Dieppe to				
Paris	201	17 0	1225	8 0
Rouen	61	5 15	3 75	2 50
Dijon to				
Paris	323	2725	1965	1275
Pontarlier	140	1190	8 50	5 65
Feignies to				
Paris	234	20 0	1440	9 40
Gannat to				
St. Germain d. F.	24	2 15	1 50	1 0
Geneva to				
Lausanne	61	5 15	3 65	2 50
Macon	161	1365	9 75	6 40
Modane	202	17 0	1225	8 0
Paris	598	5025	3625	2365
Granville to				
Cherbourg	133	1125	8 15	5 25
Paris	328	2765	1990	13 0
St. Malo	99	8 40	6 0	4 0
Grenoble to				
Lyons	131	1025	7 40	4 90
Paris	649	5465	3940	2565

	Kil.	1 Cl fr.c.	2 Cl fr.c.	3 Cl fr.c.
Havre to				
Paris	228	1925	1390	9 0
Rouen	89	7 50	5 50	3 65
Jeumont to				
Paris	240	2050	1475	9 65
Laon to				
Paris	140	12 0	8 65	5 65
Reims	52	4 50	3 25	2 15
Tergnier	29	2 25	1 75	1 15
Lille to				
Mouscron	15	1 50	1 00	0 65
Paris	247	2325	1540	1015
Lyons to				
Macon	72	6 15	4 40	2 90
Marseilles	352	2965	2140	14 0
Paris	527	4440	3190	2090
St. Germain d. F.	178	15 0	1090	7 15
Marseilles to				
Paris	872	7325	5275	3450
Ventimiglia	260	22 0	1590	1040
Nantes to				
Redon	81	7 00	5 00	3 25
Paris to				
Pontarlier	462	3890	28 0	1825
Quievrain	241	2050	1490	9 65
Reims	156	1340	9 65	6 25
Rouen	136	1150	8 25	5 40
St. Germain d. F.	362	3050	22 0	1440
Toulouse	752	6115	4400	2865
Ventimiglia	1132	9525	6865	4475
Rennes to				
Redon	72	6 15	4 40	2 90
St. Malo	82	7 0	5 0	3 25

The minimum round route must be 600 kilomètres (373 miles) from the departure station back to the same station; or, if for a route not circular, from the departure station to the terminal station the route must not be less than 600 kilomètres.

	Kil.	1 Cl fr.c.	2 Cl fr.c.	3 Cl fr.c.
Aarau to				
Brugg	19	1 65	1 15	0 75
Olten	14	1 25	0 90	0 65
Wohlen-Villm'g'n	20	1 75	1 25	0 90
Alpnachstad to				
Lucerne	14	1 25	0 90	0 65
Meiringen	33	4 15	3 0	1 50
Appenzell to				
Gais	6	—	0 75	0 50
Herisau	21	—	1 75	1 15
Arth-Goldau to				
Brunnen	12	1 0	0 75	0 50
Einsiedeln	26	3 50	2 50	1 65
Lucerne	28	2 40	1 75	1 15
Rigi Kulm	9	—	8 75	5 90
Rothkreuz	17	1 50	1 0	0 75
Zug	16	1 40	1 0	0 65
Basle to				
Biel	90	7 65	5 40	3 65
Delle	70	6 50	4 25	2 90
Olten	40	3 40	2 40	1 65
Schaffhausen	103	8 75	5 90	3 90
Stein-Säckingen	30	2 65	1 75	1 25
Bellinzona to				
Flüelen	119	1465	1025	6 90
Locarno	22	1 90	1 40	0 90
Lugano	30	3 65	2 50	1 75
Berne to				
Biel	34	2 90	2 0	1 40
Lausanne	98	8 25	5 90	3 90
Lucerne	96	8 15	5 75	3 90
Neuchatel	43	4 60	3 25	2 25
Olten	67	5 65	4 0	2 65
Thun	31	2 65	1 90	1 25
Biel to				
Delle	92	7 75	5 50	3 75
Neuchatel	30	2 65	1 75	1 25
Solothurn	25	2 15	1 50	1 0
Brienz to				
Interlaken	21	2 50	2 25	1 15
Meiringen	13	1 15	0 75	0 50
Brugg to				
Baden	9	0 75	0 65	0 40
Stein-Säckingen	28	2 40	1 75	1 15
Brunnen to				
Flüelen	12	1 0	0 75	0 50
Chur to				
Landquart	14	1 25	0 90	0 65
St. Moritz	90	1890	1265	6 40
Davos Platz to				
Landquart	50	1125	7 50	3 75
Einsiedeln to				
Wadenswil	20	2 65	1 90	1 25
Grindelwald to				
Interlaken	20	—	4 15	2 50
Lauterbrunnen	16	—	3 25	2 00
Interlaken to				
Lauterbrunnen	13	—	2 65	1 65
Schynige Platte	24	—	9 75	9 15
Spiez	17	2 25	1 50	1 0
Iselle to				
Brig	22	3 75	2 65	1 75
Domodossola	20	2 25	1 65	1 15
Lausanne to				
Pontarlier	72	6 15	4 40	2 90
Vevey	19	1 65	1 15	0 75
Locarno to				
Luino	29	2 25	2 25	1 40
Lucerne to				
Olten	56	4 75	3 40	2 25
Rothkreuz	19	1 65	1 15	0 75
Vitznau	15	1 65	1 65	0 75
Lugano to				
Chiasso	26	2 25	1 65	1 15
Luino	37	—	4 0	2 15
Menaggio	31	—	4 40	2 15
Martigny to				
St. Maurice	15	1 25	0 90	0 65
Visp	71	6 00	4 25	2 90
Montreux to				
St. Maurice	28	2 40	1 75	1 15
Vevey	7	0 65	0 50	0 40
Zweisimmen	63	1500	9 65	5 65
Neuchatel to				
Pontarlier	54	4 65	3 25	2 15
Olten to				
Solothurn	35	3 00	2 15	1 40
Pfäffikon to				
Wadenswil	10	0 90	0 65	0 40
Weesen	24	2 00	1 50	1 00
Romanshorn to				
Constance	20	1 75	1 25	0 90
Rorschach	15	1 25	0 90	0 65
Winterthur	57	4 90	3 40	2 25
Rothkreuz to				
Wohlen-Villm'g'n	28	2 40	1 75	1 15
Zug	11	1 00	0 75	0 50
Sargans to				
Buchs	16	1 40	1 0	0 65
Landquart	13	1 15	0 75	0 50
Weesen	35	3 0	2 15	1 50
Schaffhausen to				
Winterthur	30	2 65	1 75	1 25
Spiez to				
Frutigen	14	—	1 15	0 90
Scherzligen	10	1 15	0 75	0 65
Zweisimmen	36	6 75	4 50	2 40
St. Gallen to				
Gais	14	—	1 65	1 15
Herisau	9	1 00	0 75	0 50
Rorschach	17	1 50	1 0	0 75
Winterthur	58	4 90	3 50	2 40
St. Moritz to				
Pontresina	11	2 65	1 90	0 90
Thun to				
Scherzligen	2	0 25	0 15	0 15
Visp to				
Brig	9	0 75	0 65	0 40
Zermatt	36	—	13 0	7 65
Vitznau to				
Rigi Kulm	7	—	5 75	—
Zurich to				
Baden	23	2 00	1 40	1 00
Wadenswil	24	2 00	1 50	1 00
Winterthur	27	2 25	1 65	1 25
Zug	41	3 40	2 40	1 65

CIRCULAR TOURS IN **ITALY.**

Tickets are issued by the State Railway Administration to 1st, 2nd, and 3rd class passengers, to be combined at will in a manner similar to that described on page 379. The tickets cover the whole of Italy; the minimum distance travelled must be 400 chilometri (248 miles). When the round journey is of less length than 800 chilometri the tickets are valid for 15 days; more than 800 chilometri and less than 2,000 chilometri, tickets are valid 30 days; more than 2,000 chilometri and less than 3,000 chilometri tickets are valid 45 days; more than 3,000 chilometri, tickets are valid 60 days.

	Chilometri.	1 Cl l. c.	2 Cl l. c.	3 Cl l. c.
Ancona to				
Bologna	204	2110	1480	9 55
Foggia	323	3340	2340	1515
Arezzo to				
Florence	88	9 15	6 45	4 15
Terontola	35	3 70	2 55	1 65
Arona to				
Milan	67	5 70	4 0	2 55
Pallanza Fondo Toce	27	2 85	2 0	1 30
Bologna to				
Florence	133	1380	9 65	6 30
Milan	216	2335	1565	1015
Modena	37	3 90	2 75	1 75
Venice	160	1655	1165	7 55
Brindisi to				
Foggia	234	2420	17 0	11 0
Naples	386	3990	2795	1810
Taranto	70	7 30	5 10	3 30
Domodossola to				
Pallanza Fondo Toce	30	3 15	2 20	1 45
Florence to				
Pisa	79	8 20	5 75	3 75
Rome	316	3265	2290	1480
Foligno to				
Perugia	40	4 0	2 80	1 85
Terni	55	5 75	4 5	2 60
Genoa to				
Pisa	165	1710	12 0	7 75
Turin	166	1720	12 5	7 80
Ventimiglia	151	1565	1095	7 15
Milan to				
Chiasso	52	5 45	3 80	2 45
Genoa	151	1565	1095	7 15
Turin	150	1555	1090	7 5
Verona	160	1555	1090	7 5
Modena to				
Verona	102	1055	7 45	4 80
Perugia to				
Terontola	43	4 25	3 0	1 95
Reggio (Calabria) to				
Naples	476	4920	3445	2230
Taranto	476	4690	3285	2110
Rome to				
Naples	249	2580	18 5	1170
Orte	84	8 70	6 10	4 0
Pisa	338	3440	2415	1560
Terni to				
Orte	30	3 15	2 20	1 45
Turin to				
Modane	106	1080	7 55	4 90
Udine to				
Pontebba	69	7 35	5 15	3 35
Venice to				
Udine	136	14 5	9 90	6 40
Verona	116	12 0	8 45	5 50

The appropriate season for travel in France will be decided by the purpose of the traveller. Spring, summer, and early autumn for the north and west, summer and early autumn for the Pyrenees, winter for the Mediterranean coast; all the year round for Paris. A special interest attaches to Normandy and Picardy, those parts of France nearest to England; there is no wonderful scenery, but a country very like Kent and Surrey, with constant suggestions of a common history—castles, churches, abbeys, and cathedrals, the grandest in the land, erected by men with whom the mediæval Englishman was close kin. In Brittany there is a wild weird coast, old world towns, druidical remains, and a region of legend. Along the Pyrenees the scenery is ruggedly magnificent, forest, torrent, broken and towering mountain, with health resorts crushed in gorges or perched on ridges where the curative springs are most accessible.

Government.—The Republic was proclaimed on Sept. 4th, 1870, but the existing constitution dates from 25th Feb., 1875. The legislative power is exercised by two Assemblies, the Chamber of Deputies and the Senate. The Deputies (597) are elected by universal suffrage; the Senators number 300. The Deputies and Senators united form the National Assembly. The President (M. Raymond Poincaré, 1913) of the Republic is elected for seven years.

Population.—Pop. (1911) 39,601,509.

Expenditure.—1913, £186,585,615; **Revenue** £186,604,358. Total **Debt** (1912), £1,302,315,991.

Army.—(1913) 705,000. On a war footing, probably about 1,300,000 men would be available for the field army.—**Navy** (1912, including those building), Dreadnoughts 4, Battleships 22, Cruisers 31, Destroyers 85, Torpedo boats 187, Submarines 89.

Money.—1 franc=100 centimes=9½d. English. GOLD COINS: 20 and 10 francs. SILVER COINS: 5, 2, and 1 franc, 50 and 20 centimes. BRONZE COINS: 10 and 5 centimes. BANK NOTES: 1,000, 500, 200, 100, and 50 francs.

Weights and Measures.

Gramme	= 15.43 grains	Mètre	= 39.37 inches
Kilogramme	= 2.205 lbs. avoirdupois	Kilomètre	= 0.621 mile
Quintal Mètrique	= 220.5 ,, ,,	Mètre Cube } Stère }	= 35.31 cubic feet
Tonneau	= 2205 ,, ,,		
Litre, Liquid	= 1.76 pint	Hectare	= 2.47 acres
Hectolitre { Liquid	= 22 gallons	Kilomètre Carré	= 0.386 square mile
Hectolitre { Dry	= 2.75 bushels		

English and French Measures.

Inch	= 2.54 centimètres	Bushel	= 36.37 litres
Foot	= 30.48 ,,	Grain	= 0.0648 grammes
Yard	= 0.914 mètre	Ounce, Troy	= 31.103 grammes
Mile	= 1.609 kilomètre	Ounce, Avoirdupois	= 28.35 grammes
Square Yard	= 0.836 square metres (mètre carrè)	Pound, Avoirdupois	= 453.592 grammes
Acre	= 0.405 hectare	Cwt.	= 50.8 kilogrammes
Pint	= 0.568 litre	Ton	= 1016 kilogrammes
Gallon	= 4.546 litres		

Postage.—To England 25c. for 20 grammes—for every 20 grammes more 15 c.; for France 10c. for 20 grammes. Post Cards, 10c. Newspapers, 5c.

Telegraph.—To United Kingdom 20c. a word, minimum charge 1 franc. In France 50c. for 10 words, and 5c. for every additional word.

Time.—The legal time of France, according to which the railways are worked, is the same as Greenwich Time, which is 9 minutes 21 seconds later than the meridian time of Paris. The system of time reckoning from midnight to midnight—24 o'clock—has been introduced as the working time on the French railways. **Luggage**—66 lbs. allowed free; excess luggage, 1 centime per 44 lbs. per kilometre.

NOTICES OF TOWNS, WATERING PLACES, ETC.

Abbeville.—*Stat.*—Pop. 19,669.

HOTEL: TETE DE BŒUF.

A fortified port on the Somme. The fine Gothic Church of St. Wolfram, of 15th and 17th centuries, has a façade richly sculptured, and towers. Musée d'Abbeville et du Ponthieu of natural history, etc.; and the Musée Boucher-de-Perthes, paintings, sculpture, antiquities.

RAIL, pages 18, 20, 29B.

Crecy-en-Ponthieu — HOTEL DU CANON D'OR—the scene of the battle of 26th August, 1346; a cross on the west side of the village indicates the battlefield. Rail from Abbeville, page 29B.]

Abries.

HOTELS: GRAND; POSTE.

The principal village of the upper part of the valley of the Guil, 5,085 ft. above sea, in a district sometimes called the French Engadine. Dry pure air, free of fog. Interesting Romanesque Church. A good centre for excursions among the mountains of the French-Italian frontier. Sport is abundant.

The nearest Railway Station is at Mont Dauphin Guillestre (page 53B), whence is a Diligence service, page 370.

Aix.—*Stat.*—Pop. 28,923.

HOTELS: ETABLISSEMENT; NEGRE-COSTE.

The ancient capital of Provence, the Aquæ Sextiæ of the Romans, a university city and the seat of an archbishop.

The Cathedral of St. Sauveur, in the north part of the city, dates from the 11th cent.; the choir is of the 13th cent., one aisle is of the 14th cent., the other aisle of the 17th cent.; the carved doors of the portal are of the late 15th cent.; paintings and tapestry in interior. Cloister on south side of the Cathedral—next to it is the Archbishop's Palace. Opposite the Palace is the University.

In south-east part of the city is the Church of St. Jean de Malte, 14th cent., with lofty spire; tomb of Alphonse II, Count of Provence, in left transept; old paintings. Other interesting churches are La Madeleine, St. Jean Baptiste, and St. Esprit.

The Musée adjoins the church of St. Jean de Malte—collections of paintings, sculpture, and antiquities.

Hotel de Ville, at centre of city, has a tower of the 15th cent.; here is the Library of 170,000 vols. and 1190 MSS.

The Etablissement Thermal is in the north-west quarter; the waters are weak but hot (93-97° Fahr.). Only a few traces of the Roman baths remain.

RAIL, pages 49B, 63A.

Aix-les-Bains.—*Stat.*—Pop. 8,320.

SPLENDIDE HOTEL ROYAL. — Fashionable hotel, of high reputation, situated in fine elevated position, with Park. Much frequented by English families. See Advt.

HOTEL MIRABEAU.—First class hotel. Unique panorama. Opened June, 1910. See Advt.

REGINA GRAND HOTEL BERNASCON.—Large splendid hotel, beautifully situated, with terrace commanding fine view of the Lake and Mountains. Open all the year. G. Bernascon, Propr. See Adv.

HOTEL BEAU SITE.—Mr. Ch. Rivollier, proprietor. Situated, Boulevard du Parc. Elevated position, with fine views. See Advt.

HOTEL DU NORD ET GRANDE BRETAGNE.—First-class family hotel, well situated near the Bath Establishment, and facing the "Grand Cercle." See Advt.

INTERNATIONAL PALACE HOTEL.—Well situated, Avenue de la Gare, near the Casinos. Lift. See Advt.

GRAND HOTEL DU LOUVRE ET SAVOY.—First-class family hotel. Very well situated near the Baths, with garden and fine views of the Lake and Mountain. See Advt.

HOTEL DES ILES BRITANNIQUES.—First class. Connected with the Baths. Modern comforts. Pension from 10 fr. 50c. See Advt.

METROPOLE HOTEL.—Opposite the principal entrance of the Grand Cercle and near the Bath Establishment. Electric light; lift. See Advt.

HOTEL WINDSOR ET PAIX.—Family hotel, adjacent to the Bath Establishment. Garden; electric light. "Good table"; reasonable charges. Pension from 8 fr. See Advt.

AIX-LES-BAINS is pleasantly situated in a fine valley of Savoy, 850 ft. above sea, 1¼ mile from Lake Bourget, with beautiful scenery all round; the climate is very mild, the mean temperature being 55° Fahrenheit. The warm sulphur springs were known to the Romans as Aquæ Gratianæ; they are now visited annually by nearly 40,000 persons. The Etablissement Thermal, well appointed, is open all the year, and the treatment is very successful in cases of rheumatism, gout, and skin disease. At the front of the Etablissement is the Arch of Campanus, a Roman burial relic, with niches for the urns containing ashes of persons whose names may be deciphered. Handsome Casino, where splendid fêtes are given.

At the Hotel de Ville is a small Museum of antiquities, including remains of a temple of Diana.

On the south side of Aix, distant about a mile—electric tramway—is **Marlioz,** where are cold sulphur springs, chiefly for drinking. Fine park.

From the Plateau of Mont Revard (5,000 ft. high), at the foot of which Aix-les-Bains is situated, there is a magnificent view of the country all round, including Mont Blanc and its sister alps. There is a Funicular Railway to the summit, the trains taking just over an hour for the journey. Half-day excursions by coaches and cars are made daily during the season (May to September inclusive) from Aix (Parc extremity of the Avenue de la Gare), at a cost of 5 francs per passenger; these vehicles go in six different directions through most beautiful and varied scenery. There is also a day excursion made two or three times a week to La Grande Chartreuse, at a charge of 15 francs for the day.

POST OFFICE.—Rue des Ecoles, near the Etablissement.

ENGLISH CH. SERVICE, St. Swithin's Church.

GOLF.—9-hole course.

MEDICAL.—Dr. Stanley Randall; Dr. Leon Blanc; Dr. Louis Blanc; Dr. Françon; Dr. Gubb; Dr. Goddard; Dr. J. Dardel, Rue des Bains. A complete list may be seen at the Etablissement.

RAIL, pages 47, 60.

[**Lac du Bourget,** 1¼ miles to west of Aix—electric tramway—has several places of interest on its banks. A steamer makes the circuit of the lake once or twice daily in the summer. At **Hautecombe,** at the foot of Mont du Chat, is a Cistercian monastery; the church has many statues, paintings, reliefs and decorations.]

Allevard-les-Bains.—*Stat.*—Pop. 2,726.

HOTELS: LOUVRE; FRANCE; DAUPHINE.

A small town, 1,560 ft. above sea, situated in a fine valley of Dauphiny, much visited for the curative properties of its warm sulphur spring, 61° Fahrenheit. The waters are used for drinking, bathing, and inhaling. Thermal Establishment, Casino, and park. Gothic Church; Chateau of 18th cent. Iron mines close by. Many points of interest in the neighbourhood: the ruined mediæval Castle of La Bastie, the Chartreuse de St. Hugon, the Sept Laux, the Puy-Gris, and others. Mountain excursions. Resident guides.

RAIL, page 47

Ambleteuse.

A fishing village, now a quiet bathing resort, 7 miles to the north of Boulogne. Fishing may be had in the river; many pleasant walks. James II landed here in 1688 when he fled from England. Reached by railway omnibus from Wimille Wimereux station, page 18; electric tram service between Boulogne and Wimereux.

Amélie-les-Bains.—*Stat.*

HOTEL ET THERMES PUJADE.—In fine position close to the Mondony Gorge. Hot sulphur and other baths. Moderate charges. See Advt.

THERMES ROMAINS; MARTINET; BOCASSIN.

A thriving town, finely placed at the confluence of the Rivers Tech and Mondony, at the foot of Fort-les-Bains (1,225 ft.) The warm sulphur springs, 60° to 145° Fahrenheit, were known to the Romans; they are successfully used in affections of the lungs. RAIL, page 44.

Amiens.—*Stat.*—Pop. 93,207.

HOTEL DE L'UNIVERS.—Beautifully situated facing the Square St. Denis. See Advt.

HOTEL DU RHIN.—Place St. Denis, near the Railway, one of the finest in town. See Advt.

The RAILWAY STATION is at the east side of the city, less than half a mile from the centre.

Amiens, chief town of Département de la Somme, the ancient capital of Picardy, is on the River Somme and two small affluents, the Arve and the Selle. It is one of the principal manufacturing towns of France, with a great trade in linen, woollens, velvet, etc.

Running across the front of the Station is a broad boulevard. The part to the right (north) is the Boulevard d'Alsace, and the second street on the west side, Rue de Gloriette, leads in five minutes to the Cathedral.

The CATHEDRAL is one of the magnificent Gothic monuments of France, the facade being specially admired. It was erected 1220-88; the length is 470 ft., transept 213 ft., width of nave 144 ft. The towers, incomplete, are of 13th (181 ft.) and 15th (210 ft.) cents.; the spire (360 ft.) dates from 1529. Many statues and much carving on the facade; between the doors of the central porch is a figure of the Saviour, the "Beau Dieu d'Amiens." In the interior the loftiness of the nave, 147 ft., is striking, only the nave of Beauvais Cathedral being loftier; a wealth of carving in the choir; behind the high altar is an angelic figure, the "Enfant Pleureur"; reliefs in the transepts and on the choir screen, the chapels are interesting. In the open square at east end of Cathedral is a statue of Peter the Hermit, or Peter of Amiens, who preached the first Crusade.

Other churches of interest are St. Germain, 15th cent., quarter mile west of Cathedral; St. Leu, 15th cent., quarter mile north of Cathedral; and Sacré Cœur, modern, 1895, half a mile due west of Cathedral.

MUSEE, half a mile south of the Cathedral, a short distance back from north side of Boulevard St. Charles. Collections of pictures, sculpture, and antiquities. Sun., Tues., and Thurs., 12.0 to 5.0, free. Opposite east side of the Museé is the Prefecture, and on south side is the Bibliothèque Communale—80,000 vols. and 572 MSS.

The Hotel de Ville is a quarter mile west of the Cathedral; old Belfry close to north side.

The Citadel, all that is left of the old fortifications, is on the north side of the city.

H.B.M.'S VICE-CONSUL.—W. Sutcliffe, Esq.

RAIL, pages 18, 20, 21, 26, 29, 30.

Angers.—*Stat.*—Pop. 83,786.

HOTELS: GRAND; CHEVAL BLANC; ANJOU.

The principal Railway Station, Gare de St. Laud, is on the south side of the city, a quarter mile from the Castle and half a mile from the Cathedral. Minor Stations are St. Serge, on north side, and La Maitre-Ecole on east side.

Angers, chief town of the Département de Maine-et-Loire, the Andegavia of the Romans, and capital of Anjou, is situated on the Maine, in a pleasant country.

The street running from north side of the Place de la Gare if followed in a north easterly line for about half a mile will lead to the cross Rue St. Aubin; down here, a little to west, is the Cathedral.

CATHEDRAL of St. Maurice, Romanesque-Gothic, of 12th-13th cent.; carving on the facade. Interior has sculpture, tapestry, finely carved pulpit; handsome windows. On north side of the Cathedral is the Bishop's palace.

Church of St. Laud, 200 yards west of Gare St. Laud. Modern; elaborate altars.

La Trinité, in a line west of the Cathedral, across the river; no aisles.

St. Serge, an ancient abbey church, on north side of city.

The Castle, near the river, north of the Station, is still an imposing monument of feudal times, though much has been destroyed.

MUSEE. From near south side of Cathedral go down Rue Toussaint, on east side is Rue du Musée. Collections of paintings, sculpture, and natural history, Sun. and Thurs., 1.0 to 5.0.

Musée St. Jean, back from west side of river, near most northerly bridge. Antiquities.

Jardin des Plantes, north side of city.

H.B.M.'S VICE-CONSUL.—R. Richou, Esq.

RAIL pp. 39, 41A, 42A, 42B, 75, 83.

Angoulême—*Stat.*—Pop. 38,211.

HOTELS: DU PALAIS; DE FRANCE; DES POSTES.

The two Railway Stations, Gare d'Orleans and Gare de l'Etat, are close together on the north east side of the city.

Chief town of Département Charente, the old capital of the Angoumois, on a rocky hill at the confluence of the Rivers Charente and Anguienne.

A street running between the Railway Stations ascends to the city, and if followed in its bending westward will conduct to the Hotel de Ville (left), on past the Palais de Justice (right), then about third street on left leads to the Cathedral.

The Hotel de Ville, on the site of the castle of the Counts of Angoulême, of which two towers still exist, contains a Picture Gallery and an Archæological Museum.

CATHEDRAL of St. Pierre, a Romanesque-Byzantine edifice, dating from 12th cent., restored 1866-75; facade and tower are specially interesting.

RAIL, pages 34, 35, 35B, 39A, 41B, 42B.

Annecy.—*Stat.*—Pop. 12,894.

HOTEL D'ANGLETERRE ET GRAND HOTEL REUNIS.—Old renowned first class family hotel, well situated, with garden. Patronised by English families. Pension from 8.50 fr. See Advt.

GRAND HOTEL VERDUN.—First class hotel, facing the Lake. Suites with baths. Hot water heating and electric light. Pension terms from 8.50 frs. Open all the year. See Advt.

MONT BLANC.

Chief town of Département Haute Savoie, beautifully situated on the Lake of Annecy, an excellent centre for excursions into the valleys of the French Alps, but otherwise not very interesting. At the Chapel of the Visitation are good paintings. Hotel de Ville has a small Musée of industrial and natural history collections, and a library. The Cathedral is a small building without interest.

RAIL, pages 47, 61A. STEAMERS, page 366.

[**Menthon.**

HOTELS: BAINS; PALACE.

A pleasant village in a sheltered situation, a little back from the shore of the Lake of Annecy. By the lake are Sulphur Baths, near some Roman remains. St. Bernard of Menthon, founder of the hospices on the Great and Little St. Bernard, was born 923, at the ancient Chateau on a hill about 1¼ mile to the east of Menthon.

STEAMER on the Lake of Annecy, page 366.]

Antibes.—*Stat.*—Pop. 10,000.

GRAND HOTEL.—Large hotel; equipped with every modern comfort. Lift; electric light; central heating. Restaurant. Moderate tariff. See Advt.

A sheltered winter place and small seaport, in a fine situation between Golfe Juan and Bai des Anges; breakwater 1,540 ft. long. It is the ancient Antipolis, the modern town being partly built on the old ramparts. Roman remains. Museum at Hotel de Ville. On the north side of the bay is Fort Carré, whence is a magnificent view. Electric Tramway to Cannes.

ENGLISH CHURCH SERVICE. RAIL, page 54.

Cap d'Antibes (Cap de la Garoupe), a headland just west of Antibes.

GRAND HOTEL DU CAP.—Superior first class, beautifully situated in own grounds of forty-five acres, amidst pine district; entirely renovated; lift; electric light. See Advt.

The Cap d'Antibes is a beautiful peninsula about 2½ miles long, clothed with a wonderfully rich vegetation and having a wild picturesque coast. As a winter resort it is in growing favour; many villas. At Villa Thuret is a garden associated with the Jardin des Plantes at Paris. Villa Eilenrok is at the extremity of the Cape (may be visited). On La Garoupe, 245 ft., are a pilgrimage church and lighthouse. Electric Tramway between Cap d' Antibes and Antibes.

Arcachon.—*Stat.*—Pop. 9,500.

HOTEL DES PINS ET CONTINENTAL (en foret).—Lifts; electric light. B. Ferras, propr. See Advt.

NEW GRAND HOTEL.—First class hotel with 100 bed and sitting rooms, replete with every modern comfort. Full south. Excellent cuisine. Season February to October. See Advt.

FRANCE; REGINA.

A favourite sea bathing and winter resort, consisting of two parts, the town along the shore and the Ville d'Hiver (winter town) in the pine forest to the south; the exhalations of the pines with the sea air render the Ville d'Hiver a very healthy quarter. Climate temperate at all seasons. Casino.

ENG. CH. SER. at the Church of St. Thomas.

BRITISH V.-CON.—Frederick Audap, Esq.

GOLF.—9-hole course, about a mile and a quarter from centre of town.

MEDICAL.—Dr. F. Lalesque; Dr. Festal.

BANK.—Exchange. Société Generale (de Paris), 215, Boulevard de la Plage.—English spoken. Letters of Credit and Circular notes cashed. Credits opened, etc. Apply London, 65, Regent street, W.

RAIL, see pages 45A, 46A.

[**Le Moulleau.** GRAND HOTEL.

A pleasant village and rising summer and winter resort about 3 miles west of Arcachon. Dominican institution and chapel.]

Argelès-Gazost.—*Stat.*—Pop. 1,800.

HOTEL DE FRANCE.—Every modern comfort. Steam heating. English Church Service at the Hotel. Golf links free for visitors. See Advt.

A little Pyreneean town, 1525 ft. above sea, in a fine situation. Very good centre for visiting Cauterets, St. Sauveur Gavarnie, and all the Pyreneean resorts; six hours from Biarritz, one hour from Pau. Ideal winter and spring resort, with many English visitors. Stimulating bracing climate. Sulphurous waters at the Etablissement Thermal. Nervous affections treated by electricity at the Institut de Therapeutique Physique. ENGLISH CHURCH SERV. in the season.

GOLF.—18-hole course, 10 mins. walk from the Hotel de France. RAIL, page 43.

Arles.—*Stat.*—Pop. 24,567.

GRAND HOTEL DU NORD. — All modern equipment; access to Roman remains. See Advt.

The principal Railway Station, Grande Gare, is on the north side of the city, half a mile from the centre.

Arles, a very old place, on the River Rhone, is the Roman Arelate, on the Via Aurelia. There is some trade in the port, but the interest for the traveller is in the Roman remains.

Due south from the Railway Station, across the Place Lamartine, a street leads in half a mile directly to the Rond Point des Arènes, where is the Amphitheatre, about 500 yards in circumference; it dates from the beginning of the Christian era, the forty-three tiers of seats could accommodate 26,000 spectators. Bull fights take place here on Sunday in summer. Just south west of the Amphitheatre are the remains of the Theatre.

From the west side of the Amphitheatre the Rue des Arènes leads to the Place du Forum, the ancient Roman Forum—on north side are two columns. A few yards south of the Place du Forum is the Place de la Republique, where are a Roman Obelisk and other remains. A quarter mile north of the Place du Forum, just back from the river, is the Palace of Constantine.

Cathedral of St. Trophimus, just west of the ruined Roman Theatre, has a fine doorway and cloisters; a few pictures in interior.

Musée in Place de la République, immediately opposite west end of the Cathedral. Valuable collections of ancient and early Christian sarcophagi, etc.

The Aliscamps, the old Roman burial place, consecrated to Christian use by St. Trophimus, a very celebrated cemetery in the middle ages, is at the south east side of the city. The cemetery was neglected and the monuments scattered, some are collected in an Allée, others are at the Museum.

RAIL, pages 49, 51, 57, 63B, 74B.

[**Saintes Maries**, 24 miles from Arles, derives its name from Mary of Bethany, Mary the mother of James, and Mary Magdalen, who, with their servant Sara, Lazarus, and St. Maximin, landed here—so is the tradition. In the Church are relics of the saints; on May 24th-25th and Oct. 22nd many pilgrims attend. RAIL from Arles, page 51.]

Arras.—*Stat.*—Pop. 26,144.

HOTELS: UNIVERS; COMMERCE; ST. POL.

Chief town of Dept. Pas de Calais, on the Scarpe. Hotel de Ville, a fine building. Cathedral, built 1755-1833; elaborate high altar; a Descent from the Cross, said to be by Rubens, and an Entombment, said to be by van Dyck, in the ambulatory. On ground floor of old Abbey of St. Vaast is a Musée of paintings and an archeological collection. Grande Place and Petite Place have interesting old houses. Arras is a centre of the grain trade.

RAIL, pages 20, 22A, 23, 26, 28.

Auray.—*Stat.*—Pop. 6,450.

HOTELS: PAVILLON; POSTE.

A port, in Dept. Morbihan, on the River d'Auray (an inlet from Quiberon Bay); has not much interest of its own, but is a good centre for Carnac, Plouharnel, Locmariaker, etc. Adjoining Chartreuse d'Auray, to the north-west of Station, is a Votive Chapel, to the memory of 952 Emigrés, slain on the spot marked by a Chapelle Expiatoire. At Ste. Anne d'Auray, 3 miles, is a much frequented pilgrimage Church; great gatherings at Whitsuntide and on Ste. Anne's Day (July 26th). Motor service between Auray and Locmariaker.

MOTORING AND CYCLING.—E. Plunian, Rue de l'Hôpital, (Telephone No. 8). Motor cars, Bicycles, and Carriages. Free garage. Large garage with inspection pit. Stock Michelin.

RAIL pages 31, 31A, 37.

[A steamer usually leaves Port Maria, the port of **Quiberon** (HOTEL DE FRANCE) twice a day for **Belle Isle** or **Belle Ile-en-Mer**, in the Atlantic, a pleasant summer retreat, 12 m. long, with good cliffs, and a few little villages. HOTEL DE FRANCE at Le Palais, the chief port, pop. 4,900.]

Auxerre.—*Stat.*—Pop. 18,036.

HOTELS: EPEE; FONTAINE; POSTE.

Chief town of Département de l'Yonne, on the River Yonne. Railway Station on east side of city, about half mile from centre.

Cathedral of St. Etienne, 13th-15th cent., two towers, has fine portals on west front, many figures in recesses and niches; graceful interior, statue of St. Stephen, tombs, stained glass.

Church of St. Pierre, in Rue du Pont, has fine portico and tower. St. Eusèbe, in Rue du Temple; tower, wood carving, stained glass. Remains of Abbey of St. Germain, best seen from quay.

Musée, little north of Cathedral, near Hotel de Ville; collections of paintings, sculpture, antiquities, etc.

RAIL, pages 53C, 56.

Avignon.—*Stat.*—Pop. 49,304.

GRAND HOTEL DE L'EUROPE.—First class family hotel, situated full south. See Advt.

HOTEL D'AVIGNON; CRILLON.

The Railway Station is at the south west side of the city, about half a mile from the centre.

Avignon, the ancient Avenio, chief town of the Département Vaucluse, on the River Rhone, the seat of an archbishop, is a very important place in the history of the Catholic Church. Upon the river bank, which rises like a cliff, are the Papal Palace and Cathedral, and about this spot the city is picturesque. It was the residence from 1305 until 1377 of Popes in antagonism to the Popes of Rome. At the entrance to the city from the Station the old walls should be noticed.

From immediately by the Railway Station the Cours de la République, with its continuation, leads north east across the city; at the upper end of the thoroughfare, on the east side, is the PALAIS DES PAPES, a gloomy fortress-like Gothic range of buildings, with endless corridors and staircases, and chambers of grim traditions.

On north side of the Papal Palace is the Romanesque Cathedral, Notre Dame des Doms, dating from the 12th cent.; interior contains Tombs of Pope John XXII, Benedict XII, several paintings, and much decoration. Fine view from the Promenade du Rocher des Doms, on north side of Cathedral; to the left is the ruin of a bridge across the Rhone, the celebrated Pont d'Avignon, built by the Bridge Making Fraternity under St. Benezet.

St. Agricol Church, just west of Hotel de Ville 14-15th cent. Good paintings.

St. Pierre Church, 200 yards due south of the Papal Palace; Gothic, of 14th cent. Within are some paintings. Most of the other churches are worth visiting.

Musée Calvet, a hundred yards back from west side of Rue de la République, at about midway along this street. Good collections of sculpture and paintings, old and modern masters. Sunday 12.0 to 4.0. City Library in same building;

130,000 vols., 3,000 MSS.; daily 9.0 to 12.0 and 2.0 to 4.0.

Musée Requien at north end east side of Cours de la République. Natural History collection and library. Sunday 12.0 to 4.0.

In the cemetery on east side of the city is buried John Stuart Mill (died 1873).

ENGLISH CHURCH SERVICE.

RAIL, pages 49, 63A.

Avranches.—*Stat.*—Pop. 7,845.

HOTELS: DE FRANCE; ANGLETERRE; BONNEAU.

A favourite English resort in Normandy, on the River Sée; on a fine slope in view of the sea. Churches of St. Saturnin, St. Gervais, and N.D. des Champs. Museum in the old Bishop's Palace. Henry II.'s Stone (site of Cathedral, before 1790), where he did penance for Becket's murder.

ENG. CH. SERVICE, Church of St. Michael, Rue Bouillant.

RAIL, pp. 75, 75A, 85. A local line from Avranches Station to Boulevard du Sud and St. James.

Ax-les-Thermes.—*Stat.*—Pop. 1,609.

HOTELS: BOYER; SICRE; FRANCE.

An old town, in itself not attractive, at a meeting of three fine valleys, 2,350 ft. above sea, with many warm sulphur springs from 63° to 171°, used for drinking and bathing in cases of rheumatism, skin disease, scrofula, catarrhs, etc. It is a much quieter place than other Pyreneean resorts; temperature variable, nights often cold.

RAIL, page 46.

[**Andorra.** From Ax a road ascends to cross the Pyrenees, emerging on the Spanish side near Puigcerda, about 30 miles. At a little beyond l'Hospitalet, 10½ miles from Ax, a track goes off westward to Andorra. The road is practicable for carriages as far as l'Hospitalet, but the track beyond is only to be travelled on horseback or on foot. It is usual to sleep at l'Hospitalet; the journey thence occupies about 9 hours. **Andorra** (3,540 ft. above sea—an inn, CALOUNE) is the village capital, pop. 800, of a little republic, total pop. 5,231; the "country," an irregular square, is about 18 miles wide in either direction, and beside mountain includes a small fertile plain].

Bagnères de Bigorre.—*Stat.*—Pop. 8,837.

HOTELS: VICTORIA; PARIS; BEAU SEJOUR; FRASCATI; DE FRANCE.

A Pyreneean watering place, 1,805 ft. above sea, pleasantly situated on the Adour. About 20,000 visitors come annually for the waters; most of the springs are warm, containing sulphate of lime, but they vary much; four are cold chalybeate springs; rheumatism, nervous affections, female disorders, digestion troubles, anæmia, etc., are successfully treated. The principal bath establishments, the Thermes and the Neothermes, belong to the town.

In the town are the old St. Vincent Church and Tour des Jacobins. Casino. RAIL, page 45.

Ballon d'Alsace, 4,120 ft., one of the highest points of the Vosges Mountains. At the summit, near a statue of the Virgin, is an indicator showing the neighbouring heights. Magnificent extensive view all round. On the north west side is the Ballon de Servance, 3,900 ft. The ascents are marked by finger posts.

Reached from St. Maurice page 73, a two hours walk; or from Giromagny, page 74A, a three hours walk; carriages to be had.

Barèges.

HOTELS: DE L'EUROPE; ANGLETERRE.

Barèges, 4,040 ft. above sea, on the Gave de Bastan, consists of one long street. A favourite summer resort for the powerful warm sulphur springs, used for bathing and drinking in cases of obstinate wounds, ulcers, scrofula, gout, rheumatism, anæmia, and some nervous affections. Fine Bath Establishment.

DILIGENCE from Luz to Barèges, page 370.

[An easy excursion from Barèges is to the Pic du Midi de Bigorre, 9,440 ft., in about 3½ hours, or there and back in 6 hours. Guide not necessary. HOTELLERIE DU PIC DU MIDI near the top of mountain; sunrise view very fine.]

Bayeux.—*Stat.*—Pop. 7,912.

HOTELS: LUXEMBOURG; GRAND.

Cathedral of Notre Dame, half mile from Station, Gothic, of 12th cent., erected by Odo, Bishop of Bayeux, half-brother of William the Conqueror; both exterior and interior should be carefully inspected. Many old houses.

The famous Bayeux Tapestry is in a small Musée attached to the Bibliothèque in the Place du Chateau. The Tapestry, representing the invasion of England by the Normans, is 230 ft. long, 18 inches wide. Who worked it is not known absolutely, but usually it is ascribed to Matilda, wife of William the Conqueror.

RAIL, pages 74B, 75A, 78.

Bayonne.—*Stat.*—Pop. 27,192.

HOTELS: GRAND ET COMMERCE; PARIS.

An old town, 3½ miles from the Bay of Biscay, at the confluence of the Rivers Adour and Nive

The Cathedral dates from 1213, but parts are modern; interior has handsome high altar and paintings in the chapels. In the Place de la Liberté, in one large building, is the Hotel de Ville, Bibliothèque, Musée, and Theatre.

At the base of the Citadel, near the Railway Station, is a cemetery, Cimitière des Anglais, where are buried English soldiers who fell at the unsuccessful siege of 1814.

H.B.M.'s VICE-CONSUL.—P. Schœdelin, Esq.

RAIL, pages 43, 45.

Beaulieu.—*Stat.*

HOTEL BRISTOL.—First class hotel, with Verandah Restaurant and terraces extending to the sea. Electric light; lift; garden, See Advt.

HOTEL EMPRESS.—Elevated position, full south. Good sea view. Garden. Lift. Central heating (hot water system). See Advt.

MEYER'S VICTORIA HOTEL.—First class, large garden. See Advt.

HOTEL METROPOLE.—First class, beautifully situated in fine grounds, facing the sea. Lift; electric light. See Advt.

BOND'S HOTEL.—High class family hotel, beautifully situated, within short distance of Railway Station. Every modern comfort. Pension from 12 fr. See Advt.

PANORAMA PALACE HOTEL.—On sea shore, full south; quiet and comfortable. Central heating; large gardens; tennis courts; garage. Pension from 15 frs. See Advt.

A well sheltered winter resort, increasing in popularity, with excellent sea bathing. Climate mild and dry. In a beautiful Bay, has many walks and drives, with lovely mountain scenery. Golf links. Electric tram service to Nice and Monte Carlo.

MEDICAL.—Dr. Johnston-Lavis. Villa Lavis.

HOUSE AND ESTATE AGENTS.– Kurz's Agency, opposite the Station. Particulars of Apartments and Villas to be let sent on application. See Advt.

RAIL, p. 54.

[**St. Jean**, on Cap Ferrat, 1½ mile south of Beaulieu. Ruins of a Moorish fort, destroyed 1706, and of a chapel; tunny fishing in early spring. Tramway service connects with Beaulieu.]

Beauvais.—*Stat.*—Pop. 19,906.

HOTELS: DE FRANCE; CONTINENTAL.

Chief town of the Département de l'Oise, on the River Thérain, where carpets, army cloths, gold and silver lace, and buttons are extensively made; there is also a branch State Tapestry manufactory.

CATHEDRAL, St. Pierre, begun 1247, though only a part, never completed, is a magnificent imposing edifice, of gigantic proportions, with an exceptionally lofty and beautiful choir (152 ft.), and superb south transept facade. Originally there was a spire 500 ft. high, but it fell in 1573. In the chapels are paintings; tapestries; astronomical clock in choir chapel. To west of Cathedral is a part of an ancient Church, known as Basse Œuvre, supposed to belong to 6th cent. At the back of the Basse Œuvre is a small Musée of antiquities.

To south west of Place de la Cathedrale is the Palais de Justice, formerly the bishop's palace. The present Episcopal Palace is on the north side of the Cathedral.

At the Hotel de Ville is the banner taken personally by Jeanne Lainé, or Hachette, who led the women at the siege in 1472 by Charles the Bold and 80,000 men. RAIL, pages 22, 29A, 30.

Belfort.—*Stat.*—Pop. 39,371

GRAND HOTEL.-New first class hotel, centrally situated. Every modern comfort. Apartments with private baths. Electric light; central heating; lift. See Advt.

POSTE; JEANNIN.

A strongly fortified frontier town, on the River Savoureuse, in a position of great military importance, dominating the narrow way—the Trouée de Belfort—between the Vosges and Jura mountains; successful in resistance against the besieging Germans in the war of 1870-1. Citadel on a rock 220 ft. high. The Lion of Belfort, 36 ft. high, 72 ft. long, commemorates the siege. At the Hotel de Ville is a museum and collection of pictures. Entrenched Camp (will hold 20,000 men) in a valley on the Strassburg road.

RAIL, pages 52, 68, 74A.

Berck-sur-Mer.—*Stat.*—Pop. 7,500.

A rising and very healthy watering place, 27 miles to the south of Boulogne. Kursaal and Casino; the shore is dotted with villas, bungalows, and hotels.

RAIL. From Rang-du-Fliers-Verton, on main line from Calais and Boulogne to Paris (page 18) there is a branch railway to Berck, page 30A. Local line between Berck Plage and Paris Plage.

Besançon.—*Stat.*—Pop. 57,978.

HOTELS: DES BAINS; NORD; PARIS; EUROPE.

Chief town of Département du Doubs, the Roman *Vesontio*, former capital of Franche-Comté, on the River Doubs, one of the most strongly fortified places in France.

From the principal Railway Station, Gare de la Viotte, follow the road to left, it presently bears to right, crossing the river, and leading in a few minutes to Place St. Pierre, where is the Hotel de Ville; immediately behind is the Palais de Justice. Continuing along the Grande Rue from the Place St. Pierre, on the south side is seen the Palais Granvelle, occupied by learned societies; up the street just beyond the Palais Granvelle, on opposite side, is the Bibliothèque, 130,000 vols., 1,850 MSS., 10,000 medals, and curiosities; at No. 140, Grande Rue, Victor Hugo was born, 1802. At the end of the street is the Porte de Mars, erected, it is said, by Marcus Aurelius, 167 A.D. Here also is the Cathedral, with the Citadel beyond.

The Cathedral of St. Jean, much hemmed in is of the 11th-13th cent., of several styles; many paintings in interior, modern astronomical clock with 72 dials.

Just north of the west end of Grande Rue, in a Place, is the Musée, with a good collection of paintings and antiquities. RAIL, pages 52, 53.

Biarritz.—*Stat.*—Pop. 12,800.

GRAND HOTEL.-Splendid establishment, facing the sea and the baths. Rendezvous for English and American travellers. See Advt.

HOTEL D'ANGLETERRE.—In the best situation, on the border of the sea. Magnificent garden, full south. M. Campagne, Proprietor. See Advt.

HOTEL CONTINENTAL. — Situated near the Casino and opposite the British Club. Lift; electric light; garden. See Advt.

HOTEL VICTORIA ET DE LA GRANDE PLAGE.—First-class hotel. Very well situated, near to the English club. See Advt.

HOTEL DES PRINCES.—Handsome family hotel. Pension during the winter. See Advt.

HOTEL PAVILLON ALPHONSE XIII.—Recently built family hotel, near the sea. Every modern comfort. Electric light and steam heating throughout; large Garden. See Advt.

CARLTON HOTEL.—New first class hotel in fine position. Every modern comfort. Suites and single rooms with bath. See Advt.

Biarritz is favourably situated facing the Bay of Biscay, on a line of cliffs sloping to a magnificent beach; it is one of the most frequented bathing resorts in France, especially by the better classes of society. In winter the season is almost as animated as during summer. Casino, bathing establishment. The Race Course is at La Barre, near the entrance to the harbour of Bayonne.

ENG. CH. SERVICE at St. Andrew's Church (memorial porch bearing names of British officers). The Rev. Prebendary L. J. Fish, M.A. Sunday, 8.30 and 11.0 a.m., 5.30 p.m.

PRESBYTERIAN CHURCH.

H.B.M.'S VICE-CONSUL.—Nigel Bellairs, Esq.

GOLF.—18-hole course, mile from centre of town; club-house. Ladies' green, 9-hole.

MEDICAL.—Drs. Malpas, Mackew, and Welby.

BANK.—Exchange. Société Generale (de Paris), 4, Place de la Liberté.—English spoken. Letters of Credit and Circular notes cashed. Credits opened, etc. Apply London, 65, Regentstreet, W.

BENQUET'S AGENCY.—Founded in 1872. Apartments, Houses, and Villas to let. Jules Benquet, Managing Proprietor.

RAIL, p. 45; Biarritz and Bayonne local line. p. 45.

Blois.—*Stat.*—Pop. 23,542.

HOTELS: DU CHATEAU; FRANCE; BLOIS.

Chief town of Département de Loir-et-Cher, on the River Loire; a very picturesque city.

Immediately east of the Railway Station, the Avenue Victor Hugo leads in a quarter of a mile to the CHATEAU, one of the most interesting castles of France. Among the names associated with the castle are Francis I, Louis XIII, his mother Marie de Medicis, the Duke of Guise and his brother the Cardinal of Guise—both assassinated here. Open daily.

Just away from the Castle, nearer the river, is the old Abbey Church of St Nicolas, 1138-1210.

Cathedral of St. Louis, one third mile north east of the Castle—of little interest. Behind the Cathedral is the Bishop's Palace.

RAIL, pages 34, 36, 40.

[**Chambord** may be conveniently visited from Blois. The Chateau is the finest specimen in France of Renaissance architecture; built 1526 by Pierre Nepveu for Francis I. The rooms, 440, are almost all empty. Steam Tramway from Blois (Vienne suburb, on other side of river, opposite the Castle) to Bracieux-Chambord, page 46A. Motor Services from Blois to Chambord during the tourist season.]

Bordeaux.—*Stat.*—Pop. 261,678.

GRAND HOTEL ET HOTEL DE FRANCE.—First class hotel. Every modern comfort; lift, electric light, etc. Vve. Louis Peter, proprietress. See Advt.

BUFFET ET HOTEL TERMINUS.—At St. Jean Station. Property of the Sleeping Car Co. Electric light, lift, and baths. See Advt.

GRAND HOTEL METROPOLE ET EXCELSIOR.—Opposite the Place de la Comédie, Grand Theatre, Prefecture, etc. Suites, with bath room. Lift; electric light; warm water heating. See Advt.

PAIX.

There are two important RAILWAY STATIONS. Gare de la Bastide, the more central, is on the east bank of the River Garonne, a bridge immediately in front connecting with the city; at this Station passengers usually alight when coming from Paris. The Gare St. Jean, on the west bank of the Garonne, in the south east part of the city, is the Station for departure of and arrival from the South and Spain; the through express trains between Paris and the extreme south of France run into this Station. The Gare St. Louis is at north side of city.

The traveller who alights at the Gare de la Bastide has immediately a good view of this imposing city. The River Garonne here sweeps round in a broad bend, the handsome quays along the west bank are in full view, and spanning the river is a bridge justly considered one of the finest in Europe. The city is the fourth largest of France; though 60 miles from the sea the tide comes right up, enabling shipping of about two million tons annually to enter. The principal trade of the port is engaged with Bordeaux wines (Medoc, Sauterne, Graves, etc.), but much colonial produce is imported.

The central point of Bordeaux life is the Place de la Comedie, at the crossing of the two streets near the south west corner of the Place des Quinconces. Most of the leading hotels and cafés are in the immediate neighbourhood. The Place des Quinconces, the largest open square, is the site of Chateau Trompette (demolished 1789); in the middle is a monument to the Girondins.

CATHEDRAL of St. André, 11th-12th cents., Gothic, on north side two towers with spires; choir in interior much admired, statues and paintings; Richard II of England baptised here. By south east angle of Cathedral is the Clocher (Belfry) Peyberland, built 1440; the bell weighs 10 tons.

St. Seurin, the old cathedral, of 11th cent., half-mile north west of Cathedral of St. André, just off north side of Rue Judaique. Interior very obscure; beautiful stained windows; much sculpture.

Notre Dame, a few yards south west from south west corner of Place des Quinconces. Interior elaborately decorated; paintings.

St. Michel, just back from the quay to south of west end of the bridge; dates from 8th cent., rebuilt 15th-16th cents., Gothic. Tour St. Michel, by west end of church. In a vault here may be seen mummified bodies from old cemetery once on this spot.

Ste. Croix, back from the quay, west bank, mid-way between bridge and railway bridge. Romanesque of 10th cent., on an older church site of 7th cent., several times restored. The west front should be noticed.

Hotel de Ville, opposite west end of St. André Cathedral; once the archbishop's palace.

Musee, just west of the Cathedral, at back of the Hotel de Ville. In the right wing are paintings by old masters—Titian, Murillo, Rubens, etc.; in the left wing are works by modern artists. Open daily, except Monday and Friday, 12.0 to 5.0 (4.0 in winter).

Palais Gallien, or les Arènes, half-mile west of, and in a line with, north side of Place des Quinconces. Remains of an amphitheatre of the time of the Emperor Gallienus (A.D. 268).

Grand Theatre, a little back from south side of Place des Quinconces. Portico has twelve Corinthian columns. In 1871 the National Assembly held its sittings here. Prefecture, by the theatre.

Bibliotheque (Library), in Rue Mably, a few yards from south west corner of Place Quinconces. 150,000 volumes; copy of Montaigne's Essays, with MS. notes by the author. Open daily 11.0 to 4.0 and 8.0 to 10.0.

Jardin Public, a few yards from north west corner of Place des Quinconces. Museum of natural history and ethnography at south west side of Jardin.

POST OFFICE, at corner of Rue du Palais Gallien and Rue Judaique. Poste Restante here.

ENG. CHURCH, Cours du Pavé des Chartrons.

H.B.M.'s CONSUL.—A. L. S. Rowley, Esq.

VICE-CONSUL.—James Patterson, Esq.

U. S. CONSUL.—A. K. Moe, Esq.

GOLF.—9-hole course; mile from boulevard.

RAIL, pp. 35, 36, 41, 42, 42B, 45, 45A, 45B.

Bormes-les-Mimosas, see page 402.

Boulogne-sur-Mer.—*Stat.*—Pop. 57,027.

GRAND HOTEL CHRISTOL AND BRISTOL.—First class hotel, near the Railway Station and Steamers; electric light and telephone; restaurant, and table d'hote. See Advt.

GRAND HOTEL DU LOUVRE ET TERMINUS.—Facing the landing stage. Modern comfort. Reasonable charges. See Advt.

HOTEL DU PAVILLON IMPERIAL.—Facing the sea. First-class hotel. See Advt.

HOTEL FOLKESTONE.—First class, facing the harbour. Every modern comfort. Pension terms. See Advt.

HOTEL DERVAUX.—73 to 81, Grande Rue, and 24, Rue de Vieillards. First class. See Advt.

BERRY'S HOTEL, 96 to 102, Rue de Boston, Established 40 years. See Advt.

HOTEL MEURICE.—Well situated, Rue Victor Hugo, in central part of the town. Central heating. See Advt.

Furnished apartments. List sent on application to Merridew's Library.

The harbour of Boulogne is accessible at all states of the tide. The Folkestone steamers run alongside the Gare Maritime, where trains await them; the town Station, or Boulogne Ville, lies back out of view from the harbour, but is in an almost direct line from the Gare Maritime, about one-third mile distant. The third railway station, Boulogne Tintelleries, is on the Calais side of the town, away from the harbour.

Boulogne, the Roman Bononia, a favourite seaside resort, and a thriving port, ranking next in importance to Marseilles, Havre, and Bordeaux, is in Dept. Pas-des-Calais, on the Channel, at the mouth of the River Lianne, 29 land miles (25½ sea miles) from Folkestone.

The Lower town, Basse Ville, is in part modern and regularly built. Here, on the sea front, stretch the sands, where, at the height of the bathing season, the scene is most animated. Casino, with theatre (good companies). Pier, Jetée de l'Est, 650 yards—Dover lights may be sometimes seen; the light on Cap Grisnez is clearly seen. Statues of Sauvage, the French claimant to the invention of the screw propeller of Jenner; of General José de San Martin; of Mariette Bey. Museum, in summer open daily except Tuesday, in Grande Rue, contains paintings, a Library of 50,000 vols. and MSS., and collections of local fossils and of remains from primeval dwellings. Fish Market is worth visiting early in the morning.

The old Upper Town, or Haute Ville, includes the Château, in which Louis Nap. was confined, 1840, near Le Sage's House. Ancient Belfry, behind the Hôtel de Ville. Fine view from the Ramparts, now a promenade. Cathedral of Nôtre Dame, a domed building of Italian style of little architectural merit, has paintings and statues; crypt (1 fr.) The Cemetery, where many English are buried, is on the road to the right after leaving the Porte de Calais. On the heights near the Haute Ville are several Forts; a Column, 190 feet high, finished 1841. to commemorate the intended invasion of England, 1801-4, by Napoleon I, whose bronze statue by Bosio, is on the top.

POST AND TEL. OFFICE, Place Fréderic Sauvage.

ENGLISH CHURCH SERVICE.—St. John's Anglican Church: Rue des Vieillards. Holy Trinity Church, Rue de la Lampe.

WESLEYAN CHAPEL, 70, Grande Rue 7.

H.B.M.'S VICE-CONSUL.—H. F. Farmer, Esq.

GOLF.—18-hole sea-side course at Aubengues, Wimereux, reached by electric tram, or rail; club house. Lawn Tennis.

MEDICAL.—J. A. Philip, Esq., M.D.

BANK.—Exchange. Société Generale (de Paris), 32, Rue Victor Hugo. English spoken. Letters of Credit and Circular notes cashed. Credits opened, etc. Apply London, 65, Regentstreet, W. Sub. Offices: Berck sur Mer, Etaples, Montreuil, Hesdin.

ENGLISH LIBRARY AND READING ROOMS.—Merridew's, Rue Victor Hugo, depôt for the sale of Bradshaw's *Guides*.

RAIL, pp. 18, 19A. Electric tram service.

Boulouris. HOTELS; GRAND; BLANQUET.

Finely situated in a sheltered position, 2½ miles from St. Raphael.

RAIL (St. Raphael Station), pages 53c and 54.

Bourbonne-les-Bains.—*Stat.*—Pop. 4,156.

HOTELS: THERMAL; GRAND.

A bathing place, quieter rather than fashionable, in a pleasant country; warm springs, 140 to 150° Fahrenheit strongly impregnated with chloride of sodium, much in use for old wounds, scrofula, rheumatism, and paralysis. Season May to October. Good bath establishment. Casino. Church of 12th-13th cent. RAIL, p. 68.

Bourboule-les-Bains (La).—*Stat.*

PALACE HOTEL ET MAJESTIC, VILLA MEDICIS—Situated near the Baths. Good cuisine; electric light; telephone. Lift. See Advt.

HOTEL DES ILES BRITANNIQUES.—First-class establishment, near the baths. Lift. See Advt.

GRAND HOTEL CONTINENTAL AND HOTEL DE LA METROPOLE.—First class establishments, offering every modern comfort. Calorifères. See Advt.

A quite modern bathing resort in the Auvergne that not many years ago was an insignificant village. About 12,000 visitors annually to the warm mineral springs, used in cases of anæmia, rheumatism, diseases of the skin, diabetes, respiratory organs, and some forms of fever. Three bath establishments. Casino. Season mid May to end Sept.

RAIL, page 37.

Bourg.—*Stat.*—Pop. 19,000.

HOTELS: EUROPE; FRANCE; PAIX.

Chief town of Dept. of the Ain, formerly the capital of Bresse. Notre Dame Church, Gothic, of 16th cent., has choir stalls and beautiful windows. At the Hotel de Ville is a Museum of antiquities, pictures, etc.

The historically interesting Church of Brou is about a mile from the Station. Erected 1511-36; elaborate portal; sculpture and carving in interior; royal tombs—(see Matthew Arnold's poem). Former convent, adjoining church, is now a seminary.

RAIL, pages 53, 60, 62.

Bourges.—*Stat.*—Pop. 45,785.

HOTELS: DE FRANCE; BOULE D'OR; CENTRAL.

Chief town of Département du Cher, the former capital of Berry, seat of an archbishop, in a level country, at the confluence of the Rivers Yèvre and Auron.

From the Railway Station the Avenue de la Gare leads across the River Yèvre into the city. At Place Planchat, the short Rue du Commerce (left) runs into the Place Cujas, whence the Rue Moyenne runs south to the Cathedral (seen up short street to left).

Cathedral of St. Etienne, Gothic, of 13th-16th cent., one of the magnificent churches of France; imposing facade, lavishly decorated; massive towers, 190 ft. and 218 ft. high interior very impressive—370 ft. long, 130 ft. wide, nave 120 ft. high; paintings, statues and beautiful windows.

House of Jacques Cœur, in Rue Jacques Cœur, running out of south west side of Place Cujas. Dating from about middle of 15th cent.; chapel on first floor. The building is now the Palais de Justice.

Just west of Place Cujas, in Rue des Arènes, is the Musée, where are collections of paintings, sculpture, antiquities, weapons, pottery, and curiosities.

RAIL, pages 35B, 37, 38, 42B.

Brest.—*Stat.*—Pop. 90,540.

HOTELS: CONTINENTAL; MODERNE.

The chief naval port in France, and a 1st class fortress, in Dept. Finistère, with an inner land-locked Harbour formed by the Penfold, an outer Harbour or Rade, connected by a narrow channel with the Atlantic, all protected. Dockyard, not open to strangers.

H. B. M.'s VICE-CONSUL.—S. S. Dickson, Esq.

U.S. CONSULAR AGENT.

RAIL, pp. 31, 80.

Brides-les-Bains.

GRAND HOTEL DES THERMES.—First class hotel, situated in Park. Electric light. See Advt.

BAIGNEURS; GRUMEL; GRAND.

A much frequented pretty watering place in Département Savoie, in the Doran Valley. Its warm springs are used for drinking and bathing chiefly in cases of obesity. Bath Establishment. Casino. English Church in the season. Reached by tram from Moutiers Salins Station, p.62A.

Cabourg.—*Stat.*—

GRAND HOTEL; NORMANDIE.

A sea bathing resort, 4 miles west of Trouville. Spacious sandy beach. Casino.

GOLF.—18-hole course, close to sea.

RAIL (Dives-Cabourg), page 78, also page 74B.

Caen.—*Stat.*—Pop. 46,934.

HOTELS: FRANCE; ESPAGNE; ANGLETERRE.

The principal RAILWAY STATION, Gare de l'Ouest, is at the south east side of the town, nearly a mile from the centre; Steamers from Havre come to a Quai near the Station, but at opposite side of the river. A minor Station, Gare St. Martin, is for a local line to sea coast.

Caen is the chief town of Département Calvados, on the River Orne, connected with the sea by a canal (9 miles); a place with special interests for English people. Many old houses.

From the Railway Station turn to north, to the river; on the other side, a little to west, is the Place Alexandre III, here the Rue St. Jean runs in, and at north end of this street is the Church of St. Pierre.

St. Pierre, Gothic, 13th to 16th cents., with a tower 255 ft. high; decorated chapels, fine stained glass, curious figure carving on the capitals of the pillars.

On the height close by is what is left of the castle built by William the Conqueror, now a barracks.

Ste. Trinité, half a mile east of St. Pierre, founded in 1066 as the Abbaye-aux-Dames by the wife of William the Conqueror, Matilda, whose tomb is here. Adjoining the church is a Hospital, formerly the Abbaye—the nuns were of noble family, and the Abbess was styled Madame de Caen.

St. Etienne, on the west side of the town, at the west end of the line of street running in front of La Trinité. The Church of the Abbaye-aux-Hommes, founded by William the Conqueror. The building is so crushed in that it is seen to disadvantage. The empty tomb of William is before the high altar, the remains having been thrown out twice during popular disturbance, in 1562 and 1793. The rebuilt Abbaye, on south side, is now the Lycée.

Close to east side of Place du Parc, by St. Etienne, a few yards along the Rue Caumont, is a Museé des Antiquaires, with interesting collections of antiquities. Sun. and Thurs.

Hotel de Ville, in Place de la République, on west side of town. Here is a MUSEE of good paintings, engravings, and objects of art. Also the Library of 90,000 vols. and 600 MSS., and portraits. Sun. and Thurs.

ENGLISH CHURCH SERVICE.—At St. Michael's Church, Rue Richard Lenoir, on east side of town.

H.B.M.'s VICE-CONSUL.—C. Hettier, Esq.

RAIL, pp. 74B, 75, 77B, 78, 83.

Local Steamer service daily, according to tide, between Havre and Caen.

Calais.—*Stat.*—Pop. 72,322 (including St. Pierre les Calais).

TERMINUS HOTEL, Gare Maritime, opposite the Steam Packet Pier. Baths. Post and Telegraph Office; Custom House. Electric Light. See Advt.

CENTRAL HOTEL, Gare Centrale, in the centre of the town. First-class hotel, well situated. Post and Telegraph Office. Electric Light.

GRAND HOTEL.—Centrally situated, and equipped with all modern comfort. Garage. Reasonable. See Advt.

MEURICE; FRANCE.

Calais is the nearest French port to England —24¾ land miles (21½ sea miles) from Dover, and the traffic between the two countries, with the harbour trade, are its principal importance. The harbour, accessible at all states of the tide, is protected by two piers, one 1,100 yards long, and the Dover steamers run up to the Quai adjoining the Gare Maritime. The sands of Calais appear in many a painting and often in literature. The bathing is good. Casino. Lighthouse. Calais was retaken in 1558 by the French from the English, who had possessed it for two hundred years.

Hotel de Ville, in Place d'Armes, where is also a Watch Tower, founded in 9th cent., and used as a lighthouse until 1848. Notre Dame Church, a 14th cent. Gothic, with handsome altar, a relief of the Assumption, and painting by Rubens. Musée. Hôtel de Guise.

The town is joined to **St. Pierre lès Calais**, where most of the works and manufactures are carried on—viz: Ship building, flax-spinning, saw mills, foundries, machine making, and especially cotton and lace manufactures. The pop. of this part includes many English.

POST OFFICE.—Place Richelieu.

ENGLISH CHURCH SERVICE.—Holy Trinity in Rue du Moulin Brulé.

H.B.M.'s CONSUL.—C. A. Payton, Esq., M.V.O.

VICE-CONSUL.—E. H. Blomefield, Esq., M.V.O.

U. S. CONSUL.—J. B. Milner, Esq.

RAIL, pp. 18, 19A, 22A, 26.

Cambrai.—*Stat.*—Pop. 25,250.

HOTELS: DE FRANCE; BOISSY.

On the Scheldt. In the Cathedral are statues and paintings. St. Géry, with marble rood screen, and an Entombment said to be by Rubens. Hotel de Ville. Musée, with collection of paintings. Porte Notre Dame, an old town gate. Cambrai gives name to "cambric," known to the French as "batiste."

RAIL, pages 22A, 29, 29A, 29B, 30A.

Cannes.—*Stat.*—Pop. 34,051.

HOTEL METROPOLE.—Beautifully situated in its own grounds of over 30 acres. Stands high amidst pine trees. First class. Garage. Proprietors, Gordon Hotels, Ltd. See Advt.

HOTEL GALLIA, LTD.—First-class hotel, standing in its own grounds; two lifts; electric light everywhere. Winter garden. See Advt.

PARK HOTEL, formerly Château des Tours (Villa Vallombrosa).—First class hotel, very well situated. Grounds with tropical plants. See Advt.

HOTEL BRISTOL.—First class hotel, centrally situated near the Railway Station. Park. Tariff moderate. See Advt.

BEAU SITE HOTEL.—Superior first-class hotel, standing in its own grounds. Noted tennis courts. Much patronized by English and Americans. See Advt.

THE ESTEREL HOTEL.—Situated west end, in one of the finest positions. Thoroughly first class; heated by hot water. See Advt.

THE GRAND HOTEL.—Situated on the principal promenade; electric light, garden. See Advt.

GRAND HOTEL DU PAVILLON.—First class family hotel. Every up-to-date comfort. New large hall. Lift. Reasonable tariff. See Advt.

HOTEL DES ANGLAIS.—First class family hotel. Very comfortable, delightfully situated. See Adv.

GRAND HOTEL DE LA CALIFORNIE.—Renowned first class. Beautifully situated (Californie), with large park. See Advt.

CONTINENTAL HOTEL.—First class hotel. High situation (West End). Established 1879. Lift. See Advt.

HOTEL BEAU LIEU.—Beautiful situation commanding a splendid view of the sea. See Advt.

HOTEL GRAY ET D'ALBION.—Well known first class hotel; electric light; lift. See Advt.

HOTEL BELLE VUE, well situated in the west end. See Advt.

HOTEL DES PINS.—First class. Situated at Californie, amidst beautiful pine district. Large garden; lift. See Advt.

BEAU RIVAGE.—First class. Well situated on the principal promenade. Garden; lift. See Advt.

HOTEL RICHEMONT ET TERRASSE.—High class family hotel, completely renovated. Fine panorama. Hot water heating throughout. Reasonable charges. See Advt.

GD. HOTEL DE PROVENCE.—First class hotel, on elevated position and surrounded by garden; electric light, lift. See Advt.

HOTEL DU PARADIS.—First class hotel, Boulevard du Cannet, close to St. Paul's Church. With park; lift and electric light. See Advt.

HOTEL HOLLANDE ET DE RUSSIE.—Well situated in a fine park, fifteen minutes from sea. Electric light; telephone. See Advt.

WINTER PALACE ST. CHARLES.—Well known first class hotel, situated full south. Large garden. Every modern comfort. English connection. Terms from 10/-. See Advt.

HOTEL ALSACE-LORRAINE.—Family hotel, situated in a quiet and sunny position, with garden. See Advt.

HOTEL SUISSE.—Well situated, full south, with beautiful garden; lift; electric light. See Advt.

HOTEL VICTORIA.—Family hotel, well situated, full south; near Promenade. Pension from 9 fr. Open the whole year. See Advt.

HOTEL PENSION SAVOY.—First class hotel, with fine view of the sea. Modern comforts. Pension from 9 fr. See Advt.

HOTEL DES ILES BRITANNIQUES.—Centrally situated, full south. Lift; central heating throughout. Reasonable. See Advt.

HOTEL PENSION AND VILLA DE LA TOUR.—Family House. well situated at the west end of Cannes. Electric light throughout. See Advt.

PENSION ANGLO-AMERICAINE. — First class pension, standing in its own grounds. Well heated throughout. Electric light. Pension terms from 7 fr. See Advt.

Furnished houses and apartments are plentiful; it is better to arrange for them through an agent, because of French law and local custom.

The RAILWAY STATION is near the centre of the town. All the streets running south from the railway line lead in a few minutes to the sea. A minor Station at La Bocca, on the west side, is useful for residents of the Route de Frejus, but very few trains call there.

TAXIMETRE MOTOR CARS.

Electric Tramway to all parts of the town and along the coast in each direction.

The winter climate of Cannes is very favourable to persons suffering from chest and lung weakness, being mild, dry, and uniform. In the neighbourhood of the sea its tonic and stimulating effects are most marked; the suburbs are suitable for nervous disorders. Sunny days are the rule; there is no fog. The sea bathing season begins in April.

Cannes is one of the most fashionable wintering places in Europe, and has not only the advantages of a pleasant winter climate and a situation on a picturesque coast, but the plan of the town allows gardens of luxuriant vegetation to most of the larger houses, securing purity and freedom of air. Cannes is a modern town, the only old section being round Mont Chevalier, near the Lighthouse; here is the Port, so called. On Mont Chevalier is an old Church of the 13th cent., a Tower, and remains of a castle on the site of the Roman "Castrum Massilinum."

At the Hotel de Ville, by the sea, on east side of Mont Chevalier, is a Museum of Antiquities and an Ethnographical Collection; also the Municipal Library and a Natural History Collection. A statue of Lord Brougham is in the Allées de la Liberté, by the sea; on the east side, on the rising ground of La Californie, are a column and statue in memory of the Duke of Albany (died here 1884). Statue of King Edward VII (April, 1912).

Excellent music at the Casino, where is a theatre, visited by first class companies during the season.

POST OFFICE.—Rue Bivouac and Rue Notre Dame.

ENG. CH. SERV., Christ Church, West Cannes. St. George's Memorial Church. Holy Trinity, East Cannes. St. Paul's, Boulevard du Cannet. PRESBYTERIAN CHURCH.

H.B.M.'S VICE-CONSUL.-J. Taylor, Esq., M.V.O.

GOLF.—18-hole course at Napoule, 4 miles by rail; club house. Ladies' green, 9-hole. Tennis and Croquet Club, in Rue Lacour; Aviation Club, Polo ground; race-course.

MEDICAL.—Dr. Richard Bright, 11bis, Rue Hermann, 1—3. Dr. G. C. Bright, M.D., F.R.C.P., Chalet Magali. Dr. E. Wightman Ginner, 40, Rue de Fréjus; telephone 717; consultations 2-3.30. Dr. Gordon Sanders, M.B., F.R.C.P. (Edinburgh), M.D. (Montpellier), Villa Martha. Dr. Alfred Carr, 15, Rue Hermann (winter); 4, Harley Street, London (summer). Dr. McDougall.

COURT CHEMISTS. — **Pharmacie Anglaise, Ginner and Co., 40, Rue d'Antibes, opposite** Crédit Lyonnais.

ENGLISH BANK AND ESTATE AGENCY.—Messrs. John Taylor and Son, 45, Rue de Fréjus. See Advt.

HOUSE AND ESTATE AGENTS.—C. E. Clark. Particulars of Villas to be let forwarded on application. See Advt.

GENERAL ENQUIRY OFFICE at the Hotel de Ville, where information regarding the town may be obtained free of charge.

DEPOT FOR BRADSHAW'S PUBLICATIONS—Librairie Vial, 34, Rue d' Antibes, Cannes.

RAIL, pp. 53C, 54.

[Le Cannet.

STELLA HOTEL.—Family hotel in splendid situation, full south. Garden. Lift. Electric light. Central heating. Pension from 8 frs. See Advt.

A suburb at the north end of the Boulevard Carnot, about 1½ mile north of the Railway Station; it is preferred for invalids who cannot live near the sea.

La Napoule.

A pleasant quiet suburb of Cannes, on the west side of the Golfe de la Napoule. The Golf Links, amongst the finest on the Riviera, are here.

The **Isles de Lerins**, opposite Cannes. Steamers twice a day during the season, fare 2 francs (St. Marguerite); St. Honorat, 3 francs. Both islands, 4 francs. Boat leaves Cannes 10.0 a.m. and 1.30 p.m. Returns, St. Honorat, 11.30 a.m., St. Marguerite, 11.40 a.m.; St. Marguerite 4.0 p.m., St. Honorat 4.10 p.m. On Ile Ste. Marguerite, the larger island, was confined the "Man with the Iron Mask," 1686-1698; Marshal Bazaine was a prisoner here from 26th Dec., 1873, to 9th Aug., 1874, when he escaped. On the smaller island, St. Honorat, is the Monastery of Lerins.]

Cap d'Ail—*Stat.*

EDEN GRAND HOTEL.—One of the most fashionable hotels on the Riviera; fine terrace; every modern comfort; see Advt.

Three miles west of Monte Carlo, 150 feet above sea, at the base of the Tête de Chien. In a beautiful situation, one of the most salubrious and picturesque spots of the Riviera. Sheltered from north winds.

RAIL, page 54.

Cap Ferrat, 1¼ mile south of Beaulieu; tramway service.

A pleasant little place, with hotel, overlooking the Bay; at the end of the small Cap de St. Hospice are ruins of a church and of a Saracenic fortress.

Cap Martin.

CAP MARTIN HOTEL.—**One of the most aristocratic hotels on the Riviera**; unique position, surrounded by pine woods; replete with every comfort. Moorish Tea Pavilion. See Advt.

HOTEL VICTORIA.—Beautifully situated, with verandah, facing sea. Electric light; central heating. Pension from 8 fr. See Advt.

A beautiful forest-covered headland about two miles west of Menton; the views over the sea are very fine. There are a few remains of a Convent of 11th cent. The villas in the immediate neighbourhood are usually occupied by distinguished families. Here is a Signal Station. Electric tram to Mentone and Monte Carlo.

Carcassonne.—*Stat.*—Pop. 29,298.

HOTELS: BERNARD; BONNET ST. JEAN BAPTISTE.

The Railway Station is on the north side of the city.

Chief town of Dept. Aude, on the River Aude.

From the Station the Rue de la Gare, going south, with its prolongation, traverses the city to the Boulevard Barbes.

Church of St. Vincent, in Rue du Quatre Septembre, off west side of Rue de la Gare. Gothic, 14th-16th cent.; from tower of this Church the site of the meridian of Paris was calculated by Méchain and Delambre.

Cathedral of St. Michel, Gothic, 13th cent.; a little to west from south end of continuation of Rue de la Gare.

Musée, in Grande Rue, by the Square Gambetta, at east side of city. Paintings, faience, and curiosities. Bibliothèque in same building.

The Cité, or old town, to south east, across the river, on a hill, has all the appearance of a mediæval fortified place; and, with its citadel, towers, and lines of fortifications, may be considered unique. Some of the fortifications date from the 5th cent. The Church of St. Nazaire is also very interesting. RAIL, pages 45B, 46.

Carnac.—*Stat.*

HOTEL DES MENHIRS, at Plouharnel; HOTEL DES VOYAGEURS at Carnac.

The Railway Station, at Plouharnel, is named Plouharnel-Carnac. Carnac is about 2 miles south east of Plouharnel; steam tram between the two places. Many ancient stone monuments, easily found, at both villages. Small Musée at Carnac. RAIL, page 37.

Cauterets.—*Stat.*—Pop. 1,685.

GRAND HOTEL D'ANGLETERRE.—Beautiful first class establishment, with annexe and fine garden. Mr. A. Meillon, propr. See Advt.

CONTINENTAL; UNIVERS; REGINA; PARC.

A beautifully situated small town, celebrated as one of the most important thermal stations of the Pyrenees, also a principal centre for excursions in the High Pyrenees and a resort for winter sport; on the banks of a torrent, in a valley surrounded by lofty mountains. The waters contain sulphur and sodium; there are also alkaline and sulphate springs; they range in temperature from 61° to 131° Fahrenheit, and are used in cases of anæmia, chlorosis, skin diseases, rheumatism, respiratory affections, etc. Modern Gothic church; at the Mairie is a Plan in Relief of the Central Pyrenees.

POST OFFICE at Hotel de Ville.

ENGLISH CHURCH SERVICE.

GOLF LINKS. RAIL, page 47.

Chalons-sur-Marne.—*Stat.*—Pop. 26,630.

HOTEL DE LA HAUTE MERE DIEU.—Comfortable hotel. English spoken. Omnibus at the Station day and night. See Advt.

RENARD; CLOCHE D'OR.

Chief town of Département de Marne, on the River Marne, the Roman Catalaunum.

From near the Station the Rue de Marne leads into the city to the Hotel de Ville.

Cathedral of St. Etienne, Romanesque, of 13th cent., in Rue de Marne; handsome high altar, tombs. At Bishop's Palace, Rue du Cloitre, behind Cathedral, is a small collection of paintings.

By the Hotel de Ville is the Bibliothèque (70,000 vols.) and the Musée, with collections of paintings, sculpture, antiquities, furniture, etc.

Church of Notre Dame, at the back of the Hotel de Ville, of 12th-14th cent., Gothic-Romanesque; fine windows. Church of St. Alpin, close to Place de l'Hotel de Ville, 12th-16th cent., has several old paintings.

RAIL, pages 64, 67, 73.

[**L'Epine**, a village 5 miles east of Chalons, on the Ste. Menehould road, famous for a beautiful Abbey Church, built by the English it is said, 1420-1529; interior has miraculous image of Virgin, to which are many pilgrimages.

The **Camp of Chalons** is near Mourmelon (page 67), about 16 miles from Chalons. The Camp covers 29,650 acres; it was a great military centre until 1870, but is now only used for manœuvres.]

Chambéry.—*Stat.*—Population 21,762.

GRAND HOTEL DE FRANCE.—First class in every way. The best place to break the journey on the Mont Cenis Route to Italy. Centre for motoring excursions in Savoy. See Advt.

GRAND HOTEL DE LA PAIX AND TERMINUS.—Facing Station. Modern comfort. See Advt.

POSTE; PRINCES.

The old capital of Savoy, on the River Leisse, having an extensive silk industry. Cathedral, 12th to 15th centuries, has fine stained glass. Palais de Justice; immediately opposite is the Musée of miscellaneous collections, including pictures and a library of 40,000 vols. Handsome Hotel de Ville. Of the Chateau, founded 13th cent., only three towers and a chapel remain; behind the Chateau is a small museum. The Portail St. Dominique, 14th cent., was part of an old convent removed and set up in its present place.

RAIL, pages 57, 60, 62A.

Chamonix.—*Stat.*—Population of village and immediate neighbourhood about 4,000.

SAVOY PALACE.—First class family hotel, with view of Mont Blanc; electric light, baths, telephone. See Advt.

GRAND HOTEL ROYAL ET DE SAUSSURE.—First class family hotel, in a free situation, with a large park and fine view of Mont Blanc. See Advt.

GRAND HOTEL COUTTET.—Well situated in a shady garden, with fine view of Mont Blanc. Electric light; baths. See Advt.

GRANDS HOTELS DU MONT BLANC and CACHAT.—With large park and fine view. Electric light; lift. See Advt.

GRAND HOTEL BEAU RIVAGE ET DES ANGLAIS.—First class family hotel, patronised by English and Americans. Every modern comfort; reasonable charges. See Advt.

HOTEL D'ANGLETERRE ET DE LONDRES.—High class family hotel, with nice garden. All modern comforts. Suites and single rooms with private baths. See Advt.

GRAND HOTEL DES ALPES.—Well known first class hotel in fine position. Electric light. Reasonable charges. See Advt.

Chamonix, in Dept. Haute Savoie, is visited by an ever increasing number of travellers because of the surpassing grandeur of its mountain scenery; it has become a centre for winter sports.

A monument to Saussure, the naturalist, stands in the village, and there is an interesting collection of Alpine pictures by the painter Loppé.

Several Minor Ascents may be safely made without the assistance of a guide, but in all venturesome excursions, when the climbers are inexperienced, and absolutely when ladies are concerned, the services of a guide should be secured. Applications for guides are made to the Guide Chef, who employs each in his turn, the applicant having no choice except in certain specified cases, as, among others, when the applicant does not sufficiently speak French and desires a guide who understands English, when ladies desire a particular guide. The Guide-Chef will supply a Guide Tariff.

GUIDE CHARGES.

To Montenvers, Mer de Glace, Chapeau, Flegère, and return ... ... 12fr.
,, Flegère and return ... ... 6fr.
,, the Jardin, and return by Chapeau... 14fr.
Ascent of Mont Blanc .. ..100fr.

The authorities have determined that for the ascent of Mont Blanc one traveller requires two guides, each 100 fr., and one porter, 50 fr., with one guide extra for every additional traveller—the total cost per traveller for the ascent, when two or three are together, may be estimated at £10. Charges for horses and mules, only required on some excursions, are about equal to the charge for the guide, with the addition of a fee for the attendant. Climbing railway as far as Montenvers.

With favourable weather, and sufficient leisure and means, the interest of Chamonix grows. Three or four days are little enough, but when the traveller can spare no more than one day there can be pleasantly accomplished in a round—the ascent to Montenvers, the passage across the Mer de Glace to the Chapeau, then down to Les Tines, ascent of the Flegère, and descent to Chamonix. The round can be done within ten hours, and a guide is not needed except for the passage across the Mer de Glace (about 20 minutes); for the Mer de Glace a guide can be obtained at Montenvers, fee 2fr. 50c. Only robust, loosely dressed people should attempt mountain climbs; for slippery places a pair of old woollen socks, to draw over the boots, are a great help.

To the Glacier des Bossons is another excursion for a short half-day.

There are small hotels (where beds can be had) or inns at several of the most frequented points, and climbers should enquire as to these so as to avoid when possible the trouble of carrying food.

Mont Blanc, 15,730 ft. above sea, was first ascended by Jacques Balmat, a guide, in 1786, later (August) in the same year by Dr. Paccard. On the first day of the ascent the climb is usually as far as the Grand Mulets, 10,700 ft. above sea; here is an inn, with about eight rooms, the charges naturally being "season rates"—bed, 12 fr. On the second day the climb to the summit is completed, and also the descent to the Grand Mulets, where again the night is spent. On the third day the descent is completed to Chamonix; sometimes the descent from the summit to Chamonix may be made in one day. From notes made by many travellers it is to be inferred that the climb is exacting but absorbingly interesting, the near scenery awful in sublimity and grandeur, but the view at the summit often unsatisfactory, owing to snow, or cloud, or the immense distance that renders remote objects, though large, vague and indistinct.

ENGLISH CHURCH SERVICE in the English Church.

RAIL, page 61B.

Champagnole.—*Stat.*—Pop. 4,000.

A pleasant little town of the Jura Mountain district, on the River Ain, favourably known for trout fishing. Excursions in the wooded mountains. RAIL, page 57.

Chantilly—*Stat.*—Pop. 4,211.

HOTELS: GRAND CONDE; ANGLETERRE.

Chiefly visited for the Race Course, close to the Station. Two Chateaux, one with magnificent art collections; Sun. and Thurs., 1.0 to 5.0 (except race days).

ST. PETER'S ENG. CHURCH.

H.B.M.'s VICE-CONS.—E. R. Spearman, Esq., C.M.G. RAIL, pages 18, 22, 24, 28.

Charbonnieres.—*Stat.*—

HOTELS: GRAND; DE BAINS.

A pleasantly situated village, having mineral springs (cold chalybeate), with a casino.

RAIL, page 62.

Chartres.—*Stat.*—Pop. 23,182.

HOTELS: GRAND MONARQUE; DUC DE CHARTRES; DE FRANCE.

The Roman Autricum, chief town of Dept. Eure-et-Loir, on the River Eure; one of the most ancient and picturesque places in France. The CATHEDRAL of Notre Dame, one of the grandest Gothic edifices in France, dates rom the 13th cent. The towers by the west facade are 350 ft. and 375 ft. high; the spire on the north tower is greatly admired. The side portals are richly decorated. The majestic interior is 428 ft. long, transept 150 ft. long, nave 105 ft. wide, 120 ft. high. The choir wall has exquisite sculpture; beautiful stained glass. The Veil of the Virgin Mary is in the Treasury.

A quarter mile east of the Cathedral, a little south, is the mediæval Porte Guillaume. Returning towards Cathedral, but presently going south, is the Church of St. Pierre, 11th-13th cents. A little west of St. Pierre is the Hotel de Ville, with a small Museum.

Henri IV, of Navarre, was crowned King of France at Chartres in 1594. The Germans made the city a military centre in the war of 1870.

RAIL, pages 40, 42, 42A, 80, 84.

Chatel Guyon-les-Bains.—Pop. 1,700.

GRAND HOTEL DU PARC.—Spacious up-to-date first class hotel. See Advt..

SPLENDID NOUVEL HOTEL.—First class, in fine park-like garden. Garage, etc. See Advt.

A village of the Auvergne, three miles from Riom, 1,170 ft. above sea, well known for its warm alkaline springs, used in cases of anæmia, dyspepsia, etc. In the church is an 18th cent. gilded altar piece; similar altar piece at St. Bonnet, a village close by.

RAIL, page 59.

Cherbourg.—*Stat.*—Pop. 43,731.

HOTELS: DE L'AIGLE; DE L'AMIRAUTE; FRANCE.

A naval station, third in importance in France, and fortress of the first class.

Hotel de Ville, with Musée of pictures (Sunday 12-4 free). Churches of La Trinité and Notre Dame du Voeu.

H.B.M.'s VICE-CONSUL.—Captain C. D. Beresford.

U.S. CONS. AGENT.

RAIL, pp. 78, 85.

Clermont-Ferrand.—*Stat.*—Pop. 65,386.

HOTELS: POSTE; UNIVERS; LYON.

Chief town of Dépt. Puy-de-Dome, the former capital of Auvergne, pleasantly situated on a slight hill, with a fertile country on the east side and on the west a range of extinct volcanoes known as the Monts Dôme. Owing to many houses being built of lava the streets have a gloomy appearance.

From the Railway Station, on the east, the Avenue Charras, soon after entering the city turns north to the Place Delile, whence the Rue du Port runs west. Just off north side of Rue du Port is the Church of Notre Dame du Port, of 10th cent., in which it is stated Peter the Hermit preached the first crusade (1095). Rue du Port bends south at west end to the Palais de Justice, nearly adjoining which is the Hotel de Ville. About 100 yards south of the Palais de Justice is the Cathedral.

The Cathedral, Gothic, dating from 1248 but only completed in the last century, has fine windows, high altar, and modern copper work.

Musée at extreme south east; collections of paintings, sculpture, weapons, furniture; daily in morn. and aft. Library in same building, 55,000 vols., 1,100 MSS. Adjoining the Musée is the Palais de l'Academie, the seat of the University. Large statue of Vercingetorix.

RAIL, pages 31A, 36, 58, 63B.

[The **Puy-de-Dome**, 4,805 ft., is about 8 miles from Clermont-Ferrand. Upon the summit are an observatory and some ruins of a temple of Mercury; magnificent view. Local railway from Clermont-Ferrand to the summit.]

Cluses—*Stat.*—Pop. 2,500.

HOTELS: NATIONAL; REPOSOIR; CHARTREUSE.

An interesting little town, in an attractive part of Haute Savoie, 1,590 ft. above sea, where the chief industry is watch making.

RAIL, page 61A. MOTOR SERVICE, page 370.

Contrexéville.—*Stat.*—Pop. 1,000.

COSMOPOLITAIN PALACE HOTEL.—First class, on elevated position, with fine view. Lift, electric light, and central heating. See Advt.

GRAND HOTEL DE L'ETABLISSEMENT.—First class; the only hotel in the park. Comfortable; moderate charges. Up-to-date restaurant. See Advt.

HOTEL CONTINENTAL.—First class, newly built hotel, with the latest modern comfort and convenience. Apartments with baths. Facing the springs and park. Pension from 11 fr. See Advt.

CENTRAL HOTEL AND HOTEL HARMAND.—Comfortable family house, close to springs and park. Every modern convenience; large hall. Pension from 9 fr. See Advt.

A watering place in Dept. Vosges, in the valley of the Vair, of great celebrity for the cure of gout, arthritis, gravel, and other diseases of the urinary organs; the waters contain potash and magnesia, with traces of iodine and arsenic. Bath house in a pretty park. Casino. Season, May 20th until September 20th. Golf; tennis.

ENG. CH. SERVICE during the season.

MEDICAL.—Dr. D'Estrées; Dr. Barnard; Dr. Debout.

RAIL, see page 68A.

Coucy-le-Chateau.—*Stat.*

HOTELS: DES RUINES; POMME D'OR.

The ruined Chateau (public property) is one of the most impressive monuments of feudal times in Europe; an immense place, covering 10,000 square yards, dating from 13th cent. Donjon 210 ft. high, 100 ft. in diameter, walls in places 34 ft. thick. RAIL, page 29A.

Coutances.—*Stat.*—Pop. 7,493.

HOTELS: FRANCE; D'ANGLETERRE; DAUPHIN.

In Dept. Manche, over the Soule, 8 m. from the sea. The graceful and magnificent Cathedral (13th century) is one of the most beautiful churches in France, and is a perfect museum of architectural detail; the Gothic dome or lantern is a unique feature; the building is 312 feet long. Old church of St. Pierre.

RAIL, pages 75A, 85, 87.

Creusot (Le).—*Stat.*—Pop. 30,541.

HOTEL RODRIGUE.

In Dept. Saône-et-Loire, on Canal du Centre. A busy place owing its prosperity to Schneider's Iron Works, employing about 15,500 persons. The works include collieries, foundries, and engineering shops, turning out cannon, locomotives, and machinery. Statue of Schneider. Palæontological and Mineralogical Museum.

RAIL, page 53A.

Croix, La.—*Stat.*

A pleasant, bracing winter resort between Hyères and St. Raphael. In the neighbourhood are Moorish remains.

RAIL, page 53C.

Dax, or Acqs.—*Stat.*—Pop. 11,000.

THERMES DE DAX.—Large, commodious and airy establishment, well managed. Pension and Baths, Summer and Winter, under the direction of a Doctor speaking English.

PAIX; DE L'EUROPE.

The Roman Aquæ Tarbellicæ, noted for its hot sulphur springs, on the Adour, among healthy pine forests, in view of the Pyrenees. There are 5 springs (up to 140° F.), and, as well as the Mud Baths, are good for rheumatism, paralysis, diseases of the joints, and old wounds.

RAIL, pages 45, 46.

Dieppe.—*Stat.*—Pop. 22,771.

HOTEL ROYAL.—Finest and largest hotel, and nearest to the Casino. Facing sea. Every modern convenience. See Advt.

HOTEL METROPOLE ET DES BAINS.—Good in every respect. See Advt.

GRAND HOTEL.—First class, facing sea. Apartments with baths. Every modern comfort. Open all the year. Terms from 10s. 6d. See Advt.

HOTEL DES ETRANGERS.—Comfortable family hotel, situated on the Plage. Open from March to November. See Advt.

The trains connecting with the Newhaven Steamers start from the quay alongside; the Railway Station is at the end of the line of quays back to south west from Landing Place, about three quarters of a mile.

An important fishing town, but chiefly known as a fashionable watering place frequented by English families. Fine shore, good bathing; the Casino, or Etablissement de Bains, is at the west end of the plage.

Church of St. Jacques, a little back from the quay of the inner dock, Gothic, with elaborate lace-like work in the stone; Lady Chapel of interior very fine, much carving. St. Remy, south of the Casino, contains some good sculpture.

The Chateau (castle) is on the cliff at the west end of the plage; used as a barracks.

POST OFFICE.—Quai Berigny.

ENGLISH CHURCH.—Rue de la Barre.

H.B.M.'s VICE-CON.-Comm. H. C. Wallis, R.N.

GOLF.—18-hole course, 1 mile from Station; club house. Also 12-hole course at Pourville, 2½ miles west of Dieppe.

BANK.—EXCHANGE. Société Generale (de Paris), Place de la Barre (near Casino). English spoken. Letters of Credit and Circular notes cashed. Credits opened, etc. Apply London, 65, Regent Street, W.

RAIL, pp. 76, 77A, 84, 85.

[**Puys.**—HOTEL DE PUYS.

A pleasant little bathing place, a mile north east of Dieppe. A "Cæsar's Camp" on the cliff. Omnibus to and from Dieppe.]

Dijon.—*Stat.*—Pop. 76,847.

HOTEL DE LA CLOCHE.—Moderate charges, very clean and well ordered. Near the Protestant church. Wine merchant. See Advt.

DE BOURGOGNE; TERMINUS; MOROT; CONTINENTAL.

An ancient and well-built city, one of the most interesting in France, the chief town of dept. Côte d'Or, formerly the capital of Burgundy, on the rivers Ouche and Suzon, and the Canal de Bourgogne, a strongly fortified place, with a great trade in corn and wine.

From the Railway Station the Rue de la Gare leads to the Place d'Arcy and then, in a direct line, by the Rue de la Liberté, into the heart of the town at the Place d'Armes, before the Hotel de Ville.

A little beyond the town end of Rue de la Gare, a street on the right leads to the Cathedral of St. Bénigne, of 13th cent.; choir stalls and monuments. On south east side of the Cathedral is the former church of St. Philibert, 12th cent., with spire, now a warehouse. A few yards further east is Church of St. Jean, with tombs of St. Urban, St. Gregory, and Emp. Tetricus.

The Hôtel de Ville, the ancient Palace of the Dukes of Burgundy, contains the MUSEUM and PICTURE GALLERY, a collection of pictures of rare excellence, one of the best provincial collections in France, with antiquities, archives, etc.; open Sun. 12.30 to 3.30 p.m., Thurs. and Sat. 12.0 to 3.0 p.m. In the Salle des Gardes are two splendid marble tombs of Philippe le Hardi and Jean-sans-Peur, his son.

A little east of the Hotel de Ville is the Theatre, with the old church of St. Etienne opposite. Further east is the Church of St. Michel; altar-piece and frescoes. Almost immediately north of the Hotel de Ville is the church of Notre Dame, 13th cent., with a three storied porch; the clock dates from 1383.

On the east side of the town, in the Place du Trente Octobre, is the Monument to memory of inhabitants who fell in battle before Dijon, 1870. The bronze Statue of St. Bernard is in the Place St. Bernard, on north west side of town.

Palais de Justice, 16th cent., a little south of Hotel de Ville; here the Parlement of Burgundy used to meet. Cemetery to north of Railway Station; Botanical Garden, immediately south of Railway Station. The Parc is on the south side of the town.

POST OFFICE, in Place des Ducs, behind Hotel de Ville.

RAIL, see pp. 47, 48, 52, 53A, 63B.

Dinan.—*Stat.*—Pop. 10,620.

HOTELS: DE BRETAGNE; D'ANGLETERRE; POST; PARIS.

A picturesque town of Brittany, in Dept. Côtes-du-Nord, on a steep granite rock, 200 feet above the Rance; rich in old houses, walls, and towers, with an old castle (now a prison). Hotel de Ville, with Museum. St. Sauveur church, with curious sculpture, and the heart of Duguesclin in a cenotaph; statue of the hero in Place Duguesclin.

ENGLISH CH. SERV. at Christ Church.

Mr. John Le Cocq, BANKER.

RAIL, pp. 75A, 80, 82.

Dinard.—*Stat.*—Pop. 5,090.

NOUVEL HOTEL DE PROVENCE ET D'ANGLETERRE.—Comfortable hotel, open all the year round. Electric light. Pension terms 9-12 frs. See Advt.

HOTEL DES TERRASSES.—Direct on the sea front. Fine panorama. Restaurant. See Advt.

ROYAL; GRAND; WINDSOR; BAINS; PLAGE.

Furnished houses and apartments are plentiful; it is better to arrange for them through an agent, because of French law and local custom.

A beautiful sea bathing place, at the mouth of the Rance, in dept. Ille-et-Vilaine, facing St. Malo with which place there is hourly steamer service, fare, 25c. and 15c. It has two beaches. Tramway service to **St. Briac.**

ENG. CH. SER. at St. Bartholomew's Church.

MEDICAL.—Dr. Richard Bright.

GOLF.—18-hole course at St. Briac, 4 miles by tram; club house.

Mr. Jules Boutin, BANKER and HOUSE AGENT, may be applied to for particulars concerning Dinard, Dinan, St. Enogat, St. Briac, St. Lunaire. See Advt. RAIL, p. 82.

Dol.—*Stat.*—Pop. 4,762.

GRAND HOTEL; HOTEL GRAND' MAISON.

In Dept. Ille-et-Vilaine, in Brittany, with a beautiful Gothic Cathedral of 13th-16th cent., and old walls and houses. RAIL, pp. 75A, 82.

Douai.—*Stat.*—Pop. 36,314.

HOTELS: DU COMMERCE; DE FLANDRE.

An industrial town on the River Scarpe. From the Station a street leads west to the Place Carnot, whence the Rue St. Jacques leads to the Place d'Armes, where is the Hotel de Ville, a fine Gothic building of 15th cent.; belfry 130 ft.

Church of St. Pierre, between Place Carnot and Place d'Armes; paintings. South of St. Pierre, near fortifications, is the Church of Notre Dame, with celebrated altar piece in the sacristy.

Musée, in Rue Fortier, a street running from Place Carnot; very valuable collection of pictures and sculpture; also antiquarian, zoological, and ethnographical collections. Sun. and Thurs., 11.0 to 4.0 or 5.0. RAIL, pages 20, 23, 29, 29B.

Dreux.—*Stat.*—Pop. 9,718.

HOTELS: DE FRANCE; PARADIS.

A very old town. Gothic church of St. Pierre and Hotel de Ville, 16th cent. On hill above town is the handsome, richly decorated, Chapelle Royale—burial place of Louis Philippe and members of Orleans family. RAIL, pp. 82, 84, 85, 86.

Dunkirk.—*Stat.*—Pop. 38,891.

HOTELS: CHAPEAU ROUGE; FLANDRE; PYL.

A busy port—the third in commercial importance in France—and strongly fortified place, in a district where much Flemish is spoken. In Church of St. Jean, by the Bassin du Commerce, is a "Christ" by van Dyck and a "Holy Family" by Guido Reni. Belfry (295 feet) of St. Eloi, to east of St. Jean, separated from the church by Rue de l'Eglise. Musée of paintings, collections of coins, weapons, ship models, etc. Bibliothèque in same building, 30,000 vols.

POST-OFFICE and TELEGRAPH, Rue Dupouy.

ENG. CH. SERVICE, Place de la Prison.

H.B.M.'s CONSUL.—P. C. Sarell, Esq.

RAIL, pp. 19A, 26, 94.

[Tramway from Dunkirk to **Malo-les-Bains,** a sea bathing resort with sandy beach. Two bathing establishments].

Eaux Bonnes (Les).—*Stat.*—Pop. 812.

HOTELS: FRANCE; CONTINENTAL; BERNIS.

A noted warm sulphur spring 2,455 ft. above sea, in a fine part of Dept. Basses Pyrénées, at the mouth of a gorge in the Ossun valley. Seven springs (up to 89°), gassy, oily, and stimulant, good for the chest and throat, for old wounds and ulcers, and diseased bones. The waters are usually drunk. Casino.

MEDICAL.—Dr. R. Rigoulet, M.D.

RAIL, page 45A.

[**Eaux Chaudes (Les).**—HOTELS: DE FRANCE; BAUDOT.—Smaller than Eaux Bonnes, but in even a grander situation. The sulphurous waters, up to 95°, are more for bathing than drinking, and are used in cases of rheumatism and female ailments; good bath establishment. ENGLISH CHURCH SERVICE in summer. An omnibus twice a day each way between Eaux Bonnes and Eaux Chaudes, 5 miles.]

Epernay.-*Stat.*-Pop. 19,377. HOTEL EUROPE.

A very old place, the Sparnacum of the Romans, pleasantly situated on the River Marne. It is a centre of the trade in champagne.

RAIL, pages 64, 70, 74A.

Epinal.—*Stat.*—Pop. 26,125.

HOTELS: LOUVRE; DE LA POSTE.

Chief town of dept. Vosges, on the Moselle, under the Vosges hills. Church of St. Maurice; Lib. (30,000 vols.) Museum, rich in antiquities; also paintings. RAIL, pages 66, 67, 70, 72, 73.

Etretat.—*Stat.*—Pop. 1,950.

GOLF HOTELS ROCHES BLANCHES ET LA PLAGE.—First class hotels and restaurants, near the Golf Club. Lift; private bath rooms. Electric light. Motor meets steamer at Havre. See Advt.

HOTEL BLANQUET.—First class, pleasantly situated on the sea shore. Pension from 12 fr. 50 c. See Advt.

HOTEL HAUVILLE.—First class. Well situated on the sea front, close to the Casino. Modern comfort. Pension from 10 frs. See advt.

A fashionable bathing place, in Seine Inférieure, in a gap of the high Channel cliffs. Bath House and Casino. Many villas and chalets; Nôtre Dame Church. A great place for artists.

Golf Club (18 holes) and Tir au Pigeon.

RAIL, page 77A. A motor-bus service between Etretat and Havre about four times daily; through tickets issued by L. and S. W. Ry.

Eu.—*Stat.*—Pop. 5,000. HOTEL DU CYGNE.

On the River Bresle. Church of St. Lawrence, Gothic, 12th cent., interior interesting. Chapelle du College, 17th cent. RAIL, pages, 20, 30, 85.

Evian-les-Bains.-*Stat.*-Pop. 3,512

First class BATHING ESTABLISHMENT. Principal Spring: Cachat.

ROYAL HOTEL.—Most luxurious and up-to-date, patronised by French and English aristocracy. Managed by "Ritz and Carlton Hotels," London. (English Church Service). See Advt.

SPLENDIDE HOTEL.—First class family hotel. Beautifully situated in own park. Under the same management as the Royal. Terms moderate. See Advt.

GRAND HOTEL D'EVIAN.—First class. Beautifully situated, with large park on the lake. Noted cuisine. Garage. Pension from 12 fr. See Advt.

HOTEL DE PARIS ET BEAU RIVAGE.—An excellent hotel, well situated with gardens and terrace overlooking lake. Pension from 8 fr. See Advt.

L'ERMITAGE D'EVIAN.—First class. All modern comforts combined with reasonable terms. Open from May to October. See Advt.

A charming little town of the Department of Haute Savoie, in a very picturesque spot on the Lake of Geneva. Healthy climate, cool in summer, mild in winter; lake and mountain scenery all round. Beautiful vicinity. New Casino, opened June, 1913; theatre, golf links, lawn tennis, regatta, motor boats, etc. The Etablissement, for all kinds of hydropathic treatment, massage, and electricity, ranks among the first in Europe. Cure for chronic gout, dyspepsia, neurasthenia, arterial hypertension, gall stones, renal calculus, and all kindred ailments. Season from May till October.

MEDICAL.—Fifteen medical practitioners.

RAIL, page 61A. Steamer, page 364. During the summer months a motor car service connects Evian with Le Fayet St. Gervais, over the Col des Gets, 58 miles. See page 370.

Evreux.—*Stat.*—Pop. 17,766.

HOTELS: CHEVAL BLANC; GRAND CERF.

Chief town of Dept. Eure, on the Iton. Seat of a bishop. Cathedral, 11th to 18th cents., is of several styles; interior imposing—fine stained glass. Tour de l'Horloge, 15th cent., close by. Musée has mediæval curiosities and modern paintings. Hotel de Ville. RAIL, pp. 78,84,85,86.

Falaise.-*Stat.*-Pop. 8,163. H. DE NORMANDIE.

In Dept. Calvados, on a wooded cliff *(falaise)* over the Ante; the birth-place of William the Conqueror, 1027. RAIL. pp. 75, 83.

Fayet St. Gervais (Le).—*Stat.*

GRAND HOTEL SAVOIE.—First class hotel, with every modern convenience. Magnificent views of the Sallanches Valley, the Aiguilles de Varens, and the Passy ridge. (See Advt. under St. Gervais-les-Bains).

A village of Savoy, 1,860 ft. above sea. A well-known climatic station and bathing resort, and head of the Chamonix Electric Railway. The sulphur waters, which were accidentally discovered in 1806 by some shepherds, are effectually used in cases of intestinal, nervous, and skin diseases, gout, etc. The natural surroundings of the district are beautiful and invigorating. RAIL, pages 61A, 61B. Tramway to St. Gervais-les-Bains, 61B. During the summer months motor car services run from Le Fayet over the Col des Aravis to Thones, 35 miles, and from Le Fayet through the Gorges de l'Arly to Albertville, 29 miles. See page 370.

Fécamp.—*Stat.*—Pop. 14,650.

HOTELS: DES BAINS; D'ANGLETERRE; PLAGE.

A fashionable bathing place and fishing port, in Dept. Seine Inférieure, much frequented. The fine Abbey Church, in a state of admirable preservation, is all that remains of a Benedictine priory. Pilgrims come here on 15th June to obtain water at a spring. Bibliothèque and Musée de la Ville.

BRITISH V.-CONS.—Alex. G. B. Bax, Esq.

RAIL, pages 77A, 84.

Fontainebleau.—*Stat.*—Pop. 14,078.

SAVOY HOTEL AND RESTAURANT, 42, Avenue du Chemin de Fer. Single rooms and suites. Pension terms. See Advt.

AIGLE NOIR; FRANCE; MERCEDES.

The town is 1¼ mile from Station; electric tramway.

Visited for the Chateau and Forest. The Chateau is open daily, 10.0 to 5.0 in summer, 11.0 to 4.0 in winter; an attendant gives explanations when conducting visitors. It dates from the reign of Francis I, was the favourite residence of Napoleon I, and part is now occupied by the President of the Republic. Pope Pius VII was a prisoner here, 1812-1814.

The Forest of 42,500 acres is the most beautiful in France, full of picturesque alleys, glades, gorges—much frequented by artists.

BANK, EXCHANGE.—Société Generale (de Paris), 22, Rue de la Cloche. English spoken. Letters of Credit and Circular notes cashed. Credits opened, etc. Apply London, 65, Regent Street, W.

RAIL, pages 63; 48, 58.

Gérardmer.—*Stat.*—Pop. 8,800.

HOTELS: POSTE; DU LAC; BEAU RIVAGE.

A favourite summer resort, 2,200 ft. above sea, on a lake, on the French side of the Vosges, amidst fine scenery; a good centre for excursions. Weaving factories and bleach works in the neighbourhood.

RAIL, page 70; Tramway to Schlucht, page 69

Granville.—*Stat.*—Pop. 12,720.

HOTELS: DU NORD; PARIS; GRAND.

A fortified port and sea bathing resort, at the mouth of the River Bosq, almost opposite Jersey. Good firm sands; bathing establishment and casino. In the picturesque upper town is Notre Dame Church (15th cent), with good stained glass. RAIL, pages 82, 85. Steamer to Jersey.

Grasse.—*Stat.*—Pop. 15,020.

GRAND HOTEL—Charmingly situated. Formerly the residence of Queen Victoria. See Advt.

VICTORIA; BELLE VUE.

Funicular and electric tram from Station to town.

A picturesque old town with exquisite views from the promenades, famed for its perfumes extracted from the flowers cultivated in the neighbourhood. It is situated on the southern slope of the hills, 1,070 ft. above sea, 12 miles from the Mediterranean, with a peculiarly mild climate favourable to invalids for whom sea air is too exciting. Ancient tower at Hotel de Ville, church of 12th-13th cent., three paintings by Rubens at the Hospital Chapel. Golf links.

ENGLISH CHURCH, Avenue Victoria.

RAIL, pages 47, 53C.

Grenoble.—*Stat.*—Pop. 77,438.

GRAND HOTEL.—First class hotel, beautifully situated. Fine garden. See Advt.

GD. HOTEL MODERNE.—First class establishment, very well and centrally situated in the most fashionable part of the town. All modern comfort. Electric light; lift; baths. See Advt

BAYARD; EUROPE; CENTRAL.

Chief town of Département Isère, a fortress of the first class, former capital of Dauphiné, on the River Isère, magnificently situated amidst imposing mountain scenery, the best centre for excursions among the Alps of Dauphiné. Glove making employs many persons here. In the old town are narrow winding streets; the newer quarters have fine thoroughfares. In the town itself is little to interest beside the Musée, where is a very good collection of paintings, also some sculpture, and an archæological collection; in the same building is the Library of 170,000 vols. and 7,300 MSS. Cathedral. Church of St. André.

H.B.M.'s VICE-CONSUL.—James Lewis, Esq.

U.S. CONS.—Charles P. H. Nason, Esq.

RAIL, pages 62A, 63A. MOTOR SERVICE, page 370. Tramways to Claix, Vif, Eybens, Voreppe, and Veurey.

Hardelot Plage.—

HOTEL HARDELOT.—First class family hotel. Every modern comfort. Golf links; tennis; fishing, etc. See Advt.

A quiet seaside resort, 8½ miles south of Boulogne with a firm expanse of sand and a sea wall forming a parade 2,000 ft. long. The old castle, a favourite and picturesque spot, is now a restaurant. Pleasant walks in the forest; boating and fishing in two lakes.

Reached by electric tram from Pont de Briques station, fare 60 c.

Le Havre.—*Stat.*—Pop. 136,159.

GRAND HOTEL DE NORMANDIE.—Well situated, 106, 108, Rue de Paris. Comfortable and moderate. See Advt.

HOTEL CONTINENTAL.—Facing the sea and close to landing stages of Transatlantique, etc., boats. Lift. Baths. Open all the year. See Advt.

FRASCATI; TORTONI; ANGLETERRE.

STEAMERS from Southampton berth alongside the Grand Quai; electric trams from Quai to Railway Station.

The Railway Station is on the east side of the town, at east end of Boulevard de Strasbourg, a mile and a half from the Steamer landing place.

Havre is well situated at the mouth of the River Seine, having a fine appearance from the sea. Next to Marseilles it is the most important seaport of France; its trade with America is very large, three fourths of the cotton imported into France being received here. It is a handsome town, but has nothing to interest beside commercial activity.

On the Quai, to seaward of the landing place, is the Musée-Bibliothéque, with a collection of pictures and sculpture; Sun. and Thurs., 10.0 to 4.0 or 5.0. In the library are 50,000 vols., with a collection of coins; open daily.

Hotel de Ville, at north end of Rue de Paris; a building in Renaissance style.

Church of Notre Dame, in Rue de Paris; the tower was once a beacon.

POST OFFICE.—Boulevard de Strasbourg, just east of Hotel de Ville.

ENGLISH CHURCH SERVICE.—Rue Mexico.

H.B.M.'s CONSUL GEN.—H. L. Churchill, Esq.

VICE-CONS.—J. O'B. T. Walsh, Esq.

U.S. CONS.—J. B. Osborne, Esq.

GOLF.—9-hole course, 1 mile from Harfleur Station.

Local Steamer service daily, according to tide, from Havre to Caen, Honfleur, and Trouville.

RAIL, pages 76 and 84.

[**Ste. Adresse.**—HOTEL DES PHARES. 2¼ miles north west of Havre, reached by tramway. On the cliff, a favourite bathing place. Casino.]

Houlgate—*Stat.*

GRAND HOTEL; BEAUSEJOUR; BELLEVUE; IMBERT.

A pleasant village and favourite bathing resort of Normandy, having a good sandy beach. Many villa residences. Casino, where is good music in the season. The "Desert," a spot strewn with rocks fallen from the cliffs, is about 3 miles to north east. Historically interesting coast; from Dives, about 2 miles south west, William the Conqueror first set out for England in 1066—commemorative column, and in the porch of the Church (14th-15th cent.) are the names of those who accompanied William.

RAIL, page 78.

Hyères.—*Stat.*—Pop. 15,982.

At **Costebelle.**—HOTEL DE L'ERMITAGE and GD. HOTEL DE COSTEBELLE.—Splendidly situated in the Pine Forest. Honoured by Royalty. See Advt.

ZICK'S GOLF HOTEL.—First class, adjoining golf links, In an extensive pine park, with fine view over mountains, sea, and islands. Lift; electric light; central heating. See Advt.

GRAND HOTEL DES PALMIERS.—Largest first-class hotel with good garden. Lift. Electric light. Terms from 9 fr. See Advt.

THE GRAND HOTEL AND RESTAURANT ILES D'OR.—Best situated, on the hill :first class family hotel; full south; large garden. Golf links. Garage. See Advt.

HOTEL REGINA HESPERIDES. — First class family house in an elevated position, with large garden. See Advt.

GRAND HOTEL CHATEAUBRIAND AND BRITANNIQUE.—First-class hotel, beautifully situated with fine view from elevated position. See Advt.

HOTEL VICTORIA AND AMBASSADEURS.—Family hotel, entirely renovated. Electric lift; central heating. New management. Pension from 8 frs. See Advt.

The Railway Station is half a mile from the town. Two other Stations, La Plage for the coast, and Salins d'Hyères for the salt works.

Hyères is the oldest of the French Mediterranean resorts, well situated at the base of a hill, three miles from the sea. The climate is generally very dry and mild, and recommended for any derangement of the respiratory organs. Immense quantities of flowers, early fruit, and vegetables, are sent from the district to distant markets, and the palm trees, oleanders, orange and olive trees of the public promenades and gardens are famous. Many interesting excursions may be made in the immediate neighbourhood, including the Mines of Bormettes.

The modern town is at the foot of the hill, the old town on the slope. In the Place de la Rade in the Chateau Denis is the Bibliothèque and a small Musée of natural history. Church of St. Louis, dating from 12th cent.; handsome new Hotel de Ville. Jardin d'Acclimatation.

St. Paul's English Church.

All Saints' English Church, Costebelle.

H.B.M.'s V. CONS.—Jesse Hook, Esq.

GOLF.—18-hole course on the east side of Hyères, on the road to the Salins; conveyances run several times a day from Costebelle and Hyères to the Links. There is also a second 18-hole links belonging to the proprietor of the Costebelle hotels

MEDICAL.—Dr. Biden, Villa Marie Marguerite.

THE ENGLISH BANK.—R. J. Corbett and Co. See Advt.

BANK.—EXCHANGE. Société Generale (de Paris), 6, Avenue Gambetta. English spoken. Letters of Credit and Circular notes cashed. Credits opened, etc. Apply London, 65, Regent Street, W.

HOUSE & ESTATE AGENTS.—J. Hook, Director (Correspondents for Messrs. Thos. Cook and Son). Circulating Library.

DEPOT FOR BRADSHAW'S PUBLICATIONS.—The English Bank.

RAIL, pp. 53C, 54.

[**Costebelle**, about two miles south of Hyères, on a hill, with magnificent views, has many English visitors. Old Romanesque Chapel.

San Salvadour (Var), on the French Riviera.

GRAND HOTEL.—Magnificently situated first class hotel. Standing in 125 acres of park land, pine and eucalyptus trees. Terms from 12/- a day. See Advt.

Owing to its very favourable situation, sheltered from north winds, San Salvadour is a pleasant winter resort with special value in cases of arthritic disease. Thermal establishment (lithia spring) amidst palms, pines, mimosas, and eucalyptus; fine coast views. Chateau belonging to the Empress Eugenie; "Fondation Anne-Marie," a climatic cure establishment. Excursions among the hills. RAIL, page 53C.

Bormes-les-Mimosas.—*Stat.*—Pop. 2,100.

GRAND HOTEL.—First class, elevated position. Surrounded by 28 acres of park land. Magnificent view. English clientèle. Terms from 8 frs. See Advt.

An interesting little walled town, in the Vallèe des Maures, 8 miles from Hyères, in a sheltered situation on the side of a hill, enjoying as a winter station a specially mild climate—tropical flora, the eucalyptus, mimosas, etc. Ruins of an old castle; fine views. RAIL, page 53C.

Le Lavandou.—*Stat.*—Pop. about 900.

A pleasantly situated and favourably known resort, about 12½ miles from Hyères. Its name is derived from the profusion of lavender blooming on the hills. RAIL, page 53C.]

Juan-les-Pins.—*Stat*—

HOTEL: GRAND.

In Dept. Alpes Maritimes, between Cannes and Nice. A new winter and sea-bathing resort in a beautiful and sheltered part of the Riviera; shore of fine sand three miles long. Pine woods. RAIL, page 54.

Laon.—*Stat.*—Pop. 14,625.

HOTELS: DE LA HURE; NORD; ACACIA.

The Railway Station is below the town, on north west side. The street from the Station. Avenue de la Gare, leads almost directly in one-third mile to the old Cathedral.

Laon is built on a ridge in the midst of a vine growing plain; the Laudunum of the Romans. Quaint old streets

The CATHEDRAL of Notre Dame—as the bishopric was suppressed at the Revolution it is not really a cathedral—is a fine Gothic pile of 12th-14th cent., with lofty towers and spires; impressive pure Gothic facade; interesting interior. On north west side of the Cathedral is the Palais de Justice.

Musée, a few yards south east of east end of Cathedral, contains paintings and antiquities.

Citadel, a little east of the Cathedral.

RAIL, pages 21, 28, 29, 29A, 67.

La Rochelle.—*Stat.*—Pop. 36,371.

HOTELS: FRANCE; ETRANGERS; COMMERCE.

Capital of Dept. Charente Inférieure, on the Bay of Biscay, memorable for the fourteen months' siege of 1628-29, by Richelieu, which reduced the pop. from 27,000 to 5,000. Towers of St. Nicholas, La Chaine, and de la Lanterne (now a prison). Hotel de Ville (renaissance); St. Louis Cathedral; tower of St. Sauveur; Lib. of 25,000 vols. H.B.M.'s VICE-CONSUL.—C. J. H. Hamilton, Esq. RAIL, pp. 40, 41, 42A.

Le Mans.—*Stat.*—Pop. 69,361.

HOTELS: DAUPHIN; GRAND; SAUMON.

Chief town of Département de la Sarthe. From the Railway Station the Avenue Thiers leads to the (right hand) Prefecture, Musée, and church of Notre Dame de la Couture. The Musée contains a good collection of pictures, sculpture, weapons, pottery, antiquities, etc.; open daily except Mon. In same building is the Bibliothèque of 50,000 vols. and 700 MSS.

From opposite the Prefecture the short Boulevard René-Levasseur leads to the Place de la République, whence the street on north east side leads to the Place des Jacobins, where is the Cathedral.

Cathedral of St. Julien, Gothic, 10th-15th cent.; in south transept is tomb of Berengaria, wife of Richard Cœur de Lion, fine windows, some tapestry. RAIL, pages 38, 75, 80, 87.

Le Puy.—*Stat.*—Pop. 20,973.

HOTELS: GARNIER; AMBASSADEURS.

Chief town of Département Haute Loire, 2,050 ft. above sea, on the slope of Mont Anis, between the Rivers Borne and Dolezon. A curious old place, in parts a labyrinth of steep narrow streets.

Cathedral of Notre Dame, of black and white stone, dating from the 9th cent.; many peculiarities observable in the edifice. Close by is the Rocher de Corneille, a peak bearing a colossal Statue of Notre Dame de France, 52 ft. high.

Musée Crozatier, near Place du Breuil, with collections of paintings, sculpture, and antiquities. RAIL, page 52A.

Le Touquet.

HOTEL DES ANGLAIS.—With every up-to-date comfort of a first class hotel. Close to Casino and the golf course. See Advt.

HERMITAGE; GOLF.

Motor bus at Etaples Station.

A sea side resort, about 20 miles south of Boulogne, growing in favour with families; cheerful but well ordered society. Fine stretch of sands, good bathing; tennis. Two casinos. Vast pine woods; the neighbourhood is full of historic associations. GOLF.—18-hole course.

Railway station at Etaples, 2 miles distant.

Lille.—*Stat.*—Pop. 217,807.

HOTEL DE L'EUROPE.—First-class well known hotel. See Advt.

BRUXELLES; CONTINENTAL; FLANDRE.

The RAILWAY STATION is in the east part of the town. The streets to left of Station, by St. Maurice Church, lead south in five minutes to the Place de la République, the centre of activity.

Chief town of Département du Nord, having in Flemish the name "Ryssel," in a fertile plain, on the River Deûle. Lille was the capital of French Flanders, and suffered greatly in the interminable wars of the middle ages; practically no old buildings are left, the attractive town having a quite modern appearance. It is an important manufacturing centre, with a vast trade in linen, woollens, cotton, machinery, etc.

Church of St. Maurice, a few yards west of the Railway Station, almost the only mediæval building in the town. Fine interior; high altar. Church of St. Michel, quarter mile due south of Place de la République; modern Romanesque; paintings in interior.

PALAIS DES BEAUX ARTS, an imposing building on east side of Place de la République, about one-third mile south west from the Railway Station. Here are Collections of the first importance, paintings, sculpture, antiquities, etc., with ethnographical, industrial, and decorative art museums. The Picture Gallery is specially rich in works by Flemish and Dutch masters, almost all the great artists of these schools being represented. Daily, 10.0 to 4.0 or 5.0.

Prefecture, in Place de la République, opposite the Palais des Beaux Arts.

Hotel de Ville, quarter mile south west of the Railway Station. Here are the Bibliothèque Communale, 100,000 vols., and a Museum of Engravings.

Bourse (Exchange), 200 yards, in direct line west, from the Railway Station.

POST OFFICE in Place de la République.

ENGLISH CHURCH SERVICE, at Christ Ch., Rue Watteau.

H.B.M's VICE-CONSUL.—James E. Walker, Esq.

U.S. CONS. AGENT.

GOLF.—9-hole course, adjoining town.

RAIL, pp. 21, 23, 26, 28, 29, 29A, 29B, 90, 103.

Limoges.—*Stat.*—Pop. 92,181.

HOTELS: AMBLARD; BOULE D'OR; VEYRIRAS; CAILLAUD.

The Railway Station, Gare des Benedictins, is at north east side of city, less than half a mile from the centre. The Gare de Mont Jovis, on north west side, is a minor Station.

Chief town of Département Haute Vienne, the ancient capital of the Limousin, on the River Vienne. In the old part of the town, where many quaint timber-built houses may be seen, the streets are very tortuous and narrow, some are impracticable for carriages. There are many porcelain manufactories—Limoges enamel is celebrated.

The Avenue de la Gare leads south from the Benedictins Station to the Place Jourdain, thence a street on south east approaches the Cathedral.

CATHEDRAL of St. Etienne, partly Romanesque, partly Gothic, whose building has extended through centuries, beginning about 1273 and only finished in recent years. Fine north portal; interior very imposing, tombs, rood loft, windows—in Sacristy are magnificent enamels. Behind the Cathedral is Bishop's Palace.

From south west corner of Cathedral the street leads to the Hotel de Ville, where is a small Museum of pictures and sculpture.

Musée Ceramique; a very fine collection of porcelain and faience.

H.B.M.'s VICE CONSUL.—H. F. de Luze, Esq.

U.S. CONS.—E. Belisle, Esq.

RAIL, pp. 31A, 32, 35, 38, 39A.

Lisieux.—*Stat.*—Pop. 16,849.

HOTEL DE FRANCE; NORMANDIE.

In Normandy, Department Calvados. Many old houses; Gothic Cathedral, 12th cent., with a noble facade. Small Musée. Becket found refuge at the priory of St. Ouen-le-Pin, near here. Lisieux is one of the most attractive of the old-world towns of France, and full of picturesque bits. RAIL, pp. 77B, 78.

Lourdes.—*Stat.*—Pop. 6,976.

HOTELS: DE LA GROTTE; MODERNE; D'ANGLETERRE; CHAPELLE.

In Département Hautes Pyrénées, finely situated on the Gave (torrent) de Pau. The modern importance of Lourdes wholly attaches to the pilgrimages to a grotto where the Virgin appeared to a peasant girl, Bernadette Soubirous, in 1858; miraculous cures are attributed to a spring at the grotto, and thousands of pilgrims, able as well as afflicted, resort there continually.

Boulevard de la Grotte leads to right from the Railway Station in half a mile to the Grotto; the water of the spring is very cold.

Church of the Rosary; flights of steps and crescent inclines lead to the terrace; many chapels within. Basilica Church, on higher ground, Gothic; statue of the Virgin; many votive offerings on interior walls.

Several establishments for the care of the pilgrims, and charitable institutions.

RAIL, page 43.

Luc-sur-Mer.—*Stat.*—HOTEL BELLE PLAGE.

A small bathing place between Trouville and Arromanches, 7 miles from Caen. Casino, pier, and promenade. Good sandy beach; fishing from the rocks. RAIL, page 74B.

Luchon, Bagnères de.—*Stat.*—Pop. 3,258.

HOTELS SACARON; BONNE MAISON; CASINO; BAINS; CONTINENTAL.

Apartments and Furnished Rooms numerous.

Delightfully situated in the Vallée de Luchon, on the Rivers One and Pique, 2,605 ft. above sea, amidst magnificent scenery, the nearest place of any size to the central Pyrenees, with curative waters known in Roman times. The sulphurous and saline waters, drunk and inhaled, varying greatly in temperature and component parts, are specially beneficial in skin affections, rheumatism, surgical cases, scrofula, etc. The Bath Establishment is exceptionally well organised.

Luchon consists of an old town and a new. The former, where is the Railway Station, is a collection of rather mean houses in narrow streets; the modern part, much the larger, has fine streets and promenades, and many good buildings and villa residences. Allée d'Etigny is an imposing avenue. At the Casino are models in relief of the Pyrenees, geological and botanical collections, and some pictures.

ENGLISH CHURCH SERVICE in summer.

RAIL, see page 43.

[**Lac d'Oo**, 10 miles from Luchon; conveyances generally leave Luchon daily at about noon, fare about 4 fr. An interesting excursion to a Pyreneean lake, amidst wild and impressive scenery; waterfall (890 ft.) at head of lake.—**Vallée du Lys** and the **Rue d'Enfer**; brakes usually leave Luchon for the Vallée du Lys at noon daily, fare about 4 fr. The Vallée is esteemed one of the finest in the Pyrenees.]

Luz.—*Stat.*—Pop. 1,507.

HOTELS: DE L'UNIVERS; LONDRES.

A small old town, 2,425 ft. above sea, picturesquely situated in a valley. During the summer it is much visited for its waters as well as for its surroundings. The waters are chiefly used in nervous affections. The church, dating from 12th cent., is interesting. RAIL, page 47.

[**St. Sauveur.**-HOTELS: PARIS; FRANCE; BAINS. Half a mile from Luz, 100 ft. higher, a pretty modern village, with warm sulphur springs specially favourable for treatment of women and in nervous cases.

A diligence runs from Luz to **Gavarnie**, 5,085 ft. above sea. HOTEL VIGNEMALE. The immensity of the masses cause the Cirque de Gavarnie to appear close to the village, but it is an hour's walk beyond. The Cirque is a wonderful amphitheatre, 5,380 ft. above sea, enclosed by towering mountains; the principal waterfall, Cascade de Gavarnie, when the water is full has a leap of 1,385 ft.; in summer, when the water is low, the fall is in two leaps. Sunrise and sunset are very beautiful seen from here.]

Lyons, ***Fr.* Lyon.**—*Stat.*—Pop. 523,796.—(*Plan in Special Edition, or post free 3d. stamps*).

GRAND HOTEL DE LYON, a first-class hotel for families and gentlemen: moderate. See Advt.

GRAND NOUVEL HOTEL.—First class modern hotel. Centrally situated. Every modern comfort; suites with baths. See Advt.

BUFFET.—At the Perrache Station, managed by Sleeping Car Co. See Advt.

GRAND HOTEL DU GLOBE.— Situated Place Bellecour, in fashionable part of the town. Otis lift; electric light; bathrooms. See Advt.

HOTEL D'ANGLETERRE.—Well situated, Place Carnot, two minutes from Perrache Station. Lift; electric light; central heating. See Advt.

TERMINUS.

The principal RAILWAY STATION is the Gare de Perrache, on the south side of the city, but in a fairly central situation; here all the express trains to and from the directions of Paris and Marseilles run in. The Gare de Vaise is in the north west district, the Gare de Brotteaux in the north east district, both away from centre.

TAXIMETRE MOTOR CARS.

Lyons, ancient Lugdunum, capital of the Department du Rhône, is, after Paris, the first city of France for size and commercial importance. It is the centre of the French silk, velvet, and ribbon trades, the annual value of these manufactures being about £16,000,000. There are also important engineering and chemical works. Its commercial prominence is largely due to its favoured situation on two navigable rivers, the Rhône and the Saône. It is a fortified place of the first class and the seat of an Archbishop.

Place Bellecour is the centre of activity at Lyons—here are the principal cafés; in the Rue de la Republique, running out of north east side of Place Bellecour, are the best shops. Most of the mills and factories are in suburbs on high ground at Vaise (west) and Croix Rousse (north west). The working population lives chiefly in the district of Guillotiere, on east side of the Rhône.

CATHEDRALE (St. Jean), on the west bank of the Saône, just across the bridge a little from west side of Place Bellecour, 12th-15th cent. Interior has statues, marble pulpit; chapel of St. Louis very ornate; astronomical clock in transept (best seen at noon or 1.0 or 2.0 p.m.).

Notre Dame de Fourvière, clearly seen on the hill due west (quarter mile) of the cathedral. In Byzantine style, erected in pursuance of vow by clergy of Lyons during war of 1870-71. 282 ft. long, 114 ft. wide, 124 ft. high to platform of tower. Interior elaborately decorated; high altar has statue of Virgin; mosaics, paintings. Fine view from tower (50c.); Mont Blanc to be seen in clear weather. Chapelle de Notre Dame, by the church, is much visited by pilgrims.

Eglise d'Ainay, the oldest church in Lyons; a little to west of mid distance between Place Carnot and Place Bellecour. Erected 10-11th cents. on site of Roman temple. Paintings, mosaics.

St. Nizier, south of Rue de l'Hotel de Ville, between Place Bellecour and Hotel de Ville. The ancient cathedral; Gothic, of 15th cent., with later additions.

Hotel de Ville, fine building, with statuary on principal facade. Immense bronze statues of the rivers Saône and Rhône in the vestibule.

PALAIS DES ARTS, south side of Place des Tereaux, opposite the Hotel de Ville. Here are the MUSEES—Picture Gallery, Sculpture Gallery, Natural History collection, collections of antiquities and marbles, and Library. The paintings are numerous and highly esteemed, including works by Rubens, Teniers the younger, Tintoretto, Perugino, Ribera; in the Galerie des Lyonnais are paintings by local artists. The Library contains 50,000 vols. and 40,000 engravings and drawings. Picture and Sculpture Galleries open daily, except Mon., 11.0 to 4.0; other collections on Sun. and Thurs.

BOURSE (Exchange), east side of Rue de la Republique, between Place Bellecour and Hotel de Ville. A handsome structure in Renaissance style, built 1853-60. On an upper floor is a Musée Historique des Tissus (dress materials)—very interesting—open Sun. and Thurs. 11.0 to 4.0. In 1894 President Carnot was assassinated on leaving this building.

PALAIS DE JUSTICE, west bank of Saône, a few yards north of Cathedral; a long heavy looking building, with twenty-four columns on river front.

Prefecture, in Cours de la Liberté, a little way from east bank of the Rhône, quarter mile north east of Place Bellecour. In Renaissance style; in the large halls are busts, statues, and paintings.

Parc de la Tête d'Or, a pleasant park on north east side of city, where are the Zoological and Botanical Gardens.

POST OFFICE, at south east corner of Place Bellecour. Here is the Poste Restante.

ENG. CH. SERVICE, at Holy Trinity Church.

H.B.M.'s CONSUL.—E. R. E. Vicars, Esq.

VICE-CONSUL.—W. Annett, Esq.

U.S. CONS.—Dr. C. B. Hurst.

BANK.—EXCHANGE. Société Generale (de Paris), 6, Rue de la Republique. English spoken. Letters of Credit and Circular notes cashed. Credits opened, etc. Apply London, 65, Regent Street, W.

RAIL, pp. 49, 51B, 52A, 53, 56, 61B, 62, 63A, 87.

Marseilles, *Fr.* **Marseille.** — *Stat.* — **Pop.** 550,619—(*Plan in Special Edition, or post free 3d. stamps*).

GRAND HOTEL DU LOUVRE ET DE LA PAIX.—Very fine first-class hotel, latest modern comfort; full south. Lift, telephone, electric light; tariff in every room. See Advt.

HOTEL NOAILLES ET METROPOLE.—Highly reputed first class hotel, patronised by English and American visitors. Superior accommodation. Telephone; lift. List of charges in every apartment. See Advt.

GRAND HOTEL (formerly Grand Hotel Marseille).—First-class hotel, centrally situated near the Station. Affords every modern comfort. Lift; electric light; telephone. See Advt.

REGINA HOTEL.—First class modern hotel, in good situation. See Advt.

TERMINUS HOTEL (in the Marseilles Station). Property of the Sleeping Car Co. Large first-class Hotel.

GRAND HOTEL DE GENEVE.—With view over sea, Cannebière, and the Exchange. English management. See Advt.

GRAND HOTEL DE BORDEAUX ET D'ORIENT.—Well situated, in close vicinity of the Cannebière and Railway Station. Lift; electric light. See Advt.

HOTEL CONTINENTAL.—Family hotel, conveniently situated, close to the Cannebière and Quay. English clientèle. Baths. Pension from 8 fr. See Advt.

GRAND NOUVEL HOTEL (Meublé).—First class, central position, within easy distance of Station. Apartments with baths. Rooms from 4 fr. See Advt.

HOTEL DU PETIT LOUVRE.—Well situated on the Cannebière, very comfortable and moderate. Lift, central heating. Terms from 9 fr. See Advt.

RESTAURANT "LA RESERVE" ET PALACE HOTEL (Corniche-Marseilles).—First class establishment with fine view of the. Mediterranean. See Advt.

The principal RAILWAY STATION, Gare St. Charles, is well within the city, a little to north east of the centre. Immediately before the Station, across the open space, the Boulevard leads south, in a quarter of a mile, to the busiest part of the leading thoroughfare, the extension of the Cannebière. The Quai de Joliette and Docks for the large STEAMERS are within a mile of the Station, due west.

CABS.—In the interior of the town, 1 or 2-horse cabs, 1 fr. 50 c. per drive day or night per hour, 2 fr. 50 c., day or night. Auto-taxis: First 800 metres or 6 minutes, 1 fr.; every 400 metres or 3 minutes extra, 20 c.; luggage 25 c.

Marseilles, the principal seaport of France, is a handsome modern city, all that was mediæval having been practically improved out of existence, and certainly no trace remaining of the ancient Massilia, founded here by Greeks from Phocæa about 600 B.C. Trade with Algiers and Tunis, and to the East through the Suez Canal, have given a wonderful impetus to the commerce of Marseilles, but the Suez Canal has also brought Trieste and Genoa into prominent competition. Of the extensions of the harbour the most important is the cutting of a water way to connect the port of Marseilles with the River Rhone. Two very fine lines of thoroughfare, crossing each other at right angles, traverse the city; one, running from the Vieux Port (old port), south west to north east, bearing in its course the names Rue Cannebière, Rue Noailles, and Allées de Meilhan, may be fairly described as magnificent. The second fine thoroughfare runs right and left across the line of the Cannebière, leading in its southerly direction to the avenue named Promenade du Prado, the favourite evening promenade.

The principal interest is in the harbour, which at the Old Port touches the foot of the Cannebière and extends round on north west side to the docks for large steamers. There are about 14 miles of quais; more than 7,000,000 tons of merchandise are annually imported and exported, and more than 400,000 travellers annually land and embark. The imports are cereals, oil seeds, coal, sugar, coffee, hides, sheep from Algeria, wool. Large soap and candle manufactories are in the neighbourhood.

CATHEDRALE (Ste. Marie Majeure), erected 1852-93, in the neo-Byzantine style, on a terrace facing the docks, just round north west from the sea end of the Vieux Port. Two towers over the façade, several domes; length of building 460 ft. Imposing interior, rich with mosaics, marble, and other decorations; choir chapels very large. Episcopal Palace by south east corner of Cathedral. Statue of Bishop Belsunce, who remained almost alone at his post during plague of 1720, when 40,000 persons died. Close by Cathedral are remains of the old Cathedral, on site of temple of Diana.

NOTRE DAME DE LA GARDE, clearly distinguished on the summit of a hill on south side of the Vieux Port; reached by funicular railway. Handsome modern pilgrimage church on site of mediæval sanctuary; statue of Virgin over the bell tower; high altar has silver figure of Virgin; paintings and sculpture.

St. Victor, close to south side of Vieux Port, by Fort d'Entrecasteaux. All that is left of a famous abbey.

St. Vincent de Paul, at north east end of the Allées de Meilhan.

Bourse (Exchange), on north side of the Cannebière, built 1852-60. Elaborate façade, statues and reliefs by the portico.

Hotel de Ville, on the Quai, north side of Vieux Port, 1663-83. At the Santé (Quarantine Office), at sea end of north side of Vieux Port, are some paintings and reliefs.

PALAIS DE LONGCHAMPS, on a height just off extreme north end of Boulevard de la Madeleine, the northerly continuation of the Cannebière. Magnificent building in Renaissance style. Here is the MUSEE DES BEAUX ARTS, with choice collections of sculpture and paintings by old and modern masters. Daily, except Mon. and Fri., 9.0 to 12.0 and 2.0 to 5.0 (in winter 2.0 to 4.0). Museum of Natural History in same building. Jardin Zoologique on north side of Palais.

Archaeological Museum in the Chateau Borely, near the sea end of the Prado. Models, sculptures, furniture, and miscellaneous antiquities. The Egyptian section is of the highest interest. Sun. and Thurs. 2.0 to 6.0 (4.0 in winter), but visitors are always admitted on application to custodian.

Chateau d'If, on small island d'If, two miles to west of Vieux Port; frequent small steamers. Castle built 1529, dungeons are shewn.

Prado Plage, on the road to the Corniche, three miles from Marseilles. Seaside resort; good bathing. Trams start from Cours St. Louis or the Prefecture. HOTEL DE LA PLAGE.

POST OFFICE, in Rue Colbert, a street running from north end of Cours Belsunce to Rue de la Republique (both these streets run off north side of Cannebière). Here is the Poste Restante.

ENGLISH CHURCH, 4, Rue de Beloi.

H.B.M.'s CONSUL GENERAL.—Martyn C. Gurney, Esq., M.V.O. VICE-CONSULS.—P. D. W. Nutt, Esq., and W. M. Gurney, Esq.

U.S. CONSUL GENERAL.—A. Gaulin, Esq., VICE-CONSUL.—V. P. H. Cram, Esq.

MEDICAL.—Dr. Ed. Hawthorn, 286, Rue Paradis; Teleph. 3001. Dr. Paul Gouin.

DEPOT FOR BRADSHAW'S PUBLICATIONS.—Pinet, 4, Rue Noailles,

RAIL, pages, 49, 54, and 68A.

Martigny-les-Bains.—*Stat.*

A pleasantly situated village and attractive Spa of the Vosges, on a plateau of the Monts Faucilles, 1,257 ft. above sea; protected from cold wind, without sudden variations of temperature, and little humidity. The waters, used for drinking and bathing, are cold, 50°—77°, are more strongly lithiated than other Vosges springs, and are most useful in treatment of gout, gravel, liver and kidney troubles, and skin affections arising from arthritism. Season from May until end September. Hydropathic establishment; Casino; good music. Park, with lake.

ENGLISH CHURCH SERVICE.

GOLF.—9-hole course. RAIL, page 68A.

Menton (Mentone).—*Stat.*—Pop. 18,000.

HOTEL DES ILES BRITANNIQUES, fine and healthy situation, commanding a magnificent view. See Advt.

WINTER PALACE. See Advt.

HOTEL DE BELLE VUE, beautifully situated and favourably known, with pleasant garden.

HOTEL DES ANGLAIS, beautifully situated and favourably known. See Advt.

HOTEL D'ITALIE AND HOTEL GDE. BRETAGNE.—Old established hotel, with large private gardens. Every modern comfort. Lifts. See Advt.

HOTEL IMPERIAL.—New first class hotel, containing 300 rooms and 150 bathrooms. Hot and cold water supply in all apartments. Large park. See Advt.

ALEXANDRA HOTEL.—First class, modern comfort, moderate terms; splendidly situated in own grounds with a large park. See Advt.

ROYAL WESTMINSTER HOTEL.—First class, situated in one of the best positions in the town, with garden; lift. See Advt.

HOTEL NATIONAL.—First class, full south, in a sheltered position, with extensive view. Electric light; lift; garden and lawn tennis ground. See Advt.

GRAND HOTEL MONT FLEURI.—Situated in a fine position, well sheltered, full south, near the Railway Station. See Advt.

REGINA PALACE HOTEL.—BALMORAL HOTEL.—Good. Centrally situated. Facing sea. With international clientèle. Electric light. Moderate charges. Pension from 9 fr. See Advt.

GRAND HOTEL D'ORIENT ET D'ANGLETERRE.—First class hotel. Opposite the Post and Telegraph Offices, Hydraulic lift. See Advt.

GRAND HOTEL DE VENISE ET CONTINENTAL.—First class, English clientèle; large garden; electric light and lift. Pension terms from frs. 11. See Advt.

GARAVAN PALACE.—New first class hotel, with all comforts. Swiss management. Pension from 12 fr. See Advt.

THE GRAND HOTEL.—East Bay of Garavan. Beautiful situation, full south, with fine garden of palms. See Advt.

GRAND HOTEL RIVIERA PALACE.—Highly reputed fashionable hotel, splendidly situated in own grounds. Elevated position. See Advt.

GRAND HOTEL DE TURIN ET BEAU-SEJOUR.—Well situated, full south, in the central part of the town. Lift; garden. See Advt.

GRAND HOTEL DU LOUVRE.—Well known first class family hotel, with a fine large garden. See Ad.

HOTEL DES COLONIES.—Situated south, near the Public Gardens. See Advt.

HOTEL BEAU RIVAGE.—Well situated (where Rev. C. H. Spurgeon used to live), near the Garavan Station. Full south. See Advt.

HOTEL BRISTOL.—Family hotel, close to English Church, etc. Reasonable charges. See Advt.

HOTEL DU PARC.—Situated full south, in its own garden. All modern comforts. Pension terms from 9 frs. See Advt.

HOTEL ANNONCIATA.—Highest and healthiest situation in Menton. 700 ft. altitude; pure air, spring water, every modern comfort. Funicular Railway. See Advt.

CARLTON PALACE HOTEL.—New first class hotel, overlooking the sea. 70 rooms and salons with bath and toilette. Pension from 12 fr. See Advt.

HOTEL PENSION MAGALI.—First class, situated full south. Electric light and all modern comforts. Pension from 8 frs. See Advt.

CECIL HOTEL.—New high class family hotel in good position. Hot and cold water supply in every room. Pension from 10 fr. See Advt.

VILLA STELLA, Garavan.—In quiet, sheltered position facing sea. Garden. English management. Pension from frs. 8.

RESTAURANT DE L'AMIRAUTE, VILLA LES GROTTES.—First class; fine views from the Olive Gardens. See Advt.

Furnished houses and apartments abound; it is better to hire these through an agent, who will explain letting terms.

There are two Railway Stations—Menton Gare, the principal, for the west district, and Garavan Gare for the east district, but travellers are not usually met at the latter unless so arranged.

Tramway across the town and along the coast.

Menton is one of the best winter residences on the Mediterranean; it is sheltered from north winds, especially upon the east side; there is not any fog, but dews at sunset are frequent. Mean winter temperature 50°. Menton is considered quieter than Cannes or Nice.

Menton is delightfully situated on two small bays, Baie de l'Ouest and Baie de l'Est, or Garavan, with between them a rocky promontory upon which the old part of the town is built. A little east of the Principal Railway Station is the stream, Torrent de Carei, over which a bridge leads to the centre of the town. This portion, from the railway bridge to the sea, is now covered by a well kept public garden, which is a great improvement. The new Casino Municipal gives on to this garden. **All the streets running south from the line of railway lead to the sea; the Promenade du Midi is along the shore, the other chief thoroughfare, Avenue Felix Faure and Rue St. Michel, runs parallel with the east end of Promenade du Midi, just back from the sea. The small port and lighthouse are by the promontory separating the two bays. Church of St. Michel, by the port; close by, a little west, Church of the Conception, with statues of saints. At the Hotel de Ville, in Rue St. Michel, is a small Museum of local prehistoric Antiquities.**

The Municipal Casino contains a splendid theatre, with reading rooms, restaurant, skating rink, etc. Also Casino at the Roches-Rouge. At the Roches-Rouges are caves where prehistoric remains were found. Many excursions are brought within reach by the electric tram service. Luxuriant vegetation.

HOTEL MIRAMAR.—Beautifully situated just over the Italian frontier, on the Corniche road (at the Roches-Rouge). Electric light, central heating. First class restaurant. See Advt.

ENG. CH. SERVICE (in winter).—At East Bay, Christ Church; at West Bay, St. John's.

PRESBYTERIAN SERVICES. — At the Scotch Church, Rue de la Republique.

H.B.M's VICE-CONSUL.—H. H. Hill, Esq.

GOLF.—18-hole course at Sospel, 10 miles, by electric tram.

MEDICAL.—Dr. Stanley Rendall, M.D. Dr. Campbell; Dr. Samways.

ENGLISH CHEMISTS.—Pharmacie Lindewald-Blancher, Place St. Roch.

MENTONE BRITISH AGENCY LIMITED.-Directors: Mr. H. H. Hill, Mr. J. L. Churchman, Mr. Francois Dona. (Regd. 4th Feb. 1913.) BRITISH VICE-CONSULATE, MENTONE. BANK. HOUSE AGENCY. List of Villas and Flats to be Let sent free on application. Offers information and assistance to English Visitors, and undertakes business of all descriptions throughout the year.

DEPOT for BRADSHAW'S GUIDE. — Librairie Centrale, 3, Rue Saint Michel.

RAIL, page 54.

[**Carei Valley.**—On a lovely hill between this and the Borrigo Valley stands the old and interesting monastery of the Annonciata, which is reached by a funicular railway starting from the Carei Valley every quarter hour. Electric tram from town to the funicular railway.]

Montauban.—*Stat.*—Pop. 30,388.

HOTELS: DU MIDI; TERMINUS.

On the River Tarn, a town once strongly Protestant, now even partly so, having a Faculty of Protestant Theology. Cathedral of 18th cent.; Church of St. Jacques. At the Hotel de Ville is a Museum of pictures, antiquities, etc. Picturesque bridge of early 14th cent. RAIL, pp. 32, 37, 45B, 46.

Mont Dore-les-Bains.—*Stat.*-Pop. 1,758.

HOTEL SARCIRON-RAINALDY (formerly Chabaury, Ainé).-Very well situated. Lift. See Advt.

NOUVEL HOTEL AND HOTEL DE LA POSTE.—Well situated, with Villas for families. See Advt.

HOTEL GALLIA.—Recently opened. Central heating; garage. See Advt.

A small town, 3,440 ft. above sea, on the River Dordogne, beautifully situated in a valley amongst the heights of the Monts Dore. The warm mineral springs, up to 113°, known to the Romans—drinking and bathing—are used in cases of bronchitis, asthma, rheumatism, chlorosis, etc. Well managed Etablissement. Season, June to October. Casino.

GOLF.—9-hole links between Mont Dore and Sancy, about 1¼ mile from Mont Dore.

RAIL, page 37.

Mont St. Michel.—*Stat.*—Pop. 200.

HOTEL POULARD AINE; POULARD JEUNE.

A village upon an isolated rock, 160 ft. above sea, half a mile from the shore. The summit of the rock is crowned by the picturesque Benedictine Abbey. RAIL, page 75A.

Monaco and **Monte Carlo,** distant from each other about a mile and a quarter.

Monaco.—*Stat.*—Pop. 9,500.

The small principality of Monaco is about 2½ miles in length along the sea shore, with a varying width of 165 to 1100 yards—about 6 square miles in all. The reigning Prince, Albert I, born 1848, succeeded in 1889. The capital consists of the old town, Monaco proper, upon the rocky peninsula, and La Condamine, or new town, on the lower ground; La Condamine, more sheltered and much the larger, is a health resort in winter and visited for sea bathing in summer.

From the Railway Station at La Condamine the road descends to the Place d'Armes, whence a path and road ascend to the Palace, a building in Renaissance style—to be visited during the absence of Prince; beside portraits are a few pictures by old masters. The Cathedral, in Romano-Byzantine style, an imposing building, has tastefully decorated interior. Museum on Promenade St. Martin; Oceanographical Museum.

POST OFFICE, Avenue St. Martin.

ENGLISH CHURCH SERV.—St. Cyprian's Ch.

H.B.M's CONSUL.—C. J. Sim, Esq.

RAIL, page 54.

Monte Carlo.—*Stat.*—Pop. nearly 4,000.

HOTEL METROPOLE.—First-class hotel, beautifully situated, close to the Casino, and overlooking the Public Gardens. See Advt.

HOTEL DE L'HERMITAGE.—High class, splendid position, close to Casino; magnificent view. Much patronised by an upper class of English and American visitors. See Advt.

GRAND HOTEL.—Splendid first-class family hotel, well known to English travellers. See Adv.

HOTEL DU PRINCE DES GALLES.—Very favourite first class hotel. High situation, full south. 200 rooms. Large garden. Every modern comfort. Much frequented by English. See Advt.

HOTEL VICTORIA.—First class family hotel, in a large garden; lift. See Advt.

HOTEL DES ANGLAIS AND ST. JAMES.—First class family hotel, facing the Public Gardens and close to Casino. Apartments with private baths and toilette. See Advt.

HOTEL BEAU RIVAGE—First class family hotel, situated full south. Fine views Suites and single rooms. All comforts. See Advt.

HOTEL DE LONDRES.—First class. In good situation, facing Casino and gardens. Open all the year. See Advt.

HOTEL WINDSOR.—In the healthiest and most charming part of Monte Carlo. See Advt.

HOTEL ROYAL.—First-class family hotel, well situated. See Advt.

HOTEL DU HELDER.—First class, near Casino. See Advt.

NOUVEL HOTEL DE LOUVRE.—Near Casino, with fine view. Lift; electric light; central heating. Open all the year. Terms from 14 frs. See Advt.

BALMORAL PALACE.—Situated next to Grand Hotel, with view on the Sea. Lift. See Advt.

HOTEL DE LA TERRASSE.—Private residential. Fine view from elevated position. Restaurant Electric light. Terms from 11 fr. See Advt.

HOTEL ALBION ET DU LITTORAL.— Well appointed family hotel, situated full south; fine view; every modern comfort. Central heating. English patronage. Pension from 10 fr. See Advt.

GRAND HOTEL TERMINUS.—Facing the Station and Casino grounds. Restaurant. Electric light. Open all the year. Moderate. See Advt.

MONTE CARLO PALACE HOTEL.—First class, facing Casino and gardens. Latest modern improvements. Suites with bath rooms. Central heating. See Advt.

HOTEL MASSENA. — Family hotel, in fine position. Electric light and central heating. Pension from 11 fr. 50c. per day. See Advt.

Monte Carlo, in the principality of Monaco, is beautifully situated on a sheltered bay and enjoys a delightful climate, while the surrounding scenery is full of charm and variety. The Bath Establishment, on the terrace, is supplied with every form of medical and hygienic bath, and at the "bar" the mineral waters of all the best known European resorts may be obtained; the decorations and fittings are elaborate. The Casino is on a promontory on the east side of the town; beside a fully supplied Reading Room, there is an elaborately decorated Salle de Fetes and widely known Salles de Jeu (Gaming Rooms). High class music twice daily. Splendid view from terrace behind the Casino. The Salles de Jeu are open from 11.30 a.m. until midnight; tickets gratis obtained in the vestibule; inhabitants of Principality not admitted. Trente-et-Quarante and Roulette are the games played, at the former the minimum stake is 20 fr., the maximum 12,000 fr.; at roulette the minimum is 5 fr., the maximum 6,000 fr. The Gardens of the Casino are famous for their beauty.

Adjoining the Casino Terrace is the Tir aux Pigeons; the Grand Prix, competed for in January, is 20,000 fr.

In the Palais des Beaux Arts are paintings.

POST OFFICE, Avenue de Monte Carlo.

MEDICAL.—Dr. R. Pryce-Mitchell, Villa Henri. Dr. Rolla Rouse. Dr. A. S. Blackwell, Villa Ciro.

DENTISTS.—R. S. Ash and Son.

BANKERS AND EXCHANGE OFFICES.—Comptoir National d'Escompte de Paris (late Smith's Bank). Payment of cheques, circular notes, letters of credit.

GOLF.—18-hole course, on the top of the hill near La Turbie. **RAIL, pages 53c, 54.**

[Mountain Rail from Monte Carlo to **La Turbie** (page 53c), an ancient place, with remains of Roman Tropaea Augusti, erected B.C. 6. Magnificent view.]

Montpellier.—*Stat.*—Pop. 80,230.

HOTELS: GRAND; METROPOLE; MIDI.

Capital of the department of the Hérault, on a hill, at whose base is the River Lez. A town of historical importance, enjoying for several centuries great prosperity, which in modern times has passed to other centres of population in the neighbourhood. The modern quarters are handsome, but the older streets are narrow and uninviting.

The Cathedral, a little north east of the centre of the town, is of the 14th cent., restored at end of 19th cent.; at the west front is a capacious porch with lofty arch, a more attractive porta is that to the south transept. In interior are paintings; in the fifth chapel a fine marble statue of the Virgin.

The Faculté de Medicine adjoins the Cathedral on its north side. There are an anatomical museum, library of 50,000 vols., and a collection of drawings; in one of the rooms are portraits of professors since the foundation of the School of Medicine, which has always been celebrated.

The University, suppressed 1794, restored 1896, is a few yards south of the Cathedral; about 1,500 students.

The Musée, on the south side of the town, contains a very fine collection of paintings—more than 800; there are also cases of art objects. In the same building is the municipal library of 100,000 vols. and 10,000 engravings. The principal promenade and one of the great attractions of Montpellier is the Peyrou, on the north side of the town, near the Cathedral. Here are the Porte du Peyrou, a triumphal arch in honour of Louis XIV, and the Chateau d'Eau. On the south side of the Peyrou is the Palais de Justice.

RAIL, pages 45A, 57, 86. Palavas, $7\frac{1}{2}$ miles distant, is the sea-side resort nearest to Montpellier.

Nancy.—*Stat.*—Pop. 119,949.

GRAND HOTEL, in the Stanislas Square.—Modern comforts. Restaurant. Garage. See Advt.

HOTEL AMERICAIN.—3, Place St. Jean. Central position, two minutes from the Station. Large new restaurant. All modern comforts. Rooms from fr. 3.50. See Advt.

D'ANGLETERRE; EUROPE.

The Railway Station is on the west side of the city, half a mile from the centre.

Chief town of Département de Meurthe-et-Moselle, on the River Meurthe; seat of a bishop, with a University and Ecole Forestière.

Just off the north side of Place Thiers, before the Station, is the Porte Stanislas, whence the Rue Stanislas leads to the Place Stanislas, at the heart of the city; on the south side of the Place is the Hotel de Ville, on east the Episcopal Palace, on the west the Theatre, on the north (a little back) the Porte Royale.

The Hotel de Ville contains a Musée of very valuable ancient and modern paintings and sculpture. Sun. and Thurs., 12.0 to 4.0.

The Cathedral is about 200 yards due south of Place Stanislas; built 1703-40; paintings.

Palais Ducal, one third mile due north of Place Stanislas, contains a Musée of antiquities, portraits, weapons, curiosities. Adjoining Ducal Palace is the Franciscan Church—many tombs.

RAIL, pages 64, 66, 68A, 70, 72, 73.

Nantes.—*Stat.*—Pop. 170,535.

HOTELS: BRETAGNE; VOYAGEURS; FRANCE.

The principal RAILWAY STATION, Gare d'Orleans, is close to the quai on east side of city. Gare de l'Etat, on south side, is connected with the lines running into the Gare d'Orleans.

Chief town of the Département de la Loire-Inférieure, on the Loire, a flourishing commercial town with a considerable shipping trade; several sugar refineries, factories for tinning sardines and provisions; extensive works (cotton mills, iron foundries) in the suburbs.

Just west of the Gare d'Orleans, on the quai, is the Chateau, of 15th cent. Turning to north, into the Place Duchesse Anne, in a few yards on left is seen the Cathedral.

Cathedral of St. Pierre, commenced in the 15th cent. but not completed until 1892. Within are tombs and monuments; some paintings.

The Musée de Peinture is in the Rue du Lycée, directly opposite east end of Cathedral. Very good collection of paintings, old masters and many modern French masters represented.

Musée d'Histoire Naturelle and Musée Dobrée (Archæological) are close together. Follow the line of quais for nearly a mile west of Gare d'Orleans; parallel with the quai, 250 yards back, is the Rue Voltaire, where is the first named Musée; the Musée Dobrée, a little further north west, is specially interesting.

H.B.M.'s VICE-CONSUL.—Alfred Trillot, Esq.
U. S. CONSUL.—L. Goldschmidt, Esq. VICE-CONSUL.—H. D. Bennett, Esq.

RAIL, pp. 37, 39, 41, 41B, 42A, 77B, 83.

Nantua.—*Stat.*—Pop. 30,000.

HOTEL DE FRANCE.

A small town picturesquely situated between mountains, at the south east end of the Lake of Nantua. Abbey Church of 7th cent.

RAIL, page 62.

Narbonne.—*Stat.*—Pop. 29,566.

HOTELS: GRAND; DORADE.

The Roman Narbo, a flourishing place from the 5th until the 13th cent., retaining but few indications of its ancient importance.

Church of St. Just (once the Cathedral), unfinished, dates from 1272; the oldest part, the choir, is 131 ft. high; tombs; in the treasury are objects of interest. Of the old fortified Archiepiscopal Palace three towers remain; between two of the towers is the Hotel de Ville. Museum of pictures, sculpture, antiquities, etc. The Roman Forum occupied the site covered later by the Cathedral and palace. RAIL, pages 45B, 46.

Nice.—Pop. 142,940.

HOTEL DE FRANCE.—First class hotel, in best part of town; electric light, lift. See Advt.

HOTEL NEGRESCO.—New first class hotel, containing 300 bed and sitting rooms; opened in December, 1912. See Advt.

WINTER PALACE, Cimiez.—One of the finest and most comfortable hotels in Europe. See Adv.

HERMITAGE HOTEL Cimiez.—See Advt.

LANGHAM HOTEL.—First class. Moderate charges. See Advt.

GRAND HOTEL DU CIMIEZ.—PAVILLON VICTORIA. See Advt.

GRAND HOTEL D'ANGLETERRE.—First class superior hotel, pleasantly situated on the "Jardin Public"; affords extensive accommodation and great comfort. Lift. See Advt.

KRAFT'S HOTEL DE NICE.-Very good situation; excellent. See Advt.

HOTEL DU LUXEMBOURG.—First class, excellent position. Promenade des Anglais. Every modern comfort. Open all the year. See Advt.

GRAND HOTEL DES PALMIERS.—First class English family hotel. Fine situation on Boulevard Victor Hugo. Garden; great comfort. See Advt.

CARLTON HOTEL.—New family hotel, equipped with all modern comfort; well situated. See Ad.

GRAND HOTEL.-First class; 600 rooms. See Ad.

HOTEL BEAU RIVAGE.—First class hotel. Well situated, corner Jardin Public and Promenade des Anglais. Every modern comfort. See Advt.

GRAND HOTEL DU RHIN.—Strictly first class family house. Best situation, full south. Electric light; lift; central heating. See Advt.

WESTMINSTER HOTEL, first class family hotel, on the Promenade des Anglais.

HOTEL DE LA GRANDE BRETAGNE.—One of the best situated first class hotels, facing the Public Gardens. Lifts. See Advt.

SPLENDID HOTEL.—First class hotel, situated Boul. Victor Hugo; electric light; lift. Pension from 12 fr. See Advt.

TERMINUS HOTEL. — First class, opposite Central Railway Station. Every modern comfort. English patronage. Open all the year. Pension from 12 fr. See Advt.

HOTEL DE BERNE.—Opposite Railway Station. Comfortable. See Advt.

GRAND HOTEL DES ILES BRITANNIQUES.—First class hotel, situated Boulevard Victor Hugo; electric light and central heating. See Advt.

GD. HOTEL METROPOLE ET PARADIS.—First class hotel, well situated, Boulevard Victor Hugo. Electric light; lift. See Advt.

HOTEL AND PENSION SUISSE.—Family hotel. Well situated, full south. See Advt.

PALACE HOTEL, formerly MILLIET.—First class hotel, situated full south; in the best part of the town. W. Meyer, propr.

HOTEL DE BADE AND O'CONNOR.—First class family hotel, centrally situated. within easy access of Promenade des Anglais. Electric light; central heating. Pension from 8 fr. See Advt.

HOTEL DU LOUVRE.—First class residential hotel. situated in a central aristocratic quarter-Bd. Victor Hugo. All latest improvements-Terms from 10/6. See Advt.

WEST END HOTEL.—First class, on the Promenade des Anglais. Lift; electric light. Pension terms from 12 fr. See Advt.

QUEEN'S HOTEL.—Renovated. Superior first class English family hotel. See Advt.

HOTEL GALLIA.—First class family hotel, centrally situated, full south. All latest improvements, central heating throughout. Garden. Pension from frs· 10. See Advt.

HOTEL ST. PETERSBURG.—First class, well situated, in sheltered position, Promenade des Anglais. Garden. Electric light; central heating. Terms from 10s. 6d. See Advt.

MEYER'S PARK HOTEL, ST. BARTHELEMY, Villa Arson.—Splendidly situated, first class hotel. See Advt

HOTEL CONTINENTAL.—Close to Tennis Club Grounds. Lift. See Advt.

HOTEL PENSION DE FRANCE.—First class family hotel. Situated full south, with large garden, near Promenade des Anglais. Pension from 9 fr. See Advt.

HOTEL BRICE (44, Rue Cotta).—First class English house, entirely rebuilt and enlarged. Every modern comfort. Suites with baths. Terms from 9 fr. See Advt.

MARINE VILLA-PENSION ANGLAISE.—Situated 77, Promenade des Anglais, in the middle of a fine garden. See Advt.

INTERNATIONAL HOTEL.—First class; full south. Apartments with bath and w.c. Most central; quiet situation. Large garden. Hot water heating. Pension from 9 frs. See Advt.

HOTEL DE RIVOLI ET DES NEGOCIANTS.—Rue Pastorelli. Lift, electric light, central heating. Rooms from 4 frs. Pension arrangements. See Advt.

Furnished houses and apartments numerous; arrangements for these are better made through an agent, who can fully explain terms of letting.

CABS.—Auto-Taxis 90 c. per kilometre; 1-horse cab 1 fr. per course, 1 fr. 50 c. at night; 2-horse cab 1 fr. 75 c. per course, 2 fr. 75 c. at night.

The principal Railway Station—Grande Gare—is on the north west side of the town; all the streets running south from the line of railway lead through the town and eventually to the sea

the fine Avenue de la Gare, just east of the Station, within sight. crosses the main streets and ends at the Place Massena, a centre of traffic quite close to the shore. A minor Station, Nice Riquier, is to the north east; a third Station, Gare du Sud, for a local line, is in the Avenue Malaussena.

Nice is held in great favour because of its mild equable winter climate and the variety of life its size affords; there is shelter from the north, north east, and north west winds, the air is refreshing, warm, and dry. Occasionally the dust is troublesome along the shore promenades; away from the sea the air is always pure and free. There are no fogs, but for a short time after sunset the air is damp and chilly. Mean winter temperature 48°. The season is considered to begin with January and close in first week of April, but visitors throng from October to May.

Nice, the Roman Nicæa, chief town of the Department Alpes Maritimes, and seat of a bishop, is finely situated on the Baie des Anges. A small river, the Paillon, separates the old town, on the left bank, the east side, from the modern districts, which spread over by far the larger space. The Casino Municipal, a great centre of attraction, is in Place Masséna, at south end of Avenue de la Gare. Jardin Public, between the Casino and the sea, a beautiful rendezvous, with palm trees, pepper trees, and myrtles. The Promenade des Anglais runs along the sea front on the west side, the Boulevard du Midi runs along the sea front on the east side.

On the Promenade des Anglais, facing the Jardin Public, is La Jétée, a famous landmark in Nice. In addition to the celebrated gambling rooms, there is a noted restaurant, also reading and conversation rooms, and a theatre in which performances of all kinds are given. In the Grand Hall there is during the season the famous Concert Symphonique every morning. Entrance for the day, 2 fr.

The churches of Nice are without architectural or historic interest. Musée Municipal, in Avenue Notre Dame, near Avenue de la Gare; paintings, pastels, engravings, sculpture: daily 10.0 to 12.0, 2.0 to 4.0, except Sun. and Mon. Natural History Museum, Boulevard Risso; Tues., Thurs., Sat. aft.

Hotel de Ville in Rue St. Francois-de-Paule, a street running parallel with Boulevard du Midi; in the same street is the Library (90,000 vols.), with a small collection of antiquities; a little beyond the east end of this street are the Prefecture and, on the north side, the Palais de Justice. On the east, by the sea, rises the hill known as the Chateau, with splendid prospects.

POST OFFICE, Place de la Liberté, at east end of Rue de l'Hotel des Postes, a street running off east side, south end, of Avenue de la Gare.

ENG. CH. SERV. (Trinity), Rue de France, Christ Church, Avenue Notre Dame.

PRESBYTERIAN CHURCH, Bvd. Victor Hugo.

AMERICAN EPIS. CHURCH, Bvd. Vict. Hugo

H.B.M.'s CONSUL.—J. W. Keogh, Esq.

U. S. CONSUL.—W. D. Hunter, Esq.

GOLF.—18-hole course at Cagnes (rail or tram); club house; also 9-hole course.

MEDICAL.—Dr. Amy, Dr. Brandt, Dr. Gilchrist.

BANKERS.—Credit Lyonnais.

HOUSE AND ESTATE AGENCY.—Agence Lattes, below Grand Hotel, 10, Avenue Felix Faure. Established 1842. The oldest on the Riviera.

VILLAS AND FLATS.—JOHNSON'S Riviera Agency, 13, Rue Hotel des Postes, is the only English firm of House Agents at Nice.

DEPOTS FOR BRADSHAW'S GUIDE.—Levant and Chevalier, Rue St. Jean Baptiste. D. Escoffier, 14, Avenue Felix-Faure.

RAIL, pp. 47, 53C, 54; MOTOR SERVICE to Briançon, see page 370; STEAMER, see List.

[**Cimiez**, on a pleasant hill, at the north side of, and really part of Nice.

WINTER PALACE, Cimiez.—One of the finest, most comfortable, hotels in Europe. See Advt.

EXCELSIOR HOTEL REGINA, formerly the residence of H.M. the Queen; see Advt.

HERMITAGE HOTEL (at Cimiez).—First class, splendid position, midst large park. Magnificent panorama. Electric funiculaire. See Advt.

GRAND HOTEL CIMIEZ. PAVILLON VICTORIA.—Splendid situation; beautiful gardens; magnificent view. Residence of Queen Victoria in 1895-96; see Advt.

HOTEL ALHAMBRA.—First class, well situated, in proximity of the town and tramway station. See Advt.

Cimiez is on the site of the Roman Cemenelum, of which remains have been discovered—a section of an Amphitheatre, a Temple of Apollo, and traces of other buildings. The Capuchin Monastery of Cimiez (1540) is on the site of a temple of Diana.

Mont Boron.

GRAND HOTEL DU MONT BORON.—First class, on the road to Beaulieu. Beautifully situated, with fine view; garden; lift; electric light. Pension arrangements. Terms from 10 fr. See Advt.

Mont Boron, 950 ft., is a fortified height crowning the promontory on the east side of Nice; very fine views. Beautiful road to Villefranche, 3 miles. The Bay of Villefranche, at the east base of Mont Boron, is an anchorage of the French Mediterranean Fleet.]

Nimes.—*Stat.*—Pop. 80,437.

HOTELS: DE LUXEMBOURG; CHEVAL BLANC; MANIVET; MIDI.

The RAILWAY STATION is at south east side of city, about half a mile from the principal sights.

Chief town of Département Gard, the Roman Nemausus, on the southern slope of hills extending from the Cévennes, having numerous monuments of antiquity. In the modern quarters are handsome thoroughfares. Silks are manufactured, and there is a trade in wine and spirits.

Immediately before the Station extends the broad Avenue Feuchères, at whose north end is the Esplanade, where on the north west side will be seen the Place des Arènes.

The Roman AMPHITHEATRE (Les Arènes), though smaller than the Colosseum at Rome and other amphitheatres, is in a better state of preservation. It was built in the 1st or 2nd Christian century; it is 146 yards long, 111 yards wide, and 70 ft. high; there was room for 24,000 spectators. Bull fights are now held in it.

North from the Amphitheatre is the Boulevard Victor Hugo, near the north end of which, on east side, is the MAISON CARREE, an exquisite Corinthian Temple in admirable preservation; museum of antiquities in the interior.

Proceeding to north end of Boulevard Victor Hugo, and then along Quai de la Fontaine, to west, in half a mile is the Jardin de la Fontaine, with a small Temple of Diana (doubtful) to north west, and the Tour Magne directly north; the tower is an imposing relic, 90 ft. high, part of the Roman ramparts. Fine view from the top.

Cathedral of St. Castor, 250 yards east, a little south, of the Maison Carrée; facade; a few paintings in interior. 200 yards east of the Cathedral is the Boulevard Amiral Courbet, at north end of which is the Gothic Church of St. Baudile and Porte d'Auguste, a Roman arch.

MUSEE, on west side of Rue Cité Foule, running south from the Amphitheatre. Paintings, sculpture, engravings, bronzes. Open daily.

At the Ecole des Beaux Arts, in Boulevard Amiral Courbet, are lapidary collections, a collection of casts, and natural history collections.

RAIL, pages 51, 53B, 56, 57, 58, 62.

Orleans.—*Stat.*—Pop. 72,096.

GRAND HOTEL AND ST. AIGNAN.—**First-class hotel, well situated, opposite the Square Bannier and promenades.** See Advt.

BOULE D'OR; STE. CATHERINE; MODERNE.

The Railway Station is on the north side of the city, within half a mile of the centre.

Chief town of the Département du Loiret, the former capital of Orléanais, on the River Loire.

From the Railway Station, a little to west, along the broad boulevard, is the Place Bannier; thence the Rue Bannier (Church of St. Paterne at corner) goes south east to the Place du Martroi, where is a Statue of the Maid of Orleans. Just south of the Place du Martroi, the Rue Jeanne d'Arc goes east to the Cathedral.

Cathedral of Ste. Croix, 1601-1829, late Gothic, has a florid facade; two towers, 285 ft. high, with central spire. In interior is monument of Bishop Dupanloup, some carving, paintings, and good windows. Bishop's Palace on north east side of Cathedral.

Church of Notre Dame de Recouvrance, a little back from quay, north bank, 300 yards west of west bridge, erected to commemorate the deliverance of the city by Joan of Arc. Paintings. Remains of St. Aignan Church, a little back from quay near the east bridge.

Hotel de Ville (Mairie), a little north west of the Cathedral; once a royal residence—here Francis II died in 1560 in the arms of his wife, Mary Queen of Scots.

Musée, in the old Hotel de Ville, just off south side of Rue Jeanne d'Arc. Paintings and sculpture; also many engravings. Sun. and Thurs. in the afternoon. A little south, in the Rue Ste. Catherine, is a small Historical Museum

Musée Jeanne d'Arc, in the Maison Jeanne d'Arc, 37, Rue du Tabour, a street on west side of Rue Royale. Collection of objects connected with the heroine.

RAIL, pages 32, 34, 35, 36, 42A.

Paray-le-Monial.—*Stat.*—Pop. 3,855.

HOTELS: DE BOURGOGNE; POSTE.

A small town whose chief importance is as a pilgrim resort to the scene of the appearance of the Virgin to Marie Alacocque (died 1690), a nun of what is now the Convent of the Visitation; whence is derived the prominence of the worship of the Sacred Heart. Church of 12th cent.; old Hotel de Ville.

RAIL, pp. 53A, 62, 63.

PARIS.—(*Plan in Special Edition, or post free 6d. stamps*). In Dept. Seine. Population (1911) 2,888,110, of whom about 180,000 are foreigners—25,000 English and Americans.

GRAND HOTEL.—A vast establishment, in the finest situation. Railway tickets issued. See Advt.

HOTEL D'ALBANY, 202, Rue de Rivoli. Opened 1894. Modern hotel. See Advt.

HOTEL ST. JAMES.-211, Rue St. Honoré; quietest hotel in Paris, with own garden. See Advt.

ELYSEE PALACE HOTEL.—First class, in finest situation. See Advt.

HOTEL REGINA.—Well situated, 2, Place de Rivoli, with view over finest part of Tuileries Gardens. Electric light. See Advt.

HOTEL DE CALAIS.—Situated 5 and 7, Rue des Capucines, corner of Rue de la Paix. Electric light. See Advt.

HOTEL CONTINENTAL.—First class, centrally situated, 3 Rue Castiglione; fine views on the Tuileries Gardens and Champs Elysées. Electric light; lifts; central heating. See Advt.

HOTEL MAJESTIC.—Avenue Kléber. First-class; built on the grounds of the former palace and gardens of the late Queen Isabella of Spain. Single rooms from 5—12 fr. See Advt.

HOTEL EDWARD VII.—New first class hotel, Rue Edouard VII, close to the Madeleine and Opera. First class restaurant. Opening in April. See Advt.

HOTEL DE CRILLON.—Place de la Concorde. New first-class hotel. 300 rooms and bathrooms. Restaurant with terrace. See Advt.

GRAND HOTEL TERMINUS, GARE ST. LAZARE. At the centre of Paris. First-class. 500 rooms; all modern comfort. See Advt.

GRAND HOTEL DU LOUVRE.—Reduced Tariff.

PALAIS D'ORSAY HOTEL.—Well situated with view of the Champs Elysées and the Tuileries. Electric light. See Advt.

HOTEL MIRABEAU.—8, Rue de la Paix, the finest part of Paris. Entirely re-built and equipped with every up-to-date comfort. See Ad.

HOTEL BRIGHTON.—First class family house, facing the garden of the Tuileries. Electric light. lift. See Advt.

HOTEL VOUILLEMONT-15, Rue Boissy d'Anglas. Entirely rebuilt and refurnished. 150 rooms and 120 bath and dressing rooms. See Advt.

HOTEL DE LILLE ET D'ALBION.—223, Rue St. Honoré, a well conducted good family house. See Advt.

HOTEL LUTETIA AND RESTAURANT.—43, Boulevard Raspail, Square du Bon Marché. First class new hotel. All modern comforts. See Adt.

HOTEL LOTTI.—Latest first class hotel, with 200 rooms and 100 bath-rooms, situated between the Place Vendôme and the Tuileries Gardens. Every up-to-date comfort. See Advt.

HOTEL PLAZA.—25, Avenue Montaigne (Rond Point des Champs Elysées). First class. Up-to-date and home like. See Advt.

HOTEL LOUVOIS.—First class; modern and comfortable. Central. See Advt.

HOTEL DE FRANCE ET CHOISEUL.—Situated 239-241, Rue St. Honoré, between Place Vendome and Tuileries Gardens. Lifts. See Advt.

GRAND HOTEL DE MALTE.—63, Rue Richelieu, near the Palais Royal and grand boulevards. See Advt.

HOTEL CASTIGLIONE.—First class family hotel, centrally situated near Tuileries Gardens and Place Vendome. Steam heating. See Advt.

HOTEL LOUIS LE GRAND.—Centrally situated in Rue Rouget de l'Isle, 3, facing the Jardin des Tuileries. Every up-to-date comfort. Pension terms from 9 fr. See Advt.

NORMANDY HOTEL.—7, Rue de l'Echelle (corner of the Avenue de l'Opera), and 256, Rue St. Honoré. Good and moderate. See Advt.

HOTEL WAGRAM.—208, Rue de Rivoli. First class hotel in good position. Up-to-date comforts. Latest sanitary arrangements. See Advt.

MAC-MAHON PALACE HOTEL.—High class family hotel. See Advt.

SAVOY HOTEL.—Central; modern appointments. See Advt.

HOTEL ASTORIA.—Corner of the Champs Elysées and the Place de l'Etoile. 200 rooms. Every modern comfort. Restaurant. See Advt.

HOTEL CAMPBELL.—High class family hotel, Avenue Friedland. Entirely renovated. See Ad.

LONDON AND NEW YORK HOTEL.—Well known hotel, opposite St. Lazare Station. Every modern comfort. Moderate charges. See Advt.

HOTEL DE LA GRANDE BRETAGNE.—Situated 14, Rue Caumartin, near the Madeleine and Opera. See Advt.

HOTEL BEDFORD.—17, Rue de l'Arcade. Near the Madeleine; excellent in every respect. Steam heating. See Advt.

HOTEL MONTANA.—Avenue de l'Opera. Up-to-date hotel. See Advt.

HOTEL DES CAPUCINES.—Boulevard des Capucines, best situation. First class. See Advt.

HOTEL CHATHAM, 17 and 19, Rue Daunou, formerly 67 and 69, Rue Neuve St. Augustin. See Advt.

HOTEL BELLE VUE, 39, Avenue de l'Opera, and Rue d'Antin, 8; comfortable, reasonable prices. See Advt.

GRAND HOTEL SUISSE.—Situated 5, Rue Lafayette. Electric light, lift, central heating, and baths. Board from 9 fr. 50 c. See Advt.

HOTEL MEYERBEER, at Rond Point of Champs Elyseés. Every modern comfort. See Advt.

IMPERIAL HOTEL.—Situated 4, Rue Christophe Colomb, Champs Elysées. Lift; electric light. See Advt.

HOTEL TREMOILLE.—Champs Elysees. English family hotel. 150 rooms. Lift, central heating. Electric light. Terms from 9 shillings. See Advt.

HOTEL DU PALAIS.—Situated 28, Cours la Reine, near Pont Alexandre III; electric light and lift. See Advt.

ROYAL HOTEL.—33, Avenue de Friedland, Champs Elysées. Private bath rooms: central heating; modern and moderate. See Advt.

GRAND HOTEL DU PALAIS ROYAL.—4, Rue de Valois. Comfortable. Rooms from 5.50 frs. Pension from 12.50 frs. See Advt.

HOTEL AVENIDA.—New high class hotel near the Rond Point des Champs Elysées (Rue du Colisée). Moderate tariff. See Advt.

BUFFET HOTEL, GARE DU NORD.—Situated in the interior of the Station. Restaurant. Lift. Electric light. See Advt.

HOTEL BALTIMORE.—88bis, Avenue Kleber. Suites with baths. Every modern comfort. Moderate. See Advt.

HOTEL AND PENSION TETE.—9, Cité du Retiro. Entrance, 35, Rue Boissy d'Anglas, and 30, Faubourg St. Honoré. Very comfortable. See Adv.

VIATOR HOTEL.—Good small hotel, close to Gare de Lyon. All modern improvements. See Advt.

HOTEL DU PRINCE ALBERT, 5, Rue St. Hyacinthe, St. Honoré, near the Tuileries. See Advt.

HOTEL DE LONDRES ET DE MILAN.—8, Rue St. Hyacinthe. See Advt.

HOTEL KUEHNER-ROETH.—29, Avenue Victor Hugo. Equipped with every modern comfort. Reasonable charges. See Advt.

HOTEL GALLIA.—63, Rue Pierre Charron (Champs Elysées). Every modern comfort. See Advt.

HOTEL WESTMINSTER.—Rue de la Paix. Centrally situated, but very quiet. Large and small suites. See Advt.

DOMINION HOTEL.—26, Avenue Friedland, close to Arc de Triomphe. All comforts. Inclusive terms from 12 frs. See Advt.

HOTEL BURGUNDY.—8, Rue Duphot (Madeleine). Entirely renovated. Steam heating. Rooms from 3 fr. Meals en pension 7 fr. See Advt.

ROYAL PALACE HOTEL.—8, Rue Richelieu (near the Avenue de l'Opera). New modern hotel. Restaurant. Moderate charges. See Advt.

HOTEL TERMINUS DU CHEMIN DE FER DE L'EST.—Built 1911-12. First class; warm water in all rooms. Lift; telephone on each floor. See Advt.

HOTEL TERMINUS DU CHEMIN DE FER DE LYON.—Situated, 19, Boulevard Diderot, opposite Paris-Lyon Station. Electric light; telephone. See Advt.

GD. HOTEL EUROPEEN.—67, Rue Turbigo, in the centre of the grand Boulevards. Rooms from 3 frs., Pension from 8 frs. See Advt.

HOTEL FRANÇAIS.—13, Rue de Strassbourg. Facing the Gare de l'Est, and close to the Gare du Nord. Rooms from 3s. 6d. See Advt.

THE ENGLISH PRIVATE HOTEL AND PENSION.—Very comfortable. Situated 11 bis, Rue Lord Byron, Champs Elysee. Electric light; central heating. English management. Terms from 6/- See Advt.

PENSION HAWKES.—7, Avenue du Trocadèro. Place de l'Alma. Entirely renovated and under new management. Electric light; central heating. Terms: from frs. 8. Visitors received by day or month. See Advt.

ST. RAPHAEL'S FAMILY HOUSE, 5, Rue des Pyramides, near the Louvre and the Tuileries Gardens, the Opera, etc. Electric light, central heating. Pension terms from 8 frs. per day. See Advt.

CABS.—The Taximetre Motor Car is in general use. Fares: 75 c. for 1,200 mètres (1,312 yards) or nine minutes occupation, 10 c. increase for each 400 mètres (437 yards) or three minutes occupation. Luggage, each article 25 c. Between midnight and 6.0 a.m. an extra charge of 50 c.

METROPOLITAIN RAILWAY (underground).—The fares are the same for any distance, 25 c. 1st class, 15 c. 2nd class. See page 83.

PARIS, the capital of France, stands on both banks of the River Seine, the river flowing from east to west, its length within the city being about 7 miles, crossed by 31 bridges. The low lying district of Grenelle, by the river, is 80 feet above sea level, the heights of Montmartre, in the north district, rise to 420 feet above sea level. Mean winter temperature 38½°, annual 50°; average annual rainfall 23 inches.

In January, 1910, widespread distress and damage were caused in the riverside districts by the unprecedented swelling of the River Seine, the water rising nearly to the keystones of the arches of the bridges; the quays were entirely submerged and the flood covered the adjoining streets; it was estimated that the property loss reached a total of £40,000,000.

It will save time, be inexpensive, and give a better idea of the situation of the more notable buildings of interest, to hire a car for a drive round the heart of the city; an easily found and suitable starting place would be, for instance, the Place de la Concorde, by the River Seine, in the west central part of a plan of Paris. From the Place de la Concorde the drive would be eastward along the Rue de Rivoli and its continuation as far as the Place de la Bastille; almost all along this part of the drive is a line of historic buildings on the right hand—what remains of the Tuileries, then the Louvre, the towers of Notre Dame back to the right, the Hotel de Ville, a stretch of old Paris, and finally the site of the Bastille. From the Bastille the drive would turn northward by the Boulevard Beaumarchais and its continuation—comparatively uninteresting—to the Place de la Republique, where begin what are called the grand boulevards, swarming with Paris life, ending at the Church of the Madeleine, whence the short but imposing Rue Royale leads back to the Place de la Concorde.

As it is impossible within available space to treat adequately the interesting buildings and places of Paris, only those are briefly noticed whose importance demands attention, and for convenience of visiting they are grouped where in proximity.

NOTRE DAME CATHEDRAL, a noble Gothic pile, founded 1163. Two majestic towers over the west front; three recessed entrances, profusely carved—centre represents Last Judgment, immediately above statues of many French Kings. Interior very fine, rich carving in the choir choir chapels ornate; marble floor, imposing high altar, much sculpture, some beautiful paintings; gorgeous rose windows. In the treasury, several relics; in the chapter house, robes of Archbp. Darboy, murdered by Communists. Admission to choir, sacristry, treasury, and chapter house, 1 fr. inclusive.

PALAIS DE JUSTICE (Law Courts), just west of Notre Dame.

SAINTE CHAPELLE, in the Palais de Justice. Small; one of the most beautiful specimens of existing Gothic architecture. Fine stained glass.

HOTEL DE VILLE, at the east end of the Rue de Rivoli. A magnificent building in the Renaissance style. Several spacious elaborately decorated halls.

TOUR ST. JACQUES, in the Rue de Rivoli, near Hotel de Ville. View from top (10c.).

ST. GERVAIS, near Hotel de Ville. Old stalls, stained glass. Music at service much esteemed.

MUSEE CARNAVALET, in the Rue de Sévigné, near Rue Franc-Bourgeois, a little north east of the Hotel de Ville. Antiquities, pictures, and relics connected with revolutions of 1789, 1830, 1848. Sun. and Thurs, 11 to 4.

PLACE DE LA BASTILLE, at east end of Rue de Rivoli. Monument in centre. Outline of the old Bastille walls is traced in the roadway in the western corner.

TUILERIES GARDENS, in the Rue de Rivoli and Place de la Concorde. Part of the gardens was the site of the Palace—wrecked 1871, removed after. Magnificent view from here across the Place de la Concorde to the Arc de Triomphe on the height of the Champs Elysées.

The LOUVRE, in the Rue de Rivoli, with the River Seine on the south side. Most important public building of Paris. Vast Galleries of celebrated paintings (upstairs), sculpture, antiquities. Open daily, except Monday.

ST. GERMAIN L'AUXERROIS. Opposite the colonnade of the Louvre. Antique architecture; frescoes. It was the bell of this Church that boomed the signal for the massacre of the Huguenots on St. Bartholomew day.

INSTITUTE OF FRANCE, on Quai Conti, opposite the Louvre. A crescent shaped building. The Académie Francaise, with other Académies (Belles-Lettres, Sciences, Beaux-Arts, Sciences Morales), assemble here.

PALAIS ROYAL, Rue St. Honoré. A once royal palace, chiefly associated with the Orleans family, now turned to commercial uses and of little present interest.

ST. EUSTACHE. At the end of Rue Montmartre, opposite the Halles (Markets) Centrales. One of the largest and most important of the Churches of Paris. Many chapels. Music much esteemed.

ST. ROCH. In Rue St. Honoré. Architecturally insignificant. Paintings, sculpture. The services are very ornate. Outside this church many revolutionary scenes are recorded.

PALAIS DU CORPS LEGISLATIF, often called Palais Bourbon, on the Quai d'Orsay, opposite the Place de la Concorde. The Deputies assemble here.

HOTEL DES MONNAIES (Mint), on the Quai Conti, opposite the Louvre. Collection of coins Tues. and Fri., 12 to 3.

LUXEMBOURG PALACE, on south side of the Seine, in the Rue Vaugirard, ten minutes walk south of the Louvre. The Senate assembles here. Museum and Picture Gallery (modern artists) only open to public: daily, except Mon.

MUSEE DE CLUNY, on the south side of the Seine, near the Boulevard St. Germain, where the Boulevard St. Michel crosses. A museum of the greatest interest; mediæval and ancient curiosities of all kinds. Daily, Mon. excepted.

The SORBONNE, off the Boulevard Michel, to the left going south. Fine building, facade 250 feet long. University Library of 80,000 vols.; daily, except Sun.

PANTHEON, south of the Seine, in an almost direct line south of Notre Dame. Imposing domed edifice, dedicated when built to Ste. Genevieve; diverted in 1791 to the purpose of a memorial temple; in 1822 restored to its original religious use; again secularised in 1830; once more restored to the Church in 1852; finally secularised in 1885.

ST. ETIENNE DU MONT. Near the Pantheon. Interior very fine; paintings; in the chapel are relics of Ste. Genevieve.

ST. SULPICE, near the Luxembourg. Frescoes, organ especially good. A line of copper near middle of church marks the meridian of Paris.

VAL DE GRACE, south side of the Seine, in Rue St. Jacques, near south end of Boulevard St. Michel. The main building is a hospital; the church forming part has conspicuous dome.

ST. GERMAIN DES PRES. In Rue Bonaparte, directly south of the Louvre, across the river. Oldest church of Paris. Paintings. Used as a saltpetre manufactory during the Revolution.

CHURCH OF THE MADELEINE. Erected by Nap. I. as a Temple of Fame, diverted to sacred uses. Splendid facade fronting Rue Royale, 52 exterior Corinthian columns. Rich gilding, paintings, statuary. Music at services here much esteemed.

CHAPELLE EXPIATOIRE, on Boulevard Haussmann, where Rue Pasquier runs in. Sacred to the memory of Marie Antoinette and Louis XVI. Tombs of the Swiss Guard are in the cloisters.

ST. AUGUSTIN, Boulevard Haussmann. Paintings, fresco, dome decorations.

GRAND OPERA, off the north side of the Boulevard des Capucines. Finest theatre of the world, though with less seating capacity than some.

BIBLIOTHEQUE NATIONALE, Rue Richelieu. It is stated there are 3,000,000 vols., and 150,000 manuscripts, with enormous collections of maps, plans, and miscellaneous engravings, coins, medals, etc. Public admitted only to Reading Room & collections of coins, medals, antiquities.

The BOURSE (Stock Exchange), in Rue Vivienne. Public admitted to view scene from gallery.

NOTRE DAME DE LORETTE, at end of Rue Lafitte. Sumptuously provided with paintings.

LA TRINITE, Rue St. Lazare. Splendid facade.

ST. VINCENT DE PAUL, in Rue La Fayette, near Gare du Nord. Frescoes, painted roof, stained glass.

ST. LAURENT, Boulevard de Strasbourg. Facade, choir.

SACRE COEUR. On the heights of Montmartre. Imposing Byzantine fabric. The bell of this church is considered the finest in France.

PALAIS DE L'ELYSEE, near the Place de la Concorde end of the Champs Elysée, on the right hand looking up. The official residence of the President of the French Republic.

ARC DE TRIOMPHE, at the upper end of the Avenue des Champs Elysées. Erected to commemorate Napoleonic victories. Height 152 feet. Fine view from the top; small gratuity to ascend.

HOTEL DES INVALIDES; the gilded dome is distinctly seen to the south west of the Place de la Concorde. Tomb of Napoleon (Mon., Tues., Thurs., Fri., Sun., 12 to 3). Military memorials. Not many veterans housed here.

STE. CLOTILDE, in Rue St. Dominique. Frescoes in chapels, carving in choir, beautiful stained glass.

EIFFEL TOWER (984 ft.). Loftiest tower in the world. On the Champ de Mars.

BOIS DE BOULOGNE, on the west side of Paris, beyond the Arc de Triomphe. The Hyde Park of Paris. Adjoining, further west, is the race-course of Longchamp.

BOIS DE VINCENNES, on the east side of Paris.

PARC MONCEAU, near the north end of the Boulevard Malesherbes. Small; very agreeable.

PARC DES BUTTES CHAUMONT, on the north east side of Paris.

JARDIN ZOOLOGIQUE D'ACCLIMATATION, on left of Boulevard Maillot, west of the Arc de Triomphe, on north side of Bois de Boulogne.

JARDIN DES PLANTES, on Quai St. Bernard, south side of Seine, eastward from Notre Dame.

PERE LA CHAISE CEMETERY, on the east side of Paris, on Boulevard Menilmontant, facing the upper end of Rue de la Roquette, which runs up from Place de la Bastille.

CEMETERY OF MONTMARTRE, on north side of Paris, in a line north of St. Lazare Station.

CEMETERY OF MONTPARNASSE, on south side of Paris, some distance south of the Luxembourg.

THEATRES.—The classic houses are: Theatre Francais, Odéon, Vaudeville, Gymnase, Variétés, Opera, Opera Comique. The traveller who has not a good knowledge of French will find more amusement at such theatres as the Gaité, Chatelet, Bouffes Parisiéns, where ballet, tableaux, etc., are leading features.

POST OFFICE.—The principal Post Office is in the Rue du Louvre, a little to the left going from the Bourse to the Louvre. Letters addressed "Post Restante, Paris," are delivered here. The latest open post box for England is at the Gare du Nord, about 8.30 p.m. Stamps sold at all tobacco shops.

ENGLISH SPEAKING PLACES OF WORSHIP,

ENG. CHURCH (C. C. C. Soc.), Rue d'Aguesseau, opposite the British Embassy. Rev. A. S. V. Blunt. Sunday, 8.30, 10.30, 3.30. and 8.0; H. C. Sunday 8.30 a.m. and noon. ST. GEORGE'S ANGLICAN CHURCH, 7, Rue Auguste Vacquerie, at 8.30, 10.30, and 6.0. CHRIST CHURCH, 83, Boulevard Bineau, Neuilly; in connection with the "Ada Leigh" Homes for British Girls in Paris and the English Orphanage; services, 8.30 a.m., 10.30 a.m., 4.0 p.m.

WESLEYAN CHURCH, 4, Rue Roquépine, near the Chapelle Expiatoire, 11 a.m. and 8 p.m.

INDEPENDENT CHAPEL, 23, Rue Royale, 11 a.m. and 7.30 p.m.

AMERICAN PRESBYTERIAN, 21, Rue de Berri.

AMERICAN EPISCOPAL, Holy Trinity, Avenue de l'Alma. 5, Avenue Montaigne.

ST. LUKE'S CHAPEL of American Ch. of Holy Trinity, 5, Rue de la Grande Chaumière, near Boulevard Montparnasse.

CHURCH OF SCOTLAND, 17, Rue Bayard.

ENGLISH ROMAN CATHOLIC.-50, Avenue Hoche.

GIRLS' FRIENDLY SOCIETY.—50, Avenue d'Jena.

Y.M.C.A.—160, Rue Montmartre.

BRITISH AND AMERICAN EMBASSIES, ETC.

GREAT BRITAIN.—His Excellency the Hon. Sir Francis Leveson Bertie, G.C.B., G.C.M.G., G.C.V.O., 39, Faubourg St. Honoré. Secretary of Embassy.—G. D. Grahame, Esq., M.V.O Commercial Attache.—Sir Henry Austin Lee, K.C.M.G., C.B.

H.B.M.'s CONSUL GENERAL.—W. S. Harriss Gastrell, Esq. VICE-CONSULS.—H. Hall Hall, Esq., and E. Attwell Smith, Esq.

UNITED STATES.—His Excellency Hon. Myron T. Herrick. Sec. of Embassy, R. W. Bliss, Esq.

U.S. CONSUL-GENERAL.—F. H. Mason, Esq.

VICE-CONSUL.—L. Memminger, Esq.

GOLF.—18-hole course, 1¼ mile from Versailles (Chantiers) Station. Also 9-hole course at Le Pecq, by tram; club house.

BANKERS AND EXCHANGE OFFICES.—Messrs. Munroe and Co., 7, Rue Scribe, correspondents of the principal English and American Banks.

MEDICAL.—Dr. Jarvis, 81, Bd. Malesherbes; Dr. Mamlock, 20, Rue Lesueur; Dr. Robinson, 1, Rue d'Aguesseau; Dr. A. Warden, 11, Av. Bois de Boulogne.

CHEMIST.—Carteret, 9, Rue des Pyramides. English, American, and Foreign Pharmacy. Central situation, near principal hotels.

HOUSE AND ESTATE AGENCY.—W. H. Tiffen, (late firm John Arthur & Co.). Established 1818. 22, Rue des Capucines. Telephone 247—82.

DEPOTS FOR BRADSHAW'S PUBLICATIONS.—The Galignani Library, 224, Rue de Rivoli; Brentano and Co., 37, Avenue de l'Opera; W. H. Smith and Son, 248, Rue de Rivoli.

RAIL.—For Routes and Trains from Paris, see pages cxxxvii-cxl, and the Index.

Pau.—*Stat.*—Pop. 37,149.

GRAND HOTEL GASSION.—This well known first-class hotel offers advantageous arrangements for families. See Advt.

GRAND HOTEL DU PALAIS ET BEAU SEJOUR.—First class hotel, full south, with view on the Pyrénées. Lift; electric light. See Advt.

HOTEL DE FRANCE,—First-class hotel, adjoining Club, and commanding splendid views.

MAISON COLBERT, Rue Montpensier, first-class Pension and Boarding house, kept by English Ladies. See Advt.

The RAILWAY STATION is on the south side, at the foot of the plateau upon which the town is built. Vehicles go a long way round, but a foot path leads upward from the Station past the Casino to the Place Royale, whence is a magnificent view. Immediately west of Place Royale is the modern Church of St. Martin; high altar, fine windows.

Chief town of the Département Basses-Pyrénées, once the capital of Béarn, finely situated on the Gave (torrent) de Pau, in view of the Pyrenees. It is a place of great historical interest, from associations with the Court of Navarre, Henri IV of France, his mother Jeanne d'Albret, and others; but it is now generally known as a very favourable winter and spring residence for consumptive or nervously affected persons—by many it is preferred to the Riviera because of the dry air, absence of wind, and the quieter life. Pau is regarded as a favourable centre for aviation. Average winter temperature 44° Fahrenheit.

CHATEAU, quarter mile due west of Place Royale. An old towered castle, with state apartments, mediæval furniture, tapestry, and curiosities. Daily, 10.0 to 5.0 or 11.0 to 4.0.

A quarter mile north of the Place Royale is the Palais de Justice, with the church of St. Jacques on west side.

Musée, in Place Bosquet, half mile east of Place Royale; paintings, sculpture, curiosities; a natural history collection. Sun. and Thurs.

Parc Beaumont, at south east corner of town—band here; Casino. Protestant cemeteries on west side of town, reached from lower end of Route de Bordeaux.

POST OFFICE. — Rue Gambetta, near the Nouvelle Halle.

ENG. CH. SERV.—Christ Church, Rue Serviez. Holy Trinity Church, Rue des Temples. St. Andrew's, Rue O'Quin.

PRESB. AND FREE CHURCH.—Rue O'Quin.

BRITISH V.-CONS.—H. T. H. Hewetson, Esq

GOLF.—18-hole course 1 mile from centre of town; club house. Ladies' 9-hole course. Croquet Club in the Park Beaumont. Hunting; English hounds three times a week during the season.

MEDICAL.—Dr. F. L. Brown; Dr. Rigoulet.

ENGLISH BANK, EXCHANGE, AND INFORMATION OFFICE.—Messrs. Ayrton and Evans, 25, Rue du Lycée. See Advt.

BANK.—EXCHANGE. Société Generale (de Paris), 8, Rue Gambetta. English spoken. Letters of Credit and Circular notes cashed. Credits opened, etc. Apply London, 65, Regent Street, W.

RAIL, pp. 43, 44, and 45A.

Perpignan.—*Stat.*—Pop. 39,510.

HOTELS: GRAND; NORD.

Chief town of the department of the Pyrénees Orientales, formerly the old capital of Roussillon, on the River Tet. Cathedral (St. Jean), 14th-15th cents., has interesting interior. At the University, founded 1349, are the Museum (paintings, sculpture, natural history) and Library. La Loge, of 14th cent., containing the municipal offices, is a curious relic of Moorish and Gothic architecture. RAIL, pages 46, 46A

Petites Dalles.

HOTEL DES PAVILLONS.

A picturesque sea bathing resort and fishing village. Casino. Reached from Cany (page 84).

Pierrefonds les Bains.—*Stat.*—Pop. 1,750.

HOTELS: DES BAINS; ETRANGERS; DES RUINES.

A pretty village in Dept. Oise, in the forest of Compiègne. Church of 11-14th cents. Fine mediæval Castle, 1380, the finest Gothic chateau in France. Good sulphur waters at the Bath-house, useful in mucous complaints.

RAIL p. 28.

Pioule les Bains.

GRAND HOTEL DE PIOULE.

A new health resort, with thermal springs pleasantly situated, about 1¼ mile from Le Luc Station (page 54).

Plombières-les-Bains.—*Stat.*—Pop. 1,869.

GRAND HOTEL (formerly NAPOLEON).—First class, adjoining Bath Establishment. Entirely renovated and up-to-date. Highest patronage. See Advt.

METROPOLE; STANISLAUS; PAIX.

A fashionable watering place in a ravine of the Augronne, in the Vosges hills. Numerous bathing establishments, the springs varying from 59° to 160° Fahr.; specially recommended for enteritis, appendicitis, nervous diseases, rheumatism, and gout. Casino and Park, Excursions by carriage or omnibus to the Feuilleés, 3 m., to the Val d'Ajol, 5 m., to Remiremont, 9m., the latter an interesting old town of 10,500 inhabitants, on the left bank of the Moselle, with church dating from the 10th century.

MEDICAL.—Dr. Bottentuit.

RAIL, pages 66, 71.

Poitiers.—*Stat.*—Pop. 41,242.

HOTELS: DU PALAIS; EUROPE; FRANCE.

The Railway Station is on west side of the city.

Chief town of Département Vienne, the old capital of Poitou, on a hill, at the confluence of the Rivers Clain and Boivre. It is a rather dull place, with cramped, winding, steep streets; there are many religious communities.

From the Station, cross the open space to the further of the two boulevards, the Boulevard Solferino. If this boulevard is followed in its bending it will lead in its continuations to the Church of Notre Dame la Grande, with a finely detailed west facade; paintings in interior. Almost opposite the Church is the Palais de Justice. Continuing along the street from Notre Dame for a quarter of a mile any of the turnings to right lead to the Cathedral of St. Pierre, part Romanesque part Gothic, begun by Henry II of England in 1162. 200 yards north east of the Cathedral is the very old Church of St. Radegonde, whose sarcophagus within is an object of pilgrimage.

Returning to the Cathedral, the Rue St. Paul, on west side, leads to the Palais de Justice, where, turning south, the street winds to the Hotel de Ville, where is a Musée containing a picture gallery and a natural history collection.

In the Place d'Armes, before the Hotel de Ville, is the Musée des Augustins, with an interesting miscellaneous antiquarian collection.

From south west side of the Place d'Armes the Rue Victor Hugo leads to the Prefecture, where, on north side, the Boulevard de la Prefecture runs into the Boulevard Solferino, close to the Railway Station.

The battle of Poitiers, 1356—called by the French the battle of Maupertuis—was probably on ground just south of Les Barres (Station, page 34), near the hamlet Moussais-la-Bataille.

RAIL, pages 34, 38, 41A, 42A.

Pornichet.—*Stat.*

HOTELS: DU CASINO; DES BAINS.

A much frequented seaside resort of Brittany. at the mouth of the River Loire, of quite modern creation; excellent firm sands. Church. Casino.

RAIL, page 39.

[Ste. Marguerite.

HOTEL DE LA PLAGE.

Two miles from Pornichet, towards St. Nazaire, in growing favour as a sea bathing resort; good sands. Pine woods; pleasant excursions in the neighbourhood.

GOLF.—9-hole course; tennis.

Omnibus from and to Pornichet Station.]

Reims (Rheims).—*Stat.*—Pop. 115,178.

HOTEL DU LION D'OR, facing the Cathedral; very good and comfortable hotel, frequented by English travellers. English and German spoken. Pfister and Co., proprietors. See Advt.

GRAND HOTEL.—Reconstructed and enlarged. First class in every respect, near Cathedral. Lift. Garage. See Advt.

COMMERCE; NORD.

The RAILWAY STATION is on the west side of the city. From the south east corner of the Square Colbert, in front of the Station, the Place Drouet d'Erlon leads to the cross street Rue de Vesle, where just to the left, behind the houses, is the Cathedral.

Reims is situated on the River Vesle, in a plain, with vine yards on the hills all round; it is the centre of the champagne trade, and has also an important industry in woollens and merino, much of which is in British hands. Historically it is a place of great interest; with, however, but few relics of the past remaining beside the Cathedral.

The magnificent Gothic CATHEDRAL of Notre Dame, where the Kings of France were crowned, begun 1212, the building continued into the 14th cent., has a beautiful west facade, with about 530 figures in the recessed portals; the towers rise to a height of 267 feet. Other statues at the north portal, and in niches in several parts of the exterior. The interior is 453 ft. long, nave 98 ft. wide, 125 ft. high. Paintings by Titian, Tintoretto, Poussin, and other masters; old tapestries; rich windows. In the Treasury are vessels, plate, vestments, and reliquaries. On south side of the Cathedral is the Archbishop's Palace, 15th-17th cent.

Church of St. Remi, in south part of city—follow streets going south east from Cathedral, about a mile—is a vast imposing edifice, of 11th-12th cent.; very fine stained windows; statues; tomb of St. Remi.

At the Hotel de Ville, quarter mile due east of the Railway Station, are collections of paintings, faience, Japanese curiosities, and antiquities; also objects pertaining to the champagne trade. Sun. and Thurs., 1.0 to 4.0. Library of 80,000 vols. and 1,500 MSS in the Hotel de Ville.

Porte de Mars, at the north end of the boulevard, close to the Station, a Roman monument of 4th cent., so restored that little of the old work is left.

H. B. M.'S VICE-CONSUL.—John W. Lewthwaite, Esq.

U.S. VICE-CONSUL.—W. Bardel, Esq.

BANK.—EXCHANGE. Société Generale (de Paris), 2, Place Royale (formerly 18, Rue Courmeaux), and 16, Rue Colbert. English spoken. Letters of Credit and Circular notes cashed. Credits opened, etc. Apply London, 65, Regent Street, W.

RAIL, pp. 67, 70, 74A.

Rennes.—*Stat.*—Pop. 79,372.

HOTELS: MODERNE; GRAND; DE FRANCE.

The old capital of Brittany, now of Département Ille-et-Vilaine, at the confluence of the Rivers Ille and Vilaine; once a busy place, now lifeless.

From the Railway Station the Avenue de la Gare leads north into the city. Near north end of the Avenue, to left, is the Lycée, the scene of the Dreyfus Court Martial, Aug. 1899. Just by the river is the Palais Universitaire, containing a Musée of very valuable paintings, also some sculpture, and natural history collections.

U.S. CONS. AG.—Ernest Folliard, Esq.

RAIL, pages 77B, 80, 82, 83.

Roubaix.—*Stat.* (pop. 122,723—HOTELS: FERRAILLE; DE FRANCE) and **Tourcoing**—*Stat.* (pop. 82,644—HOTEL DU CYGNE) are at the centre of one of the most industrial districts in France, with populous busy villages all round. Wool-combing, and the manufacture of wool goods, tissues, and yarns. At **Croix** (pop. 12,438) ENG. CHURCH SERVICE is held in the English Church. H.B.M.'S VICE-CONSUL, at Croix, A. Faulkner, Esq.

U.S. CONSUL.—J. E. Haven, Esq.

RAIL, pages 23, 29, 90.

Rouen.—*Stat.*—Pop. 124,987.

HOTEL DE LA POSTE.—Situated in the centre of the town, opposite the Post Office. All up-to-date comforts. Garden. See Advt.

GRAND HOTEL D'ANGLETERRE.—First class, on the Quay. Electric light, central heating, and lift. Baths. Moderate terms. See Advt.

GRAND HOTEL DE PARIS.—On the Quai de Paris, opposite the Steamer Landing Place. See Advt.

GRAND HOTEL DU NORD.—Centrally situated. Comfortable. Member of the T.C.F. and A.C.F. See Advt.

FRANCE.

The principal Railway Station, GARE DE L'OUEST (RIVE DROITE), is on the north side of the city, within half a mile of the centre; at this Station the trains between Dieppe and Paris, and Havre and Paris, run in. At the Gare du Nord, on east side of city, the train service connects with Amiens and the north. From the Gare d'Orleans, on south side, the trains leave for Chartres and Orleans. The State line has a second Station on the south side (Rive Gauche), of minor importance.

ROUEN, the ancient Rotomagus of the Romans, the mediæval capital of Normandy, and the chief town of the Département Seine-Inférieure, is situated on the River Seine in a pleasant country.

Notwithstanding many demolitions to clear space for modern handsome streets, the city is full of relics of antiquity at every turn; the line of the old walls is marked by a semi-circle of fine boulevards. It is an important centre of cotton manufacture, and goods styled "Rouennerie," and is sometimes mentioned as the Manchester of France.

Upon leaving the Gare de la Rive Droite, turn to left into the Rue Verte, this leads in a minute or so to the broad Boulevard Jeanne d'Arc, here, straight in front, is one end of the Rue Jeanne d'Arc, leading down to the river. Follow the Rue Jeanne d'Arc as far as the cross street, Rue de la Grosse Horloge; this, to left, leads to the Cathedral.

The CATHEDRAL, Notre Dame, is one of the most imposing Gothic edifices in Normandy. Its building ranged from 1270 until the 16th cent. The loftier of the two towers, Tour de Beurre (funds derived from indulgences to eat butter in Lent), is 252 ft. high; the other, Tour St. Romain, is 245 ft. high; the inartistic iron spire is 465 ft. high. Much sculpture at the portals. The interior is 447 ft. long, transept 177 ft. long, nave (with aisles) 105 ft. wide and 92 ft. high. Elaborate high altar; in the Lady Chapel are magnificent monuments and good altar piece. A mutilated effigy of Richard Cœur-de-Leon (died 1199) on south side of choir; his heart was buried below, his coffin is shewn in the Treasury, where are other relics. Archbishop's palace immediately east of Cathedral.

St. Maclou, a few yards north east of Cathedral, with wonderful carving on the front.

St. Ouen, quarter mile due north of east end of Cathedral; 14th cent., with modern additions. A beautiful Gothic church, larger than the Cathedral. Interior 453 ft. long, transept 138 ft. long, nave 84 ft. wide, height 106 ft. High altar; tombs.

St. Vincent, near south end, west side, of Rue Jeanne d'Arc; small Gothic church of 16th cent.; fine windows, wood carving in choir.

PALAIS DE JUSTICE, back from east side of Rue Jeanne d'Arc. Interior highly decorated.

MUSEE, on east side, near north end, of Rue Jeanne d'Arc, with the Jardin Solferino in front. Good collections of paintings (old masters and modern and sculpture. Daily, 10.0 to 4.0 or 5.0, free on Thurs. and Sun., other days 1 fr. Behind the Musée is the Bibliothèque, containing 132,000 vols,, 3,500 MSS, and great numbers of medals, coins, and portraits.

Hotel de Ville, by St. Ouen Church, at east end of Rue Thiers, a cross street of Rue Jeanne d'Arc. Formerly part of St. Ouen monastery.

Musée d'Antiques, north end of Rue de la République, half mile due north of Hotel de Ville. Natural History Museum close by.

In the Vieux Marché, in a line with the Palais de Justice, but off west side of Rue Jeanne d'Arc, Joan of Arc was burned, 1431. The spot is supposed to be a little to west of centre. Just away south of the Vieux Marché is the Hotel du Bourgthéroulde, 15th cent., adorned with reliefs.

POST OFFICE.—Rue Jeanne d'Arc, west side.

ENG. CH. SERVICE, at All Saints, Ile Lacroix.

H.B.M.'s CONSUL.—C. B. C. Clipperton, Esq.

U.S. CONSUL.—J. Potter, Esq.

BANK.—EXCHANGE. Société Generale (de Paris), 34 Rue Jeanne d'Arc. English spoken. Letters of Credit and Circular notes cashed. Credits opened, etc. Apply London, 65, Regent Street, W.

RAIL, pages 21, 74C, 76, 84.

Royat-les-Bains.—*Stat.*—Pop. 1,560.

GRAND HOTEL AND MAJESTIC PALACE.—Large beautiful, first-class hotel; situated near the Bath Establishment. Commands the finest and most extensive view of Royat. Lift. See Advt.

ROYAT PALACE HOTEL.—High class, facing the Park and Bathing Establishment; built in 1909; up-to-date. Garden. Pension from 12 frs. See Advt.

SPLENDID; METROPOLE.

A favourite tranquil health resort situated in a beautiful valley in the volcanic district of the Puy-de-Dome, 1,450 ft. above sea, with fine views over plain and mountain; air pure and dry, no dampness, cool in summer. The waters rise in four springs, differing in mineralisation and temperature, from 55° to 96°; all are used for drinking, three for bathing. The treatment is very beneficial in cases of gouty origin, dyspepsia, throat and kindred troubles, cardiac affections, also anæmia, spasmodic contractions, and obesity. The Thermal Establishment is well supplied with modern arrangements. Church of 10-11th cent. Casino and theatre; music daily in the park, where are some Roman remains. For the geologist or botanist the neighbourhood has much to interest. Tram to Clermont Ferrand.

MEDICAL.—Dr. Brandt; Dr. Petit.

ENGLISH CHURCH SERVICE in summer.

RAIL, pages 31A, 36.

St. Cyr-sur-Mer.—*Stat.*—

THE GRAND HOTEL.—Modern comforts. Electric light. Central heating. Finely situated in about 9 acres of garden and park; overlooking the sea. See Advt.

A pleasantly situated resort, between La Ciotat and Toulon, with a fine view over the hills and the sea; many olive plantations in the neighbourhood; numerous excursions.

RAIL, page 54.

St. Etienne.—*Stat.*—Pop. 148,656.

HOTELS: DE FRANCE; EUROPE.

Chief town of Département Loire. A modern well built manufacturing town, situated in the midst of the richest coalfield of south France, a smoke blackened district teeming with thriving industries. The only "sights," apart from the activity of the place, are the immense National Arms Factory (10,000 workmen), and the Palais des Arts, containing collections. School of Mines.

U.S. CONSUL.—W. H. Hunt, Esq.

RAIL, pages 52A, 56, 63B.

St. Gervais-les-Bains.—

GRAND HOTEL DU MONT JOLY.—First class establishment; every modern comfort. Electric light throughout. Large shady park. See Advt.

THE GRAND HOTEL.—Close to Mont Blanc Railway Station, in elevated position; central heating; lift; garage. See Advt.

A pleasant resort, whence Mont Joli, 8,288 ft., may be easily ascended. The sulphur springs (temp. 103°-108° Fahr.) are a mile from the village in a wooded ravine, the gorge of the Bon Nant, and are much frequented in the summer. Many fine excursions, especially that to Mont Blanc by a broad mule track which starts from St. Gervais and leads the tourist to the foot of the mountain. See also Fayet St. Gervais (Le).

Tramway from Le Fayet Station, page 61B.

MOTOR SERVICE, page 370.

St. Jean de Luz.—*Stat.*—Pop. 3,856.

GRAND HOTEL D'ANGLETERRE.—Well situated, with fine view of the sea and Pyrenees. Open all the year round. See Advt.

GOLF HOTEL.—In fine position, commanding extensive views. Modern comforts. Tennis. See Advt.

MODERN HOTEL.—Equipped with modern comfort. Overlooking the sea. Suites with bath and toilette. See Advt.

A bathing place (good sandy beach) and frontier town, with a genuine Basque character, on a bay at the mouth of the River Nivelle. A favourite English winter resort. Church of St. John, 13th cent.

ENGLISH CHURCH SERVICE.

GOLF.—La Nivelle Links (18 holes), close to the town. 9-hole course, 5 minutes from Station.

MEDICAL.—Dr. Blazy.

RAIL, page 45.

St. Jean-pied-de-Port.—*Stat.*—Pop. 1,600.

HOTEL CENTRAL.

A small picturesque old town on the Nive de Behobie, once the capital of Basse Navarre, fortified to command the passage of the Col or Port de Roncevaux. Interesting Basque houses. Citadel dominates upper town. RAIL, page 45.

[**Roncevaux** (Spanish Roncevalles), 14 miles from St. Jean, over the frontier, where Roland was slain at the defeat of part of Charlemagne's army 778. Old Abbey.]

St. Malo.—*Stat.*—Pop. 11,476.

GRAND HOTEL DE FRANCE ET CHATEAUBRIAND. —Comfortable family hotel; modern comfort. See Advt.

GRAND HOTEL FRANKLIN; CONTINENTAL; DE L'UNIVERS; DU CENTRE.

An old fortified seaport and bathing place in Brittany, very picturesquely situated on a peninsula, with St. Servan immediately south, and Dinard opposite, across the River Rance. The RAILWAY STATION is back on the east side, midway between St. Malo (north) and St. Servan (south), about half a mile from each.

The town is hemmed in on all sides, and the streets are narrow, winding, and steep; many quaint houses. Its ancient ramparts form a pleasant promenade. Church, 15th cent.; fine choir, some modern stained glass. Library, Museum, Casino. Statue of Jacques Cartier. The first Bishop, A.D. 543, St. Malo, or St. Maclou, is said to have been a Welshman.

H.B.M.'s V.-CONSUL.-Hon. E. Henniker-Major.

RAIL, page 82.

[**St. Servan.**—Pop. 12,240. HOTEL BELLEVUE; UNION; PELICAN. Reached from St. Malo by the Pont Roulant (moving bridge) at the mouth of the harbour, or by the road passing the Railway Station. Small bathing establishment and Casino. ENGLISH CHURCH SERVICE at Trinity Ch., Rue Chapitre. Chaplain, Rev. Stuart Hall.

Paramé.—Pop. 4,826.

GRAND HOTEL DE PARAME.—Beautiful first-class hotel, agreeably situated facing the sea. See Advt.

HOTELS: PLAGE; BRISTOL.

A bathing place, growing in favour, about 2 miles east of St. Malo. Fine sandy beach. Casino. Golf links.

ENGLISH CHURCH.—St. John Baptist.

Steam Tram every half hour to St. Malo.]

St. Martin Vésubie.—Pop. 1,953.

HOTEL REGINA; VICTORIA; LONDRES; GRAND.

At the junction of the Rivers Vésubie and Borréon, 3,110 ft. above sea, growing in favour as a bracing summer resort from Nice. Splendid mountain scenery, pine forests. Cold sulphur spring in the neighbourhood. Good centre for mountain excursions. ENG. CH. SERV.

RAIL, page 53C.

Ste. Maxime-Plan-de-la-Tour.—*Stat.*-Pop. 1,020. HOTEL ST. MAXIME.

A small port on the south inlet of the Golfe de Frejus, in growing favour as a Mediterranean winter resort. Pine forests and mountains (Chaine des Maures). RAIL, page 53C.

St. Maximin.—*Stat.*—Pop. 2,420.

HOTELS: DU VAR; DE FRANCE.

A little town specially notable for its 13th cent. Gothic Church, regarded as the finest in Provence; the interior even surpasses in interest the exterior; below the church is a crypt of earlier date. RAIL, page 53C.

[About ten miles south west of St. Maximin is the Ste. Baume, a grotto where—according to tradition—Mary Magdalen retired towards the close of her life; the grotto has been transformed into a chapel. Pilgrims are received at the Hotellerie de la Ste. Baume, kept by nuns.]

St. Quentin.—*Stat.*—Pop. 55,571.

HOTELS: DU CYGNE; FRANCE; COMMERCE.

An old town, centre of a district busy with cotton and woollen manufactories. From close to the Station a street leads north across the river to the Hotel de Ville, at the heart of the town; a little east of the Hotel de Ville is the Church of St. Quentin, a beautiful Gothic of 12th-15th cent. RAIL, pages 22A, 24, 29B, 30A.

St. Raphaël.—*Stat.*—Pop. 4,250.

HOTEL CONTINENTAL ET DES BAINS. — The most central first-class house. See Advt.

GRAND HOTEL BEAU RIVAGE.—Well situated on sea shore; full south, with fine view. Central heating; baths. Pension from 9 fr. per day. See Advt.

GRAND HOTEL ST. RAPHAEL. — First-class hotel, full south, near Anglican Church. See Ad.

A bathing place and winter resort on a small bay of the Mediterranean; pure, mild, and invigorating air. A new Boulevard connects

Boulouris and St. Raphaël with St. Aygulf, on the other side of the bay. Walks and drives to Frèjus (Roman remains), to the Esterel Hills, to Mt. Vinaigre (2,400 ft.), and among the pine woods. Charming views of the snowy summits of the Alpes Maritimes. Traces of a Roman aqueduct, and of a light tower on the Lion de Terre rock. About 1 m. distant is Parc Calvet (open to visitors), with red and blue porphyry rocks running far into the sea. Here Nap. I embarked for Elba, 1814.

ENG. CHURCH SERVICE.—St. John's Church.

GOLF LINKS, Tennis and Croquet Courts.

THE ENGLISH TEA ROOMS, L'ETOILE. Permanent Exhibition of Water Colours. Miss Cecilia Blackwood and Miss Margaret Neville.

HOUSE AND ESTATE AGENTS.—The Anglo-American Agency and Bank, W. King & Co., 6, Rue Charles-Gounod. See Advt.

DEPOT FOR BRADSHAW'S GUIDE.—W. King and Co., as above.

RAIL, pp. 53C, 54.

[Anthéor.—

A very picturesque peaceful spot, between sea and forest, about 6 miles east of St. Raphael. The Esterel Hills (red porphyry covered by woods) on either side are very attractive. Fine view from Cap Roux, 1,486 ft.

Reached from Agay Station, page 54.]

St. Tropez.—*Stat.*—Pop. 3,533.

HOTELS: CONTINENTAL; COMMERCE.

A pretty spot (Dept. Var), on a little bay of the Mediterranean. RAIL, p. 53C.

Salies-de-Béarn (Basses Pyrénées).—*Stat.*—Pop. 6,240.—HOTELS: DE FRANCE; DU PARC.

A summer and winter resort, pleasantly situated in a valley. The saline waters contain nearly six times as much salt as sea water. The climate is delightful, and the numerous springs have a beneficial effect on the atmosphere.

RAIL, p. 43.

Schlucht, Col de la—see page 489.

Sedan.—*Stat.*—Pop. 20,163.

HOTELS: DE L'EUROPE; DE LA CROIX D'OR; LION D'OR.

A once strongly fortified town, now chiefly known for the battle and capitulation of Sept. 1st and 2nd, 1870. A pleasant place, with prosperous cloth manufacture. Church in the Place d'Armes. Donjon, 15th cent., all that is left of old castle.

The battlefield is best visited from the village of Bazeilles, the scene of the earliest and fiercest fighting. Take train to Bazeilles and walk back. The result of the battle was the surrender of the French army of 88,000 men; the Germans lost 10,000 men, the French 11,000 men. At Bazeilles is a small inn, "A la Dernière Cartouche," the only house in the place not destroyed; here is a small museum of relics in a room.

RAIL, pages 69, 70, 72, 74B.

Soissons.—*Stat.*—Pop. 12,373.

HOTELS: LION ROUGE; SOLEIL.

An ancient fortified city, on the River Aisne; the Roman Suessiona, celebrated for the defeat here of the Romans by Clovis, 486. As the city is entered from the Station, to the left is the Abbey of St. Jean-des-Vignes, where Thomas à Beckett lived nine years; fine portal, with towers and spires.

The CATHEDRAL, Romanesque and Gothic, is of the 12th-13th cents.; interior contains paintings, tapestry, historical tombs.

The Abbaye Notre Dame (now a barrack), in Rue du Commerce, was once very important, sheltering in the 9th cent. more than 200 nuns. The Church was long a Pilgrim resort to the tomb of St. Drausin.

At the Hotel de Ville, at north east part of the city, are a library of 50,000 vols. and a small Musée. RAIL, pages 28, 29A, 74A.

Tarbes.—*Stat.*—Pop. 25,087.

HOTELS: DE LA PAIX; DARMAN.

Chief town of Département Haut Pyrénées, on the River Adour.

Railway Station on north side of town, three quarters of mile from centre. Cathedral, 12th-14th cent.; high altar, wood carving. In the Jardin Massey, a beautiful small park, is a Musée of paintings, sculpture, medals, etc., and a natural history collection. RAIL, pages 43, 45, 45A.

Toul.—*Stat.*—Pop. 12,200.

HOTELS: GRAND; DE METZ.

A very old town, on the Moselle, the Tullum Leucorum of the Romans, the seat of a bishop during 1,200 years. A fortress of the first class, captured by the Germans in 1870, after a thirty-eight day siege. St. Etienne Church, 13th-15th cents., has fine west front and magnificent cloisters; St. Gengoult Church, 13th-15th cents. has beautiful cloisters; old stained glass. Hotel de Ville, once the bishop's palace.

RAIL, pages 64, 74, 74A.

Toulon.—*Stat.*—Pop. 104,582.

GRAND HOTEL.—First class, well situated. Full south. Open all the year. Every modern comfort. See Advt.

VICTORIA; NORD; CONTINENTAL.

The most important naval station in France after Brest, a fortress of the first-class, well situated on a bay of the Mediterranean.

The RAILWAY STATION is on the north side of the town; the Arsenal and Docks are about half a mile south west of the Station. Ave. Vauban leads from opposite Station to the heart of town.

Church of Ste. Marie-Majeure, once the cathedral, just back from west side of Cours Lafayette, at the south east part of the town. Romanesque church of 11th-12th cent. Interior has reredos, figures of the Virgin, pulpit. Near the harbour end of Cours Lafayette is Church of St. Jean, with decorated interior.

Musée, in Boulevard Strasbourg, by south end of Avenue Vauban. Paintings and sculpture. Daily except Mon. and Sat., 2.0 to 5.0 (winter 4.0). In same building is the Bibliothèque of 32,000 vols., a manuscript Bible of 1442, and collection of coins.

The Arsenal is at the south west side of the town. It is not open to visitors.

POST OFFICE, in Rue Racine, off south side, near east end, of Boulevard Strasbourg.

H.B.M.'s VICE-CONSUL.—P. Wilkinson, Esq.

U.S. CONS. AGENT.

RAIL, pages 53C, 54.

[**Tamaris**, across the roadstead from Toulon; steamers almost hourly. A small winter place, deriving its name from the tamarisks by the shore.]

Toulouse.—*Stat.*—Pop. 149,576.

HOTELS: GRAND; TIVOLLIER.

The principal RAILWAY STATION, Gare Matabiau, is at the north east side of the city. A minor Station, Gare St. Cyprien, is for the line to Auch.

Toulouse, chief town of the Département Haute Garonne, the ancient Tolosa, afterward capital of Languedoc, seat of an Archbishop, is a busy wealthy place situated in a pleasant plain, on the River Garonne.

Either of the two bridges across the Canal du Midi on the west side of the Station lead, with the continuing streets, to the Boulevard de Strasbourg and the centre of the city.

Church of St. Sernin (Saturnin), at end of Rue St. Bernard, running off west side, north end, of Boulevard de Strasbourg; a very fine Romanesque church, dating from end of 11th cent., 330 ft. long, 104 ft. wide, transept 210 ft. long, nave 70 ft. high. Carved stalls, bas reliefs behind choir. The church is regarded as the special attraction of Toulouse.

Cathedral of St. Etienne, a little back from west side of Allée St. Etienne, which is part of the south continuation of the Boulevard de Strasbourg. Owing to different periods of erection the architecture is of no special style; objects of interest in the many chapels, handsome choir, stained glass.

Church of La Daurade, at the river end of the street running west from the Cathedral; original interior decorations very rich; paintings.

The Capitole (Hotel de Ville) stands back on west side of Rue Alsace Lorraine, 200 yards west of point where Allée Lafayette joins Boulevard de Strasbourg. Here is the Academie des Jeux Floraux, one of the oldest literary institutions of Europe, distributing flowers of gold and silver to poets annually on May 3rd.

Musée, south end of Rue Alsace Lorraine, 300 yards due west of Cathedral. Good collections of paintings and antiquities, also some sculpture. Sun. and Thurs., 12.0 to 4.0 or 5.0.

Musée St. Raymond, opposite St. Sernin Church industrial art and antiquities.

Lycée, in Rue Gambetta, 200 yards south west of the Capitole. Originally the dwelling of Bernuy, the Spanish merchant who guaranteed the ransom of Francis I (2,000,000 fr.), captured at battle of Pavia, 1525. Town library in this building, 70,000 vols.

H.B.M.'s VICE-CONSUL.—T. Huggins, Esq.

RAIL, pp. 32, 43, 45B, 46, 46A, 47.

Tours.—*Stat.*—Pop. 73,398.

HOTEL METROPOLE.—First class establishment in fine position, recently opened. Every modern comfort; excellent cooking. See Advt.

GRAND HOTEL DE L'UNIVERS.—First class. Entirely renovated; excellent cooking, cellar, most careful service. Patronised by English and Americans. Maurice Rollin, manager. See Advt.

GRAND HOTEL DU FAISAN.—Hotel of old repute, facing the Royal Bridge. French cooking and excellent wines. Central heating. Garage. See Advt.

GRAND HOTEL DE BORDEAUX.—Few minutes from the station, on the boulevards. High class family hotel; newly fitted. Central heating. Garage. See Advt.

The RAILWAY STATION is a little south east of the centre of the city.

Tours, the chief town of the Département d'Indre-et-Loire, the Roman Turones, and capital of Touraine, is situated in a pleasant fertile country, on the River Loire, with suburbs extending to the River Cher.

Across the front of the Railway Station runs the Boulevard Heurteloup, and thence the second street east on the north side, Rue Nicolas Simon, leads directly to the Cathedral.

The CATHEDRAL of St. Gatien is one of the best examples of the Gothic in France; begun in 1170, the building was protracted until about 1550. Richly ornamented facade, the towers are 226 ft: and 229 ft. high; in interior the choir should be examined, tombs, stained glass. Palace of the Archbishop a little way from south side of Cathedral. A few yards due north of the Cathedral, at the corner of the Caserne, by the river, is the Tour de Guise, 11th-12th cent., part of a royal palace.

The street, Rue la Scellerie, running west from the Place de la Cathedrale. leads past the fine Theatre Municipal, across the Rue Nationale, to the Tour Charlemagne (north side) and the Tour St. Martin (south side); these towers are remains of the once magnificent basilica church of St. Martin, pulled down in 1802, when the street was driven through; under the Tour Charlemagne lies buried Luitgard, third wife of the monarch—opposite this tower is the church of St. Martin.

Musée, in the Place de l'Hotel de Ville, at south end of the Pont de Tours, middle one of three bridges over the river. Paintings, sculpture, art objects, and antiquities also a natural history collection. Sun. and Thurs. Just south of the Musée is the old abbey church of St. Julien.

Palais de Justice, just west of the Railway Station, in the boulevard; Prefecture and gardens immediately in front of the Station.

RAIL, pages 34, 37, 38, 39, 40, 42A.

[**Chenonceaux**, 20 miles from Tours, has a famous Chateau, in its day a favourite residence of royalty, of Francis I, Marie de Medicis, also for a short time of Mary Queen of Scots and her husband Francis II (1559). RAIL, page 38.]

Trayas (Le).—*Stat.*

ESTEREL HOTEL.—Comfortable hotel, situated full south, with fine sea view. Garage; carriages. Restaurant. See Advt.

In a picturesque situation on the coast, about seven miles west of Cannes. The ascent of the Grand Pic du Cap Roux, whence is a fine view, is made from Le Trayas.

RAIL, page 54.

Tréport (Le).—*Stat.*—Pop. 4,750.

HOTELS: DE FRANCE; DES BAINS; DE LA PLAGE.

A popular bathing place, especially with Parisians, situated at the mouth of the Bresle, at the base of a high cliff; the beach is partly shingle and partly sand. Casino with many attractions.

Mers, a mile distant, is also a rapidly growing resort, near which is **Les Terrasses**, upon the cliff, and connected with the shore by funicular railway.

H.B.M'S VICE-CONSUL.—E. H. Barker, Esq.

RAIL, pages 20, 21, 30, 85.

Trouville-sur-Mer.—*Stat.*-Pop., with Deauville, 8,775.

HOTELS: ROCHES NOIRES; PARIS; PLAGE ANGLETERRE; BRAS D'OR.

A fashionable bathing place, in Dept. Calvados, in the Seine's mouth, on the small river Touques. Fine sandy beach without shingle, many pretty villas, and English scenery. Nôtre Dame-des-Victoires, on the hill; N. Dame-de-Bons-Secours, Rue des Bains. Hôtel de Ville; Casino.

BANK, EXCHANGE.—Société Generale (de Paris), Rue Victor Hugo. English spoken. Letters of Credit and Circular notes cashed. Credits opened, etc. Apply London, 65, Regentstreet, W.

HOUSE AGENCY AND DEPOT FOR BRADSHAW'S GUIDES—W. King and Co.

RAIL, p. 78. Steamer to Havre daily.

[**Deauville** (GRAND HOTEL; HOTEL DE LA TERRASSE) is opposite Trouville and cheaper but not so attractive. Casino.

GOLF.—18-hole course, adjoining the racecourse. Ladies' green, 9-holes.]

Troyes.—*Stat.*—Pop. 55,486.

HOTELS: DES COURRIERS; ST. LAURENT.

Chief town of Département de l'Aube, formerly the capital of Champagne, on the River Seine. An old place of greatly reduced commercial importance.

From the Railway Station, on the west side of the city, a little south on opposite side of Boulevard Carnot, two streets go eastward—Rue de la Monnaie and the prolongation (Rue Notre Dame) of Place de la Bonneterie—both leading beyond a canal to the Cathedral.

Church of St. Jean, just off north side of Rue Notre Dame; paintings. St. Urbain, quarter mile due east of St. Jean; considered a masterpiece of Gothic architecture. All the churches are worth inspection.

Cathedral of St. Pierre, 13th-16th cent., imposing though of differing styles; fine west fron tower 242 ft. Beautiful windows; paintings.

Musée, in Rue St. Loup, at north west angle of Cathedral. Paintings (old and modern), sculpture, archæological and natural history collections. Bibliothèque, by the Cathedral; 110,000 vols., 2,500 MSS.

U.S. CONS. AGENT. RAIL, 68, 73, 74, 74A.

Uriage.—*Stat.*—Pop. 2,100.

HOTELS: GRAND; GLOBE; MIDI; ALBERGES.

A prettily situated bathing place, 1,360 ft. above sea, about 8 miles from Grenoble, with tonic sodic and sulphurous waters, used in cases of skin disease and for the weakly. Good Bath Establishment. In the church are paintings by old masters. Old Chateau. RAIL, page 62A.

Valenciennes.—*Stat.*—Pop. 31,007.

HOTELS: DU COMMERCE; NORD.

From the Station, on the right the Rue Ferrand leads into the town. In the Place Carpeaux is the Church of St. Géry, 13th cent., wood carving in choir; thence the street leads to the Place d'Armes, where is the Hotel de Ville, containing a Musée of Painting and Sculpture.

Notre Dame du Saint Cordon, in Place Verte; richly decorated.

RAIL, pages 20, 22A, 28, 29, 29A.

Valescure.

GRAND HOTEL DE VALESCURE.—First class hotel, near golf links. Situated in the midst of forests of pine and oak; magnificent view from terrace. See Advt.

HOTEL DES ANGLAIS.—First class, full south; nearest to the golf links; large garden. Pension terms. See Advt.

A delightfully situated resort two miles distant from St. Raphael, in a beautiful part of the pine woods. ENGLISH CHURCH.

MEDICAL.—Dr. Vadon.

GOLF.—12-hole course.

HOUSE AND ESTATE AGENTS.—The Anglo-American Agency and Bank, W. King & Co. 6, Rue Charles Gounod. See Advt.

DEPOT FOR BRADSHAW'S GUIDE.—W. King and Co., as above.

RAIL (St. Raphael Station), pages 53C and 54.

Vernet les Bains. *Stat.* Villefranche Vernet les Bains.—Pop. 1,300.

GRAND THERMAL AND CLIMATIC ESTABLISHMENT, situated in the splendid Park of its own four Hotels. Two Hydropathic Establishments. See Advt.

Vernet, Le, or Vernet les Bains, an old typical little Pyreneean town, situated amidst fine scenery, at the foot of Mont Canigou (9,000 ft.). Altitude 2,000 feet above sea level. A climatic health resort protected from winds by the amphitheatre of mountains by which it is surrounded. Famous for its sulphurous-sodic waters, 45° to 149° Fahrenheit, specially useful in affections of the throat, delicate chest, nose, ears, rheumatism, gout, dyspepsia, sciatica, anæmia, nerves, and convalescence.

Casino, theatre. English club with English billiards. Shooting, trout fishing; extensive pine forests. Excursions in the mountains, the French and Spanish Cerdagne.

The ancient monastery of St. Martin du Canigou, a pilgrim resort, founded by Count Guifred (1007), is about 2 miles distant.

Motors and carriages from Villefranche Vernet les Bains Station, page 46, to Vernet les Bains, drive 15 minutes.

ENGLISH CHURCH.

[The electric railway from Villefranche to Bourg Madame, on the Spanish frontier, gives access to a splendid highland district.]

Versailles.—*Stat.*—Pop. 60,458.

TRIANON PALACE HOTEL.—Modern hotel with restaurant overlooking the Park. Electric light, lift, and central heating. Sports. See Advt.

Chief town of Département Seine et Oise, a suburb of Paris, visited for the Palace. The Palace and Gardens are of intense interest from their associations, but as "sights" they are to many disappointing. The fountains play on first Sunday in month, May to Oct. ENG. CHURCH.

BANK, EXCHANGE.—Société Generale (de Paris), Rue Carnot, No. 2. English spoken. Letters of Credit and Circular notes cashed. Credits opened, etc. Apply London, Société Generale (de Paris), 65, Regentstreet, W.

Tram from Quai side of Louvre. RAIL, page 84.

Vic-sur-Cère—*Stat.*—Pop. 1,745.

HOTELS: GRAND; TOURING.

Finely situated in most interesting country—the River Cère flowing through wooded gorges. Some ruins of ancient forts; several old castles in the neighbourhood. Close by are chalybeate and gaseous springs. RAIL, page 31A.

Vichy.—*Stat.*—Pop. 10,870.

GRAND HOTEL DU PARC.—Facing Springs, Casino, and Thermal Establishment. Lift; electric light. Connected with Majestic Palace; new; bath and toilet adjoining every room. See Advt.

HOTEL CARLTON.—First class hotel. Best situation on the Park. Equipped with every modern comfort. See Advt.

THERMAL PALACE.—First class; in fine situation. Electric light. See Advt.

ASTORIA PALACE HOTEL.—New first class hotel, replete with the latest comfort. Facing Park and Casino, and close to the Springs. See Advt.

INTERNATIONAL HOTEL.—Rue de Nimes, opposite Park and Casino. Built in 1903, with every comfort. Lift; electric light; steam heating. Garden. See Advt.

GRAND HOTEL DES AMBASSADEURS, first-rate hotel, well situated. See Advt.

GRANDS HOTELS DES PRINCES.—First class, on the Park, facing Casino and Thermal establishment. Lift; electric light. See Advt.

HOTEL DE LA GRANDE BRETAGNE AND QUEEN'S HOTEL.—Very convenient and fine situation, between the two parks. Garden. See Advt.

GRAND HOTEL DES BAINS.—First class hotel, situated in the Park, near Springs. Electric light and lift; garden. See Advt.

GRAND HOTEL EXCELSIOR DE LA PAIX.—First class, on the Park, facing Casino. Electric light. See Advt.

The Railway Station is on the east side of the town, near the modern quarters. The Rue de Paris runs west from the Station to the four road crossing, Quatre Chemins, whence the Rue Lucas, on west side, leads to the principal Bathing Establishment.

Vichy, the most frequented watering place in France, owes much of its modern renown to Napoleon III, who was a frequent visitor. It is pleasantly situated on the River Allier, and has a healthy climate. The waters (warm) are chiefly for drinking, but bathing is also extensively practised. Affections of the digestive organs, liver complaints, stomach disorders, and female illness, are successfully treated; it is estimated there are nearly 100,000 visitors annually. July and August are the most fashionable months.

The Thermal Establishment, owned by the State, leased by a company, is an extensive range of buildings on the south side, west end, of the Rue Lucas; it is open all the year, and the water may be drunk gratis. The baths are, 1st class, 2fr. 50c.; 2nd class, 1fr. 50c.; and 3rd class, 60c

The Parc, immediately south of the Thermal Establishment, is the favourite promenade from 8.30 to 9.30 in the morning and from 2.30 to 3.30 in the afternoon, as well as in the evening. The Casino is on the south side of the Parc; here may be found all the usual comforts and distractions, including a card room.

Church of St. Louis, east of the Casino; paintings in interior.

The Nouveau Parc, a fine promenade, is by the side of the river.

The southern quarter is old Vichy, with little to interest. Here are the Sources Celestins—used in cases of gout, etc.—and one or two bath establishments.

POST OFFICE.—On west side of Place de l'Hotel de Ville, just west of Casino.

ENGLISH CHURCH SERVICE at St. Mark's Church, Rue du Peintre Lebrun.

GOLF LINKS.—Club House. J. Aletti, Manager. See Advt.

MEDICAL.—Ch. Cormack, M.D., in summer. Dr. Charles Cotar, 34, Rue de l' Etablissement Thermal; speaks English (in winter at Mentone).

BANKING AND STOCK EXCHANGE OPERATIONS.—Société Generale (de Paris), Place Victor Hugo. English Interpreter. Letters of Credit and Circular notes cashed. Credits opened, etc. Apply London, 65, Regent Street, W.

RAIL, pages 58, 62A.

[**Cusset**—HOTEL DU GLOBE—an old place of 6,454 inhabitants, about two miles east of Vichy, has a Bath Establishment with two cold springs.]

Vitré.—*Stat.*—Pop. 10,584.

HOTELS: DE FRANCE; DES VOYAGEURS.

An old world interesting town, with a ruined castle and many quaint houses, on the River Vilaine. The Castle dates from the 14th-15th cent.; part is a prison, in another part are the Musée and Bibliothèque. Notre Dame Church, on higher ground, has a fine Triptych in a Chapel.

RAIL, pages 77B, 80.

Vittel (Vosges).—Pop. 3,000.

PALACE HOTEL.—Splendidly situated; covered way to springs and baths. Electric light, lift, suites. See Advt.

HOTEL DE L'ETABLISSEMENT. — Comfortable first class hotel, choice table. Electric light, lift. See Advt. Also HOTEL DU PARC; CENTRAL; CONTINENTAL; and several others.

VITTEL, 1,100 ft. above sea; bracing climate, 5½ hours from Paris by corridor restaurant train, or by Calais-Rheims. Beautiful park and fine covered promenade, wooded walks; races, pigeon shooting, tennis, English croquet and bowling green. Casino with first class theatre and other attractions. Season 25th May to 25th September.

The two principal springs of alkaline carbonated and sulphated waters have now attained great renown; over ten million bottles are exported yearly.

Grande Source.-Uric acid in all its associations—gout, gouty state, gravel, neurasthenia, neuritis, neuralgias, sciatica, hysteria, kidney, and bladder diseases, albuminuria. Much used as a pleasant still table water by the gouty.

Source Salée.—Abdominal congestion of the stomach, intestinal or liver origin, whether from sedentary habits, alcohol, tropical, or other cause. Much used for gall stones and bronchial catarrh, asthma of gouty origin.

ENGLISH CHURCH.

GOLF.—9-hole course, half-mile from Station.

ENGLISH PHYSICIAN.—Dr. Johnston-Lavis.

RAIL, page 68A.

Wimereux.—*Stat.*—Pop. 1,200.

SPLENDIDE HOTEL.—First class hotel adjoining the casino. Every modern comfort. Electric light; lift. Open from June 1st. See Advt.

Wimereux, a popular watering place, 2½ miles north of Boulogne-sur-Mer, where are many chalets and several hotels. Casino and Assembly rooms. Golf links and tennis courts.

ENGLISH CHURCH SERVICE during summer.

RAIL, page 13. Electric tram to Boulogne.

BELGIUM (La Belgique).

Within narrow limits, easily travelled, Belgium offers great attractions of noble mediæval architecture, a wealth of the painter's art, and a wonderful modern industrial development. The numerous towns in many instances retain their mediæval character, the Hotels de Ville (Town Halls) and other secular buildings are the finest of their kind in Europe, and many of the Great CATHEDRALS are richly endowed with paintings and works of art; at Antwerp and Brussels the PICTURE GALLERIES are vast collections of works by old and modern masters, of surpassing interest.

Government.—Albert I, reigning king, born 1875, succeeded December 17th, 1909.

Army.—Peace Establishment, 46,574 regulars, and about 46,563 of the Garde civique; in war a total of 180,000 men. Belgium has no Navy.

Revenue (1913), £30,306,185; Expenditure £30,221,604.

Money.—100 centimes = 1 franc = 9½d. (exactly 9 3-5th d). GOLD COINS.—Pieces of 20 and 10 francs. SILVER COINS.—Pieces of 5, 2, 1, franc, and 50 centimes. BRONZE COINS.—Pieces of 1 and 2 centimes. NICKEL COINS.—Pieces of 10 and 5 centimes.

Weights and Measures.—The weights and measures of Belgium are those of the metric system. See page lxxi, also page 383.

Population (1910).—7,423,784.

Railways.—2,915 miles open, mostly belonging to the State. West Europe (Greenwich) time is kept on all lines. In Belgium railway time is reckoned from midnight to midnight, that is to 24.0 o'clock. **Luggage.**—No free luggage is allowed except hand luggage to the amount of 55 lbs.; Luggage rate, 6 centimes per 100 lbs. per kilometre. SEASON TICKETS available for 5 days over the Belgian Railway Lines are also issued at the following fares: 1st Class, £1 8s.; 2nd class, 18s. 5d.; 3rd class, 10s. 5d. Season Tickets available for 15 days at double the aforementioned rates. The tickets may be had at the Belgian Mail Packet Office, 53, Gracechurch Street, London, E.C., and 72, Regent Street, London, W., and in Dover, also at all the principal tourist agencies; photo. of applicant required.

Telegraph.—About 4,774 miles open. Tariff, 50c. (5d.) for 15 words, and an additional 10 centimes for each series of 5 words above the first 15, to any station in Belgium; to U. Kingdom 17c. a word, with charge of 50c. for the telegram. POSTAGE.—10c. per Inland letter, under ½ oz.; to Holland and Luxemburg, 20c.; and 25c. to England and other countries in the Postal Union. Cards 5c. and 10c. (foreign). Newspapers 2c. and 5c. (foreign).

NOTICES OF TOWNS, etc.

ANTWERP (in French, **Anvers**).—*Stat.*—Pop. (1911), 308,618, almost entirely Flemish. (*Plan in Special Ed., or post free 3d. stamps*).

HOTEL ST. ANTOINE.—First class hotel, situated in centre of town. Entirely renovated. Private bathrooms; lift. Every modern comfort. Cable Antonio. See Advt.

GRAND HOTEL.—First-class family hotel, with English clientèle, in centre of town. Private suites, with bathrooms. Lift, central heating, and all modern comforts. Garden. See Advt.

GRAND HOTEL WEBER.—First-class house, well and centrally situated, Avenue de Keyser; with electric light, lift, baths, and every modern comfort. See Advt.

HOTEL DE L'EUROPE, on the Place Verte, close to the Cathedral; good in every respect and charges reasonable. See Advt.

TERMINUS HOTEL.—Just opposite entrance and exit of Central Station. Electric light, lift, and steam heating. See Advt.

QUEEN'S HOTEL.—Comfortable hotel, centrally situated. Rooms, including light and attendance, from 4 frs. See Advt.

STEAMER and RAILWAY.—The steamers from Harwich arrive at and depart from the Quai d'Herbouville, at the far side of the city, up the river. Electric tramcars run from the Quai d'Herbouville to the Cathedral, near the principal hotels, and to the Gare Centrale every few minutes. As the steamer passes the quays the Cathedral is readily seen over the houses; a line drawn straight from the nearest quay to the Cathedral, if prolonged for about a mile, would go direct to the Railway Station. A train connecting with the Harwich steamer starts from the Sud Quai, close to the landing place, only taking forward travellers to places on Brussels line and beyond; similarly a train from Brussels runs down to the Sud Quai to connect with the outward steamer.

From the GARE CENTRALE trains depart for Malines, Brussels, Aix-la-Chapelle, and almost all places inland. From the SUD STATION trains depart for Malines and Brussels, and for one or two local lines. A third Station, STATION DE WAES, on opposite side of river, is for the direct line to Ghent—ferry steamers from the Quai.

CABS.—Taximètre Motor Cabs, for 1 or 2 persons, 600 mètres, about one third mile, 80c., each additional 300 metres 10c.; luggage carried outside, 25c. for 25 kilogrammes, about 55lbs. Taximètre horse cabs, for 1 or 2 persons, 800 mètres, nearly half mile, 60c., each additional 400 mètres 10c.

Tramways serve all parts of the town, and connect with the suburbs.

ANTWERP, on the River Scheldt, 55 miles from the sea, is one of the greatest ports of the Continent, much of the trade of south western Germany here finding its outlet, in addition to the trade of Belgium. The imports are chiefly raw produce—wheat, coffee, wool, hides, tobacco, timber, and petroleum. The quays and docks are of vast extent. The industries include sugar refining, brewing, tobacco manufacture, lace making, and diamond cutting. It is strongly defended by a chain of forts, and defending floods could be let in over part of the environs. Apart from its commercial importance Antwerp is especially interesting from historic and art associations—it is the heart of what may be called the country of Rubens, and within some of the mediæval houses yet standing lived and worked such men as Teniers, van Dyck, the Neefs, Jordaens, Quinten Massys, Plantin, the celebrated printer, the ecclesiastics, burgomasters, patricians, and patriotic citizens, who yet live pictorially in the Churches and Museé.

The CATHEDRAL of Notre Dame will be easily found, as the embroidered spire is high above all other buildings. It is considered the most beautiful as well as the largest of the Gothic churches of the Netherlands. It had a line of architects—Jean Amel, sometimes called Appelmans, began the work in 1352; to him succeeded his son Peter, in 1398; later, in 1434, came Jean Tac; then Everaert, in 1449; after 1500 for nearly twenty years were Herman van Waghemakere and his son Dominic, the building operations not ceasing until 1616, parts being then left, as now, unfinished. Fire in 1533, religious fanaticism in 1566, and French vandalism in 1794, in turn did much damage; the west facade was restored 1901-3. Its shape is that of a cross, its length is 384 feet, the nave is 171 feet wide and 131 feet high, the transept 213 feet wide; there are 125 pillars; the spire is 404 feet high. Relatively, it occupies about five sixths of the area covered by St. Paul's Cathedral, London. The interior is very imposing, on a fine day being beautifully clear and bright. There is fine stained glass, many elaborately decorated chapels, sumptuous altars, tombs, and much carving. It is only possible to mention a few of the numerous wonderful paintings. The High Altar piece is an Assumption, by Rubens; in the south aisle are fourteen scenes of the Passion by Vinck and Hendricks (modern), In the north transept is the Elevation of the Cross, in the south transept the Descent from the Cross, both by Rubens. In the Lady Chapel in north aisle is a head of Christ on white marble to right of altar. Cathedral generally open all day, but, when pictures are uncovered for view (12.0 to 4.0 or 5.0), entrance 1 fr.; on Sunday and Thursday, except during Lent, between 8.0 and 12.0 the view of the pictures is free. The Chimes are struck by 40 bells, the largest, cast in 1507, weighing 8 tons. Opposite west door of Cathedral, in the Marché-aux-Gants, is a Well having an iron headpiece stated to be the work of Quinten Massys (or, Matsys). At No. 11, on north west side, a tablet marks the house where David Teniers, the painter, was born.

CHURCH OF ST. JACQUES, Gothic, in Longue Rue Neuve, five minutes east of Cathedral. Dating from 1491, it was not completed until 1656. It is the most sumptuous of the Churches of Antwerp, containing elaborate memorials of distinguished Antwerp families. Rubens was buried here June 1st, 1640. From the magnificence may be selected: The Last Judgment, by B. van Orley, in third chapel of north aisle; St. Peter called to be an Apostle, by A. van Noort, in first chapel of Ambulatory, behind the choir; the Altar-piece, or St. George, by Rubens, in the fourth chapel of the Ambulatory, the Rubens chapel. The St. George is made up of portraits. St. George is Rubens; his two wives, Isabel Brandt and Helène Fourment, are there; his daughter; his father is St. Jerome, his grandfather is Time; his youngest son an angel. Pulpit, in the nave, by Willemssens. Church is usually open, but the special pictures are shewn on week days from 12.0 to 4.30, fee 1 fr.

Church of St. Paul, Gothic, a few minutes north of Cathedral, a little back from the river. Begun 1533, completed 1621. Paintings and carving. Scourging of Christ, and Adoration of the Magi, by Rubens; Bearing of the Cross, by van Dyck. When church is not open in usual way, a fee of 1 fr. In inner court is a "Mount Calvary," an arrangement of rock and statues on a mound, below is a grotto representing the Holy Sepulchre.

Church of St. Augustine, five minutes south of the Cathedral, just off Rue des Peignes. Altar-piece by Rubens, much dilapidated; Vision of St. Augustine, by van Dyck.

Church of St. André, five minutes south of Cathedral, in Rue St. André, off west side of Rue Nationale. Many paintings, several modern. Carved pulpit, by van Geel and van Hool, representing the Calling of St. Andrew and St. Peter. On a pillar in south transept is medallion portrait of Mary, Queen of Scots, two of whose maids of honour are buried here. When not open in usual way, 50 centimes.

Church of St. Antoine, ten minutes north of Cathedral, a little off west side of Avenue du Commerce. St. Antony receiving infant Jesus, by Rubens; Christ mourned by angels and disciples, by van Dyck.

Church of St. Charles (Jesuit Church), two minutes north east of Cathedral, in Rempart Ste. Cathérine. Paintings and statues.

Church of St. George, in Rue de Malines, a mile south east of Cathedral. Two spires. Modern paintings by Guffens and Swerts.

MUSEE DES BEAUX ARTS, three quarters of a mile south of Cathedral, same distance back from river as Cathedral. An imposing square building in Greek Renaissance style, erected 1879-90, by J. J. Winders and Fr. van Dyck. Here is the PICTURE GALLERY, with a collection of SCULPTURE. In the lower part of the building, in the left wing, are the Sculptures; in the right wing is what is known as the Rubens Collection, a gathering of engravings, photographs, etc., of most of Rubens works. The entrance hall and stairway are embellished with fine paintings, in one series "Antwerpia," on a throne, has round about her most of the great masters of Art of Antwerp—painters, sculptors, architects. The PICTURE GALLERY is on the upper floor, a collection of works by Old and Modern Masters of vast extent and magnificence The names of the artists are attached to the pictures, and catalogues for free consultation are sometimes to be found in the rooms. Open daily, 10.0 to 5; on Sunday and Thursday free, other days 1 fr.

MUSÉE PLANTIN-MORETUS, in Marché du Vendredi, a little south of the Cathedral, nearer to the river. Of surpassing interest to everyone concerned with Printing. The house is the old home and printing office of Christopher Plantin, a celebrated printer who lived 1514-89. In the Printing Office everything has been arranged, as far as possible, as though work has just been finished for the day. Open daily, 10.0 to 4.0 or 5.0; Sunday and Thursday, free, other days 1 franc.

HOTEL DE VILLE, in Grand' Place, just off north west corner of Cathedral. Erected 1561-65. The staircase and spacious chambers are lavishly decorated; many fine paintings, much carving, chimney-pieces, etc., open daily, 50 c. The houses in the Grand' Place are mostly Guild Houses, or Company Halls—as Coopers' Hall, Carpenters' Hall, Merchant Tailors' Hall. Van Dyck was born (1599) in the house No. 4.

BOURSE (Exchange), a little east of Cathedral, between Place de Meir and Longue Rue Neuve. Close by, in Place de Meir, on south side, by Rue de la Bascule, is the Palais du Roi; almost next to the King's Palace, a little further east, is the House of Ruben's Parents (bust of Rubens at top); only a fragment left, portico with sculptures—in a garden of No. 7, Rue Rubens, an intervening street—of house built by Rubens for himself in 1611, and where he died, 1640.

Among many statues are: Statue of Rubens, in Place Verte, by Cathedral; of Quinten Massys, in the Parc; of Hendrik Leys, in Avenue Louise Marie; of Jordaens, in Avenue Rubens; of Teniers, in Place Teniers. Monument of French Fury, in front of Flemish Theatre; Monument commemorative of Abolition of Tolls on the Scheldt, in Place Marnix.

Small Parc at about centre of city. Zoological Garden, close to Gare Centrale.

There is generally MUSIC daily during summer in the evening in the Parc, Pepinière, Place Verte, or Place St. Jean; also in the Zoological Gardens or at the Harmonie.

POST OFFICE, in Place Verte, south side of Cathedral. TELEGRAPH OFFICE, Rue des Douze Mois, on north side (west end) of Place de Meir, and at Railway Station.

ENG. CH. SERV. at St. Boniface Church, Rue Gretry.

H. B. M.'s CONSUL-GEN.—Sir E. C. Hertslet; VICE-CONSULS.—W. Lydcotte, Esq., R. H. Cox, Esq., and M. N. Kearney, Esq.

U. S. CONSUL GENERAL.—H. W. Diederich, Esq.
VICE-CONSUL —H. T. Sherman, Esq.

GOLF.—18-hole course, 15 mins. drive from centre of town; club house.

RAIL, see pp. 90, 95, 96, 99, 100, 101, 102B, 110.

STEAMER to Harwich, Hull, Grimsby, etc., see Steamer List.

Arlon.—*Stat.*—Pop. 11,300.

HOTELS: BARNESCH; DU NORD.

Capital of Belgian Luxemburg, 1,330 ft. above sea. Museum of Roman antiquities. Three miles east is the ruined Abbey of Clairfontaine.

RAIL, see page 103A.

Audenarde.—*Stat.*—Pop. 6,572.

HOTELS: SAUMON; POMME D'OR.

A picturesque place in West Flanders, with a very fine though small Gothic Town Hall of the 16th century. Churches of St. Walburga and Notre Dame de Pamele, both interesting. In 1708 the allied armies commanded by the Duke of Marlborough and Prince Eugene gained a victory here over the French.

RAIL, pp. 100, 102B.

Blankenberghe.—*Stat.*—Pop. 6,100.

CONTINENTAL AND PALACE HOTEL.—First class hotel, situated facing the sea. Lift; electric light throughout. See Advt.

A favourite bathing place, about 9¼ miles from Bruges; nearly 50,000 visitors annually. Fine beach, and Digue lined with hotels and villas. Casino; theatre; various fêtes in the bathing season. Lighthouse and small harbour.

ENG. CH. SERVICE during season.

TRAMWAY between Blankenberghe and Ostend.

RAIL, page 111.

Bruges.—*Stat.*—Pop. (1911) 53,484.

GRAND HOTEL AND GRAND HOTEL DU COMMERCE, a first-rate, old-established house, enjoying an excellent reputation. See Advt.

HOTEL DE FLANDRE.—Old-established, noted for fine wines and good dinners, which are also served in the splendid garden of the hotel. Pension from 5s. October to March. See Advt.

The principal Railway Station is on the west side of the city, about a quarter mile from the Grande Place.

Bruges was in the 15th century the commercial centre of Europe, where scholars and great painters, learning and art, were liberally encouraged; the population was 200,000, and the sumptuous apparel of the inhabitants—the wool trade was immense—was noticeable. Of all this prosperity little is left. The city is the most picturesque of the kingdom, every church is worth visiting, and quaint buildings are everywhere.

From the Station, a little to south, the Rue Sud du Sablon leads in 150 yards to the Cathedral.

CATHEDRAL of St. Sauveur, Gothic, brick, of 13th-14th cent., with many later additions. The interior is more attractive than the exterior; length 110 yards, breadth 41 yards, transepts 58 yards long, height 30 yards. Polychromatic decorations, rich wood carving, many fine paintings, monuments, brasses.

On south east side of Cathedral the Rue St. Esprit leads (100 yards) to the Church of Notre Dame, Gothic, of 13th-15th cent.; tower 395 ft. high. Interior 80 yards long, 55 yards broad, 70 ft. high. Many very fine paintings; by the altar at end of south aisle is an exquisite Statue of the Virgin and Child, ascribed to Michael Angelo; in a chapel in the ambulatory are the elaborate tombs of Charles the Bold (died 1477) and his daughter Mary (died 1482). To see pictures and tombs, 1fr., or 50c. each for a party.

Gruuthuus, on east side of Notre Dame, contains collections of antiquities. Daily, aft., 50c.

Hôpital St. Jean, opposite west side of Notre Dame; paintings by Memling, some of his best work. Daily 9.0 to 6.0 (earlier in winter), 1fr.

Musée, in Rue Ste. Catherine, going south across bridge from Notre Dame. Pictures by old masters. Sun. 11.0 to 1.0 free; other days 50c.

The Grande Place is at the end of Rue des Pierres, running north east from the Cathedral. On the south side of the Place, in the centre of the facade of the Halles, is the Belfry of Bruges, 1282-1400, 352 ft. high. with slight inclination to south east. Government buildings on east side of the Place.

Rue St. Jacques, north west corner of Grande Place, leads to Church of St. Jacques; many good paintings.

Jesuit Church, modern, in Rue Flamande, running out of north east corner of Grande Place.

Hotel de Ville, south side of Place du Bourg, 100 yards south east of Grande Place; Gothic, 14th cent. Paintings in principal hall represent scenes in Bruges history.

Chapelle du Saint Sang, on west side of Hotel de Ville. A Gothic gem, containing several good pictures—a "Descent from the Cross," by Gerard David. The Saint Sang (Holy Blood) may be seen on Friday morn. Fri. and Sun. morn free, other times 50c.

Palais de Justice, on east side of Hotel de Ville. Magnificent chimney-piece in Court Room; portraits, tapestry.

On the north side of the Place du Bourg is an open space planted with sycamore and chestnut trees, here stood the Church of St. Donatian; it is stated that the rather poor statue of Van Eyck is on the spot where was the Lady Altar of the Church; one of two rooms over the porch of this church was rented as a printing place by Colard Mansion, who here, in 1475, for William Caxton, printed the first English book. Of the Church of St. Donatian, Jean de Gerson (by some identified with Thomas à Kempis) was dean 1394-1411.

Bibliothèque, in Place Jean van Eyck, 250 yards up street running north from Palais de Justice, 50,000 vols., many old MSS. and early printed books. Daily except Sat. and Sun.

ENGLISH CHURCH.—Rue des Baudets.

H.B.M.'s V.-CONSUL.-Lieut.-Col. H. E. Boileau.

EDUCATION. — PEMBROKE BOYS' SCHOOL. — Headmaster, C. E. Laurence, M.A. Thorough English Education, also conversational French and German.

OUR DAUGHTERS ABROAD.—The Establishment of Madame B. de L., 19, Quai St. Anne, offers a refined home with superior educational advantages. Established 1887. French, German, and English spoken.

For further details respecting the foregoing Schools see the School Directory in Bradshaw's British Guide, page ii.

RAIL, pages 90, 93, 102, 111.

BRUSSELS (French, **Bruxelles.**) — *Stat.*— Pop. (1911) 646,400, including the surrounding Communes.—(*Plan in Special Edition or, post free, 3d. stamps*).

HOTEL METROPOLE.— Well situated in the centre of the town, facing the beautiful Place de Brouckère. Lift. Electric Light. See Advt.

PALACE HOTEL.—First class, opposite Northern Station and fronting Botanical Garden. Lift; electric light. See Advt.

HOTEL DE BELLE VUE ET DE FLANDRE.— Beautifully situated in the Place Royale, with electric light, lift, and central heating. Kept by Mr. Dremel, of Dresden. See Advt.

HOTEL ASTORIA (formerly Mengelle).—Family hotel. Latest creation of Brussels. See Advt.

GRAND HOTEL.—Situated in the finest part of the Boulevard Anspach, near the Post and Telegraph Offices. Lift; electric light. See Advt.

GRAND HOTEL BRITANNIQUE, well situated, Place du Trône, No. 3, near the King's Palace, and the Boulevards. E. Blondiau, proprietor. See Advt.

THE CARLTON HOTEL.—103, Avenue Louise, in the healthiest and most fashionable part of the town. Lift. Electric light. Central heating. See Advt.

WILTCHER'S HOTEL.-Removed to larger modern premises, 65-73, Avenue Louise, in the most beautiful part of the city. Electric light. Lift. Central heating. Terms from 9 frs. See Advt.

HOTEL EUROPE, in a fine open and healthy situation on the Place Royale. See Advt.

HOTEL DE FRANCE, Rue Royale, corner of the Montagne du Parc. Well known, first-class, superintended by the proprietor himself. See Adv.

HOTEL DE LA POSTE, 30 and 32, Rue Fosse aux Loups, near the Place de la Monnaie. See Advt.

PRINCE OF WALES HOTEL, 76, Rue Royale, opposite Park, not far from principal curiosities of town. See Advt.

The two principal Railway Stations are the GARE DU NORD, where trains from and to Ostend, Antwerp, Holland, and Germany, arrive and depart, and the GARE DU MIDI, where trains from and to Calais and France arrive and depart; a broad thoroughfare—at its north end called Boulevard du Nord, then Boulevard Anspach, and at its south end Boulevard du Hainaut—runs across the town from one Station to the other. The Station du Quartier Leopold, an important secondary Station, is in the east part of the city.

CABS.—Cab charges are arranged in two zones, the first zone including all the central part of Brussels. Within this zone the charges are: Taximètre Motor Cabs, 780 mètres (nearly half a mile) or 6 minutes waiting 80c., each additional 250 mètres or 2 minutes waiting 10c. Ordinary horse cab charges are the same. The charges for drives extending to the second zone are nearly a quarter higher. Each article of luggage carried outside 15c. to 25c.

TRAMWAYS run in all directions. Fares 10c.— 15c., with 5c. extra for the 1st class part of the car.

CAFÉS.—The best are in the Boulevard Anspach and in the Place de la Monnaie, off the east side north end, of Boulevard Anspach; other good cafés close by the Gare du Nord and the Gare du Midi.

BRASSERIES (Beer Saloons).—These abound, especially in the neighbourhood of the Boulevard Anspach. Some very extensive. Most of the Beer Saloons are quiet orderly places, but are hardly suitable for ladies.

The BEST SHOPS are in the Boulevard Anspach, or in the Rue de la Madeleine and Montagne de la Cour, a steep thoroughfare running from near the north side of the Hotel de Ville up to the Place Royale, and in the Rue Royale.

BRUSSELS, the capital of Belgium, on the River Senne, is situated near the centre of the Kingdom. Only here and there does the river, or one of its branches, come into view, the city being built over most of its course. The city consists of a lower and upper part; the former the old city, the latter, on high ground to the east, being modern. Consequent upon improvements very little of historic Brussels remains, nor are the local industries of great importance, the manufactures being of a restricted and light character, such as lace, leather goods, furniture, and carriages. But the city has long been

regarded as a place of pleasant residence, with a reputation as an art and educational centre. It is estimated that there are 2,000 British permanent residents, mostly in the Quartier Leopold, the healthiest quarter, on the east. The French language is spoken and understood practically all over Brussels, but in the lower town and in the suburbs Flemish maintains itself.

CHURCHES.

The CATHEDRAL, dedicated to Ste. Gudule and St. Michel. Near the centre of the city, a little north east of the Hotel de Ville; seen immediately, down below, from the Rue Royale. A Gothic edifice, dating from about 1220; an earlier church on the same site consecrated 1047. Interior plain. Stained glass very fine, especially in the Chapel of the Sacrament. Carved pulpit (brought from Church of the Jesuits at Louvain), by Verbruggen, representing the expulsion of Adam and Eve from Eden. Several monuments. Open daily (apart from hours of service) from 12.0 to 4.0. To see the objects of art, 1 fr., for a party 50 c. each.

ST. JACQUES SUR CAUDENBERG, in Place Royale, by the Palais du Roi. Built 1776-1785, on site of ancient Augustine abbey. Statue of Godefrey de Bouillon in front of church, on spot where (1097) he called upon the Flemings to join the Crusade.

NOTRE DAME DES VICTOIRES, on west side of Rue de la Regence, a little south from Place Royale. Dates from 1304, but was rebuilt in 16th cent. Monuments, reliefs, and paintings; carved pulpit.

NOTRE DAME DE LA CHAPELLE, west of Place Royale, and south of Hotel de Ville, Gothic, dating from 1216. Frescoes and paintings. High altar after designs by Rubens. Carved pulpit-Elijah in the Wilderness.

STE. CATHARINE, a little off west side, north end, of Boulevard Anspach, between the Halles Centrales and Halles aux Poissons. Designed by Poelaert, the architect of the Palais de Justice. Among the paintings is an Assumption attributed to Rubens.

STE. MARIE DE SCHAERBEEK, at north end of Rue Royale.

PUBLIC BUILDINGS.

HOTEL DE VILLE, in the GRANDE PLACE, at about the centre of the lower town. Though surrounded by narrow winding streets, the Hotel de Ville is easily found because of its lofty spire, seen over roofs and street openings from a long distance. The streets on east side of Boulevard Anspach, just south of the Bourse, lead to the Grand Place. The descending street westward from Place Royale, the Rue Montagne de la Cour, with continuations, eads eventually to near the Grande Place. The GRANDE PLACE is the great historic spot of Brussels, often described as the finest mediæval square in existence. Here, almost every prominent incident in the history of Brussels had its origin or came to its climax; perhaps the most vivid memory is that of the execution on a scaffold in the open space of twenty-five Flemish noblemen in the spring of 1568, followed in June by the execution of Count Egmont and Count Hoorn. Immediately opposite the Hotel de Ville is the modern Maison du Roi, rebuilt 1873-96 according to the original plans of the 15th-16th cents. In the old building Count Egmont and Count Hoorn were confined during the night before their decapitation (June, 1568), passing directly from the balcony to the scaffold. The Musée Communal is on the second floor of the Maison du Roi, containing a variety of objects illustrative of Brussels history—models, sculptures, banners, metal work, coins, paintings, prints, etc. Open daily 10.0 to 4.0, Tuesday 10.0 to 2.0. The GUILD HOUSES, or Halls of the Companies, much shattered during the bombardment in 1695, by Louis XIV of France, and re-built shortly after, were carefully restored 1889-1902. On the south side of the Place is Butchers' Hall, marked by a swan, and Brewers' Hall, marked by an equestrian statue of Duke Charles of Lorraine; on the west side is the Archers' Hall (Maison de la Louve), marked by a group of Romulus and Remus and the wolf; then the Merchant Captains' (seamen) Hall, with a gable like a vessel's stern and cannon shewing; then Mercers' Hall. On the other side of the Archers' Hall is the gilded Carpenters' Hall, and, further, is the Printers' Hall. Merchant Tailors' Hall is on the north side. The range of buildings on the south east side of the Place was in the old days known as the Weigh House.

The HOTEL DE VILLE, apart from its historic associations, is architecturally one of the most interesting buildings in Belgium. It is Gothic, 198 feet in length, 165 feet in depth; the east end was built first, dating from 1402, the west end dating from 1444; the tower, or spire, 370 feet, was finished 1454. Effigies of the architects, Jacob van Thienen, who began the work, and Jan van Ruysbroeck, who came after, are in the first niche of the spire. Many statues on the facade. In the courtyard are two fountains. Within the Hotel de Ville are several spacious and handsomely decorated chambers, the Salle du Conseil Communal, Salle de Maximilien, Salle des Mariages, Banqueting Chamber, and others. There are many pictures, painted ceilings, much carving, wooden statues, etc. Admission to interior 10.0 to 3, Sunday 10.0 to 12.0; 50 centimes. From spire (50 c.) is extensive view.

PORTE DE HAL, at the Junction of Boulevard du Midi and Boulevard de Waterloo; a little east of the Midi Station. An old city gate, all that is left of the ancient town wall. Built in 1381, became, while Alva governed the Netherlands, a sort of Bastille; now contains a Museum of Weapons and Armour. Open daily, 10.0 to 4.0.

PALAIS DES BEAUX ARTS. At the south west angle of the Place Royale, by the north end of Rue de la Regence. The extensive range of buildings contains a collection of paintings by Old Masters, the Royal Library, and Modern Paintings, with Sculpture. In the principal hall of the section near the Place Royale is the MUSÉE DE SCULPTURE. On the first floor is the GALLERIE DES TABLEAUX ANCIENS (Old Masters), a priceless collection of works by artists whose names are world known—Rubens, Teniers, Jan Steen, Van Dyck, Dou, Cuyp, and others, mostly of the Flemish and Dutch schools. The collection used to be ranked after that at Antwerp, but competent critics now decide there is no inferiority. The name of the artist with the subject of the painting are on the frames. The MUSÉE MODERNE (Modern Pictures) is in the west wing, beyond the Library. This is a very fine collection of paintings by Belgian artists since 1830, some of the examples having a wide fame. Artist and subject are noted on the frame. The Galleries are open, free, daily from 10.0 to 3.0, 4.0, or 5.0. The BIBLIOTHÉQUE (Royal Library), between the two picture galleries, contains 600,000 vols., 28,000 MSS., and 100,000 engravings; open daily 10.0 to 3.0.

PALAIS ARENBERG, off the east side of the Square du Petit Sablon, Rue de la Regence; restored 1753, and 1892. Small choice collection of works by Rembrandt, P. Potter, Van Dyck, Jan Steen, Teniers, Cuyp, Rubens, etc. Shown on weekdays by written application, 1.0 to 4.0; 1 fr. The old Palais was at one time the residence of Count Egmont.

MUSÉE WIERTZ, at south end of Rue Wiertz, on east side of the Quartier Leopold Railway Station. A collection of paintings by Anton Joseph Wiertz (died 1865), an accomplished but eccentric artist. The Musée is one of the curiosities of Brussels. Daily, 10.0 to 5.0; winter, 10.0 to 4.0.

PALAIS DE JUSTICE, at south end of Rue de la Regence. An immense building, on high ground, visible from almost every part of the city. It covers an area of 270,000 square feet, at its base 590 feet long and 560 feet wide, and is said to be the largest mass of building of the 19th century. Begun 1866, finished 1883, at a cost of £1,760,000. The architect was Poelaert, and, so far as the style may be classified, is described as Græco-Roman. Several colossal statues. There are about 27 courtrooms and 245 other rooms, and 8 open courts. The Salle de Pas Perdus (attendance hall), in the centre, under the dome, has an interior height of 320 ft. Attendants conduct visitors over the building, daily 9.0 to 4.0, 25 c., but much may be seen without fee.

PALAIS DU CINQUANTENAIRE, on far east side of Brussels, to north east of Parc Leopold Here is a Museum of Industrial Art, very interesting. The exhibits are of all kinds, ecclesiastical, reliquaries, tapestry, bronzes, pottery, costumes, lace, embroidery, etc. Daily 10.0 to 5.0, winter 10.0 to 4.0. In the south wing of the building is the MUSEE ROYAL DES ANTIQUITIES, containing very valuable and interesting collections, especially in the Egyptian section.

PALAIS ROYAL, residence of the King, on south side of the Parc, east of Place Royale, much altered and extended since 1905.

PALAIS DE LA NATION, erected 1779-83, restored after a fire 1884-87, on north side of Parc, where the Belgian Senate and Chamber of Deputies have their assemblies. To be seen daily except during legislative session (Nov. to May), 50c.

BOURSE (Exchange).—East side of Boulevard Anspach. Built 1873, by the architect Suys, at a cost of £160,000. The principal hall is a cross, with dome at centre. On opposite side of Boulevard is Hotel des Ventes.

CONSERVATOIRE DE MUSIQUE, east side of Rue de la Regence. Very important collection of musical instruments. Mons. and Thurs., 2.0 to 4.0.

MUSÉE D'HISTOIRE NATURELLE, on south side of Parc Leopold, to east of city. Natural History Collections, palæontological section of great interest; daily, except Saturday, 10.0 to 3.0.

The UNIVERSITY, Rue des Sols, a little north of the Palais des Beaux Arts. Established 1834 in a building of 16th cent., modified 1711; about 1,000 students.

MONUMENTS, STATUES, ETC.

COLONNE DU CONGRES, in Rue Royale, erected 1850-59, commemorative of Congress of June 4th, 1831, when the present constitution of Belgium was established.

MONUMENTS OF COUNTS EGMONT and HOORN, in Square du Petit Sablon, Rue de la Regence; also semi-circle of statues of celebrated contemporaries of the Counts.

MARTYRS' MONUMENT, in Place des Martyrs, a square a little off east side, mid distance, of Rue Neuve, a street running directly south from Station du Nord. Erected 1838 to memory of Belgians who were killed in national struggle with the Dutch in 1830.

PARKS.

The PARC, south end Rue Royale. Much frequented on summer evenings when band plays.

PARC LEOPOLD on east side of city. Very small.

BOIS DE LA CAMBRE, to south east. Avenue Louise, running out of Boulevard Waterloo, leads to the Bois. A delightful park.

CEMETERY at Laeken, a suburb to north of Brussels, has its own tranquil beauty.

THEATRES.—The principal is the Théâtre Royal de la Monnaie, standing a little back from east side, north end, of Boulevard Anspach; operas only; closed in summer. Théâtre des Galleries St. Hubert, in Passage St. Hubert, and Théâtre Royal du Parc, at north east corner of the Parc—at both theatres, comedies, dramas, lighter operas, etc. Other theatres are Olympia, Alcazar, Flamand, Vaudeville. At the Alhambra, Boulevard de la Senne, spectacular plays.

MUSIC.—In the afternoon in the Parc, from 1st May to 31st August, and also at night during summer at the Wauxhall, in the Parc. In the winter admirable popular and classical concerts are given.

POST OFFICE.—The principal Post Office is in Place de la Monnaie, just off the east side, north end, of the Boulevard Anspach, which is the middle section of the broad thoroughfare from the Nord Station to the Midi Station. Here is the Poste Restante. The office is open from 7.0 a.m. until 10.0 p.m. The branch offices are open until 8.0 p.m. Boxes to receive post letters will be found at the Railway Stations. TELEGRAPH OFFICES at the Post Offices.

ENGLISH SPEAKING PLACES OF WORSHIP.

CHURCH OF RESURRECTION, Rue de Stassart.

CHRIST CHURCH, Rue Crespel, Avenue de la Toison d'Or.

SCOTS CHURCH, 22, Rue Bodenbroeck.

BRITISH CHARITABLE FUND, 63, Avenue Brugman.

BRITISH INSTITUTE, 41, Rue du Prince Royale.

BRITISH AND AMERICAN EMBASSIES.

GREAT BRITAIN.—His Excy. Sir F. H. Villiers, G.C.V.O., K.C.M.G., C.B.

H. B. M.'s VICE-CONSUL.—T. E. Jeffes, Esq.

UNITED STATES.—His Excellency Hon. Lars Anderson. U.S. CONSUL GENERAL.—E. Watts, Esq. VICE-CONSUL.—C. R. Nasmith, Esq.

GOLF.—18-hole course, at Velvoord, 15 mins. by rail; also a course at Chateau Ravenstein, Tervueren, tram.

BANK, EXCHANGE. — Société Francaise de Banque et de Depots. 70, Rue Royale; 25, Boulevard Anspach; 3, Place Louise; and Exhibition. English spoken. Letters of Credit and Circular notes cashed. Credits opened, etc. Apply London, Société Generale (de Paris), 65, Regentstreet, W.

DEPOT FOR BRADSHAW'S PUBLICATION.—Librairie Kiessling et Cie, 48, Rue Coudenberg.

RAIL.—For Routes and Trains from Brussels, see pages cxxiv-cxxv, and the Index.

Charleroi.—*Stat.*—Pop. (1911) 28,891.

HOTELS: BEUKELEERS; LIEBERTZ.

A once strongly fortified town, besieged several times, now chiefly known as the centre of the iron trade of Belgium. In Church of St. Antoine, in Ville Basse, are paintings. Palais de Justice, in Ville Haute. Musée Archéologique in Boulevard de l'Ouest.

H.B. M.'s VICE-CONSUL.—H. Le Fanu, Esq.

RAIL, pages 90, 92, 97, 98, 100, 107.

Chaudfontaine.—*Stat.*—Pop. 1,851.

HOTELS: DES BAINS; D'ANGLETERRE.

A pretty watering place near Liége, on the River Vesdre. Warm springs, up to 97° Fahrenheit, containing salt and carbonate of lime, used in treatment of rheumatism and neuralgia.

RAIL, page 104.

Courtrai (*Flemish*, **Kortrijk**).—*Stat.*—Pop. (1911) 35,872.

HOTELS: DAMIER; ROYAL.

On the River Lys, a place where linen and lace are made. From the Railway Station the Rue du Chemin de Fer leads to the Grande Place, where is the Hotel de Ville, having elaborate chimney pieces in the principal rooms, also frescoes. Belfry almost opposite Hotel de Ville. Church of St. Martin, with good west portal; carved pulpit, paintings. Church of Notre Dame, in Rue Notre Dame, has a very fine "Elevation of the Cross," by van Dyck, and other paintings. Musée, in Rue du Béguinage, street leading from Notre Dame to St. Martin; collection of paintings.

RAIL, pages 89, 90, 102B.

Dinant.—*Stat.*—Pop. 7,700.

HOTEL DES POSTES.—First class hotel, well situated, opposite the Railway Station and River. Electric light, telephone. See Advt.

HOTEL DE LA TETE D'OR.—Not very large, but good and comfortable. Pension from 8 fr. See Advt.

HOTEL DES ARDENNES.—Well situated family hotel. Baths. Electric light. Rooms from 2 frs. Pension from 6 frs. See Advt.

FAMILLES; HALLEZ.

A town picturesquely situated on the River Meuse, at the foot of cliffs upon which is a fortress. Church of Notre Dame, Gothic, of 13th cent., with tower 200 ft. high; behind the Church are steps (408) in the rock leading up to the Citadel. At Hotel de Ville are a few paintings. Palais de Justice; Casino in Grande Rue. Fine view from the bridge crossing the river.

The beautiful valley of the Meuse is best seen on the steamer passage from Namur to Dinant (page 368).

RAIL, pages 92, 96, 101.

Ghent (*French*, **Gand**).—*Stat.*—Pop. (1911) 166,719.

HOTELS: POSTE; DE L'ETOILE; COMTE D'EGMONT.

The principal Railway Station, SUD, for the State lines, is about half a mile south of the Hotel de Ville, at the centre of the city. Other Stations are the Pays de Waes, for a line to Antwerp through Waesland; and Eecloo Station for a line via Eecloo to Bruges; both these latter Stations, close together, are to the east.

CABS.—Taximètre Motor Cabs, 1,000 mètres, 1,093 yards, 75c., each additional 200 mètres, 10c. 1-horse cab per half-hour 1 fr., each following quarter hour 50c.; 2-horse cab per half-hour 1 fr. 50c., each following quarter hour 75c. During the night 1 fr. 25c. extra;

GHENT INTERNATIONAL EXHIBITION, 1913.—This Exhibition is planned on a larger scale than the Brussels Exhibition of 1910. The Exhibition covers about 250 acres, the grounds including the Citadel Park; the Palais des Fetes alone covers seven and a half acres. Beside the exhibits concerned with Industry, Science, and Art, a very interesting feature is the Old Flanders section. Every form of sport is represented. The arrangements for music are on an exceptionally generous scale.

Ghent, the capital of East Flanders, on the Rivers Scheldt and Lys, with many branches crossed by innumerable bridges, is a city much spread out; in 16th cent. one of the largest and wealthiest cities of Europe. Linen and cotton mills, lace and leather goods made; there is also a large grain trade.

From the Sud Station the Rue de Flandre leads north west in one-third mile to the Cathedral.

Cathedral of St. Bavon, Gothic, 10th-15th cent., externally rather plain, but internally lavishly decorated. Carved pulpit; high altar has statue of St. Bavon. Very fine paintings, the most remarkable the "Adoration of the Lamb," by the brothers van Eyck, in a chapel near the choir; in another chapel is a painting by Rubens, St. Bavon renouncing the military profession to become a monk. Bishop's Palace on east side of Cathedral.

The Beffroi (Belfry) is a little north west of the Cathedral, along the Rue St. Jean. A square tower 385 ft. high to point of spire; dating from 1183; there are 44 bells. Fine view, 1 fr.

Church of St. Nicolas, a little west of the Beffroi; 13th cent.; high altar; paintings. 200 yards west of St. Nicolas is the Church of St. Michel; paintings, including a celebrated Crucifixion by van Dyck.

Hotel de Ville, a few yards north of the Beffroi. The building is considered a beautiful example of florid Gothic architecture; dating from 1516 to late in same century. Fine chambers; paintings and chimney pieces; the Archives are kept here.

200 yards due north of the Hotel de Ville is the Marché du Vendredi, the historic square of Ghent, associated with most great events in the life of the city. In centre of the Place is Statue of Jacques van Artevelde (1290-1345).

Church of St. Jacques, a little back from east side of Marché du Vendredi; of 15th or 16th cent. Paintings.

Immediately north of St. Jacques is the Bibliothèque, containing 200,000 vols., 2,100 MSS., many thousand drawings and engravings, collection of coins, etc. Behind the Bibliothèque is the Jardin Botanique.

The Grand Béguinage, a sheltering institution of the nature of an immense nunnery, for women of unblemished character, is on the east side of the city, a mile east, a little north, of the Cathedral. About 700 inmates, who are partly self supporting, devoting themselves to sick nursing, education, and useful work. The Petit Béguinage is a little off east side of Sud Station, Abbaye de St. Bavon, quarter mile due east of Cathedral; some remains of the old Abbaye, 10th cent., with tombs.

Musée des Beaux Arts, in the Parc de la Citadelle, two thirds of a mile south west of the Sud Station. A handsome building by C. van Rysselberghe, completed 1904, containing collections of sculpture and painting of the first importance. Daily 10.0 to 4.0 or 5.0; free Sun. and Thurs., other days 10c.

Musée d' Archéologie, in Rue Longue des Pierres. Interesting miscellaneous collections. Sun. and Thurs. free, other days 50c.

Chateau des Comtes de Flandre, a restored old castle, quarter mile north west of Hotel de Ville. Edward III of England and his Queen Phillipa entertained here by Jacques van Artevelde, 1339, and here their son John of Gaunt (Ghent) was born, 1340

Palais de Justice, half mile west of Sud Station, just west of Place d'Armes. Imposing building in Greek style; some modern paintings in principal hall.

University, in Rue des Foulons, 200 yards south west of Cathedral. About 1,100 students.

POST OFFICE.—Marché-aux-Grains.

ENGLISH CHURCH, Place St. Jacques. Sunday, 8.30, 10.30, 6.0.

H.B.M.'s VICE-CONS.—F. Lethbridge, Esq.

U. S. CONSUL.—H. A. Johnson Esq.

GOLF.—9-hole course, $1\frac{1}{4}$ miles from Station.

RAIL, pp. 89, 90, 93, 94, 97, 100, 101, 102, 107.

Hal.—*Stat.*—Pop. 14,300.

HOTEL DU DUC DE BRABANT.

A small town, on the River Senne, famous as a resort of pilgrims to the miracle working image of the Virgin in the Church of Notre Dame—Gothic, 14th cent.; beautiful alabaster high altar, many costly gifts from popes, emperors, kings, and others. Hotel de Ville.

RAIL, pages 98, 103, 108.

Han-sur-Lesse.—Pop. 476.

HOTELS: DE BELLEVUE; GRAND.

A village of the Ardennes where is a well known grotto. It is about two miles long, presents a succession of halls with magnificent stalactite formations, and is partly visited by boat. The entrance to the Grotto is about one mile south east of the village. See Advertisement under Brussels. Half a mile south of the Grotto is the Perte de la Lesse, where the river tumbles into a subterranean passage.

Han-sur-Lesse is $2\frac{1}{2}$ miles from Eprave and four miles from Rochefort. From Rochefort a local railway connects, at frequent intervals, with Han.

Heyst.—*Stat.*—Pop. 3,700.

HOTELS: DES BAINS; KURSAAL; PLAGE ROYAL.

A sea bathing resort, visited by English families during the summer; the dunes about here are very fine. Broad digue. Gothic Church.

RAIL from Bruges page 111; an electric tramway runs along the coast from Ostend to Heyst,

Knocke.—*Stat.*—Pop. 2,319.

HOTELS: KURSAAL; GRAND; PLAGE.

A bathing resort rapidly rising in public favour, near the Dutch frontier. Good coast views; shady avenues of trees.

GOLF.—18-hole course.

ENGLISH CHURCH SERVICE during season.

Reached by a local line from Bruges, see p. 111. Local lines also connect with Heyst and Breskens.

Laroche.—*Stat.*—

HOTELS: DE LUXEMBOURG; DES ARDENNES; NORD.

A small picturesque town and summer resort at the junction of several valleys. Casino; ruins of a castle. Interesting excursions.

RAIL, page 100.

Leau.—*Stat.*—Pop. 2,100.

A once strongly fortified place, whose chief interest now is St. Leonhard Church, a very fine example of 14th-15th cent. Gothic architecture; the interior contains a wonderful collection of 15th cent. Gothic bronze work, early Flemish and Renaissance paintings, and a magnificent sculptured Tabernacle. The Gothic Town Hall is also of interest.

RAIL, page 94.

Liége (Flemish, Luik).—*Stat.*—Pop. (1911) 167,676.

HOTEL DE SUEDE.—First class hotel, situated in the centre of the town, opposite the Royal Theatre. See Advt.

GRAND HOTEL DE L'EUROPE.—First class family hotel, centrally situated, opposite the Royal Theatre. Great comfort. See Advt.

METROPOLE; NOTGER.

There are two important Railway Stations at Liége—Station des Guillemins, on south west side of the town, where the train service to and from France, Germany, etc., runs through; and Station de Longdoz, a terminus. Minor stations are Station du Palais (near Palais de Justice), Station de Jonfosse, and Station de Vivegnis (north side of town, far from centre).

CABS.—Motors, 800 mètres, about half mile, 75 c., and 10c. for each additional 200 mètres. Horsed cabs, first half hour 1 fr.

Liége, the chief town of the Walloon part of Belgium, is picturesquely situated on the River Meuse; it is the centre of one of the most industrious districts of the country, with coal mines in the immediate vicinity, and iron foundries, engineering shops, and manufactories on all sides. The town is separated by the Meuse into two parts, in that to the west are the principal buildings and shops, in the eastern part are the factories and working class quarters.

From the Station de Guillemins the Rue des Guillemins runs north east to the handsome Parc d'Avroy, whence a line of fine boulevards leads northward in about a mile to the Place du Theâtre, the centre of Liége civic life.

The Church of St. Jean is just west of the Place du Theatre, the Church of St. Denis is a little off east side of the Place; in the latter are a handsome high altar, statues, and stained glass.

Palais de Justice, in the Place Lambert, to which the Place Verte leads north east from the Place du Theâtre. On the Place Lambert formerly stood the Cathedral of St. Lambert, destroyed by revolutionaries in 1794 and altogether removed in 1808. The episcopal palace, 1508-40, has become the Palais de Justice; some modern additions.

Hotel de Ville, in Place du Marché, just east of Palais de Justice; pictures and tapestries. The Exchange, adjacent, was formerly the Church of St. André.

The Cathedral of St. Paul, 1280-1528, is 100 yards south east of Place du Theâtre; in interior (92 yds. long, 37 yds. broad, 80 ft. high) are paintings, sculpture, elaborately carved pulpit, choir stalls, and high altar; in Treasury (1 fr.) are valuable plate and groups in gold enamel.

The University is 100 yards east of the Cathedral, at the river side. About 2,500 students.

Church of St. Jacques, 200 yards south of Cathedral. Gothic, early 16th cent.; the most interesting church of the city. Interior, 87 yards long, 33 yards broad, 75 feet high; elaborate decorations.

Other churches are St. Martin, conspicuous, on a hill; and Ste. Croix, west of Palais de Justice.

Musée des Beaux-Arts, in the Academie des Beaux Arts, Rue de l'Academie, 200 yards north west of Place du Theatre; collection of modern paintings; daily 10.0 to 4.0 or 5,0, free.

Archeological Museum in the Maison Curtius, Quai de Maastricht, east of Place du Theatre; a few yards north is the Musée d'Armes; adjacent is the Musée d'Ansembourg—an old mansion, 1735-40, preserved in its original state.

H.B.M.'s V.-CONS.—J. B. Dolphin, Esq.

U.S. CONS.—A. Heingartner, Esq.

RAIL, pp. 92, 100, 102B, 104, 111, 116.

[**Seraing**—Pop. 41,389; 3 miles south of Liége, on the River Meuse—is celebrated for the vast industrial enterprise founded 1817 by an Englishman, John Cockerill; an immense organisation including collieries, iron-mines, smelting furnaces, steel works, and engineering shops, where about 11,000 men and boys are employed. Steamer from Liége almost every half hour, an hour's ride; steam tram every quarter hour; RAIL, page 92. At **Herstal** (pop. 20,114), a suburb, on north east side of Liége, is the extensive Fabrique Nationale of weapons.]

Lierre.—*Stat.*—Pop. 25,100. HOTELS: DU COMMERCE; ANVERS.

A somewhat dull but handsome town. The Cathedral, though not one of the largest, is perhaps architecturally the most beautiful in Belgium, and has a superb Gothic jubé or rood-screen. Musée, in Rue de Malines—antiquities, pictures, etc.

RAIL, pages 99, 100, 102B.

Louvain (Flemish, **Leuven**).—*Stat.*—Pop. (1911), 42,307.

HOTELS: SUEDE; BRITANNIQUE; GARE.

On the River Dyle, a town once much more populous—in the 14th cent. there were 150,000 inhabitants; owing to disputes with the Dukes of Brabant many weavers left the place for England and Holland, and the lost prosperity has never been regained.

From the Station, on the east side of the town, the Rue de la Station leads directly to the Grande Place, where is the Hotel de Ville, 1448-59, a fine specimen of Gothic, with much sculpture upon the facade; the interior is modern—paintings and frescoes in the rooms, and also a small Musée of paintings.

Church of St. Pierre, opposite Hotel de Ville; Gothic, 1425-97. Interior—101 yards long, 29½ yards broad, 80 ft. high—has fine "jubé" or rood loft separating the choir from the nave; paintings, carved pulpit, statues, and tombs.

Church of Ste. Gertrude, quarter mile up Rue de Malines from Grande Place. Carving of choir stalls, scenes from the life of Christ and saints, regarded as equal to the best in Belgium.

Church of St. Michel, 200 yards south of Grande Place, off east side of Rue de Namur. Modern paintings.

Church of St. Jacques, one third mile west from Grande Place, in Rue de Bruxelles, has paintings by old masters and modern work. On north side of the Church is a bronze statue of Father Damien, 1840-89, the missionary to the lepers on the island of Molokai.

Church of St. Joseph, just off the Place du Peuple, a little east of Grande Place; good modern frescoes.

The University, west side of Rue de Namur, 100 yards south of Grande Place, lost its position as a Government university in 1834, and is now maintained as a Catholic university. The foundation dates from 1426, and in the 16th century it was one of the most famous universities of Europe, attended by 6,000 students. In the Library are 150,000 vols.

The Abbaye de Parc, a large monastic establishment, is about half a mile beyond the town, on the south side.

RAIL, pages 100, 101, 104.

Malines (Flemish, **Mechelen**).—*Stat.*—Pop. (1911), 59,191.

HOTELS: STATION; DE LA COUPE; EUROPE.

An old town on the River Dyle, with broad streets, in some respects picturesque but with dull and squalid quarters.

From the Railway Station, on south side of city, the Rue Conscience leads, with its prolongations, directly north east in two thirds mile to the Grande Place, where are the Hotel de Ville and the Cathedral.

Cathedral of St. Rombaut, Gothic, mostly of 14th-15th cent.; massive west tower, unfinished, 318 ft.; diameter of clock face 44 ft. Interior—length 308 ft., nave 40 ft. wide 90 ft. high; among the paintings are an altar-piece in south transept, a celebrated "Crucifixion," by van Dyck, and in the north transept an "Adoration of the Shepherds" by Erasmus Quellin; several other good paintings; carved pulpit, monuments, good modern windows. Archbishop's Palace is a little north of Cathedral, behind some houses.

Church of St. Jean, 200 yards north east from Grande Place. An altar-piece by Rubens, illustrating scenes in life of St. John the Baptist; other paintings.

Notre Dame Church, in Rue Notre Dame, a street on west side of prolongation of Rue Conscience, running from Railway Station. Behind high altar, in a chapel, is a "Miraculous Draught of Fishes," by Rubens; other good paintings.

Musée, opposite the Hotel de Ville. A few pictures, collection of antiquities, etc.

Palais de Justice, quarter mile east of Cathedral; formerly the palace of Margaret of Austria.

RAIL, pages 96, 101, 110.

Mons (*Flemish*, **Bergen**).—*Stat.*—Pop. 27,904.

HOTELS: ESPERANCE; SCHMITZ.

On the River Trouille; the centre of the Belgian coal fields. As the town is entered from the Station, to the left is the Gothic Cathedral of Ste. Waudru, dating from 1450; several monuments and paintings in interior. On high ground to left of Cathedral is the supposed site of a fortress erected by Cæsar, near by is a Belfry, 275 ft. high. The Hotel de Ville, in the Grande Place, is an interesting old building, 1458-67; some paintings. Musée, in Rue Neuve; small picture gallery and archæological collection. Visitors who require the services of an interpreter may obtain them free of charge at the Ecole Superieure Commerciale et Consulaire.

H. B. M.'s V.-CONSUL.—H. Le Fanu, Esq.

RAIL, pages 90, 94, 100. 102B, 108.

Namur.—*Stat.*—Pop. (1911), 32,444.

HOTELS: HARSCAMP; HOLLANDE; MONNAIE; COURONNE.

The Railway Station is on the north side of the city, about half a mile from the centre.

Namur is situated at the confluence of the Rivers Meuse and Sambre, and because of its important strategic position has always been strongly fortified. It has been besieged several times, one consequence being there are few old buildings.

From the Place de la Station the Rue Godefroid runs south; at the end of this street turn west into the Rue de Bruxelles, whence the first street on south side leads to the Cathedral.

Cathedral of St. Aubin, Renaissance, 1751-67, with a dome. Paintings, statues, and monuments in the interior; golden crown of 12th cent. in the treasury.

Church of St Loup, in Rue du College, a street on west side of Cathedral; much sculpture on choir ceiling.

Musée Archéologique, on south side of city, near most easterly bridge across the Sambre. Sunday, 10.0 to 1.0.

Citadel, on a height between the Sambre and the Meuse, near the confluence, built 1691; the ground behind Plateau du Donjon, is now a park.

RAIL, pages 92, 103A, 103B, 107. For Steamers on the River Meuse to Dinant, see page 368.

Nieuport, and Nieuport-Bains.—*Stat*—Pop. of Nieuport 3,500.

HOTELS: DES BAINS; PLAGE; PREVOST.

The town of Nieuport has little to interest, but to Nieuport Bains many visitors come for the sea bathing; broad sands. Digue. Kursaal.

GOLF.—18-hole course.

RAIL, pages 94, 95; an electric tram along the coast to Ostend.

Ostend, or Ostende.-*Stat.*-Pop. (1911), 42 638.

HOTEL CONTINENTAL.—Large first-class hotel, beautifully situated. See Advt.

SPLENDID HOTEL.—Very well situated, facing the Sea and Baths. See Advt.

GRAND HOTEL DU KURSAAL ET DU BEAU SITE. —English first-class family hotel and pension. Restaurant. See Advt.

HOTEL DE LA PLAGE.—First class hotel and restaurant, in excellent position, next to the Kursaal. Every modern comfort. See Advt.

GRAND HOTEL DU LITTORAL.—Facing sea. First class. See Advt.

GRAND HOTEL.—In good position, overlooking the sea, and close to all attractions. All modern comforts. Rooms from 6 frs. Pension terms from 12.50 frs. See Advt.

OCEAN HOTEL.—First class hotel, well situated, facing sea and baths. All modern comforts. See Advt.

GRAND HOTEL FONTAINE.—First class, well situated, with 350 rooms. All up-to-date comforts. See Advt.

HOTEL IMPERIAL.—Situated near the Kursaal and bathing place. See Advt.

THE ROCHESTER HOTEL.—Comfortable family hotel, near the sea and Kursaal. First class restaurant. All coupons accepted. Pension terms from 10 fr. See Advt.

GRAND HOTEL LEOPOLD II.—English family hotel and pension, under entire English management. Close to the sea and casino. See Advt.

ST. JAMES HOTEL.—English family hotel, 38, Rue de l'Eglise, near the sea, Kursaal, and Casino. See Advt.

CABS.—Taximètre motor cabs, 1,000 mètres (1,093 yards) 2 fr., each additional 800 mètres 20 c. One-horse cab, 1 r. 50 c. per drive within town.

The harbour of Ostend is accessible at all states of the tide. The Dover steamers run alongside the Station Maritime, where trains await them; the town Station, for all other traffic than the through traffic connected with the steamers, is a little back on the Quai, a quarter mile behind the Station Maritime. The town lies between the Railway and the sea; cross from the Pier (Station Maritime) or from the general Railway Station towards the houses on the other side of a sheet of water, then any of the streets northward, the principal is Rue de la Chapelle, lead to sea front.

Ostend has a special importance as one of the principal ports of passenger traffic between Great Britain and the Continent; it has also great attractions as a summer resort, the excellence of the sands for sea bathing and the gaiety of the amply provided amusements drawing thousands of visitors during the season.

In the town is very little to interest. The Hotel de Ville is in the Place d'Armes, off the Rue de la Chapelle; the Gotnic Church of SS. Peter and Paul is in a corner of the town near the Station Maritime; the Church of St. Catharine, in Rue Christine, a street running from the sea front towards the railway. Parc Léopold, near centre of town, is pleasant, with a small lake.

All the attractions are along the sea front. Here is the chief promenade, the Digue, flanked by a line of handsome buildings—hotels, restaurants, and sumptuous private villas. Midway along the Digue is the Kursaal, and a little further west is the Chalet du Roi; still further west is the Hippodrome Wellington, with a racecourse—race meetings several times during season. Concerts are given daily, afternoon and evening, at the Kursaal, and balls almost nightly; balls also in the Casino, at the Hotel de Ville, two or three times a week.

The Fishing industry of Ostend is very extensive, employing about 250 boats. The Oyster Parks (may be visited) contain immense numbers of oysters, brought mostly from the English coast. There is a large export trade in eggs, butter, rabbits, and provisions.

POST OFFICE, at corner of Avenue Henri Serruys, by east side of the Parc Leopold, at the centre of the town. Post Office also at the Railway Station, and during summer at the Kursaal.

CHURCH OF ENG. SERVICE in the Church, Rue Longue.

H.B.M.'S VICE-CONSUL.—W. G. E. Hervey, Esq.

GOLF.—18-hole course, between Ostend and Blankenberghe; club house.

RAIL, pp. 90, 95, 102.

Panne, La.—

A quiet sea bathing place, close to the French frontier, nestling among the dunes—here covered with verdure. Smooth clean beach. The village, behind the dunes, is attractive. The submarine cable to Dover begins here.

Reached by Tram from Furnes, 3½ miles, or from Adinkerke, 2 miles.

Rochefort.—*Stat.*—Pop. 2,900.

HOTEL BIRON; DE L'ETOILE.

A picturesque old town, 625 ft. above sea, on the River Lomme, once the capital of the County of Ardennes. On a height are the ruins of an old castle. Romanesque church and modern Chateau of Beauregard. In the neighbourhood are several caverns in the limestone rock. A visit to the interesting Grotte de Rochefort, at the upper end of the town, requires about two hours—charge 6 fr.

RAIL, page 101.

Spa.—*Stat.*—Pop. 8,100.

GRAND HOTEL BRITANNIQUE.—First class hotel, very well situated, standing in its own extensive grounds. See Advt.

GRAND HOTEL DE BELLE VUE ET DE FLANDRE.—On the promenade. First class hotel. Garden. See Advt.

HOTEL DE LAEKEN ET RESTAURANT.—Well situated Rue Leopold, with view on the mountains and the garden of the Kursaal; near the Post Office. Pension from 7 fr. 50. See Advt.

Spa, 820 ft. above sea, one of the oldest and most popular watering places of Europe, is pleasantly situated at the base of wooded heights, at the confluence of the Rivers Wayai or Spa and Picherotte. The number of annual visitors exceeds 20,000, and the name "Spa" has been freely adopted for mineral springs elsewhere. The waters, for drinking and bathing, are full of carbonic acid gas, sparkling, cheering, easily digested, and containing carbonate of iron, soda, lime, and magnesia. They are efficacious in anæmia, chlorosis, female disorders, etc. The mineral baths are much used in cases of heart disease; mud baths are also taken. Season, May to October.

The Railway Station is on the west side of the town, about half a mile from the centre.

The Avenue du Marteau runs by the Railway Station past the former Queen's Palace to the Place Royale, where is the imposing Etablissement des Bains; the Casino is close by, in the Rue Royale. Near the Casino, in the Place Pierre-le-Grand, is the chief spring, the Pouhon; in the Rue Dundas, adjacent, is the Pouhon du Prince de Condé; other springs, there are sixteen, are in the woods. Immense Salle de Fêtes, erected at a cost of about a quarter of a million sterling. Musée Communal, with a collection of pictures. Tennis courts.

The principal promenades are the Place Royale, Promenade de Sept-Heures, Promenade des Anglais, the Lake of Warfaaz, Promenade des Artistes, de Meyerbeer, d'Orleans, Belle Vue.

More distant excursions are to the ruined Castle of Franchimont, the valley of the Ambleuse, the Hoëgne, with its cascades, the Cascade of Coo, the grotto of Remouchamps. the Baraque Michel, 2,200 ft. (the highest point of Belgium).

Band three times daily at the Springs or in the park; frequent vocal and instrumental concerts theatrical performances; sports of all kinds including motor races and horse races.

POST OFFICE.—Rue Louise.

ENGLISH CHURCH SERVICE.—At the English Church. Sundays, 8, 11, and 3.30.

PRESBYTERIAN SERVICE (Free Ch. of Scotland), Sunday in July and August, at Chapelle Evangélique.

H.B.M.'s VICE-CONS.—Henri Hayemal. Esq.

GOLF.—Attractive 18-hole links on the old Sart racecourse. Tram from Spa Station to Verviers passes the links.

MEDICAL.—A. M. Cafferata (English, of Liverpool), M.D., consulting physician to the Spa Waters (formerly of St. George's Hospital, London), Avenue du Marteau, 5.

RAIL, page 111.

Tournai (*Flemish*, **Doornijk**).—*Stat.*—Pop. (1911) 37,108.

HOTELS: BELLEVUE; HOLLANDE; IMPERATRICE.

A very old place, on the River Scheldt (Escaut), the Civitas Nerviorum of the Romans, now a busy, prosperous, clean city, where the carpet known as "Brussels Carpet" is chiefly made—generally in the houses of the weavers, not in factories.

From the Railway Station, on the east side of the city, the Rue Royale leads west in about half a mile direct to the Cathedral.

CATHEDRAL of Notre Dame, Romanesque, 12th-14th cent. Interior—136 yards long, width of nave 78 ft., height 78 ft., length of transept 73 yards, height of choir 107 ft. Rood loft (separating choir from nave) finely sculptured; good paintings, including one by Rubens in a chapel of the ambulatory, modern stained glass. Episcopal Palace to north of Cathedral, with Bibliothèque (8,000 early printed vols.) opposite. At a few yards south west of the Cathedral is the Belfry.

Halle aux Draps (Cloth Hall), in Grande Place, a few yards west of the Cathedral, containing a Musée of paintings, old and modern masters; fee 50c. In same buldiing is a Musée Archéologique of miscellaneous antiquities. On north side Grande Place is Church of St. Quentin—some paintings.

Hotel de Ville, on west side of city, quarter mile south west of Cathedral; one chamber, "Salon de la Reine," should be seen. Musée of Natural History to east of Hotel de Ville.

Church of St. Brice, at end of Rue de l'Athenée, running south west from Railway Station; 12th cent. Some mediæval houses in the neighbourhood.

RAIL pages 89, 100, 102B, 103.

Verviers.—*Stat.*—Pop. (1911), 46,485.

HOTELS: DU CHEMIN DE FER; ALLEMAGNE.

A modern town, where much cloth is made and yarn spun. Church of St. Remacle has good windows. Napoleon III stayed a night at Hotel du Chemin de Fer, in 1870, as a prisoner on his way from Sedan to Wilhelmshöhe.

RAIL, pages 102B, 104, 111.

Villers-la-Ville.—*Stat.*—Pop. 1,020.

HOTEL DES RUINES.

A village visited for the imposing ruins of the Cistercian Abbey, the property of the State, about a quarter of a mile north of the Station. The Abbey was founded 1147; destroyed by the French 1796. Fee 25c.

RAIL, page 100.

Vilvorde.—*Stat.*—Pop. about 15,400.

An old small town on the River Senne, interesting as the scene of the martyrdom of William Tyndale, Oct. 6th, 1536. His New Testament—for whose translation he was burned—is the basis of the Authorised Version.

RAIL, page 110.

Waterloo.—*Stat.*

The village is about a mile east of the Railway Station. Within the Church is a bust of the Duke of Wellington and several memorial tablets to British officers.

Battlefield of Waterloo. — The most interesting visit is made from a commencement at the village of Waterloo. There is a light railway from Waterloo Station to Mont St. Jean and the Gordon Monument, see page 107. A shorter visit, for those who cannot spare time, is made from Braine l'Alleud Station, whence a road leads east to the Lion Monument, nearly two miles; light railway from Braine l'Alleud to Lion Monument, see page 107. One advantage of the use of the light railways is that many beggars are thus avoided; relics are generally offered for sale, but they are more than doubtful.

The lines of the British and Allied army, facing south, extended in something like crescent formation from a little behind and west of Hougomont to the farms of Papelotte and La Haye on the east. On lower ground, in front of these lines, are the farms of Hougomont and La Haye Sainte. The lines of the French army, facing north, extended similarly on the rising ground east and west of the farm of La Belle Alliance. The lines of the two armies were about a mile apart. The British and Allied army consisted of 67,600 men, of whom 24,000 were British, with 180 guns; the French army was 71,900 strong, with 246 guns. The French troops were experienced and reliable, with overwhelming superiority in artillery.

After a night of wind and rain the 18th June, 1815, broke with an overcast sky and falling rain. Occasional shots were exchanged as early as eight o'clock, but the battle did not really begin until nearly noon. The first blow was directed by the French at Hougomont; the second and almost simultaneous blow was struck at La Haye Sainte; at these two places, and over all the ground round about, the great struggles raged. Blucher approached from the south east between 4.0 and 5.0 in the afternoon and at 6.0 o'clock was in action. The final endeavour on the part of Napoleon was made between 7.0 and 8.0 in the evening when two columns of Guards, his finest soldiers, in all about 5,000 strong, advanced, one to storm Hougomont the other to pierce the Allied army to north of La Haye Sainte. The movement failed, and the Allied army at the critical moment swept down victoriously from the heights so patiently occupied. The French retreat was along the Genappe road. The total loss of life was never known, but it was estimated that 50,000 men were killed or badly wounded; the Allied army lost 14,000 men, the French more than 30,000.

The best view of the battlefield is obtained from the Lion Mound, 200 ft. high.

RAIL from Brussels to Waterloo and Braine l'Alleud, page 107.

Westend-Bains.

HOTEL BELLEVUE.—First class family hotel, on the sea front. Every up-to-date comfort, Fine terrace: tennis and golf links; garage. See Advt.

A quite recently developed coast resort, about seven miles from Ostend, to the west. The situation is exceptionally pleasant, dominating some of the most attractive country in Flanders, and the villas are of superior architecture. Life is rather quieter than at Ostend. Tennis and golf. At the village of Lombartzyde, about a mile from the sea, is a figure of Madonna, greatly venerated by the fisherfolk.

Reached by electric tram from Ostend.

Ypres.—*Stat.*—Pop. 17,400.

HOTEL DE LA CHATELLENIE; EPEE ROYALE.

An interesting clean old town, on the River Yperlee, now covered in; formerly, in 13th cent., of great importance, with a population of 200,000 and an extensive woollen trade. It gave the name to the fabric "diaper" (d'Ypres); linen and lace are now made. The Rue de la Station leads from the Railway Station to Rue du Temple, which runs towards the Grande Place, where is the large Halle des Drapiers (Drapers' Hall), dating from 1200, regarded as one of the finest remaining secular buildings of its century. At east end is the Hotel de Ville. At the rear of the Halle des Drapiers is the Cathedral of St. Martin, 13th cent.; a fine example of Transition architecture; frescoes and carving; in the cloister a stone marks the grave of Jansenius (died 1638), Bishop of Ypres, founder of the Jansenist sect. Just south west of the Halle des Drapiers is a small Musée of paintings, including works by Rubens, van Dyck, and Jordaens.

RAIL, pages 90, 95.

Zee Brugge (Bruges Port).—*Stat.*

A port at the sea end of a Canal (6¼ miles long) leading to Bruges. The Canal is 229 feet wide at water-level, with minimum depth of 26 ft. 3 in. The roadstead is protected by a breakwater 1 mile in length.

H.B.M.'s V.-CONSUL.-Lieut.-Col. H.E. Boileau.

RAIL, page 111.

HOLLAND; or, the NETHERLANDS.

HOLLAND (etymologically, Hollowland) is a flat strip of country, situated along the south-eastern coast of the North Sea; its greatest length from N.E. to S.W. being 190 miles; greatest breadth from E. to W., 123 miles. It contains the Provinces of North Holland (Amsterdam, etc.), South Holland (Hague, Rotterdam), and Zeeland, next the coast; Groningen, Drenthe, Friesland, in the North; Overijssel, Guelderland, Utrecht, in the middle; North Brabant, and Limburg (Duchy), in the South. Area, 12,648 square m.; to which the reclamation from the Zuyder Zee will add six per cent. Holland, which was once an extended swamp, alternately covered by and abandoned by the sea, presents the picture of a people owing not only their wealth and high commercial position, but even the very land, to their own labour and enterprise. It consists of the Deltas of the Rhine, Maas, etc., mostly below the level of the sea; from the encroachments of which it is defended by broad sandhills and downs—sometimes high enough to shut out the view of the water even from the church spires; or by artificial Dykes (embankments) kept up at a great annual charge, as in Zeeland and North Holland, and in Friesland, where they cost half-a-million sterling. The Canals are very numerous, and of the greatest utility in draining off the waters and in facilitating the internal trade. They are lined with trees, which tend greatly to improve the country, from which the barges seem to rise. Wide meadows are during eight months of the year covered with cattle. In the North, wheat, flax, and madder, are raised; and in the South, where agriculture has made the greatest progress, inferior tobacco is grown, and different kinds of fruit-trees cover the fields. Vast quantities of cattle and provisions are sent to England. Thousands of windmills are everywhere in use for drainage, sawing, and other purposes. Peat, the common fuel, is got from the reclaimed meres or polders. It will be noticed that away from the towns the people have preserved in their costume much that is nationally characteristic, and the traveller will find an occasional trip on the canals an interesting experience.

Population.—(1911) 6,022,452. The Protestants amount to nearly 3-5ths; the Catholics to not quite 2-5ths.

Government.—A Constitutional Monarchy, dating from 1814, and styled *Het Koningrijk der Nederlanden*, or "Kingdom of the Netherlands," the proper name of the country. Queen Wilhelmina, born 1880, succeeded 1890, married Feb. 7th, 1901, to Heinrich, Duke of Mecklenburg. The First Chamber is chosen by the Provincial States, and consists of 50 members who sit for nine years. The Second Chamber consists of 100 members, sitting four years, and chosen by ballot by the tax-payers.

Army.—Peace Establishment, (1912) 24,244; war establishment, about 125,000. The Military Commands are Amsterdam, Utrecht, Gorinchem or Gorkum, Rotterdam, and the Helder. **Navy** (1913), 10 battleships, 6 cruisers, 1 monitor, 47 torpedo-boats, 6 submarines, 12 destroyers. The national colours are red, white, and blue, in bands one above the other.

Revenue.—(1913), £17,460,955; Expenditure, £19,268,331.

Churches, Picture Galleries.—Though among the Churches of Holland are many large Gothic edifices, the material of which they are built, brick, has not the imposing effect of stone the contents, too, of the Churches, include little that is artistic beside elaborate monumental tombs. A fee of 25c. each person is usually expected by the sacristan when the Church is not open. The Picture Galleries of The Hague and Amsterdam are of world renown, and most of the larger towns possess valuable collections of paintings.

Centenary of Independence of Holland, 1813. NATIONAL FESTIVITIES and EXHIBITIONS. During the summer of 1913 several Exhibitions will be open in different towns illustrative of Dutch progress during the century 1813-1913. There will also be performances at different places of mediæval religious plays, with old-world music and pageantry. The Peace Palace at The Hague will be the centre of much interest on August 29th.

Routes to Holland—1. Via Folkestone and Flushing or Queenborough and Flushing; from Holborn Viaduct, St. Paul's, and Victoria Stations by South Eastern and Chatham Railway to Queenborough, steamer thence to Flushing, sea passage being about 6 hours; see Advt., pages vii to x. **2. Via Harwich and Hoek van Holland;** from Liverpool Street Station by Great Eastern Railway to Harwich, thence by steamer to Hoek van Holland, sea passage about 7 hours; see Advt. on page inside Cover. **3. To Rotterdam** direct from London by Batavier Line, see Advt., page 731. **4. Grimsby to Rotterdam** by the Steamers of the Great Central Co., see Advt., page 735. **5. Hull to Amsterdam, Rotterdam, and Harlingen,** the Hull and Holland Steamship Co., see Advt., page 731. **6. Leith to Amsterdam and Rotterdam,** Messrs. G. Gibson & Co. **7. Newcastle to Rotterdam,** in about 30 hours. See also Alphabetical List of Sailings, pages 336 to 360c.

Money.—100 cents=1 guilder or florin=1s. 8d. The gold coins are pieces of 10 florins (called Gouden Tientjes), and 5 florins. The silver coins are pieces of 2½, 1, and ½ florin. There are also in silver, of a lower standard, 25 cents (kwartje), 10 (dubbeltje), and 5 cent pieces. In nickel there is a piece of 5 cents. The bronze coins are pieces of 2½, 1, and ½ cents.

Weights and Measures.—The metric system of weights and measures, and, with trifling changes, the metric denominations, are adopted in Holland. See p. lxxi.

Railways.—No free allowance of Luggage. The rates are—22 lbs. for 20 kilometers, 5 cents; 22 lbs. for 50 kilometers, 10 cents; 22 lbs. for 100 kilometers, 15 cents; 22 lbs. for 200 kilometers, 25 cents; 22 lbs. for 400 kilometers, 45 cents; minimum charge, 15 cents. Bicycles are charged as 50 lbs. Children from 3 to 10 half fare. Amsterdam time (20 minutes before Greenwich time) is observed on all lines. There are 1,984 miles of Railway.

Postage.—Letters for places in Holland, 5c. per 20 grammes; letters for places outside Holland, 12½ c. per 20 grammes—7½ c. for the second 20 grammes. Post Cards for places outside Holland, 5c.

Telegraph.—To Great Britain, 5 words, 50 c.; each additional word 10 c. Inland telegrams, 10 words 25 c.

NOTICES OF TOWNS, ETC.

Amsterdam.—*Stat.*—Pop. (1911) 580,960, of whom about 65,000 are Jews, mostly living in the east part of the city. (*Plan in the Special Edition, or post free 3d. stamps*).

VICTORIA HOTEL.—First-class hotel; 100 rooms and saloons. Modern comfort; moderate prices. See Advt.

AMERICAN HOTEL.—First class; well situated. See Advt.

AMSTEL HOTEL.—First class; centrally situated, overlooking the Amstel River. Suites and single rooms with private baths. See Advt.

BRACK'S DOELEN HOTEL–First class. Patronized by English and Americans. Suites with baths and toilettes. See Advt.

HOTEL DES PAYS BAS.—First class, in central position, with every modern comfort. Patronized by English and Americans. See Advt.

HOTEL MILLE COLONNES.—Old established, well situated on the Rembrandtplein. Restaurant. Terms from 7s. 6d. per day. Rooms, with breakfast, from 4s. 2d. See Advt.

LUTKIE'S PRIVATE HOTEL—High class international family hotel, with all modern comforts. Leidschekade, 88 and 89. See Advt.

EUROPE.

The principal RAILWAY STATIONS are the CENTRAL STATION, on the north side, and the WEESPERPOORT STATION, to the south east; both Stations are within a mile of the centre of the city.

CABS.—Motor cabs, 1,200 mètres (1,310 yards) 40c., each additional 300 mètres 10c. After midnight increased charges. Large article of luggage 15c.

Electric tramways in all directions.

Amsterdam, situated at the confluence of the Rivers Amstel and Ij (or Y), is the commercial capital of Holland, as distinguished from the seat of Government, which is at the Hague; it is also one of the great financial centres of Europe. Many more ships enter and leave Rotterdam than Amsterdam, but most of the Dutch Colonial produce is brought on from the former place to be dealt with at Amsterdam. Among the arts or crafts practised here that of diamond polishing should be mentioned; the craft is mostly in the hands of Jews, employing several thousands.

From the Central Station a way leads south to continue along the west side of a square sheet of water to the Damrak, at the south end of which is the Dam, the centre of the business life of Amsterdam. At the north end of the Damrak is the Beurs (Exchange), at the south end, off the west side, are the Nieuwe Kerk, the Paleis (Royal Palace), and the Zeemanshoop, a maritime institution (seaman's hope). Kalver Straat, running from south side of the Dam, is a principal street, with many good cafés, restaurants, and shops.

The Nieuwe Kerk, Gothic, 1408–70, contains several monuments of admirals and other interesting memorials. The Oude Kerk, dating from 1300, is back from east side of Warmoes Straat, 200 yards east of the Beurs,

Het Paleis (Royal Palace) was erected in 1648 as a Stadhuis, becoming a palace at its presentation in 1808 to King Louis Napoleon. Much sculpture and many fine paintings—the Reception Chamber is especially magnificent; fine chimney piece in Throne Room. Daily, 10 to 3.0 or 4.0, 50 c.

Raadhuis (Town hall), in the Oudezyds Voorburgwal, south east of the Dam. Paintings in the council chamber.

The RIJKS MUSEUM, where are several Collections of great interest, is on the south side of the city—a mile due south of the Dam. The handsome modern building, erected 1877-85, is in Dutch Renaissance style; symbolical sculpture upon the facades. The PICTURE GALLERY (Schilderyen Verzameling), on the first floor, is, with the exception of that at The Hague, the finest in Holland; there are more than 3,000 works by old and modern masters. The names of the most celebrated Netherlands painters constantly recur, Rembrandt, Rubens, Jan Steen, Hals, Dou, etc.; many portraits. In other parts of the building are Collections of Dutch National Costumes, Naval Collections, Military Collections, Colonial Collections. Several rooms are occupied with an Ecclesiastical Exhibition. Rooms are also arranged illustrative of old Dutch life. There are Collections of Porcelain, Glass, Jewelry; cabinets of Engravings; an Admirals room of naval portraits and pictures; an Antiquarian Collection.

The Royal Library is in the Museum. Daily (in winter closed on Monday), 10.0 to 5.0 (in winter 4.0): Sunday, 12.30 to 5.0.

Stedeljik Museum (Municipal Museum), in Paulus Potter Straat, 300 yards south of the Rijks Museum. Collections of uniforms, weapons, and pictures of local military subjects; on floor above is a Collection of modern Dutch paintings, including many fine works. Daily, except Tuesday, 10.0 to 5.0; Sunday, 12.30 to 5.0. Shorter hours in winter.

Fodor Museum, on the Keizersgracht, two-thirds of a mile south east of the Dam. Modern paintings and drawings by old masters. Daily, except Tuesday, 10.0 or 11.0 to 4.0; on Sunday 25 c., other days 50 c.

Six Picture Gallery, on the Heerengracht, about half a mile south east of the Dam. A private collection of celebrated paintings. Admission through consul; fee for charitable purposes, 1 fl.

Willet-Holthuysen Museum, near east end of the Heerengracht; collection of furniture, silver articles, porcelain, glass, etc. Daily, except Friday, 10.0 to 4.0; Sunday 1.30 to 4.0; 25 c., on Sunday 10 c.

Amstelkring Museum, in the Oudezyds Voorburgwal; a collection of Roman Catholic ecclesiastical antiquities.

University, half a mile south east of the Dam, occupying an old alms house; about 1,000 students. The University Library is in the Singel, about half a mile due south of the Dam; 350,000 vols. and many valuable manuscripts.

SHIPPING EXHIBITION.—A most interesting exhibition of all that relates to Dutch Shipping, historical and modern. Also an Exhibition of Women's Work during the century 1813-1913. Both Exhibitions open until the end of September.

Zoological Garden, in east part of city, a mile east of the Dam.

Ooster Park is at the east side, Vondel Park at the south side, of the city.

POST OFFICE.—In the Nieuwe Zyds Voorburgwal, to west of the Royal Palace.

ENG. CH. SERVICE, English Episcopal Church, Groene Burgwal.

SCOTCH PRESB. CH., Begynhof, off Kalver St.

H.B.M.'s CONSUL. — W. A. Churchill, Esq.

VICE-CONSUL.—E. J. Labarre, Esq.

U.S. CONSUL.—F. W. Mahin, Esq.

RAIL, pp. 115A, 118, 118B, 119, 119B, 120.

Arnheim, or Arnhem.—*Stat.*—Pop. (1911) 64,634.

HOTELS: TOELAST; PAYS BAS.

Capital of the Province of Guelderland, on the River Rhine, a very pleasant town in the most picturesque part of Holland, with many handsome modern houses; it is the favourite residence of wealthy Hollanders from the East Indies.

The Railway Station is on the west side of the town, one third mile from the Rhine. At about a mile south east of the Station, near the river, guided by the conspicuous tower of the Groote Kerk, is the Groote Markt. The Groote Kerk, Gothic, dating from 1452, contains several monuments: tower 305 ft. On east side of the church is the Gemeentehuis (Town Hall), once a palace of the Dukes of Guelderland, often styled Duivelshuis (devils house) because of the curious decorations. In the Markt is the Museum van Oudheden en Kunst—portraits. coins, carved ivory, etc. Law courts and other government buildings on the south side of the Markt.

ENG. CH. SERVICE, Lutheran Mission Hall, Tuin Steeg.

GOLF.—9-hole course at Rosendael, 1½ miles from Velp Station.

RAIL, pages 114, 118, 119. Steamer on the Rhine, page 362.

Boskoop.—Pop. 3,297.

A pomological centre, with thousands of acres of roses, azaleas, etc., much visited in the seasons of full bloom. About two miles from Gouda, whence the steamer trip through "Polderland" is very interesting.

Breda.—*Stat.*—Pop. (1911) 27,259.

HOTELS: DE KROON; ZWAAN; WAPEN VAN NASSAU.

A once strongly fortified town on the Rivers Merk and Aa. In the Markt is the Hervormde Kerk, Gothic, dating from 1290, containing some magnificent monuments; satirical wood carving in choir. Of the old castle, completed by William III of England, all that was interesting was destroyed when it was converted into a military academy.

RAIL, pages 113, 116.

Delft.—*Stat.*—Pop. (1911) 34,485

HOTELS: WILHELMINA; LUBRECHTS; BOLK; BALKENENDE.

An old fashioned town on the River Schie, with many clean canals bordered by lime trees. Delft pottery was renowned in the 17th and 18th centuries; after a decline, interest in it has been revived.

From the Railway Station, in the south west part of the town, the tower of the Nieuwe Kerk, in the Groote Markt, is seen, half a mile to north east.

The Nieuwe Kerk, dating from 1396, has a magnificent monument of William of Orange, murdered at the Prinsenhof; other princely monuments; tomb of Grotius (Hugo de Groot, 1583-1645). On the west side of the Markt is the Stadhuis, where are some good paintings.

A quarter of a mile north west of the Groote Markt, on the west bank of the Oude Delft, is the Prinsenhof, once a monastery, later the residence of the princes of Orange, now occupied by the Gemeente Museum. Here William of Orange was murdered by Balthasar Gerhard on 10th July, 1584; an inscription on the first-floor by the stairs marks the fatal spot.

Oude Kerk, dating from 15th cent., opposite the Prinsenhof; the tower leans slightly; within are monuments of Dutch naval heroes.

RAIL, page 119.

Dordrecht, or **Dort.**—*Stat.*—Pop. (1911) 47,304.

HOTELS: BELLEVUE; ARMES DE HOLLANDE.

Situated on an island of the River Maas, a busy timber dealing, ship building place, in the 16th century one of the most important cities of Holland; famous Synod (Nov. 1618-May 1619) held here, when the Calvinist party prevailed over the Arminians. The Groote Kerk has conspicuous tower; interior bare, but finely carved choir stalls. In Museum Straat, in east part of the town, is the Zuid-Afrikaansch Museum (South African Museum), containing exhibits associated with President Kruger, President Steyn, the Boer generals, etc. Adjoining is the Municipal Museum, with a collection of paintings, mostly modern. The Groothoofd Poort, an ancient gate, at one end of Wyn Straat, contains a collection of antiquities.

H.B.M.'s VICE-CONSUL.-J. J. Vriesendorp, Esq.

RAIL, pages 116, 119.

Flushing (Dutch, **Vlissingen).**—*Stat.*—Pop. 21,778.

HOTELS: COMMERCE; ZEELAND.

A seaport on the south coast of the Island of Walcheren, at the mouth of the River Scheldt, here nearly two and a half miles wide. The steamers from Queenborough go alongside the Harbour Railway Station.

The principal importance of Flushing is derived from the traffic to and from England, but it is also a sea bathing resort. At the Gevangentoren is a collection of local antiquities. Church of St. Jacob, 14th cent. The great Dutch naval hero, Admiral de Ruyter (1607-1676) was born here.

H.B.M.'s V.-CONSUL.—P. de Bruyne, Esq.

U.S. CON.-AGENT.

RAIL, page 113. Steamer across the river to Breskens and Terneuzen several times a day.

Gouda.—*Stat.*—Pop. (1911) 24,850.

Situated at the confluence of the Rivers Gouw and Yssel. In the Markt, quarter mile from the Railway Station, are the Stadhuis (1449-59) and the Museum, the latter containing antiquities and a few paintings. Close by is the Groote Kerk, with beautiful stained glass windows.

RAIL, pages 115A, 118.

Groningen.—*Stat.*—Pop. (1911) 77,221.

HOTELS: DOELEN; FRIGGE; WILLEMS.

Capital of the Province of Groningen, situated at the confluence of the Rivers Hoornsche Diep and Drentsche Diep (or Reitdiep). Large trade in grain and rape seed.

From the Railway Station, on the south side of the town, the Stations Weg runs east to the bridge, thence the street running north in a line with the bridge leads to the Groote Markt. **The Stadhuis (Town Hall) is in the Groote Markt, where also is the Martin Kerk, Gothic, 1627, with tower 320 ft. high.**

The University, in a modern building, 1909, is 200 yards west of the Groote Markt; about 500 students; in the library is a copy of the New Testament of Erasmus bearing marginal notes by Luther. Opposite the University is the Roman Catholic Broeder Kerk—paintings in interior. In the Groningsche Museum, half a mile south west of the Groote Markt, are collections of antiquities and of modern art.

H.B.M.'s VICE-CONSUL.—A. P. Schilthuis, Esq.

RAIL, pages 115, 115A.

Haarlem.—*Stat.*—Pop. (1911) 69,988.

HOTELS: FUNCKLER; LEEUWERIK; 'T WAPPEN VAN AMSTERDAM.

A pleasant, clean, thriving town of north Holland, on the River Spaarne, the centre of a famous horticultural district, whence bulbs (hyacinths, tulips, crocuses, lilies, etc.) are exported all over Europe.

From the Railway Station, on the north side of the town, either of the streets running south leads in half a mile to the Groote Markt, at the centre of the town.

Groote Kerk (St. Bavo), in the Groote Markt, dating from 15th cent., tower 262 ft. high; interesting interior—the organ was for a long time the largest in the world. Before the Church is a statue of Coster, who was locally claimed as the inventor of printing.

By the west end of the Kerk is the Vleeschhal (Meat Markt), erected 1602-3, a very quaint building, where now the National Archives are stored.

Stadhuis (Town Hall), on west side of the Groote Markt; here is a small picture gallery, including several works by Franz Hals. Weekdays 10.0 to 4.0, 25c.; Sunday 12.0 to 3.0, free. Library at the back of the Stadhuis.

Bisschopelijk Museum (Episcopal Museum), on east side of Jans Straat, near the Groote Markt. Collection of antiquities connected with Dutch Church. Daily except Sunday, 10.0 to 5.0, 25c.

Teijler Museum, at the river end of Dam Straat, east side of the Groote Markt; small collection of paintings, a geological collection, many scientific instruments, library. Monday to Friday 11.0 to 3.0.

Paviljoen Museum, on south side of Frederiks Park, to the south of the town; an art industrial museum and a colonial museum. South of the Paviljoen is a beautiful park of beech and lime trees.

GOLF.—Course at Velsen.

RAIL, pages 119, 119B.

[The country on the west side of Haarlem, towards the sea, is very attractive, with good views from the dunes.

Zandvoort.—*Stat.*—Pop. 3,800.

HOTELS: D'ORANGE; KURSAAL; DRIEHUIZEN.

A fishing village and sea side resort 5½ miles south west of Haarlem. Good beach.

RAIL, page 119.]

The HAGUE (*Dutch*, **'s Graven Hage, or den Haag**).—*Stat.*—Pop. (1911), 288,577.

GRAND HOTEL PAULEZ.—First class. In proximity to the museums. Trams in all directions. See Advt.

HOTEL DES INDES.—First class. Write for illustrated Booklet of Hague. Proprietor, C. T. Haller. See Advt.

HOTEL D' ANGLETERRE.—First class family hotel, centrally situated, 22, Wagenstraat. Every comfort; electric light, central heating. Moderate terms, from 8s. per day. See Advt.

GRAND HOTEL-RESTAURANT "CENTRAL."—First class. Rooms with bath and toilette. Rooms with breakfast from 2.50 fl. See Advt.

PENSION ZORGVLIET.—6, Groot Hertoginnenlaan. First class, in best position. Villa. Every comfort; highest references. Pension from 6s. to 12s. See Advt.

There are two Railway Stations. The State Railway Station is on the east side of the town, the Hollandsche Station is on the south side of the town; both are within three quarters of a mile of the centre.

CABS.—Motor cabs, 1,000 mètres (1,090 yards) 50c., each additional 500 mètres 10c. Extra after midnight. Each large article of luggage 10 c.

The Hague is the political capital of Holland, the residence of the Queen, and the seat of government. It is a town of broad handsome thoroughfares, with stately public buildings and houses; there is practically no trade beyond a few small industries in furniture, metal work, pottery, etc. The Dutch name, 'S Graven Hage, signifies the Count's Enclosure (or park), and the town has grown from a hunting place in early times of the Counts of Holland.

From the Station of the State Railway proceed westward for about a third of a mile, then turn to right (north), and in a quarter of a mile the Vijver will be reached; the Vijver is a sheet of water at about the centre of the town, where fashionable life gathers. From the Hollandsche Station the way to the Vijver is due north for about three quarters of a mile.

Royal Palace (Paleis des Konings), on west side of the Noordeinde, a broad thoroughfare near west-end of the Vijver. Only to be seen during absence of royal family.

The Binnenhof, the old palace of the Stadtholders, is on the south side of the Vijver; it is an extensive range of buildings dating from 1250; some parts have been rebuilt and others restored. The west wing, near the Vijver, is occupied by the Chambers of the States General (Staten Generaal); on the east side of the inner courtyard is the turretted Ridderzaal (Hall of Knights), where the archives are kept, and on the south side of the Ridderzaal is the Gerechtshof (Law Courts). Several Government Offices occupy other parts of the Binnenhof.

The Mauritshuis, where is the famous PICTURE GALLERY, is the corner building by the Vijver, at its east end. The collection (Koninklyk Kabinet van Shilderyen) includes about 500 paintings, three fourths belonging to the Dutch School. There are paintings by Rembrandt, Potter, Ostade, Jan Steen, Gerard Dou, Terburg, Ruysdaels—all masterpieces; beside works by Rubens, Teniers, van Dyck, Holbein, van der Meer, and other well known names. The most celebrated paintings are: (155), view of Haarlem, by Jacob van Ruysdael; (146), School of Anatomy, by Rembrandt; (129), The Fiddler, by Adrian van Ostade; (145), Presentation in the Temple, by Rembrandt; (147), Susanna, by Rembrandt; (176), The Dispatch, by Gerard Terburg; (136), a Bull, by Paul Potter; (166), Poultry, by Jan Steen; (32), a Young Mother, by Gerard Dou; (170), a picture of life, by Jan Steen. Weekdays 10.0 to 5.0 (4.0 in winter), Sunday 12.30 to 4.0.

Gevangenpoort, just away from south west end of the Vijver; an old tower and gate where the brothers de Witt were murdered by the mob, 1672.

Stadhuis (Town Hall), 250 yards south west of the Vijver. Immediately opposite is the Groote Kerk (St. James), Gothic, 15th-16th cent., with monuments in interior; tower 330 ft. high. The Nieuwe Kerk, on the Spui, quarter mile south east of the Vijver, contains tombs of the de Witts and Spinoza.

Gemeente Museum (Municipal Museum) at north east end of the Vijver; a gallery of paintings, and collections of antiquities, medals, porcelain, and glass. Weekdays 10.0 to 4.0 (3.0 in winter), Sunday 1.0 to 4.0.

Mesdag Museum, in the Laan van Meerdervoort, in west part of the town. Collection of very fine modern paintings. Weekdays, 10.0 to 5.0 or 3.0; Sunday, 12.30 to 5.0 or 3.0; 25c.

Bibliotheek (Library), on north west side of Lange Voorhout, 200 yards back from west side of the Vijver. 500,000 vols.; in room on an upper floor are Bibles and prayer books with historical associations. Extensive collections of medals, coins, and gems, in the same building.

Meermanno Westreenianum, on the Nieuwe Prinsesse Gracht, quarter mile north of the Vijver. Collection of early printed books, manuscripts, coins, and curiosities.

Zoological Garden, third of a mile north west of the Vijver.

Haagsche Bosch, a beautiful park, about a mile north of the Vijver; at north east corner of the park is a royal villa, Huis ten Bosch (House in the wood)—interesting rooms.

The "Peace Palace" (Vrede Paleis), towards whose cost Mr. Carnegie has given £300,000, is on the Zorgvliet, at the beginning of the old road to Scheveningen. On August 29th the Palace will be inaugurated.

POST OFFICE.—Opposite the north side of the Groote Kerk, 350 yards south west of the Vijver.

ENG. CH. SERVICE.—St. John and St. Philip, Van den Bosch Straat.

BRITISH MINISTER.—Hon. Sir Alan Johnstone G.C.V.O. SEC. OF LEG.—Lord Acton, M.V.O. VICE-CONSUL.—G. Barger, Esq.

U.S. MIN.—His Excy. Lloyd Bryce. SEC. OF LEG.—J. G. Bailey, Esq.

GOLF.—9-hole course on Chingendael racecourse, 3 miles from The Hague.

RAIL, pp. 115A, 118, 119.

Helder.—*Stat.*—Pop. (1911), 27,156.
HOTELS: BELLEVUE; BURG; TOELAST.
Situated at the extreme north of the mainland of North Holland, where the violence of the wind and encroachment of the sea are constant dangers. The gigantic Helder Dyke is 6¼ miles long, 12 feet broad, and goes down 200 feet into the sea at an angle of 40°. Three quarters of a mile east of Heider is **Nieuwediep,** a naval station, with dockyard, arsenals, and Naval Schools.
H.B.M'S VICE-CONSUL.—W. J. van Neck, Esq.
RAIL, page 119B.

Hoek van Holland (Hook of Holland).—*Stat.*
A growing port at the mouth of the Maas, where the Harwich steamers land and embark passengers. The Quay is accessible at all states of the tide.
RAIL, page 112.

Leiden, or **Leyden.**—*Stat.*—Pop. (1911) 59,133
HOTELS: LEVEDAG; GOUDEN LEEUW; SOLEIL D'OR; CENTRAL; PLACE ROYAL.
The Railway Station is at the north west corner of the town, nearly a mile from the centre.
A very old town, situated upon numerous small islands, among which flows what is called the Old Rhine. Previous to the great siege by the Spaniards, October 1573 to March 1574, Leiden had a population of 100,000.
From the Railway Station the Stations Weg leads south towards Breede Straat, the principal thoroughfare.
Museum van Oudheden, at west end, north side, of Breede Straat. Here are collections of antiquities (Egypt well represented). Stadhuis (Town Hall), 16th cent., on north side of Breede Straat; good facade and spire.
St. Pieters Kerk, 100 yards south west of the Stadhuis, largest church in Leiden, many eminent men buried here. Just south of St. Pieters Kerk, in the Klok Steeg, is a house with an inscription stating that John Robinson, a leader of the first pilgrim fathers banished from England, lived there, 1611-25. Hooglandsche Kerk (St. Pancras), 200 yards east of the Stadhuis; monuments.
Municipal Museum, in the Oude Singel, east of south end of Stations Weg; some good paintings and a collection of local antiquities. Daily 10.0 to 4.0, 10c.
Ethnographical Museum, in the Hoogewoerd, in south east part of the town; collections from Australia, the Dutch Colonies, and the Southern Ocean. Other collections from India, China, and Japan at 69, Rapenburg, in the south west district. Natural History Museum at 28, Rapenburg. 112, Rapenburg, bears a tablet to the effect that Jean Luzac, a friend of Washington, lived there.
The University buildings (Academiegebouwen) are a distance apart. The principal building is by the Van der Werf Park, on the south side of the town; the University Library, 250 yards west of the main building, is one of the most valuable in Holland—190,000 vols. and 6,400 MSS; branch of the University by the north end of the Botanical Garden. There are about 1,500 students; founded 1575, at one time the University was famed throughout Europe.
RAIL, pages 117, 119, 119B.

[**Katwyk-aan-Zee.**—Pop. 8,000.
GROOT BADHOTEL; RHIN.
A favourite Dutch seaside resort, 6m. from Leiden by steam tramway, the road passing Endegeest, where Descartes (1596-1650) lived and wrote his chief works, and Rynsburg, where Spinoza (1660-63) lived (small Spinoza Museum). At Katwyk the Old Rhine finds its way into the sea; at high tide the sea is 12 ft. higher than the river level, at low tide the sluice gates are opened, when the confined Rhine streams out washing away the otherwise choking sand thrown up by the sea.]

Maestricht, or **Maastricht.**—*Stat.*—Pop. (1911) 38,233.
HOTELS: DU LEVRIER; EMPEREUR.
Capital of Dutch Limburg, on the River Maas; the Roman Trajectum ad Mosam. A little south of the Station, a street leads west to the bridge and across to the centre of the town at the Vrythof—about a mile. St. Servatius Kerk, in the Vrythof, dating from the 11th or 12th cent., on a much older foundation (560–599), is regarded as the oldest church in the Netherlands; over the porch is the Emperor's Hall, a domed chamber of great interest; objects of interest in the treasury. In the Groote Markt, 100 yards north east of the Vrythof, is the Stadhuis (1658-64), where are a few paintings and some tapestry; at the old Stadhuis, close by in Kleine Straat, is the Oudheidkundig Museum, a collection of antiquities. Church of Onze Lieve Vrouwe, quarter mile south east of the Vrythof, of 11th cent., restored. The Petersberg, a short distance south of the town, for centuries yielded great quantities of building stone, with a result that there is a labyrinth of galleries in the disused quarries many miles in length; it is dangerous to enter the passages without a guide.
RAIL, pages 99, 111, 114.

Middelburg.—*Stat.*—Pop. 19,150.
HOTELS: GRAND; NIEUWE DOELEN; ABDY.
Capital of the Province of Zeeland. The Gothic Stadhuis (Town Hall), dating from 16th cent. (tower 180 ft. high; many statues on the facade), contains a Museum (Oudheidkamer) of curiosities. At the Zeeuwsch Genootschap der Wetenschappen are collections of Roman and other antiquities; many maps, plans, coins; objects associated with Admiral de Ruyter; cabinets of Zeeland flora and fauna.
Abdij (Abbey), dating from 12th cent., rebuilt after a fire in 1492; in large hall is fine tapestry representing battles with the Spaniards. Nieuwe Kerk, formerly the Abbey Church, contains several monuments.
Exhibition of Dutch Costumes and popular Art, during summer of 1913.
RAIL, page 118.

Nymegen, or **Nymwegen.**-*Stat.*-Pop. (1911), 57,116.

HOTELS: KEIZER KAARL; MULDER; BELLEVUE; BERG EN DAL.

On the River Waal, situated amidst well wooded attractive environs. The Railway Station is in the south west part of the town, about two thirds of a mile from the Groote Markt, just west of which is the Groote Kerk, dating from 1272—monuments in interior. The Stadhuis, in Korte Burcht Straat, erected 1554, having statues of German monarchs on the facade, contains an interesting Museum of antiquities. On the east side of the town, on an eminence near the river, is a pleasure ground, the Valkhof, where are a few remains of a palace of the Carlovingian emperors.

During the summer of 1913 EXHIBITION of Roman and other antiquities found in the neighbourhood.

RAIL, pages 114, 118B, 119, 120A.

Rotterdam.—*Stat.*—Pop. (1911), 436,018.

HOTEL LEYGRAAFF.—First class, well situated, overlooking the park. Every modern comfort. English and American connection. Rooms from 4s. 6d. See Advt.

MAAS HOTEL.—First class; up-to-date comfort. Rooms from 5s. See Advt.

GRAND HOTEL COOMANS.—First class commercial and family hotel; 175 rooms. Electric light; lift; central heating. Room and breakfast from 2fl. See Advt.

VICTORIA; WEIMAR.

There are three RAILWAY STATIONS at Rotterdam, all on the north side of the river. BEURS Station, in a line with the railway bridge across the river, less than quarter mile from bridge; MAAS Station, on the quay, quarter mile up the river from the railway bridge; DELFTSCHE POORT Station, on north west side of town, a mile from the river.

STEAMERS of the Batavier Line from and to London berth at the quay along the north side of the river; the Hull and Netherlands Line steamers berth at the Parkhaven, also on the north side.

CABS.—Motor cabs, 1,200 mètres (1,310 yards) 60c., each additional 400 mètres 10c. Horsed cabs, 2,400 mètres 60c., each additional 800 mètres 10c. Increased charges after midnight. Large articles of luggage 10c.

Electric tramways in all directions.

Rotterdam, situated on both banks of the Maas, about 15 miles from the sea, is the principal seaport of Holland, large ships being able to come alongside the river quays. Half the import trade of Holland is received here, and the exports reach nearly the same magnitude. There are few "sights," the chief interests being in the harbour and the great commercial activity.

The broad quay on the north side of the river, extending half a mile on the seaward side of the bridge, is De Boompjes. At the end of the Boompjes a street runs off into the town by the railway, leading to the Beurs Station, and then, in 200 yards, to the cross Hoogstraat, the principal street.

Groote Kerk (Church of St. Lawrence), close to the railway, a few yards north of its intersection of Hoogstraat. A Gothic brick church, dating from 1412; tower 210 feet high; tombs of Dutch admirals in interior.

Boymans Museum, on Schiedamschedyk, a few yards south of west end of Hoogstraat; collection of pictures by old and modern Dutch masters. Daily, 10.0 or 11.0 to 3.0 or 5.0, at varying charges. In the same building, on the ground floor, is the municipal collection of antiquities.

Beurs (Exchange), opposite the Beurs Station. A little north of the Beurs, in the Groote Markt, is a statue of Erasmus.

Park, close to the river. Zoological and Botanical Garden at north west corner of town.

POST OFFICE.—In the Beursplein, opposite, on west side, the Beurs Station.

ENGLISH CHURCH SERVICE.—St. Mary's in Haringvlet. The church was built by the celebrated general the Duke of Marlborough, and has been used as barracks, hospital, storehouse, and armoury.

SCOTCH CHURCH, Vasteland 2, service at 10.30 and 6.30.

H. B. M.'s CONSUL.—H. Turing, Esq. VICE-CONSULS.—F. W. Manners, Esq., and J. W. van Dyk, Esq.

U.S. CONSUL GENERAL.—Soren Listoe, Esq. VICE-CONSUL.—G. H. Krogh, Esq.

RAIL pages 112, 115A, 116, 118, 119.

Scheveningen.—*Stat.*—Pop. 26,000.

HOTEL PALACE, and others. See Advt.

Scheveningen, formerly a quiet fishing haven, is now, during the bathing season, one of the most frequented, brightest, and fashionable seaside resorts on the Continent, the near proximity of The Hague, 3 miles distant, greatly adding to its importance. Sands are good; season June until end of Sept. Excellent concerts. Kurhaus and Kursaal; lighthouse; marine hospital for children—the Sophie Stichting; mon. to Wil. I. Charles II of England embarked here at the Restoration. Numerous villas and private lodgings. Many fishing boats.

Constant Tramway service between The Hague and Scheveningen; for service in connection with trains to and from The Hague, see page 119.

CABS.—Motor cabs, 1,000 mètres (1,090 yards) 50c., each additional 500 mètres 10c. Increased charges after midnight; luggage, 10c. each large article.

Post and Telegraph Office, Badhuisstraat; also at the Kurhaus.

ENGLISH CHURCH at the Kurhaus.

H. B. M.'s VICE-CONSUL.—G. Barger, Esq.

GOLF.—9-hole course, near to sea; separate ladies' course; club house.

RAIL, page 119.

Utrecht.—*Stat.*—Pop. (1911), 121,317.

HOTEL DES PAYS-BAS.—First class, in finest and quietest position. Every modern comfort and convenience. Moderate terms. See Advt.

EUROPE; CENTRAL.

There are two Railway Stations — Central Station, on the west side of the city, and Maliebaan Station, on the east side; each about half a mile from the Cathedral, at the centre.

CABS.—Stations to town, 60c.

Capital of the Province of Utrecht, the Roman Trajectum ad Rhenum, a very old place; the River Rhine here separates into two streams, the Old Rhine flowing into the North Sea at Katwyk, the other branch, the Vecht, flowing into the Zuyderzee near Muiden. Utrecht is in many respects a pleasant city, the line of the old ramparts is covered by promenades bordered by streams; on the east side is a famous avenue, the Maliebaan, where are many handsome houses. The so-called "Jansenists" (named after Jansenius, Bishop of Ypres, died 1638) are also called the Church of Utrecht, as the city is the seat of their Archbishop; the Church of Utrecht, or ancient Church of Holland, is in full union with the Old Catholic Churches of Germany, Switzerland, Austria, and Russian Poland.

The Dom (Cathedral of St. Martin) is half a mile due east of the Central Station, or half a mile north west of the Maliebaan Station. Erected 1254-67, it was one of the largest churches in the country, but in 1674 a storm destroyed the nave, and the tower is now separated from the choir by a wide interval; tower 338 ft. high, fine view; cloisters on south side of choir. Universiteit (University) on south side of Cathedral, founded 1636—there are about 1,000 students; the Bibliotheek (University Library) is one third mile north of the University, in Wittevrouwenstraat—about 250,000 vols., 1,500 MSS.

Aartsbisschoppelyk Museum (Archiepiscopal Museum), in the Nieuwe Gracht, 200 yards south east of the Cathedral. Collection of objects—paintings, vessels, vestments, etc.—associated with the Church. Daily except Sunday, 10.0 to 5.0, 50c.

Kunstliefde Museum, a little north of the Vredenburg, close to the Central Station. Small collection of paintings, including works by artists of Utrecht. Daily 25c.

Museum van Oudheden, at north end of the Maliebaan. Interesting collection of ancient and mediæval antiquities. Daily 10.0 to 4.0, 10c.; Sunday and Wednesday afternoon, free.

During the summer of 1913 there will be an EXHIBITION of early Dutch painting.

CHURCH OF ENGLAND SERVICE.—At Church recently erected.

H.B.M.'S VICE-CONSUL.—John Twiss, Esq.

RAIL, pages 115, 115A, 117, 118, 118B.

[**Soestdyk.** HOTEL UBBINK. 12 miles north of Utrecht, near Baarn Railway Station. Royal residence; the wood is open to the public.]

Zaandam.—*Stat.*—Pop. (1911) 25,305.

HOTEL DE ZON.

A busy town situated on the River Zaan. Most of the houses are only one or two storied, painted either green or red; innumerable windmills. The only attraction is the Hut of Peter the Great, on the west bank of river, south side of town; here Peter the Great lived for about a week in 1697 while he worked as a carpenter in the shipyard of Mynheer Kalf.

RAIL, pages 119B, 120; Steamer to and from Amsterdam several times daily.

[The **Nordzee Kanaal**, connecting the North Sea with the Zuider Zee, giving Amsterdam direct access to the North Sea, has its eastern end just south of Zaandam. The Canal is about 15 miles long, 60 to 110 yards wide, and about 30 ft. deep.]

LUXEMBURG (Grand Duchy).

A Grand Duchy, declared neutral by the great Powers of Europe, at London, May 11th, 1867. Grand Duchess, Marie, born 1894, succeeded February, 1912.

Population, 259,891; one tenth of the inhabitants not native. **Area**—998 square miles.

Money, same as in Belgium, but German money is more generally used.

Government.—A Constitutional Monarchy. The Chamber of Deputies is composed of 53 members, one for each 5,000 of the population, elected for six years.

The Grand Duchy of Luxemburg, which belonged successively to Burgundy, Spain, Austria, and France, was restored to its nationality as a member of the German Confederation under the sceptre of the Prince of Orange-Nassau, by the Congress of Vienna, 1815. The strong fortress was dismantled in accordance with the terms of the Congress of London, 1867.

Diekirch.—*Stat.*—Pop. 3,500.

HOTELS: DES ARDENNES; EUROPE.

Very picturesquely situated on the left bank of the River Sauer, at the base of the Herrenberg and the Schutzenberg. Modern Romanesque Church of St. Lawrence; one or two old churches. In the place of the old town walls are broad tree planted avenues.

RAIL, pages 212, 212B.

Echternach.—*Stat.*—Pop. 4,200.

HOTEL BELLEVUE.

On the River Sauer. The Benedictine Abbey, dating from the 7th century, is in a good state of preservation; the abbey church of St. Willibrord was founded 1017. Old Rathaus. At Echternach on Whit Tuesday there is a pilgrim procession known as the "Dancing Procession," commemorative of a cure by St. Willibrord of a convulsion that attacked the cattle of the neighbourhood. Very pretty scenery near Echternach.

RAIL, page 212B.

Larochette.—*Stat.*—Pop. 2,000.

HOTEL DE LA POSTE.

In the Valley of the Weisse Erenz, finely situated in a broken wooded country. Right over the town, on a rock, are the ruins of the old castle. In the neighbourhood is the Duke of Arenberg's Chateau of Meysemburg.

RAIL, page 212B.

Luxemburg.—*Stat.*—Pop. 20,848.

GRAND HOTEL BRASSEUR.—First class hotel, well spoken of; situated near the park and the new promenades. Omnibus at the Station. See Advt.

GRAND HOTEL DE COLOGNE.—First class hotel, in central position. Large garden. The English Club rooms are in the hotel. Rooms from M. 2.50. Motor bus at Station. See Advt.

The Railway Station is on the south side of the town, about a mile from points of interest. Trams from Station into the town.

Luxemburg, the capital of the Duchy, occupies a uniquely picturesque situation. The upper part, the Oberstadt, is on the level summit of a rocky height which rises precipitously on three sides, 200 ft.; below are the Alzette and Petrusse streams, and from their opposite banks equally precipitous rocks rise. The lower town, the Unterstädte, lies in the ravine between the heights. Of the fortifications only some of the oldest parts remain.

The tramway from the Station runs into the Place de la Constitution, whence is a fine view; within a quarter of a mile north of the Place are clustered the principal buildings of the town. The old Royal Palace, erected 1580, is now the residence of the Grand Duke. Gothic Cathedral of Notre Dame, 17th cent. Hotel de Ville, where is a collection of pictures. Municipal collection of antiquities. In the ravine of the Petrusse, towards the Station, is the ancient Chapel of St. Quirinus, cut in the rock, with old Romanesque carvings on the altar. Of the extensive castle of the Spanish Governor, Prince Mansfeld, once just outside the town on the north east side, nothing whatever remains; near here is a huge statue of St. Joseph.

H.B.M.'s MINISTER.—Hon. Sir A. Johnstone, G.C.V.O.

H.B.M.'s CONSUL.—N. le Gallais, Esq.

RAIL, pages 103A, 210, 212, 212B.

Mondorf.—*Stat.*—

HOTEL DU GRAND CHEF.

At Mondorf are warm saline springs, 68° Fahrenheit, useful in cases of rheumatism, scrofula, nervous diseases, and bronchial affections.

RAIL, page 212B.

Vianden.—*Stat.*—Pop. 1,600.

HOTEL DES ETRANGERS.

A very picturesque place on the River Our. The once celebrated castle has fallen into decay; the chapel and halls retain their interest. Victor Hugo lived here in exile; a tablet marks the house. Several most interesting walks and excursions in the neighbourhood.

RAIL, page 212B.

GERMANY—THE RHINE.

From DUSSELDORF to MANNHEIM.

The River Rhine is abundantly interesting from its impetuous source to its sluggish meeting with the sea. The quaint Dutch towns of the lower part, the giant industries of the middle part, attractive Dusseldorf, and then Cologne and a succession of vine clad hills, rugged peaks, ruined castles, and modern princely palaces, with the glamour of history and legend clinging to many a scene, make travel either up or down the river a memorable event. Travellers whose time is limited often begin their experience of the Rhine at Cologne, but those who make Dusseldorf a starting place will be amply repaid by the modernity of this interesting city.

The distance from Rotterdam to Mannheim may be travelled in one steamer, taking about three days. The length of the Rhine from Basle to the sea is 526 miles; from Mannheim to Cologne 162 miles. The breadth at Cologne is 433 yards, at Bonn 532 yards, at Coblence 399 yards, at Mayence 492 yards, at Mannheim 429 yards. The deepest part is at the Lurleiberg, 76 feet. At the two sources the waters are at a height above sea of 7,689 ft. (Vorder Rhein) and 7,268 ft. (Hinter Rhein); at Mannheim the river level is 280 ft. above sea, at Mayence 265 ft., at Coblence 190 ft., at Cologne 142 ft.

Steamers on the Rhine. See page 362.

Note.—"**Right**" and "**Left**" here mean Right and Left when looking to the bow of the boat, in going up the river.

Dusseldorf—see page 473.

COLOGNE, or KOLN.—*Stat.*— (*Plan in Special Edition, or post free 3d. stamps*).—Pop. (1910) 516,527.

EXCELSIOR HOTEL ERNST.—Entirely new first class establishment. Facing the Cathedral, and two minutes from Station. Up to date in every respect. See Advt.

HOTEL DU DOME, Dome Square, exactly opposite the Cathedral, two minutes walk from the Central Station. Electric light; baths. See Advt.

HOTEL DU NORD, an excellent hotel, near the Central Station, the Cathedral, the Rhine, etc. See Advt.

HOTEL DISCH.—Near Station, Steamboat Landing, and Cathedral, Patronised by English and American travellers; rebuilt 1911-12. See Advt.

HOTEL DE COLOGNE.—Situated opposite the Central Railway Station. Electric light; lift. See Advt.

SAVOY HOTEL (GROSSER KURFURST).—First class family hotel, near Central Station, and facing chief entrance to Cathedral. English Club in hotel. See Advt.

MONOPOL HOTEL.—Comfortable hotel, situated close to the Station and the Cathedral. See Advt.

CITY HOTEL.—First class, facing the Central Station, entirely new, and very moderate. Hot and cold water in each room. See Advt.

GRAND HOTEL BELGIQUE.—In proximate vicinity of the Central Station and Cathedral. Lift; electric light, and central heating. See Advt.

MINERVA HOTEL.—Fine new modern house, with all latest improvements, between Railway Station and Landing Pier of Steamers. Renowned house for Rhine and Moselle wines. See Advt.

STAPEL HAUS—Built 1531. One of the sights of Cologne. Beautiful location on the Rhine, between Nord and Victoria Hotels; large concert hall; restaurant. See Advt.

HOTEL CONTINENTAL.—On the Cathedral square and close to Station and Landing Stage. Entirely renewed in 1912. Every modern comfort. See Advt.

WESTMINSTER HOTEL.—Situated near the Cathedral, Central Station, and landing places of boats. Lift; baths. See Advt.

HOTEL HAMBURGER HOF.—Facing the Station, north portal. Very comfortable, new, and strictly moderate. English spoken. Rooms from 2 m. 50 pf. See Advt.

PENSION M. AND C. MIDDENDORFF—Gilbachstrasse, 11, formerly Engelbertstrasse, 67. Comfortable family home in best and quietest position. Every comfort. Highest references. Pension from M. 5. See Advt.

ZUM TREPPCHEN, 38 to 44, Am Hof, close to Cathedral. First class Wine Restaurant. Fixed price Dinners, Luncheons, and Suppers, and à la carte. Fine wines. Proprietor, Mathias Beckmann, Treppchen-Kellerei, Cologne. Shipper of Hocks and Moselles to all countries.

The principal Railway Station, the CENTRAL BAHNHOF, is close to the Cathedral.

The Rhine is east of the Central Bahnhof, less than a quarter mile. The Landing Stage of the Cologne and Dusseldorf Steamship Co. is a few yards up river from the old boat bridge—less than a mile from the Central Station. The Landing Stage of the Nederland Co. is within five minutes of the Central Station.

TAXAMETER CABS, or Motor Cabs.—1 or 2 persons, about ½ mile (800 mèters), 50 pf., with 10 pf. for each additional 400 mèters. Luggage under 22 lbs. free; 22 lbs. to 55 lbs. 25 pf.

Electric Trams traverse the town.

COLOGNE (German Köln, or Cöln), lies on the left bank of the River Rhine, 120 ft. above sea level; it is an imperial fortress, the largest town of the Rhine Provinces of Prussia, and one of the most important commercial places in Germany.

Deutz is on the opposite side of the Rhine. A handsome modern bridge—the Hohenzollern Brucke—connects Cologne and Deutz; the bridge, completed 1911, cost about £750,000 very fine view of the Cathedral from the bridge. In the modern parts of Cologne the streets are spacious, but in the older parts, near the river, the streets are narrow and gloomy.

The Dom (Cathedral) is sometimes described as the most magnificent Gothic edifice in the world. Meister Gerard is regarded as the author of the design, the immediately following architects being Meister Arnold and his son Meister Johann. It was founded 14th Aug., 1248, and completed 14th Aug. 1880, at a cost of £2,000,000. Walk

round the outside to see the full beauty of the colossal structure—its flying buttresses, choir, south transept (240 feet high by 130 feet wide), west door, and clustered spires. Width of nave and aisles 144ft.; the nave is 145ft. and the aisles are 60ft. high, on about 100 clustered pillars. The height to the ridge of the roof is over 200 ft.; the central spire is 350ft. high; and the two West Spires are 512ft. above the level of the floor from which they rise. Ascend the galleries round the choir. The painted glass in the triforium, clerestory, and aisle windows is very rich; a good deal is modern work by Munich artists. Eight choir Chapels—one being the Three Kings (or Magi) Chapel; Gold Chamber or Treasury of plated relics; Library; Kaiser Bell of 25 tons weight; Teufelsstein, or stone thrown by the Devil from the Seven Mountains; tombs of Marie de Medicis, of Archbp. Conrad von Hochstaden, the founder, and of Archbp. Anton von Schaumberg, etc. Entrance to the nave and transept free all the day, except from 9 to 10 and 3 to 3.30. To see the Choir, and the Treasury of the Three Kings, 1 mk. 50 pf. each. To ascend the tower, as far as the pinnacles (grand view), 1 mark extra. Tickets from the Domschweizer.

The CHURCHES of Cologne are numerous and all interesting. Near the centre of the city are: Gross St. Martin, between Altermarkt and the river, a fine specimen of restored Romanesque, with a tower (270 ft.). St. Maria-im-Capitol, in Marien Platz, off the south end of Hochstrasse, towards the river, of 11th cent.; paintings and sculpture. St. George, beyond south end of Hochstrasse, 16th cent. St. Peter, in Sternengasse, running west from south end of Hochstrasse; "Crucifixion" by Rubens over high altar (fee 1m. 50pf.); Rubens' father buried here. St. Cæcilia, adjoining St. Peter's church, parts as old as 10th cent. Minorites Church, adjoining the Museum, restored early Gothic, contains tomb of Duns Scotus (died 1309).

On the north side are: St. Cunibert, by the river, beyond railway bridge; fine stained glass. St. Andreas, just west of the Dom; remains of Albertus Magnus in Gothic reliquary. Jesuits' Church, west side of Central Bahnhof; pulpit and high altar much decorated; the bells of this church were cast from cannon taken by Tilly at Magdeburg (1629). St. Ursula, a little north of Central Bahnhof; the bones of the 11,000 virgins, who with the saint were slain by Huns, are in cases round the church; in the Goldene Kammer (fee 1m. 50 pf. for 1 to 3 persons) is reliquary of St. Ursula. St. Gereon, at west end of Gereonstrasse, dedicated to 318 martyrs of the Theban legion who perished here; a Romanesque church nearly 200 ft. long—a cross added to a round church.

On the west side are: Apostles Church at west end of Neumarkt, a basilica with double transept. Mauritius Church, south of the Apostles' Church, Gothic.

On the south side are: St. Pantaleon, due south of the Neumarkt, a military church, parts very old; Empress Theophano buried here (999) St. Severin, 13th cent., at south end of Severinstrasse, on site of Christian church of 4th cent.

Museum (Wallraf-Richartz Museum), a little to south west of the Dom, fine collection of stained glass, Roman antiquities, ancient and modern paintings of the Cologne School, coins, and other objects; open daily 9 to 5, winter 10 to 4, 50pf., free on Wed. and Sun. Industrial Museum opposite north side of Wallraf Museum; daily, 9 to 5. Archiepiscopal Museum opposite south door of Dom; daily, 9 to 6, 50pf. Mediæval Museum in the Hahnenthor, on west side of town; weapons, armour, standards, etc.

Rathhaus (Town Hall), in Rathhaus Platz, a little south of the Dom, has portico in Renaissance style, with inscriptions and reliefs; in the Hansa-Saal are canopies, armorial bearings, and mediæval decorations. Opposite the Rathhaus, in the Rathhaus Platz, is an old Gothic chapel. The Library is immediately to west of the Rathhaus.

The Gürzenich, surmounted by pinnacles and turrets, a little south of the Rathhaus, is the most important of the old secular buildings of Cologne. It was built 1441-52 as a "Herren Tanzhaus," and serves as a banquet-house and for great festivals, also for an Exchange. The interior has mural paintings, carvings, and stained glass. Concerts given here in winter are renowned.

Oberlandesgericht (Courts of Justice), in Comödienstrasse, west of the Dom.

Zoologischer Garten, on north side of town; Botanical Garden adjoining. Stadtgarten on west side, Volksgarten on south side.

In the Cemetery, on west side of town, half a mile from the Hahnenthor, are War Mons. of 1866 and 1870-1.

In the Holzwerft (timber dock), at the up river side of the city, is a fine large statue of a "Tauzieher" (dock labourer), by Nikolaus Friedrich, of Berlin.

POST OFFICE, in Dominikanerstrasse, a little west of Central Bahnhof.

ENG. CHURCH SERV., in Chapel, 8, Bischofsgartenstrasse (Hotel du Nord). Sun., 8.30, 11.0, and 6.0.

H.B.M.'s CONSUL.—C. A. Niessen, Esq., C.V.O.

U.S. CONS.—H. J. Dunlap, Esq.

GOLF LINKS.

MEDICAL.—Dr. Hall, Dr. Prior.

BANK. — Rheinisch-Westphalische Disconto Gesellschaft, 5 to 7, Sachsenhausen. Capital, 95 million Marks; Reserve, 18 millions. All Banking business, Letters of Credit, Deposits, etc.

EAU DE COLOGNE, Johann Maria Farina, No. 4, Jülichs Platz. Highly recommended. See Advt.

DEPOT FOR BRADSHAW'S PUBLICATIONS.—J. G. Schmitz, Station Bookstalls, and Passage, 1—3. Thomas Cook and Son, 1, Domhof.

RAIL.—For Routes and Trains from Cologne, see pages cxxvi-cxxx, and the Index.

Bonn (right).—*Stat.*—Pop. 87,978.

The Grand Hotel Royal, situated on the banks of the Rhine; replete with every modern comfort. F.C. Eisenmenger, Manager. See Advt.

Stern; Continental; du Rhin.

Steamers.—The Pier of the Cologne-Dusseldorf Steamer Co. is 200 yards south of the Bridge; the Pier of the Nederland Co. is just north of the Bridge.

The Railway Station—Bahnhof—is centrally situated, about two thirds of a mile south west of the Bridge.

Bonn, 20 miles up the river from Cologne, the Roman Bonna, is a famous University town pleasantly situated on the west bank of the Rhine.

The Münster (Minster) is about half a mile south west of the bridge, or, about 200 yards due north of the Railway Station. The Münster is an imposing edifice in later-Romanesque style, the greater part dating from the 13th cent., though portions (the crypt, and masonry above) date from the 11th cent.; lofty tower, four smaller towers; good paintings, including work by mediæval artists, statue of St. Helena, stained windows; cloisters. Beethoven statue on the Münster Platz.

A few yards east of the Münster is the University, formerly the palace of the Elector of Cologne. Founded as an Academy in 1777, it was raised to the status of a University in 1784. About 2,000 students. In the Aula (academic hall) are frescoes. Library of 250,000 vols. and 1,350 MSS. Emperor William monument in front of the University.

A few yards from the north angle of the University is the Markt Platz, the centre of business. Here is the Rathhaus (1782); close by is the church of St Remigius (Minoritenkirche), with paintings by modern artists. Off the north west of the Markt Platz is Bonngasse, where, on east side, is Beethoven's House, a museum of objects associated with the composer, Ludwig von Beethoven, born here 1770.

Provinzial Museum, in Colmantstrasse, a short distance west of the Bahnhof; collection of antiquities and picture gallery—free on Sun. and Thurs. Stadt Museum, by the Rhine, quarter mile south of bridge; collection of modern pictures and some sculpture—free on Sun. and Wed. Kunst museum, on south side of the Hof Garten, by the University, extensive collection of casts, also some antiquities; free on Monday, Wednesday, and Friday.

The Alte Zoll is a terrace by the Rhine, in a line with the University, whence are fine views; the Hof Garten is on the east side of the University; the Poppelsdorf Allee, a beautiful shady promenade, is in a line with the east side of the University, just beyond the railway—at the end of the Allee is Poppelsdorf Schloss, where are the natural history collections of the University. About two miles beyond the Schloss, on the Kreuzberg (400 ft.), are a Monastery and Church; in a chapel at the back of the altar, is a flight of "holy steps," to be ascended only on the knees.

The Alter Friedhof (Cemetery) is one-third mile north west of the Bahnhof; many eminent names are to be found here.

English Church Service, in the University Chapel.

Rail, pages 122, 126.

Godesberg (right).—*Stat.*—Pop. 18,163.

Hotels: Kaiserhof; Godesberger Hof.

A pleasant town standing where the valley commences to expand, much frequented during summer for the cool bracing air; many handsome villas. A hydropathic establishment connected with one of the hotels; also a Kurhaus at the alkaline chalybeate spring of Draisch. Above the town, on a height, 400 ft. above sea, is the ruined Castle of Godesberg, said to date from the year 1210, on the site of a Roman fort. Museum of "Arndt" (poet) memorials at the "Arndtruhe" inn.

English Church Service, Rhein Allée.

Cure and Hydropathic Establishment "Godesberg," for diseases of the nerves, etc. Dr. Staehly. Director Butin. See Advt.

Rail, page 122.

Konigswinter (left).—*Stat.*—Pop. 4,022.

Hotels: Mattern; Kaiserhof; Petersberg.

A little town animated in summer with tourists to the Seven Mountains, for which it is the best starting place. The **Drachenfels** (dragon's rock), 1,065 ft. above sea, crowned by the ruins of a castle, rises above the town, up stream. The ascent is a pleasant walk, or, beside numerous carriages, there is the climbing railway; the view from the summit is one of the finest on the Rhine. The ruined Castle was erected early in 12th cent.; the mythical dragon was slain by Siegfried, one of the heroes of the Nibelungenlied. The **Petersberg,** 1,095 ft., rising behind Konigswinter, affords another magnificent view (climbing rail to top). The Seven Mountains (Siebengebirge), are Drachenfels, Wolkenburg, Petersberg, Nonnenstromberg, Oelberg, Lohrberg, and Lowenburg; they are covered with forest, and are traversed by pleasant paths.

RAIL, page 123.

The Abbey of **Heisterbach,** the ruin of a magnificent abbey-church, is about 2½ miles east of Konigswinter; easily visited from the Petersberg. The Abbey was erected 1202-37.

—— **Honnef** (HOTEL KLEIN; WEINSTOCK), pop. 5,801, a favourite summer resort, is a straggling village in a fertile plain, about 2 miles up river from Konigswinter. It is a very attractive spot, enjoying much sunshine.

Rolandseck (right).—*Stat.*

HOTELS: BELLEVUE; ROLANDSECK.

In a beautiful situation, much frequented; many villas in the neighbourhood. On a height behind, 344 ft. above the river, is an Arch, all that is left of the Castle stated to have been built by Charlemagne's knight Roland (slain 778). A legend associates the memories of Roland and Hildegunde, daughter of Count Heribert of Drachenburg. On the island of **Nonnenwerth,** close to Rolandseck, once stood an ancient nunnery to which in grief Hildegunde retired. A girls' school occupies the existing buildings.

RAIL, page 122.

Remagen (right).—*Stat.*—Pop. 3,534.

HOTELS: FURSTENBERG, RHEIN, ANKER.

A very old town, the Rigomagus of the Romans, and a mediæval place of some note. On the Apollinarisberg, to north of the town, is the four-spired Apollinariskirche, erected 1839; in interior are good frescoes, and in the crypt is the head of St. Apollinaris, visited by pilgrims; open 7.0 a.m. until 8.0 p.m., 30 pf.

RAIL, pages 122, 123D.

[**Sinzig,** about 2½ miles beyond Remagen, and 1½ mile back from the Rhine, is a very old place, the Roman Sentiacum, once a residence of the Frankish kings. On a hill is the interesting Romanesque Parish Church, dating from 1220, containing one or two good paintings.

RAIL, page 122.

Soon after leaving Sinzig Station the train passes close to the Rheinahr Glass Bottle Factory, where the bottles are made for the famous Apollinaris Spring (see also page 487), situated in the adjoining valley of the Ahr. Visitors are admitted.]

Linz (left).—*Stat.*—Pop. 4,035.

HOTELS: WEINSTOCK; EUROPAISCHER HOF.

A little old town, with some remains of its ancient walls and gates. Church of St. Martin, 13th cent.; one or two paintings in interior. Good red wine grown in the district. A floating bridge connects with Kripp, on opposite bank of the Rhine.

RAIL, page 128.

Just before the village of Hönningen (left) is reached the Castle of Arenfels (restored) is seen. On opposite bank of river (right) is the modern Castle of Rheineck, erected 1832, with a tower on south side belonging to an old castle of 12th cent.; a little beyond is the village of Brohl (right—a local railway runs up to Kempenich, 14 miles), with Rheinbrohl facing across the river. Two miles from Rheinbrohl is the Ober Hammerstein, with the ruins of Hammerstein Castle, whither in 1105 the Emperor Henry IV retired before the usurpation of his son Henry V.

Andernach (right).—*Stat.*—Pop. 7,889.

HOTELS: HACKENBRUCH; RHEINISCHER HOF; WEBEL.

The Roman Antunnacum; in the 6th century of some importance as a residence of the Frankish Kings. The old walls in part still exist. Watch Tower, with eight-sided upper storey, by the river, erected 1451-68, restored 1880. Within the town, among the narrow streets, are the Rathhaus, 1564, where is a small collection of antiquities, and the four-towered Church of St. Genovefa, 1206. In the upper part of the town is the ruined Castle of the Electors of Cologne, of 15th cent.

RAIL, pages 122, 123B.

The Rhine just here makes a considerable bend, at the turn, on the left, the town of Neuwied coming into sight.

Neuwied (left).—Stat.—Pop. 18,177.

HOTELS: WILDER MANN; MORAVIAN.

A busy well-built little town, best known in connection with the "Settlement" of the Moravian Brethren, whose manner of life in some respects resembles that of byegone Quakerism, and whose schools are in high repute. Near the river is the Palace of the Prince of Wied; in a house close by is a collection of Roman antiquities.

RAIL, page 128.

Weissenthurm (right)—*Stat.*—Pop. 3,257. A little up river from Neuwied, on the opposite bank. At the north end of the village is the Watch Tower (1370) giving name to the place. Behind and above the village is an Obelisk to the memory of the French General Hoche, who crossed the river here with his army in 1797.

RAIL, page 122.

Between Weissenthurm and the next village on same side, Urmitz, traces of two Roman camps have been discovered, and it is conjectured that just about here was the bridge made across the Rhine by Julius Cæsar. The larger island of the two in mid stream higher up is **Niederwerth,** where Edward III of England in 1337 met the Emperor Lewis. The river narrows as at a bend the heights of Ehrenbreitstein (left) and the River Mosel and Coblence (right) are approached.

Coblence (Coblenz).—*Stat.*—Pop. 56,487.

RIESEN-FURSTENHOF AND ANCHOR.—Facing the Rhine Steamer Landing Stage. Beautifully arranged. Strictly moderate. See Advt.

GRAND HOTEL BELLE VUE—COBLENZER HOF.—New first class hotel, in fine position, with extensive views of the Rhine. Every modern comfort. See Advt.

PALAST PARK HOTEL.—Three minutes from Station. Newest and most comfortable, with strictly moderate terms. See Advt.

The Steamer Pier is just north of the boat bridge. The Railway Station—Hauptbahnhof—is on the west side of the town, two thirds mile from the Rhine.

Coblence, the Roman Confluentes, capital of the Rhenish Province of Prussia, is picturesquely situated at the confluence of the Rivers Rhine and Moselle. In addition to its attraction as a place of residence, it is favourably regarded as an educational centre; the wine trade is important.

Facing the Rhine is the imposing Regierungs-palast (Government offices) with square peaked tower. Upon the point of land at the junction of the rivers rises the Monument of Emperor William I. Southward, along the quay, is the Castorkirche, dating from the 12th cent. In the open space west of the church is the Castor-Brunnen, erected in 1812 by the French (Coblence was capital of the French Department of the Rhine, 1798-1813) to commemorate the invasion of Russia; there is a sarcastic endorsement by the Russian General St. Priest, "seen and approved" by him as commandant of the town, 1814.

The beautiful Rhein Anlagen (gardens and promenade) extends along the river front a little south of the boat bridge. Above and behind the Anlagen is the Schloss, formerly a favourite residence of the German Imperial family; the royal apartments may be seen. Small collection of pictures at the Theatre, off north west angle of the Schloss.

Cemetery on the Karthause hill, to south west of town.

Immediately opposite Coblence, connected with it by a bridge of boats, is **Ehrenbreitstein,** pop. 5,550. The way to the Fortress is to the left, along the Hofstrasse. At the last gateway up the hill tickets of admission are obtained. The existing fortress dates from 1816, though the position has for centuries been strongly fortified. Fine view. Fort Asterstein is on the height to the south of Ehrenbreitstein.

CHURCH OF ENGLAND SERVICE.

RAIL, pages 122, 123B, 124, 128, 146.

Just above Coblence is the island of Oberwerth, opposite which, on the left, is **Horchheim,** whose vineyards yield a good red wine. The view from the steamer, down river, is here very fine. 1½ mile beyond Horchheim, on same side, the River Lahn flows into the Rhine, and almost opposite the influx of the Lahn, but a little further up stream, is the village of **Capellen** (HOTEL BELLEVUE; STOLZENFELS), with the **Castle of Stolzenfels** on the wooded height, 310 ft. above the river. The Castle, rebuilt, 1836-42, is the property of the Emperor, and may be visited; frescoes in the Chapel and Rittersaal (Knights' Hall); donkeys on hire from Capellen up to the Schloss. Local steamers between Capellen and Oberlahnstein.

Oberlahnstein (left).—*Stat.* Pop. 8,007.
HOTELS: WELLER; BREITENBACH.
An old town, with a few towers remaining of the fortifications. Near the river side, in upper part of town, is Schloss Martinsburg, dating from 1394, at one time a residence of the Electors of Mayence; the modern parts were built 1712. Rathhaus, partly timber built. Behind Oberlahnstein, on a height, by the River Lahn, is the Castle of Lahneck, dating from 13th cent., restored 1860—may be visited in absence of owner.

RAIL, pages 128, 128A, 146.

1¼ mile above Capellen, on same side, is the **Königsstuhl** (King's seat), dating from 1376, rebuilt 1843; it is an eight-sided structure, 18 ft. high, 22 ft. across. Here the Electors of Cologne, Treves, Mayence, and of the Palatinate, met to elect Emperors, and here many treaties were arranged and decrees issued. Directly opposite the Konigsstuhl, on the other side of the Rhine, near Oberlahnstein, among the trees, is a white chapel, where, August 20th, 1400, the Electors deposed the Emperor Wenceslaus, conferring the imperial dignity the next day upon Rupert at the Konigsstuhl.

Rhens (right).—*Stat.*—Pop. 1,509.
HOTEL KONIGSSTUHL.
A little old town with several mediæval timbered houses, and remains of the ancient walls.

RAIL, page 122.

Braubach (left).—*Stat.*—Pop. 2,760.
HOTELS: KAISERHOF; DEUTSCHES HAUS.
An ancient town. The fine old Castle of Marksburg, 485 ft. above the river, one of the very few Rhine castles that have escaped destruction, is now partly occupied by a restaurant.

RAIL, pages 128, 128A.

The Rhine here makes one of its most considerable curves; on the right, at the bend, is a ruined chapel, all that is left of the village of Peterspay. Shortly after, on the left, above the village of Osterspay, is seen Chateau Liebeneck.

Boppard (right).—*Stat.*—Pop. 6,199.
HOTELS: BELLEVUE; SPIEGEL.
The Roman Bobobriga, still preserving some of its mediæval fortifications. Here the Order of Knights Templar had a Lodge, of which are relics at the upper end of the town. The beautiful situation renders this interesting old town a favourite place of residence. Two-towered Pfarrkirche of early 13th cent.; interior restored 1894-5. In the Carmeliterkirche, early 14th cent., are carved stalls and old paintings. Close to the river is the Castle of the Archbishops of Treves, now used as law courts. Just beyond the up-river end of the town is St. Martin Monastery, used as a Protestant reformatory. Behind the town, 100 ft. above the river, is the extensive Marienberg, once a Benedictine nunnery, now a hydropathic establishment. The environs are very attractive; excellent wine produced in the district.
RAIL, pages 122, 123B.

Camp (left).—Pop. 1,791.
HOTELS: ANKER; KAUTH.
A summer resort; local steamer service across the river to Boppard.

Bornhofen (left).
HOTELS: ZUM MARIENBERG; ZUM LIEBENSTEIN.
About 1 mile up-river from Camp. The Church, erected 1435, is a pilgrimage resort. On a height are the ruins of the two Castles of Sterrenberg (the higher) and Liebenstein, known as The Brothers, and the subject of a legend.

St. Goar (right).—*Stat.*—Pop. 1,629.
HOTELS: SCHNEIDER; LILLIE; JUNG.
An attractive town on a beautiful curve of the river. In the Protestant Church, of 15th cent., are a few monuments; at the Roman Catholic Church is a statue of St. Goar, who lived here in the 6th cent. Behind the town is the imposing ruined Castle of Rheinfels, 375 ft. above the river; erected 13th cent., destroyed 1797. Local steamer to St. Goarshausen.
RAIL, page 122.

St. Goarshausen (left).—*Stat.*—Pop. 1,586.
HOTELS: ADLER; NASSAUER HOF.
A little town crushed between the river and the hills. Above the town is the Castle of Neu Katzenelnbogen, generally known as The Katz (Cat), built 1393. Iti s celebrated in the famous song, "Trutz-Katz," by Jörg Ritzel. By the castle a pleasant valley, Schweizerthal, runs into the country; it is studded by cascades, rocks, and clear streams.
RAIL, pages 128, 128A.

A little more than a mile up river from St. Goarshausen, on the same side (left), rises the precipitous rock of the Lurlei, 430 ft. above the river. Here the Rhine flows in its narrowest and deepest channel, 220 yards wide, 76. ft. deep; the dangers of the rapids at the foot of the Lurlei and the legend of the siren luring boatmen to destruction have long inspired authors and artists. A famous echo rings from the cliffs that shut in the river, but it can only be evoked when other sounds are hushed. On the same side as the Lurlei, at the bend half a mile up river, are rocks known as the Sieben Jungfrauen (Seven Maidens), visible at low water.

Oberwesel (right).—*Stat.*—Pop. 2,913.
HOTELS: HOTEL GERTUM; GOLDENER PFROPFENZIEHER.
A delightfully situated picturesque town, the Vosavia of the Romans. By the river is the Ochsenthurm (Ox Tower), part of the old fortifications. At south end of the town is the Frauenkirche, 1307-31, regarded as a model of the Gothic style; several paintings in interior—tombs of the Schönberg family. St. Martinskirche is interesting. Above the town is the ruin of Schönburg Castle, of 12th cent., the birthplace of Marshal Schomberg, killed at the battle of the Boyne, 1690; near by is a modern chateau.
RAIL, page 122.

Caub (left).—*Stat.*—Pop. 2,410.
HOTELS: ZUM GRUNEN WALD; ADLER; PFALZ.
Some of the old fortifications still exist. Marshal Blücher had his quarters here for a few days, Dec.-Jan., 1813-14, and a statue represents him indicating the passage of the Rhine. Above the town is the restored Castle of Gutenfels; here Richard Earl of Cornwall, who became Emperor of Germany 1257, met his second wife, Guta von Falkenstein.
RAIL, page 128.

In mid stream, on a rock, is a well preserved old castle called the Pfalz, or Pfalzgrafenstein, founded 1314-17; upon a hexagonal base is a pentagonal tower, surrounded by several turrets. According to tradition heirs of the Counts Palatine were always born in this castle. Keys in charge of ferryman at Caub (75 pf.). The passage of the Rhine by Blücher was made here, Jan. 1st, 1814.

Bacharach (right).—*Stat.*—Pop. 1,901.
HOTELS: HERBRECHT; BLUCHERTAL.
A little old town, busy with a wine trade that has always been famous. The towered mediæval walls are in good preservation. In the Markt Platz is the Knight Templar Church of St. Peter; also in the Platz is the very old timbered Weber tavern, built 1568. On rising ground is the ruined Church of St. Werner, erected 1293. High above the town is the ruined Castle of Stahleck, the residence of the Counts Palatine, 1142—1253.
RAIL, page 122.

1½ mile up river from Bacharach, on same side, is the ruined Castle of Fürstenberg, above the village of Rheindiebach; immediately opposite, on the other side of the Rhine, is the ruined Castle of Nollich, at the influx of the River Wisper.

Lorch (left).—*Stat.*—Pop. 2,216.
HOTEL KRONE.
One of the oldest towns on the Rhine. Church of St. Martin, 13th-15th cent., restored, has interesting interior.
RAIL, page 128.

Up river from Lorch the principal interest is upon the right hand. Above the village of Niederheimbach (right), almost opposite Lorch, is the tower of the ruined Castle of Heimburg, 13th cent.; on same side, one mile further, is the tower of the Castle of Sooneck, 14th cent.; 1½ mile further, same side, above the village of Trechtingshausen, is Falkenburg Castle, of evil reputation as the stronghold of a robber baron. Just beyond Falkenburg is Clementscapelle, stated to have been erected for the benefit of the souls of the robber garrison of Falkenburg, who were all hanged when Rudolph of Hapsburg captured it late in 13th cent. Half a mile beyond Clementscapelle is the restored Castle of Rheinstein, of 12th cent., containing a collection of armour and antiquities.

Assmannshausen (left).—*Stat.*—Pop. 1,060.
HOTELS: KRONE; ANKER.
A wine growing village of considerable reputation; the full flavoured red wine is often preferred to Burgundy. Local steamers to and from Rudesheim and Bingen, and across the river to Rheinstein.
RAIL. pages 128. 128A.

The navigation of the Binger Loch, the rapid rocky channel of the Rhine above Assmannshausen, was for ages dangerous, the work of clearing a passage extending from Roman times down to 1832. Steamers going down stream slacken speed at the approach of up-coming steamers, and great care is required in the navigation of the large rafts. On the left, above the Binger Loch, are the ruins of the two-towered Castle of Ehrenfels, erected 1210, often the residence of the Archbishop of Mayence. In mid stream, on a small island, is the Mäusethurm (Mouse Tower), associated with a wicked Bishop Hatto, who was devoured here by mice; as, however, the bishop died about 914 and the tower was erected in the 13th cent., and the name was originally Mûsthurm (arsenal), the legend is unreliable. The tower is used for signalling purposes. The Rhine here broadens out.

Bingerbruck (right).—*Stat.*—Pop. 2,758.
HOTEL MOHRMANN.
Joined by bridges over the River Nahe to Bingen.

Bingen (right).—*Stat.*—Pop. 10,211.
HOTEL VICTORIA.—First class hotel, near the landing place. See Advt.
STARKENBURGHER HOF; ROCHENSBERG.
Situated at the influx of the River Nahe, a very old place, the scene of a battle A.D. 70 between the Romans and the Gauls. There is an extensive wine trade. Pfarrkirche of 15th cent., with a crypt much older. Above and behind the town is the Castle of Klopp, partly occupied by municipal offices, and partly by collections of antiquities. About half a mile up river from Bingen, beyond the interesting Cemetery, is the Rochusberg height (HOTEL ROCHUSBERG), upon whose east brow is the Rochuskapelle, 350 ft. above the river—very fine view. The chapel was built in 1677 in memory of the plague of 1666, destroyed by lightning 1889, rebuilt 1889-94. On the first Sunday after 16th August, at the festival of St. Roch, thousands of people assemble here.
RAIL (Bingen or Bingerbruck), pages 122, 123, 123B, 125. 134.

Rüdesheim.—*Stat.*—Pop. 5,106.
HOTEL JUNG.—First class, close to Station and boats to Bingen and Bingerbruck. Most comfortable and moderate. See Advt.
Situated at the south base of the Niederwald, just where the country spreads out into the Rhinegau, a famous wine producing district extending from a little west of Rüdesheim to Eltville. Some of the most celebrated wines are yielded by vineyards quite close to the town, near the Station; other renowned growths are nearer the river on the west towards Ehrenfels. Near the Station is the massive castle of Brömserburg (or Niederburg) part dating from the 12th cent.; in the 13th cent. it was held by the brigand Knights of Rüdesheim, later became a frequent residence of the Archbishops of Mayence; interior has been restored. Behind the Brömserburg is the tower of the Oberburg. In the Marktplatz is a Gothic Roman Catholic Church, 1390-1400; in the upper part of the town is the Adlerthurm, an old watch tower, and a Protestant Church.
RAIL, page 128; ferry to Bingen, in connection with trains, page 123. Rhine Steamers, page 362.

On the slope of the **Niederwald,** behind Rüdesheim, stands the National Monument to commemorate the united action of the German people culminating in the foundation of the new German empire in 1870–71. The figure of Germania is 33 ft. high, on a pedestal 78 ft. high. On the side of the pedestal facing the river the relief symbolises the "Wacht am Rhein," and bears portraits of the first emperor, German princes, generals, and representative soldiers. The total cost of the monument was £55,000. Fine view from the terrace. RAIL from Rüdesheim to the Monument, page 128A.

Geisenheim (left).—*Stat.*—Pop. 3,870.
HOTELS: FRANKFURTER HOF; DEUTSCHES HAUS.

A pleasant town. Church of 1510; Rathhaus, 1856. Close to the Railway Station is the Œnological and Pomological Institute for instruction in the cultivation of vines and fruit trees.

RAIL, page 128.

On a hill behind Geisenheim, in direction of Rudesheim, is the Nunnery of Eibingen, founded 1148, secularised 1802, the church being reserved for sacred uses.

Up river from Geisenheim, back from the river, on a hill among vineyards, is the Castle of Johannisberg, erected 1757-59 on the site of a Benedictine monastery; belonging to Prince Metternich. Visitors are not admitted; the vineyards yield a famous wine.

Four miles up river from Johannisberg, on the same side, is Marcobrunnen, another famous vine district.

Eltville (left).—*Stat.*—Pop. 4,115
HOTELS: REISENBACH; MAINZER HOF.

This little town was once the capital of the district—the Rheingau. Two or three handsome mediæval houses; many villas. A watch tower is the only part left of a castle erected 1330. A printing press was set up here in 1466 by the Bechtermuntze brothers, relatives of Gutenberg; a tablet indicates the house. Schlangenbad is 35 minutes by rail from Eltville.

RAIL page 128.

Biebrich (left).—*Stat.*—Pop. 22,000.
HOTELS: KAISERHOF; BELLEVUE; KRONE.

A manufacturing town. By the river is the Palace of the Grand Duke of Luxemburg, erected 1706; within the park the diminutive Castle of Moosburg, built 1806, is on the site of an ancient imperial palace.

RAIL, page 128.

Mayence (Mainz).—*Stat.*—Pop. 110,634.

HOTEL DE HOLLANDE.—First-class hotel, well situated, opposite the Landing Place. The leading family house.

ENGLISCHER HOF.—First class. Close to Landing Stage. Fine panorama. Lift; electric light; garage. Rooms from 4m., including breakfast. See Advt.

HOTEL ZUM KARPFEN.—Facing Post Office, one minute from the Rhine and Steamboats. Very moderate charges; rooms, including breakfast, from 3/6; most comfortable. See Advt.

CENTRAL HOTEL.—The only first class house near the Station. All modern comfort. Lift. Moderate prices. See Advt.

The Nederland Co's Steamer Pier is just below the bridge, the Cologne-Dusseldorf Co's Pier is just above the bridge. The RAILWAY STATION—Hauptbahnhof—is on the west side of the city, in a direct line with the bridge, two thirds mile from it.

CABS.—1-horse cab per drive within the town, for 1 or 2 persons, 50 pf., 3 or 4 persons 70 pf.; per hour, 2 m. and 2 m. 30 pf.; each large article of luggage 20 pf. To Castel (across the river) 1 m.

Mayence, the Roman Mogontiacum, one of the most strongly fortified places in Germany, is situated a little below and opposite the confluence of the Main with the Rhine. The historic interest is great; "Golden Mayence," so called because of its prosperity, was the leader of the powerful League of the Rhenish Towns, founded 1254; in modern times, down to 1866, the fortress belonged to the German Confederation, the joint garrison being supplied by Austria and Prussia. Along the river front is a very fine tree planted promenade; within the city many of the old narrow crooked streets remain. The wine trade engages most attention, but there is a large industry in furniture and leather goods.

The Dom (Cathedral of St. Martin), of various styles of architecture, is about a quarter mile from the river, from a point on the quay one third mile above the bridge. Dating from 975, the sacred edifice has undergone many vicissitudes, it has been three times destroyed by fire, in 1009, 1081, and 1191; it was used as a stronghold during struggles between the clergy and citizens, 1160, and during the French occupation, 1797-1814, it became a vast store house, in the latter year it was restored to its sacred purpose. Interior 366 ft. long, 150 ft. wide, and 89 ft. high in the nave; there are decorations and paintings, but interest is chiefly drawn to the monuments and tombstones bearing records of several centuries. From the south aisle a doorway leads to the "Memorie," the old chapter house (1243). In the cloisters are some notable monuments. At the north side of the Dom, by the Markt, is the half hidden St. Gotthard Kapelle, 1135-8, once the chapel of the archbishop's palace. Johannes Kirche, a little to south west of the Dom.

St. Stephan Kirche, on high ground, in south west part of city, 1257-1328; altar pieces, treasury, cloisters. St. Ignatz Kirche, in south part of the city, near the river.

Christus Kirche, north part of city, in Kaiserstrasse, near the Rhine. Modern (1903) domed church, one of the largest in Germany, Renaissance style; height of cupola 265 ft.; reliefs in cupola; fine windows.

A few yards west of the Dom, along the Markt, is the Statue of Gutenberg, the inventor of printing, born here at the end of 14th cent.

The Schloss is by the river just below the bridge; formerly the palace of the electors, it is now occupied by collections of Roman and Teuton art and antiquities; the pictures are mostly of the Dutch and Flemish schools, including works by Jan Steen, Ruysdael, Teniers, Dirkhals, etc. Wednesday and Sunday, free; other days 50 pf. On the upper floors are the Library (200,000 vols., 1,200 MSS), a collection of coins, and a natural history collection. In the Library is the Gutenberg Museum of exhibits relating to printing.

Within the Citadel, on south side of city—an order required—is a mass of concrete, 40 ft. high,

known as the Drusus Thurm, or Eigelstein, supposed to have been erected 9 B.C. in honour of Drusus (son in law of Augustus), killed by a fall from his horse.

In the cemetery are several elaborate monuments and a crematorium.

Near the village of Zahlbach, two thirds mile from west side of the city, are the ruins of a Roman aqueduct, of which nearly seventy columns remain.

POST OFFICE, near the Railway Station.

BANKS.—Direction der Disconto-Gesellschaft, established 1851. Ludwigstrasse, 10. Capital M.200,000,000. Reserves about M.80,000,000. All banking orders promptly executed. Letters of credit and cheques issued and cashed. Foreign moneys at current rates.

Electric Car service between Mayence and Wiesbaden.

RAIL, pages 123, 137, 139, 208.

Worms (right).—*Stat.*—Pop. 46,819.

HOTELS: EUROPAISCHER HOF; KAISERHOF; ALTER KAISER; HARTMANN.

From the Steamer Pier, close to the bridge, the Rhein Allee runs into Rheinstrasse, which leads in a quarter mile to the Rhein Thor and to the heart of the city. The RAILWAY STATION is on the north west side of the city, away from the Rhine.

Worms, the **Roman Borbetomagus,** was in mediæval times one of the principal cities of Germany; it is situated in the fertile plain of the Wonnegau, and has a considerable trade in wine and leather. Here, in April, 1521, was held the Imperial Diet, when Luther defended his doctrines in the presence of the Emperor Charles V and the Electors; in 1689 the city was sacked and fired by the French, only the Cathedral and Synagogue escaping the general ruin.

The Dom (Cathedral) is in the west part of the city, nearly a mile due west of the Steamer Pier, one third mile due south of the Bahnhof. The venerable edifice, mostly of the 12th cent., is regarded as one of the finest examples of Romanesque architecture in the Rhine countries; there are four slender towers, two domes, and a double choir. Interior is 141 yards long, 29 yards wide, 40 yards at the transept, nave 105 ft. high, monuments and reliefs.

150 yards north of the Dom is the Luther Denkmal (Luther Monument), erected 1868 after 12 years labour, the cost being £17,000. Several figures of Reformers, also reliefs on the pedestal. The Bischofshof (bishop's palace), where Luther met the Diet, was a little south of the Denkmal, the site being occupied by a stately mansion; the garden (entrance in Schloss Platz, east side of Dom) is always open.

Dreifaltigkeits Kirche (Trinity Church), in Markt Platz, a few yards south east of the Dom. Erected 1726; paintings. East of the Markt Platz is the Stadthaus. rebuilt 1884; fresco in hall.

Paulus Museum of Antiquities in Paulus Kirche, Paulusstrasse, quarter mile due east of the Dom. The building, Romanesque of early 12th cent., is of great interest. One room contains the Luther Library, with memorials of the reformer and his contemporaries.

Martins Kirche, in Ludwigs Platz, quarter mile north east of the Dom. Erected 1265, restored 1888; fine west portal. 200 yards north east of Ludwigs Platz, in Judengasse, is the Synagogue, dating from the 11th cent.

Liebfrauenkirche, in extreme north quarter, of 15th cent.; a fine specimen of late Gothic.

RAIL, pages 134, 136, 137, 139, 206, 208.

Mannheim (left).—*Stat.*—Pop. 193,902.

HOTELS: PARK; PFALZERHOF; DEUTSCHER HOF; NATIONAL.

CABS.—**From Steamer Pier or Railway Station into the town, 1 person 60 pf., 2 persons 80 pf.; ½ hour, 1 or 2 persons 1 m; 3 or more persons 1 m. 50 pf.**

The Steamer Pier is at the quay by the Schlossgarten, close to the bridge; the Railway Station—BAHNHOF—is in south west quarter, close to Schlossgarten and Rhine. Both Station and Pier are within half a mile of the centre of affairs.

A very important commercial town pleasantly situated at the confluence of the Rivers Rhine and Neckar. The central part of the town is regularly built in square blocks, the streets crossing at right angles and being distinguished by numbers and letters instead of names. The modern development of Mannheim, on the east side, is very attractive; here is the spacious Friedrichs Platz, a beautiful square surrounded by handsome buildings, and beyond are pleasant suburbs.

Along the Rhine front of the town extends the Schlossgarten, with the Grand Ducal Schloss behind the trees. The Schloss, a large building in the baroque style, erected 1720-60, contains antiquarian collections, including celebrated Gobelins tapestry, some sculpture, a natural history cabinet, a valuable collection of pictures, and a public library (over 60,000 vols., in a fine hall). Monument of Emperor William I in the courtyard.

Close to the west wing of the Schloss is the Jesuitenkirche, with ornate facade, built 1733-56. Across the open space is the Grand Ducal Theatre, built 1776-1779, where Schiller's earlier plays were first produced (1782-84).

The Rathaus, rebuilt 1903-10, on the central street running north from the Schloss, has a fine front and contains large decorated halls.

The Kunsthalle (art museum), in Friedrichs Platz, contains a good collection of modern pictures. Close by are the Wasserturm (water tower), and the Rosengarten (concert and gala hall).

Friedrichspark is a pleasant public garden, where in summer a band plays.

H.B.M.'S CONSUL.—Dr. P. Ladenburg.

U.S. CONSUL.—W. C. Teichmann, Esq.

RAIL, pages 136, 137, 139, 140, 142, 205.

Ludwigshafen (right).—*Stat.*—Pop. 83,301.

HOTELS: DEUTSCHES HAUS; PFALZERHOF.

Opposite Mannheim, with which it is connected by the Rhine bridge. A busy manufacturing and commercial place. In the Roman Catholic church are frescoes.

RAIL, pages 205, 206, 207, 208.

GERMANY—THE BLACK FOREST
(DER SCHWARZWALD.)

The Black Forest is the most extensive and the most beautiful of the wooded districts of Germany; it abounds in landscapes of varied and contrasting charms; its valleys and heights offer a tranquility hardly to be found elsewhere. It extends from north to south for nearly 100 miles, and from east to west, throughout its length, for about 35 miles; three high roads traverse the forest from north to south, namely, from Pforzheim to Basie, from Pforzheim to Waldshut, and from Pforzheim to Schaffhausen; from east to west roads enter at several places to wander in many turns before they lead out at the other side; all the roads are excellent, whether for motorist, cyclist, or pedestrian, and they are marked at frequent intervals by indications as to direction and distance.

The air is remarkably pure, there are not any large towns with teeming populations nor any smoky industries to taint the air, there is not any dust; in the heat of summer the masses of trees keep the constantly moving air cool and fragrant, and in the winter the same trees are an effective barrier to cold biting winds. The favourable climatic conditions are so generally recognised that many spots once only known for their romantic situation are now equally well known as health resorts.

The inhabitants have been content to remain within inherited dispositions, their manners are simple, and their costumes have changed little for many generations; their occupations are chiefly with timber, either with the huge rafts that later float down the Rhine, or with the smaller ways of wooden clocks, toys, and general wood-ware; there are no appearances of great wealth, on the other hand there are no beggars.

Allerheiligen.

HOTEL KLOSTER ALLERHEILIGEN.—2,030 feet above sea. Beautiful situation, near celebrated waterfall. First class hotel; pension from 6 Mks. See Advt.

A much frequented spot, 2,030 feet above sea; widely known because of the ruined abbey and several romantic legends. The abbey, founded in 1196, was greatly damaged in a storm in 1803; below the convent are the Buttenstein Falls, 270ft. All round Allerheiligen the country is very attractive; posts indicate the direction of the paths.

Motor Car service from Ottenhofen.

Antogast Bad.

Antogast, 1,585 ft. above sea, is a very pleasantly situated health resort in the Maisach valley. The reputation of its chalybeate springs, dating from the 16th cent., has greatly increased since the discovery of radium indications in the waters. The springs, stronger in radium and lithia than any other cold springs in Germany, are successfully employed in cases of anæmia, chlorosis, heart disease, nervous ailments, female ailments, etc. Forest attractions all round; good paths. In the winter tobogganing and general out door sport.

Reached by carriage from Oppenau station, 2½ miles.

Baden-Baden.—*Stat.*—Pop. 22,066.

HOTEL DE L'EUROPE.—One of the very best hotels on the Continent, combining luxury and comfort, beautifully situated. Spacious Terrace Restaurant. See Advt.

HOLLAND HOTEL, near the Kursaal, one of the best in Germany, with large park-like gardens. Proprietor, Mr. A. Roessler. See Advt.

HOTEL ZÄHRINGERHOF.—Well situated near the Promenades and Conversation House. Hydraulic lift. See Advt.

HOTEL REGINA.—First class hotel, standing on a slight elevation in its own garden, with fine views of town and mountains. Electric light. See Advt.

HOTEL DE FRANCE.—Family hotel, facing the Park and Conversation House. Hydraulic lift. Open all the year. See Advt.

HOTEL MESSMER.—First class, adjoining Kurhaus and Gardens; most beautifully arranged and enlarged. 200 rooms. Covered restaurant Verandah. See Advt.

HOTEL DE RUSSIE, Albert Moerch. Delightfully situated near the Kursaal. Hydraulic lift to each floor. See Advt.

HOTEL PETERSBURGER HOF.—Entirely renovated. Central, comfortable, and moderate. Open all the year. Pension from 6 M. See Advt.

STADT STRASSBURG HOTEL is a favourite family hotel. Fine position; entirely rebuilt 1908. All comforts. Rooms from 3 M. Pension from 8 M. 50 Pf. See Advt.

HOTEL MULLER.—Best part of Baden Baden, close to Kurhaus and gardens. Every modern comfort. Rooms from 3 marks. Pension from 7 marks. See Advt.

The RAILWAY STATION is on the north west side of the town, about two thirds of a mile from the centre of life at the Conversations Haus. From the Station the road to the left, Langestrasse, leads into the old town, the road to the right leads to the modern district—the Promenaden Platz, Conversations Haus, and Lichtenthaler Allée.

Baden-Baden, the Roman Civitas Aurelia Aquensis, in the Duchy of Baden, one of the most frequented watering places in Europe, is picturesquely situated 600 ft. above sea in the pleasant valley of the River Oosbach, among well wooded hills, bordering the Black Forest. The waters, used both for drinking and bathing, vary in temperature from 113° to 158° Fahr., and are efficacious in rheumatism, gout, and stomach complaints; careful arrangements are also made for what is known as the "Terrain Cure" for heart and lung affections, level walks are indicated by yellow signs upon the trees, a red sign denotes an easy incline, red and yellow a steep incline,

During the season, April to November, the place is alive with gaiety—concerts, theatrical entertainments, and balls are frequent, and race meetings are held at Iffezheim, near Oos; expense, however, is easily avoided, and quiet travellers will find the cost of living no greater than elsewhere. Shooting—hares, pheasants, deer, etc.

Overlooking the old town, on the north side, is the Schloss of the Grand Duke, and immediately below, on the town side, is the Stiftskirche, or abbey church, dating from the 7th cent., containing mons. of the Margraves of Baden. Rathhaus opposite south side of Stiftskirche; alongside in the old Conversations Haus. To the east of Stiftskirche are the principal Bath Establishments—the Friedrichsbad and the Kaiserin Augusta Bad, and here rise the Hot Springs, drawn into two conduits, the Hauptstollen and the Kirchenstollen. The Friedrichsbad is a handsome building in Renaissance style, where baths of all kinds, hot, cold, vapour, swimming, douches, electric, etc., are supplied, together with curative gymnastics and massage treatment. The Kaiserin Augusta Bad is a similar establishment, open during summer only, and reserved for ladies. The Landesbad, for poor patients, is a little to the east, in Leopoldstrasse; close by is the Inhalatorium.

Schloss, dating from late in 15th cent.; handsome saloons, with pictures, sculpture, etc.; winding stairs in Dagobert tower, subterranean vaults. Open daily, 1 m. Pleasant garden. Museum of Antiquities in the Palais Stephanie.

The Conversations Haus, Trinkhalle, and Theatre, are on three sides of a square in the beautiful quarters to the west of the old town. The interior decorations of the Conversation Haus are magnificent; reading rooms well supplied. The Trinkhalle, on north side of square, has frescoes in the arcades; on south side of the square is the Theatre. At the Kunstausstellung (erected 1909) is a collection of pictures—art exhibition during summer. When the band is playing before the Conversations Haus the square presents a most animated appearance. South of the square extends the Lichtenthaler Allée, a very fine promenade flanked by hotels, villas, and gardens.

Greek Church, on the Michaelsberg, one third mile due south of the Bahnhof; paintings, and elaborate decorations in gold and marble.

The Cemetery is on south east side of the own, on a slope of the Annaberg.

POST OFFICE, in Leopolds Platz, a few yards east, across the river, from the Conversations Haus.

ENGLISH CHURCH SERVICE.-All Saints Church. Daily service; weekly celebration.

Tennis courts and croquet ground in Lichtenthaler Alleé.

HOF-APOTHEKE. THE ANGLO-AMERICAN PHARMACY.—Rieffel and Dr. Hoffmann (Proprietor, Julius Wohl), 2, Langestrasse. Foreign prescriptions dispensed in strict accordance with Pharmacopœia of the respective countries. Numerous patent medicines. Separate departments for Homœopathic remedies and Surgical instruments. Goods forwarded to all parts of the World.

DR. GRODDECK'S SANATORIUM (founded in 1897) for maladies of all kinds except contagious diseases and diseases of the brain. The success of medical treatment depends largely upon the personality of the doctor. Dr. Groddeck attends to his cases personally. Only 15 beds.

SANATORIUM DR. BURGER.—Maria Viktoria Strasse, 12. For internal and nervous diseases; especially affections of the stomach and intestines, and diseases due to troubles of assimilation and nutrition.

RAIL, page 140.

[About a mile and a half south of Baden, along the Lichtenthaler Allée, is **Lichtenthal** (HOTEL LUDWIGSBAD; LOWE), pop. 3,620, where is a Cistercian Convent, founded 1245; the Church and Todten Capelle are interesting. Three miles east of Lichtenthal, near Gaisbach, are fish breeding ponds, "Fischkultur," in a pleasant valley, a favourite excursion from Baden.

The Alte Schloss Hohenbaden is about a mile due north of the Baden Bahnhof, on a height (1,550 ft.). The ruined castle dates from (it is thought) the 3rd cent.; it was the seat of the Margraves from the 11th cent. until the castle within the town was built; it was destroyed by the French in 1689. Sign posts indicate the paths from the Alte Schloss to the Felsen, masses of precipitous rocks, whence are fine views.

The **Mercuriusberg** (2,205 ft.) is the highest mountain near Baden; easy ascent, about 1½ hour, fine view from thurm at summit. Leave Baden by Scheibenstrasse.]

Badenweiler.—*Stat.*—Pop. 652.

HOTEL ROEMERBAD (Roman Baths Hotel).—Beautifully arranged first class hotel, facing Kur Park and Castle. Pension from 10 M. See Advt.

HOTEL SOMMER, with dependence "Park Villa." —Highly recommended first class old established hotel, with every modern comfort. Pension from 8 mks. See Advt.

A pleasantly situated health resort, 1,450 ft. above sea, on the western margin of the Black Forest. The springs, 77° to 80°, for bathing and drinking, have been known since Roman times, and are useful in cases of gout, rheumatism, stomach disorders, etc.; the pure air and equable temperature are regarded as favourable in cases of lung and nervous ailments. The whey cure is an important feature. During the season about 6,000 visitors. Visitor's tax, one week, 2 m.; the season, 20 m. Kurhaus, with frequent music, and park; in the park are the bath establishments, Marmorbad and Freibad. Bath House, supplied with the latest appliances. To west of the Marmorbad are the remains of the Roman baths. Grand Ducal Palace; on a hill the ruins of a castle. Concerts and theatrical representations. Town band.

ENGLISH CHURCH SERVICE in the season.

RAIL, page 140A.

[The **Belchen**, 4,640 ft., one of the finest points of view in the Black Forest, may be reached in 5 hours from Badenweiler; good paths, fingerposts; donkey, 8 marks.]

Boll Bad.

HOTEL AND KURHAUS BAD BOLL.—Reconstructed and much improved in 1913. New drawing and bath rooms. Pension from M. 5.50. See Advt.

Charmingly situated in the Wutach Valley, 2,034 feet above the sea, and surrounded by a magnificent pine forest affording pleasant and healthful walks and drives. There is good fishing in the neighbourhood, also an ancient castle and a waterfall.

Reached from Bonndorf Station (page 145), or from Reiselfingen (2 miles distant), page 144.

Donaueschingen.—*Stat.*—Pop. 3,800.

HOTEL Z. SCHUTZEN.—First class, three minutes from Station, in own large park. Most comfortable and moderate. Brine baths in the house. See Advt.

The town was partly destroyed by fire in 1908, rebuilt in mediaeval style, and is now one of the most interesting towns in Germany; 2,220 feet above sea, in a fine situation as a centre for excursions into the forest; climate excellent. Favourite hunting country of H.M. the German Emperor. A saline spring attracts summer visitors. Brine baths and inhalatorium. From the Station the principalstreet leads to the Palace and park of the Prince of Furstenberg; in the park, near the church, is a basin of water fed by a spring which is stated to be the Source of the Danube. Park always open, palace rarely. Behind the palace, on a height, is the Carlsbau, containing art and science collections. In Haldenstrasse is the Library of 90,000 vols. and 1,000 MSS (original MS. of the Nibelungen).

All information may be obtained from the Verkehrs Verein.

RAIL, pages 144, 145.

Dürrheim Bad.—*Stat.*

KURHAUS AND SALINEN HOTEL.—First class. Electric light throughout. Lift. Therapeutic treatment under supervision of Dr. Sütterlin. See Advt.

2,315 ft. above sea—the highest brine baths of Europe; very pleasantly situated in the most pleasant part of the Black Forest, about five miles from Villingen. Good centre for forest excursions, RAIL, page 145.

The Feldberg.

HOTEL FELDBERGERHOF.—First class in every detail. Central heating; electric light. 220 beds. Post in the house. Large new hotel to be built in 1914. See Advt.

The Feldberg, 4,900 ft., the highest mountain in the Black Forest, is reached from Titisee, about 9 miles distant, by a good road, partly through a beautiful pine forest. On the highest point is a tower, Friedrich-Luisen Thurm, whence is a fine view. The mountain is a popular resort, and one of the best winter sport and ski-ing grounds in Germany. At a short distance from the base of the mountain is the Feldsee, a pretty sheet of water.

DILIGENCE from Titisee, page 372; motor car from Todtnau during summer.

Freiburg-im-Breisgau.—*Stat.*—Pop. 83,324.

HOTEL SOMMER: ZAHRINGERHOF.—Facing the Station, old established first class hotel with every modern comfort; quiet position. Terrace Restaurant. See Advt.

HOTEL DE L'EUROPE.—First class, opposite the Central Station. Electric light and steam heating in all rooms. Gardens. See Advt.

HOTEL NATIONAL.—First class modern hotel, with every comfort. Best part of the town. Rooms from M.2.50; pension from M.7. See Advt.

PARK HOTEL.—New modern hotel, with every comfort. Facing Park, and five minutes from Station. Moderate charges. See Advt.

HOTEL CONTINENTAL AND PENSION.—Situated at the corner of Frederic and Bismarck Streets. Garden. See Advt.

VILLA BEAU SEJOUR—8, Werderstrasse. Entirely up-to-date. Bedrooms with bath-room. Best situation. Modern comforts. Highest references. Pension from 5.50 to 8 Marks. See Adv.

PENSION UTZ, corner of Werder and Garten Strasse; new house, with every modern comfort. Beautiful position. Excellent cuisine. Garden. Pension from M. 5. See Advt.

PENSION SCHLOSSBERGBLICK.—Ludwigstrasse, 33. Every possible comfort for visitors. Beautiful position; large garden. Pension from 5 M. See Advt.

PENSION UNIVERS.—Corner of Hilda and Urach Strasse, close to Wiehre Station. Beautiful position. Every modern comfort. Pension from from M. 5.50. See Advt.

PENSION MINERVA.—Poststrasse, 8. First class family hotel in central and quiet position. Every modern comfort. Pension from M.5.50. See Advt.

HOTEL AND PENSION PRINZ HEINRICH.—41, Günterstalstrasse. Comfortable establishment, with all modern conveniences. Newly opened. Close to the forest. Pension from M.4.50. See Advt.

CAFE SCHANZ.—Corner of Kaiserstrasse and Münsterstrasse. Elegant Café and first class Restaurant. Concerts twice daily. High class confectionery. English newspapers. Motor cars on hire. See Advt.

CAFE FRIEDRICHSBAU.—Kaiserstrasse, 148. First class, in the centre of the town. The largest café in the Grand Duchy of Baden. Afternoon and evening concerts daily. Military concert every Friday. Ladies' salon. 11 Billiard tables. English daily and illustrated papers. Tel. 235.

The RAILWAY STATION—Bahnhof—is on the west side of the town, about half a mile from the Minster.

Freiburg, 920 ft. above sea, on the River Dreisam, is a most picturesque city, situated amidst beautiful surroundings of wooded mountain and fertile plain; it is the seat of a University and of an archbishop. Beside the products of the Black Forest, which here find their principal market, pottery, silk, and machinery are manufactured.

From the Bahnhof the Eisenbahnstrasse leads east directly towards the Minster, passing, on the left, the Rathhaus (16th cent.), adorned with frescoes, and the old University.

The building of the Minster, a perfect example of German Gothic, of red sandstone, was begun sometime in the 12th cent., but not completed until 1513. The specially admired feature is the tower, 380 ft. high; in the portico is much sculpture. The interior is 354 ft. long, 102 ft. wide, 85 ft. high; monuments and paintings, good stained windows, carved woodwork (Adoration of the Magi in the transept), high altar-piece, pulpit stated to be one piece of stone. To visit choir, 50 pf.; to ascend tower, 60 pf. Archbishop's Palace opposite south side of Minster.

Kaufhaus, 1532, on south side of the Münster Platz; on the balcony above the portico are two projecting turrets. In the convent close by is a collection of antiquities.

In the Ludwigkirche (Protestant), a little beyond north end of Kaiserstrasse, quarter mile north of the Minster, are paintings.

University—about 3,500 students. New University, 1909-1912, opposite the Stadt Theater.

Handsome Stadt Theater, 1906-1910, one of the finest theatres in Germany.

On the Schlossberg, east of the city, are ruins of two castles; fine views.

POST OFFICE—in Eisenbahnstrasse.

MEDICAL.—Dr. Goldmann.

ENGLISH CHURCH SERVICE.—St. George, 59, Thurnseestrasse, two thirds mile due south of the Minster.

KODAKS.—Max Mayer, 11, Bertholdstr.

RAIL, pages 140, 143, 144, 212A.

[**Guntherstkal**, about 2 miles south of Freiburg, reached by tramway, is an attractive spot. The road to the **Schau-ins-Land**, 4,220 ft., is through Günthersthal.]

Freudenstadt.—*Stat.*—Pop. 7,270.

HOTEL AND KURHAUS WALDECK.—First class establishments; every possible comfort. Open all the year round. Winter sports. See Advt.

BLACK FOREST HOTEL.—One minute from Station, in extensive park. First class. Open all the year round. Winter sports. See Advt.

WALDLUST; RAPPEN; POST.

In a beautiful situation 2,380 feet above sea. An industrial town, founded in 1599 by a number of Protestant refugees from Salzburg. The market place is the chief attraction, as it is surrounded by arcades and picturesque buildings. In the Protestant Church are two naves for the separate use of men and women. Freudenstadt is recommended for nervous complaints, and, owing to its height and position, is suitable for both winter and summer cures. RAIL, p. 194.

Freyersbach Bad.

BATH HOTEL FREYERSBACH.—First class, with every comfort. 80 rooms, 120 beds. All kinds of mineral baths. Trout fishing; hunting. Pension from M. 6. See Advt.

A very pleasant "Cure" and health resort, 1,260 ft. above sea, in a pretty valley surrounded by high hills, with shady forest roads and paths in all directions. The sulphurous and iron springs have a considerable reputation, and draw an ever increasing number of visitors for the treatment of cases of lassitude, anæmia, chlorosis, chronic catarrh, constipation, nerve troubles, and numerous ailments. For the invalid and the healthy the surrounding forest is full of interest, and within easy reach are some of the most attractive of the towns of south Germany. The charges for the mineral baths are unusually low.

The nearest railway station is at Oppenau; the diligence between Oppenau and Peterstal, page 372, passes through Freyersbach.

Friedenweiler.—Pop. 300.

HOTEL KURHAUS.

A pretty little village, 2,965 ft. above sea, a favourite air-cure and forest resort. The once well known Benedictine and later Cistercian Abbey was burned 1725; part became the summer residence of the Prince of Furstenberg.

Reached by good road from Neustadt Station, 3 miles.

Gernsbach.—*Stat.*—Pop. 2,740.

HOTEL PFEIFFER.

An old and interesting little town, 525 feet above sea, on the River Murg. Rathaus of early 17th cent.; tombs in the Protestant Church.

At Schloss Eberstein, 1798, on a wooded height, 1,015 feet, a mile and a half from the upper end of Gernsbach, are pictures, arms, and curiosities; fine view. The Murgtal is one of the most attractive valleys of the Black Forest; good fishing in the river.

RAIL, page 146. Motor omnibuses several times daily to Baden Baden and Wildbad.

Griesbach Bad.

BATH HOTEL AND KURHAUS.—Comfortable, well equipped establishment. Pension from 6 Marks. Good trout fishing. See Advt.

A very pleasantly situated resort, 1,665 ft. above sea, in the delightful valley of the Rench (Renchtal), at the base of the densely wooded Kniebis. The curative properties of the chalybeate springs have been known for centuries; recent analyses have demonstrated the presence of significant radium emanations in the waters, which possess the highest radio activity of all the cold springs of Germany; they are successfully employed in chlorosis, anæmia, nervous ailments, heart disease, gout, rheumatism, women's ailments, etc. The baths are of all kinds.

Reached by diligence from Oppenau, 7½ miles, page 372.

Hausach.—*Stat.*—Pop. 1,560.

HOTELS: KRONE; HIRSCH; ENGEL.

A quaint little town, once dominated by a now ruined castle of the Princes of Furstenberg.

RAIL, pages 144, 145.

Herrenalb.—*Stat.*—Pop. 1,300.

On the River Alb, 1,200 ft. above sea. Kurhaus; 10,000 Kur guests annually. Only a fragment left of the once famous Benedictine Abbey, destroyed by the Swedes in 1642. Interesting church, with remains of cloisters. Excellent trout fishing.

RAIL, page 140B. Motor service between Herrenalb, Wildbad, and Baden-Baden.

Hochenschwand.—Pop. 300.

3,315 ft. above sea, one of the highest villages of Baden, a popular resort as an air cure.

Kurhaus. From the Belvedere, close to the village, are magnificent sunrise and sunset views.

Reached by a good road from St. Blasien, 4½ miles, or by a footpath.

Hornberg.—*Stat.*—Pop. 3,000.

SCHLOSS HOTEL.

An interesting old town, 1,180 ft. above sea, at one of the most attractive parts of the Black Forest; during summer much frequented as an "air cure." On a height above the town is a ruined schloss (1,500 ft.) and an hotel.

RAIL, page 144.

[A favourite excursion is to the **Althornberg**, 2,390 ft., 2½ miles south of Hornberg; very fine view; pleasant descent from the Althornberg to Triberg. Between Hornberg and St. Georgen the railway is in the highest degree interesting. There are 26 tunnels between Hornberg and St. Georgen, and many bridges, with wonderful curves as the line rises in gradients varying from 1:58 to 1:50.]

Königsfeld.—*Stat.*

An interesting village, where is a Moravian settlement. RAIL (Peterzell-Konigsfeld), p. 144.

Menzenschwand.

HOTEL ADLER.

A much frequented summer and winter resort of the southern Black Forest, 2,953 ft. above sea, at the foot of the Feldberg, well sheltered from cold winds. Reached by diligence from St. Blasien, page 372. Motor service connects Menzenschwand with Titisee and Albbruck.

Offenburg.—*Stat.*—Pop. 15,435.

HOTELS: BAHNHOF; UNION.

An old town, on the River Kinzig. Gothic Church (Protestant), with pierced tower. Statue of Sir Francis Drake, as the presumed introducer of the potato into Europe (1586). RAIL, 140, 144.

Peterstal Bad.

KUR HOTEL.

In the romantic upper valley of the Rench (Renchtal), one of the pleasantest health resorts, in a sheltered situation. The chalybeate and carbonic acid springs, known since the 16th century, are very useful in cases of poorness of blood, female ailments, dyspepsia, etc.; nearly 2,000 patients annually. The air is remarkably pure. Reached by diligence from Oppenau, 5 miles, page 372.

Pforzheim.—*Stat.*—Pop. 69,082.

HOTEL RUF.—First class, facing Station. Hot and cold water in each room. Every comfort. Splendid views. See Advt.

HANSA HOTEL.

A pleasant prosperous town, most favourably situated for excursions to all parts of the Black Forest, of which it is regarded as the northern gate. In the Schlosskirche are monuments of the Margraves of Baden of 16th cent. Rathaus; School of Industrial Art. The extensive jewellery trade employs about 33,000 hands.

RAIL, pages 141, 194A.

Rippoldsau Bad.—Pop. 700.

A village 1,855 feet above sea, at the foot of the Kniebis, 3,165 ft., in a picturesque contracted part of the Wolfthal—the most frequented health resort of the Kniebis district. For centuries the curative properties of the springs have been known, the waters (drinking and bathing) being very useful in cases of gout, rheumatism, stomach affections, female ailments, nervous troubles, etc. Modern well organised Bath Establishment; music; trout fishing and shooting. Season from May until October. Motor Car Service to and from Wolfach Station, page 372.

St. Blasien.—Pop. 1,840.

HOTEL AND KURHAUS.—First class, 200 rooms. Many medical, social, and sporting conveniences.

SANATORIUM LUISENHEIM for patients requiring distinctly medical treatment. See Advt.

Beautifully situated in a sheltered position, at the junction of two elevated valleys. 2,530 feet above the sea. Formerly celebrated for its vast Benedictine Abbey, now widely known as a summer and winter resort, where the mingled forest and mountain air is specially favourable in cases of lung weakness and nerve troubles. Many pleasant paths, marked for guidance as to grade and abundantly provided with seats, lead into the delightful surroundings, and offer points of view over grand scenery. Church, with central dome 165 ft. in diameter. The Kurhaus provides all kinds of baths, including light and air baths; Kurgarten; good music. Trout fishing and shooting in the neighbourhood.

MOTOR SERVICE to St. Blasien from Titisee and Waldshut, page 372.

Schluchsee.—Pop. 704.

STAR HOTEL (STERN)—Excellent hotel, in good position. Pension from 5 M. Branch house—Hotel Schiff. See Advt.

Fine position on the road from Titisee to St. Blasien. 3,152 feet above the sea. Specially suitable for winter cure. Pure air, and surrounded by pine forests. Shooting and fishing. Every kind of winter sport. The lake, 2½ miles long, is kept in perfect condition for skating; ski-ing taught by a professional.

Reached from Titisee Railway Station. Motor Omnibus service four times daily, see page 372.

Schönwald.—A climatic sanatorium and summer and winter resort, 3,260 feet above sea, amid meadows and pine woods. Dil., p. 372.

Singen.—*Stat.*—Pop. 9,000.

CENTRAL HOTEL SCHWEIZERHOF.—Opposite the Station, very quiet. All modern comforts. Rooms from 2—3 Mks. See Advt.

Situated at the foot of the Hohentwiel (2,253 ft.), and at the south end of the Black Forest Railway; a good centre whence to explore both the Black Forest and Switzerland. The castle on the height of Hohentwiel was destroyed by the French in 1800—it has a fine historic record. Monuments to Widerholt (defender in Thirty Years War), Bismarck, and Scheffel. From the imposing ruins is a magnificent view.

RAIL, pages 139A, 144, 260A.

Teinach.—*Stat.*—

HOTEL: BAD.

A delightfully situated spot, 1,275 ft. above sea, at the base of the Zavelstein (1,925 ft.), long known as a tourist and bathing resort. The principal springs are the Hirschquelle, Bachquelle, and Tintenquelle, and the waters are efficaciously used in cases of anæmia, catarrhs, dyspepsia, gout, and nerve affections. Ruined castle on the Zavelstein. RAIL, page 194A.

Titisee.—*Stat.*

HOTEL TITISEE.—First class. Beautiful position onl ake. Modern comforts. Central heating. Open all the year. Garage. Winter sports. See Advt.

THE BEAR HOTEL, facing Station, is highly recommended as a summer and winter hotel and pension. See Advt.

The Lake (Titisee) is a pretty sheet of water, filling the bed of a former glacier; the Seebach flows in at the south end, the Gutach flows out at the north end. Titisee is the most convenient spot from which to reach the Feldberg (p. 457). Fine winter station with every kind of sport.

RAIL, page 144. Motor service between Titisee and St. Blasien, see page 372.

Todtmoos.-Pop. 1,550. HOTELS: BAD; RUSSIE.

A village in the valley of the Wehra, 2,695 ft. above sea, much visited during summer. The Wehra Thal is one of the finest of the Black Forest valleys.

Diligence from Wehr to Todtmoos, page 372.

Triberg.—*Stat.*—Pop. 4,100.

BLACK FOREST HOTEL.—Close to the Waterfall. An excellent first class establishment, managed by the proprietor himself. See Advt.

HOTEL WEHRLE.-Very comfortable, modern, and moderate; old reputation; close to waterfall. Splendid park; noted cuisine. Pension from mks. 7. See Advt.

WALD AND KUR HOTEL BELLEVUE.—First class; well situated in its own grounds. Large terraces. Pension, 7—10 Mks. Trout fishing. See Advt.

In an elevated but sheltered situation, 2,250 ft. above sea; favourite resort all the year round. Winter sport; the bob run is one of the finest in South Germany. At the Gewerbehalle is a collection of clocks, the making of which engages many of the inhabitants. Two churches.—Protestant and Roman Catholic. The Waterfall, the most imposing in west Germany, is from a height of 500 ft., broken into seven leaps; from the path on right bank are fine views.

Tennis courts; open air theatre.

ENGLISH CHURCH SERVICE.

RAIL, page 144. Diligence, page 372

Villingen.—*Stat.*—Pop. 10,924.

A very interesting old town, 2,300 feet above sea. Two long streets cross each other—from the middle may be seen the four old towers guarding the entrances to the town. During the Thirty Years War it was three times besieged. Cathedral, built by Heinrich von Furstenberg in the thirteenth century, in Roman style. The chancel contains beautiful work of the 14th century. The industry of this town has increased very much recently, the chief manufactures being silk weaving, musical instruments, clocks, etc. Magnificent views may be obtained from the watch tower. The environs are very beautiful; the district is considered to be among the healthiest parts of the Black Forest. Excellent institutions for private education.

RAIL, pages 144, 145, 194A.

Waldshut.—*Stat.*—Pop. 4,000.

HOTEL: BLUME.

On the north bank of the Rhine, at a considerable height above the river. A busy, interesting, quaint old town, at the south end of the Schwarzwald line, convenient as a centre whence to visit either the Black Forest or parts of Switzerland. Motor car service to St. Blasien, Titisee, page 372.

RAIL, pages 139A, 262A.

Wehrawald (near Todtmoos).

WEHRAWALD SANATORIUM.—On a south spur of a lofty range of hills, thoroughly sheltered by pine forest. Complete modern installation. See Advt.

2,600 ft. above sea. A quiet sunshiny spot, where throughout the year the light, pure, balmy air is greatly valued for its restorative qualities in cases of lung weakness.

Reached in 2½ hours from Wehr station, page 142; the diligence between Wehr and Todtmoos (p. 372) passes Wehrawald.

Wildbad.—*Stat.*—Pop. 3,532.

HOTEL KLUMPP and KLUMPP'S HOTEL BELLEVUE.—First class hotels in excellent position, facing the Royal Bath House, etc. Close to the promenade and Trinkhalle. Up-to-date comforts. Lift; electric light; steam heating. See Advt.

ROYAL BATH HOTEL.—First class; the only hotel in Wildbad having its own Thermal Baths. Every possible comfort. Dependence VILLA WETZEL. See Advt.

SOMMERBERG HOTEL.—On the top of the Sommerberg, reached by funicular railway. First class; every modern comfort. All kinds of winter sports. Pension from 7 M. See Advt.

A favourite watering place of Wurttemberg, 1,413 feet above sea, on the River Enz, in a narrow pine clad valley. The springs, 90°-100° Fahr., are very beneficial in cases of gout, rheumatism, paralysis, metal poisonings, nervous diseases, female ailments, etc. Kurtax, for one week, 1 person 4 m., each additional member of family 3 m. The Konig-Karls Bad is lavishly decorated and fitted with all appliances. Handsome new Kurhaus (1910); theatre; frequent good music.

Funicular Railway up the Sommerberg, a delightful spot where every kind of winter sport may be indulged in; ascent in seven minutes, fare 1 Mark return.

ENGLISH CHURCH SERVICE at Trinity Church.

MEDICAL. — Dr. Weizsaecker, Dr. Asher, Dr. Haussmann, Dr. Grunow, Dr. Lorenz, Dr. Hiller.

RAIL, page 194A. Motor Car service twice daily between Wildbad and Baden-Baden via Gernsbach.

GERMANY.

Germany is above all other Continental lands a country of large towns, there being some 45 cities with upwards of one hundred thousand inhabitants, and about 200 besides with populations over 20,000. Partly owing to its former division into almost innumerable independent States, it is also the richest of all countries in palaces and public buildings of importance, and, next to France, it is also the richest in fine Gothic churches. The Protestant Cathedrals of Magdeburg, Halberstadt, Marburg, Nurnberg, and Ulm, and the Roman Catholic Cathedrals of Cologne, Mayence, Metz, Strassburg, Freiburg-im-Breisgau, Speyer, Bamberg, and Regensburg, are ecclesiastical buildings of the first rank, but there are scores of other churches little inferior to these. In sumptuous church furniture and carved detail the Gothic churches of Germany far surpass those of France. No country in the world can show so many nobly planned and well-built towns or cities which have preserved so perfectly their ancient character. Amongst many grand and exquisitely picturesque old cities of the later middle ages may be singled out for special study Nurnberg, Ulm, Augsburg, Regensburg, and Rothenburg, in South, and Hildesheim, Brunswick, Magdeburg, Lübeck, Wismar, and Danzig in North Germany. German scenery is generally pleasing and varied, except in the far north, and there are many pretty mountain chains of moderate elevation, and much fine river and forest scenery in different parts of the country. Parts of the Black Forest Mountains even attain to grandeur, and in the Alpine district called the Bavarian Highlands and round Berchtesgaden are many beauty spots which will compare with the best known tourist centres of Switzerland.

The German Empire (deutsches Reich) consists of the following twenty-five States and the Imperial territory of Alsace-Lorraine, in order of magnitude —

PRUSSIA.	BRUNSWICK.	SCHWARZBURG-RUDOLSTADT.
BAVARIA.	SAXE-WEIMAR.	SCHWARZBURG-SONDERHAUSEN
WURTTEMBERG.	MECKLENBURG-STRELITZ.	REUSS (younger branch).
BADEN.	SAXE MEININGEN.	SCHAUMBURG-LIPPE.
SAXONY.	ANHALT.	REUSS (elder branch)
ALSACE-LORRAINE.	SAXE-COBURG-GOTHA.	HAMBURG.
MECKLENBURG-SCHWERIN.	SAXE-ALTENBURG.	LUBECK.
HESSE.	LIPPE.	BREMEN.
OLDENBURG.	WALDECK.	

Total area, 208,780 square miles; Population (1910), 64,925,993.

Emperor (deutscher Kaiser).—Wilhelm II, German Emperor and King of Prussia, born January 27th, 1859, succeeded June 15th, 1888. Heir, Prince Friedrich Wilhelm, born May 6th, 1882.

Government.—Imperial legislation is vested in the Bundesrat (the council of the individual States of the Empire—61 members, appointed by the different States Governments), and the Reichstag (397 deputies elected by popular suffrage).

Army.—On a peace footing, 656,144; war footing, about 3,000,000. **Navy** (1913), including those building, dreadnoughts 21, battleships 20, cruisers 47, destroyers 153, torpedo boats 47, submarines 26.

Language.—In all the larger hotels, and in most of the smaller hotels, English and French are spoken. While ever so slight a knowledge of German is always a great advantage, onlyi n the by-ways of travel and remote districts is an absolute ignorance of the language likely to cause serious inconvenience.

Hotels.—German Hotels are, after those of Switzerland, the best in the world, and are generally moderate in their charges. The cuisine is hardly inferior to the French, and the restaurants and cafés are perhaps superior. The dinner hour is generally 12 to 1; in Berlin, Hamburg, and some of the larger cities, as late as 3 or 4; and, in places frequented by foreign tourists, a second table d'hôte is often provided at 6 or 7 o'clock.

Railways.—Railway carriages in Germany are generally clean and comfortable and the fares are less than in most other parts of the Continent. For ordinary trains the fares average 1$\frac{2}{5}$d. per mile first class, $\frac{9}{10}$d. second class, $\frac{3}{5}$d. third class; for express trains, "Schnell-Zuge," there is an extra charge varying from 25pf. to 2m.; no reduction for return tickets. Seats in through corridor trains are numbered and may be reserved in advance at starting station without fee. Tickets are usually available for four days, with one break allowed on journey. Mid Europe Time, one hour in advance of Greenwich Time, is observed on all lines. There is no free allowance of luggage.

Postage.—Letters to places in Germany or in Austria Hungary 10 pf. per 20 gramms (two thirds of an ounce); to other countries 20 pf. for the same weight (for United States 10 pf. if sent by direct steamer). Post cards for foreign countries 10 pf. In Bavaria only Bavarian postage stamps may be used. **Telegrams** to United Kingdom 15 pf. per word—minimum 80 pf.; to the United States 1 m. 5 pf. to 1 m. 60 pf. per word.

Money.—100 Pfennige = 1 Mark = 11$\frac{3}{4}$d. English. GOLD COINS.—20, 10 Marks. SILVER COINS.—5, 3, 2, and 1 Mark pieces, and 50 Pfennige pieces. NICKEL COINS.—20, 10, and 5 Pfennige pieces. BRONZE COINS.—2 and 1 Pfennig pieces. BANK NOTES.—20, 50, 100, 500, and 1,000 Marks.

Luggage Rates.

Only in operation in association with Passenger Ticket.

DISTANCE.	Charge for Carriage of 1 to 25	26 to 35	36 to 50	51 to 75	76 to 100	101 to 125	126 to 150	151 to 175	176 to 200
	KILOGRAMM.								
Kilometer.	Pf.	Pf.	Pf.	Pf.	Pf.	Pf.	Pf.	Pf.	Pf.
1—25	20	20	40	60	80	1 00	1 20	1 40	1 60
26—50	20	25	50	75	1 00	1 25	1 50	1 75	2 00
51—100	50	50	1 00	1 50	2 00	2 50	3 00	3 50	4 00
101—150	50	75	1 50	2 25	3 00	3 75	4 50	5 25	6 00
151—200	50	1 00	2 00	3 00	4 00	5 00	6 00	7 00	8 00
201—250	50	1 25	2 50	3 75	5 00	6 25	7 50	8 75	10 00
251—300	50	1 50	3 00	4 50	6 00	7 50	9 00	10 50	12 00
301—350	1 00	1 75	3 50	5 25	7 00	8 75	10 50	12 25	14 00

DISTANCE.	Charge for Carriage of 1 to 25	26 to 35	36 to 50	51 to 75	76 to 100	101 to 125	126 to 150	151 to 175	176 to 200
	KILOGRAMM.								
Kilometer.	Pf.	Pf.	Pf.	Pf.	Pf.	Pf.	Pf.	Pf.	Pf.
351—400	1 00	2 00	4 00	6 00	8 00	10 00	12 00	14 00	16 00
401—450	1 00	2 25	4 50	6 75	9 00	11 25	13 50	15 75	18 00
451—500	1 00	2 50	5 00	7 50	10 00	12 50	15 00	17 50	20 00
501—600	1 00	3 00	6 00	9 00	12 00	15 00	18 00	21 00	24 00
601—700	1 00	3 50	7 00	10 50	14 00	17 50	21 00	24 50	28 00
701—800	1 00	4 00	8 00	12 00	16 00	20 00	24 00	28 00	32 00
over 800	1 00	4 50	10 00	15 00	20 00	25 00	30 00	35 00	40 00

Weights and Measures.

Meter=39·3701 in=3·281 ft.=3 ft. 3⅜ in.=1·0936 yard.
Square Meter (quadratstab)=1 1-5th or 1·196 sq. yd.
Ar (or 100 sq. meters)=119·6 sq. yds.
Cubic Meter=35 1-3rd cubic ft.
Centimeter=2-5ths inch.
Kilometer=1093 yds=5-8th mile

10 Kilometers=6¼ miles.
100 Kilometers=62 1-10th miles.
Square Kilometer=2-5ths square mile.
Hecktar=2½ acres (2·471).
100 Hecktars=247·1 acres.

Gramm=15½ grains (15·432)
10 Gramms=1-3rd oz. Avoirdupois.

Kilogramm=2 1-5th lbs. (2·2) Avoir.
Pfund=1·102 lb. Avoirdupois.
Centner=110·231 lbs. Avoirdupois.
Tonne=19·684 cwt.

Liter=1·761 pint.
Hectoliter=22·009 gallons.

NOTICE OF TOWNS, WATERING PLACES, etc.

For the Rhine, see page 448; for the Black Forest, see page 455.

Ahrweiler.—*Stat.*—Pop. 5,450.

HOTEL STERN; KRONEN.

A very old busy little town, enclosed within walls, in an attractive situation. Lorenzkirche, of 14th and 15th cents. A former Franciscan monastery, on the Calvarienberg, a height to the south, is occupied as a girls' school.

1½ mile up the valley from Ahrweiler is Walporzheim, an ancient village, noted for its wines.

RAIL, page 123D.

Aix-la-Chapelle (German Aachen).—*Stat.*—Pop. 156,143.

HOTEL NUELLENS.—First-rate, airy, and delightful situation, facing the Elise Fountain with its garden and public promenade. See Advt.

NEW KAISERBAD, BRUNNEN—BAINS DE L'EMPEREUR, OR EMPEROR'S BATH AND NEW BATH.—Very superior establishment, supplied direct from the Mineral Springs.—(The proprietor, Mr. Dremel, is also proprietor of the Hote Nuellens). See Advt,

HOTEL KAISERHOF.—First class; 160 rooms and salons. Lift; electric light; central heating. Garage. See Advt.

HENRION'S GRAND HOTEL AND STADT BADHAUS CORNELIUS, BATH HOTEL, AND ROSENBAD HOTEL.—First class Establishment, with fine Mineral Baths in Hotel. See Advt.

HOYER'S UNION HOTEL, close to the Railway Station. Clean, comfortable, and reasonable. See Advt.

At **Burtscheid.**—H. WEBER'S ROSENBAD HOTEL.—First class. Own thermal springs. Large garden. Every comfort. Pension from Mks. 7.25. Note address. See Advt.

THE HAUPTBAHNHOF, the principal Railway Station, is on the south side of the city; the West Bahnhof is on the north west side of city.

AIX-LA-CHAPELLE, the Aquae Grani of the Romans, the northern capital of the empire of Charlemagne, who made it his favourite seat, is situated in a fertile country surrounded by wooded hills. Very little remains of the ancient historic city, the scene of so many important events, improvements having swept away most relics of the past; broad handsome streets and promenades now cover the lines of the mediæval fortifications, and on all sides are indications of a modern town. The warm sulphur springs, 96° to 131° Fahr., have been known from very early times; thousands of visitors use them annually in cases of skin disease, rheumatism, gout, contractions, etc. The chief industries are cloth weaving, needle making, and the making of machinery.

The Münster (or Cathedral), the bath establishments, and principal hotels, are all gathered at the centre of the city. From the Bahnhof Platz, before the Hauptbahnhof, the Bahnhofstrasse leads into the broad Hochstrasse, the line of which, north west, leads to the Theater Platz, where, at the north corner, opens out the Friedrich Wilhelm Platz—here is the Elisenbrunnen—and just away from the west side of the Platz is seen the Münster.

The MUNSTER (Minster), or Cathedral, is an irregular pile, including a Romanesque octagon erected by Charlemagne, 796-804; adjoining the east side of the octagon is the Gothic choir (1353-1413). Mosaics in the octagon, and candelabrum presented by Frederick Barbarossa (1165) hanging over a modern inscription in pavement, "Carolo Magno;" in the gallery of the octagon, the Hochmünster, is the Throne of Charlemagne, who it is conjectured was buried in one of the chapels, and whose (presumed) sarcophagus is shewn in the Chapel of the Cross on north west side. Rich stained windows in choir, high altar, episcopal throne, pulpit, statues, and carving. Within the edifice the German emperors were crowned down to Ferdinand I (1531); some of the imperial insignia are now at Vienna. On the south side of the octagon is the treasury, wonderfully rich in relics, curiosities, and gold and silver vessels; within an elaborate silver shrine are objects of great veneration—the "swaddling clothes" of the infant Jesus, the linen cloth that girded the body of the Saviour upon the Cross. the robe of the Virgin. the blood stained cloth that enshrouded the body of John the Baptist; these relics are shewn publicly, gratis, once in seven years. Fees for treasury, 1 to 3 persons, 3 m. (single travellers unite or join a party); to view throne of Charlemagne, sarcophagus, etc., 50 pf.

Marienkirche, just north west of the Bahnhof Platz, a modern Church, Gothic, has elaborately decorated interior. St. Foillan Kirche, east of Münster, oldest foundation; St. Michael Kirche, just south of west end of Münster, the Jesuit Church; St. Paul, in Jacobstrasse, 250 yards west of Münster; St. Jacob Kirche, in Jacobstrasse; St. Nicolaus Kirche, off north side of Markt Platz; many other churches.

A few yards north of the Münster. in the Markt Platz, is the RATHHAUS, on the site of Charlemagne's palace; the building, Gothic, dating from middle of 14th cent., was much injured by fire in 1883, since restored. The Kaisersaal, on floor above, is adorned with fine historic frescoes; in the Council chamber are portraits. In the Fischmarkt, at south west corner of the Münster, is the Archiv und Bibliothek, containing the archives—some documents are shewn—and library (80,000 vols.).

The SPRINGS rise in the heart of the town. The Elisenbrunnen, supplied from the Kaiserquelle (Emperor Spring) is in Friedrich Wilhelm Platz, just east of the Münster; here, in the Trinkhalle, are the chief gatherings to drink the water, from 7.30 a.m. to 8.30 a.m. and between 12.0 and 1.0 p.m. Opposite the garden side is Edelstrasse, where, or in the adjoining Buchel, are the Konigin von Ungarn bath, the Kaiserbad, Neubad, and Quirinusbad; in Corneliusstrasse, off north side of the Buchel, are Comphausbad, Rosenbad, and Corneliusbad. The Kurhaus is in Comphausbadstrasse, a little north of Friedrich Wilhelm Platz; the chief resort of visitors, containing Kursaal, concert and ball rooms, reading room, etc.

SUERMONDT MUSEUM, about 250 yards east of Friedrich Wilhelm Platz. Collection of valuable paintings by old masters—Rubens, Jordaens, Cuyp, Teniers, van Dyck, Rembrandt, etc. Also a collection of modern pictures, and collections of antiquities and objects of industrial art. Admission to old collection free on Sun. and Wed.; 50 pf. on Tues., Thurs., Fri., and Sat.; to modern pictures, Sun. and Wed., 25 pf., other days, 50 pf.

Rhenisch-Westphalian Polytechnic School (or University), in the Templergraben, one third mile north west of the Münster; about 400 students.

POST OFFICE, in the Capuzinergraben, just south of Friedrich Wilhelm Platz.

ENGLISH CHURCH SERV.—Empress Frederick Memorial Church, Couventstrasse.

U. S. CONSUL.—P. King, Esq.

RAIL, pages 99, 104, 122, 127, 134A,

Aachen-Burtscheid.

The Springs and Kurhaus of BURTSCHEID, formerly a separate town, but now incorporated with Aix-la-Chapelle, are immediately south of the Hauptbahnhof. Victoriabrunnen and Kochbrunnen are the chief springs (up to 160°); there is also a cold spring; the Kurhaus is a handsome building.]

Alexandersbad, in Bavaria, 1,935 ft. above sea, a pleasant summer resort with chalybeate baths, Curhaus. DILIGENCE, page 373.

Allerheiligen, see page 455.

Altenahr.—*Stat.*—Pop. 878.

HOTELS: KASPARI; RHEINISCHER HOF.

A favourite summer resort, in a very picturesque situation, on the River Ahr. The ruined Castle of Altenahr, on a height, 950 ft., dates from the 10th cent. Weisse Kreuz, to north of the castle, is a fine point of view; another and finer view is from the Schwarze Kreuz. on the opposite bank of the Ahr. In the district between Altenahr and Adenau floods caused great loss of life (estimated 150 lives) and destruction of property, June 12th, 1910. RAIL, page 123D.

Altona.—*Stat.*—Pop. 172,628.

HOTEL KAISERHOF—First class modern hotel, facing Station from which Atlantic and other boat expresses arrive and depart. See Advt. under Hamburg.

A thriving commercial and industrial town. practically part of Hamburg.

The broad Kaiserstrasse leads south from the Hauptbahnhof to the river; at the south end of the Kaiserstrasse, on east side, is the Palmaille, the favourite promenade. On north side of the Palmaille is a Museum with natural history and ethnographical collections. Parallel with the Palmaille, but a little north, is Konigstrasse, where, opposite the theatre, is the Real Gymnasium, containing a picture gallery.

St. Paulikirche has a copper covered dome. At the Roman Catholic Church. a little north of east end of Konigstrasse, is an altar piece said to be by Murillo. St. Johanniskirche, erected 1883, north end of the Allée, running up north east from the Hauptbahnhof, is considered one of the best of modern brick buildings in North Germany.

At Ottensen, to the west of Altona, Klopstock, the poet, lies buried.

RAIL, pages 168, 169.

Andernach, see page 450.

Ansbach.—*Stat.*—Pop. 18,478.

HOTELS: STERN; WEDEL.

On the River Rezat. Schloss, once the residence of the Margraves of Brandenburg-Ansbach, beside interesting artistic appointments has a picture gallery. Gumbertuskirche, with three towers, contains memorials of Knights of the Order of the Swan. Johanniskirche contains burial vault of the Margraves.

RAIL, pages 196, 204.

Antogast Bad, see page 455.

Arnstadt.—*Stat.*—Pop. 16,270.

HOTELS: GOLDENE HENNE; SONNE.

A well situated town with a saline spring which draws many visitors. Liebfrauenkirche, 12th-13th cent., contains tombs and sculpture. Rathhaus of 1585; Schloss.

RAIL, pages 152, 170A, 173C.

Bayreuth.—*Stat.*—Pop. 34,547.

HOTELS: REICHSADLER; BAHNHOF; SONNE.

The Railway Station—BAHNHOF—is in the north part of the town, half a mile from the centre. The Wagner Festspielhaus (theatre) is seen on high ground at end of street, right hand, on leaving the Station.

Capital of Upper Franconia. Bahnhofstrasse leads south across the narrow River Main to Luitpold Platz, where, on west side, is the Herzogspalais (palace of Duke of Wurttemberg); a little beyond is Opernstrasse, where are the Roman Catholic Church and the Opera House; still a little further south, Richard Wagnerstrasse goes off to south east—No. 48 was the house of Wagner (died 1883), who lies buried in the garden. About 250 yards south of Wagner's house, at the corner of Lisztstrasse and Wahnfriedstrasse, is the house where Liszt died, 1886. In Friedrichstrasse, to which Ludwigstrasse leads south from the Opera House, lived Jean Paul Richter (died 1825); house marked by tablet.

The Neues Schloss (1754-73) is on the Residenz Platz, 400 yards south of the Opera House; here are some pictures and historical collections. Altes Schloss, in Maximilianstrasse, a few yards west of the Opera House.

Stadt Pfarrkirche (Protestant), 100 yards south of the old Schloss.

In the Cemetery, on west side of the town, Jean Paul Richter and Franz Liszt lie buried.

About three miles east of Bayreuth is the Eremitage, a palace erected 1715; the gardens, and "temples" in them, are interesting. The Fantasie is another palace, about three miles west of Bayreuth; pleasant gardens.

RAIL, pages 202, 203, 203B, 203C.

Berchtesgaden.—*Stat.*—Pop. 2,630.

GRAND HOTEL KURHAUS.—Highest class. Finest situation, with large park and beautiful views. Electric light; baths. See Advt.

HOTEL BELLEVUE.—First class, in fine position. Baths and Inhalations. Electric light throughout. See Advt.

HOTEL VIER JAHRESZEITEN (Four Seasons Hotel).—Fine situation, very comfortable. Rooms from 1.50 Mk. to 5 Mks. Pension 6 to 10 Mks. See Advt.

A very beautifully situated small Bavarian town, 1,870 ft. above sea, among the Bavarian Alps, with rock, forest, and water scenery all round; a favourite summer resort. Schloss, once an abbey; in the abbey church are tombs and carved stalls—cloisters. Carved wares are a famous local industry. RAIL, pages 200, 203C.

BERLIN.—*Stat.*—Pop. (1910) 2,071,257 (with suburbs, 3,680,000). *(Plan in Special Edition, or post free 6d. stamps).*

HOTEL ADLON.—No. 1, Unter den Linden (corner Pariser Platz). Hotel de Luxe. See Advt.

CONTINENTAL HOTEL.—First class, facing Friedrichstrasse Station. Every modern comfort. See Advt.

BRISTOL HOTEL.—High class in every respect, n finest part of the Unter den Linden. Patronized by the leading classes. Every modern comfort. See Advt.

CENTRAL HOTEL.—First class modern hotel, facing the Friedrichstrasse Station. 500 rooms, from 3 Marks. See Advt.

HOTEL ESPLANADE, entirely new, in connection with Esplanade Hotel, Hamburg. Palatial hotel, every modern comfort. Four lifts. See Advt.

HOTEL ATLANTIC, DER KAISERHOF. — First class hotel, in Wilhelmsplatz. See Advt.

EDEN HOTEL.—New first class hotel, in best part of Berlin. 200 rooms and suites, with hot and cold water supply. Fine view of the Tiergarten. See Advt.

SAVOY HOTEL.—Opposite the Friedrichstrasse Station. 200 rooms and salons; suites with bath and toilet. See Advt.

HOTEL DER FURSTENHOF.—Potsdamer Platz. Entirely new, with every modern comfort. 300 rooms, with hot and cold water, baths. See Advt.

ELITE HOTEL.—Opened April, 1908. First class hotel, near Friedrichstrasse Station. See Advt.

GRAND HOTEL BELLEVUE AND THIERGARTEN HOTEL.—Well situated opposite the Potsdam Ry. Electric light. See Advt.

HOTEL BAUER.—Unter den Linden. First, class old established hotel with every comfort. Central and best position. See Advt.

HOTEL EXCELSIOR.—New, first class, and with every modern comfort. Facing Anhalter Bahnhof, Station for Dresden, Carlsbad, Vienna, Munich, Italy, &c. 500 rooms from 3 marks. See Advt.

WHITE HOUSE HOTEL.—1, Krausenstrasse. New first class hotel. Every modern comfort. Central position. Rooms from M. 3. See Advt.

HOTEL CUMBERLAND.—First class private hotel, in the best part of the west end. 600 rooms with baths. Latest sanitary arrangements. See Advt.

HOTEL "DER KOENIGSHOF."—New high class hotel at the corner of "Unter den Linden." Rooms from 3 M., with bath and toilette from 7 M. See Advt.

HOTEL PRINZ ALBRECHT.—First class family hotel, quiet, best position. Close to Anhalt and Potsdam Stations. Moderate tariff. See Advt.

MONOPOL HOTEL.—First class, close to Friedrichstrasse Station. Every modern comfort. Suites with baths. Single rooms from 4 mks. See Advt.

HABSBURGER HOF.—High class hotel, close to the Anhalter Bahnhof (Askanischer Platz, 1). Apartments and single rooms with bath, etc. Rooms from 3 M. Garage. See Advt.

HOTEL ZUM REICHSTAG.—27, Dorotheenstrasse, chief entrance, 2, Bunsenstrasse. Modern hotel in central quiet position, with every comfort. Rooms from Mks. 3. See Advt.

HOTEL COBURG.—Facing the main exit Friedrichstrasse Station. First class family house, modern and moderate. See Advt.

ALEXANDRA HOTEL.—New and modern family hotel. Opened 1904. Very central location; managed on English lines; moderate. See Advt.

GRAND HOTEL DE RUSSIE—First class, opposite Friedrichstrasse Station. All modern comforts. Rooms from 3 M. See Advt.

PARK HOTEL, CHARLOTTENBURG, BERLIN.—Close to Zoologischer Garten Station. First class family hotel, with every modern comfort. Quiet and healthy position. Pension arrangements. Moderate terms. See Advt.

HOTEL METROPOLE.—Unter den Linden, 20 (next to the "Passage"). Modern comforts. Rooms from 2—10 M. See Advt.

SCHLOESSER'S HOTEL.—75, Friedrichstrasse, close to Unter den Linden. Old established hotel, in central position. Entirely renovated. Every modern comfort. Rooms from M. 3. See Advt.

HOTEL PRINZ WILHELM.—14, Dorotheenstrasse. Family hotel, in quiet position, close to Unter den Linden. All modern comforts. Rooms from 3 M. See Advt.

HOTEL SANSSOUCI.—Linkstrasse, 37. Good second class house, convenient, quiet position, near Potsdamer and Anhalter Stats. Every modern comfort. Rooms from M. 2. Pension. See Advt.

PENSION KAHRN.—28, Kleiststrasse. First class Pension with all modern comforts. Homelike and good cooking. See Advt.

PENSION VON FINCK.—123a, Potsdamerstrasse, close to Potsdamer and Anhalter Stations. Central, first class, with all comfort. Pension from 5.50. See Advt.

PENSION MEHRING.—Kurfürstenstrasse, 81. Central position; comfortable house; close to Zoological Gardens. Pension from Mk. 4. Same house—Dresden, Portikusstrasse, 12. See Advt.

PENSION BAVARIA.-10, Haberlandstrasse, close to Bayerischer Platz. Most comfortable family house. Quiet position. Every modern comfort. Moderate terms. See Advt.

BERLIN - GRUNEWALD. — PENSION BISMARCK PLATZ, 16, Hubertus Allee. Station: Halensee, on the Ringbahn, next to Grunewald Station. First class. Every modern comfort. Finest and healthiest position, close to woods. Dependance: Warmbrunnerstrasse, 4. Rooms with or without board. See Advt.

CAFE BAUER.—World-renowned, Berlin's finest Café, facing Unter den Linden, corner of Friedrichstrasse. Large wall paintings by Anton von Werner. Hundreds of newspapers, reviews, and directories, from all parts of the world.

RESTAURANT HILLER. — Proprietor, Alfred Walterspiel, 62, Unter den Linden. Leading Restaurant of old reputation.

TAXI-CABS.—At the Way Out, "Ausgang," from the Railway Stations an official hands to the traveller requiring it a metal ticket having the number of a cab. On payment of fare 25 pf. must be added for this ticket. Let a porter see the ticket number and fetch the cab; surrender ticket when entering cab. Porter expects 25 pf., if luggage is bulky 50 pf.

The fares are: No. 2 Tax, "Black," 1 to 4 persons, up to 600 meters, 70 pf., each additional 300 meters, 10 pf.; No. 3 Tax, "Blue," 1 to 4 persons, up to 400 meters, 70 pf., each additional 200 meters, 10 pf. Waiting, 8 minutes, 50 pf., each additional 4 minutes, 10 pf.; one hour, 1 mk. 50 pf. All fares doubled after 12.0 night.

The Local Railways—the Stadtbahn, the Ringbahn, the Elevated, and the Underground Railways—are of great service for quick transport, the trains being very frequent; there is no first class—the fares are from 10 pf. to 30 pf. These lines are probably more useful for residents than for tourists, whose convenience is better served by the tramways.

Electric Tramways in all directions.

BERLIN, the capital of Prussia, the residence of the German Emperor, and the seat of the Imperial Government, is the most modern of the great cities of Europe. Broad streets flanked by handsome buildings cross the city in all directions, there are many spacious squares and open places rendered more attractive by trees and statues; cleanliness and order are noticeable everywhere. The site is 110 ft. to 160 ft. above sea level, on the River Spree, in the midst of a sandy plain; it is a great manufacturing and commercial place, its scientific institutions are of world wide renown, and its art collections are of the richest and worthily housed. The Berlin season, when the Court is in residence, is in January and February; the great military reviews are in May and September.

UNTER DEN LINDEN is the most imposing thoroughfare, it runs almost due east and west and derives its name from the lines of lime trees (there are also many chestnut trees); at its west end is the stately Brandenburg Gate (Brandenburger Tor) and right and left are fine buildings, the interest culminating at the east end, where are the Cathedral, the Royal Castle, and the principal museums. The busiest streets are Friedrichstrasse, which crosses the Linden at about its middle distance, and Leipzigerstrasse, which runs parallel with the Linden about half a mile south.

The west end of the Linden, at the Brandenburg Gate, widens into the Pariser Platz; here, on the north side, is the French Embassy. Proceeding eastward from the Pariser Platz within a few yards Wilhelmstrasse runs off to the right. [The British Embassy is a very short distance down Wilhelmstrasse, on the west side; this fine street is almost entirely lined by official buildings and palaces, and at its south end opens out into Leipziger Platz, where, again, are several important buildings.] Continuing along the Linden, at the further corner of Wilhelmstrasse is the Ministry of Religion and Education, and nearly the next house is the Russian Embassy, with the Ministry of the Interior on the opposite side of the road: beyond this, a little eastward, by the corner of Schadowstrasse, is the United States Embassy. Further along, on the right hand, just before Friedrichstrasse, is the Kaisergallerie, a handsome arcade. Just after crossing Friedrichstrasse the Statue of Friedrich der Grosse will be seen. On right hand of statue is the Palace of Emperor Wilhelm I, with the old Royal Library just round the corner in the Opern Platz. Here are the Empress Augusta Statue and the Kaiser Vase. [Behind the Palace of Emp. Wilhelm I Markgrafenstrasse runs south; here is a fine group, the Franzosische Kirche and the Neue Kirche with the Schauspielhaus (Theatre) between in the background; the middle space is the Schiller Platz, with the Schiller monument.] Returning to Unter den Linden, opposite Palace of Emp. Wilhelm I is the new Royal Library, erected 1909, with the University next to it. The Opera House is here, on right hand; opposite the Opera House, on left hand side of Unter den Linden, is the Konigswache (Royal Guard House—Guard Mount at 12.45 p.m.), with the Zeughaus (Arsenal) next; the palace on the right, next the Opera, is the Palace of the Crown Prince. Straight on, across the Schlossbrucke (Palace-bridge), on the right will be seen the Royal Palace, and on the left, among the trees, the Statue of Friedrich Wilhelm III, and still further to the left, the Altes Museum, Neues Museum, National Gallerie, with the Dom (Cathedral) rising over all.

Leipzigerstrasse (parallel with, half mile south of, the Linden) has at its east end a group of magnificent buildings, the principal being the Herrenhaus (Prussian House of Lords) and south of this the splendid Abgeordneten Haus (Prussian House of Commons).

The famous SIEGES ALLEE (Victory Avenue) is within a quarter of a mile of the east ends of both the Linden and Leipzigerstrasse. This fashionable promenade is a broad handsome avenue adorned with fine statues of Prussian Rulers (thirty-two); the north end opens out into the imposing Konigs Platz, where, in the centre, is the SIEGES DENKMAL (Victory Monument), 200 ft. high, with the Bismarck Monument and the Reichstags Gebaude (Imperial Diet).

CHURCHES.

DOMKIRCHE (Cathedral), on the east side of the Lustgarten. Magnificent edifice in Italian Renaissance style of architecture, by Julius and Otto Raschdorff; 344 ft. long, 246 ft. broad, 374 ft. high. The erection was begun 1894, completed 1902; consecrated 1905. Interior retains some features of the old Domkirche, as the Hohenzollern Vaults, and monuments and coffins of several Electors and Kings; the bells, also, of the 15th and 16th century, belonged to the old Domkirche. Colossal figure of Christ, by Schaper, over principal facade.

MARIENKIRCHE, a little east of Domkirche, on right hand of Kaiser Wilhelmstrasse. 14th cent., tower (295 ft.). Expiatory cross (murder of Abbot of Bernau) before entrance.

SYNAGOGUE, short distance north of the Domkirche, in Oranienburgerstrasse, near Monbijou Platz. Very fine building, dome (158 feet); paintings and sculpture.

NICOLAIKIRCHE, in Poststrasse, a little to east of Royal Palace, across river. Oldest church in Berlin. Interior interesting; grave of Pufendorf.

KLOSTERKIRCHE, Klosterstrasse, a little east of Nicolaikirche. Gothic, 13th cent., one of the few mediæval churches in Berlin.

PETER KIRCHE, Brüderstrasse, off south side of Royal Palace. Lofty tower (315 ft.).

FRIEDRICH-WERDER KIRCHE, in Werder Markt, near the Werderbrucke. Altarpiece.

HEDWIG KIRCHE (Roman Catholic), behind Opera House. Resembles Pantheon at Rome.

NEUE KIRCHE (German Cathedral), in Gensdarmen Markt. Detached towers with domes.

DOROTHEENKIRCHE, in Neustadtischekirchstr., off north side of Unter den Linden (west end).

KAISER WILHELM GEDACHTNIS KIRCHE (Emperor William Memorial Church), on south side of Zoologischer Garten. Romanesque, by Schwechten. The west tower, 370 ft., highest in Berlin. Interior very fine—frescoes, mosaics, statues.

KAISER FRIEDRICH GEDACHTNIS KIRCHE, near west end of Thiergarten, off north side of Charlottenburg Chaussee.

GNADEN KIRCHE, half mile, due north, of Konigs Platz. Empress Augusta memorial church. Daily, 12.0 to 1.0 and 5.0 to 7.0.

EMMAUS KIRCHE, in south east part of city, nearly opposite Görlitzer Bahnhof. Has two galleries; will hold 2,600 worshippers.

MICHAELS KIRCHE, in south east part of city; half mile south west of Schlesischer Bahnhof. Romanesque.

THOMAS KIRCHE, in south east part of city, quarter mile south of Schlesischer Bahnhof. Interior very fine.

PUBLIC BUILDINGS.

ROYAL PALACE (KONIGLICHE SCHLOSS). Beyond the extreme east end of Unter den Linden, over the Schlossbrucke, to the right. In form a rectangle, 650 ft. in length, 380 ft. in depth; the dome is 232 ft. high. At the entrance from the Lustgarten are two large bronze groups, the Horse Tamers, and in the first court a bronze St. George. To see the royal apartments, picture gallery, and chapel, apply to custodian in inner court, ground floor, 10 to 1. Fee 50 pf. Sundays and holidays 11.30 to 1.30.

ALTES MUSEUM, opposite the Royal Palace, on the other side of the Lustgarten. A building in Greek style, with portico of eighteen columns. Here are vast collections of sculpture, paintings, antiquities, coins, medals, etc. NEUES MUSEUM (immediately behind the Altés Museum), in the Renaissance style; elaborately decorated interior. Paintings, casts, Egyptian, and Assyrian collections, engravings, bronzes, vases, gems. Both Museums open daily, except Mon., 10 to 3; Sun., 12 to 5.

NATIONAL GALLERIE, next to the Neues Museum. In the form of a Corinthian temple, 200 ft. long, 105 ft. wide. Modern paintings. Open daily; Sun., 12 to 5; Thurs., 1 to 5; other days, 10 to 5. On Thurs. 1 m., Fri. and Sat. 50 pf., other days free. In the Pergamon Museum, behind the National Gallerie, are art treasures from Pergamon and other cities of Asia Minor.

KAISER FRIEDRICH MUSEUM, at the northern point of the island upon which are the Dom and Museums, a little north west of the National Gallerie. Erected 1903, in Italian late-renascent style. On ground floor are miscellaneous artistic collections, antiquities, etc.; on the upper floor is the Picture Gallery, with sculpture. Open daily except Mon., 10.0 to 5.0; Sun. 12.0 to 5.0. Tues. and Wed. 50pf., other days free.

SCHLOSS MONBIJOU.—A palace to the north of the Museums and National Gallerie, on opposite side of river, containing the Hohenzollern Museum—relics pertaining to the imperial family. Daily, 10 to 3. Fee, 25 pf.

RAVENE GALLERIE, in Wallstrasse, almost due south, quarter mile, of Royal Palace. Collection of modern German and French paintings. Tues. and Fri. 10.0 to 2.0.

REICHSTAGS GEBAUDE (Hall of the Imperial Diet).—In Konigs Platz, a short distance directly north from the Brandenburg Gate. Magnificent edifice, in Italian Renaissance style, by Paul Wallot. Many reliefs and figures decorate the exterior. Admission to interior, daily, at 9.0 and 9.30 a.m., and 12.0 noon and 2.30 p.m.; on

Sunday at 1.0 and 1.30 p.m.; 25 pf. Mon. of Bismarck in front.

HERRENHAUS (Prussian House of Lords) and ABGEORDNETEN HAUS (Prussian House of Commons), within a rough parallelogram formed by the extreme west end of Leipzigerstrasse on the north, by Wilhelmstrasse on the east, Prinz Albrechtstrasse on the south, and Königgrätzerstrasse on the west. The two Houses of Parliament, with adjacent dwellings of the Presidents, are an imposing group in the Renaissance style, by the architect F. Schulze. The Abgeordneten Haus is on the south side, in Prinz Albrechtstrasse; the Herrenhaus is on the north side, a little back from Leipzigerstrasse.

RATHHAUS (Town Hall), in Königstrasse, east of the Royal Palace. Fine brick building, with tower 243 ft. high. Decorated interior. Daily, except Thurs. and Fri., 10 to 3.

JUSTIZPALAST (Law Courts), in Neue Friedrichstrasse, near Alexanderplatz. Magnificent building—principal front in Grunerstrasse.

SCHAUSPIELHAUS (Theatre), in Gensdarmen Markt. Ionic portico to eastern facade.

MUSEUM FUR VOLKERKUNDE (Ethnographical Museum). In Königgratzerstrasse, near Potsdamer Bahnhof. A Renaissance building. Prehistoric, anthropological, and ethnological collections. Daily, except Tues., 10 to 3; Sun., 12 to 5.

KUNSTGEWERBE MUSEUM (Industrial Museum) In Prinz Albrechtstrasse, next to the Museum fur Völkerkunde. Very interesting collection of products of ancient and modern nations. Open daily, except Mon., 10 to 3; Sun., 12 to 5.

BORSE (Exchange), east of the Altes and Neues Museums, on the other side of the river. Handsome building, facade has double colonnade. View the scene from gallery.

UNIVERSITY, at east end of Unter den Linden, north side, opposite Opera Haus. Extensive building, garden in front, with statues. 8,000 students.

BIBLIOTHEK (Royal Library), a new building, 1909, adjoining the University, west side. 1,230,000 vols. and 30,000 MSS. (including MS. of Luther's translation of the Bible); Gutenberg's Bible, the first book printed with moveable type; miniatures by Lucas Cranach. The reading-room is open daily, 9 to 9; shown to strangers from 1 to 2, except Sat. and Sun.

OPERN HAUS (Opera House), at east end of Unter den Linden. Corinthian portico.

ZEUGHAUS (Arsenal), at extreme east end of Unter den Linden, on north side, by the river. A fine square building, each side 295 ft. long. Many sculptured heads on exterior. Interior is a Military Museum (weapons, etc.) and Hall of Fame. Open daily, except Sat., 10 to 3; Sun. 12.0 to 3.0.

TRACHTEN MUSEUM, in Klosterstrasse. Interesting collection of German peasant costumes, domestic groups, implements, etc. Daily except Mon. 10.0 to 3.0, Sun. 12.0 to 5.0.

MEERESKUNDE MUSEUM, in Georgenstrasse. Collections illustrative of oceanic interests; shipping, nautical instruments, fisheries, etc. Mon., Wed., Sat., 10.0 to 3.0, Sun. 12.0 to 4.0.

EISENBAHN (Railway) MUSEUM, Invalidenstrasse.

NATURKUNDE MUSEUM (Natural History), Invalidenstrasse.

MUSICAL INSTRUMENT collections, Fasanenstrasse, Charlottenburg. Tues. 11.0 to 1.0; Wed. and Sat. 12.0 to 1.0.

THIERGARTEN, at the north west side of the city, beyond the west end of the Unter den Linden, through the Brandenburg Thor. A beautiful park, with small lakes. The Thiergarten is traversed east and west by the Charlottenburg Chaussee, and north and south by the Sieges Allée.

ZOOLOGISCHER GARTEN, at the extreme south west of Thiergarten. Fine collection of animals.

FRIEDRICHSHAIN, on east side of Berlin. Pleasant park, with views of Berlin.

BOTANICAL GARDEN, in the suburb of Dahlem, on south west side of Berlin.

VICTORIA PARK, on north slope of the Kreuzberg, an eminence—the only one—on south side of city. Here is the National Monument of the War of Liberation.

Military reviews and Parades are generally held in the Tempelhofer Feld, beyond the Kreuzberg, on south side of city. The most important reviews are in May and September.

CEMETERIES.—In St. Matthew's Cemetery, in the suburb of Schoneberg, about two miles due south from west end of Unter den Linden, are buried many eminent Germans. Several other extensive cemeteries are also on the south side—the Alte and Neue Jerusalemer Kirchhof, the Alte and Neue Dreifaltigkeits Kirchhof. The Lützow Cemetery is at Charlottenburg.

THEATRES.—The best are: Opern Haus, Schauspielhaus, Neues Opern Theater, Deutsches, Lessing, Berliner, Westens, Schiller, Residenz, Neues, Hebel. Schiller Theater at Charlottenburg. The Wintergarten, Metropole, and Apollo are of the music hall character.

GOLF.—9-hole course, west-end of city.

POST OFFICE.—The principal Post Office (Hauptpostgebaude) is in Konigstrasse, on the left, going from Schloss Platz (south side of Royal Palace) to Alexander Platz. Letters addressed "Poste Restante" are delivered here (on such occasions passport very convenient). Another large Post Office is at the corner of Leipzigerstrasse and Mauerstrasse; here is a Postal Museum.

ENGLISH SPEAKING PLACES OF WORSHIP.

ST. GEORGE'S ENGLISH CHURCH.—In the Garden of Monbijou Palace. Rev. H.M. Williams.

AMERICAN CHURCH, 6, Motzstrasse.

BRITISH AND AMERICAN EMBASSIES, ETC.

GREAT BRITAIN.—Rt. Hon. Sir E. Goschen, G.C.M.G., G.C.V.O., 70, Wilhelmstrasse.

H.B.M.'S CONSUL GEN.—H. Boyle, Esq., 7, Margarethenstrasse; hours 10.0 to 1.0, and 3.30 to 6.0.—VICE-CONSUL.—A. C. Charlton, Esq.

UNITED STATES.—His Excellency Hon. J. G. A. Leishman, 16, Rauchstrasse.

U.S. CONSUL GENERAL.—A.M. Thackara, Esq. VICE-CONSUL.—De Witt C. Poole, Esq.

MEDICAL. — Alphonse Roman, M.D. Kiel, M.R.C.S. Eng., L.R.C.P. Lond., 18, Speyererstr (Bayerischer Platz), W., hours 3-5; Tel. Lützow 470. Dr. Fritsche.

BANKS.—Direction der Disconto-Gesellschaft, established 1851, 35, Unter den Linden, W. Capital M.200,000,000. Reserves Mk.81,300,000. All banking orders promptly executed. Letters of credit and cheques issued and cashed. Foreign moneys at current rates.

OPTICIANS.—J. Rodenstock, 101-102, Leipzigerstrasse, and 44, Joachimsthalerstrasse. Eye Glasses of all kinds. Field Glasses. Photographic Apparatus, Films, etc. See Advt. under Munich, page 962.

TRAVEL INQUIRY OFFICE.—Reliable information upon most subjects of interest to travellers may be obtained at the office of the Fremdenführer-Centrale. See Advt.

[Charlottenburg.

The road through the Thiergarten from the Brandenburg Thor leads in about three miles to Charlottenburg, a town of 305,181 inhabitants, but practically part of Berlin. Of the ROYAL PALACE only the central part is shewn —the apartments occupied by Frederick I, the Chapel, and the Porcelain Chamber. The MAUSOLEUM (tickets obtained at the Palace) is in the Palace Garden; here repose the Emperor William I (died 1888), the Empress Augusta (died 1890), and other members of the royal family. The statuary is exquisite. On the south side of Berlinerstrasse, the part of the high road between the Thiergarten and Charlottenburg, is the TECHNISCH HOCHSCHULE (Technical Academy), an imposing building adorned with sculpture; 2,300 students; the Collections are accessible on most days of the week, 10.0 to 3.0. The Porcelain Manufactory is on north side of Berlinerstrasse.]

Biebrich, see page 453.

Bingen, see page 452. **Boll Bad,** see page 457.

Bonn, see page 449A. **Boppard,** see page 451.

Bornhofen, see p. 451. **Braubach,** see p. 450A.

Braunlage.—*Stat.*

A favourite summer and winter resort of the Harz country, amidst attractive surroundings, 2,000 ft. above sea. Many visitors to the baths.

RAIL, page 153.

Bremen.—*Stat.*—Pop. 247,437.

HILLMAN'S HOTEL.—Well known first class hotel, in fine position. 160 rooms and 60 bathrooms. Restaurant. See Advt.

HOTEL DE L'EUROPE.—First class. Finest position. Every modern comfort. Rooms with bath. Near Station. See Advt.

HOTEL ALBERTI—Comfortable; facing Station. Quiet position. All modern conveniences. Rooms from Mks. 2.75. Pension. See Advt.

CENTRAL HOTEL.—Leading hotel at the Central Station. Rebuilt and entirely renovated. All modern comforts. Rooms with bath. Rooms from M.3.50. See Advt.

HOTEL ST. PETERSBURG.—Good second class hotel, with all comforts. Opposite Central Station. See Advt.

ELECTRIC CARS circle the city, and traverse some of the principal streets.

The principal Railway Station is the Haupt Bahnhof; **on the west side of the Bahnhofsplatz the street called Georgstrasse leads eventually to the river Weser and the Kaiserbrucke; the Bahnhofstrasse, in middle of Bahnhofsplatz, leads, bearing slightly to left, towards the Dom and the Grossebrucke. The Wall-Anlagen, a pleasant promenade on the site of the old ramparts, is the great attraction of the city.**

The DOM (Cathedral), Romanesque. of 11th-13th cents., restored 1888-98; the interior has rococo pulpit, reliefs on organ front, stained windows; in the Bleikeller (lead-cellar) are mummies. In the Domsheide, immediately south east of Dom, is a Statue of Gustavus Adolphus; here are the Law Courts and the Post Office. By the south side of the Dom is the Künstlerverein.

The RATHAUS, in the Marktplatz, just west of the Dom, a Gothic building with Renaissance additions; in the great hall are suspended models of ships, medallion portraits of German emperors on ceiling, and stained glass windows; in the Rathskeller, mentioned in German history and literature, are frescoes—great stock of Rhine and Moselle wines; the Stadthaus (rebuilding) adjoins the Rathaus on the north-east side. By the Rathaus are the Roland statue and statue of Emperor William I. The Börse (Exchange), in the Marktplatz, an imposing building with handsome hall (mural paintings). Opposite the Rathaus is the Schütting, or Chamber of Commerce (1538-94). Here, also, is Liebfrauenkirche (12th-13th cent.), containing monument to Count Moltke (1906).

On the north west side of the Marktplatz the Obernstrasse leads to Ansgariikirche (13th cent.), with altar piece, stained windows, and tower (375 feet); before west door is a group representing St. Ansgarius (died 865) releasing boy from paganism. The Gewerbehaus (hall of cloth merchants) is to the west of Ansgariikirche.

At the Kunsthalle, near the Osterthor, **a little east of the Dom, is a collection of pictures, sculpture, many drawings by Dürer, engravings, etc. open free, daily (except Sat.) 11.0 a.m. to 2.0 p.m. Museum of Natural History, Ethnology, and Commerce, in the Bahnhofsplatz (open in summer, free on Sun., 10.0 a.m. to 2.0 p.m., and Wed. and Sat., 2.0 p.m. to 6.0 p.m.; on Tues. and Fri., 10.0 a.m. to 2.0 p.m., 50 pf.). Town Library, 130,000 vols., on south side of the Museum. Bürger Park, north of Hauptbahnhof.**

POST and TEL. OFFICE, in the Domsheide.

H.B.M.'s CONSUL.—C. E. Scholl, Esq.

U.S. CONSUL.—W. T. Fee, Esq.

GOLF.—9-hole course at Horn; club house.

BANKS.—Direction der Disconto-Gesellschaft, established 1851. 1, Stintbrücke. Capital M.200,000,000. Reserves M.81,300,000. All banking orders promptly executed. Letters of credit and cheques issued and cashed. Foreign moneys at current rates.

DEPOT FOR BRADSHAW'S GUIDE.—Thomas Cook and Son, 36, Bahnhofstrasse.

RAIL, pp. 132, 151, 154, 159. Steamers, see list.

Bremerhaven (pop. 25,000) **and Geestemunde** (pop. 23,625), **are opposite each other where the Geeste flows into the mouth of the**

Weser. The railway station for both places is at Geestemunde. HOTELS: at Geestemunde, HANNOVER, LEHRKE; at Bremerhaven, BEERMANN, HOMFELD, LOHR. Bremerhaven, the seaport of Bremen, has extensive docks and ship building yards, and is a growing thriving place. Lighthouse, whence is fine view of surroundings, admission 25 pf. H.B.M.'s VICE-CONSUL.—N. C. Haag, Esq. RAIL, page 159.

Breslau.—*Stat.*—Pop. 512,105.

HOTELS: MONOPOL; VIER JAHRESZEITEN; NORD; KRONPRINZ.

There are four Railway Stations at Breslau—the Hauptbahnhof, on the south side; Oderthorbahnhof, on the north side; the Niederschlesisch-Markischbahnhof and the adjoining Freiburgerbahnhof, on the west side.

TAXIMETER CABS.—1 or 2 persons 1000 meters 50 pf., and 10 pf. for each additional 500 meters. 3 or 4 persons 750 meters 50 pf.

Breslau, the capital of Silesia and the second city in Prussia, is situated in a fertile plain, on both banks of the Oder, at the confluence of the Ohle. It is one of the most important centres of industry and commerce in Germany, engineering is especially prosperous, there are many distilleries, while the country round sends in great quantities of wool, grain, timber, cloth.

To westward from the open space before the Hauptbahnhof runs the Gartenstrasse, and out of this street, the first street north, on right hand, Neue Schweidnitzerstrasse leads right across the city, from south to north, through the Grosse Ring (otherwise Der Ring), the centre of Breslau street traffic.

Shortly after turning into Neue Schweidnitzerstrasse, and traversing the broad Tauenzenplatz, the old city moat is crossed, and here, right and left, are public buildings; on the right are statue of Emperor William I, and Corpus Christi Church; on the left are Government Offices and Stadt Theater, with, behind, the Palaisplatz, Royal Palace, Kunst Gewerbe Museum, and the Börse (Exchange). A little further north Schweidnitzerstrasse runs into Der Ring.

The noble RATHHAUS is on the south east side of Der Ring, it is of 15th cent.; in the Fürstensaal (princes' hall) are portraits; under the building is the Schweidnitzer Keller, a finely vaulted restaurant; on east side of building is the Staupsaule (pillory). The Stadthaus adjoins the Rathhaus. In Der Ring are statues of Frederick the Great and Frederick William III; on west side of Der Ring is a house (1500) once occupied by Kings of Bohemia.

Off the south west corner of Der Ring is Blücherplatz, with statue of Blucher, and the Alte Börse (now municipal offices). Behind the Alte Börse, in the Ross markt, is the Savings Bank, where is the City Library of 150,000 vols. 3,600 MSS., and the Civic Archives—open daily. 9.0 a.m. to 2.0 p.m.

Off the north west corner of Der Ring is Elisabethkirche, Protestant, founded 1257, tower 335 ft. high; on either side of high altar are portraits of Luther and Melancthon by Cranach; several interesting tombstones, stained glass windows. Maria Magdalenen Kirche, Protestant, is one street east of Der Ring.

The continuation of Schweidnitzerstrasse, from north east corner of Der Ring, leads to a cluster of buildings by the river. Here is the University (2,000 students), then, eastward, the Ursuline Convent and the Law Courts; across the Sandbrücke is the University Library of 350,000 vols., 3,700 vols. of MSS., and specimens of early printing — an Archaeological Museum is in same building.

The Sandkirche (Church of Our Lady on the Sand), 14th cent., is immediately north of the University Library. Across the Dombrücke, eastward, on the left of Domstrasse, is the Kreuzkirche, 13th cent.; tomb of Duke Henry IV of Silesia before the high altar. At end of Domstrasse is the DOM, or Cathedral of St. John the Baptist, 14th cent., the original building dating from 12th cent.; the interior has several monuments, statues, and paintings, including, in Chapel of St. John, north aisle Cranach's "Madonna among the pines." The Residenz of the Prince Bishop is to south west of the Dom. St. Ægidius, oldest church in Breslau, is to north of the Dom.

A little east of the Dom is the Lessingbrücke, across this, south, on the right, are Government Offices, and, next them, the Holtei Höhe, and, beyond, the Kaiserin Augusta Platz, where is a School of Art. North of the Dom is Botanical Garden.

At the MUSEUM, west of the Hauptbahnhof and south of the Palaisplatz, is a collection of modern paintings and duplicates of old masters. Open daily, except Mon., 10.0 a.m. to 2.0 p.m.; Sun., 11.0 a.m. to 4.0 p.m. In the same building is the Collection of the Silesian Art Union, open 10.0 a.m. to 4.0 p.m.; Sun. 11.0 to 2.0, 1 mk.

The principal POST OFFICE is an imposing building at the east end of Albrechtstrasse, near centre of city, due north of the Hauptbahnhof.

H.B.M.'s VICE-CONSUL.—H. Humbert, Esq.

U.S. CONS.—H. L. Spahr, Esq.

RAIL. pp. 179, 179A, 180, 217, 218, 218A, 219, 220, 220A.

The Brocken.

BROCKEN HOTEL.—On the summit of the Brocken, lately enlarged and fitted up with every modern comfort. Open all the year. Specially adapted for winter sport. See Advt.

The Brocken, 3,145 ft. above sea, the Mons Bructerus of the Romans, is the highest summit of the Harz Mountains; both in summer and winter the fine clear air makes the Brocken a favourite health resort, with the additional attractions in winter of sports of all kinds. Fine view from the tower. Meteorological Station. According to legendary lore witches gather here on Walpurgis Night (last day of April)—see Goethe's "Faust," and it is a place of pilgrimage for literary and other societies.

RAIL, page 153, 165B. In winter the railway station for The Brocken is Elend, page 165B.

Bruckenau Bad.—*Stat.*—Pop. 1,560.

HOTEL ROYAL KURHAUS; SCHLOSS.

Bruckenau Bad, in the pastoral valley of the

little River Sinn, is about two miles west of the town of Bruckenau. The waters, for drinking and bathing, are useful in cases of anemia, female complaints, disorders of urinary organs, rheumatism, breathing and digestive troubles. Kurtax, 12m., additional members of family 5m. Kursaal.

RAIL. page 203A. Diligence. page 373.

Brunswick (Braunschweig). — *Stat.* — Pop. 1910) 143,552.

PARK HOTEL.—New first class hotel in convenient position. Electric light, lift, steam heating. Suites with baths. Moderate. See Advt.

DEUTSCHES HAUS; MONOPOL; KAISERHOF.

The Railway Station–BAHNHOF–is on the south side of the town, half a mile from the centre.

CABS.—In the inner town, 60 pf. to 1 mk.

ELECTRIC CARS traverse the principal streets.

Brunswick is the capital and "Residenzstadt" of the Duchy of Brunswick; it is situated on the River Oker, in a fertile plain broken by several wooded heights. It is one of the most interesting towns of Germany; in the inner town are many splendid examples of mediæval architecture contrasting with neighbouring handsome modern buildings, and the new villa districts are very attractive. The old fortifications are now beautiful promenades. Among the residents are many government officials, and the general cheerfulness is increased by the presence of the headquarters staff of the ducal regiments. Sport of all kind in the neighbourhood. It is also a busy place, with an extensive trade in sugar, tobacco, and machinery. In addition to its own attractions, Brunswick is a good centre for excursions in the Harz Mountains.

Most of the Churches are masterpieces of the Gothic and Romanesque styles of the middle ages. The principal is the DOM, or Burgkirche, of St. Blasius, in Burgplatz, about half mile north east of the Bahnhof, a Romanesque building of 1172-1194, with Gothic additions of 14th and 15th cents.; within are many interesting monuments and old mural paintings; to see the vaults a fee required. On north side of Cathedral is a bronze Lion, erected 1166 by Henry the Lion, as symbolical of his supremacy. The Castle of Henry the Lion, several times injured by fire, is east of the Lion monument. On the east side of the platz, opposite the Dom, is the Stadthaus, and here also is the Gildehaus (Guildhall), of 1573. A few yards north is Ruhfäutchen Platz, where are the Finance Offices and the Rathaus, containing the Civic Archives and the Municipal Library of 40,000 vols. Just off the north end of Ruhfäutchen Platz is the Vaterländische Museum of arms, uniforms, national costumes, and historical curiosities, etc.

In the Hagenmarkt, a very short distance north of the Dom, is the Katharinenkirche and the Henry fountain.

Very interesting is the Alstadt-Markt, on west side of the city, a little north west of the Bahnhof; here are the fine Gothic ALTSTADT RATHHAUS, dating from 1250, a Gothic fountain of 1408, the Martinkirche, of 1180-90, and the Gewandthaus (cloth hall), a Renaissance building of 1270. In the adjacent streets are several ancient houses.

East of the Dom, a short distance through the Langehof, is the SCHLOSS; only the gardens may be visited. Further east is the Ducal Park with the DUCAL MUSEUM on the south side, open daily, 9.0 a.m. to 3.0 p.m., Sunday, 11.0 a.m. to 2.0 p.m.; collections of pictures (many of the Dutch School), enamels, sculpture, antiquities, majolica, bronzes, medals, coins, etc. Within the park, north of the Museum, is the Theatre.

In the Steintor Promenade, south of the Ducal Park, is the Municipal Museum (free on Tues. and Fri. 10.0 a.m. to 2.0 p.m., and Sun. 11.0 a.m. to 2.0 p.m., other days 10.0 a.m. to 12.0 noon, 50 pf.); collections include antiquities, musical instruments, and paintings.

Brüdernkirche and Petrikirche are west of the Dom. War Monument in Siegesplatz, east of the Bahnhof.

Statue of Lessing in Lessing Platz, north of Siegesplatz.

Fine view over the town from the Windmühlenberg, near the August Thor.

POST and TELEGRAPH OFFICE, in Friedrich Wilhelmstrasse, about quarter mile north of the Bahnhof.

U. S. CONSUL.—Talbot J. Albert, Esq.

RAIL, pp. 158, 159, 160, 162, 163, 204A.

Camp, see page 451.

Carlsruhe (Karlsruhe).—*Stat.*-Pop. 134,313.

VICTORIA HOTEL.—First class. Facing the Station; with all comfort. Moderate tariff. Rooms from 2 mks. See Advt.

GERMANIA; GROSSE; ROTES HAUS.

The Railway Station—BAHNHOF—is in a south central part of the town, close to the points of interest.

Capital of the Grand Duchy of Baden very regularly planned in the older parts, where many streets converge upon the Schloss. An important industrial centre, with engine and railway carriage works, cabinet making, and electro plating. Carlsruhe is also regarded as an art centre, where landscape painting is specially studied.

From the Bahnhof the Carl Friedrichstrasse leads north in half a mile, traversing the Markt Platz, to the Schloss. On the east side of the Markt Platz is the Evangelische Stadtkirche, with tombs of grand ducal family; on west side of the Platz is the Rathhaus. A pyramid in centre of street marks the grave of the Margrave Carl Wilhelm.

The Schloss, a crescent-shaped building with a tower 150 ft. high, was erected 1750-82; some of the apartments are elaborately decorated. In the east wing is the Zähringer Museum of art, also many exhibits connected with the ducal family; open May, June, and September, daily, 11.0 to 1.0. In the west wing is the Court Theatre, celebrated in Germany for its productions. Behind the Schloss are gardens.

Kunsthalle, 1836-45, on west side of Schloss Platz, containing the Picture Gallery; a good collection. Sun., Wed., and Fri., 11.0 to 1.0 and 2.0 to 4.0, free; strangers may visit at any time. Near the Kunsthalle, in Waldstrasse, is the gallery of the Carlsruhe Kunstverein—a collection of modern paintings by local artists. Justizpalast (law courts), 1878, to west of the Kunsthalle.

The Vereinigte Sammlungen (united Grand Ducal Collections) are in a building in Friedrichs Platz, to which either Ritterstrasse or Lammstrasse leads south from Schloss Platz. Mineralogical, Geological, and Zoological Collections; Antiquarian and Ethnographical Collections; also collections of weapons, national costumes, and of art-industrial work. On the upper floor is a Library of 165,000 vols. and a collection of coins.

Palace of the Crown Prince (Erbgrossherzogl. Schloss), in Kriegsstrasse.

Cemetery (Neuer Friedhof), on north east side of town.

POST OFFICE, in Kaiserstrasse, a fine broad thoroughfare running east and west, a little south of the Schloss.

ENGLISH CHURCH SERVICE.—In Chapel of the Ludwig Wilhelm Krankenheim, Kaiser Allée.

RAIL, pages 140, 140B, 141, 142, 145.

Cassel.—*Stat.*—Pop. 153,196

HOTELS: KASSELER HOF; ROYAL; KING OF PRUSSIA; SCHIRMER.

Cassel, seat of the Government of Hesse Nassau, on the river Fulda. Manufactures of machinery, railway carriages, and locomotives.

From the Bahnhof the short Kurfürstenstrasse leads to Friedrich-Wilhelmsplatz, whence, on opposite side, Theaterstrasse leads to Friedrichsplatz, where on the left is the old Electoral PALACE, the MUSEUM FRIDERICIANUM, the Royal Military School, and the Roman Catholic Church (a "St. Francis" from Ruben's studio); in the centre of the Platz is the statue of the Landgrave Frederick II. In the Museum Fridericianum (open Thurs., 10.0 a.m. to 1.0 p.m., in summer also Tues. and Wed., 3.0 to 5.0 p.m.) are collections of ancient sculpture, casts, coins, etc., and a library (open daily) of 200,000 vols., and 1,600 MSS. Behind the Military School, in the Steinweg, is the Natural History Museum (Mon. and Thurs., 10.0 a.m. to 1.0 p.m., in summer also Tues. and Sat., 3.0 to 5.0 p.m.). On south side of the Platz is the Aue Thor, with bronze reliefs commemorative of war of 1870-1.

At end of the Steinweg is the Schloss-Platz, where, on the east side, are the Law Courts and Government Offices; whilst at the south end is the new Hoftheater.

From the south east corner of Friedrichsplatz the Schöne Aussicht leads past the Bellevue Schloss to the BILDERGALLERIE (Picture Gallery); open, Sun., 11.0 a.m. to 1.0 p.m., Tues., Wed., Fri., and Sat., 10.0 a.m. to 1.0 p.m., and in summer also on Mon. and Thurs., 3.0 to 5.0 p.m. The collection is specially rich in the works of Dutch and Flemish masters, many by Rembrandt and Rubens; of Italian masters there are pictures by Titian, Tintoretto, Paolo Veronese. On the ground floor of the Bildergallerie are other Art Collections, and a "Hessian Temple of Fame."

The Protestant Martinskirche is in Martinsplatz, between the Bahnhof and the river; several monuments. Mon. to Landgrafen Phillipp by the Kirche.

The principal business street is the Obere Konigstrasse, which runs south east of the Konigsplatz, a central open space, a short distance east of the Bahnhof. The Neues Rathaus, completed 1909, with fine facade, faces towards the Oberer Königstrasse.

The Karlsaue is a beautiful small park on the south east side of the town; much statuary.

POST and TELEGRAPH OFF.—40, Königsplatz.

ST. ALBAN'S ENGLISH CHURCH.

RAIL, pp. 134A, 134D, 148, 156, 156C, 173A.

Electric Tram from the Konigsplatz, at Cassel, to **Wilhelmshöhe.** HOTELS: GRAND.

WILHELMSHOHE is celebrated for its Schloss and park. In the park are many beautiful spots, lakes, cascades, fountains, temples; the great fountain throws up a jet of water 200 feet; the Löwenburg is an imitation of an ancient castle.

Caub, see page 451.

Chemnitz.—*Stat.*—Pop. 287,807.

HOTELS: ROMISCHER KAISER; CAROLA; STADT GOTHA.

The principal Railway Station—HAUPT BAHNHOF—is in the east central part of the town.

TAXIMETER CABS.—1 or 2 persons, 1,000 meters 70 pf., and 10 pf. for each additional 500 meters.

Chemnitz, the largest manufacturing town of Saxony, is situated at the base of the Erzgebirge, in a fertile plain. There are few "sights" in this busy place; the leading industries are in hosiery, mixed fabrics, chemicals, foundries, and engineering works.

About 150 yards west of the Haupt Bahnhof is the spacious Schiller Platz, and a quarter mile further west is the Schloss Teich, a sheet of water, with the Schloss, once an abbey now a restaurant, in attractive grounds. The Schlosskirche, 16th cent., contains some paintings.

In the König Albrecht Museum, erected 1909, in the Neustadter Markt, are art and other collections. The new Stadttheater is also in the Neustadter Markt.

The Old Rathaus, with high tower, is in the Hauptmarkt, one third mile south west of the Haupt Bahnhof. A little east is the new Rathaus. Most of the churches are modern.

H.B.M.'S VICE-CONSUL.—E. Zeissler, Esq.

U.S. CONSUL.—T. H. Norton, Esq.

RAIL, pages 184, 184A, 185, 186, 189, 190, 190A.

Coblence, see page 450A.

Coburg.—*Stat.*—Pop. 23,789.

HOTELS: BAHNHOF; LENTHAUSER.

On the River Itz. From the Bahnhof, on north west side of the town, Bahnhofstrasse leads east; at its far end a street, Burglass, goes south to the Schloss Platz, where is the Residenz Schloss, once a monastery, altered to a ducal residence in 1549. East of the Schloss Platz is the ducal park. On a height to the east, 520 ft. above the town, is the old Festung, or Castle of Coburg, where Luther in 1530 for a time resided; the building now contains collections of Luther relics, old coaches, armour and weapons, a natural history cabinet, coins, etc.

Moritzkirche, a few yards south of Schloss Platz, contains ducal monuments. In Markt Platz, west of Schloss Platz, are the Rathhaus on the south side and Government buildings on north side.

U.S. CONSUL GENERAL.—F. Dillingham, Esq.

VICE-CONSUL.—W. H. Murphy, Esq.

RAIL, pages 173B, 174.

Colmar.—*Stat.*—Pop. 43,000.

HOTELS: ZWEI SCHLUSSEL; TERMINUS.

The interesting capital of Upper Alsace, on the River Lauch, within 2 miles of the wooded Vosges mountains.

The broad tree planted Marsfeld is a few yards east of the Station; here, on the south side, is the

Bezirks Präsidium (District Governor's Office), and, further south, the new Oberlandesgericht (law courts); on the west side is the Post Office. Just away from the north side of the Marsfeld is the Church of St. Dominik. Museum of antiquities. Church of St. Martin, dating from 1237.

RAIL, pages 208, 211, 212A, 212B.

Cologne, see page 448.

Constance (Konstanz).—*Stat.*—Pop. 27,591.

INSEL HOTEL.—Ancient Dominican convent of great historic interest. Isolated position, on small island in the Lake of Constance. Sports. Patronized by English and Americans. See Advt.

HOTEL TERMINUS.—Facing Station and boats. Comfortable and moderate. Rooms from M. 2.50. Entirely renovated. See Advt.

SEE; HALM.

At the north west end of the Lake of Constance, or Bodensee; formerly much more populous. The Münster (Minster), dating from 1052, rebuilt 1435 and 1600, has a pierced spire; carved choir stalls. A little south west of the Münster is Stephanskirche, 15th cent.; wood carving in interior. Stadt Kanzeli, in Kanzelistrasse, quarter mile south of the Münster, contains archives—good inner court; a little west of the Kanzeli is the Rosgarten Museum, where is a collection of antiquities. Kaufhaus (Merchants' Hall), by the Lake, just north of the Bahnhof, erected 1388; here the conclave of cardinals met at the Great Council of Constance, 1414-1418. About 250 yards south west of the Münster is a mass of boulder known as the Hussenstein, marking the spot where Huss and Jerome of Prague were martyred, 1415.

BANK AND EXCHANGE.—Ludwig Neuburger.

RAIL, pages 139A, 260A. Steamer, page 369.

Crefeld.—*Stat.*—Pop. 129,406.

HOTEL CREFELDER HOF.—Corner of Ostwall and St. Antonstrasse. Entirely new first class hotel, with every comfort. Rooms with private bath. Hot and cold running water supply. Moderate charges. See Advt.

BELTZ; HERFS.

Crefeld, on the west side of the River Rhine, with which it is connected by a waterway, is an important industrial town, the seat of the silk and velvet manufactories in Germany; all around is the busy district of the lower Rhine provinces. About a quarter of the out-put of the Crefeld looms (about £4,000,000 annually) is exported to Great Britain and America.

From the handsome Hauptbahnhof the spacious tree lined Ost Wall, where are several monuments, leads north right across the town; the West Wall, another avenue, runs parallel with the Ost Wall, a quarter mile distant; the Sud Wall and the Nord Wall, at each end of the Ost Wall and West Wall, complete a very fine parallelogram. In the West Wall are the Rathaus, where are frescoes, and the Kaiser Wilhelm Museum, containing paintings, carvings, furniture, weapons, etc. In the Nord Wall are the Chamber of Commerce and the Commercial School. In the south west part of the town is the Webe Schule, with an interesting Textile Museum.

RAIL, pages 120A, 121, 124, 127, 135.

Cuxhaven.—*Stat.*—Pop. 12,000.

DÖLLE'S HOTEL BELVEDERE.—Overlooking the sea. Comfortable and well furnished. See Advt.

A pleasant watering place much frequented for sea bathing, a pilot station, and of growing importance in connection with the great Hamburg transatlantic steamers, which often land and embark passengers here. Schloss of 14th cent.

H.B.M.'S VICE-CONSUL.—P. Thode, Esq.

RAIL, pages 154, 159.

Dantsic (Danzig).—*Stat.*—Pop. 170,337.

HOTELS: DANTZIGERHOF: REICHSHOF: NORD.

The Railway Station—HAUPTBAHNHOF—is on the north west side of the town, about half a mile from the centre of interest, at the Lange Markt.

Dantsic is the strongly fortified capital of the Province of West Prussia, situated about three miles from the Baltic Sea; the River Mottla flows through the town to an immediate confluence with the River Vistula; down the Vistula is brought a great quantity of corn from Poland to the vast grain stores of Dantsic. The timber trade is extensive, and there are also several manufactories. There are many fine mediæval gabled houses in the picturesque streets.

The Marienkirche, with a turretted tower 248 ft. high, is half a mile south east from the Hauptbahnhof; built 15th cent.; in interior are imposing high altar, a Crucifixion group, a painting of the Judgment by Memling in a chapel in the north aisle, and other works of art. This church is stated to be the largest Protestant church in the world, St. Paul's, London, only excepted—nave 333 ft. long, 111 ft. wide; transept 218 ft. long, by 125 ft. wide.

The Rathhaus, of 14th cent., is 50 yards south of the Marienkirche, at the north west corner of the Lange Markt. At the top of the tower, 270 ft., is the figure of King Sigismund Augustus of Poland. The interior is interesting. In the Lange Markt is also the Exchange, known as the Artus Hof, or Junkerhof, of 15th cent.; fine hall. At the east end of the Lange Markt is the Grüne Thor, where are archæological and natural history collections.

At the Franziskaner Kloster, an old Franciscan Monastery, in Fleischerergasse, half a mile south west of the Lange Markt, is a Picture Gallery and museum of antiquities and of industrial-art work. Sun., Wed., and Thurs., 11.0 to 2.0, free, other days (Sat. excepted), 50 pf.

H.B.M.'S CONSUL.—A. Maclean, Esq. VICE-CONSUL.—F. Berger, Esq.

ENGLISH CHURCH SERVICE, Heiligegeistgasse.

RAIL, pages 175, 177A, 178.

Darmstadt.—*Stat.*—Pop. 87,089.

HOTELS: TRAUBE; DARMSTADT; BRITANNIA.

Capital of the Grand Duchy of Hesse. The Schloss (Grand Ducal Palace), dating from 15th cent., was mostly built early in 18th cent. The Picture Gallery is upon the upper floor. The Library of 600,000 vols., 4,000 MSS., curiosities, etc., is also in the building.

Roman Catholic Church, in Wilhelminen Platz, quarter mile due south of Louisen Platz.

On the east side of the town rises the Mathildenhöhe, and, a little beyond, the Rosenhöhe.

RAIL, pp. 123, 135A, 136, 139

Donaueschingen, see page 457.

Dortmund.—*Stat.*—Pop. 214,226.

HOTELS: ROEMISCHER KAISER; KOLNISC. HOF.

An old town that has become an immensely active centre of mining and iron industry. It was a fortified place in the 10th cent. and imperial diets often assembled here. The Vehmgericht (14th and 15th cent.), a famous secret tribunal organised in a lawless time to protect the general welfare, had its supreme court at Dortmund.

Reinoldikirche, Marienkirche, Petrikirche, and the Roman Catholic Profsteikirche, are all near the centre of the town, where is also the old Rathhaus (restored), on the Markt Platz.

POST OFFICE—Hauptpost—in the Hiltropwall.

RAIL, pages 131, 133D, 133E, 135, 135B, 160A.

Drei Aehren.

GRAND HOTEL DREI AEHREN.—First class, beautifully situated; 240 rooms; every modern comfort. Pension from M. 8. See Advt.

Reached by electric tram from Turkheim, on the Colmar-Metzeral line, page 211. A pretty village, which is a favourite summer resort, and also a place of pilgrimage; 1,910 ft. above sea, a good place for "after cures" from Nauheim and other baths; many level walks. Fine views of the Münster valley and of the Black Forest.

DRESDEN.—*Stat.*—**Population** (1910) 548,308. (*Plan in Special Edition, or post free 3d. stamps*).

HOTEL BELLEVUE.—World renowned. Rebuilt and enlarged. Very select, unique position. Patronised by high-class English families. Private baths and toilets. Auto-Garages separately locked. See Advt.

HOTEL EUROPAISCHER HOF.—First class modern hotel, in best position, near Central Station. See Advt.

GRAND UNION HOTEL.—Well situated, near the Railway Station for Carlsbad, Vienna, etc. Moderate charges. Lift and telephone. See Advt.

SAVOY HOTEL.—High class, in quiet position. Moderate tariff; great comfort; two minutes from Central Station. See Advt.

THE CONTINENTAL HOTEL.—Facing the chief exit of the Central Station. Entirely renewed and enlarged, with every modern comfort. Two lifts; large garden. Moderate terms. See Advt.

HOTEL BRISTOL.—First-class hotel, well situated. Near Central Railway Station. See Advt.

HOTEL KAISER WILHELM.—Wiener Platz. Central situation. Modern comfort; good cooking; garden. See Advt.

HOTEL AND RESTAURANT STADT GOTHA.—Close to Palace, Opera, Museum, etc. Most comfortable. English dinners in first class wine restaurant. Rooms from 2 m. 50 pf. See Advt.

WESTMINSTER HOTEL.—First class, close to Central Station. See Advt.

CARLTON HOTEL.—1, Bismark Platz. Best and quietest position; close to Central Station. All modern comforts. Pension from Mks. 7 (in winter from Mks. 6). Rooms from Mks. 2.50. See Advt.

HOTEL STADT ROM.—Neumarkt, 10. Central position. Renovated. Modern comforts. Rooms from Mk. 1.50. See Advt.

GRAND HOTEL REICHSPOST.—Centrally situated, close to all points of interest. 90 rooms equipped with all modern comfort (hot and cold water supply), from Mk. 2.50. See Advt.

HOTEL DE SAXE.—Pragerstrasse, 56. First class, at Central Station. All modern comforts. Rooms from Mks. 2.50. Pension from Mks. 6. See Advt.

HOTEL WINDSOR.—Pragerstrasse, 50. Near Central Station. Comfortable hotel with every modern convenience. Central but quiet, overlooking gardens at the back. Rooms from Mk. 2. Pension from Mk. 6.50. See Advt.

PENSION SCHMALZ.—25, Sidonienstrasse. First class; old established. Central position. All home comforts. Pension from Mks. 4. See Advt.

PENSION MEINCKE.—47, Eisenstuckstrasse, close to Central Station; first class, comfortable, and convenient. 5 to 8 Marks daily. See Advt.

PENSION BLECH.—Two minutes from Station, in park-like grounds. Most highly spoken of. Pension from 5 M. See Advt.

PENSION DONATH.—Luttichaustrasse, corner of Struvestrasse. Comfortable pension in central position. Excellent table. English breakfast if desired. Pension from 5 M., reduction by long stay. See Advt.

PENSION KUHLEMANN.—3, Münchnerstrasse. First class and most comfortable. Finest position. Central heating. Electric light. Pension, Mks. 5 to 8. See Advt.

PENSION GAEDE.—Räcknitzstrasse 22. Opposite the new Sendig Hotel. Very comfortable. Central, quiet position. Pension from Mks. 5. See Advt.

PENSION MEHRING.—See Advt. under Berlin.

CABS.—Taximeter Cabs are of two classes. *A* For 1-2 persons 70 pf. for 800 meters, 10 pf. for each 400 meters more; 3 persons 70 pf. for 600 meters, 10 pf. for each 300 meters more. *B* Second class cabs at lower rates. Motor cabs also for hire.

Electric Cars traverse the principal streets.

DRESDEN, the capital of the Kingdom of Saxony, stands on the banks of the Elbe, which divides it into Altstadt, on the south or left side of the river, and Neustadt on the north or right side of the river. The situation is pleasant, the environs are beautiful, and the fame of the city as a centre of art attracts many students. The principal Railway Station, the HAUPTBAHNHOF, is in the Altstadt.

Dresden has always been one of the most frequented cities in Germany. There are English and American quarters, where in the last few years spacious residences and villas have sprung up on all sides. As a city offering facilities for

art, music, and good society, Dresden cannot be excelled.

The handsome bridge, Friedrich August Brücke (completed 1910), may be taken as the centre of the most interesting part of Dresden. Immediately to the east of the Fried. Aug. Brücke, on the Altstadt side, stretches the beautiful Bruhlsche Terrasse, whence are fine views over the river; looking down stream the Fried. August Brucke and the Marienbrücke for railway and ordinary traffic are seen, looking up stream the Konigin Carolabrücke and the Albertbrücke. High class concerts in the Belvedere on the Bruhl Terrace. Near the flight of steps to the terrace, facing the Royal Palace and Catholic Church, is the Standehaus, equestrian statue of King Albert in front.

The Königliche Schloss (Royal Palace), just south of the Fried. Aug. Brücke, will be discovered by its lofty tower, 331 ft., over the Grüne Thor, in the facade fronting the Hofkirche; the Grüne Thor leads into the Great Court, where, in the corner to the right is the Grünes Gewölbe (Green Vault), Within the Schloss the Ball Room, Throne Room, and Chapel are shewn; in the Grünes Gewölbe are priceless collections of curiosities, jewels, enamels, crystals, coins, medals, specimens of the goldsmiths' art, ivories, small works of art, etc.

The Zwinger, to the west of the Schloss, is a range of buildings of seven pavilions, with the Museum at one corner; view the building from the river side. In the Museum are the picture gallery, with collections of engravings and drawings; in the Zwinger are the zoological, ethnographical, and mineralogical collections, with scientific instruments. The Picture Gallery is of world renown and it is impossible here to even indicate its treasures—open on Sun., 11 to 2; Tues., Thurs., and Fri., 9 to 5; on Wed. and Sat., 9 to 5—50 pf.; on Mon., 9 to 1, 1m. 50 pf. In winter open 10.0 to 3.0 Tues., Wed., Thurs., Fri., Sat.; 11.0 to 2.0 Sun. and Mon.

The Johanneum, a little to the east of the Schloss, at the north west corner of Neu Markt, contains the Historical Museum, weapons, armour, costumes, standards, saddlery, and the Porcelain collection.

Königliche Porzellanniederlage (Royal China Depot), Schlossstrasse, 36. Exhibition and Sale of art china and china for household use. See Advt. under Dresden.

The Japanische Palais is near the Neustadt end of the Marienbrücke, to the left of the Zwinger, but on the opposite side of the river Here is the Royal Library of 500,000 vols., 6,000 MSS., 28,000 maps, many specimens of early printing, and literary curiosities.

The Albertinum is at the east end of the Bruhlsche Terrasse; collection of antiquities, Assyrian, Greek, Roman, etc.

Kunst-Gewerbe Museum (Industrial Art Museum), daily, except Mon., 9.0 a.m. to 2.0 p.m., Sun. and Fri. 9.0 to 1.0, in Eliasstrasse, a short distance from south end of Albertbrücke, contains furniture, tapestry, and porcelain. On application, the "Aula," once the banquetting room of the Brühl Palace, may be seen; painted ceilings, gilt doors, etc.

The Roman Catholic Hofkirche, between the river and the Schloss, has many statues of saints on parapets and at entrances; an altarpiece, the "Ascension"; tower (305 ft.); royal burial vaults under sacristy. Music at services much esteemed. Sophienkirche, the Protestant Hofkirche, is in the rear of the Schloss, just beyond the Prinzen Palais. Frauenkirche is in Neu Markt; lofty dome, lantern 310 ft. Kreuzkirche, in the Alt Markt, tower 312 ft.

New Rathaus (completed 1910), a very fine building, by the Kreuzkirche, one-third mile south east of Fried. Aug. Brücke—architects, Karl Roth and Franz Bräter. Open weekdays except Sat., 8.0 to 9.30 and 2.0 to 3.30; Sun., 9.0 to 12.0. Tower 320 ft. high (lift, 1 to 5 persons, 1 M. 25 Pf; without lift 10 Pf.); very fine view.

The Luther Monument is in the Neu Markt; in the Alt Markt is the Germania statue; equestrian statue of King John in Theater Platz; many other statues and some beautiful fountains.

Hof Oper, near Fried. August Brücke, opposite the Catholic Hofkirche, an imposing buiilding in Renaissance style, considered one of the finest opera houses in Europe. Albert Theater (dramas, etc.), in Albert Platz, in Neustadt, in a direct line from Fried. Aug. Brücke. Residenz Theater; Central Theater (variety),

The Grosse Garten is a pleasant park on the south east of the town, with Zoologischer Garten on its south side. This district was the scene of the defeat of the Allies by Napoleon, 1813.

The Military Barracks, a vast range of buildings, in Neustadt, are interesting.

The Cemeteries on the Neustadt side—old Neustädter Kirchhof, about three quarters of a mile north of Neustadt Bahnhof, and new Neustädter Kirchhof, one mile further, should be visited; the Roman Catholic Cemetery (Weber and F. Schlegel buried here) is in Friedrichstrasse, on the Altstadt side, west of Marienbrücke.

CHIEF POST OFFICE (also Telegraph and Telephone), in Post Platz, a little to south of the Zwinger.

ENG. CH. SERV.—All Saints' Ch., Wienerstr

PRESBYT. SERV. (Ch. of Scotland), at the Church, 2, Bernardstr.

ST. JOHN'S AMERICAN EPISCOPAL CHURCH.—Reichsplatz, 5.

H.B.M.'S MINISTER RESIDENT.—Arthur Grant-Duff, Esq. H.B.M.'S CONSUL.—C. W. Palmié, Esq. VICE-CONSUL.—F. Bassenge, Esq.

U. S. CONSUL-GENERAL.—T. St. J. Gaffney, Esq. VICE-CONSUL.—J. L. A. Burrell, Esq.

GOLF.—9-hole course.

MEDICAL.-Dr. Pusenilli, Dr. Klotz, Dr. de Souza.

CHEMIST,—THE INTERNATIONAL PHARMACY REICHS APOTHEKE—10, Bismarck Platz, close to Central Station. English and American prescriptions made up according to their respective pharmacopœias by qualified assistants. All patent medicines and foreign specialities. Mineral waters. Toilet articles. Laboratory for analyses. Free delivery. Tel. 151.

TIEDEMANN and GRAHL, 9, Seestrasse. Wine Merchants. First-class Wine Restaurant, ground and first floor.

ALLGEMEINE DEUTSCHE CREDIT-ANSTALT, 16, Altmarkt. Capital 90 million marks. Reserve 30 millions. Letters of credit and circular notes cashed.

ANGLO-AMERICAN FORWARDING & SHIPPING AGENT. Special Tourist Office.—Alfred Kohn. Packing & Warehouses, Railway & Steamer Tickets. Sole Agent for International Sleeping Car Co. By special appointment to H.R.H. Prince Johann Georg. Telephone 3422 and 18508. Telegrams: Americano. Christianstrasse, 31. Close to Central Station.

PIANOS.—F. RIES, 21, Seestrasse (Kaufhaus). BECHSTEIN and others for sale or hire. Sheet music of all countries. Circulating library. Tickets and information for all important Concerts.

J. H. BLUTH, 9, Pragerstrasse. By appointment to the Royal Court. Greatest stock of real and imitation LACE. Speciality—Saxon Lace.

LINEN.—JOSEPH MEYER (au petit Bazar).—13, Neumarkt. Speciality of Saxon Damask Table Linen, Sheeting, Handkerchiefs, &c. Ladies' Wedding Outfits. Established 1837. See Advt.

DEPOT FOR BRADSHAW'S GUIDE.—Thomas Cook and Son, 43, Pragerstrasse.

RAIL, see Routes from Dresden, page cxxxii.

STEAMERS on the Elbe, see page 367.

[Weisser Hirsch.—A well-known health resort, reached by electric car from Dresden. It is sheltered from northerly winds by a large tract of pine forest, and is a favourite resort for those living in the neighbourhood of Dresden.]

Duisburg.—*Stat.*—Pop. 229,483.

HOTELS: EUROPAISCHER HOF; PRINZ REGENT.

A manufacturing town, on a canal connecting the Rivers Rhine and Ruhr. A centre of the coal trade of the Ruhr Valley. Salvatorkirche, 15th cent. RAIL, pages 126, 135, 160A. Steamer, page 362.

Dürrheim Bad, see page 457.

Düsseldorf.—*Stat.*—Pop. 358,728.

HOTEL BREIDENBACHERHOF.-First-class hotel, situated in a fine part of the town, near the Painting Exhibition. See Advt.

PARK HOTEL.-Comfortable modern hotel, with private bath rooms. American bar. See Advt.

ROYAL HOTEL.—Family hotel, near the Central Station. All modern conveniences. See Advt.

PENSION MOELLER MARCUS. — Achenbachstrasse, 78. Comfortable family home. Best position. Every modern comfort. Pension from M. 6. See Advt.

The principal RAILWAY STATION, the HAUPTBAHNHOF, is on the east side of the town, at about a mile from the centre of activity; minor Stations are Derendorf Bahnhof, on the north east, and Bilk Bahnhof, on the south. At Obercassel, on the opposite side of the Rhine, there is a Station.

The Landing Places of the Rhine Steamers are at about the middle of the river front of the town.

Düsseldorf, the chief town of the district of Düsseldorf, is situated at the confluence of the small River Düsselbach with the Rhine. It is one of the pleasantest towns in Germany; its many attractions exciting an interest in almost every visitor. In the town are broad tree-lined streets and squares, small parks and recreation grounds, and on the Rhine is a magnificent embankment with terraces, gardens, and handsome buildings. As an art centre Düsseldorf has always been conspicuous; its school of painters is world-known, and in all that relates to music and the drama a high standard is maintained. The city is also a great commercial and industrial place, with a huge trade in iron, steel, and machinery.

On the central pier of the Rhine Bridge is the figure of a lion, the heraldic badge of Düsseldorf.

From the west side of the Wilhelms Platz, by the Hauptbahnhof, the Bismarckstrasse runs north-west to the Konigs Platz, and thence the line of the thoroughfare leads to the Konigs Allee, where, a little north, round about the Theatre, is the centre of Düsseldorf life. From the Landing Places of the Rhine Steamers the streets from the river lead in a quarter of a mile to the broad Alleestrasse, near the Theatre.

Andreaskirche just off west side of Alleestrasse, near the Theatre; dating from 1629; some paintings in the chapels, tombs. Lambertkirche, 200 yards west of Andreaskirche, Gothic, of 14th cent.

Rathhaus, on the Markt Platz, by the Rhine. In Bolkerstrasse, east side of Markt Platz, Heinrich Heine, the poet, was born, 1799 (died 1856).

Kunst Academie (Academy of Art), one third mile north west from the Theatre, near the Rhine. Handsome Renaissance building, with a small collection of works by old masters, including an Assumption, by Rubens; also collections of drawings, engravings, and water colours. In the Aula are frescoes. Week-days 50 pf., Sun. free.

Kunsthalle, in Friedrichs Platz, west side of Alleestrasse, near the Theatre; in Renaissance style. Here is the Stadtische Gemäldesammlung (Town Picture Gallery), a collection of paintings by modern Düsseldorf artists. Daily, 9.0 to 6.0 (5 in winter), 50 pf.

Gewerbe Museum (Industrial Art), on north side of Friedrichs Platz; exhibits of textile fabrics, lace, ironwork, pottery, wood-carving; also Indian and Japanese collections. Here are the Provincial and Municipal Library. Daily, except Monday, 10.0 to 4.0, 50 pf.

Oberlandesgericht (Law Courts)—fine modern building, 1911. Regierungsgebaude (Government Offices), 1911.

Provinzial Standehaus (House of the Rhenish Estates), in south east quarter.

Hofgarten, just beyond the north ends of Konigs Allee and Alleestrasse; War Monument, in memory of campaigns of 1864, 1866, and 1870-1.

Zoologischer Garten, away from town, to north east. Cemetery, beyond the town, to north, by the Rhine.

POST OFFICE.—Wilhelms Platz, opposite the Hauptbahnhof.

CHURCH OF ENGLAND.—British Chaplaincy Church, 14B, Kreuzstr. Holy Communion every Sunday 8.0 a.m., on 1st Sun. of month and after Matins, 11.30. Evensong, 6.30. British Chaplain, 123, Duisburgerstr.

H.B.M.'s CONSUL GENERAL.—Dr. F. P. Kœnig. VICE-CONSUL.—J. Schneider, Esq.

RAIL, pp. 132, 133D, 134A, 134B, 134D, 160A.

STEAMERS on the Rhine, page 362.

Eisenach.—*Stat.*—Pop. 38,362.

HOTEL DER RAUTENKRANZ.—First class hotel of old repute, situated in the Market Place, with view on the Wartburg. Baths; French restaurant. See Advt.

HOTEL THURINGER HOF.—11, Karlsplatz, opposite Luther monument. First class, built 1912, with every modern comfort. Hot and cold running water in all rooms. Rooms from M. 2.50. Garage. See Advt.

KAISERHOF; GROSSHERZOG VON SACHSEN; GOLDEN LION; ELIZABETHENRUHE.

A well situated town in the most attractive part of the Thuringian Forest, having special interests associated with Luther. The Hauptbahnhof is on the east side of the town. In the Markt Platz, at the centre of the town, is the Ducal Palace; opposite the palace is Georgskirche. In Luther Platz is the Luther Haus, where Luther is said to have lived in 1498. Johann Sebastian Bach was born at a house, marked by a tablet, in the Frauenplan. St. Nicholas Church, near the Station, is a fine Romanesque building. In the Marien Thal is the house once occupied by Fritz Reuter (poet), now a Museum.

The Wartburg. 615 feet above Eisenach, is an interesting and picturesque historic castle, occasionally the residence of the Grand Duke of Weimar; founded 1070. It consists of the Vorburg and the Hauptburg; in the Vogtei of the Vorburg are mementoes of Luther, who was in hiding here, as "Junker Georg," 1521-1522; the Hauptburg exhibits the magnificence of a castle of the 12th cent. Tickets, 50 pf., at the Hotel by the entrance to the stronghold.

The slightly saline waters of the Grand Duchess Caroline Spring, either for drinking or bathing, are successfully used in cases of gout, scrofula, female complaints, rheumatism, bowel disorders, etc. The Spring Pavilion is at the south eastern side of the town.

From the picturesque Marienhöhe are fine views of the surrounding country.

ENGLISH CHURCH SERVICE, on first Sunday in each month.

RAIL, pages 170, 173A, 173B.

Elberfeld.—*Stat.*—Pop. 170,195; in the adjoining town of **Barmen** there is a population of 169.214.

ELBERFELD HOTELS: WEIDENHOF; KLEIN; KAISER HOF.

BARMEN HOTELS; VOGELER; SCHUTZENHAUS; RHEINISCHER HOF.

The principal RAILWAY STATION at Elberfeld is Elberfeld-Döppersberg, in a central situation. Elberfeld (west) and Barmen (east), with several suburbs, are practically one large industrial town, stretching along the valley of the Wupper and up the side slopes. The manufactures are principally concerned with cotton, calico, silk, chemicals, and soap. The older and busier parts are not attractive, but the north west part of Elberfeld, at the base of the Nutzenberg, is modern and well built.

At Elberfeld is a modern Rathhaus, in Neu Markt, one third mile due north of the Döppersberg Bahnhof; of the churches the most important is the Reformiertekirche, half mile due west of the Rathhaus. In the old Rathaus is the Municipal Museum.

At Barmen there are a Ruhmeshalle (Hall of Fame), with collections, and a natural history collection at the Museum. Handsome Protestant Church; at the Missionshaus is a collection of foreign curiosities.

ENGLISH CHURCH SERVICE, in the Lutheran Church at Elberfeld.

U.S. CONSUL at Barmen.—G. E. Eager, Esq.

RAIL, pages 133E, 134A, 134D.

Elend.—*Stat.*

HOTEL: WALDHOEHE.

A well situated Harz village, 1,705 ft. above sea, frequented both in summer and winter. Forest scenery all round pure air. A centre for winter sport.

RAIL, page 165B.

Elgersburg.—*Stat.*—Pop. about 1,400.

HOTEL KURHAUS.

A picturesquely situated village, 1,790 ft. above sea, surrounded by woods, with a bracing climate, much frequented as a summer resort. On a rocky height is a restored mediæval castle.

RAIL, page 170A.

Eltville, see page 453.

Emden.—*Stat.*—Pop. 21,487.

HOTEL CENTRAL; WEISSES HAUS.

A thriving town in a fertile plain, connected by canals with the River Ems, 2½ miles distant. The Rathaus, 1574-76, in Renaissance style, contains a collection of early firearms in the armoury; extensive view from the tower. Grosse Kirche has mon. of Count Enno (1540). In Museum of the Gesellschaft für Kunst und Vaterländsche Alterthümer are a picture gallery and collections of antiquities. Museum of Natural History, with amber collection.

H.B.M.'s VICE-CONS.—Lucas Shadwell, Esq.

RAIL, pages 133A. 133C. Steamers to islands of Norderney and Borkum.

Ems (Bad Ems).—*Stat.*—Pop. 7,500.

HOTEL D'ANGLETERRE AND PARK VILLA.—Fine situation opposite Baths. Beautiful garden. English meal times (late dinner). Rooms with bath and lavatory. See Advt.

ROYAL KURHAUS HOTEL.—Re-erected 1912-13. Most modern and thoroughly first class. Handsome public and private rooms. Connecting colonnade to Kursaal. See Advt.

ROYAL HOTEL "THE ROEMERBAD."—Overlooking Kurgarten and Baths. High class, well appointed. Baths and Inhalatorium in hotel, English and American clientèle. See Advt.

FOUR SEASONS AND EUROPE HOTEL.—Best positions. English clientèle. Latest improvements. Facing Kur Gardens and Casino. See Advt.

FOUR TOWERS HOTEL.—First class. Beautifully situated, with fine garden. Apartments with bath and toilette. Pension from 9 Marks. See Advt.

Ems, 260 ft. above sea, is pleasantly situated on both banks of the River Lahn, with wooded heights on each side. The curative properties of the warm alkaline waters, used for drinking, inhaling, douching, and bathing, were known to the Romans, and for centuries the springs have been visited by persons suffering from nervous dyspepsia, catarrhs of all kinds, female ailments, gout, and rheumatism. There are about 26,000 visitors annually, the season, lasting from May to October, being very bright and animated at its height. Regatta in July, "battle of flowers," Venetian water festivals. Visitors' tax, payable after a week's stay, 18 m. for head of family, other members 9 m.

The point of attraction is the Kurhaus, at the centre of the town, the springs of drinking waters rising in the arcades — usual time for drinking 6.0 to 7.0 a.m., 10.0 a.m. to 12.0 noon, and 4.0 to 6.0 p.m. The Kursaal, with many fine rooms, and the Kur Garten are close by; during the afternoon the Garten is the fashionable resort. A tablet in the Garten marks the spot where King William of Prussia (afterward Emperor William) gave the answer to the French Ambassador (Count Benedetti) that immediately preceded the war of 1870. Mon. of Emp. William (in civil attire—unique) in the Wandelhalle, a covered promenade. Bismarck column in north west part of the town.

Music at the early drinking of the waters, at late afternoon in the Garten, and in the evening at the Kursaal; concerts and theatricals. Funicular Railway up the Malberg, 1,090 feet; charming walks. Tennis, croquet, boating, fishing.

POST OFFICE in Römerstrasse.

ENG. CH. SERV. at Church of SS. Peter and Paul.

MEDICAL.—There are many medical men practising in the town, a list of whom may be obtained on application.

RAIL, page 146.

Erfurt.—*Stat.*—Pop. 111,463.

HOTEL EUROPE (EUROPAISCHER HOF AND ROMISCHER KAISER.) First class family hotel. Finest and quietest position. All modern comforts. Close to all sights. Motor omnibus at the Station. Rooms from M. 2.50. See Advt.

On the River Gera, a very interesting old city. From the Bahnhof, on south side of the city, Bahnhofstrasse leads north west to a broad thoroughfare, the Anger. At the corner of the Anger is the Packhof, with Picture Gallery (daily 11 to 1) and the Royal Library, 55,000 vols., 7,700 MSS (week days 10.0 a.m. to 1.0 p.m.) A little beyond north end of Bahnhofstrasse, Schlosserstrasse leads west to the Fisch Markt, where is the Rathhaus—250 yards west from here is the Dom.

The Roman Catholic Dom dates from 13th cent., part is Gothic; interior is adorned with reliefs, rich stained windows, and some paintings cloisters. On south side of the Friedrich Wilhelms Platz, by the Dom, is the ancient Lilie Inn, where it is said Luther, Gustavus Adolphus, Maurice of Saxony, and other celebrities stayed.

Immediately west of the Dom is Severikirche, with three spires—reliefs in interior. Prediger-kirche is 250 yards east of the Dom; Barfusser-kirche is a few yards further east. In the north part of the city, in Augustinerstrasse, half a mile north east of the Dom, is the Augustine Monastery, where Luther was a monk, 1505-8.

U.S. VICE-CONSUL.—R. C. Busser, Esq.

RAIL, pages 152, 170, 172A.

Essen.—*Stat.*—Pop. 294,653.

KAISERHOF.—First class hotel, equipped with all modern comforts. Apartments with bath and toilette. Rooms from M. 4. See Advt.

BERLINER HOF; MONOPOL; RHEINISCHER HOF.

A town whose modern development and importance obscures its historical foundation in the 9th century. It is the centre of a coal mining, iron working, district, black with smoke from countless chimneys. Krupp's huge Works are here.

The Münsterkirche, of 9th cent., restored 1886, is one of the oldest churches in Germany; altar piece, early works of art in the treasury. Rathhaus.

RAIL, pages 130, 133D, 135, 160A.

Feldberg (The), see page 457.

Frankfort-on-the-Main (*German*, **Frankfurt-am-Main**).—*Stat.*—Pop. (1910) 414,576—(*Plan in Special Edition, or post free 3d. stamps*).

IMPERIAL HOTEL.—Very select. Highest patronage. Unique open situation, opposite Opera. Suites and single rooms with baths and toilette. See Advt.

FRANKFURTER HOF HOTEL.—First class house, well situated on the Kaiserplatz, five minutes from the Station. Electric light and lift. See Advt.

THE SWAN HOTEL.—Centre of town, first class, entirely rebuilt. The treaty of peace between France and Germany was signed here. Large airy rooms from 3 marks. See Advt.

CARLTON HOTEL.—New first class hotel, facing Central Station. Up-to-date comforts. See Advt.

HOTEL MONOPOL AND METROPOLE.—New, facing the chief exit of the Central Station. Very comfortable and moderate charges. See Advt.

HOTEL BRISTOL.—Facing Station and close to all points of interest. Apartments and single rooms, with bath. Rooms from 3 Marks. See Advt.

GRAND HOTEL CONTINENTAL.—Opposite the Central Station. Every modern comfort. Moderate. See Advt.

HOTEL PRINCE HEINRICH.—Facing the Central Station, in quiet situation. Every improvement. English comfort. Rooms from 2 Mk. See Advt.

HOTEL DEUTSCHER KAISERHOF.—Facing the Station. Hot and cold water supply. Rooms with breakfast from 4—6.50 M. Tariff in all rooms. See Advt.

HOTEL BASELER HOF (Christliches Hospiz) Wiesenhüttenplatz (near Station).-Every modern comfort. Lift; electric light; baths. Rooms from 2 Mk. See Advt.

PENSION PFAFF.—First class private hotel in central but quiet position. Every comfort. Lift. Large garden. Pension from 6 M. See Advt.

CABS (all fares double between 11.0 p.m. and 6.0 a.m.)—Taximeter Cabs: 1st zone, 1 or 2 persons for 800 meters 50 pf., each extra 400 meters 10 pf.; 2nd zone, 1 or 2 persons for 600 meters 50 pf., each extra 300 meters 10 pf.; 3 or 4 persons about quarter extra. Waiting, 10 pf. each 4 min.; luggage 25 pf. each large article.

Electric Trams in all directions.

FRANKFORT, on the River Main, belongs to Prussia; formerly it was a free town of the German Empire, and later, until 1866, it was one of the free towns of the German Confederation, and the seat of a Diet. It has always been a town of great commercial importance, and it is a centre of European financial influence.

The principal railway station, the Hauptbahnhof, is a fine building on the south west side of the town, and from the Bahnhofs Platz broad streets run towards the centre of the town. The Ostbahnhof, on the east side, is about two miles from the Hauptbahnhof.

The middle street running from before the Hauptbahnhof is one end of the principal thoroughfare of the town—under different names it runs eastward until it touches Zoologischer Garten, close to the Ostbahnhof. About three quarters of a mile from the Hauptbahnhof, the street broadens out into the Hohenzollernplatz, where, away to the left, is a cluster of public buildings and points of interest; after the Hohenzollernplatz the thoroughfare is called Die Zeil. A street on the right, the Fahrgasse, leads down to the Alte Main Brucke (to be rebuilt); just before the bridge is reached the Dom will be seen off to the right. A little west of the Dom is the Römer, then, going west, the street leads back to the Hauptbahnhof, or, going northward, the streets lead to Die Zeil or Hohenzollernplatz.

The Dom (Cathedral), Gothic, of different periods, 1235 to 1358, was half ruined by fire 1867; tower, 312 feet; the emperors of old Germany were crowned at the high altar by the Elector of Mayence—on right is the Wahlkapelle (election chapel) where the emperors were elected. Upon a house in the Platz, to the east of the Dom, No. 4. is an effigy of Luther; he is stated to have preached here when going to Worms.

Leonhard Kirche, by the river, west of Alte Main Brücke. Nicolai Kirche, on south side of the Römerberg. Paulus Kirche on north side of the Romer.

The Archiv, a Historical Museum—banners, weapons, furniture, paintings, etc.—is just south of the Dom; Sun. & Wed. free; other days 50 pf.

The Römer is perhaps the most interesting edifice of Frankfort. It is the town hall of the old free imperial city; in the Kaisersaal are portraits of the emperors; in the Wahlzimmer (election room) the electors met to deliberate. The new Rathaus is on the north side of the Römer group of buildings. Upon the Römerberg, the open space before the Römer, down to end of eighteenth century no Jew was permitted to intrude. Justitia Fountain in centre of the Römerberg, and some mediæval houses at the side.

Ethnological Museum, on Munzgasse, just west of the Romer.

Bibliothek (Library), is about half a mile east of the Dom, near the river; 215,000 vols., many MSS., and curiosities.

The Art and Industrial Museum, in Neue Mainzerstrasse, contains valuable collections; on Sun. and Wed. free; other days 50 pf.

The Stadel Art Institute is in the suburb of Sachsenhausen, immediately south (half-a-mile) of the Hauptbahnhof, but on the opposite side of the river. A handsome building in the Italian Renaissance style. Here are very fine collections of pictures, drawings, engravings, and casts, in many rooms. Sun. 11 to 1; Wed. 11 to 4; other days, 10 to 1; at other hours, 1m.

Bethmann Museum, at corner of Friedberger Landstrasse, north of Neue Zeil; sculpture.

Opernhaus, north west (one third mile) of the Hohenzollernplatz. The Theatre (Schauspielhaus), in Gallus Anlage; Bismarck mon. by the theatre. Neues Theater, on Mainzerlandstrasse, near the Hauptbanhof; Albert Schuman Theater, in the Station square; Hippodrome on the left bank of the Main.

Börse (Exchange), quarter mile north of the Hohenzollernplatz.

Goethe's house, where he was born (1749), is in the Grosser Hirschgraben, 23; interesting rooms, also Goethe Museum and Library. Daily, 8 to 6, except Sun. aft.; 1 mark. The Goethe Monument is in Goethe Platz.

War Monument in the Cemetery, Schafergasse, running out of north side of Die Zeil. Gutenberg Mon. Schiller Mon. in Schiller Platz. Eschenheimer Thurm, the only one left of the old tower gateways of the city, is at end of Gross Eschenheimerstr., running north from Schiller Platz.

The zig-zag line of the old fortifications is now laid out as pleasant promenades, under different names, encircling the town from a point on the river bank near Unter Main Brücke to a point on river bank near Ober Main Brücke. The Palmen Garten is on north west side of the town; concert occasionally in aft. and even. Zoologischer Garten is on east side; 1 mark.

POST OFFICE (Hauptpost), on the north side of Die Zeil.

Cemetery on north side of town, in Eckenheimer Landstrasse, running from Eschenheimer Anlage. Beautiful spot, many monuments. Jewish Burial Ground close by.

ENGLISH CHURCH. — Königsteinerstrasse. Chaplain, Rev. R. S. Kendall, Bohmerstrasse, 38.

H.B.M.'S CONSUL-GEN.—E. B. von Speyer, Esq. VICE-CONS.-C. Gardner, Esq., and J. W. F. Thelwall, Esq.

U S. CONSUL-GEN.—H. W. Harris, Esq. VICE-CONSUL.—W. Dawson, Esq.

BANKS.—Direction der Disconto-Gesellschaft, established 1851, Rossmarkt 18. Capital M.200,000,000. Reserves about M.80,000,000. All banking orders promptly executed. Letters of credit and cheques issued and cashed. Foreign moneys at current rates.

CHEMIST.—THE ROSEN-APOTHEKE, The Anglo-American Pharmacy. Engelhard, Successors. Dr. Curt Hoffmann, Am Salzhaus, 3, near the Goethe house. Telephone 470. English and American prescriptions made up according to their respective pharmacopœias by qualified assistants only. Largest stock of patent medicines. Laboratory for Analysis.

RAIL.—See Routes from Frankfort, page cxxxiii

Freiburg-im-Breisgau, see page 457.

Freiersbach Bad, see page 458.

Freudenstadt, see page 458.

Friedenweiler, see page 458.

Friedrichshafen.—*Stat.*—Pop. 5,200.

KURGARTEN HOTEL.—First class, overlooking the Lake. Every modern comfort. Private motor-boat and car. Sports. See Advt.

The Railway Station is situated about a mile from the Harbour, but trains run down to the quay for the convenience of steamer passengers.

Many visitors in summer for the lake bathing. In the Schloss are a few pictures by modern Wurtemberg masters. Kurhalle, amidst pleasant surroundings by the lake. Riedle Park, with fine view of the Lake and Alps. The collections of the Bodensee Verein should be visited.

RAIL, pages 139A, 193, 193A. STEAMER, p. 369.

Fulda.—*Stat.*—Pop. 21,000.

HOTELS: KURFURST; WOLFF; BAHNHOF.

An old place on the River Fulda, in an attractive country, with evidence of vanished importance in the numerous public edifices. From the Bahnhof, on east side, across the city, past the Schloss, in two thirds of a mile, to the Dom, of 18th cent., containing a very ancient figure of Charlemagne; under the high altar lies buried St. Boniface, an English missionary, martyred 755 in Friesland —the Dom was injured by fire, June 4th, 1905, the north tower suffering most. West of the Dom are the old Benedictine Convent buildings. Just north of the Dom is Michaelskirche, dating from 9th cent. RAIL, pages 149. 149A, 150.

Furtwangen see page 458.

Garmisch.—*Stat.*

PARK HOTEL ALPENHOF.—First class, modern, comfortable and moderate. Rooms with private baths. Lift; central heating. Open all the year. See Advt.

HOTEL PENSION "VILLA BETHELL."—Comfortable English hotel-pension, with all modern improvements; electric light. See Advt.

A beautifully situated summer resort, and also a centre for winter sport, 2,290 ft above sea, at the foot of the Eckenberg. This picturesque village—several old houses—is the Government centre of the district; and its proximity to Oberammergau makes it a desirable place for a stay. Kurhaus. Wittelsbach Park is on east side of the village. The Risserhauer, 2,565 ft., with lake, is a mile south of Garmisch. The Eibsee, 3,190 ft., 7 miles west of Garmisch, a lake amidst magnificent surroundings, is reached by omnibus once or twice daily. The Wetterstein range, crowned by the Zugspitze, 9,725 ft., is about 10 miles to the south. All around the Bavarian highlands are very attractive.

RAIL, pages 197B, 237B. Diligence, page 373

[**Badersee.**—

ALPENHOTEL BADERSEE.—In quiet dust-free position. All winter sports. Tennis and boating. Pension from 7 M. See Advt.

The Badersee, 2,720 ft. above sea, is a beautiful little lake, whose emerald-green waters are so clear that the bottom may be seen at the depth of 50 feet. The charming surroundings make the spot a favourite summer and winter resort. Boats on the lake. Shady walks in summer and sheltered from wind in winter. All winter sports. Interesting country all round.

A motor omnibus runs between Garmisch-Partenkirchen and the Badersee, 4½ miles.]

Geisenheim, see page 453.

Gernsbach, see page 458.

Giessen.—*Stat.*—Pop. 31,153. **HOTEL HESSEN** **On the River Lahn. Small University, founded 1607, about 1,100 students.**

RAIL, pages 133B, 146, 147, 149A, 156A.

Godesberg, see page 449A.

Gorlitz.—*Stat.*—Pop. 85,806.

HOTEL VIER JAHRESZEITEN; STADT DRESDEN.

The Railway Station—Bahnhof—is on the south west side of the town, a mile from the centre.

An ancient town, now a busy manufacturing place, on the River Neisse. From the Bahnhof Berlinerstrasse leads north to Post Platz, where are the Law Courts. A few yards north is the Frauenkirche, 15th cent.; then a few yards west is Demiani Platz, where is the Kaisertrutz, a heavy building of 15th cent. From the Demiani Platz the Obermarkt winds north east, passing the Dreifaltigkeitskirche (Trinity) and the Rathhaus to the Peterskirche, a fine specimen of late Gothic—towers 275 ft. high. Arsenal, containing objects relating to the Hohenzollern family.

RAIL, pages 179a, 180, 186.

Goslar.—*Stat.*—Pop. 20,000.

HOTELS: KAISERWERTH; HANNOVER; ACHTERMANN.

A picturesque town of the north west Harz district, with several remains—wall towers and quaint houses—of mediæval times; a good centre whence to visit a highly attractive mountain and forest neighbourhood.

Close to the Station is the two-spired Neuwerkskirche, of 12th cent., with interesting interior; opposite is the Achtermanns Turm, of 16th cent. Bahnhofstrasse leads to the heart of the town, past Jakobkirche, 12th cent., and, a little further, through Fischemakerstrasse, to the old world Marktplatz, where are the 15th cent. Rathaus (collection of pictures) and the Kaiserworth, also of the 15th cent.; on the platz is a fountain, said to date from the 12th cent. Behind the Rathaus and the Kaiserworth is the Marktkirche, and opposite is the Brusttuch, a 16th cent. house with quaint carvings. Here the street to the left leads to the Domkapelle, a portion of a former celebrated cathedral, erected 11th cent., mostly demolished 1820. Close by, on rising ground, is the Kaiserhaus, the oldest purely secular building in Germany, erected in the 11th cent., restored

19th cent.; the great hall is 56 yards long, 17 yards wide, 35 ft. high, and is adorned with frescoes; the domestic St. Ulrich Chapel contains the tomb of Henry III. Museum, near east end of Breitstrasse; collection of antiquities, geological, natural history, and ethnographical collections. RAIL, pages 163, 166.

Gotha.—*Stat.*—Pop. 39,553.

SCHLOSS HOTEL.—Modern house, built 1912, with the latest comfort and conveniences. Hot and cold running water in every room. Large garden. See Advt.

WUNSCHER; HERZOG ERNST.

A pleasant busy town of Thuringia, attractively situated. From the Bahnhof, on south side of the town, Bahnhofstrasse runs north, presently crossed by the Schloss Allee, which, on left, leads in a few minutes to the Schloss Friedenstein, the ducal residence—may be visited, 50 pf. Opposite the Schloss, to south, is the Museum, where are a Picture Gallery, some casts, and collections of antiquities and art objects.

Klosterkirche, 200 yards north west of the Schloss; Margarethenkirche, east of the Markt.

Ducal park on south side of town.

RAIL, pages 170, 172, 172A.

Gottingen.—*Stat.*—Pop. 35,806.

HOTELS: KRONE; ROYAL; GEBHARD.

An old university town, on the River Leine, having picturesque streets but few striking public buildings. Tablets indicate houses where learned men associated with the University lived. In the Markt Platz is the Rathhaus, 14th cent., with wall paintings. In Wilhelms Platz is the Aula, containing collections of pictures, casts, and coins; in Burgstrasse is a museum of antiquities. The University Library (550,000 vols., 6,500 MSS.) is in an old monastery. RAIL, pages 149, 156.

Griesbach Bad, see page 458.

Hahnenklee.—

HOTEL: HAHNENKLEE'ER HOF.

A village of the Upper Harz district, 1,700 ft. above sea, at the foot of the lofty Bocksberg; frequented both in summer and winter. Wide spreading pine forests, with stretches of meadow land; two or three small lakes. Pure air; in winter, skating, ski-ing, etc. A regular motor car and omnibus service between Goslar railway station and Hahnenklee.

Halberstadt.—*Stat.*—Pop. 48,000.

HOTELS: PRINZ EUGEN; HALBERSTADTER HOF; WEISSES ROSS.

An old manufacturing city on the River Holtemme. From the Bahnhof Magdeburgerstrasse leads west to Breite Weg and the Markt in half a mile. Here are the Rathhaus, of 14th cent., and Martinikirche; several old wood carved houses in the Markt. A few yards north west of the Markt is the Dom, of 13-15th cent., with the single exception of Magdeburg the finest Protestant Cathedral in North Germany. At west end of the Dom Platz is the Liebfrauenkirche dating from 1146. RAIL, pp. 153, 162, 166

Halle.—*Stat.*—Pop. 180,843.

HOTELS: KRONPRINZ; CONTINENTAL.

The Railway Station—HAUPT BAHNHOF—is on south east side of town, a mile from centre. An old town, on the River Saale, now an important commercial and manufacturing place. From the Haupt Bahnnof Leipzigerstrasse leads north west to the Markt Platz, where, in the middle, is the Rothe Thurm, a clock tower 276 ft. high. On south east side of the Platz is the Rathhaus, dating from 14th cent.

Marienkirche, with four towers, erected 1530-54, is on west side of Markt Platz; paintings in interior. St. Moritzkirche, the most important church, is a quarter mile south west of the Markt Platz; dating from 12th cent., carved work in interior. The Dom, of minor interest, is a quarter mile north west of Markt Platz. South of the Dom is the Provincial Museum. Paulus kirche, modern, 1903, in the Kaiser Platz.

The University, about 2,000 students, is a quarter mile north of the Markt Platz. Justizgebaude (Law Courts), erected 1905.

RAIL, pages 148, 158, 166, 170, 173A.

Hamburg.—*Stat.*—Pop. (1910) 931,035. *(Plan in Special Edition, or post free 3d. stamps).*

HOTEL ATLANTIC.—Entirely new, in best situation. First class. See Advt.

ESPLANADE HOTEL AND RESTAURANT.—Entirely new modern hotel with every comfort and improvement. Fine position. See Advt.

GRAND HOTEL VIER JAHRESZEITEN (Four Seasons).—First class hotel, overlooking the Alster Bassins. Hot and cold water supply in every room. Single rooms from M. 4. See Advt.

HAMBURGER HOF.—Palatial hotel, fine position on Jungfernstieg, facing Alster Bassins. Patronised by English and Americans. See Advt.

STREITS HOTEL.—Well known first class hotel, situated on the Alster Bassin. Rooms from M. 3.50. See Advt.

PALAST HOTEL.—In the best position. First class, modern, and moderate. See Advt.

CONTINENTAL HOTEL.—Modern, first class, and moderate. Facing Central Station. See Advt.

HOTEL REICHSHOF.—First class, every modern improvement. Garage. See Advt.

ENGLISH HOTEL.—2, Admiralitatstrasse, central and moderate. The Restaurant has English and German good cooking. See Advt.

UNION HOTEL.—Close to the Central Station. Old established, comfortable, moderate. See Adv.

HOTEL ZUM KRONPRINZEN.—On the Alster Bassins. First class family hotel; old established, moderate and modern. See Advt.

HOTEL FURST BISMARK.—Facing the Central Station, chief portal. Rooms with breakfast from M. 3.50. New, excellent restaurant; moderate. See Advt.

HOTEL SCHADENDORF.—First class family hotel, almost opposite Central Station. Every modern comfort. Moderate charges. Rooms from M. 2.50. Pension. Tel. III-2458. See Advt.

BIEBER CAFÉ AND LONDON TAVERN.—Large and most interesting Café and Restaurant, with accommodation for 2,000 people. One of the sights of Hamburg. Daily concerts. Every delicacy of the season. See Advt.

The chief Railway Station-the HAUPTBAHNHOF-is in a central situation, within a mile of the heart of the business quarter.

TAXIMETER CABS.—1 or 2 persons for 1,200 meters 80 pf., each additional 400 meters 10 pf.; 3 or 4 persons for 900 meters 80 pf., each additional 300 meters 10 pf. Also Motor Cabs.

HAMBURG, the second city of the German Empire, ranks in commercial importance before any other town on the Continent of Europe; it is favourably situated on the broad lower Elbe, 60 miles from the mouth of the river. The magnificent harbour is entered annually by nearly 16,000 vessels of a total burden of 11,000,000 tons; the imports are of the average annual value of £267,000,000, and the exports of the average value of £240,000,000. The "Free Port"—or Bonded Warehouse District—is enclosed by floating palisades in the river and the Zoll Canal on the city side; persons entering this enclosure should be careful not to take with them anything liable to duty. A tremendous fire in 1842 consumed almost all that was left of historic Hamburg; the city has fine modern streets filled by an active thriving population, whose favourite promenades are by the Alster Bassins, two attractive tree bordered sheets of water. Under the Elbe is a double tunnel for pedestrians and vehicles, 490 yards long, made at a cost of over £500,000. The art collections of Hamburg are noteworthy. Altona (see description of) adjoins Hamburg on the west.

A very fine connected thoroughfare extends in a semi-circle westward from the Hauptbahnhof, across the Alster lakes, between the Botanic Garden and several public buildings, to the great Bismarck Monument; opposite the Botanic Gardens are the Post Office, Customs Offices, and the Musikhalle, and back from the road on the Botanic Garden side are the Law Courts.

The lofty tower, 370 ft. high, of the Rathaus (Town Hall) is conspicuous over the houses near the south east corner of the Binnen Alster. The building is a fine example of the Renaissance style, erected 1886-97, having much sculpture on the exterior—on the facade are statues of 20 German emperors. A fine door, the "Brautpforte," is the entrance to the chamber for civil marriages; interior has some handsome halls decorated with paintings. Open weekdays 11.0 to 3.0, 50 pf.; Sunday, 11.0 to 3.0, 30 pf. On the south side of the Rathaus is the Borse (Exchange).

Nicolai Kirche, in the Hopfen Markt, one third mile due south of the Rathaus, has a very high tower, 485 ft.; a Gothic building, erected after the fire of 1842 by Sir Gilbert Scott; sculpture and fine windows. A few yards south east of Nicolai Kirche is Katharinen Kirche, of 17th cent., containing some old paintings. Petri Kirche, 200 yards due east of the Rathaus, has a fine relief of the Entombment in the chancel; Jakobi Kirche is a few yards further east. The large Michaelis Kirche, in Michaelistrasse, about two thirds mile south west of the Rathaus, was destroyed by fire 1906, since rebuilt; will hold 3,000 worshippers; tower 426 ft.

The Kunsthalle is 200 yards north west of the Hauptbahnhof, close to the Binnen Alster; here are extensive collections of paintings including the Schwabe collection of British masters; there are also cabinets of engravings; open daily—summer 10.0 to 5.0, winter 10.0 to 4.0, Monday, 1.0 to 4.0, free. Half mile north of the Kunsthalle, on the east side of the Aussen Alster, at 59, An der Alster, is the Galerie Weber of about 350 pictures by old masters; Mon., Wed., Thurs., Fri., 10.0 to 4.0, by introduction.

Museum for Kunst und Gewerbe (Industrial Art), just south east of the Hauptbahnhof; very interesting miscellaneous collections. Opposite, on the other side of the railway, is the Natural History Museum.

The Johanneum, a quarter mile due east of the Rathaus, along Rathausstrasse, contains a collection of local antiquities and the City Library of about 365,000 vols. and 7,000 MSS.

The Botanic Garden and adjoining Zoological Gardens are about a quarter mile from the west side of the bridge across the Alster lakes. Hagenbeck's Zoological Park is at Stellingen, on the north west side of Hamburg—reached by tramway.

POST OFFICE, in Stephansplatz, near north west corner of Binnen-Alster (Poste Restante here).

ENG. CH. SERVICE, at Church, Zeughausmarkt.

ENG. REFORMED CH., 30 Johannisbollwerk.

H. B. M.'S CONSUL-GENERAL.—W. R. Hearn, Esq. VICE-CONSULS.—A. J. Ogston, Esq., and W. R. K. Gandell, Esq.

U.S. CONSUL-GENERAL.—R. P. Skinner, Esq. VICE-CONSUL.—E. H. L. Mummenhof, Esq.

GOLF.—9-hole course at Reinbek—by train from Hamburg.

DEPOT FOR BRADSHAW'S GUIDE.—Thomas Cook and Son, 39, Alsterdamm.

RAIL, pp. 132, 154, 156, 167, 168, 169, 213A.

Hanover (*Germ.* **Hannover**).—*Stat.*—**Pop.** (1910) 302,375; with **Linden**, 375,754.

HOTEL BRISTOL.—First class, opposite Central Station. Every modern comfort. Private baths. Telephone in each room. Winter garden. Leading restaurant. See Advt.

KASTEN'S HOTEL.—Entirely renovated. with electric light, lift, central heating. See Advt.

HOTEL ROYAL.—First-class hotel, situated opposite the Central Railway Station. Garden and terrace. Electric light. See Advt.

PALAST HOTEL RHEINISCHER HOF.—Facing Central Station. Hot and cold water supply and telephone in every room. Rooms from M. 3.50. See Advt.

GRAND HOTEL MUSSMANN.—First class hotel, facing Station. Electric light, lift, central heating. Wine and beer restaurant. Rooms from M. 3. See Advt.

The Railway Station-BAHNHOF-is at the centre of the town.

TAXIMETER CABS (horse and motor).—1 or 2 persons, 800 meters, 50 pf., for each additional 400 meters, 10 pf.; 3 or 4 persons, 600 meters, 50 pf., each additional 300 meters, 10 pf. From Railway Station 25 pf. extra.

Electric Cars (fares 10 to 25 pf.) traverse the principal streets.

The capital of the Prussian province of Hanover, on the River Leine, in a well cultivated flat country.

The old quarter is most interesting, whole streets still having the ancient houses; the modern residential quarters are on the north and east sides.

From Ernst August Platz, before the Station, Bahnhofstrasse leads into Georgstrasse, the chief thoroughfare of the town; to the left is the spacious Theater Platz, in which is the Royal Theatre.

The Königliche Schloss is in Leinstrasse, between the Railway Station and the river; daily 10 to 6; 25 pf.; old Schloss immediately opposite. Markt Kirche, near back of old Schloss, is of 14th century, tower 295 feet, fine stained glass. The old Rathaus faces the Markt Kirche; close by, No. 10, Schmiedestrasse, corner of Kaiserstrasse, was once Leibnitz's house, now the Industrial Museum. Provincial Museum in Masch Park, natural history collections, historical collections, paintings, and sculpture; daily, 10 to 3, free—Sunday, 11 to 2; another collection of pictures, with some sculpture, at the Gallerie, in Prinzenstrasse.

Kestner Museum, Friedrichstrasse, has collections of Egyptian, Greek, Roman, and other antiquities, coins, cameos, paintings, engravings, and 10,000 volumes; also a mediæval collection of rare worth—books, autographs, paintings, etc.; the Town Library is in the same building.

Adjoining the Museum is the new Rathaus (erected 1901-9), with large dome.

Welfen Schloss (Palace of the Guelphs—now a Technical School) is on the east side of Herrenhausen Allee, a broad avenue of limes on the north west side of the town leading to Schloss Herrenhausen, where George I and II lived; portraits, statue of Electress Sophia (died here 1714), great Fountains 220 feet high (Wed. and Sat), sculpture gallery. Berggarten, mausoleum.

In Georgs Platz, south from Theater Platz, is the Lyceum, with statue of Schiller. Permanent Industrial Exhibition, corner of Landschaftstrasse, 11 to 12, 25 pf. Ægidientor Platz, south of Georgs Platz, is an important tramway centre. East of Ægidien Platz, in Marienstrasse, is the Gartenkirche—in the churchyard lies Charlotte Kestner (the original of Lotte in Goethe's "Werther"), who lived at No. 4, Ægidienstrasse.

From south-east end of Georgstrasse, at Theater Platz, Theaterstrasse runs eastward into Königstrasse; this latter, with Am Schiffgraben, which runs roughly parallel to it, is distinguished by numerous fine residences. At end of Königstrasse, in a circular space, is a War Monument by Voltz (1884), beyond which is the Eilenriede, a beautiful wood; Zoological Garden in south part of the Eilenriede.

POST AND TEL. OFFICE.–In Ernst-August Platz.

ENGLISH CHURCH SERVICE.—Nicolai Capelle. Klages Markt.

H.B.M.'s VICE-CONSUL.—C. C. Stevenson, Esq.

U.S. CONSUL.—A. H. Michelson, Esq.

THE FREMDENVEREIN, Schillerstrasse, 29/I, near the Railway Station, gives every information on all subjects to visitors without charge. See Advt. under Hanover.

RAIL, see pp. 154, 155, 156, 158, 159, and 160.

Harzburg Bad.—*Stat.*—Pop. 4,500.

WALDPARK HOTEL BELVEDERE.—First class; beautiful position facing springs. Every modern comfort. English Church Service in the hotel. Suites with bath. See Advt.

GRAND HOTEL SCHMELZER.—First class, in finest position. Every comfort. Open all the year. Winter sport. Pension from Mks. 6. See Advt.

HOTEL HARZBURGER HOF.—First class. 200 suites and single rooms, equipped with every modern comfort. Close to the forest. See Advt.

HOTEL LUDWIGSLUST.—First class, highest and best position. Every modern comfort. Winter sport. Open all the year. Pension from M. 6.50. See Advt.

Harzburg, a fashionable summer resort in the Harz, occupies a fine position at the entrance to the valley of the River Radau, 770 ft. above the sea. Its many villas and gardens and pleasant promenades extend along the Radau Tal and up the neighbouring hills. South of the Station (1 mile) are the Juliushall Saline Baths, also the Krodo Quelle—the latter for drinking. Kurhaus at foot of the Burgberg, whence a bridge crosses to the grounds called the "Eichen"—(Oaks). **A few remains of Schloss Harzburg are on the Burgberg, 1,555 ft., whence is a fine view; here is the well-known Canossa Monument, an obelisk with medallion of Prince Bismark. The Radau Fall is 1½ mile up the Radau Valley. The paths in the vicinity of Harzburg are indicated by posts.**

RAIL, pages 163, 166.

Hausach, see page 458.

Heidelberg.—*Stat.*—Pop. 56,016.

HOTEL PRINZ CARL.—First class, foot of the Castle and close to Berg railway. Central position. See Advt.

SCHLOSS HOTELS—First class, situated in a unique position in an open elevated position adjoining Castle and gardens. See Advt.

MULLER'S VICTORIA HOTEL.—First class. Overlooking Stadt Park, 2 minutes from Station. All modern comfort. See Advt.

HOTEL DE L'EUROPE.—First class, beautifully arranged, with every modern comfort, large garden, 2 minutes from Station. See Advt.

GRAND HOTEL.—First class, near Anlage and Station. Modern comfort. Patronised by English and Americans, old reputation. See Advt.

HOTEL METROPOLE MONOPOL.—First class, quiet position on the Promenade. Modern and comfortable. Especially patronised by English families. Rooms from M. 3, Pension from M. 7.50. See Advt.

HOTEL SCHRIEDER.—Next to station. Quiet. All rooms on garden side from Mks. 2. Moderate charges. See Advt.

HOTEL LANG.—Family hotel, in quiet position, near Station. Every modern comfort. Excellent cuisine. Garden. Pension from M. 5. See Advt.

HOTEL AND RESTAURANT "ZUM RITTER."—Built in 1592, in German Renaissance style. Very interesting; finely painted and decorated hall. Electric light, Steam heating. See Advt.

PENSION PRIMOSOLE.—3, Riedstrasse, villa in large garden. First class; very comfortable pension from 4 m. 50 pf. One minute from Post and Station. See Advt.

PENSION CHATELAINE.—3, Gaisbergstrasse, near Station and public gardens. Garden with terrace and verandah, French cuisine. Baths. Full pension from M 4 to M 6. See Advt.

PENSION ROLANDA.—Anlage, 26. Well situated on the Promenade. Large covered Verandahs. Comfortable. English spoken. Pension from Mk. 4.50. See Advt.

CABS.—Taximeter Cab to seat 4, 1000 meters in town 50 pf. with 10 pf. for each additional 500 meters.

The chief Railway Station—HAUPTBAHNHOF—is on the west side of the town; immediately to east of the Station is one end of Leopoldstrasse, the principal promenade, leading across the town to the Schloss. 1½ mile distant. The climate is mild both in winter and summer; in summer there is plenty of good music, in winter good companies visit the theatre.

Heidelberg, in the Grand Duchy of Baden, on the River Neckar, is one of the most beautifully situated as well as most historically interesting towns of Germany; it is almost surrounded by wooded hills, whence the views are very fine.

Peterskirche, Gothic, of 15th cent., is at the east end of Leopoldstrasse; here Jerome of Prague published his theses. Heilig-Geistkirche, Gothic, 15th cent., is in the Markt Platz, at east end of Hauptstrasse, which runs parallel with Leopoldstrasse; in the choir are tombs of King Rupert and his wife Elizabeth. The plain University, erected 1711-15, is in Ludwigs Platz, a little north of Peterskirche; it was founded 1386, had its most famous period towards the end of the 16th cent., and is attended by about 1,300 students; the Library (Universitäts-bibliothek, contains 400,000 vols., 4,000 MSS., 3,000 papyri, and 3,200 old documents—some of the most interesting objects are to be seen in a room on ground-floor, on Wed., 2.0 to 4.0. free, other weekdays 50 pf. The Jesuiten Kirche, of 18th cent., is on north side of the University.

Rathhaus, 1701-1703, on east side of Markt Platz; in the hall are paintings. Modern Stadthalle, 1903 imposing facade on the Neckar side.

Town Museum of Art and Antiquities in the Cheliusschen Hause, 97, Hauptstrasse.

The Schloss, the great attraction, dominating the town, on a height, 640 ft. above sea, is a most magnificent ruin, a maze of shattered courts, halls, towers, and fountains, surrounded by gardens. The earliest building was erected near the end of the 12th cent.; a more extensive building was erected in the 14th cent., this being strongly fortified during the 15th and 16th cents., the ornate parts being additions of the 16th and 17th cents. In March, 1689, the evacuating French blew up the fortifications, and burned the palace. and, after an almost complete restoration, the final catastrophe was caused by lightning in 1764. In one part of the Schloss is a collection of miscellaneous antiquities and objects of art. The "Tun" of Heidelberg, in a cellar, is a monster 49,000 gallon cask. To view interior of Schloss and collections. 1 person 1 mark, 2 persons 1 m. 50 pf., 3 or more persons 50 pf. each.

The **Molkenkur** is a point of view, 345 ft. above the Schloss, 995 ft. above sea: the road ascends from the south side of the Schloss, or there is the funicular railway from the Kornmarkt up to the Castle, the Molkenkur, and the Konigstuhl. The environs of Heidelberg are very attractive, with views from the heights. Fine view from the Philosophenweg. On the north side of the River Neckar, half a mile east of the Alt Brucke, a road leads up to the Hirschgasse, passing a well-known students' tavern and duelling place.

In the Cemetery (Friedhof), two thirds of a mile south of the Hauptbahnhof, are the graves of several eminent men associated with the University.

Städtisches Verkehrs Bureau (Information Office), 77, Hauptstrasse.

POST OFFICE.—Opposite the Hauptbahnhof.

ENGLISH CHURCH SERVICE, at 46, Plockstrasse.

MEDICAL.—Dr. Reinhardt.

DEPOT FOR BRADSHAW'S PUBLICATIONS.—Bangel and Schmitt, Leopoldstrasse, 5.

RAIL, pages 136, 139A, 140, 142, 143.

Heilbronn.—*Stat.*—Pop. 42,688.

HOTELS: ROYAL; BAHNHOF; NECKAR.

Well situated on the River Neckar, one of the most interesting towns of Wurttemberg. From the Bahnhof, on west side of the town, Bahnhofstrasse leads east across the river to the Markt Platz—half a mile. On the north side of the Platz is the late-Gothic Rathhaus, containing curious clock made in 1580. Kilianskirche, dating from 1013, is a few yards east of the Markt Platz; tower 205 ft. high; in the choir is a carved wood altar and a ciborium. 200 yards south of the Markt are the Law Courts (Landgericht) in what was once an imperial palace and afterwards belonged to the Teutonic Order; adjacent is the Roman Catholic Church. Museum of antiquities, near river side, by the bridge (up stream) leading from Bahnhofstrasse. RAIL, p. 190A, 193, 194A.

Herrenalb, see page 458.

Hildesheim.—*Stat.*—Pop. 47,061.

HOTOPP'S HOTEL.—Well reputed hotel, facing the Central Station. Modern comforts. Garage. Restaurant. Rooms from M.2.50. See Advt.

ENGLISCHERHOF; KAISERHOF.

The Railway Station—Hauptbahnhof—is on the north side of the city.

Taximeter Cabs, 1 or 2 persons, 1,000 meters, 50 pf., and 10 pf. each 500 meters extra.

A very interesting old city of North Germany which has retained much that is mediæval and picturesque. From the Bahnhofs Platz the line of thoroughfare of Bernwardstrasse leads south in half a mile to the Altstadter Markt. At the east side of the Markt is the Gothic Rathhaus, built 1443; Knochenhauer Amthaus (Butchers' Hall), built 1529, is a wonderfully fine timber building; south of the Rathhaus is the Templer Haus.

A few yards south of Altstadter Markt, in Andreas Platz, is Andreaskirche, with choir dating from 1389; tower 385 ft. high. 200 yards south west of Andreaskirche is the Romanesque Dom, dating from 1055; the edifice has suffered from several alterations; in interior are bronze reliefs, sarcophagus of St. Godehard and tomb of St. Epiphanius; many objects of church art in the Treasury; cloisters, where is a rose bush 30 ft. high, stated to be 1,000 years old.

Godehardikirche, in Godehard Platz, quarter mile south east of Dom, built 1133-72, restored. Michaeliskirche, one third mile north west of Dom, built 1001-33, restored. These two churches are regarded as among the best Romanesque churches of Germany.

Romer Museum in former Martinkirche, 200 yards due west of Dom; miscellaneous collections.

RAIL, pages 155, 157A, 159, 166.

Hochenschwand, see page 458.

Homburg Bad.—*Stat.*—Pop. 15,000.

RITTER'S PARK HOTEL.—Hotel de Luxe, greatly enlarged in 1911. High class accommodation for English and Americans. First class cooking, also dietetic treatment. Pension during April, May, and June, September, and October, from 11 Marks. See Advt.

VICTORIA HOTEL.—First class (also 3 fine villas). Magnificent garden. Most of rooms face garden. Specially patronized by English and Americans. Renowned for its cooking. Situated near Park, Springs, Bathhouse, and Kurhaus. See Advt.

HOTEL AUGUSTA.—Beautifully appointed first class hotel, near Kurhaus, Springs, and Baths. Suites of rooms with bath, facing Garden. See Advt.

THE GRAND HOTEL.—First class hotel, situated close to the Kurhaus and Park, near the mineral springs. Electric light; lift. See Advt.

WEBER'S HOTEL NATIONAL.—English family hotel of old repute in fine position (corner of Luisen and Ferdinand-strasse), near the Park. Electric light. See Advt.

HOTEL BEAU SEJOUR and VILLA BEAU SITE.—Well situated, facing park, and close to the mineral wells and bath houses. Every home comfort. See Advt.

HOTEL ADLER.—Comfortable family hotel; open all the year. Every modern improvement. Pension from M. 8. See Advt.

TAXIMETER MOTOR CABS; electric trams. Frequent electric tram service to Frankfort.

BAD HOMBURG VOR DER HOHE, 630 ft. above sea, on a spur of the Taunus Mountains, is one of the most fashionable and popular watering places of Germany. The cold sparkling saline waters—with radium emanations—for drinking and bathing, good for affections of the digestive organs, gout, rheumatism, obesity, anæmia, and female ailments, are used by about 15,000 visitors annually. The "course" lasts four weeks; visitors' tax, 1 person 20 m., 2 persons 30 m., 3 persons 38 m. Tickets for one week 6 m. each person—a slight increase during June, July, and August. The season is from March to October.

The KURHAUS, in Luisenstrasse, running north west from the Station, is the principal resort; beside several handsome rooms and reading room there is a collection of antiquities found in the neighbourhood. In the Kur Park, to north of the Kurhaus, are the Springs, the property of the town—Elisabeth Brunnen, Stahlbrunnen, Augusta Victoria Quelle, Luisenquelle, Landgrafenbrunnen; the Kaiserbrunnen and Solsprudel are more generally used for bathing. Ludwigbrunnen is of special value in throat affections. First class air-cure, also Fango-Tonschlamm treatment. Inhalation rooms of the latest system. Before the Kaiser Wilhelm Bath is a statue of Emperor William I.

Music in early morning at the Elisabeth Brunnen, in the afternoon and evening at the Kur-Garten; frequent concerts, balls, and representations by good companies at the theatre.

At the west side of the town is the Schloss, rebuilt 1820-1840, occasionally the residence of the Imperial family—fine view from the Weisse Thurm (188 ft.); fees, to view interior of Schloss, 50 pf.; to ascend tower, 25 pf.

Interesting Roman remains on the Saalburg (1,380 ft.), about 4 miles north west.

ENGLISH CHURCH SERVICE.—Christ Church, Ferdinand Strasse.

CHURCH OF SCOTLAND.—Service in the Erloser Kirche (July, August).

EDUCATIONAL.—VICTORIA COLLEGE, Dornholzhausen. Founded by H.I.M. the late Empress Frederick. Home and Educational Establishment for gentlemen's daughters. Principal, Madame Rossbach von Griesheim.

For further details see the School Directory in Bradshaw's British Guide, page iii.

GOLF.—18-hole course in Homburg Park, quarter mile from Station.

PHYSICIANS.—Dr. Hoeber. Dr. Weber, Dr. H. Richartz, Dr. Pariser, Dr. Dammert, Dr. Baumstark, Dr. Reichelman.

BANKS.—Direction der Disconto-Gesellschaft, established 1851. Capital M.200,000,000. Reserves about Mk.80,000,000. All banking orders promptly executed. Letters of credit and cheques issued and cashed. Foreign moneys at current rates.

DEPOT FOR BRADSHAW'S PUBLICATIONS.—F. Schick.

RAIL, pages 128, 150.

Hornberg, see page 458.

Ilmenau.—*Stat.*—Pop. 11,200.

HOTELS: LÖWE; TANNE.

A pleasant little town and summer resort, 1,565 ft. above sea, on the River Ilm, in the duchy of Weimar. A Kurhaus and several bath establishments. Numerous fine walks, with post indications. To the Schwalbenstein, 2,250 ft., where Goethe composed part of Iphigenia (March, 1779). RAIL, pages 152, 170A.

[The **Kickelhahn,** 2,830 ft., one of the loftiest heights of the Thuringia Forest, about 2½ miles south of Ilmenau; a delightful walk through woods, passing the grand-ducal lodge of Gabelbach. Goethe often spent the night on the summit of the Kickelhahn.]

Ilsenburg.—*Stat.*—Pop. 4,100.

HOTEL ROTHE FORELLEN.

A thriving village of iron-workers, with a Schloss of Prince Stolberg-Wernigerode, formerly a Benedictine Abbey, where is a collection of antiquities. Church of 12th cent. The chief interest of Ilsenburg is that it lies at the entrance of the Ilse Thal, one of the most romantic valleys of the Harz, a series of rock, waterfall, and forest scenes. RAIL, page 166.

Jena.—*Stat.*—Pop. 38,487.

HOTELS: SCHWARZER BAR; DEUTSCHES HAUS; SONNE.

The Station of the Weimar-Gera line is on south side of town; the Station of the Saale line is on the north side.

An old university town (about 2,000 students), pleasantly situated on the River Saale. The handsome new University building (1908) contains a valuable archæological museum. At the Stadtkirche is a figure of Luther in relief. The new University occupies the site of the old Schloss. Tablets indicate houses where illustrious men have lived. The battlefield of 14th Oct., 1806, is to the north of the town.

RAIL, pages 152, 170.

Kiel.—*Stat.*—Pop. 211, 627.

SEEBADEANSTALT DÜSTERNBROOK.-First class establishment, with every modern comfort. Open from May to October. See Advt.

HANSA HOTEL.—Facing the Central Station. Equipped with every modern comfort. Suites and single rooms with bath and toilette. Hot and cold water supply in every room. See Advt.

CONTINENTAL HOTEL.— Comfortable, near Station and Royal Mail Steamer piers. Modern comforts. Rooms from M. 3. See Advt.

A very old town, finely situated at the south end of the Kieler Hafen; the chief naval station of Germany, and a great centre of trade between the islands of Denmark and the Continent. The KAISER WILHELM CANAL, connecting the North Sea with the Baltic, flows into the Kieler Hafen at **Holtenau**, a little to the north of Kiel; it was opened in 1895, the total cost being £7,800,000; the length from the Kiel end to the North Sea end at **Brunsbuttel** near the mouth of the Elbe, is 60 miles, the depth is 30 ft., width at surface 220 ft., at bottom 70 ft.; the largest war ships may pass through. The harbour is protected by forts at Friedrichsort and Moltenort, near the north end of the Hafen.

One part of Kiel consists of narrow streets of old houses, but a fine modern quarter is on the north side. The Nicolaikirche is near the middle of the town, with interesting ancient houses close by; north east of Nicolaikirche is the Schloss, once the residence of the Dukes of Holstein—in the Garden is a war monument. North of the Schloss is the University. At the old University, in Kattenstrasse, is a Museum of National Antiquities. The Thaulow Museum, in the Sophienblatt, opposite the Railway Station, has a fine collection of wood carvings. In the Garden of the Imperial Yacht Club is a monument to Herr Krupp.

H.B.M.'s VICE-CON.—A. Sartori, Esq., M.V.O.

GOLF.—9-hole course at Kitzeberg, 20 mins. by steamer.

RAIL, pp. 166A, 168, 169.

Kissingen.—*Stat.*—4,755.

ROYAL KURHAUS HOTEL.-Beautifully situated; mineral baths in the house. First class hotel. See Advt.

HOTEL VICTORIA and HOTEL KAISERHOF.—First class family hotels; with lift; garden. G. Liebscher, proprietor. See Advt.

HOTEL DE RUSSIE.—First class hotel, overlooking the Kurgarten, opposite the mineral spring. Electric light; lift. See Advt.

GRAND HOTEL METROPOLE.—First class hotel, with every modern comfort; in the best, and open, position. See Advt.

The Railway Station—Bahnhof—is on the south side, half a mile from the Kurhaus and centre.

A favourite watering place, 660 ft. above sea, picturesquely situated in the valley of the River Saale, with wooded hills all round. The virtues of the waters were known in the 16th century; they are for drinking and bathing, and are of great service in digestive troubles, liver complaints, obesity, heart disease, rheumatism, gout, female ailments, anaemia, etc. There are many resident medical men, and about 33,980 visitors annually. The Kurtax is in three grades—1st class, 30 M.; 2nd class, 24 M.; 3rd class, 14 M.; other members of a family and accompanying servants at a reduced rate.

From the Bahnhof, Prinzregentenstrasse goes north across the handsome well built town. One third mile from the Bahnhof, back from west side of Prinzregentenstrasse, is the Royal Kurhaus, with the Kurgarten extending behind; here the scene is very animated at the early drinking of the waters, 6.0 to 8.0 a.m., and also at the evening promenade—band on each occasion. West of the Kurgarten, across the river, is the Prinz-Regent Luitpold Bad, with, close by, the Casino.

There is plenty of good music, and during the season performances at the theatre every day.

Rathhaus in the Markt, at north end of Prinzregentenstrasse. Roman Catholic church in Salinenstrasse, on east side of town; Marien Kapelle still further east, by the Cemetery. Protestant Church, east side of Prinzregentenstrasse, opposite the Kurhaus. Kissingen was the scene of a battle between the Bavarians and Prussians, July 10th, 1866, ending in the discomfiture of the former; monument to the fallen near the Cemetery.

1½ mile north of Kissingen, by the River Saale, are some Saline Springs, with an extensive lately renovated bath house (Salinenbad). Steamers from and to Kissingen about half hourly.

POST OFFICE.—Ludwigstrasse, running off east side, north end, of Prinzregentenstrasse.

ENGLISH CHURCH SERV.—At All Saints Church, north end of Salinenstrasse.

GOLF LINKS.

RAIL, page 195.

[**Bocklet.** ROYAL KURHAUS HOTEL.

A small bathing place with very strong chalybeate springs and mud baths, 6 miles north of Kissingen. Diligence, page 373.]

Kleve.—*Stat.*—Pop. 16,687.

HOTELS: PRINZENHOF; BAD; ROBBERS.

An attractive health resort, on the slope of a hill that once was the bank of the River Rhine. The waters of the chalybeate spring are beneficial in nervous complaints.

On rising ground is the former Ducal Palace, known as the Schwanenburg, used as law courts and prison; the tower, Schwanenthurm, erected 1439, is 180 ft. high.

Stiftskirche, of 14th cent., an imposing brick built Gothic edifice, in the Markt Platz, on south side of the Schwanenburg; interesting monuments. At the Rathhaus, west of the Schwanenburg, is a collection of antiquities and pictures.

On the west side of the town is the extensive Thiergarten, with, to south, the Klever Berg, 335 ft.

RAIL, pages 118B, 120A, 126.

Königsberg.—*Stat.*—Pop. 245,994.

HOTELS: DEUTSCHES HAUS; BERLINERHOF.

The principal Railway Stations—Ost Bahnhof and Sud Bahnhof—are in the south west part of the city, within half a mile of the business quarter.

An important city on the River Pregel. At a very short distance north of the Ost and Sud Stations is the river quay, and near the bridge to east are the Börse (Exchange) and Rathhaus, with, a little further, the Dom; in the Stoa Kantiana, by north side of the Dom, is the grave of Immanuel Kant (died 1804). The Schloss, a quarter mile north of the Dom, has a high tower; in the north wing is a museum of antiquities. Extending north of the Schloss is the Schloss Teich, a picturesque lake with gardens at the sides. The University lies back from the south west side of the Schloss Teich; about 1,100 students. Stadt Museum in Königstrasse, east of the Schloss—a good collection of pictures.

H.B.M.'s VICE-CONSUL.—O. Birth, Esq.

RAIL, pages 174, 174A, 175, 176, 178A, 178B.

Königsfeld, page 459.

Königssee.—*Stat.*

HOTEL SCHIFFMEISTER.—Comfortable modern hotel, having fine view over the lake. Garden; garage and pit. See Advt.

The Königssee, sometimes called the Lake of St. Bartholomew, 1,975 ft. above sea, in Upper Bavaria, is the most beautiful lake in Germany. It is about 6 miles long and 1¼ mile broad, surrounded by mountains, some of them rising sheer from the beautiful green waters to a height of 6,500 ft. The village of Königssee is on the north side of the lake; other delightful spots are the wooded point of Kessel and St. Bartholomew point, where are a chapel and former hunting box. Regular motor boat service and private motor and rowing boats on hire; duration of journey round lake, two hours. Separated by about half a mile from the Königssee is the **Obersee,** another beautiful small lake.

RAIL, page 203C; Boat service, 203C.

Konigswinter, page 449A.

Konigstein.—*Stat.*—Pop. 2,500.

An attractive little town of the Taunus region, 1,190 ft. above sea, whence several interesting excursions may be made. Imposing ruins of old Schloss; modern chateau of the Grand Duke of Luxemburg. About half a mile distant is the ruined old Schloss Falkenstein.

RAIL, page 150.

Kreuznach.—*Stat.*—Pop. 22,860.

HOTEL ORANIENHOF.—Well situated, close to the Kurhaus; baths in the hotel; large garden, etc. See Advt.

GRAND HOTEL ROYAL D'ANGLETERRE.—First class and up-to-date in every respect. Facing Kurpark. Apartments with radium, thermal, and fresh water baths. See Advt.

On the River Nahe, which separates the Neustadt, on west side, from the Altstadt and Bath quarters, on the east side. Thousands of persons come in the season to bathe in the saline waters, which are highly beneficial in scrofulous and skin diseases, affections of the eyes and ears, cancerous growths, rheumatism, heart disease, obesity, etc.; some of the waters, for drinking, contain iodine and bromine. The Kurhaus, where is a large Inhalatorium, is pleasantly surrounded by gardens—an animated scene during the morning and evening; music three times daily. Handsome new Bath House; new Kurhaus in course of construction.

In the Altstadt are Wilhelmskirche, Wolfgangskirche, Helig-Kreuzkirche, and Pauluskirche; Niklauskirche is in the Neustadt. A small museum of antiquities at the School in Kreuzstrasse (Altstadt); on north east side of the Altstadt, near the railway, is a fragment of a Roman fortification, known as the Heidenmauer (Heathen Wall). Across the river on west side of the Altstadt rises the Kauzenberg (490 ft.), where are the ruins of a castle.

The Baths of **Karlshalle** and **Theodorshalle** (HOTEL TULLIUS; SCHEIBER), with a Kurhaus, are about 1½ mile south of Kreuznach.

ENGLISH CHURCH SERVICE.—Church a little north of the Kurhaus, close to the bridge.

ENGLISH PHARMACY.—Schwanen Apotheke, near English Church. Prescriptions accurately dispensed with pure drugs. Large assortment of English and American Patent Medicines.

RAIL, pages 125, 125A.

Laach may be reached from Niedermendig, 3½ miles, by a good road (carriage 4 mk.), or by tramway from the Krahnenberg at Andernach, 7 miles, fare 1 m. 50 pf.

HOTEL MARIA LAACH, close to the Abbey.

The Laacher See, 900 ft. above sea, is an almost circular basin of water, about 1½ mile across, 5 miles round, 175 feet deep at the middle. It is not regarded as a crater, but is the result of volcanic action. Many traces of scoriæ, pumice, etc. On the south west bank of the lake is the Benedictine Abbey of Laach, founded 1093, in its day one of the wealthiest and most important of German abbeys; the noble Romanesque Church (1156) is of great architectural interest; the conventual buildings are modern.

Langenschwalbach, or Schwalbach.—*Stat.* —Pop. 3,000.

HOTEL ALLEESAAL.—Near the Royal Bath house, first class hotel. Patronized by the late King and Queen when Prince and Princess of Wales. See Advt.

GRAND HOTEL DUKE OF NASSAU.—First class hotel; every modern comfort. Electric light; lift. Rooms with bath. Arrangements for prolonged stay. English and American clientèle. Open from May to October.

HOTEL VICTORIA PENSION.—Exceedingly well situated. Patronized by English families. Electric light & electric lift. Moderate charges. See Adv.

Schwalbach, or Langenschwalbach, the principal town of the Unter Taunus district, on the north slope of the Taunus mountains, 1,043 ft. above sea, is a much frequented fashionable health resort; beautifully situated in a valley; mild dry air, refreshingly cool in summer. Average July temperature 70° Fahrenheit. The waters, impregnated with iron and carbonic acid, for drinking and bathing, are specially favourable in nervous and heart affections, anæmia, etc. The mud baths are much used in female ailments, gout, and rheumatism. Handsome new Bath House, erected at a cost of 500,000 marks. Season May until October. Kursaal (entirely rebuilt in the winter of 1912–13), with reading room, etc. Music—morning, afternoon, and evening—at the Springs or the Kursaal. Pleasant promenades connect the principal springs, and there are many walks in the woods. In the Weinbrunnenthal are lawn tennis and croquet grounds. Fishing and shooting are to be had. Visitors' tax, 6 M. for the first week, for the season 20 M.

ENG. CH. SER. at Christ Church, Frankfurterstr.

MEDICAL.—Dr. Mills, Dr. Oberstadt, Dr. Frickhoeffer, Dr. Pfeifer.

SANATORIUM LANGENSCHWALBACH DR. STRAKOSCH.—In the finest and most beautiful position in large park. All the most modern improvements and conveniences, All kinds of baths—mud, carbonic acid gas, etc., can be taken in the house, Rontgen and radium treatment. Well adapted for winter, and opportunity for all kinds of sport,

GOLF.—9-hole course.

The Kurverwaltung has offices at 35, Brunnenstrasse, and gives all information, verbally or by letter, without charge.

RAIL, page 146.

Leipsic, or Leipzig (Saxony) —*Stat.*—Pop. (1910) 589,850. (*Plan in Special Edition, or post free 3d. stamps).*

HOTEL DE PRUSSE.—First class, old established, on Promenade. Central, comfortable, and moderate. See Advt.

HOTEL HAUFFE.—First class hotel, on the Promenade, near the Stations. Electric light; lift. See Advt.

HOTEL SEDAN.—Facing Station. Most comfortable first class hotel. Lift; electric light; central heating. Baths. Moderate prices. See Ad.

GRAND HOTEL DE ROME.—Entirely new first class modern hotel, close to Station; hot and cold water in each room; moderate tariff. See Advt.

VICTORIA HOTEL.—Central position. Comfortable and moderate. Entirely renovated and enlarged. Rooms from Mks. 2.50. See Advt.

HOTEL FURSTENHOF.—First class new hotel, with the latest improvements and conveniences. Close to Central Station. Hot and cold water supply in every room. Rooms from 4 M. See Advt.

The HAUPTBAHNHOF, in the north central part of the town, is regarded as the largest railway station in Europe; the BAYERISCHE BAHNHOF is in a south central situation, less than a mile south of the Hauptbahnhof.

TAXIMETER MOTOR CABS.

Leipsic is a town of great commercial importance; it is the centre of the book and fur trades of Germany, the seat of the supreme law courts of the Empire, and its University is ancient and renowned. It lies in a flat district near the confluence of the rivers Elster, Pleisse, and Parthe.

From the Hauptbahnhof, a fine thoroughfare leads south in a few minutes to the Augustus Platz, where are the University, Museum, Post Office, and Theatre.

South of the Augustus Platz, in the Konigs Platz, is the Grassi Museum, containing Ethnographical and Art-Industrial collections, open daily (Monday excepted) 10.0 a.m. to 3.0 p.m. Westward from the Grassi Museum is a cluster of fine buildings; here are the Imperial Law Courts; the University Library, 550,000 vols., 6,000 MSS.; the Gewandhaus (Drapers' Hall); and the famous Conservatorium of Music.

North west of Königs Platz is the new Rathaus (Town Hall) which occupies the site of the Pleissenburg (Citadel), view from tower. Weekdays 1.0 p.m. to 3.30 p.m., Sun. 9.30 a.m. to 1.0 p.m.

The University is located in the Augusteum, on the west side of Augustus Platz; it was founded 1408, and there are about 4,000 students; in the Aula are Reliefs by Rietschel, statues, and mon. to students who fell in the war of 1870-1. At the Museum, also on the Augustus Platz, are collections of pictures, engravings, etc.

On the west side of Augustus Platz the busy Grimmaischestrasse leads to the Markt Platz, where is the old Rathhaus. War Mon. on north side of square. A little way off north side of Grimmaischestrasse, in Nikolaistrasse, is Nicolai Kirche, where Luther is said to have preached. In Grimmaischestrasse, near the Markt Platz, is Auerbach's Keller, a restaurant, scene of part of Goethe's "Faust."

The Booksellers' Exchange (Buchhändlerhaus), handsome building in Renaissance style, is in Hospitalstrasse, to the east of Augustus Platz; Museum, rare books and specimens of printing. Exchange (Börse).

Thomas Kirche, lofty roof—mon. of Bach; Johannes Kirche (Bach buried here), Luther Kirche, Nicolai Kirche, Matthäi Kirche, Pauliner Kirche, Peter Kirche, lofty spire. Many statues. Reformation Monument (Reformations Denkmal), on Johannes Platz, off west side of Augustus Platz.

The Battle of Leipsic, 16th–19th October, 1813, was fought over ground to south east of the city.

immense monument on the battlefield, 300 ft. high, erected at a cost of about £300,000.

West of Leipsic is the industrial suburb of Plagwitz (reached by tram) where is the Palmen Garten with ornamental grounds, concert hall, etc.

The Leipsic Fairs—Easter and Michaelmas are attended by a vast concourse of traders; New Year's Fair is not so important.

Königliche Porzellanniederlage (Royal China Depot), Göthestrasse, 6. Exhibition and Sale of Art China and China for household use. See Advt. under Dresden.

POST OFFICE, on the Augustus Platz.

ENGLISH CH. SERV.—In the Church in Seb. Bach Strasse.

AMERICAN CHURCH, Erste Bürgher Schule.

H.B.M.'s VICE-CONSUL.—R. M. Turner, Esq.

U.S. CONSUL.—R. N. Snyder, Esq.

GOLF. — 9-hole course, five minutes from Gaschwitz Station.

RAIL, pp. 158, 170, 173, 173A, 183A, 184A, 187, 188, 189A.

Lindau.—*Stat.*—Pop. 5,850.

HOTEL BAYERISCHER HOF.—Well situated on the Lake, near the Railway Station. Electric light and lift. See Advt.

LINDAUER HOF; REUTEMANN.

On an island just off the north shore of the Lake of Constance, near its east end; in mediæval times an important trading place. At the Rathhaus, erected 1422-36, is a collection of antiquities. Fine views over the Lake and of the Alps.

RAIL, pages 193A, 199. Steamer, page 369.

Linz, see page 450. **Lorch**, see page 452.

Lübeck.—*Stat.*—Pop. 98,656.

HOTELS; STADT HAMBURG; INTERNATIONAL; KAISERHOF; UNION.

A busy commercial city, once at the head of the Hanseatic League, with streets full of charming and artistic bits, reminders of mediæval greatness. The "marzipan" of Lübeck, a kind of almond cake, specially eaten at Christmas, is famous.

From the BAHNHOF, on the west side of the city, crossing the Puppen Brücke the Inner Holstentor is reached, whence Holstenstrasse leads in a quarter mile to the Markt Platz.

The noble Gothic brick Rathhaus, on north east side of Markt Platz, erected 1442, has gables, spires, and paintings on the north facade. An imposing flight of stairs ascends to the Bürgerschaftssaal and other chambers, all elaborately decorated. The Rathskeller, a restaurant below the Rathhaus, is interesting.

Marienkirche, a few yards north of the Markt Platz; erected in 13th cent.; this plain but very imposing Gothic edifice is the largest brick built church in Europe, and holds a high place in the history of architecture; it is 335 ft. long, transept 186 ft. across and 162 ft. high, nave 127 ft. high, spires 410 ft. high. Celebrated clock behind the high altar; the "Dance of Death," a painting, is in a side chapel.

Petrikirche, a few yards south west of the Markt Platz; Gothic, erected early in 14th cent.; in interior are monumental brasses, carved pulpit, curious old clock.

Domkirche (Cathedral), in south corner of the city, by the Muhlenteich, half a mile due south of the Markt Platz. Partly Gothic, built 1173-1335; towers 394 ft. In interior are high altar of 1696, and altar piece in the Greveraden Capelle; monuments and sarcophagi.

Museum, on south side of the Cathedral; built 1889-92. Collections illustrative of Lübeck industry and art, historical exhibits; natural history collection, commercial collections. On an upper floor is the Picture Gallery.

Library (120,000 vols., 1,000 incunabula, and nearly 1,000 MSS.), in the old Minorite Convent, in east central part of city, one third mile north east of the Markt Platz; in same building are collections of coins and medals.

Jacobikirche, north end of Breitstrasse, street running north from Markt Platz; Gothic, 14th cent.; altar in the Brömsen Capelle. Opposite west side of the church is the Hall of the Shipowners (Schiffergesellschaft), also the Merchants' Hall (Kaufleute)—both interesting.

Gerichts Gebaude (law courts), in north part of city, two thirds mile north of Markt Platz.

POST OFFICE in Markt Platz.

H.B.M.'s V.-CONSUL.-D.E.W. Eschenburg, Esq.

RAIL, pages 166A, 213, 213A.

Ludwigshafen, see page 454.

Magdeburg (Prus. Saxony).—*Stat.*—Pop. 279,629.

HOTEL MAGDEBURGERHOF.—First class hotel, in central position. Equipped with every modern comfort. Advt.

CENTRAL; CONTINENTAL; CITY.

Capital of the Prussian province of Saxony, a fortress of the first rank, and an important commercial and industrial town, situated chiefly on the left bank of the Elbe. Several iron foundries, engineering shops, and sugar refineries; beetroot, for the sugar, is much cultivated in the country round about. Magdeburg suffered terribly during the Thirty Years War, and when the town was stormed and sacked by Tilly, 1631, 30,000 persons perished.

From the Haupt Bahnhof the streets eastward lead to the Kaiserstrasse, a fine broad modern thoroughfare, running north and south, and a little further east, also running north and south, is Der Breite Weg, the principal business street of the town; still further east is the Elbe.

The DOM, or Cathedral (S.S. Maurice and Catherine), on the Dom Platz, off the east-central side of Der Breite Weg, is a noble edifice, erected 1208-1363, sometimes stated to have been the earliest attempt at Gothic architecture in Germany; height of tower 337 feet; in the interior are many interesting monuments.

A little north of the Dom Platz is the Liebfrauenkirche, of 11th cent., restored 1890-91. In the Kaiser Friedrich Museum are collections of pictures, sculpture, natural history, and objects illustrative of Magdeburg history.

Justizpalast (Law Courts), a fine building with two towers.

In the Altemarkt, off the north east side of Der Breite Weg, is equestrian mon. of Otho I; Rathhaus on east side of Altemarkt, here also is the Public Library. East of the Rathhaus, before the Johanniskirche, is a Luther monument. Friedrich Wilhelms Garten on south side of town.

H. B. M.'s. VICE-CONSUL.—E. Drake, Esq.

U. S. CONSUL.—A. W. Donegan, Esq.

RAIL, pp. 158, 160C, 161C, 162, 163, 164.

Mannheim, see page 454.

Marburg.—*Stat.*—Pop. 20,246.

HOTELS: PFEIFFER; RITTER.

An old University town, in a pleasant situation, on the River Lahn.

The great attraction of the town is the beautiful Gothic Church of St. Elizabeth, a gem of mediæval architecture; the two towers are 236 ft. high. The Church was erected, 1235-83, over the tomb of St. Elizabeth (died 1231), whose remains were removed and placed under the tomb of Conrad (also buried in the Church) in order to check pilgrimages. The sarcophagus of the saint is in the sacristy. High altar, screen, several monuments.

Lutheran Church of 14th cent., containing monuments. University, founded 1527; about 900 students. Rathhaus, 1512, in the Markt Platz.

The 13th cent. Schloss, on a height, 875 ft. above sea, is famous as the scene in 1529 of the argument upon the Eucharist between Luther, Melanchthon, and Zwingli, before Landgrave Philip the Generous. RAIL, pages 156A, 217.

Marienburg.—*Stat.*—Pop. 13,534.

HOTEL KONIG VON PREUSSEN; MARIENBURG.

A very old town, on the River Nogat, in east Prussia. The great Schloss, regarded as the finest mediæval secular building in Germany, was long the seat of the powerful Knights of the Teutonic Order (founded 1192). Marienkirche in the Hochschloss; in Chapel of St. Anna, close by, several of the Grand Masters lie buried. Ritter Saal, a fine hall. In the town are the Rathhaus, Catholic Church, and Marienthor, all of 14th cent.

RAIL, pages 175, 176, 178, 178A.

Mayence, see page 453.

Meiningen.—*Stat.*—Pop. 17,186.

HOTEL SACHSISCHER HOF; ERBPRINZ; HIRSCH.

Capital of the Duchy of Saxe-Meiningen, on the River Werra, with wooded hills all round.

Opposite the Station is a small park—the English Garden. To north is the Ducal Schloss, containing a picture gallery (mostly Dutch paintings), collection of coins, and a library.

At the Rathhaus, in Markt Platz, is a collection of antiquities. The Stadtkirche, rebuilt 1888, is in Markt Platz. Hof Theater, rebuilt 1909.

RAIL, pages 173B, 195.

Meissen.—*Stat.*—Pop. 35,865.

HOTELS: BLAUER STERN; ALBERTSHOF

A picturesque old city, on the River Elbe. The two towered Dom (much damaged by storm 1547, restoration completed 1908), on the Schlossberg, at the extreme north corner of the city, dates from 13th cent. The Albrechtsburg, by the Dom, 15th cent., is a large Schloss—several halls decorated with frescoes.

The Königl. Porzellan Fabrik (Royal Porcelain Manufactory) is 1½ mile south west of the city. Sale rooms and depots at Meissen, Dresden, and Leipsic. RAIL, page 183A.

Menzenschwand, see page 459.

Metz.—*Stat.*—Pop. 68,193.

GRAND HOTEL (formerly Hotel de l'Europe).—Well situated, with a fine garden before the house. Charges moderate. See Advt.

HOTEL ROYAL.—Kaiser Wilhelm Ring. First class modern hotel, opposite Station; fitted up with latest comfort and convenience. Rooms with baths. Garage. Rooms from M. 2.50. See Advt.

ANGLETERRE; METZ.

TAXIMETER CABS.—1 or 2 persons, 50pf. per 1,000 meters, and 10 pf. each additional 500 meters.

Metz is the strongly fortified capital of German Lorraine, garrisoned by about 25,000 men. The River Mosel flows by the west side of the town; an affluent, the Seille, flows on the east side. It is the Roman Divodurum; after being for centuries within the German Empire it became French by capture in 1552; in 1871 it was restored to Germany.

The Cathedral, two thirds of a mile due north of the Bahnhof, is a noble Gothic pile, of 14th-15th cent., in architectural importance little inferior to the Cathedrals of Cologne and Strassburg; the principal portal and the Porte de Notre Dame (east side) were rebuilt during recent restoration. Tower 387 ft. high; impressive interior, beautiful windows.

Opposite east side of the Cathedral is the Stadthaus, or Hotel de Ville, containing a small museum of antiquities and a few pictures. At the Bibliothek, 200 yards north east of the Cathedral, there are, besides the Library, a collection of Roman and other antiquities and a small picture gallery.

Beyond the city, on north east side, is Chambière Friedhof (Cemetery), where is a Memorial to French soldiers who fell at Metz in 1870.

RAIL, pages 210, 211, 212.

[The battlefields of Metz are principally upon the west side and east. The capitulation was signed on 27th October, 1870, at Frescati, 3 miles south of Metz; the surrender included the fortress, 3 marshals, 50 generals, 6,000 other officers, 173,000 men, flags, and all war material.]

MUNICH (*German* **München**).—*Stat.*—Pop. (1910) 596,467.

REGINA PALACE HOTEL.—New first class hotel, on the Maximilian Platz; fine position. Excellent sanitary arrangements. 200 rooms from 5 m.; 60 bath rooms. Modern comforts. See Advt.

HOTEL BAYERISCHER HOF.—Beautiful situation on the Promenade Platz. Electric light; lifts. See Advts.

GRAND HOTEL BELLEVUE.—First class. Rebuilt. Every modern convenience. See Advt.

HOTEL CONTINENTAL.—First class and up to date in every respect. Largely patronised by English and Americans. Every modern improvement and comfort. See Advt.

FOUR SEASONS HOTEL.—RUSSISCHER HOF.—Well situated. Maximilianstrasse, in the centre of the town, near the theatres, Museum, etc. Electric Light. Lift. See Advt.

RHINE HOTEL.—Situated near the Central Station. Lift; electric light. See Advt.

PARK HOTEL.—First class. 160 rooms and salons. Centrally situated, facing Maximilian Park. Every modern comfort. Garage. Moderate terms. See Advt.

HOTEL LEINFELDER.—First class family hotel, opposite Botanical Garden. Every modern comfort. Apartments with bath. Moderate terms. See Advt.

HOTEL MARIENBAD.—Barerstrasse, 11 and 20. First class renowned family hotel. Quiet but central position. All modern comforts. Garden; garage. See Advt.

CENTRAL HOTEL, facing Central Station.—Modern, comfortable, and moderate. Viennese cuisine. Under new management. Rooms from M. 2.50, Pension if desired. See Advt.

HOTEL STACHUS.—Karlsplatz. Family hotel with every modern comfort. Newly re-built, good restaurant. Rooms from M. 3. Pension from 7 Marks. See Advt.

GRAND HOTEL GRUNWALD.—First class, opposite Central Station. See Advt.

HOTEL ENGLISCHER HOF.—Centrally situated, near the Post Office and Royal Theatres. Electric light, central heating, telephone. See Advt.

HOTEL WOLFF.—Opposite Central Station. Comfortable family hotel. Modern comforts. Rooms from Mks. 2.50. See Advt.

HOTEL DEUTSCHER KAISER.—Good second class hotel, close to Central Station. 400 rooms from 2 M. Modern comforts. See Advt.

GRAND HOTEL SAVOY.-Karlstor. New, modern and central. Most comfortable and moderate. American bar. Daily concert. Rooms from 2 m. See Advt.

HOTEL DE L'EUROPE.—Facing the Central Station (southern exit), 150 rooms. Moderate terms. See Advt.

HOTEL BAMBERGERHOF.—Good second class hotel. Central. All modern comforts. Rooms from 2 Marks. Pension. See Advt.

PENSION QUISISANA.—First-class Pension, situated 84, Theresienstrasse, next the Pinakotheks. Excellent cooking. Highly recommended. See Advt.

PENSION WASHEIM.—6, Türkenstrasse. First class; very comfortable; central. Good cuisine. Baths; lift. Pension from M. 5.50. See Advt.

PENSION STELLA.—7, Prinz Ludwigstrasse. First class. Central, close to galleries, museums, theatres, &c. Excellent table. Pension from 6 marks upwards. See Advt.

PENSION TOUSSAINT, Briennerstr, 8. First class, in fine central position. Pension from 6 to 12 M. See Advt.

PENSION FELDHUTTER.—5, Elisenstrasse. Close to Station. Most comfortable. Room with breakfast Mks. 3. Pension from Mks. 6. All modern comforts. See Advt.

HOTEL PENSION HELIOS.—6, Sonnenstrasse. Most comfortable. Central and open position. All modern comforts. Rooms from Mks. 2. Pension from M. 5.50. See Advt.

RESTAURANT PREYSING PALAIS.—27, Residenzstrasse. Most-up-to-date. The building, dating from 14th century, and its decorations are most interesting. See Advt.

BEER SALOONS AND GARDENS.—These are very numerous, beer being one of the great specialities of Munich. The Hofbrauhaus, in the Platzl, to south of Maximilianstrasse, is one the sights of the town. Though these establishments are well conducted and should be seen, ladies may find the excessive smoking disagreeable.

MUNICH, capital of the Kingdom of Bavaria, in an elevated situation, 1703 ft. above sea level, on the south side of a flat sterile district, on the River Isar. Its name is derived from the monks (Mönche), who founded a convent here about 960. Modern Munich is specially identified with progress in German art, its leading position being mainly due to King Ludwig I and the eminent men who assisted him.

The Central Railway Station (Central Bahnhof) is a very fine building on the west side of the town; the Ost Bahnhof, less important, is about two miles distant from the Central, and is on the east side of the town.

TAXIMETER AND MOTOR CABS.

From Bahnhof Platz, before Central Bahnhof, short streets lead to the broad Karls Platz, which under other names stretches right and left in a semi circle. A glance at some of the important places may be obtained in a walk of about four miles by following the street on the extreme right of the Central Bahnhof, Bayerstrasse, in its windings as far as the river; then turning to left, proceed along Steindorfstrasse as far as first bridge, Maximilianbrücke; here turn sharp to left into the fine Maximilianstrasse, where objects of interest present themselves right and left; continue along the Maximilianstrasse to a little beyond Max Josefs Platz, where, at Theatinerstrasse, bear to the left while still keeping almost in line with Maximilianstrasse; soon the walk will end near the broad Karls Platz near the Central Bahnhof.

The Königliche Residenz (Royal Palace) is in Max Josefs Platz, at the west end of the Maximilianstrasse, mid way going from the Central Bahnhof to the river, bearing slightly to the left. The Palace is in three sections, the Konigsbau on the Platz, the Festsaalbau behind, fronting the Hofgarten, and the Alte Residenz between. Sumptuous apartments in the Alte Residenz; jewels and objects of great value in the Treasury; in the Reiche Capelle is pocket altar of Mary Queen of Scots, miniature altars ascribed to Benvenuto Cellini, and costly gold and silver plate. In the Festsaalbau are Hall of Charlemagne, Battle Saloon, Ball Room, Throne Room, and other spacious rooms, all decorated. The Konigsbau (not usually to be visited) is an imitation of the Pitti Palace at Florence. Admission to Alte Residenz and Festsaalbau week-days, 10.45, 1 M.; for some parts an extra fee.

Alte Pinakothek and Neue Pinakothek, the former having some resemblance to the Vatican, are about half-a-mile north east of Central Bahnhof. Here are wonderful collections of pictures, vases, antiquities, etc. In the Alte Pinakothek the pictures, old masters, are arranged chronologically, according to schools of painting; many of the pictures are of world renown. The Neue Pinakothek contains modern pictures only. Alte Pinakothek open daily, except Tues. 9 to 4 (Sun., 10 to 3). Neue Pinakothek, open daily. 1 Mark; Sunday free.

National Museum, in Prinz Regentenstrasse. Rich collections of objects of art of every kind, illustrative of progress of civilisation in all countries. Daily (Mon. excepted) 9 to 4; free on Sun. and Wed., other days 1m. Before the Museum is the small but charming Hubertustempel.

The Schack Gallery, a new building (1908), in Prinz Regentenstrasse, contains fine examples of modern German work, and good copies of Italian and Spanish masters; daily, except Thurs.

10.0 to 2.0; Sun., 11.0 to 1.0; on Monday 1 Mark, free other days.

XIth INTERNATIONAL ART EXHIBITION, in the Royal Crystal Palace, under the Most High Patronage of His Royal Highness the Prince Regent of Bavaria. Organised by the Munich Artists' Association in conjunction with the Munich "Secession." 1st of June until end of October. Open daily from 9-6. Admission 1 Mark. Season tickets.

The Glyptothek, on **Konigs Platz, is a little north of Central Bahnhof. Gallery of ancient** Sculpture in thirteen halls. **Free on Mon., Wed.,** and Fri., 9 to 2 (in winter 10 to 4), other days 1 mark. At the two sections of the Deutsches Museum, in Maximilianstrasse and Zweibruckenstrasse are collections relating to natural science and engineering.

PERMANENT FINE ART EXHIBITION. — D. Heinemann. Lenbachplatz, 5 and 6. Valuable collection of modern pictures and works of the Old English and Brabizon schools. Admission 1 Mark.

EXHIBITION OF OLD WORKS OF ART AND OLD PICTURES. A. S. Drey, purveyor to the Royal Court, Maximilians Platz, 7, close to the Regina Palace and Continental Hotels. Paris Branch: 55, Avenue Champs Elysées.

JACQUES ROSENTHAL, 47, Briennerstrasse. Fine illuminated Manuscripts, Incunabula, and other rare books. Early prints, etc., etc.

Basilika (Basilica **of St. Boniface), in Karlstrasse,** off Luisenstrasse, **running up north of** Bahnhof Platz. **A fine modern reproduction of an ancient Italian basilica. Sarcophagus of** Ludwig I and **Queen Theresa; frescoes, etc.**

Frauenkirche, **midway between Central** Bahnhof and river, off **north side of Kaufingerstrasse,** Cathedral of Archbishopric **of Munich and** Freising; a Gothic brick **built edifice; towers** (357 ft.) not **completed; good music. Peterskirche,** south east of **Marien Platz, oldest church** of Munich. Theatinerkirche, **immediately by** north west corner of **the Konigliche Residenz,** is elaborately **decorated; royal vaults. Ludwigskirche,** in **Ludwigstrasse, cruciform church;** frescoes. **Michaelskirche, in Neuhauserstrasse.** a Court Church; **music much esteemed.** Mariahilfkirche, **on east side of the Isar, away** from the centre **of the town, on the south east,** in early Gothic **style; fine stained glass. Allerheiligen-Hofkirche (All Saints), on east side of Konigliche Residenz, very ornate, good music.**

Bibliothek (Royal Library), in Ludwigstrasse, running up north of the Konigliche Residenz. More than a million volumes, 30,000 MSS.; literary curiosties in the Cimeliensaal.

Justiz Palast, an imposing baroque building, surmounted by a dome, in Karls Platz.

University, in Ludwigstrasse, on left hand from centre of town.

Maximilianeum, at east end of Maximilianbrücke; paintings, etc.

Prinz Regenten Theater, on the Gasteighöhe. Hof Theater, in Max Josefs Platz. Residenz Theater, next to Hof Theater.

The Siegesthor (Victory Gate) is at north end of Ludwigstrasse; the Propylæa, a superb gate, in Luisenstrasse.

Armeemuseum, on east side of the **Hof Garten,** erected 1900-1904, in Italian Renaissance style. Collections of old weapons, flags, trophies, etc. Richly decorated hall. Daily, except Sat., 10.0 to 1.0; Sun., 1.0 to 4.0; free Sun., Tues., Fri., other days 1 Mark.

Neues Rathhaus, in Marien Platz, handsome Gothic building; numerous paintings Old Rathhaus, close by. Daily, except Sun., 2.0 to 3.0.

The Public Gardens are very attractive; in Ludwigstrasse and Maximilianstrasse handsome buildings are right and left, and there are objects of interest almost everywhere.

The Bavaria Statue and Ruhmeshalle (Hall of Fame) are on the south west of the town.

The Southern Cemetery (Alter südlicher Friedhof and Neuer südlicher Friedhof), in Thalkirchnerstrasse, just beyond Sendlinger Thor Platz, on south side of town, is a beautiful spot. The Northern Cemetery (Nordl. Friedhof) is at end of Luisenstrasse, north of Central Bahnhof.

POST OFFICE, on south side of Max Josefs Platz, close to Hof Theater.

H. B. M.'S MINISTER RESIDENT.—Sir Vincent Corbett, K.C.V.O. CONSUL.—L. Buchmann, Esq. V.-CONS.—A. Abbott, Esq.

U.S. CONS. GEN.—T. W. Peters, Esq. VICE-CONSUL.—A. Schlesinger, Esq.

CHURCH OF ENGLAND.—St. George's Church (new) Blumenstrasse. Chaplain Rev. D. Cowling. Holy Communion every Sunday at 8.0 a.m.; on 1st and 3rd Sunday of the month at mid-day. Matins 11.30, evensong 6.0. The site of the church has been given by the city authorities free of charge.

AMERICAN CHURCH, Salvatorplatz.

MEDICAL.—Dr. Karl E. Ranke.

BANK FUR HANDEL UND INDUSTRIE, FILIALE MUNCHEN (Darmstädter Bank); established 1853; Lenbachplatz, 4. Capital and Reserve M. 192,000,000. Letters of credit and cheques issued and cashed. All general banking business transacted.

ENGLISH CHEMIST.—Theatinerstrasse, corner of Perusastrasse, International Pharmacy. Large stock of all English and American Patent Medicines. Foreign prescriptions. English qualified dispensers. Telephone 2202.

ADOLPH SCHOBER, 2, Briennerstrasse. Ladies' Tailor, Dressmaker, High class Millinery. French models. Silk and Woollen goods. See Advt.

MUNICH LODEN MANUFACTORY, JOH. GG. FREY, 7, Maffeistrasse. Oldest German factory, and the only one in Munich. Complete outfit for mountain and other tours. Ladies' and Gentlemen's Sporting Suits. Waterproof Costumes ready made or to measure. Capes, Raincoats, etc. All sporting articles.

HOSIER AND HABERDASHER.—C. Wagner & Co., 7, Theatinerstrasse (Arco Palace). Depot of the genuine Dr. Jaeger's Wool underclothing, Dr. Lahmann's Sanitary Cotton underwear, Camelhair blankets. Fixed prices. English spoken.

OPTICIANS.—J. Rodenstock, 3, Bayerstrasse. **Eye Glasses of all kinds. Field Glasses, Photographic apparatus, Films, etc. See Advt.**

TOURIST OFFICES.—Official Bavarian Tourist Offices, formerly Schenker and Co. Agency of Thos. Cook and Son. Promenadeplatz, 16, and Hauptbahnhof (central building). Railway and Steamship tickets. Train de luxe and sleeping car suppliments. Conducted and inclusive independent tours. Daily Motor Car excursions in and around Munich. Automobiles on hire. Banking. Tours to Bavarian Royal Castles. Passion Play at Erl, near Kufstein. Tickets for Wagner & Mozart festival, theatres, etc. Luggage forwarded. A.B.R. Express. Fast or slow freight. Correspondents of American Express Co. Depôt for the sale of BRADSHAW'S GUIDES.

RAIL, pp. 192, 196, 197, 197B, 199, 200, 201, 202, 203A, 203B, 203C, 203D.

Munster-am-Stein.—*Stat.*

HOTELS: PARK; BAUM; LANGMACK.

Bad Münster-am-Stein is a pleasantly situated village, with many quiet attractions, at the base of the Rheingrafenstein and the Gans, 380 feet above sea. The saline radio-active waters are successfully used in female ailments, are specially favourable for children, and in cases of rheumatism, gout, neuralgia, heart affection, scrofula, etc. About 7,000 "cure" visitors. The handsome Bath Establishment contains all modern appliances. Mild climate with little rain. On the Rheingrafenstein, 770 ft., is a ruined castle of the 11th cent. On the Ebernburg, rising on the west side of Münster, are some ruins of a castle (part has become an inn) where Ulrich von Hutten, the reformer, was for a time (1520-22) protected by Franz von Sickingen.

RAIL, pages 125, 125A, 204A, 206.

Nauheim Bad.—*Stat.*—Pop. 5,123.

GRAND HOTEL METROPOLE and MONOPOLE.—Strictly first class. Every modern comfort and luxury. Numerous suites with baths. Grand location facing park. Personally conducted by the proprietor. See Advt.

JESCHKE'S GRAND HOTEL.—New first class hotel, with 200 rooms and 100 bathrooms, equipped with the latest modern comfort. See Advt.

GRAND HOTEL KAISERHOF.—First class hotel, with balconies, central heating, and every modern comfort; fine park. See Advt.

PRINCE OF WALES HOTEL.—First class, close to Baths and Park. All comforts. Moderate. See Advt.

PARK HOTEL.—First class family hotel, well situated adjoining the Park, with electric light and lift. See Advt.

CARLTON HOTEL.—First class, and very modern and comfortable house, facing Baths and Park. Moderate prices. See Advt.

HOTEL BRITANNIA (late Hotel de Londres).—First class, near Baths, Park, and Station. Lift. Full pension from 8 Mks. See Advt.

AUGUSTA VICTORIA HOTEL.—First class family hotel, well situated; electric light, lift. See Advt.

BRISTOL HOTEL.—First class house, directly opposite the Baths. Lift; electric light; garden. Rooms from 4 m., See Advt.

HOTEL DE L'EUROPE.—First class, exactly facing Baths and Kurpark. Every comfort. Moderate terms. See Advt.

KIRSCH'S HOTEL D'ANGLETERRE.—Close to Springs, Baths, Kurhaus; first class, quiet, and comfortable. See Advt.

Bad Nauheim is one of the most delightful health resorts of Germany—a bright, wonderfully clean little town, modern in plan and all its arrangements. The situation, 400 feet above sea level, on the wooded height of Johannisberg, a spur of the Taunus mountains, the River Usa flowing through the town, is very healthy; all round is an attractive fertile country intersected by wooded paths in every direction. The roads are good for motoring. The warm and cold saline springs, rich in carbonic acid, for bathing and drinking, are highly successful in the treatment of heart disease, gout, rheumatism, anæmia, female ailments, skin diseases, etc. Bath Establishment, with the latest appliances; Inhalatorium. Season begins at mid-April, ending mid-October. Kurtax, 1 person 25 m., two members of same family 35 m., each additional member of family 5 m. Handsome Kurhaus, with reading, billiard, and game rooms, etc.; extensive beautiful park, with lakes for boating and fishing; tennis courts. The modern Gothic Dankeskirche has a sculptured font and good west window. Rathaus in Markt-platz. Town band daily, frequent concerts, performances at the theatre; organ recitals.

Several pleasant forest walks and drives in the neighbourhood. At Ziegenberg is a Schloss with associations of Goethe; modern Schloss at Cransberg.

GOLF LINKS.—9-hole course, with club house.

ENGLISH CH. SERVICE at St. John's Church.

POST OFFICE.—Corner of Ernst Ludwig Ring and Kurstrasse.

RAIL, pages 128, 156A.

Neuenahr.—*Stat.*—Pop. 3,700.

HOTELS: PALAST; KUR; HOHENZOLLERN; KRONEN.

Neuenahr, 302 ft. above sea, is situated on the picturesque little River Ahr. Frequented by over 12,000 patients annually. The warm alkaline springs, 86°—120°, contain bicarbonate of soda, and are strongly charged with carbonic acid; an important new spring, the Willibrordus Sprudel, was discovered in 1904. Liver and digestive disorders, diabetes, pulmonary affections, and cases of chronic catarrh yield to the treatment by the waters. Well appointed Bath Establishment; magnificent Kurhaus; theatre. English Divine Service from June to September. On a height, 1,119 ft., are a few remains of Neuenahr Castle, of early 13th cent.; fine view. The valley of the Ahr is charming. Trout fishing; roads and paths lead in all directions through Neuenahr Forest.

The large establishment of the famous APOLLINARIS SPRING is situated here, and is annually visited by some thousands. It is the property of the "Aktien-Gesellschaft Apollinaris-Brunnen," and the water is exported to all parts of the world. The spring was discovered in 1851, and the number of bottles annually sold exceeds 37 millions. The Apollinaris water is mostly shipped by Rhine vessels from Remagen to Belgium,

Holland, and England, and is transhipped at the seaports to all transmarine places. (See also page 450).

RAIL, page 123D.

Neuwied, see page 450.

Nurnberg (Nuremberg).-*Stat.*-Pop. 333,142.

GRAND HOTEL.—First class modern hotel, close to the Station, opposite the Frauenthor Graben. See Advt.

SENDIG'S HOTEL WURTEMBERGERHOF.—Palatial first class hotel, facing Station. See Advt.

HOTEL GOLDEN EAGLE.-First-class. In centre of the city. All comforts. 110 rooms and salons. Lift. Electric Light. Central heating. Moderate terms. See Advt.

HOTEL VICTORIA.—Situated opposite Station Electric Light, Lift, Central heating. See Advt.

HOTEL AM STERNTOR (Christliches Hospiz).—Near the Sterntor, not far from the Railway Station. Every comfort. 100 beds from 1.50 M. Excellent cuisine. See Advt.

HOTEL DEUTSCHER KAISER.—Three minutes from Station. A comfortable, moderate, and well-appointed hotel. Rooms from 2.50 M. See Advt.

HOTEL KAISERHOF.—Central position, close to the Station and all sights. Large restaurant and Ratskeller. Rooms from M. 2.50. See Advt.

PRIVATE HOTEL TREFZER, 72, Königs Strasse.—Close to the Station. Modern comforts. Rooms with breakfast from Mks. 3. See Advt.

The principal Railway Station—CENTRAL BAHNHOF—is on the south side of the town, two thirds of a mile from the centre.

Nürnberg, on the River Pegnitz, is the most striking and interesting of the mediæval towns of Germany. Within the walls there is hardly a street, public building, or individual house, that is not an object of beauty and interest, so that the town may be justly regarded as one great museum of mediæval art. Suburbs have grown in modern times all round the walls, and Nürnberg is now the most important manufacturing and commercial town of South Germany.

From the Central Bahnhof, across the Bahnhof Platz, the town is entered at the Frauen Thor, whence Konigstrasse leads past St. Lorenzkirche to the Museums Brücke over the Pegnitz and the Haupt Markt, at the heart of the old town.

St. Lorenzkirche, erected 1283-1477, Gothic; sculptured west portal, with fine window above; in the choir is a beautiful work of art, the Ciborium (receptacle for the host), 65 ft. high, elaborately carved; before the altar is a suspended carved wood representation of the Salutation; many other objects of interest. When church is closed, fee of 40 pf.

Northward, across the river, from St. Lorenzkirche, is the Haupt Markt, where is the Frauenkirche, erected 1355-61, with curious 16th cent. clock over west entrance, shewing working figures at noon; fine stained glass; the Tuchersche Altar piece is very highly regarded.

In the north west corner of the Haupt Markt is the Schöne Brunnen, erected 1385-96, one of the most beautiful Gothic fountains in existence. Behind the Frauenkirche, in the Gänsemarkt, is a quaint fountain called the Gänsemannchen.

From the north west corner of the Haupt Markt the street leads to St. Sebalduskirche, with the Rathhaus opposite. St. Sebalduskirche, dating from 10th cent. a mingling of different styles, offers much to interest upon the exterior; interior contains St. Sebald's Monument, a masterpiece in bronze, reliefs, paintings, stained windows; when closed, fee 20 pf.

The Rathhaus, of 1616-22, in Renaissance style, includes an older building of 14th cent.; the modern part at the rear, Gothic, was added 1885-89. In the principal hall are frescoes designed by Dürer; staircase and ceilings decorated. On an upper floor is a collection of modern paintings. Bibliothek, to north of the Rathhaus, in an old Dominican monastery; 70,000 vols., 2,000 MSS., many literary curiosities.

At the top of Burgstrasse is the oldest building in the town, a five-sided tower, containing torture chambers.

The Kaiserburg, to west, at top end of Burgstrasse—a royal Bavarian residence, founded 11th cent., extended by Frederick Barbarossa 12th cent., restored mid 19th cent. Fee 50 pf.

At the north end of Albrecht Dürerstarsse which runs parallel (200 yards west) with Burgstrasse, is Durer's House, marked by tablet, containing mementoes. Law Courts, 100 yards west of Haupt Markt.

St. Egidienkirche, 18th cent., 300 yards north east of the Rathhaus, contains a Pieta by van Dyck. Jacobskirche, in south west part of town, 17th cent., contains carvings and pictures.

GERMANIC NATIONAL MUSEUM, at south side of town, quarter mile north west of the Central Bahnhof, in a former Carthusian Monastery. Extensive collections of antiquities, sculpture, paintings, military objects, etc. Many fine works in the Picture Gallery. Open daily 10.0 to 1.0 and 2.0 to 4.0, 1 m.; free on Sun.

Landesgewerbeanstalt, by south side of river, at east side of town; industral collections A few yards east is a museum of railway models.

In St. Johannis Kirchhof (Cemetery), half a mile beyond north west town gate, are buried Albrecht Dürer (died 1528), and many celebrated persons. Central Friedhof is a little further north west.

POST OFFICE.—Bahnhof Platz, immediately east of Station.

ENGLISH CHURCH SERVICE in summer.

H.B.M.'s CONSUL.—S. Ehrenbacher, Esq.

U.S. CONSUL.—G. N. Ifft, Esq.

BANKERS—ANTON KOHN. Letters of Credit, Exchange, and all banking business. Travellers' letters can be addressed here, etc., etc.

RAIL, pages 195A, 197, 202, 204, 204A.

Ober-Ammergau.—*Stat.*

HOTEL OSTERBECHL; WITTELSBACH.

Applications for apartments to Burgmeister.

A village of Bavaria, 2,745 ft. above sea, celebrated for the Passion Plays commemorative of a plague visit about 1633; wood and ivory carving the principal industry. About a mile west is a group in sandstone of the Crucifixion. The Bavarian royal castle of Linderhof is 7½ miles from Ober-Ammergau, erected 1870-8 by King Ludwig II; splendidly decorated; paintings, extensive gardens, grottos, elaborate kiosks, cascades; may be visited in summer, fee 3 mk.

RAIL, page 197B. Diligence, page 373.

Oberhof.—*Stat.*

SCHLOSS HOTEL.—The leading first class hotel, fitted up with every modern comfort and convenience. Facing Kurgarten and near golf links. Suites and rooms with baths. See Advt.

GRAND HOTEL WUNSCHER.—First class; open all the year, with every comfort; beautiful views. Close to the sports ground. See Advt.

HOTEL THURINGER WALD.—Family hotel, combining every comfort and convenience with moderate prices. Rebuilt 1912; open all the year. Pension from M. 7.50. Garage. See Advt.

A favourite summer and winter resort in the Thuringian forest, 2,706 ft. above sea. Air remarkably fresh and pure; the surrounding woods are intersected by good roads to attractive points of interest—the Dietharzer, or Schmalwasser Grund, is one of the loveliest valleys of Thuringia. Kurtaxe: one person for a week 3 m., two members of a family 5 m. 50 pf., three members 8 m., each additional member 1 m. 50 pf.; for any longer stay, twice the amounts stated. Ducal shooting lodge; church; three bath establishments. Well known centre for winter sports.

GOLF LINKS. RAIL, page 170A.

Oberlahnstein, see page 450A.

Oberstdorf.—*Stat.*

HOTELS: WITTELSBACHER HOF; LUITPOLD.

A beautifully situated summer resort in Bavaria, four hours from Munich, three hours from Lindau, in the Algau Alps, 2,665 ft. above sea; pure mountain air. The neighbourhood affords many attractive excursions, as to the gorge of the Breitach, the Spielmannsau, Freiberg See, Oythal, roundings of Oberstdorf are also most favour-Birgsau, etc. Good fishing. Winter sports.

RAIL, page 195.

Oberwesel, see page 451.

Odilienberg, the, 2,470 ft., a height of the Vosges Mountains, a resort of tourists and of pilgrims to the tomb of St. Odile. Convent of St. Odile. Paths indicated by finger posts. Reached from Barr, page 207A; a three hours walk, or carriage part way.

Oeynhausen Bad.—*Stat.*—Pop. 4,000.

HOTELS: KUR; VICTORIA; PAVILION.

A picturesquely situated and much frequented watering place on the River Werre; the warm saline waters are beneficial in cases of paralysis, rheumatism, bone diseases, scrofula. Handsome Kurhaus, erected 1909. RAIL, pages 155, 160.

Offenburg, see page 459.

Oldenburg.—*Stat.*—Pop. 30,242.

HOTELS: ERBGROSSHERZOG; BAHNHOF.

A pleasant town, capital of the Grand Duchy of Oldenburg, on the River Hunte. From west side of the Bahnhof the line of thoroughfare of Bahnhofstrasse leads to the Markt Platz, where are the Rathhaus and Lambertikirche. From the south east corner of Markt Platz a short street leads to the Residenz Schloss, 17th-18th cent., now unoccupied. South east of the Schloss, across the narrow river, is the Palais, the residence of the Grand Duke. A few yards from the Palais, to south west, is the Augusteum, with the grand ducal picture gallery; open daily, 10.0 to 1.0. Gewerbe Museum (Industrial Museum). RAIL, page 151.

Partenkirchen.—*Stat.*

HOTEL HAUS GIBSON, with Park Villa and Landhaus Gibson.—First class. In own large park. Garage. Winter sport. See Advt.

ALPEN KURHAUS SCHONBLICK.—First class modern family house, in own large grounds. Open all the year. Pension arrangements. See Advt.

A beautifully situated summer and winter resort of the Bavarian Highlands, 2,350 ft. above sea, at the foot of the Eckenberg; a good starting place for several excursions in the surrounding attractive country. Gothic church of considerable interest, District school of carving and design, open to visitors. Centre for winter sport.

ENGLISH CHURCH.

RAIL (Garmisch-Partenkirchen), page 197B.

Passau.—*Stat.*—Pop. 18,735.

HOTELS: BAYRISCHER HOF; MOHR.

Picturesquely situated on a rocky point at the junction of the Rivers Danube, Inn, and Ilz. Dom, nearly a mile due east of the Bahnhof, rebuilt 17th cent., a fine example of its kind. Rathhaus, 17th cent., east of the Dom. South of the Dom the Ludwigs Brucke leads towards the pilgrimage Church of Mariahilf, on a height.

RAIL, pages 195A, 203B, 204, 239B. STEAMERS, p. 368.

Peterstal Bad, p. 459. **Pforzheim**, p. 459.

Posen—(Polish **Poznan**).—*Stat.*—Pop. 156,691.

HOTEL STADT DRESDEN; ROME; VICTORIA.

TAXIMETER CABS.—1 or 2 persons 50pf. for 800 meters, with 10pf. for each additional 400 meters.

Posen, one of the oldest of Polish towns, and a strongly fortified place, is situated at the junction of the Rivers Warthe and Cybina; it was the residence of the Kings of Poland until the end of the 13th cent.

From the Haupt Bahnhof the entrance to the town is at the Berliner Thor, thence St. Martinstrasse runs eastward past the Royal Palace, a new Romanesque building, to Viktoriastrasse, from which the Berlinerstrasse, on the right, leads to Wilhelms Platz and the broad Wilhelmstrasse, a principal thoroughfare. At the west end of Wilhelms Platz is the Theatre. Königliche Akademie, containing the Kaiser Friedrich Museum and the Kaiser Wilhelm Library. At the north end of Wilhelmstrasse is the General Kommando (military headquarters). A little east of Wilhlems Platz is the Alter Markt, where, in the north east corner, is the Rathhaus, rebuilt 1536—tower 214 ft. high. Raczynski Library of 70,000 vols.

The Dom, rebuilt 1775, is in the extreme north east quarter; in the interior is a Chapel richly decorated with mosaics and paintings.

Handsome Stadt Theater, built 1909.

POST OFFICE.—Wilhelmstrasse.

RAIL, pages 175, 177A, 178, 179, 182, 218A, 219.

Potsdam.—*Stat.*—Pop. 62,243.

HOTELS: EISENBAHN; EINSIEDLER; SANS SOUCI. Tramways pass the Railway Station.

Potsdam is a pleasantly situated garrison town on the River Havel. From the Bahnhof, on south west side of the town, a bridge leads north in five minutes to the Parade Platz and Stadt Schloss, where are interesting rooms associated with Frederick the Great. At north side of the Schloss is Nikolai Kirche; opposite the church, to east, is the Rathhaus. 150 yards west of the Parade Platz is the Garnison Kirche, where, in a vault under the pulpit, Frederick the Great lies buried.

Half a mile north west of the Garnison Kirche is the Brandenburg Thor (gate), whence an avenue leads to the Park of Sanssouci. By the park entrance is the Friedenskirche, where, in the mausoleum, lie buried the Emperor Frederick III and the Empress Frederick. The Palace of Sanssouci was the favourite residence of Frederick the Great, whose rooms are preserved as originally arranged. The Picture Gallery (separate building) has a few paintings of no great interest. Between the Palace and the Orangery is the famous Windmill; in the saloons of the Orangery are sculpture and paintings. Paths lead south west in about a mile to the Neues Palais, or Friedrichskron Palais, erected 1763-1769 by Frederick the Great, at a cost of £450,000. The principal rooms are the Shell Saloon, the rooms of Frederick the Great, the Marble (concert) room, and ball room.

The Palace of Babelsberg, away on the east side of Potsdam, on opposite side of the broadening out river, is in an attractive park—works of art in palace.

At a short distance from the north side of Potsdam is what is called the Russian colony of Alexandrovka (a few houses and a Greek church), with, one third mile east, the Marmor Palais (Marble Palace), erected 1786-96—some paintings and sculpture.

The palaces are usually open from 10.0 until 6.0 (4.0 in winter); fee to each 25 pf.

BANKS.—Direction der Disconto-Gesellschaft, established 1851, Nauenerstrasse, 34A. Capital M. 200,000,000. Reserves Mk. 81,300,000. All banking orders promptly executed. Letters of credit and cheques issued and cashed. Foreign moneys at current rates.

RAIL, pages 164, 165B.

Pyrmont.—*Stat.*—Pop 3,900.

HOTELS: KUR; BAD; KAISERHOF; RASMUSSEN.

An attractive little town in the Emmer valley, one of the oldest bathing resorts in Germany; about 25,000 visitors annually. Hauptquelle, one of the principal springs, is chalybeate; the other, Salzbrunnen, is saline; the waters (cold) are good in nervous and dyspeptic complaints. Visitor's tax, 20m., additional members of family 10m. Chateau and Park of the Prince of Waldeck. Kursaal and theatre.

MEDICAL.—Dr. Seebohm.

RAIL, page 155.

Regensburg (Ratisbon).—*Stat.*—Pop. 52,624.

HOTEL GRÜNER KRANZ.—First class family Hotel. Every modern comfort. Apartments with baths. Omnibus at the Station. Garage. See Advt.

MAXIMILIAN; NATIONAL.

Regensburg the Roman Castra Regina, pleasantly situated on the River Danube, at the influx of the River Regen, is a city of great historic and artistic interest.

The Dom, dating from 1275 but not completed until 1534, is among the finest churches of South Germany. Length of interior 306 ft., width 125 ft., nave 132 ft. high; rich stained glass, ciborium (receptacle for the host), 56 ft. high, high altar enriched with silver, other altars in the aisles, paintings, monuments. At east end of the Dom, by the garden, in an old church, is an historical museum.

Niedermünsterkirche, a few yards from east end of the Dom, with palace of the bishop adjoining; in the narrow Kallmünzergasse, behind, is the Roman Catholic Vereinshaus St. Erhard, with collections, and a Gothic Dollinger Hall.

Rathhaus, 250 yards north west of the Dom, the oldest part of 14th cent.; old tapestry in the halls, portraits, flags, etc.; dungeons and torture chambers shewn.

St. Jakobskirche, 12th cent., generally called the Schottenkirche, half mile south west of the Dom; many figures carved on north porch. To east of the Schottenkirche, in Bismarck Platz, is the big Dominikanerkirche, having cloisters on south side. St. Emmeramskirche, on north side of Palace of the Prince of Thurn und Taxis, one third mile south west of the Dom; of 11th cent.; under pavement before the altar are buried Emperor Arnulph and Emp. Ludwig; monuments, relics of saints; the old abbey has been absorbed in the palace of the prince. Obermünsterkirche, to north east of St. Emmeramskirche, has some old frescoes.

RAIL, pages 195, 195A, 202.

[The **Walhalla** (Hall of the Chosen—Temple of Fame), on a wooded hill six miles north east of Regensburg, is a fine modern Grecian Doric temple, erected 1830-42 by King Ludwig I of Bavaria. In the richly adorned hall are names and busts of Germans and others deemed worthy of national recognition. Open daily, free, in summer 8.0 to 12.0 and 1.0 to 7.0, in winter 9.0 to 12.0 and 1.0 to 4.0. Rail from Stadtamhof (north suburb of Regensburg) to the Walhalla, page 204A.]

Reichenhall Bad.—*Stat.*—Pop. 4,208.

KURHAUS AXELMANNSTEIN AND GRAND HOTEL.—New hotel de luxe with every possible comfort. Cure bath house. Splendid trout and grayling fishing. See Advt.

HOTEL PANORAMA and DEPENDANCES PARK HOTEL, VILLA PAULA, VILLA QUISISANA.—First class; comfortable and moderate. Best position. All baths in the house. Pens. from Mks. 9. See Ad.

HOTEL PENSION ASTORIA.—Comfortable family hotel. Fine position; garden; beautiful views; excellent cuisine. Pension from 8 M. See Advt.

BURKERT.

A favourite watering and climatic health resort in Bavaria, 1,545 ft. above sea, on the River Saalach, with lofty picturesque wooded mountains on three sides, affording complete shelter from cold winds. Air remarkably pure. Saline, pine needle, carbonic acid, fango, and radium baths. The inhalation and pneumatic cabinets are among the best in existence. The waters are beneficial in cases of scrofula, chlorosis, female ailments, respiratory troubles, etc. Kurtax, 1 person 15m., each additional member of family 5 m. About 40,000 visitors in the season. Kurgarten, with frequent music. Romanesque Church with frescoes. Schloss Gruttenstein on a height.

The environs of Reichenhall are very attractive; there are numerous shady woodland paths on the level or of gentle ascent leading to interesting spots—the ancient monastery of St. Zeno, the ruined Schloss of Plain, the old Church of Nonn, etc. The more distant excursions are also very pleasant.

30 miles of preserved trout and grayling fishing in the vicinity; good centre for excursions to Königssee, Salzburg, &c.

ENGLISH CHURCH SERVICE in summer.

RAIL, page 200. MOTOR SERVICE, page 370.

Remagen, see 450. **Rhens**, see 450A.

Rippoldsau Bad, see page 459.

Rolandseck, see page 450.

Rostock.—*Stat.*—Pop. 65,383.

HOTELS: FURST BLUCHER; ROSTOCKER HOF.

A picturesque town, on the River Warnow, with a considerable shipping trade. Rathhaus, erected 1265, in Neuer Markt, about a mile north east from the Haupt Bahnhof; close by, north west, is Marienkirche, Gothic, 15th cent. Petrikirche, by the river, quarter mile east of the Rathhaus. University in Blucher Platz, quarter mile west of the Rathhaus; Grand-Ducal Palace on south side of the Platz. Jacobikirche, 14th cent., a few yards north of Blucher Platz. Marshal Blucher was born here.

H.B.M.'s VICE-CONS.—Heinrich Ohlerich, Esq.

RAIL, pages 178B, 181A, 213, 213A.

Rothenburg.—*Stat.*—Pop. 7,900.

HOTEL WILDBAD.—The best and largest in the town, patronised by American Society. See Advt.

HOTEL GOLDENER HIRSCH.—Central position, magnificent view of valley. Central heating; electric light; moderate charges. Garage. See Advt.

HOTEL EISENHUT.

Rothenburg, on the Tauber, one of the few surviving German mediæval fortified towns, is a most picturesque old place, with its towers, Gothic churches, town gates, and well preserved ramparts. Healthy situation, 1,396 ft. above sea.

In the Markt Platz is the Rathhaus, with a tower 230 ft. high; the older part is Gothic, the later part is a Renaissance building of 1578; very interesting interior. Jacobskirche, 1373-1471, with two towers (175 ft.), is a fine example of Gothic architecture; carved wood altars, beautiful windows. The Franziskanerkirche (with cloisters) and Wolfgangkirche are of great interest; several ancient houses. At the west end of the town is the Wildbad, which was founded in the year 1356 by the celebrated Mayor of the town, Henry Topler, and was rebuilt the last time in 1900. It is now a first class bathing establishment and health resort. In its large and shady park there is a good hotel and restaurant. The mineral baths include a large swimming bath. Good views of the town from the walks outside the walls. RAIL, pages 196A, 204.

Rüdesheim, see p. 452. **St. Blasien**, see p. 459.

St. Goar, St. Goarshausen, see page 451.

Sassnitz.—*Stat.*—HOTEL FAHRNBERG.

A beautifully situated sea-side place on the Island of Rugen—a favourite resort in summer. Excellent bath establishment. RAIL, page 181.

Schierke.—*Stat.*—Pop. 600.

BURG HOTEL.—Beautiful position, and most comfortable. Electric light. Central heating. Headquarters for winter sport. Open the whole year. See Advt.

BARENBERGER HOF. — First class, open winter and summer. Hot and cold water supply in all the rooms. Open air treatment. Pension from 8 M. See Advt.

A pleasantly situated Harz village, 1,850 ft. above sea, on the south side of the Brocken, above the Valley of the Bode, much frequented in summer, and in growing favour as a winter resort. Pure air and striking forest scenery; wooded heights and interesting rocks; good roads and footpaths. A centre for winter sports.

RAIL, pages 153, 165B (during the winter Elend is the station for Schierke).

Schlangenbad.—*Stat.*—Pop. 411.

ROYAL KURHAUS HOTELS: the NEW, the MIDDLE, and the LOWER KURHAUSER, 130 rooms and 80 rooms respectively. Fitted with every requirement of first-class hotels. Lifts in all Houses. See Advt.

HOTEL VICTORIA.—First class hotel, facing the Royal Bath House. Every modern comfort. Reasonable charges. See Advt.

A charming village and bathing resort in the picturesque valley of the Taunus district, 985 feet above the sea level. There are nine warm springs (temperature between 81 and 89 F.), which have a special reputation in skin diseases, nervous complaints, gout, rheumatism, and the diseases of women. There are three Bath Houses, the Upper, the Middle, and the Lower, the former of which, with the Kurhaus, was erected in the winter of 1912-13. The equipment includes a Radium Inhalatorium, Fango treatment, Terrain Cure, etc.

The forest and mountain scenery of the neighbourhood is remarkably beautiful, and there are miles of shady walks through the forest surrounding the village. Many excursions may be made to the Rhine and to places in the Taunus district.

ENGLISH CHURCH SERVICE in Summer.

MEDICAL.—Dr. Müller de la Fuente; Dr. Hannappel; Dr. V. Niessen.

BANK AND EXCHANGE.—Georg Winter.

RAIL, page 128.

Schleswig.—*Stat.*—Pop. 19,032

HOTELS: STADT HAMBURG; RAVEN.

A very old town—one long winding street round an inlet of the sea. Ducal Schloss, now a barrack. Romanesque Dom, erected early 12th cent., tower 365 ft. high; the reredos is a finely carved representation of the Passion.

RAIL, page 168.

Schlucht.—

HOTELS: ALTENBERG; FRANCAIS.

The Schlucht, also known as the Col de la Schlucht, is the deep picturesque ravine or pass connecting the Gerardmer Valley on the French side of the Vosges mountains with the Münster Valley on the German side. Near the summit of the pass, 3,775 ft. above sea, are Schlucht and Altenberg, a quarter of an hour walk distant from each other. All around the scenery is of a striking character; the wild mountain peaks, pine-covered slopes, and small lakes afford a prospect of unusual beauty.

Electric train service from Münster to Schlucht, page 211, and from Schlucht to Gerardmer, p. 69.

Schluchsee, see page 459.

Schmiedeberg.—*Stat.*—Pop. 5,000.

HOTEL GOLDNER STERN.

An old town, 1,470 ft. above sea, stretching along the Eglitz valley of the Riesengebirge (Giant Mountains). Carpets are made; mines of magnetic iron ore. Much sleighing and tobogganing in the winter. RAIL, page 182.

[The ascent of the **Schneekoppe**, or Riesenkoppe, 5,260 ft., is usually made from Schmiedeberg. The Schneekoppe is the highest point of North Germany; a granite cone, with a chapel on the summit, 17 cent., on the border of Silesia and Bohemia.]

Schonwald, see page 459.

Schwerin.—*Stat.*—Pop. 42,519.

HOTELS: STERN'S; DE RUSSIE; NORD.

In a good situation on the Lake of Schwerin. A few yards east of the Bahnhof is a sheet of water, the Pfaffen Teich, and back a few yards from the south end of the Teich is the Dom, a brick building of 14th-15th cent., tower 380 ft. high; grand-ducal tombs in interior. In the cloisters is the Library, 225,000 vols. Half a mile south east of the Dom is the Schloss, in Renaissance style, one of the finest modern palaces in North Germany. In the Alter Garten, by the Schloss, is the Museum, with a Picture Gallery and other collections.

RAIL, page 213.

The **Spessart** is an extensive forest district of Germany, full of fine trees, oaks and beeches, bounded on the north by the River Kinzig and on other sides by the River Main. The roads and paths are well indicated by the Verein der Spessart-Freunde; several secluded forest inns. Near the centre rises the Geyersberg, 1,920 ft. The district is usually penetrated from Aschaffenburg, from Lohr, from Wertheim, or from Klingenberg, and **Rohrbrunn** (GASTHOF ZUM HOCHSPESSART), on the west slope of the Geyersberg, is the best point whence explorations may be made.

Singen, see page 459.

Sinzig, see page 450.

Speyer (Spires).—*Stat.*—Pop. 23,045.

HOTELS: WITTELSBACHER HOF; RHEIN. HOF.

The Dom was long the burial place of the German emperors; at a celebrated diet held here in 1529, under Charles V, the name Protestant was first applied.

The Romanesque DOM, on the east side of the city, is regarded as the grandest building of its kind in Germany. It was built 1030-1100, in 1698 it was half ruined by the French; in 1794, after devastation, it became for a time a store house, not being restored to sacred use until 1822. Over the simple but imposing edifice rise two domes and four towers; length 147 yards, transept 60 yards, width of nave 15 yards, height of nave 105 ft., the west towers are 240 ft. high.

Close to the Dom, in a picturesque building 1909) is the Historical Museum of the Palatinate.

RAIL, pages 139A, 207.

Stettin.—*Stat.*—Pop. 236,113.

HOTELS: DEUTSCHES HAUS; NORD.

The BAHNHOF is at the south side of the town.

TAXIMETER CABS.—1 or 2 persons 50 pf. for 800 meters, and 10 pf. extra for each 400 meters more.

On the River Oder, an important shipping and manufacturing town, has some quaint old parts and handsome new quarters, but for the general traveller there is little to interest.

POST OFFICE.—Immediately north east of the Bahnhof.

H.B.M.'s CONSUL.—R. Bernal, Esq.

U.S. CONSUL.—H. C. A. Damm, Esq.

RAIL, pages 175, 175A, 179, 182A, 183, 220.

Strassburg.—*Stat.*—Pop. (1910) 178,891.

GRAND HOTEL DE LA VILLE DE PARIS AND HOTEL FURSTENHOF.—Up-to-date first class hotel, well situated near the Cathedral, and affording extensive and superior accommodation. Lift. See Advt.

PALACE HOTEL MAISON ROUGE.—First class. Entirely rebuilt and up to date. Well known old established hotel. See Advt.

HOTEL NATIONAL.—First class family hotel, opposite Railway Station; recently renovated throughout; all modern improvements, private baths with toilette, etc. Managed by the proprietor. J. Fedier. See Advt.

HOTEL PFEIFFER.—Well situated opposite the Central Railway Stat. Hydraulic lift. See Advt.

GRAND HOTEL DE L'EUROPE AND HOTEL REBSTOCK.—Centre of city. Electric light. See Advt.

HOTEL UNION.—Centrally situated; equipped with up-to-date comforts. Private bathrooms. Moderate. See Advt.

HOTEL CHRISTOPH.—Strictly first class. Every modern improvement. Built 1902; right opposite Station, overlooking the square. See Advt.

The RAILWAY STATION—CENTRALBAHNHOF—a fine building, is on the west side of the city, about two thirds of a mile from the centre.

TAXIMETER CABS.—1 or 2 persons 50 pf. per 1,000 meters (within the town), 10 pf. each additional 500 meters.

Capital of Alsace and German Lorraine, seat of the provincial government, a university town; situated upon the River Ill, and connected by canals with the River Rhine, 2 miles distant. It is strongly fortified by an outer chain of forts, and an inner rampart.

From the middle of the crescent of the Bahnhof Platz the short Küssgasse leads to a bridge over the narrow River Ill; here, a few yards south, is one end of Langestrasse, which, if followed in its bending, will lead in half a mile to close to the Münster.

The erection of the Münster (or Cathedral) was begun in 1176 and continued until about 1420; originally designed as a Romanesque edifice (noticeable in the east end) it received many modifications, the nave and west end being Gothic. The facade is specially admired. Interior 121 yards long, 45 yards wide, nave 99 ft. high; sculptured pulpit, rich stained-glass windows, one or two modern frescoes; in the south transept is the famous Astronomical Clock. Very fine views from the several stages of the Tower, whose total height is 465 ft. (St. Paul's, London, 404 ft.); to platform 20 pf., to turrets 40 pf., to top 2 m.

In the Schloss Platz, opposite the south portal of the Münster, in the old Episcopal Palace, is the Municipal Museum of antiquities, below, and a Picture Gallery on an upper floor—old masters and modern works. In the south west corner of the Schloss Platz is the Frauenhaus (House of our Lady), 14th-16th cent., containing some models and curiosities.

150 yards due south from west end of the Münster, by the canal, is the Grosse Metzig 1588, the lower part being a market, with a Museum of Industrial Art above.

Church of St. Thomas, by the canal, one third mile south west of the Münster, a mingling of Romanesque and Gothic, 12th-14th cent.; in interior celebrated monument of Marshal Saxe (died 1750), sarcophagi, and busts of University professors.

The Broglie Platz, the principal promenade, where there is generally music in the afternoon, is a quarter of a mile north of the Münster. At the east end of the Broglie is the Theatre, and beyond, across the river, in the Kaiser Platz, is the Kaiser Palast, 1883-89, in Florentine Renaissance style; daily 10.0 to 6.0, 11.0 to 4.0 in winter, 25 pf. Government buildings on north side of the Platz. Opposite the Palast, on east side of the Platz, are the Universitäts Bibliothek (850,000 vols.) and the Hall of the Provincial Diet. The other University buildings (Collegiengebaude) are a quarter of a mile south east of the Bibliothek, across the river, erected 1877-84; several statues.

Orangerie, a mile north east of Broglie Platz, a pleasant park.

POST OFFICE, a few yards south east of Kaiser Platz, at one side of the Provincial Diet.

ENGLISH CH. SERVICE at 24, Manteufelstrasse.

U.S. CONSUL (at Kehl).—M. A. Jewett, Esq.

RAIL, pages 145, 207A 208, 210, 212A.

Stuttgart.—*Stat.*—Pop. (1910) 286,218.

HOTEL MARQUARDT, adjoining the Railway Station. In the finest part of the town; comfortable and well furnished. See Advt.

ROYAL HOTEL.—Opposite the Central Station. All modern comforts. Apartments with private baths. Rooms from 2.50 Mks. Lift. See Advt.

HOTEL CONTINENTAL.—New high class family hotel in central position. Apartments with baths. Rooms with breakfast from 3.80 M. See Advt.

TAXIMETER MOTOR CABS. Electric Trams from Schloss Platz traverse the town.

Stuttgart, capital of the Kingdom of Wurttemberg, pleasantly situated on a plain close to the River Neckar, with forest covered or vine clad hills all round, is one of the most attractive towns of Germany. The modern quarters are handsome, and the old parts have retained many of their picturesque features. It is a favourite summer and winter residence; there is an absence of smoke, and in winter considerable sunshine. Printing and bookselling are prominent in the business life, which is also largely engaged in making pianos, furniture, and fancy wares.

The Railway Station, HAUPT BAHNHOF, in a central situation, is in Schlossstrasse, at whose south end (100 yards) is the SCHLOSS PLATZ, one of the most beautiful public squares in Europe.

On the south east side of the Schloss Platz is the Royal Residenz Schloss, erected 1746-1807, in French Renaissance style, consisting of a main building and two wings; the finest parts of the interior are the stairs, with painted ceiling, and the marble saloon; frescoes, pictures, and statues in the saloons—in all there are 365 rooms. Entrance in south west wing, no ticket required. Extensive Schlossgarten on east side.

The Altes Schloss, of 16th cent., on south west side of the Schloss Platz, is used as Government offices. Immediately west of the Altes Schloss is the Stiftskirche (Evangelical), dating from 1436, restored 1895; fine stained glass, statues of Counts of Württemberg. Across the open space from the Altes Schloss is the Prinzenbau, erected 1694-1710—a royal residence.

The Konigsbau, a graceful colonnaded building, erected 1857-1860, on north side of the Schloss Platz, has on the upper floor a handsome concert hall. At west side of the Konigsbau is the Kronprinzenpalast. At east side of Schloss Platz is the Queen Olga Palace.

The Akademie, where is the Royal Library, is immediately behind the Residenz Schloss—in the east wing of the building are the royal stables.

Bibliothek, in Neckarstrasse, opposite south side of Residenz Schloss group of buildings; 500,000 vols., including 7,300 vols. of the Bible in 100 languages, about 3,800 MSS., and several literary curiosities. In the same building is an Archæological Museum, and valuable collections of objects in ivory, bronze, and precious metals, also coins and medals. At west side of the Bibliothek, in Neckarstrasse, is the Archives Building, containing Natural History Collections.

Museum der bildenden Künste, in Neckarstrasse, 250 yards east of the Residenz Schloss. Here are a Sculpture Gallery, and, on an upper floor, a Picture Gallery; in the latter are several works, old and modern, by Swabian artists. Tues., Wed., and Fri., 10.0 to 4.0, Sun. 11.0 to 4.0. In winter open on Sun. and Wed. only.

Landesgewerbe Museum, Schlossstrasse, 300 yards north west of the Hauptbahnhof. An interesting industrial museum. Weekdays 10.0 to 5.0, Sunday 11.0 to 1.0.

Johanneskirche, in Guttenbergstrasse, two thirds mile west of the Hauptbahnhof, a Gothic gem, 1866-76; Leonhardskirche, late Gothic, 15th cent., quarter mile south west of the Schloss Platz; Hospitalkirche, late Gothic, 15th cent., quarter mile west of the Hauptbahnhof.

Zentral Friedhof, the largest cemetery, is two thirds of a mile north east of the Hauptbahnhof.

POST OFFICE, in Schlossstrasse, nearly opposite the Haupt Bahnhof.

ENGLISH CHURCH SERVICE at the Church, Olgastrasse. WESLEYAN CHAPEL, Sophienstrasse.

H. B. M.'s MINISTER (residing at Munich). CONSUL.—J. H. Harris Gastrell, Esq. VICE-CONS.—E. Schleicher, Esq.

U.S. CONS.—E. Higgins, Esq.

DEPOT FOR BRADSHAW'S PUBLICATIONS.—Hermann Wildt, 5, Konigsstrasse.

RAIL, pages 191, 192, 192A, 193, 194.

[Just away from the north side of Stuttgart are Rosenstein Palace (paintings and sculpture), Wilhelma Palace (in Moorish style), and Berg Villa.]

Tegernsee.—*Stat.*—Pop. 1,618.

HOTEL STEINMETZ.—First class, well situated. Recently rebuilt and enlarged. Modern comforts. Suites and single rooms. Central warm water heating throughout. Rooms from 2.50 M. See Advt.

HOTEL TEGERNSEER HOF.—Comfortable family hotel, open all the year. Near Lake and winter sports ground. Pension from M. 6.50. See Advt.

SERBEN.

A village, 2,400 ft. above sea, delightfully situated on the east bank of the Tegernsee, among the Bavarian Alps. The lake, in its setting of meadows and heights, compares with the most beautiful lakes of Switzerland. Schloss, once a Benedictine abbey, founded 719.

RAIL, page 203C; DILIGENCE, page 373.

Teinach, see page 459.

Titisee, see page 460.

Tölz Bad.—*Stat.*—Pop. 4,800.

HOTELS: KAISERHOF; SEDLMAIER.

Tölz is situated on a hill, 2,155 ft. above sea, on the River Isar, in the most attractive part of the Bavarian highlands; along the river bank, on the other side from the town, are extensive woods and promenades, and just beyond these is Krankenheil, where are springs containing natron and iodine, used throughout the year with great advantage in cases of gout, affections of the nerves and eyes, and ailments of children. Resident medical men. The Bath Establishment is amply furnished. Theatre, daily concerts, reading room, tennis courts. Winter Sports.

The country all round is interesting, and many pleasant excursions may be made.

RAIL from Munich, page 203C. Diligence, page 373.

Treves (German Trier).—*Stat.*—Pop. 47,574.

HOTEL PORTA NIGRA.—First class family hotel, situated opposite the Porta Nigra. See Advt.

The Railway Station-Hauptbahnhof-is on the east side of the city, one third mile from points of interest. On west side, across the river, is a minor Station for a local line.

The oldest city in Germany, the Roman Augusta Treverorum, on the River Mosel, in a picturesque situation, with hills all round. Many ancient remains and curious old houses.

From the Bahnhof a short road and then the fine broad Nord Allee lead west in one third mile to the Porta Nigra, considered the finest Roman structure in Germany; built about A.D. 312, in the 11th cent. used as a church, restored as a gate 1817; it has three storeys, the two gateways are 23 ft. high, the length is 118 ft.; the greatest height is 95 ft. and greatest depth 69 ft.; open in morning. Simeonstrasse runs south from the Porta to the Markt Platz, where is a granite pillar of 1723, in place of one erected 958. By west side of the Platz, opposite St. Gangolphs Kirche, is the Rotes Haus, formerly the Rathaus, bearing an inscription to the effect that Treves is 1,300 years older than Rome; in the upper rooms of the Rotes Haus is a highly interesting Municipal Museum, including collections illustrative of local history and works of art; the ground floor is occupied by the Restaurant zur Steipe. A few yards east of the Markt Platz is the Dom.

The Dom, one of the oldest German Cathedrals, is on the site of a building erected by the Emperor Valentinian I (364-375); the structure was altered to the purpose of a Christian Church at an unknown early date, was wrecked by Franks and later by Normans, being restored early in 11th cent., additions being made until the 17th cent. In interior are monuments, choir screens, high altar; the "holy coat" of camel's hair, said to have been worn by Christ, is kept in a room above the cloisters—it is only shewn at rare intervals when vast numbers of pilgrims attend. In the treasury are a nail from the Cross, head of St. Matthew in a reliquary, and many other relics (treasury open on week-day morns. at about 11.30, fee 1 M.). Cathedral Museum in the cloisters.

Adjoining the Dom is the beautiful 13th cent. Gothic Liebfrauenkirche (Lady Chapel); sculptured portal; stained glass windows, figures of the Apostles on the twelve pillars, frescoes in choir, altar piece; sacristy.

The Basilica is 200 yards due south of the Dom, in Constantins Platz. A brick structure of early 4th cent. intended probably for judicial or civic purposes, after various uses becoming in 1856 a Protestant Church. It is 225 ft. long, 100 ft. wide, and 98 ft. high.

South east from the Basilica, across the Palast Platz, is the Provinzial Museum, in Renaissance Style, 1885-89, containing interesting collections of Roman remains, objects of industrial art, and pictures; free on Sun. and Wed. morn., other days 50 pf. Roman Palace, on south side of Palast Platz; an interesting ruin. A quarter mile east, outside the city, among vineyards, is the Amphitheatre (known as the Käskeller), in good preservation, where Constantine in 306 caused thousands of Franks to be slain by wild beasts, and where in 313 was a great slaughter of Bructeri prisoners.

The Library at the Gymnasium, 100 yards west of the Basilica, contains valuable MSS. and early printed works.

The bridge over the Mosel has parts dating from B.C. 28. A short distance south of east end of bridge are ruined Roman Baths, of 4th cent.

RAIL, pages 124, 125, 126, 127A.

[About a mile from the south side of Treves is the Church of St. Mathias (Matthew), of 12th cent., wherein is a sarcophagus stated to contain remains of the Apostle—much visited by pilgrims. At St. Paulin, a mile north east of Porta Nigra, is a Cross on the place where early Christians were martyred by Romans.

At **Igel**—*Stat.*—about 7 miles from Treves, is a celebrated Roman obelisk, 75 feet high, erected in 3rd cent. as a funeral monument.

The Valley of the **River Mosel** is attractive in all its length; in parts the scenery is very picturesque, with numerous pleasant small towns and villages set amidst vine clad hills, whose summits are here and there crowned by ruined castles and modern stately dwellings. There is also a welcome tranquility—as compared with the Rhine during the season. Treves is the headquarters of the Mosel Valley Railway, which is the best, and indeed the only way, to see the Valley from the train.

Triberg, see page 460.

Ulm.—*Stat.*—Pop. 56,109.

HOTELS: BAHNHOF; MUNSTER; RUSSIE.

Ulm, on the River Danube, is one of the most picturesque towns of Wurtemberg, with apparently almost entire streets dating from mediæval times. From the Bahnhof, Bahnhofstrasse leads east directly to the Münster, founded 1377, continued at intervals, completed 1890. It is one of the finest churches in Europe, quite original in its design; the facade is most imposing, the spire. 531 ft., the loftiest in existence; in interior is a magnificent organ, the largest in Germany, pulpit, choir stalls, ciborium, some paintings, rich stained windows. Open 11.0 to 12.0; at other times, 20 pf.

A little south of the Münster, in the Markt Platz, is the Rathhaus, of 16th cent.; in the Taubengasse, to east, is the Gewerbe Museum of industrial art. RAIL, p. 191, 192, 193, 194A, 201.

Villingen, see page 460.

Waldshut, see page 460.

Warmbrunn.—*Stat.*—Pop. 4,200.

HOTELS DE PRUSSE; SCHWARZER ADLER.

Pleasantly situated on the northern slopes of the Riesengebirge, 1,130 ft. above sea, visited for the warm thermal springs, 95°—104° Fahrenheit, used both in bathing and drinking, especially valuable in cases of gout and skin disease. Cursaal, theatre. Schloss of Count Schaffgotsch; the Propstei contains the Schaffgotsch library of 80,000 vols., and collection of coins, weapons, minerals, etc. RAIL, page 183A.

Wehrawald, see page 460.

Weimar.—*Stat.*—Pop. 34,582.

HOTELS. ERBPRINZ; RUSSIE; ELEFANT; KAISERIN AUGUSTA.

Capital of the Grand Duchy of Saxe Weimar, on the River Ilm; an old town, with literary associations. Goethe (died 1832) lived here for fifty-six years, and Schiller, Herder, and Wieland, also lived here, drawn thither by the Duke Charles Augustus, a patron of literature; Weimar is also known as an art centre. The Railway Station is on the north side of the town; from the Jubilaums Platz, before the Bahnhof, the Sophienstrasse leads southward directly into the town, past the Museum. The Museum has collections of sculpture, art objects, and paintings; daily, except Monday, 10.0 to 4.0. Sunday and Wednesday free other days 50 pf. The Stadtkirche (Peter-Pauls Kirche), in the Herder Platz, at the centre of the town, has a fine picture, "The Crucifixion," by the elder Cranach, containing portraits of Luther, Melanchton, and others; in front of the Church is statue of Herder (grave within church). The Schloss is a little to east of Stadtkirche—frescoes and paintings; a fee. The Grand Ducal Bibliothek, of 200,000 vols. and 8,000 maps, is on east side of Fürston Platz, just south of the Schloss; daily, except Sun., 9.0 to 2.0 and 3.0 to 6.0; 1 m.), Goethe's House, in the Goethe Platz, a little south of centre of town, the residence of the poet, has become a Goethe National Museum; open in summer daily, 11.0 to 4.0; in winter Sunday and Wednesday, 11.0 to 3.0; 1 m., Sun. 50 pf. Schiller's House, 12, Schillerstrasse (north side), north of and close to Goethe Platz; 8.0 to 12.0 and 2.0 to 6.0; 30 pf. Hoftheater (1908). Donndorf Museum of Sculpture. Liszt Museum in the house when he died. The Rathhaus is in the Markt Platz. The Cemetery (Friedhof), is on south side of town; the pleasant Park is to the south east.

ENGLISH CHURCH SERVICE.—St. Michael.

RAIL, pp. 152, 153, and 170.

Weissenthurm, see page 450.

Wernigerode.—*Stat.*—Pop. 22,000.

HOTELS: MONOPOL; ESSENER HOF; HIRSCH.

A picturesque healthy town, 770 ft. above sea, at the junction of the Zilligerbach and Holzemme streams, in one of the most attractive districts of the Harz mountains. St. Sylvestrikirche, St. Johanniskirche, St. Theobaldikirche, and other churches well repay inspection. In the Marktplatz is the quaint Rathaus of 14th cent.

Modern Gymnasium. In the Lustgarten are the Library (119,000 vols., 1,000 MSS.) and the Palm House. Stately schloss and park of the Prince of Stolberg-Wernigerode.

RAIL, pages 165B and 166.

[From Wernigerode along the valley of the Steinerne Renne to the **Brocken**, 3,415 ft. above sea, the Mons Bructerus of the Romans, the highest mountain in central Germany. RAIL pp. 153, 165B].

Wiesbaden.—*Stat.*—Pop. 109,002.

NASSAUER HOF.—First class, in fine situation, facing Kurpark. See Advt.

HOTEL FOUR SEASONS AND BATHS.—First class, facing Kurhaus, Opera, park. Rendezvous of English and Americans; moderate tariff. See Advt.

ROSE HOTEL AND BATHS.—First class and very comfortable. Opposite the Promenade, near Kurhaus and Royal Theatre. Lift. See Advt.

PALACE HOTEL.—First class hotel, conveniently situated opposite the "Kochbrunnen." Otis elevators. Telegraph office. See Advt.

HOTEL WILHELMA AND BATH.—High class; in villa quarter. Mineral baths, numerous private baths. Facing Kurhaus and Park. See Advt.

HOTEL QUISISANA.—First-class house, beautifully situated in the Park, facing the Casino. Lift; electric light. See Advt.

SENDIG EDEN HOTEL.—First class, in best position, facing Kurhaus and close to Kochbrunnen. Thermal baths in the house. Every modern comfort. See Advt.

RESIDENZ HOTEL.—3 and 5, Wilhelmstrasse, entirely new and elegant, with thermal and sweet water baths on each floor; lift, and every possible comfort. See Advt.

VICTORIA HOTEL AND BATH HOUSE.—First class in very best position, with all modern comfort; lift, etc. Arrangements for a stay. Moderate prices. See Advt.

HOTEL PRINZ NICOLAS.—Modern, close to Central Station. Thermal Baths on every floor. Rooms from 2.50 M. Garage. See Advt.

PENSION VILLA HERTHA.—24, Dambachtal. Healthy and central situation. English management. See Advt.

PENSION FORTUNA. — Kaiser Wilhelm. 11, Paulinenstrasse. First class; finest position. Every modern comfort. Excellent cuisine. Pension from M. 6. See Advt.

The HAUPTBAHNHOF is in the Kaiser Wilhelm Ring, on the south side of the town. From the Hauptbahnhof the Nikolasstrasse leads north to the spacious Rheinstrasse, where, a little east, is the Wilhelmstrasse, the principal thoroughfare, where the public gardens broaden out on the east side.

CABS.—Taximeter cabs charge 50 pf. for about two thirds of a mile, and 10 pf. for each extra third of a mile. Electric Trams in all directions.

Wiesbaden, one of the most attractive watering places and summer and winter resorts on the Rhine, is pleasantly situated in a fruit and vine country, 90 ft. above the level of the Rhine, 385 ft. above sea, at the south west base of the Taunus Mountains; many miles of beautiful forests, with the background of the Taunus range, make the view to the north west specially interesting. In the winter there is a good toboggan run in the forest. There are several hot springs rising in different parts of the town, the waters, used both for bathing and drinking, being beneficial in cases of rheumatism, neuralgia and nervous affections, gout, liver complaints, obesity, etc.; the Kochbrunnen, the chief drinking waters. have a temperature of 156° Fahr. Kurtax ((includes privileges of Kurhaus) for stay of more than 4 days and not more than 10 days, 7 M.; higher charge for lengthened visit.

The KURHAUS, a beautiful building a little back from the east side, north end, of Wilhelmstrasse, is one of the most agreeable resorts of the kind in Europe. There are a spacious hall and handsome saloons, with concert and ball rooms, and a well supplied reading room—about 300 newspapers and periodicals, including the leading English and American papers. The band is exceptionally good; concerts twice daily; balls and other entertainments are frequent. The Kurpark, the favourite afternoon promenade, is to the east of the Kurhaus.

The Trinkhalle is off the left side of the Taunusstrasse, just after this street leaves the north end of Wilhelmstrasse. Here the waters of the Kochbrunnen (15 springs), rising from below the pavilion, are drunk from 6.0 to 8.0 a.m. and throughout the day.

In the Schlossplatz, a few yards west of middle of Wilhelmstrasse, is the Markt Kirche, Gothic (1853); large statues of Christ, and Matthew, Mark, Luke, and John, in the choir. By the Church is the Rathhaus (1884). On the west side of the Schlossplatz is the old ducal Schloss (1837), now a royal palace; statues and frescoes; daily 10.0 to 4.0, sometimes later, 25pf.

Church of St. Bonifacius, north side of Luisenstrasse, running west from Wilhelmstrasse; Romanesque (1844), altarpiece; before the church is a monument to Nassau soldiers who fell at Waterloo. Ringkirche (1894), at west end of Rheinstrasse.

Museum, on west side of Wilhelmstrasse, at corner of Friedrichstrasse. A collection of good modern German paintings with some examples of early German art, beside Dutch and Italian works. Open daily. In the same building—collection of Antiquities, open almost daily during morn. and aft.; Natural History Collection; Library of 120,000 vols., many manuscripts, old miniatures, etc. on upper floor.

Music several times daily; in early morning at the Trinkhalle, at other times at the Kur Garten and Kurhaus. At the Royal Opera House, one of the finest buildings of its kind in Germany, is a permanent first class company; the other theatres have also good companies.

POST OFFICE, in Rheinstrasse.

ANGLICAN CHURCH.—S. Augustine, 3, Frankfurterstrasse. Sunday, 8.30, 11.0, 6.0. Wednesday and Friday, 11.0.

U.S. CONS. AGENT.

GOLF LINKS. Lawn tennis; in winter the courts are flooded for skating. Sleighing, tobogganing, and ski-ing.

MEDICAL.—There are over 200 doctors practising in Wiesbaden during the season.

SANATORIUM FOR COMPLAINTS OF THE STOMACH AND INTESTINES. 30, Park Strasse. DR. L. ABEND, Specialist for internal troubles and defective assimilation, formerly Assistant to Geheimrat Prof. von Leube, Würzburg.

BANKS.—Direction der Disconto-Gesellschaft, established 1851, 10a, Wilhelmstrasse. Capital M. 200,000,000. Reserves about Mk. 80,000,000. All banking orders promptly executed. Letters of credit and cheques issued and cashed. Foreign moneys at current prices.

RAIL, pages 123, 128, 135B, 146. Electric Car service between Wiesbaden and Mayence.

[On the north west side of Wiesbaden is the **Neroberg**, to which a cable tramway ascends from Beausite, at about a mile along the continuation of the Taunustrasse. Fine view. East of the summit, and a little below, is a mausoleum Greek Chapel (1848), the burial place of the Duchess Michailowna; interior very fine. About 2½ miles north of the Neroberg is the **Platte** (1,640 ft.), whence are fine views; shooting lodge of the Grand Duke of Luxemburg.]

Wildbad, see page 460.

Wildungen Bad.—*Stat.*—Pop. 3,500.

ROYAL BATH HOTEL.—First class; in the Kurpark. See Advt.

GRAND HOTEL FUERSTENHOF AND HOTEL GOECKE.—First class hotel, well situated, close to the Promenade and Springs. See Advt.

KAISERHOF.—First class hotel, on the Brunnen Promenade. Electric light; lift. See Advt.

PARK HOTEL.—Entirely new, in splendid position, close to Baths, Kurhaus, and Park. Very comfortable. See Advt.

A much frequented and pleasantly situated watering place in the south east corner of the

Principality of Waldeck, on an affluent of the River Eder, in a wooded and hilly country. The waters, containing iron and nitrogen, are of much service in cases of gout, kidney disease, affections of the bowels, etc. In the Brunnen Allée, a delightful promenade bordered by well laid out grounds, are the old and new Kurhaus. The season is from April until September; music three times daily, theatrical performances at the new Kurhaus. Golf links; shooting.

The Stadtkirche, Gothic, contains a good altar piece and some monuments.

Several pleasant walks in the neighbourhood. At Alt Wildungen is Schloss Friedrichstein. 995 ft. above sea, whence are fine views. The old Schloss of Waldeck, 1,380 ft. above sea, is 7½ miles north of Wildungen.

RAIL, page 156A.

[At **Frankenberg**—*Stat.*—20 miles west of Wildungen, is a Marienkirche of early 14th cent., with a beautiful Gothic Lady Chapel (1386) adjoining.]

Wittenberg.—*Stat.*—Pop. 20,590.

HOTEL GOLDENE WEINTRAUBE; KAISERHOF.

On the River Elbe, the residence of the Electors of Saxony until 1422, historically famous as the scene of early Reformation efforts. From the Bahnhof, half a mile distant, the town is entered at the Elster Thor, near which an oak tree in a small garden indicates the place where Luther burned the papal bull, Dec. 10th, 1520. Collegienstrasse, leading from the Thor, has on the left side the Augusteum, of 16th cent., a clergy training college; within the walls is "Luther's House," part of the old Augustine monastery where Luther lived, arranged as a Luther Museum. Melancthon's House, marked by a tablet, is in the same street. Near by is a barrack, formerly the University (merged in that of Halle 1817). In Markt Platz are the Rathhaus and the Luther monument. Schlosskirche, 15th cent; the doors to which Luther affixed his famous 95 Theses were destroyed at the bombardment of 1760—metal doors now replace them; in interior are the graves of Luther (died 1546) and Melancthon (died 1560). At the Stadtkirche, 14th cent., Luther often preached. RAIL, pages 170, 172, 187.

Worms, see page 454.

Wurzburg.—*Stat.*—Pop. 84,496.

KRONPRINZ HOTEL.—First class. Fine situation, near Station and facing Royal Palace. Auto Garage. Steam heating; lift. Garden. See Adv.

BAHNHOF HOTEL.—Exactly facing Station and Promenade. Very comfortable, well managed, and moderate. Rooms with private bath. Garage. See Advt.

The Railway Station—Bahnhof—is on the north side of the city, two thirds of a mile from the Dom.

A very pleasantly situated University city, on the River Main, in a vine growing country. From the Bahnhof, Kaiserstrasse, continuing into Theaterstrasse, leads to the Residenz Platz, where is the Residenz (Royal Palace), erected 1720-44, an imposing building, 550 ft. long, containing 312 rooms; handsome staircase, decorated Kaisersaal, Chapel, Picture Gallery; in the cellars, reputed the largest in Germany, are always hundreds of casks of wine. Shown daily at 11.0 and 2.0, 50 pf.

Hofstrasse goes west from the Residenz Platz to the Dom. Dating from 1042, the original Romanesque design of the Dom was twice altered in 12th cent., the interior, also, has suffered from 18th cent. restoration; old tapestry in the choir, crucifix suspended from roof. Opposite north west side of the Dom is the Neumünsterkirche, 11th-13th cent.; statue of Madonna in interior. At a few yards north west is the Markt Platz, where is the Marien Capelle, 1377-1441. Stifthaugerkirche (two towers and dome) is between the Dom and the Bahnhof. St. Burkard on west side of river.

The University, 100 yards due south of the Dom; about 1,500 students, more than the half medical; several collections, among them a Picture Gallery.

Fortress of Marienberg, on a hill on west side of the river.

POST OFFICE.—In Paradeplatz, east of the Dom.

RAIL, pages 143, 195A, 196, 198.

AUSTRIA AND HUNGARY.

[Austria, see page 494; Hungary, see page 508.]

Austria and Hungary are independent States, each having its own Parliament and Government; since 1867 they have agreed to unite their naval and military forces for mutual defence, and to be represented in other countries by the same diplomatic agents.

Reigning Sovereign.—Francis Joseph I, Emperor of Austria and King of Hungary, born 1830, succeeded to the Austrian throne in 1848, and crowned King of Hungary in 1867. Heir Presumptive, Archduke Franz Ferdinand (nephew of Emperor and King), born 1863.

Joint Army.—(1912), on a peace footing 402,388. **Navy** (1913), dreadnoughts 4, battleships (modern) 12, cruisers 12, torpedo gunboats 7, torpedo boats 65, destroyers 18, submarines 6.

Austrian Money.—100 heller=1 krone=10d. GOLD COINS, 20 and 10 kronen=16s. 8d. and 8s. 4d. SILVER, 5 kronen, 2 kronen, 1 krone, and 50 heller. NICKEL, 20 and 10 heller=2d. and 1d. BRONZE, 2 and 1 heller=1-5d. and 1-10d. The corresponding Hungarian coins are korona and fillér.

Weights and Measures.—The metric system of weights and measures is now legal and obligatory in both countries. See page lxxi.

Postage.—For letters within the dual monarchy, 10 heller per 20 gramms (two-thirds ounce); for foreign countries 25 heller per 20 gramms. Austria and Hungary have separate postage stamps; letters posted in Austria must bear Austrian stamps; those posted in Hungary must bear Hungarian stamps.

AUSTRIA.

Population—(1910), 28,324,940. The **Railways** are owned principally by the State. Lines owned by the State, 8,050 miles, privately owned but worked by the State, 3,585 miles; owned and worked by Companies, 2,405 miles. For Fares and Luggage Rates see page 233B.

NOTICES OF TOWNS, WATERING PLACES, etc.

Abbazia.—*Stat.*
HOTELS: STEPHANIE; GRAND; BELLEVUE.

A beautifully situated village on the Gulf of Quarnero, an arm of the north Adriatic; in great favour as a summer and winter resort. Good sea bathing. Steamers almost hourly to and from Fiume.

RAIL (Abbazia Mattuglie), pages 234, 237A.

The Achensee, 3,050 ft. above sea.

HOTEL ALPENHOF (Pertisau).—Beautifully situated. Every possible comfort. Rooms from 3 kronen, pension from 9 kronen. Patronized by English and American visitors. Wiener salon orchestra plays twice daily. See Advt.

GRAND HOTEL (Scholastika).—On the bank of the lake and close to the forest. Kur orchestra from June to Sept. See Advt.

The **Achensee** is a beautiful sheet of dark blue water, the finest lake of North Tyrol, 5½ miles long, ½ mile wide, 430 feet deep. Much visited during summer for the fresh cool air and delightful surroundings. A good road, in places hewn out of the rock, runs along the east bank, but the steamer affords a pleasanter journey. **Pertisau**, favourably situated on the west bank, near the south end of the lake, is a stretch of meadow land shut in by high mountains; fine views over the lake; the principal and most interesting excursions are made from Pertisau. [HOTEL ALPENHOF, PERTISAU.] The steamer between Seespitz (lake end) and Scholastika calls each way at Pertisau. **Scholastika** (GRAND HOTEL), one of the finest points on the lake, quite suitable for a protracted stay by reason of its climatic conditions and opportunities for excursions in the forest and on the water. It is the terminus of the steamers connecting the Bavarian Post motors with the railway between Tegernsee and Munich (see page 373). Kur band in summer.

RAIL and STEAMER, page 235A.

Adelsberg.—*Stat.*—Pop. 1,750.
HOTELS: ADELSBERGERHOF; KRONE; NATIONAL.

A summer resort, 1,800 ft. above sea. Ruined castle on the Schlossberg, 415 ft. above the village. The celebrated Grotto consists of several passages and chambers; the length of the accessible part of the cavern is about 2½ miles. Another grotto is the Ottok Grotto, about 1½ mile from Adelsberg—magnificent stalactite caverns.

RAIL, page 234.

Aquileia.—*Stat.*—Pop. 900.

Once a large frontier Roman city, strongly fortified, destroyed by Attila 452. The Cathedral is of the 11th cent. At the Archaeological Museum are collections of antiquities and sculpture; pleasant garden.

RAIL, page 235.

Arco.—*Stat.*—Pop. 3,000.
HOTEL: PALMES.

An old town, 300 feet above sea, beautifully situated in a sheltered position, mild climate—a favourite winter resort. Archduke Albrecht chateau. Ruined castle on a height, 390 ft; fine view. Pleasant level walks in the surrounding olive groves. Palm trees and the cypress flourish throughout the winter. The season is from September until May.

RAIL, page 235. Diligence, page 370.

Aussee.—*Stat.*—Pop. 1,700.
HOTELS: ERZHERZOG FRANZ CARL; HACKINGER; ERZHERZOG JOHANN; SONNE.

A finely situated town of Styria, on the River Traun, 2,155 ft. above sea; a favourite summer resort as a mountain centre and for the saline baths.

RAIL, page 240.

Bludenz.—*Stat.*—Pop. 6,000.

An interesting quaint old town, 1,905 ft. above sea, in a very fine situation, at the foot of the Scesaplana, the highest mountain of the Rhaetian Alps, the best centre for the exploration of the Vorarlberg country. Magnificent scenery all round; many huts and shelters of the Austrian and German Alpine clubs on the mountains. The road over the Arlberg is regarded as one of the best motor roads in the Alps. Schloss Gayenhofen, on a height; Pfarrkirche, with octagon tower. Winter sports of all kinds—sleighing, ski-ing, skating, etc.

RAIL, pages 238, 238A.

Botzen.—*Stat.*—Pop. 14,000.

HOTEL BRISTOL.—Situated in view of the Dolomites. Central heating; lift; baths. See Advt.

HOTEL GREIF.—Old established hotel. Moderate. See Advt.

HOTEL KONIG LAURIN.—Dependance of the two former establishments. Modern comforts. Fire proof. See Advt.

PARK HOTEL.—New first class hotel in good position. All modern comfort and latest sanitary arrangements. Winter garden. See Advt.

HOTEL STADT BOTZEN.—Walther Platz. Newly built first class hotel. Every up-to-date comfort and convenience. Rooms from Kr. 3. See Advt.

Botzen, 880 feet above sea, one of the most picturesque towns of the Tyrol, is situated at the confluence of the Rivers Talfer and Eisak, Pfarrkirche, Gothic, 14th-15th cent., has a tower of 205 ft. altar-piece. Franciscan Monastery, with carved altar in a chapel. Museum, in Kaiserin Elisabethstrasse containing collections of curiosities, costumes, a few pictures, and natural history objects. Fine views from the Calvarienberg, 950 feet. also from St. Oswald Promenade. A Schwebebahn (suspended carriage, worked on a wire rope), the first to be made in the Alps, ascends to Kollern, attaining a height of 4,592 ft., the views being superb. Winter sports.

The environs of Botzen abound with attractions. One favourite excursion is along the Sarnthal, past several castles to Sarnthein, 3,170 ft. above sea, 6 miles from Botzen. On the north east side of Botzen is the district of the Ritte Mountains, whence are fine views. On the south east side of Botzen the Eggenthal leads through picturesque scenery to Welschnofen (3,865 ft. above sea), past the Karersee, among woods, to the Karersee Pass (5,765 ft.) about 21 miles from Botzen.

RAIL, pages 235, 237A. Diligence, page 372.

[**Gries.**

A pleasant village and health resort, in a sheltered position, on the River Talfer, about a mile west of Botzen. In winter a preferred residence by persons with delicate chests. Spired Gothic evangelical Church. Kurhaus.

Mendel.

The Mendel Pass, rising to a height of 4,475 ft. above sea, traverses a district of imposing mountain and wood, with magnificent views over the Dolomites and the Adige valley. Mild climate and very pure air.

RAIL, pages 235, 237B.

Bregenz.—*Stat.*—Pop. 12,000.

ETTENBERGER'S HOTEL MONTFORT. — First class, vis-à-vis the principal Railway Station. Electric light and central heating. See Advt.

EUROPE; WEISSES KREUZ.

On the Lake of Constance. Church with old tower; Museum of antiquities, coins, etc.

RAIL, pages 237A, 238. Steamer, page 369.

Brennerbad.—*Stat.*—

HOTEL: GRAND.

A well known climatic resort, 4,390 ft. above sea, on the watershed between the Adriatic and the Black Sea, at the highest point of the celebrated Brenner railway. The waters, both for drinking and bathing, temperature about 68°, are pronounced to be radio-active; terrain cure. Magnificent scenery; pleasant excursions. Season from 1st June until 30th Sept.; resident doctor.

RAIL, page 235.

Brixen.—*Stat.*—Pop. 5,400.

HOTEL TIROL.—Newly built first class hotel. Hot and cold running water. Rooms from Kr. 2. Pension, without room, Kr. 6.50. Omnibus meets trains. See Advt.

The former capital (1100-1800) of an ecclesiastical principality, 1,860 ft. above sea. Moderately warm in summer, mild in winter, without sudden change. Two towered Cathedral of 15th cent.; in the cloisters are old wall paintings. Bishop's Palace and garden. RAIL, page 235.

Bruneck.—*Stat.*—Pop. 2,600.

HOTELS: TIVOLI; POST.

A beautifully situated little town of the Tyrol, 2,670 ft. above sea, the chief place of the west Puster Tal, at the opening of the Tauferer Tal; a much visited summer resort. In the church are altar pieces and frescoes. Ascent of the Kronplatz, 7,455 ft., by a good path; magnificent views. RAIL, page 236.

[**Taufers** (pop. 811, 10 miles from Bruneck), 2,800 ft. above sea, is the picturesque capital of the Tauferer Tal. Old castle. Close by is the attractive wooded valley of the Rain Tal, with waterfalls. Rail from Bruneck to Sand (for Taufers), page 236.]

Brunn.—*Stat.*—Pop. 125,737.

HOTELS: GRAND; KAISER VON OESTERREICH; NEUHAUSER.

The Railway Station is in the south east part of the city.

A manufacturing place, situated at the confluence of the Rivers Schwarzawa and Zwittawa. Immediately west of the Bahnhof is the Franzensberg promenade, with the Cathedral (SS. Peter and Paul), Gothic, 15th cent., on a hill close by; episcopal palace opposite west end of Cathedral. At a few yards north west of the Cathedral is the Stadthof, where are the law courts. The height to the north west is the Spielberg, upon which is the citadel; Count Silvio Pellico was a prisoner here, 1822-30; may be visited, small fee to attendant.

St. Jacob Kirche, one third mile due north of the Cathedral, 1314-1480; iron tower; beautiful stained glass windows.

Franzens Museum, a few yards east of the Cathedral; collections of antiquities, costumes, pictures, natural history, etc. In the old Landhaus, in Dominikaner Platz, 250 yards north of the Cathedral, is a gallery of modern paintings.

The pleasant Augarten is on north side of city.

H.B.M.'S VICE-CONSUL.—G. V. Neumark, Esq.

RAIL, pages 221, 223A, 252, 253.

Campiglio. Madonna di.

HOTELS: DES ALPES; RAINALTER; DOLOMITEN.

A favourite summer resort, in the eastern Alps, 4,970 ft. above sea, situated at the base of Monte Spinale (6,630 ft.), on a level of meadow land surrounded by fir woods. During the heat of summer great influx of visitors for the air cure. Marked paths lead through the woods in all directions; very fine views. Near excursions are to the Vallesinella Waterfalls, to Nambino Lake, to Monte Spinale, the Vier Wenzel Spitze, and Passo del Groste (8,005 ft.).

Campiglio is reached (20 minutes) from Carlo Magno, to which place is a motor service from Male (page 237B). Or, diligence from Pinzolo, page 371.

Carlsbad, or Karlsbad.—*Stat.*—Pop. 16,000.

HOTEL KONIGSVILLA AND VILLA TERESA.—Well situated on Schlossberg, in own park. Lift. Electric light. See Advt.

GRAND H. PUPP.—Beautiful first-class hotel, replete with every modern comfort. See Advt.

THE SAVOY "WEST END" HOTEL.—Well situated on the Schlossberg, in a healthy position opposite the American Park. Electric Light. Hydraulic Lifts. See Advt.

HOTEL BRISTOL.—First class. Situated in own park. Electric light. Lift. Apartments and single rooms with bath and toilette. See Advt.

HOTEL KROH.—First class hotel, in best part of the town, near Springs and Baths. See Advt.

HOTEL ANGER.—First class, in good position, with all the latest improvements. See Advt.

CONTINENTAL HOTEL.—Situated corner of Alte Wiese. Electric light. Lift. See Advt.

HOTEL NATIONAL.—First class family house. All modern comforts—lift, electric light, etc. Restaurant with finest terrace in town. See Advt.

RESIDENZ HOTEL.—First-class, in the centre of the town. See Advt.

POST HOTEL, with dependance Villa Romania.—Central, modern and comfortable; close to Baths and Springs. Moderate. See Advt.

HOTEL DE RUSSIE.—First class, facing Kurhaus. Table de regime. Moderate terms. Lift. See Advt.

HOTEL GERMANIA PALAIS.—New family hotel situated in "Westend" of the town, close to all places of interest. Apartments with baths. See Ad.

VISITORS' TAX, of three classes, for persons staying longer than a week: First class, 20 kronen; second class, 12 kronen; third class, 8 kronen; children and servants, 2 kronen. There is also a charge levied for music, varying according to number of family; in the first class from 10 kronen to 34 kronen, second class 6 kr. to 16 kr., third class 4 kr. to 12 kr. Physicians and surgeons with their wives and children (if under parental control) are exempted from this tax, also all who can produce a certificate of poverty.

The principal STATION (Buschterader Station), where the Ostend and Paris expresses arrive, is on the north west side of the town, about a mile from the centre of interest. The CENTRAL STATION, where the trains from Vienna arrive, is half a mile nearer.

CARLSBAD is one of the most renowned health resorts of the world. The curative qualities of the springs have been known since the thirteenth century, and the town has annually over 200,000 visitors. Seventeen springs, from 93° to 166° F. (Sprudel) are prescribed by the doctors. The waters are bicarbonated chloro-sulphate; their curative effects do not depend only on purgation. They are largely used for drinking purposes, but baths of the waters and mud and douches of all kind are given. Five large establishments, owned by the town, are provided with the newest and most perfect accommodation. The waters, considered as purgative, diuretic, and resolvent, are specially valuable in all complaints originating in derangement of the digestive organs, and also in many tropical diseases (for fuller details see page 810). The cure requires a stay of about four weeks. Wraps and warm clothing should be brought. The baths are open all the year, but the season is from April until October, with the height during June and July.

The town lies in the narrow valley of the Tepl, near its junction with the river Eger, among large pine and spruce-clad hills, 1,165 feet above the sea. The climate is healthy, and the town is entirely free from epidemics and contagious diseases. Imposing colonnades at the springs and other covered walks afford shelter on rainy days.

The walks in and about Carlsbad are numerous and beautiful; many, being upon the level, are suitable for the elderly and infirm. From the near heights are extensive views.

The centre of the town lies near the Sprudel, the Catholic Church, and the Marktplatz. The Alte Wiese, southward from the Marktplatz, is the favourite promenade, leading to Pupp's and the woods; here are the best shops. The Kurhaus and Stadtpark, in the northern part, are worth a visit. The upper part of the town, Schlossberg, with the English church and the "English quarter," is the best locality. The cure at Carlsbad is a serious one, and every visitor should place himself under a physician.

The music is good; bands playing in the early morning at the springs and afternoon at Pupp's Hotel, Posthof, or elsewhere. There are excellent performances in the theatre and a variety hall, also excellent Tennis Courts.

POST OFFICE.—Main Office, corner of Gartenzeile and Franz Josefsstrasse. Branch Office, telegraph and telephone, Marktplatz.

ENG. CH. SERVICE at St. Luke's new church.

PRESBYTERIAN SERVICE in the hall of the Kurhaus, June to August.

GOLF.—9-hole course, half-a-mile from centre of town.

MEDICAL.—There are upwards of a hundred medical men practising in Carlsbad, many of whom speak English; a full list may be obtained on application to the "Stadtrat."

BANK.—BÖHMISCHE ESCOMPTEBANK. Close to Sprudel. Foreign money exchanged circular notes cashed; payment on letters of credit. Mail matter received and forwarded free. Information given at Special Foreign Department. Safe Deposits.

H.B.M.'S VICE-CONSUL.—H. M. Gann, Esq.

U.S. CONSUL.—C. L. Hoover, Esq.

U.S. COMMERCIAL AGENCY.—Offices, Kreuzstrasse, "Goldener Schwan."

RAIL, pp. 243A. 250.

Cortina.—Population 3,450.

GRAND HOTEL MIRAMONTI.—Modern first class family hotel in fine position. 150 rooms and sitting rooms with balconies. Apartments with bath and private toilette. Moderate charges. Garage. See Advt.

PARK HOTEL FALORIA.—First class house, equipped with every modern comfort; beautifully situated. Moderate charges. See Advt.

PALACE HOTEL CRISTALLO.—First class. Delightful position with fine views and every comfort. Moderate charges. See Advt.

CONCORDIA; BELLE VUE.

A small town of the Dolomite region, 4,114 ft. above sea, in a delightful situation, on the River Boite, amidst cultivated fields, with a background of imposing mountain. Cortina is a favourite resort, the air being remarkably pure—dry and cool in summer—while as a centre for excursions it has many advantages. Church of SS. Filipo and Giacomo, built 1777, has carved wood altar by Andrea Brustolon; ceiling frescoes by a native, Ghedina bell tower 256 ft. high—fine view. Church of Our Lady at east end of town. Government Schools for mosaic work in metal and wood and silver filagree work.

Reached by diligence from Toblach (see page 372) or from Belluno on the Italian side.

Cracow.—*Stat.*—Pop. (1910) 151,886

HOTELS: GRAND; SAXE; DRESDE; CENTRAL.

CABS.—Station into the city, 80 h.

The ancient capital of Poland, situated at the confluence of the Rivers Vistula and Rudowa; a strongly fortified place. The Cathedral and Castle are on the Wawel hill, in the south west quarter. In the Cathedral, dating from 1320, are buried many Polish Kings, also the patriots John Sobieski (died 1696), Poniatowski (died 1813), and Kosciuszko (died 1817); in a silver sarcophagus, at centre of the Cathedral, are the remains of St. Stanislaus, patron saint of Poland; monuments, sculpture, paintings, vestments; Polish regalia, gold and silver plate, in treasury.

Church of St. Maria, on west side of the Ring Platz; rebuilt 14th cent.; north tower 265 ft. high; immense high altar; tombs, paintings, objects of great interest in the treasury. In the middle of the Ring Platz is a large building, the Sukiennice, containing the Polish National Museum of Art; daily, 11.0 to 3.0, 40 h.

The University Buildings are 250 yards west of the Ring Platz; library of 320,000 vols., an archæological museum and art collection.

Czartoryski Museum, in Pijarskastrasse, 300 yards north of the Ring Platz; extensive art collections, including a picture gallery. In Florianskastrasse, north east side of Ring Platz, the house of the artist Matejko has been converted into a museum of Polish costumes, etc.

Colossal statue of King Jagiello, erected 1910 by Paderewski, the pianist, in Matejko square.

RAIL, pages 221, 222, 246A, 247, 247A.

Eger.—*Stat.*—Pop. 26,000.

HOTEL KAISER WILHELM AND STATION HOTEL.—First class hotel, situated opposite the Railway Station. See Advt.

NEUBERGER; ZWEI ERZHERZOGE.

On rising ground, on the River Eger. From the Bahnhof, on south east side of the town, Bahnhofstrasse leads north west in about a mile to the Markt Platz, where, at the north end, is the Stadthaus; here Wallenstein was assassinated by Devereux, an Irishman, Feb. 25th, 1634; the upper part of the building contains a museum of antiquities, several relating to Wallenstein—tickets 60 h. At a quarter mile west, by the river, is the Burg, erected 1180 by Frederick Barbarossa—now a ruin; here Wallenstein's officers were murdered a few hours before their general. St. Nickolaus Kirche is just north of the Stadthaus.

RAIL, pages 188, 197, 202, 203, 243A, 250.

Franzensbad.—*Stat.*—Pop. 2,370.

KOPP'S KONIGSVILLA—First class family hotel. Beautifully situated in Salzquellstrasse, facing Morgenzeil Square. Lift; electric light. See Advt.

HOTEL BELVEDERE—BELLEVUE.—High class; every modern comfort. Beautiful park. See Advt.

HOTEL BRISTOL.—First class. Situated in best position, near the Baths and Springs. Family comfort. See Advt.

GRAND HOTEL.—First class hotel and restaurant, facing Kaiserbad and Salzquelle. Private baths. See Advt.

KAISERHOF HOTEL.—First class family hotel, in good position. Electric light; garage. See Advt.

The RAILWAY STATION is on the north side, about half a mile from the centre.

Franzensbad, 1,447 ft. above sea, is delightfully situated on an elevated plain, amidst forest scenery; with Carlsbad and Marienbad it forms the famous "Bader Trifolium," and possesses in its springs and mineral mud deposits (containing iron) curative treasures of infinite variety and wide application. Franzensbad is the premier mud bath of the world, as well as a most fashionable resort for ladies. The mud baths are specially valuable in cases of anæmia, chlorosis, gout, rheumatism, catarrh of the respiratory, urinary, and digestive organs, nervous diseases, and female ailments. The moderate mountain climate, rich in ozone, is absolutely dust free; lengthy well kept level promenades extend in all directions; for heart affections it is peculiarly suitable, and backward children thrive in the favourable conditions. Wraps and warm clothing should be brought. Season, May to October.

There are 14 mineral springs, the principal being the Salzquelle, the Franzensquelle, and the Natalienquelle. The natural Radium Emanatorium has its own highly active Radium springs; the natural carbonic acid gas bath, with a radioactive dry gas spring, is considered the richest in carbonic acid on the Continent—98.80% natural carbonic acid.

Kur and music tax: 1st class, 32 k.; 2nd class, 21 k.; 3rd class, 14 k.

From the Railway Station the Bahnhofstrasse leads in a few minutes to the Kurpark, to the south west of which, in the Kaiserstrasse, is the Kurhaus, whence a long colonnade leads to the principal drinking spring, the Franzensquelle. A theatre; good music in the morning between 7.0 and 9.0 a.m., during the promenade after drinking the waters, and in the afternoon in the Kurpark. Prominent artists from all countries appear at the concerts and theatre.

GOLF LINKS. Tennis (International tournament in July), croquet, boating on the lake, fishing, hunting, shooting. Fêtes in the park and on the lake.

POST OFFICE, in Postgasse, running from east side of Kaiserstrasse.

ENGLISH CHURCH SERVICE.

MEDICAL.—Dr. Leopold Fellner, M.D., Imperial Councillor, Villa Fellner (speaks English); Dr. Joseph Steinbach, M.D., F.I.R.M.S., of Vienna, Villa "Steinbach." Dr. Alfred Kraus, Haus Prinz von Preussen (speaks English).

RAIL, pp. 188, 197, 250.

Fulpmes.—*Stat.*—Pop. 1,150.

A health resort and centre for high mountain climbing, 3,300 ft. above sea, in the picturesque Stubai Valley, about 12½ miles from Innsbruck. Magnificent views. Excursions in the Stubai Dolomites, to the Schlicker Nadeln, Kalkkoegln, etc.

RAIL, page 238.

Gastein:
The Gastein Valley—Gastein Thal—extends from Lend to Wildbad Gastein. At about 2 miles from Lend the road is through the **Klamm Pass,** a gorge through which streams the River Ache.

Hof Gastein.—*Stat.*—Pop. 800.
HOTELS: CENTRAL; MOOSER; SALZBURGERHOF.
Chief town of the valley, 2,850 ft. above sea, 14 miles from Lend. In the 16th cent. Hof Gastein was a very prosperous place, owing to the gold and silver mines of the neighbourhood. The waters from Wildbad Gastein are brought here to the Marktische Badeanstalt, as also to the Hotels.

7 miles beyond Hof Gastein is

Bad Gastein, or Wildbad Gastein.—*Stat.*
GRAND HOTEL DE L'EUROPE.—New first class hotel in centre of town. 200 rooms and salons. Thermal baths in the hotel. Central heating. See Advt.
HOTEL STRAUBINGER.—First class hotel, with own thermal baths. See Advt.
GRAND HOTEL GASTEINER HOF.—First class modern establishment, with own thermal baths. See Advt.
Bad Gastein is a fashionable watering place on the steep eastern side of the valley. The hot springs, 77° to 120° Fahr., clear and pure, are highly beneficial in nervous affections, rheumatism, gout, debility, etc. Visitor's tax 9 kronen to 30 kronen, according to classification. Casino; frequent good music. The River Ache is precipitated over two very fine Falls, the upper of 207 ft., the lower of 280 ft.; in summer the Falls are illuminated about twice a week. St. Nicolaus Kirche.
Many attractive walks and longer excursions.
MEDICAL.—Dr. Gager.
RAIL, page 237C.

Gleichenberg.
HOTELS: MAILAND; HUNGARIA; STIRLING.
A celebrated bathing resort in a wooded valley, with promenade of great beauty; the saline-alkaline springs are of benefit in many diseases; about 6,000 visitors annually. Castle on a height, 1,395 feet.
DILIGENCE from Feldbach, page 370.

Gmunden.—*Stat.*—Pop. 7,100.
HOTELS: BELLE VUE; AUSTRIA; GOLDENES SCHIFF; MUCHA.
On the Traunsee, or Lake Gmunden, in Upper Austria, 20 m. from Ischl, near the finest part of the **Salzkammergut.** The prospects are splendid, taking in the Lake, the Todtes Gebirg, Alps of Salzburg and Dachstein. Falls of the Traun; view from Calvarienberg. The **Traunsee,** 8 m. by 2 m., is the finest lake in Austria; and is surrounded by high mountains, especially the Traunstein, 5,550 ft., the Erlakogl, 5,150 ft., and the Wilde Kogl, 6,865 ft.
RAIL, pp. 240, 242.

Görz.—*Stat.*—Pop. 30,995
HOTELS: POST; CENTRAL.
The chief town of a province and seat of an archbishop, pleasantly situated on the River Isonzo. Interesting Cathedral of 14th cent., having in the treasury valuable relics from destroyed Aquileia. By the Cathedral is a Museum of antiquities, natural history, etc. On a height on north side of the town is the Convent of Castagnavizza, where are buried members of the French Bourbon family.
RAIL, pages 234 237C

Gossensass.—*Stat.*—Pop. 531.
PALACE HOTEL WIELANDHOF.—Opened 1912. First class. Best position. Every comfort. All kinds of winter sport. Summer and winter season. See Advt.
GRAND HOTEL GRÖBNER.—First class modern hotel. Every comfort. Near Station. Suitable for summer and winter. Moderate terms. See Advt.
A climatic summer and winter health resort in the Tyrol, 1,200 ft. above sea, on the southern slope of the Brenner, in the valley of the River Eisak, amidst imposing surroundings of mountain, glacier, and forest. Shady and cool in summer; clear and bright in winter—no fog. Concerts by the Kur Orchestra; dances. Ice rink, toboggan run, sleighing, etc. Kurtax, per week, 2 K. The country all round is very pleasant for excursions.
RAIL, page 235.

Graz.—*Stat.*—Pop. 151,781.
GRAND HOTEL ELEFANT.—First class hotel, with all modern comfort. Fine restaurant. Omnibus meets all trains. See Advt.
HOTEL ERZHERZOG JOHANN.—First class in every respect. Lift. Finest central position. 100 bedrooms and salons. Omnibus at all trains. See Advt.
GRAND HOTEL WIESLER.—First class hotel with 100 rooms and suites, in central position. Central heating, electric light and lift. See Advt.
MOTOR CABS. Tramways to most parts of the town.
The picturesquely situated capital of Styria. 1,135 feet above sea, on the River Mur; one of the healthiest of the Austrian towns.
From the principal Railway Station—the Sudbahnhof—on the west side, Annenstrasse leads eastward to the **Franz Karl Bridge** and the centre of interest. 200 yards east of the bridge is the Haupt Platz, where, on south side, is the modern Rathhaus, 1887-92; fresco, "Old Graz," on staircase. On the east side of the Haupt Platz is the "Luegg," an old arcaded house of great interest.
From south east corner of Haupt Platz runs the Herrengasse, where (west side) are the 16th cent. Landhaus and the adjoining 16th cent. Landes-Zeughaus (Arsenal); interesting collections of weapons at latter. At south end of Herrengasse is the Joanneum, where are extensive collections of paintings, antiquities, natural history objects, and a library of 140,000 vols.
Dom, quarter mile north east of Haupt Platz. A 15th cent. Gothic building; altar piece and paintings; two celebrated reliquaries; six ivory reliefs. By the Dom is the elaborate baroque Mausoleum of Emperor Ferdinand II.
Leech Kirche, of 13th cent., Gothic, off east side of the Stadt Park; has old stained glass. Herz Jesu Kirche, half mile from south east side of the Stadt Park, is a modern Gothic building.

Justizpalast (Law Courts), on the Stadt Quai, a handsome building.

The University (about 2,000 students) is in the north east quarter, about a mile from Haupt Platz. Observatory. Botanical Gardens. Stadt Theater.

Fine view from the Schlossberg (1,545 ft.), ascent by cable tram; on the south side of the Schlossberg is an old Clock Tower. The extensive Stadt Park is half a mile east of Haupt Platz.

POST OFFICE in Neuthorgasse, a fine building in Renaissance style.

The environs of Graz are very attractive, the surrounding heights and woods offering innumerable excursions. Lurloch Grotto and dripping stone, the Schöckel, etc.

RAIL, pages 234, 237, 246.

Hall.—*Stat.*—Pop. 6,591.

HOTELS: VORDERWALDERHOF; BAD.

An historically interesting quaint old town of the Tyrol, on the River Inn, 1,835 ft. above sea, 5½ miles from Innsbruck. Old churches. At the Rathaus is a collection of industrial objects; natural history and other collections at the Obergymnasium. The brine baths are well known. Centre for winter sport.

RAIL, pages 235, 238, 238A (local line from Innsbruck).

Heiligenblut.

4,265 ft. above sea, magnificently situated at the upper end of the Moll Tal, in the Austrian Tyrol. The **Gross Glockner**, 12.455 ft., is ascended from here; Franz Josephs Höhe, 8.100 ft.; to the Pasterze Glacier, Gössnitz Fall, and several mountain excursions.

Reached by diligence from Dölsach page 370.

Iglau.—Pop. 23,716.—HOTELS: LÖWE; DREI FURSTEN. An ancient city prettily situated on the Iglawa. Gothic church (St. Jakob) with fine altar-piece. RAIL, pp. 224, 239B.

Igls.—*Stat.*—Pop. 294.

HOTELS: ALTWERT; IGLERHOF.

An "Air-Cure" and summer resort finely situated at the foot of the Patscherkofels, about 3 miles from Innsbruck. Magnificent views; excursions in the Stubaithal, etc.

RAIL from Innsbruck, p. 238A.

Innichen.—*Stat.*—Pop. 1,020.

HOTELS: BAR; STERN.

A summer resort in the Tyrol, 3,855 ft. above sea, in a pleasant situation, where the Sexten Tal opens out from the Puster Tal. Stiftskirche of 13th cent.; at one end of the village a chapel is an imitation of the Holy Sepulchre at Jerusalem. **Sexten,** pop. 1,304, 5½ miles from Innichen, is 4,320 ft. above sea; close to the Austrian-Italian frontier; grand excursions into the Dolomite region; good path over the Kreuzberg, 1,783 ft., into Venetia. RAIL, page 236.

Innsbruck.—*Stat.*—Pop. 53,194.

HOTEL DU TIROL.—Facing Station. Finest modern hotel. Two lifts. Liberal winter pension. Own skating rink adjoining the hotel. See Advt.

HOTEL GOLDENE SONNE.—First class hotel, conveniently situated, opposite Station. See Advt.

HOTEL VICTORIA.—Close to the Station. Comfortable; newly furnished. Electric light; lift; moderate charges. Restaurant with terrace. See Advt.

CARL KAYSER'S PENSION HOTEL (not Kaiserhof).—Situated twelve minutes drive from Railway Station; in own garden. See Advt.

PENSION WINTER.—3, Claudia Platz. First class, fine position, and very comfortable. Pension from 8 K.; reduction in winter. See Advt.

The Railway Station—Bahnhof—is on the east side of the town.

A most attractive town, both a summer and winter resort, situated on the River Inn, with fine views in all directions of a bold mountain region. Several streets are picturesque with carved, gabled, and painted houses, and in some streets the architecture is very imposing. For all kinds of winter sport Innsbruck is a good centre.

From a few paces north of the Bahnhof, Rudolfstrasse leads west into the town to Margarethen Platz, where is the Rudolfsbrunnen, surmounted by bronze statue of Duke Rudolf IV. From the Platz, Landhausstrasse leads into the impressive Maria Theresienstrasse, where, at the corner, is the Landhaus, and almost next to it, south, the Post Office. The Maria Theresienstrasse is continued northward by the arcaded Herzog Friedrichstrasse; at the bend of the latter is the Goldne Dachl (golden roof, or house), over the Gothic balcony of a palace erected 1425. The tower close by, Stadtthurm, or Feuerthurm, is 236 ft. high.

From the Goldne Dachl the short Hofgasse leads east to the Franziskanerkirche, or Hofkirche, in Renaissance style, erected 1553-63. In the nave is the imposing Maximilian Monument, representing the Emperor Maximilian I (died 1519, buried at Wiener Neustadt) surrounded by noble persons; the best figure is that of King Arthur of England (eighth on right); reliefs of events in the emperor's life upon sides of the sarcophagus; this remarkable monument was begun about 1509 and completed 1593. By the left aisle is the monument of Andreas Hofer (shot 1810), and opposite a mon. to patriotic Tyrolese since 1795. Silberne Kapelle (entrance, 40 heller), right aisle, named from silver statue of the Virgin, is interesting. Fee for the Silberne Kapelle includes admission to the Garde Saal and Riese Saal at the Hofburg.

To north of the Franziskanerkirche is the Hofburg (imperial palace), west, and the Stadtsäle and theatre, east, with the Hof Garten extending north. St. Jacobkirche is on north side of the Hofburg; paintings.

University, about 1,000 students, in Universitatsstrasse, running east from the Franziskanerkirche. Just beyond the domed University church is the Library, 180,000 vols. Behind is the Botanical Garden.

Ferdinandeum (Tyrolese Museum), in Museumstrasse, on south side of the group of the Franziskanerkirche and University; a Renaissance building; various collections, including a picture gallery. Daily, 9.0 to 5.0, except Sun.; 1 kr.

Triumphpforte (gate), at south end of Maria Theresienstrasse. Cemetery S.W. corner of town.

About a mile south of the town is the Isel Berg, 2,460 ft. above sea; on the summit are the Hofer

and other monuments. Frequent local railway service to Isel Berg.

Daily Concerts during the season. Electrically lighted skating rink (band).

POST OFFICE.—In Maximilianstrasse.

ENGLISH CHURCH SERVICE.

H.B.M.'s VICE CONSUL.—T. Stern, Esq.

MEDICAL. — Dr. Hubert Röck, 29, Anichstrasse (speaks English).

RAIL, pages 235, 237B, 238. Local lines to Igls and Stubai Valley pp. 238, 238A.

Bad Ischl.—*Stat.*—Pop. 2,500.

HOTEL BAUER.—With view on the Dachstein. Large park. See Advt.

HOTEL KAISERIN ELISABETH.—First class; well situated, opposite Kurpark. Modern. See Advt.

HOTEL KAISERKRONE. — Well known hotel, facing the Imperial Villa. Lift; electric light. Garden. Restaurant. Excellent trout fishing. Moderate terms. See Advt.

HOTEL ERZHERZOG FRANZ KARL.—Modern hotel in good position. Terms en pension. Open all the year. See advt.

HOTELS: POST; GOLDENES KREUZ; VICTORIA; AUSTRIA.

The Bahnhof is on the east side of the town.

Ischl, 1,535 ft. above sea, is beautifully situated at the confluence of the Rivers Traun and Ischl, at the heart of the attractive Salzkammergut. The natural beauty and the saline baths have combined to make Ischl a very fashionable resort. The waters, for drinking and bathing, are beneficial for bronchitis, rheumatism, nervous complaints, scrofula, etc. Frequent good music in the Trinkhalle or in the Kurhaus Park. Theatre. All kinds of winter sports. Visitor's tax, 2 kronen for a week; 16 kronen for a three weeks stay—an extra music tax of 6 kronen.

Church, with fine altar piece; Museum, containing natural history collection. Monumental Fountain to Archduke Franz Karl. Kaiser Hunting Mon. (Jagddenkmal)—a striking group. The Park of the Imperial Villa may be visited during absence of family.

The neighbourhood abounds with attractions, picturesque roads leading to several interesting spots. One pleasant excursion is to St. Wolfgang and the Schafberg, 5,840 ft. The Ischl Salt Mine—may be visited—is about 4 miles south of the town.

ENGLISH CHURCH SERV. in the German Church.

RAIL, pages 240, 248A.

MOTOR SERVICE to Unterach, page 370.

[**St. Wolfgang.**—*Stat.*

HOTEL ZUM WEISSEN ROSS; PETER.

In a fine situation on the St. Wolfgangsee, at the base of the Schafberg. Church has an altar piece. Grand view from the Schafberg, 5,840 ft. RAIL from Ischl page 248A.]

Joachimsthal, St.—*Stat.*—Pop. 8,000.

An ancient town of north-west Bohemia, 2,133 ft. above sea, not far distant from Carlsbad, on the slopes of the Keilberg (4,085 ft.), well known as a centre for winter sport. Interesting church; Rathaus; public library. By the discovery of Professor and Mdme. Curie of radium in the Joachimsthal, Uran Pechblende Joachimsthal has become world famous. Strongest radio-active springs—600 "Macheeinheiten" per litre. The resort has a great future on account of the application of modern radium therapeutics. Chronic rheumatism of the muscles and joints, gout, neuralgia, etc., yield to the treatment.

RAIL, page 249.

Karersee.—

HOTEL LATEMAR.—5,500 ft. First class, with every comfort. Liberal arrangements. Patronized by English and Americans. See Advt.

A delightful resort at the foot of the Rosengarten and the Lattemar Stock, reached by road through the magnificent gorge of Eggenthal, a convenient centre for exploring the Dolomite region of Botzen. Remarkably pure air. Excursions in all directions. This is one of the most attractive spots in the Austrian Alps, the scenery is not only very grand but almost unique in its character.

Reached by dil. from Botzen, p. 372.

Kitzbühel.—*Stat.*—Pop. 2,200.

GRAND HOTEL KITZBUHEL.—First class. Lift; electric light, steam heating. Sports. See Advt.

ENGLISH PENSION. SCHLOSS LEBENBERG.—3,000 ft. above sea. Electric light; central heating. Terms from 8 Kronen. Open all the year See Advt.

A pretty situated summer and winter resort in the Tyrol, 2,420 ft. above sea, at the junction of the Brixen and Leuken valleys, with an iron spring. Much frequented for pure air and grand scenery. Centre for winter sports—notably for ski-ing. The quaint little town is interesting. No wind; recommended for throat, chest, and nervous diseases, and cases of gout. Bathing in the Schwarzsee—the warmest alpine lake, 65°–80° Fahr. Magnificent views from the Kitzbühlerhorn, 6,540 ft. (inn), chapel at the summit; other fine points of view. Many pleasant excursions.

Rail, p. 238.

Klagenfurt.—*Stat.*—Pop. 26,000.

HOTEL KAISER VON OESTERREICH.—First class hotel and restaurant. 120 rooms and salons. Moderate terms. See Advt.

HOTEL VERDINO (Moser).—Modern first class hotel. Every comfort. First class Restaurant and Café. See Advt.

The capital of Carinthia, in a pleasant situation, 1,460 ft. above sea, on the River Glan. From the Bahnhof the Bahnhofstrasse runs north across the town. Dom Kirche on west side of Bahnhofstrasse. Museum in Viktringer Ring, which crosses Bahnhofstrasse—collections of works of art, antiquities, natural history objects. On west side of Bahnhofstrasse, near its north end, Paradeisergasse or Burggasse lead to the Neue Platz; a few yards north west is the Landhaus.

RAIL, pages 236, 237C.

[About 3 miles west of Klagenfurt is the **Wörther See**, a pretty lake 11 miles long. Military Swimming School. **Portschach**, near west end of Lake, is a summer resort.]

Klobenstein.—*Stat.*—Pop. 400.
A summer resort, 3,770 ft. above sea, with beautiful views over the Dolomites. In the neighbourhood are celebrated earth "pyramids."
RAIL, page 235.

Krimml.—*Stat.*
A pleasant village of the Austrian Alps, 3,500 ft. above sea, where are magnificent waterfalls from the Krimml Glacier; total depth of falls 1,400 ft. RAIL, page 237A.

Kufstein.—*Stat.*—Pop. 5,000.
HOTELS: EGGER; DREI KÖNIGE.
On the River Inn, a climatic resort, and centre for tourists and winter sports, 1,600 feet above sea, amidst mountain and lake scenery. Interesting old fortress of Geroldseck. From the Calvarienberg, about half a mile from the bridge is a fine view. Kufstein is a favourite centre whence mountain excursions among the neighbouring Eastern Alps may be made.
RAIL, pages 200, 235.

Laibach.—*Stat.*—Pop. 41,727.
HOTELS: STADT WIEN; ELEFANT; LLOYD.
The capital of Carniola, on the River Laibach; greatly injured by earthquake, April, 1895. Cathedral contains frescoes. Museum of art, natural history objects, etc., in Lattermann Allee. From the old Castle, overlooking the town, is a fine view. RAIL, pages 234, 234A, 242, 248.

Lambach.—*Stat.*—Pop. 300. HOTEL ROSSL.
Beautifully situated on the Traun, 21 m. from Linz, in Upper Austria, near salt works. Benedictine Monastery, founded 1032, contains a Library, old German pictures, and engravings. To the curious Church of Baura, built 1722.
RAIL, pages 239, 242, 243.

Lana.—*Stat.*—Pop. 3,157.
ROYAL HOTEL.
A rising resort, near Meran, about 900 feet above sea; beautiful situation, pure air and absence of wind. Fine views. Wire-rope railway to the Vigiljoch-Berg, duration of journey 20 minutes, difference of altitude nearly 4,000 feet. Electric railway to Meran. Electric tram service connecting with Lana-Burgstall station will be opened July, 1913.
RAIL, page 237A.

Landeck.—*Stat.*—Pop. 2,500
HOTEL POST.
Finely situated at the junction of the Rivers Inn and Sanna, 2,670 ft. above sea, in North Tyrol, 56 miles west of Innsbruck. Interesting old Schloss Landeck. The mild climate, freedom from wind, and total absence of fog attract many visitors. Imposing surroundings of wooded mountains and glaciers. The rail to Bludenz, traversing the **Arlberg** by a Tunnel 6¾ miles long, was opened October, 1884. Summit of the Tunnel 4,300 ft. above sea (1,600 ft. below the Pass), and slopes down to 4,270 ft. and 3,996 ft. at the east and west ends.
RAIL, page 238; Diligence, p. 371.

Lavarone.—GRAND HOTEL LAVARONE.
In South Tyrol, a favourite health resort, 4,000 ft. above sea, amidst fine mountain scenery. Reached by DILIGENCE from Roveredo (page 371) Caldonazzo (page 370) or Arsiero (page 370).

Lemberg (*Polish* **Lwów**).—*Stat.*—Pop. 206,113.
HOTELS: IMPERIAL; METROPOLE; GRAND.
The principal Railway Station, in a west suburb, is about 1½ mile from the centre.
Capital of Galicia. In a square at the centre is the Rathhaus, with a tower 260 ft. high. The Roman Catholic Cathedral is a few yards south of the Rathhaus; the Armenian Cathedral is 200 yards north of the Rathhaus; the Greek Catholic Cathedral is on a height between Station and town. The University buildings (about 1,700 students) are in the south east quarter.
H.B.M'S VICE-CONSUL.—Prof. R. Zaloziecki.
RAIL, pages 245, 246A, 247, 247A.

Lermoos.—*Stat.*—Pop. 600.
A beautifully situated village in the Tyrol, in a verdant spot, 3,245 ft. above sea. visited as an air cure in summer and winter. RAIL, page 203C.

Levico.—*Stat.*—Pop. 6,000.
HOTELS: EDEN; BELLEVUE; GRAND.
Situated at the beginning of the Valsugana, 1,663 ft. above sea. Arsenical-ferruginous springs. Gout, anæmia, malaria, nerve affections, etc., are treated. Season from April until November. Another resort, Vetriolo, is 3,000 ft. above Levico. RAIL, page 237.

Linz.—*Stat.*—Pop. 67,817.
HOTEL ERZHERZOG KARL.—First class, in good position. Apartments and single rooms with bath and toilette. Open all the year. See Advt.
Cap. of Upper Austria, 117 m. from Vienna, near the site of the Roman Lentium, in a beautiful spot on the Danube—bridge to Urfahr. Three large suburbs; old Castle, now a barrack. Mathias Kirche, with the tomb of Montecuculi (1680). The Landhaus and Museum where the States assemble. Trinity Column on the Hauptplatz. Pöstlingberg is the highest point in the neighbourhood. The fortifications consist of 32 detached forts, after a plan by Prince Max, of Este. To Klam Castle, on a height. The great gorge of the Danube between Passau and Linz is remarkably beautiful.
RAIL, pp. 237C, 239. Steamer, p. 368.

Marienbad.—*Stat.*—Pop. 5,500.
HOTEL KLINGER.—First class and largest hotel. Pretty situation on the Kurort. Large hall; vacuum cleaning. See Advt.
HOTEL WEIMAR—Well situated, near the Springs and Bath Establishments. See Advt.
HOTEL AND PENSION CASINO.—First-class family hotel, beautifully situated. Pension terms. See Advt.
HOTEL IMPERIAL.—First class house, near the Springs. Electric light; lift. See Advt.
GRAND HOTEL OTT. HOTEL EGERLANDER. HOHENHOTEL CAFE EGERLANDER.—First class houses, with every modern comfort. Conveniently situated. Moderate charges. Under personal management of proprietor, Kaspar Ott. See Advt.
HOTEL ROYAL—New first class hotel, in fine position. Close to all points of interest. All modern comforts. See Advt.
HOTEL KAISERHOF.—First class house, situated opposite the baths. Lift; electric light; baths. See Advt.
HOTEL DELPHIN.—Modern first class house, See Advt.

HOTEL "NEPTUN."—Opposite the Park and Kurhaus. Electric light; lift; omnibus at the Station. See Advt.

The RAILWAY STATION is on the south side, a mile and a half from the town.

Marienbad is a pleasant watering place, 2,200 ft. above sea, in a delightful valley surrounded by pine forests on the hills. More than 100,000 visitors annually come to drink and bathe in the waters, which are impregnated with Glauber's salt and are like those of Carlsbad, but are naturally cold (often, however, administered warm). The waters are successfully used in cases of heart disease, gout, arterioclerose, disordered stomach, liver, and digestive organs, and are often recommended as part of special treatment for ladies. Three large Bathing Establishments: New Bath, Central Bath, and Mud Bath (80,000 bathers annually); ten mineral springs.

Visitors' Tax, in three classes; First class, 20 kronen; second class, 12 kronen; third class, 8 kronen. Music Tax: First class 10 kronen, two persons 16 kronen, three persons 22 kronen; second class 8 kronen, two persons 10 kronen, three persons 12 kronen; third class 4 kronen, two persons 6 kr., three persons 8 kr.

The way from the Railway Station leads into the chief thoroughfare, the Kaiserstrasse, with fine promenades on one side and attractive houses on the other. The Kursaal is a little back to the east from the north end of Kaiserstrasse; the Theatre is a little back from the west side of Franz Josefs Platz, at the extreme north end of Kaiserstrasse. Good music at the Kreuz-Brunnen in the early morning and evening, and at the Waldquelle at about noon; also at the Ferdinands Brunnen in the early morning. Town Hall; Law Courts; attractive arcades; tennis ground.

Many fine walks in the pine forests close to the town; an extensive view from the Podhorn, 2,776 ft., about four miles to the east.

CH. OF ENGLAND SERV.—At Christ Church.

GOLF.—9-hole course, 15 mins. from town.

RAIL, page 243A.

[The springs of Marienbad are the property of the Abbey of **Tepl**, seven miles east of Marienbad. The Church, founded 1197, has modern interior; paintings in private chapel; library, zoological and geological collections, with other objects of interest.]

Meran.—*Stat.*—Pop. 24,000.

GRAND HOTEL AND MERANERHOF.—Largest establishment in Meran; most up-to-date; fire-proof. Fine situation. Open the whole year. See Advt.

HOTEL FRAU EMMA.- Near Station and promenades. Lift, electric light, steam heating. Reduced terms during winter. See Advt.

HOTEL ERZHERZOG JOHANN.—First class, honoured by visit of Emperor Francis Joseph. See Advt.

PALACE HOTEL.—First class hotel. Open the whole year. 150 rooms; private suites. See Advt.

GD. HOTEL BRISTOL.-First class modern hotel. Patronized by English and Americans. See Adv.

HOTEL HABSBURGERHOF.—First class, near Station and promenades. Electric light; lift. See Advt.

PARK HOTEL.—Modern hotel surrounded by extensive park-like grounds. See Advt.

SAVOY HOTEL.—First class family hotel, situated on the Topheimer Promenade. See Advt,

HOTEL ADERS, Obermais.—First class. Large park and winter garden. Garage. Pension. See Advt.

HOTEL MINERVA.-Family hotel, in good position. Modern comfort. Reasonable terms. See Advt.

HOTEL ERZHERZOG RAINER.—First class, with every comfort; lift, etc. Pension terms. See Adv.

HOTEL HASSFURTHER.-On the promenade, close to Wandelhalle. Garden. Open also in summer. See Advt.

The Bahnhof is on west side of the town.

The old capital of the Tyrol, 1,000 ft. above sea, in a sheltered beautiful situation on the River Passur, at the foot of the Küchelberg. As a resort Meran includes the adjoining villages of Untermais, Obermais, and Gratsch. Visited in autumn for the grape and milk cure, and in winter for the dry, mild, and equable climate; very little wind. About 31,000 visitors during the season. The town has many attractions—an interesting arcaded street, Unter den Lauben, crossing the town from east to west; the costumes of the country people adding a picturesque touch. The Giselda Promenade is bordered by grand old poplars; other favourite promenades are the Stefanie Promenade, the Untere and Obere Winter Anlage, and the Maria Valerie Garten. Tyrolese patriotic plays in March, April, September, and October. Golf links.

The Burg, 15th cent., formerly the residence of the Counts of Tyrol. Gothic Church, 14th cent.; paintings. Kurhaus. Theatre. Music two or three times daily.

Schloss Tirol, more or less ruined, on north west side of the Küchelberg, about two miles from Meran; very fine view in evening light. Several old castles in the neighbourhood; at Schloss Schonna (1,925 ft.) is a collection of arms and curiosities.

ENGLISH CHURCH in the grounds of the Meranerhof.

RAIL, page 237A. Electric railway to Lana.

Molveno.

HOTEL MOLVENO.

A favourite health resort, 2,820 feet above sea, on the delightful Lake of Molveno, surrounded by picturesque mountains, between the Brenta and Monte Gazza. Central for excursions in the Brenta Dolomites; many attractive walks in the neighbourhood.

Reached in four hours by carriage along very attractive road from Mezzolombardo, 14 miles distant.

Mostar.-*Stat.*-Pop. 16,369. HOTEL NARENTA.

Chief town of the Herzegovina, on the River Narenta; old bridge supposed to be of Roman origin. Greek Cathedral; Karagjoz Mosque.

RAIL, page 247B.

Olmütz.—*Stat.*—Pop. 23,000.

HOTELS: GOLIATH; LAUERS: PIETSCH.

A fortress, and former cap. of Moravia, 129 m. from Vienna, on the March, between the Sudeten and Carpathian Mountains; and a great market for cattle. The old Gothic Cath. has the grave of Wenceslas III. (1306); in St. Maurice's Church is an organ with 2,332 pipes. Bishop's Palace; University, restored 1827; Arsenal; and handsome Rathhaus. Holy Mountain is a place of pilgrimage.

RAIL, pages 221, 244, 247, 249, 254.

Parenzo (Istria).—*Stat.*—Pop. 3,500.

A little interesting old town on the Istrian coast of the Gulf of Venice, in a fine position; visited for sea bathing and as a health resort. Cathedral of 6th cent.

RAIL, page 235A. Frequent steamer connection with Trieste.

Pilsen (Bohemia).—*Stat.*—Pop. 80,343.

HOTELS: PILSENER; KAISER VON OESTERREICH.

On the Niess and Radbusa, near the Bohemian frontier. Gothic Rathhaus; St. Bartholomew Gothic Church; Wallenstein's House, where 24 of his followers were executed 1634. Karlstein, an old royal Castle, on a peak.

RAIL, pp. 243A, 243B, 244.

Pola.-*Stat.*-Pop. 58,081. H. CENTRAL; EUROPA.

A very old place (called Pietas Julia by the Romans), on the Adriatic, with numerous Roman remains of the highest interest—now a Naval Station. Duomo, on the quay of the Porto di Commercio; Castle, on the hill. Church of Madonna del Mare has fine facade and tower, above Romanesque portal are five statues, that of St. Barbara (central) is noteworthy. Near bend of the quay, west of the Duomo, is the Palazzo Municipio, where, adjoining, is the Temple of Augustus and Roma (B.C. 19). From the Municipio the Via Sergia leads to the Porta Aurea, and, continuing along the Via Giulia, are the Porta Erculea and the Porte Gemina; a little further east is the Amphitheatre (A.D. 150), 345 ft. broad, 79 ft. high, in three storeys.

RAIL, p. 242.

Prags.—

HOTEL WILDSEE.—First class, great comfort, up-to-date in every respect. Pension. See Advt.

The Pragser Thal is an attractive valley in the Dolomite region of the Austrian Tyrol, much visited as an Alpine air cure. At the principal village, Alt Prags, population 600, situated 4,535 ft. above sea, amidst fine scenery, are some well known alkaline baths. Beyond Alt Prags is Neu Prags, where are also baths; forest surroundings. About two miles from Neu Prags is the Pragser Wildsee, 4,920 ft. above sea, a beautiful sheet of water, shut in by the Seekofel, 9,220 ft. Shooting and fishing.

Reached by Diligence from Niederdorf Station, page 371.

PRAGUE (*Bohemian* **Praha.**)-*Stat.*—Pop. (1910) 223,741.

HOTEL ERZHERZOG STEPHAN.—First-class hotel, situated on the "Wenzelsplatz." Electric light; lifts; steam heating; telephone. See Advt.

PALACE HOTEL.—Facing the Post Office. Entirely new, large, modern hotel. Lift. Baths. Garage. Rooms from 3 Kronen. See Advt.

HOTEL BLUE STAR.—Old established, entirely remodelled and modernized. Very central; first class; two minutes from Station. See Advt.

HOTEL GOLDEN GOOSE.—New construction in central situation. Lift, electric light, and central heating. 90 single rooms, and suites with bath. See Advt.

HOTEL CENTRAL.—In central position. Modern comfort; moderate terms. See Advt.

The principal RAILWAY STATIONS—STAATS BAHNHOF, FRANZ JOSEFS BAHNHOF, and NORDWEST BAHNHOF—are on the east side of the city, and all fairly central.

INFORMATION TO TRAVELLERS given by the Boehmische Landes Verband für Fremden Verkehr; Bureau, Graben, 14.

PRAGUE, the capital of the kingdom of Bohemia, a city of great historical and religious interest, is in a picturesque situation on both banks of the River Moldau. In the neighbourhood of the Railway Stations are handsome modern districts, but the traveller will be drawn towards the north west part of the city; here, on the right bank of the Moldau, near the river bend, is the Josefstadt, the Jews' quarter, where much that was squalid has been demolished for improvements; on the opposite side of the river are the old aristocratic quarters, the Kleinseite on the lower ground, the venerable Hradschin on the height above. The principal thoroughfare runs in a south westerly course from the Nordwest Bahnhof to the Kaiser Franz Brucke, part being the thronged Graben; from the Franz Josefs Bahnhof the broad Wenzels Platz leads north west to the Graben; the Staats Bahnhof is about 250 yards east of the north end of the Graben. In and about the Graben and Wenzels Platz are the best hotels. German is generally understood, but the current language is Bohemian.

From the Railway Stations any of the thoroughfares going west lead to the river. The Kaiser Franz Brucke is a fine stone bridge, the Schützen Insel being in mid stream; a little to north is the old Karls Brucke, of 16 arches, closely associated with Prague history, the scene of a great annual pilgrimage, on 16th May, to the spot whence St. John Nepomuc, patron saint of Bohemia, was thrown into the river, 1383.

The HRADSCHIN is a cluster of buildings on the height half a mile beyond the west end of the Karls Brucke. The views from several points here are very fine. On the east side of the Hradschiner Platz is the Burg, an Imperial Palace dating from the 14th century; the Thirty

Years War is considered to have had its immediate cause in the throwing from the window of the Council Chamber here of the two councillors, Martinitz and Slawata, May 23rd, 1618. The Cathedral (Dom) of St. Veit (Vitus), on the east side of the Burg, founded 1344, though incomplete, is the finest church in Bohemia; tower 323 ft. high, once 520 ft.; in the chapels are paintings, sculpture, and elaborate altars; silver shrine of St. John Nepomuc; Royal Monument in nave, over graves of kings of Bohemia; in treasury are many curiosities. Ancient church of St. Georg, 10th century, east of Cathedral.

On the north side of the Hradschiner Platz is the Archbishop's Palace, on the south side a Convent and the Palace of Prince Schwarzenberg, and on the west side a palace of the Emperor Francis Joseph.

In Lorettogasse, running from south west side of the Hradschiner Platz, is the Church of Loretto, with a copy of the Holy House of Loretto in the courtyard. Just south of the west end of the Lorettogasse is the Abbey of Strahow, to be visited only in the morning; the Church (of the Assumption) contains tombs; picture gallery (ladies not admitted), and library of 70,000 vols. and 1,000 MSS.

At a short distance north east of the Hradschiner Platz, at the end of the Kaiser Garten, is the Belvedere, erected 1536; in the principal room are frescoes.

In the Waldstein Platz, one-third mile due east of the Hradschiner Platz, is Waldstein Palace, built 1623-30 by Albrecht von Wallenstein, or Waldstein, the famous general of the Thirty Years War; may be inspected, small fee.

The RUDOLFINUM is on the Kronprinz Rudolfs Quai, near the east end of the Kettensteg, the footbridge across the river north of the Karls Brucke. Within the Rudolfinum are the Conservatory of Music, an Art Industrial Museum, (daily except Monday, 10.0 to 5.0, free; Sat. 40 heller), and a Picture Gallery (daily, except Monday, 9.0 to 1.0).

Behind the Rudolfinum, back from the river, is the district of Josefstadt, formerly called the Judenstadt, once exclusively inhabited by Jews. Many of the old narrow crowded streets have been demolished, but there is still much to interest. At about 200 yards due east of the Rudolfinum is the sombre looking Altneuschule, an old synagogue, dating from 1338, on the site of one founded several centuries earlier. Close by is the ancient Jewish Cemetery.

BOHMISCHES MUSEUM, at south east (upper) end of Wenzels Platz. Here are several collections—historical, archæological, ethnographical, mineralogical, zoological, and botanic, besides a collection of autographs (Huss, Ziska, Wallenstein) and local antiquities; library. Daily, 9.0 o 1.0.

At the north end of Karls Platz, in south west part of the city, stood the Rathhaus of the Neustadt, the scene of a furious struggle of the people headed by Ziska for the release of the Hussite prisoners, 1419, when seven councillors were hurled from the windows; only a tower remains of the old building, which has been transformed into Law Courts.

In the Grosse Ring—to south east of the Josefstadt, third of a mile from the river between the Karls Brucke and the Kettensteg bridge—is the Teynkirche, founded 1360, the old church of the Hussites; on a pillar in south east part of interior is the tombstone of the astronomer Tycho Brahe. On the north side of the church is the Kinsky Palace. On the west side of the Ring is the Rathhaus of the Altstadt, built 1838-48; a few remains of an older building, notably the chapel, council chamber, and tower with famous clock, were preserved. In front of the Rathhaus, June 21st, 1621, many leaders of the Protestants were executed.

The UNIVERSITY is in three sections. At a short distance from the east end of the Karls Brucke, on the north side of Karlsgasse, is a range of buildings known as the Clementinum, containing the University Library of 230,000 vols., scientific collections, and lecture halls; the building for the law students is the Carolinum, one third mile due east of the Clementinum the buildings of the Medical Faculty are off the south east side of Karls Platz, about a mile due south of the Clementinum. The University was founded in 1348, and at one time had an European renown.

At the extreme south of the city, beyond the Railway Bridge, is the Wyschehrad, a modern fortification (1848) on the site of an ancient castle.

POST OFFICE.—In Heinrichgasse, running off north side of Wenzels Platz.

ENGLISH CHURCH SERVICE.—St. Martin's Church, Martinska ulice.

H.B.M.'S CONSUL.—Capt. A W. W. Forbes.

U.S. CONSUL.—J. I. Brittain, Esq.

RAIL, pages 225, 243, 243B, 246, 248, 249, 250, 252.

Reutte.—*Stat.*—Pop. 1,800.

A Tyrolese village, on the River Lech, 2,795 ft. above sea, amidst grand wooded surroundings. The picturesque Stuben Falls are at a short distance east of the village. In the neighbourhood is the Plansee, a fine sheet of water, 2¾ miles long, quarter to half mile broad.

RAIL, page 203C; Diligence, page 370.

Riva.—*Stat.*—Pop. 6,550.

LIDO PALACE HOTEL.—A vast up-to-date hotel, in the best position on the Lake. Full south; with large park. Rooms from 3 Kr.; pension from 10 Kr. See Advt.

RIVA; DU LAC; IMPERIAL.

In a beautiful situation at the north end of the Lago di Garda, a centre for numerous excursions; climate not too warm in summer. Ruins of a castle on the hill above the town; La Rocca Castle, now a barrack, on the Lake.

Grand road cut for 2 miles through the gigantic cliffs overhanging the Lake, and then ascending by zigzags into the lovely valley of the Lago di Ledro, from which to Storo through a succession of magnificent defiles: this road has no superior in Europe, and presents a succession of stupendous Alpine pictures. At Varone, 2 miles north west, is a waterfall in a gorge.

RAIL, page 235. Steamer, page 365. Dil. p. 371.

Rohitsch-Sauerbrunn.—*Stat.*

A very pleasant health resort of Steiermark, between mountains and forests. The curative properties of the waters are like those of Carlsbad; 4,500 visitors annually. RAIL, page 234.

Roncegno.—*Stat.*—Pop. 1,400.

THE GRAND AND PALACE HOTELS.—Opened 1907. Strictly first class. On a sunny plateau, commanding the panorama of the Dolomites. Own park of 30 acres of pine and fir woods. 300 rooms. Verandahs and terraces 400 feet long. Moderate pension terms. See Advt.

A pleasantly situated mountain village in the Val Sugana, 29¾ miles from Trient, with many beautiful walks and drives. The natural springs (for bathing and drinking) are the richest known in arsenic and very rich in iron, and are much recommended in anæmia, nervous troubles, female disorders, malaria, and debility. Equable climate in spring, summer, and autumn. Dry invigorating air, no dust nor humidity. The bathing establishment is quite modern and is connected with the hotels. English speaking doctors. Tennis, shooting, fishing, theatre, balls, and daily concerts. Season, May 1st to October.

RAIL, p. 237.

Rovereto.—*Stat.*—Pop. 10,475.

HOTELS: BALMORAL; GRAND.

In South Tyrol, in a fine part of the Leno, near the Adige; a flourishing centre of the silk trade. Churches of S. Marco and S. Maria del Carmine, both with frescoes. Old Venetian restored Sparkassepalast; collections at the Schulpalast. Rathaus. A wonderful route leads from here over the Fugazzà Pass to Schio.

RAIL, p. 235; Diligence, p. 371.

Salzburg.—*Stat.*—Pop. 36,188.

HOTEL DE L'EUROPE.—First class hotel, well situated, near the Station, with fine view of the mountains. Electric light; lift. See Advt.

HOTEL BRISTOL.—Centrally situated, with view of the city, Hohen-Salzburg, and mountains Lift. See Advt.

HOTEL PITTER.—Family hotel with 120 rooms. Near the principal Stations. Lift; electric light; baths. Moderate terms. See Advt.

PENSION HUBERTUS.-High class establishment, in quiet and select position. All modern comforts. Good cooking. See Advt.

The Stations of the State Railway and the Salzkammergut line are close together on the north side of the city, about a mile from the centre of the city; tramway from Stations.

SALZBURG, 1,350 ft. above sea, on both banks of the River Salzach, below some lofty hills, is regarded as one of the most beautifully situated places of Europe. Most of the existing chief buildings are survivors of the times of the Archbishops of the 17th and 18th centuries, frequent conflagrations having destroyed others.

From the Station an almost straight line of thoroughfare, Westbahnstrasse, leads directly to the Stadt Brucke and the old town, where is the Residenz Platz, in the middle of which is the Residenz Brunnen, 46 ft. high; the Residenz is on the west side of the Platz; opposite are the Law Courts, Post Office, and State Offices; on the south side is the Dom, erected 1614-28, in Renaissance style—pictures in the aisles, old font (1321), treasury, In the Kapitel Platz, on south side of the Dom, is the Archbishop's Palace; off the south west corner of this platz is the Churchyard of St. Peter, where are the Church of St. Peter, with monument of Michael Haydn (died 1806), brother of Joseph Haydn, the Church of St. Margaret, and the Benedictine Abbey of St. Peter—interesting treasury and library.

In the Platz, near the Stadt Brucke is the House of Paracelsus (died 1541), a famous physician.

Franciscan Church, 13th cent., a little west of Dom Platz; in the monastery recital every morning on the Pansymphonicum, the invention of one of the monks, ladies not admitted. Collegium Kirche in Universitäts Platz. A short distance west is the Neuthor, a tunnel through the rock.

A few yards from the south end of the Stadt Brucke is Getreidegasse, where, at No. 7, Mozart was born; the house is now a Mozart Museum. A house in Makart Platz is known as Mozart's House.

Carolino-Augusteum Museum on Franz Joseph Quai; collections of musical instruments, antiquities, pictures, costumes, handicraft objects, weapons, and miscellaneous curiosities.

The Fortress of Hohen Salzburg, above the town, is reached by a cable railway from close to St. Peter's Churchyard; Church of St. George in the Fortress, fine view. The Fortress is at the east end of the Monchsberg, a tree covered height a mile and a half long, 1,645 feet high, with many pleasant paths and glorious views. Just below the Fortress, to the east, is the Nonnberg, an ancient convent.

Mirabell Schloss, near the Stadt Park, erected 1606, rebuilt 1818; geological collections and sculpture. Kurhaus on north side of Stadt Park.

The Capuzinerberg, 2,130 ft., rises on the east side of the city; a little further up than the Capuchin Monastery is the "Mozart Hauschen," brought from Vienna, in which was composed the opera The Magic Flute. Very fine views.

The finest view is from the **Gaisberg**, 4,220 ft., east of the Capuzinerberg; reached by rack railway from the village of Parsch, about a mile from the Carolinen Brucke—tramway.

POST OFFICE, in Residenz Platz.

ENG. CH. SERV., in the German Evang. Church.

RAIL, pp. 200, 201, 203C, 239, 248A.

Semmering.—*Stat.*

HOTELS: PANHANS; STEFANIE; SUDBAHN; ERZHERZOG STEPHAN.

One of the favourite resorts, both in summer and winter, of Austria, amidst magnificent scenery. Very pure air; good roads. Many attractive excursions in the neighbourhood.

RAIL, p. 234.

Serajevo—*Stat.*—Pop. 51,949.

HOTELS: EUROPA; CENTRAL.

The picturesque capital of Bosnia, situated in a narrow valley, on the River Miljacka, at the base of hills rising to 5,250 ft. The Austrian population lives mostly by the river, the Servians and Turks live on the slopes. Between the Railway Station and the town is the Fortified Camp. Electric trams.

The centre of business and most interesting spot is the Bazaar, in the east part of the town, thronged by country people on market days. At west side of Bazaar is the Husref Beg Mosque.

Two-towered Roman Catholic Cathedral; handsome Greek Church. Close to the R.C. Cathedral is the Bosnian Museum, where are collections of national costumes, antiquities, natural history, etc. Modern brick built Rathhaus. Fine views from the Castle, on the east side of the town.

H.B.M.'s CONSUL.—F. G. Freeman, Esq.

RAIL, page 247B.

Sterzing. — *Stat.* — Pop. 1,672. HOTELS: STOETTER'S; ALTE POST; NEUE POST. An old town and a Roman station, in N. Tyrol, on the Eisach, 14 m. from Brenner Pass; visited all the year—cool in summer, much sunshine in winter. Houses curiously painted outside. The Church contains many monuments, and some quaint old pictures. Several fine mountain excursions may be made from Sterzing. RAIL, p. 235.

Sulden, or **St. Gertraud.**

SULDEN HOTEL.—Large first-class house (English Church) in splendid situation, in immediate vicinity of the forest, with fine view over the magnificent Glaciers of the Ortler Group. See Ad.

Sulden is a village in the romantic Suldenthal, 6,050 ft. above sea, a great centre for tourists and mountaineers. Many walks to easily accessible heights with grand views. Huts have been erected and roads made by the Alpine clubs. Rich flora in June and July. Ascent of the Ortlerspitze, passing the night at the Paverhütte. Reached by diligence from Spondinig Prad, see page 371.

Tai.—

A pleasant village, 2,795 ft. above sea, among the Ampezzo Alps, in a situation most convenient for mountain climbing or pedestrian excursions. Church with paintings by Cesare Vecellio, Titian's cousin. DILIGENCE, page 372.

Teplitz, or **Teplitz-Schönau** (Bohemia).—*Stat.*—Pop. 28,000.

GRAND HOTEL "ZUM ALTEN RATHAUS."—First class. Hot and cold water in all rooms. Also the HOTEL KRONPRINZ RUDOLPH, under the same proprietorship. See Advt.

A pleasantly situated town, under the Erzgebirge range, 720 feet above sea, since Roman times celebrated for its Baths, which are among the most frequented and fashionable in Austria. The highly radio-active springs are hot (some 119° Fahr.) and alkalo-saline, and are almost exclusively used and excellent for stiff joints, gout, rheumatism, neuralgia (ischias), and after-results of severe injuries, gunshot wounds (the Warriors' Bath), etc. The principal Bath Establishments are the new Kaiserbad (1912), the Kaiserin Elisabeth Bad (1911)—a magnificent building, the Stadtbad, Herrenhaus, and Schlangenbad. Shady parks are to be found throughout the whole spa, and charming walks and fine views in great variety are afforded by the wooded hills close by; the Königshöhe and Stephanshöhe are favourite resorts. The delightful Erzgebirge may be easily reached by electric railway. Teplitz-Schönau is also an important centre of intellectual culture. Amusements of all sorts abound; first class orchestra; frequent reunions are arranged by the Kurverein. Sport of all kinds may be had. Church of St. Elisabeth, Roman Catholic; Synagogue; Protestant Church. Museum of antiquities and natural history in Schulengasse. Upon the summit of the Schlossberg, 1,286 ft., is a ruined castle, partly restored. In the neighbourhood are brown coal and lignite mines.

RAIL, pages 250, 251.

Toblach (Tyrol).—*Stat.*—Pop. 1,659.

HOTELS: BELLEVUE; GERMANIA; TOBLACH; SUDBAHN.

A beautiful and much frequented place in the Tyrol. Church contains fine fresco. Ascent from here of the Pfannhorn, 8,730 ft. The Lake of Toblach is very attractive. RAIL, p. 236. Diligence p. 372.

Torbole.—*Stat.*

HOTEL: GRAND.

A pleasantly situated village at the north end of the Lago di Garda, with fine views of the Alps. Luxurious vegetation.

RAIL (Nago Torbole), page 223. Steamer, p. 365.

Trafoi.—Pop. 200.

TRAFOI HOTEL is a large up-to-date and first class establishment. English church. See Advt.

POST; SELVIO.

A village on the route of the Stelvio Pass, 5,080 ft. above sea, in the midst of splendid scenery, much frequented by Alpine tourists, also for its pure mountain air. The Three Holy Springs, a celebrated pilgrim resort, under the massive Madatsch and the Trafoier Eiswand. Ascent of the Ortler Spitze. Reached by diligence from Spondinig Prad, see page 371.

The Stelvio Pass, the highest and most beautiful road Pass in Europe, begins at Trafoi, and ascends to the summit by a series of some fifty zigzags (short cuts not recommended, especially in descending) which command magnificent views of the Ortler range and its exquisite hanging glaciers.

Trient, or **Trento.** — *Stat.* — Pop. 30,049.

IMPERIAL HOTEL TRENTO.—First class family hotel. See Advt.

BRISTOL.

The Stazione is on north west side of the town.

The ancient Tridentum, on the River Adige, among beautiful hills; thoroughly Italian in character, with many fine streets, palaces, and towers.

Duomo, 11th-15th cent., Romanesque, with lions at the north entrance. At the church of Santa Maria Maggiore, 16th cent., in west part of town, the Council of Trent assembled 1545-63—in the choir is a picture containing portraits of the councillors.

Palazzo Municipale, in Via Larga, contains a museum of antiquities, natural history collection, coins, etc. Castello del Buon Consiglio, on north east side of town, where the prince-bishop resided, now a barrack; above the Castle is a Capuchin monastery.

RAIL, pages 235, 237, 237B. Dil. p. 371.

Trieste.—*Stat.*—Pop. (1910) 229,510.

HOTEL DE LA VILLE.—First class family house, facing the sea. All modern comforts. 150 rooms. Moderate terms. See Advt.

The principal **RAILWAY STATION** is by the harbour, in the north west part of the town, about half a mile from the centre of interest. St. Andrea Station is on the extreme south side of the town.

Trieste, the Tergeste of the Romans, the principal seaport of Austria, is situated on a gulf at the north east end of the Adriatic. It is a thriving commercial place, with little to interest beside its importance as a mercantile and shipping centre. About half a mile south of the Railway Station, along the quay, is the busiest part of Trieste; here are the Teatro Comunale, the Tergesteo—a block of buildings containing the Exchange—and the Chamber of Commerce. Behind a tree-planted space on the quay is the Piazza Grande, where are the Municipal Offices.

The Byzantine Cattedrale of S. Giusto, 14th cent., on a height, about half a mile back from the quay at its busiest part, is on the site of a Roman temple, of which there are a few remains by the tower; in interior are some mosaics; tombs of the older line of the Spanish Bourbons in San Carlo chapel.

In the Via della Cattedrale is the Lapidario, a collection of antiquities in the open—here is buried Winckelmann, a famous antiquary, murdered at Trieste, 1768.

The Church of Santa Maria Maggiore, 1627-82, between the quay and the Cathedral, has a modern fresco. Close by, a few yards south, is the Piazzetta di Riccardo, so named after Richard Cœur-de-Lion, who is stated to have been imprisoned here as he returned from Palestine; the Arco di Riccardo is of Roman origin.

Church of S. Nicolo dei Greci, on the quay, with handsome interior. About a quarter mile back from S. Nicolo is the Church of S. Antonio, 1827-49, and close by the Greek Church of S. Spiridione.

The Museo Civico is in Piazza Lipsia, a hundred yards from the quay, near its south end; here is the Commercial and Nautical Academy, containing a Museum of Natural History; in the same building is the Museum of Antiquities.

Museo Civico Revoltella, close to the quay, near its south end; paintings and sculpture.

On the south side of the town is a fine avenue along the coast, the Passeggio di S. Andrea, whence are good views.

ENGLISH CHURCH SERVICE at Christ Church.

H. B. M.'s CONSUL GENERAL.—J. B. Spence, Esq. VICE-CONSUL.—N. Salvari, Esq. CONSULAR AGENT at Lissa—Serafino Topic, Esq.

U. S. CONSUL.—R. J. Totten, Esq. VICE-CONSUL.—O. de Martini, Esq.

RAIL, pp. 234, 234A, 235A, 237C, 242.

[The Castle of **Miramar** is finely placed on the coast five miles north of Trieste; the castle, once the property of the Emperor Maximilian, of Mexico, may be visited daily after 11.0 a.m., the park is always open.

Capodistria, pop. 10,690, is an ancient little town, the Roman Justinopolis, on the coast, 8 miles south of Trieste. Cathedral, Palazzo Publico on site of a temple of Cybele. Reached by steamer from Trieste to Muggia, then walk over the hill to S. Nicolo, thence by boat; or rail direct.

VIENNA (*German* **Wien**).—*Stat.*—Pop. (1910) 2,031,498. (*Plan in Special Edition, or post free 6d. stamps*).

HOTEL BRISTOL.—Well situated, near the Imperial Palace. The best situation in Vienna; patronized by English and American families. Electric light; lift. Rooms from 6 Kronen. See Advt.

GRAND HOTEL.—In the most fashionable and much frequented part of the town, 9, Kärntnerring. Table d'hote. See Advt. Also an excellent Restaurant.

HOTEL METROPOLE.—Vast first-class hotel beautifully situated. Much frequented by English and American travellers. Rooms from 5 kronen. See Advt.

HOTEL MEISSL AND SCHADN.—First class. All modern comfort. Fine central position. Patronized by English and Americans. See Advt.

PARK HOTEL SCHONBRUNN is an entirely new and up to date establishment, facing the Imperial Castle and Park, with tram communication, etc., to all parts of the city. Rooms from 6 kronen. See Advt.

HOTEL ASTORIA.—Karntnerstrasse. New first class hotel. See Advt.

HOTEL SACHER (Edward Sacher).—First-class hotel, situated opposite the Imperial Royal Court Opera. Electric light; lift. Baths. See Advt.

HOTEL KRANTZ.—Neuer Markt. Central and fashionable quarter, near Opera, Palace, etc. First class. Rooms from 7 kr. See Advt.

HOTEL ERZHERZOG KARL.-Situated I, Kärntnerstrasse, 31; with electric light and lifts. See Advt.

HOTEL IMPERIAL.—Modern first class hotel in central position. Completely renovated and refitted. See Advt.

HOTEL KAISERIN ELIZABETH.-First class family hotel; electric light, lift, telephone. Rooms from 5 kronen. See Advt.

ROYAL HOTEL.—First class family hotel, central. Stefansplatz—Graben. See Advt.

HESS' HOTEL (OESTERREICHISCHER HOF).—Well situated, I, Rothenthurmstrasse, corner of Fleischmarkt. Lift; electric light. See Advt.

HOTEL MATSCHAKERHOF.—Near the Graben and Stefansplatz. Lift; electric light; baths. Pension from 12 kronen. See Advt.

HOTEL DUNGL.—New, modern hotel, one minute from Opera, Palace, Ring, etc. Every comfort. Rooms from 5 kr. See Advt.

PARK HOTEL.—New modern hotel, facing the Sud and Staats Railway Stations. Most comfortable; lift, etc. Rooms from 4 kr. See Advt.

HOTEL VICTORIA.—Favoritenstrasse, 11—IV. Near the Opera, the Sudbahn Station, and the Staatsbahnhof. Moderate inclusive terms. Cook's coupons taken. See Advt.

HOTEL KLOMSER.—Centrally situated (Herrengasse 19). Every modern comfort. Pension terms. See Advt.

HOTEL HAMMERAND.—8, Florianigasse. English and American house. Inclusive terms. See Advt.

PENSION TATLOCK.—Ebendorferstrasse, 4. First class; modern comfort. Best and most central position. Lift. Inclusive terms from 7 kr. See Advt.

PENSION EXQUISITE.—Graben, Stefansplatz (Equitable Palace). Finest position; all modern comforts. See Advt.

PENSION WASHINGTON.—8, Ebendorferstrasse. First class family house. Central and quiet position. Moderate terms. See Advt.

PENSION SANS SOUCI.—Comfortable. Central position, near University and sights. Lift; electric light; baths, etc. Pension from Kr. 7. See Advt.

PENSION OLD ENGLAND.—First class English Boarding House, central and quiet. Close to Opera, Museums, and sights. Moderate terms. See Advt.

RESTAURANT "DEUTSCHES HAUS," Stephans Platz, facing Stephans Church, is a first class restaurant in every detail, with good cuisine, at popular prices. The wine cellar is celebrated (Deutschen Ritter Ordens). This interesting house was built 500 years ago. See Advt.

There are six large Railway Stations, all within two miles of the centre of the city:—

WESTBAHNHOF—rail to Munich, Frankfort.

FRANZ JOSEFS BAHNHOF—to Eger, Prague.

NORDBAHNHOF—to Prague, Oderberg, Cracow, Berlin, Warsaw.

NORDWESTBAHNHOF—to Prague, Dresden.

STAATSBAHNHOF—to Brunn, Prague, Dresden, Hungary, Constantinople.

SUDBAHNHOF—to Trieste, Venice.

CABS.—Taximeter motor cars and taximeter horsed cabs. Night fares, 11.0 p.m. until 6.0 a.m., half extra. TRAMWAYS in all directions.

STEAMERS.—The Danube steamer quays are at the east side of the city, 2½ to 3 miles from the centre. A small steamer leaves early morn. from close to the Radetzky Bridge, on the Danube Canal, near centre of city, to connect with the Budapest steamer.

VIENNA, the capital of Austria, lies on a plain, on the Danube Canal, into which flows the little River Wien (whence the name of the city). It is regarded as one of the brightest and healthiest of the large continental cities, with cheerful and courteous inhabitants.

A fine broad thoroughfare, the Ringstrasse, extends in a crescent two miles long round three sides of the Inner Town (Innere Stadt); within this district are most of the principal buildings and interesting phases of Vienna life. In its various sections the Ringstrasse is named Kärntnerring, Opernring, Burgring, etc. The best shops are in the Kärntnerstrasse, the Graben, Stephans Platz, the Kohlmarkt, and parts of the Ringstrasse.

CHURCHES.

Quite at the centre of the city, in Stephans Platz, is the Church or Cathedral of ST. STEPHEN (Stephans Kirche), whose lofty spire, 448 ft. high, is conspicuous. The west front dates from the middle of the 13th cent., with additions until 1579; the west towers are 210 ft. high; coloured tiles cover the roof. The Riesentor (Giant Door), at the west end, is only opened on special occasions; upon the outside wall of the choir are reliefs—Christ taking leave of the Holy Women; on the north east side is the pulpit of the monk Capistranus (1451). The rather dark interior is 354 ft. long, 105 ft. wide, 92 ft. high in the nave, 72 ft. high in the aisles; elaborately groined vaulting. Within the church are several monuments, richly carved choir stalls, stained glass windows, elaborate altars; sarcophagus of Emperor Frederick III; pulpit in nave; in the Tirna Chapel is the tomb of Prince Eugene of Savoy. From the tower (fee 40 h.) extensive view, including battlefields of Lobau, Wagram, and Essling; the great bell is on the second stage of the tower. On the north side of Stephans Platz is the Archbishop's Palace. A little to the south of Stephans Kirche, at the corner of the Graben and Kärntnerstrasse, is the "Stock im Eisen," a pine tree stump, clamped, full of nails, driven in because of some idea of sanctity associated with the tree.

MICHAEL KIRCHE, in Kohlmarkt. Gothic, paintings by Schnorr; some monuments of 16th-18th cents.

KAPUZINER KIRCHE (Capuchin Church), in Neuer Markt, 200 yards south of Stephans Kirche, containing the Imperial Vault (open daily except Sunday, 10:0 a.m. to 12.0 noon, fee for the poor expected); in the vault are more than 130 coffins, among them those of Maria Theresa, Maria Louise (wife of Napoleon) and her son, the Duke of Reichstadt, Maximilian of Mexico, Crown Prince Rudolph (died 1889), and Empress Elizabeth (died 1898).

AUGUSTINER KIRCHE, in Augustinerstrasse, a little north of the Hofgarten, with a noble Monument to Arch-Duchess Maria Christina, of Sax Teschen, by Canova. Here also are mortuary chapels of the Emp. Leop. II, of Gen. Daun, and of Pro. van Swieten; in the Loretto Chapel the hearts of all the emperors and empresses since early in the 17th cent. are preserved in silver urns.

KARLSKIRCHE, in the Wieden district, on south side of the Wien, built (in fulfilment of a vow made by the Emp. Charles VI when the plague raged in Vienna), by Fisher, of Erlach, 1716-1736; it has two slender towers, 108 ft. high, near the porch.

SCHOTTENKIRCHE, in the Freiung, with handsome high altar, paintings by Sandrart, and monument of Starhemberg.

PETERSKIRCHE, in Peters Platz, off north side of the Graben, has a dome with frescoes.

MINORITE CHURCH (1395); mosaic of Da Vinci's Last Supper, and mon. of the poet Metastasio.

St. Maria Stiegen, in Salvatorgasse, quarter mile north west of Stephans Kirche—handsome altars and stained glass.

Votivkirche (commemorating the Emperor's escape from assassination, 1853), in Maximilian Platz, a fine Gothic building, with elaborately decorated interior.

Public Buildings.

The Burgring and Franzensring parts of the Ringstrasse are flanked by the chief public buildings.

The **Hofburg**, or **Burg**, the residence of the Austrian princes since the 13th cent., an extensive range of buildings and gardens on the north side of the Burgring—the gardens stretch from the Hofgarten on the east to the Volksgarten on the west, with the buildings behind. Within the gardens are numerous statues and marble groups. The Hof Bibliothek (Library), towards the centre, open daily, except Sunday, 9.0 a.m. to 4.0 p.m. (closed from 1st Aug. to 15th Sept.), contains 800,000 vols. and 24,000 MSS.; also an immense collection of engravings and portraits. In the great hall are statues; the ceiling paintings are by Gran. In the Treasury (open Tues., Thurs., Sat., 10.0 a.m. to 1.0 p.m.; for tickets written application must be made on previous day) are family treasures of the Hapsburg house.

On the east side of the Hofgarten is the **Albertina**, or library of the Archduke Frederic, with engravings and drawings (Mon. and Thurs., 9.0 a.m. to 2.0 p.m.); there are 50,000 vols., 24,000 maps and plans, and a very valuable collection of 18,000 drawings, including 50 by Raphael, 150 by Dürer, 52 by Rubens, 147 by Rembrandt. There are also 220,000 engravings.

The **Imperial Museums** on the Burgring are handsome buildings in Italian Renaissance style, erected 1872-89. The **Kunsthistorisches Museum** (Art Museum) contains about 1,800 pictures, classed under the Italian school-Titian, Paolo Veronese, Giorgione, etc.; Dutch and Flemish school — with Van Dyck, Teniers, Rubens, Dou, etc.; Spanish school—Velazquez; French school — Poussin; German — Dürer, Holbein, etc. It also contains works of modern painters, and Canova's Theseus. There are also Egyptian and other antiquities, arms, coins, &c. The wonderful Imperial collection, the unrivalled accumulated treasures of many centuries, forms perhaps the chief attraction of the Art Museum, and is probably the richest and most valuable and historically interesting collection in existence of articles of gold and silver, gems, jewels, precious stones, crystals, etc., historical curiosities, and smaller works of art. The Ambras collection of Armour, one of the richest in existence, is on the ground floor of the Art Museum. The marble staircase leading to the vast picture gallery is a dream of gorgeous splendour. Open free, on Sun. (9.0 to 2.0), Tues., and Fri. (9.0 to 3.0); on Wed. and Sat. 1 k. The **Naturhistorisches Museum** contains mineralogical, geological, zoological, and botanical specimens, also a grand collection of meteorites. Open, free, Sun. (9.0 to 2.0); Mon. (1.0 to 4.0); and Thurs. (10.0 to 3.0); on Mon., Wed., and Sat. 1 k. Between the museums is a monument to the Empress Maria Theresa.

A few yards north of the Natural History Museum, at the bend of the Ring, behind the garden, are the Law Courts (Justiz Palast), a Renaissance building, erected 1875-81; splendid hall.

The entire west side of the Franzensring is occupied by the Parliament House, Town Hall, and University; on the opposite side are the Volksgarten and the Hofburg Theatre.

Parliament House (Reichsrats Gebaüde), in the Greek style, was erected 1883; the Chamber of Deputies is on the right, Upper Chamber on left.

Rathaus (Town Hall), with Rathaus Park in front. Gothic building, erected 1873-83; many statues; tower 320 ft. high; frescoes in council chamber. Within the building are the Municipal Library and the very interesting Historical Museum of Vienna—open daily 9.0 to 1.0 or 2.0, on Sun., Tues., and Thurs., free; other days 2k.

University, an extensive range of buildings in Renaissance style, erected 1873-84; small fee to visit the aula. There are about 5,200 students; library of 500,000 vols.

Hofburg Theatre, built 1876-89; among the busts on the exterior is that of Shakespeare; elaborately decorated interior, painting and statuary; may be visited during day on application to official.

In the Schottenring, the northerly continuation of the Franzensring, is the Exchange (Börse), a Renaissance building, erected 1872-77; fine hall and vestibule; on an upper floor is an Ethnographical Museum.

At the corner of Hessgasse, a little south of the Exchange, on the opposite side, is the Stiftungshaus, erected 1884-5 at the cost of the Emperor on the site of the Burg Theatre, burned 1881, when about 400 lives were lost; commemorative chapel on first floor.

In the eastern part of the Ringstrasse—the Parkring and Stubenring—is the pretty Stadt Park, ornamented with statues. Opposite the Park are the Dumba Palace and the Horticultural Society's buildings, with, a few yards further north, the Palace of the Archduke Eugène. On the north side of the Stadt Park is the Museum of Art and Industry; collections of decorative art, furniture, metal work, textile fabrics, library of technical books; open Mon., Tues., Wed., 60h, other days free. An Arts and Crafts School adjoins the Museum on the north side.

The **Liechtenstein Picture Gallery**, in the summer residence of the Princes of Liechtenstein, is in the Liechtensteinstrasse, about half a mile north west of the Schottenring. Open, in summer, daily except Sat., 9.0 a.m. to 4.0 p.m., on Sun., 2.0 to 4.0 p.m.; in winter, on application to the curator. A magnificent collection of about 800 paintings by celebrated artists, including many by Rubens and Van Dyck.

The **Harrach Picture Gallery**, in the Harrach Palast, is in the open place known as the Freiung, about half a mile north west of the Hofburg. About 400 pictures by old masters, many very fine. Mon., Wed., Sat., 10.0 a.m. to 4.0 p.m., during summer. Close by the Harrach

Palast, to the right, where the Freiung runs into the Renngasse, is the Schönborn Palast, where is the SCHONBORN PICTURE GALLERY (Mon., Wed., Fri., 9.0 to 3.0), a smaller collection of very choice paintings. The CZERNIN PICTURE GALLERY (May to Oct. on Mon. and Thurs., 10.0 a.m. to 2.0 p.m.), in the Palace of Count Czernin, is in Landesgerichtstrasse, facing the Rathhaus; a very fine collection of about 350 pictures, mostly of the Dutch School.

ACADEMY OF FINE ARTS, in Schiller Platz, a few yards back from south side of the Opernring. A handsome building, erected 1872-76. In the picture gallery the Dutch painters of the 17th cent. are well represented; some modern paintings; many thousand drawings, water colours, engravings, etc.

Gallery of modern pictures at the BELVEDERE, formerly the residence of Prince Eugene of Savoy, on the south east side of the city.

The Arsenal is an extensive range of buildings immediately east of the Sudbahnhof and Staatsbahnof. In the Army Museum (Heeresmuseum) are weapons, trophies, flags, uniforms, and military curiosities.

PARKS, GARDENS, ETC.

The Prater, the largest of the Parks, is on the east side of the city; the southern part, where is a lake, is at times a fashionable resort; the northern part is the popular resort; horse racing here.

The Augarten is by the Nordwestbahnhof, less than a mile from north end of the Prater.

Botanical Gardens, close to the Belvedere, in south east quarter.

Hofburg Theater, in Franzensring; tragedy and comedy.

Hofopern Theater, in Opernring; opera.

Deutsche Volkstheater, behind the Museums in the Burgring; dramas, popular plays.

Theater an der Wien, quarter mile south of Opernring; drama, operettas.

Music, military bands, in the Prater and public gardens, afternoon and evening during summer. Nearly always there is good music to be heard; consult the landlord of hotel.

The house where Haydn died (May 31st, 1809), 17, Haydngasse, about three quarters mile south west of the Opernring, is arranged as a Haydn Museum; his burial place is at Kismarton (Eisenstadt).

CEMETERIES.—In the south east suburb (tramway) is the Central Friedhof, where are buried many illustrious persons—Mozart, Beethoven, Schubert, Makart, the Littrows, Ghega, Amerling, and numerous others; some of the monuments are very fine. Matzleinsdorf Friedhof, a short distance west of the Sudbahnhof, contains the remains of Gluck; in the Protestant section of the cemetery, a little further west, are many well known names.

POST OFFICE, in Postgasse, a short distance off the west side of the Stubenring; several branch offices. Principal TELEGRAPH OFFICE, in Borsen Platz, a little off east side of the Schottenring.

CHURCH OF ENGLAND SERVICE.—At Christ Church, the Embassy, Metternichgasse, 6. Rev. A. P. Hill.

PRESBYTERIAN CHURCH.—9, Eschenbachgasse.

H. B. M.'S AMBASSADOR.—His Excellency Sir F. Cartwright, G.C.V.O., K.C.M.G. CONSUL GENERAL.—Sir F. W. Duncan, Bart. CONSUL.—O. S. Phillpotts, Esq.

U.S. AMBASSADOR.—His Excellency R.C. Kerens. SECRETARY OF LEGATION.—U. Grant-Smith. Esq.

CONSUL GENERAL.—C. Denby, Esq. VICE-CONSUL.—R. W. Heingartner, Esq.

ENGLISH AND AMERICAN CHEMIST to the British and American Embassies, etc. I, Karnthnerring, 18. See Advt.

GOLF.—9-hole course, in the Prater.

DEPOT FOR BRADSHAW'S GUIDE.—Thomas Cook and Son, 2, Stefansplatz.

Schonbrunn.

PARK HOTEL SCHONBRUNN.—See Advt. under Vienna.

At Schonbrunn, in the south west suburbs of Vienna, reached by tramway, is a Palace, the summer residence of the Emperor Mathias, and completed under Maria Theresa. The Duke of Reichstadt, son of Nap. I., died here (1832). Its garden, well attended on Sunday, contains a beautiful spring, from which the castle derives its name, the Gloriette, with a view of Vienna, a flower garden with a palm house, and a menagerie.

Laxenburg is about 11¾ miles due south of Vienna. Imperial palace and park. On an island in the park is the Franzensburg, erected 1799-1836, in mediaeval style; interesting rooms.

Mödling. Pop. 11,100. 10 miles south west of Vienna. Old Knight Templar Church of St. Othmar. The Bruhl (reached by electric railway from Mödling) is a beautiful ravine, with added artificial ruins, etc. On a hill in the neighbourhood is the Husaren Tempel. The old Abbey of Heiligenkreuz, 7½ miles west of Mödling, contains tombs of the Babenberg family.

The **Kahlenberg**, 3 miles north west of Vienna, is a height, 1,404 ft. above sea, whence is a very fine view. Climbing rail to summit, or walk up in 1 hour; a shady path near the base, Beethoven Gang, was a favourite resort of the composer. A forest path leads to Leopoldsberg, 1,380 ft. above sea, rising abruptly from the River Danube; church on site of an old castle.

Villach (Carinthia).—*Stat.*—Pop. 14,000.

PARK HOTEL.—First class hotel with 200 rooms and salons. Apartments with baths and toilette. Park. Opened 1st July, 1911. See Advt.

BAHNHOF; MOSSER; POST.

The ancient Villa ad Aquas and chief place of the Carinthian Oberland, 1,643 ft. above sea, is picturesquely situated on both sides of the River Drau, at the base of the Dobratsch, 7,110 ft. The Gothic parish Church of St. Jakob, 14 cent., contains much that is interesting; Franciscan Church, modern, high altar, frescoes; Holy Cross Church, a few minutes south east of town. At the Rathaus, 16th cent., is an archæological museum. In the park is a relief map of Carinthia.

At Bad Villach, 2 miles to south west, are warm sulphur springs, 84° to 86° Fahr.; bath establishment and Curhaus; tennis court.

Many attractive mountain and other excursions in the neighbourhood.

RAIL, pages 236, 237C, 241.

Vöslau.-*Stat.*-Pop. 3,680.

HOTELS: BELLEVUE; HALLMAYER; VOSLAUER HOF.

A favourite summer resort of the Viennese, in lower Austria, 19 m. from Vienna; noted for its fine air and beautiful scenery. It stands among pine woods, on the top of a hill. The mineral bath in Count Fries's park rises to 74° F.

RAIL, p. 234.

Wiener-Neustadt.—*Stat.*—Pop. 32,874.

HOTELS: HIRSCH; KREUZ; KRONE.

A manufacturing town, 930 ft. above sea, about 27 miles south of Vienna. The two towered Church, of 13th-14th cents., is part Gothic and part Romanesque. Neukloster Kirche—paintings in the monastery library. Collection of antiquities at the Rathhaus. Ducal Castle of the Babenbergs, dating from 12th cent.—now a Military Academy; in the Chapel are beautiful stained windows.

RAIL, pages 234, 236, 248A.

Windisch Matrei.—Pop. 1,656.

WEISSENSTEIN CASTLE HOTEL.

A finely situated village of the Tyrol, at the junction of the Tauern and Virgen valleys, between the Gross Glockner and the **Gross Venediger**, 12,055 ft. (ascent comparatively easy). Favourite centre for mountain excursions; the air is very pure and the rainfall slight. Guides for the mountains are to be found in the village.

Reached by Diligence from Lienz, page 370.

Zell-am-See.—*Stat.*

HOTELS: KAISERIN ELISABETH; BOHM.

A favourite summer resort, 2,460 feet above sea, beautifully situated on the Zeller See, a sheet of water $2\frac{1}{2}$ miles long and 1 mile broad. Cool and bracing; no wind. From east bank of lake fine view towards the south. Ascent of the Schmittenhöhe, 6,455 feet, easy; magnificent panorama.

Zell is a good centre for excursions, that into the Kaprun Valley to the Kesselfall Alpenhaus and the Mooserboden is very attractive.

RAIL, pages 237A, 238. A small steamer plys upon the lake.

DALMATIA

Cattaro.—Pop. 6,000.

HOTELS: STADT GRAZ; JAGER.

A strongly fortified town, at the extreme south of Austrian territory, on an angle of a bay, a the frontier of Montenegro, whose steep hills are immediately in front. Residence of the District Governor. Cathedral; Franciscan Monastery. Theatre. Motor car to Cettigne. STEAMERS, page 340.

Ragusa.—Pop. 13,000. Railway Station at **Gravosa**, about two miles distant.

HOTELS: IMPERIAL; VILLE.

A finely situated coast town, replete with interest, in a lovely country amidst the richest southern vegetation, under Monte Sergio, 1,350 ft.; faced by Lacroma Island, where Richard Cœur de Leon was wrecked. In the Cathedral, 17th cent., are paintings. Palace of the Rectors, 14th cent.; Museum in the Palazzo Comunale. Church of the Dominican Monastery; Jesuit Church; Franciscan Church.

H.B. M.'S VICE-CONSUL—W. N. L. Shadwell, Esq.

RAIL (Gravosa), p. 247B; STEAMERS, p. 340.

Sebenico.—*Stat.*—Pop. 8.500.

A curious old place at the mouth of the River Kerka. Cathedral of 15th cent. The Falls of the Kerka are 10 miles inland. RAIL, page 244.

Spalato.—*Stat.*—Pop. 17,000.

HOTELS: TROCCOLI; DE LA VILLE.

Finely situated on a peninsula with a background of hills in a fertile country. Much of the old town is within the circuit of the great Palace built by the Emperor Diocletian, which covered about nine acres. What is left of Diocletian's Palace is, in parts, in good preservation. Cathedral—once a temple of Diana or the mausoleum of Diocletian. Museum of antiquities.

RAIL, page 244.

Zara.—Pop. 21,000.

HOTELS: BRISTOL; GRAND; VAPORE.

The capital of Dalmatia, on a peninsula, a busy place of quite Italian character. The ancient ramparts have been turned into fine promenades. Romanesque Cathedral of 13th cent.; close by is the older Church of S. Donato, 9th cent., now used as a museum. Other interesting churches. Beautiful views from the Giardino Pubblico. Trade in silk, wool, oil, wine, and in the world renowned liqueur **Maraschino (Luxardo's).**

STEAMER, page 340.

MONTENEGRO.

Cettigne.—Pop. 4,500.

HOTEL VUKO VULETIC.

The capital of Montenegro. The Palace of the King, without pretensions, is not usually shown. The Theatre building contains a Museum of arms, trophies, etc. Government Palace contains Parliament Hall and Courts of Justice. Park. The road from Cattaro to Cettigne, regarded as a wonderful work in road making, commands magnificent views of the Adriatic and the Montenegro mountains.

BRITISH CHARGE D' AFFAIRES.—H. D. Beaumont, Esq.

Motor car service between Cettigne and Cattaro, 28 miles, in about 3 hours; also between Cettigne and Rijeka, on the Lake of Scutari, 10 miles, in about $1\frac{1}{4}$ hr. At Rijeka is a steamer service to Vir Pazar, whence is a railway to the port of Antivari.

Scutari (Turkey).—Pop. 21,000.

HOTEL EUROPA.

Chief town of the Vilayet of Scutari, on the River Bojana, flowing from the Lake of Scutari to the Adriatic. Two hours south of Scutari is the little port of Obotti, where Ragusa steamers call.

H. B. M.'S VICE-CONSUL.—N. J. Summa, Esq.

STEAMER, page 363.

HUNGARY.

Population.—(1910) 20,886,487. There are 12,903 miles of **Railways**; of these, 5,045 miles are owned by the State and 5,898 miles of privately owned Railways are worked by the State; privately owned and worked, 2,091 miles. Fares and Luggage Rates are stated on page 233B.

Books.—A series of illustrated booklets dealing with the most interesting parts of Hungary is issued by the Hungarian State Railways, and may be had on application from the Administration in Budapest or from the Office of Bradshaw's Guide.

NOTICES OF TOWNS, WATERING PLACES, etc.

Balaton Füred.—*Stat.*

HOTELS: GRAND: IPOLYHOF; ELISABETH.

A bathing resort on Lake Balaton, or Plattensee, much frequented in summer for the carbonic acid springs — beneficial in female ailments.

RAIL (Balatonfüred), page 230A.

Brassó (*German* **Kronstadt**).—*Stat.*—Pop. 41,056.

HOTELS: CONTINENTAL; EUROPA; BUKAREST.

The Principal Railway Station, in a suburb to the east, is a mile and a half from the centre.

A finely situated and important commercial town. In a large square at the centre of the town is the Rathhaus, with a tower 190 ft. high; a few yards west is the Pfarr Kirche, of 14th-15th cent., and by the church is a Museum of archæological and natural history objects. Bartholomæus Kirche, the oldest, at extreme north end of town. From the Zinne mountain, 3,153 ft., on west side of town, is a very fine view.

RAIL, pages 233, 233A.

BUDAPEST (*German* **Buda-Pesth**).—*Stat.*—Pop. 880,371. (*Plan in the Special Edition, or post free 6d. stamps*).

GRAND HOTEL ROYAL.—First class family hotel, in central position. Electric light; central heating; lift. Rooms from 4 Kronen. See Advt.

GRAND HOTEL HUNGARIA.—On the Danube, in finest position. First class, with all the improvements and comforts of the leading hotels of Europe. See Advt.

HOTEL BRISTOL.—First class in every respect, in best position on the Danube. Modern comforts. Good cuisine. Rooms from 4 Kronen. See Advt.

PALACE HOTEL.—New first class hotel, centrally situated. 150 suites and single rooms from 4 Kr. Restaurant. See Advt.

HOTEL BRITANNIA.—New first class hotel, on the Terezien Ring, close to the West Station. Opened in April, 1913. See Advt.

PARK HOTEL.—New first class hotel, facing the Central Station. 200 rooms and apartments from 4 Kronen. Every up-to-date comfort. See Advt.

HOTEL JAGERHORN.—Well situated first-class hotel. See Advt.

HOTEL CONTINENTAL.—First class family house. Best position, near the Danube and Exchange. Rooms from Kr. 4. Pension. See Advt.

PENSION SACHER.—Irányi Utca, 21. First class, up-to-date, and most comfortable. Central position. Excellent cuisine. See Advt.

PENSION GRIMM.—Vigado-utca, 2. High class pension in central position. All modern comforts. Inclusive terms from 8 Kr. See Advt.

PENSION BELLEVUE.—V. Zoltán—u, 8. First class new International Pension. Central and beautiful position. Every modern comfort and convenience. Pension from Kr. 9. See Advt.

PENSION GERO.—Lipót-Körut, 10. First class, central, and most comfortable. Close to the West Station. Pension from Kr. 10. See Advt.

There are three principal RAILWAY STATIONS, each within a mile of the centre: West Station (Nyugoti pálya udvar—Westbahnhof), in the north west part of Pest, for trains to and from Vienna via Marchegg, to Bucharest, etc.; East Station (Keleti pálya udvar—Ostbahnhof), on east side, for trains to and from Vienna via Bruck, to Belgrade, etc.; South Station (Déli vasuti pálya udvar—Sudbahnhof), for train service to Trieste, Venice, etc.

The large Danube steamers land passengers at the Ferencz József rakpart (Franz Josef Quai), on the Pest side, near the Suspension Bridge. Local steamers ply across and up and down the river, fares 10, 15, and 20 fillér.

Underground Electric Railway between Gizella Tér (near river, a little south of Suspension Bridge) and the Városliget (City Park).

BUDAPEST, capital of Hungary, is situated on both banks of the River Danube; the part upon the left bank of the river is by far the larger, though down to the 15th century it was inferior in size and importance to the part on the right bank.

Most British travellers will alight at either the West Station or the East Station. From the West Station the Váczi Körút (Waitzner Ring) leads in two-thirds of a mile to the inner city; or from the north end of the Váczi Körút any of the short streets west will lead in a quarter of a mile to the magnificent Parliament House by the river. From the East Station the Rákoczy ut leads in about a mile to the inner city and the river. It is well to begin an inspection of the city with a stroll along the quais. The Suspension Bridge (Láncz Hid), one of the longest in Europe, is the work of British engineers, Tiernay and Clark (1840-49).

The PARLIAMENT HOUSE (Uj Országház), by the river, north of the Suspension Bridge, is an immense Gothic pile, by the architect Steindl; splendid facade to the river, central dome 350 ft. high. Interior richly decorated with marble and gold; painted ceilings.

Opposite the north east corner of the Parliament House is the Curia Regia (Magyar Királyi Curia), the Supreme Law Court, in Renaissance style; handsome flight of stairs. To south of the Curia are the Ministries of Agriculture and Justice; a little back, along the Alkotmany Utcza, north side, are the Law Courts (Törvényszeki Palota).

The Hungarian National Museum of Fine Arts is in the Városliget (Town Park), on the north east side of the city. Here are extensive choice collections of Spanish, Italian, German, Flemish, and Dutch paintings, including works by the most famous masters—Murillo, Ribera, Tintoretto, Raphael, Correggio, Rubens, Van Dyck, Rembrandt, Dürer, Cranach, to name only a few. British art is represented by Gainsborough,

Reynolds, Lawrence, Constable, etc. There are also paintings by ancient Hungarian masters, and many examples by modern artists. A collection of about 100,000 designs and engravings, specially rich in illustration of the German schools of the 18th cent.; sculpture; a Japanese collection, including paintings, wood carvings, and objects of industrial art.

The AKADEMIA is in Ferencz József Tér, on the quai, just north of the Suspension Bridge. The building, in the Renaissance style, erected 1862-64, contains the Historical Picture Gallery, in which will be found the portraits of many illustrious Hungarians. Open Sun., Tues., & Fri.

The VIGADO (Redoute), on the the quai, south of the Suspension Bridge, a Moorish erection, 1862-65, intended for festive gatherings; wall paintings on the stairway and halls. A little south along the quai, by the bridge, in the Esku Tér, are the Greek Church, and the old "Parish Church" of Pest, dating from 1500—interesting interior. The new Városház (Town Hall) is a few yards south on the east side of the Veress Pálné Utcza—handsome stairway and hall.

The Fövámház (Custom House), by the Ferencz Jozsef bridge, and the immense Grain Elevator, lower down the quai, should be seen.

The Polytechnic is a handsome building on the right bank of the Danube.

The NEMZETI MUZEUM, in Muzeum Körüt, quarter of a mile in direct line from east end of Ferencz Jozsef bridge. Here are collections of antiquities and modern curiosities of great interest. The Library contains 540,000 volumes and more than 20,000 MSS.

The University (Egyetem) is in Egyetem Ter, between the Museum and the river; the University Library (220,000 vols.) is a little north, in the Ferencziek Tér.

The **Basilika Church**, dedicated to St. Stephen, **with a dome 315 ft. high, on west side of Váczi Körüt, one third mile due east of the Suspension Bridge, is interesting.**

Industrial Arts Museum, on west side, north end, of Ullöi ut, an eastern looking building with a dome 154 ft. high. Collections of industrial art, furniture, pottery, woodware, ironware, with some ecclesiastical robes and tapestry. Hungarian exhibits specially interesting.

The imposing Royal Palace (Kiraly Palota) is on the summit of the hill just south of the west end of the Suspension Bridge. The rooms number 860—only some are open to inspection in absence of the Court; the crown jewels are not shewn; the gardens, generally open, extend to the river. Lofty Heyntzi monument in memory of the General who defended the fortress against the Hungarians in 1849.

A little north of the Royal Palace, on the Disz Tér, is the Honvéd Monument—a memorial of the struggle for independence 1848-9.

Matthias Church, in Szent Háromság (Trinity) Tér, one third mile north west of Suspension Bridge; dating from 13th cent., used as a mosque during the possession of the town by the Turks (1541-1686), restored and tower (260 ft.), built 1890-96. This is the coronation Church; Francis Joseph was here crowned King of Hungary in 1867.

Very fine view from the hill of Szent Gellérthogy (the Blocksberg), on south side of Buda. Here are bathing establishments supplied by warm sulphur springs; here also is the establishment of Andreas Saxlehner, producing the Hunyadi János natural aperient water, which is so well known. There are also warm sulphur springs at the north side of Buda, close to the river.

The Városliget is a pleasant park on the north east side of the city. Here are the Zoological Garden and the highly interesting Agricultural Museum.

The working class "colonies" established by the Municipality should be visited; in the Arena ut there is a large people's hotel for workmen, and others are being built; the Municipal Bread Factory is regarded as a model for similar establishments elsewhere.

National Opera House, in Andrássy ut; will accommodate 4,000 persons.

CEMETERY (Köztemetö) **on east side of Pest; Kossuth and Deák buried here.**

POST OFFICE **in Koronaherczeg Utcza, 250 yards back from landing place of Vienna steamers.**

H.B.M.'S CONS. GEN.—E. M. Grant Duff, Esq.

CONSUL.—Ignatz Brüll, Esq., C.M.G. VICE-CONSUL.—Dr. A. Kauffmann.

U.S. CONSUL-GENERAL.————. VICE AND DEPUTY CONS.—F. E. Mallett, Esq.

RAIL, pp. **225A, 225B, 226A, 227, 230A, 231, 231A, 232, 232A, 233, 237. Steamer, p. 368.**

Debreczen.—*Stat.*—Pop. 92,729.

HOTELS: STIER; KONIGIN VON ENGLAND.

An important commercial town whose inhabitants are mostly Protestant. College (law and theology), attended by about 2,000 students. In the large Church, Kossuth, April 14th, 1849, announced the deposition of the Hapsburgs.

RAIL, pages 227B, 228.

Esztergom (*Germ.* **Gran**).—*Stat.*—**Pop. 16,000.**

HOTELS: BAD; KONIG VON UNGARN; DREI MOHREN.

In a picturesque situation on the **River Danube, near the influx of the River Gran. On a height, 215 ft. above the river, is the Cathedral, 1820-56, in Italian Renaissance style; nave 350 ft. long, transept 160 ft. long, dome 52 ft. in diameter and 260 ft. high; altar pieces, paintings, monuments; in the treasury are a Calvary, vestments, vessels, etc. Archbishop's Palace contains collections of paintings and antiquities; at the Archbishop's Library (100,000 vols.) are many ancient manuscripts.** RAIL, **pages 225B, 226A.**

Fiume.—*Stat.*—Pop. 49,806.

HOTELS: EUROPA; DEAK; LLOYD; QUARNERO.

A busy seaport, on the Bay of Quarnero. The Railway Station is on the west side of the town, about half a mile from the centre at the Piazza Adamich. Cathedral; Church of St. Veit; pilgrimage Church of Madonna del Mare, to which steps ascend from near Church of St. Veit. Governor's Palace; Archduke József mansion,

From the Corso a street at the clock tower leads to an Arch erected by the Romans. Imperial Naval Training College. Frequent steamers to and from Abbazia.

H.B.M.'s CONSUL.—G. Faber, Esq.

VICE-CONS.—A. Steinacker, Esq.

U.S. VICE-CONS.—S. H. Shank, Esq.

RAIL, pages, 231A, 234.

Herkulesfürdó.—*Stat.*

HOTELS: FRANZ-JOSEFS HOF; RUDOLFS HOF.

In a fine situation, 485 ft. above sea, in a picturesque defile of the River Cerna. The hot springs, 126°—146° Fahrenheit, known to the Romans, are beneficial in cases of rheumatism. Handsome Cursaal; bazaar. Numerous pleasant paths in the valley. A short distance south east is the Domogled, 3,360 ft. RAIL, page 227.

The **Hohe Tátra** is a wonderfully attractive part of the interesting Carpathian Mountains. Snow clad granite peaks, mountain gorges, ranges of forest, delightful valleys with numerous beautiful small lakes, combine their charms in this romantic country. Lake Csorba, the "Pearl of the Tátra," is of rare beauty, though of inconsiderable size. Owing to its mild climate and pure air, the Hohe Tátra is an ideal resort both in summer and winter. Local electric railways connect several of the places of greatest interest.

RAIL (to Popräd Felka), page 253A.

Kassa.—*Stat.*—Pop. 44,211.

HOTELS: SCHALKHAZ; EUROPA; SCHIFFBECK.

A busy old town, on the River Hernad; once a fortress. The Cathedral, 15th cent., is regarded as the best Gothic church in Hungary; in interior are a rich open work canopy, 66 ft. high, fine windows, high altar with many paintings on a gold ground. Museum of antiquities, coins, natural history. RAIL, pp. 227A, 231, 253A.

Kolozsvar (*German* **Klausenburg**).—*Stat.*—Pop. 60,808. HOTELS: NEW YORK; CENTRAL.

A University town, on the River Szamos. Roman Catholic Cathedral of St. Michael, 15th cent., in the Markt Platz; Protestant Church, 15th cent., in south east quarter. University on west side of town.

H.B.M's VICE CONSUL.—S. Tamási, Esq.

RAIL, pages 223, 233.

Nagy Szeben (*German* **Hermannstadt**).—Pop. 30,000.—HOTELS: ROMISCHER KAISER; MELTZER.

The former capital of Transylvania. Rathhaus; Protestant Church, with large painting of the Crucifixion and collection of ecclesiastical treasures. Collections in Brukenthal Palace and at the Museum. RAIL, pp. 232, 233, 233A.

Nagy Várad (*German* **Grosswardein**).—*Stat.*—Pop. 64,169.

HOTELS: RIMANOCZI; GRUNER BAUM; SZECHENYI

An ancient town, on the River Koros. Roman Catholic Cathedral, near the Railway Station; in the Museum close by are historical collections.

RAIL, pages 228, 230A, 233.

Pécs (*German* **Funfkirchen**).—*Stat.*—Pop. 49,822.

HOTELS: NADOR; WILDER MANN.

A pleasantly situated town. The four-towered Romanesque Dom, dating from 11th cent., rebuilt 1881-91, is by some considered the finest cathedral in Hungary. Three Mosques built by the Turks (1543-1686) still stand—two have become churches. Good wine from neighbouring vineyards. Sulphur springs at Harkany, 14 miles south. RAIL, pages 226A, 230.

Popräd Felka.—Population 1,700.

Former free town of the province of Zips, founded in the 12th century, on the river Popräd. Here is the museum of the Carpathian Club. Popräd Felka is an excellent centre for excursions in the Tátra region; railway to the mineral springs of Tátra-füred (page 253), and a fine mountain road to the Ice Cave of Dobsina, a natural wonder.

RAIL, page 253 A.

Pöstyén (*German* **Pistyan**).—*Stat.*—Pop. 8,000.

468 ft. above sea, in a fertile plain, at the west base of the Carpathian Mountains; the climate is mild and the country around attractive. The waters are 143° Fahr.; recommended in cases of rheumatism, sciatica, gout, neuralgia, skin diseases, and rachitis. Bath Establishments (radio-active mud-baths, 152° Fahr.), open all the year.

RAIL, page 233B.

Pozsony (*German* **Pressburg**).—*Stat.*—Pop. 78,223. HOTELS: GRUNER BAUM; NATIONAL.

An old town, at one time the capital of Hungary, in a fine situation on the Danube. At about 200 yards back from the Steamer Pier is the broad Promenaden Platz; parallel with the Promenaden Platz, a few yards distant, is Langegasse, where, at west end, is the Dom, dating from 1204—kings of the Hapsburg line crowned here; in north aisle is St. Anne's Gothic Chapel. West of the Dom, on the Schlossberg, is the ruined royal palace; fine views. Just beyond the east end of Langegasse are the Rathhaus (containing museum of antiquities, arms, etc.) and Palace of the Primate of Hungary.

RAIL, pages 226, 227. Steamer, page 368.

Szeged (*German* **Szegedin**).—*Stat.*—Pop. 118,328.

HOTELS: EUROPE; TISZA; SCHWARZER ADLER.

Two Railway Stations; Szeged Station on the River Quay, at south-east side of town, and Szeged Rokus Station at north-west of town. A commercial town on both banks of the River Theiss. Rathaus in Szechenyi Ter, at centre of town; at the Kultur Palast, in Rudolf Ter, by the bridge over the river, is a picture gallery, collections of antiquities, etc., and a library of 60,000 vols. Franciscan Monastery with old Church of St. Matthias in south part of town—ecclesiastical relics and library.

RAIL, pages 226A, 227, 227B, 230A, 254.

Tátra Lomnicz.—*Stat.*

HOTELS: NAGY SZALLODA; PALACE.

One of the most prominent health resorts of the Hohe Tátra, having a particularly mild climate and affording special facilities for winter sport. The Tarpatak Valley (two hours walk) with its beautiful falls, is the finest in the Tátra.

RAIL, page 253.

Temesvar.—*Stat.*—Pop. 72,555.

HOTELS: KRONPRINZ RUDOLF; HUNGARIA.

A busy place on the Bega Canal, the inner town and three populous suburbs being separated by parks and open spaces. Cathedrals of the Greek and Roman Catholic Churches. Museum of antiquities, natural history, etc.; also a collection of pictures. Town Hall. Monument to the defenders of the town in 1849. The old Castle built by Hunyadi in 1442, now an arsenal, has been so altered that very little of the original is left. The Siebenbürgen Barracks are an immense building.

RAIL, pages 226A, 227, 227A, 227B, 232.

Tokaj.—*Stat.*—Pop. 4,800.

HOTEL GOLDENER ADLER.

At the junction of the Bodrog with the Theiss, under a steep hill, called Kopacs Teto. Tokaj wine was first grown by K. Lajos, about 1342; the best wine is called "Aszu," the next best "Szomorodni." Government vineyards at Tarczal. RAIL, p. 227B.

Vácz (*German* **Waitzen**).—*Stat.*—Pop. 14,500.

HOTEL CURIE. A town 21m. from Budapest, on the Danube; one of the oldest settlements of the Magyars. Cathedral, and Deaf and Dumb Asylum. RAIL, pages 226A, 227.

Varasd (*German* **Warasdin**).—*Stat.*—Pop. 10,400.

HOTELS: WILDER MANN; LAMM. The frontier town of Croatia, on the Drave. Near Sulphur Baths, and good vineyards. RAIL, p. 229.

Zágráb (*German* **Agram**).—*Stat.*—Pop. 79 038.

HOTELS: KAISER VON OESTERREICH; GRAND; PRUCKNER; IMPERIAL.

Two Railway Stations: Sudbahnhof, on west side of town, for Vienna, Trieste, etc.; Staatsbahnhof, on south side, for Budapest, Fiume, etc.

The capital of Croatia, in a pleasant situation, on the River Medvescak. The Cathedral, Gothic, 15th cent., is in the north east quarter; column to the Virgin in front of Cathedral, Archbishop's palace opposite south side of Cathedral. Within a quarter mile (west) of the Cathedral are the Chamber of Deputies, St. Mark's Church, Palace of the Governor, Municipal Offices, and the Natural History Museum. A few yards south west of the Cathedral, in the lower town, is the open square, Jelacicevtig (Jellacic Platz), whence a narrow street leads south by the Synagogue to squares where are the Law Courts and Academy of Science (antiquities, pictures, etc.).

RAIL, pages 229, 231A, 235.

SWITZERLAND.

(With Map in Special Edition.)

Switzerland is the culminating ridge of the mountains bordering on France, Germany, Austria, and Italy, forming the head water-systems of the Rhône, Rhine, Aar, Ticino, and Inn. The surface is about 220 miles by 110 miles, or an area of 15,976 square miles.

Railways.—Mid-Europe Time, which is one hour before French and the same as Italian railway time, is kept on all railways. Return Tickets at a reduction of 25 per cent. Children, 3 to 12, half price. **Luggage,** 0·5 centime per 22 lbs per kilometre. **Tourist Season Tickets** available over most of the Swiss Railways (mountain lines and a few other lines not included), are issued for periods of 15, 30, or 45 days; the rates are: 15 days—1st class, £3 8s., 2nd class, £2 8s., 3rd class, £1 16s.; 30 days—£5, £3 12s., £2 12s.; 45 days—£6 12s., £4 12s., £3 8s.; two hours notice to be given at principal stations, twenty-four hours notice at minor stations, and unmounted photograph of applicant required. These tickets may be obtained in London from the General Agency of the Swiss Federal Railways, Carlton House, 11B, Regent Street, Waterloo Place, S.W.

Money.—100 centimes = 1 franc = 9½d. English. GOLD COIN.—20 franc piece, and 20 and 10 franc pieces. SILVER COIN.—5, 2, 1, ½-franc pieces. NICKEL COIN.—20, 10, and 5 centime pieces. BRONZE COIN.—2 and 1 cent. pieces.

Weights and Measures.—The *Pfund*, or pound, chief unit of weight, is legally divided into decimal Grammes, but the people generally prefer the use of the old halves and quarters (Halbpfund and Viertelpfund). 1 Centner = 50 Kilogrammes = 100 Pfund = 110 lbs. avoirdupois. 1 Quintal = 100 Kilogrammes. See also p. lxxi.

Telegraph to United Kingdom, 50 c. *Grundtaxe*, and about 30 c. per word; for Switzerland, 30 c. *Grundtaxe*, and about 2½ c. per word.

Postage.—To United Kingdom, 25 c. for ½-oz. (15 gr.); 5 c. and 10 c. in Switzerland, according to distance. Cards, 10 c. (to United Kingdom), and 5 c.

Government.—A Federal Assembly, or Legislative body, consisting of a National Council, of 167 members (1 for 20,000 pop.); and a Council of States, of 44 members—two for each Canton. A Federal Council, or Executive, of 7 members, is nominated by the Assembly for three years, under a President (M. Marc Ruchet), elected annually, seated at Berne, where the Foreign Ministers reside.—**Army** (1912), 214,022, consisting of Elite 143,220, and Landwehr 69,569. **Population** (1910), 3,741,971.

Enquiry Offices for Tourists have been established in most of the principal towns and centres in Switzerland for the purpose of furnishing information to Tourists and intending Visitors.

Adelboden.—Pop. 1,564.

REGINA HOTEL.—Excellent house, specially suitable for English families. Electric light; central heating. Open June to September and December to March. Pension from 9 fr. (summer) and 14 fr. (winter). See Advt.

NEVADA PALACE.—Fire-proof first class hotel, opened 1912, replete with every modern comfort and luxury. Large park. Terms from 13 fr. (summer) and 15 fr. (winter). See Advt.

HOTEL BEAU SITE.—Family hotel, entirely rebuilt and enlarged. Lift, electric light. Central heating. Open the whole year. Pension from 7 frs. See Advt.

GRAND HOTEL KURHAUS.—First class hotel, in a fine position, with every modern comfort. All winter sports. See Advt.

HOTEL PENSION EDELWEISS.—Comfortable and well situated. Electric light and central heating. Baths. Sports. See Advt.

HOTEL BRISTOL OBERLAND.—In quiet position, with fine view. Electric light; central heating. Open all the year. Pension from 7 fr. See Advt.

An interesting village and health resort, much frequented at all seasons, 4,450 ft. above sea, in the attractive Adelboden Valley. Church (15th cent.) with frescoes; old timber houses. Fine views of the chain of the Lohner and snowy Wildstrubel (10,670 ft.). Rich Alpine flora. Every form of winter sport is practised. A centre for mountain excursions.

ENGLISH CHURCH SERVICE at the new Church.

WINTER SPORT STORES.—Chr. Klopfenstein, next Hotel National. Skis, Skates, Ski boots, and Winter Outfits. Catalogue on application.

DILIGENCE from Frutigen, page 376.

Aigle.—*Stat.*—Pop. 3,897.

HOTELS: GRAND; BEAU SITE; VICTORIA.

A summer resort, the Roman Aquila, in Canton Vaud, in Ormont Valley, 1,335 feet above sea, near the Rhône and Lake of Geneva. Chateau. Good wine. Fine view from the Plantour, 1,604 ft., a wooded hill to south of the town. Skating and curling in winter. Golf links.

ENGLISH CHURCH SERVICE at St. John Ch. Electric Tram.

RAIL, pp. 263B, 267A. Diligence, p. 376.

Airolo.—*Stat.*—Pop. 1,697.

GRAND HOTEL MOTTA.—Very comfortable house, with electric light, baths, large terrace, and fine park. See Advt.

HOTEL LOMBARDI and DEPENDENCIES.—Good hotel, with electric light and garden; telephone. Pension 7-12 fr. per day. See Advt.

In the Val Leventina, the upper valley of the Ticino, 3,750 ft. above sea, the first village of Italian speaking Switzerland after emerging from the St. Gotthard Tunnel; favourably regarded as a summer resort. RAIL, page 259.

[From Airolo an interesting and comparatively easy way (bridle path as far as Piora) leads to **Santa Maria**, on the Lukmanier Diligence Route. On the way are Lake Ritom (at west end is HOTEL PIORA), amidst attractive surroundings, and several other small secluded lakes; beyond the lakes is the **Uomo Pass**, and then the descent to Santa Maria.]

Alpnach Stad.—*Stat.*

HOTELS: PILATUS; ROSSLI.

At one end of the Alpnacher See, an almost enclosed arm of the Lake of Lucerne.

RAIL, page 267A. Steamer, page 369.

[**Mont Pilatus**, 6,995 ft., rising prominently due south of Lucerne, affords one of the finest views of central Switzerland. The ascent is through forest and along pastures, with a rich and varied flora, to a rugged wild summit; occasional mist at noon, but clear morn. and even. HOTEL PILATUSKULM].

Altdorf.—*Stat.*—Pop. 2,551.

BLACK LION HOTEL (LION NOIR).—Well known, old established hotel, situated in the centre of the town; garden. Very reasonable charges. Pension from 6 fr. See Advt.

SCHLUSSEL; LOWE.

Pleasantly situated in a fertile mountain surrounded valley of Canton Uri, of which it is the capital; 1,490 ft. above sea. The town (a mile from the Station) is the scene of the exploits of the mythical William Tell, of whom is a statue in the principal square. During the summer Schiller's "Tell" is performed by citizens. Church; Capuchin Monastery above. At the village of Bürglen, on the hill, a mile south east, was Tell's home; a memorial chapel stands next the site of his house.

RAIL, page 259. Diligence, page 376.

Amsteg.—*Stat.* HOTELS: STERN; KREUZ.

In Canton Uri, on the Reuss, 1,712 ft. above sea, near the **Maderaner Thal**, or valley of the Kärstelen, amongst peaks 10,000 ft. high, Hüfistock and other glaciers, waterfalls, and forests. RAIL, page 259.

Andermatt.—Pop. 818.

GRAND HOTEL BELLEVUE.—First class hotel with every modern comfort. Electric light. Restaurant Francais. See Advt.

DANIOTH'S GRAND HOTEL.—First class, of old reputation. Equipped with every modern improvement. Apartments with baths. Tennis. Winter sports. Pension from 8 fr. See Advt.

Chief village of the Urseren Valley, a summer and winter resort and a centre for all kinds of winter sport; 4,738 ft. above sea. Old Church. Fine view from the Mariahilf Chapel.

ENGLISH CHURCH SERVICE at Hotel Bellevue.

Diligence from Göschenen, page 377.

[**Hospenthal.**

HOTEL MEYERHOF.—English family hotel. Terms on pension from 8 fr. in summer, from 10 fr. in winter. See Advt.

A picturesque little Alpine village above Andermatt, 1½ miles distant, 4,870 ft. above sea level, at the junction of the roads over the Furka and St. Gotthard Passes. A favourite summer and winter resort.

Reached by diligence from Andermatt, p. 377.]

Arolla, Mayens d'Arolla.

HOTELS: KURHAUS; MT. COLLON.

In the Val d'Arolla, 6,570 feet above sea, with a very dry climate; finely situated at the base of the Glacier d'Arolla and the Glacier de Vuibez, over which rises the pyramidal Mont Collon (11,955 feet). A centre for mountain climbing. One fine excursion is to Zermatt over the Col de Bertol. English Ch. Serv. in summer.

Good track between Arolla and Evolène (4 hrs.); diligence between Evolène and Sion, page 375.

Arosa.—Pop. 1,476.

HOTEL SEEHOF.—First class hotel, situated in fine position on the Lake. Every modern comfort. Electric light and central heating. English rendezvous. See Advt.

ALEXANDRA HOTEL.—An English clientèle is cultivated by the proprietor (whose wife is an Englishwoman), ten years at the London and South Western Hotel, Southampton. See Advt.

GRAND HOTEL.-First class, beautifully situated in its own grounds, midst pine woods. Frequented mostly by English and Americans. Pension from 10 fr. See Advt.

HOTEL VALSANA.—First class, occupying finest position, opposite the Skating Rink. Open all the year. Pension from 9 fr. See Advt.

EXCELSIOR HOTEL.—First class. Newest hotel. Charmingly situated, in proximate vicinity of pine woods. Pension from 8 fr. See Advt.

HOTEL PENSION BRISTOL.—Family hotel, well situated, overlooking the lake. Garden; tennis. Pension from 7 fr. See Advt.

A beautiful Alpine summer and winter health resort, about 6,000 ft. above sea, amidst superb scenery, sheltered from the north wind, a favourable residence in cases of phthisis. Pine woods, rich flora. Many mountain excursions; resident guides. Skating, ski-ing, and all winter sports. ENGLISH CHURCH SERV.

MEDICAL.—Dr. Moreland.

VILLA GENTIANA.—The only private English Sanatorium in the Alps.

DILIGENCE from Chur, page 377.

Avants, Les.—See page 526B.

Axen Fels.—*Stat.*

PALACE HOTEL AXEN-FELS.—Strictly first class, in beautiful park. Mostly frequented by English. Pension from 10 fr.—high season from 14 fr. (English Church Service). Golf links (9 holes); three tennis courts. See Advt.

Just above Brunnen, with a very fine view in both directions over the Lake of Lucerne. Numerous pleasant excursions within easy distance. Pure and invigorating air.

RAIL (Brunnen, Morschach, Axenfels Axenstein), page 259A. Steamer, page 369.

[**Morschach.**—*Stat*

HOTEL PENSION DEGENBALM.—On a height, 236 ft. above the village; electric light; baths; tennis; own farm; celebrated milk cure; terms from 6 frs. See Advt.

A little below Axen Fels and above Brunnen, in a beautiful secluded situation, favourable during summer for quiet and rest; in winter, tobogganing and ski-ing. Lake and mountain views. RAIL, page 259A.]

Axenstein.—*Stat.*

GRAND HOTEL.—Strictly first class 2,350 ft. above sea level; commanding magnificent panorama. New building, enlarged and improved surrounded by beautiful woods. Tennis. (English Chapel adjacent). See Advt.

Finely situated above Brunnen, with wide, superb views over both arms of the Lake of Lucerne; visited by Queen Victoria in 1869. In much repute as a health resort, the air being remarkably pure, light, and invigorating. In the immediate neighbourhood are several spots of historic and literary importance. In grounds near the covered promenade are erratic blocks and traces of glacier action. A pleasant path leads to a road on the Gutsch Mountain; lake excursions all round. The Stoos (4,242 ft.) and Frohnalpstock (6,295 ft.) are easily ascended from Axenstein. ENG. CH. SERV.—All Saint's Ch.

RAIL from Brunnen, page 259A.

Baden.—*Stat.*—Pop. 7,500.

A picturesque town near Zurich, on the river Limmat, noted for its hot mineral springs, most beneficial in cases of gout, rheumatism, chronic catarrhs, etc. RAIL, pages 260A, 261, 262.

Basle, or Bâle (*German* **Basel**).—*Stat.*—Pop. (1910) 131,914.

828 ft. above the sea. The key to Switzerland, where several International Railway Lines meet and the customs examinations take place. Terminus of the Gotthard Railway. Quickest and shortest connection with Paris, London, Berlin, Hamburg, Munich, Vienna, Brussels, Milan, Rome, Genoa, as well as the Riviera and the Engadine. Well known University. Basle is recommended as an intermediate station for the change of climate between the warm South and the low lying North and the Alpine districts. It offers to its visitors manifold and favourite points of interest and pleasure. Museums with collections of Holbein and Böcklin, Historical museum, large Zoological Gardens, Minster with cross-aisle, Municipal Theatre.

GRAND HOTEL VICTORIA AND NATIONAL réunis.—First class hotels, facing the Central Station. Equipped with every modern comfort. Lifts; electric light and steam heating throughout. Excellent cuisine. See Advt.

GRAND HOTEL AND HOTEL EULER.—First class hotel. Well situated, opposite the Swiss Railway Station. Lift. Garden. See Advt.

THREE KINGS HOTEL.—Well situated on the Rhine. First class in every respect. See Advt.

HOTEL SCHWEIZERHOF.—First class house. Near the Swiss Railway Station. Every modern comfort. Suites and single rooms with bath and toilet. Garden; terrace; restaurant. See Advt.

HOTEL UNIVERS.—First class; near Central Station (facing the Exit), and Promenade, Suites and single rooms with bath and toilet. Rooms from 4 frs. See Advt.

HOTEL ST. GOTHARD—TERMINUS.—Situated opposite the Swiss Station, Post, and Telegraph. See Advt.

HOTEL JURA.—Large second class hotel, facing the Central Station. All modern comforts. Rooms from 2/-. See Advt.

PARC HOTEL BERNERHOF.—Conveniently situated on the promenades, near Central Station. Electric light. Restaurant. See Advt.

HOTEL HOFER.—Close to the Central Station. All modern comforts. Rooms from fr. 2.75. See Advt.

HOTEL BRISTOL.—Opposite the Swiss Station, entirely renovated; every modern comfort. Rooms from 3 fr. Pension from 7 fr. Restaurant. See Advt.

There are two important RAILWAY STATIONS. The SCHWEIZERISCHER BAHNHOF is on the south side of the town—here the trains from Alsace

(Strassburg, etc.) run in, connecting with the principal Swiss Railways(Berne, Lucerne, Zurich. etc.). The BADISCHER BAHNHOF, on the north side of the town, is where the trains from Heidelberg, Carlsruhe, etc. run in. Both Stations are within two thirds of a mile from the Rhine and the centre of the town. Electric Tramways to all parts of the town.

BASEL, the Roman Basilea, is situated on both banks of the River Rhine; the larger and more interesting part, Gross Basel, is on the south bank; Klein Basel, where are many factories, is on the north bank.

The Gothic Münster (Minster) is close to the river, on the south bank; its two towers may be seen from all parts of the town. Prior to the Reformation (1529) it was the Cathedral of the Bishopric of Basel. Parts of the building date from 1185, but the greater part is an erection of 1365 after damage by earthquake and fire. North tower 210 ft. high, south tower 206 ft. high, Interior—213 ft. long, 107 ft. wide—contains tombstone of Erasmus (died 1536) on a pillar, several monuments, and some reliefs; good stained windows; rood loft sustaining the organ. Free on Mon. and Wed. aft., at other times 25 c. The famous Council of Basel began its sittings in the Münster in 1431. Cloisters leading to the Pfalz terrace, whence is a fine view; the Concilien Saal, in the cloisters, contains a collection of Bibles, in the adjoining Betsaal is a Palestine collection. 100 yards south east of the Münster is Baumleingasse, where at the house No. 18 Erasmus died.

St. Elisabethan Kirche, quarter mile due south of Münster, and St. Matthaus Kirche (tower 240 ft.), in Klein Basel, both modern. Paulus Kirche, 1901 (the dome is conspicuous), half mile west of the Swiss Station.

Museum, 100 yards north west of the Münster. On lower floors are ethnographical, pre-historic, and natural history collections. Picture Gallery on upper floor; paintings by Hans Holbein the younger, and German and Dutch masters, with good examples by modern Swiss artists. Free on Sun. morn. and Wed. aft., at other times 50 c.

Kunsthalle, in the Steinenberg, one sixth mile south of Münster; collection of pictures; Sunday and Wed. free, other days 50 c.

Historisches Museum in the restored Bärfusser Kirche, 250 yards south west of the Münster. Highly interesting collection of antiquities, ecclesiastical, judicial, warlike, industrial, and artistic. Sun. morn. and aft. and Wed. aft. free, other days 50 c.

Rathhaus (1508-21), in the Marktplatz, quarter mile north west of the Münster.

Close to the Spalen Thor (1400), the best of the town gates left, two thirds mile due west of the Münster, are the University buildings—library on north side, 250,000 vols. and about 4,000 MSS. 200 yards west of the Spalen Thor, in Missionstrasse, is Missions Haus, with East Indian, Chinese, and African collections.

Zoological Garden, on south side of town. Kannenfeld Gottesacker (cemetery), in north west district. St. Jakob Monument, at south end of St. Jakobstrasse, beyond Aeschenplatz, two thirds mile south east of the Münster, in memory of 1,300 Swiss who fell fighting against 30,000 French, in 1444.

POST OFFICE, in Freiestrasse, 200 yards west of the Münster.

ENGLISH CHURCH SERV. at Hotel Trois Rois.

H. B. M.'S VICE-CONSUL.—C. Oswald, Esq.

U. S. CONSUL.—George Gifford. Esq.

DEPOT FOR BRADSHAW'S PUBLICATIONS.—F. Festersen and Co., Station Bookstalls.

RAIL.-See Routes from Basle, pp. cxviii to cxx.

Beatenberg, St.—Pop. 1,082.

GRAND HOTEL VICTORIA.—First class, situated facing Lake of Thun; latest sanitary and central heating arrangements. See Advt.

GRAND HOTEL BEATENBERG KURHAUS—First class, near Funicular Station. Well situated, with full view on glaciers and lake. Very large old park. Modern comfort. See Advt.

GRAND PARK HOTEL DE LA POSTE.—First class, well situated, with fine views of the Alps, Glaciers, and Lake. Large shady garden and park. See Advt.

GRAND HOTEL BELLEVUE.—First class family hotel, beautifully situated, in close proximity to the English Church. Entirely renovated and under new management. Large garden terrace. Pension from 7 fr. See Advt.

HOTEL PENSION BLUMLISALP. — Admirably situated, 10 minutes from the Station. Lately considerably enlarged. Electric light; central heating. Open all the year. Pension from 6 fr. See Advt.

HOTEL-PENSION BEAU-REGARD.—Centrally situated on the promenade, commanding magnificent view of lake and mountains. Excellent cooking. Very reasonable charges. Pension from 5 fr. See Advt.

A beautiful spot and favourite Alpine health resort on the north side of Lake Thun, 6 m. from Interlaken, 3,822 ft. above sea, named from the Hermitage, or Cave, of St. Beatus (*Beatus höhle*). The air is remarkably pure, seven hours sunshine on the average per day; magnificent views—finest view is from the Amisbuhl, 4,383 ft. Centre for winter sports; very large skating rink.

ENGLISH CHURCH SERVICE at the Eng. Church.

Funicular railway up from Beatenbucht, where is railway station, page 268F, and steamer pier, page 363.

Bernardino, San.

HOTELS: VICTORIA; BROCCO; RAVIZZA.

The highest village, 5,335 feet, of the Val Mesocco; many visitors in the summer for the pure air and a mineral spring. DILIGENCE, p. 377.

[An often winding road leads up from the village of San Bernardino to the **San Bernardino Pass**, 6,770 ft. (an INN). The descent is to Hinterrhein and Splugen.]

Berne or **Bern.**—*Stat.*—Pop. (1910) 85,264.

HOTEL BERNERHOF.—First class hotel, delightfully situated. Full view of the Alps. See Advt.

HOTEL NATIONAL.—New modern hotel, on the Bundes-Platz, and near the Station. Lift, central heating. Rooms from 3.50 frs. See Advt.

HOTEL SCHWEIZERHOF.—Re-opened in June. 1913. Facing the Station. Hot and cold water supply and telephone in all rooms. Rooms from 3 fr. 50c. See Advt.

PARK HOTEL PENSION FAVORITE.—English family hotel, 7 minutes from Station. Elevated position; fine panorama of Berne. Lift; central heating, and electric light. Pension arrangements. See Advt.

HOTEL DU LION.—Good second class hotel, facing the Station and close to Post Office. Electric light, central heating, baths. Rooms from 3 frs. Pension term from 8 frs. See Advt.

HOTEL BRISTOL.—New high class hotel, not far from the Station. Hot and cold water supply. 130 beds from 3 fr. See Advt.

HOTEL BAREN.—Near Federal Palace and Station. Very comfortable. Rooms from 3 fr. Pension from 7 fr. 50 c. See Advt.

HOTEL DE LA POSTE. Facing the Central Station. Lift; central heating. Moderate. See Advt.

PENSION EDEN.—Comfortable pension-hotel, in quiet position, five minutes from Station. Garden. Electric light, central heating. Pension from 6 fr. See Advt.

Berne, 1,765 ft. above sea, is often mentioned as the most picturesque town in Europe. It is situated upon a rocky peninsula at whose base the River Aare, 100 ft. below, flows in a complete bend; the old arcaded streets, with wonderfully preserved mediæval towers and fountains, and the many spots commanding magnificent views, will arrest attention at every turn. Besides being the capital of the Canton, Berne is the seat of the Swiss Government.

A few yards south of the Bahnhof a broad thoroughfare—Spittalgasse, Marktgasse, Kramgasse, Gerechtigkeitsgasse—traverses the town from west to east, the latter end being at the Nydeck Brücke over the Aare; just beyond the east end of the bridge is the Bärengraben (bear pit), where the town bear is kept—the name Berne being derived from Bären. At the junction of the Marktgasse and Kramgasse is the Zeitglockenthurm (clock tower), 15th-17th cent.

Less than half a mile due south of the Bahnhof, upon a noble site over the river, is the Swiss House of Parliament (Bundeshaus), a magnificent range of buildings in Florentine style; on each side of the domed and towered central structure are extensive wings—in the west wing are the Ministries of the Interior and Justice; the central part is occupied by the two Chambers—the Nationalrath and the Ständerath; in the east wing are the Ministries of War, Industry, and Agriculture.

The Gothic Münster (Minster), one third mile due east of the Bundeshaus. The building dates from 1421-1598; length 285 ft., width 118 ft., height 77 ft. On west portal are sculptures, "The Judgment"; tower 328 ft. Interior has choir stalls, monuments, stained glass, large organ. Free on Sun. aft., other times 20c.

Town Library (150,000 vols.) between the Bundeshaus and the Münster. Rathhaus (1406-16), 200 yards due north of the Münster.

The University is about 200 yards north of the Railway Station; 1,900 students.

Historical Museum (Historisches Museum), on Helvetia Platz, just beyond the south end of Kirchenfeld Brücke (between the Bundeshaus and Münster). Archæological and ethnographical collections; warlike, ecclesiastical, artistic, domestic, and industrial objects of interest; Sun., Tues., and Sat., at certain times free, otherwise 50 c. Swiss National Library near south end of Kirchenfeld Brücke.

Kunst Museum, quarter mile north east of the Bahnhof; sculpture and painting, including several works by modern Swiss artists; free on Sun. and Tues., other days 50 c. Natural History Museum, opposite the Kunst Museum.

Handsome Stadttheater. Industrial Museum in the Kornhaus, close to the Theatre. Swiss Alpine Museum in Zeughausgasse, near the Theatre.

Botanical Garden, near north end of railway bridge.

POST OFFICE immediately north of Rail. Sta.

ENGLISH CHURCH SERVICE, in the Church of S. Ursula. Kirchenfeld. 8.30, 10.30, 5.0.

BRITISH MINISTER.—His Excy. Grant Duff, Esq. CONSUL.—Gaston de Muralt, Esq.

UNITED STATES MINISTER.—His Excy. H. S. Boutell. CONSUL.—G. Heimrod, Esq.

MEDICAL.—Dr. Sahli.

RAIL, pp. 257, 259B, 263, 265, 267; Diligence, p. 374.

Bex.—*Stat.*—Pop. 3,190.

GRAND HOTEL DES SALINES.—Well situated family hotel, with own bath establishment. Own large park. Terms from 9 frs. See Advt.

GRAND HOTEL DE BEX AND BATH.—High class family hotel, situated in its own grounds. Fine view of the Alps. Open the whole year. Pension terms from 7 fr. See Advt.

A favourite health resort, 1,427 ft. above sea, on the River Avancon. In summer the visitors are chiefly French. The strong saline waters are in great repute. ENGLISH CHURCH SERV.

RAIL, pages 263B, 267A.

[**Les Plans.**—GRAND HOTEL DES PLANS. the Vallée des Plans, about 5 miles east of Bex, among mountains, 3,612 ft. above sea.]

Biel (Bienne).—*Stat.*—Pop. 23,583.

HOTELS: COURONNE; BIELERHOF; VICTORIA.

A busy place, near the north end of the Bieler See (Lac de Bienne); a seat of the watch making trade. Part of the old town is quaint and picturesque; the modern parts are handsome. At the Museum Schwab is a collection of lacustrine antiquities, etc.; admission 50c.

RAIL, pp. 257B, 260, 264-5. Diligence, p. 374.

[The **Taubenloch Schlucht** (Gorge) is 1½ mile north of Biel.

Magglingen (Macolin).—HOTEL.

In a splendid situation on the slopes of the Juras, above Biel, 2,960 ft. above sea. Frequented as a health resort. Wooded surroundings; fine view of the whole chain of the Swiss Alps.

English Church and Roman Catholic Services in the season. Funicular Railway up from Biel, page 260.]

Brienz.—*Stat.*—Pop. 2,580.

HOTEL DE LA CROIX BLANCHE.—Comfortable, well situated; near Brunig Railway Station and opposite Landing Stage. Moderate. See Advt.

BELLEVUE; OURS.

In a pastoral situation at the north end of the Lake of Brienz, with the Brienzer Grat rising behind. Exhibits of wood carving—the principal industry here—at the Industrie Halle; there is a Wood Carving School. Fine view from church.

ENGLISH CHURCH SERVICE.

RAIL, page 267A. Steamer page 363.

[Rail (page 267A) up from Brienz to the **Rothhorn**, 7,715 feet (HOTEL ROTHHORN KULM), through beautiful meadow land. The view, best in morning and evening light, is as extensive as that from the Rigi.]

Brig (Brigue).—*Stat.*—Pop. 2,809.

GRAND HOTEL COURONNE ET POSTE.—First class hotel close to Station. Lift; electric light; central heating. Pension from 8 fr. See Advt.

VICTORIA.

A quaint old town, on the northern slope of the Simplon, 2,277 ft. above sea, near the entrance of the Simplon Tunnel. The surroundings are delightful, mountain heights and ravines, pastures and forest. Mild climate, cool in summer; in winter all kinds of season sport—toboggan run 5 miles long on the Simplon road. Within the town is the three towered Stockalper Chateau, of the 17th cent., one of the oldest castles in Switzerland; Church and Hospital of St. Antony, dating from 1304. College, 17th cent., with interesting church; fine views from terrace. Municipal School; district Hospital. The opening of the Lötschberg line has added to the importance of Brig as a tourist centre and frontier station.

RAIL, page 263B. Diligence, pages 376, 377.

At **Simplon Kulm** (diligence, page 376), the highest point of the Simplon route, is HOTEL BELLEVUE, 6,660 ft. above sea; 80 beds; electric light, central heating; garage. See Advt.

[The **Simplon Tunnel** begins, on the Swiss side, near the village of Termen, 1½ mile east of Brigue. The work was commenced in 1898, and boring completed, Feb., 1905, the cost being £3,120,000. The tunnel is 12½ miles long.]

Brissago.—Pop. 2,000.

GRAND HOTEL.—Highest order. Very beautiful situation on lake. English clientèle; from 9 fr. Auto. meets trains at Locarno, if desired at Fondotoce (Simplon). See Advt.

A picturesque little place of Canton Ticino, on Lago Maggiore, about 6 miles from Locarno, near the Italian frontier. Many fine villas. The ascents of the Limidario, 3,189 ft., and the Gridone, are very attractive. Mild climate, luxuriant vegetation. Noted mineral spring at Madonna del Monte. Numerous fine walks and excursions in the neighbourhood.

MEDICAL.—Dr. T. Vivanti.

CHEMIST.—The English Pharmacy.

ENGLISH CHURCH SERVICE during spring and autumn.

STEAMER, page 366.

Brunig.—*Stat.*

HOTEL AND KURHAUS BRUNIG.—Well situated on the Brunig Pass, close to the Railway Station. Fine shady garden and park. See Advt.

An attractive mountain resort (3,400 ft.) on the crest of the ridge above the Lungern See, close to the broad picturesque Brunig Pass, with splendid views of the Engelhörner, Faulhorn, etc., Aare Valley, and Brienzer See. Remarkably pure air; numerous fine walks and excursions in the neighbourhood. RAIL, page 267A.

Brunnen.—*Stat.*—Pop. 3,085.

GRAND HOTEL BRUNNEN.—First class hotel, every modern comfort, well situated, with large park and covered terrace. Electric light; lifts. Steam heating in every room. See Advt.

WALDSTATTERHOF, HOTEL FOUR CANTONS.—First class in every respect, beautifully situated with park on Lake shore. Electric light, lift, hot water heating; tennis. Pension from 8 frs. (English Church Service.) See Advt.

PARK HOTEL.—First class family hotel, finest position in midst of beautiful park. Lift; electric light. Pension from 7 fr. See Advt.

HOTEL EDEN.—Elevated position, with fine view on both arms of the lake. Terraces; garden. Lift from the road. Pension from fr. 7.50. See Advt.

One of the most beautiful spots on the Lake of Lucerne (or, Lake of Four Cantons), with superb lake and mountain views. The road from Brunnen to Flüelen (8 miles), the Axenstrasse, mostly hewn out of the rock, commands an exquisite panorama, the grandeur of the scenery culminating at Tell's Platte.

ENGLISH CHURCH SERVICE in summer at Waldstatterhof (Hotel Four Cantons).

RAIL, pages 259, 259A; Steamer, page 369.

[On the opposite side of the Lake from Brunnen, about 1½ mile distant, towards Flüelen, is the historic spot called the **Rüttli** (or Grutli), a clearing in a wood, 1,646 ft. above sea. Here, on Nov. 7th, 1307, thirty-three men from Uri, Schwyz, and Unterwalden, made oath to effect their country's freedom—the leaders of the confederates were Walter Fürst, of Uri, Erny (Arnold) an der Halden, of Unterwalden, and Werner Stauffacher, of Schwyz. **Tellsplatte**, 4½ miles from Brunnen, towards Flüelen, is a ledge of rock on to which Tell leaped from Gessler's boat. Tell's Chapel, adorned with frescoes, stands on the Platte.]

Cergues, St.

HOTELS: CAFT; AUBERSON; OBSERVATOIRE.

A summer resort in a valley at the base of Mont Dole, 3,500 ft. above sea level. Splendid views of the Lake of Geneva, Mont Blanc, and the Bernese Alps. ENGLISH CHURCH SERVICE.

DILIGENCE from Nyon, page 375.

[The **Dole**, 5,505 ft., the highest mountain of the Swiss Jura, is ascended in about 3 hours from St. Cergues; guide 5 fr.]

Champéry.—*Stat.*—Pop. 704.

GD. HOTEL DENT DU MIDI.—First class, with magnificent views of the mountains. 300 beds. Pension from 7 frs. See Advt.

HOTEL CROIX FEDERALE.—Old established; situated in centre of village. Electric light; central heating. Fine view; garden; terrace. Open all the year. Pension from fr. 6.50. See Advt.

ALPES.

A beautifully situated summer and winter resort, 3,450 ft. above sea, the highest village of the Val d' Illiez. Resident guides for the Dent du Midi, 10,696 ft., and other mountain climbs. Paths from Champéry to Samoens (8 hours) over the Cols de Coux and de la Golesse, and from Champéry to Sixt (10 hrs.) over Col de Sagerou; guide not necessary. All forms of winter sport.

EDUCATIONAL.—Mr. Charles J. Murray, M.A., Chalet Grenon. Preparation for all exams. Special facilities for modern languages.

ENGLISH CHURCH SERVICE at English Church.

RAIL, page 267A.

Château d'Œx.—Pop. 2,691.

GRAND HOTEL.—First class, with all up to date requirements. Open all the year. Pension from 10 frs. See Advt.

HOTEL BERTHOD.—Well known family hotel, standing in pleasant grounds; tennis. Frequented by English. Pension from 7 frs. See Adv.

HOTEL DE L'OURS.-Open all the year. Equipped with modern comfort. Terms from 7 fr. See Advt.

HOTEL BEAU SEJOUR.—Well built modern hotel, opposite the Station. Every comfort. Garden, terrace, verandah. Pension from fr. 8. See Advt.

HOTEL PENSION ROSAT.—Family hotel, in fine elevated position, overlooking the valley. Entirely rebuilt and enlarged: all latest improvements. Pension from 7 fr. See Advt.

A quiet pastoral straggling village, 3,500 feet above sea, amidst magnificent scenery; a favourite summer and winter health resort—pure, dry air. In winter much sunshine and no wind; every kind of winter sport.

ENGLISH CHURCH SERV. at St. Peter's Church.

RAIL, page 262C. Diligence, page 376.

Chaumont, The.—*Stat.*

The Chaumont, 3,845 ft. above sea, on the north side of Neuchatel, is a very fine point of view; afternoon light the best. A chapel and school near the summit. Funicular railway connects Neuchatel and the Chaumont.

Chesieres-sur-Ollon.—*Stat.*

GRAND HOTEL DU CHAMOSSAIRE.—Fine situation, opposite the Glaciers of Trient, Dents du Midi, and Morcles. Hot water heating and electric light. See Advt.

Favourably situated, with much sunshine, 100 ft. above sea, in a very pleasant district, the terminus of the Bex-Villars-Chesieres Railway. Visited both in summer and winter—winter sports of all kinds; skating rink of 20,000 square yards. Fine view of the Alps. RAIL, page 267A.

Chexbres.—*Stat.*

HOTELS: BELLEVUE; GRAND; VICTORIA.

A summer and winter resort, in a very fine situation, on a table-land, 2,145 feet above sea, commanding superb views over the Lake of Geneva. Mild pure air and much sunshine. Reached by mountain railway from Vevey in 18 minutes; or from Puidoux-Chexbres station.

ENGLISH CHURCH SERVICE in the season.

RAIL (Puidoux-Chexbres), pages 262C, 263, 264A.

Chur (Coire).—*Stat.*—Pop. 11,950.

NEW HOTEL STEINBOCK.—First class hotel, well situated, facing the Station. Electric light; lift; baths. See Advt.

LUKMANIER; WEISSES KREUZ.

Capital of the Canton of the Grisons, 1,935 ft. above sea, the Curia Rhaetorum of the Romans, in an attractive situation on the River Plessur, an affluent of the River Rhine, 1½ mile distant. In the winter, skating and ski-ing.

From the Railway Station, in the north west quarter, the Untere Bahnhofstrasse leads past the Post Office to the upper part of the town, where is the Roman Catholic Cathedral of St. Lucius, dating from the 8th cent.; several styles noticeable in interior, elaborate altars, paintings, carving; many reliquaries, crucifixes, etc., in the treasury. Just north of the Cathedral, and forming part of the Episcopal Palace, is the Roman tower of Marsoel, containing a Chapel regarded as one of the earliest of Christian edifices. A few yards west of the Cathedral is the Museum, containing miscellaneous collections, including a few pictures; 1 fr., free on Sunday.

ENGLISH CHURCH SERVICE.

RAIL. pp. 268. 268B, 268D. Diligence, pp. 377-8.

Comballaz, La.—HOTEL DE LA COURONNE.

A summer resort, delightfully situated, 4,475 ft. above sea, in the district of Ormont dessous, on the diligence road from Aigle to Chateau d'Oex. Mineral springs. ENG. CH. SERVICE.

DILIGENCE, page 376.

Corbeyrier.

HOTEL VICTORIA.—In fine position. Modern equipments, combined with moderate charges. No consumptives admitted. See Advt.

BELLEVUE; DUBUIS.

A pleasantly situated village, 3,045 ft. above sea, sheltered from cold winds; fine views of the Rhone Valley. The Tour d'Ai, 7,567 ft., and the Tour de Mayen, 7,628 ft., are easy ascents of three to four hours from Corbeyrier. In the winter tobogganing, skating, and ski-ing.

DILIGENCE from Aigle, page 376.

Davos Platz.—*Stat.*—Pop. 4,780.

SAVOY HOTEL SPLENDID.—English family hotel, in elevated, sunny position. Lift. Electric light; central heating. Open all the year. Pension from 10 frs. See Advt.

VICTORIA HOTEL.—First class hotel, well situated, full south. See Advt.

GRAND HOTEL and BELVEDERE.—First class, of old established reputation. See Advt.

HOTEL ET PENSION BUOL, large first class hotel, open the whole year. See Advt.

HOTEL D'ANGLETERRE.—First class family hotel. See Advt.

KURHAUS; KAISERHOF; ROSE; EDEN; NATIONAL

An extensive village in a lofty mountain valley of Canton Grisons, 5,115 feet above sea. A summer and winter resort favourable for persons of consumptive tendency, with a remarkably fine, dry, clear, bracing air; sheltered from north and east winds; winter temperature 21°, summer 51°. Much sunshine, with calm air, in winter, when the days are enlivened by skating and tobogganing; winter nights very beautiful. Pine woods, alpine plants. Kursaal, with frequent concerts and theatrical performances. At the Rathhaus is a collection of old weapons and miscellaneous curiosities. Several institutions for the treatment of lung affections, including two schools (boys' and girls') for delicate children. Alexandra Sanatorium, in a fine situation on the mountain side. Resident guides for mountain excursions. ENGLISH CHURCH SERVICE.

H.B.M.'s CONSUL.—Dr. B. Hudson.

MEDICAL.—Dr. Hudson; Dr. Bill.

Davos Dorf.—*Stat.*—5 164 feet above sea.

HOTELS: SEEHOF; FLUELA; CONCORDIA.

Situated a little above and 1½ mile distant from Davos Platz, on a lake, at the base of the Schiahorn (8,900 ft.).

GOLF.—Course between Davos Platz and Dorf.

RAIL, page 268D. Diligence, page 377.

[Cable Railway from Davos Platz to the **Schatzalp** (6,150 ft., INN), or by a pleasant path from near the Kurhaus through the forest.

SANATORIUM SCHATZALP.–Cure Establishment for diseases of the lungs. 985 ft. above Davos Platz. Frequented by English. Prospectus on application to the Management. Doctors: Dr. Lucius Sprengler, Dr. Neumann.]

Disentis.—*Stat.*—Pop. 1,360.

HOTELS: DISENTISER HOF; POST; KRONE.

A little town of Canton Grisons, 3,773 ft. above sea, on the Vorder Rhein, near its junction with the Mittel Rhein. Schools occupy the buildings, on a height, of the old Benedictine Abbey (dating from 7th cent.) whose abbots once were powerful in the district.

ENG. CH. SERVICE at Disentiser Hof.

RAIL, page 268D. DILIGENCE, pp. 377 and 378.

Eggishorn.— HOTEL JUNGFRAU.

A good mountain centre, in Canton Valais, 7,195 ft. above sea, much frequented in the season. The view from the summit of the Eggishorn (9,625 ft.) is strikingly grand, overlooking the Aletsch Glacier, the largest in Switzerland, and including a wide range of Alpine peaks. ENGLISH CHURCH SERVICE.

Diligence from Brig to Viesch, page 377; a bridle path from Viesch to Eggishorn.

[A good path from Eggishorn to the **Riederalp**, 6,315 feet (HOTEL RIEDERALP), in a fine situation, with mild climate; English Church Service in the season. From the Riederalp to the Rieder Furka, 6,820 ft. (PENSION RIEDER FURKA), thence across the south end of the Gross Aletsch Glacier (only at this passage is a guide needed) to **Belalp** (HOTEL BELALP)—near here is a monument to Professor Tyndall, who resided at the Villa Lüsgen.]

Einsiedeln.—*Stat.*—Pop. 4,077.

HOTELS: PFAU; SONNE.

On the Alpbach, 2,900 ft. above sea, in a pleasant valley, about 6 miles south of the Lake of Zurich. A celebrated resort of pilgrims, who, to the number of about 150,000 annually (a great throng on Sept. 14th), flock to worship before the miracle working image of the Virgin. The Abbey dates from the 9th cent., but the present buildings were erected 1704-19. Within the church, in the Chapel of the Virgin, is the small image of the Virgin and Child, decorated with gold and jewels. Library of 50,000 vols. in the Abbey, many MSS., and natural history collection; in the Fürstensaal are portraits; paintings in the Private Chapel of the Abbot. RAIL, p. 256A.

Engelberg.—*Stat.*—Pop. 471.

HOTELS CATTANI.—First class hotels, with every modern comfort. 600 beds. Beautifully situated; extensive gardens. Largely frequented by English families. Cattani Brothers, proprietors. See Advt.

HOTEL ENGEL.—Well known. See Advt.

PARK HOTEL SONNENBERG.—First class hotel, beautifully situated. Patronised by English families. Hydropathic Establishment. See Adv.

TERRACE PALACE HOTEL.—First class (opened 1906), in beautiful elevated position, with fine view; every modern comfort and luxury. Garden; terrace. Pension from 9 fr. See Advt.

HOTEL BELLEVUE.—First class, entirely renovated and enlarged. Apartments with baths. Central heating. Open all the year. Tennis. Pension from 8 frs. See Advt.

HOTEL PENSION SCHONTAL.—In beautiful, quiet situation. Electric light; central heating. Open all the year. Pension from 7 fr. See Advt.

CENTRAL HOTEL.—Newly built; eighty beds. Electric light, lift, and central heating. Open all the year. Pension from 6 fr. See Advt.

A favourite tourist centre and health resort of Canton Unterwalden, 3,340 ft. above sea, in an Alpine Valley, Engelberger Thal; mild climate, magnificent scenery. Winter Sports—tobogganing, skating, ski-ing, etc. At the higher end of the village is the Benedictine Abbey (visits not encouraged), founded 1121, rebuilt 1729; modern paintings in the church, handsome altar-piece; Library of 20,000 vols., some MSS. Important School attached to Abbey, also an extensive Farm. ENGLISH CHURCH SERVICE.

Funicular railway ascends in 7½ minutes to the **Gerschni Alp**, throughout the day, in summer almost half hourly.

The ascent of the **Titlis**, 10,627 ft., is usually made from Engelberg. Several other mountain climbs; resident guides.

Reached by Steamer from Lucerne to Stansstad; RAIL thence, page 259B.

Evolène.—Pop. 1208.

HOTELS; GRAND; BEAU SITE; BELLE VUE.

Picturesquely situated in the Val d'Hérens, 4,520 feet above sea, among meadows, flanked by larch and pine forests on the mountains. Magnificent views of the Ferpècle Glacier, the Dent d'Hérens, and the Dent Blanche. The Sasseneire (10,692 ft.), Pic d'Arzinol (9,843 ft.), and several other interesting ascents made from here. ENGLISH CHURCH SERVICE in summer.

Reached by diligence from Sion, page 375.

Faido.—*Stat.*—Pop. 835.

HOTEL SUESSE.—Facing the railway station. All modern comforts. Electric light; central heating. Lift. Garage. Trout fishing. Pension from 8 fr. See Advt.

FRANSIOLI. •

Chief place of the Val Leventina, upper valley of the Ticino, 2,485 ft. above sea. A much frequented spring and summer resort, with a dry climate. Fine scenery, mountain and forest all round. Interesting carved wooden houses, dating from the beginning of the 16th cent. Old churches in the surrounding villages. Piumogna cascade and gorge of the Monte Piottino are worth visiting. Trout fishing. ENG. CHURCH SERV.

RAIL, page 259.

Faulensee Bad.—*Stat.*—2,630 ft. above sea.
A well frequented sub-Alpine resort, on wooded slopes between Spiez and Interlaken; climate equable, temperate, and bracing. Iron spring, containing gypsum, for drinking and bathing—recommended for anæmia and debility. Fine views over lake and mountain. Excursions in all directions. Resident doctor.

ENGLISH CHURCH SERVICE.

RAIL, page 267. Diligence, page 375.

Felsenegg.
HOTELS: FELSENEGG KURHAUS SCHONFELS.
A health resort, 3,085 ft. above sea, on the Zuger Berg, overlooking the Lake of Zug. In the winter tobogganing and ski-ing.

ENGLISH CHURCH SERVICE in summer.

Electric Tramway between Felsenegg and Zug.

Finhaut (or Fins-Hauts).
GRAND HOTEL BRISTOL.—First class; every comfort. Baths and douches on every floor. See Advt.

GRAND HOTEL FINHAUT.—In elevated position. Pension from 6 fr. See Advt.

Finhaut is in a very fine situation, with views of the Trient valley and glacier. In summer, when there are many visitors, English Church service. Resident guides for the mountains (see also page 526). RAIL, page 257A.

Flims.—Pop. 790.
HOTELS: SCHWEIZERHOF; POSTE.
A little old town, 3,615 feet above sea, on the Oberalp Route. The town and near neighbourhood are a pleasant summer resort; woods of pine and beech, two or three small pretty lakes; several attractive excursions. In the winter much skating, ski-ing, etc. DILIGENCE, page 377.

Fluelen.—*Stat.*—Pop. 941.
In Canton Uri, at the south end of the Lake of Lucerne, here called the Urner See. Church; small Chateau of Rudenz. At this end of the Lake the scenery is of a very striking character; the views from the Fluelen end of the Axenstrasse (road bordering east side of the Lake) are superb.

RAIL, page 259. Steamer, page 369. Tram between Fluelen and Altdorf.

Fribourg (Freiburg).—*Stat.*—Pop. 16,741.
HOTELS: TERMINUS; SUISSE; FAUCON.
The beautifully situated and picturesque capital of the Canton of Fribourg, on the River Sarine, 2,100 ft. above sea. Parts of the old city walls and towers remain.

Church of St. Nicholas, 1470-92, tower 280 ft., has carving of the Judgment on the portal; interior contains carved stalls, a few pictures in the chapels, and an organ with 7,800 pipes and 67 stops—daily recitals in summer. Hotel de Ville, with eight-sided clock tower of 1511. Historic lime tree, the growth of a twig borne by a youthful messenger from the victorious battlefield of Morat who fell exhausted and dying upon this spot (1476). In the Lycée is the Cantonal Museum, containing sculpture, a picture gallery, collections of antiquities, coins, natural history objects, etc.

RAIL, pp. 259B, 263, 263A. Diligence, p. 374.

Gais.—*Stat.*—Pop. 2,854.
HOTELS: KRONE; FALKE.
A well known whey-cure resort, 3,075 ft. above sea, a pleasantly situated village with meadows all round.

RAIL, page 256. Diligence, page 374.

Gallen, St.—*Stat.*—Pop. (1910) 37,657.
HOTELS: HIRSCH; HECHT; SCHIFF.
Capital of the Canton of St. Gallen, with a large trade in cotton goods.

Bahnhofstrasse leads from the Station to the Markt Platz, whence the Marktgasse leads to the Church of St. Laurence. Close by is the Klosterhof, with the Abbey, founded 7th cent. by St. Gallus, an Irish monk rebuilt 18th cent., suppressed 1805; a seat of learning in 8th, 9th, and 10th cents. Municipal offices now occupy part of the buildings; in other parts are the Bishop's house and the Abbey Library (30,000 vols., and valuable MSS.).

At the Cantonal School are the Municipal Library and collections illustrative of commerce and geography. The Museum contains a Picture Gallery and natural history and historical collections; an Industrial Museum.

H.B.M.'S VICE-CONS.—E. A. Steiger-Züst, Esq.

U.S. CONSUL.—D. I. Murphy, Esq.

RAIL, pp. 256, 257B, 268, 268A. Diligence, p. 375.

[Rail from St. Gallen to **Trogen** (HOTEL KRONE), a summer resort, page 267A.]

Gemmi Pass.—The Pass of the Gemmi, or Daube, 7,640 ft. above sea, is in many respects the most wonderful in Switzerland. It is usually approached from the north west side, going from Kandersteg to Louèche-les-Bains. From Kandersteg a good bridle path leads to the Pass, a guide not being needed; magnificent views throughout. A climbing railway (or lift) from Louèche-les Bains to the top of the Gemmi is projected.

Geneva (Geneve).—*Stat.*—Pop. (1910) 125,520. *(Plan in Special Edition, or post free 3d. stamps).*

GRAND HOTEL NATIONAL.—Strictly first class, beautifully situated on the border of the Lake; the only one with a park. See Advt.

HOTEL METROPOLE AND GENEVA PALACE.—First class, beautifully situated opposite Jardin Anglais and near Landing Stage. Central heating; moderate. See Advt.

GRAND HOTEL DES BERGUES.—First class, of old reputation; central, facing Isle Rousseau; latest modern improvements. See Advt.

GRAND HOTEL BEAU RIVAGE.—First class hotel, beautifully situated with a terrace. See Advt.

GRAND HOTEL DE LA PAIX.—First class hotel, beautifully situated. Quai du Mont Blanc. See Advt.

HOTEL D'ANGLETERRE.—First class hotel, splendidly situated, commanding the most charming view of Mont Blanc. See Advt.

HOTEL DE L'ECU.—First class family hotel, well situated, overlooking the Lake, with fine view. Every modern comfort. Pension from 10 frs. See Advt.

RICHMOND FAMILY HOTEL.—Opposite the Pier. Well situated. Moderate prices. See Advt.

GRAND HOTEL DE RUSSIE AND CONTINENTAL.—First class hotel, beautifully situated Quai du Mont Blanc. See Advt.

HOTEL BELLEVUE.—First class modern hotel, beautifully situated, with terrace on the Lake. Fine view. Central heating; garden. Pension from 8 frs. See Advt.

HOTEL PENSION VICTORIA.—Very good house, well situated. and moderate. See Advt.

HOTEL SUISSE.—Situated facing the Railway Station. Lift; electric light, See Advt.

HOTEL DU LAC.—An excellent hotel, well situated near Landing Stage and Jardin des Anglais. Lift, electric light, central heating. Pension from 8 frs. See Advt.

HOTEL DE LA POSTE.—Conveniently situated in the best part of the town. See Advt.

GRAND HOTEL INTERNATIONAL.—Opposite the Station, with direct access. Modern sanitary arrangements. Electric light, etc. Rooms from 3 frs. See Advt.

HOTEL DU PARC.—Comfortable family hotel, pleasantly situated, facing Lake and near Jardin des Anglais. Lift; electric light. Very reasonable. See Advt.

HOTEL-PENSION BRISTOL.—Comfortable family hotel, centrally situated, 10, Rue Montblanc, near English Church. Pension from 8 fr. See Advt.

HOTEL BEAU SEJOUR (at Champel-les-Bains, Geneva).—Well situated, with beautiful view and fine park. See Advt.

PENSION GROTTE D'AZUR.—8, Rue de la Cloche, near the Brunswick monument. Excellent table. Pension from 6 frs. See Advt.

The principal RAILWAY STATION—Gare de Cornavin—is on the north side of the town, half a mile distant from the Lake. The Eaux-Vives Station, for Annemasse, is in the south east part of the town, 1½ mile distant from the Cornavin Station. The train service from and to French towns is according to Greenwich time; the service with other parts of Switzerland is according to Mid Europe time.

Electric Trams in the town and to the suburbs.

GENEVA is situated at the south end of the Lake of Geneva, where it narrows into the River Rhone, the town being upon both banks of the River and spreading out upon each side of the Lake. The few "sights" are in the older part, upon the south side, but the interests of Geneva are principally historic associations and the pleasant surrounding country.

From the Railway Station the broad Rue du Mont Blanc descends to the Pont du Mont Blanc across the end of the Lake. The views from the Pont and neighbouring quays are very beautiful, especially on clear summer evenings.

The Cathedral (St. Pierre) shows out prominently over the houses on the south side; though small, it is one of the most beautiful 12th-13th cent. churches of the Continent; the facade is disfigured by an incongruous Corinthian portico, but the proportions and massive grandeur of the interior are singularly impressive; monuments, Chapelle des Macchabées; chair of Calvin, who often preached here, under the finely carved pulpit. Open Tues., Thurs., Sat., 1.0 to 3.0, free, at other times 20 c. A few yards north west of the portico is one end of the Rue de Calvin, where Calvin resided.

A short distance west of the Cathedral is the Hotel de Ville, of little interest. The Rue de l'Hotel de Ville continues north into the equally narrow Grande Rue, where, at No. 40, Jean Jacques Rousseau was born 1712 (died 1778).

On the west side of the Hotel de Ville is the Promenade de la Treille, overlooking the Jardin Botanique, the Promenade des Bastions, and, beyond, the University.

Church of Notre Dame, in Place Cornavin, close to the Railway Station.

The University is a range of three buildings, erected 1868-72; about 1,100 students; Natural History Museum, Archeological Museum, and collections of coins; in the Library are 150,000 vols. and 1,500 MSS., with many portraits of reformers, statesmen, and scholars, also several curiosities (portrait of George Eliot, painted at Geneva in 1850).

At the north end of the Promenade des Bastions, in the Place Neuve, are the Conservatoire de Musique and the Theatre (a fine Renaissance building).

Musée d'Art et d'Histoire; a handsome building (1911) with several fine rooms. Here are collections of pre-historic relics, Greek, Roman, and Etruscan antiquities, objects of local historic interest, and some good pictures.

Ecole d'Horlogerie, Musée des Arts Decoratifs (valuable engravings), and Musée Industriel (machines used in boring St. Gothard Tunnel), are all within a quarter mile west of the principal Railway Station.

Brunswick Monument, on Quai du Mont Blanc; an elaborate monument in memory of the Duke Charles II, who died 1873 leaving about twenty million francs to the town.

POST OFFICE.—Rue du Mont Blanc, between the Railway Station and the Lake.

ENG. CH. SER.-Holy Trinity, Rue du Mont Blanc.

AMERICAN CH.—Rue des Voirons.

CH. OF SCOTLAND.—Service every Sunday during summer in the Cathedral (Maccabees' Chapel).

H.B.M.'s CONSUL.—R. E. A. de Candolle, Esq.

VICE-CONSUL.—L. Stein, Esq.

U.S. CONSUL.—F. B. Keene, Esq.

GOLF.—18-hole course, at Plan-les-Ouates, tram hourly; club house.

MEDICAL.—Dr. Rene Koenig. Dr. H. Treves Barber.

DENTISTS.—Dr. Francis L. Pache, University of Pennsylvania; 8, Rue Adhémar Fabri (near the Hotels Richmond and Beau-Rivage).

CHEMIST.—Grande Pharmacie Finck, 26, Rue du Mont Blanc, near the Railway Station. All English and American pharmaceutical preparations in stock. English Assistant. See Advt.

ANGLO-AMERICAN PHARMACY.—Passage des Lions. All English and American prescriptions carefully compounded; large stock of patent medicines. Telephone 1168.

BANKERS.—M. M. Lombard Odier et Cie., Principal Agents of the Banks of England and America, 23, Corraterie.

SOCIETE SUISSE DE BANQUE ET DE DEPOTS.—9, Rue du Commerce. Letters of credit, circular notes cashed, credits opened, etc. Apply London, Société Generale (de Paris), 65, Regentstreet.

EDUCATION.—Les "Hirondelles." High-class educational home for young ladies, etc,, etc. Principals: Mr. and Mme. A Dourouze.

EDUCATION.—Chateau de Lancy. First class Educational Establishment for Sons of Gentlemen. Modern Languages; commercial training; English examinations.

For further particulars regarding the foregoing School, see the SCHOOL DIRECTORY in Bradshaw's Guide for Great Britain, page ii.

MANUFACTURERS OF WATCHES AND JEWELRY. Golay Sons and Stahl, 31, Quai des Bergues. Established 1837. See Advt.

TOURIST OFFICE AND FORWARDING AGENTS.—C. H. Ackermann (Rue d'Italie). Railway tickets, Circular Tours, Storage, luggage forwarding. Agents for the Hamburg America Line. See Advt.

ENGLISH TAILOR.—A. HANSMAN, 3 and 5, Rue des Alpes. English materials only. Telephone No. 325.

RAIL, see ABC Routes from Geneva, p. cxxxiv.

[Monnetier-Mornex—
Mornex, 2,230 ft. above sea, and Monnetier, 2,625 ft. above sea, on the southern slopes of Mont Salève, about 5 miles south east of Geneva. Magnificent views. ENGLISH CHURCH SERVICE.

RAIL, page 61A, Tram from Geneva, page 255.

At **Pregny** (tram in 10 minutes), north east of Geneva, is the Ariana Museum of Art objects generally—paintings, engravings, porcelain, etc., and a library with interesting autographs in cases; free on Sun. and Thurs,; 1 fr. on Tues., Wed., Fri., Sat. An Alpine Garden between the Museum and the lake. A little beyond the Museum is the Chateau Rothschild; beautiful grounds—tickets at the Geneva hotels. Across the French frontier from Pregny is **Ferney** (4 miles from Geneva; tramway), whose existence as a village is principally owing to Voltaire; at the Chateau are memorials of Voltaire—open during summer about one day a week.]

Gersau—

HOTEL MULLER,—First class, situated in a sheltered position, facing the Lake. Nice garden; electric light; pension from 8 fr. (English Church Service.) See Advt.

BEAU SEJOUR; SEEHOF; GERSAU.

At the base of the Rigi, on the Lake side, much frequented on account of the mild sheltered position; fruit growing all round; two or three silk factories behind the village. Starting point for the Rigi Scheidegg 5,412 ft., Hochfluh 5,582 ft., and Gersauerstock 4,756 ft. Many pleasant excursions. STEAMER, page 369.

Giessbach—

HOTELS GIESSBACH, A. G.—Equipped with every comfort of an up-to-date first class hotel, in magnificent position. See Advt.

BEAU SITE.

At the north end of the Lake of Brienz, opposite Brienz, in a beautiful situation, a very popular resort in summer. The Falls descend in seven leaps and are crossed by three bridges; from near the highest bridge the stream, the Giessbach, is precipitated 190 feet down.

STEAMER, see page 363; short railway line from the Lake to the Falls.

Gimel.—*Stat*: HOTEL DES BAINS.

2,500 ft. above sea. Alkaline springs. Luxuriant pine woods. RAIL, page 261A.

Glarus.—*Stat.*—Pop. 4,877.

HOTELS: GLARNER HOF; **DREI EIDGENOSSEN.**

Capital of Canton Glarus, on the River Linth, 1,490 ft. above sea, in a fine mountain spot. Romanesque church. The Law Courts occupy the site of the old church, where Zwingli, the reformer, was pastor, 1506-16. Collections of antiquities, etc., in the Post Office building. Collection of pictures by Swiss painters at the Rathhaus. RAIL, page 262B.

[3 miles west of Glarus is the Klonthal See, the road to which is partly through an imposing gorge.]

Göschenen.—*Stat.*—Pop. 800.

GRAND HOTEL.—First class, next to the Railway Station. Electric light. Garden. Pension from 7 fr. See Advt.

A village situated in the most interesting part of the St. Gotthard Road, 3,640 ft. above sea, amidst grand scenery of peak and waterfall. In the cemetery is a monument to the engineer of the St. Gotthard Tunnel, L. Favre (died 1879).

ENGLISH CHURCH SERVICE in summer.

RAIL, page 259. Diligence, page 377.

[The **St. Gotthard Tunnel,** whose north end is at Göschenen, is 9¼ miles long, with its highest central rise 3,786 ft. above sea; it is 1,083 ft. below Andermatt; is 28 ft. wide, 21 ft. high, and has a double set of rails. It was begun June, 1872, and completed Feb. 29th, 1880, at a cost of £2,270,000.]

Grimmialp.

GRAND HOTEL.—First class, in fine position, surrounded by extensive forest. Every modern comfort. See Advt.

A summer resort, 4,134 ft. above sea, in growing favour as much for its quiet as for its pure air and pleasant surroundings of Alpine meadow, forest, and peak. Reached by Diligence, page 376, from Oey-Diemtigen.

Grimsel Hospice. The Hospice (now a minor hotel), 6,155 ft. above sea, at the west end of the small Grimsel Lake, is only inhabited during the season. The **Grimsel Pass,** 7,103 ft., 3 miles from the Hospice, offers beautiful views. Just over the Pass is the Todtensee (Lake of the Dead), the scene of fighting of French and Austrians, 1799. The **Furca Pass** route goes off at Gletsch, at the end of the Grimsel Pass route, to Hospenthal and Göschenen. At the Pass the height above sea is 7,990 ft. DILIGENCE, page 377.

Gruben-Meiden—

In a fine situation, 5,961 ft. above sea, just below the Turtman Glacier. Magnificent scenery and opportunities for mountain excursions. Reached from Sierre station by carriage to Vissoye, thence horse to St. Luc, and over the Meiden Pass to Gruben; or reached by bridle path from Turtman.

Gstaad.—*Stat.*—Pop. 298.

GRAND HOTEL ALPINA.—First class hotel. Lofty situation with fine panorama. Garden. Excursion centre. Winter sports. Terms from 8 fr. See Advt.

GRAND HOTEL DU PARC.—First class; magnificent position, fine view, own forest close by. Summer and winter sports. Open all the year. Terms from 8 fr. See Advt.

HOTEL BERNERHOF (formerly Station Hotel).—Very comfortable; recently enlarged. Electric light, central heating. Open all the year. Pension from 7 fr. See Advt.

A pleasantly situated mountain village, and a favourite resort both in summer and winter, 3,450 feet above sea, at the entrance to three valleys—the Lauenental, the Gsteigtal, and the Turbachtal. Very fine mountain and glacier scenery. In summer excursions among the mountains; resident guides. Sunny and sheltered from wind in winter; no fog—tobogganing, ski-ing, skating, etc. ENGLISH CHURCH SERVICE.

RAIL, page 262C; Diligence, page 376.

Gunten—*Stat.*

PARK HOTEL—Fire-proof construction. Fine panorama. Electric light, lift; central heating. Apartments with baths. Pension from 8 frs. See Advt.

A village pleasantly situated on the Lake of Thun, between Thun and Interlaken, with fine views all round. Gorge and Fall of the Guntenbach. From the Nussbaum, 2,625 ft., is a beautiful view.

ENGLISH CHURCH SERVICE.

RAIL, p. 268F. STEAMER, p. 363.

Heiden.—*Stat.*—Pop. 3,750.

HOTELS FREIHOF & SCHWEIZERHOF. First class, well situated, fine view. Electric light. See Advt.

An air-cure and whey-cure resort, 2,640 ft. above sea, overlooking the Lake of Constance. Kurhalle. Fine views. ENGLISH CHURCH SERVICE in summer. RAIL, page 256.

Interlaken.—*Stat.*—Pop. 7,170.

REGINA HOTEL JUNGFRAUBLICK.—First class; elevated position, midst beautiful park; honoured by the presence of H.M. Queen Mary. See Advt.

GRAND HOTEL VICTORIA.—Opposite the Jungfrau. Beautiful first class hotel. See Advt.

HOTEL JUNGFRAU.—Excellent accommodation. Lift; electric light. See Advt.

GRAND HOTEL (formerly BEAU RIVAGE.)—First class hotel, beautifully situated Open April-October. See Advt.

GRAND HOTEL METROPOLE.—Formerly Grand Hotel Ritschard. Excellent hotel, situated on the principal promenade. See Advt.

GRAND HOTEL DES ALPES AND PALACE HOTEL.—First class house; moderate. Electric light; lift. See Advt.

SCHWEIZERHOF—HOTEL SUISSE.—First class, well situated on the Grande Promenade, with fine views of the Jungfrau and Alps. Lift; electric light. See Advt.

HOTEL DU NORD.—Well situated family hotel. Electric light. View of Jungfrau. See Advt.

TERMINUS HOTEL.—Facing the Central Station and the Landing Stage. 100 beds. Electric light; baths. Restaurant. Moderate terms. See Advt. Electric light. Lift. Baths. Restarant. See Adv.

HOTEL BELVEDERE.—Modern; comfortable. See Advt.

HOTEL BEAU SITE.—First class establishment, beautifully situated. Moderate charges. See Adv.

HOTEL CENTRAL.—In quiet open position, close to Central Station and Landing Stage. Lift, electric light. Pension from 7 fr. See Advt.

The principal RAILWAY STATION, the Bahnhof, is at the west, or Lake of Thun, side of the town—here the trains arrive from Berne and Thun; the Oststation, a minor station, is on the east, or Lake of Brienz, side.

INTERLAKEN (between the lakes), 1,863 ft. above sea, lies on the small Bodeli plain, that, once probably covered by water, interposes between the Lake of Thun and the Lake of Brienz. With lake and mountain scenery of surpassing grandeur all round, it is one of the most frequented summer resorts; it is most advantageously situated as a centre whence to explore the Oberland, while the mild equable temperature and magnificent views combine to make it a delightful place of rest.

The Höheweg, where visitors throng, is a tree-shaded thoroughfare extending across the town, south-west to north-east, from near the Bahnhof to near the Oststation; here are several of the large hotels and the best shops. Near the north east end, a little back, is an old Monastery, founded 1130, with an adjoining Schloss (1750), both now used as government offices and hospital; the monastery church has been so divided that English Church, Presbyterian, French Protestant, and Roman Catholic Services are held within it. On the Höheweg is also the Kursaal, with reading, billiard, and concert rooms—music two or three times a day; there is daily music in the morning on the Höheweg, in front of the Kursaal.

On the south west side of the town, a short walk from the Höheweg (20 minutes), rises the Kleine Rugen, a wooded height commanding fine views of the Jungfrau, Mönch, and the Lakes; still finer views are obtained from the Grosse Rugen, an hour and half walk beyond.

On the north east side of the town, beyond the bridge over the River Aare, are several attractive walks in the Bruckwald; at the Hohbühl, 250 yards to west of bridge, is a small erection to commemorate visits of Weber, Mendelssohn, and Wagner. The road to east of the bridge leads to Schönegg and Goldswyl, where is a small lake (Faulensee).

Very fine view from the summit of the Harder, 4,290 ft., on the north side of Interlaken; ascent by funicular railway.

On the north west side of the town, the road at the bridge over the River Aare at Unterseen leads to St. Beatenberg (see under that name).

POST OFFICE, at south west end of the Höheweg.

ENGLISH CHURCH SERVICE in English Church.

GOLF.—9-hole course, 1½ mile from town.

RAIL, pages 256A, 267, 268F. STEAMER, p. 363.

[INTERLAKEN to LAUTERBRUNNEN, MURREN, WENGEN, the JUNGFRAU, and GRINDELWALD.

RAIL, see page 256A.

Circular tickets are issued for the round from Interlaken to Lauterbrunnen, Wengen, Kleine Scheidegg, Grindelwald, and back to Interlaken, available for six days, 2nd cl. 22 fr. 65 c., 3rd cl. 13 fr. 95 c. Pedestrians will find the tour amply repay the exertion.

The line runs from Interlaken between the villages of Wilderswyl and Gsteig (station) to Zweilütschinen (station), whence the Isenfluh, 3,610 ft., may be ascended, and on to Lauterbrunnen.

Lauterbrunnen, 2,620 ft. above sea. Pop. about 2,000. HOTEL STEINBOCK; ADLER, ETC.

A village on both sides of the River Lütschine, eight miles from Interlaken, in a valley where the sun's rays do not fall before 7.0 a.m. in summer and nearly noon in winter. The name is derived from the springs (brunnen) streaming over the rocks or rising on all sides. The road from the Station in about half a mile branches off, the way to the right leads in five minutes to the **Staubbach,** a fall that descends in a leap of 980 ft., the water spreading in spray, in sunshine resembling a misty veil, in moonlight very beautiful. The way to the left, on road from Station, leads in about two miles to the **Trümmelbach Gorge** and **Falls**—admission to path 50 c.; three rainbows form in the sunshine. Tobogganing, skating, ski-ing, in winter.

The Station of the Mürren railway at Lauterbrunnen is a short distance west of the Oberland Ry. Station. The line runs from Lauterbrunnen for about a mile due west to the Grutsch Alp, 4,890 ft., and then turns sharply southward for 2½ miles to Mürren. The walk from Lauterbrunnen to Mürren, about two and half hours, is full of attraction.

Mürren, 5,385 ft. above sea. Pop. about 400.

GRAND HOTEL.—Old and large establishment. Restaurant and terraces with fine view of glaciers. Electric light. See Advt.

GRAND HOTEL DES ALPES.—Good and comfortable. Electric light. Open from May till October 30. See Advt.

A scattered village on a terrace, a favourite resort for its pure air and beautiful scenery, embracing a wide panorama of the Oberland peaks. The summit of the Allmendhubel, 6,358 ft., may be easily reached in three quarters of an hour by pleasant paths. The ascent of the Schilthorn, 9,753 ft., in four or five hours, is more fatiguing than difficult. ENG. CH. SERV. There is also Service at **Gimmelwald,** about a mile south of Murren.

From Lauterbrunnen the Wengern Alp line ascends in a mile and a half to

Wengen, 4,190 ft. above sea.

PALACE HOTEL AND NATIONAL—First class (200 rooms); finest position. Every modern comfort. Apartments with baths. Open all the year. Pension from 10 fr. See Advt.

HOTEL PARK AND BEAU SITE.—Excellent family, charmingly situated in proximate vicinity of fine firwoods. Frequented by English families. Pension from 8 fr. See Adv.

REGINA HOTEL BLUMLISALP.—Family hotel, beautifully situated, close to Station. Garden terrace. Fine view. Pension from fr. 8.0. Open May to September. See Advt.

GRAND HOTEL BELVEDERE.—New first class hotel with 160 beds. Well situated, close to the woods and commanding fine panorama. Hot water heating throughout. See Advt.

Situated in a tract of meadow land, under the rocky Tschuggen, 8,278 ft.; sheltered from cold wind. The pure air and fine views attract many visitors; as a winter station is in growing repute—much tobogganing, skating, ski-ing, etc. ENG. CHURCH SERV.

From Wengernalp, 5 miles from Lauterbrunnen, is a celebrated view of the Jungfrau.

Scheidegg, 6,770 ft. above sea, 6¼ miles from Lauterbrunnen.

Magnificent views to south of the Mönch, Eiger, and Jungfrau, and to north over the Grindelwald valley. Ascent of the Lauberhorn, 8,120 ft., to north west, in an hour.

The **Jungfrau** Railway (page 256A), to be 7½ miles long, was begun in 1896. The line ascends from Scheidegg to the first station, at Gletscher, 7,565 ft. above sea, and thence upward through narrow tunnels to the Eismeer 10,275 ft., the Monch 10,995 ft., and Jungfrau Joch 11,090 ft., thence a lift to connect with the summit of the Jungfrau 13,670 ft. It is expected the railway will be completed in 1915.

From Scheidegg the line descends gradually to Alpligen (5,287 ft.), 8¾ miles from Lauterbrunnen, and then makes a steep descent to Grindelwald, 3 miles further.

Grindelwald, 3,415 ft. above sea. Pop. 3,346. Distant about 11½ miles from Lauterbrunnen, and about 13 miles from Interlaken by the direct line via Burglaunen.

GRAND HOTEL EIGER.—Renowned old-established hotel, centrally situated; fine view; garden, terrace. Patronised by English. Open all the year. Pension from 8 fr. See Advt.

HOTEL ALPENRUHE.—In a fine situation, with every modern comfort. Electric light; lift; central heating. Winter garden. See Advt.

HOTEL BELVEDERE (opened 1907).—First class family hotel, occupying finest position near Station; own grounds; central heating; open all the year. Pension from 8 fr. See Advt.

HOTEL TERMINUS.—At the Station. Quiet and comfortable. Electric light, central heating. Open all the year. Pension from 6 fr. 50 c. See Advt.

A favourite centre for mountain excursions, and a frequented summer and winter resort, in a sheltered situation, under the Wetterhorn (12,150 ft.) to north east, the Mettenberg (10,193 ft.) to east, and the Eiger (13,040 ft.) to south. In the winter much ski-ing, tobogganing, bobsleighing, skating, etc. The Ober Grindelwald Glacier is between the Wetterhorn and the Mettenberg, the Unter Grindelwald Glacier is between the

Mettenberg and the Eiger. To the Ober Glacier, a walk of two and half hours there and back by easy paths. From the Ober Glacier there is a cable "Aufzug—Lift," a car suspended from a cable, about 600 yards long, upward to a station at Engi. For all ascents among the mountains south and east guides should be employed, many are resident; for the ascent of the Faulhorn, 8,803 ft., about midway between Grindelwald and the Lake of Brienz, a guide is unnecessary; there and back, eight hours of walking. ENGLISH CHURCH SERVICE.

From Grindelwald the direct line to Interlaken descends to Burglauenen (2,915ft.), Lütschenthal (2,355 ft.), Zweilütschinen (2,150 ft.), and Interlaken.

INTERLAKEN to the SCHYNIGE PLATTE.
RAIL, see page 256A.

From the **Schynige Platte**, 6,463 ft. above sea, is a magnificent prospect. The ascent begins at Wilderswyl-Gsteig, whence it is 4½ miles to the Platte. It is an easy walk from the Platte to the Daube, 6,772 ft.

Kandersteg.—*Stat.*

GRAND HOTEL VICTORIA.—First class, of old reputation, much frequented by English. Open all the year. Pension from 8 fr. See Advt.

GRAND HOTEL.—First class, in fine position. Park, tennis; own skating rink. Open all the year. Moderate terms. See Advt.

BELLEVUE; KURHAUS.

At the head of the Kander Thal, 3,835 ft. above sea, both a summer and a winter resort. Finely situated in its proximity to the Blümisalp and other lofty peaks. At foot of the Blümisalp is the picturesque Oeschinen Lake, 5,000 ft. above sea, the beautiful Staubbach Fall being passed on the way. Other falls in the Gastern Thal. To the south is the Gemmi Pass, for which Kandersteg is the starting point. Mountains, glaciers, and wild valleys all round. Much winter sport—tobogganing, ski-ing, skating, etc.

Close to Kandersteg is the north end of the great **Lötschberg Tunnel**, on the line of railway connecting Berne with the Simplon line. The boring of the tunnel, begun in October, 1906, was completed March 31st, 1911; it is 9 miles long—longer than was anticipated, but owing to the tapping of the Kander River in July, 1908, when a disastrous inrush of water drowned twenty-five workmen, the original almost straight projection had to be slightly diverted. In the cemetery at Kandersteg is a monument to the overwhelmed workmen. There are two lines of railway and the traction is electric.

RAIL, page 268F.

Klosters.—*Stat.*

SPORT HOTEL SILVRETTA.—First class, with extensive park. Mostly frequented by English. Summer and winter sports. Pension from 10 fr. See Advt.

VEREINA.

A small group of villages in a pleasant mountain surrounded valley, 3,940 ft. above sea; woods and meadows all round. Visited both in summer and winter (skating, tobogganing, etc). Many attractive mountain excursions.

RAIL, page 268D.

Lausanne.—*Stat.*—Pop. 63,926.

GRAND HOTEL RICHE-MONT.—First class hotel, beautifully situated, surrounded by gardens and commanding view of the Lake. See Advt.

GRAND HOTEL BEAU SITE.—First class, well situated, with fine view of the Lake and mountains. Electric light. See Advt.

HOTEL BEAU RIVAGE, at Ouchy-Lausanne. First class establishment, well situated on the shore of the Lake. Electric Light; lifts. See Advt.

HOTEL CECIL.—First class family hotel, beautifully situated near the Station and the Montbenon garden. Fire-proof. See Advt.

SAVOY HOTEL.—First class. All comforts. See Ad.

THE ROYAL HOTEL.—First class. See Advt.

HOTEL GIBBON.—A first rate house in every respect. Near this Gibbon finished his *Decline and Fall*, 1787. See Advt.

HOTEL BEAU-SEJOUR.—First class residential hotel, standing in its own grounds, near Station. Rebuilt and enlarged. Lifts, central heating. Pension from 9 fr. See Advt.

ALEXANDRA GRAND HOTEL.—New modern hotel, in good position. 120 beds. Reasonable terms. See Advt.

HOTEL CONTINENTAL.—Situated opposite the Railway Station, the Post and Telegraph Office. Restaurant; lift. Comfort. See Advt.

HOTEL VICTORIA.—New modern hotel, in good position. Electric light; central heating. Lift. Baths. Rooms from 3.50 frs. See Advt

EDEN HOTEL.—Avenue de la Gare. Three min. from Station. Fine view. Lift, electric light, central heating. Pension from 8 fr. See Advt.

CARLTON HOTEL (opened 1908).—Well appointed modern hotel, situated between town and lake, and close to English club. All latest improvements. Pension from fr. 8. See Advt.

GRAND HOTEL DE LA PAIX.—Centrally situated, with fine views. Rooms from 3.50 frs. Pension from 10 frs. Open all the year. See Advt.

HOTEL MAJESTIC.—First class (alt. 2,133 ft.), near the Lausanne-Signal Funicular Ry. Fine view; all modern comforts. Tennis court. Pension from 10 frs. See Advt.

HOTEL MIRABEAU.—New high class hotel, close to the Station. Rooms and suites with private baths. See Advt.

MODERN HOTEL JURA-SIMPLON.—New hotel in proximity to the Station and the funicular railway. Rooms and suites with baths. Pension from 8 frs. See Advt.

HOTEL MONT-FLEURI.—Comfortable hotel; opposite the English Church. Electric light; lift. Terms from 7 fr. See Advt.

BRITISH HOTEL.—Family hotel, newly opened in beautiful quiet situation, Avenue des Alpes. Every comfort; hot and cold water supply. Pension terms. See Advt.

HOTEL METROPOLE (opened 1912).—First class family hotel, situated Avenues de Florimont et des Alpes, with fine views. Every modern comfort. Pension from 7 fr. See Advt.

PENSION GRANCY-VILLA.—Situated close to the English Church. Fine view. Pension from 6 fr. 50 c. See Advt.

HOTEL PENSION WINDSOR.—First class family house; electric light, lift, central heating; baths. See Advt.

BRISTOL HOTEL.—Comfortable pension hotel near Station. Garden; electric light, central heating. Terms from 6 fr. See Advt.

HOTEL PENSION BELVEDERE.—Family hotel, opened 1912. Elevated position, with fine view on the lake and Alps. All latest improvements. Pension from 6 fr. See Advt.

PENSION CLARENCE (newly opened).—In quiet, central position, near Station. Very comfortable and homelike. Excellent cuisine. Electric light, central heating. Pension from 6 frs. See Advt.

Lausanne, 1,584 ft. above sea, is in a very fine situation on the lower slopes of Mont Jorat, about 1¼ mile from the Lake of Geneva. The old parts of the town have many steep tortuous streets, but the modern quarters are attractive. The town and neighbourhood have long been an educational centre; in 1891 the old College was raised to the dignity of a University.

The Cathedral (Protestant) stands out prominently in the east part of the town. Erected 1235-75, restored 1875-1900, it is regarded as the most complete and important Gothic Church in Switzerland. Interior 352 ft. long, 150 ft. wide, nave 62 ft. high; several interesting monuments. Open 9.0 to 12.0 and 1.0 to 4.0.

A few yards west of the Cathedral, in the Place de la Riponne, is the Palais de Rumine (1898-1904), containing the University, Library (280,000 vols.), and Musée des Beaux-Arts; many good paintings.

Tribunal Fédéral, the supreme court of appeal of Switzerland, on Montbenon, just north west of the Railway Station—an imposing building in beautiful grounds. Close by, in the Place Montbenon, is the Casino.

A short distance north of the Chateau, to north of the Cathedral, is a point of view called the Signal, 2,125 ft. above sea.

POST OFFICE.—Place St. Francois.

ENGLISH CHURCH (Christ Church), Route d'Ouchy. PRESBYTERIAN CHURCH, Avenue de Rumine. WESLEYAN CHAPEL, Rue du Valentin.

H.B.M.'s CONSUL.—A. Galland, Esq.

MEDICAL.—Drs. Cesar Roux (surgery specialist); Muret (women's ailments); Marc Dufour (oculist); Combes (stomach); Bourget; Verrey (English); Mernod.

BRITISH AND AMERICAN PHARMACY.—Pharmacie Internationale, H. Masset, 9, Place St. Francois. American Soda Fountain.

DRUG STORES.—Pharmacie-Droguerie du Lion d'Or (Pascal fils), Rue de Bourg, 33. Chemical and Pharmaceutical Products, Photographic Chemicals, Plates. Dark room (gratis). Colours and all Materials for Artists. Perfumery from the best English and French Houses, etc.

BANKERS.—Galland and Co., English-American Bank and House Agency (British Consulate), 3, Place St. François. Booking Office to all Transatlantic S.S. Companies.

BANKERS.—Ch. Masson and Co., 2, Place St. Francois, Lausanne. English and American Bankers. Letters of Credit, Exchange.

BANK, EXCHANGE.—Société Suisse de Banque et de Depots. Avenue du Theatre, Rue Charles Monnard, 1 and 3. English spoken. Letters of Credit and Circular notes cashed. Credits opened, etc. Apply London, Société Générale (de Paris), 65, Regentstreet, W.

EDUCATION.—PENSIONNAT HEUBI.—First class Educational Establishment for young Ladies. Mr. and Mrs. Heubi, Chateau Brillantmont. See Adv.

LA BERGERONNETTE, Av. des Alpes.—Educational home for Young Ladies. Highest references, moderate terms. Principal, Miss Nicholas.

MME. VIRET, "Le Manoir," Signal.—First class Boarding School for Girls, with best opportunity for learning languages, music, painting, etc. Home comforts. Principal: Mme. Henri Viret. Highest references. See Advt.

CHATEAU DES APENNINS.—Educational home for Girls. Facilities for acquiring languages, music, drawing, needlework. Special attention to health. Prospectus on application to Mlles. Bollinger.

The "EBOR HOUSE" Preparatory School for boys (Day School). Head Master, F. A. Vaughan.

For further particulars regarding the foregoing Schools, see the School Directory in Bradshaw's Guide for Great Britain, page ii.

TOURIST AND OFFICIAL FORWARDING AGENTS.—Perrin and Co., 15, Place St. Francois, Tourist and Official Forwarding and Custom House Agents; Storage, Exchange, and Sleeping Car Offices. Depot for Bradshaw's Publications.

RAIL, pp. 263, 263B, 264, 264A, 267A.

[**Ouchy.**—*Stat.*

THE ROYAL HOTEL.—First class hotel, near the Quay. French Restauraunt. Large garden. See Advt

SAVOY HOTEL.—New modern hotel, on the border of the Lake, with magnificent view of the Alps. Garden. Pension from 10 frs. See Ad.

HOTEL DU CHATEAU (at Ouchy-Lausanne).—Comfortable hotel, situated opposite the Landing Place, with fine view of Lake and Mountains. See Advt.

On the Lake of Geneva, immediately below Lausanne, 1 mile distant.

EDUCATIONAL.—LA VILLA.—School for Boys. Head Master. Dr. M. Auckenthaler.

STEAMER. page 364; RAIL, page 267A.]

Lenk.—*Stat.*—Pop. 1,750.

PARK HOTEL BELLEVUE.—First class; open position, commanding splendid view on the mountains. All summer and winter sports. Pension from 8 frs. See Advt.

HOTEL DES BAINS; KRONE; WILDSTRUBEL.

A finely situated Alpine village, 3,527 ft. above sea. The purity of the air and the magnificent scenery of the Lenk valley have long made the village a favourite summer resort, and it has a growing reputation as a centre for winter sport. Sulphur baths. RAIL, page 262C.

Bad Leuk—(Loueche-les-Bains).-Pop. 1,600.

HOTELS: ALPES; MAISON BLANCHE; FRANCE.

A village in Canton Valais, locally known as Les Bains (or Baden), in the ravine of the River Dala, immediately below the lofty rocky wall of the Gemmi, 1,660 ft. high; because of the situation the sun is lost to view at about 5.0 p.m. even in summer. Hot springs (sulphate of calcium—93° to 123°), beneficial in cases of rheumatism and skin disease, much frequented from June to Sept.

DILIGENCE from Leuk station (page 263B) to Bad Leuk, page 374.

[Several attractive excursions from Louèche, notably over beautiful pastures to the

Torrent Alp (Hotel), 8,005 ft., whence are splendid views; ENGLISH CHURCH SERVICE For the Gemmi Pass, see page 517.]

Leysin.—*Stat.*—Pop. 450.

A finely situated village, 4,500 ft. above sea, lying above Aigle and Sepey. Three large Sanatoria, also a Sanatorium for children; the altitude and very pure air are favourable for the special treatment of lung affections. Tobogganing, skating, ski-ing, etc. See Advert. pages.

MEDICAL.-Dr. Exchaquet-Meyer, Dr. Jaquerod.

RAIL to Aigle, page 267A.

Locarno.—*Stat.*—Pop. 3,603.

GRAND HOTEL AND PENSION LOCARNO.—Beautiful situation. Large garden. See Advt.

HOTEL DU PARC.—First class, beautifully situated in its own large grounds. Apartments with bath. English clientele. Pension from 9 fr. See Advt.

HOTEL METROPOLE.—First class hotel, well situated, full south, on the Lake, near Railway Station. Garden. See Advt.

A busy little town, 680 ft. above sea, of quite Italian character, beautifully situated near the north end of Lake Maggiore, at the influx of the River Maggia. It is a favourite winter, spring, and autumn resort, because of the mild climate. Old arcaded houses in the market place. Church of Sant' Antonio. Kursaal, with theatre, reading room; salle de jeux; concerts twice daily. Funicular railway to the wooded height above the town where is the pilgrimage Church of Madonna del Sasso, containing paintings; above the church a path leads to chapels.

ENGLISH CHURCH SERVICE, at Grand Hotel.

RAIL, pages 259B, 261. Steamer, page 366. Diligence, page 374.

[**Bignasco**—HOTEL DU GLACIER—18 miles from Locarno, in a beautiful part of the Val Maggia, which is a succession of pretty villages among rock scenery, waterfalls, and cultivated fields. RAIL, p. 261. DILIGENCE, p. 374].

Locle.—*Stat.*—Pop. 12,994.

HOTEL DES TROIS ROIS; JURA.

In a valley of the Juras, 3,035 ft. above sea. A watch-making town. School of Horology.

RAIL, page 255. Diligence, page 375.

Lucerne (Luzern).—*Stat.*—Pop. 39,152.

PALACE HOTEL.—Most luxurious high class hotel. Best situation on the "Quai," close to Casino and tennis grounds. Built 1906. See Ad.

GRAND HOTEL NATIONAL.—Large beautiful first class hotel in Louvre style. New Grill Room and Tea Room. Lift. Pfyffer and Co., proprietors. See Advt.

HOTELS SCHWEIZERHOF AND LUZERNERHOF—Splendid large first class hotels, of well-known reputation. Kept by Messrs. Hauser Brothers. Beautiful situation. See Advt.

CARLTON HOTEL TIVOLI.—Situated on the principal promenade, with view of Lake and Mountains. Electric light; lift. See Advt.

HOTEL ST. GOTHARD (Terminus Hotel), opposite the Steamboat Landing Place. See Advt.

HOTEL MONTANA.—New, first-class hotel, in elevated position, on the border of the Lake. All modern hotel improvements. See Advt.

HOTEL DES BALANCES AND BELLEVUE.—Very agreeably situated. Lift electric light. Open all the year. See Advt.

HOTEL DE L'EUROPE.—Highly reputed fashionable hotel, in quiet position, facing the Lake. Entirely rebuilt and up-to-date. Garden; lift; electric light. See Advt.

HOTEL BEAU RIVAGE.—First class hotel, beautifully situated. Moderate charges. See Advt.

HOTEL SWAN AND RIGI.—First class house, well situated on the Quay, with every modern comfort. Electric light; lift. See Advt.

HOTEL BRISTOL.—First class; great comfort; near Central Station and Landing Stage. Pension from 8.50 fr. Rooms from 3 fr. Breakfast 1.60 fr., Lunch 3.50 fr., Dinner 4.50 to 5 fr. See Advt.

HOTEL DES ALPES.—Excellent position. Commanding fine views. 60 beds. Verandah; terrace; lift; baths. Rooms from frs. 2.50, pension from frs. 7.50. See Advt.

HOTEL DU NORD.—Good second class, in quiet situation near Station. Restaurant. Electric light; baths. Pension from 6 fr. See Advt.

HOTEL RUTLI AND RHINE.—Excellent second class, situated within a short distance of Central Station. Restaurant; electric light; central heating; pension from 7 fr. See Advt.

HOTEL MINERVA.—Comfortable family hotel, opposite Station. All modern comforts. Pension from fr. 8.50. See Advt.

HOTEL PENSION WALLIS.—10 min. from Central Station by tramway; large park. Lawn tennis. Own dairy. Pension from 6 frs. See Advt.

PENSION RICHEMONT.—Very comfortable, situated near the principal promenade and within two minutes of trams and Casino. Garden terrace, verandah. Pension from fr. 6.50. See Advt.

PENSION ANGLAISE.—Comfortable, on Drei Linden Hill, near town. Panorama of Alps and lake. Garden. Pension from 5 fr. 50 c. See Advt.

PENSION GYGER.—First class pension, delightfully situated on elevated position with fine view; garden, terrace. Pension from 6.50 fr. See Advt.

HOTEL PENSION BELLE RIVE.—First class pension hotel, elevated position, fine views. Terrace; garden. Pension, 7 fr. 50 c. See Advt.

HOTEL WAGNER.—New family hotel. Quietly situated, near the Station and landing stage. Modern comforts. Rooms from 3 frs. See Ad.

HOTEL DE LA PAIX.—80 beds. Lift. Electric light. Central heating. Rooms from 2.50 fr. See Advt.

The RAILWAY STATION is by the Lake. Two Steamer PIERS—one close to Station, the other directly across the water at the Schweizerhof Quai. Electric Tramways.

Lucerne, capital of the Canton of Lucerne, on the Lake of Lucerne (or, Lake of Four Cantons), is perhaps the most beautifully situated tourist centre in Europe; surrounded on three sides by exquisitely wooded hills, with a magnificent prospect over a small arm of the Lake to a background of lofty snow clad mountains. The old city is still girdled on the landside by its mediæval walls and towers, which, with the rapid flowing Reuss, and the handsome Lake front and its palatial hotels, forms a view as picturesque as it is imposing. The streets in the older parts of the town are narrow and have little altered since the 16th cent., many of the houses having richly frescoed facades and beautiful metal signs. The old Gothic and renaissance fountains are specially noteworthy. The newer quarters, with their sumptuous hotels, handsome pensions, and pretty villas, are very attractive. The walks in every direction are charming, and the more distant excursions are almost innumerable. Two quaint mediæval bridges cross the River Reuss obliquely, both are roofed and the one nearest the efflux of the river from the Lake, the Kapellbrucke, has paintings of scenes in the lives of St. Leodegar and St. Mauritius. By the Kapellbrucke is an old tower, Wasserthurm, once a lighthouse (lucerna), whence the name of the town. The other bridge, higher up the river, is called the Spreuerbrucke.

The Hofkirche, whose two towers are immediately observed, dates from early in the 16th cent.; wood carving on pulpit, in stalls, and at side altars, good organ (occasional recitals), stained windows; treasury contains interesting objects; frescoes in arcades of churchyard. A quarter mile north of the Hofkirche is the monument, "The Lion of Lucerne" (Löwen Denkmal), in memory of the Swiss guards who died in defence of French royalty at the Tuileries, August 10th, 1792; in the Chapel, close by, are memorials of the officers slain, and in the Museum is a diorama and an exhibition of pictures (1 fr.) Adjoining the monument is the Gletschergarten, where are interesting signs of a remote ice period.

The Rathhaus (1519-1605), in Kornmarkt, opposite the north end of the Reuss Steg (iron foot bridge), contains a Museum of Antiquities, prehistoric, Roman, and mediæval; in the Council Chamber above is carving on walls and ceiling. Jesuiten Kirche, on the quay, near south end of the Reuss Steg; robe of St. Nikolaus von der Flue in a chapel. Museum, with Cantonal and Town Libraries; botanical and geographical collection in the Cantonal School building, behind the Jesuiten Kirche. Kriegs und Friedens Museum (War and Peace Museum), a timber mediæval building by the Lake, close to the Railway Station. In the Zuricherstrasse are Meyer's Diorama of the Rigi and the Stauffer Museum of Alpine animals (1 fr. to each).

KURSAAL (reading room, theatre, band), in Haldenstrasse. Golf Links.

POST OFFICE.—In Bahnhof Platz, between Railway Station and bridge.

ENGLISH CHURCH SERV. at St. Mark's Church. H.B.M.'s CONSUL.—Dr. L. A. Falck.

MEDICAL.—Dr. J. Eberhardt, Theaterstrasse, 18. Dr. Karl Doepfner, formerly of the University of Chicago, above Thos. Cook's Offices.

SURGEON DENTIST.—Dr. Alfred Faller, Grendelstrasse, 3—near Cook's Office—(9.0–5.0).

THE ENGLISH PHARMACY "F. Brunck." Alpenstrasse, 7, and Haldenstrasse, 23, opposite the National. All English and American prescriptions carefully compounded.

VILLA SOMMERAU, 15c, Kapuzinerweg. Cure Establishment. Noted for its comfort; very quiet and dust free position. Magnificent views. Dietary cooking, according to medical prescription, also vegetarian cooking. Family Life.

BANKERS.—Crivelli and Co., Correspondents of all principal Banks of the United States and the Continent. Exchange Office.

SOCIETE DE CREDIT SUISSE (formerly BANK in LUZERN), established 1856. Capital 16,000,000 fr. Exchange; Letters of Credit; Correspondents of the principal Banks.

DEPOT FOR BRADSHAW'S PUBLICATIONS.—E. Gebhardt, Schweizerhof Quai; Librairie E. Haag (late Eisenring), Kappelplatz.

RAIL.—See Routes from Lucerne, page cxxxv.

[The **Gutsch** (1,720ft. above sea), is a wooded height just beyond the west side of the town, affording a splendid view over town, lake, and mountain; funicular rail from the town or winding road. Another fine point of view is at the Drei Linden, 1,810 ft. above sea, less than a mile north west of the Hofkirche.

Sonnenberg 2,560 ft. above sea, is a finely situated health-resort, amidst woods, enjoying extensive views. English Church Service in summer. Reached by electric tram from Lucerne to Kriens, and thence funicular rail, every six minutes, see page 260. Or it is a pleasant half hour walk through woods from the Gütsch.

GOLF HOTEL, first class, magnificent situation among pine woods, 2,400 ft. above sea level. 9-hole golf links. Pension from 8 fr. See Advt.

The **Lake of Lucerne** is the grandest for mountain scenery in all Switzerland, and many pleasant excursions may be made by the steamer services shown on page 369. The chief points of interest on the Lake are:—

The **Burgenstock** 2,855 ft. above sea, is much frequented for the curative properties of the pure air; fine woods, magnficent views. English Church Service in summer. HOTELS AND PENSIONS BURGENSTOCK, first class hotels, surrounded by large parks; electric light; see Advt. Reached by Steamer from Lucerne, page 369, funicular rail from pier, page 261A. The **Rigi**, see page 527A.

Brunnen, see page 514B.

Gersau, see page 519.

Hertenstein.

SCHLOSS HOTEL.—First class, beautifully situated in park of 240,000 square metres, facing lake. Convenient centre for excursions. English clientele. Terms from 9 frs. See Advt.

Finely situated on the Lake below the Rigi, has beautiful views all round. Steamer, page 369.

Seelisberg, see page 528.

Vitznau, see page 532.

Weggis, see page 532.]

Lugano.—*Stat.*—Pop. 9,394.

GRAND HOTEL DU PARC—BEAUSEJOUR.—First class, old established, in finest position, facing the Lake. Large park. Highest patronage. Pension from 10 fr. See Advt.

LE GRAND HOTEL AND LUGANO PALACE.—First class; Restaurant Francais. Highest comfort; large hall; electric light; steam heating throughout. See Advt.

GRAND HOTEL SPLENDIDE.—First class fashionable hotel, well situated on the border of the lake. Patronised extensively by English and American families. See Advt.

HOTEL EUROPE.—First class hotel, elegantly furnished. Excellent position, overlooking the Lake; large shady park. See Advt.

HOTEL BRISTOL.—First class hotel, well situated, full south aspect. Lift; electric light; central heating. See Advt.

HOTEL METROPLE and MONOPOLE.-First class. Splendidly situated, with large park. Elevated position, full south. Lift; electric light. The nearest to the English Church. See Advt.

HOTEL VICTORIA.—First class, opposite the "Paradiso" Landing Stage. Entirely renewed with every modern comfort. Lift, electric light, central heating. Pension from 7.50 fr. See Advt.

SAVOY HOTEL SOMMER—First class, near Lake and Landing Stage. Open all the year. Lift. Central heating. Electric light. Special accommodation for English. See Advt.

REGINA HOTEL (Villa Ceresio).—Situated right on the Lake, and surrounded by garden. Electric light; lift; central heating. See Advt.

HOTEL BELLEVUE AU LAC.—Well situated on the Lake. Full south. Electric light, central heating, and lift. See Advt.

HOTEL WASHINGTON.—Comfortable hotel, situated in its large park on the hill, four minutes from the Station. See Advt.

HOTEL ADLER-STADTHOF.—Quiet comfortable hotel, opposite the Station. Fine view, garden; electric light; central heating. Pension from 7 frs. See Advt.

PENSION MINERVA.—Very comfortable. In close proximity to Station. Park. Electric light; central heating. Open all the year. Pension from 7 fr. See Advt.

The Railway Station is considerably above the town, a cable tramway connecting. There are five Steamboat Piers.

In Canton Ticino, 905 ft. above sea, beautifully placed on the west shore of Lake Lugano; an old Italian town, with picturesque tortuous arcaded streets, one of the best tourists centres in the Italian lake district. Climate mild, vegetation sub-tropical, scenery as noted for rich colouring as for its own intrinsic beauty. On the hill from the Station to the town is the Church of San Lorenzo, of 15th cent. In Church of Santa Maria degli Angioli, on east side of town, 150 yards back from the Lake, are good frescoes. Palazzo Civico, by the pier. Many beautiful walks in the immediate neighbourhood.

ENGLISH CHURCH SERVICE at English Church.

H. B. M.'S VICE-CONSUL.—R. H. Hamilton, Esq.

MEDICAL.—Dr. F. Zbinden, 42, Via del Colle; speaks English; 2.0–4.0 p.m. Dr. Ed. Hartmann, 27, Via Nassa; speaks English; consultations, 2.0–4.0 p.m.

ENGLISH NURSES' HOME.—Miss Heath, "Villa Hesland," Via Coremmo, 10 (Besso-Lugano)." Fully-trained Nurses supplied; resident patients taken. Telephone 761. Telegrams: Heath, Lugano.

EDUCATIONAL.—Mlle. Cunier, "Le Lierre." First class Boarding School for Girls, with best opportunity for learning languages, science, and art. Home comforts, Highest references. See Advt.

For further details respecting the foregoing School see the School Directory in Bradshaw's British Guide, page ii.

BANKERS.—SOCIETE DE CREDIT SUISSE.—Quai Vincenza Vela. Reserved capital, 100 millions. Established 1856. Exchange, Letters of Credit. Correspondents of the principal Banks.

RAIL, pages 259, 261. Steamers, page 367. Electric trams; motor omnibus between Lugano and Ponte Tresa.

[**Monte Generoso**, 5,590 feet.

About 6 miles due south of Lugano. The view from Monte Generoso is one of the finest in the whole range of the Lombard Alps. The mountain is comparatively isolated, rising from a chain of lower hills; northward extends the range of the Swiss Alpine chain, behind is the plain of Lombardy with its many cities. The flora is wonderful.

STEAMER from Lugano to Capolago, p. 367, or RAIL from Lugano to Capolago, page 259. Mountain Railway from Capolago to Generoso, page 259A.

Monte Salvatore, 3,000 feet. HOTEL KULM.

A mile south of Lugano. Pilgrimage chapel at the summit. Beautiful views, flowers and plants of rare beauty. Mountain Railway from Lugano Paradiso, page 259A.

Monte Bre, 3,050 feet. Two miles east of Lugano: funicular railway to the summit.

Lanzo d'Intelvi.

HOTEL BELVEDERE.

A pleasantly cool summer spot, on opposite side of the lake from Lugano, 3,116 ft. above sea; fine views over the lake and mountains. English Church Service during summer.

Funicular Railway from Sta. Margherita (page 367) to Lanzo d'Intelvi.]

Maloggia (Maloja).

PALACE HOTEL.—H. Schlagenhauff, manager. First class in every respect. 300 rooms; 50 bathrooms. Luxurious public rooms. Orchestra; billiards; central heating. See Advt.

6,000 ft. above sea, on the Maloggia route, the lowest pass between Switzerland and Italy, one of the most beautiful in the Alps. Well-known and fashionable summer and winter resort, 12 miles from St. Moritz by road. Prettiest spot in the Upper Engadine. Pure, bracing air. Starting point of a great many most attractive mountain and glacier excursions. Bright sunshine, exceedingly dry climate. Magnificent mountain scenery. Well known golf links; tennis; trout fishing; rowing and sailing boats; besides many other pastimes. Post, telegraph, telephone. Summer season, June 1st to end of September; Winter season, December 1st to end of March. Skating on Sils Lake and on the rink of the Maloggia Palace; ski-ing, tobogganing, hockey, curling.

ENGLISH CHURCH SERVICE in the season.

DILIGENCE, page 378.

Martigny.—*Stat.* —Pop. 3,000.

GRAND HOTEL DU MONT BLANC.—First class, close to the Station of electric railway. Garage. See Advt.

GRAND HOTEL CLERC.—First class, of old reputation, much frequented by English and Americans. Terms from 8 fr. See Advt.

NATIONAL.

Tramway between Railway Station and town.

Martigny Ville is an old town, the Roman Octodurum, in Canton Valais, on the River

Drance, near its influx to the Rhône. During the season there is much activity with the arrival and departure of travellers over the Passes to Chamonix and Aosta. The aged and infirm monks of the St. Bernard Hospice dwell in a Monastery here. In the south part of the town some Roman remains have been discovered.

RAIL, pages 257A, 263B, 263C.

[A good road ascends from Martigny eastward, through woods, 10 miles, to the **Pierre-à-Voir,** 8,123 feet. English Church Service in Summer.]

MARTIGNY TO CHAMONIX VIA SALVAN.

RAIL from Martigny to Argentière, page 257A

RAIL from Argentière to Chamonix, page 61B.

The line runs parallel with the Rhone Valley railway from Martigny to Vernayaz, where the ascent begins; after two tunnels, and a curve partly through a third tunnel, the Plan du Sourd is traversed to

Salvan, 3,230 ft. above sea, a village much frequented during summer for the pure air and as a centre for mountain excursions; resident guides. Small collection of prehistoric carvings found in the neighbourhood. English Church Service in summer.

The line ascends in bends and through a tunnel to **Les Marécottes,** 3,385 ft. above sea, a pretty place; then, after crossing the Triège gorge, runs along a precipitous hill-side to Le Tretien (3,484 ft.) and **Finhaut** (4,060 ft.).

A little beyond Finhaut the line begins to descend to the Eau Noire valley and **Le Châtelard-Trient** (3,680 ft.), at the frontier of Switzerland and France. HOTEL SUISSE AU CHATELARD.

Between Le Châtelard and Argentière the road is up the confined valley of the Eau Noire, passing from Switzerland into Savoy, and presently a descent to a wild stream, afterwards an ascent through the narrowing valley to **Valorsine.** Thence a solitary vale, leading to the top of the **Col des Montets** (4,740 ft.), where the Col de Balme is seen towering in front, and then Mont Blanc itself. Moving onward a magnificent view of the Glacier du Tour and the Aiguille Verte is disclosed; at **Argentière,** 4,100 ft. (HOTEL COURONNE; MONT BLANC; GLACIER; BELLEVUE), the Glacier d'Argentière spreads out on the left hand. The village (pop. 500) is well known as a centre for mountain excursions. The descent is now made of the Vale of Chamonix, with the River Arve on the left hand.

MARTIGNY TO CHAMONIX VIA THE TETE NOIRE.

The route to Chamonix is frequently traversed by pedestrians (guides not needed) in about 8½ hours, in much the same time as is taken by the small omnibus that runs over the road (fare 16 fr.). Two horse carriages, for two persons, 40 fr., 3 persons 50 fr., 4 persons 60 fr.

Leaving Martigny by the St. Bernard road, at the village of Croix a notice indicates the road to Chamonix. Here the ascent begins, winding up to the hamlet of Les Chavans. The road gets steeper in the approach to the **Col de la Forclaz** (5,105 ft.), and this point passed a descent is made to **Trient** (HOTEL: GLACIER DE TRIENT), in the Val de Trient; then the road traverses the forest of Trient, emerging from it by the HOTEL DE LA TETE NOIRE, and continues along the face of the **Tête Noire**—a way having been cut in the rock at an immense precipitous height above the valley—across the Eau Noire to **Le Châtelard.** From Le Châtelard to Chamonix see previous route.

TO CHAMONIX VIA THE COL DE BALME.

This is, partly or entirely, a pedestrian route about 11 hours required. The route shewn previously is followed as far as a point in the descent from the Col de la Forclaz to Trient, where, on the left, the bridle path goes off for the Col de Balme. Guide not necessary.

Soon after leaving the carriage road a bridge is crossed, and, some meadows traversed, there is a steep zigzag climb among the trees for nearly an hour; then the path becomes easier to the **Col de Balme,** 7,221 ft. (HOTEL SUISSE). Beyond the Col de Balme, the path, entering Savoy, descends to La Tour over some rough steep ground, the River Arve flowing on the right. At **Le Tour** is the end of a carriage road leading to Argentière (see route above).

MARTIGNY TO AOSTA.

From Martigny the railway has been completed as far as **Orsières** (page 263C), whence the road (Diligence, p. 376) climbs in one or two long twists and a long ascent to **Liddes** (HOTEL GRAND ST. BERNARD; UNION). A fairly straight road leads up to **Bourg St. Pierre** (HOTEL DU DEJEUNER DE NAPOLEON), a village with 11th cent. church and an Alpine Garden belonging to a Geneva Society. Passing through a larch forest and the Défilé de Charreire, at the Cantine de Proz is a lonely Inn; then follow the stony Plan de Proz, Hospitalet (where are chalets and a dairy), and a long winding rise to the Hospice of St. Bernard.

There are two buildings at the **Hospice of Great St. Bernard,** 8,110 ft. above sea; in one are the church, dwellings of the monks, and rooms for travellers; the other, called the Hotel de St. Louis, is a house of refuge in case of fire, and where the poorer travellers are received. The piano was presented by King Edward VII (1904) to replace one given by him when Prince of Wales. Lodging and food are gratuitous, but travellers should drop into the box for offerings *at least* the amount of an hotel charge. From 20,000 to 25,000 travellers are received yearly. In an upper chamber is a Library and natural history collections, coins, relics, etc. A quarter of a mile beyond the Hospice the descent on the Italian side commences, an excellent carriage road leading down to St. Remy and Aosta.

Bagnes, Val de Bagnes.

The Val de Bagnes is a wild picturesque stretch of country on the road from Martigny to Aosta over the Col de Fenêtre. Rail from Martigny to Sembrancher, page 263C, thence diligence to Lourtier, page 376; thence bridle path. Magnificent scenery — mountain, forest, torrent, glacier.

The principal town of the valley is **Le Chable.** Pop. 1,400, 2,742 ft. above sea, 13 miles from Martigny, in a very picturesque situation, on the River Dranse; old abbey-house, once the fortified castle of the "vidames" of Bagnes; spired church.

Lourtier (HOTEL DE LOUTIER), 3,690 ft. above sea, about 17 miles from Martigny, is in a beautiful valley amidst meadows and orchards, with the gloomy Bec de Corbassière towering above. The road from Lourtier to Fionnay, 5 miles, is a series of zigzags over steep slopes; the diligence service ends at Lourtier, but mules and horses or a carriage may be had—many travellers prefer to walk.

Fionnay.

HOTEL DU GRAND COMBIN.—Well known first class hotel, much frequented on account of its proximity to the glaciers. Pension terms. See Advt.

CARROU; ALPES.

Fionnay, 4,910 ft. above sea, is a collection of old brown Swiss chalets, scattered in picturesque confusion, with meadow, Alpine flowers, and forest all round. Very pure air; no fog, and very little rain.

Mauvoisin (HOTEL MAUVOISIN), 5,570 ft., is 1½ hour beyond Fionnay, along a wild narrow valley, the River Dranse flowing 100 ft. below the bridge. Travellers to Aosta should stay the night at Mauvoisin, or, higher, at Chanrion. To the Pass from Chanrion 2 hours: guide for the Col de Fenêtre, 18 fr.

TO THE GRAND COMBIN VIA THE VAL DE BAGNES.

From Fionnay a very interesting excursion is by a track leading between the Corbassière Alp and the lower end of the Glacier de Corbassière to the Cabane de Panossière, 8,908 ft., a hut shelter on the edge of the glacier—guide about 8 fr. From the Cabane several fine ascents may be made, notably of the **Grand Combin,** 14,164 ft., in 9 to 10 hours—guide about 60 fr. The descent is often made on the other side of the mountain to Bourg St. Pierre, where is a diligence service to the Grand St. Bernard or to Orsières, whence is a railway to Martigny.

Maurice, St.—*Stat.*—Pop. 2,162.

HOTEL SIMPLON; ALPES.

A quaint old town, the Roman Agaunum, in Canton Valais. The Abbey, dating from 4th cent. is regarded as the most ancient north of the Alps; several precious works of ancient art, MS. of the Gospels, etc.—rarely shewn. Hermitage of Notre Dame du Sex, on a hill to west of Station. Grotte des Fées, a stalactite cavern with waterfall. RAIL, page 263B.

[**Lavey.** ETABLISSEMENT THERMAL.
The Bains de Lavey are about 1¼ mile from St. Maurice up the Rhone Valley. Warm saline-sulphur spring, 100° Fahr., much frequented in the season.]

Meiringen.—*Stat.*—Pop. 3,077.

HOTEL DU SAUVAGE.—First class, old established. Magnificent position, with large park. Pension from 8 fr. See Advt.

BRUNIG; KREUZ MEIRINGERHOF.

Chief village of the lovely Hasli Valley, on the River Aare, 1,968 feet above sea, amidst picturesque surroundings, a favourite resort on account of the purity and freshness of the air. Its position at the junction of five mountain roads—the Grimsel, the Grosse Scheidegg, the Susten, the Jockpass, and the Brünig—renders it one of the most frequented places of the Bernese Oberland. Church tower was once part of a castle; ruined tower of Resti to east of village. The fall of the Alpbach, pouring down upon an enormous bank of moraine, frequently displays in early morning a rainbow—illuminated every evening in the season. The natural beauties of the neighbourhood are numerous.

ENGLISH CHURCH SERVICE at Church in grounds of Hotel Wildenmann.

RAIL, page 267A. Diligence, page 377.

[**Reichenbach Falls.**
On the south side of Meiringen. In summer the Falls are illuminated by electricity. Electric rail from near Hotel Reichenbach to the upper fall; also a footpath.]

Montreux.—*Stat.*—Pop. 16,000.

GRAND HOTEL MONNEY AND BEAU-SEJOUR.—First class family hotel, with large and shady garden. Lift. See Advt.

GRAND HOTEL ET HOTEL DES ALPES.—Splendid establishments. See Advt.

HOTEL BELMONT, with large Villa. Surrounded by park, terraces, and vineyards. See Advt.

HOTEL SUISSE.—First class, opposite Central Railway Station and Landing Stage. Replete with every comfort and luxury. Garden. Terms from 10 fr. See Advt.

GRAND HOTEL EDEN.—Situated on the south Quay, near the Kursaal; lift; electric light. See Advt.

HOTEL BREUER.—First class, in good position. All comforts. See Advt.

HOTEL CONTINENTAL.—First class hotel, beautifully situated, with garden on border of Lake. Lift; electric light; central heating. See Advt.

HOTEL DE PARIS.—First class family hotel, centrally situated, near Kursaal; latest modern improvements. Pension from 7 fr. See Advt.

HOTEL DE L'EUROPE.—Excellent, in highest and finest situation, near Station. Much frequented by English families. Pension from 8 fr. See Advt.

HOTEL MIRABEAU (Clarens).—An elegant and quiet pension hotel, standing in pleasant grounds, facing the Lake. Pension from 9 fr. See Advt.

HOTEL BEAU RIVAGE.—Well situated. Winter garden. See Advt.

HOTEL VICTORIA.—Family hotel, in central position, above the Station. Electric light; central heating. Pension from 6 fr. See Advt.

HOTEL PENSION RICHEMOND.—Family hotel, in quiet position; near the Kursaal; open all the year. Pension from 7 fr. See Advt.

HOTEL MODERNE.—Comfortable hotel, of recent construction, adjoining the Station; with restaurant. See Advt.

HOTEL NATIONAL.—First class family hotel. Suites and single rooms with bath and toilette. Open all the year. See Advt.

WINDSOR HOTEL—SAVOY HOTEL ET HOLLANDE.—Family hotel, highly situated, overlooking the Lake. 50 beds. All modern comforts. Pension from 7 fr. See Advt.

Montreux is the name applied to a strip of shore, and slopes in the background, at the north east end of the Lake of Geneva. The district is one of the pleasantest residential and tourist centres in French speaking Switzerland; the scenery is of varying attraction, mountain, lake, and meadow; in summer the heat is cooled by the Lake breezes, in winter the sheltered situation secures a mild climate with clear air—not often are there frost and snow. From CLARENS, on the west side, there is a line of delightful spots along the shore through VERNEX and COLLONGES to TERRITET, at the east side, with CHARNEX, LES PLANCHES, GLION, and VEYTAUX, nestling in the hillsides behind. The district is well served by Railway (pages 262C, 263B,) and Steamer (page 364), and the electric tramway passes all along the Lake shore from Vevey to Chillon. During May the Narcissus Festival is held.

H.B.M's VICE-CONSUL.—M. Cuenod. Esq.

GOLF.—9-hole course at Aigle: club house.

ENGLISH CHURCH SERVICES: Territet—Church of St. John; Clarens-Montreux Christ Church; Presbyterian Church near Montreux Station; Roman Catholic Church, Avenue du Kursaal.

At Clarens are many villa residences; Chateau des Cretes, above the village to north west, has gardens accessible at times. In the Rue du Lac, the house where Byron lived, 1816, is marked by a tablet. Rousseau is specially associated with Clarens.

HOTEL ROYAL.—First class, on the border of the Lake. Very comfortable. See Advt.

GRAND HOTEL DE CLARENS.—First class; in good situation. Garden; garage. See Advt.

HOTEL BEAU SITE (at Baugy sur Clarens).—Family hotel, charmingly situated above Clarens, with park; electric light; central heating. Pension from 7 fr. See Advt.

Chailly is very pleasantly situated among the hills, about a mile west of the centre of Montreux, with easy access by rail up from Clarens. Several roads and paths lead through beautiful country.

HOTEL PENSION MURY.—In tranquil situation (at Chailly-sur-Clarens). Comfortable, homelike; with shady park. Electric light; central heating. Pension from fr. 5.50. See Advt.

RAIL from Clarens, page 262C.

Blonay is another delightful spot, 2,043 ft. above sea level. A little above the village is the old Chateau of Blonay; 16th cent. chapel. A famous point of view above Blonay is Les Pleiades, 4,475 ft.

RAIL from both Clarens and Vevey, page 262C.

At **Montreux-Territet** are

HOTEL EXCELSIOR ET BON PORT.—Quiet; winter garden. See Advt.

HOTEL MONT FLEURI.—Summer and winter residence. See Advt.

HOTEL D'ANGLETERRE.—Elevated situation, overlooking the Lake and the Alps. Quiet, homelike. Terms from 7 frs. See Advt.

HOTEL-PENSION LES VIOLETTES (at Veytaux, above Territet). In quiet sheltered position; renovated, every comfort. Fine view; garden. Pension from fr. 5.50. See Advt.

HYDRO L'ABRI and KURHAUS TERRITET.—First class establishment for the treatment of internal and nervous diseases. Mental or Tuberculous cases not admitted. See Advt.

MEDICAL.—Dr. Loy, specialist for internal and nervous diseases, Sanatorium l'Abri. Hours of consultation: Monday, Wednesday, Friday, 1.30 to 3.0 p.m.

Vernex (Montreux-Vernex) occupies about the middle situation along the Lake front. Here is the principal market—an animated scene; opposite the Roman Catholic Church is the Kursaal the old Church of Montreux is at Les Planches, half a mile up the hill—fine view from the terrace.

The Castle of Chillon, about a mile east of Territet, is supposed to date from the 9th cent., but the existing building is probably of the 13th cent., with some remains, as the pillars in the vaults, of the earlier work; upon the pillars many celebrities have put their names; open morn. and aft., 50 c.

AMERICAN DENTIST.—Donald L. Galbreath, D.D.S., successor to J. F. Patterson, D.D.S., 74, Grand Rue, Montreux,; Telephone 105.

THE BRITISH PHARMACY.—F. Auenmuller, Avenue du Kursaal. English prescriptions and specialities; analyses.

ENGLISH BANKERS.—Wm. Cuenod and Co., Montreux (British Vice-Consulate), successors of Cuenod, Churchill, and Sons. Head Office, Vevey; branch at Clarens.

BANQUE DE MONTREUX. also Territet and Aigle. Capital Fr. 6,000,000; Reserves, Fr. 1,875,000. Exchange; Letters of Credit.

RAIL, pp. 262C, 263B, 267A; Steamer, p. 364. During the summer a motor-car service runs between the steamer pier and the railway stations.

[**Glion.**—*Stat.*

HOTEL DU RIGHI VAUDOIS.—First class hotel, beautifully situated. See Advt.

GRAND HOTEL VICTORIA.—First class hotel, in a commanding position. See Advt.

Funicular Railway (page 267A) up to Glion, 2,270 ft. above sea, whence are fine views. Most forms of winter sport. English Church.

The line upward from Glion to Caux, Jaman, and Naye (6,710 ft.) is one of the most picturesque mountain lines in Switzerland.

Caux, 3,610 ft.

PALACE HOTEL and GRAND HOTEL.—Both first class establishments, with every modern comfort. Splendid view of the Lake and mountains. See Advt.

Frequented as a health resort, overlooking Montreux, magnificent views. Cool in summer, sunny in winter. Tobogganing, skating, ski-ing, bob-sleighing, etc., in winter. At Naye, higher up, is the Alpine Garden of the Montreux Botanical Society. The Grottes de Naye are interesting. RAIL, Territet to Glion, and Glion to Caux and Naye, page 267A.

Chamby.—*Stat.*

HOTEL DES NARCISSES.-First class, splendidly situated, in close proximity of pine woods. Suites with bath. Terrace balconies. Open all the year. Pension from 9 fr. See Advt.

In a fine prominent position above Montreux—2,461 ft. above sea. Great wealth of narcissus bloom in the season. Winter sports.

ENGLISH CHURCH SERVICE.

RAIL, page 262C.

Avants, Les.—*Stat.*

GRAND HOTEL DES AVANTS.—Recently enlarged, and fitted with every modern comfort. Famous as a sporting centre. Open all the year. Much patronised by English. Terms from 9 fr. See Advt.

HOTEL DE SONLOUP.—Newly built, 4,000 ft. above sea; close to pine woods and nearest to starting point of the toboggan runs and ski-ing slopes. Pension from 9 fr. See Advt.

A beautifully situated summer and winter health resort, 3,190 ft. above sea, on the slopes of the Pré Alpes, above Montreux. Very fine views; in early summer the narcissus blooms extensively. In the winter much skating, tobogganing, ski-ing, etc. Funicular service between Les Avants and **Sonloup** every quarter of an hour, journey 50 minutes.

ENGLISH CHURCH SERVICE. RAIL, page 262C]

Moritz, St. Canton Grisons.—*Stat.*

St. Moritz Dorf and St. Moritz Bad are about 1½ mile apart, an electric tram maintaining a frequent service between the two places.

Moritz Dorf, St. (village).—Pop. 1,600.

GRAND HOTEL.—First class hotel, affording every modern comfort. See Advt.

PALACE HOTEL.—First class hotel, up to date. 180 rooms and apartments with private baths. Winter sport. Own orchestra. See Advt.

SUVRETTA HOUSE.—High class hotel, opened December, 1912. Magnificent position, full south. Surrounded by extensive "Sporting Park." Rooms from 5 fr. Pension terms. See Advt.

HOTEL BELVEDERE (Bavier).—Well situated, overlooking the whole valley. Winter Garden. Electric light; lift. See Advt.

SCHWEIZERHOF CHATEAU (Hotel Suisse).—Central, near Post and Telegraph Offices. Central heating, electric light. See Advt.

HOTEL CASPAR BADRUTT.—First class, in good position. Renovated and enlarged. See Advt.

PRIVATE HOTEL ST. MORITZ.—In quiet sunny position, with fine view of Lake. Electric light, baths, etc. Pension from 10 frs. See Advt.

NEW ROSATSCH HOTEL.—New high class hotel, with all home comforts. Reasonable. Pension terms. See Advt.

NEW POST HOTEL.—New family hotel in central and sunny position. Rooms from 4 frs. Pension from 11 frs. See Advt.

HOTEL WALDHAUS.—New high class family hotel in sunny sheltered position. 80 rooms from frs. 3.50. Pension from frs. 10. See Advt.

WESTEND HOTEL (formerly RHAETIA).—Well appointed family hotel, situated full south, with fine view. Electric light; central heating. English clientèle. Pension from 9 fr. See Advt.

HOTEL MONOPOL.—New high class hotel, with up-to-date comforts. Suites and single rooms. Moderate charges. Open all the year. See Advt.

PENSION KOPP.—Full south, on the promenade. Exceedingly comfortable and home-like, specially suitable for English families. Electric light; central heating. Pension from 10 fr. See Advt.

HOTEL CAMPFER.—Quiet pension hotel, charmingly situated, 15 minutes from St. Moritz. Electric light; central heating. English clientèle. See Advt.

St. Moritz, 6,033 ft. above sea, the highest village in the Engadine, is situated a short distance from the north side of the Lake of St. Moritz. The purity of the air and the magnificent scenery attract both summer and winter visitors; during the winter season, when the dry air is specially favourable in the early stages of chest affections, there is much tobogganing, skating, ski-ing, etc. Several good paths to fine points of view; very pleasant walk through the woods to Pontresina.

ENGLISH CHURCH.

Easy ascents, about 1 hour each, of the Alp Laret, 6,893 ft., to north east, and of the Alp Giop, 7,160 ft., to north west.

MEDICAL.—Resident English Physician and H.B.M.'s Consul, Dr. Holland.

AMERICAN DENTIST.—Dr. Berry.

TOURIST AND FORWARDING AGENTS.—Gerber and Naegeli, Bankers and Exchange Offices. Correspondents of Thos. Cook and Son.

DEPÔT FOR BRADSHAW'S GUIDES, Librairie Branzke and Gandolfo Gallerie, opposite the Hotel du Lac.

Moritz Bad, St., 5,823 ft. above sea.

ENGADINER HOF.—First class hotel. Centrally situated, "Quartier des Bains." Pension terms from 12 fr. to 20 fr. Open winter and summer. See Advt.

HOTELS KURHAUS, NEUES STAHLBAD, VICTORIA AND DU LAC.—First class. Open from June 1st to end September. See Advt.

HOTEL NATIONAL.—Excellent house, between the Curhaus and the Stahlbad. Newly fitted up for winter season. Pension from 10 fr. See Advt.

St. Moritz Bad is situated at the south west end of the Lake of St. Moritz. The curative properties of the carbonic acid and alkaline waters, used for drinking and bathing, have been known for centuries, drawing many patients every season, which lasts from mid June to mid September. Baths at the Kurhaus and the Neue Stahlbad. Casino by the Lake; reading room and music. A favourite walk, about an hour, is to the Hahnensee, a small lake in a delightful situation.

GOLF.—9-hole course, 1 mile from station.

DEPOT FOR BRADSHAW'S GUIDE.—C. B. Faist, English Library.

RAIL, page 257A, 268B.

[Celerina.

CRESTA PALACE.—First class family hotel, recently built. Fine open position. Every modern comfort. Central heating; electric light; lift. See Advt.

A pleasant village two miles from St. Moritz; a quiet résting place. A winter sport centre.

Campfer, 6,000 ft. above sea.

A mile and a half from St. Moritz Bad, in the direction of Silvaplana. Skating, ski-ing, etc., in winter. English Church Service. DILIGENCE, see page 378.

Silvaplana, 5,958 ft. above sea.

HOTEL POSTE; SONNE.

A pleasantly situated village, about 3 miles from St. Moritz. Winter sports. ENGLISH CHURCH SERVICE.

DILIGENCE, page 378.]

Neuchatel.—*Stat.*—Pop. (1910) 23,505.

GRAND HOTEL DE BELLE VUE.—Well situated first class hotel, on the Lake, with electric light, lift, and garden. See Advt.

GRAND HOTEL TERMINUS ET HOTEL DES ALPES.—Well situated, with fine view of the whole panorama of the town and the Alps. Electric light; lift. See Advt.

Neuchatel is pleasantly situated on the Lake of Neuchatel at the base and on the slopes of the Juras. From the Railway Station. above the town, on the north east side, the Avenue de la Gare leads in about three-quarters of a mile to the neighbourhood of the hotels and Lake. From the tree planted quay, extending 1½ mile, are beautiful views of the Alps. At the middle of the quay is the small port. On the quay, at the east side of the harbour, is the Musée des Beaux Arts, a fine building, containing a Picture Gallery and a collection of antiquities; free on Sun. and Thurs., morn. and aft., other days 50 c. At the west side of the harbour is the Gymnase, containing the Natural History Museum and collection of stuffed Alpine birds; also the Public Library; open daily, Sundays excepted, from 10.0 to 12.15 and from 2.0 to 7.0.

The Collegiate Church and Chateau are adjacent on the hill in the west part of the town. The church dates from the 12th cent., the two Gothic towers are of the 15th cent.; in the choir is a monument of the Counts of Neuchatel with fifteen life size figures; cloisters on the north side. The Chateau, part of 12th cent., other parts of 15th-17th cent., is occupied by the Cantonal Government, the town being the capital.

Ethnological Museum, half mile west of the Chateau.

University (about 300 students), back from east end of the quay. Ecole de Commerce (largest in Switzerland), about 1,000 scholars of all nations.

Cercle du Musée, in the Palais Rougemont—library, garden, etc., open to strangers.

POST OFFICE.—On the Quay, facing the port; also at Railway Station.

ENGLISH CHURCH SERVICE.—At Church, Rue du Palais Rougemont.

H.B.M.'S VICE-CONSUL.—E. Chable, Esq.

GOLF.—Club house half-hour's walk from town. Tennis clubs.

MEDICAL.—Dr. Stauffer.

RAIL, pages 259B, 264, 264A, 265. Steamers page 363.

[The **Lake of Neuchatel** is 25 miles long, 4 to 6 miles broad; the outflow of the waters is at the north east end, where the River Thiele issues. Near the north end of the Lake, at La Sauge, is the canal leading into the Lake of Morat.]

Neuhausen.—*Stat.*

HOTEL SCHWEIZERHOF.—First class house, well situated, with fine view on the Falls and the Alps, Electric light; lift. See Advt.

BELLEVUE.—First class hotel, in fine situation; full view of Falls. See Advt.

The **Falls of the Rhine** are at Neuhausen, 2 miles down the river from Schaffhausen. The waters pass in three leaps over an irregular ledge, 60 ft. high near one bank, 48 ft. high near the other. Best point of view, one of the rocks that rise above the Falls; the access is by boat (no danger) and railed path; 1 or 2 persons 3 fr. and small fee, each additional person 1 fr.

The Falls are illuminated four times a week from June 1st until July 15th, and every evening after until the end of September.

ENGLISH CHURCH SERVICE.

RAIL, pages 139A, 261B, 262.

Oberhofen.—*Stat.*

HOTEL MONTANA.—New high class hotel, in good position. Suites and single rooms. Pension from 7 frs. See Advt.

MOY; VICTORIA.

A pleasant village on the north shore of the Lake of Thun. Very fine views. Chateau Harrach is picturesque.

RAIL, page 268F. STEAMER, page 363.

[**Hilterfingen.**—*Stat.*

HOTEL WILDBOLZ (opened 1909).—First class family hotel, beautifully situated, with large garden extending to lake. Every modern comfort. Boating, fishing. Pension from 7.50 fr. See Advt.

PENSION HILTERFINGEN.—Unique position in its own grounds. Commanding full view of lake and mountains. Own rowing boats free of charge. Pension from 6fr. See Advt.

Hilterfingen, ten minutes distant from Oberhofen, is in a sheltered position amidst magnificent vegetation—a delightfully quiet retreat.

RAIL, page 268F.]

Ormont, Dessous (lower), **& Dessus** (upper).

A delightful pastoral valley in Canton Vaud, about 7 miles long, from **Le Sepey,** 3,704 feet above sea (HOTEL DU MONT D'OR; CERF), at west end, to **Le Plan des Iles,** 3,815 ft. above sea (HOTEL DES DIABLERETS), at east end. Between these villages are many pensions and private houses. In winter much tobogganing, skating, and ski-ing. Ascent of the **Diablerets,** 10,650 ft., and many easier mountain climbs.

ENG. CHURCH SER. at Le Plan and Le Sepey.

DILIGENCE from Aigle, page 376.

Pfäfers Bad. HOTEL and BATH HOUSE.

In the narrow deep gorge of the River Tamina, about 3 miles beyond and 525 ft. above Ragaz. The hot springs, 99° to 102°, free of taste and smell, contain small quantities of lime, chloride of sodium, and magnesia; they rise in a gloomy part of the gorge, where it is only from 30 ft. to 50 ft. wide—admission 1 fr.

The village of Pfäfers, Pfäfers Dorf (HOTEL ADLER; LOWE), is an interesting walk of 1¼ hr. from Pfäfers Bad; the winding path requires some caution, the way being slippery in wet weather. The old Benedictine Abbey is a lunatic asylum. Pfäfers is reached by diligence from Ragaz, page 377.

Pont, Le.—*Stat.*

GRAND HOTEL DU LAC DE JOUX.—First class. Elevated situation, with splendid view. All summer and winter sports. Complete modern equipment. Pension from 10 fr. See Advt.

A favourite summer and winter health resort, 3,310 ft. above sea, in a fine situation at the north end of the pretty Lac de Joux. Golf links; winter sports. Ascent in 1½ hours of the Dent de Vaulion, 4,880 ft., grand view.

English Church Service.

RAIL, page 259B. Steamers on the Lac de Joux, page 366.

Pontresina.—*Stat.*—Pop. 500.

HOTEL KRONENHOF AND BELLAVISTA.—First class hotel, with view on the Roseg Glacier and snow mountains. Electric light; lift. See Advt.

HOTEL ROSEG.—First class in every respect. Beautifully situated on elevated position, facing Roseg glacier. Extensively patronised by English. Pension terms from 12 fr. See Advt.

SCHLOSSHOTEL ENDERLIN.—First class family hotel, in fine position. Central heating; electric light; lifts. Suites with bath, etc. See Advt.

HOTEL PONTRESINA LTD.—New first class hotel, in fine position. Open from June to October. Central heating. Large garden. Tennis. Opposite English Church. Restaurant. See Adv.

HOTEL LANGUARD.—Modern hotel, in fine position. Good cooking Electric light; lift; central heating. Baths. Moderate. See Advt.

Pontresina is a mountaineering village extending for about ¾ mile along the River Bernina, consisting of Lower Pontresina (or Laret), Upper Pontresina (or Spiert), and a cluster of houses between called Bellavita; a favourite summer resort, and a centre for winter sport. Woods, mountains, and glaciers are all round, and the flora of the neighbourhood is exceptionally interesting. The Morteratsch Glacier and Roseg Glacier, the Schafberg (8,965 ft.), and Piz Languard (10,715 ft.) are within easy distance. Several guides resident in the village.

ENG. CHURCH SERVICE in the new church.

PRESBYTERIAN SERVICE in the village church, in July and August.

RAIL, page 257A.

[The **Bernina Pass** is in some respects the finest in Switzerland; often a considerable traffic of Valtellina wine is traversing it. The road leads up to the solitary Bernina Houses, 6,720 ft. (small inn), whence it is 5 miles to the Bernina Hospice, 7,575 ft. (HOTEL), on the Lago Bianco. The summit of the Pass, 7,644 ft., is a quarter mile beyond the Hospice; thence the road descends rapidly to La Rosa, Poschiavo, and Tirano. Railway, page 257A.]

Prese, Le.—*Stat.*

A pleasant summer resort, with an Italian climate, on the Lago di Poschiavo, 3,155 ft. above sea. A spring of alkaline sulphur waters near the Kurhaus.

ENGLISH CHURCH SERVICE in summer.

RAIL, page 257A.

Ragaz.—*Stat.*—Pop. 1,866.

HOTEL BRISTOL.—Very conveniently situated; every up-to-date comfort. Carriages to the world famed Taormina and thermal springs of Pfäfers. See Advt.

HOF RAGAZ; SCHWEIZERHOF.

In a picturesque situation, 2,000 ft. above sea, on the River Tamina, one of the most frequented watering places of Switzerland; nearly 50,000 visitors annually. The Railway Station is nearly a mile distant, on the north side. The warm waters, brought to the baths, by a conduit 2¼ miles long, from Pfäfers, are good in cases of gout, rheumatism, and paralysis. Kursaal and Kur Garten. Visitors' tax of 50 c. per day.

ENGLISH CHURCH SERVICE.

GOLF.—8-hole course.

RAIL, pages 268, 268B. Diligence p. 377.

[Funicular railway from Ragaz to **Wartenstein**, 2,463 ft. above sea. A health resort. Ruins of the Castle of Wartenstein.]

Reichenau.—*Stat.*

HOTEL ADLER.

A village in Canton Grisons, 1,936 ft. above sea (in view of the Brigelser Horn, 10,555 ft.), on the Splügen road, where the two heads of the Rhine join; the Hinter Rhein (blue), from the Bernardin, the Vorder Rhein (white), from the St. Gotthard.

RAIL, pages 268B, 268D. Diligence, page 377.

Rhone Glacier, 5,750 ft. above sea.

HOTEL DU GLACIER DU RHONE.

In Canton Valais, on the Furca Route. The Rhone Glacier is the grandest of all the accessible glaciers of the Alps; the views over this wonderful sea of ice from the zigzags of the Furca Pass are very fine. The River Rhone issues from the glacier not far from the hotel.

ENGLISH CHURCH SERVICE in summer.

DILIGENCE, page 377.

Rigi, or **Righi.**

RIGI FIRST HOTEL-PENSION (open from June until end September).—Comfortable first class hotel in centre of all the Rigi hotels. Ten minutes from Vitznau, Rigi, and Arth Rigi Stations. Pension from 8 fr. See Advt. under Lucerne.

KALTBAD; RIGI KULM; SCHREIBER; RIGI STAFFEL.

The Rigi, or Righi, the old Mons Regius, in Canton Schwyz, 8 miles east of Lucerne; a well-known mountain ridge between the Lakes of Lucerne and Zug. The view from the summit (5,905 ft. above sea) is unrivalled for extent and grandeur. The horizon has a circumference of 300 miles, and includes in the prospect 13 lakes, the Oberland, the mountains of the Black Forest of Germany, and the range of the Juras from Geneva to Basle. Sunset is generally far more beautiful than sunrise, and is best seen from the Rothstock; sunrise from the Kulm. The panorama from the different Rigi Railways is magnificent.

Coming from Lucerne the ascent is usually made from Vitznau, while travellers from Zürich ascend from Arth. For pedestrians, the most favourable ascent (3 hours) is from Arth; the best descent (2 hours) is upon Weggis. There is a good path up from Kussnacht, on the Lake of Zug. Pedestrians should not attempt the climb in the afternoon. Tobogganing and ski-ing in winter at Rigi Kaltbad and Rigi Klosterli.

RAIL, page 256.

Romont.—*Stat.*—Pop. 2,110.

HOTELS; CERF; CROIX BLANCHE.

A very interesting little old town, preserving its ancient walls and watch towers, picturesquely situated on a hill, on the River Glane. Gothic Church, curious carving in the choir stalls. The Chateau, founded 10th cent., is used for municipal offices.

RAIL, pages 263, 265.

Rorschach.—*Stat.*—Pop. 9,140.
HOTEL HIRSCH; ANKER.
A thriving town and summer resort, 1,310 ft. above sea, on the Lake of Constance, in Canton St. Gall. Above the town is the old Abbey of Mariaberg, now a school. Wide view from the Rorschacher Berg.
RAIL, pages 256. 260A, 262, 268. Steamer, p. 369.

Rosenlaui Bad.
HOTEL KURHAUS.
A quiet spot, 4,363 ft. above sea, in the wooded valley of the Reichenbach. frequented for the baths and the restful seclusion. Waterfall by the Kurhaus; from the bridge opposite the Kurhaus a path leads to the Rosenlaui Glacier, a climb of nearly two hours.
ENGLISH CHURCH SERVICE in season.
Rosenlaui is reached by a bridle path from either Meiringen or Grindelwald; horse charge from either Meiringen or Grindelwald, about 10fr.

Rossinières.—*Stat.*
HOTELS; GRAND CHALET; SARINE.
A pleasant village of Canton Vaud, on the River Sarine, frequented in summer; 3,025 ft. above sea.
ENGLISH CHURCH SERVICE in summer.
RAIL, page 262C.

Saas Grund, 5,125 ft. above sea.
HOTEL MONTE MORO.
A village in the valley of the Saaser Visp; a fine centre for mountain excursions—several resident guides. The district has innumerable attractions for the pedestrian.
ENGLISH CHURCH SERVICE in summer.
Reached by bridle path (4 hours) from Stalden.
[A good path leads to **Saas Fee,** whence is superb view of the **Fee Glacier.** ENGLISH CHURCH SERVICE in summer. HOTELS LAGGER; 380 beds; every modern comfort; electric light throughout; moderate tariff; see Advt.
Another good path goes up from Saas Grund to Almagel (INN), 5,505 feet, and to the **Mattmark Lake** (HOTEL MATTMARK), 6,965 feet. From Mattmark it is a 6 hours journey over the Monte Moro Pass, 9,390 feet, to Macugnaga, whence is a good road to **Ceppomorelli**—Diligence. page 374.]

Samaden.—*Stat.*—Pop. 1,028.
THE HOTEL BERNINA.—First class family hotel. Near golf links. 200 beds; fine garden. Moderate terms. See Advt.
BELLEVUE; EDEN.
The chief place of the Upper Engadine, in the valley of the River Inn, 5,670 feet above sea. Several diligence routes cross here. In the winter, tobogganing, skating, etc.
ENGLISH CHURCH SERV. at Immanuel Church.
GOLF.—18-hole course, 7 mins. walk from Station. Course for ladies.
RAIL, pages 257A, 268B.
DILIGENCE, pages 377, 378.

Sarnen.—*Stat.*—Pop. 3,950.
HOTELS: SEILER; OBERWALDNER HOF; ADLER. At Kerns (reached by diligence), KURHAUS ST. NIKLAUSEN.
Chief place of the Obwalden division of Canton Unterwalden, on Lake Sarnen, 1,545 ft. above sea. At the Rathhaus are portraits of the Landammanns from 1381 to 1824. Church, on a hill, with pictures. Capuchin Monastery and a Nunnery. RAIL, page 267A. Diligence, p. 375.
[Just east of Sarnen is the **Melchthal,** a delightful valley, where are many chalets and some pretty villages—tobogganing and ski-ing in winter. At Ranft is the Hermitage of St. Nikolaus von der Flüe (died 1487), whose portrait, as Brother Klaus, is seen in many parts of German speaking Switzerland. Dil., p. 375.]

Schaffhausen.—*Stat.*—Pop. 16,917.
A picturesque town with many gabled houses, on the River Rhine, near the Baden frontier. Old Cathedral, 1052-1101, now a Protestant church; the cloisters are interesting. On a hill is the Castle of Munot, 1564-82; fine view from the platform. At the Imthurneum is a small picture gallery. Natural history collection, antiquities, and library at the Museum. Rathhaus of 1625.
RAIL, pp. 139A, 260A, 261B, 262. STEAMER, p. 369.

Schinznach Bad.—*Stat.*
KURHAUS.—Powerful Sulphur Baths. See Advt.
On the River Aare, in Canton Aargau. Much frequented for the sulphur baths, useful in cases of gout, rheumatism, skin diseases, and chronic catarrhs.
ENGLISH CHURCH SERVICE in summer.
RAIL, page 262.
[Above Schinznach is the Wülpelsberg, 1,686 ft., crowned by the ruins of **Hapsburg,** erected 1020, the ancestral seat of the reigning imperial family of Austria; only a tower remains.]

Schuls.—*Stat.*—Pop. 1,117.
HOTELS: BELVEDERE; POST; PARK.
Chief place of the Lower Engadine, in a fine open situation, with good views. Chalybeate and other baths at the Badehalle. Omnibus many times a day between Schuls and Tarasp.
RAIL, page 268E. DILIGENCE, pages 371, 377, 378.

Schwyz.—*Stat.*—Pop. 7,398.
HOTELS: ROSSLI; SCHWEIZERHOF.
A picturesque scattered town, at the base and on the slopes of the Little Myten and Great Myten. Historical frescoes on the Rathhaus, where are portraits of Landammans. Fine view from the Great Myten, 6,245 ft.
RAIL. page 259. Diligence. page 375.

Seelisberg, 2,637 ft. above sea.
GRAND HOTEL SONNENBERG; BELLEVUE.
Delightfully situated on a hill, above one of the most beautiful parts of the Lake of Lucerne. Omnibus connects with steamer calling at Treib.
ENGLISH CHURCH SERVICE in summer.
STEAMER to and from Treib, page 369.

Sierre (Siders).—*Stat.*—Pop. 1,833.
PENSION BEAU SITE.—Newly opened, in beautiful, quiet situation, within three minutes of Station. Electric light; central heating. Pension from 5 fr. 50 c. See Advt.
BELLEVUE; TERMINUS.
An old place of the Rhone Valley, picturesquely situated on a hill; interesting mediæval houses. In the winter, tobogganing and skating. Good centre for excursions.
ENGLISH CHURCH SERVICE.
RAIL, page 263, 263B.

[A good road south west from Sierre leads through the interesting **Val d'Anniviers** as far as **Vissoye**, 11 miles (HOTEL D'ANNIVIERS; DES ALPES).

St Luc, 5,390 feet (HOTEL BELLA TOLA; CERVIN), is reached by a path (1¼ hr.) from Vissoye. The situation is pleasant, among pastures: fine views. ENG. CH. SERVICE.

Grimentz (HOTEL DES BECS DE BOSSON). 5,151 ft. above sea, in a valley surrounded by pastures and forest. No fog; sheltered from wind. Fine views all round.

6 miles beyond Vissoye, by a bridle path, is **Zinal**, 5,505 ft. (HOTEL DES DIABLONS; DURAND); imposing scenery all round; many mountain excursions—resident guides; ENGLISH CHURCH SERVICE.

Montana-sur-Sierre.

PALACE HOTEL.—First class. Every modern convenience; large lounge and public rooms; electric light, lift, etc. Reduced golf subscription to visitors. See Advt.

HOTEL DU PARC.—Good, surrounded by large forest. Fine view. Electric light; central heating, baths. Pension from 8 frs. See Advt.

5,085 ft. above sea. 12½ miles from Sierre, 45 minutes by funicular railway. A favourite summer and winter resort, commanding views that extend from Mont Blanc to the Matterhorn; charming excursions in all directions, in the pine forests and on the small lakes. 18-hole golf links, tastefully situated, and quite sporting. Well-known centre for all forms of winter sport.

ENGLISH CHURCH SERV. RAIL, page 263.]

Simplon Kulm, see under Brig, page 514B.

Sion (Sitten).—*Stat*—Pop. 6,900.

HOTEL: GRAND; POSTE; SUISSE; TERMINUS.

The old capital of Canton Valais, the ancient Sedunum, in a picturesque situation, on the River Sionne at its confluence with the Rhone; many interesting relics in the town and immediate neighbourhood. Gothic Cathedral of 15th cent. with tower of 9th cent.; close by is the Church of St. Théodule. On a height (2,150 ft.) to north is the ruined episcopal Castle of Tourbillon, built 1294, sacked 1788; on another height (2,040 ft.), where was once a Roman fort, is the Castle of Valeria, with the restored church of Notre Dame de Valere and the Cantonal Musée.

RAIL, page 263B. Diligence, page 375.

[**Les Mayens de Sion.**—

HOTEL DE LA DENT D'HERENS.—High class family hotel in magnificent position. Close to extensive forests. Pension terms from 8-10 fr. See Advt.

Beautifully situated in the woods, 4,590 ft. above sea, about eight miles from Sion. Very fine views of the Bernese Alps. Excursions in all directions. Reached by carriage from Sion.]

Solothurn (Soleure).—*Stat.*—Pop. 10,550.

HOTELS: KRONE; TERMINUS; ADLER.

Capital of the Canton, the ancient Salodurum, on the River Aare. Cathedral of St. Ours, 1762-73, in the treasury are mediæval objects of art metal work, also vestments. Collection of armour and weapons at the Arsenal. Clock Tower, of 5th or 6th cents.; the inscription claims great antiquity for the town. Small Picture Gallery; at the Cantonal School are collections of antiquities and the Cantonal Library. Natural History Museum. Town Library of 40,000 vols., and collections of coins and medals.

RAIL, pages 255, 257, 257B.

[**Weissenstein**, 4,220 ft. above sea.

A climatic station with Kurhaus, situated amidst beautifully wooded scenery. In the St. Verena Thal is the Hermitage of St. Verena, a dwelling and chapel. Magnificent views of the Alpine Chain. Tobogganing and ski-ing in winter. Rail from Solothurn to Moutier (Munster), at the foot of the mountain, p. 255.]

Spiez.—*Stat.*—Pop. 3,031.

PARK HOTEL BUBENBERG.—First class, elevated position. With large park. Every modern comfort. Pension from 8 fr. See Advt.

A village in a pleasant situation on the west side of the Lake of Thun. Old Chateau Erlach, restored, with church.

ENGLISH CHURCH SERVICE in the season.

RAIL, page 267. Steamer, page 363. Diligence, page 375.

[A bridle path from Wimmis (next station to Spiez, page 267), ascends the **Niesen**, (funicular rail open), 7,763 ft. Exceedingly fine view—best at sunset or early morning. INN near the top.]

Splugen.—Pop. 374.

HOTELS: BODENHAUS; SPLUGEN.

An old village of the Rheinwald Thal, 4,757 ft. above sea, busy in the season with the traffic over the Splugen and Bernardino Routes.

DILIGENCE, page 377.

[The **Splugen Pass** route goes off south from Splugen to Chiavenna. The Pass, 6,945 ft. above sea, is about 6 miles from Splugen, close to the frontier of Switzerland and Italy; Italian Custom House (two INNS) 1½ mile beyond the Pass. Thence the descent is in long bends, in places protected by roofs (avalanche galleries). Near Pianazzo (an INN) is a Fall, 650 ft. high, of the Madesimo; lower is Campodolcino (HOTEL CROCE D'ORO), and the scenery softens with the approach to Chiavenna, 25 miles from Splugen.]

Stachelberg Bad.

The alkaline-sulphur waters attract during the season many visitors to the Baths, finely situated in the Linth Valley. Grand scenery.

ENGLISH CHURCH SERVICE in summer.

Stachelberg is ½ mile from Linthal Station, page 262B.

Stans.—*Stat.*—Pop. 2,798.

HOTELS: STANSERHOF; ENGEL.

Chief place of the Nidwalden division of Canton Unterwalden, in a deep valley. Rathhaus contains portraits of the Landammans from 1521, other paintings, and a collection of flags. Collections of antiquities and historical curiosities at the Museum in Bahnhof Platz. Church of 1641; a tablet by the chapel in the churchyard records the massacre here by the French in 1798.

RAIL, page 259B.

[The **Stanserhorn**, 6,233 feet.

HOTEL STANSERHORN.—First class hotel, with electric light and terrace, moderate charges. See Advt.

A wonderful panorama is surveyed from the Stanserhorn, sunrise being specially admired. Electric railway (page 259B) up from Stans to near the Stanserhorn Hotel; thence a path to the top.]

Susten Pass.

The Susten Pass is on the way connecting Meiringen with Wassen, a station on the St. Gotthard Railway. Good road from Meiringen to near the Steingletscher, passing through Innertkirchen, and upward by a pleasant meadow country to Gadmen, 3,960 ft., and on in many windings through the woods and across a wild stony tract to the Hotel at the base of the Stein Glacier. From here the Sustenhorn, 11,523 ft., may be ascended in 6 to 7 hours; also the Gwächtenhorn, 11,245 ft.

A bridle path leads from the hotel up to the **Susten Pass**, 7,420 ft., in about 1½ hour—fine view. The descent to Wassen is not so attractive as the approach on the Meiringen side. Diligence from Meiringen to Innertkirchen, page 377. Carriage from Meiringen to Steingletscher in 7 hours.

Taesch.—*Stat.*—

HOTEL TAESCHHORN.—Comfortable family hotel, with fine view of the mountains. Electric light throughout. Pension from 7 fr. See Advt.

In a magnificent situation, 4,728 ft. above sea, just below Zermatt. Grand mountain scenery all round.

RAIL from Visp, page 266.

Tarasp Bad.

In the Lower Engadine, **3,946 ft. above sea. The waters, for drinking and bathing, are impregnated with salt and carbonate of soda. Kurhaus (Hotel) and Trinkhalle. Many visitors in the season.**

ENGLISH CHURCH SERVICE at English Church.

DILIGENCE, pages 377, 378.

[Vulpera, 4,160 ft.

HOTELS: VULPERA; SCHWEIZERHOF.

About a mile from Tarasp, in a sunny situation. Music two or three times a week. Omnibus several times daily from Tarasp.

MEDICAL.—Dr. E. Balli (in winter in Locarno.]

Territet.

GRAND HOTEL ET HOTEL DES ALPES.—Splendid establishments. See Advt.

HOTEL PENSION VERNET.—Comfortable pension, situated near Railway Station and Pier. Electric light; lift; central heating. See Advt.

HOTEL BONIVARD (at Territet-Chillon).—First class. See Advt.

See also under **Montreux.**

HOTEL BYRON (see under Villeneuve).

Thun.—*Stat.*—Pop. 6,030.

GRAND HOTEL THUNERHOF, HOTEL BELLEVUE, PENSION DU PARC.—First class hotels, with electric light; lift; and baths. Fine view of the Lake and high Alps. See Advt.

GRAND HOTEL VICTORIA AND BAUMGARTEN.—First class hotels, charmingly situated, with fine view over the Lake and Mountains. Pension from 7 fr. 50 c. See Advt.

SCHLOSS HOTEL FREIENHOF.—Considerably enlarged. Every modern comfort. Electric light; central heating. Apartments. Baths. Pension terms. See Advt.

PENSION ITTEN.—First class English and American pension, pleasantly situated, with large garden. Electric light. Pension from 6 fr. 50 c. See Advt.

HOTEL NATIONAL.—New, in open position. 50 beds. Large terrace and covered verandah. Open May-November. Pension terms from 6.50 frs. See Advt.

PARK HOTEL (Gunten).—Fire-proof construction. Fine panorama. Electric light, lift; central heating. Apartments with baths. Pension from 7 frs. 50 c. See Advt.

A picturesque and attractive old town, 1,844 ft. above sea, on the River Aare, a little below its efflux from the Lake of Thun. Over the town rises the tower of the Castle of Zähringen-Kyburg, dating from 1182, containing a small museum of antiquities. From near the church, to south east of castle, the views are very beautiful. The Swiss Artillery have their head quarters here. Kur Garten and Kursaal, with music daily. Lawn tennis ground; trout fishing.

ENGLISH CHURCH SERV. at English Church.

RAIL, pages 257, 261A, 267, 268F. STEAMERS page 363. Diligence, page 375.

[The Lake of Thun, 11 miles long, 2 miles broad, has a beauty all its own. The magnificent scenery, well viewed from the steamer, is delightfully varied—wood, cliff, and mountain.]

Thusis.—*Stat.*—Pop. 1,281.

HOTEL VIAMALA.—First class hotel, in a fine position; electric light; large park. See Advt.

A very old place, the Roman Tusaun, on the Hinter Rhein, 2,450 ft. above sea, finely situated at the foot of the Heinzenberg, and at the junction of the Schyn and Splügen roads. On a rock 807 ft. above the river is the ruined castle of Hohen-Rhatien, the oldest castle of Switzerland; at north side of the rock is the old church of St. John. ENGLISH CHURCH SERVICE.

RAIL, page 268B. DILIGENCE, page 377.

[The **Via Mala**, the first part of the road from Thusis to Andeer and Splügen, is a narrow cleft or defile, the most impressive of all the Alpine gorges; the way is partly along ridges, cut in the mountain wall, partly over bridges, and partly through tunnels; in places the rocks rise on either hand straight up to a height of 1,600 ft., the Rhine thunders on its way below the road, and the alternations from sunshine to gloom are awe inspiring. Diligence, page 377.]

Vallorbes.—*Stat.*—Pop. 3,279.

HOTELS: GRAND; GENEVE.

A watch making place, 2,520 feet above sea, under Mont d'Or (4,770 ft.).

RAIL, pages 259B, 263B. Diligence, page 375,

Vernayaz.—*Stat.*

HOTELS: GORGES DU TRIENT; VICTORIA.

Just beyond the village, up the valley, to the right, is the remarkable **Gorge de Trient**, (tickets at the hotel, 1 fr.). The fall of the **Pissevache**, 215 ft., is just beyond Vernayaz, in the other direction. RAIL, pages 257A, 263B.

Vevey.—*Stat.*—Pop. 12,781.

HOTEL DU LAC (Landing Place, Vevey-la-Tour).—First class, beautifully situated, with garden and terrace facing the Lake. See Advt.

GRAND HOTEL DES TROIS COURONNES.—First class hotel. Lift. See Advt.

GRAND HOTEL AND PALACE HOTEL.—First class hotel, charmingly situated in a beautiful park (at Corsier). Terms from fr. 9. See Advt.

PARK HOTEL MOOSER.—Excellent first class family hotel. Lift. See Advt.

HOTEL PENSION DES ALPES—High class family hotel, beautifully situated in extensive grounds. Latest modern improvements. Pension terms from 6 fr. See Advt.

CHATEAU DE VEVEY HOTEL PENSION.—With garden on the shore. Electric light; central heating. Pension from 7 frs. See Advt.

HOTEL BEAU SEJOUR.—Conveniently situated. Central hot water heating, electric light and lift. Baths. See Advt.

HOTEL D'ANGLETERRE.—First class English family hotel, on the new Quay, entirely re-built and up-to-date. Apartments with baths. New management. Pension from fr. 7.50. See Advt.

HOTEL PENSION NUSS.—Equipped with all modern comfort. Well situated, with view of Lake. Pension from 6 fr. 50 c. See Advt.

In a very fine situation on the Lake of Geneva, commanding beautiful views of the head of the Lake and surrounding mountains. In the winter much tobogganing, skating, ski-ing, etc.

Just east of the Railway Station, near the Russian Church, is the Musée, containing a small picture gallery, natural history collection, and library. A little above, on a hill outside the town, is the Church of St. Martin, built 1498, where are the graves of Ludlow and Broughton, two of the judges of Charles I. Ludlow's house stood on ground now covered by part of the Hotel du Lac; on Quai Sina is a memorial tablet. Beyond the east end of the town, by the Lake, is the Tour de Peilz, of 13th cent.

Two miles north east of Vevey is the Chateau of Hauteville, whence are beautiful views; and two miles higher up, beyond the villages of St. Légier and La Chiésaz, is the mediæval Chateau of Blonay, 2,118 ft. above sea.

ENGLISH CHURCH SERVICE.—At All Saints' Church. Rev. G. W. Crawford, LL.B.

FIRST CLASS DISPENSING CHEMIST.—H. Golaz, opposite Hotel des Trois Couronnes. Founded in 1805.

BOARDING SCHOOL FOR GIRLS.—Les Charmettes, Private Villa, with garden. Modern languages (thorough). Art and Music. Summer School in the mountains. Fees from £60.

For further details see the SCHOOL DIRECTORY in Bradshaw's British Guide, page ii.

HOUSE AND ESTATE AGENTS.—Ogay and Co., Place des 3 Couronnes. Particulars of Villas and Flats to be let sent on application.

RAIL, pages 262C, 263B. Steamer page 364. An electric tramway along the Lake shore from Vevey through Montreux to Chillon.

[Funicular rail from Vevey to **Mont Pélerin**, 3,855 ft.; magnificent view from summit of Lake Leman and mountains of Savoy.

HOTEL BELVEDERE.—Delightfully situated in vicinity of beautiful pine forests. Magnificent view. Verandah: terraces; electric light. Pension from fr. 6.50 See Advt.

GRAND HOTEL DU MONT PELERIN.—First class modern hotel, situated in a charming spot on the heights above Lake Geneva. Pension from 8 fr. See Advt.

PELERIN PALACE.—2,952 ft. above sea. First class, splendidly situated, commanding unsurpassed views. Park forest adjoining. Open all the year. Terms from fr. 9. See Advt.]

Vicosoprano.

HOTEL HELVETIA.

In the Canton of the Grisons, 3,500 ft. above sea, the principal village of Val Bregaglia, on the celebrated Maloggia route from Chiavenna to the Engadine. Mild alpine climate, the surrounding forests shielding from cold wind. In winter, tobogganing and ski-ing. DILIGENCE, page 378.

Visp (Viege).—*Stat.*—Pop. 950.

HOTELS: POST; SOLEIL.

An old village, 2,160 ft. above sea, picturesquely placed at the mouth of the Visp Valley.

RAIL, pages 263B, 266.

Viesch.

HOTELS: GLACIER; DES ALPES.

3,460 feet above sea, in a pleasant situation at the junction of the Vieschbach with the River Rhone. DILIGENCE, page 377.

Villars-sur-Ollon.—*Stat.*

GRAND HOTEL DU MUVERAN and HOTEL BELLE VUE.—Both establishments are well situated. with fine view of the Rhone Valley, Glaciers of Trient, etc. Electric light. See Advt.

GRAND HOTEL.-First class hotel. with electric light and lift. See Advt.

A summer resort, 4,166 ft. above sea, with mild bracing climate, sheltered from north and east winds. Fine views of the Rhone Valley and of several mountain groups. Winter sports in the neighbourhood. The Chamossaire, 6,940 ft., is easily ascended in 2½ hrs. from Villars.

ENGLISH CHURCH SERVICE at English Church.

MEDICAL.—Dr. Bishop.

RAIL, page 267A.

Villeneuve.—*Stat.*—Pop. 1,741.

HOTEL BYRON.—Renowned first class hotel, admirably situated in own grounds, facing Lake. patronised by best English families. See Advt. under Montreux-Territet.

A very old little town—the Roman Pennilucus—in a picturesque situation, at the east end of the Lake of Geneva. Fine views. Chillon Castle within a mile.

RAIL, 263B; Steamer, page 364; Diligence, page 375.

Vitznau.—Pop. 896.

HOTEL DU PARC.—First class hotel, beautifully situated in own large park, on lake shore. Every modern comfort. Tennis. (Branch house of Rigi First). Pension from 9 fr. See Advt. under Lucerne.

HOTEL VITZNAUERHOF.—First class, situated on the border of Lake. Modern comfort. Central heating; electric light. Pension from 9 fr. See Advt. under Lucerne.

RIGI; ALPENROSE.

In a delightful situation on the Lake of Lucerne, at the foot of the Vitznauer Stock—the lake terminus of the Rigi Railway.

STEAMER, page 369; Rigi railway, p. 256.

Weesen.—*Stat.*—Pop. 741.

HOTELS: SPEER; SCHWERT; MARIAHALDEN.

A summer resort in a sheltered spot at the west end of the Walensee.

ENGLISH CHURCH SERVICE in summer.

RAIL, pages 262B, 268B.

[The **Wallensee,** or Lake of Wallenstadt, 9½ miles long, 1¼ mile broad, is a fine sheet of water, hemmed in by noble cliffs and mountains—almost equal in grandeur to the Lake of Lucerne. Electric launch service twice daily.]

Weggis.—Pop. 1,522.

HOTEL BELLEVUE.

A pleasant village on the Lake of Lucerne, in a sheltered position at the foot of the Rigi, with a reputation as a health resort. English Church Service in the season.

STEAMER, page 369.

Weissenburg.—*Stat.*

HOTEL WEISSENBURG.

In a beautiful part of the Simmen Thal, 2,418 feet above sea.

The Baths of Weissenburg are 1¼ mile north west of the village, in a narrow ravine. The waters, 70° to 81°, for drinking only, are useful in bronchial and chest complaints.

RAIL, page 267.

Winterthur.—*Stat.*—Pop. 25,066.

HOTELS: GOLDNER LOWE; KRONE; ADLER.

An industrial town with an extensive trade in cotton goods. Modern Stadthaus. A small picture gallery at the Kunsthalle. Library and collection of antiquities at the School.

U.S. CONSULAR AGENT.

RAIL, pages 256, 260A, 261B, 262, 268.

Yverdon.—*Stat.*—Pop. 7,985.

HOTELS: LONDRES; PAON.

The ancient Eburodunum, a busy little town, on the River Thièle, near the south end of the Lake of Neuchatel. In the old Chateau, erected 1135, are a Library and collections of antiquities and coins. At the Hotel de Ville is a curious collection of 18th century clocks, also a collection of Roman antiquities. The Bains d' Yverdon—sulphur waters—are nearly a mile to south east.

RAIL, pages 263A, 264. Diligence, pp. 374, 375.

[**Mauborget.**

HOTEL BELLE VUE.

About eight miles north of Yverdon, at the foot of Mont Chasseron, near the Lake of Neuchatel. A pleasant tranquil resting place amidst pastures and forests. Nearest Station is Grandson, 4 miles distant. DILIGENCE, page 374.]

Zermatt.—*Stat.*—Pop. 741.

GRAND HOTELS SEILER: RIFFELALP, MONTE ROSA, MONT CERVIN, VICTORIA, and SCHWARZ SEE. See Advt.

HOTELS GINDRAUX: BEAU SITE; ZERMATTERHOF; RIFFELBERG; KULMHOTEL (GORNERGRAT). High class, equipped with all modern requirements. See Advt.

A village, 5,315 ft. above sea, in a valley, almost surrounded by lofty peaks and glaciers—sometimes described as the very centre of the Alps. Near the English Church rest several victims of mountain disaster, and in the Churchyard are other melancholy records.

Many resident guides. The ascent of the **Matterhorn,** 14,705 ft., from the Schwarz See Hotel, takes about 10 hours, guide and porter charges about 180 fr. The ascent of **Monte Rosa,** 15,217 ft., takes about 10 hours from the Riffelhaus, guide and porter charges about 150 fr.

The Railway up from Zermatt to Gornergrat commands the grandest view obtainable in this way in the Alps of the world of ice and snow. Hotels have been erected at each station. At **Riffelalp,** 7,307 ft., is HOTEL RIFFELALP; at **Riffelberg,** 8,429 ft., is HOTEL RIFFELBERG; at **Gornergrat,** 10,290 ft., is the new KULMHOTEL (luncheons served at 4 frs. on arrival of trains). The wonderful spectacle of sunset and sunrise will repay a stay overnight. The panorama from the Gornergrat is renowned for it grandeur.

ENGLISH CHURCHES at Zermatt and Riffelalp.

RAIL, Visp to Zermatt, page 266; Zermatt to Gornergrat, page 266.

Zug.—*Stat.*—Pop. 6,510.

HOTELS: HIRSCH; OCHS; LOWE.

Capital of the smallest Canton of the Swiss Confederation, a very picturesque old place; on the Lake of Zug, 1,385 ft. above sea. Church of St. Oswald, 15th cent., and Capuchin Church—paintings at both. At east side of the town is St. Michael Church (1902), on a hill. Interesting Rathhaus, with collection of antiquities. Bee Museum on the Rosenberg. In the winter all kinds of winter sport at Schonfels.

RAIL, pages 259B, 260. Steamer, page 363.

[Road-motor car several times daily from Zug to the beautiful Ægeri Lake, at the south east end of which is **Morgarten** (battle of 1315). Omnibus thence to Sattel, Ægeri station.]

Zurich.-*Stat.*-Pop. (1910) 189,088,

HOTEL BAUR AU LAC.—First class hotel, beautifully situated. Fine garden. See Advt.

ELITE HOTEL.—New modern, centrally situated hotel, with large Café-Restaurant, 90 bedrooms from fr. 3.50. See Advt.

GRAND HOTEL VICTORIA.—First class family hotel, situated facing the Station. Restaurant. Electric light; lift. See Advt.

SAVOY HOTEL.—First class, centrally situated, entirely rebuilt, with all latest improvements. Suites with baths. Restaurant français. Pension terms. See Advt.

HOTEL HABIS-ROYAL.—Near the principal Railway Station. Comfortable house, with lift, salons, and gardens. See Advt.

HOTEL PENSION TIEFENAU.—Steinwiesstrasse, 8. Quiet situation. Central heating electric light; baths. Pension terms from 6.50 frs. See Ad.

HOTEL SCHWERT.—Centrally situated. Fine views. Recently renovated. Electric light and central heating. Baths. Excellent cooking. Pension terms. See Advt.

HOTEL NATIONAL, opposite the North-Eastern Railway Station. First class hotel, very comfortable. See Advt.

CITY HOTEL.—New modern hotel, close to Central Station. Hot and cold water supply in every room. Inclusive terms from 10 fr. See Advt.

HOTEL PELIKAN.—Excellent, in a quiet central part, three minutes from Station. All modern comforts; noted cuisine. Rooms from fr. 3.50. Pension from fr. 9. See Advt.

PENSION NEPTUN.—15, Seefeldstrasse. First class English and American pension. Garden; electric light; central heating. Pension from 6 fr. See Advt.

The RAILWAY STATION, Hauptbahnhof, is on the north side of the town; from the Bahnhof Platz the broad Bahnhofstrasse leads southward in three quarters of a mile to the Lake.

Zurich, the Roman Turicum, is finely situated in a mountain valley, 1,345 ft. above sea, at the north west end of the Lake of Zurich, where the River Limmat flows into the Lake. It is the capital of the Canton of Zurich, and commercially the most important town in Switzerland; the older parts remain in places quaint and picturesque, while the modern quarters are spacious and handsome. The principal manufacture is concerned with silk, but the engineering trade is extensive, and many cotton mills are in the neighbourhood. From the quays there is a beautiful view over the Lake and the surrounding country.

The Romanesque Gross Münster (Minster) is a few yards back from the east side of the River Limmat, by the second bridge (Münster Brücke) from the Lake. Built 11th-13th cent., old cloisters, good modern stained windows; Zwingli was pastor here from 1519 until 1531; in summer open morn. and aft.—20 c. Close to the bridge, on the Gross Münster side, in what was formerly the Wasserkirche (1479-84) is the Town Library of 160,000 vols. and 4,500 MSS.; among the latter are letters of Zwingli, Lady Jane Grey, Henry IV of France, and Frederick the Great. Near the west end of the bridge is the Frau Münsterkirche, of 12th-13th cents.

Landes Museum (Swiss National Museum), immediately north of the Bahnhof, an imposing Gothic building. The collections are of wide interest and of the highest importance. There are pre-historic, Roman, mediæval, and modern divisions, with artistic, domestic, ecclesiastic, and warlike exhibits. Daily, except Mon., from 12.0 to 4.0 or 5.0, free; in the morn., 10.0 to 12.0, 1 fr. Industrial Museum in wing near the Platzpromenade.

The University, about 1,400 students, is in part of a building known as the Polytechnikum, less than a quarter of a mile due east of the Hauptbahnhof; the other parts of the Polytechnikum are occupied by the Federal Polytechnic School. The Aula is handsomely decorated; scientific collections; fine view from terrace on the roof.

Künstlergut, 100 yards south of the Polytechnikum; gallery of pictures by Zurich artists. Sun. morn. and Sat. aft. free, other times 50 c.

Tonhalle, a handsome concert hall, on the Alpen Quai; Theatre, on the Uto Quai; both by the Lake.

Botanic Garden, at south end of Löwenstrasse, running south west from the Hauptbahnhof.

Belvoir Park is by the Lake, at the south west extremity of the town. Zurichhorn Park, by the Lake, at the south east extremity of the town.

Alt Friedhof (Cemetery), quarter mile east of bridge at Lake end of the River Limmat.

POST OFFICE, on the quay at west side of the River Limmat, near the Lake.

ENGLISH CHURCH SERVICE, St. Andrew, Hohe Promenade.

H.B.M.'S. CONSUL-GENERAL.—Sir H. Angst, K.C.M.G. VICE-CONSUL.—J. C. Milligan, Esq.

U.S. CONSUL-GENERAL.—R. E. Mansfield, Esq. VICE-CONSUL.—H. A. McBride, Esq.

GOLF.—9-hole course, on the Dolder Hill, reached by funicular railway.

ENGLISH PHYSICIAN.—Dr. Theodore Zangger, M.D., late Assistant Physician University Hosp., 66, Zeltweg (consultations, 1.0—3.0 p.m.).

RAIL, pp. 256A, 260, 261, 261B, 262, 262B, 268B. STEAMERS, p. 363. DILIGENCE, p. 375.

[Fine views from the **Zurichberg**, 2,050 ft. above sea, two miles east of the town—DOLDER GRAND HOTEL; electric tram from the Quai Brücke to Romerhof, thence ascent by cable tram. Fine sunset view.

To the **Uetliberg**, 2,865 ft. above sea, six miles south west from Zurich, is a favourite excursion. HOTEL UETLIBERG; UTO-STAFFEL. The views compare favourably with those from heights nearer the Alps in beauty if not in grandeur. Climbing rail from Zurich; Station in the Selnau suburb, three quarters mile south west of Hauptbahnhof.

The **Lake of Zurich**, 1,340 ft. above sea, 25 miles long, 2½ miles across at the widest part, though without the impressive grandeur of other Swiss lakes, has a placid beauty all its own. The slopes all round are mostly meadows, orchards, and vineyards, sprinkled everywhere with attractive villages.

STEAMERS, see page 363.]

Zweisimmen.—*Stat.*—Pop. 2,070.

HOTEL TERMINUS—Comfortable, close to the Station. Recently enlarged; 60 beds. Every modern comfort. Pension from 6.50 frs. See Advt.

Chief place of the Simmenthal, in a pleasant situation, where the river, the Kleine Simme, broadens out; a summer and winter resort, 3,100 ft. above sea. Old Church. The cattle of the district are famous. In winter, tobogganing, skating, ski-ing, etc.

RAIL, pages 262C, 267.

ITALY.

For description of the ALPINE PASSES and the LAKES see SPECIAL EDITION.

Italy consists of a long peninsula, between the Adriatic and the Mediterranean, extending from N.W. to S.E., the greatest length of which is 695 to 700 miles, from the sources of the river Tosa to Cape Cimiti, in Calabria, or Cape Lucca, in Otranto; and also of the large islands of Sicily and Sardinia. The breadth at the north is 365 miles; about 275 miles from Mount Genèvre to the mouth of the Po, through the middle of Lombardy; 156 miles from Piombino to Ancona; and only 20 miles in some parts of Calabria. **Area,** including the Islands, 110,659 square miles.

Population (1911) 34,671,377. Of these, about 65,000 Protestants, and about 35,000 Jews. **Reigning Sovereign.**—Vittorio Emanuele III, born 1869. **Senate**—numbers 375 members; Chamber of Deputies 508. **Army** (1911), peace establishment, 302,252. **Navy** (1913, including those building), dreadnoughts, 6; battle-ships, 11; cruisers, 22; torpedo gunboats, 10; destroyers, 35; torpedo boats, 111; submarines, 32. Naval stations at Naples, Spezia, Venice; and at La Plata, in South America. Coast line, 3,950 miles. **Revenue** (1913) £105,839,787. **Expenditure,** £105,206,970. **Debt,** 522 millions sterling.

Railways.—Mid Europe Time (one hour in advance of West Europe—Greenwich—Time) is observed on all lines. The time is reckoned from midnight to midnight, that is to 24.0 o'clock. **Luggage**—no free allowance of luggage—see table of fares and luggage rates, page 269. The validity of the railway ticket is according to distance, one day for each 100 chilometri (62 miles), not counting the day of issue. Journeys of 300 chil. may be broken once; 600 chil., twice; 900 chil., three times; 1,000 chil., four times; longer journeys, five times.

Money—100 centesimi = 1 lira = 9½d. Gold Coins are still somewhat scarce, and the currency consists chiefly of notes, silver, and bronze and nickel coins. NOTES: *State*—50, 25, 10, and 5 lire; *Bank*—1.000, 500, 200, and 100 lire. GOLD COINS—100, 50, 20, 10, and 5 lire. SILVER COINS—5, 2, and 1 lira, and 50 and 20 centesimi (rarely met with). NICKEL COINS—25, 20, and 10 centesimi. BRONZE COINS—1, 2, 5, and 10 centesimi.

Weights and Measures.—The weights and measures of Italy are those of the metric system, the names only being altered to the Italian form. See page lxxi.

Postage.—Letters of 15 grammes (half an ounce), 5 c. for local post, 15 c. for the rest of Italy; for abroad (Great Britain, United States of America, etc.) 25 c. for 15 grammes, and 15 c. for each additional 15 grammes. Post cards, for Italy or other countries, 10 c.

ASSOCIAZIONE NAZIONALE PER IL MOVIMENTO DEI FORESTIERI (Italian National Association for Foreigners).—An Association to facilitate, by information and otherwise, intercourse of Foreigners with Italy. The principal office is at the Palazzo Lazzaroni, Piazza Montecitorio, Rome, with Branches at 2, Via Strozzi, Florence; 14 and 15, Via S. Carlo, Naples; and 16, Via Ruggero Settimo, Palermo.

NOTICES OF TOWNS, WATERING PLACES, etc.

Abetone, 4,520 ft. above sea.

HOTEL PENSION BELLINI, Boscolungo-Abetone.

A mountain summer resort, under Monte Cimone, 7,103 ft. Fine forest scenery; a good starting point for several excursions in the north Apennines. Reached from Pracchia, on Bologna-Pistoja line, page 279. On the road from Pracchia to Abetone is **Cutigliano,** another summer resort.

MEDICAL.—Dr. Bonar (June to October).

The Abruzzi are three mountain provinces, bordering the Adriatic, of exceptional beauty and interest. The inhabitants have retained the simplicity and costumes of centuries ago, as may be seen at the village festas. The Abruzzi have given birth to many celebrities—D'Anunzio, Minchetti, Tosti, and Rosetti being amongst the best known. Spring and autumn are delightful seasons for the Abruzzi, and not too chilly.

Acqui.—*Stat.*—Pop. 16,000.

GRANDS HOTELS DES THERMES.—With every accommodation of up-to-date first class hotels. Bath treatments given in the hotels. See Advt.

The Roman Aquæ Statiellæ, on the River Bormida, known for its warm sulphur springs and mud baths, recommended for rheumatism, gout, etc. Cathedral of 12th cent.

RAIL, page 273.

Alassio.—*Stat.*—Pop. 4,200.

GRAND HOTEL ALASSIO.—In splendid position, overlooking sea. Patronised by English and American families. Pension from 8 fr. See Advt.

GRAND HOTEL MEDITERRANEE.—First class, finely situated; every modern comfort. See Advt.

THE SALISBURY HOTEL.—High class in every respect. Fine position, 250 ft. above sea. Pension from 10 fr. a day. See Advt.

THE NORFOLK HOTEL (late Val d'Olivo).—Specially adapted for English families. On the hillside, about 200 feet above sea level. 8 to 12 fr. per day. See Advt.

PALACE HOTEL.—Well situated in own garden, and equipped with modern comforts. Open all the year. See Advt.

HOTEL PENSION BELLEVUE.—Excellent family hotel. Well situated on hillside, near Station. Garden; electric light. Pension from 7 fr. See Advt.

SAVOY HOTEL.—Comfortable small hotel, Well situated on sea shore. Full south. Electric light. Pension from 6 fr. See Advt.

A very picturesque town, between Ventimiglia and Genoa, rapidly rising in favour, especially with those who prefer a place which is not too fashionable and expensive. A favourite winter resort for persons desiring quiet or in delicate health, the steady bracing climate being free of fog; in early summer the fine sands are excellent for sea bathing. English Church. Good library. The foreign colony is almost entirely English. Tennis ground. English tea room.

ENGLISH CH. SERVICE at St. John's Church.

MEDICAL.—Dr. Boon.

HERBERT J. SEALE.—Anglo-American Agency and Bank. House Agents. Forwarding and receiving goods, etc.

RAIL, p. 272.

Alessandria.—*Stat.*—Pop. 75,721.

HOTELS: EUROPA; GRAND MOGOL.

On the River Tanaro, in a low lying district, of little interest other than as a strongly fortified place. Great Citadel on left bank of River Tanaro.

RAIL, pages 269, 270, 273.

[**Marengo** (battle of 14th June, 1800—Napoleon defeated Austrians), is about 2 miles east of Alessandria—tram.]

Amalfi.—Pop. 7,000.

HOTELS: CAPUCCINI; LUNA; SYRENE.

A bustling little town of the Gulf of Salerno, in a picturesque situation at the entrance of a ravine; in mediæval times it was a thriving seaport with a population of 50,000. Encroachments of the sea and landslips have caused much damage.

The Cattedrale (Sant' Andrea), of 11th cent., with modern restorations, is interesting; bronze doors; the remains of St. Andrew are stated to have been buried in the crypt since 13th cent., being brought from Constantinople—large statue of the Saint. Church of S. Maria Dolorata, quarter mile north of Cathedral.

Reached by Diligence from Vietri Station (page 374), 10 miles. Steamers from and to Naples (about 5 hours) once or twice a week during season, October to March.

[**Ravello** (HOTEL PALUMBO), a two hours walk, or drive of 1½ hr., from Amalfi, along a winding beautiful road. Pop. 2,000; Cathedral of 11th cent. Saracenic remains at Palazzo Rufolo.]

Ancona.—*Stat.*—Pop. of the commune 63,100.

HOTELS: VITTORIA; MILANO; ROMA.

The Railway Station is to the south of the town, 1½ mile from the business quarter. The Dogana (Custom House), for arrivals by sea, is at the middle of the bend of the Porto quay.

A very ancient city, the Greek Ancon, in a fine situation, with one of the best harbours in the kingdom. From the Station the road runs along the quay of the Porto, with most of the public buildings close behind.

The Romanesque-Byzantine Duomo, 12th-13th cent., at the extreme north of the city, on a height, Monte Guasco, on the site of a temple of Venus (10 pillars included in edifice); Gothic portal; sculptures and sarcophagi in interior, in crypt of left transept are tombs of Saints Cyriacus, Marcellinus, and Liberius. At the shore end of the north pier, close by, is a Triumphal Arch of A.D. 115; a short way along the pier is a second arch, erected by Pope Clement XII. In the Via del Duomo is the Archeological Museum. In Church of S. Domenico, in Piazza del Plebiscito, a few yards back from middle of quay, is a painting by Titian. At one side of the Church is the Civica Pinacoteca Podesti.

H. B. M.'s VICE-CONSUL.—E. A. Kane, Esq.

U. S. CONS. AGENT.

RAIL, pages 283, 285.

Andorno Bagni.—*Stat.*

GRAND HOTEL.

Andorno is a very pleasantly situated village, 1,805 ft. above the sea, much visited in summer. Gothic church, dating from 1304. The Baths (Andorno Bagni) are arranged as modern hydrotherapic establishments.

RAIL, page 289.

Aosta.—*Stat.*—Pop. 6,100.

HOTELS: VICTORIA; LONDRES; CORONA.

The Roman Augusta Prætoria Salassorum, finely situated in a valley at the foot of the Alps, at the confluence of the Rivers Dora Baltea and Buthier. The town retains its old walls and towers, and Roman remains are the Porta Prætoria, the Triumphal Arch of Augustus, and remnants of the theatre and amphitheatre near the market place. Cathedral; Church of St. Ours.

Ascents of the Becca di Nona, 10,305 ft., in six to seven hours; also of Mont Emilius, 11,677 ft., more difficult, in seven to eight hours.

RAIL, page 274A.

[**Pré St. Didier** (HOTEL DE L'UNIVERS), 3,250 ft. above sea, 17½ miles from Aosta, picturesquely situated, whence an easy route leads over the Little St. Bernard (accommodation at the hospice) to Bourg St. Maurice.

Courmayeur (HOTEL ROYAL; ANGELO; MONT BLANC), 4,360 ft. above sea, at the head of the valley, 21 miles from Aosta, is much frequented during summer. The ascent of Mont Blanc is often made from here.

DILIGENCE to Courmayeur, page 373.

Cogne (HOTEL GRIVOLA), 5,033 ft. above sea, 6½ hours from Aosta, is a favourite centre for the Graian Alps. Shooting lodges of Italian royalty (the steinbock is hunted) in the neighbourhood.]

Aquila.—*Stat.*—Pop. of commune 21,942.

HOTELS: SOLE; ITALIA.

Capital of the province, 2,365 ft. above sea, cool in summer, when it is a favourite resort.

From the Railway Station, on west side, a short road, one third mile, leads north east to the Porta Romana, at one end of the Via Romana, which with its continuations traverses the town to the Corso Vittorio Emanuele. A few yards beyond the intersection of the Corso by the line of the Via Romana is the Church of S. Bernardino di Siena; good facade, mon. of saint in interior. The Duomo is a short distance south along the Corso Vittorio Emanuele; half a mile south east, outside the city gate, is the Monastery of Santa Maria di Collemaggio, with decorated interior; Chapel of Celestine V to left, with scenes from his life. Palazzo Municipio, in Corso V. Emanuele, containing picture gallery and collections.

RAIL, page 285B.

[From Aquila good road, 10 miles, carriages to be had, to Assergi, 2,780 ft., whence is made the ascent of the **Gran Sasso d'Italia**, or Monte Corno, 9,585 ft., the highest peak of the Apennines. The excursion requires about two days; food should be taken.—5½ m. north west of Aquila is the village of San Vittorino, on the site of the Sabine town of Amiternum, the birthplace of Sallust; a few remains of antiquities.]

Argegno.—

Attractively situated on the Lake of Como, at the opening of the fertile Intelvi valley; a good centre for excursions in the neighbouring pleasant country or to the surrounding mountains.

Steamer service, page 365.

Arona.—*Stat.*—Pop. 4,600.

HOTELS: TERMINUS; ITALIE.

On Lago Maggiore, near the south end. An old place. In the Church of Santa Maria is a chapel of the Borromean family, with good paintings. On a height is a colossal metal statue, 70 ft. high, of San Carlo Borromeo (died 1584); in church close by are relics of the saint.

RAIL, page 274, 274A, 275. Steamer, page 366.

Assisi.—*Stat.*—Pop. 5,000.

HOTELS: LEONE; AQUILA D'ORO.

The Roman Asisium, picturesquely situated on a hill, 1,345 ft. above sea, birthplace (1182) of St. Francis, founder of the order of Franciscans, canonised in 1228, two years after his death. Entering the town from the Station, the old Monastery of the Franciscans (1228) is on the brow of the hill to the left; the building is now partly occupied as a training school. The two churches, one above the other, are of great interest. In the lower church are many fine paintings, above the high altar are renowned frescoes by Giotto (vows of the Franciscan order); the tomb of St. Francis is in the crypt. In the upper church are many frescoes. Descending into the town, in the Piazza Vittorio Emanuele is the Church of S. Maria della Minerva, with a portico that once was part of a temple of Minerva. A little further east is the Duomo (S. Rufino), 1140-1228, and, again a few yards east, is the Church of S. Chiara (Clara), 1257, foundress of the order of the Clarissines; she is buried below the high altar.

RAIL, page 283.

Bari.—*Stat.*—Pop. of commune 103,670

HOTELS: RISORGIMENTO; CENTRALE.

The Railway Station is on the south side of the city, about 1½ mile from the port.

The Roman Barium, often mentioned in mediæval history, an important commercial place. From the Station the Strada Sparano da Bari leads north across the city to the Corso Vittorio Emanuele; 200 yards further north, back among the winding streets, is the Cattedrale di San Sabino, dating from 1027, a Byzantine edifice, much altered; paintings. 150 yards north of the Cathedral, by the sea, is the Church of S. Nicola, with the venerated bones of the saint in the crypt. The Castello is a few yards west of the Cathedral. At the Ateneo, in Strada Sparano, close to the Station, are collections of antiquities.

H.B.M.'s V.-CONS.—Emile Berner, Esq.

U.S. CONS. AGENT.

RAIL, pages 285, 285B.

Bassano.—*Stat.*—Pop. 7,600.

HOTELS: SAN ANTONIO; MONDO.

A pleasant old town, on the River Brenta, in a beautiful district. Cathedral in north quarter. At the Museo Civico are several paintings by members of the da Ponte family, surnamed Bassano from their birthplace; in one room are objects associated with Canova, who was born at Possagno, 10 miles north east.

RAIL, page 288.

Baveno.—*Stat.*—Pop. 2,800.

PALACE GRAND HOTEL.—A first class hotel with strictly moderate tariff. Every modern convenience. See Advt.

GRAND HOTEL BELLEVUE.—Large first class hotel, beautifully situated, with large park. Electric light; lift. See Advt.

HOTEL BEAU RIVAGE.—Comfortable English hotel, with fine view over the Lake and the Bay. Electric light. Pension from 7 fr. See Advt.

HOTEL SIMPLON.—Comfortable pension hotel, in beautiful quiet situation, surrounded by large garden. Fine view. Electric light. Pension from frs. 7. See Advt.

A place of growing importance, on Lago Maggiore, and on the new Simplon railway line. Many fine villas. Baveno is pleasant for a stay because of the beautiful views of the **Borromean Islands.** Upon **Isola Bella** (HOTEL DU DAUPHIN) is a large palazzo of the Borromeo family, containing a small picture gallery, and objects of art in other rooms; in the chapel are family tombs; the terraced gardens are very beautiful; open daily except Monday, palazzo 50 c., gardens 50 c. Isola Madre and Isola dei Pescatori are worth visiting.

ENGLISH CHURCH SERVICE.

MEDICAL.—Dr. Soltan Eccles, Dr. Pio Borella, English Chemist.

RAIL, page 274. Steamers, page 366.

Bellagio.—Pop. 1,100.

HOTEL GRANDE BRETAGNE.-Magnificent hotel, well managed by the proprietor, Mr. Auguste Meyer.

GRAND HOTEL BELLAGIO and HOTEL VILLA SERBELLONI.—Beautifully situated, and both surrounded by a large garden and park to which visitors only have free access. See Advt.

SPLENDIDE HOTEL DES ETRANGERS.—In fine situation, facing lake. Lift; electric light; central heating. Pension from 8 fr. See Advt.

A small town, delightfully situated on a wooded promontory separating the Lago di Como from the Lago di Lecco. Several villas (Villa Serbelloni, Villa Melzi, Villa Giulia, and others), some accessible, have beautiful gardens. Ascent of Monte S. Primo, 5,530 ft., in 4¼ hours.

ENGLISH CHURCH SERVICE.

MEDICAL.—Dr. Eliot, Dr. Bishop.

GOLF.—9-hole course at Dervio, with club house.

STEAMERS, page 365.

Belluno.—*Stat.*—Pop. of commune 20,687.

HOTELS: ALPES; CAPELLO; GRAND HOTEL VENA D'ORO.

The ancient Bellunum, capital of a province and a bishop's see, 1,303 feet above sea, on an elevation between the Rivers Ardo and Piave, which here join. Wooded hills and lofty Dolomite peaks all round. Unfinished Duomo, of 16th cent., restored after earthquake in 1873; altar pieces and paintings; fine view from the Campanile, 217 ft. high. In the Piazza del Duomo is the Prefettura, a Lombardic building, with balconies and good portico; west of the Prefettura is the Municipio, a fine Gothic building. Close by is the Museo Civico—miscellaneous collections, including pictures, books, and manuscripts. Church of S. Pietro, 14th cent., restored 18th cent., has paintings; S. Stefano has a Roman sarcophagus by its southern door.

RAIL, p. 282; Diligence p. 372.

[**Venadoro.**

About 4½ miles to the east of Belluno, pleasantly situated on the hill side, 1,650 ft. above sea, amid plantations of pine trees. The springs have medicinal properties. Fine views over the Dolomite region. Reached from Belluno by diligence, page 372.]

Bergamo.—*Stat.*—Pop. of commune 55,306.

HOTELS: ITALIA; MODERNE.

Bergamo, the ancient Bergamum, capital of a province, is situated in a beautiful country; it consists of two parts, the Citta Piana, where are several cotton and silk mills, and the Citta Alta, the historical city on the height, where most that interests the traveller will be found.

The RAILWAY STATION is on the south side, about a mile distant, from the Citta Alta. Immediately north west of the Station the Viale della Stazione leads across the lower town to the tree shaded Viale Vittorio Emanuele, where, at the bend of the road, is the station of the cable tramway to the Citta Alta (15 c.). A few yards beyond the terminus of the tramway is the Piazza Garibaldi, with the unfinished Palazzo Nuovo (a technical institute) on the right hand and the Palazzo Vecchio (Library) on the left. Behind the Palazzo Vecchio is the Romanesque Church of Santa Maria Maggiore, dating from 1137, with lion portals; in interior are some very old frescoes, carved choir stalls of great merit, and monument of the composer Donizetti (a native, died 1848). Adjoining is the Cappella Colleoni, erected by the Condottiere Bartolommeo (died 1475) as a memorial of his power; facade lavishly sculptured; beautiful monument of Medea, daughter of Colleoni. At west side of the Cappella is the Duomo, dating from 1459; paintings. At extreme east of the Citta Alta is the Accademia Carrara, containing a picture gallery, fee 1 lira.

In the Citta Bassa, on east side, is the Church of the Santo Spirito; several fine paintings. San Bartolomeo, near centre of city; interesting. San Bernardino in Pignolo.

RAIL, pages 275, 281, 287.

Bogliaco.

GRAND HOTEL.

A beautifully situated health resort on the Lake of Garda, having a wealth of tropical vegetation. Very extensive trade in lemons, olive oil, etc. Temperate climate; snow and fog are unknown. Villa of Count Bettoni; other villas; good fishing. Excursions in all directions.

STEAMER, page 365.

Bognanco.

On the Simplon route from the Italian Lakes to Switzerland, 2,083 ft. above sea, among pinewoods. Highly mineralised alkaline and iron springs, charged with natural carbonic acid gas, useful in digestive disorders, anæmia, and general debility.

Reached from Domodossola Station, 4½ miles distant.

Bologna.—*Stat.*—Pop. 172,628.

GRAND HOTEL BRUN.—Old established first class hotel, with latest modern improvements. Kept by J. F. Frank. See Advt.

GRAND HOTEL BAGLIONI.—New first class hotel in Via Indipendenza. Suites and single rooms with bath and toilette. Latest modern requirements. See Advt.

HOTEL PELLEGRINO.—Well conducted hotel, combines good accommodation with moderate charges. See Advt.

The RAILWAY STATION is on the north side of the city, about a mile from the centre. A few yards south of the Railway Station—follow the tramway lines—is an open space, whence two thoroughfares, the Via Galliera and the Via dell' Indipendenza, run in parallel lines due south, the latter leading direct to the Piazza del Nettuno and the Piazza Vittorio Emanuele, which lie at right angles to each other and are the centre of Bolognese life.

MOTOR CABS, per 500 metri, 1 lira, each additional 250 metri 20 c. Horsed cab per drive, 1 lira. Extra charge at night.

Electric trams in all directions.

BOLOGNA, the ancient Felsina and Bononia, is situated at the northern base of the Appenines, in a pleasant country watered by the Rivers Reno, Aposa, and Savena. The historic associations are numerous, the many old churches and palaces in the narrow streets having each some special interest.

At the south east corner of the Piazza Vittorio Emanuele is the Gothic Church of S. Petronio, dating from 1390; had the original design been fulfilled it would have been the largest cathedral in Italy, but the work was arrested in 1659; the length is 384 ft. (intended to be 700 ft.), breadth 157 ft., height of nave 132 ft. The beautiful interior is rich with sculpture and paintings. In this church Charles V. was crowned Emperor in 1530—the last German emperor to be crowned in Italy. At end of north aisle is a Museo di San Petronio (admission 25c.), with relics, etc.

The Duomo (S. Pietro) is in the Via della Indipendenza, a short distance north of the Piazza Vittorio Emanuele. Dates from 1575.

S. Domenico, in Piazza Galileo, quarter mile south (very slightly east), of Piazza Vittorio Emanuele. Romanesque of 13th cent.; sculpture and paintings, magnificent choir stalls. In chapel of S. Domenico is tomb of the saint, who was founder of the Inquisition.

S. Stefano, on east side of Via Santo Stefano, quarter mile due east of Piazza Vittorio Emanuele; a cluster of eight different churches, founded in 4th cent. upon the site of a temple of Isis. The principal church of the eight dates from 1637; the other churches are much older, 10th and 11th cent.

S. Giovanni in Monte, a few yards south of S. Stefano. One of the oldest foundations (A.D. 433), rebuilt 1442; good paintings, some carving.

S. Bartolommeo di Porta Ravegnana, at west end of Via Mazzini, quarter mile due east of Piazza Vittorio Emanuele; erected 1530. Good paintings in chapels and on ceiling.

Santa Maria dei Servi, on south side of Via Mazzini; dating from 1383; portico with slender columns. Several good paintings.

S. Giacomo Maggiore, on south side of Via Zamboni, one third mile north east of Piazza Vittorio Emanuele, founded 1267. Among the paintings are some fine examples. By east end of the church is the Oratory of Santa Cecilia (1481), decorated with frescoes.

S. Francesco, in Piazza Malpighi, quarter mile due west of Piazza Vittorio Emanuele. Altar piece with figures and reliefs; tomb of Alexander V.

Palazzo Comunale, on west side of Piazza Vittorio Emanuele. Erection commenced 1290. Frescoes in interior. Opposite is the Palazzo del Podesta, restored.

Museo Civico, just off south east corner of Piazza Vittorio Emanuele, in Via dell' Archiginnasio. Antique and mediæval miscellaneous collections of great interest. Free on Sunday, other days 1 lira. A few yards south, in Piazza Galvani, is the Archiginnasio Antico, containing the Biblioteca Comunale of 193,000 vols. and 5,700 MSS.; the building was the old university.

The University is on the south side of Via Zamboni, half mile north east of Piazza Vittorio Emanuele. Library of 200,000 vols. and 5,000 MSS.; daily except Sunday. Geological Museum, a few yards east of the University.

Accademia di Belle Arti, at corner of Via Zamboni and Via delle Belle Arte, opposite the University. Many paintings by Guido Reni, Lodovico Carracci, Annibale Carracci, Domenichino, Fr. Francia, and other old masters; the finest work is a "St. Cecilia," by Raphael. Sunday free, other days 1 lira.

The Leaning Towers are at the east end of Via Rizzoli, 200 yards north east of Piazza Vittorio Emanuele. Torre Asinelli, erected 1109, is 320 ft. high, and 4 ft. out of perpendicular; visitors ascend with attendant, 50c. The Torre Garisenda, erected 1110, is 156 ft. high, and 8 ft. out of perpendicular. Just south of the towers is the Mercanzia, erected 1384.

Palazzo Bevilacqua Vincenzi, 15th cent., on west side of Via d'Azeglio, running south from Piazza Vittorio Emanuele. A few yards west of the palace, in Via Urbana, is the Collegio di Spagna. Palazzo di Giustizia, the old Palazzo Bacciocchi, is in Piazza dei Tribunali, 200 yards east of Via d'Azeglio, near its south end.

Giardini Margherita, at south east corner of city, a very pleasant small park. Fine view from San Michele in Bosco, 440 ft. high, a former monastery, now an Orthopædic institute, on south side of the city.

The Certosa is the Cemetery—Campo Santo—a mile and a half west of city. Three miles to south west, on a hill, is the pilgrimage Church of Madonna di S. Luca, so called from a painting of the Virgin attributed to St. Luke, brought from Constantinople in 1160; in the arcades upon the hill are several chapels.

POST OFFICE, in the Palazzo Comunale, Piazza del Nettuno.

ENG. CHURCH SERVICE at Hotel Brun.

RAIL, see pp. 279, 279A, 282, 285, 288.

Borca.—Pop. 800.

A finely situated and interesting village, amidst pastures and woods, of the Valle di Cadore, on the River Boite. A good centre for exploring the Dolomite region. At the other side of the river from Borca is the village of Villanuova, the scene of great devastation by a landslip from Monte Antelao, April, 1814, when 257 persons perished. The library, now dispersed, of the village priest of Borca was early in 19th century one of the best in North Italy; one of its treasures, the Biblia Pauperum, is now in the Rylands Library, Manchester.

MEDICAL.—Dr. G. Ansaldi.

DILIGENCE, page 372.

Bordighera.—*Stat.*—Pop. 3,900.

HOTEL ROYAL.—First-class, elevated situation over Strada Romana, with fine view of the whole coast. Just enlarged and fitted with every improvement. Electric light; lift. See Advt.

HOTEL ANGST.—First class hotel, in a beautiful sheltered position. Lift; electric light; hot water heating throughout, as well as open fireplaces. See Advt.

HOTEL DE LONDRES.—First-class family hotel—transferred and enlarged; beautiful situation, with garden. Lift; electric light; central heating. Pension from 8 fr. See Advt.

HOTEL HESPERIA.—On the Strada Romana, with every modern convenience. See Advt.

HOTEL AND KURHAUS CAP AMPEGLIO.—Modern first class hotel, in fine position, overlooking the sea. See Advt.

HOTEL D'ANGLETERRE.-First-class hotel, close to the English Church. Large garden. See Advt

HOTEL BELVEDERE-LOMBARDI.—High class and comfortable. Sheltered position. Large garden. See Advt.

HOTEL BRISTOL.—First class, well situated; large garden. Fine view of sea and mountains. Electric light. See Advt.

GRAND HOTEL DES ILES BRITANNIQUES.—In midst of fine garden. Steam heating and electric light. Garage. See Advt.

PENSION VILLA QUISISANA.—Strada Romana. First class; full south. Home comfort; central heating; electric light. Reasonable. See Advt.

The Railway Station is by the shore, near the middle sea front of the town.

The favourite residence of foreigners is the neighbourhood of the Strada Romana, running parallel with the shore but back on the slope.

Via Vittorio Emanuele is the principal street of the old town; at the Stabilimenti Winter, in this street, is a palm branch exhibition. Bordighera has a recognised trade in palm branches for the Catholic Churches on Palm Sunday. About the middle of Strada Romana is the Nuovo Museo, a collection of flora, etc.; International Library of over 10,000 vols. Chiesa di Terrasanta. Casino. The flower culture of Bordighera (roses, carnations) is famous. Many pleasant walks and drives in neighbourhood.

ENG. CH. SERV. at All Saints' Church.

H. B. M's VICE-CONS.—Arthur E. Turton, Esq.

MEDICAL.—Dr. Bogle, Dr. G. Hamilton, Dr. Hubbard.

ENGLISH BANK, HOUSE AGENCY, AND TOURIST OFFICE.—Edward E. Berry and Co. (British Vice Consulate).. List of villas and flats to let free on application. Railway, sleeping-berth, and steamship tickets on sale.

RAIL, p. 272. Electric trams to Ventimiglia.

Bormio.—A very old little town, at the opening of Val Furva.

Two miles further up the valley are the **Bagni di Bormio.**

The hot springs were known to the Romans, they are useful in cases of paralysis, gout. rheumatism, and neuralgia; also mud baths.

Bormio is a fine centre for mountain excursions.

DILIGENCE, page 374.

Brescia.—*Stat.*—Pop. of commune 83,338.

HOTELS: BRESCIA; ITALIA; GALLO; GAMBERO.

The ancient Brixia, capital of a province, in a fine situation at the base of the Alps. Large iron and steel trade.

From the Railway Station, at south west side of city, a short broad road leads to the Piazza de Roma, whence the Corso Vittorio Emanuele leads to the centre at the Piazza della Loggia, two thirds of a mile.

Palazzo Municipio, or La Loggia, on west side of Piazza della Loggia, a magnificent building with elaborately decorated exterior, erected 1492 on site of a temple of Vulcan. Torre dell' Orologio (clock tower) at opposite side of Piazza.

In Piazza del Duomo, only a few yards south east of Piazza della Loggia, is the Duomo Nuovo, 1604-1825, containing statuary and reliefs; from the south side the Duomo Vecchio, or La Rotonda, is entered, founded 12th cent. Opposite east end of the Duomo Nuovo is the Biblioteca Queriniana; 80,000 vols., literary curiosities. By north side of the Duomo Nuovo is the Broletto, where are law courts and a prison; the campanile is called la Torre del Popolo. The street on north side of the Broletto, Via dei Musei, leads east; at a short distance, north side in a small piazza, is the Museo Civico Età Romana, in a temple built by Vespasian A.D. 72; among the antiquities is a bronze Victory of great merit. A few yards further east is the Museo Civico Età Cristiana, in the old Churches of Santa Giulia and San Salvatore, containing mediæval antiquities. A fee of 1 lira admits to both museums.

Church of S. Clemente, quarter mile eastward from south side of the Duomo Vecchio—paintings; a few paces south east, Church of Santa Maria Calchera—paintings.

At the Pinacoteca Martinengo, in Piazza Moretto, are sculptures, and a picture gallery, with paintings by Moretto and Romanino. In Church of St. Afra, close by, are paintings by Titian, Tintoretto, and P. Veronese.

Castello, on a hill, to the north east; historic collection.

In Church of S. Giovanni Evangelista, 200 yards from north west corner of Piazza Vecchia, are several fine paintings. There are paintings of merit in most of the other churches. Campo Santo (cemetery), half mile from Porta Milano, on east side of city.

RAIL, pages 280, 281, 288.

Brindisi.—*Stat.*—Pop. 17,000.

HOTEL INTERNATIONAL; EUROPA, CENTRALE.

There are two Railway Stations—Centrale and Porto. The Centrale Station is on the west side of the town, about half a mile from the Harbour. The Porto Station is close to the Quay whence the Steamers going east depart.

BRINDISI, the Brentesion of the Greeks and Brundisium of the Romans, has from the earliest historic times been of importance to travellers. It stood at the coast end of the Appian Way, and the harbour was several times crowded with ships of the Crusaders. After centuries of decay the harbour was cleared of the sand that choked it, and large steamers are now able to berth at the Quay. On a low hill near the Quay is a column bearing part of an inscription, and remains of another column are close by. The towered castle is used as a prison. Cathedral; the church of S. Giovanni has become a museum of antiquities. Virgil died here B.C. 19.

H.B.M.'s CONSUL.—S. G. Cocoto, Esq., M.V.O.

RAIL, pages 277, 285.

Cadenabbia.

GRAND HOTEL BELLEVUE.—Fashionable first class hotel, situated opposite the Landing Stage; patronized by English and Americans. Open all the year. See Advt.

HOTEL BELLE ILE.—Well situated family hotel, overlooking the Lake. Electric light; baths; garden with terrace. Pension from 8 fr. See Advt.

HOTEL BRITANNIA.—First class family hotel, in fine position, overlooking the lake; garden. Electric light. Central heating. Pension from frs. 8. See Advt.

In a beautiful sheltered situation on Lago di Como. At a short distance south west is the Villa Carlotta, containing works of art, among them celebrated reliefs by Thorwaldsen; garden of luxuriant vegetation; fee 50 c. Half way up the Sasso di San Martino, behind Cadenabbia, is the Church of Madonna di S. Martino, whence is fine view. ENGLISH CH. SER. during Summer.

MEDICAL.—Dr. Eliot, Dr. Bishop.

GOLF.—9-hole course at Dervio, with club house.

STEAMER, page 365.

[**Tremezzo.**

TREMEZZO HOTEL.—New family hotel, in good position. Electric light, lift and central heating. Moderate. See Advt.

HOTEL PENSION BAZZONI ET DU LAC.—Comfortable family hotel, pleasantly situated, with garden and terrace overlooking the Lake; very reasonable terms. See Advt.

Tremezzo is with Cadenabbia practically one place. Many villas of Italian nobility. The district, the Tremezzina, is known as the garden of Lombardy.

GOLF.—9-hole course at Dervio, with club-house.

Lenno (about 2½ miles from Cadenabbia).

REGINA HOTEL.—Family hotel in beautiful, quiet situation, facing Lake. Electric light, central heating. Open all the year. Pension from frs. 7—9. See Advt.

At Lenno, a delightful place on the Lake, is Villa Arconati; very fine view. Below the church is a little temple with marble columns. On the mountain above Lenno is the extensive Abbey of Acqua fredda, inhabited in 1906 after a century of neglect by Benedictins expelled from France.]

Calalzo.—Pop. 1,436.

HOTEL MARMAROLE.—First class hotel in splendid position. Moderate charges. Automobile garage. See Advt.

A finely situated village in the Dolomite region, in the Cadore valley, 2,825 ft. above sea, on the River Piave, amidst cultivated fields and pine woods, with a background of imposing mountains. Calalzo is a favourite resort, the air being remarkably pure, dry, and cool in summer. Excursions in the Cadore Dolomites: Antelas, Marmarole, Spalti di Toro, Monfalcone, Cridola.

Reached by diligence, page 372, from Belluno; or from Toblach on the Austrian side.

Cannero.—

HOTEL PENSION ITALIE.—Well situated on the shore of the lake, surrounded by its own gardens. Central hot water heating. Pension from 6 fr. Under new proprietorship. See Advt.

In a beautiful situation on the west shore of Lago Maggiore, on the slopes of Monte Carza, opposite Luino; vineyards and orchards all round. The romance of a sort of robber stronghold in the 15th cent. attaches to the two half-ruined Castelli di Cannero.

STEAMER, page 366.

Capua.—*Stat.*—Pop. 14,000.

ALBERGO DELLA POSTA.

A fortified town, on the River Volturno, in a very fertile country; it came into existence after the destruction of the ancient Capua, 3 miles distant. Modernised Duomo, of 11th cent. In the Museo Campano are antiquities and a few pictures. RAIL, page 276.

[**Santa Maria di Capua** is a prosperous little town on the site of the ancient Capua, destroyed by the Saracens in the 9th cent. Among the remaining ruins is the Amphitheatre, 185 yards in one direction, 152 yards in the other. RAIL, page 276.]

Carrara.—*Stat.*—Pop. 25,000.

GRAND HOTEL.

An agreeable little town whose population is almost exclusively engaged in working the world known marble quarries. Many sculptors have studios here. Sculpture is the predominant feature in the Churches of S. Andrea and of Madonna delle Grazie and at the Accademia delle Belle Arti.

RAIL, page 275.

Caserta.—*Stat.*—Pop. of commune 33,189.

HOTELS: VITTORIA; VILLA REALE; FIRENZE.

Opposite the Railway Station is the principal attraction, the Palazzo Reale, erected 1752, by Charles III; the chapel is lavishly decorated; the theatre has marble columns. Pleasant gardens. To view palazzo, 1 lira; chapel, 25 c., permit obtained at the Palazzo Reale at Naples.

RAIL, pages 276, 278, 285B.

Cassino.—*Stat.*—Pop. 13,500.

HOTEL CENTRALE.

Until 1871 the town, which occupies the site of the ancient Casinum, was called San Germano. There are remains of antiquity—colossal ruins of an amphitheatre—but otherwise the town has few attractions. The object of the traveller will be to visit the **Monastery of Monte Cassino**, 1,715 feet above sea, of castle like appearance, founded by St. Benedict in 529, on the site of a temple of Apollo. The Monastery, State property, is used as an ecclesiastical training college. The Church is decorated with mosaics and paintings; under the high altar are buried St. Benedict and St. Scholastica. The MSS. in the Library are of great value. In the Pinacoteca are good paintings. The visit requires about 5 hrs.

RAIL, page 276.

Castellammare.—*Stat.*—Pop. of the commune 32,841.

HOTEL QUISISANA.

On the site of the ancient Stabiæ, destroyed A.D. 79, at the same time as Pompei; officially named Castellammare di Stabia. A favourite sea-side resort, winter and summer; warm sulphur springs. Harbour; arsenal; old castle.

H.B.M.'s V. CONSUL.—E. S. Albanese, Esq.

U.S. CONSULAR AGENT.

ENGLISH CHURCH SERVICE at Hotel Quisisana.

RAIL, page 278. Electric **Tramway to** Sorrento.

Cava dei Tirreni.—*Stat.*—Pop. 21,000.

HOTELS: LONDRES; VICTORIA.

Finely situated, 980 ft. above sea, on a slope of Monte Albino—a favourite resort amidst delightful country. Arcaded street leads from the Station to the Piazza, where is the church. Villa Pubblica, by the Piazza, is a pleasant public garden.

RAIL, page 277.

[**Pæstum** (Pesto) is most conveniently visited from Cava dei Tirreni. The Railway Station is close to the Porta della Sirena, the entrance to the ruined city. Competent authorities describe the ruined Greek temples to be, those at Athens excepted, the finest existing. Admission to temples 1 lira, on Sunday free.]

Cernobbio.

GRAND HOTEL VILLA D'ESTE.—Beautifully situated on the bank of the Lake; with park and garden. See Advt.

HOTEL PENSION REINE OLGA.—Well situated, full south, facing the Lake; electric light and gardens; pension terms. See Advt.

A beautiful place on Lago di Como, near its south end; soft climate and fine views; several handsome villas in the neighbourhood. On Monte Bisbino, 4,390 ft., to north west, is a pilgrimage church. Tramway to Como.

MEDICAL.—Dr. Eliot.

STEAMER, p. 365.

Chiavenna.—*Stat.*—Pop. 3,100.

HOTELS: CONRADI; NATIONAL.

The Clavenna of the Romans, in a fine situation on the River Mera, at the mouth of the Val Bregaglia. Church of San Lorenzo, with clock tower. Some interesting remains—font of 1206—in the Battisterio. De Salis Castle, a ruin.

RAIL, page 281. Diligence, pages 377, 378.

Como.—*Stat.*—Pop. of commune 44,132.

GRAND HOTEL PLINIUS.—First class. On the border of the Lake, with garden. Open March 1st to November 10th. See Advt.

ITALIE; VOLTA.

Situated at the south west end of the Lake of Como, with a background of mountains; the Comum of Roman times and a mediæval place of importance, now a centre of silk manufacture.

Cathedral—Duomo, originally Gothic (1396), but diverted to Renaissance style (1486); handsome west portal; decorated interior, good paintings and wood carvings; statues of elder and younger Pliny (both born here) by principal entrance. Church of S. Fedele (Romanesque), 200 yards south west of Cathedral. Annunziata Church, 16th cent., handsome interior, on south west side of town; a little further south is the Church of Sant' Abbondio, dating from 5th cent.

Museo Civico of Roman antiquities, weapons, coins, etc., in Palazzo Giovio.

RAIL, pp. 269A, 274A, 287. STEAMERS, p. 365.

[Funicular rail up from Como to **Brunate**, on the mountain to north east.

Magnificent panorama; pure cool air. Rail from and to Como every half hour.]

Cremona.—*Stat.*—Pop. of commune 40,436.

HOTEL ROMA.

From the Porta Milano, near the Station (on the north side of the city), the Corso Garibaldi leads south east towards the Duomo (two thirds of a mile), the way being indicated by the lofty Torrazzo.

The Duomo, Romanesque-Lombard, erected 1107-90, has attractive facade; many frescoes, some celebrated, in interior; reliefs on pulpits, choir stalls. Torrazzo, 397 ft. high, connected with the Duomo by loggie. Baptistery close to south west angle of Duomo; Campo Santo (mosaics), by south east angle of Duomo.

Church of S. Pietro al Po, in Via S. Pietro, one third mile south west of the Duomo; beautiful ceiling decoration. SS. Agostino e Giacomo, one third mile north west of the Duomo; good paintings. S. Agata, quarter mile north of S. Agostino; frescoes. At Church of S. Sigismondo, two miles north east of the Duomo, outside the city, are noted pictures and frescoes.

Palazzo Municipio, opposite the Duomo; small gallery of paintings of Cremona school, chimney-piece, etc. In Piazza Roma, 200 yards north, is a house marked by tablet where Stradivari (died 1737), made many of his violins.

Museo Civico, in the Istituto Ala Ponzoni, quarter mile south west of the Duomo; sculpture, pictures, weapons, uniforms, etc.

RAIL, pages 279C, 281, 282.

Diano Marina.—*Stat.*—Pop. 2,100.

A pleasantly situated winter resort, in a fertile plain. In February, 1887, much ruin was caused by an earthquake. On a height is Diano Castello.

RAIL, page 272.

Domodossola.—*Stat.*—Pop. 3,900.

HOTEL TERMINUS.

A picturesque little town, 912 ft. above sea, the ancient Oscela, on the River Toce, at the Italian end of the Simplon Tunnel. At the Palazzo Silva, 16th cent., is a small Museum. From the Calvario hill, on south side of the town, is a fine view. Mountain excursions.

RAIL, pages 263B, 274, 274A. Diligence to Pòntebrolla (Locarno), 374.

Elba, the most important of the Tuscan islands, lies off the west coast of Italy, separated by about 5½ miles of sea from Piombino on the mainland. Pop. of island 25,043; iron mining and tunny and sardine fisheries are the principal occupations. Mild equable climate. **Portoferraio,** pop. 5,970, chief town; here is the Palazzina dei Molini, for a time the residence of Napoleon I; Villa Napoleone is four miles west of the town. Monte Capanne is 3,343 ft. high.

H.B.M.'s VICE-CONSUL.—J. C. Airey, Esq.

STEAMERS from Leghorn and Piombino, pages 354 and 355.

Faenza.—*Stat.*—Pop. 12,300.

Pleasantly situated on the River Lamone. Faenza ware, "fayence," a kind of majolica, is well known. The Cathedral of San Pietro is interesting. Some good pictures and sculpture at the Pinacoteca, in the secularized Convent of Santa Maria dell' Angelo.

RAIL, pages 285, 286.

Ferrara.—*Stat.*—Pop. of commune 95,212.

HOTELS: STELLA D'ORO; EUROPA.

The Roman Forum Alieni, once prosperous and important, the seat of the great Este family, now a city of empty streets and neglected palaces.

Immediately east of the Station a short thoroughfare leads to the broad Viale Cavour, which, in half a mile, goes south east to the heart of the city at the Castello, a four-towered building, occupied by the municipality—in the council chamber and Sala di Napoli are frescoes.

The Cattedrale of S. Giorgio (1135) is 100 yards due south of the Castello; imposing facade in the Lombard style; in interior paintings and statuary. The Campanile is in the Renaissance style. Opposite (south west) is a group of buildings including Palazzo della Ragione, where are the law courts, and the half hidden Church of S. Romano. In Via Cairoli, close by, is the Seminario Arcivescovile, containing frescoes by Garofalo; 50 c.

In the Church of S. Paolo, 100 yards south west of Cattedrale, are paintings. S. Francesco, one-sixth mile south east of Cattedrale, at end of Via Volta Paletto; a brick church of 1494, with several domes; frescoes and monuments of Este family. South west from S. Francesco, along the Via della Scienze, is the University (law, medicine, mathematics), attended by only a few students; collection of coins, library of 100,000 vols. and 2,000 MSS., among latter poems by Ariosto and Tasso. In same district, a third mile further south east, is the Palazzo Schifanoja, in Via Scandiana, a palazzo of the Este family, 1391-1469, now town property; celebrated but poorly preserved frescoes.

Ateneo Civico, west side of Corso Vittorio Emanuele, street leading north from the Castello; fine Renaissance building, 1567, called Palazzo dei Diamanti because of facets of stones, containing the Picture Gallery; many important works of the Ferrara School, with a few modern pictures; fee 1 lira.

A little way west of the Ateneo, in the Corso di Porta Po, is the Via Ariosto, where, in the part going north, west side, is the Casa dell' Ariosto, the poet's house, now town property. In a lower chamber of the Ospedale, in Corso della Giovecca, just beyond the north east corner of the Castello, the poet Tasso was confined during a time of mental alienation (1579-1586); many poets have written their names upon the walls.

RAIL, pages 279A, 288.

FLORENCE (*Ital.* **Firenze**). — *Stat.* — Pop. of the commune 232,860. — (*Plan in Special Edition, or post free 3d. Stamps*).

GRAND HOTEL BAGLIONI.—First class hotel, facing the Railway Station. Electric light; heated throughout. Lift. Apartments with bath and lavatories communicating. See Advt.

HOTEL MINERVA.—Place Sta. Maria Novella. Central situation near Railway Station. Electric light; lift. See Advt.

SPLENDIDE HOTEL PATRIA.—Centrally situated, near Piazza Signoria and Post Office. Entirely renovated. Lift; electric light; central heating. Pension from 8 fr. See Advt.

HOTEL PENSION PENDINI.—Good, centrally situated. Piazza Vittorio Emanuele. Lift. Electric light; Pension from frs. 7. See Advt.

PENSION PLUCKNETT.—7, Via dei Martelli. First class pension, well situated, close to the Duomo; every comfort; lift; electric light; central heating; English management. Pension from frs. 6.50. See Advt.

DE VILLE; GRAND; PALACE; CAVOUR.

The principal RAILWAY STATION—Stazione Centrale—is in the north central part of the city. The Stazione Campo di Marte is at the east side of the city, a considerable distance from the centre.

Electric trams and omnibuses traverse the city. Several electric railways to outside districts.

Should the traveller have but a few hours to spare, let him cross from the Stazione Centrale, bearing to the left, to the open space of Piazza dell' Unita Italiana, here the street tending south east, Via Panzani, leads very soon to the Duomo. From the Duomo proceed south along Via Calzajoli to its end in Piazza della Signoria, a busy centre, with Palazzo Vecchio on left hand, and, on south side, extending to the Arno, Palazzo degli Uffizi. By the river, the Arno, turn to right hand, westward, cross the first bridge, Ponte Vecchio, and presently, on left hand, will be seen the Palazzo Pitti, with the Boboli Gardens (Giardino di Boboli) behind. From Piazzi Pitti, just beyond south end, turn into Via Maggio; following the street, over Ponte Santa Trinita, it will lead back close to the Stazione Centrale.

FLORENCE, formerly the capital of the Grand Duchy of Tuscany, sometime the capital of the Kingdom of Italy, 1865-71, is situated on both banks of the River Arno, in a pleasant valley. It is generally conceded pre-eminence as the centre of Italian intellectual life; literature and the fine arts have attained a dignity and grace that seem fittingly to adorn a city set like a gem amidst beautiful natural surroundings. The art treasures of Florence are practically inexhaustible, while the monuments, palaces, and streets, perpetuate many famous historical or literary reminiscences. There is a resident foreign colony largely English and American.

The Duomo, or Cattedrale di Santa Maria del Fiore, in Piazza del Duomo, was erected 1294-1461; the first architect was Arnolfo di Cambio, to him succeeding Giotto, Andrea Pisano, Talenti, and, much later, Filippo Brunelleschi, to whom the dome and lantern are due. Its length is 555 feet, breadth at the transept 341 feet; dome 300 feet high, lantern 351 feet. Bronze doors. over north door a bas relief of Madonna. The vastness of the interior impresses; monuments, reliefs, statues, paintings, and stained glass. To visit dome 50 c., fine view. The Campanile (bell tower), begun by Giotto, 1334. 276 ft. high, has four storeys, and is adorned with bas reliefs and statues of patriarchs, prophets, evangelists, and symbolical figures; fee to ascend 50c.

Opposite west end of the Duomo is the Battistero (San Giovanni Battista), the cathedral church of Florence until 1128; celebrated bronze doors.

Opposite the east end of the Duomo is the Museo di Santa Maria del Fiore, or Cathedral Museum; open daily 10.0 to 3.0 or 4.0, 50c., free on Sunday. Works of art from the Cathedral and Baptistery.

Church of Or San Michele, west side of Via Calzajoli, south of Duomo. Statues on exterior. As interior is very dark the visit should be in the morning; celebrated Tabernacle by Andrea Orcagna.

Santa Croce, half-mile south **east from Duomo.** Tombs of Michael Angelo (died 1564), Alfieri (died 1803), monuments of celebrated men, Dante, Macchiavelli, and many others. Frescoes of surpassing interest by Giotto, Taddeo Gaddi, Agnolo Gaddi, and others, in the chapels. In the Piazza Santa Croce, is the Dante Monument.

Santa Maria Novella, opposite Stazione Centrale. Frescoes by Ghirlandajo, in choir; in Cappella Rucellai a celebrated Madonna, by Cimabue. On west side of Church, ancient Cloister, Il Chiostro Verde, with frescoes.

San Lorenzo, in Piazza San Lorenzo, a little north west of Duomo. Very ancient church. Paintings and monuments. Cloisters. Cappella dei Principi, sumptuous **mortuary chapel of the princely** Medici **family. Sagrestia Nuova (New Sacristy), by Michael Angelo, a mausoleum for the Medici. Admission to Cappella and Sagrestia, daily** 9.0 to 5.0, **1 lira, Sunday, free. Biblioteca Laurenziana, south side of S. Lorenzo (weekdays, 8.0 to** 12.0, **or 10.0 to 4.0), built from** a design **by Michael Angelo; 10.000 MSS. of Latin and Greek authors, MSS.** of Petrarch and Dante, Æschylus, Cicero, Virgil.

San Marco, in Piazza San Marco, to which Via Ricasoli leads north from Duomo. Paintings and Statues. Adjacent is the old Monastery, now the Museo di San Marco (10.0 to 4.0, 1 lira, Sunday, free); famous frescoes by Fra Angelico **da Fiesole; Girolamo Savonarola was an inmate** of the monastery; **historic cells of the monastery.**

Santa Trinita, near Ponte S. Trinita. Frescoes by Ghirlandajo.

Santissima Annunziata, a little north of Duomo, up Via de' Servi. Frescoes by Andrea del Sarto; in Cappella della Vergine a "miracle" picture of the Virgin.

Santo Spirito, a little west of Palazzo Pitti. many altars; paintings.

Santa Maria del Carmine, south side of and short distance from the Arno, **west of Ponte alla Carraja.** Celebrated frescoes.

Galleria degli Uffizi, south of the Piazza della Signoria, to which Via Calzajoli leads south from the Duomo. Daily 10.0 to 4.0, 1 lr., Sunday free. **It is impossible here even to indicate the principal treasures of this wonderful collection; when time is very limited it is advisable to proceed to the saloon named the Tribuna, in the Corridore Orientale, where are some of the greatest masterpieces. Also collections of gems, engravings, inscriptions, cameos, designs, miniatures, pastels.**

On first floor of Palazzo degli Uffizi is the Biblioteca Nazionale; daily, except Sunday, 10.0 to 4.0. There are about 500,000 vols. and 20,000 MSS. State Archives (Archivio di Stato), in about 200 rooms, enormous collection of papers.

Palazzo Pitti, south side of the Arno, over Ponte Vecchio. Royal apartments and Silver Room, Thurs. and Sun., 9.30 to 4.0 (fee, for Royal apartments, 50c. to 1 lira; for Silver room, 50c.). The Gallery open daily 10.0 to 4.0, 1 lira, Sunday morn. **free. The remarks under Galleria degli Uffizi apply here.**

The Pitti Palace is the residence of the King of Italy when at Florence; in the Gabinetto degli Argenti **(Silver Room) is a display of goldsmith art.** The **Boboli Gardens (Reale Giardino di Boboli),** behind **the Pitti Palace, in addition to their own** attractions **command fine views.**

Museo Nazionale in Palazzo del Podesta. generally known as Il Bargello, on east side of Via del Proconsolo, running south from east end of the Duomo. Daily, 10.0 to 4.0, 1 lira; Sunday morn. free. Collections illustrative of mediæval and modern Italian art, paintings, sculpture, weapons, goldsmiths' work, ivories, bronzes, etc.

Accademia di Belle Arti, on east side of Via Ricasoli, running north from west end of the Duomo. Daily, 10.0 to 4.0, 1 lira; Sunday morn. **free. Pictures and Sculpture. Michael Angelo's celebrated "David" (Il Gigante) in Cupola Saloon.**

Palazzo Corsini, facing the Arno, north side, by Ponte alla Carraja; Tues., Thurs., Sat., 10.0 to 3.0; entrance at back in Via di Parione. Pictures.

Museo Archeologico, in Palazzo della Crocetta, in Via della Colonna, half a mile north east of the Duomo. Beside the Archeological collections there are an Egyptian Museum and a collection of tapestry.

PALAZZO VECCHIO, in Piazza della Signoria, to which Via Calzajoli leads south from the Duomo. Statues and frescoes, decorated rooms. Offices of Municipal Council here. Loggia dei Lanzi on south side of Piazza, an open vaulted hall, with Sculpture. The Piazza della Signoria was formerly the scene of many historic popular assemblies; here Savonarola, with two other Dominican monks, was burned, May 23rd, 1498.

Several other Palaces, all having historical associations, mostly with small collections of pictures or objects of art.

Dante's House, Casa Dante, on north side of Via Dante, to which Via Magazzini runs north east from Piazza della Signoria.

Michael Angelo's House, Casa Buonarroti, at corner of Via Ghibellina (running east from Via del Proconsolo, which leads south from east end of Duomo) and Via Michael Angelo Buonarroti. Weekdays, 10.0 to 4.0, 1 lira; Sun. morn. free.

Robert and Elizabeth Browning lived at the Casa Guidi (tablet on house), in Piazza San Felice, a few yards north of Palazzo Pitti.

POST OFFICE in the Uffizi Palace, north side. The new Post Office, in Via Pellicceria, running out of south side of Piazza Vittorio Emanuele, will be opened in 1913. Telegraph Office in Palazzo Nonfinito, east side of Via Proconsolo, at east end of Duomo.

CH. ENG. SERV., at Holy Trinity, Via La Marmora. St. Mark's, Via Maggio.

AMER. EPIS. CH., Piazza del Carmini.

PRESBYTERIAN CHURCH, 11, Lung Arno Guicciardini.

H. B. M.'s CONSUL.—A. Leman, Esq. VICE-CONSUL, Gennaro Placci, Esq.

U. S. CONSUL.—L. J. Keena, Esq.

GOLF.—9-hole course at San Donato; club house.

MEDICAL, English.—Drs. A. R. Coldstream, Henderson, Gates, Garry.

ITALIAN DOCTOR.—Dr. Ernesto Riccioli, 10, Corso Tintori; consultation hours 2—3; telephone 19—16.

ENGLISH CHEMISTS. — H. Roberts and Co. (by appointment to her late Majesty Queen Victoria), 17, Via Tornabuoni.

BANKERS AND MONEY CHANGERS.—Maquay and Co., 5, Via Tornabuoni, ground floor. Correspondents of all the principal English and American Banks.

BANKERS.—Kuster and Co. Correspondents of the principal English and American Banks, 6, Via Vecchietti.

TERRACOTTAS.—The celebrated Galleries of Artistic Terracottas of the "Manifattura di Signa" are well worth a visit. Via Vecchietti, 2, and Via dei Fossi, 8.

ANTIQUITIES.—Giuseppe Salvadori. Via dei Fossi, 9. Best house for Antiquities and Works of Art.

DEPOT FOR BRADSHAW'S GUIDES.—B. Seeber, 20, Via Tornabuoni.

RAIL, pp. 270A, 271A, 279, 286.

[Electric tramway from Florence to **Fiesole**, on a hill, three miles to the north east. The old Etruscan town has a population of 5,000; straw plaiting is the chief industry. Between San Domenico di Fiesole and Fiesole the old road is steep, but the climb is well rewarded by the beautiful views. The Church of San Domenico, with the neighbouring Monastery, the Badia di Fiesole, five minutes distant, are of great interest. At Fiesole, 970 ft. above sea, nearly 500 ft. above San Domenico, is a Cathedral dating from 11th cent.; behind the Cathedral are ruins of a Roman temple and theatre. The Franciscan Monastery covers the site of the ancient Capitol. The sunset view from Fiesole is very fine.]

Gardone-Riviera.

GRAND HOTEL.—First class. Open from 15th September to 15th May. See Advt.

SAVOY HOTEL.—Entirely new first class hotel, with every modern comfort; lift, etc. Pension terms from 9 fr. One minute from Landing Stage. See Advt.

On the west bank of the Lago di Garda, regarded as the warmest winter resort north of the Apennines. Its sheltered situation, a chain of heights protecting it from north winds, is favourable for consumptive and nervous invalids; the spring climate is delightful. Luxuriant vegetation—the olive, lemon, and cypress flourish, and palms grow in the open. Many pleasant walks, free from dust, with numerous seats. On the Isola Lecchi, 3 miles distant, is a mansion of Prince Borghesi. Steam tram to Idro, at south end of Lago d'Idro.

MEDICAL.—Dr. Th. Brühl, Parkvilla (speaks English).

STEAMER, page 365.

GENOA (*Ital.* **Genova**).—*Stat.*—Pop. of the commune 272,221.

BRISTOL HOTEL.—First class hotel, centrally situated, affording every modern comfort. Electric light. See Advt.

SAVOY HOTEL.—First class hotel, situated near the Railway Station and Landing Pier, with view of the sea. Electric light. See Advt.

HOTEL DE LONDRES.—Sunny position, opposite Railway Station. Moderate. See Advt.

GRAND HOTEL MIRAMARE.—First class, near Station and Harbour. Up-to-date comfort. Latest sanitary arrangements. Rooms and suites. Magnificent views. See Advt.

EDEN PALACE HOTEL AND HOTEL DU PARC.—Standing in fine grounds, and quietly situated. Suites and single rooms with private baths, etc. Electric light and central heating; lift. See Advt.

HOTEL VICTORIA.—Very centrally situated, Piazza Annunziata, entirely renovated. Lift, electric light, central heating. Pension from 10 fr. See Advt.

GRAND HOTEL DE GENES.—First class hotel in fine position, opposite Carlo Felice Theatre; high patronage. Rooms from 5 lire. See Advt.

HOTEL DE FRANCE ET RUSSIE.—Well known old established house, situated in the centre of town, commanding fine view of harbour. Lift and electric light. See Advt.

HOTEL SMITH.—English house, well situated, overlooking the harbour; terms moderate. Pension from 8 fr. Rooms 2.50-4 fr. See Advt.

BRITANNIA HOTEL.—High class English and American hotel, facing the Station. Modern comforts. Restaurant. Pension terms. See Advt.

HOTEL FURSTENHOF (PRINCIPE). HOTEL CONTINENTAL.—Up-to-date first class hotels; near Railway Station and Landing Stage. See Advt.

HOTEL HELVETIA.—Good second class, centrally situated near Station. Lift; electric light. Central heating. Swiss management. Moderate pension terms. See Advt.

RAILWAY.—The principal Railway Station is the Stazione Piazza Principe, in the Piazza Acquaverde, on the north west side of the city, close to the old harbour; at this Station the hotel omnibuses and cabs wait. A second station, Stazione Piazza Brignole, **on the east side, is not so important.**

STEAMER.—Passengers are landed at the Ponte Federico Guglielmo or the Ponte Andrea Doria, **in the old harbour, close to the principal Railway Station.**

CABS.—Motors, drive of 1,200 metri, 1 lira; each additional 300 metri 20c. One horse cab per drive 1 lira, 2 horse cab 1 lira 50c. Extra charge at night.

Electric Tramways traverse the city.

GENOA is the chief commercial city of Italy, with an extensive transport trade, much of it obtained at the expense of Venice. Viewed from the harbour the beauty of its situation is striking, and this, associated with the number of its palaces, justifies the qualification of "La Superba." The streets in the old town are narrow and steep, but in the newer quarters are broad straight thoroughfares.

The centre of the life of Genoa is the PIAZZA DEFERRARI, where the electric cars converge. In front of the Stazione Principe is the Piazza Acquaverdi; **running out of this, on the east side, is Via Balbi, which ends in the Piazza Annunziata; just here the line of street bends south in Via Cairoli, continuing in Via Garibaldi to Piazza Fontane Marose, here at south east corner Via Carlo Felice runs into the Piazza Deferrari.**

CATTEDRALE of San Lorenzo, by Piazza Umberto, **just out, by south west corner, of Piazza** Deferrari. **Begun 1110, dome added 1567, interior restored 1896. Paintings and statues. In the chapel of S. Giovanni Battista are relics of John the Baptist. In the Sacristy (Mon. and Thurs., 1.0 to 4.0, 50c.) gold and silver shrines and vessels are shewn, with relics. On east side of Piazza** Umberto **is the church of San Ambrogio, with two pictures by Rubens—Presentation in the Temple, and St. Ignatius healing the sick.** On the north side of the Piazza is the Palazzo Ducale, where the old doges resided; sumptuous interior now utilised as public offices.

San Matteo, in Salita di S. Matteo, off west side of Piazza Deferrari. **Memorials of the Doria family**

Santa Maria di Carignano, at south end of Via Fieschi, a street on south side of Via Venti Settembre, which runs east from Piazza Deferrari. 1552-1603. Paintings and statues. View from dome; verger expects 25c.

The Ospedale di Pammatone, close to centre of the Via Venti Settembre, has a chapel adjoining where for a very small fee is shown in a glass coffin the wonderfully preserved remains of the patron saint of Genoa, Santa Caterina, dressed in rich attire and wearing quaint but beautiful rings.

Santissima Annunziata del Vastato, **east end of Via Balbi, which runs east of Stazione Principe. Frescoes.**

San Stefano, **north side of Via Venti Settembre, running east from Piazzo Deferrari. Martyrdom of Stephen, by Giulio Romano.** Part of the old church fell into ruin in 1912.

Where paintings in churches are covered a **small fee is expected.**

Accademia di Belle Arti, on north side of Piazza Deferrari; here are the Municipal Library and the Museo Chiossone, the latter containing a valuable collection of Chinese and Japanese antiquities.

Palazzo Rosso, in Via Garibaldi, south side. Mon., Thurs., Sat., **10.0 to 4.0**; 50c. **Collection** of pictures; library.

Palazzo Bianco, Via Garibaldi, opposite Palazzo Rosso. Daily, 11.0 to 4.0, 1 lira. Sculpture, pictures, antiques.

Palazzo Municipale, next to Palazzo Bianco. Frescoes. **Paganini's violin.**

Palazzo Doria, just west, south side, of Stazione Principe. Frescoes.

Palazzo Durazzo-Pallavicini, east end of Via Balbi, north side. Pictures by Rubens, Titian, several by Van Dyck. Introduction necessary.

Palazzo Reale, Via Balbi, south side. Daily, when Royalty not in residence.

Universita, Via Balbi, north side, opposite Palazzo Reale. Staircase. Natural History Museum. Library.

Villetta Dinegro, a little back from north end of Via Carlo Felice, running north from Piazza Deferrari. Pretty little park.

Campo Santo (Cemetery), about 1½ mile north from the city, on the north bank of the River Bisagno. A beautiful cemetery—Mazzini buried here.

On the headland of Capo del Faro is the Lighthouse, whence is a very fine view—best at sunset. A cable tramway to Granarolo, 775 ft., whence is another good view.

POST OFFICE, south east corner of Piazza Deferrari.

ENGLISH CHURCH SERVICE.—Church of the Holy Ghost, Piazza Marsala.

PRESBYTERIAN CHURCH.—Via Peschiera.

H. B. M.'s CONSUL-GENERAL.—W. Keene, Esq., M.V.O. VICE-CONSUL.—G. B. Beak, Esq.

U.S. CONSUL-GENERAL.—J. A. Smith, Esq. VICE-CONSUL.—J. B. Youngs, Esq.

MEDICAL.—Dr. med. C. Wild (speaks English), Via Assarotti, 11-4; hours of consultation, 1.0 p.m. to 3.0 p.m.; telephone 16.83. Prof. G. Ferrari, M.D., 12, Via Assarotti; speaks English; consultations from 2.0 p.m. to 3.0 p.m.; telephone 7-34. Ch. Breiting, M.D.; Dr. Th. Zaeslein.

DENTISTS.—Mr. Charles Bright and Dr. Mario Frizzoni, Surgeon Dentists, Via S. Giacomo Filippo, 35.

MOSCATELLI'S INTERNATIONAL PHARMACY.—33, Via Carlo Felice. English and American patent medicines.

ENGLISH BANKERS.—Kirby and Le Mesurier, 7, Via Carlo Felice. Correspondents of principal English and American banks.

DEPOT FOR BRADSHAW'S GUIDE.—Italian State Railway Office, Piazza Deferrari. Gontrand, 35, Via Venti Settembre.

RAIL, pages 269A, 270, 270A, 272, 273.

Gerace.—*Stat.*—Pop. 9,600.

An old place on the mountain slope facing the sea, on the site of the ancient Locri Epizephyrii, dating from 683 B.C. Cathedral, with antique columns. On October 23rd, 1907, the district round Gerace was devastated by earthquake, causing the collapse of the Gerace Cathedral and numerous fatalities. The village of Ferruzzano (pop. 2,111), 6 miles from Gerace, was almost entirely destroyed.

RAIL, page 278.

Grosseto.—*Stat.*—Pop. of the commune 12,442.

Capital of the Maremme; the town is nearly a mile from the railway station. The Cathedral dates from 1294. At the Municipio is a collection of Etruscan cinerary urns, vases, etc.

RAIL, pages 270, 275.

Ivrea.—*Stat.*—Pop. 6,000.

Chief town of the Canavese, on the River Dora Baltea, 875 ft. above sea, a picturesque old place, colonised by the Romans, B.C. 100. The Cathedral, of ancient foundation, has been frequently restored. In the Palazzo Municipale is the Museo Garda, with Asiatic collections.

RAIL, page 274A.

Lecco.—*Stat.*—Pop. 10,400.

HOTELS: GRAND; MAZZOLENI.

A busy little town pleasantly situated at the foot of Monte Resegane (6,160 ft.), near the south end of the Lago di Lecco, the south eastern branch of the Lago di Como. Silk, cotton, and iron manufactories. Pilgrimage church and ruined castle on the hill of San Girolamo.

RAIL, pages 274A, 281. STEAMERS, page 365.

Leghorn (*Ital.* **Livorno**).—*Stat.*—Pop. of the commune 105,315.

HOTELS: GIAPPONE; ANGLETERRE.

The RAILWAY STATION is on the north side of city, about two thirds of a mile from the centre.

Livorno stands next to Genoa as a place of commercial importance, having a great trade with eastern Mediterranean ports; local industries are ship building, iron foundries, and glass manufacture.

Half a mile due south of the Railway Station is the Piazza Carlo Alberto, from which the principal thoroughfare, Via Vittorio Emanuele, runs to the port. Proceeding from the Piazza, on south side of Via V. Emanuele is the Pinacoteca, where are small collections of paintings and coins; presently the street emerges into the Piazza Vittorio Emanuele, where are the Cattedrale, the former Ducal Palace, now the Prefettura, the Exchange, and municipal offices.

ENGLISH CHURCH, a little back from south side of Via degli Elisi, to which the Via Cairoli leads from south side of Piazza V. Emanuele. Interesting little cemetery by the church.

H. B. M.'s CONS.—M. Carmichael, Esq.

U. S. CONS.—F. Deedmeyer, Esq.

RAIL, pages 270, 270A, 271A.

Levanto.—*Stat.*—Pop. 3,000.

HOTELS: NAZIONALE; GRAND; SAVOY.

A pleasantly situated fortified old town, on the coast between Genoa and Spezia. Delightful winter residence, principally patronised by English visitors. Magnificent promenades under pine and olive trees. Sea bathing. Public gardens.

ENGLISH CHURCH SERV. in winter.

RAIL, p. 270.

Loreto.—*Stat.*—Pop. 1,178.

HOTELS: PELLEGRINO; GENELLI; ROMA.

A town of little more than a single street, whose only interest is the Chiesa della Casa Santa. The tradition is that the "house" at Nazareth, long venerated there, at a time of danger was miraculously conveyed to a place on the coast of Dalmatia, and later (three years) was again miraculously carried to its present situation, where a church was built over it.

The Chiesa della Casa Santa—Church of the Holy House—the second church built over the sacred deposit, was begun 1468, completed 1500. Good facade; in interior are reliefs, mosaics, and frescoes; under the dome, surrounded by a marble screen, is the Casa Santa, a simple stone house, 13½ ft. high, 28 ft. long, 12½ ft. deep. In the treasury are curiosities and valuables.

Opposite the church are the Jesuits' College and the Palazzo Apostolico—in the latter a small collection of pictures.

RAIL, page 285.

Lovere.—Pop. 3,500.

A busy little town at the north west end of the Lake of Iseo. Church of S. Maria in Valvendra, 15th cent., contains frescoes and other paintings; S. Giorgio church, 17th cent. A small collection of pictures at the Palazzo Tadini. Very fine view from the Santuario di San Giovanni, beyond the Convento dei Cappuccini. A tramway connects Lovere with Bergamo, in about two and a half hours.

STEAMERS on Lago d'Iseo, page 366.

Lucca.—*Stat.*—Pop. of the commune 76,160.

HOTELS: UNIVERSO; CROCE DI MALTA; CORONA; CAMPANA.

A pleasant town, the Roman Luca, situated in a fertile plain. Silk and woollen goods are manufactured; there is also a trade in oil.

From the RAILWAY STATION, on the south side of the city, the Duomo is seen towering above the ramparts.

The Duomo (S. Martino), dates from 1060, but has been several times restored, the Romanesque original receiving Gothic additions; imposing facade. Interior 91 yards long, 28 yards wide, transept 39 yards across; beautiful stained glass; elaborate pulpit, many paintings; specially fine monument of Noceto in right transept. In the Cappella del Santuario is a notable painting. Madonna with Saints Stephen and John, by Fra Bartolommeo. In the nave is a small marble chapel containing an ancient cedar wood crucifix made by St. Nicodemus and conveyed by a miracle from the Holy Land to Lucca in 782—shewn only three times a year; before the entrance is a solid gold candelabrum. A mosaic of Judgment of Solomon in pavement of nave.

Opposite north west corner of the Duomo is the Church of S. Giovanni, of 12th cent.; adjoining left transept is an ancient Baptistery. Church of S. Frediano, near the ramparts, one third mile due north of the Duomo, dating from 7th cent., has good frescoes. All the other churches are interesting.

Palazzo Provinciale, on west side of Piazza Napoleone, 100 yards west of the Duomo, contains the Picture Gallery; among several fine works two by Fra Bartolommeo are justly renowned—Madonna della Misericordia, and Mary Magdalen and Catherine of Siena in the Divine presence. Daily (Monday excepted), 10 to 2, 50c.

RAIL, pages 271A, 274A.

[About 15 miles north of Lucca, in a hilly country, are several villages collectively known as the **Bagni di Lucca**, one of the coolest summer residences in Italy, with springs varying in temperature from 98° to 130° Fahr.; the bath establishments are fitted with all modern appliances. At Ponte à Serraglio, 410 ft. above sea, the largest village, are HOTEL D'EUROPE, HOTEL NEW YORK, DES BAINS, a casino, and the Nuovo Ospedale, built by Prince Demidoff. Avenues of plane and chestnut trees lead up to Villa, 490 ft. above sea, where are HOTEL DU PARC, VICTOIRE, and a casino; rooms may be had. A mile further is Bagni Caldi (HOTEL DES THERMES), where are mud baths useful in cases of rheumatism and gout.

ENGLISH CHURCH SERVICE during season.

RAIL, page 274A.]

Luino.—*Stat.*—Pop. 3,800.

GRAND HOTEL SIMPLON-TERMINUS. — Well situated, with park, garden, and electric light. See Advt.

A busy little place on Lago Maggiore, on the frontier. Italian and Swiss customs examinations are made here. In Church of S. Pietro are frescoes.

RAIL, pages 259B, 269, 274, 367. Steamer, 366.

Macerata.—*Stat.*—Pop. of the commune, 22,940.

A picturesque busy little town, situated on hills between the Chienti and Potenza valleys. At the Church of San Giovanni are one or two good paintings; close by, in the Biblioteca Comunale, is a small collection of paintings with some antiquities and coins.

RAIL, pages 283, 285.

Mandela.—*Stat.*

A village 33½ miles from Rome, beyond Tivoli, whence the delightful valley of the Licenza is visited. The Sabine farm of Horace was in this valley, at a short distance from the village of Rocca Giovane.

RAIL, page 282.

Manfredonia.—*Stat.*—Pop. 8,500.

A quiet old town amidst luxurious vegetation; except a part of the old fortifications not anything remains of archeological interest, the Turks having destroyed everything in 1620. Two miles west of the town is the Cathedral of Santa Maria Maggiore di Siponto, a good example of Romanesque architecture.

BRITISH VICE-CONSUL.—F. Cafarelli, Esq.

RAIL, page 285B.

Mantua (*Ital.* Mantova).—*Stat.*—Pop. 32,657 (about one tenth Jews).

HOTELS: SENONER; AQUILA D'ORO.

The capital of a province, on the River Mincio, which here forms two lakes—Lago Superiore to west, Lago di Mezzo to east.

About a hundred yards south of the Railway Station is one end of the Corso Vittorio Emanuele leading east to Corso Umberto Primo, the busiest street, which, passing the Church of Sant'Andrea, continues to the Piazza Sordello, where is the Cathedral.

Sant' Andrea, a large building dating from 1472, has a wide portico, with an adjoining tower of red brick. Frescoes by Franc. Mantegna and Giulio Romano; other paintings; the Cappella S. Longino contains a sarcophagus bearing the inscription: "Longini ejus, qui latus Christi percussit, ossa."

Cattedrale (S. Pietro), not specially interesting; fine ceiling, and a few good paintings.

Opposite the Cathedral is the Reggia, once the ducal palace of the Gonzagas—in an upper room are portraits of the Gonzagas, frescoes in other rooms; a small picture gallery; fee 1 lira. A few yards north east, by the lake, is the Castello di Corte; frescoes by Mantegna, some obliterated; Renaissance Church of Santa Barbara (1565), by south side of the Castello; paintings.

Museo Civico, in the Palazzo degli Studi, short distance south of Piazza Sordello; sculpture, reliefs, and interesting antiquities; fee 50c. In the same building is the Library. Close by, a few yards east, is the Reale Accademia Virgiliana; here are the Museo del Risorgimento and the more important Museo Patrio.

Palazzo del Te, on south side of city—follow to end the street running south from Piazza delle Erbe, by Church of S. Andrea. The Palazzo, erected from designs by Giulio Romano (early 16th cent.), is decorated with frescoes and grotesques, fee 50c.

House of Giulio Romano, in Via Carlo Poma, opposite the Palazzo di Giustizia.

RAIL, pages 279C, 281, 282.

Menaggio.—*Stat.*—Pop. 1,700.

HOTEL VICTORIA.—Well and quietly situated, with large garden. Patronized by English. See Advt.

GRAND HOTEL MENAGGIO.—First class house, well situated on the shore of the Lake; garden. See Advt.

On the west shore at a central part of Lago di Como, in a beautiful situation, with a fine view of Bellagio and over the Lake. Silk is manufactured. South of the village, by the lake, is the attractive Villa Mylius. From the Villa Vigoni, on north side, are superb views.

ENGLISH CHURCH SERVICE.

GOLF.—9-hole course at Croce, $1\frac{1}{4}$ mile from Menaggio; club house; also 9-hole course at Dervio, with club house.

RAIL, page 367. Steamer page 365.

MILAN (*Ital.* **Milano**).—*Stat.*—Pop. of commune 599,200. *(Plan in Special Edition, or post free 3d. stamps).*

HOTEL CAVOUR.—First class, Place Cavour, opposite the public gardens. Good accommodation, moderate. See Advt.

HOTEL DE LA VILLE.—First class. Well situated; good rooms and excellent cuisine. On the Corso Vittorio Emanuele. Railway and Telegraph offices in the hotel. See Advt.

HOTEL MANIN.—Opposite the park, in the healthiest and most convenient part of the town. Lift, and central heating. See Advt.

GRAND HOTEL DE MILAN.—First class; close to Scala Theatre, etc., Cathedral and Galleries. Private suites. See Advt.

HOTEL DE L'EUROPE.—A select family hotel. Every modern comfort. See Advt.

HOTEL DU NORD and DES ANGLAIS.—Close to the Central Station. Every modern comfort; reasonable charges. See Advt.

HOTEL D'ITALIE.—Close to Central Station. Electric light, baths; garden; restaurant. See Adv.

HOTEL VICTORIA.—(Annexe of the HOTEL DU LION).—Lift; electric light; heated by American steam system. See Advt.

HOTEL EXCELSIOR AND SUISSE.—Near the Duomo and the Royal Palace. Electric light and steam heating. Rooms from 3 fr. Pension from 8.50 fr. See Advt.

PALACE; CONTINENTAL.

There are three Railway Stations at Milan. The Stazione Centrale, on the north side of the town, is the principal station; the Stazione Ferrovie Nord Milano, on west side of town, where the trains of the Nord Ry. arrive and depart; and the less important Stazione di Porta Ticinese, on south west side of town.

TAXIMETRO CABS, 80c. per 1,000 metri, 10c. for each 500 m. more. MOTOR CABS, 70c. per 400 m., and 10c. for each 200 m. more.

Electric Trams traverse the city in all directions. Steam Trams connect Milan with a wide stretch of country.

MILAN, the capital of Lombardy, on the small river Olona, is the most important commercial centre of Italy; great quantities of farm produce are exported; the silk trade is the largest in Europe, and the manufacture of woollen goods, machinery, railway rolling stock, and furniture are prominent industries.

On the south side of the broad open space before the Stazione Centrale, from the Porta Principe Umberti, the Via Principe Umberti leads towards the heart of the city. Continuing southward from the Via Principe along the Via Alessandro Manzoni, on the left, where the thoroughfare broadens out at the Piazza della Scala, any of the streets, or the splendid Galleria Vittorio Emanuele, conduct to the Duomo.

The magnificent CATHEDRAL covers an area of 14,000 square yards; the height of the dome is 223 ft., of the tower, 354 ft.; the pinnacles appear innumerable (there are 135): the statues decorating the exterior are stated to number about 2,300. The interior is 162 yards long, at the transept 96 yards broad, the nave is 151 ft. high; the stained-glass windows in the choir arrest attention—they are stated to be the largest in the world. The original architect is unknown, but several Italian, German, and French architects were, at different periods, associated with the building; the style is Gothic, with many variations; the building was begun in 1386, it was not consecrated until 1577, by San Carlo Borromeo; the dome, begun 1759, was finished in 1769; the facade was partly restored 1903-7. In a chapel in left aisle is a wooden crucifix carried by S. Carlo Borromeo, 1576, when ministering during the plague. There are many monuments, elaborate altars and altar pieces, and historic tombs. The Treasury contains valuable and interesting objects. In the subterranean Cappella S. Carlo Borromeo is the tomb of the saint; free until 10.0 a.m., after, 1 lr., to see relics of saint 5 lire. The roof and tower should be ascended for the view; ticket 25 c.—for the panorama of the Alps, 75 c.

In the Piazza del Duomo is an equestrian Statue of Victor Emmanuel II., with reliefs of Allies entering Milan after the battle of Magenta. On the north side of the Piazza is the Galleria Vittorio Emanuele, a handsome arcade. On the south side of the Piazza, a little to the east, is the Palazzo Reale (10.0 to 12.0, 1 lr.), frescoes and handsome saloons. To the east of the Duomo is the Palazzo Arcivescovile (Archbishop's Palace). A little beyond the north west corner of the Piazza del Duomo is the Piazza dei Mercanti, with the former Palazzo della Ragione (law courts) in the centre, and on the north side the towered Palazzo dei Giureconsulti.

A short distance west of the Piazza dei Mercanti, in the Via Dante, on the left, is the Via Meraviglia, this leads, following the street, distance less than mile, to the church of Santa Maria delle Grazie, where, to the west of the church (a door marked "Cenacolo Vinciano"), is the refectory of a suppressed monastery, containing the celebrated painting, "The Last Supper," by Leonardo da Vinci, restored 1908; other frescoes and paintings in same room; 9.30 a.m. until 4.30 p.m.; Sun., 10.0 a.m. to 1.0 p.m.; 1 lira.

The Via Caradosso, to east of S. Maria della Grazie, leads to Via Boccaccio, where turning to east, presently in an open space is seen the Stazione Nord Milano; here, any of the streets north lead to the Castello, where is the Museo Artistico, a collection of pictures, an Archaeological Museum, a Coin Collection, and an interesting Museo del Risorgimento Nazionale—a collection of patriotic objects.

On the east of the Castello the streets lead to the broad Foro Bonaparte, and here, on east side, the Via Tivoli leads to Via Fiori Chiari (both short streets), at the end of which is the Palazzo di Brera, where is the Picture Gallery, Library, and Observatory. Canova's statue of Napoleon I. is in the Court. The best known work in this famous collection is Raphael's "Sposalizio," in Room XXII; there are many rooms, ante-chambers, and vestibules; open daily, 9.0 a.m. to 3.0 p.m., 1 lr., free on Sun. from 9.0 until 12.0.

Other churches of Milan are S. Maurizio, on south side, east end, of Corso Magenta, about three quarters of a mile west of the Duomo—many paintings; Sant' Ambrogio, a mile west of the Duomo, of 12th cent., very interesting—many works of art, reliefs, etc. S. Lorenzo, a mile south west of the Duomo, the oldest church of Milan; S. Eustorgio, a little further south, very old; S. Satiro, in Via Torino, quarter mile south west from the Duomo; S. Alessandro, a little further south, is sumptuously decorated.

The Ospedale Maggiore, south east of the Duomo, one of the largest hospitals in Europe, is an extensive brick building of mixed Gothic and Renaissance architecture.

The Biblioteca Ambrosiana, off west side of Via Torino, a quarter mile south west of Piazza del Duomo, contains 250,000 vols. and 15,000 MSS.; many of the latter of great value; open daily, 10.0 a.m. to 4.0 p.m., 1 lr. In the Pinacoteca, in same building, are engravings and drawings.

Museo Poldi-Pezzoli, in Via Morone; valuable collections, including pictures, furniture, tapestry, weapons, armour, and antiquities. 9.0 to 4.0, 1 lr.

Museo Borromeo, quarter mile west of Duomo; paintings and sculpture. Tues. and Fri., 1.0 to 4.0; 50 c.

La Scala, the great theatre, is north of the Duomo, near north end of Galleria Vit. Emanuele.

The public gardens of Milan are the Giardini Publici, on north east side of city, near the Stazione Centrale, and the Parco, to the west, near the Castello.

The Cimitero Monumentale, to the north west, beyond the Porta Volta, is a beautiful cemetery; the guide expects a fee of 1 lr. 50 c.

POST OFFICE, Via della Posta, quarter mile west of the Duomo.

ENGLISH CHURCH SERVICE, All Saints Church, Via Solferino.

H.B.M.'s CONS.—J. H. Towsey, Esq.

U.S. CONSUL.—C. M. Caughy, Esq.

GAMBRINUS HALLE RESTAURANT. Café-Concert. Gallerie Vittorio Emanuele. RESTAURANT OROLOGIO, Piazza del Duomo. Good restaurants, moderate charges.

PRINCIPESSA JOLANDA HOSPITAL, Via Sassi, 4. English nurses.

DEPOT FOR BRADSHAW'S PUBLICATIONS.—Sacchi and Figli, Corso Venezia, 13.

RAIL, pp. 269, 269A, 272A, 274, 275, 279-80-81, 287, 288.

Misurina.—
HOTEL: GRAND.
A beautifully situated place, on the Lake of Misurina, 5,760 ft. above sea, close to the south Tyrol frontier of Austria, one of the most admired centres of the Dolomite region. The scenery all round is magnificent—lake, pine forests, and sharply defined variously tinted mountains. Motors travelling to Misurina via Schluderbach mount a gradient of about 1 in 4½, the road via Auronzo (coming from Venice) has a gradient of about 1 in 5. The rise does not exceed one mile in length each way.
DILIGENCE service, page 372.

Modena.—*Stat.*—Pop. of commune 70,923.
HOTELS: GRAND ROYAL; SAN MARCO.
The Roman Mutina, in a fertile situation between the River Secchia and River Panaro; capital of a province, seat of an archbishop, having a university.
A little east of the Railway Station, which is on the north side of the city, the broad Corso Vittorio Emanuele leads south to the Palazzo Reale (1634), formerly the Ducal Palace, now a military academy. On the south side of the Palazzo is the spacious Piazza Reale. Proceeding south for a quarter of a mile along one of the streets just away from the west side of the Piazza Reale, the Campanile, or La Ghirlandina, will indicate the site of the Duomo.
The Romanesque Duomo, 1099-1184, in the Piazza Grande, having rough carving upon the facade illustrative of the Creation and mankind of early ages, contains frescoes, monuments, choir stalls; in the crypt is the tomb of St. Germinianus. The adjoining Campanile, erected 1224-1319, is 335 ft. high; good view (50c.). The street running out from the south east corner of the Piazza Grande leads in two hundred yards to the University.
Church of S. Pietro, in extreme south east part of city, contains some fine groups in terra cotta (a branch of the sculptor's art specially studied at Modena in the middle ages).
The Albergo Arti is about a quarter mile due west of the Duomo. The Picture Gallery is on an upper floor (fee 1 lira). On lower floors are the Museo Civico (modern paintings, casts, collections of coins, medals, and antiquities) and the Biblioteca Estense (90,000 vols. and 3,000 MSS). In the Court is the Museo Lapidario (principally Roman remains).
Giardini Publici in north east quarter.
RAIL, pages 279, 282, 287.

Mondovi.—*Stat.*—Pop. 9,200.
Once a university town, 1560 to 1719, now industrial. At the cathedral of 15th cent. is a monument to Francesco Beccaria. Fine view of the Alps from the Belvedere.
RAIL, pages 273, 289.

Monselice.—*Stat.*—Pop. 3,600.
Picturesquely situated at the south east base of the Monte Euganei; old walls and a ruined castle. At Caoddo, two miles south of Monselice, is a famous private ornithological collection, the property of Count E. Arrigoni degli Oddi, which may be seen on application.
RAIL, pages 279A, 279C.

Monsummano.—*Stat.*
A small town on a height in the fertile valley of the Nievole. About two miles distant from Monsummano is the **Grotta Giusti**, a much frequented thermal resort possessing a natural sudatorium.
RAIL (Pieve Monsummano Station), page 271A, omnibus thence to the Grotta Giusti.

Montecatini Baths.—*Stat.*—
HOTELS: PACE; SALUS.
A favourite watering place, 100 ft. above sea, in the Val di Nievole, at the northern base of Monte Albano, 8 miles west of Pistoja. The sulphur chlorine and saline waters, for drinking and bathing, are successfully used in the treatment of digestive, stomach, and intestinal disorders, diabetes, obesity, gout, etc.; 60,000 visitors annually. The bathing establishments are handsome buildings with modern arrangements; at the Stabilimento Tettucio is a well supplied reading room, etc. Theatre and Casino. Shady walks. Funicular railway to Montecatini Alto.
MEDICAL. — Drs. Grocco, Casciani, Fedeli (English speaking).
RAIL, page 271A.

NAPLES (*Ital.* **Napoli**). — *Stat.* — Pop. of commune (1911) 678,031. (*Plan in Special Edition, or post free 3d. stamps*).
PARKER'S HOTEL.—First-class and comfortable hotel, beautifully situated. Corso Victor Emmanuel. See Advt.
BRISTOL HOTEL.—First class, in fine position. All modern comforts. Open all the year. Reasonable charges. See Advt.
GRAND HOTEL VICTORIA.—First class hotel, well situated on the Parthenope Quay. See Advt.
GRAND HOTEL DU VESUVE.—First class hotel, well situated on the new embankment (Quai Partenope), with fine view over the Bay; electric light; lift. See Advt.
BERTOLINI'S PALACE HOTEL.—First class in every respect. See Advt.
GRAND HOTEL SANTA LUCIA.—Situated on the new embankment, full south, with fine view of Bay and Vesuvius. Electric light. See Advt.
HOTEL ROYAL DES ETRANGERS.—First class hotel, well situated. Via Parthenope (New Embankment). See Advt.
In the lower part of the town and by the sea, are GRAND and SAVOY HOTELS; in the Corso Vittorio Emanuele, PALACE; in the Piazza Municipio, HOTEL DE LONDRES.

RAILWAY.—The principal Railway Station, Stazione Centrale, is on the east side of the town, two and a half miles from the district on the sea front at the west side, where is the "Strangers' Quarter."
TAXI CABS.

NAPLES, the most populous city of Italy, formerly the capital of the old Kingdom of Naples, situated at the base and on the slopes of an amphitheatre of hills, on the west side of a magnificent bay, is one of the most beautifully placed cities of the world, justifying the adage "vedi Napoli e poi mori!"—see Naples, and then die. The city lies in unequal parts on either side of the heights of Capodimonte, Sant' Elmo, and Pizzofalcone; the old and larger part, which is also the business centre, being to the east, the modern smaller district being to the west, both parts having a fine sea front on the Gulf of Naples. Though old Naples is still an intricacy of narrow streets, alleys, steep ascents, and lofty houses densely populated, much has been done to widen thoroughfares and to build more sanitary dwellings; in the west district, and on the heights where foreigners chiefly reside, there are good roads and handsome houses. The views from the beautiful roads climbing the hills are delightful. The general improvement includes an abatement of the former street noises and of the persistent begging.

Via Roma, formerly, and still often called, the Toledo, is the leading business thoroughfare, with its extensions traversing the city from south to north.

The DUOMO (Cathedral) of San Gennaro (St. Januarius), is in the Strada del Duomo, half a mile due west of the Stazione Centrale. It is a Gothic edifice, built 1272-1314; many times altered and restored. Many paintings and tombs. In third chapel of south aisle, the Chapel of St. Januarius, in the high altar, are vessels containing blood of the martyred saint, thrown to wild beasts A.D. 305; the "liquefaction" of the blood occurs thrice annually, on the first Saturday in May, on 19th Sept., and 16th Dec., the occasions being great religious functions. A door in left aisle (50c. when door is closed) leads to the Church of Santa Restituta, on the site of a temple of Apollo.

Other Churches are: Santa Chiara, in the Strada Santa Trinita, off east side, midway, of the Via Roma; 1310-1340; monument of Robert the Wise behind the high altar, reliefs, and paintings. Sant' Anna dei Lombardi, often called Monte Oliveto, also a little off east side, midway, of the Via Roma; 1411; paintings. San Domenico Maggiore, a little north of Santa Chiara, built 1289, a very fine Church with many monuments; Thomas Aquinas dwelt in the monastery here. Incoronata, in Strada Medina; 1352; frescoes. San Lorenzo, in Strada de Tribunali; 1266-1324. San Francesco di Paola, in Piazza del Plebiscito, opposite Royal Palace; high altar, paintings, statues. San Severo, Via San Severo; notable sculpture. Many other Churches, nearly 300; open from an early hour until noon, then closed until evening.

Palazzo Reale, Royal Palace, in Piazza del Plebiscito, at south end of Via Roma; open Sun. and Thurs. 11.0 to 4.0, during absence of royal family; grand staircase, throne room, banqueting room, pictures. Palazzo di Capodimonte, at end of north extension of Via Roma; gardens, pictures, sculpture. Tickets for Palazzo Reale include Capodimonte.

Museo Nazionale, on east side of northerly extension of Via Roma. Daily 10.0 to 6.0, 1 lira; Sun. 9.0 to 1.0, free. Collections of paintings, sculpture, antiquities from Herculaneum and Pompei, bronzes, weapons, papyri, coins, relics.

Museo Civico Filangieri, in the Palazzo Cuomo, west side and towards south end of Strada del Duomo. Tues. and Sat. 10.0 to 2.0, free, other days 50c. to 1 lira. Pictures, mosaics, antiques, weapons, gems, enamels.

Museo San Martino, by Castel Sant' Elmo, to west of middle of Via Roma. Daily, 10.0 to 4.0, 1 lira; Sun. 9.0 to 1.0, free. A suppressed Carthusian monastery with Church and Museum of interesting miscellaneous objects.

Museo Artistico Industriale, Via Paggeria. Daily 10.0 to 3.0, free. Exhibits from art schools furniture, pottery, carving, etc.

Museo Tesorone, Via Cariati; by permission of owner. Objects of art, medals, antiquities.

Acquario, Aquarium, in the Villa Nazionale, on west sea front, 2 lire. An institution of great value; very interesting.

Catacombs are behind the Church of San Gennaro, a short distance off west side of north extension of Via Roma. Daily, 10.0 to 1.0, 1 lira.

San Carlo Theatre, at south end of Via Roma, one of the largest theatres in Europe.

STREET SCENES.—The Rione Santa Lucia, on the sea front, almost in a line with the south end of Via Roma, is the fisher quarter. Here may be witnessed every variety of careless Neapolitan life. The Via Roma in the evening, is very animated. Near the Stazione Centrale, a little north west by Porta Capuana, reciters gather groups of listeners; also south of the Stazione, at the Villa del Popolo, the reciters are seen.

POST AND TELEGRAPH OFFICE, in Strada Montoliveto, short distance from east side, midway, of Via Roma.

ENGLISH CHURCH, Strada San Pasquale, Riviera di Chiaja.

BIBLE SOC. AGENT.—101, Strada di Chiaja.

H.B.M.'s. CONSUL.—S. J. A. Churchill, Esq., M.V.O. VICE-CONSUL.—A. Napier, Esq.

U.S. CONSUL.—W. W. Handley, Esq.

MEDICAL.—Dr. Eyre, 54, Via Chiatamone; Dr. A. Mallard, 7, Via Pontano.

INTERNATIONAL HOSPITAL.—Villa Bentinck, Corso Vittorio Emanuele; Dr. Scotti.

ENGLISH BANKERS AND STEAMSHIP AGENTS.—Messrs. Holme and Co., 24, Via Guglielmo Sanfelice. Agents for Lloyds.

Noted House for CORALS, LAVA, CAMEOS, TORTOISE SHELL. Achille Squadrilli, Piazza Vittoria. Opposite the entrance of the Villa Nazionale. Established 1836.

NAPLES SOCIETY FOR THE PROTECTION OF ANIMALS. 2, Via Vittoria (opposite American Express Co., and 150 yards from Cook's). President, Princess Mele Barese (née Mackworth-Praed). Director, Carlo Calvello. Funds urgently needed.

DEPOT FOR BRADSHAW'S PUBLICATIONS.—Detken and Rocholl. Piazza Plebiscito.

RAIL, pp. 276, 277, 277A, 278, 285B, 286.

Vesuvius.—Tramway service from Naples to Pugliano, whence there is an electric railway to the funicular line climbing to the cone of Vesuvius—see page 286. An eruption causing widespread disaster and the loss of nearly 500 lives began on April 6th, 1906, continuing until April 11th. There were two streams of lava, the lesser in the direction of Terzigno, and the greater in the direction of Bosco Trecase, a town of about 10,000 inhabitants, which was almost entirely destroyed. The loss of life was principally due to dwellings being crushed by the weight of fallen cinders and ashes.

[The Island of **Ischia,** of volcanic origin, 15 miles from Naples, population 24,000, offers during summer delightful scenery and a pleasant climate.

Casamicciola.—Pop. 3,500. HOTEL PICCOLA SENTINELLA; SAUVE. Not the largest town of the island (Ischia, the capital, has a pop. of 7,000), but the most attractive, on the north side, on the slopes of Monte Epomeo. The warm alkaline and saline springs are much visited.

STEAMER daily from Naples.

Capri, the ancient Capreae, an island in the south part of the Gulf of Naples, 4 miles from the nearest mainland, is a favourite spring and autumn residence, and a retreat from Naples during the summer heat. Population of island about 6,000. On the east coast the cliffs rise abruptly from the sea, some to a height of 900 ft.; on the west the loftiest height is Monte Solaro, 1,920 ft. The island was a favourite resort of several Roman emperors, notably Tiberius (A.D. 27), remains of whose villas are to be seen in the north east corner of the island. The air is remarkably pure. From the Marina Grande, the landing place from the steamers, is a funicular railway up to the town of Capri (460 ft.); trains about every half hour. The tour of the island by boat takes from 3 to 4 hours, and costs from 8 to 10 lire.

The town of **Capri,** capital of the island, pop. 3,700, lies in a slight hollow. Church of Santo Stefano. In the Museo d'Arte is a small collection of paintings by Capri artists.

SPLENDID HOTEL.—New first class hotel, equipped with all up-to-date comforts. Reasonable terms. See Advt.

H.B.M.'S CONS. AGENT.—Harold Trower, Esq.

MEDICAL.—Dr. Cerio (speaks English).

Anacapri (pop. 2,375), 880 ft. above sea.

A delightful summer resort, about two miles from Capri by a winding road—one point overlooked by the Castello di Barbarossa, ruined in the 16th cent.; Churches of Sta. Sofia and S. Michele. The celebrated Blue Grotto (Grotta Azzurra) is on the coast immediately north of Anacapri—the visit is made by boat; from a low entrance, hardly 3 ft. high, the roof rises to 41 ft., and the water reaches the depth of nearly 50 ft.; best time to visit between 10 a.m. and 1.0 p.m. in summer.

ENGLISH CHURCH SERVICE in winter, at All Saints Church, Capri.

MEDICAL—Dr. Vincenzo Cuomo. Dr. med. chir. Fred. Green (English). Dr. med. Mich. Romano.

STEAMER from Naples, page 354. Row boats between Capri and Sorrento.]

Nepi.—Pop. 2,200.

The Etruscan Nepete, surrounded by mediæval walls and towers. Cathedral of 10th cent. Sculpture and inscriptions at the Palazzo Municipale. At the ruined Castello on east side of the town Lucrezia Borgia at one time lived.

Reached from Civita Castellana Station, p. 279.

Nervi.—*Stat.*—Pop. 3,500.

HOTEL EDEN.—First class hotel, exceptionally well situated in extensive grounds. Fine reception rooms. Orchestra; electric light. See Advt.

LE GRAND HOTEL (late Pension Anglaise).—In the midst of the large and charming Grapallo Park. Warm sea baths on every floor. All modern improvements. Garage. Table de regime. See Advt.

HOTEL PENSION VICTORIA.—First class family hotel, situated full south, with garden; close to the Station. Lift, electric light, central heating. Pension from 9 fr. See Advt.

EDEN; BRISTOL.

A much frequented picturesquely situated health resort about 7½ miles east of Genoa. It is regarded as the most favoured winter residence of the Riviera Levante; there is a little more rain and less dust than at several other places along the coast; orange, lemon, and olive groves abound. Mean winter temperature 52° Fahr. The grounds of some of the larger villas, accessible for small fee, have luxuriant vegetation. Fine views from the road leading up behind the town to St. Ilario Church and Monte Giugo (1,595 ft.). ENGLISH CHURCH SERVICE.

RAIL, page 270.

[**Bogliasco.**

About a mile east of Nervi; fine marine views. RAIL, page 270.]

Nola.—*Stat.*—Pop. 12,000.

A very ancient Campanian city, where it is stated, in the 5th cent., church bells were first introduced by a Bishop of Nola; on June 26th a festival is held in honour of the event. Nola was also famed for its plastic art—vases, etc.

RAIL, pages 277A, 286.

Oropa.—
A pleasantly situated bathing resort among the mountains, six miles north west of Biella. Hydropathic Establishment. Pilgrimage church of Madonna d'Oropa, 3,870 ft.
Reached by diligence from Biella, page 373.

Orta.—*Stat.*—Pop. 1,100.
GRAND HOTEL BELVEDERE.—In excellent position, overlooking the lake and mountains. Open from April to October. Pension from 8 lire. See Advt.
A pleasant little town on the east bank of the Lago d'Orta, at the base of Monte d'Orta, or Sacro Monte, 1,315 ft. Piazza facing the lake; numerous villas. On the Sacro Monte are twenty chapels in honour of St. Francis d'Assisi, with illustrative frescoes and groups; fine views all the way up with extensive panorama from the Campanile at the summit. Opposite the town is the Isola San Giulio, where is interesting old church. RAIL, page 274A.

Ortona.—*Stat.*—Pop. 12,000.
HOTEL PROGRESSO.
A very old seaport town on a lofty promontory. Interesting cathedral. Ruined fort. Fine views towards the south.
RAIL, page 285.

Orvieto.—*Stat.*—Pop. 7,300.
HOTEL BELLE ARTI (ancient Bisenzi Palace).—First class, near the celebrated Cathedral. Every modern comfort; pension from 8 fr. See Advt.
An old town, 1,165 ft. above sea, on a height, the site of Volsinii, one of the capitals of the Etruscan League. From the Station, to north east, a short cable tramway up to the entrance to the town, whence, to left, runs the Corso Cavour. A little south of the Corso, one third mile from town entrance, is the Duomo, dating from 1285, one of the best of Italian Gothic churches; upon the facade are mosaics and sculpture; the paintings in the interior are very fine, miraculous image of the Virgin in the Cappella Nuova, in the Cappella del Corporale is a reliquary containing the blood stained chalice cloth of the "Bolsena Miracle" (miraculous appearance to a priest in 1263 of proof of the doctrine of transubstantiation).
Museo Municipale in the Palazzo dei Papi, a few yards south west of the Duomo; collections of Etruscan pottery, bronzes, etc.
The Etruscan Necropolis is just outside the north west corner of the town; the tombs are mostly of 5th cent. B.C. RAIL, page 279.

Ospedaletti.—
HOTELS: REINE; ROYAL; RIVIERA.
Beautifully situated between San Remo and Bordighera, this charming, well sheltered little winter resort is preferred by many English travellers. ENGLISH CHURCH SERVICE.
RAIL, page 272.

Padua (Padova).—*Stat.*—Pop. 96,230.
HOTELS: FANTI STELLA D'ORO; CROCE D'ORO.
The principal RAILWAY STATION is on the north side of the city, three quarters of a mile from the centre. S. Sofia Station, for local lines to Fusina and Venice, and Bagnoli, is on the east side, one third mile from centre. From the west side of the principal Railway Station follow the street going south—it leads to the Piazza dell' Unita d'Italia and the Duomo; or, not proceeding so far as the Duomo, turn east with the tram lines into Via Garibaldi—the continuation of this street leads to Piazza Cavour, the busiest place.
Padua, the ancient Patavium, capital of a province, is situated on the River Bacchiglione, which streams in several channels among the narrow winding, often arcaded, streets of the city. Learning (the University) and Art (Andrea Mantegna and other masters) rendered the city famous during the middle ages.
In the Piazza dell' Unita d'Italia is the Loggia del Consiglio, an arcade above some steps; on the west side of the Piazza is the Palazzo del Capitano. A few yards south of the Piazza is the Duomo, of 16th cent., with a brick Baptistery of 12th cent. adjoining. One hundred and fifty yards due east of the Piazza dell' Unita d'Italia are the Piazza dei Frutti and the Piazza delle Erbe, and between them is the Palazzo della Ragione, usually named the Salone, after its large hall, which is decorated with frescoes; fee 50c. The University is in Via Otto Febbraio, a little east of the Salone.
The Church of Sant' Antonio of Padua, generally known as Il Santo, of great interest. is in the south east part of the city, half a mile south east of the Duomo. It is an immense building with seven domes, is 126 yards long, transept 60 yards broad, 123 ft. high at the cross; begun 1232, completed 1424, the style being an attempted union of Byzantine with Gothic; in interior are frescoes and monuments, high altar in choir, the Cappella del Santo, in left transept contains the remains of St. Anthony under the altar; cloisters; in the sanctuary is a collection of plate and curios. On the south side of the church (a staircase gives access) is the Biblioteca Antoniana; 30,000 vols., many MSS.; also collections of pictures, medals, etc. The statue of Gattamelata, in front of church, has special interest, as being one of the earliest (1453) bronze castings of modern times. Immediately south west of the church is the Scuola del Santo, decorated with frescoes (three by Titian) of scenes in life of St. Anthony. In the adjoining Cappella S. Giorgio are several frescoes. The Museo Civico on the south side of the range of buildings, contains a Picture Gallery, collection of antiquities, the Library, and the Archives.
Church of Santa Giustina, at south east corner of the spacious Piazzo Vittorio Emanuele, at extreme south east part of the city; extensive structure, dating from 1501; the high altar covers the tomb of the saint; paintings, carving.
In the north east part of the city, to the left when coming from the Railway Station, in an open situation, are the Augustine Church of the Eremitini (13th cent.) and the Chapel of Madonna dell' Arena, the most famous examples of Padua art being found in both edifices; in the church are the celebrated frescoes by Andrea Mantegna, in the chapel the still more celebrated frescoes by Giotto, with other paintings and some sculpture.
RAIL, pages 279A, 280, 286, 288.

[At **Stra**, 7 miles from Padua, is the Villa Pisani, once the property of the Pisani family, bought by Napoleon I for Eugène Beauharnais, now belonging to the State; decorated rooms, beautiful garden. RAIL, page 286.]

Pallanza.—*Stat.*—Pop. 6,865.

GRAND EDEN HOTEL.—Beautifully situated, facing the Borromean Islands. Comfortably furnished. Garage. See Advt.

GRAND HOTEL AND HOTEL PALLANZA.—First class, beautifully situated. With extensive grounds. Overlooking the Lake. See advt.

SIMPLON HOTEL.—New hotel, equipped with every modern comfort. Moderate charges. Swiss management. See Advt.

A busy little town, in a delightful situation on Lago Maggiore, in full view of the Borromean Islands. Cool and bracing in summer, warm in winter, fog and snow are unknown; climate favourable in cases of rheumatism and nervous debility. Churches of S. Leonardo, near quay, and Madonna di Campagna (frescoes), at the base of Monte Rosso (3,270 ft.). There is a short electric railway between Pallanza and Fondo Toce station on the Simplon line from Lausanne to Milan; the service connects with the express trains in both directions.

ENGLISH CHURCH SERVICE.

RAIL, p. 274.

STEAMERS, page 366; Diligence, p. 374.

Palazzo Pignano.

A pleasant little place, 6¼ miles from Crema, where is a highly interesting church recently restored in its original pure Lombard style. Columns carved with biblical symbols supposed to be anterior to the 10th century; ceiling and façade.

Reached by automobile from Crema.

Parma.—*Stat.*—Pop. of commune 51,910.

HOTELS: CROCE BIANCA; LA MARINA; ITALIE.

The RAILWAY STATION is at the north side of the city, about half a mile distant from the Duomo.

Parma, capital of a province, formerly capital of the Duchy of Parma, is situated on the River Parma, an affluent of the River Po. It is a place of very old foundation, but presents a quite modern appearance.

From immediately east of the Railway Station the Strada di Colorno, continuing into the Strada Garibaldi, runs south into the city, the River Parma flowing in a parallel line on the west. At about mid distance of its length the Strada Garibaldi opens out into the Piazza della Prefettura, the Duomo being about a hundred yards due east. The Prefettura, in the Piazza, is the old ducal Farnese Palace.

The Duomo (Cathedral), 11th-13th cent., is Lombard-Romanesque; in interior are several frescoes, that on the Dome, the Assumption, is by Correggio; in the crypt are monuments. Opposite the south west corner of the Duomo is the octagon Battistero (Baptistery), 12th-13th cent.; carving upon portals. Just away from the east end of the Duomo is the Renaissance Church of S. Giovanni Evangelista, 1510-1614; among the frescoes in interior that in the dome and the St. John in the sacristy archway, north transept, are by Correggio. Other churches are Madonna della Steccata, near south end of Strada Garibaldi, with frescoes (here is the tomb of Count Neipperg, died 1829, who married the Empress Marie Louise after the death of Napoleon), and S. Antonio and San Sepolcro, in Corso Vittorio Emanuele, at east side of city.

Palazzo della Pilotta, between the river and the west side of the Piazza della Prefettura, contains collections of paintings, antiquities, and a library. In the Picture Gallery are several works by Correggio; besides the old masters there are modern paintings. In the Museo d'Antichità is a rich collection of coins. The Library contains 200,000 vols. and 4,500 MSS. In the Convento di S. Paolo, in Borgo del Parmigianino, fifty yards north west of the Duomo, are some greatly admired frescoes by Correggio. In each case a fee of 50c. or 1 lira is expected.

The University, dating from 16th cent., a little beyond the south end of Strada Garibaldi, contains an interesting Zoological collection.

Giardino Pubblico, formerly the ducal garden, is on the west bank of the River Parma, opposite the Palazzo della Pilotta.

In the Piazza Garibaldi, a few yards east of the south end of Strada Garibaldi, are the Palazzo del Governo and the Palazzo Municipale.

POST OFFICE, east side of Piazza della Prefettura.

RAIL, pages 275, 279, 281, 288.

Pavia.—*Stat.*—Pop. of commune 39,898.

HOTELS: CROCE BIANCA; TRE RE.

The Roman Ticinum, now capital of the Province of Pavia, on the River Ticino. The Railway Station is on the west side of the city. From the Porta Cavour, a few yards south of the Station, the Corso Cavour leads in half a mile to the centre at the Piazza Grande, Just east of the Piazza Grande is the Corso Vittorio Emanuele, traversing the city north and south.

The Duomo is a few yards from the south side of the Piazza Grande. Dating from 1486, the edifice has never been completed. Church of San Michele, quarter mile south east of Piazza Grande; Romanesque, old reliefs on facade. Church of San Teodoro, to west in same line of street with S. Michele: frescoes. S. Pietro, in north part of city, dating from 1100, restored; in interior is an elaborate Arch of St. Augustine.

University, 15th cent., on east side of Corso Vittorio Emanuele, just away from the Piazza Grande. At the north end of the Corso is the Castello, and at the south end is the 14th cent. covered bridge across the river.

Museo Civico in the Palazzo Malaspina, 200 yards north of Piazza Grande; a picture gallery, collections of engravings, antiquities, etc.

RAIL, pages 269A, 273, 274A, 281, 288.

[Five miles north of Pavia is the Carthusian Monastery, the **Certosa di Pavia**, of great extent, one of the finest specimens of Gothic architecture in Italy; it is now State property. The facade is specially admired; interior contains many paintings, reliefs, monuments; cloisters; small dwellings of the monks. Free on Sunday, other days 1 lira 30c. RAIL from Pavia 269A.]

Pegli.—*Stat.*—**Pop. 6,100**

HOTEL MEDITERRANEE; PENSION FORBES.

A pleasant summer sea bathing and winter resort, about six miles west of Genoa, with a very equable climate. Beautiful walks in the wooded valleys and on the hill sides. To visit the Villa Doria a permit must be obtained at Palazzo Doria, Genoa. Villa Pallavicini, fee 1 lira; numerous objects of interest in the grounds, many tropical plants and trees cultivated.

ENG. CHURCH SERVICE at St. John's Church.

RAIL, p. 272.

Perugia.—*Stat.*—Pop. of the commune 65,805.

GRAND HOTEL BRUFANI.—Unique position. Splendid view from every room; modern comfort; lift. Terms moderate. See Advt.

PALACE HOTEL.—Modern hotel with moderate terms. Full south; splendid view. Garage. See Advt.

The Railway Station is south west of the city, a mile from the centre. Electric tram from Station.

Perugia, capital of the Province of Umbria, is picturesquely situated on hills 985 ft. above the valley of the Tiber; in summer the air is pleasantly cool; good drinking water. Many buildings still remain of the 14th and 15th cent., the days of greatest prosperity, and these, with the fame of the Umbrian school of painting, of which Perugino was the chief, make Perugia most interesting.

The road from the Station ascends in curves to the Porta Nuova; at an early bend pedestrians will find a path shortening the distance. From the Porta Nuova the street runs north to the Piazza Vittorio Emanuele, where, from the north west corner, the wide Corso Vanucci leads to the Cathedral. In the Piazza Vittorio is the Prefettura; from the garden terrace is a very fine view.

Cattedrale di S. Lorenzo, Gothic, 15th cent.; in the Cappella S. Bernardino is a celebrated Descent from the Cross by Baroccio, other paintings, carved stalls, tombs of Popes; in the Library are MSS., including the Codex of St. Luke, of 6th cent. The fountain on the Piazza, Fontana Maggiore, dates from 1277.

Opposite the Cattedrale, at the corner of the Piazza and the Corso Vanucci, is the Palazzo del Municipio, built 1281-1333. On an upper floor is the Pinacoteca Vanucci, a picture gallery containing many examples of Umbrian art—the finest works are in the Sala del Pinturicchio. Open 9.0 to 3.0, 1 lira. In the same building is the Biblioteca Comunale of 70,000 vols., also rare MSS. of 11th-15th cent. A few yards south of the Palazzo Municipio, on same side of the Corso Vanucci, is the Collegio del Cambio, containing notable frescoes by Perugino (his name was Pietro Vanucci); open morning and afternoon, 50c.

Oratorio di S. Bernardino, one third mile due west of the Cattedrale, has a superb polychrome facade. Church of S. Domenico, half mile south of Cattedrale, in Corso Cavour, contains celebrated monument of Pope Benedict XI; half mile further south is Church of S. Pietro de' Cassinensi, erected early in 11th cent.—several good paintings, carved choir stalls. All the other churches should be visited.

The University, founded 1320, is in north part of city; collections of Etruscan and Roman antiquities; daily except Mon., 1 lira.

ENGLISH CHURCH SERVICE in Church of St. George, on premises of Hotel Brufani. Services (8.30, 11.0, 4.30), from Sept. until Nov. and Feb. until May.

RAIL, page 283.

[About 3 miles south of Perugia, near Ponte S. Giovanni (station, p. 283) is the ANCIENT ETRUSCAN NECROPOLIS of Perugia.]

Piacenza.—*Stat.*—**Pop.** 38,542.

HOTEL SAN MARCO.

Capital of a province, one third mile south of River Po. From the Railway Station, on east side, the Duomo is half a mile due west.

The Duomo, 12th cent., Lombard-Romanesque, has good frescoes. 250 yards south west of Duomo is Church of S. Antonino, 12th cent., with fine vestibule. S. Sisto, in north part of city, has paintings; the Sistine Madonna, the masterpiece by Raphael, painted for this church, is now at Dresden. S. Maria di Campagna, at extreme north west, has good frescoes.

RAIL, pages 273, 279.

Pinerolo.—*Stat.*—Pop. 12,600.

A little town of considerable importance in the middle ages. Cathedral of 11th cent.; at the Church of San Maurizio are tombs of eight princes of Savoy, 1334-1490.

RAIL, page 271.

Pisa.—*Stat.*—Pop. of the commune 65,232

GRAND HOTEL and DE LONDRES.—First class; full south; private baths; good cuisine, moderate prices. See Advt.

Other Hotels: HOTEL NETTUNO, modern. Near the station, with moderate tariff, HOTEL MINERVA

The RAILWAY STATION is on the south side of the city, half a mile from the quays along the Arno, the liveliest district, and about a mile from the Duomo.

Electric Tram service.

Pisa—the Pisae of the Romans—is situated on both banks of the River Arno, about 6 miles distant from the sea; it is the capital of a province, the seat of an archbishop, and possesses a university. The mild equable winter climate is favourable in cases of throat disease; average winter temperature 46°.

From the Railway Station, across the spacious Piazza Vittorio Emanuele, the Via Vittorio Emanuele leads northward to the Arno, and, if the line of thoroughfare be followed as it traverses the city, at the far end, after a turn westward, the Duomo will be found.

The Romanesque Duomo, of white marble with black and coloured lines, erected 1063-1118, is 104 yards long and 35½ yards wide, having a dome over the intersection. Imposing facade; upon the doors Biblical scenes are represented. Many fine paintings and frescoes in interior; in right transept is the ornate Cappella di S. Ranieri; elaborate high altar; carved choir stalls.

The circular Battistero, just west of the Duomo, 1153-1278, has a celebrated pulpit, with reliefs. The acoustic properties of the cupola are such that the custodian by intoning four notes will produce the sweetest sounds of an organ, lasting about a minute.

At the Church of Santo Stefano ai Cavalieri, built 1565-96, are very interesting old flags, war trophies, Turkish, Moorish, Arabian, and others, the designs and needlework being remarkable.

The Campanile, generally known as the Leaning Tower, by the east end of the Duomo, is 179 ft. high and 13 ft. out of the perpendicular. Begun 1174, finished 1350. Beautiful view (30 c.).

The Campo Santo is on the north side of the Duomo. Archbishop Ubaldo dè Lanfranchi caused 53 ship loads of earth to be brought here from the Holy Land in 1203, the burial place of holy ground being afterward inclosed by pillars and arches. Upon the walls are remains of frescoes; many monuments and much sculpture. Sunday, free; other days 1 lira.

The University (La Sapienza) is a little back from the river (north side) at the centre of the city. Founded in 12th cent.; present building erected 1493; about 1,000 students; Galileo was teacher of mathematics here in 1610. Library of 120,000 vols.

Museo Civico, in cloisters of Church of S. Francesco, on east side of city; collections of early Tuscan painting and sculpture.

POST OFFICE, on the quay, south side of river, 100 yards west of Ponte di Mezzo.

ENGLISH CHURCH, south end (near river) of Via Solferino.

MEDICAL. — Dr. Charles Layfield, Via St. Cecilia, No. 18.

RAIL, pages 270, 270A, 271A.

[About six miles from Pisa on the road to Leghorn, by S. Rossore, is the very interesting Church of S. Pietro in Grado, erected in 10th cent., on the traditional spot where St. Peter first landed in Italy.]

Pistoja.—*Stat.*—Pop. 13,400.

HOTEL GLOBO.

A pleasant place, cool in summer, in a fertile country. From the Station the street leads north into the city, at Piazza Cino the thoroughfare bends to left, and then the first street to right, Via Orari, leads to the Duomo.

The Duomo, of 12th cent., has a terracotta relief over principal entrance; in interior are paintings and reliefs, in Cappella S. Jacopo is a silver altar of 13th-14th cent. (about 450 lbs. of silver used). Opposite the Duomo is the Battistero, 1316, with pulpit on exterior. At the west corner of the Piazza is the Palazzo Pretorio, 14th cent., containing the law courts; on other side of Piazza, east, is the Palazzo del Comune, with a small picture gallery A few yards north west of the Palazzo de Comune is the Ospedale del Ceppo, ornamented with fine frieze of reliefs in terracotta.

Church of S. Andrea, in Via S. Andrea, quarter mile north west of the Duomo, of 12th cent., with a pulpit having several reliefs. 100 yards west is Church of S. Francesco al Prato, with frescoes. Other churches are S. Giovanni, in Via Cavour (pulpit and terracotta group), and S. Domenico, in Corso Umberto Primo.

RAIL, pages 271A, 279.

Pompei.—*Stat.*

HOTELS: DIOMEDE; GRAND; SUISSE.

The entrance to the ruined city is about 200 yards from the Station; on Thursday admittance is free, but guides are not provided; on other days a 2 lr. 50c. fee is charged, which does not include the guide (one speaking English should be requested—usual fee 2 lr. per hour). Persons offering services outside the entrance should be disregarded. Visitors are admitted from 7.0 a.m. to 6.0 p.m., four or five hours are required for even a superficial visit, two or three visits are really necessary, and it is hardly worth the trouble entailed to the mere passer-by who has not previously given attention to the subject.

Previously in part destroyed, but rebuilt, the final catastrophe occurred on August 24th, 79, the town, buried under 20 feet of earth, lying unknown during the middle ages; in 1748 accidental discoveries by a peasant led to excavations, which since 1860 have been systematic. It is assumed that the labour of clearing will extend to the middle of the 20th century, and cost about five million lire.

RAIL, page 277.

Porto Maurizio.—*Stat*—Pop. of the commune 7,853.

HOTEL: PALACE.

Finely situated winter resort, on a wooded promontory; olive groves everywhere. Domed church; public garden. RAIL, page 272.

Pracchia.—*Stat.*

Pracchia, 2,020 ft. above sea, is the starting place for the ascent of the Corno alle Scale, 6,380 ft. From Pracchia there is an omnibus, 5½ hours, to Boscolungo, finely situated in the forest, whence the ascent is made of Monte Cimone, 7,103 ft., the highest point of the Northern Apennines.

RAIL, page 279.

Rapallo.—*Stat.*—Pop. 7,500.

An ancient seaport and modern favourite winter resort in a beautiful situation at the head of the Golfo di Rapallo. The climate is very pleasant, the heights to north and west protecting from cold winds. Attractive Public Gardens and Kursaal (concerts). A small trade in olive oil and lace. The district abounds with pleasant points of view. On Monte Rosa, to the north east, is the pilgrimage church of Madonna di Montallegro, 2,015 ft., a walk of 2½ hours—magnificent view.

ENGLISH CHURCH SERV. at St. George's Ch.

MEDICAL.—Dr. W. Winslow.

RAIL, see p. 270.

[**Zoagli.**—*Stat.*—

NAVE HOTEL.—First class. Recently opened. Situated full south, fine view. All latest improvements. Pension from 7 frs. See Advt.

Zoagli, 2½ miles from Rapallo. Prettily situated amongst olive groves. Noted for its healthy climate. There are many beautiful walks in the neighbourhood; a statue of Canevaro, founder of the hospital; a silk manufactury.

RAIL. page 270].

Ravenna.—*Stat.*—Pop. of commune 71,581.

ROYAL HOTEL SAN MARCO. — Completely renovated and enlarged. 70 bed rooms and suites with baths. Central heating. Electric light. Lift. Auto garage. See Advt.

BYRON; ROME.

An ancient place, in a plain between the Rivers Montone and Ronco, historically of great importance, and again likely to become one of the first seaports of the Adriatic, the Government having been granted 20,000,000 lire for the necessary works. For monuments of early Christianity it is regarded as second in interest only to Rome; the bishopric was founded, it is stated, in A.D. 44 by St. Apollinaris, disciple of St. Peter.

Immediately before the RAILWAY STATION, on the east side of the city, is the spacious Piazza Farini, whence the broad Viale Farini runs westward, continuing in the narrower Via Luigi Carlo Farini to the Piazza Vittorio Emanuele, the central point. On the west side of the Piazza is the Palazzo Municipale, behind which is Piazza Venti Settembre, whence Via Gioacchino Rasponi leads south west to the Duomo.

The Duomo of Sant' Orso, built 1734-44, stands on the site of a church of the 4th cent., of which the bell tower and crypt are the only remains; in interior are several sarcophagi of early Christian saints and bishops; frescoes. By the north west side of the Duomo is the octagonal Baptistery, A.D. 449-452, having very old mosaics in the cupola. Palace of the Archbishop a few yards from east end of the Duomo; on first floor is the Chapel of St. Petrus Chrysologus, of 5th cent.

Accademia delle Belle Arti, 150 yards due east of the Duomo, at corner of Via Alfredo Baccarini; collections of pictures, sculpture, and mosaics; 50 c. A little south of the Accademia, on same side of the Via Baccarini, in a secularised monastery, is the Biblioteca Comunale, containing 80,000 vols. and 800 MSS.—among the curiosities are a prayer book of Mary Queen of Scots and a visitors' book from Dante's Tomb.

Church of San Francesco, east side of Piazza Byron, 200 yards due east of the Duomo, just east of the Accademia; ancient foundation, rebuilt 1793; monuments and sarcophagi. By north side of the church is the Tomb of Dante (died 1321), a domed square building.

Sant' Apollinare Nuovo, in Corso Giuseppe Garibaldi, quarter mile due east of S. Francesco. Erected 500 as an Arian Cathedral, 60 years later adapted to Roman services; despite restoration the interior preserves its early Christian appearance.

Church of S. Vitale, of 6th cent., with 17th cent. campanile, quarter mile north west of Piazza Vittorio Emanuele, on the site of the martyrdom of St. Vitalis; an octagonal church, 38 yards in diameter; mosaics; altar of translucent alabaster. A few yards north is the Mausoleum of Galla Placidia (Roman empress, A.D. 440), beautified with mosaics; sarcophagi.

The Museo Nazionale is in the cloisters of San Vitale; interesting collection of Roman antiquities, etc.

All the other churches are interesting

Mausoleum of Theodoric the Great, known as the Rotonda, half mile north east of the Railway Station. A 10-sided building, erected about 520, the dome being one stone 36 ft. in diameter; the "remains" were scattered at the adaptation of the structure to Catholic uses.

Church of Sant' Apollinare in Classe, three miles south east. Continue south along the Corso Giuseppe Garibaldi, leaving the city by the Porta Nuova; or train to Classe station. Erected middle of 6th cent., restored 18th cent., the largest of the basilica churches of Ravenna; mong o ther objects in interior are portraits of bishops from A.D. 74. Behind the cloisters of Sant' Apollinare are some remains of the Palace of Theodoric; close by are remains of the Palace of the Exarchs. The Pine Forest of Ravenna, the subject of several poems, begins about two miles east of the church.

RAIL, pages 279A, 283, 286.

Recoaro.

The Baths of Recoaro, 1,460 ft. above sea, are in a very fine situation, on a hill, about 26 miles north of Vicenza. About 8,000 visitors; season June to September. Attractive mountain excursions.

Reached by tramway from Vicenza to Valdagno, thence 6 miles by diligence. There is also a good road from Rovereto to Recoaro, page 371.

Reggio (Emilia).—*Stat.*—Pop. of the commune 70,419.

The ancient Regium Lepidi. At the centre of the rather poor town is the Cathedral, dating from 12th cent., with three or four partial rebuildings; on the west side of the piazza by the Cathedral, is the house where it is said the poet Ariosto (1474—1533) was born. The Church of Madonna della Ghiara, 16th cent., has a beautiful and interesting interior. Museo, with natural history and other collections; the Biblioteca Municipale contains about 56,000 vols. and 1,000 MSS.

RAIL, pages 279, 286.

[At **Canossa**, about 7 miles from Reggio, on the summit of a rock, are ivy-clad ruins of a castle where in 1077 the Emperor Henry IV did penance during three days in the presence of Pope Gregory VII; magnificent view. Other ruined castles in the neighbourhood.]

Reggio (di Calabria).—*Stat.*—Pop. of the commune 43,162.

The ancient Rhegium, on the Straits of Messina, a town that was almost entirely destroyed by earthquake and tidal wave on December 28th, 1908.

H.B.M.'s VICE-CONSUL.—E. Briglia, Esq.

RAIL, pages 277A, 278.

Regoledo.

GRAND HOTEL.

A finely situated health resort, 500 ft. above Lake Como, about half a mile from Bellano.

RAIL (to Bellano) page 281; Steamer, page 365.

Rieti.—*Stat.*—Pop. 16,800.

The ancient Reate, on the River Velino, once the chief city of the Sabines; a few inscriptions at the Municipio are all that remain of the ancient place. 15th cent. Cathedral.

RAIL, page 285B.

Rimini.—*Stat.*—Pop. of the commune 43,203.

HOTELS: GRAND; AQUILA D'ORO.

The ancient Ariminum, finely situated on the Adriatic, where the two Rivers Ansa and Marecchia flow into the sea.

From the Station, on the side nearest the sea, a broad thoroughfare leads into the heart of the city to the Corso d' Augusto and Piazza Cavour, where is the Palazzo del Comune on the west side (small picture gallery) and the theatre in the middle. South east along the Corso d' Augusto is the Piazza Giulio Cesare, the ancient forum—the pedestal is a memorial of the passage of the Rubicon by Cæsar; still further along the street is the Porta Romana, a triumphal arch erected to Augustus, B.C. 27. At extreme north west end of the Corso is Ponte d' Augusto, across the River Marecchia, a fine example of ancient work.

The Duomo is a few yards north of the Piazza Giulio Cesare. Gothic of 13th cent., remodelled in Renaissance style, 1447-55; tombs of the Malatesta family. lords of Rimini.

RAIL, pages 279A, 285.

[**San Marino,** a diminutive republic of 32 square miles and 10,489 population, is about 12 miles from Rimini. The town (ALBERGO DEL TITANO) is on a rock (820 ft.) in a bare country. Small Cathedral, Palazzo del Governo, and museum with picture gallery. Diligence from Rimini, page 374.]

Ripafratta.—*Stat.*

A small place between Lucca and Pisa, at the base of the beautiful Monte San Giuliano, mentioned by Dante.

RAIL, page 271A.

ROME (*Ital.* **Roma**).—*Stat.*—Pop. of commune (1911) 542,123. *(Plan in Special Edition, or post free stamps 6d.).*

HOTEL DU QUIRINAL.—Situated in healthiest part of Rome, close to new Opera House and American Church, patronised by English and American families. See Advt.

HOTEL REGINA.—Very first class fashionable hotel. Situated in the finest part of the town, opposite Palazzo Margherita. See Advt.

HOTEL DE RUSSIE.—First class, quiet and central. Large garden. See Advt.

THE SELECT HOTEL.—New hotel de luxe, on the new boulevard connecting Piazza Barberini and Piazza Colonna. Every luxury, no rooms without private bath and toilet. See Advt.

GRAND CONTINENTAL HOTEL.—Large first class hotel, facing the Central Railway Station. Very comfortable; up to date equipments. Arrangements made for long stay. See Advt.

SAVOY HOTEL.—First class family hotel, situated 15, Via Ludovisi. Hydraulic lift, electric light, and bathrooms. See Advt.

MAJESTIC HOTEL (late Hotel Suisse).—Via Veneto, near Piazza Barberini. With every modern comfort. Quiet; full south. See Advt.

BERTOLINI'S SPLENDID HOTEL.—Modern first class establishment, with Italian and French restaurant. See Advt.

MODERN HOTEL.—First class hotel, situated near the Trevi Fountain and Central Post Office. Electric light; lift; central heating. See Advt.

HOTEL IMPERIAL.—Modern hotel. Electric lift; steam heating Apartments with private baths. See Advt.

HOTEL WINDSOR.—Situated Via Veneto (Ludovisi Quarter). Lift; electric light; central heating. See Advt.

GRAND HOTEL DE LA MINERVE.—Centrally situated; electric light; lift; baths. See Advt.

GRAND HOTEL DE L'EUROPE.—First class, in the healthiest part of the town, with modern comfort. French restaurant. See Advt.

HOTEL BETHELL.—(Palazzo Sterbini), 41, Via Babuino, Piazza di Spagna. Lift; electric light and steam heating throughout. Rooms from 3 lire. Pension from 8 lire. See Advt.

THE GRAND HOTEL FLORA.—New first class hotel, in fine position (Via Veneto, opposite Villa Borghese Gardens). 450 beds. Suites with bath, etc. Rooms from 5 fr. See Advt.

HOTEL WESTMINSTER AND METROPOLE.—Via S. Nicola da Tolentino. Electric light; central heating throughout. Pension terms from 10 lire. See Advt.

HOTEL LAGO MAGGIORE.—Good second class hotel, opposite the Central Station. Lift, electric light, and central heating. Rooms from 2.50 frs. See Advt.

PENSION W. WHITE.—11, Via Vittoria Colonna. Quite central position, near St. Peter's and Vatican. Comfortable and home-like. English management. Open all the year. Pension from frs. 7. See Advt.

ALBION PENSION.—Centrally situated, Via Sicilia, 166, five minutes from Villa Borghese. All modern comforts. Pension from 8 fr. See Advt.

HOTEL PENSION ESEDRA.—First class hotel-pension in excellent position. Modern comforts. Lift; electric light; central heating. Pension from 8 frs. See Advt.

RESTAURANT SAN CARLO.—120, Corso Umberto, corner of Via Carrozze, facing S. Carlo. Excellent and moderate. Lunch 2.50 fr; Dinner 4 fr.

The chief Railway Station—STAZIONE TERMINI—is on the north eastern side of the city.

CABS.—Taximeter motor cabs.

Electric Trams and omnibuses traverse the city.

ROME, the capital of Italy since 1871, is situated on both banks of the Tiber (Italian Tevere), much the larger section being to the east of the river. Modern Rome covers part of a plain, some heights, and the intersecting valleys; Ancient Rome occupied the heights only; in the middle ages these heights were almost deserted, and only in comparatively recent times have they become repopulated. Standing outside the Stazione Termini, and looking westward, immediately in front, across the town is the Vatican, with the Cathedral of St. Peter; the district on the right hand includes the strangers' quarter; ancient Rome is almost entirely included in the district to the left. Competent authorities state that two weeks at least are necessary for even a hasty visit to the "sights" of Rome; space will only permit here an indication of what may be seen during a preliminary round of half-a-dozen hours from the Station.

From the Stazione Termini, cross, north-westward, the Piazza dei Cinquecento, bearing slightly to the left. In front of the Station is a monument to the 500 Italian soldiers surprised and killed in Abyssinia, 1886. Just by here were the Thermæ of Diocletian, the most extensive baths of Rome (the piazza on the left is called Piazza delle Terme); parts of the Thermæ were at various times made use of in many ways, Pope Pius IV employing Michael Angelo to convert one part into a Carthusian Convent, when the former Trepidarium was transformed into what is now the Church of S. Maria degli Angeli. The Museo Nazionale delle Terme Diocleziane (antiquities found on city public property) is to the right of the church. Proceeding a little, north west, the Via Venti Settembre is reached, here turn sharply to left, the street presently leading into the Via del Quirinale, with the gardens of the palace on the right, and the Royal Palace itself on the right in the Piazza at the end of the Via. From the Piazza del Quirinale turn into the Via Consulta, at south east corner, following the line of the street, across the Via Nazionale, into the Via dei Serpentine, which will eventually lead, keeping to the line of street, across the Via Cavour, to the Colosseum (go to east side for best view). From the Colosseum proceed westward, past the Fountain Meta Sudante, along the Sacra Via towards the Arch of Titus, with the Church of S. Francesca Romana on right, on the site of a Temple of Venus; adjoining the church are the three arches of the Basilica of Constantine. Here, and for some distance forward, as well as all about, are many vestiges of ancient Rome, columns, arches, ruins of temples, with the Forum as the way ascends the Capitoline Hill to the Palazzo del Senatore. The finest view of Rome is from the Torre Capitolina, by north east corner of Palazzo del Senatore. On the west side of the Palazzo del Senatore is the Piazza del Campidoglio (or Square of the Capitol) where, on right, is the Museo Capitolino and on the left the Palazzo dei Conservatori, both with collections of great interest. The great Temple of Jupiter was just behind the Palazzo dei Conservatori. Descend the steps on the west side of the Piazza del Campidoglio to the Piazza Aracœli, continuing, directly in a line north westward, along the Via Aracœlito where it opens broadly out at the end of the Corso Vittorio Emanuele. Turn to left into the Corso. The second street on the right, the Via dei Cestari, leads in a few minutes to the Pantheon. From the Pantheon return directly to the Corso, or thread the streets, full of interest, to west of Pantheon, gradually working south back to the Corso; the west end of the Corso leads on to the Ponte Vittorio Emanuele, over the Tiber, where, immediately to the west, on the Monte Vaticano. are the Cathedral of St. Peter and the Pontifical Palace and Gardens. From the Vatican back to the Stazione di Termini is about two miles, due east, and the way cannot be missed if the Monte Quirinale (just behind which is the Station) be kept in view.

The best SHOPS are near or in Piazza di Spagna, Via Condotti, Via del Babuino, Via Sistina, Via del Corso, and generally in the district midway between the Stazione Termini and the Vatican. At the foot of the steps in the Piazza di Spagna is the house where John Keats died (1821), now used as a Keats and Shelley museum.

Many architects were concerned in the building of the CATHEDRAL of ST. PETER, but the principal credit is assigned to Bramante, the creator of the design, and to Michael Angelo, whose chief work is the Dome. To the spectator, approaching from the Piazza di San Pietro, the majesty of the Dome is lost behind the facade, erected at the instance of Pope Paul V. at the end of the nave lengthened by him in order to work out the idea of a Latin cross; the design of Bramante was a Greek cross. The building was commenced in 1506, but was not completed until 1626; the total cost of erection was about £10,000,000, and its maintenance absorbs annually about £7,500. It covers about 18,000 square yards, almost twice the area of St. Paul's, London; the length is 232 yards, of the transept 150 yards; height of the nave 151 feet; height of the Dome from the pavement to the summit of the lantern 404 ft., to the summit of the cross 435 feet. Beside the high altar there are many other altars (29); there are tombs of popes, emperors, and kings; the high altar is immediately over the Tomb of St. Peter. Round the Confessio are 89 lamps, always alight. The bronze Statue of St. Peter, on white marble, under a canopy, is by a pillar; the right foot is worn smooth by the kisses of the devout. Many visits are necessary to appreciate the Cathedral.

The VATICAN, adjoining the Cathedral on the north side, is the residence of the Pope; the principal entrance, Portone di Bronzo, is at the Cathedral end of the colonnade on the north side of the Piazza di S. Pietro. Apart from its interest as the Papal residence, the Museums and Picture Galleries of the Vatican contain innumerable and priceless art treasures; the collections are open from 10.0 a.m. until 3.0 p.m., Saturday, 1.0 p.m.; during summer from 9.0 a.m. until

1.0 p.m.; admission by *Permessi*, good for five persons, obtained at the top of the Scala Regia, a staircase to which the Portone di Bronzo gives access. A fee of 1 lira for the Sculpture Galleries, except on Saturday, when they also are free. Permessi for the Library are obtained from the Cardinal-Secretary of State.

PALAZZO REGIO DEL QUIRINALE, the residence of the King of Italy; only a part shown when the Royal Family is in residence. The rooms are not specially interesting; some frescoes; a chapel. Sun., 1.0 p.m. to 4.0 p.m. free; permessi obtained (10.0 a.m. to 11.30 a.m.) at the Ministero della Casa Reale, Via del Quirinale.

MUSEO CAPITOLINO, on the north side of Piazza del Campidoglio, or Square of the Capitol, Sculpture and Mosaics; the "Dying Gladiator" is in room on first floor; bust of the Emperors and great men of antiquity; the "Capitoline Venus" is in the Venus Room. Daily, 10.0 a.m. to 3.0 p.m., 1 lr.; Sun., 10.0 a.m. to 1.0 p.m., free. Close by is the great monument to King Victor Emanuel; the horse and rider are gilded all over, the screen is of beautiful white marble.

PALAZZO DEI CONSERVATORI, opposite the Capitoline Museum. Collections of Antiquities, terracottas, bronzes, sculpture, coins; Picture Gallery; frescoes in the Sale dei Conservatori; relics of Garibaldi in small room. Daily, 10.0 to 3.0, 1 lr.; Sun., 10.0 to 1.0, free.

MUSEO NAZIONALE DELLE TERME DIOCLEZIANE, opposite the Stazione Termini. Antiques of rare interest. Inscriptions, sculpture, bronzes, reliefs, paintings, mosaics, weapons, ornaments, etc. Daily, 10.0 a.m. to 4.0 p.m., 1 lira; Sun., 10.0 a.m. to 1.0 p.m., free.

GALLERIA D' ARTE MODERNA, on west side of Via Nazionale. Sculpture on the ground floor. Picture Gallery above. Daily, 9.0 a.m. to 3.0 p.m. 1 lira; Sun., 10.0 a.m. to 1.0 p.m., free.

VILLA BORGHESE, on north side of city; entrance by the Porta del Popolo. The beautiful grounds are studded by various ornamental erections, but the art treasures in the Casino are the great attraction. Sculpture fils the ground floor, the Picture Gallery being above. Grounds open 9.0 a.m. until dusk. Galleries open daily, 10.0 to 4.0, 1 lira; Sunday, 10.0 to 1.0, free.

PALAZZO DORIA, on west side of Corso Umberto I. Magnificent palace, with famous Picture Gallery, Tues. and Fri., 10.0 a.m. to 2.0 p.m. (a fee).

PALAZZO COLONNA, Via della Pilotta. Gallery of famous pictures. Tues., Thurs., Sat., 10.0a.m. to 3.0 p.m., 1 lira.

PALAZZO DEL LATERANO, on south east side of city, at east end of Via S. Giovanni, a street leading east from the Colosseum. On ground floor is the Museo Profano of ancient Sculpture; Tues. and Thurs., 10.0 a.m. to 3.0 p.m., 1 lira; Sat., 10.0 a.m. to 1.0 p.m., free. The Christian Museum and Picture Gallery, Mon., Wed., Fri., 10.0 a.m. to 3.0 p.m., 1 lira.

CASTELLO S. ANGELO, by the Tiber, near the Vatican. In addition to the interest attaching to the Castle, are collections illustrating local history, as well as models, drawings, etc., relating to military engineering. Weekdays, 10.0 to 4.0, 1 lira.

The PAGAN ANTIQUITIES are legion, some of the most interesting are clustered within a parallelogram from the Colosseum to the crest of the Capitoline Hill.

POST OFFICE, in Piazza S. Silvestro, on north side of city, a little off east side of Corso Umberto I.

ENGLISH CHURCH SERVICE.—All Saints, Via Babuino, Piazza di Spagna. Trinity Church, Piazza San Silvestro.

AMERICAN EPIS. CH.—St. Paul's, Via Nazionale. Presbyterian Church, 7, Via Venti Settembre. Methodist Church, 38, Via Firenze Wesleyan Church, 64, Via della Scrofa.

ENGLISH ROMAN CATHOLIC CHURCHES.—San Silvestro, Corso Umberto I, by the Post Office. S. Thomas of Canterbury, Via Monserrato.

CATHOLIC COLLEGES.—English, in Via di Monserrato. Scotch, Via Quattro Fontane. Irish, Via Pansiperna. Canadian, Via Quattro Fontane. North American, Via dell' Universita.

BRITISH ACADEMY OF ARTS.–53B, Via Margutta.

ROME SOCIETY FOR THE PROTECTION OF ANIMALS.—66, Piazza di Spagna. Hon. Director: Leonard T. Hawksley.

BRITISH AND AMERICAN EMBASSIES.

GREAT BRITAIN.—His Excellency Rt. Hon. Sir Rennell Rodd, G.C.V.O., K.C.M.G.

H.B.M.'S CONSUL.—C. C. Morgan, Esq., 20, Via Condotti. VICE-CONSUL.—H. D. Johnson, Esq.

UNITED STATES.—His Excellency Thomas O'Brien. SEC. OF EMBASSY.—P. Wheeler, Esq.

CONS.—C. Coleman, Esq.

GOLF. — 9-hole course near Acqua Santa Station; club house.

MEDICAL.—Dr. Thomson Bonar; Dr. G. Sandison Brock; Dr. Arthur Welsford.

AMERICAN DENTIST. — Drs. Fenchelle and Bond, L.D.S., B.D.S., D.D.S., American Dentists, 93, Piazza di Spagna. Hours 9.30–1, 2.30–5.

CHEMISTS.—Mr. J. Evans (late Sinimberghi, Evans, and Co). The best and oldest established Chemist in Rome, Via Condotti. See Advt.

SANGIORGI GALLERY.—Borghese Palace. The most attractive exhibition of fine arts and furniture in Europe. Tapestries, paintings by masters, velvets, brocades, laces, ancient and modern marble sculptures, reproductions after the ancient styles.

ROMAN PEARLS.—A. Rey, 121-123, Via Babuino. Best house for Roman pearls. Visitors may inspect the process of manufacture from solid alabaster to the perfection of the pearl.

OLD ORIGINAL ENGRAVINGS, rare colour prints; old masters. Rare old books. L. Kempner, Via Condotti, 51, 52.

PERMANENT PHOTOGRAPHS.—The Compagnia Rotografica, Via Condotti, 10A, near Piazza di Spagna. Artistic Photographs and Post Cards of Italy.

DEPOT for BRADSHAW'S PUBLICATIONS.—Piale, Piazza di Spagna.

RAIL, pp. 270 271A, 275, 276, 278, 279, 282, 288.

[**Frascati.**—*Stat.*—Pop. 8,453.

A delightfully situated summer resort—though attractive at all seasons—1,056 ft. above sea, on the north slope of the Alban Mountains. Several beautiful villas belonging to wealthy Romans—Villa Torlonia, Villa Lancellotti, Villa Aldobrandini, and others—a few accessible to the public.

In the Duomo (S. Pietro), erected 1700, a tablet to left of the high altar is to the memory of Charles Edward, the Young Pretender (died 1788).

The ancient **Tusculum** is about 1½ miles south east of Frascati. Remains of an amphitheatre, of the forum, and the theatre. Villa of Cicero (doubtful).

RAIL, page 275.

Tivoli.—*Stat.*—Pop. 12,881.

HOTELS: REGINA; SIRENA; SIBILLA.

The ancient Tibur, a favourite residence of Roman nobles during the Augustan age, the villa of the Emperor Hadrian being of surpassing splendour. From the Railway Station, on east side, the town is entered at the Porta St. Angelo and the Ponte Gregoriano, at end of which, to right, a short street leads to the Temple of the Sibyl in the court of Albergo Sibilla. The entrance to the Waterfalls is on left side, entering, close to Porta St. Angelo. Following the line of thoroughfare continuing from the Ponte Gregoriano, bending to south west, the Villa d'Este will be found to left, and, in same direction, 3 miles, is Hadrian's Villa (Villa Adriana)an extensive ruin, with the gardens covering about 170 acres.

RAIL, page 282. Tram from Rome, passing the Villa Adriana, page 275.]

Rovigo.—*Stat.*—Pop. of the commune 12,224.

The small capital of a province, whose principal attraction is the very interesting collection of pictures at the Palazzo Comunale; in the same building is also a collection of antiquities.

RAIL, pages 279A, 282.

Salerno.—*Stat.*—Pop. of the commune 45,682.

HOTELS: D'ANGLETERRE; VITTORIA.

Railway Station, to east, is a mile from the town.

CAB.—Station to town, 1-horse 50c., 2-horse 1 lira, at night half extra.

The ancient Salernum, in a beautiful situation on the Gulf of Salerno. Parts of the old town are very interesting. Cattedrale San Matteo, erected 1084; bronze doors; in interior are several monuments, notably that of Pope Gregory VII (died 1085), lecterns in nave, in the decorated crypt the venerated remains of St. Matthew are stated to be deposited. Other Churches, with paintings, are S. Lorenzo, S. Giorgio, and S. Agostino. Ruined castle on the hill.

H.B.M.'s VICE-CONSUL.—P. Consiglio, Esq.

RAIL, pages 277, 278.

Salice.—*Stat.*—Pop. 1,200.

A picturesquely situated bathing resort, 600 ft. above sea. The waters, for bathing and drinking, are very rich in iodine and bromine.

RAIL, page 269A.

Salo.—Pop. 5,000.

GRAND HOTEL SALO.—Occupies one of the best positions on the shores of Lake Garda. First class; every modern comfort. See Advt.

A picturesque little town pleasantly situated on the Lago di Garda, at the foot of a mountain covered with groves of orange, lemon, and pomegranate trees. Sheltered from wind, the climate is genially mild in winter, cedars and various palms growing in the open. From the Lungo Lago, a favourite promenade, are delightful views over the bay. In the Cathedral, built 1530, are paintings by artists of Brescia and Verona, wood carving, etc.; the Church of S. Bernardino, built 1476, is interesting. At the Ateneo is a collection of old "actes," an ancient bible, and antiquities dating from the year 1200. Palazzo Martinenvo, where Lady Mary Wortley Montagu and Lady Orford resided, 1750-1755. Colonna Dorica, with the S. Marco Lion. A delicious liqueur, Acqua di Cedro, is made here.

Golf links 20 minutes from the Casino.

ENGLISH CHURCH.

STEAMER, page 365. Electric tram to Brescia, Tormini, etc.

Salsomaggiore.—*Stat.*—Pop. 1,700.

GRAND HOTEL DE MILAN.—First class, in connection with Thermal Springs; every modern comfort. Pension from 10 fr.

THERMES.

A pleasantly situated village lying in the valley between Piacenza and Parma, rapidly becoming famous for its waters, which are very rich in bromine and iodine, and the richest in the world in lithium, strontium, and ichthyol, and have been successfully used in the treatment of scrofula, rheumatism, affections of the respiratory organs, ladies' complaints, etc.

MEDICAL.—Dr. Eyre (spring and autumn), at the Hotel des Thermes.

DEPOT FOR BRADSHAW'S PUBLICATIONS.—Library and Stationery Repository Gandolfo, 174, Via Romagnosi.

RAIL, page 279B.

Sta. Margherita.—*Stat.*—Pop. 4,900.

GRAND HOTEL CONTINENTAL—First class hotel, full south, in a fine position, the most fashionable part of the town. Electric light; lift; central heating. See Advt.

STRAND HOTEL.—Superior first class hotel, finely situated, full south, overlooking the bay. With all the latest improvements. Pension from 8 fr. See Advt.

"THE EDEN" GRAND HOTEL GUGLIELMINA (opened 1910).—First class. Sunny, elevated position, with fine view. Up-to-date in every respect. Terms from 9 frs. See Advt.

GRAND HOTEL REGINA ELENA.—A most comfortable first class English family hotel, in the finest situation, and nearest to Portofino. Unique panorama. Own sea bathing place and landing stage. See Advt.

A clean picturesque little town, much developed as a winter resort, finely situated on the Monte Fino peninsula, close to Rapallo; luxurious vegetation all round. Mild invigorating climate; sheltered from north winds; no dust; good spring water. Many delightful excursions. ENGLISH CHURCH SERVICE. English library.

RAIL, page 270.

[**Portofino**, about 3 miles from Sta. Margherita—omnibus several times a day, 25 c.

THE SPLENDID HOTEL.—First class. Modern comforts. Open October–May. Park. See Advt.

A beautiful road leads from Sta. Margherita to the village of Portofino, the Roman Portus Delphini, a little port snugly sheltered in a bay near the south east extremity of a headland. Population 1,500, mostly fishermen; lace is made by the women. At the Church of San Giorgio, 12th cent., in the middle of the village, are relics of the saint. At the extreme point of the headland is an old Castle; pilgrimage Chapel of Madonna del Capo. On the road between Sta. Margherita and Portofino is the Monastery of Cervara, where Francis I of France was for a time kept a prisoner by Charles V of Spain (1525).

Portofino Kulm, Monte di Portofino.

Portofino Kulm, 2,000 ft. above sea, is about 3 miles distant, and quite distinct from, Portofino, the fishing village. The Kulm is a hill on a beautiful headland whence are obtained some of the finest views over the coast and Mediterranean; vegetation very rich, especially upon the south side; air pure, very little north wind. Below the Kulm, at San Fruttuoso, known in 10th cent., is an interesting church.

Automobile service between Recco and Portofino Kulm.]

S. Pellegrino.—*Stat.*—Pop. 1,500.

Situated on the River Brembo, in the Val Brembana, one of the pleasantest valleys of the Bergamasque Alps, 1,145 ft. above sea, with mountain scenery all round. The Thermal Establishment is one of the most important of Italy, the principal season being in July and August; more than 50,000 visitors annually. The waters, from three warm saline springs, used for bathing and drinking, are prescribed for gout, digestive and liver troubles, lumbago, intestinal ailments, stone, etc. Equable climate; in the pine woods are many attractive walks.

RAIL, page 287.

San Remo.—*Stat.*—Pop. 20,350.

SAVOY HOTEL.—First class hotel. In elevated position. Fine grounds; splendid view. Much patronised by English and American families. See Advt.

GRAND HOTEL BELLEVUE AND KURHAUS SAN REMO.—First class, on slightly elevated ground; sheltered and dust free. Fine view of the sea. See Advt.

BERTOLINI'S ROYAL HOTEL.—First class, near Station. Fine views of town and sea. Large garden; restaurant. See Advt.

GRAND HOTEL VICTORIA.—Comfortable and old established first-class hotel, with electric light, lift, and garden. See Advt.

GRAND HOTEL DES ANGLAIS. — Near the English Church and public promenade. Lift. Central heating. Electric light. See Advt.

THE WEST END HOTEL.—First class hotel. Suites and single rooms with bath and toilette. Hot water heating; lift. See Advt.

HOTEL DE L'EUROPE ET DE LA PAIX.—Conveniently situated opposite Railway Station. All modern comforts. See Advt.

RIVIERA PALACE HOTEL.—Modern hotel in fine position. Roof garden overlooking the sea. See Advt.

HOTEL DE LONDRES.—First-class hotel, delightfully situated, facing the sea. See Advt.

HOTEL BELVEDERE.—Well situated on the mountains, with fine sea view. Garden. See Advt.

HOTEL COSMOPOLITAIN. — Old established. Close to Station. Lift; electric light; central heating. Rooms from 3 fr. Pension from 8 fr. See Advt.

The Railway Station is near the shore, on the west side of the town.

Beautifully situated on a fine bay, with mild, dry, invigorating climate, sheltered from north winds. Mean winter temp. 51°.

In the old town are steep clean streets of ancient houses, archways, stairways, and picturesque corners. Vines and tender climbing plants are often seen near the roofs of the houses.

The new town is well laid out. The principal thoroughfare is the Via Vittorio Emanuele, whose west end is a little north of the Station. Close here is the Giardino Pubblico, containing palms, eucalypti, etc. The Corso Imperatrice, west of the Station, a splendid promenade, terminates at its west end in the Giardino dell' Imperatrice. On the north side of the town is a delightful hill road, running in pleasant windings, whence are beautiful views. At the Casino, opera and concerts daily in the season.

Old Cathedral Church of San Sirio. Madonna della Costa Church, finely situated on the hill behind old town, with view of bay and mountains. Ospedale close by.

Forte S. Tecla, by the Port, now a prison, was erected by the Genoese to defend the harbour.

POST OFFICE, Via Roma.

ENG. CHURCH SERV.—(Winter Chaplaincy) St. John the Baptist.

H.B.M.'s VICE-CON.—Meysey Turton, Esq.

GOLF.—9 hole course near Taggia Station; club house.

MEDICAL.—Dr. M. Foster; Dr. Miller; Dr. G. Ansaldi, of Genova and Edinburgh.

AMERICAN DENTIST.—Dr. Edward E. Powers, Phila. U.S.A. 18, Via Vittorio Emanuele, 1st fl.

BANKERS.—Messrs. Asquasciati frères, English Bankers, 26, Via Vittorio Emanuele.

HOUSE AGENCY.—Benecke and Heywood, Anglo-American House Agents and Bankers. Also Tourist Office. See Advt.

HOUSE AGENCY.—M. and A. Turton. The Anglo-American Agency and Bank. House and Estate Agents, Bankers, Wine and General Agency.

DEPOT FOR BRADSHAW'S GUIDES, Librairie Branzke and Gandolfo Gallerie, 7, Corso Imperatrice, opposite the Casino.

RAIL, p. 272.

Saronno.—*Stat.*—Pop. 8,700.

An extensive village on the Lura, with a celebrated pilgrimage church—Santuario della Beata Vergine, of late 15th cent.; interior has good frescoes. Saronno is also known for its "amaretti," a kind of gingerbread.

RAIL, page 287.

Sarzana.—*Stat.*—Pop. 6,500.

The Roman Sergiana, situated in a fertile plain. The handsome Cathedral, of early 14th cent., contains an ancient painted crucifix. The Church of San Francesco has interesting tombs. Town walls of 15th cent.

RAIL, pages 270, 275.

Savona.—*Stat.*—Pop. 25,000.

An industrial town and busy sea port, the Savo of the Romans. In the Cathedral, of early 17th cent., are several interesting objects; opposite the Cathedral is the unfinished Ateneo. At the Ospedale Civico is a small collection of pictures. Torre Pancaldo, at the harbour. It is stated that soap (sapone) was first made at Savona, thence deriving its name; extensive iron and steel works.

H.B.M.'s CONSUL.—S. Guattari, Esq.

RAIL, pages 272, 273.

Sestri Levante.—*Stat.*—Pop. 3,000.

GRAND HOTEL JENSCH.—First class; position quiet and well sheltered, with fine view of sea and mountains. Perfect Sanitary arrangements. Lift, etc. See Advt.

HOTEL MIRAMARE,—On sea shore, facing south. Much frequented by English and Americans. Moderate tariff. See Advt.

A little seaport, the Roman Segesta Tiguliorum, situated on a fertile neck of land terminating in a broad abrupt cape. The picturesque rocky coast and wooded hills attract many visitors during both winter and summer; fine view over the Mediterranean. Good coast promenade; Public gardens, Villa Piuma may be visited (small fee to gardener), also Villa Mandrella. Capuchin Monastery. Many delightful excursions may be made.

RAIL, page 270.

Siena.—*Stat.*—Pop. of the commune 41,673.

GRAND HOTEL ROYAL.—First class, in fine position, full south. All modern comforts. Terms "en pension." See Advt.

GRAND HOTEL CONTINENTAL.—First class, beautifully situated. Full south. Steam-heating and electric light. See Advt.

Tramways.

The Railway Station is on the north east side of the city, about half a mile from the Piazza del Campo and the Duomo. Emerging from the Station, immediately to right (west) is Via Garibaldi, which presently bends into Via Cavour, leading towards the Piazza del Campo.

Siena is pleasantly situated on three hills, its elevation, 1,045 ft. above sea, rendering it cool in summer. It is one of the most interesting of the smaller towns of Italy, whether regarded historically—it was once the rival of Florence with a population of 100,000—or as the seat of a famous school of art; mediæval architecture and painting are here wonderfully represented; it is also a centre of industrial activity (weaving, etc.). It is the seat of an archbishop, and has an ancient University.

At the centre of the city is the Piazza del Campo, or Piazza Vittorio Emanuele, the scene of many historic events. On the south side of the Piazza is the Palazzo Pubblico, of brick, 1289-1305; at the base of the Mangia tower, 335 ft., is the Capella di Piazza; within the Palazzo are several fine frescoes by famous Siena artists—fee 50 c. The Fonte Gaia, at the centre of the Piazza, is modern, reproducing the old fountain of 1343. A few yards from the east side of the Piazza is the Palazzo Piccolomini, 15th cent., containing the city archives, autographs, miniatures, etc. The University (about 250 students) is just east of the Palazzo Piccolomini.

The Duomo, 150 yards west of the Piazza del Campo, is on high ground, on the site of a temple of Minerva. The building dates from early in the 13th cent. it is 300 ft. long, 80 ft. wide, with a transept 165 ft. long. Upon the facade, of red, black, and white marble, are sculpture and mosaics. Pavement of interior (except in August usually covered) has mosaics of many Biblical scenes; much fine sculpture by Michael Angelo. Marinna, Pisano (the pulpit), Donatello, and others; frescoes and other paintings, many busts of popes. In the left aisle is the entrance to the Cathedral Library containing frescoes, missals, etc.

Opposite the south east side of the Duomo is the Opera del Duomo, containing sculpture, paintings, objects of ecclesiastical art, vestments, etc. To west of the Opera is the Palazzo Reale, occupied by municipal offices. On the west side of the Piazza del Duomo are the Church and Hospital of S. Maria della Scala, 13th cent.

Church of S. Agostino, quarter mile south of the Duomo, in the Piazza Giordano Bruno; paintings. S. Maria del Carmine, in Via Baldassare, quarter mile west of S. Agostino; paintings. S. Martino, immediately south of Palazzo Piccolomini; paintings and sculpture. S. Spirito, quarter mile south east of Piazza del Campo; paintings, cloisters. SS. Concezione, in extreme south east part of city; beautiful interior, paintings, sculpture. S. Francesco, quarter mile north east of Piazza del Campo; sculpture, frescoes, stained glass; adjoining, on south side, is the Oratorio di S. Bernardino, where are paintings. S. Domenico, in Piazza Mazzini, quarter mile north west of Piazza del Campo; paintings, mosaics, high altar; in Chapel of St. Catherine the head of the saint is preserved within a shrine. 100 yards east of S. Domenico, a few yards off north side of Via Benincasa, is the House of St. Catherine of Siena, whose father's name was Benincasa. She was born 1347, died 1380; the rooms of the house have been converted into Oratories, the Church is below; fee 50 c.

Accademia di Belle Arti, in Via delle Belle Arti, off west side of Via Cavour, quarter mile north of Piazza del Campo, A collection of paintings by old Siena masters, also a few modern works. Daily, 9.0 to 3.0, 1 lira. At the west side of the Accademia is the Biblioteca Comunale, containing 80,000 vols. and 5,000 MSS., including Greek Gospels of the 11th cent. and letters of St. Catherine.

POST OFFICE, Via Cavour, in the old Palazzo Spannocchi.

ENGLISH CHURCH SERVICE.

RAIL, page 275.

Sorrento.—Pop. 7,500.

GRAND HOTEL VICTORIA.—First class hotel, with fine view on the Bay and Mount Vesuvius. Electric light; steam heating; baths. See Advt.

The ancient Surrentum, beautifully situated at the south side of the Gulf of Naples, amidst lemon and orange gardens; much frequented as a health resort, cool in summer, warm in winter. There are no remains of the Roman city and little is left of the mediæval walls. Small ship building industry and fishing boats, Cathedral. Tasso (born 1554, died 1595) was a native, a house in Strada San Nicola is stated to have been the residence of his sister Cornelia.

ENGLISH CHURCH SERV. at Hotel Tramontano.

U.S. CONS. AGENT.—Francesco Ciampi, Esq.

GOLF.—9 hole course, near St. Agata.

Reached from Castellammare di Stabia Station by Electric Tramway in 1½ hour service about every half hour; fare 1 lira. Steamers from Naples, page 354.

Spezia (La).—*Stat.*—Pop. of the commune 65,612.

GRAND HOTEL ET CROCE DI MALTA; splendid situation full south overlooking the Bay. Beautiful garden in front of the hotel. See Advt.

Finely situated on the Golfo della Spezia, at the base of pleasant village covered hills; the mild bracing climate renders it a favourite winter resort, and sea bathing attracts in summer. It is a naval port, with the largest Arsenal and Dockyard in Italy.

H.B.M.'s VICE-CONS.—H. C. Ricardo, Esq.

MEDICAL.—Dr. A. E. Leeson.

RAIL, pages 270, 275.

Stresa.—*Stat.*—Pop. 2,000.

GRAND HOTEL ET DES ILES BORROMEES.—First class, unrivalled situation; self-contained suites; large grounds. Garage. Orchestra, 3 lifts; private road from station to hotel. Cook's office and Sleeping Car Agency in the grounds of the hotel. See Advt.

REGINA PALACE HOTEL.—Modern, first-class hotel. 200 rooms and apartments with baths and toilette. Garden. Garage. See Advt.

A delightful place, justly named "the Beauty Spot of Lake Maggiore"; on the widest part of the Lake, close to the Borromean Islands. Here are the summer palaces of Queen Margherita, the Duke and Duchess of Genoa, and many fine villas of the Italian nobility. A good centre for visiting the Italian lakes; headquarters of the Royal Verbano Yacht Club. Since the opening of the Simplon Tunnel Stresa has become an important transit station of traffic between the railway and lake steamers. Electric Railway to the top of the famous Mottarone, "Italian Righi"; also a Kursaal and Mineral (Arsenical) water Establishment. A great centre for all sports.

MEDICAL.—Dr. C. Lodigiani.

ENGLISH CHURCH.

RAIL, page 274; STEAMER, page 366.

[**Gignese.**

In a very fine situation on the slopes of the Mottarone, 1,500 ft. above the level of the lake, and about 1½ hour drive from Stresa. From Baveno a mule path, whence are magnificent views, leads up to Gignese. Cool fresh air, with wide panorama.]

Subiaco.—*Stat.*—Pop. 8,000.

The ancient Sublaqueum, a little town, 1,340 ft. above sea, with a castle once the residence of popes. Famous monasteries, dating from 530; at one was printed the first book published in Italy, 1465. The country round is beautiful.

RAIL, page 282.

Susa.—*Stat.*

An ancient interesting little town, the Roman Segusio, on the River Dora. The Church of S. Giusto is of the 11th cent. A few Roman remains, including a triumphal arch at the west side of the town. Ruined Castle of Brunetta.

RAIL, page 273.

Taranto.—*Stat.*—Pop. of the commune 60,733.

HOTELS: EUROPA; RISORGIMENTO; CENTRALE.

On the north side of the Golfo di Taranto, curiously situated on a rock between the Golfo and an inlet called the Mare Piccolo. An ancient place, the Tarentum of the Greeks. Owing to the cramped situation the inhabitants are densely packed in narrow streets. Cattedrale (San Cataldo), 11th cent. has in the saint's chapel rich mosaics and sculpture. In the Museo are antiquities found in the neighbourhood. Roman aqueduct, 9½ miles long, on north side of the city to the mainland.

RAIL, pages 277, 285B.

Tirano.—*Stat.*—Pop. 3,000.

HOTEL TIRANO.

In the Valtellina, on the River Adda, 1,475 ft. above sea, at the Italian end of the Bernina Route from Switzerland. Several fine old houses of patrician families.

RAIL, page 257A, 281. Diligence, page 374.

Torre Pellice.—*Stat.*—Pop. 4,000.

The chief place of the Waldensian Valleys (Vallées Vaudoises), 1,695 ft. above sea, close to the French frontier, 34 miles from Turin. The history of the persecuted Protestant communities of the Waldensian Valleys is well known. French is generally spoken. Other places in the valleys are Luserna, Villar, and Bobbio Pellice.

RAIL, page 271.

Treviso.—*Stat.*—Pop. of the Commune 41,022.

HOTELS: STELLA D'ORO; ROMA.

Capital of the Province of Treviso, on the River Sile. From the Railway Station, on south side of city, proceed northward, crossing the two arms of the river, following the thoroughfare in its slight bend westward to the Duomo.

Duomo (S. Pietro), begun 1500, unfinished, has five domes; among paintings in interior is an Annunciation by Titian in large chapel to right of choir; good frescoes. The other churches should be visited. The Galleria Comunale, in Borgo Cavour, quarter mile north west of the Duomo, contains some good paintings.

RAIL, pages 282, 283, 285A, 288.

TURIN (*Ital.* **Torino**).—*Stat.*—Pop. 427,106. *(Plan in Special Edition, or post free 3d. stamps).*

GRAND HOTEL ET HOTEL D'EUROPE, Piazza Castello, opposite the King's Palace, near the Station. First-class Hotel, entirely refurnished and replete with every modern comfort. See Advt.

PALACE HOTEL.—First class, facing the Central Station; moderate charges. Steam heating. Garage. Garden. See Advt.

GRAND HOTEL LIGURE ET D'ANGLETERRE.—Facing Station exit. Full south. Every comfort. Moderate. See Advt.

GRAND HOTEL SUISSE.—Opposite "Arrival" side, Central Station. See Advt.

The principal RAILWAY STATION—Stazione Centrale—is on the south side of the city.

TURIN, the capital of the former Kingdom of Sardinia, and from 1860 to 1865 the capital of the Kingdom of Italy, is a most regularly built city.

Immediately in front of the Stazione Centrale is Piazza Carlo Felice, with gardens and a statue of Massimo d'Azeglio; here the Via Roma leads by way of the Piazza San Carlo in about half a mile to Piazza Castello, the centre of modern Turin life.

The PALAZZO MADAMA (erected near end of 13th cent.—the name refers to Maria, mother of Vittorio Amadeo II, early in 18th cent.), in the middle of Piazza Castello, is the only remaining mediæval structure in Turin. On the north side of the Piazza is the PALAZZO REALE, a brick building, dating from 1646; Sun., Tues., Thurs., Sat., 10.0 to 12.0 and 2.0 to 4.0, 50 c. In the south east wing of the Palace is the Armería Reale (Royal Armoury); free by ticket obtained at office on staircase. Interesting collection of armour, weapons, flags, Napoleonic relics, etc. The Royal Library of 70,000 vols. and 3,000 MSS. is in same building below.

On the north west side of Palazzo Reale is the CATTEDRALE (San Giovanni Battista), in the Renaissance style, 1492-1498; behind high altar is the Cappella del Santissimo Sudario—so named because in a receptacle, a sort of urn, over the chapel altar, is preserved part of the linen cloth in which the body of Christ was wrapped. Statues of members of the House of Savoy buried here.

The PINACOTECA (PICTURE GALLERY) is in the Palazzo dell 'Accadēmia delle Scienze, on the south side of Piazza Carignano, which runs out of Piazza Castello near south east corner. Week days 10.0 to 4, summer 9.0 to 4.0, 1 lira; on Sunday (1.0 to 4.0) free. The pictures are in upper part of building. In the same building is a Museum of Antiquities.

The MUSEO CIVICO is in Via di Gaudenzio Ferrari, a street on east side of Via Rossini, which runs north from Via della Zecca (the broad street on east side of Piazza Castello). Free on Sun., Tues., and Thurs., 9.0 to 4.0; other days 1 lira; closed Mon. Collections of modern pictures, sculpture, enamels, pottery, ivories, stained glass.

Among the Churches worth attention are the Church of La Consolata, in Via della Consolata, a little north west of Piazza Castello; a much venerated Madonna in this church. Church of Gran Madre di Dio, over the bridge at south end of Via di Po. Church of Corpus Domini, a little south west of the Cattedrale.

PALAZZO DI CITTA (Town Hall), a little off north-east side of Via Garibaldi, contains a library; several statues.

UNIVERSITY, in the Via di Po, running south from Piazza Castello; about 3,000 students; the library of 275,000 vols., is open to public on weekdays 9.0 to 4.0 and 7.0 to 10.0 (in summer 9.0 to 5.0), closed in September. A fire in 1904 destroyed 24,000 vols. and 2,600 MSS.

Accademia Albertina di Belle Arti, a little east of the University. Pictures and cartoons.

Natural History Museum, in the Palazzo Carignano, in Piazza Carignano. 1.0 to 4.0, free.

The best shops are in the streets running into the Piazza Castello. The public gardens (Giardino pubblico) are at south end of Corso Vittorio Emanuele II.

POST OFFICE, in Via Alfieri, off west side of Piazza S. Carlo.

A very fine view, best in the morning, from the Monte dei Cappuccini, a wooded height to south-east, just across the river; here are an old Capuchin Church and a Club House of the Italian Alpine Club. The BASILICA DI SOPERGA, a conspicuous object on a hill to the east, is a handsome church containing the royal burial vaults; from dome magnificent view of the Alps.

ENGLISH CHURCH SERVICE, Via Pio Quinto.

H. B. M.'S CONSUL-GENERAL.—Major W. P. Chapman.

H.B.M.'s V.-CONSUL.—A. G. Linari, Esq.

U.S. CONSUL.—C. B. Perry, Esq.

RAIL, pp. 269, 270, 271, 272, 272A, 289.

Urbino.—*Stat.*—Pop. 6,889.

Situated on a hill, 1,480 ft. above sea, in a bare mountain region; a town of many historic and artistic associations. Raphael Santi was born here, 1483, in a house in the Contrada Raffaelo—died at Rome 1520; fine monument to the painter in the Piazza Duca Federigo. In the Duomo, 1801, are some good paintings. In the Palazzo Ducale, 1465, are collections of sculpture and paintings. University, about 260 students.

RAIL, page 283.

Varallo.—*Stat.*—Pop. 2,800.

HOTEL D'ITALIE.

Chief town of the Val Grande, at the entrance of the Val Mastallone. Interesting churches of S. Gaudenzio, S. Maria delle Grazie (scenes from the life of Christ), and S. Maria di Loreto. The Stabilimento Idroterapico is a well furnished hydropathic institution. The Sacro Monte, with many chapels and a fine church, commands beautiful views.

MEDICAL.—Dr. Bogle.

RAIL, p. 274A. Diligence, page 374.

Varenna.—*Stat.*

ROYAL VICTORIA HOTEL.—First class, beautifully situated, with terrace and garden overlooking the lake.

A small town, delightfully situated, where the Val d'Esino emerges upon the Lake of Como. Beautiful surroundings; much marble quarried and worked. Ruins of Torre di Vezio above the town—fine view. Golf links.

MEDICAL.—Dr. F. M. Bishop.

GOLF.—9-hole course at Dervio, with club house.

RAIL, page 281; Steamer, page 365.

Varese.—*Stat.*—Pop. 21,619.

HOTEL PENSION EUROPE.—Good second class hotel, facing the public garden. Every modern comfort. Central heating. Moderate. See Advt.

EXCELSIOR.

A prosperous town in a beautiful situation, 1,250 feet above sea, commanding fine views. Many villas of wealthy Milanese families. Church of San Vittore, with paintings. To Madonna del Monte (2,885 ft.), a pilgrim resort, 7½ miles to north west—electric tram as far as the Prima Cappella, funicular to the summit.

ENGLISH CHURCH SERVICE.

GOLF.—9-hole course, half mile from Station.

RAIL, pages 274, 287.

VENICE (*Ital.* **Venezia**). — *Stat.* — Pop. 160,719. *(Plan in Special Edition, or post free 3d. stamps).*

THE GRAND HOTEL.—Enlarged by annexation of adjoining Palace Swift. Every comfort of a first-class hotel. Finest location on the Grand Canal. Moderate charges.

DANIELI'S ROYAL HOTEL.—First-class hotel. In the best part of the town. See Advt.

HOTEL REGINA (formerly Rome et Suisse).—Advantageously situated on the Grand Canal. Moderate charges. See Advt.

HOTEL ET PENSION BEAU RIVAGE.—First-rate house, well situated on the principal quai; fine panorama. Entirely renovated; electric light; baths; terms from 9 fr. See Advt.

HOTEL DE L'EUROPE.—First-class hotel, well situated on the Grand Canal. Comfort combined with moderate charges. Electric light; lift. See Advt.

GRAND HOTEL VICTORIA.—Old established, first class, situated near S. Marc Square. See Advt.

HOTEL BRITANNIA.—Situated on the finest part of the Grand Canal, and replete with every modern comfort. See Advt.

HOTEL BAVARIA AND JOLANDA.—Situated full south, overlooking the Grand Canal. All modern and sanitary arrangements. Moderate terms. See Advt.

RAILWAY.—The Railway Station is on the north west side of the city, at the end of the Canal Grande. Gondolas, rowing and motor, always waiting at the Station.

STEAMER.—Sea-going steamers usually anchor in the Canal a little east of Piazza di San Marco. Gondola from steamer to quay 20 c.; each light article 5 c., each heavy article 20c.

The principal HOTELS are near the Piazza di San Marco, at the further end of the Canal Grande from the Railway Station.

GONDOLAS.—Regular Stations, or "Stands," as cabs. Holds (gondola) four or (barca) six persons; with one rower, first hour 1 lira 50c. (1 or 2 persons); each additional half hour 75c. When it is intended to use the gondola for a time and not for a direct passage to destination, say "all' ora," and show watch. Double fares when second rower employed; one rower sufficient for all canal trips. For distant trips on the lagoons (away from the canals) a bargain is necessary. FERRIES straight across canals, 5 c.; crossing at a slant 10c.; be sure to say "traghetto" (crossing). Small steamers and Motor Boats also ply on the Canals, but the popularity of the Gondola is not much affected.

The GRAND CANAL (Canal Grande) flows through Venice on a curved line (∿), with the Railway Station at the west end, to left, the Piazzo di San Marco near east end, to right, and the RIALTO bridge about midway.

The climate of Venice is softened by the sea and lagoons, though cold winds blow from the north east in winter. Mean temp. 37° (Jan.) to 77° (July). The humidity of the air is favourable to some throat affections, but unfavourable to rheumatism. Nervously affected persons will find the "noiseless highways" a relief, and the absence of dust is pleasant. During summer, June to October, mosquitoes abound; mosquito curtains are called "zanzarieri."

VENICE is the capital of the Province of Venezia; it lies, as an island, about 2½ miles from the mainland, in a shallow bay of the Adriatic, known as the Lagoons (Lagune). The city is an agglomeration of about 117 small islands, whereon, and also upon intermediate piles, the houses and palaces have been built, There are about 150 canals, crossed by nearly 400 bridges. The trade of Venice is principally a transport trade; there is some ship building, and an extensive industry in lace, beads, spun glass, fine goldsmiths' work, and art objects.

When the traveller has only a day or two to spare it is better to hire a gondola for a few hours—the gondolier will point out the places of interest as they are passed; spending the balance of time in such churches or palaces as are nearest to hand. The churches are usually open from 6.0 a.m. until noon.

PIAZZA DI SAN MARCO, often called simply "La Piazza," on the north side of the east end of Canal Grande. This is the centre of Venice life. On the east side is the Church of St. Mark and the Palace of the Doges; on the other sides the palaces—"Procuratie Vecchie" (north) and "Procuratie Nuove" (south), with the west flank—appear as one range of imposing buildings. The Procuratie Nuove with the adjoining Old Library now form the Palazzo Reale. The Procurators were the chief officials of the Republic after the Doge. After sunset the scene upon the Piazza is very animated; in summer a band plays about three evenings a week, in winter during the afternoon.

SAN MARCO, or Cathedral of St. Mark (whose bones are said to have been brought here from Alexandria in 829), built in the form of a Greek cross, with Byzantine domes; begun 830, rebuilt after destruction by fire in 976, reconstructed in a Byzantine style in 11th and later centuries; 250 feet long, 170 feet wide. Famous Bronze Horses over the principal portal, supposed to have once decorated an arch of Nero; mosaics on the facade, sculpture at the main entrance. The interior is magnificently decorated with statues and mosaics (those by Tintoretto are in the arch over the screens); the high altar is usually covered, but may be seen (11 to 2, 50c.); in the treasury are valuable sacred objects.

At the south west corner of Piazza San Marco is the new Campanile, erected (completed 1910) on the site of the old tower, which collapsed July 13th, 1902.

On west side of the Piazzetta is the old Library (Libreria Vecchia), of 16th cent., a magnificent building with a double row of open arches. On the Molo is the old Zecca (Mint), where is housed the Library of St. Mark, transferred from the Palazzo Ducale; 350,000 vols., 11,000 MSS.

South of San Marco, on the east side of the Piazzetta, is the PALAZZO DUCALE, the Palace of the Doges, with double arcaded exterior, the pillars exhibiting much very fine sculptor's work. The interior, of great historic interest, contains a fine collection of paintings, including works by Tintoretto and Paolo Veronese, and an Archæological Museum. Weekdays, 9.0 to 5.0, 1 lira; free on Sunday, 10.0 to 2.0. The Bridge of Sighs (Ponte dei Sospiri) connects the Palace on east side with the Prigioni (prisons).

All the churches of Venice should be seen, the most celebrated are:

San Giorgio Maggiore, on island of that name, directly south of San Marco; a church with dome; beautiful interior, paintings; view from campanile.

Frari (Santa Maria Gloriosa dei Frari), half mile south east of Railway Station and same distance south west of the Rialto bridge. Famous church; many historic personages buried here; monuments, sculpture, paintings. During restoration of interior the most valuable altar pieces are to be seen at the church of St. Toma, a short distance east.

San Sebastiano, near west end, north side, of Canal della Giudecca; paintings by Paolo Veronese.

Santa Maria della Salute, south side of Canal Grande, near its east end. Domed church; decorated exterior; handsome interior; paintings by Titian.

Il Redentore (Church of the Redeemer), on island of Giudecca, south side of city; architecturally interesting; paintings.

San Zaccaria, a little east of San Marco; paintings.

SS. Giovanni e Paolo, half a mile north of San Marco. Domed church, containing tombs of the doges; magnificent monuments, paintings.

Scuola San Giorgio degli Schiavoni, east side of Rio della Pietà, half a mile east of San Marco: paintings.

San Francesco della Vigna, near the lagoon, a mile north east of San Marco; statues and paintings.

Santa Maria Formosa, a little north of San Marco. Domed church; paintings.

San Salvatore, a little south of Rialto bridge. Domed church; statues and paintings—an Annunciation by Titian.

San Giovanni Crisostomo, a little north of Rialto bridge. Paintings.

ACCADEMIA DI BELLE ARTI, on south side of Canal Grande, near the iron bridge, about three quarters of a mile west of San Marco. Weekdays, 9.0 to 4.0, 1 lira; Sunday, 10.0 to 2.0, free. A magnificent collection of paintings by Venetian artists. Titian's masterpiece, The Assumption of the Virgin, is in Room II. Other great names are Bellini (Gentile and Giovanni), Tintoretto, Paolo Veronese, Marconi, and Carpaccio.

Scuola di San Rocco, by the Church of San Rocco, just west of the Frari Church. Daily, 9.0 to 5.0 in summer, 10.0 to 3.0 in winter; 1 lira (includes church of S. Rocco). Paintings; Tintoretto's celebrated Crucifixion in the Sala dell' Albergo.

Arsenal, half a mile east of San Marco. Weekdays, 9.0 to 3.0. In the Museum are ship models, weapons, etc.

Galleria d'Arte Moderna, in the Palazzo Pesaro, on south side of the Grand Canal, half a mile west of the Rialto bridge. Collection of paintings by modern artists. Weekdays, 9.0 to 4.0, 1 lira; Sun., 9.0 to 2.0, free.

Museo Civico Correr, in the Fondaco dei Turchi, on south side of the Grand Canal, near the Station. Art collections, library, and historical exhibits. Weekdays, 9.0 to 4.0, 1 lira; Sunday, free.

POST OFFICE.—In the Fondaco dei Tedeschi, just north of east end of the Rialto bridge, open 8.0 a.m. until 9.0 p.m. Telegraph Office, just off west side of Piazza San Marco.

Church of Eng. Service.—St. George's Church, Campo S. Vio.

H.B.M.'s Consul.—Edward de Zuccato, Esq.

U. S. Con.—J. V. Long, Esq.

Medical—Dr. W. Blaydes, Dr. Todd, Dr. Werner.

Rail, pages 279a, 280, 285a, 286, 288.

[Lido.—

Excelsior Palace Hotel.—New first class. In charming position—fine panorama. 400 bed and sitting rooms. Up to date sanitation. Moderate. Open all the year. See Advt.

Hotel Marino.—On the shore. 60 bed rooms equipped with modern comfort. Café and terrace overlooking the sea. Moderate terms. See Advt.

On the Adriatic, near Venice. Good beach. Views at sunset very fine. Castle. Reached by steamer from Venice, page 355.

If the visitor intends to stay several days at Venice a visit by the morning steamer to the small isle of Torcello (on the Lagune, about 1 hour distant) is recommended, where is to be seen a primitive Cathedral with large stone shutters, also, almost adjoining, a most picturesque Church, both built in the very early years of Christianity; in front of the Cathedral are the remains of a temple].

Verona.—*Stat.*—Pop. of commune 81,909.

Grand Hotel de Londres et Royal Deux Tours.—E. Ceresa, proprietor. First class, in good situation. Electric light; lift. See Advt.

Grand Hotel Colombe d'Or.—Situated south, close to the Roman Amphitheatre. Entirely refurnished. Steam heating, Garage. See Advt.

Hotel Riva S. Lorenzo and Cavour.—Most comfortable, with terrace overlooking the Adige. Electric light; lift. Pension from 9 fr. See Advt.

The principal Railway Station, Stazione Porta Vescovo, is on the south east side of the town, about 1½ mile from the centre of the town; the Stazione Porta Nuova, on south side, is less than a mile from the centre.

Verona is a town of ancient foundation; it was a Roman colony B.C. 89, and continuously in its history, until quite modern times, was one of the prosperous places of northern Italy—its interest now for travellers is chiefly antiquarian and artistic. It lies on both banks of the River Adige, and is strongly fortified.

When the traveller has only a short time, perhaps less than a day, to spare, it is well to ride on the tramcar that runs between the two Railway Stations—the Stazione Porta Vescovo and the Stazione Porta Nuova; in this way some of the most interesting sites are traversed, and a prompt return can be made to them.

Following the line of thoroughfare leading northward from the Stazione Porta Vescovo, at a short distance is the Porta Vescovo, then the street, slightly bending to left, becomes Via Venti Settembre, the River Adige is crossed, and presently the tram lines run into the Piazza delle Erbe.

The Piazza delle Erbe abounds in interest; it is the ancient Forum. At the centre, between the cross streets, is the canopied Capitello; a little north is the Fountain, with the statue of Verona; a Colonna of marble, with the lion of S. Mark, is at the north end. On the south-west side at the corner of Via Pelliciai, is the Casa dei Mercanti; on the north side is the stately Palazzo Trezza, of 17th cent.; at the corner, by the Corso Sant' Anastasia, is the Casa Mazzanti, built by the Scaligers—ancient outside stairs at the back. On south west side, in the Via Capello, is a house, marked by a tablet, where Juliet's parents are said to have lived.

An archway in the Via Costa leads from the Piazza delle Erbe to the Piazza dei Signori (also called Piazza Dante). On the west side is the Domus Nova, of 13th cent., rebuilt 17th cent.; on the north side is La Loggia, or Palazzo del Consiglio, a very fine example of early Renaissance architecture, erected 1476-93; on the east side is the Prefettura, once a residence of the Scaligers; on the south side is the Palazzo del Comune, or Palazzo della Ragione, dating from 12th cent., with rebuildings in 16th and 19th cents.—in the court is the entrance to the Torre del Comune, 272 ft. high, stated to have been built 1172; the Tribunali (law courts) are also in the Piazza. Between the Prefettura and the Tribunali a passage leads to the Church of S. Maria Antica and the Arche degli Scaligeri, the Tombs of the Scaligers.

On north east side of Piazza dei Signori, a short street, Via Foggie, leads to the Corso S. Anastasia; here, turning to right, at north end of the Corso, is the Gothic Church of Sant' Anastasia, dating from 1290; frescoes and sculpture.

From the Piazza Sant' Anastasia, on north west side, Via Liceo leads into Via Duomo and presently to the Duomo, a Gothic Cathedral of 15th cent., with portions (choir and facade) dating from 12th cent. Frescoes; an "Assumption," by Titian, over one of the altars. From the choir a corridor leads to the 12th cent. Baptistery of S. Giovanni in Fonte. By the facade, to left, are Romanesque Cloisters.

Close by the Duomo, to the north, on opposite side of the River Adige, is the Church of San Giorgio in Braida, where are some fine paintings in good state of preservation. Just across the river from the Duomo, a few yards south of the Ponte Pietra, on the slope of the hill, is the Roman Theatre.

From the bridge to west of the Duomo, Ponte Garibaldi, proceed by the river, on south side, along Lungadige Panvino, until about midway between Ponte Garibaldi and the next bridge, Ponte di Castel Vecchio. Here, any of the short streets lead south to the Corso Cavour, and thence all the streets southward lead to Piazza Vittorio Emanuele. On east side of the piazza is the famous Amphitheatre, or Arena, erected by Diocletian A.D. 290; entrance on west side, 1 lira, closed at sunset. Statue of Victor Emmanuel at middle of piazza. [The curious may care to visit the so-called Tomb of Juliet—Tomba di Giulietta—in a garden (50c.) on the Campo di Fiera, off Via Cappucini, a street on south side of Via Pallone, at south east corner of Piazza Vittorio Emanuele.]

PALAZZO POMPEI, on east bank of the Adige, just south of Ponte Navi, midway between centre of town and Stazione Porta Vescovo, contains the Museo Civico (summer 9.0 to 4.0, winter, 9.0 to 3.0, 1 lira). Natural history collections, antiquities, sculpture, bronzes, coins, on ground floor; in rooms above the Picture Gallery, mostly paintings of the Veronese School.

The Church of San Zeno Maggiore is at extreme north west of town; follow river bank, on west side, from the bridge of Castel Vecchio, about a mile. Reliefs on portal; interior has sculpture and frescoes. Cloisters to left of church, with small museum of Christian antiquities (50c.).

San Bernardino, on west side, directly (short distance) south of San Zeno; frescoes, paintings, cloisters.

Santa Maria in Organo, east side of town, short distance from east end of Ponte Umberto; ancient church, rebuilt 1481; frescoes, choir stalls, sacristy.

San Fermo Maggiore, at west end of Ponte Navi, opposite Palazzo Pompei; 14th cent.; sculptures and frescoes.

POST OFFICE in Piazza dell' Indipendenza, a little off east side of Piazza Erbe, and near west end of Ponte Umberto.

RAIL, pages 280, 282, 287.

Viareggio.—*Stat.*—Pop. 14,900.

GRAND HOTEL REGINA.—New first class hotel commanding position.

A well built town, sea bathing resort, and winter residence, with mild genial climate, sheltered from cold winds by a pine forest.

MEDICAL.—Dr. Munro.

RAIL, pages 270, 274A.

Vicenza.—*Stat.*—Pop. of the commune 54,555.

HOTELS: ROMA; TRE GAROFANI.

Capital of a province, the ancient Vicetia, on the Rivers Bacchiglione and Retrone, at the base of Monte Retrone. The principal interest attaches to architecture, several creations of the great master Andrea Palladio (1518-80) adorning the cramped streets; in the 15th cent. the city was also the seat of a school of painting.

From the Railway Station, in south west quarter, a broad road leads north, quarter mile, to the Porta Castello, at one end of the Corso Principe Umberto. 200 yards due east of the Porto is the Duomo, containing a few paintings; on south east side of the piazza is the Vescovado (epis. palace), of 1543. From Piazza del Duomo the Via Garibaldi leads east to Piazza de' Signori, where is the Basilica Palladiana, 1549—tower 265 ft.; opposite the Basilica is the Palazzo Municipio.

Museo Civico, in Piazza Vittorio Emanuele, at north east end of the Corso; on upper floor is gallery of valuable paintings; collections of antiquities, natural history, etc.; daily 11.0 to 2.0 free; 9.0 to 11.0, and 2.0 to 4.0, 50 c. Teatro Olimpico, 1584, on north side of the piazza. In Church of Santa Corona, a few yards back from west side of this end of the Corso, are good paintings.

Pilgrimage Church of Madonna del Monte, south side of city, on Monte Berico; paintings, and memorials of insurrection of 1848. Before reaching the church a road goes off east to the Rotonda, celebrated but in decayed state, a square structure with columns, domed hall; fee 50 c. RAIL, pages 280, 288.

Viterbo.—*Stat.*—Pop. 20,640.

HOTEL GRANDORI; ANGELO; SCHENARDI.

From the Railway Station, on north side, a broad road leads south, passing, after entering the town, and after a slight bend westward, into the Corso Vittorio Emanuele, which conducts to the Piazza del Plebiscito, at the centre. In the piazza is the Palazzo Municipale, 1264, with portico of 15th cent.; here is a museo of antiquities and paintings (50 c.). From the piazza the Via San Lorenzo leads south and then west to the Duomo (S. Lorenzo), 12th cent., Romanesque. The Piazza S. Lorenzo is the spot where July, 1155, Pope Hadrian IV compelled the Emperor Frederick I to hold his stirrup as a sign of vassalage. RAIL, page 278, 283.

SICILY.—(SICILIA).

Catania.—*Stat.*—Pop. of commune 210,703.

HOTELS: CENTRAL; EUROPE; GRANDE BRETAGNE.

The Railway Station is close to the shore, on the north east side of the town, about two thirds of a mile from the centre. Travellers arriving by Steamer are landed in small boats—50 c., luggage 1 lira.

A busy commercial place, having a large trade in the produce of the fertile neighbouring country. In 1669 Catania was almost destroyed by an eruption of Ætna, and in 1693 a terrible earthquake brought it to the ground, burying 60,000 persons under the ruins. From the Station a street runs south west in a line with the sea to the Piazza dei Martiri, where the Corso Vittorio Emanuele goes off to west across the town

The Duomo, on south side of the Corso, contains some royal sarcophagi; in the Cappella di S. Agata are the relics of the saint, martyred A.D. 252—her crown is stated to have been the gift of Richard Cœur de Lion; mon. of Bellini, the composer; fresco in sacristy. Under the piazza are remains of Roman baths.

The University is in a piazza a few yards back from the north side of the Corso, opposite the Duomo. Nearly 1,000 students; library of 91,000 vols.; collection of shells.

Roman Amphitheatre, the largest in Sicily, the greater part being under the Piazza Bellini (a few yards off south side—mid-way—of Via Lincoln).

Teatro Greco, the remains of a Græco-Roman theatre, are 200 yards west of the University, in the Via Teatro Greco; the ruins are mostly underground. In the ruins an abundant spring of clear water has been found.

Church of San Nicola, on west side of town, contains one of the largest organs in Europe;

very fine carving on the choir stalls; paintings; in the transept is a meridian mark. From the tower is a fine view of Ætna and Monte Rossi, of former craters of Nicolosi, and of the whole country where the lava flowed that destroyed Catania several times. In the old monastery, now turned to secular use, is a Museo of miscellaneous curiosities, also a library (20,000 vols. and some MSS).

Museo Biscari, in Via Museo Biscari, 100 yards east of the Duomo; collections of antiquities.

H.B.M.'s VICE-CONSUL.—W. A. Franck, Esq.
U.S. CONSUL.—A. W. Weddell, Esq.

RAIL, pages 289A, 290, 290A.

[**Mount Ætna** is usually ascended from Catania; the ascent is made by night, so that sunrise may be seen; summer is the most favourable time. Travellers should enquire at the office of the Italian Alpine Club as to guides, mules, etc.; lowest cost about 40 lire per traveller, exclusive of food, which must be taken. The climb is fatiguing, and the wind often piercingly cold. The ascent proper begins at Nicolosi, 2,266 ft. above sea, a village 9 miles north west of Catania. The crater is subject to constant modification, at times there is a single abyss, at other times there is a double abyss. Sunrise, seen from the loftiest peak, 10,742 ft., is very grand. The Observatory is 1,000 ft. below the crater. Circumference of the mountain at the base, 86 miles.]

Girgenti.—*Stat.*—Pop. of commune 26,823.

HOTELS: DES TEMPLES; BELVEDERE.

The Railway Station is 2¼ miles to north east of the town. Cab, Station to town, 2 lire.

A place of considerable commercial importance as a centre of the sulphur trade, which, however, is declining. Near the entrance of the town from the Station is the Duomo, dating from 14th cent.; paintings, in left aisle a Roman sarcophagus with reliefs. In the Church of S. Maria dei Greci are relics of a temple (either of Jupiter or of Athene). Museum.

The ruins of the ancient city, the Arcagas of the Greeks, and the Agrigentum of the Romans, are approached from the east side of the modern city. On the left is the Rupe Atenea (Rock of Athene), where it is supposed once stood a temple of Athene; to the right a road leads to the Church of San Nicola, beyond which, in ¼ mile, the road turns east to the Temple of Concord (become the Church of S. Gregorio) and the Temple of Juno Lacinia, of which twenty-five columns are standing, portions of others have been re-erected. West of the road leading up from San Nicola is the Temple of Zeus, of vast proportions, never finished.

RAIL, p. 290.

Marsala.—*Stat.*—Pop. 37,000.

HOTELS: STELLA D'ITALIA; CENTRALE.

A modern commercial town with a trade in wine, on the site of the ancient Lillybæum; some traces of the latter are near the Porta di Trapani and in the Convento dei Niccolini. Cathedral.

H.B.M.'s VICE-CONSUL.—C. E. Massey, Esq.
RAIL, page 289A.

Messina.—*Stat.*—Pop. of commune 126,557.

A once prosperous and populous town that in the early morning (about 5.0 a.m.) of Dec. 28th, 1908, was ruined by an earthquake followed immediately by a tidal wave, the devastation being continued later by the outbreak of extensive fires. Previous to the disaster the population of the commune was 168,712, of whom it is estimated that 130,000 lost their lives.

H.B.M.'s VICE-CONSUL.—J. B. Heynes, Esq.
RAIL, page 290.

PALERMO.—*Stat.*—Pop. of commune 341,088 *(Plan in Special Edition, or post free 3d. stamps).*

EXCELSIOR PALACE HOTEL.—First class; modern. In good position. Rooms from 4 fr. Pension arrangements. See Advt.

IGIEA; PALMES; FRANCE; SAVOY.

The principal RAILWAY STATION, Stazione Centrale, is on the south side of the town; a minor Station, Stazione Lolli, is to north west.

STEAMER.—Travellers arriving by steamer are conveyed to the Dogana (custom exam.), charge 1 lira per person, including luggage.

A little to left of the Stazione Centrale the Via Macqueda runs northward, with its continuations traversing the town: within half a mile of the Stazione the Via Macqueda is crossed by the Corso Vittorio Emanuele. These two streets are the principal thoroughfares, and are exactly represented by the figure +; the Stazione is at the foot, the Giardini Inglese and better residential quarter at the head, at the extremity of the right arm is the pleasant Giardino Garibaldi and the old harbour (La Cala), on the left arm is the Cattedrale with the Palazzo Reale at the end. The town itself is not imposing, but the situation is very fine, and the climate delightful.

Proceeding from the Stazione Centrale northward along the Via Macqueda the street soon becomes interesting as the crossing by the Corso Vittorio Emanuele is approached. On the east side is the Palazzo della Citta, or Municipio; immediately opposite is the University, attended by nearly 1,500 students. Next to the University is the Church of San Giuseppe de' Teatini; much decoration. Turning here to west into the Corso Vittorio Emanuele, on the right hand the Cattedrale is presently seen.

The CATTEDRALE stands on the site of an ancient Christian Church at one time used as a mosque. The existing building dates from 1169, and was erected by an Archbishop of English birth, Gualterio Offamilio, or Walter of the Mill. It has been many times restored. The interior contains the Tombs of the Kings of Sicily, and several other sarcophagi. In the Cappella di Santa Rosalia the remains of the saint are in a sarcophagus of silver, exhibited only two or three times a year.

The PALAZZO REALE is just beyond and almost opposite the Duomo, across the Piazza della Vittoria. The great attraction at the Palazzo is the Chapel, Cappella Palatina, a beautiful relic of mediæval art.

The MUSEO NAZIONALE is at the end of a short street, Via Bara, running out of east side of Via Macqueda, north of the Corso. The collections include ancient sculpture, vases, coins, inscriptions, etc. The Picture Gallery in upper part of building. Open 10.0 to 3.0, Sunday 11.0 to 3.0; 1 lira—Sunday free.

La Martorana Church, behind Municipio, off east side Via Macqueda, dates from 1143. Weekdays, 9.0 to 4.0, 1 lira; Sunday after 10.0 free. Mosaics and inscriptions.

San Giovanni degli Eremite, early Norman church, on the site of a mosque; behind Palazzo Reale.

San Salvatore, on south side of Corso Vittorio Emanuele. Interior very fine.

Carmine Maggiore, in Via Collegio, a little north west of Stazione Centrale.

San Domenico, a little back from north side of Corso Vittorio Emanuele, near its east end. Paintings and monuments. Behind the church, in Via Bambinai, is the Oratorio del Santissimo Rosario, where are good paintings.

Santa Cita, a little north of San Domenico, has reliefs and sarcophagi. Oratorio behind church.

The MARINA, or Foro Italico, is on the sea front, directly east of Stazione Centrale; promenade with fine views; band generally in morning. Villa Giulia, a public garden, on the Marina, is very beautiful; Botanic Garden adjoining.

H.B.M.'s CONSUL.-R. G. Macbean, Esq., M.V.O.

VICE-CONSUL.—W. A Morrison, Esq.

U. S. CONS.—H. de Soto, Esq.

ENG. CH. SERVICE—Church in Via Stabile.

GOLF LINKS.

RAIL pages 289A, 290. STEAMERS, see List.

Selinunte.—*Stat.*—

On the coast, facing south, near the west end of the island, the site of the ancient Greek city of Selinus, founded B.C. 628, ruined by Hannibal B.C. 409, finally destroyed B.C. 263. The ruins of the famous ancient temple are of the greatest interest. At the Casa della Commissione plans of Selinus may be seen.

RAIL, page 290A.

Syracuse.—*Stat.*—Pop. of commune 40,835.

HOTELS; ROMA; VITTORIA; ETRANGERS.

The Railway Station is close to the ruins of the ancient city, but is a mile north west of the modern city. Steamers land passengers in small boats. charge 50 c.

Ancient Syracuse covered a vast space, and had a population of 500,000; the modern city, not attractive, is confined to the little island of Ortygia, and has a population of less than 25,000. The situation is of great natural beauty, and the historic associations are of the deepest interest.

The Duomo, on the west side of the island, is on the site of a temple (to whom is not known), and at one time in its history was a Saracenic mosque. Opposite the Duomo, to south, is the Museo Archeologico. At the end of the street running south of the Duomo is the Fountain of Arethusa. At the north of the Island, near the Piazza del Popolo, is a Greek temple, ascribed by some to Diana by others to Apollo. St, Paul (Acts xxviii, 12) on the journey to Rome, stayed three days at Syracuse.

A few yards south along the road from the Railway Station is an open space, whence a road goes north east; this presently bifurcates, the road on the left leading to the principal of the ancient ruins—the amphitheatre, the Latomia del Paradiso, and the Greek Theatre, all within about two miles of the Station. Near the amphitheatre is the house of the Custode delle Antichità, who accompanies visitors, fee 50 c.

The buildings and ruins to the right hand (within 2 miles) of the Railway Station, facing north, include the Church of San Giovanni, founded 1182, on a spot sanctified by martyrdoms, and, according to tradition, by the presence of St. Paul, who it is averred preached here; near the church are the Catacombs—1 lira.

The ancient Fort Euryelus is about 6 miles north west along the road by the Station.

H.B.M.'s VICE-CONSUL.—Joseph Lobb, Esq.

RAIL, page 290, 290A. Steamer to Malta, see List.

Taormina.—Pop. 3,000.

GRAND HOTEL SAN DOMENICO.—First class, comfortable, much frequented hotel, with views of Etna and Ionian Sea. Winter Garden. See Advt.

CASTELLO; TIMEO.

The ancient Tauromenium, founded, B.C. 396, in a most beautiful situation, on a hill by the coast, about 3 miles by a winding road from the Station of Giardini-Taormina. Cab from Station, 1 to 4 persons, 3 lire, extra at night.

The Greek Theatre, re-constructed by the Romans, the great attraction, is to the east of the town, on a height; attached is a museum. Castello, the old Acropolis, on a height, 1,300 ft Cathedral; in Piazza Vittorio Emanuele is Palazzo Corvaia, with a relief on the staircase—close by are Church of Santa Caterina and a small Roman theatre. Houses in the Corso have remnants of mediaeval architecture. The views are considered among the most beautiful in Italy. Sunrise and sunset offer panorama of surpassing grandeur.

H.B.M.'s VICE-CONSUL.—Dr. S. Cacciola.

RAIL (Giardini-Taormina Station), page 290.

Trapani.—*Stat.*—Pop. of commune 59,593.
HOTELS: GRAND; TRINACRIA.
The ancient Drepana. Cathedral (S. Lorenzo) contains a Crucifixion by van Dyck; at the Oratorio di San Michele are some coloured wooden groups representing the Passion. Upon the summit of Monte San Giuliano, about 6 miles to north east, once stood a temple of Venus Erycina, the site being now occupied by a decayed little town.
H.B.M.'s VICE-CONS.—L. M. Marino, Esq.
U.S. CONSULAR AGENT.
RAIL, page 289A.

SARDINIA (Italian **Sardegna**) is, Sicily excepted, the largest island in the Mediterranean; it was once much more fertile than now, many districts having fallen out of cultivation, while forest covers a fifth of the land. During the hot months, July to October, there is much malaria in the low lying districts. Cattle, oil, and wine are exported, but the principal sources of wealth are the silver, lead, zinc, antimony, and cadmia mines. Scattered about the island are many Nuraghi, conical stone monuments, containing one or two chambers, ascribed to various ages and purposes, but most generally considered to have been places of refuge set up by early natives. A daily steamer service is maintained between Civita Vecchia, on the Italian coast, and Golfo Aranci, a port in the north east part of the island, whence there is railway to the principal towns.
RAIL, page 289A.

Cagliari.—*Stat.*—Pop. of commune 60,101.
HOTELS: SCALA DI FERRO; QUATTRO MORI.
The capital, a very old place, on the Golfo di Cagliari, at the south end of the island; though very hot in summer is usually free of fever. Cathedral; University, about 250 students; Museum of Antiquities. Roman Amphitheatre.
H.B.M.'s CONSUL.—R. H. Pernis, Esq.
U.S. CONSULAR AGENT.

Iglesias.—*Stat.*—Pop. 12,000.
ALBERGO LEON D'ORO.
On the south west coast; at the centre of the mining district. Cathedral; a School of Mines. Extensive tunny fisheries at the neighbouring island of S. Pietro, chief town **Carloforte** (pop. 6,300; H.B.M.'s VICE CONSUL—E. Armeni, Esq.)

Porto Torres.—*Stat.*—Pop. 8,500.
A malarious place on the site of the Roman Turris Libyssonis, with many Roman remains in the neighbourhood. Church of San Gavino. Steamer to Ajaccio.

Sassari.—*Stat.*—Pop. of commune 43 118.
HOTELS: ITALIA; SAN MARTINO.
Attractive new quarters of the town, with good public buildings; the Cathedral and one or two churches have paintings. University, about 150 students.
H.B.M.'s VICE-CONSUL.-Cav. G. Sechi-Pieroni.

SPAIN.

Late spring and the autumn are preferable seasons for travelling in the interior of Spain; for the Mediterranean coast, and south Spain generally, early spring and late autumn are preferred. Owing to the configuration of the country it may be said there are as many variations in climate as there are contrasts of character in the population; three fourths of the interior are treeless poor land, with an elevated central district that is bleak and sombre. Only in the south and east and along the valley of the River Ebro is the scenery pleasantly attractive—elsewhere nature often appears to frown. Only in the large towns is the hotel accommodation what the traveller has a right to expect; unfortunately great architectural attractions are often in secondary towns where the hotels are decidedly second rate.

Government.—King Alfonso XIII, born May, 1886; married May 31st, 1906, to Princess Victoria Eugénie Julia Ena, daughter of Princess Beatrice (Princess Henry of Battenberg). Heir, Prince Alfonso Pio Christino Eduardo, born May 10th, 1907. The Cortes are composed of two legislative bodies—the Senate (about 360 members), and the Chamber of Deputies (one Deputy for every 50,000 inhabitants).

Army—Peace establishment, (1912) 128,073; on a war footing about 220,000 men. **Navy** (including those building)- dreadnoughts 3, battleships 1, cruisers 7, destroyers 7, torpedo boats 24, gunboats 10.

Population (1910), 19,588,688, including the Canary Islands, etc.

Railways.—Trains run according to Greenwich Time. Railway carriages have to be changed at the French frontier, the railway gauges of France and Spain being different; the trains, however, run alongside each other. First class carriages are tolerably comfortable, second class carriages are wanting in comfort, third class carriages are unsuitable for British travellers. Railway speed is slow, rarely more than 15 miles per hour. **Luggage.**—66 lbs. allowed free. **Distance Railway Tickets**, **available for travel over a distance from 2,000 to 12,000 kilometros (1,243 miles to 7,458 miles), are issued by the Spanish Railway Companies. The fares range from 165 pesetas 1st class, and 121 p. 2nd class, for the shorter distance, to 792 pesetas 1st class, and 607 p. 20 c. 2nd class, for the longer distance, the validity extends from 3 months to 12 months.**

Money.—100 Centimos=1 Peseta=Paper about 7½d., Specie 9½d. **Gold coins are rarely seen, bank notes of the Banco de Espana taking their place.** SILVER COINS—1, 2, 5 Pesetas, and 50 Centimos. BRONZE COINS—1, 2, 5, 10 Centimos.

Postage.—Letters to Great Britain 25 c. per half ounce; post cards, 10 c.

Weights and Measures.—Though the metric system of weights and measures has been introduced in Spain the old weights and measures are still largely used. They are:—The Quintal = 220.4 lbs. avoirdupois; the Libra = 1.014 lbs. avoirdupois; the Arroba, for wine = 3½ imperial gallons, for oil = 2⅝ imperial gallons; the Square Vara = 1.09 vara = 1 yard; the Fanega = 1½ imperial bushel. See p. lxxi.

NOTICE OF PRINCIPAL TOWNS, ETC.

Algeciras.—*Stat.*-Pop. 13,300.

HOTEL REINA CRISTINA. — Modern hotel, first-class. See Advt.

ANGLO-HISPANO; MARINA.

Algeciras is well situated, on a low hill, at the mouth of the River Miel, and offers a very picturesque aspect from the sea. The climate is milder, warmer, and more equable than that of other Mediterranean resorts, the mean winter (shade) temperature being 55° F.; the air is dry and bracing without sudden changes of temperature. Algeciras is reputed to be one of the healthiest towns in Spain; the water supply is excellent. As a health resort it may be recommended as a rest cure, whilst it is also a convenient centre for visiting the most interesting towns of Andalucia and Morocco. There is a handsome Plaza, with a fountain erected by Castanos in 1807, a prettily laid out Alameda, spacious bull-ring, and also a church of some interest. In the vicinity is the splendid aqueduct built by the Moors, which still supplies the town with water.

H.B.M.'s V.-CONSUL.—Wm. James Smith, Esq.

GOLF.—9-hole course.

MEDICAL.—Dr. A. W. W. Dowding.

Rail page 299. Steamer across the bay to Gibraltar; also to Ceuta, Tangier, and Cadiz.

Alicante.—*Stat.*—51,165.

HOTELS: REINA VICTORIA; BOSSIO.

The RAILWAY STATION is on the west side of the town, half a mile from the centre.

Capital of the Province of Alicante, on a small bay of the Mediterranean, with a large export trade in fruit and Alicante wine. The situation is sheltered; in winter the climate is mild and dry. Church of San Nicolas de Bari, impressive interior; Santa Maria. Castillo de Santa Barbara, on height to east; an order necessary.

H.B.M. V. CONSUL.—J. Tato, Esq.

RAIL, pp. 293, 296. Steamers to Spanish and other ports.

[**Busot**, 10 miles north east of Alicante (diligence), 1,640 feet above sea, among pine woods, has a reputation as a winter resort.]

Almeria.—*Stat.*—Pop. 45,198.

HOTELS: DE PARIS; DE LONDRES.

Capital of the Province of Almeria, and an important Mediterranean seaport, possessing an excellent harbour. Immense quantities of fruit shipped, grapes, oranges, almonds, etc.; sugar refineries. Very pleasant winter climate. Town is dominated by the Castillo de San Cristobal and the Moorish Alcazaba. Cathedral.

H.B.M.'s VICE-CONSUL.—J. Murison, Esq.

U.S. CONSULAR AGENT.

RAIL, page 298A.

Aranjuez.-*Stat.*-Pop. of the commune 9,811.

HOTEL DE PASTOR.

Aranjuez is only visited for the Royal Palace, which is immediately opposite the end of the road from the Railway Station. Permit to view obtained from the Administrador del Real Patrimonio, in the Casa del Infante, Plaza de la Liberdad, 500 yards due east of the Station. Handsome staircases and rooms; beautiful gardens. RAIL. pages 296, 297A.

Badajoz.—*Stat.*—Pop. 33,160.

HOTELS: CENTRAL; GARRIDO.

Capital of the Province of Badajoz, a strongly fortified place on the frontier, sometimes called the "Key of Portugal." Cathedral.

RAIL. pages 297, 300.

Barcelona.—*Stat.*— Pop. (1910) 560,000.

PALACE HOTEL.—First class hotel, in the most central part of the city. English and American clientèle. See Advt.

GRAND HOTEL COLON.—First class establishment, situated Plaza Cataluña, Paseo de Gracia. Telephone, post, and telegraph services; restaurant. See Advt.

HOTEL D'ORIENT (Rambla del Centro)—First class hotel, with all modern comfort. Perfect sanitation. Electric light and bath rooms. Omnibus at the Station. See Advt.

GRAND HOTEL ET QUATRE NATIONS (CUATRO NACIONES), Rambla. First class family hotel, situated in the most fashionable part of the town. See Advert.

GRAND HOTEL FALCON.—First class family and commercial hotel. Lift; electric light. Steam heating throughout. See Advt.

GRAND HOTEL D'ANGLETERRE.—First class hotel, Plaza de Cataluna. Central heating. Hot and cold water supply laid on in bedrooms. See Advt.

The principal RAILWAY STATIONS, the Estacion de Francia and the Estacion del Norte, are in the north part of the city, but near the centre. The Estacion de Francia is close to the Puerto (Port); at this Station trains arrive from and depart for the French frontier at Portbou, thence for Narbonne, Cette, and Marseilles. The Estacion del Norte is further, about half a mile, from the Puerto; at this Station the train service connects with France on the west side of the Pyrenees, for Bordeaux, etc.

Barcelona, the capital of the Province of Barcelona, is the most important commercial and industrial city of Spain, the activity of the population contrasting with the dullness noticeable elsewhere. There are many fine streets flanked by handsome buildings, especially along the line of the old walls, where now are spacious avenues; and in the suburbs are numerous iron foundries, machine works, cotton and silk mills, etc. Climate very pleasant; summer heat not oppressive, nor winter cold severe—snow rarely falls.

On the sea front of the city, bordering the Puerto, is the fine, spacious, palm planted quay, the Paseo de Colon; the north end of the Paseo leads to the Plaza de Palacio, a centre of activity, and the Estacion de Francia; at the south end of the Paseo is the Plaza de la Paz, where is the Columbus Monument (200 ft. high)—here is one end of the Rambla, an imposing thoroughfare broadening into tree shaded avenues bearing different names.

The CATEDRAL (de la Santa Eulalia), on high ground at the centre of old Barcelona, is considered one of the finest of Spanish Gothic churches. Begun 1298, completed 1448; exterior view hindered by surrounding buildings; many paintings of varying merit in interior, some good reliefs, splendid stained glass windows, tomb of Santa Eulalia in crypt; cloisters on south west side.

Santa Maria del Mar, close to north end of the Puerto, near Estacion de Francia. Gothic (1328-83); imposing interior, with paintings. For permission to build this church the Moors, then in possession of the country, exacted a heavy tribute. Old fountain opposite the church.

The other churches of Barcelona are generally remarkable for the absence of aisles, the width often seeming greater than is really the case.

Casa de la Diputacion, in the Plaza de la Constitucion, two minutes walk south east of the Cathedral. The old House of Provincial Deputies; several paintings by modern artists in the rooms in the Capilla de San Jorge (chapel in same building) are ecclesiastical decorations. The Casa Consistorial is on the south east side of the Plaza, opposite the Casa de la Diputacion. Some interior details of the Consistorial are of interest; on an upper floor is the Archivo Municipal, with collections illustrating local history—daily 10.0 to 1.0 and 4.0 to 6.0.

Archivo General de la Corona de Aragon, a Gothic building, in the Plaza del Rey, just away from north east angle of the Cathedral. The archives are stated to number more than four million documents. Opposite the Archivo, in the old Capilla Real de Santa Aguĕda, is the Museo Provincial; collection of Roman and mediæval antiquities, coins, medals, etc.—open during the morning, 50 c.

Archæological Museum (Museo Martorell), in the Paseo de a Industria, west of the Estacion de Francia. Museum of Natural History at the corner of the Paseo de la Industria and Calle de la Princesa.

University, in Calle de las Cortes, a street on south side of the Rambla de Cataluña. Founded 1450; rebuilt 1863-73; about 2,500 students; the library contains 150,000 vols.

Palacio de Bellas Artes, at east end, south side, of Salon de San Juan, a broad avenue running east and west, a little south of Estacion del Norte. Here is the Museo Municipal de Bellas Artes interesting collection of pictures.

Palacio de Justicia (Law Courts), a handsome building on north side of Salon de San Juan. The Arco de Triunfo, at the end of the Salon de San Juan, was the entrance to an exhibition.

Castillo de Montjuich, on the heights at south side of city. Fine view from heights. In 1705 Montjuich was surprised and captured by Lord Peterborough. Cemeterio del Oeste on south west slope of the Montjuich.

Parque y Jardines de la Ciudadela, a quarter mile north of the Puerto, beyond the Estacion de Francia; rare plants and pleasant lakes; small museums in the avenues.

Cemeterio del Este, away on north side of city, close to the sea.

Bull Ring, in Plaza de Toros, east side of Estacion de Francia.

POST OFFICE (Correo), in Plaza de Urquinaona, near the Plaza de Cataluña, near west end of the Rambla. Here is the Poste Restante. Telegraph Office (Telegrafos), in Ronda de la Universidad, No. 17.

ENGLISH CHURCH, ST. GEORGE.—200, Calle Rosellon (corner of Calle Claris), 8.0, 11.0 a.m., 8.30 p.m.

H.B.M.'s CONSUL-GENERAL.—J. F. Roberts, Esq., C.M.G. V.-CONSULS.—H. Tom, Esq., and George R. Smither, Esq.

U.S. CONS.-GEN.—H. H. Morgan, Esq. VICE-CONSUL.—C. H. Albrecht, Esq.

RAIL, pages 292, 295.

Bilbao.—*Stat.*—Pop. (1910) 92,514.

HOTEL BISCAYA; LONDRES.

On the River Nervion, with wooded hills around, about 8 miles from the sea; an important commercial town, concerned in iron manufacture. Many British residents. In the new town, to west of the Station, are wide streets and modern buildings. Across the river from the Railway Station is the Paseo del Arenal, the centre of the city life—here is the Institutio, with a library and museum. Churches of Santiago, 14th cent., and San Antonio Abad, 15th cent. Casa del Ayuntamiento, by the river.

H.B.M.'s CONSUL.—Lord H. Hervey. V.-CONS. —James Innes, Esq.

U. S. CONSULAR-AGENT.

RAIL, pages 292, 294A, 298A.

[Portugalete, 7½ miles from Bilbao, a small seaport and sea side resort, with a pop. of 5,200. An English Church. RAIL, p. 294A.]

Burgos.—*Stat.*—Pop. 31,489.

GRAND HOTEL DE PARIS.—First-class hotel. Well situated. See Advt.

NORTE Y LONDRES; UNIVERSAL.

The Railway Station is to the south west, about a mile from the centre of the city.

Burgos, the capital of the Province of Burgos, stands on both banks of the small River Arlanzon, the older part being confined between the river and a hill (800 ft.) upon which are the ruins of a castle. Great interest attaches to Burgos as the home of the national hero, the Cid, while the Cathedral is justly regarded as one of the glories of Gothic architecture in Spain.

The erection of the CATHEDRAL was begun by Ferdinand III (Leon and Castile) and Bishop Maurice, an Englishman, in 1221; the towers of the west front were built 1442-58, the edifice not being completed until early in the 16th cent. The exterior presents innumerable points of interest — towers, spires, windows, portals, statues, culminating in the cimborio, or lantern, having eight pierced pinnacles adorned with statues. Interior is 350 ft. in length, transept 194 ft. long and 165 ft. high; of the fifteen chapels several are rich with elaborate altars, sculpture, and paintings; magnificent tombs in the Capilla del Condestable. In the cloisters are statues and tombs; in the Capilla del Corpus Christi, on east side of cloisters, is a relic of the Cid—a coffer.

In the church of Santa Agueda, a few yards west of the Cathedral, the Cid compelled Alfonso VI to swear his innocence of the murder of his brother Sancho. Other churches are San Nicolas, San Esteban, and San Gil, all full of interest.

Arco de Santa Maria, at west end of the Espolon; an interesting old gateway, containing a museum of curios.

Fine view from the Castle, where Edward I of England was married to Eleanor of Castile. Three stone monuments on the road near west side of the Castle mark the site of the house where the Cid was born—the Solar del Cid.

Casa Consistorial, fronting Plaza Mayor, a few yards east of the Cathedral. Part of the remains of the Cid and of his wife Ximena are in the Capilla.

Casa del Cordon, in Plaza de la Liberdad, east of Cathedral, is an imposing building.

Casa de Miranda, on south side of river, lightly to east of Cathedral, is a fine mediæval relic.

[About a mile south west of Burgos is the REAL MONASTERIO DE LAS HUELGAS, once a royal summer pleasure house, now a famous convent. Royal tombs. Cartuja de Miraflores, on a hill, two miles north east of Burgos; the monuments in the church are considered masterpieces.]

RAIL, see p. 291.

Cadiz.—*Stat.*—Pop. (1910) 67,174.

HOTELS: DE FRANCE; CONTINENTAL.

Situated at the extremity of a very narrow peninsula, about 5 miles long, joined to the mainland by a mere strip of sand, in parts only a quarter mile wide; capital of the Province of Cadiz, and a strongly fortified place. It has a singularly clean, bright, and gracious appearance; from the proximity of the sea, the absence of street traffic and noise, and other points of resemblance, it is sometimes called the Spanish Venice. It is the ancient Gades, and is constantly mentioned in maritime history.

The Catedral is a quarter mile west of the Railway Station, on the side facing the open sea; begun 1722, completed 1838; the old Cathedral (Catedral Vieja) is a few yards east. Academia de Bellas Artes, half mile north of the Railway Station, near the harbour side—valuable collection of pictures; Museo Arqueologico. Torre de Vigia, 100 feet high, a watch tower at the centre of the town, used for ship signalling. Pleasant promenades along the north west sea front.

H.B.M.'s VICE-CONSUL.—R. A. Calvert, Esq.

RAIL, page 294.

Cartagena.—*Stat.*—Pop. 96,983.

HOTELS: DE RAMOS; DE FRANCIA.

The ancient Carthago Nova, a strongly fortified town, one of the principal naval harbours of Spain. Very mild climate. Interest centres in the Arsenal (poorly maintained), to view which an order must be obtained. Ruins of a Cathedral.

H.B.M.'s VICE-CONSUL.—P. Miller, Esq.

RAIL, page 297A.

Cordoba, or **Cordova.**—*Stat.*—Pop. 65,160.

HOTELS: SUIZA; ESPANA; FRANCIA.

The RAILWAY STATION is just beyond the north west part of the city, about two thirds of a mile from the centre.

Capital of the Province of Cordoba, on the Guadalquivir, on a plain between the river and the Sierra de Cordoba. Its history is clearly traced from Roman times, and it was renowned as the capital of the Moors, but its present appearance is a mournful contrast with past glory. Almost everything that could recall the presence of the Moors has been destroyed, fragments only remain, and there is little to arrest the traveller after he has visited the Cathedral and contemplated the sierra and the river.

The Cathedral is at the south west corner of the city, just back from the river, about a mile due south of the Railway Station. It was originally the chief mosque of the Moors, and is the largest monument of Arab religious architecture in Spain, only second in size to the Kaaba of Mecca. The edifice dates from about 785, was several times extended, and was completed as a Moorish work about 990. In 1238 it passed into the possession of Christians. The interior, at first view, seems filled with short columns, of which there are between 800 and 900, of varying material—marble, jasper, porphyry, etc.; there are 19 aisles; mosaics and tracery abound. The choir is very fine, but out of harmony with the building; elaborate high altar. Just south of the Cathedral is the Moorish bridge over the river. The Alcazar is a little way from south west angle of Cathedral. The Escuela Provincial de Bellas Artas contains a museum of pictures and curios.

H. B. M.'s VICE-CONSUL.—R. E. Carr, Esq.

RAIL. pages 293, 294, 296.

[In the Sierra to the north-west, distant about 4 miles, is the Convent of S. Jerónimo, where are found remains of the celebrated Moorish palace of **Az-Zahra**. Consequent upon recent excavations discoveries of considerable architectural and archæological interest have been made.]

Corunna (La Coruña).—*Stat.*—Pop. 45,650.

HOTEL DE FRANCE.

Capital of the Province of Coruña, a prosperous trading town, and the principal military station in north Spain. Palacio Municipal, in Plaza de Maria Pita. Churches of Santa Maria and Santiago, of 13th cent. Sir John Moore (died Jan. 16th, 1809) was buried in the Jardin de San Carlos, to east of the harbour; on north wall of the garden is a tablet recording the loss of 172 officers and men of H.M.S. Serpent, lost off Cape Villano, Nov., 1890. English Cemetery to north west of town.

H. B. M.'s CONSUL.—A. H. Medhurst, Esq.

VICE-CONSUL.—T. Guyatt, Esq.

RAIL, page 293.

Figueras.-*Stat.*-Pop. of the commune 11,522.

HOTEL DE PARIS.

A town without interest except that a diligence plies from it to **Rosas** (pop. 2,805), a small port 10 miles distant, on the Gulf of Rosas, where the climate and surroundings are considered equal to parts of the Riviera.

RAIL, page 295.

Gerona.-*Stat.*-Pop. 15,951.

FONDA ITALIANA.

Capital of the Province of Gerona, an old town upon rising ground, on the River Ter, famous for the heroic defence in 1809, when, aided by a few English, the garrison for seven months resisted a French army of 35,000 men. Gothic Cathedral, dating from 1312, with unusually wide nave, 74 ft.; elaborate high altar, tombs, monuments, cloisters. San Feliu, south of Cathedral, has interesting interior. West of the Cathedral is San Pedro, in the cloisters of which is the Museo Provincial.

RAIL, pages 295, 295A.

Gibraltar. (British). — Pop. 25,367, including the garrison of 5,340 men.

BRISTOL HOTEL.—First class, in a healthy and aristocratic locality, with full south aspect and garden. Fine view. See Advt.

CECIL; BRITISH GRAND.

Some STEAMERS anchor in the Bay, at a distance off the town, travellers being landed in tenders (free). In other cases there is a landing or embarking charge of 1s. 6d., with luggage up to 56 lbs. free; in rough weather charges are increased. The small steamers in connection with the trains at Algeciras, 6 miles across the Bay, run to an extension of the Old Mole.

CABS.—Each cab bears a metal plate giving the authorised fares (in English money).

The Rock of Gibraltar, a mass of Jurassic limestone, rises in a bold headland fronting the Straits and Africa. Behind the headland is a saddle-like depression, then again a rise northward, with an abrupt fall to a sandy isthmus so flat as to be hardly discernible from the sea. The Rock runs due north and south, its length is almost 3 miles, the width ½ to ¾ mile; the east and north sides are sheer down, the south and west sides fall away in terraces. O'Hara's Tower (Sugar Loaf Hill), 1,361 ft., is to the south; Highest Point, 1,396 ft., is next in order towards the north; Signal Station, 1,295 ft., next towards the north; then Middle Hill, 1,211 ft.; finally, at north end, Mount Rockgun, 1,356 ft. The Rock has a bare, treeless aspect, but there are several grassy wooded glens; a growth of cactus on the slopes affords shelter for a small tribe of wild monkeys; rabbits and partridges are numerous. From Europa Point across the Straits to Ceuta, in Africa, the distance is about 13 miles—this is not the narrowest part, which is between Tarifa, in Spain, and the Cuchillos de Siris, in Africa, 8 miles. Two currents, one above and one below, are constantly flowing through the Straits; the upper current, from the Atlantic, sometimes flows in at the rate of five miles an hour; the heavier, because salter, waters of the Mediterranean escape below. The currents and cross winds from the two land sides render navigation at all times difficult and occasionally dangerous. The principal trade of the Harbour is as a coaling station for the many vessels entering—about 5,000 annually.

The town is along the base of the Rock on its western side, and consists of little more than two or three parallel streets. Waterport Street and the Street called Irish Town are the business thoroughfares, and here the rather mixed population throngs—many soldiers, Moors from across the Straits, numbers of Jews, and nondescripts of all nations.

The Anglican Cathedral (Trinity Church), is in Cathedral Square; close by, in Church Street, is the Roman Catholic Cathedral. In Southport Street, the southern extension of Church Street, is the Convent, the residence of the Governor. At the south end of Southport Street, is Southport Gate, with, on the left, Trafalgar Cemetery, where are buried many officers and men who fell at the battle of Trafalgar (October 21st, 1805).

At the water side, just here, are Ragged Staff Stairs, where Admiral Sir George Rooke landed at the capture of Gibraltar, July, 1704. Southward beyond Southport Gate and Prince Edward's Gate, are the Grand Parade, Alameda Gardens (fine display of sub-tropical vegetation), with a pleasant district of villa residences known as South Town.

Extensive Naval works are in course of construction on the south west side of the Rock, where are the Naval Harbour, the Dockyard, and what is called the New Mole, though dating from 1620.

The Gates are closed at evening gun fire, but a pass in or out up to 11.30 p.m. may be obtained at the Police Station. After 11.30 p.m. until sunrise no one may enter or leave the town without special permission.

The "Galleries" may be inspected, visitors having only to write their names in book at the entrance; other parts of the fortifications not open to the public.

On the north side, a mile and a half away from the Rock, across the strip known as the Neutral Ground, is the uninteresting straggling Spanish town of **La Linea de la Concepcion** (pop. 30,000), whose inhabitants are generally described as labourers and smugglers.

GOVERNOR.—General Sir Archibald Hunter, K.C.B., D.S.O.

ENGLISH CHURCH SERVICE in the Cathedral.

PRESBYTERIAN CHURCH, St. Andrew's.

H.B.M.'s VICE-CONS. at San Roque.—G. F. Cornwell, Esq., K.C.

GOLF.—9-hole course at Algeciras.

STEAMER from Gibraltar across the bay to Algeciras, thence Rail into Spain, see page 299.

Granada.—*Stat.*—Pop. 77,425.

THE NEW ALHAMBRA PALACE HOTEL AND CASINO.—First-class, with fine views of the mountains. 250 rooms and apartments. Inclusive terms from 20 pesetas. See Advt.

WASHINGTON IRVING; ALAMEDA AND VICTORIA; PARIS.

The Railway Station, in the north west district, is a mile from the centre of the city.

Granada, the chief city of the Province of Granada, was once the capital of the Moorish Kingdom. It is finely situated just below two heights, is the seat of an archbishop, and is possessed of an ancient university. It is a place of past glory and present decay; away from the principal thoroughfares, the streets are neglected and dirty, an entire quarter—the Albaicin—is inhabited by gipsies, and beggars are unusually numerous.

The height upon which is the Alhambra is clearly seen south east across the city from the Railway Station; the busiest centre is the Puerta Real, about a mile due south of the Station and a quarter mile west of the Alhambra height.

The CATEDRAL (Santa Maria de la Encarnación) is a little north of the Puerta Real. Its building extended over many years, 1523-1703, even then being left incomplete; it was begun in the Gothic style, continued in what was called the Plateresque style (from the elaborate working of silver plate), and is mentioned by authorities as the best specimen of Renaissance architecture in Spain and one of the finest churches in Europe. Elaborate sculpture about the entrances. In the interior are many fine paintings, especially in the Capilla Mayor, at east end of nave. In the Capilla Real, on south side, are tombs of Ferdinand and Isabella and other royal persons, also reliefs and relics of great historical interest. Adjoining the Cathedral at the south west corner is the Sagrario, or Church of Santa Maria de la O, on the site of the chief mosque of Granada.

San Jeronimo, a little to west between Railway Station and Cathedral. Magnificent Capilla Mayor with tomb below of the Gran Capitan Gonsalvo de Cordoba. Statues in armour. The former convent is used as a barracks.

San Juan de Dios, in direct line between Railway Station and Cathedral. Paintings and relics The church is attached to a large hospital.

Neustra Señora de las Angustias, on the Alameda de Invierno. Statues, including one of the Virgin specially revered. Frescoes.

Santa Ana, at the west base of the Alhambra height. On the site of the mosque of Almanzora. Tower resembling a minaret; painting and sculpture.

San Juan de los Reyes, San Nicolas, and San Salvador, three churches close together, near to and in a line north of the Moorish Palace on the Alhambra height.

San Miguel el Alto and San Cecilio are on the heights to north of the Alhambra. Many grottoes, "Santas Cuevas," connected with San Cecilio.

The Convento de Cartuja, at extreme north of the city, has cloisters, a Church, refectory, and sagrario—all very interesting.

The ALHAMBRA occupies the plateau of a height, Monte de la Assabica. The plateau, 800 yards long and about 200 yards broad, was enclosed by a wall with towers, and the range of buildings included a mosque, palaces, and courts; some of the Moorish erections were demolished to make space for a palace for Charles V. Disaster, neglect, and decay worked havoc to the Alhambra from 1718 until 1828, when the first attempt at restoration was commenced. The hasty visitor may experience disappointment, the chambers are empty and the fountains without water, but enthusiasts will make repeated visits. Open daily, 8 to 12 and 1.30 to 5; admission, 1 peseta.

The Palacio de Generalife, the summer residence of the Moorish princes is on a height just east of the Alhambra. The name is a rendering of the Arabic Djennat al-'Arif (garden of Arif). The palace is dilapidated, but the gardens are very pleasant.

Museo Provincial, in the Calle de los Arandas. Collection of paintings by old and modern masters, antiquities, coins, etc.

The Plaza de Bibarrambla, a few yards south west of the Cathedral, is historic ground upon which many Moorish and Christian pageants, tournaments, bull fights, and sanguinary strife have been witnessed.

University, in Calle de la Duquesa, quarter mile north west of the Cathedral; a library of 25,000 vols. and some pictures; the students number about 600.

The favourite promenades, Paseo del Salon and Paseo de la Bomba, are on the south side of the city, by the River Genil—the broad Alameda de Invierno leads to them from the Puerta Real. The Alameda de la Alhambra is a beautiful grove in the valley and on the slopes south west of the Alhambra height.

The gipsy quarter, the Albaicin, is the east part of the city; travellers should only explore this district in groups, and avoid it after dark.

POST OFFICE (Correo), in Calle de Mendez Nuñez, a little south east of the Cathedral.

H.B.M.'S VICE CONSUL.—W. Davenhill, Esq.

RAIL, pages 294, 298A.

[**Santa Fé** (Railway Station—Atarfe-Santa Fé), a little town about 5½ miles from Granada. Interesting Church. The famous contract with Columbus regarding his voyage of discovery was signed here April 17th, 1492.

Huelva.—*Stat.*—Pop. 27,699.

HOTELS: INTERNATIONAL; MADRID.

Capital of the Province of Huelva, on an inlet of the Gulf of Cadiz, near the mouths of the Rivers Tinto and Odiel. Pleasant winter climate. Much ore shipped from the Tinto and Tharsis mines.

H.B.M.'s VICE-CONSUL.—A. Attwood. Esq.

MEDICAL.—Dr. Mackay.

RAIL, pages 297, 297A.

[Up the river—a row of one or two hours—to **Palos** and the Convent of Santa Maria la Rabida, both places closely associated with Columbus. Colossal Monument to Columbus at La Rabida.

The **Rio Tinto** copper mines, 52¾ miles from Huelva, are very valuable, are the property of British and German capitalists, and extend throughout an area of nearly 13 square miles; one of the mining villages is inhabited by British miners; more than a milion tons of ore are raised annually, the bulk being sent to South Wales.]

Jerez, or Xeres de la Frontera.-*Stat.*-Pop. 62,628.

HOTELS; CISNES; VICTORIA.

A clean pleasant town, the third wealthiest in the kingdom, centre of a great wine trade—"Sherry" being a rendering of Jerez. Church of San Miguel, with handsome interior; Alcazar. The immense Bodegas (wine vaults) of the wine firms may be visited.

H.B.M.'s VICE-CONS.—Walter John Buck, Esq.

U.S. CONSUL.—W. R. Dorsey, Esq.

RAIL, pages 293, 294.

Leon.—*Stat.*—Pop. 15,974.

HOTELS: DE PARIS; NORIEGA.

Capital of the Province of Leon, pleasantly situated in a fertile plain at the confluence of the Rivers Torio and Bernesga. It was the famous capital of the Kingdom of Leon, at the height of its prosperity during the 11th, 12th, and 13th cents.; now all that is left of the ancient glory are the Cathedral and city walls, the narrow crooked streets being almost deserted.

The CATHEDRAL, though smaller than those of Toledo, Burgos, and Seville, is regarded as one of the finest examples of Gothic architecture in Spain, and one of the noblest churches in Europe. Begun in 1199, it was not finished until near the end of the 14th cent. It has been several times restored. The length is 298 ft., width 131 ft., nave 98 ft. high. Grace and lightness characterize the interior; beautiful stained glass; much sculpture; paintings. Cloisters.

Colegiata de San Isidoro, founded by Ferdinand I of Castile in 1005 partly as a royal mausoleum; the tombs were destroyed by the French in 1808. Bones of San Isidoro in shrine on high altar. Convent of San Marcos, with part used as a Museo.

RAIL, page 293.

MADRID.—*Stat.*—Pop. (1910) 571,539. (*Plan in Special Edition, or post free 3d. stamps*).

HOTEL DE PARIS.—First class. Every modern comfort. Central heating. Electric light; lift. Hot and cold water supply in every room. See Advt.

HOTEL DE ROME.—Centrally situated, with carriage entrance. Lift; electric light; telephone; garden. See Advt.

HOTEL INGLES.—Comfortable hotel, situated in centre of the town. Moderate charges. See Advt.

CAFES.—The most frequented cafés are in and round about the Puerta del Sol, at the centre of the city; they may be used without question during the day, but at night are not suitable for ladies—this remark specially applies to those cafés where music is provided in the evening.

RAILWAY STATIONS.—There are three principal railway stations, all within a mile of the centre of the city at Puerta del Sol; two, Estacion de las Delicias and Estacion de Atocha, are close together, the Delicias being a quarter mile south of the Atocha; the Estacion del Norte is about two miles north west of the Delicias and Atocha Stations. At the ESTACION DEL NORTE, north west of centre of city, trains arrive from and depart to the north and north west of Spain, including the services from France via Bordeaux and Irun; the ESTACION DE ATOCHA (or DEL MEDIODIA), south east of centre of city, is the Station for the south, for Badajos (towards Portugal), and for Saragossa (towards Barcelona); the ESTACION DE LAS DELICIAS, south of centre of city, is for the direct line for Lisbon.

Electric Tramways traverse the city.

MADRID, a fine attractive city, the capital of the kingdom of Spain, is built upon an eminence rising from a wide stretching plain, an insignificant river, Rio Manzanares, flowing by the west side of the city. Consequent upon the elevation and the treeless nature of the surrounding plain, the climate is fitful, the changes rapid and severe; the great heat of the summer day is often followed by a keen searching chilly evening air; within a day the temperature will range 30° to 35° Fahrenheit. Wraps are needed, colds and chills are easily caught; persons with lung affections cannot be too careful. Spring is a good season for visiting Madrid, also October and November; summer day heats are almost unbearable.

The most convenient point whence to guide the traveller is the PUERTA DEL SOL, a large plaza right at the centre of the city, where Madrid life is seen at greatest activity. Hotels and cafés are on all sides. Here several streets run in. The broader street on the west side, Calle del Arenal, leads to the Plaza Oriente, where is the Royal Palace; the Calle Mayor, also on west side, is more commercial, it leads to the new Cathedral (it was from a window of the top storey of No. 88 Calle Mayor that the bomb was thrown at the carriage of the King and Queen, June, 1906); the broader street on the east side, Calle de Alcalá, leads to the Paseo de Recoletos—both fashionable promenades; the Carrera de S. Jerónimo, also on east side, having the best shops, leads to the Paseo del Prado, where is the Museo del Prado.

PALACIO REAL—Royal Palace, on west side of Plaza de Oriente, to which Calle del Arenal leads from west side of Puerta del Sol. An imposing square building, on a height above the River Manzanares. State rooms, richly decorated, notably the Salon de Embajadóres (Throne Room). Chapel in north wing of Palace; here, in the Relicário de la Real Capilla, are venerated relics, as, a fragment of the Crown of Thorns, a nail from the Cross. The Palace may be seen (not easily accessible) during absence of Royal Family by written permission obtained at the Intendencia Generál. The Royal Stables are by the north wing of the Palace.

ARMERIA, at south west corner of Plaza de Armas, south side of Royal Palace. Wonderful collection of armour, arms, flags, and war trophies. Daily 10.0 until noon, 1 peseta; Saturday 2.0 until 4.0 free.

CATEDRAL—Nuestra Senora de la Almudena. South of the Royal Palace. In course of erection since 1895 from designs by the Marques de Cubas.

MUSEO DEL PRADO, on east side of Paseo del Prado, to which the Carrera de S. Jerónimo leads from the east side of Puerta del Sol. The Collection of Pictures is classed with the first in Europe; there are about 2,000 examples. The Spanish School naturally is predominant, Velasquez, Murillo, and Riba are well represented; there are also many works by Italian and Flemish artists. The Spanish masterpieces are mostly in the long chamber—Galleria Principal. There is also a Sculpture Gallery. Open daily, 8.0 until 1.0; 1 peseta.

PALACIO DE LA BIBLIOTECA Y MUSEOS NACIONALES, on east side, north end, of the Paseo de Recoletos, into which the Calle de Alcalá runs from east side of Puerta del Sol. Here, beside the National Library (about 600,000 printed volumes, and vast stores of MSS., maps, autographs, etc.) and the National Archives, are the MUSEO DE ARTE MODERNO—a collection of modern paintings and sculpture, the MUSEO ARQUEOLOGICO NACIONAL, and the MUSEO DE CIENCIAS NATURALES.

REAL ACADEMIA DE BELLAS ARTES, north side of Calle de Alcalá, very short distance from Puerta del Sol. The Gallery contains some paintings by Murillo. Daily, 9.0 until 4.0; Sunday until noon.

MUSEO DE ARTILLERIA, off east side of Salon del Prado. Interesting collection of war trophies, models, relics, and curiosities.

MUSEO NAVAL (in the Marine Ministry), north end, east side, of Calle de Bailén, just north of Royal Palace, opposite the Royal Stables. Naval collection of great interest: portraits, models, relics, etc., relating to early navigators.

PALACIO DEL CONGRESO, north side of Carrera de S. Jerónimo, street running from east side of Puerta del Sol. Public gallery during sitting of Cortes; when Cortes not in session the Palace may be visited, fee 50 c.

CASA DE AYUNTAMIENTO—Town Hall, in Plaza de la Villa, south side, west end, of Calle Mayor, street running out west from Puerta del Sol. Opposite east side of the Casa is the restored Torre de los Lujanes, where Francis I of France, taken at Battle of Pavia, was sometime a prisoner.

UNIVERSITY, in Calle de S. Bernardo, in north east quarter of the city.

CHURCHES.

San Francisco el Grande, half a mile due south of Royal Palace. Chapels, high altar, frescoes, beautiful doors.

San Ginés, south side of Calle del Arenal. Statue of Christ. Church once much visited for the purpose of disciplinary personal flagellation in vaults below.

San Isidro el Real, in Calle de Toledo, running off south side of Calle Mayor, half mile south west of Puerta del Sol. Paintings.

San Jerónimo el Real, just east of Museo Prado; here King Alfonso and Princess Ena were married, May, 1906.

Basilica de Nuestra Señora de Atocha, south east of the Prado, east of Estacion de Atocha. On site of the ancient Ermita de Atocha.

San Antonio de la Florida, by Estacion del Norte, facing Casa de Campo. Frescoes in dome.

San Andrés de los Flamencos, in Calle Claudio Coello, in north east part of city. High altar with painting by Rubens.

PUBLIC GARDENS AND PARKS.—Buen Retiro (Parque de Madrid), on east side of city; adjoining, at south west corner, is the Jardin Botanico. Campo del Moro and Casa de Campo are on west side of city, west of Royal Palace.

PLAZA DE TOROS—Bull Ring. A short distance south from east end of Calle de Alcalá, about two miles east of Puerta del Sol. Space for 14,000 spectators.

The Senado (Senate), is in Calle de Bailen, north end, opposite the Royal Stables.

THEATRES.—Teatro Real, in Plaza de Oriente, opera. Teatro Español, Calle del Principe, high class plays; Teatro de la Comedia, Calle de Principe, and Teatro de la Princesa, Calle de Tamayo, both for better class plays; Teatro de la Zarzuéla, Calle de Jovellanos, light variety performances.

POST OFFICE. — The principal Post Office, Corréo Central, is in Calle de Carretas, a street running off south side of Puerta del Sol; here is the Poste Restante. TELEGRAPH OFFICE in Calle del Corréo, close by. Stamps (Sellos) are sold at tobacco shops. The letter box is a "buzóne."

H.B.M.'s AMBASSADOR.—Rt. Hon. Sir Maurice de Bunsen, G.C.V.O., K.C.M.G., C.B. SECRETARY OF EMBASSY.—Claud Russell, Esq. CONSUL—A. Jackson, Esq.

U.S. MINISTER.—Hon. H. C. Ide. SEC. OF LEGATION. — G. Scholle, Esq. CONSUL. — F. T. F. Dumont, Esq.

BRIT. EMBASSY CHAPEL.—4, Calle Leganitos. RAIL, pp. 291, 296, 297, 298, 299.

[**El Escorial** (HOTELS: REINA VICTORIA; MIRANDA)—*Stat.*—32 miles north west of Madrid, among the mountains (Sierra de Guadarrama). The village is in two clusters, Escorial de Abajo, by the Railway Station, and Escorial de Arriba, a mile higher from the Station, and about 3,280 ft. above sea. The famous MONASTERY OF SAN LORENZO is at the latter. Admission to church and library free, to other parts 20c. to 30c. each section. The Monastery is a great gloomy structure overlooking a rocky sterile country. The courts, staircases, corridors, seem innumerable. In the Church (Templo) are many altars, some adorned with paintings —high altar is very ornate; royal tombs, statues, frescoes. On south side of the Church is the Panteon de los Reyes, the burial vault of Spanish monarchs. The Palace is in the north east wing of the range of buildings.]

Malaga.—*Stat.*—Pop. (1910) 133,045.
HOTELS: REGINA; SIMON.
The RAILWAY STATION is in the south west part of the city, west of the Puerto.
Electric tramways.

Capital of the Province of Malaga, beautifully situated on a bay of the Mediterranean, enjoying a mild equable climate, fairly cool in summer and dry in winter. The country on the west side is of wonderful fertility, and the fruit exportation (oranges, lemons, figs, etc.) is a great industry. There are also cotton mills, sugar refineries, and iron foundries.

The Cathedral, just back from the Puerto, dates from the middle of the 16th cent. — the arms of Philip II and Queen Mary of England, his wife, are to be seen—but the building was prolonged over 250 years. Interior 375 ft. long, 245 ft. wide, 130 ft. high. Many works of art in the Capilla Mayor.

Castillo de Gibralfaro, on the height east of the Puerto; in clear weather Africa can be seen. Cementerio (Cemetery) Ingles, at sea base of the Gibralfaro height.

Between the Cathedral and the Gibralfaro, on a lower height, are relics of the palace or fortress of the Alcazaba, on the supposed site of the Phœnician Settlement.

The pleasant Parque (trees, flower beds, etc.) is at one side of the Puerto.

ENG. CH. SERV.—At the Chapel in the English Cemetery on the Caleta Road.

H.B.M.'s CONSUL.—P. Staniforth, Esq. VICE-CONSUL.—E. R. Thornton, Esq.

U.S. CONSUL.—R. Frazer, Esq , jun. VICE-CONSUL.—T. R. Geary, Esq.

RAIL, page 294.

Monserrat. — The Monserrat, the sacred mountain of the Catalan people, is a wild and singular jagged mountain, 4,070 ft., rising from the plain of Catalonia. By some authorities here was located the Holy Grail, and the mountain is still a great pilgrim resort. The Monastery, about two thirds of the way up, is of very ancient foundation, dating from 880; before the altar of the church is a miracle working Image of the Virgin—here Ignatius Loyola, founder of the Jesuits, discarded the military profession and vowed himself to a religious life. Bedrooms in the Monastery; no charge, but usual to give 2p. 50c. to 5p. per night.

MOUNTAIN RAILWAY from Monistrol, page 293.

Murcia.—*Stat.*—Pop. (1910) 124,985.
HOTELS: PATRON; UNIVERSAL.

Capital of the Province of Murcia, on the River Segura, in a beautiful situation, with many suggestions of Moorish days; in the modern quarters are broad tree planted streets. Cathedral of 14th cent., Gothic, with facade of 18th cent.; interesting chapels, paintings, wood carving; tower 310 ft. high, fine view. Other churches worth inspection are San Juan, San Nicolas, San Miguel, the Ermita de Jesus. In the Calle del Principe Alfonso, leading from the Cathedral to the Plaza de Santo Domingo, are the Casino and ancient balconied houses. At the Contraste, quarter mile north west of the Cathedral, is the Museo Provincial, with small collection of pictures.

RAIL, pages 293, 297A.

Oviedo.—*Stat.*—Pop. 52,874.
HOTEL COVADONGA ; PARIS.

Capital of the Province of Oviedo, pleasantly situated on a hill by the River Nora. Several mines in the vicinity. Gothic Cathedral, dating from 14th cent.; much carving in interior, high altar; in the Camara Santa are relics, among them fragments of the Cross and the Staff of Moses, one of St. Peter's sandals, one of the thirty pieces of silver, some crumbs from the Feeding of the Five Thousand. Several other old churches. At the Universidad is a small collection of pictures.

RAIL, pages 293, 298A.

Pamplona.—*Stat.*—Pop. 27,190.
FONDA DE LA PERLA.

On a hill, on the left bank of the River Arga. Gothic Cathedral, dating from 1397, has much sculpture and beautiful cloisters. At the Sarasate Museo are objects associated with the musician.

RAIL, pages 292, 295A.

Ronda.—*Stat.*—Pop. 25,000.

HOTEL REINA VICTORIA.—2,426 feet above sea. Large public rooms. Bathrooms and sanitation of British workmanship. English management. See Advt.

STATION; ROYAL; GIBRALTAR.

A finely situated interesting town, 2,460 feet above sea, on a projection of the Sierra Nevada, in the midst of a magnificent range of mountains. The air is remarkably salubrious, cool during summer heats; rain rarely falls during daylight. The old Moorish town is separated from the modern quarter by the Tajo, an imposing gorge of the River Guadalevin, 230 feet across at its narrowest part, 350 ft. deep; two bridges, whence are splendid views. Church of Sta. Maria la Mayor, once a mosque, with Gothic additions; the choir stalls have good reliefs and figures of saints. From the terraces of the Casa del Rey Moro and the Casa de Mondragon are views down into the abyss of the Tajo. The Alameda is an attractive public promenade.

At old Ronda, Ronda la Vieja, the Roman Arunda, about 7 miles north, are remains of an amphitheatre.

RAIL, page 299.

Salamanca.—*Stat.*—Pop. 26,295.

HOTELS: PASAJE; TERMINUS.

The RAILWAY STATION is to north east of city, a mile from centre at Plaza Mayor.

Capital of the Province of Salamanca, and seat of a renowned university; on the River Tormes. The road from the Railway Station enters the city at the Puerta de Zamora, whence the street in front leads directly to the Plaza Mayor, one of the finest squares in Spain; Ayuntamiento (city hall) on north side. Immediately south of the Plaza Mayor is the Church of San Martin (paintings and tombs), and again immediately south of this church the Calle de Garcia Barrado leads to the Cathedrals.

The CATEDRAL NUEVA occupied from 1509 until 1733 in building, and though claimed as Gothic exhibits other styles. Interior 340 feet long, 158 feet wide; many statues and figures in relief; tombs. CATEDRAL VIEJA (old), next to the Nueva; dating from an uncertain time between 1100 and 1200, regarded as one of the best remaining examples in Spain of the Transition style. It was mutilated to make space for the other Cathedral; frescoes; cloisters, with chapels adjoining.

Opposite the Catedral Nueva, the Calle de Calderon de la Baria leads to the Plazuela de la Universidad, with the Universidad on east side. The once famous University, regarded about 1250, soon after its foundation, as the equal of the Universities of Oxford, Paris, and Bologna, attended in its most glorious days, during 16th cent., by 7,000 students, is now reduced to an attendance of a few hundreds.

200 yards west of Plaza Mayor, in line with its south side, is the Convento de las Augustinas Recoletas, in the church of which is a celebrated "Conception" by Ribera, and other pictures. A little further west is the Colegio de Santiago Apostol, a seminary for Irish Catholics.

A little south of **the Cathedrals is the Roman bridge across the River Tormes; the arches nearest the city are of the original structure.**

RAIL, pages 290A, 298A, 299.

San Sebastian.—*Stat.*—Pop. (1910) 47,894.

HOTELS: CONTINENTAL; LONDRES; PALAIS; EZCURRA.

Capital of the Province of Guipuzcoa, the most fashionable sea side resort in Spain. Beautifully situated on an inlet (the Concha) of the Bay of Biscay. Spanish royalty usually in residence during the summer at the Palacio Real on west side. Avenue de la Libertad, in the new town, is a fine tree shaded thoroughfare. Gothic Church of San Vicente, 1507; Church of the Buen Pastor. Palacio de la Diputacion in Plaza de Guipuzcoa. Monte Urgull, 380 ft., at sea end of old town; on north side are graves of British officers who fell here 1813 and 1836.

POST OFFICE in Plaza de Guipuzcoa.

H.B.M.'s V.-CONSUL.—A. Budd, Esq., M.V.O.

GOLF LINKS.

RAIL, pages 291, 294A.

[**Zarauz**, another fashionable sea side resort, is about 16 miles west of San Sebastian. Pop. 3,043. GRAND HOTEL. RAIL, page 294A.]

Santander.—*Stat.*—Pop. 65,209.

HOTELS: GOMEZ; EUROPA; CONTINENTAL.

Capital of the Province of Santander, an important seaport, and a delightfully situated fashionable sea side resort. Gothic Cathedral.

H.B.M.'s V.-CONSUL.—M. Pineiro, Esq.

U.S. CONSULAR AGENT.

RAIL, pp. 292, 294A, 295A, 298A.

Santiago de Compostella.-*Stat.*-Pop. 24,300.

HOTELS: VIZCAINO; SUIZA.

Once the capital of Galicia, on a slope of the Monte Pedroso, near the confluence of the Sar and Sarela; seat of an archbishop, and a university city.

From the Railway Station the way goes north east and then north to the heart of the city at Plaza de Alfonso XII, about half a mile distant, where is the cathedral.

The CATHEDRAL is considered the most important example of early Romanesque architecture in Spain. The erection dates from 1078 to 1211; on at least two occasions, in the 16th and in the 18th cents., extensive alterations were made; length 308 ft., width at transepts 207 ft., height of nave 79 ft. Immediately within the west facade is the Portico de la Gloria, described as "one of the greatest glories of Christian art." The Capilla Mayor, over the grave of St. James the Apostle, is at extreme east end of the Cathedral; in the side chapels are sculpture and tombs. The Gothic Cloisters, at south west angle, are among the best in Spain. All over the city are several convents and churches deserving attention.

University in south east part of the city.

RAIL, page 294A.

Saragossa (Zaragoza).—*Stat.*—Pop. (1910) 105,788.

HOTELS: CUATRO NACIONES; EUROPA.

TWO RAILWAY STATIONS—Estacion del Sepulcro on west side, Estacion del Arrabal on north side; both Stations are about a mile from centre of city. Estacion de Cariñena, to south west, is for a local line.

Saragossa, capital of the Province of Saragossa, on the River Ebro, 605 ft. above sea, is the seat of an archbishop and a university city.

From opposite the Estacion del Sepulcro the broad Paseo de Maria Augustin leads south east for half a mile to the Plaza de Aragon, whence, running north east, the Calle de la Independencia leads to the heart of the city at Plaza de la Constitucion. From the Estacion del Arrabal the route is an almost straight line south to the river, over the old Piedra Bridge, along the Calle de Don Jaime to the Plaza de la Constitucion—the Plaza was the scene of dreadful fighting in the siege of 1808-9, a monument to the defenders is here.

LA SEO, the old Cathedral (San Salvador), is close to the Piedra bridge over the Ebro, just off the east side of the north end of Calle de Don Jaime. Erected 1119-1520 on the site of a mosque. Interior is dark; elaborate choir and high altar; statues of San Vincente and San Lorenzo; tombs in the chapels; vestments in the sacristy.

NUESTRA SENORA DEL PILAR, the second Cathedral, by the river, a little west of the Piedra bridge; begun 1681, the building was not completed before the close of the 19th cent.; 435 ft. long, 220 ft. wide. Elaborate high altar; great object of veneration is the almost invisible pillar in the Capilla de Nuestra Señora del Pilar, on which the Virgin appeared to St. James.

Santa Engracia, a little to east of south end of Calle de Independencia, a Gothic Church of the time of Charles V; was practically destroyed in the siege of 1808-9, rebuilt at the charge of the State 1891-8. San Pablo, quarter mile south of the Ebro, in north west quarter; very old church, dating from the 13th cent.

The Lonja (Exchange), close to the Piedra bridge, to west, is a fine Renaissance building; opposite the Lonja is a Priests' Training College (Seminario Conciliar), with the Archbishop's Palace behind.

University, a little north of east end of Calle Mayor, which runs from east side of Calle de Don Jaime.

Audencia (Law Courts), Calle del Coso, 200 yards west of Plaza de la Constitucion. This building, then a private house, was the headquarters of the famous defence of 1809.

Castillo de la Aljaféria, on west side of city, a little north of the Sepulcro Station. Built by Abu Dja' far Ahmed, afterwards the residence of the Kings of Aragon, now a barracks. Handsome staircase and salons.

Where the short street from the Castillo runs into the Paseo is the special spot (of course the surroundings are all changed) of the heroism of the Maid of Saragossa, Maria Augustin, after whom the Paseo is named.

POST OFFICE on east side of Calle de la Independencia.

H. B. M.'s VICE-CON.—E. Miret, Esq.

RAIL, pages 292, 295, 297, 299.

Segovia. -*Stat.*—Pop. 14,000.

HOTEL EUROPEO; FORNOS.

The Railway Station is a mile and a half south east of the Cathedral.

Capital of the Province of Segovia, on a hill, 3,300 ft. above sea. A venerable wall enclosed city, with Roman remains, old churches and monasteries, ruined palaces and mediæval houses, in the narrow crooked streets.

CATHEDRAL, Gothic, dating from 1525; elaborate exterior decorations at east end. Length 344 ft., width 157 ft., cupola 220 ft. high. Light interior; high altar, paintings, rich windows, cloisters. Most of the churches are interesting.

Alcazar, dating from 1352, at extreme west corner of city.

Aqueduct (El Puente)—the most extensive Roman relic in Spain—back, on right hand, going from Railway Station to city.

RAIL, page 291.

[**San Ildefonso** and **La Granja.** 7 miles east of Segovia; conveyance by omnibus.

HOTELS: EUROPA; ROMA.

San Ildefonso (pop. 3,300) is a village 3,795 ft. above sea among the Guadarrama Mountains, where a grange of the Hieronymite monks was purchased by Philip V (1719) and on the site the palace of La Granja erected. Royal apartments to be seen; frescoes in the Colegiata; in the gardens are celebrated fountains, only playing about six times a year.]

Seville.-*Stat.*-Pop. (1910) 155,366.

GRAND HOTEL DE PARIS.—Well situated, near the Cathedral. Electric light; baths. Moderate charges. See Advt.

GRAND HOTEL DE MADRID, very well situated; moderate charges; see Advt. Sleeping Car Office.

ORIENTE; INGLATERRA.

Prices at hotels are doubled during Holy Week.

There are two Railway Stations: ESTACION DE CORDOBA, on west side of the city, on the bank of the Rio Guadalquivir, for train service from and to Cordoba, Alcazar, and Madrid; ESTACION DE CADIZ, to south east of city, for the trains to Cadiz.

Electric Trams in principal streets.

Seville is the capital of Andalusia and of the Province of Seville; it is situated on the banks of the River Guadalquivir, in a wide fruitful plain, is not naturally picturesque, but in the streets presents a bright cheerfulness of life and in the better class homes a charm that go far to justify the boast, "Quien no ha visto Sevilla no ha visto maravilla"—who has not seen Seville has not seen a wonder. The climate is specially favourable in winter, when almost every day has sunshine, frost and snow are rarely seen; in summer the sun shines fiercely.

Saragossa, capital of the Province of Saragossa, on the River Ebro, 605 ft. above sea, is the seat of an archbishop and a university city.

From opposite the Estacion del Sepulcro the broad Paseo de Maria Augustin leads south east for half a mile to the Plaza de Aragon, whence, running north east, the Calle de la Independencia leads to the heart of the city at Plaza de la Constitucion. From the Estacion del Arrabal the route is an almost straight line south to the river, over the old Piedra Bridge, along the Calle de Don Jaime to the Plaza de la Constitucion—the Plaza was the scene of dreadful fighting in the siege of 1808-9, a monument to the defenders is here.

LA SEO, the old Cathedral (San Salvador), is close to the Piedra bridge over the Ebro, just off the east side of the north end of Calle de Don Jaime. Erected 1119-1520 on the site of a mosque. Interior is dark; elaborate choir and high altar; statues of San Vincente and San Lorenzo; tombs in the chapels; vestments in the sacristy.

NUESTRA SENORA DEL PILAR, the second Cathedral, by the river, a little west of the Piedra bridge; begun 1681, the building was not completed before the close of the 19th cent.; 435 ft. long, 220 ft. wide. Elaborate high altar; great object of veneration is the almost invisible pillar in the Capilla de Nuestra Señora del Pilar, on which the Virgin appeared to St. James.

Santa Engracia, a little to east of south end of Calle de Independencia, a Gothic Church of the time of Charles V; was practically destroyed in the siege of 1808-9, rebuilt at the charge of the State 1891-8. San Pablo, quarter mile south of the Ebro, in north west quarter; very old church, dating from the 13th cent.

The Lonja (Exchange), close to the Piedra bridge, to west, is a fine Renaissance building; opposite the Lonja is a Priests' Training College (Seminario Conciliar), with the Archbishop's Palace behind.

University, a little north of east end of Calle Mayor, which runs from east side of Calle de Don Jaime.

Audencia (Law Courts), Calle del Coso, 200 yards west of Plaza de la Constitucion. This building, then a private house, was the headquarters of the famous defence of 1809.

Castillo de la Aljafería, on west side of city, a little north of the Sepulcro Station. Built by Abu Dja' far Ahmed, afterwards the residence of the Kings of Aragon, now a barracks. Handsome staircase and salons.

Where the short street from the Castillo runs into the Paseo is the special spot (of course the surroundings are all changed) of the heroism of the Maid of Saragossa, Maria Augustin, after whom the Paseo is named.

POST OFFICE on east side of Calle de la Independencia.

H. B. M.'s VICE-CON.—E. Miret, Esq.

RAIL, pages 292, 295, 297, 299.

Segovia. -*Stat.*—Pop. 14,000.

HOTEL EUROPEO; FORNOS.

The Railway Station is a mile and a half south east of the Cathedral.

Capital of the Province of Segovia, on a hill, 3,300 ft. above sea. A venerable wall enclosed city, with Roman remains, old churches and monasteries, ruined palaces and mediæval houses, in the narrow crooked streets.

CATHEDRAL, Gothic, dating from 1525; elaborate exterior decorations at east end. Length 344 ft., width 157 ft., cupola 220 ft. high. Light interior; high altar, paintings, rich windows, cloisters. Most of the churches are interesting.

Alcazar, dating from 1352, at extreme west corner of city.

Aqueduct (El Puente)—the most extensive Roman relic in Spain—back, on right hand, going from Railway Station to city.

RAIL, page 291.

[**San Ildefonso** and **La Granja.** 7 miles east of Segovia; conveyance by omnibus.

HOTELS: EUROPA; ROMA.

San Ildefonso (pop. 3,300) is a village 3,795 ft. above sea among the Guadarrama Mountains, where a grange of the Hieronymite monks was purchased by Philip V (1719) and on the site the palace of La Granja erected. Royal apartments to be seen; frescoes in the Colegiata; in the gardens are celebrated fountains, only playing about six times a year.]

Seville.-*Stat.*-Pop. (1910) 155,366.

GRAND HOTEL DE PARIS.—Well situated, near the Cathedral. Electric light; baths. Moderate charges. See Advt.

GRAND HOTEL DE MADRID, very well situated; moderate charges; see Advt. Sleeping Car Office.

ORIENTE; INGLATERRA.

Prices at hotels are doubled during Holy Week.

There are two Railway Stations: ESTACION DE CORDOBA, on west side of the city, on the bank of the Rio Guadalquivir, for train service from and to Cordoba, Alcazar, and Madrid; ESTACION DE CADIZ, to south east of city, for the trains to Cadiz.

Electric Trams in principal streets.

Seville is the capital of Andalusia and of the Province of Seville; it is situated on the banks of the River Guadalquivir, in a wide fruitful plain, is not naturally picturesque, but in the streets presents a bright cheerfulness of life and in the better class homes a charm that go far to justify the boast, "Quien no ha visto Sevilla no ha visto maravilla"—who has not seen Seville has not seen a wonder. The climate is specially favourable in winter, when almost every day has sunshine, frost and snow are rarely seen; in summer the sun shines fiercely.

The lofty tower of the GIRALDA, in the south part of the city, the most conspicuous object in Seville, is a convenient point whence to direct the traveller, and in the immediate neighbourhood of the Giralda will be found the places of greatest interest. The centre of public life is the narrow Calle de las Sierpes, a street running out of the north side of the Plaza de la Constitución, less than a quarter mile due north of the Cathedral—here are the best cafés and shops; the fashionable promenade is the Paseo de las Delicias, by the river, at the south side of the city.

The CATEDRAL (Santa Maria de la Sede) will be found immediately if the tower of the Giralda be looked for, as the tower is at one of the Cathedral corners. The Cathedral is a Gothic edifice of surpassing architectural and historic interest, apart from sacred associations. It was erected 1402-1506 by unknown architects on the site of the Mosque of the Sultan Abu Ya'Kub Yûsuf; it has suffered much from earthquake, and two or three times the dome has collapsed, the last collapse being on August 1st, 1888. The exterior has innumerable turrets, lanterns, pinnacles, and flying buttresses, and the puertas (doorways) are lavishly sculptured; the interior is majestic in architectural simplicity, enriched in all the chapels with many works of art. The total length is about 400 feet, width 250 feet, the nave is 132 feet high; the area covered is 124,000 square feet, nearly half as much again as the space occupied by St. Paul's Cathedral, London. The Capilla Mayor contains a silver effigy of the Virgin, with scenes illustrative of her life; in the side chapels are, besides elaborate decorations, paintings by Murillo, Luis das Vargas, Alonso Cano, Juan de las Roelas, and other celebrated masters. The Sacristia Mayor, at south east corner, contains the Treasury of costly plate, crosses, silver altars, reliquaries, gorgeous vestments, etc. At the extreme east end is the Capilla Real, with tombs of royalty; body of St. Ferdinand (King of Spain, died May 1st, 1252), in a shrine at lower altar; "Virgen de los Reyes" at high altar. At the north west corner of the Cathedral is the Sagrario, with statues and paintings. Columbus monument in south transept; the sarcophagus contains the remains of the great discoverer. The Cathedral is usually open from 12.0 to 3.30.

Adjoining the north side of the Cathedral, on the east side of the Patio de los Naranjos, is the BIBLIOTECA COLUMBINA, containing about 34,000 volumes, many relating to the discovery of America; the chief treasures are Manuscripts of Columbus, Bible of Alfonso the Learned, and some ancient Missals.

The GIRALDA, the most ancient building in Seville, was originally a minaret of the chief Moorish Mosque. The figure at the top, the "Giraldillo," moving with the wind, weighs a ton and a quarter; it is 305 ft. from the ground. Ascend for the view, 25 c.

Just north east of the Giralda is the Palacio Arzobispal; small collection of paintings.

The CASA LONJA (Exchange) is immediately opposite the south side of the Cathedral. It is a Renaissance building dating from 1583-98. Handsome Patio; fine marble stairs up to the Archivo General de Indias, a collection of documents relating to the conquest and government of America and Phillippine Islands. Daily in winter 10.0 to 4.0, in summer 8.0 to 11.0.

The ALCAZAR, a castle-like building with towers, is opposite the south east corner of the Cathedral. This was the palace of the Moorish Kings, and is now the royal residence. The salons and chambers are richly decorated, especially the Salon de Embajadores (Ambassadors); the Patio de las Doncellas, a cloistered Court of the Maidens, has beautiful Moorish arches. Extensive gardens behind the palace. Weekdays 11.0 to 4.0; 1 peseta to guide.

The MUSEO PROVINCIAL, in the old Convento de la Merced, is a quarter of a mile north east of the Estacion de Cordoba. The collection of paintings—in the convent church—is small, but includes some famous works, several by Murillo; some sculpture and antiquities. Daily 10.0 to 3.0; 50 c.

The Casa de Pilatos is at the east end of Calle de Aguilas, about half mile north east of the Giralda. The building is a combination of Moorish, Gothic, and Renaissance architecture, dating from early in 16th cent. The name is from a once popular idea of a resemblance to the house of Pilate. The rooms are decorated with "azulejos" (tiles) and ancient sculpture.

Casa de Ayuntamiento, in Plaza de la Constitucion, a few yards north of the Cathedral. Interior has superb ceilings; fine staircase; Municipal Library.

The churches are numerous. Of special interest are the Church of the Hospital de la Caridad, a hundred yards south west of the Cathedral, where are celebrated paintings by Murillo; the Church of the Universidad (University), half a mile due north of the Giralda, where are many fine pictures and statues; San Lorenzo, in north west part of city—many fine works of art. There are many Conventual institutions.

Murillo's House, where the painter died April 3rd, 1682, is 7, Plaza de Alfaro, two hundred yards west from the Alcazar, facing the Alcazar Gardens.

The Fabrica de Tabacos is usually included among the "Sights" of Seville. It is immediately south of the Alcazar Gardens. It is an immense building, where are employed about 5,000 Cigarreras. Daily, in the afternoon (between 2.0 and 3.0). Attendant 1 peseta, forewoman of each room a few centimos.

POST OFFICE (Correo), Calle de San Acasio, on west side of Calle de las Sierpes, half mile north of the Giralda.

ENGLISH CHURCH SERVICE at the Church of the Ascension. Plaza Murillo (Winter Chaplaincy).

H.B.M's CONS.—A. L. Keyser, Esq. VICE-CONSUL.—A. A. Henderson, Esq.

U.S. CONSUL.—C. S. Winans, Esq.

ENGLISH PHYSICIAN.—Dr. John Dalebrook.

RAIL, pages 294, 296A, 297, 297A.

Tarragona.—*Stat.*—Pop. of the commune 26,099.

HOTEL DE PARIS; FONDA DE EUROPA.

Capital of the Province of Tarragona, and seat of an archbishop who, with the Archbishop of Toledo, is Primate of Spain. Picturesquely situated on a high sloping cliff, it is historically of great interest; its modern importance is associated with a very prosperous wine trade. The Cathedral, a fine example of late Romanesque, is at the north east corner of the city; majestic interior; beautiful cloisters. Museo Arqueologico Provincial, collection of ancient and mediæval objects. Fragments of Roman sculpture, etc., to be seen everywhere; remains of the Roman walls. Roman Aqueduct, 2½ miles distant, an imposing relic.

The Carthusian monks expelled from the Grande Chartreuse in France established (in 1905) a liqueur distillery here.

H.B.M.'s VICE-CONSUL.—I. Navarro, Esq.

U.S. CONSULAR AGENT.

RAIL, pp. 292, 295, 298.

Toledo.—*Stat.*—Pop. of the commune 25,970.

HOTELS: CASTILLA; FONDA DE LINO; FONDA IMPERIAL.

The RAILWAY STATION is to the north east of the city, on the opposite side of the River Tagus, three quarters of a mile from the centre of the city.

Capital of the Province of Toledo, a celebrated ancient city, the Roman *Toletum*, built on a rocky eminence, three of whose deep sides are washed by the Tagus, and whose fourth side is connected with the plain of Castile by a narrow isthmus. The aspect of the city is sombre, the cramped situation only permitting narrow crooked streets without any open spaces, the houses also show blank outer walls, the windows being on the interior sides. On the other hand its attractions are described as a "gigantic open-air museum of the architectural history of Spain," and as a city with which few others can compete in artistic interest. It is stated that the population was once 200,000.

Beyond indicating the position of the Cathedral and one or two other places it is almost impossible to direct the traveller, the streets being a labyrinth. Guides should be obtained at hotel only.

The road from the Railway Station enters the city by the Puente de Alcantara over the Tagus; here a broad road runs to north west, and soon after the corner is turned, and before the Puerto del Sol is reached, a street is seen on left hand, Calle de Venancio Gonzalez, which leads south into the Calle del Comercio, the principal street, whose continuation winds eventually to the Cathedral.

The CATHEDRAL is so crushed in that no good view can be obtained of the exterior. The present edifice dates from 1227, the work not being completed before 1493. The general style is decided to be Gothic. but in the protracted building other styles exerted an influence. Total length 395 feet; width 195 feet; nave 100 feet high. The interior is a veritable museum of statues, paintings, tombs, and every sort of Church splendour in the many chapels and choir. Cloisters at north west angle. Archbishop's Palace opposite west front of Cathedral, and on south side of the Plaza here is the Ayuntamiento (city hall).

Church of Santo Tomé, quarter mile west of Cathedral; go along street opposite west side of Ayuntamiento into the cross street Calle de la Trinidad, follow line of this latter street. Celebrated painting by Theotocopuli of Burial of Count Orgaz. Going west along line of Calle de Santo Tomé, in quarter mile is Convent and Church of San Juan de los Reyes. Convent used as a Museo of pictures, sculpture, and miscellaneous objects.

The Puente de San Martin, on river side of San Juan, should be seen. Immediately south east of San Juan is Santa Maria la Blanca, and, a little further south east, the Sinagoga del Transito. Thence the streets north east wind eventually back to near Cathedral.

The Alcazar, on high ground, is about 200 yards north east of the Cathedral; follow winding of street opposite mid east front of the Cathedral. Imposing facades and patio.

Hospital de Santa Cruz, on west side of Plaza de la Concepcion, opposite west end of Puente de Alcantara. The building is considered a masterpiece of Spanish Renaissance.

POST OFFICE in Calle de Alfonso Doce, 100 yards due west of Cathedral.

RAIL, page 296.

Valencia.—*Stat.*—Pop. 233,348.

REINA VICTORIA HOTEL.-New first class hotel equipped with all modern comfort. Restauran français. See Advt.

PARIS; GRAND; CONTINENTAL.

The principal RAILWAY STATION, Estacion del Norte, is in the south east district, about half a mile from the centre of the city; the Madrid, Barcelona, and Alicante trains run in here.

Electric Tramways.

Valencia is the capital of the Province of Valencia, the seat of an archbishop and a university city; situated in a fertile plain, on the River Turia, or Guadalaviar. Though the sea is near, 2½ miles, it can only be seen from lofty positions. The climate is genial, and, with the cheerful animation and colour of the streets, despite their narrowness, justify the affectionate regard of the inhabitants.

From the Estacion del Norte the traveller should proceed across the open space in front to where it narrows at its north end, here a short street leads to the busy Calle de San Vicente, which, if for five minutes the line of the street northward be followed in its bending to left along the Calle de Zaragoza, will lead to the Cathedral.

The CATHEDRAL, La Seo, 1262-1482, is a Gothic building on the site it is thought of a temple of Diana, to which followed a Christian Church and a Moorish mosque; the bell tower, El Miguelete, is 152 ft. high. The interior, 320 ft. long, 200 ft. wide at the transepts, has a beautiful high altar and good paintings in the chapels; in the sacristy and relicario are many treasures. Archbishop's Palace faces east side of Cathedral.

A bridge leads from the north end of the Cathedral, across Plaza Almoina, to the Capilla de Nuestra Señora de los Desamparados (the Forsaken); over the high altar is a greatly revered Image of the Virgin.

From the Plaza de la Constitucion, at north end of Cathedral, the Calle de Caballeros runs south west. Here, on the right hand, is the AUDENCIA (Law Courts), a handsome Renaissance building of 16th cent., the old Palacio de la Diputacion (House of Deputies) of the Kingdom of Valencia; historical paintings. Just beyond the Audencia, on right hand, is the Church of San Bartolomé; and further south along the Calle de Caballeros, after the Plaza Conde de Buñol, in a street on east side, is the Church of San Nicolas, with good paintings.

One of the most interesting centres of Valencia is the Plaza del Mercado, to which the short Calle de San Fernando leads from the Calle de San Vicente, just where the latter is entered from the Estacion del Norte. Tournaments and festivals were held here; here the Cid burned alive Ahmed Ibn Dji'haf. On the north side is the Lonja de la Seda (Silk Exchange), with an imposing hall.

MUSEO PROVINCIAL DE PINTURAS, in the former Convento del Carmen, in the north west corner of the city. The Calle Baja, near south end of Calle de Caballeros, leads to almost opposite the Museo. There is also an Archæological collection. Daily, 50 c.; free on Sunday.

The UNIVERSITY, founded 1441, is a quarter of a mile south east of the Cathedral. There are about 1,700 students. Library of 0,000 vols., and many MSS. At the west side of the University is the COLEGIO DEL PATRIACA, where, besides Archives, Library, etc., is a Capilla de la Purisima Concepcion, containing fine tapestry and some good pictures; at the south west corner of the building is the Iglesia del Corpus Christi—impressive celebration of Miserere on Friday morn; ladies must be attired in black.

The old Citadel is at the extreme north east corner of the city. Immediately before the Citadel is the Paseo de la Glorieta, a beautiful pleasure ground, and on the south east side of the Glorieta is the Fabrica de Tabacos. Beyond the Citadel, on the further side of the River Turia, is the Alameda, the fashionable afternoon promenade.

Old Gate, Torres de Serranos, on north side of city; another old Gate, Torres de Cuarte, on the west side.

The Bull Ring (Plaza de Toros) is just south east of Estacion del Norte.

The Harbour of Valencia, El Grao, three miles from the city, is of little interest.

POST OFFICE (Correo), at corner of Calle del Palau, 200 yards east of the Cathedral.

H.B.M.'s V. CONSUL.—E. Harker, Esq.
U.S. CONS.—C. I. Dawson, Esq.

RAIL, pages 298, 299.

Valladolid.—*Stat.*—Pop. 67,742.

HOTELS: MODERNO; FRANCIA.

The principal RAILWAY STATION, Estacion del Norte, is in the south west district, half a mile from centre of city.

On the River Pisuerga, in a fertile plain; capital of the Province of Valladolid, seat of an archbishop and university city, once the favourite residence of the Kings of Castile.

From the Estacion del Norte the broad Campo Grande narrows to the Calle de Santiago, at the end of which is the Plaza Mayor, the centre of Valladolid life. Just where the Campo touches the Calle de Santiago, on east side, is the Calle de Miguel Iscar, where is the House of Cervantes, 1603-1606, belonging to the State.

The CATHEDRAL is less than a quarter of a mile due east of the Plaza Mayor. It is in Renaissance style, dating from 1585, never completed. Interior 402 ft. long, 207 ft. wide; some paintings, in the sacristy a silver custodia 6½ ft. high. Close to Cathedral, on east side, is the Church of Santa Maria la Antigua, of 12th-13th cents.; high altar.

The University is just away from the south east angle of the Cathedral, on south side of Plaza Santa Maria. Statues on the facade; about 1,400 students; in the library (34,000 vols., 300 MSS.) is a collection of Bibles in different languages. 200 yards south of the Plaza Santa Maria, to east, is the Colegio de Santa Cruz, 1480-92, containing the Museo—modern paintings and sculpture in wood. A few yards east of the Museo is the Calle de Cristobal Colon (Columbus), where, at a decayed house marked by an inscription, Christopher Columbus died, May 21st, 1506.

Church of San Pablo, quarter mile due north of Cathedral, dating from 1276, two or three times restored; ornamented facade. Opposite San Pablo is the Capitania General, formerly the Palacio Real, of 17th cent. Immediately to east of San Pablo is the Colegio de San Gregorio (now municipal offices), with magnificent facade; fine staircase.

RAIL, pages 291, 295A, 297A.

PORTUGAL.

The most favourable time for a visit to Portugal is from November until May, when the specially rich vegetation is fresh and luxuriant; winter conditions are very mild along the coast, notably so in the southern part of the Kingdom. At its best the country presents a charming variety of natural beauty; inland are mountain and valley, along the rugged coast are bold headlands of bare rock and stretches of huge sand downs broken into marsh and lagoon. Helped by the abundance of moisture, the fertility of the soil is remarkable, grain of all kinds and fruit trees being easily cultivated, but there are whole districts where the land has been allowed to fall out of cultivation and become poor pasture. The fisheries of the coast are very rich. In the large towns are good hotels; minor hotels should be avoided, they are generally dirty and otherwise unsatisfactory.

Government, a republic, proclaimed on Wednesday, October 5th, 1910, upon the departure from the country of King Manuel II. President of the Republic, Senhor Manoel Arriaga. **Population** (1911) 5,957,985 (including Madeira and Azores.)

Army—peace establishment 30,000.

Railways—66 lbs. of Luggage allowed free.

Money.—The new monetary unit is the Escudo = about 4s. 2d. to 4s. 5d., equivalent to 1,000 reis of the old system; the escudo is divided into 100 parts, named centavos. GOLD COINS—10, 5, and 2 escudo pieces. SILVER COINS—Escudo, and pieces of ½ escudo, and 20 and 10 centavos. NICKEL COINS—Pieces of 4 centavos, 2 centavos, 1 centavo, and ½ centavo. A piece of 10 centavos = about 5d.; one centavo = about ½d. The old system of reckoning in reis is still in general use: 1,000 reis = 1 milreis = paper 3s. 6d., specie 4s. 5½d. The British sovereign has legal currency in Portugal, with value at par of 4½ escudos.

Old Currency: **SILVER COINS—Pieces of 500, 200, 100, and 50 reis, called respectively 5, 2, 1, and ½ testoon pieces. BILLON COINS—Pacato of 40 reis. BRONZE COINS—20 reis (vintem), 10 reis, and 5, and 3 reis pieces.**

Weights and Measures.—The metric system of weights and measures (see page lxxi) is the legal standard. **Postage.**—Letters to England, etc., 5 c. per half ounce.

NOTICES OF TOWNS.

Alcobaça.—Four miles from Vallado Station, page 299A.

HOTEL ALCOBACENSE.

The Mosteiro de Santa Maria — Cistercian Abbey of Alcobaça—was one of the wealthiest and most important convents of the world. Built 1148-1222, it was sacked by the French in 1810, and secularized in 1834, part now being used as a barracks. The extensive buildings form an immense square, and it is stated that the uninterrupted celebration of Mass at one time engaged the attention of 900 monks. In the Church are the tombs of Pedro I and his unfortunate wife Inez de Castro. Fine cloisters.

Eight miles north of Alcobaça is the little town of **Batalha.** Midway is Aljubarrota, where, following the conflict at the village of Canoeira (the site of Batalha), was the decisive battle of Aug. 14th, 1385, securing the independence of Portugal from Spain. In thankfulness for victory John I began the erection of the imposing Mosteiro de Santa Maria da Victoria, or Mosteiro da Batalha, which occupies all the north part of the town. The French in 1810 greatly damaged the buildings, which were declared a national monument in 1840 and carefully restored. In the Church are royal and other tombs; cloisters, chapter house. Capellas Imperfeitas (unfinished chapels)—all interesting. Total fees about 500 reis.

Braga.—*Stat.*—Pop. 24,300.

HOTELS: GRAND; FRANQUEIRA.

On the River Cavado; seat of an archbishop, who is Primate. Cathedral dates from 12th cent.; tombs, wood carving, relics in sacristy. Three miles east of Braga, on the crest of a hill, is the Church of Bom Jesus do Monte, visited by thousands of pilgrims at Whitsuntide.

RAIL, page 301.

Bussaco.—*Stat.*

HOTEL DA MATTA DO BUSSACO.

A pleasantly situated health resort, amidst luxurious vegetation; magnificent cedars, cypresses, and palms; paths through the woods in all directions, leading often to hermitages and other reminders of the old extensive Trappist monastery, of which practically nothing is left. A monument marks the site of the Battle of Sept. 27th, 1810, where Massena was defeated by Wellington. Ascent of the Cruz Alta, 1,775 ft., commanding fine view.

GOLF.—9-hole course.

RAIL, Luso-Bussaco station, **page 301.**

Cintra.—*Stat.*—Pop. 5,000.

HOTELS: CENTRAL; NETTO; NUNES.

A town set amidst beautiful surroundings—mountain, sea, and luxuriant vegetation—at the north base of the Sierra de Cintra, 17½ miles from Lisbon. Here are the summer residences of many wealthy families.

Half a mile from the Station, at the centre of the town, is the Palacio Real, of 14th-15th cents.; fee 200 reis. A pleasant path leads to the rocky height of the Pena (1,735 ft.) and the Castello da Pena; apart from fine views the castello has not much to interest; fee 150 to 200 reis. Below the Castello da Pena is the ancient Castello dos Mouros (80 to 100 reis), whence a beautiful road, Caminho de Collares, leads to the Quinta de Monserrate (2 miles from Cintra), the property of Sir F. Cook, who is also Visconde de Monserrate. The grounds of the Quinta contain a wealth of vegetation.

RAIL, page 301.

Coimbra.—*Stat.*—Pop. 18,500.

HOTELS: AVENIDA; BRAGANCA; MONDEGO.

Capital of the Province of Beira, and seat of a University, on a hill by the River Mondego—the situation and climate have always been extolled.

Sé Velha (old Cathedral), at the centre of the town, quarter mile due east of the Railway Station; a massive Romanesque building of 12th cent., interior has paintings, tile decorations, and tombs. A quarter mile north east of the Sé Velha is the Sé Nova, a Renaissance edifice of 1580; paintings, vestments, and rich Church plate. The University is in the south part of the city; about 1,200 students; the Library contains 100,000 vols. and many MSS. On the north side of the city is the secularized Mosteiro (Monastery) de Santa Cruz, with many objects of historical interest. A short distance east from the south side of the bridge over the river is the Quinta das Lagrimas, once the residence of the ill-fated Inez de Castro.

RAIL, page 300.

Evora.—*Stat.*—Pop. 20,000.

HOTEL EBORENSE.

The ancient Ebora, chief town of the Province of Almetejo, seat of an archbishop, very interesting historically. Cathedral, 1186-1204; Church of São Francisco, 15th cent. In the old palace of the Archbishops is the public library and a small museum. Remains of the Roman Temple of Diana. RAIL, page 299A.

LISBON.—Pop. 357,700 (with suburbs, 708,750). *(Plan in Special Edition, or post free 3d. stamps).*

GRAND HOTEL CENTRAL.—First-class hotel, finely situated on the Tagus. Very comfortable. See Advt.

AVENIDA PALACE HOTEL.—Every comfort and luxury. The property of the International Sleeping Car Co. See Advt.

HOTEL DURAND; BORGES; DE L'EUROPE.

RAILWAY.—There are two principal Railway Stations, ESTACAO CENTRAL, generally called ESTACAO ROCIO, and ESTACAO DO BARREIRO. Estaçao Rocio is at the centre of the city, here the express services connecting with Spain. Badajoz, and Oporto, arrive and depart; Estaçao Barreiro is on the opposite side of the Tagus, and connecting railway steamers depart from and arrive at the Quai of the Praça do Commercio, this station is for the train service to the south of Portugal. A line drawn south from the Estaçao Rocio will lead in about three quarters of a mile to the Praça do Commercio, the embarking place of the southern railway. The minor Estaçao Caes dos Soldados, on the East Quay, is for slow trains on the northern line; another minor station, on the West Quay, Estaçao Caes do Sodré, is for a local line to Cascaes.

STEAMER.—Large Steamers anchor in the Tagus, below the city, passengers landing in small boats at the Quay, Praça do Commercio. No rates for boatmen, bargain must be made. Custom House, Alfándega, in Praça do Commercio, open until sunset.

INCLINED RAILWAYS, connecting higher and lower parts of city; fares, 20 reis to 50 reis. Electric Tramways.

LISBON is pre-eminent for the natural beauty of its situation, lying in and upon an amphitheatre of hills on the north bank of the Tagus. Regarded from the sea the city seems to rise in picturesque terraces; from the shore the view is over two broad river scenes, on the one hand the mouth of the Tagus, on the other the spacious land locked harbour. The luxuriance of the vegetation in the public gardens is wonderful.

PRACA DO COMMERCIO, a handsome square, having one side open to the Tagus, may be described as the centre of Lisbon life. It is a little eastward of mid-distance of the city's river front; is about three quarters of a mile due south of Estaçao Rocio, and is at that part of the Quay where passengers land from Steamers. On the east side of the Praça are the Bolsa (Exchange) and Alfándega (Custom House); on the west side is the Post Office; nearly all the buildings in the square are government offices. In the middle is an equestrian statue of Joseph I, and near the quay the Caes de Columnas (two marble columns). In the river opposite here many ships and thousands of people perished in a whirlpool during the great Earthquake of 1755. It was at the north west corner of the square, at the opening of the Rua do Arsenal, that on February 1st, 1908, King Carlos and the Crown Prince Luiz were assassinated.

The Avenida da Liberdade is a magnificent tree planted avenue about two thirds of a mile long, running northward from the Estacao Central. The Praca de Luiz de Camoes, where is the Monument of Camoes (Camoens), is a quarter mile south west of the Rocio.

The CATHEDRAL—Sé Patriarchal, lying a little back, just east of Praça do Commercio, is the oldest church in Lisbon. The earthquake, and later a fire, destroyed nearly all the original building. In the Capilla de São Vicente are the remains of St. Vincent. In a chapel in the cloisters is a crucifix with miraculous attributes.

São Vicente de Fóra, east of the Cathedral, on rising ground, back from the river. Much marble decoration in interior; baldachino of high altar by de Castro. Here are the tombs of King Carlos and the Crown Prince, assassinated 1908. A little south east is the church of Santa Engracia, never completely built, and now used as an artillery depot.

Nossa Senhora de Graça, half mile back from river, on high ground, just north east of the Castello de São Jorge. Miracle working image of "Our Lord."

São Roque, just west of Estaçao Rocio. Decorated chapels, handsome altar columns of lapis lazuli. Adjoining is the Santa Casa da Misericordia, where about 200 children (expostos) are annually received. Just here is the Alameda de Sao Pedro de Alcantara, whence is a beautiful view.

Basilica do Santissimo Coraçao de Jesus, generally known as the Estrella Church, on west side of city, easily found because of its prominence. Interior elaborately decorated; high altar. Fine view from Dome. On the north side of the Passeio da Estrella is the Cemeterio dos Inglezes; graves of Doddridge, the divine, and Fielding, the novelist.

Nossa Senhora da Conceiçao Velha, Rua da Alfandega, off east side of Praça do Commercio. Magnificent facade.

PALACIO DAS NECESSIDADES, at extreme west of city, quarter mile back from river. Formerly the residence of the Kings of Portugal.

Castello de São Jorge, quarter mile north east from Praça do Commercio. The old Moorish citadel. Now a barracks, military prison, and small church of Santa Cruz do Castello, where is much reverenced figure of St. George.

Palacio das Cortes, in Largo de São Bento, in west part of city. Parliament House of Lisbon. National archives kept here.

MUSEU NACIONAL DAS BELLAS ARTES, on the Quay, a mile west of Praça do Commercio. Picture Gallery of works by ancient and modern masters. Sun. and Thurs., 11.0 to 4.0, free; other days, 12.0 to 2.0, on application.

MUSEU ARCHEOLOGICO, in the old Igreja (Church) do Carmo, just off south west corner of Praça Rocio, by Estaçao Rocio. Interesting collections of antiquities, musical instruments, minerals, etc. Daily 10.0 to 4, 100 reis.

Museu de Artilheria, in the Arsenal do Exercito, on the Quay, half mile east of Praça do Commercio. Cannon and exhibits relating to war.

Museu Naval, in Arsenal da Marinha, just west of Praça do Commercio. Daily.

Academia das Sciencas, in Rua do Arco de Jesus, half mile due west of Estaçao Rocio. Anthropological, Geological, and Pre-Historic collections. Weekdays, 10.0 to 3.

JARDIN BOTANICO, quarter mile north west of Estaçao Rocio. Regarded as the finest Botanical Garden in Europe. Tropical plants; magnificent palms.

MAE D'AGUA (Mother of Water), in the north west quarter; an immense stone hall containing the reservoir, with acqueduct.

BIBLIOTHECA NACIONAL (Library), on the Largo da Bibliotheca Publica, a few yards north west of the Praca do Commercio; 400,000 vols., 15,000 MSS., 40,000 coins; daily, 12.0 to 4.0, and 7.0 to 11.0.

PRACA DOS TOUROS—Bull Ring, in Praça do Campo, about a mile north east of Estaçao Rocio. Bull Fights in summer.

POST OFFICE.—The principal Post and Telegraph Office is on the west side of Praço do Commercio.

ENGLISH CHURCH SERVICE.—St. George's, Rua da Estrella.

PRESBYTERIAN CHURCH, 7, Rua da Arriaga.

H. B. M.'s MINISTER.—His Excy. Sir Arthur Hardinge, K.C.B., K.C.M.G. SEC. LEGATION.—H. W. Gaisford, Esq.

CONSUL.—P. A. Somers Cocks, Esq., C.M.G. VICE-CONSUL.—H. E. Jones, Esq., V-CONS. at Belem.—C. J. Ffrench Duff, Esq.

U.S. MINISTER.—His Excellency C. E. Woods.

U.S. CONSUL GENERAL.—W. L. Lowrie, Esq. VICE-CONSUL.—K. S. Patton, Esq.

RAIL, pages 299A, 300, 301.

Belem and **Ajuda**, close together, are just away from Lisbon, on the west side. Tramway from Lisbon to Belem, or rail from Caes do Sodre station (page 301). The Convento dos Jeronymos de Belem, an extensive range of buildings, now mostly an Orphanage, was where Vasco de Gama stayed the night before departing on his voyage of discovery. At the south east corner, next the Tagus, is the Church of Santa Maria, of which the principal entrance is very fine; much to see in the interior; Vasco de Gama and Camoens buried here; Cloisters (fee 200 reis) of rare beauty. Torre de São Vicente, or Tower of Belem, by the river; fine view from platform. The PALACE of AJUDA is finely placed on a hill above Belem; not shewn.

Mont 'Estoril.—*Stat.*

GRAND HOTEL D'ITALIE.—First class hotel, with fine sea views. Telephone. See Advt.

GRAND HOTEL ESTRADE.—First class hotel, charmingly situated. Every modern comfort. Renowned cooking. See Advt.

About 15 miles west of Lisbon. A winter resort in a beautiful situation at the mouth of the River Tagus, facing the sea, on the slope of a hill, surrounded by eucalyptus, pine, and palm trees. Casino, with gaming rooms. Many wealthy Lisbon merchants reside here.

RAIL, page 301.]

Mafra.—The town is six miles from Mafra Railway Station; public conveyance between the two, fare 200 reis.

HOTELS: MOREIRA; DUARTE.

The Convent of Mafra is a range of buildings, including a church, a monastery, and a palace, built by John V, 1717-1730, the cost exceeding £4,000,000. Hours are required to merely perambulate the courts and chambers of this vast monument of a flat taste in art. The Church has a noteworthy high altar. In the palace are paintings of scenes from the national history.

RAIL, page 299A.

Monchique.—Pop. 5,000.

A small town, in the province of Algarve, finely situated at the base of the Serra de Monchique (2,960 ft.). The Caldas de Monchique, 1,490 feet above sea, have a wide reputation for the cure of skin diseases. Thermal establishment and casino.

Reached by diligence from Portimao (p. 299A), from which place Monchique is 16¼ miles distant.

Oporto.—*Stat.*—Pop. 180,215.

HOTELS; PORTO; PARIS; FRANCFORT; UNIVERSAL.

Electric tramways.

The principal RAILWAY STATION is the Estação Central, at the centre of the town—here all trains from and to distant places arrive and depart; Campanha Station is a mile and a half from centre of town, on east side. Boa Vista Station, in north west district, is or a minor line to Povoa and Famalicao.

Oporto (o Porto—the harbour), on the River Douro, is very pleasantly placed in a hemmed in situation on hill slopes descending to the river, with a background of high land, and with the river broadening out to a spacious harbour. The principal trade is connected with port wine.

The PRAÇA DE DOM PEDRO, a few yards north west of the Estação Central, is the centre of activity. On the north side of the Praça is the Casa de Camara (town hall). The steep street running from south west side of the Praça leads to the Igreja (church) dos Clérigos, with the Torre dos Clérigos close by; fine view from the Torre. Just west of the Clérigos is the Jardim da Cordoaría (or Campo dos Martyres da Patria), a well laid out pleasure ground, with public buildings on each side.

The SE (Cathedral), a quarter mile south of the Praça de Dom Pedro, has little to interest beside the cloisters on the south side. The Ch. of São Francisco (by the Bolsa—Exchange), west of the Sé, nearer the river, contains some fine carved wood-work of 17th-18th cents. West of São Francisco, behind the Alfandega (Custom House), is the old church of São Pedro. Other churches are: Nossa Senhora da Lapa, at north end of Rua do Almada, a street running from north west side of Praça de Dom Pedro; São Ildefonso, a little east of Praça de Dom Pedro; and São Martinho de Cedofeita, 12th cent., in north west part of town.

The Bridge of Oporto—Ponte de Dom Luiz Primeiro, is a quarter mile south of the Praça de Dom Pedro. The bridge crosses the Douro in one arch of 560 ft. span. During and after the winter rains the River Douro sometimes rises 20 feet above its usual level.

At the Palacio do Crystal, at the west side of the city, is a small zoological garden.

POST OFFICE (Correio), in Praça Batalha, a few yards east of the Estação Central.

ENG. CH. SERV.—St. James Church.

H. B. M.'s CONSUL.—H. Grant, Esq.

GOLF LINKS.

RAIL, pages 300, 301.

Thomar.—Reached from Payalvo Station (page 300) by public conveyance—4½ miles, fare 200 reis. HOTEL UNIAO COMERCIAL.

Thomar is one of the most interesting small towns of Portugal. It came into existence under the protection of the Knights Templar; upon the suppression of that Order King Denis established the Order of Christ, with the seat of the Great Chapter here. Prince Henry the Navigator was Grand Master from 1418 to 1460. The Convento de Christo includes the beautiful Church of the Order with the older Temple Church attached; there are also cloisters and corridors, the latter flanked by cells. In the town are mediæval Churches of great historical interest.

ISLANDS.

IN THE MEDITERRANEAN and ATLANTIC. (For SICILY, See p. 562

CORFU (*Greece*).—Pop. of Island (1907) 99,571; of town, about 28,978.

GRAND HOTEL ST. GEORGE; first class, well situated, and one of the most comfortable. Pension terms. See Advt.

Travellers land from the Steamers in small boats, charge 1 dr., with luggage 2 dr. As the boatmen are often troublesome it is well to let the hotel porter settle the boat charges.

Corfu is the most attractive island of the Ionian group. From 1386 until 1797 the island was under the domination of the Venetians; from 1815 until 1864 it was held by the English, who ceded it to Greece. In spring and autumn the climate is delightful. Archbishops of the Greek and Roman Catholic Churches have seats here.

The town, with the suburbs of Kastrades and Mandoukio, is a busy commercial place, having a large export trade in olive oil. The street Nikephorus leads from the harbour in a few minutes to La Spianata (Esplanade), where on the north side is the Royal Palace, formerly the residence of the British Lord High Commissioner —in throne room portraits of British sovereigns, in council chamber portraits of presidents of the Ionian Senate. Before the Palace is a Statue of Sir Frederick Adam (High Commissioner 1823-32). The avenue of trees traversing the Esplanade leads to the Fortezza Vecchia, built by the Venetians, destroyed by the English 1864—now a barracks and military hospital. From the platform, 230 ft., is a magnificent view.

From south side of the Esplanade a street descends to the Empress Elisabeth boulevard, leading to Fort San Salvador, in the suburb of Kastrades. At the foot, on east side, of the fort, is the Tomb of Menecratès, a small round building of 6th or 7th cent. B.C. Half a mile beyond is the Royal Villa of Monrepos, with fine gardens. At a short distance from Monrepos, at the village of Analipsis, are some remains of an ancient Temple. Casino.

H.B.M.'S CONSUL.—G. Raymond. Esq., M.V.O.

VICE-CONSUL.—P. Papadachi, Esq.

U.S. CONS.-AGENT.—C. E. Hancock, Esq.

ENGLISH CH. SERVICE in the English Church. The British Cemetery has a special interest.

MONEY.—Drachmai, 25 = 1£.

STEAMERS to Brindisi, etc., see Steamer List.

Many delightful excursions may be made from the capital to other parts of the island over good roads. It is well to be provided with a passport and Turkish "visa."

To Benizza, 11 miles, an orange growing district, where are remains of a Roman villa; two miles before reaching Benizza is the Villa Achilleion, a favourite residence of the late Empress of Austria. To Monte San Deca, 1,860 ft., whence is grand view of the Albanian coast. To Govino, where are remains of a Venetian arsenal. To Palaeokastritza, where is a Monastery—crossing the hills by the Pass of San Pantaleone. The views of coast, sea, and sunset are very beautiful; there are many classical associations.

Other islands of the Ionian group:

Santa Maura (or Leucadia), near the scene of the naval defeat of Antony and Cleopatra by Augustus, B.C. 30.

Kephalonia, the largest island, where the roads and other improvements made by the English have lapsed into ruin. (British Vice-Consul at Argostoli, J. Saunders, Esq.) Black Mountain, 5,260 ft.

Ithaca (Thiaki), the island of Ulysses and Penelope.

Zante.—See under Greece, *Special Edition*.

CORSICA, or **La Corse** (*France*), is an island of wonderful natural attraction. The scenery is almost always fine, often grand; vegetation is luxuriant—massive in forest, fragrant in lemon and almond trees, brilliant in colour; the climate is mild and equable, the atmosphere clear, with plenty of sunshine. In winter the coast temperature is higher than that of the French Riviera, in summer the elevated towns are pleasantly cool. Population, 288,820. The troubled history of Corsica either prevented the erection or the survival of historic buildings, and there is practically nothing to interest the archeologist. After two years of British sovereignty the island, in 1796, was definitely ceded to France. Coal, iron, marble, porphyry, and various granites are found. Copper, silver, lead, antimony, and asbestos, are worked. See Black's "Corsica" and Reynolds-Ball's "Mediterranean Winter Resorts.

STEAMERS from Leghorn, Marseilles, Nice, etc., see page 356.

RAIL, page 41A.

Ajaccio.—*Stat.*—Pop. 21,779.

GRAND ET CONTINENTAL HOTEL.—First class. Elevated position with fine view. Extensive own grounds. Sunny Hall. Orchestra. See Advt.

ETRANGERS; SUISSE; FRANCE.

When the STEAMERS do not go alongside the quay, the landing charge in small boat is 1 fr. The RAILWAY STATION is close to the shore, on the north side of the town. The Quartier des Etrangers is in the south west part.

An excellent winter station, on the north-west side of a beautiful bay, with a good harbour, open to the south, and well sheltered by surrounding hills. The principal thoroughfares are lined by lemon, orange, and other trees. From Ajaccio as headquarters the island may be explored by motor car in all directions over good roads.

At about mid distance along the harbour front is the spacious Place des Palmiers, at one corner of which is the Hotel de Ville, where is a small museum of objects relating to the Buonaparte family. From the south side of the Place runs the Rue Napoléon, leading to the little Place Letitzia, where is the Maison Bonaparte—not the original house, which was burned, but one erected by the Fesch family. In the Rue Napoléon is the house of another celebrated family—Pozzo di Borgo. The Cathedral, late 16th cent., a domed building, is without special interest. North of the Place des Palmiers, in the Rue Fesch, is the Palais Fesch, including the Collège Fesch, where are collections of pictures and other objects, and a library of 35,000 vols.; in the right wing of the palace is the chapel, where is the tomb of Napoleon's mother, Letitia. Other buildings are the Military Hospital and Great Seminary, in the Place du Diamant; Church of St. Roch; Prefecture; Theatre; and Hotel Sebastiani.

The environs of Ajaccio are very pleasant, Monte Salario, 965 ft., about 3 miles to west, commands beautiful views. Monte Pozzo di Borgo, 2,560 ft., on north west side of Ajaccio, is a favourite excursion; 8 miles from the town, drive or walk—at the Castello della Punta are pictures and antiques. ENG. CH. SERV. in winter.

H.B.M'S VICE-CONSUL.—Hon. H. Dundas.

Bastia.—*Stat.*—Population, 25,425.

CYRNOS PALACE HOTEL.—First class, in fine position. Every modern comfort. Pension terms. See Advt.

DE FRANCE; LINGENIEUR.

Chief commercial town of the island; good harbour. Cathedral of S. Giovanni Battista contains tombs; Church of S. Croce is of interest. Natural history collections and library of 30,000 vols. at the former College of the Jesuits. Old forts erected by the Genoese; Citadel. Some of the houses are seven and eight storeys high. Fine views from several points along coast to north.

H.B.M'S V.-CONS.—W. F. Routley, Esq.

[From Bastia an arm of the island projects northward to **Cap Corse**, a road skirting both sides of the peninsula; public conveyance daily from Bastia to Rogliano. Delightful country. To the little town of St. Florent, 14 miles, over the Col de Teghime, 1,800 ft.]

Bonifacio.—Pop. 4,188. HOTEL: FRANCE.

At the south end of the island, the Pallas Civitas of Ptolemy, in a picturesque situation on a rock. Cathedral of S. Maria Maggiore, in the middle of the town; near by are the Citadel and the Torrione, 78 ft. high; from the latter 217 steps cut in the rock (King of Aragon's stairs) descend to the sea. Knight Templar Ch. of St. Dominique, Gothic, with incomplete tower; other churches are S. Maria Maddalena, S. Francis, S. Anthony.

At opposite side of the harbour is the Punta della Madonetta, and behind this point some Camere, or grottoes explored by boat when weather favourable.

Motor Car between Bonifacio and Ajaccio, staying some hours or the night at **Sartene**, pop. 5,096, one of the most interesting places in the island—HOTEL CESAR; UNIVERS. Motor Car Service also between Bonifacio and Ghisonaccio.

Calvi.—*Stat.*—Pop. 1,898.

Once an important fortified place; Nelson was bombarding it when he lost his right eye. Columbus is stated to have been born here. Cathedral contains tombs.

Corte.-*Stat.*-Pop. 5,425. HOTEL PAOLI; NORD.

A picturesque town of historic interest, specially associated with the patriot Pasquale Paoli, whose rooms, with other objects, are shown at the Pallazzo di Corte. Citadel above the town.

Monte Rotondo, 8,775 ft., is best ascended from Corte—two days required. Magnificent view from summit. The mouflon—a wild horned sheep—is met on the mountain.

Vizzavona.—*Stat.* HOTEL VIZZAVONA.

3,000 feet above sea, among forests of beech and pine, with a delightfully invigorating climate even in summer.

MADEIRA (*Portugal*).—In lat. 32° N., long. 17° W., distant from Southampton 1,309 sea miles, from Lisbon, 520 sea miles. Greatest length, 38 miles, greatest breadth, 15 miles. Geologically regarded as a mass of lava beds and basalt dykes, based on a volcano; Pico Ruivo is 6,059 ft. high;

some of the sea cliffs are 1,000 to 1,935 ft. high. This delightful health resort is remarkable for its genial winter, pleasant cool summer, and equable day and night temperature. Mean winter temp. 60½°; annual average of rainy days 88. The vine is much cultivated, with abundance of oranges, bananas, dates, figs, flowers, ferns, potatoes, etc. MONEY.—Portuguese bank notes and silver; there is very little gold.

STEAMERS from London, Southampton, Liverpool, Lisbon, etc.; the large steamers and local smaller steamers maintain frequent services between Madeira, the Canary Islands, and the Azores. See Steamer List.

Funchal, the capital of the island, on the south side; population 44,049.

HOTELS: REIDS; PALACE HOTEL (late New Hotel); MILES'-CARMO HOTEL; REID'S MOUNT HOTEL, 2,000 ft. above the sea—See Advts. All are comfortable and beautifully situated, with fine views, large grounds of several acres, and are lighted by electricity.

Noon at Funchal is 1 hour 7 minutes 40 seconds after Greenwich.

Funchal is a picturesque town in a beautiful situation; the sanitary state is good, the water sweet; the town is lighted by electricity. Landing from sea going steamers is by steam launches or boats at the jetty; usual charge about 1s.

The Cathedral, of 15th cent., has highly decorated interior; the Jesuit Church, Igreja do Collegio, is also much decorated; annual procession on 1st May to Church of N. S. do Socorro. In the chapel of the Convent of Santa Clara is the tomb of Zargo, the discoverer of the island. Church of N. S. do Monte, 15th cent., 1,965 ft. above sea, reached by climbing railway.

Governor's Palace (Palacio Sao Lourenço), a Japanese looking building; Town Hall (Camara Municipal). At the Museum, in the old Convento da Encarnaçao, are small but interesting collections, including good map in relief of Madeira. Opera house. Fine view from Forte Sao Joao do Pico (Peak Fort); another fort on the Loo Rock; on east side of the town is the Fort of Sao Thiago, used as a barracks.

English Church; Scotch Church; Methodist Epis. Church of America.

BRITISH CONSUL.—Captain Boyle, M.V.O. VICE-CONSUL.—E. Sarsfield, Esq.

MEDICAL.—Dr. Michael Grabham; Dr. Scott; Dr. R. H. Stevens; Dr. Pitta; Dr. N. Porto.

MAJORCA, or Mallorca (*Spain*).—The largest of the Balearic Islands, the others being Minorca, Iviza, and Formentera, with a few small isles.

Majorca is situated 135 miles south of Barcelona, about midway in a direct line between Barcelona and Algiers; its area is 60 miles by 40 miles, with a chain of hills running along the north side, 4,000 feet high at the highest peak—Puig Mayor. The climate of this beautiful island is very pleasant in winter and spring, at other times it is warm and relaxing. Snow is rare; winds prevail; the roads are good. Majolica pottery derives its name from the island. Population of island, 240,000.

STEAMERS from Alicante, Barcelona, and Marseilles, see page 355. RAIL, page 295A.

Palma.—*Stat.*—Pop. 68,359.

The GRAND and VICTORIA HOTEL.—First class, affording every modern comfort. Electric light; lift; steam heating. Pension from 8 ps. See Adv.

A pleasant lively town, in the sorth west part of the island, situated on a bay, the shores being picturesquely dotted by numerous windmills. Several interesting old mansions of local Spanish nobility; in the Calle de la Palma is the ancient house of the Bonaparte family (until 1411), before its migration to Corsica. The Gothic Cathedral contains tombs of early kings of Majorca, of the Marquis Romana (associated with the Duke of Wellington during the Peninsular War), and other notable persons. Good rose window; plate in the treasury. Church of San Francisco has the tomb of Raymond Lully (born 1234); beautiful cloisters; the convent is used as a prison. 16th cent. Casa Consistorial; Lonja (Exchange) of 15th cent. Theatre and Bull-ring. Bellver Castle is on a hill.

H.B.M.'s VICE-CONSUL.-Don B. Bosch y Cerda.

Manacor, Pop. 15,000, is the second town of the island. Artá (pop. 5,300), two hours drive from Manacor, has a celebrated Cave of Artá. Another cave near Manacor is the cave of the Dragon.

Alcudia is a small port in the north east corner of the island, about 8 miles from Puebla (*Station*).

Soller, pop. 10,000, is in a fine situation at the base of Puig Mayor (4,740 ft.). The lemon is extensively cultivated. The harbour of Soller is about two miles north of the town.

Other interesting places in Majorca are:

Valldemosa, regarded as one of the loveliest spots in Europe. Here are the Chateau of Raxa and a 15th cent. Convent.

Miramar, the magnificent domain of the Austrian Archduke Luis Salvator. The pilgrimage Convent of Lluch—now a boys' school.

Pollensa and Castillo del Rey, in wild scenery.

Minorca, or **Menorca**.—The easternmost of the Balearic Islands, 27 miles E.N.E. of Majorca; 33 miles by 13 miles in extent; chiefly flat country, rising to a cone at Monte Toro, 1,000 ft., above sea. Population, 37,654.

Mahon.—Pop. 17,140. HOTELS: DEL VAPORE; BUSTAMENTE. About three miles of protected water-way leads from the sea at Port Mahon to Mahon. The fort La Mola, at the north entrance of the Port, is very strong—visitors not admitted. The British held possession of Port Mahon from 1708 until 1756 (when Admiral Byng, failing to retain it, was shot by judgment of court-martial), and again, with two intervals, until 1802. The British strong positions were on the side opposite to La Mola, and are now mere ruins with a few tombs among them. The town of Mahon claims its name from its Carthaginian founder, Magon, and it is also claimed that Hannibal was born here. Traces of the British occupation linger in a few words and manners.

H.B.M's V.-CONSUL.—Bartolomé Escudero, Esq., M.V.O.

Ciudadela, an interesting little town, has several fine old houses in its arcaded streets.

Alayor and Mercadel are two other small towns; near Mercadel is Monte Toro, where are a pilgrimage church and convent ruins. Scattered over

Minorca are several groups of prehistoric stone remains known as Talayots, of whose signification not anything is positively known; they are variously described as Phœnician, "Druidic," or merely abodes of a rude age.

Iviza, the third in size of the Balearic Islands, is 42 miles south west of Majorca, and only 50 miles from the Spanish coast. Population of island, 25,000, of an unruly reputation. The town of Iviza, on a poor harbour, is not without interest—there are old heavy fortifications and crumbling mansions. Hotel accommodation is practically absent from the island; the pure dry air of the interior, where are almond orchards, is an attraction.

H.B.M.'s VICE-CONSUL.—J. S. Lopez, Esq.

Formentera, population 1,700, is a little island, 6 miles south of Iviza, with a very healthy climate, recommended in cases of chest complaints.

MALTA (Great Britain).

Malta is the largest of a group of three islands —the others being Gozo and Comino—situated 56 miles south of Sicily and 187 miles from the coast of Africa.

Total population 228,534, exclusive of the garrison (usually about 10,000). In summer the climate is hot, but the winter climate, apart from much wind, is pleasant—mean temperature in January 61°. The language (lingua Maltese) is a mingling of corrupt Arabic with Italian; English, the official language, is becoming more generally understood. British money is the currency.

COMMANDER-IN-CHIEF OF THE MEDITERRANEAN FORCES.—General Sir Ian S. M. Hamilton.

GOVERNOR.—Lieut.-Gen. Sir H. M. L. Rundle.

Malta has an almost daily Steamer service connecting with SYRACUSE (Adria Line, Advt., page 731; Navigazione Generale Italiana Line, and a weekly service connecting with TUNIS (Cie. Générale Transatlantique, Advt., page 729), whence there is a frequent service to Marseilles. The Peninsular and Oriental Co.'s steamers from and to LONDON (Advt., page 726). The Papayanni and Ellerman Lines from LIVERPOOL.

Valletta.—Pop. 80,000.

HOTELS: ROYAL; ANGLETERRE; GREAT BRITAIN; IMPERIAL.

CABS.—Drive within town, 3d; extra fare after dark.

Capital of the island of Malta, on a rocky promontory; between two deep and almost land locked harbours—an immensely strong natural position. Fort St. Elmo is at the sea end of the promontory; opposite, on the left (entering), is Fort Ricasoli; on the right, Fort Tigne. The streets are mostly very steep, in places there are only stairways, but the general cleanliness is a pleasing contrast with other Mediterranean ports. The principal thoroughfare, Strada Reale, runs through the middle of the town, from Fort St. Elmo to Porta Reale, about half a mile.

The Governor's Palace is in a central situation, in the Strada Reale and Strada Teatro. Handsome interior, with tapestry, collection of weapons, documents, and memorials of the Order of the Knights of Malta; fee to view, 6d. A short distance south west of the Palace is the Cathedral of San Giovanni, dating from 1576, with many monuments of Grand Masters and officers of the Maltese Order; paintings in the chapels. Between the Palace and the Cathedral is the Library (40,000 vols.), with a Museum of antiquities. The "Auberges" of the Knights have been diverted to various uses; the most interesting, the Auberge de Castile, is now occupied by the artillery and engineers; the Union Club occupies the Auberge de Provence. Beyond the Porta Reale are the Argotti and Maglio Gardens and the garrison drill ground.

CHURCH OF ENGLAND SERV.—St. Paul's Ch.

GOLF.—9 hole course, at Marsa, two miles from Valletta.

An ENGLISH NURSING INSTITUTE and HOME, under the patronage of His Excellency the Governor of Malta and the Commander-in-Chief of His Britannic Majesty's Fleet in the Mediterranean, is established in Valletta.

Città Vecchia, connected by rail with Valletta. The old capital, sometimes called Notabile, 6 miles west of Valletta. The Cathedral is stated to be on the site of the house of Publius, governor of the island when St. Paul was shipwrecked; in a chapel is an image of St. Paul, covered with a silver cloth; fine stalls in choir. In the south quarter of the town, by the Church of St. Francis, is the Church of San Paolo, erected over a grotto where, it is stated, St. Paul lived during his three months stay in the island. St. Paul's Bay, on the north side of the island, 5½ miles from Città Vecchia, is the supposed scene of the shipwreck of St. Paul; large statue of the Apostle on the islet of Selmun.

Gozo (steamer twice a day from Valletta, returning same day). The principal town, Victoria (Duke of Edinburgh Hotel), formerly Rabato, is nearly 4 miles from the landing place in Migiarro Bay. On the island are the Torre de' Giganti, a Phœnician stone pile (fee 6d.) and a stalactite grotto. The little island of **Comino**, between Malta and Gozo, has very few inhabitants.

CANARY ISLANDS *(Spain)*.—The old Fortunate Islands, a volcanic group of 13, in the Atlantic, off the north west coast of Africa. Seven of the islands are inhabited: Teneriffe, Gran Canaria, Fuerteventura, Lanzarote, La Palma, Gomera, and Hierro. Genial exhilarating winter climate; not too warm in summer; generally, the Canaries are breezier than Madeira; very little rain in winter.

STEAMERS from London, Liverpool, Southampton, Cadiz, etc.; see Steamer List. Local Steamers maintain a frequent service between the Canary Islands.

Teneriffe, the largest of the islands, is 52½ miles long and 31½ miles at its broadest; population, 138,008.

Santa Cruz de Santiago.—Pop. 53,403.

GRAND HOTEL QUISISANA.-First class modern hotel, in extensive grounds. See Advt. under "Canary Islands."

Santa Cruz, the chief town of Teneriffe, is a picturesque place, with a bright cheerful population. The water supply has been improved, the streets are lighted by electricity, and electric trams connect with other towns. Pleasant shady public gardens. English Club. Theatre.

Palace of the Governor General; Gobierno Civil, with fine patio; modern Courts of Justice; Museum and Library in the old Franciscan monastery. Plaza de Toros (bull ring) and cock pit.

The Iglesia de la Concepcion, 16th cent., is sometimes called the Cathedral; the exterior is unattractive, tower 166 ft. high; carved woodwork in interior; among the relics is a piece of the true cross; handsome vestments and plate; here are two of Nelson's flags, captured 1797, when he lost his arm. Church of S. Francisco, 17th cent.; close by is the Capilla de Dolores.

ENGLISH CHURCH in upper part of the town.

H.B.M.'s CONSUL.—J. E. Croker, Esq. VICE-CONSUL.—R. C. Griffiths, Esq.

U.S. CONSUL.—W. W. Kitchen, Esq.

Puerto Orotava.—Pop. 5,562.

HOTEL MARTIANEZ.—First class, situated near the sea and Martianez springs; large garden, with shady verandahs. See Advt.

An attractive town and favourite health resort on the north side of Teneriffe, 27 miles from Santa Cruz; good water supply. The Valley of Orotava was pronounced by Humboldt the most beautiful in the world.

The Church of N. S. de la Peña de Francia has an agreeable interior. English Church and resident chaplain. English cemetery.

H.B.M.'s VICE-CONSUL.—T. M. Reid, Esq.

GOLF.—9-hole course on Santa Ursula promontory, about six miles from Puerto Orotava.

Villa Orotava.—Pop. 9,192. 1,300 ft. above sea, 3½ miles from Puerto Orotava, with a climate more bracing than at the Puerto. Iglesia de la Concepcion, a handsome church, with some silver plate that once belonged to St. Paul's Cathedral, London; Iglesia de San Juan. Casa Municipal and gardens. In a garden is a chestnut tree of 27½ ft. girth, planted 1496.

Realejo Alto.—Pop. 4,077. 1,160 ft. above sea. About 5 miles from Puerto Orotava. Iglesia de Santiago is interesting. The ascent of The Peak, 12,192 ft., is usually made from here.

Icod de los Vinos.—Pop. 6,706; 700 ft. above sea, about 10 miles from Realejo. Chief attractions are the views of The Peak. Near the church is the largest dragon tree of the island. Below the town are Guanche sepulchral caves. Four miles from Icod is Garachico, pop. 2,929, once the chief port of the island, practically ruined in 1706 by lava streams. Several old churches.

La Laguna.—Pop. 13,704.

HOTEL AGUERE AND CONTINENTAL.—First class, surrounded by fine country. See Advt.

The old capital of the island, a pleasant summer residence and winter resort, 1,804 ft. above sea; 5½ miles from Santa Cruz, a tramway connecting.

At the Municipio are old paintings on the staircase. Universidad de San Fernando, with library of 20,000 vols., some early printed books, and curious Dutch manuscript of 15th cent. Close by is the Bishop's Palace, a handsome building.

Cathedral, 16th cent., restored, has good altars and pulpit, tomb of Don Alonso de Lugo, conqueror of the island. Iglesia de la Concepcion, 16th cent., with lofty tower; miraculous picture of St. John in altar to north of chancel. Other churches and convent chapels.

Tacoronte.—Pop. 4,204. ENGLISH HOTEL.

A picturesque spot, 12½ miles from Santa Cruz, reached by tram in 1½ hours. Iglesia de Santa Catalina has rich collection of gold and silver plate. In the Church of the Convento de San Augustin is the famous wooden Christ of Tacoronte, to which many miracles are attributed.

Grand Canary.—34½ miles long by 29½ miles broad. The highest point is the Pico del Pozo de las Nieves, 6,400 ft. Temperature rather high, but cool and bracing on the hills; invalid season from October to March.

The chief port is **Puerto de la Luz**, pop. about 10,000. A steam tramway, 3½ miles long, connects with Las Palmas. H.B.M.'s CONSUL, P. Swanston, Esq.

Las Palmas.—Pop. 53,824.

SANTA CATALINA HOTEL.—First class English hotel, in its own beautiful garden, covering about 20 acres, overlooking the sea. See Advt.

METROPOLE; QUINEY'S.

Capital of Grand Canary, a cheerful town, lighted by electricity, with a good water supply.

Cathedral of S. Cristobal, rebuilt 1781, unfinished; lofty interior; the lectern is stated to have belonged to the old St. Paul's Cathedral, London. Church of S. Francisco, 1689; curious interior. At San Telmo are many votive offerings by mariners. The Gobierno Militar is the residence of the Governor. At the Municipio (Town Hall) are a Museum and Library. Opera House. Casino in the gardens of the Alameda—the favourite promenade. ENGLISH CHURCH.

GOLF.—13-hole course; club house.

Several interesting excursions by good roads. At **Cuesta de Silba** are over 300 caves formerly inhabited by the Canarios. At Montaña de las Cuatro Puertas the most sacred burial ground of the Canarios remains almost in the original state.

La Palma, 29 by 17¼ miles, is by many regarded as the most beautiful of the Canary Islands. Pop. 41,994. Highest point, 7,768 ft. Chief town, **Santa Cruz**, pop. 7,024. HOTEL ARIDANE; FONDA MARINA. Good water; town lighted by electricity. Some interesting churches; small museum. The chief object of interest in the island is the Gran Caldera, a crater four miles across, and 7,000 ft. deep. Weird volcanic scenery. H.B.M.'s V.-CONSUL, R. F. Millar, Esq.

Lanzarote, 36 by 13½ miles. Pop. 17,546. Chief town, **Arrecife**, pop. 3,082; good harbour; an ill built unattractive place. Many extinct volcanoes in the island.

For Pages 585 to 712, see SPECIAL EDITION, price 3s. 6d., published the 1st of each Month, containing an additional amount of useful Information with Maps not to be found in the 2s. Edition.

LONDON BRIGHTON & SOUTH COAST RAILWAY.

Via NEWHAVEN & DIEPPE.

ROYAL MAIL ROUTE TO

PARIS AND THE CONTINENT

THE PICTURESQUE & CHEAPEST ROUTE.

24-KNOT TURBINE STEAMERS CROSSING CHANNEL IN 2¾ HOURS.

TWO EXPRESS SERVICES DAILY, SUNDAYS INCLUDED.

Through Carriages (Corridor-Bogie, latest type) by Day Service between Dieppe and Milan, via Lausanne and Simplon.

LONDON to PARIS.	DAY EXPRESS. 1 & 2 Class.	NIGHT EXPRESS. 1, 2, 3 Class.
VICTORIA (West End) dep.	10 0 a.m	8 45 p.m
London Bridge (City) "	....	8 45 "
Newhaven Harbour.. "	11 30 "	10 25 "
Dieppe .... "	3 11 p.m	3 8 a.m
Rouen .... arr.	.... | 5 19 p.m	.... | 7 14 a.m
PARIS (St. Lazare) ... "	6¶ 3 p.m |	6¶ 30 a.m | ....

PARIS to LONDON.	DAY EXPRESS. 1 & 2 Class.	NIGHT EXPRESS. 1, 2, 3 Class
PARIS (St. Lazare)....dep.	10¶ 0 a.m |	9 20 p.m
Rouen .... "	.... | 1112a.m	11 37 "
Dieppe............... "	1 0 p.m	1 25 a.m
Newhaven Harbour .. "	4 45 "	6 0 "
London Bridge (City)..arr.	....	7 30 "
VICTORIA (West End) "	6 10 "	7 30 "

¶ Via Pontoise.

A Corridor-Lavatory Train runs between Dieppe and Paris—St. Lazare and Paris—Lyon in connection with the Day Service in both directions, and 1st, 2nd, and 3rd Class Corridor-Lavatory Carriages are run in the Night Boat Train to and from Dieppe and Paris—St. Lazare and Paris—Lyon.

A Restaurant Car (1st and 2nd) is run both ways between Dieppe and Paris—St. Lazare in the Day Trains.

FARES including Harbour Passenger Taxes) from	SINGLE JOURNEY TICKETS.				RETURN TICKETS. Available One Month.		
	1st Class.	2nd Class.	3rd Class.	Available for	1st Class.	2nd Class.	3rd Class.
LONDON to	s. d.	s. d.	s. d.		s. d.	s. d.	s. d.
Dieppe	28 7	20 0	14 9	Three Days.	45 3	31 1	22 10
Rouen	33 7	24 0	15 8	Seven Days.	53 3	38 1	27 3
Havre	39 4	27 5	19 7	Seven Days.	61 2	42 8	30 6
PARIS (St. Lazare)	38 7	28 0	18 7	Seven Days.	66 3	47 1	33 3
Paris (Lyon)	39 8	29 0	19 6	Seven Days.	68 5	49 1	35 1

Change of Cabin.—Second Class Passengers may use the First Saloon of the Steamboats by payment on board, or at the time of booking, of 5s. by Day or Night Service, and Third Class Passengers may use the Second Saloon of the Night Boats on payment of 3s. 6d.

The journey may be broken at all intermediate Stations. Tickets are available via Brighton.

Switzerland, Italy, South of France, South Germany, Austria, Hungary, Spain, Algeria, &c.—Through Bookings and Registration of Luggage.

1 to 15 DAY EXCURSIONS to DIEPPE, ROUEN, and PARIS, July 12th and 13th, July 31st to August 4th, &c. Passengers may return any day within 15 days.

GREATLY ACCELERATED SERVICES BETWEEN LONDON AND PARIS.

The Day Service to and from Paris and the Night Service to Paris have been greatly accelerated, and pass by the New Pontoise Route. The Night Service from Paris continues via Rouen.

Passengers have still the option of travelling by Rouen in the case of all Services.

Three 24-knot Turbine Steamers are now on the Service, and cross the Channel in 2¾ hours.

Full particulars of Continental Manager, Brighton Railway, Victoria Station, London, S.W.

34

BELGIAN STATE RY. & MAIL PACKET SERVICE

VIA DOVER-OSTEND.

SHORT SEA PASSAGE and Accelerated MAIL SERVICE between

LONDON and THE RHINE,

GERMANY, SWITZERLAND, ITALY, RUSSIA,

And CAIRO (Egypt).

THE NEW TURBINE STEAMERS,

"PRINCESSE ELISABETH" "JAN BREYDEL" and "PIETER DE CONINCK"

beating the record of all Channel packet boats afloat, and

the splendid and Fast New Steamers, "Princesse Clementine," "Rapide," "Leopold II.," "Marie Henriette," "Princesse Henriette," "Princesse Josephine," perform thrice daily the

SEA PASSAGE IN THREE HOURS.

Two additional Turbine Steamers, the "Stad Antwerpen" and the "Ville de Liége," will be placed on the service shortly.

Through Carriages from Ostend to Bad-Nauheim, Brussels, Cologne, Lucerne, Milan, Genoa, Munich, Nuremberg, Spa Ulm, Vienna, Budapest, BERLIN, WIRBALLEN (St. Petersburg), Warsaw, and Moscow, also to Switzerland, Carlsbad, Marienbad, and most watering places on the Continent. Sleeping Carriages between Ostend, Bale, Cologne, Vienna Belgrade, Constantinople, Kustendje (for Constantinople), and Berlin, Wirballen (St. Petersburg), and vice versa.

THREE SERVICES DAILY.

Route	Frequency / Via		
LONDON-OSTEND-BRUSSELS	THRICE DAILY	IN 8	HOURS
LONDON-OSTEND-SWITZERLAND	THRICE DAILY	IN 18	HOURS
LONDON-OSTEND-MILAN-ITALY	THRICE DAILY	IN 27	HOURS
LONDON-OSTEND-VIENNA-BUDAPEST	DAILY	IN 37	HOURS
LONDON-CONSTANTINOPLE DAILY.	(Three Times Via OSTEND-BUCAREST-KUSTENDJE.)	IN 72	HOURS
	(Four Times Via OSTEND-BELGRADE-SOFIA)	IN 71	HOURS
LONDON-CAIRO, WEEKLY	(Via OSTEND-TAUERN-TRIESTE.)	IN $4\frac{1}{2}$	DAYS
LONDON-OSTEND-BERLIN (NORD EXPRESS)	DAILY	IN 21	HOURS
LONDON-OSTEND-ST. PETERSBURG	(TWICE WEEKLY.)	IN 51	HOURS

LONDON-OSTEND-WARSAW-MOSCOW IN 58 HOURS. WEEKLY

GHENT EXHIBITION, 1913.

For Information, Guides (free), Private Cabins and Tickets, see opposite page.

BELGIAN STATE RY. & MAIL PACKET SERVICE

THREE DAILY EXPRESS TRAINS

VIA DOVER-OSTEND

SWITZERLAND and ITALY

in both directions between **LONDON, OSTEND, BRUSSELS, STRASBURG, SWITZERLAND,** and **ITALY.** Connections: at **Strasburg,** to and from the **Black Forest;** at **Bale,** to and from the whole of **Switzerland;** at **Milan,** to and from **Venice, Genoa, Bologna, Florence, Rome, Naples, Brindisi,** &c.; at **Brindisi,** for **Egypt,** every Tuesday, Saturday, and Sunday, and the 15th and 30th of every month; every Sunday for **Bombay, British India, French India, Persia,** by the Indian Mail; for **Ceylon,** the **Straits Settlements, Annam, Cambodia, Tonquin, Cochinchina, China, Japan, Dutch Indies,** and **Australasia,** every alternate Sunday from July 6th; for **Zanzibar,** and **Mozambique,** every fourth Sunday from July 27th; at **Naples,** for **Egypt,** every Thursday; for **Australia** every second Sunday from July 13th; for the **Dutch Indies,** every alternate Friday from July 11th; for **China,** every alternate Friday from July 11th; for **Zanzibar** and **Mozambique** the 13th and 29th July.

The Ostend Route is thus rendered not only the best served in its connections all the year round, but also the most advantageous as regards the number of its through communications, the rapidity of the various services it provides (London-Bale in 18 hours), the non-changing of trains, and the comfort and moderate fares which it offers to travellers.

THIRD CLASS SERVICE FOR SWITZERLAND.

Passengers for Switzerland with 3rd class tickets leaving London at *2.20 p.m., arrive in Bâle next morning at 11.15 a.m.; those leaving London at 9.0 p.m. arrive in Bale next evening at 5.32 p.m.; passengers leaving Dover at 11.0 a.m. arrive in Bâle next morning at 5.50 a.m. Through carriage, third class, between Ostend and Bale, and *vice versa.*

* Holders of 3rd class tickets to Antwerp, Brussels, Liège, Verviers, and to all intermediate stations can travel by this train.

FARES:—Dover-Bale, 3rd class, single, £1 9s. 5d. (15 days); Return, £2 12s. 3d. (60 days).

Passengers for and through Alsace-Lorraine are not affected by the Passport Regulations provided they travel by the Dover-Ostend Route. They land and embark both at **Dover and Ostend** alongside the Piers. Trains arrive at and start from the Steamers' side. **Through Carriages** are run by the Mail Trains between **Ostend** and Principal Stations, such as **Brussels, Strasburg, Bale, Zurich, Milan, Salzburg, Carlsruhe, Stuttgart, Innsbruck,** and Watering Places. The Steamers carrying H.M. Mails are the fastest in the Channel, have superior accommodation, and are fitted with the Marconi System of Wireless Telegraphy.

SAILINGS THREE TIMES DAILY (SUNDAYS INCLUDED) AS UNDER:

	a.m.	p.m.	p.m.		a.m.	p.m	p.m.
FROM ADMIRALTY PIER DOVER	11 0	4 30	11 0	**FROM PIER OSTEND HARBOUR**	10 37	3 30	10 58

Two new Turbine Steamers, the "Stad Antwerpen" and the "Ville de Liége," will be placed on the service shortly.

Fridays and Saturdays, special tourist tickets London-Ostend and back.

Fares from Dover to Ostend: Single Tickets: 1st Class, **9/-**; 2nd Class, **7/2.**—Return Tickets: 1st Class, **15/-**; 2nd Class, **12/-** (30 days). Private Cabins Small Cabin, **7** frs.; Centre Cabin, **14** frs.; Special Cabin, **28** frs.; State Room **75** frs.; can be engaged in advance by making application in Dover, as at foot, or at Ostend-Quay to Station Master. Through Tickets from London to the Continent allow break of journey at most places *en route,* and Return Tickets are available if to Belgium for one month, if beyond Belgium for 60 days from date of issue. **Luggage** can be registered to and from all Chief Stations on the Continent, 56 lbs. being allowed each passenger gratis to and through Belgium. Tickets issued and luggage registered in London at Charing Cross Station (South Eastern and Chatham Railway); in Dover, **BELGIAN TICKET OFFICE,** on the Pier and Strond Street. For tickets, single, return, combined tours, information, timebooks and Illustrated Continental Tour Books, apply to the **BELGIAN TICKET OFFICES, 53, GRACECHURCH STREET, E.C., 72, REGENT STREET, LONDON, W., or NORTHUMBERLAND HOUSE, DOVER.**

For information and timebooks *only,* apply to **Mr. DEFRANCE, Commercial Representative of the Belgian State Railways,** 47, Cannon Street, E.C.

FARES:—For fares from London, see pages lxxiii to cxvii of this Guide (A B C Direct Routes).

Continental Daily Parcels Express, in correspondence with the Belgian State Railway, Imperial German Post, Federal Swiss Post, Italian Railways, etc.—Three Services Daily, in both directions, for the conveyance of parcels by Mail Express. Tariffs and other information to be had gratis at 53, Gracechurch Street E.C.; and 72, Regent Street, W.

July, 1913.

LONDON AND SOUTH WESTERN RAILWAY. **JULY, 1913.**

LONDON AND GUERNSEY AND JERSEY.

OUTWARD.—LONDON to GUERNSEY and JERSEY.	*Via* SOUTHAMPTON and L. & S. W. Ry. Daily (Sundays excepted).	*Via* WEYMOUTH and G. W. Ry. Daily (Sundays excepted).
Boat Train leaves London	Waterloo 9.45 aft.	Paddington 9 35 a.m.
Steamer leaves at	12.30 night	1 45 p.m.
HOMEWARD.—JERSEY and GUERNSEY to LONDON.	*Via* SOUTHAMPTON and L. & S. W. Ry. Daily (Sundays excepted).	*Via* WEYMOUTH and G. W. Ry. Daily (Sundays excepted).
Steamer leaves Jersey	8 0 mrn	8 30 a.m.
Steamer leaves Guernsey	10 0 mrn	10 15 a.m.

FARES.—London to Guernsey or Jersey:—1st cl. 33s.; 2nd cl. 22s. 2d.; 3rd cl. 20s. Return Tickets available for 6 months 1st cl. 48s.; 2nd cl. 37s. 6d.; 3rd cl. 30s.

SERVICES BETWEEN JERSEY AND FRANCE.

From Jersey to St. Malo.—Every Monday and Wednesday	FARES.—Single	1st class. 8s. 10d.	2nd class.	5s. 10d.
From St. Malo to Jersey.—Every Monday and Thursday	„ —Return	„ 13s. 8d.;	„	9s. 2d.
From Jersey to Granville.—Every Tuesday and Friday	„ —Single	„ 8s. 5d.;	„	5s. 5d.
From Granville to Jersey.—Every Tuesday and Saturday	„ —Return	„ 12s. 10d.	„	8s. 4d.

London and Paris

Via SOUTHAMPTON, HAVRE, and ROUEN,

OPEN SEA PASSAGE ONLY 5 HOURS.

THE PICTURESQUE NORMANDY ROUTE.

For Etretat, Honfleur, Caen, Trouville, Rouen, Paris, South of France, and Switzerland.

Every night (except Sunday) all the year round. The 1st class accommodation is in separate cabins of 1 (Cabines de Luxe), 2, and 4 berths each. Electric Lights.

Fares:—London to Paris, or *vice versa*, 1st cl. 36s. 10d.; 2nd cl. 26s. 10d.; Double Journey, 62s. 4d. and 44s. 4d. London to Havre, or *vice versa*, 1st cl. 30s. 6d.; 2nd cl. 21s. 6d.; Double Journey 47s. 0d. and 35s. 0d.

London to Honfleur & Trouville, or *vice versa*, 1st cl. 31s. 4d.; 2nd cl. 22s. 2d.; Double Journey 48s. 7d. and 36s. 3d.

Two new large Turbine Steamers are now performing this service.

LONDON TO PARIS.	Every Week-day.	Sats. from 26th July.
Boat Train from London (Waterloo)	9.45 aft.	8.57 a.m.
Steamer leaves Southampton	12.15 night.	11.15 a.m.
Train leaves Havre	*8.0 morn.	6.43 p.m.
Train arrives Paris (St. Lazare)	11.22 morn.	11.18 p.m.
PARIS TO LONDON.	Every Week-day—and Sundays from 27th.	
Boat Train from Paris (St. Lazare)	7.48 aft.	
Steamer leaves Havre	12.0 night	
Train leaves Southampton	7.0 morn.	
Train due London (Waterloo)	about 9.0 morn.	

*—Failing connection with the 8.0 a.m. a special Boat Train is run immediately after Steamer's arrival.

SERVICE BETWEEN LONDON AND ST. MALO, via Southampton.

SOUTHAMPTON to ST. MALO.

Boat Train leaves Waterloo Station (1) July.	Steamer leaves Southampton.	Boat Train leaves Waterloo Station. (1) July.	Steamer leaves Southampton.
Tues. 1...... 2 55 p.m.	6 0 p.m.	Tues. 22...... 9 45 p.m.	12 0 midn't
Thur. 3...... 4 50 p.m.	7 15 p.m.	Wed. 23...... 6 55 p.m.	9 30 p.m.
Sat. 5...... 4 50 p.m.	7 15 p.m.	Thur. 24...... 9 45 p.m.	12 0 midn't
Tues. 8...... 6 55 p.m.	9 30 p.m.	Fri. 25...... 8 15 p.m.	11 15 p.m.
Thur. 10...... 8 15 p.m.	11 15 p.m.	Sat. 26...... 7 30 p.m.	10 0 p.m.
Sat. 12...... 7 30 p.m.	10 0 p.m.	Mon. 28...... 6 30 p.m.	9 0 p.m.
Tues. 15...... 2 55 p.m.	6 0 p.m.	Tues. 29...... 7 30 p.m.	10 0 p.m.
Thur. 17...... 4 50 p.m.	7 15 p.m.	Wed. 30...... 2 25 p.m.	5 0 p.m.
Sat. 19...... 7 30 p.m.	10 0 p.m.	Thur. 31...... 6 30 p.m.	9 0 p.m.
Mon. 21...... 6 55 p.m.	9 15 p.m.		

ST. MALO to SOUTHAMPTON.

July.	July.
Wed. 2... 5 30 p.m.	Wed. 23... 8 0 p.m.
Fri. 4... 7 30 p.m.	Thur. 24... 8 0 p.m.
Mon. 7... 8 0 p.m.	Fri. 25... 9 0 p.m.
Wed. 9... 8 0 p.m.	Sat. 26... 9 30 p.m.
Fri. 11...10 0 p.m.	Mon. 28...12 0 mid.
Mon. 14... 4 0 p.m.	Tues. 29... 3 0 p.m.
Wed. 16... 6 0 p.m.	Wed. 30... 4 0 p.m.
Fri. 18... 7 0 p.m.	Thur. 31... 5 30 p.m.
Mon. 21... 8 0 p.m.	
Tues. 22... 8 0 p.m.	

(1) Passengers may travel by any previous train.

Fares.—London to St. Malo, or *vice versa*, 1st cl. 35s. 10d.; 2nd cl. 25s. 10d. Return, 53s. 8d. and 41s. 2d., available for Six Months.

SERVICE BETWEEN LONDON AND CHERBOURG, VIA SOUTHAMPTON.

Southampton to Cherbourg every Tuesday, Thursday, and Saturday at 11.15 midnight. Boat Train leaves Waterloo Station, London, at 8.15 aft.

Cherbourg to Southampton, every Mon., Wed. and Fri. at 11.0 aft., or as soon after as tide and circumstances permit.

Fares.—London to Cherbourg, or *vice versa*, 1st cl. 30s. 4d.; 2nd cl. 20s. 10d. Return, 46s. 8d. & 31s. 8d. available for Six Months.

For further information, &c., apply to Mr. H. HOLMES, Superintendent of the Line, Waterloo Station, London; Mr. BENNETT, 253, Rue St. Honoré, Paris; Mr. LANGSTAFF, 67, Grand Quai, Havre; or to **Mr. T. M. WILLIAMS, Dock and Marine Manager, Southampton.**

July 1st, 1913. By order, **H. A. WALKER,** General Manager, Waterloo Station, London.

Red Star Line

Regular Mail Steamers between

Antwerp—New York. Dover—New York.
Antwerp—Boston. Antwerp—Baltimore.
Antwerp—Philadelphia.

PROPOSED SAILINGS (subject to change).

1913. From ANTWERP to NEW YORK. 1913.

TWIN SCREW STEAMERS OF 13,000 TO 19,000 TONS.

Fitted with Wireless Telegraph System, as well as with Submarine Signalling Apparatus.

Steamer	Day	Date	Time
Finland	Saturday	5 July	1 0 p.m.
Lapland	Saturday	12 July	7 0 a.m.
Vaderland	Saturday	19 July	1 0 p.m
Zeeland	Saturday	26 July	7 0 a.m
Finland	Saturday	2 August	1 0 p.m.
Kroonland	Saturday	9 August	7 0 a.m.
Vaderland	Saturday	16 August	1 0 p.m.
Lapland	Saturday	23 August	2 30 p.m.
Zeeland	Saturday	30 August	11 0 a.m.
Kroonland	Saturday	6 September	2 15 p.m.
Finland	Saturday	13 September	11 0 a.m.
Lapland	Saturday	20 September	2 0 p.m.

From ANTWERP to BOSTON.
Fortnightly by First Class Steamers.

From ANTWERP to PHILADELPHIA.
Fortnightly by First Class Steamers.

From ANTWERP to BALTIMORE.
Fortnightly by First Class Cargo Steamers.

Passage Rates from Antwerp to New York and Boston, subject to change.

Class	Steamers	Rate	Notes
FIRST CLASS.	Lapland	£19 10 0	and higher, according to location and size of staterooms, and number of persons occupying them: for further particulars see cabin tariff.
	Other Steamers to New York	£17 0 0	
SECOND CLASS.	Lapland	£12 0 0	
	Other Steamers to New York, Aug. 10—Oct. 15	£11 10 0	
	Other Steamers to New York, Oct. 16—Aug. 9	£11 0 0	
	Steamers to Boston	£11 0 0	
THIRD CLASS.	All Steamers	£8 0 0	plus 16 - Head Tax collected by the United States.

RED STAR LINE, 22, Kammenstraat, ANTWERP.

AACHEN, 22, Hochstrasse.
BASLE, 58, Elisabethenstrasse.
BERLIN, 6, Unter den Linden.
BRUSSELS, 6, Boulevard Anspach.
BUDAPEST, VIII Köztemetö út 12a.
COLOGNE, 13, Unter Fettenhennen.
CREFELD, Crefelder Hof.
DOVER, 2, Strond Street.
DRESDEN, 31, Christianstrasse.
DUSSELDORF, 10, Wilhelmsplatz.
FRANKFURT a. M. 18, Kaiserstrasse.
INNSBRUCK, 2, Südbahnstrasse.
LEIPZIG, 3, Georgiring.
LIVERPOOL, 27-29, James Street.
LONDON. 1, Cockspur Street, S.W.; 38, Leadenhall Street, E.C.
LUCERNE, J. Baumeler, Schweizerhofquai-Schwanenplatz.
LUXEMBURG, Maria-Theresien Strasse
MANNHEIM, 7, Bahnhofsplatz.
MAYENCE, 12, Stiftstrasse.
MUNICH, 18, Maximiliansplatz.
PARIS, 9, Rue Scribe.
SOUTHAMPTON, Canute Road.
STRASSBURG i. E., 6, Bahnhofsplatz.
STUTTGART, 21, Königstrasse.
VIENNA, 14, Kärntnerring.
WIESBADEN, 3, Kaiser-Friedrichplatz
ZURICH, 8, Lintheschergasse.

KHEDIVIAL MAIL LINE OF STEAMERS.

Service between TURKEY, GREECE, and EGYPT.—Express Mail Service by first-class British steamers. Departure from Constantinople every *Tuesday afternoon* for Mitylene, Smyrna, Piræus, and Alexandria.

Arrival at Alexandria *Saturday morning.* Passengers have time to visit Athens during stay of steamer at Piræus, and journey may be broken at any port without extra charge.

The steamers run in connection with the Oriental Railways Express trains from and to Budapest, Vienna, Berlin, Paris, and London.

Service between TURKEY, SYRIA, HOLY LAND, and EGYPT. Every fortnight fast steamers leave Constantinople on *Saturdays* for Gallipoli, Dardanelles, Mitylene, Smyrna, Chios, Rhodes, Mersina, Alexandretta, Tripoli, Beyrouth, Caiffa, Jaffa (for Jerusalem), Port Said, and Alexandria.

Arrival at Alexandria on *Wednesday mornings*, the voyage taking 10 days, and affording an unequalled opportunity of seeing the Greek Islands, Asia Minor, and Syrian Ports. Return from Egypt and Syria every fortnight.

EGYPT to SYRIA and HOLY LAND.—Departures from Alexandria *every Saturday* and from Port Said every *Sunday* for Jaffa, Caiffa, Beyrouth, Tripoli, Alexandretta, and Mersina, and returning via same ports.

Every second week the steamers proceed along the Syrian Coast to Mersina, return thence to Beyrouth, and leave on Fridays for Rhodes, Smyrna, and Constantinople, affording the quickest communication between Syria and Constantinople.

EGYPT to CYPRUS.—Steamers under mail contract leave Alexandria every Tuesday and Port Said every Wednesday for Famagusta, Larnaca, Limassol, & Paphos. Return from last Cyprus Port Saturdays. This service runs in connection with the P. & O. Brindisi Mail Steamers.

EGYPT to SUDAN and UPPER NILE.—Best and cheapest Route to Khartoum. Express steamers leave Suez Docks *Wednesdays* at 5 p.m. for Port Sudan (and Suakim) in connection with the Sudan Government Railways Express Service de Luxe to Khartoum, and connecting outwards and homewards with the P. & O. Brindisi Mail Steamers.

RED SEA COASTING MAIL SERVICE.—Steamers from Suez Docks every *Monday evening* at 5 p.m. for Jeddah, calling one week at Tor (for Sinai), El-Wedj, Yambo, and Jeddah; and in the following week at Jeddah, Port Sudan, Suakim, Massowah Hodeidah, and Aden.

Itineraries being subject to occasional alteration from quarantine and other causes, enquiry should be made of agency at port of departure.

Information may be obtained and passages booked at the Co.'s London Office, 87, Bishopsgate; at the Co.'s Agencies at ports called at; at all the Offices of Messrs. Thomas Cook & Son, of the Hamburg-Amerika Linie Reise Bureau and at most Tourist Agencies.

P & O Mail and Passenger Services

Under Contract with His Majesty's Government.

EGYPT, INDIA, CHINA, JAPAN, AUSTRALASIA, &c.

Conveying Passengers and Merchandise to ALL EASTERN PORTS.

From London (Tilbury Dock):—Weekly, to Gibraltar, Marseilles, Port Said, Aden and Bombay; fortnightly to Colombo, Straits, China, Australia, and New Zealand. From Brindisi, weekly to Port Said, Aden, and Bombay; fortnightly to Colombo, Australasia, Straits, China, &c.

Intermediate Steamers usually leave London (Royal Albert Dock) every Saturday for Malta, and alternate Saturdays (1.) for Colombo and Calcutta, and (2.) for Straits, China, and Japan, as a rule carrying Passengers at reduced fares.

Return Tickets at a Fare and a half to all ports East of Egypt, available for 24 months. Six-months' Return Tickets, London to the Mediterranean. For further information apply at the Company's Offices, London:—122, Leadenhall Street, E.C., and Northumberland Avenue, W.C.; Paris:—Captain A. W. Churchward, 14, Rue du 4 Septembre; Hernu Peron & Co., 61, Boulevard Haussmann; and Thomas Cook & Son, 1, Place de l'Opera; Marseilles:—Estrine & Co., 18, Rue Colbert.

BIBBY LINE.

TWIN-SCREW STEAMERS.

TO MARSEILLES, EGYPT, COLOMBO, SOUTHERN INDIA (VIA TUTICORIN), AND RANGOON.

	Tons.	Liverpool.	Marseilles.
s.s. Gloucestershire	8,124	July 10th	July 18th.
s.s. Oxfordshire	8,623	July 24th	Aug. 1st.
s.s. Worcestershire	7,169	Aug. 7th	Aug. 15th.

Also Fortnightly from London, dates on application.

These fast mail steamers, built by Messrs. Harland & Wolff, of Belfast, have their accommodation amidships, are supplied with electric light throughout, and fitted with electric fans, mechanical ventilators, and refrigerators, and carry a Surgeon and Stewardess. This line is recognised by the Indian Government for Officers returning at expiry of furlough.

Apply to BIBBY BROS. & CO., 26, Chapel Street, Liverpool; or 10 and 11, Mincing Lane, London.

N.Y.K.—NIPPON YUSEN KAISHA.

From **ANTWERP & LONDON, via MARSEILLES,** to

JAPAN In 45 DAYS.

FORTNIGHTLY.

CALLING AT COLOMBO, SINGAPORE, AND HONG KONG,

By New Twin Screw Steamers of 8,500 Tons Register. Superior Passenger Accommodation.

	Antwerp.	London.	Marseilles.
IYO MARU	———	July 5th.	July 12th.
HIRANO MARU	July 13th.	July 19th.	July 26th.
TANGO MARU	July 27th.	Aug. 2nd.	Aug. 9th.
KAMO MARU	Aug. 10th.	Aug. 16th.	Aug. 23rd.

Fares to Japan, £54 First Class, £37 10s. Second Class; to other Ports at equally Moderate Rates.

For Handbooks and all particulars apply to the Company's Offices, 4, LLOYD'S AVENUE, LONDON, E.C.

MOSS LINE.

Regular Services of well appointed Passenger and Cargo Steamers from Liverpool, Glasgow, and Swansea to the Mediterranean and Black Sea.

LIVERPOOL to ALEXANDRIA.

Via Gibraltar, Algiers, and Malta.

"Seti" .... 14th July.
"Meroe" .... 4th August.

LIVERPOOL to CONSTANTINOPLE,

Via Gibraltar, Malta, Syra, and Smyrna.

"Esneh" .... 22nd July.

LIVERPOOL to BORDEAUX—Weekly—On Fridays.
s.s. "Vendie" and s.s. "Vosges" alternatively.

Glasgow, Swansea, and Newport to Alexandria at regular intervals.

Excellent accommodation for passengers 1st and 2nd class.

**JAMES MOSS & CO., Managers,
31, James Street, Liverpool.**

M.M.—MESSAGERIES MARITIMES CO.'S

MAIL STEAMERS.

Departures from MARSEILLES. Special Return Tickets issued.

Route	Frequency
Djibouti, Colombo, Singapore, Saigon, China, and Japan	Every 14 days.
Pondicherry, Madras, Calcutta	Every 28 days.
Aden, Bombay, Australia, New Caledonia, New Zealand, and Tasmania	Every 28 days.
Djibouti, Mombassa, Zanzibar, Madagascar, Réunion, and Mauritius	Every 28 days.
Djibouti, Aden, Mahé, Madagascar, Réunion, and Mauritius	Every 28 days.
Alexandria and Beyrouth	Weekly.
Greek Ports, Smyrna, Constantinople, and Black Sea	Weekly.
Syrian Coast and Jaffa	Fortnightly.
London to Marseilles (Cargo only for all Ports)	Weekly.

OFFICES—Dixon House, 72 to 75, Fenchurch Street, LONDON, E.C.; 1, Rue Vignon, PARIS; 3, Place Sadi Carnot, MARSEILLES; and at 62, Pall Mall, LONDON, S.W.

COMPAGNIE de NAVIGATION MIXTE, French Mail Steamers to ALGERIA, TUNIS, TRIPOLI, SPAIN, & MOROCCO.

HEAD OFFICE:—54, Cannebière, Marseilles. (Telegraphic Address, "Navimixte, Marseille").
PORT VENDRES AGENCY:—Gare Maritime. CETTE AGENCY:—17, Quai du Sud.
LYONS AGENCY:—41, Rue de la Republique. (Telegraphic Address, "Rapide, Lyon").

PARIS AGENTS:—MM. PH. MARZOLFF ET CIE., 51, Rue du Faubourg Poissonniere; also the Agencies of Messrs. COOK, LUBIN, DUCHEMIN, LE BOURGEOIS. PASSAGE OFFICES:—CIE. MIXTE, 9, Rue de Rome; et 5, Rue Edouard VII.

Departures from Marseilles.

To Algiers (direct), Mon., 6.0p.m., and Thurs.(rapid), 11.45 a.m.

To Tunis (rapid) ... Saturday noon.

To Tunis (rapid), **Susa, Monastir, Mehedia, Sfax, Gabes, Djerbah, and Tripoli—Return calling at same Ports.** Wednesday noon.

To Oran (direct), **Nemours, Melilla, Tangiers, Wednesday,** 6.0 p.m., and alternately—each fortnight—to Beni Saf, Tetuan, Gibraltar, and Malaga

To Philippeville (rapid) **and Bona** ... Thursday 12.0.

Departures from Port Vendres and Cette.

Port Vendres to Oran (rapid) ... Friday, 1.30 p.m.
" " **to Algiers** (rapid) ... Sunday, 1.30 p.m.
Cette to Oran ... Thursday, 10.0 p.m.
" **to Algiers** ... Saturday, 10.0 p.m.

Algiers to Marseilles (direct) ... Saturday, 6.0 p.m.

Tunis to Marseilles (rapid Monday, 2.0 p.m. & Wed. 9.0 a.m

Combined Railway and Steamer Service.—At all French Railway Stations circular tickets at reduced price are delivered (subject to the common tariff conditions, G.V., No. 205 of Railways), arranged at the choice of the traveller, available 90 days, entitling to journey by rail and passage on the steamers of the Cie. de Navigation Mixte. These tickets allow a break of travel at all ports and stations included in their respective itineraries. The Compagnie de Navigation Mixte is also associated with the combined tickets of the "Verein" (German Railway Union).

COMPAGNIE NAVIGATION MAROCAINE ET ARMENIENNE.

N. PAQUET & CIE., 4, Place Sadi-Carnot, MARSEILLES.

Morocco Line.—The 1st and 16th of each month at 8.0 a.m., a "Rapide Direct" departure for Oran (optional), Tangiers, Casablanca, Mazagan, Saffi, and Mogador. Other supplementary monthly departures at varying dates for Gibraltar, Tangiers, and other ports of the Morocco Coast.

Constantinople and Black Sea Line.—Calling at Dardanelles, Constantinople, Samsoun, Trebizonde, Batoum, and Novorossisk. Departures from **Marseilles**, every Wednesday fortnight, at 11.0 a.m. Next departures: July 9th and 23rd; August 6th and 20th; September 3rd and 17th. Departures from **Batoum** every Thursday fortnight. Next departures: July 3rd, 17th, and 31st; August 14th and 28th; September 11th and 25th.

PARIS AGENCIES FOR PASSENGERS.—Société Générale de Transports Maritimes, 8, Rue Ménars
" " " GOODS.—MM. F. Puthet & Cie, 22, Rue Albouy. (Rue du 4 Septembre).
LYONS AGENCY.—MM. F. Puthet & Cie., 2, Quai St. Clair.
LONDON. For Passengers, Bureau P.L.M. 179/180, Piccadilly.

MAIL STEAMER CONTINENT SCANDINAVIA. ROUTE.

KIEL-KORSÖR.

COPENHAGEN, STOCKHOLM, CHRISTIANIA.

Two Services Daily in each direction by the Steamers of the

Danish State Railways

(NIGHT PASSAGE),

"Freja," "Skirner," "Aegir,"

From Kiel ... ... 1 32 a.m. | From Korsör ... ... 10 0 p.m.

Impl. German Day Mail Steamer Service Kiel=Korsör

(DAY PASSAGE),

"Prinz Waldemar," "Prinz Adalbert," "Prinz Sigismund,"

From Kiel ... ... 9 15 a.m. | From Korsör ... ... 2 54 p.m.

2 hours at sea, 3 hours sheltered in the Kiel Bay and between the Danish Islands.

8 p35	10 a0	dep.	London *via* Vlissingen	arr.	7 p34	7 a48
8 p30	...	,,	London *via* H. v. Holland	,,	...	8 a0
9 p0	9 a0	,,	London *via* Ostende	,,	10 p0	5 a43
10a28	9 p0	,,	Amsterdam	,,	8 a37	3 p15
9 a55	8 p22	,,	Rotterdam	,,	9 a8	3 p48
11p15	1 p45	,,	Paris	,,	4 p0	10p46
5 a45	5 p22	,,	Brussels	,,	11a26	6 p57
1 p45	11p40	,,	Cologne	,,	7 a10	3 p2
7 p55	5 a8	,,	Bremen	,,	1 a4	9 a25
9 p42	6 a55	arr.	Hamburg H.	dep.	11p14	7 a39
11p55	9 a0	dep.	Rome	arr.	7p15	7p15
5 p40	7 p35	,,	Genoa	,,	9a20	9 a20
9 p 5	11p35	,,	Milan	,,	6 a22	6 a22
7 a53	2 p33	,,	Basle	,,	2 p55	8 p55
12p48	8 p55	,,	Frankfort-a-M.	,,	9 a21	3 p59
9 a 0	4 p25	,,	Munich	,,	2 p0	8 p55
7 p38	3 a50	,,	Hanover	,,	2 a2	10a12
10p26	6 a44	arr.	Hamburg H.	dep.	11 p4	7 a18

1 p45	11p40	dep.	Cologne	arr.	7 a10	3 p2
11 p8	7 a5	,,	Hamburg Haupt.	,,	11 p 4	7 a27
11p33	7 a25	,,	Altona	,,	10 p38	6 a51
1 a16	9 a5	arr.	Kiel	dep.	9 p0	5 a27
‡1 a32	*9 a15	dep.	Kiel (Steamer)	arr.	*8 p25	‡4 a55
‡7 a30	*2 p38	arr.	Korsör (Steamer)	dep.	*2 p55	‡10 p 0
8 a3	3 p0	dep.	Korsör	arr.	2 p44	9 p46
10 a4	4 p48	arr.	Copenhagen	dep.	12p55	7 p50
10a55	9 p5	dep.	Copenhagen	arr.	8 a29	5 p33
12p50	11 p7	,,	Helsingborg	,,	6 a38	3 p32
6 p34	4 a20	arr.	Gothenburg	dep.	1 a33	10 a0
...	12 0	arr.	Christiania	dep.	5 p45	...
11 a5	7 p50	dep.	Copenhagen F.	arr.	9 a40	2 p55
3p 0	10 p12	,,	Malmö	dep.	8 a10	1 p25
6a58	8 a49	arr.	Stockholm	dep.	8 p30	10 p0

*—German Day Steamer.
‡—Danish Night Steamer.

SHORT, SHELTERED, AND PLEASANT PASSAGE.

Direct communication with the through fast trains to and from Scandinavia and the Continent.
Sleeping Cars Cologne—Kiel, and vice versa; Throughgoing Cars Paris—Brussels—Cologne—Kiel, and vice versa.

Through tickets and baggage registration to and from all principal places.
Information and Tickets in BERLIN also from the Travel=Bureau Norden, 3, Unter den Linden (Corner of Wilhelm-Strasse).

Great Central Railway

Direct Route via Grimsby.

TO - -

HAMBURG.

ROYAL MAIL.

DAILY SERVICE (except Sundays)

Leaving GRIMSBY after arrival of BOAT TRAINS.

RETURNING from Sandthor Quay DAILY (except Sundays), about 9-0 p.m., German time (one hour in advance of English).

Average Passage under 30 hours.

Six fine new Steamers with luxurious passenger accommodation amidships.

TO - -

ANTWERP,

For Ghent International Exhibition, April-October, 1913.

Leaving GRIMSBY every MONDAY, WEDNESDAY, and SATURDAY after arrival of Boat Trains. RETURN from (d'Herbouville Quay, Antwerp) every TUESDAY, THURSDAY, and SATURDAY, at 7-0 p.m.

Average Passage, 20 hours.

TO - -

ROTTERDAM.

Leaving Grimsby every TUESDAY, THURSDAY, and SATURDAY, after arrival of Boat Trains. RETURN (from St. Jobshaven) every TUESDAY, THURSDAY, and SATURDAY, at 7 p.m. Dutch time (6-40 Greenwich).

Sea Passage about 12 hours.

The sailings are subject to alterations or suspension on Bank Holidays or other special occasions.

CHEAP 16 DAYS EXCURSION and 45 DAYS TOURIST TICKETS, also for INCLUSIVE TOURS are issued to HAMBURG, ROTTERDAM, and ANTWERP, and beyond.

For particulars, see Folders and Booklet of Continental arrangements and Tours obtainable Free at G. C. R. Stations, Dean & Dawson's Offices, Steamship Passenger Office, Grimsby Docks, and Publicity Office, 216, Marylebone Road, London, N. W.

SAM FAY, General Manager.

ROYAL DANISH MAIL ROUTE TO
DENMARK, NORWAY, AND SWEDEN

By REGULAR STEAMERS of DET FORENEDE LINE, in connection with the Great Eastern Railway Company, *via* HARWICH (Parkeston Quay) and ESBJERG.

The Fine Steamers **"J. C. LACOUR,"** 1,700 Tons, 3,600 H.P. indicated, **"N. J. FJORD,"** 1,500 Tons, 2,300 H.P. indicated, **"PRIMULA,"** 1,500 Tons, 2,500 H.P., or other of the Company's Fine Steamers. will run as under, weather and other circumstances permitting. The new fast Steamer, **"A. P. BERNSTORFF,"** 2,300 Tons, 3,300 H.P. indicated, will be placed on the service during the summer months. **—(Sea Passage about 22 Hours).**

PARKESTON QUAY for ESBJERG.

MONDAYS, WEDNESDAYS, FRIDAYS, SATURDAYS — Steamers leave about 9.45 p.m. after arrival of the 7.12 p.m. train from Liverpool Street Station (Dining and Restaurant Cars from London to Maninngtree).

ESBJERG for PARKESTON QUAY.

MONDAYS, TUESDAYS, WEDNESDAYS, SATURDAYS — Steamers leave about 5.0 p.m. after arrival of the 8.20 a.m. train from Copenhagen.

Through Carriages, Copenhagen to Esbjerg harbour.

Passengers from the North and Midland Counties are due to arrive at Parkeston Quay at 9.30 p.m.

FARES.

		SINGLE.		RETURN.	
		1st Rail and Saloon.	2nd Rail and Saloon.	1st Rail and Saloon.	2nd Rail and Saloon.
A	LONDON to ESBJERG	£2 8 3	£2 5 6	£3 14 11	£3 11 4
A	LONDON to COPENHAGEN	3 10 2	2 19 2	5 18 6	4 18 5
A	LONDON to FREDERIKSHAVN	3 12 2	3 0 3	6 2 6	5 0 7
A	LONDON to STOCKHOLM	5 10 3	4 4 4	9 18 7	7 8 8
A	LONDON to GOTHENBURG	4 9 6	3 10 9	7 17 2	6 1 6
A	LONDON to CHRISTIANIA	6 1 8	4 11 8	10 13 5	7 17 8
	HARWICH to ESBJERG	Saloon. 2 0 0	......	Saloon 3 2 6	......

A—These fares apply also from any G. E. Railway Country Station (Peterborough excepted).
Return Tickets are available 60 days. The Second Class Tickets are available 3rd Class Rail only in England.

Sleeping Carriages from Esbjerg Quay by the Night Train to Copenhagen.
Through Carriages from Copenhagen to Esbjerg harbour by the 8.20 a.m. train.

For full particulars, Pamphlet, and Tickets, apply to THE UNITED SHIPPING CO. Ltd., 108, Fenchurch St. London, E.C. or to the Continental Traffic Manager, Great Eastern Railway, Liverpool Street Station London, E.C

WILSON LINE

TO

NORWAY AND SWEDEN.

The **Wilson Line** of **Royal Mail Passenger Steamers** have been built specially for the Scandinavian Tourist Services. They are all luxuriously fitted with the latest improvements for the comfort of Passengers, the Saloons and Staterooms being entirely amidships, and lighted by electricity. These Steamers are of high speed, and their route for Norway are so arranged that they get within shelter of the outlying islands on the Coast as quickly as possible, thus making over-sea passages very short.

DURING THE PASSENGER SEASON THE INTENDED SAILINGS ARE

HULL FOR CHRISTIANSAND AND CHRISTIANIA.—OPEN-SEA PASSAGE, 22 HOURS.

R.M.S. "ESKIMO," every Saturday at 6.30 p.m.; leaving **Christiania** for **Hull**, every Wednesday at 1 p.m., calling at **Christiansand**, Wednesdays, midnight, due Hull, 2 a.m. Fridays.

SUPPLEMENTARY SERVICE for 2nd and 3rd Class Passengers, S.S. "SPERO" from **Hull**, Wednesdays, July 2nd, 16th, and 30th; returning from **Christiania**, Fridays, July 11th and 25th, calling at **Christiansand** on Saturdays at 9 a.m. due Hull Sunday night.

S.S. "KOLPINO," from **Grimsby**, Wednesdays, July 9th and 23rd; returning from **Christiania**, Friday, July 18th, calling at **Christiansand**, Saturday, at 9 a.m., due Grimsby, Sunday night.

HULL TO STAVANGER, BERGEN, AALESUND, CHRISTIANSUND, AND DRONTHEIM.

R.M.S. "OSLO," or R.M.S. "AARO" Thursdays, 6.30 p.m.

Drontheim to **Hull** .... Thursday, 10 p.m.
Christiansund to **Hull** .... Friday, 8 a.m.
Aalesund to **Hull** .... Friday, 3 p.m.
Bergen to **Hull** .... Saturday, noon.
Stavanger to **Hull** .... Saturday, 10 p.m.

HULL FOR GOTHENBURG.—OPEN-SEA PASSAGE, 35 HOURS.

The route to Stockholm (by railway or canal) and St. Petersburg. The R.M.S. "CALYPSO," every Tuesday at 6.30 p.m.; leaving **Gothenburg** for **Hull**, every Friday at 10 p.m., due Hull, Sunday noon.

In connection with the above sailings which are to and from Hull (Riverside Quay), Special Boat Trains will be run to and from the Hull (Riverside Quay) Station, as under:—

Special Train will leave King's Cross, every Thursday and Saturday at 2 p.m., Peterbro' 3.28 p.m., Grantham, 4.6 p.m., due Riverside Quay 6.5 p.m., to 23rd August (21st August excepted).

Through Carriages from York at 3.55 p.m., Newcastle at 1.40 p.m., Leeds 3.52 p.m., Liverpool (Exchange) 2.10 p.m., Manchester (Victoria) 2.55 p.m., and Wakefield 3.57 p.m., arriving at the Riverside Quay Station at 5.28 p.m.

Through Train from Hull (Riverside Quay) at 9.10 a.m. for London (King's Cross) every Monday and Friday to 3rd October

GRIMSBY FOR GOTHENBURG.—OPEN-SEA PASSAGE, 35 HOURS.

The Royal Mail Steam Ship "SALMO," every Saturday evening; leaving **Gothenburg** for **Grimsby**, every Wednesday, 9 a.m., due Grimsby Thursday nights.

HULL TO STETTIN.

S.S. "RUNO" and S.S. "NOVO," every Friday night. Leaving **Stettin** via Gothenburg every Saturday noon.

HULL FOR RIGA.

EVERY FRIDAY NIGHT.
RIGA for HULL every Wednesday noon.

HULL TO ST. PETERSBURG,

EVERY MONDAY NIGHT.
ST. PETERSBURG for HULL, every Tuesday noon.

HULL FOR COPENHAGEN.

Every Wednesday Evening.
Leaving COPENHAGEN for HULL every Thursday.

NEWCASTLE FOR COPENHAGEN.

Every Thursday noon.
COPENHAGEN for NEWCASTLE every Thursday.

SPECIAL HOLIDAY TOURS

Have been arranged to Norway and Sweden, including First Class Return Tickets, with victualling on board, and Hotel and travelling expenses. First Class throughout.
Illustrated Handbooks of the above Tours may be obtained on application.

For Passage and Freight apply to THOS. WILSON, SONS, & CO. LIMITED, Owners, HULL; or to UNITED SHIPPING CO. LTD., 108, Fenchurch Street, E.C.; GELLATLY, HANKEY, & Co., 51, Pall Mall; SEWELL & CROWTHER, 18, Cockspur Street; or THOS. COOK & SON, Ludgate Circus, London.

AACHEN—AIX-LA-CHAPELLE—Continued on next page.

TRAVEL and HOTEL ENQUIRIES—See page xii.

TRAVEL and HOTEL ENQUIRIES—See page xii.

AIX-LES-BAINS—Continued on next page.

AIX-LES-BAINS

Magnificent

Panorama.

Private Park.

Auto Garage.
(Boxes).

Tennis, etc. ::

Opened in 1911.

The most up-to-date Hotel. Aristocratic Clientele.

SEASON: APRIL TO SEPTEMBER.

. . AIX-LES-BAINS. . .

Regina-Gd. Hotel Bernascon

ELEVATED position, near Baths and Casinos. Entirely First Class, opened in 1900. Latest comfort and luxury. 250 rooms with hot and cold running water. 50 private baths. Splendid view of the Lake and the Valley. Large shady Gardens and Dining Terraces. Garages for 50 cars. Branch House, the handsome "VILLA REGINA," opened in 1907, and standing in its own magnificent grounds.

J. EDMUNDTS, Manager.

HOTEL BEAU SITE.

130 ROOMS AND SALOONS.

First Class Hotel. Beautifully situated in the Park, near the Baths. Magnificent view. Garden. Omnibus. Hydraulic Lift. Electric Light. Bathrooms.

VILLA BEAU SITE.

Private Apartments for families.

Proprietor: LOUIS RIVOLLIER.

INTERNATIONAL PALACE HOTEL.

FIRST CLASS FAMILY HOTEL.

With every Modern comfort. Near the Bath and opposite the Casino. **Open all the year.** Apartments with private baths and latest appliances. Hotel Garage free to guests; also private boxes. *Branch House:* **HOTEL du PAVILLON.** Steam Heating. Electric Light. — Baths. — Facing the Station. **Pavillon Rivollier Restaurant,** the most fashionable in Aix.

P. RIVOLLIER, Proprietor.

 AIX-LES-BAINS—Continued on next page

AJACCIO (Island of Corsica).—See page 581.

TRAVEL and HOTEL ENQUIRIES—See page xii.

ALGECIRAS (Andalusia).—See page 566.

HOTEL REINA CRISTINA

OPPOSITE GIBRALTAR. Modern Hotel; furnished by Maples; electric light; best sanitary arrangements; golf; sea bathing; private omnibus; frequent saloon steamers daily to and from Gibraltar.

J. THOMSON, Manager, Algeciras, Andalusia, Spain.

ALGIERS.—See page 679, Special Edition.

. ALGIERS . .

GRAND HOTEL EXCELSIOR.

UP TO DATE.

This Magnificent Hotel was inaugurated by the reception of T.R.H. The Duke and Duchess of Connaught and Royal Family, during their visit to Algiers.

American Bar. — CLEVEN, Manager.

HOTEL ST. GEORGE

Mustapha Superior.

High Class . . English House. **HOTEL DE LUXE.** **Illustrated Booklet and Tariff on application.**

Numerous large suites and bed-rooms with private bath-rooms and toilet.

2 Lifts. Electric Light. Large beautiful garden.

3 Tennis courts and a Croquet lawn. — Golf Links,

The Electric tramway passes the garden entrance every quarter of an hour.

FR. BOLLBUCK, Manager.

Alger-Mustapha. * Hotel de Luxe

Grand Hotel Continental

UNDER ROYAL PATRONAGE. Greatly enlarged and improved in 1911. **200 Bedrooms. 50 Bathrooms.** Extensive Grounds. Best situation. All rooms facing South. Magnificent view of Bay and Atlas Mountains. Lift, Banqueting Hall, Restaurant Francais, Salons, Billiard Room, Smoking Rooms, Bridge Salon, large Lounge. Winter Garden. **The most Up-to-Date Hotel. — In summer: HOTEL d'ANGLETERRE, Bad Nauheim.**

For all information apply to the Proprietors: **Messrs. KIRSCH & EDLICH.**

ALEXANDRA HOTEL. HOTEL KIRSCH.

THIS well known select Hotel has been rebuilt with every modern comfort. Lift. Electric Light. Central Heating. Suites of apartments with Private Dining Room and Bath-Room. Large Garden and Terrace. Croquet Lawn. Garage. Unrivalled view of Algiers Bay and Djurdjura Mountains. Renowned Cuisine. Electric Tram stops at Garden Entrance.

Cook's Coupons accepted. * J. SOLLBERGER, Proprietor and Manager.

TRAVEL and HOTEL ENQUIRIES—See page xii.

ALLERHEILIGEN (Black Forest) Germany.—See page 455.

ALTDORF (Switzerland).—See page 512.

ALTONA see under HAMBURG.

ANTWERP

Make Your Head Quarters the

NEW

HOTEL ST. ANTOINE

ENTIRELY RENOVATED IN 1910.

Considerably Enlarged . .
50 Private Bathrooms added.
Finest Situation in the City.
Facing the noble Cathedral and the Place Verte. . . .

Establishment of the highest order.
Furnished by Maple & Co., Paris.
. . . Splendid Garden-Terrace.
Excellent French Cuisine. . . .
. . . Carefully selected Wines.

Telegraphic Address: "ANTONIO."

Antwerp is now connected with Brussels by Fast Trains (30 MINUTES JOURNEY).

ANTWERP.

THE GRAND HOTEL

RUE GÉRARD.

Quiet and Select, Central, with Garden.

OPENED 1902. – ANTWERP. – OPENED 1902.

GRAND HOTEL WEBER.

Corner of AVENUE DE KEYSER, 1 minute from Station.

NEWEST FIRST CLASS HOTEL.

Beautifully furnished by MAPLE & CO. of London.

Every Modern Comfort. Otis Electric Elevator. Electric Light. Central Heating. HALL. LARGE SUITES and SINGLE BED ROOMS with PRIVATE BATHS. Table d'Hôte and à la Carte Restaurant. Grill Room and Bar. Band plays during Dinner. Omnibus meets all Trains and Steamers.

ANTWERP—Continued on next page.

ANTWERP—*Continued.*

HOTEL de l'EUROPE

Lovely open situation in the celebrated PLACE VERTE, the heart of old ANTWERP.

Facing the Cathedral. Very quiet and airy rooms.

MODERN FIRST CLASS FAMILY HOTEL.

TERMINUS HOTEL ANTWERP.

Largest Hotel of Antwerp.

Just opposite Entrance and Exit of Central Station, SO NO CAB CHARGES for Travellers. Every modern comfort.

Lift. Electric Light throughout. Steam Heating. Bedrooms from frs. 4.

QUEEN'S HOTEL.

FINEST VIEW OF RIVER. — Renowned for its comfort, cuisine, and excellent wines. Room, Electric Light, and Service from frs. 4. Dinner, frs. 4. Bus meets Trains and Boats. Every assistance given to tourists and business men.

Bradshaw's Guide.

TRAVEL ENQUIRY DEPARTMENT.—This Department has proved of efficient service both to hotel-keepers and the travelling public. Prospectuses of clients whose announcements appear in Bradshaw's Guide are kept for inspection or distribution at the Company's Offices in London, Liverpool, Manchester, Glasgow, and Dublin. For further particulars see page xii.

ARCACHON (France).—See page 386.

ARCACHON.

HOTEL DES PINS ET CONTINENTAL

(IN FOREST).

Constructed with most modern comfort. Comfort, Cleanliness, Attentive Service Moderate Charges. Apartments with Bath and Toilet.

LIFTS. * ELECTRIC LIGHT. * TELEPHONES. * CENTRAL HEATING.

B. FERRAS, Proprietor.

NEW GRAND HOTEL

FIRST CLASS. Open since July, 1910.

100 Bed and Sitting Rooms. Every modern comfort. Moderate charges. Only Hotel which has Dressing-rooms attached to all its Bed-rooms with Hot and Cold running water and most of them with Private Bath. Stands in the midst of its own Park, facing Sea and Full South. Special arrangements for a long stay. No consumptive cases taken.

Hot and Cold Sea-water Bath Establishment in the Hotel. Renowned for its good Cuisine and Cellar.
Open from 1st of February till end of October. — A. PACHLER, General Manager.

TRAVEL and HOTEL ENQUIRIES—See page xii.

ARGELES (Htes. Pyrenées).—See page 386.

HOTEL de FRANCE

J. PEYRAFITTE, Proprietor.

Comfortable First Class Establishment,

STEAM HEATING. — SPECIAL ARRANGEMENTS FOR LONG VISITS.

ENGLISH CHURCH IN THE HOTEL.

FREE GOLFING from October to March on the Hotel's 18 hole GOLF LINKS.

ARLES, sur Rhone (France).—See page 386.

GRD. HOTEL DU NORD—PINUS (First Class)

Only Hotel contiguous to Roman Forum. Only Entrance to Roman Catacombs in the Hotel.

Best equipped Hotel in Arles. Furnished with all modern accommodation and Sanitary arrangements. Electric Light. **Telephone. English spoken.** Omnibus meets every train. Table d'Hôte. Private Dining Saloons, Smoking Room, Bath Room, &c. **Every comfort afforded to Families. Moderate prices. — Managing Proprietor: F. BESSIERE.**

AROSA (Grisons), Switzerland.—See page 513.

AROSA.

GRISONS, SWITZERLAND. 6,000 feet above sea level.

Splendid Winter Resort. **Recommended by the greatest medical authorities.**

HOTEL SEEHOF.

FIRST-CLASS HOTEL.

FINEST SITUATION IN AROSA. ON THE LAKE. Specially adapted for English Visitors. Electric light and central heating throughout. **Lift.** New drawing room and billiard room, with English and French billiards. Curling Rink in front of the Hotel. Skating, Tobogganing, and Skying. For Prospectus and all particulars apply to the Proprietor: **P. Wieland-Brunold.** — Telegrams: "*SEEHOF, AROSA.*"

AROSA (Ct. GRISONS, Switzerland), 6,000 feet above sea level.

Lift. ALEXANDRA HOTEL Lift.

FIRST Class House (opened July, 1905), beautifully situated, south aspect, well appointed throughout. Every modern convenience. Surrounded by Pine Woods, two minutes from the Upper Lake, close by the Skating Rink, Bobsleigh run. Large covered Verandahs facing south with splendid view. Spacious Lounge with English Fire-place, Drawing Room, Reading and Smoking Room, Dark Room, Bathroom on each floor. Electric Light, Central Heating, and best sanitary arrangements. New Billiard Room with English Table (by Burroughes & Watts). ***For Prospectus and further information apply to* A. GRUBER, Propr. for 10 years at the L. S. W. Railway Co.'s South Western Hotel, Southampton.**

Grand Hotel.

FIRST CLASS HOUSE.

BEAUTIFULLY situated, surrounded by Pine Forests. Tennis Court. **Own Toboggan Run and Skating Rink.** All Winter and Summer Sports. Tea-Concerts. **No consumptive cases taken.** Extensively patronized by English and Americans. Terms en pension from **9 fr.**

Proprietor: K. L. JACOBI-CLAUS.

AROSA—Continued on next page.

ATHENS.—See page 684, Special Edition.

AVIEMORE.—See page 1093.

AVIGNON (France).—See page 387.

TRAVEL and HOTEL ENQUIRIES—See page xii.

BADEN-BADEN.—See page 455.

HOTEL de l'EUROPE

Strictly First Class and Up-to-Date.

Opposite Kurhaus.

THIS HOTEL is now entirely reconstructed with the most modern improvements. Apartments and Rooms with Bath and W.C. en suite. Hot and cold running water and Telephone in all rooms.

RESTAURANT FRANCAIS
ON THE
MAGNIFICENT NEW TERRACE.

Electric Light and Steam Heating throughout. | Patronised by the best English and American Society.

FRIEDRICH RUPPEL, New Proprietor.

HOLLAND HOTEL

With a Large Park.
FORMERLY
Duke of Hamilton's.

FIRST CLASS ESTABLISHMENT
OF OLD STANDING.

Sophien Allee, nearest Bathing Establishments and Kur-haus.

SINCE 1900 MODERN PALATIAL BUILDING.

With all improvements Up-to-Date.

Lifts. Electric Light. Steam Heating. Apartments and Single Rooms with Private Baths and Lavatories. Motor Garage with Inspection Pit, Electric Charging Apparatus, etc.

A. RÖSSLER, Proprietor.

BADEN-BADEN—Continued on next page

BADEN-BADEN—*Continued.*

Hotel Petersburger Hof

ENTIRELY RENOVATED.

Central Position, close to the Kurhaus and Baths. Every modern comfort. Central Heating.
∴ Restaurant. ∴ Open all the year. ∴

Pension from Mks. 6. New Proprietor: **A. WALDELE.**

STADT STRASSBURG HOTEL.

Favourite Family Hotel in extremely quiet position close to Kurhaus and Baths.
Entirely rebuilt in 1908 and fitted up with every modern comfort.

Renowned Restaurant with open and covered Terraces. Large shady Garden. Private Rooms with Baths. Rooms from **Mk. 3.** Pension from **Mk. 8.50.** **Propr.: FRITZ HOLLISCHER.**

Hotel Müller

IN the best part of Baden Baden, close to Curhaus and Parks. Renovated 1913. This Hotel can be very confidently recommended to English and Americans. While strictly moderate, every modern comfort and convenience is offered. The Cuisine, Service, and Management leave nothing to be desired. Rooms with Bath. Lift. Rooms from 3 **mks.** Pension from **7 mks.**

THEODORE MÜLLER, Proprietor.

BADENWEILER (Germany).—See page 456.

HOTEL RÖMERBAD

First Class Hotel, with every comfort and modern appliance.

THIS Beautifully arranged House is highly recommended to English and American Families for its open and quiet position, opposite the Grand Ducal Castle, commanding views over the Kurpark, the Valley of the Rhine, and the Vosges. — Large Garden. — Lawn Tennis. 180 Rooms. Suites of Apartments with Private Bath Rooms. Thermal Baths in the House.

Electric Light. 2 Lifts. Central Heating. **Restaurant.**

OPEN FROM APRIL TO OCTOBER.
PENSION FROM MK. 10 UPWARDS.

JONER BROTHERS, Proprietors.

HOTEL SOMMER (Karlsruher Hof.)

First Class House. With dependance "Park Villa." Opposite the Kurpark & the new Markgrafenbad.

LARGE PARK. LIFT. ELECTRIC LIGHT. CENTRAL HEATING. BATHS.

—— LARGE HALL. PENSION TERMS from Mk. 8 upwards. ——

Highly recommended to English and American Families.

Prospectus from the Proprietor, **ERNST GLOESER,** *also from Bradshaw's Office.*

TRAVEL and HOTEL ENQUIRIES—See page xii.

BARCELONA—Continued on next page.

BARCELONA—*Continued.*

Grand Hotel de Oriente

RAMBLA DEL CENTRO.

—— VERY FIRST CLASS HOTEL. ——

150 BEDROOMS. All new and modern comforts. Apartments with private Bathroom. Every room with Lavatory, Central Heating, Telephone, and Parquet. Splendid Summer Garden and Restaurant. Best French cooking. Moderate terms. — Garage. — Omnibus meets all Trains and Steamers.

C. BRAMBILLA, Manager. — **O. ZENATELLO, Proprietor.**

GRAND HOTEL et 4 NATIONS

Telegraphic Address: "SLEEPING."

THE acknowledged leading and best appointed Hotel in Town. All modern comfort. 40 Private Bathrooms. Moderate Charges. Inclusive Terms. Magnificent Restaurant, also open to non-residents. Concerts by the Hotel Orchestra. Sole Agent of the Sleeping Car Company in Barcelona. Most centrally situated on the Rambla, the most fashionable quarter. Southern aspect.

GRAND HOTEL FALCON

Beautiful situation in the Rambla.

FIRST CLASS HOTEL, entirely renewed during summer, 1911. All meals served at separate tables. New Drawing Room for ladies with piano. **Steam Heating throughout.** Otis Electric Lift. Modern Sanitary arrangements. Bath rooms on every floor. Moderate terms. Interpreters and Special Omnibuses of the Hotel at every train. .·. .·. .·.

NEW GRAND

HOTEL d'ANGLETERRE

PLAZA DE CATALUNA, the largest Square in Europe.

FIRST CLASS HOTEL. Lavabos with Hot or Cold running water. Electric Lift. Central Heating.

Moderate Prices.

BASLE.—See page 513.

BASLE.

GRAND HOTEL VICTORIA ET NATIONAL.

Opposite the Central Station, and close to the Public Gardens.

Free from noise of trains.

THE most convenient, largest, and up-to-date Hotel in Town. Apartments and single rooms with private bath and toilette attached. Rooms fitted with running hot and cold water. Vacuum Cleaner. Large Halls and covered Terrace. Open Air Restaurant. — **PAUL OTTO, Proprietor.**

TRAVEL and HOTEL ENQUIRIES—See page xii.

BASLE—*Continued.*

BASLE—Continued on next page.

TRAVEL and HOTEL ENQUIRIES—See page xii.

BASTIA (Corsica),—See page 581.

Bastia CYRNOS PALACE HOTEL

(CORSICA.)

First Class House with all modern comfort.

BEAUTIFUL LOCATION. BOARD.

BAVENO (Lac Majeur) Italie (on the Simplon Road)—See page 536.

BAVENO (Lago Maggiore).

PALACE GRAND HOTEL.

On the main Simplon Line, between Milan and Geneva.

THIS MAGNIFICENT HOTEL occupies an enchanting position on the Lake, with a commanding view of the Borromean Islands and the mountains. The Hotel contains 100 rooms and salons and is equipped with every requirement of modern Hotels of the first class. Lift. Central heating. Large Lounge and Verandah. Orchestra. Private rooms with toilettes en suite. Tennis Courts. — Garage with Pit. — The Hotel Omnibus meets all Trains and Steamers. Motor boat for excursions. Tariff strictly moderate. Open from March to November.

PAUL BORGO, Proprietor, also of the Grand Hotel Pavillon, Cannes.

BAVENO. Gd. HOTEL BELLE VUE

HIGHEST ORDER.

FACING the Borromean Islands. Extensive Park. Overlooking the Lake. Lawn Tennis. English Church. Lift. Electric Light and Central Heating throughout. Baths and Dressing Rooms, Auto Garage. Best change station for all travellers going from St. Gothard by the Simplon lines, and vice versa. Motor boat for excursions. **T. PEDRETTI.**

HOTEL BEAU-RIVAGE. Baveno

The Eden of the Lake Maggiore, on the Simplon Ry. Line.

IN 1913 ENTIRELY RENOVATED AND REBUILT. 90 BEDS.

COMFORTABLE ENGLISH HOTEL, situated opposite the Borromean Islands, commanding a splendid view over the Lake and fine Bay. Large Park. Every modern comfort. Central Heating. Bath. Electric Light. Omnibus meets trains. Excellent Cuisine. Garage. Boat. Pension from **Frs. 7.** Reduction in March and October. Cook's Coupons accepted. The nearest to the English Church. Also HOTEL SUISSE, ILES BORROMEES, facing the Pier. — **POZZETTI & CO., Proprietors.**

Baveno. HOTEL SIMPLON.

WELL known English Hotel. Recently rebuilt and equipped with every modern comfort. Lift, Central Heating, Baths on every floor. 50 large airy rooms. Balconies. Splendid view of the Lake and Mountains. The Hotel stands in its own beautiful grounds; best and quietest position. Garage with pit. Dark room. Terms from **7 frs.** per day. Telephone No. 11.

E. CANTI, Managing Proprietor.

ST. BEATENBERG (Canton de Berne, Switzerland).—See page 514.

GRAND HOTEL VICTORIA — ST. BEATENBERG, Switzerland.

1st Class, 200 Beds. Summer and Winter Resort.

4,000 ft. above Sea Level

The most important and largest First Class Hotel in St. Beatenberg Specially frequented by ENGLISH Families.

Apartments "en suite" with Private Bath Rooms.

Orchestra. Lift.

Two Tennis Lawns.

Central heating throughout.

Hydro and Electro-therapeutic Establishment. Resident Physician.

Winter Sports. P. MARGUET, Managing Proprietor.

4,000 Feet above the Sea.

GRAND HOTEL BEATENBERG

KURHAUS.

FIRST CLASS HOTEL, **frequented by English families.** Modern building. 160 Beds. Nearest the Funicular Railway. **Best prominent position.** Especially preferred for the fine mountain scenery, the freshness of the air, and the open surroundings, with the old park, the playing grounds, and promenades. **Electric Light. Lift. Hot Water Heating throughout.** Bathrooms on the floors. Post, Telegraph, Telephone. **Lawn Tennis.** Physician. English Church.

R. MULLER EGLI, Prop. and Manager

ST. BEATENBERG. — Lake of Thoune.

1,150 m. above Sea level, First Class Climatic Station.

GRAND PARC HOTEL DE LA POSTE

First Class House.

STONE BUILDING. 120 Beds. All modern comforts. The finest and most healthy situation in the centre of a beautiful Promenade. Splendid view of the Alps, the Glaciers, and the Lake of Thoune. Surrounded by a Shady Park. Lawn Tennis. Good attendance and first class cooking. Electric Light. Lift. Hot Water Heating. Post, Telegraph, and Telephone Office in the Hotel. English Protestant and Roman Catholic Churches. Physician. Moderate Terms.

EGLI-BRUNNER, Proprietor.

TRAVEL and HOTEL ENQUIRIES—See page xii.

ST. BEATENBERG (Canton de Berne, Switz.)—*Continued.*

GRAND HOTEL BELLEVUE.

MOST Comfortable First Class Family Hotel. Entirely renovated. Large public Rooms. Baths, Electric Light, Central Heating. Splendid situation, commanding extensive views of Lake, facing the Jungfrau, Monch, and Eiger. **Summer Sports.** Orchestra. Moderate Charges.

Prospectus and particulars from the Proprietor-Manager—**S. BILL-ANDEREGG.**

HOTEL PENSION BLUMLISALP Beatenberg.

OPEN ALL THE YEAR. **(Summer and Winter Sports).**

ENGLISH FAMILY HOUSE in a pleasant situation. 10 Minutes from the Station. Lately considerably enlarged; with every modern comfort. Electric Light. Central Heating. Shady Garden and Terrace. TERMS from 6 frs. upward. Prospectus on application.

FAMILY HOWARD.

HOTEL & PENSION BEAU-REGARD.

3,773 FEET ABOVE THE SEA. **OPEN ALL THE YEAR ROUND.**

COMFORTABLE HOUSE, recently refurnished. Magnificent view of the Jungfrau, the Schreckhörner, the Lake of Thun, and the mountains. Many balconies. Electric Light. Excellent cooking. Moderate prices and every attention. Pension terms from **5-8 Frs.** Skating Rink. Tobogganing. Ski-ing. Winter Sports. — **D. JAGGI, Propr.**

BEAULIEU (Alpes Maritimes, France).—See page 388.

HOTEL BRISTOL

Delightful situation midway between Nice and Monte Carlo. Refinement and luxury amidst perfect surroundings. Conductive to health and pleasure. Sumptuous appointments. English sanitation. Open December to May.

The "ULTIMA RATIO" of HOTEL LIFE.

Write HOTEL RUSSELL, LONDON, . . . for Tariff and Brochure.

BEAULIEU.

HOTEL EMPRESS

FIRST CLASS ENGLISH HOUSE.

MAGNIFICENT ELEVATED POSITION, full South, near Station, English Church, and Sea. Extensive view. All modern comforts and improvements. Lift. Hot Water Heating throughout. Baths. Garden. Arrangements for a stay. TELEPHONE 1, 06. * **E. EXNER, Proprietor.**

MEYER'S VICTORIA HOTEL.

Commanding the most beautiful scenery in Beaulieu; on elevated position with Garden. Electric Light and Water Heating throughout.

FULL SOUTH. — **J. V. MEYER, Proprietor.**

BEAULIEU—Continued on next page.

BEAULIEU—(ALPES MARITIMES, FRANCE).—*Continued.*

HOTEL METROPOLE

High Class Hotel and Restaurant, the only one on the Sea shore.

WELL renowned for its excellent Cuisine and Cellar. The Hotel stands in its own beautifu Park, in the finest and most healthy position, full South, with magnificent Panorama. Large Terrace on Sea shore. Suites of Apartments with private Baths and Dressing Rooms. Hot water heating throughout. — **CH. FERRAND, Managing Proprietor.**

Bond's Hotel

BEAULIEU.

FIRST CLASS FAMILY HOTEL. Well Situated on High Ground, looking Full South. Within five minutes of the Railway Station, Church, and Sea. Specially recommended for its **Comfort and Excellent Cuisine.** Bath Rooms. Electric Light and central heating throughout. Lift. Inclusive terms from 12 fr. (Telephone 1-12). **J. BOND, Proprietor.**

BEAULIEU.

PANORAMA PALACE HOTEL.

Full South.

1st Class. * 120 Rooms and Salons. * 50 Bathrooms.

New Veranda RESTAURANT facing the Sea.

Under the management of the New Proprietor: **G. POZZO di BORGO.**

Summer: Hermitage & Atlantic Hotels—Le Touquet-Paris-Plage.

BEAULIEU (South of France).

KURZ'S AGENCY.

OPPOSITE STATION. Founder of the first House and Estate Agency in Beaulieu. Publishers of the Visitors' Yearly Guide Book of Information about Beaulieu. Furnished and Unfurnished Houses and Apartments to let, also Land and Houses to be sold. Correspondents of Thos. Cook & Son and Sleeping Car Co. —— Telegrams :—" Kurz, Beaulieu-sur-Mer."

BELFORT (France)—**See page 389.**

GRAND HOTEL ET DU TONNEAU d'OR.

Opened in January, 1907.

Apartments with private baths. Every modern comfort. Electric Light.
Central Heating. — Lift. — Garage. — Baths. — Telephone 2.28.

Proprietor: EUGENE GARTEISER.

BELGRADE (Servia).—**See page 667, Special Edition.**

BELGRAD (Servia).

First Class. Newly built.
—LIFT.—

HOTEL BRISTOL

Central Heating. Baths. Reading Room. Garage.

Rooms from Frs. 3. Propr.: GEORG POPARA.

TRAVEL and HOTEL ENQUIRIES—See page xii.

BELLAGIO on the Lake of Como (Italy).—See page 536.

HOTEL GRANDE BRETAGNE.

HYDRAULIC LIFT AND ELECTRIC LIGHT.

ONE OF THE LARGEST AND BEST MANAGED HOTELS to be found on the Italian Lakes. **It is magnificently situated** in the midst of extensive gardens overlooking the two Lakes. The Proprietor spares no effort to give satisfaction to his visitors. **Central Heating.** English Divine Service is held in a Chapel belonging to the Hotel Grande Bretagne.

A. MEYER, Proprietor.

GRAND HOTEL ET DE BELLAGIO.

CENTRAL Heating throughout. Lift. Electric Light, and every up to date comfort. One of the finest Hotels in Europe. Magnificently situated on the shore of the lake. Splendid Garden. Connected with it is "**Hotel Villa Serbelloni,**" amidst the famous gardens overlooking three parts of the lake. Ten miles of walks in the grounds. *N.B.*—Visitors of the Grand Hotel have free access to Serbelloni Garden. **L. BREITSCHMID, Proprietor.**

SPLENDIDE HOTEL DES ETRANGERS

EXPRESSLY BUILT and handsomely furnished FIRST CLASS HOTEL in magnificent situation opposite the Lake. Lift. Electric Light throughout. Central Hot Water Heating. Bath and Douches. Spring Water. Large Garden and Restaurant Francaise on the Lake. Table d'Hote at separate Tables. Auto-Garage Omnibus meets all the Boats. Rooms from **3 frs.** Pension from **8 frs.** Cook's Coupons accepted. Moderate Terms.

F. FERRARIO, Proprietor.

BERCHTESGADEN (Germany).—See page 465.

The Leading Hotel of the Bavarian Alps.

Proprietor: H. ROTHE, Purveyor to the Court.

EVERY COMFORT.

Late Summer residence of The German Imperial Family.

BERCHTESGADEN

Summer and Health Resort in the Bavarian Highlands.

HOTEL BAD BELLE VUE.

Modern Comforts. Apartments with Bath and Toilette. Hot Water Heating. Garage. Inhalations and Medical Baths. — **Proprietor: A. HANREICH, Jnr.**

HOTEL VIER JAHRESZEITEN.

HOTEL 4 SEASONS.

BEAUTIFULLY situated and very comfortable Hotel. — **60 Rooms from 1.50 to 5 Mks.** Pension 6 to 10 Mks. Summer and Winter season. Specially recommended for Winter sport. Central Heating. Recommended to English and Americans. **Proprietor : A. MILLER.**

BERLIN.—See page 465.

TRAVEL and HOTEL ENQUIRIES—See page xii.

BERLIN:

Conrad Uhl's

Hôtel Bristol-Berlin.

Unter den Linden. 5/6a.

The world renowned "Leading Hôtel" of the German capital.

Frequented by the ÉLITE of English Society.

→ *Every modern comfort*

TARIFFS AND EVERY INFORMATION AT THE DORLAND AGENCY, 3, REGENT STREET, LONDON, S.W OR THE VARIOUS OFFICES OF BRADSHAW'S GUIDES.

BERLIN—*Continued.*

BERLIN.

EDEN HOTEL

Opened December, 1912.

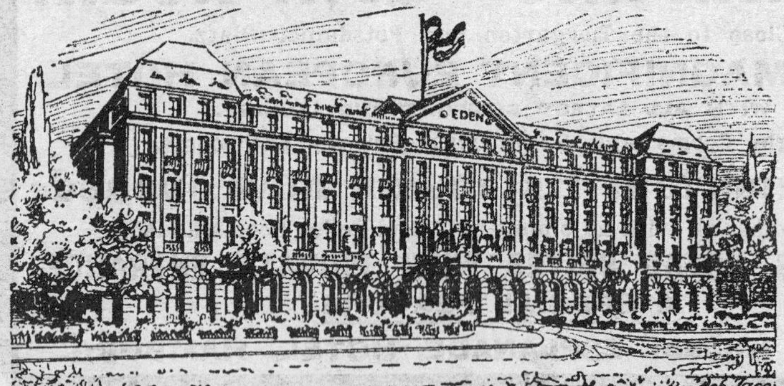

Finest Situation, facing Zoological Gardens and . . Tiergarten Park.

Two minutes from Zoological Gardens Station.

The most Up-to-Date and Fashionable Hotel. — International Aristocratic Clientele.

200 Rooms and Suites with private Bathroom and Toilet.
Telephone and Running Hot and Cold water throughout.

FIRST CLASS FRENCH and OPEN-AIR RESTAURANT,
5 o'clock Tea.

Berlin's Latest Creation—
ROOF RESTAURANT
Magnificent views overlooking Tiergarten.

Telegrams: EDENHOTEL, BERLIN.

A. WALTERSPIEL, Proprietor.

UNDER THE SAME MANAGEMENT:

HILLER'S RESTAURANT,

UNTER DEN LINDEN, 62 and 63.

The World-renowned Rendezvous of leading Society.

Proprietor: A. WALTERSPIEL.

BERLIN—Continued on next page.

BERLIN—*Continued.*

BERLIN—Continued on next page.

BERLIN—*Continued.*

*

KURFÜRSTENDAMM

193/194.

*

HOTEL CUMBERLAND BERLIN

*

KURFÜRSTENDAMM

193/194.

*

In the CENTRE of the WEST END.

The Leading Apartment Hotel and Boarding Establishment; 600 Rooms with private Baths; running hot and cold water. All sanitary comfort. Tariff on application.

J. C. SCHWEIMLER, General Manager.

Purveyor to His Imperial Majesty the German Emperor.

BERLIN, S.W. — First Class Family Hotel.

HOTEL "PRINZ-ALBRECHT."

Close to Anhalt and Potsdam Stations, most central, quiet, and finest part of Berlin, opposite the House of Commons. Suites with Private Bath and Toilet.

Rooms from 3 Mk. Pension Arrangements.

BERLIN—*Continued.*

BERLIN—Continued on next page.

BERLIN—*Continued.*

WHERE TO STAY IN BERLIN ! !

Alexandra Hotel.

MITTELSTRASSE, 16/17.

An inexpensive Hotel, 3 minutes walk from Central Railway Station—Friedrichstrasse. Next street to Unter den Linden (Berlin's most Fashionable thoroughfare). Near all sights, Royal Castle, Theatres, English Embassy, and the beautiful Tiergarten Park.

Cook's Coupons accepted.

Most convenient for visitors to Berlin whether on business or on pleasure. 100 Front and Garden Rooms from **2/6** upwards.

What English Guests say:—
Central, Homelike, Comfortable, Courtesy.

Managing Proprietor: C. H. MÜLLER.

BERLIN. UNTER DEN LINDEN, 20 (Close to Friedrich-Strasse, and next to the "Passage").

HOTEL METROPOLE.

Fine modern Hotel, equipped with every up-to-date comfort. Lift. Electric Light. Baths. 60 Rooms with single bed from 2 to 5 M.; with 2 beds from 4.50 to 10 M.

Proprietor: J. LEISTER.

TRAVEL and HOTEL ENQUIRIES—See page xii.

BERLIN—*Continued.*

BERLIN—Continued on next page.

BERLIN—*Continued.*

PENSION VON FINCK

123a, POTSDAMER STRASSE.

FIRST CLASS in every respect. Close to the Potsdamer and Dresden Stations (Anhalter Bahn.), with tram communication everywhere in the City. 2 minutes from Thiergarten. . . . EXCELLENT TABLE . .

Full Board from M. 5.50 per day.

*** Spacious Establishment well recommended to English and Americans. ***
Leading Clientele. — — — Large elegant airy rooms.

PENSION KÄHRN

28, KLEIST-STRASSE.

FIRST CLASS PENSION. Spacious and refined Home. Situated in the most fashionable part of Berlin, and well known for its Home Comforts and good Cuisine. Tram and under-ground communication in all directions.

PENSION MEHRING.

81a, I, Kurfürsten Strasse, 81a, I.

First Class Pension founded 1885. Good position, 5 minutes from the Zoological Garden Station. Trams in all directions. Full Pension from **Marks 4.** Baths.

Same House—**DRESDEN, 12, Portikus Strasse.** Best position. Pension from **Mks. 4.** Bath.

PENSION BAVARIA

10, Haberland Strasse. Close to Bayerischer Platz. 10, Haberland Strasse.

Distinguished Family Home, quiet position, very elegantly furnished rooms.
Every modern comfort. ROOMS with Running HOT and COLD Water. Roof-garden.
First Class Cooking. Moderate Terms. Best References. English and French spoken.
Telephone: Nollendorf 457. — MISS CLOTILDE SCHROETTER.

Berlin—Grunewald.

PENSION BISMARCKPLATZ

16, HUBERTUS ALLEE, close to Halensee Station.

FIRST CLASS, with every modern comfort. Villa with garden. Own private woods.
Easy Train communication in all directions. Tel: Pfalzburg, 379.

DEPENDANCE: Warmbrunner Strasse 4. Rooms with or without board. Lift.
Proprietress: Mrs. SPRAGUE.

Berliner Fremdenführer-Centrale, Berlin W. 8

Tel.: Centrum 8345. Behrenstrasse 48, Kerkaupalast.

Reliable, expert Guides (Ladies or Gentlemen).

Travel Inquiry Office—Rooms secured for Visitors.

TRAVEL and HOTEL ENQUIRIES—See page xii.

BERNE—Continued on next page.

BEX-LES-BAINS (Switzerland).—See page 514A.

BIARRITZ (France).—See page 389.

BINGEN (Rhine-Germany).—See page 452.

BIRMINGHAM.—See page 1093.

BLANKENBERGHE (Belgium).—See page 428

BAD BOLL, near Bonndorf (Black Forest), Germany.—See page 457.

HOTEL AND KURHAUS BAD BOLL.

In the wild and romantic Wutachtal, with large Pine Forests.
14 miles of fishing reserved for Hotel guests. — Post and Telegraph in Hotel.
The Hotel has just been reconstructed and its comforts greatly increased.
Rooms from **2 Mks.** Pension from **5.50—7 Mks.** Railway Stations: Bonndorf and Reiselfingen.
PAUL BOGNER, Proprietor.

BOLOGNA (Italy).—See page 537.

BOLOGNA (Italy).

The Gd. Hotel Baglioni

— Via Indipendenza, 6-8. —

The new LEADING and "UP-TO-DATE" HOTEL of Bologna.

120 Rooms and Suites. **30** Private Bath and Toilet Rooms.
Splendid Hall. — Modern Garage.
— 3 Auto Busses at Railway Station. Every Comfort. —
Cables: Hotel Baglioni, Bologna. **GUIDO BAGLIONI, Proprietor.**

TRAVEL and HOTEL ENQUIRIES—See page xii.

BONN (Germany).—See page 449A.

BORDEAUX.—See page 390.

TRAVEL and HOTEL ENQUIRIES—See page xii.

BORDIGHERA—*Continued.*

BORDIGHERA.
HOTEL d'ANGLETERRE

First Class Family Hotel—Old established reputation.

BEST Central situation. Full South with large magnificent Garden. Newly ronovatod. Now Hall. Perfect Sanitary arrangements. Lift. Electric Light and Hot Water Heating in every Room. Table d'Hote at separate Tables. Garage for Automobiles. Moderate Terms. **New Proprietor: X. FURRER (Swiss)**

HOTEL BELVEDERE-LOMBARDI

STRADA ROMANA, BORDIGHERA.

KNOWN as the really English Homely High Class Hotel. Full South. Sheltered position on elevated ground. Beautiful garden. Every modern comfort. Patronised by English nobility. Hot Water Heating throughout. **Entirely renovated and enlarged, 1910.**

Same Proprietor, **Hotel Kurhaus, Westerland,** *Sylt (Germany).*

HOTEL BRISTOL.

BORDIGHERA.

Formerly Hotel de Londres.

FIRST CLASS FAMILY HOTEL, near Cap Ampeglio, well situated in its own grounds. Fine Garden. Extensive view of the coast as far as the Estere Mountains. Central Heating and Electric Light throughout. Bath Room. Cuisine Soignée. Madame Biamonti is English. **Propr.: G. BIAMONTI.**

GRAND HOTEL & DES ILES BRITANNIQUES

BORDIGHERA. First Class.

FINEST Position, quiet and dust free, surrounded by own large Park (20,000 square metres). 5 minutes from the Casino and the Parade. Family Hotel, equipped with all modern comforts. **All rooms situated full South.** Central Heating. Completely renovated and refurnished in 1912. Pension Terms from **10 frs.** **DELLA VALLE.**

BORDIGHERA.
PENSION VILLA QUISISANA

STRADA ROMANA.

FIRST CLASS PENSION, situated **full South** on elevated ground. Nice garden. Every home comfort. Hot Water Heating and Electric Light throughout. Moderate Terms. **Apply: Mrs. MÜLLER, also Proprietress of English Lodge, Coblence o/Rhine (Germany).**

BORMES-LES-MIMOSAS (France).—See page 402.

BORMES-LES-MIMOSAS (Line Toulon-Hyères-St. Raphael).

One of the finest and healthiest spots of the Riviera.

GRAND HOTEL AND PAVILLON DE L'ORANGERIE

UNDER English Patronage. Entirely rebuilt and refurnished. Of moderate size but up-to-date in every respect. Apartments with Private Bath and Toilette. Elevated, sheltered position, offering the most marvellous panorama of the Riviera. Park of 28 acres Tennis Court (full size) and Croquet. Terms moderate. English Church. Hotel Autobus meets trains at Bormes or Hyères. * **G. BAGGENSTOSS, Swiss-Proprietor** (Formerly at the "RITZ." London)

BOULOGNE-SUR-MER.—See page 391.

Grand Hotel Christol & Bristol

A FIRST CLASS HOTEL,

Situated near the Railway Station, Landing Stage and the Postal Telegraph Office.

ELECTRIC LIGHT and Lift. Central heating throughout. Telephone. Motor Garage. Bath Rooms. Suites of private apartments and bedrooms with bathroom and toilette. Omnibus. Tariff in each Room. No charge for service or Electric light.

∴ RESTAURANT à la CARTE. ∴

Telegraphic Address: Bristol, Boulognesurmer.

L. SAGNIER, Proprietor.

BOULOGNE-SUR-MER.

GRAND HOTEL DU LOUVRE ET TERMINUS.

Unique Hotel facing the Landing Stage and Railway Station.

GARAGE.

ALL MODERN COMFORT COMBINED WITH MODERATE CHARGES.

BOULOGNE-SUR-MER.

HOTEL du PAVILLON IMPERIAL

FIRST CLASS. — THE ONLY HOTEL IMMEDIATELY FACING THE SEA.
Electric Light and Lift. Bath Rooms. Motor Garage.
No Charge for Service and Electric Light.
SPECIAL TERMS FOR A STAY BEFORE AND AFTER THE SEASON.

HOTEL FOLKESTONE (Bayly's).

FIRST CLASS. **Facing Harbour and near Casino.**
Electric Ligh and Lift. ∴ **Bath Rooms.** ∴ **Central Heating.** ∴ **Garage.**
Special Terms out of Season. *Same Management as the* "Imperial Pavillon Hotel.'

BOULOGNE-SUR-MER—Continued on next page.

BOULOGNE-SUR-MER—*Continued.*

Boulogne-Sur-Mer.

HOTEL DERVAUX, GRANDE RUE and . . RUE des VIEILLARDS.

UP-TO-DATE HOTEL open all the year round. Highly recommended to Families. 200 Rooms. Bath Rooms. Extensive Promenade Hall. Electric Light, Central Heating, Lift, Telephone. Motor Garage, with Pit. Moderate prices per Day, and Pension terms per Week or Month.

PAUL DERVAUX, Proprietor.

BERRY'S HOTEL BOULOGNE.

96/102, Rue de Boston.

Splendid Open Position. Sea view, adjoining the Casino and Sands, facing the English Steamers. Extensive Gardens. — Open all the year. Terms moderate. — **Cook's Coupons accepted.**

F. BERRY, Proprietor.

HOTEL MEURICE.

FIRST CLASS. Recommended to Tourists. Select Company. Situated in the most central part. Choice Cuisine and Wines. Arrangements for protracted stay. Moderate charges. Central heating.

LA BOURBOULE-LES-BAINS (France).—See page 391.

BOURBOULE . . PALACE HOTEL ET MAJESTIC . . VILLA MEDICIS.

SELECT HOUSE. At entrance to Parc Fenestre. Near the Etablissement. Enlarged and completely renovated. Central Heating, and hot and cold water supply in all toilettes. Apartments with Baths and Douches on every floor. Perfect sanitation. Rooms from **5 fr.** **Tables de Regime** according to Medical advice. First Class cuisine. Restaurant. Pension from **13 frs.** Reduced terms during May, June, and Sept. Private Villas. Lift. Electric Light. Dark Room. Telephone. Omnibus. Interpreter. Garden. Tennis. Skating Rink. Large Garage with pit and closed boxes, Toilet Room for Tourists. Rooms for Chauffeurs.

Vve A. SENNEGY, Proprietress.

HOTEL DES ILES BRITANNIQUES.

C. DONNEAUD, Proprietor.

First-class Establishment. Near the Baths. Best Sanitary arrangements.

LIFT. OPEN FROM THE 25th MAY UNTIL 30th SEPTEMBER.

Electric Light. Telephone. English spoken. Se habla Español.

TRAVEL and HOTEL ENQUIRIES—See page xii.

LA BOURBOULE-LES-BAINS (France)—*Continued.*

THE GRAND——— LA BOURBOULE.

METROPOLE AND CONTINENTAL HOTELS

have private Baths-Toilettes with W.C.

They are the Most Up-to-Date in every respect. — 300 Rooms. — Reasonable terms.

. . . Private Band. . . .

Apply for information and booklet to— **FERREYROLLES JUNR. & SONS, Proprietors.**

BOURNEMOUTH.—See pages 1093 1094.

BREGENZ (Austria).—See page 495.

BREGENZ.—HOTEL MONTFORT

On the Lake of Constance.

MODERN FIRST CLASS HOTEL,
Facing the Central Station.
G. ETTENBERGER, Propr.

BREMEN.—See page 467B.

HILLMANN'S HOTEL

Unrivalled Location.

160 Rooms.
60 Private Bath Rooms.

New Restaurant. — H. VOLLMER, Manager.

HOTEL de l'EUROPE.

FIRST CLASS. IN BEST POSITION. LATELY REBUILT.

Every modern comfort. Rooms with Bath. Close to the Station.

Proprietor: F. STEINECKE.

HOTEL ALBERTI

COMFORTABLE HOTEL IN QUIET POSITION, FACING STATION.

Every modern convenience. Central Heating. Electric Light. Lift. Baths.
Rooms from Mks. 2.75. Pension if desired. Tel. 444. Proprietor: H. W. EICKE.

BREMEN—Continued on next page

BREMEN—*Continued.*

BRIDES-LES-BAINS (Near Aix, Savoy).—See page 392.

BRIENZ (Switzerland).—See page 514B.

BRIGUE (Brig), Switzerland.—See page 514B.

TRAVEL and HOTEL ENQUIRIES—See page xii.

BRISSAGO (Switzerland).—See page 514B.

BRISSAGO (The Pearl of the Lago Maggiore).

SWITZERLAND.

The Grand Hotel

One of the LEADING HOTELS on this superb Lake.

EXQUISITE Situation in the middle of its magnificent Park. **Tennis, Boating, Fishing, Sport. English Church.** All steamers stop at Brissago. During Spring and Autumn season the **New** and **Fine Auto** of the Hotel meets trains at Locarno (20 minutes); if desired also to Fondotoce, on the Simplon, near Pallanza (50 minutes). Tariff free. Pension from **9 francs.**

SOMAZZI and RIGANTI, Proprietors.

BRIXEN (S. Tyrol).—See page 495.

HOTEL TIROL.

NEWLY Built Modern First Class Hotel, in the centre of the Town. Central Heating. Electric Light. Lift. Suites with Baths. All rooms with hot and cold running water. Elegant Restaurant and Café. Rooms from **Kr. 2.** Pension, not including room, **Kr. 5.50.** Omnibus at the Station. — Garage.

THE BROCKEN.—See page 468.

BROCKEN (Harz Mountains), 3,415 feet above Sea.

BROCKEN HOTEL

COMFORTABLE HOTEL on the summit of the Brocken, lately enlarged and renovated. Own Electric Light. Steam Heating. Also open in Winter. Best opportunities for all kinds of Winter Sport. Pension. Tel. Schierke No. 7. Prospectus from Bradshaw's Offices and the—

Branch House: Hotel Weisses Ross, Halberstadt. — Proprietor, RUDOLPH SCHADE.

BRUGES (Belgium).—See page 428.

GRAND HOTEL

– AND –

GRAND HOTEL DU COMMERCE.

First Class Establishment. **THE LARGEST IN BRUGES. In the Centre of the Town.**

CHIEFLY patronised by English and American Society. **All modern comfort.** Electric Light and Steam Heating in all the rooms. Suites and Bedrooms with automatic Bath and Toilet. Splendid Garden. **AUTOMOBILE at every Train.** Auto-Garage at the Hotel.

Cable and Telegraphic Address: "GRAND HOTEL, BRUGES."

C. VAN DEN BERGHE & SON, Proprietors.

BRUGES—Continued on next page.

BRUGES—*Continued.*

— BRUGES. —

HOTEL DE FLANDRE

ENTIRELY RENOVATED WITH COMFORT AND LUXURY. LEADING HOTEL.

Hot and cold water supply in most of the rooms. Meals served in splendid garden.

Patronised by Royalty and English and American Society.

Telegrams—"Flandre-Bruges." — October-March full pension from **5/-**

Automobile Association and Motor Union of Great Britain. American Automobile Club. American Automobile Association.

Touring Automobile Association of America.

Vve. E. H. BENSEL, Proprietress.

BRUNIG (Bernese Oberland, Switzerland).—See page 514B.

GRAND HOTEL & KURHAUS BRÜNIG.

RAILWAY STATION 2 HOURS FROM LUCERNE AND INTERLAKEN.

3,400 ft. above the Sea. Splendid health resort. Most comfortable Hotel with 150 beds. Electric Light. Central heating. Lift. Dark room. Post, telegraph, telephone Carriages. Garage. Orchestra. Resident doctor. Pension terms for May and June from **8-14 Frs.**, after July 1st from **9 Frs.** — Arrangements for families. — **English Church Service at the Hotel.** Bedrooms with Private Bath and Toilette. — **Ed. HAUBENSAK, Proprietor.**

BRUNNEN (Switzerland).—See page 514B.

BRUNNEN (Lake of Lucerne).

Grand Hotel Brunnen

NEWLY OPENED. Entirely Fire-proof built.

THOROUGHLY FIRST CLASS HOTEL.

IN the best situation of Brunnen. Extensive park with Lawn Tennis and shady private walks. Latest modern comfort. Three Lifts. Electric Light. 250 Rooms and Saloons. Steam Heating in every Room. American Bar. English and French Billiards. French Cuisine. Table d'Hote at separate Tables. Covered Terrace, 100 yards long, 4 yards wide, a lovely Promenade during bad weather. The only Hotel highly situated.

Brunnen Near LUCERNE, Lake of 4 Cantons, Gotthard Railway station

LIFT **THE WALDSTATTER HOF** Private baths

First Class Hotel, 250 beds, best situation with park on the Lake, hot water heating English Church Service, Pension from 8 fr. :: Managed by the Proprietor **F. Fassbind**

TRAVEL and HOTEL ENQUIRIES—See page xii.

BRUNNEN—*Continued.*

Park Hotel

FIRST CLASS HOTEL.

WITH every modern comfort. Large Park. Finest and quiet situation. Specially adapted for English families. Bathrooms on every floor. Private apartments with baths. Large Verandahs. Electric Light. Lawn Tennis. Billiard table. Pension arrangements from **francs 7** upward, according to the Rooms. Garage. **BROTHERS AUFDERMAUR, Proprs. and Managers.** also of **HOTEL ADLER**, opposite the Landing Place of Steamers. Lift in both Hotels. Prospectus on application.

Eden Hotel.

FIRST CLASS.

50 BEDS.

In magnificent elevated position on the border of the Lake. ∴ ∴ ∴ ∴ Close to the Landing Stage. — Lift. Terraces. Large Garden.

Pension from 7.50 francs.

BRUNSWICK.—See page 469.

PARK HOTEL.

BRUNSWICK.

FACING the Ducal Theatre, the Park, and Abt's Monument. Close to the Ducal Castle, the Dom, Castle Dankwarderode, the Ducal and Municipal Museums. The leading Hotel. Opened 15th October, 1909. Equipped with the latest modern comfort. Suites with Baths and Telephone. Hot and cold water supply. Central Heating. Electric Light. Lift. Garage. Restaurant with Terrace Garden. Wholesale Wine Merchants. Telephone Nos. 193, 363, 364. **KARL KALMS,** Purveyor to the Courts.

BRUSSELS.—See page 429.

HOTEL MÉTROPOLE.

FIRST CLASS HOTEL

With all Modern Comfort, in the best and most central part of Brussels.

Leading Hotel in Belgium.

500 Bedrooms and Private Salons, provided with Bath.

Telephone to ∴ Foreign Countries ∴ in all Rooms.

NEW WING

Splendid Palm Garden. American Bar. Steam Heating.

Offices of the Sleeping Cars at the Hotel.

WIELEMANS-CEUPPENS, Proprietor.

BRUSSELS—Continued on next page.

BRUSSELS—*Continued.*

BRUSSELS.

PALACE HOTEL

The Most Comfortable Hotel in Europe.

OPPOSITE NORTHERN STATION.
FRONTING BOTANICAL GARDEN.

500 Rooms with Bathroom attached to each room. | Telephone in all places. From Francs **7.50.**

High Class French Restaurant. Moderate Charges.

BRUSSELS. NEXT TO THE KING'S PALACE.

HOTEL de BELLE VUE et de FLANDRE.

The most aristocratic Hotel of Belgium. Place Royale.

Large and small Apartments with or without Bathroom and Toilet.
Central Heating. Electric Light. Lift. Modern Comfort. Winter Garden.
Hot and Cold Water supply in most of the Rooms.
Garage with pit for Automobiles.
Member of the AUTOMOBILE CLUB of France, Germany, and America.

Brussels. LE GRAND HOTEL. Belgium.

Tariff for Rooms, Attendance, Light and Heating included.

ROOMS.	1st Floor	2nd Floor	3rd Floor	4th Floor	RESTAURANT.
1 Bed, 1 Person... ... ... fcs.	from 10	from 9	from 7	from 5	Breakfast 1.50
1 Bed, 2 Persons	,, 13	,, 11	,, 9	,, 8	Luncheon 4.0
2 Beds	,, 18	,, 13	,, 12	,, 10	Dinner... ... ... 6.0
1 Large Bed, Bath Room, Lavatory & W C	,, 18	,, 15	—	,, 10	Arrangements *en Pension* Price
2 Beds, Bathroom, Lavatory and W.C....	,, 20	,, 17	,, 15	—	Lists and all information sent
New Lavatories with hot and cold water in every Room.					post free on demand.

TRAVEL and HOTEL ENQUIRIES—See page xii.

BRUSSELS—*Continued.*

BRUSSELS—Continued on next page.

TRAVEL and HOTEL ENQUIRIES—See page xii.

BUDAPEST—Continued on next page.

TRAVEL and HOTEL ENQUIRIES—See page xli.

BURGOS (Spain).—See page 567.

TRAVEL and HOTEL ENQUIRIES—See page xii.

CADENABBIA (Lake of Como), Italy.—See page 540.

CADENABBIA (Lake of Como, Italy).

HOTEL BELLE VUE

Very 1st Class Establishment. * Highest Comfort and Reputation.

.... EXCELLENT CUISINE. ....

IN MARCH — JUNE — JULY — AUGUST—OCTOBER—NOVEMBER :— Special Reduced Prices.

Golf. — Auto Garage. — Orchestra.

Five minutes walk from the English Church. **A. FEDELE, General Manager.**

HOTEL BELLE ILE.

CADENABBIA (Lake of Como).

FIRST CLASS FAMILY HOTEL, beautifully situated in the best, sunny and quiet position on the Lake. Fine view of the Lake and mountains. Near the steamboat pier and English Church. Electric light. Lift. Baths. Golf. — Large gardens and terrace on the Lake. — Modern comfort. — Pension from **Francs 8.**

G. MELLA, Proprietor.

HOTEL BRITANNIA.

CADENABBIA.

1ST CLASS ENGLISH FAMILY HOTEL. Situated in a very fine, sheltered position. Lift. **Recently enlarged and renovated.** Moderate inclusive terms. Splendid view of the lake and mountains from all the rooms. Large Garden. Central Heating. All modern comfort. Lift. Boating.

C. GANDOLA.

"THE BEST AND HANDIEST POCKET CONVERSATIONAL GUIDES PUBLISHED."

Price 1/-

Will fit the waistcoat pocket.

BRADSHAW'S

Foreign Phrase Books.

ENGLISH—FRENCH.
ENGLISH—GERMAN.
ENGLISH—ITALIAN.
ENGLISH—SPANISH.

BRADSHAW HOUSE, SURREY STREET, STRAND, LONDON, W.C.
Henry Blacklock & Co., Ltd., Proprietors and Publishers.

Remittances may be made in stamps of any country of 5 centimes value (or equivalent).

TRAVEL and HOTEL ENQUIRIES—See page xii.

CALAIS.—See page 393.

TERMINUS HOTEL ET BUFFET (Gare Maritime.)

OPPOSITE the Steam Packet Pier. The only Hotel with a view of the sea. All travelling arrangements made. Lift, Electric Light. Renowned *cave* and *cuisine.* Travellers passing through Calais have always time for lunching at the Buffet. Official notice is given of the departure of trains five minutes beforehand. *Under the same management:*

CENTRAL HOTEL and BUFFET

(GARE VILLE).

Situated in centre of the Town. First Class Hotel. . . . Central Heating. . . . Electric Light. — Garden. — Moderate charges.

GRAND HOTEL.

.·. IN CENTRE OF TOWN .·.

First Class House with modern comfort. Large Garage. Moderate terms.

CALALZO (Italian Dolomites).—See page 540.

CALALZO—CADORE, 2,829 feet above sea. (ITALIAN DOLOMITES).

HOTEL MARMAROLE

SEASON: MAY—OCTOBER. The Railway Line is now open to Perarolo (Longarone-Perarolo).

FIRST CLASS HOUSE in quiet position near pine woods, amidst Dolomites of majestic grandeur. Centre for excursions and mountaineering (Antelao, Marmarole, Spalti di Toro, Monfalcone, Cridola). Ideal place for tourists, artists, health and holiday seekers. Very salubrious air and water. A mile from Pieve (Titian's birth place). Moderate charges. Motor garage. Comfortable carriages and motor cars to Belluno and Toblach **FANTON BROS., Proprs.**

CANARY ISLANDS (Las Palmas).—See page 584.

CANARY ISLANDS (LAS PALMAS).

UNION CASTLE LINE DIRECT SERVICE.

SANTA CATALINA HOTEL

(ENGLISH).

(Patronised by H.M. the King of Spain.)

Beautiful Gardens of about 20 acres facing sea. Golf, Tennis, Croquet, etc. English Church. — English Physician and Trained Nurse.

The Secretary, Canary Islands Company Limited, Finsbury Pavement House, London, E.C.

CANARY ISLANDS. — Finest Climate in the World.

GRAND HOTEL QUISISANA

TENERIFFE.

Most Modern Hotel in the Canary Islands. Furnished in luxurious style by London firm. English Sanitation. Bathrooms on every floor. Hotel stands in own grounds of 60 acres. All rooms exceptionally lofty and ventilated perfectly. Superb scenery. Golf. Finest Cuisine. Cables: "Quisisana, Teneriffe." Passages booked by all lines; rooms reserved. Illustrated booklets, tariff, and all particulars free of charge from CANARY ISLANDS and MADEIRA AGENCY, 11, ADAM STREET, STRAND, London, W.C. — (Telephone, Gerrard 8616).

CANNERO (Italy).—See page 540.

CANNERO—LAC MAJEUR (opposite Luino).

HOTEL PENSION ITALIE.

FINELY situated on the shore of the Lake. Absolutely quiet. No noise from motor cars, or railway. In its own grounds, in the midst of orange, mandarin, and lemon trees. Beautiful climate. — All modern comforts. — Hot water heating throughout. — Many splendid walks. Open all the year. Terms "*en pension*" from 6 frs. according to room.

V. DESTEFANIS, Managing New Proprietor.

CANNES.—See page 393.

CANNES. **C. E. Clark**

(THE ANGLO-AMERICAN AGENCY). 7, Rue Felix Faure—Cannes.

PARTICULARS OF VILLAS TO LET FORWARDED ON APPLICATION. **HOUSE AND ESTATE AGENT.**

Official Agency { South Eastern and Chatham Railway, London and North Western Rly., and North German Lloyd Co. — Telegrams: "CECLARK, CANNES."

CANNES.

GALLIA PALACE

Situated in grounds of 5 hectares, in one of the best positions of Cannes.

250 Rooms and Saloons with Balconies. Built on the latest modern princip es, and entirely fire-proot. Kitchen under the management of a well known Chet.

2 LIFTS. — ELECTRIC LIGHT EVERYWHERE.

NEW SYSTEM OF VENTILATION AND STEAM HEATING COMBINED.

Private Dressing Cabinets, 60 Private Bath Rooms, etc.; Hot and Cold Water to every Room.

Concerts by the Hotel Orchestra, twice daily, in the large Winter Garden, capable of accommodating 250 persons.

Theatre, which can be entirely shut off from the Hotel.

Large Ball Room. English and French Billiards.

Public Rooms all face South. Lawn Tennis and other Pastimes.

— GARAGE FOR 50 AUTOMOBILES. —

Write for Prospectus to the Manager, **ED. SMART**

Same Proprietors: MALOJA PALACE, MALOJA, ENGADINE.

CANNES MOST RENOWNED PARK.

HÔTEL DU PARC

Well Known First Class Family Hotel. Formerly "Chateau Vallombrosa."

M. ELLMER, Proprietor.

CANNES—Continued on next page

CANNES—*Continued.*

HOTEL METROPOLE

OPEN DECEMBER TO MAY.

BEAUTIFULLY SITUATED in own private park, over 30 acres in extent, affording magnificent unobstructed views over the Golfe Juan. Faces due south. Luxuriously furnished suites with private bathrooms. Fine Tennis Courts and Croquet lawn. Golf, Hunting, Yachting, Motoring, etc. Garage. **The Hotel is connected with Town Station, Golf Links, and Polo Ground by private Motor Car Service.** Under same management as Hotel Metropole, Monte Carlo, and Hotel Royal, Dieppe.

ILLUSTRATED TARIFF BOOKLETS FROM ANY OF THE GORDON HOTELS, or the COMPANY'S CENTRAL OFFICES, 2, ADELPHI TERRACE, LONDON, W.C.

Open from October 1st to June 1st. Renowned Cuisine. Lift. Steam Heat. Large Park. Perfect Sanitation. Electric Light throughout.

HOTEL DES ANGLAIS

The Recognised Leading First Class English Hotel.

Numerous self-contained apartments with private Bathrooms, etc.

Beautifully situated close to St. Paul s Church. Prop.: G. MOREL.

CANNES.

HOTEL BRISTOL

— CENTRAL. —

FIRST CLASS FAMILY HOTEL. Rooms with Baths and w.c. Central Heating throughout. The Hotel stands in a large Park, full South. Beautiful new Dining Room and Hall. J. SCHAER & SONS, Proprietors (Swiss).

CANNES. THE WELL KNOWN

HOTEL BEAU-SITE

Entirely Renovated. — 50 Bathrooms.

Beautiful Lounge. Orchestra. Ball twice weekly.

NEAREST to GOLF and POLO. 3 Club Tennis Courts.

E. Schmid, Director. In Summer: "Grand Hotel Thunerhof," Thun.

CANNES HOTEL DE L'ESTEREL.

Nearest Golf Links. Thoroughly First Class. Hot Water Heating in every room.

Excellent Cuisine. Lovely Grounds connected with "Beau Site" Park. Ideal place for health and comfort. **MODERATE TARIFF. — Manager: F. BERTL.**

CANNES

LE

Grand Hotel

H. MENGE, Proprietor.

TRAVEL and HOTEL ENQUIRIES—See page xii.

TRAVEL and HOTEL ENQUIRIES—See page xii.

CANNES—*Continued.*

.. CANNES ..

THE PAVILLON GRAND HOTEL

ENGLISH QUARTER.

1st class house with modern comforts.

New Large Hall. Splendid Garden. Terms moderate.

P. BORGO, of the Hotels Baveno, Lake Maggiore, Italy.

CANNES.—RIVIERA.

GRAND HOTEL CALIFORNIE

FIRST CLASS.

Splendid and sheltered position, 100 Metres above Sea level.
Large Park. Central Heating. Electric Light. Lift. Apartments with Baths.

A. KEES, Manager.

CANNES.

HOTEL DES PINS.

FIRST CLASS. Full South. Surrounded by Pine Trees. Lawn Tennis. Special Tram Service from Hotel to Town.

LIFTS. TELEPHONES.

HOTEL BEAU-RIVAGE.

FIRST CLASS. Large Garden. Exceptional position on the "Croisette" and on the border of Sea.

FREDERIC HAINZL, Manager.

CANNES.

HOTEL CONTINENTAL

HIGHLY reputed and fashionable FIRST CLASS FAMILY HOTEL. High situation, with beautiful views over the Town, the Sea, the Islands, and the Esterel Mountains. Full South, in a large and entirely sunny Garden. Lift. Central Hot Water Heating, Rooms and Suites with Private Bath.

H. ROST.

LIFT. ..

HOTEL BEAU LIEU.

ELECTRIC LIGHT.

FIRST CLASS HOTEL. Highly recommended and patronised by English families for its home comfort and beautiful situation, facing full south. The Hotel has all up-to-date sanitary arrangements. Large Garden and Forest. Lawn Tennis. Auto bus service with the town. Every attention. Moderate charges. Central Water Heating throughout. Open from October 15th to the end of May. — H. GIMBERT, Proprietor.

HOTEL GRAY et d'ALBION.

FIRST CLASS.

Newly Enlarged. Contains 200 Rooms and 100 private Bath Rooms.
Perfect Sanitary Arrangements.
Large Dining Room and Restaurant. Finest Park on the Riviera.

P. L'HERMITE, Director.

CANNES—Continued on next page

CANNES—*Continued.*

TRAVEL and HOTEL ENQUIRIES—See page xii.

CANNES—*Continued.*

HOTEL SUISSE.

Best central situation in the "QUARTIER du CERCLE NAUTIQUE."
Every modern comfort. * Auto-Garage.
Pension from 12 Frs. — *Managing Proprietor* **: A. KELLER-KIENBERGER.**

HOTEL VICTORIA.

Central situation. Fine Garden. Near Sea. Comfortable Rooms. Very Good Table.
OPEN WHOLE YEAR. Hot Water Heating throughout. Tramway at the door.
Pension from 9 frs. L. W. PILATTE, Proprietor.

CANNES.

HOTEL-PENSION SAVOY.

FIRST CLASS FAMILY HOTEL. — UNRIVALLED POSITION.
Magnificent views of the Mediterranean. Hot Water Heating in every Room.
Electric Light & Lift. Tennis. Swiss Management. **Terms from 9 Frs.**

CANNES.

HOTEL DES ILES BRITANNIQUES.

CENTRAL SITUATION, FULL SOUTH. LARGE GARDEN. LIFT.
Central Heating in all the Rooms.
Moderate Prices. Pension from 11 frs. **A. BODE, new Proprietor.**

CANNES. WEST END.

HOTEL PENSION DE LA TOUR.

COMFORTABLE Quiet First Class Family House. — Elevated situation free from dust. Very large Garden and sunny Grounds. Lovely view over the Sea and the Esterel Mountains. Easy communication by electric tram with the Town, the Golf Links, Polo, etc. Telephone. Tennis. Electric Light. Auto-Garage. Excellent Cooking. Moderate Charges.
E. BENZ, Proprietress (Swiss).
— (Close by, NICELY FURNISHED VILLA to let, Board and Service if required). —

PENSION ANGLO-AMERICAINE (VILLA CAMPESTRA).

BOULEVARD CARNOT.
First Class English House. — Full South. — Large Grounds.
Ten minutes walk from Station and English Church.
Telephone. Electric Light. Billiards. House heated by a Calorifere.
Terms from 7 frs. per day. Open from September 20th to June 20th.

THE ENGLISH BANK AND ESTATE AGENCY,

JOHN TAYLOR & SON.

HOUSE AND ESTATE AGENTS. BAGGAGE AGENTS.
Wine and Spirit Merchants, etc., etc.
Offices of the British Vice-Consulate.

CARLSBAD (Austria).—See page 495.

Bohemia CARLSBAD Austria

2 Railway Stations, on Buschtehrad Railway and Central Station. Direct Carriages to all Capitals of the Continent. Sleeping and Restaurant Cars. "Trains de Luxe" and Express Trains. Ostend (London), Paris, Vienna, and Berlin Express.

The Carlsbad Waters are the first of Alkaline Mineral Waters containing Sulphate of Sodium besides Alkaline Carbonates and free Carbonic Acid.

16 Mineral Springs

varying from 95° 3 F. to 162° 5 F., of which the SPRUDEL, MUHLBRUNN, MARKTBRUNN, and SCHLOSSBRUNN are the most frequented.

FIVE LARGE BATHING ESTABLISHMENTS. THE KAISERBAD, The most remarkable in Europe.

1912 — ***70,935 BATHERS. 200,000 TOURISTS AND PASSING VISITORS.***

Indications:—Diseases of Stomach and Intestines, Swelling of the Spleen and Liver, Gallstones, Kidneys, Bladder and Prostrata, Gravel and Urinary stones, Hæmorrhoids, Obesity, Glykosuria, Diabetes, Gout, Rheumatism, Urinary disorders, Oxaluria, Sciatica.

Remedies : 16 Mineral Springs, Drinking and Bathing cures.

5 Large Bathing Establishments.—Hot Baths, Carbonic Acid Baths, Mud Baths, Spring and River Water Baths, Steam and Hot Air Baths, Vapour Baths (Private if required), Electric Light and Water Baths. 2 Hydrotherapeutic Institutes, Swedish Gymnasium, Massage.

NUMEROUS FIRST CLASS HOTELS.
1,200 Houses and Villas, furnished with every modern comfort.

Lighting by Electricity. High Pressure Water Pipes. Macadamised or Wood-paved Streets. Reconstructed Drains.

THEATRE, VARIETY HALL, CONCERTS, ORCHESTRAS. MILITARY BAND. HORSE RACING. DANCING SOIRÉES. GOLF. LAWN TENNIS. SWIMMING. FISHING.

Large Ring of magnificent Promenades (110 Kilometers) in the Mountains and Woods surrounding the Town, with numerous and splendid points of view.

FOR INFORMATION AND PROSPECTUSES APPLY TO THE STADTRAT.

CARLSBAD—Continued on next page.

TRAVEL and HOTEL ENQUIRIES—See page xii.

CARLSBAD—*Continued*

CARLSBAD—Continued on next page

CARLSBAD—*Continued.*

CARLSRUHE.—See page 469.

TRAVEL and HOTEL ENQUIRIES—See page xii.

CHAMONIX (France).—See page 395.

CHAMONIX—*Continued.*

✱ GRANDS HOTELS CACHAT ET DU MONT BLANC ✱

THE LEADING UP-TO-DATE HOTELS OF CHAMONIX.

Large Park. Finest view and position. Apartments with Baths. Garage.
Patronized by the Nobility and Gentry.
—— Opening in 1914 of the CACHAT'S MAJESTIC PALACE Grand Luxe. ——
Family CACHAT, Managing Proprietors.

CHAMPERY (Switzerland).—**See page** 515.

CHAMPERY (Switzerland). 3,600 Ft. above Sea. * Electric Railway from AIGLE to MONTHEY. Charming Summer and Winter Resort at the foot of the renowned Dent du Midi.

GRAND HOTEL DENT du MIDI

FIRST CLASS IN EVERY WAY. 380 BEDS. DANCES. CONCERTS. PLAY ROOM. TENNIS. Delightful walks and Mountain excursions. Magnificent scenery. Ideal for Summer and Winter sports. Terms from **7 frs.** in Summer and **9 frs.** in Winter. *Full information from the Proprietor*: TH. EXHENRY.

HOTEL CROIX FÉDÉRALE

Open all the year.

CENTRAL Heating. Electric Light. Telephone. Cuisine of old repute. Table d'hote and à la carte. Lunch at 12.30, Dinner at 7 o'clock. Dining room with verandah. Reading room. Billiards. Smoking room. Baths and Douches. Terraces and shady garden. Excellent spring water in the house. Terms from **fr. 6.50** in Summer and **fr. 7** in Winter. **V. DEFAGO, Proprietor.**

CHATEAU D'ŒX (Vaud), Switzerland.—**See page** 515.

CHATEAU d'ŒX.

Grand Hotel

3,500 feet above sea level, in an elevated situation. First Class, newly opened, with all up to date requirements. Suites, Double and Single Bedrooms with lavatories, bath, and dressing rooms attached. Open all the year. English and French Billiard Tables.
— Pension Terms from 10 francs upwards. —

HOTEL-PENSION BERTHOD, 3,300 FEET.

Well-known Family Hotel, facing full south and fitted with modern improvements.
Central heating. Pension Terms **7 to 12 frs.** Open all the year. 3 Tennis, 2 Croquet Grounds.
Berthod's Hotels.—*Orchestra.—House Dances.—Centre of Amusements.*
Winter Sports. The Berthod Hotel's Skating Rink, one of the largest artificial rinks, with a surface of 22,000 sq. ft. and known as one of the best of Switzerland. Curling.

Hotel de l'Ours

CHATEAU d'OEX. **3,280 ft. above sea level. Montreux-Oberland.** CHATEAUX d'OEX.

OPEN ALL THE YEAR. — Summer and Winter Station. — Central Heating. Baths. Billiards. Garden with Covered Terrace. Large Hall. Troute "du Vivier" a speciality. Telephone No. 57. Garage. Terms en Pension from **7 frs.** in Summer and **8 frs.** in Winter
N. FROSSARD, Manager.

CHATEAU D'OEX—Continued on next page

CHATEUX D'ŒX (Vaud), Switzerland—*Continued.*

CHATEAU d'ŒX.

GRAND HOTEL BEAU-SEJOUR & KURHAUS

NEW FIRST CLASS HOTEL. Central Heating. Baths. Electric Light. Lift. Restaurant. Renowned Cooking. Billiards. Large covered Verandah. Perfect Sanitation. Tennis. Own Skating Rink. Park and Garden. Terms from **8 frs.** **C. CLAUSEN, Manager.**

N.B.—Well known as a Winter and Summer Station, Chateau d'Œx may be also highly recommended in Spring and Autumn . .

HOTEL - PENSION ROSAT

Recently Rebuilt and Enlarged.

Equipped with every modern Comfort. Unique Position, overlooking the Valley. Specially patronised by English families. Verandah. Central Heating. Tennis Lawn. Sleigh drives. Tobogganing. — **Pension from 7 Francs.** — **Winter terms from 8 Francs.** Special arrangements for families. **Proprietor ALFRED ROSAT.**

CHATEL GUYON-LES-BAINS.—See page 397.

CHATEL GUYON-LES-BAINS (Auvergne)

GRAND HOTEL du PARC

MOST UP-TO-DATE.

200 Rooms. — 50 Bathrooms.

Opened from 1st May to 15th October.

VEDRINE BROTHERS.

CHATEL-GUYON (Puy de Dôme).

SPLENDID NOUVEL HOTEL

Private Park. Auto-Garage (Boxes). Tennis, etc. Telephone.

CHESIERES, Alps Vaudoises (Switzerland)—See page 515.

GRAND HOTEL DU CHAMOSSAIRE.

- Alpes Vaudoises. - **CHESIERES.** 4,100 ft. above Sea level.

Terminus of the Electric Ry. Bex-Villars-Chesières. 7 Minutes from Villars. Electric Light. Central Hot Water Heating. — Three Doctors.

Open Winter and Summer.

For Prospectus and Information apply to **H. AMIGUET and Family,** *Managing Proprietors.*

TRAVEL and HOTEL ENQUIRIES—See page xii.

CHRISTIANIA (Norway). See page 637, Special Edition.

Grand Hotel.

FIRST CLASS. WORLD REPUTATION.

Splendid situation on the Carl Johan's Square. Principal Promenade. Electric Light. PERFECT SANITATION. Steam Heating. Lifts. Baths, etc. Omnibus. MODERATE CHARGES. Billiards, etc. — The Management.

CHUR—Coire (Switzerland).—See page 515.

COIRE. — COIRE.

NEW HOTEL STEINBOCK

OPENED JULY 1901.

NEWLY CONSTRUCTED and highly recommended First Class Hotel, with every modern comfort. Delightfully situated **facing the Station.** Splendid views from every window. **140 Beds from frs. 3 upward, including Light and Service.** Large Garden, full South, with covered Verandah. Private Apartments with Bath attached. Ladies' Drawing, Billiard, and Smoking Rooms. Vestibule. Café-Restaurant. Lift. Electric Light. Central Heating. Baths on each floor. Best Sanitary arrangements. Pension. **The Manager: E. BÜTIKOFER.**

COBLENCE (Rhine).—See page 450A.

Grd. Hotel Belle Vue

COBLENZER HOF.

Modern Construction de Luxe.

FIRST CLASS, EQUIPPED WITH ALL COMFORTS.
∴ RUNNING WATER IN EVERY ROOM. ∴

Opened Spring, 1913.

Magnificent covered Terrace overlooking the Rhine.

Unique Panorama from Horchheim to Vallendar.

English Church Service in the Hotel.

Management: K. A. KARCHER.

COBLENCE—Continued on next page.

COBLENCE—*Continued.*

PALAST-PARK HOTEL.

THE NEWEST AND MOST COMFORTABLE HOTEL, NEAREST THE STATION

Unique, quiet, open situation, with splendid view from each room. 3 minutes from Central Station. Electric Light. Steam Heating. Omnibus to all Trains.

Strictly Moderate Terms. — J. PIES PROPRIETOR.

RIESEN FÜRSTENHOF & ANCHOR

First Class, facing the Steamer Landing Stage.

THIS Famous Hotel, known as the "Giant," has been thoroughly reconstructed and renovated. Every modern comfort and convenience. Views up and down the Rhine from all rooms. Restaurant on Rhine Terrace. Facing the Fortress of Ehrenbreitstein. Moderate prices. Omnibus at all trains. Daily Concerts. Cook's Coupons.

J. HANSEN, Proprietor.

—H.R.H. The PRINCE OF WALES stayed here in March, 1913.—

COLOGNE (Rhine).—See page 448.

EXCELSIOR HOTEL.

—OPPOSITE CATHEDRAL.—

NEWLY BUILT. — *200 Rooms and Private Baths.*

Branch House of HOTEL BAUR au LAC, Zurich.

DOM-HOTEL

COLOGNE. Opposite the . . RAILWAY AND BOAT STATIONS.

Hotel du Nord

STRICTLY FIRST CLASS. Between the Cathedral and the Rhine.

Patronised by the Prince and Princess of Wales.

TABLE d'HOTE at 1 and 6 p.m.

TELEGRAPH AND POST OFFICES IN THE HOTEL.

ENGLISH CHURCH FROM JUNE 15th, 1879.

TRAVEL and HOTEL ENQUIRIES—See page xii.

COLOGNE—*Continued.*

COLOGNE—Continued on next page.

TRAVEL and HOTEL ENQUIRIES—See page xii.

COLOGNE—*Continued.*

Pension M. & C. MIDDENDORFF

Gilbachstrasse 11, formerly Engelbertstrasse 67II.

Situated in the best and quietest part of the City.

Own house with Garden and Balconies. Large airy rooms. Every comfort. Excellent cuisine.
Trams Nos. 20 and 18 from Central Station.
Highest references. Pension from Mks. 5. Pensionnaires received by the day. Tel. B 793.

COMO (Italy).—See page 541.

GRAND

HOTEL PLINIUS

– COMO. –

FIRST CLASS HOUSE.

On the border of the Lake, with Garden and Terraces. Modern comfort. Private suites with bath, etc.

Rooms from 3.50 frs. Inclusive Pension from 10 frs. Cook's Office close to the Hotel. — **J. COSTA, Manager.**

Branch House :—

Villa d'Este, Cernobbio.

COMO (Cernobbio).—See page 541.

GRAND HOTEL VILLA D'ESTE

GOLF LINKS. **& REINE d'ANGLETERRE.**

FIRST CLASS HOTEL, with extensive and most beautiful Park and Gardens, on the border of the Lake. Formerly the residence of H.M. Queen Caroline of England and H.M. the late Empress of Russia. **Centre of excursions in the Lakes District.** Every modern comfort. Lawn Tennis. Roller Skating Rink. English Chaplain. English Doctor. Post and Telegraph. **Private Suites with Baths, etc. Lifts, Electric Light, and Central Heating throughout. International Telephone.** American Bar. Perfect Sanitary arrangements. Motor Garage. Moderate charges. Pension. Telegraphic address: VILLAESTE CERNOBBIO.

Auto-Car meets every train at COMO and Steamers at CERNOBBIO.

— **T. DOMBRE, Manager.** —

SPRINGS AND AUTUMNS ON THE LAKE OF COMO.

HOTEL REINE OLGA

CERNOBBIO. Close to Villa d'Este.

THE most charming stopping and resting place. On the border of the Lake. Highly recommended. Full South. Comfortable Family Hotel. Spacious Bedrooms. All modern comfort. Good table. Large and shaded Garden. Pensions from 7 to 11. Open all the year round. Cook's Coupons. Post, Telegraph, and Telephone in the Hotel. Motor Garage. Motor Launch. Roller Skating Rink. **Central Heating.** — **N. MORO, Proprietor and Manager.**

COPENHAGEN.—See page 648, Special Edition

COPENHAGEN.

HOTEL D'ANGLETERRE.

Beautiful open location in the most select part of the Town and right opposite the Royal Opera.

LEADING HOTEL IN COPENHAGEN.

Entirely re-built and re-furnished by Messrs. Waring & Gillow, of London.

All Suites with Private Baths and Toilet.

MAGNIFICENT RESTAURANT AND GRILL ROOM OPEN TO NON-RESIDENTS.

Five o'clock Tea served in the Palm Court. Beautiful Lounge.

Single Bedrooms from **4 Kr.** including **Attendance, Electric Light,** and **Central Heating.**

Omnibus at the Station & Landing Pier. Dark Room. | Telegrams: "ANGLETERRE. COPENHAGEN"

COPENHAGEN.

HOTEL COSMOPOLITE KONGENS NYTORV

FIRST CLASS HOTEL. NEWLY BUILT.

150 Elegantly Furnished Rooms. Electric light. Elevator.

CENTRAL HEATING.

Grand Dining Saloon connected with a Beautiful Palm Garden.

SPECIAL COSY DRAWING ROOM FOR LADIES.

Only Fireproof Hotel in Copenhagen. Moderate Prices.

THE MANAGEMENT.

HOTEL DAGMAR COPENHAGEN. V.

FIRST CLASS HOTEL. 75 elegantly furnished rooms with all modern comfort. Beautiful large Restaurant and Café. Reading and Conversation Rooms. Situation: most fashionable part of Copenhagen, overlooking the Boulevard. Excellent French Cooking.

All modern comforts.

JULIUS NIELSEN, Proprietor.

THE CENTRAL HOTEL

Raadhuspladsen 16. Copenhagen B. Best Position. 2 Minutes from Railway Station.

60 Rooms from **Kr. 2**, including Electric Light and Central Heating.

Telephones: H 1037 and 5087. Telegraphic address: Centralhotel. Telephone in each room. Lift.

Restaurant. | Breakfast .... **Kr. 1,00.** Lunch .... „ **1,50.** | Dinner ...... **Kr. 2—3,50.** Pension from ... **Kr. 7,00.** | **POUL MOLLER. Proprietor.**

CORTINA d'AMPEZZO—Continued on next page.

CREFELD (Germany).—See page 471.

CUXHAVEN (North Sea Bathing Place) Germany.— See page 471.

(Canton des Grisons.) DAVOS PLATZ. (Switzerland).— See page 515.

TRAVEL and HOTEL ENQUIRIES—See page xii.

DAVOS PLATZ—*Continued.*

(France). DAX (Landes, France).—**See page 397.**

DIEPPE (France).—See page 398.

TRAVEL and HOTEL ENQUIRIES—See page xii.

DIJON (France).—See page 398.

DIJON

The Right Place to break the Journey on your way to Switzerland, Italy, or the Riviera. . . .

FIRST CLASS. **Hotel de la Cloche** UP-TO-DATE.

Hotel Moderne & du Jura Near the Station.

Bradshaw's Guide.

TRAVEL ENQUIRY DEPARTMENT.—This Department has proved of efficient service both to hotel-keepers and the travelling public. Prospectuses of clients whose announcements appear in Bradshaw's Guide are kept for inspection or distribution at the Company's Offices in London, Liverpool, Manchester, Glasgow, and Dublin. For further particulars see page xii.

DINANT-sur-Meuse (Belgium).—See page 432.

★HOTEL DES POSTES★

Opposite the Railway Station and Landing Place of Steamers.

VERY FIRST CLASS HOTEL.

IN the finest situation of the town, on the banks of the Meuse, with Terraces, Balconies, Reading Room, Smoking Room, Telephone. Electric Light in all the Rooms. Carriages for Excursions. Omnibus at all Trains and Steamers. Pension from **8 francs** per day.

Restaurant à la Carte. Auto-Garage.

Motor Cars for Hire.

Mme. Vve. A. DEGRAA, Proprietress.

✱ HOTEL DE LA TETE D'OR. ✱

MOUSSOUX-DISIERE, Proprietor.

VERY FIRST CLASS HOUSE, situated Grand Place, opposite the Landing Stage, in the most agreeable part of the town. Large picturesque Garden belonging to the Hotel. Apartments with Balconies. Reading Room, Smoking Room. Carriages for Excursions. Omnibus meets all Trains and Steamers. Covered shelter for Cycles and Motor-Cars. Pension from **8 frs.**

Electric Light. Telephone 24.

Dinant-sur-Meuse, BELGIUM.

VERY COMFORTABLE.

Largely patronised by English people.

Baths. Electric Light.

Recommended.

Rooms from 2 fr. Pension from 6 fr.

DINARD (near St. Malo), France.—See page 398.

DINARD—NEAR ST. MALO.

12 **Hours from London, via Southampton.** The most fashionable Sea-bathing place in the West of France. English Church, Club, Tennis, Golf. Every facility for education, etc. Illustrated Guide sent on receipt of P.O. or stamps for one shilling, For further particulars about Dinard, Dinan, St. Enogat, St. Briac, St, Lunaire, Paramé, apply to **JULES BOUTIN, Banker and House Agent, Dinard.**
All persons travelling in Brittany and Normandy should supply themselves with "Boutin's Travellers' Cheques," which are cashed in the principal Hotels.

WINTER and SUMMER . Resort for Golfers .

DINARD Golf Links

ONE OF THE BEST GOLF LINKS ON THE CONTINENT.

HOTEL des PANORAMAS & du GOLF.

(The only Hotel on the Links).

Entirely Renovated. Under the direction of the Golf Club. Will be open in June.

"COTE d'EMERAUDE." (DINARD).

NOUVEL HOTEL DE PROVENCE ET D'ANGLETERRE.

Every modern Comfort. **Electric Light.**

Special terms for a long stay. Open all the year round. Baths in the Hotel.

Telegraphic Address: Hotel Provence-Dinard. ✱ **A. JOUBERT, Proprietor.**

HOTEL des TERRASSES.

Open from 1st of May.

Incomparable position on the Sea front. Magnificent view. Private bath rooms.

RESTAURANT. *Telegram Address: Manager, Terrasses Hotel.* **New Management.**

DONAUESCHINGEN (Germany).—See page 457.

DONAUESCHINGEN

2,296 feet above Sea level.

BRINE BATH AND HEALTH RESORT. SALINE SPRINGS.

With Municipal Bathing Establishment. — Electric Baths. — Carbonic Acid Baths. Inhalatorium. Medicinal Baths of every description. Magnificent Forests with well kept Promenades. — Residence of the Prince of Fürstenberg. — Splendid Park. **Hunting ground of the German Emperor.** Princely Library. Collection of Pictures and Engravings. Fürstl. Fürstenberg Brewery. Information and Prospectus on application to the **VERKEHRS-VEREIN, I.**

HOTEL z. SCHUTZEN

BRINE BATHS IN THE HOTEL.

FIRST Class old established Hotel and Kurhaus in its own large park, 3 minutes from the Station. Every modern comfort. Central Heating. Summer and Winter Pension, the latter at reduced prices. Good Fishing and Shooting. Highly recommended for its comfort and moderate charges. GARAGE. — **J. BURI, Proprietor.**

DOVER.—See pages 1092-1094.

DREI AEHREN (Germany).—See page 472.

DRESDEN.—See page 472.

DRESDEN—Continued on next page

DRESDEN—*Continued.*

Savoy Hotel.

Patronized by H.R.H. the Princess of Wales, now H.M. Queen Mary of England.

HIGH CLASS MODERN HOTEL, in the finest position in Dresden. Two minutes from Central Station. Fashionable quarter. Trams in all directions. Great comfort. Apartments with Bath. Strictly moderate tariff. Good Rooms from **3 Marks.** Pension from **6 Marks.** First rate Cuisine. Highly recommended to English and Americans for a stay or a visit.

Manager: CHARLES SCHMITT.

THE Grand Union Hotel

BISMARK SQUARE, CLOSE TO CENTRAL STATION.

ENTIRELY RENEWED 1909-10. Magnificent high class English family establishment. **"A home away from home."** Situated in the finest and quietest part of the town (the English quarter). **Latest improvements. Suites with Bath.** Garden. Lift. Central heating. Moderate charges. Special terms for a stay. Close to English Church.

A. BECKER-LANDRY,

formerly manager of the Hotel Bristol, Naples, and Excelsior Palace, Palermo.

BRANCH HOUSES:

THE METROPOLE & VICTORIA, Chamonix; HOTEL ST. GOTHARD, Lugano.

HOTEL CONTINENTAL

Exactly facing the chief exit of the Central Station.

FIRST CLASS HOTEL, recently ENLARGED and EQUIPPED with every modern comfort.

This Hotel can be confidently recommended to English and Americans.

The terms are strictly moderate and everything is up-to-date. Apartments and Single Rooms with bath and toilet. Very fine garden. Position unique and very quiet. Two Electric Lifts. Heated throughout.

Rooms from 3 M. and Pension from 8 M. ED. POSSEL, Manager.

HOTEL BRISTOL.

FIRST CLASS, situated on the Bismark Square, the healthiest and finest part of Dresden.

Highly recommended by English and American Families. Real English Home comfort.

EVERY MODERN COMFORT. — MODERATE TERMS. — PENSION.

TRAVEL and HOTEL ENQUIRIES—See page xii.

DRESDEN—*Continued.*

HOTEL KAISER WILHELM.

Wiener Platz. Central Position.

FIRST Class Hotel, specially adapted to the requirements of English visitors to Dresden. Excellent Cuisine, with pension terms arranged so that visitors may take their meals at the hours most convenient to themselves. Perfect Sanitation. Central Heating. Large Beautiful Garden. — **ALBIN PANSDORF** **Purveyor to the Court.**

HOTEL "STADT GOTHA"

FIRST CLASS RESTAURANT—WINE MERCHANTS.

SITUATED in the most central and convenient part of the town—close to the King's Palace, Opera House, Picture Gallery, Museum, etc. A most comfortable and old established moderate Hotel, excellent Cuisine. **Rooms from 2 Marks 50.** **A. KÖGEL, Proprietor** (Court Purveyor).

DRESDEN.

In quietest position close to the Central Station. Select Family Hotel, equipped with all modern and hygienic comfort.

Westminster Hotel.

HOT and COLD WATER supply in all Bed Rooms.
Self-contained Apartments with Private Baths.
MAGNIFICENT HALL. — MODERATE TERMS.

CARLTON HOTEL

1, Bismarck Platz. — Quiet position close to Central Station. First Class with every modern comfort. 70 Rooms. Rooms from **Mks. 2.50.** Pension from **6 Mks.** **GUSTAVE HARTIG, Propr.**

HOTEL STADT ROM.

NEUMARKT, 10.

Comfortable Family and Commercial Hotel in Central Position, entirely renovated. Elegant lofty Rooms. Electric Light. Lift. Central Heating. Large Restaurant.
Rooms from Mks. 1.50 to Mks. 6. **Propr. FRITZ LOOS.**

GRAND HOTEL REICHSPOST

DRESDEN-A.

Magnificent NEW BUILDING in CENTRAL POSITION. ∴ ∴ FIRST CLASS. ∴ EVERY COMFORT. ROOMS including BREAKFAST from 3.50 Marks.

COMFORTABLE RESTAURANT. EXCELLENT COOKING. Close proximity to the MUSEUMS, the ROYAL THEATRE, the CASTLE. Telephone No. 215.

Hotel de Saxe

DRESDEN-A. Prager Strasse, 56.

Telephone No. 18742. Modern House. Fitted Up-to-date. Telephone on each floor. Fine large rooms looking on to the street. Garden. Rooms with baths, partitioned. Apartments for Families. Reading and Writing Rooms. Acknowledged good Kitchen.
Full Pension from 6 M. (at least 3 days stay). — **MAX SCHLEGEL, Proprietor.**

DRESDEN—Continued on next page

DRESDEN—*Continued.*

DURRHEIM (Germany).—See page 457.

DUSSELDORF.—See page 473.

EASTBOURNE.—See page 1095.

TRAVEL and HOTEL ENQUIRIES—See page xii.

EMS BAD (Germany).—See page 474.

Bad EMS (English Church * Fishing * Shooting * Tennis.)

HOTEL d'ANGLETERRE

("ENGLISCHER HOF")

AND

PARK VILLA

First Class in every respect. Largely improved during the past years, especially in the Winter 1912 - 1913.

LATEST CREATIONS:

Central Hot Water Heating, Suites and Rooms with connecting bathroom and toilet, Rooms with cold and hot running water.

Pleasant airy situation, directly opposite Royal Baths and the shady Ems Park.

INHALING INSTITUTION CLOSE BY.

PRIVATE GARDENS, in which air and rest cures may be taken, and in which meals can be served. Theatre, Tennis & Croquet Grounds close to Hotel. Own Trout Fishing.

Splendid Hall, Drawing, Music, Reading, and Smoking Rooms. Table d'Hote Room and fine **Restaurant** LATE DINNER served in both.

Electric Light. Vacuum Cleaner. Lift. Perfect Sanitary arrangements.

Omnibus at Station. Motor Car to let. Auto Garage.

The "Park Villa"

"an ideal home for families."

Stands in its own gardens, within a two minutes' walk from the Hotel.

Special Feature: Self contained suites with private Bath and Toilet.

Apply for illustrated Prospectus to the Proprietor :— **F. SCHMITT.**

TRAVEL and HOTEL ENQUIRIES—See page xii.

EMS BAD—Continued on next page

EMS BAD—*Continued.*

ENGELBERG (Switzerland).—See page 516.

TRAVEL and HOTEL ENQUIRIES—See page xli.

ENGELBERG—*Continued.*

ENGELBERG—Continued on next page.

ETRETAT (Seine Inférieure, France).—See page 399.

THE GOLF HOTELS

"ROCHES BLANCHES" AND "LA PLAGE"

MOST UP-TO-DATE.

Electricity.

The only Hotel having a Lift.

MODERATE TERMS.

Central Heating.

Open all the year.

Pension from 10 Frs.

PRIVATE BATH ROOMS

REGULAR MOTOR BUS SERVICE between the "Hotels" and the Steamer at Havre. Through Tickets, London—Etretat. Telephone *38*.

HOTEL BLANQUET

ON THE SEA SHORE.

Pension from 12 francs 50 cmes. upward. House highly recommended.

HOTEL HAUVILLE AND RESTAURANT

ON THE SEA FRONT. QUITE NEAR GOLF LINKS. NEXT DOOR TO THE CASINO
120 Bedrooms and Private Apartments. Magnificent views of Sea, Cliffs, and Golf Link.
Pension from 10 fr. and upward. Modern Comfort. Electric Light. Telephone No. 5.
In Winter: Hotel Pension de France, Nice. — **J. MARTIN-BARRAT, Proprietor.**

EVIAN-LES-BAINS (France).—See page 399.

EVIAN

LAKE OF GENEVA, on the . . French Border, facing Ouchy.

SOURCE CACHAT, famous since the 18th century. Recommended by German, English, and French physicians for chronic gout, dyspepsia, neurasthenia, arterial hypertension, gall stones, renal calculus, and kindred ailments. The Etablissement ranks among the first in Europe. Annual export exceeds 13,000,000 bottles. Casino. Theatre. Golf Links. Lawn Tennis. Regatta, Motor Boats, etc. — **Train de Luxe from Paris.**

EVIAN-LES-BAINS—Continued on next page.

TRAVEL and HOTEL ENQUIRIES—See page xii.

FAIDO (Switzerland).—See page 516.

FELDBERG (Germany).—See page 457.

FINS-HAUTS (Switzerland).—See page 517.

FIONNAY (Val de Bagnes, Switzerland).—See page 526A.

TRAVEL and HOTEL ENQUIRIES—See page xii.

FLORENCE—*Continued.*

PENSION PLUCKNETT

Palazzo Ruspoli, Via dei Martelli 7 (close to the Cathedral), Florence.

FIRST CLASS ENGLISH PENSION, renovated, under New Management (Unrivalled Situation). Central, and near all tram lines. Lift, Central Heating, Electric Light, Bath, and Smoking Rooms. Certified Sanitation. Open all the year. PENSION from **7** to **10 francs,**

—— Recommended by the Travel Editor of the "Queen." ——

FOLKESTONE.—See pages 1092 and 1096-1097.

FONTAINEBLEAU (France).—See page 400.

Telephone: **195.** | **FONTAINEBLEAU.** | Telephone: **195.**

42, Avenue du Chemin de Fer.

Savoy Hotel & Restaurant

EVERY BEDROOM HAS A BATH ROOM OR A DRESSING ROOM ATTACHED.
RUNNING HOT AND COLD WATER. — **Inclusive terms.**

FRANKFORT-ON-THE-MAIN.—See page 475.

HOTEL IMPERIAL

HIGH CLASS FAMILY HOTEL,

Magnificently situated on the Promenade, opposite the Opera, (close to the Palmengarten).

Numerous Suites and . .
Rooms with private bath.

On the Kaiserplatz. 80 Private Bath Rooms. First Class throughout.

FRANKFURTER-HOF

GRAND HOTEL de FRANCFORT

Ritz-Restaurant with Garden Terrace.

FRANKFORT-ON-THE-MAIN—Continued on next page

FRANZENSBAD (Austria).—See page 496A.

The INCREASE in ENGLISH VISITORS ∴ ∴ from 1911 to 1912 amounted to— **45%**

The Cosmopolitan Health Resort.
. . . The Garden City. . . .

FRANZENSBAD

Approved by the Medical Profession as the Health Resort for:—

Women's Complaints, Sterility, Excessive Perspiration, Appendicitis, Myom, Diseases of the Blood and the Assimilation, Nervous Disorders, Rheumatism, Gout, Kidney Diseases, etc., etc.

Advantages: Iron Mineral Mud Deposits, unequalled in quality and quantity. Radio-active Spring for drinking cure. Natural Radium Emanatorium. Ferruginous Springs for Anæmia and Neurasthenia.

Diseases of the Heart, Weakness of the Heart, Disorders of the Valve, Cardiac Neurosis, Fatty Degeneration of the Heart. ARTERIOSCLREOSIS, etc., etc.

Advantages: Only natural Carbonic Acid Baths. The most perfect method on the Continent for individual graduation of the percentage of CO_2 and the temperature. Level ground (1,477 feet above Sea). Rontgen and Zander Institute. Electro-Cardiograph; Inhalatorium. Combination of Radium and Drinking Cures (the diuretic Natalie Spring, the aperient "Kalter Sprudel").

Radio-active CO_2 Gas baths as a specific against Sterility, Lassitude, as well as premature weakness ∴ ∴ ∴

(See also descriptive part of Guide).

Art ✶ Sport ✶ Society ✶ Tennis ✶ Golf ✶ Hunting ✶ Fishing, etc.

Season: May 1st to September 30th.

Illustrated Prospectus free on application to the— **BÜRGERMEISTER-AMT in FRANZENSBAD (Austria).**

Reached from London (via Hook of Holland) in 29¼ hours.
Reached from London (via Calais) in 30 hrs.

Reached from London (via Flushing) in 29¼ hours.
Reached from London (via Ostend) in 27 hrs.

TRAVEL and HOTEL ENQUIRIES—See page xii.

FREIBURG (im Breisgau, Baden).—See page 457.

FREIBURG—Continued on next page.

TRAVEL and HOTEL ENQUIRIES—See page xii.

FREIBURG—Continued on next page.

FREIBURG (im Breisgau, Baden)—*Continued.*

PENSION UNIVERS

CORNER of HILDA and URACHSTRASSE.

FIRST CLASS FAMILY PENSION in open, quiet position, close to the Forest. Near the **Station Wiehre, on the Höllental Railway.** Large sunny rooms. Every modern comfort. Central Heating. Excellent Cuisine. **Moderate Terms.** Best opportunities for Winter Sport. Telephone 344.

Prospectus on application from Bradshaw's Offices. O. MAYER-SARTORI.

Pension Minerva.

First Class Modern House in quiet and Central position, close the Station. Central Heating. Electric Light. Lift. Excellent Cuisine. Highly recommended to English and Americans. Proprietress: FRAU MEVI.

8, POST STRASSE, 8.

NEWLY BUILT. Family Hotel. NEWLY BUILT.

Hotel and Pension PRINZ HEINRICH

NEWLY OPENED. 41, Günterstal Strasse. NEWLY OPENED.

Comfortable Family Hotel and Pension, close to the Forest.
Fitted up with every modern convenience. Central Heating, etc.

Pension from **Mks. 4.50** to **Mks. 6.** Tel. 74. **Propr.: AUGUST SCHÖPPERLE.**

CAFÉ SCHANZ and Restaurant

Corner of Kaiser and Münster Strasse.

Most elegant and up to date Establishment. — Own First Class Confectionery. Five o'clock Tea. Concerts every afternoon and evening English daily and illustrated papers. Motor Cars of all kinds on hire. Telephone Nos. 25 and 66.

FREUDENSTADT (Germany).—See page 458

Hotel & Kurhaus Waldeck.

FIRST CLASS. ABSOLUTELY NEW BUILDING WITH EVERY MODERN COMFORT.

APARTMENTS WITH PRIVATE BATH. — CENTRAL HEATING.

French Cooking. Trout Fishing. Own Private Orchestra.

Proprietor: CARL LUZ.

TRAVEL and HOTEL ENQUIRIES—See page xii.

GARDONE-RIVIERA (Lago di Garda).—See page 544.

GARDONE-RIVIERA, Italy. On the Lake of Garda.
Season: 15th SEPTEMBER to 15th MAY.

GRAND HOTEL

Illustrated Prospectus gratis on application. — CHR. LUTZELSCHWAB.

Savoy Hotel.

LATEST HOTEL construction in Gardone, with every modern comfort. Finest and quietest position, 1 minute from Landing Stage, on the strand promenade. Highly recommended to English and American Families. Large private garden. Moderate terms. Open the whole year, Consumptives not admitted. — C. SCHUMACHER, New Proprietor

GARMISCH (Bavarian Highlands), Germany.—See page 477.

PARK HOTEL ALPENHOF.

FIRST CLASS MODERN HOUSE WITH EVERY COMFORT.
Rooms with Private Baths. Central Heating. Lijt. Garage. Summer and Winter Season.
Winter Sport. — Lawn Tennis. — Pension Arrangements.
Proprietor: H. KILIAN.

GARMISCH (BAVARIAN HIGHLANDS). Frequent Trains from Munich and Innsbruck.

FIRST CLASS ENGLISH HOTEL PENSION

VILLA BETHELL.

. . Beautiful . . Summer Resort. Lovely scenery.

Centre of district for Excursions to Royal Bavarian Castles. Easily reached, half-hour Motor from Ammergau.
Frequent trains from Munich. — Moderate Terms. — First Class Winter Sports.
Address: Mrs. H. SLINGSBY BETHELL. Winter—HOTEL BETHELL, ROME.

BADERSEE, Near Garmisch-Partenkirchen.—See page 477.

"ALPENHOTEL BADER-SEE."

MOUNTAIN AIR-CURE RESORT, 2,625 feet above Sea level. Modern Family Hotel, specially recommended for after cure. Electric Light and Central Heating. Reading and Smoking Rooms, etc. Excellent cooking and renowned cellar. Post and Telegraph at the Hotel. Telephone No. 37 Garmisch. Pension from 7 M. Motor 'bus to Garmisch-Partenkirchen 8 times daily. ENGLISH SPOKEN. — *Prospectus on application to the Proprietor:* GUSTAV SCHUH.

TRAVEL and HOTEL ENQUIRIES—See page xii.

BAD-GASTEIN (Austria).—See page 497.

BAD GASTEIN—Continued on next page.

BAD GASTEIN.
GRAND HOTEL GASTEINER HOF

OWN THERMAL BATHS.

First Class Modern Hotel.

Proprietors: WINDISCHBAUER BROTHERS.

GENEVA (Switzerland).—See page 517.

GRAND HOTEL NATIONAL.

FIRST CLASS.

THE only Hotel with large Garden on the shore of the Lake. Splendid view of Mont Blanc and the Alps.

Restaurant in the open air.

Concert twice daily.

Apartments with Bathrooms.

Garage for Automobiles.

Dark Room for Photographers.

Hotel MÉTROPOLE et Geneva PALACE

FIRST CLASS.

Opposite the "Jardin Anglais." The nearest to Station for Chamonix. Close to the Steamboat Landing Place. Extensive view on the Lake and Juras. — Entirely renewed and refurnished. Numerous apartments with Bath Toilette. Vacuum Cleaner.

Moderate Prices. OPEN ALL THE YEAR ROUND.

GRAND HOTEL DES BERGUES

FIRST CLASS.

Near Steamboat Landing Place and next to English Church. Central situation, the finest of the Town. Opposite the Island of J. J. Rousseau. View of Mont Blanc. American Heating throughout. Winter Garden. Dark Room for Photographers, Garage and Accessories for Automobiles,

OPEN ALL THE YEAR ROUND.

TRAVEL and HOTEL ENQUIRIES—See page xii.

GENEVA (Switzerland)—*Continued.*

(GENEVA—Continued on next page

GENEVA (Switzerland)—*Continued.*

TRAVEL and HOTEL ENQUIRIES—See page xii.

GENEVA—Continued on next page.

GENEVA—*Continued.*

GOLAY SONS and STAHL, GOLAY-LERESCHE & SONS

31, QUAI DES BERGUES. Established 1837.

Manufacturers of Watches and Jewelry. Dealers in Diamonds. and Precious Stones.

Branch House in Paris: 239, Rue St. Honorée (Place Vendôme), Paris.

GRAND PHARMACIE FINCK.

English and American Chemist.

26, Rue du Mont Blanc; 2, Rue Pradier. Near the Railway Station.

LARGEST stock in Switzerland of English and American Patent Medicines. Special Shop over the Pharmacy for all kinds of Surgical appliances. India Rubber goods, etc. "à La Croix Rouge." HIGH CLASS CHEMIST. ENGLISH ASSISTANTS.

TOURIST OFFICE. — FORWARDING AGENCY.

Storage. Furniture Removers. Railway Tickets.

C. H. ACKERMANN, GENEVA,

1, Rue d'Italie. Switzerland.

AGENTS of THE HAMBURG AMERICAN LINE and SLEEPING CARS.

BRADSHAW'S CONTINENTAL GUIDE

SPECIAL EDITION 3/6

including the following matter in addition to the information contained in the 2/- Book:—

Routes through FRANCE, SWITZERLAND, ITALY, and GERMANY,

AN ITINERARY OF THE ITALIAN LAKES,

Condensed Descriptions of the Principal Towns, etc., in the following Countries:

Algeria	Egypt	Lapland	Norway	Sweden
Bulgaria	Finland	Holy Land	Rumania	Tunis
Cyprus	Greece	Levant	Russia	Turkey in Europe
Denmark	Iceland	Morocco	Servia	

With a Vocabulary in English, French, German, and Italian.

Also Maps of Europe, Switzerland, and the Rhine, and Plans of the following Cities:

Amsterdam	Cologne	Florence	Madrid	†Rome
Antwerp	Constantinople	Geneva	Marseilles	†St. Petersburg
†Berlin	Copenhagen	Hamburg	Milan	Stockholm
Brussels	Dresden	Leipsic	Naples	Turin
†Budapest	Frankfort-on-the-Main	Lisbon	Palermo	Venice
Christiania		Lyons	†Paris	†Vienna

For the convenience of persons using the 2/- Continental Guide, SINGLE Plans of the above towns (as sold with the 3/6 edition) will be forwarded upon receipt of stamps (3d.), except towns marked † when stamps (6d.) must be sent.

Address: BRADSHAW HOUSE, SURREY STREET, STRAND, W.C.

TRAVEL and HOTEL ENQUIRIES—See page xii.

GENOA.—See page 545.

BRISTOL HOTEL.

NEW.

HIGH CLASS IN EVERY RESPECT.

Patronised by Royalty.

Centrally located in the Magnificent Via XX Settembre, the Finest part of the town.

SUPERIOR RESTAURANT SERVICE also open to non-residents.

SAVOY HOTEL

Entirely renovated with the latest comfort.

Opposite the Railway Station, and close to Landing Pier and Custom House. (NO SMOKE OR NOISE FROM THE TRAINS.)

Patronised by H. M. the Empress Frederic and H. R. H. Princess Beatrix of Battenberg, H. M. the Queen of Holland, Their R. H. Prince and Princess Henry of Prussia, The Swiss President during his official visit to Genoa, The King of Saxony, H.M. the Queen Carola of Saxony, H.R.H. Prince Johann George of Saxony, The Maharajah of Burwen, the Crown Prince of Persia etc., etc.

HOTEL DE LONDRES

First Class. Moderate Terms. Sunny Position.

OPPOSITE CENTRAL RAILWAY STATION & CLOSE TO LANDING PIER.

Main Street paved with noiseless Asphalt. Luggage stored Free.

Both Hotels are close to the Garage International, one of the best of the Littoral.

GENOA—Continued on next page.

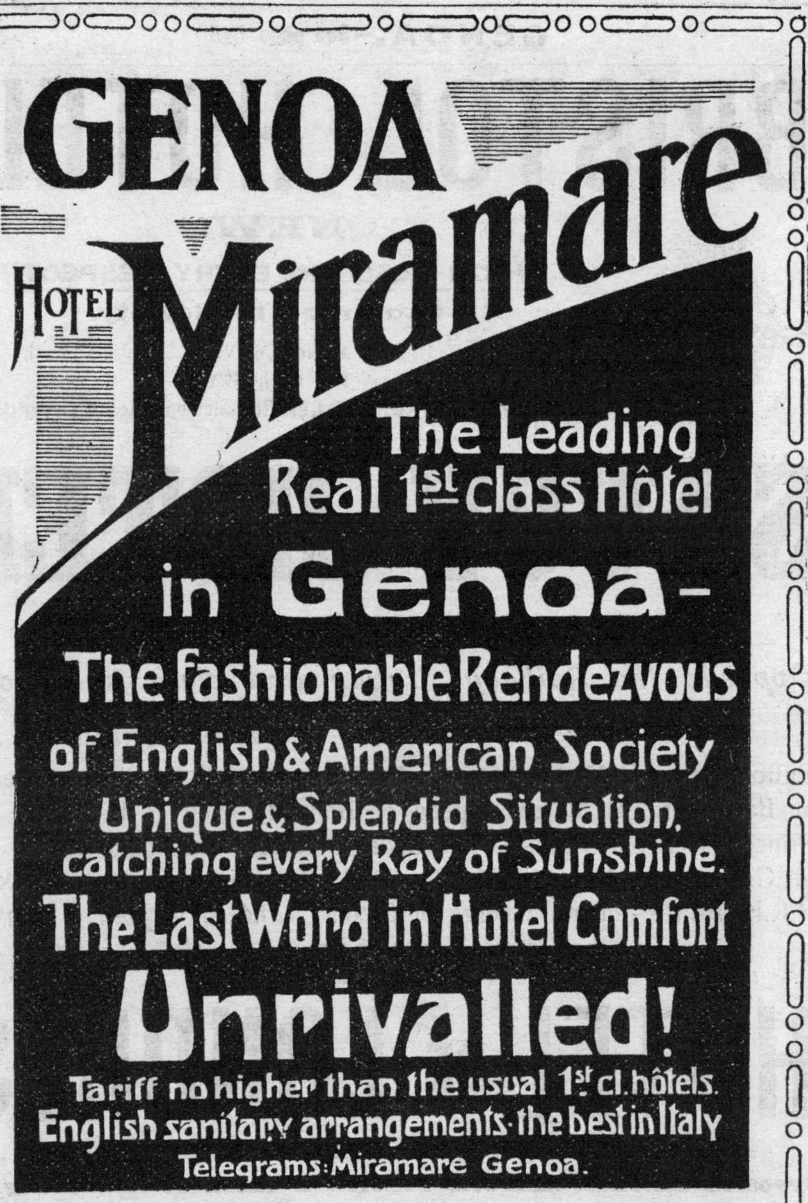

TRAVEL and HOTEL ENQUIRIES—See page xii.

GENOA—*Continued.*

EDEN PALACE HOTEL

(HOTEL DU PARC.)

THE ONLY QUIET POSITION OF THE TOWN.

5 minutes from Station and Harbour by Hotel Autobus.

Electric Light. Lift. Central Heating. Standing in a magnificent Park.

Suites of Private Apartments, with Bath Rooms. American Bar.

HOTEL VICTORIA.

PIAZZA ANNUNZIATA

COMPLETELY redecorated and enlarged by 30 rooms. Specially recommended to families. Every modern comfort. Lift. Central Heating. Apartments and Single Rooms with Baths. Warm and Cold Water in all rooms. Moderate Terms. — **D. MELANO, Proprietor.**

GRAND HOTEL de GÊNES

GENOVA.

Full South. In the best situation facing the Opera House. Furnished with every modern comfort. Rooms and suites with bath. Quiet rooms. Restaurant, Garage.

G. and R. BONERA, Proprietors and Managers.

BRITANNIA HOTEL. GENOA.

FIRST CLASS HOTEL. Patronised by English and Americans. Moderate terms. Opposite the Station and close to the Landing Piers. Open all the year round. Lift. Electric Light. Steam Heating. Bathrooms on every floor. Restaurant. Full pension.

HOTEL SMITH ET PENSION

ENGLISH HOUSE. PIAZZA CARICAMENTO.

Full view of the Sea. Table d'Hote. Restaurant. Lift. Central Heating and Electric Light in every Room. Moderate and inclusive terms from 8 Frs. a day. Rooms 2.50—4 Frs., including Light and Heating. — Omnibus at the Station.

SMITH BROTHERS, Proprietors and Managers.

HOTEL DE FRANCE ET RUSSIE. Genoa.

Good Family Hotel, frequented by Americans, English, and Netherlanders, commanding fine views on the Harbour, and close to the Steam-ship AGENTS.

All modern comfort.

Good French Cooking. — Omnibus meets all Trains and Steamers (Cook's Coupons).

CERESIO & BADANELLI, Proprietors.

GENOA—Continued on next page.

GENOA—*Continued.*

GENOA.

Hotel Fürstenhof-Principe

The best equipped First Class Hotel in close proximity to the Central Station. No bus required. Quiet rooms with view of the Sea.

Hotel Continental

In the Centre of the Town, next to Cook's and the North German Lloyd. Up-to-date Comforts.

Both Hotels have rooms with hot and cold water supply. TARIFF: Rooms from **4** frs., with bath from **8** frs.

HOTEL HELVETIA

(**Piazza Annunziata.** *No fare from Station.*)

A Comfortable, well kept Swiss Family House at a reasonable tariff. Most Central Position, in close proximity to the Station. Recommended to English and American families. Lift, Electric Light, Central Heating, Baths. Rooms from **fr. 2.50,** Breakfast with honey, **fr. 1.25,** Lunch **2.50,** Dinner **3.50,** Moderate Pension terms. Cook's Coupons accepted. English spoken.

Garage. — Ask for Omnibus. — **Swiss Proprietor.**

GERSAU (Lac IV Cantons), Switzerland.—See page 519.

HOTEL ET PENSION MÜLLER.

FINE POSITION ON THE LAKE. Bathing. Fishing. Mild climate. Large shady Garden. Well recommended as a Family Hotel. Moderate charges. **Pension from Frs. 8.** Motor Screw Boat. Carriages. Lawn Tennis. Hydaulic Lift. Electric Light in every Room. Private Apartments and Baths. 120 Rooms.

ALB. MÜLLER, Proprietor.

GIBRALTAR.—See page 569.

Bristol Hotel

Situated in a most healthy and aristocratic locality.
Only Hotel with full South aspect, and a Garden for its visitors.
Perfect Sanitary conditions in Hotel and in the City.
Splendid view of surroundings from top terraces of Hotel.
Telegraphic Address: "BRISTOL," Gibraltar.

GIESSBACH (Lake of Brienz, Switzerland).—See page 519.

GIESSBACH-FALLS

—LAKE OF BRIENZ— Between Interlaken & Lucerne. ∴ 20 Steamers every day ∴

SUMMER RESORT, 2,360 above sea level.

Grand Hotel, Hotel Kurhaus and Pension Beau-Site.

with all modern comfort. Delightfully situated, sheltered from the wind and free from dust. Extensive private grounds and adjacent fir woods. Great number of walks and Excursions. Orchestra, Tennis, Post, Telegraph and Railway Office. English Service. Illumination of the celebrated Cascades every evening.

J. STROHL, Manager.

GLASGOW.—See page 1097.

TRAVEL and HOTEL ENQUIRIES—See page xii.

GOTHA (Germany).—See page 478.

GOTHA.

Schloss Hotel

FIRST CLASS. Suites with Private Baths.

Splendid Hall (Lounge) and Public Rooms. Fine Restaurant. Hot and cold running water in every room. Own large Garden. The Hotel answers all sanitary and modern requirements.

Managed by the Proprietor: M. O. SCHMID.

GOTHENBURG (Sweden).—See page 641, Special Edition.

GOTHENBURG.

GRAND HOTEL HAGLUND

Near the Railway Station.

LARGEST and LEADING HOTEL. Patronised by English and American tourists. Entirely renovated and under new management. Apartments and single rooms with private baths. New smoking lounge. Ladies' drawing room. Magnificent Palm Court. Hot and cold water supply throughout. Central Heating. **Restaurant and Grill Room.**

Rooms from Kr. 3.50. *Telegraphic Address:*— **GRAND.**

HOTEL GOTA KALLARE (Under same Management.)

Commercial House in the Business Centre. Comfortable Rooms.

Restaurant. Moderate. **Rooms from Kr. 3.** Swedish Cooking.

Telegraphic Address:— **Gota Kallare.** —— **E. HAGLUND, Manager.**

HOTEL EGGERS GOTHENBURG.

THE BEST patronised First Class Hotel, in central position, facing the Botanical Garden. 100 Rooms and Salons. Apartments and Single Rooms with Bath. Hot and Cold Water supply and Telephone in every Room. Large Restaurant and Open air Terrace. Well renowned German and French Cooking. — **AXEL EGGERS, Proprietor.**

GRANADA (Spain).—See page 570.

The New Alhambra Palace Hotel and CASINO.

GRANADA. ——UP TO DATE HOTEL—— GRANADA.

Overlooking the Valley and Sierra Nevada.

250 rooms with Bath. — Inclusive terms from 20 pesetas upwards.

GRASSE (Near Cannes).—See page 400.

Grand Hotel.

FIRST CLASS FAMILY HOTEL.

FINEST and HEALTHIEST SITUATION, 1,150 feet altitude. Splendid view of valley, mountains, and sea. Bracing air, yet sheltered. Central heating. Lift. Electric light. Suites with bath. Famous Restaurant. Afternoon tea. Concerts. Open 15th Oct. till June.
Inclusive terms from Francs 12.50. H. ROST, Proprietor.

TRAVEL and HOTEL ENQUIRIES—See page xii.

TRAVEL and HOTEL ENQUIRIES—See page xii.

TRAVEL and HOTEL ENQUIRIES—See page xii.

HAMBURG.—See page 478.

HAMBURG—Continued on next page

HAMBURG—*Continued.*

TRAVEL and HOTEL ENQUIRIES—See page xii.

HAMBURG—*Continued.*

HAMBURG—Continued on next page.

TRAVEL and HOTEL ENQUIRIES—See page xii.

HANOVER—Continued on next page.

HARDELOT.—See page 401.

HARROGATE.—See page 1092 & 1098.

TRAVEL and HOTEL ENQUIRIES—See page xii.

HEIDELBERG (Germany).—See page 480.

HOTEL PRINZ CARL.

∴ **FIRST CLASS.** ∴

FINEST SITUATION AT FOOT OF THE CASTLE AND FUNICULAR RAILWAY.

SUITES with BATH and W.C. ✱ **Auto Garage.**
PAUL GÄRTNER.

HEIDELBERG.

SCHLOSS HOTELS

First Class Family Hotels. Unique position next to the Castle ruins.

SPLENDID VIEW. — ROOMS and SUITES with BATH and TOILET
Garage with latest improvements. Automobile and Porter at the Station.

HOTEL VICTORIA

FIRST CLASS. Entirely renovated and enlarged.

Apartments with Baths. Big Terrace and RESTAURANT. Garden. Concerts. Garage.
Specially recommended to English and American travellers.

H. MÜLLER and F. PIGUERON, Proprietors.

HOTEL DE L'EUROPE.

HEIDELBERG.

Thoroughly First Class and most Up-to-Date. All latest comforts and luxury. The position of the EUROPE in its own Park is the finest in town and near Station. Specially frequented by the élite of English and American Society. — **F. GABLER, Propr.**

HEIDELBERG.

GRAND HOTEL

FIRST CLASS FAMILY HOTEL.

NEAR TOWN PARK AND STATION.

With fine Garden and Terraces. Fitted up with every modern comfort and luxury.
Suites with Baths. Frequented by Americans.

SCHAEFER & MICHEL, Proprietors.

TRAVEL and HOTEL ENQUIRIES—See page xii.

HEIDELBERG—*Continued.*

TRAVEL and HOTEL ENQUIRIES—See page xii.

HOSPENTHAL (Switzerland).—See page 512.

HYERES (Var—France).—See page 401.

HYERES—Continued on next page

HYERES—*Continued.*

Le Golf Hotel

IN an Extensive Pine Park, bordering own Golf Links, with splendid view over Mountains, Sea, and Islands. 250 Rooms. All public Rooms full south. Electric Light. Lifts. Central Heating. Suites with Private Baths and Toilettes. Afternoon Tea-Concerts. Garage and Boxes. Three Tennis Courts. **Six full-size Croquet Lawns.** Motor-Bus to all trains. New Golf Club House. — Sole Proprietor of the Hyères Golf Links (18 holes).

The GOLF HOTEL, BEAUVALLON s/MER, is under the same Management.

Hyeres, Cote d'Azur.

LE GRAND HOTEL (& ILES D'OR).

By Motor-Bus 3 Minutes from Railway Station.

(Branch House of the Gd. Hotel Louvre and Paix of Marseilles).

ENTIRELY Renovated, a New Hall and New Drawing and Music Room have been added (in 1911). Elevated and sheltered position; fine Sea view. Large Garden and Tennis. English and French Billiards. Electricity. Central Heating. Garage. Single and Double Rooms with Bath attached. **Pension Terms from 10 frs.** (Regime). All Public Rooms full South. Auto to Costebelle Golf Links and Croquet.

Owners: L. ECHENARD-NEUSCHWANDER. — Manager: FORNALLAZ-SPEAK.

GRAND HOTEL DES PALMIERS

HYÈRES.

FIRST Class Hotel of universal reputation. Most healthy and beautiful; central position, near the English Church, free from noise and dust, and protected from cold winds. Surrounded by delightful gardens and fine avenues. All the rooms are sunny and provided with large balconies, enjoying splendid view over Mountains, Sea, and Islands. **Entirely renovated, 1912.** Central Heating and Electricity in all the rooms. Suites with Bath and W.C. New enlarged Hall. English Billiards. Perfect Sanitation. Garage. Tennis. Afternoon Teas.

Under the personal management of the New Proprietor E. GLOGG-MAILLÉ.

HYERES.

REGINA HESPERIDES HOTEL.

Recommended by the Travel Editor of the "Queen" and Medical Press for its comfort and most moderate Pension Terms.

First Class Family Hotel, conveniently situated. Elevated, on the hill. Large Private Garden. Opposite English and French Church. Perfect Sanitation. Pension Terms from £2 per Week, reduced prices in October—November. — *Telegraphic Address:* **"Hesperides, Hyères."**

BERTRAND VIDAL, Proprietor.

Chateaubriand & Britannique Hotel.

ENTIRELY RENOVATED.

SITUATED in the most sheltered part of Hyères. Enjoying a splendid view over the Sea and the Islands. Large Park and Private Garden. Only ten minutes walk from the Golf Links. Electric Light and Central Heating throughout. Lift. — **P. ROBIN, Proprietor.**

TRAVEL and HOTEL ENQUIRIES—See page xii.

HYÈRES—*Continued.*

GD. HOTEL VICTORIA-AMBASSADEURS

Centrally situated; full South. ENTIRELY RENOVATED IN 1911.

Central Heating and Electric Light throughout. Dressing rooms attached to every room. **Pension terms from 8 frs. Excellent Cooking. Mmes. LANDOT-DECK, Managing Proprietors.**
In Summer: Hotel Mont Blanc, Argentieres, Hte. Savoie.

THE ENGLISH BANK—HYÈRES.

(Correspondent of all the principal English and American Banks).

House and Estate Agency,
Correspondent for
Messrs. Thos. Cook & Son.
J. HOOK, Director.

*

CIRCULATING LIBRARY.

BRITISH VICE-CONSULATE.

SAN SALVADOUR (Var) near Hyeres.—**See page 402.**

SAN SALVADOUR (Var) On the French Riviera. Between Marseilles and Nice (near Hyères). The most Sunny Sea Side Resort. — The Healthiest Climate. Lithia Water Springs. Thermal Establishment. Health Resort for Arthritis.

THE GRAND HOTEL

THE LAST WORD IN HOTEL COMFORT.
Terms from 12/- a day.
G. A. PAILLARD, Manager.

For illustrated booklet apply to the Manager, "Hotel San Salvadour" (Var).
Cable Address:—SAN SALVADOUR, Hyères.

Golf • Tennis • Croquet • Fishing • Boating • Garage • Motor Cars.

INNSBRUCK (Tyrol).—**See page 498.**

HOTEL du TIROL.

First Class Establishment, facing the Station.

With all the comforts of the large . . Modern Hotels of Europe . .

2 LIFTS
ROOMS WITH BATH ROOM

Most liberal arrangements for Winter pension.

INNSBRUCK IS NOTED for its EQUABLE CLIMATE and WINTER SPORTS.

C. LANDSEE, Proprietor.

(Golden Sun) HOTEL GOLDENE SONNE.

OPPOSITE THE STATION.

FIRST CLASS HOTEL. Recently refurnished and equipped with every modern comfort. Apartments with bath and toilette. Terms "en pension." Renowned for its superior Cuisine and Wine. Splendid Dining Room. Verandah and Garden.

A. GRABNER, Manager.

INNSBRUCK—Continued on next page.

INNSBRUCK—*Continued.*

HOTEL VICTORIA.

NEAR THE STATION.

Favourite Family Hotel. Comfortably equipped and newly furnished. Baths. Nice surroundings and Gardens, considerably enlarged. Nice Dining Room and Restaurant, with verandah. Special Cuisine. Meals à la Carte. Pilsen and Munich Beer from the cask, also Foreign and Tyrolese Wines. Reading and Writing Room. Steam Heating. Electric Light and Lift. Garage. Moderate Prices. No Omnibus necessary. Porter meets trains.

JEAN SCHLEGEL, Proprietor.

CARL KAYSER'S (NOT KAISERHOF.)

PENSION, PARK AND FAMILY HOTEL.

12 Minutes Drive from Railway Station. Splendidly situated in a large Garden, overlooking the River and Valley. Homelike, (no luxuries), quiet, (no motors). English and American Newspapers. Library, Baths, Tennis, Electric Light, Telephone, Telegraph. Conducted under the personal care of the Proprietor. December and January winter sport.

Summer terms: 7–9 Kr. Winter terms: 6–8 Kr. Apply for Prospectus.

PENSION WINTER

3, CLAUDIA PLATZ.

First Class Family Pension in the best and healthiest part of the town, close to the mountains. Large airy rooms. Every comfort. Excellent cuisine.

Pension from Kr. 8. Reduction in Winter.

Prospectus from Bradshaw's Office or the Proprietress FRAU. DR. RABL.

INTERLAKEN (Switzerland).—See page 520.

INTERLAKEN.

REGINA HOTEL JUNGFRAUBLICK

FIRST CLASS RESIDENTIAL HOTEL.

Visited in 1903 by Her Majesty Queen Mary.

Elevated Position.

Finest View. Immense Private Park. Lawn Tennis.

TRAVEL and HOTEL ENQUIRIES—See page xii.

INTERLAKEN—*Continued.*

THE INTERLAKEN.

Grd. HOTEL VICTORIA

AND

Grd. HOTEL JUNGFRAU

are in the Finest situation on the HÖHEWEG and

∴ facing the Jungfrau and Glaciers. ∴

Both Hotels have been entirely renovated and offer every modern comfort. Pension Arrangements during the whole Season.

RESTAURANT FRANCAIS
AND OPEN AIR RESTAURANT.
Afternoon Tea Concerts.

LARGE SPORT GROUNDS.
AUTOMOBILE - GARAGE.

A. MULLER, General Manager.

GRAND HOTEL

(Formerly the BEAU RIVAGE).

This beautiful FIRST CLASS FAMILY HOTEL is situated . . in its own Park . . on the Principal Promenade.

OPEN AIR RESTAURANT.
Table d'Hote at separate tables.

SPECIAL ARRANGEMENTS for PROLONGED STAY.

Private Bathrooms . . and Suites . . * . . OPEN . . MAY-OCTOBER.

ALBERT DOEPFNER, Proprietor.

IN WINTER: AT NAPLES, GRAND HOTEL HAUSER & DOEPFNER.

INTERLAKEN—Continued on next page.

·· GRAND ··
HOTEL METROPOLE

First Class, in central situation on the Hoeheweg.

PRIVATE APARTMENTS WITH BATHS AND TOILETTES.

Table d'Hôte at small tables.
RESTAURANT.

E. SEILER, Proprietor.

Grand Hotel des Alpes
AND
PALACE HOTEL

FIRST CLASS. **Pension from 9 Frs.**

THE GRAND HOTEL des ALPES is situated on the principal promenade, "Höheweg," with splendid view of the Jungfrau and other Mountains. Near the "Kursaal" as well as the Mountain-Railway Stations, etc. Large Gardens. Baths. Electric Light. Comfortable Rooms. — **Lifts.** — **Perfect sanitary installations.** — **Garage.** **Specially recommended to English families who wish to make a prolonged stay**

INTERLAKEN.

SCHWEIZERHOF (Hotel Suisse)

FIRST CLASS. **Pension from 10 frs.**

Best position on the Grande Promenade. Lift. Electric Light throughout. **Apartments and Rooms with Private Baths.** First Class Restaurant. Terrace. Motor Shed.

Managed by the Proprietors
FAMILY
WIRTH—STRUBIN.

Terminus-Hotel & Pension BRISTOL

INTERLAKEN.

Rooms from Frs. 3. **Pension from Frs. 8.**

150 BEDS. Best Position, opposite Central Station and Landing Stage. Splendid view from every room. Recently built with all modern comfort. Lift. Hall. Drawing Rooms. Apartments with Baths. — Central Heating.

Lovely Garden.

OPEN ALL THE YEAR ROUND.

IRELAND.—See page 1099.

BAD ISCHL (Ischl Baths), Austria.—See page 499.

BAD ISCHL—Continued on next page

BAD ISCHL (Ischl Baths)—*Continued.*

JERSEY.—See page 1099.

KANDERSTEG (Switzerland).—See page 521.

KARERSEE (Dolomites—Tyrol—Ortler).—See page 499.

TRAVEL and HOTEL ENQUIRIES—See page xii.

KIEL (Germany).—See page 483.

KISSINGEN (Bavaria).—See page 483.

KISSINGEN—Continued on next page

KITZBÜHEL (Tyrol) Austria.—See page 499.

TRAVEL and HOTEL ENQUIRIES—See page xii.

KLAGENFURT (Austria).—See page 499.

KLAGENFURT.

Hotel and Restaurant

KAISER von OESTERREICH

HIGH CLASS HOTEL.

120 Rooms and Salons.

Central Heating.

Notwithstanding great comfort moderate terms.

FRANZ LERCH, Propr.

KLAGENFURT, on the Tauern Railway (Austria).

HOTEL VERDINO (MOSER)

First Class Hotel.

Highly recommended to English and American Families. Every modern comfort. Special terms for a longer stay. — Proprietor J. VERDINO.

KLOSTERS (Switzerland).—See page 521.

KLOSTERS. **FAVOURITE SUMMER and WINTER RESORT** 4,030 feet above sea level, on the "Rhætian Railway." ∴

SPORT HOTEL SILVRETTA

1st Class. 200 rooms. Open all the year. Entirely renovated and enlarged. Terms from **Frs. 10.** Magnificent grounds for ski-ing. Own skating rink, Ideal bobsleigh run 2½ miles long. Dances, Concerts, Gymkhanas, etc. For Prospectus address: **MEISSER et Cie.,** Proprs. and Managers.

KÖNIGSSEE (Bavarian Highlands).—See page 483A.

THE MOST BEAUTIFUL LAKE IN GERMANY.

Regular Motor Boat Service see page **203c**, also Motor and Rowing boats always for hire.

HOTEL SCHIFFMEISTER.

REBUILT 1911-12; modern construction with Radiators, Baths, etc. Adjoining the Lake, with beautiful view; large Garden and Terraces; garage with pit, etc. Pension. Tel.: Berchtesgaden. 67. Prospectus from Bradshaw's Offices and the Proprietors:— **C. & J. MODEREGGER.**

KREUZNACH (or CREUZNACH) (Germany).—See page 483A.

Radium Brine Baths.

KREUZNACH.

The only German Spa where RADIUM is obtained from the Springs.

CURATIVE MEANS: Bathing Establishment for Radium Treatment, Radium Baths, Radium Drinking Cures, Radium Inhalation.

INDICATIONS: Gout, Rheumatism, Sciatica, Scrofula, Women's Complaints, Diseases of the Heart.

FINEST POINT IN THE VALLEY OF THE NAHE.

Prospectuses on application to the Kurverwaltung.

KREUZNACH—Continued on next page.

KREUZNACH (or CREUZNACH)—*Continued.*

LANGEN SCHWALBACH (Germany).—See page 484.

TRAVEL and HOTEL ENQUIRIES—See page xii.

LAUSANNE—*Continued.*

LAUSANNE

CECIL HOTEL.

3 Minutes from the Station. 150 Beds.

Rooms from 4 Frs. Pension from 9 Frs.

French Restaurant.

Tennis Lawn. Concerts.

J. SUMSER, Managing Proprietor.

OUCHY . .

SAVOY HOTEL.

OPENED MARCH, 1911.

150 Beds. 50 Bath Rooms. The most Up-to-Date as regards Comfort. — Salle Hydrotherapique. Quiet and magnificent position, close to the Lake, in own large and shady Park. Three excellent Tennis Lawns. Pension from **10 Frs.**

Under the same Management as "HOTEL CECIL."

OUCHY-LAUSANNE.

THE ROYAL HOTEL

THE NEWEST CREATION on the LAKE OF GENEVA.

200 Beds. — 70 Bathrooms. — 3 Minutes from the Quay. — Opened 1909.

		With dressing room (hot & cold water).	With private bath-room.
Single Rooms	from Frs. 4	from Frs. 5	from Frs. 9
Rooms with 2 Beds	from Frs. 7	from Frs. 8	from Frs. 14

TARIFF OF MEALS:—

Lunch served in the Large Dining Room at any time from 12.0—1.30 (carving table on wheels) Frs. 4.50.

Dinner served in the Large Dining Room at any time from 7.0—8.30 (carving table on wheels) Frs. 6.

Inclusive Terms from 10—28 Frs.

Roof Garden. *RESTAURANT FRANCAIS.* **Large Park.**

Commanding Position. — Extensive Garage. — Vacuum Cleaner.

O. A. KAELIN, Managing Director.

Late of Cap Martin Hotel, near Mentone; Splendid Hotel, Aix-les-Bains.

Branch House: HOTEL de la FORET, Morgins-les-Bains.

LAUSANNE— Continued on next page

THE "Beau Sejour"

FIRST CLASS HOTEL

Recomended for Families.
Special arrangements.

Newly enlarged, with all modern comfort.
160 Beds. Apartments with Baths.
Central position in a large Park. Tennis.
Terms from 9 Francs.

R. PASCHE, Manager. Telegraphic Address:— **SEJOURBO.**

HOTEL GIBBON

THIS FIRST CLASS HOTEL, in finest and central position of the town, Place St. Francois, next the new Post Office, and near the Railway Station and Funiculaire Lausanne—Ouchy, commands most admirable view over the Lake and Alps. Furnished with all elegance and modern comfort for English travellers. Lift, Baths, Electric Light and central heating in every room. Beautiful shaded Terrace and Garden. — **L. LIEBERMANN, Manager.**

LAUSANNE.

Alexandra Grand Hotel

FIRST CLASS. *AND RESTAURANT.*

RECENTLY BUILT AND EQUIPPED WITH EVERY MODERN COMFORT.

120 Beds. 15 private Bath Rooms. In the midst of own Park.

Rooms from 3.50 Frs. PENSION (for stay of at least 8 days) from 9 Frs.

CH. F. BUTTICAZ Proprietor.

HOTEL CONTINENTAL.

FIRST CLASS. Opposite the Railway Station, the Post and Telegraph Office. Newly built and furnished with every modern comfort. Large and small apartments, and special arrangements made for families. Restaurant "à la Carte" and Table d'Hôte. Pension. Excellent Cooking and Wines. Moderate charges. Reading and Smoking Rooms. Baths on each Floor. Lift and Central Heating. The first Hotel in Switzerland with the Electric-Alarm-Clock.
H. BUNDT & SONS, New Proprietors.

OUCHY-LAUSANNE.

HOTEL du CHATEAU

FIRST CLASS. Open all the year round. Entirely renovated.
Splendid view on the Lake. Large Terrace and Winter Garden.
Apartments with private baths. New management. J. REISSER, Manager.

LAUSANNE—Continued on next page

LAUSANNE.

HOTEL VICTORIA.

The Most Recently Built . . . . . . | All Modern Comforts. — Garden.
First Class Family Hotel, near the Station. | View of the Lake. Moderate terms

F. IMSENG, Proprietor.

LAUSANNE.

EDEN HOTEL.

FIRST CLASS.

Close to Railway Station (Avenue de la Gare). Highly recommended to English and American Families. — All modern comforts. — Apartments with private bath. — Vacuum Cleaner. Rooms from **3.50 frs.** inclusive. Pension terms in Winter from **8 frs.**, in Summer from **9 frs.**

Telegraphic Address: EDENOTEL. G. GERCKÉ, Proprietor.

CARLTON HOTEL.

Splendid situation, between the TOWN and the LAKE.

—— *LATEST CREATION* ——

Terms:—
Winter from **8 frs.**, **Summer** from **9 frs.** Ls. MÜLLER, Prop. Manager.

GRAND HOTEL de la PAIX

LAUSANNE.

In Centre of Town, with panorama of Lake and Alps. Fire-proof building equipped with the newest comfort, Rooms from **3.50 Frs.** Pension from **10 Frs.** Café Restaurant with terrace. Billiards. Bowling. Open the whole year.

Lausanne-Signal (2,133 feet above the Sea).

HOTEL MAJESTIC

OPENED AUGUST, 1910.

FIRST CLASS with every modern comfort. Every room with toilette and hot and cold water supply. Elevated and healthy situation close to the Forest "Sauvabelin." Magnificent Panorama of the Sea and the Alps. OWN PARK with tennis lawns, etc. Garage. Specially recommended to Families and for a protracted stay.

Moderate Terms. —— TH. SACHS, Manager.

LAUSANNE.

HOTEL MIRABEAU.

Recently opened. The one FIRST CLASS Hotel and Restaurant near the Station. Entirely up to date. Apartments with Baths. Fine view. Perfect sanitation. Vacuum cleaner. Manager: TH. RAHM-SCHÖRI.

HOTEL METROPOLE

Avenues de Florimont et des Alpes.
New First Class Hotel.

OPENED AUGUST, 1912. Situated in a fashionable and quiet part of the town. Unrivalled view over the Lake and Alps. Five minutes from Railway Station and centre of town. Electric Light and Central Heating in every room. Large Public rooms. Lift. Terrace. Garage and Pit. Library, 1,000 volumes. Rooms Fr. 3, upwards. Pension Fr. 7, upwards.

Règime de Table. New Proprietor: FRANCOIS RUDMANN.

British Hotel

LAUSANNE.

NEW First Class English Family House. Beautifully situated on the new Avenue des Alpes, and commanding fine view over the lake and mountains. Rooms with hot and cold running water. Elevator, large lounge, central heating, etc. FULL TERMS from 6—12 frs.

A. H. DUNER, Proprietor, late of Maloja Palace.

LAUSANNE—*Continued.*

TRAVEL and HOTEL ENQUIRIES—See page xii.

LEIPSIC.—See page 484.

LEIPSIC—Continued on next page

LENK (Switzerland).—See page 522.

LENNO (near Cadenabbia, Lake of Como)—See page 540.

TRAVEL and HOTEL ENQUIRIES—See page xii.

LEYSIN (Switzerland).—See page 523.

Alpine Health Resort for Chest Complaints.

LEYSIN

FRENCH-SPEAKING SWITZERLAND.

—On the Simplon Railway.—

5,000 ft. above Sea Level. * OPEN ALL THE YEAR ROUND.

Four Sanatoriums ;—

GRAND HOTEL	... ...	13	frs., upwards
MONTBLANC	... ...	11	" "
CHAMOSSAIRE	... ...	8	" "
SANATORIUM BELVEDERE		12	" "

Board and Medical attendance included.

Special treatment for Pulmonary Tuberculosis by Sanatorium Methods assisted by Alpine Atmosphere.

Prospectus free on application to the Directors.

LIEGE (Belgium).—See page 434.

HOTEL DE SUEDE.

Central Heating. — Rooms with Bathrooms en Suite.

AMERICAN BAR.

LEADING HOTEL. **Proprietor: Ad. D. MICHOTTE.**

HOTEL de l'EUROPE.

FIRST CLASS. OPPOSITE THE ROYAL THEATRE.

Newly Furnished. Baths. Electric Light. Central Heating.
Much frequented by English Families. Cook's Coupons accepted.

H. HENRARD, Proprietor.

IN THIS ESTABLISHMENT EXISTS THE MOST IMPORTANT AND MOST RENOWNED RESTAURANT OF THE TOWN.

LILLE (France).—See page 403.

HOTEL de l' EUROPE.

ELECTRIC LIGHT. Central Heating. Running hot and cold water in all bedrooms. Bathrooms. Shampooing. Chiropodist in the Hotel. Drawing Room and Smoking Room. Very large Yard with Garden. FIRST CLASS COOKING.

English and German spoken. — Auto meets Trains. — **LIFT.** — Telephone : 4·75.

COOK'S TICKETS (first class) are accepted.

TRAVEL and HOTEL ENQUIRIES—See page xii.

LINDAU (Bavaria).—See page 484A.

LINZ (Austria).—See page 500.

LISBON.—See page 578.

LIVERPOOL.—See page 1100.

LOCARNO (Switzerland).—See page 523.

LONDON.—See Pages 1080-1092.

LUCERNE (Switzerland).—See page 523.

TRAVEL and HOTEL ENQUIRIES—See page xii.

LUCERNE—Continued on next page

TRAVEL and HOTEL ENQUIRIES—See page xii.

LUCERNE—*Continued.*

GRAND EUROPE HOTEL

FIRST CLASS ENGLISH AND AMERICAN FAMILY HOUSE.

IN FINEST POSITION, with shady **Garden** on the **Border** of the **Lake.** Splendid Public Rooms. **New Restaurant Terrace.** Grand Hall. Single and Double Rooms with private Bath and Toilet. Rooms with hot and cold water Toilet. Hot water heating. **Full Pension : Spring and Autumn from Fr. 8.50 and Fr. 9.50 upward, August from Fr. 11.** Auto Garage. Open March to October.

RICH. MATZIG, Managing Proprietor.

LUCERNE "BEAU RIVAGE" Quai National.

The Hotel "Beau Rivage" Entirely renovated. **Situated in front of the** lovely Lake. Patronised by English visitors. Central Heating. Fine Hall. Private Bathrooms. Table d'hote at separate tables. Excellent Cooking. Open early March to middle October. **Inclusive terms from 9 frs. Full Season from 12 frs.** *Recommended by the Travel Editor of the "QUEEN."* **C. GIGER, Propr.**

Branch House PENSION FALLER, above the Beau Rivage. Full Terms from **6** to **10** frs., according to season.

HOTEL SWAN AND RIGI

LUCERNE.

FIRST CLASS HOUSE of old reputation, situated on the Quay, patronised by English and Americans. **Both houses connected by ENCLOSED bridge.** Electric Light and Hot Water Heating throughout. Apartments with Private Bathrooms. RESTAURANT with open Terrace. OPEN ALL THE YEAR. **HAEFELI BROTHERS, Proprietors.**

HOTEL BRISTOL LUCERNE SUISSE

EXQUISITELY FURNISHED.

Close to the Station and the landing stages. Quiet position.

Rooms from **3** frs., Pension from **9** frs.

Prospectus on application to the— **Proprietor: GUSTAV MUTH.**

LUCERNE.

Hotel des Alpes

FINEST and most quiet situation on the border of the Lake and River Reuss. Splendid view of the mountains. 60 Beds. Reading Room and Ladies. Drawing Room. — Verandah. — Terrace. — Lift. — Baths. — Heated by Steam.

BEDROOMS FROM 2.50 FR. PENSION FROM 7.50 FR.

LUCERNE.

Hotel du Nord

——GOOD SECOND CLASS HOUSE——

NEAR the Post, Pier, and Station, but without the noise of the Railway. Every modern comfort, enlarged and completely renovated. Open all the year round. Electric Light. Central Heating. Lift. Baths. Restaurant on the ground floor. Table d'Hote. 90 Beds. Nicely furnished cosy rooms from **2.50 fr** DINNER from **2.50 fr.** — SUPPER, **2.50 fr.** — PENSION, **7—9 fr.** — Porter meets all trains.

LUCERNE - Continued on next page.

TRAVEL and HOTEL ENQUIRIES—See page xii.

LUCERNE—*Continued.*

LUCERNE-BÜRGENSTOCK.—See page 524.

LUCERNE—continued on next page

LUGANO (Switzerland.)—See page 524.

LUGANO.

PARK-HOTEL

1st CLASS, OF HIGH COMFORT AND REPUTATION.

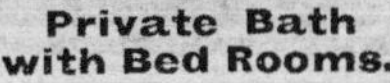

Unrivalled Position in large Park.

During Spring and Autumn Season Hotel Orchestra Band.

Open the whole year.

Special arrangements for prolonged stay.

Managing Proprietors: EHRET and ZÄHRINGER.

LE GRAND HOTEL AND PALACE.

The Leading First Class Hotel.

HIGHEST COMFORT.

Occupying the finest site on the LAKE in own magnificent PARK and GARDENS.

Private Apartments.
Baths and Toilette Rooms.
Restaurant Francais.
Auto Garage.

Lawn Tennis.
House Orchestra.
Moderate Charges.
Special Arrangements.

Open the Whole Year.

THE BUCHER-DURRER HOTELS.

LUGANO—Continued on next page.

LUGANO—*Continued.*

TRAVEL and HOTEL ENQUIRIES—See page xii.

LUGANO—*Continued.*

LUINO (Lac Majeur), Italy.—See page 546A.

GRAND HOTEL SIMPLON-TERMINUS.

FIRST CLASS HOUSE.

WITH large Park and Garden on the shore of the Lake. Electric Light in every room. Central Heating. Luino, being a centre of railway communication, is the most favourite place for a long stay. This place is also recommended for its magnificent shaded Promenades on the shore of the Lake, in the Forest, and on the Mountain, with splendid points of view. Direct Electric Train from Milan and Varese. G. MORANDI, Proprietor.

LUXEMBURG.—See page 447.

GRAND HOTEL BRASSEUR.

First Class Hotel.

IN an exceptional situation, near to the Park, best and finest Promenades. Replete with every modern comfort. Lift. Central Heating. 100 Rooms and Saloons. Restaurant. Baths and Douches. — English, French, and German spoken. — Omnibus to all Trains. Electric Light. **P. BEYENS, Manager.**

GRD. HOTEL de COLOGNE

First Class Hotel with every modern comfort.

Best central position. — Large Garden. — ROOMS from Mks. 2.50. Motor Bus at the Station. The English Club Rooms in the Hotel are open to guests.

Proprietor: FERD C. WEBER.

Bradshaw's Guide.

TRAVEL ENQUIRY DEPARTMENT.—This Department has proved of efficient service both to hotel-keepers and the travelling public. Prospectuses of clients whose announcements appear in Bradshaw's Guide are kept for inspection or distribution at the Company's Offices in London, Liverpool, Manchester, Glasgow, and Dublin. For further particulars see page xii.

LYONS.—See page 404.

LYONS

THE GRAND HOTEL

PLACE DE LA BOURSE.

A complete Hotel, throughout up-to-date.

Hot and cold running water. — 40 Rooms with Bath.

J. DUFOUR, Manager.

TRAVEL and HOTEL ENQUIRIES—See page xii.

LYONS—*Continued.*

.. 11, Rue Grolee and .:
11, Quai de l'Hopital.

Gd. NOUVEL HOTEL.

The most Central and the most Comfortable.
200 Rooms. Apartments with Bath, etc., etc.
Garage on the premises.

MAGNIFICENT VIEW ON THE RHÔNE. —Cable Address: NOUVOTEL.—

BUFFET AT THE LYONS PERRACHE STATION.

UNDER THE MANAGEMENT OF THE INTERNATIONAL SLEEPING CAR CO.

Finest Cuisine. The wines, liquors, and mineral waters are of the best quality. Moderate Tariff.

The TERMINUS HOTEL at this Station is under the same management.

A HIGH CLASS HOTEL OF PERFECT MODERN EQUIPMENT AND SANITATION

GRAND HOTEL du GLOBE

Rue Gasparin, Place Bellecour.

FIRST CLASS FAMILY HOTEL. LATEST IMPROVEMENTS.

Rooms and Suites with Bath. — Fine Winter Garden.

Rooms from 3.50 frs. Pension from 11 frs. New Proprietors: DE PREUX & BLANCHOUD.

HOTEL d'ANGLETERRE

Facing PERRACHE STATION. The best situated on the Place Carnot.

Completely modernised. Central Heating. Lift. Electric Light. Baths. * Rooms from 3 Frs. Breakfast 1.25 Frs. Lunch 3 Frs. Dinner 4 Frs.

Arrangements for Families. — Telephone 0.69. — E. VRAY, Proprietor.

MADEIRA (Funchal).—See page 582.

REID'S HOTELS.—

Winter average 61° F. Complete freedom from dust. — Established 1850.

3½ Days voyage from England, 7 from New York.

REID'S PALACE HOTEL (late New Hotel) and annexes.—Situated on the Cliffs to the West of Funchal, standing in the largest hotel gardens in Madeira; overlooking the Sea, grand view of the Mountains. Lift. Sea Bathing and Boating. Terms 10/- to 25/- daily pension. — Swiss Manager.

REID'S CARMO HOTEL.—In sheltered central position. Terms 9/- to 18/-

These FIRST CLASS HOTELS are lighted by electricity, and afford every comfort for families and travellers. French and English Cuisine of highest class, and Choice Wines. Tennis Courts, large Gardens. Billiards. The SANITARY arrangements are by the Banner Sanitation Co., London. Water direct from a Mountain Spring. Sanitary Steam Laundry. All Steamers met.

REID'S MOUNT PARK HOTEL, Monte, 2,000 ft. above sea. Telegrams: REID FUNCHAL. A.B.C. Code, Unicode, and Lieber Code. — Pamphlet free of MADEIRA AGENCY, 11, Adam Street (Strand), W.C.; "Hotel Tariff Bureau," 275, Regent St. London Messrs. Thos Cook & Son, London; at the Steamship Companies; or W. and A. Reid, Madeira.

MANCHESTER.—See page 1101.

MARIENBAD.—See page 500.

MARIENBAD—Continued on next page

TRAVEL and HOTEL ENQUIRIES—See page xii.

MARSEILLES.—See page 405.

MARSEILLES—Continued on next page.

MARSEILLES—*Continued.*

TRAVEL and HOTEL ENQUIRIES—See page xii.

Canton de Valais. MARTIGNY (Switzerland).—See page 525.

MARTIGNY

Terminus of the Electric Railway—MARTIGNY-CHAMONIX
Starting Point of the International Highway, MARTIGNY. AOSTA-TURIN over the GRAND ST. BERNARD.

GRAND HOTEL du MONT BLANC

Close to the Station of the Electric Railway, Martigny-Chamonix.
Modern Comforts. Carriages for all directions. Garage. GEORGES MORAND, Proprietor.

MARTIGNY

(VALAIS-SUISSE).

Terms from Frs. 8 per day.

Grand Hotel Clerc

FIRST CLASS HOTEL, well known to American and English travellers. At head of Martigny-Chamonix Electric Rly. Most pleasantly situated. Carriages at any time for the Grand St. Bernard, etc. Large garage.

Mme. Vve OSCAR-CORNUT-BRUNNER, Propr.

Terms from Frs. 8 per day.

MAYENCE (Germany).—See page 453.

HOTEL DE HOLLANDE

WELL-KNOWN First Class Hotel. Thorough comfort, finest and best situated Hotel in the Town, affording an open view of the River. Favourite and quiet stopping place for excursions in the neighbourhood.

Opposite the Landing Place.

Omnibus meets all Trains at Central Station. Steam Heating. Lift. Electric Light. Fire-proof Staircase. The Hotel is arranged to suit requirements of single Travellers as well as families, and is moderate in its charges.

The only Hotel with Suites and rooms with private bath and toilette.

Auto. Garage. — Imperial Automobile Club.

ENGLISCHER-HOF

HOTEL D'ANGLETERRE.

First Class House on the Rhine.

NEXT TO THE LANDING PLACE.

Splendid view on the Mountains.

LIFT. ELECTRIC LIGHT. AUTO-GARAGE.

Apartments and Single Rooms with Bath.

Rooms from 4 M. including Breakfast.

OTTO ENGEL, Proprietor.

TRAVEL and HOTEL ENQUIRIES—See page xii.

MAYENCE—*Continued.*

HOTEL ZUM KARPFEN (CARP HOTEL)

IMMEDIATELY facing the Post Office, and 1 minute from Rhine Boats Landing Stage. Most comfortable old established Hotel, with essentially moderate charges. Rooms from 3/6 with Breakfast. Good Cuisine and Wines. Well recommended to English and American families and Tourists desiring a quiet comfortable Hotel. Omnibus meets all trains. Electric light. Central heating; modern improvements, etc. — **Proprietor: C. MEINTZINGER, Wine Merchant.**

CENTRAL HOTEL.

FIRST CLASS HOTEL FACING THE CENTRAL STATION.

ENTIRELY renovated with all modern improvements. Large Restaurant with Terrace. Baths. Vacuum Cleaner. Lift. Steam Heating. Electric Light. Moderate Terms. Cook's coupons accepted. Telephone 186. Well recommended. **FRANZ SEYFRIED, Propr.**

MAYENS-SUR-SION (Switzerland).—See page 529.

Switzerland. LES MAYENS DE SION. Valais. Altitude 4,593 feet. Station: SION.

HOTEL de la DENT d'HERENS

FIRST Class Summer Resort. Carriage drive to Hotel. Unsurpassable panorama, finest in Wallis; view of glaciers of Bernese Alps, Dent Blanche, Cervin, etc. Dry and pure air. Extensive forests. Centre of excursions. Pension terms from **8-10 frs.** Specially recommended to families. The St. Maurice Station Buffet is under same management. Well arranged Luncheon baskets for train leaving Lausanne at 9.10 a.m. Applications to conductor at Lausanne. **CRESCENTINO BROS., Proprietors.**

MEIRINGEN (Switzerland).—See page 526A.

MEIRINGEN (Brunig Railway).
Starting point for the Grimsel-Rhone Glacier, and Scheidegg Pass.

GRD. HOTEL DU SAUVAGE (WILDENMANN).

LIFT. First Class, leading Hotel in Meiringen. Magnificent position near Station and Post Office. English Church in the Park of the Hotel. **Terms "en Pension" stay of 5 Days.** *Prospectus on application. Terms from* **Frs. 8.** **W. GUNTER, Managing Proprietor.**

MENAGGIO (Lake of Como) Italy.—See page 547.

VICTORIA HOTEL

Every modern comfort. Open also during winter. Tennis, Golf, Motor Launch, Fishing, Lake Baths, Drives. Resident English Physician and Surgeon: Dr. E. F. Eliot. 90°/₀ of the visitors are English. GIANELLA & BULLO, Propr.

MENAGGIO—Lake of Como.

GRAND HOTEL MENAGGIO.

COMFORTABLE FIRST CLASS FAMILY HOTEL, in a quiet position, though near Pier and Station. — Surrounded by beautiful garden which gives right on the Lake. Lift. Central Heating. Golf. Moderate Terms. — **Open from February to November.**

A. RICCHINI, Proprietor.

MENTONE (Alpes Maritimes).—See page 406.

MENTONE

Owes its world-wide celebrity to its magnificent natural advantages.

Its **Situation**, immediately between the Maritime Alps and the most picturesque part of the Mediterranean Coast, with its undisputed consequence, a pre-eminently healthy and invigorating climate, is **Unique in Europe.**

(Mentone's death rate for the 6 months, 1st April to 30th September, 1911, was 9 per annum per 1,000 of the population).

The 1910-1911 Season marked **a New Era in Mentone's Existence** on account of the great additions to the many attractions provided for its visitors.

The Casino Municipal,

inaugurated on the **4th December, 1909**, is second to none on the coast for beauty, size, and for the varied and up-to-date attractions offered. There is a **Splendid Theatre** with constant performances (Opera Comique, Comedie, Concerts Classiques, &c.), Salles de reunion, High Class Restaurant, Skating Rink, Bowling, &c., &c.

The Mentone Golf Links

(OF 18 HOLES)

Situated in the verdant and beautiful valley of Sospel are classed as **among the very best**, if not the best on the Continent.

BEN SAYERS of North Berwick says:—

"Never more surprised in my life! They are the best links I have seen abroad."

The New Electric Tram

TO SOSPEL,

which follows a special and most picturesque route, brings the **Links within three quarters of an hour of Mentone** and at the same time place a new centre of excursions (Moulinet, L'Authion, Peira-Cava, Les Cols de Braus, Bruis, &c.) within easy reach of the Mentone Visitor.

TRAVEL and HOTEL ENQUIRIES—See page xii.

MENTONE—Continued on next page.

MENTONE (Alpes Maritime)—*Continued.*

TRAVEL and HOTEL ENQUIRIES—See page xii.

MENTONE—Continued on next page

MERAN—Continued on next page

MERAN (South Tyrol)—*Continued.*

HOTEL FRAU EMMA

NEAR the STATION and the PROMENADE.

260 BEDS.

Magnificent views of the Mountains. 160 Rooms and Apartments, with Bath and Toilette. Lift and Electric Light. Steam heating. Vacuum Cleaner.

REDUCED TERMS DURING THE WINTER MONTHS.

H. & F. HELLENSTAINER, Proprietors. — (In Summer: HOTEL EMMA, PRAGSER WILDSEE.)

Hotel Erzherzog Johann.

220 Beds. 150 Rooms and Apartments with Bath.

View of the Promenade. Central position.

Every modern comfort.

OPEN all the YEAR. Proprietor: ROBERT WENTER.

PALAST HOTEL

OPEN ALL THE YEAR ROUND.

220 Beds. Near the Promenades. 150 Rooms and Apartments with Bath.

Garage. FRANZ LEIBL, Proprietor.

HOTEL BRISTOL

190 BEDS

Up-to-Date Construction de Luxe.

Sunny Central Position. 130 Rooms and Apartments, with Baths.

Warm Water Heating.

GARAGE. Proprietors: WALTER BROS.

MERAN (South Tyrol)—*Continued.*

HOTEL HABSBURGER HOF

155 Beds.

Close to the Station, the Promenade, and the Kur- and Bath Houses. 120 Rooms.
Apartments with Bath. Warm Water Heating. Open, sunny position. Garage.

Proprietor: Jos. FUCHS.

PARK HOTEL

Obermais.

140 BEDS.

Modern Family Hotel.

Open Position. • Large Park. • Proprietor: H. PANZER.

In Summer: San Martino di Castrozza, DOLOMITEN HOTEL and HOTEL FRATAZZA.

MERAN.

SAVOY HOTEL

Stephanie-Promenade.

Select House. Very quiet position.

EVERY UP-TO-DATE COMFORT.

120 Rooms and Salons.

SUITES and SINGLE ROOMS with PRIVATE BATH.

Large elegant Lounge and Public Rooms. Auto-Garage.

Proprietor: F. BRUNNER.

Obermais.

Hotel Aders

90 Beds.

LARGE PARK. * WINTER GARDEN.

Modern comfort. Garage. *Proprietor: F. BAUDUIN.*

OBERMAIS.

HOTEL MINERVA

85 BEDS.

UP-TO-DATE COMFORTS.
In Fine elevated position. Tramway connection; close to Kurpark.
Apartments with Bath and Toilette.
PROSPECTUS.

In Summer: HOTEL SALEGG, Seis am Schlern.

MERAN—Continued on next page.

MILAN—Continued on next page

MILAN—*Continued*

HOTEL VICTORIA.

(Annexe of the Hotel du Lion) MILAN.

SITUATED in the finest part of the Town, near the Cathedral. The accommodation is of such character that Families and Tourists will find it a most desirable place of residence. Reading and Smoking Rooms. Elevator. Lighted by Electricity and heated by the new American Steam System. Baths. Pension. Moderate charges. Cook's Coupons.

CH. FONTANA. Proprietor.

HOTEL EXCELSIOR et SUISSE

Via Rastrelli 20. — Opened in 1906.

QUIET position near the Duomo and the Royal Castle. Recommended to families. Every modern comfort. Dinners served at small tables. Electric light. Central heating. Pension from 8.50 Francs. — Rooms from 3 Francs. — Omnibus meets trains.

CLEMENTI-NEGRI, New Proprietor.

MONTANA SUR SIERRE (Switzerland).—See page 529.

PALACE HOTEL

(5,000 feet above sea level.) **MONTANA-SUR-SIERRE.**

Magnificent 18-hole GOLF COURSE adjoining the Hotel.

A fine natural course situated on an undulating plateau, 5,000 feet above sea level.
Funicular Railway from Sierre.

—— Season—May to October. ——

Full particulars from The Secretary, 5, Endsleigh Gardens, London, N.W.

GRAND HOTEL du PARC MONTANA. ON THE SIMPLON LINE.

*** * CONSUMPTIVES ARE NOT RECEIVED. * ***

5012 FEET ABOVE SEA LEVEL. Magnificent panorama from the Simplon to Mont Blanc. Best situation. Open all the year. Very first class Winter Sport: Luging, Ski-ing, Skating, and Curling on the Lake close to the Hotel. — Central Heating, Electric Light English Church, and R.C. services. Montana is reached from Sierre in 45 minutes by funicular railway. Prospectus gratis. **LS. ANTILLE, Proprietor.**

MONT-DORE-LES-BAINS (France).—See page 407.

HOTEL SARCIRON-RAINALDY.

FIRST CLASS. 300 ROOMS and SALONS.

Opposite the Establishment and the Park.

Hygienic Installation. Lifts.

ELECTRIC LIGHT. VILLAS FOR FAMILIES.

Garage for Automobiles.

Apply to: SARCIRON RAINALDY.

MONTE CARLO—Continued on next page

MONTE CARLO—*Continued.*

GRAND HOTEL DU PRINCE DE GALLES

Of the Very First Class.

SPECIALLY Recommended to English Families. Situated in the midst of large Garden. Elevated, quiet, and climatic position. Superb view of Sea and Town. Suites of apartments with private Bath and Toilette, entirely up-to-date. Magnificent Restaurant facing south; view from every table. 200 Rooms, large Hall and public rooms. Heating throughout. Special terms in October, November, December, and April-May.

MARCEL REY and B. ROLANDAIS, Managing Proprietors.

HOTEL VICTORIA.

Entirely refurnished and newly decorated.

LARGE PUBLIC ROOMS FACING SOUTH.

Suites of apartments with private Bath-rooms and toilette.

Large Garden. — Auto-Car shed.

Vve. E. REY, Proprietress.

Hotel des Anglais AND St. James.

FIRST CLASS FAMILY HOTEL.

Apartments with Private Baths and Toilette.

Hot Water Heating throughout.

Best Sanitation.

G. LUDWIG, Proprietor.

MONTE-CARLO.

HOTEL BEAU RIVAGE

Full South.

Beautiful View. First Class. Most modern arrangements. Hot and Cold Water supply in all rooms. Suites consisting of Bed Room, Drawing Room, and Bath Room. — **OTTO ROHRER, New Proprietor.**

MONTE CARLO.

HOTEL de LONDRES

FIRST CLASS. Best position, full south. Facing Casino and Gardens. Splendid view on the Sea. Entirely renewed this summer. Every modern comfort. Perfect sanitation. Bath Rooms on each floor. Lift. Electric Light. Central Heating. Excellent Cuisine. Moderate Charges. **Inclusive Terms from Frs. 14.** Open all the year. **H. KAISER, Manager.**

MONTE CARLO—*Continued.*

HOTEL WINDSOR

SITUATED in the most charming and healthy part of Monte Carlo, and recently enlarged and redecorated. Sanitary arrangements by George Jennings, London. Suites with bath and toilette and single rooms with all the latest comfort. All public and most of the private rooms are heated by hot water radiators. Verandahs facing full south have been added to the Salons and the Dining room. Arrangements made for a protracted stay. Lift. Electric Light in every Room

A. GAILLARD and FAU, Proprietors.

MONTE CARLO.—HOTEL ROYAL.

One of the best situations, high and healthy.

70 Rooms and Saloons, newly fitted up with every modern convenience and comfort.

FIRST-CLASS FAMILY HOTEL. OPEN ALL THE YEAR.

CRETTAZ BROTHERS, Proprietors.

HOTEL ET RESTAURANT DU HELDER

FIRST CLASS HOUSE, well situated in proximate vicinity of the Casino. Enlarged in 1911. 100 Rooms and Saloons. New Apartments with Bath and Toilette. Central Heating in all Rooms. Baths and Douches. Electric Light. Lift. **ALBERT BREMOND, Proprietor.**

BALMORAL PALACE.

AVENUE DE LA COSTA.

Family Hotel of the Highest Class. — Every Modern Comfort. — Finest Situation. View on the Sea. Full South. **100** Rooms. Apartments with Bath Rooms.

Central Heating in every room. Pension Terms from 14 Frs.

Under the same Management as **Hotels Metropole and Continental, La Bourboule, France.**

HOTEL DE LA TERRASSE

FIRST CLASS HOTEL, recommended to families.

ELECTRIC LIGHT. CENTRAL HEATING. RESTAURANT.

Arrangements for prolonged stay. Terms from 11 frs. 50. Looking on the Boulevard.

L. GARRÉ, Proprietor (Swiss).

HOTEL d'ALBION ET DU LITTORAL

Situated full South.

MAGNIFCENT view of the Sea and the Mountains. Near the Casino. Open all the year. Electric light and lift. Central heating. Constant hot and cold water supply in every room, Dark room. Baths on every floor. Omnibus. Telephone. **Inclusive terms from 10 Frs.**

STALLE, Brothers, Proprietors.

MONTE CARLO—Continued on next page

MONTE CARLO—*Continued.*

NOUVEL HOTEL de LOUVRE

OPEN . . ALL THE YEAR.

FIRST CLASS. Near Casino, with splendid view on sea. Specially constructed for a Hotel, and furnished with every modern comfort. Lift. Electric Light. Central Heating Apartments and bedrooms, with private bathrooms attached. **Terms from Frs. 14 per day**

J. BOURBONNAIS, Proprietor.

MONTE-CARLO.

Gd. HOTEL RESTAURANT TERMINUS.

OPEN ALL THE YEAR.

Opposite the Railway Station, the Gardens, and the "Escaliers du Casino." Electric Light. Central Heating. Telephone. Pension from 10 francs.

English spoken. **GEORGES ROLFO, Proprietor.**

Monte Carlo.

Monte Carlo Palace & Alexandra Hotel

Facing the Casino and the Public Gardens. Open all the year round.

NEW FIRST CLASS ESTABLISHMENTS equipped with Up-to-Date Comforts.

Running hot and cold water in all Bed Rooms.

Toilette attached to all sitting rooms. Suites with private bath rooms and W.C.

MONTE CARLO.

HOTEL MASSENA

23, BOULEVARD des MOULINS.

Magnificent position, on the border of the Sea. Close to the Casino. Auto-Station of the Golf Club. Electric light, Central heating, Baths. Grill room. Pension from **11.50 Frs.** per day. **A. BERNARD, Propr.**

Open all the year.

MONT 'ESTORIL (Portugal).—(Winter Resort).— **See page 579.**

MONT'ESTORIL.—The Riviera of Portugal.

Grand Hotel d'Italie.

NEW FIRST CLASS HOTEL, recently enlarged. Specially built as a Winter residence. Water supply from the **Valle de Cavallos**, a source certified by doctors to be one of the purest of Portugal. Large sunny garden with covered lounge. Electric Light throughout. Excellent French Cuisine. English chaplain in residence during winter months. Full size Tennis Court. Moderate terms. — **PETRACCHI FELICE, Proprietor and Manager.**

TRAVEL and HOTEL ENQUIRIES—See page xii.

MONTREUX (Switzerland). See page 526A.

MONTREUX—Continued on next page

MONTREUX—*Continued.*

Montreux.

Grand

Hotel Excelsior et Bon Port.

200 Rooms and Salons. 30 private Bath-rooms. Latest comfort and up-to-date requirements. Modern English Sanitation. Magnificently situated on the shores of the lake, near the Kursaal and Promenade. Large Public rooms, beautifully decorated, with a fine view of the Lake and Mountains. Large Restaurant, American Bar, (English & French Billiards). Fine shady Garden & Terrace on the border of the lake. Moderate terms. Omnibus at the Montreux-station, Steamer and Landing stage. Telegraph address: Excelsior-Montreux.

L. BARONI, Manager.

MONTREUX.

GRAND HOTEL SUISSE.

One of the Finest and most Up to date Hotels in Montreux.

Opposite the Landing Stage and near the Station. Terms from **10 frs.**
Every Room with Balcony overlooking the Lake. — Renowned for its excellent Cuisine.

MONTREUX.

GRAND HOTEL EDEN

FIRST CLASS ENGLISH FAMILY HOTEL.

Magnificent situation on the border of the Lake.

Promenade "QUAI DU MIDI."

Next to the Kursaal. Every Modern Comfort. Lift. Central Heating. Rooms and Apartments with Bath and Toilette. Garden. Garage. Moderate Terms. PENSION FROM 9 FRS. Cook's Coupons accepted.

E. EBERHARD, Proprietor.

HOTEL CONTINENTAL.

Family Hotel with Up-to-Date Comfort, in quiet position.

Large Park on the new Quay. Central Heating. Lift. Open all the year round. Omnibus meets trains and boats. Rooms from **3 Frs.** Pension from **8-18 Frs.**

Self-Contained Suites with Bath, Toilette, and W.C.

Golf Links. **H. EULENSTEIN. New Proprietor.**

MONTREUX Continued on next page

MONTREUX—*Continued.*

HOTEL DE PARIS.

HOTEL specially recommended for families. Excellent situation in the centre of Montreux, facing the Kursaal, and near the Catholic Church. Lounge. Salons. Winter Garden. Recreation Room. Central Heating. Electric Light throughout. Lift. Renowned Cuisine. Arrangements for prolonged stay from 8 francs per day. Tariff on application.

L. MOINAT, Proprietor.

Montreux.

HOTEL DE l'EUROPE.

FIRST CLASS FAMILY HOTEL.

Especially patronised by English Society. Unrivalled position. Close to the Station. Standing up high from the Lake. Replete with all modern comfort.

Terms from Frs. 8. — FAMILLE BETTSCHEN.

Branch House: **GRAND HOTEL, Mont Barry-les-Bains, in the Gruyeres Alps.**

Finest Scenery. * 3 hours from Montreux by the new Electric Railway: Montreux—Mont Bovon—Bulle. Station, Le Paquir. * Finest Scenery.

Special terms Spring and Autumn. Season from May to September. Pension from **frs. 7.**

HOTEL MIRABEAU

First Class. Apartments with bath. Garage.

Large shady park on the border of the Lake. Pension from 9 francs.

HOTEL BEAU RIVAGE.

FIRST CLASS FAMILY HOTEL, in the most sheltered position. Much frequented by English Families. Central for Sports, Amusements, Church, and English Club. Central Heating. Electric Light. Billiards. Golf. Tennis. Dances. Concerts. Pension from 7 Frs. Lift. **J. M. SPALINGER, Proprietor.**

HOTEL VICTORIA.

COMFORTABLE FAMILY HOTEL, nicely situated above the stations, in the centre of all excursions. Electric Light. Warm Water Heating. Hall. Salons. Garden. Terms from 6 fr. per day according to season. — **Meals served at separate tables.**

J. DECASPER, Proprietor.

Hotel Pension Richemond

MONTREUX.

WELL KNOWN ENGLISH FAMILY HOTEL. Charming quiet position, near the Lake and Kursaal, between the Promenades. Modern comfort. Central Heating. **Excellent Table.** Special arrangements for families and long stay. Pension Terms from **Frs. 7.** Open all the year.

HOTEL des PALMIERS—same management. Entirely renovated 1912. Open all the year. Terms from **Frs. 7.** — **G. WOERNER,** Managing Propr.

TRAVEL and HOTEL ENQUIRIES—See page xii.

MONTREUX—Continued on next page

TRAVEL and HOTEL ENQUIRIES—See page xii.

MONTREUX—Continued on next page

MUNICH—Continued on next page.

MUNICH—The Art Centre of Germany.

HOTEL CONTINENTAL

The Most Refined, Artistic, and Up-to-Date Hotel de Luxe.

Rebuilt and Refurnished with all the latest comforts and conveniences in 1912.

Grand Hotel Bellevue

ENTIRELY REBUILT.  **ENTIRELY REBUILT.**

Opened April, 1913.

Leading First Class Hotel, with every modern comfort and luxury. 150 Rooms and Sitting Rooms. 60 Bathrooms; private Suites with Bathroom and Toilet. Hot and cold running water and long distance telephone in every room. Magnificent public Rooms. Elegant Restaurant with Terrace. Garage. Rooms from Mks. **4,** upwards.

Proprietor: W. FRANTZMANN. — Manager: H. KREITTMAYR.

TRAVEL and HOTEL ENQUIRIES—See page xii.

MUNICH—*Continued*

MUNICH—Continued on next page.

MUNICH—*Continued.*

MUNICH—Continued on next page.

MUNICH—*Continued.*

TRAVEL and HOTEL ENQUIRIES—See page xii.

MUNICH—*Continued.*

Bradshaw's Guide.

TRAVEL ENQUIRY DEPARTMENT.—This Department has proved of efficient service both to hotel-keepers and the travelling public. Prospectuses of clients whose announcements appear in Bradshaw's Guide are kept for inspection or distribution at the Company's Offices in London, Liverpool, Manchester, Glasgow, and Dublin. For further particulars see page xii.

MÜNSTER-am-Stein.—See page 487.

NAPLES—*Continued.*

NAUHEIM BAD *-Continued.*

NAUHEIM—Continued on next page.

TRAVEL and HOTEL ENQUIRIES—See page xii.

NAUHEIM BAD—*Continued.*

TRAVEL and HOTEL ENQUIRIES—See page xii.

NEUHAUSEN—SCHAFFHAUSEN (Switzerland).—See p. 528.

NICE.—See page 409.

NICE.

HOTEL DE FRANCE

AVENUE MASSENA (Jardin Public).

Opened 1st of October.

Private Baths WITH Bedrooms AND Apartments.

BEST SITUATION.

Steam Heating.

LIFT.

New Proprietor, **E. WEBER, Junr.**

Late Manager, Hotel Beausite, Cannes.
" " Hotel Victoria, Homburg.

Branch Houses
- HOTEL de la PAIX, Geneva.
- HOTEL VICTORIA, Homburg (Bad), near Frankfort.
- HOTEL VICTORIA, Beatenberg, near Interlaken.

TRAVEL and HOTEL ENQUIRIES—See page xii.

NICE

37, Promenade des Anglais, 37.

HOTEL NEGRESCO

First Class Hotel and Restaurant.

300 Bed Rooms and Sitting Rooms, each Bed Room with private Bath Room adjoining. Telephone in each Room.

Opened in December, 1912.

MODERATE TARIFF THROUGHOUT THE HOUSE.

Under the Personal Direction and Management of— **H. NEGRESCO** of the RESTAURANT du CASINO MUNICIPAL de NICE.

NICE—Continued on next page.

TRAVEL and HOTEL ENQUIRIES—See page xii.

NICE—*Continued.*

NICE—Continued on next page

NICE—*Continued.*

TRAVEL and HOTEL ENQUIRIES—See page xii.

NICE—*Continued.*

NICE. LE TERMINUS HOTEL.

THE only Up-to-date First Class House opposite Railway Station. Open the whole year. Numerous Single Rooms and private Suites with Baths. 200 Beds. Vacuum Cleaner Rooms from 4.50 frs. Luggage carried up to the Hotel free of charge. Propr.: HENRI MORLOCK.

NICE. HOTEL de BERNE.

OPPOSITE RAILWAY STATION. Open the whole year. Every comfort. Rooms from 3 frs. Very advantageous inclusive terms. — Luggage carried up to the Hotel free of charge.

Proprietor: HENRI MORLOCK.

GRAND HOTEL DES ILES BRITANNIQUES.

— BOULEVARD VICTOR HUGO. —

FIRST CLASS, with every modern comfort. Central Heating and Electric Light throughout. Lift. Large Hall. Beautiful Dining Rooms. Apartments with bath and toilette attached. 200 Beds. Terms from 10 frs. per day. Patronized by English. BAEBLER & BUCHLI, New Proprs.

NICE.

HOTEL METROPOLE & PARADIS.

FIRST CLASS HOTEL.

Best position Boulevard Victor Hugo, with all modern comfort.

L. KOMMERELL, Proprietor.

NICE. HOTEL SUISSE.

— FIRST CLASS SWISS HOUSE. —

English Sanitation. — Splendidly situated near sea. — Lift. — Garden. Baths. Central Heating. Reputed for comfort, cleanliness, moderate charges.

J. P. HUG, Proprietor.

— NICE. —

PALACE HOTEL PLACE MAGENTA. 2 à 6, Rue Alphonse Karr.

EVERY MODERN COMFORT. — UP-TO-DATE.

VERY CENTRAL. LARGE GARDEN. W. MEYER, Proprietor.

NICE. HOTEL DU LOUVRE. Boulevard Victor Hugo

Modern First Class Family Hotel. Situated in the most central and most aristocratic part of Nice. Lately completely renovated; all the latest improvements including latest sanitary arrangements. — Renowned French Cuisine. — INCLUSIVE TERMS from 10/6. — Special arrangements for protracted stay.

New Proprietor: CHS. BOMMER. *(In Summer: Villa Maria, Lucerne).*

NICE—Continued on next page.

TRAVEL and HOTEL ENQUIRIES—See page xii.

NICE (Mont-Boron).—See page 410.

OBERHOF—Continued on next page

OBERHOF—*Continued.*

Hotel Thüringer Wald.

WELL KNOWN First Class Family Hotel, rebuilt in 1912, and fitted up with **every modern comfort and convenience.** The oldest established and largest Hotel in Oberhof. Open the whole year. Hot and cold running water in every room. Electric Lift. Patronised by the highest Society. Pension from **Mks. 7.50**. Garage. Prospectus from Bradshaw's Offices or the—

Proprietor: FRITZ FLEISCHER.

OBERHOFEN (Switzerland).—See page 527.

OBERHOFEN (Lake of Thun, Switzerland).

Hotel Montana.

Newly built First Class Family Hotel. Up-to-date in every respect. Apartments with Baths and Toilets. Large shady Park. Tennis Court designed by English expert. Pension from **7 fr.** upwards. — CH. JMMER, Propr.

OBERHOFEN-HILTERFINGEN, Switzerland.—See page 527.

HOTEL WILDBOLZ.

JUST COMPLETED, with all latest comforts. Elevated position with magnificent view of the lake and Alps. Large hall and verandah, numerous balconies, electric light, central heating, lift, baths. Delightful garden right down to lake, with own bath house and row boats. **Fishing.** Good steamer connexion with Thun and Interlaken (Kursaal). Pension from **7.50 Frs.** Open all year. Illustrated Prospectus free.

FAMILY WILDBOLZ, Propr.

OBERHOFEN-HILTERFINGEN 10 minutes from Steamer Landing Stage and 30 from Thun.

PENSION HILTERFINGEN THUNERSEE.

HIGH CLASS. Perfect Sanitation. Central Heating. Open all the year. Situated in its own extensive grounds. Commanding full view of Lake and snow mountains. Own rowing boats. on Lake of Thun free of charge. Pension from **6 Francs.**

Own Bathing Establishment on the Lake. **A. MARBACH, Proprietor.**

ORLEANS (France).—See page 411

GRAND HOTEL AND HOTEL ST. AIGNAN

FIRST CLASS HOUSE.

REPLETE with every comfort. European Reputation. Table d'Hôte and meals served at separate tables. Smoking and Ladies' Drawing Room. Private Apartments with Drawing Room, Bath Room, and Toilette. Lift. Electric Light throughout. Central Heating in each Room. Telephone. Large Auto-Garage. Situation exceptionally pleasant on the Square Bannier. Special arrangements for families during Winter. English spoken.

Pension Terms for a stay of at least 3 days.

Dr. DESCHAMPS-LEMAÌRE, Proprietor.

TRAVEL and HOTEL ENQUIRIES—See page xii.

OSTEND—Continued on next page

OSTEND.—*Continued.*

THE SPLENDID

Finest situation, facing the Sea and Baths, and next to the Palace of the Royal Family.

ALL MODERN COMFORT.

400 BEDS AND SALOONS.

Rooms from 6 frs., light and attendance included.
Pension, 16 shillings to £1 a day according to location of room.
Meals served at tables séparées.

Cable Address:

'SPLENDID, OSTEND.'

The GAND ET ALBION HOTEL,
In town, close to the Sea.
Popular Prices. Apply for Tariff.

GRAND HOTEL KURSAAL

AND BEAU SITE.

The best situated on the Sea, all Rooms being front.

PATRONIZED MOSTLY BY ENGLISH AND AMERICAN FAMILIES.

Lift. — Lighted throughout by Electricity. — Lift.

Arrangements, full board 12 to 16 shillings a day, according to floor; all meals at separate tables. Rooms from 4 francs.

Address for Letters and Cablegrams: **HOTEL KURSAAL, OSTEND.**

The GAND et ALBION HOTEL, in town, close to the Sea. Popular Prices. Apply for Tariff.

OSTEND—Continued on next page

TRAVEL and HOTEL ENQUIRIES—See page xii.

OSTEND—*Continued.*

PALERMO (Sicily—Italy).—See page 563.

PALLANZA (Italy).—See page 551.

GRAND EDEN HOTEL

UNRIVALLED SITUATION, on Cape Castagnola, with famous Deer Park. Open the year round. Renovated throughout and enlarged. Best Sanitary Fittings. Apartments with Bath and w.c. Well known for cleanliness and superior catering. Steam Heating in all the Rooms. Lift. Garage. Pension terms. — **J. & P. STAMM, Swiss Managing Proprietors.**

Branch Hotel: Holland Hotel. Baden Baden. For many years Caterers in England and British Colonies.

Pallanza

(Simplon Line),

Lago Maggiore.

Gd. Hotel et Hotel Pallanza.

OPEN all the Year round. First Class. Apartments with Private Bath Rooms. Central Heating. Lift. Electric Light. English Church Services. Railway tickets and booking office. Extensive gardens overlooking the Lake and facing the Borromean Islands.

Auto-Garage. — **G. and A. ANZANI, Proprietors.**

PALLANZA (Lago Maggiore).

NEW

SIMPLON HOTEL.

NEW

Every Modern Comfort at reasonable terms.

FAMILY A. FANCONI, from Samaden, Engadine.

PALMA.—See page 582.

BALEARIC ISLANDS. PALMA, MAJORCA.

Best Winter Resort.

Mild Climate.

GRAND HOTEL

In the Centre of the City.

With a Branch House: HOTEL VILLA VICTORIA,

Quite on the edge of the Sea, with Large Gardens and Terraces, at about 1¼ miles from the Grand Hotel. **First Class Houses, open all the year.**

Central Heating. Electric Lift. Smoking and Billiard Rooms. Moderate Terms.

Special Motor Cars and Carriages for Excursions on Hire. Prospectus on application.

Departures: from MARSEILLES Every Wednesday; from BARCELONA 5 times a Week.

TWO EXPRESS SERVICES WEEKLY from BARCELONA—Tuesday and Friday.

PARAMÉ (near St. Malo) France.—See page 419.

PARAMÉ IS THE MOST CHARMING SEA SIDE RESORT.

GRAND HOTEL DE PARAMÉ.

Near St. Malo, Brittany.

Large Garage. Omnibus meets all trains and steamers.

FIRST CLASS ESTABLISHMENT, overlooking the finest sandy sea shore in France. Close to Casino and Bathing. Charming panoramas, picturesque scenery. Sunny and very salubrious Climate. Interesting excursions, such as Mont St. Michel, Jersey, etc. **200 Rooms and Sitting Rooms. Beautiful Dining Room.** Large shady gardens. Splendid Terrace. Hot Baths and Telegraph in the Hotel. Hair Dresser's Room. Dark Room for Photographers.

Pension terms from **10** frs. LAFOSSE, Propr.

PARIS.—See page 411.

PARIS.

GRAND HOTEL

CLOSE TO THE GRAND OPERA.

ENTIRELY RENOVATED.

All modern comfort. Telephone in every room.

250 Private bathrooms. Hot & cold running water.

ROOMS from 6 Frs.

LUNCHEON, 5 Frs. • DINNER, 7 Frs.

APPLY FOR PAMPHLET No. 12 TO THE MANAGER.

PARIS—Continued on next page

PARIS—*Continued.*

TRAVEL and HOTEL ENQUIRIES—See page xii.

PARIS—Continued on next page

PARIS—*Continued.*

TRAVEL and HOTEL ENQUIRIES—See page xii.

PARIS—Continued on next page.

TRAVEL and HOTEL ENQUIRIES—See page xii.

PARIS—Continued on next page.

TRAVEL and HOTEL ENQUIRIES—See page xii.

PARIS—*Continued.*

PARIS—Continued on next page.

PARIS—*Continued.*

PARIS—*Continued.*

ALL LATEST IMPROVEMENTS.

First Class in every respect.

LIFT.

Beautiful Hall and Public Rooms.

IN ALL THE ROOMS RUNNING HOT AND COLD WATER and CENTRAL HEATING.

TELEPHONE: 242-71.

HOTEL DE LILLE ET D'ALBION

Situated between the Place Vendôme, the Tuileries Garden, the Opéra House, and the Comédie-Francaise.

INCLUSIVE TERMS.

223, Rue Saint-Honoré.

NUMEROUS PRIVATE AND PUBLIC BATHROOMS.

CH. GENEYNE, Manager.

Telegraphic Address: LILLALBION-PARIS.

Paris

HOTEL LUTETIA

— AND —

RESTAURANT.

43, Boulevard Raspail, Square du Bon Marché.

10 Minutes by the Metropolitan from the Madeleine and Grand Boulevards.

230

ROOMS AND SUITES WITH BATHS.

90 BATH-ROOMS.

ROOM from **5** Francs, Attendance and Light inclusive.

I. CADILLAT. Manager.

PARIS—Continued on next page

PARIS—*Continued.*

Hotel de France et Choiseul.

239–241, Rue St. Honoré, Place Vendome. Near the Tuileries Gardens.

Small and large apartments with private Bathrooms and Single Bedrooms.

APARTMENTS AND ROOMS HEATED BY STEAM.

MODERATE PRICES. — LIFTS. — TELEPHONE. — ELECTRIC LIGHT.

Luncheons and Dinners at separate tables. Restaurant à la Carte.

Telegraphic Address: FRANCHEUL—PARIS.

HOTEL LOUVOIS

SQUARE LOUVOIS, Near the Opera and Grand Boulevards.

NEW. = Hot and Cold Water. Private Bathrooms. = Central and quiet.

Telegraphic Address: HOTEL LOUVOIS, PARIS.

F. MOLLARD, Managing Proprietor.

HOTEL CASTIGLIONE.

PARIS. — 12, RUE CASTIGLIONE. — PARIS.

FIRST CLASS FAMILY HOTEL.

Near the Tuileries Garden and Place Vendome. Very Central.

EVERY SUITE OF ROOMS HAS ITS OWN BATH.

Steam Heating Throughout. — J. BORGO, Proprietor.

HOTEL LOUIS-LE-GRAND

Re-opened at 3, RUE ROUGET de l'ISLE.

Most quiet situation opposite Continental Hotel and facing the Tuileries Garden.

ENTIRELY remodelled and fitted throughout with all modern improvements. Electric Lift. Central Heating. Telephone and **Hot and Cold running water** in every room. Vacuum cleaning process. Apartments with Private Bath and Toilet. Renowned for its excellent cooking.

Very Moderate Inclusive Terms.

Telegraphic Address: "OTELBLET, PARIS." — EMILE BLET, Proprietor.

PARIS—Continued on next page.

PARIS—Continued on next page.

PARIS—*Continued.*

LONDON & NEW YORK HOTEL

13 & 15, PLACE DU HAVRE.

Opposite St. Lazare Station. The most central situation in Paris.

Entirely Renovated. Every Modern Comfort.

Hot and Cold Running Water. . .
Rooms with Private Baths attached. • English Sanitary Plumbing.

Established 75 years, well known for comfort and moderation of prices.

Patronized by English Families.

Telegraphic Address: "LONDORK, PARIS." H. DEHOUVE, Proprietor-Manager.

HOTEL G[de] BRETAGNE

14, Rue Caumartin. Near the Madeleine and Opera, in proximity to the Grand Boulevards and Gare St. Lazare.

Special terms for a long stay. Reduced prices during the Winter Season.

ENTIRELY rebuilt and fitted throughout with all improvements, and possesses now 100 most comfortably furnished Bed rooms and about 30 Bath rooms, as well as a great number of private sitting rooms. Each Bed room has a special toilette room with constant supply of hot and cold running water. Large Entrance Hall. Winter Garden. Roof Garden. Tastefully decorated Drawing Rooms. Bar. Smoking and Dining Rooms. Steam heating. Lift.

HOTEL MEYERBEER.

ROND POINT des CHAMPS ELYSÉES, PARIS.

FULL SOUTH. FINEST SITUATION. EVERY MODERN COMFORT.

Steam Heating. Private Bath Rooms. SEGUIN, Proprietor.

HOTEL CHATHAM

19, Rue Daunou, PARIS

BETWEEN RUE DE LA PAIX AND THE BOULEVARDS

THIS Old Established Hotel has been partially rebuilt; has suites of rooms with bathrooms attached. **Luxurious New Volney Restaurant.** Very old wine cellars. Verandah on large, airy, and quiet courtyard. Excellent cuisine. Electric Light. Lift. Modern Sanitation.

Telegrams: "Chathamel-Paris." **Manager: C. MICHAUT.** Telephone 247 53.—Ligne Interurbaine No. 68.

HOTEL BELLEVUE

39, AVENUE de l'OPERA, PARIS.

FINEST CENTRAL SITUATION. Facing the Opera House. Table d'Hote: Luncheon and Dinner served at separate tables. Reading and Smoking Rooms. Lift. Baths. Electric Light throughout. Steam Heating in every Room. Single Rooms from 5 frs.; Double Rooms 9 frs.; attendance and light included. Special moderate terms for the winter. **Telephone No. 232-76.**

Cable Address "HOTEL BELLEVUE, PARIS." Mme. V. L. HAUSER, Proprietress.

TRAVEL and HOTEL ENQUIRIES—See page xii.

PARIS—*Continued.*

PARIS—Continued on next page.

PARIS—*Continued.*

TRAVEL and HOTEL ENQUIRIES—See page xii.

PARIS—*Continued.*

PARIS—Continued on next page.

PARIS—*Continued.*

HOTEL FRANCAIS

13, RUE DE STRASBOURG.

Facing the EASTERN STATION and only 2 minutes from the NORD STATION.

Rooms from 3/6 per day.

Excellent Table; moderate Service. — Telegraphic Address: HOTEFRANC, PARIS.

PARIS. **HOTEL SUISSE.** PARIS.

5, RUE LAFAYETTE. Near the Opera and the Grands Boulevards. DEROSSI, Proprietor.

Lift. Central Heating. Electricity. Baths.

Rooms from 5 francs and upwards. Board from 9.50 (Service at separate tables).

Telegraphic Address: SCHWEIZERHOF. PARIS. Telephone 232-55.

The English Private Hotel Pension

11 bis, Rue Lord Byron (Champs-Elysées).

VERY Comfortable Boarding House. Conveniently situated in the most fashionable part of Paris. Close to Churches, Museums, Art Schools. Underground, Tramways, Omnibuses to all parts of the city. Bath Room. Electric Light. Steam heating. French and English spoken. Terms from **6/-** per day; from **£8** per month. Highest references. — **MISS CAHILL.**

PENSION HAWKES.

7, Avenue du Trocadero, Champs Elysées.

Easy access to all parts. Baths. Central Heating. Electric Light. Good Cellar.

PENSION TERMS from **frs. 8.** BED and BREAKFAST from **frs. 4.**

Visitors received by Day or Month. Telephone 655, 33. **Madame LASCOMBE, Successor.**

HOTEL-PENSION ST. RAPHAEL.

5, Rue des Pyramides.

HIGHLY RECOMMENDED. — Situated in one of the nicest and most convenient parts of Paris, near the Louvre, Tuileries Gardens, Place Vendôme, Opera, and all the leading theatres. Entirely renovated. Lift. Electric Light. Central Heating. Bath Rooms. Excellent cooking. Comfortable bed rooms with or without board. FULL BOARD from **10 Frs.** per day.

BERTHE KUHLING & CO., Proprietors.

PARTENKIRCHEN (Bavaria).—See page 488.

PARTENKIRCHEN (Bavarian Highlands).

HOTEL HAUS GIBSON.

With Park-Villa and Landhaus Gibson.

FIRST CLASS Family Hotel, in finest position, adjoining the woods, in own large Park. Every modern comfort. Apartments with Bath and Toilet. Tennis Court. Sun and Swimming Baths. Garage. Open all the year. Winter sport. Telephone 1181. **Fr. STANNER, Proprietor.**

PARTENKIRCHEN (Bavarian Highlands).

Alpen-Kurhaus "Schönblick."

2,395 Feet above Sea Level.

NEW Modern Family Hotel, quietly situated in a very large Park. Elegant public rooms. Warm water heating. Hot water in all toilettes and on every floor. Passenger and luggage lift. Electric light. Vacuum cleaner. Single rooms and apartments. Terms "en Pension,"

PAU (France).—See page 415.

PAU. **GRAND HOTEL GASSION**

Newly and thoroughly re-furnished and greatly improved by the present Proprietor, M. MEILLON.

FIRST CLASS ESTABLISHMENT, of remarkable construction, situated Boulevard du Midi, near the Chateau Henry IV. Splendid Panoramic View. Winter Garden. Excellent accommodation combined with moderate charges. Suites with Baths. Bath-rooms. Best Sanitary arrangements. Electric Light. Railway Tickets. **Steam Heating throughout. Telephone. Lift. OPEN ALL THE YEAR.**

GD. HOTEL DU PALAIS ET BEAU-SEJOUR

SITUATED NEXT TO THE PALAIS D'HIVER, ON THE BOULEVARD DU MIDI.

FIRST CLASS HOTEL. 160 Rooms and 25 Salons. Unique view of the Pyrenees. Due South. Lift. Telephone. Steam Heating and Electric Light throughout. Recommended to Families. Open all the year round. **F. BONNAFON,** Propr

Hotel de France

F. CAMPAGNE, New Proprietor.

Entirely Rebuilt. Refurnished by Maple & Co. Magnificent Hall and Salons. Apartments and rooms with Baths. — Unsurpassed View of the Pyrenées. — Electric Lift. — Modern Garage free to Visitors. .... STEAM HEATING THROUGHOUT. ....

The "GRAND RESTAURANT," EQUAL TO THE BEST OF PARIS, IS OPEN ALL THE YEAR.

MAISON COLBERT. PAU.

— (RUE MONTPENSIER). —

First Class Pension (kept by the daughters of an English Physician). Highly recommended for its good table and every comfort and attention. Nearest the English Churches. Not far from the Golf Links. Large Garden. Tennis. Croquet. Perfect Sanitation. Electric Light. Telephone 2.78. Moderate Charges. Apply to the Proprietors.

PAU. The ENGLISH BANK F. J. Ayrton.

ANGLO AMERICAN WINE AND ESTATE AGENCY.

27, RUE DU LYCÉE.

Depot for Messrs. BARTON & GUESTIER, Bordeaux. AYALA & CO., Ay. SANDEMAN & CO., London. ACKERMAN-LAURANCE, Saumur.

Pau representative of—

Messrs. Thos. COOK & Son. | All information gratis. | Depot of English Tea, China and Ceylon.

PERUGIA (Italy).—See page 551A.

PERUGIA.

BRUFANI'S GRAND HOTEL

The only Establishment built expressly for an Hotel.

With all modern comfort. —— Commands one of the finest views in Italy. Apartments with bath and toilet en suite. Electric Lifts. Central hot-water) heating in every room. Large Library. Moderate terms. Auto Garage. Special Electric Car meets all trains.

GEORGE J. COLLINS, Proprietor.

PERUGIA—Continued on next page.

PERUGIA—*Continued.*

PERUGIA

Palace Hotel.

Opened 1903. — The Newest and most Modern Hotel. — Full South — Splendid View.

POST AND TELEGRAPH OFFICES IN THE HOTEL. GARAGE.

Special Electric Omnibus at the Station Terms fr. 10 frs. F. CHIARI & C. GAGLIARDI, Proprs.

PFORZHEIM (Germany).—See page 459.

HOTEL RUF

FIRST CLASS, in finest position facing the Station.

Splendid view of the Black Forest. *** The Finest Hotel in Pforzheim.
Cold and Warm Water in each Room. Many private apartments with Bath.

Every Comfort. Proprietor, E. RUF.

PISA (Italy).— See page 551A.

PISA.

FIRST CLASS.

Grand Hotel & de Londres

UNRIVALLED POSITION facing the ARNO (with 48 Windows and Balconies). FULL SOUTH

Electric Lift. Electric Light. Central (Hot Water) Heating.

Apartments with Private Bath and Lavatory.

RESTAURANT. GARAGE. MODERATE CHARGES.

Telephone No. 3-43. — Proprietor: NEW COMPANY, Ltd.

PLOMBIÈRES (Vosges—France).—See page 416.

LE GRAND HOTEL (ex NAPOLEON).

The only Hotels connected with the Bath Establishment.

All modern comforts.

BOXES & CARAGES FOR 20 CARS. APARTMENTS WITH PRIVATE BATH ROOMS.

CAROLET, Proprietor. In Winter, West End Hotel, Nice.

TRAVEL and HOTEL ENQUIRIES—See page xii.

Engadine—PONTRESINA (Switzerland).—See page 527A

Altitude 5,915 feet. Altitude 5,915 feet.

GRAND HOTEL KRONENHOF & BELLAVISTA

FIRST CLASS. 250 BEDROOMS. Greatly Enlarged and Embellished.

THE new Bedrooms are in a sunny position with fine view on the Roseg Glacier. Large Hall with open fire places. Lift. Fire-proof staircase. Baths on each floor. Beautiful Public Rooms. Electric Light and steam heating throughout. English drainage. Cuisine and Wines excellent. Reduced terms in Spring and Autumn. The Hotel is largely frequented by English and American visitors. *Recommended by the Travel Editor of "The Queen."* Private Tennis Court.

Summer and Winter Season.

GREDIG, Managing Proprietor.

PONTRESINA (Engadine).

HOTEL ROSEG

FIRST CLASS, in the very best and most elevated position of the Spot, out of the village, facing the beautiful Roseg Glacier. Large Garden and private Tennis Court. Every modern comfort, best table, and excellent wines. Large new Hall. Suites with private baths, toilette and w.c. Best sanitary arrangements. Mostly patronised by English clientele. Moderate charges. Central Hot Water Heating throughout.

A. F. ZAMBAIL, Proprietor-Manager.

PONTRESINA—Continued on next page.

Engadine—PONTRESINA (Switzerland)—*Continued.*

Pontresina

Upper-Engadine.

SELECT FIRST CLASS HOTEL. 200 Beds.
Summer and Winter Season. OPENED 1908.

SCHLOSSHOTEL-ENDERLIN.

Proprietors: FAMILY ENDERLIN. Manager: U. GREDIG-ENDERLIN.

PONTRESINA (Engadine).

HOTEL PONTRESINA.

(OPEN SUMMER AND WINTER).

FIRST Class Hotel. Magnificent situation. Full South. 150 Rooms and Apartments with Bath. Central Hot Water Heating in every room. Large Garden and private woods. Lawn Tennis. Winter Sports. English Church. **H. BECK, Manager.**

PONTRESINA. ENGADINE (Switzerland).

HOTEL LANGUARD

First Class, in open position.

Magnificent views of the Mountains. — Quiet, recommended for a protracted stay. Excellent Cooking. Fine Wines. Moderate terms.

Electric Light. Lift. Central Heating. Baths. — Omnibus meets trains.

GREDIG BROS. & CO., Propr s.

PORTOFINO (Italy).—See page 556.

N.B.—Portofino is invisible from "Portofino-Kulm," which is 22 Kilometers distant. Travellers should distinguish between Portofino and Portofino-Kulm.

PORTOFINO—HOTEL SPLENDID

QUEEN OF THE MEDITERRANEAN RESORTS. OPEN OCTOBER 1 TO MAY 31. The only First Class Hotel in Portofino and district. 25 minutes from Santa Margherita Railway Station. Omnibuses and Carriages meet all trains. All Rooms full South. Beautiful Park, Gardens, and Pine Woods. Complete shelter facing the unrivalled Gullio Bay. — *Telegraphic Address:* "SPLENDID," PORTOFINO.

E. KUHN, Manager.

PRAGS (Tyrol).—See page 502.

HOTEL WILDSEE

(4,920 feet above Sea).

FIRST CLASS charmingly situated Hotel, on the Lake, with all comforts:

1¼ hour from Niederdorf Station.

Lovely part of the Dolomites. Pine Forests.

Good Fishing, free.

Specially recommended to English and Americans as an ideal Alpine Resort.

TRAVEL and HOTEL ENQUIRIES—See page xii.

PRAGUE (Bohemia).—See page 502.

RAGAZ (Switzerland).—See page 527A.

RAPALLO, near Sta. Margherita (Italy).—See page 552.

ONE HOUR FROM GENOA (GENOA—SPEZIA LINE.)

IMPERIAL PALACE HOTEL

FIRST CLASS HOUSE. Greatest modern comfort. Lift. Baths. Central Heating. Electric light. Spring Water. Luxuriously furnished. Sumptuous apartments. Magnificent palm garden. Tranquil situation. View of the entire panorama of the charming gulf from Portofino to Sestri Levante. **Arrival Stations—Santa Margherita (the nearest to the Hotel), and Rapallo. Omnibus at both Stations.** Telephone No. 148.25. **ANTONIO and LUCA, BROTHERS CUBA, and G. MARAGLIANO.**

HELVETIA PALACE PARC HOTEL

FULL SOUTH, First Class Family House, expressly built as a hotel with every modern improvement and comfort. Splendid Ladies' Drawing room, Billiard, and Smoking rooms. All front rooms with large balconies. The only Hotel in Rapallo with beautiful Garden right to the Sea, with Terrace and Private Boat landing-stage. Wonderful outlook over the Golf Tigulio and Portofino. Private suites with baths. Open all the year. Garage. Tel. 148-20.

G. CAMPO, Proprietor.

THE NEW BRISTOL HOTEL

STRICTLY FIRST CLASS. Expressly built for an Hotel, and equipped with every modern comfort. Most Perfect Sanitation. Unquestionably the most Healthy; unrivalled position, facing full South, in midst of large Garden, and commanding magnificent view of the whole Gulf and surrounding mountains. Every room with large balcony. American Bar. Roller Skating Rink. Billiards. Splendid Large Lounge. All Public Rooms Full South. Apartments with Private Bath, Dressing Room, and Toilette attached. *Apply for Illustrated Brochure.*

Proprietors : **AGRIFOGLIO & BIANCHI.** — **ROBERT STALDER,** *Manager.*

TRAVEL and HOTEL ENQUIRIES—See page xii.

RHEIMS (France).—See page 417.

HOTEL du LION d'OR

FIRST CLASS HOTEL, facing the Cathedral. Most healthy position. Comfortable Public and Private Rooms. Apartments for Families. Smoking Room. Bath Rooms. Electric Light. Steam Heating. Table d'Hote and Restaurant à la Carte. Famous Cuisine and Cellar. American Bar. Large Court and Gardens. Garage. Motor-bus meets all trains.

Telephone No. 668. * English and German spoken.

PFISTER & CO., Proprietors.

LE GRAND HOTEL

RHEIMS.

VERY FIRST CLASS, the largest in the district, near the Cathedral. The only hotel with lift. Steam Heating throughout. Electricity. Rooms with private baths and toilet. English sanitary arrangement. Recommended Restaurant. Large Lounge Hall. Roof Garden with beautiful view of the Cathedral. Garage with pit. Telephone 530. E. MULATIER, Manager.

RIPPOLDSAU BAD (Black Forest).—See page 459.

BAD RIPPOLDSAU

BLACK FOREST. 2,000 ft.

Railway Stations { WOLFACH—from Frankfurt, Strassburg, and Constanz. FREUDENSTADT—from Stuttgart.

FERRUGINUS BATHS. — IRON MUD BATHS. — DIETETIC MEDICAL INSTITUTE.

Most Modern New First Class Hotel. Every comfort.

RIVA (Lake of Garda, Tyrol).—See page 503.

RIVA (Lake of Garda, South Tyrol).

LIDO PALACE HOTEL

FIRST CLASS. — UP-TO-DATE.

Unsurpassed position, directly on the Lake, amidst own large and splendid Park. Suites and Rooms with private Bath and Toilet attached. Modern Garage (boxes) Fishing, Boating, Climbing, Lawn Tennis, and other pastimes. Own Bathing Establishment in the Lake. — Terms Moderate.

EUGEN SCHLAGENHAUFF, Manager (formerly PICCADILLY HOTEL, LONDON).

TRAVEL and HOTEL ENQUIRIES—See page xii.

ROME—See page 554.

The QUIRINAL Hotel

The Hotel which combines true Home Comfort and Luxury.

Unequalled position on famous VIA NAZIONALE (finest street of Rome), in highest and Healthiest part of City.

BEAUTIFUL GARDEN FULL SOUTH.

PRIVATE BATH-ROOMS THROUGHOUT. RESTAURANT FRANCAIS.

Afternoon Concert Teas served in the magnificent Winter Garden.

BUCHER-DURRER, Managing Proprietor.

Branch Houses:—

PALACE HOTEL, Milan. — MEDITERRANEE, Pegli. — PALACE, Lugano.
PALACE, Lucerne. STANSERHORN & BUERGENSTOCK HOTELS near Lucerne.

Rome.

VILLA LUDOVISI

Opposite Queen Margherita's Residence.

By Special Appointment to the Dowager Queen Margherita.

"THE REGINA"

OPENED IN 1905.

By Special Appointment to H.R.H. The Duke of Genoa.

IS

The Hotel

WHICH COMBINES

Comfort and Luxury.

G. BARBIANI, Proprietor.

ROME—Continued on next page.

ROME—*Continued.*

ROME—*Continued.*

ROME—Continued on next page.

ROME—*Continued.*

TRAVEL and HOTEL ENQUIRIES—See page xii.

ROME—*Continued.*

HOTEL LAGO MAGGIORE.

Second Class Hotel, facing the Central Station.

IN finest and healthiest position of the town. Next the Post and Cook's Office and Opera House. Lift, Baths. Electric Light and Central Heating in every room. Rooms from 2.50-4 frs. and 6-8 frs., Light, Heating, and Attendance included. **BETTOJA BROS., Proprietors.**

HOTEL MASSIMO d'AZEGLIO. 250 Rooms. Under same management.

PENSION W. WHITE

Entire 3rd floor of the PALAZZO SIMONETTI, 11, Via Vittorio Colonna.

Central Position: 10 minutes walk to the Piazza di Spagna and the Spanish Steps, also near St. Peter's and the Vatican. Winter terms from **8 frs.** (afternoon tea included). Summer terms from **6.50 frs.** Open all the year. Lift. **Mrs. & Miss WEINREICH-WHITE.**

ALBION PENSION ROME.

(Ludovisi Quarter).

166, Via Sicilia (corner of Via Dogali). Private Villa surrounded by its own garden; situated full South. In the vicinity of all the modern and fashionable Hotels. Quiet and homely. Hot water heating and electric light throughout. Large airy dining-room; separate tables. Excellent cuisine. Five minutes walk from the public gardens (Villa Borghese). Electric Cars to all parts close by. Pension from **8 francs**; special terms to parties.

Telephone 92-87. English Proprietress and Management.

HOTEL PENSION ESEDRA.

PIAZZA TERMINI; Entrance 117, Torino Street (same building as Cook's Office).

FIRST Class Family Hotel in a splendid palace on the Esedra d'Termini. The healthiest and highest location in Rome. Convenient to all trams. Central Heating. Electric Light. Lift. Baths. Table d'hote at separate tables. — Telephone 88—23. — Pension from **8 francs.**

A. ANDREANI, Proprietor.

J. EVANS.

(Late SINIMBERGHI EVANS & Co.)

Chemist to the British and American Embassies.

64, 66, VIA CONDOTTI, ROME.

ENGLISH and American Prescriptions dispensed by qualified English Assistants. Special Agent for Apollinaris and all kinds of Mineral Waters.

RONCEGNO (South Tyrol).—See page 504.

RONCEGNO

FAMOUS CLIMATIC HEALTH RESORT.

1½ Hours from Trient, 3½ from Venice by train. **1,683** feet. Renowned for the Curative Powers of its **Arsenic-Iron Waters** for drinking or bathing. **Ideal Spring-Summer-Autumn Resort.** Most charming situation. Dolomites' view. Invigorating Climate. No Wind. No humidity.

Grand and Palace Hotels

1st Class. 30 Acres of private century old Park of Pines and Fir Woods.

Tennis. Orchestra. Terms moderate. **May-October.**

RONDA (Spain).—See page 573.

RONDA (Andalusia).

HOTEL REINA VICTORIA.

Modern Hotel; furnished by Maple.

Electric Light. — Best Sanitary arrangements. — 2,426 feet above sea level.
Striking Situation. THREE HOURS BY STEAMER and RAIL from GIBRALTAR.

MARK LAW, Manager, Ronda (Andalusia), Spain.

ROTHENBURG (Bavaria)—See page 489.

HOTEL AND KURHAUS WILDBAD.

Rothenburg o.-T.
Bavaria.

THIS FIRST CLASS FAMILY HOTEL is situated in its own Park, with a fine view of the Tauber Valley. Open all the year. Highest comfort. Private Apartments with Baths and Toilette. Electric Light. Central Heating. Lift. Open Air Restaurant. Table d'Hote at separate tables. Special arrangements for prolonged stay. Omnibus from 15th April to 15th October at the Station. Auto Garage. Illustrated Prospectus gratis.

HOFRAT FR. HESSING.

HOTEL GOLDENER HIRSCH. First Class.

CENTRAL AND BEST POSITION.

Beautiful Views. — Every Comfort. — Central Heating. — Electric Light.
Moderate Charges. Garage. **Proprietor: F. BECK.**

ROTTERDAM.—See page 445.

HOTEL LEYGRAAFF Rotterdam.

WESTPLEIN

FOR MERCHANTS, TOURISTS, AND FAMILIES.

PREFERRED for its fine position and great comfort. — TERMS MODERATE.

Telegrams: "LEYGRAAFF, ROTTERDAM."

SPEND A DAY IN ROTTERDAM, the most flourishing and picturesque town of Holland, and stop at the

MAAS HOTEL

A First Class House combining modern comfort with moderate charges

Rooms from 5 shillings upwards.

TRAVEL and HOTEL ENQUIRIES—See page xii.

ROUEN (France).—See page 417.

ROYAT-LES-BAINS (France).—See page 418.

TRAVEL and HOTEL ENQUIRIES—See page xii.

ST. CYR-SUR-MER (France).—See page 418.

THE GRAND HOTEL.

Surrounded by 9 acres of Park and Garden sloping in terraces down to the Sea.

Unique Panorama of Sea and Hills. — Specially recommended for a recreative sojourn. Latest Comforts. Hot and Cold Water supply. Central Heating. Suites with Bath. Telephone and Telegraph. Numerous Excursions and walks.

ST. GERVAIS-LES-BAINS (France).—See page 418.

MONT-JOLY PALACE.

MOST UP-TO-DATE AND FASHIONABLE.

Single Rooms and Suites with Bath. Hot and Cold running water throughout. Large Garden and shady Park. English Church Service at the Hotel.

Next to the Mont Blanc Railway Station. — **G. DORIN, Managing Proprietor.**

Saint-Gervais-les-Bains.

LE GRAND HOTEL FIRST CLASS.

NEAR THE MONT BLANC RAILWAY STATION.

INCOMPARABLE view of the Glaciers and the Mont Blanc Chain. Large Hall. Three Verandah and Terrace. Shady Park. Tennis Lawn. Suites of Apartments with Bath. Rooms with hot and cold water supply. Electric Lift. Central Heating. Telephone No. 5. Garage. Reduced prices during May, June, & Sept.

Address: MARTIN, LE GRAND HOTEL, ST. GERVAIS-LES-BAINS.

LE FAYET BAINS—St. Gervais-les-Bains.—See page 400.

Foot of Mont Blanc. Haute Savoie, France. Hydropathic Establishment and Mineral Spa. Specific for Skin and Nervous Diseases, Eczemas, etc.

GRAND HOTEL DE LE SAVOIE.

Nearest to the Springs. Modern Comforts. Private Park of 120 acres. Golf Links.

ST. JEAN-DE-LUZ (Pyrenées), France.—See page 419.

GRAND HOTEL d'ANGLETERRE

THE HIGH CLASS HOTEL.

TRAVEL and HOTEL ENQUIRIES—See page xii.

ST. JEAN-DE-LUZ—*Continued.*

GOLF HOTEL

THE NEWEST. FULL SOUTH. MAGNIFICENT VIEW OF THE BAY AND PYRENEES. SUITES WITH PRIVATE BATH ROOMS. 2 GARDENS. TENNIS. ELECTRIC LIGHT. **L. FOURNEAU.**

MODERN HOTEL

Best situation on the Beach between the two Golf Links.

ALL MODERN COMFORTS.

Suites with private bath rooms. — For terms apply to— **THE PROPRIETOR.**

ST. MALO (France).—See page 419.

·· ST. MALO. ··

Gd. Hotel de France et Chateaubriand.

Entrance on the Beach.

135 Rooms with Sea View. All modern comforts. Sanitary arrangements. Bath Rooms. Genuine Family Hotel. — Cook's Coupons accepted.

Open from April 1st to October 31st. — **MAISONNEUVE,** Manager

STA. MARGHERITA (Levante), Italy.—See page 556.

THE STRAND HOTEL —Very— First Class.

BUILT on the border of the magnificent Gulf of Tigulio. Full South. It offers to its Visitors the greatest comfort amidst the most pleasant surroundings. Latest Sanitary arrangements. Parquet Floor, Double Doors and Windows to every Room. Electric Light. Central Heating, Baths and Douches, Warm Sea Baths. Lawn Tennis, Garage, etc. Pension from **8 Frs.**

Omnibus meets trains. — Annexe: **HOTEL BELLEVUE.** Pension from **7 Francs.**

Sta. Margherita, Ligure.

GRAND HOTEL CONTINENTAL

VERY First Class with every modern improvement, full South, the best situated, having the largest uninterrupted Park and Garden 20,000 sqr. metres, right down to the Sea, with Terrace and Boat landing stage. Open all the year round. Terms from **9 Lire** upwards, according to Season. Cooks' coupons accepted. Tennis Lawn.

A. CIANA, Proprietor and Manager, Same House **HOTEL BELVEDERE, Orta,** Lake of Orta.

STA. MARGHERITA LIGURE (Levantine Riviera). 45 minutes from Genoa. (Near Rapallo; Line Genoa-Pisa-Rome).

"THE EDEN" GRAND HOTEL GUGLIELMINA

First Class Hotel, Healthy Situation. The Driest, Sunniest, and Warmest position. Magnificent Views of Land and Sea. All the Front Rooms with Balcony. Vast English Hall and grand Verandah. Sheltered from Wind and Dust. Automobile at the Station. Telegraphic Address: Hotel Guglielma, Santa Margherita, Ligure. Inclusive terms from **9 Frs.** per day. ⁂ **GUGLIELMINA BROS., Proprietors.**

STA. MARGHERITA—Continued on next page

TRAVEL and HOTEL ENQUIRIES—See page xii.

ST. MORITZ—Continued on next page

TRAVEL and HOTEL ENQUIRIES—See page xii.

ST. MORITZ—Continued on next page.

ST. MORITZ DORF (Engadine), Switzerland—*Continued.*

St. Moritz (Engadine).	THE HOTEL WALDHAUS
	—70 BEDS— Apartments and Suites with Bathroom. The distinguished FAMILY HOUSE, in finest open situation over Lake. Full South. Summer and Winter Residence. Lawn Tennis. Private Skating Rink. Arrangements from **Frs. 11** per day. Indoor amusements.

St. Moritz-Dorf. **WEST-END HOTEL**

OPEN ALL THE YEAR.

English Family Hotel. Finest sunny position with splendid views.
Excellent Plain Cooking. Balconies. Electric Light. Central Heating. Baths. Latest Sanitary arrangements.
PENSION from **Frs. 9** inclusive. — **J. RUNGGER-CORAY'S ERBEN, Proprietor.**

St. Moritz-Dorf. **HOTEL MONOPOL**

OPENED 1912.

Newest Comfort. * Suites and Single Rooms, with Bath and Toilette
Large elegant RESTAURANT. Moderate Terms. Open all the year.
Management: R. LIPS, Proprietor.

"PENSION KOPP"

ENGLISH and American House. 1st class, beautiful sunny situation, suitable for **Winter and Summer.** Central heating, electric light, bath, cosy ladies' drawing rooms. Meals served at table d'hote and separate tables. Terms from **10 Francs.** For Prospectus address:— **MISS KOPP** (who speaks English), or Bradshaw House, London.

CAMPFER, near ST. MORITZ.—See page 526c.

CAMPFER, near ST. MORITZ. — Summer and Winter Season.

HOTEL CAMPFER

Formerly HOTEL D'ANGLETERRE. 15 minutes drive from St. Moritz.

ONE of the healthiest and prettiest spots in the Upper Engadine. Sunny sheltered position. Excursions in the wood. Electric Light. Central Heating. Modern comfort. Excellent Winter Sports. Well recommended English Hotel. Pension from 10 Frs. **J. MARK, Proprietor.**

BRADSHAW'S SCHOOL DIRECTORY.

Enquiries as to Schools at Home or on the Continent will be answered gratis if particulars of Locality, Age, Approximate Fees, &c., are forwarded to the London Office, Bradshaw House, Surrey Street, Strand, W.C

TRAVEL and HOTEL ENQUIRIES—See page xii.

ST. PETERSBURG.—See page 654, Special Edition.

GRAND HOTEL D'EUROPE

ST. PETERSBURG.

ST. PETERSBURG. **GRAND HOTEL d'EUROPE.**

LEADING ESTABLISHMENT OF THE RESIDENCE.

Most Central Position on the Newski Prospect.

Entirely reconstructed, and fitted up with the greatest comfort.

350 rooms. Apartments with private bath and lavatory.

Bedrooms from **3 roubles** upwards.

Rooms with private Bath from **7 roubles** upwards.

Under Swiss Management.

ONLY HOUSE with Perfect English Sanitary arrangement and vacuum cleaner.

Largest roof garden in Europe with splendid view.

First Class Restaurant and excellent orchestra.

Telegraphic Address:— EUROPOTEL, PETERSBURG.

J. WOLFLISBERG-GIGER, General Manager.

ST. PETERSBURG—Continued on next page.

ST. PETERSBURG—*Continued.*

TRAVEL and HOTEL ENQUIRIES—See page xii.

ST. PETERSBURG—*Continued.*

HOTEL DE FRANCE.

Kept by E. RENAULT.

GREAT MORSKAI, BEST SITUATION IN THE TOWN.

OPPOSITE THE WINTER PALACE, ERMITAGE, FOREIGN OFFICE, & NEWSKI PROSPECT.

Tramway communication through the whole town. ROOMS from 2r. to 25 roub. DINNERS from 1r. 50k. to 3 roub. Renowned Cuisine.

LARGE READING ROOM WITH ALL EUROPEAN NEWSPAPERS.

POST AND TELEGRAPH OFFICE. BATHS.

EXCELLENT GUIDES, AND ALL LANGUAGES SPOKEN.

By the same Proprietor is kept the **Hotel Belle Vue,** just opposite the **Hotel de France.**

ST. PETERSBURG. * Nevsky Prosp. 118.

GRAND HOTEL DU NORD

FIRST CLASS HOTEL with every modern comfort. Central situation just opposite the Moscow Station. 200 Rooms from 2 rbl. to 25 rbl., with Hot and Cold Water. Apartments with Private Bath and Lavatory. Large Dining and splendid Reading and Conversation Rooms. Electric Light. 2 Lifts. Billiards. Hotel Autobus at every train. Correspondence: English, French, German. **W. J. SOLOVIOFF, Proprietor.**

ST. RAPHAEL (near Cannes).—See page 419.

HOTEL CONTINENTAL ET DES BAINS.

Near the Casino and English Church. Open all the year round.

FULL SOUTH. First Class. Highly recommended and worthy of the patronage of English and American Travellers. Every Comfort. Good Cooking. Moderate Charges. Omnibus to all Trains. Heated Throughout. Drainage perfect. Latest Sanitary arrangements (English System). ALFRED MÜLLER, Proprietor.

GRAND HOTEL BEAU RIVAGE.

FIRST CLASS. Unique Situation on Sea Shore. Magnificent View. Full South. Self-contained Apartments with Bath and Toilette. Central Heating in all the rooms. Baths Douches. Excellent French Cuisine. Renowned Cellar. Omnibus at every Train. Pension from 10 francs per day. Lift. Electric Light. — BRUNET, Proprietor.

ST. RAPHAEL.—Continued on next page.

ST. RAPHAEL—*Continued.*

GRAND HOTEL ST. RAPHAEL.

FIRST CLASS HOTEL. Full South. Beautifully situated in its own Garden; splendid view over the Mediterranean, outskirts of the Town, and inland from the Sea. Close to the Anglican Church. Golf Links. Electric Light and Central heating in every room. Latest English Sanitary arrangements. Moderate Charges. Arrangements for Families. Auto-Garage.

W. WAGNER, Proprietor of the HOTEL OBERLAND, INTERLAKEN, SWITZERLAND.

SAINT - RAPHAEL - VALESCURE.

The Anglo-American Agency & Bank

Telegrams: *KING, ST. RAPHAEL.*

W. F. KING.

6, RUE CHARLES GOUNOD

Telephone — 78 —

House and Estate Agents. Railway and Steamship Agency. Banking and Exchange.

VALESCURE—ST. RAPHAEL, see under VALESCURE.

SAN REMO (Riviera—Italy).—See page 556.

SAN REMO (Riviera, Italy).

Savoy Hotel.

— THE MOST MODERN FIRST CLASS HOTEL IN SAN REMO. —

PATRONISED by English and American Society 150 Rooms. Apartments with Private Bath and Lavatory. In elevated position, commanding extensive view of sea and coast; full south. Sheltered from winds, dust, and noise. Large and beautiful garden. Close to the municipal Casino. Hot water heating in all the rooms. Restaurant français. Motor Garage. Golf Links. Afternoon Tea Concert. **PAUL MARINI, Proprietor.**

SAN REMO.

The Royal Hotel

and RESTAURANT. — Auto Garage.

Large Garden. Orchestra. Golf Links. M. BERTOLINI, Proprietor.

SAN REMO.

OPENED
—AUTUMN, 1912.—

Grand Hotel Bellevue & Kurhaus Sanremo.

Season: October 15th to end of May.

Sheltered and dust free, in the midst of old Palm Gardens. 27 apartments with baths. — Dietetic Treatment.

Electro Hydro - Therapeutics. Warm Sea Baths. Reduced Terms until January 1st.

Under the same Management:

HOTEL and KURHAUS ST. BLASIEN (Black Forest).

HÔTEL VICTORIA ET DE ROME

Pension from 8-12 Frs
CENTRAL HEATING.
LIFT. FINE GARDEN.
In Summer: -
TAESCHHORN HOTEL,
TAESCH, near Zermatt (Switzerland).
EMILE LAGGER, Propr.

SAN REMO—Continued on next page.

SAN REMO—*Continued.*

SAN SALVADOUR—See page 886.

SAAS FEE (Switzerland).—See page 528.

SALO (Lago di Garda, Italy).—See page 555.

SALSOMAGGIORE (Italy).—See page 555.

SAMADEN (Switzerland).—See page 528.

TRAVEL and HOTEL ENQUIRIES—See page xii.

SCHEVENINGEN, The HAGUE (Holland).—See page 445.

Fashionable Sea-Side Resort on the North Sea.

(SEASON—JUNE TO SEPTEMBER 30.)

SCHEVENINGEN

THE HAGUE—HOLLAND.

Programme of Entertainments.

Concerts daily by the **Berlin Philharmonic Orchestra** of 80 Performers, including Soloists of the first rank.

Every Friday a **Grand Symphony Concert.**

Every Wednesday, **Concert, assisted by renowned** Soloists.

Every Evening *Réunion dansante* in the Drawing Room.

Large Balls in the Kursaal, small ones in the Theatre. In July and August (in fine weather) Fireworks; also splendid Children's Fêtes and open-air Balls on the Terrace.

In the Theatre, **French Performances by Parisian Actors.**

On the Königin Wilhelmina Pier the Scheveningen Kur-Band plays every day. Magnificent electrical illumination of the Entire Sea Front.

SEA TRIPS BY SALOON STEAMERS.

Circus Performances. Café Concerts. In the Kurhaus-Bar Concerts given by the renowned **Neapolitan Band** and Cercle d'Été.

HORSE RACING. — GOLF CLUB. — LAWN TENNIS.

Splendid Roads for Motoring and Cycling.

PALACE HOTEL — *SAVOY HOTEL*
HOTEL KURHAUS — *GRAND HOTEL*
HOTEL d'ORANGE — *HOTEL RAUCH*

All situated on Scheveningen's splendid Sea Front.

TRAVEL and HOTEL ENQUIRIES—See page xii.

Burg Hotel.

Most Comfortable Hotel.

BEAUTIFULLY situated above the Valley of the "Bode." First Class Cuisine. Electric Light. Central Heating. All International Languages. Instructions in Winter Sport. Head quarters for Bobsleigh and Ski Sport. Open all the Year. Highly recommended by English Families.

Proprietor, A. DRYER.

BARENBERG (near Schierke), Germany.—See page 489.

BARENBERGER HOF formerly KURHOTEL WALDPARK

(GARDEN CITY BARENBERG).

Open Summer & Winter. In Winter reached from Elend Station. **FIRST CLASS.**

Most MODERN House in BEST and HEALTHIEST position.
Hot and Cold Water supply throughout. ∴ Large Public Rooms.
Verandahs. Terraces. Open-Air Treatment.
Well kept level Promenades. Own Rodel Course in Winter.

Excellent cooking, also dietetic cooking if required. Pension from 8 M.

Prospectus on application to the Manager: F. LOESCHER.

SCHINZNACH BAD (Switzerland).—See page 528.

SCHINZNACH (SWITZERLAND), RAILWAY STATION.

BATHS AND HEALTH RESORT.

The strongest Sulphur Springs. Rich in Sulphur and Carbonic Acid. The supply at the Sulphur Springs: half-a-million gallons a day. **Thermal Sulphur Baths, Inhalations, Drinking, and first rate arrangements for Pulverization (great success for perfecting the complexion of young and old).**

Indications: Gout; Rheumatism; Neuralgia; Skin Diseases (Acne disseminata et rosacea, Eczema, Psoriasis, Urticaria, Furunculosis, etc.); Chronic Catarrhs (which are not of a consumptive character) of the Respiratory Organs.

Large Wooded Park. Excellent Residence for Ladies and Children. Catholic and Protestant Divine Service in private Chapel. Kurmusik. Auto-Garage. Sixteen miles trout fishing in excellent brooks.

Through Booking from London to Schinznach les Bains. Luggage can also be registered.

Physician in the Hotel. Prospectus from the Manager.

SCHLANGENBAD (near Wiesbaden).—See page 489.

ROYAL BATHS OF SCHLANGENBAD

ROYAL KURHAUSER.

New Kurhaus. 130 Rooms, with the most modern equipment. Suites with Baths. Beautiful covered Promenades. Lift to Baths.

Middle and Lower Kurhaus. 80 Rooms. Large, airy, and well furnished. Beautiful situation, leading direct to the Forest. Mineral Baths in the house; lift.

Berliner Hof and Schweizerhaus Villas, to let separately or together, 7 and 6 Rooms. Charming situation. Kitchen utensils provided.

The New Kurhaus and Colonnades.

SCHLANGENBAD—Continued on next page

SIENA (Italy).—See page 557.

2 hours from Florence. **SIENA.** 5 hours from Rome

THE TOWN OF ART, HISTORY. AND MEDIÆVAL ARCHITECTURE.

GRAND HOTEL ROYAL.

Beautifully situated on the famous Lizza Promenade.

Close to the new Post and Telegraph Office and all the principal Curiosities of the town. Entirely renovated and enlarged with every modern comfort. — Moderate Charges. Special arrangements for Winter and Summer Seasons.

G. BONDENTE, Manager. L. BETTI, Propr.

SIENA.

GRAND HOTEL CONTINENTAL

FIRST CLASS HOTEL, OPENED 1885.

THE most advantageously situated, facing the Post and Telegraph Office. Southern aspect. 50 Windows overlook the most splendid Panorama of the surrounding Country. Apartments with private bath. Steam heating and Electric light throughout. Electric Lift. Grand Hall. **Arrangements made for Pension.**

Patronized by H.M The Queen Margherita of Savoy. **A. ZAZZERA, Proprietor.**

SIERRE (Switzerland).—See page 528.

SIERRE—1,804 feet above Sea.

PENSION BEAU SITE (Formerly Pension d'Etrangers-Villa Beaulieu)

Exceptionally fine position. Entirely new Building. Electric Light. Central Heating. Baths. Cuisine Soignee (dietary cooking). Sun cure (on terrace nearly 100 yards long). Fine walks. Grapes cure in September. PENSION from **5.50 Frs.** **AD. FARDEL, Proprietor.**

Under the same management: HOTEL des BECS de BOSSON, Grimentz (Val d'Anniviers). Summer Resort, situated 4,700 feet above the Sea. Pension from 6 Frs.

SIMPLON-KULM (Switzerland).—See page 514B.

SIMPLON-KULM (Switzerland). Altitude 2,010 m.

HOTEL BELLEVUE

ON THE CULMINATE POINT OF THE SIMPLON ROUTE.

Centre for Excursions. Health Resort. 80 Beds. Electric Light. Central Heating. Post. Telegraph. Garage. — **O. KLUSER-LAGGER, Proprietor.**

SINGEN (Germany).—See page 459.

CENTRAL HOTEL SCHWEIZERHOF.

FACING STATION AND POST OFFICE.

New Fireproof Construction, equipped with every modern comfort. Lift. Central Heating. Electric Light. Baths. Garage. Very Quiet.

Rooms from 2—3 M. — Telephone No. 60. — **Proprietor, AUG. ROWALD.**

STOCKHOLM.—See page 643, Special Edition.

GRAND HOTEL and GRAND HOTEL ROYAL

STOCKHOLM.

THE two finest Hotels in SCANDINAVIA, situated opposite the Royal Palace with a magnificent view on the North-Strom and Lake of Mälaren. 250 Bedrooms and Drawing-rooms. The most modern fittings in Bath-rooms attached to many of these apartments.

NILS TRULSSON, Managing-Director.

FIRST CLASS.

HOTEL RYDBERG

FACING the ROYAL CASTLE.

Up-to-Date Comforts.

Fashionable Restaurant, Café and American Bar.

— Proprietor ÅUG. ÅHLFELDT —

One of the Finest and Most Elegant Hotels in Scandinàvia.

Opened in June, 1909. Warm and cold water in every room. A beautiful inside garden. Latest improvements; every convenience. For tariff apply to the Manager.

Hotel Pension Belfrage

VICTORIA PALACE, BRUNKEBERGSTORG 2.

FIRST CLASS FAMILY HOTEL, with all modern improvements, in the most central, select and quiet locality, convenient to the Galleries, Theatres, and other places of interest. Excellent table. — Electric Light. — Central Heating. — Highest English references.

Pension terms from 6 Kr., or rooms without board from Kr. 2.50.

STRASSBURG (Alsace—Germany).—See page 489A.

STRASSBURG.

GRAND HOTEL VILLE DE PARIS

AND

HOTEL FÜRSTENHOF

The Leading Hotel.

MOST CENTRAL POSITION, NEXT TO THE CATHEDRAL. • ELEGANT ROOMS AND SUITES WITH PRIVATE BATHS, ETC.

Telegrams: **"PARISHOTEL."** **RESTAURANT FRANÇAIS.** **AUTO-GARAGE.**

STRASSBURG—Continued on next page.

STRASSBURG—*Continued.*

TRAVEL and HOTEL ENQUIRIES—See page xii.

(Simplon Road) STRESA (Lago Maggiore).—See page 558.

"The beauty spot on Lake Maggiore" **STRESA** (Simplon-Lötschberg Line) Italy.

Grand Hotel et des Iles Borromées

Highest Order. 300 Rooms and 75 Private Bath-rooms with Toilet.

Favourite resort for English and American travellers. — Nearest to the Borromean Islands.

FINEST PANORAMIC VIEW.

Extensive Park and Gardens with Tennis, Croquet, Skating Rink, and Children's play grounds. 3 Lifts. Electric Light and Central Heating throughout. English and French Billiards. Large complete Auto Garage. Luxurious self-contained Suites with private entrances. Magnificent Lounge Hall and Foyer. Splendid Dining Rooms. French and Open Air Restaurant.

AMERICAN BAR.

Orchestra. Nice shops and travelling Agency in the grounds. English Church in the Hotel.

ROMEO OMARINI.

STRESA, Lake Maggiore, Simplon Road, Italy.

REGINA PALACE HOTEL.

Opened MARCH, 1908.

Beautiful Modern Hotel. FIRST CLASS.

200 Rooms and Salons.

Private Apartments with Bath Rooms.

Large Gardens. Tennis. Auto-Garage.

GUIDO GUIDI, Manager.

STUTTGART (Germany).—See page 490.

HOTEL MARQUARDT STUTTGART

FIRST CLASS HOTEL.

BEAUTIFULLY SITUATED OVERLOOKING THE SCHLOSSPLATZ.

Rooms from Mk. 4.50 including Breakfast.

All rooms fitted with HOT and COLD Water supply. Telephone connection in every apartment.

STUTTGART.

ROYAL HOTEL

FACING THE . . . CENTRAL STATION.

First Class Hotel with every modern comfort.

100 ROOMS and APARTMENTS with PRIVATE BATHS from **Mks. 2.50**, including ELECTRIC LIGHT and CENTRAL HEATING.

Lift. Large RESTAURANT with Garden. Recommended. **Proprietor: AUG. BANZHOF.**

HOTEL CONTINENTAL.

STUTTGART.

NEW FIRST CLASS FAMILY HOTEL. Every modern comfort. Hot and Cold Water supply in every room. Apartments and Single Rooms with private Bath. Best Sanitary arrangements. Central Heating throughout. Garage. Omnibus at Station. Moderate terms. Advantageous arrangements for a prolonged stay. — **E. HASMANN, Manager.**

TRAVEL and HOTEL ENQUIRIES—See page xii.

TOURS—Continued on next page.

TOURS—*Continued.*

TRAFOI (Tyrol).—See page 505.

TRAYAS (Le), near Cannes, France.—See page 421.

TREMEZZO, Lac de Como (Italy).—See page 540.

TRENTO (Trient), South Tyrol.—See page 505.

TREVES (German: Trier), Germany.—See page 491.

TRIBERG (Germany).—See page 460.

In the middle of the celebrated Railroad of the Black Forest.

UTRECHT (Holland).—See page 446.

VALENCIA (Spain).—See page 576.

. . VALENCIA. . .

Reina Victoria Hotel

OPENED 1913. OPENED 1913.

FIRST CLASS SWISS HOTEL
with every modern comfort.

Restaurant Français.

Telegrams:—
— VICTOREL VALENCIA, SPAIN. —

VALESCURE (France).—See page 422.

Valescure—Riviera.

COIRIER'S GRAND HOTEL

FIRST CLASS IN EVERY RESPECT. All latest improvements. Apartments and single Rooms with bath rooms. PATRONISED BY BEST ENGLISH FAMILIES. Vacuum Cleaner. — Motor to Golf Links. — PERSONAL MANAGEMENT.

HOTEL des ANGLAIS.

Valescure—St. Raphael. Var—Riviera.

FULL South, in midst of a large Garden and Pine Forest. Splendid walks in the Esterel. Lawn Tennis. Near the English Church. On the way and nearest to the new Valescure Golf Links. Sanitary Drainage. Bath. Douches. Heated. Sheltered from winds and no dust. Moderate Prices. JOSEPH BICKEL, Proprietor, (Swiss.)

THE ANGLO-AMERICAN AGENCY & BANK,

W. F. KING.

MAGNIFICENT VILLAS TO LET AND FOR SALE. — All particulars gratis.
Visitors' Correspondence may be addressed here.
See ST. RAPHAEL. page 1032

VARENNA (Italy).—See page 559A.

VARESE (Italy).—See page 559A.

SPRING AND AUTUMN HEALTH RESORT.

HOTEL PENSION DE L'EUROPE.

Excellent Second Class Family House. — Facing the Magnificent Public Garden. Entirely re-furnished. Splendid Reading and Drawing Room. Large Hall. Electric Light throughout. CENTRAL HEATING. Baths. Garden. Cook's Coupons. VERY MODERATE PENSION TERMS. — CAPELLO & STABILINI, Proprietors.

VENICE.—See page 559A.

VENICE.

THE GRAND HOTEL

FIRST CLASS HOUSE with all modern improvements. Occupies the three finest Palaces on the Grand Canal. With an immense Terrace. Situated on the most picturesque and healthiest location of the Grand Canal. Accommodation for 300 persons. 30 magnificent parlours. Every home comfort. New apartments with private Bathrooms.

Patronised by the elite of English and American Society.

A. PIANTA. Manager.

HOTEL ROYAL DANIELI.

On the Grand Canal and Riva degli Schiavoni.

Finest view of the Town.

THIS FIRST CLASS ESTABLISHMENT enjoys the reputation of being one of the best kept Houses on the Continent. It has been entirely refitted, and is now replete with all modern comforts. New apartments with private Bath Rooms. Railway Ticket and Booking Office on the premises.

A. BOZZI. Manager.

VENICE.

HOTEL REGINA (formerly ROME et SUISSE)

SITUATED on one of the finest positions of the Grand Canal, at a few minutes walk from St. Mark's Square. It has recently been entirely re-built and re-furnished, and now stands amongst the most complete of modern hotels, combined with its usual moderate charges. Electric Light throughout. Baths. Steam heating. Electric Lift. A spacious terrace full South. All its windows overlooking either the Grand Canal or the private Garden. **J. OSIO, Manager.**

HOTEL AND PENSION BEAU RIVAGE

SITUATED on the Riva degli Schiavoni, near the Doges' Palace and St. Mark's Square. From its windows one enjoys the finest view of the Town. Recently entirely re-fitted with all modern comforts. This High Class Boarding House is most convenient for a prolonged stay. Moderate charges.

VENICE—Continued on next page

TRAVEL and HOTEL ENQUIRIES—See page xii.

VENICE—*Continued.*

ALBERGO MARINO.

Beside the HOTEL EXCELSIOR, on the Sea shore.

60 Rooms. * Bath Rooms. * Dining Rooms. * Reading Room.

Grand Cafe and Magnificent Terrace on the "Plage."

EVERY MODERN COMFORT. MODERATE CHARGES.

Telephone N. 108. — **Proprietor: A. VIANELLI.**

VERNET-LES-BAINS (France).—See page 422.

VERNET LES BAINS

The "PARADISE of the Pyrenees."

SOUTH OF FRANCE (Near PERPIGNAN).

Railway Station: VILLEFRANCHE—VERNET-LES-BAINS. Through Booking from London (see page CXV); through carriage (2nd and 1st class couchettes, lits-toilette) from Paris (quai d'Orsay) 7 p.m. daily (see pages 32 and 46).

REMARKABLE CLIMATE. Not Windy. Not Damp. 12 Natural Hot Sulphur Springs (45° Fahr. to 150° Fahr.). At all seasons, invaluable cure for Rheumatism, Gout, Neuralgia, Dyspepsia, Sciatica, Nervous and General Weakness, affections of the Respiratory Organs, Convalescences. **Up to Date** Bath and Hydropathic Establishments, in direct floor communication with **FIRST CLASS HOTELS** (Lifts, Electric Light, Central Heating, English Sanitation, bath and dressing rooms, suites, halls, modern furniture, etc.)—newly furnished apartments and Chalets. Casino. Good Club with English Billiards, Ladies' Bridge Rooms, Orchestra, etc. Tennis Excursions, etc. Putting Golf. Garage, atelier, etc. Apply for Illustrated English Brochure—

EMILE KIECHLE, Directeur Etablissement Thermal, Vernet-les-Bains (Pyr. Or)

VERNET-les-BAINS (PYR. OR.) — THE "PARADISE OF THE PYRENEES."

Grand Hotel du Portugal
Hotel du Parc * Hotel des Bains Mercader

Up-to-Date, Open all the Year,

AND WELL KNOWN FOR THEIR GOOD COOKING AND ATTENDANCE.

VERONA (Italy).—See page 561.

GRAND HOTEL DE LONDRES & ROYAL DEUX TOURS.

THE LEADING FIRST CLASS HOTEL IN VERONA.

Entirely re-furnished with all latest improvements by the new Proprietor.

English Sanitary Arrangements. ELECTRIC LIGHT. LIFT. Central Heating.

Winter Garden. Bath Rooms. Auto-omnibus at the principal Station (Porta Vescovo).

EMILIO CERESA, Proprietor.

VERONA—Continued on next page

TRAVEL and HOTEL ENQUIRIES—See page xii.

VEVEY—*Continued.*

VEVEY—Continued on next page.

VEVEY—*Continued.*

VEVEY. **Hotel Pension NUSS** — Open — all the year.

NEW HOUSE.

Latest Comforts. — 50 Rooms with Balconies. - Completely Fireproof. SPLENDID POSITION on the border of the LAKE. Private Port. Park. Cuisine renommée.

Pension from 6.50 francs. Garage.

VEVEY (Mont-Pelerin).—See page 531.

MONT PELERIN, above Vevey.

HOTEL BELVEDERE Altitude 970 M.

FAMILY HOTEL. Exceptional Situation in the middle of woods. Splendid view on the Lake Leman and the Alps. Pine Forests in the vicinity. Air Cure. Open all the year round. Central Heating. Electric Light. Large covered Verandah. French Restaurant. Cremerie. Telephone. Lawn Tennis. Winter sports. 10 minutes from the Station, terminus of Funicular "Vevey-Pélerin." — Moderate Charges. — Pension from **6.50 Francs.**

C. CHAPPUIS, Proprietor.

THE GRAND HOTEL MOUNT-PELERIN

ABOVE VEVEY (FUNICULAR) 3,000 FEET.

DELIGHTFUL RESORT all the year round. Winter Sports. 130 Rooms all with balcony and finest view. The Grand Hotel of Mont Pèlerin is a model of comfort and good taste. All modern requirements are catered for in order to make the house worthy of the colony of residents and tourists who expect, amidst such splendid natural beauty, repose with comfort, well being with tranquillity. Telegram address: "GRANDPELERIN VEVEY."

NIESS & CO., Proprietors.

Branch Houses: THE GRAND HOTEL, Aigle; HOTEL VICTORIA, Geneva.

PÉLERIN PALACE HOTEL

2,952 feet above the sea. — MONT PELERIN, above Vevey.

OPEN all the year round. First Class Hotel. Modern Sanitation. 140 Bedrooms. Ten family suites with private bathrooms, &c. Hot water heating. English and French billiards. Dark room. Lift. Large park. Orchestra. Motor garage. Medical attendance at the hotel. Terms from **9 frs.** Telephone 411. No cases of tuberculosis can be admitted. K. SCHERTENLEIB, Manager

VIAREGGIO (Italy).—See page 562.

VICHY-LES-BAINS (France).—See page 423.

Golf Links Finest Links in France.

Professional: J. B. BOMBOUDIAC.

CLUB HOUSE. — J. ALETTI, Manager.

TRAVEL and HOTEL ENQUIRIES—See page xii.

VICHY-LES-BAINS—*Continued.*

HOTEL du PARC

ENTIRELY REBUILT AND REFURNISHED.
Opposite the New Bath Establishment,
Springs, and Casino.
FINEST RESTAURANT ROOM IN EUROPE.

MAJESTIC PALACE

NEWLY BUILT. **HOTEL.** NEWLY BUILT.

WITH BATH OR TOILET ADJOINING EACH ROOM.

BRANCH HOUSE **PAVILLON SEVIGNÉ** In its own Park.

General Manager: **J. ALETTI.**

VICHY-LES-BAINS—Continued on next page.

VICHY-LES-BAINS—*Continued.*

CARLTON HOTEL

ON THE PARK.
Beautiful Garden.

RECONSTRUCTED.
Latest Comfort.

OPEN-AIR
RESTAURANT.

Manager: F. HAINZL.

THERMAL PALACE HOTEL

OVERLOOKING THE
PARK.

OPPOSITE THE CASINO.

MOST UP TO DATE
COMFORT..

Manager: E. REY.

TRAVEL and HOTEL ENQUIRIES—See page xii.

VICHY-LES-BAINS—*Continued.*

ASTORIA PALACE HOTEL

Recently Opened with all Up-to-date Comfort.

MODERN SANITARY ARRANGEMENTS.

Best Situation, overlooking the PARC, and facing the CASINO.
Near the Principal VICHY SPRINGS and medical establishments,
and close to Post and Telegraph.

TELEPHONE No. 3·20.

INTERNATIONAL HOTEL.

Opposite the PARC and CASINO. — Well known for its comfort.

LARGE GARDEN. AUTO GARAGE.

Special attention paid to the Meals in accordance with medical prescription.

Under the same management as—ASTORIA PALACE HOTEL. L. SOALHAT, Proprietor.

Gd. HOTEL et VILLAS des AMBASSADEURS

ON THE PARK. FACING THE CASINO.

ENTIRELY RENOVATED.

Rooms and Suites with Bath and Toilet. . . . *G. ROUBEAU, Proprietor.*

GRANDE BRETAGNE & QUEEN'S HOTEL

FIRST CLASS.

Renovated 1912. In Magnificent Park. Opposite Golf Links.

A. MURIS, Proprietor.

VICHY-LES-BAINS—continued on next page.

VIENNA.—See page 506.

TRAVEL and HOTEL ENQUIRIES—See page xii.

VIENNA—*Continued.*

THE GRAND HOTEL

VIENNA. I. KARNTNERRING, 9. VIENNA.

Owing to extensive alterations undertaken in 1912, and the opening of the magnificent Annex in Spring, 1913, this Hotel, in close proximity to the Imperial Opera and the Museums, is the most fashionable up-to-date Hotel of the Austrian capital.

350 Rooms. 100 private bathrooms. Telephone connection in 200 rooms. The entire Hotel is provided with hot water radiators and with modern optical signals (no ringing of bells). Concert in the large dining room from 8 p.m., and in the magnificent large new hall during 5 o'clock tea. Cabin booking office of the Norddeutscher Lloyd and Sleeping Car Ticket Office.

HOTEL METROPOLE

Vienna—Franz Josefs-Kai Ring.

FIRST CLASS in every appointment. Mostly patronised by English and American Families. Unrivalled situation in the centre of Vienna; Rooms overlooking the Danube and Kahlenberg. 300 Rooms; Running Water; Suites and single Rooms with private Baths Toilets, and Telephone. Central hot water heating throughout. Comfortable Public Reception Rooms. Winter Garden. Banqueting Hall. Evening Concert in the dining room. Excellent French and Viennese Cooking. Electric Ozone Installation. Lifts day and night. Safe deposit. Vacuum Cleaner. Post and Telegraph Office. Branch of Länder Bank. Typewriter. Ladies' and Gentlemen's Hairdresser. Rooms from **Kronen** 3.50. Plan-tariff on application.

J. RUESS, Manager.

Hotel Meissl & Schadn

I. Kärntnerstrasse, 16.

1st Class Hotel — AND — **Restaurant.**

HIGHLY RECOMMENDED. Private Apartments and single rooms with baths and telephone.

Park Hotel Schönbrunn

VIENNA. HIETZING.

FIRST CLASS FAMILY HOTEL, with most beautiful and healthy position in Vienna, facing the Imperial Castle Schönbrunn. This magnificent new Hotel contains all the most modern improvements. All rooms with Baths and Toilet. High class French and Viennese Cuisine. Pension arrangements. Lift. Electric Light. Steam Heating. Auto Garage. Good communication with all parts of the city. Own Automobiles.

Proprietors: PAUL HOPFNER & SON, also Restaurant Hopfner, Vienna, I, Kärtnerstasse, No. 61, and Graben Restaurant, Graben, 29. The Tariff plan is sent free on application.

VIENNA—Continued on next page

TRAVEL and HOTEL ENQUIRIES—See page xii.

VIENNA—Continued on next page

VIENNA—*Continued.*

TRAVEL and HOTEL ENQUIRIES—See page xii.

VIENNA—*Continued.*

I. KÄRNTHNERRING, 17. OPPOSITE SCHWARZENBERGPLATZ.

ENGLISH AND AMERICAN CHEMIST

To the BRITISH AND AMERICAN EMBASSIES, etc., etc.

Adler-Apotheke, F. WISINGER. — Pharmacie Française.

RESTAURANT "DEUTSCHES HAUS."

STEPHANS PLATZ.

FIRST CLASS RESTAURANT, situated in the centre of the City, behind and exactly facing St. Stephan's Church. Magnificent Garden and cool Dining-Rooms and Saloons. Water Cascade. Finest Cooking and renowned Cellar of Wine of the **Deutschen Ritter Ordens.** Popular Prices. This house is a curiosity in Vienna, having been built over 500 years ago. Recommended to English and Americans. **FRIEDRICH KARGL, Proprietor.**

VILLACH (Austria).—See page 506c.

VILLACH-PARK HOTEL.

VERY FIRST CLASS HOTEL, equipped with up-to-date comforts, in dust-free position with magnificent Park. View of the Mountains. 200 Rooms and Salons with Bath and Toilette. Lounge. Café. Garage (boxes). **Open all the year.** Most suitable for break of the journey when travelling north or southwards, or to and from Meran.

VILLARS-SUR-OLLON (Switzerland).—See page 531.

ALPES-VAUDOISES. VILLARS-sur-OLLON (SUISSE)

Jura Simplon Ry. Station: BEX. Electric Tram: Bex-Villars—Altitude 4,300 ft.

GRAND HOTEL MUVERAN
HOTEL BELLE VUE.

Manager: CHARLES GENILLARD. * Summer and Winter Season.

ALTITUDE 4,300 feet. Large Park. Splendid view on the Rhone Valley, the "Dent du Midi," Glacier of Trient, etc. — Pine Forest and numerous walks in the neighbourhood. Post and Telegraph Office. English Church. Catholic Chapel. Baths and Douches on each Floor. Theatre. Smoking Rooms. Billiard Rooms (English Tables) Promenoir. Tennis. Electric Light. — Central Heating. — Lift. — Pension inclusive from 8 Francs.

VILLARS-SUR-OLLON—Continued on next page

VILLARS-SUR-OLLON—*Continued.*

GRAND HOTEL

OPENED 1896.

Proprietor : J. FREUDWEILER.

Every modern comfort: Lift. Electric Light, Bathroom each Floor. Tennis, Gymnasium. Dark Room, etc., etc.

Church of England close by—Services regularly from 10th June until 30th September.

VILLENEUVE (Switzerland)—See Montreux.

VITTEL (Vosges—France).—See page 423.

GRAND HOTEL de l'ETABLISSEMENT

THIS HOTEL is situated in the Parc de l'Etablissement des Eaux Minerales, near the "Grand Source," the "Source Salée," and the "Hydropathic Establishment," with which it is connected by covered galleries. An annexe of the Hotel, constructed in 1905, contains rooms and apartments furnished with the greatest taste and comfort and with due regard to hygiène. — Passenger Lifts. — Electric Light.

VITTEL PALACE.

AN ENTIRELY NEW HOTEL specially recommended to English Visitors.

This Hotel is situated upon an eminence commanding a view over the Race Course and the Golf Links, and in close proximity to the Springs and the Park.

Private Suites with Salon and separate Bath and Toilet.

This Hotel is Recommended by its Hygienic and Picturesque Situation, being in the Open Country. Electric Light Lift. — G. RADLE, Manager.

VITZNAU, see LUCERNE-VITZNAU, page 913.

WEHRAWALD (Germany).—See page 460.

WEHRAWALD (Baden) near Todtmoos, in south part of the Black Forest. **2,825 feet above sea.**
Railway Station Wehr (railway line Basle [Badischer Bahnhof] -Schopfheim-Säckingen).

SANATORIUM WEHRAWALD.

HIGHEST situated health establishment of Germany for persons of CONSUMPTIVE TENDENCY. Sunny wind-sheltered position surrounded with magnificent pine woods. Most perfect hygiene. 100 Beds. Modern improvements. Electric Light. Lift. Central heating. Röntgenkabinett, Inhalatorium. Many permanent cures. Open all the year round. — Especially favourable residence in light cases of phthisis. — Prospectus sent by the medical directorate. **Dr. FR. LIPS, Head Physician.**

TRAVEL and HOTEL ENQUIRIES—See page xii.

WIESBADEN, BATHS OF.—See page 492.

WIESBADEN.

NASSAUER HOF

(HOTEL NASSAU).

— With Magnificent Bath House. —

FINEST POSITION,

FACING THE CURPARK AND ROYAL THEATRE.

Bath House and private Bath Rooms supplied direct from the hot springs (Kochbrunnen).

Select Home of International Society.

WORLD WIDE REPUTATION

Telegraphic Address: **NASSAUERHOF, WIESBADEN.**

TRAVEL and HOTEL ENQUIRIES—See page xii.

WIESBADEN. BATHS OF—Continued on next page

TRAVEL and HOTEL ENQUIRIES—See page xii.

WIESBADEN Continued on next page.

WIESBADEN BATHS OF—*Continued.*

PENSION VILLA HERTHA—WIESBADEN.

TEL. 4182. **DAMBACHTAL 24.** **BUILT 1909.**

Under English Management. Near Springs, Kurhaus, Woods. Trams. Terms from **35/-** to **70/-** per week. Mineral baths. **Pension Villa Hertha,** a **Modern** up-to-date **Villa** in the beginning of the beautiful Dambachtal. Large Garden. 13 balconies. Large Reception, Dining, and Smoking Rooms. Separate tables if desired. Afternoon Tea. Hot Water **Central Heating.** Electric Light Splendid position for winter.

MISS RODWAY, FRL. ANDRÉ.

WIESBADEN.

PENSION FORTUNA

KAISER WILHELM.

11, **Paulinen Strasse.** — First Class Pension, in best position, close to the Kurhaus, Theatre, and Kochbrunnen. Every modern comfort. Central Heating, Lift, Electric light. Thermal Baths on each floor. Renowned for its excellent cuisine. Pension from **Marks 6.**

Proprietress: L. KNIPPER.

WILDBAD (Black Forest—Germany).—**See page 460.**

HOTEL KLUMPP AND KLUMPP'S HOTEL BELLEVUE.

THESE First Class Hotels are beautifully situated, facing the Royal Bath Buildings and Conversation House, at the entrance of the Promenade and Trinkhalle. Every modern comfort. Excellent Cuisine and Wines. Table d'Hote. RESTAURANT. Arrangements made for a prolonged stay. Lift, Electric Light, Steam Heating. Exchange Office; Correspondents of the Principal Banking Houses. Trout Fishing. Hunting. Reduced prices for Rooms till middle of June and from the middle of August. — **Propr.: FAMILY KLUMPP.**

For Tariff apply to the Managers.

Royal Bath Hotel

with Dependance **Villa Victoria.**

ABSOLUTELY FIRST CLASS.

Only Hotel with Thermal Bath. Electric Light, Lift. 100 elegant and comfortably furnished Rooms and Salons. Table d'hote at separate tables. Pension from **10 Mks.** upwards. Gardens and Terrace. Omnibus meets all trains. The rooms of the Hotel are connected by easy stairs and lift (without being outside) with the Thermal Bath.

Entirely renovated 1913. — **New Proprietor, OSW. JÜPTNER.**

SOMMERBERG HOTEL

HIGH CLASS new hotel, open all the year, on the top of the Sommerberg, standing in its own grounds. Every modern comfort is here installed. 10 Minutes from Wildbad by Funicular Railway. In winter the sports, such as Ski-ing, Bob-sleighing, etc. are very attractive. Electric Light. Vacuum cleaner. Lift. All kinds of Baths, etc. Unique in every respect. 75 Rooms and Salons. — Arrangements for Pension from 7 Marks. — First Class Cuisine.

Proprietors: CARL BATZNER and EMIL WENTZ.

BAD-WILDUNGEN—Continued on next page.

ZERMATT (Switzerland).—See page 532.

ZURICH (Switzerland).—See page 532.

TRAVEL and HOTEL ENQUIRIES—See page xii.

ZURICH— Continued on next page

MIDLAND GRAND HOTEL

The Tubes and Taxicabs bring the West End and City within a few minutes of

LONDON'S MOST COMFORTABLE HOTEL

W. TOWLE, Manager,
Midland Railway Hotels.

LONDON—Continued on next page.

THE GORDON HOTELS IN LONDON.

First-class Hotels owned and managed by the Gordon Hotels Limited. All conveniently situated, well equipped, and equally comfortable.

HÔTEL MÉTROPOLE

Northumberland Avenue,
Trafalgar Square.

CONVENIENTLY situated for all places of interest. Most theatres within half a mile radius. Telephones in all bedrooms and sitting rooms. Finest Hotel Lounge in London.

Telegrams : "Metropole, London."
Telephone 8130 Gerrard (20 lines).

GRAND HOTEL.

UNEQUALLED POSITION, overlooking Trafalgar Square. Numerous suites with luxuriously-fitted bathrooms, also bedrooms with bathrooms communicating, on every floor.

Telephones in bedrooms and sitting rooms

Telegrams : "Granotel, London."
Telephone 766 Gerrard (7 lines).

TRAVEL and HOTEL ENQUIRIES—See page xii

LONDON—Continued on next page

HOTEL CECIL LONDON

3 minutes from Charing Cross.

Most Central and Modern First Class Hotel in London.

ACCOMMODATION—800 GUESTS.

RESTAURANT

(Open to non-residents).

Telegrams: "CECELIA, LONDON."
Telephone: 60 GERRARD.

PALM COURTS

RENDEZVOUS OF CONTINENTAL SOCIETY IN LONDON.

F. W. KAISER, General Manager.

TRAVEL and HOTEL ENQUIRIES—See page xii.

THE

HYDE PARK HOTEL

Albert Gate, London, S.W.,

HAS AN UNINTERRUPTED VIEW OVER HYDE PARK.

The Finest Position in London.

View of Hyde Park Hotel from the Serpentine Lake.

Suites unequalled in Luxurious Accommodation, Every Suite having its own Bathroom.

"An Ideal Family Hotel."

LONDON - Continued on next page.

LONDON—Continued on next page

LONDON—Continued on next page.

TRAVEL and HOTEL ENQUIRIES—See page xii.

LONDON—Continued on next page

TRAVEL and HOTEL ENQUIRIES—See page xii.

BOURNEMOUTH—*Continued.*

CANTERBURY.

DOVER.

DOVER—Continued on next page.

DOVER—*Continued.*

Telegraphic Address:—"GRAND, DOVER." — TELEPHONE 589 (*2 lines*).

GRAND HOTEL

LEADING FAMILY AND RESIDENTIAL HOTEL IN DOVER.

LUXURIOUSLY FURNISHED and Electric Light throughout. Bright and Airy Rooms, overlooking Channel (S.W. aspect) and Granville Gardens. Private Suites of Rooms (communicating) with Balconies, High Class Cuisine. Choice Vintage Wines. Passenger Lift to all Floors. Grand Hotel Bus meets all Trains and Mail Boats. The Hotel is comfortably warmed throughout. New Grill Room now open.

Moderate Terms inclusive, or à la Carte. Special Week End Terms.

A. A. & M. C. A. AFFILIATED. MOTOR GARAGE. INSPECTION PIT. **Manager,**

Opposite Granville Gardens & Band Stand. *Telephone No. 589 (2 lines).* **O. F. BERGANN.**

EASTBOURNE.

ALEXANDRA HOTEL,

GRAND PARADE.

The finest position on Grand Parade. Facing the Sea, near Wish Tower.

EVERY MODERN COMFORT AND CONVENIENCE.

Spacious Dining Hall.
New Lounge.
Smoking, Reading and Billiard Rooms.

Table d'Hote at Separate Tables.
Fully Licensed.

À La CARTE or EN PENSION.

W. E. WOOD,
Proprietor.

(21 years Manager, Trinity College, Cambridge.)

Telephone: 132. Telegrams: "ALEXANDRA," Eastbourne.

TRAVEL and HOTEL ENQUIRIES—See page xii.

EASTBOURNE.—*Continued.*

FOLKESTONE.

FOLKESTONE—Continued on next page

FOLKESTONE—*Continued.*

WEST CLIFF HOTEL

FOLKESTONE.

LEADING and MOST FASHIONABLE HOTEL.

FACING SEA and the Leas. 220 Magnificent Apartments and Suites. Up-to-date. Luxurious. Moderate. Electric Light. Lift. Motor Garage. 2 Acres Private Gardens. Tennis, Croquet, Bowls, etc.

Under the personal direction of

ANGUS MACDONALD,

Late of the Hotel Beau Site, Cannes.

WAMPACH'S HOTEL LTD.

CASTLE HILL AVENUE, FOLKESTONE.

First-class, most up-to-date. New Lounge and Smoke Room. Lift. Garage. Moderate Tariff. Book Central Station. 'Bus meets all Trains.

Telephone: 39. Telegrams: "WAMPACH." O. LINDHEIMER, Manager.
(Late Manager Queen's Hotel, Leeds.)

VICTORIA PRIVATE HOTEL

MARINE CRESCENT, FOLKESTONE.

Facing Sea. **Close to Harbour Station, Piers,** and Lift to Leas. New Lounge. Electric Light.
Inclusive Moderate Terms. — Table d'Hote 7 o'clock. — **Proprietress: MISS POPE.**

FOLKESTONE.

BATH HOTEL, Clifton Crescent, The Leas.

Old Established First-class Private Hotel. *South Aspect, Sea View, Separate Tables, Electric Light.*

Telephone: 117. **Inclusive terms from 7/6 per day.** **Mrs. GRIFFITHS JONES**
Telegrams: "Bath Hotel, Folkestone." PROSPECTUS. (Late of the York House Hotel, Bath).

TRAVEL and HOTEL ENQUIRIES—See page xii.

GLASGOW.

GLASGOW. ST. ENOCH STATION HOTEL

Adjoins the Glasgow Terminus of the Glasgow & South Western and Midland Railways.

CONVENIENTLY SITUATED. ELECTRIC LIGHT. PASSENGER ELEVATOR.

AYR. STATION HOTEL. BEAUTIFUL DISTRICT FOR TOURISTS.

DUMFRIES. STATION HOTEL. ADJOINS THE STATION.

J. H. THOMAS, Manager, Glasgow and South Western Railway Company's Hotels.
Chief Office: ST. ENOCH STATION HOTEL, GLASGOW.

Bradshaw's Guide.

TRAVEL ENQUIRY DEPARTMENT.—This Department has proved of efficient service both to hotel-keepers and the travelling public. Prospectuses of clients whose announcements appear in Bradshaw's Guide are kept for inspection or distribution at the Company's Offices in London, Liverpool, Manchester, Glasgow, and Dublin. For further particulars see page xii.

GUERNSEY.

GUERNSEY.

OLD GOVERNMENT HOUSE HOTEL.

ALL MODERN IMPROVEMENTS.

The HOTEL GROUNDS command an unequalled view of entire Channel Group.

SPLENDID HEALTH RESORT.

Special Tariff for Winter Months.

PATRONISED BY ROYALTY.

Private Omnibus and Porters to meet all Steamers.

Telegrams: "GOV., GUERNSEY."

Mrs. JOHN GARDNER,
Managing Director.

IRELAND.

BRADSHAW'S GUIDE

HAND BOOK

1. 2. 3. 4.

Bradshaw-Mitchell's

RAIL TIMES

Winter Revision

MP Middleton Press

ISBN 978-1-906008-45-1